Chromosome 9

- Interferon deficiency
- Galactosemia
- Tuberous sclerosis
- Fructose intolerance
- Citrullinemia
- Acute hepatic porphyria
- Lead poisoning, susceptibility to
- Nail-patella syndrome
- Hemolytic anemia due to adenylate kinase deficiency
- Chronic myeloid leukemia *
- C5 deficiency
- Coproporphyria
- Harderoporphyria

Chromosome 12

- C1r/C1s deficiency, combined
- Hemolytic anemia due to triosephosphate isomerase deficiency
- von Willebrand disease
- Colorectal adenoma
- Colorectal cancer
- Stickler syndrome
- ?Spondyloepiphyseal dysplasia congenita
- ?Kniest dysplasia
- ?Langer-Saldino achondrogenesis
- ?Osteoarthrosis, precocious
- Glioma *
- Lipoma *
- Acyl-CoA dehydrogenase, short chain, deficiency
- Immune interferon deficiency
- Phenylketonuria [Hyperphenylalaninemia, mild]
- Acute alcohol intolerance
- ?Fetal alcohol syndrome
- ?Brody myopathy

Chromosome 8

- Hyperlipoproteinemia I
- Hemolytic anemia due to glutathione reductase deficiency
- Plasminogen activator deficiency
- Spherocytosis II
- ?Hypogonadotropic hypogonadism due to GNRH deficiency
- Adrenal hyperplasia, congenital, due to 11-hydroxylase deficiency
- CMOII deficiency
- Renal tubular acidosis-osteopetrosis syndrome
- Langer-Giedion syndrome *
- [Trichorhinophalangeal syndrome-1]
- ?Adolescent multinodular goiter
- Hereditary congenital hypothyroidism (1 or more forms)
- Burkitt lymphoma *
- Epidermolysis bullosa, Ogna type
- Macular dystrophy, atypical vitelliform

Chromosome 7

- Craniosynostosis
- Argininosuccinicaciduria
- Mucopolysaccharidosis VII
- Ehlers-Danlos syndrome type VII A2
- Osteogenesis imperfecta (2 or more forms)
- Marfan syndrome, atypical
- Cystic fibrosis
- Trypsinogen deficiency
- Tritan colorblindness
- Pyruvate dehydrogenase complex deficiency

Chromosome 11

- ?Beckwith-Wiedemann syndrome *
- Manic-depressive illness
- MODY
- Diabetes mellitus, rare form
- Hereditary persistence of fetal Hb]
- Sickle cell anemia
- β-thalassemias
- β-methemoglobinemias
- β-erythremias
- β-Heinz body anemias
- HPFH, deletion type
- Wilms tumor *
- Acatalasemia
- Aniridia-2 *
- T-cell leukemia/lymphoma
- Combined apoA-I/C-III deficiency
- Hypertriglyceridemia (1 form)
- Hypoalphalipoproteinemia
- Exertional myoglobinuria due to LDH-A deficiency
- Liver cell carcinoma
- Hypoprothrombinemia
- Dysprothrombinemia
- Angioedema, hereditary
- B-cell leukemia *
- McArdle disease
- Epidermolysis bullosa dystrophica, recessive
- Acute intermittent porphyria

Chromosome 6

- Factor XIIIA deficiency
- Orofacial cleft
- Methylmalonicaciduria, one type
- Spinocerebellar ataxia-1
- Long Q-T syndrome
- Hemochromatosis
- Congenital adrenal hyperplasia due to 21-hydroxylase deficiency
- C2 deficiency
- C4 deficiency
- Atrial septal defect (one form)
- [Renal glucosuria]
- Argininemia
- Plasminogen Tochigi disease

(partially obscured labels)
- ...lic anemia due to ...inase deficiency
- ...endocrine neoplasia
- ...romatic leukodystrophy ...p lack of SAP-1
- ... T-cell acute lymphocytic *
- ...an ...sease
- ...steral ester storage disease
- ...inemia, ...responsive & B6-unresponsive
- ...plasia-
- ...ng protein, deficiency of

(Continued)

SIXTH EDITION

THE
METABOLIC BASIS
OF
INHERITED DISEASE

Editors

Charles R. Scriver, M.D.C.M.
Professor of Biology, Human Genetics and Pediatrics, Departments of Biology and Pediatrics and Center for Human Genetics, McGill University, Montreal, Canada

Arthur L. Beaudet, M.D.
Investigator, Howard Hughes Medical Institute; Professor, Institute for Molecular Genetics and Departments of Pediatrics and Cell Biology, Baylor College of Medicine, Houston, Texas

William S. Sly, M.D.
Alice A. Doisy Professor of Biochemistry and Professor of Pediatrics; Chairman, Edward A. Doisy Department of Biochemistry and Molecular Biology, St. Louis University School of Medicine, St. Louis, Missouri

David Valle, M.D.
Investigator, Howard Hughes Medical Institute; Professor of Pediatrics, Medicine, and Molecular Biology & Genetics, The Johns Hopkins University School of Medicine, Baltimore, Maryland

Consulting Editors

John B. Stanbury, M.D.
Honorary Physician, Massachusetts General Hospital; Division of Health Science and Technology, Massachusetts Institute of Technology, Boston, Massachusetts

James B. Wyngaarden, M.D.
Director, National Institutes of Health, Bethesda, Maryland

Donald S. Fredrickson, M.D.
Researcher, Molecular Disease Branch, National Heart, Lung and Blood Institute; Scholar, National Library of Medicine, National Institutes of Health, Bethesda, Maryland

SIXTH EDITION

THE
METABOLIC BASIS
OF
INHERITED DISEASE

Editors

Charles R. Scriver, M.D.C.M.
Arthur L. Beaudet, M.D.
William S. Sly, M.D.
David Valle, M.D.

Consulting Editors

John B. Stanbury, M.D.
James B. Wyngaarden, M.D.
Donald S. Fredrickson, M.D.

McGRAW-HILL INFORMATION SERVICES COMPANY
Health professions Division
New York   St Louis   San Francisco   Colorado Springs   Auckland
Bogotá   Caracas   Hamburg   Lisbon   London   Madrid   Mexico   Milan   Montreal
New Delhi   Panama   Paris   San Juan   São Paulo   Singapore   Sydney   Tokyo   Toronto

1234567890HALHAL8932109

ISBN 0-07-909254-3 (set)
ISBN 0-07-060727-3 (v. 1)
ISBN 0-07-060728-1 (v. 2)

This book was set in Plantin by The Clarinda Company.
The editors were J. Dereck Jeffers and Gail Gavert.
The production supervisor was Robert R. Laffler.
The designer was Charles A. Carson.
The cover was designed by M N' O Production Services, Inc.
Arcata Graphics/Halliday was printer and binder.

Library of Congress Cataloging-in-Publication Data

The Metabolic basis of inherited disease/editors, Charles R. Scriver
. . . [et al.]; consulting editors, John B. Stanbury, James B.
Wyngaarden, Donald S. Fredrickson.—6th ed.
    p.   cm.
    Includes bibliographies and index.
    1. Metabolism, Inborn errors of.   I. Scriver, Charles R.
    [DNLM: 1. Hereditary Diseases.   2. Metabolic Diseases.
3. Metabolism, Inborn Errors.   WD 2300 M587]
RC627.8.M47 1989
616.3'9042—dc19
DNLM/DLC
for Library of Congress

88-39722
CIP

CONTENTS

VOLUME II

LIST OF CONTRIBUTORS

Milton B. Adesnik, Ph.D. [3]
Professor, Department of Cell Biology, New York University School of Medicine, New York, New York

Björn A. Afzelius, Ph.D. [112]
Professor, Wenner-Gren Institute, University of Stockholm, Stockholm, Sweden

Robert J. Alpern, M.D. [103]
Associate Professor of Medicine; Chief, Division of Nephrology, University of Texas Southwestern Medical Center, Dallas, Texas

D. Bernard Amos, M.D. [4]
James B. Duke Professor of Immunology and Experimental Surgery; Chief, Division of Immunology, Department of Microbiology and Immunology, Duke University Medical Center, Durham, North Carolina

Donald C. Anderson, M.D. [113]
Professor of Pediatrics, Microbiology and Immunology and Cell Biology; Head, Section of Leukocyte Biology, Baylor College of Medicine, Houston, Texas

Thomas E. Andreoli, M.D. [78]
Professor and Chairman, Department of Internal Medicine, University of Arkansas for Medical Sciences, Little Rock, Arkansas

Irwin M. Arias, M.D. [53]
Chairman of Physiology, Department of Physiology and Medicine, Tufts University Medical School, Boston, Massachusetts

Gerd Assmann, M.D. [50, 64]
Professor of Clinical Chemistry; Director of the Institute for Clinical Chemistry and Laboratory Medicine, Central Laboratory; Director of the Institute for Arteriosclerosis Research, Westphalian-Wilhelms University, Münster, West Germany

Salvatore Auricchio, M.D. [121]
Professor of Pediatrics, Department of Pediatrics, and 2nd Faculty of Medicine, University of Naples, Naples, Italy

John A. Barranger, M.D., Ph.D. [67]
Professor of Pediatrics and Biochemistry, University of Southern California; Head, Division of Medical Genetics, Children's Hospital of Los Angeles, Los Angeles, California

Arthur L. Beaudet, M.D. [1, 63, 108]
Investigator, Howard Hughes Medical Institute; Professor, Institute for Molecular Genetics and Department of Pediatrics, Baylor College of Medicine, Houston, Texas

David M. O. Becroft, M. D. [43]
Pathologist in Charge, Princess Mary Hospital for Children, Auckland, New Zealand

Pamela S. Becker, M.D., Ph.D. [95]
Fellow in Hematology, Yale University, School of Medicine, New Haven, Connecticut

Merrill D. Benson, M.D. [97]
Professor of Medicine and Medical Genetics, Indiana University School of Medicine, Indianapolis, Indiana

Michel Bergeron, M.D. [104]
Professor and Chairman, Department of Physiology, Faculty of Medicine, University of Montreal, Montreal, Canada

David F. Bishop, Ph.D. [70]
Associate Professor of Pediatrics and Genetics, Mount Sinai School of Medicine, New York, New York

Ingemar Bjorkhem, M.D., Ph.D. [51]
Professor, Department of Clinical Chemistry at Huddinge Hospital, Karolinska Institutet, Stockholm, Sweden

R. Michael Blaese, M.D. [110]
Deputy Chief, Metabolism Branch, National Cancer Institute, National Institutes of Health, Bethesda, Maryland

Thomas F. Boat, M.D. [108]
Professor and Chairman, Department of Pediatrics, University of North Carolina at Chapel Hill, Chapel Hill, North Carolina

Thomas H. Bothwell, M.D., D.Sc. [55]
Professor and Head of Department of Medicine, University of the Witwatersrand Medical School; Director, Medical Research Council Iron and Red Cell Metabolism Unit, Johannesburg, South Africa

Jan L. Breslow, M.D. [49]
Frederick Henry Leonhardt Professor, The Rockefeller University, New York, New York

H. Bryan Brewer, Jr., M.D. [50]
Chief, Molecular Disease Branch, National Heart, Lung, and Blood Institute, Bethesda, Maryland

Michael S. Brown, M.D. [48]
Paul J. Thomas Professor of Medicine and Genetics, University of Texas Southwestern Medical Center, Dallas, Texas

John D. Brunzell, M.D. [45]
Professor of Medicine, Division of Metabolism, Endocrinology and Nutrition, University of Washington, Seattle, Washington

Saul W. Brusilow, M.D. [20]
Professor of Pediatrics, The Johns Hopkins University School of Medicine, Baltimore, Maryland

Joseph L. Butler, M.D. [109]
Associate Professor of Pediatrics and Medicine, Division of Developmental and Clinical Immunology, Departments of Medicine, Pediatrics and Microbiology and The Comprehensive Cancer Center, University of Alabama at Birmingham, Birmingham, Alabama

Peter H. Byers, M.D. [115]
Professor, Departments of Pathology and Medicine (Medical Genetics), Center for Inherited Disease, University of Washington, Seattle, Washington

John W. Callahan, Ph.D. [66]
Associate Professor of Biochemistry and Pediatrics, Hospital for Sick Children, University of Toronto, Toronto, Canada

C. Thomas Caskey, M.D. [38]
Investigator, Howard Hughes Medical Institute; Professor and Director, Institute for Molecular Genetics, Baylor College of Medicine, Houston, Texas

Webster K. Cavenee, Ph.D. [9]
Director, Montreal Branch, Ludwig Institute for Cancer Research, Royal Victoria Hospital, Montreal, Canada

Robert W. Charlton, B.Sc., M.D. [55]
Senior Physician, Department of Medicine, University of the Witwatersrand Medical School, Johannesburg, South Africa

Winston W. Chen, Ph.D. [65]
Associate Professor of Neurology, The Johns Hopkins University, Baltimore, Maryland

Dominic Chung, Ph.D. [85]
Research Associate Professor, Department of Biochemistry, University of Washington, Seattle, Washington

James E. Cleaver, Ph.D. [120]
Professor of Radiology, Laboratory of Radiobiology and Environmental Health, University of California, San Francisco, California

J. B. Clegg, M.A., Ph.D. [93]
Reader, M. R. C. Molecular Haematology Unit, Nuffield Department of Clinical Medicine, University of Oxford, John Radcliffe Hospital, Oxford, England

Paul M. Coates, Ph.D. [33]
Research Associate Professor, Department of Pediatrics, University of Pennsylvania School of Medicine, Philadelphia, Pennsylvania

Harvey R. Colten, M.D. [111]
Harriet B. Spoehrer Professor and Chairman, Department of Pediatrics, Washington University School of Medicine, St. Louis, Missouri

Ernst Conzelmann, Ph.D. [72]
Wissenschaftlicher Assistant, Institute of Organic Chemistry and Biochemistry, Rheinische Friedrich-Wilhelms Universität, Bonn, Germany

David N. Cooper, B.Sc., Ph.D. [1]
Lecturer in Molecular Genetics, Haematology Department, King's College Hospital School of Medicine and Dentistry, University of London, London, England

Max D. Cooper, M.D., Ph.D [109]
Professor of Pediatrics and Microbiology, Division of Developmental and Clinical Immunology, Departments of Medicine, Pediatrics and Microbiology and The Comprehensive Cancer Center, University of Alabama at Birmingham, Birmingham, Alabama

Diane Wilson Cox, Ph.D. [96]
Professor, Research Institute, The Hospital for Sick Children; Departments of Paediatrics, Medical Genetics and Medical Biophysics, University of Toronto, Toronto, Canada

Rody P. Cox, M.D. [21]
Dean and Professor of Internal Medicine, University of Texas Southwest Medical Center at Dallas, Dallas, Texas

Joseph Dancis, M.D. [21]
Professor and Chairman, Department of Pediatrics, New York University School of Medicine, New York, New York

David M. Danks, M.D. [54]
Director, Murdoch Institute for Research into Birth Defects, Royal Children's Hospital; Professor of Pediatric Research, University of Melbourne, Melbourne, Australia

Dean J. Danner, Ph.D. [22]
Associate Professor, Division of Medical Genetics, Department of Pediatrics, Emory University School of Medicine, Atlanta, Georgia

Earl W. Davie, Ph.D. [84]
Professor of Biochemistry, University of Washington, Seattle, Washington

Thierry de Barsy, M.D. [12]
Professor, Laboratorire de Chimie Physiologique and Departement de Neuropsychiatrie, Faculté de Medecine, Université Catholique de Louvain, Brussels, Belgium

Jehan-François Desjeux, M.D. [98]
Chief, Research Unit on Intestinal Functions, Metabolism and Nutrition, Institut National de la Santé et de la Recherche Medicale, Paris, France

Robert J. Desnick, Ph.D., M.D. [70]
Arthur J. and Nellie Z. Cohen Professor of Pediatrics and Genetics; Chief, Division of Medical and Molecular Genetics, Mount Sinai School of Medicine, New York, New York

Thomas D. DuBose, Jr., M.D. [103]
Professor of Medicine, Physiology and Biophysics; Chief, Division of Nephrology, The University of Texas Medical Branch at Galveston, Galveston, Texas

J. E. Dumont, M.D., Ph.D. [73]
Professor of Biochemistry; Head, Institute of Interdisciplinary Research, School of Medicine, University of Brussels; Head, Euratom Radioprotection Contract, E.E.C., Brussels, Belgium

Bo Dupont, M.D. [74]
Professor of Immunology, Graduate School of Medicine; Director, Histocompatibility Testing Laboratory and Clinical Immunology Laboratory, Memorial Sloan-Kettering Cancer Center, New York, New York

John W. Eaton, Ph.D. [60]
Professor of Medicine, Laboratory Medicine and Pathology, Dight Laboratories, University of Minnesota, Minneapolis, Minnesota

Louis J. Elsas II, M.D. [22]
Professor, Division of Medical Genetics, Department of Pediatrics, Emory University School of Medicine, Atlanta, Georgia

Charles J. Epstein, M.D. [7]
Professor of Pediatrics and Biochemistry, University of California, San Francisco, California

Wayne A. Fenton, Ph.D. [29, 82]
Research Scientist in Human Genetics, Yale University School of Medicine, Department of Human Genetics, New Haven, Connecticut

Thomas B. Fitzpatrick, M.D., Ph.D., D.Sc. (Hon.) [119]
Wigglesworth Professor of Dermatology, Harvard Medical School, Massachusetts General Hospital, Boston, Massachusetts

Gebhard Flatz, M.D. [122]
Professor of Human Genetics, Department of Human Genetics, Medizinische Hochschule, Hannover, Germany

John R. Forehand, M.D. [114]
Assistant Professor, Department of Pediatrics, University of Pennsylvania School of Medicine and The Children's Hospital of Philadelphia, Philadelphia, Pennsylvania

Daniel W. Foster, M.D. [10]
The Jan and Henri Bromberg Professor and Chair, Internal Medicine, The University of Texas Southwestern Medical Center, Dallas, Texas

Irving H. Fox, M.D. [37]
Professor of Internal Medicine and Biological Chemistry; Director, Clinical Research Center, University of Michigan, University Hospital, Ann Arbor, Michigan

Frank E. Frerman, Ph.D. [30, 34]
Professor of Pediatrics and Microbiology, University of Colorado School of Medicine, Denver, Colorado

Kazuo Fujikawa, Ph.D. [88]
Research Professor, Department of Biochemistry, University of Washington School of Medicine, Seattle, Washington

William A. Gahl, M.D., Ph.D. [107]
Head, Section on Human Biochemical Genetics and Chief (Acting), Human Genetics Branch, National Institute of Child Health and Human Development, National Institutes of Health, Bethesda, Maryland

Richard A. Galbraith, M.D., Ph.D. [52]
Assistant Professor and Physician, The Rockefeller University, New York, New York

Edward I. Ginns, M.D., Ph.D. [67]
Head, Neurogenetics Section, Clinical Neuroscience Branch, National Institute of Mental Health, Bethesda, Maryland

Richard Gitzelmann, M.D. [11]
Professor, Division of Metabolism, University Pediatric
Department, Kinderspital Zurich, Zurich, Switzerland

Egil Gjone, M.D. [46]
Professor, Department of Medicine, Rikshospitalet
University Hospital, University of Oslo, Oslo, Norway

John A. Glomset, M.D. [46]
Professor, Howard Hughes Medical Institute Research
Laboratories/Seattle, University of Washington School of
Medicine, Seattle, Washington

Lowell A. Goldsmith, M.D. [16]
James H. Sterner Professor of Dermatology and Chairman,
Department of Dermatology, University of Rochester School
of Medicine and Dentistry, Rochester, New York

Joseph L. Goldstein, M.D. [48]
Paul J. Thomas Professor of Genetics and Chairman,
Department of Molecular Genetics, University of Texas
Southwestern Medical Center, Dallas, Texas

Stephen I. Goodman, M.D. [30, 34]
Professor of Pediatrics, University of Colorado School of
Medicine, Denver, Colorado

André Gougoux, M.D. [104]
Professor, Department of Medicine and Department of
Physiology, University of Montreal, Montreal, Canada

James E. Griffin, M.D. [75]
Associate Professor of Internal Medicine, The University of
Texas Southwestern Medical Center, Dallas, Texas

Peter S. Harper, M.D. [118]
Professor and Consultant in Medical Genetics, Institute of
Medical Genetics, University of Wales College of Medicine,
Cardiff, Wales

Richard J. Havel, M.D. [44]
Director, Cardiovascular Research Institute and Professor of
Medicine, University of California School of Medicine, San
Francisco, California

Gregory S. Heard, Ph.D. [83]
Assistant Professor of Human Genetics, Department of
Human Genetics, Medical College of Virginia, Richmond,
Virginia

Ulla Hedner, M.D. [84]
Professor of Clinical Coagulation, University of Goteborg,
Sweden; Director of Hematology Research, Novo Industri
A/S, Bagsvaerd, Denmark

Henry-Géry Hers [12]
Professor of Biochemistry, Laboratoire de Chimie
Physiologique, Université Catholique de Louvain and
International Institute of Cellular and Molecular Pathology,
Brussels, Belgium

Michael S. Hershfield, M.D. [40]
Associate Professor of Medicine and Assistant Professor of
Biochemistry, Duke University Medical Center, Durham,
North Carolina

Howard H. Hiatt, M.D. [14]
Professor of Medicine, Harvard Medical School; Professor of
Medicine, Harvard School of Public Health; Senior
Physician, Brigham & Women's Hospital, Boston,
Massachusetts

D. R. Higgs, M.B., B.S. [93]
Honorary Consultant in Haematology, Nuffield Department
of Clinical Medicine, University of Oxford, John Radcliffe
Hospital, Oxford, England

Richard E. Hillman, M.D. [35]
Professor of Child Health and Biochemistry; Director of
Metabolic Genetics, University of Missouri Hospital and
Clinics, Columbia, Missouri

Edward W. Holmes, M.D. [41, 42]
Professor of Medicine, Associate Professor of Biochemistry,
Division of Metabolism, Endocrinology and Genetics, Duke
University Medical Center, Durham, North Carolina

Arthur L. Horwich, M.D. [20]
Associate Professor of Human Genetics and Pediatrics, Yale
University School of Medicine, New Haven, Connecticut

Donald E. Hultquist, Ph.D. [92]
Professor of Biological Chemistry, University of Michigan
Medical School, Ann Arbor, Michigan

Akitada Ichinose, M.D., Ph.D. [85]
Research Assistant Professor, Department of Biochemistry,
University of Washington, Seattle, Washington

Ernst R. Jaffé, M.D. [92]
Distinguished University Professor of Medicine, Albert
Einstein College of Medicine, Bronx, New York

Jean L. Johnson, Ph.D. [56]
Assistant Medical Research Professor, Department of
Biochemistry, Duke University Medical Center, Durham,
North Carolina

Richard B. Johnston, Jr., M.D.   [114]
William H. Bennett Professor and Chairman, Department of Pediatrics, University of Pennsylvania School of Medicine and The Children's Hospital of Philadelphia, Philadelphia, Pennsylvania

Michael M. Kaback, M.D.   [72]
Professor and Chairman, Department of Pediatrics, University of California San Diego School of Medicine, San Diego, California

John P. Kane, M.D., Ph.D.   [44]
Professor of Medicine; Professor of Biochemistry and Biophysics, University of California, School of Medicine, San Francisco, California

Attallah Kappas, M.D.   [52]
Sherman Fairchild Professor, Vice-President and Physician-in-Chief, The Rockefeller University, New York, New York

Seymour Kaufman, Ph.D.   [15]
Chief, Laboratory of Neurochemistry, National Institute of Mental Health, Bethesda, Maryland

Richard A. King, M.D., Ph.D.   [119]
Professor, Department of Medicine and Institute of Human Genetics, University of Minnesota School of Dentistry, Minneapolis, Minnesota

Edwin H. Kolodny, M.D.   [69]
Professor of Neurology, Harvard Medical School, Boston; Director, Eunice Kennedy Shriver Center for Mental Retardation, Inc., Waltham, Massachusetts

Donna D. Kostyu, Ph.D.   [4]
Assistant Medical Research Professor, Department of Microbiology and Immunology, Duke University Medical Center, Durham, North Carolina

Kenneth H. Kraemer, M.D.   [120]
Research Scientist, Laboratory of Molecular Carcinogenesis, National Cancer Institute, National Institutes of Health, Bethesda, Maryland

Nicholas M. Kredich, M.D.   [40]
Professor of Medicine and Biochemistry, Duke University Medical Center, Durham, North Carolina

Claude Laberge, M.D.   [16]
Professor of Genetic Medicine, Laval University Medical Center, Department of Medicine, Quebec, Canada

Bert N. La Du, Jr., M.D., Ph.D.   [27]
Professor, Department of Pharmacology, University of Michigan Medical School, Ann Arbor, Michigan

Jean Marc Lalouel, M.D., D.Sc.   [6]
Professor, Department of Human Genetics; Investigator, Howard Hughes Medical Institute, University of Utah Medical Center, Salt Lake City, Utah

Agne Larsson, M.D.   [31]
Department of Pediatrics, University Hospital, Uppsala, Sweden

Richard M. Lawn, Ph.D.   [86]
Staff Scientist, Department of Cardiovascular Research, Genentech, Inc., South San Francisco, California

Paul B. Lazarow, Ph.D.   [57]
Associate Professor, The Rockefeller University, New York, New York

David H. Ledbetter, Ph.D.   [8, 9]
Associate Professor, Institute for Molecular Genetics, Baylor College of Medicine, Houston, Texas

Harvey L. Levy, M.D.   [17, 23, 101]
Associate Professor of Neurology, Harvard Medical School; Assistant Neurologist and Pediatrician, Massachusetts General Hospital, Boston, Massachusetts

Samuel E. Lux, M.D.   [95]
Chief, Division of Hematology and Oncology, The Children's Hospital, Boston, Massachusetts

Lucio Luzzatto, M.D.   [91]
Professor of Hematology, Royal Postgraduate Medical School; Consultant Hematologist, Hammersmith Hospital, University of London, London, England

Robert W. Mahley, M.D., Ph.D.   [47]
Director, Gladstone Foundation Laboratories for Cardiovascular Disease, Cardiovascular Research Institute, Departments of Pathology and Medicine, University of California, San Francisco, California

Philip W. Majerus, M.D.   [90]
Professor of Medicine and Biological Chemistry, Washington University School of Medicine, St. Louis, Missouri

Stephen J. Marx, M.D.   [80]
Chief, Mineral Metabolism Section, National Institute of Diabetes, and Digestive and Kidney Diseases, National Institutes of Health, Bethesda, Maryland

Edward R. B. McCabe, M.D., Ph.D.   [36]
Associate Professor of Molecular Genetics and Pediatrics; Director, Robert J. Kleberg, Jr., Clinical Center, Institute for Molecular Genetics, Baylor College of Medicine, Houston, Texas

Rodger P. McEver, M.D. [90]
Investigator, St. Francis Medical Research Institute and Associate Professor of Medicine, University of Oklahoma Health Sciences Center; Affiliated Associate Member, Oklahoma Medical Research Foundation, Oklahoma City, Oklahoma

Victor A. McKusick, M.D. [1]
University Professor of Medical Genetics, The Johns Hopkins University School of Medicine; Physician, The Johns Hopkins Hospital, Baltimore, Maryland

Atul Mehta, M.D. [91]
Consultant Hematologist, Department of Hematology, Royal Free Hospital, University of London, London, England

Alton Meister, M.D. [31]
Professor and Chairman, Department of Biochemistry, Cornell University Medical College, New York, New York

Ann B. Moser, A.B. [58, 65]
Assistant in Neurology, The Johns Hopkins University, Baltimore, Maryland

Hugo W. Moser, M.D. [57, 58, 65]
University Professor of Neurology and Pediatrics, The Johns Hopkins University; Director, Neurogenetics Unit, John F. Kennedy Institute for Handicapped Children, Baltimore, Maryland

Björn Mossberg, M.D. [112]
Associate Professor, Department of Medicine 1, South Hospital, Stockholm, Sweden

Arno G. Motulsky, M.D., Sc.D. [55]
Professor of Medicine and Genetics; Director, Center for Inherited Diseases, University of Washington, Seattle, Washington

S. Harvey Mudd, M.D. [23]
Chief, Section on Alkaloid Biosynthesis, Laboratory of General and Comparative Biochemistry, National Institute of Mental Health, Bethesda, Maryland

Joseph Muenzer, M.D., Ph.D. [61]
Assistant Professor, Department of Pediatrics, The University of Michigan Medical School, Ann Arbor, Michigan

William M. Nauseef, M.D. [114]
Associate Professor, Department of Internal Medicine, College of Medicine, University of Iowa, Iowa City, Iowa

Elizabeth F. Neufeld, Ph.D. [61, 72]
Professor and Chair, Department of Biological Chemistry, University of California Los Angeles School of Medicine, Los Angeles, California

Maria I. New, M.D. [74]
Harold and Percy Uris Professor of Pediatric Endocrinology and Metabolism; Chief of Pediatric Endocrinology; Chairman, Department of Pediatrics, The New York Hospital–Cornell Medical Center, New York, New York

Catherine M. Nolan, Ph.D. [62]
Research Associate, Edward A. Doisy Department of Biochemistry and Molecular Biology, St. Louis University School of Medicine, St. Louis, Missouri

Yves Nordmann, M.D. [52]
Professor and Chief, French Center of Porphyria (Hospital Louis Mourier), Faculty Xavier Bichat University, Paris, France

Kaare R. Norum, M.D. [46]
Professor, Institute for Nutrition Research, School of Medicine, University of Oslo, Oslo, Norway

Robert L. Nussbaum, M.D. [8]
Associate Investigator, Howard Hughes Medical Institute; Assistant Professor, Departments of Human Genetics and Pediatrics, University of Pennsylvania School of Medicine, Philadelphia, Pennsylvania

William L. Nyhan, M.D., Ph.D. [25]
Professor, Department of Pediatrics, University of California, San Diego School of Medicine, La Jolla, California

John S. O'Brien, M.S., M.D. [71]
Professor, Department of Neurosciences, University of California, San Diego School of Medicine, La Jolla, California

Stuart H. Orkin, M.D. [2]
Leland Fikes Professor of Pediatric Medicine, Harvard Medical School; Investigator, Howard Hughes Medical Institute, Boston, Massachusetts

Donald E. Paglia, M.D. [94]
Professor, Department of Pathology, University of California School of Medicine, Los Angeles, California

Thomas D. Palella, M.D. [37]
Assistant Professor of Internal Medicine; Chief, Division of Rheumatology; Director, Rackham Arthritis Research Unit, University of Michigan School of Medicine, Ann Arbor, Michigan

Songya Pang, M.D. [74]
Professor of Pediatrics, Division of Pediatric Endocrinology, University of Illinois School of Medicine, Chicago, Illinois

Morag Park, Ph.D. [5]
Head of Molecular Oncology Section, Ludwig Institute for Cancer Research, Montreal, Canada

Thomas L. Perry, M.D. [26]
Professor, Department of Pharmacology and Therapeutics, University of British Columbia, Vancouver, Canada

James M. Phang, M.D. [18]
Chief, Endocrinology Section, Metabolism Branch, National Cancer Institute, National Institutes of Health, Bethesda, Maryland

John A. Phillips, III, M.D. [77]
Professor of Pediatrics and Biochemistry; Director, Division of Genetics, Vanderbilt University School of Medicine, Nashville, Tennessee

Walter C. Quevedo, Jr., Ph.D. [119]
Professor of Biology, Division of Biology and Medicine, Brown University, Providence, Rhode Island

Stanley C. Rall, Jr., Ph.D. [47]
Senior Scientist, Gladstone Foundation Laboratories for Cardiovascular Disease, Cardiovascular Research Institute, University of California, San Francisco, California

Howard Rasmussen, M.D., Ph.D. [105]
Professor of Medicine, Cell Biology and Physiology, Department of Internal Medicine, Yale University School of Medicine, New Haven, Connecticut

W. Brian Reeves, M.D. [78]
Assistant Professor, Department of Internal Medicine, Division of Nephrology, University of Arkansas for Medical Sciences, Little Rock, Arkansas

Samuel Refetoff, M.D. [73]
Professor of Medicine and Pediatrics, University of Chicago, Chicago, Illinois

Martin Renlund, M.D. [107]
Attending Neonatologist, Department of Obstetrics, Helsinki University Hospital; Researcher, Finnish Academy of Science, Helsinki, Finland

Brian H. Robinson, Ph.D. [32]
Professor, Departments of Biochemistry and Pediatrics, University of Toronto and Research Institute, The Hospital for Sick Children, Toronto, Canada

Charles R. Roe, M.D. [33]
Professor, Department of Pediatrics, Duke University School of Medicine, Durham, North Carolina

Leon E. Rosenberg, M.D. [29, 82]
Dean, School of Medicine; C. N. H. Long Professor of Human Genetics, Professor of Pediatrics and Internal Medicine, Yale University School of Medicine, New Haven, Connecticut

David S. Rosenblatt, M.D. [81]
Director, Division of Medical Genetics, Department of Medicine, McGill University; Principal Investigator, Medical Research Council of Canada Genetics Group; Professor, Medicine and Pediatrics, McGill University, Montreal, Canada

Jayanta Roy Chowdhury, M.D. [53]
Professor of Medicine and Director, Division of Gastroenterology, Albert Einstein College of Medicine, Bronx, New York

David D. Sabatini, M.D., Ph.D. [3]
Frederick L. Ehrman Professor and Chairman, Department of Cell Biology, New York University School of Medicine, New York, New York

Richard L. Sabina, Ph.D. [41]
Assistant Professor, Department of Anatomy and Cellular Biology, Medical College of Wisconsin, Milwaukee, Wisconsin

J. Evan Sadler, M.D., Ph.D. [87]
Associate Investigator, Howard Hughes Medical Institute and Departments of Medicine and Biological Chemistry, Washington University School of Medicine, St. Louis, Missouri

Amrik S. Sahota, Ph.D. [39]
Research Associate, Department of Medical Genetics, Indiana University Medical Center, Indianapolis, Indiana

Hidehiko Saito, M.D. [88]
Professor, First Department of Internal Medicine, Nagoya University School of Medicine, Nagoya, Japan

Konrad Sandhoff, Ph.D. [72]
Professor and Director, Institute of Organic Chemistry and Biochemistry, Rheinische Friedrich-Wilhelms Universität, Bonn, Germany

Shigeru Sassa, M.D., Ph.D. [52]
Associate Professor and Physician, The Rockefeller University, New York, New York

Jörg Schmidke, M.D. [1]
Professor, Institute of Human Genetics, University of Gottingen, Gottingen, West Germany

Gerd Schmitz, M.D. [50, 64]
Privatdozent, Institut für Klinische Chemie und Laboratoriumsmedizin, Westphalian-Wilhelms University, Münster, West Germany

Andre W. Schram, Ph.D. [65]
Senior Scientific Officer, Department of Biochemistry, Academic Medical Center, Amsterdam, The Netherlands

C. Ronald Scott, M.D.   [24]
Professor, Department of Pediatrics, University of
Washington School of Medicine, Seattle, Washington

Charles R. Scriver, M.D.C.M.   [1, 15, 18, 26, 102]
Professor of Biology, Human Genetics and Pediatrics,
Departments of Biology and Pediatrics and Center for
Human Genetics, McGill University, Montreal, Canada

Stanton Segal, M.D.   [13, 99]
Professor of Pediatrics and Medicine, University of
Pennsylvania School of Medicine; Director, Division of
Biochemical Development and Molecular Diseases,
Children's Hospital of Philadelphia, Philadelphia,
Pennsylvania

Giorgio Semenza, M.D.   [121]
Professor of Biochemistry, Co-chairman, Department of
Biochemistry, ETH, Zurich, Switzerland

Larry J. Shapiro, M.D.   [76]
Professor of Pediatrics and Biological Chemistry, UCLA
School of Medicine; Investigator, Howard Hughes Medical
Institute; Chief, Division of Medical Genetics, Harbor/UCLA
Medical Center, Torrance, California

Olli Simell, M.D.   [19, 100]
Professor and Chairman, Department of Pediatrics,
University of Turku Hospital, Turku, Finland

H. Anne Simmonds, Ph.D.   [39]
Director, Purine Research Laboratory, UMDS Guy's & St.
Thomas' Hospitals, London, England

Flemming Skovby, M.D.   [23]
Associate Professor of Pediatrics, Section of Clinical Genetics,
Department of Pediatrics, Rigshospitalet, University of
Copenhagen, Copenhagen, Denmark

Sverre Skrede, M.D.   [51]
(*Deceased, March 10, 1987*) Institute of Clinical
Biochemistry, Rikshospitalet, University of Oslo, Oslo,
Norway

William S. Sly, M.D.   [1, 62, 117]
Alice A. Doisy Professor of Biochemistry and Professor of
Pediatrics; Chairman, Edward A. Doisy Department of
Biochemistry and Molecular Biology, St. Louis University
School of Medicine, St. Louis, Missouri

C. Wayne Smith, M.D.   [113]
Associate Professor of Pediatrics, Baylor College of Medicine,
Houston, Texas

Phyllis W. Speiser, M.D.   [74]
Assistant Professor of Pediatrics, Division of Pediatric
Endocrinology; Associate Program Director of the Pediatric
Clinical Research Center, The New York Hospital–Cornell
Medical Center, New York, New York

Matthew W. Spence, M.D., Ph.D.   [66]
Director, Atlantic Research Centre for Mental Retardation;
Professor of Pediatrics and Biochemistry, Dalhousie
University, Halifax, Nova Scotia, Canada

Oded Sperling, Ph.D.   [106]
Professor of Chemical Pathology and Chairman of the
Department of Chemical Pathology, Sackler School of
Medicine, Tel-Aviv University; Director of Clinical
Biochemistry and Chairman of the Division of Laboratories,
Beilinson Medical Center, Petah Tekva, Israel

Allen M. Spiegel, M.D.   [79]
Chief, Molecular Pathophysiology Branch, National Institute
of Diabetes, Digestive, and Kidney Diseases, National
Institutes of Health, Bethesda, Maryland

Timothy A. Springer, Ph.D.   [113]
Associate Professor of Pathology, Center for Blood Research,
Harvard Medical School, Boston, Massachusetts

Daniel Steinberg, M.D., Ph.D   [59]
Professor, Department of Medicine and Head, Division of
Endocrinology and Metabolism, University of California, San
Diego, School of Medicine, La Jolla, California

Beat Steinmann, M.D.   [11]
Privatdozent, Division of Metabolism, Department of
Pediatrics, University of Zurich, Kinderspital Zurich,
Zurich, Switzerland

J. Timothy Stout, Ph.D.   [38]
Institute for Molecular Genetics, Baylor College of Medicine,
Houston, Texas

D. Parker Suttle, Ph.D.   [43]
Assistant Member, Division of Biochemical and Clinical
Pharmacology, St. Jude's Children's Research Hospital,
Memphis, Tennessee

Kinuko Suzuki, M.D.   [72]
Professor, Department of Pathology, School of Medicine,
University of North Carolina, Chapel Hill, North Carolina

Kunihiko Suzuki, M.D.   [68]
Professor of Neurology and Psychiatry; Director, Biological
Sciences Research Center, University of North Carolina
School of Medicine, Chapel Hill, North Carolina

Yoshiyuki Suzuki, M.D. [68]
Vice Director, The Tokyo Metropolitan Institute of Medical Science, Tokyo, Japan

Judith L. Swain, M.D. [41]
Associate Professor of Medicine, Assistant Professor of Microbiology, Duke University Medical Center, Durham, North Carolina

Lawrence Sweetman, Ph.D. [28]
Professor of Pediatrics, Department of Pediatrics, University of California School of Medicine, San Diego, La Jolla, California

Kouichi R. Tanaka, M.D. [94]
Professor of Medicine, University of California School of Medicine, Los Angeles, California; Chief, Division of Hematology, Department of Medicine, Harbor-UCLA Medical Center, Torrance, California

Harriet S. Tenenhouse, Ph.D. [105]
Associate Professor of Pediatrics, McGill University; Associate Professor, McGill Center for Human Genetics; Auxiliary Professor of Biology, McGill University, Montreal, Canada

Samuel O. Thier, M.D. [99]
President, Institute of Medicine, National Academy of Sciences, Washington, D.C.

Jess G. Thoene, M.D. [107]
Professor, Departments of Pediatrics and Biological Chemistry, University of Michigan Medical School, Ann Arbor, Michigan

George H. Thomas, Ph.D. [63]
Associate Professor of Pediatrics, The Johns Hopkins University School of Medicine; Director, The Kennedy Institute Genetics Laboratory, Baltimore, Maryland

Douglas M. Tollefsen, M.D., Ph.D. [89]
Associate Professor of Medicine, Hematology-Oncology Division, Washington University Medical School, St. Louis, Missouri

Edward G. D. Tuddenham, M.D. [86]
Director, Haemostasis Research Group, Medical Research Council (U.K.) Clinical Research Centre, Harrow, Middlesex, England

William N. Valentine, M.D. [94]
Professor Emeritus, Department of Medicine, University of California Center for Health Sciences, Los Angeles, California

David Valle, M.D. [1, 19]
Investigator, Howard Hughes Medical Institute; Professor of Pediatrics, Medicine, and Molecular Biology & Genetics, The Johns Hopkins University School of Medicine, Baltimore, Maryland

Karel J. Van Acker, M.D. [39]
Professor, Department of Pediatrics, University of Antwerp, Wilrijk, Belgium

Georges Van den Berghe, M.D. [11]
Research Director, Laboratory of Physiological Chemistry, International Institute of Cellular and Molecular Pathology, Brussels; Consultant Physician, Department of Pediatrics, University of Leuven, Leuven, Belgium

George F. Vande Woude, Ph.D. [5]
Director, BRI-Basic Research Program, NCI-Frederick Cancer Research Facility, Frederick, Maryland

François Van Hoof, M.D. [12]
Professor of Biochemistry, Laboratoire de Chimie Physiologique, Université Catholique de Louvain and International Institute of Cellular and Molecular Pathology, Brussels, Belgium

Gilbert Vassart, M.D., Ph.D. [73]
Head, Molecular Genetics, Institute of Interdisciplinary Research and Department of Medical Genetics, Hospital Erasme, University of Brussels, Belgium

Gordon A. Vehar, Ph.D. [86]
Director, Department of Cardiovascular Research, Genentech, Inc., South San Francisco, California

Sybe K. Wadman, Ph.D. [56]
Professor of Biochemistry of Inherited Metabolic Disease, University Children's Hospital, Het Wilhelmina Kinderziekenhuis, Utrecht, The Netherlands

Margaret R. Wallace, Ph.D. [97]
Associate, Howard Hughes Medical Institute, University of Michigan, Ann Arbor, Michigan

D. J. Weatherall, M.D. [93]
Nuffield Professor of Medicine, Nuffield Department of Clinical Medicine, University of Oxford, John Radcliffe Hospital, Oxford, England

Dianne R. Webster, Ph.D. [43]
Deputy Director, National Testing Center, Auckland, New Zealand

Michael Welsh, M.D. [108]
Professor, Pulmonary Disease Division, Department of Internal Medicine, University of Iowa College of Medicine, Iowa City, Iowa

Perrin C. White, M.D.   [74]
Assistant Professor of Pediatrics, Division of Pediatric Endocrinology; Director, Laboratory of Molecular Endocrinology, The New York Hospital–Cornell Medical Center, New York, New York

Ray White, Ph.D.   [6]
Professor and Co-Chairman, Department of Human Genetics; Investigator, Howard Hughes Medical Institute, University of Utah Medical Center, Salt Lake City, Utah

Michael P. Whyte, M.D.   [116]
Associate Professor of Medicine, Division of Bone and Mineral Diseases, Departments of Medicine and Pediatrics, The Jewish Hospital of St. Louis, Washington University School of Medicine; Director, Metabolic Research Unit, Shriners Hospital for Crippled Children, St. Louis, Missouri

Jean D. Wilson, M.D.   [75]
Professor of Internal Medicine, The University of Texas Southwestern Medical Center, Dallas, Texas

Jerry Winkelstein, M.D.   [111]
Eudowood Professor of Pediatrics, Director, Division of Allergy and Immunology, The Department of Pediatrics, The Johns Hopkins University School of Medicine, Baltimore, Maryland

Carl J. Witkop, Jr., D.D.S., M.S.   [119]
Professor and Chairman, Division of Human Genetics, University of Minnesota School of Dentistry, Minneapolis, Minnesota

Barry Wolf, M.D., Ph.D.   [83]
Professor, Departments of Human Genetics and Pediatrics, Medical College of Virginia, Richmond, Virginia

Allan W. Wolkoff, M.D.   [53]
Professor of Medicine, Albert Einstein College of Medicine, Bronx, New York

Savio L. C. Woo, Ph.D.   [15]
Professor, Department of Cell Biology and Molecular Genetics; Investigator, Howard Hughes Medical Institute, Baylor College of Medicine, Houston, Texas

W. G. Wood, Ph.D.   [93]
Senior Scientist, M.R.C. Molecular Haematology Unit, Nuffield Department of Clinical Medicine, University of Oxford, John Radcliffe Hospital, Oxford, England

William I. Wood, Ph.D.   [86]
Senior Scientist, Department of Development Biology, Genentech, Inc., South San Francisco, California

James B. Wyngaarden, M.D.   [42]
Director, National Institutes of Health, Bethesda, Maryland

This edition of *The Metabolic Basis of Inherited Disease* marks a transition, a changing of the guard, as it were, among the editors. The sixth edition also reflects a transformation in the field of endeavor it encompasses; and there is a challenge too—for future editions. Transitions can be difficult and transformations sometimes produce unhappy results; neither need be the case here. Challenges can invigorate.

THE TRANSITION

Stanbury-Wyngaarden-'n-Fredrickson, collectively, were one famous "author" known to everyone in the field. This extraordinary editorial organism piloted the novel and timely book they had introduced and then edited through four successful editons. By a remarkable fision—or was it fusion?—the fifth edition was placed under the care of Stanbury-Wyngaarden-'n-Fredrickson, Goldstein 'n Brown. Now that giant has stepped aside, handing the challenge to a new team. The new editors have discovered how great the former ones were—if they hadn't known it before. Very large shoes had to be filled!

THE TRANSFORMATION

The sixth edition has many new features, notably the evidence of molecular genetics in one chapter after another. If *The Metabolic Basis of Inherited Disease* has had an abiding rationale, it was that the cause of all diseases listed in it was Mendelian and the diseases (so-called inborn errors of metabolism) were exceptions to be treasured for their illumination of human biology and for the insight they gave into pathogenesis of disease. But always there was a feeling that one did not understand cause as well as one should because not much was known about the genes. That situation is changing. There are new data about loci and structure of numerous normal genes and about the mutations affecting the phenotype encoded by them.

With 31 new chapters, the book is approximately one third larger than it was. Accordingly this edition appears for the first time in a two-volume format. It is a change undertaken with reluctance, but size of type, weight of paper, and the like had been adapted to the limit in the previous edition to accommodate the mass of information presented there. We elected to revise and print all chapters instead of using a précis of some, as in the last edition. Authors were encouraged to focus on up-to-date material and to use previous editions as archives of older material. But the wealth of new information neutralized contraction of the old. Hence the option taken here; to divide the book into two volumes, between separate covers.

New topics in the sixth edition include the following: There is a formal discussion of gene mapping and the medical use of genome markers (Chap. 6). Down syndrome (Chap. 7) and fragile X syndrome (Chap. 8) illustrate how any genetic disorder can eventually accommodate to our views of molecular genetics. They are the thin edge of the wedge toward understanding a great deal about human genetic disease and the editors introduce these chapters with some trepidation, realizing they could well be the very thin edge of a very big wedge—one of our challenges for future editions. One new chapter (122) covers the lactase deficiency polymorphism in whites. This disorder does not fit the paradigm of a rare inborn error because it is so common; on the other hand, it does represent a Mendelian disadaptive phenotype for some individuals. There is a whole new section on peroxisomal diseases (Chaps. 57–60) and Chap. 3 covers organelle biogenesis. Contiguous gene syndromes appear in this edition for the first time. The retinoblastoma story (Chap. 9) began as a contiguous gene syndrome; the new chapter encompasses this and analogous phenomena. Chap. 5 on oncogenes is new. The genes for retinoblastoma, chronic granulomatosus disease, and Duchenne muscular dystrophy are now known through techniques of "reverse" or "indirect" genetics. They are harbingers of what is to come in other diseases and they are topics developed at some length in this edition. Two appendices to Chap. 1, experiments in this edition, list: (1) the Mendelian disorders that can be diagnosed at the DNA level through oligonucleotide probes or by tightly linked markers that associate with alleles encoding mutant gene products; useful probes and their sources are catalogued in this appendix and (2) the mapped loci and their chromosomal assignments, the most current version of Victor McKusick's famous catalog available as we went to press. Perhaps a future edition will also catalog what we know about the mutant alleles at the loci encoding disease. Meanwhile the summary table grows in Chapter 1. It was introduced for the first time in the fifth edition and it is continued here for two reasons: first to show, in a simple manner, the growth of subject material between the last and present editions; second, to show how the white spaces in the fifth edition table are being filled in.

THE CHALLENGE

The future holds the potential for a separate chapter delineating the biochemical basis of each variant listed in *McKusick's Mendelian Inheritance in Man*. If this is the case, there will be many hundred chapters in subsequent editions of MBID. In addition, most monogenic disorders are not monogenic but modified through other loci by definable biochemical mechanisms; and most diseases are caused by polygenic and multifactorial mechanisms which also have a biochemical basis. Cytogenetic disorders have a biochemical basis as well, and in some instances the phenotypes may be determined by one or a few loci. These all represent effects of the constitutional genotype on the phenotype, but there is also the role of somatic mutation in the pathogenesis of malignancies whether inherited or sporadic. With the explosion of information virtually assured, the challenge of how to focus and mold future editions is a daunting one.

This book has not grown unattended. In addition to the herculean efforts of some 200 authors and their assistants, others assured a safe passage during the development of the book, notably Dereck Jeffers and Gail Gavert at McGraw-Hill; Loy Denis, who served as coordinator for the editors and authors; and our own assistants: Lynne Prevost and Huguette Rizziéro (CRS), Grace Watson (AB), Elizabeth Torno (WS), and Sandy Muscelli (DV). But especially we thank our extraordinary predecessors for their nurture and care of a book many of us have come to admire and need. If this edition meets with the approval of its former editors, we will have partially done the job we acquired; the readers will ultimately decide whether it was done satisfactorily.

Last, an acknowledgement to our families; they know more about this book than they bargained for. . . !

Charles R. Scriver
Arthur L. Beaudet
William S. Sly
David Valle

SIXTH EDITION

THE
METABOLIC BASIS
OF
INHERITED DISEASE

PART 10

PEROXISOMES

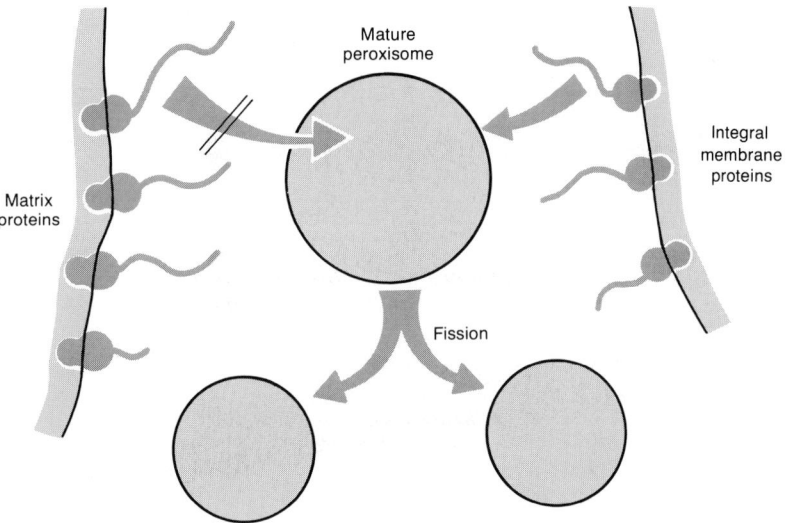

Mature peroxisome

Matrix proteins

Integral membrane proteins

Fission

Disorders of peroxisomal function

CHAPTER 57

DISORDERS OF PEROXISOME BIOGENESIS

PAUL B. LAZAROW
HUGO W. MOSER

INTRODUCTION AND HISTORY

In 1964 Bowen et al. described an apparently similar pattern of multiple malformations apparent at birth in two unrelated pairs of sibs in Iowa and Maryland.[1] Major abnormalities included severe hypotonia, high forehead, a large anterior fontanelle; midface hypoplasia; glaucoma, cloudy corneas, and cataracts; multiple joint contractures; an enlarged liver; chondrodysplasia punctata; and multiple subcapsular cysts in the kidney. Passarge and McAdams reported five similarly affected sisters and introduced the name *cerebro-hepato-renal syndrome*.[2]

Opitz et al. reappraised the Bowen report in 1969[3] and concluded that while the Iowa and Maryland cases did not represent the same entity, the Iowa cases were similar to those reported by Smith et al.,[4] Punnett and Kirkpatrick,[5] and Passarge and McAdams.[2] In recognition of Hans Zellweger's seminal role in identifying the Iowa cases, Opitz proposed the name *Zellweger cerebro-hepato-renal syndrome*,[6] and this is now the generally accepted designation. Hundreds of similar cases have been reported or referred to[6] including three cases reported prior to 1964 which, in retrospect, are examples of Zellweger syndrome.[7] Wilson et al. have presented a clinical analysis of 90 cases,[8] and Heymans has summarized 114 cases reported in the literature.[9]

In 1969 the Zellweger syndrome was assigned by Opitz to the "multiple congenital anomaly" disease category.[3] In 1973 Goldfischer et al. provided the first evidence that it should be reassigned to the metabolic category when they reported that Zellweger patients lacked demonstrable peroxisomes in liver and kidney and that the mitochondria were also structurally and functionally abnormal.[10] The deficiency of peroxisomes has been confirmed in all subsequent studies, but the nature of the mitochondrial defect has been found to be variable[11,12] and is now considered to be secondary to the lack of peroxisomes. The significance of the peroxisome defect was highlighted when it was demonstrated that the first two steps of ether-glycerolipid biosynthesis, which Hajra had localized to the peroxisome,[13,14] are deficient in all Zellweger patients.[15–18] Zellweger patients also show defects in other reactions known to be localized to this organelle. These include the degradation of very long chain fatty acids,[19–21] the metabolism of bile acid intermediates,[22,23] and the catabolism of pipecolic acid.[24] It is the congruence of the anatomic finding—lack of peroxi-

somes—and the biochemical results—deficiencies of biochemical reactions known to be localized to this organelle—that has led to the general acceptance that the peroxisomal defect is the primary abnormality in the Zellweger syndrome. Opitz has emphasized the significance of this conclusion for the quest to understand the mechanisms of human malformations:

> Now, 20 years after discovery of the Zellweger syndrome, it has undergone one of the most dramatic of changes in modern medical history, namely [reassignment], from that of a true multiple congenital anomaly (i.e., static nonmetabolic malformation) syndrome to the metabolic dysplasia–malformation category. Simply a semantic difference? No, rather a true one of such fundamental importance that the very concept "Zellweger syndrome" has become paradigmatic of a whole new class of genetic disorders.[6]

Recently it has been shown that deficiencies of peroxisome structure and multiple peroxisomal biochemical defects also exist in somewhat more mildly involved patients diagnosed as having neonatal adrenoleukodystrophy (ALD),[25] infantile Refsum disease,[26] hyperpipecolic acidemia,[27–29] and one type of Leber congenital amaurosis.[30] Recent results indicate that there is genetic as well as phenotypic heterogeneity. Failure of peroxisome biogenesis has been shown to represent the basic defect in the Zellweger syndrome, and complementation studies suggest that this is likely to be the case in the other peroxisome deficiency disorders as well. Therefore, we have taken the liberty of using the term "disorders of peroxisome biogenesis" for this group of diseases.

PEROXISOME PROPERTIES, APPEARANCE, AND DISTRIBUTION

Peroxisomes are probably present in most, if not all, mammalian cells other than mature erythrocytes, but their size and abundance vary considerably.[31,32] Liver (Fig. 57-1A and B) and kidney are tissues in which peroxisomes are particularly abundant. In these tissues, peroxisomes appear in transmission electron microscopy as round or oval organelles, bounded by one membrane, with an average diameter of approximately 0.5 μm (range 0.2 to 1 μm). In rat liver, but not in human liver, a characteristic crystalloid inclusion facilitates their identification. Peroxisome ultrastructure has been reviewed by Hruban and Rechcigl.[33]

Nonstandard abbreviations used in this chapter are: ALD = adrenoleukodystrophy; DHAP = dihydroxyacetone phosphate; DHAPAT = acyl-CoA:dihydroxyacetone phosphate acyltransferase; DHCA = 3α,7α-dihydroxy-5β-cholestanoic acid; ER = endoplasmic reticulum; HMG-CoA = hydroxymethylglutaryl-CoA; RCDP = rhizomelic chondrodysplasia punctata; THCA = 3α,7α,12α-trihydroxy-5β-cholestanoic acid; VLCFA = very long chain fatty acids ($\geq C_{24}$).

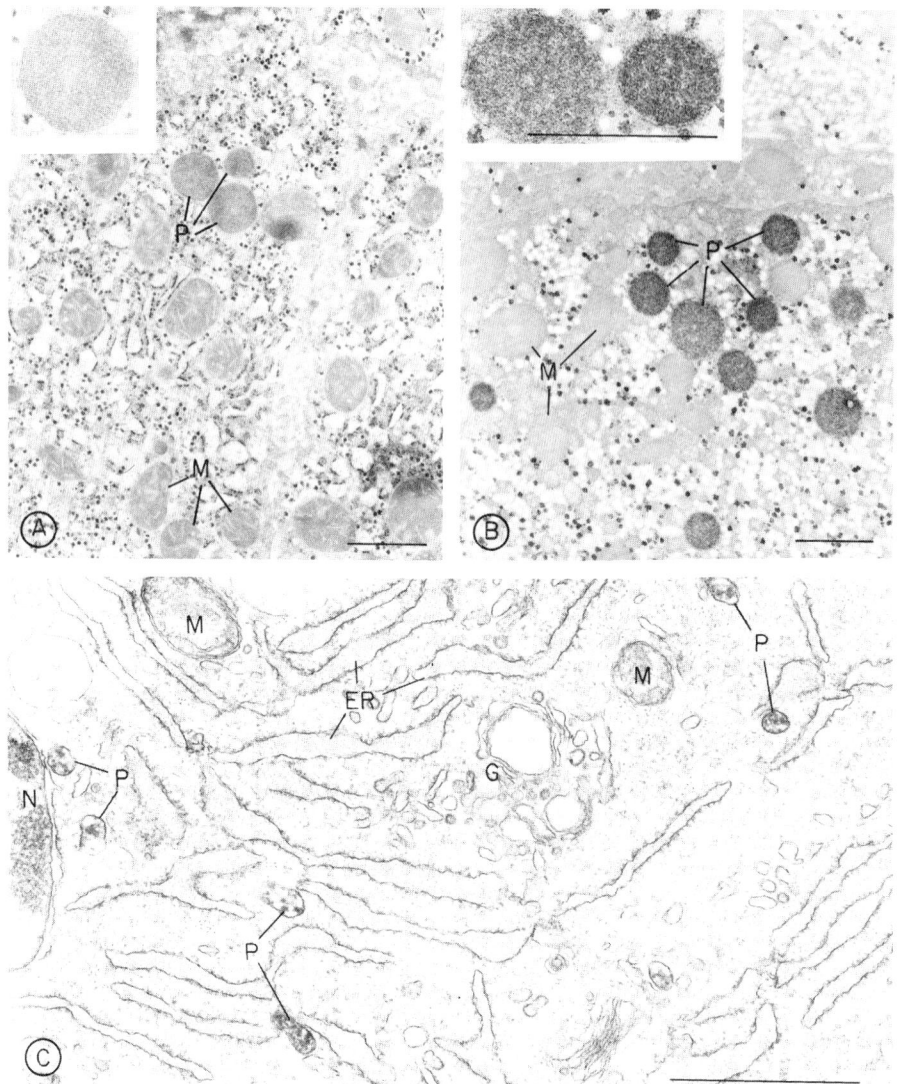

Fig. 57-1 Electron microscopy of human liver (*A,B*) and normal human amniocyte (*C*). *A* and *C*. Morphology. *B*. Catalase cytochemistry showing a cluster of diaminobenzidine-positive peroxisomes (P). Bar = 1 μm. Magnification = 11,000 for *A* and *B*, and 26,000 for *C* and insets in *A* and *B*. M = mitochondrion, G = Golgi apparatus, ER = endoplasmic reticulum, N = nucleus. (*A* and *B* from Lazarow et al.[190] *C* from H. Shio and P.B. Lazarow.)

Peroxisomes, which are sometimes referred to in discussions of morphology as "microbodies," occupy approximately 1.5 to 2 percent of the liver parenchymal cell volume in the rat.[34,35] They are distributed fairly uniformly throughout the liver lobule and throughout hepatocytes.[34] Because they tend to occur in clusters, morphometric analysis is necessary to evaluate changes in abundance caused by experimental manipulations or disease. Some of the peroxisomes may be interconnected, as shown by serial section analysis of mouse liver.[36]

The amniocyte (Fig. 57-1C) and the fibroblast are examples of cell types in which peroxisomes are much less abundant and, moreover, small, with diameters of approximately 0.1 to 0.25 μm.[37–38a] In between these extremes of peroxisome abundance are steroid-secreting cells (adrenal cortex),[39] sebaceous gland cells (which synthesize unusual ether lipids and waxes),[40–42] myelin-forming cells (glia),[43] and many cells of the digestive tract. In certain cell types, notably in the sebaceous glands, peroxisomes do not exist as individual spherical entities, but rather are interconnected into an elaborate, contorted intracellular compartment,[42] referred to as "peroxisomal reticulum."[44]

Peroxisomes do not contain DNA[45] and probably also lack glycoproteins.[46] Compared with other organelles, peroxisomes have an unusually high equilibrium density in sucrose, metrizamide, or Nycodenz gradients, typically 1.23 g/cm³. This is due to the fact that the peroxisome membrane contains aqueous protein pores[47] which permit the free passage of sucrose and Nycodenz, as well as metabolites, such as amino acids and hydroxy acids, and even cofactors like ATP.

The peroxisomal membrane is 6.5 to 7 nm thick with a typical trilaminar appearance.[48] The rat liver peroxisomal membrane has a unique polypeptide composition with some 10 characteristic integral membrane proteins.[49–52] Although peroxisomes are the site of the initial reactions in plasmalogen biosynthesis (see below), the peroxisomal membrane is not especially enriched in plasmalogens (Amiya K. Hajra, University of Michigan, personal communication).

ANABOLIC FUNCTIONS OF PEROXISOMES

Plasmalogen Biosynthesis

Plasmalogens constitute some 5 to 20 percent of the phospholipids in most mammalian cell membranes.[53] Plasmalogens contain a 1,2-unsaturated, long-chain alcohol in vinyl ether linkage to the glycerol backbone of the phospholipid (Fig. 57-2A) in place of the ester-linked fatty acid found in conven-

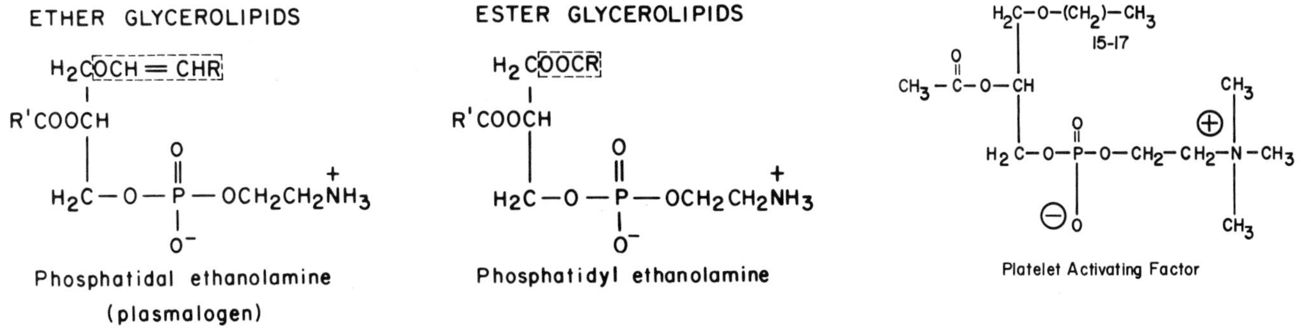

ETHER GLYCEROLIPIDS

$H_2\overline{COCH = CHR}$

$R'COOCH$

$H_2C—O—\overset{O}{\underset{O^-}{\overset{\|}{P}}}—OCH_2CH_2\overset{+}{N}H_3$

Phosphatidal ethanolamine

(plasmalogen)

A.

ESTER GLYCEROLIPIDS

$H_2\overline{COOCR}$

$R'COOCH$

$H_2C—O—\overset{O}{\underset{O^-}{\overset{\|}{P}}}—OCH_2CH_2\overset{+}{N}H_3$

Phosphatidyl ethanolamine

B.

$H_2C—O—(CH_2)—CH_3$

$\underset{15\text{-}17}{}$

$CH_3—\overset{O}{\overset{\|}{C}}—O—CH$

$H_2C—O—\overset{\oplus}{\underset{\ominus}{\overset{O}{\overset{\|}{P}}}}—O—CH_2—CH_2—\overset{+}{N}—CH_3$

$\underset{CH_3}{}$ $\underset{CH_3}{}$

Platelet Activating Factor

C.

Fig. 57-2 Phospholipid structures. A. A plasmalogen. B. Phosphatidyl ethanolamine. C. Platelet activating factor.[63] A and C are ether lipids whereas B is an ester-linked phospholipid. The plasmalogens (A) are distinguished from other ether lipids (C) by the double bond between the first two carbons of the long-chain alcohol. R and R' represent the long tails of the fatty acids or fatty alcohols.

tional phospholipids (Fig. 57-2B). Plasmalogens are especially abundant in nervous tissue, and in white matter they preponderate in certain classes of phospholipids. For example, in myelin the ethanolamine phospholipid class is 80 to 90 percent plasmalogens.[54]

In contrast to the more common ester-linked phospholipids that are synthesized in the endoplasmic reticulum (ER), the first reactions in the synthesis of the ether-linked phospholipids, including the plasmalogens, occur in peroxisomes.[13,14] Plasmalogen synthesis begins with dihydroxyacetone phosphate (DHAP), which is acylated by a peroxisomal acyltransferase (Fig. 57-3). The resulting 1-acyl-DHAP is then the substrate for alkyl-DHAP synthase, which replaces the long-chain fatty acid with a long-chain alcohol. The 1-alkyl-DHAP is reduced to 1-alkyl-glycerol-3-phosphate by a reductase that uses NADPH as the cofactor (Fig. 57-3). The enzymes that catalyze these three reactions are all found in peroxisomes, as determined by differential and equilibrium density centrifugation of liver and brain.[13,14] At least the first two of these enzymes are membrane-bound proteins whose active sites face the luminal space of the peroxisomes.[55] NADP[+] generated in peroxisomes by the third reaction may be reduced by the peroxisomal isoenzyme of isocitrate dehydrogenase.[56]

The subsequent reactions in ether lipid biosynthesis are the same as the corresponding steps in ester lipid assembly.[53] Enzymes catalyzing these reactions are present in the ER[57,58] and have not been detected in peroxisomes.[14,59,60] The alkyl-glycerol-3-phosphate intermediate, which is relatively water soluble, evidently travels from peroxisomes to ER, where the synthesis of the plasmalogens is completed.

The long-chain alcohol required in the second peroxisomal plasmalogen-synthesizing reaction is formed by the reduction of a long-chain acyl-CoA by two molecules of NADPH. Bishop and Hajra[61] suggested, on the basis of differential centrifugation experiments, that the acyl-CoA reductase catalyzing this reaction may also be a peroxisomal enzyme.

Sebaceous tissues such as the mouse preputial gland produce waxes and ether lipids.[62] It may not be coincidental that these cells contain an abundant peroxisomal reticulum.[42] Platelet activating factor is also an ether lipid, namely, 1-alkyl-2-acetyl-glycerophosphorylcholine (Fig. 57-2C).[63]

Cholesterol Biosynthesis

Hydroxymethylglutaryl-CoA (HMG-CoA) reductase is the rate-limiting enzyme in cholesterol biosynthesis and is located in the ER[64] (see Chap. 48). This enzyme activity may be induced in peroxisomes by cholestyramine treatment of rats, according to cell fractionation and immunoelectron microscopy.[65,66] In contrast to the ER enzyme, which is a glycosylated transmembrane protein,[67,68] the peroxisomal enzyme is a soluble protein found in the matrix space of the organelle. The peroxisomal and ER isoenzymes also differ in their diurnal fluctuations.[69] Thompson et al.[70] have recently reported that rat liver peroxisomes, together with a high speed supernatant (cytosol) fraction, are capable of converting mevalonic acid to cholesterol.

Bile Acid Biosynthesis

Bile acids are formed from cholesterol by hydroxylations of the ring structure and the oxidative shortening of the side

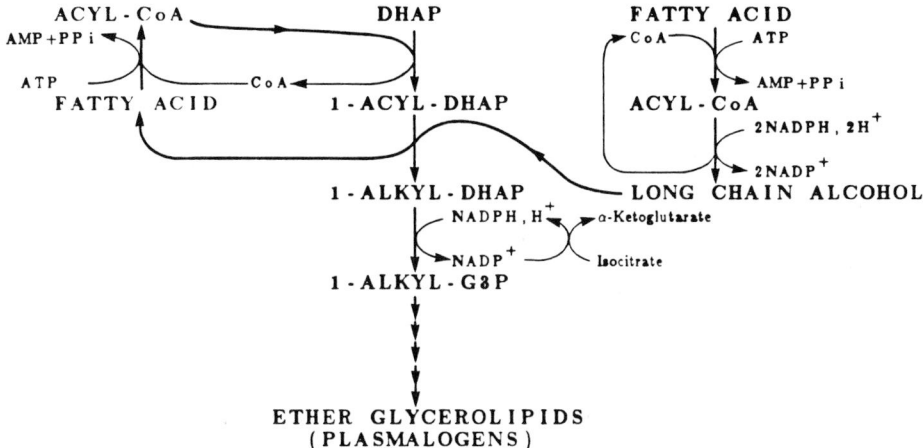

Fig. 57-3 The initial reactions in plasmalogen biosynthesis. DHAP = dihydroxyacetone phosphate. (*From P.B. Lazarow, Journal of Inherited Metabolic Disease 10 (Suppl.1) 11–22, 1987. Used by permission.*)

chain (see Chap. 53). Among these reactions, there is a β-oxidative cleavage of the side chain. This is catalyzed[71,72] by the peroxisomal β-oxidation system described below. Peroxisomes appear to be essential for bile acid formation because abnormal intermediates in bile acid synthesis accumulate in peroxisomal disorders (see later in this chapter).

Gluconeogenesis

Conversion of amino acids to glucose is a physiologically important response to high protein diets and to starvation, when tissue protein is utilized to maintain the blood glucose level. Gluconeogenesis occurs in the liver and, to a lesser extent, in the kidney. Conversion of amino acids to glucose often begins with deamination, to which peroxisomes contribute. In rat liver, a glyoxalate aminotransferase acts on L-amino acids: alanine, aspartate, asparagine, glutamine, histidine, and phenylalanine.[73] A liver D-amino acid oxidase converts D-amino acids that may arise from digestion of bacteria in the gut to keto-acids. In human liver, serine:pyruvate and alanine:glyoxalate aminotransferases are located in peroxisomes.[74,75] In rat kidney, a variety of L-amino acids are irreversibly oxidized to their keto-acid analogues by L-amino acid oxidase.[76]

Glyoxalate Transamination and Primary Hyperoxaluria, Type I

Glyoxalate is formed from glycolate by a peroxisomal oxidase[76] and may then be further oxidized to oxalic acid. The alanine:glyoxalate aminotransferase removes glyoxalate before the further oxidation.[77] There is a species difference in the subcellular localization of this aminotransferase. In rat liver two isoenzymes exist, one of which is found in peroxisomes and the other in mitochondria.[78] In human liver, the enzyme is found mainly, if not exclusively, in peroxisomes.[75] Deficiency of the peroxisomal alanine:glyoxalate aminotransferase is the cause of primary hyperoxaluria, type I[79,80] (see Chap. 35). Catalase and glutamate:glyoxalate aminotransferase are unaffected in this disease.

CATABOLIC FUNCTIONS OF PEROXISOMES

H_2O_2-Based Cellular Respiration

De Duve and his collaborators discovered that peroxisomes contain a group of enzymes that use O_2 to oxidize a variety of substrates and thereby form hydrogen peroxide.[76] The H_2O_2 thus produced is efficiently decomposed within the organelle by catalase (Fig. 57-4), which is present at concentrations as high as 40 mg/ml. De Duve named the peroxisome not for peroxidases, but for its peroxide-based respiration. The oxidases' substrates include D- and L-amino acids, L-α-hydroxy acids, and urate;[76] glutaryl-CoA;[81] oxalate;[82] and CoA derivatives and polyamines, as will be discussed below. The decomposition of H_2O_2 may occur either catalatically (in which two H_2O_2 combine to form water and oxygen) (Fig. 57-4, *top*) or peroxidatically (Fig. 57-4, *bottom*). Peroxidation substrates include ethanol, methanol, nitrites, quinones, and formate.[83] This peroxisomal respiration is estimated to account for some 20 percent of the oxygen consumption by liver.[76]

One function of peroxisomal respiration is to protect cells against H_2O_2 by the compartmentalization of most H_2O_2 metabolism within the organelle. The bulk of H_2O_2 generated inside peroxisomes is probably decomposed peroxidatically, with the catalatic reaction serving as a safety valve in case of excess H_2O_2 production.[83] Any H_2O_2 escaping from peroxisomes would encounter a second protective system, glutathionine peroxidase, in the cytosol (see review of H_2O_2 metabolism by Chance et al.[84]

A second function of peroxisomal respiration is to dispose of excess reducing equivalents. The peroxisomal oxidases are free of the constraint imposed by respiratory control, which regulates mitochondrial activity. Therefore they may function even when the intracellular ATP/ADP ratio is high (see de Duve[85] and the comprehensive review by de Duve and Baudhuin[76]).

A possible third function of peroxisomal respiration may be to contribute to thermogenesis. Since the energy of the peroxisomal oxidations is not conserved as ATP, this energy is dissipated as heat. Peroxisomes proliferate strikingly in brown adipose tissue during cold adaptation,[86] despite the fact that the principal means of heat production in this specialized tissue is the burning of fatty acids by uncoupled mitochondria.[87]

Polyamine Catabolism

Spermine and spermidine are oxidized by a single peroxisomal enzyme, polyamine oxidase.[88] The end products of this catabolism are putrescine, 3-aminopropionaldehyde, and H_2O_2. A peroxisomal localization of this enzyme has been demonstrated in liver by cell fractionation[88] and in kidney by EM cytochemistry.[82]

Purine Catabolism

In most animals, purines are degraded via xanthine and uric acid to allantoin, which is excreted.[89] In rats, urate oxidase, the enzyme converting urate to allantoin, is located exclusively in the peroxisomes, where it is the major, if not the only, constituent of the paracrystalline core. Human beings and other primates lack urate oxidase, and uric acid is excreted as the end product of purine catabolism. The result is that we are susceptible to gout and our peroxisomes lack cores.

Ethanol Oxidation

Peroxisomes make a minor contribution to ethanol clearance, especially when ethanol is present at high concentrations. Al-

Fig. 57-4 Peroxisomal respiration. Catalase can convert 2 H_2O_2 to O_2 and 2 H_2O (upper reaction) or can use 1 H_2O_2 to oxidize a substrate peroxidatically (lower reaction). Peroxidation substrates (R'H_2) include ethanol, methanol, nitrites, quinones, and formate. Substrates for the oxidases (RH_2) include D- and L-amino acids, L-α-hydroxy acids, urates, glutaryl-CoA, oxalate, polyamines, and certain CoA derivatives. (*From de Duve and Baudhuin.*[76])

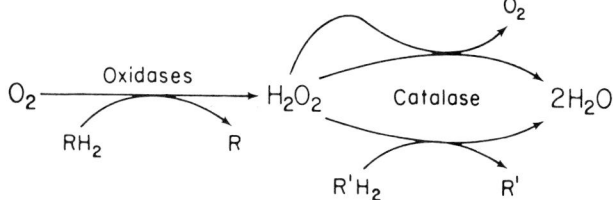

though most ethanol is oxidized by the cytosolic alcohol dehydrogenase, some 5 to 25 percent of ethanol clearance is insensitive to inhibitors of alcohol dehydrogenase.[90] Part of this is oxidized by the peroxidatic reaction of catalase.[91,92] This peroxisomal ethanol oxidation may be increased experimentally by supplying substrates of the peroxisomal oxidases to rats or to perfused liver.[92,93] Possible practical applications of increasing peroxisomal ethanol clearance have been discussed.[93]

Pipecolic Acid Catabolism

L-Pipecolic acid, a minor intermediate in lysine catabolism (see Chap. 21), is oxidized to α-aminoadipic acid within peroxisomes in human beings and other primates, but in mitochondria in rats and rabbits.[94]

β Oxidation of Fatty Acids, Very Long Chain Fatty Acids, Long Chain Dicarboxylic Acids, Prostaglandins, Xenobiotics, and the Side Chain of Cholesterol

Reactions. Peroxisomes catabolize fatty acids to acetyl-CoA and short acyl-CoA or acylcarnitine end products[95,96] (Fig. 57-5). Other CoA derivatives also undergo β oxidation in peroxisomes. Four parts of this process may be distinguished.

1. *Activation.* Peroxisomes activate fatty acids with chain lengths of 12 carbons or more to the corresponding acyl-CoA compounds by means of an acyl-CoA synthetase, ATP, and CoA.[97–99] The synthetase is a membrane-bound enzyme. Very long chain fatty acids (VLCFA) (i.e., those with chain lengths of 24 or more carbons) may be activated by a second, distinct peroxisomal synthetase.[100,101] It is suggested that deficiency of this latter synthetase (see Chap. 58 on adrenoleukodystrophy) prevents peroxisomes from oxidizing lignoceric acid (C_{24}), despite the presence of another synthetase capable of activating lignoceric acid in the endoplasmic reticulum.[101] This implies that peroxisomes must themselves activate the fatty acids they will oxidize. The peroxisomal capacity to activate palmitate is

approximately equal to the peroxisomal capacity to β-oxidize it.[98]

2. β *Oxidation per se.* Peroxisomes shorten fatty acyl-CoAs and other substrates 2 carbons at a time by means of four reactions shown in Fig. 57-5. In the first of these reactions, a double bond is introduced with the concomitant reduction of O_2 to H_2O_2; thus this pathway feeds the peroxisomal respiratory system. The second and third reactions, a hydration of the double bond and an NAD-linked dehydrogenation, are catalyzed by a single bifunctional protein. Lastly, acetyl-CoA is produced by a thiolytic cleavage.

The enzymes catalyzing the four reactions of β oxidation (three proteins) were purified from rat liver and characterized by Hashimoto and his colleagues.[102] The amino acid sequences of the oxidase and thiolase have been deduced from the sequences of the corresponding cDNA clones.[103,104] All three proteins are located in the matrix space inside the peroxisomes. While thiolase is soluble and leaks readily from damaged peroxisomes, the oxidase and bifunctional protein appear to be aggregated and/or associated in some fashion with the membrane.[105]

The peroxisomal β-oxidation system shows maximal catalytic activity toward saturated acyl-CoAs with chain lengths of C_{12}–C_{16} (Fig. 57-6A). Its activity declines with increasing chain length such that it has much less absolute activity for the VLCFA (e.g., lignoceroyl-CoA), but this small activity is nevertheless physiologically very important.[19–21] Long chain unsaturated fatty acids are well oxidized by peroxisomes, in general more efficiently than their saturated counterparts.[106,107] Rat liver peroxisomes appear not to be able to oxidize butyryl-CoA and other short-chain fatty acids.[96] As a result, peroxisomal β oxidation of long-chain fatty acids in this tissue would be expected to go almost, but not quite, to completion. This has been experimentally verified: palmitoyl-CoA undergoes five cycles of β oxidation (sufficient to form five acetyl-CoA and one hexanoyl-CoA) rather than the theoretical maximum of seven cycles.[96]

3. *Carnitine acyltransferases.* Removal of the end products of peroxisomal β oxidation may be facilitated by carnitine acetyltransferase and carnitine octanoyltransferase.[108,109] Transferase activity is substantial for acetyl-CoA, maximal for hexanoyl-CoA, and declines with further increases in chain length.[110,111]

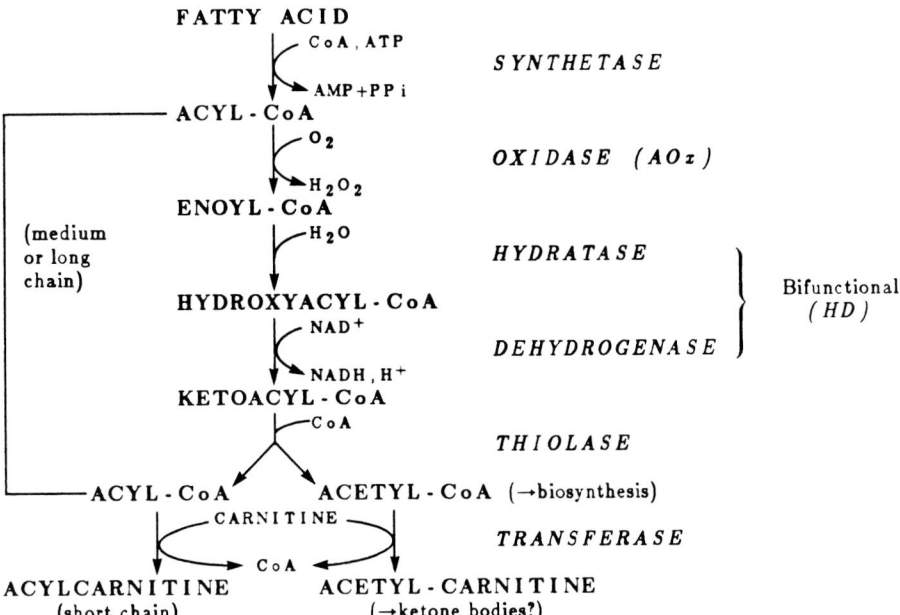

Fig. 57-5 Peroxisomal fatty acid catabolism. (*From P.B. Lazarow, Journal of Inherited Metabolic Disease 10 (Suppl. 1):11–22, 1987. Used by permission.*)

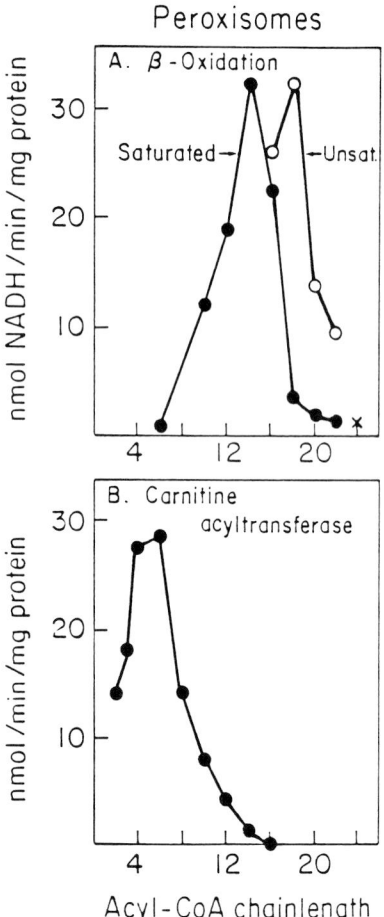

Peroxisomes

Fig. 57-6 Peroxisomal fatty acid catabolism—chain length specificities. *A.* β Oxidation assayed by NADH oxidation. Solid symbols, saturated fatty acyl-CoAs. Open symbols, monounsaturated fatty acid-CoAs. (*Redrawn from Osmundsen et al.*[106] The X indicates the activity toward lignoceroyl-CoA (C_{24}, saturated), extrapolated from the results of Singh et al.[20] *B.* Carnitine acyltransferase activity. (*Drawn from Markwell et al.*[109])

The specific activities of peroxisomal β oxidation and peroxisomal carnitine transferases are complementary (Fig. 57-6), supporting the idea that rat liver peroxisomes β-oxidize fatty acids down to the short fatty acids, which then can be trans-acylated to carnitine. The carnitine octanoyltransferase is a soluble protein located in the matrix space of the organelle.[109,110]

4. *Auxiliary enzymes.* The double bonds of unsaturated fatty acids may fall in the wrong position (3,4-unsaturation) or be in the wrong stereoisomeric configuration (cis) to be oxidized by the peroxisomal β-oxidation enzymes. These problems are handled by 2,4-dienoyl-CoA reductase and enoyl-CoA isomerase.[112–114] Fatty acid–binding protein may transport fatty acids through the cytosol to peroxisomes.[115]

Functions Peroxisomal β oxidation is apparently ubiquitous: it occurs in animals,[95,96] plants,[116] and unicellular eukaryotes.[117,118] In contrast, mitochondrial β oxidation seems to occur only in animal cells.[116,118,119] The animal mitochondria oxidize fatty acids to supply energy. Muscle mitochondria convert fatty acids to acetyl-CoA, and then burn the acetyl-CoA in the Krebs cycle to make ATP. Liver mitochondria condense much of the acetyl-CoA they produce to ketone bodies, which are exported to support ATP production elsewhere in the body.

Peroxisomes in plants and yeasts oxidize fatty acids (completely) to acetyl-CoA, which is then condensed to succinate within the peroxisomes (via the glyoxalate cycle). The succinate is further converted to glucose by mitochondrial and cytosolic reactions. Thus this peroxisomal β oxidation serves an essential anabolic function: gluconeogenesis.

In rat liver, where both peroxisomes and mitochondria carry out β oxidation, there are significant differences between the two systems. The enzymes in the two organelles have different structures and no antigenic cross-reactivity.[102] Exceptionally, peroxisomal and mitochondrial acyl-CoA synthetases have similar properties.[120] Functionally, peroxisomes use a flavoprotein acyl-CoA oxidase, which forms H_2O_2, whereas mitochondria use a flavoprotein acyl-CoA dehydrogenase, which is tightly coupled to the electron transport chain. Carnitine facilitates the entrance of fatty acids into mitochondria, while from peroxisomes it aids the exit of end products of β oxidation. Peroxisomal β oxidation is stimulated by increases in the intracellular ATP concentration,[121] whereas mitochondrial β oxidation is inhibited by increases in the intramitochondrial ATP concentration (by respiratory control).[119]

These facts, together with the role of peroxisomal β oxidation in plants and yeasts, strongly suggest that in animal cells, one function of peroxisomal β oxidation is to supply acetyl-CoA for anabolic reactions (e.g., cholesterol and bile acid biosynthesis and acetylations) when the cells are well supplied with energy.[122] The physiological contribution of peroxisomes to palmitate β oxidation may depend on metabolic conditions. It has been variously estimated at 5 to 30 percent.[123–125] Peroxisomes might also contribute acetyl-CoA for ketone body formation (via acetyl-carnitine) during times of maximal ketogenesis. Bremer and colleagues[126] demonstrated the involvement of peroxisomes in diet-induced ketogenesis.

Other important functions of mammalian peroxisomal β oxidation are the catabolism of a variety of substrates that are poorly oxidized by mitochondrial β oxidation. VLCFA such as lignoceric acid ($C_{24:0}$) and cerotic acid ($C_{26:0}$) are preferentially oxidized in peroxisomes.[19–21] A characteristic feature of human peroxisomal diseases, discussed in detail below, is the accumulation of VLCFA in tissues and plasma.

Long-chain dicarboxylic acyl-CoAs appear to be preferentially oxidized in peroxisomes.[127] C_6 and C_8 dicarboxylic acids appear in urine in cases of defective mitochondrial fatty acid oxidation.[128] This appears to be the result of a compensatory increase in microsomal ω oxidation plus peroxisomal β oxidation. This chain-length pattern in human urine (predominately C_8 and C_{10}) is consistent with the chain-length specificity of peroxisomes in rat liver mentioned above.

Prostaglandins are frequently inactivated and catabolized by a process that includes two cycles of β oxidation, resulting in a shortening of the molecules by four carbons prior to their excretion in urine.[128a] The site of this β-oxidative catabolism has been reexamined recently for prostaglandins $F_{2\alpha}$ and E_2, and has been shown to occur predominantly in peroxisomes.[128b,128c]

Xenobiotic compounds with acyl side chains likewise are degraded by β oxidation and excreted. The peroxisomal β-oxidation system has been found to carry out this process for several xenobiotic drugs and model compounds.[128d–128f]

As mentioned previously, the β-oxidative side chain cleavage of cholesterol, as it is converted to bile acids, occurs in peroxisomes.[71,72]

Another function of peroxisomal β oxidation may be the chain shortening of long unsaturated acyl-CoAs, which under some circumstances appear to undergo only a few cycles of β oxidation.[129]

Tissue Distribution and Induction. Peroxisomal fatty acid oxidation has been found in liver,[95,96] kidney, intestine, lung, muscle, spleen,[130] brown adipose tissue,[131] heart,[132] and adrenal cortex.[133] Hepatic peroxisomal β oxidation can be increased severalfold by fasting[134] or high fat diets[135–137] and tenfold or more by hypolipidemic drugs and plasticizers.[138] Clofibrate, typical of the hypolipidemic drugs, also increases peroxisomal β-oxidation activity in small intestine and kidney.[139] Brown fat peroxisome β oxidation is strikingly induced by cold adaptation.[140]

Inferences from Diseases

As will be seen subsequently in this chapter, there is a good correlation between the enzymatic capacity of peroxisomes, determined in large part by the biochemical analysis of rat tissues (described above), and the biochemical defects that have been found in patients with peroxisome deficiency diseases. This has led to the conclusion that there is a one-to-one correlation between biochemical abnormalities seen in these diseases and deficient peroxisomal enzymes. Useful as this has been to generate testable hypotheses, some caution is required. First, there is some overlap in function between the peroxisomes and other organelles, including the mitochondria and endoplasmic reticulum (e.g., in fatty acid oxidation). Second, some abnormalities in the mitochondrial electron transport chain have been noted in peroxisomal disorders.[10,141] Third, there may be species differences in the subcellular localization of an enzyme, as, for example, in pipecolic acid metabolism.[94]

A case in point concerns phytanic acid oxidation. Phytanic acid accumulates in peroxisomal diseases (see below). However, at least in rat, it would appear to be oxidized in mitochondria.[142] Thus far, the location of phytanic acid oxidation has not been determined in human tissues. Therefore at the present time there is no direct experimental evidence for including "adult" Refsum disease (see Chap. 59) among the peroxisomal disorders.

PROLIFERATION OF PEROXISOMES AND ENZYME INDUCIBILITY

Not only does the abundance of peroxisomes vary normally among cell types, but it may be altered considerably within a cell type by physiological and pharmacological agents. Adrenocorticotrophin causes peroxisome proliferation in adrenal cortex,[143] cold adaptation causes the number of peroxisomes in brown fat to increase,[86,140] and hypolipidemic drugs cause peroxisomes to proliferate strikingly in rats and mice, but generally not in primates (reviewed by Reddy et al.[138]). These proliferations are accompanied by alterations in the protein composition of the peroxisomes. For example, clofibrate causes a preferential increase in the β-oxidation enzymes relative to catalase and oxidases.[95,144,145]

Some peroxisomal enzymes may be induced without marked changes in the number of peroxisomes. Low doses of hypolipidemic drugs have this effect on the liver β-oxidation enzymes[146] as do high fat diets.[135–137] Renal peroxisomal D-

amino acid oxidase is induced by exposure of germ-free mice to bacteria, which results in the appearance of D-amino acids in the gut.[147]

Hepatic catalase activity is decreased to as little as 5 percent of the normal value in rats bearing carcinomas, lymphomas, or sarcomas.[148] Prolonged treatment of rodents with high doses of hypolipidemic agents eventually leads to liver tumors, which Reddy has suggested might be related to the peroxisome-proliferating effect of these compounds.[138] Carcinogenicity has not seemed to be a side effect in humans treated with therapeutic doses of hypolipidemic drugs.

BIOGENESIS AND TURNOVER OF PEROXISOMES

Biogenesis of Proteins

Peroxisomal proteins are encoded by nuclear genes and synthesized on free polyribosomes in the cytosol (reviewed in Ref. 46). The newly synthesized proteins diffuse through the cytosol (typical half-times are 1 to 15 min[149]) and are imported posttranslationally into preexisting peroxisomes (Fig. 57-7). This leads to the progressive enlargement of the peroxisomes, which then divide to form new ones. In those cell types in which peroxisomes are extensively interconnected into a peroxisomal reticulum, formation of new peroxisomes consists of an elaboration of, or budding from, this peroxisomal reticulum.

A characteristic feature of peroxisome biogenesis is that proteins of the organelle are generally synthesized at their final sizes, without the cleavable amino-terminal topogenic sequences found on most secretory,[150,151] mitochondrial,[152,153] and chloroplast[154] proteins. Among the 10 rat liver peroxisomal proteins whose biosynthesis has been investigated thus far, only thiolase is made as a larger precursor, some 3 to 6 kDa larger than the mature protein.[155,156] In this exceptional case, proteolytic processing occurs gradually and is *not* linked to import into the organelle.[157] Thus, in general, the topogenic information directing proteins to peroxisomes is inherent to the mature polypeptides, and posttranslational translocation into peroxisomes is not accompanied by proteolytic processing.

The conclusions summarized above apply to matrix,[155–164] core,[160] and integral membrane proteins.[52,165–167] Most of the

Fig. 57-7 Current understanding of peroxisome biogenesis. (*From Lazarow and Fujiki.[46] Used by permission.*)

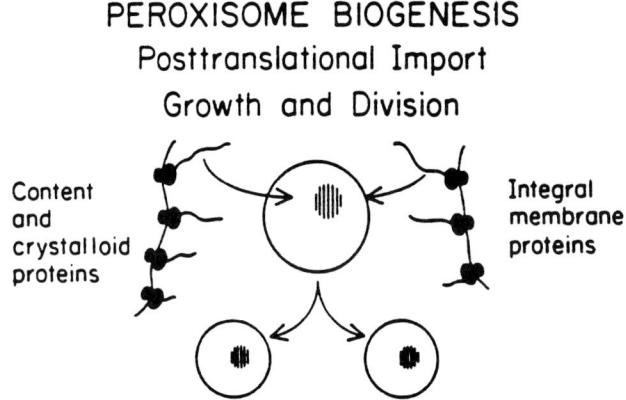

PEROXISOME BIOGENESIS
Posttranslational Import
Growth and Division

Content and crystalloid proteins

Integral membrane proteins

five rat liver peroxisomal matrix proteins whose biosynthesis has been studied are oligomeric proteins. Catalase is a tetrameric hemoprotein.[168,169] It enters peroxisomes as an apomonomer; heme addition and oligomerization occur inside.[158] The amino-terminal and carboxy-terminal sequences of the mature catalase are identical to those predicted from the cloned cDNA sequence,[170] except for removal of the initiator methionine. No other modification of the primary structure of catalase was detected by one- and two-dimensional peptide mapping.[161]

Acyl-CoA oxidase of rat liver is a homodimeric flavoprotein.[171,172] After assembly in peroxisomes, the polypeptides are gradually cleaved, over a time frame of hours, into two subunits.[157] Cleavage does not go to completion, and both subunits remain part of the mature enzyme.[171,172] Hence this proteolytic maturation (or perhaps it is proteolytic aging) is quite different from the typical proteolytic processing of organelle protein precursors, in which the cleaved amino-terminal topogenic peptide disappears.

The bifunctional hydratase-dehydrogenase is a monomer as purified[173] but shows a strong tendency to aggregate in the organelle.[105] Thiolase is dimeric.[174] Only the carnitine octanoyl transferase appears to be a soluble monomeric matrix protein.[110]

Four integral membrane proteins of rat liver peroxisomes have been investigated with respect to their biosynthesis. These have masses of 22, 26, 53, and 69 kDa. All four are synthesized on free polyribosomes at their final sizes, and insert posttranslationally into preexisting peroxisomes.[52,165–167]

Biosynthesis of Lipids

The phospholipids of peroxisomes, like those of mitochondria, are synthesized by the endoplasmic reticulum (ER). They may be conveyed to their final destination by phospholipid carrier proteins.[175] So far as is presently known, this is the only role of the ER in peroxisome assembly; the view of a decade ago that peroxisomes form by budding from the ER is no longer credible.[46]

Import in Vitro and Targeting

The posttranslational import of proteins into rat liver peroxisomes has been reconstituted efficiently in vitro.[176–178] This has permitted investigation of the details of the import process, which has been dissected into binding and translocation steps. Import of acyl-CoA oxidase into peroxisomes requires ATP hydrolysis but not a membrane potential.[176] A membrane protein (or proteins) is required for import, likely functioning as a receptor.[52]

A mammalian peroxisomal topogenic sequence has not yet been identified. Yeast peroxisomal acyl-CoA oxidase contains two, redundant, topogenic sequences. One is in the middle and the other is at or near the amino-terminus.[177,178] Each is capable alone of targeting the mouse cytosolic protein dihydrofolate reductase into peroxisomes. A carboxy-terminal 12-amino acid peptide of firefly luciferase has been shown to target bacterial chloramphenicol acetyltransferase to peroxisomes of cultured monkey cells.[179]

In summary, peroxisomes enlarge by the posttranslational accretion of newly synthesized matrix and membrane proteins, targeted by internal sequences. New peroxisomes form by division or budding from preexisting ones. This process resembles the biogenesis of DNA-containing organelles (mitochon-

dria and chloroplasts), thus raising interesting questions about the possible endosymbiont origin of peroxisomes.[180,181] This model of peroxisome biogenesis implies that peroxisomes do not form de novo. Thus, every cell must have at least one peroxisome if that cell or its progeny are ever to make more peroxisomes. This is clearly critical for germ cells and for peroxisomal diseases (discussed below) where peroxisome assembly is defective.

Turnover

Peroxisomes are degraded randomly, as wholes, by autophagy.[76,182] Consistent with this, rat liver peroxisomal proteins appear to turn over synchronously, with half-lives of approximately 1.5 days.[183,184]

PHENOTYPE OF "CLASSIC" ZELLWEGER SYNDROME

Physical Examination and Clinical Course

Newborn infants with "classic" Zellweger syndrome show striking and consistent abnormalities that are easily recognized. Table 57-1, reproduced from Hugo S. A. Heymans' doctoral dissertation,[9] lists the most common physical findings and their relative frequency in a series of 114 patients. Of central diagnostic importance are the typical face (high forehead,

Fig. 57-8 Newborn infants with Zellweger syndrome. Note prominent forehead, hypertelorism, epicanthal folds, hypoplastic supraorbital ridge, and depressed bridge of nose. (*Courtesy of Dr. Hans Zellweger, Iowa*).

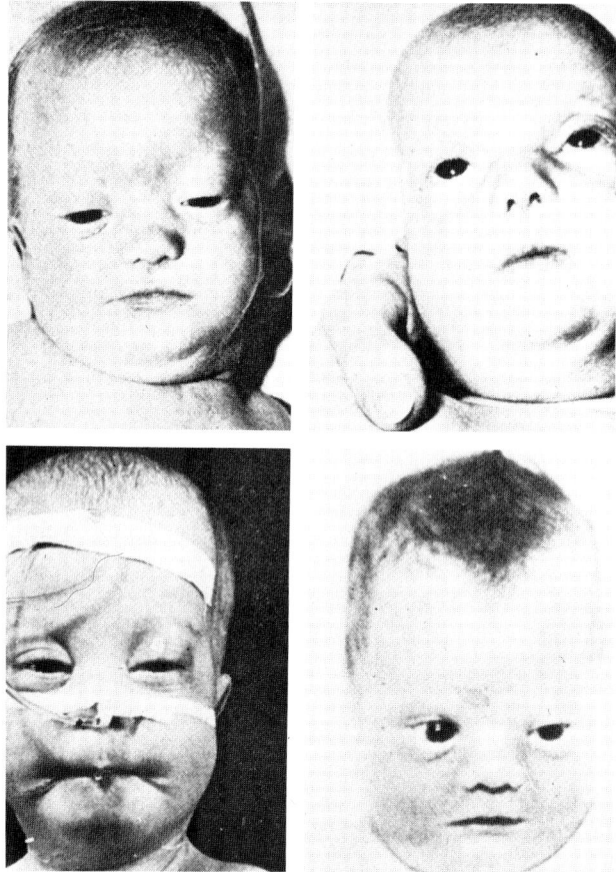

Table 57-1   Main Clinical Abnormalities in Zellweger Syndrome

Abnormal feature	Cases in which information about the feature was available		Cases in which the feature was present	
	Number	Percent	Number	Percent
High forehead	60	53	58	97
Flat occiput	16	14	13	81
Large fontanelle(s), wide sutures	57	50	55	96
Shallow orbital ridges	33	29	33	100
Low/broad nasal bridge	23	20	23	100
Epicanthus	36	32	33	92
High arched palate	37	32	35	95
External ear deformity	40	35	39	97
Micrognathia	18	16	18	100
Redundant skin folds of neck	13	11	13	100
Brushfield spots	6	5	5	83
Cataract/cloudy cornea	35	31	30	86
Glaucoma	12	11	7	58
Abnormal retinal pigmentation	15	13	6	40
Optic disk pallor	23	20	17	74
Severe hypotonia	95	83	94	99
Abnormal Moro response	26	23	26	100
Hyporeflexia or areflexia	57	50	56	98
Poor sucking	77	68	74	96
Gavage feeding	26	23	26	100
Epileptic seizures	61	54	56	92
Psychomotor retardation	45	39	45	100
Impaired hearing	21	18	9	40
Nystagmus	37	32	30	81

SOURCE: From H.S.A. Heymans' survey of 114 patients with Zellweger syndrome reported in the literature.[9]

upslanting palpebral fissures, hypoplastic supraorbital ridges, epicanthal folds) (Fig. 57-8); severe weakness and hypotonia; neonatal seizures; and eye abnormalities (cataracts, glaucoma, corneal clouding, Brushfield spots, pigmentary retinopathy, and optic nerve dysplasia). Because of the hypotonia and "mongoloid" appearance, these infants are sometimes suspected to have Down syndrome.[185] The physical features and clinical findings are detailed in several reviews.[8,185–187] Infants with classic Zellweger syndrome rarely live more than a few months due to the severe hypotonia, feeding difficulty, seizures, liver involvement, and frequent cardiac defects. More than 90 percent show postnatal growth failure. In Wilson's literature survey of 90 patients, 79 had died at an average age of 12.5 weeks.[8] Some apparently classic Zellweger patients live longer. At least two factors may be operative here. Longer-surviving patients may have a somewhat milder disease such as neonatal ALD (see below) or may have been correctly diagnosed but survived longer because of extraordinary care or the late onset of fatal complications such as aspiration or cardiac failure. Distinction between these two factors may be aided by assessment of psychomotor development. Most patients with the somewhat milder forms do achieve some psychomotor development, albeit very limited, whereas most patients with classic Zellweger syndrome fail to do so (H. Zellweger, personal communication).

PATHOLOGICAL FINDINGS

Absent Peroxisomes

Goldfischer et al. first reported that patients with Zellweger syndrome lack peroxisomes in the liver and kidney.[10] The or-

ganelle could not be demonstrated either by exhaustive electron microscopy or by electron-microscopic cytochemistry for catalase. All subsequent studies have confirmed this finding.[11,188–190] Absence of liver peroxisomes is now considered an essential criterion for the diagnosis of Zellweger syndrome. Peroxisomes are also markedly reduced in number or absent in cultured skin fibroblasts of Zellweger patients.[37,38]

Brain

The most striking and intriguing neuropathological abnormality is a disorder of neuronal migration that has been studied by Volpe and Adams[191] and Evrard et al.[192] This disordered migration leads to characteristic and unique cytoarchitectonic abnormalities, which involve the cerebral hemispheres (Fig. 57-9), the cerebellum, and the inferior olivary complex. In the cerebral hemispheres neurons that are normally destined for outer cortical layers are distributed within the inner cortical layers and in the underlying white matter. This migration failure causes the cerebral convolutions to be abnormally small (microgyria) or thick (pachygyria). The migrational defect involves mainly the perisylvian and medially adjacent frontoparietal convexity, while other areas, such as the anterior frontal and occipital regions, may show a normal convolutional pattern. Evrard et al. concluded that the mechanism of migration was disturbed continuously from the third month of gestation,[192] a conclusion that has been confirmed in subsequent studies of fetuses with Zellweger syndrome.[193] A unique and characteristic feature of the Zellweger brain malformation is that while there is a disturbed migration of multiple neuronal classes throughout the greater duration of the migratory epoch, the defect is restricted to certain regions of the cerebral hemispheres with sufficient consistency that it can be distin-

NEOCORTEX CYTOARCHITECTONIC ANALYSIS

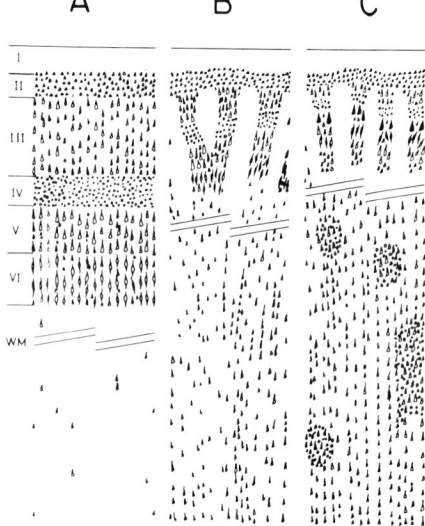

A: normal
B: Zellweger microgyria
C: Zellweger pachygyria

A.

Fig. 57-9 *A. Schematic representation of cell pattern in normal (A), microgyric (B), and pachygyric (C) neocortical regions. Roman numerals to left correspond to normal cortical layers. White matter and horizontal slashes mark junction of cortex and central white matter. The white matter in B and C contains numerous heterotopic neurons that failed to reach their normal location in the neocortex. In addition, in the abnormal cortex (B and C) the neurons are arranged in fascicles that contain three to six neurons abreast of*

DISTRIBUTION OF CYTOARCHITECTONICS IN ZELLWEGER CEREBRAL HEMISPHERE

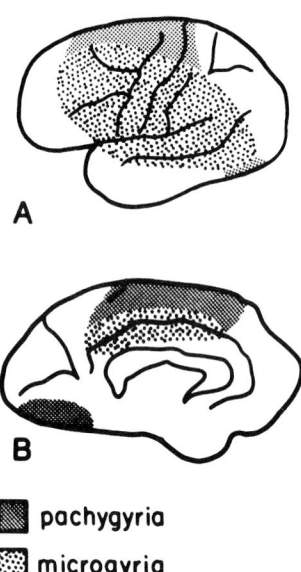

■ pachygyria
▨ microgyria

B.

*each other. (Modified from Evrard et al.[192] Used by permission.)
B. Patterns of pachygyric (fine stippling) and microgyric (coarse stippling) gyral abnormalities on lateral (A) and medial (B) surface of cerebral hemispheres in Zellweger syndrome. The abnormality is restricted, and its pattern is characteristic (see text). The gyri in the unshaded areas are normal. (Modified from Evrard et al.[192] Used by permission.)*

guished from all other cerebral malformations. Other characteristic features are migrational defects that involve large Purkinje cells in the cerebellum and laminar discontinuities in the principal nucleus of the inferior olivary complex. There is also hypoplasia of the olfactory bulbs[194] and a neuroaxonal dystrophy of the dorsal nucleus of Clarke and the lateral cuneate nucleus.[195,196]

In addition to the neuronal migrational defects, there is also an abnormality of white matter. While the extent and significance of this had been disputed, recent biochemical advances provide insight about its mechanism. Passarge and McAdams had noted a severe myelin deficiency and accumulation of sudanophilic lipids and concluded that this finding was consistent with a sudanophilic leukodystrophy.[2] In contrast, brain myelin content was considered to be nearly normal in the Volpe and Adams case.[191] While a destructive myelin process was present, it was restricted to the periventricular region, and its location and restricted distribution suggested to the authors that it was related to hypoxic-ischemic episodes associated with seizures and aspiration.[191] Agamanolis et al., in consonance with Passarge and McAdams, noted a general deficiency of myelin and an active demyelinative process. They were also the first to note the presence of longitudinal or fiberlike inclusions in both the white and gray matter.[194] Recent studies by Powers and associates[193,195] have demonstrated that these lamellar inclusions are similar to those present in X-linked adrenoleukodystrophy (see Chap. 58) and contain cholesterol es-

terified with VLCFA. These recent findings suggest that the white matter abnormality in Zellweger syndrome is related to the defect in very long chain fatty acid metabolism, and the mechanism may resemble that in X-linked ALD (see Chap. 58). As will be discussed, Zellweger syndrome patients have multiple metabolic defects in contrast to the single defect in X-linked ALD. These additional defects, particularly the inability to synthesize a major myelin constituent, plasmalogen,[197] probably also contribute to the white matter abnormality.

Eye

Abnormalities of the anterior segment include corneal clouding, congenital cataract, and congenital glaucoma. The posterior segment demonstrated ganglion cell loss, gliosis of the nerve fiber layer and optic nerve, optic atrophy, and changes resembling those of retinitis pigmentosa in the retina and pigment epithelium.[198] The electroretinogram is extinguished.[199]

Liver

Heymans reviewed 114 Zellweger cases reported in the literature.[9] The liver was enlarged in 78 percent and fibrotic in 76 percent. Thirty-seven percent had micronodular cirrhosis, and cholestasis was present in 59 percent. The changes were more severe in the older infants. In the first 2 months after birth microscopic abnormalities were absent or only mild, while nearly all patients older than 20 weeks showed advanced changes consisting of severe fibrosis and micronodular cirrhosis. Excessive iron deposits in liver were reported in an early study[200] and were at first thought to be a factor in the pathogenesis of the cirrhosis. This is now considered unlikely, since Gilchrist et al. showed that the liver iron levels diminished with time and were normal in infants living beyond 20 weeks.[201]

Kidney

Renal cysts were observed in 78 of 80 patients who were studied pathologically[9] (Fig. 57-10). The cysts vary from glomerular microcysts to large cortical cysts of glomerular and tubular origin.[202] The cysts are already present in the fetus.[193]

Adrenal

The adrenal pathology of Zellweger patients is similar to that in adrenoleukodystrophy. The reticularis–inner fasciculata zones contain striated cells, some of which are ballooned. Ultrastructural examination demonstrates the lamellar inclusions identical to those found in adrenoleukodystrophy.[203] While overt adrenal insufficiency has not been reported in the Zellweger syndrome, adrenocortical function has been shown to be impaired.[204]

Cartilage

Calcific stippling of the patella (Fig. 57-11) and synchondrosis of the acetabulum occurs in 50 percent of Zellweger patients.[1,9,205,206] Abnormal mineralization of the patella was already observed at midgestation in two fetuses with Zellweger syndrome.[193] Mineralization of the patella normally begins at 2 to 4 years of age and is completed at about 6 years.[207] Powers et al. suggest that the alteration in Zellweger syndrome represents a premature rather than a dysplastic mineralization.[193]

Cardiovascular System

Congenital cardiovascular malformations occur frequently in Zellweger patients. In Heymans' review, ventricular septal defects occurred in 32 percent, and 22 percent had various abnormalities of the aorta.[9]

Thymus

While two cases showed aplasia of the thymus,[208] postmortem studies of six additional patients[201] and assays of cellular immune responses in peripheral blood lymphocytes[209] have failed to show evidence of cellular immunodeficiency. Study of a related illness, neonatal ALD (see below), has shown lipid inclusions in the thymus.[210,211]

Muscle

While muscle has not been studied in detail in Zellweger patients, a myopathy has been demonstrated in a patient with

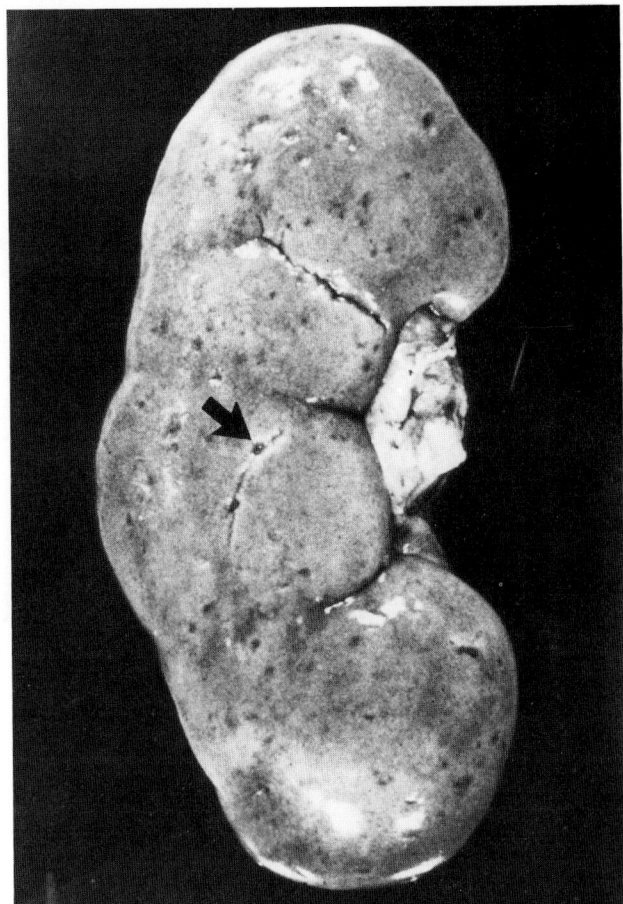

A.

B.

Fig. 57-10 Gross (A) and microscopic (B) appearance of renal cysts in a patient with Zellweger syndrome. Note that many of the cysts are small (arrow, A) and thus may escape detection on ultrasound studies. These cysts are not pathognomic of Zellweger syndrome. They occur also in a number of nonperoxisomal disorders.[7] (Courtesy of Dr. Hans Zellweger.)

neonatal ALD[212] and muscle cells cultured from a patient with Zellweger syndrome showed defective plasmalogen synthesis and cytosolic subcellular localization of catalase,[213] the biochemical abnormalities characteristic of disorders of peroxisomal biogenesis (see below).

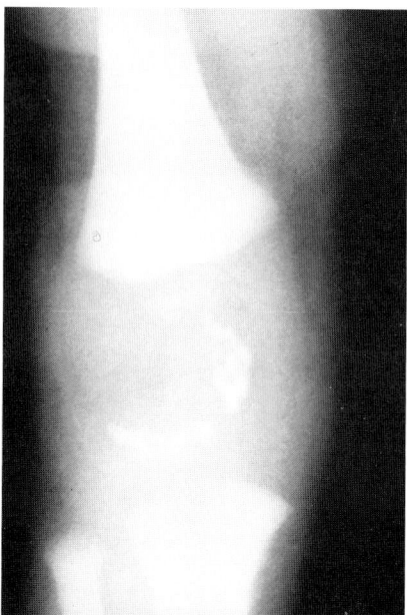 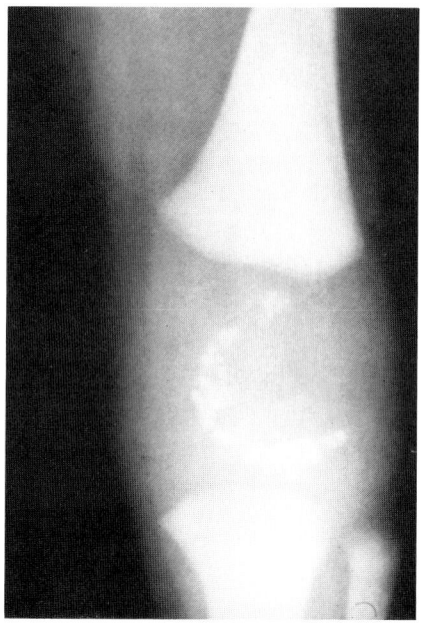

Fig. 57-11 Abnormal calcific stippling of the patella in an infant with Zellweger syndrome. (*Courtesy of Dr. Hans Zellweger.*)

BIOCHEMICAL ABNORMALITIES

Table 57-2 summarizes the key morphologic and biochemical abnormalities in Zellweger syndrome patients.

Catalase and Some Oxidases are Cytosolic Rather Than Particle-Bound

While liver cells or cultured skin fibroblasts of Zellweger patients contain normal or above normal amounts of catalase and the structure and properties of the enzyme appear normal,[214] its subcellular localization is abnormal.[37,190,215–217] Normally, at least 50 to 65 percent of catalase activity is inside peroxisomes. In Zellweger patients, essentially all of the catalase activity is cytosolic. The amount of catalase inside peroxisomes may be assessed by measuring latency or sedimentability: the absence of particle-bound catalase in Zellweger patients represents a biochemical counterpart to the previously mentioned morphologic demonstration that this organelle is lacking. In our experience, there has been excellent correlation between subcellular catalase distribution in cultured skin fibroblasts and the status of peroxisomes in liver biopsies or postmortem specimens. Liver peroxisomes have been lacking in those patients with cytosolic fibroblast catalase, whereas they have been present in patients in whom this enzyme was found in the particulate fibroblast fraction (H.W. Moser, unpublished observations). Some peroxisomal oxidases are also mislocalized to the cytosol but, in contrast to catalase, have somewhat subnormal activity.[215,217]

Defective Synthesis and Decreased Tissue Levels of Plasmalogens

As already noted, Hajra et al. have demonstrated that the first two steps of plasmalogen biosynthesis normally take place in the peroxisome,[13,14] catalyzed by acyl-CoA:dihydroxyacetone phosphate acyltransferase (DHAPAT) and alkyl-dihydroxyacetone phosphate synthase. DHAPAT has been shown to be deficient in tissues, cultured skin fibroblasts, cultured amniocytes and chorion villus cells, leukocytes, and thrombocytes of

Zellweger patients,[16,17,218–220] and a deficiency of alkyl-dihydroxyacetone phosphate synthase has been demonstrated in tissues and cultured skin fibroblasts.[221] Roscher et al.[222] have devised a convenient and sensitive assay which utilizes a double label, double substrate incubation, namely [1-^{14}C]hexadecanol and [9'10'-^{3}H]-*sn*-hexadecylglycerol. Incorporation of the ^{14}C substrate requires the peroxisomal reactions (Fig. 57-3), while that of the tritiated substrate bypasses the peroxisomal steps and requires only the subsequent microsomal reactions, serving as an internal control. The ratio of ^{3}H to ^{14}C incorporation into the plasmalogen fraction thus provides an accurate and reproducible measure of the peroxisomal reactions (Fig. 57-13C). In Zellweger patients this ratio is more than 15 times greater than in controls.[222] Webber et al. have shown that the K_m for DHAP and other properties of the residual DHAPAT activity in Zellweger fibroblasts are normal, suggesting that the enzyme is not defective but is present at a reduced level.[223]

Plasmalogen levels are generally less than 5 percent of control in the brain, liver, kidney, muscle, and heart of Zellweger patients (Fig. 57-12).[16,224] There is a less striking, but significant, reduction of red blood cell plasmalogen levels.[224] The degree of red blood cell plasmalogen reduction is a function of age. During the first 5 weeks levels were 5 to 10 percent of control. Normal levels were observed in Zellweger patients whose age was 20 weeks or older.[225] Serial measurements in the same patient are not yet available. It is therefore not known whether the normal levels in the older patients are due to their having a less severe metabolic defect than the young

Table 57-2 Diagnostically Significant Abnormalities in Zellweger Syndrome

1. Peroxisomes absent or reduced in number
2. Catalase in cytosol
3. Deficient synthesis and reduced tissue levels of plasmalogens
4. Defective oxidation and abnormal accumulation of very long chain fatty acids
5. Deficient oxidation and age-dependent accumulation of phytanic acid
6. Defects in certain steps of bile acid formation and accumulation of bile acid intermediates
7. Defect in oxidation and accumulation of L-pipecolic acid
8. Increased urinary excretion of dicarboxylic acids

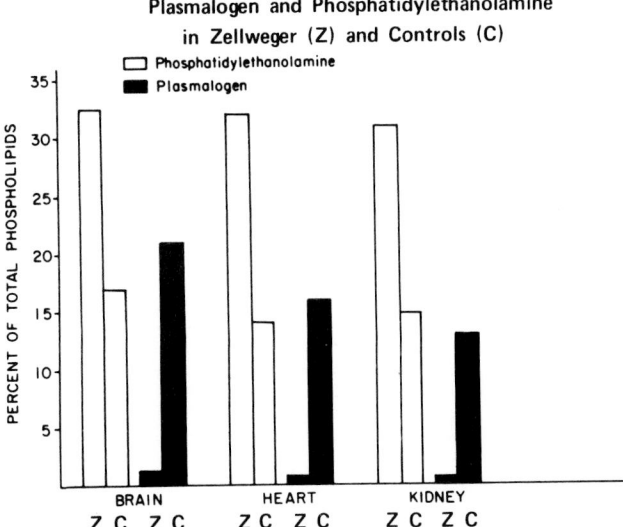

Fig. 57-12 Plasmalogen levels in postmortem tissues of patients with Zellweger syndrome. Note that levels of plasmalogens are reduced to less than 5 percent of control. There is a (compensatory?) increase in phosphatidyl ethanolamine, the ester-linked phospholipid analogue of plasmalogen. (*Modified from Heymans et al.[16] and Heymans et al.[224] Used by permission.*)

infants, or whether normalization with age is attributable to provision of plasmalogens in the diet. Bjorkhem et al. have devised a sensitive assay for red blood cell plasmalogen levels. A lipid extract of red blood cells is subjected to methyl trans-esterification, which forms a dimethylacetal from plasmalogens (ether lipids), whereas a methylated acid is produced from ester lipids. The ratio of the dimethylacetal to the methylated fatty acid is a measure of plasmalogen content.[226] The same method can also be applied to dried blood samples on filter paper obtained during neonatal screening.[227]

Increased Tissue Levels and Impaired Capacity to Degrade Very Long Chain Fatty Acids

Increased levels of VLCFA are present in all of the more than 250 patients with disorders of peroxisome biogenesis in whom this test has been performed (Fig. 57-13D). Increases of unbranched saturated or monounsaturated fatty acids with a chain length of 24 or more carbons have been observed in plasma, red blood cells, white blood cells, amniocytes, chorion villus cultures, and tissues.[228–233]

In Zellweger syndrome, plasma hexacosanoic acid ($C_{26:0}$) levels are increased ninefold or more over control. Unlike X-linked ALD, the monounsaturated VLCFA levels are also increased. The plasma level of hexacosenoic acid ($C_{26:1}$) was seven times control.[228] It has been proposed that the ($C_{26:1}$) moiety that is increased consists of *cis*-17 and *cis*-19 hexacosenoic acids.[231] At the same time, the levels of docosanoic ($C_{22:0}$) fatty acid are decreased in the plasma of Zellweger syndrome patients.[229] This leads to a strikingly abnormal $C_{26:0}/C_{22:0}$ ratio: 0.49 ± 0.03 in Zellweger syndrome patients compared to 0.014 ± 0.0076 in controls.[234] Poulos et al. have reported that Zellweger brain tissue also contains an excess of C_{26} to C_{38} polyenoic fatty acids.[235] The increased VLCFA plasma levels are already present on the first day after birth. There appears to be little diurnal variation or change with age (H.W. Moser, unpublished observation).

The VLCFA accumulation in Zellweger syndrome is due to an impaired capacity to degrade these acids,[228,232,236,237] a pro-

cess that normally takes place in the peroxisome.[19–21] Immunoblot studies have provided the explanation for the defective peroxisomal β oxidation. Zellweger liver is deficient in all of the peroxisomal β-oxidation proteins: acyl-CoA oxidase, the bifunctional protein with enoyl-CoA hydratase (EC 4.2.1.17) and 3-hydroxyacyl-CoA dehydrogenase (EC 1.1.1.35) activities, and 3-oxoacyl-CoA thiolase (acetyl-CoA acyltransferase: EC 2.3.1.16).[190,237–240] Small amounts of the high molecular weight precursor form of 3-oxoacyl-CoA thiolase were detected.[237,238,240]

The reason for the deficiency of the peroxisomal β-oxidation enzyme has been clarified by continuous label and pulse-chase experiments with cultured skin fibroblasts by Schram et al.[240] and by studies of in vitro protein synthesis.[237] In one study fibroblasts were labeled continuously for 4 days with [14C]leucine. Under these circumstances Zellweger and control cell lines synthesized and accumulated comparable amounts of catalase. This was not unexpected since Zellweger cells are known to contain approximately normal catalase levels. In contrast, the cells contained no demonstrable 14C-labeled acyl-CoA oxidase or mature 3-oxoacyl-CoA thiolase.[240] In a second experiment, the fibroblasts were labeled for 1 h with [35S]methionine. During this short interval, Zellweger and control fibroblasts synthesized comparable amounts of the precursors of the acyl-CoA oxidase. In a final experiment, the cells that had been exposed for 1 h to [35S]methionine were "chased" for 24 h with a medium containing unlabeled methionine. In the normal cell lines the precursor β-oxidation enzymes were converted to the mature enzyme form, but this failed to occur in the Zellweger cell lines, and furthermore, the total amount of labeled protein diminished greatly. It was concluded that the Zellweger cells were capable of synthesizing precursors of acyl-CoA oxidase and 3-oxoacyl-CoA thiolase, but that these proteins failed to be processed normally and that they were degraded more rapidly than normal. Studies with cell-free systems lead to similar conclusions, since they demonstrated that Zellweger liver produces normal amounts of mRNA for peroxisomal fatty acid oxidation enzymes.[237] Similarly, Chen et al. demonstrated that cultured skin fibroblasts of a neonatal ALD patient contained mRNA for the bifunctional peroxisomal fatty acid oxidation enzyme, while this enzyme was lacking in postmortem liver of the same patient.[241]

These studies lead to the conclusion that patients with disorders of peroxisomal biogenesis are capable of synthesizing peroxisomal β-oxidation enzymes but that the enzymes fail to be processed and are degraded. As a result the patients are deficient in mature peroxisomal fatty acid oxidation enzymes, and this results in the accumulation of VLCFA in the tissues. It is not yet determined why in Zellweger syndrome there is accumulation of both unsaturated and saturated VLCFA, while in X-linked ALD only saturated VLCFA are found in excess. The peroxisomal enzyme 2,4-dienoyl-coenzyme A reductase (EC 1.3.1.34) appears to have a major role in the oxidation of unsaturated fatty acids.[113,114] The activity of this enzyme has not yet been evaluated in Zellweger patients.

Medium- and Long-Chain Dicarboxylic Aciduria

Zellweger syndrome and neonatal ALD patients excrete in the urine modestly elevated amounts of medium-chain-length dicarboxylic acids.[242–244] These include those with an even number of carbon atoms, such as adipic (C_6), suberic (C_8), and

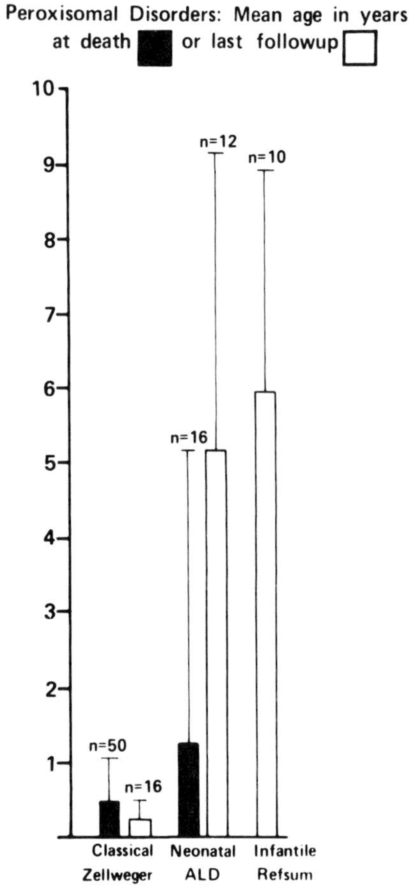

Peroxisomal Disorders: Mean age in years
at death ■ or last followup □

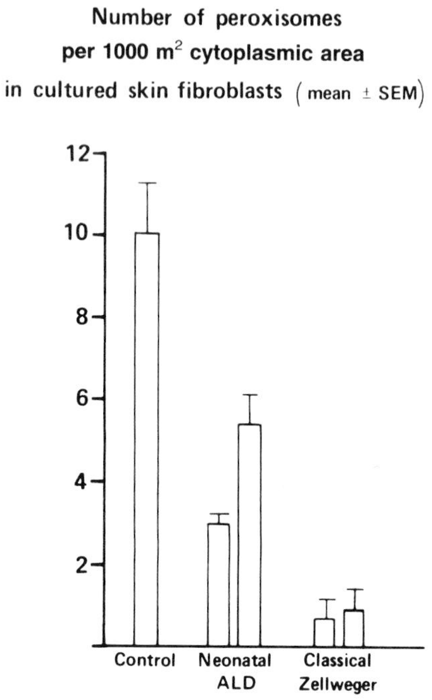

Number of peroxisomes
per 1000 m² cytoplasmic area
in cultured skin fibroblasts (mean ± SEM)

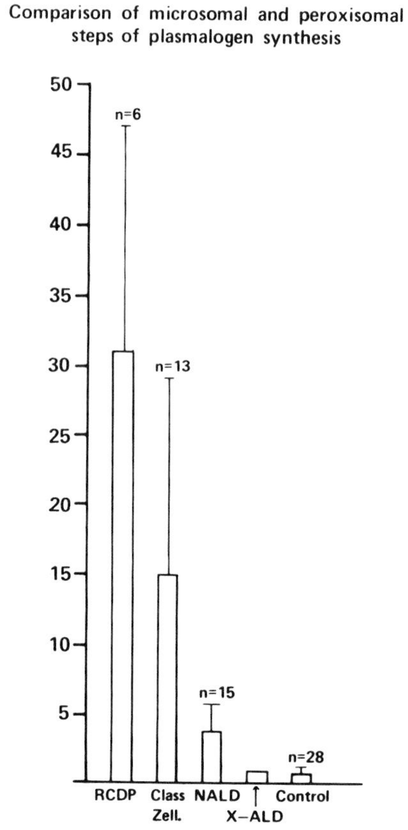

Comparison of microsomal and peroxisomal
steps of plasmalogen synthesis

A.

B.

C.

Peroxisomal Disorders: C26:0 □ and C26:1 ■
Fatty Acid levels in plasma (μg/ml)

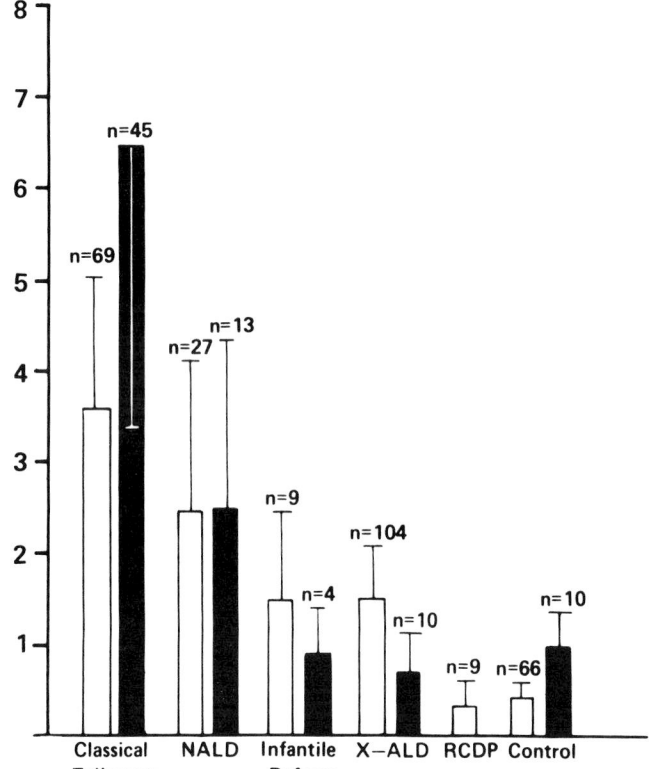

D.

Fig. 57-13 Comparisons among Zellweger syndrome, neonatal ALD, and infantile Refsum syndrome in respect to age of survival (A), numbers of peroxisomes in cultured skin fibroblasts (B), ratios of microsomal to peroxisomal steps of plasmalogen synthesis[222] (C), and extent of VLCFA excess in plasma (D). For the two parameters which are available for comparison, values for neonatal ALD are intermediate between those for Zellweger syndrome and infantile Refsum disease. Values for A, C, and D are calculated from cases studied at Kennedy Institute (see Table 57-3), while those for B are taken from Arias et al.[38] The cases designated as "neonatal ALD" in B are described in Ref. 25 (patients 5 and 7). While in Ref. 38 they were referred to "as clinically atypical patients who had features of both Zellweger syndrome and neonatal ALD," a recent review of their records indicates that with current state of knowledge the diagnosis of neonatal ALD is most appropriate. The $^3H/^{14}C$ ratio plotted in C indicates the relative incorporation into plasmalogens of ^{14}C hexadecanol, which requires peroxisomal reactions, and of ^3H-hexadecylglycerol, which bypasses the peroxisomal steps and uses only subsequent reactions in the pathway of plasmalogen synthesis that takes place in the microsomes.

sebacic (C_{10}) acids, as well as those with an odd number of carbon atoms, such as pimelic (C_7) and azelaic (C_9) acids, and 2-hydroxy odd- and even-chain dicarboxylic acids. In addition, the ratio of sebacic (C_{10}) to adipic (C_6) acids is abnormally increased compared to that in normal urine. Small, but nonetheless abnormally increased, amounts of longer chain ($\geq C_{12}$) dicarboxylic acids are also present in the urine of Zellweger and neonatal ALD patients.

Medium-chain-length dicarboxylic acids are formed both by P_{450}-mediated ω oxidation of medium-chain-length free fatty acids and by ω oxidation of long-chain fatty acids followed by degradation by β oxidation, principally in peroxisomes. Although mitochondria are capable of transporting C_{10} and C_{12} dicarboxylic acids and degrading them to shorter-chain-length dicarboxylic acids, including succinate (C_4), by β oxidation, the tenfold higher K_ms for this process in mitochondria compared to peroxisomes[245] suggest that the mitochondrial degradation of dicarboxylic acids is of relatively little importance except, perhaps, during fasting. In normal urine, it is likely that the strong predominance of adipic acid reflects the basal metabolism of dicarboxylic acids to (mostly) adipic and suberic acids by peroxisomes. Thus, in the absence of the efficient degradation of dicarboxylic acids by peroxisomes, the cytoplasmic levels of dicarboxylic acids should increase up to limits dictated by the alternate, low affinity mitochondrial system. Moreover, the cytoplasmic pattern of dicarboxylic acids in the absence of peroxisomal function would also be expected to reflect more the usual abundance of medium-chain free fatty acids (C_{12}, C_{10}, and C_8) and the chain length dependency of ω oxidation. The urinary pattern of dicarboxylic acids found in Zellweger syndrome and neonatal adrenoleukodystrophy[246] is consistent with the absence or severe depression of peroxisomal β oxidation, modified by the greater water solubility and lesser protein binding of the shorter chain dicarboxylic acids. Although abnormally increased, the dicarboxylic aciduria characteristic of patients with peroxisomal disorders is relatively mild, far less than that of primary defects of mitochondrial β oxidation[128] and of little diagnostic or clinical significance.

Defective Oxidation and Tissue Accumulation of Phytanic Acid

Phytanic acid oxidation activity in cultured skin fibroblasts of Zellweger patients is reduced as severely as in "adult" Refsum disease.[247,248] Plasma phytanic acid levels vary with age.[249] Wanders et al. reported that in Zellweger patients up to 17 weeks of age they were normal (3 to 7 μg/ml) but were significantly increased (25 to 59 μg/ml) in patients who were 40 weeks of age or older. Figure 57-14 shows the plasma phytanic acid levels of the 42 Zellweger patients up to 20 months of age who were tested at the Kennedy Institute. In one 6-week-old patient this level was 38 μg/ml. In all of the other patients it was below 8 μg/ml with a mean value of 3.3 μg/ml ± 6.8 μg/ml (SD). Since phytanic acid is of dietary origin exclusively, the moderately increased levels in the older infants almost certainly are due to the combined effects of dietary phytanic acid intake and impaired capacity to degrade this substance.

Accumulation of Intermediates of Bile Acid Metabolism

Abnormally high plasma levels of 3α,7α,12α-trihydroxy-5β-cholestanoic acid (THCA) and of 3α,7α-dihydroxy-5β-choles-

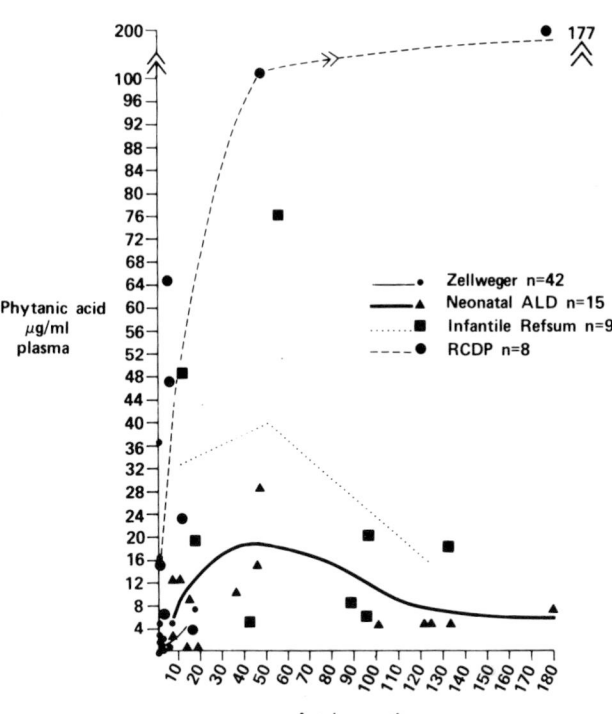

Plasma Phytanic Acid Level as a Function of Age

Fig. 57-14 Variation with age of plasma phytanic acid levels in patients tested at the Kennedy Institute. These are "cross-sectional" results in that all points represent different patients. Due to the scale only a small proportion of the 42 Zellweger patients are shown on this graph. Twenty-eight of these patients (ages 0 to 6 months) had normal plasma phytanic levels, that is, below 3 μg/ml. While neonatal ALD and infantile Refsum patients had higher levels, this appears to be related to their longer survival, since the youngest neonatal ALD patients had levels similar to the Zellweger patients. For unknown reasons the neonatal ALD and infantile Refsum patients who are older than 80 months appear to have somewhat lower plasma levels than those age 30 to 60 months, even though in all cases the phytanic acid oxidation in cultured skin fibroblasts was less than 2 percent of control (H.W. Moser, unpublished observation). In the RCDP patients plasma phytanic levels are higher and become elevated at an earlier age than in patients in the other disease groups.

tanoic acid (DHCA) are present consistently in Zellweger syndrome patients.[22,23,250-254] Total bile acid levels are normal except when there is liver damage. In Zellweger syndrome, THCA, DHCA, varanic acid, and certain other metabolites may account for 30 to 50 percent of total plasma bile acids, while normally these metabolic intermediates are absent or present in very low concentration.

Defects in peroxisomal function can readily account for these abnormalities. Normally, conversion of THCA into cholic acid and of DHCA into desoxycholic acid takes place in the peroxisome.[71,255,256] Kase et al. have shown these reactions to be deficient in Zellweger syndrome both in vivo and in vitro.[257]

Accumulation and Impaired Catabolism of Pipecolic Acid

Danks et al. first reported elevated levels of pipecolic acid in plasma and urine[24] of Zellweger syndrome patients. This finding has been confirmed repeatedly.[186,258,259] Dancis and Hutzler have reported that 4-day- and 10-day-old infants with Zellweger syndrome had normal pipecolic acid levels in plasma. The levels increased postnatally subsequent to age 3½ weeks.[258] Lam, Hutzler, and Dancis also made the important observation that the urine of Zellweger patients contained the L-isomer of pipecolic acid almost exclusively.[260] Thus L-pipecolic acid rather than the D-isomer or the DL-racemic mixture should be utilized in metabolic studies.

The locus of the metabolic defect has been delineated in part by loading studies with lysine and pipecolic acid. There was no significant increase of pipecolic acid levels in plasma, urine, or cerebrospinal fluid following an oral L-lysine load.[259] L-Lysine in liver is metabolized via the saccharopurine pathway, which does not involve pipecolic acid. The pipecolic acid pathway of lysine degradation is used mainly in brain.[261] Failure of an oral lysine load to increase pipecolic acid levels probably is due to failure of substantial amounts of lysine to cross the blood-brain barrier. Substantial differences between Zellweger and control patients were observed when they were administered DL-pipecolic acid (150 mg/kg).[259] The Zellweger patient showed a greater and more prolonged increase in plasma pipecolic acid levels, and a lesser increment in the excretion of α-aminoadipic acid, the eventual metabolic product of pipecolic acid oxidation. This finding suggests that Zellweger patients have a diminished capacity to metabolize pipecolic acid, albeit subject to the caution that the load consisted of DL- rather than L-pipecolic acid. Degradation of DL-pipecolic acid has been localized to the rat liver peroxisome,[262] but this may reflect a relatively nonspecific D-amino acid oxidase activity which is also known to be present in the peroxisome.[76,263] This activity has in fact been shown to be reduced in the kidney of a patient with Zellweger syndrome.[190]

The most meaningful studies are those which involve the L-isomer. The subcellular localization of L-pipecolic acid metabolism is species-dependent. Mihalik and Rhead have shown recently that in rats and rabbits this reaction takes place in the mitochondrion, while in human beings and other primates, it occurs in the peroxisome.[94] The conversion of pipecolic acid to α-aminoadipic acid involves a two-step process.[264] Mihalik and Watkins have studied this reaction in the liver of primates, where as already noted, it takes place in the peroxisomes, and found that this reaction requires two separate enzymes.[264] It will be of great interest to study the activities of these two enzymes in Zellweger syndrome patients.

Mitochondrial Abnormalities in Zellweger Syndrome

Patients with Zellweger syndrome have normal lactate/pyruvate and β-hydroxybutyrate/acetoacetate ratios in blood, and their cultured skin fibroblasts metabolize [1-^{14}C] and [2-^{14}C] pyruvate at a normal rate.[12] Mitochondrial structure was normal in a liver biopsy specimen.[190] While these observations exclude consistent alterations in mitochondrial function and structure, there are indications of mitochondrial abnormalities in some patients.[10,11,141,265,266] Kelley and Corkey[141] found that Zellweger cultured skin fibroblasts showed five times normal sensitivity to the complex III inhibitor antimycin A. Trijbels et al. also suggested involvement of complex III and proposed that there was impairment of the interaction between ubiquinone and succinate dehydrogenase. They postulated that this could result from changes in mitochondrial membrane lipid composition secondary to a primary peroxisomal defect.[12] Full evaluation of the mitochondrial defect requires further study.

Liver Function

In Heymans' literature survey >85 percent of Zellweger patients had elevated transaminases, and hyperbilirubinemia was reported in 13 of 19 cases (60 percent).[9] Hypoprothrombinemia responsive to vitamin K administration was reported in 18 patients. Liver enlargement was common.

Iron

An early report by Vitale et al.[200] noted the presence of hypersideremia, and elevated iron levels or total iron-binding capacity was reported in 17 of 30 cases.[9] However, Gilchrist et al.[201] reported that liver iron levels were increased only prior to 18 weeks of age, and that they were normal in patients who were 20 weeks or older. Patton et al. noted that even in the young infants the iron excess was small compared to that in hemochromatosis.[267] These observations suggest that excess iron deposition has little or no pathogenetic significance in the Zellweger syndrome.

Glycogen Deposition and Hypoglycemia

Glycogen deposits in the liver and neurons and glia of the central nervous system have been reported in one case.[268] Hypoglycemia has been reported in five other cases.[9] In two cases this was associated with hyperplasia of pancreatic islets.[267]

Neurophysiological Studies

Neurophysiological studies show profound abnormalities.[269] Continuous negative sharp waves were observed on the electroencephalogram. Brain stem auditory evoked responses were not elicitable or prolonged, and somatosensory evoked responses showed a severe propagation defect. In 6 of 11 patients there was no recognizable audiometric response to 70 decibels. The electroretinogram is extinguished.[199]

DISORDERS OF PEROXISOMAL BIOGENESIS WITH PHENOTYPE OTHER THAN THE CLASSIC ZELLWEGER SYNDROME

Current Classification

Absent or greatly diminished numbers of peroxisomes and the full panel of Zellweger syndrome biochemical defects are now known to occur in a series of disorders with several different phenotypes. These disorders were described and named before the peroxisomal abnormality was recognized, and the names of the disorders—neonatal ALD, infantile Refsum disease, hyperpipecolic acidemia—reflect the features that attracted the attention of the original observers. This traditional classification will be used here in view of the large number of literature citations and the lack of availability, at this time, of a more meaningful system. Table 57-3 lists the patients studied at the Kennedy Institute classified in accordance with this traditional system. As discussed below, a classification based on complementation analyses is emerging.

Neonatal Adrenoleukodystrophy

Neonatal ALD was first described in 1978 by Ulrich et al.[270] and has been reviewed comprehensively.[25,271,272] Ulrich's patient was weak and severely hypotonic at birth, developed seizures at 4 days and a hypsarrhythmic electroencephalogram at 2 months. Seizures continued to be severe, there was no psychomotor development, and the boy died at 20 months. Postmortem examination showed widespread demyelination and micropolygyria involving the cortex and the insula of the temporal operculum. The adrenals were small with atrophic cortices which contained ballooned cells with lamellar cytoplasmic inclusions similar to those in X-linked ALD. Postmortem studies of brain cholesterol ester fractions showed a marked excess of hexacosanoic acid (25 percent of total fatty acid) (B. Molzer, H. Bernheimer, unpublished results). On the basis of these findings Ulrich et al. named this disorder *connatal ALD*. The disorder is now referred to as *neonatal ALD*.

Neonatal ALD must be differentiated sharply from X-linked ALD (Chap. 58). The differences are fundamental. Hepatic peroxisomes are absent or greatly diminished in neonatal ALD, while they have a normal structure in X-linked ALD.[20,272,273] Neonatal ALD patients have an impaired capacity to synthesize plasmalogens[274] and oxidize phytanic acid[248] and have increased plasma levels of pipecolic acid[275] and bile acid intermediates.[276,277] None of these abnormalities are present in X-linked ALD. X-linked and neonatal ALD have never occurred in the same family. While tissue accumulation of VLCFA is a feature common to both disorders, this results from a different mechanism: In neonatal ALD there is absence or deficiency of all peroxisomal β-oxidation enzymes,[241] while in X-linked ALD the basic defect appears to involve the activation of VLCFA (see Chap. 58).

Table 57-3 Patients with Peroxisomal Disorders Tested at the Kennedy Institute (Excluding X-Linked Adrenoleukodystrophy and Adult Refsum Disease)

Disorder	Number of cases
Classic Zellweger	101
Neonatal ALD	38
"Mild Zellweger"	5
Infantile Refsum	10
Hyperpipecolic acidemia	5
Leber amaurosis	2
Phenotype resembling Zellweger but peroxisome structure intact	13
Rhizomelic chondrodysplasia punctata	14
Clinical information insufficient to permit classification	47
Total	235

NOTE: Samples tested were referred from United States, Canada, and Western Europe. Classification is based upon clinical information from referring physicians in accordance with criteria described in the text. The category "phenotype resembling Zellweger, but peroxisome structure intact" includes one case with thiolase deficiency;[291,292] two cases with acyl-CoA oxidase deficiency;[293] one case with bifunctional hydratase-dehydrogenase deficiency (P.A. Watkins, unpublished observation); and one case with an as yet undefined defect in VLCFA oxidation.[294]

Many of the phenotype differences between neonatal ALD and Zellweger syndrome can be summarized by the statement that neonatal ALD is a slightly less severe illness (Fig. 57-13). Neonatal ALD patients live longer. In the Kennedy Institute series, the mean age of death in neonatal ALD is 15 ± 31 months (n=16), compared to 5.7 ± 6.8 months (n=50) in classic Zellweger syndrome (Fig. 57-13A). Dysmorphic features are less striking than in Zellweger syndrome and may be absent.[25] A few residual peroxisomes have been seen in liver,[272,273] and substantial numbers have been reported in fibroblasts of neonatal ALD patients (Fig. 57-13B).[38] The defects in plasmalogen synthesis (Fig. 57-13C) and the degree of VLCFA accumulation (Fig. 57-13D) in neonatal ALD are less severe than in Zellweger syndrome. The neuronal and gray matter changes in neonatal ALD are less consistent and less severe. While some neonatal ALD cases showed striking micropolygyria,[270] other cases showed only mild neuronal migrational defects and heterotopias,[271] and in yet others the cortex and neurons appeared normal.[210,276] The olivary nucleus apparently was normal in all cases. Most neonatal ALD cases showed a widespread sudanophilic leukodystrophy, often associated with perivascular accumulation of lymphocytes, as in X-linked ALD, and the white matter involvement actually is more striking than in Zellweger syndrome. This is probably attributable to the longer survival in neonatal ALD, since the white matter lesion is known to advance with age. Chondrodysplasia punctata and renal cysts are not observed in neonatal ALD.

The clinical course of neonatal ALD varies from that of a severely involved infant who never made psychomotor gains and died at 4 months[212] to patients who are in stable albeit handicapped conditions in their midteens.[233,277] These long-surviving patients are severely retarded and moderately dysmorphic. Impaired hearing and retinopathy initially had led to the diagnosis of Usher syndrome. Most neonatal ALD patients have an impaired cortisol response to ACTH, but overt adrenal insufficiency is infrequent. While neonatal ALD patients may achieve the ability to walk and to say a few words, their mental age rarely advances beyond 10 to 12 months. They may also experience regression at 3 to 5 years of age, presumably due to progression of the leukodystrophy.

Infantile Refsum Disease

This disorder was described first by Scotto et al. in 1982.[278] These authors had evaluated a 5-year-old boy who had an enlarged liver and in addition was mentally retarded and had sensorineural deafness, pigmentary degeneration of the retina, anosmia, and dysmorphic features. Ultrastructural study of a liver biopsy specimen revealed lamellar structures which resembled those normally found in plant chloroplasts which are known to contain bound phytol. This microscopic observation led the authors to measure the plasma phytanic acid level, which was found to be 50 to 100 μg/ml (normal less than 3 μg). This important and unexpected finding led to a comparison with "adult" Refsum disease (Chap. 59). Elevated phytanic acid levels, pigmentary degeneration of the retina, sensorineural hearing loss, and anosmia are observed in both, but dysmorphic features and mental retardation do not occur in "adult" Refsum disease. These considerations led to the designation *infantile phytanic acid storage disease*. It was also noted that Kahlke et al. had described a similar case in 1974.[279]

It is fortuitous that the ultrastructural changes on liver biopsy led Scotto et al. to focus initially on the phytanic acid abnormality in infantile Refsum disease. Subsequent studies, many of them carried out by the original group of investigators, have demonstrated that infantile Refsum disease is a disorder of peroxisomal deficiency. Peroxisomes are absent or severely diminished in number;[280] plasmalogen synthesis is impaired;[281] VLCFA,[247] bile acid intermediates,[282] and pipecolic acid[26] accumulate; and, as expected, phytanic acid oxidative activity is deficient.[247] The phytanic acid oxidation deficiency and phytanic acid accumulation in Zellweger or neonatal ALD patients who survive beyond the fortieth week is equivalent to that in infantile Refsum disease (Fig. 57-14). The emphasis on the phytanic acid abnormality and the name thus reflect a historical sequence rather than a fundamental difference.

Perhaps because the first patient identified by Scotto et al.[278] was already 5 years old (an age at which most Zellweger and neonatal ALD cases would have succumbed), the infantile Refsum disease category includes the most mildly involved patients with disordered peroxisomal biogenesis (Fig. 57-13A). The patients included in the Kennedy series all were living at ages 3 to 11 years. All infantile Refsum patients have learned how to walk, although gait may be ataxic and broad-based, and their cognitive function is in the severely retarded range[283] compared to profound retardation in neonatal ALD and Zellweger syndrome. All the patients have had sensorineural hearing loss. They have pigmentary degeneration of the retina. The electroretinogram demonstrates severely subnormal rod- and cone-mediated responses, with greater involvement evident for responses generated by middle and inner retinal neurons compared with responses mediated by photoreceptors.[284] Patients have moderately dysmorphic features including epicanthal folds, flat bridge of nose, and low set ears.[285] Early hypotonia and enlarged liver with impaired function were common.[278,283] For unknown reasons, levels of plasma cholesterol and high and low density lipoproteins are often moderately reduced. Chondrodysplasia punctata and renal cortical cysts are absent. Postmortem study has been performed in only one infantile Refsum patient, who died at 12 years of age.[285] This revealed micronodular liver cirrhosis and small, hypoplastic adrenals. The brain showed no malformations except for a severe hypoplasia of the cerebellar granule layer and ectopic locations of the Purkinje cells in the molecular layer. A mild and diffuse reduction of axons and myelin was found in the corpus callosum, the periventricular white matter, corticospinal tracts, and optic nerves. While large numbers of perivascular macrophages were present in the same areas, there was no active demyelination. The retina and cochlea showed severe degenerative changes.

Mild Variants of Zellweger Syndrome

Barth et al.[286] and Bleeker-Wagemaker et al.[287] have reported 3 patients with mild variants of Zellweger syndrome. Clinical features and laboratory data (including phytanic acid levels of 34 and 62 µg/ml) resemble those in patients that have been included in the infantile Refsum category.

Hyperpipecolic Acidemia

The first case of hyperpipecolic acidemia was reported in 1968 by Gatfield et al.[27] They described a boy who presented at 6 months with an enlarged liver and hypotonia. He was severely retarded, had pigmentary degeneration of the retina, and died at 27 months following progressive neurologic deterioration. Postmortem study showed cirrhosis of the liver and a sudanophilic leukodystrophy with intracellular lamellar inclusions. Pipecolic acid levels were elevated in plasma, urine, and tissues. Loading studies indicated impaired catabolism of pipecolic acid, but no abnormalities of lysine metabolism. At the time of the initial report the disturbance in pipecolic acid metabolism was considered to be the main abnormality. Subsequent studies of cultured skin fibroblasts and plasma samples of this patient have revealed elevated levels of VLCFA equivalent to those in ALD (H.W. Moser, unpublished observation), and the disturbance of pipecolic acid metabolism appears similar to that in Zellweger syndrome. It is likely that this case represented a disorder of peroxisome deficiency. The clinical course and the absence of renal cysts and dysmorphic features suggest that it should be assigned to the neonatal ALD category, even though in the autopsy report the adrenals were described as "not remarkable." However, the adrenal pathology in X-linked or neonatal ALD may be subtle and not recognized unless specifically looked for (J.M. Powers, personal communication).

Three other cases of hyperpipecolic acidemia have been reported in the literature.[288,289] In each of these cases, retrospective studies of frozen plasma and cultured skin fibroblast samples (H.W. Moser, unpublished observation) have revealed VLCFA abnormalities characteristic of ALD and the disorders of peroxisome biogenesis. There are many clinical and biochemical similarities among hyperpipecolic acidemia, the Zellweger syndrome, and neonatal ALD. Points of difference include the facial appearance of the patient reported by Thomas et al.,[289] which does not resemble that of Zellweger syndrome patients. Challa et al. reported periodic acid–Schiff–positive inclusions in the astrocytes of their patient, an abnormality that they did not observe in Zellweger syndrome.[290] Potentially the most significant difference is the report by the same authors that peroxisomes were normal in the postmortem liver of their patient.[290] However, the report did not include photomicrographs and did not specify whether catalase cytochemistry was performed. Furthermore we have studied cultured fibroblasts of this same patient and found that catalase activity was cytosolic (P.A. Watkins, H.W. Moser, unpublished observation). As already noted, in our experience in patients with intact liver peroxisomes, catalase activity in cultured skin fibroblasts has been located in the particulate fraction. The points of resemblance between hyperpipecolic acidemia, Zellweger syndrome, and, particularly, neonatal ALD outweigh the reported differences, and in our view, there is insufficient reason at present to assign these patients with hyperpipecolic acidemia to a separate disease category.

Presentation Resembling Leber Congenital Amaurosis

Ek et al.[30] reported a boy who at age 7 months presented with eye findings characteristic of Leber congenital amaurosis. He was hypotonic and retarded and had an enlarged liver, but lacked dysmorphic features and chondrodysplasia punctata. Liver biopsy demonstrated lack of peroxisomes, and biochemical results were characteristic of the disorders of peroxisome biogenesis. This report demonstrates that eye abnormalities may be a prominent symptom of peroxisome deficiency disorders and that they represent at least one of the causes of Leber congenital amaurosis.

ZELLWEGER-LIKE PHENOTYPE IN PATIENTS WITH STRUCTURALLY INTACT PEROXISOMES

Peroxisomal 3-Oxoacyl-Coenzyme A Thiolase Deficiency

In 1986 Goldfischer et al.[291] reported a girl with dysmorphic features resembling those of the Zellweger syndrome who was profoundly weak and hypotonic at birth, at 24 h developed intractable seizures, and failed to make psychomotor gains prior to her death at 11 months. Postmortem study demonstrated renal cortical cysts, atrophic adrenal glands, a sudanophilic leukodystrophy, and heterotopias of large neurons in the cerebellum. Levels of VLCFA and bile acid intermediates were similar to those in the disorders of peroxisomal biogenesis.

It came as a surprise when the liver was found to contain abundant peroxisomes. Additional biochemical studies revealed key differences between this case and the disorders of peroxisomal biogenesis. Plasmalogen biosynthesis was normal and immunoblot studies of peroxisomal fatty acid β-oxidation enzymes revealed that only one of the enzymes—3-oxoacyl-coenzyme A thiolase—was deficient, while the other enzymes were present in normal quantity.[292] Addition of the thiolase enzyme to a liver homogenate from this patient restored peroxisomal β oxidation to normal in a concentration-dependent manner. The fact that the isolated thiolase deficiency was associated with both VLCFA and bile acid intermediate excess suggests that this enzyme is involved in the metabolism of both groups of compounds.

Peroxisomal Acyl-CoA Oxidase Deficiency

Poll-The et al.[293] have described two brothers with an isolated deficiency of peroxisomal acyl-CoA oxidase. The patients presented with hypotonia, neonatal seizures, and severe psychomotor retardation. Biochemical abnormalities were confined to VLCFA excess. Bile acids, plasmalogens, and pipecolic acid were normal. Liver peroxisomes were present and, in fact, appeared to be enlarged. Naidu et al.[294] reported a girl with similar clinical presentation, including retinopathy and adrenal involvement, in whom the metabolic defect was also confined to VLCFA metabolism. Unlike the patients reported by Poll-The et al., immunoblot studies revealed normal amounts of material reacting with antibody to peroxisomal acyl-CoA oxidase. These cases, as well as the previously cited 3-oxoacyl-coenzyme A thiolase deficiency, indicate that a Zellweger-like phenotype can be associated wtih isolated defects of peroxisomal enzymes and intact peroxisome structure. Thirteen cases in this category have been identified at the Kennedy Institute (Table 57-3).

RHIZOMELIC CHONDRODYSPLASIA PUNCTATA

Heymans et al.[295,296] demonstrated impaired plasmalogen biosynthesis and phytanic acid accumulation in rhizomelic chondrodysplasia punctata (RCDP) patients and assigned this disorder to the peroxisome disease category. Liver peroxisomes are demonstrable, but their distribution and structure may be abnormal. Many hepatocytes appear to lack peroxisomes, while other liver cells contain an increased number of irregularly shaped huge peroxisomes (Hugo S.A. Heymans, personal communication). Catalase in cultured skin fibroblasts is in the particulate fraction.[297] Thus, while peroxisome structure may be abnormal, RCDP differs from the disorders of peroxisome biogenesis in that a substantial number of peroxisomes are present. Hoefler et al.[297] have shown that RCDP is associated with three biochemical abnormalities: The first is a defect in plasmalogen biosynthesis which is significantly more severe than in the Zellweger syndrome. Heymans et al.[295] had previously demonstrated deficient DHAPAT activity. The second is a phytanic acid oxidation defect equivalent to that in Refsum disease and Zellweger syndrome. Plasma phytanic acid levels as a function of age in RCDP patients are higher than in patients with disorders of peroxisome biogenesis (Fig. 57-14), suggesting that the phytanic acid oxidation defect may be different. The third defect is the presence of 3-oxoacyl-coenzyme A thiolase in the unprocessed form.[297] In spite of this last abnormality VLCFA oxidation is normal. Levels of bile acid intermediates are not increased.

The RCDP phenotype differs from that of Zellweger syndrome. RCDP patients have striking shortening of proximal limbs (Fig. 57-15), severely disturbed endochondrial bone formation, and coronal clefts of vertebral bodies on lateral roentgenograms of the spine. Most RCDP patients have ichthyosis and cataracts. The chondrodysplasia punctata is more widespread than in Zellweger syndrome and may involve the vertebral columns and some extraskeletal tissues, whereas in the Zellweger syndrome it is usually confined to the patella and acetabulum. RCDP must be differentiated from other forms of chondrodysplasia punctata. These include the Conradi-Hunermann form, which has an autosomal dominant mode of inheritance, while RCDP inheritance is autosomal recessive. Limb length in Conradi-Hunermann syndrome patients is normal, and they have normal cognition and a longer life span.[298] There are also X-linked dominant[299] and X-linked recessive[300] forms of chondrodysplasia punctata, the latter being associated also with defective steroid sulfatase activity. Metabolic defects associated with peroxisomes are present only in the rhizomelic form of chondrodysplasia punctata (H.W. Moser, R. Schutgens, unpublished observations).

PROSPECTS OF CLASSIFICATION BASED UPON COMPLEMENTATION ANALYSIS

A promising new development is the utilization of complementation analysis to clarify the pathogenesis and classification of peroxisomal disorders. Complementation is demonstrated by the acquisition of the capacity to synthesize plasmalogens, and to form peroxisomes as evidenced by formation of particle-bound catalase. Cultured cell lines from different patients

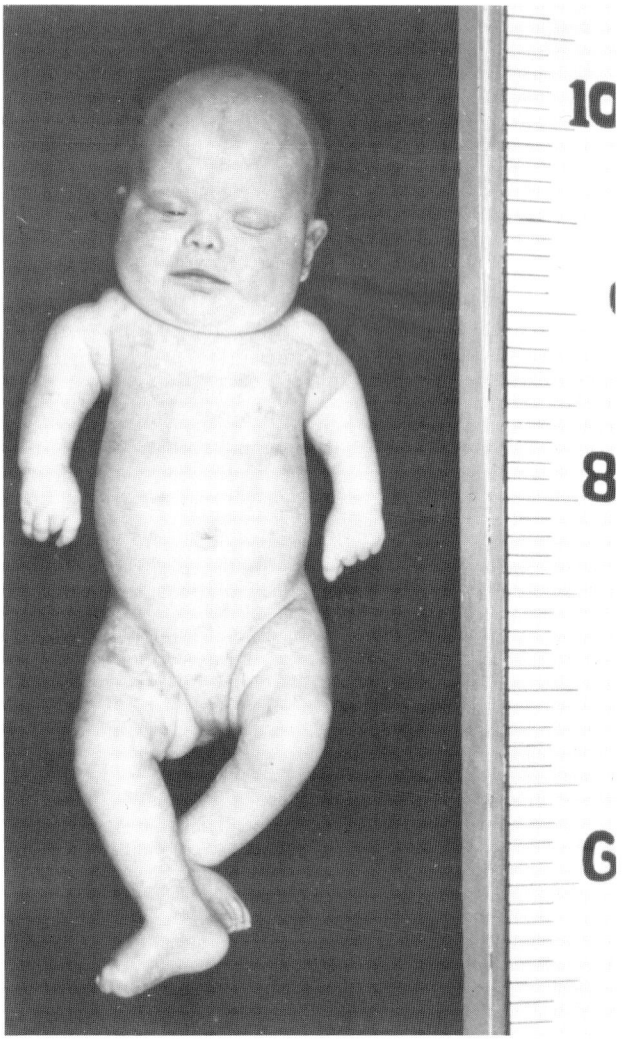

A.

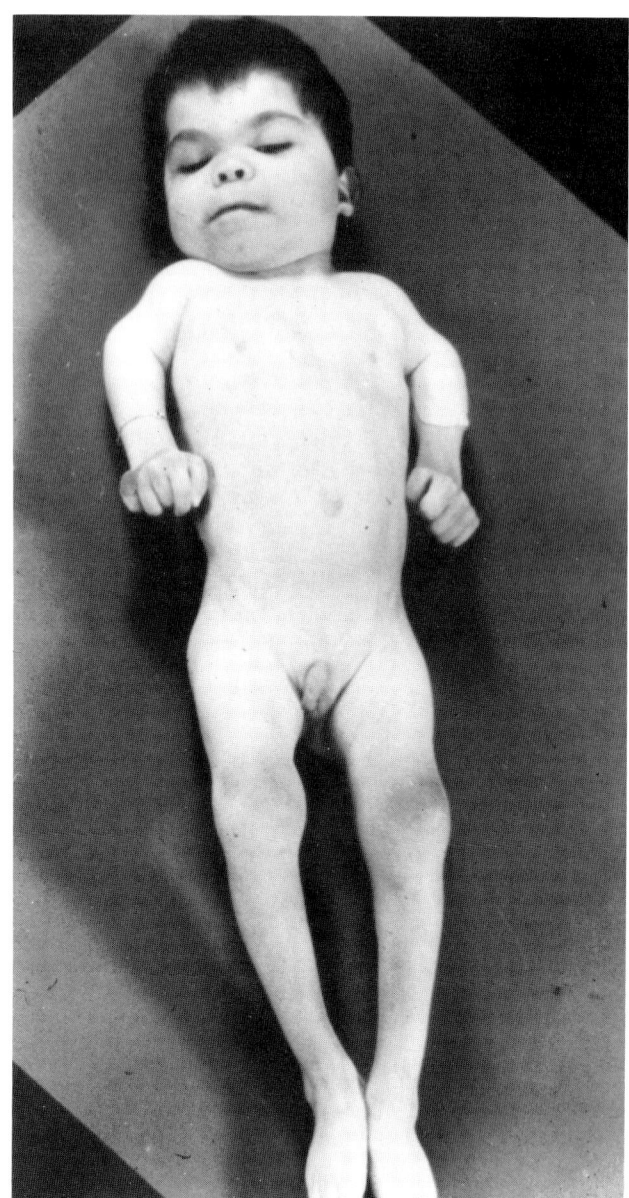

B.

Fig. 57-15 A newborn female (A) and a 12-year-old boy (B) with rhizomelic chondrodysplasia punctata (RCDP). Note severe shortening of proximal limbs, depressed bridge of nose, hypertelorism, and widespread erythematous and scaling skin lesions in patient A. Patient A is case 2 in Ref. 297. Patient B is case 7 in Ref. 297a. Both patients had the biochemical defects characteristic of RCDP (see Ref. 297). (*Photo A courtesy of Dr. B. McGillivary, Vancouver, B.C.; photo B courtesy of Dr. R.B.H. Schutgens, Amsterdam, The Netherlands.*)

are fused by the addition of polyethylene glycol and dimethylsulfoxide, and compared with cell lines that have been co-cultivated but not fused and with self-fusion controls. A complementation analysis is positive when cells that are unable to synthesize plasmalogens or to form particle-bound catalase acquire this capacity after fusion.

So far, six complementation groups have been established[301,302] (Table 57-4). Group 1 comprises RCDP. Group 2 includes cell lines from patients with Zellweger syndrome, infantile Refsum disease, and hyperpipecolic acidemia. Groups 3 and 5 include Zellweger patients who died at ages 3 and 5 months, respectively, presumably examples of the severe "classic" form of the disease. The Zellweger patients in complementation group 2 ranged in age from 2 to 6 years and thus may represent a somewhat milder form of the disease. Complementation group 4 includes patients with neonatal ALD.

This group is probably heterogeneous, since Roscher et al.[302] have found two neonatal ALD complementation groups.

The complementation analyses reported so far indicate that five distinct genetic defects can lead to disordered peroxisome biogenesis (see Table 57-4) (Brul et al.[301]): groups 2 to 5, plus the two neonatal ALD groups of Roscher et al.[302] Group 1 (RCDP) is clearly distinct, since peroxisome structure is intact in this disorder. Complementation studies so far have been applied only to a limited number of cell lines, and thus it is possible that additional groups will be identified. Furthermore, while existence of complementation establishes that cell lines are genotypically distinct, failure to demonstrate complementation does not prove identity.[302]

It is likely that careful analysis of phenotype within each of the complementation groups will result in a revised classification of peroxisomal disorders and that this classification will

Table 57-4 Peroxisomal Disorder Complementation Groups

Group 1	RCDP
Group 2	Zellweger syndrome 1, infantile Refsum, hyperpipecolic acidemia
Group 3	Zellweger syndrome 2
Group 4	Neonatal adrenoleukodystrophy
Group 5	Zellweger syndrome 3

SOURCE: From Brul et al.[301] Roscher et al.[302] have demonstrated two complementation groups within group 4 (neonatal adrenoleukodystrophy).

modify or replace the one in current use. Biochemical and genetic study of the factors involved in the complementation events may also contribute to the precise definition of the defects (see Addendum.)

PATHOGENESIS OF PEROXISOMAL DISORDERS

Nature of the Defect in Zellweger Syndrome

Defective formation of the peroxisomal membrane was originally considered as a likely cause for the absence of the organelle. Recent studies indicate that a different mechanism is involved. By means of immunoblot studies, the livers of Zellweger and infantile Refsum disease patients were found to contain normal amounts of the 69-, 53-, and 22-kDa integral membrane proteins of peroxisomes.[303,304] These membrane proteins were also found in normal and Zellweger fibroblasts.[305,306] In homogenates from Zellweger cells, these proteins sedimented in a membrane fraction, albeit at the abnormally low density of 1.10 g/cm^3, compared to the usual fibroblast peroxisome density of 1.17.[306] With immunofluorescence techniques, the peroxisomal integral membrane proteins were located in unusual membrane structures that were much larger in size (though fewer in number) than normal peroxisomes[305] (Fig. 57-16). As discussed above, the enzymes that should be inside these peroxisomal membrane vesicles are either absent or mislocalized to the cytosol. These results indicate that peroxisomes are not entirely absent in Zellweger syndrome, but rather consist of (nearly) empty membrane ghosts. These ghosts have been visualized by immunoelectron microscopy.[306] The results suggest that the primary defect(s) involves the machinery for the posttranslational import of peroxisomal proteins. Obvious candidates include the receptor and the ATPase that are involved in the import mechanism.[52,176]

The complementation studies described above indicate that disorders of peroxisome deficiency involve at least five distinct genetic defects,[301,302] indicating that peroxisome assembly may be disturbed by a variety of genetic abnormalities.

Enzymatic Consequences of Disordered Peroxisomal Biogenesis

The observed pattern of enzyme deficiencies and subcellular distributions in the peroxisome deficiency disorders is in good agreement with the nature of the defect and with the known manner of assembly of the organelle. Because these proteins are synthesized on cytoplasmic free polyribosomes and imported into preexisting peroxisomes posttranslationally from

the cytosol,[46] a defect in the import machinery would cause newly made peroxisomal proteins to remain in the cytosol. Many of them, not belonging there, would probably be degraded rapidly, but some could accumulate. The steady state concentrations of peroxisomal enzymes in Zellweger syndrome would be expected to vary, because each protein would turn over at an idiosyncratic rate determined by its individual interaction with the protein degradation machinery of the cytosol. This is in contrast to the synchronous turnover of peroxisomal proteins in normal cells,[183,184] where degradation occurs by the autophagic sequestration of entire peroxisomes.[76,182]

Studies of the formation and turnover of peroxisomal β-oxidation enzymes[240] indicate that the oxidase and thiolase enzymes are formed normally in Zellweger syndrome, but that they are degraded rapidly and fail to be processed normally. The same phenomenon may apply to DHAPAT. Webber et al.[223] found that DHAPAT in Zellweger fibroblasts had a normal K_m, but was present in abnormally low concentrations. L-α-hydroxy acid oxidase is present at approximately half of its usual concentration.[215] The activity of D-amino acid oxidase is normal in liver[215] but reduced in kidney.[190] Catalase accumulates to as much as twice its usual level[37,190,215]; consistent with

Fig. 57-16 Immunofluorescence analysis of peroxisomal proteins in control and Zellweger fibroblasts. Top row (A,E), anticatalase; second row (B,F), antiserum against several peroxisomal integral membrane proteins; third row (C,G), affinity-purified antibody to 69-kDa membrane protein; bottom row (D,H), preimmune serum. For details see text and Ref. 305. (*From Santos et al.*[305] *Used with permission.*)

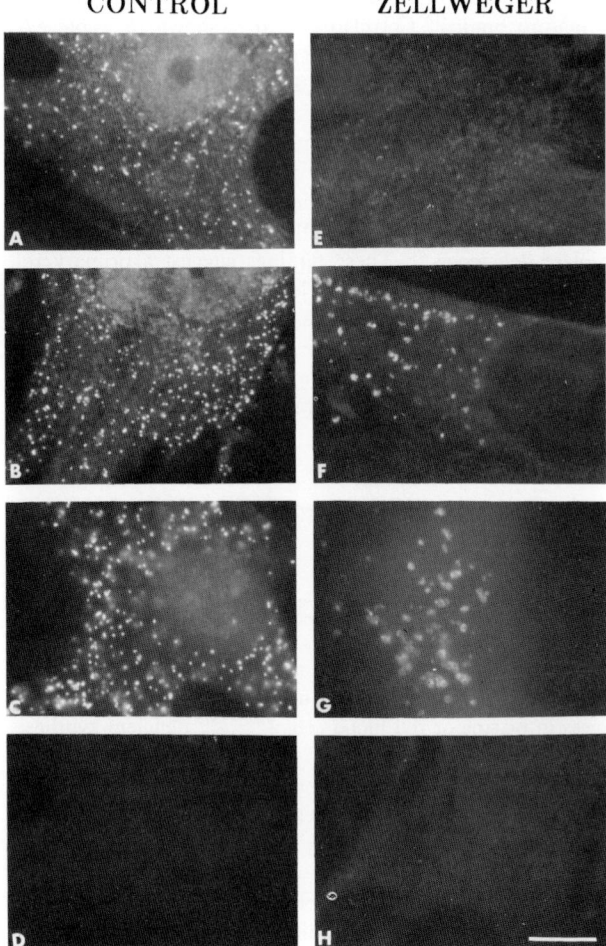

CONTROL   ZELLWEGER

this, the rate of degradation of catalase in Zellweger fibroblasts is distinctly slower than normal (Fig. 3 in Ref. 214). Failure to process 3-oxoacyl-CoA thiolase is not necessarily attributable to the defective peroxisome structure, since this enzyme also fails to be processed in RCDP[297] where the structure of the organelle is at least partially intact.[296]

Pathological Consequences of Peroxisome Enzyme Defects

Zellweger syndrome is associated with profound malformations in many organs, and its very existence indicates that peroxisomes play an important role in organ development. While studies in human beings can provide important correlative data, an animal model may be required for precise delineation of pathogenesis. No animal model is available at this time. Search for such a model will be facilitated by recently developed techniques which make it possible to use Guthrie capillary blood spots to screen for these disorders.[227,307]

Elucidation of the neuronal migrational defect is of particular interest. This profound defect has been studied in detail in postmortem studies of both postnatal[191,192] and fetal[308] brain tissue. As noted above, the defect has a restricted and characteristic distribution and acts throughout the neuronal migrational period, and is readily demonstrable at 14 weeks after conception.[308] Disorders of neuronal migration have been recently reviewed.[309] Particular interest focuses on the interaction between migrating neurons and the radial glia, which act as guidewires. Glia contain more peroxisomes than do neurons, and peroxisomes are more abundant in developing than in mature brain.[310] Correlative studies shown in Table 57-5 provide clues about which peroxisomal functions may be most critical. It will be recalled that in RCDP plasmalogen biosynthesis is severely affected, while VLCFA metabolism is normal.[297] Conversely, in 3-oxoacyl thiolase deficiency VLCFA metabolism is affected, while plasmalogen synthesis is intact.[292] Preliminary studies indicate that there are no defects in neuronal migration in RCDP,[297] while it is disturbed in thiolase deficiency.[291] These findings suggest a primary role for the VLCFA abnormality. Neuronal interactions are influenced by cell adhesion molecules such as the neural cell adhesion molecule.[311] This molecule is acylated and, conceivably, alterations in its fatty acid composition could affect its properties. These complex issues are discussed in a recent publication.[308]

DIAGNOSIS

Diagnosis of the Affected Child

A variety of biochemical assays are available for the diagnosis of affected children. These include demonstration of VLCFA excess in plasma or red blood cells;[228,312,313] deficient synthesis of plasmalogens in cultured skin fibroblasts, white blood cells, or thrombocytes;[16,219,222] diminished levels of plasmalogen in red blood cells,[226] a measurement that is meaningful only in children less than 20 weeks old; increased level of plasma and urinary pipecolic acid,[275,314,315] with the observation that this increase may not be demonstrable in infants less than 4 weeks old; elevated levels of bile acid intermediates in serum;[227,256,282,316] and consistent deficiency of phytanic acid

Table 57-5 Correlation Between Biochemical and Neuronal Migrational Defects

Diagnosis	VLCFA	Plasmalogen	Neuron migration
Zellweger	Increased	Decreased	Abnormal
Neonatal ALD	Increased	Decreased	Abnormal
"Pseudo-Zellweger"[291,292]	Increased	Normal	Abnormal
RCDP[297]	Normal	Decreased	Normal

oxidation[248] in the presence of normal or moderately increased plasma phytanic acid levels (Fig. 57-14).[248,271]

Absence or deficiency of liver peroxisomes can be demonstrated directly by electron microscopy of liver biopsies, provided that catalase cytochemistry and appropriate controls are included.[317] Electron-microscopic identification of the small peroxisomes in cultured skin fibroblasts is feasible but more difficult due to their scarcity,[318] and we do not recommend it for routine diagnosis. Peroxisomes are more easily observed in fibroblasts by immunofluorescence microscopy.[305] The integrity of peroxisome structure can also be assessed by determining the subcellular distribution of catalase in liver or cultured skin fibroblasts.[37,190,215,216] When peroxisomes are lacking, virtually all of the catalase is present in the cytosolic fraction, while normally 50 percent or more is recovered in the particulate fraction.

The indications and selection of diagnostic assays are under current review. The phenotype of peroxisomal disorders is more varied than had been recognized in the past. In particular, the dysmorphic features associated with classic Zellweger syndrome may be lacking. Clinical features that may serve as indications for these diagnostic assays include: severe psychomotor retardation; weakness and hypotonia; dysmorphic features; neonatal seizures; retinopathy, glaucoma or cataracts; hearing deficits; enlarged liver and impaired liver function; and chondrodysplasia punctata. The combined presence of one or more of these abnormalities adds weight to the indication.

Test selection is influenced by availability of laboratory resources. In our own experience, assay of plasma VLCFA represents the least invasive and consistently informative procedure. Other laboratories utilize assays of plasmalogen synthesis in fibroblasts or white blood cells, or plasma levels of bile acid intermediates or pipecolic acid. Since VLCFA levels are normal in RCDP, and plasmalogen synthesis is normal in 3-oxoacyl-CoA thiolase or acyl-CoA oxidase deficiency, reliance on a single assay may be insufficient for the identification of complex or unusual cases. For such cases we recommend plasma assays of VLCFA, bile acid intermediates, phytanic acid, and pipecolic acid; determination of plasmalogen levels in red cells; and measurement of plasmalogen biosynthesis, phytanic acid oxidase, and subcellular distribution of catalase in cultured skin fibroblasts.

Prenatal Diagnosis

A variety of techniques are available for the prenatal diagnosis of peroxisomal disorders. They include demonstration of increased VLCFA levels or their impaired oxidation[228,319,320] and deficient plasmalogen synthesis[218,321] in cultured amniocytes or chorion villus samples, or demonstration that peroxisomes are absent or deficient by cytochemical techniques[322] or by demonstrating the mislocalization of catalase to the cell cytosol.[38a,323] At the Kennedy Institute we have monitored 76

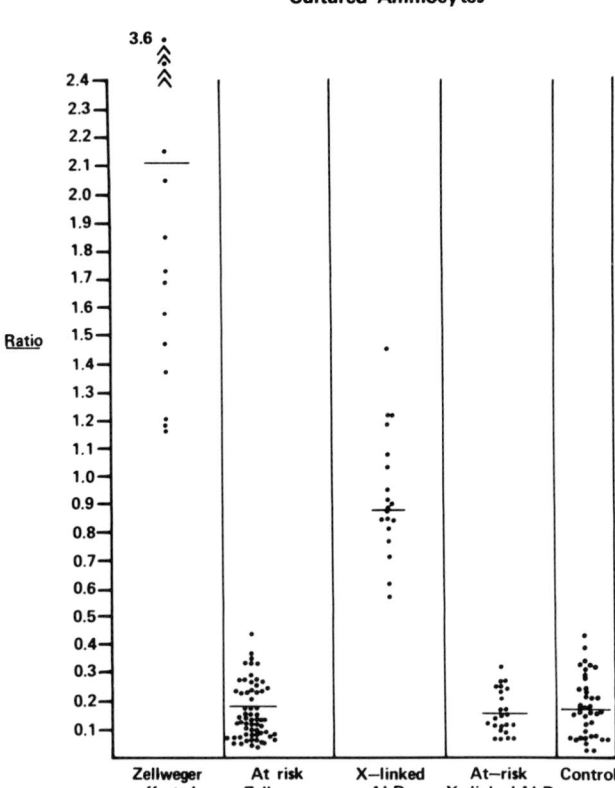

Fig. 57-17 Prenatal diagnosis of peroxisomal disorders by assay of $C_{26:0}$ to $C_{22:0}$ ratio in cultured amniocytes, as described in Ref. 228. The ratio is increased in Zellweger syndrome and X-linked ALD. Diagnoses were verified postnatally or by postmortem examination of fetuses. There is no overlap between values for affected Zellweger fetuses (n = 14) or those hemizygous for X-linked ALD (n = 20), and at-risk fetuses shown to be unaffected (n = 86) or the controls (n = 44).

pregnancies at risk for disorders of peroxisome biogenesis and 4 pregnancies at risk for RCDP and have identified 14 affected fetuses. In each instance, diagnosis was confirmed by postnatal studies or postmortem examination of the fetus, and there have been no false negative tests (Fig. 57-17). We have utilized cultured amniocytes or chorion villus samples. Other investigators have been successful with direct measurement of VLCFA levels in chorion villus samples.[319] When cultured chorion villus samples are used, the possibility of a false negative result due to maternal overgrowth must be kept in mind.[324]

At this time we continue to recommend use of cultured amniocytes or chorion villus samples for the prenatal diagnosis of the disorders of peroxisome biogenesis. Performing two different assays, VLCFA levels and plasmalogen biosynthesis, provides a valuable cross-check.[321] In our previous experience, direct analysis of VLCFA in chorion villus samples failed to provide sufficiently reliable differentiation, but the recent results by Rocchiccioli et al. suggest that this is feasible.[319] Another approach to the direct analysis of chorion villus samples is by cytochemical staining for plasmalogens, which would be expected to be absent. This interesting approach has been proposed by Roels et al.[322]

For the prenatal diagnosis of X-linked ALD, and of 3-oxoacyl-CoA thiolase or acyl-CoA oxidase deficiencies, reliance

must be placed on VLCFA studies, since plasmalogen synthesis is not affected. Prenatal diagnosis of RCDP depends upon measurement of plasmalogen synthesis and phytanic acid oxidation activities.[325] VLCFA metabolism is not affected in this condition.

Heterozygote Identification

No techniques are available at present for the identification of persons who are heterozygous for disorders of peroxisomal biogenesis. This is probably a reflection of the fact that all the biochemical abnormalities that have been delineated so far probably are secondary to as yet unidentified primary defect(s).

Genetics of Disorders of Peroxisome Biogenesis

The pattern of inheritance of Zellweger syndrome and neonatal ALD is compatible with an autosomal recessive mode of inheritance. In Heymans' review of the literature two or more sibs were involved in 17 of the 90 families studied, and parental consanguinity was noted in 17 percent of the 78 cases in which data were available.[9] An X-linked mode of inheritance is suggested in two unrelated families in which two half-brothers were affected by neonatal ALD. In both families the boys had different fathers. The diagnosis of the usual form of X-linked ALD (Chap. 58) was excluded by the demonstration of cytosolic catalase and multiple peroxisomal enzyme defects. (H.W. Moser, unpublished observation). This observation suggests that there may exist a "subset" of neonatal ALD with an X-linked inheritance.

Danks et al. had estimated that the incidence of Zellweger syndrome was 1 in 100,000.[24] More recent estimates place the combined frequency of disorders of peroxisome biogenesis at 1 in 25,000 to 1 in 50,000.[7] During the last 5 years 207 new patients with disorders of peroxisome biogenesis have been identified through the study of samples sent to the Kennedy Institute (H.W. Moser, unpublished observation). Sixty-nine percent of the samples were from the United States and 22 percent from Canada. With approximately 3.6 million births a year in the United States, the experience in the Kennedy Institute laboratory alone would account for an incidence of 0.79 cases per 100,000 births in the USA.

TREATMENT

The potential of postnatal treatment is limited by the multiple malformation and defects that originate in fetal life. Wilson et al.[8] and Holmes[326] have administered ether lipids orally to mildly affected patients with Zellweger syndrome, and achieved a partial normalization of red blood cell plasmalogen levels. Plasma VLCFA can also be normalized at least in part by a dietary regimen now being tested in X-linked ALD.[327] This regimen also minimizes phytanic acid intake and has brought about normalization of phytanic acid levels (H.W. Moser, unpublished observation). This "triple" dietary approach is now being tested in patients with the somewhat milder forms of disordered peroxisome biogenesis.[328] Administration of clofibrate has failed to induce liver peroxisomes in Zellweger disease patients.[190,329]

ADDENDUM

Brul et al. have examined the kinetics of assembly of peroxisomes after fusion of complementary cell lines from patients with disorders of peroxisome biogenesis.[330] In two combinations of cell lines assembly was rapid and insensitive to cycloheximide. In three other combinations of cell lines assembly of peroxisomes was slow and sensitive to this inhibitor.

Roscher et al.[331] have carried out complementation studies in cell lines from 18 patients with disorders of peroxisome biogenesis. They demonstrated six groups. One 12-member group included five classical Zellweger syndrome, three neonatal ALD, three infantile Refsum, and one hyperpipecolic acidemia patient. A second group included one classical Zellweger and one neonatal ALD patient. There were three groups with single classical Zellweger cases and one group with a single neonatal ALD case. These findings, taken together with those of Brul et al.,[301] fail to establish a discernible relationship between genotype and phenotype. The large complementation groups of Roscher and Brul include all phenotypes as currently defined, whereas the most common phenotype (classical Zellweger syndrome) is distributed among at least four complementation groups.

Watkins et al. have identified one patient with an isolated deficiency of the bifunctional enzyme enoyl-CoA hydratase/3-hydroxyacyl-CoA dehydrogenase.[332] The patient was hypotonic, had neonatal seizures and profound psychomotor retardation, and died at 5½ months of age. The brain showed polymicrogyria and a severe defect in neuronal migration.

Wanders et al.[333] investigated the ability of human liver to oxidize L-pipecolic acid. They found that human liver contains an H_2O_2-producing L-pipecolic acid oxidase and that the activity of this enzyme was deficient in the liver of patients with Zellweger syndrome. These results are consonant with those of Mihalik and Rhead[94] and Mihalik and Watkins,[264] who partially purified from primate liver enzymes that oxidize L-pipecolic acid to α-amino adipic acid[264] and found that this activity was deficient in the liver of a patient with Zellweger syndrome.[94]

REFERENCES

1. BOWEN P, LEE CSN, ZELLWEGER H, LINDENBERG R: A familiar syndrome of multiple congenital defects. *Bull Johns Hopkins Hosp* 114:402, 1964.
2. PASSARGE E, MCADAMS AJ: Cerebro-hepato-renal syndrome. A newly recognized hereditary disorder of multiple congenital defects including sudanophilic leukodystrophy, cirrhosis of the liver, and polycystic kidneys. *J Pediatr* 71:691, 1967.
3. OPITZ JM, ZURHEIM BM, VITALE L, SHAHIDI NT, HOWE JJ, CHOU SM, SHANKLIN DR, SYBERS HD, DOOD AR, GERRITSEN T: The Zellweger syndrome (cerebro-hepato-renal syndrome), in Bergsma D (ed): *Malformation Syndromes*, Part II. Baltimore, Williams and Wilkins for the National Foundation—March of Dimes BD, 1969, vol 2, p 144.
4. SMITH DW, OPITZ JM, INHORN SL: A syndrome of multiple developmental defects including polycystic kidneys and intrahepatic biliary dysgenesis in two siblings. *J Pediatr* 67:617, 1965.
5. PUNNETT HH, KIRKPATRICK JA: A syndrome of ocular abnormalities, calcification of cartilage and failure to thrive. *J Pediatr* 73:602, 1968.
6. OPITZ JM: The Zellweger syndrome: Book review and bibliography. *Am J Med Genet* 22:419, 1985.
7. ZELLWEGER H: The cerebro-hepato-renal (Zellweger) syndrome and other peroxisomal disorders. *Dev Med Child Neurol* 29:821, 1987.
8. WILSON GN, HOLMES RG, CUSTER J, LIPKOWITZ JL, STOVER J, DATTA N, HAJRA A: Zellweger syndrome: Diagnostic assays, syndrome delineation, and potential therapy. *Am J Med Genet* 24:69, 1986.
9. HEYMANS HSA: Cerebro-hepato-renal (Zellweger) syndrome. Clinical and biochemical consequences of peroxisomal dysfunction. Thesis, University of Amsterdam, 1984.
10. GOLDFISCHER S, MOORE CL, JOHNSON AB, SPIRO AJ, VALSAMIS MP, WISNIEWSKI HK, RITCH RH, NORTON WT, RAPIN I, GARTNER LM: Peroxisomal and mitochondrial defects in the cerebro-hepato-renal syndrome. *Science* 182:62, 1973.
11. VERSMOLD HT, BREMER HJ, HERZOG V, SIEGEL G, BASSEWITZ DBV, IRLE U, VOSS HV, LOMBECK I, BRAUSER B: A metabolic disorder similar to Zellweger syndrome with hepatic acatalasia and absence of peroxisomes, altered content and redox state of cytochromes, and infantile cirrhosis with hemosiderosis. *Eur J Pediatr* 124:261, 1977.
12. TRIJBELS JMF, BERDEN JA, MONNENS LAH, WILLEMS JL, JANSSEN AJM, SCHUTGENS RBH, VAN DEN BROEK-VAN ESSEN M: Biochemical studies in the liver and muscle of patients with Zellweger syndrome. *Pediatr Res* 17:514, 1983.
13. HAJRA AK, BURKE CL, JONES CL: Subcellular localization of acyl-coenzyme A: Dihydroxyacetone phosphate acyltransferase in rat liver peroxisomes (microbodies). *J Biol Chem* 254:10896, 1979.
14. HAJRA AK, BISHOP JE: Glycerolipid biosynthesis in peroxisomes via the acyl-dihydroxyacetone phosphate pathway. *Ann NY Acad Sci* 386:170, 1982.
15. BORST P: Animal peroxisomal (microbodies), lipid biosynthesis and the Zellweger syndrome. *Trends Biochem Sci* 8:269, 1983.
16. HEYMANS HSA, SCHUTGENS RBH, TAN R, VAN DEN BOSCH H, BORST P: Severe plasmalogen deficiency in tissues of infants without peroxisomes (Zellweger syndrome). *Nature* 306:69, 1983.
17. DATTA NS, WILSON GN, HAJRA AK: Deficiency of enzymes catalyzing the biosynthesis of glycerol-ether lipids in Zellweger syndrome: A new category of metabolic disease involving the absence of peroxisomes. *N Engl J Med* 311:1080, 1984.
18. SCHUTGENS RBH, ROMEYN GJ, WANDERS RJA, VAN DEN BOSCH H, SCHRAKAMP G, HEYMANS HSA: Deficiency of acyl-CoA: Dihydroxyacetone phosphate acyltransferase in patients with Zellweger (cerebro-hepato-renal) syndrome. *Biochem Biophys Res Commun* 120:179, 1984.
19. KAWAMURA N, MOSER HW, KISHIMOTO Y: Very long chain fatty acid oxidation in rat liver. *Biochem Biophys Res Commun* 99:1216, 1981.
20. SINGH I, MOSER AE, GOLDFISCHER S, MOSER HW: Lignoceric acid is oxidized in the peroxisome: Implications for the Zellweger cerebro-hepato-renal syndrome and adrenoleukodystrophy. *Proc Natl Acad Sci USA* 81:4203, 1984.
21. SINGH H, DERWAS N, POULOS A: Very long chain fatty acid beta-oxidation by rat liver mitochondria and peroxisomes. *Arch Biochem Biophys* 259:382, 1987.
22. HANSON RF, SZCZEPANICK-VAN LEEUWEN P, WILLIAMS GC, GRABOWSKI G, SHARP HL: Defects of bile acid synthesis in Zellweger's syndrome. *Science* 203:1107, 1979.
23. MONNENS L, BAKKEREN J, PARMENTIER G, JANSSEN G, VAN HAELST U, TRIJBELS F, EYSSEN H: Disturbances in bile acid metabolism of infants with the Zellweger (cerebro-hepato-renal) syndrome. *Eur J Pediatr* 133:31, 1980.
24. DANKS DM, TIPPETT P, ADAMS C, CAMPBELL P: Cerebro-hepato-renal syndrome of Zellweger. A report of eight cases with comments upon the incidence, the liver lesion, and a fault in pipecolic acid metabolism. *J Pediatr* 86:382, 1975.
25. KELLEY RI, DATTA NS, DOBYNS WB, HAJRA AK, MOSER AB, NOETZEL MJ, ZACKAI EH, MOSER HW: Neonatal adrenoleukodystrophy: New cases, biochemical studies, and differentiation from Zellweger and related peroxisomal polydystrophy syndromes. *Am J Med Genet* 23:869, 1986.
26. POLL-THE BT, SAUDUBRAY JM, OGIER H, SCHUTGENS RBH, WANDERS RJA, SCHRAKAMP G, VAN DEN BOSCH H, TRIJBELS JMF, POULOS A, MOSER HW, VAN ELDERE J, EYSSEN HJ: Infantile Refsum's disease: Biochemical findings suggesting multiple peroxisomal dysfunction. *J Inherited Metab Dis* 9:169, 1986.
27. GATFIELD PD, TALLER E, HINTON GG, WALLACE AC, ABDELNOUR GM, HAUST MD. Hyperpipecolatemia: A new metabolic disorder associated with neuropathy and hepatomegaly. *Can Med Assoc J* 99:1215, 1968.
28. BURTON BK, REED SP, REMY WT: Hyperpipecolic acidemia: Clinical and biochemical observations in two male siblings. *J Pediatr* 99:729, 1981.
29. THOMAS GH, HASLAM RHA, BATSHAW ML, CAPUTE AJ, NEIDENGARD L, RANSOM JL: Hyperpipecolic acidemia associated with hepatomegaly, mental retardation, optic nerve dysplasia and progressive neurological disease. *Clin Genet* 8:376, 1975.
30. EK J, KASE BF, REITH A, BJORKHEM I, PEDERSEN JI: Peroxisomal dysfunction in a boy with neurological symptoms and amaurosis (Leber disease): Clinical and biochemical findings similar to those observed in Zellweger syndrome. *J Pediatr* 108:19, 1986.
31. HRUBAN Z, VIGIL EL, SLESERS A, HOPKINS E: Microbodies: Constituent organelles of animal cells. *Lab Invest* 27:184, 1972.

32. NOVIKOFF AB, NOVIKOFF PM, DAVIS C, QUINTANA N: Studies on microperoxisomes. V. Are microperoxisomes ubiquitous in mammalian cells? *J Histochem Cytochem* 21:737, 1973.

33. HRUBAN Z, RECHCIGL M: *Microbodies and Related Particles*. New York, Academic, 1969.

34. LOUD AV: A quantitative stereological description of the ultrastructure of normal rat liver parenchymal cells. *J Cell Biol* 37:27, 1968.

35. WEIBEL ER, STAUBLI W, GNAGI HR, HESS FA: Correlated morphometric and biochemical studies on the liver cell. I. Morphometric model, stereologic methods, and normal morphometric data for rat liver. *J Cell Biol* 42:68, 1969.

36. GORGAS K: Serial section analysis of mouse hepatic peroxisomes. *Anat Embryol* 172:21, 1985.

37. SANTOS MJ, OJEDA JM, GARRIDO J, LEIGHTON F: Peroxisomal organization in normal and cerebro-hepato-renal (Zellweger) syndrome fibroblasts. *Proc Natl Acad Sci USA* 82:6556, 1985.

38. ARIAS JA, MOSER AB, GOLDFISCHER SL: Ultrastructural and cytochemical demonstration of peroxisomes in cultured fibroblasts from patients with peroxisomal deficiency disorders. *J Cell Biol* 100:1789, 1985.

38a. LAZAROW PB, SMALL GM, SANTOS M, SHIO H, MOSER A, MOSER H, ESTERMAN A, BLACK V, DANCIS J: Zellweger syndrome amniocytes: Morphological appearance and a simple sedimentation method for prenatal diagnosis. *Pediatr Res* 24:63, 1988.

39. BLACK VH, BOGART BI: Peroxisomes in inner adrenocortical cells of fetal and adult guinea pigs. *J Cell Biol* 57:345, 1973.

40. GORGAS K, ZAAR K: Peroxisomes in sebaceous glands. III. Morphological similarities of peroxisomes with smooth endoplasmic reticulum and Golgi stacks in the circumanal gland of the dog. *Anat Embryol* 169:9, 1984.

41. GORGAS K, VOLKL A: Peroxisomes in sebaceous glands. IV. Aggregates of tubular peroxisomes in the mouse Meibomian gland. *Histochem J* 16:1079, 1984.

42. GORGAS K: Peroxisomes in sebaceous glands. V. Complex peroxisomes in the mouse preputial gland: Serial sectioning and three-dimensional reconstruction studies. *Anat Embryol* 169:261, 1984.

43. HOLTZMAN E: Peroxisomes in nervous tissue. *Ann NY Acad Sci* 386:523, 1982.

44. LAZAROW PB, SHIO H, ROBBI M: Biogenesis of peroxisomes and the peroxisome reticulum hypothesis, in Bucher T, Sebald W, Weiss H (eds): *Biological Chemistry of Organelle Formation. 31st Mosbach Colloquium*. New York, Springer-Verlag, 1980, pp 187–206.

45. KAMIRYO T, ABE M, OKAZAKI K, KATO S, SHIMAMOTO N: Absence of DNA in peroxisomes of Candida tropicalis. *J Bacteriol* 152:269, 1982.

46. LAZAROW PB, FUJIKI Y: Biogenesis of peroxisomes. *Annu Rev Cell Biol* 1:489, 1985.

47. VAN VELDHOVEN PP, JUST WW, MANNAERTS GP: Permeability of the peroxisomal membrane to cofactors of beta-oxidation. Evidence for the presence of a pore-forming protein. *J Biol Chem* 262:4310, 1987.

48. LAZAROW PB: The peroxisomal membrane, in Bitter EE (ed): *Membrane Structure and Function*. New York, Wiley, 1984, vol 5, pp 1–31.

49. FUJIKI Y, FOWLER S, SHIO H, HUBBARD AL, LAZAROW PB: Polypeptide and phospholipid composition of the membrane of rat liver peroxisomes. Comparison with endoplasmic reticulum and mitochondrial membranes. *J Cell Biol* 93:103, 1982.

50. HASHIMOTO A, KUWABARA T, USUDA N, NAGATA T: Purification of membrane polypeptides of rat liver peroxisomes. *J Biochem* 100:301, 1986.

51. HARTL FU, JUST WW: Integral membrane polypeptides of rat liver peroxisomes: Topology and response to different metabolic states. *Arch Biochem Biophys* 255:109, 1987.

52. IMANAKA T, REDWOOD CS, SHIO H, SMALL GM, LAZAROW PB: Peroxisomal integral membrane polypeptides: Topology, site of synthesis, and requirement for protein translocation. Manuscript submitted, 1988.

53. SNYDER F (ed): *Ether Lipids*. New York, Academic, 1972.

54. WYKLE RL: Brain, in Snyder F (ed): *Lipid Metabolism in Mammals*. New York, Plenum, 1977, vol 1, pp 317–366.

55. BISHOP JE, SALEM M, HAJRA AK: Topographical distribution of lipid biosynthetic enzymes on peroxisomes (microbodies). *Ann NY Acad Sci* 386:411, 1982.

56. LEIGHTON F, POOLE B, BEAUFAY H, BAUDHUIN P, COFFEY JW, FOWLER S, DE DUVE C: The large scale separation of peroxisomes, mitochondria and lysosomes from the livers of rats injected with Triton WR-1339. *J Cell Biol* 37:482, 1968.

57. WYKLE RL, SNYDER F: Microsomal enzymes involved in the metabolism of ether-linked glycerolipids and their precursors in mammals, in Martonosi A (ed): *The Enzymes of Biological Membranes*. New York, Plenum, 1976, vol 2, pp 87–117.

58. BELL RM, COLEMAN RA: Enzymes of glycerolipid synthesis in eukaryotes. *Annu Rev Biochem* 49:459, 1980.

59. BALLAS LM, LAZAROW PB, BELL RM: Glycerolipid synthetic capacity of rat liver peroxisomes. *Biochim Biophys Acta* 795:297, 1984.

60. DECLERCQ PE, HAAGSMAN HP, VAN VELDHOVEN P, DEBEER LJ, VAN GOLDE LMG, MANNAERTS GP: Rat liver dihydroxyacetone-phosphate acyltransferases and their contribution of glycerolipid synthesis. *J Biol Chem* 259:9064, 1984.

61. BISHOP JE, HAJRA AK: Mechanism and specificity of formation of long chain alcohols by developing rat brain. *J Biol Chem* 256:9542, 1981.

62. SANSONE G, HAMILTON JG: Glyceryl ether, wax ester and triglyceride composition of the mouse preputial gland. *Lipids* 4:435, 1969.

63. HANAHAN DJ, DEMOPOULOS CA, LIEHR J, PINCKARD RN: Identification of platelet activating factor isolated from rabbit basophils as acetyl glyceryl ether phosphorylcholine. *J Biol Chem* 255:5514, 1980.

64. BROWN MS, GOLDSTEIN JL: Multivalent feedback regulation of HMG CoA reductase, a control mechanism coordinating isoprenoid synthesis and cell growth. *J Lipid Res* 21:505, 1980.

65. KELLER G-A, BARTON MC, SHAPIRO DJ, SINGER SJ: 3-Hydroxy-3-methylglutaryl-coenzyme A reductase is present in peroxisomes in normal rat liver cells. *Proc Natl Acad Sci USA* 82:770, 1985.

66. KELLER GA, PAZIRANDEH M, KRISANS S: 3-Hydroxy-3-methylglutaryl-coenzyme A reductase localization in rat liver peroxisomes and microsomes of control and cholestyramine-treated animals: Quantitative biochemical and immunoelectron microscopical analyses. *J Cell Biol* 103:875, 1986.

67. LISCUM L, CUMMINGS RD, ANDERSON RGW, DEMARTINO GN, GOLDSTEIN JL, BROWN MS: 3-Hydroxy-3-methylglutaryl-coenzyme A reductase: A transmembrane glycoprotein of the endoplasmic reticulum with N-linked "high-mannose" oligosaccharides. *Proc Natl Acad Sci USA* 80:7165, 1983.

68. LISCUM L, FINER-MOORE J, STROUD RM, LUSKEY KL, BROWN MS, GOLDSTEIN JL: Domain structure of 3-hydroxy-3-methylglutaryl-coenzyme A reductase, a glycoprotein of the endoplasmic reticulum. *J Biol Chem* 260:522, 1985.

69. RUSNAK N, KRISANS SK: Diurnal variation of HMG-CoA reductase activity in rat liver peroxisomes. *Biochem Biophys Res Commun* 148:890, 1987.

70. THOMPSON SL, BURROWS R, LAUB RJ, KRISANS SK: Cholesterol synthesis in rat liver peroxisomes. Conversion of mevalonic acid to cholesterol. *J Biol Chem* 262:17420, 1987.

71. PEDERSEN JI, GUSTAFSSON J: Conversion of 3alpha, 7alpha, 12alpha-trihydroxy-5beta-cholestanoic acid into cholic acid by rat liver peroxisomes. *FEBS Lett* 121:345, 1980.

72. KRISANS SK, THOMPSON SL, PENA LA, KOK E, JAVITT NB: Bile acid synthesis in rat liver peroxisomes: Metabolism of 26-hydroxycholesterol to 3beta-hydroxy-5-cholenoic acid. *J Lipid Res* 26:1324, 1985.

73. HSIEH B, TOLBERT NE: Glyoxylate aminotransferase in peroxisomes from rat liver and kidney. *J Biol Chem* 251:4408, 1976.

74. NOGUCHI T, TAKADA Y: Peroxisomal localization of serine:pyruvate aminotransferase in human liver. *J Biol Chem* 253:7598, 1978.

75. NOGUCHI T, TAKADA Y: Peroxisomal localization of alanine:glyoxylate aminotransferase in human liver. *Arch Biochem Biophys* 196:645, 1979.

76. DE DUVE C, BAUDHUIN P: Peroxisomes (microbodies and related particles). *Physiol Rev* 46:323, 1966.

77. ROWSELL EV, SNELL K, CARNIE JA, ROWSELL KV: The subcellular distribution of rat liver L-alanine-glyoxylate aminotransferase in relation of a pathway for glucose formation involving glyoxylate. *Biochem J* 127:155, 1972.

78. TAKADA Y, MORI T, NOGUCHI T: The effect of vitamin B6 deficiency on alanine:glyoxylate aminotransferase isoenzymes in rat liver. *Arch Biochem Biophys* 229:1, 1984.

79. DANPURE CJ, JENNINGS PR, WATTS RW: Enzymological diagnosis of primary hyperoxaluria type 1 by measurement of hepatic alanine:glyoxylate aminotransferase activity. *Lancet* 1:289, 1987.

80. DANPURE CJ, JENNINGS PR: Peroxisomal alanine:glyoxylate aminotransferase deficiency in primary hyperoxaluria type I. *FEBS Lett* 201:20, 1986.

81. VAMECQ J, VAN HOOF F: Implication of a peroxisomal enzyme in the catabolism of glutaryl-CoA. *Biochem J* 221:203, 1984.

82. BEARD ME, BAKER R, CONOMOS P, PUGATCH D, HOLTZMAN E: Oxidation of oxalate and polyamines by rat peroxisomes. *J Histochem Cytochem* 33:460, 1985.

83. CHANCE B, OSHINO N: Kinetics and mechanisms of catalase in peroxisomes of the mitochondrial fraction. *Biochem J* 122:225, 1971.

84. CHANCE B, SIES H, BOVERIS A: Hydroperoxide metabolism in mammalian organs. *Physiol Rev* 59:527, 1979.

85. DE DUVE C: Evolution of the peroxisome. *Ann NY Acad Sci* 168:369, 1969.

86. AHLABO I, BARNARD T: Observations on peroxisomes in brown adipose tissue of the rat. *J Histochem Cytochem* 19:670, 1971.

87. SMITH RE, HORWITZ BA: Brown fat and thermogenesis. *Physiol Rev* 49:330, 1969.

88. HOLTTA E: Oxidation of spermidine and spermine in rat liver: Purification and properties of polyamine oxidase. *Biochemistry* 16:91, 1977.

89. SCOTT PJ, VISENTIN LP, ALLEN JM: Enzymatic characteristics of peroxisomes of amphibian and avian liver and kidney. *Ann NY Acad Sci* 168:244, 1969.

90. KHANNA JM, ISRAEL Y: Ethanol metabolism, in Javitt NB (ed): *Liver and Biliary Tract Physiology* I. Baltimore, University Park Press, 1980, pp 275–315.

91. OSHINO N, CHANCE B, SIES H, BUCHER T: The role of H_2O_2 generation in perfused rat liver and the reaction of catalase compound I and hydrogen donors. *Arch Biochem Biophys* 154:117, 1973.

92. OSHINO N, JAMIESON D, SUGANO T, CHANCE B: Optical measurement of the catalase-hydrogen peroxide intermediate (compound I) in the liver of anaesthetized rats and its implication to hydrogen peroxide production in situ. *Biochem J* 146:67, 1975.

93. THURMAN RG, MCKENNA W: Activation of ethanol utilization in perfused liver from normal and ethanol-pretreated rats. The effect of hydrogen peroxide generating substrates. *Hoppe-Seyler's Z Physiol Chem* 355:336, 1974.

94. MIHALIK SJ, RHEAD WJ: L-Pipecolic acid is oxidized to aminoadipic acid in the peroxisome of the human and monkey: Subcellular localization and initial characterization of the pathway. *Pediatr Res* 21:292A, 1987.

95. LAZAROW PB, DE DUVE C: A fatty acyl-CoA oxidizing system in rat liver peroxisomes: Enhancement by clofibrate, a hypolipidemic drug. *Proc Natl Acad Sci USA* 73:2043, 1976.

96. LAZAROW PB: Rat liver peroxisomes catalyze the beta-oxidation of fatty acids. *J Biol Chem* 253:1522, 1978.

97. SHINDO Y, HASHIMOTO T: Acyl-coenzyme A synthetase and fatty acid oxidation in rat liver peroxisomes. *J Biochem* 84:1177, 1978.

98. KRISANS S, MORTENSEN RM, LAZAROW PB: Acyl-CoA synthetase in rat liver peroxisomes. Computer-assisted analysis of cell fractionation experiments. *J Biol Chem* 255:9599, 1980.

99. MANNAERTS GP, VELDHOVEN P VAN, BROEKHOVEN A VAN, VANDEBROEK G, DEBEER LJ: Evidence that peroxisomal acyl-CoA synthetase is located at the cytoplasmic side of the peroxisomal membrane. *Biochem J* 204:17, 1982.

100. WANDERS RJA, VAN ROERMUND CWT, VAN WIJLAND MJA, SCHUTGENS RBH, SCHRAM AW, VAN DEN BOSCH H, TAGER JM: Studies on the peroxisomal oxidation of palmitate and lignocerate in rat liver. *Biochim Biophys Acta* 919:21, 1987.

101. WANDERS RJA, VAN ROERMUND CWT, VAN WIJLAND MJA, SCHUTGENS RBH, HEIKOOP J, VAN DEN BOSCH H, SCHRAM AW, TAGER JM: Peroxisomal fatty acid beta-oxidation in relation to the accumulation of very long chain fatty acids in cultured skin fibroblasts from patients with Zellweger syndrome and other peroxisomal disorders. *J Clin Invest* 80:1778, 1987.

102. HASHIMOTO T: Individual peroxisomal beta-oxidation enzymes. *Ann NY Acad Sci* 386:5, 1982.

103. MIYAZAWA S, HAYASHI H, HIJIKATA M, ISHII N, FURUTA S, KAGAMIYAMA H, OSUMI T, HASHIMOTO T: Complete nucleotide sequence of a cDNA and predicted amino acid sequence of rat acyl-CoA oxidase. *J Biol Chem* 262:8131, 1987.

104. HIJIKATA M, ISHII N, KAGAMIYAMA H, OSUMI T, HASHIMOTO T: Structural analysis of cDNA for rat peroxisomal 3-ketoacyl-CoA thiolase. *J Biol Chem* 262:8151, 1987.

105. ALEXSON SEH, FUJIKI Y, SHIO H, LAZAROW PB: Partial disassembly of peroxisomes. *J Cell Biol* 101:294, 1985.

106. OSMUNDSEN H, NEAT CE, NORUM KR: Peroxisomal oxidation of long chain fatty acids. *FEBS Lett* 99:292, 1979.

107. HOVIK R, OSMUNDSEN H: Peroxisomal beta-oxidation of long-chain fatty acids possessing different extents of unsaturation. *Biochem J* 247:531, 1987.

108. MARKWELL MAK, MCGROARTY EJ, BIEBER LL, TOLBERT NE: The subcellular distribution of carnitine acyltransferases in mammalian liver and kidney. A new peroxisomal enzyme. *J Biol Chem* 248:3426, 1973.

109. MARKWELL MAK, TOLBERT NE, BEIBER LL: Comparison of the carnitine acyltransferase activities from rat liver peroxisomes and microsomes. *Arch Biochem Biophys* 176:479, 1976.

110. MIYAZAWA S, OZASA H, OSUMI T, HASHIMOTO T: Purification and properties of carnitine octanoyltransferase and carnitine palmitoyltransferase from rat liver. *J Biochem* 94:529, 1983.

111. FARRELL SO, FIOL CJ, REDDY JK, BIEBER LL: Properties of purified carnitine acyltransferases of mouse liver peroxisomes. *J Biol Chem* 259:13089, 1984.

112. DOMMES B, BAUMGART C, KUNAU WH: Degradation of unsaturated fatty acids in peroxisomes. *J Biol Chem* 256:8259, 1981.

113. HILTUNEN JK, KARKI T, HASSINEN IE, OSMUNDSEN H: Beta oxidation of polyunsaturated fatty acids by rat liver peroxisomes. A role for 2,4-dienoyl-coenzyme A reductase in peroxisomal beta oxidation. *J Biol Chem* 261:16484, 1986.

114. SCHULZ H, KUNAU WH: Beta-oxidation of unsaturated fatty acids: A revised pathway. *Trends Biochem Sci* 12:403, 1987.

115. APPELKVIST EL, DALLNER G: Possible involvement of fatty acid binding protein in peroxisomal beta-oxidation of fatty acids. *Biochim Biophys Acta* 617:156, 1980.

116. BEEVERS H: Glyoxysomes of castor bean endosperm and their relation to gluconeogenesis. *Ann NY Acad Sci* 168:313, 1969.

117. BLUM JJ: Localization of some enzymes of beta-oxidation of fatty acids in the peroxisomes of *Tetrahymena*. *J Protozool* 20:688, 1973.

118. TANAKA A, OSUMI M, FUKUI S: Peroxisomes of alkane-grown yeast: Fundamental and practical aspects. *Ann NY Acad Sci* 386:183, 1982.

119. MCGARRY JD, FOSTER DW: Regulation of hepatic fatty acid oxidation and ketone body production. *Annu Rev Biochem* 49:395, 1980.

120. MIYAZAWA S, HASHIMOTO T, YOKOTA S: Identity of long-chain acyl-coenzyme A synthetase of microsomes, mitochondria, and peroxisomes in rat liver. *J Biochem* 98:723, 1985.

121. LEIGHTON F, NICOVANI S, SOTO U, SKORIN C, NECOCHEA C: Peroxisomal properties with potential regulatory implications: Selective ATP requirement for fatty acid oxidation and membrane protein phosphorylation, in Fahimi HD, Sies H (eds): *Peroxisomes in Biology and Medicine.* Heidelberg, Springer-Verlag, 1987, pp. 177–188.

122. LAZAROW PB: Compartmentation of beta-oxidation of fatty acids in peroxisomes, in Sies H (ed): *Metabolic Compartmentation.* New York, Academic, 1982, pp 317–329.

123. MANNAERTS GP, DEBEER LJ, THOMAS J, DESCHEPPER PJ: Mitochondrial and peroxisomal fatty acid oxidation in liver homogenates and isolated hepatocytes from control and clofibrate-treated rats. *J Biol Chem* 254:4585, 1979.

124. FOERSTER E-C, FAHRENKEMPER T, RABE U, GRAF P, SIES H: Peroxisomal fatty acid oxidation as detected by H_2O_2 production in intact perfused rat liver. *Biochem J* 196:705, 1981.

125. KONDRUP J, LAZAROW PB: Flux of palmitate through the peroxisomal and mitochondrial beta-oxidation systems in isolated rat hepatocytes. *Biochim Biophys Acta* 835:147, 1985.

126. BERGSETH S, CHRISTIANSEN EN, BREMER J: The effect of feeding fish oils, vegetable oils and clofibrate on the ketogenesis from long chain fatty acids in hepatocytes. *Lipids* 21:508, 1986.

127. MORTENSEN PB, KOLVRAA S, GREGERSEN N, RASMUSSEN K: Cyanide-insensitive and clofibrate enhanced beta-oxidation of dodecanedioic acid in rat liver. *Biochim Biophys Acta* 713:393, 1982.

128. RHEAD WJ, AMENDT BA, FRITCHMAN KS, FELTS SJ: Dicarboxylic aciduria: Deficient [1-^{14}C] octanoate oxidation and medium-chain acyl-CoA dehydrogenase in fibroblasts. *Science* 221:73, 1983.

128a. PACE-ASCIAK C, GRANSTRÖM E: *Prostaglandins and Related Substances.* Amsterdam, Elsevier, 1983.

128b. DICZFALUSY U, ALEXSON SEH, PEDERSEN JI: Chain-shortening of prostaglandin $F_{2\alpha}$ by rat liver peroxisomes. *Biochim Biophys Res Commun* 144:1206, 1987.

128c. SCHEPERS L, CASTEELS M, VAMECQ J, PARMENTIER G, VAN VELDHOVEN PP, MANNAERTS GP: β-Oxidation of the carboxyl side chain of prostaglandin E_2 in rat liver peroxisomes and mitochondria. *J Biol Chem* 263:2724, 1988.

128d. YAMADA J, HORIE S, WATANABE T, SUGA T: Participation of peroxisomal β-oxidation system in the chain-shortening of a xenobiotic acyl compound. *Biochem Biophys Res Commun* 125:123, 1984.

128e. YAMADA J, ITOH S, HORIE S, WATANABE T, SUGA T: Chain-shortening of a xenobiotic acyl compound by the peroxisomal β-oxidation system in rat liver. *Biochem Pharmacol* 35:4363, 1986.

128f. YAMADA J, OGAWA S, HORIE S, WATANABE T, SUGA T: Participation of peroxisomes in the metabolism of xenobiotic acyl compounds: Comparison between peroxisomal and mitochondrial β-oxidation of ω-phenyl fatty acids in rat liver. *Biochim Biophys Acta* 921:292, 1987.

129. BREMER J, OSMUNDSEN H: Fatty acid oxidation and its regulation, in Numa S (ed): *Fatty Acid Metabolism and Its Regulation.* Amsterdam, Elsevier, 1984, pp 113–154.

130. SMALL GM, BROLLY D, CONNOCK MJ: Palmityl-CoA oxidase: Detection in several guinea pig tissues and peroxisomal localization in mucosa of small intestine. *Life Sci* 27:1743, 1980.

131. KRAMAR R, HUTTINGER M, GMEINER B, GOLDENBERG H: Beta-oxidation in peroxisomes of brown adipose tissue. *Biochim Biophys Acta* 531:353, 1978.

132. CONNOCK MJ, PERRY SR: Detection of acyl-CoA beta-oxidation enzymes in peroxisomes (microperoxisomes) of mouse heart. *Biochem Int* 6:545, 1983.

133. RUSSO JJ, BLACK VH: Hormone-dependent changes in peroxisomal enzyme activity in guinea pig adrenal. *J Biol Chem* 257:3883, 1982.

134. ISHII H, HORIE S, SUGA T: Physiological role of peroxisomal beta-oxidation in liver of fasted rats. *J Biochem* 87:1855, 1980.

135. ISHII H, FUKUMORI N, HORIE S, SUGA T: Effects of fat content in the diet on hepatic peroxisomes in the rat. *Biochim Biophys Acta* 617:1, 1980.

136. NEAT CE, THOMASSEN MS, OSMUNDSEN H: Induction of peroxisomal beta-oxidation in rat liver by high-fat diets. *Biochem J* 186:369, 1980.

137. NEAT CE, THOMASSEN MS, OSMUNDSEN H: Effects of high-fat diets on hepatic fatty acid oxidation in the rat. *Biochem J* 196:149, 1981.

138. REDDY JK, WARREN JR, REDDY MK, LALWANI ND: Hepatic and renal effects of peroxisome proliferators: Biological implications. *Ann NY Acad Sci* 386:81, 1982.

139. SMALL GM, BURDETT K, CONNOCK MJ: Clofibrate-induced changes in enzyme activities in liver, kidney, and small intestine of male mice. *Ann NY Acad Sci* 386:460, 1982.

140. NEDERGAARD J, ALEXSON S, CANNON B: Cold adaptation in the rat: Increased brown fat peroxisomal beta-oxidation relative to maximal mitochondrial oxidative capacity. *Am J Physiol* 239:C208, 1980.

141. KELLEY RI, CORKEY BE: Increased sensitivity of cerebro-hepato-renal syndrome fibroblasts to antimycin A. *J Inherited Metab Dis* 6:158, 1983.

142. SKJELDAL O, STOKKE O: The subcellular localization of phytanic oxidase in rat liver. *Biochim Biophys Acta* 921:38, 1987.

143. BLACK VH, RUSSO JJ: Stereological analysis of the guinea pig adrenal: Effects of dexamethasone and ACTH treatment with emphasis on the inner cortex. *Am J Anat* 159:85, 1980.

144. LAZAROW PB, FUJIKI Y, MORTENSEN R, HASHIMOTO T: Identification of beta-oxidation enzymes among peroxisomal polypeptides: Increase in Coomassie blue-stainable protein after clofibrate treatment. *FEBS Lett* 150:307, 1982.

145. HESS R, STAUBLI W, RIESS W: Nature of the hepatomegalic effect produced by ethyl-chlorophenoxy-isobutyrate in the rat. *Nature* 208:856, 1965.

146. LAZAROW PB, SHIO H, LEROY-HOUYET MA: Specificity in the action of hypolipidemic drugs: Increase of peroxisomal beta-oxidation largely dissociated from hepatomegaly and peroxisome proliferation in the rat. *J Lipid Res* 23:317, 1982.

147. LYLE LR, JUTILA JW: D-amino acid oxidase induction in the kidneys of germ-free mice. *J Bacteriol* 96:606, 1968.

148. GREENSTEIN JP. *Biochemistry of Cancer*. New York, Academic, 1947.

149. LAZAROW PB, ROBBI M, FUJIKI Y, WONG L: Biogenesis of peroxisomal proteins in vivo and in vitro. *Ann NY Acad Sci* 386:285, 1982.

150. BLOBEL G: Intracellular protein topogenesis. *Proc Natl Acad Sci USA* 77:1496, 1980.

151. WALTER P, LINGAPPA VR: Mechanism of protein translocation across the endoplasmic reticulum. *Annu Rev Cell Biol* 2:499, 1986.

152. SCHATZ G, BUTOW RA: How are proteins imported into mitochondria? *Cell* 32:316, 1983.

153. HAY R, BOHNI P, GASSER S: How mitochondria import proteins. *Biochim Biophys Acta* 779:65, 1984.

154. SCHMIDT GW, MISHKIND ML: The transport of proteins into chloroplasts. *Annu Rev Biochem* 55:879, 1986.

155. FURUTA S, HASHIMOTO T, MIURA S, MORI M, TATIBANA M: Cell-free synthesis of the enzyme of peroxisomal beta-oxidation. *Biochem Biophys Res Commun* 105:639, 1982.

156. FUJIKI Y, RACHUBINSKI RA, MORTENSEN RM, LAZAROW PB: Synthesis of 3-ketoacyl-CoA thiolase of rat liver peroxisomes on free polyribosomes as a larger precursor. Induction of thiolase mRNA activity by clofibrate. *Biochem J* 226:697, 1985.

157. MIURA S, MORI M, TAKIGUCHI M, TATIBANA M, FURUTA S, MIYAZAWA S, HASHIMOTO T: Biosynthesis and intracellular transport of enzymes of peroxisomal beta-oxidation. *J Biol Chem* 259:6397, 1984.

158. LAZAROW PB, DE DUVE C: The synthesis and turnover of rat liver peroxisomes. V. Intracellular pathway of catalase synthesis. *J Cell Biol* 59:507, 1973.

159. ROBBI M, LAZAROW PB: Synthesis of catalase in two cell-free protein-synthesizing systems and in rat liver. *Proc Natl Acad Sci USA* 75:4344, 1978.

160. GOLDMAN BM, BLOBEL G: Biogenesis of peroxisomes: Intracellular site of synthesis of catalase and uricase. *Proc Natl Acad Sci USA* 75:5066, 1978.

161. ROBBI M, LAZAROW PB: Peptide mapping of peroxisomal catalase and its precursor: Comparison to the primary wheat germ translation product. *J Biol Chem* 257:964, 1982.

162. RACHUBINSKI RA, FUJIKI Y, MORTENSEN RM, LAZAROW PB: Acyl-CoA oxidase and hydratase-dehydrogenase, two enzymes of the peroxisomal beta-oxidation system, are synthesized on free polysomes of clofibrate-treated rat liver. *J Cell Biol* 99:2241, 1984.

163. FUJIKI Y, RACHUBINSKI RA, LAZAROW PB: Synthesis of a major integral membrane polypeptide of rat liver peroxisomes on free polysomes. *Proc Natl Acad Sci USA* 81:7127, 1984.

164. OZASA H, MIYAZAWA S, OSUMI T: Biosynthesis of carnitine octanoyl-transferase and carnitine palmitoyltransferase. *J Biochem* 94:543, 1983.

165. FUJIKI Y, RACHUBINSKI RA, LAZAROW PB: Synthesis of a major integral membrane polypeptide of rat liver peroxisomes on free polysomes. *Proc Natl Acad Sci USA* 81:7127, 1984.

166. KOSTER A, HEISIG M, HEINRICH PC, JUST WW: In vitro synthesis of peroxisomal membrane polypeptides. *Biochem Biophys Res Commun* 137:626, 1986.

167. SUZUKI Y, ORII T, TAKIGUCHI M, MORI M, HIJIKATA M, HASHIMOTO T: Biosynthesis of membrane polypeptides of rat liver peroxisomes. *J Biochem* 101:491, 1987.

168. NICHOLLS P, SCHONBAUM GR: Catalases, in Boyer PD, Lardy H, Myrback K (eds): *The Enzymes*, 2d ed. New York, London, Academic, 1963, vol 8, pp 147–225.

169. MURTHY MRN, REID TJ, SICIGNANO A, TANAKA N, ROSSMANN MG: Structure of beef liver catalase. *J Mol Biol* 152:465, 1981.

170. FURUTA S, HAYASHI H, HIJIKATA M, MIYAZAWA S, OSUMI T, HASHIMOTO T: Complete nucleotide sequence of cDNA and deduced amino acid sequence of rat liver catalase. *Proc Natl Acad Sci USA* 83:313, 1986.

171. INESTROSA NC, BRONFMAN M, LEIGHTON F: Purification of the peroxisomal fatty acyl-CoA oxidase from rat liver. *Biochem Biophys Res Commun* 95:7, 1980.

172. OSUMI T, HASHIMOTO T, UI N: Purification and properties of acyl-CoA oxidase from rat liver. *J Biochem* 87:1735, 1980.

173. FURUTA S, MIYAZAWA S, OSUMI T, HASHIMOTO T, UI N: Properties of mitochondrial and peroxisomal enoyl-CoA hydratases from rat liver. *J Biochem* 88:1059, 1980.

174. MIYAZAWA S, FURUTA S, OSUMI T, HASHIMOTO T, UI N: Properties of peroxisomal 3-ketoacyl-CoA thiolase from rat liver. *J Biochem* 90:511, 1981.

175. WIRTZ KWA: Phospholipid transfer proteins, in Jost P, Griffith OH (eds): *Lipid-Protein Interactions*. New York, Wiley, 1982, vol 1, pp 151–231.

176. IMANAKA T, SMALL GM, LAZAROW PB: Translocation of acyl-CoA oxidase into peroxisomes required ATP hydrolysis but not a membrane potential. *J Cell Biol* 105:2915, 1987.

177. SMALL GM, LAZAROW PB: Import of the carboxyterminal portion of acyl-CoA oxidase into peroxisomes of Candida tropicalis. *J Cell Biol* 105:247, 1987.

178. SMALL GM, SZABO LJ, LAZAROW PB: Acyl-CoA oxidase contains two targeting sequences each of which can mediate protein import into peroxisomes. *EMBO J* 7:1167, 1988.

179. GOULD SJ, KELLER G-A, SUBRAMANI S: Identification of a peroxisomal targeting signal at the carboxy terminus of firefly luciferase. *J Cell Biol* 105:2923, 1987.

180. DE DUVE C: Peroxisomes and related particles in historical perspective. *Ann NY Acad Sci* 386:1, 1982.

181. DE DUVE C: Microbodies in the living cell. *Sci Am* 248(5):74, 1983.

182. PFEIFER U: Inhibition by insulin of the formation of autophagic vacuoles in rat liver. *J Cell Biol* 78:152, 1978.

183. POOLE B, LEIGHTON F, DE DUVE C: The synthesis and turnover of rat liver peroxisomes. II. Turnover of peroxisome proteins. *J Cell Biol* 41:536, 1969.

184. POOLE B: The kinetics of disappearance of labeled leucine from the free leucine pool of rat liver and its effect on the apparent turnover of catalase and other hepatic proteins. *J Cell Biol* 246:6587, 1971.

185. KELLEY RI: The cerebro-hepato-renal syndrome of Zellweger, morphologic and metabolic aspects. *Am J Med Genet* 16:503, 1983.

186. GOVAERTS L, MONNENS L, TEGELAERS W, TRIJBELS F, VAN RAAY-SELTEN A: Cerebro-hepato-renal syndrome of Zellweger: Clinical symptoms and relevant laboratory findings in 16 patients. *Eur J Pediatr* 139:125, 1982.

187. SCHUTGENS RBH, HEYMANS HSA, WANDERS RJA, VAN DEN BOSCH H, TAGER JM: Peroxisomal disorders: A newly recognized group of genetic diseases. *Eur J Pediatr* 144:430, 1986.

188. ENDRES W, MUELLER-HOECKER J, VAN DEN ENDE A, SCHUTGENS RBH, BIESE K, HUEBNER G, WADMAN SK: Cerebro-hepato-renal syndrome of Zellweger: Absence of liver peroxisomes; hypocatalasia and renal excretion of pipecolic and trihydroxycoprostanoic acid. *Eur J Pediatr* 135:331, 1981.

189. MOOI WJ, DINGEMANS KP, VAN DEN BERGH WEERMAN MA, JOBSIS AC, HEYMANS HSA, BARTH PG: Ultrastructure of the liver in the cerebro-hepato-renal syndrome of Zellweger. *Ultrastruct Pathol* 5:135, 1983.

190. LAZAROW PB, BLACK V, SHIO H, FUJIKI Y, HAJRA AK, DATTA NS, BANGARU BS, DANCIS J: Zellweger syndrome: Biochemical and morphological studies on two patients treated with clofibrate. *Pediatr Res* 19:1356, 1985.

191. VOLPE JJ, ADAMS RD: Cerebro-hepato-renal syndrome of Zellweger. An inherited disorder of neuronal migration. *Acta Neuropathol* 20:175, 1972.

192. EVRARD P, CAVINESS VS JR, PRATS-VINAS J, LYON G: The mechanism of

arrest of neuronal migration in the Zellweger malformation: An hypothesis based upon cytoarchitectonic analysis. *Acta Neuropathol (Berl)* 41:109, 1978.

193. POWERS JM, MOSER HW, MOSER AB, UPSHUR JK, BRADFORD BF, PAI SG, KOHN PH, FRAIS J, TIFFANY C: Fetal cerebro-hepato-renal (Zellweger) syndrome: Dysmorphic, radiologic, biochemical pathologic findings in four affected fetuses. *Hum Pathol* 16:610, 1985.

194. AGAMANOLIS DP, ROBINSON HB, TIMMONS GD: Cerebro-hepato-renal syndrome. Report of a case with histochemical and ultrastructural observations. *J Neuropathol Exp Neurol* 35:226, 1976.

195. POWERS JM, TUMMONS RC, MOSER AB, MOSER HW, HUFF DS, KELLEY RI: Neuronal lipidosis and neuroaxonal dystrophy in cerebro-hepato-renal (Zellweger) syndrome. *Acta Neuropathol* 73:333, 1987.

196. DELEON GA, GROVER WD, HUFF DS, MORINIGO-MESTRE G, PUNNETT HP, KISTENMACHER ML: Globoid cells, glial nodules, and peculiar fibrillary changes in the cerebro-hepato-renal syndrome of Zellweger. *Ann Neurol* 2:473, 1977.

197. NORTON WT: Isolation and characterization of Myelin, in Morell P (ed): *Myelin*. New York, London, Plenum, 1977, pp 161–199.

198. COHEN SMZ, BROWN FR III, MARTYN L, MOSER HW, CHEN W, KISTENMACHER M, PUNETT H, GROVER W, DE AL CRUZ C, CHAN NR, GREEN WR: Ocular histopathological and biochemical studies of the cerebro-hepato-renal (Zellweger) syndrome and its relation to neonatal adrenoleukodystrophy. *Am J Ophthalmol* 96:488, 1984.

199. HITTNER HM, KRETZER FL, MEHTA RS: Zellweger syndrome. Lenticular opacities indicating carrier status and lens abnormalities characteristic of homozygotes. *Arch Ophthalmol* 99:1977, 1981.

200. VITALE L, OPITZ JM, SHAHIDI NT: Congenital and familial iron overload. *N Engl J Med* 280:642, 1969.

201. GILCHRIST KW, GILBERT EF, GOLDFARB S, GOLL U, SPRANGER JW, OPITZ JM: Studies of malformation syndromes of man XIB: The cerebro-hepato-renal syndrome of Zellweger: Comparative pathology. *Eur J Pediatr* 121:99, 1976.

202. BERNSTEIN J, BROUGH AJ, MCADAMS AJ: The renal lesions syndromes of multiple congenital malformations: Cerebro-hepato-renal syndrome, Jeune asphyxiating thoracic dystrophy; Tuberous sclerosis; Meckel syndrome, in Bergsma D et al (eds): *The Clinical Delineation of Birth Defects: Part XVI, Urinary System and Others.* New York: R Liss for the National Foundation, March of Dimes BD: OASX (4), p 35.

203. GOLDFISCHER S, POWERS JM, JOHNSON AB, AXE S, BROWN FR III, MOSER HW: Striated adrenocortical cells in cerebro-hepato-renal (Zellweger) syndrome. *Virchows Arch (A)* 401:355, 1983.

204. GOVAERTS L, MONNENS L, MELIS T, TRIJBELS F: Disturbed adrenocortical function in cerebro-hepato-renal syndrome of Zellweger. *Eur J Pediatr* 143:10, 1984.

205. POZNANSKI AK, NOSANCHUK JS, BAUBLIS J, HOLT JF: The cerebro-hepato-renal syndrome (CHRS) Zellweger's syndrome. *Am J Roentgenol* 109:313, 1970.

206. WILLIAMS JP, SECREST L, FOWLER GW, GWINN JL, DUMARS KC. Roentgenographic features of the cerebro-hepato-renal syndrome of Zellweger. *Am J Roentgenol* 115:607, 1972.

207. GRAHAM CB: Assessment of bone maturation—Methods and pitfalls. *Radiol Clin North Am* 10:185, 1972.

208. HONG R, HOROWITZ SD, BORZY MF, GILBERT EF, ARYA S, MCLEOD N, PETERSON RDA: The cerebro-hepato-renal syndrome of Zellweger: Similarity to and differentiation from the DiGeorge Syndrome. *Thymus* 3:97, 1981.

209. BAKKEREN J, CARPAY I, WEEMAES C, MONNENS L: Cellular immunity in cerebro-hepato-renal syndrome of Zellweger. *Lancet* II:1029, 1976.

210. HAAS JE, JOHNSON ES, FARRELL DL: Neonatal-onset adrenoleukodystrophy in a girl. *Ann Neurol* 12:449, 1982.

211. JAFFE R, CRUMRINE P, HASHIDA Y, MOSER HW: Neonatal adrenoleukodystrophy. Clinical, pathologic and biochemical delineation of a syndrome affecting both males and females. *Am J Pathol* 108:100, 1982.

212. WOLFF J, NYHAN WL, POWELL H, TAKAHASHI D, HUTZLER J, HAJRA AK, DATTA NS, SINGH I, MOSER HW: Myopathy in an infant with a fatal peroxisomal disorder. *Pediatr Neurol* 2:141, 1986.

213. WANDERS RJA, BARTH PG, VAN ROERMUND CWT, OFMAN R, WOLTERMAN R, SCHUTGENS RBH, TAGER JM, VAN DEN BOSCH H, BOLHUIS PA: Peroxisomes and peroxisomal functions in muscle. Studies with muscle cells from controls and a patient with cerebro-hepato-renal (Zellweger) syndrome. *Exp Cell Res* 170:147, 1987.

214. WANDERS RJA, STRIJLAND A, VAN ROERMUND CWT, VAN DEN BOSCH H, SCHUTGENS RBH, TAGER JM, SCHRAM AW: Catalase in cultured skin fibroblasts from patients with the cerebro-hepato-renal (Zellweger) syndrome: Normal maturation in peroxisome-deficient cells. *Biochim Biophys Acta* 923:478, 1987.

215. WANDERS RJA, KOS M, ROEST B, MEIJER AJ, SCHRAKAMP G, HEYMANS HSA, TEGELAERS WHH, VAN DEN BOSCH H, SCHUTGENS RBH, TAGER JM: Activity of peroxisomal enzymes and intracellular distribution of catalase in Zellweger syndrome. *Biochem Biophys Res Commun* 123:1054, 1984.

216. SANTOS M, LEIGHTON F: Subcellular distribution of peroxisomal enzymes in Zellweger syndrome fibroblasts, in Seno S, Okada Y (eds): *International Cell Biology.* Japan Society for Cell Biology, Tokyo, 1984, p 284.

217. WANDERS RJA, SCHUTGENS RBH, TAGER JM: Peroxisomal matrix enzymes in Zellweger syndrome: Activity and subcellular localization in liver. *J Inherited Metab Dis* 8 suppl 2:151, 1985.

218. SCHUTGENS RBH, SCHRAKAMP G, WANDERS RJA, HEYMANS HSA, MOSER HW, MOSER AE, TAGER JM, VAN DEN BOSCH H, AUBOURG P: The cerebro-hepato-renal (Zellweger) syndrome: Prenatal detection based on impaired biosynthesis of plasmalogens. *Prenat Diagn* 5:337, 1985.

219. WANDERS RJA, VAN WERINGH G, SCHRAKAMP G, TAGER JM, VAN DEN BOSCH H, SCHUTGENS RBH: Deficiency of acyl-CoA: Dihydroxyacetone phosphate acyltransferase in thrombocytes of Zellweger patients: A simple postnatal test. *Clin Chim Acta* 151:217, 1985.

220. BESLEY GTN, BROADHEAD DM: Dihydroxyacetone phosphate acyltransferase deficiency in peroxisomal disorders. *J Inherited Metab Dis* 10, suppl 2:236, 1987.

221. SCHRAKAMP G, ROOSEBOOM CFP, SCHUTGENS RBH, WANDERS RJA, HEYMANS HSA, TAGER JM, VAN DEN BOSCH H: Alkyldihydroxyacetone phosphate synthase in human fibroblasts and its deficiency in Zellweger syndrome. *J Lipid Res* 26:867, 1985.

222. ROSCHER A, MOLZER B, BERNHEIMER H, STOCKLER S, MUTZ I, PALTAUF F: The cerebro-hepato-renal (Zellweger) syndrome. An improved method for the biochemical diagnosis and its potential for prenatal diagnosis. *Pediatr Res* 19:930, 1985.

223. WEBBER KO, DATTA NS, HAJRA AK: Properties of the enzymes catalyzing the biosynthesis of lysophosphatidate and its ether analogy in cultured fibroblasts from Zellweger syndrome patients and normal controls. *Arch Biochem Biophys* 254:611, 1987.

224. HEYMANS HSA, VAN DEN BOSCH H, SCHUTGENS RBH, TEGELAERS WHH, WALTHER JU, MULLER-HOCKER J, BORST P: Deficiency of plasmalogen in the cerebro-hepato-renal (Zellweger) syndrome. *Eur J Pediatr* 142:10, 1984.

225. WANDERS RJA, PURVIS YR, HEYMANS HSA, BAKKEREN JAJM, PARMENTIER GG, VAN ELDERE J, EYSSEN H, VAN DEN BOSCH H, TAGER JM, SCHUTGENS RBH: Age-related differences in plasmalogen content of erythrocytes from patient with the cerebro-hepato-renal (Zellweger) syndrome: Implications for postnatal detection of the disease. *J Inherited Metab Dis* 9:335, 1986.

226. BJORKHEM I, SISFONTES L, BOSTROM B, KASE BF, BLOMSTRAND R: Simple diagnosis of the Zellweger syndrome by gas-liquid chromatography of dimethylacetals. *J Lipid Res* 27:786, 1986.

227. GUSTAFSSON J, SISFONTES L, BJORKHEM I: Diagnosis of Zellweger syndrome by analysis of bile acids and plasmalogens in stored dried blood collected at neonatal screening. *J Pediatr* 111:264, 1987.

228. MOSER AE, SINGH I, BROWN FR III, SOLISH GI, KELLEY RI, BENKE PJ, MOSER HW: The cerebro-hepato-renal (Zellweger) syndrome: Increased levels and impaired degradation of very long chain fatty acids and their use in prenatal diagnosis. *N Engl J Med* 310:1141, 1984.

229. BAKKEREN JAJM, MONNENS LAH, TRIJBELS JMF, MAAS JM: Serum very long chain fatty acid pattern in Zellweger syndrome. *Clin Chim Acta* 138:325, 1984.

230. GOVAERTS L, BAKKEREN J, MONNENS L, MAAS J, TRIJBELS F: Disturbed very long chain (C24-C26) fatty acid pattern in fibroblasts of patients with Zellweger's syndrome. *J Inherited Metab Dis* 8:5, 1985.

231. MOLZER B, KORSCHINSKY M, BERNHEIMER H, SCHMIDT R, WOLF C, ROSCHER A: Very long chain fatty acids in genetic peroxisomal diease fibroblasts: Differences between the cerebro-hepato-renal (Zellweger) syndrome and adrenoleukodystrophy variants. *Clin Chim Acta* 161:81, 1986.

232. POULOS A, SINGH H, PATON B, SHARP P, DERWAS N: Accumulation and defective beta-oxidation of very long chain fatty acids in Zellweger's syndrome, adrenoleukodystrophy and Refsum's disease variants. *Clin Genet* 29:397, 1986.

233. BROWN FR III, MCADAMS AJ, CUMMINS JW, KONKOL R, SINGH I, MOSER AB, MOSER HW: Cerebro-hepato-renal (Zellweger) syndrome and neonatal adrenoleukodystrophy: Similarities in phenotype and accumulation of very long chain fatty acids. *Johns Hopkins Med J* 151:344, 1982.

234. MOSER HW, MOSER AE, SINGH I, O'NEILL BP: Adrenoleukodystrophy. Survey of 303 cases: Biochemistry, diagnosis and therapy. *Ann Neurol* 16:628, 1984.

235. POULOS A, SHARP P, SINGH H, JOHNSON D, FELLENBERG A, POLLARD A: Detection of a homologous series of C26-C38 polyenoic fatty acids in the brain of patients without peroxisomes (Zellweger's syndrome). *Biochem J* 235:607, 1986.

236. WANDERS RJA, VAN ROERMUND CWT, VAN WIJLAND MJA, HEIKOOP J, SCHUTGENS RBH, SCHRAM AW, TAGER JM, VAN DEN BOSCH H, POLL-THE

BT, SAUDUBRAY JM, MOSER HW, MOSER AB: Peroxisomal very long chain fatty acid beta-oxidation in human skin fibroblast, activity in Zellweger syndrome and other peroxisomal disorders. *Clin Chim Acta* 166:255, 1987.

237. SUZUKI Y, ORII T, MORI M, TATIBANA M, HASHIMOTO T: Deficient activities and proteins of peroxisomal beta oxidation enzymes in infants with Zellweger syndrome. *Clin Chim Acta* 156:191, 1986.

238. TAGER JM, VAN DER BEEK WATH, WANDERS RJA, HASHIMOTO T, HEYMANS HSA, VAN DEN BOSCH H, SCHUTGENS RBH, SCHRAM AW: Peroxisomal β-oxidation enzyme proteins in the Zellweger syndrome. *Biochem Biophys Res Commun* 126:1269, 1985.

239. SUZUKI Y, ORII T, HASHIMOTO T: Biosynthesis of peroxisomal β oxidation enzymes in infants with Zellweger syndrome. *J Inherited Metab Dis* 9:292, 1986.

240. SCHRAM AW, STRIJLAND A, HASHIMOTO T, WANDERS RJA, SCHUTGENS RBH, VAN DEN BOSCH H, TAGER JM: Biosynthesis and maturation of peroxisomal β-oxidation enzymes in fibroblasts in relation to the Zellweger syndrome and infantile Refsum disease. *Proc Natl Acad Sci USA* 83:6156, 1986.

241. CHEN WW, WATKINS PA, OSUMI T, HASHIMOTO T, MOSER HW: Peroxisomal β-oxidation enzyme proteins in adrenoleukodystrophy: Distinction between X-linked adrenoleukodystrophy and neonatal adrenoleukodystrophy. *Proc Natl Acad Sci USA* 84:1425, 1987.

242. BJORKHEM I, BLOMSTRAND S, HAGA P, KASE BF, PALONEK E, PEDERSEN JI, STRANDVIK B, WIKSTROM SA: Urinary excretion of dicarboxylic acids from patients with the Zellweger syndrome. Importance of peroxisomes in β-oxidation of dicarboxylic acids. *Biochim Biophys Acta* 795:15, 1984.

243. ROCCHICCIOLI F, AUBOURG P, BOUGNERES PF: Medium and long-chain dicarboxylic aciduria in patients with Zellweger syndrome and neonatal adrenoleukodystrophy. *Pediatr Res* 20:62, 1986.

244. ROCCHICCIOLI F, CARTIER PH, AUBOURG P, BOUGNERES PF: Mass spectrometric identification of 2-hydroxy-sebacic acid in the urines of patients with neonatal adrenoleukodystrophy and Zellweger syndrome. *Biomed Environ Mass Spectrom* 13:315, 1986.

245. KOLVRAA S, GREGERSEN N: In vitro studies on the oxidation of medium-chain dicarboxylic acids in rat liver. *Biochim Biophys Acta* 876:515, 1986.

246. PAMPOLS T, RIBES A, PINEDA M, BALLESTER A, FERNANDEZ-ALVAREZ E, MOSER AE, MOSER HW: Medium chain dicarboxylic and hydrodicarboxylic aciduria in a case of neonatal adrenoleukodystrophy. *J Inherited Metab Dis* 10 (suppl 2):217, 1987.

247. POULOS A, SHARP P, WHITING M: Infantile Refsum's disease (phytanic acid storage disease): A variant of Zellweger's syndrome? *Clin Genet* 26:579, 1984.

248. POULOS A, SHARP P, FELLENBERG AJ, DANKS DM: Cerebro-hepato-renal (Zellweger) syndrome, adrenoleukodystrophy, and Refsum's disease: Plasma changes and skin fibroblast phytanic acid oxidase. *Hum Genet* 70:172, 1985.

249. WANDERS RJA, SMIT W, HEYMANS HSA, SCHUTGENS RBH, BARTH PG, SCHIERBEEK H, SMIT GPA, BERGER R, PRZYREMBEL H, EGGELTE TA, TAGER JM, MAASWINKEL-MOOY PD, PETERS ACB, MONNENS LAH, BAKKEREN JAJM, TRIJBELS JMF, LOMMEN EJP, BEGANOVIC N: Age-related accumulation of phytanic acid in plasma from patients with the cerebro-hepato-renal (Zellweger) syndrome. *Clin Chim Acta* 166:45, 1987.

250. MATHIS RK, WATKINS JB, SZCZEPANIK-VAN LEEUWEEN P, LOTT IT: Liver in the cerebro-hepato-renal syndrome: Defective bile acid synthesis and abnormal mitochondria. *Gastroenterology* 79:1311, 1980.

251. EYSSEN H, EGGERMONT E, VAN ELDERE J, JAEKEN J, PARMENTIER G, JANSSEN G: Bile acid abnormalities and the diagnosis of cerebro-hepato-renal syndrome (Zellweger syndrome). *Acta Paediatr Scand* 74:539, 1985.

252. GUSTAFSSON J, GUSTAVSON KH, KARLAGANIS G, SJOVALL J: Zellweger's cerebro-hepato-renal syndrome—Variation in expressivity and in defects of bile acid synthesis. *Clin Genet* 24:313, 1983.

253. LAWSON AM, MADIGAN MJ, SHORTLAND D, CLAYTON PT: Rapid diagnosis of Zellweger syndrome and infantile Refsum's disease by fast atom bombardment—Mass spectrometry of urine bile salts. *Clin Chim Acta* 161:221, 1986.

254. CLAYTON PT, LAKE BD, HALL NA, SHORTLAND DB, CARRUTHERS RA, LAWSON AM: Plasma bile acids in patients with peroxisomal dysfunction syndromes: Analysis by capillary gas chromatography-mass spectrometry. *Eur J Pediatr* 146:166, 1987.

255. KASE F, BJORKHEM I, PEDERSEN JI: Formation of cholic from 3 alpha, 7 alpha, 12 alpha-trihydroxy-5 beta cholestanoic acid by rat liver peroxisomes. *J Lipid Res* 24:1560, 1983.

256. KASE BF, PEDERSEN JI, STRANDVIK B, BJORKHEM I: In vivo and in vitro studies on formation of bile acids in patients with Zellweger syndrome. *J Clin Invest* 76:2393, 1985.

257. KASE BF, PEDERSEN JI, STRANDVIK B, BJORKHEM I: In vivo and in vitro studies on formation of bile acids in patients with Zellweger syndrome.

Evidence that peroxisomes are of importance in the normal biosynthesis of both cholic and chenodeoxycholic acid. *J Clin Invest* 76:2393, 1985.

258. DANCIS J, HUTZLER J: The significance of hyperpipecolatemia in Zellweger syndrome. *Am J Hum Genet* 38:707, 1986.

259. TRIJBELS JMF, MONNENS LAH, BAKKEREN JAJM, VAN RAAY-SELTEN AHJ, CORTIAENSEN JMB: Biochemical studies in the cerebro-hepato-renal syndrome of Zellweger: A disturbance in the metabolism of pipecolic acid. *J Inherited Metab Dis* 2:39, 1979.

260. LAM S, HUTZLER J, DANCIS J: L-Pipecolaturia in Zellweger syndrome. *Biochim Biophys Acta* 882:254, 1986.

261. CHANG YF: Lysine metabolism in the rat brain: The pipecolic acid-forming pathway. *J Neurochem* 30:347, 1978.

262. TRIJBELS JMF, MONNENS LAH, MELIS G, VAN ESSEN VDB, BRUCKWILDER M: Localization of pipecolic acid metabolism in rat liver peroxisomes: Probable explanation for hyperpipecolataemia in Zellweger syndrome. *J Inherited Metab Dis* 10:128, 1987.

263. ZAAR K, ANGERMULLER S, VOLKL A, FAHIMI HD: Pipecolic acid is oxidized by renal and hepatic peroxisomes. Implications for Zellweger's cerebro-hepato-renal syndrome (CHRS). *Exp Cell Res* 164:267, 1986.

264. MIHALIK SJ, WATKINS PA: Partial purification of L-pipecolic acid oxidase. *FASEB*, 2:A1763, 1988.

265. MULLER-HOCKER J, WALTHER JV, BISE K, PONGRATZ D, HUBNER G: Mitochondrial myopathy with loosely coupled oxidative phosphorylation in a case of Zellweger syndrome: A cytochemical-ultrastructural study. *Virchow's Arch (B)* 45:125, 1984.

266. SARNAT HB, MACHIN G, DARWISH HZ, RUBIN SZ: Mitochondrial myopathy of cerebro-hepato-renal (Zellweger) syndrome. *Can J Neurol Sci* 10:170, 1983.

267. PATTON RG, CHRISTIE DL, SMITH DW, BECKWITH JB: Cerebro-hepato-renal syndrome of Zellweger. *Am J Dis Child* 124:840, 1972.

268. AGAMANOLIS DP, PATRE S: Glycogen accumulation in the central nervous system in the cerebro-hepato-renal syndrome. *J Neurol Sci* 41:325, 1979.

269. GOVAERTS L, COLON E, ROTTEVEEL J, MONNENS L: A neurophysiological study of children with the cerebro-hepato-renal syndrome of Zellweger. *Neuropediatrics* 16:185, 1985.

270. ULRICH J, HERSCHKOWITZ N, HEITZ P, SIGRIST T, BAERLOCHER P: Adrenoleukodystrophy: Preliminary report of a connatal case. Light and electron microscopical, immunohistochemical and biochemical findings. *Acta Neuropathol* 43:77, 1978.

271. AUBOURG P, SCOTTO J, ROCCHICCIOLI F, FELDMANN-PAUTRAT D, ROBAIN O: Neonatal adrenoleukodystrophy. *J Neurol Neurosurg Psychiatry* 49:77, 1986.

272. VAMECQ J, DRAYE JP, VAN HOOF F, MISSON JP, EVRARD P, VERELLEN G, EYSSEN HJ, VAN ELDERE J, SCHUTGENS RBH, WANDERS RJA, ROELS F, GOLDFISCHER SL: Multiple peroxisomal enzymatic deficiency disorders. A comparative biochemical and morphological study of Zellweger cerebro-hepato-renal syndrome and neonatal adrenoleukodystrophy. *Am J Pathol* 125:524, 1986.

273. GOLDFISCHER SJ, COLLINS J, RAPIN I, COLTOFF-SCHILLER C-H, CHANG M, NIGRO VH, BLACK NB, JAVITT NB, MOSER HW, LAZAROW PB: Peroxisomal defects in neonatal onset and X-linked adrenoleukodystrophy. *Science* 227:67, 1985.

274. WANDERS RJA, SCHUTGENS RBH, SCHRAKAMP G, TAGER JM, VAN DEN BOSCH, MOSER AB, MOSER HW: Neonatal adrenoleukodystrophy. Impaired plasmalogen biosynthesis and peroxisomal beta oxidation due to deficiency of catalase-containing particles (peroxisomes) in cultured skin fibroblasts. *J Neurol Sci* 77:331, 1987.

275. KELLEY RI, MOSER HW: Hyperpipecolic acidemia in neonatal adrenoleukodystrophy. *Am J Med Genet* 19:791, 1984.

276. MANZ HJ, SCHUELEIN M, MacCULLOUGH DC, KISHIMOTO Y, EIBEN RM: New phenotypic variant of adrenoleukodystrophy. Pathologic, ultrastructural, and biochemical study in two brothers. *J Neurol Sci* 45:245, 1980.

277. NOETZEL MJ, CLARK HB, MOSER HW: Neonatal adrenoleukodystrophy with prolonged survival. *Ann Neurol* 14:379, 1983.

278. SCOTTO JM, HADCHOUEL M, ODIEVRE M, LAUDAT MH, SAUDUBRAY JM, DULAC O, BEUCLER I, BEAUNE P: Infantile phytanic acid storage disease, a possible variant of Refsum's disease: Three cases, including ultrastructural studies of the liver. *J Inherited Metab Dis* 5:83, 1982.

279. KAHLKE W, GOERLICH R, FEIST D: Erhohte Phytansaurespiegel im plasma und Leber bei einen Kleinkind mit unklaren Hirnschaden. *Klin Wochenschr* 52:651, 1974.

280. ROELS F, CORNELIS A, POLL-THE BT, AUBOURG P, OGIER H, SCOTTO J, SAUDUBRAY JM: Hepatic peroxisomes are deficient in infantile Refsum disease: A cytochemical study of 4 cases. *Am J Med Genet* 25:257, 1986.

281. WANDERS RJA, SCHUTGENS RBH, SCHRAKAMP G, VAN DEN BOSCH H, TAGER JM, SCHRAM AW, HASHIMOTO T, POLL-THE BT, SAUDUBRAY JM: Infantile Refsum disease: Deficiency of catalase-containing particles (per-

oxisomes), alkyldihydroxyacetone phosphate synthase and peroxisomal β oxidation enzyme proteins. *Eur J Pediatr* 145:172, 1986.

282. POULOS A, WHITING MJ: Identification of 3-alpha, 7 alpha, 12 alpha trihydroxy 5 beta cholestan-26-oic acid, an intermediate in cholic acid synthesis, in the plasma of patients with infantile Refsum's disease. *J Inherited Metab Dis* 8:13, 1985.

283. BUDDEN SS, KENNAWAY NG, BUIST NRM, POULOS A, WELEBER RG: Dysmorphic syndrome with phytanic acid oxidase deficiency, abnormal very long chain fatty acids, and pipecolic acidemia: Studies in four children. *J Pediatr* 108:33, 1986.

284. WELEBER RG, TONGUE AC, KENNAWAY NG, BUDDEN SS, BUIST NRM: Ophthalmic manifestations of infantile phytanic acid storage disease. *Arch Ophthalmol* 102:1317, 1984.

285. TORVIK A, TORP S, KASE BF, EK J, SKJELDAL O, STOKKE O: Infantile Refsum's disease—A generalized peroxisomal disorder. Case with postmortem examination. *J Neurol Sci* 85:39, 1988.

286. BARTH PG, SCHUTGENS RBH, WANDERS RJA, HEYMANS HSA, MOSER AE, MOSER HW, BLEEKER-WAGEMAKERS EM, JANSONIUS-SCHULTHEISS K, DERIX M, NELCK GF: A sibship with a mild variant of Zellweger syndrome. *J Inherited Metab Dis* 10:253, 1987.

287. BLEEKER-WAGEMAKERS EM, OORTHUYS JWE, WANDERS RJA, SCHUTGENS RBH: Long term survival of a patient with the cerebro-hepato-renal (Zellweger) syndrome. *Clin Genet* 29:160, 1986.

288. BURTON BK, REED SP, REMY WT: Hyperpipecolic acidemia: Clinical and biochemical observations in two male siblings. *J Pediatr* 99:729, 1981.

289. THOMAS GH, HASLAM RHA, BATSHAW ML, CAPUTE AJ, NEIDENGARD L, RANSOM JL: Hyperpipecolic acidemia associated with hepatomegaly, mental retardation, optic nerve dysplasia and progressive neurological disease. *Clin Genet* 8:376, 1975.

290. CHALLA VR, GEISINGER KR, BURTON BK: Pathologic alterations in the brain and liver in hyperpipecolic acidemia. *J Neuropathol Exp Neurol* 42:627, 1983.

291. GOLDFISCHER SL, COLLINS J, RAPIN I, NEUMANN P, NEGLIA A, SPIRO AJ, ISHII T, ROELS F, VAMECQ F, VAMECQ J, VAN HOFF F: Pseudo-Zellweger syndrome: Deficiencies in several peroxisomal oxidative activities. *J Pediatr* 108:25, 1986.

292. SCHRAM AW, GOLDFISCHER S, VAN ROERMUND CWT, BROUWER-KELDER EM, COLLINS J, HASHIMOTO T, HEYMANS HSA, VAN DEN BOSCH H, SCHUTGENS RBH, TAGER JM, WANDERS RJA: Human peroxisomal 3-oxoacyl-coenzyme A thiolase deficiency. *Proc Natl Acad Sci USA* 84:2494, 1987.

293. POLL-THE BT, ROELS F, OGIER H, SCOTTO J, VAMECA J, SCHUTGENS RBH, WANDERS RJA, VAN ROERMUND CWT, VAN WIJLAND MJA, SCHRAM AW, TAGER JM, SAUDUBRAY JM: Pseudo neonatal adrenoleukodystrophy: A new peroxisomal disorder with enlarged peroxisomes and a specific deficiency of acyl-CoA oxidase (Pseudo-Neonatal Adrenoleukodystrophy). *Am J Hum Genet* 42:422, 1988.

294. NAIDU S, HOEFLER G, HOEFLER S, WATKINS P, CHEN W, RANCE N, POWERS JM, BEARD M, GREEN WR, HASHIMOTO T, MOSER HW: Neonatal seizures and retardation in a female with biochemical changes resembling X-linked adrenoleukodystrophy: A probable new peroxisomal disease entity. *Neurology* 38:1100, 1988.

295. HEYMANS HSA, OORTHUYS JWE, NELCK G, WANDERS RJA, SCHUTGENS RBH: Rhizomelic chondrodysplasia punctata: Another peroxisomal disorder. *N Engl J Med* 313:187, 1985.

296. HEYMANS HSA, OORTHUYS JWE, NELCK G, WANDERS RJA, DINGEMANS KP, SCHUTGENS RBH: Peroxisomal abnormalities in rhizomelic chondrodysplasia punctata. *J Inherited Metab Dis* 9, suppl 2:321, 1986.

297. HOEFLER G, HOEFLER S, WATKINS PA, CHEN WW, MOSER AB, BALDWIN B, MCGILLIVARY B, CHARROW J, FRIEDMAN JM, RUTLEDGE L, HASHIMOTO T, MOSER HW: Biochemical abnormalities in rhizomelic chondrodysplasia punctata. *J Pediatr* 112:726, 1988.

297a. SCHUTGENS RBH, HEYMANS HSA, WANDERS RJA, OORTHUYS JWE, TAGER JM, SCHRAKAMP G, VAN DEN BOSCH H, BEEMER FA: Multiple peroxisomal enzyme deficiencies in rhizomelic chondrodysplasia punctata, in Goldberg DM, Moss DW, Schmidt, E et al. (eds): *Advances in Clinical Enzymology*. Karger, Basel, 1988, vol 6, pp 1–9.

298. SPRANGER JW, OPITZ JM, BIDDER U: Heterogeneity of chondrodysplasia punctata. *Hum Genet* 11:190, 1971.

299. HAPPLE R: X-Linked dominant chondrodysplasia punctata. Review of literature and report of a case. *Hum Genet* 53:65, 1979.

300. CURRY CJR, MAGENIS RE, BROWN M, LANMAN JT, TSAI J, O'LAGUE P, GOODFELLOW P, MOHANDAS T, BERGNER EA, SHAPIRO LJ: Inherited chondrodysplasia punctata due to a deletion of the terminal short arm of an X-chromosome. *N Engl J Med* 311:1010, 1984.

301. BRUL S, WESTERVELD A, STRIJLAND A, WANDERS RJA, SCHRAM AW, HEYMANS HSA, SCHUTGENS RBH, VAN DEN BOSCH H, TAGER JM: Genetic heterogeneity in the cerebro-hepato-renal (Zellweger) syndrome and other inherited disorders with a generalized impairment of peroxisomal func-

tions: A study using complementation analysis. *J Clin Invest* 81:1710, 1988.

302. ROSCHER A, HOEFLER S, HOEFLER G, PASCHKE E, PALTAUF F: Neonatal adrenoleukodystrophy (NALD) and cerebro-hepato-renal syndrome (CHRS): Genetic complementation analysis of impaired peroxisomal plasmalogen biosynthesis. *Abstracts 24, Annual Symposium of the Society for the Study of Inborn Errors of Metabolism.* Amersfoort, The Netherlands, 1986.

303. LAZAROW PB, FUJIKI Y, SMALL GM, WATKINS P, MOSER H: Presence of the peroxisomal 22-kDa integral membrane protein in the liver of a person lacking recognizable peroxisomes (Zellweger syndrome). *Proc Natl Acad Sci (USA)* 83:9193, 1986.

304. SMALL GM, SANTOS MJ, IMANAKA T, POULOS A, DANKS DM, MOSER HW, LAZAROW PB: Peroxisomal integral membrane proteins in livers of patients with Zellweger syndrome, infantile Refsum's disease and X-linked adrenoleukodystrophy. *J Inherited Metab Dis*, in press.

305. SANTOS MJ, IMANAKA T, SHIO H, SMALL GM, LAZAROW PB: Peroxisomal membrane ghosts in Zellweger syndrome—Aberrant organelle assembly. *Science* 239:1536, 1988.

306. SANTOS MJ, IMANAKA T, SHIO H, LAZAROW PB: Peroxisomal integral membrane proteins in control and Zellweger fibroblasts. *J Biol Chem* 263:10502, 1988.

307. NISHIO H, KODAMA S, YOKOYAMA S, MATSUO T, MIO T, SUMINO K: A simple method to diagnose adrenoleukodystrophy using a dried blood spot on filter paper. *Clin Chim Acta* 159:77, 1986.

308. POWERS JM, TUMMONS RC, CAVINESS VS, MOSER AB, MOSER HW: Structural and chemical alterations in the cerebral maldevelopment of cerebro-hepato-renal (Zellweger) syndrome. *J Neuropathol Exp Neurol*, in press.

309. BARTH PG: Disorders of neuronal migration. *Can J Neurol Sci* 14:1, 1987.

310. ARNOLD G, HOLTZMAN E: Microperoxisomes in the central nervous system of the postnatal rat. *Brain Res* 155:1, 1978.

311. CUNNINGHAM BA, HEMPERLY JH, MURRAY BA, PREDIGER EA, BRACKENBURY R, EDELMAN GM: Neural cell adhesion molecule: Structure, immunoglobulin-like domains, cell surface modulation, and alternative RNA splicing. *Science* 236:799, 1987.

312. TSUJI S, SUZUKI M, ARIGA T, SEKINE M, KURIYAMA M, MIYATAKI T: Abnormality of long-chain fatty acids in erythrocyte membrane sphingomyelin from patients with adrenoleukodystrophy. *J Neurochem* 36j:1046, 1981.

313. AUBOURG P, BOUGNERES PF, ROCCHICCIOLI F: Capillary gas-liquid chromatographic-mass spectrometric measurement of very long chain (C22 to C26) fatty acids in microliter samples of plasma. *J Lipid Res* 26:263, 1985.

314. VAN DEN BERG GA, BREUKELMAN H, ELZINGA H, TRIJBELS JMF, MONNENS LAH, MUSKIET FAJ: Determination of pipecolic acid in urine and plasma by isotope dilution mass fragmentography. *Clin Chim Acta* 159:229, 1986.

315. HUTZLER J, DANCIS J: The determination of pipecolic acid: Method and results of hospital survey. *Clin Chim Acta* 128:75, 1983.

316. BJORKHEM I, FALK O: Assay of the major bile acids in serum by isotope dilution-mass spectrometry. *Scand J Clin Lab Invest* 43:163, 1983.

317. ROELS F, GOLDFISCHER S: Cytochemistry of human catalase: The demonstration of hepatic and renal peroxisomes by a high temperature procedure. *J Histochem Cytochem* 27:1471, 1979.

318. BEARD ME, MOSER AB, SAPIRSTEIN V, HOLTZMAN E: Peroxisomes in infantile phytanic acid storage disease: A cytochemical study of skin fibroblasts. *J Inherited Metab Dis* 9:321, 1986.

319. ROCCHICCIOLI F, AUBOURG P, CHOISET A: Immediate prenatal diagnosis of Zellweger syndrome by direct measurement of very long chain fatty acids in chorionic villus cells. *Prenat Diagn* 7:349, 1987.

320. WANDERS RJA, VAN WIJLAND MJA, VAN ROERMUND CWT, SCHUTGENS RBH, VAN DEN BOSCH H, TAGER JM, NIJENHUIS A, TROMP A: Prenatal diagnosis of Zellweger syndrome by measurement of very long chain fatty acid (C26:0) beta-oxidation in cultured chorionic villous fibroblasts: Implications for early diagnosis of other peroxisomal disorders. *Clin Chim Acta* 165:303, 1987.

321. HAJRA AK, DATTA NS, JACKSON LG, MOSER AB, MOSER HW, LARSEN JW JR, POWERS J: Prenatal diagnosis of Zellweger cerebro-hepato-renal syndrome. *N Engl J Med* 312:445, 1985.

322. ROELS F, VERDONCK V, PAUWELS M, FOULON W, LISSENS W, LIEBAERS I: Visualization of peroxisomes and plasmalogens in first trimester chorionic villus. *J Inherited Metab Dis* 10, suppl 2:233, 1987.

323. WANDERS RJA, SCHRAKAMP G, VAN DEN BOSCH H, TAGER JM, SCHUTGENS RBH: A prenatal test for the cerebro-hepato-renal (Zellweger) syndrome by demonstration of the absence of catalase-containing particles (peroxisomes) in cultured amniotic fluid cells. *Eur J Pediatr* 145:136, 1986.

324. CAREY WF, ROBERTSON EF, VAN CRUGTEN C, POULOS A, NELSON PV: Prenatal Diagnosis of Zellweger's Syndrome by Chorionic Villus Sampling—and a caveat. *Prenat Diagn* 6:227, 1986.

325. HOEFLER S, HOEFLER G, MOSER AB, WATKINS PA, CHEN WW, HASHIMOTO T, MOSER HW: Prenatal Diagnosis of Rhizomelic Chondrodysplasia Punctata. *Prenat Diagn*, in press.

326. HOLMES RD, WILSON GN, HAJRA AK: Oral ether lipid therapy in patients with peroxisomal disorders. *J Inherited Metab Dis* 10 suppl 2:239, 1987.

327. MOSER AB, BOREL J, ODONE A, NAIDU S, CORNBLATH D, SANDERS DB, MOSER HW: A new dietary therapy for adrenoleukodystrophy. Biochemical and preliminary clinical results in 36 patients. *Ann Neurol* 21:240, 1987.

328. GREENBERG CR, HAJRA AK, MOSER AB: Triple therapy of a patient with a generalized peroxisomal disorder. *Am J Hum Genet* 41, *suppl* A-64, 1987.

329. BJORKHEM I, BLOMSTRAND S, GLAUMANN H, STRANDVIK B: Unsuccessful attempts to induce peroxisomes in two cases of Zellweger disease by treatment with clofibrate. *Pediatr Res* 19:590, 1985.

330. BRUL S, WIEMER EAC, WESTERVELD A, STRIJLAND A, WANDERS RJA, SCHRAM AW, HEYMANS HSA, SCHUTGENS RBH, VAN DEN BOSCH H, TAGER JM. Kinetics of the assembly of peroxisomes after fusion of complementary cell lines from patients with the cerebro-hepato-renal (Zellweger) syndrome and related disorders. *Biochem Biophys Res Commun* 152:1083, 1988.

331. ROSCHER A, HOEFLER S, HOEFLER G, PASCHIKE E, PATAULF F, MOSER AB, MOSER HW. Genetic and phenotypic heterogeneity in disorders of peroxisome biogenesis. A study involving cell lines from 18 patients. Submitted.

332. WATKINS PA, CHEN WW, HARRIS CJ, HOEFLER G, HOEFLER S, BLAKE DC JR, BALFE A, KELLEY RI, MOSER AB, BEARD ME, MOSER HW. Peroxisomal bifunctional enzyme deficiency. Submitted.

333. WANDERS RJA, ROMEYN GJ, VAN ROERMUND CWT, SCHUTGENS RBH, VAN DEN BOSCH H, TAGER JM. Identification of L-pipecolate oxidase in human liver and its deficiency in Zellweger syndrome. *Biochem Biophys Res Commun* 154:33, 1988.

CHAPTER 58

ADRENOLEUKODYSTROPHY (X-Linked)

HUGO W. MOSER
ANN B. MOSER

1. *The term adrenoleukodystrophy is used to describe at least two genetically determined disorders that cause varying degrees of malfunction of the adrenal cortex and nervous system myelin and are characterized by abnormally high levels of saturated very-long-chain fatty acids in tissues and body fluids.*

2. *Two types of adrenoleukodystrophy must be distinguished. The first type is X-linked, the biochemical abnormalities appear to be confined to very-long-chain fatty acid metabolism, and peroxisome structure is normal. The second type is referred to as neonatal adrenoleukodystrophy. This disorder has an autosomal recessive mode of inheritance and resembles the Zellweger cerebrohepatorenal syndrome in that the number and size of peroxisomes are diminished and the function of at least five peroxisomal enzymes is impaired. This chapter is concerned with X-linked adrenoleukodystrophy. Neonatal adrenoleukodystrophy is discussed in Chap. 57.*

3. *The childhood form is the most common phenotype of X-linked adrenoleukodystrophy. Affected boys develop normally until 4 to 8 years, then suffer dementia and progressive neurologic deficit leading to a vegetative state. Second in frequency is adrenomyeloneuropathy. With this phenotype young men, over a period of decades, experience progressive paraparesis and sphincter disturbance due to spinal cord involvement. Ninety percent of patients in these two groups have varying degrees of adrenal insufficiency. Less common phenotypes include adrenal insufficiency without nervous system involvement, progressive cerebral dysfunction in adults, and biochemically affected persons who are asymptomatic. The various phenotypes commonly occur within the same kindred. Ten to fifteen percent of female heterozygotes develop neurologic disturbances that resemble those of adrenomyeloneuropathy.*

4. *The gene for X-linked adrenoleukodystrophy has been mapped to Xq28. It is linked to those for glucose-6-phosphate dehydrogenase, red-green color vision, and the DXS52 recombinant human DNA probe.*

5. *Tissues and body fluids of patients with X-linked adrenoleukodystrophy contain abnormally high levels of unbranched saturated very-long-chain fatty acids, particularly hexacosanoic ($C26:0$), pentacosanoic ($C25:0$), and tetracosanoic ($C24:0$). This excess is most striking in the cholesterol ester and ganglioside fractions of brain white matter and adrenal cortex but is present to varying degrees in virtually all tissues and body fluids.*

6. *It is likely that the very-long-chain fatty acid accumulation is due to impaired capacity to degrade them, a process that normally takes place in the peroxisome. The precise nature of the enzyme defect has not been determined.*

7. *Diagnosis of X-linked adrenoleukodystrophy hemizygotes is based upon demonstration of a characteristic pattern of increased very-long-chain fatty acid levels in plasma, red blood cells, or cultured skin fibroblasts. These techniques also permit identification of 85 percent of heterozygotes. Accuracy of heterozygote identification can approach 100 percent when fatty acid analyses are combined with the use of the DXS52 DNA probe. Prenatal identification of affected hemizygotes is achieved by demonstration of increased levels of very-long-chain fatty acids in cultured amniocytes or chorion villus biopsy samples; DXS52 linkage also can be used in appropriate families.*

8. *Adrenal hormone replacement therapy is effective in correcting the adrenal insufficiency associated with adrenoleukodystrophy. At present there is no proven method to prevent or ameliorate the neurologic manifestations, but several approaches are under investigation. These include dietary regimens that have been shown to normalize plasma very-long-chain fatty acid levels, bone marrow transplantation, and immunosuppression.*

HISTORY

In 1923, Siemerling and Creutzfeldt[1] reported a 7-year-old boy who had been well until age 3 or 4 years, when he was first noted to be hyperpigmented. At 6½ years he became disturbed, and his speech and gait deteriorated. He became spastic, unable to walk or swallow, and died at 7 years. Postmortem examination showed adrenal atrophy and extensive demyelination combined with perivascular accumulation of lymphocytes and plasma cells in the central nervous system. In 1963, Fanconi et al.[2] proposed an X-linked recessive mode of inheritance on the basis of pedigree analysis of 10 reported cases.

The key to all subsequent knowledge about the disease was the observation by Powers, Schaumburg, and Johnson[3–6] that adrenal cells of these patients contained characteristic lipid inclusions, followed by the demonstration that these inclusions consisted of cholesterol esters that contained a striking and characteristic excess of very-long-chain fatty acids (VLCFA).[7] Identification of a biochemical "handle" led to the development of assays capable of demonstrating more subtle increases in VLCFA levels in cultured skin fibroblasts,[8] plasma,[9] or red blood cells[10] and amniocytes.[11] These techniques have permitted precise postnatal and prenatal diagnosis, the facilitation of genetic studies and gene mapping,[12–14] and the evaluation of

---

Nonstandard abbreviations used in this chapter are: ACTH = adrenal corticotropin hormone; ALD = adrenoleukodystrophy; AMN = adrenomyeloneuropathy; BAER = brain-stem auditory evoked responses; CT = computed tomography; G-6-PD = glucose-6-phosphate dehydrogenase; MRI = magnetic resonance imaging; VLCFA = very-long-chain fatty acids.

therapeutic approaches.[15,16] Metabolic studies of VLCFA metabolism in patients with adrenoleukodystrophy (ALD) indicate that they have an impaired capacity to degrade these substances.[17-20] Subcellular localization studies indicate that VLCFA oxidation takes place in the peroxisome,[21] and X-linked ALD is now generally assigned to the peroxisomal disease category.[22,23] The precise enzyme defect in X-linked ALD has not been identified, although circumstantial evidence suggests a defect in a VLCFA CoA synthetase.[20,24]

CLINICAL FEATURES OF X-LINKED ALD

The phenotype of X-linked ALD is more varied than had been originally thought. Since the specificity of the biochemical abnormality involving VLCFA has now been confirmed, this assay can be used as the method of ascertainment. In this section we review the clinical changes observed in persons who display this biochemical abnormality. With this approach we have tentatively established seven clinical subtypes of X-linked ALD in males. These subtypes, as well as their relative frequencies, are listed in Table 58-1, which lists the experience at the Kennedy Institute and all cases reported in the literature up to December 1985. The results may be skewed by ascertainment biases. Since tests have focused mainly on symptomatic persons, it is likely that we have underestimated the number of persons who are asymptomatic or who have symptoms that do not fit what we now believe to be the clinical presentation of ALD. The various subtypes frequently occur within the same kindred (Table 58-2).

CHILDHOOD ALD

The clinical characteristics of childhood ALD have been analyzed in several large series.[25-28] Mean age of onset is 7.2 ±

Table 58-2 Phenotype Patterns in 146 Adrenoleukodystrophy (ALD) Pedigrees in Which More Than One Male Was Affected*

Pattern	No. of pedigrees
Neurologic involvement childhood type only (childhood or adolescent ALD)	79
Neurologic involvement adult type only (adrenomyeloneuropathy or adult cerebral)	21
Childhood and adult neurologic types present in same pedigree	43
Addison disease without neurologic involvement	2
Information incomplete	1
Total	146
Addison disease and neurologically involved males in same pedigree	24
Symptomatic and asymptomatic males in same pedigree	37

*Studied at the Kennedy Institute up to December 1985. SOURCE: Moser et al.[28] Used by permission.

1.7 years with a range of 2.75 to 10 years. Psychomotor development up to 3 years or later has been normal in all reported cases. Neurologic symptoms began prior to age 3 years in only one case, namely at 2¾ years. In 86 percent of the 167 childhood ALD patients tested at the Kennedy Institute, neurologic symptoms preceded signs of adrenal insufficiency, but 85 percent of the neurologically involved cases showed diminished cortisol response to ACTH at the time of neurologic diagnosis.[28]

Early behavioral changes consist of emotional lability, withdrawn or hyperactive behavior, and/or school failure. Difficulty in understanding speech in a noisy room or over the telephone are common early symptoms, and reflect impaired auditory discrimination, often with retention of normal pure tone perception. Diagnosis of an attentional deficit disorder and therapy with stimulants are a frequent part of the early history. The attention deficit disorder evolves rapidly to include clear-cut signs of parietal lobe dysfunction such as constructional and dressing apraxia, higher cortical sensory loss,

Table 58-1 X-Linked Adrenoleukodystrophy Cases in 321 Pedigrees Tested at the Kennedy Institute and Those Reported in Literature up to December 1985

	Cases tested at Kennedy Institute			
	Biochemically confirmed cases	Cases diagnosed on basis of clinical or morphologic findings, but not tested biochemically	Cases reported in literature from pedigrees not tested at Kennedy Institute	Total
Clinical subtype				
Childhood ALD	167	147	134	448
Adolescent ALD	42	4	9	55
Adult cerebral ALD	13	8	23	44
AMN	86	47	14	147
Addison disease only	29	24	14	67
Presymptomatic	29		2	31
Asymptomatic	25			25
Information insufficient to classify phenotype	18	2		20
Total	409	232	196	837

NOTE: The patients included in column 3 are relatives of the biochemically confirmed cases in column 2. Column 4 includes ALD patients reported in the literature but who were not tested at the Kennedy Institute. Reference 28 lists the literature citations for all these cases.
SOURCE: Moser et al.[28] Used by permission.

e.g., astereognosis and graphesthesia, and poor body orientation in space. The resultant behavior from bilateral cerebral hemispheric involvement may be labeled as dementia. Strabismus is not uncommon. Visual impairment is an early symptom in approximately one-third of the patients and includes field cuts and impaired visual acuity. In the later stages of the disease vision is lost totally and there is optic atrophy. Approximately one-third of the patients have focal or generalized seizures, and a seizure may be the initial symptom. Once the neurologic symptoms become manifest, progression is often rapid; the mean interval between first neurologic symptoms and an apparently vegetative state was 1.9 ± 2 years.[28] In this state the child is bedridden, unable to see or speak, and is fed via nasogastric tube or gastrostomy. The child or adolescent may remain in a vegetative state for several years, in some instances more than 5 years.

ADOLESCENT ONSET ALD

In one series[28] there were 42 patients in whom first symptoms occurred between age 11 and 21 years. Symptoms and progression in these patients resemble those in the childhood form.

ADRENOMYELONEUROPATHY

Adrenomyeloneuropathy (AMN) was first described in Austria by Budka et al.[29] and by Griffin et al. in the United States.[30] Characteristically, a man in his twenties, who previously had been well, notes stiffness or clumsiness in his legs. Generalized weakness, weight loss, pigmentation and attacks of nausea and vomiting may be noted before, after, or concurrent with the neurologic symptoms and lead to the diagnosis of Addison disease. The neurologic disability is slowly progressive, so that within the next 5 to 15 years the gait disturbance becomes severe and requires the use of a cane or a wheelchair. Urinary disturbances are noted in the twenties or thirties. Neurologic examination reveals a spastic paraparesis, with the upper extremities usually intact. Impaired vibration sense in the distal lower extremities as well as long tract signs and a relatively mild peripheral neuropathy are noted. Motor conduction velocity may be reduced in the lower extremities. Brain computed tomography (CT) is usually intact, but magnetic resonance imaging (MRI) studies may reveal subtle changes. Intellectual function usually appears intact, but detailed psychological tests may detect cognitive defects which may progress as the disease advances. Depression or emotional disturbances are not uncommon and become more severe as the illness advances. Impotence beginning in the late twenties or thirties is a common occurrence in AMN.[31] In one case hypogonadism preceded by 12 years the other manifestations of AMN. In spite of the eventual impairment of sexual function, it is not uncommon for AMN patients to have offspring.

It was found in retrospect that some men who later developed AMN had been hyperpigmented since early childhood. At the time that AMN is diagnosed, plasma adrenal corticotropin hormone (ACTH) levels usually are greatly elevated. Presumably, these men had abnormally high ACTH (and melanocyte stimulating hormone) levels and in this way were able to maintain relatively normal adrenal function during infancy

and childhood. In the Kennedy Institute series adrenal insufficiency preceded neurologic deficit in 42 percent of AMN patients, and 88 percent showed impaired adrenal reserve at the time of initial neurologic diagnosis. In two cases Addison disease preceded neurologic dysfunction by 22 and 27 years. Occasionally adrenal function is normal.[32]

CEREBRAL SYMPTOMS IN ADULTS

The Kennedy Institute series includes 21 patients with predominantly cerebral symptoms beginning in adulthood, and 23 such cases have been reported in the literature.[28]

In most instances these men present in the twenties or thirties with symptoms that resemble schizophrenia, with dementia or a specific cerebral deficit. One 29-year-old man, who at postmortem examination was found to have bilateral temporal lobe lesions, had symptoms characteristic of the Kluver-Bucy syndrome.[33] Another 34-year-old man presented with dysphasia and a right homonymous hemianopsia.[34] The presence of Addison disease is a crucial diagnostic clue. The occurrence of psychotic disturbance in a patient with Addison disease must alert the clinician to the possibility of ALD, although psychotic symptoms may occur in other forms of Addison disease also. CT and study of very-long-chain fatty acids permit differentiation. Adrenal function was normal in two cases.[35] White matter lesions demonstrated by CT were the first diagnostic clue, with the specific diagnosis being established by biochemical assays.

ADDISON DISEASE ONLY

The Kennedy Institute series included 29 persons with the biochemical defect of ALD who have Addison disease but were neurologically intact. Their mean age was 12.8 ± 6.6 years (SD), with a range of 3 to 35 years. It is not known how many will remain free of neurologic involvement. As already noted, in some AMN or adult cerebral cases the interval between the diagnosis of Addison disease and first neurologic symptom was in excess of 20 years. We know of two ALD pedigrees in which all affected male members had Addison disease but were neurologically intact. X-linked adrenal insufficiency may also be associated with deficiency of glycerol kinase whose locus is at Xp21 (see Chap. 36).[36] Wakefield and Brown[37] reported another family with X-linked congenital Addison disease. It is likely that there are a variety of causes of X-linked Addison disease. Investigations to differentiate such cases should include assays of VLCFA and of glycerol kinase activity.

PERSONS WHO HAVE THE BIOCHEMICAL DEFECT OF ALD BUT WHO ARE FREE OF DISABILITY

We know of 54 persons with the biochemical defect of ALD who appear to be free of disability. Twenty-nine of the asymptomatic individuals are less than 10 years old and are at risk of developing the disability later on. Twenty-five are 11 years or older, and most of them are older than their symptomatic proband relatives. Since AMN and ALD occur frequently within the same kindred, it is likely that some of these persons will develop AMN when they become adults. However, we know of two 62-year-old men who have the biochemical defect of ALD but who are free of demonstrable neurologic or adrenal dysfunction. One man is the grandfather of an ALD patient; the other, the brother of a patient with adult cerebral ALD. Both were identified as part of a systematic biochemical survey of members of the pedigree. The biochemical abnormality in these men is comparable to that in their severely affected relatives. This suggests that the biochemical defect of ALD in some persons does not lead to disability. We do not know how frequently this occurs, since biochemical tests are rarely performed in persons without symptoms.

SYMPTOMATIC ALD HETEROZYGOTES

Women who are heterozygous for ALD may develop progressive spastic paraparesis, moderate vibratory sense loss, long tract signs, and peripheral neuropathy manifesting first at age 43 ± 11 years (SD). These abnormalities resemble those in AMN, but are milder and of later onset. O'Neill et al.[38] found that 9 of 21 ALD heterozygotes (42 percent) had spastic paraparesis beginning in the third decade. The myelopathy was judged to be mild in four, moderate in two, and severe in three. We know of 42 women who have spastic paraparesis. Systematic surveys have not yet been carried out.[28] We estimate that significant neurologic disability occurs in 10 to 15 percent of women heterozygous for ALD. Unlike AMN, adrenal function is almost always intact[28] (Table 58-3).

One 14-year-old girl who was heterozygous for ALD developed Addison disease and cerebral disease and thus presented with a clinical picture which resembled but was of later onset and slightly less severe than the typical childhood ALD in her affected brother.[40] This girl had a normal karyotype and to our knowledge is the only female who presented with the cerebral form of the disease in adolescence. As already noted, most symptomatic heterozygotes present with the clinical picture of AMN. Two heterozygote women had a severe dementing illness.[41,42] Postmortem studies of symptomatic ALD heterozygotes have shown morphologic and biochemical changes characteristic of ALD.[42,43]

Most ALD heterozygotes with paraparesis had previously been diagnosed as having multiple sclerosis.[44] Another was di-

Table 58-3 Comparison Between Male Adrenomyeloneuropathy (AMN) Patients and Symptomatic Women Who Are Heterozygous for ALD

Characteristics	AMN	Heterozygotes
No. of patients	86	42
Paraparesis	100% (By definition)	41/42
Cerebral involvement (excluding "cerebral adult" category)	20% (Estimated)	2/42
Impaired vibration sense or other sensory disturbance	Varying degrees in most patients	20/22
Adrenal dysfunction	65/74	1/15
Age at onset of symptoms	28 ± 7.0	43 ± 11
Range	15–53	23–73

SOURCE: Moser et al.[28] Used by permission.

agnosed as having a dorsolateral cord syndrome of unknown etiology.[45] In all instances the diagnosis was changed to the manifesting ALD heterozygote state only because they had a male child with ALD. One previously reported ALD heterozygote[44] had noted intermittent paresthesias in her left arm and leg since age 40. At age 44 impaired vibration sense, hyperreflexia in lower extremities, and the demonstration of oligoclonal bands in cerebrospinal fluid led to the diagnosis of multiple sclerosis. When she was 47 years old, the diagnosis of ALD was established in her son and she herself was shown to have unequivocal elevations of VLCFAs.[44] A similar sequence has been noted in an Australian patient. These histories highlight the phenotypic resemblance between multiple sclerosis and the manifesting ALD heterozygote. The diagnostic difficulty is confounded by the fact that most neurologically impaired ALD heterozygotes have normal adrenal function. We know of only three heterozygotes who had clinically evident adrenal insufficiency.[28]

RARER ALD PHENOTYPES

There are four reports of prominent cerebellar disturbances in patients with ALD.[46–49] One 54-year-old patient showed a clinical and radiologic picture that resembled olivopontocerebellar degeneration. He had developed Addison disease at age 10, while neurologic disability did not manifest until age 52.[48]

PATHOLOGY OF ALD

Nervous System

The pathology of ALD has been reviewed recently.[50] Postmortem studies of the brain in childhood or adult cerebral ALD show that the cortex is usually intact but that the centrum semiovale is replaced by large areas of gray-to-brown firm, translucent tissue. This confluent and often bilaterally symmetric demyelination is most commonly observed in the parietooccipital region. CT and MRI studies have shown that caudorostral progression is a feature in 85 percent of the cases, although in some cases the initial lesion is frontal. The arcuate fibers are often spared, but the posterior cingulum, corpus callosum, fornix, hippocampal commissure, posterior limbs of the internal capsule, and optic pathways are characteristically involved. Histopathologically the demyelination and sclerotic lesions exhibit marked loss of myelinated axons and oligodendrocytes. Both isomorphic and anisomorphic astrogliosis is seen. Diffuse infiltrations and large perivascular collections of mononuclear cells, mostly lymphocytes, are seen frequently (Fig. 58-1). This feature, which bears a resemblance to multiple sclerosis, is characteristic of ALD, and as discussed below, may be an important clue to pathogenesis. Griffin et al.[51] typed the lymphocytes in these perivascular cuffs and concluded that the distribution of cells resembles that found in the central nervous system during a cellular immune response.

The central nervous system lesions in AMN differ from those in childhood and cerebral ALD. Here it is the spinal cord which bears the brunt of the disease process. The pattern of fiber loss is consistent with a distal axonopathy. The great-

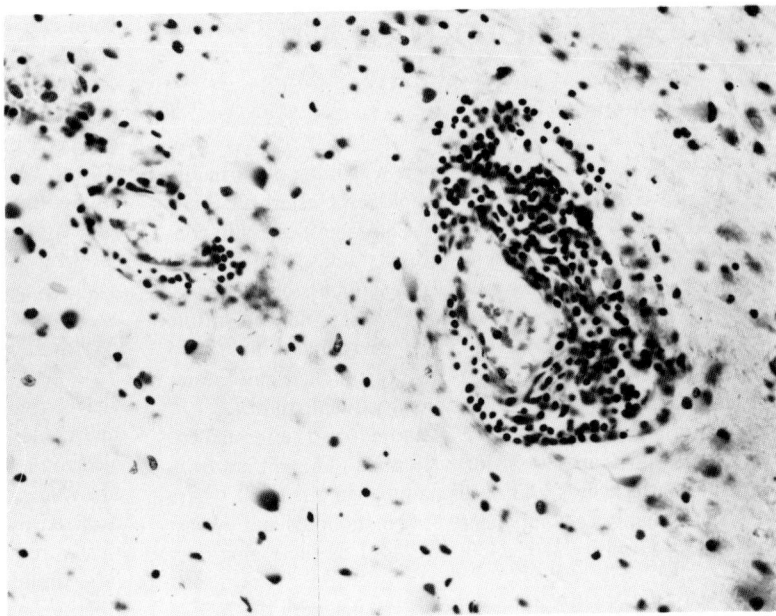

Fig. 58-1 Hematoxylin-eosin stained section of white matter of a 22-year-old patient with adult cerebral ALD,[9] showing intense perivascular infiltration of mononuclear cells. *(From Powers et al.[52] Used by permission.)*

est fiber losses are observed in the lumbar corticospinal, cervical gracile, and dorsal spinocerebellar tracts. In contrast to childhood and adult ALD, sudanophilia and inflammation are minimal to absent, and astrogliosis is moderate. Perivascular accumulations of lymphocytes or macrophages are present but less prominent than in the childhood form.

Peripheral nerve involvement in ALD and AMN is less severe than the central nervous system lesion. Sural and peroneal nerves may display a loss of large- and small-diameter myelinated fibers and endoneurial fibrosis.

Adrenal Cortex and Testis

In the adrenal cortex cells become ballooned first in the inner fasciculate and reticular zone and striated due to the accumulation of lamallae, lamellar lipid profiles, and fine lipid clefts. As the disease advances, the adrenal cortex becomes severely atrophic. In fetuses affected by X-linked ALD the prominent fetal adrenal zone is mainly involved.[52] Postpubertal males show lamellae and lipid-laden profiles in the Leydig cell cytoplasm similar to those observed in adrenocortical cells. Changes in seminiferous tubules are nonspecific and include loss of germ cells and vacuolated Sertoli cells.[53]

Ultrastructural Changes

Powers and Schaumburg[4] were the first to describe electron-dense bileaflet structures lying free in the cytoplasm of adrenocortical cells (Fig. 58-2). These leaflets, referred to as lamellae, have been demonstrated also in Schwann cells, Leydig cells, and macrophages in CNS white matter lesions. Curiously, they have not been positively identified in oligodendrocytes. The extent to which these lamellae can be classified as truly specific for ALD and generalized peroxisomal disorders (see Chap. 57) depends on morphologic features, which have been described clearly by Powers et al.[52,53] Johnson et al.[6] showed that these lamellae contain VLCFA, probably in the form of cholesterol ester. Ultrastructural demonstration of the

characteristic lamellae (as defined by Powers) and biochemical demonstration of an excess of saturated VLCFA thus are a reflection of the same abnormality which is characteristic of X-linked ALD and related peroxisomal disorders.

Fig. 58-2 This adrenocortical cell contains both unilamellate and multilamellate inclusions which are both free in the cytoplasm and attached to various organelles (arrows), ×18,538. Electron micrograph was taken from uranyl acetate–lead citrate stained thin sections. *(From Moser et al.[28] Used by permission.)*

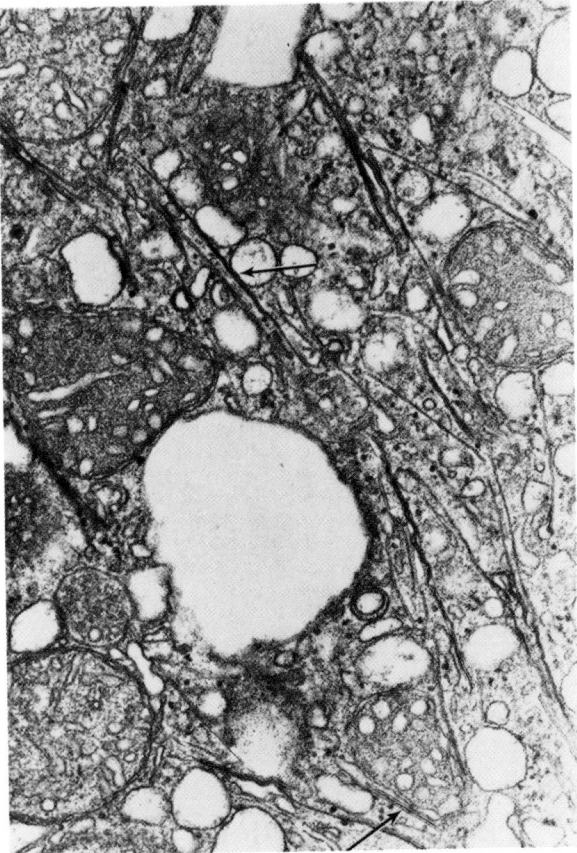

CHEMICAL PATHOLOGY OF ALD

Cholesterol Ester

Igarashi et al.[7] were the first to report a striking abnormality in the fatty acid composition of cholesterol esters in ALD brain and adrenal cortex (Fig. 58-3). Cholesterol esters in control brain contain mostly C16 to C20 fatty acids, while cholesterol esters in ALD brain contain large amounts of very-long-chain fatty acids (C24 to C30 or more), where they constitute 20 to 67 percent of total fatty acids, compared with 0 to 5 percent in controls.[54] The abnormality of cholesterol ester fatty acids has been confirmed in all subsequent studies.[42,55–58] The abnormal fatty acids are saturated and unbranched. C25:0 and C26:0 are the major fatty acids. This differs from the usual pattern of VLCFA in mammalian tissues,[54] where they occur mainly as components of sphingolipids and consist of C22 to C27 with 22:0, 24:0, and 24:1 as the major fatty acids.

The cholesterol ester abnormality correlates with the histology. The greatest excess of cholesteryl ester levels and VLCFA enrichment is observed in the actively demyelinating areas.[58–60] In two studies cholesterol ester levels and fatty acid composition were normal in those regions of ALD brain that appeared histologically intact,[58,59] while in one other patient the cholesterol esters in a histologically intact area did contain abnormally high VLCFA levels.[60] "Burned out" gliotic areas of brain contain normal or slightly increased levels of cholesterol esters, with increased VLCFA content.[59]

Gangliosides

Gangliosides are the second lipid fraction in which ALD tissues show a major and consistent alteration in fatty acid composition. Fatty acids with a chain length greater than 22 account for 28 to 50 percent of total fatty acids in ALD brain gangliosides, compared with 2.5 percent in controls.[54,61] C24:0 and C24:1 (and not C25:0 or C26:0) represent the predominant VLCFA in ALD gangliosides, thus differing slightly from the pattern noted in the ALD cholesterol ester fraction. All the VLCFAs were attached to the ganglioside by the usual amide linkage. The VLCFA excess was present in all ganglioside species, with those containing multiple sialic acid units showing the greatest excess.

Myelin

Correlation with morphologic studies indicates that the abnormal cholesterol esters in ALD brain—demonstrable with the electron microscope as lamellar inclusions—are located mainly in invading macrophages.[15] When ALD white matter is fractionated by standard techniques,[62] the myelin content is drastically reduced compared with normal,[51,56] while there is a large amount of less dense material, referred to as the floating fraction, which contains large quantities of the abnormal cholesterol esters. Brown et al.[57] reported that myelin isolated from ALD brain contained up to 10 percent of cholesterol ester and that these cholesterol esters were enriched in VLCFA. Normal myelin does not contain cholesterol ester. Such an abnormality in the composition of ALD myelin might cause it to be unstable; however, it was not possible to exclude that the ALD myelin was contaminated with "floating fraction" material, even though steps were taken to minimize this.[57]

Other brain constituents show lesser or no VLCFA excess. Studies of the cerebroside and sulfatide fractions are particularly difficult to interpret since these myelin constituents normally contain VLCFA, and their long-chain and VLCFA content is known to be diminished when there is demyelination, as occurs in ALD. In two studies a 1.5- to 2-fold increase in VLCFA content of cerebrosides and sulfatides was noted,[7,57] while in another study their level was unchanged.[58] VLCFA content in the free fatty acid and triglyceride fractions is moderately increased.[56–59] The phospholipid VLCFA content is usually not significantly altered.[7,56] A recent study noted an eightfold increase in the VLCFA content of the glycerophosphatide fraction in a histologically intact area of ALD brain.[59]

As discussed in "Diagnosis of ALD," below, a two- to tenfold VLCFA excess has been demonstrated in the red blood cells, plasma, and cultured skin fibroblasts of more than 1000 ALD hemizygotes and heterozygotes, and the specificity of this finding has been confirmed. These studies have confirmed the significance of the VLCFA abnormality which was first demonstrated in postmortem tissues, and indicate that this biochemical abnormality is an integral part of the disease process.

VERY-LONG-CHAIN FATTY ACIDS

Occurrence and Metabolism

Occurrence and Source of VLCFA. Normally VLCFA occur in highest concentration in myelin lipids and red blood cell sphingomyelin. Hexacosanoic acid (C26:0) accounts for approximately 1 percent of total fatty acids in brain cerebrosides and sulfatides[7] and red blood cell sphingomyelin.[16] VLCFA

Fig. 58-3 Gas chromatographic tracings of fatty acid methyl esters of brain cholesterol esters. Technical details are described in Ref. 7. The top is from a normal brain, and the bottom from an ALD patient. Note the large amounts and the bell-shaped distribution of very-long-chain fatty acids in the ALD specimen. The major peak marked X in the ALD sample is unidentified. (From Igarashi et al.[7] Used by permission of the International Society of Neurochemistry.)

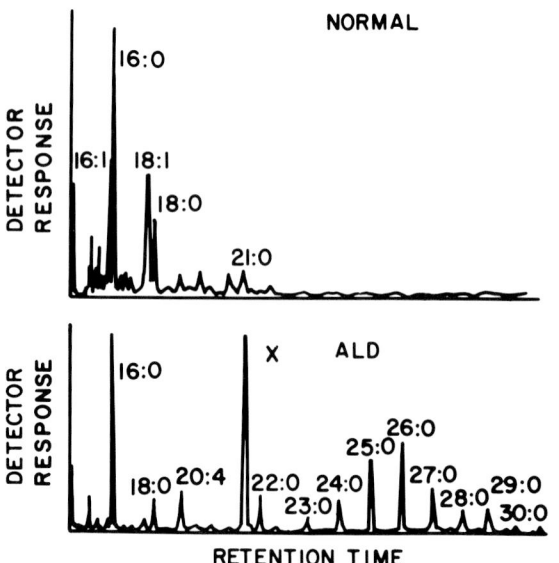

are present in much lower concentration in other tissues and lipid moieties. C26:0 constitutes less than 0.01 percent of total fatty acids[9] in normal plasma and in adipose tissue (H. W. Moser, unpublished observation). Because of their low tissue content and technical difficulties, most older published reports do not provide quantitative data about fatty acids with greater than 24 carbon chain length.

VLCFA are constituents of cutin, the outer waterproofing membrane of plants.[63] Cutin contains very-long-chain alkanes, with chains containing up to 32 carbons. These alkane chains are produced by the decarboxylation of corresponding VLCFA, which are formed in turn by the elongation of palmitic (C16:0) and stearic (C18:0) acids.[64] As part of a dietary therapy program for ALD (see "Dietary Therapy," below), we have analyzed the VLCFA of more than 200 foods. VLCFA levels were found to be high not only in fats but also in the outer layers of many fruits and vegetables and in yeast.[65]

The VLCFA present in the human body appear to be derived from both the diet and endogenous synthesis. This information is based upon studies in two ALD patients. In the first study a terminally ill ALD patient each day received 10 mg of $(3,3,5,5)-{}^2H_4$ hexacosanoic (C26:0) acid by nasogastric tube for a 100-day period. This quantity of C26:0 is equivalent to the C26:0 of the usual American diet. Postmortem study demonstrated that in certain parts of the brain up to 90 percent of C26:0 contained the label, indicating that in this patient a substantial portion of brain C26:0 was of dietary origin.[66] Studies in another ALD patient indicated that endogenous synthesis also is a source of VLCFA. This patient each day received 50 ml of D_2O by mouth for a 196-day period. At the end of the study deuterium enrichment of lignoceric acid (C24:0) and hexacosanoic acid (C26:0) was 72 to 79 percent that of palmitic (C16:0) and stearic (C18:0) acids[67] (Fig. 58-4). This result differs sharply from the findings in respect to phytanic acid in a Refsum disease patient. When this patient received the same amount of oral D_2O over the same time period, plasma phytanic acid was essentially free of label.[68] This result led to the conclusion that phytanic acid in humans is of dietary origin only. The results in the ALD patients indicate that C26:0, and presumably other VLCFA, are of both dietary and endogenous origin. The results do not permit conclusions about the relative importance of the two pathways, although the high level of VLCFA label following D_2O administration suggests that the endogenous synthesis is more important. Recent dietary studies in ALD patients lead to the same conclusion. Dietary restriction of C26:0 failed to lower plasma C26:0 levels,[65] while a reduction is achieved by measures that are presumed to diminish endogenous VLCFA synthesis.[15,16]

Biosynthesis of VLCFA. Synthesis of fatty acids with chain length greater than 16 carbons is carried out by the fatty acid elongation system. This system occurs in both mitochondria and microsomes. The microsomal system appears to be more active and to have greater physiological significance.[69]

The stoichiometry of the elongation reaction in the microsomal system is

$$\text{Palmityl CoA} + \text{malonyl CoA} + \text{NADPH} + \text{H}^+ \rightarrow$$
$$\text{stearoyl CoA} + \text{CO}_2 + \text{NADP}^+ + \text{CoA} + \text{H}_2\text{O}$$

With this reaction a C16 fatty acid (palmitic) is elongated to C18 (stearic acid). VLCFA synthesis is achieved by repeated cycles of the same reaction, two carbon units being added until the desired chain length is achieved. Fatty acid synthesis and elongation are complex and highly regulated processes involving the coordinated action of multiple enzymes and acyl carrier proteins.[70]

The maturational changes in activity of the brain microsomal fatty acid elongation system correlate with the deposition of myelin.[71] This correlation is significant, since myelin lipids contain large amounts of long-chain fatty acids. The activity of the microsomal system also is reduced in mouse mutants that are deficient in myelin.[69]

The characteristics of the elongation system vary among tissues.[71] Formation of saturated VLCFA, including C26:0, from $[1-{}^{14}C]C18:0$ was first demonstrated in rat sciatic nerve,[72] and subsequently in normal and ALD cultured human skin fibroblasts.[73] The factors that control the rate of the elongation are still poorly understood. The chain length of the substrate is an important factor. In a study utilizing swine cerebral microsomes it was found that elongation of C20:0 CoA yielded C22:0 and C24:0 concomitantly, whereas elongation of C22:0 CoA yielded only negligible amounts of C24:0. Kinetic studies in this system suggested that elongation of C20:0 CoA and of C22:0 CoA are carried out through two separate pathways, with that for the C_{20} substrate being more active. Bourre et al. concluded that a single enzyme is responsible for the elongation of behenic acid (C22:0) and its monounsaturated counterpart, erucic acid (C22:1).[74] This finding is relevant to current dietary therapy. It has been shown that administration of monounsaturated fatty acids diminishes synthesis of saturated VLCFA,[75] presumably through competition for the elongating system machinery. On the other hand, the elongation system for polyunsaturated fatty acid is distinct from that for saturated fatty acids.[76]

Degradation of VLCFA. Three lines of evidence indicate that the peroxisome plays a significant, and possibly the major, role in the β oxidation of VLCFA. In 1976 Lazarow and de Duve demonstrated a peroxisomal fatty acid oxidizing system in rat liver,[77] and it was found that this system was most active toward medium- and long-chain fatty acids.[78] Patients who lack peroxisomes invariably have impaired degradation and elevated levels of VLCFA.[79,80] Subcellular fractionation studies in rat liver have demonstrated that C24:0 is oxidized mainly in the fractions that contain peroxisomes.[21] Studies of VLCFA degradation present technical problems because of their insolubility and apparent low rates of oxidation and the difficulty of separating peroxisomes from mitochondria. For these reasons the relative contribution of peroxisomes and mitochondria to the degradation of VLCFA is not fully established. While there is no doubt that peroxisomes play a role, a mitochondrial contribution cannot be excluded.

Figure 58-5 compares the peroxisomal and mitochondrial β-oxidation system. The peroxisomal system is discussed in more detail in Chapter 57. It should be noted that the peroxisomal enzymes (2 to 4 in Fig. 58-5) are distinct from their mitochondrial counterparts (enzymes 5 to 8 in Fig. 58-5).[81] Enzymes 2 to 4 have been purified from rat liver, their amino acid sequence has been determined, and their cDNA clones isolated.[82-85]

The study of lignoceroyl CoA synthetase (enzyme 1, Fig. 58-5) has been hampered by the insolubility of the substrate. Singh and associates were able to test its activity in rat brain microsome fractions with the combined use of the solubilizing agent α-cyclodextrin and detergents.[86] A 100-fold purification

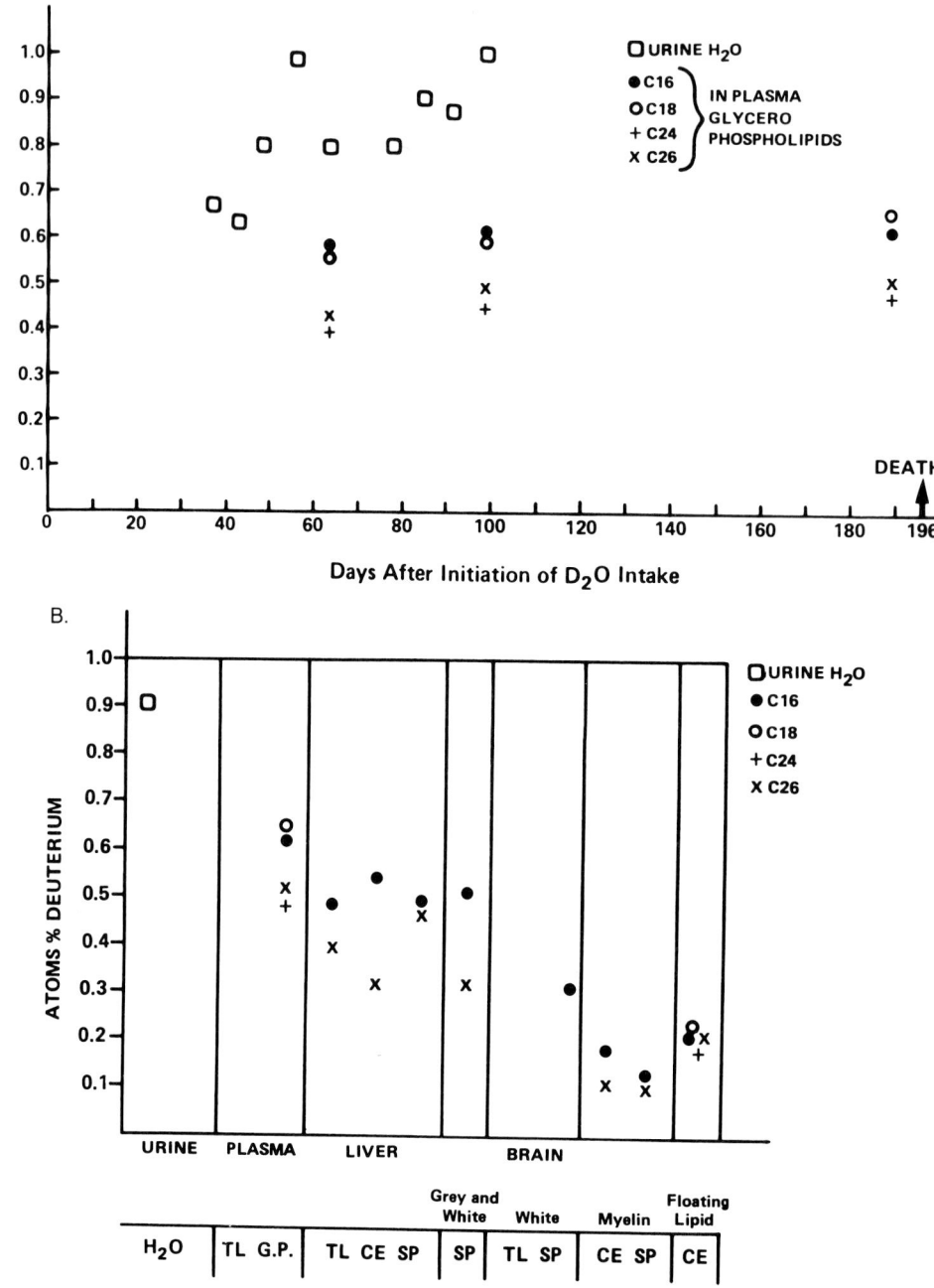

Fig. 58-4 Deuterium content (atoms %) in a 6-year-old patient with ALD: A. in urine H_2O and plasma fatty acids following the oral administration of D_2O (50 ml/d) and B. in postmortem tissues and plasma following oral administration of D_2O (50 ml/d) for 196 days.

All the fatty acid analyses refer to saturated compounds. TL = total lipids; G.P. = glycerophosphatides; CE = cholesterol esters; SP = sphingomyelin.

of the rat brain and liver enzymes was achieved by Nagamatsu et al.[87] The partially purified enzyme was 100-fold more active toward CoA ester synthesis from palmitic acid than lignoceric acid. Palmitoyl CoA and lignoceroyl CoA synthetase activities co-purified during all steps of the procedure, and it was considered likely that a single enzyme catalyzes both reactions.[86] In contrast, Bhushan et al. concluded that palmitoyl and lignoceroyl CoA synthetase are separate enzymes, since the enzyme activities were differentially enriched in three fractions obtained by hydroxylapatite chromatography, and the detergent triton X-100 inhibited the lignoceroyl CoA but not the palmitoyl CoA synthetase activity.[88] Since it has been proposed that in X-linked ALD there is a specific involvement of lignoceroyl-CoA synthetase (see "Update," below), resolution of these discrepant results is of special importance.

The Enzyme Defect in X-Linked ALD

An impaired capacity to degrade saturated VLCFA has been a consistent finding in various cell preparations of ALD patients. The defect was first demonstrated by Singh et al.[17,90] [^{14}C]CO$_2$ production from [1-^{14}C]C24:0 in ALD cells was reduced to 17 percent of control. Similar impairments were also demonstrated in respect to the degradation of [1-^{14}C]C26:0 and in homogenates of white blood cells and cultured amniocytes. [1-^{14}C]C16:0 and C18:0 were degraded at a normal rate by all these cells. Defective VLCFA degradation has also been demonstrated by three other groups of investigators.[18,19,89] Two of these studies utilized whole fibroblast cultures,[18,19] and, in these systems, the VLCFA oxidation in ALD cell lines was 27 to 50 percent of control. In the other study which uti-

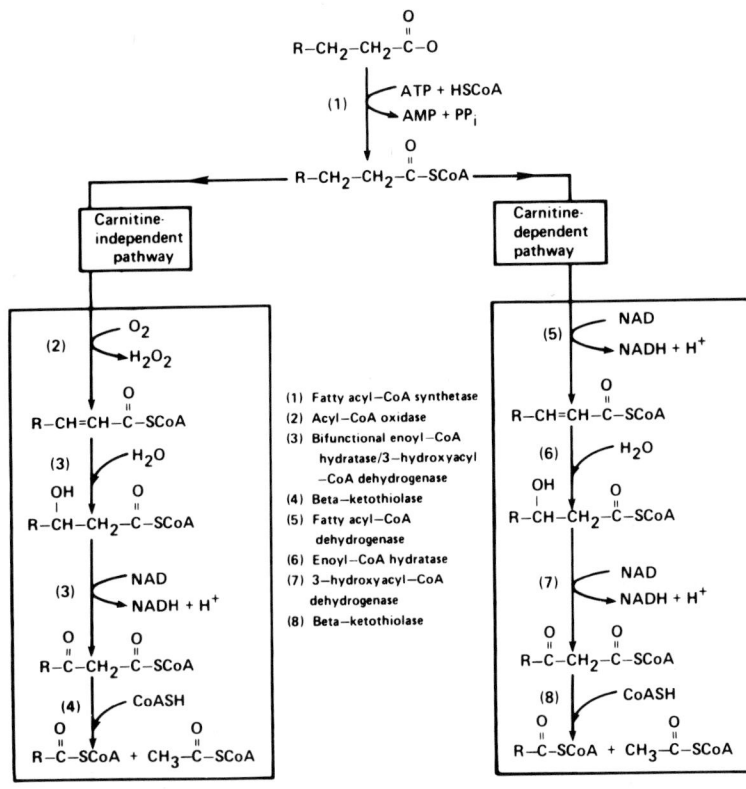

Fig. 58-5 β-Oxidation pathway in peroxisomes and mitochondria. See text for discussion.

lized homogenates of cultured skin fibroblasts, [1-^{14}C]C24:0 oxidation was reduced to 5 percent of control.[89] Tsuji et al. have conducted a carefully controlled study of VLCFA synthesis in cultured skin fibroblasts in ALD patients.[73] They demonstrated that in the ALD samples the activity of the microsomal fatty acid elongation system was increased 50 to 80 percent over that in the controls. Fatty acid synthetase activity was unaltered. In a later publication the same authors also confirmed the impaired VLCFA degradation in ALD cell lines.[91]

The increased VLCFA levels in ALD tissues thus may be caused both from impaired degradation and increased synthesis. Determination of the relative importance of these two factors requires kinetic studies which have not yet been performed. We believe that the degradative defect is the most significant factor, since the defect is more severe and has been reported independently by four groups. The factors that control VLCFA synthesis are complex and in need of further study. The importance of defining them is highlighted by the recent finding that perturbations which are thought to alter VLCFA synthesis have a profound effect on the plasma VLCFA levels of ALD patients (see "Dietary Therapy," below).

It is generally postulated that the impaired VLCFA degradation in X-linked ALD is due to the defective function of an as yet unidentified peroxisomal enzyme. This formulation is based upon the observation that the impaired degradative capacity is confined to those fatty acids that are metabolized mainly by the peroxisome,[21] and the resemblance of the VLCFA accumulation in ALD to that in the generalized peroxisomal disorders (see Chap. 57). In the latter group there is firm evidence that the fatty acid disorder is due to peroxisomal dysfunction. While most authors, ourselves included, designate X-linked ALD as a peroxisomal disorder,[22,23] it must be cautioned that such an assignment is still tentative. Unlike what is observed in the Zellweger syndrome and the generalized peroxisomal disorders, peroxisomes in X-linked ALD patients are normal in size and number.[92] Table 58-4 shows that there are substantial differences between the VLCFA abnormalities in X-linked ALD and Zellweger syndrome. Zellweger patients show a greater accumulation of saturated VLCFAs and a more severe defect in their degradation. In Zellweger

Table 58-4 Comparison of VLCFA Abnormalities in X-Linked ALD and Zellweger Syndrome

	X-Linked ALD	Zellweger	Controls
Plasma C26:0	1.62 ± 0.87 (282)	3.06 ± 1.23 (40)	0.33 ± 0.18 (1900)
Plasma C26:1	0.77 ± 0.33 (10)	5.4 ± 3.4 (10)	0.96 ± 0.51 (10)
C24:0 oxidation in cultured fibroblasts, % control	23	3	100
Immunoblot analysis of enzymes 2 to 4 (Fig. 58-5)	Normal	Absent or present in precursor form	

NOTE: Units are in micrograms per milliliter (μg/ml) of plasma.

syndrome there is accumulation of unsaturated VLCFAs (see Chap. 57), whereas in X-linked ALD only the saturated VLCFAs are present in excess.[79,93] Finally, immunoblot studies of the peroxisomal fatty acid oxidation enzymes in post-mortem tissues have shown profound abnormalities in Zellweger syndrome, while studies in X-linked ALD have shown no abnormalities.[94,95]

A final decision about whether X-linked ALD is a peroxisomal disorder must be deferred until the basic defect has been defined. Because of the evidence that there is an overall impairment of peroxisomal fatty acid oxidation, research has focused mainly on the peroxisomal β-oxidation enzymes shown in Fig. 58-5. A defect involving an α-oxidation system is considered unlikely because of the high concentration of odd-numbered VLCFA, such as C25:0, in ALD brain.[54] These odd-numbered fatty acids are known to be formed by an α-oxidation system. Measurement of the activities of the peroxisomal β-oxidation enzymes has been hampered by technical problems. Since fatty acid β-oxidation takes place both in mitochondria and peroxisomes, measurement of peroxisomal activity alone requires physical separation of the organelles, or a procedure that will inhibit the mitochondrial component without affecting peroxisomal function. These goals have not yet been achieved. While immunoblot studies indicate that X-linked ALD tissue contains normal quantities of protein reacting with antibodies to acyl CoA oxidase, bifunctional enzyme, and thiolase (enzymes 2 to 4, Fig. 58-5), the activities of these enzymes have not been assessed in ALD tissues.

Two groups of investigators have provided provocative but as yet circumstantial evidence that the enzyme defect in X-linked ALD involves lignoceroyl-CoA synthetase (enzyme 1, Fig. 58-5). While oxidation of [1-^{14}C]C24:0 in ALD fibroblasts was reduced to 32 percent of control, the CoA derivative of C24:0 was oxidized at a normal rate.[20,24] This finding has lead to the hypothesis that the defect in X-linked ALD involves the activation of C24:0 and other VLCFA. Overall activity of lignoceroyl-CoA synthetase ALD fibroblasts was only partially reduced.[96] As noted in the previous section, it is not known whether VLCFA CoA synthetase is distinct from palmitoyl-CoA synthetase. This question is significant since palmitoyl-CoA synthetase appears to function normally in X-linked ALD. A defect confined to lignoceroyl-CoA synthetase would imply that it is a separate enzyme. Additional data are required to resolve these questions.

In conclusion, available evidence indicates that the enzyme defect in ALD involves the impaired capacity to degrade VLCFA, and there is circumstantial evidence that the defect involves some aspect of the peroxisomal β-fatty acid oxidation system. The specific enzyme defect has not been identified. As described in the next section, the ALD gene has been mapped to Xq28. Mapping of "candidate enzymes" may aid the identification of the defective enzyme.

GENETICS OF X-LINKED ALD

Pattern of Inheritance and Incidence

Pedigree analysis in over 300 kindreds has confirmed X-linked recessive mode of inheritance in all instances.[28] Reevaluation of the single instance of possible father-son transmission reported in the literature[97] indicated that the son did not have

ALD.[98] ALD has been reported in all geographic locations and races, including 9 black, 9 Jewish, and 1 Maori family.[28] The incidence of the disorder is not known. During the last 4 years, our laboratory has diagnosed 50 to 80 new cases a year, approximately 60 percent of them from the United States. On the basis of 3.6 million U.S. births per year, this yields a minimum incidence of 1.1 per 100,000. This is clearly a minimum value. We do not know what proportion of ALD cases are diagnosed, and our laboratory obviously does not test samples from all cases that exist.

There is as yet no accurate information about the proportion of cases that represent new mutations. To gain information about this question, we have carried out a preliminary comparison of families in which there was an isolated case of ALD with those in which multiple cases have been identified. In this analysis we used a classification function to assess heterozygote status.[99] This function was abnormal in 88 percent of 74 mothers who belonged to multiple case pedigrees and were obligate heterozygotes. The function was abnormal in 73 percent of 30 women who were mothers of boys in families with only isolated ALD cases (Fig. 58-6). The relatively small difference between these two groups, coupled with our experience that thorough study of extended pedigrees often leads to the identification of affected relatives of apparently isolated cases, suggests to us that new mutations are relatively infrequent.

Mapping the ALD Gene; Linkage to Glucose-6-Phosphate Dehydrogenase, the DXS52 DNA Probe, and Red-Green Color Vision

Linkage to glucose-6-phosphate dehydrogenase (G-6-PD) was established by studies of families with women heterozygous for both ALD and electrophoretic variants of G-6-PD. No recombinants between these genes were observed in the offspring of 18 doubly heterozygous women.[12] Since G-6-PD has been mapped to Xq28,[100] this result localizes the ALD gene to the same segment of that chromosome. Skin fibroblast clones from heterozygotes were of two types: one with normal fatty acid pattern, the other showing a pattern similar to that of affected males. This indicates that the locus is subject to inactivation.[12]

Localization to Xq28 has been confirmed through the use of the DXS52 recombinant DNA probe, which recognizes polymorphic loci in that region.[101] Linkage to this probe was established in studies involving seven ALD families. The total logarithm of the odds (lod) score was 13.766 at a theta value of 0. This result confirms that the ALD gene maps to Xq28.[13] Subsequent to this publication we have noted one recombination event between ALD and the DXS52 probe. This event occurred in a family in whom we also studied the color vision gene (see Fig. 58-1 and Ref. 14), and in this instance there was no recombination between ALD and the red-green color vision genes, suggesting that these genes may be linked more closely to ALD than is the DXS52 probe.

Of great current interest are recent studies of the relationship between ALD and red-green color vision defects. We have demonstrated recently that red-green color vision defects occur more frequently in ALD patients than in the general population.[102] Utilizing the Farnsworth-Munsell 100 hue discrimination test,[103] we have demonstrated defects in red-green color vision in 60 percent of ALD patients (H. W. Moser, unpublished observation), compared with 8 to 10 percent in

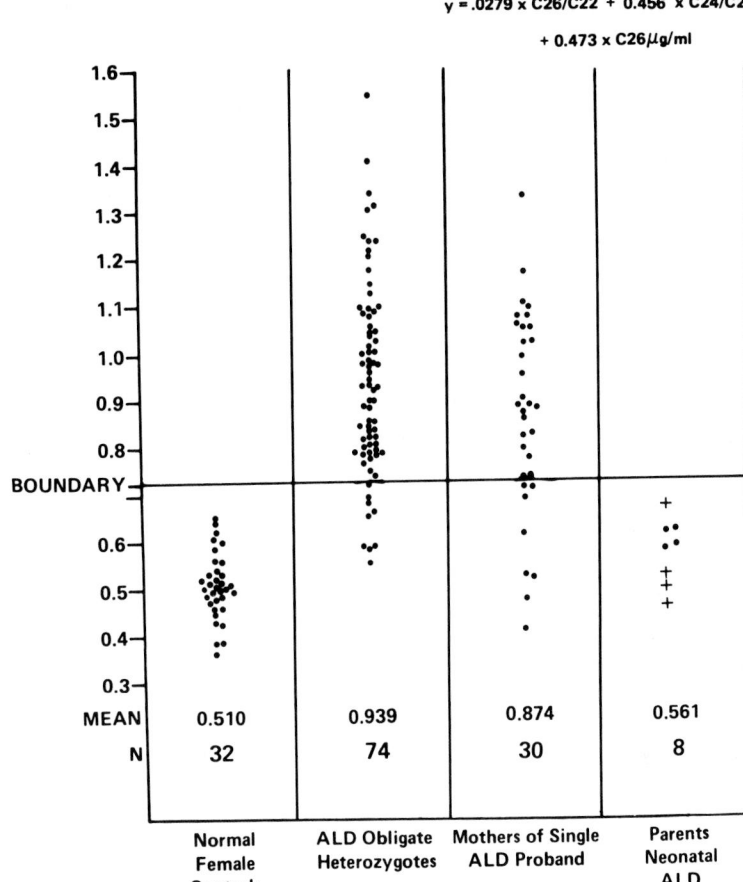

$$y = .0279 \times C26/C22 + 0.456 \times C24/C22$$
$$+ 0.473 \times C26\mu g/ml$$

	Normal Female Controls	ALD Obligate Heterozygotes	Mothers of Single ALD Proband	Parents Neonatal ALD
MEAN	0.510	0.939	0.874	0.561
N	32	74	30	8

• Mother

Fig. 58-6 Identification of ALD heterozygotes by assay of plasma VLCFA based on classification function (y) using discriminant analysis. *(From Martin-DeLeon.[100] Used by permission.)*

the general population.[102] These tests were conducted in AMN patients who had intact cognition and who were free of demonstrable lesions in optic nerves, optic tracts, and visual cortex.

Studies of the red-green visual pigment genes were conducted in 16 men hemizygous for ALD or AMN, in 12 women heterozygous for ALD, and in 13 unaffected male relatives of ALD patients.[14] These persons belonged to eight kindreds. Results within a kindred were consistent, but differed between kindreds. Abnormalities of color vision genes were present in five of the eight kindreds (60 percent), compared with 8 percent within the general population.[104,105] No recombination between altered pigment genes and the ALD locus occurred in 28 meioses. This indicates close linkage between ALD and the red-green color vision genes. Figure 58-7 depicts the proposed structure of red and green visual genes based upon hybridization studies in these five kindreds. The varied patterns encountered suggest that overlapping deletions and reorganizations may occur in the ALD patients. Probes from the extreme ends of the deletion break points may be useful in identifying the ALD gene itself. The observations support the possibility that genetic lesions of varying structure may underlie ALD in different kindreds, a situation which has been recognized in other X-chromosome disorders, such as muscular dystrophy (see Chap. 118). The exciting prospect is that study of families with such deletions will facilitate isolation of the ALD gene, utilizing procedures similar to those used for the identification of the Duchenne muscular dystrophy gene.

The knowledge about the locus of the ALD gene is ex-

pected to facilitate identification of the enzyme defect. We have shown that clones for rat liver acyl CoA oxidase (enzyme 2, Fig. 58-5), rat liver bifunctional enzyme (enzyme 3), and thiolase (enzyme 4) do not hybridize to human X-chromosomal DNA (P. Aubourg and G. Sack, unpublished observation). This makes it unlikely that defects in these enzymes represent the primary defect in ALD. Study with human en-

Fig. 58-7 Proposed chromosomal structures for human red and green visual pigment genes in 5 ALD kindreds (labeled B, C, D, H, and O). Normal pattern (N) shows one red and two green genes in tandem array as described.[104] Our interpretation of the alterations in these five kindreds is based on hybridization with CDNA fragments from 5′, middle, and 3′ portions of color vision pigment genes.[105] The red gene in kindreds C, D, H, and O showed hybridization with the green gene or other rearrangements discussed in Ref. 14.

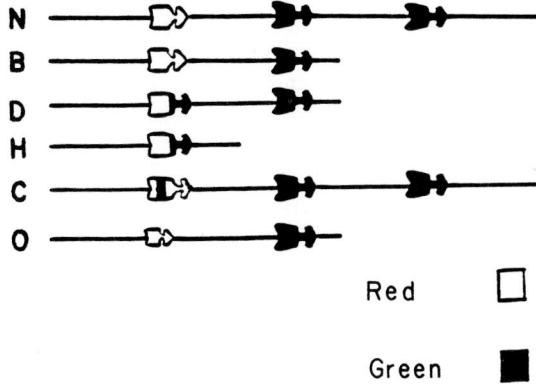

Red □

Green ■

zymes is required to confirm this conclusion, and the possibility of organ-specific enzymes must also be kept in mind. This is particularly relevant since the major pathology in ALD is confined to nervous tissue, adrenal cortex, and testis. The chromosomal localization of lignoceryol-CoA synthetase is unknown.

THE PATHOGENESIS OF X-LINKED ALD

While there is no doubt that there is an association between ALD and VLCFA accumulation, it remains uncertain whether the fatty acid abnormality is the direct cause of pathology, whether secondary pathogenetic factors are required, or whether the VLCFA excess is an epiphenomenon. Direct toxicity of saturated VLCFA could result from decreased membrane fluidity caused by accumulation of these rigid abnormally long acyl chains. Knazek et al.[106] have demonstrated that membrane microviscosity is increased in erythrocytes of AMN and ALD patients whose red cells showed increased VLCFA levels. Altered membrane viscosity could have profound physiological effects in a variety of organs. Possibly related to such a change is the intriguing recent report that the white blood cells of an ALD patient had no detectable ACTH binding sites.[107] Studies are in progress to determine if this abnormality can be reversed when VLCFA levels are normalized by dietary manipulation (see "Therapy" below).

Pathogenesis of Adrenal Insufficiency

Since there is suggestive evidence that different mechanisms are responsible for the adrenal and nervous system lesions, we consider these issues separately.

There is substantial evidence that the accumulation of abnormal cholesterol esters is detrimental to adrenal cortical cells. The abnormal cholesterol esters are seen ultrastructurally as lamellar lipid profiles and clefts. The cells that contain these abnormal profiles show decreased amounts of rough endoplasmic reticulum, depression of several histochemically demonstrable enzymes, and a diminished capacity to adapt to changes in the microenvironment.[108] In contrast to brain, there is little or no inflammatory response in the ALD adrenal gland.[50]

A possible contributing factor to the adrenal dysfunction is that the abnormal fatty acid composition of the adrenal cholesterol esters may limit the capacity for steroidogenesis. The supply of cholesterol from stored cholesterol esters is one of the rate limiting factors in steroidogenesis. The cholesterol ester hydrolase involved is stimulated by ACTH.[109] In both normal subjects and ALD patients cholesterol esterified with VLCFA is a poor substrate for cholesterol ester hydrolases.[110] This may limit the capacity of the ALD cholesterol esters to serve as precursors of adrenal steroids. Allen et al.[111] proposed that in ALD there also is a partial block of 11-hydroxylase, one of the enzymes involved in converting cholesterol to cortisone. As already noted, there is a recent report that the ACTH receptor malfunctions in ALD patients.[107] Such an abnormality could clearly contribute to ACTH unresponsiveness.

Pathogenesis of Nervous System Lesions

The pathogenesis of the nervous system lesions in ALD remains unresolved. Supportive of a direct toxic effect of VLCFA are the finding of Theda et al.[59] and Reinecke et al.[60] that in postmortem ALD brain there is a statistically significant correlation between the extent of histological abnormality and VLCFA excess and the finding of Brown et al.[57] that ALD myelin has an abnormal composition. However, there are several findings that remain unexplained. These include the marked variability of phenotype. Some persons who have the biochemical defect remain free of neurologic disability even in adult life. Table 58-5 shows that there is no correlation between plasma VLCFA levels and the severity of neurologic disability. There is also a lack of correlation between the severity of neurologic deficit and adrenal insufficiency. It is our hypothesis that the ALD biochemical defect is necessary but not sufficient for the expression of the neurologic defect—and that there are other unidentified factors that influence the severity of neurologic involvement.

We are currently testing the hypothesis that immunologic factors influence the expression of neurologic disease in ALD. It will be recalled that, unlike the other leukodystrophies, active ALD brain lesions show a striking and characteristic perivascular accumulation of lymphocytes (Fig. 58-1). Griffin et al.[51] have typed these cells in autopsy material from four ALD patients. On the average they consisted of 59 percent T cells, 34 percent T4 cells, 16 percent T8 cells, 24 percent B cells, and 11 percent monocyte/macrophages. Mononuclear cells in the cerebrospinal fluid from six ALD patients with active central nervous system disease were, on the average, 61 percent T cells, 40 percent T4 cells, 16 percent T8 cells, 3 percent B cells, and 18 percent monocyte/macrophages. This distribution of cells is similar to that found in the central nervous system during a cellular immune response. Cerebrospinal fluid from 8 of 10 ALD patients had increased IgG concentrations. Bernheimer and coworkers[112] have demonstrated increased levels of free IgG and IgA in ALD brain tissue, comparable to those found in brain tissue of patients with multiple sclerosis and 2 to 10 times higher than control levels, and accumulation of lymphoid cells staining for IgG, IgA, and IgM has been observed. Unlike the finding in multiple sclerosis, bound immunoglobulins were not detected cytochemically. The free immunoglobulins in ALD brain may represent soluble immune complexes or exudative serum protein secondary to the inflammatory compromise of the blood-brain barrier. We have used enzyme-linked immunoabsorbent assay (ELISA) and complement fixation techniques[113] to test for the presence of antibodies to ALD and normal myelin in the plasma of 27 patients with various forms of X-linked ALD, and we have

Table 58-5 Comparison of Plasma VLCFA Levels in Various X-Linked ALD Phenotypes

Phenotype	No. of patients	Hexacosanoic acid (C26:0) μg/ml plasma (mean and SD)
Childhood ALD	160	1.36 ± 0.52
Adrenomyeloneuropathy	62	1.47 ± 0.78
Asymptomatic ALD	14	1.27 ± 0.39
Controls	1858	0.24 ± 0.16

SOURCE: Moser et al.[28] Used by permission.

demonstrated that these antibody levels were increased significantly compared to control (D. E. Griffin and C. L. Koski, unpublished observation). While the above results suggest strongly that immunologic responses do play a role in the pathogenesis of ALD, there is no information about whether such reactions are primary or secondary. To help answer this question we are conducting studies to compare immunologic responses in neurologically intact ALD patients with those who have neurologic lesions.

How can these proposed immunologic events be related to the primary genetic defect in ALD, which almost certainly involves a disturbance of lipid metabolism? The metabolic defect leads to an abnormal fatty acid pattern in a variety of lipids—a consistent finding in all patients. It is possible that in some, but not all, patients these abnormal lipids become antigenic and that the extent to which this occurs influences the severity of neurologic involvement. Gangliosides are of particular interest in this respect. Ganglioside fatty acid composition is markedly abnormal in ALD patients,[54,61] and ganglioside fatty acid composition has been shown to influence their antigenic properties.[114]

Elucidation of the pathogenesis of ALD is essential for the planning of therapeutic interventions. It has recently become possible to lower VLCFA levels in ALD patients by dietary manipulations. Studies are in progress to determine if normalization of VLCFA levels will alter the course of the disease. Immunosuppression regimens so far have not shown a demonstrable favorable effect.[115,116] At this time there is no animal model of ALD.

DIAGNOSIS OF ALD

Differential Diagnosis on Basis of Clinical Presentation

Table 58-6 lists the conditions that have been mistaken for one of the ALD phenotypes. Reference 28 provides a detailed discussion of the differential diagnosis.

Biochemical Assays

Postnatal Diagnosis of Affected Males. Biochemical assays used for the diagnosis of ALD depend on the demonstration of abnormally high levels of saturated VLCFA in accessible tissues or body fluids, such as cultured skin fibroblasts,[8,120] white blood cells,[121] red blood cells,[10,122] cultured amniocytes,[11] plasma,[9,123–125] and cultured muscle.[126] The analytic procedures used are capillary gas liquid chromatography,[8,9,11,121] which may be combined with mass spectrometry,[121] or high performance liquid chromatography.[27,125]

Provided that care is exercised, these techniques are highly effective for the diagnosis of ALD hemizygotes. In accessible tissues VLCFAs are present in low concentration. In ALD plasma they make up approximately 0.1 percent of total fatty acids compared with 0.01 to 0.02 percent in normal plasma. Great care must be used to validate the identity of peaks, to provide standardization, and to avoid contaminants. Table 58-7 lists results obtained in our laboratory with the plasma capillary gas liquid chromatography method.[8] We consider the

Table 58-6 Differential Diagnosis of ALD

Phenotype	Symptom or sign
Childhood neurologic deficit *without* overt adrenal insufficiency	Hyperactivity, attention deficit, minimal brain damage, emotional disturbance
	Seizure disorder
	Brain tumor
	Metachromatic or globoid leukodystrophy
	Batten disease
	Encephalitis
	Subacute sclerosing panencephalitis
	Schilder's myelinoclastic diffuse sclerosis[118]
Childhood neurologic deficit *with* adrenal insufficiency	Hypoglycemic or anoxic damage associated with Addison disease
	X-linked glycerol kinase deficiency[36]
	Central pontine myelinolysis[117]
	Glucocorticoid deficiency with achalasia and deficient tear production[119]
Addison disease only	All other types of adrenal insufficiency
Adrenomyeloneuropathy	Multiple sclerosis
	Familial spastic paraparesis[32]
	Spinocerebellar or olivopontocerebral degeneration[47–49]
	Cervical spondylosis
	Spinal cord tumor
Adult cerebral	Schizophrenia
	Depression
	Seizure disorders, organic psychosis[35]
	Alzheimer's disease
	Brain tumor
Symptomatic heterozygote	Multiple sclerosis[44]
	Chronic nonprogressive spinal cord disease[45]
	Spinal cord tumor
	Cervical spondylosis

NOTE: Numbers indicate references in which cases are described.

diagnosis secure if the plasma shows significantly elevated C26:0 levels, as well as abnormal C26:0/C22:0 and C24:0/C22:0 ratios. Elevated levels of VLCFA are also observed in neonatal ALD, the Zellweger cerebrohepatorenal syndrome, hyperpipecolic acidemia, and infantile Refsum disease (Chap. 57). The clinical manifestations of these latter disorders differ greatly from those of X-linked ALD, and the pattern of the VLCFA often is different.

Plasma VLCFA levels of affected males show the characteristic abnormalities in cord blood and in the neonatal period, and the levels show little or no variation with age.[15] Diagnostic ambiguity has been observed in two sets of circumstances. Plasma level abnormalities similar to those in ALD may occur in children who are being treated with a ketogenic diet for epilepsy. Their plasma levels return to normal after a prolonged period on the diet or after it is discontinued, but the fibroblast assay[8] gives normal results at all times. The second source of ambiguity occurs in the occasional non-ALD patient in whom the plasma C26:0 level is elevated, but the C26:0/C22:0 and C24:0/C22:0 ratios are normal. These persons can be distinguished from ALD patients by demonstrating normal

Table 58-7 Experience with Assays for VLCFA in Plasma and Cultured Skin Fibroblasts*

Diagnostic category	Plasma			Cultured skin fibroblasts	
	C26:0, μg/ml plasma	C24:0/C22:0 ratio	C26:0/C22:0 ratio	C26:0, μg/ml protein	C26:0/C22:0 ratio
Childhood ALD-AMN hemizygotes (n = 282)	1.6 ± 0.84	1.6 ± 0.17	0.075 ± 0.02	0.42 ± 0.15	0.67 ± 0.21
Heterozygotes for X-linked ALD (n = 268)	0.81 ± 0.33	1.3 ± 0.20	0.039 ± 0.017	0.26 ± 0.16	0.41 ± 0.25
Neonatal ALD (n = 20)	2.4 ± 0.73	1.8 ± 0.35	0.30 ± 0.14	0.37 ± 0.14	0.80 ± 0.43
Zellweger syndrome (n = 36)	2.5 ± 0.85	2.0 ± 0.24	0.49 ± 0.03	0.78 ± 0.24	2.0 ± 1.2
Hyperpipecolic acidemia (n = 4)	1.7	1.4	0.16	0.42 ± 0.06	0.90 ± 0.11
Normal controls (n = 65)	0.33 ± 0.15	0.83 ± 0.15	0.014 ± 0.0076	0.079 ± 0.066	0.080 ± 0.029
Other diseases (n = 1858)	0.24 ± 0.16	0.81 ± 0.09	0.014 ± 0.0056	0.066 ± 0.035	0.093 ± 0.062

*Assays performed at the Kennedy Institute, January 1979-February 1984.
SOURCE: Moser et al.[28] Used by permission.

C26:0 levels in repeat plasma samples obtained in the fasting state and in cultured skin fibroblasts. ALD patients show consistent elevations of VLCFA in plasma and fibroblasts. With the utilization of these follow-up procedures we have not observed false positives in tests of samples from approximately 10,000 persons. False negatives are difficult to exclude, since we do not have follow-up on all persons whose test results were negative, but at this time we do not know of a documented false negative test.

VLCFA Analysis and Other Techniques for the Prenatal Identification of Affected Male Fetus. Table 58-8 summarizes the Kennedy Institute experience with prenatal diagnosis. We have monitored 93 pregnancies and have identified 21 affected male fetuses. Families elected to continue pregnancy in three instances, and the fetus was aborted in 18 instances. In each instance the prenatal diagnosis was confirmed by pathologic or biochemical study of the fetus[11,52] or by postnatal plasma assay. The DXS52 DNA probe has also been used to identify an affected male fetus.[127] Because of our relatively large experience and so far invariably accurate results with the VLCFA assay, we consider this the procedure of choice for the prenatal identification of affected male fetuses, but linkage analysis with the DXS52 DNA probe can be used in informative families.[13] The more limited recent experience with cultured chorion villus samples suggests that results parallel those with cultured amniocytes. Measurements of VLCFA

levels in amniotic fluid have not provided reliable differentiation. We are also testing the possibility of measuring VLCFA β-oxidation in direct or cultured chorion villus samples. Wanders et al. have used this approach for the early prenatal diagnosis of Zellweger syndrome.[128] This technique may shorten the time required to achieve diagnosis, since only a small tissue sample is required.

HETEROZYGOTE IDENTIFICATION

We utilized VLCFA assays in a study of 74 women who were obligate heterozygotes for X-linked ALD.[100] With the aid of discriminant analysis we developed a classification function which permitted us to identify as abnormal 65 of the 74 obligate heterozygotes (Fig. 58-6). When studies of cultured skin fibroblasts were performed in the nine heterozygotes who had normal plasma VLCFA levels, six showed clearly abnormal or probably abnormal levels in this second tissue. We concluded that 94 percent of obligate ALD heterozygotes have abnormally high VLCFA levels in either plasma or cultured skin fibroblasts, thus yielding a 6 percent false negative rate. Since the publication of this report, we have studied an additional 130 obligate ALD heterozygotes and have observed an 8 percent false negative rate.

While these results are encouraging, there is need for im-

Table 58-8 VLCFA Assays of Amniocyte and Chorion Villus Cultures in Pregnancies at Risk for ALD

	Male ALD fetus	Male non-ALD fetus	Female fetus	Normal results, follow-up incomplete	Control
Amniocyte					
C26:0	0.43 ± 0.20 (19)	0.068 ± 0.038 (24)	0.15 ± 0.18 (22)	0.070 ± 0.15 (11)	0.10 ± 0.07 (23)
Range	0.20-0.94	0.03-0.15	0.041-0.74	0.052-0.095	0.02-0.24
C26:0/C22:0	0.93 ± 0.22 (19)	0.17 ± 0.076 (24)	0.43 ± 0.62 (22)	0.16 ± 0.044 (11)	0.17 ± 0.10 (23)
Range	0.57-1.5	0.060-0.28	0.029-2.3	0.10-0.20	0.06-0.44
Chorion villus					
C26:0	0.44 (2)	0.093 ± 0.042 (8)	0.17 ± 0.14 (6)	0.063 (1)	0.036 ± 0.010 (7)
Range	0.33-0.50	0.046-0.18	0.12-0.40		0.027-0.058
C26:0/C22:0	1.3 (2)	0.13 ± 0.041 (8)	0.29 ± 0.34 (6)	0.15 (1)	0.059 ± 0.02 (7)
Range	1.1-1.6	0.083-0.19	0.028-0.40		0.023-0.082

NOTE: The values listed are means and standard deviations. Numbers in parentheses indicate number of cases studied. C26:0 levels are expressed as micrograms per milligram of protein. The diagnoses for the male fetuses were confirmed by postnatal studies or pathologic and biochemical studies of fetus. The female fetuses include those who were homozygous normal as well as those who were heterozygous and this is reflected in the large standard deviation. Control values are taken from Refs. 11 and 127, which also describe the methods.

provement because of the existence of false negatives and the difficulty in the interpretation of small deviations from normal. Since the linkage between ALD and the DXS52 DNA probe has been established, the combined use of these approaches offers a great deal of promise. The DXS52 probe is highly polymorphic and is informative in more than 90 percent of families in which samples from affected and unaffected males are available for study. The lod score of 13.77 indicates that the marker is closely linked to ALD,[13] although, as already mentioned, we noted one recombination event subsequent to the publication of this article. Because of the relative ease of the plasma VLCFA assay, we rely on it as the initial determinant of heterozygote status, and when the result is unequivocally abnormal we designate the woman as a carrier. If the result is normal or ambiguous, we follow it up with fibroblast VLCFA assay. In the future, we plan to use the DNA probe as the follow-up test in those families where informative relatives are available for study.

Biopsy Diagnosis of ALD

Martin et al.[129-131] and Arsenio Nunes et al.[132] have shown the value of conjunctival or skin biopsy for the diagnosis of ALD. In most cases careful electron-microscopic study of nerve twigs contained in these specimens reveals characteristic curved clefts and leaflets in Schwann cells surrounding myelinated axons. Characteristic lamellar inclusions have also been observed in sural nerve biopsy specimens.[133] The availability of biochemical assays has lessened the need for biopsy procedures.

Neurophysiological Studies

Brain-stem auditory evoked responses (BAERs) in most patients with ALD or AMN show abnormalities in waveforms beyond wave 1. One AMN patient showed no demonstrable waveforms subsequent to this wave; in most others waves 2 to 5 were delayed.[134-136] Women heterozygotes for ALD also may have abnormal BAER. In one study, the I-V interwave was increased in all three women who were tested.[137] In another study abnormal BAERs were noted in two out of seven[134] and one out of five ALD carriers.[138] In the study by Garg et al.[134] prolonged somatosensory responses were observed in four of seven ALD heterozygotes, compared with two of seven abnormal BAER responses. Tobimatsu et al.[139] studied BAER, visual evoked, and somatosensory evoked responses in three ALD patients and two heterozygotes and found that at least one of these modalities was abnormal in every subject.

The electroencephalogram in childhood ALD patients often shows irregular large amplitude slow activity which is more prominent over the posterior region of the brain.[140,141] The electroretinogram was normal, while the visual evoked responses were abnormal in 4 of 14 cases.[140] Motor conduction velocity in peripheral nerves is reduced in approximately 50 percent of patients with AMN. The motor nerve conduction velocity, distal latency, and amplitude of compound action potentials were normal in six of eight patients with childhood ALD, while two of the children showed moderate abnormalities.[139]

In summary, BAER and sensory evoked potential studies are sensitive indicators of neurologic abnormalities, particularly in patients with AMN and in heterozygotes. Abnormalities in peripheral nerve are observed relatively frequently in AMN patients and adult heterozygotes and uncommonly in affected boys.

Adrenal Function

Thirty-five to forty-five percent[26,27] of patients with childhood ALD have overt adrenal insufficiency, but 90 percent show subnormal cortisol increases in response to ACTH stimulation.[26] Approximately 10 percent of ALD patients show normal cortisol increases in response to ACTH stimulation.[98] Increased plasma ACTH levels are observed very frequently. This was first reported by Rees et al.[142] All of Aubourg's 17 childhood ALD patients in whom this measurement was obtained had increased plasma ACTH levels.[27] We have already referred to the intriguing recent report that ACTH binding sites were lacking in the white blood cells of an ALD patient.[108]

The need for adrenal function tests to establish the diagnosis of ALD has diminished somewhat now that the more specific VLCFA assays are available. Nevertheless, it continues to be of importance to assess adrenal function in every case. It is essential to be aware of the extent of impaired adrenal reserve so that replacement therapy can be instituted promptly. In addition, in some localities adrenal function tests are more readily available than VLCFA measurements. The great majority of ALD patients do show clinical or laboratory evidence of impaired adrenal function or reserve, and this is not a feature in most of the other disorders from which ALD must be differentiated.

Imaging Techniques: CT and MRI

The most common initial lead toward the diagnosis of childhood ALD is provided by characteristic abnormalities demonstrable by CT[143-145,151] or MRI. A common chain of events is that a boy who is failing in school and demonstrates progressive behavioral disturbances is examined by a pediatrician or neurologist, and CT or MRI scans are obtained as part of this evaluation. Striking and characteristic abnormalities are often demonstrated even relatively early in the course of the illness and then lead to confirmation by biochemical assays. MRI scans also provide the opportunity for precise structure-function correlations and will be of great value for the evaluation of the effects of therapeutic intervention.

Eighty percent of childhood ALD cases[143] show cerebral white matter lesions that are characteristic with respect to location and attenuation patterns. The lesions are symmetric and involve the periventricular white matter in the posterior parietal and occipital lobes. Noncontrast CT scans show bilateral hypodensities in this location.[148] The second characteristic feature is observed following the intravenous injection of contrast material. This technique demonstrates a garland of accumulated contrast material adjacent and anterior to the posterior hypodense lesions shown on the noncontrast CT[148] (Fig. 58-8A). These patterns can be correlated with the pathologic findings described by Schaumburg et al.[26] These studies demonstrated caudorostral progression of white matter pathology and the striking accumulation of perivascular lymphocytes at the advancing edge of the lesion. This latter zone corresponds

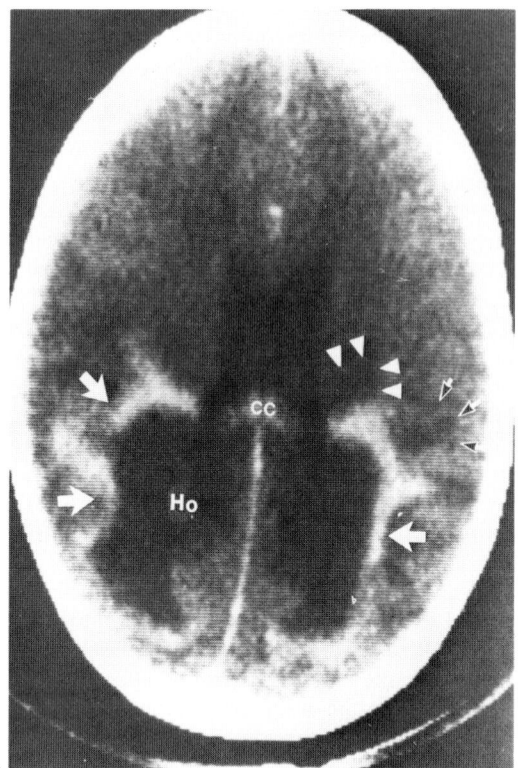
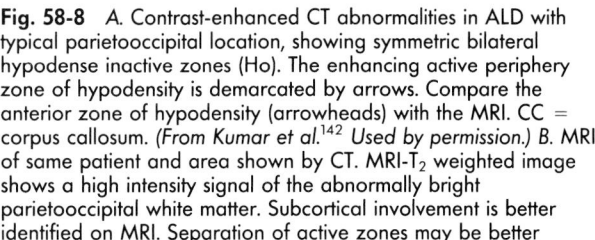

A.

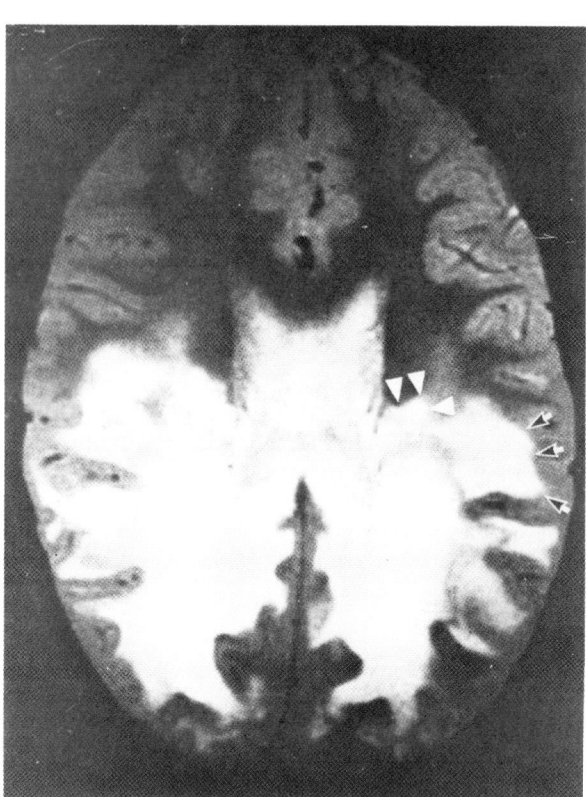

B.

Fig. 58-8 *A.* Contrast-enhanced CT abnormalities in ALD with typical parietooccipital location, showing symmetric bilateral hypodense inactive zones (Ho). The enhancing active periphery zone of hypodensity is demarcated by arrows. Compare the anterior zone of hypodensity (arrowheads) with the MRI. CC = corpus callosum. *(From Kumar et al.[142] Used by permission.) B.* MRI of same patient and area shown by CT. MRI-T_2 weighted image shows a high intensity signal of the abnormally bright parietooccipital white matter. Subcortical involvement is better identified on MRI. Separation of active zones may be better appreciated by CT since both inactive and active zones are seen at high signal areas on MRI. However, it is assumed that such major distinctions afforded by CT will also be demonstrable when IV enhancement (paramagnetic enhancement) becomes readily available. Note the hypodense involvement of CT (arrowheads and arrows) in *A* compared to the well resolved lesions on MRI in *B.* *(MRI scan courtesy of Louis Wener, M.D., Medical Director, Magnetic Resonance Associates, Clinton, Maryland. From Moser et al.[28] Used by permission.)*

to the CT region with contrast material accumulation. While caudorostral progression is most common, initial lesions were frontal in 12 percent of patients.[143,146] In other cases, referred to as the Di Chiro type II form, there is marked contrast enhancement of the internal capsule, corpus callosum, corona radiata, forceps major, and cerebral peduncles,[147] which may also be observed in combination with the classic pattern.[148] Unilateral lesions,[149] which may produce a mass effect strongly suggestive of brain tumor[150] may also occur. Calcification within hypodense lesions was observed in 8 percent of cases[143,148,151] and corresponds to small deposits in "burned out" gliotic white matter lesions.[26]

Recent experience indicates that MRI is superior to CT in demonstrating nervous system involvement in ALD. In a study comparing the two techniques,[143] it was found that MRI provided a clearer distinction between normal and abnormal white matter and permitted better delineation of subcortical lesions. MRI may demonstrate abnormalities that fail to be detected by CT (Fig. 58-8*B*). Analysis of MRI also permits precise structure-function correlation of lesions involving auditory or visual pathways and specific defects in cognitive function.[143] This is of particular interest in studies of brainstem structures, which on CT scans are obstructed by the surrounding bones. MRI scans have demonstrated small unilateral lesions involving the lateral lemniscus or inferior colliculus that corresponded to ipsilaterally delayed wave intervals on brain-stem auditory evoked responses. Indeed, such correla-

tive studies may provide new insights about the normal location of pathways and brain regions involved in auditory discrimination and specific cognitive functions. Because MRI permits precise determination of the size and location of white matter lesions, it provides an objective and precise gauge of the effects of therapeutic interventions. The lesions demonstrable by MRI in ALD patients differ from those in multiple sclerosis. The multiple sclerosis lesions show a patchy distribution, whereas in ALD the demyelination appears to be contiguous within the larger white matter bundles.[143] While the sensitivity and precision of MRI offer diagnostic advantages over CT, it cannot replace the insight into disease dynamics provided by a comparison of contrast and noncontrast CT. The zone of contrast accumulation permits delineation of the most active disease zone, and alterations in the extent of contrast accumulation may provide another measure of the effect of potential therapies.

THERAPY

Adrenal Insufficiency

Steroid replacement therapy for adrenal insufficiency is effective and of great importance. While glucocorticoid therapy was followed by neurologic improvement in one AMN patient,[151] the general experience has been that correction of adrenal insufficiency does not alter the course of the neurologic disease.

Symptomatic Therapy

The progressive behavioral and neurologic disturbances associated with the childhood form of ALD provide an extreme challenge for the family. Confirmation of the diagnosis of ALD requires the establishment of a comprehensive management program and partnership between the family, physician, visiting nurses, school authorities, and counselors.[153] In addition, parent support groups such as the United Leukodystrophy Foundation, 2304 Highland Drive, Sycamore, Illinois 60178, have proven to be of great value. Genetic counseling for the immediate family and other relatives who may be at risk is an indispensable part of the management plan. The importance of this preventive effort cannot be overemphasized. The task is complicated by the fact that individuals at risk often include distant relatives who may have had little contact with the immediate family. Communication with school authorities is important, since under the provision of Public Law 94-142, Education for All Handicapped Children, children with conditions such as ALD qualify for special services. Children with leukodystrophies are classified as "other health impaired" or "multihandicapped." Depending on the rate of progression of the disease, special needs might range from relatively low-level resource services within a regular school program (to correct deficiencies in isolated academic subjects) to self-contained services (for children with attention deficit disorder and multiple academic deficiencies) to home- and hospital-based teaching programs for children who are not mobile.[153]

Management challenges vary with the stage of the illness. The early stages are characterized by subtle changes in affect, behavior, and attention span. Counseling and communication with school authorities are of prime importance. Changes in sleep-wake cycle can be benefited by the judicious nighttime use of sedatives such as chloral hydrate (10 to 50 mg/kg), pentobarbitol (5 mg/kg), or diphenhydramine (2 to 3 mg/kg).

As the leukodystrophy progresses, major areas of concern are modulation of muscle tone and support of bulbar muscular function. Acute episodic exacerbations of muscle tone may present as painful muscle spasms. In our experience, baclofen in gradually increasing doses (5 mg twice a day to 25 mg four times a day) has been the most effective pharmacologic agent. Other agents may also be used, care being taken to monitor for the occurrence of side effects and drug interaction.[153] As the leukodystrophy progresses, bulbar muscular control is lost. While initially this can be managed by changing to soft and pureed foods, most patients eventually require nasogastric tubes or surgical procedures such as gastrostomy or lateral esophagostomy. At least one-third of the patients have focal or generalized seizures, which usually respond readily to standard anticonvulsant medications.

Search for Specific Therapy to Prevent or Ameliorate Neurologic Disability

The challenge to develop methods to prevent neurologic damage in ALD is heightened by the fact that diagnosis can be made years or even decades before neurologic symptoms develop and that during this time interval neurologic and intellectual functions are entirely intact. At this time there is no validated therapy, but several approaches are under active investigation. These include diet, bone marrow transplants, immunosuppression, plasma exchange, and pharmacologic agents.

Dietary Therapy

Dietary restriction of C26:0 and VLCFA failed to lower plasma VLCFA levels or to alter clinical progression.[65,154] An important new approach is based upon the observation by Rizzo et al. that the addition of oleic acid to the tissue culture medium reduced the rate of C26:0 synthesis by ALD fibroblasts.[16] Oral administration of a glycerol trioleate oil combined with dietary restriction of VLCFA has been shown to lower plasma and red blood cell levels of saturated VLCFA in 30 of 40 patients.[15,16] This is an encouraging observation, since all previous attempts to normalize VLCFA levels had been unsuccessful. In possibly analogous disorders, such as Refsum disease and cerebrotendinous xanthomatosis, normalization of the levels of "offending" metabolites such as phytanic acid and cholestanol, respectively, has brought about unquestionable neurologic improvement (see Chaps. 59 and 48). Preliminary data suggest that the trioleate dietary regimen has improved peripheral nerve function.[15] A prospective randomized therapeutic trial is now in progress in our clinic.

The mechanism through which trioleate oil reduces saturated VLCFA levels requires additional investigation. Bourre et al.[74] concluded that the elongation of the monounsaturated fatty acid C22:1 (erucic acid) and its saturated counterpart C22:0 (behenic acid) is catalyzed by the same enzyme system. A high concentration of monounsaturated fatty acids—such as oleic acid—thus may favor synthesis of monounsaturated VLCFA and diminish that of saturated VLCFA. The available data are consistent with this hypothesis (Fig. 58-9). The levels of monounsaturated VLCFA increased coincident with the diminution of saturated VLCFA. For unknown reasons the plasma levels of monounsaturated VLCFA (C22:1, C24:1) are diminished in untreated ALD patients, and the administration of the trioleate oil first leads to a normalization of these levels and then to moderate increases up to two times normal.[15]

The glycerol trioleate regimen as currently used has several limitations. Preliminary observations suggest that when it is administered to boys already symptomatic with childhood ALD, it fails to stem the rapid progression of the disease. This failure may be related to the fact that 30 to 90 days is required before significant VLCFA reduction is achieved, and the natural course of symptomatic childhood ALD is associated with serious deterioration during this time interval. Furthermore, while the diet reduces plasma VLCFAs by approximately 50 percent, it fails to return them to normal, even in fully compliant patients. While over 30 patients have been able to follow the diet without side effects,[15] it does involve a significant change in lifestyle. We view it as an experimental approach, in need of further evaluation and modification.

An exciting modification of the dietary approach is suggested by the recent observation that the addition of oral erucic acid (C22:1) brings about normalization of plasma and red blood cell saturated VLCFA levels in a short time period (W. Rizzo et al., unpublished observation). This finding clearly offers exciting new therapeutic possibilities, but its general use must be restricted until its possible toxicity is evaluated. Erucic acid is a component of rapeseed oil, an important nutrient

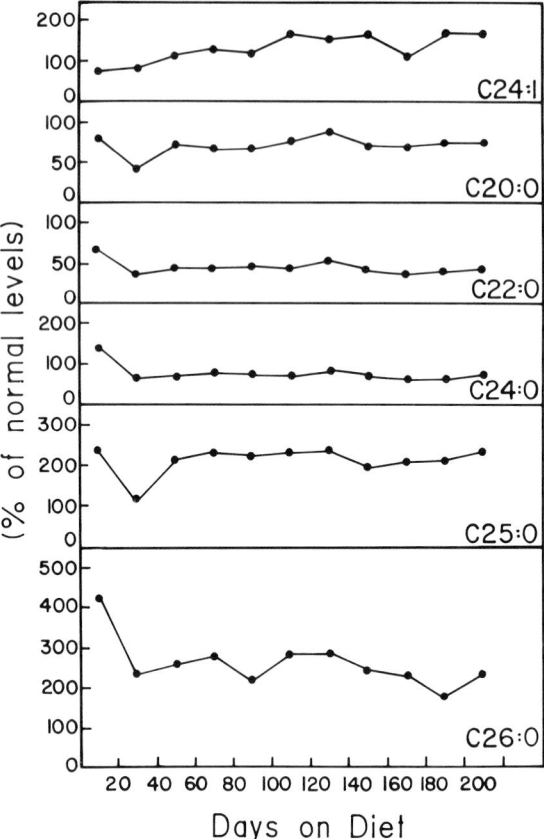

Fig. 58-9 Effect of low VLCFA intake and glycerol trioleate on plasma VLCFA levels in 11 patients with ALD. See Ref. 15 for description of diet.

used in many parts of the world.[155] Erucic acid produces a transient cardiac lipidosis in rats and pigs,[156] but probably not so in monkeys and humans.[155,157] The lipidosis is transient, probably because of an adaptive response brought about by induction of increased activity of a peroxisomal oxidative system which degrades the erucic acid.[157] The concern about erucic acid toxicity in general human nutrition has been side-stepped by the use of techniques which convert rapeseed oil to a low erucic acid product.[155] In contrast, the diet proposed here depends on the retention of a high erucic acid content. Preliminary short-term administration of erucic acid to ALD patients did not produce signs of cardiac or other toxicity. Careful evaluation of the possible beneficial and toxic effects of this substance is indicated.

Bone Marrow Transplantation

Bone marrow transplantation in a 12-year-old patient with progressive childhood ALD was successful in replacing the recipient's circulating white blood cells with cells that had normal capacity to degrade VLCFA, and there was a significant reduction of plasma VLCFA levels. The patient died of an adenovirus infection 141 days after transplant. It was not possible to evaluate the effect of the transplant on neurologic status.[158] Bone marrow transplants have been performed in two additional ALD patients who are brothers (K. Weinberg et al., unpublished observation). The older, severely symptomatic boy succumbed within 3 weeks to complications of the transplant procedure. His 4-year-old asymptomatic brother, who underwent transplantation recently, withstood the proce-

dure well and has remained asymptomatic. The place of bone marrow transplantation in ALD poses difficult ethical questions. The experience with the two severely symptomatic patients has not been favorable, and the procedure probably has greatest chance of success if it is performed in boys who are still free of neurologic disease. This potential but unproven benefit must be balanced against the 20 to 30 percent mortality risk of the procedure, and the fact that at this time it is not possible to predict whether an asymptomatic boy with the biochemical defect is destined to develop the fatal childhood form or the less severe disease type or even remain normal for life (see Table 58-1). Because of these ethical dilemmas and the potential benefit of the less dangerous dietary approaches, we do not recommend bone marrow transplants in asymptomatic boys at this time, but this position may be modified with additional experience.

Immunosuppression

The effects of immunosuppression has been tested in five patients with childhood ALD. Stumpf et al. administered cyclophosphamide 100 mg/m² body surface and cortisone 2 mg/kg per day to one patient for a 4-month period,[115] while our group used shorter courses of cyclophosphamide in larger dosages (350 to 700 mg/m²) in four symptomatic children and one patient with the adult cerebral form.[116] Both groups concluded that they had failed to alter the neurologic progression of the disorder.

Other Therapeutic Approaches

A course of 14 plasma exchanges over a 12-week time period reduced plasma VLCFA levels to normal for 24 to 48 h after each exchange. Toward the end of the procedure the preexchange plasma level was reduced by one-third. The patient's condition appeared to remain stable during the plasma exchange period, to deteriorate further 2 weeks after the exchange period, and to deteriorate further 2 weeks after the exchange was discontinued.[159] Because of the small amount of C26:0 removed per exchange (1 to 4 mg) and the burden of the procedure, long-term trials have not been attempted. Plasma exchange may prove of value when combined with dietary therapy, since it brings about a rapid lowering of VLCFA levels which can be maintained until the effects of the diet assert themselves.

We have tested the effects of orally administered clofibrate and carnitine in separate trials. Carnitine failed to change plasma VLCFA levels in two patients.[154] Clofibrate reduced the total plasma C26:0 level but did not alter the ratio of C26:0 and C24:0 to C22:0 or total fatty acids, and the effect was thought to represent a redistribution of lipids rather than a specific effect on VLCFAs. No effect on clinical status was demonstrable during the 12- to 18-month period of this limited therapeutic trial.[154]

UPDATE

Two groups of investigators[160,161] have prepared peroxisome enriched fractions from cultured skin fibroblasts and have demonstrated that in this fraction lignoceroyl CoA and hexacosanoyl CoA ligase activities were reduced, namely 19.6 ±

6.7[160] and 17 percent[161] of control, respectively. These are the first direct demonstrations that this enzyme activity is deficient and that the defect is peroxisomal.

Whitcomb et al. have shown that human adrenocortical cells cultured in the presence of 5 mM C26:0 or C24:0 showed decreased basal and ACTH-stimulated cortisol release compared with cells cultured without exogenous fatty acids or in the presence of linoleic acid (C18:2).[162] This is the first demonstration that abnormally high levels of saturated VLCFA impair adrenal function.

The minimally symptomatic 3⁸/₁₂-year-old ALD patient who received a bone marrow transplant 2 years ago continues to be in stable condition without progression of the neurological deficit.[163]

Erucic acid (C22:1) has now been administered to nine adrenoleukodystrophy patients for periods up to 11 months. Levels of saturated VLCFA have been normalized, albeit in association with a 25-fold increase in plasma C22:1 levels. No toxic effects have been observed. The rate of neurological progression in severely symptomatic boys does not appear to have been altered (W. B. Rizzo, unpublished observation). Provided that further investigations confirm lack of significant toxicity, therapeutic trials of this regimen will be conducted in presymptomatic or more mildly involved patients.

REFERENCES

1. SIEMERLING E, CREUTZFELDT HG: Bronzekrankheit und sklerorisende Encephalomyelitis (diffuse sclerose). *Arch Psychiatry* 68:217, 1923.

2. FANCONI A, PRADER A, ISLER W, LUTHY F, SIEBENMANN R: Morbus Addison mit Hirnsklerose im Kindesalter. Ein hereditares syndrom mit X-chromosomaler vererbung. *Helv Paedr Acta* 18:480, 1963.

3. POWERS JM, SCHAUMBURG HH: The adrenal cortex in adrenoleukodystrophy. *Arch Pathol* 96:305, 1973.

4. POWERS JM, SCHAUMBURG HH: Adrenoleukodystrophy: Similar ultrastructural changes in adrenal cortical cells and Schwann cells. *Arch Neurol* 30:406, 1974.

5. POWERS JM, SCHAUMBURG HH: Adrenoleukodystrophy (sex linked Schilder's disease). A pathogenetic hypothesis based on ultrastructural lesions in adrenal cortex, peripheral nerve and testis. *Am J Pathol* 76:481, 1974.

6. JOHNSON AB, SCHAUMBURG HH, POWERS JM: Histochemical characteristics of the striated inclusions of adrenoleukodystrophy. *J Histochem Cytochem* 24:725, 1976.

7. IGARASHI M, SCHAUMBURG HH, POWERS JM, KISHIMOTO Y, KOLODNY E, SUZUKI K: Fatty acid abnormality in adrenoleukodystrophy. *J Neurochem* 26:851, 1976.

8. MOSER HW, MOSER AB, KAWAMURA N, MURPHY J, SUZUKI K, SCHAUMBURG HH, KISHIMOTO Y, MILUNSKY A: Adrenoleukodystrophy: Elevated C26 fatty acid in cultured skin fibroblasts. *Ann Neurol* 7:542, 1980.

9. MOSER HW, MOSER AB, FRAYER KK, CHEN W, SCHULMAN JD, O'NEILL BP, KISHIMOTO Y: Adrenoleukodystrophy: Increased plasma content of saturated very long chain fatty acids. *Neurology* 31:1241, 1981.

10. TSUJI S, SUZUKI M, ARIGA T, SEKINA M, KURIJAMA M, MIYATAKE T: Abnormality of long-chain fatty acids in erythrocyte membrane sphingomyelin from patients with adrenoleukodystrophy. *J Neurochem* 36:1046, 1981.

11. MOSER HW, MOSER AB, POWERS JM, NITOWSKY HM, SCHAUMBURG HH, NORUM RA, MIGEON BR: The prenatal diagnosis of adrenoleukodystrophy: Demonstration of increased hexacosanoic acid in cultured amniocytes and fetal adrenal gland. *Pediatr Res* 16:172, 1982.

12. MIGEON BR, MOSER HW, MOSER AB, AXELMAN J, SILLENCE D, NORUM RA: Adrenoleukodystrophy: Evidence for X-linkage, inactivation and selection favoring the mutant allele in heterozygous cells. *Proc Natl Acad Sci USA* 72:5066, 1981.

13. AUBOURG PR, SACK GH JR, MEYERS DA, LEASE JJ, MOSER HW: Linkage of adrenoleukodystrophy to a polymorphic DNA probe. *Ann Neurol* 21:349, 1987.

14. AUBOURG PR, SACK GH JR, MOSER HW: Frequent alterations of visual pigment genes in adrenoleukodystrophy. *Am J Hum Gen* 42:408, 1988.

15. MOSER AB, BOREL J, ODONE A, NAIDU S, CORNBLATH D, SANDERS DB, MOSER HW: A new dietary therapy for adrenoleukodystrophy. Biochemi-

16. RIZZO WB, PHILLIPS MW, DAMMANN A, LESHNER RT, JENNINGS SS, AVIGAN JL, PROUD VK: Adrenoleukodystrophy: Dietary oleic acid lowers hexacosanoate levels. *Ann Neurol* 21:232, 1987.

17. SINGH I, MOSER AB, MOSER HW, KISHIMOTO Y: Adrenoleukodystrophy: Impaired oxidation of very long chain fatty acids in white blood cells, cultured skin fibroblasts and amniocytes. *Pediatr Res* 18:286, 1984.

18. RIZZO WB, AVIGAN J, CHEMKE J, SCHULMAN JD: Adrenoleukodystrophy: Very long chain fatty acid metabolism in fibroblasts. *Neurology* 34:163, 1984.

19. POULOS A, SINGH H, PATON B, SHARP P, DERWAS N: Accumulation and defective beta-oxidation of very long chain fatty acids in Zellweger's syndrome, adrenoleukodystrophy and Refsum's disease variants. *Clin Genet* 29:397, 1986.

20. WANDERS RJA, VAN ROERMUND CWT, VAN WYLAND MJA, NIJENHUIS AA, TROMP A, SCHUTGENS RBH, BROUWER-KELDER EM, SCHRAM AW, TAGER JM, VAN DEN BOSCH H, SCHALWIJK C: X-linked adrenoleukodystrophy: Defective peroxisomal oxidation of very long chain fatty acids but not of very long chain fatty acyl-CoA esters. *Clin Chim Acta* 165:321, 1987.

21. SINGH I, MOSER AE, GOLDFISCHER S, MOSER HW: Lignoceric acid is oxidized in the peroxisome: Implications for the Zellweger cerebro-hepato-renal syndrome and adrenoleukodystrophy. *Proc Natl Acad Sci USA* 81:4203, 1984.

22. MOSER HW: Peroxisomal disorders (editorial). *J Pediatr* 108:89, 1986.

23. SCHUTGENS RBH, HEYMANS HSA, WANDERS RJA, VAN DEN BOSCH H, TAGER JM: Peroxisomal disorders: A newly recognized group of genetic diseases. *Eur J Pediatr* 144:430, 1986.

24. HASHIMI M, STANLEY W, SINGH I: Lignoceroyl-CoA ligase: Enzyme defect in fatty acid beta-oxidation system in X-linked childhood adrenoleukodystrophy. *FEBS Lett* 196:247, 1986.

25. BLAW ME: Adrenoleukodystrophy, in Vinken PJ, Bruyn CW (eds): *Handbook of Clinical Neurology.* Amsterdam, North Holland, 1970, vol 10, p 128.

26. SCHAUMBURG HH, POWERS JH, RAINE CS, SUZUKI K: Adrenoleukodystrophy. A clinical and pathological study of 17 cases. *Arch Neurol* 32:577, 1975.

27. AUBOURG P, CHAUSSAIN JL, DULAC O, ARTHUIS M: Adrenoleucodystrophie chez L'Enfant: A propos de 20 observations. *Arch Fr Pediatr* 39:663, 1982.

28. MOSER HW, NAIDU S, KUMAR AJ, ROSENBAUM AE: Adrenoleukodystrophy: Toward a biochemical definition of a disease with varied presentations. *CRC Crit Rev Neurobiol* 31:29, 1987.

29. BUDKA H, SLUGA E, HEISS WD: Spastic paraplegia associated with Addison's disease: Adult variant of adrenoleukodystrophy. *J Neurol* 213:237, 1976.

30. GRIFFIN JW, GOREN E, SCHAUMBURG HH, ENGEL WK, LORIAUX L: Adrenomyeloneuropathy: A probable variant form of adrenoleukodystrophy. *Neurology* 27:1107, 1977.

31. POWERS JM, SCHAUMBURG HH: A fatal cause of sexual inadequacy in men: Adrenoleukodystrophy *J Urol* 124:583, 1980.

32. O'NEILL BP, SWANSON J, BROWN FR III, GRIFFIN JW, MOSER HW: Familial spastic paraparesis: An adrenoleukodystrophy phenotype? *Neurology* 35:1233, 1985.

33. POWERS JM, SCHAUMBURG HH, GAFFNEY CL: Kluver-Bucy syndrome caused by adrenoleukodystrophy. *Neurology* 30:1131, 1980.

34. CHAZOT G, SASSOLAS G, KOPP N, TRILLET M, SCHOTT B: Adrenomyeloneuropathie: Forme adulte d'adrenoleucodystrophie. *Rev Neurol (Paris)* 135:211, 1979.

35. ESIRI MM, HYMAN NM, HORTON WL, LINDENBAUM RR: Adrenoleukodystrophy: Clinical, pathological and biochemical findings in two brothers with the onset of cerebral disease in adult life. *Neuropathol Appl Neurobiol* 10:429, 1984.

36. WISE JE, MATALON R, MORGAN AM, MCCABE AM, MCCABE ERB: Phenotypic features of patients with congenital adrenal hypoplasia and glycerol kinase deficiency. *Am J Dis Child* 141:744, 1987.

37. WAKEFIELD MA, BROWN RS: X-linked congenital Addison's disease. *Arch Dis Child* 56:73, 1981.

38. O'NEILL BP, MOSER HW, SAXENA KM, MARMION LC: Adrenoleukodystrophy: Clinical and biochemical manifestations in carriers. *Neurology* 34:798, 1984.

40. HEFFUNGS W, HAMEISTER H, ROPERS HH: Addison disease and cerebral sclerosis in an apparently heterozygous girl: Evidence for inactivation of the adrenoleukodystrophy locus. *Clin Genet* 18:184, 1980.

41. MORARIU MA, CHASAN JL, NORUM RA, MOSER HW, MIGEON BR: Adrenoleukodystrophy variant in a heterozygous female. *Neurology* 32:81, 1982.

42. MOLZER B, BERNHEIMER H, BUDKA H, PILZ P, TOIFL K: Accumulation of very long chain fatty acids in common to 3 variants of adrenoleukodystro-

phy (ALD) "classical" ALD, atypical ALD (female patient) and adreno-myeloneuropathy. *J Neurol Sci* 51:301, 1981.

43. POWERS JM, MOSER HW, MOSER AB, CHAN KM, ELIAS SB, NORUM RA: Pathological findings in adrenoleukodystrophy heterozygotes. *Arch Pathol Lab Med* 111:151, 1987.

44. DOOLEY JM, WRIGHT BA: Adrenoleukodystrophy mimicking multiple sclerosis. *Can J Neurol Sci* 12:73, 1985.

45. NOETZEL MJ, LANDAU WM, MOSER HW: Adrenoleukodystrophy: Carrier state presenting as a chronic nonprogressive spinal cord disorder. *Arch Neurol* 44:566, 1987.

46. KURODA S, HIRANO A, YUASA S: Adrenoleukodystrophy. Cerebello-brain-stem dominant case. *Acta Neuropathol* 60:149, 1983.

47. MARSDEN CD, OBESO JA, LANG AE: Adrenomyeloneuropathy presenting as spinocerebellar degeneration. *Neurology* 32:1031, 1982.

48. OHNO T, TSUCHIDA M, FUKUHARA N, YUASA T, HARAYAMA H, TSUJI S, MIYATAKE T: Adrenoleukodystrophy: A clinical variant presenting as olivopontocerebellar atrophy. *J Neurol* 231:167, 1984.

49. TAKADA K, ONODA K, TAKAHASHI K, NAKAMURA H, TAKETOMI T: An adult case of adrenoleukodystrophy with features of olivo-ponto-cerebellar atrophy. Clinical and pathological studies. *Jpn J Exp Med* 57:53, 1987.

50. POWERS JM: Adreno-leukodystrophy (adreno- testiculo- leuko- myelo-neuropathic- complex): A review. *Clin Neuropathol* 4:181, 1985.

51. GRIFFIN DE, MOSER HW, MENDOZA Q, MOENCH TR, O'TOOLE S, MOSER AB: Identification of the inflammatory cells in the central nervous system of patients with adrenoleukodystrophy. *Ann Neurol* 18:660, 1985.

52. POWERS JM, MOSER HW, MOSER AB, SCHAUMBURG HH: Fetal adrenoleukodystrophy: The significance of pathologic lesions in adrenal glands and testis. *Hum Pathol* 13:1013, 1982.

53. POWERS JM, SCHAUMBURG HH: The testis in adrenoleukodystrophy. *Am J Pathol* 102:90, 1981.

54. KISHIMOTO Y, MOSER HW, SUZUKI K: Adrenoleukodystrophy, in Lajtha A (ed): *Handbook of Neurochemistry.* New York, Plenum, 1985, vol 10, p 125.

55. MENKES JH, CORBO LM: Adrenoleukodystrophy: Accumulation of cholesterol esters with very long chain fatty acids. *Neurology* 27:928, 1977.

56. RAMSEY RB, BANIK NL, DAVISO AN: Adrenoleukodystrophy: Brain cholesteryl esters and other neutral lipids. *J Neurol Sci* 40:189, 1979.

57. BROWN FR III, CHEN WW, KIRSCHNER DA, FRAYER KL, POWERS JM, MOSER AB, MOSER HW: Myelin membrane from adrenoleukodystrophy brain white matter—Biochemical properties. *J Neurochem* 41:341, 1983.

58. TAKETOMI T, HARA A, KITAZAWA N, TAKADA K, NAKAMURA H: An adult case of adrenoleukodystrophy with features of olivo-ponto-cerebellar atrophy: II. Lipid biochemical studies. *Jpn J Exp Med* 57:59, 1987.

59. THEDA C, MOSER AB, MOSER HW, DEBUCH H: Temporal evolution of brain biochemical changes in adrenoleukodystrophy. *J Neurochem* 48 (Suppl):S35, 1987.

60. REINECKE CJ, KNOLL DP, PRETORIUS PJ, STEYN HS, SIMPSON RHW: The correlation between biochemical and histopathological findings in adrenoleukodystrophy. *J Neurol Sci* 70:21, 1984.

61. IGARASHI M, BELCHIS D, SUZUKI K: Brain gangliosides in adrenoleukodystrophy. *J Neurochem* 27:327, 1976.

62. NORTON WT, PODUSLO ES: Myelination in rat brain: Method of myelin isolation. *J Neurochem* 21:749, 1973.

63. KOLATTUKUDY PE: Biopolyester membranes of plants: Cutin and suberin. *Science* 208:990, 1980.

64. KOLATTUKUDY PE, CROTEAU R, BROWN L: Structure and biosynthesis of cuticular lipids. *Plant Physiol* 34:670, 1974.

65. VAN DUYN MA, MOSER AE, BROWN FR III, SACKTOR N, LIU A, MOSER HW: The design of a diet restricted in saturated very long chain fatty acids: Therapeutic application in adrenoleukodystrophy. *Am J Clin Nutr* 40:277, 1984.

66. KISHIMOTO Y, MOSER HW, KAWAMURA N, PLATT M, PALLANTE SL, FENSELAU C: Adrenoleukodystrophy: Evidence that abnormal very long chain fatty acids of brain cholesterol esters are of exogenous origin. *Biochem Biophys Res Commun* 96:69, 1980.

67. MOSER HW, PALLANTE SL, MOSER AB, RIZZO WB, SCHULMAN JD, FENSELAU C: Adrenoleukodystrophy: Origin of very long chain fatty acids and therapy. *Pediatr Res* 17:293A, 1983.

68. STEINBERG D, MIZE CE, AVIGAN J, FALES HM, ELDJARN K, STOKKE O, REFSUM S: Studies on the metabolic error in Refsum's disease. *J Clin Invest* 45:1076, 1966; 46:313, 1967.

69. MURAD S, KISHIMOTO Y: Chain elongation of fatty acid in brain: A comparison of mitochondrial and microsomal enzyme activities. *Arch Biochem Biophys* 185:300, 1978.

70. VOLPE JJ, VAGALOS RP: Mechanism and regulation of biosynthesis of saturated fatty acids. *Physiol Rev* 56:339, 1976.

71. CHRISTIANSEN N, RORTVEILT T, NORUM KR, THOMASSEN MS: Fatty acid chain elongation in rat small intestine. *Biochem J* 237:293, 1986.

72. CASSAGNE C, DARRIET D, BOURRE JM: Biosynthesis of very long chain fatty acids by the sciatic nerve of the rabbit. *FEBS Lett* 90:336, 1978.

73. TSUJI S, OHNO T, MIYATAKE T, SUZUKI A, YAMAKAWA T: Fatty acid elongation activity in fibroblasts from patients with adrenoleukodystrophy (ALD). *J Biochem* 96:1241, 1984.

74. BOURRE JM, DAUDU O, BAUMANN N: Nervonic acid biosynthesis by erucyl-CoA elongation in normal and quaking mouse brain microsomes. Elongation of other unsaturated fatty acyl-CoAs (mono and polyunsaturated). *Biochim Biophys Acta* 424:1, 1976.

75. RIZZO WB, WATKINS PA, PHILLIPS MW, CRANIN D, CAMPBELL B, AVIGAN J: Adrenoleukodystrophy: Oleic acid lowers fibroblast C22-26 fatty acids. *Neurology* 36:357, 1986.

76. LUDWIG SA, SPRECHER H: Substrate specificity on the malonyl-CoA-dependent chain elongation of all-cis polyunsaturated fatty acids by rat liver microsomes. *Arch Biochem Biophys* 197:333, 1979.

77. LAZAROW PB, de DUVE C: A fatty acyl-CoA oxidizing system in rat liver peroxisomes; enhancement by clofibrate, a hypolipidemic drug. *Proc Natl Acad Sci USA* 73:2043, 1976.

78. OSMUNDSEN H, THOMASSEN MS, HILTUNEN JK, BERGE RK: Physiological role of peroxisomal beta-oxidation, in Fahimi HD, Sies H (eds): *Peroxisomes in Biology and Medicine.* Berlin, Springer-Verlag, 1987, p 152.

79. MOSER AE, SINGH I, BROWN FR III, SOLISH GI, KELLEY RI, BENKE PJ, MOSER HW: The cerebro-hepato-renal (Zellweger) syndrome. Increased levels and impaired degradation of very long chain fatty acids and their use in prenatal diagnosis. *N Engl J Med* 310:1141, 1984.

80. SCHUTGENS RBH, HEYMANS HSA, WANDERS RJA, VAN DEN BOSCH H, TAGER JM: Peroxisomal disorders: A newly recognized group of genetic diseases. *Eur J Pediatr* 144:430, 1986.

81. HASHIMOTO T: Individual peroxisomal beta-oxidation enzymes. *Ann NY Acad Sci* 386:5, 1982.

82. MIYAZAWA S, HAYASHI H, HIJIKATA M, ISHII N, FURUTA S, KAGAMIYAMA H, OSUMI T, HASHIMOTO T: Complete nucleotide sequence of a cDNA and predicted amino acid sequence of rat acyl-CoA oxidase. *J Biol Chem* 262:8131, 1987.

83. OSUMI T, ISHII N, MIYAZAWA S, HASHIMOTO T: Isolation and structural characterization of the rat acyl-CoA oxidase gene. *J Biol Chem* 262:8138, 1987.

84. ISHII N, HIJIKATA M, OSUMI T, HASHIMOTO T: Structural organization of the gene for rat enoyl-CoA hydration: 3 Hydroxyacyl-CoA dehydrogenase bifunctional enzyme. *J Biol Chem* 262:8144, 1987.

85. HIJIKATA M, ISHII N, KAAMIYAMA H, OSUMI T, HASHIMOTO T: Structural analysis of cDNA for rat peroxisomal 3-ketoacyl-CoA thiolase. *J Biol Chem* 262:8151, 1987.

86. SINGH I, SINGH R, BHUSHAN A, SINGH AK: Lignoceroyl-CoA ligase activity in rat brain microsomal fraction: Topographical localization and effect of detergents and alpha-cyclodextrin. *Arch Biochem Biophys* 236:418, 1985.

87. NAGAMATSU K, SOEDA S, MORI M, KISHIMOTO Y: Lignoceroyl-coenzyme A synthetase from developing rat brain: Partial purification, characterization and comparison with palmitoyl-coenzyme A synthetase activity and liver enzyme. *Biochim Biophys Acta* 836:80, 1985.

88. BHUSHAN A, SINGH RP, SINGH I: Characterization of rat brain microsomal acyl-coenzyme A ligases: Different enzymes for the synthesis of palmitoyl-coenzyme A and lignoceroyl-coenzyme A. *Arch Biochem Biophys* 246:374, 1986.

89. WANDERS RJA, VAN ROERMUND CWT, VAN WIJLAND MJA, HEIKOOP J, SCHUTGENS RBH, SCHRAM AW, TAGER JM, VAN DEN BOSCH H, POLL-THE BT, SAUDUBRAY JM, MOSER HW, MOSER AB: Peroxisomal very long chain fatty acid beta-oxidation in human skin fibroblasts: Activity in Zellweger syndrome and other peroxisomal disorders. *Clin Chem Acta* 166:255, 1987.

90. SINGH I, MOSER HW, MOSER AB, KISHIMOTO Y: Adrenoleukodystrophy: Impaired oxidation of long chain fatty acids in cultured skin fibroblasts and adrenal cortex. *Biochem Biophys Res Commun* 102:1223, 1981.

91. TSUJI S, SANO-KAWAMURA T, ARIGA T, MIYATAKE T: Metabolism of [17, 18-^{3}H$_2$] hexacosanoic acid and [15, 16-^{3}H$_2$] lignoceric acid in cultured skin fibroblasts from patients with adrenoleukodystrophy (ALD) and adrenomyeloneuropathy (AMN). *J Neurol Sci* 71:359, 1985.

92. GOLDFISCHER SJ, COLLINS J, RAPIN I, COLTOFF-SCHILLER C-H, CHANG M, NIGRO VH, BLACK NB, JAVITT NB, MOSER HW, LAZAROW PG: Peroxisomal defects in neonatal onset and X-linked adrenoleukodystrophy. *Science* 227:67, 1985.

93. MOLZER B, KORCHINSKY M, BERNHEIMER H, SCHMID R, WOLF C, ROSCHER A: Very long chain fatty acids in genetic peroxisomal disease fibroblasts: Differences between the cerebro-hepato-renal (Zellweger) syndrome and adrenoleukodystrophy variants. *Clin Chim Acta* 161:81, 1986.

94. TAGER JM, VAN DER BEEK WATH, WANDERS RJA, HASHIMOTO T, HEYMANS HSA, VAN DEN BOSCH H, SCHUTGENS RBH, SCHRAM AW: Peroxisomal beta-oxidation enzyme proteins in the Zellweger syndrome. *Biochem Biophys Res Commun* 126:1269, 1985.

95. CHEN WW, WATKINS PA, OSUMI T, HASHIMOTO T, MOSER HW: Peroxisomal beta-oxidation enzyme proteins in adrenoleukodystrophy: Distinction between X-linked adrenoleukodystrophy and neonatal adrenoleukodystrophy. *Proc Natl Acad Sci USA* 84:1425, 1987.

96. WANDERS RJA, VAN ROERMUND CWT, VAN WIJLAND MJA: Peroxisomal fatty acid beta-oxidation in human skin fibroblasts: X-linked adrenoleukodystrophy, a peroxisomal very long chain fatty acyl-CoA synthetase deficiency. *J Inherited Metab Dis* 10(Suppl. 2):220, 1987.

97. O'NEILL BP, MARMION LC, FERINGA ER: The adrenomyeloneuropathy complex: Expression of four generations. *Neurology* 31:151, 1981.

98. MOSER HW, MOSER AB, SINGH I, O'NEILL BP: Adrenoleukodystrophy: Survey of 303 cases: Biochemistry, diagnosis and therapy. *Ann Neurol* 16:628, 1984.

99. MOSER HW, MOSER AB, TROJAK JE, SUPPLEE SW: Identification of female carriers of adrenoleukodystrophy. *J Pediatr* 103:54, 1983.

100. MARTIN-DeLEON PA, WOLF SF, PERSICO G, TONIOLO D, MARTINI G, MIGEON BR: Localization of glucose-6-phosphate dehydrogenase in mouse and man by in situ hybridization: Evidence for a single locus and transposition of homologous X-linked genes. *Cytogenet Cell Genet* 39:87, 1985.

101. OBERLE I, DRAYNA D, CAMERINO G, WHITE R, MANDEL JL: The telomere of the human X-chromosome long arm: Presence of a highly polymorphic DNA marker and analysis of recombination frequency. *Proc Natl Acad Sci USA* 82:2824, 1985.

102. HAUPT I: The Nela test for color blindness applied to school children. *J Comp Psychiatry* 6:291, 1926.

103. FARNSWORTH D: The Farnsworth-Munsell 100-hue and dichromatous tests for colour vision. *J Opt Soc Am* 33:568, 1943.

104. NATHANS J, THOMAS D, HOGNESS DS: Molecular genetics of human color vision: The genes encoding blue, green and red pigments. *Science* 232:193, 1986.

105. NATHANS J, PIANTIANIDA TP, EDDY RL, SHOWS TB, HOGNESS DS: Molecular genetics of inherited variation in human color vision. *Science* 232:205, 1986.

106. KNAZEK RA, RIZZO WB, SCHULMAN JD, DAVE JR: Membrane microviscosity is increased in the erythrocytes of patients with adrenoleukodystrophy and adrenomyeloneuropathy. *J Clin Invest* 72:245, 1983.

107. MEYER WJ III, SMITH EM, RICHARDS GE, GREGER NS, BROSNAN PG, KEENAN BS: ACTH receptor defect in adrenoleukodystrophy (ALD). *Pediatr Res* 21:251A, 1987.

108. POWERS JM, SCHAUMBURG HH, JOHNSON AB, RAINE CS: A correlative study of the adrenal cortex in adrenoleukodystrophy. Evidence for a fatal intoxication with very long chain saturated fatty acids. *Invest Cell Pathol* 3:353, 1980.

109. BECKETT GJ, BOYD GS: Purification and control of bovine adrenal cortical cholesterol ester hydrolase and evidence for the activation of the enzyme by a phosphorylation. *Eur J Biochem* 72:223, 1977.

110. OGINO T, SUZUKI K: Specificities of human and rat brain enzymes of cholesterol ester metabolism toward very long chain fatty acids: Implications for biochemical pathogenesis of adrenoleukodystrophy. *J Neurochem* 36:776, 1981.

111. ALLEN JP, KEPIC T, GARWACKI D, YUNUS M: Adrenal defect in adrenomyeloneuropathy. *South Med J* 75:877, 1982.

112. BERNHEIMER H, BUDKA H, MULLER P: Brain tissue immunoglobulins in adrenoleukodystrophy: A comparison with multiple sclerosis and systemic lupus erythematosus. *Acta Neuropathol (Berl)* 59:95, 1983.

113. KOSKI CL, HUMPHREY R, SHIN ML: Anti-peripheral myelin antibody in patients with demyelinating neuropathy: Quantitative and kinetic determination of serum antibody for complement component 1 fixation. *Proc Natl Acad Sci USA* 82:905, 1985

114. KANNAGI R, NUDELMAN E, HAKOMORI SI: Possible role of ceramide in defining structure and function of membrane glycolipids. *Proc Natl Acad Sci USA* 79:3470, 1982.

115. STUMPF DA, HAYWARD A, HAAS R, FROST M, SCHAUMBURG HH: Adrenoleukodystrophy: Failure of immunosuppression to prevent neurological progression. *Arch Neurol* 38:48, 1981.

116. NAIDU S, BRESNAN MJ, GRIFFIN DE, O'TOOLE S, MOSER HW: Intensive immunosuppression fails to alter neurological progression in childhood adrenoleukodystrophy. *Arch Neurol*, in press.

117. KANDT RS, HELDRICH FJ, MOSER HW: Recovery from probable central pontine myelinolysis associated with Addison's disease. *Arch Neurol* 40:118, 1983.

118. POSER CM, GOUTIERES F, CARPENTIER MA, AICARDI J: Schilder's myelinoclastic diffuse sclerosis. *Pediatrics* 77:107, 1986.

119. ALLGROVE J, CLAYDEN GS, GRANT DB, MACAULAY JC: Familial glucocorticoid deficiency with achalasia of the cardia and deficient tear production. *Lancet* 1:1284, 1978.

120. TONSHOFF B, LEHNERT W, ROPERS HH: Adrenoleukodystrophy: Diagnosis and carrier detection by determination of long-chain fatty acids in cultured fibroblasts. *Clin Genet* 22:25, 1982.

121. MOLZER B, BERNHEIMER H, HELLER R, TOIFL K, VETTERLEIN M: Detection of adrenoleukodystrophy by increased C26:0 fatty acid levels in leukocytes. *Clin Chim Acta* 125:299, 1982.

122. ANTOKU Y, SAKAI T, GOTO I, IWASHITA H, KUROIWA Y: Adrenoleukodystrophy: Abnormality of very long chain fatty acids in erythrocyte membrane phospholipids. *Neurology* 34:1499, 1984.

123. AUBOURG P, BOUGNERES PF, ROCCHICCIOLI F: Capillary gas-liquid chromatographic-mass spectrometric measurement of very long chain (C22 to C26) fatty acids in microliter samples of plasma. *J Lipid Res* 26:263, 1985.

124. KOBAYASHI T, KATAYAMA M, SUZUKI S, TOMODA H, GORO I, KUROIWA Y: Adrenoleukodystrophy: Detection of increased very long chain fatty acids by high-performance liquid chromatography. *J Neurol* 230:209, 1983.

125. ALBERGHINA M, FIUMARA A, PAVONE L, GIUFFRIDA AM: Determination of C20-C30 fatty acids by reversed-phase chromatographic techniques: An efficient method to quantitate minor fatty acids in serum of patients with adrenoleukodystrophy. *Neurochem Res* 9:1719, 1984.

126. ASKANAS V, McLAUGHLIN J, ENGEL KW, ADORNATO BT: Abnormalities in cultured muscle and peripheral nerve of a patient with adrenomeyloneuropathy. *N Engl J Med* 301:588, 1979.

127. BOUE J, OBERLE I, HEILIG R, MANDEL JM, MOSER A, MOSER H, LARSEN JW Jr, DUMEZ Y, BOUE A: First trimester prenatal diagnosis of adrenoleukodystrophy by determination of very long chain fatty acid levels and by linkage analysis to a DNA probe. *Hum Genet* 69:272, 1985.

128. WANDERS RJA, VAN WIJLAND MJA, VAN ROERMUND CWT, SCHUTGENS RBH, VAN DEN BOSCH H, TAGER JM, NIJENHUIS A, TROMP A: Prenatal diagnosis of Zellweger syndrome by measurement of very long chain fatty acid (C26:0) beta oxidation in cultured choriomic villus fibroblasts: Implications for early diagnosis of other peroxisomal disorders. *Clin Chim Acta* 165:303, 1987.

129. MARTIN JJ, CEUTERIC C, MARTIN L: Skin and conjunctival biopsies in adrenoleukodystrophy. *Acta Neuropathol* 38:247, 1977.

130. MARTIN JJ, CEUTERIC C: Morphological study of skin biopsy specimens: A contribution to the diagnosis of metabolic disorders with involvement of the nervous system. *J Neurol Neurosurg Psychiatry* 41:232, 1978.

131. MARTIN JJ, CEUTERIC C, LIBERT J: Skin and conjunctival nerve biopsies in adrenoleukodystrophy and its variants. *Ann Neurol* 8:291, 1980.

132. ARSENIO NUNES ML, GOUTIERES F, AICARDI J: An ultramicroscopic study of skin and conjunctival biopsies in chronic neurological disorders of childhood. *Ann Neurol* 9:163, 1981.

133. JULIEN J, VALLAT JM, VITAL C, LAGUENY A, FERRER X, DARRIET D: Adrenomyeloneuropathy: Demonstration of inclusions at the level of the peripheral nerve. *Eur Neurol* 20:367, 1981.

134. GARG BP, MARKAND ON, DEMYER WE, WARREN C JR: Evoked response studies in patients with adrenoleukodystrophy and heterozygous relatives. *Arch Neurol* 40:356, 1983.

135. OCHS R, MARKAND ON, DEMYER WE: Brainstem auditory evoked responses in leukodystrophies. *Neurology* 29:1089, 1979.

136. GRIMES AM, ELKS ML, GRUNBERGER G, PIKUS AM: Auditory brainstem responses in adrenomyeloneuropathy. *Arch Neurol* 40:574, 1983.

137. MOLONEY JBM, MASTERSON JC: Detection of adrenoleukodystrophy carriers by means of evoked potential. *Lancet* 2:852, 1982.

138. O'NEILL BP, WESTMORELAND BF, TIFFANY C, MOSER HW: Brainstem auditory evoked potentials in adrenoleukodystrophy carriers. *Ann Neurol* 34 (Suppl) 1:163, 1984.

139. TOBIMATSU S, FUKUI R, KATO M, KOBAYASHI T, KUROIWA Y: Multimodality evoked potentials in patients and carriers with adrenoleukodystrophy and adrenomyeloneuropathy. *Electroencephalogr Clin Neurophysiol* 62:18, 1985.

140. BATTAGLIA A, HARDEN A, PAMPIGLIONE G, WALSH PJ: Adrenoleukodystrophy: Neurophysiological aspects. *J Neurol Neurosurg Psychiatry* 44:781, 1981.

141. MAMOLI B, GRAF M, TOIFL M: EEG, pattern-evoked potentials and nerve conduction velocity in a family with adrenoleukodystrophy. *Electroencephalogr Clin Neurophysiol* 47:411, 1979.

142. REES LH, GRANT DB, WILSON J: Plasma corticotrophin levels in Addison-Schilder's disease. *Br Med J* 3:201, 1975.

143. KUMAR AJ, ROSENBAUM AE, NAIDU S, WENER L, CITRIN CM, LINDENBERG R, KIM WS, ZINREICH SJ, MOLLIVER ME, MAYBERG HS, MOSER HW: Role of magnetic resonance imaging in adrenoleukodystrophy. *Radiology* 165:497, 1987.

144. DUDA EE, HUTTENLOCHER PR: Computer tomography in adrenoleukodys-

trophy: Correlation of radiological and histological findings. *Radiology* 120:349, 1976.

145. GREENBERG HS, HALVERSON D, LANE B: CT scanning and diagnosis by adrenoleukodystrophy. *Neurology* 27:884, 1977.

146. MARLER JR, O'NEILL BP, FORBES GS, MOSER HW: Adrenoleukodystrophy (ALD): Clinical and CT features of a childhood variant. *Neurology* 33:1203, 1983.

147. DiCHIRO GD, EIBEN RM, MANZ HJ, JACOBS IB, SCHELLINGER D: A new CT pattern in adrenoleukodystrophy. *Radiology* 137:687, 1980.

148. DUBOIS PJ, FREEMARK M, LEWIS D, DRAYER BP, HEINZ ER, OSBORNE D: Atypical findings in adrenoleukodystrophy. *J Comput Assist Tomogr* 5:88, 1981.

149. AUBOURG P, DIEBLER C: Adrenoleukodystrophy—Its diverse CT appearances and an evolute or phenotypic variant: The leukodystrophy without adrenal insufficiency. *Neuroradiology* 24:33, 1982.

150. YOUNG RSK, RAMER JC, TOWFIGHI J, WEIDNER W, LEHMAN R, MOSER HW: Adrenoleukodystrophy. Unusual computed tomographic appearance. *Arch Neurol* 39:782, 1982.

151. INOUE Y, FUKUDA T, TAKASHIMA S, OCHI H, ONOYAMA Y, KUSUDA S, MATSUOKA O, MURATA R: Adrenoleukodystrophy: New CT findings. *AJNR* 4:951, 1983.

152. PECKHAM RS, MARSHALL MC JR, ROSMAN PM, FARAG A, KABADI U, WALLACE EZ: A variant of adrenomyeloneuropathy with hypothalamic pituitary dysfunction and neurologic remission after glucocorticoid replacement therapy. *Am J Med* 72:173, 1982.

153. BROWN FR III, STOWENS DW, HARRIS JC JR, MOSER HW: The leukodystrophies, in Johnson RT (ed): *Current Therapy in Neurologic Disease*. Philadelphia, Dekker, 1985, p. 313.

154. BROWN FR III, VAN DUYN MA, MOSER AB, SCHULMAN JD, RIZZO WB, SNYDER RD, MURPHY JV, KAMOSHITA S, MIGEON CJ, MOSER HW: Adrenoleukodystrophy: Effects of dietary restriction of very long chain fatty acids and of the administration of carnitine and clofibrate on clinical status and plasma fatty acids. *Johns Hopkins Med J* 151:164, 1982.

155. KRAMER JKG, SAVER FD, PIDGEN WJ (eds): *High and Low Erucic Acid Rapeseed Oils. Production, Usage, Chemistry and Toxicological Evaluation.* Toronto, Academic, 1983.

156. BREMER J, NORUM KR: Metabolism of very long chain monounsaturated fatty acids (C22:1) and the adaptation to their presence in the diet. *J Lipid Res* 23:243, 1982.

157. LOEW FM, SCHIEFER B, LAXDAL VA, PRASAD K, FORSYTH GW, ACKMAN RG, OLFERT ED, BELL JM: Effects of plant and animal lipids rich in docosenoic acids on the myocardium of cynomolgus monkeys. *Nutr Metab* 22:201, 1978.

158. MOSER HW, TUTSCHKA PJ, BROWN FR III, MOSER AB, YEAGER AH, McDONELL JH, WHITE CL, SINGH I, MARK SA, MAUMENEE IH, GREEN WR, POWERS JM, SANTOS GW: Bone marrow transplant in adrenoleukodystrophy. *Neurology* 34:1410, 1984.

159. MURPHY JV, MARQUARDT KM, MOSER HW, VAN DUYN MA: Treatment of adrenoleukodystrophy by diet and plasmapheresis. *Ann Neurol* 12:220, 1982.

160. WANDERS RJA, VAN ROERMUND CWT, VAN WIJLAND MJA, SCHUTGENS RBH, VAN DEN BOSCH H, SCHRAM AW, TAGER JM: Direct demonstration that the deficient oxidation of very long chain fatty acids in X-linked adrenoleukodystrophy is due to an impaired ability of peroxisomes to activate very long chain fatty acids. *Biochem Biophys Res Commun*, 153:618, 1988.

161. LAZO O, CONTRERAS M, HASHMI M, STANLEY W, IRAZU C, SINGH T: Peroxisomal lignoceroyl-CoA ligase deficiency in childhood adrenoleukodystrophy and adrenomyeloneuropathy. *Proc Natl Acad Sci USA*, in press.

162. WHITCOMB RW, LINEHAN WM, KNAZEK RA: Effects of long-chain saturated fatty acids on membrane microviscosity and adrenocorticotropin responsiveness of human adrenocortical cells in vitro. *J Clin Invest* 81:185, 1988.

163. WEINBERG K, MOSER A, WATKINS P, LENARSKY C, WINTER S, MOSER HW, PARKMAN R: Bone marrow transplantation for adrenoleukodystrophy. *Pediatr Res* 23:334A, 1988.

CHAPTER 59

REFSUM DISEASE

DANIEL STEINBERG

1. *Refsum disease is a rare inborn disorder of lipid metabolism inherited as an autosomal recessive trait and first recognized clinically as a predominantly neurologic syndrome. As described by Sigvald Refsum in 1946, the cardinal manifestations of the syndrome are retinitis pigmentosa, peripheral neuropathy, cerebellar ataxia, and elevated cerebrospinal fluid protein concentration. Less constant features include nerve deafness, anosmia, skeletal abnormalities, ichthyosis, and nonspecific electrocardiographic abnormalities.*

2. *Almost without exception, Refsum syndrome is associated with the accumulation in blood and tissues of an unusual 20-carbon, branched chain fatty acid—phytanic acid (3,7,11,15-tetramethylhexadecanoic acid). Patients with the classic clinical syndrome and with accumulation of phytanic acid should be designated as having Refsum disease. Accumulation of phytanic acid reliably distinguishes Refsum disease from the large number of neurologic disorders with which it shares one or more clinical features. However, accumulation of phytanic acid is not unique to Refsum disease. It also occurs in a number of peroxisomal disorders (e.g., Zellweger syndrome; infantile Refsum disease; and autosomal recessive infantile adrenoleukodystrophy). These are readily differentiated from Refsum disease on clinical grounds.*

3. *Phytanic acid is exclusively exogenous in origin; endogenous biosynthesis has not been demonstrated. Dietary phytanic acid itself is the major source; dairy products and ruminant fats are especially rich sources of phytanic acid, but small amounts are found in many dietary fats. Free phytol is readily converted to phytanic acid, but the phytol in chlorophyll (the major dietary source of phytol) is poorly absorbed.*

4. *The major mechanism for phytanic acid degradation is via a novel α-oxidative pathway, involving an initial α-hydroxylation followed by decarboxylation to generate the 19-carbon lower homologue, pristanic acid. The further degradation of pristanic acid occurs by a series of β-oxidative steps analogous to those involved in oxidation of straight-chain fatty acids.*

5. *Patients with Refsum disease appear to have an isolated phytanic acid α-hydroxylase deficiency. Its activity is also missing in patients with global peroxisomal defects. Because many additional metabolic functions are defective in the latter disorders, onset is earlier and clinical expression is more general and severe than in Refsum disease.*

6. *Skin fibroblasts from patients with Refsum disease (and from patients wtih peroxisomal disorders) oxidize phytanic acid at less than 10 percent the normal rate; fibroblasts from obligate Refsum heterozygotes oxidize phytanic acid at about 50 percent of the normal rate. Heterozygotes do not accumulate phytanic acid and remain asymptomatic. The carrier state can be demonstrated in fibroblast cultures.*

7. *Treatment with diets low in phytanic acid reduces plasma phytanic acid levels and brings about significant improvement in peripheral nerve function, in skin abnormalities, and in electrocardiographic patterns. However, full restoration of function is seldom achieved, and cranial nerve dysfunction, while stabilized, does not regress. Plasmapheresis combined with diet can be used to effect more rapid decreases in phytanic acid stores. Treatment that keeps plasma phytanate levels low arrests progress of the disease and prevents relapses. It should be instituted as early as possible and continued for life.*

HISTORICAL OVERVIEW

In 1946 Sigvald Refsum published his definitive monograph identifying a new familial neurologic syndrome which he designated *heredopathia atactica polyneuritiformis*.[1] The primary clinical features, almost all of them seen in Refsum's original cases, are listed in Table 59-1. Individually, none of the findings was unique, but Refsum astutely concluded that the pattern in his five original cases, occurring in two inbred Norwegian families, could be distinguished from those seen in the many clinically similar heredoataxic syndromes previously described.

The first direct evidence that the syndrome described by Refsum stemmed from a specific biochemical defect was published by Klenk and Kahlke in 1963.[2] They analyzed postmortem tissues from a 7-year-old girl diagnosed as having Refsum disease by Richterich and coworkers in Berne.[3] Liver and kidney were grossly infiltrated with lipid, mostly neutral lipid, but no unusual complex lipids were detected. Gas-chromatographic analysis revealed a large, abnormal peak that accounted for over 50 percent of the total fatty acids in liver lipids. This component was isolated in pure form and fully characterized as phytanic acid, a 20-carbon, branched chain acid not previously reported in human tissues (Fig. 59-1). In the plasma of patients with Refsum disease, phytanic acid was found in amounts corresponding to 5 to 30 percent of the total fatty acids.[4] Normal human plasma contains only traces of phytanic acid (less than 0.3 mg/dl), amounts so small that they are generally undetectable in routine analyses.[5,6]

Two general hypotheses suggested themselves concerning the origin of the accumulated phytanic acid.[7,8] The polyisoprenoid structure of phytanic acid suggested a biosynthetic origin by pathways related to that for sterol synthesis. However, studies in patients with Refsum disease[9,10] and in experimental

---

Although the subcellular localization of phytanic acid oxidase in humans is not known, we have placed this chapter in the section on peroxisomal disorders because deficiency of phytanic acid oxidase and accumulation of phytanic acid are part of the constellation of abnormalities observed in patients with genetic defects in peroxisomal biogenesis (see Chap. 57 and Dr. Steinberg's discussion of the possible peroxisomal involvement in Refsum disease). The Editors.

Table 59-1 Clinical Features in Refsum Disease

Retinitis pigmentosa: failing night vision,* progressive constriction of visual fields, lenticular opacities
Peripheral polyneuropathy: generally symmetrical, motor and sensory losses, absent or diminished deep tendon reflexes
Cerebellar ataxia: dyscoordination out of proportion to the degree of peripheral neuropathy, unsteady gait, positive Romberg sign, intention tremor, nystagmus
Elevated cerebrospinal fluid protein level without pleocytosis
Familial incidence with autosomal recessive pattern of inheritance
Nerve deafness, anosmia, pupillary abnormalities, nystagmus
Nonspecific ECG changes
Ichthyosislike changes ranging from mild hyperkeratosis of palms and soles to florid ichthyosis on trunk
Epiphyseal dysplasia: short fourth metatarsal, syndactyly, hammer toe, pes cavus, osteochondritis dissecans

*Some authors have used the term hemeralopia to designate poor vision in dim light, whereas medical dictionaries define the term to mean "day blindness." We shall use the less ambiguous term *night blindness*.

animals[11] failed to demonstrate any endogenous synthesis. These results pointed to an exogenous origin for the accumulated phytanic acid and a defect in catabolism as the basis for its accumulation. Phytol, a component of the chlorophyll molecule, was shown to be readily convertible to phytanic acid, and both phytol and phytanic acid itself were shown to be potential dietary sources since phytanate accumulated when they had been fed in large doses to experimental animals.[9–17]

A series of studies by Steinberg and coworkers beginning in 1966 established the major pathway for phytanic acid oxidation in humans and experimental animals (Fig. 59-2).[18–22] It involves (1) an unusual initial α oxidation to yield α-hydroxyphytanic acid and then, by decarboxylation, the $(n - 1)$ fatty acid, pristanic acid; and (2) a series of successive β-oxidation steps for the further degradation of pristanic acid. Rates of phytanic acid oxidation in patients were shown to be less than 5 percent of normal,[9,10,23,24] and the defect was shown to persist in fibroblast cell cultures.[25] The latter finding greatly facilitated further studies, which led to identification of the site of the metabolic block. Evidence from clinical observations[24] and cell culture studies[25–27] indicated that the primary enzyme defect is in the first step in the new metabolic pathway, i.e., in the conversion of phytanic acid to α-hydroxyphytanic acid. Results of studies with model substrates structurally related to phytanic acid were compatible with this conclusion.[28,29]

As soon as it was established that phytanic acid had an exogenous origin, the possibility of therapeutic intervention by eliminating dietary sources of phytanate and its precursors was investigated. It was clearly shown that dietary modification reduces levels of phytanic acid in plasma and tissues.[23,30–32] Experience to date shows that dietary treatment with reduction of phytanate levels arrests progress and leads to partial remission (see "Treatment," below).

Fig. 59-1 Structure of phytanic acid, a 20-carbon, fully saturated fatty acid. The branched chain structure is that characteristic of terpenes, presumably derived from four 5-carbon isoprenoid precursors.

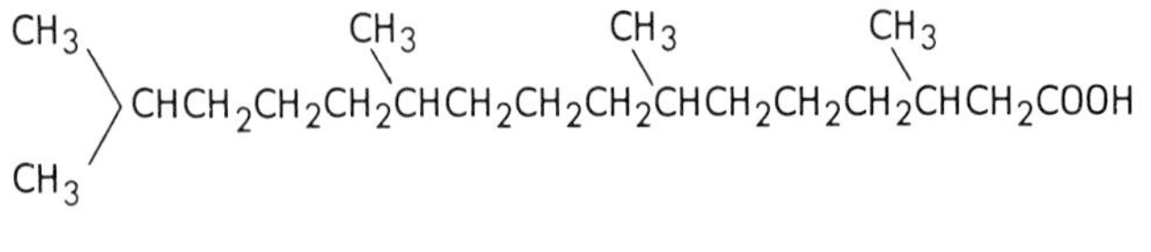

PHYTANIC ACID

(3, 7, 11, 15 - tetramethylhexadecanoic acid)

For many years it was thought that accumulation of phytanic acid was limited to patients with Refsum disease. However, in 1974 Kahlke et al.[33] described an infant with cerebral damage, arrested development, icterus, and hepatomegaly in whom phytanic acid was unequivocally elevated in the serum and in a liver biopsy. The clinical picture was decidedly not that of Refsum disease. Over the following years a series of studies demonstrated that phytanic acid accumulation accompanies a number of inherited diseases now believed to represent peroxisomal disorders (e.g., Zellweger syndrome; infantile Refsum disease; and autosomal recessive infantile adrenoleukodystrophy). As discussed in detail in Chap. 57, these disorders are characterized by an almost complete absence of peroxisomes and both structural and functional abnormalities in mitochondria. Phytanic acid oxidation was originally reported by Tsai et al.[22,34] to be present in the mitochondrial fraction. This was confirmed by others,[35–37] although in only one instance were enzyme markers used to characterize the fractions.[37] The severe deficit in phytanic acid oxidase activity in the peroxisomal disorders could be secondary to the still poorly characterized mitochondrial abnormality described in those patients.[38,39] However, with the new evidence regarding peroxisomal disorders in hand, it becomes important to reexamine the question of enzyme localization. The well-established, almost complete deficiency in phytanic acid oxidation in patients with peroxisomal deficiencies strongly suggests a key role for the peroxisome in phytanic acid metabolism. Another possibility is that the first steps in phytanic acid oxidation require peroxisomes and that the further metabolism of the products requires the mitochondria (or vice versa). It may be that in Refsum disease there is a specific, limited mutation affecting phytanic acid α-hydroxylase, whereas in the other disorders, with more global defects in peroxisome structure and function, there is defective phytanic acid oxidation *together with* many other defects that lead to the more severe clinical expression in these syndromes.

Emphasis in this chapter will be placed primarily on the metabolic pathway for phytanic acid oxidation, the nature of the enzymatic deficiency, genetic aspects, and pathogenesis. Space limitations preclude reference to all of the many papers dealing with this disease. Readers are referred to previous editions of this book[40] and to other reviews[23,41–44] for more complete documentation of the clinical aspects.

TERMINOLOGY

As discussed above, until recently it was thought that phytanic acid storage was unique to Refsum disease, but it is now clear that phytanic acid can accumulate in other disorders that have a very different clinical course than the one described by Refsum. Thus far, these all appear to involve peroxisomal deficiency, and they all are characterized by early onset, failure to grow and develop normally, and hepatic failure—features not present in patients with Refsum disease. Because phytanic acid is stored in several disorders, the designation *phytanic acid storage disease* is no longer sufficiently restrictive. The designation *phytanic acid α-hydroxylase deficiency* to replace *Refsum disease* could be considered, since that is the specific deficiency demonstrated in all eight patients with Refsum disease so far tested for it;[24,27,45] however, not all patients have been studied in that detail, nor are they likely to be in the future. I propose, then, to continue to use the term *Refsum disease* for those pa-

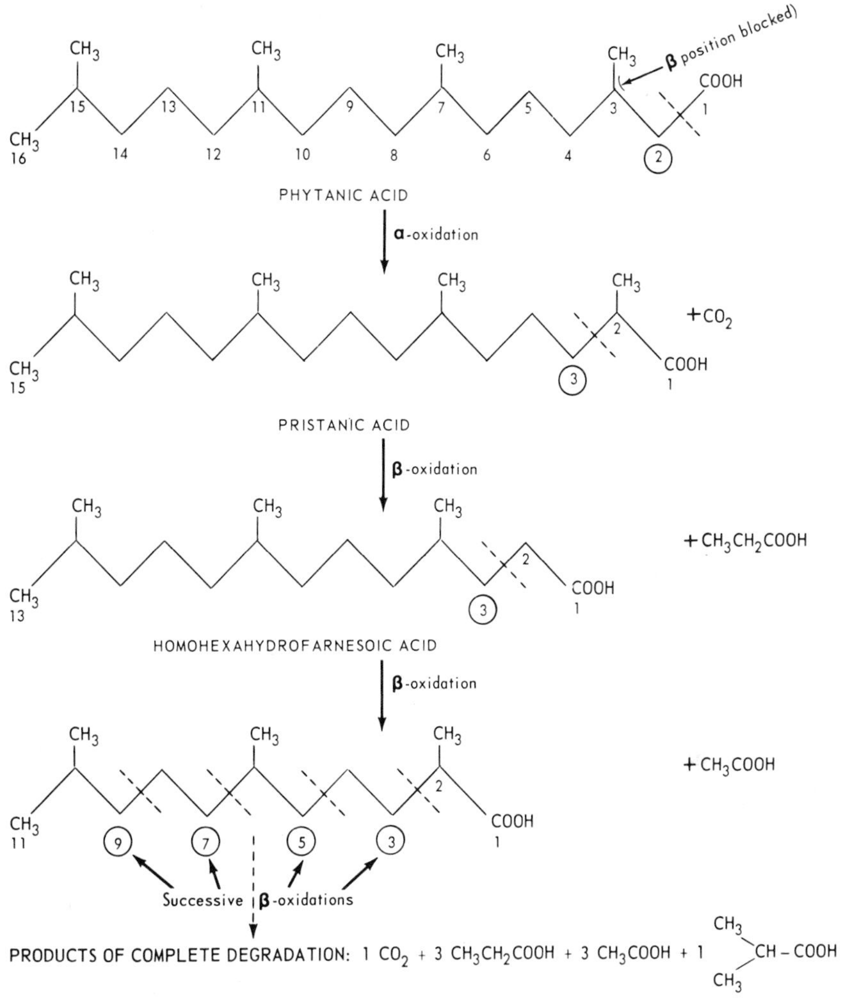

Fig. 59-2 The major pathway for oxidation of phytanic acid in mammals. The first step, introduction of a hydroxyl function at the α position, is the site of the metabolic block in phytanic acid storage disease. This is followed by decarboxylation to yield the $(n-1)$ lower homologue, pristanic acid, and then by a series of successive β oxidations. Direct β oxidation of phytanic acid is not possible because the methyl group at position 3 prevents the dehydrogenation step in the β-oxidation cycle (see Eq. 59-2).

tients who have the classic clinical syndrome described by Refsum together with phytanic acid storage. When sufficient biochemical sophistication allows it, we would designate each of the phytanic acid storage diseases according to the specific gene defect involved.

The designation *infantile Refsum disease* may be confusing, suggesting a closer relationship to Refsum disease than actually exists. For that reason, I propose that the designation be dropped in favor of *infantile phytanic acid storage disease* or, even better, some new designation that relates it to the demonstrated peroxisomal defect. Patients with Refsum disease appear to have a normal number of peroxisomes and have a specific, limited defect in phytanic acid α oxidation.

CLINICAL FINDINGS AND DIFFERENTIAL DIAGNOSIS

The diagnostic tetrad of retinitis pigmentosa, peripheral polyneuropathy, cerebellar ataxia, and high cerebrospinal fluid protein concentration in the absence of pleocytosis has been found in virtually every patient with Refsum disease. Additional clinical findings are listed in Table 59-1. The various clinical features of the syndrome may appear sequentially as the disease progresses; thus, incomplete syndromes early in the course are to be expected and have been described in patients already showing storage of phytanic acid.

Patients destined to develop Refsum disease appear to be perfectly normal as infants and do not show any obvious defects in growth and development. Onset has occasionally been detected in early childhood but not until the fifth decade in others. Most patients have clear-cut manifestations before age 20. Presenting complaints relate to failing vision and weakness in extremities or unsteadiness of gait. The earliest symptom is almost always night blindness, although it may require careful questioning to elicit this history and establish the true date of onset.

The course is one of gradually progressive deterioration, interrupted in over half of the patients by unexplained and sometimes lengthy periods of remission. Dramatic exacerbation associated with a poorly defined febrile illness, a surgical procedure, or pregnancy has been noted, as in Friedreich ataxia. Gradual recovery of function following such episodes is the rule, but residual neurologic deficits remain.

A number of deaths have occurred suddenly and without obvious cause. In view of the electrocardiographic changes that accompany the disease, which are nonspecific in most cases but include a few examples of impaired atrioventricular conduction and bundle branch block, a cardiac arrhythmia is suspected as the cause of sudden death. Two deaths were attributed to respiratory paralysis and two to bacterial pneumonia, respiratory insufficiency not being mentioned explicitly as a factor.

Much increased levels of phytanic acid have been demonstrated in the serum of virtually every patient with Refsum disease who was examined for them. Conversely, no increases in phytanic acid levels have been found in any of a wide variety of other neurologic syndromes closely related clinically to Refsum disease. Some of the more important disorders with negative results for phytanic acid accumulation are Dejerine-Sottas hypertrophic peripheral neuropathy, Friedreich ataxia, multiple sclerosis, retinitis pigmentosa of both the recessive and dominant types, a larger number of nonspecific heredo-ataxias, peroneal muscular atrophy (Charcot-Marie-Tooth syndrome), abetalipoproteinemia, high density lipoprotein deficiency (Tangier disease), amyotrophic lateral sclerosis, Sjögren-Larsson syndrome, Spielmeyer-Vogt disease, and Tay-Sachs disease.

Phytanic acid accumulation in plasma is not unique, nor is it pathognomonic for Refsum disease. In 1974 Kahlke, Goerlich, and Feist[33] described an infant with cerebral damage, arrested development, icterus, and hepatomegaly in whom phytanate was unequivocally elevated in plasma and in a liver biopsy. The clinical picture was decidedly atypical for Refsum disease, in which early childhood is generally uneventful. Similar cases were later described by Scotto et al.[46] and by Poulos et al.[47,48] Subsequent studies have established that these patients also accumulate very long chain, straight-chain fatty acids, pipecolic acid, and abnormal bile acids,[48-57] characteristic features of peroxisomal disorders. Indeed, peroxisomes are deficient in these cases,[52,53] whereas peroxisomes are present in normal numbers in fibroblasts of patients with Refsum disease.[54] Thus, "infantile Refsum disease" might better be renamed and classified along with related peroxisomal disorders such as Zellweger syndrome and infantile adrenoleukodystrophy (see Chap. 57). All of these are now recognized as peroxisomal disorders and may even represent variations of a single underlying metabolic disease. Phytanic acid accumulates either because phytanic acid oxidation in some way involves peroxisomes or because these disorders are accompanied by additional defects affecting the mitochondria, which have been reported by several laboratories to be the primary site of phytanic acid oxidation.[35-37] It should be noted that the distribution of phytanic acid oxidase in *human* tissues has yet to be reported; the data available thus far are from studies of rat and guinea pig liver only. In any case, the peroxisomal disorders are readily distinguished clinically from Refsum disease. They have a much earlier onset, include strong elements of cerebral and hepatic dysfunction, and produce arrested development, often with death in infancy or early childhood.

Concordance between clinical diagnosis of Refsum disease and phytanic acid storage has been established in at least 100 cases, but there are a few exceptions. Several patients with clinical features difficult to distinguish from those typically found in Refsum disease have been described in whom there was no demonstrable accumulation of phytanate.[32,55-60] In one of these,[55] later metabolic studies and cell culture studies showed that the patient oxidized phytanate normally, and autopsy failed to show the findings characteristic of Refsum disease.[60] Further work may clarify the relationship between pathogenesis in the rare cases *without* phytanate and that in the more usual cases *with* phytanate. At present it is preferable to designate as examples of people with Refsum disease only those patients with both (1) the typical clinical syndrome and (2) demonstrated accumulation of phytanic acid or demonstrated reduction in capacity to oxidize phytanic acid. The latter stipulation is included since even patients with drastically reduced capacity to metabolize phytanate may all but free themselves of the stored acid when kept on the appropriate diet.[31,32] Their capacity to oxidize phytanate, however, remains deficient.[24]

An even narrower definition at the biochemical level can be proposed. In 14 clinically typical patients studied in vivo, in cell culture, or both, the oxidation of pristanic acid, the α-oxidation product of phytanic acid, was normal. This established that the metabolic error is a phytanic acid α-oxidase deficiency.[46,61] In 8 of the 14 patients thus far tested, oxidation of α-hydroxyphytanate was also normal.[24,27,45] Thus, these patients, and perhaps most or all others with Refsum disease, have a *phytanic acid α-hydroxylase deficiency*.

Presumed heterozygotes (parents or sibs of clinical cases) have occasionally shown phytanate accumulation without evidence of neurologic involvement.[62,63] Since heterozygotes have about a 50 percent reduction in capacity to oxidize phytanate,[46] it is understandable that these individuals may tend to accumulate phytanic acid to a much more limited extent than homozygotes. The normal level of oxidative capacity is far in excess of that needed to dissimilate the usual intake of phytanate and precursors in the diet. On the other hand, it is conceivable that under the appropriate circumstances (excessive dietary load or imposition of extrinsic factors accentuating the metabolic defect) these heterozygotes may store phytanic acid to a limited degree (and possibly even develop clinical disease).

A definitive diagnosis of Refsum disease requires demonstration of abnormal levels of phytanic acid in blood or tissues accompanying the typical clinical syndrome. Gas-liquid chromatography of the fatty acid methyl esters is the method of choice.[64] Because of its branched structure, methylphytanate behaves like a straight-chain, 17-carbon fatty acid on gas-liquid chromatography. Mass spectroscopy may be needed for unequivocal identification. A satisfactory preliminary screening tool is provided by thin-layer chromatography, which is based on the greater mobility of triglycerides that contain phytanate.[65-67] Even when phytanate accounts for only 10 percent of total serum fatty acids, the phytanate-containing glycerides can be identified. Verification can then be made by gas-liquid chromatography.

METABOLIC BASIS FOR ACCUMULATION OF PHYTANATE

Evidence Against Endogenous Synthesis

The polyisoprenoid structure of phytanic acid suggested that it might be endogenously synthesized by addition of a fourth isoprene unit to farnesol, generating the 20-carbon compound geranylgeraniol.[7,8] Geranylgeranyl pyrophophate is a normal intermediate in carotene biosynthesis in plants, and its synthesis has been reported in mammalian liver. In plants, phytol is formed from mevalonic acid by such a pathway, and thus there is precedent for the reduction of double bonds in the polyisoprenoid series. The postulated conversion of the alcohol to a carboxylic acid would be analogous to the demonstrated oxidation of farnesol to farnesoic acid.

However, attempts to demonstrate biosynthesis of phytanic acid from [2-^{14}C]mevalonic acid in a patient with Refsum disease were negative, and neither labeled acetate nor mevalonate was incorporated into phytanate in experimental animals.[9-11] To rule out the possibility of a very slow rate of endogenous synthesis and to test for alternative pathways of biosynthesis from small molecules, clinical studies were carried out in two patients using deuterium oxide as a precursor.[10,31] The patients' body water levels were held at a constant level of enrichment over 4 to 5 months. Plasma cholesterol levels showed the expected progressive enrichment in deuterium, but plasma phytanate levels showed minimal enrichment, corresponding to replacement of only two to four hydrogen atoms. Some enrichment would be expected as a result of the conversion of dietary phytol to phytanic acid (see below). The results make it unlikely that much, if any, of the phytanate that accumulates in this disease arises from endogenous *de novo* biosynthesis. The fact that elimination of phytanate from the diet reduces body stores of the compound (see below) clearly establishes the quantitative importance of exogenous sources. Nevertheless, the postulated pathway via geranylgeranyl pyrophosphate may operate at a low level and may be induced by environmental or genetic factors. Dulaney et al.[68] and Evans and Dulaney[68a] have reported the occurrence of small amounts of a monounsaturated ($\triangle^{15}$) and a triunsaturated ($\triangle^{6,10,14}$) form of phytanic acid in the serum and urinary lipids of patients (but not of normal subjects). These compounds could represent metabolites of geranylgeranyl pyrophosphate, with one or three of its four double bonds reduced, the pyrophosphate cleaved, and the alcohol function oxidized. Further metabolic studies have not been reported.

Origin from Dietary Phytanic Acid

Addition of phytanic acid to the diet of rats or mice leads to its accumulation in blood and tissues.[9,16,17] Large amounts must be fed to exceed the large capacity of the normal animal to catabolize phytanate. In mice fed diets containing phytanate 2 percent by weight for 2 weeks, the phytanate levels in liver and serum reached values of 20 to 30 percent of total fatty acids, levels approaching those seen in affected patients. It should be noted that daily dietary intake of phytanate in humans is less than 100 mg/day or about 1 mg/kg/day; the intake needed to cause significant accumulation in mice and rats is about 1000 mg/kg/day! Since phytanic acid is efficiently absorbed by way of the lymph—as efficiently as palmitic acid[69]—these feeding experiments indicate that the compound is rapidly metabolized. This is confirmed by the rapid disappearance of stored phytanate (within a week or two) when the animals are returned to a normal diet.

Dairy products and ruminant fats in the human diet are probably the major sources of phytanic acid.[70–73] Ruminants ingest large quantities of chlorophyll, and the resident bacteria in the rumen effectively degrade it, liberating the phytol from its linkage to the propionic acid side chain of the porphyrin. Free phytol is then readily converted to phytanic acid, as discussed below. Some conversion occurs even within the rumen.[74] Phytanic acid can account for as much as 5 to 10 percent of the total fatty acids in bovine plasma, whereas plasma of nonruminant animals and of normal humans contains only traces. Butterfat can contain more than 100 mg phytanate per 100 g wet weight.[74] On the other hand, skim milk, chicken, pasta, and safflower oil contain less than 0.5 mg/100 g.[72,73] The daily phytanic acid intake from an ordinary diet has been estimated to be somewhere between 50 and 100 mg/day.[23,75] Dietary sources of phytanic acid are considered in more detail in "Treatment," below.

In the rat, orally administered phytanic acid is well absorbed even when fed in large doses, and most of the absorption occurs by way of the lymph.[69] Direct studies of phytanic

acid absorption in humans are not available. Since phytol absorption in humans is similar to that in the rat,[9,13–15] it may be reasonable to assume that at least 50 to 75 percent of the phytanic acid in the daily diet is, in fact, absorbed.

Origin from Dietary Phytol

Free Phytol. Phytol, differing in structure from phytanic acid only in having a $\triangle^2$ double bond and an alcohol rather than a carboxylic acid function at the 1 carbon (Fig. 59-3), is readily converted to phytanic acid.[9–15] Two pathways are possible, depending on the sequence in which the double bond reduction and the oxidation of the alcohol function occur. Both the 2,3-unsaturated acid (phytenic acid; $\triangle^2$-3,7,11,15-tetramethylhexadecanoic acid) and the saturated alcohol (dihydrophytol) can be converted to phytanic acid, so that both pathways are potentially available.[11,14] However, after administration of phytol to experimental animals, large amounts of phytenic acid are found but little or no dihydrophytol. This suggests that oxidation of the alcohol function is normally the initial step.[11,69] Studies in rat liver show that the phytol-phytanate conversion is effected without detectable production of dihydrophytol.[76]

Orally administered phytol is efficiently absorbed by normal human subjects (61 to 94 percent of a tracer dose), and similar values have been found in two patients with phytanic acid storage disease.[10] Studies in rats show that absorption is mainly by way of the thoracic duct,[69] and in the course of absorption about 10 to 20 percent of the dose is converted to phytanic acid. Since similar values were found in a germ-free rat, it is unlikely that the intestinal flora play any major role in the phytol–phytanic acid conversion.

Klenk and Kremer, on examining the liver fatty acids of phytol-fed rats, noted the presence of three or four different isomeric forms of phytenic acid, but these were not further characterized.[14] Baxter and Milne developed chromatographic methods that improved resolution of these isomers and made possible their individual isolation on a preparative scale.[77] They showed that the usual saponification procedures lead to isomerization but transesterification under acid conditions

Fig. 59-3 Two alternative pathways for the conversion of phytol to phytanic acid. The operation of the pathway shown on the right has been demonstrated. Conversion of dihydrophytol to phytanic acid has been demonstrated, but the overall pathway shown at the left has not yet been verified experimentally.

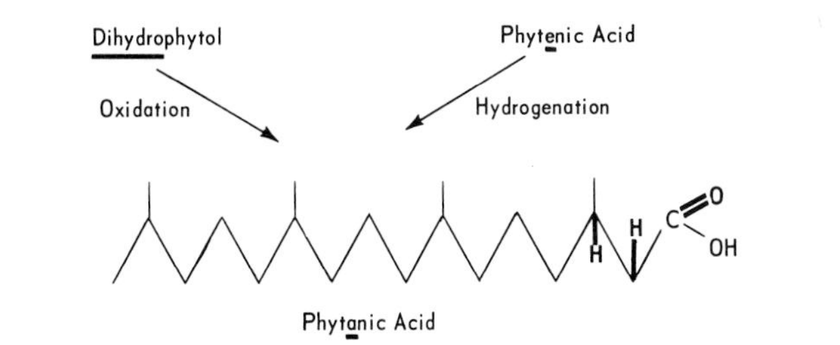

does not. Five isomers were demonstrated in the lymph of phytol-fed rats: the cis and trans forms of $\triangle^2$-phytenic acid, the cis and trans forms of $\triangle^3$-phytenic acid, and the 3-methylene isomer. The *trans*-$\triangle^2$ form predominated (70 percent of total phytenic acid). These findings are interesting in relation to the question of the mechanism of the phytol-phytanate conversion and may also be relevant to the question of the variable ratios of phytanic acid diastereoisomers found in different animal species and different patients with phytanic acid storage disease.[70,78,79]

Chlorophyll-Bound Phytol. The ubiquitous presence of chlorophyll in green vegetables suggested that this might be an important dietary precursor since it contains 1 mol phytol per mole, bound in ester linkage to a propionic acid side chain of one of the pyrrole rings. However, Baxter and Steinberg, using high specific activity [^{14}C]pheophytin *a* (Mg^{2+}-free chlorophyll *a*), showed that in the thoracic duct–cannulated rat not more than 2 percent of bound phytol was absorbed.[80] Baxter's clinical balance studies showed that 95 percent of the phytol administered orally as [^{14}C]pheophytin was recovered in the feces, both in normal control subjects and in two patients with phytanic acid storage disease.[81] He also fed 180 g spinach to a human subject with the thoracic duct cannulated and recovered only 2 percent of the spinach phytol in a 24-h lymph collection. From these results it is clear that while free phytol is an excellent precursor of phytanic acid, the bound phytol in the chlorophyll molecule cannot be a quantitatively important dietary source of stored phytanate. In the course of preparing vegetables for the table some of the phytol may be released from ester form and become available. However, even the total amount of phytol in the usual diet is less than 10 percent of the amount of preformed phytanic acid.[31,71]

Other Precursors

Billeter et al.,[82] studying the metabolism in pigeons of orally administered phylloquinone labeled both in the nucleus and in the phytyl side chain, found that the phytyl side chain was split off by intestinal bacteria. The fate of the side chain was further studied using a side chain–labeled phylloquinone. It was possible to isolate an acidic lipid with the properties of phytanic acid from breast muscle. Data are not available to assess the quantitative importance of this pathway.

It is possible that the intestinal flora contribute to the stored phytanate in patients. Some bacteria can synthesize phytanate itself, and others may synthesize related isoprenoid compounds convertible to phytanate.[83,84] If such synthesis occurs *de novo* in the bacteria (from acetate by way of mevalonate), the clinical studies with deuterium oxide described above should have detected it, since the total-body water, including that in the intestine, was presumably all at the same level of enrichment with deuterium. On the other hand, if the bacteria were to modify the structure of higher molecular weight branched chain compounds in the diet, such structural modification might not necessarily entail incorporation of hydrogen from water and would go undetected. Additional evidence against a quantitatively important contribution by intestinal bacteria comes from clinical studies of phytanic acid excretion in feces. After 10 days on a formula diet low in phytanic acid, fecal excretion of phytanate fell to about 2 mg/day.[31]

There is some reason to suspect that not all of the dietary precursors are known. The amounts of phytanic acid accu-

mulated in the tissues of patients, as estimated from biopsies and postmortem analysis, are considerable—up to 200 to 400 g. Even assuming a dietary intake of 100 mg/day and no degradation or excretion at all, it would take 5 to 10 years to accumulate such large stores. While this is by no means unfeasible, the possibility must be considered that there are additional sources of phytanate. The possibility that there is endogenous biosynthesis in infants and children should be tested, other branched chain dietary constituents should be considered as precursors, and production by unusual intestinal flora should be explored.

DEFECTIVE OXIDATION OF PHYTANIC ACID

Normal Oxidative Capacity

A number of lines of evidence indicate that normal animals, including human beings have a large capacity to dissimilate phytanic acid and prevent its accumulation even at high levels of intake. [U-^{14}C]phytanic acid injected intravenously into normal humans as the albumin complex is converted to $^{14}CO_2$ at a rate comparable to that for [1-^{14}C]palmitic acid.[24] This is so even though the initial rate of disappearance of the labeled free phytanic acid from the plasma is distinctly lower than that of palmitic acid. Orally administered [U-^{14}C]phytol, which is probably oxidized to $^{14}CO_2$ in large part only after prior conversion to phytanic acid, is also efficiently oxidized—about 21 percent of the absorbed dose in the first 12 h.[10]

The capacity of experimental animals to oxidize and excrete phytanate can be exceeded, but this requires the addition of relatively large amounts of phytanic acid or phytol to the diet, as discussed above. In humans, according to Avigan, even after ingestion of 9.5 g phytol in a single dose by a normal subject, plasma phytanate had risen only to 2.4 mg/dl after 18 h.[5] In a heroic study this same volunteer ate 3.5 kg boiled spinach over a 60-h interval; his plasma phytanic acid level did not change perceptibly! Further evidence comes from studies showing that the fractional rate of oxidation of phytol to CO_2 in normal volunteers is the same whether only a tracer dose is given or whether a full 1-g dose of carrier phytol is given with it.[10]

Defective Oxidation in Patients with Refsum Disease

Clinical Studies. The first demonstration of the reduced capacity of patients to oxidize phytanic acid utilized [U-^{14}C]phytol as a precursor.[9] Observed rates of $^{14}CO_2$ production in two patients were only about one-fifth those in normal volunteers. Subsequent studies in three additional cases, using intravenously injected [U-^{14}C] phytanic acid itself, showed an even more striking defect, initial rates of $^{14}CO_2$ production being less than 5 percent of those of control subjects.[24] The apparent difference in the degree of block suggested by the clinical studies using these two different precursors probably does not reflect basic differences in the degree of enzyme block in the patients studied. Later cell culture studies using fibroblasts derived from skin biopsies showed that all five patients had comparably severe deficits, phytanic acid being oxidized at rates less than 5 percent of those observed in normal fibroblast cultures.[61] The results suggest the possibility that phytol can be oxidized to a significant degree by a pathway not involving phytanate as an intermediate.

After intravenous injection of labeled phytanic acid, less than 0.001 percent of the dose was recovered in the feces of either controls or patients, showing that biliary excretion or other mechanisms of excretion by way of the intestinal tract are quantitatively unimportant.[24] Less than 6 percent of the injected radioactivity appeared in the urine, 95 percent of it in nonlipid forms.

Eldjarn and coworkers compared controls and patients with regard to oxidation of model compounds[85–87] but not phytanic acid itself. These model compounds (3,6-dimethyloctanoic acid and 3,14,14-trimethylpentadecanoic acid) resemble phytanate in having a methyl substituent on the 3 carbon and, like phytanate itself, are not susceptible to ordinary β oxidation. Moreover, the substituents at the ω end of these molecules should prevent β oxidation from that end also. 3,6-Dimethyloctanoic acid, labeled in the ω terminus (carbon 8), was oxidized to a limited extent by normal controls—2 to 3 percent in 10 h—but in two patients with phytanic acid storage disease, no $^{14}CO_2$ could be detected above background. One of these patients was restudied after plasma phytanate levels had been drastically reduced by dietary means.[87] At that time there was a small but significant yield of $^{14}CO_2$—0.5 to 1 percent of the administered dose. The oxidation of the other model compound, 3,14,14-trimethylpentadecanoic acid, which was labeled with tritium by catalytic exchange, was determined by measuring the release of tritium to body water. In control subjects, 31 to 37 percent of the dose was found in body water at the maximum, but in two patients only 8 and 17 percent, respectively, was found.[87] The metabolic pathway by which the trimethylpentadecanoic acid was degraded was not established, and the cumulative yield of labeled metabolites in the urine was apparently no different in patients and controls. The other model compound, 3,6-dimethyloctanoic acid, was largely degraded by ω oxidation, a small fraction undergoing α oxidation as discussed below.

Fibroblast Cell Culture Studies. As is true of a growing list of inherited diseases of metabolism, the defect in Refsum disease persists in cultured fibroblasts.[25] Normal human fibroblasts derived from skin biopsies oxidized added phytanate at rates comparable to those for added palmitate. Cells derived from patients with phytanic acid storage disease, on the other hand, while oxidizing palmitate at a normal rate, oxidized phytanate at only about 5 percent of the normal rate. The low rate of phytanate oxidation was not due to a defect in uptake since the rate of incorporation of phytanate into cell lipids was in fact greater in the patients' cells than in the controls' cells. The sum of [^{14}C]phytanate in cell lipids and in $^{14}CO_2$ was almost exactly the same. This indicated a normal uptake mechanism.[27] Poulos[88] and Sjkeldal et al.[89,90] have confirmed and extended the evidence for the concordance between clinically diagnosed Refsum disease and phytanic acid oxidase deficiency in cultured fibroblasts. However, the severity of the defect in the cell culture studies did not correlate well either with the clinical severity of the syndrome or with levels of phytanate in the plasma. The level in the plasma will obviously depend on the severity of the deficiency, the amount of phytanic acid in the diet, and the efficacy of possible alternative routes of metabolism of phytanic acid.

The possibility that phytanic acid storage might be due in part to a defect in the rate at which it is released by hydrolytic enzymes from ester linkages has been considered. However,

studies of the rate of release of phytanate previously incorporated into cultured cells during incubation in unlabeled medium showed no difference in this regard between the cells of patients and those of controls.[27] Laurell has shown that the phytanyl ester bonds in glyceryl triphytanate are extremely resistant to hydrolysis by lipoprotein lipase.[91] Since the plasma of patients contains diphytanyl and monophytanyl triglycerides but no detectable triphytanyl triglycerides,[65–67,92] this finding leaves undecided the question of whether the phytanyl ester bonds in the naturally occurring mixed glycerides also are resistant to hydrolysis. Studies by Avigan and Steinberg, using the serum of a patient with phytanic acid storage disease or the chyle from a phytanic acid–fed rat as substrate, indicated that even in mixed glycerides the phytanyl ester bond is resistant to the action of lipoprotein lipase.[93] Ellingboe and Steinberg, using synthetic mixed glycerides containing phytanate, showed that the phytanyl ester bond is relatively resistant to hydrolysis by pancreatic lipase as well as by lipoprotein lipase from rat adipose tissue.[94] These findings may explain the fact that phytanic acid in the depot fat of patients or phytanic acid–fed rats accounts for a much lower percentage of total fatty acids than it does in their plasma. No difference has thus far been reported between control subjects and patients in their ability to hydrolyze phytanyl ester bonds.

The studies summarized to this point establish that there is little or no endogenous biosynthesis of phytanic acid, that phytol and phytanic acid are potential dietary precursors (as are, perhaps, other compounds), and that the metabolic error lies in a degradative pathway (Fig. 59-4).

Defective Oxidation in Patients with Peroxisomal Disorders

There is a clear-cut defect in phytanic acid oxidation in skin fibroblasts from patients with Zellweger syndrome and related peroxisomal disorders.[89,90,95] The logical inference at first glance would be that phytanic acid oxidation is localized in the peroxisomes. Yet studies performed in the rat and in the guinea pig[22,34–37] have localized the activity primarily in the mitochondrial fraction. When the studies were carried out, the potential importance of the peroxisome had not yet been appreciated and the fractions were not characterized by use of enzyme markers. Thus, there is a possibility that peroxisomes were "smeared" into the mitochondrial fractions. However, the recent study by Skjeldal and Stokke,[37] using catalase as a marker for peroxisomal localization, led to the conclusion that α oxidation of phytanic acid is exclusively a mitochondrial process in rat liver. They could not confirm the requirement for a cytosolic cofactor as reported by Muralidharan and Kish-

Fig. 59-4 The metabolic error in phytanic acid storage disease.

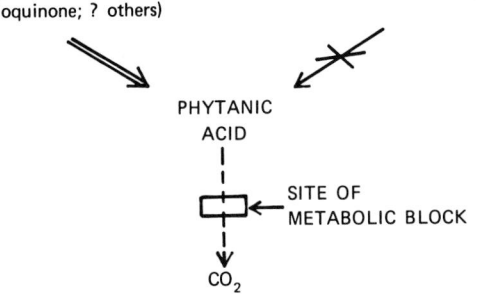

EXOGENOUS ORIGIN
(Phytanic acid; Phytol; Phylloquinone; ? others)

ENDOGENOUS ORIGIN
(Acetate; Mevalonate; D_2O)

PHYTANIC ACID

SITE OF METABOLIC BLOCK

CO_2

imoto.[36] If phytanic acid oxidase activity is really a mitochondrial process and not a peroxisomal process, how do we explain its disappearance or near-disappearance in patients with peroxisomal disorders? We must postulate either (1) that these patients have an additional defect involving a mitochondrial system for branched chain fatty acid oxidation; (2) that the studies of subcellular distribution are incorrect; (3) that there are important species differences; or (4) that interaction between mitochondria and peroxisomes is involved. Subcellular distribution studies have not yet been reported using human liver; the activity could be predominantly peroxisomal in human tissues. The conversion of phytanic acid to CO_2 may require peroxisomes (presumably carrying out the α-hydroxylase reaction) *and* mitochondria. For example, the mitochondria might be able more rapidly to convert uniformly labeled phytanic acid to $^{14}CO_2$. However, even when phytanic acid labeled in the 1 position is used, the conversion to $^{14}CO_2$ seems to occur in the mitochondria. It is probably best to reserve judgment until more research is done. Whatever the nature of the defect in Zellweger syndrome and related peroxisomal disorders, it certainly involves phytanic acid oxidase in some way but also many other metabolic pathways. In contrast, the only metabolic defect so far identified in patients with Refsum disease is the specific inability to carry out α oxidation of phytanic acid.

PATHWAY FOR PHYTANIC ACID OXIDATION IN RELATION TO PREVIOUSLY DESCRIBED PATHWAYS FOR FATTY ACID OXIDATION

The theoretically possible modes of initial attack on the phytanic acid molecule based on the present knowledge of fatty acid–oxidizing mechanisms are indicated in Fig. 59-5, and each will be discussed in turn.

β Oxidation

This ubiquitous mitochondrial system for successive cleavage of two carbon fragments from the carboxyl end of the chain is quantitatively the most important pathway for fatty acid oxidation. Five basic steps, repeated in cyclic fashion, are involved:

Activation (acylthiokinase, long chain):
$$RCH_2CH_2COOH + CoASH + ATP \longrightarrow$$
$$RCH_2CH_2COSCoA + AMP + PP_i \quad [59\text{-}1]$$

Dehydrogenation (acyl-CoA dehydrogenase):
$$RCH_2CH_2COSCoA + \text{flavoprotein} \longrightarrow$$
$$RCH{=}CHCOSCoA + \text{reduced flavoprotein} \quad [59\text{-}2]$$

Hydration (enoyl hydrase):
$$RCH{=}CHCOSCoA + H_2O \longrightarrow$$
$$RCHOHCH_2COSCoA \quad [59\text{-}3]$$

Dehydrogenation (L($+$)-β-hydroxyacyl-CoA dehydrogenase):
$$RCHOHCH_2COSCoA + NAD^+ \longrightarrow$$
$$\overset{O}{\overset{\|}{R}}CCH_2COSCoA + NADH + H^+ \quad [59\text{-}4]$$

Thiolytic cleavage (β-ketoacyl-CoA thiolase):
$$\overset{O}{\overset{\|}{R}}CCH_2COSCoA + CoASH \longrightarrow$$
$$\overset{O}{\overset{\|}{R}}CSCoA + \overset{O}{\overset{\|}{CH_3}}CSCoA \quad [59\text{-}5]$$

Phytanic acid could undergo metabolism by way of this pathway only through Eq. 59-3. Because of the 3-methyl substituent, it could not be dehydrogenated at this stage to yield the β-keto intermediate.

Fatty acids with 2-methyl substituents can be oxidized by the classic β-oxidation system. The reactions are presumably entirely analogous except that Eq. 59-5 generates not acetyl-CoA but rather propionyl-CoA, as in the oxidation of α-methylbutyrate:

$$\overset{O}{\overset{\|}{CH_3}}C{-}\overset{CH_3}{\overset{|}{C}}HCOSCoA + CoASH \longrightarrow$$
$$\overset{O}{\overset{\|}{CH_3}}CSCoA + \overset{O}{\overset{\|}{CH_3}}CH_2CSCoA \quad [59\text{-}6]$$

There are two ways in which phytanate could be modified initially that would bring it under the jurisdiction of the β-oxidation system. First, it could undergo an α-oxidative decarboxylation:

$$\overset{CH_3}{\overset{|}{R}}CHCH_2COOH \longrightarrow \overset{CH_3}{\overset{|}{R}}CHCOOH \quad [59\text{-}7]$$
(Phytanate; 20 carbons) (Pristanate; 19 carbons)

This reaction converts a β-methyl fatty acid to an α-methyl fatty acid. It effects a "frame shift" such that the branch

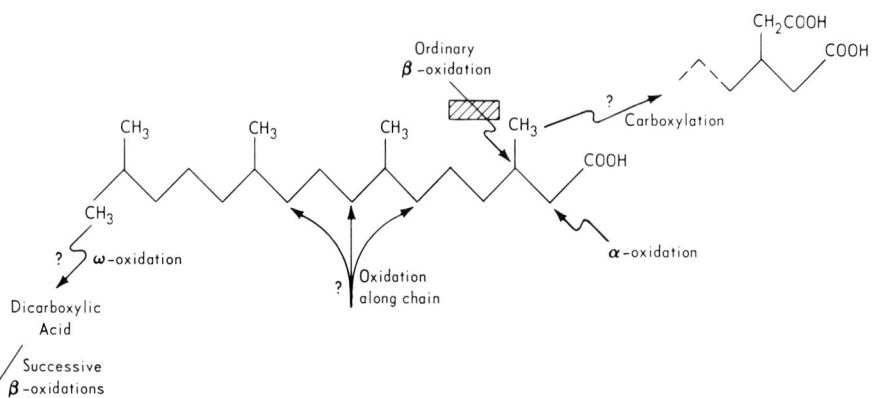

Fig. 59-5 Schematic representation of the theoretically possible initial modes of oxidative attack on the phytanic acid molecule. The shaded box indicates the blocking effect of the methyl group at position 3 on ordinary β oxidation.

methyl groups no longer impede normal β oxidation. The first β-oxidation cycle would release propionyl-CoA (see Eq. 59–6). A second cycle of β oxidation would then yield acetyl-CoA and an α-methyl fatty acid, whereupon the full cycle could repeat itself. As discussed below, this is in fact probably the major pathway after formation of the $(n - 1)$ acid, pristanic acid.

Second, the molecule could undergo an initial oxidation at the terminal carbon, i.e., ω oxidation:

$$
\begin{array}{ccc}
CH_3 & CH_3 & CH_3 \\
| & | & | \\
\underline{CH_3}CHCH_2CH_2(CH_2CHCH_2CH_2)_2CH_2CHCH_2COOH & \longrightarrow \\
\end{array}
$$

$$
\begin{array}{ccc}
CH_3 & CH_3 & CH_3 \\
| & | & | \\
\underline{HOOC}CHCH_2CH_2(CH_2CHCH_2CH_2)_2CH_2CHCH_2COOH
\end{array}
$$

[59-8]

Note that at the ω-carboxyl end of the molecule, the branch-methyl substituent is in the α position. Thus oxidation could, after activation, proceed from this end of the molecule by β oxidation, yielding propionyl-CoA and acetyl-CoA, alternately.

α Oxidation[96]

Straight-Chain Fatty Acids. Oxidation of long-chain, straight-chain fatty acids, including the common fatty acids such as palmitate and stearate, appears to be an important pathway in plants, but in mammalian systems only brain and nerve oxidize straight-chain fatty acids by attack at the α position. The longer-chain fatty acids, C_{20} and above, appear to be preferred substrates. The uniquely high concentrations of α-hydroxy acids in nerve tissue are probably due to the operation of this pathway. Similarly, the significant levels of odd-numbered, long-chain acids (e.g., 21:0, 23:0, 25:0) in nerve tissue reflect in part 1-carbon shortening of even-numbered acids by this mechanism while some may arise from additions of 2-carbon units to propionate. The α-hydroxy and α-keto acids are believed to be intermediates, free or enzyme-bound. The overall sequence from even-numbered acid to $(n - 1)$ acid has been difficult to demonstrate in cell-free systems, particularly the initial α hydroxylation. In any case, as discussed below, it appears that the system for α oxidation of phytanate is *not* identical with the system for α oxidation in nerve.

Phytanic Acid: Conversion to Pristanic Acid. Conversion of labeled phytanic acid to its $(n - 1)$ lower homologue, pristanic acid, was first demonstrated by Avigan and coworkers in 1966.[18] The rate and extent of this conversion strongly suggested that this is the major normal pathway for phytanate oxidation, and subsequent studies in vivo and in vitro bear this out.[18–22] Unambiguous proof of direct conversion was provided by studies in which phytanic acid labeled with deuterium at the 2 and 3 positions was injected into rats. Pristanic acid was recovered from the liver and identified by mass spectrometry; one-half of the deuterium was lost, as expected, as a result of oxidation of the 2 carbon, but the enrichment at position 3 was nearly the same as that of the injected phytanate.[18] This result also served to rule out the possibility that phytanate might first be dehydrogenated to phytenic acid (3,7,11,15-tetramethylhexadec-2-enoic acid) and then hy-

drated to form the α-hydroxy acid (see "Phytanic Acid: Further Oxidation of Pristanic Acid," below).

Net accumulation of pristanic acid has been demonstrated in mice and rats fed phytanic acid,[19,90,97,98] and trace amounts have been found in normal human tissues, including plasma,[5] and in butterfat[99] and ruminant depot fat.[100] No systematic surveys of the relative capacities of different tissues to oxidize phytanate have been reported, but it seems likely that the system will prove to be widely distributed.

Phytanic Acid: Role of α-Hydroxyphytanate as an Intermediate. α-Hydroxyphytanic acid was first isolated from incubations of phytanic acid with rat liver mitochondria, which appeared to contain all of the enzymes necessary for the complete oxidation of phytanic acid.[21,22] That it is an obligatory intermediate was suggested by the following: (1) the rate of its formation relative to the rate of appearance of pristanic acid was consistent with such a role; (2) when labeled α-hydroxyphytanate was added as substrate, it was converted to pristanic acid and further degradation products identical to those formed from labeled phytanate itself; and (3) unlabeled α-hydroxyphytanate reduced the yield of labeled CO_2 from labeled phytanate. In the latter connection, the radioactivity recovered in the form of α-hydroxyphytanate was too small to account adequately for the reduced yield of labeled CO_2. Thus, the hydroxy intermediate may not ordinarily be released from the enzyme surface during the phytanate-pristanate conversion.

Studies on the mechanism of the hydroxylation in subcellular fractions of rat liver have shown that the activity is confined to the mitochondria.[22] The reaction is stimulated by NADPH and requires molecular oxygen. In these respects it resembles the several NADPH-dependent mixed-function oxygenase reactions linked to the cytochrome P_{450} system in liver microsomes, but the distinctly different subcellular localization distinguishes it clearly from them. Another unique property, not fully understood, is the marked stimulation of the hydroxylation caused by the addition of ferric iron, whereas ferrous iron inhibits the reaction. These properties further distinguish the phytanate-oxidizing system in the liver from the straight-chain α-oxidation system in the brain. The latter is primarily microsomal and is stimulated by ferrous iron.[101,102] As noted above, the evidence for the conversion of long-chain, straight-chain fatty acids to the α-hydroxy form in subcellular preparations of mammalian brain is mostly indirect. The hydroxy acid may remain tightly bound as is proposed for hydroxyphytanate; the latter, however, is to some extent dissociable and can be readily demonstrated as a major product.

Phytanic Acid: Further Oxidation of Pristanic Acid. The pathway for degradation beyond pristanic acid was first established by studies in mice fed phytanic acid.[19] This species, for reasons not fully understood, when fed phytanic acid accumulates much larger quantities of pristanic acid and also significant quantities of lower degradation products. The latter were clearly demonstrable by gas-liquid chromatography of liver fatty acids and could be completely characterized by the use of combined gas-liquid chromatography and mass spectrometry.[20] Confirmation of their direct formation from phytanic acid was obtained by injecting [U-^{14}C]phytanic acid and demonstrating the presence of radioactivity in the relevant gas-liquid chromatography peaks. The compounds shown in Fig. 59-2 have all been characterized as products of phytanic acid in vivo, in vitro, or both. The products obviously form the series that would be expected from successive β oxidations of pristanic acid.

When labeled pristanic acid was incubated with rat liver mitochondria, a new component, with a retention time on gas-liquid chromatography greater than that of the starting material, was detected. This was identified as the 2,3-unsaturated form of pristanic acid, Δ^2-pristenic acid.[22] This would be the expected dehydrogenation product in the classic β-oxidation sequence. The demonstrated formation of the α,β-unsaturated derivative supports the interpretation that further degradation of pristanic acid occurs by way of a β-oxidation pathway.

If the scheme shown in Fig. 59-2 is correct, 3 mol propionic acid should be formed during the degradation of each mole of phytanic acid. Direct evidence for propionate as a degradation product was provided by studies in rat liver homogenates and, most convincingly, in studies utilizing mutant human skin fibroblasts.[103,104] [U-^{14}C]phytanic acid was incubated with cell lines from patients with inherited disorders blocking propionate degradation (propionic acidemia and methylmalonic acidemia). In both cell lines there was a striking accumulation of [^{14}C]propionate and a decrease in the rate of $^{14}CO_2$ generation relative to that in normal fibroblasts. The latter would be anticipated since the degradation scheme predicts that almost half of the carbon atoms in phytanate reach CO_2 by way of propionate. Thus, the results considerably strengthen the case for the postulated pathway.

ω Oxidation

ω Oxidation is initiated by oxygen attack at the ω carbon or at the penultimate (ω − 1) carbon of straight-chain fatty acids. The major primary product is a dicarboxylic acid of the same number of carbon atoms as the substrate. While straight-chain fatty acids can readily be shown to undergo this form of oxidation in an isolated microsomal system, there is evidence that the mitochondrial β-oxidation system is quantitatively much more important, at least for the long-chain, straight-chain fatty acids.[105,106]

As discussed above, initial ω oxidation of phytanic acid would make it possible for β oxidation to proceed from the ω end without interference from the branch methyl groups. Try has presented evidence suggesting ω oxidation of phytanic acid in rat liver homogenates.[107] Proof of structure was not presented, the conclusion being based mainly on the finding of radioactivity in fatty acids with properties similar to those of dicarboxylic acids. In any case, it was concluded that ω oxidation proceeded at a low rate at best. In the course of studies of phytanate oxidation by the mouse, which allowed the isolation of a large number of degradation products, and in studies of phytanic acid oxidation in isolated rat liver mitochondria, where many of the same degradation products could be identified, careful search was made for the formation of dicarboxylic acids but none was found.[20,22] The evidence available suggests that under ordinary conditions ω oxidation is probably a minor pathway. However, in patients lacking the α-oxidation pathway, ω oxidation might become significant and account for the limited rate of phytanate oxidation that has been observed in patients.[23,24]

After an initial ω oxidation, successive β oxidations from the ω end would generate propionic acid and acetic acid in successive cleavages and include as potential products 3,7-dimethyloctanedioic acid (dimethylsubaric acid), 3-methylhexa-

nedioic acid (methyladipic acid), and 3-methylbutanedioic acid (3-methylsuccinic acid). Normal individuals excrete 3-methyladipic acid,[108] and there is some evidence that this excretion is somewhat greater in patients with Refsum disease,[109–112] but other laboratories find no difference.[113] Better evidence that ω oxidation of phytanate can occur, at least in patients with Refsum disease, comes from the work of Greter, Lindstedt, and Steen[112] showing that 3,7-dimethylsubarate is not detectable in normal urine but is excreted by patients with Refsum disease. The calculated amount of phytanic acid degraded by this ω-oxidation pathway was 30 mg daily. It is quite remarkable to note that in order to achieve therapeutic benefit, it has been found best to reduce the daily intake—normally about 60 mg/day—to 21 mg/day and that best results were obtained with a liquid formula diet providing less than 3 mg/day.[31,114,115] Additional evidence that ω oxidation may contribute to the degradation of phytanate comes from studies showing that the excretion of 3-methyladipate is increased in rats fed phytol.[116]

Removal of Methyl Groups after Fixation of CO_2

A β-substituted fatty acid (β-methylbutyric acid) is formed in the course of the oxidative degradation of leucine. This fatty acid (as the acyl-CoA) could undergo the second and third steps of the usual β-oxidation cycle, namely, α,β-dehydrogenation and hydration to form the β-hydroxyacyl-CoA derivative (see "β Oxidation" earlier in this chapter). The second dehydrogenation to form the β-keto acid would be blocked. Degradation depends upon fixation of CO_2 to the β-methyl group of the α,β-unsaturated acid. Hydration yields hydroxymethylglutaryl-CoA, which is cleaved to yield acetoacetic acid and acetyl-CoA:

A similar CO_2-fixation "trick" has been shown by Seubert and Remberger[117] to function in bacteria in the oxidation of geranoic acid and farnesoic acid, β-methyl-substituted branched chain acids. The only difference in this case is that after fixation of CO_2 to the branch methyl group, free acetic acid is cleaved instead of acetyl-CoA. This leaves a β-keto acyl-CoA derivative, which can then be β-oxidized in the usual fashion. The general similarity in structure of these unsaturated polyisoprenoid fatty acids and phytanic acid (see Fig. 59-2) suggested the possibility that phytanic acid might undergo an analogous oxidation. Eldjarn and coworkers[85] initially reported a CO_2 requirement for the oxidation of a model compound structurally related to phytanic acid (3,6-dimethyloctanoic acid) but were unable to confirm this in later studies.[118,119] Tsai and coworkers[22] were unable to demonstrate a CO_2 dependency for the oxidation of phytanic acid itself in rat liver mitochondria. Moreover, in none of the systems in which the oxidation of phytanic acid itself has been studied has there been evidence for the appearance of the expected 20-carbon dicarboxylic acid intermediate, the 19-carbon 3-keto derivative, or the 17-carbon lower homologue that would be expected in such a pathway.

LOCALIZATION OF THE SITE OF THE ENZYMATIC ERROR

The site of the enzymatic block in phytanic acid oxidation in patients has been localized to the initial α oxidation, probably in the α-hydroxylation step itself. This conclusion is based on studies of the rates of oxidation of phytanic acid and of its degradation products in cell cultures and is supported by studies in vivo in patients.

1. While the rate of phytanic acid oxidation in cell cultures derived from patients is only 1 percent of that seen in control cell cultures, the rates of oxidation of labeled pristanic acid (Fig. 59-6) are comparable to the rates in control cells.[25–27,61] The rate of oxidation of α-hydroxyphytanic acid has been found to be normal also,[27] implying that the mutation involves the α-hydroxylation step.

2. The rate of oxidation of intravenously injected phytanic acid is depressed in patients, but the rate of oxidation of pristanic acid or of α-hydroxyphytanic acid is comparable to that seen in normal subjects.[23,24]

3. After incubation of normal fibroblasts with labeled phytanic acid, the cell lipids can be shown to contain α-hydroxyphytanic acid and labeled pristanic acid as well as labeled 4,8,12-trimethyltridecanoic acid.[27] In contrast, the cell lipids in fibroblasts derived from patients contain only labeled phytanic acid and no degradation products.

4. Careful study of serum and tissue lipids from patients with phytanic acid storage disease and of postmortem tissues has failed to reveal the accumulation of any branched chain congeners other than phytanic acid itself. Were the metabolic block at some lower point in the degradation pathway, one might expect to find at least some concentrations of accumulated intermediates.[25]

5. After administration to normal subjects of a branched chain model compound related to phytanic acid in having a β-methyl substitution ([8-^{14}C]3,6-dimethyloctanoic acid), a small fraction of the administered dose of radioactivity is recovered in the urine in the form of the α-oxidation product (2,5-dimethylheptanoic acid).[86] In contrast, patients failed to show any α-oxidation product in the urine. Normal subjects oxidized a small percentage of the administered radioactivity to CO_2, but patients oxidized none.[85,86] If it is assumed that the model compound is metabolized by the same systems that oxidize phytanic acid itself, which is supported by the results in patients, these results support the conclusion that there is a defect in α oxidation.

On the basis of indirect evidence obtained by using model compounds, it was proposed by Eldjarn that the accumulation of phytanic acid might reflect a defect in ω oxidation.[120] However, later studies showed that other compounds subject to ω oxidation were handled normally,[121] and even the oxidation of the model compound used originally (tricaprin) returned toward normal in the patients after they had been maintained on a low phytanate diet.[122] Possibly the stores of phytanate secondarily affect some ω-oxidation systems. As discussed above, there is no evidence for a major role of ω oxidation in the metabolism of phytanic acid in normal animals or in normal humans. On the other hand, the residual capacity of patients with phytanic acid storage disease to catabolize phytanate may be due in part to ω oxidation and in part to a residual capacity for α oxidation.

Fig. 59-6 Rates of phytanic acid and pristanic acid oxidation in fibroblast cell cultures. The almost complete deletion of the phytanic acid–oxidizing activity in homozygous patients is shown, as well as the normal rates of pristanic acid oxidation in patients. The rate of oxidation of phytanic acid in the obligate heterozygotes (parents) is approximately 50 percent of control values.

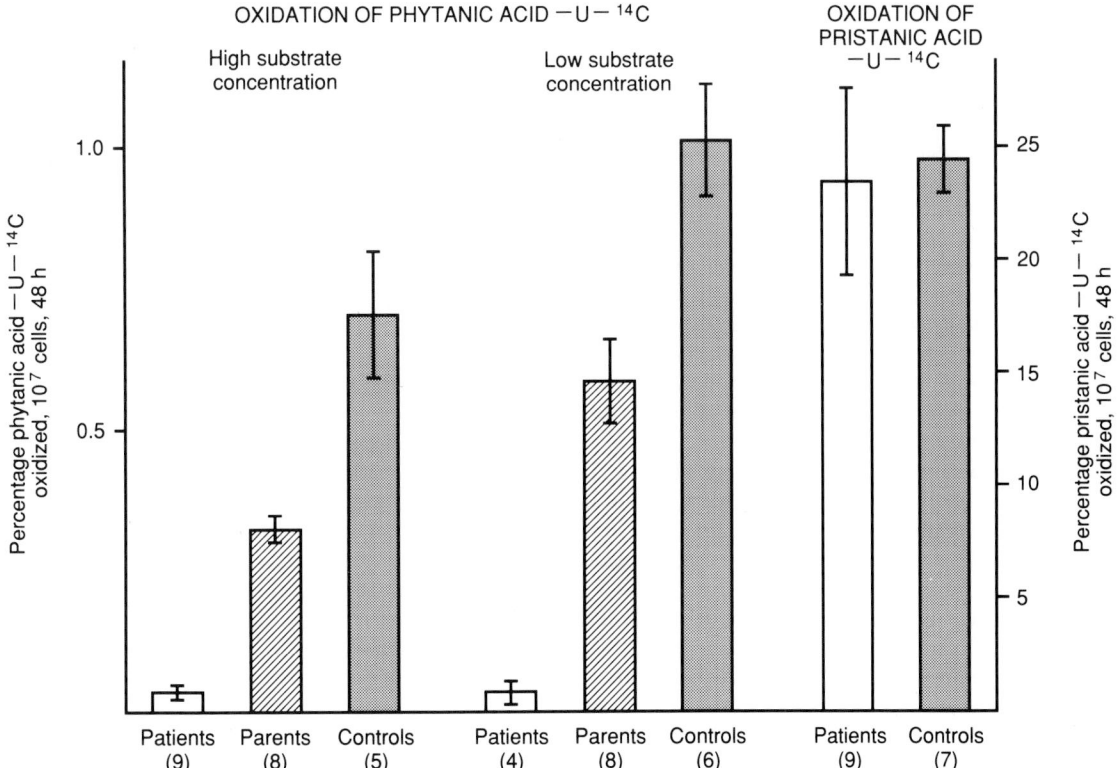

GENETICS

The observed inheritance pattern in Refsum disease is that expected for autosomal recessive transmission. The classic criteria appear to be well-satisfied, viz., (1) parents of patients and children of patients are clinically unaffected, (2) the prevalence of consanguinity between parents of affected children is high, (3) prevalence in males and females is approximately equal, and (4) the proportion of cases in affected sibships approximates the theoretical 25 percent. The demonstration of a partial defect in phytanic acid oxidation in cell cultures derived from presumed heterozygotes firmly established the recessive mode of inheritance.[61] Cultures derived from affected children were shown to oxidize phytanic acid at less than 3 percent of the rate seen in control cultures. Cultures from the parents, on the other hand, oxidized phytanic acid at 46 to 59 percent of the normal rate. There was no overlap between results in controls and results in the presumed heterozygotes when oxidation was measured at a high concentration of substrate (Fig. 59-6). None of the parents had clinically manifested neurologic disease, but one had been reported to have some elevation of phytanic acid in plasma. This exceptional case was chosen for study particularly in view of the report of phytanic acid accumulation.

Serum phytanic acid analyses have been reported in about 20 obligate heterozygotes. None showed clinical stigmata of Refsum disease, and, with three exceptions, phytanic acid levels were within normal limits. Thus, it appears that one-half the normal capacity for oxidation of phytanic acid is ordinarily adequate to prevent significant accumulation on ordinary diets. One of the exceptional parents was the mother of patient E.H., who was originally reported by Kahlke and Richterich[62] to have a phytanate level as high as that of her affected son. A serum sample obtained from this same patient in 1967 showed only the usual normal trace levels of phytanate (Herndon and Steinberg, unpublished results). Unless the single analysis originally reported represents analytical error, one has to conclude that this presumed heterozygote accumulated phytanic acid transiently. The second exception is the mother of patients E.S. and J.S., reported by Nevin et al. in 1967.[63] Her plasma phytanate accounted for 2.6 percent of total fatty acids. The fact that she was herself symptom-free seems to rule against her being homozygous. The cell culture results classify her as a heterozygote rather unambiguously. Gibberd et al.[123] reported a phytanate level of 4 mg/dl in the asymptomatic mother of a bona fide case. With a 50 percent reduction in capacity to oxidize phytanate, it is conceivable that under some conditions (e.g., changes in diet or alterations in the expression of the enzyme defect) heterozygotes may accumulate phytanate. There are no recorded examples of established heterozygotes with clinical disease.

The number of confirmed cases reported totals about 100. Since the syndrome is now well recognized by neurologists, it seems unlikely that very many bona fide cases are going unrecognized and unreported. It can be concluded that the gene frequency is very low.

For purposes of genetic counseling, especially helpful in the case of clinically unaffected individuals in affected sibships, the carrier state can be diagnosed using the fibroblast cell culture method. It may be possible to design a simpler and more direct clinical "loading" test. A preliminary report suggests that plasma phytanate levels in a heterozygote may reach higher levels after ingestion of 10 g phytol than are reached in a control subject, but more extensive studies are needed to establish the usefulness of such a test.[124] The cell culture method is becoming increasingly accessible. Normal amniotic cells have been shown to have the capacity to oxidize phytanic acid,[95,125] and so it should be possible to make a diagnosis of the homozygous or heterozygous state ante partum. Poulos et al.[95] have shown that cultured amniocytes and cultured chorionic villus cells can also be used to make a prenatal diagnosis of Zellweger syndrome and of infantile Refsum disease.

The biochemical evidence available is compatible with the postulate of a single mutation leading to the loss of a functional phytanic acid hydroxylase (Fig. 59-2). It is possible that the primary defect might lie in a system necessary for phytanic acid hydroxylation (e.g., a cofactor regenerating system), but not in the phytanic acid α-hydroxylase itself. Defective phytanate oxidation due to generation of a metabolic inhibitor has been tested by hybridizing a fibroblast line from a patient with a normal cell line (D 98); the cloned hybrid cells oxidized added [^{14}C]phytanate at a rate equal to or greater than that of the normal parent line (D. Hutton and D. Steinberg, unpublished observations). The possibility of multiple gene defects is always difficult to rule out, but thus far no biochemical errors have been established beyond the defect in phytanic acid α oxidation.

As discussed above, the defect in phytanic acid oxidation in fibroblasts from patients with peroxisomal disorders can be fully as great as it is in fibroblasts from patients with Refsum disease. However, in these disease states many more metabolic abnormalities are present in addition to the defect in phytanic acid oxidation. It is possible that the latter is secondary to the loss of peroxisomal functions but the possibility that some interaction between peroxisomal and mitochondrial function is necessary for optimal phytanic acid oxidation cannot be ruled out.

PATHOGENESIS

While much insight has been gained into the biochemical basis for phytanic acid accumulation, it remains to be established how the accumulation of phytanic acid leads to the clinical manifestations of the disease. Indeed, it is not firmly established whether or not phytanic acid accumulation per se is the necessary and sufficient basis for *all* of the clinical signs and symptoms of Refsum disease.

Molecular Distortion Hypothesis

The simplest hypothesis is that the incorporation of the multiple-branched, "thorny" phytanic acid molecule into tissue lipids in place of the normal straight-chain fatty acids interferes with myelin function or at least increases its susceptibility to damage.[23] The cross-sectional area of the phytanic acid molecule is at least 50 percent greater than that of the straight-chain fatty acids,[126] and the binding forces at close range would be considerably less than those of straight-chain fatty acids. Thus, in highly ordered structures like that of myelin or membrane lipids generally, the displacement of straight-chain acids by phytanic acid might in itself lay the basis for evolution of the clinical disease. If this were the case, then elimination of phytanic acid and its precursors from the diet should prevent the development of lesions in very young patients and arrest the progress or even lead to some reversal of symptoms in older patients. As discussed in the next section in more detail, this appears to be the case.

Attempts to produce the disease in animals by feeding large amounts of phytanic acid or its precursors have yielded negative results.[12–14,16,19,20,118] In the five species studied (rat, rabbit, chinchilla, mouse, and polecat), it has been possible to increase the phytanic acid levels in serum and in most tissues to values similar to those reported in postmortem tissues of patients with phytanic acid storage disease. The levels reached in nerve and brain, however, have been low relative to those reported in the human disease. Consequently, the negative experimental results do not militate strongly against the hypothesis that phytanic acid storage in the nervous system is pathogenetic. Higher levels could not be attained because increasing the levels of intake still further caused serious toxic effects, including the arrest of growth and the death of the test animals. The mechanism of this marked toxicity of phytol or phytanic acid remains unknown. The administration of large doses of fat-soluble vitamins and polyunsaturated fats afforded no protection (see Ref. 17 and unpublished results).

Dubois-Dalcq et al.[127,128] observed degenerative changes in explant cultures of mouse spinal ganglia exposed for several weeks to phytanic acid (60 to 100 mg/liter) complexed to albumin. There were similar changes, although less intense and slower to develop, in cultures exposed to equimolar concentrations of palmitic acid. Because phytanic acid binds less tightly to albumin than palmitic acid,[129] the concentration of unbound phytanate was probably somewhat higher than that of palmitate. Thus, the observed changes may represent general responses to long-chain fatty acids rather than any specific response to phytanic acid per se.

Antimetabolite Hypothesis

The close structural similarity between phytanic acid and the isoprenoid side chains of the fat-soluble vitamins, particularly vitamins E and K, led to the suggestion that phytanic acid might be toxic by interfering with the function of these fat-soluble vitamins. However, the arrest in the growth of rats or mice fed large doses of phytanate was not prevented by the simultaneous administration of large doses of fat-soluble vitamins. These negative results do not completely rule out the hypothesis. Phytanic acid might be competing successfully, even noncompetitively, at the site of vitamin function. One reason this hypothesis has received attention follows from the resemblance between some of the clinical features of abetalipoproteinemia (in which fat-soluble vitamin transport may be deficient) and the clinical features of phytanic acid storage disease. Other possibilities, such as interference with the function of coenzyme Q or other polyisoprenoid compounds can be mentioned speculatively, but no relevant data are as yet available.

Another hypothesis, not strictly in this "antimetabolite" category, is that advanced by Laurell.[66] He noted the low levels of linoleate in the patients' glycerides and speculated that there may be an induced relative linoleate deficiency. Displacement of linoleate and arachidonate has been noted in the phospholipids of liver, kidney, heart, and skin.[130,131] Since ichthyosis is also seen in essential fatty acid deficiency, it was suggested that phytanate might be pathogenetic in a related fashion.[131] It has also been proposed that the high concentrations of phytanate in skin, some of it in cholesterol esters, may induce ichthyosis by reducing the amount of free cholesterol available.[132]

"Double-Function" Hypothesis

It could be proposed that the α-oxidation system necessary for the metabolism of phytanic acid (and deleted in patients) plays a physiologically important role in one or more additional biochemical pathways. One specific hypothesis along these lines relates to the possibility of a generalized deficiency in α hydroxylation. α Hydroxylation of fatty acids in animals has been observed only in nerve tissue (as discussed under "α Oxidation," above). Thus, a deficiency in this system might understandably manifest itself primarily in nervous system disease. Studies on the properties of the phytanic acid–oxidizing system show clearly that it is distinct from the long-chain, straight-chain fatty acid α-oxidation system. Moreover, analyses of postmortem tissues failed to show any abnormality in concentration or composition of the straight-chain α-hydroxy fatty acids in brain or nerve.[133,134] Analysis of skin biopsies in two cases showed an α-hydroxy fatty acid concentration at the lower limits of normal and with a normal distribution.[135] Finally, rats fed a phytanic acid–rich diet have shown no abnormality in α-hydroxy fatty acid concentration or composition in brain. Thus, there is no evidence that patients with phytanic acid storage disease have any difficulty in making α-hydroxy acids in the straight-chain fatty acid series.

Multiple Gene Defects

Thus far there is no evidence of a consistent defect in any other biochemical pathway. The karyotype, when reported, has been normal. Nevertheless, the possibility of still undiscovered biochemical defects always remains open. One can ask whether the clinical features reported are all reasonably attributed to nerve damage or in some other way to phytanic acid accumulation. Certainly most of the clinical features are readily attributed to nerve damage, but not all. The electrocardiographic abnormalities may be caused by damage to the conduction system, but there are reports also of myocardial fibrosis. Patients have been reported to have shortening of the metacarpal and metatarsal bones, pes cavus, epiphyseal dysplasia, and ichthyosis. These are not readily attributable to nerve damage. They may be due to incorporation of phytanic acid into and distortion of the membranes of other cells.

TREATMENT

If the conclusion drawn from biochemical and clinical studies is correct—that the stored phytanate is exclusively of exogenous origin—then elimination of phytanate and its precursors from the diet should prevent further accumulation. To the extent that the patients retain some capacity to degrade phytanate (or excrete it unchanged), it should be possible to deplete body stores. In fact, reduction of plasma phytanate levels by dietary treatment has now been reported in at least 23 cases.[23,41,42,72,114,115,123,136–144,147,148,154] The fall can be quite dramatic, e.g., from 174 to 13.5 mg/dl in one case[140] and in another case, with plasma exchange in addition to diet, from

145 to 13 mg/dl.[154] In a few cases normal levels have been achieved, but in most the plasma level plateaus at about 10 to 30 mg/dl. As long as phytanic acid intake is kept at a suitably low level the plasma concentration stays down although there can be a temporary partial "escape," particularly if there is weight loss, as discussed below.

The response in plasma levels may be delayed for months after initiating the diet. This suggests that tissue stores are mobilized when intake is reduced. Adipose tissue biopsies taken before and after diet treatment show that this storage site shows the expected fall in concentration.[31]

Evaluation of plasma phytanate levels is more complex than in the case of water-soluble compounds such as galactose. Almost all of the phytanate is present in the phospholipids and triglycerides of the plasma lipoproteins. The lipoproteins are synthesized and secreted primarily by the liver (very low density and high density lipoproteins) and to a lesser extent by the intestine. Precursors for the fatty acids in the lipoproteins include not only fatty acids synthesized de novo but also free fatty acids mobilized from adipose tissue and fatty acids stored in liver phospholipids and triglyceride. Phytanate can account for as much as 50 percent of the fatty acids in liver lipids, i.e., a higher concentration than that found in plasma. Thus, if liver lipids are mobilized, the percentage of phytanate in plasma will tend to rise and may do so quite rapidly. In adipose tissue the percentage of phytanate is relatively low (1 to 5 percent of total fatty acids). Thus, if adipose tissue lipids are rapidly mobilized, the percentage of phytanate in plasma may not increase immediately and may even fall while the absolute concentration rises (especially if the patient develops significant hyperlipidemia). However, the normal straight-chain fatty acids can go on to be oxidized while the phytanate, because of the metabolic block, will tend to accumulate and increase in both absolute and relative concentration. For these reasons it is best to follow responses to diet both in terms of absolute phytanate levels (milligrams per deciliter) and in terms of relative phytanate content (percentage of total fatty acids).

A potential hazard of dietary treatment arises if the patient, in attempting to adapt to a new and rigorous diet, reduces his or her calorie intake and begins to lose weight. In several cases this has been associated with a paradoxical rise in plasma phytante levels and an accompanying clinical relapse, which at times has been quite drastic.[72,123,138,140,142] While not proved, this may well be explained by the mobilization of phytanate from lipids stored in the liver and in the adipose tissue, as discussed above.

The total mass of phytanate stored in adipose tissue is enormous, even though phytanate accounts for only 5 percent or less of adipose tissue fatty acids. In one patient in whom total-tissue analyses were carried out, 286 out of 381 g stored phytanic acid was found in adipose tissue.[130] To put this in perspective, consider that the average daily intake of phytanate in the diet is less than 100 mg/day. Thus, 286 g phytanic acid corresponds to over 7 years of daily dietary phytanic acid intake! Turning the proposition around, phytanic acid accounts for only approximately 0.1 percent of the fatty acids taken in daily (100 mg or less phytanic acid versus a total daily fat intake of approximately 100 g). Thus, the phytanic acid in the adipose tissue stores is present at a concentration 10 to 50 times that in the diet. Thus, mobilization of stored depot fat provides an "input" 10 to 50 times that provided by the usual diet on a gram-for-gram basis.

Several reports of relapses in patients experiencing weight loss not associated with an intercurrent illness suggest a possible reinterpretation of the relapses reported in patients experiencing various stresses such as surgery, pregnancy, viral infections, or other intercurrent illnesses. Is it possible that the common denominator in all of these instances is the loss of weight and the mobilization of depot fat? One case report in particular is strongly suggestive.[145] This patient experienced a progressive and rapid neurologic deterioration associated with marked weight loss following the development of hyperthyroidism together with diabetes mellitus. However, it is equally likely that neural function is adversely affected during intercurrent illnesses by additional mechanisms not directly related to weight loss and the accompanying increases in plasma phytanic acid. Patients with other neurologic syndromes, such as Friedreich ataxia, have also been noted to suffer relapses associated with intercurrent illnesses. The pathophysiologic basis remains unclear. At any rate, the association between weight loss and relapse in patients with phytanic acid storage disease is strong enough that rapid weight loss at any time should be avoided in patients with the established disease state.

Dietary Prescription

Management consists in eliminating from the diet as rigorously as possible all sources of phytanic acid. Unfortunately, data are not yet available on all foodstuffs. Dairy products of all kinds, ruminant fats, and ruminant meats are the major sources, and these must be absolutely proscribed. Green vegetables were originally excluded from the diet because of the possibility that the phytol in chlorophyll might be absorbed and converted to phytanate.[31] However, chlorophyll phytol is very poorly absorbed,[81] and the exclusion of green vegetables may be unnecessary (although cooking may release some bound phytol). In any case phytol is relatively unimportant compared to phytanic acid itself as a dietary component. Some values for phytanate content of foods are presented in Table 59-2, and more information on dietary management is available in several publications.[23,31,72,73,115,123,141,146] The papers by Masters-Thomas and coworkers[72,73] are particularly helpful in providing data on the phytanic acid content of many ordinary foodstuffs and suggesting a practical dietary regimen to maintain phytanic acid intake at less than 10 mg daily.

The magnitude and rate of fall in plasma phytanate levels depend on the rigor with which sources of phytanic acid are eliminated from the diet. Reducing intake from that in the usual diet—about 60 mg/day—to 21 mg/day caused less of a response and a slower response than was obtained on a drastically modified diet (mostly liquid formula) that contained less than 3 mg/day.[31,114] Because phytanic acid is widely distributed (Table 59-2), it is difficult to reduce intake much below 10 to 20 mg/day using generally available foods. A regimen of a liquid formula as a major source of calories—supplemented with solid foods poor in phytanate—may be the best approach.

Periodic plasmapheresis or plasma exchange has been used in several clinics to reduce body stores[123,138,141,147,148,154] of phytanate and, combined with dietary management, has helped keep plasma levels low. A lifetime program of such treatment may be unreasonably burdensome, but repeated plasmapheresis or plasma exchange during the early stages of

Table 59-2 Examples of Phytanic Acid Content of Foodstuffs

Food	Phytanate content in mg/100 g wet weight
Butter	5–500
Tunafish, canned in oil	57
Lamb, cooked, minced	49
Cheeses	5–50
Beef, stewed	24
Cod, grilled	4.2
Haddock, steamed	2.6
White bread	1.6
Cornflakes	1.2
White rice, boiled	1.0
Potato, boiled	0.66
Egg yolk	0.22

NOTE: The values given represent in many cases analyses of only a single sample and should not be generalized. The wide variations in phytanate content of dairy products in part reflect seasonal differences in cattle feeding practices or differences in total fat content (cheeses). SOURCE: Data from Refs. 25, 71–73, 146.

management appears to be a rational way to obtain a good initial response. It cannot be regarded as a substitute for dietary management, only as a supplement.

Response to Diet

In those patients responding with a good fall in plasma phytanate levels, there has been an arrest in the progress of the peripheral neuropathy and objectively documented regression. Improvement in nerve conduction velocity has been demonstrated in nine cases,[31,114,115,138,139,141,143] with return to normal in some. In some instances unobtainable nerve response has given way to velocities above 25 to 30 m/s, and previously unobtainable reflexes have been restored. Lenz et al.[148] examined sural nerve biopsies before and after about two years of dietary treatment. They noted that demyelination had stopped and that there was considerable remyelination and regeneration.

Muscle strength and gait have improved, and sensory deficits have receded. Ichthyotic changes can regress early after start of treatment. It may be particularly significant that the nonspecific electrocardiographic abnormalities have been corrected in some cases. Indeed, in the patients maintaining low plasma phytanate there have been no relapses; some of them have now been under treatment for 5 to 15 years.[149–152] One of the patients (T.E.) started on diet therapy in Oslo in the mid-1960s, responded well to diet initially[30] but died of a cerebral hemorrhage 5 years later; the second Oslo patient (K.M.) continues to thrive 34 years after his disease was first noted.[149] The sister (K.S.) of the siblings treated at the National Institutes of Health in the 1960s[23,114] died in 1981, apparently of renal failure. No other deaths have been reported. This should be interpreted in the context of the experience prior to the initiation of diet therapy, when one-half of the untreated patients died before age 30 according to Hansen and Refsum.[150]

No convincing regression has been noted in auditory or visual deficits, but two reports suggest that at least there may not be further progression.[149,153]

The now much expanded experience with diet treatment supports the conclusion that exogenously derived phytanic acid is the source of the storage lipid in this disease and that it is pathogenetic, directly or indirectly. It is reasonable to expect that any therapeutic benefits will be more significant if treatment is initiated early. Once demyelination is extensive, restoration of function is unlikely even if progression is arrested. Every effort should be made to establish the diagnosis at an early age and institute treatment.

REFERENCES

1. REFSUM S: Heredopathia atactica polyneuritiformis. *Acta Psychiatr Scand (Suppl)* 38:9, 1946.
2. KLENK E, KAHLKE W: Über das Vorkommen der 3,7,11,15-Tetramethyl-hexadecansaure (Phytansäure) in den Cholesterinestern und anderen Lipoidfraktionen der Organe bei einem Krankheitsfall unbekannter Genese (Verdacht auf Heredopathia atactica polyneuritiformis, Refsum's syndrom). *Hoppe-Seyler's Z Physiol Chem* 333:133, 1963.
3. RICHTERICH R, VAN MECHELEN P, ROSSI E: Refsum's disease (heredopathia atactica polyneuritiformis): An inborn error of lipid metabolism with storage of 3,7,11,15-tetramethylhexadecanoic acid. *Am J Med* 39:230, 1963.
4. KAHLKE W: Refsum-Syndrome—Lipoidchemische Untersuchungen bei 9 Fallen. *Klin Wochenschr* 42:1011, 1964.
5. AVIGAN J: The presence of phytanic acid in normal human and animal plasma. *Biochim Biophys Acta* 116:391, 1966.
6. KREMER GJ: Über das Vorkommen der 3,7,11,15-Tetramethylhexadecansäure in den Lipoiden von Normalseren. *Klin Wochenschr* 43:517, 1965.
7. STEINBERG D: Remarks on the biochemical basis of Refsum's disease. *Nord Med* 73:570, 1965.
8. ELDJARN L: Biokjemiske synspunkter på phytansyrens opprinnelse. *Nord Med* 73:569, 1965.
9. STEINBERG D, AVIGAN J, MIZE C, ELDJARN L, TRY K, REFSUM S: Conversion of U-C14-phytol to phytanic acid and its oxidation in heredopathic atactica polyneuritiformis. *Biochem Biophys Res Commun* 19:783, 1965.
10. STEINBERG D, MIZE CE, AVIGAN J, FALES HM, ELDJARN K, STOKKE O, REFSUM S: Studies on the metabolic error in Refsum's disease. *J Clin Invest* 45:1076, 1966; 46:313, 1967.
11. MIZE CE, AVIGAN J, BAXTER JH, FALES HM, STEINBERG D: Metabolism of phytol-U-14C and phytanic acid-U-14C in the rat. *J Lipid Res* 7:692, 1966.
12. STEINBERG D, AVIGAN J, MIZE C, BAXTER JH: Phytanic acid formation and accumulation in phytol-fed rats. *Fed Proc* 24:290, 1965.
13. STEINBERG D, AVIGAN J, MIZE C, BAXTER J: Phytanic acid formation and accumulation in phytol-fed rats. *Biochem Biophys Res Commun* 19:412, 1965.
14. KLENK E, KREMER GJ: Untersuchungen zum Stoffwechsel des Phytols, Dihydrophytols, und der Phytansäure. *Hoppe-Seyler's Z Physiol Chem* 343:39, 1965.
15. STOFFEL W, KAHLKE W: The transformation of phytol into 3,7,11,15-tetramethylhexadecanoic (phytanic) acid in heredopathia atactica polyneuritiformis (Refsum's syndrome). *Biochem Biophys Res Commun* 19:33, 1965.
16. HANSEN RP, SHORLAND FB, PRIOR IAM: The fate of phytanic acid when administered to rats. *Biochim Biophys Acta* 116:178, 1966.
17. STEINBERG D, AVIGAN J, MIZE CE, BAXTER JH, CAMMERMEYER J, FALES HM, HIGHET PF: Effects of dietary phytol and phytanic acid in animals. *J Lipid Res* 7:684, 1966.
18. AVIGAN J, STEINBERG D, GUTMAN A, MIZE CE, MILNE GWA: Alpha-decarboxylation, an important pathway for degradation of phytanic acid in animals. *Biochem Biophys Res Commun* 24:838, 1966.
19. MIZE CG, STEINBERG D, AVIGAN J, FALES HM: A pathway for oxidative degradation of phytanic acid in mammals. *Biochem Biophys Res Commun* 25:359, 1966.
20. MIZE CE, AVIGAN J, STEINBERG D, PITTMAN RC, FALES HM, MILNE GWA: A major pathway for the mammalian oxidative degradation of phytanic acid. *Biochim Biophys Acta* 176:720, 1969.
21. TSAI S-C, HERNDON JH Jr, UHLENDORF BW, FALES HM, MIZE CE: The formation of alpha-hydroxyphytanic acid from phytanic acid in mammalian tissues. *Biochim Biophys Res Commun* 28:571, 1967.
22. TSAI S-C, AVIGAN J, STEINBERG D: Studies on the alpha-oxidation of phytanic acid by rat liver mitochondria. *J Biol Chem* 244:2682, 1969.
23. STEINBERG D, VROOM FQ, ENGEL WK, CAMERMEYER J, MIZE CE, AVIGAN J: Refsum's disease—A recently characterized lipidosis involving the nervous system. *Ann Intern Med* 66:365, 1967.

24. MIZE CE, HERNDON JH Jr, BLASS JP, MILNE GWA, FOLLANSBEE C, LAUDAT P, STEINBERG D: Localization of the oxidative defect in phytanic acid degradation in patients with Refsum's disease. *J Clin Invest* 48:1033, 1969.

25. STEINBERG D, HERNDON JH Jr, UHLENDORF BW, MIZE CE, AVIGAN J, MILNE GWA: Refsum's disease: Nature of the enzyme defect. *Science* 156:1740, 1967.

26. STEINBERG D, AVIGAN J, MIZE CE, HERNDON JH Jr, FALES HM, MILNE GWA: The nature of the metabolic defect in Refsum's disease. *Pathol Eur* 3:450, 1968.

27. HERNDON JH Jr, STEINBERG D, UHLENDORF BW, FALES HM: Refsum's disease: Characterization of the enzyme defect in cell culture. *J Clin Invest* 48:1017, 1969.

28. ELDJARN L, STOKKE O, TRY K: Alpha-oxidation of branched-chain fatty acids in man and its failure in patients with Refsum's disease showing phytanic acid accumulation. *Scand J Clin Lab Invest* 18:694, 1966.

29. STOKKE O, TRY K, ELDJARN L: Alpha-oxidation as an alternative pathway for the degradation of branched-chain fatty acids in man, and its failure in patients with Refsum's disease. *Biochim Biophys Acta* 144:271, 1967.

30. ELDJARN L, TRY K, STOKKE O, MUNTHE-KAAS AW, REFSUM S, STEINBERG D, AVIGAN J, MIZE C: Dietary effects on serum-phytanic-acid levels and on clinical manifestations in heredopathia atactica polyneuritiformis. *Lancet* 1:691, 1966.

31. STEINBERG D, MIZE CE, HERNDON JH Jr, FALES HM, ENGEL WK, VROOM FQ: Phytanic acid in patients with Refsum's syndrome and response to dietary treatment. *Arch Intern Med* 125:75, 1970.

32. REFSUM S, ELDJARN L: Heredopathia atactica polyneuritiformis—An inborn defect in the metabolism of branched-chain fatty acids, in Banner HG (ed): *Future of Neurology*. Stuttgart, Thieme, 1967, p 36.

33. KAHLKE W, GOERLICH R, FEIST D: Erhöhte Phytansäurespiegel in Plasma und Leber bei einem Kleinkind mit unclarem Hirnschaden. *Klin Wochenschr* 52:651, 1974.

34. TSAI S-C, STEINBERG D, AVIGAN J, FALES HM: Studies on the sterospecificity of mitochondrial oxidation of phytanic acid and of α-hydroxyphytanic acid. *J Biol Chem* 248:1091, 1973.

35. STOKKE O: The degradation of a branched chain fatty acid by alternations between α- and β-oxidations. *Biochim Biophys Acta* 176:54, 1969.

36. MURALIDHARAN VB, KISHIMOTO Y: Phytanic acid α-oxidation in rat liver: Requirement of cytosolic factor. *J Biol Chem* 259:13021, 1984.

37. SKJELDAL OH, STOKKE O: The subcellular localization of phytanic acid oxidase in rat liver. *Biochim Biophys Acta* 921:38, 1987.

38. GOLDFISCHER S, MOORE CL, JOHNSON AB, SPIRO AJ, VALSAMIS MP, WISNIEWSKI HK, RITCH RH, NORTON WT, RAPIN I, GARTNER LM: Peroxisomal and mitochondrial defects in the cerebro-hepato-renal syndrome. *Science* 182:62, 1973.

39. GOLDFISCHER S: Peroxisomes and human metabolic diseases: The cerebrohepatorenal syndrome (CHRS), cerebrotendinous xanthomatosis, and Schilder's disease (adrenoleukodystrophy). *Ann NY Acad Sci* 386:528, 1982.

40. STEINBERG D: Phytanic acid storage disease (Refsum's disease), in Stanbury JB, Wyngaarden JB, Fredrickson DS, Goldstein JL, Brown MS (eds): *The Metabolic Basis of Inherited Disease*, 5th ed. New York, McGraw-Hill, 1983, p 731.

41. REFSUM S: Heredopathia atactica polyneuritiformis (Refsum's disease), in Dyck PG, Thomas PK, Lambert EH, Bunge R (eds): *Peripheral Neuropathy*. Philadelphia, Saunders, 1984, vol II, chap 71.

42. STEINBERG D, HERNDON JH Jr: Refsum's disease: Phytanic acid storage disease, in Goldensohn ES, Appel SH (eds): *Scientific Approaches to Clinical Neurology*. Philadelphia, Lea and Febiger, 1977, p 994.

43. TRY K: Heredopathia atactica polyneuritiformis (Refsum's disease): The diagnostic value of phytanic acid determination in serum lipids. *Eur Neurol* 2:296, 1969.

44. CAMMERMEYER J: Neuropathological changes in hereditary neuropathies: Manifestation of the syndrome heredopathia atactica polyneuritiformis in the presence of interstitial hypertrophic polyneuropathy. *J Neuropathol Exp Neurol* 15:340, 1956.

45. HUTTON D, STEINBERG D: Localization of the enzymatic defect in phytanic acid storage disease (Refsum's disease). *Neurology (Minneap)* 23:1333, 1973.

46. SCOTTO JM, HADCHOUEL M, ODIEVRE M, LAUDAT M-H, SAUDUBRAY J-M, DULAC O, BEUCLER I, BEAUNE P: Infantile phytanic acid storage disease, a possible variant of Refsum's disease: Three cases, including ultrastructural studies of the liver. *J Inherited Metab Dis* 5:83, 1982.

47. POULOS A, POLLARD AC, MITCHELL JD, WISE G, MORTIMER G: Patterns of Refsum's disease: Phytanic acid oxidase deficiency. *Arch Dis Child* 59:222, 1984.

48. POULOS A, SHARP P, WHITING M: Infantile Refsum's disease (phytanic acid storage disease): A variant of Zellweger's syndrome? *Clin Gen* 26:579, 1984.

49. BUDDEN SS, KENNAWAY NG, BUIST NRM, POULOS A, WELEBER RG: Dysmorphic syndrome with phytanic acid oxidase deficiency, abnormal very long chain fatty acids, and pipecolic acidemia: Studies in four children. *J Pediatr* 108:33, 1986.

50. POULOS A, SINGH H, PATON B, SHARP P, DERWAS N: Accumulation and defective β-oxidation of very long chain fatty acids in Zellweger's syndrome, adrenoleukodystrophy and Refsum's disease variants. *Clin Gen* 29:397, 1986.

51. POLL-THE BT, SAUDUBRAY JM, OGIER H, SCHUTGENS RBH, WANDERS RJA, SCHRAKAMP G, van den BOSCH H, TRIJBELS JMF, POULOS A, MOSER HW, van ELDERE J, EYSSEN HJ: Infantile Refsum's disease: Biochemical findings suggesting multiple peroxisomal dysfunction. *J Inherited Metab Dis* 9:169, 1986.

52. OGIER H, ROELS F, CORNELIS A, POLL-THE BT, SCOTTO JM, ODIEVRE M, SAUDUBRAY JM: Absence of hepatic peroxisomes in a case of infantile Refsum's disease. *Scand J Clin Lab Invest* 45:767, 1985.

53. WANDERS RJA, SCHUTGENS RBH, SCHRAKAMP G, van den BOSCH H, TAGER JM, SCHRAM AW, HASHIMOTO T, POLL-THE BT, SAUDUBRAY JM: Infantile Refsum disease: Deficiency of catalase-containing particles (peroxisomes), alkyldihydroxy-acetone phosphate synthase and peroxisomal β-oxidation enzyme proteins. *Eur J Pediatr* 145:172, 1986.

54. BEARD ME, SAPIRSTEIN V, KOLODNY EH, HOLTZMAN E: Peroxisomes in fibroblasts from skin of Refsum's disease patients. *J Histochem Cytochem* 33:480, 1983.

55. KOLODNY EH, HASS WK, LANE B, DRUCKER WD: Refsum's syndrome: Report of a case including electron microscopic studies of the liver. *Arch Neurol* 12:583, 1965.

56. SHY GM, SILBERBERG DH, APPEL SH, MISHKIN MM, GODFREY EH: A generalized disorder of nervous system, skeletal muscle, and heart resembling Refsum's disease and Hurler's syndrome. *Am J Med* 42:163, 1967.

57. SOLCHER H: Über Hirnveränderungen bei Heredopathia atactica polyneuritiformis (Refsum). *Acta Neuropathol (Berl)* 24:92, 1973.

58. RON MA, PEARCE J: Refsum's syndrome with normal phytate metabolism. *Acta Neurol Scand* 47:646, 1971.

59. BRYNIARSKA D, GOLDSZTAJN M: A degenerative syndrome resembling Refsum's disease. *Neurol Neurochir Pol* 6:895, 1972.

60. KAYDEN HJ, REAGAN TJ, MIZE CE, HERNDON JH Jr, STEINBERG D: Diffuse cerebral sclerosis. *Arch Neurol* 28:304, 1973.

61. HERNDON JH, STEINBERG D, UHLENDORF BW: Refsum's disease: Defective oxidation of phytanic acid in tissue cultures derived from homozygotes and heterozygotes. *N Engl J Med* 281:1034, 1969.

62. KAHLKE W, RICHTERICH R: Refsum's disease (heredopathia atactica polyneuritiformis), an inborn error of lipid metabolism with storage of 3,7,11,15-tetramethyl hexadecanoic acid. II. Isolation and identification of the storage product. *Am J Med* 39:237, 1965.

63. NEVIN NC, CUMINGS JN, McKEOWN F: Refsum's syndrome heredopathia atactica polyneuritiformis. *Brain* 90:419, 1967.

64. PITTMAN R, STEINBERG D: Isolation and measurement of phytanic acid and related isoprenoid compounds by gas chromatography, in Olsen RE (ed): *Methods in Medical Research*. Chicago, Year Book Medical Publishers, 1970, vol 12, p 84.

65. KARLLSSON KA, NORRBY A, SAMUELSSON B: Use of thin-layer chromatography for the preliminary diagnosis of Refsum's disease (heredopathia atactica polyneuritiformis). *Biochim Biophys Acta* 144:162, 1967.

66. LAURELL S: Separation and characterization of phytanic acid-containing plasma triglycerides from a patient with Refsum's disease. *Biochim Biophys Acta* 152:75, 1968.

67. MOLZER B, BERNHEIMER H, BARLOLIN GS, HOFINGER E, LENZ H: Di-, mono- and nonphytanyl triglycerides in the serum: A sensitive parameter of the phytanic acid accumulation in Refsum's disease. *Clin Chim Acta* 91:133, 1979.

68. DULANEY JT, WILLIAMS M, EVANS JE, COSTELLO CE, KOLODNY EH: Occurrence of novel branched-chain fatty acids in Refsum's disease. *Biochim Biophys Acta* 529:1, 1978.

68a. EVANS JE, DULANEY JT: Location of double bonds in two unsaturated forms of phytanic acid from Refsum disease as determined by mass spectrometry. *Biochim Biophys Acta* 752:346, 1983.

69. BAXTER JH, STEINBERG D, MIZE CE, AVIGAN J: Absorption and metabolism of uniformly ^{14}C-labeled phytol and phytanic acid by the intestine of the rat studied with thoracic duct cannulation. *Biochim Biophys Acta* 137:277, 1967.

70. ACKMAN RG, HANEN RP: The occurrence of diastereoisomers of phytanic and pristanic acids and their determination by gas-liquid chromatography. *Lipids* 2:357, 1967.

71. GOERLICH R: Phytol und Phytansäure in Nahrungstoffen. Ihre Bedeutung bei der Refsum-Krankheit. Doctoral dissertation. Ruprecht Karl Universität, Heidelberg, 1974.

72. MASTERS-THOMAS A, BAILES J, BILLIMORIA JD, CLEMENS ME, GIBBERD FB,

PAGE NGR: Heredopathia atactica polyneuritiformis (Refsum's disease). 1. Clinical features and dietary management. *J Hum Nutr* 34:245, 1980.

73. MASTERS-THOMAS A, BAILES J, BILLIMORIA JD, CLEMENS ME, GIBBERD FB, PAGE NGR: Heredopathia atactica polyneuritiformis (Refsum's disease). 2. Estimation of phytanic acid in foods. *J Hum Nutr* 34:251, 1980.

74. PATTON S, BENSON AA: Phytol metabolism in the bovine. *Biochim Biophys Acta* 125:22, 1966.

75. PRIOR IAM, ALEXANDER WE, STEINBERG D, MIZE CE, HERNDON JH Jr: Unpublished results.

76. MURALIDHARAN FN, MURALIDHARAN VB: In vitro conversion of phytol to phytanic acid in rat liver: Subcellular distribution of activity and chemical characterization of intermediates using a new bromination technique. *Biochim Biophys Acta* 835:36, 1985.

77. BAXTER JH, MILNE GWA: Phytanic acid: Identification of five isomers in chemical and biological products of phytol. *Biochim Biophys Acta* 176:265, 1969.

78. ELDJARN L, TRY K: Different ratios of the LDD and DDD diastereoisomers of phytanic acid in patients with Refsum's disease. *Biochim Biophys Acta* 164:94, 1968.

79. LOUGH AK: The stereochemistry of phytanic acid in Refsum's syndrome. *Lipids* 5:201, 1969.

80. BAXTER JH, STEINBERG D: Absorption of phytol from dietary chlorophyll in the rat. *J Lipid Res* 8:615, 1967.

81. BAXTER JH: Absorption of chlorophyll phytol in normal man and in patients with Refsum's disease. *J Lipid Res* 9:636, 1968.

82. BILLETER M, BOLLIGER W, MARITIUS C: Untersuchungen über die Umwandlung von verfutterten K-Vitaminen durch Austausch der Seitenkette und die Rolle der Darmbakterien hierbei. *Biochem Z* 340:290, 1964.

83. VELICK SK, ANDERSON RJ: The chemistry of phytomonas tumefaciens. III. Phytomonic acid, a new branched-chain fatty acid. *J Biol Chem* 152:523, 1944.

84. KATES M, YENGOYAN LW, SASTRY PS: A diether analog of phosphatidyl glycerophosphate in *Halobacterium cutirubrum*. *Biochim Biophys Acta* 98:252, 1965.

85. ELDJARN L, TRY K, STOKKE O: The existence of an alternative pathway for the degradation of branched-chain fatty acids, and its failure in heredopathia atactica polyneuritiformis (Refsum's disease). *Biochim Biophys Acta* 116:395, 1966.

86. STOKKE O, TRY K, ELDJARN L: α-Oxidation as an alternative pathway for the degradation of branched-chain fatty acids in man, and its failure in patients with Refsum's disease. *Biochim Biophys Acta* 144:271, 1967.

87. TRY K: Indications of only a partial defect in the alpha-oxidation mechanism in Refsum's disease. *Scand J Clin Lab Invest* 20:255, 1967.

88. POULOS A: Diagnosis of Refsum's disease using [1-^{14}C]phytanic acid as substrate. *Clin Gen* 20:247, 1981.

89. SKJELDAL OH, STOKKE O, NORSETH J, LIE SO: Phytanic acid oxidase activity in cultured skin fibroblasts. Diagnostic usefulness and limitations. *Scand J Clin Lab Invest* 46:283, 1986.

90. SKJELDAL OH, STOKKE O, REFSUM S, NORSETH J, PETIT H: Clinical and biochemical heterogeneity in conditions with phytanic acid accumulation. *J Neurol Sci* 77:87, 1987.

91. LAURELL S: The action of lipoprotein lipase on glyceryl triphytanate. *Biochim Biophys Acta* 152:80, 1968.

92. LAUDAT P, WOLF L-M: Repartition des esters phytaniques parmi les triglycerides plasmatiques de cinq patients atteints de maladie de Refsum: Étude par chromatographie en couche mince. *Biochim Biophys Acta* 176:245, 1969.

93. AVIGAN J, STEINBERG D: Unpublished results.

94. ELLINGBOE J, STEINBERG D: Differential susceptibility of phytanyl and palmityl ester bonds to enzymatic hydrolysis. *Biochim Biophys Acta* 270:92, 1972.

95. POULOS A, van CRUGTEN C, SHARP P, CAREY WF, ROBERTSON E, BECROFT DMO, SAUDUBRAY JM, POLL-THE BT, CHRISTENSEN E, BRANDT N: Prenatal diagnosis of Zellweger syndrome and related disorders: Impaired degradation of phytanic acid. *Eur J Pediatr* 145:507, 1986.

96. BOWEN DM, RADIN NS: Hydroxy fatty acid metabolism in brain. *Adv Lipid Res* 6:255, 1968.

97. SHORLAND FB, HANSEN RP, PRIOR IAM: The effect of phytanic acid on the fatty acid composition of the lipids of the rat with further observations on its metabolism, in *Proceedings of the Seventh International Congress of Nutrition*. West Germany, Verlag Friedr Vieweg & Sohn, 1966, vol V, p 399.

98. HANSEN RP, SHORLAND FB, PRIOR IAM: The occurrence of 4,8,12-trimethyltridecanoic acid in the tissues of rats fed high levels of phytanic acid. *Biochim Biophys Acta* 152:642, 1968.

99. HANSEN RP, MORRISON JD: The isolation and identification of 2,6,10,14-tetramethylpentadecanoic acid from butter fat. *Biochem J* 93:225, 1964.

100. HANSEN RP: Occurrence of 2,6,10,14-tetramethylpentadecanoic acid in sheep fat. *Chem Ind* 1964, p 1258.

101. LEVIS GM, MEAD JF: An α-hydroxy acid decarboxylase in brain microsomes. *J Biol Chem* 239:77, 1964.

102. DAVIES WE, HAJRA AK, PARMAR SS, RADIN NS, MEAD JF: Decarboxylation of 2-keto fatty acids by brain. *J Lipid Res* 7:270, 1966.

103. HUTTON D, STEINBERG D: Identification of propionate as a degradation production of phytanic acid oxidation in rat and human tissues. *J Biol Chem* 248:6871, 1973.

104. STEINBERG D, HUTTON D: Phytanic acid storage disease, in Volk BW, Aronson SM (eds): *Sphingolipids, Sphingolipidoses, and Allied Disorders*. New York, Plenum, 1972, p 515.

105. BERGSTROM S, BORGSTROM B, TRYDING N, WESTOO G: Intestinal absorption and metabolism of 2,2-dimethylstearic acid in the rat. *Biochem J* 58:604, 1954.

106. ANTHONY GJ, LANDAU BR: Relative contributions of alpha, beta, and omega-oxidative pathways to in vitro fatty acid oxidation in rat liver. *J Lipid Res* 9:267, 1968.

107. TRY K: The in vitro omega-oxidation of phytanic acid and other branched chain fatty acids by mammalian liver. *Scand J Clin Lab Invest* 22:224, 1968.

108. PETTERSEN JE, STOKKE O: Branched short-chain dicarboxylic acids in human urine. *Biochim Biophys Acta* 304:316, 1973.

109. BRENTON DP, DURAN M, GALE A, KRYWAWYCH S, STERN GM, WADMAN SK: Refsum's disease—Excretion of 3-methyladipate. *Proc Int Symp on IEM in Humans*, Switzerland, 1980, p 11.

110. BRENTON DP, KRYWAWYCH S: 3-Methyladipate excretion in Refsum's disease. *Lancet* 1:624, 1982.

111. BILLIMORIA JD, GIBBERD FB, CLEMENS ME, WHITELAW MN: Metabolism of phytanic acid in Refsum's disease. *Lancet* 1:194, 1982.

112. GRETER J, LINDSTEDT S, STEEN G: 2,6-Dimethyloctanedioic acid—A metabolite of phytanic acid in Refsum's disease. *Clin Chem* 29:434, 1983.

113. STOKKE O, REFSUM S: Refsum's disease and metabolism of phytanic acid. *Lancet* 1:906, 1982.

114. KARK RAP, ENGEL WK, BLASS JP, STEINBERG D, WALSH GO: Heredopathia atactica polyneuritiformis (Refsum's disease): A second trial of dietary therapy in two patients, in *Nervous System, Birth Defects*. New York, The National Foundation, 1971, vol VII, no 1, p 53.

115. LAUDAT PH: Intolerance au phytol: Maladie de Refsum. *Biochimie* 54:735, 1972.

116. KRYWAWYCH S, BRENTON DP, JACKSON MJ, FORTE C, WALKER DK: 3-Methyladipate excretion in animals fed a phytol supplement with reference to Refsum's disease. *J Inherited Metab Dis* 8:147, 1985.

117. SEUBERT W, REMBERGER U: Untersuchungen über den bakteriellen Abbau von Isoprenoiden. II. Die Rolle der Kohlensäure. *Biochem Z* 338:245, 1963.

118. STOKKE O: Alpha-oxidation of fatty acids in various mammals, and a phytanic acid feeding experiment in an animal with a low alpha-oxidation capacity. *Scand J Clin Lab Invest* 20:305, 1967.

119. STOKKE O: Evidence against a CO_2-fixation mechanism in the degradation of a beta-methyl substituted fatty acid in mammals. *Biochim Biophys Acta* 176:230, 1969.

120. ELDJARN L: Heredopathia atactica polyneuritiformis (Refsum's disease)—A defect in the omega-oxidation mechanism of fatty acids. *Scand J Clin Lab Invest* 17:178, 1965.

121. ELDJARN L, TRY K, STOKKE O: The ability of patients with heredopathia atactica polyneuritiformis to omega-oxidize and degrade several isoprenoid branch-chained fatty structures. *Scand J Clin Lab Invest* 18:141, 1966.

122. TRY K, ELDJARN L: Normalization of the tricaprin test for omega-oxidation in Refsum's disease upon lowering of serum phytanic acid. *Scand J Clin Lab Invest* 20:294, 1967.

123. GIBBERD FB, BILLIMORIA JD, PAGE NGR, RETSAS S: Heredopathia atactica polyneuritiformis (Refsum's disease) treated by diet and plasma-exchange. *Lancet* 1d:575, 1979.

124. GAUTIER JC, LAUDAT PH, ROSA A, GRAY F, LHERMITTE F: Maladie de Refsum: Test de charge en phytol chez un descendant. *Nouv Presse Med* 2:2029, 1973.

125. UHLENDORF BW, JACOBSON CB, SLOAN HR, MUDD SH, HERNDON JH, BRADY RO, SEEGMILLER JE, FUJIMOTO W: Cell cultures derived from human amniotic fluid: The possible application in the intrauterine diagnosis of heritable metabolic disease. *In Vitro* 4:158, 1969.

126. O'BRIEN JB: Cell membranes—Composition, structure, function. *J Theor Biol* 15:307, 1967.

127. DUBOIS-DALCQ M, GORGE F: Neurocytologie—Action de l'acide phytanique sur le systeme nerveux peripherique in vitro. *C R Acad Sci[D] (Paris)* 270:2325, 1970.

128. DUBOIS-DALCQ M, MENU R, BUYSE M: Influence of fatty acids on fine structure of cultured neurons. *J Neuropathol Exp Neurol* 31:645, 1972.

129. ARVIDSSON EO, GREEN FA, LAURELL S: Branching and hydrophobic bonding: Partition equilibria and serum albumin binding of palmitic and phytanic acids. *J Biol Chem* 246:5373, 1971.

130. MALMENDIER CL, JONNIAUX G, VOET W, VAN DEN BERGEN CJ: Fatty acid composition of tissues in Refsum's disease (heredopathia atactica polyneuritiformis). Estimation of total phytanic acid accumulation. *Biomedicine* 20:398, 1974.

131. REYNOLDS DJ, MARKS R, DAVIES MG, DYKES PJ: The fatty acid composition of skin and plasma lipids in Refsum's disease. *Clin Chim Acta* 90:171, 1978.

132. ANTON-LAMPRECHT I, KAHLKE W: Zur Ultrastruktur Hereditater Verhornungsstörungen. V. Ichthyosis beim Refsum-syndrom (heredopathia atactica polyneuritiformis). *Arch Dermatol Form* 250:185, 1974.

133. KISHIMOTO Y, RADIN NS, STEINBERG D: Cited in [84].

134. MacBRINN MC, O'BRIEN JS: Lipid composition of the nervous system in Refsum's disease. *J Lipid Res* 9:552, 1968.

135. BLASS JP, AVIGAN J, CLARK RG: Effects of phytol feeding and experimental allergic encephalomyelitis on myelin synthesis. *Fed Proc* 28:838, 1969.

136. WOLF LM, LAUDAT PH, CHAUMONT P, BONDUELLE M: Maladie de Refsum: Evolution clinique et bio-chimique sous regime sans phytol: Investigations biochimiques complementaires. *Rev Neurol (Paris)* 120:89, 1969.

137. QUINLAN CD, MARTIN EA: Refsum's syndrome: Report of three cases. *J Neurol Neurosurg Pyschiatry* 33:817, 1970.

138. LUNDBERG A, LILJA LG, LUNDBERG PO, TRY K: Heredopathia atactica polyneuritiformis (Refsum's disease): Experiences of dietary treatment and plasmapheresis. *Eur Neurol* 8:309, 1972.

139. SAHGAL V, OLSEN WO: Heredopathia atactica polyneuritiformis (phytanic acid storage disease): A new case with special reference to dietary treatment. *Arch Intern Med* 135:585, 1975.

140. DRY J, PRADALIER A, DELPORTE M-P, LEYNADIER F: A propos de deux nouveaux cas de maladie de Refsum. Evolution sous regime. *Semin Hop Paris* 52:1675, 1976.

141. THUMLER R, ATXPODIEN W, KREMER GJ, HAFERKAMP G: Refsumsyndrom (Heredopathia atactica polyneuritiformis). Klinik, Diägnostik und Diätetische Behandlung. *Dtsch Med Wochenschr* 102:1454, 1977.

142. PENOVICH PE, HOLLANDER J, NUSBACHER JA, GRIGGS RC, MacPHERSON J: Note on plasma exchange therapy in Refsum's disease. *Adv Neurol* 21:151, 1978.

143. BAROLIN GS, HODKEWITSCH E, HOFINGER E, SCHOLZ H, BERNHEIMER H, MOLZER B: Klinisch-biochemische Verlaufsuntersuchungen bei Heredopathia atactica polyneuritiformis (Morbus Refsum). *Fortschr Neurol Psychiatr* 47:53, 1979.

144. MOSER HW, BATSHAW ML, MURRAY C, BRAINE H, BRUSILOW SW: Management of heritable disorders of the urea cycle and of Refsum's and Fabry's diseases, in Papadatos C, Eartsocas C (eds): *The Management of Genetic Disorders.* New York, AR Liss, 1979, p 183.

145. FRYER DG, WINCKELMAN AL, WAYS PO, SWANSON AG: Refsum's disease. A clinical and pathological report. *Neurology* 21:162, 1971.

146. ACKMAN RG, HOOPER SN: Isoprenoid fatty acids in the human diet: Distinctive geographical features in butterfats and importance in margarines based on marine oils. *Can Inst Food Technol J* 6:159, 1973.

147. HUNGERBUHLER JP, MEIER C, ROUSSELLE L, QUADRI P, BOGOUSSLAVSKY J: Refsum's disease: Management by diet and plasmapheresis. *Eur Neurol* 24:153, 1985.

148. LENZ H, SLUGA E, BERNHEIMER H, MOLZER B, PURGYI W: Refsum Krankheit und ihr Verlauf bei diätetischer Behandlung durch 2½ Jahre. *Nervenarzt* 50:52, 1979.

149. DJUPESLAND G, FLOTTORP G, REFSUM S: Phytanic acid storage disease: Hearing maintained after 15 years of dietary treatment. *Neurology* 33:237, 1983.

150. HANSEN E, REFSUM S: Heredopathia atactica polyneuritiformis. Phytanic acid storage disease (Refsum's disease). A biochemically well defined disease with a specific dietary treatment, in Huber A, Klein D (eds): *Neurogenetics and Neuro-ophthalmology.* New York, Elsevier, p 333.

151. DRY J, PRADALIER A, CANNY M: Maladie de Refsum: Quatorze années de régime sans phytol. *Ann Med Interne* 133: 488, 1982.

152. DRY J, PRADALIER A, CANNY M: Maladie de Refsum: Dix ans de régime diététique pauvre en acide phytanique et phytol. *Ann Med Interne* 133:483, 1982.

153. HANSEN E, BACHEN NI, FLAGE T: Refsum's disease: Eye manifestations in a patient treated with low phytol low phytanic acid diet. *Acta Ophthalmologica* 57:899, 1979.

154. FELDMANN H: Refsum-syndrom Heredopathia atactica polyneuritiformis in der sicht des HNO-arztes. *Laryngol Rhinol* 60:235, 1981.

CHAPTER 60

ACATALASEMIA

JOHN W. EATON

1. *Catalase is a ubiquitous enzyme, present in almost all aerobic organisms. With other enzymes, such as superoxide dismutase and glutathione/glutathione peroxidase, catalase subserves a central function in organismal oxidant defense.*

2. *Despite the central role of catalase in oxidant defense, rare cases of acatalasemia do occur, having been found primarily in Japan and Switzerland. This genetically heterogenous disorder is inherited as an autosomal recessive, and approximately 100 homozygotes have been reported, most arising from consanguinous marriages.*

3. *In acatalasemia, the erythrocyte is the cell most severely affected, often having less than 1 percent of normal activity. Other tissues may display variable levels of enzyme deficiency. In some forms of acatalasemia, heterozygotes typically have half-normal red cell catalase activity (hypocatalasemia).*

4. *The various types of acatalasemia appear to be caused both by the synthesis of abnormally unstable enzyme forms and by enzymes which have low specific activity.*

5. *In Japan, acatalasemia is associated with ulcerating, often gangrenous, oral lesions, and the syndrome is known as Takahara disease, after the discoverer of human acatalasemia. This disease, which formerly occurred in about half of the younger Japanese patients, is now much rarer. Indeed, most patients with acatalasemia have no associated health problems.*

6. *Worldwide, the frequency of the gene(s) for acatalasemia appears to fall between 0.001 and 0.005 as variously assessed by the frequencies of hypo- and acatalasemic patients.*

7. *Hypo- and acatalasemia also occur in a number of nonhuman species such as ducks and dogs. Acatalasemic mice have been developed by selective breeding of hypocatalasemic animals.*

NATURE AND DISTRIBUTION

Catalase (EC 1.11.1.6; H_2O_2 oxidoreductase) aids in the clearance of hydrogen peroxide, and practically all aerobic organisms have very efficient catalases and peroxidases for this purpose. The very existence of organisms with hypo- or acatalasemia is startling in view of the destructive potential of free H_2O_2. The first humans deficient in this enzyme were found in Japan.[1] Numerous subsequent reports clearly show that this rare—but physiologically very interesting—condition has a worldwide distribution.[2–12]

Acatalasemia is a genetically heterogenous condition which probably has arisen as the result of a number of different mutations. In practically all cases, the term *acatalasemia* is actually a misnomer; there is usually a small amount of residual enzyme activity detectable even in the erythrocytes, so that the term *hypocatalasemia* may be more correct. However, for the sake of convenience, *acatalasemia* will be employed here to denote severe, near-total deficiency of activity in the erythro-cytes, whereas *hypocatalasemia* will indicate variants with intermediate levels of catalase deficiency, usually heterozygotes for alleles causing acatalasemia in homozygotes.

BIOCHEMICAL ASPECTS OF CATALASE

Early Investigations

As catalase effects the decomposition of peroxide to water and oxygen, bubbles of oxygen form. It was this property of catalase which led to the early observation by Thènard (in 1818) that animal and plant tissues would decompose hydrogen peroxide. Later, Warburg found that cyanide inhibited this activity and suggested that the enzyme was iron-dependent.[13] Catalase was purified in crystalline form by Sumner and Dounce.[14] Much of the basic information on the enzymatic activity of catalase was developed by Chance, who was first to demonstrate the existence of enzyme/substrate complexes during the catalatic activity of catalase.[15] As detailed below, the complete amino acid sequences for catalases from several species are known. Furthermore, the chromosomal location and base sequences for the structural genes for human, bovine, and rat catalases have now been established.

Enzyme Structure and Activity

Catalase is a tetramer of approximately 240,000 daltons. It comprises four identical subunits, each 60,000-dalton subunit having a single ferriprotoporphyrin (heme) group. The resting state of catalase contains a high-spin ferric (heme) iron[16,17] which reacts readily with H_2O_2. The heme within catalase is the same as that within methemoglobin and metmyoglobin, and, in the case of all three proteins, the heme can be removed from the protein by treatment with acid acetone. The heme group of catalase is wedged within a 20-Å wide hydrophobic channel, and the iron is probably stabilized by interactions with adjacent amino acids[18–20] (see Fig. 60-1). The complete amino acid sequence of bovine liver and erythrocyte catalase and partial sequence of human erythrocyte catalase[21–23] are known, and the crystal structure has been determined.[18,24–26] The monomer of human erythrocyte catalase comprises 526 amino acid residues, and the four monomeric subunits are arranged in a tetrahedrally symmetric ellipsoid tetramer, the diameter of which varies from 70 to 95 Å.[18,26,27]

The catalase tetramer can be dissociated by agents such as urea into dimers and monomers.[28] In the process, the enzyme loses catalytic activity which can be regenerated by reformation of the tetramer. It is interesting to note that, as catalatic activity is lost, the enzyme gains peroxidatic activity at an equal rate.[28] In some conditions, the monomers and dimers of catalase can be reassociated and will regain normal activity.[28–32]

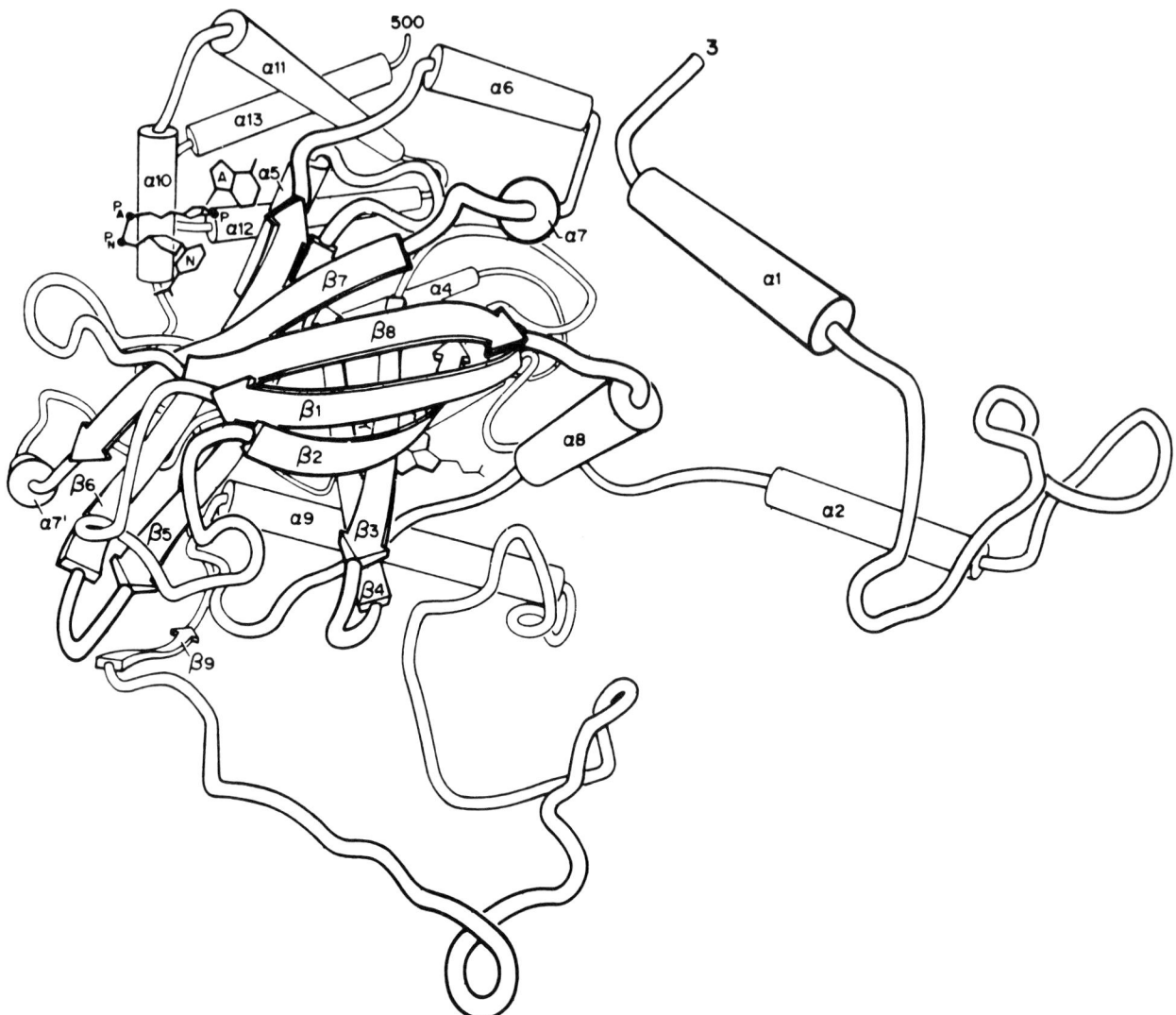

Fig. 60-1 Diagrammatic representation of one monomer of beef liver catalase. It is likely that human catalase has an almost identical structure. Cylinders labeled α represent α helices and ribbons labeled β represent β sheets, which combine in an antiparallel manner to form an 8-stranded β-barrel extending from residues 76 to 320. A portion of the heme group can be seen in the central portion of the molecule, and the tightly bound molecule of NADP(H) is apparent in the upper left overlying α10. (From Fita and Rossman.[19] Used by permission.)

Considerable heterogeneity in the molecular weight and electrophoretic mobility of catalase has been observed.[28,33–38] This may derive, in part, from artifacts introduced during purification procedures,[39] posttranslational modifications such as glycosylation,[40] sialation,[41] in vitro proteolysis during preparation,[42] or oxidation of the protein sulfhydryl groups (of which catalase has 16).[34,35,43,44] It has recently been found that hepatic catalases from rat, mouse, and guinea pig are all glycoproteins and have sialylated carbohydrate moieties.[45]

Catalase will decompose H_2O_2 two different ways. In the so-called catalitic mode,[15,46] the enzyme produces water and oxygen in a two-step reaction involving a $Fe^{IV}=O$ (ferryl-oxo) intermediate[47,48]:

$$\text{Cat}:Fe^{3+} + H_2O_2 \rightarrow$$
$$\text{cat}:Fe^{4+}=O \text{ (compound I)} + H_2O \quad [60\text{-}1]$$

$$\text{Cat}:Fe^{4+}=O \text{ (compound I)} + H_2O_2 \rightarrow$$
$$\text{cat}:Fe^{3+} + H_2O + O_2 \quad [60\text{-}2]$$

According to Chance et al.,[49] the rate constant for reaction (60-1) is 1.7×10^{-7} $M^{-1} \cdot s^{-1}$ and reaction (60-2) is 2.6×10^{-7} $M^{-1} \cdot s^{-1}$ (for catalase from rat liver).

In the peroxidatic mode, catalase compound I ($R=O$) can oxidize a proton donor (AH_2):

$$R=O + AH_2 \rightarrow R + A(ox) + H_2O \quad [60\text{-}3]$$

In the course of the first reaction, water is formed from the heterolysis of H_2O_2. One of the oxygens is left double-bonded to an Fe^{IV} [see reaction (60-1) above], and the heme group becomes an organic radical.[47] In reaction (60-2) above, it has been established that both atoms evolved as O_2 derive from the second H_2O_2.[50] In the event that compound I of catalase is exposed to high levels of peroxide, it may react with a second mole of H_2O_2 forming compound II, which is inactive. Compound II can be reactivated via a peroxidatic reaction with substrates such as alcohols[51–53] or NAD(P)H.[54] Further exposure of compound II to H_2O_2 will lead to the formation of compound III, an inactive form of the enzyme.

There are several unusual features of the enzymatic function of catalase. First, its reaction with H_2O_2 is first-order and dependent strictly on the concentration of H_2O_2. The rate of reaction is unusually rapid; catalase accelerates the decomposition of H_2O_2 by more than 100,000,000-fold.[55] Put another way, 1 mol of catalase can dispose of more than 40,000 mol of H_2O_2 per second at O°C.[56] Second, high concentrations of the substrate will cause inhibition of the enzyme via reaction between catalase compound I and H_2O_2. Third, very little energy change is involved in the catalatic (as opposed to peroxidatic) decomposition of H_2O_2. Therefore, catalase activity is practically independent of temperature, and the pH optimum is fairly broad.[57] For further details on the enzymatic characteristics of catalase, consult the excellent review by Chance et al.[58] Finally, catalase is one of the most copious enzymes in the mammalian body. One estimate is that more than 0.1 percent of the protein within normal human erythrocytes is catalase.[59] The liver is also rich in catalase activity, but most of the hepatic catalase resides within peroxisomes.[60] The steps involved in postsynthetic insertion of the enzyme into the peroxisome are not yet fully elucidated.[61]

Recently, it has been discovered that catalase binds NADPH with extraordinarily high affinity.[62] The binding is in a ratio of 4 mol of NADPH per mole of catalase tetramer (i.e., 1 NADPH per heme-containing sub-unit), and the dissociation constant for this binding is less than 1×10^{-8} M. Catalase will also (competitively) bind, with somewhat lesser affinity, NADH, $NADP^+$, and NAD^+. The tight binding of NADPH has helped explain an anomaly in the electron density map of beef liver catalase.[19,20] In this enzyme, the NADP(H) is bound near the carboxyl end of two α helices and lies within 14 Å of the heme group (see Fig. 60-1). The function of this very high affinity binding of NADPH close to the heme group is not known; however, the NADPH may help prevent the inactivation of catalase by low amounts of H_2O_2,[62] perhaps through peroxidatic decomposition of catalase complex II, as previously suggested.[54]

Synthesis and Turnover

Relatively little is known about the rates of synthesis and degradation of catalase. Several investigators have failed to find significant decrements in catalase activity in young versus old (i.e., lighter versus more dense) erythrocytes, suggesting that little degradation of the enzyme occurs during the 120-day life span of the normal human red cell.[63] In contrast to the red cell, in which almost all the catalase is cytosolic (except for a small fraction which is membrane-associated),[64] almost all catalase activity within the liver resides within specialized organelles such as the mitochondria and peroxisomes[65,66] (see Chap. 57). Although hepatic catalase is synthesized in the endoplasmic reticulum, it is rapidly translocated to peroxisomes. The half-life of liver catalase in several rodent species has been variously estimated to be between 19 h and 5 days.[66-70]

Techniques of Measurement

The simplest and most routinely applied assay of catalase involves the measurement of the rate of catalase-mediated decomposition of H_2O_2.[71] In this spectrophotometric procedure, very dilute red cell lysates or tissue homogenates (prepared with a detergent to ensure complete exposure of catalase within organelles) are added to a very dilute H_2O_2 solution at neutral pH. The time required for absorbance (at 240 nM) to decrease a set amount is taken as a measure of the catalase activity. Catalase may also be measured by immunoassay, fluorometrically, photometrically, manometrically, with an oxygen electrode, or by determining its peroxidatic decomposition of substrates such as formate. Details of many of these assays are available elsewhere.[57,59,72-77] It should be noted that, in performing assays on individuals with suspected hypo- or acatalasemia, it may be wise to keep the temperature of the assay as low as possible. This is because some variants are heat-labile, and assays performed at room temperature or 37°C may be compromised by enzymatic decomposition. Aebi and coworkers[78-80] have also devised immunologic and cytochemical techniques for assessing catalase and its activity within individual red cells.

PHYSIOLOGICAL FUNCTIONS OF CATALASE

Tissue Distribution

The highest catalase activities in mammals are found in the erythrocytes, liver, and kidney. Catalase is also present in phagocytic cells. In pulmonary alveolar macrophages the enzyme is evidently localized within intracellular granules.[81] Connective tissues such as fibroblasts, by comparison, have very little catalase.[82,83] One recent report[84] indicates that endothelial cells and vascular smooth muscle entirely lack catalase activity. As might be expected, cultured smooth muscle and endothelial cells were found to be exceptionally sensitive to superoxide- and peroxide-generating systems. Furthermore, the destabilization and destruction of these cells could be prevented by the addition of exogenous catalase.[84] These observations may help explain the exaggerated sensitivity of endothelial cells to destruction by activated phagocytes.[85]

In liver, catalase is present largely within peroxisomes, organelles designed to carry out coupled oxidation reactions. In comparison, the cytoplasm of hepatocytes contains very little catalase activity. This seclusion of the enzyme in peroxisomes may also occur within fibroblasts and amniotic fluid cells[86,87] and has been recently proposed as a possible diagnostic technique for cerebrohepatorenal (Zellweger) syndrome wherein peroxisomes are absent. Cultured amniotic fluid cells from fetuses with Zellweger syndrome fail to show normal compartmentation of catalase; instead, all the enzyme present within these cells is cytoplasmic.[87] Thus, prenatal diagnosis of Zellweger syndrome may involve simple determination of the fraction of amniocyte catalase activity which is cytoplasmic (see Chap. 57).

Enzymatic Functions

Without question, the main function of catalase is the conversion of hydrogen peroxide to water and oxygen. As shown in Fig. 60-2, catalase is part of a cluster of antioxidant enzymes which act in concert to protect cells against activated oxygen species. In the course of orderly aerobic metabolism, oxygen is reduced to water, and the intermediates in this reduction include superoxide (O_2^-) and H_2O_2, both of which may occa-

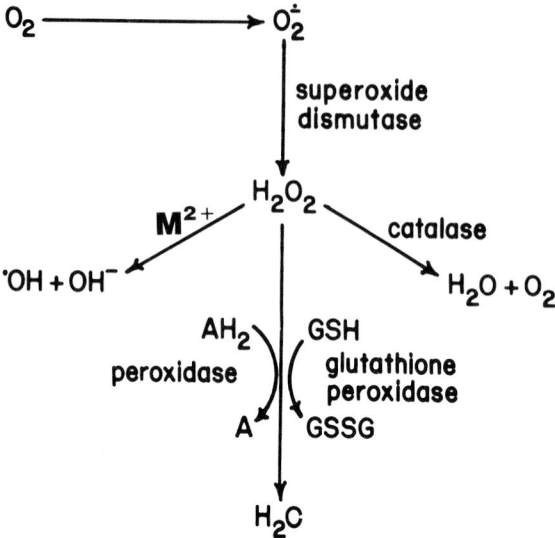

Fig. 60-2 The catabolism of activated oxygen species. In the course of normal metabolism, oxygen is reduced, in a series of 4 one-electron steps, to water. Superoxide dismutase, catalase and peroxidases combine to speed the clearance of activated oxygen species, thereby avoiding damage to cellular constituents from species such as H_2O_2 and the hydroxyl radical (·OH).

sionally escape the metabolic cascade.[58] For example, it has been estimated that 5 to 50 percent of all oxygen consumed by the liver is converted to H_2O_2,[58] an amount sufficient to keep about one-third of the hepatic catalase in the form of compound I.[51,88] In addition, O_2^- and H_2O_2 may also arise from stimulated phagocytes, spontaneous oxidative events, and γ and uv radiation.

Enzymes such as superoxide dismutase and catalase are designed precisely to prevent damage from these reactive oxygen species. For example, Nicholls[289] has estimated that over 99 percent of added H_2O_2 which enters the erythrocyte is destroyed by catalase, thereby supplying almost perfect protection to hemoglobin against oxidation by H_2O_2. There is also some evidence suggesting a role for erythrocyte catalase in the protection of heterologous cells against oxidant challenge,[90] and catalase may also prevent peroxide-mediated damage to DNA.[91]

There has been a great deal of argument concerning the quantitative importance of catalase-mediated detoxification of H_2O_2 because catalase has a rather low affinity for substrate when it acts in the catalatic mode. By contrast, the reduced glutathione/glutathione peroxidase system has greater affinity for substrate, leading both Keilin and Hartree[92] and Cohen and Hochstein[93] to argue that, at low H_2O_2 concentrations ($<10^{-7} M$), catalase plays almost no role in H_2O_2 detoxification. However, catalase has a substantially higher substrate affinity when acting peroxidatically. Although the peroxidatic donors which have been studied—such as ethanol and formate—are not often present in vivo, reduced pyridine nucleotides may also act to support the peroxidatic action of catalase.[54] In fact, one estimate is that, even when the H_2O_2 concentrations are as low as 10^{-8} to $10^{-9} M$, catalase may function in a peroxidatic mode to clear H_2O_2.[46] Therefore, even under conditions of low substrate concentrations, the peroxidatic activity of catalase probably does play a part in the clearance of H_2O_2 in vivo.[51]

Because alcohols such as ethanol will act as donors for the peroxidatic decomposition of catalase complex I, catalase has the potential to contribute to the conversion of ethanol to acet-

aldehyde in vivo. It is likely that hepatic microsomal/peroxisomal catalase, acting as a peroxidase, catabolizes a significant fraction of ethanol, converting it to acetaldehyde.[94–97] Oshino et al. have estimated that hepatic catalase will oxidize 10 percent of administered ethanol but, when stimulated, will clear up to 30 percent.[88,98] Vatsis and Schulman[95,96] have used normal and acatalasemic mice to address this question experimentally. They conclude that, in the case of the microsomal ethanol oxidizing system (MEOS), as much as 60 to 70 percent of MEOS-dependent ethanol oxidation occurs via the action of catalase and only 30 to 40 percent by way of alcohol dehydrogenase.[96] Hepatic catalase can also mediate the oxidation of methanol and formate.[99,100]

An additional interesting activity of catalase may be in acting as an L-dopa peroxidase, i.e., 3-(3′,4′-dihydroxphenyl-L-alanine peroxidase).[101] Snyder et al.[102] made the observation that L-dopa would protect against Heinz body formation in glucose-6-phosphate dehydrogenase-deficient erythrocytes under oxidant stress. However, the physiological import of this L-dopa peroxidase activity in normal circumstances remains to be established. The lack of any evident disorder in L-dopa metabolism in acatalasemic subjects argues against any vital importance for this enzymatic activity of catalase.

Finally, there is the unexpected observation[103,104] that catalase may also function in the metabolism of a carcinogen. The enzyme which converts hydroxyanthranilic acid to cinnabarinic acid (cinnabarinate synthase) is very likely identical with catalase because the activity of this enzyme is low in acatalasemic mice and because the liver enzyme is inhibited by 3-amino-1,2,4-triazole, which also inhibits hepatic catalase.

CLINICAL DESCRIPTIONS OF CATALASE DEFICIENCIES

Takahara Disease

In general, acatalasemia is a relatively benign disease. It is, therefore, ironic that the initial discovery of this condition in humans was through an associated pathology. In 1946, Takahara, practicing at the Okayama Medical School, removed a tumor from the nasal cavity and maxillary sinus of a young girl. Upon postoperative application of dilute hydrogen peroxide, he was surprised to find that the exposed tissues turned black and did not bubble. Takahara subsequently ascribed this to a deficiency in catalase. The parents were first cousins, and three of the five siblings of the propositus were similarly affected. Following the first report of this disorder,[1] a number of other families with the condition were identified. Acatalasemia was subsequently found to be inherited as an autosomal recessive, with heterozygotes having intermediate levels of red cell catalase activity[105] (Fig. 60-3).

A syndrome of oral gangrene and ulcerations is associated with Japanese acatalasemia in roughly half the cases. The reasons for the variable expression of these symptoms are not known at present. Possibly important factors include heterogeneity in the severity of catalase deficiency at the tissue level,[106] differences in oral flora, idiosyncracies in oral hygiene, or environmental (dietary) factors. Support for the latter is provided by the observation that the frequency of the syndrome has declined markedly in recent years.[56] One additional factor affecting expression of the syndrome is age; patients are rarely affected after puberty.

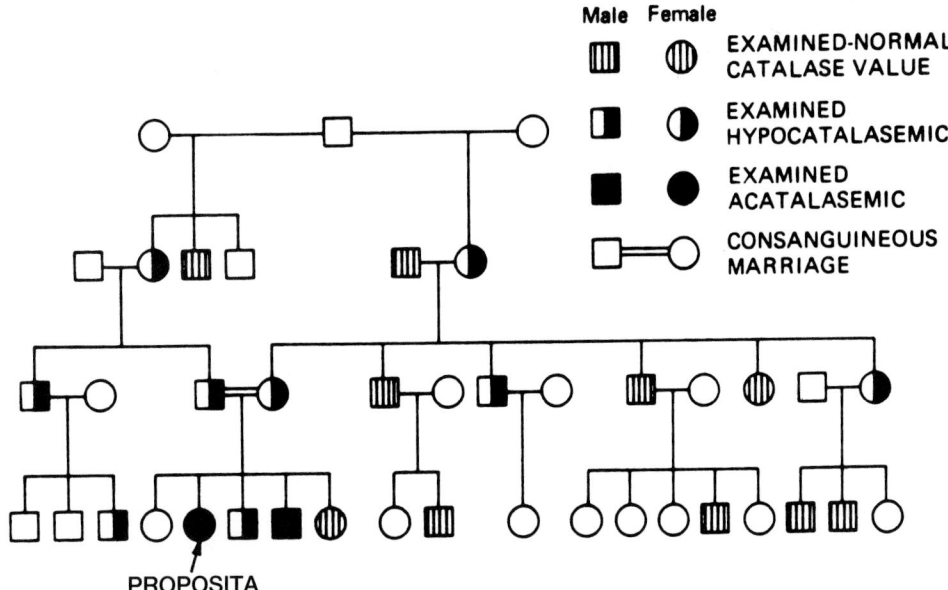

Fig. 60-3 Genealogy of a Japanese kindred in which several members are hypocatalasemic (heterozygous) or acatalasemic. Note the consanguineous mating in the third generation, which yielded two acatalasemic children. (*Redrawn from Nishimura et al.[105] Used by permission.*)

The deficiency of catalase activity evidently predisposes the patient to infection by peroxide-generating bacteria such as streptococci and pneumococci. The infections, which start as small lesions around the gingival-dental border or the tonsillar lacunae, develop into fulminating inflammatory processes and may cause extensive tissue destruction.[107] There is often destruction of the gums, and some of the affected patients are eventually left edentulous by this process. Takahara[7] reported that surgical debridement of the affected areas was effective in limiting the process in most cases.

The ulcerations and consequent gangrene are clearly associated with the lack of catalase activity in the affected tissues and/or in the erythrocytes. However, the reasons for this association are not presently clear. It has been suggested[90] that erythrocyte catalase may serve to protect heterologous tissues against damage by exogenous peroxide. Alternatively, the catalase activity within the affected tissue, and not that within red cells, may be an important determinant of the susceptibility to inflammation and gangrene. Finally, Matsunaga et al.[108] have suggested that the H_2O_2 accumulated in areas of infection may serve to induce neutrophil dysfunction. In support of this, they find that preincubation of (Swiss-type) acatalasemic neutrophils with H_2O_2 leads to depressed cellular function.

Aside from the occurrence of this severe syndrome of oral infections and gangrene, patients with acatalasemia have no other serious pathologies. There is, however, one interesting anomaly in the catabolism of heme. According to Takahara and Ogata,[109] the urinary excretion of heme degradation products—coproporphyrin and bilirubin—is five times normal. Changes in hepatic catalase or, for that matter, the enhanced (i.e., induced) synthesis and turnover of catalase itself may be partially responsible for this anomaly.

Other Catalase Deficiencies

Sometime after Takahara's pioneering studies, roughly 73,000 blood donors were screened for acatalasemia in Switzer-land.[110,111] As a result, three acatalasemic individuals were identified, indicating a gene frequency of 0.0064 and a frequency of heterozygotes of about 0.01. Care should be taken in calculation of actual gene frequencies because the abnormal genes involved in causation of acatalasemia may differ between affected Swiss individuals. The results of several other random population screenings for acatalasemia have revealed frequencies approximately the same as those in the Japanese and Swiss samples.[9,112]

Interestingly, and in stark contrast with the Japanese patients, none of the Swiss acatalasemics had oral gangrene or any other health problem associated with the deficiency.[111] This may be attributable to the fact that Swiss acatalasemics have easily detectable catalase activity in other tissues.[8] Although comparable direct determinations have not been made on Japanese cases, Krooth et al.[113,114] and Sadamoto[115] found that, whereas cultured fibroblasts from Swiss acatalasemic patients maintained ≈15 percent of normal enzyme activity, those from Japanese patients had only 2 to 4 percent. This suggests that the tissues of Japanese patients may be entirely without protection from H_2O_2, perhaps explaining the predisposition to oral gangrene.

In addition to these cases of severe catalase deficiency, a number of cases of hypocatalasemia have been uncovered. Many of these are from Japanese kindreds within which acatalasemic propositi were intially found, and they represent the heterozygous expression of the enzyme deficiency.[116] Interestingly, Aebi et al.[117] report that Swiss heterozygotes fail to show the expected hypocatalasemia, their catalase activity falling within the normal range. This may be due to a normal stability of the catalase heterotetramers composed of normal and variant monomers. Szeinberg et al.[3] report an interesting coincidence of glucose-6-phosphate dehydrogenase deficiency and hypocatalasemia in three members of a single large kindred. Although the authors conclude that the two traits are inherited independently of each other, the possibility exists that the severe glucose-6-phosphate dehydrogenase deficiency might have led to diminution of catalase activity through depletion of cellular NADPH levels which may help maintain catalase activity.[54] However, some members of the kindred were found to have hypocatalasemia while also exhibiting normal levels of glucose-6-phosphate dehydrogenase activity. As is discussed below, hypocatalasemia is also a frequent finding in patients with the complex of aniridia and Wilms tumor (see "Molecular Genetics of Catalase").

Subnormal levels of catalase have also been reported in fibroblasts from patients with xeroderma pigmentosum (an hereditary condition characterized by marked sensitivity to ultraviolet radiation and predisposition to skin cancer). Cultured fibroblasts from such patients have about 25 percent of the catalase activity of normal cultured fibroblasts.[118] Unfortunately, it is not known whether this decrement in catalase is reflective of a hypocatalasemia in the patients from whom the fibroblasts were derived or whether the enzyme deficit developed during the process of culturing the fibroblasts.

In some rare circumstances, there can be acquired hypocatalasemia. During the administration of oxidant drugs to individuals with glucose-6-phosphate dehydrogenase deficiency, erythrocyte catalase activity may temporarily decline but rebound almost immediately after discontinuation of oxidant drug exposure. This temporary decrement in catalase activity may be due to a decline in the amounts of NAD(P)H which, in turn, may be necessary for continued reduction of catalase compound II to the native form of the enzyme.[54] In addition, certain solid tumors produce uncharacterized substances which inhibit or block the synthesis of hepatic catalase.[119–122] Finally, there are isolated reports of rare electrophoretic variants of human red cell catalase.[2,123] None of these has been associated with hypo- or acatalasemia.

CELLULAR AND MOLECULAR ASPECTS OF CATALASE DEFICIENCIES

Affected Tissues

Without question, the erythrocyte is the cell most affected by acatalasemia. This is because the mature erythrocyte is incapable of compensatory induction of additional catalase once the reticulocyte has left the bone marrow. Some early reports (e.g., Ref. 124) suggested that the deficiency of catalase might be as severe in other tissues as it was in the red cell. Indeed, Ogata et al.[125] found that the leukocytes of Japanese hypo- and acatalasemic patients had catalase activities as low as those of the red cells. However, other reports suggest that substantial residual catalase activity is present in a variety of nonerythroid tissues from acatalasemic patients.[8,126] Thus, it is likely that, as in a number of enzyme disorders such as glucose-6-phosphate dehydrogenase deficiency, the erythrocyte is preferentially affected and other nucleated cell types less so.

The profound deficiency of catalase activity in the erythrocytes of some acatalasemic individuals does not, however, sensitize these cells to destruction by most oxidative challenges. Jacob et al.,[127] studying acatalasemic Swiss individuals, found that, upon in vitro challenge with oxidant drugs, acatalasemic erythrocytes compensated by acceleration of the pentose phosphate shunt. Indeed, erythrocyte survival in acatalasemic individuals is normal, even during the administration of oxidant drugs such as primaquine.[127] These investigators and others[128] concluded that catalase and glutathione-dependent systems are capable of substituting for each other in the prevention of oxidant damage to the cell.

Molecular Mechanisms of Deficiencies

It has been shown that one Swiss-type variant enzyme can be electrophoretically separated from normal and that hybrid catalases (comprising equal parts normal catalase and catalase from obligatory heterozygotes) have intermediate electrophoretic mobility.[28] By contrast, the Japanese variants which have been investigated show no significant variations in isoelectric point.[129] In fact, the residual enzyme obtained from acatalasemic erythrocytes cannot be distinguished on the basis of heat stability, ion-exchange chromatographic behavior or subunit molecular weight.[129–132] Erythrocytes from Japanese acatalasemics appear to contain less antigenically cross-reactive material, suggesting either impaired synthetic rate or instability of the variant enzyme.[130] Results of studies on individual red cells stained with fluorescent anticatalase antibodies support this impression.[80,133]

Investigations of the residual catalase in erythrocytes from Swiss who are homozygous and heterozygous for acatalasemia indicate that the abnormal enzyme from homozygotes is more heat-labile.[117] This increased lability can evidently be traced to an instability of the abnormal homotetramer. Indeed, in the homozygotes, most of the detectable catalase activity resides within the very youngest erythrocytes. On the level of individual red cells, Aebi and coworkers found that only reticulocytes showed immunologic or enzymatic staining for the protein. The difference in catalase from youngest to oldest red cells may be as much as 300:1.[78–80]

In contrast, Swiss-type obligatory heterozygotes fail to show a gene dosage effect and their red cell catalase activities fall within the normal range.[117] This may be attributable to a stabilization of the abnormal monomer when it is included with normal catalase chains in a heterotetramer[134] even though the abnormal enzyme from heterozygotes may form less stable tetramers with normal catalase monomers.[28] Overall, it may be concluded that the deficiency of enzyme in Swiss homozygotes is attributable to instability of the homotetramer, a situation with many precedents in abnormal proteins and enzymes.

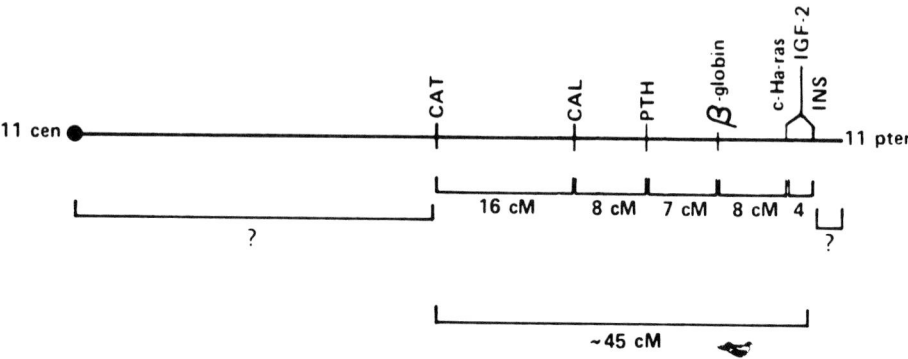

Fig. 60-4 Linkage map for human chromosome 11 showing the distances between catalase (CAT) and the loci for calcitonin (CAL), parathyroid hormone (PTH), β-globin gene cluster (β-globin), c-Harvey-ras oncogene, insulinlike growth factor II (IGF-2), and insulin (INS). (Reproduced from Kittur et al.[141] Used by permission.)

GENETICS OF HUMAN CATALASE VARIANTS

Mendelian Inheritance of Hypo- and Acatalasemia

As indicated earlier, hypo- and acatalasemia are clearly genetically heterogeneous entities. The deficiency of catalase activity may arise either from the production of an unstable form of the enzyme (as in some Swiss variants),[117] from the synthesis of a form of the enzyme with low specific activity, or from diminished synthesis (as in some Japanese variants). It should, however, be emphasized that neither the Swiss nor the Japanese cases are homogeneous. Regardless of the molecular basis of the acatalasemia, heterozygotes would be expected to exhibit some degree of hypocatalasemia, especially in erythrocyte-associated activity. Thus, as one might predict, most patients with acatalasemia arise from consanguinous marriages between two hypocatalasemic partners.[109,135,136]

Frequencies and Population Genetics

The reason that most patients with acatalasemia are offspring of consanguineous marriages[109] is that the gene frequency is quite low. Assuming a gene frequency of 0.01, the likelihood of unrelated parents both being heterozygous would be low (around 1/10,000). The frequency of hypocatalasemia (i.e., probably heterozygosity) in East Asia ranges between 0.2 and 0.4 percent (i.e., gene frequencies of 0.002 and 0.004).[109,112] Hypocatalasemia occurs with a frequency of about 0.5 percent in two Iranian populations.[12] As noted earlier, the first screening of the Swiss population uncovered three acatalasemics out of 73,000 blood donors, implying a frequency of heterozygotes of about 0.01. Based on these gene frequencies (and in the absence of significant inbreeding), the frequency of homozygous acatalasemic patients in most human populations would be expected to fall between 1/25,000 and 1/250,000. Because the estimates of gene frequency are compromised by inbreeding effects, the latter figure is probably nearer the mark.

Molecular Genetics of Catalase

The single locus coding for human catalase (CAT) has been mapped to chromosome 11, p13 (i.e., the short arm of chromosome 11; Fig. 60-4).[137–139] It is interesting to note that the loci coding for β-like chains of hemoglobin are located nearby on chromosome 11.[140] However, the genetic distance between the catalase locus and the β-globin cluster is such that linkage between the two is undetectable.[141] In addition to catalase and the β-globin cluster, 11p also contains the loci for calcitonin,[142,143] the c-Ha-ras-1 oncogene,[144,145] the lactate dehydrogenase A subunit,[146,147] insulin,[144,148] insulinlike growth factor,[149,150] and parathyroid hormone[151] (see Chap. 6).

Gravel and his coworkers earlier succeeded in isolating and sequencing a partial cDNA clone extending from amino acid 76 to the carboxyl terminus of human catalase.[152] More recently, the entire sequence of full length catalase cDNA clones has been reported by two separate groups.[153,154] The gene is 34 kb in length and contains 12 introns and 13 exons[153] (see Fig. 60-5). It appears that the 5′ flanking region of the gene lacks a TATA box but does contain several CCAAT and GGGCGG sequences which may subserve the same promoter function. The DNA sequence suggests that the gene actually codes for a protein 526 amino acid residues long, whereas the human erythrocyte enzyme is 517 residues long.[23] Either post-synthetic processing of the protein or proteolytic modification[155] may account for the structural differences between the liver and erythrocyte forms of the enzyme. Furuta et al.[155] have reported the nucleotide sequence of cDNA for rat liver catalase. The nucleotide sequence of the rat, like that of the human, predicts a product of 526 amino acids. The sequence reported for rat liver catalase suggests a high degree of conservation; in fact, complete conservation was found between human, bovine, and rat catalases in 39 amino acid residues which are in contact with the heme.[155]

One important application of probes for the catalase gene is in the study and diagnosis of Wilms tumor, a frequent renal neoplasm (nephroblastoma) in young children. About 2 percent of children with Wilms tumor also have aniridia, while one-third of those with nonfamilial (sporadic) aniridia will develop Wilms tumor. In both cases, the aniridia-Wilms tumor syndrome is usually accompanied by mental retardation and urogenital abnormalities in addition to the tumor.[156] This complex disorder is influenced by loci which may reside near the gene for catalase within 11p13. When the aniridia-Wilms tumor syndrome is accompanied by visible deletions of 11p13, the patients usually also have hypocatalasemia.[137–139,157–161] On the other hand, patients lacking cytogenetic evidence of chromosomal deletion in 11p13 generally have normal catalase, suggesting that the linkage between aniridia-Wilms tumor and the catalase locus is not too close.[157] In the genesis of this tumor, it is likely that a somatic mutation—consisting of replicative loss of an uncharacterized normal allele and duplication of a recessive allele which predisposes to Wilms tumor—is a necessary secondary event in the genesis of this neoplasm[162–166] (see Chap. 9). However, Boyd et al.[167] have recently found no deletion of the catalase gene in one patient with the Wilms-aniridia syndrome and five others with nonfamilial aniridia (one of whom had a visible deletion of 11p13). Furthermore, analysis of restriction fragment length polymorphisms indicates that full dosage of both the catalase and parathyroid hormone genes may be present and the loci may be heterozygous within the tumor.[168] This observation implies that the catalase and Wilms tumor loci are sufficiently distant so that loss of the normal allele at the Wilms tumor locus is not necessarily accompanied by loss of one catalase allele. Indeed, based on studies of partial deletion of band 11p13, it has been concluded that the gene for catalase may reside several thousand kilobases proximal to the loci for Wilms tumor and aniridia.[169]

ANIMAL MODELS

A murine model of acatalasemia was developed by Feinstein et al.,[170] who repetitively back-crossed selected mice which had lower than normal catalase activity. This strain, C3H-Csb-ANL (for Argonne National Laboratory) produces normal amounts of a catalase with abnormal subunit association.[171] This leads to deficient catalase activity in the erythrocyte (≈50 percent of normal in heterozygotes and 1 percent of normal in homozygotes), while other tissues are less severely affected.[170,172,173] In the liver, although the catalatic activity of catalase is either labile[96] or lacking,[174] the peroxidatic activity may be completely normal and can be precipitated with antibodies prepared against normal mouse catalase. Therefore,

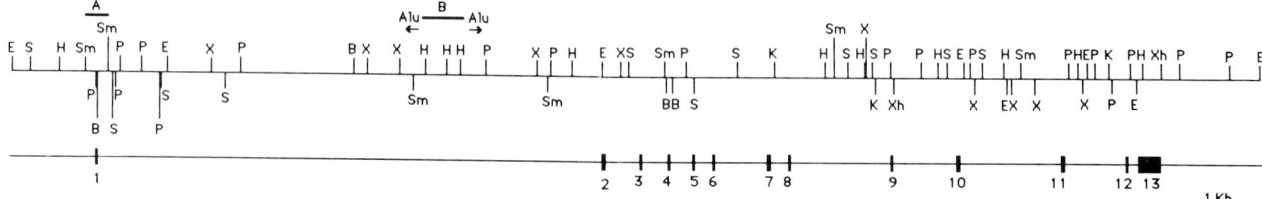

Fig. 60-5 Structure of the human catalase gene. The 13 exons and 12 introns within the gene are shown in the lower portion. The upper diagram shows the approximate position of restriction endonuclease sites B (BamHI), E (EcoRI), H (HindIII), I (KpnI), P (PstI), S (SstI), S_m (SmaI), X (XbaI), and X_h (XhoI). The entire gene is 34 kb long, and the coding sequence occupies about 2.2 kb. (Redrawn from Quan et al.[153] Used by permission.)

when this mutant enzyme dissociates, the subunits express peroxidatic activity but lack catalase activity.[175] However, the mutant enzyme is immunologically indistinguishable from normal.[176] These animals have no spontaneous health problems but, interestingly, are very readily killed by the injection of H_2O_2 solutions.[170] The enhanced lethality of H_2O_2 is directly attributable to the deficiency of catalase; prior injection of purified catalase (even subcutaneously) abrogates the lethal effect of H_2O_2.[170] As indicated above, it has been found that microsomal preparations from the livers of these animals, when preincubated to deplete active catalase, are much less active than normal in supporting the NADPH-dependent oxidation of ethanol to acetaldehyde.[95,96] These results imply that catalase may normally play an important role in the hepatic clearance of ethanol. The locus coding murine catalase has not been placed. However, linkage analysis indicates that the gene causing acatalasemia (which is probably the structural catalase gene) is located on linkage group V between the Danforth shorttail and agouti loci.[177]

In addition to the acatalasemia in mice caused by an abnormal catalase allele, there are very large interspecies variations in erythrocyte catalase activity. Duck red cells are almost devoid of catalase activity (roughly 0.1 percent of normal human), and dog red cells are also quantitatively deficient (approximately 3 percent of human).[128] It is not surprising that the exposure of erythrocytes from these two species to added hydrogen peroxide results in the generation of substantial amounts of methemoglobin, whereas human erythrocytes are quite resistant to such a peroxide challenge.[128]

I owe a particular debt to the late Dr. Hugo Aebi and to Dr. Sonja Wyss for their extensive contributions to the field and their very scholarly and thorough treatment of this subject in the previous edition. I thank Ms. Diane Konzen for assistance in preparation of this manuscript. Completed February 1987.

REFERENCES

1. TAKAHARA S, MIYAMOTO H: Three cases of progressive oral gangrene due to lack of catalase in the blood. *Jpn J Otol* 51:163, 1948.
2. BAUR EW: Catalase abnormality in a Caucasian family in the United States. *Science* 140:816, 1963.
3. SZEINBERG A, de VRIES A, PINKHAS J, DJALDETTI M, EZRA R: A dual hereditary red blood cell defect in one family. Hypocatalasemia and glucose-6-phosphate dehydrogenase deficiency. *Acta Genet Med Gemellol (Roma)* 12:247, 1963.
4. ENGSTEDT L, PAUL KG: Non-hereditary hypocatalasia. *Scand J Clin Lab Invest* 17:295, 1965.
5. TAYLOR EH, HAUT A: Hypocatalasia in two American men. *Clin Res* 15:289, 1967.
6. AEBI H, BOSSI E, CANTZ M, MATSUBARA S, SUTER H: Acatalasemia in Switzerland, in Beutler E (ed): *Hereditary Disorders of Erythrocyte Metabolism.* New York, Grune & Stratton, 1968, p 41.
7. TAKAHARA S: Acatalasemia in Japan, in Beutler E (ed): *Hereditary Disorders of Erythrocyte Metabolism.* New York, Grune & Stratton, 1968, p 21.
8. AEBI H, SUTER H: Acatalasemia. *Adv Hum Genet* 2:143:1971.
9. SALDIVAR AA, CARRASCO RMD, REYES GR: Deficiencia de catalasa entrocitica en la ciudad de Puebla. *Rev Invest Clin (Mex)* 26:47, 1974.
10. GROSS J, SCHERZ B, WYSS S, KÜNZEL W, MAIWALD HJ, HARTWIG A, POLSTER H: Characterization of the catalase of erythrocytes of a patient with the symptoms of Takahara's disease. *Acta Biol Med Ger* 36:793, 1977.
11. DELGADO W, CALDERÓN R: Acatalasia in two Peruvian siblings. *J Oral Pathol* 8:358, 1979.
12. OHKURA K, MIYASHITA T, NAKAJIMA H, MATSUMOTO H, MATSUTOMO K, RAHABAR S, HEDAYAT S: Distribution of polymorphic traits in Mazandaranian and Guilanian in Iran. *Hum Hered* 34:27, 1984.
13. WARBURG O: Über die antikatalytische Werkung der Blausäure. *Biochem Z* 136:266, 1923.
14. SUMNER JB, DOUNCE AL: Crystalline catalase. *J Biol Chem* 121:417, 1937.
15. CHANCE B: An intermediate compound in the catalase-hydrogen peroxide reaction. *Acta Chem Scand Ser B* 1:236, 1947.
16. TORII K, IIZUKA T, OGURA Y: Magnetic susceptibility and EPR measurements of catalase and its derivatives: A thermal equilibrium between the high and low spin states in the catalase-azide compound. *J Biochem (Tokyo)* 68:837, 1970.
17. MAEDA Y, TRAUTWEIN A, GONSER U, YOSHIDA K, KIKUCHI-TORII K, HOMMA T, OGURA Y: Mössbauer effect in bacterial catalase. *Biochim Biophys Acta* 303:230, 1973.
18. REID TJ III, MURTHY MRN, SICIGNANO A, TANAKA N, MUSICK WDL, ROSSMANN MG: Structure and heme environment of beef liver catalase at 2.5 Å resolution. *Proc Natl Acad Sci USA* 78:4767, 1981.
19. FITA I, ROSSMANN MG: The NADPH binding site on beef liver catalase. *Proc Natl Acad Sci USA* 82:1604, 1985.
20. FITA I, ROSSMANN MG: The active center of catalase. *J Mol Biol* 185:21, 1985.
21. SCHROEDER WA, SHELTON JR, SHELTON JB, ROBERTSON B, APELL G: The amino acid sequence of bovine liver catalase: A preliminary report. *Arch Biochem Biophys* 131:653, 1969.
22. SCHROEDER WA, SHELTON JR, SHELTON JB, ROBERTSON B, APELL G, FANG RS, BONAVENTURA J: The complete amino acid sequence of bovine liver catalase and the partial sequence of bovine erythrocyte catalase. *Arch Biochem Biophys* 214:397, 1982.
23. SCHROEDER WA, SHELTON JR, SHELTON JB, APELL G, EVANS L, BONA VENTURA J, FANG RS: The partial amino acid sequence of human erythrocyte catalase. *Arch Biochem Biophys* 214:422, 1982.
24. KISELEV NA, SHPITSBERG CI, VAINSHTAIN BK: Crystallization of catalase in the form of tubes with monomolecular walls. *J Mol Biol* 25:433, 1967.
25. KISELEV NA, de ROSIER DJ, KLUG A: Structure of the tubes of catalase: Analysis of electron micrographs by optical filtering. *J Mol Biol* 35:561, 1968.
26. MURTHY MRN, REID TJ III, SICIGNANO A, TANAKA N, ROSSMANN MG: Structure of beef liver catalase. *J Mol Biol* 152:465, 1981.
27. VAINSHTAIN BK: The quaternary structure of catalase, in Thurman RG, Williamson JR, Yonatani T, Chance B (eds): *Alcohol and Aldehyde Metabolizing Systems.* New York, Academic, 1974.
28. SCHERZ B, KUCHINSKAS EJ, WYSS SR, AEBI H: Heterogeneity of erythrocyte catalase: Dissociation, recombination and hybridization of human erythrocyte catalases. *Eur J Biochem* 69:603, 1976.
29. SHPITSBERG VL: Dissociation and re-association of catalase of human erythrocytes. *Biofizika* 11:766, 1966.
30. SAMEJIMA T, McCABE WJ, YANG JT: Reconstitution of alkaline-denatured catalase. *Arch Biochem Biophys* 127:354, 1968.
31. FURUTA H, HACHIMORI A, OHTA Y, SAMEJIMA T: Dissociation of bovine liver catalase into subunits on acetylation. *J Biochem* 76:481, 1974.
32. AEBI H, SCHERZ B, BEN-YOSEPH Y, WYSS SR: Dissociation of erythrocyte catalase into subunits and their reassociation. *Experientia* 31:397, 1975.

33. HOLMES RS, MASTERS CJ: Catalase heterogeneity. *Arch Biochem Biophys* 109:196, 1965.

34. HEIDRICH HG: New aspects on the heterogeneity of beef liver catalase. *Hoppe-Seyler's Z Physiol Chem* 349:873, 1968.

35. MORIKOFER-ZWEZ S, CANTZ M, KAUFMANN H, von WARTBURG JP, AEBI H: Heterogeneity of erythrocyte catalase. Correlations between sulfhydryl group content, chromatographic and electrophoretic properties. *Eur J Biochem* 11:49, 1969.

36. HOLMES RS, MASTERS CJ: Species specific features of the distribution and multiplicity of mammalian liver catalase. *Arch Biochem Biophys* 148:217, 1972.

37. JONES GL, MASTERS CJ: On the synthesis and degradation of the multiple forms of catalase in mouse liver. *Arch Biochem Biophys* 161:601, 1974.

38. MASTERS C, PEGG M, CRANE D: On the multiplicity of the enzyme catalase in mammalian liver. *Mol Cell Biochem* 70:113, 1986.

39. ROBBI M, LAZAROW PB: Synthesis of catalase in two cell-free protein-synthesizing systems and in rat liver. *Proc Natl Acad Sci USA* 75:4344, 1978.

40. FURUTA S, LeDONNE N, TOLBERT NE: In Seno S, Okada Y (eds): *International Cell Biology*. Tokyo, Japanese Society for Cellular Biology, 1984, p 284.

41. JONES GL, MASTERS CJ: On the nature and characteristics of the multiple forms of catalase in mouse liver. *Arch Biochem Biophys* 169:7, 1975.

42. MAINFERME F, WATTIAUX R: Effect of lysosomes on rat liver catalase. *Eur J Biochem* 123:343, 1982.

43. CANTZ M, MORIKOFER-ZWEZ S, BOSSI E, KAUFMANN H, von WARTBURG JP, AEBI H: Alternative molecular forms of erythrocyte catalase. *Experientia* 24:119, 1968.

44. MIYAHARA T, TAKEDA A, HACHIMORI A, SAMEJIMA T: On the heterogeneity of catalase from goat liver. *J Biochem* 84:1267, 1978.

45. PEGG M, CRANE D, MASTERS C: Confirmation that catalase is a glycoprotein. *Biochem Int* 12:831, 1986.

46. CHANCE B: Enzyme-substrate compounds. *Adv Enzymol* 12:153, 1951.

47. HANSON LK, CHANG CK, DAVIS MS, FAJER J: Electron pathways in catalase and peroxidase enzymic catalysis. Metal and macrocycle oxidations of iron porphyrins and chlorins. *J Am Chem Soc* 103:663, 1981.

48. La MAR GN, de ROPP JS, LATOS-GRATZYNSKI L, BALCH AL, JOHNSON RB, SMITH KM, PARISH DW, CHENG R-J: Proton NMR characterization of the ferryl group in model heme complexes and hemoproteins: Evidence for the Fe^{IV}=O group in ferryl myoglobin and compound II of horseradish peroxidase. *J Am Chem Soc* 105:782, 1982.

49. CHANCE B, GREENSTEIN DS, ROUGHTON FJW: The mechanism of catalase action. I. Steady-state analysis. *Arch Biochem Biophys* 37:301, 1952.

50. MARNAGIN RC, WANG JH: Investigation of the catalytic mechanisms of catalase and other ferric compounds with doubly labeled O^{18} hydrogen peroxide. *J Am Chem Soc* 80:786, 1958.

51. CHANCE B, OSHINO N: Kinetics and mechanisms of catalase in peroxisomes of the mitochondrial fraction. *Biochem J* 122:225, 1971.

52. OSHINO N, CHANCE B: The role of H_2O_2 generation in perfused rat liver and the reaction of catalase compound I and hydrogen donors. *Arch Biochem Biophys* 154:117, 1973.

53. OSHINO N, OSHINO R, CHANCE B: The characteristics of the "peroxidatic" reaction of catalase in ethanol oxidation. *Biochem J* 131:555, 1973.

54. EATON JW, BORAAS M, ETKIN NL: Catalase activity and red cell metabolism, in Brewer GJ (ed): *Hemoglobin and Red Cell Structure and Function*. New York, Plenum, 1972, p 121.

55. FORMAN HJ, FISHER AB: Antioxidant defenses, in Gilbert DL (ed): *Oxygen and Living Processes*. New York, Springer-Verlag, 1981, p 235.

56. AEBI H, WYSS SR: Acatalasemia, in Stanbury JB, Wyngaarden JB, Frederickson DS (eds): *The Metabolic Basis of Inherited Disease*, 4th ed. New York, McGraw-Hill, 1978, p 1792.

57. AEBI H: Catalase in vitro, in Packer L (ed): *Methods in Enzymology*. New York, Academic, 1984, vol 105, p 121.

58. CHANCE B, SIES H, BOVERIS A: Hydroperoxide metabolism in mammalian organs. *Physiol Rev* 59:527, 1979.

59. BEN-YOSEPH Y, SHAPIRA E: Specific immunoassay for quantitative determination of human erythrocyte catalase. *J Lab Clin Med* 81:133, 1973.

60. NOVIKOFF AB, GOLDFISCHER S: Visualization of peroxisomes (microbodies) and mitochondria with diaminobenzidine. *J Histochem Cytochem* 17:675, 1969.

61. GOLDMAN BM, BLOBEL G: Biogenesis of peroxisomes: Intracellular site of synthesis of catalase and uricase. *Proc Natl Acad Sci USA* 75:5066, 1978.

62. KIRKMAN HN, GAETANI GF: Catalase: A tetrameric enzyme with four tightly bound molecules of NADPH. *Proc Natl Acad Sci USA* 81:4343, 1984.

63. THORUP OA JR, CARPENTER JT, HOWARD P: Human erythrocyte catalase: Demonstration of heterogeneity and relationship to erythrocyte ageing in vivo. *Br J Haemat* 10:542, 1964.

64. ALLEN DW, CADMAN S, McCANN SF, FINKEL B: Increased membrane binding of erythrocyte catalase in hereditary spherocytosis and in metabolically stressed normal cells. *Blood* 49:113, 1977.

65. de DUVE C, BAUDHUIN P: Peroxisomes (microbodies and related particles). *Physiol Rev* 46:323, 1966.

66. LAZAROW PB, de DUVE C: The synthesis and turnover of rat liver peroxisomes. *J Cell Biol* 59:491, 1973.

67. THEORELL H, BEZNAK M, BONNISCHEN R, PAUL KG, AKESON A: On the distribution of injected radioactive iron in guinea pigs and its rate of appearance in some hemoproteins and ferritins. *Acta Chem Scand* 5:554, 1951.

68. RECHCIGL M JR, HESTON WE: Genetic regulation of enzyme activity in mammalian system by the alteration of rates of enzyme degradation. *Biochem Biophys Res Commun* 27:119, 1967.

69. POOLE B, LEIGHTON F, de DUVE C: The synthesis and turnover of rat liver peroxisomes. II. Turnover of peroxisome proteins. *J Cell Biol* 41:536, 1969.

70. OGATA M, MIZUGAKI J, TAKAHARA S: Recovery of catalase activity after inhibition with aminotriazole in acatalasemia mice. *Tohoku J Exp Med* 116:39, 1975.

71. BEERS RF JR, SIZER IW: A spectrophotometric method for measuring the breakdown of hydrogen peroxide by catalase. *J Biol Chem* 195:133, 1952.

72. FEINSTEIN R, HOWARD JB, BALLONOFF LB, SEAHOLM JE: A rapid blood catalase screening technique adjustable to any level of activity. *Anal Biochem* 8:277, 1964.

73. LAMY J-N, LAMY-PROVANSAL J, JUND R, WEILL JD: Methode automatique de dosage de la catalase dans le sang et les erythrocytes. *Ann Biol Clin (Paris)* 26:417, 1968.

74. LEIGHTON F, POOLE B, BEAUFAY H, BAUDHUIN P, COFFEY JW, FOWLER S, de DUVE C: The large-scale separation of peroxisomes, mitochondria, and lysosomes from the livers of rats injected with Triton WR-1399: Improved isolation procedures, automated analysis, biochemical and morphological properties of fractions. *J Cell Biol* 37:482, 1968.

75. AEBI H, SUTER H: Catalase, in Yunis JJ (ed): *Biochemical Methods in Red Cell Genetics*. New York, Academic, 1969, p 255.

76. GROSS J: Katalase-Siebtest für Massenuntersuchungen auf Hypo- und Akatalasie. *Z Med Labortech* 10:90, 1969.

77. OHKURA K, NUMATA N, ANAN K: A single screening test for the blood catalase activity. *Jpn J Hum Genet* 13:208, 1968.

78. AEBI H, CANTZ M, SUTER H: Cellular distribution of catalase activity in red cells of homozygous and heterozygous cases of acatalasia. *Experientia* 21:713, 1965.

79. AEBI H, CANTZ M: Ueber die cellulare Verteilung der Katalase im Blut Homozygoter und heterozygotes Defektträger (Akatalasie). *Humangenetik* 3:50, 1966.

80. HOSOI T, SUTER H, YAHARA S, AEBI H: Pseudomosaicism in acatalasemic red cells visualized by fluorescent antibody technique. *Experientia* 25:313, 1969.

81. DAVIES P, DRATH DB, ENGEL EE, HUBER GL: The localization of catalase in the pulmonary alveolar macrophage. *Lab Invest* 40:221, 1979.

82. DEISSEROTH A, DOUNCE AL: Catalase: Physical and chemical properties, mechanisms of catalysis, and physiological role. *Physiol Rev* 50:319, 1970.

83. SCHONBAUM GR, CHANCE B: Catalase, in Boyer PD (ed): *The Enzymes*. New York, Academic, 1976, p 363.

84. SHINGU M, YOSHIOKA K, NOBUNAGA M, YOSHIDA K: Human vascular smooth muscle cells and endothelial cells lack catalase activity and are susceptible to hydrogen peroxide. *Inflammation* 9:309, 1985.

85. SACKS T, MOLDOW CF, CRADDOCK PR, BOWERS TK, JACOB HS: Oxygen radicals mediate endothelial cell damage by complement-stimulated granulocytes. An in vitro model of immune vascular damage. *J Clin Invest* 61:1161, 1978.

86. WANDERS RJA, KOS M, ROEST B, MEIJER AJ, SCHRAKAMP G, HEYMANS HSA, TEGELAERS WHH, van den BOSCH H, SCHUTGENS RBH, TAGER JM: Activity of peroxisomal enzymes and intracellular distribution of catalase in Zellweger syndrome. *Biochem Biophys Res Commun* 123:1054, 1984.

87. WANDERS RJA, SCHRAKAMP G, van den BOSCH H, TAGER JM, SCHUTGENS RBH: A prenatal test for the cerebro-hepato-renal (Zellweger) syndrome by demonstration of the absence of catalase-containing particles (peroxisomes) in cultured amniotic fluid cells. *Eur J Pediatr* 145:136, 1986.

88. OSHINO N, JAMIESON D, CHANCE B: The properties of hydrogen peroxide production under hypoxic and hyperoxic conditions of perfused rat liver. *Biochem J* 146:53, 1975.

89. NICHOLLS P: Activity of catalase in the red cell. *Biochim Biophys Acta* 99:286, 1965.

90. AGAR NS, SADRZADEH SMH, HALLAWAY PE, EATON JW: Erythrocyte catalase: A somatic oxidant defense? *J Clin Invest* 77:319, 1986.

91. JONES GM, SANFORD KK, PARSHAD R, GANTT R, PRICE FM, TARONE RE:

Influence of added catalase on chromosome stability and neoplastic transformation of mouse cells in culture. *Br J Cancer* 52:583, 1985.

92. KEILIN D, HARTREE EF: Properties of catalase. Catalysis of coupled oxidation of alcohols. *Biochem J* 39:293, 1945.

93. COHEN G, HOCHSTEIN P: Glutathione peroxidase: The primary agent for the elimination of hydrogen peroxide in erythrocytes. *Biochemistry* 2:1420, 1963.

94. CHANCE B, OSHINO N, SUGANO T, JAMIESON D: Role of catalase in ethanol metabolism, in Thurman RG, Williamson JR, Yonatani T, Chance B (eds): *Alcohol and Aldehyde Metabolizing Systems*. New York, Academic, 1974.

95. VATSIS KP, SCHULMAN MP: Absence of ethanol metabolism in "acatalasemic" hepatic microsomes that oxidize drugs. *Biochem Biophys Res Commun* 52:588, 1973.

96. VATSIS KP, SCHULMAN MP: Pathways of ethanol oxidation in hepatic microsomes of acatalasemic (Csb) mice. *Adv Exp Med Biol* 85A:303, 1977.

97. BOSRON WF, LI T-K: Alcohol dehydrogenase, in Jacoby WB (ed): *Enzymatic Basis of Detoxification*. New York, Academic, 1980, vol 1, p 231.

98. OSHINO N, JAMIESON D, SUGANO T, CHANCE B: Optical measurement of the catalase-hydrogen peroxide intermediate (compound I) in the liver of anesthetized rats, and its implication to hydrogen peroxide production in situ. *Biochem J* 146:67, 1975.

99. AEBI H, FREI E, KNAB R, SIEGENTHALER P: Untersuchungen über die Formiatoxydation in der Leber. *Helv Physiol Pharmacol Acta* 15:150, 1957.

100. AEBI H, KOBLET H, von WARTBURG JP: Ueber den Mechanismus der biologischen Methanoloxydation. *Helv Physiol Pharmacol Acta* 15:384, 1957.

101. AWASTHI YC, SRIVASTAVA SK, SNYDER LM, EDELSTEIN L, FORTIER NL: L-Dopa peroxidase activity of human erythrocyte catalase. *J Lab Clin Med* 89:763, 1977.

102. SNYDER LM, EDELSTEIN L, FORTIER N, CARIGLIA N, JACOBS J, CIPRO C: The protective effect of L-Dopa on Heinz body formation in G6PD deficient red cells. *Experientia* 30:85, 1974.

103. SAVAGE N, PRINZ W: Cinnabarinate synthase from Baboon (Papio ursinus) liver: Identity with catalase. *Biochem J* 161:551, 1977.

104. FEINSTEIN RN: Cinnabarinate synthase activity in normal and acatalasemic mice. *Proc Soc Exp Biol Med* 158:398, 1978.

105. NISHIMURA ET, HAMILTON HB, KOBARA TY, OGURA Y, DOI K: Carrier state in human acatalasemia. *Science* 130:333, 1959.

106. OGATA M, SADAMOTO M, TAKAHARA S: On minimal catalitic activity in Japanese acatalasemic blood. *Proc Jpn Acad Sci* 42:828, 1966.

107. TAKAHARA S: Progressive oral gangrene probably due to lack of catalase in blood (acatalasemia): Report of nine cases. *Lancet* ii:1101, 1952.

108. MATSUNAGA T, SEGER R, HOGER P, TIEFENAUER L, HITZIG WH: Congenital acatalasemia: A study of neutrophil functions after provocation with hydrogen peroxide. *Pediatr Res* 19:1187, 1985.

109. TAKAHARA S, OGATA M: Metabolism in Japanese acatalasemia with special reference to superoxide dismutase and glutathione peroxidase, in Hayaishi O, Asada K (eds): *Biochemical and Medical Aspects of Active Oxygen*. Baltimore, University Park Press, 1977, p 275.

110. AEBI H, HEINIGER JP, BUTLER R, HASSIG A: Two cases of acatalasia in Switzerland. *Experientia* 17:466, 1961.

111. AEBI H: The investigation of inherited enzyme deficiencies with special reference to acatalasia, in Crow JF, Neel JV (eds): *Proc Third Internatl Congr Hum Genet, 1966*. Baltimore, Johns Hopkins Press, 1967, p 189.

112. OHKURA K, OGURA Y, TAKAHARA S: Population studies of acatalasemia and hypocatalasemia in Japan, Ryukyu and Taiwan. Communication to the Third International Congress on Human Genetics. Chicago, 1966.

113. KROOTH RS, HOWELL RR, HAMILTON HB: Properties of acatalasemic cells growing in vitro. *J Exp Med* 115:313, 1962.

114. KROOTH RS: Some properties of diploid cell strains developed from the tissues of patients with inherited biochemical disorders. *In Vitro* 2:82, 1967.

115. SADAMOTO M: Nature of cultured cells of the skin from acatalasemic individuals with Takahara's disease. *Acta Med Okayama* 20:193, 1966.

116. OGATA M, MIZUGAKI J: Properties of erythrocyte catalase from heterozygotes for Japanese type acatalasemia. *Acta Med Okayama* 33:205, 1979.

117. AEBI H, WYSS SR, SCHERZ R, GROSS J: Properties of erythrocyte catalase from homozygotes and heterozygotes for Swiss-type acatalasemia. *Biochem Gen* 14:791, 1976.

118. VUILLAUME M, CALVAYRAC R, BEST-BELPOMME M, TARROUX P, HUBERT M, DECROIX Y, SARASIN A: Deficiency in the catalase activity of xeroderma pigmentosum cell and simian virus 40-transformed human cell extracts. *Cancer Res* 47:538, 1986.

119. MATUO Y: In vivo liver catalase-depressing substance from rhodamine sarcoma. *Gann* 59:405, 1968.

120. MATUO Y, NISHIKAWA K, HORIO T, OKUNUKI K: Effect of growth on rhodamine sarcoma in rat on some liver enzyme activities. *Gann* 59:299, 1968.

121. NAKAMURA T, MATUO Y, NISHIKAWA K, HORIO T, OKUNUKI K: Effects on various types of liver catalase by growth of rhodamine sarcoma and by administration of in vivo catalase-depressing substance prepared from the tumor. *Gann* 59:317, 1968.

122. KASHIWAGI K, TOBE T, HIGASHI T, WARABIOKA K: Impaired synthesis of liver catalase in tumor-bearing rats. *Gann* 63:57, 1972.

123. NANCE WE, EMPSON JR, BENNETT TW, LARSON L: Haptoglobin and catalase loci in man: Possible genetic linkage. *Science* 160:1230, 1968.

124. KAZIRO K, KIKUCHI G, NAKAMURA H, YOSHIYA M: Die Frage nach der physiologischen Funktion der Katalase in menschlichen Organismus: Notiz über die Entdeckung einer Konstitutionsanomalie "Anenzymia catalasea." *Chem Ber* 85:886, 1952.

125. OGATA M, MIZUGAKI J, TAKETA K, TAKAHARA S: Activities of catalase in leukocytes and glucose-6-phosphate dehydrogenase in erythrocytes of hypocatalasemia and acatalasemia. *Tohoku J Exp Med* 122:93, 1977.

126. OGATA M, MIZUGAKI J, TAKAHARA S: Catalase activity in the organs of Japanese acatalasemics. *Tohoku J Exp Med* 113:239, 1974.

127. JACOB HS, INGBAR SH, JANDL JH: Oxidative hemolysis and erythrocyte metabolism in hereditary acatalasia. *J Clin Invest* 44:1187, 1965.

128. PANIKER NIV, IYER GYN: Erythrocyte catalase and detoxification of hydrogen peroxide. *Can J Biochem* 43:1029, 1965.

129. OGATA M, MIZUGAKI J, IZUMI M, TAKETA K: Polyacrylamide gradient gel electrophoretic studies of residual catalase in acatalasemia. *Physiol Chem Phys Med NMR* 15:31, 1983.

130. OGATA M, MIZUGAKI J: Residual catalase in Japanese type acatalasemia. *Cell Struct Funct* 3:279, 1978.

131. OGATA M, MIZUGAKI J: Heterogeneity of erythrocyte catalase in Japanese-type acatalasemia by electrofocusing. *Biochem Gen* 20:265, 1982.

132. OGATA M, MIZUGAKI J: Properties of catalase subfractions separated by chromatofocusing of acatalasemia hemolysates. *Acta Med Okayama* 36:73, 1982.

133. HOSOI T: Fluorescent antibody technique utilized for studies on cellular distribution of erythrocytic antigens. *Acta Hemat Jap* 31:138, 1968.

134. AEBI H, WYSS SR: The role of enzyme variants, polymorphisms and enzyme hybrids in enzyme deficiency conditions. *Acta Biol Med Germ* 40:537, 1981.

135. TAKAHARA S: Acatalasemia and hypocatalasemia in the Orient. *Semin Hematol* 8:397, 1971.

136. OGATA M, HAYASHI S, TAKAHARA S: Estimation of the frequency of the recessive gene of acatalasemia in Japan. *Acta Med Okayama* 25:193, 1971.

137. JUNIEN C, TURLEAU C, de GROUCHY J, SAID R, RETHOVE MO, TENCONI R, DUFIER JC: Regional assignment of catalase (CAT) gene to band 11p13. Association with the aniridia-Wilms' tumor-gonadoblastoma (WAGR) complex. *Ann Genet* 23:165, 1980.

138. WIEACKER P, MUELLER CR, MAYEROVA A, GRZESCHIK KH, ROPERS HH: Assignment of the gene coding for human catalase to the short arm of chromosome 11. *Ann Genet* 23:73, 1980.

139. JUNIEN C, TURLEAU C, LENOIR GM, PHILIP T, SAID R, DESPOISSE S, LAURENT C, RETHORE MO, KAPLAN JC, de GROUCHY J: Catalase determination in various etiologic forms of Wilms' tumor and gonadoblastoma. *Cancer Genet Cytogenet* 7:51, 1983.

140. GUSELLA J, VARSANYI-BREINER A, KAO F, JONES C, PUCK T, KEYS C, ORKIN SH, HOUSMAN D: Precise localization of human β-globin gene complex on chromosome 11. *Proc Natl Acad Sci USA* 76:5239, 1979.

141. KITTUR SD, HOPPENER JWM, ANTONARAKIS SE, DANIELS JDJ, MEYERS DA, MAESTRI NE, JANSEN M, KORNELUK RG, NELKIN BD, KAZAZIAN HH Jr: Linkage map of the short arm of human chromosome 11: Location of the genes for catalase, calcitonin, and insulin-like growth factor II. *Proc Natl Acad Sci USA* 82:5064, 1985.

142. HOPPENER JWM, STEENBERG PH, ZANDBERG J, BAKKER E, PEARSON PL, GEURTS van KESSEL AHM, JANSZ HS, LIPS CJM: Localization of the polymorphic human calcitonin gene on chromosome 11. *Hum Genet* 66:309, 1984.

143. PRZEPIORKA D, BAYLIN SB, MCBRIDE OW, TESTA JR, de BUSTROS A, NELKIN BD: The human calcitonin gene is located on the short arm of chromosome 11. *Biochem Biophys Res Commun* 120:493, 1984.

144. de MARTINVILLE B, FRANCKE U: The c-Ha-ras-1, insulin and β-globin map outside the deletion associated with aniridia-Wilms' tumour. *Nature* 305:641, 1983.

145. de MARTINVILLE B, GIACALONE J, SHIH C, WEINBERG RA, FRANCKE U: Oncogene from human EJ bladder carcinoma is located on the short arm of chromosome 11. *Science* 219:498, 1983.

146. FRANCKE U, GEORGE DL, BROWN MG, RICCARDI VM: Gene dose effect: Intraband mapping of the LDH A locus using cells from four individuals with different interstitial deletions of 11p. *Cytogenet Cell Genet* 19:197, 1977.

147. LEWIS WH, COGUEN JM, POWERS VE, WILLARD HF, MICHALOPOULOS EE: Gene order on the short arm of human chromosome 11: Regional assign-

ment of the LDH A gene distal to catalase in two translocations. *Hum Genet* 71:249, 1985.

148. de MARTINVILLE B, LEARY J, ULLRICH A, FRANCKE U: The human insulin gene (INS) maps on the short arm of chromosome 11. Human gene mapping 6. *Cytogenet Cell Genet* 32:265, 1982.

149. BRISSENDEN JE, ULLRICH A, FRANCKE U: Human chromosomal mapping of genes for insulin-like growth factors I and II and epidermal growth factor. *Nature* 310:781, 1984.

150. TRICOLI JV, RALL LB, SCOTT J, BELL GI, SHOWS TB: Localization of insulin-like growth factor genes to human chromosomes 11 and 12. *Nature* 310:784, 1984.

151. ANTONARAKIS SE, PHILLIPS JA III, MALLONEE RL, KAZAZIAN HH Jr, FEARON ER, WABER PG, KRONENBERG HM, ULLRICH A, MEYERS DA: β-Globin locus is linked to the parathyroid hormone (PTH) locus and lies between the insulin and PTH loci in man. *Proc Natl Acad Sci USA* 80:6615, 1983.

152. KORNELUK RG, QUAN F, LEWIS WH, GUISE KS, WILLARD HF, HOLMES MT, GRAVEL RA: Isolation of human fibroblast catalase cDNA clones. *J Biol Chem* 259:13819, 1984.

153. QUAN F, KORNELUK RG, TROPAK MB, GRAVEL RA: Isolation and characterization of the human catalase gene. *Nucleic Acids Res* 14:5321, 1986.

154. BELL GI, NAJARIAN RC, MULLENBACH GT, HALLEWELL RA: cDNA sequence coding for human kidney catalase. *Nucleic Acids Res* 14:5561, 1986.

155. FURUTA S, HAYASHYI H, HIJIKATA M, MIYAZAWA S, OSUMI T, HASHIMOTO T: Complete nucleotide sequence of cDNA and deduced amino acid sequence of rat liver catalase. *Proc Natl Acad Sci USA* 83:313, 1986.

156. MILLER RW, FRAUMENI JF, MANNING MD: Association of Wilms' tumor with aniridia, hemihypertrophy and other congenital malformations. *N Engl J Med* 270:922, 1964.

157. FERRELL RE, RICCARDI VM: Catalase levels in patients with aniridia and/or Wilms' tumor: Utility and limitations. *Cytogenet Cell Genet* 31:120, 1981.

158. NIIKAWA N, FUKUSHIMA Y, TANIGUCHI N, IIZUKA S, KAJII T: Chromosome abnormalities involving 11p13 and low erythrocyte catalase activity. *Hum Genet* 60:373, 1982.

159. BARLETTA C, CASTELLO MA, FERRANTE E, MAVELLI I, CLERICO A, CIRIOLO MR, VIGNETTI P: 11p13 Deletion and reduced RBC catalase in a patient with aniridia, glaucoma and bilateral Wilms' tumor. *Tumori* 71:119, 1985.

160. BATEMAN JB, SPARKES MC, SPARKES RS: Aniridia: Enzyme studies in an 11p-chromosomal deletion. *Invest Ophthalmol Vis Sci* 25:612, 1984.

161. TURLEAU C, de GROUCHY J, TOURNADE M-F, GAGNADOUX M-F, JUNIEN C: Del 11p/aniridia complex. Report of three patients and review of 37 observations from the literature. *Clin Genet* 26:356, 1984.

162. KOUFOS A, HANSEN MF, LAMPKIN BC, WORKMAN ML, COPELAND NG, JENKINS NA, CAVENEE WK: Loss of alleles at loci on human chromosome 11 during genesis of Wilms' tumour. *Nature* 309:170, 1984.

163. KOUFOS A, HANSEN MF, COPELAND NG, JENKINS NA, LAMPKIN BC, CAVENEE WK: Loss of heterozygosity in three embryonal tumors suggests a common pathogenetic mechanism. *Nature* 316:330, 1985.

164. ORKIN SH, GOLDMAN DS, SALLAN SE: Development of homozygosity for chromosome 11p markers in Wilms' tumour. *Nature* 309:172, 1984.

165. REEVE AE, HOUSIAUX PJ, GARDNER RJM, CHEWINGS WE, GRINDLEY RM, MILLOW LJ: Loss of a Harvey ras allele in sporadic Wilms' tumour. *Nature* 309:174, 1984.

166. FEARON ER, VOGELSTEIN B, FEINBERG AP: Somatic deletion and duplication of genes on chromosome 11 in Wilms' tumours. *Nature* 309:176, 1984.

167. BOYD P, van HEYNINGEN V, SEAWRIGHT A, FEKETE G, HASTIE N: Use of catalase polymorphisms in the study of sporadic aniridia. *Hum Genet* 73:171, 1986.

168. RAIZIS AM, BECROFT DM, SHAW RL, REEVE AE: A mitotic recombination in Wilms' tumor occurs between the parathyroid hormone locus and 11p13. *Hum Genet* 70:344, 1985.

169. van HEYNINGEN V, BOYD PA, SEAWRIGHT A, FLETCHER JM, FANTES JA, BUCKTON KE, SPOWART G, PORTEOUS DJ, HILL RE, NEWTON MS, HASTIE ND: Molecular analysis of chromosome 11 deletions in aniridia-Wilms' tumor syndrome. *Proc Natl Acad Sci USA* 82:8592, 1985.

170. FEINSTEIN RN, BRAUN JT, HOWARD JB: Reversal of H₂O₂ toxicity in the acatalasemic mouse by catalase administration: Suggested model for possible replacement therapy of inborn errors of metabolism. *J Lab Clin Med* 68:952, 1966.

171. LEWIS WH: Establishment of mouse cell lines homozygous for temperature sensitive mutation in the catalase gene. *Somatic Cell Mol Genet* 11:319, 1985.

172. FEINSTEIN RN, HOWARD JB, BRAUN JT, SEAHOLM JE: Acatalasemic and hypocatalasemic mouse mutants. *Genetics* 53:925, 1966.

173. FEINSTEIN RN, BRAUN JT, HOWARD JB: Acatalasemic and hypocatalasemic mouse mutants. II. Mutational variations in blood and solid tissue catalase. *Arch Biochem Biophys* 120:165, 1967.

174. FEINSTEIN RN: Acatalasemia in the mouse and other species. *Biochem Genet* 4:135, 1970.

175. SRIVASTAVA SK, ANSARI NH: The peroxidatic and catalatic activity of catalase in normal and acatalasemic mouse liver. *Biochim Biophys Acta* 633:317, 1980.

176. FEINSTEIN RN, SUTER H, JAROSLOW BN: Blood catalase polymorphism: Some immunological aspects. *Science* 159:638, 1968.

177. DICKERMAN RC, FEINSTEIN RN, GRAHN D: Position of the acatalasemia gene in linkage group V of the mouse. *J Hered* 59:177, 1968.

PART 11

LYSOSOMAL ENZYMES

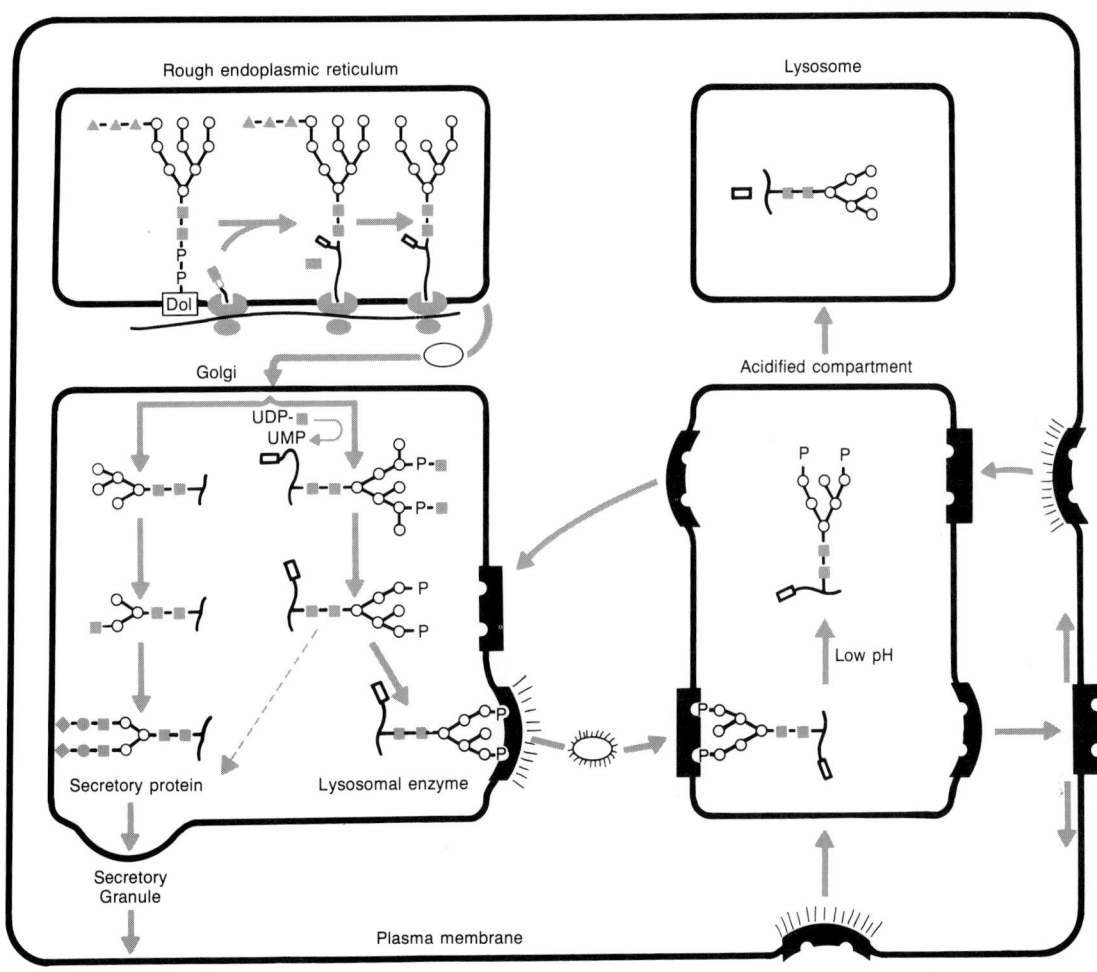

CHAPTER 61

THE MUCOPOLYSACCHARIDOSES

ELIZABETH F. NEUFELD
JOSEPH MUENZER

1. The mucopolysaccharidoses (MPS) are a group of disorders caused by deficiency of lysosomal enzymes needed for the stepwise degradation of glycosaminoglycans (mucopolysaccharides). Depending on the enzyme deficiency, the catabolism of dermatan sulfate, heparan sulfate, or keratan sulfate may be blocked, singly or in combination; chondroitin sulfate may also be involved. Undegraded glycosaminoglycan molecules are stored in lysosomes. Their accumulation eventually results in cell, tissue, or organ dysfunction. Glycosaminoglycan fragments generated by alternate pathways are excreted in urine. To date, 10 enzyme deficiencies that give rise to MPS have been identified. The enzyme deficiencies, affected glycosaminoglycans, and corresponding syndromes and syndrome subtypes are presented in Table 61-1.

2. The enzymes of glycosaminoglycan degradation that are relevant to MPS include four glycosidases, five sulfatases, and one nonhydrolytic transferase. These have been extensively purified, in many cases to homogeneity. Properties of the enzymes as well as biosynthesis and processing of several enzyme proteins have been elucidated. Cloning and characterization of the genes encoding the enzymes have been undertaken in many laboratories; precise identification of the mutations that cause the MPS is expected to result from these molecular studies.

3. The MPS share many clinical features, though in variable degrees, including a chronic and progressive course, multisystem involvement, organomegaly, dysostosis multiplex, and abnormal facies. Hearing, vision, cardiovascular function, and joint mobility may be affected. Profound mental retardation is characteristic of the Hurler syndrome, the severe form of the Hunter syndrome, and all subtypes of the Sanfilippo syndrome, but normal intellect may be retained in other MPS. The bony lesions of the Morquio syndrome are specific to that disorder. There is clinical similarity between different enzyme deficiencies, and conversely, a wide spectrum of clinical severity within any one enzyme deficiency. Thus, diagnosis and prognosis must be based on both enzymatic and clinical evaluation. In the absence of specific therapy, supportive management (with particular attention to respiratory and cardiovascular complications, hearing loss, and hydrocephalus) can greatly improve the quality of life for patients and their families.

4. Simple enzyme assays are available for the diagnosis of the MPS, using fibroblasts, leukocytes, or serum. Prenatal diagnosis following amniocentesis or chorionic villus biopsy is routine for some MPS and theoretically possible for all. By contrast, identification of heterozygotes remains difficult because of an overlap of normal and heterozygous levels of enzyme activity. Considerable progress has been made in the identification of carriers of the Hunter syndrome, the only X-linked MPS, but the procedures remain cumbersome, and the results are sometimes uninformative.

5. Except for the Hunter syndrome (iduronate sulfatase deficiency), the MPS are transmitted in autosomal recessive manner. The loci of several autosomal genes encoding enzymes of glycosaminoglycan degradation have been identified; the locus of the iduronate sulfatase gene has been assigned to Xq28.

Multiple allelism at each locus has been proposed to explain the clinical variability within each enzyme deficiency.

6. Several animal models of MPS have been developed: canine MPS I and MPS VII and feline MPS I and MPS VI. These are proving useful for evaluating new therapies such as bone marrow transplantation.

7. The MPS have been considered potentially amenable to enzyme replacement therapy, based in part on the ease with which biochemical correction occurs when cells cultured from MPS patients are provided with appropriate exogenous enzyme. Some recent success in altering the course of MPS I and VI by bone marrow transplantation suggests that sufficient enzyme can be provided by hematopoietic cells to check the storage of glycosaminoglycans. These encouraging results have been confirmed in animal models. However, the high risk and uncertain long-term effectiveness of bone marrow transplantation limit its value at the present time.

The mucopolysaccharidoses (MPS) are a family of heritable disorders caused by deficiency of lysosomal enzymes needed to degrade mucopolysaccharides (for which the preferred term is *glycosaminoglycans*). The undegraded or partially degraded glycosaminoglycans are stored in lysosomes (Fig. 61-1) and/or excreted in urine. Each of the known mucopolysaccharidoses involves the deficiency of one of 10 enzymes needed for the stepwise degradation of dermatan sulfate, heparan sulfate, or keratan sulfate, singly or in combination; chondroitin sulfate may also be affected. The disorders are chronic and progressive, and often display a wide spectrum of clinical severity within one enzyme deficiency. The classification and major features of the MPS are summarized in Table 61-1.

The discoveries that led to our understanding of the biochemical basis of the mucopolysaccharidoses are summarized elsewhere.[1,2] The reader is referred to the previous edition of this text and to earlier sources for comprehensive reviews of clinical and pathological aspects of the MPS.[3-5a]

ENZYMOLOGY OF GLYCOSAMINOGLYCAN DEGRADATION

Understanding the normal pathways of glycosaminoglycan catabolism is closely tied to the elucidation of enzyme deficiencies in the mucopolysaccharidoses. The role of many of the enzymes involved became apparent only through the consequences of their absence. Figures 61-2 to 61-5 illustrate enzymology of lysosomal degradation of dermatan sulfate, heparan sulfate, keratan sulfate, and chondroitin sulfate and enzyme deficiencies in the mucopolysaccharidoses. The glycosaminoglycans themselves are degradation product

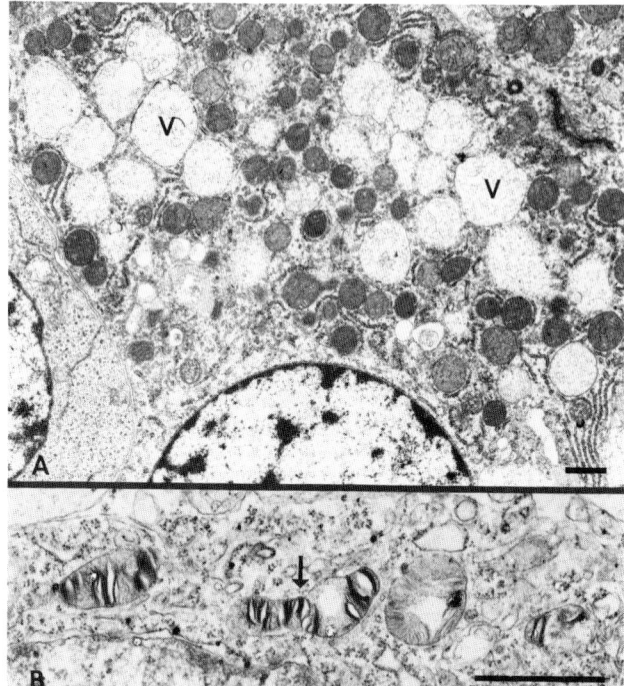

Fig. 61-1 Characteristic appearance of cells in mucopolysaccharidoses. *Upper panel:* large vacuoles (V) that may appear empty or contain fine granular material, in a hepatocyte from a Hurler patient. *Lower panel:* inclusion bodies (arrow), named zebra bodies for their striated appearance, in a cerebral neuron of a Hunter patient. The vacuoles are lysosomes engorged with stored glycosaminoglycans, whereas the zebra bodies also contain glycolipids. The bars represent 1 μm. *(Courtesy of Dr. A.J. Garvin, Medical University of South Carolina, Charleston, S.C.)*

by proteolytic cleavage of proteoglycans, the macromolecular forms in which they exist in connective tissue.

Most of the enzyme deficiencies were discovered in the 1970s; the literature of that decade is summarized in the previous edition.[5] Subsequently, interest focused on purification and characterization of the normal enzymes and elucidation of their synthesis and transport to lysosomes. The cloning and sequencing of the corresponding genes have begun. Such studies will provide the background for understanding the disease-producing mutations at the level of protein and nucleic acid.

Enzymes of Dermatan Sulfate Catabolism

Dermatan sulfate consists of sulfated N-acetylgalactosamine alternating with uronic acid residues.[6] The latter are predominantly L-iduronic acid, some of which are sulfated; there are also occasional glucuronic acid residues. Degradation proceeds stepwise from the nonreducing end, as shown schematically in Fig. 61-2, by the sequential action of three glycosidases and two sulfatases.

Glycosidases. α-L-Iduronidase, the enzyme that is deficient in MPS I, hydrolyzes terminal α-L-iduronic acid residues of dermatan sulfate (Fig. 61-2, reaction 2) and of heparan sulfate (see below). The enzyme is present in tissues in low abundance; between 20,000- and 200,000-fold enrichment was required for its purification to homogeneity from human kidney,[7] liver,[8,9] and lung.[10,11]

Biosynthetic labeling experiments in human fibroblasts have shown that α-L-iduronidase is synthesized as a precursor of

approximately 75 kDa and processed to a mature form of 66 kDa.[12] Smaller polypeptides have been found in purified preparations of α-L-iduronidase, but these probably represent products of proteolytic nicking in vivo or during purification rather than true subunits. The enzyme is active as a monomer. In the course of its synthesis, the precursor form of α-L-iduronidase is modified by formation of mannose 6-phosphate residues that serve to bind the enzyme to the phosphomannosyl receptor and to target it to lysosomes.[13,14] A small fraction of the newly made enzyme is secreted and may be taken up by receptor-mediated endocytosis.[15] The secreted, phosphorylated precursor form of α-L-iduronidase is identical to the "Hurler corrective factor" that normalizes the degradation of glycosaminoglycans in MPS I fibroblasts.[2]

β-Glucuronidase, the enzyme deficient in MPS VII, removes the glucuronic acid residues present in dermatan sulfate (Fig. 61-2, reaction 5) as well as in heparan sulfate and the chondroitin sulfates (see below). It is no doubt the best studied of the lysosomal enzymes of glycosaminoglycan degradation. It has been purified to homogeneity from a number of mammalian sources (see, e.g., Refs. 16 to 18). It has a dual localization in some tissues, particularly rodent liver, where it also occurs in microsomes in association with the protein egasyn.[19,20] The active enzyme is a tetramer of subunits of 75 kDa; these are synthesized in precursor form and are proteolytically processed at the carboxy terminus but not at the amino end, except for loss of the signal peptide.[21] Studies of β-glucuronidase have figured prominently in the elucidation of lysosomal enzyme transport, for it was the recognition marker of this enzyme that was first identified as mannose 6-phosphate (Ref. 22; see Chap. 62). Full-length cDNA has been cloned from human and rodent sources, sequenced, and expressed.[23,24]

The glycosidase thought to be required for hydrolysis of the N-acetylgalactosamine residues of dermatan sulfate (Fig. 61-2, reaction 4) is β-hexosaminidase A or β-hexosaminidase B. Both isoenzymes are deficient in the G_{M2} gangliosidosis known as Sandhoff disease (see Chap. 72). This suggests that Sandhoff disease patients should have as prominent dermatan sulfate storage as patients with MPS I, II, VI, or VII. Yet such is not the case,[25] and glycosaminoglycan accumulation in fibroblasts from Sandhoff disease patients appears to be only moderately elevated.[26] It is possible that the S isoenzyme of β-hexosaminidase, which is present in these patients, can participate in the degradation of dermatan sulfate.

Sulfatases. Iduronate sulfatase, the enzyme deficient in MPS II, specifically removes the sulfate group from the 2 position of L-iduronic acid present in dermatan sulfate (Fig. 61-2, reaction 1) and in heparan sulfate (see below). It has been purified to near homogeneity from human plasma and placenta and shown to exist as a monomer of about 80 kDa.[27,28] The enzyme was originally studied as the "Hunter corrective factor" which normalizes the defective glycosaminoglycan degradation of fibroblasts from Hunter patients.[2] The factor is presumed to be the secreted form of iduronate sulfatase, bearing a mannose 6-phosphate recognition marker. However, direct studies of the synthesis and transport of this interesting enzyme are not yet available.

A different sulfatase, lacking in MPS VI, is required to hydrolyze the sulfate groups in the 4 position of N-acetylgalactosamine residues (Fig. 61-2, reaction 3). Desulfation of N-acetylgalactosamine 4-sulfate is a property of the enzyme arylsulfatase B, which was known in different contexts long before its deficiency in Maroteaux-Lamy syndrome was appreci-

Table 61-1 Classification of the Mucopolysaccharidoses

Number	Eponym	Clinical manifestations	Enzyme deficiency	Glycosaminoglycan affected
MPS I H	Hurler	Corneal clouding, dysostosis multiplex, organomegaly, heart disease, mental retardation, death in childhood	α-L-Iduronidase	Dermatan sulfate, heparan sulfate
MPS I S	Scheie	Corneal clouding, stiff joints, normal intelligence, and life span	α-L-Iduronidase	Dermatan sulfate, heparan sulfate
MPS I H/S	Hurler-Scheie	Phenotype intermediate between I H and I S	α-L-Iduronidase	Dermatan sulfate, heparan sulfate
MPS II (severe)	Hunter (severe)	Dysostosis multiplex, organomegaly, no corneal clouding, mental retardation, death before 15 years	Iduronate sulfatase	Dermatan sulfate, heparan sulfate
MPS II (mild)	Hunter (mild)	Normal intelligence, short stature, survival to 20s to 60s	Iduronate sulfatase	Dermatan sulfate, heparan sulfate
MPS III A	Sanfilippo A	Profound mental deterioration, hyperactivity, relatively mild somatic manifestations	Heparan N-sulfatase	Heparan sulfate
MPS III B	Sanfilippo B	Phenotype similar to III A	α-N-Acetylglucosaminidase	Heparan sulfate
MPS III C	Sanfilippo C	Phenotype similar to III A	Acetyl-CoA:α-glucosaminide acetyltransferase	Heparan sulfate
MPS III D	Sanfilippo D	Phenotype similar to III A	N-Acetylglucosamine 6-sulfatase	Heparan sulfate
MPS IV A	Morquio A	Distinctive skeletal abnormalities, corneal clouding, odontoid hypoplasia; milder forms known to exist	Galactose 6-sulfatase	Keratan sulfate, chondroitin 6-sulfate
MPS IV B	Morquio B	Spectrum of severity as in IV A	β-Galactosidase	Keratan sulfate
MPS V	No longer used	—	—	—
MPS VI	Maroteaux-Lamy	Dysostosis multiplex, corneal clouding, normal intelligence; survival to teens in severe form; milder forms known to exist	N-Acetylgalactosamine 4-sulfatase (arylsulfatase B)	Dermatan sulfate
MPS VII	Sly	Dysostosis multiplex, hepatosplenomegaly; wide spectrum of severity	β-Glucuronidase	Dermatan sulfate, heparan sulfate, chondroitin 4-, 6-sulfates
MPS VIII	No longer used	—	—	—

ated. The enzyme has been purified to homogeneity from human placenta and liver, where it exists as a monomer, and from feline liver, where it exists as a dimer.[29] In the presence of reducing agents, the monomer from human tissues dissociates into subunits of 43 kDa and 13 kDa.[29a] Biosynthetic studies in human fibroblasts have shown that arylsulfatase B is synthesized as a precursor of 64 kDa that becomes phosphorylated and proteolytically processed to a mature form.[30]

Hyaluronidase. The enzymes described above are exoglycosidases and exosulfatases; they can hydrolyze linkages only at the nonreducing terminus of the glycosaminoglycans. Hyaluronidase is an endohexosaminidase that can cleave dermatan sulfate internally between N-acetylgalactosamine and the occasional adjoining glucuronic acid residues.[6] Though the fragments of dermatan sulfate found in urine of MPS patients are probably generated by hyaluronidase, the role of the enzyme in the normal degradation of dermatan sulfate is not known. Cleavage by hyaluronidase followed by excretion of the resulting fragments may be considered an alternate catabolic route when the primary pathway is blocked; it is limited to certain tissues, such as liver, and does not occur in fibroblasts.[31]

Enzymes of Heparan Sulfate Catabolism

Heparan sulfate consists of glucuronic acid and L-iduronic acid residues, some of which are sulfated, alternating with α-linked glucosamine residues.[6] The latter are either sulfated or acetylated on the amino group and may also be sulfated on the 6-hydroxyl. Heparan sulfate is found in nearly all cells in association with the cell membrane. Though it shares with heparin a similarity in name and in carbohydrate composition, heparan sulfate is not an effective anticoagulant.

Heparan sulfate is degraded stepwise, as shown schematically in Fig. 61-3, by the action of three glycosidases, three or perhaps four sulfatases, and one enzyme that is not a hydrolase but an acetyltransferase.

Glycosidases. Terminal L-iduronic acid and glucuronic acid residues of heparan sulfate are hydrolyzed by α-L-iduronidase and β-glucuronidase, respectively (Fig. 61-3, reactions 2 and 7). These enzymes have been discussed in the context of dermatan sulfate degradation. Individuals with α-L-iduronidase deficiency (MPS I) or β-glucuronidase deficiency (MPS VII) are therefore blocked in the degradation of heparan sulfate as well as of dermatan sulfate.

α-N-Acetylglucosaminidase, the enzyme deficient in MPS III B, is required for the removal of the N-acetylglucosamine residues that exist in heparan sulfate or are generated during lysosomal degradation of this polymer by the action of acetyl-CoA transferase (Fig. 61-3, reaction 5). It has been purified to homogeneity from human urine, where it exists in oligomeric form.[32] Its biosynthesis in fibroblasts proceeds from a precursor form of 87 kDa to mature forms of 76 and 73 kDa.[33]

Sulfatases. Iduronate sulfatase is required for the desulfation of 2-sulfated iduronic acid residues in heparan sulfate (Fig. 61-

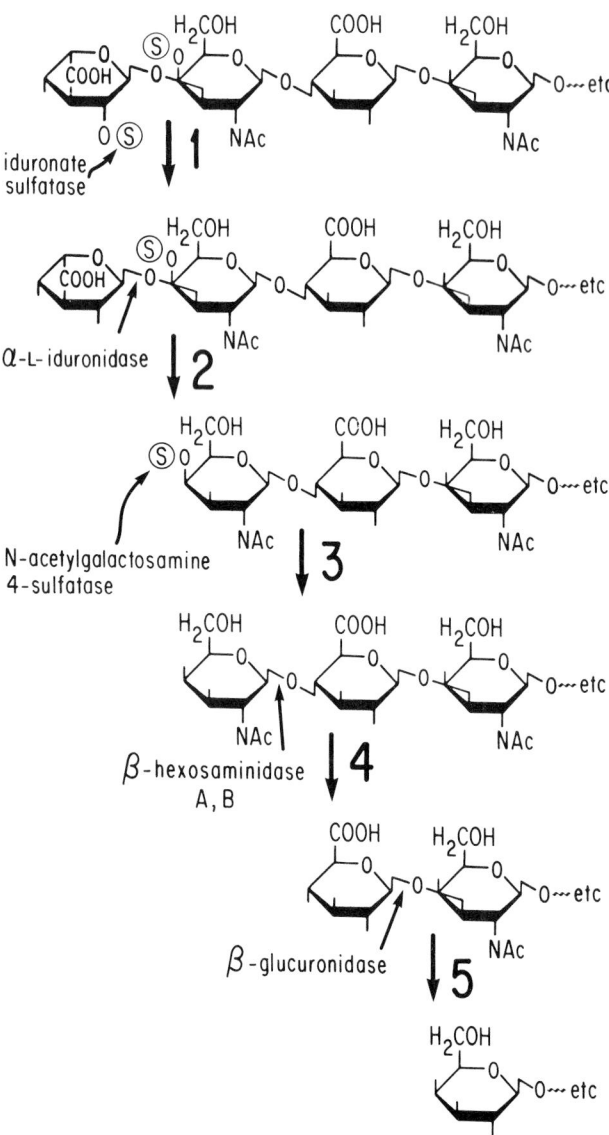

Fig. 61-2 Stepwise degradation of dermatan sulfate. The deficiency diseases corresponding to the numbered reactions are: 1 = MPS II, Hunter syndrome; 2 = MPS I, Hurler, Scheie, and Hurler-Scheie syndromes; 3 = MPS VI, Maroteaux-Lamy syndrome; 4 = Sandhoff disease; and 5 = MPS VII, Sly syndrome. This schematic drawing depicts all structures known to occur within dermatan sulfate, and does not imply that they occur in equal proportion. For instance, only a few of the L-iduronic acid residues are sulfated, and L-iduronic acid occurs much more frequently than glucuronic acid.

3, reaction 1). This enzyme has been discussed in the context of dermatan sulfate degradation, for which it is also required. Patients with iduronate sulfatase deficiency (MPS II) are blocked in the catabolism of both dermatan sulfate and heparan sulfate.

Glucuronate 2-sulfatase is a newly discovered lysosomal enzyme[34] for which there is as yet no known deficiency disease. It hydrolyzes the rare sulfated glucuronic acid residue present in heparan sulfate (Fig. 61-3, reaction 6). Glucuronate sulfatase is present in fibroblasts of patients with MPS II and is therefore distinct from iduronate sulfatase. The 2-sulfated glucuronic acid structure itself was discovered only recently in heparin,[35] heparan sulfate,[36] and chondroitin sulfate.[37] Its presence in dermatan sulfate has been suggested but not

proven. As has been the case with many other enzymes of glycosaminoglycan catabolism, the role of glucuronate sulfatase may be appreciated only when a deficiency disease is found. The enzyme has recently been purified to homogeneity from human liver.[37a]

Heparan N-sulfatase, the enzyme deficient in MPS III A, is specific for sulfate groups linked to the amino group of glucosamine (Fig. 61-3, reaction 3). Technically, such groups are sulfamate rather than sulfate, and the enzyme is often designated as "sulfamate sulfohydrolase" or "sulfamidase." It has recently been purified to homogeneity from human tissues, where its subunits of 56 kDa exist as dimers.[38]

N-acetylglucosamine 6-sulfatase (Fig. 61-3, reaction 8) is deficient in mucopolysaccharidosis III D. The enzyme was previously described as specific for the sulfated N-acetylglucosamine residues of heparan sulfate which are in α-linkage, and to be inactive toward the same residues in keratan sulfate, which are in β-linkage.[39] However, the earlier data have been reinterpreted in the light of new findings which will be discussed in the section on keratan sulfate degradation. The sulfatase is in fact able to desulfate 6-sulfated N-acetylglucosamine present in α- or in β-linkage or even free as a monosaccharide.[40,40a] The enzyme has been purified to homogeneity from human liver, where it exists in two forms; one consists of a monomer of 78 kDa, and the other of two subunits, of 32 and 48 kDa.[40b]

Acetyltransferase. Perhaps the most intriguing of the catabolic enzymes is acetyl-CoA:α-glucosaminide N-acetyltransferase, the enzyme that is deficient in MPS III C.[41] It is the only known degradative lysosomal enzyme that is not a hydrolase. It catalyzes the acetylation of the glucosamine amino groups that have become exposed by the action of heparan N-sulfatase (Fig. 61-3, reaction 4). Free glucosamine can be substituted in vitro for the glycosaminoglycan substrate, making studies much easier.[42,43] Although the enzyme has been purified only to a modest degree,[44,45] much is known about its mechanism of action.[46] On the cytoplasmic side, the enzyme acetylates itself by transfer of acetyl groups from acetyl-CoA; this half-reaction occurs at a neutral pH. On the luminal side, where the pH is acidic, the enzyme transfers its acetyl group to a glucosamine residue. A histidine is implicated at the active site.[47] The two-step mechanism, proposed on the basis of kinetic studies,[46] has been confirmed by genetic evidence; cells from one group of MPS III C patients can catalyze the first half-reaction but not the second, whereas cells from the other group lack this activity.[48]

Endoglycosidases. Endoheparanases may also participate in the catabolism of heparan sulfate by cleaving the polymer into smaller fragments, some of which escape in urine.[49] Both endo-N-acetylglucosaminidase and endoglucuronidase activities have been reported,[50,51] but more recent studies have identified only an endoglucuronidase.[51a] As in the case of dermatan sulfate cleavage by hyaluronidase, cleavage of heparan sulfate by endoglucuronidase may provide an alternative pathway that limits the amount of glycosaminoglycan stored in tissues of patients with MPS I, II, III, or VII.

Enzymes of Keratan Sulfate Catabolism

Keratan sulfate is the only glycosaminoglycan that contains no uronic acid. Instead, galactose residues, mostly sulfated, alter-

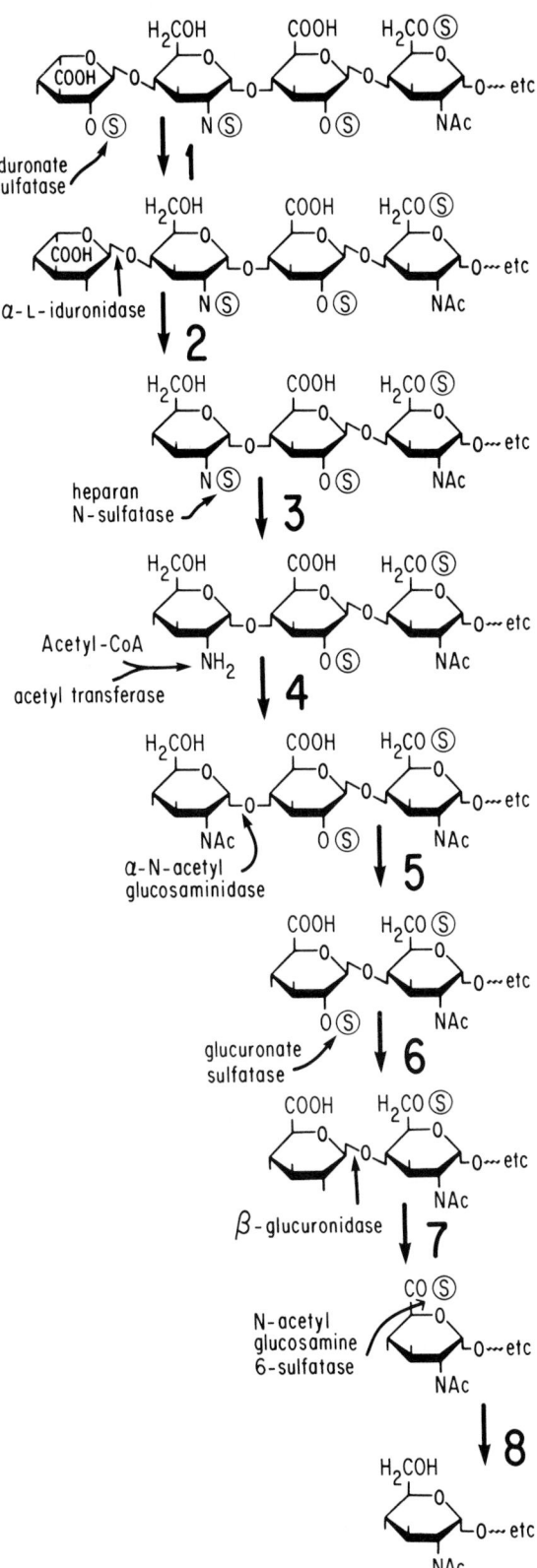

Fig. 61-3 Stepwise degradation of heparan sulfate. The deficiency diseases corresponding to the numbered reactions are: 1 = MPS II, Hunter syndrome; 2 = MPS I, Hurler, Scheie, and Hurler-Scheie syndromes; 3 = MPS III A, Sanfilippo A syndrome; 4 = MPS III C, Sanfilippo C syndrome; 5 = MPS III B, Sanfilippo B syndrome; 6 = no deficiency disease yet known; 7 = MPS VII, Sly syndrome; 8 = MPS III D, Sanfilippo D syndrome. The schematic drawing depicts all structures known to occur within heparan sulfate, and does not imply that they occur stoichiometrically. Very few of the glucuronic acid residues are sulfated.

nate with sulfated N-acetylglucosamine.[6] Inability to degrade keratan sulfate gives rise to MPS IV, the Morquio syndrome. The unique clinical manifestations of this disorder may be attributed to the restricted tissue distribution of keratan sulfate (corneas and cartilage) in contrast to the much wider distribution of dermatan sulfate and heparan sulfate. Like the two other glycosaminoglycans, keratan sulfate is degraded sequentially from the nonreducing end by the action of glycosidases and sulfatases, as shown in Fig. 61-4.

Glycosidases. The galactose residues of keratan sulfate are removed by β-galactosidase (Fig. 61-4, reaction 2). Normal β-galactosidase is a well-characterized lysosomal enzyme (e.g., Refs. 52, 53). The monomer is synthesized in human fibroblasts as a precursor of 85 kDa and processed to a smaller mature form;[54,55] the native enzyme exists as a very large multimer aggregate of 600 kDa.[55] The normal enzyme hydrolyzes terminal β-linked galactose residues found in G_{M1} ganglioside, glycoproteins, oligosaccharides, as well as in keratan sulfate. Total absence of β-galactosidase activity results in G_{M1} gangliosidosis (see Chap. 71). A mutation that selectively impairs catalytic activity toward keratan sulfate results in MPS IV B.[5,54–56]

β-N-Acetylhexosaminidase (β-hexosaminidase) is a well-known enzyme that has been studied extensively and is discussed in this volume in the context of G_{M2} gangliosidosis (see Chap. 72). Its role in the degradation of keratan sulfate appears unique in that it can participate in two alternative reactions. One is the conventional removal of a terminal N-acetylglucosamine residue, which can be catalyzed by both the A and B isoenzymes of β-hexosaminidase (Fig. 61-4, reaction 4). However, in addition, the A isoenzyme, though not the B, can remove N-acetylglucosamine 6-sulfate *en bloc* (Fig. 61-4, reaction 5).[57] This is the first instance of a mammalian glycosidase that does not require the substrate sugar to be free of substituents. The 6-sulfated amino sugar is thought to occupy the anionic site that is also used for G_{M2} ganglioside.[58] It is likely that the S isoenzyme of β-hexosaminidase also has such activity, since it catalyzes the hydrolysis of p-nitrophenyl or 4-methylumbelliferyl β-N-acetylglucosamine 6-sulfate. There is evidence that this one-step removal of sulfated N-acetylglucosamine occurs in vivo,[59] but the precise contribution of each of the two alternative reactions to the normal degradation of keratan sulfate is not known.

Sulfatases. The sulfatase that cleaves the sulfate from galactose residues (Fig. 61-4, reaction 1) is deficient in patients with MPS IV A. The enzyme and the deficiency were discovered by use of oligosaccharide substrates that had been prepared from chondroitin 6-sulfate and therefore contained sulfated N-acetylgalactosamine; as a result, the enzyme was called N-acetylhexosamine or N-acetylgalactosamine 6-sulfatase.[60,61] The enzyme has been extensively purified and shown to be specific for the "galacto" configuration—that is, it utilizes 6-sulfated galactose or N-acetylgalactosamine but not 6-sulfated N-acetylglucosamine.[62–64] It is therefore specific for the 6-sulfated galactose residues of keratan sulfate and the 6-sulfated N-acetylgalactosamine residues of chondroitin 6-sulfate. Degradation of the latter polymer is also impaired in MPS IV A.

The N-acetylglucosamine 6-sulfatase that catalyzes reaction 3 in Fig. 61-4 is now known to be the same enzyme that cleaves the 6-sulfate from N-acetylglucosamine in heparan sulfate (reaction 8 in Fig. 61-3). It is lacking in patients with

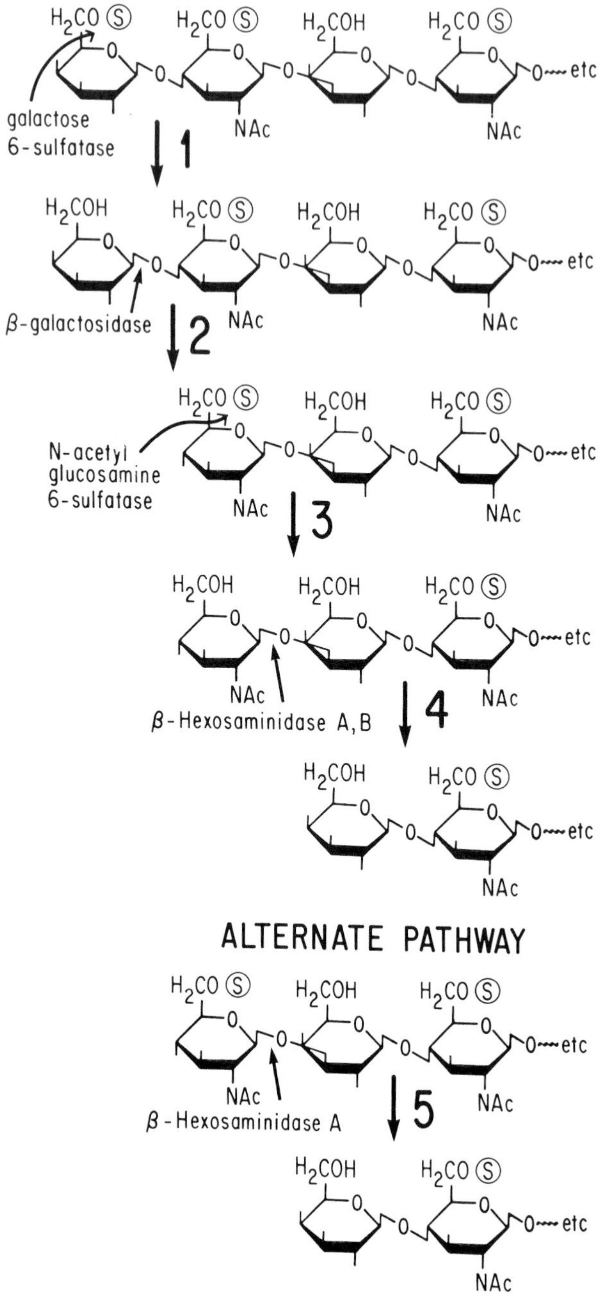

Fig. 61-4 Stepwise degradation of keratan sulfate. The deficiency diseases corresponding to the numbered reactions are: 1 = MPS IV A, Morquio A syndrome; 2 = MPS IV B, Morquio B syndrome; 3 = MPS III D, Sanfilippo D syndrome; 4 = Sandhoff disease; and 5 = Tay-Sachs and Sandhoff disease. The alternate pathway releases intact N-acetylglucosamine 6-sulfate, a departure from the usual stepwise cleavage of sulfate and sugar residues.

MPS III D.[39] But since hexosaminidase A can bypass the block (reaction 5 in Fig. 61-4), patients with MPS III D excrete massive amounts of N-acetylglucosamine 6-sulfate rather than of keratan sulfate.[59,65,66]

Comments on Enzyme Deficiencies

Glycosaminoglycan Storage and Excretion. The type of glycosaminoglycans stored or excreted by MPS patients can generally be predicted from the enzyme deficiency and from the glycosaminoglycan synthesized by a particular tissue. With respect to fine structure, the prediction is that the nonreducing

terminus of the stored glycosaminoglycan would be the residue that is the normal substrate for the missing enzyme. This has been documented in a few cases; for instance, MPS II fibroblasts, lacking iduronate sulfatase, accumulate dermatan sulfate with the predicted 2-sulfated iduronic acid termini.[67,68] As pointed out above, endoglycosidases may bypass the block, and in a special case a glycosidase, β-hexosaminidase A, can remove a sulfated sugar when the sulfatase is absent. The low molecular weight compounds generated by the endocleavages or by β-hexosaminidase A can be found in urine, though they are often missed by the usual analyses, which are geared toward the larger polymers.

The lack of massive chondroitin sulfate storage and excretion in MPS IV, VI, and VII has been puzzling. Chondroitin 4-sulfate and chondroitin 6-sulfate require desulfation by N-acetylgalactosamine 4-sulfatase (arylsulfatase B) and N-acetylgalactosamine 6-sulfatase (galactose 6-sulfatase), respectively. The former enzyme is deficient in MPS VI and the latter in MPS IV A. In fact, MPS IV A patients excrete some chondroitin 6-sulfate, though not massive amounts; urinary chondroitin 4-sulfate is not elevated in MPS VI. This may be attributed to the ability of lysosomal hyaluronidase, an endo-hexosaminidase, to bypass the block at the position shown by arrows in Fig. 61-5. The same argument applies to the modest, if any, elevation of chondroitin 4- and 6-sulfate excretion in MPS VII[69] and in Sandhoff disease.[25]

Several cases of chondroitin sulfaturia were reported in patients who were subsequently found to have α-L-iduronidase deficiency.[69a,69b] The excretion of chondroitin 4- and 6-sulfates in MPS I remains unexplained; analytical error is possible, or alternatively, the chondroitin sulfate may be a degradation product of dermatan sulfate–chondroitin sulfate "hybrid" molecules.

There have been two reports describing patients with N-acetylglucosamine 6-sulfatase deficiency and combined heparan and keratan sulfaturia.[70,71] When the first report appeared, it was thought to represent a new enzyme deficiency and disease entity, which was designated MPS VIII. However, that report was subsequently retracted[72] and the classification of MPS VIII was declared void.[73] The enzymatic basis for the second case of combined heparan-keratan sulfate excretion is not known. Fibroblasts from the patient lack N-acetylglucosamine 6-sulfatase activity. According to Fig. 61-4, this should not result in keratan sulfaturia unless β-hexosaminidase A

Fig. 61-5 Degradation of chondroitin sulfate. Arrows show potential sites for cleavage of chondroitin 4-sulfate (*top*) and chondroitin 6-sulfate (*bottom*) into oligosaccharide fragments by hyaluronidase. The oligosaccharides are hydrolyzed further by stepwise action of N-acetylgalactosamine 4-sulfatase or N-acetylgalactosamine 6-sulfatase, β-hexosaminidase A or B, and β-glucuronidase.

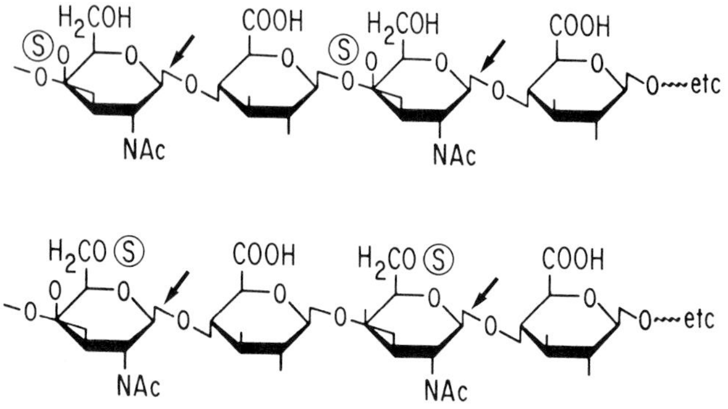

were also absent. Yet the patient's cells have a normal level of β-hexosaminidase A[74] and the biochemical basis for the double mucopolysacchariduria is not known.

Residual Enzyme Activity. One might expect an inverse relationship between clinical severity and level of residual enzyme activity.[75] This appears not to be the case in the mucopolysaccharidoses; in the assays commonly used, it is not possible to distinguish between the Hurler and Scheie syndromes or between the mild and severe forms of Hunter syndrome as the relevant enzyme appears to be equally inactive at both ends of the clinical spectrum. But as pointed out for the G_{M2} gangliosidoses (Ref. 76; Chap. 72) meaningful residual activity may not be apparent with synthetic substrate. Hopwood and colleagues[77-81] as well as others[82,83] have prepared oligosaccharide substrates which more closely resemble the natural glycosaminoglycans. Some success in discriminating between Hurler and Scheie syndromes[80] and between severe and mild forms of Morquio type A[82] has been achieved by use of the oligosaccharides. Matalon et al.[84] have reported discrimination of the Hurler syndrome from the clinically milder Scheie and Hurler-Scheie syndromes by use of desulfated dermatan and heparan as substrates.

Schuchman and Desnick[84a] have reported that the residual activity of MPS I fibroblasts could be greatly enhanced by treatment with thiol reducing agents, $MgCl_2$, and pyridoxal phosphate.

Cross-Reactive Protein. Antibodies raised against normal enzymes have been used to detect immunologically cross-reactive but enzymatically inert polypeptides produced by the patients. Such studies have often been carried out in the course of biosynthetic labeling experiments. Cells cultured from patients with MPS IV B[55] and MPS VI[30] were found to synthesize and process cross-reactive β-galactosidase and arylsulfatase B polypeptides, respectively, whereas cells from patients with MPS I[12] and MPS III B[33,85] were found to synthesize no cross-reactive α-L-iduronidase or α-N-acetylglucosaminidase polypeptides. Cross-reactive material has been found by conventional immunologic techniques in MPS II[86] and VII,[87] but not in MPS IV A.[88] These results should be interpreted with caution. On the one hand, an antiserum that is not absolutely specific for the enzyme of interest might give false positive results, and on the other, antiserum that is overly specific for the native configuration might fail to detect altered polypeptides. We believe the latter problem might have occurred in studies of α-L-iduronidase biosynthesis in Hurler syndrome,[12] as others have found cross-reactive material in all MPS I cell strains tested.[84a] Finally, it is likely that molecular heterogeneity will be found within each MPS, as has been the case in other disorders, and no generalizations should be made from studies of a small number of patients.

Glycosphingolipid Accumulation. In addition to glycosaminoglycans, several gangliosides (G_{M2}, G_{M3}, and G_{D3}) accumulate in the brain of MPS patients.[89-91] The lipids are probably stored in zebra bodies (Fig. 61-1, *panel B*), which are reminiscent of the lysosomal inclusions seen in the sphingolipidoses. The accumulation of gangliosides has been puzzling, since their catabolism does not require the enzymes of glycosaminoglycan degradation. However, the activity of several additional lysosomal enzymes is reduced in the MPS, probably as a result of inhibition by accumulated glycosaminoglycans.[92,93] The inhibition of ganglioside neuraminidase may be particu-

larly relevant.[93] It may be significant that lipid accumulation was found in brains of several patients with mental retardation (MPS IH, MPS II severe, and MPS III A and III B) but not in the brain of a patient with MPS I S, whose intelligence was normal.[89,91]

CLINICAL MANIFESTATIONS AND MANAGEMENT

Mucopolysaccharidosis I (Hurler, Scheie, and Hurler-Scheie Syndromes)

Deficiency of α-L-iduronidase can result in a wide range of clinical involvement, with three major recognized clinical entities. Hurler and Scheie syndromes represent phenotypes at the two ends of the clinical spectrum and the Hurler-Scheie syndrome represents a phenotype of intermediate clinical severity.[5] In addition, there are some patients that do not precisely fit into one of these three clinical entities.[94,95] The clinical phenotypes are not distinguishable biochemically by current methods, since they all have the following features: excessive urinary dermatan and heparan sulfate excretion, absence of α-L-iduronidase activity, and accumulation of glycosaminoglycan in cultured fibroblasts that is correctable by uptake of α-L-iduronidase. At the present time, assignment of the type of MPS I can be made only on the basis of clinical criteria.

MPS I H (Hurler Syndrome). Although the Hurler syndrome has been the prototype for the description of mucopolysaccharidoses, this may be misleading since it is not representative of all mucopolysaccharidoses, but only of the most severe end of a clinical spectrum[3-5] (Fig. 61-6). It is a progressive disorder with multiple organ and tissue involvement that leads to premature death, usually by 10 years of age. An infant with Hurler syndrome appears normal at birth but may have inguinal or umbilical hernias. Diagnosis of Hurler syndrome is commonly made between 6 and 24 months of age; a combination of enlarged liver and spleen, skeletal deformities, coarse facial features, enlarged tongue, prominent forehead, and joint stiffness first prompt medical attention. Patients with Hurler syndrome may be unusually large in infancy, but a deceleration of growth commonly occurs between 6 and 18 months with a maximum stature of 110 cm reported. Developmental delay is usually apparent by 12 to 24 months with a maximum functional age obtainable of 2 to 4 years followed by progressive deterioration. Most children with Hurler syndrome develop only limited language skills because of the developmental delay, chronic hearing loss, and an enlarged tongue. Some degree of hearing loss is probably universal, usually due to a combination of conductive and neurosensory problems; hearing aids are helpful in some children. Most Hurler children have recurring upper respiratory tract and ear infections, noisy breathing, and persistent, copious nasal discharge. Progressive clouding of the cornea also begins during the first year of life. Communicating hydrocephalus is present after the age of 2 to 3 years in most children but can occur as early as 6 months. The communicating hydrocephalus in Hurler syndrome is usually associated with increased intracranial pressure. Shunting procedures have been beneficial in some children. Obstructive airway disease, respiratory infection, and cardiac complications are the usual causes of death.

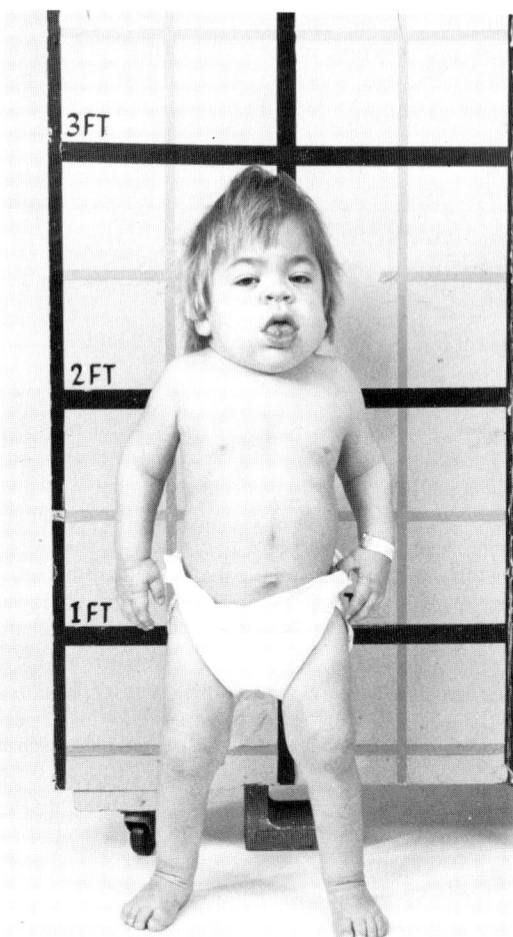

Fig. 61-6 MPS I H (Hurler syndrome) in a 4-year-old boy. Diagnosis was made at the age of 15 months at which time he had developmental delay, hepatomegaly, and skeletal involvement. At the time of the picture, the patient had short stature, an enlarged tongue, persistent nasal discharge, stiff joints, and hydrocephalus. Verbal language skills consisted of four to five words. The patient had a severe hearing loss and wore hearing aids. He was able to learn some sign language, which greatly improved communication. A ventriculoperitoneal shunt was placed after progressive ventricular enlargement was observed and elevated central nervous system pressure measured under anesthesia.

Radiologic changes seen in Hurler syndrome typify the constellation of skeletal abnormalities in mucopolysaccharidoses known as "dysostosis multiplex."[3,96] The skull is large with thickened calvarium, premature closure of lamboid and sagittal sutures, shallow orbits, enlarged J-shaped sella, and abnormal spacing of the teeth with dentigerous cysts. Anterior hypoplasia of lumbar vertebrae with kyphosis is seen early. The diaphyses of the long bones are enlarged with irregular appearances of the metaphyses. Epiphyseal centers are not well developed. The pelvis is usually poorly formed, with small femoral heads and coxa valga. Clavicles are short, thickened, and irregular. The ribs have been described as oar-shaped, narrowed at their vertebral ends, and flat and broad at their sternal ends. Phalanges are shortened and trapezoidal in shape with widening of the diaphysis.

MPS I H/S (Hurler-Scheie Syndrome). This classification is used to describe a clinical phenotype that is intermediate between the Hurler and Scheie syndromes. It is characterized by progressive somatic involvement, including dysostosis mul-

tiplex, with little or no intellectual dysfunction (Fig. 61-7).

Corneal clouding, joint stiffness, deafness, and valvular heart disease can develop by the early to midteens and cause significant impairment and loss of function. Some patients with MPS I H/S have micrognathism that creates a characteristic facies. *Pachymeningitis cervicalis*, compression of the cervical cord due to mucopolysaccharide accumulation in the dura, occurs in MPS I H/S, but communicating hydrocephalus appears to be uncommon in patients with normal intelligence. The onset of symptoms is usually observed between 3 and 8 years, and survival to adulthood is common. Cardiac involvement and upper airway obstruction contribute to clinical mortality.

MPS I S (Scheie Syndrome). This mild form of MPS I is characterized by joint stiffness, aortic valve disease, corneal clouding, and few other somatic features. Intelligence and

Fig. 61-7 MPS I H/S (Hurler-Scheie syndrome) in a 14 ½-year-old boy who demonstrates short stature, stiff joints, micrognathia, corneal clouding, umbilical hernia, hepatosplenomegaly, a systolic murmur, and normal intelligence. Diagnosis was made at the age of 1 year based on skeletal abnormalities consistent with mucopolysaccharidosis. At age 10, during attempted endotracheal intubation for carpal tunnel surgery, the patient had a respiratory arrest. Progressive joint restriction and corneal clouding had been the major clinical problem until the age of 16, when the patient developed symptoms of obstructive apnea and congestive heart failure. Nasal CPAP (continuous positive airway pressure) while sleeping has dramatically relieved the obstructive apnea, alleviating the need for a tracheostomy. He has had increasing visual loss with the development of glaucoma, which has been difficult to treat. He has graduated from high school and at age 19 is preparing to attend college.

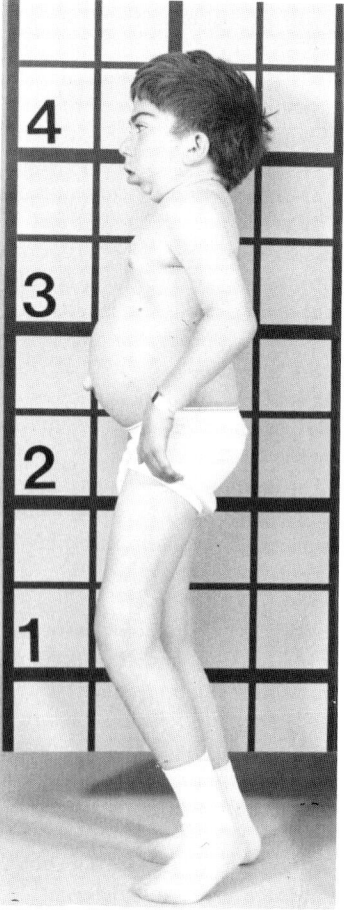

stature are normal. The joint deformity in the hands and development of carpal tunnel syndrome can lead to limitation of function. Ophthalmologic manifestations include glaucoma and retinal degeneration, which, in addition to the severe corneal clouding, may contribute to significant visual impairment. Aortic valvular disease is more likely to occur than mitral-valvular disease, with stenosis and/or regurgitation occurring due to buildup of mucopolysaccharide deposits on valves and chordae tendineae. Valve replacement has been reported in MPS I S and MPS I H/S, although experience is limited.[97] Compression of the cervical cord by thickened dura, pachymeningitis cervicalis, with resulting myelopathy can occur in MPS I S, though less commonly than in MPS I H/S. Deafness has been reported in some patients, but the etiology is unknown. The onset of significant symptoms is usually after the age of 5 years, with the diagnosis commonly made between 10 to 20 years of age.

Mucopolysaccharidosis II (Hunter Syndrome)

The Hunter syndrome comprises two recognized clinical entities, mild and severe, that represent two ends of a wide spectrum of clinical severity.[3-5,98-101] The mild and severe forms of Hunter syndrome can only be separated on clinical grounds, since the degree of iduronate sulfatase deficiency is similar in both forms. The severe form of Hunter syndrome has features similar to Hurler syndrome, except for the lack of corneal clouding and slower progression of somatic and central nervous deterioration. The mild form is somewhat analogous to MPS I S with a prolonged life span, minimal to no central nervous system involvement, and a slow progression of somatic deterioration. The occurrence of a pebbly, ivory-colored skin lesion over the back, upper arms, and lateral aspects of the thigh is distinctive to MPS II; the presence or absence of the skin lesion does not correlate with the severity of the disease. An X-linked recessive pattern of inheritance is found in both forms of Hunter syndrome; the inheritance of all the other MPS is autosomal recessive.

MPS II (Severe). The severe type of Hunter syndrome is characterized by coarse facial features, short stature, skeletal deformities, joint stiffness, and mental retardation (Fig. 61-8). The onset of the disease usually occurs between 2 and 4 years of age with progressive neurologic and somatic involvement.[3-5,101] The MPS II patients can have severe retinal degeneration, but the cornea characteristically remains clear (with one recorded exception[102]). Chronic diarrhea, due to autonomic nervous system involvement and perhaps also to mucosal dysfunction, is a troublesome problem in many of the younger patients. Recurrent ear infections and progressive hearing impairment occur in most patients. The central nervous system deterioration is probably exacerbated by moderate to severe communicating hydrocephalus with increased intracranial pressure after the age of 7 to 10 years. The communicating hydrocephalus may be present at the time of diagnosis and slowly progress over many years. Extensive neurologic involvement, similar to that of the late stages of Sanfilippo syndrome, precedes death, which usually occurs between 10 and 15 years. Obstructive airway disease and cardiac failure due to valvular dysfunction, myocardial thickening, pulmonary hypertension, coronary artery narrowing, and myocardial infarction are superimposed on severe neurologic disease and are the usual causes of death.

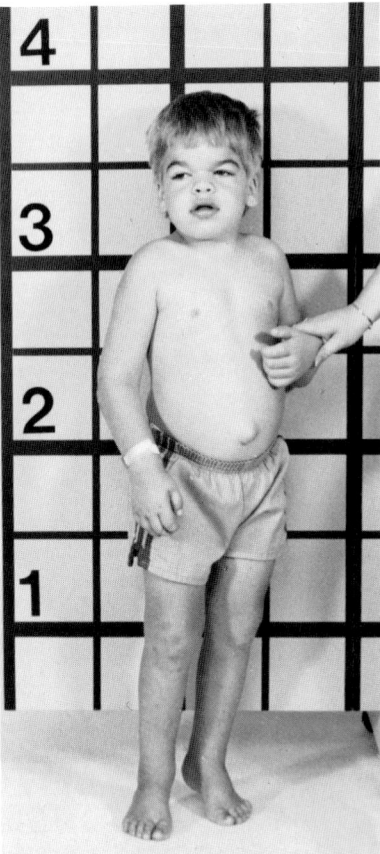

Fig. 61-8 Severe MPS II (Hunter syndrome) in a 6-year-old boy. Diagnosis was suspected at 1 year of age because of facial appearance, but a urine mucopolysaccharide screen was negative. Enzymatic diagnosis was made at age of 22 months after a family history of a maternal uncle with mental retardation and coarse facial features became known to the parents. At the time the picture was taken, the patient had hepatomegaly, joint stiffness, severe hearing loss, developmental delay, recurrent ear infections, and hyperactivity. At 8 years of age, he has an unsteady gait, refuses to eat solid foods, and has had significant loss in overall skills.

MPS II (Mild). A milder form of MPS II has been recognized with preservation of intelligence and survival into late adult life, but with obvious somatic involvement.[3-5,100] The adult patients can develop somatic features similar to those seen in severely affected Hunter patients, but at a greatly reduced rate of progression (Fig. 61-9). Hearing impairment is probably universal, and hearing aids are beneficial. Carpal tunnel syndrome and joint stiffness are common and can result in loss of function. Discrete corneal opacities detectable only by slit-lamp examination have been observed.[102] Electroretinography gives evidence of retinal dysfunction, but to a much lesser extent than in the severe form.[103] Chronic papilledema has been reported in patients with mild Hunter syndrome without raised intracranial pressure,[104,105] perhaps due to deposition of glycosaminoglycans within the sclera, with compression of the optic nerve at the intrascleral level. With one possible exception,[106] hydrocephalus has not been observed in the mild Hunter patients. A familial history of the disease appears to be much more common in the mild form than in the severe type. Patients with mild Hunter syndrome can survive into the fifth and sixth decades of life, with the longest known survival to age 87;[107] however, death may occur in early adulthood, usually from airway obstruction and cardiac failure.

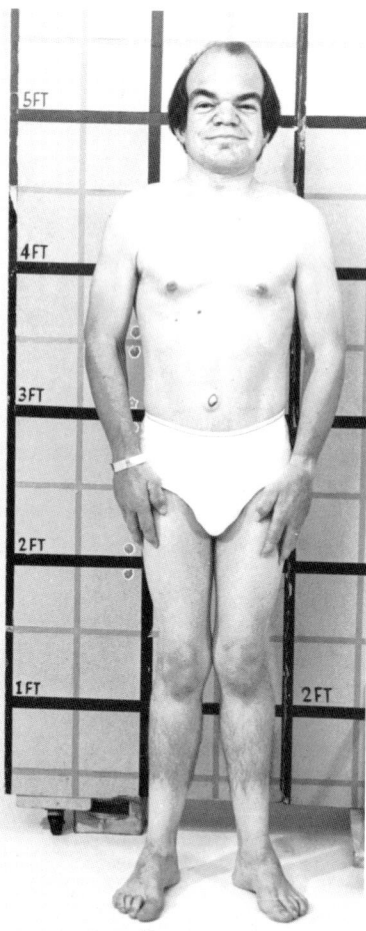

Fig. 61-9   Mild MPS II (Hunter syndrome) in a 28-year-old man. At the age of 13, when the diagnosis was made, he had joint stiffness, coarse facial features, heart murmur, and normal intelligence. The patient has had surgery for inguinal hernia and carpal tunnel syndrome. Two maternal uncles and a nephew also have Hunter syndrome. He is married and has a career as a minister and counselor.

Mucopolysaccharidosis III (Sanfilippo Syndrome)

Patients with Sanfilippo syndrome make up a biochemically diverse but clinically similar group of four recognized types. The deficient enzymes for the Sanfilippo subtypes are heparan N-sulfatase (type A); α-N-acetylglucosaminidase (type B); acetyl-CoA:α-glucosaminide acetyltransferase (type C); and N-acetyl glucosamine-6-sulfatase (type D). The four enzymes are required for the degradation of heparan sulfate.

The Sanfilippo syndrome is characterized by severe central nervous system degeneration, but only mild somatic disease (Figs. 61-10 and 61-11). Such disproportionate involvement of the central nervous system is unique among the MPS. Although intertype and intratype variability is observed,[108] the usual clinical findings are of a severe progressive neurologic disease. Onset of clinical features usually occurs between 2 and 6 years in a child who previously appeared normal. Presenting features can include hyperactivity with aggressive behavior, delayed development, coarse hair, hirsutism, and mild hepatosplenomegaly (the latter is found in young patients, but is uncommon in teenagers and adults with MPS III). There may be a significant delay in the diagnosis of MPS III after the onset of symptoms due to the mild somatic and radiographic features and to a high incidence of false negative results in the urinary screening test for mucopolysaccharides.

Coarse facial features are not a prominent component of Sanfilippo syndrome compared to other MPS. Some patients have normal features as adults. Skeletal involvement is minimal with only mild dysostosis multiplex, usually normal stature for age, and mild joint stiffness which rarely causes loss of function. Recurrent and sometimes severe diarrhea is unexplained but usually improves in older children. Speech development is often delayed with poor articulation and content. Proper speech is seldom acquired, and some patients may never learn to speak. Severe hearing loss is common in the moderate to severely involved patient. Seizures commonly occur in the older patient, but are usually easily controlled.

Severe neurologic degeneration occurs in most patients by 6 to 10 years of age, accompanied by rapid deterioration of social and adaptive skills. Cranial computed tomography (CT) at the onset of mental deterioration demonstrates mild to moderate cortical atrophy in most patients. Progression to severe cortical atrophy occurs in the late stages of the disease. Patients can be very withdrawn and lose contact with the environment as a result of the progressive dementia. Sleep disturbances and insomnia are common. Severe behavior problems are usual and can include poor attention span, uncontrollable

Fig. 61-10   MPS III A (Sanfilippo syndrome, A subtype) in a 7-year-old girl. The patient had normal developmental skills until about 5 years of age, at which time she was toilet trained, was able to feed and dress herself, and spoke in complete sentences. She was starting to learn to read and write. At the time of the picture, she had a normal physical appearance with mild hepatomegaly, but showed a significant loss in function. Now 11 years old, she is still toilet trained and able to feed herself and functions at a 3- to 4-year age level. She continues to have temper tantrums, but hyperactivity is not a major problem. Her language skills are limited, but she is usually able to communicate her needs. She has had minimal deterioration in skills over the last 2 to 3 years. She has a severely affected older brother, whose disease has progressed more rapidly.

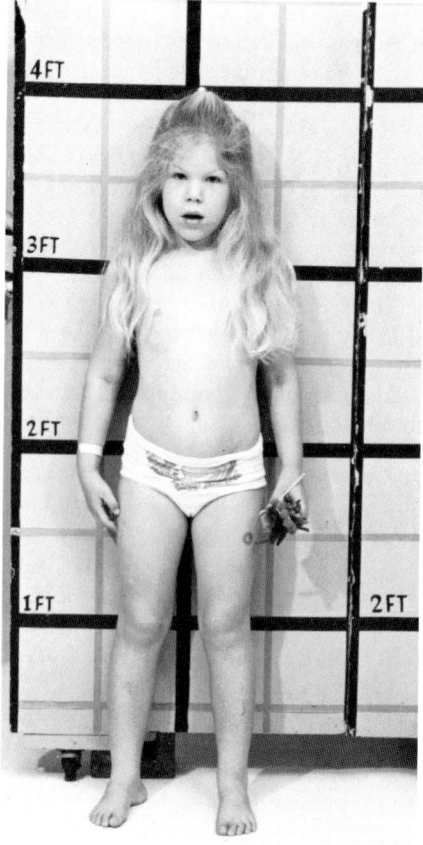

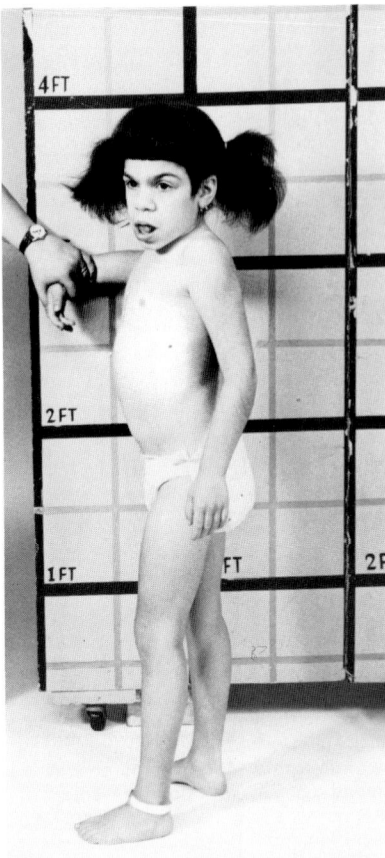

Fig. 61-11 MPS III B (Sanfilippo syndrome, type III B) in a 7-year-old girl. Enzymatic diagnosis was made at 14 months of age, when the child presented with slight coarsening of facial features, increased body hair, and a family history of an older brother with MPS III A, who was diagnosed at 3½ years of age. At the time of the picture, the patient had mild hepatomegaly, cardiomegaly, severe hearing loss, recurrent ear infections, hirsutism, marked hyperactivity, and aggressive behavior which limited her ability to interact with other children. Her speech was restricted to a few words, and she was not toilet trained. At age 11 years her hyperactivity is decreasing, allowing her to interact more with other children. She has no language skills, but is able to feed herself. She continues to attend a special school and in general is a happy child. She recently had her first seizure. Her brother's disease is more severe and progressed more rapidly.

hyperactivity, temper tantrums, destructive behavior, and physical aggression. Profound mental retardation and behavior problems often occur in patients with normal physical strength, making management particularly difficult. Pharmacologic management of the behavior problems is generally unsuccessful; behavior modification may occasionally be effective.[109] In a study of MPS III in the Netherlands,[108] dementia was noticed at an earlier age in type A (83 percent before age 6) than in types B and C. In three sibships (the families originated from two small adjacent villages in the Netherlands) with MPS III B, the 14 affected members developed dementia only in the third and fourth decades of life and had minimal somatic involvement; these may represent unusually mild cases.[109a]

Although individual patients with any of the four types of MPS III may be difficult to distinguish clinically, there are some differences among the four disorders. On the whole, type A is the most severe, with earlier onset, more rapid progression of symptoms, and shorter survival.[108] A particularly grave form of type A Sanfilippo syndrome occurs in the Cayman Islands.[110] Type B may be the most heterogeneous, with severe and mild forms reported even within the same family.[111,112] Type C appears intermediate between type A and the milder type B forms. Type D, of which only five patients have been described to date,[113,114] also appears heterogeneous. We emphasize that these differences between the four types of Sanfilippo syndrome are averages and that differential diagnosis must be performed by enzymatic tests.

Mucopolysaccharidosis IV (Morquio Syndrome)

Morquio syndrome is caused by defective degradation of keratan sulfate. Two enzyme deficiencies resulting in Morquio syndrome are now recognized, each with a wide spectrum of clinical manifestations; a deficiency of N-acetylgalactosamine 6-sulfatase, also known as galactose 6-sulfatase (type A) or of β-galactosidase (type B). The two types of Morquio syndrome are both characterized by short trunk dwarfism, fine corneal deposits, a skeletal (spondyloepiphyseal) dysplasia distinct from that in the other MPS, and preservation of intelligence (Fig. 61-12).

The predominant clinical features of Morquio syndrome are those related to the skeleton and its effects on the central nervous system. As in most mucopolysaccharidoses, patients with Morquio syndrome appear to be normal at birth. The appearance of genu valgus, kyphosis, growth retardation with short trunk and neck, and waddling gait with a tendency to fall are early symptoms of Morquio syndrome. Holzgreve et al.[115] report that the first symptoms caused by the disease in 11 patients with MPS IV A occurred between 1 and 3.5 years of age, but the diagnosis of Morquio syndrome was not made until 3 to 15 years of age. Typical skeletal anomalies of Morquio syndrome[5,5a] include: dwarfism with short trunk, platyspondyly, odontoid hypoplasia, kyphosis, hyperlordosis, scoliosis, ovoid deformities of the vertebrae, genu valgus, ulnar deviation of the wrist, valgus deformity of the elbow, inclinations of distal ends of radius and ulna toward each other, deformities of metacarpals and short phalanges, epiphyseal deformities of the tubular bones, widened metaphyses, and osteoporosis. Joints tend to be hypermobile secondary to ligamentous laxity, but decreased joint mobility can occur in the large joints (especially hips, knees, and sometimes elbows).

Odontoid hypoplasia is a universal clinical finding with grave medical consequences for patients with Morquio syndrome. The instability of the hypoplastic odontoid process with ligamentous laxity can result in life-threatening atlantoaxial subluxation. Cervical myelopathy can develop early in the patients with the severe form of Morquio syndrome. Patients with the severe form may not survive beyond their twenties or thirties. Paralysis from the myelopathy, restrictive chest wall movement, and valvular heart disease all contribute to their shortened life span. Surgery to stabilize the upper cervical spine, usually by spinal fusion, can be lifesaving.

Extraskeletal manifestations may include mild corneal clouding, hepatomegaly, cardiac valvular lesions, and small teeth with abnormally thin enamel and frequent caries formation. Unusual facial features (coarsening of facies, prognathism and broad mouth) are commonly found. Hearing loss has been reported to be frequent in Morquio syndrome[5] but was not found in any of the patients reported by Holzgreve et al.[115] They also report that in 11 MPS IV A patients (aged 3 to 15 years) hernias, aortic regurgitation, or congenital heart defects were not detected on routine clinical examination.

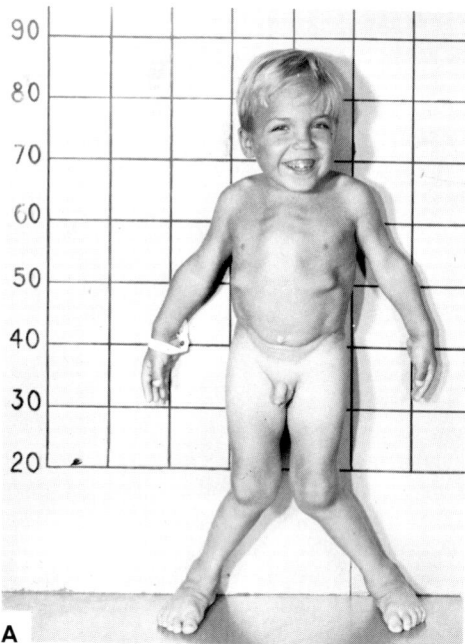

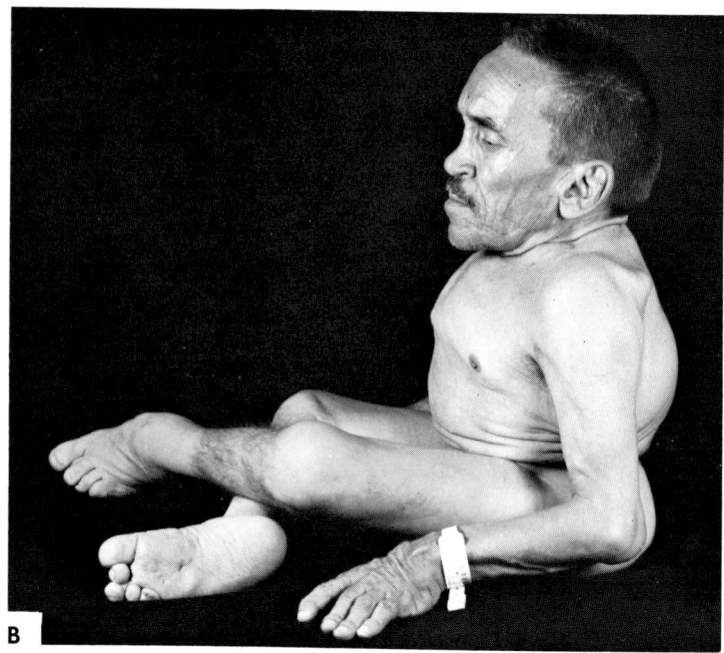

Fig. 6-12 MPS IV (Morquio syndrome). *A.* Clinically and radiologically this 8½-year-old boy shows the skeletal deformities typical of the Morquio syndrome. The mother noted flaring of the lower ribs at birth, flat feet at age 3 years, and a small size at age 4 when the diagnosis was made. *B.* At the age of 55, when this picture was taken, this man showed pectus carinatum, bilateral genu valgum, diffuse corneal clouding, atlantoaxial subluxation, and bilateral sensorineural deafness. He was always short. A protuberance of the chest was first noted at age 2. He attended a school for the handicapped and performed well academically. He worked all his life in a brother's architectural firm. Now age 68, he is probably the oldest patient with type A Morquio syndrome. A similarly affected brother died at age 24. (Both patients were described in Refs. 5 and 5a.)

A late onset variant of Morquio syndrome has been recognized with β-galactosidase deficiency, MPS IV B,[116,117] and was initially considered to be the mild form of Morquio syndrome because the progression of skeletal dysplasias and stunting of growth were less pronounced than in MPS IV A. However, subsequent reports have described patients with MPS IV B whose clinical disease was as severe as that seen in the severe form of MPS IV A.[118,119] On the other hand, patients with a mild form of Morquio syndrome due to deficiency of *N*-acetylgalactosamine 6-sulfatase (MPS IV A) have been reported who have almost normal stature, mild skeletal abnormalities with dyplastic hips, corneal clouding, and absent keratosulfaturia.[120–122] The severe and mild forms of Morquio syndrome are not caused by unique enzyme deficiencies, but each enzyme deficiency has a wide spectrum of clinical manifestations.

Maroteaux et al.[123] described two patients with a clinical picture consistent with Morquio disease, but with normal *N*-acetylgalactosamine 6-sulfatase and β-galactosidase activities. The biochemical defect is not yet known, but the finding suggests that yet another biochemical form of Morquio syndrome may exist.

Mucopolysaccharidosis VI (Maroteaux-Lamy Syndrome)

Maroteaux-Lamy syndrome was first recognized in 1963 by Maroteaux and coworkers as a Hurler-like syndrome, but with preservation of intelligence and excretion of predominantly dermatan sulfate. Milder forms of MPS VI have been recognized since the initial description of the disorder.[5] All forms of Maroteaux-Lamy syndrome are known to be due to a deficiency of a lysosomal enzyme, arylsulfatase B (also known as *N*-acetyl-galactosamine 4-sulfatase, which describes its function).

Mental development is usually normal in patients with Maroteaux-Lamy syndrome though physical and visual impairments may impede psychomotor performance. Although mental retardation has been reported in two families with arylsulfatase B deficiency,[124,125] it is not clear that the retardation was caused by the MPS.

The somatic involvement in the severe form of Maroteaux-Lamy syndrome is similar to that in Hurler syndrome (Fig. 61-13). An enlarged head and a deformed chest may be present at birth. Umbilical and/or inguinal hernias are common. Growth can be normal for the first few years of life but seems to virtually stop after the age of 6 or 8 years, with the ultimate height of severely affected patients ranging from 110 to 140 cm.[124] Corneal opacities are easily detected by slit-lamp examination. Obvious corneal clouding develops in some patients and can result in visual impairment. Restriction of joint movement (knee, hip, and elbow) develops in the first years of life, and the children assume a crouched stance. Claw hand deformities are seen in children secondary to flexion contractures of the fingers. Nerve entrapment syndromes, particularly of the carpal tunnel, are common and can be improved with surgery. The facies can remain relatively mildly affected in some patients, but others assume the coarseness characteristic of Hurler syndrome. Hepatomegaly is always present after the age of 6 years, and an enlarged spleen is found in one-half of the patients.[126] The skin usually is described as "tight," and mild hirsutism is found. The typical severe MPS VI patient at the end of the first decade of life has a shortened trunk with protuberant abdomen and prominent lumbar lordosis. Aortic valvular dysfunction due to a calcified stenotic valve is the most prominent clinical cardiac involvement. Most reported patients with the severe form of MPS VI died of heart failure in the second to third decades.

The skeletal changes associated with the severe MPS VI are similar to radiographic findings of Hurler syndrome and are

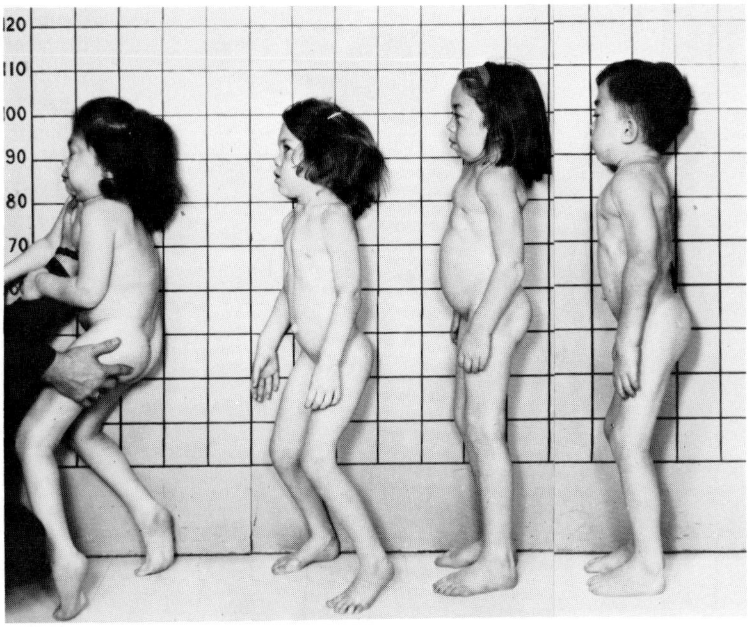

Fig. 61-13 MPS VI (Maroteaux-Lamy syndrome). These four sibs, all with the severe form of MPS VI, were aged 14, 9, 13, and 11 (from left to right) at the time of the picture.[5] In the oldest, noisy breathing was noted at 2 years of age, flexion contractures at the knees at 4 years. She was a good student. At the age of 9, she slowly developed generalized weakness to the point where she could not feed herself but remained alert. She was hospitalized at age 11 for her first episode of congestive heart failure and died at age 15½. The three other sibs have had a similar course.

striking examples of dysostosis multiplex. The pelvic changes are particularly severe with acetabulum hypoplasia and small flared iliac wings. The prominent radiologic features also include macrocephaly with a large sella, ovoid deformity of vertebral bodies, a hook-shaped deformity or blunt anterior hypoplasia of vertebral bodies of L1 to L2, epiphyseal dysplasia of the proximal femur, an elongated femoral neck in a valgus position, and irregular diaphyseal distension of tubular bones.

Spinal cord compression from thickening of the dura in the upper cervical spinal canal with resultant myelopathy is a frequent occurrence in patients with the milder forms of MPS VI. A 41-year-old woman with a mild to intermediate form of MPS VI had an insidious development of compressive cervical myelopathy with resulting spastic tetraparesis.[127] There was substantial improvement following laminectomy and excision of the markedly thickened dura (5 mm). The spinal cord compression with resultant myelopathy may be associated with developmental abnormalities of the vertebral bodies and dural thickening. The compression usually occurs in the cervical spine, but a compression myelopathy associated with a kyphoscoliotic deformity of thoracolumbar spine in a 10-year-old patient with MPS VI has been described.[128]

The mild and intermediate forms of Maroteaux-Lamy syndrome can be confused with MPS I S.[129] The short stature of patients with Maroteaux-Lamy syndrome appears to distinguish MPS VI from the Scheie syndrome.

Mucopolysaccharidosis VII (Sly Syndrome)

β-Glucuronidase deficiency was first recognized in a patient with a phenotype reminiscent of MPS I H or MPS II.[130] The patient had an unusual facies, protruding sternum, hepatosplenomegaly, umbilical hernia, thoracolumbar gibbus, marked vertebral deformities, and moderate mental deficiency (Fig. 61-14). Granulocytes showed striking coarse metachromatic granules. Fine corneal opacities were not noted until 8 years of age. Moderate mental retardation was evident by age 3 but appeared not to be progressive. In addition, neurologic regression did not occur after 3 to 4 years of age. Radiographic changes of dysostosis multiplex were moderately severe. Since

the description of the original patient, fewer than 20 patients with β-glucuronidase deficiency have been reported (reviewed in Refs. 69, 131). The patients have presented with a wide range of clinical severity. The factors common to all patients with β-glucuronidase deficiency are excess glycosaminoglycan excretion and coarse granulocyte inclusion. The early onset or more severe patients present with hepatosplenomegaly, inguinal and/or umbilical hernias, moderate skeletal abnormalities, history of repeated episodes of pneumonia in the first years of life, short stature, and developmental delay. Corneal clouding has been a variable finding. A severe neonatal form of β-glucuronidase deficiency has been reported in two infants who presented with hydrops fetalis, dysostosis multiplex, and clinical and pathologic findings of a lysosomal storage disorder.[132,133] This most severe form of β-glucuronidase deficiency is one of the few lysosomal storage diseases that may present at birth.

A milder form with later onset (after 4 years of age) is characterized by normal stature, completely normal intelligence, no facial dysmorphism, minimal skeletal change, and no significant corneal clouding.

Management

Since no specific treatment is available (see below, "Replacement Therapy—A Viable Concept?"), management of MPS patients consists of supportive care and treatment of complications. The progressive nature of organ involvement in MPS patients dictates the need for constant evaluation of their clinical status. Systematic evaluation of such areas as hearing, vision, and joint function coupled with treatment can lead to improved quality of life by minimizing the handicapping effects of diffuse systemic disease.

Hydrocephalus. Ventricular enlargement is known to occur in patients with MPS and may be due to the combination of cortical atrophy secondary to central nervous system degeneration or a defect in cerebrospinal fluid reabsorption.[134–139] The defective reabsorption of cerebrospinal fluid in MPS is presumably due to thickening of the meninges and dysfunction of the

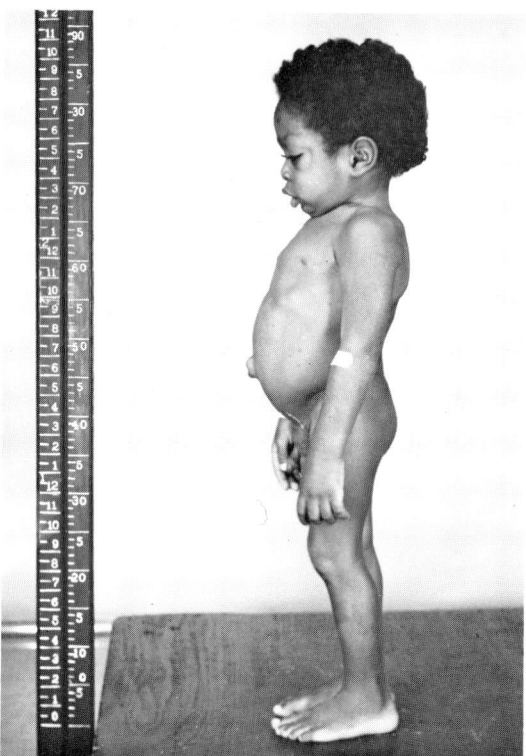

Fig. 61-14 MPS VII (Sly syndrome). This is the original patient with β-glucuronidase deficiency.[130] Aged 3 at the time this picture was taken, he showed flared ribs, pigeon breast, hepatosplenomegaly, and umbilical hernia. Now age 18, his major problems are orthopedic. Progressive kyphoscoliosis has been treated by a body brace. Because of odontoid hypoplasia, he wears a neck brace to stabilize his neck. Progressive deformity of the hips made walking painful for several years, but symptoms have abated, and he uses either a cane or walker when on his feet for prolonged periods. Mental retardation has been moderate but nonprogressive. Despite these limitations, he attends special school regularly, is happily adjusted, and appears to enjoy life and bring much joy to his family.

pacchionian granulation in the arachnoid villi. Thickened meninges and ventricular enlargement have been reported to be a common finding at autopsy in MPS. Acute communicating hydrocephalus has been reported in two patients with MPS I H.[138]

Computed tomographic (CT) studies on 12 patients with MPS showed that the development of hydrocephalus was variable and suggested that shunting procedures are sometimes indicated to improve quality of life.[137] Noncontrast cranial CT studies have been performed on 42 MPS patients (MPS I, II, and III) ranging in age from 18 months to 26 years (Ref. 140; J. Muenzer, unpublished). Mild to severe hydrocephalus was found in 32 out of 42 MPS patients. Ventricular enlargement was unsuspected in most patients at the time of initial evaluation. All patients with ventricular enlargement had mental retardation, with the degree of ventricular enlargement correlating with the severity of mental retardation, whereas only two of the ten patients with normal CT scans had mental retardation. Two patients with Hurler syndrome, who were less than 2 years of age, had minimally abnormal CT scans and mild developmental delay. The eight MPS patients with normal CT scans and normal intelligence represent only two MPS types, Hurler-Scheie and mild Hunter syndromes. The ventricular enlargement in Hurler and severe Hunter syndrome is usually associated with increased central nervous system pressure and a communicating hydrocephalus as demonstrated by lumbar cisternography. The CT scans in the older patients with San-

filippo syndrome showed ventricular enlargement with evidence of diffuse cortical atrophy. No evidence of papilledema was found in patients with hydrocephalus and documented increased intracranial pressure when examined under anesthesia.

Ventriculoperitoneal shunting in MPS patients with moderate to severe hydrocephalus is generally palliative. The degree to which hydrocephalus contributes to the neurologic deterioration in MPS is unknown. Few patients have been shunted at the onset of their hydrocephalus; early recognition of hydrocephalus and shunting may provide a better outcome. The presence of increased central nervous system pressure and progressive ventricular enlargement can be used as indications for a shunting procedure. The ventricular enlargement in Sanfilippo syndrome is probably secondary to cortical atrophy and these patients are not likely to benefit from shunting.

Vision. Corneal clouding is common in MPS I, MPS IV, MPS VI, and MPS VII and can lead to significant visual disability.[141,142] Corneal transplantation has been performed, but the long-term outcome is not always successful.[142a,b] Patients with clear grafts may still have poor vision because of associated retinal and/or optic nerve disease. Glaucoma is a complication in several of the MPS. Open-angle glaucoma has been reported in MPS I.[143,144] The trabecular meshwork is usually engorged with glycosaminoglycans, and the sclera and cornea are thickened, causing shallow anterior chambers.

Hearing. Deafness, usually of combined conductive and neurosensory origin, commonly occurs in MPS.[145–147] The deafness has been attributed to three causes: frequent middle ear infections, deformity of the ossicles, and probable abnormalities of the inner ear. Auditory brain stem response is abnormal in a nonspecific way, probably reflecting a mixture of middle ear, cochlear, eighth nerve, and lower brain stem anomalies.[147] Ventilating tubes can minimize the long-term sequelae of the frequent episodes of acute otitis media and chronic middle ear effusions which are commonplace in most MPS patients. The majority of MPS patients have significant hearing loss and would benefit from hearing aids, but few are using them. Aggressive audiologic management strategies are needed to maintain the highest quality of life.

Joint Stiffness. Joint stiffness is a common feature of all MPS, except for Morquio syndrome, where there is ligamentous laxity. Limitation of motion and joint stiffness can cause significant loss of function. The abnormal joint function probably results from a combination of metaphyseal deformities and thickened joint capsules secondary to glycosaminoglycan accumulation and fibrosis. Range of motion exercises appear to offer some benefit in preserving joint function, and should be started early in the clinical course. Once significant limitation has occurred, increased range of motion may not be achieved, although further limitation may be minimized. The indications for physical therapy and its benefits in MPS should be further studied.

Obstructive Airway Disease. A narrowed trachea, thickened vocal cords, redundant tissue in the upper airway, and an enlarged tongue all contribute to airway obstruction.[148–150] Intermittent obstruction in the severely involved MPS patient is common and may lead to sleep apnea.[151] Obstructive apnea has been reported in two patients with Scheie syndrome who had loud snoring and daytime sleepiness.[152] Tracheostomy can produce a dramatic symptomatic improvement in patients with obstructive apnea, but experience is limited. Few severely involved MPS patients have had sleep studies to determine the extent of compromise. Tonsillectomy and adenoidectomy are frequently performed in patients with MPS to correct Eustachian tube dysfunction and decrease airway obstruction.

Anesthesia. Patients with MPS present major anesthesia risks.[153–156] In Morquio syndrome in particular, but also in MPS I, II, and VI, the atlantoaxial joint is unstable, requiring careful positioning and avoidance of hyperextension of the neck. Induction of anesthesia can be difficult because of inability to maintain an adequate airway. Visualization can be limited during intubation and smaller than anticipated endotracheal tubes may be required. Recovery from anesthesia may be slow, and postoperative airway obstruction is common. Death has been reported secondary to anesthesia complication. MPS patients should undergo general anesthesia only in centers staffed with anesthesiologists experienced in these disorders.

Cardiovascular Disease. Clinical evidence of heart disease occurs in most patients with MPS who have moderate to severe somatic disease (reviewed in Ref. 97). Valvular disease, myocardial thickening, systemic and pulmonary hypertension, and narrowing of the coronary arteries with ischemia, if not infarction, all contribute to congestive heart failure and instances of sudden cardiovascular collapse. Mitral regurgitation is the most common valvular disease in MPS I H and MPS II severe, while aortic valvular disease is more likely to occur in MPS I H/S, MPS I S, MPS IV, and MPS VI. Valve replacement has been reported in MPS I H/S, MPS I S, and MPS VI, although experience is limited. Cardiac evaluation at regular intervals with echocardiography is useful in the management of patients through serial monitoring of ventricular function and size.

BIOCHEMICAL DIAGNOSIS

Differential Diagnosis

Analysis of urinary glycosaminoglycans was the earliest biochemical procedure available for diagnosis of MPS. Numerous methods have been devised, ranging from semiquantitative spot tests to precise qualitative and quantitative measurements (critically reviewed in Refs. 4, 157). Urinary glycosaminoglycan analysis can discriminate between broad classes of glycosaminoglycans but cannot distinguish subgroups. Spot tests are quick, inexpensive, and useful for preliminary evaluation, but are subject to both false positive and false negative results. In particular, MPS III and MPS IV are often missed. In view of the specificity and reliability of enzyme assays, we believe that it is more efficient to omit extensive analysis of urinary glycosaminoglycans and to proceed directly to the enzyme tests that appear relevant to the clinical problem. At the present time urinary glycosaminoglycan analysis is most useful as a research tool to characterize new disorders and to monitor the results of experimental therapies.

Definitive diagnosis of the MPS is established by enzyme assays.[158,159] Cultured fibroblasts may be used for all the MPS, leukocytes for most, and serum or plasma for MPS I, II, III B, and VII. The glycosidases can be assayed with chromogenic (p-nitrophenyl) or fluorigenic (4-methylumbelliferyl) sub-

strates. Fluorimetric assays for α-L-iduronidase[160–162] and α-N-acetylglucosaminidase[163] have become available recently and have simplified the diagnosis of MPS I and MPS III B.

Assays for the sulfatases relevant to MPS II, III A, III D, and IV A as well as for the acetyltransferase of MPS III C are not as convenient, since they require radioactive substrates that are often not available commercially and chromatographic or electrophoretic separation of reaction products from residual substrates. Though such assays are more tedious than assays that depend on the formation of a colored or fluorescent product, they are as reproducible and reliable. The sulfatase deficiency of MPS VI is an exception since it can be assayed with a chromogenic substrate for arylsulfatase B.

Prenatal Diagnosis

Prenatal diagnosis is possible for all the mucopolysaccharidoses and is routine for MPS I and II. All enzyme assays developed for cultured fibroblasts may be used on cells grown from amniotic fluid. Measurement of radiolabeled [35S]-glycosaminoglycan accumulation[164] may also be used for the prenatal diagnosis of the MPS (except for MPS IV). The technique is especially valuable when the enzyme deficiency-at-risk cannot be established in time.[165]

The long waiting time for culturing and testing amniotic fluid cells has encouraged the development of more rapid procedures. Some laboratories have focused on miniaturization of tests to reduce the number of cells required (reviewed in Ref. 166). We developed a test for prenatal diagnosis of Hunter syndrome by measuring iduronate sulfatase activity in cell-free amniotic fluid.[167] To the best of our knowledge, MPS II is the only mucopolysaccharidosis that can be diagnosed from enzyme activity in amniotic fluid. Users should be aware of a significant maternal contribution to the activity. Other tests using amniotic fluid, such as measurement of glycosaminoglycans[168] or electron microscopy of uncultured cells[169] have led to misdiagnoses; however, an improved procedure for glycosaminoglycan analysis appears reliable if performed with extreme care.[170]

Chorionic villus biopsies are rich in enzymes of glycosaminoglycan degradation and are becoming the tissue of choice for the rapid diagnosis of MPS. Our experience[165] and that of other laboratories[171–175a] has shown the value of homogenates of chorionic villi for the diagnosis of MPS II, III A, III B, III C, and IV A. Diagnosis of MPS I presents some difficulty in that normal villi occasionally have very low activity.[165,175] Cells cultured from villus biopsies should be used only if it can be determined (e.g., by cytogenetics) that they are not of maternal origin.[165]

The Hunter syndrome poses a special problem in prenatal diagnosis because the X-linked mode of inheritance results in mosaicism in heterozygous females. Iduronate sulfatase activity in material obtained from female fetuses can occasionally be almost as low as for an affected male. This is particularly true of cultured amniotic fluid cells, which may be of clonal origin,[167,176] but the problem may also occur when cell-free amniotic fluid or homogenates of chorionic villi are used.[165] Thus a prenatal diagnosis of Hunter syndrome should always include a determination of sex.

A totally noninvasive procedure has been proposed for prenatal diagnosis of MPS II, based on an increase in iduronate sulfatase activity in the mother's serum when the fetus is normal.[177] Though its reliability remains to be demonstrated (in fact, a contradictory report has been presented[178]) this intriguing suggestion deserves further evaluation.

Carrier Detection

Carrier testing is the service most often requested by MPS families, second only to demands for effective therapy. Carrier detection for the autosomal recessive MPS generally depends on measurement of the relevant enzyme in leukocytes or serum. Although statistically heterozygotes have half the normal level of activity, the wide range and the overlap between the heterozygous and normal groups makes classification of a particular individual difficult and at times impossible (see "Heterozygote Detection" in Chap. 1). As has been pointed out,[179] a major difficulty is lack of standardized methods and of a sufficient data base in any one laboratory. The frequency of MPS carriers in the general population is low; for MPS I H, it is estimated at 1 in 150, and for the other autosomal recessive MPS, even lower (see below). For purposes of genetic counseling, an assessment of risk based on these numbers may be as accurate as a laboratory test, except in cases of consanguineous marriage or of isolates with high carrier frequency. In such special cases, even imperfect tests are of value.

The situation is clearly different in the case of MPS II, which is X-linked. Female relatives of Hunter patients need to know their genetic status, particularly if they do not consider prenatal diagnosis and selective abortion to be an acceptable option. Some procedures for detecting heterozygosity for MPS II take advantage of the Lyon mechanism of X inactivation. Mosaicism of normal and Hunter cells may be observed in cloned fibroblast cultures and in hair roots.[180–183] Uncloned fibroblast cultures have also been used, even though such cultures degrade glycosaminoglycans in normal fashion because the normal cells provide iduronate sulfatase to the deficient cells (a process known as "correction"). It is possible to interfere with correction by adding to the medium specific inhibitors of endocytosis such as mannose 6-phosphate or fructose 1-phosphate. A carrier test based on [^{35}S]glycosaminoglycan accumulation in the presence or absence of fructose 1-phosphate was reported to detect most Hunter heterozygotes.[184–186]

Early attempts to detect heterozygotes by measurement of iduronate sulfatase in serum or lymphocytes did not appear promising, probably because the long incubation time used did not give a measure of the initial rate.[188] Improved protocols are reported to detect 80 to 90 percent of all carriers by analysis of enzyme in serum, or in a combination of serum and leukocytes or hair roots.[189,190] Use of polymorphic DNA probes for regions close to the Hunter locus[191] may permit even better discrimination in families with informative polymorphisms.

GENETICS

Inheritance

All mucopolysaccharidoses are inherited in autosomal recessive manner, with the exception of MPS II, the Hunter syndrome. As an X-linked recessive trait, MPS II is expected to occur only in hemizygous males; yet there are four reported

cases of affected females. One of those, T.L. in Ref. 192, was later shown to have multiple sulfatase deficiency, an autosomal recessive disorder; the basis for the second case in Ref. 192, M.C., is not understood.[165] A third case was shown to be caused by inactivation of the normal X in a heterozygote.[193] The fourth and most informative case is that of a 46,XX patient with a balanced X autosome translocation.[194] Presumably the break disrupted or inactivated the iduronate sulfatase locus on the translocated X chromosome, whereas the intact X chromosome was inactivated. The breakpoint was originally localized to Xq26-q27[193] but was later found to be at Xq28.[195]

Incidence

The mucopolysaccharidoses are rare disorders, and epidemiological data are scarce. Incidence of the Hunter syndrome, an X-linked disorder, was found to be 1 per 78,000 *male* live births in British Columbia,[196] 1 per 132,000 in Great Britain,[197] and 1 per 36,000 in Israel.[198] The Israeli figures represent complete ascertainment, whereas the incidence reported in the Canadian and British surveys is probably an underestimate. But in addition to showing a higher incidence than previously reported, the Israeli report pointed out a concentration of the disease in the Jewish population. This was attributed to genetic drift by one group of investigators[199] and to selection of the Hunter allele in Ashkenazi Jews by another.[200]

There is even less information on the other mucopolysaccharidoses. The same British Columbia survey, which covered the years 1952 to 1968, reports the incidence of Hurler syndrome to be 1 in 100,000, that of Morquio syndrome to be 1 in 300,000, and that of Scheie syndrome to be 1 in 600,000 total live births.[196] These figures are undoubtedly low, particularly for the milder disorders. The Sanfilippo syndrome, MPS III, is thought to be significantly underdiagnosed because the mental retardation is not accompanied by striking physical features. Thus, the relatively high incidence found in the Netherlands, 1 in 24,000 births, may be the result of a special effort to ascertain all cases.[108,201] Of the 73 patients in the Dutch survey, 36 had MPS III A, 23 MPS III B, and 14 MPS III C. On the other hand, the A subtype was found in 28 of 29 MPS III patients in Great Britain,[202] whereas the B subtype was present in 10 of 11 MPS III cases in Greece.[203] There is an isolate in the Cayman Islands with an exceptionally high incidence of MPS III A;[110] a carrier frequency of 0.1 has been found.[204] Only a few cases of MPS III D have been reported.

The Maroteaux-Lamy syndrome, MPS VI, is rarer than MPS I. The Sly syndrome, MPS VII, is rarer still, with fewer than 20 cases described.[69]

Allelism

It is characteristic of the MPS that one enzyme deficiency may underlie a wide variety of clinical phenotypes. The most dramatic example is that of the Hurler and Scheie syndromes, MPS I H and I S, which are so different that they had been classified as different mucopolysaccharidoses until shown to be biochemically related.[205,206] At that point, McKusick et al.[207] proposed that the mutations leading to Hurler and Scheie syndromes were allelic, and predicted the existence of compound heterozygotes, designated Hurler-Scheie, who would have an intermediate clinical phenotype. The suggestion of allelism is supported by the lack of complementation between Hurler,

Scheie, and Hurler-Scheie fibroblasts.[208,209] However, the compound heterozygote status of Hurler-Scheie patients has been disputed because of significant parental consanguinity and a variety of phenotypes among patients with MPS I of clinical severity intermediate between Hurler and Scheie syndromes.[94] At the present time it is implausible to assume that there exist only two alleles at the α-L-iduronidase locus. Where studies of other genetic diseases have progressed to analysis of mutant protein or mutant gene, great heterogeneity has usually emerged. It is therefore reasonable to anticipate a multiplicity of alleles at the α-L-iduronidase locus, with compound heterozygosity within as well as between clinical subgroups. A multiplicity of alleles is also expected in each of the other mucopolysaccharidoses.

Chromosomal Assignment

The loci for several autosomal genes encoding enzymes of glycosaminoglycan degradation (and by implication, of the deficiency diseases) have been determined from studies of human × mouse cell hybrids. The gene for α-L-iduronidase (MPS I) has been localized to chromosome 22pter-q11;[210] for β-glucuronidase (MPS VII) to 7q11.2-q22;[211] for arylsulfatase B (MPS VI), to 5p11-qter[212] and 5pter-q13,[213] indicating a localization at 5p11-q13; and for β-galactosidase (MPS IV B as well as G$_{M1}$ gangliosidosis), to chromosome 3p21-cen.[214]

The first clue to the localization of the iduronate sulfatase gene on the X chromosome was provided by discovery of a female Hunter patient with a balanced X:5 translocation.[194] The iduronate sulfatase gene was presumed to be at or near the breakpoint, which was localized at the time to Xq26-q27. However, a more distal assignment, Xq28 (close to the Xq27 site of fragile X) was made on the basis of restriction fragment length polymorphisms.[191] The apparent discrepancy was resolved when the translocation breakpoint was found to be also at Xq28.[195]

ANIMAL MODELS

Several animal models of human mucopolysaccharidoses have become available in recent years. This important development is attributable to the interest of investigators in schools of veterinary medicine, who are the ones to spot and characterize the index case—usually a lame animal brought in by its owner. The initial study is generally followed by identification and breeding of heterozygotes in order to establish a colony. Models that have become available in this manner are feline[215] and canine[216] MPS I, feline MPS VI,[217] and canine MPS VII.[218]

The animal models are essentially identical to their human counterparts with respect to pathology and to the chemistry of stored material.[219–222] Where the enzymes have been studied in any depth, interspecies similarities[223] as well as differences[29] have been found.

Feline MPS VI is to date the only animal mucopolysaccharidosis to have been detected in two unrelated kindreds. The different properties of the residual arylsulfatase B showed that the mutations were different but allelic.[224]

Clinical manifestations in the affected animals are similar though not identical to those in human patients. MPS I dogs have cloudy corneas, lameness, and stunted growth, but they live to adulthood and occasionally reproduce. Their disorder most closely resembles the human disease of intermediate severity, MPS I H/S. MPS I in cats is said to resemble MPS I H, but the animals also live to adulthood and can reproduce. MPS I appears to predispose cats, but not humans, to meningiomas.[225] MPS VI cats have corneal clouding, a flattened face, and skeletal abnormalities. They may develop spinal cord compression and hind limb paresis.[226] The MPS VII dog had major skeletal abnormalities and was compared to the more severely affected human patients.[218]

Availability of animal models is of particular value for testing new therapies. Bone marrow transplantation has been performed in MPS VI cats[227,228] and MPS I dogs,[229] as will be discussed below.

REPLACEMENT THERAPY—A VIABLE CONCEPT?

Rationale

The discovery of lysosomal storage disease by Hers and his colleagues at the University of Louvain was accompanied by the optimistic prediction that such disorders should be treatable with exogenous enzymes, which would reach lysosomes by the process of endocytosis.[230] Hope was stimulated by the finding that enzyme replacement worked extremely well in cell culture. The catabolism of glycosaminoglycans, which is blocked in fibroblasts from MPS patients, could be restored to normal by the addition of specific "corrective factors."[231] The factors were later identified as the missing lysosomal enzymes that have a mannose 6-phosphate recognition marker for efficient, receptor-mediated endocytosis into fibroblasts.[22,232] Other recognition markers that were found to be potentially useful for lysosomal enzyme replacement were the galactose system of hepatocytes and the mannose–N-acetylglucosamine system of Kupffer cells.[233]

These findings added a complication to the hypothesis of the Louvain group. If enzymes were to be prepared for therapeutic purposes, they would have to be not only highly active, pure, and nonantigenic, but also would have to bear the requisite recognition marker for uptake into target cells. The requirements seemed to present insurmountable technical difficulties, given the low abundance of the enzymes, the probable loss of the recognition marker during purification, and ignorance about the recognition systems of target cells, particularly of those in the nervous system.

Therapeutic Trials

Plasma and Leukocytes. Not surprisingly, investigators looked for ways of supplying enzyme that would bypass the labor-intensive purification process. A precedent had been set in the early 1970s by DiFerrante and colleagues for infusing large quantities of plasma or leukocytes into patients with MPS I and MPS II.[234,235] These procedures appeared at first to give positive results in the form of improved joint mobility, but retesting by many investigators showed the improvement, if any, to be transient.[236–242] The activities of the enzymes of interest were not measured in most of these studies, which were carried out before the identification of enzyme deficiencies in the MPS. Exceptions are to be found in a study of β-glucuronidase replacement by plasma infusion[243] and one of iduronate sulfatase replacement by plasma exchange.[244] The enzymes were cleared from the recipients' circulation relatively slowly, no doubt because enzymes present in plasma are sialylated[245] and have no exposed recognition marker for endocytosis.

Cultured Fibroblasts and Amnion Membranes. Disappointing results with plasma and leukocytes were attributed (in retrospect, incorrectly) to instability of the enzymes in the circulation and prompted a search for some procedure that would provide a renewable source of lysosomal enzymes, e.g., tissue or organ transplantation. A skin graft was attempted,[246] but rejection problems led to trials with fibroblasts cultured from skin biopsies.[247,248] One group of investigators reported biochemical changes[248] whereas another group found no changes other than an increase in urinary excretion of lower molecular weight glycosaminoglycans that was induced by the immunosuppressive drugs.[249] Fibroblast transplantation did not alter the clinical course of the disease.

Similarly unrewarding results were seen after transplantation of amnion. This tissue (which is a sheet of epithelial cells) was tested because the cells are not immunogenic and are rich in lysosomal enzymes, at least in culture.[250] A report of transient rise in enzyme level[251] was not confirmed.[252,253] A study of 19 transplanted patients, divided about equally between MPS I, II, III A, and III B, showed no appearance of enzyme in serum or leukocytes, minor changes in urinary glycosaminoglycan excretion in two patients, subjective reports from families and hospital staff of behavioral improvement in a few patients, but no objective signs other than some increase in joint mobility.[253] Amnion transplantation is not a useful therapy for MPS.

Bone Marrow Transplantation. Hobbs et al.[254] reported a dramatic change in the clinical course of Hurler syndrome after allogenic bone marrow transplantation: clearing of the corneas, decrease in hepatosplenomegaly, and arrest in the progressive deterioration that is usual in this disease. Since the original report, a number of patients with MPS I,[255,256] MPS II,[257] and MPS VI[258,259] have received bone marrow transplants and have been followed over several years. There have been a number of consistent changes, including: normalization of glycosaminoglycan excretion and of ultrastructural morphology of the liver; decrease in hepatosplenomegaly; clearing of corneas (except for the MPS VI patient[258]); and increase in joint mobility. Skeletal abnormalities were not reversed, though they could be partially prevented if transplantation was performed very early in life.[255] Whether neurologic function can be improved is a key question for the MPS associated with mental retardation. Some positive changes have been observed in the brain by magnetic resonance imaging.[260] Hugh-Jones[255] reported that the progression of mental deterioration could be slowed down if not completely halted, but that pregraft changes were not reversed.

Animal models have proved particularly useful in evaluating bone marrow transplantation. Two MPS VI cats[227,228] and three MPS I dogs[229] have survived the procedure. Liver biopsies showed one-fifth the arylsulfatase B and one-third the α-L-iduronidase activities in transplanted cats and dogs, respectively. The transplanted dogs had only a trace of enzyme in brain and the cats none at all. Yet the transplanted dogs had measurable α-L-iduronidase activity in cerebrospinal fluid, and most surprisingly, a marked decrease in glycosaminogly-

can level in brain and cerebrospinal fluid. Perithelial cells and neurons had a more normal (less vacuolated) ultrastructure, indicating an effect across the blood-brain barrier.[260a] Whether the effect was direct or indirect and whether the results can be extrapolated to human patients is not known.

Bone marrow transplantation is a major procedure that carries a high risk of mortality and morbidity from graft-versus-host disease and other complications. In a survey that included 23 MPS patients, mortality was found to be 30 percent when HLA-identical sibs were used as donors and was much higher with noncompatible donors.[261] In view of its high risk, high cost, and uncertain outcome, bone marrow transplantation should be considered an experimental procedure to be used in carefully selected cases and with systematic long-term monitoring of the results.

Gene Transfer

Insertion of the normal gene into the patients' own hematopoietic stem cells would provide the equivalent of bone marrow transplantation without the immunological complications. The strategy currently deemed most promising is delivery of the cloned gene or cDNA of interest by a recombinant vector derived in part from a retrovirus (e.g., Refs. 262 to 264). To be useful for therapeutic purposes, the recombinant vector should insert into the genome of the human cells but not be further infectious, and should express the gene in descendants of the hematopoietic stem cells. To date, this has not been achieved. Although recombinant retroviral vectors have been used successfully to transfer foreign genes into hematopoietic cells in culture, little or no expression of the inserted genes has been observed when the stem cells were returned to repopulate the marrow of irradiated mice.[265] The problem is believed to be a temporary one that will be solved with better understanding of the regulation of gene expression in hematopoietic cells. At this point, the mucopolysaccharidoses should be considered candidates for gene replacement in bone marrow, since patients respond biochemically and clinically to allogenic bone marrow transplantation. Animal models are available to test the efficacy and safety of the procedure. In view of the number of laboratories pursuing this goal, it is likely that answers will be available before the next edition of this compendium.

REFERENCES

1. MCKUSICK VA: Genetic nosology—Three approaches. *Am J Hum Genet* 30:105, 1978.

2. NEUFELD EF: Lessons from genetic disorders of lysosomes. *Harvey Lect* 75:41, 1981.

3. SPRANGER J: The systemic mucopolysaccharidoses. *Ergeb Inn Med Kinderheilkd* 32:165, 1972.

4. SLY WS: The mucopolysaccharidoses, in Bondy PD, Rosenberg LE (eds): *Metabolic Control and Disease.* Philadelphia, Saunders, 1980, p 545.

5. MCKUSICK VA, NEUFELD EF: The mucopolysaccharide storage diseases, in Stanbury JB, Wyngaarden JB, Fredrickson DS, Goldstein JL, Brown MS (eds): *The Metabolic Basis of Inherited Disease.* New York, McGraw-Hill, 1983, p 751.

5a. MCKUSICK V: The mucopolysaccharidoses, in McKusick VA: *Heritable Disorders of Connective Tissue.* St. Louis, MO, CV Mosby, 1972, p 521.

6. RODEN L: Structure and metabolism of connective tissue proteoglycans, in Lennarz WJ (ed): *The Biochemistry of Glycoproteins and Proteoglycans.* New York, Plenum, 1980, p 267.

7. ROME LH, GARVIN AJ, NEUFELD EF: Human kidney α-L-iduronidase: Purification and characterization. *Arch Biochem Biophys* 189:344, 1978.

8. CLEMENTS PR, BROOKS DA, SACCONE GTP, HOPWOOD JJ: Human α-L-iduronidase 1. Purification, monoclonal antibody production, native and subunit molecular mass. *Eur J Biochem* 152:21, 1985.

9. CLEMENTS PR, MULLER V, HOPWOOD JJ: Human α-L-iduronidase 2. Catalytic properties. *Eur J Biochem* 152:29, 1985.

10. SCHUCHMAN EH, GUZMAN NA, DESNICK RJ: Human α-L-iduronidase. I. Purification and properties of the high uptake (higher molecular weight) and the low uptake (processed) forms. *J Biol Chem* 259:3132, 1984.

11. SCHUCHMAN EH, GUZMAN NA, TAKADA G, DESNICK RJ: Human α-L-iduronidase II. Comparative biochemical and immunologic properties of the purified low and high uptake forms. *Enzyme* 31:166, 1984.

12. MYEROWITZ R, NEUFELD EF: Maturation of α-L-iduronidase in cultured human fibroblasts. *J Biol Chem* 256:3044, 1981.

13. SLY WS, FISCHER HD, GONZALEZ-NORIEGA A, GRUBB JH, NATOWICZ M: Role of the 6-phosphomannosyl-enzyme receptor in intracellular transport and adsorptive pinocytosis of lysosomal enzymes. *Methods Cell Biol* 23:191, 1981.

14. VON FIGURA K, HASILIK A: Lysosomal enzymes and their receptors. *Annu Rev Biochem* 55:167, 1986.

15. SANDO GN, NEUFELD EF: Recognition and receptor-mediated uptake of a lysosomal enzyme, α-L-iduronidase, by cultured fibroblasts. *Cell* 12:619, 1977.

16. STAHL PD, TOUSTER O: β-Glucuronidase of rat liver lysosomes. *J Biol Chem* 246:5398, 1971.

17. HIMENO M, NISHIMURA Y, TSUJI H, KATO K: Purification and characterization of microsomal and lysosomal β-glucuronidase from rat liver by use of immuno-affinity chromatography. *Eur J Biochem* 70:349, 1976.

18. BROT FE, BELL CE, SLY WS: Purification and properties of β-glucuronidase from human placenta. *Biochemistry* 17:385, 1978.

19. TOMINO S, PAIGEN K: Egasyn, a protein complexed with microsomal β-glucuronidase. *J Biol Chem* 250:1146, 1975.

20. STRAWSER LD, TOUSTER O: Demonstration of a rat liver microsomal binding protein specific for β-glucuronidase. *J Biol Chem* 254:3716, 1979.

21. ERICKSON AH, BLOBEL G: Carboxyl-terminal proteolytic processing during biosynthesis of the lysosomal enzymes β-glucuronidase and cathepsin D. *Biochemistry* 22:5201, 1983.

22. KAPLAN A, ACHORD DT, SLY WS: Phosphohexosyl components of a lysosomal enzyme are recognized by pinocytosis receptors on human fibroblasts. *Proc Natl Acad Sci USA* 74:2026, 1977.

23. OSHIMA A, KYLE JW, MILLER RD, HOFFMAN JW, POWELL PP, GRUBB JH, SLY WS, TROPAK M, GUISE KS, GRAVEL RA: Cloning, sequencing and expression of cDNA for human glucuronidase. *Proc Natl Acad Sci USA* 84:685, 1987.

24. NISHIMURA Y, ROSENFELD MG, KREIBICH G, GUBLER U, SABATINI DD, ADESNIK M, ANDY R: Nucleotide sequence of rat preputial β-glucuronidase cDNA and *in vitro* insertion of its encoded polypeptide in microsomal membranes. *Proc Natl Acad Sci USA* 83:7292, 1986.

25. APPLEGARTH DA, BOZOIAN G: Mucopolysaccharide storage in organs of a patient with Sandhoff's disease. *Clin Chim Acta* 39:269, 1972.

26. CANTZ M, KRESSE H: Sandhoff disease—Defective glycosaminoglycan catabolism in cultured fibroblasts and its correction by β-N-acetylhexosaminidase. *Eur J Biochem* 47:581, 1974.

27. WASTESON A, NEUFELD EF: Iduronate sulfatase from human plasma. *Methods Enzymol* 83:573, 1982.

28. DI NATALE P, DANIELE A: Iduronate sulfatase from human placenta. *Biochim Biophys Acta* 839:258, 1985.

29. MCGOVERN MM, VINE DT, HASKINS ME, DESNICK RJ: Purification and properties of feline and human arylsulfatase B isozymes. *J Biol Chem* 257:12605, 1982.

29a. GIBSON GJ, SACCONE GTP, BROOKS DA, CLEMENTS PR, HOPWOOD JJ: Human N-acetylgalactosamine-4-sulphate sulphatase. Purification, monoclonal antibody production and native and subunit M_r values. *Biochem J* 248:755, 1987.

30. STECKEL F, HASILIK A, VON FIGURA K: Biosynthesis and maturation of arylsulfatase B in normal and mutant cultured human fibroblasts. *J Biol Chem* 258:14322, 1983.

31. KLEIN U, VON FIGURA K: Characterization of dermatan sulfate in mucopolysaccharidosis VI. Evidence for the absence of hyaluronidase-like enzymes in human skin fibroblasts. *Biochim Biophys Acta* 630:10, 1980.

32. VON FIGURA K: Human α-N-acetylglucosaminidase. 1. Purification and properties. *Eur J Biochem* 80:525, 1977.

33. VON FIGURA K, HASILIK A, STECKEL F, VAN DE KAMP J: Biosynthesis and maturation of α-N-acetylglucosaminidase in normal and Sanfilippo B fibroblasts. *Am J Hum Genet* 36:93, 1984.

34. SHAKLEE PN, GLASER JH, CONRAD HE: A sulfatase specific for glucuronic acid 2-sulfate residues in glycosaminoglycans. *J Biol Chem* 260:9146, 1985.

35. BIENKOWSKI MJ, CONRAD HE: Structural characterization of the oligosaccharides formed by depolymerization of heparin with nitrous acid. *J Biol Chem* 260:356, 1985.

36. FEDARKO NS, CONRAD HE: A unique heparan sulfate in the nuclei of hepatocytes: Structural changes with the growth state of the cells. *J Cell Biol* 102:587, 1986.

37. YAMAGATA M, KIMATA K, OIKE Y, TANI K, MAEDA N, YOSHIDA K, SHIMOMURA Y, YONEDA M, SUZUKI S: A monoclonal antibody that specifically recognizes a glucuronic acid 2-sulfate determinant in intact chondroitin sulfate chains. *J Biol Chem* 262:4146, 1987.

37a. FREEMAN C, HOPWOOD JJ: Personal communication, 1988.

38. FREEMAN C, HOPWOOD JJ: Human liver sulphamate sulphohydrolase. *Biochem J* 234:83, 1986.

39. KRESSE H, PASCHKE E, VON FIGURA K, GILBERG W, FUCHS W: Sanfilippo disease type D: Deficiency of N-acetylglucosamine 6-sulfatase required for heparan sulfate degradation. *Proc Natl Acad Sci USA* 77:6822, 1980.

40. HOPWOOD JJ, ELLIOTT H: N-Acetylglucosamine 6-sulfate residues in keratan sulfate and heparan sulfate are desulfated by the same enzyme. *Biochem Int* 6:141, 1983.

40a. FREEMAN C, HOPWOOD JJ: Human liver N-acetylglucosamine-6-sulphate sulphatase. Catalytic properties. *Biochem J* 246:355, 1987.

40b. FREEMAN C, CLEMENTS PR, HOPWOOD JJ: Human liver N-acetylglucosamine-6-sulphate sulphatase. Purification and characterization. *Biochem J* 246:347, 1987.

41. KLEIN U, KRESSE H, VON FIGURA K: Sanfilippo syndrome type C: Deficiency of acetyl-CoA-α-glucosaminide N-acetyltransferase in skin fibroblasts. *Proc Natl Acad Sci USA* 75:5185, 1978.

42. HOPWOOD JJ, ELLIOTT H: The diagnosis of the Sanfilippo C syndrome using monosaccharide and oligosaccharide substrates to assay acetyl-CoA:2-amino-2-deoxy-α-glucoside N-acetyltransferase activity. *Clin Chim Acta* 112:67, 1981.

43. PALLINI R, LEDER IG, DI NATALE P: Sanfilippo type C diagnosis; assay of acetyl-CoA: α-glucosaminide N-acetyltransferase using [^{14}C]glucosamine as substrate and leukocytes as enzyme source. *Pediatr Res* 18:543, 1984.

44. FREEMAN C, CLEMENTS PR, HOPWOOD JJ: AcetylCoA:α-glucosaminide N-acetyltransferase: Partial purification from human liver. *Biochem Int* 6:663, 1983.

45. BAME KJ, ROME LH: AcetylCoA:α-glucosaminide N-acetyltransferase from rat liver. *Methods Enzymol* 138:667, 1987.

46. BAME KJ, ROME LH: Acetyl coenzyme A: α-glucosaminide N-acetyltransferase. Evidence for a transmembrane acetylation mechanism. *J Biol Chem* 260:11293, 1985.

47. BAME KJ, ROME LH: Acetyl coenzyme A: α-glucosaminide N-acetyltransferase. Evidence for an active site histidine residue. *J Biol Chem* 261:10127, 1986.

48. BAME KJ, ROME LH: Genetic evidence for transmembrane acetylation by lysosomes. *Science* 233:1087, 1986.

49. KNECHT J, CIFONELLI JA, DORFMAN A: Structural studies on heparitin sulfate of normal and Hurler tissues. *J Biol Chem* 242:4652, 1967.

50. KINDLER A, KLEIN U, VON FIGURA K: Characterization of glycosaminoglycans stored in mucopolysaccharidosis IIIA: Evidence for a generally occurring degradation of heparan sulfate by endoglycosidases. *Hoppe-Seyler's Z Physiol Chem* 358:1431, 1977.

51. KLEIN U, VON FIGURA K: Substrate specificity of a heparan-degrading endoglucuronidase from human placenta. *Hoppe-Seyler's Z Physiol Chem* 360:1465, 1979.

51a. VON FIGURA K: Personal communication, 1988.

52. DISTLER J, JOURDIAN GW: β-Galactosidase from bovine testes. *Methods Enzymol* 50:514, 1978.

53. PASCHKE E, NIEMANN R, STRECKER G, KRESSE H: Aggregation properties of β-galactosidase in normal urine and degradation of its natural substrate by a purified preparation of the enzyme. *Biochim Biophys Acta* 704:134, 1982.

54. PASCHKE E, KRESSE H: Morquio disease type B: Activation of G_{M1}-β-galactosidase by G_{M1} activator. *Biochem Biophys Res Commun* 109:568, 1982.

55. HOOGEVEEN AT, GRAHAM-KAWASHIMA H, D'AZZO A, GALJAARD H: Processing of human β-galactosidase in G_{M1} gangliosidosis and Morquio B syndrome. *J Biol Chem* 259:1974, 1984.

56. VAN DER HORST GTJ, KLEIJER WJ, HOOGEVEEN AT, HUIJMANS JGM, BLOM W, VAN DIGGELEN OP: Morquio B syndrome: A primary defect in β-galactosidase. *Am J Med Genet* 16:261, 1983.

57. KRESSE H, FUCHS W, GLOSSL J, HOLTFRERICH D, GILBERG W: Liberation of N-acetylglucosamine 6-sulfate by human β-N-acetylhexosaminidase A. *J Biol Chem* 256:12926, 1981.

58. KYTZIA HJ, SANDHOFF K: Evidence for two different active sites on human β-hexosaminidase A. *J Biol Chem* 260:7568, 1985.

59. FUCHS W, BECK M, KRESSE H: Intralysosomal formation and metabolic

fate of N-acetylglucosamine 6-sulfate from keratan sulfate. *Eur J Biochem* 151:551, 1985.

60. MATALON R, ARBOGAST B, JUSTICE P, BRANDT IK, DORFMAN A: Morquio's syndrome—deficiency of a chondroitin sulfate N-acetylglucosamine sulfate sulfatase. *Biochem Biophys Res Commun* 61:759, 1974.

61. SINGH J, DIFERRANTE N, NIEBES P, TAVELLA D: N-acetylgalactosamine 6-sulfate sulfatase in man. *J Clin Invest* 57:1036, 1976.

62. HORWITZ AL, DORFMAN A: The enzymic defect in Morquio's disease: The specificity of N-acetylhexosamine sulfatases. *Biochem Biophys Res Commun* 80:819, 1978.

63. GLOSSL J, TRUPPE W, KRESSE H: Purification and properties of N-acetylgalactosamine 6-sulfate sulfatase from human placenta. *Biochem J* 181:37, 1979.

64. GLOSSL J, KRESSE H: Impaired degradation of keratan sulfate by Morquio fibroblasts. *Biochem J* 203:335, 1982.

65. HOPWOOD JJ, ELLIOTT H: Isolation and characterization of N-acetylglucosamine 6-sulfate from the urine of a patient with Sanfilippo type D syndrome and its occurrence in normal urine. *Biochem Int* 6:831, 1983.

66. HOPWOOD JJ, ELLIOTT H: Urinary excretion of sulphated N-acetylhexosamines in patients with various mucopolysaccharidoses. *Biochem J* 229:579, 1985.

67. BACH G, EISENBERG F JR , CANTZ M, NEUFELD EF: The defect in the Hunter syndrome: Deficiency of sulfoiduronate sulfatase. *Proc Natl Acad Sci USA* 70:2134, 1973.

68. SJOBERG L, FRANSSON LA, MATALON R, DORFMAN A: Hunter's syndrome: A deficiency of L-iduronosulfate sulfatase. *Biochem Biophys Res Commun* 54:1125, 1973.

69. LEE JES, FALK RE, NG WG, DONNELL GN: β-Glucuronidase deficiency: A heterogeneous mucopolysaccharidosis. *Am J Dis Child* 139:57, 1985.

69a. BABARIK A, BENSON PF, DEAN MF, MUIR H: Chondroitinsulphaturia with α-L-iduronidase deficiency. *Lancet* 2:464, 1974.

69b. LEISTI J, RIMOIN DL, KABACK M, SHAPIRO LJ, MATALON R: Allelic mutations in the mucopolysaccharidoses. *Birth Defects* 12(6):81, 1976.

70. GINSBURG LC, DONNELLY PV, DIFERRANTE DT, DIFERRANTE NM, CASKEY CT: N-acetylglucosamine 6-sulfate sulfatase in man: Deficiency of the enzyme in a new mucopolysaccharidosis. *Pediatr Res* 12:805, 1978.

71. MATALON R, WAPPNER R, DEANCHING M, BRANDT IK, HORWITZ A: Keratan and heparan sulfaturia: Glucosamine 6-sulfate sulfatase deficiency. *Ann Clin Lab Sci* 12:234, 1982.

72. DIFERRANTE N: N-acetylglucosamine-6-sulfate sulfatase deficiency reconsidered. *Science* 210:448, 1980.

73. MCKUSICK VA: *Mendelian Inheritance in Man*, 7th ed. Baltimore, Johns Hopkins, 1986.

74. MATALON R: Personal communication, 1987.

75. CONZELMANN E, SANDHOFF K: Partial enzyme deficiencies: Residual activities and the development of neurologic disorders. *Dev Neurosci* 6:58, 1983/84.

76. CONZELMANN E, KYTZIA HJ, NAVON R, SANDHOFF K: Ganglioside G_{M2} N-acetyl-β-D-galactosaminidase activity in cultured fibroblasts of late-infantile and adult G_{M2} gangliosidosis patients and of healthy probands with low hexosaminidase levels. *Am J Hum Genet* 35:900, 1983.

77. MULLER VJ, HOPWOOD JJ: Radiolabeled disaccharides for the assay of β-D-glucuronidase activity and the detection of mucopolysaccharidosis type VII. *Clin Chim Acta* 123:357, 1982.

78. HOPWOOD JJ, ELLIOTT H: Diagnosis of Sanfilippo type A syndrome by estimation of sulfamidase activity using a radiolabelled tetrasaccharide substrate. *Clin Chim Acta* 123:241, 1982.

79. HOPWOOD JJ, ELLIOTT H: Detection of Morquio A syndrome using radiolabelled substrates derived from keratan sulphate for the estimation of galactose 6-sulphate suphatase. *Clin Sci* 65:325, 1983.

80. MULLER VJ, HOPWOOD JJ: α-L-iduronidase deficiency in mucopolysaccharidosis type I against a radiolabelled sulfated disaccharide substrate derived from dermatan sulfate. *Clin Genet* 26:414, 1984.

81. HOPWOOD JJ, ELLIOTT H, MULLER VJ, SACCONE GTP: Diagnosis of Maroteaux-Lamy syndrome by the use of radiolabelled oligosaccharides as substrates for the determination of arylsulfatase B activity. *Biochem J* 234:507, 1986.

82. GLOSSL J, MAROTEAUX P, DI NATALE P, KRESSE H: Different properties of residual N-acetylgalactosamine-6-sulfate sulfatase in fibroblasts from mild and severe forms of Morquio disease Type A. *Pediatr Res* 15:976, 1981.

83. THOMPSON JN, RODÉN L, REYNERTSON R: Oligosaccharide substrates for heparin sulfamidase. *Anal Biochem* 152:412, 1986.

84. MATALON R, DEANCHING M, OMURA K: Hurler, Scheie and Hurler/Scheie "compound": Residual activity of α-L-iduronidase toward natural substrates suggesting allelic mutations. *J Inherited Metab Dis (suppl)* 6:133, 1983.

84a. SCHUCHMAN EH, DESNICK RJ: Mucopolysaccharidosis type I subtypes.

85. SALVATORE D, DANIELLE A, DINATALE P: Biosynthesis of α-N-acetylglucosaminidase in normal and Sanfilippo B fibroblast. *Perspect Inherited Metab Dis* 6:113, 1985.

86. DANIELE A, DI NATALE P: Hunter syndrome: Presence of material cross-reacting with antibiodies against iduronate sulfatase. *Hum Genet* 75:234, 1987.

87. BELL CE, SLY WS, BROT FE: Human β-glucuronidase deficiency mucopolysaccharidosis. Identification of cross-reactive antigen in cultured fibroblasts of deficient patients by enzyme immunoassay. *J Clin Invest* 59:97, 1977.

88. GLÖSSL J, LEMBECK K, GAMSE G, KRESSE H: Morquio's disease type A: Absence of material cross-reacting with antibodies against N-acetylgalactosamine-6-sulfate sulfatase. *Hum Genet* 54:87, 1980.

89. CONSTANTOPOULOS G, DEKABAN AS: Neurochemistry of the mucopolysaccharidoses: Brain lipids and lysosomal enzymes in patients with four types of mucopolysaccharidosis and in normal controls. *J Neurochem* 30:965, 1978.

90. CONSTANTOPOULOS G, EIBEN RM, SCHAFER IA: Neurochemistry of the mucopolysaccharidoses: Brain glycosaminoglycans, lipids and lysosomal enzymes in mucopolysaccharidosis type IIIB (α-N-acetylglucosaminidase deficiency). *J Neurochem* 31:1215, 1978.

91. CONSTANTOPOULOS G, IQBAL K, DEKABAN AS: Mucopolysaccharidosis types IH, IS, II, and IIIA: Glycosaminoglycans and lipids of isolated brain cells and other fractions from autopsied tissues. *J Neurochem* 34:1399, 1980.

92. KINT JA, DACREMONT G, CARTON D, ORYE E, HOOFT C: Mucopolysaccharidosis: Secondarily induced abnormal distribution of lysosomal isoenzymes. *Science* 181:352, 1973.

93. BAUMKOTTER J, CANTZ M: Decreased ganglioside neuraminidase activity in fibroblasts from mucopolysaccharidosis patients. *Biochim Biophys Acta* 761:163, 1983.

94. ROUBICEK M, GEHLER J, SPRANGER J: The clinical spectrum of α-L-iduronidase deficiency. *Am J Med Genet* 20:471, 1985.

95. COLAVITA N, ORAZI C, FILENI A, LEONE PC, RICCI R, SEGNI G: A further contribution to the knowledge of mucopolysaccharidosis I H/S compound. Presentation of two cases and review of the literature. *Australas Radiol* 30:142, 1986.

96. GROSSMAN H, DORST JP: The mucopolysaccharidoses and mucolipidoses, in Kaufmann HJ (ed): *Progress in Pediatric Radiology*. Basel, Karger, 1973, vol 4, p 495.

97. PYERITZ RE: Cardiovascular manifestations of heritable disorders of connective tissue, in Steinberg AG, Bearn AG, Motulsky AG, Childs B (eds): *Progress in Medical Genetics*. Philadelphia, Saunders, vol 5, 1983.

98. YOUNG ID, HARPER PS, ARCHER IB, NEWCOMBE RG: A clinical and genetic study of Hunter's syndrome. 1. Heterogeneity. *J Med Genet* 19:401, 1982.

99. YOUNG ID, HARPER PS, NEWCOMBE RG, ARCHER IM: A clinical and genetic study of Hunter's syndrome. 2. Differences between the mild and severe forms. *J Med Genet* 19:408, 1982.

100. YOUNG ID, HARPER PS: Mild form of Hunter's syndrome: Clinical delineation based on 31 cases. *Arch Dis Child* 57:828, 1982.

101. YOUNG ID, HARPER PS: The natural history of the severe form of Hunter's syndrome: A study based on 52 cases. *Dev Med Child Neurol* 25:481, 1983.

102. SPRANGER J, CANTZ M, GEHLER J, LIEBAERS I, THEISS W: Mucopolysaccharidosis II (Hunter disease) with corneal opacities. *Eur J Pediatr* 129:11, 1978.

103. CARUSO RC, KAISER-KUPFER MI, MUENZER J, LUDWIG IH, ZASLOFF MA, MERCER PA: Electroretinographic findings in the mucopolysaccharidoses. *Ophthalmology* 93:1612, 1986.

104. BECK M, COLE G: Disc oedema in association with Hunter syndrome: Ocular histopathological findings. *Br J Ophthalmol* 68:590, 1984.

105. BECK M: Papilloedema in association with Hunter's syndrome. *Br J Ophthalmol* 67:174, 1983.

106. VAN AERDE J, PLETS C, VAN DER HAUWAERT L: Hydrocephalus in Hunter syndrome. *Acta Paediatr Belg* 34:93, 1981.

107. HOBOLITH N, PEDERSEN C: Six cases of a mild form of the Hunter syndrome in five generations: Three affected males with progeny. *Clin Genet* 13:121, 1978.

108. VAN DE KAMP JJP, NIERMEIJER MF, VON FIGURA K, GIESBERTS MAH: Genetic heterogeneity and clinical variability in the Sanfilippo syndrome (types A, B and C). *Clin Genet* 20:152, 1981.

109. NIDIFFER FD, KELLY TE: Developmental and degenerative patterns associated with cognitive, behavioral, and motor difficulties in Sanfilippo syndrome: An epidemiology study. *J Ment Defic Res* 27:185, 1983.

109a. VAN SCHROJENSTEIN-DE VALK HMJ, VAN DE KAMP JJP: Follow-up on seven adult patients with mild Sanfilippo B disease. *Am J Med Genet* 28:125, 1987.

110. MATALON R, DEANCHING M, NAKAMURA F, BLOOM A: A recessively inherited lethal disease in a Caribbean isolate—A sulfamidase deficiency. *Pediatr Res* 14:524, 1980.

111. ANDRIA G, DINATALE P, DEL GIUDICE E, STRISCUGLIO P, MURINO P: Sanfilippo B syndrome (MPS IIIB): Mild and severe forms within the same sibship. *Clin Genet* 15:500, 1979.

112. BALLABIO A, PALLINI R, DINATALE P: Mucopolysaccharidosis IIIB: Hybridization studies on fibroblasts from a mild case and fibroblasts from severe patients. *Clin Genet* 25:191, 1984.

113. COPPA GV, GIORGI PL, FELICI L, GABRIELLI O, DONTI E, BERNASCONI S, KRESSE H, PASCHKE E, MASTROPAOLO C: Clinical heterogeneity in Sanfilippo disease (mucopolysaccharidosis III) type D: Presentation of two new cases. *Eur J Pediatr* 140:130, 1983.

114. KAPLAN P, WOLFE LS: Sanfilippo syndrome type D. *J Pediatr* 110:268, 1987.

115. HOLZGREVE W, GROBE H, VON FIGURA K, KRESSE H, BECK H, MATTEI JF: Morquio syndrome: Clinical findings in 11 patients with MPS IVA and 2 patients with MPS IVB. *Hum Genet* 57:360, 1981.

116. O'BRIEN JS, GUGLER E, GIEDION A, WIESSMANN U, HERSCHKOWITZ N, MEIER C, LEROY J: Spondyloepiphyseal dysplasia, corneal clouding, normal intelligence, and acid β-galactosidase deficiency. *Clin Genet* 9:495, 1976.

117. ARBISSER AI, DONNELLY KA, SCOTT CI, DIFERRANTE N, SINGH J, STEVENSON RE, AYLESWORTH AS, HOWELL RR: Morquio-like syndrome with beta galactosidase deficiency and normal hexosamine sulfatase activity. *Am J Med Genet* 1:195, 1977.

118. VAN GEMUND JJ, GIESBERTS MAH, EERDMANS RF, BLOM W, KLEIJER WJ: Morquio-B disease, spondyloepiphyseal dysplasia associated with acid β-galactosidase deficiency: Report of three cases in one family. *Hum Genet* 64:50, 1983.

119. VAN DER HORST GTJ, HOOGEVEEN WJK, HUIJMANS JGM, BLOM W, VAN DIGGELEN OP: Morquio B syndrome: A primary defect in β-galactosidase. *Am J Med Genet* 16:261, 1983.

120. FUJIMOTO A, HORWITZ AL: Biochemical defect on non-keratan-sulfate-excreting Morquio syndrome. *Am J Med Genet* 15:265, 1983.

121. HECHT JT, SCOTT CI, SMITH TK, WILIAMS JC: Mild manifestations of Morquio syndrome. *Am J Med Genet* 18:369, 1984.

122. BECK M, GLOSSL J, GRUBISIC A, SPRANGER J: Heterogeneity of Morquio disease. *Clin Genet* 29:325, 1986.

123. MAROTEAUX P, STANESCU V, STANESCU R, KRESSE H, HORS-CAYLA MC: Heterogeneité des formes frustes de la maladie de Morquio. *Arch Fr Pediatr* 39:761, 1982.

124. TAYLOR HR, HOLLOWS FC, HOPWOOD JJ, ROBERTSON EF: Report of a mucopolysaccharidosis occurring in Australian aborigines. *J Med Genet* 15:455, 1978.

125. VESTERMARK S, TONNESEN T, ANDERSON MS, GUTTLER F: Mental retardation in a patient with Maroteaux-Lamy. *Clin Genet* 31:114, 1987.

126. SPRANGER JW, KOCH F, MCKUSICK VA, NATZSCHKA J, WIEDEMANN HR, ZELLWEGER H: Mucopolysaccharidosis VI (Maroteaux-Lamy's disease). *Helv Paediatr Acta* 25:337, 1970.

127. YOUNG R, KLEINMAN G, OJEMANN RG, KOLODNY E, DAVIS K, HALPERIN J, ZALNERAITIS E, DELONG GR: Compressive myelopathy in Maroteaux-Lamy syndrome: Clinical and pathological findings. *Ann Neurol* 8:336, 1980.

128. WALD SL, SCHMIDEK HH: Compressive myelopathy associated with type VI mucopolysaccharidosis (Maroteaux-Lamy syndrome). *Neurosurgery* 14:83, 1984.

129. CONSTANTOPOULOS G, STOWENS DW, BARRANGER JA: Reclassification of previously reported cases of mucopolysaccharidosis type IS to mucopolysaccharidosis type VI. *Clin Chim Acta* 124:137, 1982.

130. SLY WS, QUINTON BA, MCALISTER WH, RIMOIN DL: β-Glucuronidase deficiency: Report of clinical, radiologic and biochemical features of a new mucopolysaccharidosis. *J Pediatr* 82:249, 1973.

131. SEWELL AC, GEHLER J, MITTERMAIER G, MEYER E: Mucopolysaccharidosis type VII (β-glucuronidase deficiency): A report of a new case and a survey of those in the literature. *Clin Genet* 21:366, 1982.

132. NELSON A, PETERSON L, FRAMPTOM A, SLY WS: Mucopolysaccharidosis VII (β-glucuronidase deficiency) presenting as nonimmune hydrops fetalis. *J Pediatr* 101:574, 1982.

133. WILSON D, MELNIK E, SLY W, MARKESBERY WR: Neonatal beta-glucuronidase deficiency mucopolysaccharidosis (MPS VII): Autopsy findings. *J Neuropathol Exp Neurol* 41:344, 1982.

134. FOWLER GW, SUKOFF M, HAMILTON A, WILLIAMS JP: Communicating hydrocephalus in children with genetic inborn errors of metabolism. *Childs Brain* 1:251, 1975.

135. YATZIV S, EPSTEIN CJ: Hunter syndrome presenting as macrocephaly and hydrocephalus. *J Med Genet* 14:445, 1977.

136. VAN AERDE J, PLETS C, VAN DER HAUWAERT L: Hydrocephalus in Hunter syndrome. *Acta Paediatr Belg* 34:93, 1981.

137. WATTS RWE, SPELLACY E, KENDALL BE, DU BOULAY G, GIBBS DA: Computed tomography studies on patients with mucopolysaccharidoses. *Neuroradiology* 21:9, 1981.

138. SHINNOR S, SINGER HS, VALLE D: Acute hydrocephalus in Hurler's syndrome. *Am J Dis Child* 136:556, 1982.

139. VAN AERDE J, CAMBELL A: Hydrocephalus and shunt placement. *Am J Dis Child* 137:187, 1983.

140. MUENZER J: The mucopolysaccharidoses. *Adv Pediatr* 33:269, 1986.

141. SUGAR J: Corneal manifestation of the systemic mucopolysaccharidoses. *Ann Ophthalmol* 11:531, 1979.

142. MAUMENEE IH: The eye in connective tissue diseases, Daentl DL (ed): *Clinical, Structural and Biochemical Advances in Hereditary Eye Disorders.* New York, AR Liss, 1980, p 53.

142a. SCHWARTZ MF, WERBLIN TP, GREEN WR: Occurrence of mucopolysaccharide in corneal grafts in the Maroteaux-Lamy syndrome. *Cornea* 4:58, 1985/86.

142b. NAUMANN G: Clearing of cornea after perforating keratoplasty in mucopolysaccharidosis type VI (Maroteaux-Lamy syndrome). *N Engl J Med* 312:995, 1985.

143. QUIGLEY HA, GOLDBERG MF: Scheie syndrome and macular corneal dystrophy. *Arch Ophthalmol* 85:553, 1971.

144. SPELLACY E, BANKES JL, CROW L, DOURMASHKIN R, SHAH D, WATTS RWE: Glaucoma in a case of Hurler disease. *Br J Ophthalmol* 64:773, 1980.

145. HAYES E, BABIN R, PLATZ C: The otologic manifestations of mucopolysaccharidosis. *Am J Otol* 2:65, 1980.

146. PECK JE: Hearing loss in Hunter's syndrome-mucopolysaccharidosis II. *Ear Hear* 5:243, 1984.

147. PIKUS AT, MUENZER J: Personal communication.

148. RAMI I, GAY I, FEINMESSER R, SPRINGER C: Upper airway obstruction in Hunter syndrome. *Int J Pediatr Otorhinolaryngol* 11:229, 1986.

149. SASAKI CT, RUIZ R, KIRCHNER JA, GAITO R JR, SESHI B: Hunter's syndrome: A study in airway obstruction. *Laryngoscope* 97:280, 1987.

150. PETERS ME, ARYA S, LANGER LO, GILBERT EF, CARLSON R, ADKINS W: Narrow trachea in mucopolysaccharidoses. *Pediatr Radiol* 15:225, 1985.

151. SHAPIRO J, STROME M, CROCKER AC: Airway obstruction and sleep apnea in Hurler and Hunter syndrome. *Ann Otol Rhinol Laryngol* 94:458, 1985.

152. PERKS WH, COOPER RA, BRADBURY S, HORROCKS P, BALDOCK N, ALLEN A, VAN'T HOFF W, WEIDMAN G, PROWSE K: Sleep apnea in Scheie's syndrome. *Thorax* 35:85, 1980.

153. BAINES D, KENEALLY J: Anaesthetic implications of the mucopolysaccharidoses: A 15-year experience in a children's hospital. *Anaesth Intensive Care* 11:198, 1983.

154. KEMPTHORNE PM, BROWN TC: Anaesthesia and the mucopolysaccharidoses: A survey of techniques and problems. *Anaesth Intensive Care* 11:203, 1983.

155. BROWN TC: The airway in mucopolysaccharidoses. *Anaesth Intensive Care* 12:178, 1984.

156. SJOGREN P, PEDERSEN T, STEINMETZ H: Mucopolysaccharidoses and anaesthetic risks. *Acta Anaesthiol Scand* 32:214, 1987.

157. PENNOCK CA: A review and selection of simple laboratory methods used for glycosaminoglycan excretion and the diagnosis of the mucopolysaccharidoses. *J Clin Pathol* 29:111, 1976.

158. HALL CW, LIEBAERS I, DI NATALE P, NEUFELD EF: Enzymic diagnosis of the genetic mucopolysaccharide storage disorders. *Methods Enzymol* 50:439, 1978.

159. KRESSE H, VON FIGURA K, KLEIN U, GLOSSL J, PASCHKE E, POHLMANN R: Enzymic diagnosis of the genetic mucopolysaccharide storage disorders. *Methods Enzymol* 83:559, 1982.

160. STIRLING LJ, ROBINSON D, FENSOM AH, BENSOM PH, BAKER JE: Fluorimetric assay for prenatal detection of Hurler and Scheie homozygotes and heterozygotes. *Lancet* 1:147, 1978.

161. HOPWOOD JJ, MULLER V, SMITHSON A, BAGGETT N: A fluorometric assay using 4-methylumbelliferyl α-L-iduronide for the estimation of α-L-iduronidase activity and the detection of Hurler and Scheie syndromes. *Clin Chim Acta* 92:257, 1979.

162. ROME LH: α-L-Iduronidase from human kidney. *Methods Enzymol* 52:578, 1982.

163. MARSH J, FENSOM AH: 4-Methylumbelliferyl-α-N-acetylglucosaminidase activity for diagnosis of Sanfilippo B syndrome. *Clin Genet* 27:258, 1985.

164. FRATANTONI JC, NEUFELD EF, UHLENDORF BW, JACOBSON CB: Intrauterine diagnosis of the Hurler and Hunter syndromes. *N Engl J Med* 169:73, 1970.

165. NEUFELD EF: Unpublished results.

166. GALJAARD H: *Genetic Metabolic Diseases—Early Diagnosis and Prenatal Analysis.* Amsterdam, Elsevier, 1980.

167. LIEBAERS I, DI NATALE P, NEUFELD EF: Iduronate sulfatase in amniotic fluid can aid in the prenatal diagnosis of the Hunter syndrome. *J Pediatr* 90:423, 1977.

168. MATALON R, DORFMAN A, NADLER HL: A chemical method for the antenatal diagnosis of mucopolysaccharidosis. *Lancet* 1:798, 1972.

169. HUG G, SOUKUP S, CHUCK G, RYAN M: Antenatal diagnosis of mucopolysaccharidosis type I (Hurler's disease) is not possible by electron microscopy of uncultured amniotic fluid cells. *J Med Genet* 21:359, 1984.

170. MOSSMAN J, PATRICK AD: Prenatal diagnosis of mucopolysaccharidosis by two-dimensional electrophoresis of amniotic fluid glycosaminolycans. *Prenat Diagn* 2:169, 1982.

171. KLEIJER WJ, VAN DIGGELEN OP, JANSE HC, GALJAARD H, DUMEZ Y, BOUE J: First trimester diagnosis of Hunter syndrome on chorionic villi. *Lancet* 2:472, 1984.

172. KLEIJER WJ, JANSE HC, VOSTERS RPL, NIEJMEIER MF, VAN DE KAMP JJP: First trimester diagnosis of mucopolysaccharidosis IIIA (Sanfilippo A disease). *N Engl J Med* 314:185, 1986.

173. YUEN M, FENSOM AH: Diagnosis of classical Morquio's disease: N-acetylgalactosamine 6-sulphate sulphatase activity in cultured fibroblasts, leukocytes, amniotic cells and chorionic villi. *J Inherited Metab Dis* 8:80, 1985.

174. DI NATALE P, PANNONE N, D'ARGENIO G, GATTI R, RICCI R, LOMBARDO C: First trimester prenatal diagnosis of Sanfilippo C disease. *Prenat Diagn* 7:603, 1987.

175. POENARU L: First trimester prenatal diagnosis of metabolic diseases. *Prenat Diagn* 7:333, 1987.

175a. MINELLI A, DANESINO C, LO CURTO F, TENTI P, ZAMPATTI C, SIMONI G, ROSSELLA F, FOIS A: First trimester prenatal diagnosis of Sanfilippo disease (MPS III) type B. *Prenat Diagn* 8:47, 1988.

176. KLEIJER WJ, MOOY PD, LIEBAERS I, VAN DE KAMP JJP, NIERMEIJER MF: Prenatal monitoring for the Hunter heterozygotes: The heterozygous female fetus. *Clin Genet* 15:113, 1979.

177. ZLOTOGORA J, BACH G: Hunter syndrome: Prenatal diagnosis in maternal serum. *Am J Hum Genet* 38:253, 1986.

178. APPLEGARTH D, TOONE JR, WILSON RD, RUDD N, LOWRY RB: Prenatal diagnosis of a Hunter carrier fetus by CVS assay in a pregnancy without an increase in maternal serum Hunter enzyme. *Am J Hum Genet* 39:A249, 1986.

179. SHAPIRO LJ: Current status and future direction for carrier detection in lysosomal storage diseases, in Callahan JW, Lowden JA (eds): *Lysosome and Lysosomal Storage Diseases.* New York, Raven, 1981, p 343.

180. DANES BS, BEARN AG: Hurler's syndrome: A genetic study of clones in cell culture with particular reference to the Lyon hypothesis. *J Exp Med* 126:509, 1967.

181. MIGEON BR, SPRENKLE JA, LIEBAERS I, SCOTT JF, NEUFELD EF: X-linked Hunter syndrome: The heterozygous phenotype in cell culture. *Am J Hum Genet* 29:448, 1977.

182. YUTAKA T, FLUHARTY AL, STEVENS RL, KIHARA H: Iduronate sulfatase analysis of hair roots for identification of Hunter syndrome heterozygotes. *Am J Hum Genet* 30:575, 1978.

183. NWOKORO N, NEUFELD EF: Detection of Hunter heterozygotes by enzymatic analysis of hair roots. *Am J Hum Genet* 31:42, 1979.

184. TØNNESEN T, LYKKELUND C, GUTTLER F: Diagnosis of Hunter's syndrome carriers; radioactive sulphate incorporation into fibroblasts in the presence of fructose 1-phosphate. *Hum Genet* 60:167, 1982.

185. PETRUSCHKA L, MACHILL G, WEHNERT M, SEIDLITZ G, KNAPP A: Reliability of the Tønnesen technique for the identification of Hunter carriers. *Hum Genet* 64:404, 1983.

186. TØNNESEN T, GUTTLER F, LYKKELUND C: Reliability of the use of fructose 1-phosphate to detect Hunter cells in fibroblast cultures of obligate carriers of the Hunter syndrome: *Hum Genet* 64:371, 1983.

187. TØNNESEN T: The use of fructose 1-phosphate to detect Hunter heterozygotes in fibroblast cultures from high-risk carriers. *Hum Genet* 66:212, 1984.

188. LIEBAERS I, NEUFELD EF: Iduronate sulfatase activity in serum, lymphocytes and fibroblasts—Simplified diagnosis of the Hunter syndrome. *Pediatr Res* 10:733, 1976.

189. ARCHER IM, HARPER PS, WUSTEMAN FS: An improved assay for iduronate 2-sulphate sulphatase in serum and its use in the detection of carriers of the Hunter syndrome. *Clin Chim Acta* 112:107, 1981.

190. ZLOTOGORA J, BACH G: Heterozygote detection in Hunter syndrome. *Am J Med Genet* 17:661, 1984.

191. UPADHYAYA M, SARFARAZI M, BAMFORTH JS, THOMAS NST, OBERLE I, YOUNG I, HARPER PS: Localization of the gene for Hunter syndrome on the long arm of the X chromosome. *Hum Genet* 74:391, 1986.

192. NEUFELD EF, LIEBAERS I, EPSTEIN CJ, YATSIV S, MILUNSKY A, MIGEON BR: The Hunter syndrome in females: Is there an autosomal recessive form of iduronate sulfatase deficiency? *Am J Hum Genet* 29:455, 1977.

193. BROADHEAD DM, KIRK JM, BURT AJ, GUPTA V, ELLIS PM, BESLEY GTM: Full expression of Hunter's disease in a female with an X-chromosome deletion leading to non-random inactivation. *Clin Genet* 30:392, 1986.

194. MOSSMAN J, BLUNT S, STEPHENS R, JONES EE, PEMBREY M: Hunter's disease in a girl: Association with X:5 chromosomal translocation disrupting the Hunter gene. *Arch Dis Child* 58:911, 1983.

195. ROBERTS SH, UPADHYAYA M, SARFARAZI M, HARPER PS: Further evidence localizing the gene for Hunter syndrome to the most distal band of the X-chromosome long arm. *Cytogen Cell Genet* 46:683, 1987.

196. LOWRY RB, RENWICK DHG: Relative frequency of the Hurler and Hunter syndromes. *N Engl J Med* 284:221, 1971.

197. YOUNG ID, HARPER PS: Incidence of Hunter's syndrome. *Hum Genet* 60:391, 1982.

198. SCHAAP T, BACH G: Incidence of mucopolysaccharidoses in Israel: Is Hunter disease a "Jewish disease"? *Hum Genet* 56:221, 1980.

199. CHAKRAVARTI A, BALE SJ: Differences in the frequency of X-linked deleterious genes in human populations. *Am J Hum Genet* 35:1252, 1983.

200. ZLOTOGORA J, SCHAAP T, ZEIGLER M, BACH G: Hunter syndrome among Ashkenazi Jews in Israel; evidence for prenatal selection favoring the Hunter allele. *Hum Genet* 71:329, 1985.

201. VAN DE KAMP JJP: The Sanfilippo syndrome. A clinical and genetical study of 75 patients in the Netherlands (Doctoral Thesis). S'Gravenhage, JH Pasmans, 1979.

202. WHITEMAN P, YOUNG E: The laboratory diagnosis of Sanfilippo disease. *Clin Chim Acta* 76:139, 1977.

203. BERATIS NG, SKLOWER SL, WILBUR L, MATALON R: Sanfilippo disease in Greece. *Clin Genet* 29:129, 1986.

204. MATALON R: Personal communication.

205. WIESMANN U, NEUFELD EF: Scheie and Hurler syndromes: Apparent identity of the biochemical defect. *Science* 169:72, 1970.

206. BACH G, FRIEDMAN R, WEISSMANN B, NEUFELD EF: The defect in the Hurler and Scheie syndromes: Deficiency of α-L-iduronidase. *Proc Natl Acad Sci USA* 69:2408, 1972.

207. MCKUSICK VA, HOWELL RR, HUSSELS IE, NEUFELD EF, STEVENSON RE: Allelism, non-allelism and genetic compounds among the mucopolysaccharidoses. *Lancet* 1:993, 1972.

208. FORTUIN JJH, KLEIJER WJ: Hybridization studies of fibroblasts from Hurler, Scheie and Hurler/Scheie compound patients: Support for the hypothesis of allelic mutants. *Hum Genet* 53:155, 1980.

209. MUELLER OT, SHOWS TB, OPITZ JM: Apparent allelism of the Hurler, Scheie and Hurler/Scheie syndromes. *Am J Hum Genet* 18:547, 1984.

210. SCHUCHMAN EH, ASTRIN KH, AULA P, DESNICK RJ: Regional assignment of the structural gene for human α-L-iduronidase. *Proc Natl Acad Sci USA* 81:1169, 1984.

211. FRYDMAN M, STEINBERGER J, SHABTAI F, STEINHERZ R: Interstitial 7q deletion [46, XY, del(7) (pter cen:q112 qter)] in a retarded quadriplegic boy with normal β-glucuronidase. *Am J Med Genet* 25:245, 1986.

212. FIDZIANSKA E, ABRAMOWITZ T, CZARTORYSKA B, GLOGOWSKA I, GORSKA D, RODO M: Assignment of the gene for arylsulfatase B, ARSB, to chromosome region 5p11-5qter. *Cytogenet Cell Genet* 38:150, 1984.

213. FOX MF, DUTOIT DL, WARNICH L, RETIEF AE: Regional localization of alpha-galactosidase (GLA) to Xpter-q22, hexosaminidase B (HEX B) to 5q13-qter, and arylsulfatase B (ARSB) to 5pter-q13. *Cytogenet Cell Genet* 38:45, 1984.

214. SHOWS TB, SCRAFFORD-WOLFF LR, BROWN JA, MEISLER M: Assignment of a β-galactosidase gene (β-Gal-α) to chromosome 3 in man. *Cytogenet Cell Genet* 22:219, 1978.

215. HASKINS ME, JEZYK PF, DESNICK RJ, MCDONOUG SK, PATTERSON DF: Alpha-L-iduronidase deficiency in a cat: A model of mucopolysaccharidosis I. *Pediatr Res* 13:1294, 1979.

216. SHULL RM, MUNGER RJ, SPELLACY E, HALL CW, CONSTANTOPOULOS G, NEUFELD EF: Canine α-L-iduronidase deficiency, a model of mucopolysaccharidosis I. *Am J Pathol* 109:224, 1982.

217. JEZYK P, HASKINS ME, PATTERSON DF, MELLMAN WJ, GREENSTEIN M: Mucopolysaccharidosis in a cat with arylsulfatase B deficiency: A model of Maroteaux-Lamy syndrome. *Science* 198:834, 1977.

218. HASKINS ME, DESNICK RJ, DIFERRANTE N, JEZYK PF, PATTERSON DF: β-Glucuronidase deficiency in a dog: A model of human mucopolysaccharidosis VII. *Pediatr Res* 18:980, 1984.

219. HASKINS ME, AGUIRRE GD, JEZYK PF, DESNICK RJ, PATTERSON DF: The pathology of the feline model of mucopolysaccharidosis I. *Am J Pathol* 112:27, 1983.

220. SHULL RM, HELMAN RG, SPELLACY E, CONSTANTOPOULOS G, MUNGER RJ, NEUFELD EF: Morphologic and biochemical studies of canine mucopolysaccharidosis I. *Am J Pathol* 114:487, 1984.

221. CONSTANTOPOULOS G, SHULL RM, HASTINGS N, NEUFELD EF: Chemical characterization of canine α-L-iduronidase deficiency disease (model of human mucopolysaccharidosis I). *J Neurochem* 45:1213, 1985.

222. HASKINS ME, AGUIRRE GD, JEZYK PF, PATTERSON DF: The pathology of the feline model of mucopolysaccharidosis IV. *Am J Pathol* 101:657, 1980.

223. SPELLACY E, SHULL RM, CONSTANTOPOULOS G, NEUFELD EF: A canine model of human α-L-iduronidase deficiency. *Proc Natl Acad Sci USA* 80:6091, 1983.

224. MCGOVERN MM, MANDELL N, HASKINS M, DESNICK RJ: Animal model studies of allelism: Characterization of arylsulfatase B mutations in homoallelic and heteroallelic (genetic compound) homozygotes with feline mucopolysaccharidosis VI. *Genetics* 110:733, 1985.

225. HASKINS ME, MCGRATH JT: Menangiomas in young cats with mucopolysaccharidosis I. *J Neuropathol Exp Neurol* 42:664, 1983.

226. HASKINS ME, BINGEL SA, NORTHINGTON JW, NEWTON CD, SANDE RD, JEZYK PF, PATTERSON DF: Spinal cord compression and hind limb paresis in cats with mucopolysaccharidosis VI. *J Am Vet Med Assoc* 182:983, 1983.

227. GASPER PW, THRALL MA, WENGER DA, MACY DW, HAM L, DORNSIFE RE, MCBILES K, QUACKENBUCH SL, KESEL ML, GILLETTE EL, HOOVER EA: Correction of feline arylsulphatase B deficiency (mucopolysaccharidosis VI) by bone marrow transplantation. *Nature* 312:467, 1984.

228. WENGER DA, GASPER PW, THRALL MA, DIAL SM, LE COUTEUR RA, HOOVER EA: Bone marrow transplantation in the feline model of arylsulfatase B deficiency. *Birth Defects* 22:177, 1986.

229. SHULL RM, HASTINGS NE, SELCER RR, JONES JB, SMITH JR, CULLEN WC, CONSTANTOPOULOS G: Bone marrow transplantation in canine mucopolysaccharidosis I. Effects within the nervous system. *J Clin Invest* 79:435, 1987.

230. BAUDHUIN P, HERS HG, LOEB H: An electron microscopic and biochemical diagnosis of Type II glycogenesis. *Lab Invest* 13:1139, 1964.

231. FRATANTONI JC, HALL CW, NEUFELD EF: The defect in Hurler and Hunter syndromes, II. Deficiency of specific factors involved in mucopolysaccharide degradation. *Proc Natl Acad Sci USA* 64:360, 1969.

232. NEUFELD EF, LIM TW, SHAPIRO LJ: Inherited disorders of lysosomal metabolism. *Annu Rev Biochem* 44:357, 1975.

233. NEUFELD EF, ASHWELL G: Carbohydrate recognition systems for receptor-mediated pinocytosis, in Lennarz WJ (ed): *The Biochemistry of Glycoproteins and Proteoglycans.* New York, Plenum, 1980, p 241.

234. DIFERRANTE N, NICHOLS BL, DONNELLY PV, NERI G, HRGOVCIC R, BERGLUND RK: Induced degradation of glycosaminoglycans in Hurler's and Hunter's syndromes by plasma infusion. *Proc Natl Acad Sci USA* 68:303, 1971.

235. KNUDSON AG, DIFERRANTE N, CURTIS JE: Effect of leukocyte transfusion in a child with type II mucopolysaccharidosis. *Proc Natl Acad Sci USA* 68:1738, 1971.

236. ERICKSON RP, SANDMAN R, ROBERTSON WB, EPSTEIN CJ: Inefficacy of fresh frozen plasma therapy of mucopolysaccharidosis II. *Pediatrics* 50:693, 1972.

237. DEKABAN AS, HOLDEN KR, CONSTANTOPOULOS G: Effects of fresh plasma or whole blood transfusions on patients with various types of mucopolysaccharidosis. *Pediatrics* 50:688, 1972.

238. BOOTH CW, NADLER HL: Plasma infusions in the Hurler syndrome. *J Pediatr* 82:273, 1973.

239. MOSER HW, O'BRIEN JS, ATKINS L, FULLER TC, KLIMAN A, JANOWSKA S, RUSSELL PS, BARTSOCAS CS, COSIMI B, DULANEY JT: Infusion of normal HL-A identical leukocytes in Sanfilippo disease type B. *Arch Neurol* 31:329, 1974.

240. DEAN MF, MUIR H: Mobilization of glycosaminoglycans by plasma infusion in mucopolysaccharidosis type III. *Nature* 243:143, 1973.

241. HUSSELS IE, EIKMAN EA, KENYON KR, MCKUSICK VA: Treatment of mucopolysaccharidoses. *Birth Defects* 10:212, 1974.

242. YATSIV S, STATTER M, ABELIUK P, MESHULAM M, RUSSELL A: The therapeutic trial of fresh plasma infusions over a period of 22 months in two siblings with Hunter syndrome. *Isr J Med Sci* 8:802, 1975.

243. SLY WS: Multiple recognition forms of human β-glucuronidase and their pinocytosis receptors: Implications for gene therapy. *Birth Defects* 16:115, 1980.

244. BROWN FR, HALL CW, NEUFELD EF, MUNOZ LL, BRAINE H, ANDRZEJEWSKI S, CAMARGO EE, MARK SA, RICHARD JM, MOSER HW: Administration of iduronate sulfatase by plasma exchange to patients with the Hunter syndrome. *Am J Med Genet* 13:309, 1982.

245. WILLCOX P, RENWICK AGC: Effect of neuraminidase on the chromatographic behavior of eleven acid hydrolases from human liver and plasma. *Eur J Biochem* 13:579, 1977.

246. DEAN MF, MUIR H, BENSON PF, BUTTON LR, BATCHELOR JR, BEWICK M: Increased breakdown of glycosaminoglycans and appearance of corrective enzyme after skin transplants in Hunter syndrome. *Nature* 257:609, 1975.

247. DEAN MF, MUIR H, BENSON PF, BUTTON LR, BOYLSTON A, MOWBRAY J: Enzyme replacement therapy by fibroblast transplantation in a case of Hunter syndrome. *Nature* 261:323, 1976.

248. DEAN MF, STEVENS RL, MUIR H, BENSON PF, BUTTON LR, ANDERSON RL, BOYLSTON A, MOWBRAY J: Enzyme replacement therapy by fibroblast transplantation. *J Clin Invest* 63:138, 1979.

249. GIBBS DA, SPELLACY E, TOMPKINS R, WATTS RWE, MOWBRAY JF: A clinical trial of fibroblast transplantation for the treatment of mucopolysaccharidoses. *J Inherited Metab Dis* 6:62, 1983.

250. ADINOLFI M, AKLE CE, MCCOLL I, FENSOM AH, TANSLEY L, CONNOLLY P, HSI BL, FAULK WP, TRAVERS P, BODMER WF: Expression of HLA antigens, β2-microglobulin and enzymes by human amniotic epithelial cells. *Nature* 295:327, 1982.

251. ADINOLFI M, BROWN S: Strategies for the correction of enzymatic deficiencies in patients with mucopolysaccharidoses. *Dev Med Child Neurol* 26:404, 1984.

252. YEAGER AM, SINGER HS, BUCK JR, MATALON R, BRENNAN S, O'TOOLE SOD, MOSER HW: A therapeutic trial of amniotic epithelial cell implantation in patients with lysosomal storage diseases. *Am J Med Genet* 22:347, 1985.

253. MUENZER J, NEUFELD EF, CONSTANTOPOULOS G, CARUSO RC, KAISER-KUPFER MI, PIKUS A, MCDONALD HD, ZASLOFF MA: Amniotic membrane implantation in mucopolysaccharidoses. *Pediatr Res* 19:251a, 1985.

254. HOBBS JR, HUGH-JONES K, BARRETT AJ, BYROM N, CHAMBERS D, HENRY K, JAMES DCO, LUCAS CF, ROGERS TR, BENSON PF, TANSLEY LR, PATRICK AD, MOSSMAN J, YOUNG EP: Reversal of clinical features of Hurler's disease and biochemical improvement after treatment by bone marrow transplantation. *Lancet* 2:709, 1981.

255. HUGH-JONES K: Psychomotor development of children with mucopolysaccharidoses type 1-H following bone marrow transplantation. *Birth Defects* 22:25, 1986.

256. WHITLEY CB, RAMSAY NKC, KERSEY JH, KRIVIT W: Bone marrow transplantation for Hurler syndrome: Assessment of metabolic correction. *Birth Defects* 22:7, 1986.

257. WARKENTIN PI, DIXON MS, SCHAFER I, STRANJORD SE, COCCIA PF: Bone marrow transplantation in Hunter syndrome: A preliminary report. *Birth Defects* 22:31, 1986.

258. KRIVIT W, PIERPONT ME, AYAZ K, TSAI M, RAMSAY NKC, KERSEY JH, WEISDORF S, SIBLEY R, SNOVER D, MCGOVERN MM, SCHWARTZ MF, DESNICK RJ: Bone marrow transplantation in the Maroteaux-Lamy syndrome (mucopolysaccharidosis type VI). *N Engl J Med* 311:1606, 1984.

259. MCGOVERN MM, LUNDMAN MD, SHORT MP, STEINFELD L, KATTAN M, RAAB EL, KRIVIT W, DESNICK RJ: Status of bone marrow transplantation in Maroteaux-Lamy syndrome (MPS type 6): Status 40 months after BMT. *Birth Defects* 22:42, 1986.

260. JOHNSON MA, DESAI S, HUGH-JONES K, STARER F: Magnetic resonance imaging of the brain in Hurler syndrome. *AJNR* 5:816, 1984.

260a. SHULL RM, BREIDER MA, CONSTANTOPOULOS GC: Long term neurological effects of bone marrow transplantation in a canine lysosomal storage disease. *Pediatr Res*, in press.

261. PEARSON ADJ: Survey of preparative regimens and complications of bone marrow transplantation in patients with lysosomal storage diseases. *Birth Defects* 22:153, 1986.

262. ANDERSON WF: Prospects for human gene therapy. *Science* 226:401, 1984.

263. MANN R, MULLIGAN RC, BALTIMORE D: Construction of a retrovirus packaging mutant and its use to produce helper-free defective viruses. *Cell* 33:153, 1983.

264. YU SF, VON RUDEN T, KANTOFF PW, GARBER C, SEIBERG M, RUTHER U, ANDERSON WF, WAGNER EF, GILBOA E: Self-inactivating retroviral vectors designed for transfer of whole genes into mammalian cells. *Proc Natl Acad Sci USA* 83:3194, 1986.

265. WILLIAMS DA, ORKIN SH, MULLIGAN RC: Retrovirus-mediated transfer of human adenosine deaminase gene sequences into cells in culture and into murine hematopoietic cells *in vivo. Proc Natl Acad Sci USA* 83:2566, 1986.

I-CELL DISEASE AND PSEUDO-HURLER POLYDYSTROPHY: Disorders of Lysosomal Enzyme Phosphorylation and Localization

CATHERINE M. NOLAN
WILLIAM S. SLY

1. I-cell disease (mucolipidosis II or ML-II) and pseudo-Hurler polydystrophy (mucolipidosis III or ML-III) are biochemically related genetic diseases with rare occurrence and autosomal recessive inheritance.

2. I-cell disease shows many of the clinical and radiographic features of Hurler syndrome, but it presents earlier and does not show mucopolysacchariduria. There is severe progressive psychomotor retardation, and death usually occurs in the first decade. Pseudo-Hurler polydystrophy is milder and presents later, and survival into adulthood is possible.

3. In both diseases, there is abnormal lysosomal enzyme transport in cells of mesenchymal origin. In these cells, newly synthesized lysosomal enzymes are secreted into the extracellular medium instead of being targeted correctly to lysosomes. Affected cells show dense inclusions filled with storage material, and lysosomal enzymes are present at elevated levels in the serum and body fluids of affected patients.

4. In normal cells, targeting of lysosomal enzymes to lysosomes is mediated by receptors that bind mannose-6-phosphate recognition markers on the enzymes. The recognition marker is synthesized in a two-step reaction in the Golgi complex, and it is the enzyme which catalyzes the first step in this process, UDP-N-acetylglucosamine:lysosomal enzyme N-acetylglucosaminyl-1-phosphotransferase, which is defective in ML-II and ML-III.

5. The phosphotransferase is a low abundance membrane-bound enzyme. Genetic studies suggest that more than one gene product contributes to the functional enzyme. Biochemical studies suggest that the enzyme possesses two domains, one of which is associated with its catalytic activity and the other with the specific recognition of lysosomal enzymes.

6. While all cells and tissues of affected individuals are deficient in phosphotransferase activity, not all cells are deficient in lysosomal enzyme content. This indicates that there are other mannose-6-phosphate-independent pathway(s) which function in transport of lysosomal enzymes. The nature of the alternate pathway(s) in these cell types is unknown.

7. Diagnosis of ML-II and ML-III can be made biochemically by estimation of serum lysosomal enzyme levels. The characteristic pattern of enzyme deficiencies in fibroblasts can also be used, as can the ratio of extracellular to intracellular enzyme activities. The phosphotransferase activity can also be measured. In general, ML-II and ML-III must be distinguished

on clinical criteria and on progression of the disease. Prenatal diagnosis is reliable, and carrier detection is also possible.

8. There is no definitive treatment.

INTRODUCTION/HISTORY

In 1967, a disease was described which resembled Hurler syndrome but was without the mucopolysacchariduria and presented earlier.[1,2] One exceptional feature of this new condition was the presence of numerous phase-dense inclusions in the cytoplasm of fibroblasts from the affected individuals (Fig. 62-1). These cells were termed *inclusion cells* (abbreviated I cells), and the disease was subsequently termed I-cell disease.[3] Such inclusions were also seen in cells from patients with another condition, pseudo-Hurler polydystrophy, which was clinically milder and presented later than I-cell disease.[4,5] This was the first indication of a relationship between these two conditions.

By the early 1970s, a number of biochemical defects had been observed in I-cell disease. These included a deficiency of

Fig. 62-1 Cultured skin fibroblast from patient with I-cell disease. Note the dense inclusions, from which the disease acquired its name, present throughout the cytoplasm. Magnification ×740.

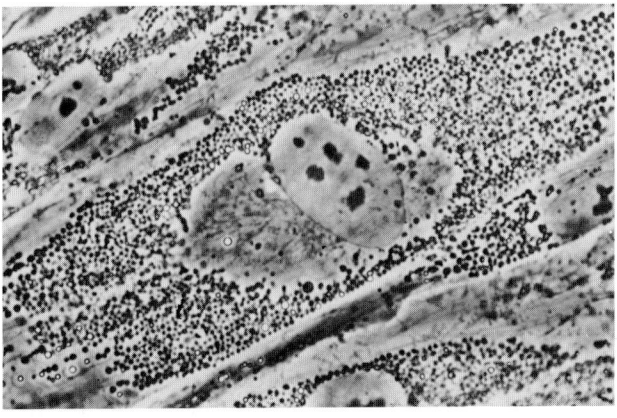

Nonstandard abbreviations used in this chapter are: CD-MPR = cation-dependent mannose-6-phosphate receptor; CI-MPR = cation-independent mannose 6-phosphate receptor; ER = endoplasmic reticulum; IGF-II = insulinlike growth factor II; Man-6-P = mannose-6-phosphate; MPR = mannose-6-phosphate receptors; SRP = signal recognition particle.

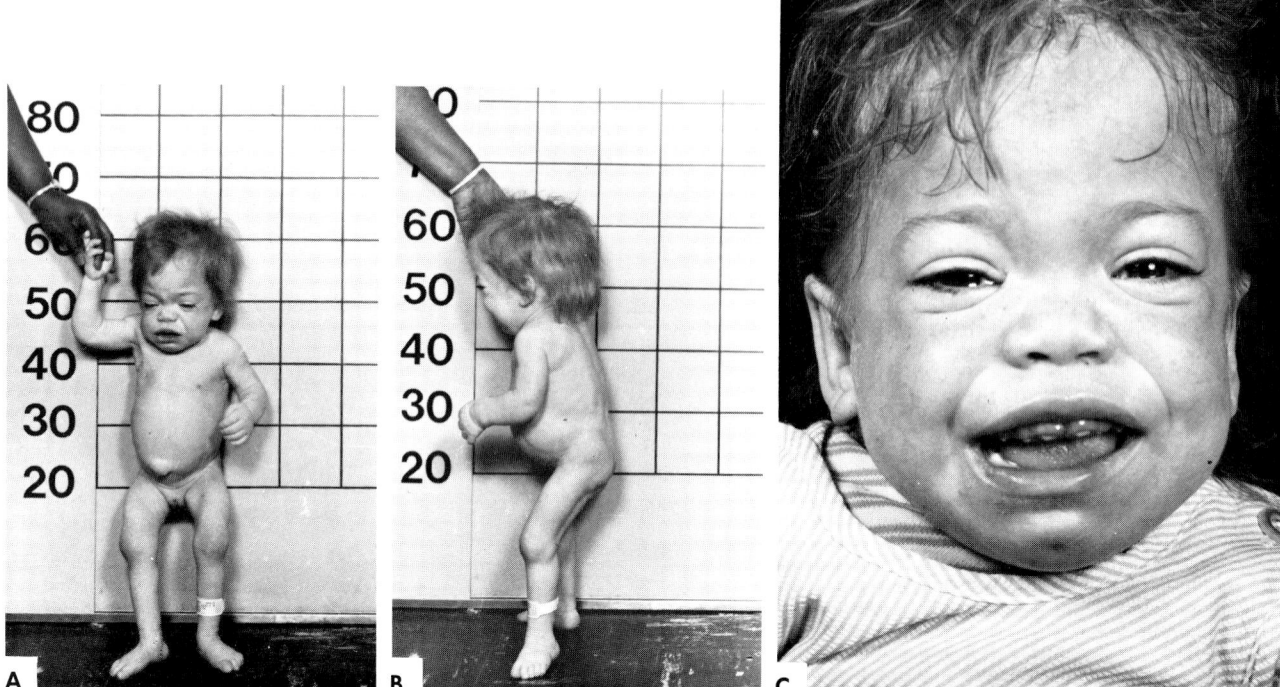

Fig. 62-2 I-cell disease (ML-II) in a 27-month-old child. Although abnormalities in appearance were noted by the parents at 2 months, the patient was diagnosed as having Down syndrome and later Hurler syndrome. At 27 months, I-cell disease was diagnosed on clinical and biochemical bases. The patient showed severe dysostosis multiplex, mental retardation, hepatomegaly, cardiomegaly, recurrent upper respiratory infections, umbilical hernias, and diastasis recti abdominis—all progressive. Corneal clouding was apparent on slit-lamp examination and subsequently became grossly evident. A and B. front and side views showing coarse facies, prominent abdomen, umbilical hernia, joint contractures, and upper lumbar kyphosis. C. detail of facies, showing characteristic gingival hyperplasia.

multiple lysosomal enzymes in cultured fibroblasts[3,6–8] and their presence in the culture medium at abnormally high levels.[8,9] The serum and body fluids of patients with I-cell disease also showed elevated levels of lysosomal enzymes.[10] Hickman and Neufeld made key observations that I-cell disease fibroblasts were capable of endocytosis of the lysosomal enzymes secreted by normal cells but that normal cells were incapable of internalizing the enzymes secreted by I-cell disease fibroblasts.[8] These observations suggested that lysosomal enzymes contained a recognition marker for uptake and transport to lysosomes and that enzymes from I-cell fibroblasts lacked this marker. The idea of a recognition marker was subsequently confirmed, and it was ultimately identified as mannose-6-phosphate, a sugar phosphate for which there was no precedent on mammalian glycoproteins.[11–13]

The biosynthetic pathway by which mannose-6-phosphate is added to lysosomal enzymes was later elucidated, and I-cell disease (and pseudo-Hurler polydystrophy) cells were shown to be defective in a key enzyme in this pathway (UDP-N-acetylglucosamine:lysosomal enzyme N-acetylglucosaminyl-1-phosphotransferase).[14,15] This enzyme is present at low levels in most cells and has not yet been purified to homogeneity. Neither has its cDNA or its gene been cloned. However, genetic studies indicate that more than one gene product contributes to the functional enzyme.

The term *mucolipidosis* was coined by Spranger and Wiedemann to denote diseases which combined clinical features common to both the mucopolysaccharidoses and the sphingolipidoses.[16] In this classification, I-cell disease was designated ML-II and pseudo-Hurler polydystrophy ML-III. (The relationship between them was not yet realized.) This classification is not ideal, as I-cell disease and pseudo-Hurler polydystrophy are fundamentally different from other known lysosomal storage diseases. However, the terms *ML-II* and *ML-III* are so well established in the literature, they will be used in this chapter as synonyms for I-cell disease and pseudo-Hurler polydystrophy, respectively.

CLINICAL MANIFESTATIONS

Mucolipidosis II (I-Cell Disease)

I-cell disease is characterized by severe psychomotor retardation and by many of the clinical features and radiologic changes that are seen in the Hurler syndrome (Fig. 62-2).[17] However, the earlier onset of signs and symptoms, the absence of excess mucopolysacchariduria, and the more rapidly progressive course leading to death between 5 and 8 years allow clinical differentiation of ML II from the Hurler syndrome (see Chap. 61). As in the Hurler syndrome, patients have coarse facial features and severe skeletal abnormalities which include kyphoscoliosis, anterior beaking and wedging of the vertebral bodies, a lumbar gibbus deformity, widening of the ribs, and proximal pointing of the metacarpals.[18–20] The abnormal inclusions seen in I-cell disease have been demonstrated in utero and in the placenta.[21–23] The clinical features are evident much earlier than in the Hurler syndrome and may be obvious at birth.[24] Neonates with I-cell disease usually show coarse facial features, craniofacial abnormalities, and restricted joint movement despite generalized hypotonia. Presenting features may also include congenital hip dislocation, hernias, and bilateral talipes equinovarus.[25] Striking gingival hyperplasia is a unique clinical feature which distinguishes ML II from Hurler syndrome.[24–26] Birth weight and birth length are often below normal. Congenital fractures may also be a manifestation of neonatal ML II.[27]

The clinical course is characterized by progressive failure to thrive and by developmental delay. The facial features become characteristic, with a high forehead, puffy eyelids, prominent epicanthal folds, flat nasal bridge, anteverted nostrils, gingival hyperplasia, and macroglossia. Psychomotor retardation is usually obvious by 6 months. Linear growth decelerates during the first year, and stops during the second year. Joint immobility progresses with development of claw-hand deformities and kyphoscoliosis. Head size remains unchanged. Abdominal protuberance with hepatomegaly is prominent, as are umbilical and inguinal hernias. Splenomegaly is minimal. Respiratory infections are frequent, as are bouts of otitis media. Corneal haziness is common, and corneal opacities are evident on slit-lamp examination as diffuse stromal granularities. Cardiomegaly and cardiac murmurs are common, and aortic insufficiency is not infrequent.[24,28]

Mental retardation is somewhat variable, but usually severe and slowly progressive. However, Okada et al. pointed out that motor development was more severely retarded than mental development in the 21 patients whose clinical courses they summarized.[28] Cardiorespiratory complications usually lead to death between the fifth and seventh year of life, but there are now several reports of patients surviving into the teens.[28,29]

Mucolipidosis III (Pseudo-Hurler Polydystrophy)

ML III is a much milder disorder with later onset of clinical signs and symptoms (2 to 4 years). The clinical course is more slowly progressive also, permitting survival into adulthood.[30] Affected patients (Fig. 62-3) share many clinical features with patients with the mild to moderately severe forms of mucopolysaccharidoses types I and VI (see Chap. 61). However, unlike patients with MPS I and MPS VI, patients with ML III have no mucopolysacchariduria. Stiffness of the hands and shoulders suggestive of rheumatoid arthritis is one of the commonest early manifestations. These symptoms often make it difficult for patients to dress themselves without assistance. By 4 to 6 years of age, most patients have claw-hand deformities, scoliosis, and short stature. Progressive destruction of the hip joints is one of the most disabling features of ML III, and often leads to a characteristic waddling gait. Carpal tunnel syndrome is frequently seen. Mild coarsening of the facial features and thickening of the skin become apparent after the sixth year. Although visual complaints are uncommon, and corneas usually appear clear, slit-lamp examination usually reveals stromal granularities by the seventh year. Traboulsi and Maumenee concluded that ML III patients develop a characteristic triad of ophthalmologic findings which include corneal clouding, mild retinopathy, and hyperopic astigmatism.[31] Cardiac valvular involvement, evidenced by the murmur of aortic insufficiency, is usual by the end of the first decade, but symptomatic cardiac insufficiency is rare. Puberty is normal.

Fig. 62-3 Pseudo-Hurler polydystrophy (ML-III) in (A) a brother age 11 and (B) a sister age 9½ years. As is usually the case in affected brother-sister pairs, the male is more severely affected. At age 2 years, the boy was observed to have deformed hands and was unable to raise his arms above his head. Growth was severely retarded after age 6, and at age 11 he showed extensive radiographic skeletal changes, including severe and characteristic changes in the hips. He also showed stiffness of the joints and claw hands, and the murmur of aortic regurgitation was present. At this age there was no corneal clouding, even by slit-lamp examination, but by age 17 clouding was clearly evident.

The sister showed similar abnormalities at age 3½ to 4 years, and there was evidence of a corneal haze on slit-lamp examination. At age 13 the murmur of aortic regurgitation was present. In both individuals IQ was estimated to be about 70. Attempts at correction of severe bilateral hip disease by hip replacement were only partially successful.

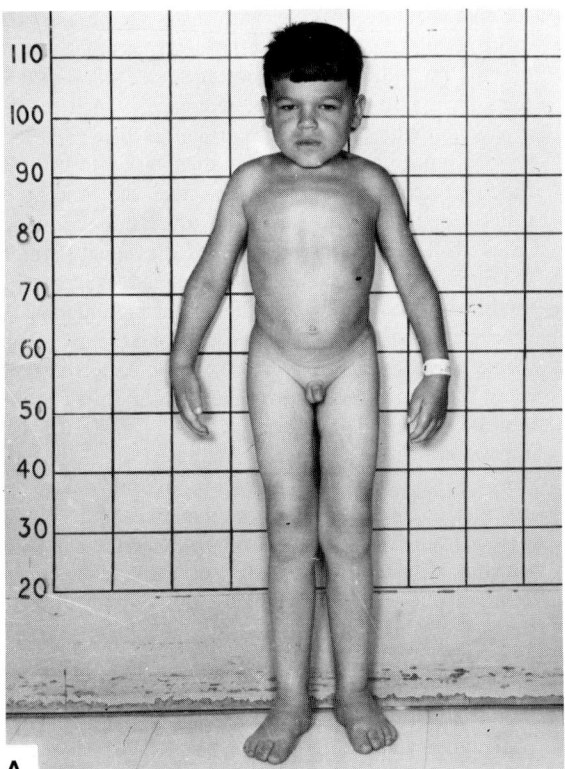

A

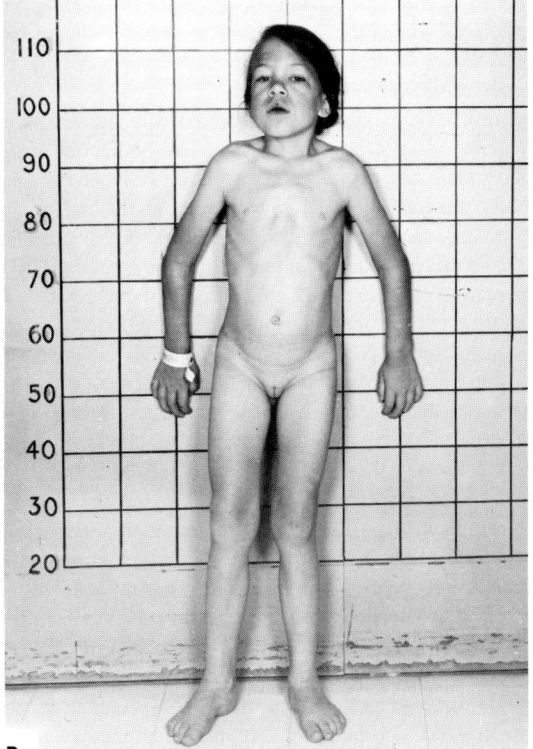

B

The skeletal dysplasia in the hands, hips, elbows, and shoulders is slowly progressive through the first two decades. Radiographic findings of dysostosis multiplex are moderately severe, and certain pelvic and vertebral changes are considered characteristic of ML III. These findings include low iliac wings with hypoplastic bodies, flattening and irregularity of the proximal femoral epiphyses with valgus deformity of the femoral necks, underdevelopment of the posterior parts of the vertebral bodies of the dorsal spine, and hypoplasia of the anterior third of the vertebral bodies of the lumbar spine.[32] For reasons that are unclear, the radiologic changes appear consistently more severe in affected males than affected females.

Nearly 50 percent of reported patients have some learning disability or mental retardation.[30] Although patients are known to survive to the fourth or fifth decades, relatively little is known with certainty about the life expectancy or the natural course of the illness beyond the third decade.

PATHOLOGY

Mucolipidosis II

A characteristic feature of ML-II is the presence of numerous membrane-bound vacuoles containing electron-lucent or fibrillogranular material in the cytoplasm of mesenchymal cells, especially fibroblasts. These are the "inclusion bodies" for which the disease was named. The contents of such vacuoles have not been well characterized but probably include oligosaccharides, mucopolysaccharides, and lipids.[33-36] Pathologic changes have been observed in mesenchymal cells of tissues of a 15-week-old fetus[21] and in placenta at the 14th week of pregnancy.[23]

The skeletal system is very seriously affected, and the radiologic features described above correlate well with abnormalities of bone structure seen on microscopic examination.[37,38] Abnormalities of cartilage structure have also been seen in patients with I-cell disease.[37,39] All this appears to indicate impaired production or maintenance of extracellular matrix by several types of mesenchymal cells.

The central nervous system shows essentially normal morphology except for the presence of lamellar bodies in spinal ganglia neurons[40] and in the anterior horn cells of one patient.[41] Only minimal alterations were seen in the peripheral nervous system, and while some vacuoles were seen in Schwann cells around unmyelinated axons, they were thought to be unlikely to interfere with the process of myelination.[41] Skeletal muscle fibers appear normal by light and electron microscopy, but satellite cells have some vacuoles.[41] Consistent with this observation, it has been noted that myoblasts in culture show the I-cell defect both biochemically and morphologically and are slower to fuse than normal myoblasts.[42] Once myotubes are formed, however, they do not exhibit the morphologic or biochemical defects. There is one report of a deficiency of type I muscle fibers, in the absence of denervation, in a quadriceps muscle biopsy of an ML-II patient, suggesting a developmental disruption of motor unit organization.[43] Such features may be correlated with the neuromuscular disability of patients with I-cell disease.

The muscular tissue of the heart appears normal, but heart valves show impressive thickening due to the presence of numerous vacuolated fibroblasts.[37,41] In liver, damage to fibro-

blasts in the periportal spaces is visible, while Kupffer cells and hepatocytes are essentially normal.[37,41] In the kidney, the glomerular podocytes, which are thought to represent mesenchymal cells, are the most severely affected.[41,44] In one study, these cells were essentially normal in the longest surviving patient (10 years), while patients who died at earlier ages (2 weeks to 4 years) showed much heavier vacuolation.[41] It is not clear what the functional significance of this finding is, but it appears to represent the only histologic difference in visceral organs between ML-II patients who die in infancy or early childhood and those who survive well into the first decade of life.[41]

ML-II patients often have repeated upper respiratory infections. Examination of one patient showed no radiographic abnormality of the trachea, but at autopsy the epiglottis, larynx, trachea, and base of the tongue were thickened with balloon cells filled with acid mucopolysaccharide and mucolipids.[45]

Mucolipidosis III

The pathology of ML-III is not as well documented as that of ML-II. Fibroblasts cultured from ML-III patients show inclusion bodies similar to those of ML-II cells though these may not be as prominent.[5,46] We are not aware of any reports of autopsy studies of ML-III patients.

NORMAL PATHWAYS OF BIOSYNTHESIS AND TRANSPORT OF LYSOSOMAL ENZYMES

The biosynthesis of lysosomal enzymes possessing the mannose-6-phosphate marker utilizes the cellular machinery for the synthesis of other glycoproteins as well as two specific enzymes involved in the addition of mannose-6-phosphate. Lysosomal enzymes, together with many membrane proteins and proteins destined for secretion, are synthesized on endoplasmic reticulum-bound ribosomes (see Chap. 3). Such proteins have a so-called signal sequence, which mediates their interaction with a signal recognition particle (SRP).[47] This lysosomal enzyme-SRP complex then binds to the SRP-recognition protein (docking protein), and the nascent protein is translocated into the lumen of the endoplasmic reticulum (ER), with subsequent cleavage of the signal peptide.[47] As is the case with most other glycoproteins, acid hydrolases are modified in the ER by the addition of high mannose oligosaccharides donated by a dolichol pyrophosphate intermediate.[48] These oligosaccharides are then subjected to the typical trimming reactions which have been shown to occur in the ER, and the nascent glycoproteins are then transferred to the Golgi apparatus, where further trimming and modification takes place. In the cis-Golgi, many acid hydrolases are specifically modified by the addition of the mannose-6-phosphate marker. This marker is generated through the concerted action of two enzymes (Fig. 62-4).[49-52] The first step in the process is the addition of an α-N-acetylglucosamine-1-phosphate residue to the 6 position of a mannose on the high mannose oligosaccharide on the hydrolase. This gives rise to a phosphodiester intermediate. The enzyme catalyzing the reaction is UDP-N-acetylglucosamine:lysosomal enzyme N-acetylglucosaminyl-1-phosphotransferase (termed *the phosphotransferase*). The sec-

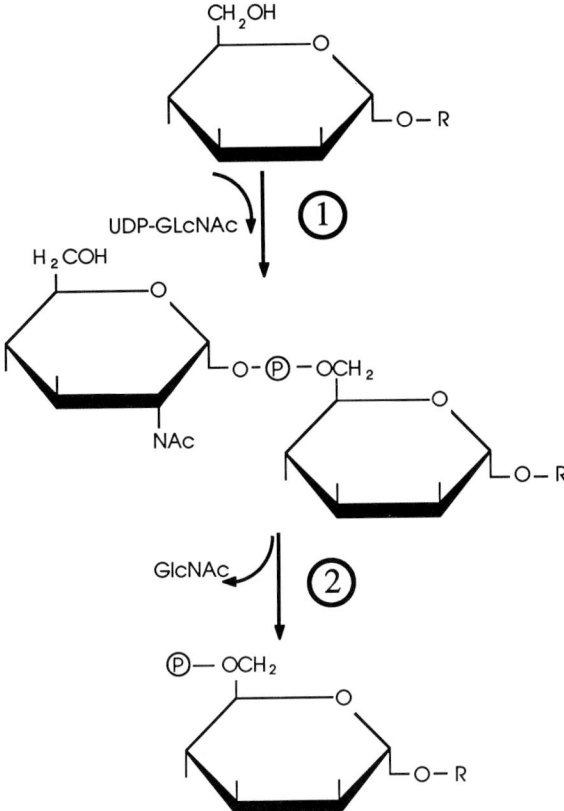

Fig. 62-4 The biosynthesis of the mannose-6-phosphate recognition marker. R represents the oligosaccharide on the nascent lysosomal enzyme. Reaction 1 is catalyzed by UDP-*N*-acetylglucosamine: lysosomal enzyme *N*-acetylglucosaminyl-1-phosphotransferase. Reaction 2 is catalyzed by *N*-acetylglucosamine-1-phosphodiester-*N*-acetylglucosaminidase.

ond step of the process involves the removal of the *N*-acetyl-glucosamine residue, catalyzed by the enzyme *N*-acetylglucosamine 1-phosphodiester-*N*-acetylglucosaminidase, to expose the mannose-6-phosphate marker. This enzyme was initially called *the phosphodiesterase,* but mechanistic studies showed it to be a glycosidase.[53]

Mannose-6-Phosphate Receptors

Following acquisition of the mannose-6-phosphate marker, acid hydrolases can be recognized by specific receptors which direct their transfer to lysosomes. Two such mannose-6-phosphate-specific receptors (MPR) are known. The first receptor to be identified was originally thought to have a mass of 215 kDa.[54–57] Recently, however, the cDNA for the receptor has been cloned from human and bovine sources, and it is apparent that the true molecular weight is much larger.[58–60] The amino acid sequence suggests a mass of about 270 kDa for the protein moiety alone, and the addition of carbohydrate would further increase its molecular weight. This receptor does not require divalent cations for binding activity and recognizes, in addition to phosphate monoesters, the so-called "covered phosphates" (phosphodiesters) found on the acid hydrolases of the slime mold *Dictyostelium discoideum*.[61–64] This has been termed the cation-independent MPR (CI-MPR) to distinguish it from the second receptor, which has a mass of 46 kDa and has an absolute requirement for divalent cations for binding activity.[65,66] The smaller receptor, which has come to be called

the cation-dependent MPR (CD-MPR), does not recognize the covered phosphates.[65,66] The role of the larger MPR in the targeting of lysosomal enzymes has been well established, while that of the smaller receptor is less well understood. The cDNA for this receptor has also been cloned.[67,68]

The cloning of the cDNAs for the two mannose-6-phosphate receptors has shown an interesting relationship between them. Both receptors consist of an extracytoplasmic amino-terminal domain, a transmembrane region, and a cytoplasmic carboxy terminal domain. The cytoplasmic regions of the two receptors are not homologous. The extracytoplasmic domain of the CI-MPR consists of 15 repeating homologous units, each of which is homologous to and similar in size to the extracellular domain of CD-MPR (Fig. 62-5).

The relative role of these two receptors in the targeting of mannose-6-phosphate-containing lysosomal enzymes is not yet clear. In cells which contain both receptors, it appears that both receptors contribute to the targeting of newly synthesized enzymes.[69] The CD-MPR, however, does not appear to mediate endocytosis of lysosomal enzymes from the extracellular environment.[69] There are subtle differences in the binding of lysosomal enzymes by the two receptors, and it has been hypothesized that small variations in the pH of the Golgi apparatus, where lysosomal enzymes potentially bind to the receptors, may modulate the extent of binding to both receptors.[70]

Fig. 62-5 A diagram of the human cation-independent MPR and cation-dependent MPR. The number of amino acids in each domain is shown.[58,67] The extracellular domain of the CD-MPR is homologous to each of the repeating units of the extracellular portion of CI-MPR. The hatched region in repeat number 13 of the CI-MPR represents the sequence which is similar to sequences found in the collagen binding domain in the fibronectin receptor in bovine seminal fluid protein and in factor XII.[58]

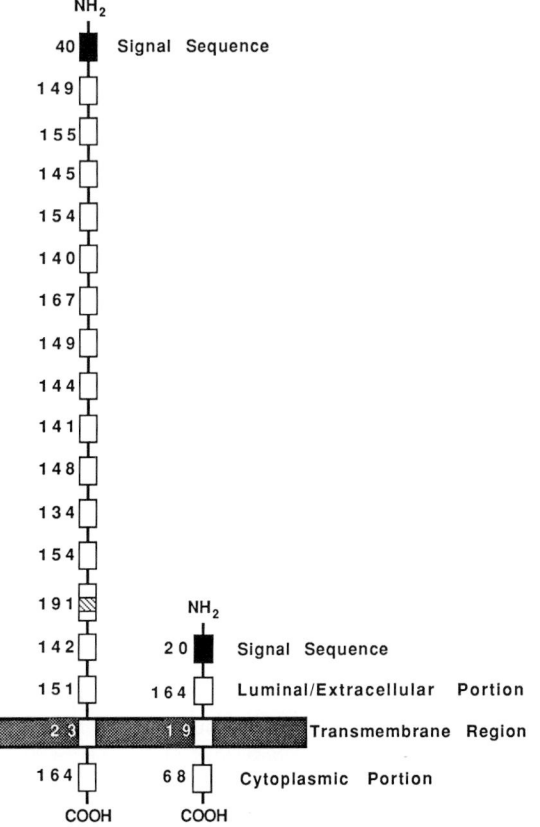

CI-MPR   CD-MPR

The availability of these receptor cDNA clones should be useful in the further elucidation of the role of the mannose-6-phosphate marker in lysosomal enzyme traffic.

An interesting observation which has emerged from the isolation of the cDNA for the cation-independent MPR is that this receptor appears to be identical with the receptor for insulinlike growth factor II (IGF-II).[58,60,71] IGF-II is a mitogenic polypeptide hormone whose physiological role is not known.[72] Thus, the CI-MPR is a multifunctional binding protein. The IGF-II- and lysosomal enzyme-binding sites of the receptor are distinct from one another, and the binding of IGF-II to the receptor is not dependent on mannose-6-phosphate.[73–75]

Lysosomal enzymes acquire the mannose 6-phosphate recognition marker in the cis-region of the Golgi apparatus and could theoretically be targeted to the lysosome from there.[76,77] Based on immunocytochemical localization of the cation-independent MPR in rat tissues, this was postulated to be the case.[78] Other immunocytochemical studies of receptor distribution in rat liver and human hepatoma cells suggest that acid hydrolases traverse the entire Golgi apparatus prior to being diverted from the pathway followed by secretory and other glycoproteins.[79,80] This is supported by the presence of complex-type carbohydrate structures on cellular lysosomal enzymes.[81] Such carbohydrate modification is thought to occur in the trans region of the Golgi apparatus.[48] Recent evidence suggests that the localization of this receptor differs from cell type to cell type,[82] which may explain the discrepancy between different studies of receptor localization.

Binding of acid hydrolases to the MPR is followed by the movement of the complexes to a prelysosomal compartment, where under the influence of a low pH, the acid hydrolases dissociate from the receptors. The acid hydrolases are transported to lysosomes while the receptors are recycled to the Golgi area and can mediate further rounds of transport.[83,84] The identity of the prelysosomal compartment is not known, but it is thought to be an endosomelike vesicle, or a vesicle intermediate between the biosynthetic and endocytic pathways to lysosomes.[85,86]

The Endocytic Pathway

In some cell types such as fibroblasts, acid hydrolases may be transported from the extracellular milieu to lysosomes through receptor mediated endocytosis.[83,84] These cells possess cell surface cation-independent MPRs which constitute 10 to 20 percent of the total cellular complement of these receptors. Following internalization in endocytic vesicles, the acid hydrolases dissociate from the receptors in a prelysosomal acidic compartment; the acid hydrolases are transported to lysosomes while the receptors recycle and can partake in further rounds of endocytosis. Both pools of receptors, cell surface and intracellular, are in fairly rapid equilibrium.[87–90] Although it appears that the CD-MPR is present on the cell surface, it does not appear that this receptor mediates endocytosis.[69] This question has not yet been examined extensively in many cell types.

The transport pathway from the cell surface to lysosomes was discovered first and originally thought to be the major route of delivery of newly synthesized acid hydrolases to lysosomes. It was suggested that the enzymes were first delivered to the extracellular environment and then reinternalized for delivery to lysosomes.[8] It is now clear that, in most cell types, the bulk of lysosomal enzymes are transported to lyso-

somes by the intracellular pathway. Transport of enzymes from the plasma membrane accounts for only a small portion of total delivery.[91] Nonetheless, the ability of I-cell disease fibroblasts to internalize normal lysosomal enzymes by this pathway was a key factor in identifying the defect in these cells.

The two routes whereby lysosomal enzymes are transported to lysosomes in a mannose-6-phosphate-dependent manner are shown schematically in Fig. 62-6. The pathway of internalization of the CI-MPR from the plasma membrane and its subsequent recycling to the cell surface are similar to that seen with a number of other cell surface receptors, including the transferrin receptor and the receptor for low density lipoprotein[92] (see Chap. 48). These receptors have also been cloned, and examination of the mechanisms involved in each of their transport pathways should be of use in elucidating common features.

Alternate Pathways to Lysosomes

One unexplained feature of the ML-II and ML-III syndromes is the fact that not all cells are deficient in lysosomal enzyme content,[93,94] even though all cells and tissues so far examined have been shown to be deficient in the phosphotransferase activity. Many cell types (including hepatocytes, Kupffer cells, and leukocytes) and several organs (including liver, spleen, kidney, and brain) have nearly normal levels of intracellular acid hydrolases. These results suggest that there is an alternate pathway for lysosomal enzymes to be transported to lysosomes that does not require the mannose-6-phosphate recognition marker. One possibility is that lysosomal enzymes present at high concentration in the serum of ML-III and ML-III patients could be internalized via other systems which recognize carbohydrates, such as galactose, N-acetylglucosamine, mannose, and L-fucose, present in the enzymes.[94] Alternatively, another intracellular pathway may be involved.

Another interesting fact is that two lysosomal enzymes are present at nearly normal levels in ML-II and ML-III fibroblasts. These are β-glucocerebrosidase, a membrane associated enzyme, which is not normally phosphorylated,[95] and acid phosphatase, a soluble enzyme, at least some of which is phosphorylated in normal fibroblasts.[96] It has been postulated that membrane associated lysosomal enzymes, such as β-glucocerebrosidase, and other proteins associated with the lysosomal membrane, for which functions have not yet been described, reach lysosomes by a pathway that does not require phosphorylation.[97,98] It is not known how these proteins are directed to the lysosome. The presence of nearly normal levels of acid phosphatase in I cells is puzzling, however, since in normal fibroblasts its targeting to lysosomes appears to be MPR-dependent.[96] It may be that an increased stability of this enzyme in lysosomes of I-cell-disease fibroblasts explains its accumulation.

PRIMARY BIOCHEMICAL DEFECT IN ML-II AND ML-III

The identification of mannose-6-phosphate as the recognition marker which mediates the internalization of acid hydrolases by fibroblasts[11–13] and the observation that I-cell disease fibroblasts are defective in the incorporation of ^{32}P into several lysosomal enzymes[99,100] suggested that these cells were defective

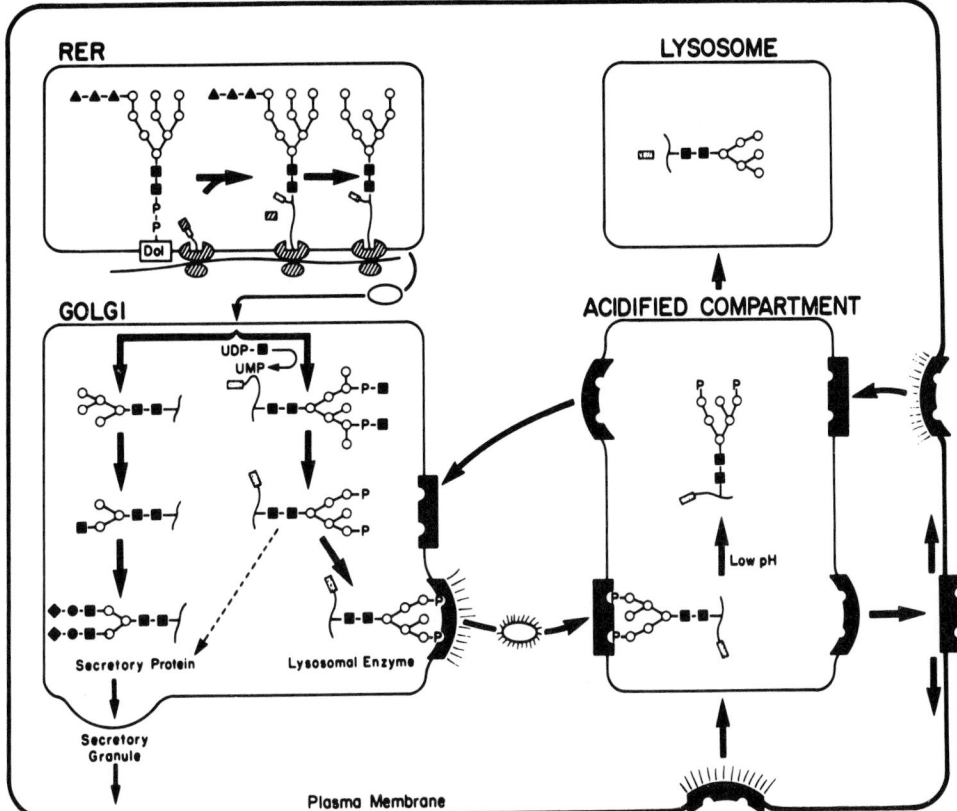

Fig. 62-6 Targeting of lysosomal enzymes to lysosomes. Lysosomal enzymes are synthesized in the rough endoplasmic reticulum (RER), transferred to the Golgi apparatus, where addition of the mannose-6-phosphate recognition marker and binding to mannose-6-phosphate receptors occur, and are subsequently transported to lysosomes. Plasma membrane MPRs bind extracellular lysosomal enzymes, and mediate their internalization in coated vesicles and their transfer to lysosomes. (From Kornfeld.[84] Used by permission of FASEB J.)

in the synthesis of this marker. The elucidation of the biosynthetic pathway of mannose-6-phosphate demonstrated the involvement of two enzymes, a phosphotransferase and a phosphodiesterase.[49–52] Assays were developed to allow the estimation of both enzymes, and it was shown that the first enzyme in the pathway, the phosphotransferase, was deficient in both I-cell disease and in pseudo-Hurler polydystrophy.[14,15] No patients have been found who lack the second enzyme.

Phosphotransferase Assay

The assay for the phosphotransferase is sensitive and reliable. The original assay used [^{32}P]UDP-GlcNAc as the donor substrate and α-methyl-mannoside or purified lysosomal enzymes as the acceptor substrates.[101] Using this assay, with α-methyl mannoside as the acceptor, it was shown that in fibroblasts from I-cell patients, the phosphotransferase was absent or barely detectable, while in cells from ML-III patients there was residual activity of from 2 to 20 percent of normal levels.[102] Also a lower level of activity could be seen in the parents of affected individuals (obligate heterozygotes) than in normal subjects.[103] In a recent study of Japanese patients with I-cell disease, there was <2 to 13 percent of control activity.[28] In this study, the patients had a somewhat mild I-cell phenotype, and the severity of the clinical phenotype did not correlate with the level of enzyme activity.[28]

The assay using ^{32}P-labeled substrate was inconvenient, however, in that the donor substrate was not commercially available, and it was therefore necessary to synthesize and pu-

rify it. In addition, the substrate had a limited shelf life due to the half-life of the isotope. UDP-[^{3}H or ^{14}C]GlcNAc can also be used in the assay. These substrates are commercially available and have long half-lives. However, the use of these substrates initially resulted in assays with high backgrounds and therefore low sensitivity. The assay has since been modified to improve the sensitivity and reliability using these commercially available substrates, and the results obtained with the modified assay are reported to be comparable to those seen using the ^{32}P-labeled substrate.[104,105]

It should be noted that when assayed with artificial acceptors such as α-methyl mannoside, the less common variant of ML-III patients (group C of the complementation groups discussed below) will show normal levels of activity. This is also true of obligate heterozygotes of this variant.

Complementation Studies/Heterogeneity of ML-II and ML-III

Clinical variability has long been observed in patients with ML-II and ML-III. In an effort to understand the basis of this variability, complementation analyses of fibroblasts from many patients were initiated. In these studies, fibroblasts from individual patients were fused with cells from other patients using polyethylene glycol as a fusogen. Complementation of pairs of fibroblasts was indicated by the increased intracellular lysosomal enzyme activity of the heterokaryons compared with the unfused homokaryon mixtures, and by the correction of the abnormal forms of these enzymes seen on polyacrylamide gel electrophoresis.[106–108] Complementation has also been monitored by measuring the phosphotransferase activity of the heterokaryons.[109]

One such study of ML-III patient fibroblasts showed the existence of three complementation groups (groups A, B, and C), though one of these (group B) was represented by a single cell line.[106] Complementation was also observed among ML-II fibroblasts, though this was less conclusive than that seen with ML-III fibroblasts,[107] and in another study several instances of complementation between ML-II and ML-III fibroblasts were seen.[108] These complementation studies indicate genetic heterogeneity and suggest that the phosphotransferase may be a heteropolymeric enzyme.

Biochemical evidence for heterogeneity also emerged from kinetic studies of phosphotransferase activity. During the development of the phosphotransferase assay, it was noticed that while most ML-III patients were defective in enzyme activity, whether this was measured using lysosomal enzymes or artificial substances as the acceptor substrates, enzyme from one sibship (GM3391) had normal activity toward α-methyl-mannoside despite very low activity with lysosomal enzymes.[102] This prompted the hypothesis that the phosphotransferase possessed two distinct domains, a catalytic domain and a domain which was important in specific recognition of lysosomal enzymes. Further studies have supported this hypothesis. Careful analysis of the kinetic parameters and of the temperature sensitivity of the residual activity of a number of ML-III fibroblasts has shown the existence of two types of defects.[109-111] In one group (group A) the catalytic activity of the enzyme is reduced both with artificial substrates and with lysosomal enzymes. The affinity of the residual activity for the lysosomal enzymes is normal, however, and activity can be somewhat normalized by assaying at 23°C rather than at 37°C.[109-111] The group C mutation appears to result in an enzyme which is defective in recognition of lysosomal enzymes but which has normal activity toward the artificial substrates.[109-111] Thus the enzyme in group A fibroblasts has a defective catalytic domain, while, in group C fibroblasts, the domain which recognizes the lysosomal enzymes is defective. This model for lysosomal enzyme recognition by *N*-acetylglucosaminophosphotransferase is shown in Fig. 62-7.

Recognition of Lysosomal Enzymes by the Phosphotransferase

The phosphotransferase is a key enzyme in the generation of mannose-6-phosphate-containing acid hydrolases. Not only does it catalyze the first step in the synthesis of the recognition marker itself, but it also is responsible for the specificity of the process. It is this enzyme which specifically selects lysosomal enzymes from the large number of other glycoproteins present in the lumen of the Golgi apparatus.[50,112] It is not yet clear how this selectivity is achieved.

The affinity of the phosphotransferase for lysosomal enzymes is 100 times greater than its affinity for nonlysosomal glycoproteins.[50,112] The oligosaccharide units of lysosomal enzymes, however, are not significantly different from those of other glycoproteins, which are poor substrates for the phosphotransferase.[113-118] The specificity of the enzyme toward the oligosaccharides of lysosomal enzymes seems to be of minor importance. Rather it seems that it is primarily the protein conformation of the lysosomal enzymes that is recognized by the phosphotransferase. This is inferred from the fact that de-

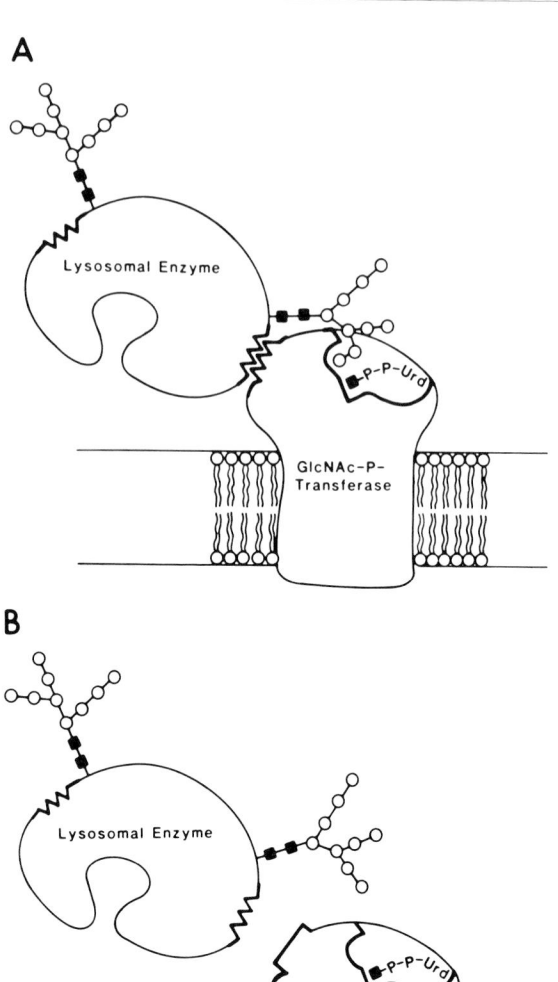

Fig. 62-7 A model for the recognition of lysosomal enzymes by *N*-acetylglucosaminylphosphotransferase. *A.* Enzyme from normal individuals. The proposed protein domain of the lysosomal enzyme which is recognized by the phosphotransferase is represented as ⌁. *B.* Phosphotransferase from individuals with the variant form of ML III, where the defect appears to be in the recognition of lysosomal enzymes rather than in the catalytic site. *(From Kornfeld.[84] Used by permission of FASEB J.)*

glycosylated lysosomal enzymes are potent inhibitors of the phosphotransferase, and this inhibition is relieved by heat treatment or proteolysis of the deglycosylated enzymes.[119] The exact nature of the determinant recognized by the phosphotransferase has not yet been elucidated. Several lysosomal enzymes have now been cloned and sequenced.[120-127] No simple sequence homology which can account for their selective recognition by the phosphotransferase has been identified.[128] Perhaps such a simple sequence exists but is only recognized when in the proper conformation. Alternatively, it has been suggested that the recognition determinant could be a conformational feature consisting of several simple sequences or amino acids from different parts of the molecule, which are brought into the correct orientation by proper folding of the molecule.[128] The application of the techniques of molecular biology to this question should help in its resolution.

Other Biochemical Defects in ML-II and ML-III

While it is now clear that the primary defect in the ML-II and ML-III syndromes is the deficiency of the phosphotransferase activity, cells from these patients also exhibit a number of other secondary defects. The cells are deficient in the activities of a large number of lysosomal enzymes and secrete abnormally large amounts of these.[3,6–9] In addition, it has been reported that many of the lysosomal enzymes synthesized by the cells show abnormal electrophoretic patterns.[129,130] This may be explained in two ways: (1) The sugar side chains are qualitatively different. The addition of mannose-6-phosphate to the oligosaccharide side chain of the nascent acid hydrolase normally prevents mannose trimming and subsequent complex-chain glycosylation of that particular side chain.[131] In the absence of this addition (as in I-cell disease), the nonphosphorylated mannose side chains undergo trimming by mannosidases and all become further processed to complex-type units; the result is that the enzymes in these cells differ from their normal counterparts. They show greater "terminal" glycosylation (galactose and sialic acid addition) and thus have more negative charge. (2) Polypeptides are also different. Lysosomal enzymes are normally synthesized as preproenzymes; they are initially proteolytically processed in the endoplasmic reticulum by removal of the signal sequence.[132] Later they undergo further proteolytic modification in the lysosome.[133] This lysosomal processing may be related to activation of some enzymes or to stabilization in the acidic environment of the lysosome.[84] In the absence of proper targeting to the lysosome, this processing does not occur. As a result, the enzymes secreted from these cells have higher molecular weights than those normally found for the same enzymes in lysosomes.

Several studies have shown excessive accumulation of free (nonpeptide) cystine in lysosomes of ML-II fibroblasts.[134–137] Such storage is also seen in fibroblasts from patients with benign and nephropathic cystinosis, another inherited lysosomal storage disease (see Chap. 107). It has been suggested (see Chap. 107) that the cystine transport protein which mediates cystine egress from lysosomes may not be processed properly in I-cell lysosomes which lack a full contingent of hydrolytic enzymes. The relationship between the defects in these two cell types is not clear.

One interesting secondary defect in I-cell disease fibroblasts is the abnormally high content of sialic acid in these cells, which seems to confer increased sensitivity to freezing.[138] It has been demonstrated that neuraminidase treatment of the cells prior to preservative freezing in liquid nitrogen enables the cells to adapt more easily to thawing and subsequent subculture.[139]

Several years ago it was reported that β-glucosidase activities were deficient in ML-II fibroblasts when assayed in the absence of detergents but that the same cells were normal for this enzyme when tested in the presence of detergents.[140] It was hypothesized that the deficiency of β-glucosidase was due to the deficiency of an activator protein required for in vivo activity of the enzyme. Several other activator proteins are known for lysosomal enzymes, and these appear to be located in lysosomes. Inui and colleagues have provided immunologic evidence for a partial deficiency of activator protein for the hydrolysis of G_{M1} ganglioside and sulfatide in skin fibroblasts, liver, and brain of ML-II patients.[141,142] An activator protein which activates β-glucocerebrosidase and also β-galactocerebrosidase and sphingomyelinase has also been shown to be ab-

normal in ML-II and ML-III fibroblasts.[143,144] All these findings suggest that activator proteins may be targeted to the lysosome in a mannose-6-phosphate-dependent manner and that lysosomal enzymes that are not affected by the primary defect in ML-II and ML-III may exhibit lower enzyme activity than in normal cells due to inappropriate targeting of their activator proteins.

DIAGNOSIS

Homozygotes

Biochemical confirmation of the diagnosis of ML-II and ML-III can be made in two ways. (1) The activities of lysosomal enzymes in serum or in cultured fibroblasts can be measured. In general, a ten- to twentyfold increase in serum β-hexosaminidase, iduronate sulfatase, and arylsulfatase A is diagnostic of the two disorders.[30,145,146] If cultured fibroblasts are available, the characteristic pattern of lysosomal enzyme deficiencies may be used as can the ratio of extracellular to intracellular enzyme activities.[7,30,147,148] The assay of lysosomal enzyme activities in white blood cells is not reliable for this diagnosis.[149,150] (2) The level of GlcNAc-phosphotransferase activity in white blood cells or in cultured fibroblasts can be measured directly.[102,103] As discussed above, this assay can now be reliably performed using commercially available substrates.[104,105]

ML-II cannot be distinguished from ML-III on the basis of residual acid hydrolase activity or localization, as these are similar in the two disorders. Varki et al. reported that there is a general correlation between the degree of deficiency of GlcNAc-phosphotransferase activity and clinical severity. In their study it was found that in ML-II patients the level of the GlcNAc-phosphotransferase activity was nonexistent or barely detectable, while ML-III patients had from 2 to 20 percent of normal levels.[102] A more recent study of Japanese patients diagnosed as having ML-II by clinical and biochemical criteria reported levels of phosphotransferase activity 2 to 13 percent of control levels.[28] In this study, the degree of deficiency did not correlate with clinical severity.

Prenatal Diagnosis

Prenatal diagnosis of ML-II has been made following amniocentesis, using the elevated lysosomal enzyme activity of amniotic fluid and the decreased activity of lysosomal enzymes in cultured amniotic cells as criteria for diagnosis.[21,151–153] This method is considered reliable but gives a late diagnosis (20 to 22 weeks of pregnancy). There have been two first trimester prenatal diagnoses of ML-II, following lysosomal enzyme determination on trophoblast biopsy material obtained at 10 weeks of gestation.[154] While it was possible to make the diagnosis on the basis of fresh biopsy material, the authors of the report concluded that diagnosis was more reliable when made on cultured material. Even with the 2- to 4-week delay for cell culture following chorionic villus biopsy, this procedure may be more acceptable than amniocentesis to couples at risk for ML-II.

A case of fetal ML-II has been diagnosed in a pregnancy at risk for the disorder, by monitoring the serum hexosaminidase level of the mother during pregnancy and comparing this with those of controls not at risk for this disorder.[155] While this preliminary observation needs further investigation, it may be of use as a simple means of early diagnosis of ML-II.[155]

One important complicating factor in the prenatal diagnosis of ML-II is the heterogeneity in lysosomal enzyme expression. It is therefore important to examine carefully the index-case fibroblasts in every case.

Heterozygote Identification

Cells from ML-II patients demonstrate very low or undetectable levels of the phosphotransferase activity, while ML-III cells possess 2 to 20 percent of normal levels of the enzyme.[102] Fibroblasts and white blood cells from parents of patients (obligate heterozygotes) have intermediate levels of phosphotransferase activity.[103] These obligate heterozygotes also have somewhat elevated levels of serum β-hexosaminidase compared to normals. The use of these two criteria has allowed the scoring of individuals at risk for the carrier state.[103,105]

It should be stressed that heterozygotes for the complementation group C variant of ML-III (see above) will show normal activity and kinetic parameters when assayed using α-methyl mannoside as acceptor substrate.

TREATMENT

There is no specific or definitive treatment for I-cell disease or mucolipidosis III. Generally, the same principles apply that are discussed for the mucopolysaccharidoses (Chap. 61). Symptomatic treatment of frequent respiratory infections with antibiotics is important. Physical therapy may slow the progression of joint immobility in ML-III patients. At least one patient with I-cell disease has responded favorably to bone marrow transplantation.[156] Although progressive hip disability may require total hip replacement in ML-III, results of long term follow-up of treated patients are not documented in the literature.

S.E. Kopits (personal communication, May 1988) indicated that he has had no success with any form of corrective hip reconstruction with ML-III patients. Based on his experience, he advises patients to defer hip surgery until after puberty. Total hip replacement has been effective in postpubertal patients with ML-III.

This chapter was authored by Dr. Elizabeth Neufeld and Dr. Victor McKusick in the previous edition. We gratefully acknowledge the fine example their chapter provided and the clinical illustrations (Figs. 62-1, 62-2, and 62-3) used from that chapter.

REFERENCES

1. LEROY JG, DeMARS RI: Mutant enzymatic and cytological phenotypes in cultured human fibroblasts. *Science* 157:804, 1967.
2. DeMARS RI, LEROY JG: The remarkable cells cultured from a human with Hurler's syndrome: An approach to visual selection for *in vitro* genetic studies. *In Vitro* 2:107, 1967.
3. TONDEUR M, VAMOS-HURWITZ E, MOCKEL-POHLS S, DEREUME JP, CREMER N, LOEB H: Clinical, biochemical, and ultrastructural studies in a case of chondrodystrophy presenting the I-cell phenotype in culture. *J Pediatr* 79:366, 1971.
4. MAROTEAUX P, LAMY M: La pseudopolydystrophie de Hurler. *Presse Med* 55:2881, 1966.
5. TAYLOR HA, THOMAS GH, MILLER CS, KELLY TE, SIGGERS D: Mucolipidosis III (pseudo-Hurler polydystrophy): Cytological and ultrastructural observationns of cultured fibroblast cells. *Clin Genet* 4:388, 1973.
6. LIGHTBODY J, WEISSMAN U, HADORN B, HERSCHKOWITZ N: I-cell disease: Multiple lysosomal-enzyme defect. *Lancet* 1:451, 1971.
7. LEROY JG, JO M, MCBRINN MC, ZIELKE K, JACOB J, O'BRIEN JS: I-cell disease: Biochemical studies. *Pediatr Res* 6:752, 1972.
8. HICKMAN S, NEUFELD EF: A hypothesis for I-cell disease: Defective hydrolases that do not enter lysosomes. *Biochem Biophys Res Commun* 49:922, 1972.
9. WIESMANN UN, LIGHTBODY J, VASELLA F, HERSCHKOWITZ N: Multiple enzyme deficiency due to enzyme leakage. *N Engl J Med* 284:109, 1971.
10. WIESMANN U, VASELLA F, HERSCHKOWITZ N: I-cell disease: Leakage of lysosomal enzymes into extracellular fluids. *N Engl J Med* 285:1090, 1971.
11. KAPLAN A, ACHORD DT, SLY WS: Phosphohexosyl components of a lysosomal enzyme are recognized by pinocytosis receptors on human fibroblasts. *Proc Natl Acad Sci USA* 74:2026, 1977.
12. NATOWICZ MR, CHI MM-Y, LOWRY OH, SLY WS: Enzymatic identification of mannose 6-phosphate on the recognition marker for receptor-mediated pinocytosis of β-glucuronidase by human fibroblasts. *Proc Natl Acad Sci USA* 76:4322, 1979.
13. DISTLER J, HIEBER V, SAHAGIAN G, SCHMICKEL R, JOURDIAN GW: Identification of mannose 6-phosphate in glycoproteins that inhibit the assimilation of β-galactosidase by fibroblasts. *Proc Natl Acad Sci USA* 76:4235, 1979.
14. REITMAN AL, VARKI A, KORNFELD S: Fibroblasts from patients with I-cell disease and pseudo-Hurler polydystrophy are deficient in uridine 5'-diphosphate-N-acetylglucosamine: Glycoprotein N-acetyl-glucosaminyl-phosphotransferase activity. *J Clin Invest* 67:1574, 1981.
15. HASILIK A, WAHEED A, VON FIGURA K: Enzymatic phosphorylation of lysosomal enzymes in the presence of UDP-N-acetylglucosamine. Absence of the activity in I-cell fibroblasts. *Biochem Biophys Res Commun* 98:761, 1981.
16. SPRANGER JW, WIEDEMANN HR: The genetic mucolipidoses. *Humangenetik* 9:113, 1970.
17. LEROY JG, SPRANGER JW, FEINGOLD M, DOPITZ JM: I-cell disease: A clinical picture. *J Pediatr* 79:360, 1971.
18. TABER P, GYEPES MT, PHILIPPANT M, LING S: Roentgenographic manifestations of Leroy's I-cell disease. *Am J Roentgenol* 118:213, 1973.
19. PATRIQUIN HB, KAPLAN P, KIND HP, GIDEON A: Neonatal mucolipidosis II (I-cell disease): Clinical and radiologic features in three cases. *Am J Roentgenol* 129:37, 1977.
20. LEMAITRE L, REMY J, FARRIAUX JP, DHONDT JL, WALBAUM R: Radiological signs of mucolipidosis II of I-cell disease. *Pediatr Radiol* 7:97, 1978.
21. AULA P, RAPOLA J, AUTIO S, RAIVIO K, KARJALAINEN O: Prenatal diagnosis and fetal pathology of I-cell disease (mucolipidosis type II). *J Pediatr* 87:221, 1975.
22. ERICKSON RP, PFLEUGER OH, SANDMAN R, HALL BD: Placental pathology in ML II. Selected abstracts: Diseases of connective tissue. *Birth Defects* 11(6):365, 1975.
23. RAPOLA J, AULA P: Morphology of the placenta in fetal I-cell disease. *Clin Genet* 11:107, 1977.
24. SPRITZ RA, DOUGHTY RA, SPACKMAN TJ, MURNANE MJ, COATES PM, KOLDOVKSY O, ZACKAI EH: Neonatal presentation of I-cell disease. *J Pediatr* 93:954, 1978.
25. CIPOLLONI C, BOLDRINI A, DONTIETT, MAIORANA A, COPPA GB: Neonatal mucolipidosis II (I-cell disease): Clinical, radiological and biochemical studies in a case. *Helv Paediatr Acta* 35:85, 1980.
26. WHELAN DT, CHANG PL, COCKSHOTT PW: Mucolipidosis II. The clinical, radiological and biochemical features in three cases. *Clin Genet* 24:90, 1983.
27. MICHELS VV, DUTTON RV, CASKEY CT: Mucolipidosis II: Unusual presentation with a congenital angulated fracture. *Clin Genet* 21:225, 1982.
28. OKADA S, OWADA M, SAKIYAMA T, YUTAKA T, OGAWA M: I-cell disease: Clinical studies of 21 Japanese cases. *Clin Genet* 28:207, 1985.
29. SATOH Y, SAKAMOTO K, FUJIBAYASHI Y, UCHIYAMA T, KAJIWARA N, HATANO M: Cardiac involvement in mucolipidosis: Importance of non-invasive studies for detection of cardiac abnormalities. *Jpn Heart J* 24:149, 1983.
30. KELLY TE, THOMAS GH, TAYLOR HA: Mucolipidosis III (pseudo-Hurler polydystrophy): Clinical and laboratory studies in a series of 12 patients. *Johns Hopkins Med J* 137:156, 1975.
31. TRABOULSI E, MAUMENEE IH: Ophthalmologic findings in mucolipidosis III (pseudo-Hurler polydystrophy). *Am J Ophthalmol* 102:529, 1986.
32. SPRANGER JW, LANGER LO Jr, WIEDEMANN HR: in *Bone Dysplasias, an Atlas of Constitutional Disorders of Skeletal Development*. Philadelphia, Saunders, 1974, p 183.

33. DAWSON G, MATALON R, DORFMAN A: Glycosphingolipids in cultured human skin fibroblasts: II. Characterization and metabolism in fibroblasts from patients with inborn errors of glycosphingolipid and mucopolysaccharide metabolism. *J Biol Chem* 247:5951, 1972.

34. HIEBER V, DISTLER J, JOURDIAN GW, SCHMICKEL R: Accumulation of ^{35}S-mucopolysaccharides in cultured mucolipidosis cells. *Birth Defects* 6:307, 1975.

35. THOMAS GH, TILLER GE Jr, REYNOLDS LW, MILLER CS, BACE JW: Increased levels of sialic acid associated with sialidase deficiency in I-cell disease (mucolipidosis II) fibroblasts. *Biochem Biophys Res Commun* 71:188, 1976.

36. STRECKER G, PEERS MC, MICHALSKI JC, HONDI-ASSAH T, FOURNET B, SPIK G, MONTREUIL J, FARRIAUX J-P, MAROTEAUX P, DURAND P: Structure of nine sialyloligosaccharides accumulate in urine of 11 patients with three different types of sialidosis: Mucolipidosis II and two new types of mucolipidosis. *Eur J Biochem* 75:390, 1977.

37. MARTIN JJ, LEROY JG, FARRIAUX JP, FONTAINE G, DESNICK RJ, CABELLO A: I-cell disease (mucolipidosis II). *Acta Neuropathol (Berl)* 33:285, 1975.

38. BABCOCK DS, BOVE KE, HUG G, DIGNAN PSJ, SOUKUP S, WARREN NS: Fetal mucolipidosis II (I-cell disease): Radiologic and pathologic correlation. *Pediatr Radiol* 16:32, 1986.

39. NOGAMI H, OOHIRA A, SUZUKI F, TSUDA K: Cartilage of I-cell disease. *Pediatr Res* 15:330, 1981.

40. NAGASHIMA K, SAKAKIBARA K, ENDO H, KONISHI Y, NAKAMURA N, SUZUKI Y, ABE T: I-cell disease (mucolipidosis II): Pathological and biochemical studies of an autopsy case. *Acta Pathol Jpn* 27:251, 1977.

41. MARTIN JJ, LEROY JG, VAN EYGEN M, CEUTERICK C: I-cell disease: A further report on its pathology. *Acta Neuropathol (Berl)* 64:234, 1984.

42. SHANSKE S, MIRANDA AF, PENN AS, DIMAURO S: Mucolipidosis II (I-cell disease): Studies of muscle biopsy and muscle cultures. *Pediatr Res* 15:1334, 1981.

43. KULA RW, SHAFIQ SA, SHER JH, QAZI QH: I-cell disease (mucolipidosis II): Differential expression in satellite cells and mature muscle fibers. *J Neurol Sci* 63:75, 1984.

44. CASTAGNARO M, ALROY J, UCCI AA, JAFFE R: Lectin histochemistry and ultrastructure of kidneys from patients with I-cell disease. *Arch Pathol Lab Med* 111:285, 1987.

45. PETERS ME, ARYA S, LANGER LO, GILBERT EF, CARLSON R, ADKINS W: Narrow trachea in mucopolysaccharidoses. *Pediatr Radiol* 15:225, 1985.

46. STEIN H, BERMAN ER, LIONI N, MERIN S, SLESKIN J, COHEN T: Pseudo-Hurler polydystrophy (mucolipidosis III): A clinical, biochemical, and ultrastructural study. *Isr J Med Sci* 10:463, 1974.

47. WALTER P, LINGAPPA VR: Mechanism of protein translocation across the endoplasmic reticulum membrane. *Annu Rev Cell Biol* 2:499, 1986.

48. KORNFELD R, KORNFELD S: Assembly of asparagine-linked oligosaccharides. *Annu Rev Biochem* 54:631, 1985.

49. REITMAN ML, KORNFELD S: UDP-N-Acetylglucosamine: Glycoprotein N-acetylglucosamine-1-phosphotransferase. *J Biol Chem* 256:4275, 1981.

50. REITMAN ML, KORNFELD S: Lysosomal enzyme targeting N-acetylglucosaminylphosphotransferase selectively phosphorylates native lysosomal enzymes. *J Biol Chem* 256:11977, 1981.

51. VARKI A, KORNFELD S: Identification of a rat liver α-N-acetylglucosaminyl phosphodiesterase capable of removing "blocking" α-N-acetylglucosamine residues from phosphorylated high mannose oligosaccharides of lysosomal enzymes. *J Biol Chem* 255:8398, 1980.

52. WAHEED A, HASILIK A, von FIGURA K: Processing of the phosphorylated recognition marker in lysosomal enzymes. *J Biol Chem* 256:5717, 1981.

53. VARKI A, SHERMAN N: Demonstrations of the enzymatic mechanisms of α-N-acetyl-D-glucosamine-1-phosphodiester N-acetylglucosaminidase (formerly called α-N-acetylglucosaminylphosphodiesterase) and lysosomal α-N-acetylglucosaminidase. *Arch Biochem Biophys* 222:145, 1983.

54. SAHAGIAN GG, DISTLER J, JOURDIAN JW: Characterization of a membrane-associated receptor from bovine liver that binds phosphomannosyl residues of bovine testicular β-galactosidase. *Proc Natl Acad Sci USA* 78:4289, 1981.

55. STEINER AW, ROME LH: Assay and purification of a solubilized membrane receptor that binds the lysosomal enzyme α-L-iduronidase. *Arch Biochem Biophys* 214:681, 1982.

56. GOLDBERG DE, GABEL CA, KORNFELD S: Studies of the biosynthesis of the mannose 6-phosphate receptor in receptor-positive and -deficient cell lines. *J Cell Biol* 97:1700, 1983.

57. CREEK KE, SLY WS: Biosynthesis and turnover of the phosphomannosyl receptor in human fibroblasts. *Biochem J* 214:353, 1983.

58. OSHIMA A, NOLAN CM, KYLE JW, GRUBB JH, SLY WS: The human cation-independent mannose 6-phosphate receptor. *J Biol Chem* 263:2553, 1988.

59. LOBEL P, DAHMS NM, BREITMEYER J, CHIRGWIN JM, KORNFELD S: Cloning of the bovine 215 kDa cation-independent mannose 6-phosphate receptor. *Proc Natl Acad Sci USA* 84:2233, 1987.

60. LOBEL P, DAHMS NM, KORNFELD S: Cloning and sequence analysis of the cation-independent mannose 6-phosphate receptor. *J Biol Chem* 253:2563, 1988.

61. ROME LH, WEISSMAN B, NEUFELD EF: Direct demonstration of binding of a lysosomal enzyme, α-L-iduronidase, to receptors in cultured fibroblasts. *Proc Natl Acad Sci USA* 76:2331, 1979.

62. FISCHER HD, GONZALEZ-NORIEGA A, SLY WS: β-glucuronidase binding to human fibroblast membrane receptors. *J Biol Chem* 255:5069, 1980.

63. FREEZE HH, MILLER AL, KAPLAN A: Acid hydrolases from *Dictyostelium discoideum* contain phosphomannosyl recognition markers. *J Biol Chem* 255:11081, 1980.

64. GABEL CA, COSTELLO CE, REINHOLD VN, KURTZ L, KORNFELD S: Identification of methylphosphomannosyl residues as components of the high mannose oligosaccharides of *Dictyostelium discoideum* glycoproteins. *J Biol Chem* 259:13762, 1984.

65. HOFLACK B, KORNFELD S: Lysosomal enzyme binding the mouse P388D$_1$ macrophage membranes lacking the 215-kDa mannose 6-phosphate receptor: Evidence for the existence of a second mannose 6-phosphate receptor. *Proc Natl Acad Sci USA* 82:4428, 1985.

66. HOFLACK B, KORNFELD S: Purification and characterization of a cation-dependent mannose 6-phosphate receptor from murine P388D$_1$ macrophages and bovine liver. *J Biol Chem* 260:12008, 1985.

67. POHLMANN R, NAGEL G, SCHMIDT B, STEIN M, LORKOWSKI G, KRENTLER C, CULLY J, MEYER HE, GRZESCHIK K-H, MERSMANN G, HASILIK A, von FIGURA K: Cloning of a cDNA encoding the human cation-dependent mannose 6-phosphate specific receptor. *Proc Natl Acad Sci USA* 84:5575, 1987.

68. DAHMS NM, LOBEL P, BREITMEYER J, CHIRGWIN JM, KORNFELD S: 46 kD mannose 6-phosphate receptor: Cloning, expression, and homology to the 215 kd mannose 6-phosphate receptor. *Cell* 50:181, 1987.

69. STEIN M, ZIJDERHAND-BLEEKEMOTEN JE, GEUZE H, HASILIK A, von FIGURA K: Mr 46,000 mannose 6-phosphate specific receptor: Its role in targeting of lysosomal enzymes. *EMBO J* 6:2677, 1987.

70. HOFLACK B, FUJIMOTO K, KORNFELD S: The interaction of phosphorylated oligosaccharides and lysosomal enzymes with bovine liver cation-dependent mannose 6-phosphate receptor. *J Biol Chem* 262:123, 1987.

71. MORGAN DO, EDMAN JC, STANDRING DN, FRIED VA, SMITH MC, ROTH RA, RUTTER WJ: Insulin-like growth factor II receptor as a multifunctional binding protein. *Nature* 329:301, 1987.

72. ROTH RA: Structure of the receptor for insulin like growth factor II: The puzzle amplified. *Science* 239, 1269, 1988.

73. BRAULKE T, CAUSIN C, WAHEED A, JUNGHANS U, HASILIK A, MALY P, HUMBLE RE, von FIGURA K: Mannose 6-phosphate/insulin like growth factor II receptor: Distinct binding sites for mannose 6-phosphate and insulin like growth factor II. *Biochem Biophys Res Commun* 150:1287, 1988.

74. TONG PY, TOLLEFSEN SE, KORNFELD S: The cation-independent mannose 6-phosphate receptor binds insulin-like growth factor II. *J Biol Chem* 263:2585, 1988.

75. MacDONALD RG, PFEFFER SR, COUSSENS L, TEPPER MA, BROCKLEBANK CM, MOLE JE, ANDERSON JK, CHEN E, CZECH MP, ULLRICH A: A single receptor binds both insulin-like growth factor II and mannose 6-phosphate. *Science* 239:1134, 1988.

76. POHLMANN R, WAHEED A, HASILIK A, von FIGURA K: Synthesis of phosphorylated recognition marker in lysosomal enzymes is located in the *cis* part of Golgi apparatus. *J Biol Chem* 257:5323, 1982.

77. GOLDBERG DE, KORNFELD S: Evidence for extensive subcellular organization of asparagine-linked oligosaccharide processing and lysosomal enzyme phosphorylation. *J Biol Chem* 258:3159, 1983.

78. BROWN WJ, FARQUHAR MG: The mannose 6-phosphate receptor for lysosomal enzymes is concentrated in *cis* Golgi cisternae. *Cell* 36:295, 1984.

79. GEUZE JH, SLOT JW, STROUS GJAM, HASILIK A, von FIGURA K: Ultrastructural localization of the mannose 6-phosphate receptor in rat liver. *J Cell Biol* 98:2045, 1984.

80. GEUZE HF, SLOT JW, STROUS GJAM, HASILIK A, von FIGURA K: Possible pathways for lysosomal enzyme delivery. *J Cell Biol* 101:2253, 1985.

81. FEDDE KN, SLY WS: Ricin-binding properties of acid hydrolases from isolated lysosomes implies prior processing by terminal transferases of the *trans*-Golgi apparatus. *Biochem Biophys Res Commun* 133:614, 1985.

82. BROWN WJ, FARQUHAR MG: The distribution of 215 kDa mannose 6-phosphate receptors within cis (heavy) and trans (light) Golgi subfractions varies in different cell types. *Proc Natl Acad Sci USA* 84:9001, 1987.

83. CREEK KE, SLY WS: The role of the phosphomannosyl receptor in the transport of acid hydrolases to lysosomes, in Dingle JT, Dean RT, Sly WS (eds): *Lysosomes in Biology and Pathology.* Amsterdam, Elsevier, 1984, vol 7, p 63–82.

84. KORNFELD S: Trafficking of lysosomal enzymes. *FASEB J* 1:462, 1987.

85. BROWN WJ, GOODHOUSE J, FARQUHAR MG: Mannose 6-phosphate receptors for lysosomal enzymes cycle between the Golgi complex and endosomes. *J Cell Biol* 103:1234, 1986.

86. GRIFFITHS G, HOFLACK B, SIMONS K, MELLMAN I, KORNFELD S: The mannose 6-phosphate receptor and the biosynthesis of lysosomes. *Cell* 52:329, 1988.

87. von FIGURA K, GIESELMANN V, HASILIK A: Antibody to mannose 6-phosphate specific receptor induces receptor deficiency in human fibroblasts. *EMBO J* 3:1281, 1984.

88. GARTUNG C, BRAULKE T, HASILIK A, von FIGURA K: Internalization of blocking antibodies against mannose 6-phosphate specific receptors. *EMBO J* 4:1725, 1985.

89. SAHAGIAN GG: The mannose 6-phosphate receptor function, biosynthesis and translocation. *Biol Cell* 51:207, 1984.

90. NOLAN CM, CREEK KE, GRUBB JH, SLY WS: Antibody to the phosphomannosyl receptor inhibits recycling of receptor in fibroblasts. *J Cell Biochem* 35:137, 1987.

91. von FIGURA K, WEBER E: An alternative hypothesis of cellular transport of lysosomal enzymes in fibroblasts. *Biochem J* 176:943, 1978.

92. GOLDSTEIN JL, BROWN MS, ANDERSON RGW, RUSSELL DW, SCHNEIDER WJ: Receptor-mediated endocytosis: Concepts emerging from the LDL receptor system. *Annu Rev Cell Biol* 1:1, 1985.

93. OWADA M, NEUFELD EF: Is there a mechanism for introducing acid hydrolases into liver lysosomes that is independent of mannose 6-phosphate recognition? *Biochem Biophys Res Commun* 105:814, 1982.

94. WAHEED A, POHLMANN R, HASILIK A, von FIGURA K, van ELSEN A, LEROY JG: Deficiency of UDP-N-acetylglucosamine: Lysosomal enzyme N-acetylglucosamine-1-phosphotransferase in organs of I-cell patients. *Biochem Biophys Res Commun* 105:1052, 1982.

95. AERTS JMFG, BRUL S, DONKER-KOOPMAN WE, van WEELY S, MURRAY GJ, BARRANGER JA, TAGER JM, SCHRAM AW: Efficient routing of glucocerebrosidase to lysosomes requires complex oligosaccharide chain formation. *Biochem Biophys Res Commun* 141:452, 1986.

96. LEMANSKY P, GIESELMANN V, HASILIK A, von FIGURA K: Synthesis and transport of lysosomal acid phosphatase in normal and I-cell fibroblasts. *J Biol Chem* 260:9023, 1985.

97. GRANGER BL, PLUTNER H, GREEN SA, MELLMAN I, HELENIUS A: Defining the lysosome membrane: Characterization of specific glycoproteins. *J Cell Biol* 101:54a, 1985.

98. BARRIOCANAL JG, BONIFACINO JS, YUAN L, SANDOVAL IV: Biosynthesis, glycosylation, movement through the Golgi system, and transport to lysosomes by an N-linked carbohydrate-independent mechanism of three lysosomal integral membrane proteins. *J Biol Chem* 261:16755, 1986.

99. BACH G, BARSAL R, CANTZ M: Deficiency of extracellular hydrolase phosphorylation. *Biochem Biophys Res Commun* 91:976, 1979.

100. HASILIK A, NEUFELD EF: Biosynthesis of lysosomal enzymes in fibroblasts. Phosphorylation of mannose residues. *J Biol Chem* 255:4946, 1980.

101. REITMAN ML, LANG L, KORNFELD S: UDP-N-acetylglucosamine: Lysosomal enzyme N-atetylglucosamine-1-phosphotransferase. *Methods in Enzymology* 107:163, 1984.

102. VARKI AP, REITMAN ML, KORNFELD S: Identification of a variant of mucolipidosis III (pseudo-Hurler polydystrophy): A catalytically active N-acetylglucosaminylphosphotransferase that fails to phosphorylate lysosomal enzymes. *Proc Natl Acad Sci USA* 78:7773, 1981.

103. VARKI A, REITMAN NL, VANNIER A, KORNFELD S, GRUBB JH, SLY WS: Demonstration of the heterozygous state for I-cell disease and pseudo-Hurler polydystrophy by assay of N-acetylglucosaminyl phosphotransferase in white blood cells and fibroblasts. *Am J Hum Genet* 34:719, 1982.

104. BEN-YOSEPH Y, BAYLERIAN MS, NADLER HL: Radiometric assays of N-acetylglucosaminyl phosphotransferase and alpha-N-acetylglucosaminyl phosphodiesterase with substrates labeled in the glucosamine moiety. *Anal Biochem* 142:297, 1984.

105. MUELLER OT, LITTLE LE, MILLER AL, LOZZIO CB, SHOWS TB: I-cell disease and pseudo-Hurler polydystrophy: Heterozygote detection and characteristics of the altered N-acetyl-glucosamine-phosphotransferase in genetic variants. *Clin Chim Acta* 150:175, 1985.

106. HONEY NK, MUELLER OT, LITTLE LE, MILLER AL, SHOWS TB: Mucolipidosis III is genetically heterogeneous. *Proc Natl Acad Sci USA* 79:7420, 1982.

107. SHOWS TB, MUELLER OT, HONEY NK, WRIGHT CE, MILLER AL: Genetic heterogeneity of I-cell disease is demonstrated by complementation of lysosomal enzyme processing mutants. *Am J Med Genet* 12:343, 1982.

108. MUELLER OT, HONEY NK, LITTLE LE, MILLER AL, SHOWS TB: Mucolipidosis II and III. The genetic relationship between two disorders of lysosomal enzyme biosynthesis. *J Clin Invest* 72:1016, 1983.

109. BEN-YOSEPH Y, PACK BA, MITCHELL DA, ELWELL DG, POTIER M, MELAN-

CON SB, NADLER HL: Characterization of the mutant N-acetylglucosaminylphosphotransferase in I-cell disease and pseudo-Hurler polydystrophy: Complementation analysis and kinetic studies. *Enzyme* 35:106, 1986.

110. LANG L, TAKAHASHI T, TANG J, KORNFELD S: Lysosomal enzyme phosphorylation in human fibroblasts. *J Clin Invest* 76:2191, 1985.

111. LITTLE LE, MUELLER OT, HONEY NK, SHOWS TB, MILLER AL: Heterogeneity of N-acetylglucosamine 1-phosphotransferase within mucolipidosis III. *J Biol Chem* 261:733, 1986.

112. WAHEED A, HASILIK A, von FIGURA K: UDP-N-acetylglucosamine: Lysosomal enzyme precursor N-acetylglucosamine-1-phosphotransferase. *J Biol Chem* 257:12322, 1982.

113. TAKAHASHI TI, SCHMIDT PG, TANG J: Oligosaccharide units of lysosomal cathepsin D from porcine spleen. *J Biol Chem* 258:2819, 1983.

114. HASILIK A, KLEIN U, WAHEED A, STRECKER G, von FIGURA K: Phosphorylated oligosaccharides in lysosomal enzymes: Identification of α-N-acetylglucosamine(1)phospho(6) mannose diester groups. *Proc Natl Acad Sci USA* 77:7074, 1980.

115. GOLDBERG DE, KORNFELD S: The phosphorylation of β-glucuronidase oligosaccharides in mouse P388D$_1$ cells. *J Biol Chem* 256:13060, 1981.

116. NATOWICZ M, BAENZIGER JU, SLY WS: Structural studies of the phosphorylated high mannose type oligosaccharides on human β-glucuronidase. *J Biol Chem* 257:4412, 1982.

117. MIZUOCHI T, NISHIMURA Y, KATO K, KOBATA A: Comparative studies of asparagine linked oligosaccharide structures of rat liver microsomal and lysosomal β-glucuronidases. *Arch Biochem Biophys* 209:298, 1981.

118. NAKAO Y, KOZUTSUMI Y, KAWASAKI T, YAMASHIMA I, VAN HALBEEK H, VLIEGENTHART JFG: Oligosaccharides on Cathepsin D from porcine spleen. *Arch Biochem Biophys* 229:43, 1984.

119. LANG L, REITMAN ML, TANG J, ROBERTS RM, KORNFELD S: Lysosomal enzyme phosphorylation. *J Biol Chem* 259:14663, 1984.

120. FAUST PL, KORNFELD S, CHIRGWIN JM: Cloning and sequence analysis of cDNA for human cathepsin D. *Proc Natl Acad Sci USA* 82:4910, 1985.

121. FUKUSHIMA H, de WET Jr, O'BRIEN JS: Molecular cloning of a cDNA for human α-L-fucosidase. *Proc Natl Acad Sci USA* 82:1262, 1985.

122. MYEROWITZ R, PIEKARZ R, NEUFELD EF, SHOWS TB, SUZUKI K: Human β-hexosaminidase α chain: Coding sequence and homology with the β chain. *Proc Natl Acad Sci USA* 82:7830, 1985.

123. BISHOP DF, CALHOUN DH, BERNSTEIN HS, HANTZOPOULOS P, QUINN M, DESNICK RJ: Human α-galactosidase A: Nucleotide sequence of a cDNA clone encoding the mature enzyme. *Proc Natl Acad Sci USA* 83:4859, 1986.

124. KORNELUK RG, MAHURAN DJ, NEOTE K, KLAVINS MH, O'DOWD BF, TROPAK M, WILLARD HF, ANDERSON MJ, LOWDEN JA, GRAVEL RA: Isolation of cDNA clones coding for the α-subunit of human β-hexosaminidase. *J Biol Chem* 261:8407, 1986.

125. NISHIMURA Y, ROSENFELD MG, KREIBICH G, GUBLER U, SABATINI DD, ADESNICK M, ANDY R: Nucleotide sequence of rat preputial gland β-glucuronidase cDNA and *in vitro* insertion of its encoded polypeptide into microsomal membranes. *Proc Natl Acad Sci USA* 83:7292, 1986.

126. TSUJI S, CHOUDARY PV, MARTIN BM, WINFIELD S, BARRANGER JA, GINNS EJ: Nucleotide sequence of cDNA containing the complete coding sequence for human lysosomal glucocerebrosidase. *J Biol Chem* 261:50, 1986.

127. OSHIMA A, KYLE JW, MILLER RD, HOFFMANN JW, POWELL PP, GRUBB JH, SLY WS, TROPAK M, GUISE KS, GRAVEL RA: Cloning, sequencing, and expression of cDNA for human β-glucuronidase. *Proc Natl Acad Sci USA* 84:685, 1987.

128. KORNFELD S: Trafficking of lysosomal enzymes in normal and disease states. *J Clin Invest* 77:1, 1986.

129. VLADUTIU GD, RATTAZZI MC: Abnormal lysosomal hydrolases excreted by cultured fibroblasts in I-cell disease (mucolipidosis II). *Biochem Biophys Res Commun* 67:956, 1975.

130. HONEY NK, MILLER AL, SHOWS TB: The mucolipidoses: Identification by abnormal electrophoretic patterns of lysosomal hydrolases. *Am J Med Genet* 9:239, 1981.

131. GOLDBERG D, GABEL C, KORNFELD S: Processing of lysosomal enzyme oligosaccharide units, in Dingle JT, Dean RT, Sly WS (eds): *Lysosomes in Biology and Pathology*. New York, Elsevier, 1984, pp 45–62.

132. SKUDLAREK MD, NOVAK K, SWANK RT: Processing of lysosomal enzymes in macrophages and kidney in Dingle JT, Dean RT, Sly WS (eds): *Lysosomes in Biology and Pathology*. New York, Elsevier, 1984, vol 7, pp 17–43.

133. HASILIK A, von FIGURA K: Processing of lysosomal enzymes in fibroblasts, in Dingle JT, Dean RT, Sly WS (eds): *Lysosomes in Biology and Pathology*. Amsterdam, Elsevier, 1984, pp 3–16.

134. TIETZE F, BUTLER JD: Elevated cystine levels in cultured skin fibroblasts from patients with I-cell disease. *Pediatr Res* 13:1350, 1979.

135. STEINHERZ R, MAKOV N, NARINSKY R, MEIDAN B, KOHN G: Comparative study of cystine clearance in cystinotic and I-cell fibroblasts upon exposure to cystine dimethyl ester. *Enzyme* 32:126, 1984.

136. GREENE AA, JONAS AJ, HARMS E, SMITH ML, PELLETT OL, BUMP EA, MILLER AL, SCHNEIDER JA: Lysosomal cystine storage in cystinosis and mucolipidosis type II. *Pediatr Res* 19:1170, 1985.

137. TIETZE F, ROME LH, BUTLER JD, HARPER GS, GAHL WA: Impaired clearance of free cystine from lysosome enriched granular fractions of I-cell disease fibroblasts. *Biochem J* 237:9, 1986.

138. SLY WS, LAGWINSKA E, SCHLESINGER S: Enveloped virus acquires the membrane defect when passaged in fibroblasts from I cell disease patients. *Proc Natl Acad Sci USA* 73:2443, 1976.

139. VLADUTIU GD, FIKE RM, AMIGONE VT: Influence of sialic acid on cell surface properties in I cell disease fibroblasts. *In Vitro* 17:588, 1981.

140. VARON R, KLEIJER JW, THOMPSON EJ, D'AZZO A: Evidence for the deficiency of beta-glucosidase-activating factor in fibroblasts of patients with I-cell disease. *Hum Genet* 62:66, 1982.

141. INUI K, EMMETT M, WENGER DA: Immunological evidence for deficiency in an activator protein for sulfatide sulfatase in a variant form of metachromatic leukodystrophy. *Proc Natl Acad Sci USA* 80:3074, 1983.

142. INUI K, WENGER DA: Biochemical, immunological and structural studies on a sphingolipid activator protein (SAP-1)'. *Arch Biochem Biophys* 233:556, 1984.

143. FUJIBAYASHI S, WENGER DA: Studies on a sphingolipid activator protein (SAP-2) in fibroblasts from patients with lysosomal storage diseases, including Neimann-Pick disease Type C. *Clin Chim Acta* 146:147, 1985.

144. RANIERI E, PATON B, POULOS A: Preliminary evidence for a processing error in the biosynthesis of Gaucher activator in mucolipidosis disease types II and III. *Biochem J* 233:763, 1986.

145. HERD JK, DVORAK AD, WILTSE HE, EISEN JD, KRESS BC, MILLER AL: Mucolipidosis type III—Multiple elevated serum and urine enzyme activities. *Am J Dis Child* 132:1181, 1978.

146. LIEBAERS I, NEUFELD EF: Iduronate sulfatase activity in serum, lyphocytes and fibroblasts—Simplified diagnosis of the Hunter syndrome. *Pediatr Res* 10:733, 1976.

147. HALL CW, LIEBAERS I, DINATALE P, NEUFELD EF: Enzymatic diagnosis of the genetic mucopolysaccharide storage disorders. *Methods Enzymol* 50:439, 1978.

148. LIE KK, THOMAS GH, TAYLOR HA, SENSENBRENNER JA: Analysis of N-acetyl-β-D-glucosaminidase in mucolipidosis II (I-cell disease). *Clin Chim Acta* 45:243, 1978.

149. KATO E, YOKOI T, TANIGUCHI N: Lysosomal acid hydrolases in lymphocytes of I-cell disease. *Clin Chim Acta* 95:285, 1979.

150. TANAKA T, KOBAYASHI M, FUKUDA T, TSUZI Y, USUI T: I-cell disease: Nine lysosomal enzyme levels in lymphocytes and granulocytes. *Hiroshima J Med Sci* 28:190, 1979.

151. HUIJING F, WARREN RJ, MCLEOD AGW: Elevated activity of lysosomal enzymes in amniotic fluid of a fetus with mucolipidosis II (I-cell disease). *Clin Chim Acta* 44:453, 1973.

152. MATSUDA I, ARASHUMA S, MITSUYAMA T, OKA Y, IKEUCHI T, KANEKO Y, ISHIKAWA M: Prenatal diagnosis of I-cell disease. *Hum Genet* 30:69, 1975.

153. GEHLER J, CANTZ M, STOECKENIUS M, SPRANGER J: Prenatal diagnosis of mucolipidosis II (I-cell disease). *Eur J Pediatr* 122:201, 1976.

154. POENARU L, CASTELNAU L, DUMEZ Y, THEPOT F: First trimester prenatal diagnosis of mucolipidosis II (I-cell disease) by chorionic biopsy. *Am J Hum Genet* 36:1379, 1984.

155. HUG G, BOVE KE, SOUKUP S, RYAN M, BENDON R, BABCOCK D, WARREN NS, DIGNAN PS: Increased serum hexosaminidase in a woman pregnant with a fetus affected by mucolipidosis II (I-cell disease). *N Engl J Med* 311:988, 1984.

156. KUROBANE I, INOUE S, GOTOH Y-H, KATO S, TAMURA M, NARISAWA K, TADA K: Biochemical improvement after treatment by bone marrow transplantation in I-cell disease. *Tohoku J Exp Med* 150:63, 1986.

CHAPTER 63

DISORDERS OF GLYCOPROTEIN DEGRADATION:
Mannosidosis, Fucosidosis, Sialidosis, and Aspartylglycosaminuria

ARTHUR L. BEAUDET
GEORGE H. THOMAS

1. Glycoproteins are synthesized by two pathways. The glycosyl-transferase pathway synthesizes oligosaccharides linked O-glycosidically to serine or threonine, while the dolichol, lipid-linked pathway synthesizes oligosaccharides linked N-glycosidically to asparagine. The oligosaccharides are degraded in the lysosome by (1) a group of exoglycosidases acting at the nonreducing termini, (2) an endo-β-N-acetylglycosaminidase, and (3) aspartylglycosaminidase. Specific deficiencies of these enzymes cause glycoprotein storage diseases.

2. The clinical phenotypes of the glycoprotein storage diseases generally resemble those of a mild mucopolysaccharidosis. Mannosidosis is divided into types I and II for infantile and juvenile-adult disease, respectively. Fucosidosis type I patients show infantile onset and an abnormal sweat chloride test, while type II patients survive to adulthood and have angiokeratoma. A juvenile phenotype is seen primarily with galactosialidosis. Sialidosis type II includes infantile and congenital phenotypes with increasingly severe mucopolysaccharidosis-like phenotypes. Patients with aspartylglycosaminuria have a very mild mucopolysaccharidosis-like phenotype with progressive mental deterioration.

3. Pathologic studies in these disorders show vacuolation of cells in most body tissues, with a reticulogranular pattern as the most frequent appearance of membrane-bound vacuoles on electron microscopy.

4. The biochemical accumulation in urine and tissues results primarily from incomplete degradation of N-glycosidically linked oligosaccharides. Multiple products are identified in these disorders, but only oligosaccharides are found in mannosidosis and sialidosis, only glycoasparagines in aspartylglycosaminuria, and both oligosaccharides and glycoasparagines in fucosidosis. There is also accumulation of glycolipid in fucosidosis.

5. The lysosomal enzyme defects are as follows: α-D-mannosidase in mannosidosis, α-L-fucosidase in fucosidosis, glycoprotein-specific α-neuraminidase in sialidosis (the ganglioside-specific α-neuraminidase is normal), and aspartylglycosaminidase in aspartylglycosaminuria. The enzyme defects may be studied in cultured skin fibroblasts.

6. All of the disorders are autosomal recessive genetic defects. Ethnic predilections include fucosidosis in southern Italians, possibly sialidosis type I in Italians, and aspartylglycosaminuria in Finns. The genetic loci for the deficient enzymes are mapped to human chromosomes as follows: α-D-mannosidase to

19p13→q13, α-L-fucosidase to 1p34, α-neuraminidase to 10pter→q23, and aspartylglycosaminidase to 4q.

7. Molecular cloning has been reported for α-L-fucosidase and for aspartylglycosaminidase.

8. Although no definitive treatment of these disorders is available, prenatal diagnosis is possible and has been accomplished for mannosidosis, fucosidosis, sialidosis, and aspartylglycosaminuria.

This chapter primarily considers lysosomal storage diseases involving well-defined loci causing defects in the degradation of glycoproteins. Glycoproteins are characterized by the presence of oligosaccharide chains covalently attached to a peptide backbone. These include peptides linked with oligosaccharides through the hydroxyl groups of serine or threonine, or through the free amino group of asparagine. Proteoglycans and oligosaccharides linked to collagen and basement membrane proteins are considered separately in Chaps. 61 and 115, respectively. Genetic defects in degradation may be restricted to glycoproteins or may involve other macromolecules as well. This is because certain oligosaccharide linkages may be found in glycolipids and proteoglycans as well as in glycoproteins. Hence, a deficiency of a single lysosomal enzyme may result in accumulation of more than one class of oligosaccharide-containing macromolecules (Table 63-1).

The glycoprotein storage diseases considered here conform to the general conceptual framework of lysosomal storage diseases. They each demonstrate deficiency of a lysosomal hydrolase, accumulation of substrates ordinarily degraded by that enzyme, a progressive clinical course, and considerable variation of the phenotype associated with different defects at a single locus. In addition, these disorders often manifest clinical features that usually would be considered as part of the mucopolysaccharidosis phenotype, such as coarse facies and dysostosis multiplex.

In addition to collagen and mucopolysaccharides, mammalian tissues contain two major groups of glycoproteins with distinct structural differences and separate synthetic pathways (Table 63-2). The biosynthesis and structure of glycoproteins were reviewed briefly in the previous edition of this chapter,[1] and more detailed reviews are available.[2-6] The oligosaccha-

---

Nonstandard abbreviations used in this chapter are: Asn = asparagine; ER = endoplasmic reticulum; Fuc = fucose; Gal = galactose; GalNAc = *N*-acetylgalactosamine; Glc = glucose; GlcNAc = *N*-acetylglucosamine; Man = Mannose.

Table 63-1 Disorders of Glycoprotein Degradation

	Extent of degradative defect	
	Glycoproteins	Glycolipids
α-Mannosidosis	Major	None
Fucosidosis	Major	Present
Aspartylglycosaminuria	Major	None
Sialidosis	Major	?Minimal
Galactosialidosis*	Major	?Minimal
β-Mannosidosis	Major	?None
G_{M1} Gangliosidosis*	Present	Major
G_{M2} Gangliosidosis (Sandhoff)†	Present	Major
Salla and related diseases‡	Sialic acid	None
Schindler disease§	Probable	Unknown
Mucolipidosis II and III¶	Generalized degradative defect	

*See Chap. 71.
†See Chap. 72.
‡See Chap. 107.
§See Chap. 70.
¶See Chap. 62.

rides are synthesized as the proteins pass from the rough endoplasmic reticulum (ER) to the smooth ER and through the Golgi apparatus. The protein portions of the glycoproteins are synthesized on membrane-bound polysomes. The sugar nucleotide synthetic pathway involves the transfer to the growing oligosaccharide chain of single sugars from sugar nucleotides. Oligosaccharides synthesized by this pathway are found linked to protein through an O-glycosidic linkage of GalNAc (N-acetylgalactosamine) to serine or threonine. There is extensive diversity of the oligosaccharide structures within this category.[2,5] A specific example of an O-glycosidic oligosaccharide is the blood group megalosaccharide shown in Fig. 63-1. The oligosaccharides of glycolipids that are synthesized by this pathway and related structures found on lipids are discussed in Chap. 70. Most of the degradative defects to be discussed involve structures of the N-glycosidic type discussed below, but defective degradation of the O-glycosidic oligosaccharides is involved in some instances.

The dolichol pathway for synthesis of oligosaccharides utilizes lipid-linked intermediates.[3,6] A complex pathway is involved to produce the structure shown in Fig. 63-2. This structure is thought to be the common intermediate that is transferred to the peptide backbone. The entire oligosaccharide structure is linked to protein through an N-glycosidic linkage of GalNAc to asparagine. Once transferred to the protein, the oligosaccharide structure undergoes a series of trimming and elongation steps, resulting in a final structure of either the "high mannose" or "complex" type. These changes are summarized in Fig. 63-3, where structure A represents the final

Table 63-2 Characteristics of Synthesis and Structure of Glycoproteins

Sugar nucleotide pathway	Dolichol pathway
1. Sequential transfer of single sugars.	1. Use of dolichol-linked intermediates.
2. O-Glycosidic linkage of GalNAc to serine or threonine.	2. N-Glycosidic linkage of GlcNAc to asparagine.
3. Tunicamycin-resistant.	3. Tunicamycin-sensitive.
4. Blood group substance and submaxillary mucins are examples.	4. Subtypes are high mannose and complex.
	5. Thyroglobulin and IgM are examples.

lipid intermediate, shown in detail in Fig. 63-2. Structure B represents a typical high mannose oligosaccharide unit, and structure C represents a typical complex oligosaccharide unit. Again, there is extensive diversity in the detail of oligosaccharide structures.[2,5]

DEGRADATION OF GLYCOPROTEINS

Since glycoproteins occur widely within cells, on the cell surface, and extracellularly, normal turnover requires degradation of a large amount of material. Glycoproteins are also abundant in nervous tissue,[4] which may explain the neurologic involvement of some of these disorders. There is considerable evidence, not the least of which stems from study of the diseases considered here, that the bulk of this degradation occurs in lysosomes. The protein backbone must be degraded by a series of lysosomal peptidases. The major mechanism of oligosaccharide degradation involves a sequence of hydrolytic steps whereby each unit is removed from the nonreducing ends of the oligosaccharide. The enzymes involved in these steps include neuraminidase (sialidase), β-galactosidase, β-N-acetylhexosaminidase, β-mannosidase, α-mannosidase, and α-fucosidase. In addition, there is evidence for an important role for an endo-β-N-acetylglucosaminidase that hydrolyzes the chitobiose linkage between the two N-acetyl glucosamine (GlcNAc) residues adjacent to the asparagine in oligosaccharides synthesized by the dolichol pathway. Lysosomal aspartylglycosaminidase is specifically required to hydrolyze the N-glycosidic linkage between GlcNAc and asparagine. Although the majority of mannose residues are α-linked, a Man(β1→4)GlcNAc linkage occurs in the core region (Fig. 63-2). Studies of caprine β-mannosidosis provide strong evidence for a requirement for β-mannosidase in the degradation.[7] A composite complex type N-glycosidic oligosaccharide and the proposed hydrolytic steps are shown in Fig. 63-4. The deficiency of any of the required lysosomal enzymes results in accumulation of products of partial degradation of the glycoproteins. Although these partial degradative products will be discussed further as stored materials under the specific disease sections, some of the findings are summarized in Fig. 63-5. It is satisfying that almost all of the stored materials in these lysosomal diseases can be viewed as expected products of incomplete degradation of known oligosaccharide structures as a result of specific enzyme deficiencies. These structures demonstrate the results of the three major types of hydrolysis: (1) single sugar removal from the nonreducing end, (2) endoglycosidic hydrolysis at the chitobiose linkage, and (3) hydrolysis of the glycoasparagine linkage. Almost all of the storage disease structures in Fig. 63-5 can be found within typical high mannose or complex glycoproteins. Fucose can occur as a terminal residue on outer chains of complex structures. The Gal-GlcNAc-Asn (Asn, asparagine) structure found in aspartylglycosaminuria is an unusual one.

Some storage products seen in four glycoprotein storage diseases are presented in Fig. 63-5. Only oligosaccharides accumulate in mannosidosis and sialidosis. Only glycopeptides are found in aspartylglycosaminuria, while both oligosaccharides and glycopeptides accumulate in fucosidosis. The data from β-mannosidosis and sialidosis suggest the existence of an endo-β-N-acetylglucosaminidase. The multiplicity of higher glycoasparagines suggests that the endo-β-N-acetylglucosamini-

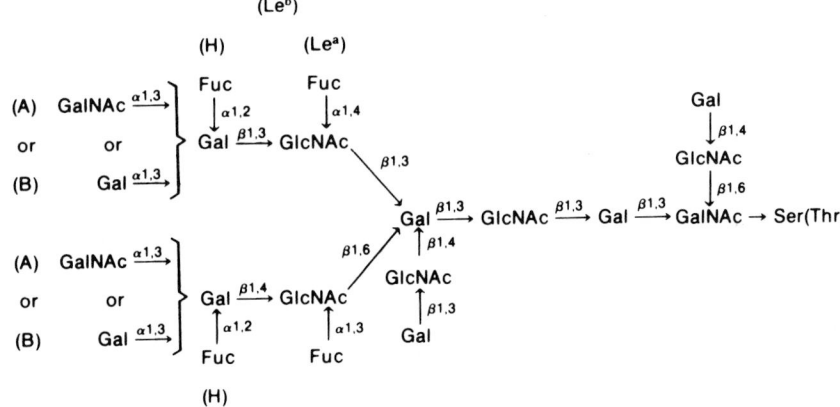

Fig. 63-1 Composite megalosaccharide proposed for blood group substance. (From Kornfeld and Kornfeld,[2] as modified from Feizi et al. J. Immunol. 106:1578, 1971.)

dase and other glycosidases may be less effective if asparagine is still present. The chitobiose linkage is not found intact if asparagine is removed. Based on the findings in fucosidosis, the presence of fucose on the GlcNAc linked to Asn probably reduces the activity of the endoglycosidase and of aspartylglycosaminidase.

HISTORY OF CLINICAL DISORDERS

In the late 1960s a group of unusual patients with phenotypes resembling mucopolysaccharidosis were characterized clinically[8,9] and biochemically.[10] These patients were described variously as having mucopolysaccharidosis, lipomucopolysaccharidosis, or mucolipidosis. A number of these patients were identified ultimately as having mannosidosis, which was first described by Öckerman in 1967.[11] The same year, Jenner and Pollitt described a brother and sister with mental retardation and large quantities of aspartylglycosamine in the urine,[12] and aspartylglycosaminidase deficiency was promptly demonstrated.[13] In 1968, fucosidosis was described by Durand et al.,[14] and the enzyme defect was reported concomitantly by Van Hoff and Hers.[15] Sialidosis due to neuraminidase deficiency was not reported until 1977[16,17]; the patient had been classified earlier as having lipomucopolysaccharidosis[8] and mucolipidosis I.[9] It was soon recognized that neuraminidase deficiency also was associated with the cherry-red spot–myoclonus syndrome. Other early reports are reviewed in a text on the lysosomal storage diseases.[18] Considerable clarification of the distinction of sialidosis from galactosylsialidosis (Chap. 71) has evolved only since the last edition of this text. A small book entitled *Genetic Errors of Glycoprotein Metabolism* was published in 1982 with chapters on sialidosis,[19] fucosidosis,[20] mannosidosis,[21] and aspartylglycosaminuria.[22] These chapters provide some greater detail than space permits here, regarding clinical features, enzymology, biochemical storage, and electron microscopy.

MANNOSIDOSIS

Clinical Features

Clinical heterogeneity is evident for mannosidosis from the reports of over 60 cases,[11,21,23–47] and from numerous unreported cases that are known. A list of affected patients is available.[42] The severe infantile phenotype is referred to as type I and a milder juvenile-adult phenotype as type II.[21,31] Virtually all patients have psychomotor retardation, facial coarsening, and some degree of dysostosis multiplex (Fig. 63-6, Table 63-3), although these features can be very mild in occasional patients.[46] Frequent findings include recurrent bacterial infections, deafness, hepatomegaly, hernias, and lenticular or corneal opacities. Susceptibility to infection may be related to a defect in leukocyte chemotaxis.[48] The ocular findings are distinctive and include posterior opacities in a spokelike pattern in the lens and superficial opacities in the cornea.[32,35,49] The skeletal dysplasia[33] includes thickening of the calvaria in the majority of patients. The vertebral bodies are prominently involved with ovoid configurations, flattening, and beak appearance, sometimes in association with gibbus deformity. The more severe infantile or type I phenotype includes rapid progression of mental deterioration, obvious hepatosplenomegaly, more severe dysostosis multiplex, and often death between 3 and 10 years of age. The milder juvenile-adult or type II phenotype is characterized by more normal early development but appearance of mental retardation during childhood and adolescence. Hearing loss is particularly prominent in type II patients. Dysostosis multiplex is milder, with survival into adulthood. Destructive synovitis,[43,45] hydrocephalus,[50] spastic paraplegia,[47] and pancytopenia[51] have been reported in type II patients. There may be a continuum of phenotypes rather than a clear separation of two phenotypes. Attempts to evaluate the clinical course of mannosidosis often describe a gradual, sometimes imperceptible, progression.[42,52]

Laboratory findings include the presence of vacuolated lym-

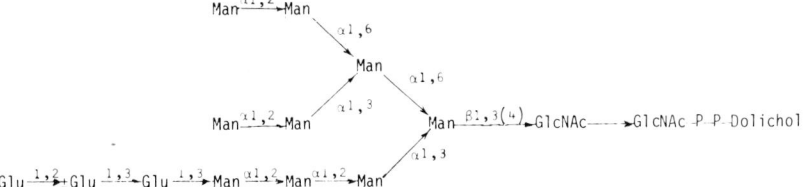

Fig. 63-2 Proposed structure of the lipid-linked oligosaccharide precursor in glycoprotein synthesis. (From S. Kornfeld, J. Biol. Chem., 253:7762, 1978. Used by permission.)

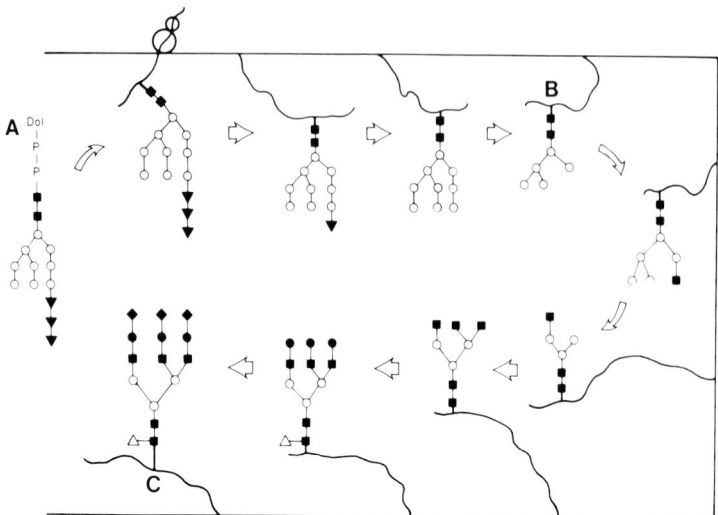

Fig. 63-3 Proposed sequence for the synthesis of complex type oligosaccharides. Dol = dolichol. The symbols are: ■ = GlcNAc; ○ = Man; ▼ = Glc; ● = Gal; ◆ = SA; △ = Fuc. The precursor, shown in detail in Fig. 63-2, is indicated as A; B indicates a high mannose structure; and C indicates a complex structure. *(With modification from S. Kornfeld, J. Biol. Chem., 253:7771, 1978. Used by permission.)*

phocytes in almost all cases. Most patients have been found not to have mucopolysacchariduria. Decreased serum IgG can occur, and a decreased PR interval on ECG has been reported.[53]

Pathology

Pathologic studies of biopsy[54] and autopsy[23,47,50,55] material are available. Light microscopy of the liver demonstrates a granular or foamy cytoplasm in the hepatocytes. Periodic acid–Schiff (PAS) staining varies with the histochemical extraction procedure. Electron microscopy demonstrates multiple vacuoles in hepatocytes and Kupffer cells, often with a reticulogranular pattern, although many other types of inclusions are observed. Examination of the central nervous system reveals marked and widespread ballooning of the nerve cells. The cytoplasm has an empty or vacuolated appearance. Electron microscopy again demonstrates membrane-bound vacuoles with a predominantly reticulogranular pattern.

Fig. 63-4 Probable steps for degradation of complex type oligosaccharide structure.

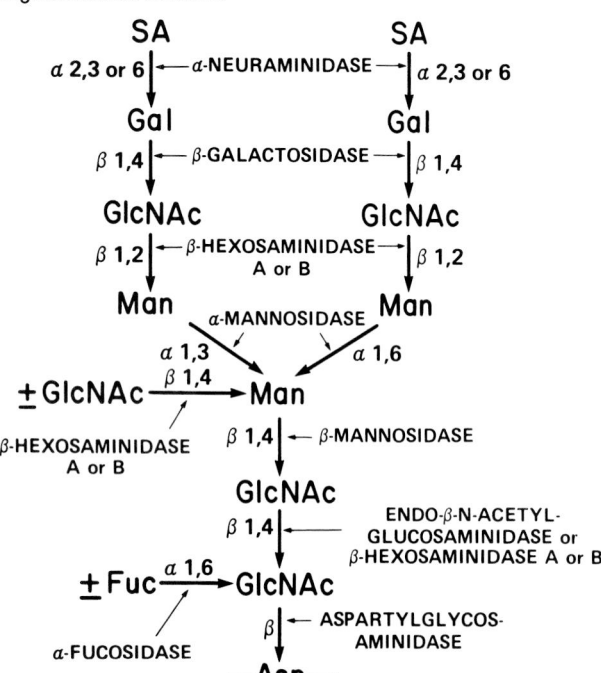

Biochemical Storage

While it is known that mannose-rich compounds accumulate in the tissues of at least some mannosidosis patients,[11,56] very few studies have been performed on material from this source. Instead, most of the analyses to date have been carried out on mannose-rich fractions isolated from the urine of these patients.

Early investigations showed the chemical structure of the three major urinary metabolites to be the following[57]:

1. Man(α1→3)Man(β1→4)GlcNAc
2. Man(β1→2)Man(α1→3)Man(β1→4)GlcNAc
3. Man(β1→2)Man(β1→2)Man(α1→3)Man(β1→4) GlcNAc.

Subsequently, Strecker et al.[58] and Yamashita et al.[59] extended these observations by isolating and characterizing additional urinary mannose-containing oligosaccharides. While these two groups found the structures to be the same for several of the newly discovered compounds, they differed on others.[58,59] More recently, 17 mannose-rich oligosaccharides were isolated and identified from pooled urine obtained from two patients with mannosidosis.[60,61] Three of these compounds were identical to the major metabolites noted above, 13 agreed with structures reported previously,[59] and one represented a newly discovered compound.

Each of the oligosaccharides isolated from the urine of patients with mannosidosis has a Man(β1→4)GlcNAc residue at the reducing end. This observation has led to the suggestion that these products may be the result of enzymatic digestion of the sugar side chains of glycoproteins and their oligosaccharide precursors by β-N-acetylglucosaminidase.[21] Comparative studies have also demonstrated that the urinary oligosaccharides differ in bovine, feline, and human mannosidosis,[62] and it was suggested that this may be due to differences in the catabolic pathways among these species.

Enzyme Defect

An α-mannosidosis activity was known for some time to exist in a variety of tissue types and sources,[21] but the interest of human geneticists dates from the first report of a patient who both lacked this enzyme and accumulated mannose-rich oligosaccharides.[11]

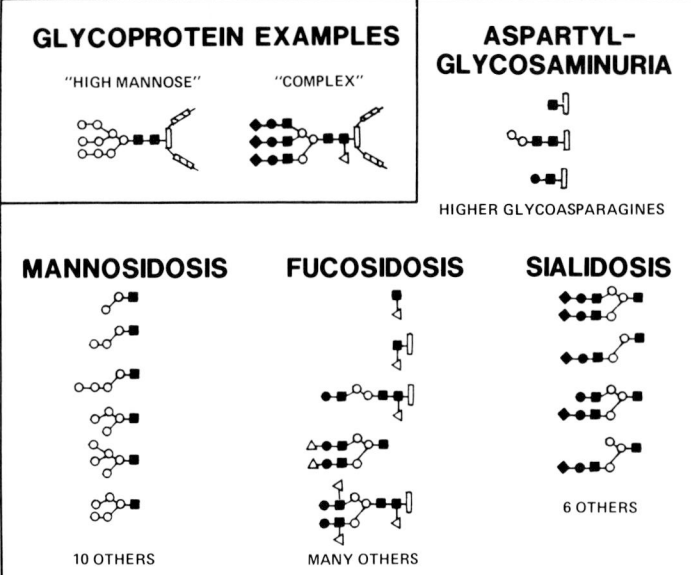

Fig. 63-5 Graphic summary of storage products in four glycoprotein storage diseases. The symbols are as for Fig. 63-3, and the rectangle represents asparagine.

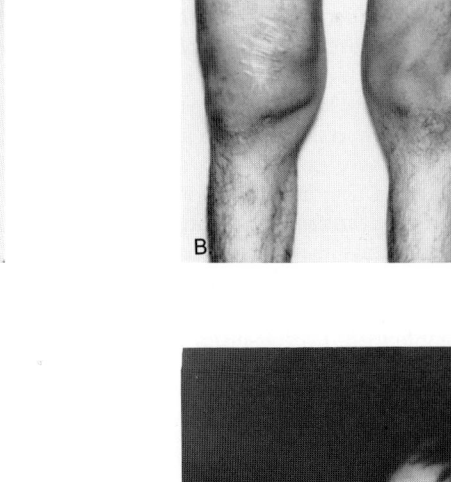

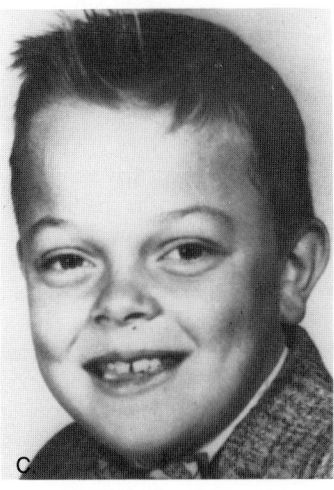

Fig. 63-6 Clinical features of mannosidosis. *A* and *B*, A 22-year-old male with mannosidosis type II showing facial appearance and destructive synovitis of the knees. *C* and *D*, A patient with mannosidosis at the age of 12 and 30 years. (*C and D are from Montgomery, Thomas, and Valle.*[44] *By permission of Johns Hopkins Medical Journal.*)

Table 63-3 Clinical Features of Mannosidosis, Fucosidosis, Sialidosis, and Aspartylglycosaminuria

Disorder	Age of onset	Facies	Dysostosis multiplex	Neurologic	Hepatosplenomegaly	Eye findings	Hematologic	Other
Mannosidosis:								
Type I	3–12 mo	Coarse	+ + +	Severe mental retardation	+ + +	Cataracts, corneal opacities	Vacuolated lymphocytes	Hearing loss
Type II	1–4 yr	Coarse	+ +	Mental retardation	+ +	Cataracts, corneal opacities	Vacuolated lymphocytes	Hearing loss prominent
Fucosidosis:								
Type I	3–18 mo	Mild coarsening	+ +	Mental retardation, seizures	+ +	Infrequent	Vacuolated lymphocytes	Sweat NaCl increased
Type II	1–2 yr	Mild coarsening	+ +	Mental retardation	+ +	Tortuous conjunctival vessels	Vacuolated lymphocytes	Angiokeratoma, anhidrosis
Sialidosis:								
Type I	8–25 yr	Normal	−	Severe myoclonus, generalized seizures, neuropathy, ↓ DTR	−	Blindness, cherry-red spot	Vacuolated lymphocytes rarely	
Type II:								
Juvenile*	2–20 yr	Mild coarsening	+ +	Myoclonus, mental retardation	−	Reduced acuity, cherry-red spots	Vacuolated lymphocytes	Angiokeratoma
Infantile	0–12 mo	Coarse	+ + +	Mental retardation	+/−	Cherry-red spots	Vacuolated lymphocytes	Renal involvement
Congenital	In utero	Coarse	+ + +	Mental retardation	+ +	?	Vacuolated lymphocytes	Hydrops fetalis, stillbirth
Aspartylgly-cosaminuria	1–5 yr	Coarse, sagging skin	+	Mental retardation	−	Lens opacities	Vacuolated lymphocytes	Acne, sun sensitivity

*A juvenile phenotype is seen primarily in galactosialidosis rather than in sialidosis.

Mannosidase activity in normal tissue results from the actions of both Golgi membrane mannosidase(s) having neutral or intermediate pH optima[63] and from lysosomal forms having acidic pH optima.[64] While the molecular and genetic relationships of these various forms of mannosidase have not been completely elucidated, it is known that mannosidosis patients lack the acidic form(s) of the enzyme while retaining the neutral enzyme.[21,65] The presence of heterogeneity within this group of patients has been suggested by reports of individuals having high residual mannosidase activity.[39,66–69] In the majority of these patients the residual activity appears to have increased heat lability and a marked increase in the K_m against certain artificial substrates. In addition, there have been reports that the mutant enzyme is activated by cobalt and variably by zinc.[31,70] Immunologic studies of this residual material have yielded conflicting results. Specifically, while antihuman liver α-mannosidase antibodies failed to react with this activity, rabbit anti-human placenta and anti-pig kidney mannosidase antibodies have yielded positive reactions.[31,71,72] It is uncertain if this residual activity represents mutant gene product or an activity from some other enzyme.

Interestingly, several investigators have found that culture media in which mannosidosis fibroblasts have been cultured accumulate acid mannosidase activity.[73–76] These findings were interpreted by one group as suggesting that "the defect in mannosidosis is expressed only after the enzyme has been delivered to lysosomes and presumably undergone some form of processing there."[75] In a later paper, evidence was presented that mannosidosis fibroblasts do not synthesize acid mannosidase and that the enzyme secreted by these cells is not related, immunologically, to lysosomal mannosidase.[76]

Genetics

Based on reports of a large number of families with affected offspring, human mannosidosis is an autosomal recessive disorder.[21] Direct evidence supporting this conclusion is provided by gene mapping. In 1977, the gene encoding acidic mannosidase was assigned to chromosome 19 by two groups.[77,78] Subsequent studies have mapped the gene locus to 19p13→q13.[79,80] To date, the gene has not been linked to any of the other loci assigned to this chromosome.[81]

Diagnosis

Patients affected with mannosidosis excrete increased amounts of several oligosaccharides, the major one being Man(α1→3)-Man(β1→4)GlcNAc.[57,82] The presence of increased amounts of this and related compounds can most easily be demonstrated by the thin-layer chromatography technique widely utilized for the detection of a variety of inherited oligosaccharide disorders (Fig. 63-7).[83–86] As with individuals affected with other errors of glycoprotein degradation, mannosidosis patients have a unique pattern of oligosaccharide excretion. A diagnostic method using lectins to analyze paraffin-embedded sections for detection of specific sugars in stored material was described,[87] but this technique is not widely utilized.

Direct measurement of α-mannosidase in leukocytes, fibroblasts, cultured fetal cells, or tissues such as brain or liver is required for confirmation or exclusion of the diagnosis. The measurement of enzyme activity in plasma has not been as reliable as the assay of the cellular enzyme levels, probably as the result of forms of mannosidase enzymes in plasma that are not decreased in mannosidosis patients.[21]

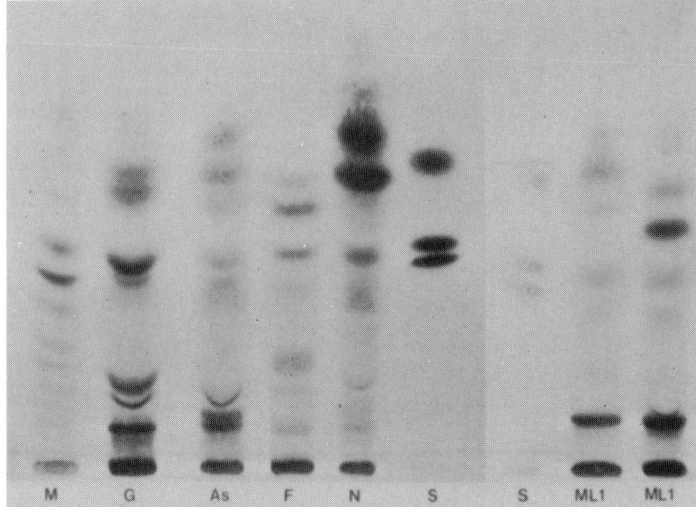

Fig. 63-7 Thin-layer chromatogram of urines with orcinol detection. M = mannosidosis; G = G$_{M1}$ gangliosidosis; As = aspartylglycosaminuria; F = fucosidosis; N = normal control; S = standard mixture of fructose, lactose, and raffinose; ML1 = sialidosis. (*From Sewell.[83] Used by permission.*)

Prenatal Diagnosis

As with the other inherited disorders of glycoprotein catabolism, there are several reports regarding the successful prenatal diagnosis of mannosidosis. These include the report of an affected fetus, later confirmed,[88] and the experience with two families in which two fetuses were found to be affected while a third was found to be free of the disease.[89] While these studies were carried out with no serious difficulties, the presence of both residual activity and forms of mannosidase not affected in mannosidosis patients must be taken into account when interpreting the results of a prenatal study for this disorder.[67]

Animal Models

There are at least two and perhaps three unrelated animal models for human mannosidosis. The best known, and most studied, of these is bovine mannosidosis, an autosomal inherited disorder found in Aberdeen Angus cattle.[90,91] The disorder has also been found in a number of related breeds of cattle, i.e., Red Angus, Murray Grey, Galloway, and shorthorns.[92] The disease in these animals is characterized by ataxia, incoordination, tremor, and aggressive behavior. As with human mannosidosis, animals affected with the bovine form of this disorder have only small amounts of the acidic form of α-D-mannosidase.[91]

Additionally, mannosidosis has been found in a domestic shorthair cat having similar clinical findings, i.e., multiple skeletal deformities, retarded growth, ataxia, intention tremors, and a deficiency of α-mannosidase activity.[93,94] More recently a similar deficiency has been described in a Persian cat, and a colony of affected cats was established.[95] A phenocopy of mannosidosis occurs in livestock grazing on a legume of the genus *Swainsona*. The plant contains a potent inhibitor of lysosomal α-mannosidase.[96]

FUCOSIDOSIS

Clinical Features

There are reports or personal knowledge of over 60 patients with fucosidosis.[20,97] A careful review indicates repetitive reporting of cases, but at least 40 definite cases are in the literature.[98–125] Other reports include an unclassified case with prominent bone involvement[126] and one with multiple partial enzyme deficiencies.[114] A fatal infantile form is referred to as type I, which accounts for about 60 percent of patients. A milder phenotype with adult survival is designated type II. The type I phenotype has onset of psychomotor retardation recognizable at about 1 year of age. Coarse facies, growth retardation, dysotosis multiplex, and neurologic deterioration are present uniformly. Hepatosplenomegaly, cardiomegaly, seizures, and infections occur frequently but are variable. The sodium chloride content of sweat is increased markedly. The type II phenotype is associated with onset of psychomotor retardation between 1 and 2 years of age. The coarse facies, growth retardation, dysotosis multiplex, and neurologic signs are similar or slightly milder. The major distinguishing features of the type II phenotype are the presence of angiokeratoma (Fig. 63-8), longer survival, often to adult years, and a more normal sweat sodium chloride value, although anhidrosis may be present.

The angiokeratomata that occur in fucosidosis are essentially indistinguishable from those seen in Fabry disease, and the distribution is similar.[100,107,127–130] Telangiectatic lesions can occur in the mouth.[131] The ocular findings in fucosidosis are not prominent, but tortuosity of conjunctival vessels occurs and a pigmentary retinopathy has been described.[129,132] The skeletal findings are those of a mild dysostosis multiplex.[109,120,133] Changes in the vertebrae are prominent, with ovoid configuration and beaking. The acetabula are often deformed and sclerotic. The shaft of the long bones may be widened. Vacuolated lymphocytes have been present where examined.

Pathology

Postmortem examination of type I patients[98,117] has revealed enlargement of the brain, heart, liver, spleen, and pancreas. The adrenal glands are atrophic. The gallbladder is described as strawberrylike. Biopsy studies from liver indicate the presence of foamy cytoplasm in some hepatocytes and Kupffer cells. Ultrastructural studies indicate the presence of vacuoles with heterogeneous content, some appearing empty, some with reticulum formation, and some with lamellar structure.[99,101] Ultrastructural studies of biopsy material from brain indicate a similar heterogeneity in the appearance of storage

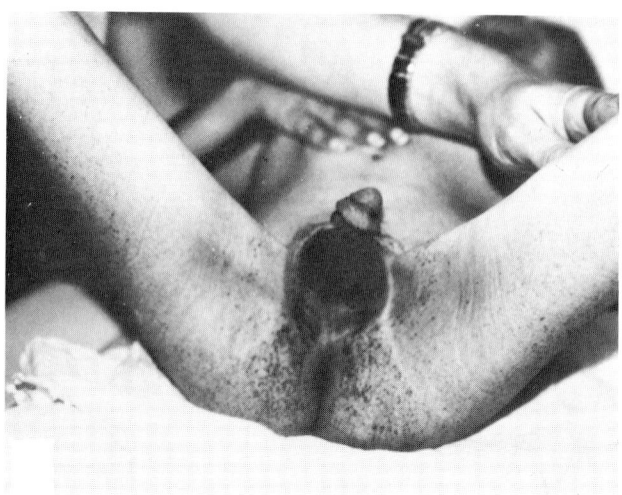

Fig. 63-8 Angiokeratoma in fucosidosis type II. *(From Snyder et al.*[113] *Used by permission.)*

vacuoles.[99] There is a striking vacuolization of the epithelial cells of the sweat glands[107,110,128] and of the conjunctiva.[110]

Biochemical Storage

It was recognized from the earliest report[14] that fucosidosis probably represented faulty degradation of both sphingolipids and polysaccharides. The major glycolipid accumulating is the H-antigen glycolipid Fuc(α1→2)Gal(β1→4)GlcNAc-α-Gal-ceramide.[134,135] There is a major accumulation of glycolipid in liver, but only minor storage in brain. Studies of the oligosaccharides found in the tissues and urine of patients with fucosidosis have indicated the presence of a decasaccharide, Fuc(α1→2)Gal(β1→4)GlcNAc(β1→2)Man[Fuc(α1→2) Gal(β1→4)GlcNAc(β1→2)Man](α1→3/6)Man(β1→4) GlcNAc, and a disaccharide, Fuc(α1→6)GlcNAc[135,136] (see Fig. 63-5). Subsequent studies[137–140] identified numerous other oligosaccharides and glycoasparagines in the urine and tissues of fucosidosis patients. In one excellent study,[141] 22 glycopeptides were identified in the urine of a patient, but the presence of the decasaccharide could not be confirmed. All of the glycopeptides contained a fucosyl residue on the GlcNAc which is linked to asparagine. There is a suggestion that fucosidosis types I and II can be distinguished by the pattern of urinary excretion.[142] Oligosaccharide accumulation predominates as the storage material in the brain of patients. The suggestion of increased keratan sulfate in the urine in fucosidosis requires further study.[143]

The relationships to blood group substances in fucosidosis deserve special mention. These substances are determined by oligosaccharide chains linked to proteins or lipids. The H, Le^a, and Le^b antigens are determined by the presence of fucosyltransferases. On the one hand, the genotype at these loci may determine the exact nature of the stored material in fucosidosis patients. On the other hand, the presence of fucosidosis may increase the expression of these antigens.[107,144] Data are insufficient at present to determine if blood type affects the clinical course of fucosidosis.

Enzyme Defect

Human tissue α-L-fucosidase has a basic subunit of approximately 50 kDa.[20] The enzyme has been purified and its ki-

netic, electrophoretic, and immunologic properties studied extensively, as reviewed elsewhere.[20] Evidence from interconversion studies suggest that various forms of fucosidase are explained in part by the existence of monomer, dimer, and tetramer forms. However, two groups[145,146] have presented evidence for heterogeneity of the subunits and the possibility of the existence of nonidentical subunits was reviewed.[20] Molecular studies have suggested that the enzyme is a homotetramer and that the cDNA for the subunit was cloned.[147] Recently, detailed kinetic studies have revealed four active sites per tetrameric complex and suggest that the enzyme is a homotetramer.[148]

Johnson and Dawson,[149] using fibroblasts, reported the existence of a discrete precursor of the α-L-fucosidase subunit. Specifically, they provided evidence that a 50-kDa mature subunit is processed from a 53-kDa precursor.

Fukushima et al.,[147] using molecular cloning techniques, isolated cDNA from a human hepatoma library which coded for a least 80 percent of the mature α-L-fucosidase. This cDNA was found to contain 1058 base pairs and to code for 347 amino acids of the subunit of the enzyme. Extensive colinearity between the nucleotide sequence and the amino acid sequence of the α-L-fucosidase was demonstrated.[147] In addition four potential glycosylation sites were identified which could add 6 to 10 kDa to the processed enzyme.

Recent studies have provided the first molecular evidence for the presence of heterogeneity among fucosidosis patients. In one investigation, using a polyclonal antibody, it was shown that liver from a single fucosidosis patient lacked detectable α-L-fucosidase protein.[150] In a larger study, however, it was found that while fibroblasts from 8 of 11 fucosidosis patients also had no detectable fucosidase enzyme protein, the cells of two additional patients synthesized the 53-kDa precursor but contained none of the mature processed enzyme.[149] The cells of the remaining patient in this study contained small amounts of cross-reacting material.

Genetics

As with the other errors of glycoprotein metabolism, fucosidosis is an autosomal recessive disease. While the disorder is panethnic, a concentration of patients has been reported from the Calabria region of southern Italy.[97] In 1975, the locus for acidic α-fucosidase was provisionally assigned to chromosome 1.[151] This assignment was confirmed, and the fucosidase locus was shown to be linked to the Rh locus.[152] More recently, the gene locus for this enzyme was mapped to band p34 of human chromosome 1.[153] The structural locus for the enzyme is designated *FUCA1*. This locus is associated with an electrophoretic polymorphism with three alleles, Fu^1, Fu^2, and Fu^0, the last being the silent allele causing fucosidosis.[154–155] The assignment has been confirmed using the cloned cDNA for Southern blotting, and a homologous DNA sequence occurs on chromosome 2.[156] A restriction fragment length polymorphism mapping to chromosome 1 was identified with the cDNA clone.[157]

There is also a genetic polymorphism involving the level of fucosidose activity in plasma. The locus for this polymorphism is designated *FUCA2*, although this locus may involve a regulatory process rather than a structural gene. Additional studies have shown that the *FUCA2* locus is linked to the plasminogen gene,[158] originally believed to be on chromosome 4, but now known to be on chromosome 6.[159]

Enzyme Defect

Both type I and type II sialidosis are the result of inherited deficiencies of a neuraminidase which normally cleaves terminal 2→3 and 2→6 sialyl linkages of several oligosaccharides and glycoproteins.[213–215] Deficiencies of this enzyme were demonstrated with a wide variety of both natural (sialyllactose, sialylhexasaccharides, and fetuin) and synthetic (3-methoxyphenyl-N-acetylneuraminic acid and 4-methylumbelliferyl-α-D-N-acetylneuraminic acid) substrates. In contrast to its action on the above substrates, this enzyme does not cleave the sialyl linkage of a variety of ganglioside substrates.[214–216] These results provide evidence for the existence of at least two forms of neuraminidase, i.e., one specific for oligosaccharides, glycoproteins, and synthetic substrates and a second one reactive with gangliosides. This conclusion is also supported by the genetic evidence for at least two separate and distinct inherited defects resulting in one case in sialidosis and in the other, in mucolipidosis IV (see Chap. 71).

An inherited, primary deficiency of neuraminidase was first demonstrated in the severe (type II) form of sialidosis.[16,17] Shortly thereafter, several investigators (Durand et al.,[179] O'Brien,[180] and Thomas et al.[182]) described a similar deficiency in a milder clinical disorder, the so-called cherry-red spot–myoclonus syndrome, now classified as *sialidosis type I*. Intermediate sialidase levels in parents of affected patients[177] and gene mapping studies[217] provide direct evidence that the enzyme deficiencies in these individuals result from an autosomal recessive inherited primary enzyme defect involving the neuraminidase.

Biochemical and genetic evidence now exists to separate sialidosis due to a primary deficiency of neuraminidase from galactosialidosis which demonstrates a combined deficiency of neuraminidase and β-galactosidase (see Chap. 71). Current evidence indicates that the combined deficiency results from loss of a protective protein required to interact with the galactosidase and neuraminidase complex.[218]

To date, human α-neuraminidase has not been well-characterized. Both the clinical and research efforts involving this enzyme have been complicated because neuraminidase is unstable, i.e., is quickly destroyed by freezing, sonication, solubilization, and/or most purification procedures.[219,220] Most of the information that is available regarding the properties of this enzyme was obtained with crude preparations of cultured skin fibroblasts either from normal controls[219,220] or from individuals affected with sialidosis.[177,182,219] Lysosomal neuraminidase was partially purified from human placenta, and evidence for a complex between β-galactosidase and a 32-kDa protein was obtained.[221] There is evidence of two genetically distinct forms of neuraminidase in leukocytes in addition to a ganglioside neuraminidase.[222]

Genetics

To date, all the clinical forms of sialidosis appear to be inherited in an autosomal recessive manner. The presence of consanguinity, multiple affected sibs, and intermediate sialidase levels in parents of affected patients and the absence of multiple affected generations support this conclusion.[19] Type I sialidosis may be more frequent in Italians. Numerous reports of a juvenile phenotype in the Japanese represent galactosialidosis rather than sialidosis.

Mueller et al.[217] have provided evidence that the expression of the glycoprotein-specific α-neuraminidase, absent in sialidosis patients, requires the presence of two genes for normal expression. Complementation analysis indicated that the sialidase deficiency in a sialidosis type II patient was caused by a mutation in a structural gene encoded on the pter→q23 region of chromosome 10. In contrast, the neuraminidase deficiency found in a galactosialidosis patient was shown to be caused by a mutation in a gene located on chromosome 20. Suggestions that a neuraminidase deficiency gene may map to chromosome 6 were based, in part, on the combined occurrence of congenital adrenal hyperplasia and neuraminidase deficiency in a patient[195] and in part on the linkage of a gene controlling hepatic neuraminidase to the *H-2* locus in the mouse.[223] The mouse mutation affects multiple hydrolases, and the question of a locus on human chromosome 6 requires further study.

Diagnosis

As with the other inherited disorders of glycoprotein catabolism, sialidosis patients excrete increased amounts of several oligosaccharides[205,224] and sialylglycopeptides[209] derived from glycoproteins. As the metabolic block in these individuals results in an inability to cleave the terminal sialic acid residues, the accumulated complex sugars are rich in sialic acid. This is in contrast to the other inborn errors of glycoprotein metabolism in which the sialic acid is removed prior to the enzymic block, thus resulting in excessive levels of oligosaccharides poor in this compound.

While detailed analysis of the accumulated oligosaccharides is too time-consuming for routine clinical diagnosis, several useful screening tests based on the demonstration of abnormal patterns and/or amounts of these compounds by thin-layer chromatography have been described.[83–86] Following application of the urine samples, the thin-layer plates are developed in an appropriate solvent and then stained. Staining with orcinol utilized for the detection of other disorders of glycoprotein degradation is usually suitable for the routine detection of the abnormal pattern of urinary oligosaccharide characteristic of this group of disorders. When desired, the sialic acid–containing oligosaccharides can also be specifically localized with resorcinol.[86] Urine samples from both type I and type II patients,[177] including newborns with the congenital or hydropic form of this disorder,[202] yield abnormal patterns by these techniques.

The definitive diagnosis of sialidosis is based on the direct measurement of neuraminidase activity in appropriate fresh tissue samples, i.e., fibroblasts, cultured amniotic fluid cells, or white blood cells. In contrast to most other lysosomal enzymes, care must be taken to ensure that the tissue to be examined has not been frozen or exposed to prolonged sonication.[220] While several substrates can be utilized for this enzyme assay, the substrate of choice appears to be 4-methylumbelliferyl-α-N-acetylneuraminic acid.[226] The use of this sensitive substrate is particularly important with leukocytes, as these cells contain only about one-tenth of the sialidase activity found in cultured fibroblast cells. One group recommends against the use of leukocytes for diagnosis,[222] and fibroblasts appear to offer better demonstration of enzyme deficiency than leukocytes using 4-methylumbelliferyl-α-N-acetylneuraminic acid as substrate.[227] At times it may be difficult to distinguish sialidosis from galactosialidosis if intermediate levels of β-galactosidase are observed, and in these exceptional cases, complementation testing could be used.[217,218]

Prenatal Diagnosis

Neuraminidase activity is readily detectable in fresh, normal cultured amniotic fluid cells. Note should be taken of the fact that these cells must be handled with special care as enzyme activity is quickly destroyed by freezing, sonication, and/or exposure to temperatures of 37°C.[220] If possible, the enzyme activity should be determined with a sensitive assay, i.e., a fluorescent technique based on the enzymatic cleavage of 4-methylumbelliferyl-α-N-acetylneuraminic acid.[226]

To date, there have been at least three reports of successful prenatal diagnostic procedures for families at risk for various forms of sialidosis. These include both affected and unaffected fetuses in a family at risk for congenital sialidosis,[201] and an unaffected fetus in a family at risk for sialidosis type II.[227]

Animal Models

A strain of mice (SM/J) has been shown to have a deficiency of neuraminidase in some but not all tissues.[228] Specifically, while there is a decrease in the levels of neuraminidase in liver, the enzyme levels in other tissues are either normal or only slightly diminished. Additionally, no increase in the sialic acid content of the liver was demonstrated in these animals. It has, therefore, been suggested that this strain of mice may not be a good model for the various types of human sialidosis.[229]

ASPARTYLGLYCOSAMINURIA

Clinical Features

By 1982, 138 patients from 108 families were diagnosed with aspartylglycosaminuria in Finland.[22,230] Other cases include eight Finnish patients in Norway,[231,232] four English cases,[12,22] three cases in the United States,[233,234] and three Italian cases, one of whom is also affected with methemoglobinemia.[22,235-237] The Finnish phenotype is quite consistent, as described in detail by Finnish investigators.[22,238] The patients were healthy for the first few months of life. Recurrent infections, diarrhea, and hernias were noted during the first year of life. Head circumference and stature were decreased later in childhood in some patients, and hepatomegaly was found infrequently. Coarsening of the facies and sagging skin folds were subtle in the first decade and more obvious thereafter (Fig. 63-10). Increased acne and sun sensitivity were found. Crystal-like lens opacities were observed in 8 of 25 patients. Joint laxity, macroglossia, hoarse voice, short stature, and brachycephaly were described in some patients. Mental development was relatively normal until about age 5, except for delayed speech. Mental deterioration occurred between the ages of 6 and 15 with IQ values usually below 40 in adults. Clumsiness and hypotonia were reported in some, and spasticity occurred in only a few older patients. Behavior frequently was uncontrolled, and the patients were excitable. Ten patients died in the third to fifth

decade, with pneumonia or pulmonary abscess being the cause in 8 of 10.[22] The patients scattered elsewhere in the world have all demonstrated mental retardation and skeletal dysplasia. Cardiac valvular involvement is reported,[22,233,234] and angiokeratoma occurred in one patient.[235]

Vacuolated lymphocytes were observed in 19 of 25 Finnish patients, while neutropenia was found in 13 of 25. The prothrombin time was decreased in 13 of 25, and the EEG was abnormal in 11 of 25. Marked aspartylglycosaminuria was present in all patients. Radiographic changes indicate a very mild dysostosis multiplex, with wedge-shaped vertebral bodies later in life and thickening of the cortex of the skull. Cerebral atrophy can be demonstrated.

Pathology

Pathologic studies of bone marrow, small intestine, skin, lymph node, kidney, and brain are available from biopsy specimens.[22,239,240] One autopsy examination has been reported,[241] and one fetal pathological study is available.[242] Light-microscopic examination of all tissues has demonstrated vacuolated cytoplasm with variable PAS staining. Hepatocytes may contain a large central vacuole and may superficially resemble advanced fatty metamorphosis. Electron-microscopic examination of all tissues has demonstrated small and huge vacuoles bounded by a single membrane. Much of the material is electron-lucent, but electron-dense granular bodies occur, particularly in brain. The brain did not show lysosomal abnormalities in one fetal study.[242]

Biochemical Storage

Aspartylglycosamine (GlcNAc-Asn) is the major storage compound that has been isolated from a variety of tissues of aspartylglycosaminuria patients. The content of GlcNAc-Asn is particularly high in the liver, spleen, and thyroid, with moderate increases in kidney and brain.[243] Detailed analysis of the brain has shown the accumulated GlcNAc-Asn to be rather evenly distributed throughout this organ.[244] Normal tissues appear to lack this compound, at least in the free state.[243]

GlcNAc-Asn is also the major abnormal metabolite excreted in the urine of affected patients, with a reported range of 0.15 to 1.88 mmol/24 h.[245] This is in contrast to normal urine in which only small amounts of this compound are found.[245,246] Urine from aspartylglycosaminuria patients contains, in addition, several other glycoasparagines, e.g., the galactosyl derivative of aspartylglycosamine (Gal-GlcNAc-Asn), Man-Man-GlcNAc-GlcNac-Asn, as well as several sialylated derivatives.[247] Most of the structures reported, to date, could be derived by partial degradation of known N-glycosidically linked oligosaccharides in glycoproteins.

Enzyme Defect

The metabolic alterations in aspartylglycosaminuria result from a deficiency of aspartylglycosaminidase (1-aspartamido-β-N-acetylglucosamine amidohydrolase). This enzyme cleaves the N-acetylglucosamine-asparagine linkages found in a variety of glycopeptides and glycoproteins. This enzyme was purified and characterized by Dugal and Dugal,[248] and later

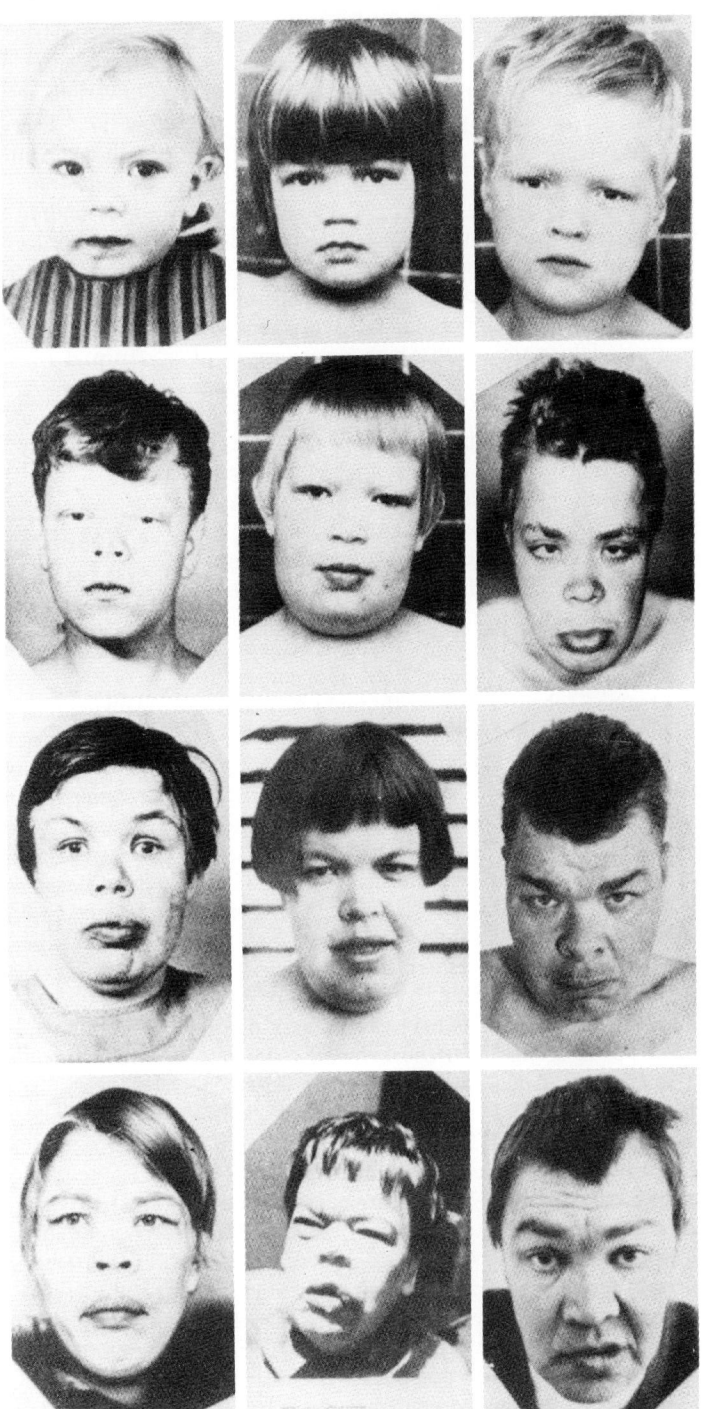

Fig. 63-10 Facial appearance in aspartylglycosaminuria. Twelve patients at various age groups are shown. *Upper horizontal line = patients below 10 years of age; second line = from 10 to 20 years; third line = from 20 to 30 years; lower line = 30 years and older.* (From Autio.[238] Used by permission.)

McGovern et al., using normal human liver, purified the enzyme to apparent homogeneity.[249] The isolated protein consisted of a thermostable monomer of 76 kDa, with a pH optimum of 6.1 and an isoelectric point of 5.7.[249] Earlier studies showed the amidase activity to be enriched in the lysosomal fraction.[250]

Aspartylglycosaminidase cleaves aspartylglucosamine to aspartic acid and 1-amino-*N*-acetylglucosamine. In 1968, deficiency of enzyme activity was demonstrated in the seminal fluid of a patient with aspartylglycosaminuria.[13] Subsequent studies have shown this enzyme activity to be absent in a variety of tissues and fluids of aspartylglycosaminuria patients. All genetic and biochemical data indicate that this is the pri-

mary defect in this disorder. There is a preliminary report that a cDNA for aspartylglycosaminidase has been isolated.[250a]

Genetics

Aspartylglycosaminuria is inherited as an autosomal recessive disorder. While isolated cases of this disorder have been reported from widespread parts of the world, the majority of affected individuals encountered have been Finnish.[22]

The structural gene encoding for aspartylglycosaminidase has been assigned to the long arm of chromosome 4.[251] Analysis of two somatic cell hybrids containing hamster-human chromosomal translocations indicates that the presence of human aspartylglycosaminidase is correlated with the presence of 4q21→qter.[251]

Diagnosis

As the name indicates, patients with aspartylglycosaminuria excrete large amounts of 2-acetamido-1-(β-L-aspartamido)-1,2-dideoxy-β-D-glucose (aspartylglucosamine).[252] The urine of these patients also contains a number of other compounds that are similar to aspartylglucosamine but which have a variety of additional carbohydrate residues.[253] Several screening tests for the detection of increased concentrations of these compounds are based on the qualitative analysis of urine by thin-layer chromatography, paper chromatography, or electrophoresis.[83-86] Following separation, the chromatogram or electrophoresis strip is stained with a mixture of orcinol and sulfuric acid or with ninhydrin. Results with the latter reagent have been improved by heating the freshly stained thin-layer plate or paper, e.g., at 120°C for 5 to 15 min.[162,163,254] Aspartylglucosamine, when stained at this higher temperature, forms a bright-blue reaction product, not the nonspecific brown color obtained when stained with ninhydrin at the lower temperatures usually utilized for amino acid analysis. Care must be taken, however, not to confuse the aspartylglucosamine with the normal urinary constituent, 1-methylhistidine, that also yields a similarly colored spot on the additional heating step.[163] A screening test based on the enzymatic determination of aspartylglucosamine levels in urine has also been described.[255] While this procedure has the advantage of yielding quantitative results, it has not found wide acceptance as a general screening tool. Acquired aspartylglycosaminuria was reported in a laxative-abusing patient.[256]

While the urinary screening tests have proved very useful, the final diagnosis of aspartylglycosaminuria relies on the measurement of aspartylglycosaminidase activity in an easily obtained tissue source, i.e., sonicates of white blood cells, fibroblasts, or amniotic fluid cells.[22,230,242] For this determination, crude tissue sonicates are incubated in the presence of the synthetic aspartylglycosamine at pH 7.0 for a prolonged period of time (usually 20 h). Under these conditions, aspartylglycosaminidase, if present, cleaves the substrate to aspartic acid and 1-amino-N-acetylglucosamine. Following nonenzymatic conversion of the latter compound to ammonia and N-acetylglucosamine, the amino sugar is measured by the Morgan-Elson reaction. Tissues from aspartylglycosaminuria patients demonstrate little or no enzyme activity, while heterozygotes usually show levels that are intermediate between the affected patients and normal individuals.

Prenatal Diagnosis

Results from several laboratories have established that cells cultured from normal amniotic fluid contain measurable amounts of aspartylglycosaminidase activity, suggesting that it should be possible to offer prenatal diagnosis for this disorder. Direct proof that this could be done was provided by Aula et al., who followed five pregnancies in which there was a high risk for aspartylglycosaminuria.[242] Cultured amniotic cells from four of the pregnancies yielded normal or carrier levels of enzyme activity while the fifth lacked activity in amniotic

cells obtained at 17 weeks of gestation. Following termination of the latter pregnancy, the enzyme deficiency was confirmed in various fetal tissues.[242] The four other pregnancies resulted in the delivery of healthy babies. Cells cultured from chorionic villi taken after the termination of the affected pregnancy also demonstrated a deficiency of aspartylglycosaminidase activity. This finding suggests that it should be possible to diagnosis this disorder by the analysis of chorionic villus biopsy material.

Animal Models

There are, at the present time, no reported animal models of aspartylglycosaminuria.

OTHER DISORDERS OF GLYCOPROTEIN CATABOLISM

β-Mannosidosis

Although, as shown in Fig. 63-4, the complex oligosaccharides include the Man(β1→4)-N-acetylglucosamine linkage, there have been, until recently, no reports of humans lacking the enzyme responsible for the cleavage of this bond. In 1986, however, Wenger et al.[257] and Cooper et al.[258] simultaneously described a total of three individuals who lacked β-mannosidase, the enzyme believed to be responsible for degradation of this chemical linkage.

The patient described by Wenger et al.[257] was a 46-month-old male with mildly coarse facies, mild bone disease, delayed speech, hyperactivity, and developmental delay. Screening for lysosomal disorders established that he lacked acidic β-mannosidase activity in leukocytes, fibroblasts, and plasma. Increased levels of a disaccharide identified as Man(β1→4)-N-acetylglucosamine were found in his urine. In addition to the deficiency of β-mannosidase activity and the associated disaccharide excretion, this patient was also found to have low levels of sulfaminidase activity and increased concentrations of urinary heparin sulfate. The relationship, if any, between the two enzymatic alterations in this patient is unclear.

The patients described by Cooper et al.[258] were 19- and 44-year-old mentally retarded brothers with scrotal angiokeratoma and tortuosity of conjunctival vessels. They were reported to lack facial dysmorphism, hepatosplenomegaly, or radiologic evidence of skeletal alterations. Both lacked β-mannosidase activity in plasma, leukocytes, and cultured fibroblasts. Urinary analysis showed the presence of large amounts of a disaccharide that yielded mannose and glucosamine following acid hydrolysis. No information was provided regarding mucopolysaccharide metabolism.

The clinically normal, unrelated parents of the patients in both reports had intermediate or low levels of mannosidase activity in one or more tissues or fluids.[257,258] These findings are compatible with and suggestive of an autosomal mode of inheritance.

The relatively mild course of the disease in these patients is in marked contrast to that found in goats, where a fatal disorder is associated with a severe alteration involving demyelination and/or dysmyelination.[7,259]

GLUTAMYL RIBOSE-5-PHOSPHATE GLYCOPROTEINOSIS

Only one patient with the disorder known as *glutamyl ribose-5-phosphate glycoproteinosis* has been reported. This disorder was described in a 6-year-old boy, who died of renal failure at 8 years of age.[260] At age 6, the major findings included mildly coarse facies, optic atrophy, muscle wasting, failure to thrive, seizures, proteinuria, neurologic deterioration, and progressive renal failure.

Glutamyl ribose-5-phosphate was isolated from the brain and kidney at autopsy.[261] As this compound could not be isolated from normal tissue, its presence in this patient was taken as evidence that this patient suffered from an inherited storage disorder. At the present time, however, it cannot be concluded that this represents a lysosomal storage disorder. Indeed many of the findings reported to date in this single patient are inconsistent with findings generally associated with known lysosomal disorders.[262] The alteration responsible for the storage of glutamyl ribose-5-phosphate in this patient has not yet been identified. For these reasons, the inclusion of this disorder in this chapter is, at the present time, tentative. The identification of the enzyme defect responsible for this disorder will be required to delineate the condition.

REFERENCES

1. BEAUDET AL: Disorders of glycoprotein degradation: Mannosidosis, fucosidosis, sialidosis and aspartylglycosaminuria, in Stanbury JB, Wyngaarden JB, Fredrickson DS, Goldstein JL, Brown MS (eds): *The Metabolic Basis of Inherited Disease*, 5th ed. New York, McGraw-Hill, 1983, chap 38, p 788.
2. KORNFELD R, KORNFELD S: Structure of glycoproteins and their oligosaccharide units, in Lennarz WJ (ed): *The Biochemistry of Glycoproteins and Proteoglycans*. New York, Plenum, 1980, p 1.
3. STRUCK DK, LENNARZ WJ: The function of saccharide-lipids in synthesis of glycoproteins, in Lennarz WJ (ed): *The Biochemistry of Glycoproteins and Proteoglycans*. New York, Plenum, 1980, p 35.
4. SCHACHTER H, ROSEMAN S: Mammalian glycosyltransferases: Their role in the synthesis and function of complex carbohydrates and glycolipids, in Lennarz WJ (ed): *The Biochemistry of Glycoproteins and Proteoglycans*. New York, Plenum, 1980, p 85.
5. MARGOLIS RK, MARGOLIS RU: Structure and distribution of glycoproteins and glycosaminoglycans, in Margolis RU, Margolis RK (eds): *Complex Carbohydrates of Nervous Tissue*. New York, Plenum, 1970, p 45.
6. WAECHTER CJ, SCHER MG: Biosynthesis of glycoproteins, in Margolis RU, Margolis RK (eds): *Complex Carbohydrates of Nervous Tissue*. New York, Plenum, 1979, p 75.
7. JONES MZ, DAWSON G: Carpine β-mannosidosis: Inherited deficiency of β-D-mannosidase. *J Biol Chem* 256:5185, 1981.
8. SPRAINGER J, WIEDEMANN H-R, TOLKSDORF M, GRAUCOB E, CAESAR R: Lipomucopolysaccharidose: Eine neue speicherkrankheit. *Z Kinderheilk* 103:285, 1968.
9. SPRANGER JW, WIEDERMANN H-R: The genetic mucolipidoses: Diagnosis and differential diagnosis. *Humangenetik* 9:113, 1970.
10. VAN HOOF F, HERS HG: The abnormalities of lysosomal enzymes in mucopolysaccharidoses. *Eur J Biochem* 7:34, 1968.
11. ÖCKERMAN P-A: A generalised storage disorder resembling Hurler's syndrome. *Lancet* 2:239, 1967.
12. JENNER FA, POLLITT RJ: Large quantities of 2-acetamido-1 (β-1-aspartamido)-1,2-dideoxyglucose in the urine of mentally retarded siblings. *Biochem J* 103:48p, 1967.
13. POLLITT RJ, JENNER FA, MERSKEY H: Aspartylglycosaminuria: An inborn error of metabolism associated with mental defect. *Lancet* 2:253, 1968.
14. DURAND P, BORRONE C, DELLA CELLA G, PHILIPPART M: Fucosidosis. *Lancet* 1:1198, 1968.
15. VAN HOFF F, HERS HG: Mucopolysaccharidosis by absence of α-fucosidase. *Lancet* 1:1198, 1968.
16. CANTZ M, GEHLER J, SPRANGER J: Mucolipidosis I: Increased sialic acid

content and deficiency of an α-N-acetylneuraminidase in cultured fibroblasts. *Biochem Biophys Res Commun* 74:732, 1977.
17. SPRANGER J, GEHLER J, CANTZ M: Mucolipidosis I-A sialidosis. *Am J Med Genet* 1:21, 1977.
18. HERS HG, VAN HOOF F: *Lysosomes and Storage Diseases*. New York, Academic, 1973.
19. O'BRIEN JS: Sialidosis, in Durand P, O'Brien JS (eds): *Genetic Errors of Glycoprotein Metabolism*. Berlin, Springer-Verlag, 1982, p 3.
20. DURAND P, ROSSANNA G, BORRONE G: Fucosidosis, in Durand P, O'Brien JS (eds): *Genetic Errors of Glycoprotein Metabolism*. Berlin, Springer-Verlag, 1982, p 49.
21. CHESTER MA, LUNDBLAD A, ÖCKERMAN P-A, AUTIO S: in Durand P, O'Brien JS (eds): *Genetic Errors of Glycoprotein Metabolism*. Berlin, Springer-Verlag, 1982, p 89.
22. AULA P, AUTIO S, RAIVIOKO, RAPOLA J: Aspartylglucosaminuria in Durand P, O'Brien JS (eds): *Genetic Errors of Glycoprotein Metabolism*. Berlin, Springer-Verlag, 1982, p 123.
23. KJELLMAN B, GAMSTORP I, BRUN A, ÖCKERMAN P-A, PALMGREN B: Mannosidosis: A clinical and histopathologic study. *J Pediatr* 75:366, 1969.
24. AUTIO S, NORDEN NE, ÖCKERMAN P-A, RIEKKINEN P, RAPOLA J, LOUHIMO T: Mannosidosis: Clinical, fine-structural and biochemical findings in three cases. *Acta Paediatr Scand* 62:555, 1973.
25. NORDÉN NE, ÖCKERMAN P-A, SZABO L: Urinary mannose in mannosidosis. *J Pediatr* 82:686, 1973.
26. TSAY GC, DAWSON G, MATALON R: Excretion of mannose-rich complex carbohydrates by a patient with α-mannosidase deficiency (mannosidosis). *J Pediatr* 84:865, 1974.
27. FARRIAUX JP, LEGOUIS I, HUMBEL R, DHONDT JL, RICHARD P, STRECKER G, FOURMAINTRAUX A, RINGEL J, FONTAINE G: La mannosidose: A propos de 5 observations. *Nouv Presse Med* 4:1867, 1975.
28. LOEB H, TONDEUR M, TOPPET M, CREMER N: Clinical, biochemical and ultrastructural studies of an atypical form of mucopolysaccharidosis. *Acta Paediatr Scand* 58:220, 1969.
29. BOOTH CW, CHEN KK, NADLER HL: Mannosidosis: Clinical and biochemical studies in a family of affected adolescents and adults. *J Pediatr* 88:821, 1976.
30. AYLSWORTH AS, TAYLOR HA, STUART CF, THOMAS GH: Mannosidosis: Phenotype of a severely affected child and characterization of α-mannosidase activity in cultured fibroblasts from the patient and his parents. *J Pediatr* 88:814, 1976.
31. DESNICK RJ, SHARP HL, GRABOWSKI GA, BRUNNING RD, QUIE PG, SUNG JH, GORLIN RJ, IKONNE JU: Mannosidosis: Clinical, morphologic, immunologic, and biochemical studies. *Pediatr Res* 19:985, 1976.
32. MURPHREE AL, BEAUDET AL, PALMER EA, NICHOLS BL: Cataract in mannosidosis. *Birth Defects* 12:319, 1976.
33. SPRANGER J, GEHLER J, CANTZ M: The radiographic features of mannosidosis. *Radiology* 119:401, 1976.
34. YUNIS JJ, LEWANDOWSKI RC, SANFILIPPO SJ, TSAI MY, FONI I, BRUHL HH: Clinical manifestations of mannosidosis—A longitudinal study. *Am J Med* 61:841, 1976.
35. ARBISSER AI, MURPHREE AL, GARCIA CA, HOWELL RR: Ocular findings in mannosidosis. *Am J Ophthalmol* 82:465, 1976.
36. VIDGOFF J, LOVRIEN EW, BEALS RK, BUIST NRM: Mannosidosis in three brothers—A review of the literature. *Medicine (Baltimore)* 56:335, 1977.
37. KISTLER JP, LOTT IT, KOLODNY EH, FRIEDMAN RB, NERSASIAN R, SSHNUR J, MIHM MC, DVORAK AM, DICKERSIN R: Mannosidosis: New clinical presentation, enzyme studies, and carbohydrate analysis. *Arch Neurol* 34:45, 1977.
38. MILLA PJ, BLACK IE, PATRICK AD, HUGH-JONES K, OBERHOLZER V: Mannosidosis: Clinical and biochemical study. *Arch Dis Child* 52:937, 1977.
39. BACH G, KOHN G, LASCH EE, EL MASSRI M, ORNOY A, SEKELES E, LEGUM C, COHEN MM: A new variant of mannosidosis with increased residual enzymatic activity and mild clinical manifestation. *Pediatr Res* 12:1010, 1978.
40. GORDON BA, CARSON R, HAUST MD: Unusual clinical and ultrastructural features in a boy with biochemically typical mannosidosis. *Acta Pediatr Scand* 69:787, 1980.
41. MITCHELL ML, ERICKSON RP, SCHMID D, HIEBER V, POZNANSKI AK, HICKS SP: Mannosidosis: Two brothers with different degrees of disease severity. *Clin Genet* 20:191, 1981.
42. AUTIO S, LOUHIMO T, HELENIUS M: The clinical course of mannosidosis. *Ann Clin Res* 14:93, 1982.
43. PATTON MA, BARNES IC, YOUNG ID, HARPER PS, PENNOCK CA: Mannosidosis in two brothers: Prolonged survival in the severe phenotype. *Clin Genet* 22:284, 1982.
44. MONTGOMERY TR, THOMAS GH, VALLE DL: Mannosidosis in an adult. *Johns Hopkins Med J* 151:113, 1982.

45. WEISS SW, KELLY WD: Bilateral destructive synovitis associated with alpha mannosidase deficiency. *Am J Surg Pathol* 7:487, 1983.

46. WARNER TG, MOCK AK, NYHAN WL, O'BRIEN JS: α-mannosidosis: Analysis of urinary oligosaccharides with high performance liquid chromatography and diagnosis of a case with unusually mild presentation. *Clin Genet* 25:248, 1984.

47. KAWAI H, NISHINO H, NISHIDA Y, YONEDA K, YOSHIDA Y, INUI T, MASUDA K, SAITO S: Skeletal muscle pathology of mannosidosis in two siblings with spastic paraplegia. *Acta Neuropathol (Berl)* 68:201, 1985.

48. QUIE PG, CATES KL: Clinical conditions associated with defective polymorphonuclear leukocyte chemotaxis. *Am J Pathol* 88:711, 1977.

49. LETSON RD, DESNICK RJ: Punctate lenticular opacities in type II mannosidosis. *Am J Ophthalmol* 85:218, 1978.

50. HALPERIN JL, LANDIS DMD, WEINSTEIN LA, LOTT IT, KOLODNY EH: Communicating hydrocephalus and lysosomal inclusions in mannosidosis. *Arch Neurol* 41:777, 1984.

51. PRESS OW, FINGERT H, LOTT IT, DICKERSIN CR: Pancytopenia in mannosidosis. *Arch Intern Med* 143:1268, 1983.

52. NOLL RB, KULKARNI R, NETZLOFF ML: Development in patients with mannosidosis. *Arch Neurol* 43:157, 1986.

53. MEHTA J, DESNICK RJ: Abbreviated PR interval in mannosidosis. *J Pediatr* 92:599, 1978.

54. MONUS Z, KONYAR E, SZABO L: Histomorphologic and histochemical investigations in mannosidosis. *Virchows Arch (B)* 26:159, 1977.

55. SUNG JH, HAYANO M, DESNICK RJ: Mannosidosis: Pathology of the nervous system. *J Neuropathol Exp Neurol* 36:807, 1977.

56. ÖCKERMAN P-A: Mannosidosis: Isolation of oligosaccharide storage material from brain. *J Pediatr* 75:360, 1969.

57. NORDÉN NE, LUNDBLAD A, SVENSON S, AUTIO S: Characterization of two mannose-containing oligosaccharides isolated from the urine of patients with mannosidosis. *Biochemistry* 13:871, 1974.

58. STRECKER G, FOURNET B, BOUQUELET S, MONTREUIL J, DHONDT JL, FARARIAUX JP: Étude chimique des mannosides urinaires excretes au cours de la mannosidose. *Biochimie* 58:579, 1976.

59. YAMASHITA K, TACHIBANA Y, MIHARA K, OKADA S, YABUUCHI H, KOBATA A: Urinary oligosaccharides of mannosidosis. *J Biol Chem* 255:5126, 1979.

60. MATSUURA F, NUNEZ HA, GRABOWSKI GA, SWEELEY CC: Structural studies of urinary oligosaccharides from patients with mannosidosis. *Arch Biochem Biophys* 207:337, 1981.

61. JARDIN I, MATSUURA F, SWEELEY CC: Electron ionization mass spectra of reduced and parmethylated urinary oligosaccharides from patients with mannosidosis. *Biomed Mass Spectrom* 11:562, 1984.

62. ABRAHAM D, BLAKEMORE WF, JOLLY RD, SIDEBOTHAM R, WINCHESTER B: The catabolism of mammalian glycoproteins. *Biochem J* 215:573, 1973.

63. TOBAS I, KORNFELD S: Purification and characterization of a rat liver Golgi α-mannosidase capable of processing asparagine-linked oligosaccharides. *J Biol Chem* 254:11655, 1979.

64. OPHEIM DJ, TOUSTER O: Lysosomal α-D-mannosidase of rat liver. *J Biol Chem* 253:1017, 1978.

65. TAYLOR HA, THOMAS GH, AYLSWORTH A, STEVENSON RE, REYNOLDS LW: Mannosidosis: Deficiency of a specific α-mannosidase component in cultured fibroblasts. *Clin Chim Acta* 59:93, 1975.

66. BEAUDET AL, NICHOLS BL: Residual altered α-mannosidase in human mannosidosis. *Biochem Biophys Res Commun* 68:292, 1976.

67. POENARU L, MIRANDA C, DREYFUS J-C: Residual mannosidase activity in human mannosidosis. Characterization of the mutant enzyme. *Am J Hum Genet* 32:354, 1980.

68. BURDITT L, CHOTAI K, HALLEY D, WINCHESTER B: Comparison of the residual acidic α-D-mannosidase in three cases of mannosidosis. *Clin Chim Acta* 104:201, 1980.

69. TSVETKOVA IV, ROSENFELD EL, PRIGOZINA IG: An unusual case of mannosidosis with severe deficiency of acid mannosidase in leukocytes and high residual enzymatic activity in skin fibroblasts. *Clin Chim Acta* 107:37, 1980.

70. HULTBERG B, MASSON PK: Activation of residual acidic α-mannosidase activity in mannosidosis tissues by metal ions. *Biochem Biophys Res Commun* 67:1473, 1980.

71. MERSMANN G, BUDDECKE E: Evidence for material from mannosidase fibroblasts crossreacting with anti-acidic α-mannosidase antibodies. *FEBS Lett* 73:123, 1977.

72. BURDITT LJ, CHOTAI KA, WINCHESTER BG: Evidence that the mutant enzyme in fibroblasts of a patient with mannosidosis does not crossreact with antiserum raised against normal acidic α-mannosidase. *FEBS Lett* 91:186, 1978.

73. HULTBERG B, MASSON PK: Normal extracellular excretions of acidic α-mannosidase activity by mannosidosis fibroblast cultures. *Biochim Biophys Acta* 481:573, 1977.

74. HALLEY DJJ, WINCHESTER BG, BURDITT LJ, D'AZZO A, ROBINSON D, GALJAARD H: Comparison of the α-mannosidase in fibroblast cultures from patients with mannosidosis and mucolipidosis II and from controls. *Biochem J* 187:541, 1980.

75. BEN-YOSEPH Y, DEFRANCO CL, CHARROW J, HAHN LC, NADLER HL: Apparently normal extracellular acidic α-mannosidase in fibroblast cultures from patients with mannosidosis. *Am J Hum Genet* 34:100, 1982.

76. POHLMANN R, HASILIK A, CHENG S, PEMBLE S, WINCHESTER B, VON FIGURA K: Synthesis of lysosomal α-mannosidase in normal and mannosidosis fibroblasts. *Biochem Biophys Res Commun* 115:1083, 1983.

77. CHAMPION MJ, SHOMS TB: Mannosidosis: Assignment of the lysosomal α-Mannosidase B gene to chromosome 19 in man. *Proc Natl Acad Sci USA* 74:2968, 1977.

78. INGRAM PH, BRUNS GAP, REGINA VM, EISENMAN RE, GERALD PS: Expression of α-D-mannosidase in man-hamster somatic cell hybrids. *Biochem Genet* 15:455, 1977.

79. BROOK JD, SHAW DJ, MEREDITH L, BRUNS GAP, HARPER PS: Localization of genetic markers and orientation of the linkage group of chromosome 19. *Hum Genet* 68:282, 1984.

80. MARTINVIK F, ELLENBOGEN A, HIRSCHHORN K, HIRSCHHORN R: Further localization of the genes for human acid alpha glucosidase (GAA), pepidase D (PEPD) and α-mannosidase B (MANB) by somatic cell hybridization. *Hum Genet* 69:109, 1985.

81. SHAW DJ, BROOK JD, MEREDITH AL, HARLEY HG, SARFARAZ M, HARPER PS: Gene mapping and chromosome 19. *J Med Genet* 23:2, 1986.

82. NORDÉN NE, LUNDBLAD A: A mannose-containing trisaccharide isolated from urines of three patients with mannosidosis. *J Biol Chem* 248:6210, 1973.

83. SEWELL AC: An improved thin-layer chromatographic method for urinary oligosaccharide screening. *Clin Chim Acta* 92:411, 1979.

84. SEWELL AC: Urinary oligosaccharide excretion in disorders of glycolipid, glycoprotein, and glycogen metabolism. *Eur J Pediatr* 134:183, 1980.

85. SEWELL AC: Simple laboratory determination of excess oligosacchariduria. *Clin Chem* 27:243, 1981.

86. HOLMES EW, O'BRIEN JS: Separation of glycoprotein-derived oligosaccharides by thin-layer chromatography. *Anal Biochem* 93:167, 1979.

87. ALROY J, ORGAD U, UCCI AA, PEREIRA MEA: Identification of glycoprotein storage diseases by lectins. *J Histochem Cytochem* 32:1280, 1984.

88. MAIRE I, ZABOT MT, MATHIEU M, COTTE J: Mannosidosis: Tissue culture studies in relation to prenatal diagnosis. *J Inherited Metab Dis* 1:19, 1978.

89. POENARU L, GIRARD S, THEPOT F, MADELENAT P, HURAUX-RENDU C, VINET M-C, DREYFUS J-C: Antenatal diagnosis in three pregnancies at risk for mannosidosis. *Clin Genet* 16:428, 1979.

90. WHITTEM JM, WALKER D: "Neuronopathy" and "Pseudolipidosis" in Aberdeen Angus calves. *J Pathol Bacteriol* 74:281, 1957.

91. JOLLY RD, SLACK PM, WINTER PJ, MURPHY CE: Mannosidosis: Patterns of storage and urinary excretion of oligosaccharides in the bovine model. *Aust J Exp Biol Med Sci* 58:421, 1980.

92. DORLING PR: Lysosomal storage diseases in animals, in Dingle JT, Dean RT, Sly W (eds): *Lysosomes in Biology and Pathology.* Amsterdam, Elsevier, 1984, vol 7, p 347.

93. BURDITT LJ, CHOTAI K, HIRANI S, NUGENT PG, WINCHESTER BG, BLAKEMORE WF: Biochemical studies on a case of feline mannosidosis. *Biochem J* 189:467, 1980.

94. WALKLEY SU, BLAKEMORE WF, PURPURA DP: Alterations in neuronomorphology in feline mannosidosis. A Golgi study. *Acta Neuropathol* 53:75, 1981.

95. VANDEVELDE M, FAUKHAUSER R, BICHSEL P, WEISMANN V, HERSCHKOWITZ N: Hereditary neurovisceral mannosidosis associated with α-mannosidase deficiency in a family of Persian cats. *Acta Neuropathol* 58:64, 1982.

96. DORLING PR, HUXTABLE CR, VOGEL P: Lysosomal storage in Swainsona SPP toxicosis: An induced mannosidosis. *Neuropathol Appl Neurobiol* 4:285, 1978.

97. DURAND P, GATTI R, BORRONE C, COSTANTINO G, CAVALIER S, FILOCAMO M, ROMEO G: Detection of carriers and prenatal diagnosis for fucosidosis in Calabria. *Hum Genet* 51:195, 1979.

98. DURAN P, BORRONE CX, DELLA CELLA G: Fucosidosis. *J Pediatr* 75:665, 1969.

99. LOEB H, TONDEUR M, JONNIAUX G, MOCKEL-POHL S, VAMOS-HURWITZ E: Biochemical and ultrastructural studies in a case of mucopolysaccharidosis "F" (fucosidosis). *Helv Paediatr Acta* 24:519, 1969.

100. PATEL V, WATANABE I, ZEMAN W: Deficiency of α-L-fucosidase. *Science* 176:426, 1972.

101. FREITAG F, KUCHEMANN K, BLUMCKE S: Hepatic ultrastructure in fucosidosis. *Virchows Arch (B)* 7:99, 1971.

102. ZIELKE K, OKADA S, O'BRIEN JS: Fucosidosis: Diagnosis by serum assay of α-L-fucosidase. *J Lab Clin Med* 79:164, 1972.

103. MATSUDA I, ARASHIMA S, ANAKURA M, EGE A, HAYATA I: Fucosidosis. *Tohoku J Exp Med* 109:41, 1973.

104. MATSUDA I, ARASHIMA S, OKA Y, MITSUYAMA T, ARIGA S, IKEUCHI T, ICHIDA T: Prenatal diagnosis of fucosidosis. *Clin Chim Acta* 63:55, 1975.

105. BORRONE E, GATTI R, TRIAS X, DURAND P: Fucosidosis: Clinical, biochemical, immunologic, and genetic studies in two new cases. *J Pediatr* 84:727, 1974.

106. KOUSSEFF BG, BERATIS NG, DANESINO C, HIRSCHHORN K: Genetic heterogeneity in fucosidosis. *Lancet* 2:1387, 1973.

107. KOUSSEFF BG, BERATIS NG, STRAUSS L, BRILL PW, ROSENFIELD RE, KAPLAN B, HIRSCHHORN K: Fucosidosis type 2. *Pediatrics* 57:205, 1976.

108. NG WG, DONNELL GN, KOCH R, BERGREN WR: Biochemical and genetic studies of plasma and leukocyte α-L-fucosidase. *Am J Hum Genet* 28:42, 1976.

109. TACONIS WK, VAN WIECHEN PJ, VAN GEMUND JJ: Radiological findings in a case of type II fucosidosis: A case report. *Radiol Clin (Basel)* 45:258, 1976.

110. LIBERT J, VAN HOOF F, TONDEUR M: Fucosidosis: Ultrastructural study of conjunctiva and skin and enzyme analysis of tears. *Invest Ophthalmol* 15:626, 1976.

111. POENARU L, DREYFUS J-C, BOUE J, NICOLESCO H, RAVISE N, BAMBERGER J: Prenatal diagnosis of fucosidosis. *Clin Genet* 10:260, 1976.

112. MacPHEE GB, LOGAN RW: Fucosidosis in a native-born Briton. *J Clin Pathol* 30:278, 1977.

113. SNYDER RD, CARLOW TJ, LEDMAN J, WENGER DA: Ocular findings in fucosidosis. *Birth Defects* 12(3):241, 1976.

114. TROOST J, STAAL GEJ, WILLEMSE J, VAN DER HEIJDEN MCM: Fucosidosis: 1. Clinical and enzymological studies. *Neuropaediatrie* 8:155, 1977.

115. ROMEO G, BORRONE C, GATTI R, DURAND P: Fucosidosis in Calabria: Founder effect or high gene frequency? *Lancet* 1:368, 1977.

116. GIOVANNINI M, RIVA E, BELUFFI G, PEREGO O: Fucosidosis: Description of a clinical case. *Minerva Pediatr* 30:1307, 1978.

117. LARBRISSEAU A, BROUCHU J, JASMIN G: Fucosidose de type 1: Étude anatomique. *Arch Fr Pediatr* 36:1013, 1979.

118. SCHOONDEWALDT HC, LAMERS KJB, KLEIJNEN FM, VAN DEN BERG CJMG, DE BRUYN CHMM: Two patients with an unusual form of type II fucosidosis. *Clin Genet* 18:348, 1980.

119. ALHADEFF JA, ANDRES SMITH GL, O'BRIEN JS: Biochemical studies on an unusual case of fucosidosis. *Clin Genet* 14:235, 1978.

120. LEE GA, DONNELL GN, GWINN JL: Radiographic features of fucosidosis. *Pediatr Radiol* 5:204, 1977.

121. SOVIK O, LIE SO, FLUGE G, VAN HOOF F: Fucosidosis: Severe phenotype with survival to adult age. *Eur J Pediatr* 135:211, 1980.

122. BOUDET CE, MAISONGROSSE G, ECHENNE B: A propos de deux nouveaux cas de fucosidose de type II.

123. CHRISTOMANOU H, BEYER D: Absence of α-fucosidase activity in two sisters showing a different phenotype. *Eur J Pediatr* 140:27, 1983.

124. IKEDA S, KONDO K, OGUCHI K, YANAGISAWA N, HORIGOME R, MURATA F: Adult fucosidosis: Histochemical and ultrastructural studies of rectal mucosa biopsy. *Neurology* 34:561, 1984.

125. BLITZER MG, SUTTON M, MILLER JB, SHAPIRA E: Brief clinical report: A thermolabile variant of α-L-fucosidase—clinical and laboratory findings. *Am J Med Genet* 20:535, 1985.

126. SCHAFER IA, POWELL DW, SULLIVAN JC: Lysosomal bone disease. *Pediatr Res* 5:391, 1971.

127. EPINETTE WW, NORINS AL, DREW AL: Angiokeratoma corporis diffusum with α-L-fucosidase deficiency. *Arch Dermatol* 107:754, 1973.

128. KORNFELD M, SNYDER RD, WENGER DA: Fucosidosis with angiokeratoma: Electron microscopic changes in the skin. *Arch Pathol Lab Med* 101:478, 1977.

129. SMITH EB, GRAHAM JL, LEDMAN JA, SNYDER RD: Fucosidosis. *Cutis* 19:195, 1977.

130. DVORETZKY I, FISHER BK: Fucosidosis. *Int J Dermatol* 18:213, 1979.

131. PRINDIVILLE DE, STERN D: Oral lesions in fucosidosis. *J Oral Surg* 34:603, 1976.

132. SNODGRASS MB: Ocular findings in a case of fucosidosis. *Brit J Ophthalmol* 60:508, 1976.

133. BRILL PW, BERATIS NG, KOUSSEFF BG, HIRSCHHORN K: Roentgenographic findings in fucosidosis type 2. *Am J Roentgenol* 124:75, 1975.

134. DAWSON G, SPRANGER JW: Fucosidosis: A glycosphingolipidosis. *N Engl J Med* 285:122, 1971.

135. TSAY GC, DAWSON G: Oligosaccharide storage in brains from patients with fucosidosis, G$_{M1}$-gangliosidosis and G$_{M2}$-gangliosidosis (Sandhoff's disease) *J Neurochem* 27:733, 1976.

136. TSAY GC, DAWSON G, SUNG S-SJ: Structure of the accumulating oligosaccharide in fucosidosis. *J Biol Chem* 251:5852, 1976.

137. NISHIGAKI M, YAMASHITA K, MATSUDA I, ARASHIMA S, KOBATA A: Urinary oligosaccharides of fucosidosis: Evidence of the occurrence of X-antigenic

138. STRECKER G, FOURNET B, MONTREUIL J, DORLAND L, HAVERKAMP J, VLIEGENTHART JFG, DUBESSET D: Structure of the three major fucosylglycosasparagines accumulating in the urine of a patient with fucosidosis. *Biochemie* 60:725, 1978.

139. NG YING, KIN NMK, WOLFE LS: Urinary excretion of a novel hexasaccharide and a glycopeptide analogue in fucosidosis. *Biochem Biophys Res Commun* 88:696, 1979.

140. LUNDBLAD A, LUNDSTEN J, NORDEN NE, SJOBLAD S, SVENSSON S, OCKERMAN P-A, GEHLHOFF M: Urinary abnormalities in fucosidosis: Characterization of a disaccharide and two glycoasparagines. *Eur J Biochem* 83:513, 1978.

141. YAMASHITA K, TACHIBANA Y, TAKADA S, MATSUDA I, ARASHIMA S, KOBATA A: Urinary glycopeptides of fucosidosis. *J Biol Chem* 254:4820, 1979.

142. NG YING, KIN NMK: Comparison of the urinary glycoconjugates excreted by patients with type I and type II fucosidosis. *Clin Chem* 33:44, 1987.

143. GREILING H, STUHLSATZ HW, CANTZ M, GEHLER J: Increased urinary excretion of keratan sulfate in fucosidosis. *J Clin Chem Clin Biochem* 16:329, 1978.

144. STAAL GEJ, VAN DER HEIJDEN MCM, TROOST J, MOES M, BORST-EILERS E: Fucosidosis and Lewis substances. *Clin Chim Acta* 76:155, 1977.

145. CHIEN S-F, DAWSON G: Purification and properties of two forms of human α-L-fucosidase. *Biochim Biophys Acta* 614:476, 1980.

146. ALHADEFF JA, ANDREWS-SMITH GL: Subunit composition of human liver α-L-fucosidase. *Biochem J* 177:753, 1979.

147. FUKUSHIMA H, DEWET JR, O'BRIEN JS: Molecular cloning of a cDNA for human α-L-fucosidase. *Proc Natl Acad Sci USA* 82:1262, 1985.

148. WHITE WJ, SCHRAY KJ, LEGLER G, ALHADEFF JA: Further studies on the catalytic mechanism of human liver α-L-fucosidase. *Biochim Biophys Acta* 912:132, 1987.

149. JOHNSON K, DAWSON G: Molecular defect in processing α-fucosidase in fucosidase. *Biochem Biophys Res Commun* 133:90, 1985.

150. ANDREWS-SMITH GL, ALHADEFF JA: Radioimmunoassay determination of decreased amounts of α-L-fucosidase in fucosidosis. *Biochim Biophys Acta* 715:90, 1982.

151. TURNER VS, TUNRER BM, KUCHERLAPATI R, RUDDLE FH, HIRSHCHHORN K: Assignment of the human α-L-fucosidase gene locus to chromosome 1 by use of a clone panel. *Birth Defects* 12 (7):238, 1976.

152. CORNEY RL, FISHER PJL, COOK J, NOADES J, ROBSON EB: Linkage between α-fucosidase and the rhesus blood group. *Ann Hum Genet* 40:403, 1977.

153. CARRITT B, KING J, WELCH HM: Gene order and localization of enzyme loci on the short arm of chromosome 1. *Ann Hum Genet* 46:329, 1982.

154. TURNER BM, TURNER VS, BERATIS NG, HIRSCHHORN K: Polymorphism of human α-fucosidase. *Am J Hum Genet* 27:651, 1975.

155. TURNER BM, BERATIS NG, TURNER VS, HIRSCHHORN K: Silent allele as genetic basis of fucosidosis. *Nature* 257:391, 1975.

156. FOWLER ML, NAKAI H, BYERS MG, FUKUSHIMA H, EDDY RL, HENRY WM, HALEY LL, O'BRIEN JS, SHOWS TB: Chromosome 1 localization of the human α-L-fucosidase structural gene with a homologous site on chromosome 2. *Cytogenet Cell Genet* 43:103, 1986.

157. DARBY JK, JOHNSEN J, NAKASHIMA P, WILLEMS PJ, O'BRIEN JS, FOWLER ML, SHOWS TB, SHOOTER EM, CAVALLI-SFORZA LL: Pvu II RFLP at the human chromosome 1 α-L-fucosidase gene locus (FUCA 1). *Nucleic Acids Res* 14:9543, 1986.

158. EIBERG H, MOHR J, NIELSEN LS: Linkage of plasma α-L-fucosidase (FUCA2) and the plasminagen (PLG) system. *Clin Genet* 26:23, 1984.

159. MURRAY JC, SADLER E, EDDY RL, SHOWS TB, BUETOW KJ: Evidence for assignment of plasminogen (PLG) to chromosome 6, not chromosome 4. *Cytogenet Cell Genet* 40:709, 1985.

160. STRECKER G, FOURNET B, SPIK G, MONTREUIL J, DURAND P, TONDEUR M: Structure de 9 oligosaccharides et glycopeptides riches en fucose secretes dans l'urine de deux sujets atteints de fucosidose. *C R Acad Sci Paris D* 284:85, 1977.

161. MCLAREN J, NG WG: Radial and linear thin layer chromatographic procedures compared for screening urines to detect oligosaccharidoses. *Clin Chem* 25:1289, 1979.

162. SIMELL O, SIPILA I, AUTIO S: Extra heating of TLC plates detects two lysosomal storage diseases, aspartylglucosaminuria and fucosidosis, during routine urinary amino acid screening. *Clin Chim Acta* 133:227, 1983.

163. HENDERSON MJ, ALLEN JT, HOLTON JB, GOODALL R: Extra heating of amino acids. *Clin Chim Acta* 146:203, 1985.

164. ZIELKE K, VEATH ML, O'BRIEN JS: Fucosidosis: Deficiency of α-L-fucosidase in cultured skin fibroblasts. *J Exp Med* 136:197, 1972.

165. WOOD S: A sensitive fluorometric assay for α-L-fucosidase. *Clin Chim Acta* 58:251, 1975.

166. WOOD S: Human α-L-fucosidase: A common polymorphic variant for low

serum enzyme activity, studies of serum and leukocyte enzyme. _Hum Hered_ 29:226, 1979.

167. WOOD S: Plasma α-L-fucosidase: Presence of a low activity in some normal individuals. _J Lab Clin Med_ 88:469, 1976.

168. DICIOCCIO RA, BARLOW JJ, MATTA KL: Specific activity of α-L-fucosidase in sera with phenotypes of either low, intermediate, or high total enzyme activity and in a fucosidosis serum. _Biochem Genet_ 24:115, 1986.

169. BUTTERWORTH J, GUY GJ: α-L-fucosidase of human skin fibroblasts and amniotic fluid cells in tissue culture. _Clin Genet_ 12:297, 1977.

170. KELLY WR, CLAGUE AE, BARNS RJ, BATE MJ, MacKAY BM: Canine α-L-fucosidosis: A storage disease of springer spaniels. _Acta Neuropathol (Berl)_ 60:9, 1983.

171. HARTLEY WJ, CANFIELD PJ, DONNELLY TM: A suspected new canine storage disease. _Acta Neuropathol (Berl)_ 56:225, 1982.

172. FRIEND SCE, BARR SC, EMBURY D: Fucosidosis in an English springer spaniel presenting as a malabsorption syndrome. _Aust Vet J_ 62:415, 1986.

173. HEALY PJ, FARROW BRH, NICHOLAS FW, HEDBERG K, RATCLIFFE R: Canine fucosidosis: A biochemical and genetic investigation. _Res Vet Sci_ 36:354, 1984.

174. ABRAHAM D, BLAKEMORE WF, DELL A, HERRTAGE ME, JONES J, LITTLEWOOD JT, OATES J, PALMER AC, SIDEBOTHAM R, WINCHESTER B: The enzyme defect and storage products in canine fucosidosis. _Biochem J_ 221:25, 1984.

175. TAYLOR RM, FARROW BRH, STEWART GJ, HEALY PJ: Enzyme replacement in nervous tissue after allogenic bone-marrow transplantation for fucosidosis in dogs. _Lancet_ 2:772, 1986.

176. TAYLOR RM, FARROW BR, STEWART GJ: Correction of enzyme deficiency by allogenic bone-marrow transplantation following total lymphoid irradation in dogs with lysosomal storage disease (fucosidosis). _Transplant Proc_ 18:326, 1986.

177. LOWDEN JA, O'BRIEN JS: Sialidosis: A review of human neuraminidase deficiency. _Am J Hum Genet_ 31:1, 1979.

178. SPRANGER J, CANTZ M: Mucolipidosis I, the cherry-red spot-myoclonus syndrome and neuraminidase deficiency. _Birth Defects_ 14(6B):105, 1978.

179. DURAND P, GATTI R, CAVALIERI S, BORRONE C, TOUNDEUR M, MICHALSKI J-C, STRECKER G: Sialidosis (mucolipidosis I). _Helv Paediatr Acta_ 32:391, 1977.

180. O'BRIEN JS: Neuraminidase deficiency in the cherry red spot-myoclonus syndrome. _Biochem Biophys Res Commun_ 79:1136, 1977.

181. RAPIN I, GOLDFISHER S, KATZMAN R, ENGEL J, O'BRIEN JS: The cherry red spot-myoclonus syndrome. _Ann Neurol_ 3:234, 1978.

182. THOMAS GH, TIPTON RE, CH'IEN LT, REYNOLDS LW, MILLER CS: Sialidase (α-N-acetyl neuraminidase) deficiency: The enzyme defect in an adult with macular cherry-red spots and myoclonus without dementia. _Clin Genet_ 13:369, 1978.

183. GOLDSTEIN ML, KOLODNY EH, GASCON GG, GILLES FH: Macular cherry-red spot, myoclonic epilepsy, and neurovisceral storage in a 17 year old girl. _Trans Am Neurol Assoc_ 99:110, 1974.

184. THOMAS PK, ABRAMS JD, SWALLOW D, STEWART G: Sialidosis type I: Cherry red spots-myoclonus syndrome with sialidase deficiency and altered electrophoretic mobilities of some enzymes known to be glycoproteins. _J Neurol Neurosurg Psychiatry_ 42:873, 1979.

185. STEINMAN L, THARP BR, DORFMAN LJ, FORNO LS, SOGG RL, KELTS KA, O'BRIEN JS: Peripheral neuropathy in the cherry-red spot-myoclonus syndrome (sialidosis type I). _Ann Neurol_ 7:450, 1980.

186. FEDERICO A, CECIO A, APPONI BATTINI G, MICHALSKI JC, STRECKER G, GUAZZI GC: Macular cherry-red spot and myoclonus syndrome. _J Neurol Sci_ 48:157, 1980.

187. HARZER K, CANTZ M, SEWELL AC, DHARESHWARM SS, ROGGENDORF W, HECKL RW, SCHOFER O, THUMLER R, PEIFFER J, SCHLOTE W: Normomorphic sialidosis in two female adults with severe neurologic disease and without sialyl oligosacchariduria. _Hum Genet_ 74:209, 1986.

188. TILL JS, ROACH ES, BURTON BK: Sialidosis (neuraminidase deficiency) types I and II: Neuro-ophthalmic manifestations. _J Clin Neuro Ophthalmol_ 7:40, 1987.

189. RAPIN I: Myoclonus in neuronal storage and Lafora diseases. _Adv Neurol_ 43:65, 1986.

190. KELLY TE, GRAETZ G: Isolated acid neuraminidase deficiency: A distinct lysosomal storage disease. _Am J Med Genet_ 1:31, 1977.

191. BERARD M, TOGA M, BERNARD R, DUBOIS D, MARIANI R, HASSOUN J: Pathologic findings in one case of neuronal and mesenchymal storage disease: Its relationship to lipidoses and to mucopolysaccharidoses. _Pathol Eur_ 3:172, 1968.

192. MAROTEAUX P, POISSONNIER M, TONDEUR M, STRECKER G, LEMONNIER M: Sialidose par deficit en alpha (2-6) neuraminidase sans atteinte neurologique. _Arch Fr Pediatr_ 35:280, 1978.

193. MAROTEAUX P, HUMBEL R, STRECKER G, MICHALSKI J-C, MANDE R: Un nouveau type de sialidose avec atteinte renale: La nephrosialidose, 1.

Étude clinique, radiologique et nosologique. _Arch Fr Pediatr_ 35:819, 1978.

194. WINTER RM, SWALLOW DM, BARAITSER M, PURKISS P: Sialidosis type 2 (acid neuraminidase deficiency): Clinical and biochemical features of a further case. _Clin Genet_ 18:203, 1980.

195. OOHIRA T, NAGATA N, AKABOSHI I, MATSUDA I, NAITO S: The infantile form of sialidosis type II associated with congenital adrenal hyperplasia: Possible linkage between HLA and the neuraminidase deficiency gene. _Hum Genet_ 70:341, 1985.

196. LAVER J, FRIED K, BEER SI, IANCU TC, HEYMAN E, BACH G, ZEIGLER M: Infantile lethal neuraminidase deficiency (sialidosis). _Clin Genet_ 23:97, 1983.

197. YOUNG ID, YOUNG EP, MOSSMAN J, FIELDER AR, MOORE JR: Neuraminidase deficiency: Case report and review of the phenotype. _J Med Genet_ 24:283, 1987.

198. KELLY TE, BARTOSHESKY L, HARRIS DJ, McCAULEY RGK, FEINGOLD M, SCHOTT G: Mucolipidosis I (acid neuraminidase deficiency). _Am J Dis Child_ 135:703, 1981.

199. LOUIS JJ, MAIRE I, HERMIER M, NICOLAS A, GUIBAUD P: Une observation de mucolipidose de type I par deficit primaire en alpha D neuraminidase. _J Genet Hum_ 31:79, 1983.

200. AYLSWORTH AS, THOMAS GH, HOOD JL, MALOUF N, LIBERT J: A severe infantile sialidosis: Clinical, biochemical, and microscopic features. _J Pediatr_ 96:662, 1980.

201. JOHNSON WG, THOMAS GH, MIRANDA AF, DRISCOLL JM, WIGGER JH, YEH MN, SCHWARTZ RC, COHEN CS, BERDON WE, KOENIGSBERGER MR: Congenital sialidosis: Biochemical studies: Clinical spectrum in four sibs; two successful prenatal diagnoses. _Am J Hum Genet_ 32:43A, 1980.

202. BECK M, BENDER SW, REITER H-L, OTTO W, BASSLER R, DANCYGIER H, GEHLER J: Neuraminidase deficiency presenting as non-immune hydrops fetalis. _Eur J Pediatr_ 143:135, 1984.

203. MAROTEAUX P, HUMBEL R, STRECKER G, MICHALSKI J-C, MANDE R: Un nouveau type de sialidose avec atteinte renale: La nephrosialidose, 1. étude clinique, radiologique et nosologique. _Arch Fr Pediatr_ 35:819, 1978.

204. KING M, COCKBURN F, MacPHEE GB, LOGAN RW: Infantile type 2 sialidosis in a Pakistani family—A clinical and biochemical study. _J Inherited Metab Dis_ 7:91, 1984.

205. STRECKER G, PEERS M-C, MICHALSKI J-C, HONDI-ASSAH T, FOURNET B, SPIK G, MONTREUIL J, FARRIAUX J-P, MARTEAUX P, DURAN P: Structure of nine sialyl-oligosaccharides accumulated in urine of eleven patients with three different types of sialidosis. _Eur J Biochem_ 75:391, 1977.

206. DORLAND L, HAVERKAMP J, VLIEGENTHART JFG, STRECKER G, MICHALSKI J-C, FOURNET B, SPIK G, MONTREUIL J: 360 MHz^{1}H nuclear-magnetic resonance spectroscopy of sialyloligosaccharides from patients with sialidosis (mucolipidosis I and II). _Eur J Biochem_ 87:323, 1978.

207. STRECKER G, MICHALSKI JC: Biochemical basis of six different types of sialidosis. _FEBS Lett_ 85:20, 1978.

208. KURIYAMA M, ARIGA T, ANDO S, SUZUKI M, YAMADA T, MIYATAKE T: Four positional isomers of sialyloligosaccharides isolated from the urine of a patient with sialidosis. _J Biol Chem_ 256:12316, 1981.

209. LECAT D, LEMONNIER M, DERAPPE C, LHERMITTE M, VAN HALBEEK H, DORLAND L, VLIEGENTHART JFG: The structure of sialyl-glyco-peptides of the O-glycosidic type, isolated from sialidosis (mucolipidosis I) urine. _Eur J Biochem_ 140:415, 1984.

210. SCOCCA J, THOMAS GH, REYNOLDS LW, MILLER CS: Accumulation of [^{3}H] sialyl-conjugates in sialidosis (sialidase deficient) fibroblasts cultured in the presence of [^{3}H] α-N-acetyl-mannosamine. _J Inherited Metab Dis_ 9:79, 1986.

211. THOMAS GH, SCOCCA J, MILLER CS, REYNOLDS LW: Accumulation of N-acetylneuraminic acid (sialic acid) in human fibroblasts cultured in the presence of N-acetylmannosamine. _Biochim Biophys Acta_ 37:846, 1985.

212. SCOCCA JR, THOMAS GH, MILLER CS, REYNOLDS LW: Purification and characterization of sialic acid containing materials accumulated in cultured skin fibroblasts from a patient with type II sialidosis. _J Inherited Metab Dis_ 10:33, 1987.

213. FRISCH A, NEUFELD EF: A rapid and sensitive assay for neuraminidase: Application to cultured fibroblasts. _Anal Biochem_ 95:222, 1979.

214. CANTZ M: Sialidases, in Schauer R (ed): _Sialic Acids, Chemistry, Metabolism and Functions. Cell Biology Monographs_ 10. Vienna, Springer-Verlag, 1982, p 307.

215. CANTZ M, MESSER H: Oligosaccharide and ganglioside neuraminidase activities of mucolipidosis I (sialidosis) and mucolipidosis II (I-cell disease) fibroblasts. _Eur J Biochem_ 97:113, 1979.

216. WENGER DA, TARBY TJ, WHARTON C: Macular cherry-red spots and myoclonus with dementia: Coexistent neuraminidase and β-galactosidase deficiencies. _Biochem Biophys Res Commun_ 82:589, 1978.

217. MUELLER OT, HENRY WM, HALEY LL, BYERS MG, EDDY RL, SHOWS TB:

Sialidosis and galactosialidosis: Chromosomal assignment of two genes associated with neuraminidase deficiency disorders. *Proc Natl Acad Sci USA* 83:1817, 1985.

218. D'AZZO A, HOOGEVEEN A, REUSER AJJ, ROBINSON O, GALJAARD H: Molecular defect in combined β-galactosidase and neuraminidase deficiency in man. *Proc Natl Acad Sci USA* 79:4535, 1982.

219. WARNER TG, O'BRIEN JS: Synthesis of 2′-(4-methylumbelliferyl)-α-D-N-acetylneuraminic acid and detection of skin fibroblast neuraminidase in normal humans and in sialidosis. *Biochemistry* 18:2783, 1979.

220. THOMAS GH, REYNOLDS LW, MILLER CS: Characterization of neuraminidase activity of cultured human fibroblasts. *Biochem Biophys Acta* 568:39, 1979.

221. VERHEIJEN FW, PALMERI S, HOOGEVEEN AT, GALJAARD H: Human placental neuraminidase activation, stabilization and association with β-galactosidase and its "protective" protein. *Eur J Biochem* 149:315, 1985.

222. VERHEIJEN FW, JANSE HC, VAN DIGGELEN OP, BAKKER HD, LOONEN MCB, DURAND P, GALJAARD H: Two genetically different MU-NANA* neuraminidases in human leucocytes. *Biochem Biophys Res Commun* 117(2):135, 1983.

223. WOMACK JE, YAN DLS, POTIER M: Gene for neuraminidase activity on mouse chromosome 17 near H-2: Pleiotropic effects on multiple hydrolases. *Science* 212:63, 1981.

224. KURIYAMA M, ARIGA T, ANDO S, SUZUKI M, YAMADA T, MIYATAKE T, IGATA A: Two positional isomers of sialylheptasaccharides isolated from the urine of a patient with sialidosis. *J Biochem (Tokyo)* 98:1949, 1985.

225. BECK M, BENDER SW, REITER H-L, OTTO W, BASSLER R, DANCYGIER H, GEHLER J: Neuraminidase deficiency presenting as non-immune hydrops fetalis. *Eur J Pediatr* 143:135, 1984.

226. MYERS RW, LEE RT, LEE YC, THOMAS GH, REYNOLDS LW, UCHIDA Y: The synthesis of 4-methylumbelliferyl α-ketoside of N-acetyl-neuraminic acid and its use in a fluorometric assay for neuraminidase. *Anal Biochem* 101:166, 1980.

227. MUELLER OT, WENGER DA: Mucolipidosis I: Studies of sialidase activity and a prenatal diagnosis. *Clin Chim Acta* 109:313, 1981.

228. POTIER M, YAN LA, WOMACK E: Neuraminidase deficiency in the mouse. *FEBS Lett* 108:345, 1979.

229. MCKUSICK VA: *Mendelian Inheritance in Man*, 7th ed. Baltimore, Johns Hopkins University Press, 1986, p 1159.

230. AULA P, AUTIO S, RAIVIO K, NANTO V: Detection of heterozygotes for aspartylglucosaminuria (AGU) in cultured fibroblasts. *Humangenetik* 25:307, 1974.

231. BORUD O, TORP KH: Aspartylglycosaminuria in northern Norway. *Lancet* 1:1082, 1976.

232. BORUD O, STROMME JH, LIE SO, TORP KH: Aspartylglycosaminuria in northern Norway in eight patients: Clinical heterogeneity and variations with the diet. *J Inherited Metab Dis* 1:95, 1978.

233. ISENBERG JN, SHARP HL: Aspartylglucosaminuria: Psychomotor retardation masquerading as a mucopolysaccharidosis. *J Pediatr* 86:713, 1975.

234. HREIDARSSON S, THOMAS GH, VALLE DL, STEVENSON RE, TAYLOR H, MCCARTY J, COKER SB, GREEN WR: Aspartylglucosaminuria in the United States. *Clin Genet* 23:427, 1983.

235. GEHLER J, SEWELL AC, BECKER C, HARTMANN J, SPRANGER J: Clinical and biochemical delineation of aspartyl-glycosaminuria as observed in two members of an Italian family. *Helv Paediatr Acta* 36:179, 1981.

236. GEHLER J, SEWELL AC, BECKER C, SPRANGER J: Aspartylglycosaminuria in an Italian family: Clinical and biochemical characteristics. *J Inherited Metab Dis* 4:229, 1981.

237. MUSUMECI S, SALVATI A, SCHILLIRO G, SALVO G, DI DIO R, CAPRARI P: Homozygous NADH-methemoglobin reductase and aspartylglucosaminidase deficiencies in a moderately retarded Sicilian child. *Am J Med Genet* 19:643, 1984.

238. AUTIO S: Aspartylglycosaminuria: Analysis of thirty-four patients. *J Ment Defic Res Monogr Ser* 1:1, 1972.

239. ARSTILA AU, PALO J, HALTIA M, RIEKKINEN P, AUTIO S: Aspartylglucosaminuria I: Fine structural studies on liver, kidney and brain. *Acta Neuropathol (Berl)* 20:207, 1971.

240. ISENBERG JN, SHARP HL: Aspartylglucosaminuria: Unique biochemical and ultrastructural characteristics. *Hum Pathol* 7:469, 1976.

241. HALTIA M, PALO J, AUTIO S: Aspartylglucosaminuria: A generalized storage disease: Morphological and histochemical studies. *Acta Neuropathol (Berl)* 31:243, 1975.

242. AULA P, RAPOLA J, VONKOSKULL H, AMMALA P: Prenatal diagnosis and fetal pathology of aspartylglucosaminuria. *Am J Med Genet* 19:359, 1984.

243. MAURY CPJ, PALO J: N-Acetylglucosamine-asparagine levels in tissues of patients with aspartylglucosaminuria. *Clin Chim Acta* 108:293, 1980.

244. MAURY CPJ, HALTIA M, PALO J: Regional distribution of glycoasparagine storage material in the brain in aspartylglycosaminuria. *J Neurol Sci* 50:291, 1981.

245. MAURY CPJ: Quantitative determination of 4-N-2-acetamido-2-deoxy-β-D-glucopyranosyl-L-asparagine in the urine of patients with aspartylglycosaminuria by gas-liquid chromatography. *J Lab Clin Med* 93:718, 1979.

246. O'NEILL ROWLEY B, HAMILTON PB: Isolation of 2-acetamido-1-β-(L-β-aspartamido)-1,2-d: deoxy-D-glucose from normal human urine. *Clin Chem* 18:951, 1972.

247. MAURY CPJ: Urinary sialic acid levels in aspartylglycosaminuria. *Clin Chim Acta* 109:219, 1981.

248. DUGAL B, DUGAL R: 1-aspartamido-β-N-acetylglucosamine amidohydrolase purification, kinetics and its role in aspartylglucosaminuria. *J Mol Med* 3:7, 1978.

249. MCGOVERN MM, AULA P, DESNICK RJ: Purification and properties of human hepatic aspartylglucosaminidase. *J Biol Chem* 258:10743, 1983.

250. SOMER H, PALO J, SAVOLAINEN H, KNOTTINEN A: Studies on N-aspartyl-β-glucosaminidase in aspartylglucosaminuria. *Clin Chim Acta* 60:219, 1975.

250a. PELTONEN L, AULA P: Characterization of cDNA coding for human aspartylglucosaminidase (AGA). *Am J Hum Genet* 41:A233, 1987.

251. AULA P, ASTRIN JH, FRANKE U, DESNICK RJ: Assignment of the structural gene encoding human aspartylglycosaminidase to the long arm of chromosome 4 (4q21–4qter). *Am J Hum Genet* 36:1215, 1984.

252. MAURY CPJ: Aspartylglycosaminuria: An inborn error of glycoprotein catabolism. *J Inherited Metab Dis* 5:192, 1982.

253. POLLITT RJ, PRETTY KM: The glycoasparagines in urine of a patient with aspartylglycosaminuria. *Biochem J* 141:141, 1974.

254. HUMBEL R, MARCHAL C: Screening test for aspartylglycosaminuria. *J Pediatr* 84:456, 1974.

255. SUGAHARA K, NISHIMURA K, AULA P, YAMASHINA I: Enzymatic determination of urinary aspartylglycosylamine: A rapid and sensitive method to detect aspartylglycosylaminuria (AGA). *Clin Chim Acta* 72:265, 1976.

256. MALMQUIST J, HULTEN-NOSSLIN M-B, JEPPSSON J-O: Finger clubbing and aspartylglucosamine excretion in a laxative-abusing patient. *Postgrad Med J* 56:862, 1980.

257. WENGER DA, SUJANSKY E, FENNESSEY PV, THOMPSON JN: Human β-mannosidase deficiency. *N Engl J Med* 315:1201, 1986.

258. COOPER A, SARDHARWALLA IB, ROBERTS MM: Human β-mannosidase deficiency. *N Engl J Med* 315:1231, 1986.

259. JONES MZ, DAWSON G: Caprine β-mannosidosis: Inherited deficiency of β-D-mannosidase. *J Biol Chem* 256:5185, 1981.

260. WILLIAMS JC, BUTLER IJ, ROSENBERG HS, VERANI R, SCOTT CI, CONLEY SB: Progressive neurological deterioration and renal failure due to storage of glutamyl ribose-5-phosphate. *N Engl J Med* 311:152, 1984.

261. WILLIAMS JC, CHAMBERS JP, LIEHR JG: Glutamyl ribose-5-phosphate storage disease. A hereditary defect in the degradation of poly (ADP-ribosylated) proteins. *J Biol Chem* 259:1037, 1984.

262. WILLIAMS JC, VERANI R, ALCALA H, BUTLER IJ, ROSENBERG HS: Glutamyl ribose-5-phosphate storage disease: Nephrotic syndrome and cerebral atrophy. *Pediatr Pathol*, 5:277, 1986.

CHAPTER 64

ACID LIPASE DEFICIENCY:
Wolman Disease and Cholesteryl Ester Storage Disease

GERD SCHMITZ
GERD ASSMANN

1. Deficient activity on lysosomal acid lipase results in massive accumulation of cholesteryl esters and triglycerides in most tissues of the body. Both of these lipids are substrates for the enzyme, one of the major functions of which is the hydrolysis of cholesteryl esters in various lipoproteins as they are removed from plasma by tissues in the periphery. The deficiency state is expressed in two major phenotypes: Wolman disease and cholesteryl ester storage disease.

2. Wolman disease occurs in infancy and is nearly always fatal before the age of 1 year. Hepatosplenomegaly, steatorrhea, abdominal distension, other gastrointestinal symptoms, adrenal calcification demonstrable by x-rays, and failure to thrive are observed in the first weeks of life.

3. Cholesteryl ester storage disease can be more benign. It may not be detected until adulthood. Lipid deposition is widespread although hepatomegaly may be the only clinical abnormality. Hyperbetalipoproteinemia is common, and premature atherosclerosis may be severe. Adrenal calcification is rare.

4. Diagnosis of both disorders is based on the clinical picture combined with demonstration of acid lipase deficiency in cultured skin fibroblasts, lymphocytes, or other tissues. Both Wolman disease and cholesteryl ester storage disease are autosomal recessive disorders. The structural gene for the acid lipase enzyme is on chromosome 10. There is no specific therapy, but the suppression of cholesterol synthesis and apolipoprotein B production by HMG-CoA reductase inhibitors might be considered as a useful therapeutic principle.

Two diseases have been independently discovered in which prodigious amounts of cholesteryl esters and often triglycerides accumulate in lysosomes. Wolman disease is the more severe form. It is associated with hepatosplenomegaly and adrenal calcification and is nearly always fatal in the first year of life. Cholesteryl ester storage disease (CESD) is more benign, is usually compatible with survival to adulthood, and is very rarely associated with adrenal calcification.[1,2]

It appears that these disorders are allelic, involving mutations at loci controlling the activity of a hydrolase which cleaves cholesteryl esters and triglycerides under acidic conditions (Fig. 64-1). The enzyme has been variously called lysosomal acid lipase (EC 3.1.1.13), acid lipase, or acid esterase.

HISTORY

In 1956, Abramov, Schorr, and Wolman described an infant with abdominal distension, hepatosplenomegaly, and massive calcification of the adrenal glands.[3] In 1963, Wolman et al. reported two more affected sibs in this same family.[4] In the first report, Wolman and his colleagues[3] noted the accumulation of both cholesterol and triglycerides in the liver, adrenal glands, spleen, and lymph nodes. The disorder was first called "generalized xanthomatosis with calcified adrenals" or "primary familial xanthomatosis with adrenal calcification."[3-5] Later Crocker et al.[6] suggested the eponym *Wolman disease*. In retrospect, a patient described by Alexander in 1946[7] as having "Niemann-Pick disease" may have been the first with this disorder to appear in the literature.

About 40 examples of Wolman disease have been discovered. The clinical and morphologic findings of the individual patients are described in patient reports[3,4,6,8-50] and in previous editions of this book.[1,2] In patients with Wolman disease, the abnormality of lipid metabolism becomes clinically evident in the first weeks of life. The most important clinical features include hepatosplenomegaly, digestive difficulties, steatorrhea, and enlargement and calcification of the adrenal glands. The condition is usually fatal by the age of 6 months.

In 1961, Wolman et al. demonstrated that most of the accumulated cholesterol was in the esterified form.[5] Later studies repeatedly confirmed these observations. In 1969, Patrick and Lake[23] demonstrated that activity of an acid hydrolase catalyzing the hydrolysis of both cholesteryl esters and triglycerides was severely deficient in the liver and spleen of patients with Wolman disease. This has been confirmed in tissues,[29,51] including cultured fibroblasts[38,52-54] and leukocytes[37,50,55] of other patients. In 1976, Cortner et al. demonstrated that lysosomal acid lipase activity of circulating lymphocytes and cultured fibroblasts can be separated by cellogel electrophoresis into isoenzymes A and B. Both Wolman disease and CESD cells showed complete absence of the A isoenzyme.[38,56]

Brief published mention of CESD was first made by Fredrickson in 1963 in reference to a child with marked hyperli-

---

Nonstandard abbreviations used in this chapter are: ACAT = acyl-CoA:cholesterol acyltransferase; CESD = cholesteryl ester storage disease.

acid lipase deficiency

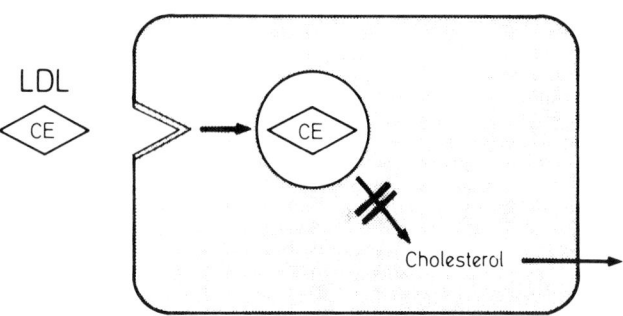

Fig. 64-1 Schematic representation of the hydrolytic site affected by the enzyme deficiency underlying the disorders described in this chapter.

pidemia, whose enlarged liver was found to contain 18 percent of its wet weight as cholesteryl esters. He called the disorder *hepatic cholesterol ester storage disorder.*[57] In 1967, Lageron et al.[59] and Infante et al.[60] reported a 43-year-old man with apparently the same disease under the name *polycorie cholésterolique de l'adulte.* He had been known to have had hepatomegaly since age 14. At about the same time, Schiff et al. reported a brother and sister with similar clinical, morphologic, and biochemical abnormalities.[61] Four of their five younger sibs also had hepatomegaly. Biopsy specimens of liver from three of these sibs were interpreted as showing minimal morphologic abnormalities, suggesting a milder expression of the same inherited defect. These authors pointed out the presence of minimal cirrhosis in the liver, in addition to the fat loading of all hepatocytes seen in the other cases.

The following year Partin and Schubert[62] described detailed studies of jejunal and duodenal biopsy specimens in the two most severely affected children of the kindred of Schiff et al.[61] The evidence they presented of cholesterol storage in the intestine was the first to indicate that the involvement of CESD extends beyond the liver. This concept has been substantiated by necropsy studies in three patients with CESD.[1,58,63] The less limited term *cholesterol (or cholesteryl) ester storage disease* proposed by Partin and Schubert has subsequently been used for the disorder. A total of 27 reported cases of this disease have been recognized (Table 64-1). As in Wolman disesae, the metabolic defect in CESD consists of severe deficiency in the activity of the acid cholesteryl ester hydrolase, or acid lipase, which catalyzes the hydrolysis of both cholesteryl esters and triglycerides (Tables 64-2 and 64-3).

The enzymatic defect has been demonstrated in several types of cells and tissues, including liver, spleen, lymph nodes, aorta, peripheral blood leukocytes, and cultured skin fibroblasts. More recently the defect has been related to the sequence of events involved in catabolism of cholesteryl esters entering the cell during removal of plasma low density lipoproteins[81,82] (see Chap. 48).

CLINICAL MANIFESTATIONS

Wolman Disease

Most of the patients with Wolman disease have had a remarkably similar clinical course. Increasing vomiting and diarrhea, hepatosplenomegaly, abdominal distension, anemia, and in-

anition are major clinical signs, and the child's general condition progresses rapidly downhill. Death usually occurs by age 3 to 6 months but has been protracted to as long as 14 months.[21]

The disease usually has its onset in the first weeks of life. In most cases, the abnormality first noticed by the parents is persistent and forceful vomiting associated with marked abdominal distension. Several patients have also had frequent and watery stools in the first few weeks of life.[18,21,26] In a few patients jaundice[4,6,10,33] or persistent low grade fever has been observed.[4,6]

Anemia usually appears by the sixth week and becomes more severe as the disease progresses; the hemoglobin may fall to 6 g/dl. Thrombocytopenia has not been observed. Vacuolization of lymphocytes has been noted repeatedly. The vacuoles are both intracytoplasmic and intranuclear. Lipid-laden histiocytes, or foam cells, have been observed in bone marrow aspirates as early as at 40 days of age. In the later stages of the illness, the marrow almost invariably contains large numbers of foam cells. Similar cells have been observed in the peripheral blood.[4] Acanthocytosis has been reported in one patient.[24] Plasma lipids are usually at the low end of the normal range.

Hepatosplenomegaly has been observed as early as the fourth day of life.[26] It is an invariable feature of the disease and may be of massive proportions.

A most striking feature of Wolman disease is calcification of the adrenal glands. This abnormality has been consistently demonstrated ante mortem by roentgenographic examination in all but four patients. The adrenals are markedly and symmetrically enlarged (up to 3.5 × 2.5 cm), and their normal pyramidal or semilunar shape is retained. They are extensively seeded with finely stippled or punctate calcific deposits. The enlarged adrenals may flatten the superior poles of the kidneys,[6] but they do not deform the caliceal system or interfere with renal function. More recently, with the use of computed tomography (Fig. 64-2), it has been shown that the density of the enlarged liver and the cortical calcification of the enlarged adrenals can be monitored with high sensitivity.[90]

Specific symptoms related to the central nervous system are uncommon in Wolman disease, but neurologic development is not normal. Typically alert and active at birth, the infants show a progressive mental deterioration within a few weeks after the onset of symptoms. Several case reports have noted that the optic fundi were normal and that a cherry-red spot was not present. In one patient a Babinski sign was elicited.[6] Konno et al. described a patient who had exaggerated tendon reflexes, ankle clonus, and opisthotonus.[10] Paralysis and convulsions have not been observed.

There are no specific routine laboratory observations that suggest the diagnosis. Liver function tests are frequently abnormal. Laboratory studies support the clinical observations of malabsorption and malnutrition. As determined by feeding ^{131}I-labeled triolein[24] or unlabeled fats,[26] there appears to be a significant impairment of fat absorption. ACTH-stimulation studies have indicated depressed adrenal responsiveness.[6,26] No gross abnormalities of the electroencephalogram have been observed in several patients.[6,10,14,24] Chromosomal analyses in two patients were normal.[10,41]

Cholesteryl Ester Storage Disease

The history and clinical course of the original patients affected with CESD are extensively discussed in previous editions of

Table 64-1 Patients with Cholesteryl Ester Storage Disease

Patient	Refs.	Sex	Age at detection Years	Age at last report or (death) Years	Hm	Sm	Ev	Hf	TC	TG	Other
1 L.Mc.	1, 51	F	3	(21)	+	+	0	+	402	150	Aortic stenosis, coronary arteriosclerosis
2 Mc.	1, 51	F	¹/₁₂	(¹/₁₂)	+	+	0	0	−	−	Respiratory distress
3 Lem.	59, 60, 69	M	14	43	+	0	0	+	275	140	Jaundice, polyposis coli
4 T.H.	61, 62, 77, 78	M	2	18	+	+	+	+	276	192	Early familial hepatic cirrhosis, serum bile acids elevated
5 W.H.T.	61	F	−	19	+	0	0	+	356	413	Eosinophilia
6 E.M.N.	65	F	7	17	+	0	+	+	400	353	Eosinophilia
7 Rad.	67 to 69	F	23	44	+	0	0	0	335	−	Recurrent abdominal pain
8 T.R.	63	F	6	(9)	+	+	+	+	−	−	Aortic arterial plaques, enlarged adrenal glands, hepatic coma
9 R.R.	63	F	−	(7)	+	+	0	+	−	−	Enlarged adrenal glands
10. J.R.	38, 63, 79, 82, 83, 84a, 89	F	2	(18)	+	+	0	+	230	69	Adrenal calcification, pulmonary hypertension, death from liver failure
11 K.W.	54, 63	F	−	8	+	0	0	−	363	214	
12 A.L.	64	M	2	7	+	0	0	−	−	−	Eosinophilia
13 L.O.	69 to 71	M	1	8	+	0	−	−	300	−	Recurrent abdominal pain
14 M.S.	69 to 71	F	9	12	+	−	−	+	390	150	Febrile icterus
15 M.A.	69	F	6	9	+	−	−	+	285	160	Febrile icterus
16 C.N.	69	F	11	11	+	−	−	+	360	135	
17 K.N.	73, 74	M	2	8	+	0	−	+	301		
18 A.C.d.O.	72	M	4	6	+	0	0	−	380	122	Recurrent abdominal pain with fever
19 B.Z.	75	M	4	13	+	−	0	+	403	334	Vitamin D–resistant rickets
20 T.S.	75	M	3	12	+	0	−	+	247	121	Factor V deficiency
21 N.S.	75	F	7	11	+	0	−	+	252	187	Factor V deficiency, recurrent abdominal pain
22 J.M.	75	M	4	5	+	0	0	+	423	302	
23 B.U.	76, 84	F	10	15	+	+	0	+	275	191	HDL₂ > HDL₃
24 Le.M.	66, 71	F	1	12	+	0	−	0	385	310	Febrile icterus, short stature, no adrenal calcification, but necrotic areas
25 K.H.	81	F	2	9	+	+	0	+	386	217	
26 A.R.	84b	F	6	16	+	+	+	+	111	125	Hepatic failure and liver transplant at age 14
27 A.W.	84c, 114	F	2	2	+	+	0	−	215	270	

NOTE: + = present; 0 = absent; − = not specifically mentioned; Hm = hepatomegaly; Sm = splenomegaly; Ev = esophageal varices; Hf = hepatic fibrosis; TC = total serum cholesterol; TG = serum triglycerides.

this book.[1,2] Table 64-1 summarizes some features of the 27 patients who are known to have CESD and one additional patient whom we regard as a probable case of CESD.[64] The principal and sometimes only sign, hepatomegaly, may be evident at birth or in early childhood. Occasionally it is delayed until the second decade of life (patients 3, 5, and 7). Hepatomegaly apparently increases with time and eventually leads to hepatic fibrosis. The spleen has been found to be enlarged in about a third of the patients. Esophageal varices have occasionally been detected. Four patients from two families of Mexican descent have developed liver failure. Two (patients 8 and 9) developed acute liver failure while their sibling (patient 10) and patient 26 from another family developed chronic liver

failure.[63,79,84a,84b] Patient 26 received a liver transplant because of chronic liver failure. Jaundice has been noted in several other patients. Gallstones have not been found in any of the patients. A number of patients have had recurrent abdominal pain. Patient 4, a boy, and patients 6 and 22, two girls, had some delay in onset of puberty. Patients 1 and 10 had recurrent epistaxes, and several have had episodes of gastrointestinal bleeding. Patients 19 and 20 had a decreased concentration of blood clotting factor V, and patient 8, hypoprothrombinemia.

Malabsorption, malnutrition, or abnormalities involving the tonsils have not been described. The only neurologic changes have occurred in patient 3, who has had unexplained episodes

Table 64-2 Acid Lipase Activity in Liver in Cholesteryl Ester Storage Disease

Patient	Ref.	Activity expressed in	[¹⁴C]Cholesteryl oleate	[¹⁴C]Cholesteryl palmitate	[¹⁴C]Trioleate	4-Muo*
1 L.Mc.	51	pmol substrate/(mg wet tissue · h)	1	1.7	660	—
Control			107 ± 23	150 ± 32.8	5730 ± 3600	—
4 T.H.	77	μmol FFA liberated/ (mg nitrogen · h)	—	—	—	—
Control			0.26–0.6	—	—	—
5 W.H.T.	62	Reduced esterase activity	?	?	?	?
18 A.C.d.O.	72	mmol substrate/(g wet tissue · min)	1.7	—	—	—
Control			5.6–15.4	—	—	—
23 B.U.	84	nmol substrate/(h · mg protein)	0.6	—	—	1.5
Control			3.5–10.4	—	—	105
27 A.W.	114	pmol substrate/min/mg wet tissue	32% normal	—	—	—

*4-Muo = 4-methylumbelliferyl oleate

of headache, vertigo, hypersomnia, and loss of consciousness. Patient 10 has been found (at age 13) to have calcified adrenal glands detectable on abdominal roentgenograms. Patient 1 had roentgenographic evidence of calcification of the hepatic artery. Exclusive of the plasma lipids, there are no other distinc-

tive abnormalities in routine laboratory tests. Patient 3 is said to have had an indirect bilirubin of 6 mg but no jaundice.[59] Patients 6 and 11 had hyperglobulinemia. Total bile acids were grossly elevated in patient 4, and the ratio of cholic to chenodeoxycholic acid was low. Bone marrow aspirates in pa-

Table 64-3 Acid Lipase Activity in Cultured Fibroblasts or Circulating Leukocytes in Cholesteryl Ester Storage Disease

Patient	Refs.	Cells	Substrates	Patient	Control	Expressed in
1 L.Mc.	51	Fibroblasts	4-Muo	1.4	25.8 ± 8.2	nmol substrate/(min·mg protein)
			[¹⁴C]Trioleate	0.1	36.5 ± 4.6	pmol substrate/(h·mg protein)
			[¹⁴C]C oleate	14.0	138.1 ± 53.9	
6 E.M.N.	38	Fibroblasts	Tridecanoate	0	0.4303	nmol substrate/(min·mg protein)
10 J.R.	38, 63	Leukocytes	p-Nitrophenyl laurate	0.88	8.39 − 20.17	nmol substrate/(min·mg protein)
	79, 82, 83	Fibroblasts	[¹⁴C]Trioleate	4.8	268 ± 39	pmol (min·mg protein)
			[¹⁴C]C oleate	0	40.2 ± 6.9	
			p-Nitrophenyl laurate	1.2	26.6 ± 5.1	nmol/(min·mg protein)
			[³H]C linoleate	0.77	5.7	pmol [³H]cholesterol/ (h·mg protein)
11 K.W.	54	Fibroblasts	[¹⁴C]Trioleate	0.8	11.8 ± 1.7	nmol/(h·mg protein)
			[¹⁴C]C oleate	0.4	3.8 ± 1.0	
			4-Muo	170.2	778.5 ± 123.2	
12 A.L.	64	Leukocytes	p-Nitrophenyl carboxylic esters	Deficiency of E-600–resistant acid esterase		
18 A.C. d.O.	72	Fibroblasts Leukocytes	[¹⁴C]C oleate [¹⁴C]Triolate 4-Muo [¹⁴C]C oleate	2.1 15.6 1000 3.4	49–326 236 2800 20–105	nmol/(min·g protein)
19 B.Z.	75	Fibroblasts	p-Nitrophenyl palmitate	Deficiency of acid esterase		
20 T.S.	75	Fibroblasts	1. 4-Muo 2. [¹⁴C]Trioleate	1. 10% of control activity 2. 4% of control activity		
22 J.M.	75	Fibroblasts		Reduced activity of acid esterase		
23 B.U.	84	Fibroblasts	[¹⁴C]Trioleate	1.1	13.2 ± 1.4	nmol/(h·mg protein)
			[¹⁴C]C oleate	0.6	5.1 ± 0.9	
			4-Muo	157.5	644 ± 142	
25 K.H.	81	Lymphocytes Fibroblasts	[¹⁴C]C oleate [¹⁴C]C oleate	≈ 4% of control activity		
26 A.W.	84c, 114	Fibroblasts	[¹⁴C]C oleate	6.1	306	pmol/(min·mg protein)

NOTE: 4-Muo = 4-methylumbelliferyl oleate; [¹⁴C]Trioleate = [¹⁴C]oleoyl triacylglycerol; [¹⁴C]C oleate = [1–¹⁴C]cholesteryl oleate.

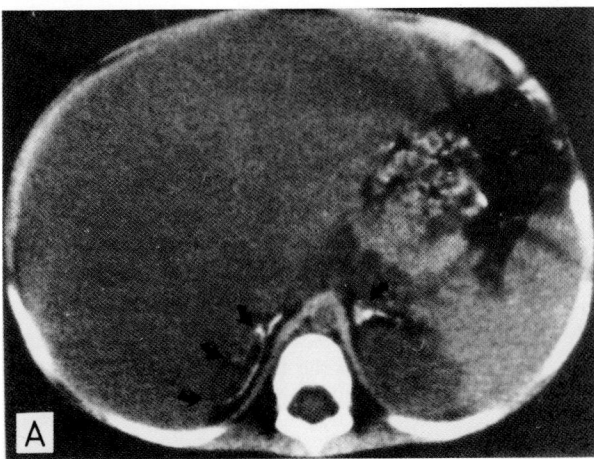

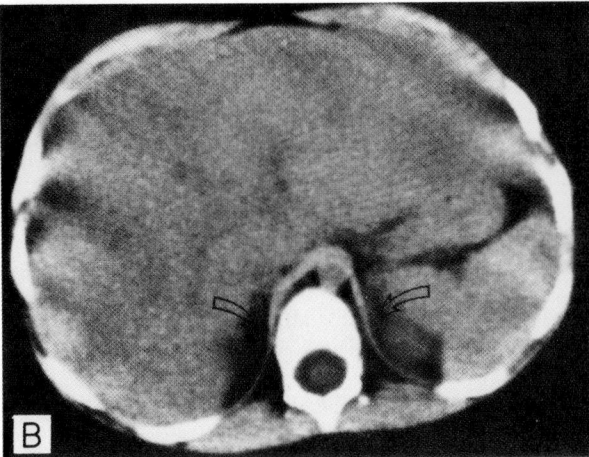

Fig. 64-2   Computed tomography. *A.* Wolman disease: The liver is enlarged and has a diffuse homogeneous reduction in density. The spleen is normal in size and density. There is bilateral adrenal enlargement with linear cortical calcification (arrows). *B.* CESD: There is diffuse homogeneous enlargement of the liver. The spleen is normal in size and density. The adrenal glands (arrows) are normal in size with no calcification. *(Courtesy of Drs. S.C. Hill, and J.M. Hoeg and reprinted from Ref. 90 with permission.)*

tients 1, 10, and 11 contained numerous large macrophages filled with birefringent droplets. Bone marrow appeared normal in patients 4 and 7.

PATHOLOGY

Liver

Hepatomegaly is a constant feature in Wolman disease; the liver appears to increase in size throughout the course of the illness and by age 4 months may weigh 400 g, which is about twice the normal weight.[14] The liver has a firm consistency, and the cut surface is yellow and greasy.

The normal architecture of the liver is sometimes preserved[29] but may be so distorted that the portal spaces, even though infiltrated with lymphoid cells, provide the only readily recognizable landmarks.[3,4,6,21,26] The hepatic parenchymal cells are enlarged and vacuolated, and grossly enlarged and vacuolated Kupffer cells are prominent. Large numbers of foamy histiocytes are found in the portal and periportal areas and frequently in clusters between parenchymal cells. Portal and periportal fibrosis may be marked, and there may even be frank cirrhosis. Under the electron microscope one sees that the organelles of the parenchymal cells have accumulated large osmiophilic lipid droplets. Most of these droplets are found within lysosomes[24] (Fig. 64-3). The smooth and rough endoplasmic reticulum may appear dilated and distended.[26] It is not certain from histochemical studies whether both glycerides and cholesterol accumulate in the Kupffer and parenchymal cells.[4,6,21,26] The liver in CESD also has an extraordinary orange or butter-yellow color and a smooth, soft texture. It is usually markedly enlarged, sometimes to twice the normal weight. Microscopic examination of the CESD liver reveals many of the same abnormalities as in Wolman disease, with some possible differences related to a disease process of much longer standing. There are: (1) lipid droplets in hepatic parenchymal cells resembling those in ordinary fatty infiltration; (2) enlargement of Kupffer cells by smaller vacuoles and by PAS-positive granules; (3) variable amounts of septal fibrosis which has progressed in some patients to micronodular cirrhosis with esophageal varices; (4) focal periportal accumulations of lymphocytes, plasma cells, and foamy

Fig. 64-3   Wolman disease. Electron microscopy of liver. *A.* Liver sinusoid lining cells distended by dropletlike and cleftlike lysosomes (Ly). Dropletlike lysosomes in liver parenchymal cell (P). Magnification, ×4500. *B.* Membrane (arrows) of a droplet like lysosome (Ly) in liver parenchymal cell. Glycogen granules (Gl). Magnification, ×106,000. *C.* High resolution of crystal cleftlike lysosomes (Ly) in liver sinusoidal cells. Magnification, ×30,000. *(Courtesy of Dr. D.B. von Bassewitz.)*

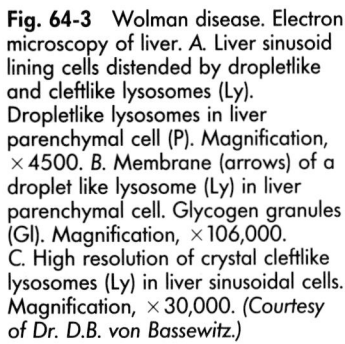

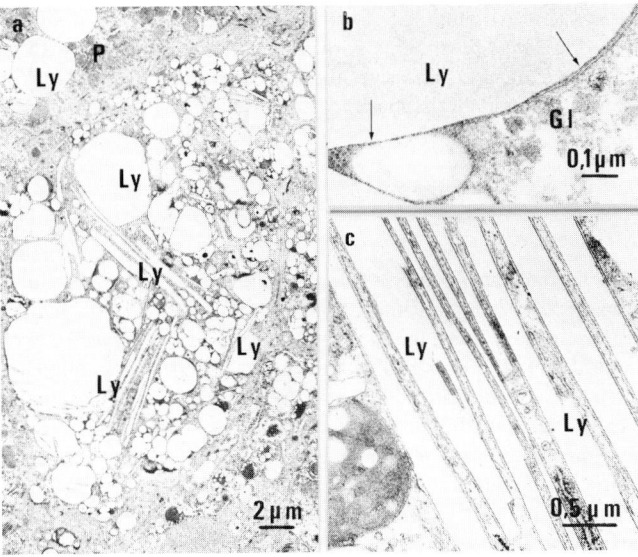

macrophages with little or no birefringence; and (5) vacuolization and massive storage of birefringent material in hepatocytes. The Kupffer cells are greatly enlarged; have several small, indented, darkly staining nuclei; and appear more finely and uniformly vacuolated than do hepatocytes. The deposits of cholesteryl esters and triglycerides in hepatocytes appear relatively stable, while those in macrophages are transformed by peroxidation and polymerization of their fatty acids to insoluble ceroid, both in CESD and in Wolman disease.[27] The gradual formation of ceroid deposits from accumulated neutral lipid has been observed in a variety of other disease states.[85,86] In CESD the deposits in macrophages in bone marrow, spleen, lymph nodes, and other organs tend to resemble histiochemically and ultrastructurally those in hepatic macrophages, while the deposits in smooth-muscle cells, perivascular cells, and endothelial cells are more similar to those in hepatocytes.

Electron microscopy of liver tissue in CESD[2,74] reveals:

1. There are cytoplasmic inclusions in the hepatocytes, containing material which in part seems to solubilize during the preparation and tends to form crystals after formalin fixation and storage at 4°C.

2. These inclusions are limited by trilaminar membranes of 13 to 14 nm thickness, consisting of a true vacuole membrane and a submembranous "halo" which is characteristic for lysosomes. There is also a thin, limiting layer which has also been described in Tangier disease (Chap. 50), in which the inclusions contain cholesteryl esters but are not limited by a membrane.

3. Heterogeneous storage material is found in Kupffer cells.

4. There are membrane-limited vacuoles containing partly dissolved, partly osmiophilic lipid (unsaturated fatty acids) in the epithelial cells of small bile ducts as well as in endothelial cells.

An animal model partly resembling the morphologic findings in hepatocytes and Kupffer cells of CESD and Wolman disease has been described by Drevon and Howig.[87] These authors fed a semisynthetic diet containing 10 percent cottonseed oil and 1 percent cholesterol to guinea pigs and observed the accumulation of multivacuolated, secondary lysosomes, membrane-bound lipid vacuoles (lipolysosomes), and myelin figures in liver. These microscopic changes were due to a marked accumulation of cholesteryl esters.

Lipolysosomes (lysosomes containing large lipid droplets) can also be observed in livers of patients with various forms of hepatic injury.[87] Their numbers and sizes increase with the degree of fatty infiltration and probably represent a nonspecific finding.

Adrenal Glands

The adrenal glands in Wolman disease are bright-yellow and grossly and symmetrically enlarged; their configuration is, however, normal. Each gland may weigh as much as 13 g, compared with a normal weight of 5 g. The adrenals are usually quite firm, contain flecks of gritty calcified tissue, and are difficult to cut. In cut section, the outer rim of cortex is intensely yellow, and the central zone is gray or white.

Under microscopic examination it can be seen that the architecture of the outer and part of the middle zones of the cortex, i.e., the zona glomerulosa and the zona fasciculata, are

relatively well preserved. Many of the cells are swollen, vacuolated, and contain sudanophilic lipid.[4,21] The areas corresponding to the inner fasciculata and the entire zona reticularis (the innermost portion of the cortex) are replaced by a broad zone of haphazardly arranged large cells with a vacuolated, foamy cytoplasm. Many of the cells contain anisotropic crystals or large clefts in the shape of cholesterol crystals.[26] Other foam cells seem necrotic, and their contents appear to have been released to form confluent lipid cysts. In the necrotic areas, calcification may be quite prominent. Most of the calcium occurs in finely granular deposits, but there may be areas in which it is condensed into dense lumps.[21] There is frequently extensive fibrosis in the inner half of the cortex.[4,21] The adrenal medulla is usually very narrow but normal in appearance.

Electron micrographs of the adrenals show that the histiocytes contain lipid in both the crystalline and droplet forms.[26] In the severely affected portions of the cortex, histochemical techniques indicate the presence of large amounts of lipid with staining properties suggestive of cholesteryl esters and triglyceride.[4,6,16,26]

Adrenal calcification is not visually observed in CESD. Extensive chemical and histopathologic examination of the adrenals in CESD has not been done.

Intestine

The small intestine of patients affected with Wolman disease is usually thickened and dilated, with a dull, opaque yellow serosa and a swollen yellow mucosa with thick, flattened, yellow villi. The changes are generally most marked in the proximal parts of the small intestine and least apparent in the terminal ileum. In the small intestine, and to some extent in the colon, the lamina propria of the mucosa is infiltrated by foamy histiocytes. Some of the mucosal cells are also foamy. The infiltration of the mucosa by foam cells converts the villi into thick, club-shaped structures.[2] Some foam cells extend through the muscularis mucosa to form small clusters in the submucosa, and similar cells are also present in the lymphoid tissue. Some of the cells of the muscularis mucosa also stain positively for neutral lipid with Sudan stains. Sudanophilic staining may also be present in the myenteric plexus and in foamy endothelial cells within the intestinal adventitial layer.

Partin and Schubert originally described changes in jejunal and duodenal biopsy specimens from patients 4 and 5 (Table 64-1) with CESD.[78] The epithelium was normal. Beneath the epithelium in the regions of the lacteals were collections of autofluorescent foam cells, which were especially densely packed in the villous tips. Large amounts of extracellular lipid were present throughout the lamina propria. This lipid appeared birefringent and stained similarly to the fat in the foam cells but was more nonpolar and gave only a weakly positive Schultz reaction. Under the electron microscope the lipid appeared electron-lucent with dense rims. Ultrastructural study of the lamina propria of the small intestine of patients 4 and 5 revealed several interesting features.[62] The lacteal endothelium was filled with round vacuoles that distended the smooth endoplasmic reticulum and looked as though they contained lipid taken up by pinocytosis. Many macrophages surrounded the lacteals and contained numerous vacuoles that were limited by membranes and were filled with material similar to those in hepatic macrophages. Lucent lipid droplets were present in adjacent smooth-muscle cells, vascular pericytes, fibroblasts, and supporting cells of nerve fibers. The ultra-structural localization of membrane-limited lipid deposits in various cell types in intestinal mucosa and submucosa was similar in other patients. In patient 1, foam cells were few and small in the lamina propria of the colon and the esophagus.

Other Tissues

In Wolman disease the spleen is always grossly enlarged and by age 3 months may weigh over 200 g, compared with the normal weight of 15 g.[4] The spleen is firm, and the cut surface is red or reddish-yellow; the surface may be mottled with yellow or brown flecks. The normal follicular architecture is replaced by a homogeneous appearance. Microscopically, only a small number of follicles are present, and they are small and compressed. Most of the reticulum cells are transformed into large foam cells, which make up the bulk of the organ. There is also swelling and vacuolization of the endothelial cells lining the sinusoids. Lymph nodes throughout the body, particularly those in the mesentery, are enlarged, orange-yellow, firm, and elastic. Their cut surfaces are yellow and appear homogeneous. The microscopic and histochemical changes are quite similar to those found in the spleen. The bone marrow, thymus, and tonsils in Wolman disease undergo changes that are almost identical to those in the spleen and lymph nodes. Vacuolization of lymphocytes in the blood and bone marrow has often been noted in Wolman disease but is not specific. Excessive vacuolization of granulocytes has been reported in one case of Wolman disease.[50]

There are no gross kidney abnormalities in Wolman disease. Under the light microscope, the tubules appear normal, but mesangial cells of the glomeruli may contain lipid droplets that are both sudanophilic and also stain for cholesterol.[14,21] There also may be foam cells in the interstitium. Foam cells have been observed in the thyroid,[14] testes,[6,14,21] and ovaries.[21] Wolman et al. observed sudanophilic droplets in the endothelium of capillaries of the gray matter and in swollen neurons in the medulla oblongata and the retina.[4] Crocker et al. later described the presence of foamy histiocytes in the leptomeninges.[6] They also noted a moderate decrease in the number of cortical neurons and found retarded myelination. Foam cells also occur in the interstitium of the choroid plexus.[10] Lipid storage in neurons, including Purkinje cells,[16] and sudanophilic granules within swollen microglia, periadventitial histiocytes, and, possibly, astrocytes have been observed in some

patients.[16,20,21] One of the most extensive studies of the central nervous system in Wolman disease was made by Guazzi et al.[14,15] These investigations found an abundance of sudanophilic material and diffuse isomorphic fibrillary gliosis of the white matter, which they interpreted as sudanophilic leukodystrophy directly related to abnormal lipid storage. The autopsy was delayed for 2 days after death, however, and some of the reported changes may have been artifactual. Byrd and Powers[48] examined ultrastructurally the peripheral and central nervous system following autopsy of a four-month-old child affected with Wolman disease. They demonstrated lipid storage in Schwann cells, perineural cells, and endoneural cells. In the central nervous system, the oligodendrocytes were the principal sites of lipid accumulation, especially in areas of active myelination.

Kamoshita and Landing[17] first made the observation in Wolman disease that ganglion cells of the plexuses of both Auerbach and Meissner were packed with sudanophilic granules. These changes were found in the stomach, duodenum, and small intestine and have been repeatedly confirmed. The storage of sudanophilic lipids in the sympathetic neurons has also been observed in one patient.[16]

In CESD, lipid storage in most tissues is more discrete. In patient 1, foam cells were described in the interstitium in lung and renal glomeruli. Endothelial cells in numerous anatomic sites contained fine lipid droplets, as did smooth-muscle cells in certain arterioles, particularly in the spleen. Electron microscopy showed that the droplets in endothelium also were limited by single, trilaminar membranes. Histologic study of the central nervous system of patient 1 showed no evidence of lipid storage. Abnormal lipid deposits can also be detected in lymphocytes (Fig. 64-4), monocytes, and cultured skin fibroblasts of CESD patients (Fig. 64-5).[63,70,78–80] In lymphocytes (fresh, unstained preparations), secondary lysosomes storing cholesteryl esters can be visualized by birefringence in polarized light. These secondary lysosomes can be histochemically identified by acid phosphatase staining. α-Naphthylbutyrate esterase activity, normally present in lymphocytes, is completely absent from lymphocytes in CESD patients.[80] In electron microscopy, the storage lysosomes can be easily visualized through their typical trilaminar membranes. Except for lymphocytes and monocytes, all other blood cells are unaffected in CESD.

In cultured skin fibroblasts of CESD patients both birefringence in plane polarized light and the absence of α-naphthylbutyrate esterase staining permit the rapid identification of acid lipase deficiency.

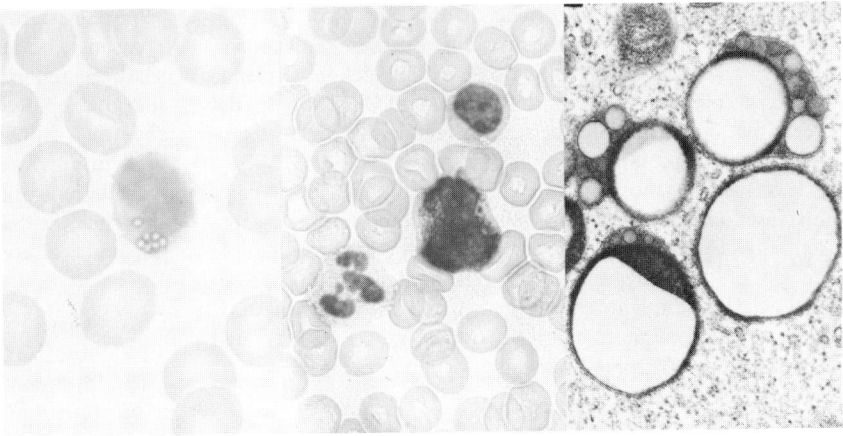

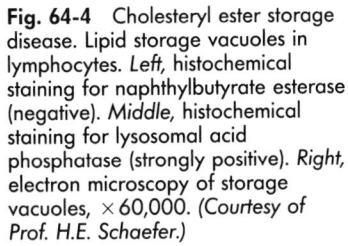

Fig. 64-4 Cholesteryl ester storage disease. Lipid storage vacuoles in lymphocytes. *Left,* histochemical staining for naphthylbutyrate esterase (negative). *Middle,* histochemical staining for lysosomal acid phosphatase (strongly positive). *Right,* electron microscopy of storage vacuoles, ×60,000. (*Courtesy of Prof. H.E. Schaefer.*)

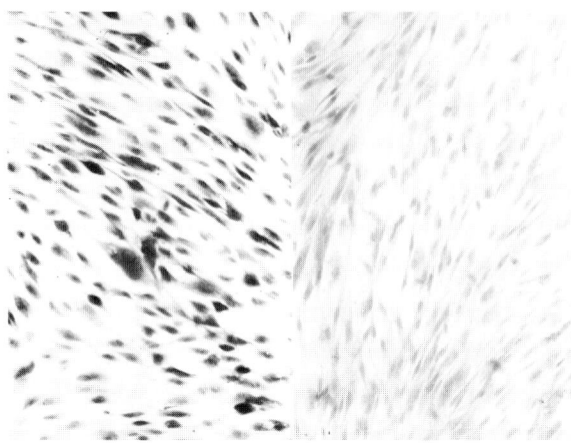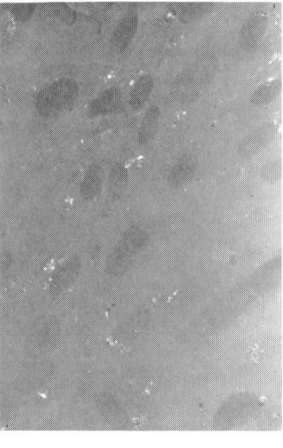

Fig. 65-5 Cholesteryl ester storage disease. *Left,* normal fibroblasts stained for naphtylbutyrate esterase (strongly positive). *Middle,* CESD fibroblasts stained for naphthylbutyrate esterase (negative). *right,* CESD fibroblasts visualized in plane polarized light birefringence (positive). *(Courtesy of Prof. H.E. Schaefer.)*

Atherosclerosis

Upon gross examination, the heart and lungs of patients with Wolman disease appear normal. Routine histologic examination of the heart also reveals no abnormalities, but in frozen sections many sudanophilic droplets may be found in the muscles[14] and vascular endothelium.[6,14] Lipid deposition in the aorta may be extensive,[27] but frank atherosclerosis has not been seen. Nevertheless, most patients affected with Wolman disease in whom postmortem examination of the arteries was made showed some degree of fat accumulation.[6,21,27,29,30,34,39] The lungs contain variable numbers of foam cells in the alveoli and intestinal tissue.[6,14,21]

With the exception of CESD patient 10, who developed obstructive pulmonary vascular disease at 15 years of age[89] and died of liver failure at age 18,[84a] none of the patients known to have CESD, including two who are in their fourth decade of life, have had clinical evidence of coronary or systemic atherosclerosis. Three of the four patients with CESD who came to necropsy, however, have had anatomic evidence of a much accelerated atherosclerosis process. Patient 1, who died at age 21, had severe (up to 75 percent) coronary arterial luminal narrowing by atheromatous plaques, as well as striking, but functionally less severe, lesions in the circle of Willis, the abdominal aorta, and the common iliac arteries. This patient died a cardiac death, and at necropsy she also had recent cardiac necrosis, but her death appeared to be related to severe aortic valvular stenosis rather than to coronary artery disease. Patient 8, who died at age 9, had a few elevated yellow plaques in the ascending aorta. Her affected sib, who died at age 8, had no abnormalities of the aorta or coronary arteries. Extensive lipid deposits in the systemic and pulmonary circulation were present in patient 10, who died at age 18.[84a] It is not known how much of the atherosclerosis in these patients was directly related to CESD or to associated hypercholesterolemia and hyperbetalipoproteinemia. Patients with CESD do not develop xanthomas of the type seen in familial hypercholesterolemia (see Chap. 48).

The fact that most patients affected with CESD may be at increased risk of developing premature atherosclerosis is potentially of great importance. It could support a hypothesis of de Duve,[93] who suggested that a relative deficiency of lysosomal acid lipase might lead to the accumulation of cholesteryl esters within lysosomes of arterial smooth-muscle cells[91,92] and thus promote atheroma formation.

LIPID ABNORMALITIES

Wolman Disease

The principal stored lipids present in increased quantities in various tissues are cholesteryl esters and triglycerides.[1,2] The triglyceride content of the liver may be 2 to 10 times the normal value. In the spleen, the triglycerides may be elevated from eight- to a hundred-fold. The triglyceride content of the adrenals has been reported in only one case[26] and was one-half the normal value. The concentrations of mono- and diglycerides were elevated five- to fifteen-fold in the liver and spleen of the two patients in which they were measured;[10,26] they were modestly, if at all, elevated in the adrenals of one patient.[26]

The total cholesterol concentration of liver and spleen has been elevated in every case of Wolman disease in which measurements have been reported. Although the free cholesterol concentration has frequently been greater than normal, the bulk of the increase in total cholesterol is due to the accumulation of cholesteryl esters. The cholesteryl ester content of the liver may be 5 to 160 times the normal value. It was shown in one case[26] that cholesteryl esters were elevated eightfold in the adrenals.[2] Analyses of the fatty acids of triglycerides and cholesteryl esters in the liver, spleen, and other tissues of patients with Wolman disease revealed no consistent abnormality.[2] Upon examining chromatographs of published tissue analyses[21] as well as their own, Assman and coworkers concluded that oxygenated steryl esters were also present in Wolman disease.[94] They were identified as esters of 7α- and 7β-hydroxycholesterol, 7-ketocholesterol, and $5,6\beta$- and $5,6\alpha$-epoxycholesterol, in this order of preponderance.

An increase in free fatty acid content of the liver and spleen has been reported in Wolman disease.[10,23] The phospholipid and glycolipid contents of the liver and spleen have not been abnormal. Lin and coworkers[95] have reported increased quantities in alkyl and alk-1-enyl glycolipids in the liver, spleen, and adrenals of a patient with Wolman disease. No consistent abnormalities have been detected in the neutral lipids, phospholipids, or glycolipids of the nervous systems.

Cholesteryl Ester Storage Disease

Chemical abnormalities in tissues in CESD are thus far known to be present in the liver, intestine, spleen, lymph node, aorta, and cultured skin fibroblasts. Lipid analyses of liver of CESD patients (Table 64-4) revealed an increase in cholesteryl esters, the concentration being 120 to 350 times normal. In patient 1, 94 percent of the glyceride fraction was triglyceride, there being only small amounts of di- and monoglycerides as determined chromatographically.[2] The percentage distribution of hepatic phospholipids was phosphatidylcholine plus phosphatidylinositol, 49 percent; phosphatidylethanolamine, 31 percent; sphingomyelin, 11.5 percent; and lysophosphatidylcholine, 7 percent.[2] In patient 3, it was concluded that the liver sphingomyelin might be increased and the phosphatidylethanolamine decreased.[60] Liver glycolipids or glyceryl ethers have not been studied adequately in any patient with CESD.

In patient 1, the content of triglycerides and cholesteryl esters was increased in the spleen and aorta; in patients 8 and 9, cholesterol and triglyceride analyses of spleen, kidney, lung, and cerebral gray matter were reported as normal. In cultured skin fibroblasts of several patients, the total concentration of cholesterol was close to that in controls, while the concentration of cholesteryl esters was markedly elevated. The acyl groups in the cholesteryl esters in CESD liver have been reported to be predominantly oleic and linoleic acids,[60,61,65,74,84] a pattern which is grossly similar to that seen in esters stored in Tangier disease, eosinophilic granuloma, or atheromas.[96] The fatty acid composition of cholesteryl esters in the intestinal mucosa of patient 4 did not differ markedly from that in controls or from the liver.[61]

Plasma Lipids and Lipoproteins

Plasma cholesterol and triglycerides have been normal in most patients with Wolman disease in whom such measurements have been made. Elevated triglycerides and VLDL (very low density lipoproteins) were reported in three patients.[21,50] Five patients have had unquestionable decreases in plasma HDL (high density lipoproteins) as determined by electrophoresis or chemical tests.[28,29,50] The severely malnourished patient described by Eto and Kitagawa had a cholesterol level of 100 mg/dl, decreased LDL and HDL, and acanthocytosis.[24]

All CESD patients in whom plasma lipid levels have been reported had hypercholesterolemia (Table 64-1). In some this has been associated with hypertriglyceridemia. The plasma lipoprotein pattern is either II-A or II-B. Patient 1 had a persistent, marked increase in LDL, in concentrations of about 330 mg LDL cholesterol per deciliter of plasma, and variable increases in VLDL. The LDL concentrations in patient 6 were elevated at both 11 and 17 years of age. Her father (age 50) and sister (age 22) both had hepatomegaly and hypercholesterolemia; the mother (age 50) had no clinical or lipid abnormalities.

The cholesteryl ester/free cholesterol ratio and the pattern of cholesteryl ester fatty acid in serum is normal in CESD.[1,65,84] Direct investigation of the enzymatic activity of lecithin:cholesterol acyltransferase has not been done. The plasma lipoprotein abnormalities in CESD may include the HDL. Patient 1, observed over a long period of time, had extremely low levels of HDL, with concentrations varying from 6 to 26 mg HDL cholesterol per deciliter of plasma, well below the 5 percent lower limit of normal and not explained by her modest hypertriglyceridemia. Patient 4 was also said to have low HDL (in terms of α-lipoproteins on the electrophoretic pattern). Patient 23 had low HDL cholesterol values on repeated determinations. An analysis of the distribution of the subfractions HDL_2 and HDL_3 in patient 23 by zonal centrifugation has revealed a remarkable discrepancy from normal: instead of the usual 1:10 ratio of HDL_2 and HDL_3, a 10:1 ratio was discovered.[84]

PROPERTIES OF LYSOSOMAL ACID LIPASE

Intracellular Processing and Secretion

Newly synthesized proteins destined for the plasma membrane, secretory vesicles, and lysosomes share a common route until they reach the Golgi apparatus, where they are sorted to

Table 64-4 Concentration of Liver Lipids in Cholesteryl Ester Storage Disease

Patient	Ref.	TC	FC	EC	TG	PL	Expressed in
1 L.Mc.	51		9	95–187	33–64	—	mg/g wet tissue
Control				1	19	—	
3 Lem.	69	—	11	174	36	21	mg/g wet tissue
4 T.H.	77	148.3	—	146.9	16.6	—	mg/g wet tissue
Control		4.8	—	1.1	10.1	—	
8 T.R.	63	—	3.6		—	—	mg/g wet tissue
9 R.R.	63	—	3.5		—	—	mg/g wet tissue
13 L.O.	70	—	30	244	—	—	μg/g wet tissue
Control		—	30	20	—	—	
17 K.N.	73	—	Normal		Normal	—	
18 A.C.,d.O.	72	259	—		Slightly elevated	—	mg/g wet tissue
21 N.S.	75	—	Normal		Slightly elevated	—	
23 B.U.	84	210	16	194	Normal	Double of control	mg/g wet tissue
Control		1.8	0.4	1.4	Normal	PS/SPM normal	
24 Le.M.	70	—	68	603	—	—	μg/mg protein
Control		—	30	20	—	—	
27 A.W.	84c, 114	10.6	0.4	10.2	5.1	—	% total net weight

NOTE: TC = total cholesterol; FC = free cholesterol; EC = esterified cholesterol; TG = triglycerides; PL = phospholipids.

their correct destinations (Fig. 64-6). The targeting of lysosomal proteins has been elaborated in detail,[97–99] and it is assumed that upon arrival in the Golgi apparatus, newly synthesized acid hydrolases are recognized by an N-acetylglucosaminylphosphotransferase,[100,101] which couples N-acetylglucosamine phosphate to terminal α-1,2 mannose residues.[102] A specific phosphodiesterase[103,104] then removes N-acetylglucosamine (GlcNAc) to generate the common recognition marker, mannose-6-phosphate (Man-6-P), which mediates binding of the acid hydrolases to Man-6-P receptors in the Golgi apparatus.[97–99]

The receptor-bound acid hydrolases are then transported to an acidic prelysosomal compartment, where the ligand is released for transport to lysosomes. The free receptor cycles back to the Golgi apparatus,[97,98] while the newly synthesized acid hydrolases, trapped within the lysosomes, are dephosphorylated by a resident phosphatase.[105]

Two types of Man-6-P receptors have been identified. One is a single polypeptide of 215 kDa,[106,107] while the second Man-6-P receptor appears to be a glycoprotein composed of three 46-kDa subunits.[108,109] The latter receptor requires divalent cations, while the 215-kDa receptor is cation-independent.[108] There is recent evidence that the 215-kDa Man-6-P receptor cycles constitutively between intracellular compartments, independent of the presence of newly synthesized ligands.[110]

The normal intracellular route for processing and secretion of precursor enzyme can be altered, when cells are treated with lysosomotropic drugs (ammonium chloride, monensin, cyanate).[102,111] Under these conditions only a small percentage of the newly synthesized acid hydrolases enter the lysosomal organelle, while the majority of the precursors undergo further processing of carbohydrate moieties in the Golgi apparatus, and are then secreted in a manner similar to secretory proteins.[111] In lysosomal enzyme trafficking (Fig. 64-6) of newly synthesized acid hydrolases, several defects could be postulated, some of which have been identified (Table 64-5).

It has been shown with purified preparations of acid lipase from fibroblast secretions that acid lipase is efficiently internalized by the Man-6-P receptor system.[112,113,173] Additional evidence for the involvement of the Man-6-P receptor system in the processing of acid lipase is derived from CESD and

Table 64-5 Possible Defects Underlying Lysosomal Enzyme Disturbances

1. No enzyme synthesis (e.g., Hurler disease)
2. Synthesis of defective enzymes
3. Posttranslational processing defects (phosphorylation/dephosphorylation; acylation; glycosylation; protein trimming)
4. No addition of recognition marker (I-cell disease)
5. No recapture of secreted enzymes
6. No pH drop in the lysosomal route
7. Defective binding and internalization of ligands which have to be hydrolyzed (e.g., LDL-receptor defect)

Wolman disease, since it could be demonstrated that the enzymatic defect can be corrected by addition of purified acid lipase to deficient fibroblasts.[112,113,173] However, coculture and cell fusion of fibroblasts from both Wolman disease and CESD subjects did not lead to correction of the enzyme deficiency, indicating that these disorders might be allelic.[114]

Biochemical Assay

At present, no standardized procedure has been established for the assay of acid lipase/cholesteryl ester hydrolase (see Tables 64-2 and 64-3), though the properties of the enzyme are influenced substantially by the assay method employed.[115] The substrates presented to the enzyme vary in their substrate class (cholesteryl ester, glycerides, and synthetic acyl esters) in the nature of acyl moieties (chain length and extent of unsaturation), and in the dispersion of the substrate (detergent, solubilizing agent, application of heat or sonication and concentration of substrate used). In addition, phospholipids and bile salts appear to stimulate the enzyme, and albumin or other proteins can serve as traps for the released fatty acids. Finally, the nature of the enzyme preparation itself (subcellular fractions, or more or less purified enzyme) considerably affects the properties of the enzyme. Since this wide variety of assay procedures exists, it is not surprising that substantial differences in pH optimum, substrate specificity, and cofactors have been reported.

The substrates used most often are [1-14C]trioleoylglycerol

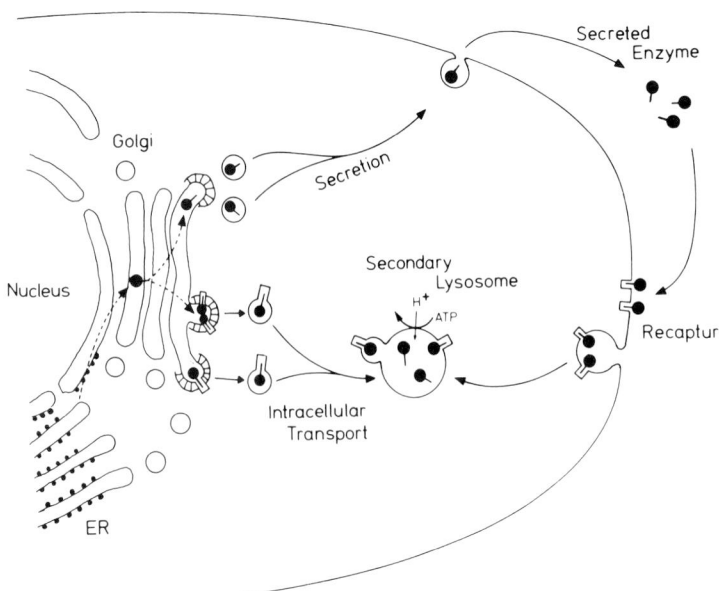

Fig. 64-6 Trafficking of lysosomal acid hydrolase. Solid circle = newly synthesized acid hydrolase; Solid circle with attached line = Man-6-P-coupled acid hydrolase; Open circle = secretory vesicle; Open keyhole shape = primary lysosome with Man-6-P receptor.

and cholesteryl [1-^{14}C]oleate (Tables 64-2 and 64-3). Labeled oleic acid liberated by enzyme action is measured after separation by thin-layer chromatography[116] or separation from substrate by solvent extraction.[117,118] The use of synthetic substrates has the advantage of sensitivity and simplicity, but unfortunately they lack specificity. The best recommendation for dispersal of acid lipase/cholesteryl ester hydrolase substrates seems to be the use of phospholipid vesicles for incorporation of radiolabeled cholesteryl esters[119] or triacylglycerols.[120] The recent presentation of fluorescent cholesteryl esters, containing fluorescent fatty acids, for acid lipase analysis may add a promising nonradioactive alternative, which can be easily used in clinical laboratories.[121–124]

Unlike many of the lysosomal hydrolases, acid cholesteryl ester hydrolase is not very stable. It does not store well when frozen and is rapidly inactivated at elevated temperatures. For acid cholesteryl esterase activity, phospholipids and bile salts are essential,[116,125,126] but there is general agreement that Ca^{2+}, Mg^{2+}, EDTA, and dithiothreitol do not significantly alter enzymatic activity.[116,127–129] However, the enzyme is inhibited by heavy metals such as copper and mercury,[116,126,128,130,131] and by agents, such as N-ethylmaleinimide, iodoacetate, and p-chloromercuribenzoate, that are reactive toward sulfhydryl groups.[125,127–129,131–133] Diisopropyl fluorophosphate and protamine sulfate have little inhibitory effect on acid lipase activity.[116,128] Since the enzyme is lysosomal, some activity may be latent. Latent activity can be measured by using 0.005% digitonin,[126] which completely disrupts the organelles prior to the assay. Most investigators find the enzyme activity toward triacylglycerols considerably higher than that toward cholesteryl esters. The significance of this is unclear.

Drug and Hormone Influences

A number of drugs inhibit acid lipase activity. These include chloroquine,[134–137] sulfonylureas,[138] 4,4-diethylamino-ethoxyhexesterol,[139] and several local anesthetics.[140–142] These drugs have the properties of weak bases that are trapped in the lysosomal compartment.[143] Bezafibrate or clofibrate do not affect acid cholesteryl esterase in aortic cells.[144] Fatty acyl CoA and acyl carnitine may have an inhibitory effect on heart acid lipase activity.[145] Cardiolipin has been shown to increase V_{max} without altering K_m of partially purified acid lipase.[146] Acid lipase activity was found enhanced in the liver following in vivo administration of glucagon but not following injections of insulin, epinephrine, or norepinephrine.[147] In other studies acid lipase activity has been reported as reduced[148,149] or unchanged[150] in mononuclear leukocytes from diabetic patients; insulin treatment has been found to markedly increase[148] or marginally reduce[150] this enzyme activity. Insulin may normalize acid cholesteryl esterase and acid triacylglycerol lipase activity in diabetic rat heart and aorta.[151–153]

Ethinylestradiol in large doses has been shown to reduce acid lipase in rat liver,[154] and the activity of the enzyme has also been found to vary with oral contraceptive use.[155] However, treatment of rats with 17α-ethinylestradiol to increase the hepatic degradation of lipoproteins did not change acid cholesteryl esterase activity in the liver.[156] Acid lipase activity is low in hypothyroid states in human beings as well as in experimental animals,[157–162] and can be normalized by restoration of thyroid function. Addition of prostacylin, 6-keto-prostaglandin F_{1a}, or 6-keto-prostaglandin E_1 to cultured arterial smooth-muscle cells significantly enhances acid choles-

teryl esterase activity, while preincubation of the cells with dideoxyadenosine (inhibitor of adenylate cyclase) abolished the effect, and addition of dibutyrl-cAMP increased acid cholesteryl esterase activity in smooth-muscle cells[163] and macrophages.[164,165] Interestingly, this effect seems to be specific for acid cholesteryl esterase since other lysosomal enzyme levels remained unaffected. Nifedipine, a slow calcium channel antagonist, enhances intracellular cyclic-AMP (cAMP) and thereby activates lysosomal acid cholesteryl ester hydrolase activity.[164–166]

Acid cholesteryl ester hydrolase activity of rat liver exhibits a diurnal rhythm with maxima at 06.00 h and minima at 18.00 h which is dependent upon dietary, but not on adrenal hormone influence.[167] In addition to diurnal rhythms, changes in cell differentiation may also modulate lysosomal acid lipase activity.[168]

Esterasin, a β-lactone derivative of myeloic acid isolated from cultures of Actinomyces, was recently described as an inhibitor of acid lipase (IC$_{50}$ ~ 80nM), while other lysosomal enzymes were not affected.[169]

Properties of Purified Lysosomal Acid Lipase

Acid lipase, although soluble, exhibits a high affinity for hydrophobic surfaces and is salt-sensitive. Since acid lipase and acid cholesteryl esterase activities copurify, it is suggested that a single enzyme hydrolyzes both triacylglycerols and cholesteryl esters. Purification of the lysosomal acid lipase has been attempted from several sources (reviewed in Ref. 115), including human liver,[170] placenta,[131,171] aorta,[172] leukocytes,[133] fibroblasts,[173] and cardiac myocytes.[146] The apparent molecular weight of the secreted human fibroblast acid lipase was estimated to be 47 to 49 kDa, while the intracellular enzyme was smaller at 41 kDa.[173] The purified enzyme is susceptible to hydrolysis by endo-β-N-acetylglucosaminidase H, resulting in a reduction (4 to 6 kDa) of the molecular weight of the two enzyme forms. Treatment with the endoglycosidase does not alter the catalytic activity or heat stability of the enzyme. However, the treated enzyme is no longer internalized by the Man-6-P receptor and thereby loses the capacity to correct cholesteryl ester accumulation in cultured lipase deficient cells.[112] Purified acid lipase hydrolyzes tri-, di- and mono-oleylglycerol as well as cholesterol oleate.[174,175] The positional specificity of purified lysosomal acid lipase was tested with tri-, di- and mono-oleylglycerols and a preference for 1(3)-ester bonds was recognized.[170,176] The main lipolytic reaction sequence catalyzed is triacylglycerol →1,2- or 2,3-diacylglycerol→2-monoacylglycerol. Nonionic phospholipids such as phosphatidylcholine increase the activity of purified acid lipase, while anionic phospholipids such as phosphatidylserine, phosphatidylinositol, and cardiolipin were ineffective.[176a,176b,177] Among a series of unsaturated phosphatidylcholines, the increase in enzyme activity parallels the number of double bonds.

Lysosomal Acid Lipase Inhibitory Proteins

A serum protein inhibitor of acid lipase has been recently reported which strongly inhibits acid lipase in cultured fibroblasts.[178] The protein is present in Cohn fraction IV, is heat labile, is nondialyzable, is destroyed by trypsin, and has a molecular weight of 50,000. There are also reports for the presence of a cytosolic protein that competitively inhibits cholesteryl ester hydrolase in the guinea pig gallbladder mucosa[179] and in various rat tissues.[180] The first cytosolic inhibitor was found to be associated with a protein fraction of 20 to 50 kDa, and the inhibitory properties are similar to the inhibitor proteins of δ-aminolevulinate dehydratase in bone marrow cells[181] and phospholipase A_2 in neutrophils.[182] The other inhibitor corresponded to a protein of 80 kDa, and the inhibitory activity was not affected by sulfhydryl reagents.[180] Similar inhibitory effects have been recognized for human apolipoprotein A-I and A-II, which inhibit triglyceride hydrolysis by hepatic triglyceride lipase.[183] These findings suggest that the described inhibitors may be related to the utilization of cholesterol by the cells. However, any physiological significance of the inhibitors of acid lipase remains to be established.

PATHOPHYSIOLOGY

Function of Lysosomal Acid Lipase in Cellular Cholesterol Metabolism

Excluding erythrocytes, acid lipase is present in virtually all tissues of the body. Lysosomal acid lipase plays an important role in the cellular processing of plasma lipoproteins, and thus contributes both to homeostatic control of lipoprotein levels in blood and to prevention of cellular lipid overloading in the arterial wall.[51,91–93,116,184–189] In a series of elegant studies, Brown and Goldstein and their coworkers have established the obligatory role of lysosomal acid lipase in the cellular degradation of plasma low density lipoproteins (see Chap. 48). Using in vitro studies with cultured fibroblasts, they demonstrated a process whereby LDL is taken up by peripheral cells. This process involves a specific receptor on the plasma membrane of the cell which binds LDL and mediates its endocytosis. The endocytotic vesicles fuse with lysosomes, after which the apolipoproteins, cholesteryl esters, and probably other lipid constituents undergo hydrolysis by lysosomal enzymes.

The lysosomal degradation of LDL cholesteryl esters is catalyzed by the acid lipase activity (Fig. 64-7) that is deficient in CESD and Wolman disease.[82,83] The free sterol liberated is transferred from lysosomes to cellular membranes and initiates three important regulatory events. First, cellular synthesis of cholesterol is reduced through suppression of the activity of 3-hydroxy-3-methylglutaryl-CoA reductase, which controls the rate-limiting step in cholesterol metabolism. Second, synthesis of LDL receptors is repressed, leading gradually to a substantial reduction in the number of receptors on the cell surface and to reduced uptake of LDL. Third, cellular formation of cholesteryl esters is stimulated through activation of the microsomal membrane-bound acyl-CoA: cholesterol acyltransferase (ACAT). In the reaction catalyzed by this enzyme, the bulk of incoming plasma cholesterol, which was mainly esterified to linoleic acid in LDL, now becomes esterified with oleic (C18:1) acid, or other C_{14} to C_{18} saturated or monounsaturated fatty acids. Under certain conditions, the reesterified cholesterol may accumulate as cytoplasmic lipid droplets that resemble the droplets seen in the foam cells of atherosclerotic lesions. The hydrolysis of cytoplasmic cholesteryl esters appears to be mediated by a cytoplasmic cholesteryl ester hydrolase whose activity is resistant to lysosomal inhibitors such as chloroquine or ammonium chloride.[190,191] The failure of the lysosomotropic drugs to prevent cholesteryl ester mobilization suggests that cytoplasmic cholesteryl esters do not reenter lysosomes for hydrolysis prior to mobilization, but are hydrolyzed in the cytoplasm. The accumulation of cholesteryl ester–rich lipid droplets in cytoplasm might be at least in part due to a reduced neutral cholesteryl esterase activity that can be reactivated by agonists of adenylate cyclase (EC 4.6.11) and cyclic AMP–dependent protein kinase (EC 2.7.1.3.7).[118,163,166,192–195] These data suggest that both lysosomal and cytoplasmic cholesteryl ester catabolism are regulated by similar mechanisms.[195]

Macrophages, which play an important role in body cholesterol metabolism, take up and degrade (using lysosomal acid lipase) significant amounts of cholesterol derived from cell membranes and plasma lipoproteins. Since these cells cannot metabolize cholesterol, they need potent cholesterol release mechanisms to prevent the accumulation of cytoplasmic cholesteryl esters. It is generally accepted that HDL promotes cholesterol efflux from various cells[196] (see Chap. 49). It has been demonstrated that apo A-I–containing HDL_3 bind to specific receptor sites on macrophages, are internalized, and take up unesterified cholesterol from the cytoplasmic lipid droplets.[197,198] At the margin of the lipid droplets, cholesterol-

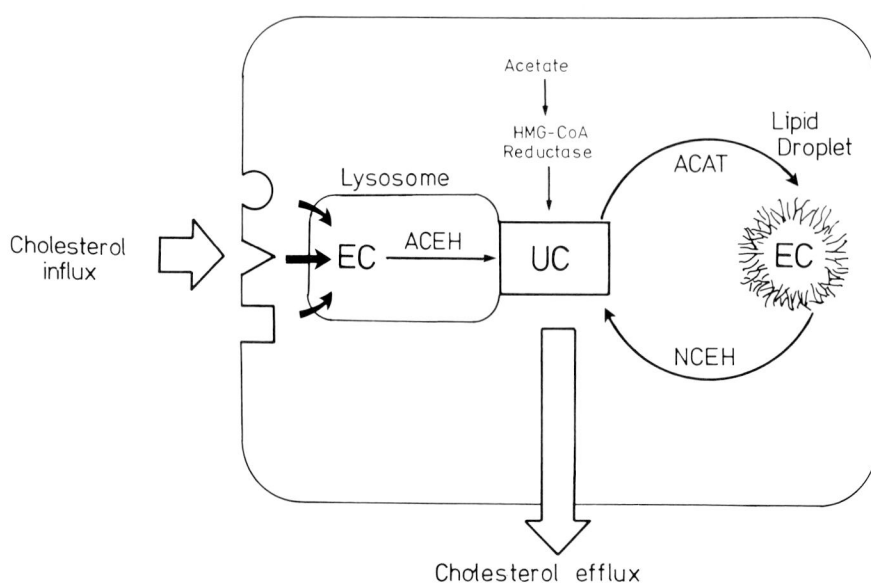

Fig. 64-7 Enzymes involved in intracellular cholesterol homeostasis. ACEH = acid cholesteryl ester hydrolase; NCEH = neutral cholesteryl ester hydrolase; ACAT = acyl CoA:cholesterol acyltransferase; EC = esterified; UC = unesterified cholesterol.

and phospholipid-rich "lamellar bodies" are formed upon attachment of smooth and rough endoplasmic reticulum.[164,165] These "lamellar bodies" are enveloped by a membrane which interacts with HDL-containing endosomes. The cholesterol-enriched HDL particles are ultimately secreted from the cells. Increased influx of cholesterol as well as inhibition of the cytoplasmic cholesterol-esterifying enzyme ACAT lead to a significant increase in HDL binding and HDL-mediated cholesterol efflux. In addition to the HDL-mediated release of cholesterol, macrophages and possibly other cells secrete upon cholesterol loading a second type of cholesterol containing "lamellar bodies" (Fig. 64-8), which originate from the lysosomal compartment.[158,159] The latter mechanism of cholesterol release, which has strong similarities with the mechanism described for the release of lung surfactant,[199–203] is independent of the presence of a cholesterol acceptor in the surrounding medium. Substances that stimulate acid hydrolase via cAMP-dependent kinases[163–166] and calcium antagonists[164,165] induce the formation and secretion of these vesicles. The latter effect can be best explained by the interaction of the calcium antagonists with adenosine A_1 receptors, thus leading to an increase in cellular cAMP levels.[204,205] It is suggested from these data and the observation that the formation of lamellar bodies is significantly impaired in CESD-fibroblasts[84] that lysosomal acid lipase activity plays a key role in the formation of the lysosomally derived lamellar bodies and may be also important for the secretion of these particles into the plasma compartment.

Plasma cholesteryl esters are derived from two main sources: (1) esterification of cholesterol in the intestine and transport of the esters into plasma by way of the lymph, in the company of dietary fat in chylomicrons, and (2) esterification of plasma lipoprotein–associated cholesterol by lecithin:cholesterol acyltransferase (see Chap. 46). Many details of the metabolism of chylomicrons are presented in Chaps. 45, 49, and 50. Once in plasma, these triglyceride-rich particles lose their triglycerides to extrahepatic tissues through the action of capillary-bound lipase, lipoprotein lipase, which has an alkaline pH optimum. The particles are reduced to "core remnants" rich in cholesterol, phospholipids, and certain surface apolipoproteins. In addition to the "core remnants," surface-derived discoidal cholesterol particles (surface remnants) are formed which contain cholesterol, phospholipid, and apolipoprotein A-I.[196] These "surface remnants" probably bind to the HDL-binding site of leukocytes and possibly other cells and

are transformed to spherical HDL.[206] The core remnants are removed by the liver at a rate which appears to be directly dependent upon the apolipoprotein composition in the remnant.[207,208] Present data suggest that apo E fosters the hepatic uptake of the "core remnant," while other apolipoproteins, such as apo C-III, may inhibit this function.[208,209] The cholesteryl esters taken up are hydrolyzed,[210–213] a process which is inhibited by chloroquine.[210,214]

Therefore, the hydrolysis of cholesteryl esters in macrophages and in the liver appears to occur inside lysosomes in a manner similar to the fate of LDL cholesteryl esters taken up by fibroblasts. The hepatic uptake of lipoproteins is not confined to parenchymal cells. Both parenchymal and nonparenchymal liver cells are active in binding and uptake of lipoproteins from the blood and have the capacity to degrade protein and cholesteryl ester moieties of lipoproteins.[215–218] In rat liver cells, about 50 percent of the total acid cholesteryl esterase activity is present in nonparenchymal cells.[218] This is compatible with the observation that cholesteryl ester storage occurs in both hepatocytes and Kupffer cells in patients affected with lysosomal acid lipase deficiency.

Lysosomal Acid Lipase and Atherogenesis

The deposition of lipids within diseased cells in arterial lesions occurs in two distinct forms, as cytoplasmic lipid droplets and as lipid-filled lysosomes.[91,184,187–189] The principal lipid accumulating in the lysosomes of aortic cells is the degradation product cholesterol, not the substrate cholesteryl ester,[187] and lipid-laden atheromatous cells display up to 3.5 times the acid cholesteryl esterase activity of normal aortic cells.[126] Cholesterol feeding of rabbits is associated with increased aortic acid lipase activity as well as other lysosomal enzyme activities, when compared to control animals.[126,219,220] Under these conditions acid lipase exhibits both a cholesteryl ester hydrolytic (pH optimum at 6.6) and a cholesteryl ester synthesizing (pH optimum at 6.2) activity, the latter at a rate approximately one-tenth the rate of hydrolysis.[221–223] Increased concentrations of cholesterol may stimulate esterification and diminish hydrolysis, while high concentrations of lecithin produce opposite effects.[221] Such conditions might well exist in lipid-laden lysosomes of arterial foam cells,[223] since both ACAT activity at neutral pH and cholesteryl ester synthesis at acid pH (possibly due to the reverse action of acid lipase) were found

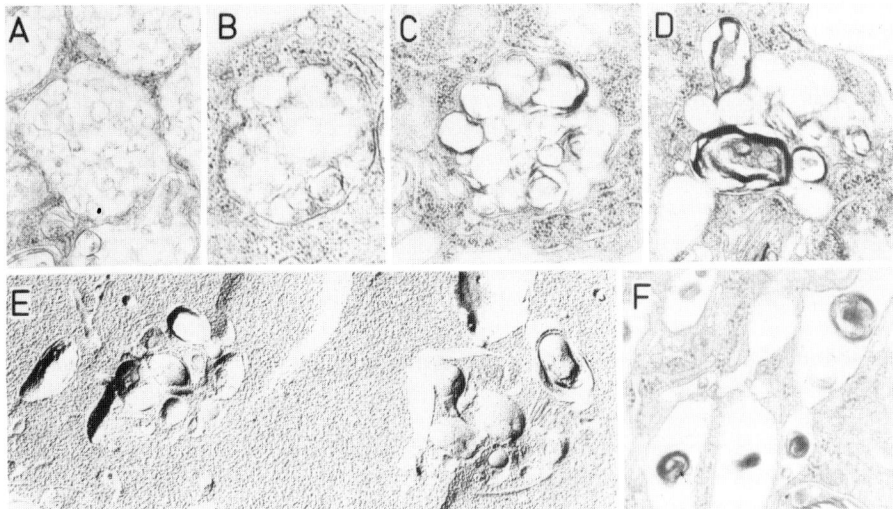

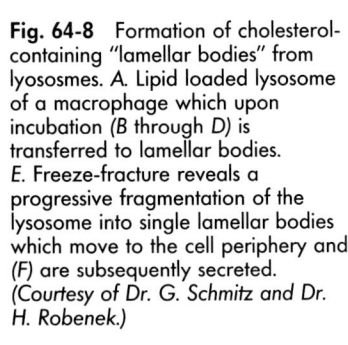

Fig. 64-8 Formation of cholesterol-containing "lamellar bodies" from lysosomes. A. Lipid loaded lysosome of a macrophage which upon incubation (B through D) is transferred to lamellar bodies. E. Freeze-fracture reveals a progressive fragmentation of the lysosome into single lamellar bodies which move to the cell periphery and (F) are subsequently secreted. (Courtesy of Dr. G. Schmitz and Dr. H. Robenek.)

to be increased in atherosclerotic lesions[224–227] and in foam cells isolated from lesions.[228,229]

Further considerations suggest that low activity of acid lipase can contribute under certain conditions to cholesteryl ester accumulation and foam cell formation in atherosclerotic lesions. In studies where acid lipase activity was measured in mononuclear leukocytes from patients with premature coronary heart disease,[230] the enzyme activity was significantly lower in the patients compared to age-matched controls. However, no correlation was observed between hypercholesterolemia or hypertriglyceridemia and acid lipase activity. Analysis of acid lipase in the patients' families provided evidence for an autosomal mutation associated with (or responsible for) the reduced enzymatic activity. This genetic factor could represent an independent risk factor for premature coronary heart disease.

Similar reductions in cholesteryl ester hydrolase activity were measured in freshly isolated mononuclear cells from patients with primary type II hypercholesterolemia, heterozygous familial hypercholesterolemia, and familial combined hyperlipidemia.[231] Diminished acid lipase activities also occurred in patients with atherosclerosis of the carotid arteries.[232]

Since aortic acid lipase activity has been found to be lower in those animal species relatively susceptible to atherosclerosis (rabbit, swine) than in relatively resistant species (rat, dog, guinea pig),[233] a relative deficiency of aortic acid lipase may explain the susceptibility to cholesterol-induced atherosclerosis. In spontaneously hypertensive rats, prolonged hypertension caused a decrease in aortic acid cholesteryl ester hydrolase activity.[234,235] However, in other experimentally induced types of hypertension, acid cholesteryl ester hydrolase was found either elevated concomitantly with other lysosomal enzymes (induction with desoxycorticosterone acetate) or unchanged, while other lysosomal enzymes were increased (induced by renal arterial constriction).[235,236] These data indicate that factors associated with some forms of hypertension may influence aortic acid cholesteryl ester hydrolase activity, but there are distinct differences in the response of lysosomal enzymes to etiologically different forms of hypertension.

Hajjar et al.,[237] who studied the atherogenic effect of Mareck disease herpes virus on cholesterol metabolism of cultured chicken arterial smooth-muscle cells, reported that infection of these cells with Mareck disease virus resulted in: (1) a decreased acid cholesteryl esterase activity, (2) decreased excretion of cholesterol, (3) increased ACAT activity, and (4) decreased cytoplasmic neutral cholesterol esterase activity. In addition, in the vessel wall from patients with premature coronary heart disease, antigens of herpes virus type 1, herpes virus type 2, and cytomegalovirus have been detected.[238,239] These findings suggest that infection of arterial wall cells by distinct viruses could promote the atherosclerotic process by alterations of cellular cholesteryl ester metabolism. In CESD, extensive premature atherosclerotic changes accompany the enzyme deficiency, whereas patients with Wolman disease usually succumb to adrenal or liver failure in infancy before vascular changes have had a chance to become manifest.

Lysosomal Acid Lipase in CESD and Wolman Disease

The activity of lysosomal acid lipase activity in cultured fibroblasts from patients with Wolman disease and CESD has been characterized by various methods, including enzymatic analy-

sis and histochemical and chemical procedures (Tables 64-2 and 64-3). With natural substrates, the acid lipase activity is less than 10 percent of controls in homozygotes and about 50 percent in heterozygotes in both conditions. Similar results can be obtained with a variety of artificial substrates (Tables 64-2 and 64-3), such as synthetic derivatives of nitrophenol or 4-methylumbelliferone. Acid lipase is distinct from phospholipase A, for there is no accumulation of phospholipids in patients affected with Wolman disease or CESD. Phospholipase A may be responsible for some of the residual activity measured with artificial substrates in the patients.

Immunologic quantification of the enzyme protein with antibodies to acid lipase in three patients with Wolman disease and three CESD patients revealed normal concentrations in both mutant cells while enzyme activity was greatly reduced.[240]

Cellogel electrophoresis of normal fibroblast extracts followed by staining for lysosomal acid lipase using 4-methylumbelliferyl oleate exhibits at least three acid lipase bands or isoenzymes, labeled A, B, and C.[38] The least anodal band, A, is the most prominent one in control fibroblasts but is reduced in heterozygotes (Wolman disease) and is undetectable in both Wolman disease and CESD cells.[38] The acid lipase isoenzyme pattern observed in cultured skin fibroblasts is also present in amniotic fluid cells, lymphocytes, and several tissues (liver, spleen, lymph nodes, aorta).[38] Prenatal diagnosis of Wolman disease has been established by the combined recognition of deficiency of acid lipase and deficiency of the A band in electrophoresis of amniotic cell extracts.[241,242]

The gene for the A band of acid lipase (LIPA) in humans has been localized to chromosome 10, while the B and C bands are probably controlled by one gene (LIPB) localized on chromosome 16.[243–247] This assignment was based on electrophoretic analysis of the enzyme in hybrid cells formed from human and mouse fibroblasts. Results with various inhibitors against the different bands favor the existence of a third gene (LIPI) independent of genes LIPA and LIPB.[246,247]

Studies of acid lipase with native emulsified substrates have shown that in both Wolman disease and CESD fibroblasts, acid cholesteryl ester hydrolase and triacylglycerol hydrolase activities are reduced proportionately,[72,248] while neutral cholesteryl ester hydrolase activity is preserved[249] but possibly down-regulated.[72,242] Moreover, proportional deficiencies of the two activities have also been measured in fibroblasts from patients with I-cell disease or pseudo-Hurler polydystrophy.[250] The latter conditions are characterized by multiple lysosomal enzyme deficiencies due to a defect of posttranslational glycosylation as related to the Man-6-P receptor cycle (see Chap. 62).

These findings, taken together, suggest that cholesteryl ester hydrolase and triacylglycerol hydrolase activities in fibroblasts reside in the same enzyme molecule (A isoenzyme). It is not clear at present to what extent the B and C isoenzymes which are retained in Wolman disease and CESD fibroblasts may account for the residual enzyme activity measured in mutant cells with both artificial and radiolabeled native substrates. Wide variation in the reported residual acid lipase activities in Wolman disease and CESD[38,54,230,248] suggests that definite diagnosis rests on the use of natural substrates.

The comparison of the rate of hydrolysis of cholesteryl esters with various chain length of fatty acids in lymphoid cell lines from normal subjects and from Wolman disease patients has shown that three cholesteryl esterases are present in normal lymphoid cell lines.[122,251–253] The first, active at pH 4.0, hydrolyzed preferentially cholesteryl esters of acyl chain length more than eight carbons. This activity is severely deficient in Wolman lymphoid cell lines and corresponds to acid lipase. The second and the third cholesteryl esterases, active at pH 6.0 and 8.0, respectively, hydrolyze shorter-chain derivatives. The pH 6.0 and 8.0 enzymes are not deficient in Wolman lymphoid cell lines. The pH 6.0 cholesterol esterase probably corresponds to the microsomal Mn^{2+}-dependent enzyme hydrolyzing cholesteryl oleate,[254] and the pH 8.0 enzyme could correspond to a microsomal carboxylesterase.[255]

In addition to cultured fibroblasts, leukocyte extracts can be used to establish the diagnosis of acid lipase deficiency (Table 64-4). The acid lipase activity assayed with 4-methylumbelliferyl esters is 10 to 15 times higher in mononuclear than in polymorphonuclear leukocytes.[56] Studies performed by Patsch et al.[256] suggested that the acid glycerol ester hydrolase and acid cholesteryl ester hydrolase in human mononuclear cells are different proteins (or at least involve different catalytic sites on the same protein). These authors measured both enzyme activities in different subcellular leukocyte fractions and noted that cholesteryl ester hydrolase activity is strongly associated with the lysosomal membrane and differs from the main glycerol ester hydrolase activity in solubilization properties.[256] However, from studies with purified acid lipase, it is suggested that a single enzyme hydrolyzes both triacylglycerols and cholesteryl esters.[170,173–176] In three patients affected with Wolman disease, low leukocyte activity of β-galactosidase has been reported in addition to the near absence of acid lipase activity.[50,55] The reason for this is not clear, but might be somehow related to the possible defects listed in Table 64-5.

Goldstein et al. compared the relative rates of hydrolysis of [³H] cholesteryl linoleate-LDL in normal and mutant CESD cells. They compared fibroblast extracts incubated at acid pH and intact fibroblast monolayers.[82] While the cholesteryl esterase activity of mutant cell lysates was less than one-twentieth that of normal lysates, the intact mutant cells showed rates of cholesteryl ester hydrolysis that were nearly one-third of normal cells. The origin of this discrepancy is not known, but it could be related to differences in the concentration or availability of substrate in the different conditions employed. The residual enzyme activity in intact CESD fibroblasts could be abolished by treatment of the cells with chloroquine, which suggested that the activity resided in the lysosomes.

Similar findings have been reported with various substrates in intact fibroblasts and fibroblast lysates from both Wolman disease and CESD patients.[257] Although acid lipase in cell lysates was less than 1 percent of control activity in both disorders, considerable differences were observed in intact fibroblasts from Wolman disease (10 to 22 percent of control) and CESD patients (28 to 49 percent of control). The findings in intact cells appear to provide a biochemical explanation for the different phenotypes associated with the two disorders.

Normally, cholesteryl esters bound to LDL demonstrate a strong regulatory effect on cholesterol metabolism in fibroblasts. When the fibroblasts are exposed to LDL, the activity of HMG-CoA reductase falls and that of fatty acyl-CoA:cholesterol acyltransferase (EC 2.3.1.26) (ACAT) rises. In both CESD and Wolman disease cells exposed to LDL, this effect of LDL is decreased. The inability to release free cholesterol from lysosomal cholesteryl esters obviously results in elevated synthesis of endogenous cholesterol and increased production of apo B–containing lipoproteins.[258] The reduced responsiveness to LDL in acid lipase-deficient fibroblasts can be restored when the mutant cells are cocultivated with normal fibroblasts.[83] It appears, therefore, that cholesteryl ester

hydrolase is secreted by normal fibroblasts into the culture medium and can be taken up in an active form by the mutant cells via Man-6-P receptors.[112,113] Studies in CESD fibroblasts have further revealed that hydrolysis of those cholesteryl esters synthesized within the cell is not impaired.[83] Thus, the lysosomal acid lipase is essential for the hydrolysis of cholesteryl esters entering the cell bound to lipoproteins.

In view of the extensive cholesteryl ester storage in the adrenals of patients affected with Wolman disease, it is interesting to note that the adrenal glands possess high concentrations of receptors for lipoproteins and are able to take up and utilize cholesteryl esters carried in plasma LDL[259,260] and HDL.[261] The steroids secreted by the adrenals are derived in large part from lipoprotein cholesterol. However, failure of lysosomal hydrolysis of lipoprotein cholesteryl esters in adrenal glands does not necessarily imply impairment of hormone production. Potentially, there are at least three major sources of cholesterol available to cells to meet their metabolic needs. These include cholesterol delivered directly from the uptake of lipoproteins into cells (involving lysosomal cholesteryl ester hydrolase), hydrolysis of stored cytoplasmic cholesteryl esters (involving neutral cholesteryl ester hydrolase), and cholesterol synthesized de novo. The study of patients with Wolman disease and CESD might add information about the quantitative importance of these pathways in different tissues, but steroidogenesis has not been investigated in these syndromes.

The precise origin of plasma LDL and the decreased concentrations of plasma HDL in CESD are not yet understood. Of particular interest is the abnormal ratio of HDL_2 to HDL_3 in patient 23.[84] In this patient with elevated plasma cholesterol but normal triglycerides, lipoprotein lipase activity was found to be normal, while hepatic lipase activity was significantly reduced. Moreover, the HDL_2 fraction contained considerable amounts of apolipoprotein C-III₃, which represents the excess sialylated precursor form of apolipoprotein C-III, while C-III₂ was almost absent in this lipoprotein fraction (Fig. 64-9). In contrast to HDL_2, the VLDL and HDL_3 fraction did not contain detectable amounts of apolipoprotein C-III₃ but revealed a normal pattern of the other sialylated forms of apolipoprotein C-III. Thus, the regular interaction of HDL_2 with hepatocytes might be disturbed in CESD, either due to the presence of excess sialylated apolipoprotein C-III or due to a down-regulation or defective function of the heparin-releasable liver lipase. Down-regulation of hepatic LDL receptors due to the high concentration of intracellular cholesterol could also explain the elevated plasma LDL concentrations.

In patient 19, who had elevated plasma cholesterol and triglyceride levels, lipoprotein lipase was found normal while hepatic lipase values were increased.[262] This patient exhibited very low levels of high density lipoproteins which consisted almost exclusively of HDL_3. The authors speculated that the

Fig. 64-9 Apolipoprotein C-III₃ in HDL_2 from CESD patient 23.

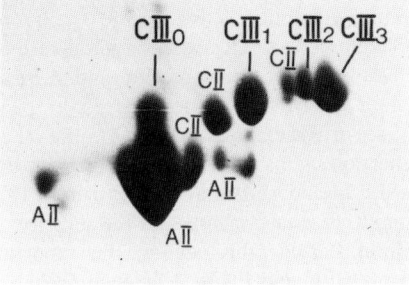

low plasma HDL levels in this patient could be a consequence of increased hepatic lipase activity.

The comparison of acid lipase activity in fibroblasts and hepatocytes from CESD and Wolman disease patients revealed the virtual absence of the enzyme activity in the fibroblasts of both patients, while hepatic acid lipase activity was 23 percent of normal in CESD and only 4 percent of normal in Wolman disease.[114] The hepatic neutral lipase activity was normal in Wolman disease but was more than twofold increased in CESD.

It appears from the very different clinical course of CESD and Wolman disease that the residual acid lipase activity directed against LDL cholesteryl esters is sufficient in CESD to keep the lysosomal accumulation of cholesteryl esters and subsequent cellular damage in most extrahepatic tissues to a level compatible with fairly normal life. In Wolman disease the residual activity is insufficient and causes overwhelming accumulation of cholesteryl esters and destruction of cell function.

GENETICS

Mode of Inheritance

Wolman disease is inherited as an autosomal recessive disorder. Males and females are affected in about equal numbers. In the original family reported by Wolman and his colleagues,[3,4] three sibs died of the disease, and numerous families since have had more than one affected child. The parents of the original patients and several subsequent pairs of parents were related,[29,32,34,36] although consanguinity has been denied in the majority of affected families.[1,2] At least six cases, possibly seven,[22] have been reported in Israel, and all but one of these have apparently been Jews of Iraqi or Iranian origin.[29] The other patients have been reported from North America, Western Europe, Pakistan, China, or Japan.

CESD is also inherited as an autosomal recessive disorder. Patients 4, 6, and 8 had esophageal varices and seemingly a more severe disorder than the others. Some patients have not been diagnosed by enzymatic assays or tissue analyses, and the presence of hepatomegaly in relatives cannot be accepted as evidence of vertical transmission of CESD. No consanguinity in parents has yet been documented.

In general, Wolman disease and CESD can be distinguished by their very different clinical course. In Wolman disease, there is marked accumulation of both triglycerides and cholesteryl esters, whereas storage of cholesteryl esters is much more pronounced in CESD. Enzymatic data do not explain why tissue triglycerides are not elevated in most cases with CESD. There is, however, a certain degree of phenotypic variation among the patients with acid lipase deficiency, a phenomenon common to most inborn lysosomal diseases. Besides the acute infantile form of Wolman disease, other forms may also exist which are of later onset and follow a less severe and more prolonged course.[43] Suzuki et al. described an atypical case of Wolman disease with absence of splenomegaly and normal adrenal glands.[37] Lack of adrenal calcification was also emphasized in two further cases of Wolman disease.[21,50] On the other hand, adrenal calcification, considered pathognomonic for Wolman disease, has also been observed in CESD (patient 10). The time of manifestation of liver cirrhosis and the severity of related symptoms differ considerably among the reported cases of CESD. Patients with acid lipase deficiency probably

represent not only homozygous expression of different alleles but occasionally also genetic compounds. The four Mexican American children with CESD (patients 8, 9, 10, and 26) have suffered acute or chronic liver failure before adulthood, and a more severe allele for CESD may exist in that ethnic group.

Heterozygote Detection

It is now established that heterozygotes for acid lipase deficiency are detectable by enzyme assay. Young and Patrick[55] reported that leukocytes of the mother, father, and a sib of one patient with Wolman disease contained about half the normal activity of the acid hydrolase. Lake[263] reported intermediate activity in lymphocytes on blood films prepared from obligate heterozygotes affected with Wolman disease. Schaub et al.[50] demonstrated subnormal levels of acid lipase activity with both the natural and synthetic substrates in the parents of one patient with Wolman disease. These authors further noted that the patient's father and mother had elevated activity of other lysosomal hydrolases in their leukocytes. A fluorometric assay of acid lipase in human leukocytes has been described which requires only 1 ml blood.[264] The test should be sensitive enough to distinguish subnormal levels of the enzyme in obligate carriers of Wolman disease. In addition to leukocytes, cultured skin fibroblasts can be used to establish subnormal levels of acid lipase in heterozygous patients.[52,264]

In CESD, the parents and two sibs of patients 8, 9, and 10 had about 50 percent of the mean activity of acid lipase in control leukocytes and cultured fibroblasts.[63] Leukocytes from the mother of patient 11 contained about 40 percent of control acid lipase activity.[64]

Thus, present data suggest that heterozygotes for both forms of acid ester hydrolase deficiency will have detectable abnormalities in enzyme assays, but that the two forms of the disease cannot be separated by such measurements alone. Vacuolation of peripheral lymphocytes does not permit heterozygote detection, since this is also seen in homozygous abnormal patients and is also a common nonspecific finding in other lysosomal hydrolase deficiencies. Prenatal diagnosis of Wolman disease has been established by quantitative assays and electrophoresis of lysosomal acid lipase in cultured amniotic fluid cells.[241,242]

DIAGNOSIS

Wolman disease must be considered in any infant with hepatosplenomegaly, gastrointestinal symptoms, and failure to thrive. The earliest examination should include careful attention to neurologic development. X-rays should be taken of the lungs and bones and of the abdomen to observe the calcification of the adrenals that is almost invariably present. Calcification of the adrenals may be observed in many other conditions such as Addison disease,[212] adrenal teratomas,[265] hemorrhage,[3,18,21] neuroblastoma, ganglioneuroma, adrenal cysts, adrenal cortical carcinoma, and pheochromocytoma.[3,18] The presence of bilateral adrenal calcification associated with hepatosplenomegaly and gastrointestinal symptoms strongly supports the diagnosis of Wolman disease. It is noteworthy that adrenal calcification has never been seen in Niemann-Pick disease. The decreased adrenal responsiveness that has been observed in some cases of Wolman disease must be differentiated from the syndrome of X-linked adrenoleukodystrophy with adrenal insufficiency and cutaneous melanosis (see Chap. 58).[266] This syndrome has a more protracted course, definite signs of central nervous system involvement, and is not easily confused with Wolman disease. Moreover, acid lipase activity is normal in fibroblasts[267] and brain tissue homogenates[268] of patients affected with adrenoleukodystrophy. Wolman disease should be further distinguished from conditions in which triglycerides instead of cholesteryl esters accumulate in tissues.[71,269] One patient with triglyceride accumulation in liver without cholesteryl ester storage has been described in association with acid lipase deficiency.[72] Numerous metabolic diseases (galactosemia, fructose intolerance, certain disorders of amino acid metabolism) may result in secondary triglyceride accumulation. *Triglyceride storage disease* is a separate biochemical and clinical entity accompanied by excessive extralysosomal triglyceride accumulation in various tissues due to a number of different metabolic defects in the pathways of triglyceride mobilization.[269,270]

A severe congenital triglyceride storage disorder leading to death in the neonatal period has been reported in a unique family under the name of "fatty metamorphosis of the viscera."[271] Other patients have been described with phenotypes similar to those of Wolman disease but with a longer life span.[23,55,272] Another generalized accumulation of neutral lipids also due to a profound deficiency of acid lipase with features of the senior syndrome has been reported.[273,274]

CESD may be easily confused with glycogen storage disease (Chap. 12). In both disorders, marked hepatomegaly and hyperlipemia without splenic enlargement may appear in a child whose mental and physical development is otherwise unremarkable. Provocative tests for adequacy for glycogenolysis could be performed, but enzymatic assay of acid lipase on leukocytes or fibroblasts should be diagnostic and should preclude the need for liver biopsy to establish a diagnosis of CESD. The absence of jaundice in any patient with CESD except late in the disease suggests that the disorder need not be confused with congenital biliary cirrhosis. A normal proportion of esters in the total cholesterol in plasma should help exclude biliary obstruction. Vacuolation of hepatocytes can also be observed by light microscopy in Niemann-Pick disease type B; several forms of mucopolysaccharidoses; and G_{M1} gangliosidosis. The latter disorders can be easily distinguished from CESD by enzyme assay and appear different on examination of cryostat sections of liver under polarized light. In CESD, liver tissue reveals birefringence, which disappears upon heating the tissue to 50 to 60°C and reappears upon cooling. Heat-sensitive birefringence of liver tissue is highly suggestive of CESD or Wolman disease and is not observed in other lysosomal deficiency states.

A child suspected of having CESD should have biochemical study of acid lipase activity in leukocytes and cultured skin fibroblasts. Definitive diagnosis of acid lipase deficiency is feasible by analysis of the clinical picture and assay of acid ester hydrolase activity in cultured skin fibroblasts or peripheral leukocytes. Substrates for the determination of acid ester hydrolase include artificial compounds, such as nitrophenyl laurate and umbelliferyl oleate, as well as cholesteryl oleate solubilized by detergents or incorporated into LDL. Natural substrates are more specific for acid lipase determinations and should be preferred. Sufficient control data must be obtained, and the tissue from the patient with either Wolman disease or cholesteryl ester storage disease should have only 1 to 10 percent of normal activity. It should rarely if ever be necessary to employ open biopsy of the liver for confirmation of enzyme deficiency or abnormal storage of cholesteryl esters and triglycerides.

TREATMENT

There is no specific treatment for Wolman disease and CESD. Replacement of the missing enzyme activity has not been attempted. However the suppression of cholesterol synthesis and apolipoprotein B production induced by HMG-CoA reductase inhibitors might be considered a useful therapeutic principle. It has been recently demonstrated in a patient with CESD that the HMG-CoA reductase inhibitor lovastatin (20 mg twice daily) resulted in significant reductions in plasma cholesterol, triglycerides, and LDL cholesterol.[258] Therapy also reduced apo B in VLDL and LDL and urine mevalonate levels. In addition to these changes in plasma lipoproteins, this therapy might also have a beneficial effect on hepatosplenomegaly and adrenal dysfunction. Patient 26 with CESD underwent liver transplantation for chronic liver failure and is well 2 years after the procedure,[84b] but a detailed report is not available.

REFERENCES

1. FREDRICKSON DS, FERRANS VJ: Acid cholesteryl ester hydrolase deficiency (Wolman's disease and cholesteryl ester storage disease), in Stanbury JB, Wyngaarden JB, Fredrickson DS (eds): *The Metabolic Basis of Inherited Disease*, 4th ed. New York, McGraw-Hill, 1978, p 670.
2. ASSMANN G, FREDRICKSON DS: Acid lipase deficiency: Wolman's disease and cholesteryl ester storage disease, in Stanbury JB, Wyngaarden JB, Fredrickson DS, Goldstein JL, Brown MS (eds): *The Metabolic Basis of Inherited Disease*, 5th ed. McGraw-Hill, New York, 1983, p 803.
3. ABRAMOV A, SCHORR S, WOLMAN M: Generalized xanthomatosis with calcified adrenals. *J Dis Chil* 91:282, 1956.
4. WOLMAN M, STERK VV, GATT S, FRENKEL M: Primary familial xanthomatosis with involvement and calcification of the adrenals: Report of two more cases in siblings of a previously described infant. *Pediatrics* 28:742, 1961.
5. WOLMAN M: Histochemistry of lipids in pathology, in Graumann W, Neumann K (eds): *Handbuch der Histochemie*. Stuttgart, Fischer-Verlag, 1964, vol 5, p 228.
6. CROCKER AC, VAWTER GF, NEUHAUSER EBD, ROSOWSKY A: Wolman's disease: Three new patients with a recently described lipidosis. *Pediatrics* 35:627, 1965.
7. ALEXANDER WS: Niemann-Pick-disease: Report of a case showing calcification in the adrenal glands. *NZ Med J* 45:43, 1946.
8. NEUHAUSER EBD, KIRKPATRICK JA, WEINTRAUB H: Wolman's disease: A new lipidosis. *Ann Radiol (Paris)* 8:175, 1965.
9. ROSOWSKY A, CROCKER AC, TRITES DH, MODEST EJ: Gas-liquid chromatography analysis of the tissue sterol fraction in Wolman's disease and related lipidoses. *Biochim Biophys Acta* 98:617, 1965.
10. KONNO T, FUJI M, WATANUKI T, KOIZUMI K: Wolman's disease: The first case in Japan. *Tohoku J Exp Med* 90:375, 1966.
11. SPIEGEL-ADOLF M, BAIRD HW, MCCAFFERTY M: Hematologic studies in Niemann-Pick and Wolman's disease (cytology and electrophoresis). *Cofin Neurol* 28:399, 1966.
12. CAFFEY J, SILVERMANN FN: *Pediatric X-ray Diagnosis*, 5th ed. Chicago, Year Book Medical Publishers, 1967, pp 672–674.
13. SLOVITER HA, JANIC V, NAIMAN JL: Lipid synthesis by red blood cell preparations in Wolman's disease (a familial lipidosis). *Clin Chim Acta* 20:423, 1968.
14. GUAZZI GC, MARTIN JJ, PHILIPPART M, ROELS H, VAN DER ERCKEN H, DELBEKE MJ, VRINTS L: Wolman's disease. *Eur Neurol* 1:334, 1968.
15. GUAZZIA GC, MARTIN JJ, PHILIPPART M, ROELS H, HOOFT C, VAN DER ERCKEN H, DELBEKE MJ, VRINTS J: Wolman's disease: Distribution and significance of the central nervous system lesions. *Pathol Eur* 3:266, 1968.
16. KAHANA D, BERANT M, WOLMAN M: Primary familial xanthomatosis with adrenal involvement (Wolman's disease): Report of a further case with

nervous system involvement and pathogenetic considerations. *Pediatrics* 42:70, 1968.

17. KAMOSHITA S, LANDING BH: Distribution of lesions in myenteric plexus and gastrointestinal mucosa in lipidoses and other neurological disorders of children. *Am J Clin Pathol* 49:312, 1968.

18. MARKS M, MARCUS AJ: Wolman's disease. *Can Med Assoc J* 99:232, 1968.

19. PARTIN JC, MEREU TR, SCHUBERT WK: Intestinal absorptive epithelium in Wolman's cholesterol lipidoses, in Arcenaux CJ (ed): *Proc 26th Ann Meeting Electron Microscope Soc Am* Baton Rouge, Claitor's, 1968, pp 194–195.

20. WOLMAN M: Involvement of nervous tissue in primary familial xanthomatosis with adrenal calcification. *Pathol Eur* 3:259, 1968.

21. MARSHALL WC, OCKENDEN BC, FOSBROOKE AS, CUMINGS JN: Wolman's disease: A rare lipidosis with adrenal calcification. *Arch Dis Child* 44:331, 1968.

22. WERBIN BZ, WOLMAN M: Primary familial xanthomatosis with involvement and calcification of the adrenals (Wolman's disease). *Harefuah* 74:283, 1968.

23. PATRICK AD, LAKE BD: Deficiency of an acid lipase in Wolman's disease. *Nature* 222:1067, 1969.

24. ETO Y, KITAGAWA T: Wolman's disease with hypolipoproteinemia and acanthocytosis: Clinical and biochemical observations. *J Pediatr* 77:862, 1970.

25. LAKE BD, PATRICK AD: Wolman's disease: Deficiency of E600-resistant acid esterase activity with storage of lipids in lysosomes. *J Pediatr* 77:862, 1970.

26. LOUGH J, FAWCETT J, WIEGENSBERG B: Wolman's disease: An electron microscopic, histochemical and biochemical study. *Arch Pathol* 89:103, 1970.

27. LOWDEN JA, BARON AJ, WENTWORTH P: Wolman's disease: A microscopic and histochemical and biochemical study showing accumulation of ceroid and esterified cholesterol. *Can Med Assoc J* 102:402, 1970.

28. KYRIAKIDES EC, FILIPPONE N, PAUL B, GRATTAN W, BALINT JA: Lipid studies in Wolman's disease. *Pediatrics* 46:431, 1970.

29. WALLIS K, GROSS M, KOHN R, ZAIDMAN J: A case of Wolman's disease. *Helv Paediat Acta* 26:98, 1971.

30. LECLERC JL, HOULD F, LELIEVRE M, GAGNE F: Maladie de Wolman: Étude anatomo-clinique d'une nouvelle observation avec absence de calcifications radiologiques et macroscopiques des surrenales. *Laval Med* 42:461, 1971.

31. PHILIPPART M: Wolman's disease. *J Pediatr* 79:173, 1971.

32. RAAFAT R, HASHEMIAN MP, ABRISHAMI MA: Wolman's disease: Report of two new cases with a review of the literature. *Am J Clin Pathol* 59:490, 1973.

33. KAMALIAN N, DUDLEY AW, BEROUKHIM F: Wolman's disease with jaundice and subarachnoid hemorrhage. *Am J Dis Child* 126:671, 1973.

34. UNO Y, TANIGUCHI A, TANAKA E: Histochemical studies in Wolman's disease: Report of an autopsy case accompanied with a large amount of milky ascites. *Acta Pathol Jap* 23:779, 1973.

35. WOLF H, NOLTE K, NOLTE R: Das neue Syndrom: Wolman-Syndrom. *Monatsschr Kinderheilkd* 121:697, 1973.

36. LAJO A, GRACIA R, NAVARRO M, NISTAL M, ROBODAN B: Enfermedad de Wolman en su forma aguda infantil. *An Esp Pediatr* 7:438, 1974.

37. SUZUKI Y, KAWAI S, KOBAYASHI A, OHBE Y, ENDO H: Partial deficiency of acid lipase with storage of triglycerides and cholesterol esters in liver. *Clin Chim Acta* 69:219, 1976.

38. CORTNER JA, COATES PM, SWOBODA E, SCHNATZ JD: Genetic variation of lysosomal acid lipase. *Pediatr Res* 10:927, 1976.

39. ELLIS JE, PATRICK D: Wolman disease in a Pakistani infant. *Am J Dis Child* 130:545, 1976.

40. HARRISON RB, FRANCKE P JR: Radiographic findings in Wolman's disease. *Radiology* 124:188, 1977.

41. OZSOYLU S, GÜRGERY A, KOCAK N, OZORAN Y, OZORAN A, KERSE I, CILIV G: Wolman's disease: A case report with lipid, chromosome and electron-microscopic studies. *Turk J Pediatr* 19:57, 1977.

42. von BASSEWITZ DB, ROGGENKAMP K, STREHL H, OTTO H: Wolmansche Erkrankung. *Verh Dtsch Ges Pathol* 62:530, 1978.

43. OZORAN Y, OZORAN Y, KERSE I, GÜRGEY A, OZSOYLU S, KOCAK N, CILIV G: An ultrastructural study in a case of Wolman's disease (clinical, biochemical, light and electron microscopic study). *Turk J Pediatr* 20:100, 1978.

44. HO FC, LIN HJ, CHAN WC: Wolman's disease: The first reported Chinese patient. *Mod Med Asia* 14:23, 1978.

45. SCHAFFNER T, ELNER VM, BAUER M, WISSLER RW: Acid lipase: A histochemical and biochemical study using triton X 100-naphtylpalmitate micelles. *J Histochem Cytochem* 26:696, 1978.

46. STY JR, STARSHAK RJ: Scintigraphy in Wolman's disease. *Clin Nucl Med* 3:397, 1978.

47. YOUNG LW, STY JR, BABBITT JP: Wolman's disease. *Am J Dis Child* 133:959, 1979.

48. BYRD JC, POWERS JM: Wolman's disease: Ultrastructural evidence of lipid accumulation in central nervous system. *Acta Neuropathol (Berl)* 45:37, 1979.

49. PERMANETTER W, MÜLLER-HÖCKER J, HÜBNER G, SCHAUB J: Wolman's disease. *Med Welt* 30:1783, 1979.

50. SCHAUB J, JANKA GE, CHRISTOMANOU H, SANDHOFF K, PERMANETTER W, HÜBNER G, MEISTER P: Wolman's disease: Clinical, biochemical and ultrastructural studies in an unusual case without striking adrenal calcification. *Eur J Pediatr* 135:45, 1980.

51. SLOAN HR, FREDRICKSON DS: Enzyme deficiency in cholesteryl ester storage disease. *J Clin Invest* 51:1923, 1972.

52. KYRIAKIDES EC, PAUL B, BALIN JA: Lipid accumulation and acid lipase deficiency in fibroblasts from a family with Wolman's disease, and their apparent correction in vitro. *J Lab Clin Med* 80:810, 1972.

53. GUY GJ, BUTTERWORTH J: Acid esterase activity in cultured skin fibroblasts and amniotic fluid cells using 4-methylumbelliferyl palmitate. *Clin Chim Acta* 84:361, 1978.

54. BURTON BK, EMERY D, MUELLER HW: Lysosomal acid lipase in cultivated fibroblasts: Characterization of enzyme activity in normal and enzymatically deficient cell lines. *Clin Chim Acta* 101:25, 1980.

55. YOUNG EP, PATRICK AD: Deficiency of acid esterase activity in Wolman's disease. *Arch Dis Child* 45:664, 1970.

56. COATES PM, CORTNER JA, HOFFMAN GM, BROWN SA: Acid lipase activity of human lymphocytes. *Biochim Biophys Acta* 572:225, 1979.

57. FREDRICKSON DS: Newly recognized disorders of cholesterol metabolism. *Ann Intern Med* 58:718, 1963.

58. FREDRICKSON DS, SLOAN HR, FERRANS VJ, DEMOSKY SJ JR: Cholesteryl ester storage disease: A most unusual manifestation of deficiency of two lysosomal enzyme activities. *Trans Assoc Am Physicians* 85:109, 1972.

59. LAGERON A, CAROLI J, STRALIN H, BARBIER P: Polycorie cholésterique de l'adulte. I. Étude clinique, electronique, histochimique. *Presse Med* 75:2785, 1967.

60. INFANTE R, POLONOVSKI J, CAROLI J: Polycorie cholésterique de l'adulte. II. Étude biochimique. *Presse Med* 75:2829, 1967.

61. SCHIFF L, SCHUBERT WK, MCADAMS AJ, SPIEGEL EL, O'DONNELL JF: Hepatic cholesterol ester storage disease, a familial disorder. I. Clinical aspects. *Am J Med* 44:538, 1968.

62. PARTIN JC, SCHUBERT WK: Small intestinal mucosa in cholesterol ester storage disease: A light and electron microscope study. *Gastroenterology* 57:542, 1969.

63. BEAUDET AL, FERRY GD, NICHOLS BL, ROSENBERG HS: Cholesterol ester storage disease: Clinical, biochemical and pathological studies. *J Pediatr* 90:910, 1977.

64. ORME RLE: Wolman's disease: An unusual presentation. *Proc R Soc Med* 63:489, 1970.

65. WOLF H, HUG G, MICHAELIS R, NOLTE K: Seltene angeborene Erkrankung mit Cholesterinester-Speicherung in der Leber. *Helv Paediat Acta* 29:105, 1974.

66. ALAGILLE D, COURTECUISSE V: Surcharge hepatique a esters du cholesterol (deux observations). *J Parisiennes Pediatr* 3:465, 1970.

67. LAGERON A, LICHTENSTEIN H, BODIN F, CONTE M: Polycorie cholesterolique de l'adulte: A propos d'une nouvelle observation. *Nouv Presse Med* 3:1233, 1974.

68. LAGERON A, LICHTENSTEIN H, BODIN F, CONTE M: Polycorie cholesterolique de l'adulte: Aspects cliniques et histochemiques. *Med Chir Dig* 4:9, 1975.

69. LAGERON A: Histoenzymologie de la polycorie cholesterolique. *Med Chir Dig* 7:155, 1978.

70. GAUTIER M, LAPONS D, RAULIN J: Maladie de surcharge a esters du cholesterol chez l'enfant. Étude biochimique comparative de cultures d'hepatocytes et de fibroblastes. *Arch Fr Pediatr (suppl)* 35:38, 1978.

71. LAGERON A, GAUTIER M, SCOTTO J: Particularités clinique et histoenzymologique del la polycorie cholesterolique chez deux enfants d'une meme fratie. *Arch Fr Pediatr (suppl)* 42:605, 1985.

72. AUBERT-TULKENS G, van HOOF F: Acid lipase deficiency: Clinical and biochemical heterogeneity. *Acta Paediatr Belg* 32:239, 1979.

73. KELLER E, KÜNNERT B, BRAUN W: Cholesterinspeicherkrankheit der Leber im Kindesalter. *Dtsch Z Verdau Stoffwechselkr* 37:231, 1977.

74. KÜNNERT B, COSSEL L, KELLER E: Zur Diagnostik und Morphologie der Leber bei Cholesterinester-Speicherkrankheit. *Zentralbl Allg Pathol Anat* 123:71, 1979.

75. PFEIFFER U, JESCHKE R: Cholesterylester-Speicherkrankheit. *Virchows Arch (B)* 33:17, 1980.

76. KUNTZ HD, MAY B, SCHEJBAL V, ASSMANN G: Cholesterinester-Speicherkrankheit der Leber. *Leber Magen Darm* 11:258, 1981.

77. BURKE JA, SCHUBERT WK: Deficient activity of hepatic acid lipase in cholesterol ester storage disease. *Science* 176:309, 1972.

78. PARTIN JC, SCHUBERT WK: The ultrastructural and lipid composition of cultured skin fibroblasts in cholesterol ester storage disease. *Pediatr Res* 6:393, 1972.

79. BEAUDET AL, LIPSON MH, FERRY GD, NICHOLS BL JR: Acid lipase in cultured fibroblasts: Cholesterol ester storage disease. *J Lab Clin Med* 84:54, 1974.

80. SCHÄFER HE, ASSMANN G, SCHMITZ G, MAY B: Histochemical and electron microscopic studies in cholesterol ester storage disease. In preparation.

81. DESAI PK, ASTRIN KH, THUNG SN, GORDON RE, SHORT MP, COATES PM, DESNICK RJ: Cholesteryl ester storage disease: Pathologic change in an affected fetus. *Am J Med Genet* 26:689, 1987.

82. GOLDSTEIN JL, DANA SE, FAUST JR, BEAUDET AL, BROWN MS: Role of lysosomal acid lipase in the metabolism of plasma low density lipoprotein: Observations in cultured fibroblasts from a patient with cholesteryl ester storage disease. *J Biol Chem* 250:8487, 1975.

83. BROWN MS, SABHANI MK, BRAUNSCHEDE GY, GOLDSTEIN JS: Restoration of a regularly response to low density lipoprotein in acid lipase-deficient human fibroblasts. *J Biol Chem* 251:3277, 1976.

84. SCHMITZ G, ROBENEK H, BRENNHAUSEN B, ASSMANN G: Tissue culture studies and HDL subclass analysis in cholesteryl ester storage disease. *J Lipid Res* (submitted) 1988.

84a. CAGLE PT, FERRY GD, BEAUDET AL, HAWKINS EP: Clinicopathologic conference: Pulmonary hypertension in an 18-year-old girl with cholesteryl ester storage disease (CESD) *Am J Med Genet* 24:711, 1986.

84b. FERRY GD, BEAUDET AL: Personal communication.

84c. KELLY DR, HOEG JM, DEMOSKY S JR, BREWER HB: Characterization of plasma lipids and lipoproteins in cholesteryl ester storage disease. *Biochem Med* 33:29, 1985.

85. FERRANS VJ, BUJA LM, ROBERTS WC, FREDRICKSON DS: The spleen in type I hyperlipoproteinemia: Histochemical, biochemical, microfluorimetric, and electron microscopic observations. *Am J Pathol* 64:67, 1971.

86. FERRANS VJ, ROBERTS WC, LEVY RI, FREDRICKSON DS: Chylomicrons and the formation of foam cells in type I hyperlipoproteinemia: A morphologic study. *Am J Pathol* 70:253, 1973.

87. DREVON CA, HOVIG T: The effects of cholesterol/fat feeding on lipid levels and morphological structures in liver, kidney and spleen in guinea pigs. *Acta Pathol Microbiol Scand* 85A:1, 1977.

88. HAYASHI H, WINSHIP DH, STERNLIEB I: Lipolyosomes in human liver: Distribution in livers with fatty infiltration. *Gastroenterology* 73:651, 1977.

89. MICHELS VV, DRISCOLL DJ, FERRY GD, DUFF DF, BEAUDET AL: Pulmonary vascular obstruction associated with cholesteryl ester storage disease. *J Pediatr* 94:621, 1979.

90. HILL SC, HOEG JM, DWYER AJ, VUCICH JJ, DOPPMAN JL: CT findings in acid lipase deficiency: Wolman's disease and cholesteryl ester storage disease. *J Comput Assist Tomogr* 7:815, 1983.

91. GOLDFISCHER S, SCHILLER B, WOLINSKY H: Lipid accumulation in smooth muscle cell lysosomes in primate atherosclerosis. *Am J Pathol* 78:497, 1975.

92. PETERS TT, TAKANO R, de DUVE C: in Potter R, Knight J (eds): *Atherogenesis, Initiating Factors, Ciba Foundation Symposium 12.* Amsterdam, Elsevier, 1973, p 197.

93. De DUVE C: Exploring cells with a centrifuge. *Science* 198:186, 1975.

94. ASSMANN G, FREDRICKSON DS, SLOAN HR, FALES HM, HIGHET RJ: Accumulation of oxygenated steryl esters in Wolman's disease. *J Lipid Res* 16:28, 1975.

95. LIN HJ, LIE KEN JIE MS, HO FC: Accumulation of glyceryl ether lipids in Wolman's disease. *J Lipid Res* 17:53, 1976.

96. FREDRICKSON DS: Tangier disease, in Stanbury JB, Wyngaarden JB, Fredrickson DS (eds): *The Metabolic Basis of Inherited Disease*, 2d ed. New York, McGraw-Hill, 1966, p 486.

97. KORNFELD S: Trafficking of lysosomal enzymes in normal and disease states. *J Clin Invest* 77:1, 1986.

98. SAHAGIAN GG: The mannose-6-phosphate receptor and its role in lysosomal enzyme transport, in Parent B, Olden K (eds): *Recent Research on Vertebrate Lectins, Advanced Cell Biology Monographs.* New York, Van Nostrand Reinhold, 1987, pp 46–64.

99. von FIGURA K, HASILIK A: Lysosomal enzymes and their receptors. *Annu Rev Biochem* 55:167, 1986.

100. HASILIK A, WAHEED A, von FIGURA K: Enzymatic phosphorylation of lysosomal enzymes in the presence of UDP-N-acetylglucosamine; absence of the activity in I-cell fibroblasts. *Biochem Biophys Res Commun* 98:761, 1981.

101. REITMAN ML, KORNFELD S: Lysosomal enzyme targeting: N-acetylglucosaminyl-phosphotransferase selectively phosphorylates native lysosomal enzymes. *J Biol Chem* 756:11977, 1981.

102. CIECHANOVER A, SCHWARTZ AL, DAUTRY-VARSAT A, LODISH HF: Kinetics of internalization of transferrin and the transferrin receptor in a human hepatoma cell line: Effect of lysosomotropic agents. *J Biol Chem* 258:681, 1983.

103. VARKI A, KORNFELD S: Purification and characterization of rat liver α-N-acetylglucosaminyl phosphodiesterase. *J Biol Chem* 256:9937, 1981.

104. WAHEED A, HASILIK A, von FIGURA K: Processing of the phosphorylated recognition marker in lysosomal enzymes: Characterization and partial purification of a microsomal α-N-acetylglucosaminyl phosphodiesterase. *J Biol Chem* 256:5717, 1981.

105. SLY WS, FISCHER HD: The phosphomannosyl recognition system for intracellular and intercellular transport of lysosomal enzymes. *J Cell Biochem* 18:67, 1982.

106. SAHAGIAN GG, DISTLER J, JOURDIAN GW: Characterization of a membrane associated receptor from bovine liver that binds phosphomannosyl residues of bovine testicular β-galactosidase. *Proc Natl Acad Sci USA* 78:4289, 1981.

107. STEINER AW, ROME LH: Assay and purification of a solubilized membrane receptor that binds the lysosomal enzyme α-L-iduronidase. *Arch Biochem Biophys* 214:681, 1982.

108. HOFLACK B, KORNFELD S: Lysosomal enzyme binding to mouse P388D₁ macrophage membranes lacking the 215 KDa mannose-6-phosphate receptor: Evidence for the existence of a second mannose-6-Phosphate receptor. *Proc Natl Acad Sci USA* 82:4428, 1985.

109. HOFLACK B, KORNFELD S: Purification and characterization of a cation-dependent mannose-6-phosphate receptor from murine P388 D₁ macrophages and bovine liver. *J Biol Chem* 260:12008, 1985.

110. PFEFFER SR: The endosomal concentration of a mannose-6-phosphate receptor is unchanged in the absence of ligand synthesis. *J Cell Biol* 105:229, 1987.

111. BROWN JA, NOWACK EK, SWANK RT: Effect of ammonia on processing and secretion of precursor and mature lysosomal enzyme from macrophages of normal and pale ear mice, evidence for two distinct pathways. *J Cell Biol* 100:1894, 1985.

112. SANDO GN, HENKE VL: Recognition and receptor-mediated endocytosis of the lysosomal acid lipase secreted by cultured human fibroblasts. *J Lipid Res* 23:114, 1982.

113. NEUFELD EF, SANDO GN, GARVIN AJ, ROWL L: The transport of lysosomal enzymes. *Supramol Structure* 6:95, 1977.

114. HOEG JM, DEMOSKY SJ JR, PESCOVITZ OH, BREWER HB JR: Cholesteryl ester storage disease and Wolman's disease: Phenotypic variants of lysosomal acid cholesteryl ester hydrolase deficiency. *Am J Hum Genet* 36:1190, 1984.

115. FOWLER SD, BROWN WJ: Lysosomal acid lipase in Borgström B, Brockmann HL (eds): *Lipases.* Amsterdam, Elsevier, 1984, p 329.

116. TAKANO T, BLACK WJ, PETERS TJ, de DUVE C: Assay, kinetics, and lysosomal localization of an acid cholesteryl esterase in rabbit aortic smooth muscle cells. *J Biol Chem* 249:6732, 1974.

117. BELFRAGE P, VAUGHAN M: Simple liquid-liquid partition system for isolation of labeled oleic acid from mixtures with glycerides. *J Lipid Res* 10:341, 1969.

118. PITTMAN RC, KHOO JC, STEINBERG D: Cholesterol esterase in rat adipose tissue and its activation by cyclic adenosine 3′,5′-monophosphate-dependent protein kinase. *J Biol Chem* 250:4505, 1975.

119. BRECHER P, CHOBANIAN J, SMALL DM, CHOBANIAN AV: The use of phospholipid residues for in vitro studies on cholesteryl-ester hydrolysis. *J Lipid Res* 17:239, 1976.

120. BRECHER P, PYNN HY, CHOBANIAN AV: Cholesteryl ester and triglyceride hydrolysis by an acid lipase from rabbit aorta. *Biochim Biophys Acta* 530:112, 1978.

121. SALVAYRE R, NÉGRE A, MARET A, RADOM J, DOUSTE-BLAZY L: Maladie de Wolman et polycorie cholestérolique de l'adulte. *Ann Biol Clin (Paris)* 44:611, 1986.

122. NÈGRE A, SALVAYRE R, ROGALLE P, DANG QQ, DOUSTE-BLAZY L: Acyl chain specificity and properties of cholesterol esterases from normal and Wolman lymphoid cell lines. *Biochim Biophys Acta* 918:76, 1987.

123. NÈGRE A, SALVAYRE R, DAGAN A, GATT S: New fluorometric assay of lysosomal acid lipase and its application to the diagnosis of Wolman's and cholesteryl ester storage diseases. *Clin Chim Acta* 149:81, 1985.

124. NÈGRE A, SALVAYRE R, MARET A, FARRE G, GATT S: Incorporation of fluorescent fatty acids in normal and acid lipase deficient cultured cells. *Cell* 57:38, 1986.

125. SMITH AG, BROOKS CJW, HARLAND WA: Acid cholesterol ester hydrolase in pig and human aortas. *Steroid Lipids Res* 5:150, 1974.

126. HALEY NJ, FOWLER S, de DUVE C: Lysosomal acid cholesteryl esterase activity in normal and lipid-laden aortic cells. *J Lipid Res* 21:961, 1980.

127. MAHADEVAN S, TAPPEL AL: Lysosomal lipases of rat liver and kidney. *J Biol Chem* 243:2849, 1968.

128. HAYASE K, TAPPEL AL: Specificity and other properties of lysosomal lipase of rat liver. *J Biol Chem* 245:169, 1970.

129. BROWN WJ, SGOUTAS DS: Purification of rat liver lysosomal cholesteryl ester hydrolase. *Biochim Biophys Acta* 617:305, 1980.

130. SHINOMIYA M, MATSUOKA N, SHIRAI K, SAITO Y, KUMAGAI A: Studies on cholesterol esterase in rat arterial wall. *Atherosclerosis* 33:343, 1979.

131. BURTON BK, MUELLER HW: Purification and properties of human placental acid lipase. *Biochim Biophys Acta* 618:449, 1980.

132. HAYASAKA S, HARA S, MIZUMO K: Partial purification and properties of acid lipase in the bovine retinal pigment epithelium. *Exp Eye Res* 25:317, 1977.

133. RINDLER-LUDWIG R, PATSCH W, SAILER S, BRAUNSTEINER H: Characterization and partial purification of acid lipase from human leukocytes. *Biochim Biophys Acta* 488:294, 1977.

134. SEVERSON DL, FLETCHER T: Properties of acid and neutral cholesterol ester hydrolases in rat and pigeon aortas. *Atherosclerosis* 41:1, 1982.

135. GOLDSTEIN JL, BRUNSCHEDE GY, BROWN MS: Inhibition of proteolytic degradation of low density lipoprotein in human fibroblasts by chloroquine, concanavalin A, and Triton WR 1339. *J Biol Chem* 250:7854, 1975.

136. STEIN Y, EBIN V, BARON H, STEIN O: Chloroquine-induced interference with degradation of serum lipoproteins in rat liver, studied in vivo and in vitro. *Biochim Biophys Acta* 486:286, 1977.

137. RICHES DWH, STANWORTH DR: Evidence for a mechanism for the initiation of acid hydrolase secretion by macrophages that is functionally independent of alternative pathway complement activation. *Biochem J* 202:639, 1982.

138. DEBEER LJ, THOMAS J, MAMAERTS G, de SCHEPPER PJ: Effect of sulfonylureas on triglyceride metabolism in the rat liver. *J Clin Invest* 59:185, 1977.

139. KASAMA K, YOSHIDA K, TAKEDA S, TSUJIMURA R, HASEGAURA S: Inhibition of acid esterase in rat liver by 4,4'-diethylaminoethoxyhexesterol. *Lipids* 11:718, 1976.

140. TRAYMOR JR, KUNZE H: Inhibition of rat liver cholesterol esterase by local aneasthetics. *Biochim Biophys Acta* 409:68, 1975.

141. RUTH RC, OWENS K, WEGLICKI WB: Inhibition of lysosomal lipases by chlorpromazine: A possible mechanism of stabilization. *J Pharmacol Exp Ther* 212:361, 1980.

142. BECKMAN JK, OWENS K, KNAUER TE, WEGLICKI WB: Hydrolysis of sarcolemma by lysosomal lipases and inhibition by chlorpromazine. *Am J Physiol* 242:4652, 1982.

143. WILO M, POOLE B: Protein degradation in cultured cells. II. The uptake of chloroquine by rat fibroblasts and the inhibition of cellular protein degradation and cethepsin B₁. *J Cell Biol* 63:430, 1974.

144. HUDSON K, DAY AJ: The effect of bezafibrate and clofibrate on microsomal ACAT and lysosomal cholesterol ester hydrolase activity in the cholesterol-fed rabbit aorta. *Atherosclerosis* 45:109, 1982.

145. SEVERSON DL, HURLEY B: Regulation of rat heart triacylglycerol ester hydrolases by free fatty acids, fatty acyl CoA and fatty acyl carnitine. *J Mol Cell Cardiol* 14:467, 1982.

146. KNAUER TE, WEGLICKI WB: Characteristics of multiple forms of the acidic triacylglycerol lipases of canine cardiac myocytes. *Biochim Biophys Acta* 753:173, 1983.

147. VAVRÍNKOVÁ H, MOSINGER B: Effect of glucagon, catecholamines and insulin on liver acid lipase and acid phosphatase. *Biochim Biophys Acta* 231:320, 1971.

148. HENZE K, CHAIT A: Lysosomal enzyme activities and low density lipoprotein receptors in circulating mononuclear cells. Effect of insulin therapy in diabetic patients. *Diabetologia* 20:625, 1981.

149. YATSU FM: Lysosomal cholesterylester hydrolase activity in mononuclear cells with atherosclerosis risk: Hyperlipidemia and diabetes mellitus. *Ann Neurol* 10:104, 1981.

150. FINEGOLD DN, COATES PM: Effect of diabetes and insulin therapy on human mononuclear leukocyte lysosomal acid lipase activity. *Metabolism* 33:85, 1984.

151. WOLINSKY J, GOLDFISCHER S, CAPRON L, CAPRON F, COLTOFF-SCHILLER B, NESAK L: Hydrolase activities in the rat aorta I. Effect of diabetes mellitus and insulin treatment. *Circ Res* 42:821, 1978.

152. RÖSEN P, BUDDE T, REINAUER H: Triglyceride lipase activity in the diabetic rat heart. *J Mol Cell Cardiol* 13:539, 1981.

153. SEVERSON DL, FLETCHER T: Effect of hyperinsulinemia on acid cholesterol ester hydrolase activity in liver, heart and epididymal fat pad preparations from rat and mice. *Biochim Biophys Acta* 718:144, 1982.

154. VALETTE A, VÉRINE A, SALERS P, BOYER J: Estrogen hormones and lipid metabolism. Effect of ethinylestradiol on liver lipases. *Endocrinology* 101:627, 1977.

155. HAGEMENAS FC, YATSU FM, MANAUGH LC: The effect of oral contraceptives on mononuclear cell cholesteryl ester hydrolase activity. *Lipids* 15:39, 1980.

156. SEVERSON DL, HAYDEN LJ, FLETCHER T: Hormonal regulation of acid cholesterol ester hydrolase activity: Effects of triiodothyronine and 17α-ethinylestradiol. *Can J Physiol Pharmacol* 62:244, 1984.

157. COATES PM, BROWN SA, LAU H, KRULICH L, KOLDOVSKI O: Effect of thyroxine on acid lipase activity of adult rat liver. *FEBS Lett* 86:45, 1978.

158. COATES PM, LAU H, KRULICH L, BROWN SA, KOLDOVSKI O: Increase in liver acid lipase of thyroidectomized rats by thyroid hormones and its inhibition by actinomycin D. *Biochim Biophys Acta* 584:358, 1979.

159. COATES PM, HOFFMANN GM, FINEGOLD DN: Effect of thyroid hormones on human mononuclear leukocyte lysosomal acid lipase activity. *J Clin Endocrinol Metab* 54:559, 1982.

160. De MARTINO GN, GOLDBERG AL: A possible explanation of myxedema and hypercholesterolemia in hypothyroidism: Control of lysosomal hyaluronidase and cholesterol esterase by thyroid hormones. *Enzyme* 26:1, 1981.

161. SEVERSON DL, FLETCHER T: Effect of thyroid hormones on acid cholesterol ester hydrolase activity in rat liver, heart and epididymal fat pads. *Biochim Biophys Acta* 675:256, 1981.

162. KATZ-FEIGENBAUM D, BRAUN L, WOLINSKY H: Hydrolase activity in the rat aorta: V Comparison to activities in liver and kidney after thyroidectomy and relation to dynamic clearance of circulating low-density lipoproteins. *Circ Res* 49:733, 1981.

163. HAJJAR DP, WEKSLER BB, FALCONE DJ, HEFTON JM, TACK-GOLDMAN K, MINICK CR: Prostacyclin modulates cholesteryl ester hydrolytic activity by its effect on cyclic adenosine monophosphate in rabbit aortic smooth muscle cell. *J Clin Invest* 70:479, 1982.

164. SCHMITZ G, ROBENEK H, BEUCK M, KRAUSE R, SCHUREK A, NIEMANN R: Calcium antagonists and ACAT inhibitors promote cholesterol efflux from macrophages by different mechanisms. I. Characterization of cellular lipid metabolism. *Arteriosclerosis* 8:47, 1988.

165. ROBENEK H, SCHMITZ G: Calcium antagonists and ACAT inhibitors promote cholesterol efflux from macrophages by different mechanisms. II. Characterization of intracellular morphological changes. *Arteriosclerosis* 8:57, 1988.

166. ETIGIN OR, HAJJAR DP: Nifedipine increases cholesteryl ester hydrolytic activity in lipid-laden rabbit arterial smooth muscle cells. *J Clin Invest* 75:1554, 1985.

167. TANAKA M, YONEKURA R, IIO T, TABATA T: A diurnal variation of hepatic cholesteryl ester hydrolase activity in the rat. *Lipids* 20:46, 1985.

168. SAURO VS, KLAMUT HJ, LIU C-H, STRICKLAND KP: Lysosomal triacylglycerol lipase activity in L6 myoblasts and its changes on differentiation. *Biochem J* 227:383, 1985.

169. IMANAKA T, MORIYAMA Y, ECSEDI GG, AOYAGI T, AMANUMA-MUTO K, OKKUMA S, TAKANO T: Esterasin: A potent inhibitor of lysosomal acid lipase. *J Biochem* 94:1017, 1983.

170. WARNER TG, DAMBACH LM, SHIN JH, O'BRIAN JS: Purification of the lysosomal acid lipase from human liver and its role in lysosomal lipid hydrolysis. *J Biol Chem* 256:2952, 1981.

171. CHEN L, MORIN R: Purification of a human placental cholesteryl ester hydrolase. *Biochim Biophys Acta* 231:194, 1971.

172. SAKURADA T, ORIMO H, OKABE H, NAMA A, MURAHAMI M: Purification and properties of cholesteryl ester hydrolase from human aortic intima and media. *Biochim Biophys Acta* 424:204, 1976.

173. SANDO GN, ROSENBAUM LM: Human lysosomal acid lipase/cholesterylester hydrolase. *J Biol Chem* 260:15186, 1985.

174. IMANAKA T, MUTO K, OKKUMA S, TAKANO T: Purification of acid lipase from rabbit liver. *FEBS Lett* 137:115, 1982.

175. IMANAKA T, AMANUMA-MUTO K, OKKUMA S, TAKANO T: Characterization of lysosomal acid lipase purified from rabbit liver. *J Biochem* 96:1089, 1984.

176. IMANAKA T, YAMAGUCHI M, OKKUMA S, TAKANO T: Positional specificity of lysosomal acid lipase purified from rat liver. *J Biochem* 98:927, 1985.

176a. KARIYA M, KAPLAN A: Effects of acidic phospholipids, nucleotides, and heparin on the activity of lipase from rat liver lysosomes. *J Lipid Res* 14:243, 1973.

176b. TENG M-H, KAPLAN A: Purification and properties of rat liver lysosomal lipase. *J Biol Chem* 249:1064, 1974.

177. IMANAKA T, AMANUMA-MUTO K, OKKUMA S, TAKANO T: Effects of phospholipids on lysosomal acid lipase purified from rabbit liver. *J Biochem* 93:1517, 1983.

178. GORIN E, GONEN H, DICKBUCH S: A serum protein inhibitor of acid lipase and its possible role in lipid accumulation in cultured fibroblasts. *Biochem J* 204:221, 1982.

179. NEIDERHISER DH: Cholesteryl ester hydrolase in gall bladder mucosa: Evidence for the presence of an inhibitor protein in the cytosol. *Biochim Biophys Res Commun* 105:328, 1982.

180. TANAKA M, YONEKURA R, IIO T, TABATA T: Characterization of a cytosolic protein inhibiting lysosomal acid cholesteryl ester hydrolase. *Lipids* 19:714, 1984.

181. KONDO M, KAJIMOTO M, KIMURA H, SUZUKI T, SASAKI A, NIVA M, URATA G: A specific inhibitor to delta-aminolaevulinate dehydratase in rat bone marrow cells. *Arch Biochem Biophys* 208:189, 1981.

182. HIRATA F, SCHIFFMANN E, VEUKATASUBRAMANIAN K, SALOMON D, AXELROD J: A phospholipase A2 inhibitory protein in rabbit neutrophils induced by glucocorticoids. *Proc Natl Acad Sci USA* 77:2533, 1980.

183. KUBO M, MATSUZAWA Y, YOKOYAMA S, TAJIM S, ISHIKAWA K, YAMAMOTO A, TARNI T: Apo A-I and apo A-II inhibit hepatic triglyceride lipase from human postheparin plasma. *Biochem Biophys Res Commun* 106:261, 1981.

184. PETERS TJ, de DUVE C: Lysosomes of the arterial wall. II. Subcellular fractionation of aortic cells from rabbits with experimental atheroma. *Exp Mol Pathol* 20:228, 1974.

185. SUKARADA T, ORIMO H, OKABE H, NOMA A, MURAKAMI M: Purification and properties of cholesterol ester hydrolase from human aortic intima and media. *Biochim Biophys Acta* 424:204, 1976.

186. BROWN MS, KOVANEN PT, GOLDSTEIN JL: Regulation of plasma cholesterol by lipoprotein receptors. *Science* 212:628, 1981.

187. SHIO H, HALEY NJ, FOWLER S: Characterization of lipid-laden aortic cells from cholesterol fed rabbits III. Intracellular localization of cholesterol and cholesteryl ester. *Lab Invest* 41:160, 1979.

188. SHIO H, FARQUHAR MG, de DUVE C: Lysosomes of the arterial wall. IV. Cytochemical localization of acid phosphatase and catalase in smooth muscle cells and foam cells from rabbit atheromatous aorta. *Am J Pathol* 76:1, 1974.

189. SHIO H, HALEY NJ, FOWLER S: Characterization of lipid-laden aortic cells from cholesterol-fed rabbits. II. Morphometric analysis of lipid-filled lysosomes and lipid droplets in aortic cell populations. *Lab Invest* 39:390, 1978.

190. HO YK, BROWN MS, GOLDSTEIN JL: Hydrolysis and excretion of cytoplasmic cholesteryl esters by macrophages: Stimulation of high density lipoprotein and other agents. *J Lipid Res* 21:204, 1980.

191. BROWN MS, HO YK, GOLDSTEIN JL: The cholesteryl ester cycle in macrophage foam cells. *J Biol Chem* 255:9244, 1980.

192. KHOO JC, MAHONEY EM, STEIN J: Neutral cholesterol esterase activity in macrophages and its enhancement by cAMP-dependent protein kinase. *J Biol Chem* 256:12659, 1981.

193. PITTMAN RC, STEINBERG D: Activatable cholesterol esterase and triacylglycerol lipase activities of rat adrenal and their relationship. *Biochim Biophys Acta* 487:431, 1977.

194. HAJJAR DP, WEKSLER BB: Metabolic activity of cholesterol esters in aortic smooth muscle cells is altered by prostaglandins I$_2$ and E$_2$. *J Lipid Res* 24:1176, 1983.

195. HAJJAR DP: Regulation of neutral cholesteryl esterase in arterial smooth muscle cells: Stimulation by agonists of adenylate cyclase and cyclic AMP-dependent protein kinase. *Arch Biochem Biophys* 247:49, 1986.

196. EISENBERG S: High density lipoprotein metabolism. *J Lipid Res* 25:1017, 1984.

197. SCHMITZ G, ROBENECK H, LOHMANN U, ASSMANN G: Interaction of high density lipoproteins with cholesteryl ester-laden macrophages: Biochemical and morphological characterization of cell surface receptor binding, endocytosis and resecretion of high density lipoproteins by macrophages. *EMBO J* 4:613, 1985.

198. SCHMITZ G, NIEMANN R, BRENNHAUSEN B, KRAUSE R, ASSMANN G: Regulation of high density lipoprotein receptors in cultured macrophages: Role of acyl-CoA:cholesterol acyltransferyse. *EMBO J* 4:2773, 1985.

199. GONIAKOWSKA-WITALINSKA L: A peculiar mode of formation of the surface linsing layer in the lungs of Salamander Salamandra. *Tissue Cell* 12:539, 1980.

200. GONIAKOWSKI-WITALINSKA L: Tubular myelin structures in the lung of amphibia. The mode of formation. *Eur J Cell Biol* 33:127, 1984.

201. WRIGHT JR, WAGNER RE, HAMILTON RL, HUANG M, CLEMENTS JA: Uptake of lung surfactant subfractions into lamellar bodies of adult rabbit lungs. *J Appl Physiol* 60:817, 1986.

202. STERN N, RIKLIES S, KALINA M, TIETZ A: The catabolism of lung surfactant by alveolar macrophages. *Biochim Biophys Acta* 877:323, 1986.

203. HARWOOD JL, RICHARDS RJ: Pulmonary surfactant: Its isolation, characterization and function. *Biochem Soc Trans 613th Meeting, Cardiff 1985*, 13:1079.

204. CHEUNG WT, SHI MM, YOUNG JD, LEE C-M: Inhibition of radioligand binding to A$_1$ adenosine receptors by BAY K8644 and Nifedipine. *Biochem Pharmacol* 36:2183, 1987.

205. DAUGHERTY A, RATERI DL, SCHONFELD G, SOBEL BE: Inhibition of cholesteryl ester deposition in macrophages by calcium entry blockers: An

effect dissociable from calcium entry blockade. *Br J Pharmacol* 91:113, 1987.

206. SCHMITZ G, BÖTTCHER A, BRÜNING T: Purification and characterization of the 110 KD HDL-binding protein from human white blood cells. *EMBO J* (submitted), 1988.

207. FAERGEMAN O, HAVEL RJ: Metabolism of cholesteryl esters of rat very low density lipoproteins. *J Clin Invest* 55:1210, 1975.

208. SHELBURNE FA, HANKS J, MEYERS W, QUARFORDT SH: Effect of apoproteins on hepatic uptake of triglyceride emulsions in the rat. *J Clin Invest* 65:652, 1980.

209. QUARFORDT S, HANKS J, JONES RS, SHELBURNE F: The uptake of high density lipoprotein cholesteryl ester in the perfused rat liver. *J Biol Chem* 255:29, 1980.

210. STEIN O, STEIN Y, GOODMAN DS, FIDGE NH: The metabolism of chylomicron cholesteryl esters in rat liver. A combined radioautographic-electron microscopic and biochemical study. *J Cell Biol* 418:410, 1969.

211. FLOREN CH, NILSSON A: Degradation of chylomicron remnant cholesteryl ester by rat hepatocyte monolayers. Inhibition by chloroquine and colchicine. *Biochim Biophys Res Commun* 74:520, 1977.

212. GOODMAN ZD, LEQUIRE VS: Transfer of esterified cholesterol from serum lipoproteins to the liver. *Biochim Biophys Acta* 398:325, 1975.

213. COOPER AD, YU PYS: Rates of removal and degradation of chylomicron remnants by isolated perfused rat liver. *J Lipid Res* 19:635, 1978.

214. FLOREN CH, NILSSON A: Binding, interiorization and degradation of cholesteryl ester-labeled chylomicron remnant particles by rat hepatocyte monolayer. *Biochem J* 168:483, 1977.

215. van BERKEL THJC, van TOL A: In vivo uptake of human and rat low density and high density lipoprotein by parenchymal and nonparenchymal cells from rat liver. *Biochim Biophys Acta* 530:299, 1978.

216. van BERKEL THJC, van TOL A, KOSTER JF: Iodine labeled human and rat low-density and high-density lipoprotein degradation by human liver and parenchymal and nonparenchymal cells from rat liver. *Biochim Biophys Acta* 529:138, 1978.

217. van BERKEL THJC, van TOL A: Role of parenchymal and nonparenchymal rat liver cells in the uptake of cholesteryl ester-labeled serum lipoproteins. *Biochem Biophys Res Commun* 89:1097, 1979.

218. van BERKEL THJC, VAANDRAGER H, KRUYT JK, KOSTER JF: Characteristics of acid lipase and acid cholesteryl esterase in parenchymal and nonparenchymal rat liver cells. *Biochim Biophys Acta* 617:446, 1980.

219. COREY JE, ZILVERSMIT DB: Effect of cholesterol feeding on arterial lipolytic activity in the rabbit. *Atherosclerosis* 27:201, 1977.

220. BRECHER P, PYUN HY, CHOBANIAN AY: Effect of atherosclerosis on lysosomal cholesterol esterase activity in rabbit aorta. *J Lipid Res* 18:154, 1977.

221. NILSSON A, NORDÉN H, WILHELMSSON L: Hydrolysis and formation of cholesterol esters with rat liver lysosomes. *Biochim Biophys Acta* 296:593, 1973.

222. DOUSSET JC, DOUSSET N, El BABA AM, SOULA G, DOUSTE-BLAZY L: Holesteryl ester synthetase in lysosomes of rabbit aorta. Effect of membrane bound cholesterol and physical state of substrate. *Artery* 5:432, 1979.

223. KRITCHEVSKY D, KATHARI HV: Arterial enzymes of cholesteryl ester metabolism. *Adv Lipid Res* 16:221, 1978.

224. PROUDLOCK JW, DAY AJ: Cholesterol esterifying enzymes of atherosclerotic rabbit intima. *Biochim Biophys Acta* 26:716, 1972.

225. BRECHER PI, CHOBANIAN AV: Cholesterol ester synthesis in normal and atherosclerotic aortas of rabbit and rhesus monkeys. *Circ Res* 35:692, 1974.

226. HASHIMOTO S, DAYTON S, ALFIN-SLATER RB, BUI PT, BAKER N, WILSON L: Characteristics of the cholesterol-esterifying activity in normal and atherosclerotic rabbit aortas. *Circ Res* 34:176, 1974.

227. DAVIS HR, GLAGOV S, ZARINS CK: Role of acid lipase in cholesteryl ester accumulation during atherogenesis. *Atherosclerosis* 55:205, 1985.

228. SCHAFFNER T, TAYLOR K, BARTUCCI J, FISCHER-DROGA K, BEESON JH, GLAGOV S, WISSLER RW: Arterial foam cells with distinctive immunomorphologic and histochemical features of macrophages. *Am J Pathol* 100:57, 1980.

229. PROUDLOCK JW, DAY AJ, TUME RK: Cholesterol-esterifying enzymes of foam cells isolated from atherosclerotic rabbit intima. *Atherosclerosis* 18:451, 1973.

230. COATES PM, LANGER T, CORTNER JA: Genetic variations of human mononuclear leukocyte lysosomal acid lipase activity. Relationship to atherosclerosis. *Atherosclerosis* 62:11, 1986.

231. HAGEMENAS FC, MANAUGH LC, ILLINGWORTH DR, SUNDBERG EE, YATSUN FM: Cholesteryl ester hydrolase activity in mononuclear cells from patients with Type III hypercholesterolemia. *Atherosclerosis* 50:335, 1984.

232. YATSU F, HAGEMENAS F, MANAUGH L, GALUMBOS T: Cholesteryl ester hydrolase activity in human symptomatic atherosclerosis. *Lipids* 15:1019, 1980.

233. BONNER MJ, MILLER BF, KOTHARI HV: Lysosomal enzymes in aortas of species susceptible and resistant to atherosclerosis. *Proc Soc Exp Biol Med* 139:1359, 1972.

234. TOMITA T, SHIRASAKI Y, TAKIGUCKI Y, OZALARI Y, HAYASHI E: Hemodynamic effects on aortic enzyme activities in spontaneously hypertensive rats. *Atherosclerosis* 37:409, 1980.

235. WOLINSKY H, CAPRON L, GOLDFISCHER S, CAPRON F, COLTOFF-SCHILLER B, KASAK LE: Hydrolase activities in the rat aorta, Part 2 (Effect of hypertension alone and in combination with diabetes melltius). *Circ Res* 42:837, 1978.

236. TOMITA T, SHIRASAKI Y, TAKIGUCHI T, OKADA T, HAYASHI E: Aortic cholesterol esterase and other lysosomal enzyme activities in Doca-salt, renal and spontaneous hypertension in the rat. *Atherosclerosis* 39:453, 1981.

237. HAJJAR DP, FALCONE DJ, FABRICANT CG, FABRICANT J: Altered cholesteryl ester cycle is associated with lipid accumulation in herpes virus-infected arterial smooth muscle cells. *J Biol Chem* 260:6124, 1985.

238. MELNICK JL, DRESSMAN GR, McCOLLUM CH, PETRIE BL, BUREK J, De-BAKEY ME: Cytomegalovirus antigen within human arterial smooth muscle cells. *Lancet* 2:644, 1983.

239. FABRICANT CG, HAJJAR DP, MINICK J: Herpesvirus infection enhances cholesterol and cholesteryl ester accumulation in cultured arterial smooth muscle cells. *Am J Pathol* 105:176, 1983.

240. BURTON BK, REED SP: Acid lipase cross-reacting material in Wolman's disease and cholesterol ester storage disease. *Am J Hum Genet* 33:203, 1981.

241. COATES PM, CORTNER J: Acid lipase in cultured amnionic fluid cells. Implications for the prenatal diagnosis of Wolman's disease. *Pediatr Res* 12:450, 1978.

242. CHRISTOMANOU H, CAP C: Prenatal monitoring of Wolman's disease in a pregnancy at risk 1st case in W-Germany. *Hum Genet* 57:440, 1981.

243. KOCH GA, McAVOY M, SHOWS TB: Lysosomal acid lipase assignment of A gene LIPA associated with Wolman's disease and cholesterol ester storage disease to human chromosome 10. *Am J Hum Genet* 32:24, 1980.

244. van GONG N, WEIL D, HORS-CAYLA MC, GROSS MS, HEUERTZ S, FOUBERT C, FRESAL J: Assignment of the genes for human lysosomal acid lipases A and B to chromosomes 10 and 16. *Hum Genet* 55:375, 1980.

245. KOCH G, LALLEY PA, McAVOY M, SHOWS TB: Assignment of LIPA, associated with human lipase deficiency to human chromosome 10 and comparative assignment to mouse chromosome 19. *Somatic Cell Genet* 7:345, 1981.

246. KOCH G, LALLEY PA, SHOWS TB: Acid lipase 1 (LIP-I) is on mouse chromosome 19: Evidence for homologous regions of human chromosome 10 and mouse 19. *Cytogenet Cell Genet* 32:291, 1982.

247. GROSS MS, van GONG N, HORS-CAYLA M-C, WEIL D, HEUERTZ S, FOUBERT C: Acid lipases and Wolman and cholesteryl ester storage diseases. *Ann Genet* 26:10, 1983.

248. HOEG JM, DEMOSKY SJ, BREWER HB: Characterization of neutral and acid ester hydrolase in Wolman's disease. *Biochim Biophys Acta* 711:59, 1982.

249. MESSIEH S, CLARKE JTR, COOK HW, SPENCE MW: Abnormal neutral lipase activity in acid lipase deficient cultured human fibroblasts. *Pediatr Res* 17:770, 1983.

250. PITTMAN RC, WILLIAMS JC, MILLER A, STEINBERG S: Acid acylhydrolase deficiency in I-cell diseae and pseudo-Hurler polydystrophy. *Biochim Biophys Acta* 575:399, 1979.

251. NÈGRE A, SALVAYRE R, VUILLAUME M, DURANT P, DOUSTE-BLAZY L: Acid lipase EC-3.1.1.3. and carboxylesterases EC-3.1.1.1. in Epstein-Barr virus transformed lymphoid cell line from Wolman's disease influence of fatty-acid structure of substrate. *Enzyme* 31:241, 1984.

252. NÈGRE A, SALVAYRE R, DURANT P, LENOIR G, DOUSTE-BLAZY L: Enzyme studies on Epstein-Barr virus transformed lymphoid cell lines from Wolman's disease lipases EC-3.1.1.3 cholesterol esterase and 4-methylumbelliferyl acyl ester hydrolases. *Biochim Biophys Acta* 794:89, 1984.

253. SALVAYRE R, NÈGRE A, MARET A, RADOM J, ROGALLE P, DANG QQ, GATT S, DOUSTE-BLAZY L: Lipases cholesterylesterases and carboxylesterases in lymphoid cell lines: Substrate specificity and relation to Wolman's, cholesteryl ester storage diseases and lipid storage myopathy, in Freysz L and Dreyfus H (eds): *Enzymes of Lipid Metabolism II*. New York, Plenum, 1986, p. 809.

254. COLEMAN RA, HAYNES EB: Differentiation of microsomal from lysosomal triacylglycerol lipase activities in rat liver. *Biochim Biophys Acta* 751:230, 1983.

255. KEOUGH DT, De JERSEY J, ZERNER B: The relationship between the carboxylesterase and monoacylglycerol lipase activities of chicken liver microsomes. *Biochim Biophys Acta* 829:164, 1985.

256. PATSCH W, RINDLER-LUDWIG R, SAILER S, BRAUNSTEINER H: Acid cholesterol ester and glycerol ester hydrolase activities. *Biochim Biophys Acta* 618:337, 1980.

257. BURTON BK, REMY WT, RAYMON L: Cholesterol ester triglyceride metabolism in intact fibroblasts from patients with Wolman's disease and cholesterol ester storage disease. *Pediatr Res* 18:1242, 1984.

258. GINSBERG HN, LE N-A, SHORT MP, RAMAKRISHNAN R, DESNICH RJ: Suppression of apolipoprotein B production during treatment of cholesterol ester storage disease with Lovastatin. *J Clin Invest* 80:1692, 1987.

259. FAUST JR, GOLDSTEIN JL, BROWN MS: Receptor-mediated uptake of low density lipoprotein and utilization of its cholesterol for steroid synthesis in cultured mouse adrenal cells. *J Biol Chem* 252:4861, 1977.

260. HALL PF, NAKAMARA M: The influence of adrenocorticotropin on transport of a cholesteryl linoleate-low density lipoprotein complex into adrenal tumor cells. *J Biol Chem* 254:12547, 1979.

261. ANDERSON JM, DIETSCHY JM: Relative importance of high and low density lipoproteins in the regulation of cholesterol synthesis in the adrenal gland, ovary, and testis of the rat. *J Biol Chem* 253:9024, 1978.

262. KOSTNER GM, HADAM B, ROSCHER A, ZECHNER A: Plasma lipids and lipoproteins of a patient with cholesteryl ester storage disease. *J Inherited Metab Dis* 8:9, 1985.

263. LAKE BD: Histochemical detection of the enzyme deficiency in blood films in Wolman's disease. *J Clin Pathol* 24:617, 1971.

264. KELLY S, BAKHRU-KISHORE R: Fluorimetric assay of acid lipase in human leukocytes. *Clin Chim Acta* 97:239, 1979.

265. MEYERS MA: Disease of the adrenal glands, in *Radiologic Diagnosis*. Springfield, IL, Charles C Thomas, 1963.

266. AQUILAR MJ, O'BRIEN JS, TABER P: The syndrome of familial leukodystrophy, adrenal insufficiency, and cutaneous melanosis, in Aronson SM, Volk BW (eds): *Inborn Disorders of Sphingolipid Metabolism. Third International Symposium, Cerebral Sphingolipidoses*. New York, Pergamon, 1967, p 149.

267. MICHELS VV, BEAUDET AL: Cholesteryl lignocerate hydrolysis in adrenoleukodeptrophy. *Pediatr Res* 14:21, 1980.

268. OGINO T, SCHAUMBURG HH, SUZUKI K, KISHIMOTO Y, MOSER AE: Metabolic studies of adrenoleicodystrophy. *Adv Exp Med Biol* 100:601, 1978.

269. GALTON DJ, GILBERT CH, LUCEY JJ, PATH MRC, WALKER-SMITH JA: Triglyceride storage disease: A defect in activation of lipolysis in adipose tissue. *Pediatrics* 59:442, 1977.

270. GALTON DJ, RECKLESS JPD, GILBERT CH: Triglyceride storage disease, in Collip PJ (eds): *Childhood Obesity*. Acton, MA, Publishing Sciences Group, 1975, p 149.

271. PEREMANS J, De GRAF PJ, STRUBBE G, De BLOCK G: Familial metabolic disorder with fatty metamorphosis of the viscera. *J Pediatr* 69:1108, 1966.

272. DEN TANDT WR, PHILIPPART M, NAKATANI S, DURAND P: Triglyceride and acid lipase deficiency in triglyceride storage disease, a possible variant of Wolman's disease. *Pediatr Res* 7:346, 1973.

273. PHILIPPART M, DURAND P, BORRONE C: Neutral lipid storage with acid lipase deficiency: A new variant of Wolman's disease with features of the senior syndrome. *Pediatr Res* 16:954, 1983.

274. DURAND P, BUGIANI O, PALLADINI G, BARRONE C, DELLA CELLA G SILIATO: Nephropathie tubulo-interstitielle chronique, degenerescence tapeto-retinienne et lipidase generalisee. *Arch Fr Pediatr* 28:915, 1971.

CHAPTER 65

CERAMIDASE DEFICIENCY:
Farber Lipogranulomatosis

HUGO W. MOSER
ANN B. MOSER
WINSTON W. CHEN
ANDRE W. SCHRAM

1. *Farber disease is a genetically determined disorder of lipid metabolism, associated with deficiency of a lysosomal acid ceramidase and tissue accumulation of ceramide.*

2. *The previously recognized clinical manifestations are painful and progressively deformed joints, subcutaneous nodules, particularly near the joints and over pressure points, and progressive hoarseness due to laryngeal involvement. These tissues show granulomas and the accumulation of lipid-laden macrophages. There may be moderate nervous system dysfunction related to the accumulation of ceramide and gangliosides in neurons. The lungs, heart, and lymph nodes may also be involved. The illness often leads to death within the first few years, but a more prolonged course has also been observed. Two additional phenotypes have been recognized recently. In the first type hepatosplenomegaly is noted in the neonatal period. This serious disorder, which may be mistaken for malignant histiocytosis, leads to death before age 6 months. In the second type the clinical picture is dominated by progressive loss of psychomotor function after the first year. The subcutaneous nodules and the laryngeal involvement may be relatively subtle in both of these phenotypes.*

3. *Specific diagnosis depends upon demonstration of a deficiency of acid ceramidase in cultured skin fibroblasts or in white blood cells. Acid ceramidase activity in heterozygotes is usually reduced. Prenatal diagnosis has been accomplished by demonstrating acid ceramidase deficiency in cultured amniotic fluid cells.*

4. *The mode of inheritance is autosomal recessive. The disorder is rare.*

5. *There is no specific therapy.*

CLINICAL MANIFESTATIONS

Table 65-1 summarizes the clinical manifestations in 40 Farber disease patients. Of these cases, 27 were described in Table 40-1 of the fifth edition of this book[1] and Refs. 2 to 34 are keyed to that table. To construct the table in the present chapter we have added data from 13 additional cases. Nine of these cases have been reported.[35–42] Diagnosis was confirmed in all instances by ceramidase assay and in most instances by morphologic studies of biopsy or autopsy tissues.

The phenotype has been subdivided into six subtypes. Types 1 to 3 have been described in the previous edition. Types 4 and 5 have been recognized only since 1983, and indicate that the phenotype is more varied than had been rec-

ognized previously. It is likely that the diagnosis was previously missed in cases of this type. Type 6 is a tentative category. It includes a single patient who has the combined biochemical defects of Farber disease and Sandhoff disease.[40] This child, whose clinical manifestations are those of type 1 Farber disease, was the offspring of consanguineous parents, and may represent the coincidental co-occurrence of two unrelated genetic disorders.

Type 1

The clinical expression of the classic form of Farber disease is so striking that diagnosis can almost be made at a glance. The characteristic features are painful swelling of joints (particularly the interphalangeal, metacarpal, ankle, wrist, knee, and elbow), palpable nodules in relation to the affected joints and over pressure points, a hoarse cry which may progress to aphonia, feeding and respiratory difficulties, poor weight gain, and intermittent fever.

Symptoms usually first appear between ages 2 weeks and 4 months. The initial finding in most patients is painful and swollen joints or hoarseness. Attention is first drawn to the limbs and joints by diffuse swelling and hyperesthesia. Later the generalized swelling of the extremities diminishes, and nodular thickenings around the joints and tendon sheaths indicate the articular involvement. The fingers are held flexed at the interphalangeal joints, and passive motion causes pain. Joint contractures develop. The older, more mildly affected patients have shown moderate flexion contractures of the knees, wrists, and fingers. The discrete nodular subcutaneous swellings increase in size and number as the disease advances (Figs. 65-1 and 65-2). They are found most often near the interphalangeal, ankle, wrist, and elbow joints. Other frequent locations are points subject to mechanical pressure, such as the occiput and the lumbosacral region of the spine (Fig. 65-1D). Nodules have also been observed in the conjunctiva, on the external ear, on the nostrils, and in the mouth (Fig. 65-2B). In a few instances they have regressed spontaneously.

Disturbances in swallowing, vomiting, and repeated episodes of pulmonary consolidation associated with fever occur frequently in the severely involved children, and pulmonary disease is the usual cause of death. The disturbances in swallowing and respiration often are due to swelling and granuloma formation in the epiglottis and larynx. Rib and sternal

Table 65-1 The Farber Disease Phenotype*

	Type 1, classic	Type 2, intermediate	Type 3, mild	Type 4, neonatal visceral	Type 5, neurologic, progressive	Type 6, combined with Sandhoff
Number of cases	21	6	5	3	3	1
Age of onset	2 wk–4 mo	Neonatal–9 mo	2½ mo–20 mo	Neonatal	1 yr–2½ yr	6 wk
Mean age of death	1.2 yr	4.7	16–18 yr	7 wk–6 mo	35 mo	
Mean age last follow-up	2.4 yr	38 mo–6 yr	9–17 yr		20 mo–5½ yr	13 mo
Nodules	100%	100%	100%	33%	100%	+
Joint involvement	100%	100%	100%	33%	100%	+
Hoarseness	100%	100%	100%	33%	66%	+
Large liver	47%	33%	0%	100%	33%	+
Large spleen	12%	17%	0%	100%	33%	0
Lung infiltrates	76%	0%	0%	2/2	0%	0
Macular cherry-red spot	12%	0%	0%	0%	66%	+
Corneal opacities	6%	17%	0%	33%	0%	0
Cataracts	6%	0%	0%	0%	0%	0
Lower motor neuron involvement	71%	17%	1/1	—	66%	—
CNS normal	26%	67%	60%			
CNS impaired	42%	17%	40%			
CNS progressive dysfunction	11%	17%			100%	+
CNS: insufficient information	21%			100%		

*CNS = central nervous system; — = information not available.

retraction and asthmatic breathing attest to the obstructive element of the respiratory disease and may require tracheostomy (Fig. 65-2). Other organs are also involved relatively frequently. Seven of the severely involved patients had moderate generalized lymphadenopathy. An enlarged tongue has been reported in six patients. Six have had cardiac involvement, and one developed a grade 3/6 systolic murmur. The murmur was probably related to granulomatous lesions of the heart valves. Such lesions have been reported in three patients. Moderate enlargement of the liver has occurred in seven patients; a moderately enlarged spleen has been reported only once.

Evaluation of nervous system function in the severely affected young children is difficult because movement causes pain. Severe and progressive impairment of psychomotor development was reported in 10 cases; of these one was complicated by probably unrelated hydrocephalus severe enough to require a shunt. Two patients had normal intelligence. Several other patients were thought to be mildly retarded or to have borderline intelligence. Salaam-type seizures or infantile spasms were reported in two patients. Other signs of nervous system dysfunction arise mainly from the peripheral nerve involvement. Deep-tendon reflexes were diminished or absent in 12 patients. Hypotonia and muscular atrophy, which is observed frequently, may be related to the almost invariable storage of lipid in the anterior horn cells or to peripheral nerve involvement[11] and to immobility and inanition. The electromyogram may show signs of denervation. In addition, two patients showed evidence of myopathy. The cerebrospinal fluid protein level was reported in 10 patients: In eight it was elevated, often markedly, and in two it was normal.

Abnormalities of the eye have been detected in six patients. Cogan et al.[8] reported a diffuse, grayish opacification of the retina about the foveola, with a cherry-red center, but without disturbance of visual function. This abnormality, which resembles that seen in metachromatic leukodystrophy, is more subtle than the cherry-red spot of Tay-Sachs disease. A second eye abnormality is a granulomatous lesion of the conjunctiva.

One patient showed corneal opacity and another lenticular opacity.

Types 2 and 3

Subcutaneous nodules, joint deformities, and laryngeal involvement dominate the clinical manifestations in these patients. They survive longer. Several type 3 patients are in relatively stable condition near the end of the second decade. Liver and lung appear not to be involved. The presence of normal intelligence in two-thirds of the patients and postmortem studies[27] suggest that the brain is affected to only a slight extent or not at all. One patient included in the type 2 category has shown progressive psychomotor deterioration,[32] which indicates that this category may overlap type 5.

Type 4

The three patients included in this category have been reported in two publications.[35,36] The patients presented with hepatosplenomegaly and severe debility in the neonatal period or during the first few weeks, and they all died before age 6 months. The patients showed massive histiocytic infiltration of liver, spleen, lungs, thymus, and lymphocytes. Subcutaneous nodules were lacking in two of the three patients. Because of their variance from the "classic" Farber phenotype and the fact that ceramidase assays are not included in the customary lysosomal enzyme "screens," the diagnosis is difficult to achieve in these cases. Case 1[36] had not been recognized even after postmortem study, and the diagnosis of Farber disease was considered only retrospectively, when subcutaneous nodules were noted in a subsequently born sib.

Type 5

In these three patients, belonging to two families, the clinical manifestations are dominated by psychomotor deterioration

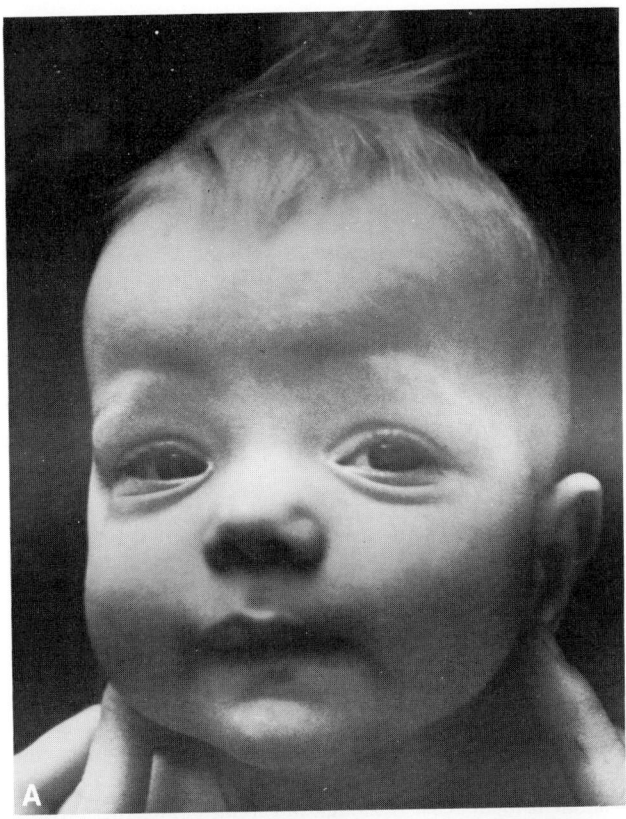

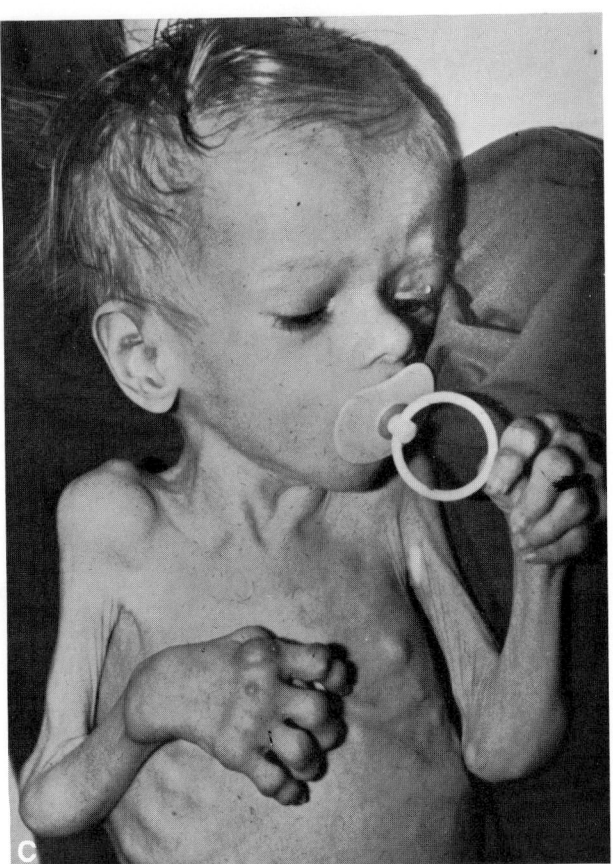

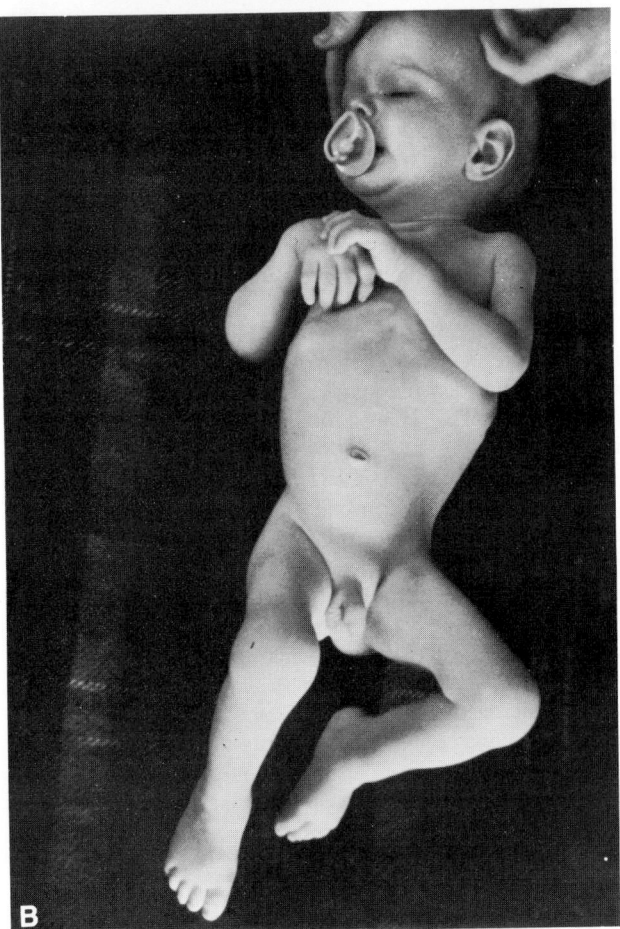

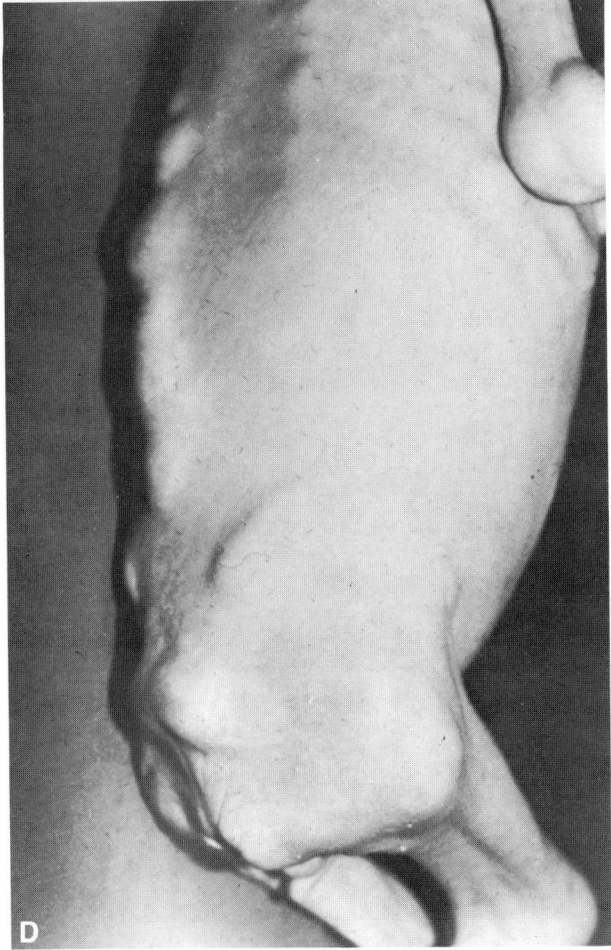

Fig. 65-1 A type 1 Farber disease. Patient at 12 months (*A,B*) and at 21 months (*C,D*). (*Courtesy of Dr. Neils Hobolth.*)

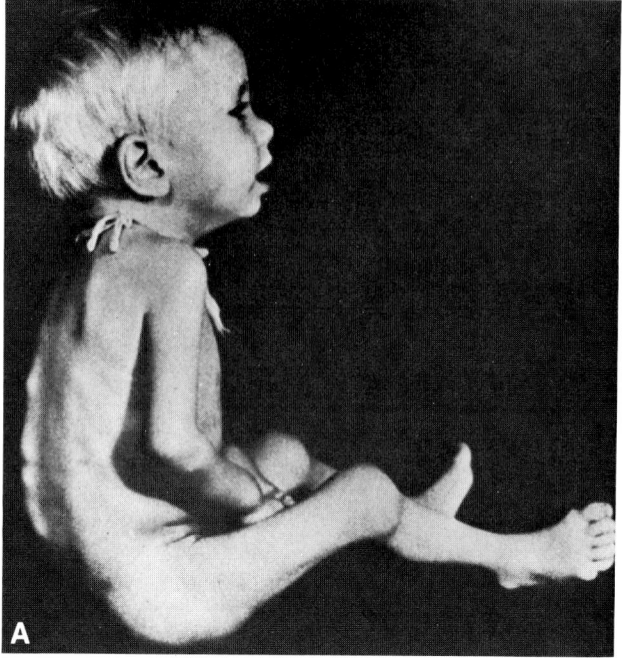

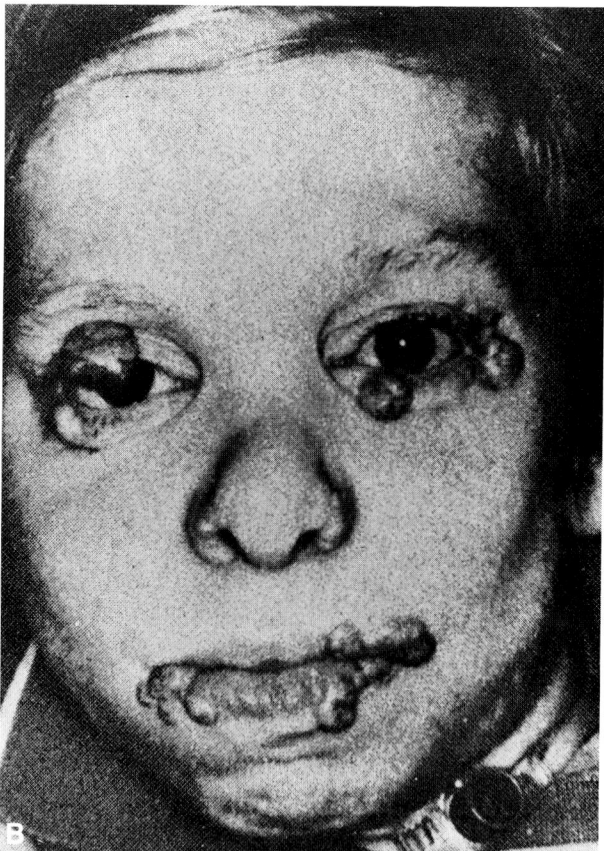

Fig. 65-2 A type 3 Farber disease. A. Patient at 23 months. Note joint swelling and contractures and subcutaneous nodules over spinous processes. Tracheostomy was performed as a lifesaving procedure at age 15 months. (*From Zetterstrom.*[25]*Used by permission.*) B. Patient at 16 years. Granulomas over lips, nostrils, eyelids. Tracheostomy still in place. He was cachectic, weighed 20.3 kg, and had atelectasis of the left lung and severe respiratory difficulties. Intelligence was normal, and he had learned to communicate well with the aid of an electric typewriter. He died 1 month later, due to cardiac arrest associated with the administration of a general anesthetic when granulomas were being removed from the eyelids. (*From Samuelsson, Zetterstrom, and Ivemark.*[27]*Used by permission.*)

beginning at 1 to 2½ years of age.[38,39] The first family included two girls from a marriage between a Korean national and a Caucasian male. Both children showed prominent macular cherry-red spots, had approximately normal development until 1 year of age, and then developed ataxia, loss of speech, and progressive quadriparesis. Postmortem study showed extensive neuronal loss and vacuolization of the cytoplasm of neurons and histiocytes with PAS-positive lipids. In contrast to type 1 Farber cases, the viscera were spared. The third case we have assigned to this category is a black child who at age 2½ years developed progressive ataxia, tremors, rigidity, seizures, polymyoclonia, and dementia.[39] While all three patients did demonstrate subcutaneous nodules and moderate joint involvement, these were overshadowed by the progressive neurologic deterioration.

MORPHOLOGIC CHANGES

Histopathology

Studies with the light microscope show granulomatous infiltrations in the subcutaneous tissues, joints, and many other organs. The earliest lesion appears to be the accumulation of macrophages or histiocytes, and in some areas this remains the principal pathologic feature. In other instances there are prominent foam cells. Although in certain tissues these foamy macrophages appear to have come from elsewhere, in other tissues (such as cartilage or in the heart valve) the storage material accumulates in the chondrocytes or endocardial cells which normally exist in these locations.[15] In some instances the lesions advance to an organized and full-blown granuloma, in which macrophages, lymphocytes, and multinucleated cells surround a core of foam cells. Older lesions show a prominent fibrotic reation. In other lesions the most prominent feature is the accumulation of abnormal material with the histochemical properties of a glycolipid or glycoprotein, with relatively little cellular reaction.[5]

The periarticular tissues, skin, and larynx have shown granulomatous lesions in all autopsied patients. Some of these lesions have invaded the joint capsule and on occasion the adjacent bone. The marrow in the diaphysis is much less involved.

The lungs have been involved in all the severely affected patients. They appear consolidated, and the interalveolar septums and the alveoli are infiltrated by massive numbers of macrophages. Granulomatous nodules are found on the parietal pleura. There is variability with respect to the degree of foam cell and granuloma formation. The heart has been involved in 6 of 17 autopsied patients. In three there was thickening and nodule formation on the mitral and aortic valves and the chordae tendineae. Lesions are variably found in other sites, including lymph nodes, intestine, spleen, kidney, tongue, thymus, gallbladder, epithelium, and liver.

Histochemical studies of paraffin-fixed sections which had been dehydrated with lipid solvents showed material with the staining properties of mucopolysaccharides.[15] This, together with chemical assays in one patient,[12] led to the supposition that Farber disease is one of the mucopolysaccharidoses.[12,15] However, when initial sample preparation avoided lipid solvents, two types of lipid-soluble storage materials were demonstrated: one of these had the tinctorial properties of ceramide,[26] while the other was periodic acid Schiff (PAS)–positive and had the staining properties of a glycolipid[5,7,8] or ganglioside.[27] These findings are consistent with biochemical assays (see below).

Except in two patients,[12,26] the nervous system has been abnormal in all autopsied cases. The main change was the accumulation of storage material in neuronal cytoplasm. This accumulation has been particularly prominent in the anterior horn cells in the spinal cord, but large nerve cells of the brainstem nuclei, basal ganglia, cerebellum, and retinal ganglion cells, and, to a lesser extent, the cortical neurons were also involved. Similar abnormalities occur in the peripheral nervous system, such as the autonomic ganglia, in posterior root cells, and, in some instances, in the Schwann cells. The storage material is PAS-positive, and much of it is extracted with lipid solvents, which suggests that it is glycolipid.[5,7,8]

Ultrastructural Studies

Ultrastructural studies have been performed in 14 patients.[10,11,14,17,22,30,37,38-42] These have shown cytoplasmic vacuoles of irregular shape up to 2 to 3 μm in size, which probably represent lysosomes since they have a single limiting membrane and show acid phosphatase activity. While these vacuoles contain a variety of materials, the most characteristic feature is comma-shaped curvilinear tubular structures, which are referred to as Farber bodies[30] or banana bodies.[44] These consist of two dark lines separated by a clear space (Fig. 65-3). Although markedly variable, the diameter of the tubules is 14 nm on the average. It is likely that these tubular structures represent ceramide, since they can be produced in cultured fibroblasts from patients by adding ceramides containing nonhydroxy fatty acids to the growth medium.[45] Neurons and endothelial cells may also contain "zebra" bodies. These are often found in the neurons of patients with mucopolysaccharidoses or the gangliosidoses and are considered to be an ultrastructural expression of stored gangliosides. This is consistent with the increased ganglioside level of some Farber disease tissues, as has been demonstrated biochemically[7] and histochemically.[27]

BIOCHEMICAL STUDIES

Alterations in Chemical Composition

Accumulation of Ceramide. Accumulation of ceramide has been reported in all of the eight Farber disease patients in whom the tissue level of this lipid has been analyzed (see Ref. 1, Table 40-2). High ceramide levels have been found in the subcutaneous nodules of seven patients, and ceramide may make up 20 percent of total lipids. Ceramide levels are also increased in the kidney. For the other tissues the extent of ceramide excess appears to vary with the severity of the disease. The severely involved patients[7,9,11] showed high ceramide levels in the liver, as well as in the lungs and brain, whereas in a more mildly affected patient, liver, lung, and brain ceramide levels were normal.[26]

Unlike those of normal subjects, the ceramides of patients with Farber disease may contain significant proportions of 2-hydroxy fatty acids. In a severely involved patient, 43 percent of kidney ceramides, 39 percent of those in the cerebellum, and 10 percent of those in the liver contained 2-hydroxy fatty

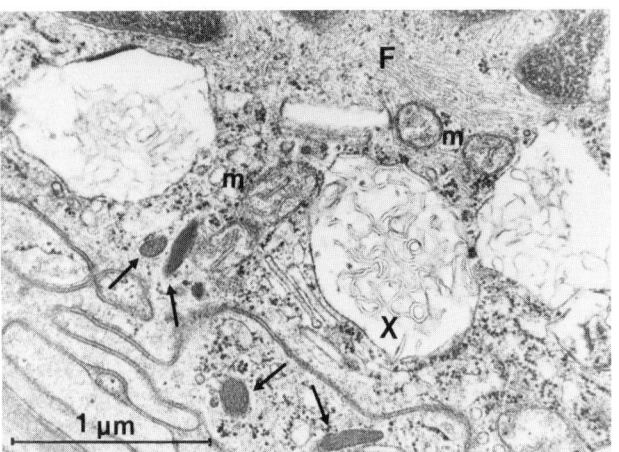

Fig. 65-3 Farber disease. Thin section of an endothelial cell with filaments (F), Wiebel-Palade bodies (arrows), mitrochondria (m), and three vacuoles, one of which (x) contains "Farber bodies." Reduced from × 45,000. (From Schmoeckel.[80])

acids.[7,47] The 2-hydroxy acids in ceramide from the Farber disease patient consisted of cerebronic acid, which has a 24-carbon chain, and lesser amounts of C_{22}, C_{20}, and C_{28} 2-hydroxy acids.[26,47] This hydroxy fatty acid pattern closely resembles that normally seen in galactocerebrosides and sulfatides. No hydroxy fatty acids were demonstrable in the ceramides isolated from the subcutaneous nodule.[26] In other respects the composition of fatty acid and the long-chain bases in ceramide from patients with Farber disease resembled those found in control tissues. The structural differences among the ceramides which accumulate in various tissues suggest that they are produced within these tissues.[26]

Alterations in Other Tissue Components. Farber et al.[2] isolated an abnormal "lipoglycoprotein complex" from the heart, liver, and lung of their patients. This complex accounted for as much as 8 to 30 percent of total lipid but was not fully characterized. One severely involved patient had a three- to tenfold increase in ganglioside levels in the liver, kidney, lymph nodes, and subcutaneous nodules. The ganglioside consisted mainly of hematoside, and the extent of ganglioside accumulation correlated with the extent to which the tissue was infiltrated with foam cells containing PAS-positive material.[7] While all these studies suggest an accumulation of glycolipid, there is variation in the extent of accumulation and type of compound. Furthermore, the chemical structure of some of these materials has not been completely defined. Nevertheless, they probably all contain ceramide, and this is consistent with the defect in ceramide degradation.

Accumulation of mucopolysaccharides was reported in one patient,[12] but tissue and urinary polysaccharides were normal in four other patients.[4-7,25-27,33] As already noted, one patient with both Farber and Sandhoff disease has been reported,[40] and this patient also shows the biochemical changes associated with the latter disorder.

Normal Ceramide Metabolism

Figure 65-4 shows the key role of ceramide in sphingolipid metabolism. It is an intermediate for the synthesis and degradation of gangliosides; myelin constituents, such as galactosylceramide and sulfatide; and membrane components such as sphingomyelin and the complex glycolipids.

A.

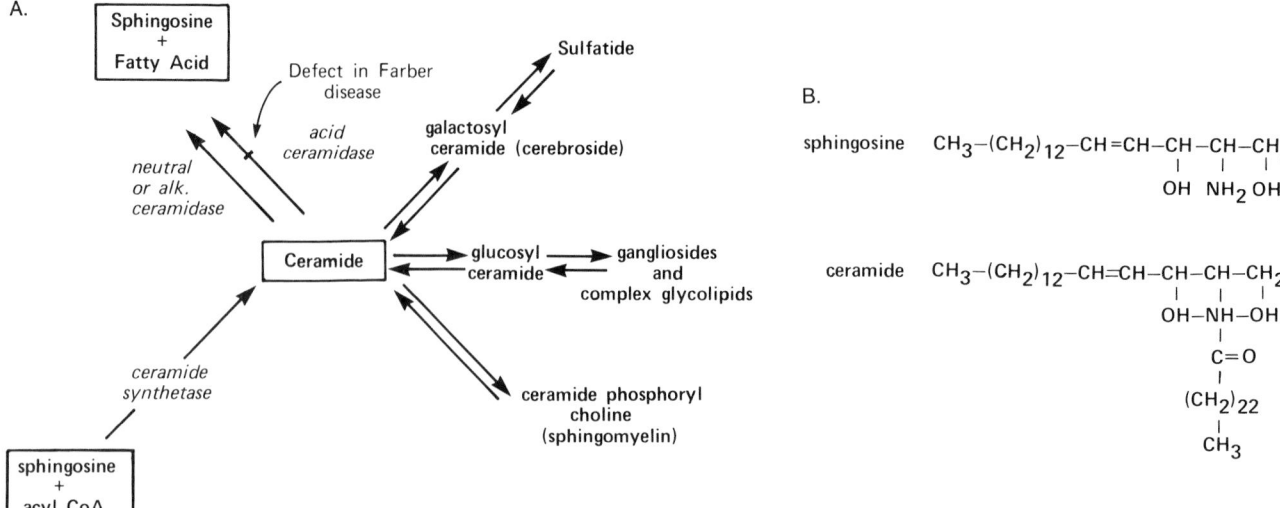

B.

Fig. 65-4 *A. Ceramide metabolism and the metabolic defect in Farber disease. The degradative direction of the ceramidase reaction is not shown, since its physiological significance is uncertain (see text). B. Formulas for sphingosine and ceramide. The fatty acid* shown in this figure is lignoceric acid, but a large variety of other fatty acids, including those with an α-hydroxy group, may be involved, and there is also variability with respect to long-chain bases, shown here as sphingosine.[26]

Ceramide Biosynthesis. Three biosynthetic pathways have been identified: (1) microsomal synthesis from long-chain base and the fatty acid-CoA derivative; (2) the "reverse ceramidase" reaction; and (3) a brain-specific ceramide synthetase. Reactions 2 and 3 utilize the free fatty acids rather than their CoA derivatives. The first pathway is probably the most significant one.

Synthesis of ceramide from sphingosine in vitro was first demonstrated by Scribney:[51]

Long-chain base + fatty acid CoA → ceramide + CoA

This reaction is catalyzed by acyl-CoA:sphingosine N-acyltransferase (EC 2.3.1.24). The reaction has a pH optimum of 7.5 and occurs in the microsome. Free fatty acids are not reactive. The rates of conversion of stearoyl-, lignoceroyl-, palmitoyl-, and oleoyl-CoA were in approximate ratios of 60:12:3:1.[52] These ratios resemble the distribution of these fatty acids in brain sphingolipids, which suggests that the ceramide synthesis reaction determines the fatty acid composition of sphingolipids. There is much less specificity with respect to the long-chain base.[53,54]

There are several distinct acyl-CoA:sphingosine N-acyltransferases, which differ in respect to their specificity for the fatty acid-CoA moiety. Thus, in mouse brain preparations the enzyme which reacts with stearoyl-CoA differs in subcellular localization and maturational pattern from that which is most reactive with lignoceroyl-CoA (C_{24}).[55] This conclusion is also supported by results obtained in "quaking" mice, mutants with a deficiency of myelin. Brain microsomes from the "quaking" mouse have normal stearoyl-CoA:sphingosine N-acyltransferase activity, while the corresponding activity toward lignoceroyl-CoA is reduced by 55 percent.[56] There is suggestive evidence that the sphingosine acyltransferase for 2-hydroxy-stearoyl-CoA and that for cerebronoyl-CoA are also distinct.[55]

Ceramidases are the enzymes responsible for degradation of ceramide. Acid, neutral, and alkaline ceramidases have been described. The acid and the alkaline ceramidases also appear to catalyze the reverse reaction, i.e., the synthesis of ceramide from sphingosine and free fatty acid.[57–59] The existence of this reverse reaction has recently been questioned, since it was reported that the reaction product was not ceramide but a condensation between long-chain fatty acids and ethanolamine which formed part of the buffer system.[60] This question is not fully resolved, since the reverse reaction had been demonstrated in a variety of buffer systems which did not contain ethanolamine.[59] It seems likely that the reaction has limited physiological significance.[51]

Recently a novel pathway for ceramide synthesis has been described in rat brain.[61] It utilizes free fatty acid and ATP. The physiological role of this reaction, which occurs only in nervous tissue, has not yet been fully assessed.

Ceramide Degradation

Acid Ceramidase. Ceramidase (EC3.5.1.23) catalyzes the reaction:

Ceramide + H_2O →long-chain base + fatty acid

A ceramidase has been purified from rat brain. The enzyme has a pH optimum of 4.8, appears to be associated with the lysosome, is stimulated by cholate or taurocholate, and is inhibited by sphingosine and fatty acid.[57,58] A greater than two hundred-fold purification was achieved by taking advantage of the fact that it withstands prolonged treatment with trypsin and chymotrypsin.

An acid ceramidase with analogous properties has been demonstrated in human kidney and cerebellum,[59] cultured skin fibroblasts,[62] and rat kidney.[63] The activity of the enzyme in human fibroblasts varies with the fatty acid composition of the ceramide substrate. For saturated fatty acids it is most active with the C12:0 (lauroyl) compound. Activity diminishes progressively for saturated acids with longer chain length, and activity is greater with ceramides containing unsaturated fatty acid.[62] The acid ceramidase from human placenta was partially purified.[64] Recently, a more complete purification and characterization was achieved for human spleen acid ceramidase.[65] The enzyme was purified to apparent homogeneity by sequential chromatography on concavalin-A-sepharose, octyl-sepharose, and DEAE-cellulose. The final preparation was purified about three hundred-fold and showed one major 47-kDa band when analyzed by polyacrylamide gel electrophoresis. While this purified preparation was free of most other lysosomal activities, acid sphingomyelinase activity was found to be purified to the same extent as acid ceramidase, suggesting that these two enzymes may form a complex. Separation of the two enzymes was achieved through the use of a monoclonal antibody which precipitated the ceramidase but not the sphingomyelinase, and immunoaffinity chromatography with this antibody permitted slightly greater purification of the enzyme. Under reducing conditions the 47-kDa protein resolved into 36-kDa and 14-kDa subunits. The larger subunit contains oligosaccharides of the high mannose type, while the small subunit is not glycosylated. The studies of Chen and coworkers support the lysosomal localization of acid ceramidase.[66,67] Studies on the molecular biology of Farber disease are being initiated in several laboratories. The phenotypic variability suggests that several types of defect will be identified at the molecular level.

Neutral and Alkaline Ceramidases. Certain tissues also show ceramidase activity in alkaline pH. This is true at least for small intestine,[68] cerebellum,[59] rat kidney,[63] cultured skin fibroblasts, and white blood cells. These neutral and alkaline ceramidases resemble the acid ceramidase in that the reactions appear reversible and in the synthetic reaction they act upon free fatty acids rather than their CoA derivatives. The small intestine alkaline ceramidase has a pH optimum of 7.6 and may be concentrated in the brush border.[68] No systematic study has yet been reported on the normal distribution of the alkaline ceramidases or of their substrate specificities. Of the tissue studied so far, human kidney appears to lack the alkaline ceramidase,[59] but this enzyme is present in rat kidney.[63] The alkaline ceramidase is clearly distinct from acid ceramidase. It is not precipitated by a monoclonal antibody against acid ceramidase,[69] and it is not deficient in Farber disease.[59,70]

Acid Ceramidase Deficiency and the Pathogenesis of Farber Disease

A deficiency of acid ceramidase was first demonstrated in postmortem tissue of two patients[70] and in the cultured skin fibroblasts and/or white blood cells of all patients who have been studied since then.[1,72] The defect in this degradative enzyme accounts for the tissue accumulation of ceramide. The alkaline ceramidases appear to function normally in Farber disease.[59,70]

When Farber disease cultured fibroblasts were incubated with [³H]oleoylsphingosine (ceramide), the rate of uptake of ceramide was the same as in the control, but the rate of ceramide degradation was impaired, presumably secondary to the defect in acid ceramidase. The finding that retained radioac-

tive ceramide was present in the lysosomal fraction provided further evidence that the defect involves a lysosomal enzyme.[66] Convincing additional evidence for a degradative defect is provided by the studies of Kudoh and Wenger,[72] who demonstrated that degradation of ceramides in cultured skin fibroblasts from patients with Farber disease was reduced to 15 percent of control. These conclusions are reinforced by morphologic studies. When ceramides are added to the culture medium in which Farber disease fibroblasts are growing, these cells develop large lysosomal inclusions that contain the curvilinear structures (Fig. 65-3)[45] which are characteristic of this disease. It is of interest, but so far unexplained, that these inclusions were produced by ceramides which contained nonhydroxy fatty acids, but not by those which contained the hydroxy fatty acids which normally occur in high concentration in brain and are found in Farber disease tissues.

It is plausible that the deficiency of acid ceramidase leads to ceramide accumulation. The accumulation of gangliosides and other glycolipids may be a secondary phenomenon, since ceramide is on the degradative pathway of these substances. The granuloma formation and histiocytic response appears to be a consequence of ceramide accumulation, since subcutaneous injection of ceramide in rats produces lesions which resemble those observed in Farber disease patients.[7]

The distribution of lesions in Farber disease and the variability of expression of the disease can only be partially explained. Neuronal storage is not unexpected, since ceramide metabolism in brain is known to be active. The striking involvement of subcutaneous tissues may be accounted for by recent observations that ceramide has an important role in normal skin. Ceramide makes up 16 to 20 percent of the total lipids in the stratum corneum[73] and forms an essential part of the intercellular barrier which preserves the water impermeability of normal skin.[74] The role of ceramide in synovial membranes has not been investigated. The absence or relatively mild involvement of the bone marrow and reticuloendothelial system in Farber disease is surprising, since these tissues are known to have a very active ceramide metabolism and are involved so strikingly in Gaucher and Niemann-Pick disease. It is possible that in these tissues ceramide is degraded by the alkaline or neutral ceramidases which are uninvolved in Farber disease or that the ceramide which cannot be degraded is reutilized for the synthesis of glycolipids or sphingomyelin (Fig. 65-4). The observed variation in severity and tissue involvement in the disease is unexplained. The enzyme defect in vitro is equally severe in the mild and severe cases. The recent purification of acid ceramidase and the availability of an antibody[65,69] may help to clarify these questions.

DIAGNOSIS

The Affected Patient

The diagnosis of classic type 1 Farber disease can be easily made clinically, since the triad of subcutaneous nodules, arthritis, and laryngeal involvement is unique for this disease. Diagnostic concerns arise when one or more of these features is missing, as in juvenile rheumatoid arthritis, in multicentric reticulohistiocytosis,[75] or in disorders such as fibromatosis hyalinica multiplex juvenilis.[76] We have found normal acid ceramidase activities in patients with these disorders and in other persons who lacked the above triad, and conversely, all patients with the triad studied so far showed reduced enzyme activity.

Acid ceramidase activity in Farber disease patients is less than 6 percent of control values. The test can be applied to postmortem tissues,[59] cultured skin fibroblasts,[71] white blood cells,[36] and amniocytes.[77]

The utilization of the acid ceramidase assay has been limited by the fact that it depends upon the use of a synthetic substrate, N-[1-^{14}C]oleoylsphingosine,[71,77,78] which is not commercially available. As a result, the assay is not included in the usual screening procedures for lysosomal enzymes, and is available only in a few laboratories. The lack of general availability and underutilization of the technique has several drawbacks. In "classic" cases, steps are usually taken to obtain enzymatic confirmation of the diagnosis. This may not be the case when the clinical picture is less typical, such as in phenotypes 4 and 5. In our own experience, this led to failure to diagnose a case with type 4 phenotype, and as a result specific prenatal studies were not offered for a subsequent pregnancy.[36] To help remedy this problem we have recently simplified the acid ceramidase assay procedure.[79] Momoi et al. have proposed that N-[1-^{14}C]lauroylsphingosine may be a better substrate for the diagnosis of Farber disease than N-[1-^{14}C] oleoylsphingosine.[62] A different and valuable approach to the enzymatic diagnosis of Farber disease has been provided by Kudoh and Wenger.[72] These investigators incubated cultured skin fibroblasts with [^{14}C]stearic acid–labeled cerebroside sulfate and measured its rate of degradation. Cells from Farber disease patients had a deficient capacity (15 percent of control) to degrade the ceramide that is formed from the cerebroside sulfate. The technique also permits diagnosis of metachromatic leukodystrophy and globoid leukodystrophy.

Other diagnostic tests include demonstration of the characteristic morphologic features on a biopsy specimen of a subcutaneous nodule or other tissue. These features include granuloma formation and the presence of macrophages with lipid cytoplasmic inclusions,[2] which are PAS-positive and are extracted by lipid solvents[7] and which show curvilinear inclusions under the electron microscope.[30,31,43,44,45,80] Sural nerve biopsy specimens may also show a characteristic ultrastructural abnormality.[11]

The third approach involves the demonstration of ceramide accumulation in tissues or body fluids. Ceramide excess can easily be demonstrated qualitatively by thin-layer chromatography,[7,21] or quantitated by high-performance liquid chromatography,[46,49,50] or by gas-liquid chromatography combined with mass spectrometry.[26] These techniques have been applied to biopsy specimens of subcutaneous nodules[14,17,18,29,30] and liver[23] and to postmortem tissues.[7,21,26] It is helpful to determine separately the ceramides containing α-hydroxy fatty acids. Most normal tissues contain only ceramides with nonhydroxy fatty acids, whereas both types are found in Farber disease tissue.[7,26,47,48] The level of ceramides in the subcutaneous nodule may constitute 20 percent of total lipids. Although such a finding may be diagnostic of Farber disease, this is not fully established, since at present there are no valid comparison samples, and it has been shown that the outer layers of normal skin contain large quantities of ceramide.[73,74] We demonstrated a 200-fold ceramide excess in the urine of one patient,[81] but four others gave normal results.

Indentification of Heterozygote

All of the obligate heteroygotes tested so far had reduced acid ceramidase activity in cultured skin fibroblasts or white blood cells (see Ref. 1, Table 40-1, and Refs. 17,28,62,71,77,78).

Prenatal Diagnosis

Ten pregnancies at risk for Farber disease have been monitored in our laboratory. One of the studies utilized a cultured chorion villus sample, while cultured amniocytes were used in the other nine. The chorion villus sample had normal acid ceramidase activity, but the procedure was followed by spontaneous abortion. In six instances acid ceramidase assays of cultured amniotic fluid cells led to the prediction that the fetus was either normal or heterozygous for Farber disease, and these diagnoses were confirmed postnatally. In three pregnancies acid ceramidase activity in cultured amniotic fluid cells was less than 10 percent of controls, and pregnancy was terminated. Postmortem tissues showed elevated ceramide levels in kidney and liver, and greatly reduced acid ceramidase activity in brain and cultured skin fibroblasts.[77]

GENETICS

The reduced acid ceramidase activity in obligate heterozygotes and pedigree data indicates an autosomal recessive mode of inheritance. Of the known cases, 24 have been female and 16 male. Except for the Jewish race, all nationalities appear to be represented. Two families are black. Among the 35 families about whom some information is available, consanguinity was present in 5. In three additional families parents or grandparents came from the same relatively small communities. In 11 families more than one sib was affected. When the index cases are omitted from enumeration, 44 were unaffected and 12 had Farber disease. In no instances were parents involved, and no cases were reported in previous generations.

The prevalence of Farber disease is unknown. The fact that it has been reported in only 40 cases, coupled with the high frequency of consanguinity, suggests that it is a rare disorder. However, the recent demonstration of previously unrecognized phenotypes, coupled with the difficulty in achieving the diagnosis in such cases, raises the possibility that the incidence exceeds current estimates.

THERAPY

At this time there is no specific therapy. Corticosteroids may provide some relief. The laryngeal and pulmonary involvement require close supervision of respiratory function, and tracheostomy may be needed. Cosmetic surgery may be useful for some of the unsightly granulomas. One patient had hypercalcemia, possibly related to an osteolytic lesion,[36] and this complication may require therapy.

In the future, Farber disease patients should be considered for bone marrow transplantation. A major portion of the disability and disfigurement associated with the disease is due to subcutaneous and periarticular nodules and viceral infiltrates.

The nodules appear to be caused by ceramide accumulation followed by macrophages and mononuclear cell infiltrates, cells which in these patients are incapable of degrading ceramides. It is plausible, and indeed likely, that replacement with enzymatically competent cells could lead to dissolution of the nodules. This approach would offer greatest hope for those patients with intact nervous system function and should be considered at an early age, before pulmonary and liver function are severely compromised.

REFERENCES

1. MOSER HW, CHEN WC: Ceramidase deficiency: Farber's lipogranulomatosis, in Stanbury JB, Wyngaarden JB, Fredrickson DS, Goldstein JL, Brown MS (eds): *The Metabolic Basis of Inherited Disease*, 5th ed. New York, McGraw-Hill, 1983, p 820.

2. FARBER S, COHEN J, UZMAN LL: Lipogranulomatosis. A new lipoglycoprotein "storage" disease. *J Mt Sinai Hosp* 24:816, 1957.

3. SCHOENENBERG H, LINDENFELSER R: Farber-Syndrom (diseminierte Lipogranulomatose). *Monatsschr Kinderheilkd* 122:153, 1974.

4. RAMPINI S, CLAUSEN J: Farbersche Krankheit (disseminierte Lipogranulomatose: Klinisches Bild und Zusammenfassung der chemischen Befunde. *Helv Paediat Acta* 22:500, 1967.

5. MOLZ G: Farbersche Krankheit: Pathologisch-anatomische Befunde. *Virchows Arch (A)* 344:86, 1966.

6. CLAUSEN J, RAMPINI S: Chemical studies of Farber's disease. *Acta Neurol Scand* 46:313, 1970.

7. MOSER HW, PRENSKY AL, WOLFE JH, ROSMAN NP, with technical assistance of CARR S, FERREIRA G: Farber's lipogranulomatosis: Report of case and demonstration of an excess of free ceramide and ganglioside. *Am J Med* 47:869, 1969.

8. COGAN DG, KUWABARA T, MOSER HW, HAZARD GW: Retinopathy in a case of Farber's lipogranulomatosis. *Arch Ophthalmol* 75:752, 1966.

9. PRENSKY AL, FERRIERA G, CARR S, MOSER HW: Ceramide and ganglioside accumulation in Farber's lipogranulomatosis. *Proc Soc Exp Med* 126:725, 1967.

10. RIVEL J, VITAL C, BATTIN J, HEHEUNSTRE JP, LEGER H: La Lipogranulomatose disseminée de Farber. Étude anatomo-clinique et ultrastructurable, de deux observations. *Arch Anat Cytol Pathol* 25:37, 1977.

11. VITAL C, BATTIN J, RIVEL J, HEHEUNSTRE JP: Aspects ultrastructuraux des lesions due nerf peripherique dans un cas de maladie de Farber. *Rev Neurol* 132:419, 1976.

12. BIERMAN SM, EDGINGTON T, NEWCOMBER VD, PEARSON CM: Farber's disease: A disorder of mucopolysaccharide metabolism with articular, respiratory, and neurologic manifestations. *Arthritis Rheum* 9:620, 1966.

13. SCHANCHE AF, BIERMAN SM, SOPHER RL, O'LOUGHLIN BJ: Disseminated lipogranulomatosis: Early roentgenographic changes. *Radiology* 82:673, 1964.

14. BECKER H, AUBOCK L, HAIDVOGL M, BERNHEIMER H: Disseminated lipogranulomatosis (Farber). Case report of the 16th case of a ceramidase deficiency. *Verh Dtsch Ges Pathol* 60:254, 1976.

15. ABUL-HAJ SK, MARTZ DG, DOUGLAS WF, GEPPERT LJ: Farber's disease: Report of a case with observations on its histogenesis and notes on the nature of the stored material. *J Pediatr* 61:221, 1962.

16. SCHULTZE G, LANG EK: Disseminated lipogranulomatosis: Report of a case. *Radiology* 74:428, 1960.

17. TOPPET M, VAMOS-HURWITZ E, JANNIAUX G, CREMER N, TONDEUR M, PELC S: Farber's disease as a ceramidosis: Clinical, radiological and biochemical aspects. *Acta Paediat Scand* 67:113, 1978.

18. DUSTIN P, TONDEUR M, JONNIAUX G, VAMOS-HURWITZ E, PELC S: La Maladie de Farber: Étude anatomo-clinique et ultrastructurale. *Bull Acad Med Belg* 128:733, 1973.

19. HOBOLTH N, RESKE-NIELSON E: To be published.

20. MOORE R: Personal communication.

21. OZAKI H, MIZUTANI M, OKA E, OHTAHARA S, KIMOTO H, TANAKA T, HAKOZAKI H, TAKAHASHI K, SUZUKI Y: Farber's disease (disseminated lipogranulomatosis): The first case reported in Japan. *Acta Med Okayama* 32:69, 1978.

22. TANAKA T, TAKAHASHI K, HOKOZAKI H, KIMOTO H, SUZUKI Y: Farber's disease (disseminated lipogranulomatosis). A pathological, histochemical and ultrastructural study. *Acta Pathol Jpn* 29:135, 1979.

23. NEVILLE BGR, TURNER DR: To be published.

24. PACHMAN LM, FRANK J, LIU M, MOSER HW: Lipogranulomatosis (Farber's disease). *J Pediatr* 93:320, 1978.

25. ZETTERSTROM R: Disseminated lipogranulomatosis (Farber's disease). *Acta Paediat* 47:501, 1958.

26. SAMUELSSON K, ZETTERSTROM R: Ceramides in a patient with a lipogranulomatosis (Farber's disease) with chronic course. *Scand J Clin Lab Invest* 27:393, 1971.

27. SAMUELSSON K, ZETTERSTROM R, IVEMARK BI: Studies on a case of lipogranulomatosis (Farber's disease) with protracted course, in VOLK BW, ARONSON SM (eds): *Sphingolipids, Sphingolipidoses and Allied Disorders.* New York, Plenum, 1972, p 533.

28. PAVONE L, MOSER HW, MOLLICA F, REITANO C, DURAND P: Farber's lipogranulomatosis: Ceramide deficiency and prolonged survival of three relatives. *Johns Hopkins Med J* 147:193, 1980.

29. AMIRHAKIMI GH, HAGHIGHI P, GHALAMBOR MA, HONARI I: Familial lipogranulomatosis (Farber's disease). *Clin Genet* 9:625, 1976.

30. SCHMOECKEL C, HOHLFED M: A specific ultrastructural marker for disseminated lipogranulomatosis (Farber). *Arch Dermatol Res* 266:187, 1979.

31. HOROWITZ S, ERICKSON C, STRUBLE R: Personal communication.

32. COLEMAN RA: Personal communication.

33. BARRIERE H, GILLOT F: La Lipogranulomatose de Farber. *Nouv Presse Med* 2:767, 1973.

34. CROCKER AC, COHEN J, FARBER S: The "lipogranulomatosis" syndrome: Review, with report of patient showing milder involvement, in Aronson SM, Volk BW (eds): *Inborn Disorders of Sphingolipid Metabolism.* Oxford, Pergamon, 1967, p 485.

35. PIERPONT ME, WENGER DA, MOSER HW: Heterogeneity of clinical expression of Farber's lipogranulomatosis. Presented at American Society of Human Genetics, 111A, 1983.

36. ANTONARAKIS SE, VALLE D, MOSER HW, MOSER A, QUALMAN SJ, ZINKHAM WH: Phenotypic variability in siblings with Farber disease. *J Pediatr* 104:409, 1984.

37. BURCK U, MOSER HW, GOEBEL HH, GRUETTNER R, HELD KR: A case of lipogranulomatosis (Farber): Some clinical and ultrastructural aspects. *Eur J Pediatr* 143:203, 1985.

38. ZARBIN MA, GREEN WR, MOSER HW, MORTON SJ: Farber's disease: Light and electron microscopic study of the eye. *Arch Ophthalmol* 103:73, 1985.

39. EVIATAR L, SKLOWER SL, WISNIEWSKI K, FELDMAN RS, GOCHOCO A: Farber (lipogranulomatosis): An unusual presentation in a black child. *Pediatr Neurol* 2:371, 1986.

40. FUSCH C, HUENGES R, MOSER HW, SEWELL AC, ROGGENDORF W, KUSTERMANN-KUHN B, POULOS A, CAREY WF, HARZER K: A case of combined Farber's and Sandhoff's disease. *Eur J Ped*, in press.

41. CARTIGNY B, LIBERT J, FENSOM AH, MARTIN JJ, DHONDT JL, WYART D, FONTAINE G, FARRIAUX JP: Clinical diagnosis of a new case of ceramidase deficiency (Farber's disease). *J Inherited Metab Dis* 8:8, 1985.

42. PALCOUX JB, DESVIGNES V, MALPUECH G, CHARBONNE F, KANTELIP B, RAYNAUD EJ: Farber's (lipogranulomatosis): Apropos of a case. *Arch Fr Pediatr* 42:535, 1985.

43. VAN HOOF F, HERS HG: Farber's disease, in Hers HG, Van Hoof F (eds): *Lysosomes and Storage Disease.* New York, Academic, 1973, p 559.

44. RAUCH HJ, AUBOECK L: "Banana bodies" in disseminated lipogranulomatosis (Farber's disease). *Am J Dermatopathol* 5:263, 1983.

45. RUTSAERT J, TONDEUR M, VAMOS-HURWITZ E, DUSTIN P: The cellular lesions of Farber's disease and their experimental reproduction of tissue culture. *Lab Invest* 36:474, 1977.

46. SUGITA M, IWAMORI M, EVANS J, MCCLEUR RH, DULANEY JT, MOSER HW: High performance liquid chromatography of ceramides: Application to analysis in human tissues and demonstration of ceramide excess in Farber's disease. *J Lipid Res* 15:223, 1974.

47. SUGITA M, CONNOLLY P, DULANEY JT, MOSER HW: Fatty acid composition of free ceramides of kidney and cerebellum from a patient with Farber's disease. *Lipids* 8:401, 1973.

48. LAUTER CJ, TRAMS EG: A spectrophotometric determination of sphingosine. *J Lipid Res* 3:136, 1962.

49. IWAMORI M, COSTELLO C, MOSER HW: Analysis and quantitation of free ceramide containing non-hydroxy and hydroxy fatty acids, and phytosphingosine by high performance liquid chromatography. *J Lipid Res* 20:86, 1979.

50. YAHARA S, MOSER HW, KOLODNY EH, KIGHIMOTO Y: Reverse phase high performance liquid chromatography of cerebrosides, sulfatides and ceramides: Microanalysis of homolog composition without hydrolysis and application to cerebroside analysis in peripheral nerves of adrenoleukodystrophy patients. *J Neurochem* 34:694, 1980.

51. SCRIBNEY M: Enzymatic synthesis of ceramide. *Biochim Biophys Acta* 125:542, 1966.
52. MORELL P, RADIN NS: Specificity in ceramide biosynthesis from long chain bases and various fatty acyl coenzyme A's by brain microsomes. *J Biol Chem* 245:342, 1970.
53. BRAUN PE, MORELL P, RADIN NS: Synthesis of C18 and C20 dihydrosphingosines, ketodihydrosphingosines and ceramides by microsomal preparations from mouse brain. *J Biol Chem* 245:335, 1970.
54. BORTZ WM: Specificity of the enzymatic synthesis of ceramide. *Biochim Biophys Acta* 152:628, 1968.
55. ULLMAN MD, RADIN NS: Enzymatic formation of hydroxy ceramides and comparison with enzymes forming non-hydroxy ceramides. *Arch Biochem Biophys* 152:767, 1972.
56. ZALC B, POLLET SA, HARPIN ML, BAUMANN NA: Ceramide biosynthesis in mouse brain microsomes: Comparison between C57 BL controls and quaking mutants. *Brain Res* 81:511, 1974.
57. GATT S: Enzymatic hydrolysis of sphingolipids. I. Hydrolysis and synthesis of ceramides by an enzyme from rat brain. *J Biol Chem* 241:3724, 1966.
58. YAVIN E, GATT S: Enzymatic hydrolysis of sphingolipids. VIII. Further purification and properties of rat brain ceramidase. *Biochem* 8:1692, 1969.
59. SUGITA M, WILLIAMS M, DULANEY JT, MOSER HW: Ceramidase and ceramide synthesis in human kidney and cerebellum. Description of a new alkaline ceramidase. *Biochim Biophys Acta* 398:125, 1975.
60. STOFFEL W, MELZNER I: Studies in vitro on the biosynthesis of ceramide and sphingomyelin. A re-evaluation of proposed pathways. *Hoppe-Seyler's Z Physiol Chem* 361:755, 1980.
61. SINGH I: Ceramide synthesis from free fatty acids in rat brain: Function of NADPH and substrate specificity. *J Neurochem* 40:1565, 1983.
62. MOMOI T, BEN-YOSEPH Y, NADLER HL: Substrate-specificities of acid and alkaline ceramidases in fibroblasts from patients with Farber disease and controls. *Biochem J* 205:419, 1982.
63. SPENCE MW, BEED S, COOK HW: Acid and alkaline ceramidase of rat tissues. *Biochem Cell Biol* 64:400, 1986.
64. CHEN WW, MOSER HW: Purification of acid ceramidase from human placenta. *Fed Proc* 38:405, 1979.
65. AL EJM, TIFFANY CW, WERDMULLER B, VAN DER FLIET R, AERTS JFGM, HILGERS JHM, MOSER AB, MOSER HW, TAGER JM, SCHRAM AW: Biochemical and immunological studies on acid ceramidase of human spleen. Submitted for publication.
66. CHEN WW, MOSER AB, MOSER HW: Role of lysosomal acid ceramidase in the metabolism of ceramide in human skin fibroblasts. *Arch Biochem* 208:444, 1981.
67. CHEN WW, DECKER GL: Abnormalities of lysosomes in human diploid fibroblasts from patients with Farber's disease. *Biochim Biophys Acta* 718:185, 1982.
68. NILSSON A: The presence of sphingomyelin and ceramide cleaving enzymes in the small intestinal tract. *Biochim Biophys Acta* 176:339, 1969.
69. TIFFANY C, AL E, TAGER J, MOSER HW, KISHIMOTO Y: The use of antibody to characterize control and Farber disease ceramidase. *J Neurochem* 48(Suppl):S35, 1987.
70. SUGITA M, DULANEY JT, MOSER HW: Ceramidase deficiency in Farber's disease (lipogranulomatosis). *Science* 178:1100, 1972.
71. DULANEY JT, MILUNSKY A, SIDBURY JB, HOBOLTH N, MOSER HW: Diagnosis of lipogranulomatosis (Farber's disease) by use of cultured fibroblasts. *J Pediatr* 89:59, 1976.
72. KUDOH T, WENGER DA: Diagnosis of metachromatic leukodystrophy, Krabbe disease, and Farber disease after uptake of fatty acid-labeled cerebroside sulfate into cultured skin fibroblasts. *J Clin Invest* 70:89, 1982.
73. GRAY GM, WHITE JR: Glycosphingolipids and ceramides in human and pig epidermis. *J Invest Dermatol* 70:336, 1978.
74. ELIAS PM, BROWN BE, FRITSCH P, GOERKE J, GRAY GM, WHITE RJ: Localization and composition of lipids in neonatal mouse stratum granulosum and stratum corneum. *J Invest Dermatol* 73:339, 1979.
75. BARROW MV, HOLUBAR K: Multicentric reticulohistiocytosis. A review of 33 patients. *Medicine* 48:287, 1969.
76. DRESCHER E, WOYKE S, MARKIEWICZ C, TEGI S: Juvenile fibromatosis in siblings (fibromatosis hyalinica multiplex juvenilis). *J Pediatr Surg* 2:427, 1967.
77. FENSOM AH, BENSON PF, NEVILLE BRG, MOSER HW, MOSER AB, DULANEY JT: Prenatal diagnosis of Farber's disease. *Lancet* 2:990, 1979.
78. DULANEY JT, MOSER HW: Farber's disease (lipogranulomatosis), in Glew RH, Peters SP (eds): *Practical Enzymology of the Sphingolipids.* New York, AR Liss, 1977, p 283.
79. TIFFANY CW, AL B, MOSER HW: A modified assay system for the measurement of ceramidase activity. Submitted for publication.
80. SCHMOECKEL C: Subtle clues to diagnosis of skin diseases by electron microscopy. "Farber bodies" in disseminated lipogranulomatosis (Farber's disease). *Am J Dermatopathol* 2:153, 1980.
81. IWAMORI M, MOSER HW: Above normal urinary excretion of ceramides in Farber's disease, and the characterization of their components by high performance liquid chromatography. *Clin Chem* 21:725, 1975.

CHAPTER 66

SPHINGOMYELIN-CHOLESTEROL LIPIDOSES:
The Niemann-Pick Group of Diseases

MATTHEW W. SPENCE
JOHN W. CALLAHAN

1. Sphingomyelin-cholesterol lipidoses (the Niemann-Pick group of diseases) can be divided into two broad types on the basis of etiology, with each type being subdivided into three clinical forms. Both types are characterized by varying degrees of hepatosplenomegaly and of formation of foam cells in bone marrow, and variably increased amounts of sphingomyelin, cholesterol, glycosphingolipids, and bis(monoacylglycero)-phospate in visceral organs. Within each broad group there is sufficient clinical and biochemical variability to indicate substantial genetic heterogeneity.

2. Type I disease includes subjects who are sphingomyelinase-deficient, with activity less than 10 percent of normal, and a storage profile in tissues in which sphingomyelin and cholesterol are the major components.

3. Type II disease includes subjects with elevation in one or more of sphingomyelin, cholesterol, glycolipid, or bis(monoacylglycero)phosphate in spleen and liver. Sphingomyelin storage, when present, is less marked than in type I disease. Lysosomal sphingomyelinase activity is often normal in solid tissues and may be normal or reduced by as much as 80 percent in cultured fibroblasts. A decrease in cholesterol esterification in cultured fibroblasts has been demonstrated in some patients.

4. The acute forms (IA and IIA) are characterized by hepatosplenomegaly and nervous system involvement in early infancy, and a rapid progression with death prior to 6 years of age. Type IIA patients have jaundice in some cases, and the degree of organomegaly and progression of nervous system involvement can be less than for type I.

5. Type IS (subacute) presents in infancy or early childhood with hepatosplenomegaly. The disease is more slowly progressive, and many patients demonstrate little clinical evidence of central nervous system involvement. Type IIS (subacute) presents in the first decade with varying degrees of psychomotor retardation, hepatosplenomegaly, seizures, and vertical supranuclear ophthalmoplegia. Death in the second or third decade from progressive central nervous system involvement is usual. Presentation and course are variable, and the description of groupings of symptom complexes and tissue findings in various demes suggests genetic heterogeneity.

6. Patients with type IC (the chronic form) have hepatosplenomegaly or foam cells usually first discovered in adulthood. Some patients have signs of central nervous system involvement. Type IIC (chronic) presents in adulthood with dementia, extrapyramidal signs, and modest or absent organomegaly.

7. The metabolic defect in type I disease is a deficiency of lysosomal sphingomyelinase. The presence of enzyme protein in

fibroblasts from types IA and IS subjects suggests point mutations in the structural gene. The nature of the metabolic defect in type II is uncertain and may involve sphingomyelinase and cholesterol esterification to varying degrees.

8. The diagnosis of type I disease may be confirmed by measuring sphingomyelinase activity in leukocytes, fibroblasts, or tissue biopsy specimens. For type II disease, evidence of a partial deficiency of sphingomyelinase or a defect in cholesterol esterification may be helpful, but no single procedure has been demonstrated to give reliable results in all circumstances.

9. The inheritance of types I and II disease is consistent with an autosomal recessive condition. Carrier detection and prenatal diagnosis of type I disease are by measurement of sphingomyelinase activity and are established procedures. No reliable single procedure has been demonstrated to predict carriers for type II disease, although intermediate levels of cholesterol esterification or sphingomyelinase activity have been described in some cases. Prenatal diagnosis has been done, but the reliability of available methodology remains uncertain at this time.

10. There is no specific treatment.

The development of knowledge pertaining to the Niemann-Pick group of inherited metabolic diseases can be traced through the chapters on Niemann-Pick disease in previous editions of this book. In the second edition, in 1966, Fredrickson[1] assembled the current knowledge of the disease in a masterful summary that included the tabulation of reports of 165 patients. In the third edition, in 1972, Fredrickson was joined by Sloan[2] and the chapter included a section on the nature of the metabolic block and a description of five types of the disease, types A through E, differentiated according to clinical, pathological, and biochemical criteria. For the fourth[3] and fifth[4] editions, in 1978 and 1983, authorship passed to Brady, who had described with Fredrickson and others in 1966 the sphingomyelinase deficiency characteristic of some forms of the disease.[5] In both editions, Brady summarized advances in knowledge with particular emphasis on the enzyme defect.

In this edition, we propose a new classification that splits the old Niemann-Pick group in two. The body of knowledge on which we base this proposed separation is impressive and compelling, albeit incomplete. The new classification is intended to refocus our thinking on the evidence of today and, we hope, to facilitate investigation of this group of diseases in the future.

HISTORY

In 1914, Albert Niemann, a pediatrician in Berlin, reported the case of "Irene D," a Polish-Jewish female infant who had hepatosplenomegaly and who died when 18 months old of a progressive illness.[6] At autopsy, her visceral organs contained large foam cells, and she was felt to have had a fulminant form of Gaucher disease. In the next 10 years, several similar cases were reported, and Ludwig Pick[7] identified these as examples of a single entity, distinct from Gaucher disease, to which the eponym *Niemann-Pick disease* was eventually applied. Case reports and studies appeared steadily thereafter, among them descriptions of increased tissue phospholipids, particularly a major increase in sphingomyelin.[8] The variability in age of onset and in clinical expression was noted in various reviews,[7,9,10] and this, together with the variability in lipid storage, led Crocker[11] to propose four subgroups of the disease: type A (acute neuronopathic), type B (chronic with marked visceral involvement but sparing the nervous system), type C (subacute with nervous system involvement), and type D (subacute with nervous system involvement and ancestry from southwestern Nova Scotia). Fredrickson and Sloan[2] later added type E (indeterminate form in adults).

The discovery by Brady et al.[5] in 1966 that sphingomyelinase (sphingomyelin phosphodiesterase, EC 3.1.4.12) was severely deficient in type A Niemann-Pick disease and the later demonstration of a similar deficiency in type B placed the biochemical phenotype of these forms of the disease on a firmer footing. However, the nature of the metabolic abnormality in other types of Niemann-Pick disease, including C and D, remained uncertain. The increasing sophistication of complex lipid analysis of tissues, and the increasing use of tissues and fluids for enzyme diagnosis of inherited disease and for carrier detection and prenatal diagnosis,[3,4] produced a large body of evidence that made it clear that all clinical phenotypes considered examples of Niemann-Pick disease could not be attributed to a single enzyme defect and allelic mutation.

CLASSIFICATION

We propose a classification that takes into account (1) the wide variations in clinical phenotype and in the nature and extent of the lipid storage among the groups,[1-4,11-19] (2) reports of chronic adult forms,[2,20-36] and (3) the reports of patients with partial deficiencies of sphingomyelinase activity,[37-48] heat labile sphingomyelinase activity,[49] or normal activity.

First, we distinguish persons who are clearly sphingomyelinase-deficient (with activity levels less than 10 percent of normal) and have a storage profile in tissues in which sphingomyelin and cholesterol are the major components from persons in whom the nature of the metabolic defect is uncertain. The former we describe as having type I disease; the latter, type II. Each type is further subdivided into 3 forms—acute, subacute, and chronic—that reflect the age at which symptoms appear, the severity of symptoms, and the prognosis. However, there is sufficient clinical and biochemical variability within the main groups and the subdivisions to indicate genetic heterogeneity or modification by other genetic or environmental factors as yet poorly understood. Included in type II disease are a wide spectrum of patients with visceral or neurovisceral lipidosis. All have some elevation in one or more

of sphingomyelin, cholesterol, glycolipid, or bis(monoacylglycero)phosphate in spleen and liver, and accumulation of sphingomyelin is often less than that of the other lipids. Lysosomal sphingomyelinase activity is either normal or reduced by as much as 80 percent, and the reduction in activity affects some tissues but not others. Some patients may have a defect in cholesterol esterification, perhaps with a secondary decrease in sphingomyelinase activity. Alternatively, the basic defect may reside in the sphingomyelin-degrading system or some other metabolic pathway, with secondary changes in cholesterol processing.

We have retained both types under the broad Niemann-Pick heading, to maintain some continuity with the previous literature. Further, the observations that varying amounts of sphingomyelin and cholesterol are stored in all of these disorders, and the evidence for a close physical interaction between these lipids in normal tissues, suggest that defects in the metabolism or processing of one lead to secondary changes in the other. Accordingly, both groups may be usefully considered together.

The proposed classification is in Table 66-1, together with the classification of previous editions and the names that have been applied to various diseases in these groups at various times. Some of the major clinical manifestations of the groups are summarized in Table 66-2.

CLINICAL MANIFESTATIONS

Type I: Lipidosis with Sphingomyelinase Deficiency and Primary Sphingomyelin Storage

Type IA: Acute Form. The acute form of type I disease is characterized by massive visceromegaly, nervous system involvement in early infancy, a rapid progression with death usually prior to 5 years of age, and sphingomyelinase activity generally less than 5 percent of normal in all tissues examined.[2-4,65] Up to 1965, this form accounted for 75 percent of cases described in the literature.[2] The incidence may have been slightly reduced by prenatal diagnosis and termination of pregnancy.[4,66-74] The relative paucity of recent reports[75-77] could reflect a lack of novelty and consequent lack of interest among journals rather than a major decrease in true incidence.

Lipid storage in fetal liver, brain, and kidney and in placenta have been documented prior to birth.[1,2,71,72,78,79] Enlargement of the placenta has been demonstrated by ultrasound,[73] and placental storage may have led to spontaneous abortion at 5 months in one case.[2] Hepatosplenomegaly has been noted at birth,[2] is readily apparent within the first 6 months of life, and is massive by 1 year of age. SGOT and SGPT are elevated in some cases.[2,80] Diffuse granular or reticular infiltrates are seen in the lung fields on x-ray.[1] Development can be relatively normal up to 3 to 4 months, or occasionally for a year or more.[2,11] However, feeding problems, vomiting, diarrhea, pyrexia, and failure to thrive are reported,[81-83] and infants with type IA disease rarely sit, and demonstrate a generalized, progressive loss of motor and intellectual function by 1 year of age. Cherry-red spots are present in the macula in 50 percent of cases; brownish-yellow discoloration of the skin has been reported.[84] Vacuolation is seen in peripheral lymphocytes, and bone marrow, spleen, and lymph nodes contain many foamy storage cells.

Table 66-1 Classification of the Niemann-Pick Group of Diseases

Disease groupings		Previous groupings
Type I	Lipidosis with sphingomyelinase deficiency and primary sphingomyelin storage	Sphingomyelinase-deficient group[51,52]
	IA—acute	Type A;[2,11] type I[50]
	IS—subacute	Type B;[2,11] type II;[50] type F[49]
	IC—chronic	Type E;[2] types V and VI[50]
Type II	Lipidosis with primary defect uncertain and secondary sphingomyelin storage	Sphingomyelinase-nondeficient group[51,52]
	IIA—acute	Neonatal hepatitis-like syndromes;[53–56] psychomotor retardation[57]
	IIS—subacute	Type C;[2,11] type D;[2,11,13,58] juvenile dystonic lipidosis;[59–61] neurovisceral storage disease with vertical supranuclear ophthalmoplegia, type III;[50] juvenile Niemann-Pick with sea-blue histiocytes;[62] type IV;[50] DAF syndrome[63]
	IIC—chronic	Neurovisceral storage disease in adulthood;[20,28,64] type E;[2] type VI[50]

Type IS: Subacute Form. Type IS includes type B of Crocker[11] and Fredrickson and Sloan,[2] type II of Neville,[50] type F of Schneider et al.,[49] and the juvenile patients reported with severe sphingomyelinase deficiency (<10 percent of normal) with or without evidence for central nervous system involvement.[85–94] This departure from previous classifications is intended to suggest that a relative lack of central nervous system involvement in a patient may reflect variations in the temporal sequence of central nervous system changes rather than complete lifetime sparing of the central nervous system.

Patients with type IS may develop visceral changes as early as type IA patients, usually splenomegaly followed by hepatomegaly. Most cases are detected in infancy or early childhood.[4] In these early-onset cases, the lung fields show diffuse infiltration and these changes may contribute to increased susceptibility to respiratory problems such as asthma and infections.[4,65]

In many of these patients with visceromegaly and sphingomyelinase deficiency, there is little evidence of central nervous system dysfunction.[2,5,65] Patients 17 and 18 of Crocker and Farber[10] were free of neurological abnormalities for at least 20 years.[2] However, central nervous system involvement as evidenced by ocular changes such as an abnormal macula with gray discoloration and granular pigmentation[85,94–96] or granular opacities about the fovea[34,90,93,97] has been observed in patients whose only other signs were visceromegaly and foam cell infiltration. Other patients have been reported to have mental retardation at 9 and 18 years of age[98] or cerebellar ataxia.[2] Elleder and Cihula[99] reported three sibs with hepatosplenomegaly, foam cells, and sphingomyelinase deficiency. A girl died at 7 years with no clinical evidence of brain disease but discrete neuronal storage at autopsy. One brother (age 22) had marked extrapyramidal signs and retardation, whereas another (age 18) had a cherry-red spot in the fundus but no other neurological signs.

Thus, the subacute group demonstrates marked phenotypic heterogeneity particularly with respect to the nature and extent of nervous system involvement. The elucidation of the reasons for this variation must await more definitive knowledge of the molecular defect, and of the differences in lipid metabolism between the nervous system and peripheral tissues.

Type IC: Chronic Form. The chronic form, or adult form, includes patients in whom the first signs and symptoms of the disease appear in adulthood, and in whom either the type of

Table 66-2 Some Major Clinical Features of the Niemann-Pick Group of Diseases

Feature	IA	IS	IC	IIA	IIS	IIC
Genetics	AR	AR	?	AR	AR	Probably AR
Age at onset	In utero–1 yr	0–3 yr	> 20	0–2 yr	0–18 yr	> 20
Age at death	< 5 yr	?	?	< 8 yr	0–37 yr	?
Neonatal jaundice				±	±	
Hepatosplenomegaly	+ +	+ +	+	+	+	±
Feeding difficulties, failure to thrive	+					
Psychomotor retardation	+ +	±	±	+ +	+ +	+
Seizures					+	
Lung infiltration	+ +	+			±	
Vertical supranuclear ophthalmoplegia					+	+
Retinal cherry-red spot	+	±	±		±	
Other ocular changes	+	±				
Foam cells	+ +	+ +	+ +	+ +	+ +	±
Sea-blue histiocytes		+	+		+	+

NOTE: AR = autosomal recessive. Blank, not commented upon; ±, sometimes present; +, usually present; + +, present.

lipid storage or the low levels of sphingomyelinase in all tissues examined indicates a primary sphingomyelinase deficiency.

The usual history is of accidental discovery of splenomegaly and/or hepatomegaly and foam cells and/or sea-blue histiocytes in bone marrow during medical investigations.[24,27] In two patients, signs attributable to hypersplenism and splenic rupture were present.[27] Another died at age 42 with hepatosplenomegaly and a 4-year history of biliary cirrhosis and hepatitis.[100] One patient presented at age 48 with respiratory problems.[65] Signs of central nervous system involvement are absent in some,[27,32] but cerebellar ataxia and cherry-red spots in the macula have been described in others.[3,4] The absence of detailed biochemical studies in some of these cases makes it difficult to determine whether they are part of the chronic type I or chronic type II group. Further, whether some of those with type IC disease are a separate category, or are part of the spectrum of the subacute form (type IS) in whom organomegaly was not detected in childhood, remains to be determined.

Type II: Lipidoses with Uncertain Primary Defect and Secondary Sphingomyelin Storage

Type IIA: Acute Form. The acute cases of type II disease are characterized by hepatosplenomegaly, psychomotor symptoms appearing between the first days of life and age 2, and death by 8 years of age, usually from respiratory infection.[55–57,101] Some patients develop jaundice in infancy and a clinical pattern similar to neonatal hepatitis.[53–56,102,103] Since many patients with type IIS disease also have jaundice in infancy, the more fulminating course of the acute form may reflect complications of liver involvement and the gene defect may be similar in type IIA and type IIS. Jaundice in infancy is fatal in at least 15 percent of the type IIS patients of southwestern Nova Scotia.[103,104] The cause of the early and sometimes transient hyperbilirubinemia is not known. Obstruction of the porta hepatis by enlarged lymph nodes has been reported,[10] but exploratory laparotomy has failed to show obstruction in other cases.[56] Lipid storage per se has also been discounted as a cause.[56] Other patients, even the sibs of those with jaundice and liver involvement, have normal development to age 1 to 2 years and then develop progressive psychomotor retardation. The motor symptoms include hypertonicity of limbs and loss of coordination and truncal control.

Type IIS: Subacute Form. Type IIS patients include many of the subjects reported as having Niemann-Pick disease type C,[1,2,4,11,47,55,57,65,101,102,105,106,108–128] type D,[2,4,13,58,103,104,129] juvenile dystonic lipidosis,[47,59–61,130,131] neurovisceral storage with vertical supranuclear ophthalmoplegia,[50,132–134] juvenile Niemann-Pick disease with vertical supranuclear ophthalmoplegia,[62] juvenile Niemann-Pick disease with sea-blue histiocytes,[48] and DAF syndrome (down gaze, ataxia, athetosis, foam cell).[63,135]

Patients with type IIS are characterized by progressive psychomotor retardation and storage in foam cells, and often by presence of sea-blue histiocytes and hepatosplenomegaly. Beyond that, the clinical presentation is varied, with a wide range in age of onset (infancy to age 18) and death (infancy and up, with subjects reported living at age 37) and in the numbers of subjects reported with vertical supranuclear ophthalmoplegia, seizures, and jaundice in infancy.

In the patients reported as having type C, infantile jaundice was observed in fewer than one-third of cases. Hepatosplenomegaly was a feature of most. Except where hepatitis and ascending cholangitis were presenting features, findings of liver function studies were normal. The subjects lose previously acquired skills and develop clumsiness and moderate ataxia, and psychomotor retardation progresses until secondary infections, usually respiratory, result in death between 5 and 15 years of age. Delays in acquiring postural control, progressive difficulty with learning in school, and seizures are features in some patients.[65] Cataplexy has been observed in at least nine subjects,[136,137] and myoclonus and narcolepsy have been presenting symptoms.[113,118] Vertical supranuclear ophthalmoplegia was specifically noted in 20 percent of cases.

Type D patients share common ancestors in the Acadian population of southwestern Nova Scotia. At least 50 percent of the group have a history of jaundice in infancy which is fatal in roughly one-third of the jaundiced group. Development to age 6 is normal apart from hepatosplenomegaly. By age 8, personality changes, emotional lability, clumsiness, ataxia, and hyperreflexia are observed, and the disease continues to progress to seizures, incontinence, and profound psychomotor retardation, with death in the teens from a combination of pneumonia and cachexia. Cataplexy was present in one, and vertical supranuclear ophthalmoplegia was observed in two subjects.[103,104,129]

Patients with a combination of vertical supranuclear ophthalmoplegia, foam cells and/or sea-blue histiocytes in their bone marrow, and varying degrees of slow or subnormal psychomotor development have been reported by several groups.[50,59–61,130,132] Other manifestations include progressive mental deterioration, seizures, cerebellar and extrapyramidal signs and symptoms, modest hepatosplenomegaly, and death in the second or third decade. The average age of onset has been 9 years, with a range from 1 to 18 years. Subjects reported eyes getting stuck in elevation and difficulty walking downstairs, and they would blink and thrust their heads when asked to perform vertical eye movements. The sequence of ocular motor abnormalities was loss of vertical saccadic movements, loss of vertical pursuit movements, and loss of convergence. The abnormalities may be explained by involvement of the corticobulbar fibers in the subthalamic and pretectal areas of brain.[50,132]

Vertical supranuclear ophthalmoplegia was also a feature of six of seven patients among nine subjects of Spanish-American descent,[48] as were large foamy histiocytes and variable numbers of sea-blue histiocytes in bone marrow. Eight of the nine patients had fibroblast sphingomyelinase activity of 12 to 50 percent of control values, whereas one patient had a level that was 130 percent of controls.

Type IIC: Chronic Form. At least three cases have been reported of a neurovisceral storage disease of the Niemann-Pick type with onset in adulthood.[20,28] Two subjects were brothers who presented at age 30 with progressive dementia, vertical supranuclear ophthalmoplegia, cerebellar ataxia, mild hypersplenism, and foam cells in bone marrow, spleen, and liver biopsies. Sphingomyelinase and glucocerebrosidase activities were above normal.[20] The third patient, the mother of two healthy children, had mild mental deficiency starting at age 26. She gradually developed a left spastic hemiparesis and dystonic symptoms, paresis of upward gaze, and dementia, but no organomegaly, and she died at age 46. Postmortem examination demonstrated storage in spleen, in brain, and to a lesser extent in liver of a pattern considered more typical of type II than of type I subjects.[28]

There may be a second group of type IIC patients in whom cerebral pathology is minimal or absent. Fredrickson and Sloan[2] reported a 27-year-old male in excellent health whose spleen was removed following accidental injury. The spleen contained foamy macrophages, and examination of formalin-fixed tissues showed fourfold and two- to threefold elevations of sphingomyelin and cholesterol, respectively. Sphingomyelinase activity was normal in cells cultured from bone marrow but was depressed in skin fibroblasts. Poulos et al.[64] reported the case of a 72-year-old patient in whom unexplained hepatosplenomegaly had been investigated 3 years earlier. Sphingomyelinase was less than 5 percent of normal in leukocytes and was reduced variably in liver (30 percent of lowest control value) and fibroblasts (40 to 60 percent of lowest control value). Sphingomyelin storage was not observed but bis(monoacylglycero)phosphate was 20 times normal.

PATHOLOGY

The Storage Cells (Foam Cell, Niemann-Pick Cell)

The foam cell (Fig. 66-1) is a relatively consistent feature of, but is not exclusive to, the Niemann-Pick group of diseases.[2,4] Found in the reticuloendothelial system of spleen, bone marrow, lungs, and lymph nodes, these cells are large (20 to 90 μm in diameter); and on phase microscopy of unstained smears or sections, their cytoplasm is filled with droplets or particles of uniform size that give the cell a foamy or "mulberry," appearance. In polarized light, the droplets are birefringent; in ultraviolet light, they have a greenish-yellow fluorescence.[2] Similar cells are present in type II disease, but the quantity and appearance of the droplets is more variable, and the birefrigence never reaches the intensity or uniformity of those seen in type I disease.[51,138] Further, the degree of cellular morphological change in type II is often out of proportion to the storage of lipid and/or lipopigment.

Histochemical examination can be done with paraffin blocks or with frozen sections fixed in calcium-formalin or glutaraldehyde.[2] Differential extraction of stored material before staining may be helpful.[138] In frozen sections, droplets in the foam cells stain blue-black with Smith-Dietrich stain, black

with Sudan black B, red with oil red O, blue-violet with Nile blue sulfate, violet with mercuric nitrate, negative or red with PAS, and blue-black with acid hematin. Lipopigment, or ceroid, is more predominant than the lipid droplets in subacute or chronic forms of the diseases. Naturally light-yellow or amber, it exhibits autofluorescence under ultraviolet light and stains with Sudan black B and oil red O, and with PAS after diastase treatment.[27] This lipopigment may be part of the reason that stains such as Wright and May-Grünwald-Giemsa stain the cytoplasm blue. Cells thus stained are called *sea-blue histiocytes*, and the patients from whom they are obtained are said to have the "syndrome of the sea-blue histiocyte."[23,27] However, sea-blue histiocytes appear to be part of an evolving pathological process in a variety of diseases, rather than a characteristic of any one.[23,27,139]

On electron microscopy, the foam cells have a small, eccentrically located nucleus, and inclusion bodies (cytosomes) in the cytoplasm.[4,140] The latter are polymorphic, are 0.5 to 5 μm in diameter, and contain whorls of loosely packed, concentrically arrayed membranes spaced about 50 Å apart. Some cells contain cores of dense granular material with "fingerprint lamellae" characteristic of ceroid deposition, and others may contain varying mixtures of inclusion bodies and dense granular material. The ceroid looks like that described in other storage diseases, as well as in atheromas and in aging cells.[4]

Organ and System Involvement in the Niemann-Pick Group of Diseases

Spleen, Lymphoid Tissue, and Bone Marrow. Possibly because they contain so many reticulum cells, spleen, lymphoid tissue, and bone marrow are the earliest and most severely involved tissues in all diseases of the Niemann-Pick group.[4] The spleen is enlarged, firm, and lighter in color than usual. On cut section, the malpighian bodies appear as reddish-yellow spots. Foamy storage cells are distributed throughout the organ, especially in the pulp and around its arteries. Cytosomes characteristic of lipid storage have been seen in spleen at 19 weeks of gestation.[141] Hematological changes (microcytic anemia and thrombocytopenia) are moderate in the acute and subacute forms but are more prominent in the chronic forms.[20,23,94]

Enlarged lymph nodes are found in the mesentery, hilum of the spleen, liver, and lungs.[4] The normal architecture can be completely replaced by masses of foam cells.

Foam cells crowd out normal hematopoietic elements in the bone marrow in some cases of type I disease but can be relatively few in other cases of type I or type II disease.[142] There are fewer foam cells in the chronic forms of type II disease, and repeated bone marrow examinations may be necessary to demonstrate their presence.[132]

There is no characteristic distribution or appearance of the storage in these organs with disease type, and the morphological differences generally relate to the degree of storage. Particularly for type II disease, the subacute and chronic forms tend to have less obvious changes, and there is a suggestion that an evaluation of disease in the later stages may find less obvious changes than would one earlier in the course of the disease.[2]

Liver. Hepatomegaly is proportional to the acuteness of the disease process, and more striking in type I than in type II

Fig. 66-1 Unstained foam cell in Niemann-Pick disease under phase microscope. Magnitude × 430 (reproduced at 75% of original size). (From Fredrickson and Sloan.[2] Used by permission.)

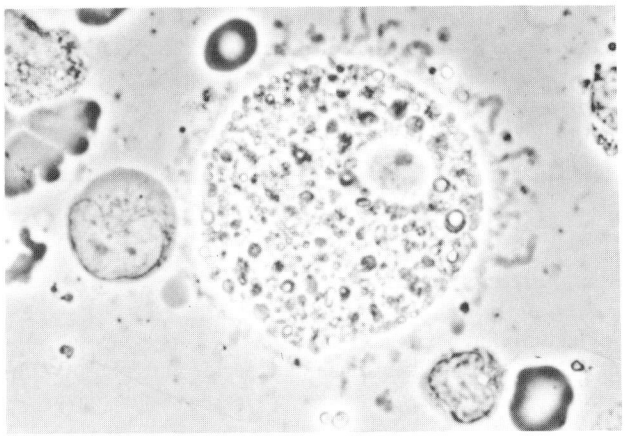

disease. In general, the acute forms involve both the hepatocytes and Kupffer cells, with lysosomal storage having the staining characteristics of sphingolipids and cholesterol.[2,4] Where hyperbilirubinemia exists there are intralobular cholestasis, fine microvesiculation of parenchymal cells, portal infiltration by lymphocytes, and early fibrosis.[120,143] In the nonacute type II disease, the changes seem more confined to the Kupffer cells and macrophages, the foamy cytoplasm of which contains vesicular membranous structures, often with dense cores.[121]

Bones. The bone marrow contains foam cells and, in later stages of nonacute type II disease, cells that stain like sea-blue histiocytes.[132] In type I disease, the extent of other bone involvement seems proportional to the severity of the disease; osteoporosis, metaphyseal splaying, and a quadrate appearance of the lumbar vertebrae have been described.[1,4,81]

Lungs and Heart. A fine nodular or diffuse reticular pattern throughout the lungs is demonstrable radiographically in most patients with type I disease, and the degree and extent varies with the severity and length of disease.[2,81] Foam cells are present in the alveoli but are not seen in sputum. Even major amounts of foam cell infiltration rarely cause respiratory difficulties, although cor pulmonale has been described in a chronic case.[29] Foam cells have been described adjacent to myocardial fibers in the heart, and endocardial fibroelastosis has been reported in an acute-onset patient.[4] Pulmonary pathology is not usually commented upon in type II disease.

Ocular Changes. A cherry-red spot in the retina has been observed in 50 percent of patients with acute type I disease.[2,4] Also described are ballooned, lipid-laden retinal ganglion cells, vacuolated cells in the inner and outer nuclear layers and in the choroid, and lamellar deposits in the corneal and lens epithelium.[144-146] Changes have been noted as early as the twenty-third week of gestation.[147] The term *macula halo syndrome* has been applied to the crystalloid opacities that are seen in some patients with subacute type I disease.[93,97] They form a halo approximately one-half the disk diameter at their outer edge and are scattered throughout the various layers of the retina, concentrated mainly in the Henle fiber layer.[93] They do not interfere with vision. Other changes are abnormal maculae with gray discoloration and granular pigmentation.[85,94-96] In type IIS disease, pleomorphic lamellar inclusions with electron-lucent zones containing variable amounts of granular material have been observed in fibrocytes and endothelial cells of the conjunctiva.[115] More extensive ocular involvement was documented in an 11-year-old girl, including storage in the keratocytes of the cornea, the lens epithelium, the retinal ganglion cells, the pigment epithelium, the corneal tract, and the fibrous astrocytes of the optic nerve.[124] The clinical sequelae of such extensive involvement were optic nerve pallor and a perimacular gray discoloration.[94,124]

Gastrointestinal Tract. Failure to thrive and chronic diarrhea and malabsorption occur in some cases of acute type I disease.[2,82] Distended intestinal loops with a loss of normal mucosal markings and prolongation of transit time have been observed in radiologic studies of gut function.[81,82] The lamina propria is infiltrated with storage cells, and the ganglion cells of the intestine are swollen with foamy cytoplasm.[83]

In rectal mucosal biopsies examined by electron microscopy, Schwann cells and axons contain pleomorphic dense bodies and lamellar bodies with large electron-lucent areas. Similar structures are seen in fibroblasts, endothelial cells, leukocytes, and plasma cells. The inclusions are similar in type I and type II disease.[83]

Other Organs. Large, yellow adrenal glands containing foam cells in the medulla are present without signs of adrenal insufficiency.[4,122] Other endocrine organs and exocrine glands also contain abnormal amounts of lipid but function normally.[4,148] Foam cells in the glomeruli and swollen tubular cells are present in the kidney without evidence of functional impairment. Brownish-yellow elevated patchy discoloration of the skin of the cheeks and occasional frank suppurative lesions with foam cell infiltration have been reported in patients with type IA disease.[11,84]

Nervous System. Patients' survival with all forms of the Niemann-Pick group of diseases is inversely correlated with the degree of central nervous system involvement.[2] Severe progressive psychomotor retardation is a feature of the acute forms, and seizures, dementia, and vertical supranuclear ophthalmoplegia are features of nonacute type II disease. Even among patients with type IS disease referred to as nonneuropathic (Crocker type B), some patients have subtle findings suggestive of a very slow involvement of the nervous system.[2-4,85,90,93-99]

At autopsy, the brain is often atrophic (weighing 50 to 90 percent of normal) and firm. Neural cells are swollen, with a pale, vacuolated cytoplasm, and storage is often restricted to certain cell types.[2,110] Only in type IA disease has the stored material stained as a lipid; it usually fails to stain with lipophilic dyes and is weakly PAS-positive. Electron micrographs show cytoplasmic inclusions—variously described as polymorphic cytoplasmic bodies, oligomembranous bodies, spherical membranous sacs, or multilamellar bodies[28]—consisting of laminated membranes with some electron-dense cores and amorphous electron-dense material similar to lipofuscin.[117] Deposition in axons with a resultant neuroaxonal dystrophy has been described.[28,110] In addition to the more usual cytoplasmic bodies, paired helical filaments similar to those of Alzheimer's disease were noted at autopsy in brain neurons from a 29-year-old patient with type II disease.[131] A severe loss of cells occurs in some areas of the cerebral or cerebellar cortex while adjacent areas may be unaffected. Demyelination, if present, is quite variable. Foam cells or lipid-laden glial cells are distributed about the leptomeninges and the tela choroidea and in the perivascular spaces, and foam cells are found in the endothelium of blood vessels[2] and in the cerebrospinal fluid.[142] The cerebellum, basal ganglia, brainstem, and spinal cord may be similarly affected, and the spinal ganglia and roots, autonomic ganglia including the Auerbach's and Meissner's plexus, and peripheral nerves may undergo morphological changes similar to those of the central nervous system.[4,149]

BIOCHEMISTRY

Accumulating Lipids

Sphingomyelin. Sphingomyelin (Fig. 66-2) is composed of a long-chain base, a long-chain fatty acid, and phosphocholine.[150,151] The long-chain base is usually sphingenine (4-amino-2-octadecene-1,3-diol), which has asymmetric carbon

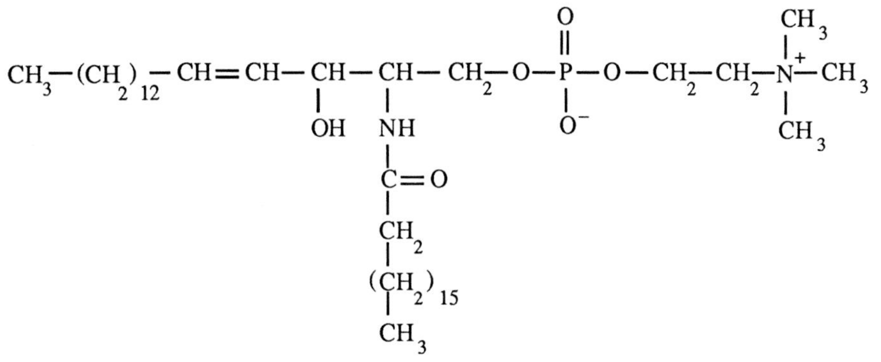

$$CH_3-(CH_2)_{12}-CH=CH-CH-CH-CH_2-O-\overset{\overset{O}{\|}}{\underset{\underset{O^-}{|}}{P}}-O-CH_2-CH_2-\overset{\overset{CH_3}{|}}{\underset{\underset{CH_3}{|}}{N^+}}-CH_3$$

with substituents on the sphingosine backbone: OH and $NH-C(=O)-CH_2-(CH_2)_{15}-CH_3$

Fig. 66-2 Structure of sphingomyelin.

atoms at the 2 and 3 positions (of the four possible diastereo-isomers, only the 2S,3R or D(+) erythro sphingenine is found in large amounts); the saturated base D(+)-sphinganine is also found. The fatty acids' carbon-chain length and degree of unsaturation vary; saturated acids, such as stearic acid, predominate.

Sphingomyelin constitutes about 7 to 14 percent of all phospholipids in normal liver, spleen, and brain.[2,12–14,17,36] Patients with type I or type II disease have elevated levels of total lipids and phospholipids in their liver and spleen (Table 66-3). The acute type I disease is characterized by massive accumulation of sphingomyelin in liver and spleen tissues (Table 66-3) but small accumulations in brain (Table 66-4).[11,15,16,18,19,152,153] Sphingomyelin was 47.9 percent of the total lipid of membranous inclusion bodies isolated from the brain of a patient with type IA disease.[18] Elevated levels have also been documented in lymph nodes, kidney, lungs, and blood plasma.[2,10,154] Sphingomyelin deposition in liver and spleen increases with age in type I patients but may decrease in some variants of type II disease.[2]

Patients with type IS disease accumulate sphingomyelin in their viscera to about the same degree as those with type IA disease, but in the few studies of the brain in this type, accumulation was not found (Table 66-4).[71,154] In contrast to the type I patients, type II patients show only slight to moderate accumulation of sphingomyelin in their visceral organs and virtually no elevation in brain.

Bis(Monoacylglycero)Phosphate. This lipid was first discovered in 1968 in tissues of a patient with type IA disease; it was elevated 85-fold in the liver, and elevated amounts were noted in the spleen, kidney, heart, and lung.[155] Structurally, this lipid resembles lysophosphatidylglycerol with an additional fatty acid—18:1 (n-9) in humans and 22:6 (n-3) in rats—attached to the terminal hydroxyl of the glycerol. Its stereochemistry was initially reported[156,157] as 1-sn-(monoacyl)-glycero-1-phospho-sn-1'-(monoacyl)glycerol, 3-sn-(monoacyl)-glycero-1-phospho-sn-1'(monoacyl)glycerol appears to be more probable.[158]

Normal human tissues have trace amounts of this lipid. Several reports have confirmed its accumulation in patient visceral tissues, notably from type IIS patients; indeed, the degree of accumulation of bis(monoacylglycero)phosphate is often more impressive than the net accumulation of sphingomyelin.[13,17,48,51,57,60,64,86,159–161] The total amount in affected tissues is usually a few percent of the total phospholipid, but levels as high as 23 percent of the phospholipid pool were reported in the spleen of a patient with type IIC disease.[64] This patient had received drug therapy but of a type not usually associated with phospholipid accumulation.[162,163] There have been few reports of elevated levels of this lipid in the brains of patients: in one study it was not found,[160] but in another study a slight increase in levels in cerebellum and frontal cortex was observed in a patient with type IIS disease.[51]

Cholesterol. The cholesterol levels in visceral tissues from patients with Niemann-Pick disease vary from below normal to 10 times normal (Table 66-3). For those with type I disease, the elevations are not as massive as for sphingomyelin or for bis(monoacylglycerol)phosphate and may be secondary to the

Table 66-3 Tissue Lipid Elevations in Niemann-Pick Disease

Type	Age, yr	Sphingomyelin		Cholesterol		Reference
		Liver	Spleen	Liver	Spleen	
IA	1.2	26 (12)*	15.7 (15)	3.5 (11)	4.1 (12)	2, 12, 14
	Fetus–2.6	1.0–50.4	2.0–43.8	0.8–7.0	2–10	
IS	8.5	22.5 (8)	16.5 (4)	3.8 (7)	—	2, 12, 14, 17, 36
	2–56	1.8–33.5	15.5–18.7	0.8–7.0	1.6, 4.2	
IC	47	—	3.9 (3)	—	—	24, 27, 100
	42–61	6.0, 11.7	2.0–5.8	0.4	0.6	
IIA	4.2	2.8 (5)	—	2.3 (3)	—	17, 54–57
	0.3–5.5	1.6–4.0	5.0, 7.8	1 7–4.0	4.3, 6.5	
IIS	9.5	2.0 (14)	6.2 (14)	2.0 (14)	2.7 (10)	2, 12–14, 17
	0.3–22	0.9–8	1.7–17	0.8–4.3	1.8–6.1	
IIC	—	—	—	—	—	28
	46	1.8 (1)	3.6 (1)	—	—	

*Because of the variable basis of calculation of results in the literature, data are presented as fold elevation above controls, calculated from the upper end of the control range for ref. 2 and from the mean control values for other references. The first number is the median. The number following in parentheses is the number of values from which the median was calculated. The range for three or more figures is given immediately below the median. The individual values are given rather than the range for two figures or fewer.

Table 66-4 Lipids in the Central Nervous System in Niemann-Pick Disease

| Type | Gray matter | | White matter | | Reference |
	Sphingomyelin	Cholesterol	Sphingomyelin	Cholesterol	
IA	3.0 (4)*	1.3 (3)	0.8 (4)	0.35 (3)	11, 15, 16, 18
	2.7–3.3	1.2–1.6	0.6–1.0	0.3–0.4	
IS	—	—	—	—	71, 154
	1.0, 1.3†	—	1.0	—	
IIA	—	—	—	—	17
	2.1, 1.6†	—	2.1	—	
IIS	0.8 (10)	1.1 (10)	0.7 (10)	0.5 (10)	11, 15, 19, 152, 153
	0.5–1.4	0.6–1.7	0.2–1.3	0.4–0.9	

*Median fold elevation above control levels, number of values, and range. Tee Table 66-3 for further details.
†These samples were not separated into gray and white matter. The data cited under group IS were from fetal specimens from fetuses at risk for type IS disease.

primary storage of sphingomyelin. In the brain, cholesterol is slightly elevated in the gray matter but is below normal in white matter (Table 66-4). Patients with type II disease display moderate elevations of this sterol in their visceral tissues, elevations that may, on a molar basis, exceed sphingomyelin; and there is no strict correlation between the molar ratios of sphingomyelin and cholesterol elevation, as might be predicted from studies on synthetic membrane bilayers.[164,165]

Glycosphingolipids and Lysosphingolipids. The major glycosphingolipids of the normal visceral tissues are glucosylceramide (GL-1), lactosylceramide (GL-2), and G_{M3} ganglioside. Liver and spleen tissues from patients with the Niemann-Pick diseases have markedly elevated levels of GL-1 and smaller but definite elevations of GL-2, GL-3, and GL-4 (Table 66-5). GL-1 accumulation was noted in spleen of a patient with type IIA.[101] The total ganglioside in these tissues was normal or elevated, the major form being G_{M3} ganglioside. Storage of GL-1 and GL-2 has been reported in brains from patients with type IA,[18] type IIA,[101] and type IIS.[13] Brain tissue from patients contains all the normal gangliosides, although the composition is slightly different from normal, and the amount is slightly elevated, especially in white matter.[18,166]

Recently, small amounts of sphingosylphosphocholine, which is structurally similar to galactosylsphingosine (described in connection with Krabbes' disease, Chap. 68) and glucosylsphingosine (described in connection with Gaucher disease, Chap. 67), were isolated from the spleen of a patient with type IS disease.[167]

Synthesis and Degradation of Sphingomyelin, Cholesterol, and Bis(monoacylglycero)phosphate

Sphingomyelin

GENERAL METABOLISM. At least three pathways of sphingomyelin biosynthesis have been described (Fig. 66-3). Initial studies showed that the final step was the transfer of phosphocholine from cytidine-5'-diphosphocholine (CDP-choline) to ceramide.[168] Later studies confirmed this and showed that, in vitro, the L-threo(2S,3S) enantiomers are better substrates than the much more common D-erythro(2S,3R) isomeric compounds.[168,169] A second reaction sequence has been reported in brain mitochondria, in which sphingosine acts as the acceptor for CDP-choline and the sphingosylphosphocholine formed is an acceptor for fatty acyl CoA to form sphingomyelin.[170] The third pathway, the direct transfer of phosphocholine from phosphatidylcholine to ceramide, has been demonstrated in normal and SV40-transformed mouse fibroblasts,[171,172] mouse liver,[173] and rat liver and baby hamster kidney cells.[174] The existence of these latter two reactions has been questioned.[169]

Table 66-5 Glycolipid Elevations in Patients with Niemann-Pick Disease

Type	Tissue	GL-1	GL-2	GL-3	GL-4	Gangliosides	Reference
IA	Liver	8.8 (3)*	7.2 (3)	3.9 (3)	2.0 (3)	—	12, 161
		6.8–11.1	2.9–7.5	1.3–4.4	1.0–2.9	4.1, 4.9	
IS	Liver	—	—	—	—	—	161
		11.7	2.3	1.0	1.3		
IIS	Liver	13.1 (5)	3.8 (5)	2.7 (5)	2.0 (5)	1.8 (5)	12
		12.2–16.9	2.3–7.2	1.6–4.8	0.8–2.6	1.3–3.3	
IA	Spleen	—	—	—	—	—	12
		11.1	3.7	3.2	1.6	1.3	
IS	Spleen	18.1 (3)	3.2 (3)	3.9 (3)	2.6 (3)	1.0 (3)	12
		10.8–20.7	1.7–3.7	2.9–4.4	1.9–2.7	0.6–1.2	
IIA	Spleen	—	—	—	—	—	57
		6.0	—	—	—	—	
IIS	Spleen	33.3 (6)	3.8 (6)	4.0 (6)	2.6 (6)	1.4 (6)	12
		27.5–46.6	2.1–7.2	2.8–7.4	1.9–3.8	0.9–1.6	
IA	Plasma	—	—	—	—	—	161
		3.3	1.0	1.1	1.2	—	
IS	Plasma	3.0 (3)	0.8 (3)	1.0 (3)	0.9 (3)	—	161
		2.1–4.3	0.7–1.0	0.9–1.1	0.7–1.0		

*Median fold elevation above control values, number of values, and range. See Table 66-3 for further details.

The direct-transfer reaction does not appear to be via a CDP-choline intermediate and is enriched in plasma membrane fractions.[172,174,175] Its activity may account, in part, for the relative enrichment of sphingomyelin in the plasma membrane. The incorporation of phosphocholine from radiolabeled sphingomyelin into phosphatidylcholine has been documented in normal fibroblasts and in fibroblasts from subjects with type I disease.[41,71,176–179] Studies with fluorescent sphingolipid analogues in cultured Chinese hamster ovary fibroblasts and human fibroblasts have provided evidence for intracellular synthesis of sphingomyelin and translocation via the Golgi apparatus to the cell surface, and for a major degradative role for the lyosome.[180,181] Each pathway's relative contribution in individual tissues and to the overall metabolism of sphingomyelin in mammalian tissues remains to be determined.

The major pathway for degradation of sphingomyelin involves sphingomyelinase, which cleaves the lipid into ceramide and phosphocholine via a phospholipase C type of reaction. Several different sphingomyelinases have been described in mammalian tissues.

PROPERTIES OF LYSOSOMAL SPHINGOMYELINASE. Lysosomal sphingomyelinase has an acidic pH optimum (4.6 to 5.0) in all tissues. K_m values of 10 to 66 μM have been reported with tritiated substrate, and values of 25 to 500 μM were obtained with [methyl-^{14}C]sphingomyelin.[182–185] Studies of the effects of pH on reaction rate using purified placental sphingomyelinase have shown that the maximal velocity for the hydrolysis of sphingomyelin is independent of pH in the pH range from 3.5 to 5.2 while the K_m value shows a pH dependence, the values being lowest near the pH optimum.[183] These results suggest that a carboxyl group and a protonated histidine are involved in sphingomyelin binding to the enzyme. The hydrophobic binding of the substrate involves a site that is specific for linear aliphatic moieties of at least 8 carbons. With purified urine enzyme, mono-, di-, and triacylglycerols or free fatty acids of a minimum of 12 carbons in chain length stimulate enzyme activity (182).

Sphingomyelinase activity is strongly inhibited by certain nucleotide phosphodiesters, such as 5'-AMP.[182,183,186,187] The observation that others, such as 5'-UMP, 5'-CMP, and 3'5'-AMP (cyclic AMP),[182,183] do not inhibit with the same potency argues against simple nonspecific inhibition.[182,188]

Lysosomal sphingomyelinase has been purified from human placenta,[188–191] brain,[184] and urine.[46,182] It is glycoprotein. Initial estimates of the enzyme's molecular mass, in the presence of detergents, were 180,000 to 300,000 daltons.[191,192] More recent work has shown that the minimum mass of the active enzyme is a monomer which has the same mass as the polypeptide chain. In placenta and spleen, this was 80,000 to 90,000 daltons in two studies[188,193] and about 70,000 daltons in a third.[190] For brain,[183] urine,[182] and fibroblasts,[194] the estimated size is 70,000 daltons. X-ray irradiation predicts that the fibroblast enzyme is near 105,000 daltons.[195] Using a polyclonal antiserum raised against purified placental sphingomyelinase and Western blots, Jobb and Callahan[196] detected a smaller polypeptide (about 80,000 daltons) in urine and brain, a larger one (108,000 to 120,000 daltons) in fibroblasts, spleen, and liver, and both forms in kidney. Freeman et al.[197] described a monoclonal antibody against placental sphingomyelinase that reacted with the enzyme in a variety of tissues and gave the same M_r for the placental enzyme as the polyclonal serum.[196,198] These results show that the polypeptide of sphingomyelinase is heterogeneous in human tissues, but the reasons for this are not known.

OTHER SPHINGOMYELINASES. Gray matter of the brain contains a high concentration of a nonlysosomal form of sphingomyelinase.[186,199] The enzyme has a pH optimum of 7.4 and is stimulated by Mg^{2+}. Enzyme activity increases during development of brain in parallel with neuronal maturation,[200] and activity levels are particularly high in basal ganglia.[201] The activity is present on the external surface of the plasma membrane of cultured neuroblastoma cells.[202] Levels of activity are much lower in nonneural tissues. The enzyme is a lipophilic integral membrane protein that is solubilized by neutral detergents. Its M_r is greater than 600,000 daltons as found by column chromatography,[203] equal to 165,000 daltons by radiation inactivation,[204,205] and less than 150,000 daltons by sedimentation, indicating a hydrophobic protein with extensive detergent binding. The particularly high activity levels in basal ganglia structures of brain are not changed significantly by acute changes in the dopaminergic system.[206] Activity levels do rise in the rat neurohypophysis during dehydration, suggesting a possible role in neurosecretion.[207] In calf brain synaptosomes and cultured neuroblastoma cells, the activity is stimulated by volatile anesthetics,[208,209] and in the latter, stimulation is dose-dependent and is correlated with anesthetic potency.[209] Activity levels are within normal limits in all brain specimens examined from patients with type I and type II disease.[154,199]

Another sphingomyelinase active at physiological pH has been described in hen erythrocytes.[210,211] Others not requiring metal ions for activity have been found in rat intestine and human myelin, but they have been little studied and their levels in tissues affected by Niemann Pick disease are not known.[212,213]

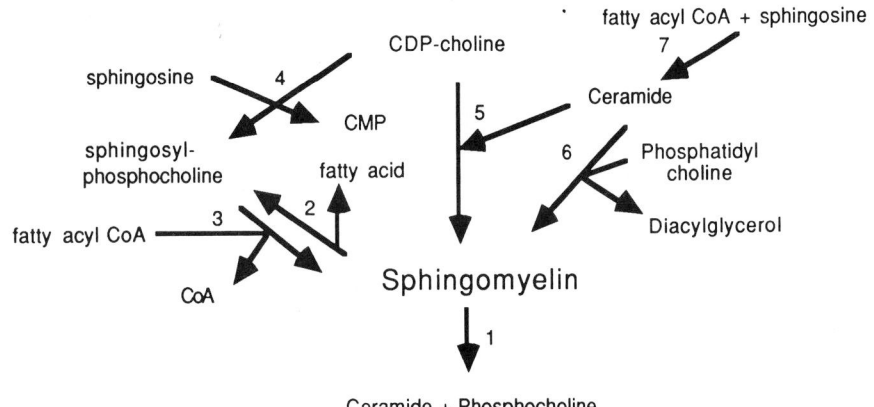

Fig. 66-3 Biosynthesis and metabolism of sphingomyelin. Numbers represent the following enzymes: (1) sphingomyelinase; (2) sphingomyelin deacylase; (3) fatty acyl CoA:sphingosyl phosphocholine acyltransferase; (4) CDP-choline:sphingosine phosphocholine transferase; (5) sphingomyelin synthase; (6) phosphatidylcholine:ceramide phosphocholine transferase; (7) fatty acyl CoA:sphingosine acyltransferase.

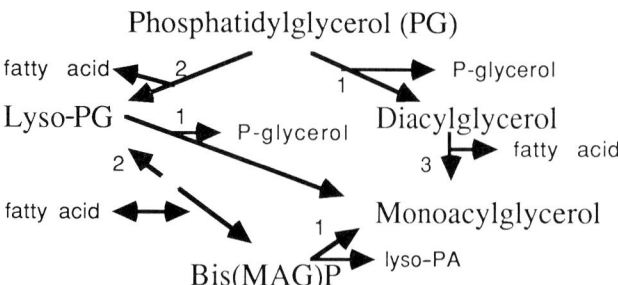

Fig. 66-4 Metabolism of bis(monoacylglycerol)phosphate, or bis(MAG)P. Numbers represent enzymes: (1) phospholipase C or sphingomyelinase; (2) phospholipase A; (3) lipase. Lyso-PA and lyso-PG denote lysophosphatidic acid and lysophosphatidylglycerol, respectively.[43]

Bis(monoacylglycero)phophate. Why bis(monoacylglycero)-phosphate (Fig. 66-4) accumulates in the Nieman-Pick diseases is unclear. In fact, since there is a general elevation in the content of tissue phospholipids in virtually all forms, the changes in this lipid may be nonspecific. Phospholipids such as phosphatidylcholine, phosphatidylglycerol, and lysophosphatidylglycerol are substrates for lysosomal sphingomyelinase,[43,44,182,214] suggesting that it may act as a phospholipase C in the lysosome, which could explain the accumulation of bis(monoacylglycero)phosphate in type I disease. The principal source of phosphatidylglycerol and diphosphatidylglycerol in tissues is the mitochondria, and fusion of portions of the mitochondrial membrane and lysosomes during autophagic digestion is probably a part of cell turnover. Phosphatidylglycerol and diphosphatidylglycerol are the immediate precursors of lysophosphatidylglycerol (Fig. 66-4).[158] In lysosomes, lysophosphatidylglycerol is rapidly converted to bis(monoacylglycero)phosphate.[158] The failure to degrade lysophosphatidylglycerol in patients with sphingomyelinase deficiency may lead to diversion of this lipid to the synthesis of bis(monoacylglycerol)phosphate (Fig. 66-4). This explanation does not entirely account for the accumulation of bis-(monoacylglycero)phosphate in type II disease, where there is a variable reduction in sphingomyelinase activity (Table 66-6). However, the biochemical phenotype of type II tissues suggests a general disturbance in membrane lipid turnover in this variant, and this may have a similar result.

Cholesterol: Intracellular Metabolism

CHOLESTEROL. In the Niemann-Pick group of diseases, the molar ratio of sphingomyelin to cholesterol varies from organ to organ and between various phenotypes (Tables 66-3 and 66-4).[1,2,12,13] In general, patients with the type I disease tend to have higher ratios (for example, 1.5 to 2.5 in liver and 1.0 to 2.5 in spleen versus control values of 0.2 to 0.3) than those with type II disease (0.2 to 0.4 in liver and spleen). Indeed, in some patients with type II disease, the increases in cholesterol and bis(monoacylglycero)phosphate are the most striking findings.[13] These findings, and the recent observations of abnormal cholesterol esterification in cultured fibroblasts from type IIS patients, have directed renewed interest to the possible role of the intracellular disposition and metabolism of cholesterol in the pathogenesis of type II Niemann-Pick disease.

Cholesterol and related sterols are components of biological membranes of most organisms.[164] Mammals maintain the cellular levels of cholesterol by a closely regulated balance between endogenous synthesis and external supply (Chap. 48).[215] The liver and intestine synthesize most cholesterol, but up to 25 percent of net total body cholesterol synthesis takes place in peripheral tissues. The other major source of cholesterol is from dietary intake or, for peripheral tissues, import from liver and intestine. This cholesterol is transported to peripheral tissues predominately as esters in lipoproteins (chiefly LDL in humans). The LDL is bound and internalized via a receptor-mediated process. The internalized endocytotic vesicle containing LDL and the receptor fuse with lysosomes, where the cholesterol esters are hydrolyzed by a lysosomal acid lipase. The unesterified cholesterol crosses the lysosomal membrane, enters the intracellular cholesterol pools, and is used for membrane synthesis and to help regulate intracellular cholesterol homeostasis (Chap. 48).[215] In regulation, the exogenously derived cholesterol suppresses 3-hydroxy-3-methylglutaryl-CoA reductase (HMG-CoA reductase) activity, generally considered to be the rate-limiting step in endogenous cholesterol biosynthesis, and thus decreases intracellular cholesterol biosynthesis. At the same time, the exogenously derived cholesterol activates acyl CoA:cholesterol acyltransferase (ACAT), so that excess cholesterol in the cell is stored as cholesterol esters (Chap. 48).[215] Finally, the exogenously derived cholesterol decreases the synthesis of LDL receptors, reducing further entry of lipoprotein into the cell and slowing the uptake of exogenous cholesterol.

Of equal interest, because of the predilection for storage in the reticuloendothelial system in type II disease, is the scavenger-cell LDL receptor–independent pathway of lipoprotein degradation (Chap. 48).[216] This pathway may account for up to 15 percent of LDL removal per day in normal individuals. The scavenger pathway can be demonstrated both in vivo and in vitro with modified LDL, but the physiological modification that normally directs lipoproteins to this pathway is not known. The cholesterol esters of the modified lipoproteins are hydrolyzed in the lysosome, and the excess cholesterol is esterified chiefly with oleic acid by ACAT in the microsomes. As a consequence of uptake of modified LDL, the synthesis of cholesterol ester by macrophages can be stimulated 100-fold, and cholesterol content elevated 38-fold.[217] The cholesterol ester is stored in droplets in macrophages and is continuously hydrolyzed and reesterified, with a half-life of about 24 h.[216] Hydrolysis of the cytoplasmic esters is not inhibited by lysosomotropic agents, suggesting that the cholesterol esterase either is in a separate compartment or is separate in its activity from the cholesterol esterase of the lysosome. The esterification by ACAT requires activation of fatty acids to fatty acyl CoA with the consumption of ATP, and the continuous hydrolysis and reesterification of cholesterol constitutes an energy-consuming cycle,[216] which may be of significance in type II Niemann-Pick disease.

In addition to the enzyme proteins concerned with endogenous synthesis of cholesterol and with the formation and hydrolysis of cholesterol esters, there are at least three low–molecular mass (10,000 to 50,000 daltons) lipid-binding proteins concerned with intracellular cholesterol and cholesterol ester metabolism. The nomenclature and the properties attributed to these proteins are not universally agreed upon, but their central importance in cellular sterol and fatty acid metabolism seems clear.[218–220] Fatty acid binding protein (FABP, Z protein, protein A) is a protein of molecular mass 14,200 daltons that modulates the activities of some enzymes of lipid metabolism. It may facilitate intracellular transport of fatty acids in aqueous compartments and contribute to compartmentation of fatty acids and fatty acyl CoA's in the cell. In the latter capacity, it may temporarily store or buffer fatty acids during hydrolysis and esterification cycles. A second protein, sterol carrier protein 1 (SCP_1, 47,000 daltons), participates in the microsomal conversion of squalene to cholesterol.[219] A third protein, sterol carrier protein 2 (SCP_2, 13,500 daltons) participates in the conversion of lanosterol to cholesterol, the conversion of cholesterol to cholesterol ester, and intracellular cholesterol transfers.

The process governing the intracellular transport of cholesterol and its efflux from the cell are not well understood. Studies of the rate of transfer of cholesterol from its site of synthesis in the cell to the plasma membrane have given widely varying results, from virtually no transfer over several hours to a half-time of 10 min.[221] The transfer is vectorial from the cell interior to the surface, and there is little evidence of a reverse process.[221] There is rapid transmembrane movement of cholesterol in the plasma membrane, and the half-time in Chinese hamster ovary cells and in red cells is in the order of seconds.[222]

Most of the free cholesterol in the cell is in the plasma membrane, and the efflux of cholesterol from this compartment to acceptor molecules outside the cell is part of the maintenance of cellular cholesterol balance.[223–225] Except for steroid hormone–producing tissues, extrahepatic tissues cannot catabolize cholesterol, and so it must be returned to the liver for excretion as cholesterol or bile acid.[223] Evidence suggests that cholesterol leaves the cell from the plasma membrane by a process of desorption out of the membrane into the extracellular space.[225] Since it has limited solubility in the aqueous phase, the process may be helped by carrier proteins, such as HDL in plasma and, for internal membranes, SCP_2 in cytoplasm. When the concentration of acceptor molecules is high, the rate of cholesterol efflux is a function of the lipid and protein in the surrounding membrane;[224,225] when it is low, the rate-limiting step in desorption from the membrane is diffusion of the sterol molecule in the unstirred water layer adjacent to the membrane.

INTERACTIONS OF CHOLESTEROL WITH PHOSPHOLIPIDS AND IN PHOSPHOLIPID METABOLISM. Cholesterol and phospolipids are two of the major structural components of mammalian membranes,[164] and the complex interactions between the two lipid classes are important to membrane function. In general, adding cholesterol to crystalline phospholipid mixtures causes liquefaction, whereas adding it to liquid crystalline mixtures causes condensation; either leads to an intermediate gel state of the mixture.[226] Like sphingomyelin, cholesterol is not uniformly distributed in the cell and generally tends to be concentrated in the plasma membrane.[164] Nonuniform distribution may be maintained in part, by the phospholipid composition of the membrane. In artificial systems, cholesterol preferentially associates with phosphatidylcholine-containing membranes with acyl chain lengths of 16 carbons.[227] By contrast, sphingomyelin seems to bar cholesterol exit from, and entrance to, sphingomyelin bilayers and hence may retain cholesterol in sphingomyelin-enriched structures. The fact that LDL contains more sphingomyelin and has a higher radius of curvature than HDL may account for the comparatively slower exchange of cholesterol from LDL.[228] This association of sphingomyelin and cholesterol is maintained in some normal and disease states also, as in the elevated levels of cholesterol and sphingomyelin in the various forms of type I Niemann-Pick disease, during aging, in atherosclerosis in arteries in humans,[164] in aging fibroblasts from rat heart,[229] and cultured heart cell reaggregates.[230] The association is not always seen, however; sphingomyelin accumulation is not a notable feature of Wolman disease, or cholesterol ester storage disease (Chap. 64).

There are also several suggestions of interactions between cholesterol and sphingomyelin metabolism. Incorporation of sphingomyelin from liposomes into cultured human skin fibroblasts reduces LDL binding and degradation and increases acetate incorporation into sterol.[231] Serum and LDL inhibit the incorporation of palmitate into long-chain bases of sphingomyelin, possibly by inhibiting serine palmitoyltransferase (3-ketosphinganine synthase).[232] The inhibition was receptor-dependent and was not observed in fibroblasts from patients with familial hypercholesterolemia, in which the uptake and degradation of exogenous sphingomyelin is impaired.[179] The synthesis of cholesterol from $[2-{}^{14}C]$ acetate is increased in fibroblasts from patients with type IA disease, and the incoporation of $[1-{}^{14}C]$ oleic acid and ${}^{125}I$-LDL is reduced.[233] These findings were variable, however, and some subjects fell within the control range. Incubating normal fibroblasts with cholesterol or 7-dehydrocholesterol decreases sphingomyelin catabolism in intact cells and modestly (25 percent) decreases sphingomyelinase activity measured subsequently in vitro.[234]

Taken together, these findings suggest a close relationship between sphingomyelin and cholesterol in vivo at a molecular and functional level in the membrane, as well as a functional relationship between the enzymes and receptors that control the intracellular metabolism of these two lipids. Accordingly, it is not surprising that mutations affecting the metabolism of either lipid could alter the metabolism of the other and cause clinical phenotypes with many similarities.

METABOLIC ABNORMALITIES IN NIEMANN-PICK DISEASE

Type I Disease: Sphingomyelinase Deficiency

The metabolic defect in type I Niemann-Pick disease is a deficiency of lysosomal sphingomyelinase, which degrades sphingomyelin to ceramide and phosphocholine.[5,37–42,45–47,65,85,87,92,111,235–237] The basic defects are probably several distinct alterations in the DNA for sphingomyelinase. Patients with either the acute or the subacute form have low levels of enzyme activity (Table 66-6 and Fig. 66-5), although the range of values is larger in patients with the subacute form. However, patients with either form synthesize sphingomyelinase polypeptide in normal amounts and normal size, so the genetic defects in each are likely point mutations.[198,238] Besley et al.[239] and Nelson and Carey[240] demonstrated that no restoration of enzyme activity occurred upon fusion of fibroblasts from these patients. Poulos et al.[241] were able to stimulate the residual enzyme activity of fibroblasts from patients with type IS disease by altering culture conditions and using activator proteins, but could produce little or no such response in cells from patients with type IA disease.

The phenotypic heterogeneity of type I patients—the fact that some have minimal brain involvement, others have severe involvement, and all have visceral involvement and low sphin-

Table 66-6 Sphingomyelinase Activity in Type I and Type II Niemann-Pick Disease*

Type	Tissue	Median	Range	Reference
IA	LIV	0.7 (7)	0.7–7.0	14
IA	SPL, BMR, KID, URN	0.1 (4)	0.0–0.8	5, 37, 38, 46
IA	LEU	0.0 (3)	0.0–3.0	233–235
IA	FIB	1.1 (7)	0.2–5.8	39, 42, 43–45, 65, 111
IS	SPL, BMR, LIV, URN	2.0 (4)	0.0–6.2	37, 38, 46, 87
IS	LEU	4.8 (18)	1.2–19.1	14, 85, 87, 233–235
IS	FIB	3.3 (8)	0.0–4.0	40–43, 45, 65, 85, 92
IC	FIB	8.0 (1)	—	65
IC	LIV	<5.0 (1)	—	27
IIA	LEU	85.2 (4)	61–117	14, 55, 56
IIA	BRN	128 (3)	84–140	17, 57
IIA	LIV	133 (5)	117–667	14, 57
IIA	SPL	133 (5)	81.6–345	14, 17, 57
IIA	FIB	55.4 (5)	15.3–91.7	54–56
IIS	SPL	131 (10)	23–241	2, 14, 37
IIS	FIB	50.0 (9)	27.0–90.5	39, 41–45, 47, 65
IIS	LIV	180 (13)	70–670	14, 45, 111
IIS	LEU, BRN, URN, BRM	81 (5)	53–104	14, 38, 46, 47, 111
IIC	FIB	15 (1)	—	64

*All values were recalculated as percent of the control value and were determined using the natural substrate.
NOTE: Abbreviations used are: BMR = bone marrow; BRN = brain; FIB = fibroblasts; KID = kidney; LEU = leukocyte; LIV = liver; SPL = spleen; URN = urine. Median, number of values in parentheses, and range.

gomyelinase activity—also argues for the presence of more than one mutation and more than one functional form of the enzyme in various tissues. So do observations of different rates of sphingomyelin hydrolysis in cultured cells in these subgroups (Table 66-6, Fig. 66-5)[65,242] and of apparent differences in size of the sphingomyelinase polypeptide in various tissues. The relative sparing of brain in some type IS patients may reflect the high levels of the neutral, Mg^{2+}-stimulated enzyme in that tissue,[186,201] which could help to relieve the substrate burden on a partially defective enzyme. Other mutations, such as those that occur in type IA disease, may so severely limit enzyme activity as to render ineffective the activity contributed by the neutral enzyme.

Why the decrease in sphingomyelinase activity that the structural gene mutation causes should so severely compro-

mise cell function is unclear. Changes in the amounts and cellular location of sphingomyelin and cholesterol may alter membrane function.[164] Sphingomyelin has been postulated to be a membrane stabilizer[164] and to modulate diacylglycerol-stimulated phospholipases.[243] Unusual metabolites as a consequence of the metabolic block may contribute also. Sphingosylphosphocholine is one of the lysosphingolipids that have been postulated to cause the progressive cellular dysfunction of sphingolipidoses.[244] Possible mechanisms of action include interference with the normal activity of protein kinase C[244] or the disruption of mitochondrial function through binding to the membranes, leading to swelling of the organelle and a disturbance of oxidative phosphorylation.[167,245]

The accumulation of bis(monoacylglycerol)phosphate has been attributed to a secondary proliferation of lysosomes in the affected tissues,[4] as well as to the deficiency of sphingomyelinase. Abnormalities in acid sphingomyelinase, an integral lysosomal-membrane protein, may so alter the lysosomal membrane as to secondarily affect the catabolism of other lipids, such as neutral glycolipids and gangliosides.

Type II Disease—Primary Defect Uncertain

Given the profile of accumulating lipids (Tables 66-3 to 66-5), the metabolic defects in type II Niemann-Pick disease could be in pathways of the metabolism of glycolipids, bis(monoacylglycero)phosphate, sphingomyelin, or cholesterol. A primary defect in any of these pathways (or in some other) could secondarily affect the others. Glucosylceramidase activity was 50 to 60% of normal in fetal tissues (brain and liver) from the offspring of a woman with a previous child with type IIA disease;[57] activity measured in liver and spleen in types IIS[12] and IIC[20] patients was normal or above normal. Glycosyl hydrolases were above normal in one liver sample of a type IIS patient[13] and were apparently unremarkable in fibroblasts of a group of other type IIS patients.[48] Specific defects in the metabolism of bis(monoacylglycero)phosphate have not been reported in type II disease. The two pathways in which abnormalities are reported in at least some patients with type II disease are in sphingomyelin degradation and cholesterol esterification.

A partial deficiency of in vitro sphingomyelinase activity in some forms of type II disease has been shown in several laboratories (Table 66-6; Fig. 66-5). The deficiency is most consistent in cultured fibroblasts, with activity levels ranging from 15 percent of normal to normal values;[4,48,51,55,65,119,242] values

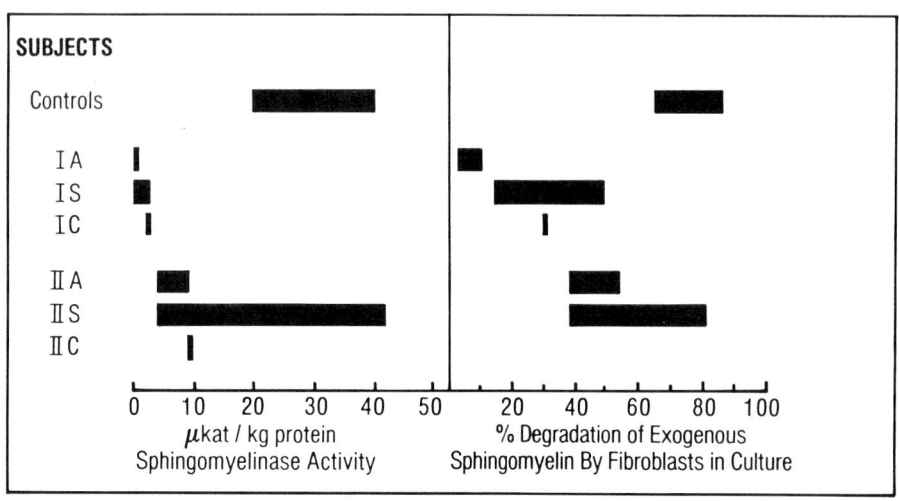

Fig. 66-5 Comparison of sphingomyelinase activity in vitro and in culture of fibroblasts from normal subjects and subjects with type I and type II disease. *(Left)* Fibroblast sphingomyelinase activity measured in vitro (refs. in Table 66-6). *(Right)* Sphingomyelinase activity measured in culture.[41,65,129]

in other tissues have tended to be closer to or within the normal range or to exceed normal values (Table 66-6; Fig. 66-5).[4,13] When measured in one laboratory, the activity level in fibroblasts seems to correlate with the severity of disease, being lower in type IIA and higher in type IIS.[65] However, there is little difference in the median and range between the groups when data pooled from several sources are compared (Table 66-6). Parallel results have come from all experimental paradigms used in studies measuring the degradation of [³H] sphingomyelin added to the medium of cultured fibroblasts for periods of up to 96 h (Fig. 66-5).[41,65,176,177,242] Patients with type IIS disease from southwestern Nova Scotia have normal levels of activity in fibroblasts whether measured in vitro or in culture.[41,215] A deficiency of activator proteins has not been shown in type II disease.[238–240] Whether the abnormality of lysosomal sphingomyelinase in some variants of type II disease is primary or secondary remains unknown.

An increasing body of evidence from two laboratories suggests there is a defect in the processing of exogenous cholesterol in some forms of type II disease. Pentchev et al.[246] found that BALB/C mice with an autosomal recessive mutation resulting in lysosomal storage of sphingomyelin, glucocerebroside, and cholesterol and decreased activity of sphingomyelinase and glucocerebrosidase accumulated cholesterol before the changes in other lipids occurred. Cultured fibroblasts from these mice formed markedly less cholesterol ester from exogenous cholesterol.[247,248] To determine whether this defect in esterification was related to deficiencies in activity of glucocerebrosidase and sphingomyelinase, they examined fibroblasts from subjects with Niemann-Pick or Gaucher disease.[105,106,248] Using filipin (a fluorescent antibiotic that forms complexes with cholesterol), they observed many intense inclusions (presumably local accumulations of cholesterol) in fibroblasts from patients with type IIS disease but none in those from patients with either type IA or type IS disease. They also observed a variable increase in the uptake of [³H]cholesterol from the medium by type II cells previously incubated in lipoprotein-deficient serum (LPDS) and a marked reduction—to 1 to 26 percent of normal—in the formation of cholesterol esters (Table 66-7). Cholesterol [³H]oleate formation by cells incubated with chemically modified LDL was less than 50 percent of normal in 6 of 8 cell lines and was normal in the remaining two; in cells incubated with normal LDL it was less than 50 percent of normal in 10 of 11 cell lines tested and normal in the other.

Subsequent studies of the uptake and metabolism of cholesterol and of normal and modified LDL by cultured fibroblasts from normal subjects and from homozygotes and heterozygotes for type IIA or type IIS disease have shown the following:

1. Cholesterol is increased above control levels in mutant cells in some circumstances. Incubating cells that had grown in LPDS in fetal bovine serum (FBS) or LDL-containing medium for up to 48 h causes a two- to threefold increase in cholesterol in fibroblasts from some type IIS patients.[107] Increases are observed in cells from the heterozygotes in some experiments but not in others. Cholesterol ester mass is also variably affected, being modestly increased in cells from homozygous affected persons in some experiments and decreased in others.[105,249]

2. The formation of cholesterol ester from exogenous [³H]oleic acid is reduced in the early stages of LDL-stimulated cholesterol ester synthesis (6 percent of normal on day 1 and 37 percent of normal by day 2) but approaches normal levels as the incubation time is increased (Table 66-8). This reduction is also observed when the cells are incubated with chemically modified LDL or with [³H]cholesterol (Table 66-7); in the latter circumstance, levels of esterification tend to be lower in patients with type IIA disease than in those with IIS disease.[242]

3. The LDL-stimulated or 25-hydroxycholesterol–stimulated formation of cholesterol esters from endogenous cholesterol is also reduced two- to tenfold in mutant cells.

4. The normal down regulation of cell surface binding, uptake, and catabolism of ¹²⁵I-LDL in cells treated with LDL is slightly reduced in cells from type II patients.

5. The in vitro activity of acyl CoA:cholesterol acyl transferase from cells grown in lipoprotein-deficient medium (ACAT down-regulated) or in medium containing LDL (ACAT up-regulated) is normal.

6. The LDL-mediated reduction of HMG-CoA reductase activity is not affected.

The apparent defect in esterification of cholesterol derived from receptor-dependent and receptor-independent pathways, and a similar defect in receptor-dependent stimulation of esterification of endogenously synthesized sterol, suggests a primary or secondary defect in the intracellular transport of cholesterol and/or fatty acid to ACAT or in the activity of ACAT in fibroblasts at least, and possibly in all peripheral tissues. A

Table 66-7 Esterification of Exogenous Nonlipoprotein Cholesterol by Cultured Fibroblasts from Subjects with Types I and II Niemann-Pick Disease and Controls

	Cholesterol Esterification*					
		Niemann-Pick Disease				
Control	IA	IS	IIA	IIS	Reference
15 ± 5 (5)	10 ± 6 (5)	14 ± 6 (8)	0.1–3.8 (20)†		105
11.7 ± 3.9 (17)	7–19 (3)	7–17 (6)	0.3 ± 0.2 (8)	0.6–6 (13)	242
5.0 ± 0.3	—	—	0.6 (2)‡	0.5 (2)§	107

*Cells were cultured in medium with 10% lipoprotein-deficient serum for 48 h. Fresh medium containing [³H]cholesterol was added and the cells were harvested 24 h later and analyzed for free and esterified [³H]cholesterol. Data are [³H]cholesterol ester, expressed as a percentage of total [³H]cholesterol and ester in the cell.
†Subjects reported as Crocker type C with no differentiation as to severity of the phenotype. Five of the type II subjects may also be reported in Ref. 242. Number of subjects in parentheses.
‡Subjects reported as Crocker type C.
§Subjects reported as Crocker type D.

Table 66-8 Cholesterol [³H]Oleate Synthesis in Cultured Human Fibroblasts from Control, Type I, and Type II Subjects Incubated ± LDL

Preincubation*				Cell type					
Medium	Time, h	Label time, h	LDL	Control	IA	IS	IIS (homozygous)	IIS (heterozygous)	Reference
LPDS, SF	24; 72†	2	–	50 ± 30 (5)‡	90 ± 70 (4)	50 ± 25 (7)	140 ± 285 (11)		105
LDL	24	2	+	3000 ± 1000	3100 ± 1600	2000 ± 800	850 ± 900		
LPDS; SC (LPDS)	72; 48		–	7 ± 4 (5)			4 ± 2 (5)	4 ± 1 (6)	249
LDL	3	6	+	340 ± 70			4 ± 2	136 ± 50	
LPDS	48		–	7 (2)			26 ± 2 (2)	3 (1)	107
LDL	0	6	+	175 ± 15			32 (2)	67 (1)	

*LDL = low-density lipoprotein; LPDS = 10% lipoprotein-deficient serum; SC = subculture; SF = serum-free. LDL remained in the incubation medium throughout the labeling.
†Time(s) of incubation in the various media.
‡pmol/h/per milligram of protein, determined from original figures and time of incubation with [³H]oleic acid (label time in table). Number of patient fibroblast cultures studied in parentheses.

scheme of locations of mutation is shown in Fig. 66-6, and includes the following possibilities.

First (Fig. 66-6, step 1), there may be a defect affecting the sequence of steps between cholesterol ester hydrolysis in the lysosome, diffusion of cholesterol to the lysosomal membrane, and the entry of cholesterol into the lysosomal membrane. The defect might reside in cholesterol metabolism and transport per se, or be secondary to defects in the sphingomyelin-hydrolyzing system or defects in bis(monoacylglycero)phosphate metabolism. The net result of such a mutation would be to limit the rate of efflux of cholesterol from the lysosome, reducing the cholesterol concentration at the ACAT site, with a resulting failure to maximally stimulate the enzyme. Lysosomal cholesterol hydrolase activity seems intact as judged by

the marked contrast in phenotypes between type II disease and Wolman and cholesterol ester storage disease (Chap. 64). However, it may be inhibited in some manner, since cholesterol ester mass tends to rise under certain experimental conditions in the cultured fibroblasts of type II patients. Whether the products of the hydrolase are passed directly into the lysosomal membrane, or passed to an intervening carrier, or diffuse to the membrane is uncertain, but any or all of these could be affected by the mutations.

The next two steps are desorption from the membrane to an acceptor particle (Fig. 66-6, step 2) and transport to the ACAT (step 3). Although not known in detail, it is likely that these steps are similar to and have the same rate-limiting sequences as those at the plasma membrane (reviewed earlier

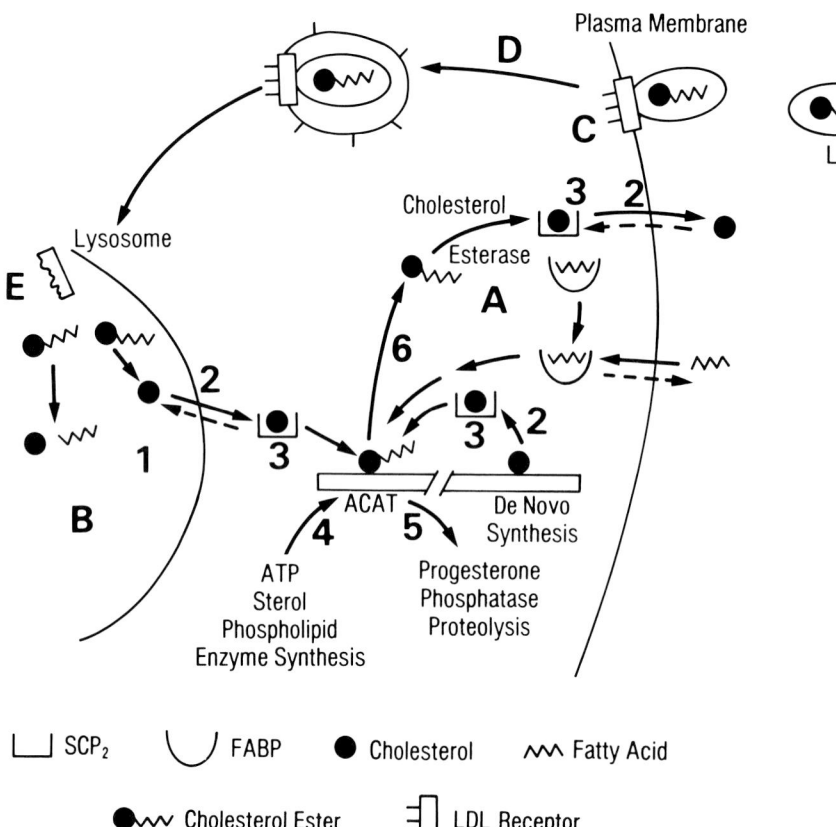

Fig. 66-6 Schematic representation of the possible sites of the metabolic defect in type II disease. (1) Cholesterol ester hydrolysis, transport, and entry into the lysosomal membrane. (2) Changes in the rate of desorption of cholesterol from the membrane. (3) Alterations in the sterol carrier protein(s). (4) Activation of ACAT. (5) Inactivation of ACAT. (6) Defects in the release of cholesterol ester from ACAT and its sequestration in storage droplets in the cell. Important secondary manifestations of these metabolic defects might be: (A) an increased metabolic demand in cells due to increased hydrolysis and esterification of cholesterol; (B) variable decreases in acid lysosomal sphingomyelinase activity; and (C, D, and E) modifications in the binding, internalization, and degradation of LDL.

under "Cholesterol: Intracellular Metabolism"). The transit of cholesterol across the lysosomal membrane or, more likely, its desorption on the cytoplasmic surface could be affected secondarily by changes in the membrane's lipid and protein composition, such as the accumulation of bis(monoacylglycero)-phosphate, sphingomyelin, or glycolipid.[224,225] There may also be mutations in proteins specific to the lysosomal membranes.[250] Some of these changes might also affect the plasma membrane and constrain the efflux of cholesterol from the cell.

A third series of defects (Fig. 66-6, step 3) might involve the sterol carrier protein or proteins that are somehow concerned with cholesterol metabolism and/or transport. Mutations affecting the amount or properties of these proteins could limit their effectiveness and decrease substrate availability or substrate regulation of ACAT activity, or could interfere with the primary regulatory activity of these proteins in ACAT activity.[217]

Another series of defects (Fig. 66-6, steps 4 and 5) concern the activation or inactivation of ACAT, such that there is a delay in reaching maximal activity and maximal activity may not be achieved. ACAT activity measured in vitro is normal in type II patients, but the conditions of assay preclude study of the potential regulatory responses that may pertain in vivo. In vivo stimulation of ACAT activity by LDL cholesterol, or by exogenous sterols, is mediated via endocytosis, so that confounding effects due to mutations in the lysosomal system (step 1 or 2) are difficult to exclude.

It is not known how cholesterol esters leave the ACAT active site and enter the storage droplets (Fig. 66-6, step 6), but presumably this process has some regulatory implications for the cholesterol esterification process.

The cytoplasmic cholesterol ester hydrolase may also play an important additional secondary role (Fig. 66-6, at A), particularly in the foam cells and the reticuloendothelial system. This enzyme is in a different cellular compartment from the lysosomal hydrolase, but they are probably genetically linked, as neutral hydrolase activities are reduced in cells from subjects with acid cholesterol esterase deficiency.[251] The cholesterol formed by the enzyme can enter the plasma membrane possibly via a sterol carrier protein–catalyzed step, and leave the cell through desorption from the external surface. Should efflux from the cell be limited for some reason (e.g., a block at step 2), the cholesterol would return to the cholesterol ester pool via esterification by ACAT. As pointed out earlier, this hydrolysis and reesterification cycle is active in macrophages and consumes ATP for fatty acid activation.[216] Increases in activity of this cycle may compromise the metabolism of these cells and lead to the accumulation of lipopigments and typical storage cells.

Other effects secondary to these primary defects have been alluded to and might include variable decreases is lysosomal sphingomyelinase activity (B in Fig. 66-6), as reported in some patients with type II disease, and (at C, D, and E) modification in the binding, internalization, and degradation of LDL.

While the exact nature of the genetic defect remains to be elucidated, the combination of a deficiency in cholesterol esterification in the homozygous affected individual with intermediate levels of esterification in the heterozygote is evidence of a lesion somewhere in this system, or in some other system that directly affects the cholesterol-processing pathways. It also seems likely that there are genotypic differences underlying the phenotypic differences in clinical presentation.[107,242]

DIAGNOSIS

Homozygotes

A presumptive diagnosis of Niemann-Pick disease can be made on the basis of hepatosplenomegaly, lipid-laden foam cells in the bone marrow, and—for the acute and some subacute forms—psychomotor retardation. Demonstrating increased quantities of sphingomyelin and cholesterol in tissue biopsy specimens can support the diagnosis of type I disease but is less reliable (although possibly helpful) in type II disease, since the degree of storage is usually less (Table 66-3). Measuring glycolipid levels is a complex and exacting procedure but may be helpful (Table 66-5).

The most readily available way to confirm type I disease and/or to differentiate it from type II disease is to assay sphingomyelinase activity in tissue extracts or fluids (Table 66-6). Absolute values are affected by the differing detergent and substrate concentrations and differing assay pH used in different laboratories. Activity levels are lower in the absence of detergents and with liposomal suspensions of sphingomyelin, but the deficiency in type I disease can be demonstrated.[42] With liposomal sphingomyelin, activator proteins for sphingomyelinase have been shown,[241,252,253] and including these proteins in the assay may discriminate type IA disease from type IS disease.[241] To date, no cases of sphingomyelinase deficiency have been attributed to faulty or absent activator proteins.

Radiolabeled sphingomyelin prepared by reduction of the double bonds in ceramide with [^{3}H], or the incorporation of [^{3}H]methyl or [^{14}C]methyl from methyl iodide into the methyl groups of the choline moiety, has been used as a substrate for pre- and postnatal diagnosis and for carrier detection[39,65,67,154,236] and remains the preferred substrate. Deficiencies in hydrolytic activity of sphingomyelinase have also been demonstrated using phosphatidylcholine[43,44,182,214] and phosphatidylglycerol.[43,182] Several promising nonradioactive alternative substrates have been developed. Colorimetric substrates include 2-hexadecanoylamino-4-nitrophenylphosphocholine (HDA-PC),[29,185,236,254] N-trinitrophenylaminolauryl-sphingosylphosphocholine (TNPAL-SM),[185,254,255] and N-(10-(1-pyrene)-decanoyl)-sphingomyelin (P10-SM).[254] Fluorescent substrates include 11-(9-anthroyloxy)-undecanoyl sphingomyelin (AOUD-SM)[185,255] and bis(4-methylumbelliferyl)-phosphate.[256] The latter is not recommended for diagnostic purposes but is useful for assaying the enzyme during purification.

Confirming a diagnosis of type II disease by in vitro enzyme assay for sphingomyelinase presents more difficulties: activity levels have ranged from 20 to 150 percent of normal in various tissues and fluids. Even with cultured fibroblasts, which provide better separation from the control range (Table 66-6),[65] results from some patients overlap the control range. Studying the metabolism of [^{3}H]sphingomyelin added to the medium of cultured cells[41,65,176,177,242] clearly separates patients with type I disease from control subjects and separates patients with the acute form of type I disease from those with the subacute form (Fig. 66-6).[65,242] Among patients with type II disease, those with acute symptoms (type IIA) have lower hydrolysis of sphingomyelin, and those with more slowly progressive disease have values in the control range.

Current evidence suggests that some cases of type II disease may be diagnosed by measuring the esterification of exogenous cholesterol by cultured fibroblasts (Tables 66-7 and 66-8). Activity may be measured after [³H]cholesterol or [³H]oleic acid is added to the culture medium, by comparing the amount of incorporation into cholesterol ester by a patient's fibroblasts with that by control fibroblasts.[105,242,249] Because acyl CoA:cholesterol acyl transferase (ACAT) activity is inducible and subject to complex control mechanisms, conditions of cell growth and the lipoprotein composition of the medium must be carefully controlled.

Heterozygotes

Heterozygotes for the Niemann-Pick group of diseases are generally asymptomatic, and clinical manifestations are rarely of diagnostic value. The splenomegaly found in the grandparents and father of one patient[10] is unusual. Foam cells have been reported in bone marrow in some obligate heterozygotes with type IIS disease.[257]

For types IA and IS, the heterozygous state can be reliably determined by measuring sphingomyelinase activity with either natural or artificial substrates. Whether carriers of the chronic form can be reliably determined is not known; since patients with type IC disease are usually adults when diagnosed, there is limited availability of surviving obligate heterozygous parents.

For type II disease, some heterozygotes—for example, the parents of patient 9 in the Spanish-American kindred[48]—show reduced levels of sphingomyelinase in fibroblasts; in the main, however, heterozygote detection by means of sphingomyelinase assays is unreliable. Using [³H]oleic acid and LDL-stimulated nonconfluent fibroblasts to measure cholesterol esterification holds some promise;[249] values for four obligate heterozygotes were 38 percent of control values. The detection of heterozygotes may require use of exogenous LDL cholesterol, since Vanier et al.[242] could not detect carriers by measuring esterification with exogenous nonlipoprotein [³H]cholesterol. Alternatively, the time of measurement may be critical, as Pentchev and colleagues[106,249] have shown the putative defect to be most readily demonstrated within the first 24 h of incubation of fibroblasts with LDL (Table 66-8).

Prenatal Diagnosis

Several reports have demonstrated the reliability of using measurements of lysosomal sphingomyelinase activity to make prenatal diagnosis of type IA and type IS disease.[41,65–68,70,71,74,140] Most have used cultured amniocytes, but a recent report documents diagnosis by chorionic villus sampling followed by direct analysis of the biopsy and of the cultured cells derived from the biopsy.[71] Analyses of fetal tissues after termination of pregnancy have shown five- to tenfold increases in the level of sphingomyelin in liver and spleen and near-normal values in the brain.[141] Increases in bis(monoacylglycero)phosphate have also been noted in visceral tissues. The lysosomal sphingomyelinase activity is markedly deficient, but the activity of the Mg^{2+}–pH 7.4 enzyme is within normal limits. Measurement of sphingomyelin turnover by cultured amniocytes loaded with radiolabeled sphingomyelin in vivo is also effective for discriminating between control and type I cells.[41,65]

The prenatal diagnosis of type II disease based on lowered sphingomyelinase activity in amniotic fluid was reported in

1978.[57] Diagnosis was confirmed by finding elevated sphingomyelin and cholesterol levels in fetal liver and reduced sphingomyelinase activity in cultured amniocytes. Another prenatal diagnosis has also been reported.[242] Knowing fetal sphingomyelinase activity would be helpful only in families in which affected members have fibroblast sphingomyelinase activity clearly different from that of control subjects. Even so, the caution from experienced laboratories, that this is not always a reliable procedure for prenatal monitoring, should be borne in mind.[65]

Defects in LDL receptor activity and intracellular cholesterol metabolism in cultured amniotic fluid cells have been shown in a fetus at risk for familial hypercholesterolemia.[258] The apparent defects in cholesterol metabolism in type II disease have not yet been demonstrated in amniotic fluid cells.

GENETICS

All evidence so far indicates an autosomal recessive inheritance of all forms of Niemann-Pick disease. There is a high frequency of the acute and subacute forms of type I disease among Ashkenazic Jews, but the overall distribution is panethnic.[1,2] Obligate heterozygotes of type IA and type IS disease have the expected intermediate levels of sphingomyelinase activity;[39,235–237] carrier detection in type IC has not been reported. The grandparents and father of one patient were noted to have splenomegaly,[10] suggesting the possibility of genetic compounds between subtypes of the type I group. The lack of complementation between fibroblasts of patients with type IA disease and those with type IS disease[239,240] is further evidence for an intragenic series of defects. The chromosomal location of the gene is not known.

As documented throughout this chapter, the series of mutations that cause type II disease and those which cause type I disease are not the same. Type II disease is an autosomal recessive condition and is panethnic in origin. The recessive mode of inheritance is supported by the relatively equal distribution of affected persons between the sexes, occurrence in more than one family member, and the increased frequency in certain populations from the same geographic area and/or of similar ethnic background.[2,48,58] The inheritance of the different phenotypes within the type II group variously described as "neurovisceral storage disease with vertical supranuclear ophthalmoplegia" or "dystonic lipidoses" is also compatible with an autosomal recessive mode of inheritance.[50,132] All known cases of type IIS that were classified as type D disease have been traced to a couple born in Nova Scotia, Canada, in the 1600s; this is compatible with a single mutation in one of the founders of this community.[58]

Whether the phenotypes grouped in type II are manifestations of two or more mutations or of one mutation but subject to other genetic and environmental modification remains to be determined. Clinical heterogeneity with both acute and subacute forms in the same sibship has been noted.[55] The disease has been reported in children of marriages between members of families at risk for type D disease and persons of Italian[2] or Quebec French stock,[107] and whether these are homozygous for the same mutation or heteroallelic remains to be determined. The patients of mixed Quebec French and Acadian ancestry seem to have a defect in cholesterol esterification that differs from that of other patients with type II disease.[107]

TREATMENT

There is no specific treatment for the Niemann-Pick group of diseases. Splenectomy has been done on patients with type IS disease either for mechanical reasons or for the occasional patient who has hemorrhagic problems. Patients who have upper respiratory problems are treated symptomatically. There has been one report of liver transplantation in a patient with type IA disease, but this procedure conferred little therapeutic benefit and the patient eventually died.[259] Similarly, after a 7-year-old girl with type IIS disease underwent orthotopic liver transplantation for hepatocellular carcinoma, her neurological symptoms continued to progress and storage material was seen in the transplanted liver.[133]

After bone marrow cells were transplanted in an inbred strain of mice with a phenotype resembling type II Niemann-Pick disease, there was a reduction in the sphingomyelin and cholesterol levels in the spleen of the mice but no improvement in their neurological status.[260,261] However, discovery of animal models of this group of diseases will make more trials of various therapies possible.

MODELS OF THE NIEMANN-PICK DISEASE GROUP

Animal Models of Type I

Two animal models analogous to type IA Niemann-Pick disease have been described. Bundza et al.[262] described a 5-month-old miniature poodle that presented with ataxia and continuous head shaking. Sphingomyelin was increased in the dog's brain, liver, and kidney, and abnormal deposits were seen in other tissues on ultrastructural analysis. Sphingomyelinase activity was markedly depressed in the brain and liver. Wenger et al.[263] described a similar disease in three unrelated litters of Siamese cats. The animals were ataxic and tremulous, with hind-leg weakness, loss of appetite, and a lack of awareness of their surroundings. Sphingomyelin was increased in the liver, and the brain ganglioside pattern resembled that seen in humans with type IA disease. Lysosomal sphingomyelinase activity was deficient in the brain and leukocytes, but the neutral Mg^{2+}–stimulated sphingomyelinase was within normal limits.

Animal Models of Type II

Adachi et al.[264] described accumulation of sphingomyelin and other phospholipids in the liver of an inbred mouse strain (FM). The disease appeared to be confined to this organ and did not appear to be a primary defect in sphingomyelinase. In 1980, Pentchev et al.[246] described a strain of BALB/C mice with many of the major features of subacute type II Niemann-Pick diseases: progressive loss of coordination, posterior paresis, weight loss, and premature death. Their lipid abnormalities included a several-fold elevation of sphingomyelin, cholesterol, glucocerebroside, lactosylceramide, G_{M3} and G_{M2} gangliosides, and bis(monoacylglycero)phosphate in the liver, spleen, kidney, and other tissues. Of the lysosomal hydrolases assayed, sphingomyelinase and glucocerebrosidase activities

were reduced to low levels, but the attenuation of sphingomyelinase was more consistent and more severe. The accumulation of unesterified cholesterol before the changes in other lipids and the onset of symptoms occurred suggests a defect in cholesterol esterification. Study of cultured fibroblasts from affected and normal mice[247,248] showed (1) increases comparable to controls in intracellular cholesterol on addition of exogenous cholesterol but no comparable increase in cholesterol esters; (2) markedly reduced formation of [³H]cholesterol esters on incubation with [³H]oleic acid and LDL; (3) similar acyl CoA:cholesterol acyl transferase (ACAT) activities measured in vitro using cell homogenates from cells grown in the absence or the presence of LDL, but a higher activity in microsomes prepared from affected mouse fibroblasts than in control microsomes (247); and (4) normal or accelerated conversion of desmosterol to cholesterol, suggesting that transfer of sterol intermediates to the microsomal compartment was unaffected. An intermediate level (48 percent of control) of esterification was noted in fibroblasts from heterozygous mice. The authors speculate that the defect resides in the ability of exogenously derived cholesterol to leave the lysosomal compartment or in the sterol carrier proteins that mediate the transfer of cholesterol between cellular compartments and ACAT.

Drug-Induced Lipidosis

Patients treated with the coronary vasodilator 4,4-diethylaminoethoxyhexestrol accumulate bis(monoacylglycero)phosphate in their livers.[162,163] When given to experimental animals over a period of weeks or when present in the medial of cultured cells, many amphiphilic cationic drugs (e.g., AY-9944, gentamicin, chloroquine) lead to a generalized phospholipidosis in affected tissues or cells, particular accumulation of bis(monoacylglycero)phosphate, and substantially reduced sphingomyelinase activity.[265–267] AY-9944 also arrests cholesterol biosynthesis at the 7-dehydrocholesterol stage. Gentamicin-treated rats develop a severe nephrotoxicity and a dramatic reduction of renal sphingomyelinase activity. The effect of gentamicin on sphingomyelinase activity appears to be specific, since it alone of the many enzymes assayed is affected. The drugs inhibit sphingomyelinase in intact cells only and not when added to in vitro assays, suggesting than an intact lysosomal system is required for these effects.

This work was supported in part by grants from the Medical Research Council of Canada, and by a Medical Research Council of Canada Career Investigator Award to Spence.

REFERENCES

1. FREDRICKSON DS: Sphingomyelin lipidosis: Niemann-Pick disease, in Stanbury JB, Wyngaarden JB, Fredrickson DS (eds): *The Metabolic Basis of Inherited Disease*, 2d ed. New York, McGraw-Hill, 1966, p 586.
2. FREDRICKSON DS, SLOAN HR: Sphingomyelin lipidoses: Niemann-Pick disease, in Stanbury JB, Wyngaarden JB, Fredrickson DS (eds): *The Metabolic Basis of Inherited Disease*, 3d ed. New York, McGraw-Hill, 1972, p 783.
3. BRADY RO: Sphingomyelin lipidosis: Niemann-Pick disease, in Stanbury JB, Wyngaarden JB, Fredrickson DS (eds): *The Metabolic Basis of Inherited Disease*, 4th ed. New York, McGraw-Hill, 1978, p 718.
4. BRADY RO: Sphingomyelin lipidoses: Niemann-Pick disease, in Stanbury JB, Wyngaarden JB, Fredrickson DS, Goldstein JL, Brown MS (eds):

The Metabolic Basis of Inherited Disease, 5th ed. New York, McGraw-Hill, 1983, p 831.

5. BRADY RO, KANFER JN, MOCK MB, FREDRICKSON DS: The metabolism of sphingomyelin.II.Evidence of an enzymatic deficiency in Niemann-Pick disease. *Proc Natl Acad Sci USA* 55:367, 1966.

6. NIEMANN A: Ein unbekanntes Krankheitsbild. *Jahrb Kinderheilkd* 79:1, 1914.

7. PICK L: Über die kipoidzellige Splenohepatomegalie typus Niemann-Pick als Stoffwechselerkrankung. *Med Klin* 23:1483, 1927.

8. KLENK E: Über die Natur der Phosphatide und anderer Lipoide des Gehirns und der Leber bei der Niemann-Pickschen Krankheit. *Z Physiol Chem* 235:24, 1935.

9. THANNHAUSER SJ: in *Lipidoses: Disease of Cellular Lipid Metabolism*, 2d ed. New York, Oxford University Press, 1950.

10. CROCKER AC, FARBER S: Niemann-Pick disease: A review of eighteen patients. *Medicine (Baltimore)* 37:1, 1958.

11. CROCKER AC: The cerebral defect in Tay-Sachs disease and Niemann-Pick disease. *J Neurochem* 7:69, 1961.

12. VANIER MT: Biochemical studies in Niemann-Pick disease. I. Major sphingolipids of liver and spleen. *Biochim Biophys Acta* 750:178, 1983.

13. RAO BG, SPENCE MW: Niemann-Pick disease type D: Lipid analyses and studies on sphingomyelinases. *Ann Neurol* 1:385, 1977.

14. BARATON G: Maladies hereditaires par surcharge en sphingomyelines ou maladie de Niemann-Pick. Lyon, University of Lyon. Thesis. 1977.

15. NORMAN RM, FORRESTER RM, TINGEY AH: The juvenile form of Niemann-Pick Disease. *Arch Dis Child* 42:91, 1967.

16. BRUNNGRABER EG, BERRA B, ZAMBOTTI V: Altered levels of tissue glycoproteins, gangliosides, glycosaminoglycans and lipids in Niemann-Pick's disease. *Clin Chim Acta* 48:173, 1973.

17. BESLEY GT, ELLEDER M: Enzyme activities and phospholipid storage patterns in brain and spleen samples from Niemann-Pick disease variants: A comparison of neuropathic and non-neuropathic forms. *J Inherited Metab Dis* 9:59, 1986.

18. KAMOSHITA S, ARON AM, SUZUKI K, SUZUKI K: Infantile Niemann-Pick disease: A chemical study with isolation and characterization of membranous cytoplasmic bodies and myelin. *Am J Dis Child* 117:379, 1969.

19. OPPENHEIMER DR, NORMAN RM, TINGEY AH, AHERNE WA: Histological and chemical findings in juvenile Niemann-Pick disease. *J Neurol Sci* 5:575, 1967.

20. WHERRETT JR, REWCASTLE NB: Adult neurovisceral lipidosis [abstract]. *Clin Res* 17:665, 1969.

21. BRIERE J, CALMAN F, LAGERON A, HINGLAIS N, EMERIT J, BERNARD J: Maladie de Niemann-Pick de l'adulte suive de la naissance a l'age de 26 ans: Forme viscerale pure avec surcharge en sphingomyeline et deficit en sphingomyelinase. *Nouve Rev Fr Hematol Blood Cells* 16:185, 1976.

22. WEGMANN W, SIEBENMANN R, AMMANN R: Niemann-Picksche, Krankheit im Erwachsenenalter. *Verh Dtsch Ges Pathol* 263, 1976.

23. LONG RG, LAKE BD, PETTIT JE, SCHEUER PG, SHERLOCK S: Adult Niemann-Pick disease: Its relationship to the syndrome of the sea-blue histiocyte. *Am J Med* 62:627, 1977.

24. CHAN WC, LAI KS, TODD D: Adult Niemann-Pick disease—A case report. *J Pathol* 121:177, 1977.

25. UHDE J: "Erwachsenenform" einer Niemann-Pickschen Erkrankung (letter). *Dtsch Med Wochenschr* 103:873, 1978.

26. D'ASSIS JL, SCAFF M, TAKAHASHI W: Doenca de Niemann-Pick forma do adulto associata a sindrome de Osler-Rendu-Weber: Registro de um cason. *Arq Neuropsiquiatr* 37:71, 1979.

27. DAWSON PG, DAWSON G: Adult Niemann-Pick disease with sea-blue histiocytes in the spleen. *Hum Pathol* 13:1115, 1982.

28. ELLEDER M, JIRASEK A, VLK J: Adult neurovisceral lipidosis compatible with Niemann-Pick disease type C. *Virchows Arch (A)* 401:35, 1983.

29. LEVER AML, RYDER JB: Cor pulmonale in an adult secondary to Niemann-Pick disease. *Thorax* 38:873, 1983.

30. MYLLA NETO G, COSTA R, FERNANDES PM, LIMA EC, RIBEIRO FM, STOLF NA: Niemann-Pick disease in adult: Report of a case surgically treated. *Rev Hosp Clin Fac Med Sao Paulo* 38:83, 1983.

31. VACHER-LAVENU MC, BARON-SELME V, ABELANET R, BOISSONNAS A, LAROCHE C: Le syndrome des histiocytes bleus: Revue de la litterature apropos d'une observation de splenomegalie idiopathique chez l'adulte. *Sem Hop Paris* 60:1333, 1984.

32. LANDAS S, FOUCAR K, SANDO GN, ELLEFSON R, HAMILTON HE: Adult Niemann-Pick disease masquerading as sea blue histiocyte syndrome: Report of a case confirmed by lipid analysis and enzyme assays. *Am J Hematol* 20:391, 1985.

33. KAN'SHINA NF, CHEMIAKIN AI, OZHIGANOVA IN: Prizhiznennaia diagnostika bolezni Nimanna-Picka u vzroslogo. *Arkh Patol* 48:78, 1986.

34. LOWE D, MARTIN F, SARKS J: Ocular manifestations of adult Niemann-Pick disease: A case report. *Aust NZ J Ophthalmol* 14:41, 1986.

35. ELLEDER M, BENESOVA E: Adultni forma Niemannova-Pickova onemocneni typu B, projevujici se jako "syndrom modreho histiocytu." *Vnitr Lek* 32:1114, 1986.

36. WILSON JAP, RAUFMAN J-P: Hepatic failure in adult Niemann-Pick disease. *Am J Med Sci* 292:168, 1986.

37. SCHNEIDER PB, KENNEDY EP: Sphingomyelinase in normal human spleens and in spleens from subjects with Niemann-Pick disease. *J Lipid Res* 8:202, 1967.

38. SLOAN HR, UHLENDORF BW, KANFER JN, BRADY RO, FREDRICKSON DS: Deficiency of sphingomyelin-cleaving enzyme activity in tissue cultures derived from patients with Niemann-Pick disease. *Biochem Biophys Res Comm* 34:582, 1969.

39. GAL AE, BRADY RO, HIBBERT SR, PENTCHEV PG: A practical chromogenic procedure for the detection of homozygotes and heterozygous carriers of Niemann-Pick disease. *N Engl J Med* 293:632, 1975.

40. CALLAHAN JW, KHALIL M: Sphingomyelinases in human tissues. III. Expression of Niemann-Pick disease in cultured skin fibroblasts. *Pediatr Res* 9:914, 1975.

41. KUDOH T, VELKOFF MA, WENGER DA: Uptake and metabolism of radioactively labeled sphingomyelin in cultured skin fibroblasts from controls and patients with Niemann-Pick disease and other lysosomal storage diseases. *Biochim Biophys Acta* 754:82, 1983.

42. POULOS A, SHANKARAN P, JONES CS, CALLAHAN JW: Enzymatic hydrolysis of sphingomyelin liposomes by normal tissues and tissues from patients with Niemann-Pick diseases. *Biochim Biophys Acta* 751:428, 1983.

43. HUTERER S, WHERRETT JR, POULOS A, CALLAHAN JW: Deficiency of phospholipase C acting on phosphatidylglycerol in Niemann-Pick disease. *Neurology* 33:67, 1983.

44. WHERRETT JR, HUTERER S: Deficiency of taurocholate-dependent phospholipase C acting on phosphatidylcholine in Niemann-Pick disease. *Neurochem Res* 8:89, 1983.

45. BESLEY GTN, MOSS SE: Studies on sphingomyelinase and B-glucosidase activities in Niemann-Pick disease variants: Phosphodiesterase activities measured with natural and artificial substrates. *Biochim Biophys Acta* 752:54, 1983.

46. WEITZ G, DRIESSEN M, BROUWER-KELDER EM, SANDHOFF K, BARRANGER JA, TAGER JM, SCHRAM AW: Soluble sphingomyelinase from human urine as antigen for obtaining anti-sphingomyelinase antibodies. *Biochim Biophys Acta* 838:92, 1985.

47. FEDERICO A, PALMERI S, DIGGELEN OV, FERRARI E, GUAZZI GC: Juvenile dystonia without vertical gaze paralysis: Niemann-Pick type C disease. *J Inherited Metab Dis* 9 suppl 2:314, 1986.

48. WENGER DA, BARTH G, GITHENS JH: Nine cases of sphingomyelin lipidosis, a new variant in Spanish-American children: Juvenile variant of Niemann-Pick disease with foamy and sea-blue histiocytes. *Am J Dis Child* 131:955, 1977.

49. SCHNEIDER EL, PENTCHEV PG, HIBBERT SR, SAWITSKY A, BRADY RO: A new form of Niemann-Pick disease characterized by temperature-labile sphingomyelinase. *J Med Genet* 15:370, 1978.

50. NEVILLE BGR, LAKE BD, STEPHENS R, SANDERS MD: A neurovisceral storage disease with vertical supranuclear ophthalmoplegia and its relation to Niemann-Pick disease. *Brain* 96:97, 1973.

51. ELLEDER M, JIRASEK A: Niemann-Pick disease: Report on a symposium held in Hlava's Institute of Pathology, Charles University, Prague 2nd-3rd September, 1982. *Acta Univ Carol [Med] (Praha)* 29:259, 1983.

52. LEVADE T, SALVAYRE R, DOUSTE-BLAZY L: Sphingomyelinases and Niemann-Pick disease. *J Clin Chem Clin Biochem* 24:205, 1986.

53. GUIBAUD P, VANIER M-T, MALPUECH G, GAULME J, HOULLEMARE L, GODDON R, ROUSSON R: Forme infantile precoce, cholestatique, rapidement mortelle, de la sphingomyelinase type C: a propos de 2 observations. *Pediatrics* 34:103, 1979.

54. JAEKEN J, PROESMANS W, EGGERMONT E, VAN HOOF F, DEN TANDT W, STANDAERT L, VAN HERCK G, CORBEEL L: Niemann-Pick type C disease and early cholestasis in three brothers. *Acta Paediatr Belg* 33:43, 1980.

55. YATZIV S, LEIBOVITZ-BEN BERSHON Z, ORNOY A, BACH G: Clinical heterogeneity in a sibship with Niemann-Pick disease type C. *Clin Genet* 23:125, 1983.

56. SEMERARO LA, RIELY CA, KOLODNY EH, DICKERSON GR, GRYBOSKI JD: Niemann-Pick variant lipidosis presenting as "neonatal hepatitis." *J Pediatr Gastroenterol Nutr* 5:492, 1986.

57. HARZER K, SCHLOTE W, PEIFFER J, BENZ HU, ANZIL AP: Neurovisceral lipidosis compatible with Niemann-Pick disease type C: Morphological and biochemical studies of a late infantile case and enzyme and lipid assays in a prenatal case of the same family. *Acta Neuropathol (Berl)* 43:97, 1978.

58. WINSOR EJT, WELCH JP: Genetic and demographic aspects of Nova Scotia Niemann-Pick disease (type D). *Am J Hum Genet* 30:530, 1978.

59. ELFENBEIN IB: Dystonic juvenile idiocy without amaurosis: A new syndrome: Light and electron microscopic observations of cerebrum. *Johns Hopkins Med J* 123:205, 1968.

60. KARPATI G, CARPENTER S, WOLFE LS, ANDERMANN F: Juvenile dystonic lipidosis: An unusual form of neurovisceral storage disease. *Neurology* 27:32, 1977.

61. MARTIN JJ, LOWENTHAL A, CEUTERICK C, VANIER MT: Juvenile dystonic lipidosis (variant of Niemann-Pick disease type C). *J Neurol Sci* 66:33, 1984.

62. BREEN L, MORRIS HH, ALPERIN JB, SCHOCHET SS JR: Juvenile Niemann-Pick disease with vertical supranuclear ophthalmoplegia: Two case reports and review of the literature. *Arch Neurol* 38:388, 1981.

63. COGAN DG, CHU FC, BACHMAN DF, BARRANGER J: The DAF syndrome. *Neuroophthamology* 2:7, 1981.

64. POULOS A, BECKMAN K, ELLIS DH, POLLARD AC: Hepatic storage of bis(monoacylglycerol) phosphate without concomitant storage of sphingomyelin in a 72-year-old patient with a partial deficiency of sphingomyelinase. *Clin Genet* 22:234, 1982.

65. VANIER MT, ROUSSON R, GARCIA I, BAILLOUD G, JUGE M-C, REVOL A, LOUISOT P: Biochemical studies in Niemann-Pick disease. III. In vitro and in vivo assays of sphingomyelin degradation in cultured skin fibroblasts and amniotic fluid cells for the diagnosis of the various forms of the disease. *Clin Genet* 27:20, 1985.

66. PATRICK AD, YOUNG E, KLEIJER WJ, NIERMEIJER MF: Prenatal diagnosis of Niemann-Pick disease type A using chromogenic substrate [letter]. *Lancet* 2:144, 1977.

67. CHAZAN S, ZITMAN D, KLIBANSKY C: Prenatal diagnosis of Gaucher's and Niemann-Pick diseases: Assays of glucocerebrosidase and sphingomyelinase in tissue cultures using natural substrates. *Clin Chim Acta* 86:45, 1978.

68. HIGAMI S, OMURA K, NISHIZAWA K, YAMASHITA T, TADA K: Prenatal diagnosis and fetal pathology of Niemann-Pick disease. *Tohoku J Exp Med* 125:11, 1978.

69. MAZIERE JC, MAZIERE C, HOSLI P: An ultramicrochemical assay for sphingomyelinase: Rapid prenatal diagnosis of a fetus at risk for Niemann-Pick disease. *Monogr Hum Genet* 9:198, 1978.

70. WENGER DA, WHARTON C, SATTLER M, CLARK C: Niemann-Pick disease: Prenatal diagnoses and studies of sphingomyelinase activities. *Am J Med Genet* 2:345, 1978.

71. VANIER MT, BOUE J, DUMEZ Y: Niemann-Pick disease type B: First-trimester prenatal diagnosis on chorionic villi and biochemical study of a foetus at 12 weeks of development. *Clin Genet* 28:348, 1985.

72. SCHOENFELD A, OVADIA J, NERI A, ABRAMOVICI A, KLIBANSKI C: Chemical and biochemical studies in fetuses affected with Niemann-Pick disease type A. *Prenat Diagn* 2:177, 1982.

73. SCHOENFELD A, ABRAMOVICI A, KLIBANSKI C, OVADIA J: Placental ultrasonographic biochemical and histochemical studies in human fetuses affected with Niemann-Pick disease type A. *Placenta* 6:33, 1985.

74. KLIBANSKY C, CHAZAN S, SCHOENFELD A, ABRAMOVICI A: Chemical and biochemical studies in human fetuses affected with Niemann-Pick disease type A. *Clin Chim Acta* 91:243, 1979.

75. DONAGHEY SF, RAINE DN, CROSSLEY JE: Chemical studies on postmortem tissues from an infant with a sphingomyelin storage disorder. *J Inherited Metab Dis* 6:190, 1983.

76. MUKHAMEDIEVA SM, BRYZHEVA TS: Sluchai sfingomielinoza (bolezn' Nimanna-Pika) u Rebenka 1 goda 9 mes. *Pediatriia* 59, 1983.

77. IWANSKA K, SZALECKI M, BASZCZYK A: Choroba Niemanna-Picka 2-miesiecanego niemowlecia. *Przegl Lek* 41:501, 1984.

78. SCHNEIDER EL, ELLIS WG, BRADY RO, MCCULLOCH JR, EPSTEIN CJ: Prenatal Niemann-Pick disease: Biochemical and histologic examination of a 19-gestational week fetus. *Pediatr Res* 6:720, 1972.

79. SARRUT S, BELAMICH P: Étude du placenta dans trois observations de dylipidosie à révélation neonatale. *Arch Anat Cytol Pathol* 31:187, 1983.

80. TAMARU J, IWASAKI I, HORIE H, TAKAYANAGI M, OHTAKE A, SHIMOJYO N, IDE G: Niemann-Pick disease associated with liver disorders. *Acta Pathol Jap* 35:1267, 1985.

81. GRUNEBAUM M: The roentgenographic findings in the acute neuronopathic form of Niemann-Pick disease. *Br J Radiol* 49:1018, 1976.

82. DINARI G, ROSENBACH Y, GRUNEBAUM M, ZAHAVI I, ALPERT G, NITZAN M: Gastrointestinal manifestations of Niemann-Pick disease. *Enzyme* 25:407, 1980.

83. YAMANO T, SHIMADA M, OKADA S, YUTAKA T, YABUUCHI H: Ultrastructural study of biopsy specimens of rectal mucosa: Its use in neuronal storage diseases. *Arch Pathol Lab Med* 106:673, 1982.

84. MARKINI MK, GERGEN P, AKHTAR M, GHANDOUR M: Niemann-Pick disease: Report of a case with skin involvement. *Am J Dis Child* 136:650, 1982.

85. HAMMERSEN G, OPPERMANN HC, HARMS E, BLASSMANN K, HARZER K:

86. REICH D, KEDAR A, KLIBANSKY C: Clinical and biochemical study of a child with the non-neuronopathic-Type B form of Niemann-Pick disease. *Eur J Pediatr* 131:133, 1979.

87. KONISHI Y, KONISHI K, TOMISAWA T, MOMOI T, SUDO M, YAMADA E, HAZAMA F: A report of a patient with Niemann-Pick disease type B and a review of the patients in Japan. *Jinrui Idengaku Zasshi* 26:207, 1981.

88. LAWLOR E, BESLEY GT, PIERCE P, TEMPERLEY IJ: Niemann-Pick disease type B in an Irish family. *Ir J Med Sci* 150:182, 1981.

89. FRIED K, LANGER R: Childbirth in a woman with chronic Niemann-Pick (type B) disease [letter]. *Clin Genet* 22:47, 1982.

90. SHAH MD, DESAI AP, JAIN MK, KULKARNI V, PATEL P, WARADKAR AM, BHUI PS, KOPPIKAR GV: Niemann-Pick disease type B with oculoneural involvement. *Indian Pediatr* 20:521, 1983.

91. RICCA V, LANDI M, CALI M, AIMAR A, LALA R, CORRIAS A, JAVARONE A: La malattia di Niemann-Pick tipo B: Aspetti clinici. *Minerva Pediatr* 38:477, 1986.

92. PAVONE L, FIUMARA A, LAROSA M: Niemann-Pick disease type B: Clinical signs and follow-up of a new case. *J Inherited Metab Dis* 9:73, 1986.

93. MATTHEWS JD, WEITER JJ, KOLODNY EH: Macular halos associated with Niemann-Pick type B disease. *Ophthalmology* 93:933, 1986.

94. LIPSON MH, O'DONNELL J, CALLAHAN JW, WENGER DA, PACKMAN S: Ocular involvement in Niemann-Pick disease type B. *J Pediatr* 108:582, 1986.

95. HARZER K, RUPRECHT KW, SEUFFER-SCHULZE D, JANS U: Morbus Niemann-Pick Type B: Enzymatisch gesichert mit unerwarteter retinaler Beteiligung. *Albrecht Von Graefes Arch Klin Ophthalmol* 206:79, 1978.

96. COGAN DG, KUWABARA T: The sphingolipidoses and the eye. *Arch Ophthalmol* 79:437, 1968.

97. COGAN DG, CHU FC, BARRANGER JA, GREGG RE: Macula halo syndrome: Variant of Niemann-Pick disease. *Arch Ophthalmol* 101:1698, 1983.

98. SOGAWA H, HORINO K, NAKAMURA F, KUDOH T, OYANAGI K, YAMANOUCHI T, MINAMI R, NAKAO T, WATANABE A, MATSUURA Y: Chronic Niemann-Pick disease with sphingomyelinase deficiency in two brothers with mental retardation. *Eur J Pediatr* 128:235, 1978.

99. ELLEDER M, CIHULA J: Niemann-Pick disease (variation in the sphingomyelinase deficient group): Neurovisceral phenotype (A) with an abnormally protracted clinical course and variable expression of neurological symptomatology in three siblings. *Eur J Pediatr* 140:323, 1983.

100. CONNOLLY CE, KENNEDY SM: Primary biliary disease and Niemann-Pick disease [letter]. *Hum Pathol* 15:97, 1984.

101. ELLEDER M, JIRASEK A, SMID F, LEDVINOVA J, BESLEY GT: Niemann-Pick disease type C: Study on the nature of the cerebral storage process. *Acta Neuropathol (Berl)* 66:325, 1985.

102. BURY F, JAEKEN J, EGGERMONT E, LIBERT J, DEN TANDT W, MARIEN J, DE VOS R, VAN DAMME B, CORBEEL L: Cholostase d'apparition precose dans la maladie de Niemann-Pick: a propos d'un cas de type C. *Pediatrie* 34:351, 1979.

103. TIBBLES JAR, WELCH JP: Clinical and genetic data on twelve new cases of Type D Niemann-Pick disease. *Pediatr Res* 6:643, 1972.

104. TIBBLES JAR: Personal communication.

105. PENTCHEV PG, COMLY ME, KRUTH HS, VANIER MT, WENGER DA, PATEL S, BRADY RO: A defect in cholesterol esterification in Niemann-Pick disease (type C) patients. *Proc Natl Acad Sci USA* 82:8247, 1985.

106. PENTCHEV PG, KRUTH HS, COMLY ME, BUTLER JD, VANIER MT, WENGER DA, PATEL S: Type C Niemann-Pick disease: A parallel loss of regulatory responses in both the uptake and esterification of low density lipoprotein-derived cholesterol in cultured fibroblasts. *J Biol Chem* 261:16775, 1986.

107. BUTLER JD, COMLY ME, KRUTH HS, VANIER M, FILLING-KATZ M, FINK J, BARTON N, WEINTROUB H, QUIRK JM, TOKORO T, MARSHALL DC, BRADY RO, PENTCHEV PG: Niemann-Pick variant disorders: Comparison of errors of cellular cholesterol homeostasis in group D and group C fibroblasts. *Proc Natl Acad Sci USA* 84:556, 1987.

108. ARSENIO-NUNES ML, GOUTIERES F: Morphological diagnosis of Niemann-Pick disease type C by skin and conjunctival biopsies. *Acta Neuropathol [Suppl] (Berl)* 7:204, 1981.

109. BESLEY GTN: Sphingomyelinase defect in Niemann-Pick disease, type C, fibroblasts. *FEBS Lett* 80:71, 1977.

110. BRAAK H, BRAAK E, GOEBEL HH: Isocortical pathology in type C Niemann-Pick disease: A combined Golgi-pigmentoarchitectonic study. *J Neuropathol Exp Neurol* 42:671, 1983.

111. CALLAHAN JW, KHALIL M, PHILIPPART M: Sphingomyelinases in human tissues. II. Absence of a specific enzyme from liver and brain of Niemann-Pick disease, type C. *Pediatr Res* 9:908, 1975.

112. ELLEDER M, JIRASEK A, SMID F: Niemann-Pick disease (Crocker's type C): A histological study of the distribution and qualitative differences of the storage process. *Acta Neuropathol (Berl)* 33:191, 1975.

113. KUNISHITA T, TAKETOMI T: Sphingomyelin storage in a patient with my-

oclonus epilepsy as a main clinical symptom: A variant in Niemann-Pick disease type C. *Jpn J Exp Med* 49:151, 1979.

114. CHRISTOMANOU H: Niemann-Pick disease, type C: Evidence for the deficiency of an activating factor stimulating sphingomyelin and glucocerebroside degradation. *Hoppe-Seyler's Z Physiol Chem* 361:1489, 1980.

115. MERIN S, LIVNI N, YATZIV S: Conjunctival ultrastructure in Niemann-Pick disease type C. *Am J Ophthalmol* 90:708, 1980.

116. PINEDA M, FERNANDEZ-ALVAREZ E, VIDAL J, FERRER J, ESTELLA JM, FABREGAS I: La enfermedad de Niemann-Pick typo C. *Arch Neurobiol (Madr)* 44:139, 1981.

117. GILBERT EF, CALLAHAN J, VISESKUL C, OPITZ JM, Niemann-Pick disease type C: Pathological, histochemical, ultrastructural and biochemical studies. *Eur J Pediatr* 136:263, 1981.

118. MIYAKE S, INOUE H, OHTAHARA S, OKADA S, YAMANO T: [A case of Niemann-Pick disease type C with narcolepsy syndrome.] *Rinsho Shinkeigaku* 23:44, 1983.

119. POULOS A, HUDSON N, RANIERI E: Sphingomyelinase in cultured skin fibroblasts from normal and Niemann-Pick type C patients. *Clin Genet* 24:225, 1983.

120. ELLEDER M, JIRASEK A, SMID F, LEDVINOVA J, BESLEY GTN, STOPEKOVA M: Niemann-Pick disease type C with enhanced glycolipid storage: Report on further case of so-called lactosylceramidosis. *Virchows Arch [A]* 402:307, 1984.

121. ELLEDER M, SMID F, HYNIOVA H, CIHULA J, ZEMAN J, MACEK M: Liver findings in Niemann-Pick disease type C. *Histochem J* 16:1147, 1984.

122. ELLEDER M, SMID F: Adrenal changes in Niemann-Pick disease: Differences between sphingomyelinase deficiency and type C. *Acta Histochem (Jena)* 76:163, 1985.

123. FUJIBAYASHI S, WENGER DA: Studies on a sphingolipid activator protein (SAP-2) in fibroblasts from patients with lysosomal storage diseases, including Niemann-Pick disease Type C. *Clin Chim Acta* 146:147, 1985.

124. PALMER M, GREEN WR, MAUMENEE IH, VALLE DL, SINGER HS, MORTON SJ, MOSER HW: Niemann-Pick disease—type C: Ocular histopathologic and electron microscopic studies. *Arch Ophthalmol* 103:817, 1985.

125. CEUTERICK C, MARTIN JJ, FOULARD M: Niemann-Pick disease type C: Skin biopsies in parents. *Neuropediatrics* 17:111, 1986.

126. HARDER A, WIDJAJA F, DEBUCH H: Studies on lipids from liver and spleen of a child (O.L.) with Niemann-Pick's disease type C. *J Clin Chem Clin Biochem* 22:199, 1984.

127. LEVADE T, MARET A, SALVAYRE R, LIVNI N, ROGALLE P, DOUSTE-BLAZY L: Biochemical and ultrastructural studies on an Epstein-Barr virus-transformed lymphoid cell line from a Niemann-Pick disease type C patient. *Biochim Biophys Acta* 877:414, 1986.

128. PAMPOLS T, PINEDA M, FERRETER M, FERNANDEZ E: Enfermedad de Niemann-Pick tipo C en dos hermanos. Bases bioquimicas del diagnostico. *An Esp Pediatr* 24:250, 1986.

129. SPENCE MW, WELCH JP, WINSOR EJT, TIBBLES JAR: Unpublished observations.

130. DE LEON GA, KABACK MM, ELFENBEIN IB, PERCY AK, BRADY RO: Juvenile dystonic lipidosis. *Johns Hopkins Med J* 125:62, 1969.

131. HOROUPIAN DS, YANG SS: Paired helical filaments in neurovisceral lipidosis (juvenile dystonic lipidosis). *Ann Neurol* 4:404, 1978.

132. YAN-GO FL, YANAGIHARA T, PIERRE RV, GOLDSTEIN NP: A progressive neurologic disorder with supranuclear vertical gaze paresis and distinctive bone marrow cells. *Mayo Clin Proc* 59:404, 1984.

133. GARTNER JC, BERGMAN I, MALATACK JJ, ZITELLI BJ, JAFFE R, WATKINS JB, SHAW BW, IWATSUKI S, STARZL TE: Progression of neurovisceral storage disease with supranuclear ophthalmoplegia following orthotopic liver transplantation. *Pediatrics* 77:104, 1986.

134. KORNFELD M, APPENZELLER J, SAIKI J, TROUP GM: Sea-blue histiocytes and sural nerve in neurovisceral storage disorder with vertical ophthalmoplegia. *J Neurol Sci* 25:291, 1975.

135. COGAN DG, CHU FC, REINGOLD D, BARRANGER J: Ocular motor signs in some metabolic diseases. *Arch Ophthalmol* 99:1802, 1981.

136. PHILIPPART M, ENGEL J JR, ZIMMERMAN EG: Gelastic cataplexy in Niemann-Pick disease group C and related variants without generalized sphingomyelinase deficiency [letter]. *Ann Neurol* 14:492, 1983.

137. KANDT RS, EMERSON RG, SINGER HS, VALLE DL, MOSER HW: Cataplexy in variant forms of Niemann-Pick disease. *Ann Neurol* 12:284, 1982.

138. ELLEDER M, HRODEK J, CIHULA J: Niemann-Pick disease: Lipid storage in bone marrow macrophages. *Histochem J* 15:1065, 1983.

139. VARELA-DURAN J, ROHOLT PC, RATLIFF NB JR: Sea-blue histiocyte syndrome: A secondary degenerative process of macrophages? *Arch Pathol Lab Med* 104:30, 1980.

140. LUDATSCHER RM, NAVEH Y, AUSLAENDER L, GELLEI B: Electron microscopic studies in lipid storage disease. *Isr J Med Sci* 17:323, 1981.

141. EPSTEIN CJ, BRADY RO, SCHNEIDER EL, BRADLEY RM, SHAPIRO D: In utero diagnosis of Niemann-Pick disease. *Am J Hum Genet* 23:533, 1971.

142. CHILCOTE RR, MILLER M, DAWSON G, MATALON R: Foamy histiocytes in the CSF of a patient with infantile Niemann-Pick disease. *Am J Dis Child* 135:76, 1981.

143. ELLEDER M, SMID F, HARZER K, CIHULA J: Niemann-Pick disease: Analysis of liver tissue in sphingomyelinase-deficient patients. *Virchows Arch (B)* 385:215, 1980.

144. ROBB RM, KUWABARA T: The ocular pathology of Type A Niemann-Pick disease: A light and electron microscopic study. *Invest Ophthalmol* 12:366, 1973.

145. WALTON DS, ROBB RM, CROCKER AC: Ocular manifestations of group A Niemann-Pick disease. *Am J Ophthalmol* 85:174, 1978.

146. LIBERT J, TOUSSAINT D, GUISELINGS R: Ocular findings in Niemann-Pick disease. *Am J Ophthalmol* 80:991, 1975.

147. HOWES EL JR, WOOD IS, GOLBUS M, HOGAN ML: Ocular pathology of infantile Niemann-Pick disease: Study of fetus of 23 weeks' gestation. *Arch Ophthalmol* 93:494, 1975.

148. O'BRIEN JS, BERNETT J, VEATH ML, PAA D: Lysosomal storage disorders: Diagnosis by ultrastructural examination of skin biopsy specimens. *Arch Neurol* 32:592, 1975.

149. GUMBINAS M, LARSEN M, LIU HM: Peripheral neuropathy in classic Niemann-Pick disease: Ultrastructure of nerves and skeletal muscles. *Neurology* 25:107, 1975.

150. ROUSER G, BERRY JF, MARINETTI G, STOTZ E: Studies on the structure of sphingomyelin. I. Oxidation of products of partial hydrolysis. *J Am Chem Soc* 75:310, 1953.

151. MARINETTI G, BERRY JF, ROUSER G, STOTZ E: Studies on the structure of sphingomyelin. II. Performic and periodic acid oxidation studies. *J Am Chem Soc* 75:313, 1953.

152. PHILIPPART M, MARTIN L, MARTIN JJ, MENKES JH: Niemann-Pick disease: Morphologic and biochemical studies in the visceral form with late central nervous system involvement (Crocker's group C). *Arch Neurol* 20:227, 1969.

153. TJIONG HB, SENG PN, DEBUCH H, WIEDEMANN H-R: Brain lipids of a case of juvenile Niemann-Pick disease. *J Neurochem* 21:1475, 1973.

154. WENGER DA, KUDOH T, SATTLER M, PALMIERI M, YUDKOFF M: Niemann-Pick disease type B: Prenatal diagnosis and enzymatic and chemical studies on fetal brain and liver. *Am J Hum Genet* 33:337, 1981.

155. ROUSER G, KRITCHEVSKY G, YAMAMOTO A, KNUDSON AG JR, SIMON G: Accumulation of a glycerolphospholipid in classical Niemann-Pick disease. *Lipids* 3:287, 1968.

156. BROTHERUS J, RENKONEN O, FISCHER W, HERRMAN J: Novel stereoconfiguration in lysoso-bis-phosphatidic acid of cultured BHK-cells. *Chem Phys Lipids* 13:178, 1974.

157. JOUTTI A, BROTHERUS J, RENKONEN O, LAINE R, FISCHER W: The stereochemical configuration of lysobisphosphatidic acid from rat liver, rabbit lung and pig lung. *Biochim Biophys Acta* 450:206, 1976.

158. POORTHUIS BJHM, HOSTETLER KY: Conversion of diphosphatidylglycerol to bis(monoacylglyceryl)phosphate by lysosomes. *J Lipid Res* 19:309, 1978.

159. SENG PN, DEBUCH H, WITTER B, WIEDEMANN H-R: Bis(monoacylglycerin)phosphosaure-Vermehrung bei Sphingomyelinase (M. Niemann-Pick). *Hoppe-Seyler's Z Physiol Chem* 352:280, 1971.

160. MARTIN J-J, PHILIPPART M, VAN HAUWAERT J, CALLAHAN JW, DEBERDT R: Niemann-Pick disease (Crocker's group A): Late onset and pigmentary degeneration resembling Hallervorden-Spatz syndrome. *Arch Neurol* 27:45, 1972.

161. DACREMONT G, KINT JA, CARTON D, COCQUYT G: Glucosylceramide in plasma of patients with Niemann-Pick disease. *Clin Chim Acta* 52:365, 1974.

162. YAMAMOTO A, ADACHI S, ISHIBE T, SHINJI Y, KAKI-UCHI Y, SEKI KT, KITANI T: Accumulation of acidic phospholipids in a case of hyperlipidemia with hepatosplenomegaly. *Lipids* 5:566, 1970.

163. KASAMA K, YOSHIDA K, TAKEDA S, AKEDA S, KAWAI K: Bis-(monoacylglyceryl)phosphate and acyl phosphatidylglycerol isolated from human livers of lipidosis induced 4,4'-diethylaminoethoxyhexesterol. *Lipids* 9:235, 1974.

164. BARENHOLZ Y, THOMPSON TE: Sphingomyelins in bilayers and biological membranes. *Biochim Biophys Acta* 604:129, 1980.

165. MARTINEK K, LEVASHOV AV, KLYACHKO N, KHMELNITSKI YL, BEREZIN IV: Micellar enzymology. *Eur J Biochem* 155:453, 1986.

166. SEITER CW, MCCLUER RH: Analysis of the structure of two gangliosides which accumulate in the brain in Niemann-Pick disease. *J Neurochem* 17:1525, 1970.

167. STRASBERG PMS, CALLAHAN JW: Psychosine and sphingosylphosphorylcholine bind to mitochondrial membranes and disrupt their function, in Salvayre RL, Douste-Blazy L, Gatt S (eds): *Lipid Storage Disorders (Biological and Medical Aspects)*. New York, Plenum Press, in press, 1988.

168. SRIBNEY M, KENNEDY EP: The enzymatic synthesis of sphingomyelin. *J Biol Chem* 233:1315, 1958.

169. STOFFEL W, MELZNER I: Studies in vitro on the biosynthesis of ceramide and sphingomyelin: A reevaluation of proposed pathways. *Hoppe-Seyler's Z Physiol Chem* 361:755, 1980.

170. FUJINO Y, NEGISHI T: Investigation of the enzymatic synthesis of sphingomyelin. *Biochim Biophys Acta* 152:428, 1968.

171. DIRINGER H, KOCH MA: Biosynthesis of sphingomyelin: Transfer of phosphorylcholine from phosphatidylcholine to erythro-ceramide in a cell-free system. *Hoppe-Seyler's Z Physiol Chem* 354:1661, 1973.

172. MARGGRAF WD, ZERTANI R, ANDERER FA, KANFER JN: The role of endogenous phosphatidylcholine and ceramide in the biosynthesis of sphingomyelin in mouse fibroblasts. *Biochim Biophys Acta* 710:314, 1982.

173. ULLMAN MD, RADIN NS: The enzymatic formation of sphingomyelin from ceramide and lecithin in mouse liver. *J Biol Chem* 249:1506, 1974.

174. VOELKER DR, KENNEDY EP: Cellular and enzymic synthesis of sphingomyelin. *Biochemistry* 21:2753, 1982.

175. VAN DEN HILL A, VAN HEUSDEN PH, WIRTZ KWA: The synthesis of sphingomyelin in the Morris hepatomas 7777 and 5123D is restricted to the plasma membrane. *Biochim Biophys Acta* 833:354, 1985.

176. BEAUDET AL, MANSCHRECK AA: Metabolism of sphingomyelin by intact cultured fibroblasts: Differentiation of Niemann-Pick disease types A and B. *Biochem Biophys Res Commun* 105:14, 1982.

177. SPENCE MW, CLARKE JTR, COOK HW: Pathways of sphingomyelin metabolism in cultured fibroblasts from normal and sphingomyelin lipidosis subjects. *J Biol Chem* 258:8595, 1983.

178. MAZIERE JC, MAZIERE C, MORA L, ROUTIER JD, POLONOVSKI J: In situ degradation of sphingomyelin by cultured normal fibroblasts and fibroblasts from patients with Niemann-Pick disease type A and C. *Biochem Biophys Res Commun* 108:1101, 1982.

179. MAZIERE JC, MAZIERE C, MORA L, POLONOVSKI J: Impairment of exogenous sphingomyelin degradation in cultured fibroblasts from familial hypercholesterolemia. *FEBS Lett* 173:159, 1984.

180. LIPSKY NG, PAGANO RE: Intracellular translocation of fluorescent sphingolipids in cultured fibroblasts: Endogenously synthesized sphingomyelin and glucocerebroside analogues pass through the Golgi apparatus en route to the plasma membrane. *J Cell Biol* 100:27, 1985.

181. SUTRINA SL, CHEN WW: Lysosomal involvement in cellular turnover of plasma membrane sphingomyelin. *Biochim Biophys Acta* 793:169, 1984.

182. QUINTERN LE, WEITZ G, NEHRKORN H, TAGER JM, SCHRAM AW, SANDHOFF, K: Acid sphingomyelinase from human urine: Purification and characterization. *Biochim Biophys Acta* 922:323, 1987.

183. CALLAHAN JW, JONES CS, DAVIDSON DJ, SHANKARAN P: The active site of lysosomal sphingomyelinase: Evidence for the involvement of hydrophobic and ionic groups. *J Neurosci Res* 10:151, 1983.

184. YAMANAKA T, SUZUKI K: Acid sphingomyelinase of human brain: Purification to homogeneity. *J Neurochem* 38:1753, 1982.

185. GATT S, BARENHOLZ Y, GOLDBERG R, DINUR T, BESLEY G, LEIBOVITZ-BEN GERSHON Z, ROSENTHAL J, DESNICK RJ, DEVINE EA, SHAFIT-ZAGARDO B, TSURUKI F: Assay of enzymes of lipid metabolism with colored and fluorescent derivatives of natural lipids. *Methods Enzymol* 72:351, 1981.

186. RAO BG, SPENCE MW: Sphingomyelinase activity at pH 7.4 in human brain and a comparison to activity at pH 5.0. *J Lipid Res* 17:506, 1976.

187. FREEMAN SJ, SHANKARAN P, WOLFE LS, CALLAHAN JW: Phosphatidylcholine and 4-methylumbelliferyl phosphorylcholine hydrolysis by purified placental sphingomyelinase. *Can J Biochem Cell Biol* 63:272, 1985.

188. JONES CS, SHANKARAN P, CALLAHAN JW: Purification of sphingomyelinase to apparent homogeneity by using hydrophobic chromatography. *Biochem J* 195:373, 1981.

189. ROUSSON R, VANIER M-T, LOUISOT P: Chromatofocusing of purified placental sphingomyelinase. *Biochimie* 65:115, 1983.

190. SAKURAGAWA N: Acid sphingomyelinase of human placenta: Purification, properties, and ^{125}iodine labeling. *J Biochem (Tokyo)* 92:637, 1982.

191. PENTCHEV PG, BRADY RO, GAL AE, HIBBERT SR: The isolation and characterization of sphingomyelinase from human placental tissue. *Biochim Biophys Acta* 488:312, 1977.

192. GATT S, GOTTESDINER T: Solubilization of sphingomyelinase by isotonic extraction of rat brain lysosomes. *J Neurochem* 26:421, 1976.

193. MARET A, POTIER M, SALVAYRE R, DOUSTE-BLAZY L: Modification of subunit interaction in membrane-bound acid B-glucosidase from Gaucher disease. *FEBS Lett* 160:93, 1983.

194. WEITZ G, LINDL T, HINRICHS U, SANDHOFF K: Release of sphingomyelin phosphodiesterase (acid sphingomyelinase) by ammonium chloride from CL 1D mouse L-cells and human fibroblasts in partial purification and characterization of the exported enzymes. *Hoppe-Seyler's Z Physiol Chem* 364:863, 1983.

195. DAWSON G, ELLORY JC: Functional lysosomal hydrolase size as determined by radiation inactivation analysis. *Biochem J* 226:283, 1985.

196. JOBB E, CALLAHAN JW: The subunit of human sphingomyelinase is not the same size in all tissues: Studies with a polyclonal rabbit serum. *J Inherited Metab Dis* 10 suppl 2:326, 1987.

197. FREEMAN SJ, DAVIDSON DJ, SHANKARAN P, CALLAHAN JW: Monoclonal antibodies against human placental sphingomyelinase. *Biosci Rep* 3:545, 1983.

198. JOBB E: Acid sphingomyelinase in normal tissues and biosynthesis in normal and Niemann-Pick fibroblasts. Toronto, University of Toronto. Thesis. 1987.

199. GATT S, DINUR T, KOPOLOVIC J: Niemann Pick disease: Presence of the magnesium-dependent sphingomyelinase in brain of the infantile form of the disease. *J Neurochem* 31:547, 1978.

200. SPENCE MW, BURGESS JK: Acid and neutral sphingomyelinases of rat brain: Activity in developing brain and regional distribution in adult brain. *J Neurochem* 30:917, 1978.

201. SPENCE MW, BURGESS JK, SPERKER ER: Neutral and acid sphingomyelinases: Somatotopographical distribution in human brain and distribution in rat organs: A possible relationship with the dopamine system. *Brain Res* 168:543, 1979.

202. DAS DVM, COOK HW, SPENCE MW: Evidence that neutral sphingomyelinase of cultured murine neuroblastoma cells is oriented externally on the plasma membrane. *Biochim Biophys Acta* 777:339, 1984.

203. SPENCE MW, BURGESS JK, SPERKER ER, HAMED L, MURPHY MG: Neutral sphingomyelinases of brain, in Callahan JW, Lowden JA (eds): *Lysosomes and Lysosomal Storage Diseases*. New York, Raven, 1981, p 219.

204. LEVADE T, POTIER M, SALVAYRE R, DOUSTE-BLAZY L: Molecular weight of human brain neutral sphingomyelinase determined in situ by the radiation inactivation method. *J Neurochem* 45:630, 1985.

205. LEVADE T, SALVAYRE R, POTIER M, DOUSTE-BLAZY L: Interindividual heterogeneity of molecular weight of human brain neutral sphingomyelinase determined by radiation inactivation method. *Neurochem Res* 11:1131, 1986.

206. SPERKER ER, SPENCE MW: Neutral and acid sphingomyelinases of rat brain: Somatotopographical distribution and activity following experimental manipulation of the dopaminergic system in vivo. *J Neurochem* 40:1182, 1983.

207. GUY NC, CLARKE JTR, SPENCE MW, COOK HW: Stimulation of neutral, magnesium-stimulated sphingomyelinase activity in the neurohypophysis of the rat by hypertonic saline ingestion. *Brain Res Bull* 10:603, 1983.

208. PELLKOFER R, SANDHOFF K: Halothane increases membrane fluidity and stimulates sphingomyelin degradation by membrane-bound neutral sphingomyelinase of synaptosomal plasma membranes from calf brain already at clinical concentrations. *J Neurochem* 34:988, 1980.

209. MOOIBROEK MJ, COOK HW, CLARKE JTR, SPENCE MW: Catabolism of exogenous and endogenous sphingomyelin and phosphatidylcholine by homogenates and subcellular fractions of cultured neuroblastoma cells: Effects of anesthetics. *J Neurochem* 44:1551, 1985.

210. RECORD M, LOYTER A, GATT S: Utilization of membranous lipid substrates by membranous enzymes: Hydrolysis of sphingomyelin in erythrocyte "ghosts" and liposomes by the membranous sphingomyelinase of chicken erythrocyte "ghosts." *Biochem J* 187:115, 1980.

211. ALLAN D, THOMAS P, LIMBRICK AR: Microvesiculation and sphingomyelinase activation in chicken erythrocytes treated with ionophore A23187 and Ca2 + . *Biochim Biophys Acta* 693:53, 1982.

212. NILSSON A: The presence of sphingomyelin—and ceramide-cleaving enzymes in the small intestinal tract. *Biochim Biophys Acta* 176:339, 1969.

213. YAMAGUCHI S, SUZUKI K: A novel magnesium-independent neutral sphingomyelinase associated with rat central nervous system myelin. *J Biol Chem* 253:4090, 1978.

214. BEAUDET AL, HAMPTON MS, PATEL K, SPARROW JT: Acidic phospholipases in cultured human fibroblasts: Deficiency of phospholipase C in Niemann-Pick disease. *Clin Chim Acta* 108:403, 1980.

215. FIELDING CJ, FIELDING PE: Metabolism of cholesterol and lipoproteins, in Vance DE, Vance JE (eds): *Biochemistry of Lipids and Membranes*. Menlo Park, CA, The Benjamin/Cummings Publishing Co, 1985, p 404.

216. BROWN MS, HO YK, GOLDSTEIN JL: The cholesterol ester cycle in macrophage foam cells: Continual hydrolysis and esterification of cytoplasmic cholesteryl esters. *J Biol Chem* 255:9344, 1980.

217. SUCKLING KE, STRANGE EF: Role of acyl-CoA:cholesterol acyltransferase in cellular cholesterol metabolism. *J Lipid Res* 26:647, 1985.

218. DEMPSEY ME: Sterol carrier protein. *Methods Enzymol* 111:293, 1985.

219. SCALLEN TJ, NOLAND BJ, GRAVEY KL, BASS NM, OCKNER RK, CHANDERBHAN R, VAHOUNY GV: Sterol carrier protein 2 and fatty acid-binding protein: Separate and distinct physiological functions. *J Biol Chem* 260:4733, 1985.

220. GLATZ JFC, VEERKAMP JH: Intracellular fatty acid-binding proteins. *Int J Biochem* 17:13, 1985.

221. LANGE Y, MATTHIES HJG: Transfer of cholesterol from its site of synthesis to the plasma membrane. *J Biol Chem* 259:14624, 1984.

222. LANGE Y, RAMOS BV: Analysis of the distribution of cholesterol in the intact cell. *J Biol Chem* 258:15130, 1983.

223. DANIELS RJ, GUERTLER LS, PARKER TS, STEINBERG D: Studies on the rate of efflux of cholesterol from cultured human skin fibroblasts. *J Biol Chem* 256:4978, 1981.

224. BELLINI F, PHILLIPS MC, PICKELL C, ROTHBLAT GH: Role of the plasma membrane in the mechanism of cholesterol efflux from cells. *Biochim Biophys Acta* 777:209, 1984.

225. RANDOLPH RK, HOFF HF: Exchange and mass efflux of cholesterol in macrophages: Evidence for a common mechanism and a role for plasma membrane proteins. *J Lipid Res* 27:307, 1986.

226. DEMEL RA, DE KRUIJFF B: The function of sterols in membranes. *Biochim Biophys Acta* 457:109, 1976.

227. YEAGLE PL, YOUNG JE: Factors contributing to the distribution of cholesterol among phospholipid vesicles. *J Biol Chem* 261:8175, 1986.

228. LUND-KATZ S, PHILLIPS MC: Packing of cholesterol molecules in human low-density protein. *Biochem J* 25:1562, 1987.

229. YECHIEL E, HENIS YI, BARENHOLZ Y: Aging of rat heart fibroblasts: Relationship between lipid composition, membrane organization and biological properties. *Biochim Biophys Acta* 859:95, 1986.

230. YECHIEL E, BARENHOLZ Y: Cultured heart cell reaggregates: A model for studying relationshps between aging and lipid composition. *Biochim Biophys Acta* 859:105, 1986.

231. GATT S, BIERMAN EL: Sphingomyelin suppresses the binding and utilization of low density lipoproteins by skin fibroblasts. *J Biol Chem* 255:3371, 1980.

232. VERDERY RB III, THEOLIS R JR: Regulation of sphingomyelin long chain base synthesis in human fibroblasts in culture: Role of lipoproteins and the low density lipoprotein receptor. *J Biol Chem* 257:1412, 1982.

233. MAZIERE JC, MAZIERE C, GARDETTE J, MORA L, POLONOVSKI J: Changes in cholesterol metabolism in cultured fibroblasts from patients with Niemann-Pick disease. *Biochim Biophys Res Commun* 102:113, 1981.

234. MAZIERE JC, MAZIERE C, MORA L, GALLIE F, POLONOVSKI J: Cholesterol and 7-dehydrocholesterol inhibit the in situ degradation of sphingomyelin by cultured human fibroblasts. *Biochem Biophys Res Commun* 112:860, 1983.

235. KAMPINE JP, BRADY RO, KANFER JN: Diagnosis of Gaucher's disease and Niemann-Pick disease with small samples of venous blood. *Science* 155:86, 1967.

236. GAL AE, BRADY RO, BARRANGER JA, PENTCHEV PG: The diagnosis of type A and type B Niemann-Pick disease and detection of carriers using leukocytes and a chromogenic analogue of sphingomyelin. *Clin Chim Acta* 104:129, 1980.

237. ZITMAN D, CHAZAN S, KLIBANSKY C: Sphingomyelinase activity levels in human peripheral blood leukocytes, using [3H]sphingomyelin as substrate: Study of heterozygotes and homozygotes for Niemann-Pick disease variants. *Clin Chim Acta* 86:37, 1978.

238. ROUSSON R, VANIER MT, LOUISOT P: Immunological studies on acidic sphingomyelinase, in Freysz L, Dreyfus H, Massarelli R, Gatt S (eds): *Enzymes of Lipid Metabolism II.* New York, Plenum, 1986, p 273.

239. BESLEY GTN, HOOGEBOOM AJM, HOOGEVEEN A, KLEIMJER WJ, GALJAARD H: Somatic cell hybridisation studies showing different gene mutations in Niemann-Pick variants. *Hum Genet* 54:409, 1980.

240. NELSON PV, CAREY WF: A method for enrichment of hybrid somatic cells: Complementation studies in certain lysosomal enzymopathies. *J Inherited Metab Dis* 8:95, 1985.

241. POULOS A, RANIERI E, SHANKARAN P, CALLAHAN JW: Studies on the activation of sphingomyelinase activity in Niemann-Pick type A, B, and C fibroblasts: Enzymological differentiation of types A and B. *Pediatr Res* 18:1088, 1984.

242. VANIER MT, ROUSSON R, ZEITOUNI R, PENTCHEV PG, LOUISOT P: Sphingomyelinase and Niemann-Pick disease, in Freysz L, Dreyfus H, Massarelli R, Gatt S (eds): *Enzymes of Lipid Metabolism II.* New York, Plenum, 1986, p 791.

243. DAWSON RMC, HEMINGTON N, IRVINE RF: The inhibition of diacylglycerol-stimulated intracellular phospholipases by phospholipids with a phosphocholine-containing polar group: A possible physiological role for sphingomyelin group. *Biochem J* 230:61, 1985.

244. HANNUN YA, BELL RM: Lysosophingolipids inhibit protein kinase C: Implications for the sphingolipidoses. *Science* 235:670, 1987.

245. STRASBERG PM: Cerebrosides and psychosine disrupt mitochondrial functions. *Biochem Cell Biol* 64:485, 1986.

246. PENTCHEV PG, GAL AE, BOOTH AD, OMODEO-SALE F, FOUKS J, NEUMEYER BA, QUIRK JM, DAWSON G, BRADY RO: A lysosomal storage disorder in mice characterized by a dual deficiency of sphingomyelinase and glucocerebrosidase. *Biochim Biophys Acta* 619:669, 1980.

247. PENTCHEV PG, BOOTHE AD, KRUTH HS, WEINTRUB H, STIVERS J, BRADY RO: A genetic storage disorder in BALB/C mice with a metabolic block in esterification of exogenous cholesterol. *J Biol Chem* 259:5784, 1984.

248. PENTCHEV PG, COMLY ME, KRUTH HS, PATEL S, PROESTEL M, WEINTRUB H: The cholesterol storage disorder of the mutant BALB/C mouse: A primary genetic lesion closely linked to defective esterification of exogenously derived cholesterol and its relationship to human type C Niemann-Pick disease. *J Biol Chem* 261:2772, 1986.

249. KRUTH HS, COMLY ME, BUTLER JD, VANIER MT, FINK JK, WENGER DA, PATEL S, PENTCHEV PG: Type C Niemann-Pick disease: Abnormal metabolism of low density lipoprotein in homozygous and heterozygous fibroblasts. *J Biol Chem* 261:16769, 1986.

250. RODMAN JS, SEIDMAN L, FARQUHAR MG: The membrane composition of coated pits, microvilli, endosomes, and lysosomes is distinctive in the rat kidney proximal tubule cell. *J Cell Biol* 102:77, 1986.

251. MESSIEH S, CLARKE JTR, COOK HW, SPENCE MW: Abnormal neutral lipase activity in acid-lipase-deficient cultured human fibroblasts. *Pediatr Res* 17:770, 1982.

252. CHRISTOMANOU H, KLEINSCHMIDT T: Isolation of two forms of an activator protein for the enzymatic sphingomyelin degradation from human Gaucher spleen. *Biol Chem Hoppe Seyler* 366:245, 1985.

253. CHRISTOMANOU H, AIGNESBERGER A, LINKE RP: Immunochemical characterization of two activator proteins stimulating enzymic sphingomyelin degradation in vitro: Absence of one of them in a human Gaucher disease variant. *Biol Chem Hoppe Seyler* 367:879, 1986.

254. LEVADE T, SALVAYRE R, BES J-C, NEZRI M, DOUSTE-BLAZY L: New tools for the study of Niemann-Pick disease: Analogues of natural substrate and Epstein-Barr virus-transformed lymphoid cell lines. *Pediatr Res* 19:153.

255. GATT S, DINUR T, BARENHOLZ Y: A fluorometric determination of sphingomyelinase by use of fluorescent derivatives of sphingomyelin, and its application to diagnosis of Niemann-Pick disease. *Clin Chem* 26:93, 1980.

256. JONES CS, DAVIDSON DJ, CALLAHAN JW: Complex kinetics of bis(4-methylumbelliferyl)phosphate and hexadecanoyl(nitrophenyl)phosphorylcholine hydrolysis by purified sphingomyelinase in the presence of Triton X-100. *Biochim Biophys Acta* 701:261, 1982.

257. VETHAMANY VG, WELCH JP, VETHAMANY SK: Type D Nieman-Pick disease (Nova Scotia variant): Ultrastructure of blood, skin fibroblasts, and bone marrow. *Arch Pathol* 93:537, 1972.

258. BROWN MS, KOVANEN PT, GOLDSTEIN JL, EECKELS R, VAN DEN BERGHE K, VAN DEN BERGH H, FRYNS JP, CASSIMAN JJ: Prenatal diagnosis of homozygous familial hypercholesterolaemia: Expression of a genetic receptor disease in utero. *Lancet* 1:526, 1978.

259. DALOZE P, DELVIN EE, GLORIEUX FH, CORMAN JL, BETTEZ P, TOUSSI T: Replacement therapy for inherited enzyme deficiency: Liver orthotopic transplantation in Niemann-Pick disease type A. *Am J Med Genet* 1:229, 1977.

260. SAKIYAMA T, TSUDA M, OWADA M, JOH K, MIYAWAKI S, KITAGAWA, T: Bone marrow transplantation for Niemann-Pick mice. *Biochem Biophys Res Commun* 113:605, 1983.

261. SAKIYAMA T, KITAGAWA T, JHOU H, MIYAWAKI S: Bone marrow transplantation for Niemann-Pick mice. *J Inherited Metab Dis* 6:129, 1983.

262. BUNDZA A, LOWDEN JA, CHARLTON KM: Niemann-Pick disease in a poodle dog. *Vet Pathol* 16:530, 1979.

263. WENGER DA, SATTLER M, KUDOH T, SNYDER SP, KINGSTON RS: Niemann-Pick disease: A genetic model in Siamese cats. *Science* 208:1471, 1980.

264. ADACHI M, VOLK BW, SCHNECK L: Animal model of human disease: Niemann-Pick disease type C. *Am J Pathol* 85:229, 1976.

265. SAKURAGAWA N, SAKURAGAWA M, KUWABARA T, PENTCHEV PG, BARRANGER JA, BRADY RO: Niemann-Pick disease experimental model: Sphingomyelinase reduction induced by AY-9944. *Science* 196:317, 1977.

266. AUBERT-TULKENS G, VAN HOOF F, TULKENS P: Gentamicin-induced lysosomal phospholipidosis in cultured rat fibroblasts: Quantitative ultrastructural and biochemical study. *Lab Invest* 40:481, 1979.

267. MORIN JP, VIOTTE G, VANDEWALLE A, VAN HOOF F, TULKENS P, FILLASTRE JP: Gentamicin-induced nephrotoxicity: A cell biology approach. *Kidney Int* 18:583, 1980.

CHAPTER 67

GLUCOSYLCERAMIDE LIPIDOSES:
Gaucher Disease

JOHN A. BARRANGER
EDWARD I. GINNS

1. *Gaucher disease is the most prevalent lysosomal storage disorder.*

2. *The eponym includes several clinical subtypes of the disease. Type 1 (nonneuronopathic) is the chronic form of Gaucher disease. It may occur at any age and does not involve the nervous system clinically. It is highly variable in both severity and progression. Clinical signs include splenomegaly, pancytopenia, hepatomegaly, and osteolytic and osteopenic degeneration of the skeleton. Type 1 is panethnic but occurs more frequently in individuals of Eastern European Jewish extraction. The disease is usually less severe in this group than in the general population, but more severe among afflicted blacks. Type 2 (acute neuronopathic) Gaucher disease is a rare disorder with no ethnic predilection. It is a clinically stereotypic, rapidly progressive neuroviseral storage disease that results in an early death. Type 3 (subacute neuronopathic) is less rapidly progressive, but is also a neuroviseral storage disorder. Patients develop ataxia, myoclonus, seizures, and dementia. There is a variable degree of hepatosplenomegaly and skeletal involvement. Death occurs in early childhood. The disease is rare and panethnic. A genetic isolate of type 3 cases has been identified in Northern Sweden (Norrbottnian Gaucher disease.)*

3. *All types of Gaucher disease are inherited as autosomal recessive disorders.*

4. *Patients with Gaucher disease are deficient in glucocerebrosidase, a specialized lysosomal acid β-glucosidase.*

5. *Glucosylceramide accumulates primarily in the lysosomes of reticuloendothelial cells.*

6. *The diagnosis of Gaucher disease should be considered in any patient with unexplained splenomegaly. It is strongly suggested by an elevation of serum tartrate noninhibitable acid phosphatase and the presence of characteristic Gaucher cells in the bone marrow. The diagnosis is confirmed by assay of glucocerebrosidase in white cells or fibroblasts. Deficiency of this activity is the hallmark of the disorder. Carrier detection is unreliable, failing in approximately 5 to 20 percent of known heterozygotes. Carriers of the disorder have no clinical signs or symptoms. The 4-methylumbelliferyl-β-D-glucopyranoside substrate provides the most convenient assay of the enzymatic activity.*

7. *Prenatal diagnosis of affected cases is dependable using either amniocytes or chorionic villi.*

8. *Glucocerebrosidase is a membrane-associated, monomeric glycoprotein with a molecular weight of 65,000. The structural protein is composed of 497 amino acids and four "complex-type" oligosaccharide chains N-linked to the polypeptide. The enzyme is synthesized as a nascent polypeptide which is translocated from the ribosomes to the endoplasmic reticulum by a* signal sequence consisting of 19 amino acids. The protein has catalytic activity for the hydrolysis of β-glucosidic ester bonds and is specialized for complex lipid substrates.

9. *Biochemical, immunologic, ultramicroscopic, and molecular genetic studies demonstrate several different mutations in the gene for the enzyme but do not explain the differences in severity encountered.*

10. *The gene for glucocerebrosidase has been cloned and mapped to chromosome 1q21. Point mutations have been described in type 1 and type 2 disease.*

11. *Organ transplantation and enzyme replacement have met with little success as therapeutic modalities. Allogeneic bone marrow transplantation has resulted in partial clinical improvement of visceral symptoms in several cases. Many of the features of the disease are related to storage either in bone marrow or in bone marrow–derived macrophages. Thus, the disease is one which may respond to autologous marrow transplantation with marrow progenitor cells into which the normal gene for glucocerebrosidase has been introduced. The possibility of somatic cell gene therapy is being studied in this disorder.*

INTRODUCTION AND HISTORY

The inherited disorders of glucosylceramide catabolism (Fig. 67-1) are collectively known as *Gaucher disease*. These disorders are related biochemically in that all accumulate the lipid, and all are deficient in lysosomal glucocerebrosidase (also called acid β-glucosidase). The disorders are clinically very different and are divided into subtypes as originally proposed by Knudson and Kaplan.[1,28] Each subtype should not be thought of as a single genotype, but as a grouping of similar phenotypes which may or may not be representatives of different mutations.

The first example of Gaucher disease occurred in a patient with hepatosplenomegaly described in the doctoral thesis of Phillippe C.E. Gaucher.[3] In this work, completed in 1882, the disorder was presented as an epithelioma of the spleen. The characteristic appearance of storage in reticuloendothelial cells was noted as early as 1907.[4] The first step toward the description of the chemistry of the material accumulating in these cells evolved from the identification of its "lipoid" character by morphologists. Later, Epstein demonstrated that spleens from Gaucher patients yielded considerable amounts of an alcohol-soluble substance.[5] In 1924, Lieb characterized this material as a cerebroside of the type of compounds described by Thudichum about 50 years earlier.[6,7] The correct identification

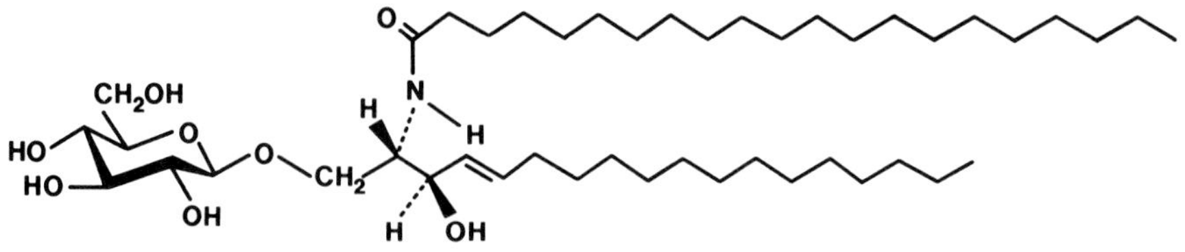

Glucocerebroside
(D-glucosylceramide)

Fig. 67-1 Structure of glucocerebroside.

of the sugar in the sphingolipid compound was not achieved until 1934, when Aghion demonstrated that the lipid accumulating in the tissues of patients with Gaucher disease was a glucosyl, not a galactosyl, derivative of ceramide.[8] This was confirmed by a number of investigators.[28]

The discovery of the lysosome as an organelle in 1955 by DeDuve and coworkers changed the approach to the definition of the metabolic errors in storage disorders. Within a very short time, the first lysosomal storage disorder was described and was shown to be due to a deficiency of α-glucosidase in a patient with Pompe disease.[16] Other storage disorders quickly became recognized as diseases resulting from the lack of a degradative capacity—notably a lysosomal enzyme—with the expected lysosomal accumulation of substrate.[146,147] The accumulation of glucosylceramide was already well known in patients with Gaucher disease. Following the rejection of the hypothesis that the excess tissue lipid was due to overproduction,[17] attention was focused on the possibility that the material accumulated because of a specific deficiency in its degradative pathway. In 1965, two groups independently described the deficiency of glucocerebrosidase in tissues of patients with Gaucher disease.[18,19] It had been recognized that a variety of clinical disorders were related to glucosylceramide storage. Although these subtypes were originally thought to be distinguished by the relative amount of residual enzyme present,[20] this correlation has not been consistent (see Ref. 21 for review). The precise genetic and biochemical reasons for phenotypic differences are being studied and are most likely to be related to different mutations in the gene for glucocerebrosidase.[22–25,327]

CLINICAL ASPECTS

On the basis of clinical signs and symptoms, Gaucher disease has been divided into three subtypes: type 1 (nonneuronopathic), type 2 (acute neuronopathic), and type 3 (subacute neuronopathic).[1] All three types of Gaucher disease are caused by a deficiency of glucocerebrosidase resulting in the accumulation of glucosylceramide within the cells of the reticuloendothelial system.[11,203] The principal difference between the subtypes is the presence and progression of neurologic complications. We have retained the classification proposed earlier[1,28] because it has provided a guide to the clinical understanding of the disease and has directed the study of the biochemical and genetic abnormalities that result in this disorder. Since symptoms in all of the three different types may begin in infancy and because the discrimination of subtypes depends on the evolution of clinical manifestations, especially nervous system involvement, this classification is more appropriate than one which includes reference to age of onset, i.e., "adult," "infantile," and "juvenile" forms of Gaucher disease (Table 67-1). The assignment of type, especially in children,

should be made only after a careful examination for the presence and progression of related neurologic abnormalities.

Type 1: Chronic Nonneuronopathic Gaucher Disease

The age of onset and the severity of symptoms within this subtype vary widely. Although the genetic defect is present from conception, the diagnosis is frequently made later in life. Diagnosis has been made in infants[66,67,205] and in adolescents, but in some instances has not been discovered until as late as the eighth decade.[68] Early diagnoses may be made in sibs of affected patients. In the Ashkenazi Jewish population, the incidence has been estimated to be between 1 in 600 and 1 in 2500.[35,46,206] It is likely that many patients with type 1 disease are not diagnosed because of a lack of significant clinical manifestations. In the authors' experience, the majority of cases in the Ashkenazi Jewish group are not identified until adulthood, and their affected sibs may have only minimal symptoms.

Although exceptions occur, painless splenomegaly with thrombocytopenia, anemia, and leukopenia are the usual initial signs.[28,68,69] In most patients these complications are not life-threatening and may go unrecognized for many years. Patients may have platelet counts below 50,000 without an accompanying bleeding diathesis. Conversely, some patients with Gaucher disease who have a normal prothrombin time, partial thromboplastin time, and platelet count (greater than 100,000) may have abnormal bleeding times, excessive bruising, and unexpected perioperative bleeding. This variability in hematologic features provides little guidance to the practitioner and necessitates an individualized approach which may require the administration of platelets and fresh frozen plasma prior to and after surgical procedures. Although hepatomegaly is often noted at the time splenomegaly is observed, the liver may not become enlarged until later in the course of the disease. Moderate hepatic dysfunction is discerned by elevation of liver enzymes in serum, reduced sulfobromophthalein clearance, or reduced and nonhomogeneous uptake of radionuclide tracers.[71] Hepatic failure is a rare occurrence. Portal hypertension leading to esophageal varices is an infrequent complication, occurring in only a few patients.[72,73,122] Degenerative changes in the skeleton are the leading cause of disability in patients with type 1 disease. Some degree of osteopenia and osteolysis occurs in virtually all patients. However, the extent of bone disease is also extremely variable.[69,74] Some patients have neither radiographic, scintigraphic, nor histologic evidence of bone involvement; others have such severe involvement that they are confined to a wheelchair early in life because of pain, pathologic fracture, or skeletal instability.[127,134] Many patients experience episodic pain lasting for days to months in the hips, legs, back, and shoulders. These episodes have been referred to as "bone crises." Patients may have abnormal diffuse yellow-brown skin pig-

Table 67-1 Subtypes of Gaucher Disease

	Type 1 *Nonneuronopathic Chronic*	*Type 2* *Acute Neuronopathic*	*Type 3* *Subacute Neuronopathic*
Clinical characteristics	1. Heterogeneous presentation 2. Marked differences in age of symptoms (from birth to 80 yrs) 3. Marked differences in rate of progression of signs and symptoms 4. Marked differences in number of organ systems involved and rate of progression in organ systems 5. No neurologic involvement 6. Common signs: Hepatosplenomegaly; osseous lesions: osteopenia, lytic lesions, osteonecrosis, failed remolding 7. Rare signs: Pulmonary infiltration; pulmonary hypertension; cyanosis; clubbing; renal involvement; cirrhosis and liver failure; pericarditis	1. Stereotypic presentation 2. Onset of clinical signs at 3 mo 3. Death before 2 yrs 4. Common signs: hepatosplenomegaly, hypertonic posture, strabismus, trismus, brain stem signs, seizures	1. Heterogeneous presentation 2. Variable age of onset of systemic signs; variable progression 3. Onset of neurologic signs in childhood or adolescence 4. Common signs: hepatosplenomegaly; osseous lesions: osteopenia, lytic lesions, osteonecrosis, failed remolding; slowly progressive dementia; myoclonus; supranuclear ophthalmoplegia
Pathology	1. Gaucher cells and variable degree of fibrosis in all organs 2. Perivascular Gaucher cells in brain 3. Storage in reticuloendothelial cells causing eccentric nucleus and expanded fibrillar cytoplasm	1. Gaucher cells in all organs including both perivascular and parenchyma of brain 2. Areas of mild gliosis, cell death neuronophagia especially occipital cortex	1. Gaucher cells in all organs but without marked changes in brain
Biochemistry	1. Deficiency of glucocerebrosidase 2. Accumulation of glucosylceramide in all organs except brain 3. Cross reactive material (CRM) to normal enzyme present	1. Deficiency of glucocerebrosidase 2. Accumulation of glucosylceramide in all tissues including brain 3. CRM present, but altered	1. Deficiency of glucocerebrosidase 2. Accumulation of glucosylceramide in all tissue including brain, but to a lesser extent than in type 2 3. CRM present, but altered
Genetics	1. Autosomal recessive inheritance 2. Incidence among Ashkenazim 1/600–1/2500 3. Incidence among general population: rare 4. Suspect many allelic mutations different from types 2, 3	1. Autosomal recessive inheritance 2. Incidence: rare 3. No ethnic predilection 4. Suspect allelic mutations different from types 1, 3	1. Autosomal recessive inheritance 2. Incidence: rare 3. Panethnic with large Norrbottnian subgroup 4. Suspect allelic mutations, different from types 1, 2

mentation on their face and legs[76,77,207] as well as delays of growth, menarche, and dentition.[78] Less frequently observed signs are clinical renal involvement,[79–81] pulmonary hypertension,[82,83] and cardiac abnormalities.[80,84] The life expectancy in most individuals with type 1 disease is normal.[28,69]

Type 2: Acute Neuronopathic Gaucher Disease

In contrast to the variability seen within type 1 Gaucher disease, it is evident from the extensive review of type 2 cases by Fredrickson and from our experience with more than 10 cases, that type 2 Gaucher disease is more uniform in its presentation. It has no ethnic predilection.[28] The average age of onset is 3 months. The presenting sign is usually hepatosplenomegaly. By 6 months, neurologic complications develop. Signs indicative of cranial nerve nuclei and extrapyramidal tract involvement appear in nearly all patients. The classic triad of trismus, strabismus, and retroflection of the head appears in the majority of patients, accompanied by progressive spasticity, hyperreflexia, positive Babinski signs, and other pathologic reflexes (Fig. 67-2). Dysphagia and difficulty in handling secretions develop, often followed by aspiration pneumonia.[225] Seizures may occur. As neurologic deterioration proceeds, the child usually becomes apathetic and motionless. Death occurs from either apnea or aspiration pneumonia at an average age of 9 months with a range of 1 month to 2 years. It must be reemphasized that children with type 1 Gaucher disease are often diagnosed before 2 years of age. They may have rapid progression in bone, liver, and spleen manifestations. Some of these cases have been erroneously diagnosed as type 2. It is essential that central nervous system involvement be documented and established as an associated finding prior to making a diagnosis of type 2 disease.

Type 3: Subacute Neuronopathic Gaucher Disease

The clinical features of type 3 Gaucher disease, apart from those referable to the nervous system, are common to the other types of Gaucher disease.[28] Hepatosplenomegaly usually precedes neurologic abnormalities. The variability in systemic organ involvement is similar to that seen in type 1. In the well-documented and biochemically proven cases, of which the Swedish collection is the largest, there is marked variation in age of onset and severity of organ involvement.[224] Neurologic abnormalities include ataxia, spastic paraparesis, grand mal and/or psychomotor seizures, supranuclear ophthalmoplegia, and dementia[85,86,208,221,245] The name given to the Swedish group of cases is *Norrbottnian Gaucher disease*. Non-Swedish cases have been described with progressive neurologic deterioration during childhood presenting with ataxia, spasticity, akinetic and myoclonic seizures, and variable degrees of supranuclear ophthalmoplegia and dementia. The reports of other patients with only supranuclear oculomotor abnormalities and an electroencephalogram showing diffuse, mild background slowing, but without other neurologic deterioration,

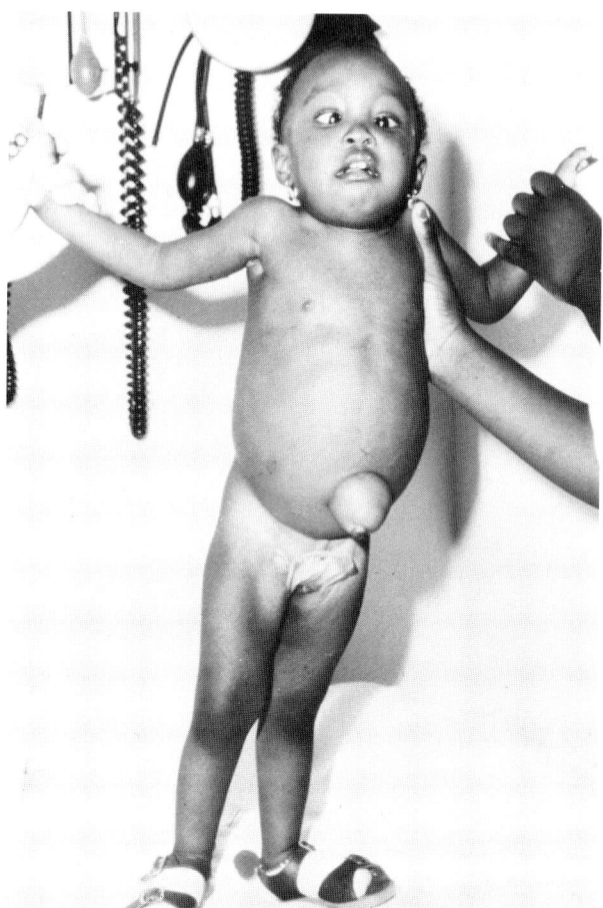

Fig. 67-2 Infant with acute neuronopathic Gaucher disease.
(Courtesy of Dr. Julian Williams, University of Southern California.)

seizures, or myoclonus are further evidence of the clinical diversity seen within type 3 Gaucher disease.[87] The neurodegenerative features occur at an older age than in type 2 disease and are more slowly progressive.[88-90]

The precise genetic and biochemical reasons for the phenotypic differences in Gaucher disease are being studied and are likely to be related to different mutations in the gene for glucocerebrosidase.[11,22-25,45,327]

CLINICOPATHOLOGIC CORRELATIONS

The Gaucher Cell

A consistent feature of Gaucher disease is the presence of lipid-laden reticuloendothelial cells within the tissues of patients. These cells are particularly abundant within the red pulp of the spleen, sinusoids of the liver, the sinusoids and medullary portions of the lymph nodes, alveolar capillaries, and the bone marrow. They are also found in the adventitia and inner walls of arterioles, veins, lymphatic vessels, and capillaries. These cells are derived from histiocytes in spleen, Kupffer cells in the liver, alveolar macrophages in the lung, osteoclasts and macrophages within the bone marrow, and periadventitial cells within the Virchow-Robin space of the brain. Gaucher cells have the same surface markers and ultrastructure as monocyte-histiocyte cell lines,[91,92] and may be seen in the pituitary,[93] pancreas,[94] thyroid,[95] adrenal cortex and medulla,[96] kidneys, and choroid layer of the eyes.

Gaucher cells are 20 to 100 μm in size and have an eccentric nucleus and a "wrinkled tissue paper" or "crumpled silk" appearance of their cytoplasm[97,98] (Fig. 67-3). They may give a weak reaction with the periodic acid–Schiff (PAS) reagent.[99] Most give a strongly positive reaction for acid phosphatase.[100] Rodlike inclusions in the cytoplasm can be seen by Nomarski interference microscopy. It has been suggested that the accumulated glycolipid is aggregated with protein to form tubular structures[101,102] (Fig. 67-4). The appearance of the cell is distinctive enough to permit its use as a diagnostic criterion. It is easily distinguished from the "foam cells" seen in other sphingolipidoses. "Gaucher-like" cells are found in leukemias,[103-105] thalassemia,[106] and in congenital dyserythropoietic anemia.[107] The "pseudo-Gaucher" cells found in multiple myeloma resemble Gaucher cells by light microscopy, but have a completely different ultrastructure.[108]

Spleen

Painless splenomegaly is usually the earliest sign in all types of Gaucher disease. Even when the spleen is not palpable by physical examination, it usually can be demonstrated to be enlarged by ultrasonography or radionuclide scans.[109,126] The rate of enlargement of the spleen is helpful in judging the rate of progression of the disease. Therefore, careful measurement by radionuclide scan or some other rigorous method should be performed. The rate of splenic enlargement is consistent for each case and does not vary significantly. Changes in that rate have been associated with malignancy or other intercurrent disease. Spontaneous rupture of the spleen is uncommon. The majority of cases will develop hypersplenism manifested by pancytopenia and a bleeding diathesis. Red cell and platelet survival time is shortened. Splenectomy should be limited to those patients having severe bleeding diathesis, high output cardiac failure, or mechanical interference of bowel, diaphragm, or kidney, or to children with severe failure to thrive. Splenic tissue has been extensively studied. Fibrosis with distortion of the splenic architecture is commonly observed. The spleen is enlarged, firm, and contains pale areas caused by infarcts.[110,111] The process of infarction can lead to abdominal pain and should be considered in the differential diagnosis of an acute abdomen in patients with Gaucher disease. The red pulp of the spleen is replaced by white collections of Gaucher cells. The surface and body of the spleen may contain dark-purple nodules that are foci of extramedullary hemato-

Fig. 67-3 Gaucher cell: typical storage cell obtained from bone marrow aspirate.

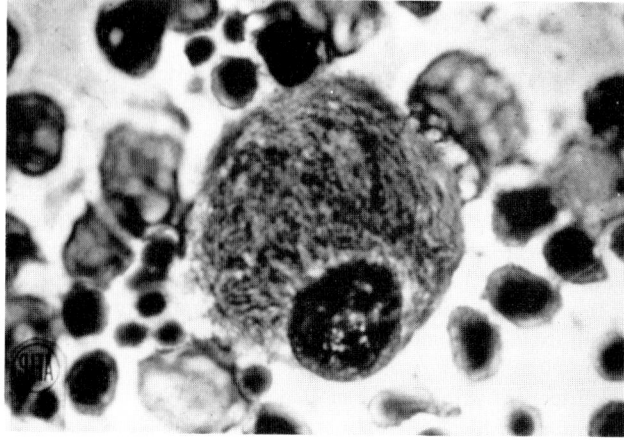

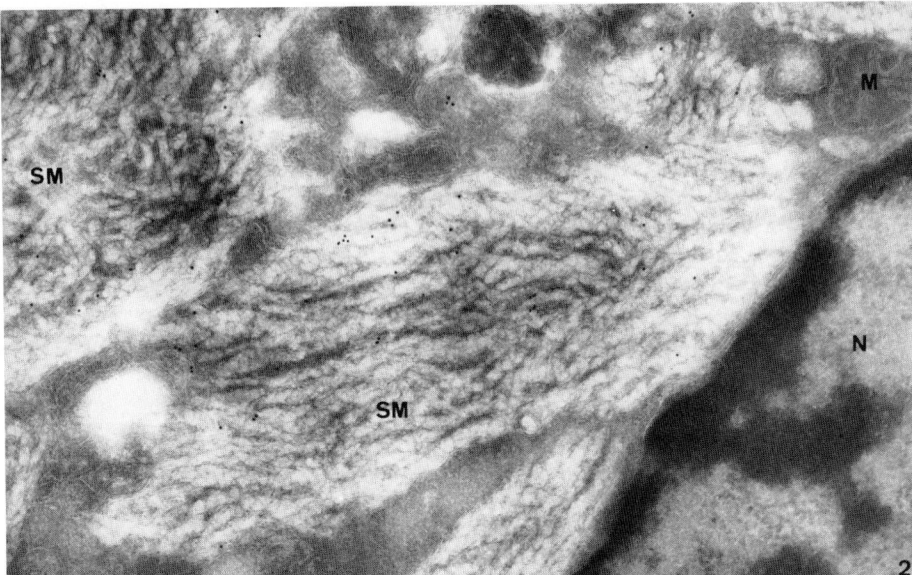

Fig. 67-4 Ultrastructure of a histiocyte from the spleen of a Gaucher patient. Tubular structures of the storage material (SM) are plainly visible in lysosomes adjacent to the nucleus (N) and mitochondria (M). ×46,000. (Courtesy of Drs. R. Willemsen and A. Reuser, Erasmus University, Rotterdam.)

poeiesis.[111] Splenectomy is almost always followed by correction of cardiac and hematologic abnormalities, but several instances of persistent anemia have been reported. These cases may be steroid-responsive. Although not characteristic of Gaucher disease, increased intravascular coagulation and hemolytic anemia have been noted and have been corrected by splenectomy.[112,113] It has often been argued that the spleen serves as a reservoir for glucosylceramide and that its removal results in deterioration in other organs.[2,69,110,128,210–213,218] Little quantitative clinical data exists to support this opinion. Lee has reviewed several hundred cases from a registry of Gaucher patients. He concluded that splenectomy had no effect on the progression of the disease.[111] Others have reached a similar conclusion based on clinical and biochemical findings.[12,119,214–216] In the Norbottnian subgroup, clinical and biochemical data suggest that splenectomy results in increased plasma and tissue lipid accumulation and a more rapid clinical course.[10,12,15,186] This difference in opinion cannot be settled at this time. The answer lies in studies which clearly document the rate of progression of the disease before and after splenectomy. Until data of this kind are available, the best

approach is a conservative one. Because of the immune and other functions of the spleen, splenectomy should not be performed until necessitated by appropriate clinical criteria.[222,223] The efficacy of partial splenectomy is currently being evaluated.[114–117]

Lymphatic System

In children with Gaucher disease, lymph nodes may be enlarged and contain Gaucher cells. The thymus, Peyer patches in the intestine,[118] and the pharyngeal tonsils[119] are frequently affected.

Liver

Despite the frequent occurrence of hepatomegaly in Gaucher disease, hepatic failure is only rarely observed.[72,121,122] Gaucher cells are seen within the sinusoids (Fig. 67-5). In the more severely affected cases, fibrosis distorts the architecture, forming small regenerating nodules that are infiltrated by

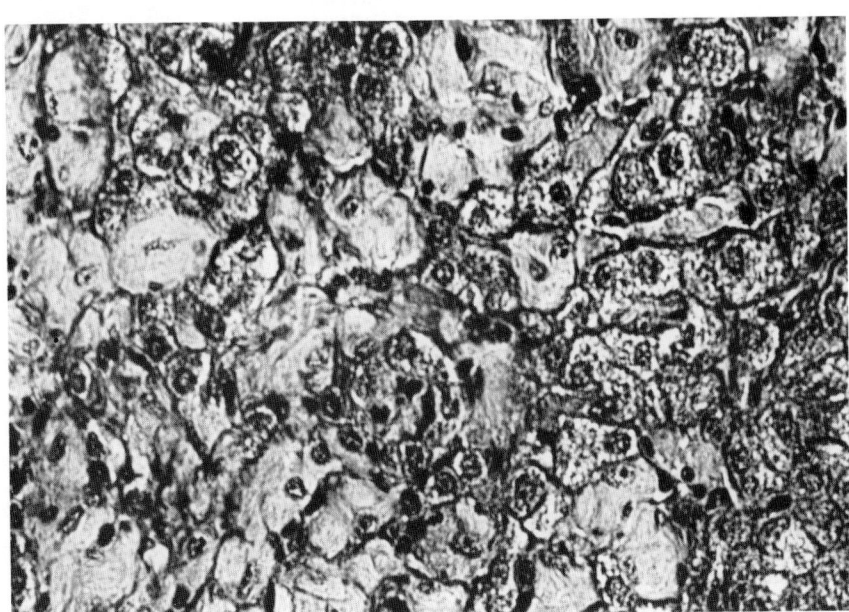

Fig. 67-5 Storage in Kupffer cells in liver sinusoids. ×228.

Fig. 67-6 Micronodular cirrhosis in an advanced case of Gaucher disease involving the liver. ×52.

Gaucher cells.[123,124] These cases have been described as cirrhotic (Fig. 67-6). In contrast to other lipidoses (such as Neimann-Pick disease), hepatocytes are not involved in storage. The enlarged liver may contain sites of extramedullary hematopoiesis. The majority of patients have abnormal liver function tests,[122] but the elevation of alkaline phosphatase is probably due to the bone involvement. Marked portal hypertension and consequent complications such as ascites and esophageal varices do occur, but are not common.[217] Radionuclide scans show a shift in tracer from liver to spleen in the majority of cases, indicating a degree of portal hypertension. Recurrent bleeding from esophageal varices has been successfully treated with a combination of aggressive medical management and sclerotherapy.[120] Jaundice is a serious sign in this disease and represents either intercurrent infectious or chronic-active hepatitis[198] or preterminal hepatic failure. In the authors' experience, only four cases out of several hundred have died of hepatic failure. In cases where liver involvement is profound, early intervention with either liver transplantation or bone marrow transplantation may be indicated.

Bone

In type 1 and 3 Gaucher patients, roentgenographic abnormalities of bone are frequent, occurring in 50 to 75 percent of all patients, but the severity and onset of symptoms are extremely variable.[69,127,128] Joint pain and "arthritic" bone pain are common. These pains are caused by deterioration of the skeleton in the periarticular regions of bone and are relieved by analgesics. Particularly useful are nonsteroidal anti-inflammatory agents. The expansion of the cortex in the distal femur (Erlenmeyer flask deformity) (Fig. 67-7)[129,130] along with fractures and other abnormalities of the acetabulum and head and neck of the femur is frequent[131-134] (Fig. 67-8). Prosthetic hip replacement has been invaluable in permitting patients to remain ambulatory.[133,134] The hip lesions in some cases may be confused with Legg-Calvé-Perthes disease. Destruction of vertebral bodies may produce collapse and gibbus formation and spinal cord or nerve dysfunction.[135] Computerized tomography, radionuclide scan, and magnetic resonance imaging[136-138] have been useful in assessing the extent of bone abnormalities. The hypothesis that bone crises are the result of progressive compromise produced directly by occlusion of vessels by Gaucher cells is not supported by scintigraphic or histologic studies. In fact, perfusion scans of bones are often en-

hanced.[127,134] Vascular occlusion by Gaucher cells would not explain the combination of osteopenia, osteonecrosis, and osteosclerosis seen in the disorder. Moreover, other vascular complications such as premature stroke, myocardial infarction, or renal failure are not features of the disease, making a simple vascular occlusive process a less attractive explanation of the skeletal involvement. Metabolic and endocrinologic studies suggest an imbalance in calcium homeostasis.[127,134] However, the entire skeleton is not affected uniformly. On the contrary, the lesions consist of collections of Gaucher cells scattered throughout the bone substance. Bone complications probably result from a toxic process around these foci, which then leads secondarily to edema, vascular compromise, and infarction. From existing information, it is not likely that infarction is incited by vascular occlusion by Gaucher cells but rather by the vascular compromise alluded to above. The infarction of the bone produces the "bone crises." This process affects the femoral heads and distal femur more frequently than other bones. These ep-

Fig. 67-7 Erlenmeyer flask deformity of the distal femur.

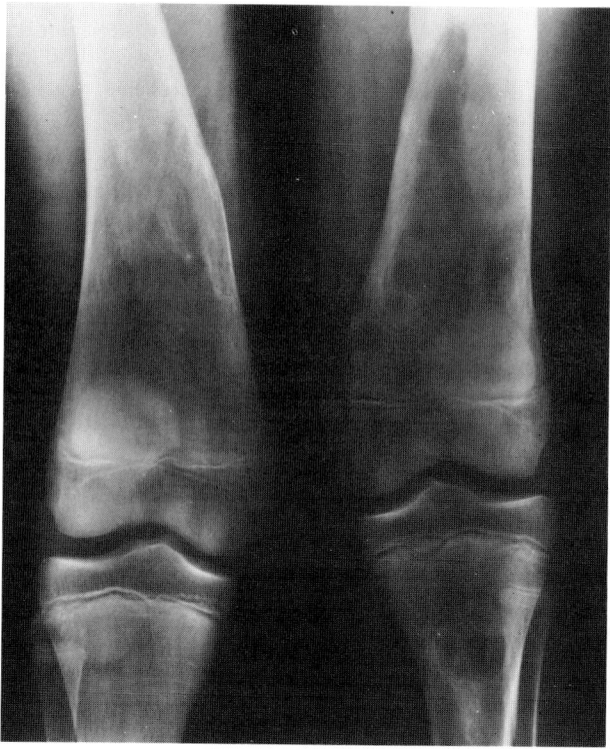

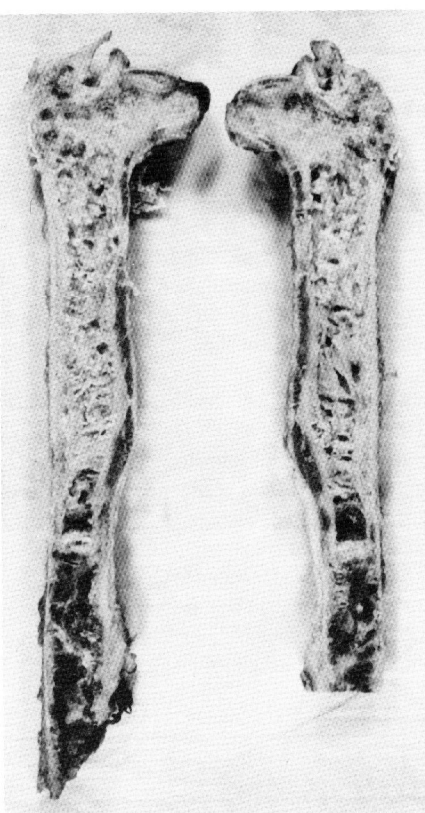

Fig. 67-8 Femoral head collapse and marked bone involvement.

isodes are usually self-contained and last approximately 2 weeks, but may be extended to months. During the first days of the crisis, analgesia is difficult to accomplish and may require hospitalization. Bed rest is always indicated until the episode is completely resolved. The infarction process sometimes resolves completely, but typically a region of osteosclerosis and/or bone deformity or fracture develops. There is a possibility that the infarcted region will become secondarily infected, producing a true osteomyelitis. However, this is the exception, and the episode should be treated conservatively unless infection is highly suspected. Instrumentation of the infarcted bone may lead to secondary infection and development of a sinus tract.[214] It should be avoided unless clearly indicated. X-rays and technetium scans are usually not helpful in distinguishing infarction from osteomyelitis, but gallium scans may assist in this sometimes difficult decision.[125] As a general measure, one should ensure that adequate calcium intake is maintained. Some patients have decreased calcium absorption from the gut.[134] Thus, if urinary calcium is low, the diet should be fortified with calcium and vitamin D. In addition, the storage of glucosylceramide in tissue macrophages may alter the generation of competent osteoclasts and result in a failure to maintain a healthy bone matrix.[127,134] Further research is needed to delineate the pathogenesis of this disorder before any effective therapy for bone complications can be developed.

Cardiopulmonary System

Most patients with type 1 disease do not have clinically symptomatic involvement of the heart or lungs. Although Gaucher cells are present in alveoli and the surrounding pulmonary arterioles, clinical complications of the respiratory system are

infrequent.[140,141] A small number of patients with type 1 and type 3 disease have severe chronic pulmonary disease without cardiac lesions. They have hypoxia, cyanosis, and clubbing[83] secondary to shunting within the lung. This complication occurs only in patients with extensive liver disease and is probably the effect of some humoral factor on the capillary bed. In α_1-antitrypsin deficiency, pulmonary complications are reversed following liver transplantation. In the only known patient with Gaucher disease who underwent liver transplantation, a similar marked improvement in oxygenation occurred immediately after surgery.[201] In those patients with kyphoscoliosis secondary to vertebral collapse, restrictive pulmonary compromise occurs. This complication is frequent in the Norrbottnian subgroup. Several cases of restrictive pericarditis have been reported. Rarely, interstitial infiltration of the myocardium resulting in decreased left verticular compliance and decreased cardiac output has been observed.[80] Asystole and sudden death have been seen in a case of non-Swedish type 3 disease.[143]

Renal

Gaucher cells can be found in the cortex, medulla, or glomeruli, but renal function in Gaucher patients is usually normal.[79–81] In a few cases, proteinuria or hematuria has been reported.[79–81] The cause of these signs is uncertain but has been attributed to the infiltration of Gaucher cells.

Gastrointestinal

Focal collections of Gaucher cells are found within Peyer patches and the lamina propria of the gastrointestinal tract.[118] Patients may complain of bloating, cramps, and diarrhea. Abnormal uptake of calcium may be one of several factors affecting bone in the disorder.[134]

Endocrine

Growth retardation and delay in skeletal maturation can be observed in children. Growth hormone deficiency and hypothyroidism have been recorded in patients with Gaucher disease, but are rare complications. Conversion of vitamin D to its active metabolites is abnormal in those patients with severe liver abnormalities. Urine calcium level is low in type 1 cases with moderate to severe bone degeneration, and osteopenia occurs without an increase in serum parathyroid hormone.[134] These secondary abnormalities in calcium homeostasis may contribute to the skeletal manifestations of the disease.

Skin

A diffuse yellow-brown pigmentation can be seen over the face or lower legs in some children and adults with Gaucher disease.[76,77,207] Although Gaucher cells are not found in the skin, increased iron pigment and melanin have been described.

Eyes

The cherry-red spot that appears in the macula in some sphingolipidoses and mucolipidoses does not occur in Gaucher disease. However, white patches containing Gaucher cells have been seen in the choroid and retina of some patients.[148,149,226] Pingueculae are fatty deposits in the conjunctiva which occur frequently in the general population. It is not certain that they occur more frequently in patients with Gaucher disease. They are not collections of Gaucher cells.[209]

Immune System

A deficiency of T lymphocytes in the spleen and peripheral blood and a decreased response to skin tests have been reported in Gaucher patients.[91] In addition, antibody responses to specific antigens are delayed. Despite these observations, the majority of Gaucher patients do not have frequent infectious complications, nor do they demonstrate clinical immune disorders. Monoclonal and polyclonal gammopathies have also been reported.[151-155] Amyloidosis,[156,157] multiple myeloma,[158-160] leukemia,[161,162] Hodgkin's disease,[163-165] cerebral astrocytoma,[166] and bronchogenic carcinoma[167] have been reported in association with Gaucher disease. These associations may be due to compromise of the immune surveillance systems secondary to macrophage dysfunction.[168]

Plasma

Levels of acid phosphatase,[169,170] angiotensin-converting enzyme,[171,172] lysosomal hydrolases,[173-175] lysozyme,[172,176] and immunoglobulins are elevated in the plasma of Gaucher patients. Patients may have prolonged partial thromboplastin, prothrombin, and bleeding times[177] because of liver involvement. In addition, it has been suggested that increased amounts of plasma glucosylceramide may interfere with the clotting cascade.[178] Glucosylceramide is elevated in the plasma and may be as high as tenfold normal. Although the level of plasma glucosylceramide has been shown to increase following splenectomy in some Norrbottnian cases,[10,12] this has not been reported in cases of other subtypes of the disease.

Nervous System

An understanding of the involvement of the brain in Gaucher disease has increased in the last several years, but is far from complete because of the limited number of postmortem cases available for study. Type 1 Gaucher disease patients do not have clinical symptoms or signs referable to the nervous system. In this group anatomic and biochemical examinations of the brain have been infrequent. Consequently, little is certain about the pathology of the brain in type 1 Gaucher disease. The earlier reports of hypophyseal[93] and leptomeningeal[94] Gaucher cells in type 1 require confirmation. Glucosylceramide is not elevated in the brains of patients with this type of Gaucher disease except in the periadventitial spaces around blood vessels.[186]

In types 1, 2, and 3 Gaucher disease, perivascular Gaucher cells have been observed within the Virchow-Robin spaces.[181] In type 2 patients' brains, free Gaucher cells have been demonstrated within the parenchyma accompanied by gliosis and microglial nodules.[12,15,182,183] These changes are present but much less frequent in type 3 patients' brains. Although increased levels of glucosylceramide have been reported in brains of both type 2 and type 3 patients,[12,15] significant neu-

ropathologic abnormalities have been observed only in the brains of type 2 patients.[184] Neuronal storage of lipid has been suggested in several reports,[15,183,189] but this has not been confirmed ultrastructurally in any case of Gaucher disease. In type 2 disease, neuronophagia and neuronal cell death in the deeper layers of the cortex, thalamus, basal ganglia, brainstem nuclei, cerebellum, and spinal cord have been reported.[12,15,225] Variable degrees of demyelination have been described in brains of type 2 patients.[143,185] From the available information, one would have to conclude that the accumulation of glucosylceramide in brain produces dysfunction in surrounding cells long before discrete pathologic changes are seen.[184] Even then, the lesions described are small and focal and not of the profound nature seen in other neurovisceral storage disorders.[225] These facts have prompted the hypothesis that there must be some toxic effect on the brain. Glucosylsphingosine has been implicated in this role, but remains to be confirmed as the toxic agent in neuronopathic Gaucher disease.[10,12,186] Recently, Hannun and Bell have shown that lysosphingolipids, including glucosylsphingosine, inhibit protein kinase C and result in nerve cell dysfunction and death.[227] They postulate that these compounds may be the agents responsible for the pathogenesis of neuronal dysfunction in the sphingolipidoses.

PATHOPHYSIOLOGY AND PATHOGENESIS

Plasma and Tissue Glucosylceramide

All patients with Gaucher disease accumulate glucosylceramide in their tissues. The lipid collects in the lysosomes of reticuloendothelial cells. Glucosylceramide is very insoluble in water and is carried in the circulation exclusively in lipoproteins.[259,323] Levels in plasma are usually elevated two- to tenfold. Among storage disorders, the accumulation of the lipid only in reticuloendothelial cells is unusual. How the lipid comes to reside in this particular cell is not known with certainty. Whether it derives from autophagy of its own membranes, endocytosis of other membranes, or uptake of circulating glucosylceramide has not been established. A single, unconfirmed study suggests that the amount of glucosylceramide derived from white blood cell membranes is quite high.[13] If this is correct, then only a small percent of the total glucosylceramide becomes stored. Knowing how the majority of the lipid is disposed of would be important to therapeutic strategies. If at least some of the accumulated brain glucosylceramide is derived from sources outside the nervous system,[12,15] then steps might be taken to decrease the amount of circulating lipid.

The level of glucosylceramide accumulated in liver and spleen is between ten- and a thousandfold that found in normal tissue. The median hepatic concentration in a series of patients was 20 mg per gram of tissue. There was no apparent correlation between liver concentration in liver biopsies and severity of disease, probably because of the nonuniform pattern of glucocerebroside storage. Only in cases in which the architecture of the organ is well-preserved can random needle biopsy of the liver give representative data.[187,228] Frequently, significant fibrosis occurs and the accumulation is inhomogeneous, making these measurements less reliable. In fact, in severe cases, almost entire lobes of liver or entire segments are fibrosed and laden with lipid-engorged macrophages.

Although few quantitative measurements of the lytic lesions in bone have been made, the same sort of inhomogeneous accumulation of Gaucher cells is seen by radionuclide scan, nuclear magnetic imgaing, and xenon scan.[134,137] Similarly, the clinical complications of osteonecrosis, osteosclerosis, osteopenia, and pathologic fracture are focal and multifocal in nature, occurring sometimes within an otherwise normal skeleton. Similar focal accumulations have been described in brain as discussed elsewhere in this chapter.

Pathogenetic Speculation

It is apparent that the accumulation of the lipid and the collection of Gaucher cells is a multifocal process in every tissue and that changes occur in tissues around collections of storage cells. This suggests a toxic process. The source of the toxin could be the storage cell itself or could result from the failure of lipid-laden macrophages to detoxify a circulating toxin. Studies have shown that the uptake of glucosylceramide by cultured macrophages causes the liberation of lysosomal enzymes, interleukins, fibroblast-stimulating factors, and other macrophage-derived factors.[168] It is possible that these agents play a role in the injury and death of neighboring cells as well as in stimulation of fibroblasts. This process may be complicated by the inability of storage cells to carry out normal functions. Such a problem is seen in animal models during macrophage blockade. In this situation, hepatocytes sustain damage because Kupffer cells cannot phagocytose and degrade potentially toxic material.[188] These processes could be operating in any tissue and probably contribute to the variety and variability of the signs, symptoms, and laboratory abnormalities seen in the disease.

Clinical Genetics

All types of Gaucher disease are inherited as an autosomal recessive trait. The collective subtypes of Gaucher disease constitute the most prevalent form of sphingolipidosis or lysosomal storage disorder. Most of the cases are type 1, or the chronic form. Although panethnic, this subtype is much more common among Ashkenazi Jews. In this group, it occurs with an incidence that has been estimated to be between 1 in 600 and 1 in 2500, making it the most prevalent Jewish genetic disorder.[35,46,206] The other subtypes are infrequent and have no ethnic predilection. These subtypes are so rare that no collective incidence figure is available, but it would possibly be less than 1 in 50,000.

Although it is more frequent among Eastern European Jews, type 1 Gaucher disease is usually less severe in this group. It is more severe among blacks. This generalization is helpful in counseling, but there are exceptions. It is therefore important to know the types of complications of the disease that have occurred in a family. In general, the severity of the disorder tends to be similar among sibs. A single exceptional family has been reported in which one type 1 and one type 2 case occurred in full sibs.[190] Testing and genetic counseling of immediate family members of affected patients are recommended. The differences in clinical subtypes and variability of some forms of the disease should be pointed out. Because of the high carrier frequency among the Ashkenazim, wide-scale carrier testing has been recommended. Since the disease among this group is not uniformly catastrophic (in fact, many cases do not come to medical attention until late in life), this kind of testing, if desired, should be done within a system providing careful counseling which can provide adequate information about the disorder and an explanation of the limitations of carrier detection.

DIAGNOSIS

Detection of Homozygotes

The diagnosis of Gaucher disease should be considered in any case of unexplained splenomegaly with or without a bleeding diathesis or other manifestations of the disease in the skeleton or liver. The disorder should be considered likely in any infant with hepatosplenomegaly and a neurodegenerative course. Elevation of tartrate noninhibitable acid phosphatase in serum is very suggestive of the disease. Demonstration of characteristic Gaucher cells in bone marrow biopsies narrows the diagnostic possibilities. The definitive diagnosis is made by assay of glucocerebrosidase in leukocytes,[29,30,235–238] fibroblasts,[29,230–234] or urine.[191] Glucocerebrosidase activity in leukocytes of patients and obligate heterozygotes is shown in Table 67-2. A variety of natural and artificial substrates provide accurate assays for homozygotes, but all have the same limitations when used for heterozygote detection (see Ref. 29 for review). The best substrate employed for the assay is the 4-methylumbelliferyl-β-D-glucopyranoside.[192] Modifications and improvements in the original description of the assay involving the addition of taurocholate have made it very useful as a diagnostic tool[21,29,193] and equivalent to assays employing the natural substrate.[238] The assay is easy to use and the substrate is widely available, making it the method of choice for a diagnostic laboratory. Conduritol B-epoxide is a specific inhibitor of mammalian glucocerebrosidase and permits confirmation of the enzyme deficiency in systems where nonspecific β-glucosidase may be interfering.[194,195] Leukocytes and fibroblasts may be prepared and shipped to laboratories for assay as whole cells or extracts. Because of the very different clinical courses of patients with Gaucher disease, researchers have tried to develop a laboratory test which would discriminate subtype. Enzymatic assay and kinetic measurements have not been useful for this purpose

Table 67-2 Glucocerebrosidase Activity in Leukocytes (by Reference)

	236	237	235	11
Control, n	42	65	38	242
Mean ± SD	18.3 ± 2.2	4.9 ± 1.2	8.8 ± 1.8	13.5 ± 3.7
Range	15.0–22.5	2.8–8.2	5.1–12.3	4.0–20.2
Type 1, n	26	8	4	92
Mean ± SD	2.5 ± 0.7	1.2 ± 0.3	1.5 ± 0.6	4.2 ± 2.3
Range	1.8–4.1	1.0–1.9	0.5–2.0	0.0–9.0
Type 2, n	—	—	—	9
Mean ± SD	—	—	—	3.3 ± 3.0
Range	—	—	—	0.4–7.3
Type 3, n	—	—	—	11
Mean ± SD	—	—	—	2.7 ± 0.9
Range	—	—	—	1.8–4.0
Obligate heterozygotes, n	32*	12†	18*	57‡
Mean ± SD	10.0 ± 2.2	3.0 ± 0.5	5.0 ± 0.9	9.4 ± 4.6
Range	6.0–14.5	2.4–3.8	2.3–6.5	2.9–24.6

*Subtype not specified.
†Ashkenazi Jewish type 1.
‡Type 1 carriers, all ethnic groups.

(see Ref. 21 for review).[33,34] Western blotting using a monoclonal antibody and polyclonal antiserums prepared against the homogeneous placental glucocerebrosidase was initially encouraging as a method to distinguish the neurologically affected cases from their counterparts.[36] In these studies and others,[40] the neurologically affected type 2 and type 3 variants had a different pattern of cross-reacting material (CRM) than type 1 cases and controls. Using a monoclonal antibody, Ginns et al.[37] reported that in five unrelated cases of type 2, no CRM was detected on Western blots. In a recent report, similar differences in CRM were observed between subtypes.[38] However, several cases of type 1 from South African kindreds gave patterns indistinguishable from those of type 2 cases. These results show that study of CRM alone is insufficient to distinguish all subtypes. Thus, no laboratory analysis to date differentiates all subtypes of Gaucher disease. Molecular genetic methods may provide some solutions to this difficult diagnostic problem.

Carrier Detection

From the time of the introduction of the assay of glucocerebrosidase, it has been observed that there is some overlap in the values of heterozygotes with those of control subjects for the activity of glucocerebrosidase in leukocytes and leukocyte subpopulations. This subject has been reviewed extensively.[21,29] A variety of chromogenic, fluorometric, and radiochemical methods have been developed, but all have the same problem in the detection of heterozygotes.[29] In studies of known heterozygotes, approximately 5 to 20 percent of the carriers fall into the normal range[29] (Table 67-2). Fibroblasts have a higher specific activity of glucocerebrosidase than do leukocytes. However, a wide range of activity in control cells, which varies with time in culture and conditions, makes it unlikely that these cells will be any more useful in heterozygote detection.[231–234,239–241] It is possible that current studies of the gene for glucocerebrosidase and its mutations may lead to more definitive carrier detection.[25,196,327]

Prenatal Diagnosis

Affected fetuses with any form of Gaucher disease can be diagnosed prenatally by enzymatic assay of cultured amniocytes. This is particularly important in families in whom the neuronopathic subtypes have occurred. Recent studies of chorionic villi reveal that this tissue contains adequate amounts of enzyme that does not vary extensively with age of the fetus.[197] Therefore, it is possible to use this material for prenatal diagnosis in fetuses at risk. Two cases of type 2 disease have been diagnosed prenatally by the authors at 8 to 10 weeks gestation and confirmed in fetal tissue. Because of the difficulty of the assay for carriers and the lack of appropriate control data, prenatal carrier detection is unreliable. Application of molecular genetic methods will most likely improve the potential for prenatal diagnosis.

BIOCHEMISTRY AND MOLECULAR BIOLOGY

Chemistry of Glucosylceramide

Glucosylceramide is a compound of ceramide and glucose (Fig. 67-1). The glucose moiety is esterified to the C-1 of ceramide in a β-glucosidic linkage. The compound is similar in structure and properties to the group of sugar-containing lipids isolated from brain by Thudichum.[7] These *cerebrosides* are composed of ceramide esterified to a variety of different substituents at C-1. This carbon may participate in reactions with (1) phosphorylcholine to produce the sphingomyelins, (2) an unsubstituted monosaccharide or oligosaccharide to produce the neutral glycosphingolipids, or (3) an oligosaccharide containing one to four molecules of sialic acid to produce the gangliosides (Fig. 67-9). The common unit among these compounds is ceramide. Ceramide is derived from a long-chain base named *sphingosine* (D(+)-erythro-1,3-dihydroxy-2-amino-4-transoctadecene, or C_{18} sphingosine). This lipid is joined by

Fig. 67-9 Structure of the sphingolipids.

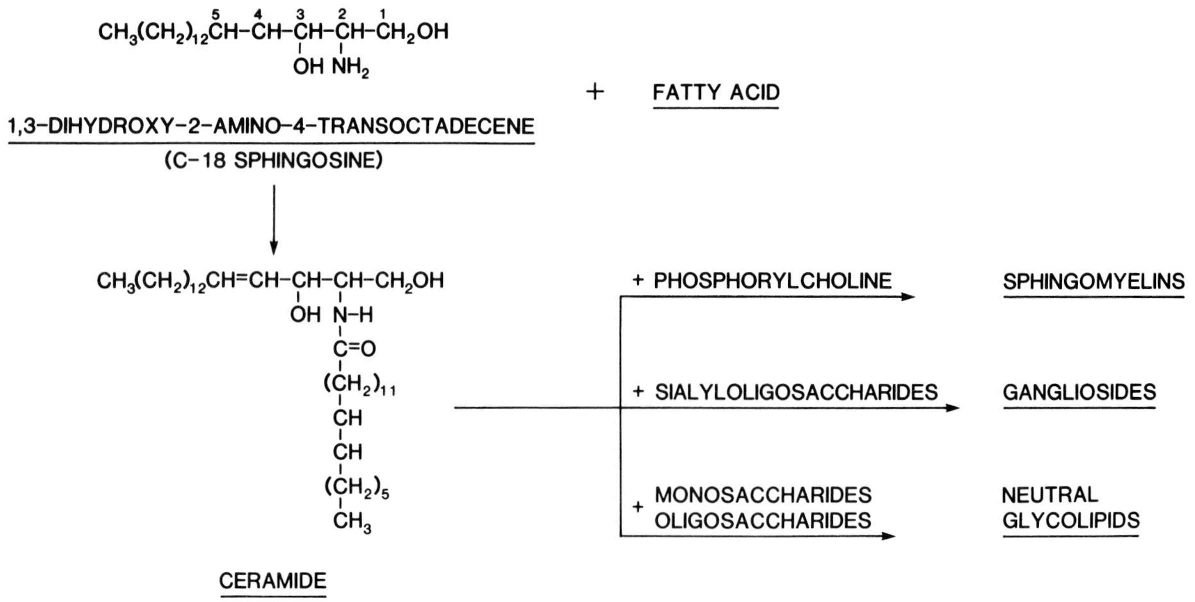

an amide bond at C-2 to a long-chain fatty acid to form ceramide (Fig. 67-9). The fatty acid chain length varies. In general, the neutral glycosphingolipids and sphingomyelins contain C_{20} to C_{24} fatty acids, whereas the gangliosides contain C_{18} fatty acids.[242] It is from sphingosine that the group of disorders of lipid catabolism obtains its name (i.e., *sphingolipidoses*) because the accumulating lipid compounds are derived from it.

Glucosylceramide is at the end of the glycosphingolipid catabolic pathway. The higher glycosphingolipids and gangliosides are degraded in a stepwise fashion by specific acid hydrolases, resulting in the formation of glucosylceramide, which is normally degraded to ceramide and glucose by glucocerebrosidase.[18,19] The compounds that contribute to the pool of glucosylceramide in peripheral organs are globoside, globotriose, and lactosylceramide. These are derived from the degradation of membranes, the major source of which is white blood cells.[13]

It is important to note that the glucosylceramide found in spleen, liver, kidney, plasma, and red cells contains fatty acids with chain length of approximately C_{22} to C_{24}.[28] The glucosylceramide in the brains of patients with type 2 disease is composed primarily of C_{18} (stearic acid).[14,186] This conclusion has been confirmed and extended to type 3 cases.[10,15] These data have been interpreted to mean that the glucosylceramide accumulating in brain derives from gangliosides within the brain itself. This is consistent with the known fatty acid content of gangliosides. However, the suggestion has been made that some of the glucosylceramide in certain type 3 cases may be derived from sources outside the central nervous system.[15] If the data are confirmed, it should have important consequences, especially since it has been suggested that levels of plasma and tissue glucosylceramide increase following splenectomy in Norrbottnian cases.[10,82]

A high performance liquid chromatography (HPLC) method developed by Ullman and McCluer permits precise quantification of glucosylceramide in the picomole range.[202,243,244] This is the best available method and is useful in measuring the small differences in the concentration of the lipid.[9,62,184]

Biochemistry of Glucocerebrosidase

Isolation and Purification of the Enzyme. Following the description of the deficiency of glucocerebrosidase (D-glucosyl-N-acylsphingosine glucohydrolase, E.C.3.2.1.45) in Gaucher disease,[18,19] the activity was partially purified from human placenta.[246] These preparations were subject to aggregation and yielded only small amounts of enzyme, but these problems were overcome by the use of butanol and cholate extraction, which efficiently removed the activity from membranes.[247] Subsequent hydrophobic chromatography steps resulted in highly purified enzyme in yields of approximately 30 percent. This material could be purified to homogeneity without loss of yield using a preparative HPLC gel-filtration procedure.[248] The product has a single amino terminus and is a monomeric glycoprotein approximately 65,000 daltons in size. This has been confirmed in several laboratories and by radiation inactivation[276] (Table 67-3). Other preparations employing substrate affinity analogues give a similarly pure product, but with less yield.[249–251,283] Recently, an immunoaffinity method

Table 67-3 Mammalian β-Glucosidase

	Neutral β-Glucosidase		*Glucocerebrosidase*
Localization	Cytosol*†	Membrane†	Membrane-bound
Substrate specificity	Glucosides	Glucosides	Glucocerebroside
	Galactosides	Galactosides	Glucosides
	Fucosides	Fucosides	
pH optimum	7.0	7.0	4.5–6.0
Effect of taurocholate	Inhibition	Inhibition	Stimulation
Effect of conduritol B-epoxide	None	None	Marked inhibition
Heat stability	Labile	Stable	Labile
pI	4.6–5.0	4.5–5.0	4.0–6.0
Molecular weight	54,000		65,000
Cross-reactivity to purified placental glucocerebrosidase	None‡		Positive
Deficient in Gaucher disease	No	?	Yes

*Daniels et al.[60]
†Maret et al.[53]
‡Unpublished data of Drs. Glew and Barranger.

has been published which allows rapid purification in high yield of placental glucocerebrosidase in two steps without the use of organic solvent extraction. The product of the purification does not differ in its properties from the material purified by the methods cited above.[252]

Stimulators and Inhibitors of the Enzyme. It has long been recognized that bile salts and negatively charged detergents stimulate the activity of glucocerebrosidase in vitro.[21,29,31,193,257,277,281,282] This has been useful in diagnostic procedures as a means of stimulating glucocerebrosidase activity and inhibiting other interfering β-glucosidases, thus improving the sensitivity and specificity of the test for enzyme activity. Taurocholate has been particularly suitable for this purpose.[193,238] Phosphatidylserine also stimulates the activity, as do a number of other negatively charged compounds.[279,284] These effects were thought by several groups to have value in diagnosing subtypes.[284,285] This has led to controversy regarding the utility of this approach. More recent data suggest that only the glucocerebrosidase of Ashkenazi Jewish type 1 cases shows a significant response to activators and stimulators.[286] The activity of the enzyme from these patients was stimulated, while there was no effect on the enzyme from controls and other subtypes. Also noted in this study were an increase in K_i for sphingosine, N-hexylglycosphingosine, and glycosphingosine. Again, this was noted only for the Ashkenazi Jewish type 1 cases, as was a fivefold increase in the half-life of inactivation of the enzyme by conduritol B-epoxide.[286] None of these effects was seen in controls and other subtypes. These potentially important and unique observations have not yet been confirmed in other laboratories. Some of the differences in the results with detergents remain unresolved[279,284–286] and merit further study.

There are different classes of inhibitors of glucocerebrosidase. 1,5-D-gluconolactone is a competitive inhibitor. Conduritol B-epoxide is a specific, irreversible, noncompetitive inhibitor of the enzyme.[194,195,287] It was first identified as an inhibitor of plant glucosidases.[298,299] Alkyl-β-glucosides are mixed inhibitors that bind to a site different from that of the activating phospholipids.[288] Sphingosine, glucosylsphingosine, and their N-hexyl derivative are potent reversible inhibitors and are thought to bind to the activating phospholipid site.[288,289] In addition, castanospermine[290] and 1-deoxynojirimycin[291] have been reported to be reversible inhibitors, while methyl-*p*-nitrophenyltriazene-β-glucoside is an irreversible "suicide substrate" inhibitor.[292] Differences in opinion exist with respect to the effects of negatively charged phospholipids and glucosylsphingosine and the apparent K_m of glucocerebrosidase for artificial substrate. One group has reported that neither compound has an effect on K_m,[288] while others have reported that anionic phospholipids decrease the apparent K_m[31] and glucosylsphingosine increases the apparent K_m for artificial substrate.[277] Resolution of these differences requires further experimentation.

Based on the kinetic analysis of activators and inhibitors of glucocerebrosidase discussed above, three domains of the active site have been proposed.[288] The model has the following elements: (1) A catalytic site: a hydrophobic region that recognizes β-glucosyl moieties and conduritol B-epoxide (CBE); (2) an aglycone site: a hydrophobic site that binds alkyl or acyl substrate and some inhibitors; and (3) a hydrophobic domain or "allosteric" site that binds activating phospholipids and sphingosine analogue inhibitors. In addition, an activator protein binding site has been proposed.[258] Recent studies by Sarmientos et al. confirm that an aglycone binding site is important to the catalytic activity.[294] Additional support for this model has been generated using inhibitors and substitutions in the fatty acid chain of glucosylceramide.[326] Radiolabeled CBE has been used to tentatively assign the active site near the carboxy terminus of glucocerebrosidase.[296] Unfortunately, the amino acid to which CBE binds could not be identified by amino acid sequence analyses.

A protein factor that stimulates glucocerebrosidase is present in spleen and other tissues. The protein, or "factor P," was initially identified by Ho and O'Brien.[255] This heat-stable protein has been called *coglucosidase*[258,261] or *sphingolipid activity protein 2* (SAP-2).[260] In vitro it stimulates the activity of glucocerebrosidase several-fold and can substitute for negatively charged phospholipids as stimulators.[32,258,262–264] In tissue and cell extracts, the activator protein is bound to some of the glucocerebrosidase activity, changing the properties of that fraction of activity. The bound activity has an apparent molecular weight of 200,000, does not bind to concanavalin A Sepharose, and is not stimulated by phospholipids or taurocholate in reaction.[266] This is in agreement with earlier studies on the activator protein.[32,278–280] The physiological role of the activator protein is not completely known. It has been speculated that it serves to transfer activating lipids such a phosphatidylserine to glucocerebrosidase, resulting in increased catalytic activity of the enzyme. One patient with Gaucher disease with normal glucocerebrosidase activity has been shown to be deficient in the activator protein.[325]

Biosynthesis of Glucocerebrosidase. Glucocerebrosidase, like all other lysosomal enzymes studied so far, is a glycoprotein. Oligosaccharides have been prepared from homogeneous placental enzyme[75] (Fig. 67-10). The majority of these oligosaccharide chains are "complex-type," containing sialic acid, galactose, *N*-acetylglucosamine, mannose, and fucose. Approximately 20 percent of the oligosaccharides are high mannose chains of five to seven residues each.[75] These results, the presence of multiple activities of glucocerebrosidase separated by isoelectric focusing,[51,53,256,257] and the detection of several cross-reacting species by Western blots of cell and tissue extracts[36] suggested that the enzyme is extensively posttransla-

Trisialylated Oligosaccharide

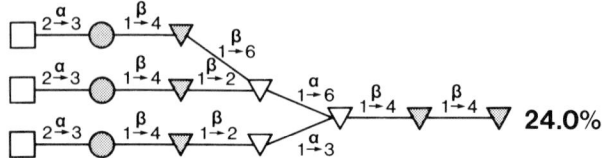

24.0%

Disialylated Oligosaccharides

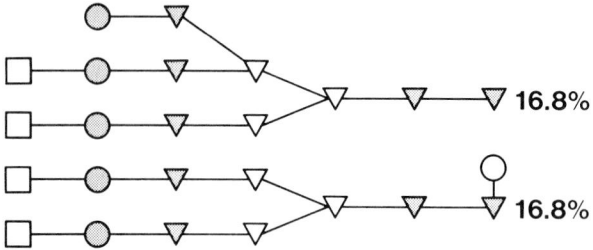

16.8%

16.8%

Monosialylated Oligosaccharides 21.1%

High Mannose Oligosaccharides

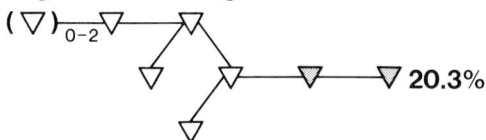

20.3%

Fig. 67-10 Structure of the oligosaccharides of glucocerebrosidase. □ = sialic acid; ● = galactose; ▼ = *N*-acetylglucosamine; ▽ = mannose; ○ = fucose.

tionally processed. Using an affinity-purified polyclonal antiserum which identified the same cross-reacting species as a monoclonal antibody,[253] Erickson et al. demonstrated by pulse-labeling studies in porcine cells that glucocerebrosidase is synthesized as a single polypeptide with a "signal sequence" at the amino terminus.[39] This polypeptide is acted upon by signal peptidase cotranslationally removing a 2-kDa signal sequence. The polypeptide is also core glycosylated cotranslationally. The addition of oligosaccharide is typical for the biosynthesis of complex-type glycoproteins:[219,229] the earliest species detected contained "high mannose" oligosaccharides sensitivie to endoglycosidase H. Later forms in the pulse-chase scheme acquire resistance to digestion by endoglycosidase H, but are sensitive to endoglycosidase H, indicating that these later species contain "complex-type" oligosaccharide chains (Fig. 67-11). These results are qualitatively in agreement with the oligosaccharide chemical analyses.

In the studies of Erickson et al.,[39] there was no indication of posttranslational proteolytic cleavage. Furthermore, glucocerebrosidase had no cytoplasmic domain in microsomes as demonstrated by the results of pronase digestion.[39] Similar steps in the processing of glucocerebrosidase in human cells have been demonstrated in two collaborating laboratories.[40,42] The multiple species of glucocerebrosidase activity and cross-reacting material undoubtedly are the result of posttranslational processing of the enzyme. A summary of these findings is presented in Fig. 67-12. A recent report from another group confirms the presence of three cross-reactants with molecular weights similar to those reported in earlier studies.[38] This work employed antibodies against placental glucocerebrosidase

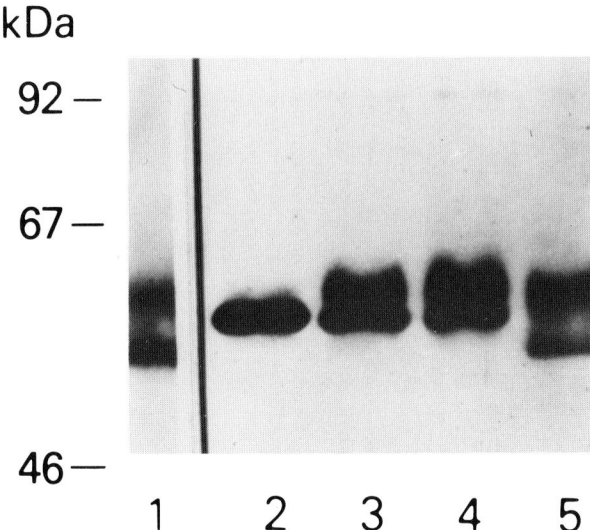

Fig. 67-11 Pulse-chase labeling of glucocerebrosidase. Glucocerebrosidase was labeled in human fibroblasts with a 30-minute pulse of ^{32}S-methionine (lane 2). Cells were chased with unlabeled methionine for 2 h (lane 3), 12 h (lane 4), and 24 h (lane 5). The figure is an SDS-polyacrylamide gel electrophoresis of glucocerebrosidase precipitated from the cell extract by monospecific rabbit antiserum prepared against homogeneous enzyme protein. Molecular weight markers are shown on the left margin. Lane 1 is a Western blot of a fibroblast extract to show correlation of cross-reactive material with biosynthetic intermediates of glucocerebrosidase. The studies demonstrate that the multiple cross-reactants are biosynthetic intermediates.

prepared independently.[38] Although one study reported fewer cross-reactants,[41] four different laboratories[36,38,40,44] have now reported the presence of three cross-reacting species of glucocerebrosidase in normal human fibroblasts. The relationship of these forms is summarized in Table 67-4.

In Jewish patients with type 1 Gaucher disease, the biosynthetic steps are apparently normal,[40] as are the number of cross-reacting species.[36,38] However, the mutant protein is somewhat unstable, since one sees less of it in pulse-labeling studies.[40] In the type 2 and type 3 cells studied, the lowest molecular weight (M_r) species is virtually absent in immunologic studies. In biosynthetic studies of these neurologically affected cases, very little low M_r species is seen unless very long labeling is done in the presence of protease inhibitors. Then, a small amount of the lower M_r material can be seen.[40] These data indicate that the mutant proteins in the type 2 and 3 cases studied are very unstable and lead to less cross-reactive material, a conclusion confirmed by other approaches.[38,43] This concept is further supported by studies of the cross-reacting material present in cells examined by immunohistochemistry.[44] Although these conclusions cannot be generalized to all cases of type 1, 2, and 3, these differences are consistent in the cases studied in the reports cited. Other mutations may result in differences in mutant proteins which have different immunoreactive species and different labeling characteristics.[38] It can be concluded from these studies that there are different mutant glucocerebrosidases, some of which can be discriminated by biochemical means. The limitation of these approaches in diagnosis is discussed elsewhere in this chapter.

During its posttranslational maturation, glucocerebrosidase does not become phosphorylated in its oligosaccharide moieties like most other lysosomal enzymes.[39,254,304–309] Since most lysosomal enzymes are routed to the lysosome via a mannose-6-phosphate (M-6-P) ligand as a recognition marker, glucocer-

ebrosidase represents a class of molecules which reach the lysosome by some other route. This is consistent with its normal concentration in cells from patients with mucolipidosis II in which the phosphotransferase necessary for constructing the M-6-P ligand is absent.[26] Approaches to the purification of glucocerebrosidase suggest that it is a membrane-associated, hydrophobic protein, although not an integral membrane protein. Interference with the formation of complex-type oligosaccharides by swainsonine results in decreased lysosomal content of glucocerebrosidase.[70] The nature of the oligosaccharide chain may be important to protein folding, membrane binding, and consequentially to lysosomal content of the enzyme, though this is speculative at present.[75,267–275]

A combination of chemical sequence and amino acid sequence deduced from the sequence of cDNA clones has revealed the entire sequence of the structural protein.[22,23] The details of these approaches will be presented in the following sections. The protein is rich in hydrophobic amino acids, although no very long hydrophobic sequences are apparent. Thus, no putative membrane-spanning region can be readily identified. A few short hydrophobic regions are candidates as membrane anchors, but assignment of this characteristic should be delayed until a three-dimensional structure is available from x-ray diffraction or other studies. It is known that seven cysteine residues participate in three disulfide bridges, but the exact position of these bridges has not yet been defined.[293] Six of these residues occur within the first half of the 497-amino-acid structural protein. Four cysteine residues are present in the first 23 amino acids and have been confirmed by direct amino acid sequence of protein.[55] Experience with a synthetic 30-amino-acid peptide from the amino terminus strongly suggests that these residues contribute to the potential for aggregation of glucocerebrosidase. Computer searches have not revealed any similarities to other proteins, including other β-glucosidases.[295] This applies as well to the domains surrounding the oligosaccharide attachment sites. There are no sequence similarities to the few lysosomal glycoproteins whose primary structures are known.

Molecular Biology of Glucocerebrosidase

Isolation and Characterization of a cDNA for Glucocerebrosidase. In order to more completely understand the nature of the defects responsible for the heterogeneity in Gaucher disease, isolation and characterization of the gene for glucocerebrosidase was undertaken by several groups. Complementary cDNA clones encoding both the signal sequence and mature glucocerebrosidase have been isolated from human hepatoma[22,24] and fibroblast libraries.[23] The abundance of glucocerebrosidase cDNA clones in the human hepatoma library was estimated to be 0.004 percent. This may be a low estimate particular to this library since mRNA studies suggest a higher abundance.[52,204] The identities of cDNAs were confirmed by comparing the amino acid sequence derived from the nucleotide sequence of cloned cDNA[22–24] to the amino acid sequence of human placental glucocerebrosidase obtained independently by chemical methods.[22,24] In addition to the 5′ and 3′ untranslated regions, the cDNA contains 1548 base pairs encoding human glucocerebrosidase.[24] The M_r of 58,000 calculated from the 516 amino acids deduced from cDNA sequence is in good agreement with that estimated by SDS-polyacrylamide of the product of in vitro translation of human placental mRNA.[39,47] Five potential glycosylation sites (Asp-X-Ser/Thr)

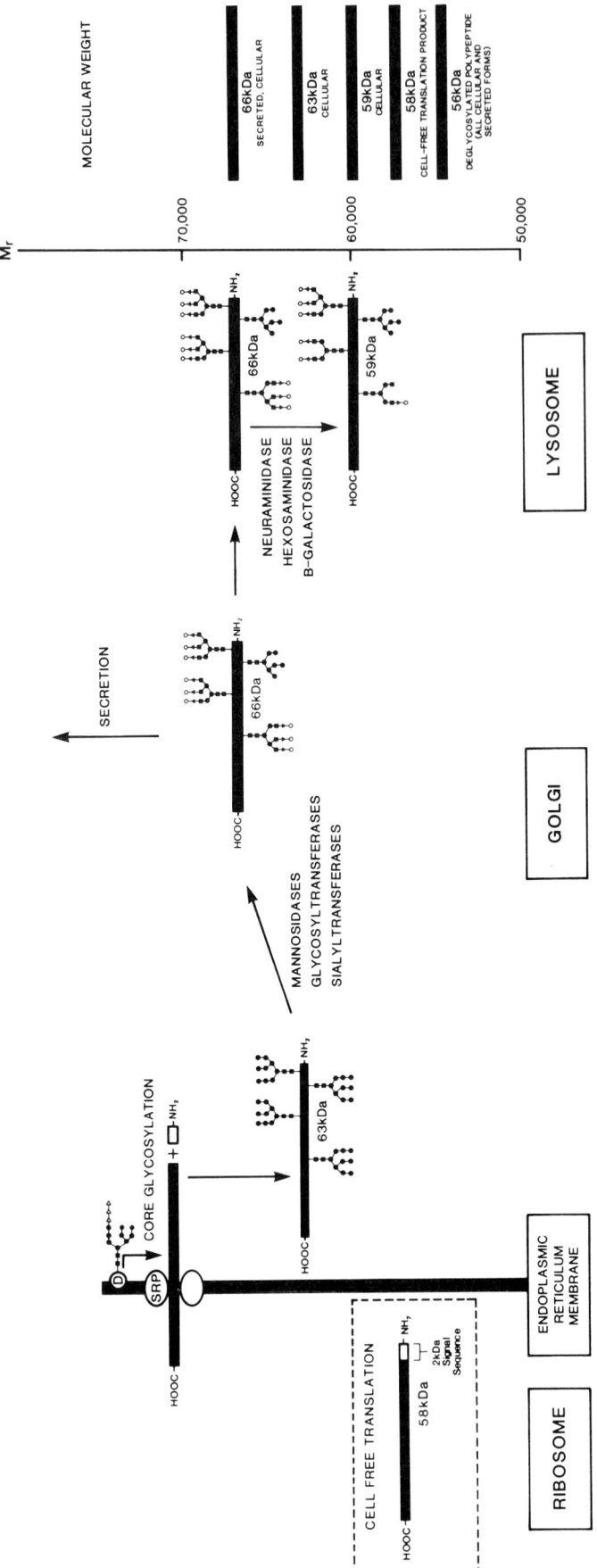

Fig. 67-12 Schematic representation of the details of the biosynthesis of glucocerebrosidase. Glucocerebrosidase is synthesized by mechanisms similar to other translocated glycoproteins.[310–322] In a cell free translation system (as indicated by the box on the lower left), a polypeptide of 58 kDa is synthesized on ribosomes. This polypeptide contains a signal sequence which facilitates its translocation to the lumen of the endoplasmic reticulum (ER). The translocation is mediated by the interaction of the signal sequence with a signal recognition particle (SRP) permitting the polypeptide to slide through the ER membrane as it is peeling off the ribosome while its translation is ongoing. As the first part of the polypeptide chain enters the ER, but before its translation is complete, two events occur. The signal sequence is cleaved from the polypeptide, and the growing chain is core glycosylated. Glycosylation occurs by the en bloc transfer of a 14-member oligosaccharide unit from a lipid in the ER membrane called dolichol (D). The "high mannose" precursor of 63 kDa is posttranslationally processed in the ER and Golgi apparatus without further proteolytic cleavage to form a 66-kDa intermediate which is also secreted in small amounts. This intermediate contains "complex-type" oligosaccharide chains (see Fig. 67-10) and is further processed in the lysosome to the mature form with a molecular weight of 59 kDa. The right side of the figure shows the molecular weight of the various forms.

Table 67-4 Apparent Molecular Weight of Different Species of Glucocerebrosidase*

Species of glucocerebrosidase	M_r, kDa	Localization
1. Cell-free translation product formed in the absence of microsomes	58	Ribosomes
2. High mannose precursor	62–63	Endoplasmic reticulum
3. Intermediate containing highly sialylated complex-type oligosaccharide chains	66	Golgi, lysosomes, secreted into media
4. Mature form containing both complete complex-type chains and incompletely sialylated and glycosylated chains	59	Lysosomes
5. N-glycanase™ and endoglycosidase F–treated intermediate and mature forms: all species resolve to a single molecular weight species	56	

*The M_r of the different species depends on the electrophoretic conditions and commercially available standards used. The values given in the table were obtained using standard 10% polyacrylamide gels. ¹⁴C-methylated molecular weight standards were obtained from New England Nuclear (Boston, Mass.). Nearly identical molecular weights were obtained by Fabbro et al.[38] for the cellular and deglycosylated forms. Somewhat lower molecular weights were obtained by Erickson et al.[39] using different conditions, gradient gels, and markers. However, it should be noted that the number and relationship of different species of glucocerebrosidase in normal cells has been consistent in most reports.[36-40,44]

were identified. Quantitative carbohydrate analysis indicates that only four are glycosylated.[75] This has been confirmed by direct analysis of the amino acid sequence.[55] In addition to the amino acid sequence of the structural protein, the reading frame of the cDNA codes for 19 additional amino acids upstream of the amino terminus.[23,24] This signal polypeptide contains a hydrophobic core consisting of Gly-Leu-Leu-Leu-Leu and in addition has glycine at the peptidase cleavage site. These features are consistent with the properties of signal peptides of other translocated proteins. Furthermore, the cDNA sequence confirms the presence of a 2-kDa signal sequence identified by pulse-labeling studies.[39]

Organization of the Gene for Glucocerebrosidase. The structural gene for glucocerebrosidase was assigned to chromosome region 1q21-1q31, using Chinese hamster–human cell hybrids.[48] A more precise localization to 1q21 was obtained using the cDNA for glucocerebrosidase as an *in situ* molecular hybridization probe to high resolution chromosome preparations from normal human lymphocyte cultures.[49] This locus is directly adjacent to bands 1q11-1q12, the 1qh region, rich in banding heteromorphisms. The cDNA for human glucocerebrosidase was used as a probe to isolate genomic clones from a control subject,[50] a type 2 patient,[25] and a type 1 patient.[327] The normal glucocerebrosidase gene has at least 11 exons and 10 introns contained within approximately 7 kb. At approximately 150 base pairs upstream to exon 1, there are two segments containing sequences that are putative promoter sequences. When examined for promoter activity, a subclone containing these regions was found to be active. In exon 11, there is a nonconsensus polyadenylation signal within 30 bases of the polyadenylation site that is located approximately 470 base pairs downstream of the translational termination site.

At locus 1q21, there is another region that is highly homologous to glucocerebrosidase cDNA but which lacks parts of several exons and splice junctions. These sequence deletions,

as well as data from Southern blot analyses of total genomic DNA from control subjects and Gaucher patients, suggest that this latter region is a pseudogene.[25,50]

Northern blot analysis revealed the presence of three poly(A)⁺ mRNAs of approximately 5600, 2500, and 2000 nucleotides.[52] The longer RNA is probably an unspliced nuclear RNA precursor. S-1 nuclease analysis indicated that the 2500 and 2000 RNA differed at both 5′ and 3′ ends. This has been interpreted to mean that an alternative 5′ splice site and 3′-polyadenylation signal may be used in the gene.[52]

Mutations in the Glucocerebrosidase Gene. Northern blot analyses and quantitation of glucocerebrosidase mRNA from normal subjects and type 1, 2, and 3 Gaucher patients have not provided definition of the mutations that are responsible for the different phenotypes of Gaucher disease.[52,204] However, sequencing of genomic DNA has provided information on the putative mutation in type 1 and type 2 disease.[25,327] The comparison of the nucleotide sequences of all exons, splice junctions, and the 5′-flanking region of a type 2 Gaucher (acute neuronopathic) glucocerebrosidase gene with those of a normal gene revealed a single base substitution (T → C) in exon 10.[25] This mutation, which generates a new *Nci*I restriction site (CCTGG → CCCGG), results in the substitution of proline for leucine at residue 444. This amino acid change is predicted to destroy the α-helical structure of the protein in this region. In vitro mutagenesis of the normal gene followed by transient expression of the mutagenized DNA confirms that the mutation results in loss of glucocerebrosidase activity. Southern blot analysis of restriction fragments resulting from digestion with *Nci*I revealed that the type 2 case studied is homoallelic for the mutation. None of the 29 control cell lines carried the mutation. Cell lines from 4 of 20 type 1 cases were heteroallelic for the mutation. Fifteen of sixteen cell lines from patients with neuronopathic disease had at least one mutated allele. Of the five type 2 cell lines tested, two were homoallelic and two were heteroallelic for the mutation. One cell line did not carry this mutation. The other 11 were type 3 cell lines, all of which were reported to carry the mutated gene. Seven of these were homoallelic for it. These data indicate several problems. First, it is likely that different mutations result in the same phenotype. This is to be expected in rare diseases in unrelated families. This fact will limit the facile application of molecular genetic methods to the diagnosis of the rarer phenotypes of the disease. Second, dissimilar phenotypes may have the same genotype. This suggests that other influences, as parts of the genetic background of the individual, may influence the clinical phenotype. If these data are correct, molecular genetic approaches to the diagnosis of subtypes of Gaucher disease will not be straightforward.[324] The results of these studies require confirmation.

Nucleotide sequence analysis of the genomic clone from an Ashkenazi Jewish patient with type 1 Gaucher disease revealed an A to G transition in exon 9 of the glucocerebrosidase gene resulting in the substitution of serine for asparagine at position 370.[327] Computer modeling predicted that from amino acid 366 to 377 the normal protein would have a β-pleated-sheet structure with an interruption as asparagine 370. In contrast, the entire region from amino acid 366 to 377 in the type 1 mutant protein is predicted to be a β-pleated sheet. Allele-specific hybridization using an oligonucleotide probe could demonstrate this mutation only in patients with the type 1 phenotype. None of the six type 2 nor the 11 type 3 patients nor the 12 normal controls had this allele. In contrast, 15 of

24 type 1 patients had one allele with this mutation, and three others were homozygous for the mutation. Thus, three genotypes were found in type 1 patients.[327] These genotypes were (1) 370 Ser/370 Ser, (2) 370 Ser/444 Pro, and (3) 370 Ser/X, where X is another mutation that has not yet been identified. Furthermore, one type 1 patient in this study had one allele with the 370 Asn-to-Ser and one with the 444 Leu-to-Pro mutation. This suggests that the presence of mutant glucocerebrosidase coded by the allele having the 370 Asn-to-Ser mutation does not lead to the development of central nervous system complications.

EXPERIMENTAL THERAPY

Organ Transplantation

In certain lysosomal disorders, organ transplantation may be palliative in end-stage disease limited to a single organ. Thus, it is reasonable to consider renal transplantation in Fabry patient with renal failure or liver transplantation in the Gaucher patient with hepatic failure. The hypothesis that organ transplantation might be an approach to systemic therapy of Gaucher disease has not been confirmed. Splenic and renal transplantation have had little or no effect on the disease process in patients with Gaucher disease.[139,144] Even in Fabry disease where α-galactosidase A is a soluble enzyme found in plasma, renal transplantation has not been of any value as a systemic therapy for the enzyme deficiency, nor has it had any effect on the course of the storage disease.[180] The hope that the transplanted organ would act either as an enzyme source for other organs or as substrate sink has not been realized. On the other hand, bone marrow transplantation has been of some value in the treatment of certain clinical aspects of storage disorders.[179] Organomegaly has been reversed in some of these disorders. However, improvement in the central nervous system has been a less certain consequence of bone marrow transplantation.[59] In some disorders, e.g., Krabbe disease, the blood-brain barrier may be altered by the disease itself, thus permitting the entry of marrow-derived progenitors into the brain.[220,303] Whether this will result in clinical utility remains to be demonstrated. Bone marrow transplantation has been reported in seven patients with Gaucher disease.[62,63,265] Rapid resolution of the enzyme deficiency in circulating white cells was achieved, indicating successful engraftment. In the first case, biochemical and morphologic parameters slowly improved.[62] However, there was little change in other clinical parameters. In the second case, organomegaly and general health improved significantly, suggesting a positive clinical response.[63] Subsequent cases have all shown regression of organomegaly.[265] In cases that warrant the risk, allogeneic bone marrow transplantation may be a useful therapy for the subtypes without significant neurologic involvement.

Enzyme Replacement

Early studies of enzyme replacement produced great hope and excitement that Gaucher disease might be amenable to therapy by infusions of enzyme.[145] The initial encouraging biochemical and clinical reports have not been confirmed. Even though amounts of enzyme in subsequent trials were increased significantly, no changes could be measured in response to enzyme.

It was considered that these trials failed to target the enzyme to the proper cell in sufficient quantity. A method was devised to improve that aspect of the problem.[150] Using enzymatic degradation of the oligosaccharide side chains of glucocerebrosidase to expose mannose residues, the enzyme molecule was tailored to bind to the naturally occurring mannose receptors on macrophage plasma membranes. In animal model studies, this engineered glucocerebrosidase was delivered to Kupffer cells in quantities tenfold greater than the unmodified native enzyme.[142] Preliminary results in clinical trials of this specially prepared glucocerebrosidase have been disappointing. These developments suggest that the pharmacology of glucocerebrosidase as a "protein drug" is complicated and that multiple variables still need clarification before enzyme replacement is a practical therapy. Recently developed cell culture models of Gaucher disease may be useful in this regard.[199,200] In these studies, murine peritoneal macrophages were loaded with glucosylceramide and their glucocerebrosidase was irreversibly inhibited with conduritol B-epoxide. During the period when no murine activity was present, the efficiency of these cells to endocytose exogenous enzyme and degrade stored glucosylceramide was examined. This model may provide information for designing studies of enzyme replacement in naturally occurring genetic equivalents such as the Gaucher dog[300] or a transgenic mouse model, should the latter become available. These approaches may provide the information needed to consider the value of this therapeutic approach.

Somatic Cell Gene Transfer

The availability of cDNA and genomic DNA for human glucocerebrosidase permits one to consider using gene transfer not only to study the regulation of the gene and the cell biologic consequences of mutation but also to contemplate the potential application of somatic cell gene therapy to patients with Gaucher disease.

Retroviral vectors have been investigated as efficient vehicles for the insertion of a foreign gene into host cell lines and organisms.[56–58,64,65] Retrovirus-mediated gene transfer provides a strategy for potential therapy of selected inherited disorders.[27,59,61,179] This approach has been examined with the glucocerebrosidase gene by several laboratories.[219] The cDNA encoding glucocerebrosidase from the Okayama-Berg shuttle vector, pCD-GC, was inserted into a site downstream from a chicken B-actin promoter in the retroviral vector pWE.[297,328] Mammalian cells tranfected with this chimeric retroviral vector expressed active glucocerebrosidase several-fold above background.[54,301] Type 2 Gaucher cells infected with the retrovirus carrying the human cDNA were corrected to normal levels of glucocerebrosidase activity (Table 67-5).[328] Similar results have been obtained by Sorge et al.[302] Other groups have had similar results with other enzymes and proteins in cell culture, but have found that expression in whole animals was not what was expected from tissue culture studies.[61] Thus, there are still obstacles to achieving long-term expression of glucocerebrosidase (or other gene products) in mouse models of gene transfer into hematopoietic progenitors. However, in principle, Gaucher disease is an excellent candidate for somatic cell gene therapy, if that approach can be developed and perfected. It is a bone marrow disorder that has responded to allogeneic bone marrow transplantation. Moreover, most cases would not require that genetically reconstituted cells enter the

Table 67-5 Expression of Normal Human Glucocerebrosidase in Type 2 Gaucher Fibroblasts Following Retroviral-Mediated Gene Transfer*

	Glucocerebrosidase, nmol/h·mg	α-Galactosidase, nmol/h·mg
Type 2 fibroblasts	7.4	126
Type 2 fibroblasts +$_p$WE vector	6.8	154
Type 2 fibroblasts +$_p$WE.GC	499	137
Normal fibroblasts	355	142

*4-methylumbelliferyl substrate used for assay. The contribution of cytosolic β-glucosidase to the observed activity of glucocerebrosidase is negligible under the conditions of the assay.[21,29] Activity in these cells has been stable for more than 24 months.

central nervous system, thus avoiding the serious limitation of use of this procedure in other lysosomal storage disorders. Although a variety of obstacles to somatic cell gene therapy remain to be overcome[61] and it may require several years of experimentation to evaluate its potential as a therapeutic modality for inherited disorders, Gaucher disease may be the first lysosomal storage disease to be treated in this way.

REFERENCES

1. KNUDSON AG, KAPLAN WD: Genetics of the sphingolipidoses, in Aronson SM, Volk BW (eds): *Cerebral Sphingolipidoses*. New York, Academic, 1962, p 395.
2. HERRLIN KM, HILLBORG PO: Neurological signs in a juvenile form of Gaucher's disease. *Acta Paediatr Scand* 51:137, 1962.
3. GAUCHER P: De l'epithelioma primitif de la rate. Paris, Thèse, 1882.
4. MARCHAND F: Uber soq. idiopathische splenomegalie-typus Gaucher. *Muench Med Wochenschr* 54:1102, 1907.
5. EPSTEIN E: Beitrag zur chemie der Gaucherschen krankheit. *Hoppe-Seyler's Z Physiol Chem* 271:211, 1924.
6. LIEB H: Der zucker im cerebrosid der milz bei der Gaucher krankheit. *Hoppe-Seyler's Z Physiol Chem* 271:211, 1924.
7. THUDICHUM JLW: Die chemische konstitution des gehirns des Menschen und der tiere. Tübingen, Franz Pietzcker, 1901.
8. AGHION A: La maladie de Gaucher dans l'enfance. Paris, Thèse. 1934.
9. ULLMAN MD, PYERITZ RE, MOSER HW, WENGER DA, KOLODNY EH: Application of high performance liquid chromatography to the study of sphingolipidoses. *Clin Chem* 26:1499, 1984.
10. NILSSON O: Glycolipid changes in Gaucher disease. Goteborg, Thesis. 1982.
11. BARRANGER JA, MURRAY GJ, GINNS EI: In Barranger JA, Brady RO (eds): *Genetic Heterogeneity of Gaucher's Disease in Molecular Basis of Lysosomal Storage Disorders*. New York, Academic, 1984, p 311.
12. NILSSON O, SVENNERHOLM L: Accumulation of glucosylceramide and glucosylsphingosine (psychosine) in cerebrum and cerebellum in infantile and juvenile Gaucher disease. *J Neurochem* 39:709, 1982.
13. KATTLOVE HE, WILLIAMS JC, GAYNOR E, SPIVACK M, BRADLEY RM, BRADY RO: Gaucher cells in chronic myelocytic leukemia: An acquired abnormality. *Blood* 33:379, 1969.
14. SVENNERHOLM L: The metabolism of gangliosides in cerebral lipidoses, in Aronson SM, Volk BW (eds): *Inborn Disorders of Sphingolipid Metabolism*. New York, Pergamon, 1967, p 169.
15. CONRADI NG, SOURANDER P, NILSSON O, SVENNERHOLM L, ERIKSON A: Neuropathy of the Norrbottnian type of Gaucher disease. *Acta Neuropathol (Berl)* 65:99, 1984.
16. HERS HG: α-Glucosidase deficiency in generalized glycogen storage disease (Pompe's disease). *Biochem J* 86:1, 1963.
17. TRAMS EG, BRADY RO: Cerebroside synthesis in Gaucher's disease. *J Clin Invest* 39:1546, 1960.
18. PATRICK AD: A deficiency of glucocerebrosidase in Gaucher's disease. *Biochem J* 97:17C, 1965.
19. BRADY RO, KANFER JN, SHAPIRO D: Metabolism of glucocerebrosides. II. Evidence of enzymatic deficiency in Gaucher's disease. *Biochem Biophys Res Commun* 18:221, 1965.
20. SNYDER RA, BRADY RO: The use of white cells as a source of diagnostic material for lipid storage disease. *Clin Chim Acta* 25:331, 1969.
21. WENGER DA, OLSON GC: Heterogeneity in Gaucher's disease, in Callahan JW, Lowden JA (eds): *Lysosomes and Lysosomal Storage Disorders*. New York, Raven Press, 1981, p 157.
22. GINNS EI, CHOUDARY PV, MARTIN BM, WINFIELD S, STUBBLEFIELD B, MAYOR J, MERKLE-LEHMAN D, MURRAY GJ, BOWERS LA, BARRANGER JA: Isolation of cDNA clones for human β-glucocerebrosidase using the λt11 expression system. *Biochem Biophys Res Commun* 123:574, 1984.
23. SORGE J, WEST C, WESTWOOD B, BEUTLER E: Molecular cloning and nucleotide sequence of human glucocerebrosidase cDNA. *Proc Natl Acad Sci USA* 82:7289, 1985.
24. TSUJI S, CHOUDARY PV, MARTIN BM, WINFIELD S, BARRANGER JA, GINNS EI: Nucleotide sequence of cDNA containing the complete coding sequence for human lysosomal glucocerebrosidase. *J Biol Chem* 261:50, 1986.
25. TSUJI S, CHOUDARY PV, MARTIN BM, BARRANGER JA, STUBBLEFIELD BR, MAYOR JA, GINNS EI: A mutation in the human glucocerebrosidase gene in neuronopathic Gaucher disease. *N Engl J Med* 316:570, 1987.
26. REITMAN M, VARKI A, KORNFELD S: Fibroblasts from patients with I-cell disease and pseudo-Hurler polydystrophy are deficient in uridine 5'-diphosphate-N-acetylglucosamine: glycoprotein N-acetylglucosaminylphosphotransferase activity. *J Clin Invest* 67:1574, 1981.
27. CHOUDARY PV, BARRANGER JA, TSUJI S, MAYOR J, La MARCA ME, CEPKO CL, MULLIGAN RC, GINNS EI: Retrovirus mediated transfer of the human glucocerebrosidase gene to Gaucher fibroblasts. *Mol Biol Med* 3:293, 1986.
28. FREDRICKSON DS, SLOAN HR: In Stanbury JB, Wyngaarden JB, Fredrickson DS (eds): *The Metabolic Basis of Inherited Disease*. New York, McGraw-Hill, 1978, p 731.
29. DANIELS LB, GLEW RH: β-glucosidase assays in the diagnosis of Gaucher's disease. *Clin Chem* 28:569, 1982.
30. BEUTLER E, KUHL WL: Detection of the defect of Gaucher's disease and its carrier state in peripheral blood leukocyte. *Lancet* i:612, 1970.
31. BASU A, GLEW RH, DANIELS LB, CLARK LS: Activators of spleen glucocerebrosidase from controls and patients with various forms of Gaucher's disease. *J Biol Chem* 259:1714, 1984.
32. PRENCE E, CHAKRAVORTI C, BASU A, CLARK LS, GLEW RH, CHAMBERS JA: Further studies on the activation of glucocerebrosidase by heat-stable factor from Gaucher spleen. *Arch Biochem Biophys* 236:98, 1985.
33. DEVINE EA, BEIGHTON P, PETERSEN EM, DESNICK RJ: Genetic heterogeneity in type 1 Gaucher disease. *Prog Clin Biol Res* 95:495, 1982.
34. GRABOWSKI GA, GOLDBLATT J, DINUR T, KRUSE J, SVENNERHOLM L, GATT S, DESNICK RJ: Genetic heterogeneity in Gaucher disease: Physicokinetic and immunologic studies of the residual enzyme in cultured fibroblasts from nonneuronopathic and neuronopathic patients. *Am J Med Genet* 21:529, 1985.
35. KOLODNY EH, ULLMAN MD, MANKIN HJ, SRINIVASSA S, RAGHAVEN, TOPOL J, SULLIVAN JL: Phenotypic manifestations of Gaucher disease: Clinical features in 48 biochemically verified type 1 patients and comments on type 2 patients. *Prog Clin Biol Res* 95:33, 1982.
36. GINNS EI, BRADY RO, PIRRUCCELLO S, MOORE C, SORRELL S, FURBISH FS, MURRAY GJ, TAGER JM, BARRANGER JA: Mutations of glucocerebrosidase: Discrimination of neurologic and non-neurologic phenotypes of Gaucher disease. *Proc Natl Acad Sci USA* 79:5607, 1982.
37. GINNS EI, TEGELAERS FPW, BARNEVELD R, GALJAARD H, REUSER AJJ, TAGER JM, BRADY RO, BARRANGER JA: Determination of Gaucher's disease phenotypes with monoclonal antibody. *Clin Chim Acta* 131:283, 1983.
38. FABBRO D, DESNICK RJ, GRABOWSKI GA: Gaucher disease: Genetic heterogeneity within and among the subtypes detected by immunoblotting. *Am J Hum Genet* 40:15, 1987.
39. ERICKSON AH, GINNS EI, BARRANGER JA: Biosynthesis of the lysosomal enzyme glucocerebrosidase. *J Biol Chem* 260:14319, 1985.
40. JONSSON LMV, MURRAY GJ, SORRELL S, STRIJLAND A, AERTS JFGM, GINNS EI, BARRANGER JA, TAGER JM, SCHRAM AW: Biosynthesis and maturation of glucocerebrosidase in Gaucher fibroblasts. *Eur J Biochem* 164:171, 1987.
41. BEUTLER E, KUHL W, SORGE J: Glucocerebrosidase "processing" and gene expression in various forms of Gaucher disease. *Am J Hum Genet* 37:1062, 1985.
42. JONSSON LV, MURRAY GJ, GINNS EI, STRIJLAND A, SCHRAM AW, TAGER JM, BARRANGER JA: Processing of beta-glucocerebrosidase in normal human fibroblasts and fibroblasts from patients with Gaucher's disease. *Fed Proc* 44:1742, 1985.
43. BEUTLER E, KUHL W, SORGE J: Cross-reacting material in Gaucher disease fibroblasts. *Proc Natl Acad Sci USA* 81:6506, 1984.
44. WILLEMSEN R, van DONGEN JM, GINNS EI, SIPS HJ, SCHRAM AW, TAGER JM, BARRANGER JA, REUSER AJJ: Ultrastructural localization of glucocere-

brosidase in cultured Gaucher's disease fibroblasts by immunocytochemistry. *J Neurol* 234:44, 1987.

45. GRAVEL RA, LEUNG A: Complementation analysis in Gaucher disease using single cell microassay techniques. Evidence for a single "Gaucher gene." *Hum Genet* 65:112, 1983.

46. KOLODNY EH, ULLMAN MD, MANKIN HJ, RAGHAVAN SS, TOPOL J, SULLIVAN JL: Gaucher's disease: Estimate of gene frequency among Ashkenazim by leukocyte β-glucosidase assay. *Abstr Int Soc Neurochem* p 425, 1979.

47. ERICKSON AH, GINNS EI, BARRANGER JA, BRADY RO, BLOBEL G: Biosynthesis and processing of glucocerebrosidase, a lysosomal hydrolase. *Fed Proc* 42:1912, 1983.

48. BARNEVELD RA, KEIJZER W, TEGELAERS FPW, GINNS EI, GEURTS Van KESSEL A, BRADY RO, BARRANGER JA, TAGER JM, GALJAARD H, WESTERVELD A, REUSER AJJ: Assignment of the gene coding for human β-glucocerebrosidase to the region of q21–q31 of chromosome 1 using monoclonal antibodies. *Hum Genet* 64:227, 1983.

49. GINNS EI, CHOUDARY PV, TSUJI S, MARTIN B, STUBBLEFIELD B, SAWYER J, HOZIER J, BARRANGER JA: Gene mapping and leader polypeptide sequence of human glucocerebrosidase: Implications for Gaucher disease. *Proc Natl Acad Sci USA* 82:7101, 1985.

50. CHOUDARY PV, GINNS EI, BARRANGER JA: Molecular cloning and analysis of the human β-glucocerebrosidase gene. *DNA* 4:74, 1985.

51. GINNS EI, BRADY RO, STOWENS DW, FURBISH FS, BARRANGER JA: A new group of glucocerebrosidase isozymes found in human white blood cells. *Biochem Biophys Res Commun* 97:1103, 1980.

52. GRAVES PN, GRABOWSKI GA, LUDMAN MD, PALELE P, SMITH FI: Human acid beta-glucosidase: Northern blot and S1 nuclease analysis of mRNA from HeLa cells and normal and Gaucher disease fibroblasts. *Am J Hum Genet* 39:763, 1986.

53. MARET A, SALVAYRE R, NEGRE A, DOUSTE-BLAZY L: Substrate specificity of the human splenic non-specific soluble beta-glucosidase. *Eur J Biochem* 133:283, 1983.

54. CHOUDARY PV, HOROWITZ M, BARRANGER JA, GINNS EI: Gene transfer and expression of active human glucocerebrosidase in mammalian cell cultures. *DNA* 5:78, 1986.

55. MARTIN B: Unpublished data.

56. MANN R, MULLIGAN RC, BALTIMORE D: Construction of a retrovirus packaging mutant and its use to produce herpes-free defective retrovirus. *Cell* 33:153, 1983.

57. CEPKO C, ROBERTS BE, MILLIGAN RC: Construction and application of a highly transmissible murine retrovirus shuttle vector. *Cell* 31:1053, 1984.

58. CONE R, MULLIGAN RC: High efficiency gene transfer into mammalian cells: Generation of helper-free recombinant retrovirus with broad mammalian host range. *Proc Natl Acad Sci USA* 81:6349, 1984.

59. BARRANGER JA: Marrow transplantation in genetic disease. *N Engl J Med* 311:1629, 1984.

60. DANIELS LB, COYLE PJ, CHIAO YB, GLEW RH, LABOW RS: Purification and characterization of a cytosolic broad specificity beta-glucosidase from human liver. *J Biol Chem* 256:13004, 1981.

61. WILLIAMS DA, ORKIN SH: Somatic gene therapy. *J Clin Invest* 77:1053, 1986.

62. RAPPEPORT JM, BARRANGER JA, GINNS EI: Bone marrow transplantation in Gaucher disease. *Birth Defects* 22:101, 1986.

63. SVENNERHOLM L, MANSSON JE, NILSSON O, TIBBLIN E, ERIKSSON A, GROTH CG, LUNDGREN G, RINGDEN O: Bone marrow transplantation in the Norrbottnian form of Gaucher's, in Barranger JA, Brady RO (eds): *Molecular Basis of Lysosomal Storage Disorders*, New York, Academic, 1984, p 441.

64. WILLIAMS DA, LEMISCHKA IR, NATHAN DG, MULLIGAN RC: Introduction of new genetic material into pluripotent hematopoietic stem cells of mice. *Nature* 310:475, 1984.

65. SORIANO P, CONE RD, MULLIGAN RC, JAENISCH R: Tissue-specific and ectopic expression of genes introduced into transgenic mice by retroviruses. *Science* 234:1409, 1986.

66. HODSON P, GOLDBLATT J, BEIGHTON P: Non-neuronopathic Gaucher's disease presenting in infancy. *Arch Dis Child* 54:707, 1979.

67. BERNSTEIN J, SHELDON WE: A note on the development of Gaucher cells in a newborn infant. *J Pediatr* 55:577, 1959.

68. BRINN L, GLAUBMAN S: Gaucher's disease without splenomegaly: Oldest patient on record, with review. *NY J Med* 62:2346, 1962.

69. MATOTH Y, FRIED K: Chronic Gaucher's disease: Clinical observations on 34 patients. *Isr J Med Sci* 1:521, 1965.

70. AERTS JM, BRUL S, DONKER-KOOPMAN WE, van WEELY S, MURRAY GJ, BARRANGER JA, TAGER JM, SCHRAM AW: Efficient routing of glucocerebrosidase to lysosomes requires complex oligosaccharide chain formation. *Biochem Biophys Res Commun* 141:452, 1986.

71. ISREAL O, JERUSHALMI J, FRONT D: Scintigraphic findings in Gaucher's disease. *J Nucl Med* 27:1556, 1986.

72. MORRISON AN, LANE M: Gaucher's disease with ascites: A case report with autopsy findings. *Ann Intern Med* 42:1321, 1955.

73. JAVETT SN, KEW MC, LIKNAITSKY D: Gaucher's disease with portal hypertension: Case report. *J Pediatr* 68:810, 1966.

74. GOLDBLATT J, SACKS S, BEIGHTON P: The orthopedic aspects of Gaucher disease. *Clin Orthop* 137:208, 1978.

75. TAKASAKI S, MURRAY GJ, FURBISH FS, BRADY RO, BARRANGER JA, KOBATA A: Structure of the N-asparagine-linked oligosaccharide units of human placental glucocerebrosidase. *J Biol Chem* 259:10112, 1984.

76. THANNHAUSER SJ: *Lipidoses, Diseases of Intracellular Lipid Metabolism*. New York, Grune & Stratton, 1958.

77. BLOOM TF, GROEN J, POSTMA C: Gaucher's disease. *Q J Med* 5:517, 1936.

78. BENDER IB: Dental observations in Gaucher's disease. *Oral Surg Oral Med Oral Pathol* 12:546, 1969.

79. HORSLEY JS Jr, BAKER JP, APPERLY FL: Gaucher's disease of late onset with kidney involvement and huge spleen. *Am J Med Sci* 190:511, 1935.

80. SMITH RRL, HUTCHINS GM, SACK GH, RIDOLFI RL: Unusual cardiac, renal and pulmonary hypertension, and fatal bone marrow embolization. *Am J Med* 65:352, 1978.

81. CHANDER PN, NURSE HM, PIRANI CL: Renal involvement in adult Gaucher's disease after splenectomy. *Arch Pathol Lab Med* 103:440, 1979.

82. ROBERTS WC, FREDRICKSON DS: Gaucher's disease of the lung causing severe pulmonary hypertension with associated acute recurrent pericarditis. *Circulation* 35:783, 1967.

83. SCHNEIDER EL, EPSTEIN CJ, KABACK MJ, BRANDES D: Severe pulmonary involvement in adult Gaucher's disease. Report of three cases and review of the literature. *Am J Med* 63:475, 1977.

84. BENBASSAT J, BASSAN H, MILWIDSKY H, SACKS M, GROEN JJ: Constrictive pericarditis in Gaucher's disease. *Am J Med* 44:647, 1968.

85. DREBROG S, ERIKSON A, HAGBERG B: Gaucher disease—Norrbottnian type 1. General clinical description. *Eur J Pediatr* 133:107, 1980.

86. BLOM S, ERIKSON A: Gaucher disease—Norrbottnian type. Neurodevelopmental, neurological, and neurophysiological aspects. *Eur J Pediatr* 140:136, 1983.

87. COGAN DG, CHU FC, REINGOLD D, BARRANGER JA: Ocular motor signs in some metabolic diseases. *Arch Ophthalmol* 99:1802, 1981.

88. NEIL JF, MERIKANGAS JR, GLEW RH: EEG findings in adult neuronopathic Gaucher's disease. *Clin Electroencephalogr* 10:198, 1979.

89. NISHIMURA RN, BARRANGER JA: Neurologic complications of Gaucher's disease type 3. *Arch Neurol* 37:92, 1980.

90. NISHIMURA RN, OMOS-LAU C, AJAMONE-MARSAN C, BARRANGER JA: Electroencephalographic findings in Gaucher's disease. *Neurology* 30:152, 1980.

91. BURNS GF, CAWLEY JC, FLEMANS RJ, HIGGY KE, WORMAN CP, BARKER CR, ROBERTS BE, HAYHOE FGJ: Surface marker and other characteristics of Gaucher cells. *J Clin Pathol* 30:981, 1977.

92. DJALDETTI M, FISHMAN P, BESSLER H: The surface ultrastructure of Gaucher cells. *Am J Clin Pathol* 71:146, 1979.

93. TEILUM G: Die Gauchersche krankheit mit der beschreibung eines falles, der veranderungen in der hypophyse und im hypothalamus zeigte. *Acta Med Scand* 116:191, 1944.

94. CHANG-LO M, YAM LT, RUBENSTONE AI: Gaucher's disease. *Am J Med Sci* 254:303, 1967.

95. RISEL WL: Über die gross zellige splenomegalie (typus Gaucher) und über das endotheliale sarkom der milz. *Beitr Pathol Anat* 46:241, 1909.

96. Case Records of the Massachusetts General Hospital. *N Engl J Med* 222:680, 1940.

97. BLOCK M, JACOBSON LO: The histogenesis and diagnosis of the osseous type of Gaucher disease. *Acta Haematol (Basel)* 1:165, 1948.

98. PITTALUGA PG, GAYANES J: Contribution a l'etude de la cellule de Gaucher. *Arch Mal Coeur* 26:65, 1933.

99. MORRISON RW, HACK MH: Histochemical studies in Gaucher's disease. *Am J Pathol* 25:497, 1949.

100. CROCKER AC, LANDING BH: Phosphatase studies in Gaucher's disease. *Metabolism* 9:341, 1960.

101. LEE RE: The fine structure of the cerebroside occurring in Gaucher's disease. *Proc Natl Acad Sci USA* 61:484, 1968.

102. ABE T, YAMEKAWA T, ENDOU H, NAGASHIMA K: Disc gel electrophoresis of proteins of membranous cytoplasmic inclusion bodies from the spleen of the patient with Gaucher's disease. *Jpn J Exp Med* 48:177, 1978.

103. ALBRECHT M: "Gaucher-zellen" bei chronisch myeloidischer leukemie. *Blut* 13:169, 1966.

104. LEE RE, ELLIS LD: The storage cells of chronic myelogenous leukemia. *Lab Invest* 24:261, 1971.

105. HAYHOE FGJ, FLEMANS RJ, COWLING DC: Acquired lipidosis of marrow

macrophages: Birefringent blue crystals and Gaucher-like cells, sea-blue histiocytes, and grey-green crystals. *J Clin Pathol* 32:420, 1979.

106. ZAINO ED, ROSSI MB, PHAM TD, AZAR HA: Gaucher's cells in thalassaemia. *Blood* 38:457, 1971.

107. ENQUIST RW, GOCKERMAN JP, JENIS MC, RAPHAEL ML, DILLON E: Type II congenital dyserythropoietic anemia. *Ann Intern Med* 77:371, 1972.

108. SCULLIN DC, SHELBURNE JD, COHEN JD: Pseudo-Gaucher cells in multiple myeloma. *Am J Med* 67:347, 1979.

109. HILL SC, REINIG JW, BARRANGER JA, FINK J, SHAWKER TH: Gaucher disease: Sonographic appearance of the spleen. *Radiology* 160:631, 1986.

110. SALKY B, KREEL I, GELERNT I, BAUER J, AUFSES AH JR: Splenectomy for Gaucher's disease. *Ann Surg* 190:592, 1979.

111. LEE RE: The pathology of Gaucher disease. *Prog Clin Biol Res* 95:177, 1982.

112. CARLING ER, CARLILL H, PULVERTAFT RJ: Splenectomy in Gaucher's disease with haemoglobinuria. *Proc R Soc Med* 26:361, 1933.

113. MANDELBAUM H, BARBER L, LEDERER M, SOBEL AE, KAYE IA: Gaucher's disease. *Ann Intern Med* 16:438, 1942.

114. BAR-MAOR JA, GOVRIN-YEHUDAIN J: Technique of covering the raw surface of the spleen after partial splenectomy. *Z Kinderchir* 40:176, 1985.

115. RUBIN M, ZIV Y, BILIK R, YAMPOLSKI I, FEIGENBERG Z, DINTSMAN M: Preservation of the spleen in children. *Isr J Med Sci* 21:922, 1985.

116. RUBIN M, YAMPOLSKI I, LAMOROZO R, ZAIZOV R, DINTSMAN M: Partial splenectomy in Gaucher's disease. *J Pediatr Surg* 21:125, 1986.

117. GUZETTA PC, CONNORS R, FINK J, BARRANGER JA: Operative technique and results of subtotal splenectomy for Gaucher disease. *Surg Gynecol Obstet* 164:359, 1987.

118. MANDELBAUM FS: A contribution to the pathology of primary splenomegaly (Gaucher type), with the report of an autopsy on a male child four and one half years of age. *J Exp Med* 16:797, 1912.

119. REICH C, SEIFE M, KESSLER BJ: Gaucher's disease: A review and discussion of twenty cases. *Medicine* 30:1, 1951.

120. LIEBERMAN DA: Sclerotherapy for bleeding esophageal varices after randomized trials. *Clin Med* 145:481, 1986.

121. ISHAK KG, SHARP HL: Metabolic errors and liver disease, in Mac Sween RNM, Anthony PP, Scheuer PJ (eds): *Pathology of the Liver*. Edinburgh, London, New York, Churchill Livingstone, 1979, p 88.

122. JAMES SP, STROMEYER FW, CHANG C, BARRANGER JA: Liver abnormalities in patients with Gaucher's disease. *Gastroenterology* 80:126, 1981.

123. VOLK BW, WALLACE BJ: The liver in lipidosis: An electron microscopic and histochemical study. *Am J Pathol* 49:203, 1966.

124. EDLIN P, KEPLER WE JR, KANBE GW: Gaucher's disease. *Gastroenterology* 28:120, 1955.

125. MILLER JH, ORTEGA JA, HEISEL MA: Juvenile Gaucher disease simulating osteomyelitis. *AJR* 137:880, 1981.

126. SHAWKER TH, MORAN B, LINZER M, PARKS SI, JAMES SP, STROMEYER FW, BARRANGER JA: B-scan echo-amplitude measurement in patients with diffuse infiltrative liver disease. *J Clin Ultrasound* 9:293, 1981.

127. STOWENS DW, TEITELBAUM SL, KAHN AJ, BARRANGER JA: Skeletal complications of Gaucher disease. *Medicine* 64:310, 1985.

128. SILVERSTEIN MN, KELLY PJ: Osteoarticular manifestations of Gaucher's disease. *Am J Med Sci* 253:569, 1967.

129. LEVIN B: Gaucher's disease: Clinical and roentgenologic manifestations. *Am J Roentgenol* 85:685, 1961.

130. TENNENT W: Gaucher's disease: Gaucher's disease—The early radiological diagnosis. *Br J Radiol* 18:356, 1945.

131. SCHEIN AJ, ARKIN AM: The classic hip joint involvement in Gaucher's disease. *Clin Orthop* 90:4, 1973.

132. LAU MM, LICHTMAN DM, HAMATI YI, BIERBAUM BE: Hip arthroplasties in Gaucher's disease. *J Bone Joint Surg* 63A:591, 1981.

133. STRICKLAND B: Skeletal manifestations of Gaucher's disease with some unusual findings. *Br J Radiol* 31:246, 1958.

134. MANKIN HJ, DOPPELT S, ROSENBERG AE, BARRANGER JA: Metabolic bone disease in patients with Gaucher's disease, in Alvioli LV, Krane SM (eds): *Metabolic Basis of Bone Disease*. 1988, in press.

135. RAYNOR RR: Spinal cord compression secondary to Gaucher's disease. *J Neurosurg* 19:902, 1962.

136. HERMANN JG, GOLDBLATT J, LEVY RN, GOLDSMITH SJ, DESNICK RJ, GRABOWSKI GA: Gaucher's disease type 1: Assessment of bone involvement by CT and scintigraphy. *Am J Radiol* 147:943, 1986.

137. ROSENTHAL DI, SCOTT JA, BARRANGER JA, MANKIN HJ, SIANI S, BRADY TJ, OSIER LK, DOPPELT S: Evaluation of Gaucher disease using magnetic resonance imaging. *J Bone Joint Surg* 68:802, 1986.

138. WISNER GL, ROSEN BR, BUXTON R, STARK DD, BRADY TJ: Chemical shift imaging of bone marrow: Preliminary experience. *Am J Radiol* 145:1031, 1985.

139. DESNICK SJ, DESNICK RJ, BRADY RO, PENTCHEV PG, SIMMONS RL, NAR-

140. MYERS B: Gaucher's disease of the lungs. *Br Med J* 2:8, 1937.

141. DONAT R: Die beteiligung der lungen beim morbus Gaucher. *Zentralbl Allg Pathol Anat* 78:273, 1941.

142. MURRAY GJ, DOEBBER TW, WU MS, POMPIPOM MM, BUGIANESI RL, SHEN TY, BARRANGER JA: Targeting of synthetically glycosylated human placental glucocerebrosidase. *Biochem Med Metab Biol* 34:241, 1985.

143. WILSON ER, BARTON NW, BARRANGER JA: Vascular involvement in type 3 neuronopathic Gaucher's disease. *Arch Pathol Lab Med* 109:82, 1985.

144. GROTH CG, COLLSTE H, CREBORG S, HAKANSSON G, LUNDGREN G, SVENNERHOLM L: Attempt at enzyme replacement in Gaucher disease by renal transplantation, in Desnick RJ (ed): *Enzyme Therapy in Genetic Disease 2*. New York, AR Liss, 1980, p 475.

145. BRADY RO, PENTCHEV PG, GAL AE, HIBBERT SR, DEKABAN AS: Replacement therapy for inherited enzyme deficiency: Use of purified glucocerebrosidase in Gaucher's disease. *N Engl J Med* 291:989, 1974.

146. HERS HG: Inborn lysosomal diseases. *Gastroenterology* 48:625, 1965.

147. DE DUVE C: Lysosomes revisited. *Eur J Biochem* 123:391, 1983.

148. CARBONE AO, PETROZZI C: Gaucher's disease: Case report with stress on eye findings. *Henry Ford Hosp Med J* 16:55, 1968.

149. REDSLOB E, GERY L: Localisations oculaires de la "maladie du Gaucher." *Ann Oculist (Paris)* 169:865, 1932.

150. FURBISH FS, STEER CJ, KRETT NL, BARRANGER JA: Uptake and distribution of placental glucocerebrosidase in rat hepatic cells and effects of sequential deglycosylation. *Biochim Biophys Acta* 673:425, 1981.

151. BLATTNER RJ: Gaucher's disease: Abnormalities in immunoglobulin. *J Pediatr* 73:626, 1968.

152. PRATT PW, ESTREN S, KOCHWA S: Immunoglobulin abnormalities in Gaucher's disease. Report of 16 cases. *Blood* 31:633, 1968.

153. MacDONALD M, MCCATHIE M, FAED MJW, PRINGLE R, GOODHALL HB, BECK JS, TUDHOFE GR, MITCHELL PEG, WOOD AJJ, GUTHRIE W, SHAW D: Gaucher's disease with biclonal gammapathy. *J Clin Pathol* 28:757, 1975.

154. WOLF P: Monoclonal gammopathy in Gaucher's disease. *Lab Med* 4:28, 1973.

155. TURESSON I, RAUSING A: Gaucher's disease and benign monoclonal gammopathy. A case report with immunofluorescence study of bone marrow and spleen. *Acta Med Scand* 197:507, 1975.

156. DIKMAN SH, GOLDSTEIN M, KAHN T, LEO MA, WEINRED N: Amyloidosis: An unusual complication of Gaucher's disease. *Arch Pathol Lab Med* 102:460, 1978.

157. HANASH SM, RUCKNAGEL DL, HEIDELBERGER KP, RADIN NS: Primary amyloidosis associated with Gaucher's disease. *Ann Intern Med* 89:639, 1978.

158. PINKHAS J, DJALDETTI M, YARON M: Coincidence of multiple myeloma with Gaucher's disease. *Isr J Med Sci* 1:537, 1965.

159. BENJAMIN D, JOSHUA H, DJALDETTI M, HAZAZ B, PINKHAS J: Nonsecretory IgD-kappa multiple myeloma in a patient with Gaucher's disease. *Scand J Haematol* 22:179, 1979.

160. RUESTOW PC, LEVINSON DJ, CATCHATOURIAN R, SREEKANTH S, COHEN H, ROSENFELD S: Coexistence of IgA myeloma and Gaucher's disease. *Arch Intern Med* 140:1115, 1980.

161. GELFAND MI, GRIBOFF SI: Gaucher's disease and acute leukemia. *J Mt Sinai Hosp NY* 28:278, 1961.

162. KRAUSE JR, BURES C, LEE RE: Acute leukemia and Gaucher's disease. *Scand J Haematol* 23:115, 1979.

163. SHAVER LR, BRANDES JA, SILVER RT, GRAY GF: Association of Hodgkins' disease and Gaucher's disease. *Arch Pathol* 98:376, 1964.

164. CHO SY, SASTRE M: Coexistence of Hodgkins' disease and Gaucher's diseae. *Am J Clin Pathol* 65:103, 1976.

165. BRUCKSTEIN AH, KARANAS A, DIRE JJ: Gaucher's disease associated with Hodgkins' disease. *Am J Med* 68:610, 1980.

166. DAVIS M, DORFMAN J: Gaucher's disease associated with a cerebral astrocytoma. *Am Pract* 12:673, 1961.

167. TSUNG SW, COTES E: Coexistence of bronchogenic carcinoma and Gaucher's disease. *Arch Pathol Lab Med* 101:56, 1977.

168. GERY I, ZIGLER JS JR, BRADY RO, BARRANGER JA: Selective effects of glucocerebroside (Gaucher's storage material) on macrophage cultures. *J Clin Invest* 68:1182, 1981.

169. ROBINSON DB, GLEW RH: Acid phosphatase in Gaucher's disease. *Clin Chem* 26:371, 1980.

170. TUCHMAN LR, SUNA H, CARR JJ: Elevation of serum acid phosphatase in Gaucher's disease. *J Mt Sinai Hosp* 23:277, 1956.

171. LIEBERMAN J, BEUTLER E: Elevation of serum angiotensin-converting enzyme in Gaucher's disease. *N Engl J Med* 294:1442, 1976.

172. SILVERSTEIN E, FRIEDLAND J: Elevated serum and spleen angiotensin

JARIAN JS, SWAIMAN K, SHARP HI, KRIVIT W: Renal transplantation in type II Gaucher disease. *Birth Defects* IX (2): March 1973.

converting enzyme and serum lysozyme in Gaucher's disease. *Clin Chim Acta* 74:21, 1977.

173. OCKERMAN PA, KAHLIN P: Acid hydrolases in plasma in Gaucher's disease. *Clin Chem* 15:61, 1969.

174. MOFFITT KD, CHAMBERS JP, DIVEN WF, GLEW RH, WENGER DA, FARRELL DF: Characterization of lysosomal hydrolases that are elevated in Gaucher's disease. *Arch Biochem Biophys* 190:247, 1978.

175. HULTBERG B, ISAKSSON A, SJOBLOD S, OCKERMAN PA: Acid hydrolases in serum from patients with lysosomal disorders. *Clin Chem Acta* 100:33, 1980.

176. WEINREB NJ: Serum and splenic lysozyme in Gaucher's disease. *Clin Res* 24:295A, 1976.

177. BOKLAN BF, SAWITSKY A: Factor IX deficiency in Gaucher's disease. An *in vitro* phenomenon. *Arch Intern Med* 136:489, 1976.

178. BENJAMIN D, JOSHUA H, DOUER D, SHAKLAI M, KRUGLIAC Y, PINKHAS J: Circulating anticoagulant in patients with Gaucher's disease. *Acta Haematol* 61:233, 1979.

179. PARKMAN R: The application of bone marrow transplantation to the treatment of genetic diseases. *Science* 232:1373, 1986.

180. SUTHERLAND DE, MATAS AJ, NAJARIAN JS: The mutual impact of transplantation and advances in the understanding and treatment of metabolic diseases. *Transplant Proc* 12(4):643, 1980.

181. DEBRE R, BERTRAND I, GRUMBACH R, BARGETON G: Maladie de Gaucher du Norrisson. *Arch Fr Pediatr* 8:38, 1951.

182. NORMAN RM, URICH H, LLOYD OC: The neuropathology of infantile Gaucher's disease. *J Pathol Bacteriol* 72:121, 1956.

183. BANKER BQ, MILLER JO, CROCKER AC: The cerebral pathology of infantile Gaucher's disease, in Aronson SM, Volk BW (eds): *Cerebral Sphingolipidoses*. New York, Academic, 1962, p 73.

184. KAYE EM, ULLMAN MD, WILSON ER, BARRANGER JA: Type 2 and type 3 Gaucher disease: A morphological and biochemical study. *Ann Neurol* 20:223, 1986.

185. SCARAVILLI F, TAVOLATO B: Neuropathological aspects of the intangile form of Gaucher's disease. *Acta Neurol Belg* 68:674, 1968.

186. NILSSON O, GRABOWSKI GA, LUDMAN MD, DESNICK RJ, SVENNERHOLM L: Glycosphingolipid studies of visceral tissues and brain from type 1 Gaucher disease variants. *Clin Genet* 27:443, 1985.

187. SHERLOCK S: Needle biopsy of the liver: A review. *J Clin Pathol* 15:291, 1962.

188. BRADFIELD JWB, SOUHAMI RL: Hepatocyte damage secondary to Kupffer cell phagocytosis, in Liehr H, Grun M (eds): *The Reticuloendothelial System and the Pathogenesis of Liver Disease*. New York, Elsevier, 1980, p 165.

189. ADACHI M, WALLACE BJ, SCHNECK L, VOLK BW: Fine structure of central nervous system in early infantile Gaucher's disease. *Arch Pathol (Chicago)* 83:513, 1967.

190. WENGER DA, ROTH S, SATTLER M: Acute neuronopathic (infantile) and chronic nonneuronopathic (adult) Gaucher disease in full siblings. *J Pediatr* 100:252, 1982.

191. AERTS JMFG, DONKER-KOOPMAN WE, KOOT M, BARRANGER JA, TAGER JM, SCHRAM AW: Deficient activity of glucocerebrosidase in urine from patients with type 1 Gaucher disease. *Clin Chim Acta* 158:155, 1986.

192. BEUTLER E, KUHL W: The diagnosis of the adult type of Gaucher's disease and its carrier state in peripheral blood leukocytes. *J Lab Clin Med* 76:747, 1970.

193. PETERS SP, COYLE P, GLEW RH: Differentiation of beta-glucosidase in human tissues using sodium taurocholate. *Arch Biochem Biophys* 175:569, 1976.

194. LEGLER G: Untersuchungen zum Wirkungemechanisms glykosidspalten der enzyme. I. Darstellung und eigenschaften spezifischer inaktivaturen. *Hoppe-Seyler's Z Physiol Chem* 345:197, 1966.

195. DANIELS LB, GLEW RH, RADIN NS, VUNNAM RR: A revised fluorometric assay for Gaucher's disease using conduritol-beta-epoxide with liver as the source of beta-glucosidase. *Clin Chem Acta* 106:155, 1980.

196. SORGE J, GELBART T, WEST C, WESTWOOD D, BEUTLER E: Heterogeneity in type I Gaucher disease demonstrated by restriction mapping of the gene. *Proc Natl Acad Sci USA* 82:5442, 1985.

197. EVANS MI, MOORE C, KOLODNY EH, CASASSA M, SCHULMAN JD, LANDESBERGER EJ, KARSON EM, DORFMANN AD, LARSEN JW, BARRANGER JA: Lysosomal enzymes in chorionic villi, cultured amniocytes, and cultured skin fibroblasts. *Clin Chim Acta* 157:109, 1986.

198. PATEL SC, DAVIS GL, BARRANGER JA: Gaucher's disease in a patient with chronic active hepatitis. *Am J Med* 80(3):523, 1986.

199. NEWBURG DS, YATZIV S, MCCLUER RH, RAGHAVAN S: Beta-glucosidase inhibition in murine peritoneal macrophages by conduritol-B-epoxide: An *in vitro* model of the Gaucher cell. *Biochim Biophys Acta* 877:121, 1986.

200. DAS PK, MURRAY GJ, GAL AE, BARRANGER JA: Glucocerebrosidase deficiency and lysosomal storage of glucocerebroside induced in cultured macrophages. *Exp Cell Res* 168:463, 1987.

201. BUSSUTIL R, BARRANGER J, unpublished data.

202. ULLMAN DM, MCCLUER RH: Quantitative analysis of plasma neutral glycosphingolipids by high performance liquid chromatography of their perbenzoyl derivatives. *J Lipid Res* 18:371, 1977.

203. SVENNERHOLM L, MANSSON J, ROSENGREN B: Cerebroside-β-glucosidase activity in Gaucher brain. *Clin Genet* 30:131, 1986.

204. REINER O, WILDER S, GIVOL D, HOROWITZ M: Efficient *in vitro* and *in vivo* expression of human glucocerebrosidase cDNA. *DNA* 6:101, 1987.

205. SUN CC, PANNY S, COMBS J, GUTBERLETT R: Hydrops fetalis associated with Gaucher disease. *Pathol Res Pract* 179:101, 1984.

206. MATOTH Y, CHAZAN S, CNAAN A, GELERNTER I, KLIBANSKY C: Frequency of carriers of chronic (type I) Gaucher disease in Ashkenazi Jews. *Am J Med Genet* 27:561, 1987.

207. GOLDBLATT J, BEIGHTON P: Cutaneous manifestations of Gaucher disease. *Br J Dermatol* III:331, 1984.

208. ERIKSON A: Gaucher disease—Norrbottnian type (III). Neuropaediatric and neurobiological aspects of clinical patterns and treatment. *Acta Paediatr Scand Suppl* 326:1, 1986.

209. CHU FC, RODRIGUES MM, COGAN DG, BARRANGER JA: The pathology of pingueculae in Gaucher's disease. *Ophthalmic Paediatr Genet* 4:7, 1984.

210. ROSE JS, GRABOWSKI GA, BARNETT SH, DESNICK RJ: Accelerated skeletal deterioration after splenectomy in Gaucher type 1 disease. *AJR* 139:1202, 1982.

211. HILLBORG PO: Morbus Gaucher i Norrbotten. *Nord Med* 61:303, 1959.

212. YOSSIPOVITCH ZH, HERMAN G, MAKIN M: Aseptic osteomyelitis in Gaucher's disease. *Isr J Med Sci* I:531, 1965.

213. LOGAN VH: The results of splenectomy in Gaucher's disease. *Surg Gynecol Obstet* 72:807, 1941.

214. BEIGHTON P, GOLDBLATT J, SACKS S: Bone involvement in Gaucher's disease. *Prog Clin Biol Res* 95:603, 1982.

215. SHILONI E, BITRAN D, RACHMILEWITZ E, DURST AL: The role of splenectomy in Gaucher's disease. *Arch Surg* 118:929, 1983.

216. MARKS C, RAM MD, ZAAS R: Surgical considerations in Gaucher's disease. *Surg Gynecol Obstet* 132:609, 1971.

217. ADERKA D, GARFINKEL D, ROTHEM A, PINKHAS J: Fatal bleeding from esophageal varices in a patient with Gaucher's disease. *Am J Gastroenterol* 77:838, 1982.

218. ASHKENAZI A, ZAIZOV R, MATOTH Y: Effect of splenectomy on destructive bone changes in children with chronic (Type I) Gaucher disease. *Eur J Pediatr* 145:138, 1986.

219. KOHN DB, NOLTA JA, HONG CM, BARRANGER JA: Expression of the human glucocerebrosidase gene by retrovirus vectors in Verna I, Mulligan RO, Beaudet A (eds): *Gene Transfer in Animals*, New York, AR Liss, 1988, in press.

220. ICHIOKA T, KISHIMOTO Y, BRENNAN S, SANTOS GW, YEAGER AM: Hematopoietic cell transplantation in murine globoid cell leukodystrophy (the twitcher mouse): Effects on levels of galactosylceramidase, psychosine, and galactocerebrosides. *Proc Natl Acad Sci USA* 84:4259, 1987.

221. BLOM S, ERIKSON A: Gaucher disease—Norrbottnian type. Neurodevelopmental, neurological, and neurophysiological aspects. *Eur J Pediatr* 140:316, 1983.

222. BALFANZ JR, NESBIT ME, JARVIS C, KRIVIT W: Overwhelming sepsis following splenectomy for trauma. *J Pediatr* 88:458, 1976.

223. DIAMOND LK: Splenectomy in childhood and the hazard of overwhelming infection. *Pediatrics* 43:886, 1969.

224. DREBORG S, ERIKSON A, HAGBERG B: Gaucher disease—Norrbottnian Type, I. General Clinical Description. *Eur J Pediatr* 133:107, 1980.

225. KAGA M, AZUMA CH, IMAMURA T, MURAKAMI T, KAGA K: Auditory brainstem response (ABR) in infantile Gaucher's disease. *Neuropediatrics* 13:207, 1982.

226. COGAN DG, CHU FC, GITTINGER J, TYCHSEN L: Fundal abnormalities of Gaucher's disease. *Arch Ophthalmol* 98:2202, 1980.

227. HANNUN YA, BELL RM: Lysophingolipids inhibit protein Kinase C: Implications for the sphingolipidoses. *Science* 235:670, 1987.

228. GAL AE, PENTCHEV PG, BARRANGER JA, DAMBROSIA JM, BRADY RO: The distribution of glucocerebroside in the liver of patients with Gaucher's disease. *Analyt Biochem* 85:127, 1979.

229. SCHACHTER H, ROSEMAN S: Mammalian glucosyltransferases: Their role in the synthesis and function of complex carbohydrates and glycolipids, in Lennarz WL (ed): *The Biochemistry of Glycoproteins and Proteoglycans*. New York, Plenum, 1980, chap 3.

230. BARNS RJ, CLAGUE AE: An improved procedure for diagnosis of Gaucher disease using cultured skin fibroblasts and the chromogenic substrate, 2-hexadecanoylamino-4-nitrophenyl-β-D-glucopyranoside. *Clin Chim Acta* 120:57, 1982.

231. TURNER BM, HIRSCHHORN K: Properties of β-glucosidase in cultured skin

fibroblasts from controls and patients with Gaucher disease. *Am J Hum Genet* 30:346, 1978.

232. BEUTLER E, KUHL W, TRINIDAD F, TEPLITZ R, NADLER H: β-glucosidase activity in fibroblasts from homozygotes and heterozygotes for Gaucher's disease. *Am J Hum Genet* 23:62, 1971.

233. HO MW, SECK J, SCHMIDT D, VEATH ML, JOHNSON W, BRADY RO, O'BRIEN JS: Adult Gaucher's disease: Kindred studies and demonstration of a deficiency of acid β-glucosidase in cultured fibroblasts. *Am J Hum Genet* 24:37, 1972.

234. HARZER K: Enzymatic diagnosis in 27 cases with Gaucher disease. *Clin Chim Acta* 106:9, 1980.

235. GOODMAN C, O'BRIEN JS: A modified method for the identification of heterozygotes for Gaucher's disease using differential thermal inactivation. *Clin Genet* 18:226, 1980.

236. RAGHAVAN SS, TOPOL J, KOLODNY EH: Leukocyte β-glucosidase in homozygotes and heterozygotes for Gaucher disease. *Am J Hum Genet* 32:158, 1980.

237. GRABOWSKI GA, DINUR T, GATT S, DESNICK RJ: Gaucher type 1 (Ashkenazi) disease: A new method for heterozygote detection using a novel fluorescent natural substrate. *Clin Chim Acta* 124:123, 1982.

238. WENGER DA, CLARK C, SATTLER M, WHARTON C: Synthetic substrate β-glucosidase activity in leukocytes: A reproducible method for the identification of patients and carriers of Gaucher's disease. *Clin Genet* 13:145, 1978.

239. JOLLY RD, DESNICK RJ: Inborn errors of lysosomal catabolism—Principles of heterozygote detection. *Am J Med Genet* 4:293, 1979.

240. HEUKELS-DULLY MJ, NIERMEIJER MF: Variation in lysosomal enzyme activity during growth in culture of human fibroblasts and amniotic fluid cells. *Exp Cell Res* 97:304, 1976.

241. HULTBERG B, SJOBLAD S, OCKERMAN PA: Properties of five acid hydrolases in human skin fibroblast cultures. *Acta Paediatr Scand* 62:474, 1973.

242. MARTENSSON E: Glycosphingolipids of animal tissue. *Prog Chem Fats Lipids* 10:367, 1969.

243. KAYE EM, ULLMAN MD: Separation and quantitation of Perbenzoylated glucocerebroside and galactocerebroside by high-performance liquid chromatography. *Anal Biochem* 138:380, 1984.

244. STRASBERG PM, WARREN I, SKOMOROWSKI MA, LOWDEN JA: HPLC analysis of neutral glycolipids: An aid in the diagnosis of lysosomal storage disease. *Clin Chim Acta* 132:29, 1983.

245. ERIKSON A, WAHLBERG I: Gaucher disease—Norrbottnian type ocular abnormalities. *Acta Ophthalmol* 63:221, 1985.

246. PENTCHEV PG, BRADY RO, HIBBERT SR, GAL AE, SHAPIRO D: Isolation and characterization of glucocerebrosidase from human placental tissue. *J Biol Chem* 248:5256, 1973.

247. FURBISH FS, BLAIR HE, SHILOACH J, PENTCHEV PG, BRADY RO: Enzyme replacement therapy in Gaucher's disease: Large-scale purification of glucocerebrosidase suitable for human administration. *Proc Natl Acad Sci USA* 74:3560, 1977.

248. MURRAY GJ, YOULE RJ, GANDY SE, ZIRZOW GC, BARRANGER JA: Purification of beta-glucocerebrosidase by preparative-scale high-performance liquid chromatography: The use of ethylene glycol-containing buffers for chromatography of hydrophobic glycoprotein enzymes. *Anal Biochem* 147:301, 1985.

249. CHOY FY: Purification of human placental glucocerebrosidase using a two-step high-performance hydrophobic and gel permeation column chromatography method. *Anal Biochem* 156:515, 1986.

250. STRASBERG PM, LOWDEN JA, MAHURAN D: Purification of glucosylceramidase by affinity chromatography. *Can J Biochem* 60:1025, 1982.

251. GRABOWSKI GA, DAGAN A: Human lysosomal β-glucosidase: Purification by affinity chromatography. *Anal Biochem* 141:267, 1984.

252. AERTS JM, DONKER-KOOPMAN WE, MURRAY GJ, BARRANGER JA, TAGER JM, SCHRAM AW: A procedure for the rapid purification in high yield of human glucocerebrosidase using immunoaffinity chromatography with monoclonal antibodies. *Anal Biochem* 154:655, 1986.

253. BARNEVELD RA, TEGELAERS FP, GINNS EI, VISSER P, LAANEN EA, BRADY RO, GALJAARD H, BARRANGER JA, REUSER AJ, TAGER JM: Monoclonal antibodies against human beta-glucocerebrosidase. *Eur J Biochem* 134:585, 1983.

254. MURRAY GJ, JONSSON LV, SORRELL SH, GINNS EI, TAGER JM, SCHRAM AW, BARRANGER JA: Phosphorylation of β-glucocerebrosidase in cultured human fibroblasts. *Fed Proc* 44:1742, 1985.

255. HO MW, O'BRIEN JS: Gaucher's disease: Deficiency of "acid" β-glucosidase and reconstitution of enzyme activity in vitro. *Proc Natl Acad Sci USA* 68:2810, 1971.

256. MARET A, SALVAYRE R, NEGRE A, DOUSTE-BLAZY L: Proprietes des formes moleculaires de la β-glucosidase et de la β-glucocerebrosidase de rate humaine normale et de maladie de Gaucher. *Eur J Biochem* 115:455, 1981.

257. MUELLER OT, ROSENBERG A: Activation of membrane-bound glucosylceramide:β-glucosidase in fibroblasts cultured from normal and glucosylceramidotic human skin. *J Biol Chem* 254:3521, 1979.

258. BERENT SL, RADIN NS: β-glucosidase activator protein from bovine spleen ("Coglucosidase"). *Arch Biochem Biophys* 208:248, 1981.

259. DAWSON G, OH JY: Blood glucosylceramide levels in Gaucher's disease and its distribution amongst lipoprotein fractions. *Clin Chim Acta* 75:149, 1977.

260. FUJIBAYASHI S, WENGER DA: Studies on a sphingolipid activator protein (SAP-2) in fibroblasts from patients with lysosomal storage diseases, including Niemann-Pick disease Type C. *Clin Chim Acta* 146:147, 1985.

261. IYER SS, BERENT SL, RADIN NS: The cohydrolases in human spleen that stimulate glucosyl ceramide β-glucosidase. *Biochim Biophys Acta* 748:1, 1983.

262. PETERS SP, COFFEE CJ, GLEW RH, LEE RE, WENGER DA, LI S, LI Y: Isolation of heat-stable glucocerebrosidase activators from the spleens of three variants of Gaucher's disease. *Arch Biochem Biophys* 183:290, 1977.

263. CHIAO Y, CHAMBERS JP, GLEW RH, LEE RE, WENGER DA: Subcellular localization of the heat-stable glucocerebrosidase activator substance in Gaucher spleen. *Arch Biochem Biophys* 186:42, 1978.

264. PETERS SP, COYLE P, COFFEE CJ, GLEWS RH: Purification and properties of a heat-stable glucocerebrosidase activating factor from control and Gaucher spleen. *J Biol Chem* 252:563, 1977.

265. HOBBS JR, JONES KH, SHAW PJ, LINDSAY I, HANCOCK M: Beneficial effect of pre-transplant splenectomy on displacement bone marrow transplantation for Gaucher's syndrome. *Lancet* 1:May 16, III, 1987.

266. AERTS JM, DONKER-KOOPMAN WE, van-LAAR C, BRUL S, MURRAY GJ, WENGER DA, BARRANGER JA, TAGER JM, SCHRAM AW1: Relationship between the two immunologically distinguishable forms of glucocerebrosidase in tissue extracts. *Eur J Biochem* 163:583, 1987.

267. CHEN JF, PAN W, D'SOUZA MP: Lysosome-associated membrane proteins: Characterization of LAMP-1 in macrophage P388 and mouse embryo 3T3 cultured cells. *Arch Biochem Biophys* 239:574, 1985.

268. LEWIS V, GREEN SA, MARSH M, VIHKO P, HELENIUS A, MELLMAN I: Glycoproteins of the lysosomal membrane. *J Cell Biol* 100:1839, 1985.

269. LIPPINCOTT-SCHWARTZ J, FAMBROUGH DM: Lysosomal membrane dynamics: Structure and interorganellar movement of a major lysosomal membrane glycoprotein. *J Cell Biol* 102:1593, 1986.

270. MADDEN EA, STORRIE B: Identification of membrane proteins from isolated Chinese hamster ovary cell lysosomes. *J Cell Biol* 105:356, 1986.

271. CROZE E, IVANOV I, SNITKIN H, KREIBICH G, SABATINI DD, ROSENFELD MG: Biosynthesis of a cysteine-rich, highly glycosylated protein present in lysosomal and endosomal membranes. *J Cell Biol* 105:335, 1986.

272. BARRIOCANAL JG, BONIFACINO JS, YUAN L, SANDOVAL IV: Biosynthesis, glycosylation, movement through the Golgi system, and transport to lysosomes by an N-linked carbohydrate independent mechanism of three lysosomal integral membrane proteins. *J Biol Chem* 261:16755, 1986.

273. BARRIOCANAL JG, SUAREZ-QUIAN CA, BONIFACINO JS, YUAN L, SANDOVAL IV: Biosynthesis, processing in the Golgi system, transport to lysosomes and half lives of three lysosomal integral membrane proteins (LIMPs). *J Cell Biol* 105:355, 1986.

274. VON FIGURA K, HASILIK A: Lysosomal enzymes and their receptors. *Annu Rev Biochem* 55:167, 1986.

275. FARQUHAR MG: Progress in unraveling pathways of Golgi traffic. *Annu Rev Cell Biol* 1:447, 1985.

276. MARET A, POTIER P, SALVAYRE R, DOUSTE-BLAZY L: Modification of subunit interaction in membrane-bound acid β-glucosidase from Gaucher disease. *FEBS Lett* 160:93, 1983.

277. BASU A, GLEW RH: Characterization of the phospholipid requirement of a rat liver β-glucosidase. *Biochem J* 224:515, 1984.

278. SHEH L, GLEW RH: High-resolution proton nuclear magnetic resonance studies of the glucocerebrosidase activator protein from Gaucher spleen. *Biochemistry* 24:6645, 1985.

279. GLEW RH, COFFEE CJ: Calmodulin and Parvalbumin: Activators of human liver glucocerebrosidase. *Arch Biochem Biophys* 229:55, 1984.

280. GARRETT KO, PRENCE EM, GLEW RH: Sucrose gradient analysis of phospholipid-activated β-glucosidase in type 1 and type 2 Gaucher's disease. *Arch Biochem Biophys* 238:344, 1985.

281. RADIN NS: Inhibitors and stimulators of glucocerebrosidase metabolism. *Prog Clin Biol Res* 95:357, 1982.

282. BASU A, PRENCE E, GARRETT K, GLEW RH, ELLINGSON JS: *Arch Biochem Biophys* 243:28, 1985.

283. OSIECKI-NEWMAN KM, FABBRO D, DINUR T, BOAS S, GATT S, LEGLER G, DESNICK RJ, GRABOWSKI GA: Human acid beta-glucosidase: Affinity purification of the normal placental and Gaucher disease splenic enzymes on N-alkyl-deoxynojirimycin-sepharose. *Enzyme* 35:147, 1986.

284. GLEW RH, DANIELS LB, CLARK LS, HOYER SW: Enzymatic differentiation of neurologic and nonneurologic forms of Gaucher's disease. *J Neuropathol Exp Neurol* 41:630, 1982.

285. CHOY FYM: Gaucher disease: The effects of phosphatidylserine on gluco-cerebrosidase from normal and Gaucher fibroblasts. *Hum Genet* 67:432, 1984.

286. GRABOWSKI GA, GOLDBLATT J, DINUR T, KRUSE J, SVENNERHOLM L, GATT S, DESNICK RJ: Genetic heterogeneity in Gaucher disease: Physico-kinetic and immunologic studies of the residual enzyme in cultured fibroblasts from nonneuronopathic and neuronopathic patients. *Am J Med Genet* 21:529, 1985.

287. LEGLER G: Labelling of the active centre of a beta-glucosidase. *Biochim Biophys Acta* 151:728, 1968.

288. GRABOWSKI GA, GATT S, KRUSE JR, DESNICK RJ: Human lysosomal β-glucosidase: Kinetic characterizaton of the catalytic, aglycon and hydrophobic binding-sites. *Arch Biochem Biophys* 231:144, 1984.

289. WARREN KR, SCHAFER IA, SULLIVAN JC, PETRELLI M, RADIN NS: The effects of N-hexyl-O-glucosylsphingosine in normal cultured human fibroblasts: A chemical model for Gaucher disease. *J Lipid Res* 17:132, 1976.

290. SAUL R, CHAMBERS JP, MOLYNEUX RJ, ELBEIN AD: Castanospermine, a tetrahydroxylated alkaloid that inhibits β-glucosidase and β-glucocerebrosidase. *Arch Biochem Biophys* 221:593, 1983.

291. LEGLER G, LIEDTKE H: Glucosylceramidase from calf spleen. Characterization of its active site with β-N-alkylumbelliferyl-β-glucosides and N-alkyl-derivatives of 1-deoxynojirimycin. *Biol Chem Hoppe Seyler* 366:1113, 1985.

292. VAN DIGGELEN OP, GALJAARD N, SINNOTT ML, SMITH J: Specific inactivation of lysosomal glycosidases in living fibroblasts by the corresponding glycosylmethyl-p-nitrophenyltriazenes. *Biochem J* 188:337, 1980.

293. TOMICH J, MARTIN B, BARRANGER J: Unpublished data.

294. SARMIENTOS F, SCHWARZMANN G, SANDHOFF K: Specificity of human glucosylceramide beta-glucosidase towards synthetic glucosylsphingolipids inserted into liposomes. Kinetic studies in a detergent-free assay system. *Eur J Biochem* 360:527, 1986.

295. Searches were performed using the Protein Identification Resource (PIR) sponsored by the National Biomedical Research Foundation and Division of Research Resources, NIH.

296. DINUR T, OSIECKI KM, LEGLER G, GATT S, DESNICK RJ, GRABOWSKI A: Human acid β-glucosidase: Isolation and amino acid sequence of a peptide containing the catalytic site. *Proc Natl Acad Sci USA* 83:1660, 1986.

297. The retroviral vector, pWE, was kindly provided by Dr. Richard C. Mulligan.

298. LEGLER G, HARDER A: Amino acid sequence at the active site of beta-glucosidase A from bitter almonds. *Biochim Biophys Acta* 524:102, 1978.

299. BAUSE E, LEGLER G: Isolation and amino acid sequence of a hexadecapeptide from the active site of beta-glucosidase A3 from Aspergillus wentii. *Hoppe-Seyler's Z Physiol Chem* 355:438, 1974.

300. HARTLEY WJ, BLAKEMORE WF: Neurovisceral glucocerebroside storage (Gaucher's disease) in a dog. *Vet Pathol* 10:191, 1973.

301. CHOUDARY PV, GINNS EI, CEPKO CL, MULLIGAN RC, TSUJI S, MAYOR J, BARRANGER JA: Gene transfer by retrovirus and expression of active human glucocerebrosidase. *Fed Proc* 45:1772, 1986.

302. SORGE J, KUHL W, WEST C, BEUTLER E: Complete correction of the enzymatic defect of type I Gaucher disease fibroblasts by retroviral-mediated gene transfer. *Proc Natl Acad Sci USA* 84:906, 1987.

303. YEAGER AM, BRENNAN S, TIFFANY C, MOSER HW, SANTOS GW: Prolonged survival and remyelination after hematopoietic cell transplantation in the twitcher mouse. *Science* 225:1052, 1984.

304. NEUFELD EF, ASHWELL G: Carbohydrate recognition systems for receptor-mediated pinocytosis, in Lennarz WL (ed): *The Biochemistry of Glycoproteins and Proteoglycans*. New York, Plenum, 1980, chap 6.

305. KAPLAN A, ACHORD DT, SLY WS: Phosphohexosyl components of a lysosomal enzyme are recognized by pinocytosis receptors on human fibroblasts. *Proc Natl Acad Sci USA* 74:2026, 1977.

306. VON FIGURA K, WEBER E: An alternative hypothesis of cellular transport of lysosomal enzymes in fibroblasts. *Biochem J* 176:943, 1978.

307. FISCHER HD, GONZALEZ-NORIEGA A, SLY WS, MORRE DJ: Phosphomannosylenzyme receptors in rat liver. *J Biol Chem* 255:9608, 1980.

308. VARKI A, KORNFELD S: Structural studies of phosphorylated high mannose-type oligosaccharides. *J Biol Chem* 255:10847, 1980.

309. REITMAN ML, KORNFELD S: Lysosomal enzyme targeting; N-acetylglucos-aminyl-phosphotransferase selectively phosphorylates native lysosomal enzymes. *J Biol Chem* 256:11977, 1981.

310. MILSTEIN C, BROWNLEE G, HARRISON T, MATTHEWS MB: A possible precursor of immunoglobulin light chains. *Nature New Biol* 239:117, 1972.

311. DEVILLERS-THIERY A, KINDT T, SCHEELE G, BLOBEL G: Homology in amino-terminal sequence of precursors to pancreatic secretory proteins. *Proc Natl Acad Sci USA* 72:5016, 1975.

312. BLOBEL G, DOBBERSTEIN B: Transfer of proteins across membranes, II. Reconstitution of functional rough microsomes from heterologous components. *J Cell Biol* 67:852, 1975.

313. WALTER P, BLOBEL G: Translocation of proteins across the endoplasmic reticulum, III. Signal recognition protein (SRP) causes signal sequence-dependent and site-specific arrest of chain elongation that is released by microsomal membranes. *J Cell Biol* 91:557, 1981.

314. WICKNER W: Assembly of proteins into membranes. *Science* 210:861, 1980.

315. KORNFELD R, KORNFELD S: Comparative aspects of glycoprotein structure. *Annu Rev Biochem* 45:217, 1976.

316. GIBSON R, KORNFELD S, SCHLESINGER S: A role for oligosaccharides in glycoprotein biosynthesis. *Trends Biochem Sci* 5:290, 1980.

317. WAGH PV, BAHL OP: Sugar residues on proteins. *CRC Crit Rev Biochem* 10:307, 1981.

318. STRUCK D, LENNARZ W: The function of saccharide lipids in synthesis of glycoproteins, in Lennarz WJ (ed): *The Biochemistry of Glycoproteins and Proteoglycans*. New York, Plenum, 1980, chap 2.

319. HUBBARD SC, IVATT RJ: Synthesis and processing of asparagine-linked oligosaccharides. *Annu Rev Biochem* 50:555, 1981.

320. HASILIK A: Biosynthesis of lysosomal enzymes. *Trends Biochem Sci* 5:237, 1980.

321. ERIKSON AH, CONNER GE, BLOBEL G: Biosynthesis of a lysosomal enzyme. *J Biol Chem* 256:11224, 1981.

322. WAHEED S, POHLMANN R, HASILIK A, VON FIGURA K: Subcellular location of two enzymes involved in the synthesis of phosphorylated recognition markers in lysosomal enzymes. *J Biol Chem* 256:4150, 1981.

323. VAN DER BERGH FA, TAGER JM: Localization of neutral glycosphingo lipids in human plasma. *Biochim Biophys Acta* 441:391, 1976.

324. BEAUDET A: Gaucher's disease. *N Engl J Med* 316:619, 1987.

325. CHRISTOMANOU H, AIGNESBERGER A, LINKE RP: Immunochemical characterization of two activator proteins stimulating enzymic sphingomyelin degradation in vitro. Absence of one of them in a human Gaucher disease variant. *Biol Chem Hoppe Seyler* 367:879, 1986.

326. OSIECKI-NEWMAN K, FABBRO D, LEGLER G, DESNICK RJ, GRABOWSKI GA: Human acid beta-glucosidase: Use of inhibitors, alternative substrates and amphiphiles to investigate the properties of the normal and Gaucher disease active sites. *Biochim Biophys Acta* 915:87, 1987.

327. TSUJI S, MARTIN BM, BARRANGER JA, STUBBLEFIELD B, LAMARCA M, GINNS EI: Genetic heterogeneity in Type 1 Gaucher disease: Multiple genotypes in Ashkenazic and non-Ashkenazic individuals. *Proc Natl Acad Sci USA* 85:2349, 1988.

328. CHOUDARY PV, TSUJI S, MARTIN BM, GUILD BC, MULLIGAN RC, MURRAY GJ, BARRANGER JA, GINNS EI: The molecular biology of Gaucher disease and the potential for gene therapy. *Cold Spring Harbor Symp Quant Biol* LI:1047, 1986.

CHAPTER 68

GALACTOSYLCERAMIDE LIPIDOSIS:
Globoid-Cell Leukodystrophy (Krabbe Disease)

KUNIHIKO SUZUKI
YOSHIYUKI SUZUKI

1. *Krabbe globoid-cell leukodystrophy is a rapidly progressive, invariably fatal disease of infants. The onset of symptoms is usually between ages 3 to 6 months. The disease usually begins with ambiguous symptoms such as irritability or hypersensitivity to external stimuli, but soon progresses to severe mental and motor deterioration. Pyrimidal tract signs are prominent. There is hypertonicity with hyperactive reflexes in the early stages, but patients later become flaccid and hypotonic. Blindness and deafness are common. Patients rarely survive the second year. There are clinical and laboratory signs of peripheral neuropathy. Systemic manifestations are rare. The disease is transmitted as an autosomal recessive trait. The clinical picture is relatively uniform, but atypical or late onset forms of the disease are known.*

2. *The presence of numerous multinucleated globoid cells in the white matter is the morphologic basis for diagnosis. The globoid cells are macrophages of mesodermal origin that contain undigested galactocerebroside. Severe myelin loss and astrocytic gliosis complete the pathologic picture in the white matter. Segmental demyelination, axonal degeneration, fibrosis, and histiocytic infiltration are also common in the peripheral nervous system.*

3. *Consistent with myelin loss, the white matter is depleted of all lipids, particularly glycolipids. The ratio of galactocerebroside to sulfatide is abnormally high. Galactocerebroside (galactosylceramide) (Fig. 68-1) is a sphingoglycolipid containing sphingosine, fatty acid, and galactose normally found almost exclusively in the myelin sheath.*

4. *The cause of Krabbe disease is a genetic deficiency of galactosylceramidase (galactocerebroside β-galactosidase). This lysosomal enzyme normally cleaves galactocerebroside to ceramide and galactose. It is postulated that accumulation of a related metabolite, psychosine, which is also a substrate for the missing enzyme, leads to early destruction of the oligodendroglia. The total brain content of galactocerebroside is thus not increased.*

5. *Assays of galactosylceramidase in leukocytes, serum, or cultured fibroblasts with the use of appropriate natural glycolipid substrates provide the means for definitive antemortem diagnosis.*

6. *There is no specific therapy for affected patients, but preventive measures are available through genetic counseling and intrauterine diagnosis of affected fetuses by galactosylceramidase assays on amniotic fluid cells or biopsied chorionic villi.*

7. *Globoid-cell leukodystrophy occurs in other mammalian species, most notably in certain strains of dogs and mice. Clinical and pathologic features are similar to those in the human disease. The animal diseases are also caused by a genetic deficiency of galactosylceramidase, thus providing an invaluable tool for study of this rare disease.*

HISTORY

In 1916 Krabbe described clinical and histologic findings in two sibs who died of an "acute infantile familial diffuse sclerosis of the brain."[1] He noted familial occurrence, early onset of spasticity, and a rapidly progressive course to death. He gave a detailed description of the globoid cells, the histologic hallmark of the disease. A retrospective search of the neuropathologic literature revealed two earlier descriptions of similar abnormal cells.[2,3] Collier and Greenfield[4] were the first to coin the term *globoid* to describe the numerous abnormal cells in the white matter.

Hallervorden's earlier suggestion[5] that globoid cells might contain kerasin (a cerebroside) received the support of chemical[6,7] and histochemical studies.[8–10] The experimental induction of the globoid-cell reaction by intracerebral implantation of galactosylceramide, a reaction not duplicated by any other lipids tested,[11–13] further supported the close relationship between the globoid cells and cerebroside. Analytically, the most consistent abnormality in the white matter appeared to be the reduced ratio of sulfatide to cerebroside.[14,15] In 1970 a profound deficiency of galactosylceramidase as the underlying genetic defect of the disease was demonstrated in the brain, liver, spleen, and kidney.[16–18] The same deficiency was then also found in peripheral leukocytes, serum, and cultured fibroblasts,[19] and prenatal diagnosis of an affected fetus was first accomplished in 1971.[20] The hypothesis of toxic effect of a related metabolite, galactosylsphingosine (psychosine), first proposed in 1972 as the critical biochemical pathogenetic mechanism of the disease,[21] has been largely substantiated in human and animal models of the disease.[22] No molecular genetic information is available due to the difficulty of obtaining sufficiently pure enzyme or antibody.

INCIDENCE AND HEREDITY

Globoid-cell leukodystrophy is a rare disease. The mode of inheritance is autosomal recessive. Both sexes are equally affected. The number of biochemically confirmed cases has been increasing since enzyme assays became common for the diagnosis of this disease, with synthetic colored and fluorescent substrates as well as natural lipid substrate, such as galactosylceramide or lactosylceramide.[19,23–26] The geographic distri-

Fig. 68-1 Galactosylceramide (galactocerebroside) and the defect in Krabbe disease.

bution is widespread. The disease has been recorded in England, Germany, France, Italy, Switzerland, the Netherlands, Poland, Russia, the United States, Canada, Japan, India, Spain, Thailand, and other countries. The incidence among the general population is not known; however, it appears to be higher in the Scandinavian countries. Hagberg et al.[27] reported 32 Swedish cases during the period from 1953 through 1967 and calculated the incidence as 1.9×10^{-5} per birth. Metzke et al.[28] found six patients in 6 years in Germany, although they did not calculate the incidence of the disease there. One of the authors (Y.S.) found at least 25 cases in Japan between 1972 and 1986 reported on the basis of enzymatic diagnosis. The incidence was calculated approximately as 1 in 100,000 to 200,000 births. Recently a report appeared of a very high incidence in a large Druze kindred in Israel.[29] The diagnosis of 12 children was confirmed by enzymatic diagnosis between 1969 and 1983. There were approximately 2000 births. The calculated incidence was 6 in 1000 live births, and the carrier frequency was 0.15 in this community.

CLINICAL MANIFESTATIONS

Age of Onset and Clinical Course

Typical infantile patients develop first clinical signs and symptoms at 3 to 6 months after birth, but there are cases of very early or late onset with atypical clinical manifestations. Neurologic or nonneurologic signs were detected in some cases during the neonatal period or within several weeks after birth. Stiffness was observed during the neonatal period in the patient of Schochet et al.[30]; fists were clenched and the extremities extended. A patient showed pronounced irritability and twitching soon after birth.[31] Subsequently, progressive feeding difficulty, wasting, and drowsiness appeared, and generalized muscle weakness and flaccidity was noted on admission at 8 weeks of age. Vomiting was the prominent initial sign during the first week of life in one patient.[32]

Cases of late onset have been reported with increasing frequency in recent years. Until enzymatic diagnosis was possible, diagnosis was made on the basis of the characteristic neuropathology in late infancy,[33] childhood,[34,35-38] and adulthood.[39-43] In rare cases, clinical onset is delayed until late infancy.[41] Recently there have been increasing reports of even later onset of globoid-cell leukodystrophy, either in childhood[2,4,34,39,42-45] or in adulthood.[46-50] Eighteen enzymatically proven cases are known to the authors.[34,44-53] The age of onset was up to 2 years in six cases, 2 to 5 years in nine cases, and 5 to 10 years in three cases. Clinical manifestations of these patients are significantly different from those of typical infantile patients.

Infantile Globoid-Cell Leukodystrophy

The clinical course and manifestations are rather stereotypical in typical infantile cases. However, clinical heterogeneity has become obvious since the advent of widely available enzymatic diagnosis.

Krabbe's original report[1] of five patients is the classic description of the typical clinical course and manifestations of the disease. The course of the disease is steadily and rapidly progressive. Hagberg[54] has divided it into three stages. Stage I is characterized by generalized hyperirritability, hyperesthesia, episodic fever of unknown origin, and some stiffness of the limbs. The child, apparently normal for the first few months after birth, becomes hypersensitive to auditory, tactile, or visual stimuli and begins to cry frequently without apparent cause. Slight retardation or regression of psychomotor development, vomiting with feeding difficulty, and convulsive seizures may occur as initial clinical symptoms. The cerebrospinal fluid protein level is already increased. In stage II, rapid and severe motor and mental deterioration develops. There is marked hypertonicity, with extended and crossed legs, flexed arms, and the backward-bent head. Tendon reflexes are hyperactive. Minor tonic or clonic seizures occur. Optic atrophy and sluggish pupillary reactions to light may be observed. Stage III is the "burnt-out stage," attained often within a few weeks or months. The infant is decerebrate and blind and has no contact with the surroundings. Deafness may appear. The final stage may last for many years, although patients rarely survive for more than 2 years.

Head size is often small,[55-58] but may be large.[33,59] Hydrocephalus has been observed.[60] Convulsive seizures occur frequently, but infantile spasms are unusual.[61,62]

The symptoms and signs are usually confined to the nervous system. No visceromegaly is present. Vomiting is sometimes prominent, resulting in progressive loss of weight and emaciation. The patient of Hagberg et al.[32] started vomiting during the first week of life, which caused malnutrition and necessitated hospitalization at 10 weeks of age. An infant was hospitalized at 8 weeks of age because of progressive feeding difficulty, generalized weakness, tachypnea, and minor motor seizures.[31] The clinical course was characterized by rapidly progressive respiratory failure and neurologic deterioration culminating in death at age 15 weeks. The lung biopsy revealed widespread distension of alveoli and alveolar ducts by numerous large macrophage-like cells containing amorphous, electron-dense, membrane-bound cytoplasmic inclusions. However, no crystalloid or tubular inclusions typical of globoid cells were found. Bouts of hyperthermia, possibly caused by involvement of the hypothalamic system, have been reported in the absence of infection.[1,32,63] Obesity in one patient[55] was not explained by lesions in the hypothalamus. Generalized ichthyosis was present from early infancy in one patient.[64]

Involvement of the peripheral nerves was once considered uncommon in globoid-cell leukodystrophy. Since the first report of the peripheral nervous system pathology by Matsuyama et al.,[65] extensive clinical and pathologic studies have been carried out on peripheral nerve lesions. Clinical examination does not always reveal neuropathy, especially in the early stages, because symptoms and signs of central nervous system involvement are overwhelming. Krabbe[1] pointed out that knee jerks could not be elicited in any of his original five patients and also that stiffness passed into a flaccid state toward the end of the disease. Since then several authors have reported absent or depressed tendon reflexes in a single examination[55,58,62,66–71] or disappearance of tendon reflexes in the course of the disease.[44,56,71,72] There are descriptions of patients with normal[33] or hyperactive[73] tendon reflexes at age 15 months.

Some patients showed slow development for the first few months after birth,[7,34,35,74] possibly because of early undetected symptoms. One patient, whose diagnosis had been established by amniocentesis at 5 months' gestation,[75] was normal neurologically during the neonatal period, but deep-tendon reflexes were already absent at 5 weeks of age, although movement and muscle tone of the extremities were apparently normal. Electromyography revealed reduced insertional activity. At 7 weeks, the peripheral nerve conduction velocity was markedly reduced. Clinically, psychomotor development was normal for the first 2 months, and weakness of neck muscles was first found at 3 months of age. These findings suggest that previously reported patients with this disease may also have developed clinical manifestations earlier than the described age of onset, if examined carefully.

Atypical Cases

Some patients have atypical or misleading clinical histories. Wallace et al.[66] reported a patient who developed mental deterioration, apparently after mumps, at age 5 months. Convulsions started at age 7 months, and the disease progressed. The clinical diagnosis was mumps encephalitis, and the final diagnosis was established only at autopsy. A patient with a rapid course (total 3 months) was diagnosed as having encephalitis.[67] Another patient[60] was irritable from the neonatal period, and her psychomotor development was markedly retarded by age 4 months, with intermittent opisthotonus and increasing feeding difficulties. The head circumference increased progressively, with a bulging fontanelle and a right abducens palsy 2 weeks after pneumoencephalography. The hydrocephalus persisted in spite of a ventriculoperitoneal shunting operation.

Late Onset Globoid-Cell Leukodystrophy

The late onset form of the disease is probably genetically distinct from the more common infantile form. Globoid cells in the central nervous system were the only diagnostic hallmark of globoid-cell leukodystrophy before the enzymatic diagnosis.[19] Because of the unusual clinical course, patients with late onset globoid-cell leukodystrophy were commonly diagnosed as having diffuse sclerosis of other types or "Schilder disease,"[76] and the correct diagnosis was made only by histologic examination. Eighteen case reports with enzymatic confirmation of the diagnosis have been collected by the authors. All of these patients developed initial clinical signs and symptoms by 10 years of age, and no case has been reported with onset in later years, although some patients have survived up to adult ages with protracted clinical courses.

Loonen et al.[51] divided the 18 late onset patients including their own case into two groups: late infantile (or early childhood) and juvenile (late childhood) types. In the first group (onset at 6 months to 3 years), irritability, psychomotor regression, stiffness, ataxia, and loss of vision were observed as initial symptoms. The course of most cases was progressive, resulting in death approximately 2 years after the onset. In the second group (onset 3 to 8 years), the patients developed loss of vision, together with hemiparesis, ataxia, and psychomotor regression. The course was generally protracted, and none of the patients died during the follow-up period, which varied from 10 months to 7 years. Most patients with the late onset form of the disease showed rapid deterioration initially, followed by a more gradual progression lasting for years. Developmental delay was recorded in some cases prior to the onset of deterioration.[34,44,45,47] In only two patients[46,49] were convulsive seizures observed during the course of the disease.

The case of Fluharty et al.[52] may be classified as "late infantile" although the disease became manifest at 3½ years of age, if the clinical signs and symptoms are considered. The genetic relationship of the late and infantile onset groups should be further evaluated, because there are reports of sibling cases with variable ages of onset and different clinical manifestations. In the reports of Crome et al.[34] and Hanefeld et al.[45]

Table 68-1 Clinical Forms of Globoid-Cell Leukodystrophy

Clinical forms	Age of onset, years	Duration, years	Clinical signs and symptoms	Peripheral neuropathy	CSF protein	Pathology	Galactosylceramidase
Infantile	¼–½	<1	Psychomotor deterioration Irritability Pyramidal signs Optic atrophy Convulsion	+	Increased	Globoid cells	Deficient
Late infantile	½–3	1–3	Psychomotor deterioration Irritability Pyramidal signs Ataxia Loss of vision	+	Increased	Globoid cells	Deficient
Juvenile	3–10	>5	Psychomotor deterioration Loss of vision Hemiparesis Ataxia	− or +	Normal or increased	Not described	Deficient
Adult	10–35	2–5	Mental retardation Pyramidal signs Loss of vision	Not described	Normal	Globoid cells	Not described

(same cases), the sister (case 1) developed loss of vision at 5½ years of age, while her brother (case 2) became ataxic and irritable at 2¾ years. They can be classified as juvenile and late infantile types, respectively, by the criteria of Loonen et al.[51] (These reports described the same patients but they were listed separately by Loonen et al.[51]). Therefore, the number of cases they collected was actually 15. These clinical types are summarized in Table 68-1 on the previous page.

The cerebrospinal fluid protein was elevated in most cases of late infantile type, while it was normal or only mildly elevated in the juvenile-type patients reported. Peripheral nerve conduction velocity is generally reduced in late infantile patients and normal in juvenile patients, with some exceptions. In one late onset case (4 years), the conduction velocity of the median nerve was markedly reduced, although the sural nerve biopsy was normal.[36]

CLINICAL DIAGNOSIS

In the infantile cases, globoid-cell leukodystrophy should be strongly suspected with the following clinical features: early onset in infancy, irritability and muscle hypertonicity with progressive neurologic deterioration, signs of peripheral neuropathy, and elevation of cerebrospinal fluid protein levels. The disease can be differentiated from nonprogressive CNS disorders of congenital or perinatal origin on the basis of a history of normal development for the first few months after birth followed by psychomotor deterioration. Rarely, the disease may first be considered to be of traumatic, inflammatory, or neoplastic origin in atypical cases, but careful evaluation of the clinical picture and appropriate laboratory investigation usually exclude these possibilities.

Differentiation from other heredodegenerative diseases of infancy is often a major problem. Metachromatic leukodystrophy usually begins in the second year of life, with slowly progressive motor disturbance as the initial symptom. Spongy degeneration of white matter begins in early infancy and is characterized by an enlarged head, initial hypotonia, and normal CSF protein concentration. Alexander disease includes megalocephaly as a characteristic sign, but otherwise there are no specific clinical manifestations. Pelizaeus-Merzbacher disease may occur in the first year of life. The disease has a slowly progressive course, and abnormal involuntary eye movements, often described as nystagmus, are prominent and of diagnostic help. The cerebrospinal fluid protein concentration is normal. Inheritance of Pelizaeus-Merzbacher disease is generally considered to be X-linked recessive. Tay-Sachs disease (see Chap. 72) is manifested in early infancy; the presence of cherry-red spots is characteristic. The initial clinical findings is sluggishness or apathy rather than hyperirritability. G_{M1} gangliosidosis (see Chap. 71) has an early onset and, both clinically and radiologically, more resembles Hurler-Hunter disease than it does Krabbe disease. Gaucher disease (Chap. 67) and Niemann-Pick disease (Chap. 66) can be differentiated from Krabbe disease by visceromegaly.

In patients with atypical symptoms or courses, and in patients with the late onset form of the disease, it is practically impossible to make a clinical diagnosis of globoid-cell leukodystrophy. In any patients with progressively deteriorating diseases of the central nervous system of obscure origin, especially with peripheral nerve and cerebellar signs, the possibility of globoid-cell leukodystrophy should always be considered. Assays of serum, leukocytes, or cultured fibroblasts for activities of galactosylceramidase provide the most reliable means of antemortem diagnosis.

LABORATORY FINDINGS

No specific abnormalities can be found in blood chemistry tests and routine urinalysis.

The protein concentration is high in the spinal fluid of patients with the infantile or late infantile forms. The cell count is normal. The electrophoretic pattern may be of some diagnostic help; albumin and α_2-globulin levels are elevated, and β_1- and γ-globulin levels are decreased.[32,71] This pattern remains constant throughout the course of the disease and is found only in metachromatic and globoid-cell leukodystrophies.[77]

Allen and Reagan[78] found much-increased β-glucuronidase activity in the cerebrospinal fluid in globoid-cell leukodystrophy as well as in diffuse meningeal dissemination of neoplasm and in acute necrotic myelopathy. It was suggested that the increased β-glucuronidase activity was of diagnostic value in globoid-cell leukodystrophy if the clinical features are fully considered.[79]

Radiologic examinations usually reveal only diffuse and symmetric cerebral atrophy. Rarely is asymmetry demonstrated by pneumoencephalography or CT scan.[59,80,81] The latter can provide more information if carefully evaluated. CT scan in the early stage of the disease can be normal.[82] Later, lucencies in the white matter appear,[83] and diffuse cerebral atrophy develops involving both gray and white matter at the third stage.[80] These findings are nonspecific and are observed in many white matter diseases. Baram et al.[84] reported CT and magnetic resonance imaging (MRI) patterns associated with evolution of the disease. At first, discrete and symmetric dense areas on CT were found in deep gray matter of the cerebral hemispheres, thalamus, posterior limb of the internal capsule, quadrigeminal plate and cerebellum, and also in periventricular and capsular white matter. MRI showed decreased T1 values with normal or slightly decreased T2 values in white matter of the centrum semiovale. Later, both CT and MRI showed diffuse reduction in gray matter and, more profoundly, in the white matter mass.

The electroencephalogram is normal in the initial stages, but the cerebral rhythms gradually become abnormal. Background activity becomes slow and disorganized[30,33,55,57,59,73,85–91] with changes that may be asymmetric.[59] This is often accompanied by multifocal paroxysmal or epileptic discharges.[30,33,55,61,74,88,89,92–94]

In accord with the clinical and pathologic observations of peripheral neuropathy, various abnormal results have been obtained by electrophysiological procedures. These include a mild increase in polyphasic motor unit potentials,[57] presence of a high amplitude neuromuscular unit with a decrease in the number of units,[61] and a few fibrillations[55,57] in the routine electromyogram. Motor nerve conduction velocity has been low in all patients examined.[44,55,57,61,63,64,91–97] Distal sensory latency of the median nerve was also prolonged in one patient.[57]

PATHOLOGY

All important pathologic changes are confined to the nervous system. Austin found abnormal droplets in the renal tubular epithelial cells, which stained bluish with toluidine blue.[70,98] Although its significance is uncertain, this is a noteworthy finding, because the kidney is the only extraneural organ that normally contains significant amounts of galactosylceramide. Multinucleated giant cells have been occasionally observed outside the nervous system, but they differ morphologically and can be distinguished from typical globoid cells.[87,99] In only one patient have giant cells similar to the globoid cells in white matter been observed in lung, lymph nodes, and spleen.[100] Congenital muscle-fiber-type disproportion has been reported.[101]

Central Nervous System

Gross Anatomy. The brain is usually markedly and uniformly reduced in size with shrunken gyri and widened sulci. On cut section the white matter is markedly reduced in volume and is of whitish-gray appearance and firm, rubberlike consistency. This appearance is due to widespread diffuse demyelination and severe astrocytic gliosis. White matter changes are often more severe posterosuperiorly within the cerebral hemispheres. The subcortical arcuate fibers tend to be spared. Phylogenetically newer tracts are usually more severely involved. In contrast to the grossly abnormal appearance of the white matter, the gray matter appears relatively normal, except for reduced cortical thickness.

Histology. Histologic involvement of the white matter is always much more severe than that of the gray matter. The major abnormalities are presence of numerous globoid cells, astrocytic gliosis, and severe lack of myelin (Fig. 68-2).

Fig. 68-2 Typical light-microscopic appearance of the white matter of globoid-cell leukodystrophy. Conspicuous clusters of globoid cells occupy a considerable portion of whole white matter. Globoid cells are PAS-positive as shown here, and many contain multiple nuclei. The remainder of the tissue is mostly occupied by reactive astrocytes. PAS stain, × 120. (Courtesy of Dr. Kinuko Suzuki.)

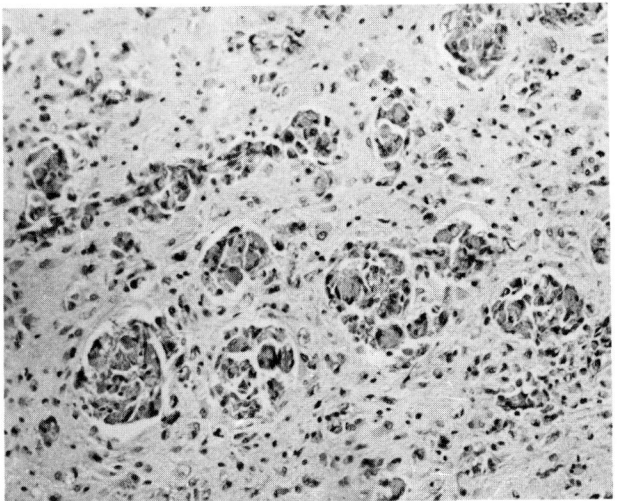

Globoid Cells. Conventionally, the characteristic abnormal cells, abundantly present in the white matter, are classified into two categories: epithelioid cells (globoid cells) and globoid bodies.[102,103] The epithelioid cells are medium-sized, round or oval mononuclear cells. The globoid bodies are large, irregular, multinucleated cells, ranging from 20 to 50 μm in diameter, with as many as 15 to 20 nuclei located near the plasma membrane. Aside from the number of nuclei, these cells are identical in staining characteristics, and among them are always cells which could be considered transitional. Experimental evidence strongly indicates that these two types of cells have the same origin.[11–13]

The mononuclear globoid cells are scattered in white matter, most typically as perivascular packets of 10 to 20 cells. These cells are more common in recently affected areas than in the old lesions in the deep white matter. The globoid cells contain pale nuclei with prominent nucleoli. The cytoplasm is abundant and stains moderately positive with periodic acid–Schiff stain, and faintly positive with Sudan black B and Sudan IV. The cytoplasm is not metachromatic with the cresyl violet stain at acid pH. The globoid cells exhibit intense acid phosphatase activity.[56,66,98,104,105] The similarities in the morphologic and histochemical characteristics between the globoid cells and the glucosylceramide-containing abnormal cells in Gaucher disease have often been pointed out.[5,8]

A transient globoid-cell reaction virtually indistinguishable from the reaction in globoid-cell leukodystrophy can be produced experimentally in rats by intracerebral injection of solid galactosylceramide.[11–13] The experimental globoid cells are identical in appearance and staining properties to the globoid cells in Krabbe disease. Galactosylceramide appears to be the only compound capable of inducing the histologic globoid-cell reaction; sulfatide, glucosylceramide, ceramide, ganglioside, and acid mucopolysaccharides are all ineffective. Similar multinucleated cells also have been produced in tissue culture of the retina by the addition of cerebroside to the media.[106]

The origin of the globoid cells in Krabbe disease has been a subject of considerable controversy. They have been stated to be of glial origin,[4] including microglia,[7] microglia and astrocytes,[107] astrocytes and adventitial cells,[108] and oligodendroglia.[109] However, the experimental production of globoid cells provided strong evidence that globoid cells are derived from nonneural, mesodermal cells. No transition from oligodendroglial cells or astrocytes to globoid cells was observed. The predominantly perivascular localization of globoid cells is difficult to explain on the basis of oligodendroglial or astrocytic origin. Recently, Oehmichen and Gruninger[110] suggested an interesting possibility. On the basis of DNA labeling with thymidine, they concluded that globoid cells experimentally produced in animal brain by galactosylceramide implantation are derived from mesodermal cells, but that the multinucleated globoid cells in the brains of patients are of astrocytic origin and only the mononuclear epithelioid cells are of mesodermal origin. The interpretation was made on the basis of light microscopy. However, ultrastructural studies of affected human brains from other laboratories have failed to demonstrate glial fibers within the globoid cells, leaving the suggestion of Oehmichen and Gruninger open to question. There is substantial morphologic and biochemical evidence to support the view that globoid cells are derived from mesodermal cells and that they are essentially macrophages. This view has been further supported recently in an immunohistochemical study of globoid cells in a murine model of the disease, the twitcher mutant.[111] The globoid cells were negative for glial fibrillary acidic protein and were positive for MAC-1, a macrophage marker.

Lack of Myelin. Myelin deficiency in the white matter of patients with globoid-cell leukodystrophy is generally profound, but the subcortical U fibers tend to be spared except in unusually severe cases, in which practically no myelin can be demonstrated within the cerebral hemispheres. Among the various white matter systems, phylogenetically newer areas tend to be more severely affected. Thus, the fornix, hippocampus, mamillothalamic tract, and white matter of basal ganglia tend to be less involved than the centrum semiovale or cerebellar white matter.[98,112,113] In the spinal cord, the pyramidal tracts are more severely affected than the dorsal columns. The areas with the most intense globoid-cell infiltration are usually the areas with the least amount of preserved myelin, and vice versa. Axons degenerate as they lose myelin. The oligodendroglial population is also severely diminished, and in the terminal state of some unusually severe cases oligodendrocytes may be difficult to find. Generally, there are no inflammatory changes or deposits of amorphous sudanophilic material. The white matter is not spongy or edematous.

Astrocytic Gliosis. Aside from the globoid cells, the areas of white matter previously occupied by axons, myelin, and oligodendroglial cells are filled with dense fibrous astrocytic proliferation. Although unusually severe, this appears to be fundamentally the same reactive astrocytic gliosis found in many other pathologic conditions.

Changes in Gray Matter. In contrast to the devastated white matter, the gray matter is generally much less affected. The cases reported by de Vries[114] and by Schenk et al.[115] are exceptional in that there were severe degenerative changes in the cerebral cortex. Typically, changes in the gray matter are limited to mild focal or laminar degenerative changes in the cerebral cortex and regressive changes in neurons of the pons, dentate nuclei, thalamus, and other areas.[7,67,107,114] A recent study of the cerebral cortex with the Golgi technique also indicated remarkable preservation of the neuronal processes.[116]

Evolution of Morphologic Changes. It is difficult to determine the chronological sequence of the various histologic changes described above, because it is rarely possible to follow morphologic changes in the same patient during the course of the illness. Even if this were possible, there are always great regional variations. D'Agostino et al.[74] attempted to formulate the chronological evolution of the morphologic changes through a study of multiple sections from three patients. Utilizing the degree of demyelination, they divided the course into four stages: (1) early, (2) advanced, (3) late, and (4) final. The early lesions are characterized by "the presence of both intracellular and extracellular PAS-positive material, with subsequent formation of mononuclear globoid cells and only a slight decrease in the intensity of myelin staining." In the advanced stage, the amounts of myelin and axons are decreased and astrocytic gliosis becomes prominent. The globoid cells are more numerous, tend to cluster around blood vessels, and may become multinucleated. In the late stage, the globoid cells become fewer in number and are mostly clumped around blood vessels. The amounts of myelin and axons are markedly diminished at this stage. The final stage is characterized by predominant astrocytic gliosis, few remaining globoid cells, and total loss of myelin and axons.

ULTRASTRUCTURE. Numerous reports describe the ultrastructural histopathology of globoid-cell leukodystrophy.[30,33,36,55,59,71,94,95,110,117–126] Mononuclear and multinucleated globoid cells appear similar, except for the number of nuclei. They both contain numerous fine tortuous cytoplasmic

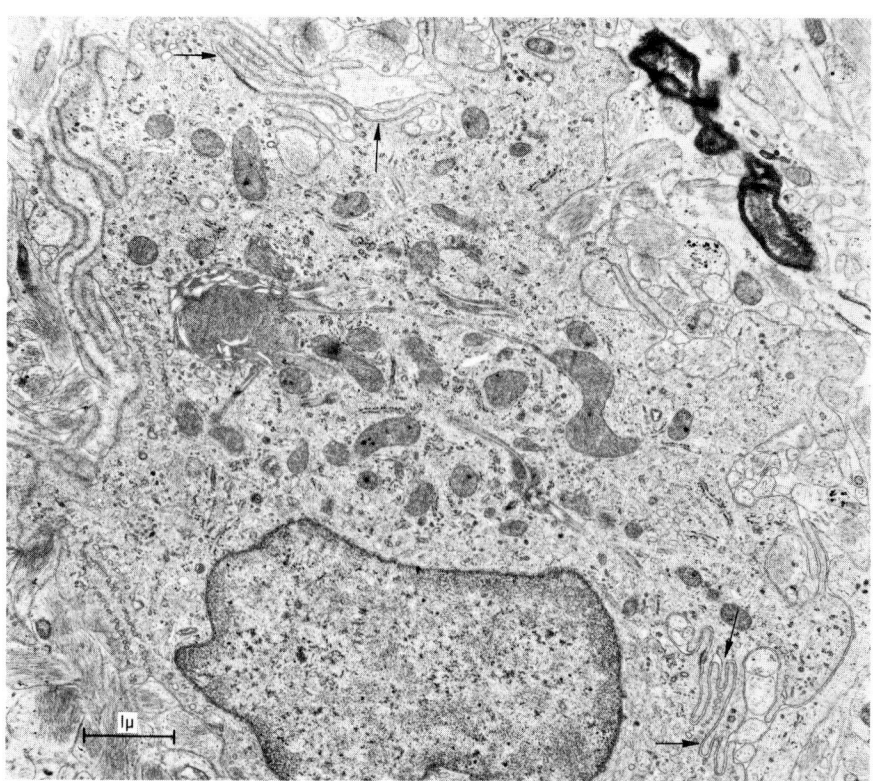

Fig. 68-3 A low magnification electron micrograph showing a globoid cell. Only one nucleus is visible. There are numerous tortuous pseudopods *(arrows)* which characterize this cell as a macrophage. Within the cytoplasm, near the center of the picture, there are many abnormal tubular inclusions (for details see Figs. 68-4 and 68-5). The line indicates a scale of 1 μm. *(Courtesy of Dr. Kinuko Suzuki.)*

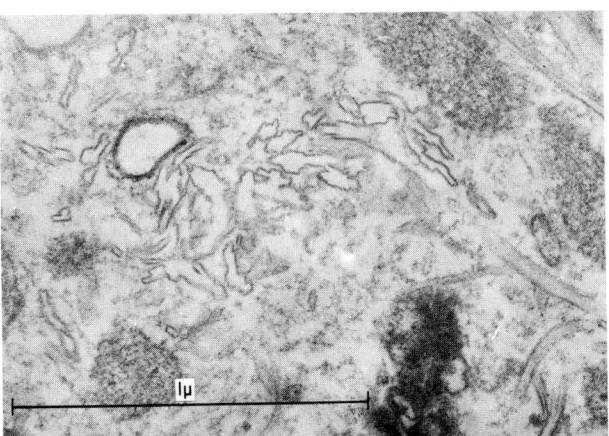

Fig. 68-4   An electron micrograph showing the characteristic hollow, polygonal, or crystalloid cut sections of the abnormal inclusions in the cytoplasm of a globoid cell. Several longitudinal sections of tubules of the same type are seen in the right side of the picture. The line indicates 1 μm. *(Courtesy of Dr. Kinuko Suzuki.)*

processes (pseudopods) which are characteristic of macrophages, moderately electron dense granular cytoplasm containing prominent rough endoplasmic reticulum, many free ribosomes, abundant fine filaments of approximately 9 to 10 nm, and scattered or clustered abnormal cytoplasmic inclusions (Fig. 68-3). The inclusions have moderately electron dense straight or curved hollow tubular profiles in longitudinal sections and appear irregularly crystalloid in cross sections (Figs. 68-4 and 68-5). Often they are freely scattered among the normal cytoplasmic organelles, but sometimes they are packed in an electron-lucent space in the cytoplasm, with or without an outer limiting membrane. These tubules often have longitudinal striations of variable density, approximately 6 nm in width. Another type of abnormal tubular inclusion, first described by Yunis and Lee,[59] has the structure of twisted tubules with 4- to 5-nm longitudinal striations and rectangular or irregularly round cross sections (Fig. 68-6). This second type of tubule is similar to those in Gaucher disease, but the first, larger tubules, with irregular, polygonal, or crystalloid cross sections, appear to be unique to globoid-cell leukodystrophy. Yunis and Lee[121] pointed out the morphologic similarities of these abnormal inclusions to negatively stained pure brain galactosylceramide. Ultrastructural studies of experimental globoid cells produced by intracerebral injection into rat brain of pure galactosylceramide showed both types of tu-

Fig. 68-5   The abnormal hollow tubules show longitudinal striations approximately 6 nm wide. The line indicates a scale of 1 μm.

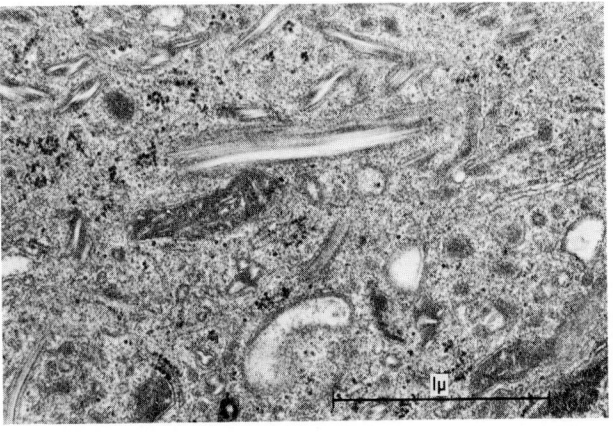

bules.[127,128] In fact, the ultrastructure of experimental globoid cells is essentially identical to that of human globoid cells (Figs. 68-7 and 68-8).

The ultrastructural appearance of human and experimental globoid cells, particularly the presence of numerous pseudopods, supports the view that these cells are macrophages. Astrocytes, identified by glial filaments, rarely contain the abnormal tubular inclusions. The few remaining oligodendroglial cells, identifiable by their dense cytoplasm and microtubules, were also free of the tubules. On the other hand, endothelial and perithelial cells often contained cytoplasmic inclusions similar to those in globoid cells.[55]

Degeneration of myelin, with or without associated axonal degeneration, is found in the white matter, but the remaining myelin has normal multilamellar configuration with normal periodicity. Cortical neurons appear normal ultrastructurally.

Peripheral Nervous System

Earlier, pathologic changes in peripheral nerves had been reported rather sporadically.[56,65,70] Some investigators did not find morphologic changes in peripheral nerves.[10,32,72,112] More recent histologic and ultrastructural studies have shown that the peripheral nervous system is commonly affected.[55,57,71,119,120,129–133] Dunn et al.[71] found peripheral nerve lesions in all of seven patients. Under light microscopy the peripheral nerve lesions consist of minimal to severe degenerative changes in axons and the myelin sheaths, associated with endoneurial fibrosis and the accumulation of foamy histiocytes around endoneurial blood vessels or trabeculae of the endoneurium. Segmental demyelination is common.[55,71,119,132] Typical globoid cells are not found in peripheral nerves. Ultrastructurally, straight or curved tubular inclusions, similar to those in globoid cells in the brain, are found scattered or clustered in the cytoplasm of histiocytes, in the proliferated endoneurial collagenous tissue, or around small blood vessels. These abnormal inclusions are often found in the Schwann cells also.[120,132] Axonal degeneration without segmental demyelination has been recorded.[134]

Peripheral nervous system lesions may be found also in the late onset form of the disease at autopsy. Pathologic findings of peripheral nerves are variable in late infantile patients at biopsy or autopsy; clear or minimal changes of segmental demyelination,[46] demyelination and remyelination in the paranodal regions,[49] or no abnormalities.[34] Partial myelination and loss of axons were reported in one autopsy case.[71]

BIOCHEMISTRY OF GALACTOSYLCERAMIDE

Chemistry of Galactosylceramide and Related Compounds

Galactosylceramide (galactocerebroside) belongs to the group of lipids generically called *sphingoglycolipids*. This name indicates that the molecule contains a long-chain base, sphingosine, and a sugar moiety. The major sphingosine found in nature is C_{18}-sphingosine, having the structure D(+)-erythro-1,3-dihydroxy-2-amino-4-trans-octadecene. In the galactosylceramide and sulfatide of normal adult human brains, C_{18}-sphingosine constitutes 95 percent or more of the total sphin-

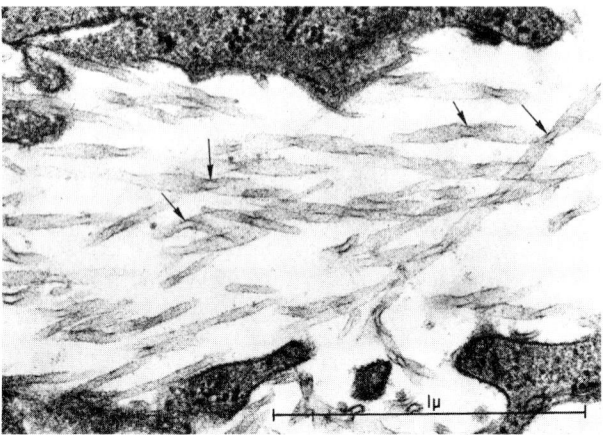

Fig. 68-6 Another type of abnormal inclusions in globoid cells. They have the structure of twisted tubules with 4- to 5-nm striations (arrows). The line indicates a scale of 1 μm. *(Courtesy of Dr. Eduardo J. Yunis.)*

gosine, the remainder being C_{18}-dihydrosphingosine and much smaller amounts of a shorter-chain analogue, C_{16}-sphingosine. In immature human brains there are higher proportions of C_{18}-dihydrosphingosine, sometimes comprising 10 percent of the total.[135]

The amino group of sphingosine is almost always acylated with long-chain fatty acid (C_{14} to C_{26}). *N*-Acylsphingosine is generically called *ceramide*, the basic common building block of almost all sphingolipids. Generally, the fatty acids of galactosylceramide and sulfatide in the brain are characterized by the predominance of longer-chain fatty acids (C_{20} to C_{26}), lack of polyunsaturated fatty acids, and the presence of α-hydroxy acids. Approximately two-thirds of the fatty acids in cerebrosides and one-third of those in sulfatides are α-hydroxy fatty acids. These are generally absent in other lipids of the brain, including glycerophospholipids, sphingomyelin, ceramide oligohexosides, and gangliosides. In galactocerebrosides and sulfatides, particularly those in white matter, 65 to 80 percent of the total unsubstituted fatty acids have chain lengths longer

Fig. 68-7 A high magnification electron micrograph of cytoplasm of a globoid cell experimentally produced in rat brain by intracerebral injection of solid galactocerebroside. Abnormal hollow tubules, identical to those seen in human globoid cells (Figs. 68-4 and 68-5), are scattered within the cytoplasm. Note the similarities of the overall appearance to Fig. 68-5, which was taken from a human globoid cell. The line indicates a scale of 1 μm. *(Courtesy of Dr. Kinuko Suzuki.)*

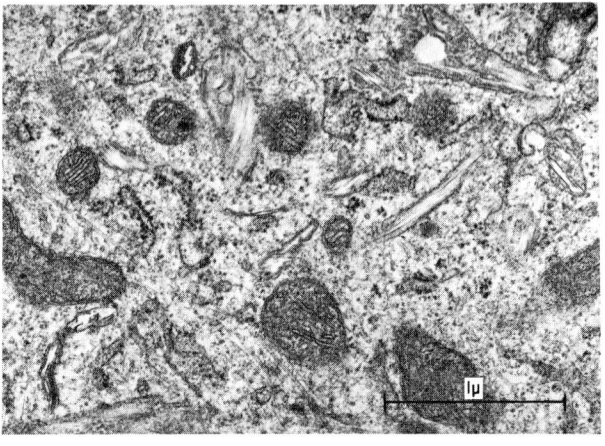

than 20 carbons. In the α-hydroxy fatty acids, the proportion of longer-chain fatty acids is even greater.

The hydroxyl group at C-1 of ceramide can be substituted for by a variety of compounds. Cerebroside is defined as a monohexosyl ceramide, the hexose being linked to the C-1 of ceramide by a glycosidic linkage. The hexose is either D-glucose or D-galactose. Depending on the nature of the hexose, the cerebroside is named *glucocerebroside* (glucosylceramide) or *galactocerebroside* (galactosylceramide). Both the glucose and galactose are in the β-anomeric configuration. Glucosylceramides occur predominantly in systemic tissues other than the nervous system and are essentially absent in normal human brain after age 1 year. They are present in small amounts in brains of normal human fetuses and newborns[136] and in the brains of older children with certain diseases, notably ganglioside storage disorders.[137,138] In contrast, galactosylceramide is characteristically a lipid of the nervous system, particularly of the myelin sheath (Fig. 68-9). Brain sulfatide is derived from galactosylceramide, having an additional sulfate group, esterlinked to the C-3 of galactose. Sulfatide is also present at high concentrations in myelin.

There are two other compounds chemically and metabolically related to galactosylceramide that are important biochemically and enzymologically in the pathogenesis of globoidcell leukodystrophy. *Galactosylsphingosine* (psychosine) is structurally galactosylceramide minus fatty acid. Although the compound is essentially absent in normal brain,[139-141] it is of potential importance when the dynamic behavior of galactosylceramide is considered in relation to the pathogenesis of the disease. Another related compound important in globoid-cell leukodystrophy is *lactosylceramide*, which has a lactose moiety, instead of galactose, at C-1 of ceramide. Lactosylceramide is distributed ubiquitously in most tissues, although its concentration is generally low.

Though detailed structures of the individual moieties, such as fatty acids or sphingosines, differ among these glycosphingolipids, the simplified notations are convenient for purposes of most discussions in this chapter. Figure 68-10 depicts chemical, and to a large extent also metabolic, relationships among galactosylceramide and related compounds using such simplified notations.

Metabolism of Galactosylceramide and Related Compounds

Two alternate pathways have been proposed for biosynthesis of galactosylceramide (Fig. 68-10). One is through psychosine, which is enzymatically synthesized from sphingosine and UDP-galactose.[142] Psychosine, in turn, could be acylated by acyl-CoA to form galactosylceramide.[143] However, enzymatic acylation of psychosine has not been unequivocally demonstrated. Meanwhile, it has been conclusively demonstrated that galactosylceramide can be synthesized through ceramide.[144,145] Biosynthesis of sulfatide occurs through cerebroside, with the "active sulfate," 3'-phosphoadenosine-5'-phosphosulfate (PAPS), as sulfate donor.[146]

The initial step in degradation of sulfatide is removal of the sulfate group to convert it to galactocerebroside. This reaction is catalyzed by cerebroside sulfate sulfatase, which is present in the arylsulfatase A fraction.[147] Deficiency of this enzyme characterizes another inherited leukodystrophy, metachromatic leukodystrophy, in which abnormal accumulation of sulfatide occurs[148,149] (also see Chap. 69).

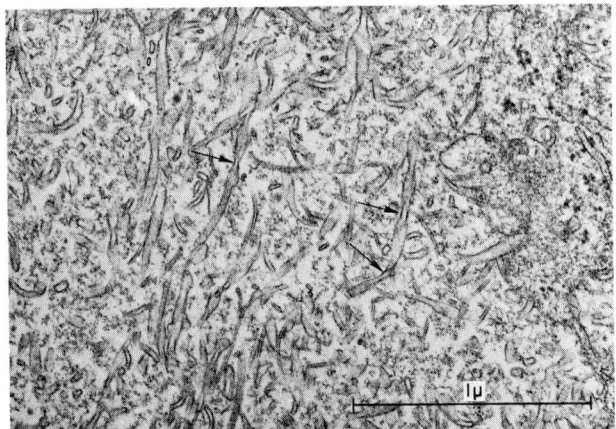

Fig. 68-8 Numerous slender, twisted tubules that were produced within experimental globoid cells in rat brain by the intracerebral injection of galactocerebroside purified from the brain of a human patient with globoid-cell leukodystrophy. The twisted configurations of the tubules are clearly seen (arrows). The ultrastructural appearance of these tubules is identical to those described by Yunis and Lee[59] in human globoid-cell leukodystrophy (Fig. 68-6). The line indicates a scale of 1 μm. (Courtesy of Dr. Kinuko Suzuki.)

Galactosylceramide is degraded to ceramide and galactose by a lysosomal hydrolytic enzyme, galactosylceramidase (galactocerebroside β-galactosidase), thus:

$$
\begin{array}{ccc}
& \text{galactosylceramidase} & \\
\text{Fatty acid} & | & \text{fatty acid} \\
| & | & | \quad + \text{ galactose} \\
\text{Sphingosine-galactose} & \longrightarrow & \text{sphingosine} \\
\text{(Galactosylceramide)} & & \text{(ceramide)}
\end{array}
$$

This enzyme in brain was first studied in detail by Radin and coworkers.[150–153] Ultracentrifugal fractionation indicated that it was associated with the lysosomal fraction. The pH optimum of the enzyme is 4.5. It is active on galactosylceramide with either unsubstituted or α-hydroxy fatty acids. In rat brain, galactosylceramidase is present before myelination when little galactosylceramide is present in the brain (at age 4 days), but the enzyme level then rises to three to four times the 4-day level during the period of active cerebroside deposition and myelination. The activity remains high in mature animals. In humans, the enzyme activity in gray matter of a 72-year-old brain was the same as that in a 21-year-old brain, but in white matter was decreased to 60 percent of the activity of the young brain.[16]

The enzyme is hydrophobic and exceedingly difficult to purify. Despite intensive efforts of several laboratories, there is

Fig. 68-9 Structure of galactocerebroside (galactosylceramide). The molecule consists of sphingosine, fatty acid, and galactose. R = —(CH$_2$)$_n$CH$_3$.

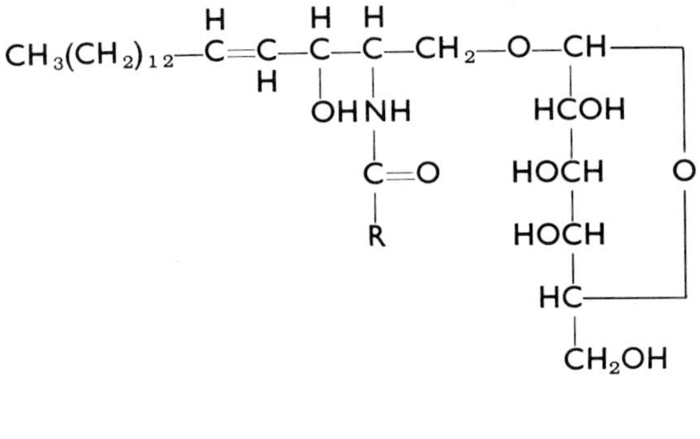

no reproducible procedure available to purify galactosylceramidase.[154–162] No polyclonal or monoclonal antibodies are available. This recalcitrant behavior of galactosylceramidase has hampered use of recombinant DNA technology in studies of Krabbe disease.

On the other hand, substrate specificity of galactosylceramidase has been substantially clarified. While galactosylceramide is clearly the main natural substrate, the enzyme is also active in catalyzing hydrolysis of terminal galactose from galactosylsphingosine (psychosine),[21,163–165] monogalactosyldiglyceride,[166] and under specific assay conditions, also from lactosylceramide.[23,24,167–175] The information on the substrate specificity of the enzyme provides an important basis when we consider the pathogenetic mechanism, as well as enzymatic diagnosis of the disease. Attempts to replace the unnatural bile salt with biologically more plausible components resulted in the demonstration that phosphatidylserine could specifically activate human brain galactosylceramidase.[176,177] While a protein factor has been described that activates galactosylceramidase in the absence of bile salt, it is not clear whether the enzyme requires such a specific natural activator protein for *in situ* hydrolysis of galactosylceramide.[178]

Galactosylceramide, Myelin, and Their Metabolism

The distribution of galactosylceramides in mammalian organs is uniquely restricted. They are practically absent in systemic organs except in the kidney, which normally contains appreciable amounts of galactosylceramide, although much less than the brain.[179–180] The brain, particularly the white matter, is rich in galactosylceramide and its sulfate ester, sulfatide. Gray matter contains much smaller amounts. Galactosylceramide is mostly, if not exclusively, localized in the myelin sheath and synthesized in the oligodendroglia and the Schwann cells. Thus, galactosylceramide is virtually absent in the brain before myelination and is present at abnormally low concentrations in pathologic conditions where severe loss of myelin occurs. The amounts of total brain galactosylceramide correlate precisely with the amounts of myelin that can be isolated from the brain, whereas amounts of other lipids do not.[181]

Myelin of adult mammalian brain generally contains galactosylceramide at a concentration of 15 to 18 percent of dry weight. The sum of galactosylceramide and sulfatide amounts to 20 percent of the dry weight of myelin. The content of galactosylceramide in myelin from the peripheral nerve is somewhat less than that of CNS myelin.[182] There are numerous original reports on the chemical composition and metabolism of myelin, and readers are referred to a recent book on this subject.[183] In view of the unusually high concentrations of galactosylceramide and sulfatide in the myelin sheath, metabolic diseases involving these lipids would be expected to manifest themselves primarily as disorders of white matter and peripheral nerves (globoid-cell leukodystrophy and metachromatic leukodystrophy).

The metabolism of brain galactosylceramide is closely linked to the metabolism of myelin. The most significant metabolic features of CNS myelin are its high rate of formation and turnover during the relatively short period of active myelination and its relative inertness in the adult brain. The period of active myelination in humans probably extends from the perinatal period to about age 18 months. Myelination does not stop after this period, and in the human brain, it may not be complete until age 20 years.[184] The amount of galactosyl-

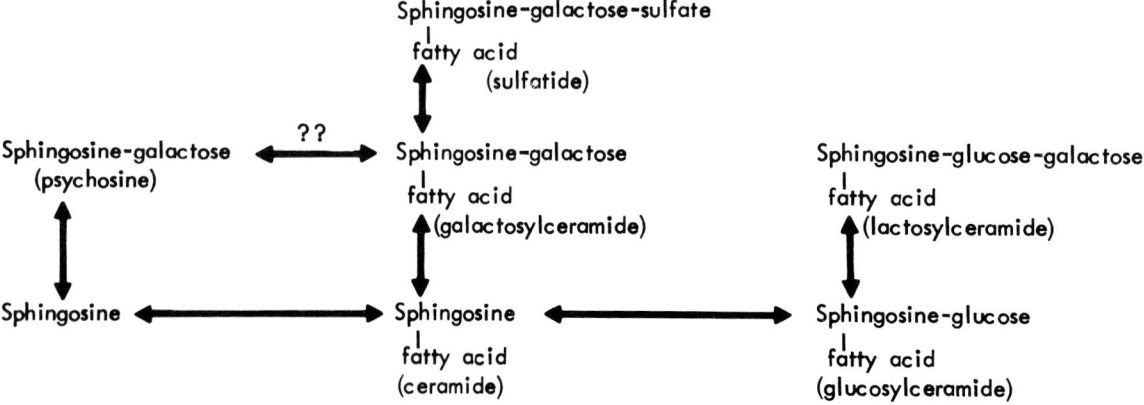

Fig. 68-10 Chemical and metabolic relationship among galactosylceramide and related compounds.

ceramide in immature brain is very low and, compared to concentrations of cholesterol and phospholipids, is relatively far below that in mature brain. When measured by incorporation of labeled galactose administered in vivo, the rate of galactosylceramide synthesis in rat brain reaches a peak at 15 to 20 days, coinciding well with the most active period of myelination.[185] A similar sharp peak is observed in the activity of UDP-galactose:ceramide galactosyltransferase, an enzyme that catalyzes the last step of galactosylceramide synthesis.[186] Synthesis and turnover of galactosylceramide occur at a much lower rate in the adult. The half-life of cerebroside and sulfatide in the mature human brain is 1 year or longer.

Some aspects of the chemistry and metabolism of galactosylceramide are critical in considering the pathophysiology of globoid-cell leukodystrophy:

1. Galactosylceramide consists of sphingosine, fatty acid, and galactose.

2. Galactosylceramide is the precursor of sulfatide.

3. Both galactosylceramide and sulfatide are highly concentrated in the myelin sheath.

4. Sulfatide is normally degraded through galactosylceramide.

5. A lysosomal hydrolytic enzyme, galactosylceramidase (cerebroside β-galactosidase), is responsible for the first step in normal degradation, in which galactosylceramide is cleaved to ceramide and galactose.

6. A few related galactolipids also serve as substrates for the same enzyme, including galactosylsphingosine (psychosine), monogalactosyldiglyceride, and lactosylceramide.

7. Biosynthesis of galactosylceramide reaches a peak coincident with the maximum period of myelination (during the first year and a half in humans).

8. Galactosylceramidase activity is low before myelination and increases sharply during the active period of myelination, when myelin also turns over relatively rapidly.

9. Once formed, adult myelin is relatively stable metabolically, although by no means completely inert.

CHEMICAL PATHOLOGY

Analytical Chemistry. Hallervorden was the first to point out the morphologic similarities of the globoid cells to the storage cells in Gaucher disease and to suggest that the globoid cells also might contain cerebroside in excess.[5] Austin[6] obtained

fractions enriched in globoid cells from seven patients with globoid-cell leukodystrophy. He concluded that globoid cells contain unusually large amounts of galactosylceramide but little sulfatide. Such increases in galactosylceramide are confined to globoid cells. Both galactosylceramide and sulfatides are almost invariably much lower than normal in the whole white matter.[9,14,15,32,69,73,139–141,187–198] An increased total concentration of cerebroside in the brains of patients with globoid-cell leukodystrophy, as reported by Blackwood and Cumings[7] is unusual. Pilz reported that α-hydroxy fatty acid–containing cerebrosides were decreased more than were those with unsubstituted fatty acids.[195]

The most consistent and perhaps the most important analytical finding is the presence of substantial amounts of galactosylsphingosine (psychosine), primarily in the white matter but also in other organs.[139–141,199] It should be noted that the absolute amounts of psychosine found in white matter of patients are very small, approximately two orders of magnitude less than galactosylceramide. Even such small amounts are significant because psychosine is essentially undetectable in normal tissues, and because it is highly cytotoxic. These analytical findings provide the strongest evidence in support of the psychosine hypothesis for the pathogenetic mechanism of the disease, which will be discussed later.

Besides the abnormalities of the major glycolipids of white matter—galactosylceramides and sulfatides—Menkes et al.[191] found an abnormal amount of dihexosyl ceramide and possibly a trihexosyl ceramide. The dihexosyl ceramide has been shown to be lactosylceramide.[192,200,201] In the brain of one patient, 16 percent of the white matter cerebroside was glucosylceramide, and two other sphingoglycolipids, digalactosylglucosyl ceramide and globoside (N-acetylgalactosaminyldigalactosylglucosyl ceramide), were also present in significant amounts.[192] These "visceral-type" sphingoglycolipids in white matter were considered intrinsic lipids of globoid cells, consistent with the idea that the globoid cells are of mesodermal origin (Table 68-2). A more recent detailed study by Vanier and Svennerholm also demonstrated alteration of gangliosides in brains of patients.[139] Levels of gangliosides G_{D1a} and G_{M1} were reduced throughout, while G_{D1b} and G_{T1} levels were slightly decreased in cerebral cortex and increased in white matter. Amounts of normally minor gangliosides, G_{D2}, G_{D3}, and G_{M3}, which are metabolically related to G_{D1b} and G_{T1}, were increased throughout the brain. Similar results were reported by Berra et al.,[202] who found no abnormalities in the composition of glycosaminoglycans and glycoproteins in the brains of patients. The fatty acid composition of sphingomyelin indicates contribution from mesodermal tissues.[203]

Unless specifically eliminated, the abnormal tubular inclusions are isolated in the conventional myelin fraction, giving erroneous analytical results. In one study[204] the abnormal tubular inclusions were present in an even larger amount than myelin. When they were carefully eliminated, the yield of the myelin was, as expected from histologic findings, only 0.4 percent of normal. The myelin had a normal ultrastructural configuration, and lipid composition was quite similar to that of normal myelin. Particularly, the amounts of glycolipids (cerebrosides and sulfatides) were normal. The cerebrosides were all galactocerebrosides, and none of the ceramide oligohexosides found in the whole white matter was present in the myelin (Table 68-3). Thus, in globoid-cell leukodystrophy the brain is capable of forming myelin with normal morphologic appearance and normal chemical composition. The finding is in contrast to what occurs in metachromatic leukodystrophy, in which myelin is formed with an excess sulfatide content.[205–207]

Besides these specific chemical abnormalities, white matter in globoid-cell leukodystrophy typically shows increased water content and drastic reduction of proteolipid protein and total lipid content, with a consequent relative, but not absolute, increase in protein. Cholesterol, lecithin, sphingomyelin, and ethanolamine and serine phospholipids are all reduced in similar degrees. These findings merely reflect the devastating myelin loss. As expected from the histologic absence of sudanophilia, cholesteryl ester is not present in white matter (Table 68-2). In contrast to the white matter, the chemical composition of the gray matter is relatively normal (Table 68-2).

In keeping with the normal histologic appearance, nonneural tissues do not show conspicuous compositional changes except for the large relative increase in psychosine.[199] Suzuki[208] examined galactosylceramide levels in the kidneys of

Table 68-3 Chemical Composition of Isolated Myelin

	Globoid-cell leukodystrophy	Normal control*
Yield, mg/10 g wet wt	3.8	1000
Chloroform-methanol-insoluble residue	25.7	12.4
Proteolipid protein	12.3	21.0
Total lipid	62.0	66.6
Cholesterol	12.2	15.6
Total phospholipid	30.3	30.1
Ethanolamine phospholipid	7.6	9.7
Lecithin	12.9	9.2
Sphingomyelin	5.0	5.1
Monophosphoinositide and serine phospholipid	4.2	5.8
Total galactolipid	17.0	17.4
Cerebroside	12.4	13.6
Sulfatide	4.6	3.8

*Average of two myelin preparations from normal brains, patients' ages 2.5 and 5.5 years.
NOTE: Expressed as percent dry weight except for the yield.
SOURCE: Data from Eto et al.[204]

five patients and found them to be approximately 30 percent higher than normal. Since the glucosylceramide level was also similarly high in patients' kidneys, it was concluded that there was no specific abnormal increase of galactosylceramide in the kidney. On the other hand, Dawson reported highly elevated levels of galactosylceramide in livers of three patients,[209] although the actual amounts were still minute. This finding has been contradicted by a more recent report.[141] Hof et al.[210] examined gangliosides in cultured fibroblasts and reported a moderate increase.

ENZYMATIC DEFECT

The fundamental genetic defect of globoid-cell leukodystrophy is a deficiency of galactosylceramidase (galactocerebroside β-galactosidase),[16,17] the enzyme that catalyzes the first step of galactosylceramide degradation[150–153] (Table 68-4). The deficiency is specific in the sense that no other lysosomal enzymes are defective; the deficiency is found not only in the brain and peripheral nerves, which are pathologically abnormal, but in all tissue sources examined, including liver, spleen, kidney, serum, leukocytes, cultured fibroblasts, cultured amniotic fluid cells, and chorionic villi. Galactosylceramidase deficiency of similar degree has not been observed in any other genetic disorders, except in cases of the so-called pseudodeficiency state (see "Diagnosis and Treatment," below).

As expected for the fundamental genetic defect in a Mendelian autosomal recessive disorder, the obligate heterozygous parents of patients with Krabbe disease show galactosylceramidase activity intermediate between those of normal individuals and patients.[211–213]

Deficient activity of galactosylceramidase can also be demonstrated with other natural substrates, galactosylsphingosine (psychosine),[21,164] monogalactosyldiglyceride,[166] or lactosylceramide.[23,24,167–175,212] Demonstration of the enzymatic deficiency with the use of lactosylceramide as the substrate requires a carefully standardized assay procedure, because another lysosomal β-galactosidase, genetically distinct from

Table 68-2 Analytical Chemistry of Globoid-Cell Leukodystrophy

	Gray matter		White matter	
	Globoid	Normal	Globoid	Normal
Water content, % fresh wt	87.0	82.1	83.5	73.0
Chloroform-methanol-insoluble residue	58.1	51.0	70.0	29.3
Total lipid	27.4	31.8	18.0	54.0
Proteolipid protein	0.7	3.2	0.5	8.6
Upper phase solids	13.6	14.0	11.5	8.0
Cholesterol	5.8	7.6	3.5	15.0
Phospholipid, total	21.4	22.1	12.9	23.9
Ethanolamine phospholipid	6.8	7.2	3.1	8.1
Lecithin	8.7	9.0	5.1	6.8
Sphingomyelin	2.5	1.8	2.3	4.3
Monophosphoinositide	0.8	0.7	0.5	0.4
Serine phospholipid	2.8	3.2	1.7	4.2
Glycolipids, total	0.44	0.92	1.6	14.6
Cerebroside*	0.25	0.50	0.99	12.5
Sulfatide	0.16	0.14	0.22	2.2
Ceramide dihexoside†	Trace	0.07	0.09	Trace
Ceramide trihexoside‡	—	—	0.04	—
Globoside§	—	—	0.20	—
Ceramide tetrahexoside¶	—	Trace	0.04	—

*Glucocerebroside constituted 32 and 13 percent of total cerebroside in gray and white matter, respectively, in the brain of a patient with globoid-cell leukodystrophy, whereas only galactocerebroside was present in the normal brain. The patient was somewhat atypical in that the cerebroside/sulfatide ratio in white matter was normal.
†Galactosylglucosyl ceramide.
‡Visceral-type trihexoside, i.e., digalactosylglucosyl ceramide.
§N-Acetylgalactosaminyldigalactosylglucosyl ceramide.
¶Asialo-G_{M1} ganglioside.
NOTE: Expressed as percent dry weight except for the water content.
SOURCE: Data from Eto and Suzuki.[192]

Table 68-4 Galactosylceramidase in Globoid-Cell Leukodystrophy

		Galactosylceramidase, nmol/(h·g)
Gray matter:		
Krabbe disease	1	12.1
	2	10.8
	3	5.7
Pathologic controls (n = 9)*		123 + 32
Normal controls (n = 4)		123 + 17
White matter:		
Krabbe disease	1	17.7
	2	21.8
	3	7.5
Pathologic controls (n = 9)*		197 + 59
Normal controls (n = 4)		199 + 55
Liver:		
Krabbe disease	3	6.4
Normal controls (n = 2)		125 and 113
Spleen:		
Krabbe disease	3	20.4
Normal controls (n = 2)		157 and 186

*Pathologic controls included metachromatic leukodystrophy, adrenoleukodystrophy, early and late onset G_{M1} gangliosidosis, Tay-Sachs disease, G_{M2} gangliosidosis with total hexosaminidase deficiency, Hurler syndrome, Gaucher disease, and Niemann-Pick disease.

NOTE: Activities of four lysosomal p-nitrophenyl glycosidases were all normal in globoid-cell leukodystrophy.

SOURCE: Data from Suzuki and Suzuki.[16]

galactosylceramidase, can also hydrolyze lactosylceramide under appropriate assay conditions.[168]

Globoid-cell leukodystrophy is one of the two known human genetic disorders caused by a deficiency of a lysosomal β-galactosidase. The other disease is G_{M1} gangliosidosis, in which G_{M1}-ganglioside β-galactosidase is deficient. Mammalian tissues contain the two genetically distinct lysosomal β-galactosidases with different, although overlapping, substrate specificities. Comparison of the enzymatic profiles of these two disorders is instructive (Table 68-5). Deficiencies of the respective enzymes result in entirely different disorders because of the different natural substrates involved. Both β-galactosidases share lactosylceramide as a common substrate, and consequently lactosylceramide accumulation does not occur to any significant degree in either globoid-cell leukodystrophy or G_{M1} gangliosidosis. It can further be predicted that under these circumstances a specific disorder with accumulation of lactosylceramide probably does not occur in humans.[214] More re-

Table 68-5 β-Galactosidase Profile of Globoid-Cell Leukodystrophy and G_{M1} Gangliosidosis

Substrates	Globoid-cell leukodystrophy	G_{M1} gangliosidosis
4-Methylumbelliferyl or p-nitrophenyl β-galactoside	Normal	Deficient
G_{M1} ganglioside	Normal	Deficient
Asialo-G_{M1} ganglioside	Normal	Deficient
Lactosylceramide	Normal*	Deficient*
Lactosylceramide	Deficient†	Normal†
Galactosylceramide	Deficient	Normal
Galactosylceramide	Normal‡	Deficient‡
Galactosylsphingosine	Deficient	Normal
Monogalactosyldiglyceride	Deficient	Expected to be normal

*With the assay system of Tanaka and Suzuki.[168]
†With the assay system of Wenger et al.[214]
‡With the assay system in the presence of cholate.[215]

cently, Kobayashi et al.[215] demonstrated that under certain assay conditions, particularly in the presence of sodium cholate, G_{M1}-ganglioside β-galactosidase could also hydrolyze galactosylceramide but not psychosine. The complex interrelationship of substrate specificity between the two β-galactosidases is important in understanding the pathogenetic mechanism of the disease.

Nonspecific enzyme abnormalities secondary to pathology have been reported for globoid-cell leukodystrophy. The increased CSF β-glucuronidase activity due to the presence of globoid cells has been already mentioned. Because of the almost total loss of the myelin sheath and oligodendroglia, activity of any enzymes that are highly localized in these tissue components is expected to be abnormally low. The sulfatide-synthesizing enzyme, PAPS:cerebroside sulfotransferase, is in this category.[216] In 1967, Austin and coworkers reported that the activity of PAPS:galactosylceramide sulfotransferase was deficient in the gray and white matter and in the kidneys of two patients with globoid-cell leukodystrophy.[217] Lees et al.[218] studied two enzymes localized in myelin, carbonic anhydrase and 2′,3′-cyclic nucleotide-3′-phosphohydrolase. Myelin isolated from white matter of a patient showed lower activities of these enzymes. While these abnormalities are not directly related to the genetic cause of the disease, they are of interest because they suggest that the myelin sheath in Krabbe disease may be intrinsically abnormal. Myelin isolated from the brain of a patient with metachromatic leukodystrophy was normal in the activities of these enzymes.

Pathophysiology

If a genetic defect of galactosylceramidase is the underlying cause of globoid-cell leukodystrophy, we should be able to explain the morphologic and biochemical characteristics of the disease on the basis of this deficiency. These include (1) almost total loss of myelin and oligodendroglia, (2) normal chemical composition of remaining myelin,[204] (3) morphologic evidence of decrease in the amount of myelin during the illness,[74] (4) massive infiltration by globoid cells, and (5) absence of excess accumulation of cerebroside in the brain despite a block in the degradative pathway.

Earlier Suzuki and Suzuki[16] formulated a plausible hypothesis based on the two apparently unique features of galactosylceramide. (1) Galactosylceramide is almost exclusively a constituent of myelin and oligodendroglia, as indicated by its virtual absence in the brain before myelination and its almost complete loss in the white matter of severely demyelinated brains. (2) Galactosylceramide appears to be unique among sphingoglycolipids in its ability to elicit the globoid-cell reaction when injected into normal rat brain.[11–13]

According to this hypothesis, the following steps could occur in the brain of a patient with genetic galactosylceramidase deficiency: Before myelination there is practically no cerebroside in the brain. Therefore, lack of enzyme activity is of little consequence, although it is normally present at low activity even at the premyelination stage.[153] As soon as myelination begins, just before birth in humans, newly formed myelin begins to undergo normal turnover. This period coincides with a rapid rise of galactosylceramidase activity in normal brain.[153] In the brain of patients with Krabbe disease, galactosylceramide from catabolized myelin cannot be disposed of because of the lack of the enzyme. This undegraded cerebroside elicits globoid-cell infiltration. When globoid cells are produced experimentally by injection of cerebroside into normal brain, the globoid-cell reaction subsides as excess cerebroside is digested. In Krabbe disease, the globoid cells remain because galactosylceramide is not degraded. As myelination proceeds, more free galactosylceramide is formed, stimulating more globoid-cell infiltration. However, myelination cannot proceed indefinitely, because the ever-increasing globoid cells overwhelm the oligodendroglial cells, which soon die. When the stage of massive death of oligodendroglial cells is reached, rapid myelin breakdown occurs. Because myelin is an extension of the oligodendroglial cell membrane, myelin breakdown contributes more free cerebrosides, and these prompt a further rapid increase of globoid cells. Finally, all the oligodendroglial cells die and all the myelin is broken down. The maximum globoid-cell infiltration is achieved, for there is no further production of myelin cerebrosides. Therefore, the total amount of cerebroside that can accumulate in the brain during the short life span of the patient is limited by the small amount of myelin produced before the death of all the oligodendroglial cells, and such total destruction usually takes place at what would have been normally a very early stage of myelination.

This hypothesis appears to explain most of the characteristic features of globoid-cell leukodystrophy satisfactorily. The most crucial part of any hypothesis about the pathophysiology of this disease is the explanation of the lack of increase in the total galactosylceramide content in the brain. The above hypothesis considered an early disappearance of the oligodendroglia and the consequent early cessation of myelination to explain the lack of abnormally high galactosylceramide accumulation. The recent finding by Kobayashi et al.[215] that the other β-galactosidase, G_{M1}-ganglioside β-galactosidase, could under specific assay conditions also hydrolyze galactosylceramide provided another possibility that galactosylceramide might be catabolized in vivo by both β-galactosidases. This is consistent with a relatively rapid decrease of galactosylceramide when it is loaded in cultured fibroblasts from patients.[219,220]

Critical to the hypothesis is the selective and almost complete loss of oligodendroglia. This question would be of particular importance if the two lysosomal β-galactosidases can degrade galactosylceramide, as postulated by Kobayashi et al.[215] A competition between globoid cells and oligodendroglia as the possible mechanism of the oligodendroglial loss would seem contrived. In an analogous genetic disorder, metachromatic leukodystrophy, the amount of sulfatide in white matter becomes excessive as a result of defective sulfatide degradation, but there is no massive oligodendroglial loss, and excess sulfatide accumulation does occur primarily within oligodendroglial cells (see Chap. 69). Therefore, there must be something unique about the block of galactosylceramide catabolism.

Miyatake and Suzuki advanced the psychosine hypothesis in order to explain the unusually rapid and complete destruction of the oligodendroglia in globoid-cell leukodystrophy.[21] Psychosine can be formed through UDP-galactose and sphingosine (Fig. 68-10). Although not firmly established, it is likely that UDP-galactose:ceramide galactosyltransferase also catalyzes galactosylation of sphingosine. Another potential route for psychosine formation—deacylation of galactosylceramide—could not be demonstrated in the author's laboratory or by Lin and Radin.[221] Psychosine with its free amino group is known to be highly cytotoxic.[222–224] Psychosine is also a substrate for galactosylceramidase, and patients with globoid-cell leukodystrophy are unable to degrade it. On the other hand,

psychosine appears to be a very poor substrate for G_{M1}-ganglioside β-galactosidase.[215] Thus, it is conceivable that psychosine generated within oligodendroglia during the period of active myelination might reach a toxic level. Oligodendroglia are selectively destroyed because psychosine formation occurs primarily in these cells. This hypothesis seems to explain early destruction of oligodendroglial cells and the resultant cessation of myelination. Recent analytical studies[139–141,199] provided strong support for this hypothesis by reporting up to hundred-fold increases of psychosine. In canine and murine models of the disease, similar increases of psychosine were found (see below).[22]

Malone et al.[225,226] recently suggested formation of abnormal myelin on the basis of higher proportions of lighter, loosely compacted myelin. It is possible that their data reflect instead the early cessation of the normal myelination process. There is currently no solid evidence that the destruction of myelin is due to the formation of chemically abnormal myelin in Krabbe disease.

Involvement of the peripheral nervous system is expected, for here the myelin also contains galactocerebroside. Histiocytes in peripheral nerves contain abnormal inclusions similar to those in the brain, but it is not clear why they are not transformed to the typical multinucleated globoid cells. The absence of discernible morphologic and functional abnormalities outside the nervous system is understandable, because normally galactosylceramide is practically absent in most nonneural tissues. The residual activity of galactocerebroside β-galactosidase results in normal turnover of minute amounts of galactocerebroside. Such appears to be the case in the kidney.[208]

There is a fixed pattern of regional differences in susceptibility of the white matter to pathologic alterations. This question was approached recently by utilizing the canine globoid-cell leukodystrophy model (see below).[227] In normal dogs, no consistent regional differences were found in galactosylceramidase activity, but in vivo turnover of galactosylceramide appeared to be more rapid in those areas of the white matter which are consistently more severely affected by the disease. Therefore, such regional differences in the metabolic activity of galactosylceramide might be at least partially responsible for the regional differences in severity of the disease.

KRABBE DISEASE AS A SPHINGOLIPIDOSIS

The two major criteria of Hers for an inborn lysosomal disease are (1) genetic deficiency of one of the acid hydrolases that is normally localized within the lysosome and (2) consequent accumulation of undigested material within single membrane-bound organelles that are pathologically altered lysosomes.[228] Globoid-cell leukodystrophy easily satisfies the first criterion but not so clearly the second. At the stage of the disease in which brain tissues are usually examined very few oligodendroglia remain; the rare ones left contain no inclusions. Instead, numerous globoid cells are present that do contain abnormal inclusions, consisting of galactosylceramide. The abnormal inclusions appear, for the most part, to be scattered freely within the cytoplasm. Although they are occasionally found embedded within an electron-lucent or electron-dense matrix, only very rarely are they surrounded by a single limiting membrane. One could argue that the lack of the limiting membrane is seen in the terminal picture, similar to the typical full-fledged membranous cytoplasmic bodies in Tay-Sachs disease. However, the essentially identical ultrastructure of the experimental globoid cells, even at an early stage, appears to be against this explanation. Specimens from patients have not been studied for ultrastructural localization of the lysosomal marker enzyme, acid phosphatase. In experimental globoid cells, acid phosphatase activity could not be demonstrated to be associated with the abnormal tubular inclusion or the surrounding matrix, although the enzyme was present within normal-appearing lysosomes that were occasionally found. Therefore, at present, there is no morphologic, histochemical, or biochemical evidence for an association of the abnormal galactocerebroside-rich inclusions and lysosomes.[229]

The fundamental metabolic defect of Krabbe disease corresponds to those in other inherited disorders of sphingolipid metabolism in which lysosomal hydrolytic enzymes involved in the degradation of particular sphingolipids are genetically defective. Of particular interest is the relationship of globoid-cell leukodystrophy to Gaucher disease. The sphingolipid involved in Gaucher disease is glucocerebroside, and the missing enzyme is glucocerebrosidase (glucosylceramidase). Glucocerebroside and galactocerebroside differ only in the sugar moiety, and the missing enzymes are those which cleave these sugars from the respective cerebrosides. The fundamental metabolic derangements in these diseases are therefore quite similar, as are the morphologic appearances of the globoid cells and the Gaucher cells. Nevertheless, the clinical and overall pathologic features of the two diseases are entirely different. These are the consequences of the entirely different tissue distributions of galactosyl- and glucosylceramides. Galactosylceramide is almost exclusively localized in the nervous system, while glucosylceramide is normally present in visceral organs and is nearly absent in the normal brain except in the early developmental stages. A massive accumulation of glucosylceramide occurs in systemic organs of Gaucher patients, while Krabbe disease is unique among the sphingolipidoses in that the total content of galactosylceramide is not elevated. It is also informative to compare globoid-cell leukodystrophy with metachromatic leukodystrophy[230] (see Chap. 69). Because galactosylceramide and sulfatide are both highly concentrated in the myelin sheath and because they are next to each other in the synthetic and catabolic pathways, both disorders manifest themselves as classical genetic disorders of myelin. On the other hand, there are several aspects where the analogy breaks down. There is an abnormal accumulation of sulfatide in the brain in metachromatic leukodystrophy while, as stressed, galactosylceramide is less than normal in the brain in Krabbe disease. Loss of the oligodendroglia is much earlier and more complete in Krabbe disease. Galactosylsphingosine (psychosine) is elevated in globoid-cell leukodystrophy, but the equivalent compound, lysosulfatide, is not known in metachromatic leukodystrophy, probably due to absence of the precursor, galactosylsphingosine. Many of these unusual features of globoid-cell leukodystrophy appear to be due to the overlapping substrate specificities of the two genetically distinct β-galactosidases.

MOLECULAR GENETICS

The present technology for isolating cDNA and genomic clones is based on availability of either specific antibodies or

at least a portion of the amino acid sequence of the product proteins. Study of globoid-cell leukodystrophy lags behind that of many other lysosomal disorders in which the recombinant DNA technology has been intensively exploited, because galactosylceramidase has not been sufficiently purified for amino acid sequencing or polyclonal antibody production. Attempts at producing monoclonal antibodies have so far been unsuccessful in the authors' and other laboratories. Thus, even the location on the chromosome of the galactosylceramidase gene is not known. However, recent developments of technologies for cloning genes without either antibodies or amino acid sequences, for the most part relying on expression systems for functional activities of the gene products, provide a hope of bringing this disorder into the era of molecular genetics.

DIAGNOSIS AND TREATMENT

Brain biopsy has long been the final resort for the definitive antemortem diagnosis of globoid-cell leukodystrophy, since Blackwood and Cumings[7] emphasized the presence of the characteristic globoid cells. Because of the wide variations of morphologic changes at different stages of the disease and in different areas of the brain, brain biopsy does not always establish the diagnosis. The diagnostic value of the peripheral nerve biopsy has not been fully explored, but, in view of consistent pathologic changes, particularly on the ultrastructural level, it may prove useful.

Assays of galactosylceramidase activity in readily available materials, such as serum, peripheral leukocytes, or cultured fibroblasts, unquestionably offer the best and most reliable means for definitive antemortem diagnosis of Krabbe disease. The same assays are also useful for prenatal diagnosis of the affected fetus, using cultured amniotic fluid cells as the enzyme source. Since the first prenatal detection of the disease and confirmation of the diagnosis by histologic examination and by additional enzymatic assays on the fetal specimens (Table 68-6),[20,231] a considerable number of affected fetuses have been detected. Although no comprehensive statistics exist, the following statistics were obtained in 1981 from major centers:

Table 68-6 Prenatal Diagnosis of Globoid-Cell Leukodystrophy

Enzyme source	Galactosylceramidase, nmol/(h·mg protein)	4-Methylumbelliferyl β-galactosidase, nmol/(h·mg protein)
Cultured amniotic fluid cells:		
Fetus at risk	0.09 and 0.10	698 and 542
Control 1	1.98 and 2.10	410 and 447
Control 2	1.80 and 1.56	485 and 467
Fetal brain:		
Affected	0.03	70.0
Control 1	5.89	81.7
Control 2	6.28	84.7
Fetal liver:		
Affected	0.03	265
Control 1	2.04	331
Control 2	2.77	337

NOTE: Amniocentesis was carried out at 14 gestational weeks, and the pregnancy was terminated at 20 weeks.
SOURCE: From Suzuki et al.[20]

Table 68-7 Comparison of Two Human Lactosylceramidases

	Lactosylceramidase I	Lactosylceramidase II
Genetic relationship	Same as galactosylceramidase	Same as G_{M1}-ganglioside β-galactosidase
Normal tissue distribution:		
Brain	Major	Minor
Liver	Minor	Major
Krabbe disease	Deficient	Normal or high
G_{M1} gangliosidosis	Normal or high	Deficient
Effect of assay system:		
Pure taurocholate	+ + +	−
Crude taurocholate	+	+ + +
Pure taurodeoxycholate	+	+ +
Oleic acid	+ +	+
Chloride	+	+
Wenger assay system[257]	+ + +	−
Tanaka-Suzuki assay system[197]	+	+ + +

Goteborg-Lyon (10 affected out of 40 prenatal tests),[232] Denver (8 out of 33), New York (4 out of 18), Japan (2 out of 8). These cases add up to 24 affected cases in 107 pregnancies at risk. Other cases are sporadically reported in the literature.[25,62,233–241] It is probably a reasonable estimate that more than 50 cases of globoid-cell leukodystrophy have been diagnosed in utero. As in other lysosomal disease, galactosylceramidase assays on chorionic villi are used increasingly because they provide an advantage of early and rapid prenatal diagnosis. A recent survey of prenatal diagnosis on chorionic villi in European countries indicates a total of 21 cases of which 4 were found affected.[241a]

Because of the broad specificity of galactosylceramidase, other natural substrates can, in principle, also be used for enzymatic diagnosis of globoid-cell leukodystrophy. Galactosylsphingosine (psychosine)[21,163–165] or monogalactosyldiglyceride[166] does not provide practical advantage, however, over the original assay for galactosylceramide hydrolysis. These substrates are more difficult to obtain and harder to label radioactively. The assay procedures are more complicated, and tissue activities may be lower than they are toward galactosylceramide. The enzyme is more active toward lactosylceramide,[212] but caution must attend use of this substrate for diagnosis of globoid-cell leukodystrophy. Both of the two lysosomal β-galactosidases can hydrolyze lactosylceramide. For diagnosis of globoid-cell leukodystrophy, therefore, one must use an assay system which determines exclusively the lactosylceramide-hydrolyzing activity of galactosylceramidase. The procedure developed by Wenger et al.[212] is excellent for this purpose. The important requirements are oleic acid, use of relatively small amounts of the substrate and pure sodium taurocholate, and absence of chloride ion. When these precautions are taken, G_{M1}-ganglioside β-galactosidase is essentially inactive toward lactosylceramide.[172,242] The properties of the lactosylceramide-hydrolyzing activities of the two β-galactosidases and their distributions in tissues of patients with globoid-cell leukodystrophy and G_{M1} gangliosidosis are compared in Table 68-7. A recent uptake and degradation study of lactosylceramide by cultured fibroblasts indicated that not only in vitro, but in intact cells, both of the β-galactosidases are active toward lactosylceramide and both globoid-cell leukodystrophy and G_{M1}-gangliosidosis fibroblasts could degrade lactosylceramide at or near normal rate.[219] Conditions of assays with natural sphingolipid substrates have been carefully examined in several laboratories in recent years.[215–220,243–250]

Assays of galactosylceramidase are also useful for detection of heterozygous carriers. Suzuki et al.[211] found fresh serum to be the most reliable enzyme source for carrier detection. The enzyme activity in serum is low and unstable, and activity is lost in storage. Carrier detection is inherently less reliable than diagnosis of affected patients, although the average activity of heterozygotes always falls in the middle between that of the normal and affected groups when sufficiently large numbers of individuals are tested.[211,248,250] While a part of the reason for the overlap may be technical, the main reason appears to be the wide variation of the activity in the normal population. Since galactosylceramidase activity can easily vary over a threefold range in both normal and carrier populations, overlap is inevitable since the averages of the two populations differ only by a factor of 2. Identification of heterozygous carriers is attracting attention beyond the usual genetic counseling purposes because of a recent suggestion that carriers of serious genetic neurologic disorders, including Krabbe disease, might not be completely normal clinically.[251,252] While studies on human heterozygotes are exceedingly difficult to control, a recent neurologic and neurobehavioral study on carriers in the murine model of the disease[253] appears to support a similar conclusion. Carrier mice, particularly males, fell significantly behind normal mice in motor development during the period of 15 to 30 days of hangtime and rotorod experiments. However, they eventually caught up with normal mice, and no significant differences could be demonstrated after 35 days.

One of the technical drawbacks of the enzymatic diagnosis of globoid-cell leukodystrophy is the need for radioactively labeled natural substrates. Kato and Suzuki[240,254,255] developed a micromethod in which the galactosylceramidase reaction was coupled to the galactose dehydrogenase reaction with NAD as the acceptor. Although this procedure eliminates the need for the radioactive substrates and is highly sensitive, it is technically even more elaborate than the radioactivity assay. A chromogenic substrate developed by Gal et al.[256] (2-hexadecanoylamino-4-nitrophenyl-β-D-galactopyranoside) appears to be less specific for galactosylceramidase than the natural substrates.[25,237] A new series of colored and fluorescent artificial substrates has been developed.[26,241,257,258] These are essentially galactosylceramide chemically modified with an additional colored or fluorescent group at the ω end of the fatty acid. They appear to be as specific a substrate as the unmodified galactosylceramide. The fluorescent substrate has an additional advantage of high sensitivity.

Although profound deficiency of galactosylceramidase activity is almost always diagnostic of globoid-cell leukodystrophy, the correspondence is not perfect. Wenger et al.[259] found a family in which some of the apparently healthy adult members showed levels of galactosylceramidase deficiency similar to those found in affected infants. Significance of this finding in relation to the pathogenetic mechanism of the disease is unclear, but it must be kept in mind when enzymatic diagnosis is attempted. Such pseudodeficiency could be an especially troubling problem in prenatal diagnosis.

None of the other laboratory procedures advocated earlier for the diagnosis of globoid-cell leukodystrophy, such as the pattern of CSF protein[32] or the elevated β-glucuronidase activity in CSF,[78] is specific, and they should no longer be used for diagnosis.

There is no specific treatment for patients with globoid-cell leukodystrophy other than supportive care, nor is it expected that any effective specific treatment can be developed in the near future. Bone marrow transplantation has been found to prolong the life span of mice affected by the same genetic galactosylceramidase deficiency (see below), but it has not been attempted in human patients. There are many fundamental obstacles. Any therapeutic attempt must deliver the agent or the enzyme to the brain across the blood-brain barrier. Furthermore, considerable neuropathologic changes are doubtless present at birth. Therapy must therefore start in utero, or ways must be found to overcome the essential irreversibility of damage to the brain.

ANIMAL MODELS

Globoid-cell leukodystrophy caused by genetic deficiency of galactosylceramidase also occurs in a few mammalian species other than human beings.[260,261] The disease in the cat was not characterized enzymatically.[262] In the single report of the disease in the sheep,[263] galactosylceramidase activity in the brain was 6 percent of normal, and characteristic clinical and pathologic abnormalities were present. The best-characterized animal models occur in the dog and the mouse. These models, particularly the more recently discovered murine globoid-cell leukodystrophy, are useful for further research.

Canine Globoid-Cell Leukodystrophy

In 1963, Fankhauser et al.[264] first reported that globoid-cell leukodystrophy occurs in certain strains of dogs. The strains in which the disease is known are West Highland and cairn terriers. The disease, which has been studied extensively from the clinical, morphologic, and biochemical standpoints,[227,265–284] is transmitted as an autosomal recessive trait. The clinical picture is quite similar to that of the human disease.

Morphologically, there are remarkable similarities between the human and the canine forms of globoid-cell leukodystrophy. The most conspicuous changes are the massive infiltration of globoid cells in the white matter, with morphologic changes, distribution pattern, and staining characteristics identical to those in human globoid cells. There is severe loss of myelin, oligodendroglia, and axons, with concomitant marked astrocytic gliosis. Ultrastructurally, canine globoid cells are quite similar to human globoid cells, containing the characteristic abnormal tubular inclusions. There are peripheral nerve lesions, again similar to those in human patients.[274,275] Unlike the human disease, the kidney of affected

dogs contains occasional abnormal inclusions, most commonly in the distal tubular epithelium.[284] Information regarding the lipid composition of the brain is limited, but one author reported decreased total lipid, decreased sulfatide, and slightly increased galactosylceramide.[268] Perhaps most importantly, there was a progressive accumulation of psychosine in affected dog brains.[22] Consistent with the presence of the abnormal inclusions, galactosylceramide was moderately increased in the kidney. The degree of the increase, however, was much smaller than that in the kidney of the murine disease (see below).

Suzuki et al.[285] demonstrated that canine globoid-cell leukodystrophy is also caused by deficient galactosylceramidase activity. As in human globoid-cell leukodystrophy, peripheral leukocytes provide a convenient source for enzymatic diagnosis of affected and heterozygous carriers.[286] The enzymatic deficiency can also be demonstrated with psychosine[287] or lactosylceramide[288] as substrates.

Several pieces of evidence indicate that the canine disease is not identical with human globoid-cell leukodystrophy. The presence of pathology and the corresponding increase in galactosylceramide in the kidney have been mentioned above. Serum is the most reliable enzyme source for diagnosis and carrier detection of human globoid-cell leukodystrophy, but activities of galactosylceramidase are identical in serums of affected, heterozygous, and normal control dogs.[211] This led to an observation that out of three electrofocusing peaks of hepatic galactosylceramidase, only the major peak is deficient in the canine globoid-cell leukodystrophy, while all three peaks are essentially absent in the human disorder.[287]

Costantino-Ceccarini et al.[289] used the canine model to investigate the biosynthetic activities of affected dog brains at various stages of the disease. Activity of UDP-galactose:ceramide galactosyltransferase was normal before the onset of clinical manifestations and then declined in white matter to approximately half-normal as the disease progressed. When radioactive galactose was injected in vivo, the synthesis of important myelin components, such as galactosylceramide, cholesterol, and chloroform-methanol-soluble protein, was decreased, while the synthesis of gangliosides and glycoproteins was unaffected.

A colony of the canine model was maintained earlier for research purposes at the University of Minnesota School of Veterinary Medicine. Regrettably, it was dissolved a few years ago due to lack of funds. Thus, there is no longer a steady source of canine globoid-cell leukodystrophy. The West Highland and cairn terriers are popular breeds of dogs for pets, and sporadic cases of affected dogs are identified from time to time among dog breeders.

A histologically similar disorder has also been described in blue-tick hound dogs[290] and in a beagle.[291] They were not characterized enzymatically.

Murine Globoid-Cell Leukodystrophy (The Twitcher)

A new neurologic mutation was discovered recently in the mouse. It is a genetically and enzymatically authentic model of human globoid-cell leukodystrophy. This mutant, called *twitcher*, was first detected at the Jackson Laboratory, Bar Harbor, Maine. Affected mice develop clinical signs at approximately 20 days, with stunted growth, twitching, and hind leg weakness. By 40 days, they reach a near-terminal stage, and even with intensive maintenance care they die before 3 months of age. Histopathologic findings are similar to those of human and canine globoid-cell leukodystrophy, both by light and electron microscopy.[292-294] Enzymatic studies with galactosylceramide and lactosylceramide as the substrate unequivocally demonstrated that galactosylceramidase deficiency is the underlying lesion in this mutant.[295,296] As a research tool, the canine and murine models offer complementary advantages and disadvantages. The canine model is more suitable for experiments that require relatively large amounts of tissue or dissection of different regions. On the other hand, the small size, rapid reproduction, and ease of maintenance make the mouse model far more convenient for experiments that require a large number of affected or heterozygous animals, or for in vivo injection of isotopes. The genetic status of individual mice can be conveniently and reliably determined by galactosylceramidase assays on homogenates of clipped tips of the tail within a few days of birth.[297] This permits morphologic and biochemical studies of the disease process during the early critical period well before the clinical onset of the disease. This mutant is now even more important because the canine model is no longer available on a regular basis for research.

As anticipated, studies on the twitcher mouse have been appearing at an accelerated pace in the past several years. They include clinical-diagnostic studies,[253,298,299] studies on pathology and morphology,[300-312] analytical biochemistry,[22,313-318] metabolic studies,[319-322] and trials on treatment.[323-329]

REFERENCES

1. KRABBE K: A new familial, infantile form of diffuse brain sclerosis. *Brain* 39:74, 1916.
2. BULLARD WN, SOUTHARD EE: Diffuse gliosis of the cerebral white matter in a child. *J Nerve Ment Dis* 33:188, 1906.
3. BENEKE R: Ein Fall hochgradigster ausgedehnter Sklerose des Centralnervensystems. *Arch Kinderheilkd* 47:420, 1908.
4. COLLIER J, GREENFIELD JG: The encephalitis periaxialis of Schilder: A clinical and pathological study with an account of two cases, one of which was diagnosed during life. *Brain* 47:489, 1924.
5. HALLERVORDEN J: Eine Speicherungshistiocytose des kindlichen Gehirens (Gauchersche Krankheit?). *Verh Dtsch Ges Pathol* 32:96, 1948.
6. AUSTIN JH: Studies in globoid (Krabbe) leukodystrophy. II. Controlled thin-layer chromatographic studies of globoid body fractions in seven patients. *J Neurochem* 10:921, 1963.
7. BLACKWOOD W, CUMINGS JN: A histochemical and chemical study of three cases of diffuse cerebral sclerosis. *J Neurol Neurosurg Psychiatry* 17:33, 1954.
8. DIEZEL PB: Histochemische Untersuchungen an den Globoidzellen der familiaren infantilen diffusen Sklerose vom Typus Krabbe. *Virchows Arch (A)* 327:206, 1955.
9. DIEZEL PB: Histochemical investigation of degenerative diffuse sclerosis (leucodystrophy and diffuse sclerosis of the Krabbe type), in Cumings JN, Lowenthal A (eds); *Cerebral Lipidoses: A Symposium.* Springfield, IL, Charles C Thomas, 1957, p 52.
10. STAMMLER A: Klinik, Pathologie und Histochemie der infantilen diffusen Sklerose vom Typus Krabbe. *Dtsch Z Nervenheilkd* 174:505, 1956.
11. AUSTIN J, LEHFELDT D, MAXWELL W: Experimental "globoid bodies" in white matter and chemical analysis in Krabbe's disease. *J Neuropathol Exp Neurol* 20:284, 1961.
12. AUSTIN JH, LEHFELDT D: Studies in globoid (Krabbe) leucodystrophy. III. Significance of experimentally produced globoid-like elements in rat white matter and spleen. *J Neuropathol Exp Neurol* 24:265, 1965.
13. OLSSON R, SOURANDER P, SVENNERHOLM L: Experimental studies on the pathogenesis of leucodystrophies. I. The effect of intracerebrally injected sphingolipids in the rat brain. *Acta Neuropathol (Berl)* 6:153, 1966.
14. AUSTIN JH: Recent studies in the metachromatic and globoid body forms of diffuse sclerosis, in Folch-Pi J, Bauer H (eds): *Brain Lipids and Lipoproteins, and the Leucodystrophies.* Amsterdam, Elsevier, 1963, p 120.
15. SVENNERHOLM L: Some aspects of biochemical changes in leucodystro-

16. phy, in Folch-Pi J, Bauer H (eds): *Brain Lipids and Lipoproteins and the Leucodystrophies.* Amsterdam, Elsevier, 1963, p 104.
16. SUZUKI K: Globoid cell leucodystrophy (Krabbe's disease): Deficiency of galactocerebroside β-galactosidase. *Proc Natl Acad Sci USA* 66:302, 1970.
17. SUZUKI K, SUZUKI Y, ETO Y: Deficiency of galactocerebroside β-galactosidase in Krabbe's globoid cell leucodystrophy, in Bernsohn J, Grossman HJ (eds): *Lipid Storage Diseases: Enzymatic Defect and Clinical Implications.* New York, Academic, 1971, p 396.
18. AUSTIN J, SUZUKI K, ARMSTRONG D, BRADY R, BACHHAWAT BK, SCHLENKER J, STUMPF D: Studies in globoid (Krabbe) leukodystrophy (GLD). V. Controlled enzymic studies in ten human cases. *Arch Neurol* 23:502, 1970.
19. SUZUKI Y, SUZUKI K: Krabbe's globoid cell leukodystrophy: Deficiency of galactocerebrosidase in serum, leukocytes, and fibroblasts. *Science* 171:73, 1971.
20. SUZUKI K, SCHNEIDER EL, EPSTEIN CJ: In utero diagnosis of globoid cell leukodystrophy (Krabbe's disease). *Biochem Biophys Res Commun* 45:1363, 1971.
21. MIYATAKE T, SUZUKI K: Globoid cell leukodystrophy: Additional deficiency of psychosine galactosidase. *Biochem Biophys Res Commun* 48:538, 1972.
22. IGISU H, SUZUKI K: Progressive accumulation of toxic metabolite in a genetic leukodystrophy. *Science* 224:753, 1984.
23. WENGER DA, SATTLER M, HIATT W: Globoid cell leukodystrophy: Deficiency of lactosyl ceramide beta-galactosidase. *Proc Natl Acad Sci USA* 71:584, 1974.
24. TANAKA H, SUZUKI K: Lactosylceramidase assays for diagnosis of globoid cell leukodystrophy and G_{M1}-gangliosidosis. *Clin Chim Acta* 75:267, 1977.
25. BESLEY GT, BAIN AD: Use of a chromogenic substrate for the diagnosis of Krabbe's disease with special reference to its application in prenatal diagnosis. *Clin Chim Acta* 88:229, 1978.
26. BESLEY GTN, GATT S: Spectrophotometric and fluorimetric assays of galactocerebrosidase activity, their use in the diagnosis of Krabbe disease. *Clin Chim Acta* 110:19, 1981.
27. HAGBERG B, KOLLBERG H, SOURANDER P, AKESSON HO: Infantile globoid cell leucodystrophy (Krabbe's disease): A clinical and genetic study of 32 Swedish cases 1953–1967. *Neuropaediatrie* 1:74, 1970.
28. METZKE H, BERG U, ULRICH U: Zur Häufigkeit der diffusen infantilen familiären Hirnsklerose (Typ Krabbe). *Klin Paediatr* 184:151, 1972.
29. ZLOTOGORA J, REGEV R, ZEIGLER M, IANCU TC, BACH G: Krabbe disease: Increased incidence in a highly inbred community. *Am J Med Genet* 21:765, 1985.
30. SCHOCHET SS JR, HARDMAN JM, LAMPERT PW, EARLE KM: Krabbe's disease (globoid leukodystrophy): Electron microscopic observations. *Arch Pathol* 88:305, 1969.
31. CLARKE JTR, OZERE RL, KRAUSE VW: Early infantile variant of Krabbe globoid cell leukodystrophy with lung involvement. *Arch Dis Child* 8:640, 1981.
32. HAGBERG B, SOURANDER P, SVENNERHOLM L: Diagnosis of Krabbe's infantile leucodystrophy. *J Neurol Neurosurg Psychiatry* 26:195, 1963.
33. NELSON E, AUREBECK G, OSTERBERG K, BERRY J, JABBOUR JT, BORNHOFEN J: Ultrastructural and chemical studies on Krabbe's disease. *J Neuropathol Exp Neurol* 22:414, 1963.
34. CROME L, HANEFELD F, PATRICK D, WILSON J: Late onset globoid cell leukodystrophy. *Brain* 96:84, 1973.
35. CHRISTENSEN E, MELCHIOR JC, ANDERSEN H: Diffuse infantile familial sclerosis (Krabbe-type). *Acta Psychiatr Neurol Scand* 35:431, 1960.
36. LIU HM: Ultrastructure of globoid leukodystrophy (Krabbe's disease) with reference to the origin of globoid cells. *J Neuropathol Exp Neurol* 29:441, 1970.
37. NEUBURGER K: Zur Histopathologie der multiplen Sklerose im Kindesalter. *Z Neurol Psychiatr* 76:384, 1972.
38. MCNAMARA ED: Encephalitis periaxialis (Schilder). *Proc R Soc Med* 26:297, 1933.
39. VERHAART WJC: A case of multiple sclerosis in an Indian in the Dutch East Indies. *Psychiatr Neurol Bladen (Amst)* 35:511, 1931.
40. GULLAIN G, BERTRAND I, GRUNER J: Sur un type anatomoclinique spécial de leucoencéphalite à nodules morulé gliogenes. *Rev Neurol (Paris)* 73:401, 1941.
41. FERRARO A: Familial form of encephalitis periaxialis diffusa. *J Nerve Ment Dis* 66:329, 1927.
42. FERRARO A: Familial form of encephalitis periaxialis diffusa. *J Nerve Ment Dis* 66:479, 1927.
43. FERRARO A: Familial form of encephalitis periaxialis diffusa. *J Nerve Ment Dis* 66:616, 1927.
44. DUNN HG, DOLMAN CL, FARRELL DF, TISCHLER B, HASINOFF C, WOLF LI: Krabbe's leukodystrophy without globoid cells. *Neurology* 26:1035, 1976.

45. HANEFELD F, WILSON J, CROME L: Die juvenile Form der Globoidzell-Leukodystrophie. *Monatsschr Kinderheilkd* 121:293, 1973.

46. MALONE MJ, SZOKE MC, LOONEY GL: Globoid leukodystrophy. I. Clinical and enzymatic studies. *Arch Neurol* 32:606, 1975.

47. KOLODNY EH, ADAMS RD, HALLER JS, JOSEPH J, CRUMRINE PK, RAGHAVAN SS: Late-onset globoid cell leukodystrophy. *Ann Neurol* 8:219, 1980.

48. FARRELL DF, SWEDBERG K: Clinical and biochemical heterogeneity of globoid cell leukodystrophy. *Ann Neurol* 10:364, 1981.

49. VOS AJM, JOOSTEN EMG, GABREELS-FESTEN AAWM, GABREELS FJM: An atypical case of infantile globoid cell leukodystrophy. *Neuropediatrics* 14:110, 1983.

50. THOMAS PK, HALPERN J-P, KING RHM, PATRICK D: Galactosylceramide lipidosis: Novel presentation as a slowly progressive spinocerebellar degeneration. *Ann Neurol* 16:618, 1984.

51. LOONEN MCB, VAN DIGGELEN OP, JANSE HC, KLEIJER WJ, ARTS WFM: Late-onset globoid cell leukodystrophy (Krabbe's disease). Clinical and genetic delineation of two forms and their relation to the early infantile form. *Neuropediatrics* 16:137, 1985.

52. FLUHARTY AL, NEIDENGARD L, HOLTZMAN D, KIHARA H: Late-onset Krabbe disease initially diagnosed as cerebroside sulfatase activator deficiency. *Metab Brain Dis* 1:187, 1986.

53. KUROKAWA T, CHIN Y-J, HASUO K, KOBAYASHI T, NAGATA M, KITAGUCHI T: Late infantile Krabbe leukodystrophy: MRI and evoked potentials in a Japanese girl. *Neuropediatrics*, 18:182, 1987.

54. HAGBERG B: The clinical diagnosis of Krabbe's infantile leucodystrophy. *Acta Paediatr Scand* 52:213, 1963.

55. SUZUKI K, GROVER WD: Krabbe's leukodystrophy (globoid cell leukodystrophy): An ultrastructural study. *Arch Neurol* 22:385, 1970.

56. ALLEN N, DE VEYRA E: Microchemical and histochemical observations in a case of Krabbe's leukodystrophy. *J Neuropathol Exp Neurol* 26:456, 1967.

57. HOGAN GR, GUTMANN L, CHOU SM: The peripheral neuropathy of Krabbe's (globoid) leukodystrophy. *Neurology (Minneapolis)* 19:1093, 1969.

58. SCHOCHET SS JR, MCCORMICK WF, POWELL GF: Krabbe's disease. A light and electron microscopic study. *Acta Neuropathol* 36:153, 1976.

59. YUNIS EJ, LEE RE: The ultrastructure of globoid (Krabbe) leukodystrophy. *Lab Invest* 21:415, 1969.

60. LAXDAL T, HALLGRIMSSON K: Krabbe's globoid cell leucodystrophy with hydrocephalus. *Arch Dis Child* 49:232, 1974.

61. YOKOTA K, YUSA T, MITSUDOME A, TAKASHIMA S, KUROKAWA T, TAKESHITA K: An autopsy case of globoid cell leukodystrophy (Krabbe's disease). *Brain Dev (Tokyo)* 5:296, 1973.

62. GULLOTTA F, PAVONE L, MOLLICA F, GRASSO S, VALENTI C: Krabbe's disease with unusual clinical and morphological features. *Neuropaediatrie* 10:395, 1979.

63. TAORI GM, SHALINI KCM, MARTIN KB, BHAKTAVIZIAM A, BACHHAWAT BK: Globoid leukodystrophy (Krabbe's disease). *Indian J Med Res* 58:993, 1970.

64. MOOSA A: Peripheral neuropathy and ichthyosis in Krabbe's leukodystrophy. *Arch Dis Child* 46:112, 1971.

65. MATSUYAMA H, MINOSHIMA I, WATANABE I: An autopsy case of leucodystrophy of Krabbe type. *Acta Pathol Jpn* 13:195, 1963.

66. WALLACE BJ, ARONSON SM, VOLK BW: Histochemical and biochemical studies of globoid cell leucodystrophy (Krabbe's disease). *J Neurochem* 11:367, 1963.

67. OSETOWSKA E, GAIL H, LUKASEWICZ D, KARCHER D, WISNIEWSKI H: Leucodystrophie infantile précoce (type Krabbe): (Remarques sur les proliferations gliales et les atrophies de système qui peuvent s'y observer). *Rev Neurol (Paris)* 102:463, 1960.

68. KASS A: Acute infantile sclerosis of the brain (Krabbe's disease). *Acta Paediatr* 42:70, 1953.

69. BIGNAMI A, TINGEY AH, TORRE C: La sclerosi cerebrale diffusa tipo Krabbe. *Riv Neurol* 31:712, 1961.

70. AUSTIN JH: Recent studies in the metachromatic and globoid forms of diffuse sclerosis. *Res Publ Assoc Res Nerv Ment Dis* 40:189, 1962.

71. DUNN HG, LAKE BD, DOLMAN DL, WILSON J: The neuropathy of Krabbe's infantile cerebral sclerosis (globoid cell leukodystrophy). *Brain* 92:329, 1969.

72. SACREZ R, LEVY HM, GRUNER JE, BILLUART J, GARLIER G: La leucodystrophie de Krabbe. *Arch Fr Pediatr* 22:641, 1965.

73. CUMINGS JN, ROZDILSKY B: The cerebral lipid composition of the brain in six cases of Krabbe's disease. *Neurology (Minneapolis)* 15:177, 1965.

74. D'AGOSTINO AM, SAYRE GP, HAGLES AB: Krabbe's disease. *Arch Neurol* 8:82, 1963.

75. LIEBERMAN JS, OSHTORY M, TAYLOR RG, DREYFUS PM: Perinatal neuropathy as an early manifestation of Krabbe's disease. *Arch Neurol* 37:446, 1980.

76. POSER CM, VAN BOGAERT L: Natural history and evolution of the concept of Schilder's diffuse sclerosis. *Acta Psychiatr Scand* 31:285, 1956.

77. HAGBERG B, SVENNERHOLM L: Metachromatic leucodystrophy—A generalized lipidosis: Determination of sulfatides in urine, blood plasma and cerebrospinal fluid. *Acta Paediatr* 49:690, 1960.

78. ALLEN N, REAGAN E: Beta-glucuronidase activities in cerebrospinal fluid. *Arch Neurol* 11:144, 1964.

79. ALLEN NE, SHUTTLEWORTH C, CLENDENON NR, GORDAN WA: Cerebrospinal fluid β-glucuronidase activity in the diagnosis of Krabbe's leukodystrophy. *Int Congr Ser 193*. Amsterdam, Excerpta Medica, 1969, p 181.

80. LANE B, CARROLL BA, PEDLEY TA: Computerized cranial tomography in cerebral diseases of white matter. *Neurology* 28:534, 1978.

81. HEINZ ER, DRAYER BP, HAENGGELI CA, PAINTER MJ, CRUMRINE P: Computed tomography in white matter disease. *Radiology* 130:371, 1979.

82. BARNES DM, ENZMANN DR: The evolution of white matter disease as seen on computed tomography. *Radiology* 138:379, 1981.

83. IESHIMA A, EDA S, MATSUI A, YOSHINO K, TAKASHIMA S, TAKESHITA K: Computed tomography in Krabbe's disease: Comparison with neuropathology. *Neuroradiology* 25:323, 1983.

84. BARAM TZ, GOLDMAN AM, PERCY AK: Krabbe disease: Specific MRI and CT findings. *Neurology* 36:111, 1986.

85. OCHIAI Y, ARIMA M, TAKAHASHI K: A case of globoid cell leukodystrophy. *Jpn J Pediatr (Tokyo)* 27:1092, 1974.

86. WADA Y, ARAKAWA T, CHIDA N, ONUMA A, NAKAGAWA H, IINUMA K, YOSHIMURA Y, NAKAJIMA S, SUZUKI Y: Globoid cell leukodystrophy: The first case with antemortem diagnosis in Japan. *Tohoku J Exp Med* 115:53, 1975.

87. AUSTIN JH: Some newer findings in Krabbe (globoid) leucodystrophy. *Trans Am Neurol Assoc* 87:66, 1962.

88. BLOM S, HAGBERG B: EEG findings in late infantile metachromatic and globoid cell leukodystrophy. *Electroencephalogr Clin Neurophysiol* 22:253, 1967.

89. KLIEMANN FA, HARDEN A, PAMPIGLIONE G: Some EEG observations in patients with Krabbe's disease. *Dev Med Child Neurol* 11:475, 1969.

90. IINUMA K, ONUMA A: Electroencephalographic findings in a case of globoid cell leukodystrophy. *Tohoku J Exp Med* 115:75, 1975.

91. EGGERS C, LEDERER V, SCHEFFNER D: EEG-Befunde im Verlaufe progredienter Hirnerkrankungen im Kindesalter. *Monatsschr Kinderheilkd* 125:8, 1977.

92. BUGIANI O, MASTROPAOLO C, DE NEGRI M: Association d'une leucodystrophy à cellules globoides d'une gliomatose et d'une abiotrophie. *Acta Neurol Belg* 68:799, 1968.

93. ANDREWS JM, CANCILLA PA, GRIPPO J, MENKES JH: Globoid cell leukodystrophy (Krabbe's disease): Morphological and biochemical studies. *Neurology* 21:337, 1971.

94. ANZIL AP, BLINZINGER K, MEHRAEIN P, DORN G, NEUHAUSER G: Cytoplasmic inclusions in a child affected with Krabbe's disease (globoid leucodystrophy) and in the rabbit injected with galactocerebrosides. *J Neuropathol Exp Neurol* 31:370, 1972.

95. LYON G, JARDIN L, AICARDI J: Étude au microscope électronique d'un nerf périphérique dans un cas de leucodystrophie de Krabbe. *J Neurol Sci* 12:263, 1971.

96. WILSON J, LAKE BD, DUNN HG: Krabbe's leucodystrophy: Some clinical and pathogenetic considerations. *J Neurol Sci* 10:563, 1970.

97. GUTMANN L, HOGAN G, CHOU SM: The peripheral neuropathy of Krabbe's (globoid) leucodystrophy. *Electroencephalogr Clin Neurophysiol* 27:715, 1969.

98. AUSTIN JH: Histochemical and biochemical studies in diffuse cerebral sclerosis (metachromatic and globoid-body forms). *IVth Int Congr Neuropathol*. Stuttgart, Thieme, 1962, vol 1, p 35.

99. DIEZEL PB: Die Stoffwechselstörungen der Sphingolipoide. Berlin, Springer-Verlag, 1957.

100. HAGER H, OEHLERT W: Ist die diffuse Hirnsklerose des Typ Krabbe eine entzündliche Allgemeinerkrankung? *Z Kinderheilkd* 80:82, 1957.

101. MARTIN JJ, CLARA R, CEUTERICK C, et al.: Is congenital fiber type disproportion a true myopathy? *Acta Neurol Belg* 76:335, 1976.

102. GREENFIELD JG, NORMAN RM: Demyelinating diseases, in Blackwood W, McMenemy WH, Meyer A, Norman RM, Russell DS (eds): *Greenfield's Neuropathology*, 2d ed. Baltimore, Williams & Wilkins, 1963, p 475.

103. AUSTIN JH: Globoid (Krabbe) leukodystrophy, in Minkler J (ed): *Pathology of the Nervous System*. New York, McGraw-Hill, 1968, p 843.

104. OEHMICHEN M, WIETHOLTER H, GENCIC M: Cytochemical markers for mononuclear phagocytes as demonstrated in reactive microglia and globoid cells. *Acta Histochem* 66:243, 1980.

105. OEHMICHEN M: Enzyme-histochemical differentiation of neuroglia and

microglia: A contribution to the cytogenesis of microglia and globoid cells. *Pathol Res Pract* 168:244, 1980.

106. SOURANDER P, HANSSON HA, OLSSON Y, SVENNERHOLM L: Experimental studies on the pathogenesis of leucodystrophies. II. The effect of sphingolipids on various cell types in cultures from the nervous system. *Acta Neuropathol (Berlin)* 9:231, 1966.

107. PFEIFFER J: Zur formalen Genese der Globoidzellen bei der diffusen Sklerose vom Typus Krabbe. *Arch Psychiatr Nervenkr* 195:446, 1957.

108. EINARSON L, STROMGREN E: Diffuse progressive leucoencephalopathy (diffuse cerebral sclerosis) and its relationship to amaurotic idiocy: Histological and clinical aspects. *Acta Jutland* 33:5, 1961.

109. CHRISTENSEN E, MELCHIOR JC, NEGRI S: A comparative study of 16 cases of diffuse sclerosis with special reference to the histopathological findings. *Acta Neurol Scand* 37:163, 1961.

110. OEHMICHEN M, GRUNINGER H: The origin of multinucleated giant cells in experimentally induced and spontaneous Krabbe's disease (globoid cell leukodystrophy). *Beitr Pathol* 153:111, 1974.

111. KOBAYASHI S, KATAYAMA M, BOURQUE EA, SUZUKI K, SUZUKI K: The twitcher mouse: Positive immunohistochemical staining of globoid cells with monoclonal antibody against Mac-1 antigen. *Dev Brain Res* 20:49, 1985.

112. EINARSON L, NEEL AF, STROMGREN E: On the problem of diffuse brain sclerosis with special reference to the familial form. *Acta Jutland* 16:1, 1944.

113. HALLERVORDEN J: Die degenerative diffuse Sklerose, in Lubarsch H, Rossle B (eds): Handbuch der speziellen pathologischen Anatomie und Histologie. Berlin, Springer-Verlag, 1956, vol XII, part 1, p 758.

114. de VRIES E: Gliomatous polio- and leucodystrophy in young child. *J Neuropathol Exp Neurol* 17:501, 1958.

115. SCHENK VW, GLUSZCZ A, ZELMAN IB: Atypical form of Krabbe-type leucodystrophy in two siblings accompanied by poliodystrophic changes. *Neuropathol Pol* 11:117, 1973.

116. WILLIAMS RS, FERRANTE RJ, CAVINESS VS JR: The isolated human cortex. A Golgi analysis of Krabbe's disease. *Arch Neurol* 36:134, 1979.

117. ANDREWS JM, CANCILLA P: Cytoplasmic inclusions in human globoid cell leukodystrophy. *Arch Pathol* 89:53, 1970.

118. SHAW C-M, CARLSON CB: Crystalline structures in globoid-epithelioid cells: An electron microscopic study of globoid leukodystrophy (Krabbe's disease). *J Neuropathol Exp Neurol* 29:306, 1970.

119. LAKE BD: Segmental demyelination of peripheral nerves in Krabbe's disease. *Nature* 217:171, 1968.

120. BISCHOFF A, ULRICH J: Peripheral neuropathy in globoid cell leukodystrophy (Krabbe's disease): Ultrastructural and histochemical findings. *Brain* 92:861, 1969.

121. YUNIS EJ, LEE RE: Tubules of globoid leukodystrophy: A right-handed helix. *Science* 169:64, 1970.

122. BLINZINGER K, ANZIL AP: Non-membrane bound cytoplasmic deposits in Krabbe globoid leukodystrophy. Further evidence of a revised concept of lysosomal storage diseases. *Experientia* 18:780, 1972.

123. YUNIS EJ, LEE RE: Further observations on the fine structure of globoid leukodystrophy: Peripheral neuropathy and optic nerve involvement. *Hum Pathol* 3:371, 1972.

124. HARCOURT B, ASHTON N: Ultrastructure of the optic nerve in Krabbe's leukodystrophy. *Br J Ophthalmol* 57:885, 1973.

125. BROWNSTEIN S, MEAGHER-VILLEMURE K, POLOMENO RC, LITTLE JM: Optic nerve in globoid leukodystrophy (Krabbe's disease). Ultrastructural changes. *Arch Ophthalmol* 96:864, 1978.

126. YAJIMA K, FLETCHER TF, SUZUKI K: Sub-plasmalemmal linear density: A common structure in globoid cells and mesenchymal cells. *Acta Neuropathol* 39:195, 1977.

127. SUZUKI K: Ultrastructural study of experimental globoid cells. *Lab Invest* 23:612, 1970.

128. ANDREWS JM, MENKES JH: Ultrastructure of experimentally produced globoid cells in the rat. *Exp Neurol* 29:483, 1970.

129. SOURANDER P, OLSSON Y: Peripheral neuropathy in globoid cell leukodystrophy (Morbus Krabbe). *Acta Neuropathol (Berlin)* 11:69, 1968.

130. SCHLAEPFER WW, PRENSKY AL: Quantitative and qualitative study of sural nerve biopsies in Krabbe's disease. *Acta Neuropathol* 20:55, 1972.

131. JOOSTEN EM, KRIJGSMAN JB, BAGREELS-FESTEN AA, GABREELS FJ, BAARS PEC: Infantile globoid cell leukodystrophy (Krabbe's disease). Some remarks on clinical and sural nerve biopsy findings. *Dev Med Child Neurol* 16:228, 1974.

132. MARTIN JJ, CEUTERICK C, MARTIN L, LEROY JG, NUYTS JP, JORIS C: Globoid cell leukodystrophy (Krabbe's disease): Peripheral nerve lesion. *Acta Neurol Belg* 74:356, 1974.

133. WATANABE K, HARA K, IWASE K: The evolution of neurological and neurophysiological features in a case of Krabbe's globoid cell leukodystrophy. *Brain Dev (Tokyo)* 8:432, 1976.

134. DEHKHARGHANI F, SARNAT HB, BREWSTER MA, ROTH IS: Congenital muscle fiber-type disproportion in Krabbe's leukodystrophy. *Arch Neurol* 38:585, 1981.

135. ISAACSON E, MOSCATELLI EA: Sphingolipids of developing human central nervous tissue: Changes in composition of sphingosine bases. *J Neurochem* 17:365, 1970.

136. SVENNERHOLM L: The distribution of lipids in the human nervous system. I. Analytical procedure: Lipids of foetal and newborn brain. *J Neurochem* 11:839, 1964.

137. SUZUKI K, SUZUKI K, KAMOSHITA S: Chemical pathology of G_{M1}-gangliosidosis (generalized gangliosidosis). *J Neuropathol Exp Neurol* 28:25, 1969.

138. SUZUKI Y, JACOB JC, SUZUKI K, SUZUKI K: G_{M1}-gangliosidosis with total hexosaminidase deficiency. *Neurology (Minneapolis)* 21:313, 1971.

139. VANIER M-T, SVENNERHOLM L: Chemical pathology of Krabbe's disease. III. Ceramide hexosides and gangliosides of brain. *Acta Paediatr Scand* 64:641, 1975.

140. VANIER M, SVENNERHOLM L: Chemical pathology of Krabbe's disease: The occurrence of psychosine and other neutral sphingoglycolipids. *Adv Exp Med Biol* 68:115, 1976.

141. SVENNERHOLM L, VANIER M-T, MÅNSSON JE: Krabbe disease: A galactosylsphingosine (psychosine) lipidosis. *J Lipid Res* 21:53, 1980.

142. CLELAND WW, KENNEDY EP: The enzymatic synthesis of psychosine. *J Biol Chem* 235:45, 1960.

143. BRADY RO: Studies on the total enzymatic synthesis of cerebrosides. *J Biol Chem* 237:PC2416, 1962.

144. MORELL P, RADIN NS: Synthesis of cerebroside by brain from uridine diphosphate galactose and ceramide containing hydroxy fatty acid. *Biochemistry* 8:506, 1969.

145. MORELL P, COSTANTINO-CECCARINI E, RADIN NS: The biosynthesis by brain microsomes of cerebrosides containing nonhydroxy fatty acids. *Arch Biochem Biophys* 141:738, 1970.

146. BALASUBRAMANIAN AS, BACHHAWAT BK: Studies on enzymic synthesis of cerebroside sulfate from 3'-phosphoadenosine-5'-phosphosulfate. *Indian J Biochem* 2:212, 1965.

147. MEHL E, JATZKEWITZ H: Ein Cerebrosid Sulfatase aus Schweineniere. *Z Physiol Chem* 339:260, 1964.

148. AUSTIN JH, ARMSTRONG D, SHEARER L: Metachromatic form of diffuse cerebral sclerosis. V. The nature and significance of low sulfatase activity: A controlled study of brain, liver and kidney in four patients with metachromatic leucodystrophy (MLD). *Arch Neurol* 13:593, 1965.

149. MEHL E, JATZKEWITZ H: Evidence for the genetic block in metachromatic leucodystrophy (ML). *Biochem Biophys Res Commun* 19:407, 1965.

150. HAJRA AK, BOWEN DM, KISHIMOTO Y, RADIN NS: Cerebroside galactosidase of brain. *J Lipid Res* 7:379, 1966.

151. BOWEN DM, RADIN NS: Purification of cerebroside galactosidase from rat brain. *Biochim Biophys Acta* 152:587, 1968.

152. BOWEN DM, RADIN NS: Properties of cerebroside galactosidase. *Biochim Biophys Acta* 152:599, 1968.

153. BOWEN DM, RADIN NS: Cerebroside galactosidase: A method for determination and a comparison with other lysosomal enzymes in developing rat brain. *J Neurochem* 16:501, 1968.

154. SUZUKI K: Galactosylceramide galactosidase, in Ginsburg V (ed): *Methods in Enzymology. Complex Carbohydrates.* New York, Academic, 1972, vol 28, part B, p 839.

155. SUZUKI Y, SUZUKI K: Glycosphingolipid β-galactosidases. I. Standard assay procedures, and characterization by electrofocusing and gel filtration of the enzymes in normal human liver. *J Biol Chem* 249:2098, 1974.

156. SUZUKI Y, SUZUKI K: Glycosphingolipid β-galactosidases. II. Electrofocusing characterization of the enzymes in human globoid cell leukodystrophy (Krabbe's disease). *J Biol Chem* 249:2105, 1974.

157. SUZUKI Y, SUZUKI K: Glycosphingolipid β-galactosidases. IV. Electrofocusing characterization in G_{M1}-gangliosidosis. *J Biol Chem* 249:2113, 1974.

158. MIYATAKE T, SUZUKI K: Partial purification and the characterization of β-galactosidase from rat brain hydrolyzing glycosphingolipids. *J Biol Chem* 250:585, 1975.

159. AWASTHI YC, LUND HW, LO JT, SRIVASTAVA SK: Sphingolipid β-galactosidases in globoid cell leukodystrophy. *Birth Defects* 14:113, 1978.

160. BEN-YOSEPH Y, HUNGERFORD M, NADLER HL: The nature of mutation in Krabbe disease. *Am J Hum Genet* 30:644, 1978.

161. BEN-YOSEPH Y, HUNGERFORD M, NADLER HL: Galactosylceramide β-galactosidase in Krabbe disease: Partial purification and characterization of the mutant enzyme. *Arch Biochem Biophys* 196:93, 1979.

162. BEN-YOSEPH Y, HUNGERFORD M, NADLER HL: The interrelationship between high- and low-molecular weight forms of normal and mutant (Krabbe disease) galactocerebrosidase. *Biochem J* 189:9, 1980.

163. MIYATAKE T, SUZUKI K: Galactosylsphingosine galactosyl hydrolase: Par-

tial purification and properties of the enzyme in rat brain. *J Biol Chem* 247:5398, 1972.

164. MIYATAKE T, SUZUKI K: Additional deficiency of psychosine galactosidase in globoid cell leukodystrophy: Implication to enzyme replacement therapy, in *Proceedings of Symposium on Enzyme Therapy in Genetic Diseases, Birth Defects*, 9(2):136, 1973.

165. MIYATAKE T, SUZUKI K: Galactosylsphingosine galactosyl hydrolase in rat brain: Probable identity with galactosylceramide galactosyl hydrolase. *J Neurochem* 22:231, 1974.

166. WENGER DA, SATTLER M, MARKEY SP: Deficiency of monogalactosyl diglyceride β-galactosidase activity in Krabbe's disease. *Biochem Biophys Res Commun* 53:680, 1973.

167. WENGER DA: Studies on galactosylceramide and lactosylceramide β-galactosidase. *Chem Phys Lipids* 13:327, 1974.

168. TANAKA H, SUZUKI K: Lactosylceramide β-galactosidase in human sphingolipidoses: Evidence for two genetically distinct enzymes. *J Biol Chem* 250:2324, 1975.

169. SVENNERHOLM L, HÅKANSSON G, VANIER MT: Chemical pathology of Krabbe's disease. IV. Studies of galactosylceramide and lactosylceramide β-galactosidases in brain, white blood cells, and amniotic fluid cells. *Acta Paediatr Scand* 64:649, 1975.

170. WENGER DA, SATTLER M, CLARK C: Effect of bile salts on lactosylceramide β-galactosidase activities in human brain, liver, and cultured skin fibroblasts. *Biochim Biophys Acta* 409:297, 1975.

171. TANAKA H, SUZUKI K: Specificities of the two genetically distinct β-galactosidases in human sphingolipidoses. *Arch Biochem Biophys* 175:332, 1976.

172. TANAKA H, SUZUKI K: Substrate specificities of the two genetically distinct human brain β-galactosidases. *Brain Res* 122:325, 1977.

173. HARZER K: The two human lactosylceramidases and their respective enzyme activity deficiency disease: Inhibition studies using p-nitrophenyl β-D-galactoside. *Hum Genet* 41:341, 1978.

174. SUZUKI K, TANAKA H, YAMANAKA T, VAN DAMME O: The specificities of β-galactosidase in the degradation of gangliosides, in Svennerholm L, Mandel P, Dreyfus H, Urban P-F (eds): *Structure and Function of Gangliosides*. New York, Plenum, 1980, p 307.

175. POULOS A, BECKMAN K: A comparison of the properties and bile salt specificities of galactosylceramide and lactosylceramide β-galactosidase activities in human leukocytes and fibroblasts. *Clin Chim Acta* 28:277, 1980.

176. HANADA E, SUZUKI K: Activation of human brain galactosylceramidase by phosphatidylserine. *Biochim Biophys Acta* 575:410, 1979.

177. HANADA E, SUZUKI K: Specificity of galactosylceramidase activation by phosphatidylserine. *Biochim Biophys Acta* 619:396, 1980.

178. WENGER DA, SATTLER M, ROTH R: A protein activator of galactosylceramide β-galactosidase. *Biochim Biophys Acta* 712:639, 1982.

179. MAKITA A: Biochemistry of organ glycolipids. II. Isolation of human kidney glycolipids. *J Biochem (Tokyo)* 55:269, 1964.

180. MARTENSSON E: Neutral glycolipids of human kidney: Isolation, identification and fatty acid composition. *Biochim Biophys Acta* 116:296, 1966.

181. NORTON WT, PODUSLO SE: Myelination in rat brain: Changes in myelin composition during brain maturation. *J Neurochem* 21:759, 1973.

182. O'BRIEN JS, SAMPSON EL, STERN MB: Lipid composition of myelin from the peripheral nervous system. *J Neurochem* 14:357, 1967.

183. MORELL P (ed): *Myelin*, 2d ed. New York, Plenum, 1984.

184. YAKOVLEV P, LECOURS AR: The myelogenetic cycles of regional maturation of the brain, in Minkowski A (ed): *Regional Development of the Brain in Early Life*. Oxford, Blackwell, 1967, p 3.

185. BURTON RM, SODD MA, BRADY RO: The incorporation of galactose into galactolipids. *J Biol Chem* 233:1053, 1958.

186. COSTANTINO-CECCARINI E: Biosynthesis of brain sphingolipids and myelin accumulation in the mouse. *Lipids* 7:656, 1972.

187. NORMAN RM, OPPENHEIMER DR, TINGEY AH: Histological and chemical findings in Krabbe's leucodystrophy. *J Neurol Neurosurg Psychiatry* 24:223, 1961.

188. AUSTIN J: Studies in globoid (Krabbe) leukodystrophy. I. The significance of lipid abnormalities in white matter in 8 globoid and 13 control patients. *Arch Neurol* 9:207, 1963.

189. TINGEY AH, EDGAR GWF: A contribution to the chemistry of the leucodystrophies. *J Neurochem* 10:817, 1963.

190. JATZKEWITZ H: Die Leukodystrophie, Typ Scholz (metachromatische form der diffusen Sklerose) als Sphingolipoidose (Cerebrosidschwefelsaurester Speicherkrankheit). *Z Physiol Chem* 318:265, 1960.

191. MENKES JH, DUNCAN C, MOOSSY J: Molecular composition of the major glycolipids in globoid cell leucodystrophy. *Neurology (Minneapolis)* 16:581, 1966.

192. ETO Y, SUZUKI K: Brain sphingoglycolipids in Krabbe's globoid cell leucodystrophy. *J Neurochem* 18:503, 1971.

193. LEES MB, MOSER HW: The chemical pathology of Krabbe's disease and

194. ROBINSON N, CUMINGS JN: Biochemical and histochemical observations on Krabbe's disease (globoid body diffuse sclerosis). *Acta Neuropathol (Berlin)* 9:280, 1967.

195. PILZ H: Sphingolipoidveränderungen bei der Leukodystrophie Typ Krabbe im Vergleich zum akuten und chronischen sudanophilen Markzerfall. *Acta Neuropathol (Berlin)* 4:16, 1964.

196. SVENNERHOLM L, VANIER MT: Brain gangliosides in Krabbe disease, in Volk BW, Aronson SM (eds): *Sphingolipids, Sphingolipidoses and Allied Disorders*. New York, Plenum, 1972, p 499.

197. VANIER MT, SVENNERHOLM L: Chemical pathology of Krabbe's disease. I. Lipid composition and fatty acid patterns of phosphoglycerides in brain. *Acta Paediatr Scand* 63:494, 1974.

198. BRANTE G: Studies on lipids in the nervous system, with special reference to quantitative chemical determination and topical distribution. *Acta Physiol Scand* 18, suppl 63:164, 1949.

199. KOBAYASHI T, SHINODA H, GOTO I, YAMANAKA T, SUZUKI Y: Globoid cell leukodystrophy is a generalized galactosylsphingosine (psychosine) storage disease. *Biochem Biophys Res Commun* 144:41, 1987.

200. EVANS JE, MCCLUER RH: The structure of brain dihexosylceramide in globoid cell leukodystrophy. *J Neurochem* 16:1393, 1969.

201. NEIMANN N, MARCHAL C, VIDAILHET M, PHILIPPART M, FALL M, FLOQUET J: Étude clinique, anatomopathologique, ultrastructurale, biochimique et enzymatique de deux cas de maladie de Krabbe. *Ann Med Nancy* 10:163, 1971.

202. BERRA B, BRUNNGRABER EG, AGUILAR V: Gangliosides, glycoproteins, and glycosaminoglycans in Krabbe's disease. *Clin Chim Acta* 47:325, 1973.

203. VANIER MT, SVENNERHOLM L: Chemical pathology of Krabbe's disease. II. Fatty acid composition of cerebrosides, sulfatides and sphingomyelins in brain. *Acta Paediatr Scand* 63:501, 1974.

204. ETO Y, SUZUKI K, SUZUKI K: Globoid cell leukodystrophy (Krabbe's disease): Isolation of myelin with normal glycolipid composition. *J Lipid Res* 11:473, 1970.

205. CUMINGS JN, THOMPSON EJ, GOODWIN H: Sphingolipids and phospholipids in microsomes and myelin from normal and pathological brains. *J Neurochem* 15:243, 1968.

206. O'BRIEN JS, SAMPSON EL: Myelin membrane: A molecular abnormality. *Science* 150:1613, 1965.

207. NORTON WT, PODUSLO SE: Metachromatic leucodystrophy: Chemically abnormal myelin and cerebral biopsy studies of three siblings, in Ansell GB (ed): *Variations in the Chemical Composition of the Nervous System*. Oxford, Pergamon, 1966, p 82.

208. SUZUKI K: Renal cerebroside in globoid cell leukodystrophy (Krabbe's disease). *Lipids* 6:433, 1971.

209. DAWSON G: Hepatic galactosylceramide in globoid cell leukodystrophy (Krabbe's disease). *Lipids* 8:154, 1973.

210. HOF L, MATALON R, DORFMAN A: Gangliosides in human skin fibroblasts and their enrichment in the "Hurler variant" and Krabbe's disease. *Z Physiol Chem* 352:1329, 1971.

211. SUZUKI K, SUZUKI Y, FLETCHER TF: Further studies of galactocerebroside β-galactosidase in globoid cell leukodystrophy, in Volk BW, Aronson SM (eds): *Sphingolipids, Sphingolipidoses and Allied Disorders*. New York, Plenum, 1972, p 487.

212. WENGER DA, SATTLER M, CLARK C, MCKELVEY H: An improved method for the identification of patients and carriers of Krabbe's disease. *Clin Chim Acta* 56:199, 1974.

213. FARRELL DF, PERCY AK, KABACK MM, MCKHANN GM: Globoid cell (Krabbe's) leukodystrophy: Heterozygote detection in cultured skin fibroblasts. *Am J Hum Genet* 25:604, 1973.

214. WENGER DA, SATTLER M, CLARK C, TANAKA H, SUZUKI K, DAWSON G: Lactosylceramidosis: Normal activity for two lactosylceramide β-galactosidases. *Science* 188:1310, 1975.

215. KOBAYASHI T, SHINNOH N, GOTO I, KUROIWA Y: Hydrolysis of galactosylceramide is catalyzed by two genetically distinct acid β-galactosidases. *J Biol Chem* 260:14982, 1985.

216. BENJAMINS JA, GUARNIERI M, MILLER K, SONNEBORN M, MCKHANN GM: Sulfatide synthesis in isolated oligodendroglial and neuronal cells. *J Neurochem* 23:751, 1974.

217. BACHHAWAT BK, AUSTIN J, ARMSTRONG D: A cerebroside sulphotransferase deficiency in a human disorder of myelin. *Biochem J* 104:15C, 1967.

218. LEES MB, SAPIRSTEIN VS, REISS DS, KOLODNY EH: Carbonic anhydrase and 2′,3′-cyclic nucleotide 3′-phosphohydrolase activity in normal human brain and in demyelinating diseases. *Neurology* 30:719, 1980.

219. TANAKA H, SUZUKI K: Globoid cell leukodystrophy (Krabbe's disease): Metabolic studies with cultured fibroblasts. *J Neurol Sci* 38:409, 1978.

220. KOBAYASHI T, SHINNOH N, GOTO I, KUROIWA Y, OKAWAUCHI M, SUGIHARA G, TANAKA M: Galactosylceramide- and lactosylceramide-loading

studies in cultured fibroblasts from normal individuals and patients with globoid cell leukodystrophy (Krabbe's disease) and G_{M1}-gangliosidosis. *Biochim Biophys Acta* 835:456, 1985.

221. LIN YN, RADIN NS: Alternate pathways of cerebroside catabolism. *Lipids* 8:732, 1973.

222. TAKETOMI T, NISHIMURA K: Physiological activity of psychosine. *Jpn J Exp Med* 34:255, 1964.

223. SUZUKI K, TANAKA H, SUZUKI K: Studies on the pathogenesis of Krabbe's leukodystrophy: Cellular reaction of the brain to exogenous galactosylsphingosine, monogalactosyl diglyceride and lactosylceramide, in Volk BW, Schneck L (eds): *Current Trends in Sphingolipidoses and Allied Disorders*. New York, Plenum, 1976, p 99.

224. IGISU H, NAKAMURA M: Inhibition of cytochrome c oxidase by psychosine (galactosylsphingosine). *Biochem Biophys Res Commun* 137:323, 1986.

225. MALONE MJ, SZOKE MC, DAVIS DA: Globoid leukodystrophy. II. Ultrastructure and chemical pathology. *Arch Neurol* 32:613, 1975.

226. MALONE MJ, SAKURAGAWA N, SZOKE M: A comparative study of myelin fractions from metachromatic and globoid leukodystrophies. *Neurology* 25:827, 1975.

227. YAMANAKA T, FLETCHER TF, TIFFANY CW, SUZUKI K: Galactosylceramide metabolism in different regions of the central nervous system: Possible correlation with regional susceptibility in genetic leukodystrophies, in Callahan JW, Lowden JA (eds): *Lysosomes and Lysosomal Storage Diseases*. New York, Raven, 1981, p 147.

228. HERS HG: Inborn lysosomal diseases. *Gastroenterology* 48:625, 1965.

229. SUZUKI K, SUZUKI K: Globoid cell leukodystrophy (Krabbe's disease), in Hers HG, van Hoof F (eds): *Lysosomes and Storage Diseases*. New York, Academic, 1973, p 395.

230. SUZUKI K: Biochemical pathogenesis of genetic leukodystrophies: Comparison of metachromatic and globoid cell leukodystrophy (Krabbe disease). *Neuropediatrics* 15(Suppl):32, 1984.

231. ELLIS WG, SCHNEIDER LE, MCCULLOUGH JR, SUZUKI K, EPSTEIN CJ: Fetal globoid cell leukodystrophy (Krabbe disease): Pathological and biochemical examination. *Arch Neurol* 29:253, 1973.

232. VANIER MT, SVENNERHOLM L, MÅNSSON JE, HÅKANSSON G, BOUF A, LINDSTEN J: Prenatal diagnosis of Krabbe disease. *Clin Genet* 20:79, 1981.

233. HARZER K, BENZ HU, KNORR-GARTNER H, JONATHA WD, KNORR K: Pränatale Diagnose der Globoidzell-Leukodystrophie (Morbus Krabbe). *Dtsch Med Wochenschr* 101:821, 1976.

234. LARGET-PIET L, VANIER MT, BERTHFLOT J, GUITIET J, LARGET-PIET A, BEUCHER A, OURY C: Maladie de Krabbe. *Pediatrie* 32:539, 1977.

235. HARZER K: Prenatal diagnosis of globoid cell leukodystrophy (Krabbe's disease). Third documented case. *Hum Genet* 35:193, 1977.

236. FARRELL DF, SUMI SM, SCOTT CR, RICE G: Antenatal diagnosis of Krabbe's leukodystrophy: Enzymatic and morphological confirmation in affected fetus. *J Neurol Neurosurg Psychiatry* 41:76, 1978.

237. BESLEY GT: The use of natural and artificial substrates in the prenatal diagnosis of Krabbe's disease. *J Inherited Metab Dis* 1:115, 1978.

238. MARTIN JJ, LEROY JG, CEUTERICK C, LIBERT J, DODINVAL P, MARTIN L: Fetal Krabbe leukodystrophy. A morphometric study of two cases. *Acta Neuropathol* 53:87, 1981.

239. KUDOH T, WENGER DA: Prenatal diagnosis of Krabbe disease: Galactosylceramide metabolism in cultured amniotic fluid cells. *J Pediatr* 101:754, 1982.

240. TSUTSUMI O, SATOH K, SAKAMOTO S, SUZUKI Y, KATO T: Application of a galactosylceramidase microassay method to early prenatal diagnosis of Krabbe's disease. *Clin Chim Acta* 125:265, 1982.

241. ZEIGLER M, ZLOTOGORA J, REGEV A, DAGAN A, GATT S, BACH G: Prenatal diagnosis of Krabbe disease using a fluorescent derivative of galactosylceramide. *Clin Chim Acta* 142:313, 1984.

241a. POENARU L.: First trimester diagnosis of metabolic diseases: A survey in countries from the European Community. *Prenatal Diag* 7:333, 1987.

242. TANAKA H, MEISLER M, SUZUKI K: Activity of human hepatic β-galactosidase toward natural glycosphingolipid substrates. *Biochim Biophys Acta* 398:452, 1975.

243. BESLEY GT, BAIN AD: Krabbe's globoid cell leukodystrophy. Studies on galactosylceramide β-galactosidase and non-specific β-galactosidase of leukocytes, cultured skin fibroblasts, and amniotic fluid cells. *J Med Genet* 13:195, 1976.

244. SUZUKI K: Globoid cell leukodystrophy (Krabbe's disease) and G_{M1}-gangliosidosis, in Glew RH, Peters SP (eds): *Practical Enzymology of Sphingolipidoses*. New York, AR Liss, 1977, p 101.

245. SUZUKI K: Enzymatic diagnosis of sphingolipidoses. *Methods Enzymol* 50C:456, 1978.

246. SVENNERHOLM L: Diagnosis of the sphingolipidoses with labelled natural substrates. *Adv Exp Med Biol* 101:689, 1978.

247. SVENNERHOLM L, HÅKANSSON G, MÅNSSON JE, VANIER MT: The assay of sphingolipid hydrolases in white blood cells with labelled natural substrates. *Clin Chim Acta* 92:53, 1979.

248. SVENNERHOLM L, VANIER MT, HÅKANSSON G, MÅNSSON JE: Use of leukocytes in diagnosis of Krabbe disease and detection of carriers. *Clin Chim Acta* 112:333, 1981.

249. KUDOH T, WENGER DA: Diagnosis of metachromatic leukodystrophy, Krabbe disease, and Farber disease after uptake of fatty acid-labeled cerebroside sulfate into cultured skin fibroblasts. *J Clin Invest* 70:89, 1982.

250. MÅNSSON J-E, SVENNERHOLM L: The use of galactosylceramide with uniform fatty acids as substrates in the diagnosis and carrier detection of Krabbe disease. *Clin Chim Acta* 126:127, 1982.

251. CHRISTOMANOU H: Biochemical, psychometric and neurophysiological studies in heterozygotes for various lipidoses. *Hum Genet* 55:103, 1980.

252. CHRISTOMANOU H: Biochemical, genetic, psychometric and neuropsychological studies in heterozygotes of a family with globoid cell leukodystrophy (Krabbe). *Hum Genet* 58:179, 1981.

253. OLMSTEAD CE: Neurological and neurobehavioral development of the mutant "twitcher" mouse. *Behav Brain Res* 25:143, 1987.

254. KATO T, SUZUKI Y: Enzymatic microdetermination method for galactocerebrosidase in tissue samples. *Proc Jpn Acad* 55B:69, 1979.

255. KATO T, SUZUKI Y: Enzymatic determination of galactosylceramide galactosidase in tissues by NAD cycling. *Anal Biochem* 126:44, 1982.

256. GAL AE, BRADY RO, PENTCHEV PG, FURBISH FS, SUZUKI K, TANAKA H, SCHNEIDER EL: A practical chromogenic procedure for the diagnosis of Krabbe's disease. *Clin Chim Acta* 77:53, 1977.

257. OKADA S, KATO T, YABUUCHI H, YOSHINO K, NAOI M, KIUCHI K, YAGI K: Use of a fluorescent analogue of a galactocerebroside for assay of galactocerebroside β-galactosidase activity in skin fibroblasts from patients with Krabbe's disease. *Clin Chim Acta* 136:57, 1984.

258. SALVAYRE R, GATT S: Use of mixed dispersion of fluorescent galactosylceramide and sodium dodecylsulfate for assaying galactosylceramide β-galactosidase and diagnosing Krabbe disease. *Enzyme* 33:175, 1985.

259. WENGER DA, RICCARDI VM: Possible misdiagnosis of Krabbe disease. *J Pediatr* 88:76, 1976.

260. SUZUKI K: "Authentic animal models" for biochemical studies of human genetic diseases, in Arima M, Suzuki Y, Yabuuchi H (eds): *Proceedings of the 4th International Symposium on Development Disabilities*. Tokyo, University of Tokyo Press, 1984, p 129.

261. SUZUKI K, SUZUKI K: Genetic galactosylceramidase deficiency (globoid cell leukodystrophy, Krabbe disease) in different mammalian species. *Neurochem Pathol* 3:53, 1985.

262. JOHNSON KJ: Globoid leukodystrophy in the cat. *J Am Vet Med Assoc* 157:2057, 1970.

263. PRITCHARD DH, NAPTHINE DV, SINCLAIR AJ: Globoid cell leukodystrophy in polled Dorset sheep. *Vet Pathol* 17:399, 1980.

264. FANKHAUSER R, LUGINBUHL H, HARTLEY WJ: Leukodystrophie vom Typus Krabbe beim Hund. *Schweiz Arch Tierheilkd* 105:198, 1963.

265. FLETCHER TF, KURTZ HJ, LOW DG: Globoid cell leukodystrophy (Krabbe type) in the dog. *J Am Vet Med Assoc* 149:165, 1966.

266. JORTNER BS, JONAS AM: The neuropathology of globoid cell leucodystrophy in the dog: A report of two cases. *Acta Neuropathol (Berlin)* 10:171, 1968.

267. AUSTIN J, ARMSTRONG D, MARGOLIS G: Studies of globoid leukodystrophy in dogs. *Neurology (Minneapolis)* 18:300, 1968.

268. AUSTIN J, ARMSTRONG D, MARGOLIS G: Canine globoid leukodystrophy: A model demyelinating disorder. *Trans Am Neurol Assoc* 93:181, 1968.

269. FLETCHER T: Leukodystrophy in the dog. *Minn Vet* 9:19, 1969.

270. AUSTIN J: Recent studies in two inborn errors of glycolipid metabolism, in Bogoch SE (ed): *The Future of the Brain Sciences*. New York, Plenum, 1969, p 397.

271. MCGRATH J, SCHUTTA H, YASHEN A, STEINBERG A: A morphology and biochemical study of canine globoid leukodystrophy. *J Neuropathol Exp Neurol* 28:171, 1969.

272. HIRTH RS, NIELSEN SW: A familial canine globoid cell leukodystrophy ("Krabbe type"). *J Small Anim Pract* 8:569, 1967.

273. FLETCHER TF, KURTZ HJ: Animal model: Globoid cell leukodystrophy in dog. *Am J Pathol* 66:375, 1972.

274. KURTZ HJ, FLETCHER RF: The peripheral neuropathy of canine globoid cell leukodystrophy (Krabbe-type). *Acta Neuropathol (Berlin)* 16:226, 1970.

275. FLETCHER TF, KURTZ HJ, STADLAN EM: Experimental Wallerian degeneration in peripheral nerves of dogs with globoid cell leukodystrophy. *J Neuropathol Exp Neurol* 30:593, 1971.

276. FLETCHER TF: Electroencephalographic features of leukodystrophic disease in the dog. *J Am Vet Med Assoc* 157:190, 1970.

277. FLETCHER TF, LEE DG, HAMMER RF: Ultrastructural features of globoid cell leukodystrophy in the dog. *Am J Vet Res* 32:177, 1971.

278. YUNIS EJ, LEE RE: The morphologic similarities of human and canine glo-

boid leukodystrophy. Thin section and freeze-fracture studies. *Am J Pathol* 85:99, 1976.

279. YAJIMA K, FLETCHER TF, SUZUKI K: Canine globoid cell leukodystrophy. Part I. Further ultrastructural study of the typical lesion. *J Neurol Sci* 33:179, 1977.

280. FLETCHER TF, JESSEN CR, BENDER AP: Quantitative evaluation of spinal cord lesions in canine globoid leukodystrophy. *J Neuropathol Exp Neurol* 36:84, 1977.

281. YAJIMA K: Canine globoid cell leukodystrophy: Chronological neuropathological observation in the early lesions. *Brain Dev* 12:153, 1980.

282. ROSZEL JF, STEINBERG SA, McGRATH JT: Periodic acid-Schiff-positive cells in cerebrospinal fluid of dogs with globoid cell leukodystrophy. *Neurology* 22:738, 1972.

283. KURCZYNSKI TW, KONDELEON SK, MacBRIDE RF, DICKERMAN LH, FLETCHER TF: Studies of a synthetic substrate in canine globoid cell leukodystrophy. *Biochim Biophys Acta* 672:297, 1981.

284. SUZUKI K: Characteristic inclusions in the kidney of canine globoid cell leukodystrophy. *Acta Neuropathol* 69:33, 1986.

285. SUZUKI Y, AUSTIN J, SUZUKI K, ARMSTRONG D, SCHLENKER J, FLETCHER T: Studies in globoid leukodystrophy: Enzymatic and lipid findings in the canine form. *Exp Neurol* 29:65, 1970.

286. FLETCHER TF, SUZUKI K, MARTIN F: Galactocerebrosidase activities in canine globoid leukodystrophy. *Neurology* 27:758, 1977.

287. SUZUKI Y, MIYATAKE T, FLETCHER TF, SUZUKI K: Glycosphingolipid β-galactosidases. III. Canine form of globoid cell leukodystrophy: Comparison with the human disease. *J Biol Chem* 249:2109, 1974.

288. KURCZYNSKI TW, FLETCHER TF, SUZUKI K: Lactosylceramidases in canine globoid cell leukodystrophy. *J Neurochem* 29:37, 1977.

289. COSTANTINO-CECCARINI E, FLETCHER TF, SUZUKI K: Glycolipid metabolism in the canine form of globoid cell leukodystrophy, in Volk BW, Schneck L (eds): *Current Trends in Sphingolipidoses and Allied Disorders.* New York, Plenum, 1976, p 127.

290. BOYSEN GB, TRYPHONAS L, HARRIES NW: Globoid cell leukodystrophy in the blue-tick hound dog. I. Clinical manifestations. *Can Vet J* 15:303, 1974.

291. JOHNSON GR, OLIVER JE Jr, SELCER R: Globoid cell leukodystrophy in a beagle. *J Am Vet Med Assoc* 167:380, 1975.

292. DUCHEN LW, EICHER EM, JACOBS JB, SCARAVILLI F, TEIXEIRA F: A globoid cell type of leukodystrophy in the mouse: The mutant twitcher, in Baumann N (ed): *Neurological Mutations Affecting Myelination.* Amsterdam, Elsevier, 1980, p 107.

293. DUCHEN LW, EICHER EM, JACOBS JM, SCARAVILLI F, TEIXEIRA F: Hereditary leucodystrophy in the mouse: The new mutant twitcher. *Brain* 103:695, 1980.

294. SUZUKI K, SUZUKI K: The twitcher mouse: A model of human globoid cell leukodystrophy (Krabbe's disease). *Am J Pathol* 111:394, 1983.

295. KOBAYASHI T, SCARAVILLI F, SUZUKI K: Biochemistry of twitcher mouse: An authentic murine model of human globoid cell leukodystrophy, in Baumann N (ed): *Neurological Mutations Affecting Myelination.* Amsterdam, Elsevier, 1980, p 253.

296. KOBAYASHI T, YAMANAKA T, JACOBS J, TEIXEIRA F, SUZUKI K: The twitcher mouse: An enzymatically authentic model of human globoid cell leukodystrophy (Krabbe disease). *Brain Res* 202:479, 1980.

297. KOBAYASHI T, NAGARA H, SUZUKI K, SUZUKI K: The twitcher mouse: Determination of genetic status by galactosylceramidase assays on clipped tail. *Biochem Med* 27:8, 1982.

298. TOYOSHIMA E, YEAGER AM, BRENNAN S, SANTOS GW, MOSER HW, MAYER RF: Nerve conduction studies in the twitcher mouse (murine globoid cell leukodystrophy). *J Neurol Sci* 74:307, 1986.

299. RAGHAVAN S, KRUSELL A: Optimal assay conditions for enzymatic characterization of homozygous and heterozygous twitcher mouse. *Biochim Biophys Acta* 877:1, 1986.

300. TAKAHASHI H, SUZUKI K: Globoid cell leukodystrophy: Specialized contact of globoid cell with astrocyte in the brain of twitcher mouse. *Acta Neuropathol* 58:237, 1982.

301. NAGARA H, KOBAYASHI T, SUZUKI K, SUZUKI K: The twitcher mouse—Normal pattern of early myelination in the spinal cord. *Brain Res* 244:289, 1982.

302. JACOBS JM, SCARAVILLI F, DEARANDA FT: The pathogenesis of globoid cell leukodystrophy in peripheral nerve of the mouse mutant twitcher. *J Neurol Sci* 55:285, 1982.

303. POWELL HC, KNOBLER RL, MYERS RR: Peripheral neuropathy in the twitcher mutant—A new experimental model of endoneurial edema. *Lab Invest* 49:19, 1983.

304. TAKAHASHI H, IGISU H, SUZUKI K, SUZUKI K: Murine globoid cell leukodystrophy (the twitcher mouse)—The presence of characteristic inclusions in the kidney and lymphnodes. *Am J Pathol* 112:147, 1983.

305. TAKAHASHI H, IGISU H, SUZUKI K, SUZUKI K: Murine globoid cell leuko-

dystrophy, the twitcher: Presence of inclusions in the kidney and lymphnode. *J Neuropathol Exp Neurol* 42:328, 1983.

306. TAKAHASHI H, IGISU H, SUZUKI K, SUZUKI K: The twitcher mouse: An ultrastructural study of the oligodendroglia. *Acta Neuropathol* 59:159, 1983.

307. TAKAHASHI H, SUZUKI K: Demyelination in the spinal cord of murine globoid cell leukodystrophy (the twitcher mouse). *Acta Neuropathol* 62:298, 1984.

308. MIKOSHIBA K, FUJISHIRO M, KOHSAKA S, OKANO H, TAKAMATSU K, TSUKADA Y: Disorders in myelination in the twitcher mutant. Immunohistochemical and biochemical studies. *Neurochem Res* 10:1129, 1985.

309. KOBAYASHI S, KATAYAMA M, BOURQUE EA, SUZUKI K, SUZUKI K: The twitcher mouse: Positive immunohistochemical staining of globoid cells with monoclonal antibody against Mac-1 antigen. *Dev Brain Res* 20:49, 1985.

310. ALROY J, UCCI AA, GOYAL V, AURILIO A: Histochemical similarities between human and animal globoid cells in Krabbe disease—A lectin study. *Acta Neuropathol* 71:26, 1986.

311. KOBAYASHI S, CHIU F-C, KATAYAMA M, SACCHI RS, SUZUKI K, SUZUKI K: Expression of glial fibrillary acidic protein (GFAP) in the CNS and PNS of murine globoid cell leukodystrophy (GLD), the twitcher. *Am J Pathol* 125:227, 1986.

312. KOBAYASHI S, KATAYAMA M, SATOH J, SUZUKI K, SUZUKI K: The twitcher mouse: An alteration of the unmyelinated fibers in the PNS. *Am J Pathol* 131:308, 1988.

313. IDA H, UMEZAWA F, KASAI E, ETO Y, MAEKAWA K: An accumulation of galactocerebroside in kidney from mouse globoid cell leukodystrophy (twitcher). *Biochem Biophys Res Commun* 109:634, 1982.

314. IGISU H, TAKAHASHI H, SUZUKI K, SUZUKI K: Abnormal accumulation of galactosylceramide in the kidney of twitcher mouse. *Biochem Biophys Res Commun* 110:940, 1983.

315. IGISU H, SHIMOMURA K, KISHIMOTO Y, SUZUKI K: Lipids of developing brain of twitcher mouse—An authentic murine model of human Krabbe disease. *Brain* 106:405, 1983.

316. SUZUKI K: Biochemical pathogenesis of Krabbe disease (globoid cell leukodystrophy), in Vanier M-T (ed): *Proceedings of the International Symposium on Recent Advances in Neurolipidoses and Allied Disorders.* Lyon, Fondation Merieux, 1984, p 35.

317. IGISU H, SUZUKI K: Analysis of galactosylsphingosine (psychosine) in the brain. *J Lipid Res* 25:1000, 1984.

318. SHINODA H, KOBAYASHI T, KATAYAMA M, GOTO I, NAGARA H: Accumulation of galactosylsphingosine (psychosine) in the twitcher mouse: Determination by HPLC. *J Neurochem* 49:92, 1987.

319. KODAMA S, IGISU H, SIEGEL DA, SUZUKI K: Glycosylceramide synthesis in the developing spinal cord and kidney of the twitcher mouse, an enzymatically authentic model of human Krabbe disease. *J Neurochem* 39:1314, 1982.

320. KOBAYASHI T, SUZUKI K: The twitcher mouse: The fate of exogenously administered [³H]galactosylsphingosine, in Makita A, Handa S, Taketomi T, Nagai Y (eds): *New Vistas in Glycolipid Research.* New York, Plenum, 1982, p 253.

321. BOURQUE EA, BORNSTEIN MB, PETERSON ER, SUZUKI K: The twitcher mouse: Myelinogenesis in organotypic culture. *Brain Res* 261:295, 1983.

322. KOBAYASHI T, SHINNOH N, KUROIWA Y: Metabolism of galactosylceramide in the twitcher mouse, an animal model of human globoid cell leukodystrophy. *Biochim Biophys Acta* 879:215, 1986.

323. SCARAVILLI F, JACOBS JM, TEIXEIRA F: Quantitative and experimental studies on the twitcher mouse, in Baumann N (ed): *Neurological Mutations Affecting Myelination.* Amsterdam, Elsevier, 1980, p 115.

324. SCARAVILLI F, JACOBS JM: Peripheral nerve grafting without immunological suppressive treatment in the twitcher mouse, a murine model of a human leucodystrophy. *Nature* 290:56, 1981.

325. SCARAVILLI F, JACOBS JM: Improved myelination in nerve grafts from the leukodystrophic twitcher into trembler mice: Evidence for enzyme replacement. *Brain Res* 237:163, 1982.

326. SCARAVILLI F, SUZUKI K: Enzyme replacement in grafted nerve of twitcher mouse. *Nature* 305:713, 1983.

327. YEAGER AM, BRENNAN S, TIFFANY C, MOSER HW, SANTOS GW: Prolonged survival and remyelination after hematopoietic cell transplantation in the twitcher mouse. *Science* 225:1053, 1984.

328. SELLER MJ, PERKINS KJ, FENSOM AH: Galactosylcerebrosidase activity in tissues of twitcher mice with and without bone marrow transplantation. *J Inherited Metab Dis* 9:234, 1986.

329. UMEZAWA F, ETO Y, TOKORO T, ITO F, MAEKAWA K: Enzyme replacement with liposomes containing β-galactosidase from *Charonia lampas* in murine globoid cell leukodystrophy (twitcher). *Biochem Biophys Res Commun* 127:663, 1985.

CHAPTER 69

METACHROMATIC LEUKODYSTROPHY AND MULTIPLE SULFATASE DEFICIENCY: Sulfatide Lipidosis

EDWIN H. KOLODNY

1. Metachromatic leukodystrophy (MLD) is an inherited disorder of myelin metabolism. It is characterized by accumulation of galactosyl sulfide (cerebroside sulfate) in the white matter of the central nervous system and in the peripheral nerves. Galactosyl sulfatide and, to a smaller extent, lactosyl sulfatide also accumulate within the kidney, gallbladder, and certain other visceral organs and are excreted in excessive amounts in the urine. In histologic preparations, they form spherical granular masses that stain metachromatically.

2. The disease may appear at any age. The late infantile form is first recognized in the second year of life and is fatal within a few years. There are also juvenile forms presenting between ages 4 and 12 and a more rare adult form that may begin at any time between the midteens and the seventh decade. In each of these variants the earliest signs are a gait disturbance, mental regression, and urinary incontinence. In the childhood variants, other common signs are blindness, loss of speech, quadriparesis, peripheral neuropathy, and seizures. In the adult, behavior disturbances and dementia are the major presenting signs, and the disease may progress slowly over several decades.

3. Multiple sulfatase deficiency *is a rare form of MLD that resembles the late infantile variant but also includes features of a mucopolysaccharidosis. It presents at the same age as late infantile MLD, but the affected child does not develop speech or the ability to walk. Additional findings are ichthyosis, coarse facial features, hepatosplenomegaly, abnormalities of the spine, and a mucopolysacchariduria.*

4. Cerebroside sulfate is normally metabolized by the hydrolysis of the 3-O-sulfate linkage to form galactocerebroside through the combined action of arylsulfatase A and a heat-stable nonenzymatic protein activator. The artificial compound p-nitrocatechol sulfate is the substrate most often employed to determine the level of arylsulfatase A activity.

5. Deficiency of arylsulfatase A activity occurs in the late infantile, juvenile, and adult forms of MLD. The deficiency of sulfatide catabolism is most marked in the late infantile variant and is less extreme in the juvenile form. The highest residual sulfatidase activity is found in the adult form, and this activity can be increased by the action of thiol proteinases. In multiple sulfatase deficiency there is a deficiency not only of arysulfatase A but also of other sulfatases, including steroid sulfatase and the mucopolysaccharide sulfatases. A defect in post-translational glycosylation of multiple sulfatases leads to the production of unstable enzyme.

6. Several patients with many of the signs of juvenile MLD including a sulfatiduria have normal arylsulfatase A activity. These individuals are missing a sphingolipid activator protein, SAP-1, that is necessary for in vivo hydrolysis of sulfatide. The gene for SAP-1 has been cloned and is located on chromosome 10.

7. Arylsulfatase A activity is occasionally deficient in some relatives of patients with MLD, in normal individuals, and in patients with other neurologic diseases due to the frequent presence in the general population of a gene for pseudodeficiency of arylsulfatase A. The enzyme deficiency in these pseudodeficiency cases is due to a catalytically normal but unstable arylsulfatase A with reduced N glycosylation. Sulfatiduria does not occur and some cerebroside sulfate sulfatase activity can be found, whereas in true MLD this particular activity is totally deficient.

8. MLD is transmitted as an autosomal recessive trait. Different gene mutations probably account for each form, but a separate allele has thus far only been demonstrated for multiple sulfatase deficiency. The locus that determines the expression of arylsulfatase A activity is on chromosome 22, probably in the region of q13.

9. The MLD heterozygote is identified by assaying leukocytes or cultured skin fibroblasts for their arylsulfatase A or cerebroside sulfate sulfatase activity. Similarly, prenatal diagnosis also can be performed by enzyme testing of cultured amniotic fluid cells or chorionic villi provided that all cell pellets with arylsulfatase A deficiency are further checked with radioactively labeled sulfatide as substrate in in vitro or in situ tissue culture studies.

HISTORICAL ASPECTS

Metachromatic staining of the nervous system was first reported by Alzheimer[1] in 1910 in an adult patient with a clinical picture resembling general paresis. In 1921, Witte[2] described a similar patient with accumulation of metachromatic material not only in the brain but also in the liver, kidneys, and testes. Scholz, in his detailed account in 1925[3] of three children from one family with progressive leukodystrophy, proposed that the myelin abnormality that he observed might be due to a glial cell defect. However, he failed to notice metachromatic properties in the tissues that he examined because they had been treated with alcohol, which removed the lipid responsible for the metachromasia. Thirty years later, von Hirsch and Peiffer[4] showed that an acetic acid–cresyl violet stain would change to a brown color in tissues from patients with MLD. Using this stain, Peiffer found striking metachromasia in frozen sections from the original patient of Scholz.[5] The descriptions of Scholz and Peiffer thus represent the first comprehensive report on the clinical and pathologic aspects of juvenile MLD. A third type of MLD that begins in the late infantile period was reported by Greenfield[6] in 1933. Feigin is credited with the first description of a congenital form.[7]

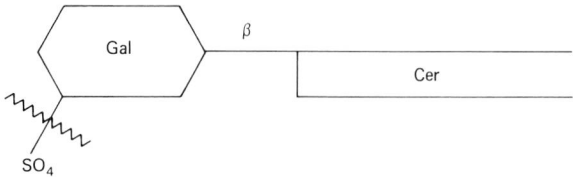

Fig. 69-1 Galactosyl-3-sulfate ceramide, the major accumulating material in metachromatic leukodystrophy, and the site of the primary defect, a deficiency in arylsulfatase A.

Known for many years as "diffuse brain sclerosis," the disease was renamed "metachromatic leucoencephalopathy" in 1938 by Einarson and Neel.[8] Norman later suggested that it be classified as a lipidosis.[9] This was proven to be correct by the independent discoveries in 1958 by Jatzkewitz[10] and Austin[11] of a large excess of sulfatides in tissues from patients with MLD. The accumulation of this acidic lipid causes the metachromasia characteristic of this disease. Austin[12] in 1963 reported the deficiency of arylsulfatase A in MLD, and the following year Mehl and Jatzkewitz[13] demonstrated a block in the metabolism of cerebroside sulfate (Fig. 69-1). Arylsulfatase A was subsequently identified as the heat-labile component of cerebroside sulfate sulfatase.[14] Mehl and Jatzkewitz[15] also described a heat-stable factor that activates cerebroside sulfate sulfatase activity several-fold. In a rare patient with MLD[16] it is this factor rather than arylsulfatase A that is deficient. Another variant with associated signs of a mucopolysaccharidosis has been reported several times since 1965.[17] In this disorder, known as *multiple sulfatase deficiency*, at least seven different sulfatases are deficient.[18]

SULFOLIPIDS

Structure and Biosynthesis

The term *sulfolipid* is applied to all sulfur-containing lipids. These consist of lipids containing sulfur in the sulfate form and proteolipids containing amino acids that include sulfur in

a different oxidation state. The non-amino acid lipid sulfur exists in three major classes of compounds (Fig. 69-2):

1. The sulfated sphingolipids, galactosyl sulfatide and lactosyl sulfatide, are the major sulfate-containing lipids in the nervous system (Fig. 69-2A and B).
2. Sulfate is present in certain galactose-containing glycerolipids that are found predominantly in the testes after puberty (Fig. 69-2C).
3. Steroid sulfates are of particular importance in the adrenal, testis, and placenta, and are also normally present in plasma, red blood cells, and brain (Fig. 69-2D).

In MLD, the catabolism of sulfatides and sulfogalactoglycerolipids is impaired; in the rare variant of MLD associated with multiple sulfatase deficiency, the metabolism of steroid sulfates is also affected.

Sulfatides

Structure. Thudichum[19,20] first recognized the existence of a sulfur-containing lipid and named it *sulfatide*. In 1933 Blix[21] reported the isolation of this substance and showed it to contain equimolar amounts of cerebronic acid, sphingosine, galactose, and sulfate. It was eventually shown to be a sulfate ester of cerebroside with the sulfate joined by an ester linkage to the C-3 hydroxyl of galactose.[22,23] As is true for cerebrosides, the sphingosine base of sulfatides consists predominantly of C-18 sphingosine.[24] The structural formula of galactosyl sulfatide appears in Fig. 69-2A.

Both sulfatides and cerebrosides contain a high proportion of long-chain fatty acids and of fatty acids that contain a 2-hydroxy group. In fact, nearly all of the 2-hydroxy fatty acids found in brain lipids are constituents of these two glycolipids. In adult brain, 20 to 25 percent of sulfatide fatty acids contain the 2-hydroxy group with cerebronic (C24h:O), oxynervonic (C24h:1), and the 22- and 23-carbon saturated fatty acids predominating. In fetal and immature brain, the proportion of hydroxy fatty acids is smaller. The major nonhydroxy fatty

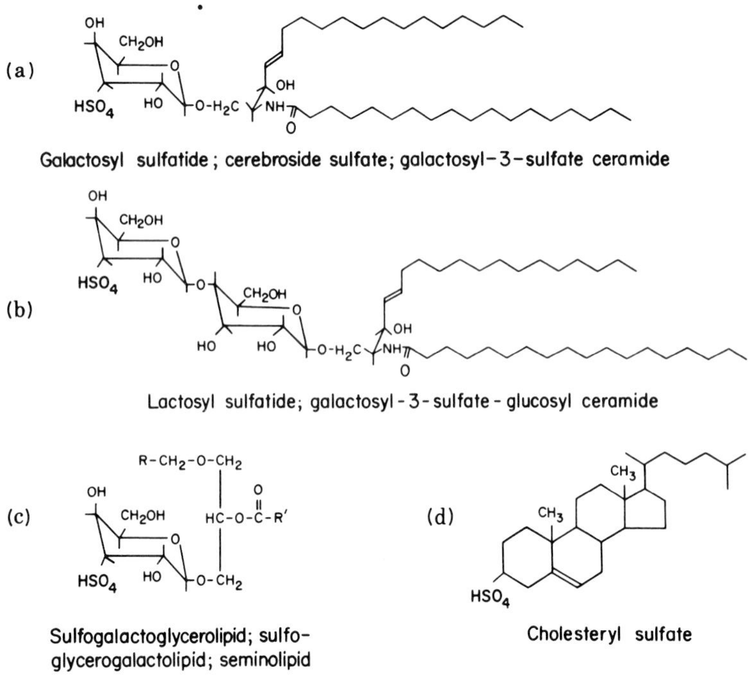

(a)

Galactosyl sulfatide; cerebroside sulfate; galactosyl-3-sulfate ceramide

(b)

Lactosyl sulfatide; galactosyl-3-sulfate-glucosyl ceramide

(c)

Sulfogalactoglycerolipid; sulfo-glycerogalactolipid; seminolipid

(d)

Cholesteryl sulfate

Fig. 69-2 The structure of some sulfolipids. Note that a variety of fatty acyl groups and of sphingosine long-chain bases are found in naturally occurring sulfatides.

acids in sulfatide of adult brain are nervonic acid (C24n:1) and lignoceric acid (C24n:O), whereas in fetal and immature brain medium-chain fatty acids (C16n:O, C18n:O, and C18n:1) predominate. The development of the pattern characteristic of adult brain coincides with myelination.

The kidney is second to brain in relative abundance of sulfatide, but its concentration is only about one-tenth that of brain. Lesser amounts may be found in the small intestine, placenta, and sublingual glands.[25] Kidney sulfatides contain more than 10 times as much behenic acid (C22n:O) as those in brain and also contain a higher proportion of lignoceric than nervonic acid.[26,27] A similar fatty acid pattern has been found in urine sulfatides, indicating that they probably originate from the kidney.[28] Brain and kidney sulfatides also differ in their long-chain base composition with the presence of some phytosphingosine in urine sulfatide but not in the sulfatide of brain.[28,29]

Lactosylceramide sulfate (Fig. 69-2B) is also present in human kidney[27,30,31] and urine. It contains sulfate joined in an ester linkage to the C-3 of the galactose moiety.[32] As in galactosyl sulfatide, the predominant sphingosine base is C-18 sphingosine. Its fatty acid composition is also similar to galactosyl sulfatide. Lactosyl sulfatide is three times more concentrated in the kidney cortex than in the kidney medulla[31] and is absent from brain.[33] There is also evidence for a trihexosyl sulfatide in human kidney.[34]

Biosynthesis. The major synthetic pathway for the formation of cerebroside sulfate is probably through sulfation of galactocerebroside[35] by reaction with 3′-phosphoadenosine-5′-phosphosulfate (PAPS) as follows:

$$PAPS + cerebroside \longrightarrow cerebroside\text{-}3\text{-}sulfate + PAP$$

The reaction is catalyzed by a microsomal sulfotransferase that has been demonstrated in a variety of mammalian tissues.[36-39] A precursor-product relationship between cerebroside and sulfatide is supported by the close compositional relationship that exists between these two glycosphingolipids in the brain and in the kidney. The same enzyme will also transfer the sulfate moiety of PAPS to lactosylceramide to form lactosyl sulfatide.[38-40] A second sulfotransferase has also been described that will sulfate galactosylsphingosine and lactosylsphingosine.[38-41]

Sulfatide accounts for 3.5 to 4 percent of the total lipids of myelin.[42] Its synthesis is maximal during the period of myelination and proceeds more slowly in the adult. It is stimulated by cortisol[43] and reduced in neonatal hypothyroidism.[44] Both neurons and oligodendroglial cells have sulfatide-synthesizing capability, but sulfotransferase activity is much more active in cells of glial origin.[45,46] Established cell lines from renal tubule epithelium have also been shown to synthesize sulfatide.[47]

Sulfogalactoglycerolipid. Diacyl and alkylacyl glycerol forms of sulfogalactoglycerolipid have been characterized. Together these two lipids account for 2.1 to 7.2 percent of the total sulfolipids in rat brain.[48] The structure of the alkylacyl form is 1-O-alkyl-2-O-acyl-3(β-3′-sulfogalactosyl) glycerol (Fig. 69-2C). Its common name, seminolipid, reflects the fact that it is the major sulfolipid of mammalian testes and sperm.[49] A sulfotransferase step is involved in the synthesis of each lipid, but it is not certain whether the same or different sulfotransferases are responsible.[50,51]

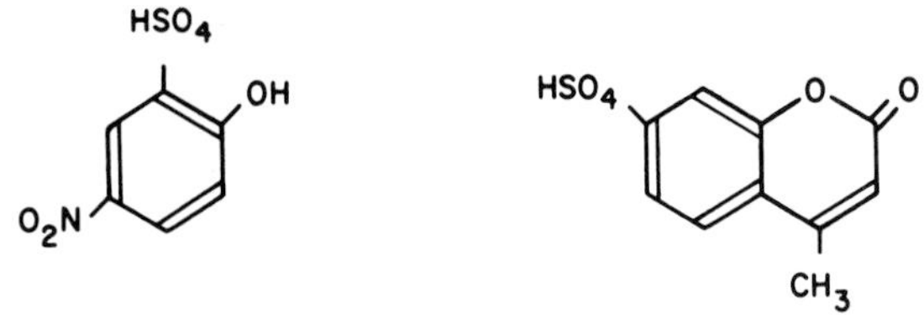

p-Nitrocatechol sulfate   4-Methylumbelliferyl sulfate

Fig. 69-3 *Synthetic substrates of arylsulfatase.*

Steroid Sulfates. Steroid sulfates found in human tissues include conjugates of cholesterol, dehydroepiandrosterone, estrogen, androgen, and corticosteroid. Their synthesis is catalyzed by one or more steroid sulfotransferases with PAPS, serving as the sulfate donor (for review see Ref. 52).

Sulfolipid Degradation

Desulfation is the first step in the enzymatic hydrolysis of the sulfolipids. Each of these sulfate esters with the exception of the steroid sulfates is a substrate for arylsulfatase A. This lysosomal enzyme was so designated because of its ability to desulfate such unphysiological aromatic sulfate esters as *p*-nitrocatechol sulfate and 4-methylumbelliferyl sulfate (Fig. 69-3). The hydrolysis of these synthetic compounds leads to a chromogenic or fluorigenic product that simplifies the quantitative analysis of this enzyme. These substrates are also hydrolyzed by arylsulfatase B, another lysosomal enzyme involved in mucopolysaccharide metabolism, and by arylsulfatase C, a microsomal enzyme active in steroid sulfate catabolism (see Table 69-1). In the pathogenesis of MLD, arylsulfatase A is significant because its deficiency in classic cases of this disease leads to the accumulation of its major physiological substrate, cerebroside sulfate. In multiple sulfatase deficiency, all three arylsulfatases as well as other sulfate ester hydrolases, listed in Table 69-1, are deficient.

Arylsulfatase A

Structural and Physical Properties. The arylsulfatases are found in all body tissues and fluids. Arylsulfatase A has been purified from a variety of sources including human liver,[53-56] placenta,[57,58] and urine.[59-61] It is an acidic glycoprotein with a low isoelectric point due to a high content of aspartic and glutamic acids. It also contains large amounts of proline.[61] Arylsulfatase A undergoes a pH-dependent polymerization forming a dimer at pH 4.5. Above pH 6.5, the enzyme exists as a monomer with a molecular weight of approximately 100 kDa. In human urine, the enzyme consists of two nonidentical subunits of 63 and 54 kDa.[61] Arylsulfatase A purified from human liver, placenta, and fibroblasts also consists of two subunits of slightly different sizes varying between 55 and 64 kDa.[54,62-66] As in the case of other lysosomal enzymes, arylsulfatase A is synthesized on membrane-bound ribosomes as a glycosylated precursor. It then passes through the endoplasmic reticulum and Golgi where its N-linked oligosaccharides are processed with the formation of phosphorylated and sulfated oligosaccharide of the complex type.[67,68] In normal cultured fibroblasts a precursor polypeptide of 62 kDa is produced which is then processed to mature 61.5- and 57.0-kDa forms.[62,66,69]

Multiple molecular forms of arylsulfatase A have been demonstrated on electrophoresis and isoelectric focusing of enzyme preparations from human urine,[60] leukocytes,[70-72] cultured fi-

Table 69-1 Human Arylsulfatases and Glycosaminoglycan Sulfatases

Enzyme	Natural substrates	Deficiency states
Arylsulfatase A (EC 3.1.6.1, lysosomal) (EC 3.1.6.8, cerebroside sulfatase)	Galactosyl sulfatide Lactosyl sulfatide Sulfogalactosylsphingosine Sulfogalactoglycerolipid Ascorbic acid-2-sulfate	Metachromatic leukodystrophy Multiple sulfatase deficiency
Arylsulfatase B (EC 3.1.6.1, lysosomal N-Acetylgalactosamine-4-sulfate sulfatase)	UDP-N-acetylgalactosamine-4-sulfate Dermatan sulfate Chondroitin-4-sulfate	Maroteaux-Lamy disease Multiple sulfatase deficiency
Arylsulfatase C (EC 3.1.6.1, microsomal) (EC 3.1.6.2, sterol sulfate, sulfohydrolase)	Dehydroepiandrosterone sulfate Pregnenolone sulfate Androstenediol-3-sulfate Estrone sulfate Cholesteryl sulfate	X-Linked ichthyosis Multiple sulfatase deficiency
Iduronide-2-sulfate sulfatase	Dermatan sulfate Heparan sulfate	Hunter disease Multiple sulfatase deficiency
Heparan-N-sulfamidase	Heparan sulfate	Sanfilippo disease type A Multiple sulfatase deficiency
N-Acetylgalactosamine-6-sulfate sulfatase	Keratan sulfate	Morquio disease, type A Multiple sulfatase deficiency
N-Acetylglucosamine-6-sulfate sulfatase	Chondroitin-6-sulfate	Mucopolysaccharidosis VIII Multiple sulfatase deficiency

broblasts,[62,73,74] and liver.[73-76] Treatment with endoglycosidase H, sialidase, and alkaline phosphatase reduces the molecular size and complexity of the electrophoretic pattern, suggesting that the charge heterogeneity of arylsulfatase A is due to variations in the carbohydrate content of the enzyme. In tumor tissues, both the amount of enzyme[77] and its molecular size[67,78] are increased, the latter due to an increase in sialylation and phosphorylation. In one study, electrophoretic variants of arylsulfatase A have been detected in a larger percentage of hospitalized alcoholic patients than normal individuals, prompting the suggestion that people with variant arylsulfatase A may be at increased risk for the neuropathologic effects of alcohol.[79,80]

Catalytic Site. The active site of arylsulfatase A contains an essential histidine residue[81] and two or more arginine residues.[82] Many anions are inhibitors of the enzyme at concentrations in the millimolar range or lower. These include SO_4^{2-}, PO_4^{3-}, SO_3^{2-}, and F^-. The reaction is also inhibited by Ag^+, Cu^{2+}, and by carbonyl reagents in the presence of Cu^{2+}.

Kinetics. A time-dependent inactivation of arylsulfatase A occurs during its reaction with p-nitrocatechol sulfate (Fig. 69-4). Partial reactivation results on exposure to SO_4^{2-} or certain other anions. It has been proposed that the reaction between enzyme and substrate substantially modifies the enzyme with loss of secondary structure.[83] An enzyme-antibody complex also shows anomalous kinetics, but the enzyme inactivation is significantly lower than for the native enzyme; presumably, this is because the antibody retards the process of structural rearrangement or covalent modification of the enzyme.[84] A similar inactivation of arylsulfatase A occurs during its hydrolysis of cerebroside sulfate, but no reactivation results on addition of SO_4^{2-}.[85] The anomalous kinetics of arylsulfatase A render it impossible to determine initial reaction rates. This property may have little if any physiological significance, since it occurs only with the monomeric form of the enzyme, whereas in its natural state in the lysosome the enzyme is probably in the dimeric form.[86]

Substrate Specificity. The cleavage of both p-nitrocatechol sulfate and cerebroside sulfate is catalyzed by the same enzyme. This conclusion is based on the copurification of both activities and their common deficiency in MLD. For optimal in vitro activity of cerebroside sulfate sulfatase (sulfatidase) at ionic concentrations in the physiological range, a bile salt such as sodium cholate or taurodeoxycholate and Mn^{2+} are needed. The metal ion facilitates the formation of mixed micelles of detergent and cerebroside sulfate.[87] A heat-stable activator protein substitutes for the bile salt in vivo. This complementary factor, known as SAP-1 (sphingolipid activator protein), is a nonenzymatic lysosomal glycoprotein with an apparent molecular weight as determined by gel filtration of 27,000 and two isoelectric points, 4.1 and 4.5.[88] It begins in cultured cells as a 65-kDa translation product that is first processed by gly-

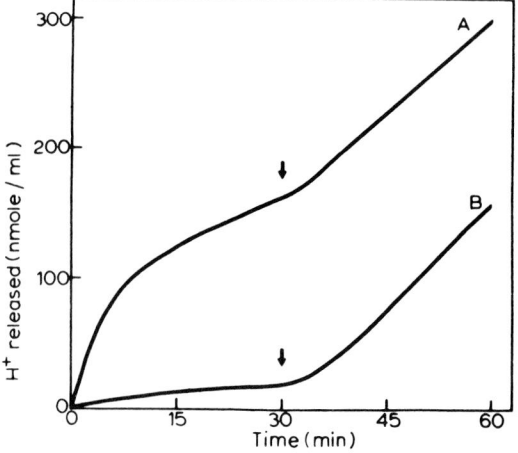

Fig. 69-4 Time curves of "native" and "modified" ox liver arylsulfatase A. Modified arylsulfatase A was obtained by gel filtration and dialysis of a conventional assay mixture. Both native (A) and modified (B) enzymes were then incubated with p-nitrocatechol sulfate under standard conditions in a pH-stat, and the rate of cleavage was determined. At 30 min (arrow) SO_4^{2-} was added to both assays. Note the diminished activity of modified enzyme compared with native, prior to addition of SO_4^{2-}. (From Nicholls and Roy.[222])

cosylation to a 70-kDa form and subsequently, in a series of steps, to an 8- to 11-kDa intralysosomal species.[89] On a weight basis it is more effective than taurocholate. It forms a one-to-one complex with sulfatide that serves as the actual substrate of the enzyme.[90] It also promotes the hydrolysis of G_{M1} ganglioside and globotriaosylceramide.[91,92] In a system of very low ionic strength, purified arylsulfatase A can also hydrolyze cerebroside sulfate without the activator present.

Other galactosyl-3-sulfates can also be hydrolyzed by arylsulfatase A. These include lactosyl sulfatide,[93] seminolipid,[94,95] and psychosine sulfate.[95,96] The rates of hydrolysis for several natural and artificial substrates of arylsulfatase A are shown in Table 69-2. The activator of sulfatidase activity also stimulates the hydrolysis of seminolipid and the deacylated derivatives, lysoseminolipid and psychosine sulfate.[95] Ascorbic acid-2-sulfate is also a substrate for the enzyme[97,98] The latter compound occurs throughout the body, but it apparently does not accumulate in MLD.[99]

Arylsulfatase A does not hydrolyze chondroitin sulfate, cerebroside-6-sulfate, or galactose-6-sulfate. It only feebly attacks tyrosine-O-sulfate, is inactive toward 5-hydroxytryptamine-O-sulfate, and has no phosphatase activity. Arylsulfatase B is discussed in Chap. 61 and arylsulfatase C in Chap. 76.

Histochemical Localization. Histochemical detection of arylsulfatase A has been accomplished using p-nitrocatechol sulfate and a copper ferricyanide incubation mixture that produces a brown precipitate in the presence of enzyme activity. In kidney and adrenal tissues, the enzyme activity localizes to cytoplasmic particles resembling lysosomes.[100] If the brown precipitate is coupled to 3, 3'-diaminobenzidine, it produces an osmiophilic polymer that is visible under the electron microscope. In cultured fibroblasts analyzed in this way, arylsulfatase A localizes to periplasmic vesicles located near the cell surface.[101] Immunochemical staining of cultured fibroblasts with fluorescent-labeled antibody to the enzyme produces a coarse granular appearance on a diffusely stained background.[102]

Physiological Role

Sulfolipids share with other membrane lipids the dual capability of hydrophilic and hydrophobic interactions. In addition, their anionic charge allows combination with inorganic cations or organic amines to maintain the electrical neutrality of the membrane. Cerebroside sulfate (sulfatide), a major component of the myelin sheath,[103] is located on the surface of this membrane[104] and is linked to basic proteins by ionic interactions.[105] It is believed to be involved in active sodium transport, serving as a cofactor for Na^+, K^+-dependent ATPase. In many tissues, sulfatide concentrations are closely correlated with Na^+ K^+-ATPase activity,[106] and the removal of sulfatide from membranes rich in ATPase by the action of arylsulfatase A causes inactivation of the ouabain-sensitive phosphatase activity.[107]

There is also evidence implicating sulfatide in the opiate-binding site. It fulfills most of the structural requirements of an opiate receptor, and the affinity with which it binds various opiates correlates well with their pharmacologic potency.[108,109] Antibodies to sulfatide antagonize the effects of morphine and β-endorphin on the periaqueductal gray region, which con-

Table 69-2 Rate of Hydrolysis of Various Sulfate Esters by Arylsulfatase A

Substrate	Rate, μmol/min per milligram protein
p-Nitrocatechol sulfate	160.0
4-Methylumbelliferyl sulfate	40.0
Ascorbic acid-2-sulfate	85.0
Cerebroside-3-sulfate	6.6
Seminolipid	5.0
Psychosine sulfate	3.0

SOURCE: Farooqui and Mandel.[379]

tains a high concentration of opiate and endorphin receptors.[110] Decreasing the available sulfatide sites by treatment with azure A, a dye with high affinity for sulfolipids,[111] or with sulfatidase[111,112] also decreases the analgesic response to morphine. In aqueous solutions of sulfatide, human β-endorphin adopts a partial helical conformation, possibly facilitating the electrostatic interaction between the protonated nitrogen of the opiates and the anionic groups at the binding site.[113] The sulfatide in myelin is probably not accessible for opiate binding because it is bound internally to basic protein.[105]

A sulfolipid also appears to serve as a component of the GABA recognition site.[114] Preincubation of synaptic membrane suspensions with arylsulfatase A inhibits their ability to bind [³H]GABA. This effect can be blocked by known inhibitors of arylsulfatase A. Furthermore, the degree of inhibition correlates directly with the p-nitrocatechol sulfate cleaving activity of the enzyme. There is also evidence implicating sulfatide in the serotonin receptor.[115]

Three adhesive glycoproteins, laminin, thrombospondin, and von Willebrand factor, bind specifically and with high affinity to sulfatide.[34] Blockade of thrombospondin binding to sulfatides by monoclonal antibodies inhibits its hemagglutination activity.[116] Sulfatide also induces the activation of at least three other clotting substances, prekallikrein, factor XI, and factor XII.[117,118] In this report it is significant that platelet sulfatide concentrations are five times that of erythrocytes.[106] Sulfatide also appears to play a role in the cytotoxicity of natural killer cells. Inhibition of their arylsulfatase activity with sodium sulfate or a synthetic substrate analogue suppresses their cytotoxicity, suggesting that membrane sulfatide is involved in the cell-to-cell contact required for the lytic process.[119,120]

The sulfogalactoglycerolipids, because they are a myelin component and turn over rapidly during myelination, may have an important role in brain maturation.[48] They are also a major glycolipid of testes and spermatozoa and are thus important in spermatogenesis.[49] Steroid sulfates participate in detoxification reactions but may fulfill other membrane functions as well.

CLINICAL MANIFESTATIONS

The seven disorders that comprise the MLD group of diseases are summarized in Table 69-3. They are classified according to age of onset and biochemical defect. The most common forms are associated with deficiency of arylsulfatase A and are divided into late infantile, early juvenile, late juvenile, and adult types.

Most patients with the late infantile type develop clinical

Table 69-3 Characteristics of MLD Variants

Type	Age at onset, years	Main clinical manifestations	Spinal fluid protein	Nerve conduction velocity	Urinary sulfatide excretion	Arylsulfatase A activity	Other
Congenital	Birth	Apnea, cyanosis, seizures, generalized weakness	Unknown	Unknown	Unknown	Unknown	
Late infantile	1–2	Developmental delay, ataxia, weakness, loss of speech, optic atrophy, progressive spastic quadriparesis	Elevated	Slowed	Elevated	Deficient	
Early juvenile	4–6	Mental confusion, ataxia, clumsiness, postural abnormalities, optic atrophy, progressive spastic quadriparesis	Elevated	Slowed	Elevated	Deficient	
Late juvenile	6–12	Cognitive difficulties preceding gait disturbance, pyramidal and extrapyramidal signs, slow progression	Elevated	Slowed	Elevated	Deficient	
Adult	>16	Dementia, psychotic thinking, incontinence, ataxia, progressive spastic quadriparesis	Normal or elevated	Normal or slowed	Elevated	Deficient	
Multiple sulfatase deficiency	<1	Signs of late infantile MLD plus coarse facial features, deafness, ichthyosis, hepatosplenomegaly, skeletal anomalies	Elevated	Slowed	Elevated	Deficient	Excess urine mucopolysaccharide, Alder-Reilly granules in white blood cells, multiple sulfatases deficient
Cerebroside sulfate sulfatase activator deficiency	4–6	Signs of juvenile MLD	Elevated	Slowed	Elevated	Normal or mildly reduced	Deficiency of cerebroside sulfate sulfatase activator factor

signs between ages 15 months and 2 years. Thereafter, the tempo of their disease is relatively rapid, with death occurring 1 to 7 years later. The age of onset and duration of illness are far less stereotyped in the juvenile and adult variants. Many juvenile onset patients develop symptoms at about age 5 years, but a scattering of cases beginning later in childhood also suggests the possibility of two subgroups of juvenile MLD: an early onset and a later onset form. A similar subdivision occurs among the adult onset cases. At least one-third become symptomatic by age 18, while the others develop the disease in the third, fourth, or a later decade. Those MLD patients whose symptoms begin after age 16 follow a clinical course that more closely resembles that of adult MLD than of juvenile MLD. Also, there have been occasional reports of the disease first appearing at age 16 or 17 in the sib of a patient whose symptoms did not begin until after age 18.[121–123] Clearly the same disease was present in both, so age criteria should be established for the designation that will encompass both sibs.

Late infantile and juvenile cases of MLD tend to have a shorter course than the adult cases, but the age of onset is not an entirely dependable indicator of duration of disease. For example, very slow progression beyond a single decade has been observed in late infantile MLD,[124,125] and in a juvenile case we have studied, more than 20 years have passed since symptoms first appeared at age 5. In adult MLD, instances have been recorded of survival for 36[126] and 42 years[127,128] after the onset of clinical signs. For convenience, therefore, we retain the customary grouping of cases into late infantile, juvenile, and adult variants, but acknowledge the heterogeneity that exists within each group with regard to age of onset and duration of illness.

There may be some regional variation in the relative frequency of the various forms of MLD (Table 69-4). In a report from Sweden[129] the late infantile form was found in 13 of 15 children (87 percent) and in two English reports, 24 of 38 (63 percent)[125] and 13 of 17 (76 percent)[130] were thus affected. A Finnish report[131] describes only two of nine patients with an onset before age 3. The authors of this report regard all of these patients as juvenile variants because they survived the age of 9 years. However, using the age-of-onset concept to define the MLD variants separates these two cases into the late infantile class. The pre-1964 literature survey of Hollander[132] disclosed 67 percent of 60 cases with an onset of MLD typical of the late infantile variant. Also, our own patient experience and that of Farrell[133] suggest that approximately equal numbers of patients with these two variants are now being diagnosed. The adult variant occurred in 15 percent of Hollander's series.[132] In the case experience of this author, the adult onset variant accounts for 20 percent of all cases (Table 69-4). These

Table 69-4 Types of MLD by Geographical Location

Geographical location	Number of cases			
	Late infantile	Juvenile	Adult	Reference
Sweden	13	2		129
England	13	4		130
England	24	14		125
Finland	2	7		131
Worldwide*	40	11	9	132
Washington State	6	4		133
New England	17	16	8	Author's experience

*1964 survey.

somewhat higher frequencies are due in part to our use of 16 as the lower age limit for the onset of clinical signs in the adult-type case. Better techniques of diagnosis including more widespread use of enzyme analyses are also contributing to greater recognition of and therefore a greater relative frequency of the juvenile and adult onset variants of MLD. Thus, one-fifth to one-quarter of all patients with MLD are probably of the adult onset variety, and a very small percentage represents rare variants, such as the congenital form, multiple sulfatase deficiency, and the sulfatase activator deficiency disorder. The majority of cases that remain are equally divided between the late infantile and juvenile forms.

Congenital MLD

The evidence for a separate congenital form of MLD has been based on histologic studies of two cases.[7,134] Direct biochemical proof of either tissue storage of sulfatide or an enzyme deficiency is lacking.

Feigin[7] described deposits of granular metachromatic material in severely degenerated cystic white matter of a male infant born 6 weeks prematurely. From birth, he had periodic spells of apnea, cyanosis, and tonic-clonic movements. He died 6 weeks after birth. The other case was a newborn female who developed cyanosis, dyspnea, and generalized weakness and died 20 h after birth.[134] Metachromatic material was scattered throughout white matter. In addition, ballooned nerve cells were found, and there was marked gliosis in the cerebral cortex and centrum semiovale. No metachromatic material was demonstrated in these enlarged neurons or in the kidney, liver, or lymph nodes, where large vacuolated cells were found.

It is conceivable that these cases represent an early stage in the clinical progression of late infantile MLD. Until both the pathology and pathologic chemistry of further congenital cases can be documented, the existence of a genetically distinct congenital variant must remain conjectural.

Late Infantile MLD

The late infantile form of MLD begins insidiously between the first and second year. In some patients development is delayed even before 1 year, and there is poor speech acquisition and slowness in learning to walk. Staggering with frequent falling and toe walking are common presenting signs. In one series, 8 of 23 patients never walked independently.[125] Another review of 67 cases described fewer than 60 percent able to walk by 16 months and 15 percent as never walking.[135] Occasionally, ataxia and weakness may occur precipitously in association with an intercurrent infection, then subside in a few weeks, only to recur and progress 1 or 2 months later. In a few cases the disease is ushered in by the appearance of a peripheral neuropathy.[136] Between age 2 and 3 years, the ability to sit without support is lost and seizures may develop. Other clinical signs include absent ankle jerks and extensor plantar responses.

Hagberg has subdivided the clinical course of late infantile MLD into four stages, based primarily on the degree of motor handicap.[137]

Clinical Stage I. Initially, most patients have flaccid weakness and hypotonia of both legs or of all four limbs. The deep-tendon reflexes may be diminished or absent. Genu recurvatum is often present. A child who has already learned to walk becomes unsteady and requires support to stand or walk (Fig. 69-5). This stage lasts from a few months to 1 year or more.

Clinical Stage II. In this stage the patient can sit up but can no longer stand. Mental regression is obvious. Speech deteriorates as a result of dysarthria and aphasia. Optic atrophy and a grayish discoloration of the macula are observed.[138,139] Nystagmus is present. Muscle tone is increased in the legs, but the arms may remain hypotonic. Ataxia and truncal titubation become obvious. Intermittent pain occurs in the arms and legs, probably as a manifestation of peripheral nerve or root involvement. The progress of the disease is now rapid, so that this stage lasts only a few months.

Clinical Stage III. At this stage the child is bedridden and quadriplegic. Muscle tone is variable. There may be decorticate, decerebrate, or dystonic posture upon which hypertonic fits may be superimposed. Bulbar and pseudobulbar palsies occur, causing difficulty in feeding and in maintaining the airway. The mental deficit is much more severe and speech is no longer distinct, but these children may still be able to smile and respond to their parents.

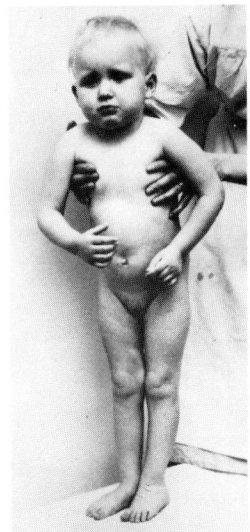 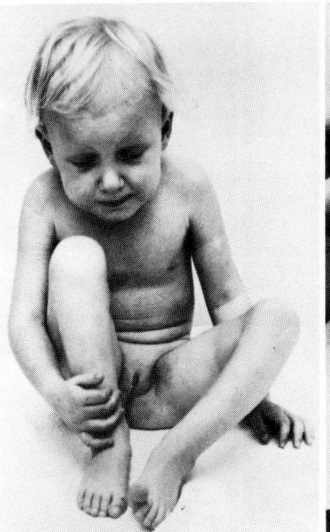 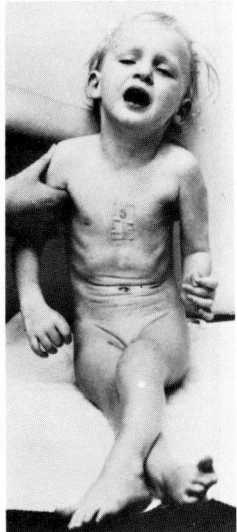

Fig. 69-5 Metachromatic leukodystrophy in late infancy. *Left.* The child needs to be supported when standing. *Center.* She can no longer stand, even with support. *Right.* In the late stage of the disease the patient is no longer able to sit; note the plantar flexion of the foot and the general debility. (*From* Hagberg.[137])

Clinical Stage IV. In this final stage, patients appear to have lost all meaningful contact with their surroundings. They are blind, without speech, and without volitional movement. Usually they must be fed through a nasogastric or gastrostomy tube. In late infantile MLD, this final stage lasts for a few months to several years.

Juvenile MLD

Juvenile MLD designates those cases with an age of onset between 4 and 12 years. The majority present during their first or second year of formal schooling with a fall-off in performance, confusion in following directions, daydreaming, and abnormal, sometimes bizarre, behavior[140] (Fig. 69-6). Incontinence and gait clumsiness also occur early in the disease. Speech becomes slurred, and signs of extrapyramidal dysfunction appear including postural abnormalities, increased muscle tone, and tremor. Within a year the child is no longer able to walk. The child then rapidly moves into stage III of the disease, with pseudobulbar palsy, rigidly flexed arms, leg scissoring, and tonic spasms. Seizures occur in more than half of the cases. Some authors distinguish between early and late onset forms of juvenile MLD.[125,141] In the early onset form, a gait disorder develops between age 4 and 6, accompanied or followed by intellectual deterioration. In the later onset form, educational, behavioral, and social difficulties appear first between 6 and 10 years followed by a disturbance in gait. The disease in the juvenile variants progresses more slowly than in late infantile MLD, with some cases having a course lasting longer than 20 years.[124,142–144] However, the majority of juvenile MLD patients do not live beyond their teens.

Adult MLD

Adult MLD may begin at almost any age beyond puberty. The first appearance of the disease has been recorded in patients as young as 15[123] and 16 years of age[122] and as old as 62.[145] A 5- to 10-year survival is common, but in a few patients the course is much more rapid,[145,146] and in others the illness may progress slowly over several decades.[126–128,143] Formerly, the diagnosis was not often suspected during life, so that most cases were brought to light by a postmortem examination. In the last several years, numerous living cases of adult MLD have been reported. These have come to light because of the increased awareness of this disease as a cause of psychiatric symptoms and more widespread use of CT scanning[147–152] and lysosomal enzyme assays in the study of degenerative nervous system diseases.

A change in personality and poor school or job performance herald the onset of the disease. The individual becomes anxious, bewildered, apathetic, and emotionally labile. Defective visual-spatial discrimination, poor memory, disorganized thinking, and decreased mental alertness are found. Psychiatric attention is frequently sought because of symptoms of

Fig. 69-6 Juvenile MLD. *Left.* At age 5½ years, 1 year before onset of symptoms, the child is entirely normal. *Center.* At age 6¹¹/₁₂ years the child has increasing gait difficulty and is unable to stand without support. *Right.* At age 8¹⁰/₁₂ years the patient is bedridden, has increasing difficulty in swallowing, and requires tube feeding. He is no longer able to speak, but recognizes his family and displays pleasure when people pay attention to him.

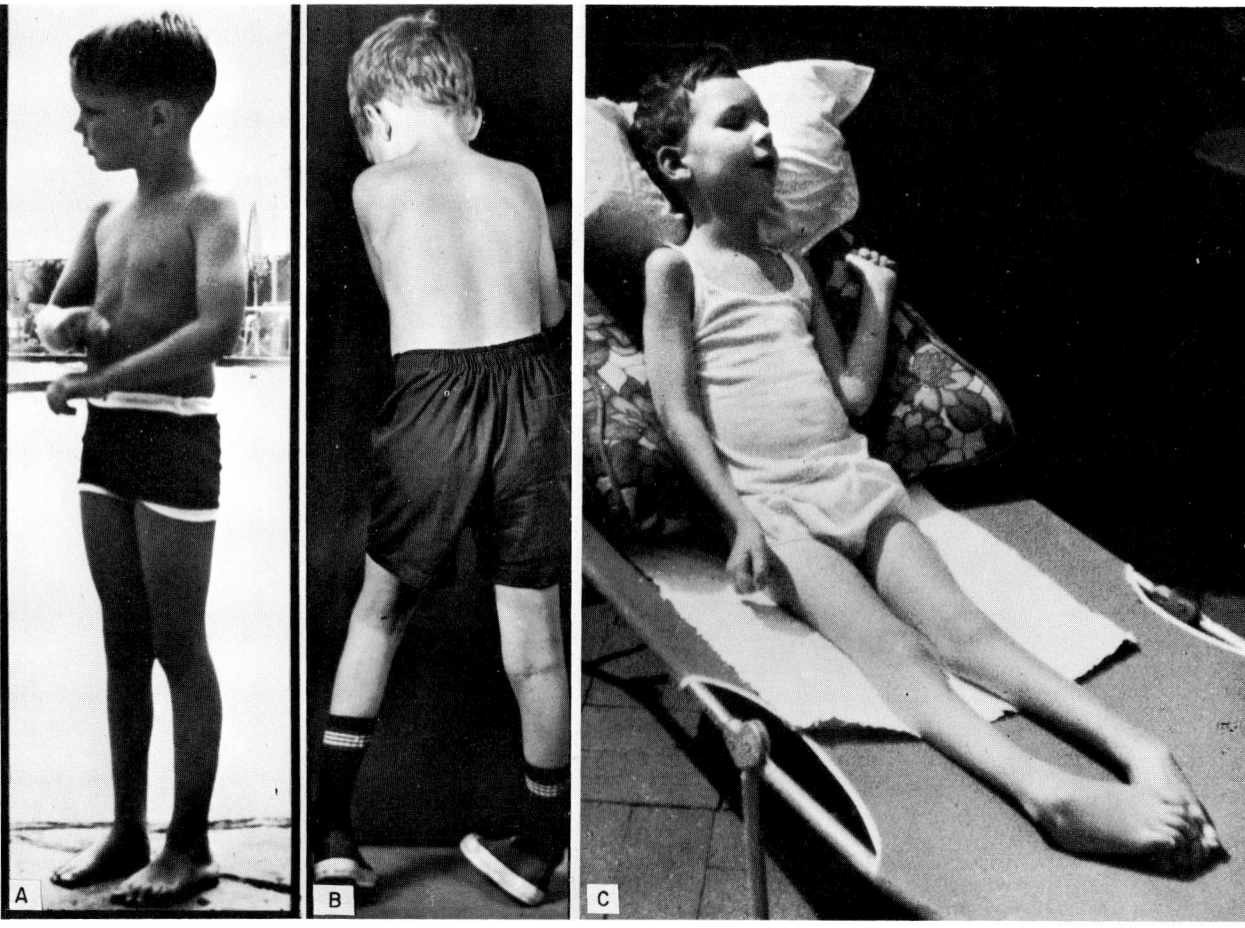

depression, schizophrenialike psychosis, or chronic alcoholism. The patient may express feelings of depersonalization or paranoia and display an inappropriate affect. Actual loss of contact by the patient with the surroundings does not occur until late in the course of the disease. Combined with these intellectual and emotional changes are a general slowness and clumsiness of movement and urinary and sometimes fecal incontinence.

Rarely, the disease may first appear as a peripheral neuropathy,[145,153] but not all patients with adult MLD develop a peripheral neuropathy. Even in the presence of a neuropathy, deep-tendon reflexes are hyperactive and muscle tone is increased, indicating that the involvement of pyramidal and extrapyramidal systems is more significant in the pathophysiology of the disease. Dystonic movements and pareses may occur, sometimes involving one side of the body more than the other. In a more advanced stage of the disease, spastic tetraparesis, decorticate posturing, and pathologic reflexes are present. Optic atrophy and horizontal nystagmus develop, and occasionally there are generalized seizures. During the final stages of the disease, the patient is in a severely deteriorated state and is mute, blind, bedridden, and unresponsive.

Multiple Sulfatase Deficiency

At least seven sulfatases are deficient in this combined storage disease that presents with features of both late infantile MLD and a mucopolysaccharidosis (Fig. 69-7). More than 40 cases of multiple sulfatase deficiency (MSD) have been reported (for review see Ref. 154; also Refs. 18, 155 to 160). Early development may be normal or delayed. Affected children usually attain the ability to pull themselves to a standing position and to say a few words, but their development is less advanced in the presymptomatic period than that of children with late infantile MLD. During the second year they lose the ability to sit, stand, and speak. They become inattentive and develop staring spells, spasticity, and blindness. Hearing is diminished, swallowing becomes difficult, and death usually occurs before the end of the first decade. However, survival into the third decade has occurred.

Mucopolysaccharidosislike features may be evident early in the course of the disease[157] or may not be appreciated until later. These include mild coarsening of the facial features, hepatosplenomegaly, stiff joints, growth retardation, and skeletal anomalies such as rib flaring, deformities of the acetabulum and sternum, and beaking of the lumbar vertebrae. Coarse facial features have not been reported in all cases, and where present are less severe than in the classic mucopolysaccharidoses. The eye findings have included skew deviation, optic atrophy, retinal degeneration,[154] and in two patients a cherry-red macula.[161,162] Corneal clouding is not usually present. Ichthyosis develops at 2 to 3 years of age.

An early onset form of the disease has been described in two infants who presented at birth with facial dysmorphism, short neck, hepatomegaly, hypoplasia of vertebral bodies, and epiphyseal dysplasia. Both developed hydrocephalus and also had corneal clouding and ichthyosis. In comparison with other MSD patients, they had a more severe deficiency of all sulfatases.[155,159]

The laboratory findings also reflect the concurrence of two separate disease processes. The usual clinical pathologic features of late infantile MLD are present, along with findings that are typical of many mucopolysaccharidoses. Among those

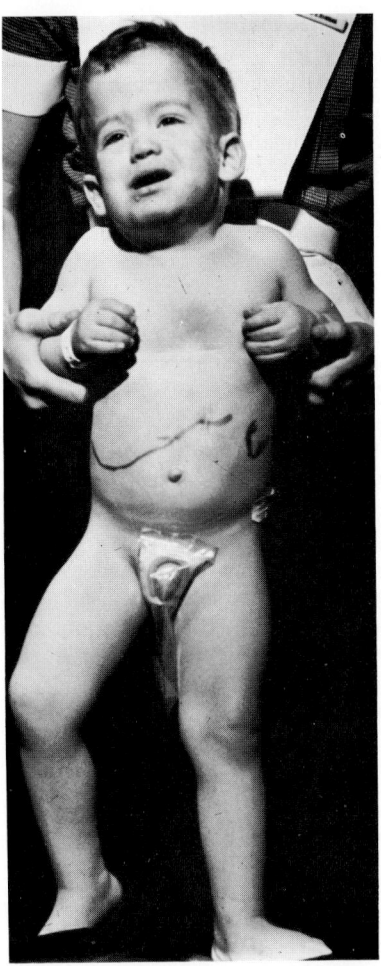

Fig. 69-7 MLD variant with multiple sulfatase deficiencies in a child 26 months of age. Note enlarged head circumference, depressed bridge of nose, enlarged liver and spleen, pectus excavatum and incurved little finger. (*From Murphy et al.*[258])

are Alder-Reilly granules in bone marrow and peripheral blood leukocytes, bone x-ray changes such as a J-shaped sella turcica and broad phalanges, and an increased urinary content of dermatan sulfate and heparan sulfate. Besides the arylsulfatase A deficiency, there is a loss of activity of arylsulfatases B and C and four other sulfatases that help to degrade mucopolysaccharidoses.[18,102]

Atypical Cases

Atypical cases with an unusual clinical expression or anomalous biochemical finding have been reported. In most of these patients, developmental delay and neurologic deficits were evident before 1 year of age,[154,163–166] and in one, the disease has been nonprogressive or has progressed more slowly than in classic variants of MLD. Several older patients have had dystonia.[163,167,168] While increased urinary excretion of sulfatides or nerve biopsy have documented sulfatide accumulation in certain of these patients, the presence of normal white matter on the CT scan[166] and normal nerve conduction and evoked potential studies[165] raises the possibility that some of the atypical cases actually represent individuals with pseudodeficiency of arylsulfatase A with coexisting but unrelated neurologic disease. In one case, arylsulfatase A activity was inducible to 38 to 74 percent of the mean by modification of the tissue culture medium,[154] and in another with a near-normal result in the cerebroside sulfate loading test, in vitro cerebroside sulfatase activity was almost totally absent. These types of unusual cases require complete clinical evaluation, including neurophysiological studies, neuroimaging, and sural nerve biopsy as well as measurements of urine sulfatides and cerebroside sulfate turnover in both the $^{199}CO_2$ medium and the MEMHEPES medium. Additionally, electrophoresis or isoelectricfocusing of arylsulfatase A subunits may be needed for unequivocal separation of pseudoarylsulfatase A deficiency from true MLD.

MLD Without Arylsulfatase A Deficiency

Three patients have been reported who have a form of juvenile MLD without arylsulfatase A deficiency.[16,169,170] Two were sibs whose parents were first cousins.[16,169] Their early development was normal. In one, a girl, behavioral abnormalities first appeared at age 4½ years. She also presented with an abnormal gait, a decrease in fine motor ability, and hyporeflexia. By age 6 years, she was functioning below a 6-month level and demonstrated a marked increase in muscle tone and hyperreflexia. Her nerve conduction times were slowed. Light- and electron-microscopic studies of a sural nerve biopsy demonstrated the histopathologic features of MLD, and the sulfatide content of her urinary sediment was markedly elevated.

Her brother began to deteriorate at age 6 years and had a similar but more slowly progressive course. At age 19, he was incontinent, nonambulatory, and uncommunicative, with extreme spasticity and hyperreflexia.

Enzyme studies of these two patients have demonstrated a dissociation between the ability of their cultured skin fibroblasts to degrade cerebroside sulfate in vitro and *in situ*. The activity of arylsulfatase A and sulfatidase in their fibroblast homogenates was in the range typical of heterozygotes for MLD, but with intact growing fibroblasts loaded with [^{35}S]sulfatide a defect in sulfatide cleavage comparable to that in MLD patients was observed.[169] This defect was normalized by the addition of exogenous purified cerebroside sulfate sulfatase activator factor.[16] Complete deficiency of the activator was confirmed in their leukocytes,[171] fibroblasts,[92] and urine[172] using specific antibody raised to the purified protein.

A third patient reported with this syndrome was also born to consanguineous parents.[170] She is now 21 years old and has had a history of developmental delay, clumsiness, ataxia, muscle weakness, and progressive psychomotor deterioration. On recent examination, her motor nerve conduction velocities were markedly slowed, and her sensory action potentials were unrecordable. Sural nerve biopsy and urinary excretion of sulfatide were typical of patients with classic MLD. Nevertheless, the arylsulfatase A activity in urine and leukocytes was normal. Presumably, she too lacks the activator protein needed for the in vivo hydrolysis of sulfatide; however, tissue culture correction experiments with added activator have not been reported in this case.

Pseudodeficiency of Arylsulfatase A (Arylsulfatase A Deficiency Without MLD)

Deficiency of arylsulfatase A may occur in the absence of any other laboratory evidence of MLD. Most cases of this type have been found in otherwise normal older relatives of patients with MLD.[144,173–181] These individuals do not have metachromatic deposits in peripheral nerve tissues, and their urine content of sulfatide is normal.[144,181,182] Thus, they themselves do not have MLD, nor are they in a preclinical stage of MLD. This phenomenon has been termed *pseudo-arylsulfatase A deficiency* or *pseudodeficiency of arylsulfatase A*. Arylsulfatase A deficiency has also been found in a few patients without any family history of MLD.[183–188] In many of these cases neurologic disabilities were present that suggested disease of the central nervous system white matter. In these cases also the clinical signs differed from those of the classic forms of MLD, and ancillary studies failed to disclose any evidence of MLD. A major distinguishing feature is their retention of some sulfatidase activity in leukocytes. In contrast, patients with MLD are totally deficient in leukocyte sulfatidase activity.[184] It is possible that some cases previously described as unusual variants of MLD[189] may actually be examples of this association of arylsulfatase A deficiency with a non-MLD type of neurologic disease.

Available data do not make clear the relationship between the neurologic disease and the enzyme deficiency. In two families without MLD that the authors have studied, the younger member of a pair of sibs with arylsulfatase A deficiency also had neurologic disease. The healthy older sib was detected only in the course of a family study of the enzyme abnormality. The lack of complete congruence between the biochemical defect and clinical state even in the same family casts some doubt on a cause-and-effect relationship. However, there is the possibility that in some unspecified way this type of arylsulfatase A deficiency predisposes to demyelinating disease[187] or neuropsychiatric disease.[190] In fact, several studies[190–192] have shown a slight but constant preponderance of lower arylsulfatase A activity in psychiatric patients, supporting the view that a disturbance in sulfatide metabolism may predispose to mental illness. This could occur through alterations in neurotransmitter function since sulfatide has been implicated in the opiate receptor[111,112] and in the CNS binding sites of GABA[114] and serotonin.[115] Nevertheless, there does not appear to be a significant difference in leukocyte sulfatidase activity between psychiatric patients and normal controls,[192] and the actual proportion of psychiatric patients with a very low level of arylsulfatase A activity does not differ from the general population.[193] Thus, the evidence for a possible relationship between low arylsulfatase A activity and psychiatric disease remains unclear.

The gene for this low enzyme variant appears to be allelic with the MLD gene locus,[194–196] and its frequency is common.[179] This would account for its frequent occurrence in MLD obligate heterozygotes, resulting in an apparent arylsulfatase A deficiency in such individuals. It is not possible to differentiate the MLD gene from this other allele by in vitro measurement of arylsulfatase A activity, since both are expressed in the heterozygote state by a reduction in enzyme activity to approximately 50 percent of normal. In the prenatal diagnosis of MLD it is important to determine whether either parent at risk for an MLD offspring also carries this additional mutation. The presence of this gene in the fetus together with a single dose of the MLD gene could lead to a false positive diagnosis of MLD. Assays of sulfatide-cleaving activity in the cultured amniotic fluid cells or chorionic villi can be used to circumvent this difficulty.[177,180]

CLINICAL LABORATORY FINDINGS

Cerebrospinal Fluid Protein

In the early stages of late infantile MLD, the cerebrospinal fluid protein may be normal, but as the disease progresses through stage II the spinal fluid protein level may continue to rise. Eventually, in the chronic stages of the disease, the level of total protein may reach or exceed 100 mg/dl. A similar elevation in spinal fluid protein occurs in the cases of juvenile MLD that begin before age 7. The later onset cases of juvenile MLD may or may not exhibit any increase in spinal fluid protein. In most adult onset cases of MLD, cerebrospinal fluid protein is normal, but raised levels have been recorded in a few patients.[127,145]

Neurophysiological Studies

The electroencephalogram may be normal early in the course of the disease. It also sometimes occurs that the electroencephalogram is abnormal prior to the clinical appearance of the disease. As the disease advances, it becomes diffusely slow and increases in amplitude, exhibiting mainly 4- to 7-Hz activity but also some 2- to 4-Hz activity. In a few cases, occasional bursts of spikes or of asymmetric slow wave activity have been recorded. Sudden noises may stimulate a marked startle response.[197–199]

In most cases, motor nerve conduction velocity is decreased, and sensory nerve action potentials are diminished in amplitude with prolonged latency to peak. These nerve conduction abnormalities may be present prior to the appearance of clinical symptoms and thus provide evidence of MLD in a presymptomatic stage.[200–202] Different nerves are affected, each in multiple areas.[203] The most marked slowing is in late infantile MLD.[199] The delay in the afferent nerves may precede that in the efferent nerves.[204] Later on, motor conduction velocity is more slowed than sensory conduction.[199] Some patients with the later onset form of juvenile MLD and those with adult MLD may exhibit little or no slowing of nerve conduction or any other electrophysiological evidence of a peripheral neuropathy, even in a clinically advanced stage of their disease.

In tests of brainstem auditory evoked responses (BAER) in late infantile MLD, prolongation of interpeak latencies, and loss of wave components are noted, indicating delay or block in conduction in the eighth cranial nerve and brainstem.[199,205–209] These changes may occur at a time when the peripheral nerve conduction is still normal.[206] In juvenile MLD, interpeak latencies of the BAER are normal or moderately increased.[200] The BAER in adult MLD has been reported to be normal.[202] Abnormalities in visual evoked responses[207,209] and in somatosensory evoked potentials[207] have also been described in patients with late infantile MLD, one patient with juvenile onset MLD,[210] and also in adult MLD.[202]

Computerized Brain Tomography

Computerized tomography (CT) of patients with MLD reveals symmetric decrease in the attenuation of the cerebral white

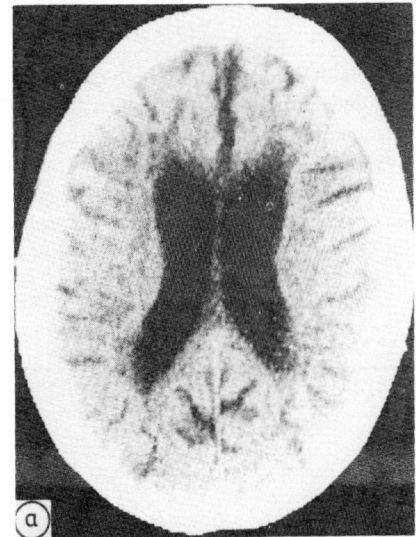

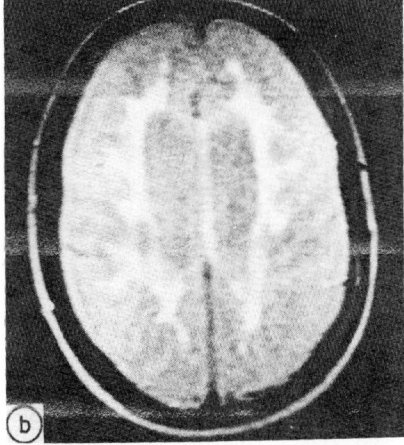

Fig. 69-8   CT and MRI scans of late juvenile onset MLD. The CT scan (A) at age 26 demonstrates cerebral atrophy with white matter hypodensity around the anterior and posterior horns of the lateral ventricles. The MRI scan (B) at age 29 shows an abnormal signal appearing diffusely throughout the periventricular white matter. (From Fisher et al.[151] with thanks to the Multiple Sclerosis Society NMR Research Group.)

matter that is not enhanced by administration of contrast (Fig. 69-8).[148,150] This change results from gradual myelin loss and the increased water content of the remaining structures. The abnormal low density may appear first in the white matter adjacent to the lateral ventricles and may be evident at a very early stage in the disease. In the late infantile and juvenile cases, there is rapid progression with involvement of the entire centrum semiovale producing ventricular enlargement. Mild cerebral atrophy also occurs.

The CT changes in adult onset MLD may be present before clinical signs appear and progress more slowly. The white matter attenuation is most noticeable near the frontal and occipital horns. It may appear as large multifocal, symmetric, well-defined periventricular lucencies rather than as a uniformly diffuse leukodystrophy.[147,150] As the disease progresses, there is significant enlargement of the ventricules and considerable cortical atrophy. With magnetic resonance imaging (MRI) (Fig. 69-8), the white matter change in adult onset MLD is more impressive and appears more diffuse than that seen in CT scans.[150–152]

Gallbladder Imaging

Extensive deposition of sulfatide may occur on the mucosal surface of the gallbladder and interferes with its normal functioning. Serial examination of the gallbladder with oral cholecystography[211] or radionuclide scanning may show progressive loss of function. A completely nonfunctioning gallbladder has been demonstrated in patients as young as 2 years of age.[212] Polypoid filling defects have also been seen on oral cholecystography.[213,214] In one patient with adult MLD, symptoms dramatically worsened after gallbladder surgery.[215]

HISTOPATHOLOGY

Metachromatic Deposits

The pathology of MLD consists primarily of demyelination and deposits of metachromatic granules in the central and peripheral nervous system. The metachromatic deposits are spherical masses 15 to 20 μm in diameter that stain brown in frozen tissue sections when treated with a 1% solution of acidified cresyl violet.[4] These masses have been observed not only in the nervous system but also in the kidney, urine, gallbladder, liver, pancreas, pituitary gland, adrenal cortex, retina, and testes.

When viewed with polarized light, the lipid deposits stained with acidified cresyl violet show a lime-green or yellow-green dichroism.[216,217] Pseudoisocyanin,[218] acriflavine,[219] and trypaflavine-phosphotungstic acid[219] have also been used to demonstrate metachromatic granules in MLD. The material in the granules can also be stained with alcian blue in the presence of 0.8 M magnesium chloride,[220] Sudan black, the periodic acid–Schiff reaction, and Hale's colloidal iron method.[217] Preextraction of the tissue with lipid solvents such as alcohol, pyridine, petroleum ether, and chloroform-methanol abolishes the reaction with these stains. These staining characteristics suggest that the stored material is acidic glycolipid of the sulfatide type. Actual chemical analysis of metachromatic granules isolated from the white matter of an MLD brain has revealed a sulfatide content amounting to 39 percent of their total lipid content. The other lipid components were cholesterol and phosphatides.[221] Energy dispersive x-ray microanalysis of the membrane-bound granules in dermal nerves has demonstrated a pronounced sulfur peak, further strengthening

the concept that the specific storage materials in the metachromatic granules are sulfatides.[222]

High resolution analysis of the storage granules by electron microscopy suggests that they are composed of several different types of inclusions. Most are surrounded by a single unit membrane suggesting their lysosomal origin.[217] Prismatic and Tuffstone inclusions are expecially characteristic. The lipid leaflets of prismatic inclusions appear in the form of little disks stacked in parallel prisms with a periodicity of 58 Å. The orientation of the disks in adjacent leaflets may be oblique to one another, creating a herringbone pattern (Fig. 69-9). A cross section of this type of inclusion assumes a hexagonal honeycomb pattern.[223] This type of inclusion has also been observed in cultured fibroblasts from MLD cases grown in the presence of sulfatides.[224]

Tuffstone bodies consist of concentrically or radially arranged lamellae with a 58 Å spacing in a granular matrix and several vacuoles of varying sizes contained within a membrane-bound lysosomal-like body (Fig. 69-10).[225,226] The term *Tuffstone* derives from the fact that these inclusions resemble volcanic limestone. Inclusions common to other types of lipid storage disease may also be observed in MLD. These include concentric lamellar osmiophilic inclusions somewhat resembling membranous cytoplasmic bodies, striated zebra bodies, granular bodies with weak osmophilia, and myelin figures.[142,217]

Central Nervous System

The central white matter is reduced in amount and is firmer than normal, has a gray or sometimes brown discoloration, and in severely affected regions may show cavitation or spongy degeneration. Usually there is sparing of the U fibers, the subcortical association fibers between adjacent convolutions, and of myelin sheaths within the central gray nuclei and optic radiation. There is a moderate to severe loss of myelin sheaths, a diminished number of interfascicular oligodendrocytes,[6] and a striking accumulation of metachromatic granules. These deposits are present in macrophages that are prominent in perivascular spaces and also may appear as free-lying bodies within the tissues. They also are found within oligodendrocytes even in areas where the myelin sheaths are relatively spared, and have been observed within the neurons of certain nuclei such as the dentate nucleus of the cerebellum, some nuclei of the brainstem, hypothalamus, thalamus, basal gan-

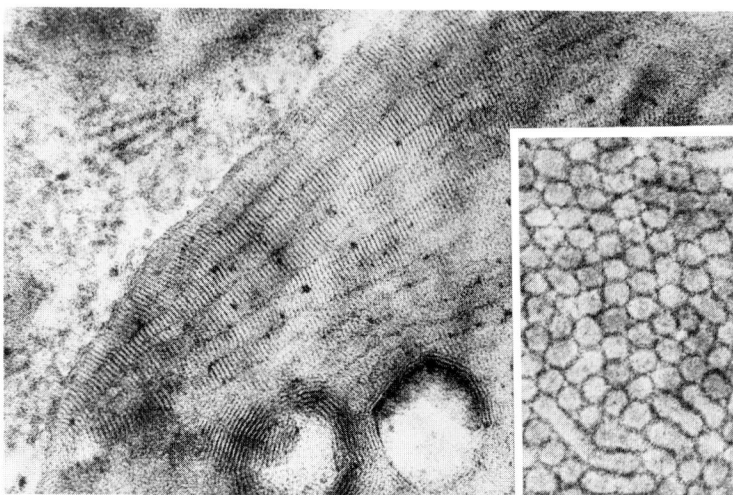

Fig. 69-9 Inclusions found at autopsy in the brain of a patient with infantile MLD. The preparation was stained with a combination of uranyl acetate and lead acetate. Note the lamellar lipid leaflets with a herringbone pattern, and *(inset)* the honeycomb aspect of the same type of structure seen in a section approximately parallel to the lamellas. ×200,000. *(From Rutsaert et al.[224])*

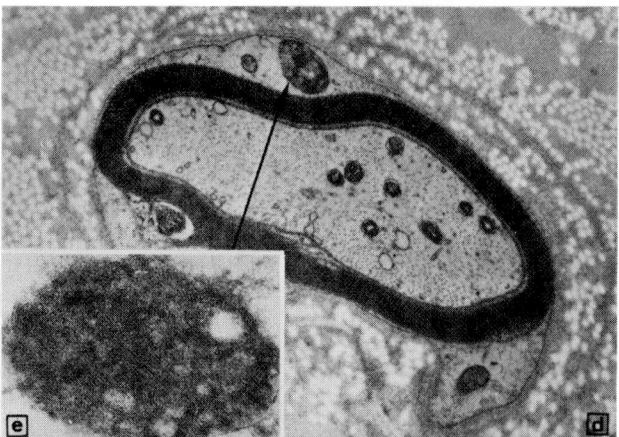

Fig. 69-10 Tuffstone inclusion in the Schwann cell of a myelinated axon from a cutaneous nerve. ×23,000. The inset shows the inclusion at higher magnification. ×120,000. Note the granular matrix containing a mosaic of slender lamellae surrounding electron lucent vacuoles of varying sizes. (*From Gebhart et al.*[237])

glia, pons, anterior horns, and spinal root ganglia.[5,217,227,228] Demyelination in the brainstem and spinal cord is prominent in late infantile MLD, much less striking in juvenile MLD, and absent from cases of adult onset.[229]

The nerve cells of the cerebral cortex are usually spared. A reactive gliosis is found in the areas of demyelination, and there may be partial or complete loss of axis cylinders. An immunochemical study of MLD white matter has described intensive staining of the myelin remnants with antiserum to basic protein, but severely affected white matter remained unstained by antiserum to myelin-associated glycoprotein.[230]

The cerebellum is atrophic, with severe demyelination, prominent gliosis, and storage granules. There is a marked reduction in Purkinje cells and granule cells, and some of the surviving Purkinje cells show torpedolike swellings in the granular layer. The axon terminals of climbing fibers and mossy fibers in the cerebellar granular layer and molecular layer also are missing.[231]

The retinal ganglion cells also accumulate metachromatic granules that appear under the electron microscope as laminated bodies with increased acid phosphatase activity, similar to the lysosomal bodies of Tay-Sachs disease.[138,232] Accumulations of metachromatic material also have been observed in retinal glial cells. The prismatic and Tuffstone inclusions characteristic of MLD have not been described in the retina but have been found in optic nerve.[233]

Peripheral Nervous System

A segmental demyelination occurs in the peripheral nervous system,[234–236] with metachromatic granules present singly or in clusters in Schwann cells in endoneural macrophages, and to a lesser degree in the Remak cells associated with unmyelinated nerve fibers. They are also seen as free-lying bodies between nerve fibers. The accumulation of metachromatic material may be found in the Schwann cells at an early stage while nerve conduction is still normal.[123] Computer-assisted morphometric analysis of sural nerves[123,236] has revealed reduced myelin sheath thickness for both the thick fibers and fibers of small axon diameter. Fibers of greater axon diameter are more severely affected than the fibers with smaller axon diameter. In one study[236] actual loss of myelinated fibers was relatively mild in the late infantile and juvenile patients, but

two of the three adult patients described in this study lost more than half of their myelinated fibers. The thick myelinated fibers are thus replaced by a new population of fibers with abnormally thin sheaths. This process of remodeling in the later onset cases causes hypertrophic changes that are reflected in palpably enlarged nerves. The microscopic appearance is of dense collagen deposits surrounding clusters of myelinated and unmyelinated axons in small onion-bulb formations.[121,123,131,142]

The sural nerve, a sensory nerve in the leg, is frequently biopsied for diagnostic purposes. The inclusions present in this nerve are varied and have the same ultrastructural appearance as those described above.[236] Nerve specimens from the different clinical variants of MLD do not show any striking differences in the types of inclusions present. Observations similar to those in sural nerve have been made on cutaneous nerves[237] and intramuscular nerve fibers.[145,232]

Visceral Organs

Involvement of visceral organs has been observed in all patients whose tissues have been carefully examined.[239] Tissues with an excretory function are particularly affected. In the kidney, metachromatic material is present in the cells of the distal convoluted tubules (especially on the luminal side), the thin limb of the loop of Henle, and the collecting tubules, as well as in the tubule lumen and urine. The inclusions consist mainly of large lamellae, but some prismatic inclusions have been observed. The glomerulus and proximal convoluted tubule are normal.[215,240,241] A proximal renal tubular acidosis has been described in one patient with the late infantile form of MLD.[212] In the fetus with MLD, the findings in the kidney, which is the major focus of pathology, include metachromatic granules and myelinlike membrane-bound inclusions.[242,243]

The gallbladder is small and fibrotic, and the mucosal cells and villi are distended with macrophages containing metachromatic material. In some cases multiple large polypoid masses or papillomatous fronds have been noted projecting from the mucosa into the lumen of the gallbladder.[213,214,244] Liver parenchymal cells, particularly at the periphery of the lobules, and the epithelial cells of the intrahepatic bile ducts contain abundant metachromatic material. There is similar but less striking involvement of the Kupffer cells and portal histiocytes.[211,240,245] Deposits of metachromatic lipids have been demonstrated in the islets of Langerhans,[211,246] the anterior pituitary,[2,239] and the adrenal cortex.[2,239] Accumulation of metachromatic material in the testes has been reported only in adult patients.[3,165] It is possible that this material was not sulfatide but seminolipid, whose metabolism is also impaired in MLD. This sulfolipid normally is not formed in the testes until after puberty and therefore would not accumulate in patients with MLD who died before then. The reticuloendothelial system generally is not involved.

CHEMICAL PATHOLOGY

Central Nervous System

In late infantile MLD, white matter sulfatide levels are increased three- to tenfold (see Table 69-5). The levels of other

Table 69-5 Composition of Cerebral White Matter and Kidney in Metachromatic Leukodystrophy, Percent of Dry Weight

	Cerebral white matter				*Kidney*		
		Metachromatic leukodystrophy				*Metachromatic leukodystrophy, infantile*	
		Infantile		*Adult*			
Components	*Normal, 6 subjects, age range 4-5 yr*	*Age 3¾ yr*	*Age 4½ yr*	*Age 29 yr*	*Normal, 3 subjects, all age 2 mo*	*Age 3¾ yr*	*Age 4½*
Total lipids	55.6-61.9	39.9	40.9	50.1	9.4-10.5	10.8	12.5
Cholesterol	12.2-15.7	8.1	7.8	13.5	1.3-1.7	1.7	1.6
Phospholipids	28.0-30.6	17.1	14.1	22.4	7.4-8.5	6.8	5.6
Cephalins	14.4-16.5	8.1	5.1	9.0	3.3-4.0	2.0	1.6
Lecithins	8.5-9.9	6.9	7.9	8.7	2.6-3.4	3.6	3.0
Sphingomyelin	4.1-5.2	2.5	2.2	4.7	1.0-1.22	1.1	1.0
Cerebrosides	10.3-13.8	2.8	3.2	7.8	0.41-0.45	1.21	0.71
Sulfatides	1.7-4.1	12.8	15.8	6.5	0.09-0.17	1.26	4.60
Lipid hexosamine	0.05	0.08	0.09	0.03			
Nonlipid hexosamine	0.23	0.7	0.65				

SOURCE: From Svennerholm.[374]

myelin lipids, such as cholesterol and sphingomyelin, may be decreased by 30 to 50 percent, presumably secondary to the loss of myelin. Levels of cerebroside are diminished out of proportion to those of other myelin lipids. They vary from less than 10 percent up to 50 percent of normal. Consequently, the cerebroside/sulfatide ratio, which in normal white matter is approximately 4, may be reduced in late infantile MLD to 0.5[247] The excess of sulfatide also has been noted in isolated myelin,[42] including a preparation from a fetus with MLD.[248] An increased concentration of sulfatide has also been shown in the cerebellum, brainstem, and spinal cord of a 24-week fetus with MLD but was normal in the still unmyelinated cortex.[249] Its chemical structure in late infantile MLD is the same as the sulfatide of normal white matter. Chemical analyses of a few cases of adult MLD have disclosed differences from late infantile MLD. In adult MLD,[247] the white matter sulfatide level is only moderately increased and contains more short-chain and saturated fatty acid and less unsaturated fatty acid than the sulfatide from normal white matter.[250] Also, there is more gray matter sulfatide accumulation in adult MLD than in late infantile MLD. In both types of MLD, a significant alteration also occurs in the fatty acid composition of white matter sphingomyelin[42,251] and cerebrosides.[26] The proportion of long-chain fatty acids is diminished, probably reflecting the loss of myelin with the proportionate increase in the nonmye-

lin compartment typical of unmyelinated or immature white matter.

This hypothesis is supported by the data of Norton and Poduslo[42] on myelin from a juvenile case of MLD. While their yield of myelin was only 4 percent of normal, the fatty acid pattern was much closer to normal than that of MLD white matter. Cerebrosides in the peripheral nerves do not show the deficit in long-chain fatty acids.[252]

Extraneural Tissues

Sulfatide concentrations are increased in the liver, gallbladder, kidney, and urine of MLD patients. Sulfolipids of fetal and mutant MLD tissues are compared in Table 69-6. The level in the liver is at least 10 times normal[253]; it is 10 to 75 times normal in the kidney,[26,254] and 10 to 100 times normal in the urine.[28,29,255] In one asymptomatic child with late infantile MLD, urine sulfatide per milligram creatinine was increased 100-fold at age 14 months and was more than twice this amount at age 19 months.[206] Both cerebroside sulfate and lactosylceramide sulfate are found. The ratio of these two sulfatides in the liver is less than 1,[243,247,256] in the gallbladder it is 5.8,[256] in the kidney it is 4,[243,255] and in the urine it is 20 to 30.[33,255] The chemical structure of the sulfatides is typical of

Table 69-6 Sulfolipid Content of Fetal and Infant MLD Tissues*

| | *Fetus* | | *Infant* | |
	Control, age 25 wk	*MLD, age 23 wk*	*Control, age 3 yr*	*MLD, age 4 yr*
Brain				
Cerebroside sulfate	ND	ND	4840	13300
Liver				
Cerebroside sulfate	6	24	ND	226
Lactosylceramide sulfate	28	160	40	385
Kidney				
Cerebroside sulfate	74	204	116	3263
Lactosylceramide sulfate	20	52	25	726

*ND = not detected. Measurements are in micrograms per gram of wet tissue.
SOURCE: From Eto et al.[243]

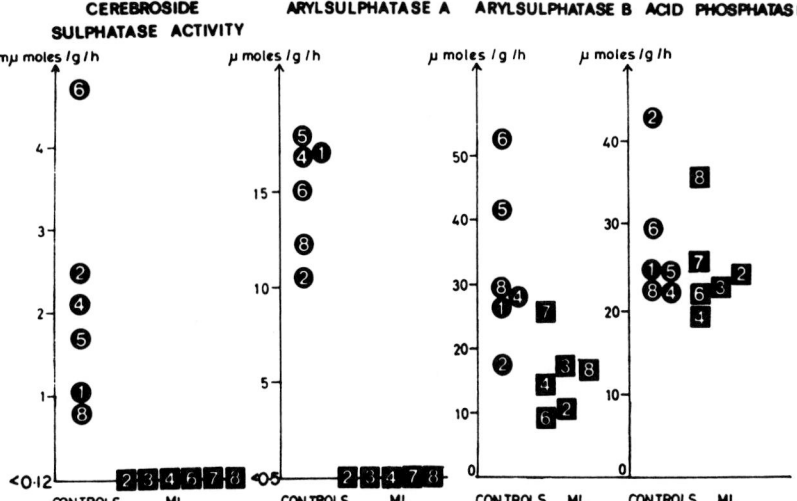

Fig. 69-11   Deficiency of cerebroside sulfatase activity and arylsulfatase A activity in the renal cortex of patients with late infantile MLD. Circles represent the enzyme activities in control subjects, and the squares those in patients with late infantile MLD. (*From Jatzkewitz and Mehl.*[14])

sulfatides present in normal kidney and differs from brain sulfatide.[26] The close resemblance to normal kidney sulfatides of the fatty acid pattern in urine of the sulfatides of MLD patients and the absence of an increase in plasma sulfatide[33,257] supports the notion that the urine sulfatides reflect the chemical pathology of the kidney.

Multiple Sulfatase Deficiency

As in late infantile MLD, tissues from patients with multiple sulfatase deficiency contain the expected sulfatide excess. Urine and cerebrospinal fluid sulfatide levels are also increased. In addition, an increase in mucopolysaccharide has been demonstrated in the brain, liver, kidney, urine, and cultured skin fibroblasts. Both dermatan sulfate and heparan sulfate have been detected. Accumulation of cholesteryl sulfate has also been reported in the liver, kidney, plasma, and urine. An abnormality in the gray matter ganglioside pattern resembling that seen in Hurler syndrome has also been detected.[155–157,159,258–261]

ENZYME DEFECTS

Late Infantile, Juvenile, and Adult MLD

Arylsulfatase A Deficiency. Deficiency in the activity of arylsulfatase A, the heat-labile component of cerebroside sulfatase, has been established as the primary enzymatic abnormality in the late infantile, juvenile, and adult variants of MLD. This deficiency was first demonstrated by Austin in the urine[262] and tissues[17] of patients with MLD. At the same time, Mehl and Jatzkewitz reported that MLD kidney was deficient in cerebroside sulfatase activity[13]; later they discovered that both enzyme activities were absent from the kidney, liver, and brain tissues of seven patients with MLD[14] (Fig. 69-11). Many other tissues and fluids from MLD patients have since been examined and also have been found deficient in arylsulfatase A activity. Those most frequently studied have been urine,[179–181] peripheral leukocytes,[191,265,266] and cultured skin fibroblasts[267] (Fig. 69-12), but the enzyme defect has also been demonstrated in serum,[268,269] tears,[139,270] saliva,[271] cultured lymphocytes,[272] and cultured bone marrow

cells.[273] The loss of cerebroside sulfate sulfatase activity in MLD has also been repeatedly confirmed, particularly in peripheral leukocytes[184,274,275] and cultured skin fibroblasts.[274,276–280] In addition, there is defective catabolism of other natural substrates of arylsulfatase A. These include lactosylceramide sulfatide,[93] sulfogalactosylsphingosine,[96] seminolipid,[281] and ascorbate-2-sulfate.[99]

Some reports have described reduced arylsulfatase B activity in kidney and brain white matter,[14] leukocytes,[191,282] cultured bone marrow fibroblasts,[273] and tears,[139] but most studies have not shown any consistent abnormality of this enzyme in patients with MLD. Other lysosomal enzyme activities have been normal.[283] The presence of normal concentrations of the heat-stable activator of arylsulfatase A has also been documented in the common variants of MLD.[284]

Properties of the Mutant Enzyme. The most frequently used method for the determination of arylsulfatase A activity was developed for use with human urine and employs the chromogenic substance *p*-nitrocatechol sulfate.[285] Under a different

Fig. 69-12   Fluorescent bands of arylsulfatase activity after electrophoresis of skin fibroblast extracts on cellulose acetate gel strips. Extracts were prepared from skin fibroblasts of a normal individual (1), an individual heterozygous for MLD (2), and a patient with MLD (3). After application at the point indicated by the arrow, and subsequent electrophoresis and incubation of the strip in the presence of 4-methylumbelliferyl sulfate, bands of arylsulfatase A and B activity appeared under ultraviolet light, as indicated. (*From Rattazzi et al.*[375] *Originally published in Ref. 345.*)

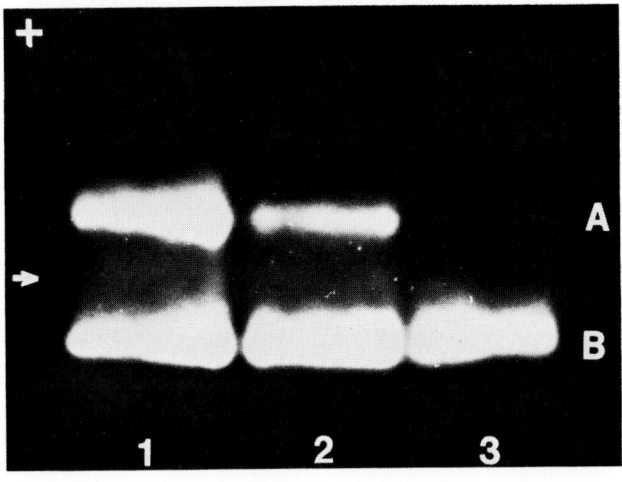

set of reaction conditions, this artificial substrate will also measure arylsulfatase B activity. The assay conditions established for the assay of arylsulfatase A activity are supposed to minimize any contribution from the arylsulfatase B present. With this method, specimens from patients with MLD invariably demonstrate the presence of a small amount of residual enzyme activity. Several groups of investigators[286–288] have examined this activity by immunologic methods to determine whether it represents true arylsulfatase A activity or a spillover of arylsulfatase B activity. Monospecific antibodies were prepared to purified arylsulfatase A and used to examine the antigenicity of the residual enzyme in Ochterlony double-diffusion plates. In each instance precipitin lines formed between the antibody and the MLD enzyme and indicated the presence of cross-reacting material. The precipitin line of the normal enzyme-antibody complex exhibited arylsulfatase A activity, but no enzyme activity was observed in the precipitin line from the MLD samples.

There is, however, direct substantial evidence for the presence in MLD patients of arylsulfatase A-like protein. Mutant arylsulfatase A has been purified from the livers of two patients with the late infantile form of MLD and from one patient with early juvenile MLD and found to have identical chromatographic behavior and peptide maps as normal human liver arylsulfatase A.[56] Antiserum to human arylsulfatase A cross-reacts with polypeptides synthesized by cultured skin fibroblasts from patients with all three forms of classic MLD. In late infantile MLD, a normal-sized immunoprecipitable glycoprotein is produced which is rapidly degraded by the cell.[65] Immunofluorescence staining of late infantile MLD cells also reveals immunologic reactivity with anti-arylsulfatase A antibody.[102] Cells from patients with the juvenile and adult forms of MLD synthesize and secrete arylsulfatase A polypeptide with an apparent rate of synthesis of 20 to 70 percent that of control cells. However, when the mutant enzyme is transported into the lysosome, it is rapidly degraded. Inhibitors of cysteine proteinases partially restore the arylsulfatase A and cerebroside sulfatase activity of fibroblasts from patients with juvenile and adult MLD.[279,289]

Biochemical Basis for Varying Ages of Onset in MLD. The difference in ages of onset between the late infantile, juvenile, and adult forms of MLD cannot be explained on the basis of quantitative differences in the level of mutant enzyme in cell-free homogenates. Most studies that have examined this question show no differences between clinical subtypes in their activity in vitro of residual arylsulfatase A.[14,274,290,291] This result would be expected if the residual arylsulfatase A activity were unstable or had otherwise lost its catalytic activity after disruption of its intracellular milieu. The findings of *in situ* tissue culture experiments suggest that this may be the case.[121,290,292,293]

Cultured skin fibroblasts from patients with MLD incorporate sulfatide that has been added to the growth media, accumulating it in sufficient amounts to stain metachromatically.[292] Normal cells also incorporate sulfatide but degrade it and do not develop metachromasia. Using [^{35}S]sulfatide, Porter et al.[290] found that the amount of this lipid that accumulated intracellularly was largest in cells derived from a patient with late infantile MLD and least in cells from a patient with adult MLD. Cells from patients with juvenile MLD stored an intermediate amount of sulfatide (Fig. 69-13). Also, the amount of hydrolysis, determined by the release of [^{35}S]sulfatide into the medium, directly correlated with the latency of onset of symptoms. Use of HEPES buffer in the cell culture medium increased the intracellular accumulation of cerebroside sulfate not only in MLD cell lines but also in cells from patients with pseudodeficiency of arylsulfatase A. This effect, which is believed to be mediated by an upward shift in the intralysosomal pH, can be used to differentiate pseudodeficiency cells from normal cells during a loading test.[293,294]

Multiple Sulfatase Deficiency

In this disease sulfate-containing glycolipids, mucopolysaccharides, and steroids accumulate because of a deficiency of several different sulfatases.[253,258–261] Cultured skin fibroblasts from patients are deficient in arylsulfatases A, B, and C (including cholesteryl sulfatase and dehydroepiandrosterone sulfatase), iduronide-2-sulfate sulfatase, heparan-N-sulfamidase, N-acetylgalactosamine-6-sulfate sulfatase, N-acetylgalactosamine-4-sulfate sulfatase (arylsulfatase B), and N-acetylglucosamine-6-sulfate sulfatase.[18,261] Less complete studies of tissue sulfatases have disclosed deficits of multiple arylsulfatases in kidney, brain, and liver.[258,260,295] Tissue levels of steroid sulfatase activities also are reduced to the limit of detection.

Patients have been classified according to their levels of re-

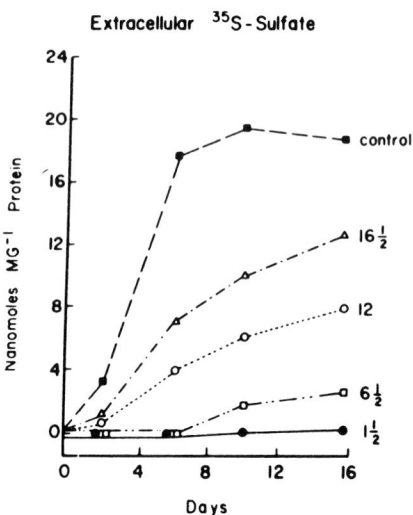

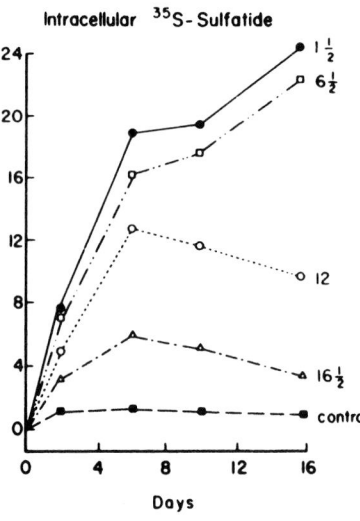

Fig. 69-13 Correlation of intracellular cerebroside sulfatase activity of skin fibroblasts with age of clinical onset. ^{35}S-Labeled cerebroside sulfate was added to fibroblasts in culture; on the days indicated, cultures were analyzed for extracellular and intracellular label. Numbers beside each plot indicate the age of the patients from whom cells originated; the older the individual, the less sulfatide was accumulated (*right*) and the more inorganic sulfate appeared in the medium (*left*). (*From Kihara et al.*[376])

sidual sulfatase activity in cultured fibroblasts.[18,69,296,297] In group I patients, the activity of all sulfatases is less than 10 percent that of controls. Group II patients have residual sulfatase activities up to 90 percent those of controls. Clinically, the group I patients have the more severe neonatal form of the disease, and their skin fibroblasts incorporate into acid mucopolysaccharides significantly greater amounts of ^{35}S-labeled sodium sulfate than do those of typical MSD.[296]

The arylsulfatase A gene in multiple sulfatase deficiency is intact and can be expressed under suitable environmental conditions. In cultured skin fibroblasts grown in mediums containing an MEM-CO_2 buffer (pH < 7.0), arylsulfatase A activity is less than one-tenth of normal. With the use of an MEM-HEPES buffer (pH > 7.4) in the mediums, arylsulfatase A activity is expressed at levels 30 to 100 percent of normal.[298] Other sulfatases deficient in this disease do not appear to manifest these pH-dependent differences in activity. The addition of sodium thiosulfate to the culture medium results over a period of weeks in higher intracellular levels of all deficient sulfatases with the possible exception of heparan-N-sulfamidase.[296-299] This effect is most pronounced for arylsulfatase A but does not completely restore its activity to normal. It is not observed in normal cells nor in neonatal MSD cells and is not present simply upon addition of this sulfate to cell homogenates.

The arylsulfatases A and B show the same properties including pH optima, isoelectric points, and heat stability as the normal enzymes,[261,300,301] but their catalytic properties and stability are impaired in MSD. The apparent rate of synthesis for these enzymes varies from 30 percent to normal in both group I and group II fibroblasts.[69] The ratio of catalytic activity to protein antigen, precipitated with antibodies specific for the normal arylsulfatases A and B, is reduced. In group I cells, the molecular activity of both enzymes is one-tenth of normal. In group II fibroblasts, arylsulfatase A activity is two- to threefold lower, and the activity of arylsulfatase B is half normal. The extent of processing of the two sulfatases is similar in control and MSD fibroblasts. However, arylsulfatase A and the 47-kDa polypeptide of arylsulfatase B[302] as well as arylsulfatase C[377] in MSD cells are unstable and more rapidly turned over. Thus, Steckel, et al.[302] believe that the MSD mutation affects an enzyme in the endoplasmic reticulum that modifies sulfatase polypeptides post-translationally.

MLD Without Arylsulfatase A Deficiency

Three living cases of this disorder have been investigated. In one case,[169] leukocyte and fibroblast arylsulfatase A activity was reduced to one-half of that present in normal controls. In another unrelated case,[170] the arylsulfatase A activity in leukocytes, fibroblasts, and urine was above the control range. The properties of the fibroblast enzyme from both cases were identical to the properties of normal fibroblast arylsulfatase A.[16,170]

In spite of apparently adequate arylsulfatase A activity, the hydrolysis of cerebroside sulfate by the cultured skin fibroblasts from these patients is markedly attenuated (Fig. 69-14). Supplementation of the fibroblasts from one case[170] with cerebroside sulfate sulfatase activator factor corrected the defect in cerebroside sulfate hydrolysis. Antibodies prepared against the activator give no immunologic reaction with extracts of leukocytes,[171] cultured skin fibroblasts,[92] and urine[172] from

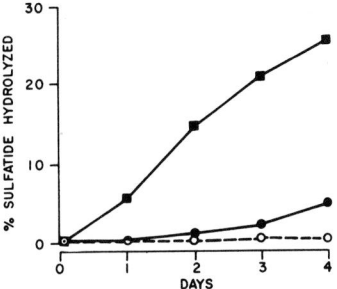

Fig. 69-14 Hydrolysis of [^{35}S]sulfatide by intact growing fibroblasts from an MLD patient without arylsulfatase A deficiency ●—●, a patient with classic late infantile MLD ○———○, and a normal control cell line ■—■. The free [^{35}S]sulfate present in the media on 4 consecutive days was analyzed and expressed as a percent of the labeled lipid added to the mediums at the beginning of the experiment. Note that the MLD variant cells cannot degrade sulfatide in vivo in spite of the substantial amounts of arylsulfatase A activity present in these cells. (*From Shapiro et al.*[169])

these patients, indicating a deficiency in the activator protein. A partial deficiency has also been demonstrated in the parents of one child by rocket immunoelectrophoresis of their leukocyte protein.[171]

Pseudodeficiency of Arylsulfatase A

Various studies have shown that normal lysosomal turnover of substrate is possible with intracellular levels of enzyme at the level of 10 to 20 percent of normal.[303-305] The residual arylsulfatase A activity in subjects with pseudodeficiency is in this same range and appears sufficient to prevent accumulation of sulfatide. The reduction in amount of immunoprecipitable cross-reacting material (Fig. 69-15) is equivalent to the observed level of arylsulfatase A activity, indicating that the enzyme has normal catalytic activity. Numerous other properties are also normal, including pH optimum, substrate affinity, sensitivity to inhibitors, and heat stability.[69,179,196]

The arylsulfatase A subunits in cultured fibroblasts from pseudodeficient subjects is consistently smaller than normal by 3 to 4 kDa (Fig. 69-15).[64,65,306] In other tissues, there is a similar decrease in the molecular size of the enzyme.[306] The amount of enzyme produced by fibroblasts is 20 percent of normal, but in the presence of ammonium chloride, which stimulates the secretion of lysosomal enzymes, the amount synthesized increases to 80 percent of normal.[307] The secreted enzyme is identical in size to the subunits of precursor enzyme[65] and forms a simpler isoelectric focusing pattern than enzyme from normal fibroblasts.[196] The enzyme is also more rapidly degraded,[307] but the use of a protease inhibitor in the culture medium does not increase the amount of residual arylsulfatase A activity.[179]

It appears likely, therefore, that there is a structural alteration affecting the glycosylation site so that there is a deficiency in the carbohydrate side chain of the enzyme. Waheed et al.[66] have shown that the arylsulfatase A polypeptide contains two oligosaccharides of the high mannose type. Their removal by endo-β-N-acetylglucosaminidase H reduces the apparent molecular weight by 5 kDa. Lack of the carbohydrate would account for the smaller subunit size, simpler isoelectric focusing pattern, and instability of the molecule with preservation of its kinetic properties. The studies of Chang[308] confirm this hypothesis. In four pseudodeficiency cell lines, the mutant enzyme incorporated three- to tenfold less mannose than normal

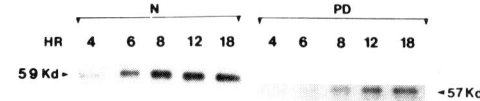

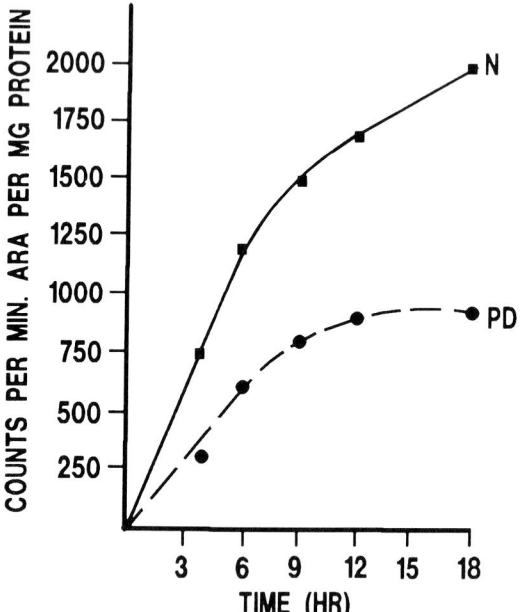

Fig. 69-15 Synthesis of arylsulfatase A by normal (N) and pseudodeficiency (PD) fibroblasts. The cells were labeled with [³H]leucine in the presence of NH₄Cl. The cell protein was extracted and immunoprecipitated with goat anti-arylsulfatase A antiserum. The immunoprecipitates were analyzed by SDS-polyacrylamide electrophoresis. Note the reduced rate of synthesis in the PD cells. The normal cells produced a major arylsulfatase A subunit of 59 kDa, whereas the PD cells synthesized a smaller subunit of 57 kDa. (*From Ameen and Chang.*[307])

and contained 30 percent less phosphorylated oligosaccharides than the normal. These results suggest that the mutation in pseudoarylsulfatase A deficiency is associated with underglycosylation and reduced phosphorylation of arylsulfatase A. However, the mutation does not affect the ability of the enzyme to target lysosomes or its catalytic activity.

PATHOGENESIS OF MLD

The accepted biochemical defect in all forms of MLD is a deficiency in the enzymatic hydrolysis of sulfatide. This leads to a progressive accumulation of sulfatides, mainly within lysosomes. The storage process is not uniform in all tissues and organs, and functional loss is not directly proportional to the amount of sulfatide that is deposited. On this basis, four categories of tissues may be defined:

1. Tissues that show little or no sulfatide accumulation and no tissue damage. These tissues include the heart, lung, spleen, skin, bones, and intestinal tract.

2. Tissues in which there is accumulation of sulfatide but no demonstrable impairment of functions. These tissues include the liver, kidney, pancreas, adrenal, and intestinal tract.[239]

3. Tissues in which there are sulfatide accumulation and evidence of impaired function but which do not appear to con-

tribute to the fatal outcome of the disease. This applies to the gallbladder, which, as already noted, shows sulfatide accumulation and progressive functional impairment.[213,214]

4. Tissues in which there are sulfatide accumulation and impaired function contributing to fatal outcome. This is restricted to the white matter of the nervous system.

The accumulation of sulfatide probably occurs independently in each organ. It is unlikely, for example, that sulfatide from the central nervous system is deposited within the kidney. The fatty acid composition of brain and kidney sulfatide are different,[26] the sulfatide concentration in MLD serum is normal,[33,257] and massive subcutaneous injections of sulfatide fail to produce kidney deposits in infant rats.[309] It is more probable that the increase in sulfatide observed in extraneural tissues reflects an *in situ* failure in the turnover of sulfatide that is normally present in plasma membranes of these tissues and serves other purposes than as a structural component of myelin. The tolerance of the kidney, gallbladder, and other extraneural tissues for sulfatides may relate to the fact that the cells most involved in the storage process fulfill an excretory function and therefore can discharge the accumulating lipid from the cell into the urine, bile, or other fluid.

The demyelination that occurs in MLD appears to be secondary to sulfatide-induced changes within the cells responsible for myelin maintenance, namely the Schwann cells in the peripheral nervous system and the oligodendrocytes in the central nervous system. Changes in the subcellular organelles of these cells have been observed before any morphologic abnormalities in the myelin sheaths associated with them were detected. In a fetus with MLD aborted in the fifth month of gestation,[310] an increase in lysosomes, some containing lamellar structured material, had been found in the cerebrum and cerebellum, even though these tissues did not stain metachromatically and myelination had not yet begun. This increase in lysosomal bodies was even more marked in the oligodendroglial cells of the spinal cord. Although accumulations of metachromatic material were observed in the spinal cord oligodendrocytes, the morphologic appearance of the spinal cord myelin at this stage was normal. An increase in the number of lysosomes thus appears to be the earliest pathologic change that results from the failure of sulfatide catabolism.

Neuropathologic studies of two other MLD fetuses aborted in the fifth month of gestation have also demonstrated cellular abnormalities at a stage at which myelin had either not yet developed or had appeared morphologically normal.[242,248] Also, in nerve biopsies from patients with MLD, a normal myelin sheath is often observed together with abundant storage material in the Schwann cell belonging to the same internodal segment of the myelin sheath.[311–313] Therefore, it is the abnormal accumulation of sulfatide within the lysosomes of oligodendroglial and Schwann cells and the metabolic failure of these cells that precede and trigger the events that cause demyelination. Early focal areas of demyelination would preferentially affect long tracts. This could produce delay in nerve conduction, in synaptic transmission, and in the latency period of evoked potentials. Intellectual impairment is a later event resulting from secondary damage to neurons and the scrambling of information produced by slowed nerve conduction.[314]

It has been suggested that myelin breakdown in MLD results from defective resorption of sulfatide from the innermost part of the myelin sheath. Catabolism of this layer of myelin is necessary for the axon to increase its cross-diameter during growth.[315] Even after maturity is reached, enzymatic failure in the resorption of myelin would prevent normal restructuring of the myelin sheath. Experiments with isotopic sulfate have confirmed the presence of two myelin compartments in adult rat myelin, one with a slow turnover rate and the other with a fast turnover rate.[316] Thus, both during growth and after the active growth phase is completed, sulfatase activity is needed to maintain the normal integrity of myelin.

Alternative pathogenic mechanisms have also been suggested, but there is less evidence to support them. One is that the myelin formed in MLD has an abnormal composition and is therefore unstable. While it is true that the chemical composition of the myelin present in MLD white matter is abnormal,[42,221,317,318] the quantity of metachromatic lipid that accumulates in an area of demyelination is considerably more than would be expected based upon the amount of sudanophilic lipid that is normally present. Another proposed mechanism is that sulfogalactosylsphingosine, a compound closely related to galactosylsphingosine, which is known to be highly cytotoxic, might accumulate and cause myelin breakdown because of the deficiency of sulfogalactosylsphingosine sulfatase in MLD.[96] There is, however, no evidence for the enzymatic deacylation of sulfatide to sulfogalactosylsphingosine.[319] Furthermore, the sulfogalactosylsphingosine present in normal brain is believed to arise *de novo* from sphingosine, and its concentration is not increased in MLD patients.[372]

The delay in appearance of clinical signs in the later onset forms of MLD is difficult to explain in terms of the timetable of brain development. The period of most rapid turnover of sulfatide is presumably early in development during the peak time of myelin formation. One would expect that the failure of enzymatic hydrolysis of sulfatide would affect brain white matter more severely at this time than at some later time. To explain this anomaly, Norton has proposed a differential distribution for the residual enzyme with higher activity in oligodendroglial cells so that after a long period of time neurons become disabled from sulfatide accumulation preferentially (Norton, quoted in Ref. 314). He has also suggested that turnover of galactolipids is normally a slow process so that the absence of metabolic degradation may not become a problem until myelination is well advanced.[320] Another hypothesis suggested by Suzuki is that the myelin laid down late in development is less metabolically stable and therefore more subject to turnover (Suzuki, quoted in Ref. 314).

GENETICS

The various forms of MLD—late infantile, juvenile, adult, and multiple sulfatase deficiency—appear to be genetically distinct. This is evident clinically in families that have more than one affected member. In such cases, the chronology of symptomatology and progression of the disease is the same. For at least one form, the multiple sulfatase deficiency syndrome, the difference in clinical subtypes of MLD is also expressed on the molecular level. Intergenic complementation experiments demonstrate that the gene for multiple sulfatase deficiency and those for other types of MLD are nonallelic. In somatic cell hybrids produced by fusing cultured fibroblasts from patients with these two conditions, arylsulfatase A activity is restored.[299,321,322] Similarly, complementation occurs between MSD cells and cells from other single sulfatase deficiency disorders (Hunter disease, Sanfilippo disease type A,

and Morquio disease type A), indicating that the mutations in these disorders are also nonallelic.[322–324] There is also metabolic cooperativity in somatic cell hybrids formed from activator deficiency and MLD fibroblasts, supporting the view that these diseases are genetically distinct.[325]

Conversely, hybridizing cell lines from patients with late infantile and adult MLD does not restore arylsulfatase A activity, suggesting that the loci for these two variants are situated on the gene map too close to one another for intergenic complementation to occur, and thus are allelic.[326,327] Also, crosses between the two types of MSD, group I and group II, do not restore arylsulfatase A and B activity, demonstrating that the neonatal and usual forms of MSD are too closely related genetically for enzyme correction to occur.[296]

All varieties of MLD are transmitted through an autosomal recessive pattern of inheritance. This is deduced from the appearance of approximately equal numbers of affected individuals of each sex, the frequent occurrence of more than one affected individual in a sibship, the occasional association of parental consanguinity, and the presence of approximately one-half the normal level of arylsulfatase A in the parents of patients. In a few parents or siblings, the level of enzyme activity is reduced to 20 percent or less without any of the signs or symptoms of MLD present. These individuals appear to have two recessive traits, one for MLD and another for pseudodeficiency of arylsulfatase A.[180,194,195] Assays for cerebroside sulfate sulfatase activity are the most reliable way to differentiate between these individuals and patients with true MLD. Such assays, however, do not distinguish carriers of an MLD gene apart from those carrying this other pseudodeficiency allele. This is because the genes for pseudodeficiency of arylsulfatase A and MLD are allelic,[196] and their expression in the heterozygote results in levels of enzyme activity that are approximately half normal. Possible combinations of mutant alleles for arylsulfatase A are shown in Table 69-7.

The overall incidence of MLD and the frequency of the trait for MLD are unknown. In northern Sweden, the incidence of late infantile MLD has been estimated to be 1 in 40,000.[129] This probably represents a somewhat higher figure than can be expected elsewhere due to a clustering of 6 of the 13 cases surveyed in a single restricted geographic isolate. In France, the reported incidence of late infantile MLD is 1 in 130,000,[328] and in Washington State it is 1 in 40,000.[329] The Habbanite Jewish community in Israel has a particularly high incidence of late infantile MLD (1.3 percent) due to a 17 percent carrier frequency and a marked tendency to consanguineous marriages.[330] Our own case experience would suggest an aggregate incidence figure for all forms of MLD of approximately 1 per 100,000 births.

The gene for the pseudodeficiency allele not associated with MLD is probably quite common, since it is often found in the parents of patients with MLD. By virtue of their status as obligate heterozygotes, these individuals already carry one allele for reduced enzyme activity. Thus, the presence of another allele that also reduces their ability to produce active enzyme becomes readily apparent. The frequency of the pseudodeficiency gene in the general population has been estimated to be about 15 percent.[179] This is the same frequency found among Habbanite Jews, a population which also has a relatively high frequency of MLD.[331]

The locus determining the expression of arylsulfatase A activity has been mapped with human-rodent somatic cell hybrids to chromosome 22.[332–334] Evidence from one study of a deleted ring chromosome 22 suggests that the gene is probably

Table 69-7 Genetic Mutations at the Arylsulfatase A (ARA) Locus

Type	Clinical state	Genotype	In vitro ARA	Sulfatide catabolism	Sulfatide excretion
Normal	Normal	ARA$^+$/ARA$^+$	Normal	Normal	Normal
MLD*	Late infantile	ARA$^-$/ARA$^-$	0-15%	0-10%	Increased
	Juvenile	ARA$^-$/ARA$^-$	0-15%	15-30%	Increased
	Adult	ARA$^-$/ARA$^-$	0-15%	30-50%	Increased
MLD heterozygote	Normal	ARA$^+$/ARA$^-$	30-50%	Normal	Normal
Pseudodeficient heterozygote	Normal	ARA$^+$/ARA$_p$	30-50%	Normal	Normal
Pseudodeficient homozygote	Normal	ARA$_p$/ARA$_p$	10-30%	Normal	Normal
Double heterozygote	Normal	ARA$^-$/ARA$_p$	10-30%	Normal	Normal

*For simplicity, the different alleles of MLD are all designated as ARA$^-$.
SOURCE: From Schaap et al.[331] as modified by McKhann.[141]

located on the long arm in the region of the q13 band.[335] Von Figura and his associates have isolated a cDNA for arylsulfatase A that has a signal peptide 18 amino acids in length and an open reading frame of 1524 base pairs coding for 508 amino acids. The predicted sequence contains three potential N-glycosylation sites. The cDNA detects an mRNA of about 2.2 kb in human liver. Using this cDNA as a probe, they have examined DNA from 26 cell lines of patients with various forms of MLD but have not detected any with abnormal fragments.[336]

The gene for the SAP-1 sphingolipid activator protein has been mapped to chromosome 10[337] and has been cloned and sequenced.[338,339] Its coding sequence of 1449 bases is equivalent to a polypeptide of ~ 53 kDa which is similar to the molecular mass of proSAP-1.

The gene for arylsulfatase B has been mapped to chromosome 5,[333] and those for iduronate sulfatase and steroid sulfatase are on the X chromosome. Shapiro and colleagues independently cloned this gene and have studied the genetics of steroid sulfatase deficiency extensively (see Chap. 76). Stein and von Figura have also isolated a cDNA for steroid sulfatase that has a coding region of 1749 base pairs equivalent to 583 amino acids. The length of the signal peptide is 21 or 23 amino acids and within the open reading frame are four potential N-glycosylation sites.[336]

The chromosome assignment of a gene that might regulate the post-translational processing of sulfatases and could be involved in the multiple sulfatase deficiency disorder remains unknown.

DIAGNOSIS

Clinical Evaluation

The initial signs of MLD may appear at any age from birth to the seventh decade. Therefore, this diagnosis should be considered whenever progressive white matter disease is encountered, regardless of the patient's age. The most common ages for the disease to begin are 1½ to 2 years for the late infantile variant, 4 to 6 years for the juvenile variant, and 16 to 26 years for the adult variant. Intellectual loss, weakness, and incoordination are early signs that might suggest the diagnosis. Further involvement of the long tracts leads eventually to spastic tetraparesis and incontinence. Specific signs that help at this stage to confirm the diagnosis are the presence of optic atrophy and peripheral neuropathy.

The clinician with a high index of suspicion for MLD will pursue this diagnostic possibility with certain clinical laboratory tests. The most useful are a cerebrospinal fluid examination for elevated protein, measurements of nerve conduction velocity, evoked potential studies, and brain CT scanning or MRI study. In adult patients without peripheral neuropathy, nerve conduction and the level of cerebrospinal fluid protein may be normal, but all patients with a significant amount of symptomatology show changes on the CT scan and MRI that are characteristic of brain white matter disease. The clinical investigation of the dysmorphic child with possible diagnosis of multiple sulfatase deficiency should, in addition, include a skeletal x-ray series, examination of the peripheral smear for Alder-Reilly granules, and a urine spot test to rule out mucopolysacchariduria.

Biochemical Confirmation

Until recently, the diagnosis of MLD was most often confirmed by histologic examination of a sural nerve biopsy. Less invasive attempts to identify accumulations of metachromatic material have employed biopsies of conjunctiva,[139] skin,[237] or cells of the urinary sediment.[340] As the molecular defects of the MLD group of diseases have become better understood, there has been increasing reliance on biochemical determinations for diagnosis so that tissue biopsies for histologic study are now being done only in exceptional circumstances.

The most common biochemical parameter studied is the activity of arylsulfatase A. This enzyme can be assayed using peripheral leukocytes and cultured skin fibroblasts. Arylsulfatase A activity is also present in urine, but this is not a reliable source for diagnostic assays because the enzyme normally has a low specific activity in this fluid.[262-264] Various modifications[59,131,265,341] of the p-nitrocatechol sulfate method of Baum et al.[285] are used for the analysis. Each takes advantage of the fact that the contribution from arylsulfatase B to the total enzyme activity can be minimized by inhibition of this enzyme with a high NaCl content in the reaction mixture. An alternative method has been developed that utilizes the fluorogenic substrate 4-methylumbelliferyl sulfate and Ag$^+$ ions to inhibit arylsulfatase A activity specifically.[342] Measurements of enzyme activity are made in the presence and absence of Ag$^+$. The difference between the two activities represents the contribution for arylsulfatase A.

In order to improve the accuracy of the arylsulfatase A assay, several procedures have been developed to separate arylsulfatase A and B physically prior to their quantification.

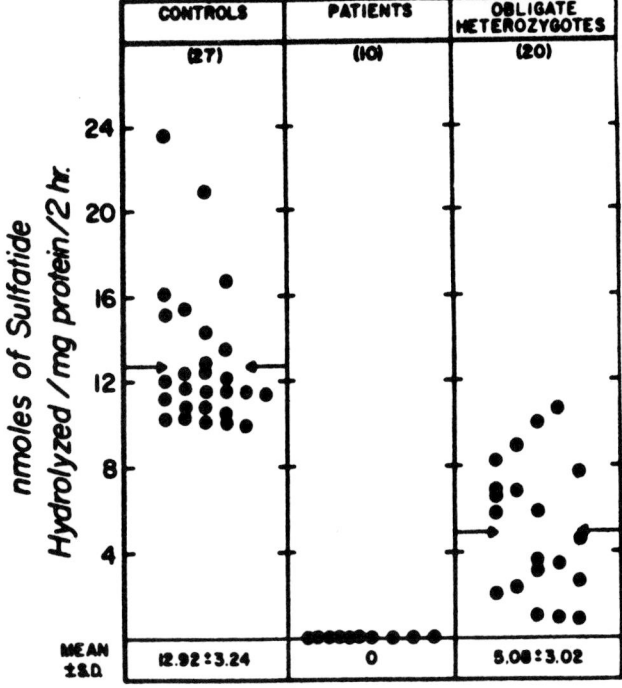

Fig. 69-16 Leukocyte sulfatidase activity in normal controls, patients with MLD, and obligate heterozygotes. A dialyzed leukocyte sonicate was incubated for 2 h with [³H]sulfatide labeled in the sphingosine portion of the molecule. The mean for each group is indicated by arrows. Note that the enzyme activity in some heterozygotes was quite low but that only in the MLD cases was it totally absent. (*Adapted from Raghavan et al.[184]*)

These have employed various forms of ion-exchange chromatography,[343,344] electrophoresis,[345-347] and isoelectric focusing.[74,276,347] With several of these techniques it is possible to visualize directly individual bands of enzyme activity. This provides the clinical chemist with an extra measure of confidence, particularly when assessing the significance of a deficiency in enzyme activity in vitro. A radioimmunoassay has also been developed.[280,294,378]

Several procedures have been described for labeling cerebroside sulfate for use as an enzyme substrate.[85,184,191,278,280,348] The advantage of the cerebroside sulfate sulfatase assay is that it can distinguish between the few normal individuals who have unusually low arylsulfatase A activity and patients with MLD (Fig. 69-16). Those with true MLD are totally deficient in activity toward this natural substrate, whereas the normal

Fig. 69-17 Response of pseudo-arylsulfatase A–deficient fibroblasts to the cerebroside sulfate loading test in MEMHEPES. ● = Normal fibroblasts. Open symbols = pseudodeficiency fibroblasts. (*From Kihara et al.[293]*)

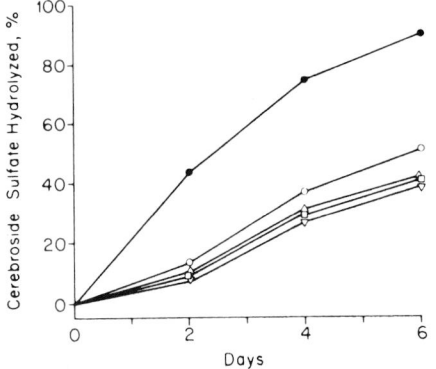

individuals with low arylsulfatase A activity will hydrolyze a small amount of cerebroside sulfate.[184] The labeled substrate is also useful in tissue culture loading experiments for diagnosing the variant with cerebroside sulfate sulfatase activator deficiency[16] or pseudodeficiency (Fig. 69-17).[280,294]

Urine sulfatide determinations are a useful adjunct to the enzyme analyses in the diagnosis of MLD.[29,255] All MLD patients, including those with multiple sulfatase deficiency and those with a deficiency of the cerebroside sulfate sulfatase activator protein, excrete large amounts of sulfatide in the urine. Fresh urine is filtered, and the cellular debris trapped on the filter is then extracted with organic solvents and its lipid content analyzed. A less rigorous screening procedure for urine sulfatide has also been described.[349] Two types of presenting patients specifically require an assessment of urinary sulfatide excretion: the patient with clinical signs of MLD but normal arylsulfatase A activity, and the patient with arylsulfatase A deficiency without other signs of MLD or with neurologic signs not typical of MLD. In the first of these two classes of patients, an increase in urine sulfatide will suggest the diagnosis of cerebroside sulfate sulfatase activator protein deficiency. In the case of the second type of patient, the increased excretion of sulfatide will alert the clinician to a presymptomatic or atypical case of MLD, whereas a finding of normal urine sulfatide will exclude the MLD genotype.

Heterozygote Identification

Leukocyte and fibroblast assays for arylsulfatase A and cerebroside sulfatase can also be used to determine whether an individual is a carrier of the trait for MLD. This is most frequently done for the sibs and other family members of a patient with MLD and for their spouses. This information permits an estimate of their risk for having children with MLD.[330] There is some overlap in enzyme values at both ends of the heterozygote range, between those for normal individuals and carriers, and between those for affected homozygotes and carriers[266] (Fig. 69-16). This spread in activity is due partly to the protein polymorphism that characterizes any diverse population and partly to the relatively frequent occurrence of the non-MLD low activity pseudodeficiency allele in the normal population. If the pseudodeficiency allele is present in an MLD heterozygote, the amount of leukocyte arylsulfatase A activity present may be so low as to suggest the disease state. When this occurs, further enzyme testing using the natural substrate, cerebroside sulfate, is desirable, including the use of sulfatide loading in cultured fibroblasts. Heterozygote levels of enzyme activity vary less within a given family than among unrelated persons. Therefore, it is helpful in doing carrier ascertainment to test as many members of the same family as possible and compare their results with those obtained for the obligate heterozygotes in the family.

Prenatal Diagnosis

Prenatal diagnosis has been repeatedly and successfully accomplished for the late infantile and juvenile forms of MLD[228,243,290,291] and is theoretically possible for other variants. The usual procedure is to determine the activity of arylsulfatase A in cultured amniotic fluid cells. Activity is normally low during the log phase of cell growth. Only after the cultured cell monolayer has reached confluency does a significant amount of enzyme activity appear. Therefore, careful attention must be paid to cell culture conditions and time of harvesting. In families that carry both the MLD allele and the allele for pseudodeficiency, the cerebroside sulfate loading test should also be done using amniotic fluid cells in culture.[177,180,278,350] Direct assays of arylsulfatase A activity in amniotic fluid have also been used for the prenatal diagnosis of MLD,[243,351,352] but most authorities feel that this procedure is less reliable than enzyme methods utilizing cultured amniotic fluid cells. Determination of arylsulfatase A activity in chorionic villi has also been used to diagnose MLD prenatally.[353] However, arylsulfatase C is a major component in this tissue,[354] and therefore precautions must be taken to avoid a false negative diagnosis. This can be accomplished by separating the arylsulfatase isoenzymes using electrophoresis[355] or column chromatography (Fig. 69-18).[354] In one case of MSD, a low estriol level was found in maternal urine during gestation,[356] and in another MSD case with neonatal onset, placental hormone insufficiency was noted at 28 and 36 weeks of gestation.[155]

TREATMENT

Symptomatic Therapy

Currently, there exists no specific treatment that will halt the progression of MLD or reverse its fatal outcome. The objectives in management of a child or adult with this disease are to maintain useful function and meaningful interaction for as long as possible. The educational program of the juvenile MLD patient in kindergarden or first grade is adjusted to lowered expectations so that the child's participation in the school environment can continue. Patients with the adult onset variant can frequently continue for several years to enjoy the company of their family and perform useful chores in the familiarity of their own homes. Eventually all mobility is lost and total supportive care becomes necessary. A permanent gastrostomy tube may be needed to assist in feeding and to maintain adequate nutrition. Passive physical therapy is utilized to prevent contractures that would otherwise cause nursing problems in the bedridden patient.

Attempts have been made to reduce sulfatide synthesis by the use of a diet low in vitamin A[28,357-359] or low in sulfur.[360] The rationale is that both vitamin A and sulfur are required for sulfatide synthesis. Unfortunately, neither approach has had favorable long-lasting effects.

Drug Therapy

Activation or stabilization of the mutant arylsulfatase A protein is also theoretically possible. For example, long-term thiosulfate treatment of skin fibroblasts cultured from patients with multiple sulfatase deficiency substantially increases their arylsulfatase A activity[296] and improves their capacity to catabolize sulfatide.[299] Consequently, thiosulfate has been proposed as a treatment for this particular disease.[361] Similarly, the ability to degrade sulfatide can be restored to fibroblasts from patients with late onset MLD by the addition of cysteine proteinases to their culture mediums.[289] However, the thiol proteinases are likely to affect the action of many proteins rendering therapy with these agents impractical. One patient with adult MLD has received acetosalicylate in an attempt to in-

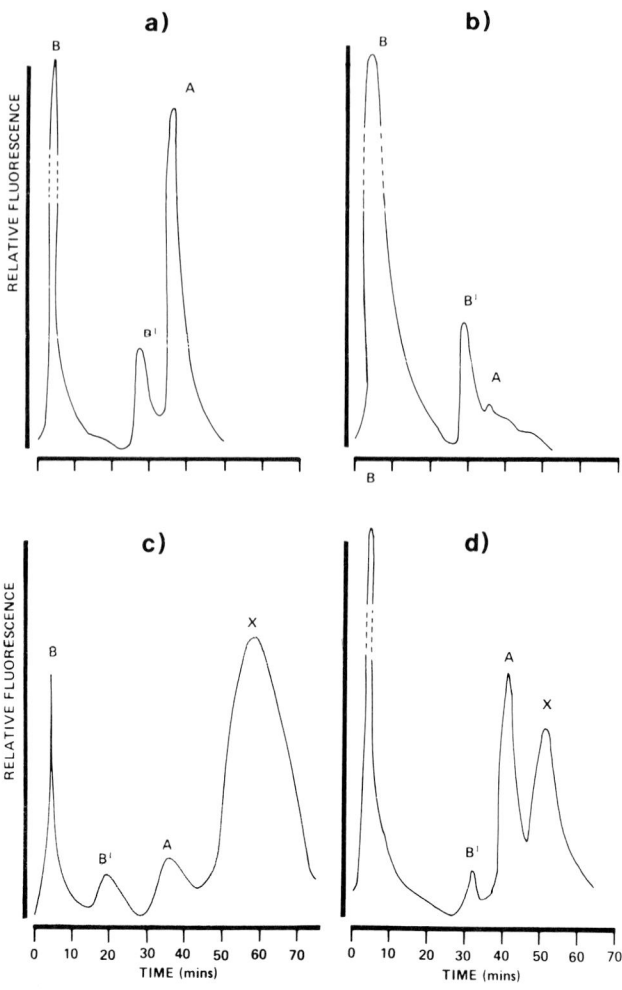

Fig. 69-18 Separation of arylsulfatases by DEAE cellulose chromatography. A, normal fibroblasts, B, fibroblasts from a patient with MLD, C, chorionic villi, and D, fibroblasts and chorionic villi mixed. Enzyme activity was determined with 4-methylumbelliferyl sulfate. (*From Giles et al.*[354])

crease his residual arylsulfatase A activity. This treatment nearly doubled his leukocyte enzyme activity but it was still less than 10 percent of the mean for the control group.[109]

Enzyme Replacement Therapy

Replacement therapy by infusion with normal enzyme has never been successfully applied to a lysosomal storage disease with central nervous system pathology. It is possible to show in tissue culture that arylsulfatase A supplied to the nutrient mediums of cells deficient in enzyme is capable of being endocytosed and can degrade [^{35}S]sulfatide previously stored within these cells. This has been accomplished with MLD skin fibroblasts[277,279,289,362] and with explants and dissociated cells from the brain of a fetus with MLD.[248]

The targeting of enzyme into an oligodendroglial cell in vivo is a much more difficult task. Purified enzyme has twice been injected into children with MLD. In one instance, a pyrogenic reaction occurred[363]; in the second, high levels of enzyme activity were present transiently in the liver, but no activity could be detected in a brain biopsy 8 h after an intrathecal injection of the enzyme.[364] Because human amnion does not provoke immunologic rejection, it has been proposed for enzyme replacement therapy in the storage diseases. Two chil-

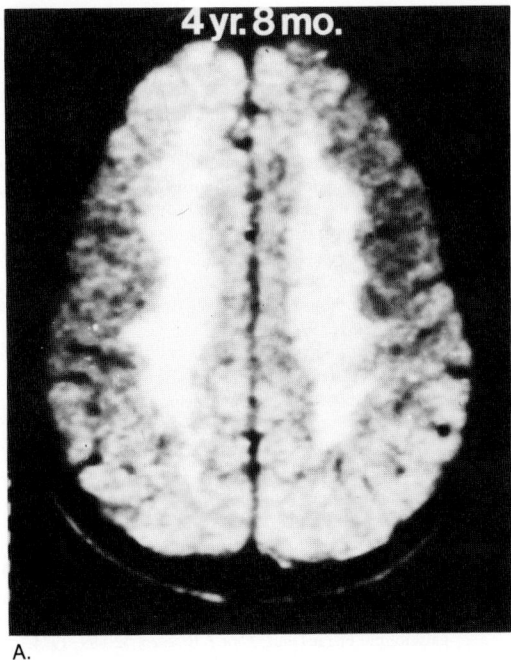
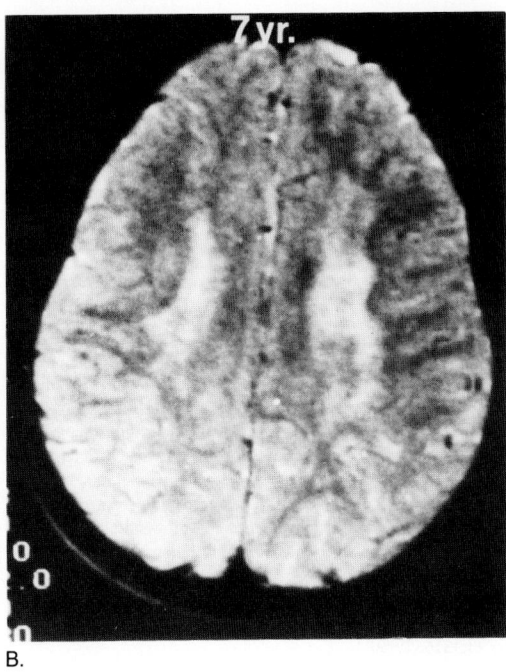
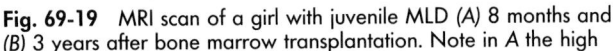

A.   B.

Fig. 69-19   MRI scan of a girl with juvenile MLD (A) 8 months and (B) 3 years after bone marrow transplantation. Note in A the high intensity confluent areas in the periventricular white matter typical of MLD and the improvement in B. (*From Krivit et al.*[373])

dren with MLD have been treated by subcutaneous implantation of sheets of amnion within 6 h after their procurement. Neither child responded, and after follow-up periods of 14 and 6 months there was no change in serum or leukocyte arylsulfatase A activity.[365]

Bone Marrow Transplantation

Several patients have received bone marrow transplants in a bold attempt to correct their low arylsulfatase A levels and retard their central nervous system deterioration. At least two with infantile MLD died soon after transplantation.[366,367] However, two others, an 11-month-old boy with late infantile MLD[368,369] and a 4-year-old girl with juvenile MLD, appear to have benefited from the procedure.[370,371] In both cases the donors were HLA-identical female sibs. The boy at age 44 months was reported to have circulating leukocyte arylsulfatase A levels in the heterozygote range and to be making continued developmental progress. However, peripheral nerve function continued to deteriorate. In contrast, at this age, one of his sibs with MLD had died, and the other was completely unresponsive and required tube feeding. The karyotype of every leukocyte cultured from his cerebrospinal fluid was female, indicative of their donor origin.

At age 6, 2½ years after her transplant, the girl with juvenile onset MLD continued to have a mild intention tremor but was able to run and dance and was performing well in the first grade. She had less toe walking, and the Achilles tendon contractures were less prominent than before the transplant. Her leukocyte arylsulfatase A levels were in the normal range. Interpeak latencies on the brainstem auditory evoked potential test had begun to improve, and the electroencephalogram had remained normal. Serial MRI scans demonstrated a reversal or stabilization of the demyelinating process (Fig. 69-19).[373] However, her motor nerve conduction velocities and visual evoked responses worsened slightly in the 2 years since the transplant. By age 5 years, her affected sister had lost the abil-

ity to speak and had to be tube-fed, and by age 6 years, she had become decerebrate and unresponsive. In neither patient with successful bone marrow engraftment did urine sulfatides change significantly. However, in one, the post-transplantation urine showed a significant concentration of cerebroside not present in the urine of an untreated patient.

Longer term follow-up is needed to assess whether this form of therapy will halt the progression of MLD and improve central nervous system functioning in children with clinical signs. The appearance of cells from the donor marrow within the cerebrospinal fluid suggests that these cells can penetrate the blood-brain barrier and seed the central nervous system. Colonization of the brain by hematogenously derived glial cells is likely to be a slow process, but their action, both as scavengers of sulfatide and as secretors of enzyme, provides a rationale for additional trials of this form of therapy.

REFERENCES

1. ALZHEIMER A: Beitrage zur Kenntnis der pathologischen Neurologia und ihrer Beziehung zu den Abbauvorgangen im Nervengewebe. *Nissl-Alzheimer's Histol Histopathol Arb* 3:493, 1910.
2. WITTE F: Über pathologische Abbauvorgange im Zentralnervensystem. *Munch Med Wochenschr* 68:69, 1921.
3. SCHOLZ W: Klinische, pathologisch-anatomische und erbbiologische Untersuchungen bei familiarer, diffuser Hirnsklerose im Kindesalter. *Z Gesamte Neural Psychiatr* 99:42, 1925.
4. VON HIRSCH T, PEIFFER J: Über histologische Methoden in der Differentialdiagnose von Leukodystrophien und Lipoidosen. *Arch Psychiatr Nervenkr* 194:88, 1955.
5. PEIFFER J: Über die metachromatischen Leukodystrophien (Typ Scholz). *Arch Psychiatr Nervenkr* 199:386, 1959.
6. GREENFIELD JG: A form of progressive cerebral sclerosis in infants associated with primary degeneration of the interfascicular glia. *J Neurol Psychopathol* 13:289, 1933.
7. FEIGIN I: Diffuse cerebral sclerosis (metachromatic leuko-encephalopathy). *Am J Pathol* 30:715, 1954.
8. EINARSON L, NEEL AV: Beitrag zur Kenntnis sklerosierender Entmarkungsprozesse in Gehirn mit besonderer Berucksichtigung der diffusen Sklerose. *Acta Jutlandica* 10:1, 1938.
9. NORMAN RM: Diffuse progressive metachromatic leucoencephalopathy. A

form of Schilder's disease related to the lipidoses. *Brain* 22:234, 1947.

10. JATZKEWITZ H: Zwei Typen von Cerebrosid-schwefelsaureestern als Sog. "Pralipoide" und Speichersubstanzen bei der Leukodystrophie, Typ Scholz (metachromatische Form der diffusen Sklerose). *Z Physiol Chem* 311:279, 1958.

11. AUSTIN J: Metachromatic sulfatides in cerebral white matter and kidney. *Proc Soc Exp Biol Med* 100:361, 1959.

12. AUSTIN JH, BALASUBRAMANIAN AS, PATTABIRAMAN TN, SARASWATHI S, BASU DK, BACHHAWAT BK: A controlled study of enzymatic activities in three human disorders of glycolipid metabolism. *J Neurochem* 10:805, 1963.

13. MEHL E, JATZKEWITZ H: Evidence for the genetic block in metachromatic leukodystrophy (ML). *Biochem Biophys Res Commun* 19:407, 1965.

14. JATZEWITZ H, MEHL E: Cerebroside-sulphatase and arylsulfatase A deficiency in metachromatic leukodystrophy (ML): *J Neurochem* 16:19, 1969.

15. MEHL E, JATZEWITZ H: Eine Cerebrosidsulfatase aus Schweineniere. *Hoppe-Seyler's Z Physiol Chem* 339:260, 1964.

16. STEVENS RL, FLUHARTY AL, KIHARA H, KABACK MM, SHAPIRO LJ, MARSH B, SANDHOFF K, FISCHER G: Cerebroside sulfatase activator deficiency induced metachromatic leukodystrophy. *Am J Hum Genet* 33:900, 1981.

17. AUSTIN JH, ARMSTRONG D, SHEARER L: Metachromatic form of diffuse cerebral sclerosis. V. The nature and significance of low sulfatase activity: A controlled study of brain, liver and kidney in four patients with metachromatic leukodystrophy (MLD). *Arch Neurol* 13:593, 1965.

18. BASNER R, von FIGURA K, GLOSSL J, KLEIN U, KRESSE H, MLEKUSCH W: Multiple deficiency of mucopolysaccharide sulfatases in mucosulfatidosis. *Pediatr Res* 13:1316, 1979.

19. THUDICHUM JLW: *A Treatise on the Chemical Constitution of Brain.* London, Baliere, 1884.

20. THUDICHUM JLW: Die chemische Konstitution des Gehirns des Menschen und der Tiere. Tubingen, Franz Pietzeker, 1901.

21. BLIX G: Zur Kenntnis der schwefelhaltigen Lipid Stoffe des Gehirns: Über cerbron Schwefelsaure. *Z Physiol Chem* 219:82, 1933.

22. YAMAKAWA T, KIOS N, HANDA S, MAKITA A, YOKOYAMA S: On the structure of brain cerebroside sulfuric ester and ceramide dihexoside of erythrocytes. *J Biochem (Tokoyo)* 52:226, 1962.

23. STOFFYN P, STOFFYN A: Structure of sulfatides. *Biochim Biophys Acta* 70:218, 1963.

24. STOFFYN PJ: The structure and chemistry of sulfatides. *J Am Oil Chem Soc* 43:69, 1966.

25. SHIMOMURA K, KISHIMOTO Y: An improved procedure for the quantitative determination and characterization of sulfatides in rat kidney and brain by high-performance liquid chromatography. *Biochim Biophys Acta* 754:93, 1983.

26. MALONE MJ, STOFFYN P: A comparative study of brain and kidney glycolipids in metachromatic leukodystrophy. *J Neurochem* 13:1037, 1966.

27. MARTENSSON E: Sulfatides of human kidney: Isolation, identification, and fatty acid composition. *Biochim Biophys Acta* 116:521, 1966.

28. NISHIO H, KODAMA S, MATSUO T: Analysis of fatty acids and sphingosines from urinary sulfatides in a patient with metachromatic leukodystrophy by gas chromatography-mass spectrometry. *Brain Dev* 7:614, 1985.

29. PHILIPPART M, SARLIEVE L, MEURANT C, MECHLER L: Human urinary sulfatides in patients with sulfatidosis (Metachromatic leukodystrophy). *J Lipid Res* 12:434, 1971.

30. MARTENSSON E: On the sulfate containing lipids of human kidney. *Acta Chem Scand* 17:1174, 1963.

31. SAMUELSSON B: Regional distribution of glycosyceramide-sulfates in human kidney. *Lipids* 17:160, 1982.

32. STOFFYN A, STOFFYN P, MATENSSON E: Structure of kidney ceramide dihexoside sulfate. *Biochim Biophys Acta* 152:353, 1968.

33. STRASBERG PM, WARREN I, SKOMOROWSKI M-A, LOWDEN JA: HPLC analysis of urinary sulfatide: An aid in the diagnosis of metachromatic leukodystrophy. *Clin Biochem* 18:92, 1985.

34. ROBERTS DD, RAO CN, LIOTTA LA, GRALNICK HR, GINSBURG V: Comparison of the specificities of laminin, thrombospondin, and von Willebrand factor for binding to sulfated glycolipids. *J Biol Chem* 261:6872, 1986.

35. HAUSER G: Labeling of cerebrosides and sulfatides in rat brain. *Biochim Biophys Acta* 84:212, 1964.

36. BALASUBRAMANIAN AS, BACHHAWAT BK: Formation of cerebroside sulphate from 3'-phosphoadenosine 5'-phosphosulphate in sheep brain. *Biochim Biophys Acta* 106:218, 1965.

37. MCKHANN GM, HO W: The in vivo and in vitro synthesis of sulphatides during development. *J Neurochem* 14:717, 1967.

38. CUMAR FA, BARRA HS, MACCIONI HJ, CAPUTTO R: Sulfation of glycosphingolipids and related carbohydrates by brain preparations from young rats. *J Biol Chem* 243:3807, 1968.

39. FARRELL DF, MCKHANN GM: Characterization of cerebroside sulfotransferase from rat brain. *J Biol Chem* 246:4694, 1971.

40. FARRELL DF: Enzymatic sulphation of some galactose-containing sphingolipids in developing rat brain. *J Neurochem* 23:219, 1974.

41. NUSSBAUM JL, MANDEL P: Enzymic synthesis of psychosine sulphate. *J Neurochem* 19:1789, 1972.

42. NORTON WR, PODUSLO SE: Biochemical studies of metachromatic leukodystrophy in three siblings. *Acta Neuropathol (Berl)* 57:188, 1982.

43. DAWSON G, KERNES SM: Induction of sulfogalactosylceramide (sulfatide) synthesis by hydrocortisone (cortisol) in mouse G-26 oligodendroglioma cell strains. *J Neurochem* 31:1091, 1978.

44. HARRIS RA, LOH HH: Brain sulfatide and non-lipid sulfate metabolism in hypothyroid rats. *Res Commun Chem Pathol Pharmacol* 24:169, 1979.

45. BENJAMINS JA, GUANIERI M, MILLER K, SONNEBORN CM, MCKHANN GM: Sulfatide synthesis in isolated oligodendroglial and neuronal cells. *J Neurochem* 23:751, 1974.

46. SARLIEVE LL, NESKOVIC NM, FREYSZ L, MANDEL P, REBEL G: Ceramid galactosyltransferase and cerebroside sulphotransferase in chicken brain cellular fractions and glial and neuronal cells in culture. *Life Sci* 18:251, 1976.

47. ISHIZUKA I, TADANO K, NAGATA N, NHMURA Y, NAGAI Y: Hormone-specific responses and biosynthesis of sulfolipids in cell lines derived from mammalian kidney. *Biochim Biophys Acta* 541:467, 1978.

48. ISHIZUKA I, INOMATA M, UENO K, YAMAKAWA T: Sulphated glyceroglycolipid in rat brain. Structure, sulphation in vivo and accumulation in whole brain during development. *J Biol Chem* 253:898, 1978.

49. KORNBLATT MJ, KNAPP A, LEVINE M, SCHACHTER H, MURRAY RK: Studies on the structure and formation during spermatogenesis of sulphoglycerogalactolipid of rat testis. *Can J Biochem* 52:689, 1974.

50. SUBBA RAO G, NARCIA LN, PIERINGER J, PIERINGER RA: The biosynthesis of sulphogalactosyldiacylglycerol of rat brain in vitro. *Biochem J* 166:429, 1977.

51. HANDA S, YAMATO K, ISHIZUKA I, SUZUKI A, YAMAKAWA T: Biosynthesis of seminolipid. *J Biochem (Tokyo)* 75:77, 1974.

52. ROBERTS KD, LIEBERMAN S: The biochemistry of the 3 β-hydroxy- Δ ^{5}-steroid sulfates, in Bernstein S, Solomon S (eds): *Chemical and Biological Aspects of Steroid Conjugation.* New York, Springer-Verlag, 1970, p 219.

53. SHAPIRA E, NADLER HL: Purification and some properties of soluble human liver arylsulfatases. *Arch Biochem Biophys* 170:179, 1975.

54. DRAPER RK, FISKUM GM, EDMOND J: Purification, molecular weight, amino acid, and subunit composition of arylsulfatase A from human liver. *Arch Biochem Biophys* 177:525, 1976.

55. JAMES GT, AUSTIN JH: Studies in metachromatic leukodystrophy. XIV. Purification and subunit structure of human liver arylsulfatase A. *Clin Chim Acta* 98:103, 1979.

56. JAMES GT, THACH AB, KLASSEN L, AUSTIN JH: Studies in metachromatic leukodystrophy: XV. Purification of normal and mutant arylsulfatase A from human liver. *Life Sci* 37:2365, 1985.

57. FAROOQUI AA: Purification and properties of arylsulfatase A from human placenta. *Arch Int Physiol Biochim* 84:479, 1976.

58. GNIOT-SZULZYCKA J: Some properties of highly purified arylsulfatase A from human placenta. *Acta Biochim Pol* 21:247, 1974.

59. STEVENS RL, FLUHARTY AL, SKOKUT MH, KIHARA H: Purification and properties of arylsulfatase A from human urine. *J Biol Chem* 250:2495, 1975.

60. LUIJTEN JAFM, VAN DER HEIJDEN MCM, RIJKSEN G, STAAL GEJ: Purification and characterization of arylsulfatase A from human urine. *J Mol Med* 3:213, 1978.

61. LAIDLER PM, WAHEED A, van ETTEN RL: Structural and immunochemical characterization of human urine arylsulfatase A purified by affinity chromatography. *Biochim Biophys Acta* 827:73, 1985.

62. WAHEED A, HASILIK A, von FIGURA K: Synthesis and processing of arylsulfatase A in human skin fibroblasts. *Hoppe-Seyler's Z Physiol Chem* 363:425, 1982.

63. SARAFIAN TA, FLUHARTY AL, KIHARA H, HELFAND G, EDMOND J: Large-scale purification of pyrogen-free human arylsulfatase A. *J Appl Biochem* 4:126, 1982.

64. FLUHARTY AL, MEEK WE, KIHARA H: Pseudo arylsulfatase A deficiency: Evidence for a structurally altered enzyme. *Biochem Biophys Res Commun* 112:191, 1983.

65. BACH G, NEUFELD EF: Synthesis and maturation of cross-reactive glycoprotein in fibroblasts deficient in arylsulfatase A activity. *Biochem Biophys Res Commun* 112:198, 1983.

66. WAHEED A, STECKEL F, HASILIK A, von FIGURA K: Two allelic forms of human arylsulfatase A with different numbers of asparagine-linked oligosaccharides. *Am J Hum Genet* 35:228, 1983.

67. WAHEED A, van ETTEN RL: Phosphorylation and sulfation of arylsulfatase A accompanies biosynthesis of the enzyme in normal and carcinoma cell lines. *Biochim Biophys Acta* 847:53, 1985.

68. BRAULKE T, HILLE A, HUTTNER HB, HASILIK A, von FIGURA K: Sulfated

oligosaccharides in human lysosomal enzymes. *Biochem Biophys Res Commun* 143:178, 1987.

69. STECKEL F, HASILIK A, von FIGURA K: Synthesis and stability of arylsulfatase A and B in fibroblasts from multiple sulfatase deficiency. *Eur J Biochem* 151:141, 1985.

70. MANOWITZ P, GOLDSTEIN L, BELLOMO F: An improved method for arylsulfatase A detection of polyacrylamide slab gels. *Anal Biochem* 89:423, 1978.

71. DUBOIS G, TURPIN JC, BAUMANN N: Arylsulfatases isoenzymes in metachromatic leukodystrophy/Detection of a new variant by electrophoresis. Improvement of quantitative assay. *Biomedicine* 23:116, 1975.

72. MANOWITZ P, FINE L-AV, NORA R, CHOKROVERTY S, NATHAN PE, FAZZARO JM: A new electrophoretic variant of arylsulfatase A. *Biochem Med Metabol Biol* 39:117, 1988.

73. STEVENS RL, FLUHARTY AL, KILLGROVE AR, KIHARA H: Microheterogeneity of arylsulfatase A from human tissues. *Biochim Biophys Acta* 445:61, 1976.

74. FARRELL DF, MacMARTIN MP, CLARK AF: Multiple molecular forms of arylsulfatase A in different forms of metachromatic leukodystrophy (MLD). *Neurology* 29:16, 1979.

75. DUBOIS G, BAUMANN N: *Identification of 2 Forms of Arylsulfatase A. Relations with Cerebroside in Liver and Brain.* Seventh Meeting International Society for Neurochemistry, Jerusalem, 1979, p 306.

76. SARAFIAN TA, TSAY KK, JACKSON WE, FLUHARTY AL, KIHARA H: Studies on the charge isomers of arylsulfatase A. *Biochem Med* 33:372, 1985.

77. MITSUHASHI K, MARU A, KOYANAGI T, ISHIBASHI T, IMAI Y, GASA S, TANIGUCHI N, MAKITA A: Arylsulfatase A activities in urine and tissues taken from bladder cancer patients. *Jpn J Exp Med* 54:211, 1984.

78. NAKAMURA M, GASA S, MAKITA A: Arylsulfatase A from normal human lung and lung tumors showed different patterns of microheterogeneity. *J Biochem* 96:207, 1984.

79. HULYALKAR AR, NORA R, MANOWITZ P: Arylsulfatase A variants in patients with alcoholism. *Alcoholism: Clin Exp Res* 8:337, 1984.

80. MANOWITZ P, FINE LV, NORA R, PERNICANO K, NATHAN P, CHOKROVERTY S: Electrophoretic variants of arylsulfatase A in alcoholic patients and controls. *Ann NY Acad Sci* 492:341, 1987.

81. LEE GD, van ETTEN RL: Evidence for an essential histidine residue in rabbit liver arylsulfatase A. *Arch Biochem Biophys* 171:424, 1975.

82. JAMES GT: Essential arginine residues in human liver arylsulfatase A. *Arch Biochem Biophys* 197:57, 1979.

83. WAHEED A, van ETTEN RL: The structural basis of the anomalous kinetics of rabbit liver arylsulfatase A. *Arch Biochem Biophys* 203:11, 1980.

84. RYBARSKA-STYLINSKA J, van ETTEN RL: Antigen-antibody interactions and the anomalous kinetics of arylsulfatase A. *Biochim Biophys Acta* 570:107, 1979.

85. STINSHOFF K, JATZKEWITZ H: Comparison of the cerebroside sulphatase and the arylsulphatase activity of human sulphatase A in the absence of activators. *Biochim Biophys Acta* 377:126, 1975.

86. WAHEED A, van ETTEN RL: The monomer-dimer association or rabbit liver arylsulfatase A and its relationship to the anomalous kinetics. *Biochim Biophys Acta* 194:215, 1979.

87. JERFY A, ROY AB: Comparison of the arylsulfatase and cerebroside sulfatase activities of sulphatase A. *Biochim Biophys Acta* 293:128, 1973.

88. INUI K, WENGER DA: Properties of a protein activator of glycosphingolipid hydrolysis isolated from the liver of a patient with G_{M1} gangliosidosis, type 1. *Biochem Biophys Res Commun* 105:745, 1982.

89. FUJIBAYASHI S, WENGER DA: Biosynthesis of the sulfatide/G_{M1} activator protein (SAP-1) in control and mutant cultured skin fibroblasts. *Biochim Biophys Acta* 875:554, 1986.

90. FISHER G, JATZKEWITZ H: The activator of cerebroside sulphatase. Binding studies with enzyme and substrate demonstrating the detergent function of the activator protein. *Biochim Biophys Acta* 481:561, 1977.

91. LI Y-T, MUHIVDEEN IA, DEGASPERI R, HIRABAYASHI Y, LI S-C: Presence of activator proteins for the enzymic hydrolysis of G_{M1} and G_{M2} gangliosides in normal human urine. *Am J Hum Genet* 35:629, 1983.

92. INUI K, EMMETT M, WENGER DA: Immunological evidence for deficiency in an activator protein for sulfatide sulfatase in a variant form of metachromatic leukodystrophy. *Proc Natl Acad Sci USA* 80:3074, 1983.

93. HARZER K, BENZ HU: Deficiency of lactosyl sulfatide sulfatase in metachromatic leukodystrophy (sulfatidosis). *Hoppe-Seyler's Z Physiol Chem* 355:744, 1974.

94. FLUHARTY AL, STEVENS RL, MILLER RT, KIHARA H: Sulfoglycerogalactolipid from rat testis: A substrate for pure human arylsulfatase A. *Biochem Biophys Res Commun* 61:348, 1974.

95. FISHER G, REITER S, JATZKEWITZ H: Enzymic hydrolysis of sulphosphingolipids and sulphoglycerolipids by sulphatase A in the presence and absence of activator protein. *Hoppe-Seyler's Z Physiol Chem* 359:863, 1978.

96. ETO Y, WIESMANN U, HERSCHKOWITZ NN: Sulfogalactosylsphingosine sulfatase: Characteristic of the enzyme and its deficiency in metachromatic leukodystrophy in human cultured skin fibroblasts. *J Biol Chem* 249:4955, 1974.

97. FLUHARTY AL, STEVENS RL, MILLER RT, SHAPIRO SS, KIHARA H: Ascorbic acid-2-sulfate sulfohydrolase activity in human arylsulfatase A. *Biochim Biophys Acta* 419:508, 1976.

98. INOUE H, SEYAMA Y, YAMASHITA S: Specific determination of arylsulfatase A activity. *Experientia* 42:33, 1986.

99. MANOWITZ P, SHAPIRO SS, GOLDSTEIN L: Ascorbate-2-sulfate levels in metachromatic leukodystrophy patients. *Biochem Med* 18:274, 1977.

100. PARTANEN S: A direct-colouring, metal precipitation method for the demonstration of arylsulphatases A and B. *Histochem J* 16:501, 1984.

101. CHANG PL, MOUDGIL G: A specific ultrastructural stain for arylsulfatase A activity in human cultured fibroblasts. *J Histochem Cytochem* 32:617, 1984.

102. TAMAKA A, HIGAMI S, ISSHIKI G, MATSUMOTO T, FURUSAWA M: Immunofluorescence staining, and immunological studies of arylsulphatase deficiency (MSD) and metachromatic leukodystrophy (MLD) fibroblasts. *J Inherited Metab Dis* 6:21, 1983.

103. NORTON WT, PODUSLO SE: Myelination in rat brain: Changes in myelin composition during brain maturation. *J Neurochem* 21:759, 1973.

104. DUPOUEY P, ZALC B, LEFROUT-JOLY M, GOMES D: Localization of galactosylceramide and sulfatide at the surface of the myelin sheath: An immunofluorescence study in liquid medium. *Cell Mol Biol* 25:269, 1979.

105. LONDON Y, VOSSENBERG FGA: Specific interaction of central nervous system myelin basic protein with lipid. *Biochim Biophys Acta* 478:478, 1973.

106. HANSSON CG, KARLSSON KA, SAMUELSSON BE: The identification of sulphatides in human erythrocyte membrane and their relation to sodium-potassium dependent adenosine triphosphatase. *J Biochem* 83:813, 1978.

107. GONZALEZ E, ZAMBRANO F: Possible role of sulphatide in the K + -activated phosphatase activity. *Biochim Biophys Acta* 728:66, 1983.

108. LOH HH, CHO TM, WU YC, HARRIS RA, WAY EL: Opiate binding to cerebroside sulfate: A model system for opiate-receptor interaction. *Life Sci* 16:1811, 1975.

109. LOH HH, LAY PY, OSTWALD T, CHO TM, WAY EL: Possible involvement of cerebroside sulfate in opiate receptor binding. *Fed Proc* 37:147, 1978.

110. CRAVES FB, ZALC B, LEYBIN L, BAUMANN N, LOH HH: Antibodies to cerebroside sulfate inhibit the effects of morphine and β-endorphin. *Science* 207:75, 1980.

111. LAW PY, HARRIS RA, LOH HH, WAY EL: Evidence for involvement of cerebroside sulfate in opiate receptor binding: Studies with azure A and Jimpy mutant mice. *J Pharmacol Exp Ther* 207:458, 1978.

112. SANCHEZ-BLAZQUEZ P, GARZON J, LEE NM: Functional opiate receptor in mouse vas deferens: Evidence of a complex interaction. *J Pharmacol Exp Ther* 226:706, 1983.

113. WU C-SC, LEE NM, LOH HH, YANG JT, LI CH: β-endorphin: Formation of α-helix in lipid solutions. *Proc Natl Acad Sci USA* 76:3656, 1979.

114. EBADI M, CHWEH A: Inhibition by arylsulfatase A of Na-independent [^{3}H]-GABA and [^{3}H]-muscinol binding to bovine cerebellar synaptic membranes. *Neuropharmacology* 19:105, 1980.

115. MIYAKAWA A, ISHITANI R: Butanol extracts from myelin fragments: Identification of 5-hydroxytryptamine binding components. *Life Sci* 31:1427, 1982.

116. ROBERTS DD, HAVERSTICK DM, DIXIT VM, FRAZIER WA, SANTORO SA, GINSBURG V: The platelet glycoprotein thrombospondin binds specifically to sulfated glycolipids. *J Biol Chem* 260:9405, 1985.

117. WEERASINGHE KM, SCULLY MF, KAKKAR VV: Inhibition of the cerebroside sulphate (sulphatide)-induced contact activation reactions by platelet factor four. *Thromb Res* 33:625, 1984.

118. SCHIFFMAN S, ROSENFELD R, RETZIOS AD: Interaction of factor XI and sulfatide. *Thromb Res* 41:575, 1986.

119. ZUCKER-FRANKLIN D, GRUSKY G, YANG J-S: Arylsulfatase in natural killer cells: Its possible role in cytotoxicity. *Proc Natl Acad Sci USA* 80:6977, 1983.

120. ZUCKER-FRANKLIN D, NABI ZF, COREY EJ, COREY DR: A substrate analog inhibitor for arylsulfatase reduces NK cell cytotoxicity. *Biochem Biophys Res Commun* 126:540, 1985.

121. PERCY AK, KABACK MM, HERNDON RM: Metachromatic leukodystrophy: Comparison of early and late-onset forms. *Neurology* 27:933, 1977.

122. MANOWITZ P, KLING A, KOHN H: Clinical course of adult metachromatic leukodystrophy presenting as schizophrenia. *J Nerv Ment Dis* 166:500, 1978.

123. ALVES D, PIRES MM, GUIMARAES A, MIRANDA MC: Four cases of late onset metachromatic leucodystrophy in a family: Clinical, biochemical and neuropathological studies. *J Neurol Neurosurg Psychiatry* 49:1423, 1986.

124. KIHARA H: Metachromatic leukodystrophy, an unusual case with a subtle cerebroside sulfatase defect, in Buchwald N, Brazier MAB (eds): *Brain Mechanisms in Mental Retardation.* New York, Academic, 1975, p 501.

125. MacFAUL R, CAVANAGH N, LAKE BD, STEPHENS R, WHITFIELD AE: Metachromatic leucodystrophy: Review of 38 cases. *Arch Dis Child* 57:168, 1982.

126. AUSTIN J, ARMSTRONG D, FOUCH S, MITCHELL C, STUMPF D, SHEARER L, BRINER O: Metachromatic leukodystrophy (MLD). VIII. MLD in adults: Diagnosis and pathogenesis. *Arch Neurol* 18:225, 1968.

127. MARKIEWICZ D, ADAMCZEWSKA-GONCERZEWICZ Z, ZELMAN IB, DYNECKI J, BIENIASZ J: A case of metachromatic leukodystrophy with a chronic course (clinical-morphological-biochemical study). *Neuropathol Pol* 16:233, 1978.

128. ROIZIN L, SCHEINESSON G, EROS G: Comparative histological and histochemical studies of infantile and adult metachromatic leukodystrophy. *Pathol Eur* 3:286, 1968.

129. GUSTAVSON K-H, HAGBERG B: The incidence and genetics of metachromatic leucodystrophy in northern Sweden. *Acta Pediatr Scand* 60:585, 1971.

130. SCHUTTA HS, PRATT RTC, METZ H, EVANS KA, CARTER CO: A family study of the late infantile and juvenile forms of metachromatic leukodystrophy. *J Med Genet* 3:86, 1966.

131. HALTIA T, PALO J, HALTIA M, ICEN A: Juvenile metachromatic leukodystrophy: Clinical, biochemical and neuropathologic studies in nine cases. *Arch Neurol* 37:42, 1980.

132. HOLLANDER H: Über metachromatische Leukodystrophie. II. Relation zwischen Erkrankungsalter und Verlaufsdauer. *Arch Psychiatr Z Neurol* 205:300, 1964.

133. FARRELL D: Personal communication.

134. BUBIS JJ, ADLESBERG L: Congenital metachromatic leukodystrophy. Report of a case. *Acta Neuropathol* 6:298, 1966.

135. ZLOTOGORA J, COSTEFF H, ELIAN E: Early motor development in metachromatic leukodystrophy. *Arch Dis Child* 56:309, 1981.

136. DESILVA KL, PEARCE J: Neuropathy of metachromatic leukodystrophy. *J Neurol Neurosurg Psychiatr* 36:30, 1973.

137. HAGBERG B: Clinical symptoms, signs and tests in metachromatic leukodystrophy, in Folch-Pi J, Bauer H (eds): *Brain Lipids and Lipoproteins and the Leukodystrophies*. Amsterdam, Elsevier, 1963, pp 134–146.

138. COGAN DG, KUWABARA T, MOSER H: Metachromatic leukodystrophy. *Ophthalmology* 160:2, 1970.

139. LIBERT J, vanHOFF F, TOUSSAINT D, ROOZITALAB H, KENYON KR, GREEN WR: Ocular findings in metachromatic leukodystrophy: An electron microscopic and enzyme study in different clinical and genetic variants. *Arch Ophthalmol* 97:1495, 1979.

140. GORDON N: The insidious presentation of the juvenile form of metachromatic leukodystrophy. *Postgrad Med J* 54:335, 1978.

141. McKHANN GM: Metachromatic leukodystrophy: Clinical and enzymatic parameters. *Neuropediatrics* 15:4, 1984.

142. THOMAS PK, KING RHM, KOCEN RS, BRETT EM: Comparative ultrastructural observations on peripheral nerve abnormalities in the late infantile, juvenile and late onset forms of metachromatic leukodystrophy. *Acta Neuropathol (Berl)* 39:237, 1977.

143. TAGLIAVINI F, PIETRINI V, PILLERI G, TRABATTONI G, LECHI A: Case report. Adult metachromatic leukodystrophy: Clinicopathological report of two familial cases with slow course. *Neuropathol Appl Neurobiol* 5:233, 1979.

144. KOLODNY EH, RAGHAVAN S, SPIELVOGEL C, GAJEWSKI A, LASCON AC, JUNGALWALA FB, LOTT IT, DULANEY JT, HOEFNAGEL D: Genetic heterogeneity in arylsulfatase A deficiency. *Neurology* 29:576, 1979.

145. BOSCH EP, HART MN: Late adult-onset metachromatic leukodystrophy: Dementia and polyneuropathy in a 63 year old man. *Arch Neurol* 35:475, 1978.

146. HOES MJAJM, LAMERS KJ, HOMMES OR, TER HAAR B: Adult metachromatic leukodystrophy: Arylsulfatase-A values in four generations of one family and some reflections about the genetics. *Clin Neurol Neurosurg* 80:174, 1978.

147. SKOMER C, STEARS J, AUSTIN J: Metachromatic leukodystrophy (MLD) XV. Adult MLD with focal lesions by computed tomography. *Arch Neurol* 40:354, 1983.

148. SCHIPPER HI, SEIDEL D: Computed tomography in late-onset metachromatic leucodystrophy. *Neuroradiology* 26:39, 1984.

149. FINELLI PF: Metachromatic leukodystrophy manifesting as a schizophrenic disorder: Computed tomographic correlation. *Ann Neurol* 18:94, 1985.

150. WALTZ G, HARIK SI, KAUFMANN B: Adult metachromatic leukodystrophy. Value of computed tomographic scanning and magnetic resonance imaging of the brain. *Arch Neurol* 44:225, 1987.

151. FISHER NR, COPE SJ, LISHMAN WA: Metachromatic leukodystrophy: Conduct disorder progressing to dementia. *J Neurol Neurosurg Psychiatry* 50:488, 1987.

152. REIDER-GROSSWASSER I, BORNSTEIN N: CT and MRI in late-onset metachromatic leukodystrophy. *Acta Neurol Scand* 75:64, 1987.

153. PILZ H, DVENSING I, HEIPERTZ R, SEIDEL D, LOWITZSCH K, HOPF HC, GOEBEL HH: Adult metachromatic leukodystrophy. I. Clinical manifestation in a female aged 44 years, previously diagnosed in the preclinical state. *Eur Neurol* 15:301, 1977.

154. BATEMAN JB, PHILIPPART M, ISENBERG SJ: Ocular features of multiple sulfatase deficiency and a new variant of metachromatic leukodystrophy. *J Pediatr Ophthalmol Stradismus* 21:133, 1984.

155. VAMOS E, LIEBAERS I, BOUSARD N, LIBERT J, PERLUMUTTER N: Multiple sulphatase deficiency with early onset. *J Inherited Metab Dis* 4:103, 1981.

156. NEVSIMALOVA S, ELLEDER M, SMID F, ZEMANKOVA M: Multiple sulphatase deficiency in homozygotic twins. *J Inherited Metab Dis* 7:38, 1984.

157. BURK RD, VALLE D, THOMAS GH, MILLER C, MOSER A, MOSER H, ROSENBAUM KN: Early manifestations of multiple sulfatase deficiency. *J Pediatr* 104:574, 1984.

158. BHARUCHA BA, NAIK G, SAVLIWALA AS, JOSHI RM, KUMTA NB: Siblings with Austin variant of metachromatic leukodystrophy multiple sulfatidosis. *Indian J Pediatr* 51:477, 1984.

159. BURCH M, FENSOM AH, JACKSON M, PITTS-TUCKER T, CONGDON PJ: Multiple sulphatase deficiency presenting at birth. *Clin Genet* 30:409, 1986.

160. SOONG B-W, HOROWITZ AL, CASSAMASSIMA A, CONSTANTOPOULOS G: Multiple sulfatase deficiency (MSD). *Neurology* 36(suppl 1):114, 1986.

161. RAYNAUD EJ, ESCOUROLLE R, BAUMANN N, TURPIN J-C, DUBOIS G, MALPUECH G, LAGARDE R: Ultrastructural and enzymatic study of a case of variant O form. *Arch Neurol* 32:834, 1975.

162. HOGAN K, MATALON R, BERLOW S, LANGER L, PAULI R, GILBERT E, HECOX K: Multiple sulfatase deficiency: Clinical, radiologic, electrophysiologic, and biochemical features. *Neurology* 33(suppl 2):245, 1983.

163. YATZIV S, RUSSELL A: An unusual form of metachromatic leukodystrophy in three siblings. *Clin Genet* 19:222, 1981.

164. KIHARA H, FLUHARTY AL, O'BRIEN JS, FISH CH: Metachromatic leukodystrophy caused by a partial cerebroside sulfatase defect. *Clin Genet* 21:253, 1982.

165. TONNESEN T, VRANG C, WIESMANN UN, CHRISTOMANOU H, LOU HO: Atypical metachromatic leukodystrophy? Problems with the biochemical diagnosis. *Hum Genet* 67:170, 1984.

166. DANESINO C, d'AZZO A, ARICO M, PODESTA AF, BELUFF G, BAINCHI E: Non-progressive psychomotor retardation in a child with severe deficiency of arylsulphatase A activity. *Clin Genet* 26:462, 1984.

167. NORDENBO AM, TONNESEN T: A variant form of metachromatic leucodystrophy in a patient suffering from another congenital degenerative neurological disease. *Acta Neurol Scand* 71:31, 1985.

168. LANG AE, CLARKE JTR, RESCH L, STRASBERG P, SKOMOROWSKI MA, O'CONNOR P: Progressive long-standing "pure" dystonia: A new phenotype of juvenile metachromatic leukodystrophy (MLD). *Neurology* 35(suppl 1):194, 1985.

169. SHAPIRO LJ, ALECK KA, KABACK MM, ITABASHI H, DESNICK RJ, BRAND N, STEVENS RL, FLUHARTY AL, KIHARA H: Metachromatic leukodystrophy without arylsulfatase A deficiency. *Pediatr Res* 13:1179, 1979.

170. HAHN AF, GORDON BA, FELEKI V, HINTON GG, GILBERT JJ: A variant form of metachromatic leukodystrophy without arylsulfatase deficiency. *Ann Neurol* 12:33, 1982.

171. FUJIBAYASHI S, INUI K, WENGER DA: Activator protein-deficient metachromatic leukodystrophy: Diagnosis in leukocytes using immunologic methods. *J Pediatr* 104:739, 1984.

172. LI S-C, KIHARA H, SERIZAWA S, LI Y-T, FLUHARTY AL, MAYES JS, SHAPIRO LJ: Activator protein required for the enzymatic hydrolysis of cerebroside sulfate. Deficiency in urine of patients affected with cerebroside sulfatase activator deficiency and identity with activators for the enzymatic hydrolysis of G$_{M1}$ ganglioside and globotriaosylceramide. *J Biol Chem* 260:1867, 1985.

173. DUBOIS G, TURPIN JC, BAUMANN N: Absence of ASA activity in healthy father of a patient with metachromatic leukodystrophy. *N Engl J Med* 293:302, 1975.

174. LOTT IT, DULANEY JT, MILUNSKY A, HOEFNAGEL D, MOSER HW: Apparent biochemical homozygosity in two obligatory heterozygotes for metachromatic leukodystrophy. *J Pediatr* 89:438, 1976.

175. DUBOIS G, HARZER K, BAUMANN N: Very low arylsulfatase A and cerebroside sulfatase activities in leukocytes of healthy members of metachromatic leukodystrophy family. *Am J Hum Genet* 29:191, 1977.

176. FLUHARTY AL, STEVENS RL, KIHARA H: Cerebroside sulfate hydrolysis by fibroblasts from a metachromatic leukodystrophy parent with deficient arylsulfatase. *J Pediatr* 92:782, 1978.

177. KIHARA H, HO C-K, FLUHARTY AL, TSAY KK, HARTLAGE PL: Prenatal diagnosis of metachromatic leukodystrophy in a family with pseudo arylsulfatase A deficiency by the cerebroside sulfate loading test. *Pediatr Res* 14:224, 1980.

178. KIHARA H, MEEK WE, FLUHARTY AL: Genotype assignments in a family with the pseudo arylsulfatase A deficiency trait without metachromatic leukodystrophy. *Pediatr Res* 18:1021, 1984.

179. HERZ B, BACH G: Arylsulfatase A in pseudo deficiency. *Hum Genet* 66:147, 1984.

180. BALDINGER S, PIERPONT ME, WENGER DA: Pseudo deficiency of arylsulfatase A: A counseling dilemma. *Clin Genet* 31:70, 1987.

181. TONNESEN T, BRO PV, BRONDVIN NIELSEN K, LYKKELUND C: Metachromatic leukodystrophy and pseudoarylsulfatase A deficiency in a Danish family. *Acta Paediatr Scand* 72:178, 1983.

182. LOTT IT, DULANEY JT: Sulfatide excretion in metachromatic leukodystrophy. *Am J Hum Genet* 29:228, 1977.

183. BUTTERWORTH J, BROADHEAD DM, KEAY AJ: Low arylsulfatase A activity in a family without metachromatic leukodystrophy. *Clin Genet* 14:213, 1978.

184. RAGHAVAN SS, GAJEWSKI A, KOLODNY EH: Leukocyte sulfatidase for the reliable diagnosis of metachromatic leukodystrophy. *J Neurochem* 36:724, 1981.

185. WEITER JJ, FEINGOLD M, KOLODNY EH, RAGHAVAN SS: Retinal pigment epithelial degeneration associated with leukocyte arylsulfatase A deficiency. *Am J Ophthalmol* 90:768, 1980.

186. FARRELL K, APPLEGARTH DA, TOONE JR, MCLEOD PM, SAVAGE AV: Pseudoarylsulfatase-A deficiency in the neurologically impaired patient. *Can J Neurol Sci* 12:274, 1985.

187. PEIFFER J, HARZER K, SCHLOTE W: Diffuse-disseminated sclerosis combined with partial arylsulfatase A (ASA) deficiency. Mixed heterozygosity of ASA and pseudo-ASA-deficiency? *Neuropediatrics* 15:59, 1984.

188. VIDGOFF J, BUXMAN MM, SHAPIRO LJ, DIMOND RL, WILSON TG, HEPBURN CA, TABEL T, HEINRICHS WL: Placental steroid sulfatase deficiency: Association with arylsulfatase A deficiency. *Am J Hum Genet* 34:434, 1982.

189. NYBERG-HANSEN R: Metachromatic leukodystrophy: Two unusual cases of the late infantile form. *Z Neurol* 203:145, 1972.

190. PROPPING P, FRIEDL W, HUSCHKA M, SCHLOR K-H, REIMER F, LEE-VAUPEL M, CONZELMANN E, SANDHOFF K: The influence of low arylsulfatase A on neuropsychiatric morbidity: A large-scale screening in patients. *Hum Genet* 74:244, 1986.

191. DUBOIS G, TURPIN JC, GEORGES MC, BAUMANN N: Arylsulfatase A and B in leukocytes: A comparative statistical study of late infantile and juvenile forms of metachromatic leukodystrophy and controls. *Biomedicine* 33:2, 1980.

192. SHAH SN, JOHNSON RC, STONE RK, MAHON-HAFF H: Prevalence of partial cerebroside sulfate sulfatase (arylsulfatase A) defect in adult psychiatric patients. *Biol Psychiatry* 20:50, 1985.

193. HERSKA M, MOSCOVICH DG, KALIAN M, GOTTLIEB D, BACH G: Arylsulfatase A deficiency in psychiatric and neurologic patients. *Am J Med Genet* 26:629, 1987.

194. LANGENBECK U, DUNKER P, HEIPERTZ R, PILZ H: Inheritance of metachromatic leukodystrophy. *Am J Hum Genet* 29:639, 1977.

195. ZLOTOGORA J, COHEN T, ELAIN E, BACH G: About the inheritance of the arylsulfatase A. *Pediatr Res* 14:963, 1980.

196. CHANG PL, DAVIDSON RG: Pseudo arylsulfatase A deficiency in healthy individuals: Genetic and biochemical relationship to metachromatic leukodystrophy. *Proc Natl Acad Sci USA* 80:7323, 1983.

197. BLOM S, HAGBERG B: EEG findings in late infantile metachromatic and globoid cell leucodystrophy. *Electroencephalogr Clin Neurophysiol* 22:253, 1967.

198. MASTROPAOLO C, PAMPIGLIONE G, STEPHENS R: EEG studies in 22 children with sulphatide lipidosis (metachromatic leukodystrophy). *Dev Med Child Neuro* 13:20, 1971.

199. LUTSCHG J: Pathophysiological aspects of central and peripheral myelin lesions. *Neuropediatrics* 15(Suppl):24, 1984.

200. CLARK JR, MILLER RG, VIDGOFF JM: Juvenile-onset metachromatic leukodystrophy: Biochemical and electrophysiologic studies. *Neurology* 29:346, 1979.

201. PILZ H, HOPF HC: A preclinical case of late adult metachromatic leukodystrophy? *J Neurol Neurosurg Psych* 35:360, 1972.

202. WULFF CH, TROJABORG W: Adult metachromatic leukodystrophy: Neurophysiologic findings. *Neurol* 35:1776, 1985.

203. MILLER RG, GUTMANN L, LEWIS RA, SUMNER AJ: Acquired versus familial demyelinative neuropathies in children. *Muscle Nerve* 8:205, 1985.

204. CRUZ AM, FERRER MT, FUEYO E, GALDOS L: Peripheral neuropathy detected on an electrophysiological study as the manifestation of MLD in infancy. *J Neurol Neurosurg Psychiatry* 38:169, 1975.

205. OCHS R, MARKAND ON, DEMYER WE: Brainstem auditory evoked responses in leukodystrophies. *Neurology* 29:1089, 1979.

206. BROWN FR, SHIMIZU H, MCDONALD JM, MOSER AB, MARQUIS P, CHEN WW, MOSER HW: Auditory evoked brainstem response and high-performance liquid chromotography sulfatase assay as early indices of metachromatic leukodystrophy. *Neurology* 31:980, 1981.

207. MARKAND ON, GARG BP, DEMYER WE, WARREN C, WORTH RM: Brain stem auditory, visual and somatosensory evoked potentials in leukodystrophies. *Electroenceph Clin Neurophysiol* 54:39, 1982.

208. MAVER K, RACHEL M, KOWITZSCH K: Early auditory evoked potentials: Developmental aspects and validity in neuropaediatric and audiologic disorders. *Eur J Pediatr* 143:13, 1984.

209. TAKAKURA H, NAKAMO C, KASAGI S, TAKASHIMA S, TAKESHITA K: Multimodality evoked potentials in progression of metachromatic leukodystrophy. *Brain Dev* 7:424, 1985.

210. CARLIN L, ROACH ES, RIELA A, SPUDIS E, MCLEAN WT JR: Juvenile metachromatic leukodystrophy: Evoked potentials and computed tomography. *Ann Neurol* 13:105, 1983.

211. HAGBERG B, SOURANDER P, SVENNERHOLM L: Sulfatide lipidosis in childhood: Report of a case investigated during life and at autopsy. *Am J Dis Child* 104:644, 1962.

212. RODRIGUEZ-SORIANO J, RIVERA JM, VALLO A, PRATS-VINAS JM, CASTILLO G: Proximal renal tubular acidosis in metachromatic leukodystrophy. *Helv Paediatr Acta* 33:45, 1978.

213. KLEINMAN P, WINCHESTER P, VOLBERT F: Sulfatide cholecystosis. *Gastrointest Radiol* 1:99, 1976.

214. BURGESS JH, KAFFAYAN B, SLUNGAARD RK, GILBERT E: Tapillonatosis of the gallbladder associated with metachromatic leukodystrophy. *Arch Pathol Lab Med* 109:79, 1985.

215. JOOSTEN E, HOES M, GABREELS-FESTEN A, HOMMES O, SCHUURMANS STEKHOVEN H, SLOOF JL: Electron microscopic investigation of inclusion material in a case of adult metachromatic leukodystrophy: Observations on kidney biopsy, peripheral nerve and cerebral white matter. *Acta Neuropathol (Berl)* 33:165, 1975.

216. DAYAN AD: Dichromism of cresyl violet-stained cerebroside sulfate ("sulfatide"). *J Histochem Cytochem* 15:421, 1967.

217. TAKAHASHI K, NAITO M: Lipid storage disease: Part II. Ultrastructural pathology of lipid storage cells in sphingolipidoses. *Acta Pathol Jpn* 35:385, 1985.

218. BENZ HU, HARZER K: Metachromatic reaction of pseudoisocyanine with sulfatides in metachromatic leukodystrophy (MLD). I. Technique of histochemical staining. *Acta Neuropathol* 27:177, 1974.

219. HOLLANDER H: A staining method for cerebroside-sulfuric esters in brain tissue. *J Histochem Cytochem* 11:118, 1963.

220. LAMPERT IA, LEWIS PD: Staining of sulfatides in metachromatic leukodystrophy with Alcian blue at high salt concentrations. *Histochemistry* 43:269, 1975.

221. SUZUKI K, SUZUKI K, CHEN GC: Isolation and chemical characterization of metachromatic granules from a brain with metachromatic leukodystrophy. *J Neuropathol Exp Neurol* 26:537, 1967.

222. NICHOLLS RG, ROY AB: The sulphatase of ox liver. XV. Changes in the properties of sulphatase A in the presence of substrate. *Biochim Biophys Acta* 242:141, 1971.

223. GREGOIRE A, PERIER O, DUSTIN P: Metachromatic leukodystrophy, an electron microscopic study. *J Neuropathol Exp Neurol* 25:617, 1966.

224. RUTSAERT J, MENU R, RESIBOIS A: Ultrastructure of sulfatide storage in normal and sulfatase-deficient fibroblasts in vitro. *Lab Invest* 29:527, 1973.

225. BISCHOFF A, ULRICH J: Amaurotische Idiotie in Verbindung mit Metachromatischer Leukodystrophie. *Acta Neuropathol (Berl)* 8:292, 1967.

226. SEITELBERGER F: Structural manifestations of leukodystrophies. *Neuropediatrics* 15:53, 1984.

227. NASCIMENTO OJ, FREITAS MR, ALENCAR AA, COUTO BH: Metachromatic leukodystrophy: Report of a case. *Arq Neuropsiquiatr* 38:287, 1980.

228. MULLER D, PILZ H, MUELEN VT: Studies on adult metachromatic leukodystrophy. Part 1. Clinical, morphological and histochemical observations in two cases. *J Neurol Sci* 9:567, 1969.

229. TAKASHIMA S, MATSUI A, FUJII Y, NAKAMURA H: Clinicopathological differences between juvenile and late infantile metachromatic leukodystrophy. *Brain Dev* 3:365, 1981.

230. ITOYAMA Y, STERNBERGER N, QUARLES R, WEBSTER HDEF, RICHARDSON EP JR, COHEN S, MOSER HW: Successful immunocytochemical localization of myelin components in paraffin sections of human nervous tissue with preliminary observations on multiple sclerosis and metachromatic leukodystrophy lesions. *Trans Am Neurol Assoc* 103:216, 1978.

231. YAMANO T, OHTA S, SHIMADA M, OKADA S, YOTAKA T, SUGITA T, YABUCHI H: Neuronal depletion of cerebellum in late infantile metachromatic leukodystrophy. *Brain Dev* 2:359, 1980.

232. GOEBEL HH, SHIMOKAWA K, ARGYRAKIS A, PILZ H: The ultrastructure of the retina in an adult metachromatic leukodystrophy. *Am J Ophthalmol* 85:841, 1978.

233. GOEBEL HH, ARGYRAKIS A: Adult metachromatic leukodystrophy. *Am J Ophthalmol* 88:270, 1979.

234. WEBSTER HDEF: Schwann cell alterations in metachromatic leukodystrophy: Preliminary phase and electron microscope observations. *J Neuropathol Expo Neurol* 21:534, 1962.

235. MARTIN JJ, CEUTORICK C, MERCELIS R, JORIS C: Pathology of peripheral nerves in metachromatic leukodystrophy. A comparative study of ten cases. *J Neurol Sci* 53:95, 1982.

236. BARDOSI A, FRIEDE R, ROPTE S, GOEBEL HH: A morphometric study on sural nerves in metachromatic leucodystrophy. *Brain* 110:683, 1987.

237. GEBHART W, LASSMANN H, NIEBAUER G: Demonstration of specific storage material within cutaneous nerves in metachromatic leukodystrophy. *J Cutan Pathol* 5:5, 1978.

238. LADISCH S, BAYEVER E, PHILIPPART M, FEIG SA: Biochemical findings after bone marrow transplantation for metachromatic leukodystrophy: A preliminary report, in Krivit W, Paul NW (eds): *Bone Marrow Transplantation for Treatment of Lysosomal Storage Diseases*, March of Dimes Original Article Series 22:69, 1986.

239. WOLFE HJ, PEITRA GG: The visceral lesions of metachromatic leukodystrophy. *Am J Pathol* 44:921, 1964.

240. RESIBOIS A: Electron microscopic studies of metachromatic leukodystrophy. IV Liver and kidney alterations. *Pathol Eur* 6:278, 1971.

241. TOGA M, BERARD-BADIER M, PINSARD N, GAMBATELLI D, HASSOUN J, TRIPIER MF: Étude clinique, histologique et ultrastructurale de quarte cas de leucodystrophie metachromatique infantile et juvenile. *Acta Neuropathol (Berl)* 21:23, 1972.

242. LEROY JG, van ELSEN A, MARTIN JJ, DUMAON JE, HULET AE, OKADA S, NAVARRO C: Infantile metachromatic leukodystrophy: Confirmation of a prenatal diagnosis. *N Engl J Med* 288:1365, 1973.

243. ETO Y, TAHARA T, KODA N, YAMAGUCHI S, ITO F, OKUNO A: Prenatal diagnosis of metachromatic leukodystrophy. A diagnosis by amniotic fluid and its confirmation. *Arch Neurol* 39:29, 1982.

244. WARFEL KA, HULL MT: Villous papilloma of the gallbladder in association with leukodystrophy. *Hum Pathol* 15:1192, 1984.

245. BARGETON E: The metachromic form of leucodystrophy and its relationship to lipidosis and demyelination in other metabolic disorders, in Folch-Pi J, Bauer HJ (eds): *Brain Lipids and Lipoproteins, and the Leucodystrophies*. Amsterdam, Elsevier, 1963, p 90.

246. DENNY-BROWN DE, RICHARDSON EP Jr, COHEN RB: Difficulty in walking and petit mal attacks in a child. *N Engl J Med* 267:1198, 1962.

247. HARZER K, KUSTERMANN-KUHN B: Brain glycolipid content in a patient with pseudoarylsulfatase A deficiency and coincidental diffuse disseminated sclerosis, and in patients with metachromatic adreno-, and other leukodystrophies. *J Neurochem* 48:62, 1987.

248. PODUSLO SE, TENNEKOON G, PRICE D, MILLER K, MCKHANN GM: Fetal metachromatic leukodystrophy: Pathology, biochemistry and a study of in vitro enzyme replacement in CNS tissue. *J Neuropathol Exp Neurol* 35:622, 1976.

249. BAIER W, HARZER K: Sulfatides in prenatal metachromatic leukodystrophy. *J Neurochem* 41:1766, 1983.

250. PILZ H, HEIPERTZ R: The fatty acid composition of cerebrosides and sulfatides in a case of adult metachromatic leukodystrophy. *Z Neurol* 206:203, 1974.

251. STALLBERG-STENHAGEN S, SVENNERHOLM L: Fatty acid composition of human brain sphingomyelin: Normal variation with age and changes during myelin disorders. *J Lipid Res* 6:46, 1965.

252. MALONE MJ, STOFFYN P: Peripheral nerve glycolipids in metachromatic leukodystrophy. *Neurology* 17:1033, 1967.

253. MOSER HW, SUGITA M, HARBISON MD, WILLIAMS M: Liver glycolipids, steroid sulfates and steroid sulfatases in a form of metachromatic leukodystrophy associated with multiple sulfate deficiencies, in Volk BW, Aronson SM (eds): *Sphingolipids, Sphingolipidoses and Allied Disorders (Advances in Experimental Medicine and Biology*, vol 19). New York, Plenum, 1972, p 429.

254. MARTENSSON E, PERCY A, SVENNERHOLM L: Kidney glycolipids in late infantile metachromatic leukodystrophy. *Acta Paediatr Scand* 55:1, 1966.

255. PILZ H, MULLER D, LINKE L: Histochemical and biochemical studies of urinary lipids in metachromatic leukodystrophy and Fabry's disease. *J Lab Clin Med* 81:7, 1973.

256. ABE T, ISHIBA S, FUKUYAMA Y: The lipid analysis and some characterization of sulfate-containing glycolipids of the mucous layer of the gall bladder from a patient with metachromatic leukodystrophy. *Jpn J Exp Med* 47:129, 1977.

257. SVENNERHOLM E, SVENNERHOLM L: Isolation of blood serum glycolipids. *Acta Chem Scand* 16:1282, 1962.

258. MURPHY JW, WOLFE HJ, BALASZ EA, MOSER HW: A patient with deficiency of arylsulfatase A,B,C and steroid sulfatase, associated with storage of sulfatide, cholesterol sulfate and glycosaminoglycans, in Bernsohn J,

259. Grossman HJ (eds): *Lipid Storage Diseases: Enzymatic Defects and Clinical Implications*. New York, Academic, 1971, p 67.

259. RAMPINI S, ISLER W, BAERLOCHER K, BISCHOFF A, ULRICH J, PLUSS H: Die Kombination von metachromatischer Leukodystrophie und Mucopolysaccharidose als selbstandiges Krankheitsbild (Mukosulfatidose). *Helv Paediatr Acta* 25:436, 1970.

260. AUSTIN J: Studies in metachromatic leukodystrophy. XII. Multiple sulfatase deficiency. *Arch Neurol* 28:258, 1973.

261. ETO Y, WEISMANN UN, CARSON JH, HERSCHKOWITZ NN: Multiple sulfatase deficiences in cultured skin fibroblasts: Occurrence in patients with a variant form of metachromatic leukodystrophy. *Arch Neurol* 30:153, 1974.

262. AUSTIN J, MCAFEE D, SHEARER L: Metachromatic form of diffuse cerebral sclerosis. IV. Low sulfatase activity in the urine of nine living patients with metachromatic leukodystrophy (MLD). *Arch Neurol* 12:447, 1965.

263. THOMAS GH, HOWELL RR: Arylsulfatase A activity in human urine: Quantitative studies on patients with lysosomal disorders including metachromatic leukodystrophy. *Clin Chim Acta* 36:99, 1972.

264. HULTBERG B: Fluorometric assay of the arylsulphatases in human urine. *J Clin Chem Clin Biochem* 17:795, 1979.

265. PERCY AK, BRADY RO: Metachromatic leukodystrophy: Diagnosis with samples of venous blood. *Science* 161:594, 1968.

266. KIHARA H, PORTER MT, FLUHARTY AL, SCOTT ML, de la FLOR SD, TRAMMELL JL, NAKAMURA RN: Metachromatic leukodystrophy: Ambiguity of heterozygote identification. *Am J Ment Defic* 77:389, 1973.

267. PORTER MT, FLUHARTY AL, KIHARA H: Metachromatic leukodystrophy: arylsulfatase-A deficiency in skin fibroblast cultures. *Proc Natl Acad Sci USA* 62:887, 1969.

268. HASHIMOTO T, MINATO H, KURODA Y, TOSHIMA K, OHARA K, MIYAO M: Monozygotic twins with presumed metachromatic leukodystrophy: Activity of arylsulfatase A in serum of patients and family. *Arch Neurol* 35:689, 1978.

269. BERATIS NG, ARON AM, HIRSCHHORN K: Metachromatic leukodystrophy: Detection in serum. *J Pediatr* 83:824, 1973.

270. JORDAN TW, CASEY B, WESTON HJ: Enzymic detection of metachromatic leukodystrophy patients and heterozygotes. *NZ Med J* 85:369, 1977.

271. DENTANDT WR, JAEKEN J: Determination of lysosomal enzymes in saliva: Confirmation of the diagnosis of metachromatic leukodystrophy and fucosidosis by enzyme analysis. *Clin Chim Acta* 97:19, 1979.

272. BERATIS NG, DANESINO C, HIRSCHHORN K: Detection of homozygotes and heterozygotes for metachromatic leukodystrophy in lymphoid cell lines and peripheral leukocytes. *Ann Hum Genet Lond* 38:495, 1975.

273. BERATIS NG, FLEISHER LD, DANESINO C, HIRSCHHORN K: Arylsulfatase A deficiency in bone marrow fibroblasts of two different forms of metachromatic leukodystrophy. *J Lab Clin Med* 84:49, 1974.

274. PERCY AK, KABACK MM: Infantile and adult-onset metachromatic leukodystrophy: Biochemical comparisons and predictive diagnosis. *N Engl J Med* 285:785, 1971.

275. DUBOIS G, ZALC B, LESAUX F, BAUMANN N: Stearoyl [1-^{14}C] sulfogalactosylsphingosine ([^{14}C] sulfatide) as substrate for cerebroside sulfatase assay. *Anal Biochem* 102:313, 1980.

276. CHRISTOMANOU H, SANDHOFF K: Variation of arylsulfatase A: Comparative studies of arylsulfatase A with synthetic and natural substrates in three families with metachromatic leukodystrophy. *Neuropadiatrie* 9:385, 1978.

277. PORTER MT, FLUHARTY AL, KIHARA H: Correction of abnormal cerebroside sulfate metabolism in cultured metachromatic leukodystrophy fibroblasts. *Science* 172:1263, 1971.

278. KUDEH T, WENGER DA: Diagnosis of metachromatic leukodystrophy, Krabbe disease, and Farber disease after uptake of fatty acid–labeled cerebroside sulfate into cultured skin fibroblasts. *J Clin Invest* 70:89, 1982.

279. von FIGURA K, STECKEL F, HASILIK A: Juvenile and adult metachromatic leukodystrophy: Partial restoration of arylsulfatase A (cerebroside sulfatase) activity by inhibitors of thiol proteinases. *Proc Natl Acad Sci USA* 80:6066, 1983.

280. BACH G, DAGEN A, HERZ B, GATT S: Diagnosis of arylsulfatase A deficiency in intact cultured cells using a fluorescent derivative of cerebroside sulfate. *Clin Genet* 31:211, 1987.

281. YAMAGUCHI S, AOKI K, HANDA S, YAMAKAWA T: Deficiency of seminolipid sulphatase activity in brain tissue of metachromatic leucodystrophy. *J Neurochem* 24:1087, 1975.

282. HALTIA T, ICEN A, PALO J: Arylsulphatase A and B in juvenile metachromatic leukodystrophy. *Clin Chim Acta* 95:255, 1979.

283. HULTBERG B, ISAKSSON A, SJOBLADS S, OCKERMAN PA: Acid hydrolases in serum from patients with lysosomal disorders. *Clin Chim Acta* 100:33, 1980.

284. JATZKEWITZ H, STINSHOFF K: An activator of cerebroside sulphatase in human normal liver and in cases of congenital metachromatic leukodystrophy. *FEBS Lett* 32:129, 1973.

285. BAUM H, DODGSON KS, SPENCER B: The assay of arylsulphatases A and B in human urine. *Clin Chim Acta* 4:453, 1950.

286. STUMPF D, NEUWELT E, AUSTIN J, KOHLER P: Metachromatic leukodystrophy (MLD). X. Immunological studies of the abnormal sulfatase A. *Arch Neurol* 25:427, 1971.

287. SHAPIRA E, NADLER HL: The nature of the residual arylsulfatase activity in metachromatic leukodystrophy. *J Pediatr* 86:881, 1975.

288. LUIJTEN JAFM, van der HEIJDEN R, RIJKSEN G, WILLEMSE J, STAAL GEJ: Characterization of arylsulfatase A of three cases of metachromatic leukodystrophy: One of the late infantile, one of the juvenile and one of the adult variant. *J Mol Med* 3:227, 1978.

289. von FIGURA K, STECKEL F, CONARY J, HASILIK A, SHAW E: Heterogeneity in late-onset metachromatic leukodystrophy. Effect of inhibitors of cysteine proteinases. *Am J Hum Genet* 39:371, 1986.

290. PORTER MT, FLUHARTY A, TRAMMELL J, KIHARA H: A correlation of intracellular cerebroside sulfatase activity in fibroblasts with latency in metachromatic leukodystrophy. *Biochem Biophys Res Commun* 44:660, 1971.

291. PERCY AK, FARRELL DF, KABACK MM: Cerebroside sulphate (sulphatide) sulphohydrolase: An improved assay method. *J Neurochem* 19:233, 1972.

292. PORTER MT, FLUHARTY AL, HARRIS SE, KIHARA H: The accumulation of cerebroside sulfates by fibroblasts in culture from patients with late infantile metachromatic leukodystrophy. *Arch Biochem Biophys* 138:646, 1970.

293. KIHARA H, TSAY KK, FLUHARTY AL: Effect of Hepes on the fibroblast cerebroside sulfate loading test. *Biochem Med* 29:278, 1983.

294. HREIDARSSON SJ, THOMAS GH, KIHARA H, FLUHARTY AL, KOLODNY EH, MOSER HW, REYNOLDS LW: Impaired cerebroside sulfate hydrolysis in fibroblasts of sibs with "pseudo" arylsulfatase A deficiency without metachromatic leukodystrophy. *Pediatr Res* 17:701, 1983.

295. ETO Y, RAMPINI A, WIESMANN U, HERSCHKOWITZ NN: Enzymic studies of sulphatases in tissues of the normal human and in metachromatic leukodystrophy with multiple sulphatase deficiencies: Arylsulfatases A, B, and C. Cerebroside sulphatase, psychosine sulphatase and steroid sulphatases. *J Neurochem* 23:1161, 1974.

296. ETO Y, TOKORO T, LIEBAERS I, VAMOS E: Biochemical characterization of neonatal multiple sulfatase deficient (MSD) disorder cultured skin fibroblasts. *Biochem Biophys Res Commun* 106:429, 1982.

297. CHANG PL, ROSA NE, BALLANTYNE ST, DAVIDSON RG: Biochemical variability of arylsulphatases -A, -B, and -C in cultured fibroblasts from patients with multiple sulphatase deficiency. *J Inherited Metab Dis* 6:167, 1983.

298. FLUHARTY AL, STEVENS RL, de la FLOR SD, SHAPIRO LJ, KIHARA H: Arylsulfatase A modulation with pH in multiple sulfatase deficiency disorder fibroblasts. *Am J Hum Genet* 31:574, 1979.

299. KRESSE H, HOLTFRERICH D: Thiosulfate-mediated increase of arylsulfatase activities in multiple sulfatase deficiency disorder fibroblasts. *Biochem Biophys Res Commun* 97:41, 1980.

300. HARZER K, STINSHOFF K, MRAZ W, JATZKEWITZ H: The patterns of arylsulfatases A and B in human normal and metachromatic leucodystrophy tissues and their relationship to the cerebroside sulphatase activity. *J Neurochem* 20:279, 1973.

301. FLUHARTY AL, STEVENS RL, DAVIS LL, SHAPIRO LJ, KIHARA H: Presence of arylsulfatase A (ARS A) in multiple sulfatase deficiency disorder fibroblasts. *Am J Hum Genet* 30:249, 1978.

302. STECKEL F, HASILIK A, von FIGURA K: Multiple sulfatase deficiency: degradation of arylsulfatase A and B after endocytosis in fibroblasts. *Eur J Biochem* 151:147, 1985.

303. BACH G, FRIEDMAN A, WEISSMANN B, NEUFELD EF: The defect in the Hurler and Scheie syndromes; deficiency of α-L-iduronidase. *Proc Natl Acad Sci USA* 69:2048, 1972.

304. ELIAHU R, SEKELES E, COHEN R, BACH G: The correction of Hunter fibroblasts by exogenous iduronate sulfate sulfatase: Biochemical and ultrastructural studies. *Am J Hum Genet* 33:576, 1981.

305. KIHARA H, PORTER MT, FLUHARTY AL: Enzyme replacement in cultured fibroblasts from metachromatic leukodystrophy. In Desnick RJ, Bernlohrs RW, Krivit W (eds): *Enzyme Therapy in Genetic Diseases.* Baltimore, Williams & Wilkins, 1973, p 19.

306. KIHARA H, MEEK WE, FLUHARTY AL: Attenuated activities and structural alterations of arylsulfatase A in tissues from subjects with pseudo arylsulfatase A deficiency. *Hum Genet* 74:59, 1986.

307. AMEEN M, CHANG PL: Pseudo arylsulfatase A deficiency. Biosynthesis of an abnormal arylsulfatase A. *FEBS Lett* 219:130, 1987.

308. CHANG PL: Personal communication.

309. AUSTIN J: Recent studies in metachromatic and globoid forms of diffuse sclerosis, in Folch-Pi J, Bauer H (eds): *Brain Lipids and Lipoproteins and the Leukodystrophies.* Amsterdam, Elsevier, 1963, p 120.

310. MEIER C, BISCHOFF A: Sequence of morphological alterations in the nervous system of metachromatic leukodystrophy: Light- and electronmicroscopic observations in the central and peripheral nervous system in a prenatally diagnosed foetus of 22-weeks. *Acta Neuropathol (Berl)* 36:369, 1976.

311. ARGYRAKIS A, PILZ H, GOEBEL HH, MULLER D: Ultrastructural findings of peripheral nerve in a preclinical case of adult metachromatic leukodystrophy. *J Neuropathol Exp Neurol* 36:693, 1977.

312. AUREBECK G, OSTERBERG K, BLAW M, CHOU S, NELSON E: Electron microscopic observations on metachromatic leukodystrophy. *Arch Neurol* 11:273, 1964.

313. GREGOIRE A, PERIER O, DUSTIN P: Metachromatic leukodystrophy, an electron microscopic study. *J Neuropathol Exp Neurol* 25:617, 1966.

314. MORELL P, WIESMANN V: A correlative synopsis of the leukodystrophies. *Neuropediatrics* 15:62, 1984.

315. AUSTIN J: Metachromatic leukodystrophy (sulfatide lipidosis), in Hers HG, Van Hoof F (eds): *Lysosomes and Lysosomal Storage Diseases.* New York, Academic, 1973, p 411.

316. DAVISON AN, GREGSON NA: Metabolism of cellular membrane sulpholipids in the rat brain. *Biochem J* 98:915, 1966.

317. O'BRIEN JS, SAMPSON EL: Myelin membrane: A molecular abnormality. *Science* 150:1613, 1965.

318. LEES MB, SAPIRSTEIN VS, REISS DS, KOLODNY EH: Carbonic anhydrase and 2′3′ cyclic nucleotide 3′-phosphohydrolase activity in normal human brain and in demyelinating diseases. *Neurology* 30:719, 1980.

319. SUZUKI K: Biochemical pathogenesis of genetic leukodystrophics: Comparison of metachromatic leukodystrophy and globoid cell leukodystrophy (Krabbe's disease). *Neuropediatrics* 15:32, 1984.

320. NORTON WT: Some thoughts on the neurobiology of the leukodystrophies. *Neuropediatrics* 15:28, 1984.

321. HOROWITZ AL: Genetic complementation studies of multiple sulfatase deficiency. *Proc Natl Acad Sci USA* 76:6496, 1979.

322. CHANG PL, DAVIDSON RG: Complementation of arylsulfatase A in somatic hybrids of metachromatic leukodystrophy and multiple sulfatase deficiency disorder fibroblasts. *Proc Natl Acad Sci USA* 10:6166, 1980.

323. HOROWITZ AL: Genetic complementation studies of multiple sulfatase deficiency. *Proc Natl Acad Sci USA* 76:6496, 1979.

324. FEDDA K, HOROWITZ AL: Complementation of multiple sulfatase deficiency in somatic cell hybrids. *Am J Hum Genet* 36:623, 1984.

325. KIHARA H, TSAY KK, FLUHARTY AL: Genetic complementation in somatic cell hybrids of cerebroside sulfatase activator deficiency and metachromatic leukodystrophy fibroblasts. *Hum Genet* 66:300, 1984.

326. KABACK MM, PERCY AK, KASSELBERG AG: In vitro studies in sulfatide lipidosis, in Volk BW, Aronson SM (eds): *Sphingolipids, Sphingolipidoses and Allied Disorders (Adv Exp Med Biol, vol 19).* New York, Plenum, 1972, p 451.

327. CHANG PL, ROSA NE, DAVIDSON RG: Somatic cell hybridization studies on the genetic regulation and allelic mutations in metachromatic leukodystrophy. *Hum Genet* 61:231, 1982.

328. GUIBAUD P, GARCIA I, GUYONNET CL: La Detection de l'heterozyotisme pour la sulfatidase. *Lyon Med* 229:1215, 1973.

329. FARRELL DF: Heterozygote detection in MLD. Allelic mutations at the ARA locus. *Hum Genet* 59:129, 1981.

330. ZLOTOGORA J, BACH G, VARAK V, ELIAN E: Metachromatic leukodystrophy in the Habbanite Jews: High frequency in a genetic isolate and screening for heterozygotes. *Am J Hum Genet* 32:663, 1980.

331. SCHAAP T, ZLOTOGORA J, ELIAN E, BARAK Y, BACH G: The genetics of the aryl sulfatase A locus. *Am J Hum Genet* 33:531, 1981.

332. BRUNS GAP, MINTZ BJ, LEARY AC, REGINZ VM, GERALD PS: Expression of human arylsulfatase-A in man-hamster somatic cell hybrids. *Cytogenet Cell Genet* 22:182, 1978.

333. DELUCA C, BROWN JA, SHOWS TB: Lysosomal arylsulfatase deficiencies in humans: Chromosome assignments of arylsulfatase A and B. *Proc Natl Acad Sci USA* 76:1957, 1979.

334. HORS-CAYLA MC, HEUERTZ S, van CONG N, WEIL D, FREZAL J: Confirmation of the assignment of the gene for arylsulfatase A to chromosome 22 using somatic cell hybrids. *Hum Genet* 49:33, 1979.

335. GUSTAVSON K-H, ARANCIBIA W, ERIKSSON U, SVENNERHOLM L: Deleted ring chromosome 22 in a mentally retarded boy. *Clin Genet* 29:337, 1986.

336. von FIGURA K: Personal communication.

337. INUI K, KAO F-T, FUJIBAYASHI S, JONES C, MORSE HG, LAW ML, WENGER DA: The gene coding for a sphingolipid activator protein, SAP-1, is on human chromosome 10. *Hum Genet* 69:197, 1985.

338. DEWJI N, WENGER D, FUJIBAYASHI S, DONOVIEL M, ESCH F, HILL F, O'BRIEN JS: Molecular cloning of the sphingolipid activator protein-1 (SAP-1), the sulfatide sulfatase activator. *Biochem Biophys Res Commun* 134:989, 1986.

339. DEWJI NN, WENGER DA, O'BRIEN JS: Nucleotide sequence of cloned cDNA for human sphingolipid activator protein 1 precursor. *Proc Natl Acad Sci USA* 84:8652, 1987.

340. READ CR: Screening for metachromatic leukodystrophy. *J Clin Pathol* 20:301, 1967.
341. LEE-VAUPEL M, CONZELMANN E: A simple chromogenic assay for arylsulfatase A. *Clin Chim Acta* 164:171, 1987.
342. CHRISTOMANOU H, SANDHOFF K: A sensitive fluorescence assay for the simultaneous and separate determination of arylsulphatases A and B. *Clin Chim Acta* 79:527, 1977.
343. KOLODNY EH, MUMFORD RA: Arylsulfatases A and B in metachromatic leukodystrophy and Maroteaux-Lamy syndrome: Studies with 4-methylumbelliferyl sulfate, in Volk BW, Schneck L (eds): *Current Trends in Sphingolipidosis and Allied Disorders (Adv Exp Med Biol, vol 68)*. New York, Plenum, 1976, p 239.
344. HUMBEL R: Rapid method for measuring arylsulfatase A and B in leucocytes as a diagnosis for sulfatidosis, mucosulfatidosis and mucopolysaccharidosis VI. *Clin Chim Acta* 68:339, 1976.
345. RATTAZZI MC, MARKS JS, DAVIDSON RG: Electrophoresis of arylsulfatase from normal individuals and patients with metachromatic leukodystrophy. *Am J Hum Genet* 25:310, 1973.
346. DUBOIS G, BAUMANN N: Arylsulfatase A and B of human leukocytes: Specific inhibitors and electrophoretic characterization. *Biochem Biophys Res Commun* 50:1129, 1973.
347. CHANG PL, ROSA NE, VAREY PA, KIHARA H, KOLODNY EH, DAVIDSON RG: Diagnosis of pseudo-arylsulfatase A deficiency with electrophoretic techniques. *Pediatr Res* 18:1042, 1984.
348. FLUHARTY AL, DAVIS ML, KIHARA H: Simplified procedure for preparation of ^{35}S-labeled brain sulfatide. *Lipids* 9:865, 1974.
349. AUSTIN JH: Metachromatic form of diffuse cerebral sclerosis. 2. Diagnosis during life by isolation of metachromatic lipids from urine. *Neurology* 7:716, 1957.
350. KIHARA H, FLUHARTY AL, TSAY KK, BACHMAN RP, STEPHENS JD, WON NG: Prenatal diagnosis of pseudo arylsulfatase A deficiency. *Prenat Diagn* 3:29, 1983.
351. RATTAZZI MC, DAVIDSON RG: Prenatal diagnosis of metachromatic leukodystrophy by electrophoretic and immunologic techniques. *Pediatr Res* 11:1030, 1977.
352. BORRENSEN A-L, van DERHAGEN CB: Metachromatic leukodystrophy. II. Direct determination of arylsulphatase A activity in amniotic fluid. *Clin Genet* 4:442, 1973.
353. SANGUINETTI N, MARSH J, JACKSON M, FENSOM ATT, WARREN RC, RODECK CH: The arylsulphatases of chorionic villi: Potential problems in the first-trimester diagnosis of metachromatic leucodystrophy and Maroteaux-Lamy disease. *Clin Genet* 30:302, 1986.
354. GILES L, COOPER A, FOWLER B, SARDHARWALLA IB, DONNAI P: Aryl sulphatase isoenzymes of chorionic villi: Implications for prenatal diagnosis. *Prenat Diagn* 7:244, 1987.
355. POENARU L, KAPLAN L, DUMEZ J, DREYFUS JC: Evaluation of possible first trimester prenatal diagnosis in lysosomal diseases by trophoblast biopsy. *Pediatr Res* 18:1032, 1984.
356. STEINMANN B, MIETH D, GITZELMANN R: A newly recognized cause of low urinary estriol in pregnancy: Multiple sulfatase deficiency of the fetus. *Gynecol Obstet Invest* 12:107, 1981.
357. MELCHIOR JC, CLAUSEN J: Metachromatic leukodystrophy in early childhood: Treatment with a diet deficient in vitamin A. *Acta Pediatr Scand* 57:2, 1968.
358. MOOSA A, DUBOWITZ B: Late infantile metachromatic leukodystrophy: Effect of low vitamin A diet. *Arch Dis Child* 46:381, 1972.
359. WARNER JO: Juvenile onset metachromatic leucodystrophy: Failure of response on a low vitamin A diet. *Arch Dis Child* 50:735, 1975.
360. MOSER HW, MOSER AB, MCKHANN GM: The dynamics of a lipidosis: Turnover of sulfatide, steroid sulfate, and polysaccharide sulfate in metachromatic leukodystrophy. *Arch Neurol* 17:494, 1967.
361. WAHEED A, HASILIK A, von FIGURA K: Enhanced breakdown of arylsulfatase A in multiple sulfatase deficiency. *Eur J Biochem* 123:317, 1982.
362. WIESMANN UN, ROSSI EE, HERSCHKOWITZ NN: Treatment of metachromatic leukodystrophy in fibroblasts by enzyme replacement. *N Engl J Med* 284:672, 1971.
363. AUSTIN JH: Studies in metachromatic leukodystrophy. XI. Therapeutic considerations, in Bergsma D, Desnick RJ, Bernlohr PW, Krivit W (eds): *Enzyme Therapy in Genetic Diseases (Birth Defects, vol IX, no 2)*. Baltimore, Williams & Wilkins, for the National Foundation—March of Dimes, 1973.
364. GREENE HL, HUG G, SCHUBERT WK: Metachromatic leukodystrophy: Treatment with arylsulfatase A. *Arch Neurol* 20:147, 1969.
365. YEAGER AM, SINGER HS, BUCK JR, MATALOW R, BRENNAN S, O'TOOLE SO, MOSER HW: A therapeutic trial of amniotic epithelial cell implantation in patients with lysosomal storage diseases. *Am J Med Genet* 22:347, 1985.
366. JOSS V, ROGERS TR, HUGH-JONES K, BEILBY B, JOSHI R, WILLIAMSON S, FOROOZANFAR N, RICHES P, TURNER M, BENSON PD, HOBBS JR: A bone marrow transplant for metachromatic leukodystrophy. *Exp Hematol* 10(suppl 10):52, 1982.
367. ABROMS K: Personal communication.
368. BAYEVER E, LADISCH S, PHILIPPART M, BRILL N, NUWER M, SPARKES RS, FEIG SA: Bone-marrow transplantation for metachromatic leucodystrophy. *Lancet* 2:471, 1985.
369. LADISCH S, BAYEVER E, PHILIPPART M, FEIG SA: Biochemical findings after bone marrow transplation for metachromatic leukodystrophy: A preliminary report, in Krivit W, Paul NW (eds): *Bone Marrow Transplantation for Treatment of Lysosomal Storage Diseases*, March of Dimes original Article Series 22:69, 1986.
370. KRIVIT W, LIPTON ME, LOCKMAN LA, TSAI M, DYCK PJ, SMITH S, RAMSAY NKC, KERSEY J: Prevention of deterioration in metachromatic leukodystrophy by bone marrow transplantation. *Am J Med Sci* 294:80, 1987.
371. LIPTON M, LOCKMAN LA, RAMSAY NKC, KERSEY JH, JACOBSON RI, KRIVIT W: Bone marrow transplantation in metachromatic leukodystrophy, in Krivit W, Taul NW (eds): *Bone Marrow Transplantation for Treatment of Lysosomal Storage Diseases*, March of Dimes Original Article Series 22:57, 1986.
372. SVENNERHOLM L: Personal communication.
373. KRIVIT W, WHITLEY CB, LUND G, RAMSAY NKC, KERSEY TH: Improvement of clinical expression of central nervous system manifestations in lysosomal storage diseases treated by bone marrow transplantation: Experimental hematology today—1987, in Baum SJ, Santos GW, Takaku F (eds): *Recent Advances and Future Directions on Bone Marrow Transplantation*. New York, Springer-Verlag, 1988, p 189.
374. SVENNERHOLM L: Some aspects of the biochemical changes in leucodystrophy, in Folch-Pi J, Bauer H (ed): *Brain Lipids and Lipoproteins, and the Leucodystrophies*. New York, 1963, p 104.
375. RATTAZZI MC, CARMODY PJ, DAVIDSON RG: Studies on human lysosomal β-D-N-acetyl hexosaminidase and arylsulfatase isoenzymes, in Markert CL (ed): *Isozymes*, II. *Physiological Function*. New York, Academic, 1974, p 439.
376. KIHARA H, PORTER MT, FLUHARTY A: Enzyme replacement in cultured fibroblasts from metachromatic leukodystrophy, in Bergsma D, Desnick RJ, Bernlohr RW, Krivit W (eds): *Enzyme Therapy in Genetic Diseases (Birth Defects, vol IX, no 2)*. Baltimore, Williams & Wilkins, for the National Foundation—March of Dimes, 1973.
377. HOROWITZ AL, WARSHAWSKY L, KING J, BURNS G: Rapid degradation of steroid sulfatase in multiple sulfatase deficiency. *Biochem Biophys Res Commun* 135:389, 1986.
378. LAIDLER PM, SILBERRING J, van ETTEN RL: A modified radioimmunoassay for arylsulfatase A in human serum and urine. *Clin Chim Acta* 158:23, 1986.
379. FAROOQUI AA, MANDEL P: Recent developments in the biochemistry of globoid and metachromatic leucodystrophies. *Biomedicine* 26:232, 1977.

CHAPTER 70

FABRY DISEASE: α-Galactosidase Deficiency; SCHINDLER DISEASE: α-N-Acetylgalactosaminidase Deficiency

ROBERT J. DESNICK
DAVID F. BISHOP

1. *Fabry disease is an inborn error of glycosphingolipid catabolism resulting from the defective activity of the lysosomal hydrolase α-galactosidase in tissues and fluids of affected hemizygous males. Most heterozygous female carriers of the gene have an intermediate level of enzymatic activity.*

2. *The enzymatic defect leads to the systemic deposition of glycosphingolipids with terminal α-galactosyl moieties, predominantly globotriaosylceramide and, to a lesser extent, galabiosylceramide and blood group B substances. Hemizygous males have extensive deposition of these glycosphingolipid substrates in body fluids and in the lysosomes of the endothelial, perithelial, and smooth-muscle cells of blood vessels. Deposition also occurs in ganglion cells, and in many cell types in the heart, kidneys, eyes, and most other tissues.*

3. *Typical clinical manifestations include the onset of pain and paresthesias in the extremities, vessel ectasia (angiokeratoma) in skin and mucous membranes, and hypohidrosis during childhood or adolescence. Corneal and lenticular opacities are early findings. With increasing age, proteinuria, hyposthenuria, and lymphedema appear. Severe renal impairment leads to hypertension and uremia. Death usually occurs from renal failure or from cardiac or cerebrovascular disease.*

4. *Heterozygous females may have an attenuated form of the disease. They can be asymptomatic, or, rarely, as severely affected as hemizygous males. The most frequent clinical finding in females is the characteristic whorllike corneal epithelial dystrophy observed by slit-lamp microscopy.*

5. *Confirmation of the clinical diagnosis in hemizygotes and heterozygotes requires the demonstration of deficient α-galactosidase activity in plasma, leukocytes, or tears or increased levels of globotriaosylceramide in plasma or urinary sediment. Heterozygous females may have intermediate levels of enzymatic activity and accumulated substrate. More accurate diagnosis of heterozygous females can be accomplished by demonstration of a molecular lesion in the α-galactosidase gene or by restriction fragment length polymorphism (RFLP) analysis.*

6. *The disorder is transmitted by the X-linked gene encoding α-galactosidase which has been localized by somatic cell and in situ hybridization as well as by RFLP studies to the region on the long arm of the X chromosome, Xq21.33→q22. The human α-galactosidase cDNA and genomic sequences have been isolated, characterized, and used to analyze the mutations causing α-galactosidase deficiency. Partial deletions, duplications, splice-junction defects, and point mutations have been identified, emphasizing the heterogeneity of the molecular lesions causing this disease.*

7. *Prenatal diagnosis can be accomplished by demonstration of deficient α-galactosidase activity and an XY karyotype or by molecular demonstration of the specific α-galactosidase mutation in chorionic villi or cultured amniotic cells.*

8. *Low maintenance dosages of diphenylhydantoin or carbamazepine may provide relief of the excruciating pain and constant discomfort. Renal dialysis and transplantation are effective in the treatment of end-stage renal disease. Exploratory trials of direct enzyme replacement indicate the potential value of this therapeutic approach.*

9. *Schindler disease is a newly recognized autosomal recessive disorder due to the deficient activity of α-N-acetylgalactosaminidase, a lysosomal hydrolase previously known as α-galactosidase B. The nature of the accumulated glycopeptide and/or glycosphingolipid substrates has not been determined.*

10. *The disease was identified in two affected brothers and was characterized by normal development for the first 9 to 15 months of life, followed by a rapid neurodegenerative course resulting in severe psychomotor retardation, cortical blindness, and frequent myoclonic seizures by 2 to 3 years of age. The affected brothers had no visceral manifestations of a storage disease. The total absence of α-N-acetylgalactosaminidase activity and enzyme protein was demonstrated in the cultured lymphocytes from the affected sibs.*

11. *Diagnosis of affected homozygotes and heterozygous carriers can be made by determination of α-N-acetylgalactosaminidase activity in various sources. Affected individuals have an abnormal urinary oligosaccharide profile. Prenatal diagnosis should be feasible by demonstration of the enzymatic defect in chorionic villi or cultured amniocytes.*

12. *The cDNA encoding α-N-acetylgalactosaminidase has been isolated and has 47 and 56 percent amino acid and nucleotide homology with the coding region for human α-galactosidase, respectively. The availability of the cDNA should facilitate isolation of the chromosomal gene previously localized to 22q11 as well as characterization of the molecular defect(s) in unrelated individuals with Schindler disease.*

α-GALACTOSIDASE DEFICIENCY: FABRY DISEASE

Fabry disease, an inborn error of glycosphingolipid metabolism, results from the defective activity of the lysosomal enzyme α-galactosidase. The enzymatic defect, transmitted by

Fig. 70-1 Globotriaosylceramide (galactosyl-galactosylglucosylceramide).

an X-linked recessive gene, leads to the progressive deposition of neutral glycosphingolipids with terminal α-galactosyl moieties in most visceral tissues and body fluids. The predominant glycosphingolipid accumulated is globotriaosylceramide, or galactosyl-(α1→4)-galactosyl-(β1→4)-glucosyl-(β1→1')ceramide (Fig. 70-1). The birefringent deposits are primarily found in the lysosomes of the vascular endothelium. Progressive endothelial glycosphingolipid accumulation results in ischemia and infarction and leads to the major clinical manifestations of the disease. The glycosphingolipids also accumulate in perithelial and smooth-muscle cells of the cardiovascular-renal system, and, to a lesser extent, in reticuloendothelial, myocardial, and connective tissue cells, in epithelial cells of the cornea, kidney, and other tissues, and in ganglion and perineural cells of the autonomic nervous system. Clinically, hemizygous males have a characteristic skin lesion, which led to the descriptive name of *angiokeratoma corporis diffusum universale*. They also have acroparesthesias, episodic crises of excruciating pain, corneal and lenticular opacities, hypohidrosis, and cardiac and renal dysfunction. Death usually occurs in adult life from renal, cardiac, and/or cerebral complications of their vascular disease. Heterozygous females are usually asymptomatic and are most likely to show the corneal opacities.

HISTORICAL ASPECTS

In 1898, two dermatologists, Anderson[1] in England and Fabry[2] in Germany, independently described the first patients with angiokeratoma corporis diffusum. Anderson designated his case as one of angiokeratoma. His original patient was a 39-year-old male who had proteinuria, finger deformities, varicose veins, and lymphedema. Because of the proteinuria, Anderson suspected that the disease was a generalized disorder and astutely suggested that abnormal vessels might be present in the kidneys as well as in the skin. He also correctly noted that "the vascular lesion was not a new formation, as implied by the suffix 'oma,' but an ectasia of cutaneous capillaries."[1] Fabry originally made the diagnosis of purpura nodularis in a 13-year-old male whom he followed over the next 30 years. He documented the presence of albuminuria, further described the cutaneous lesions, noting the presence of small vessel aneurysms,[3] and subsequently classified his case to be one of *angiokeratoma corporis diffusum*, a designation that has persisted, particularly among dermatologists.

Several individuals made early contributions to the clinical description of the disease. Steiner and Voerner[4] and Gunther[5] described a hemizygous male with anhidrosis and intermittent acroparesthesias that were aggravated by hot or cold weather. Examination of a skin biopsy showed atrophy of the sweat glands and aneurysmal dilatation of the capillaries. Weicksel[6] first described the characteristic corneal opacities and the vascular abnormalities in the conjunctiva and retina. In 1947, Pompen and coworkers[7] reported the first postmortem findings in two affected brothers who died from renal failure. The most significant observation was the presence of abnormal vac-

uoles in blood vessels throughout their bodies. From these findings, they suggested that the disease was a generalized storage disorder. Subsequently, Scriba definitively established the lipid nature of the storage material,[8] and Hornbostel and Scriba were the first to confirm the diagnosis histologically in a living patient by demonstrating the refractile lipid deposits in vessels of a skin biopsy specimen.[9] Although the familial occurrence of the disease was recognized earlier,[10] it was not until 1965 that Opitz et al.[11] documented the X-linked inheritance of the disorder by pedigree analysis.

In 1963, Sweeley and Klionsky[12] isolated and characterized two neutral glycosphingolipids—globotriaosylceramide (Gal-Gal-Glc-Cer) and galabiosylceramide (Gal-Gal-Cer)—from the kidney of a Fabry hemizygote obtained at autopsy. On the basis of these findings, they classified Fabry disease as a sphingolipidosis. Subsequent chemical analyses of various Fabry tissues and fluids[13-16] have demonstrated the marked accumulation of globotriaosylceramide, and to a lesser extent, galabiosylceramide.[12,14,16] In addition, the abnormal accumulation of blood group B substances, glycosphingolipids with terminal α-galactosyl moieties, has been reported in affected individuals with B or AB blood types.[17]

In 1967, Brady et al.[18] demonstrated that the enzymatic defect was in ceramide trihexosidase, a lysosomal galactosyl hydrolase required for the catabolism of globotriaosylceramide (Fig. 70-1). Kint,[19] using synthetic substrates, characterized the defective enzymatic activity as an α-galactosyl hydrolase. Shortly thereafter, it was recognized that there were two enzymes (designated α-galactosidases A and B) that hydrolyzed synthetic substrates with α-galactosyl moieties, α-galactosidase A being deficient in Fabry disease. It was shown subsequently that α-galactosidase B was an α-N-acetylgalactosaminidase,[20,21] the lysosomal hydrolase shown to be deficient in a recently described neurodegenerative lysosomal disease, Schindler disease.[22] Thus, there appears to be only one lysosomal α-galactosidase, the enzyme defective in Fabry disease.

The elucidation of the specific enzymatic defect in Fabry disease permitted the enzymatic diagnosis of affected hemizygous males, presumptive identification of heterozygous carrier females,[23,24] and the prenatal diagnosis of hemizygous fetuses.[25,26] In addition, pilot trials of α-galactosidase replacement have been reported.[27-29] The recent isolation of the full-length cDNA[30-32] and the entire genomic sequence[32] for human α-galactosidase has permitted the characterization of disease mutations, improved the accuracy of carrier identification, and stimulated efforts to treat the disease using recombinant DNA techniques.

Various designations have been used to identify this disorder. In keeping with the terminology applied to other lipidoses and for the benefit of information retrieval, it would seem advisable to refer to the disease by its specific enzymatic defect and to retain the commonly used eponym. Thus, an appropriate designation is *α-galactosidase deficiency: Fabry disease*. Comprehensive reviews on the clinical, pathologic, biochemical, and genetic aspects of the disease are available.[33-37]

CLINICAL MANIFESTATIONS

The Classic Hemizygote

The clinical manifestations of Fabry disease result predominantly from the progressive deposition of globotriaosylceram-

Table 70-1 Major Clinical Manifestations in Hemizygotes with Fabry Disease

Vascular glycolipid deposition	Manifestation
Skin	Angiokeratoma
Peripheral nerves (autonomic system)	Excruciating pain, acroparesthesias, hypohidrosis
Heart	Ischemia and infarctions
Brain	Transient ischemic attacks, strokes
Kidney	Renal failure

NOTE: Average age at death, 41 years.[73]

ide in the vascular endothelium (Table 70-1). Clinical onset usually occurs during childhood or adolescence, but may be delayed until the second or third decade. Early manifestations include periodic crises of severe pain in the extremities (acroparesthesias), the appearance of vascular cutaneous lesions (angiokeratoma), hypohidrosis, and characteristic corneal and lenticular opacities.

The frequency of Fabry disease has not been determined; the disease is rare, and it is estimated that the incidence is about 1 in 40,000. Of the over 400 described cases of hemizygous males, most are Caucasian; however, Black, Latin, American Indian, Egyptian, and Oriental cases have been observed.[33]

Pain. The single most debilitating symptom of Fabry disease is the pain. Two types have been described: episodic crises and constant discomfort.[10,38] The painful crises most often begin in childhood or early adolescence and signal clinical onset of the disease. Lasting from minutes to several days, these "Fabry crises" consist of agonizing, burning pain initially in the palms and soles. Often the pain will radiate to the proximal extremities and other parts of the body. Attacks of abdominal or flank pain may simulate appendicitis or renal colic.[39] The painful crises are usually triggered by exercise, fatigue, emotional stress, or rapid changes in temperature and humidity. With increasing age, the periodic crises usually decrease in frequency and severity; however, in some patients, they may occur more frequently, and the pain can be so excruciating that the patient may contemplate suicide.[40,41] Because the pain usually is associated with a low-grade fever and an elevated erythrocyte sedimentation rate, these symptoms frequently have led to the misdiagnosis of rheumatic fever, neurosis, or erythromelalgia.[38,41–43]

In addition to these intermittent crises, most patients complain of a nagging, constant discomfort in their hands and feet characterized by burning, tingling paresthesias.[38] These acroparesthesias may occur daily, usually during late afternoon, and may represent an attenuated form of the excruciating episodic crises. Although pain is a hallmark of the disease, it should be noted that about 10 to 20 percent of older patients deny any history of Fabry crises or acroparesthesias.

Skin Lesion. Angiectases may be one of the earliest manifestations and may lead to diagnosis in childhood. There is a progressive increase in the number and size of these cutaneous vascular lesions with age. Classically, the angiokeratomas develop slowly as clusters of individual punctate, dark-red to blue-black angiectases in the superficial layers of the skin (Fig. 70-2). The lesions may be flat or slightly raised and do not blanch with pressure. There is a slight hyperkeratosis notable in larger lesions. The clusters of lesions are most dense between the umbilicus and the knees and have a tendency toward bilateral symmetry. The hips, back, thighs, buttocks, penis, and scrotum are most commonly involved, but there is a wide variation in the pattern of distribution and density of the lesions. Involvement of the oral mucosa and conjunctiva is common, and other mucosal areas may also be involved. Variants without the characteristic skin lesions have been reported[44–47] (see "Atypical Hemizygotes"). Although the angiectases may not be readily apparent in some patients, careful examination of the skin, especially the scrotum and umbilicus, may reveal the presence of isolated lesions. In addition to these vascular lesions, anhidrosis, or more commonly hypohidrosis, is an early and almost constant finding.

Cardiac, Cerebral, and Renal Vascular Manifestations. With increasing age, the major morbid symptoms of the disease result from the progressive deposition of glycosphingolipid in the vascular system. Cardiac disease occurs in most hemizygous males. Early findings include left ventricular enlargement, valvular involvement, and conduction abnormalities.[48,49] Mitral insufficiency is the most frequent valvular lesion and is typically present in childhood or adolescence. Involvement of the myocardium and possibly the conduction system results in electrocardiographic abnormalities which may show left ventricular hypertrophy, ST segment changes, and T wave inversion. Other abnormalities including arrhythmias, intermittent supraventricular tachycardias, and a short PR interval have been reported.[50,51] Intracardiac pacing has shown rapid conduction through the AV node.[52] The PR interval decreased over a 10-year period in two hemizygotes, indicating an accelerated atrioventricular conduction with progressive lipid deposition in the bundle of His.[53] Several cases

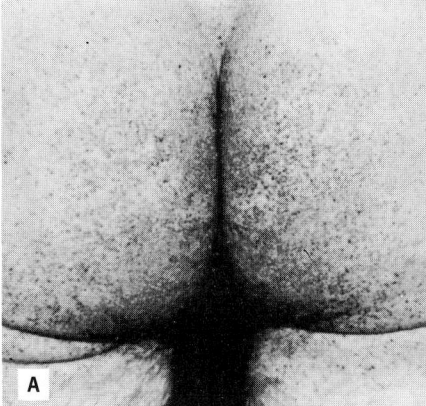

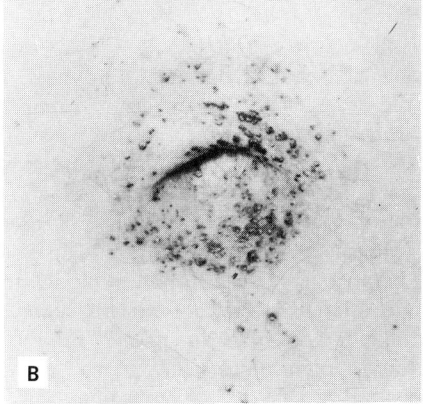

Fig. 70-2 Clusters of dark-red to blue angiokeratomas (telangiectases) on the buttocks (A) and in the umbilical area (B) of a hemizygote with Fabry disease.

with electrocardiographic changes indicating infarction had no evidence of myocardial necrosis at postmortem examination; the ECG changes were probably related to glycosphingolipid deposition in the myocardium.[49] Echocardiographic studies reveal an increased incidence of mitral valve prolapse and an increased thickness of the interventricular septum and the left ventricular posterior wall, particularly in adult hemizygous males.[54–56] The similarity of the two-dimensional and M-mode echocardiographic findings in cardiac amyloidosis patients and in a 53-year-old Fabry hemizygote has been noted.[57] In addition, hypertrophic obstructive cardiomyopathy secondary to glycosphingolipid infiltration in the interventricular septum has been reported.[58] Late manifestations may include angina pectoris, myocardial ischemia and infarction, congestive heart failure, and severe mitral regurgitation.[48,49] These findings may be accentuated by systemic hypertension related to vascular involvement of renal parenchymal vessels.

Cerebrovascular manifestations result primarily from multifocal small vessel involvement and may include thromboses, transient ischemic attacks, basilar artery ischemia and aneurysm, seizures, hemiplegia, hemianesthesia, aphasia, labyrinthine disorders, or frank cerebral hemorrhage.[10, 59–66] Personality changes and psychotic behavior may become manifest with increasing age.[66–68] A transient state of disorientation and confusion may occur in association with electrolyte imbalance secondary to renal disease. Severe neurologic signs may be present without evidence of major thrombosis or hypertension and are due presumably to multifocal small vessel occlusive disease.[69,70]

Progressive glycosphingolipid deposition in the kidney results in proteinuria and other signs of renal impairment, with gradual deterioration of renal function and development of azotemia in middle age. During childhood and adolescence, protein, casts, red cells, and desquamated kidney and urinary tract cells may appear in the urine. Birefringent lipid globules with characteristic "Maltese crosses" can be observed free in the urine and within desquamated urinary sediment cells by polarization microscopy. With age, progressive renal impairment is evidenced by significant proteinuria, isosthenuria (specific gravities of 1.008 to 1.012), and alterations of other renal tubular functions including tubular reabsorption, secretion, and excretion.[71] Polyuria and a syndrome similar to vasopressin-resistant diabetes insipidus occasionally develop. Gradual deterioration of renal function and the development of azotemia usually occur in the third to fifth decades of life, although renal failure has been reported in the second decade.[72] Death most often results from uremia unless chronic hemodialysis or renal transplantation is undertaken. The mean age at death of 94 hemizygous males who were not treated for uremia was 41 years,[73] but occasionally an affected male has survived into his sixties.

Ocular Features. Ocular involvement is most prominent in the cornea, lens, conjunctiva, and retina.[74–76] A characteristic corneal opacity, observed only by slip-lamp microscopy, is found in males with the disease and in most heterozygous females (Fig. 70-3). The earliest lesion is a diffuse haziness in the subepithelial layer. In more advanced cases, the opacities appear as whorled streaks extending from a central vertex to the periphery of the cornea. Typically, the whorllike opacities are inferior and cream-colored; however, they range from white to golden-brown and may be very faint.[76] An identical, familial corneal dystrophy, termed *cornea verticillata*, was described by Gruber in 1946;[77] subsequent investigation of these

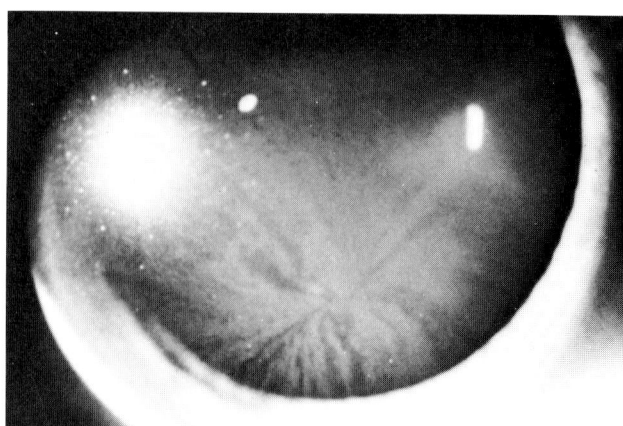

Fig. 70-3 Corneal opacity in a heterozygote observed by slit-lamp microscopy. The corneal involvement results from subepithelial glycosphingolipid deposition. *(From Sher et al.[74] Used by permission.)*

patients revealed that they were hemizygous and heterozygous for Fabry disease.[78] An indistinguishable, drug-induced phenocopy of the Fabry corneal dystrophy occurs in patients on long-term chloroquine or amiodarone therapy (see "Diagnosis").

Two specific types of lenticular changes have been described (Fig. 70-4). A granular anterior capsular or subcapsular de-

Fig. 70-4 Lenticular changes include the anterior capsular opacity shown with a "propellerlike" distribution (above) and the posterior opacity or "Fabry cataract," (below) which is best seen by retroillumination and may be unique to Fabry hemizygotes and heterozygotes. *(From Sher et al.[74] Used by permission.)*

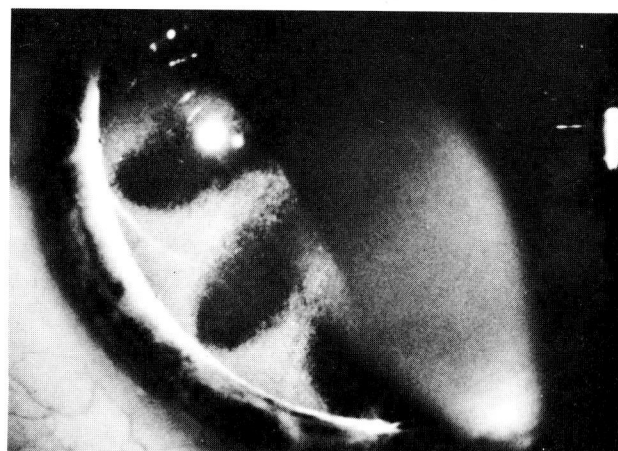

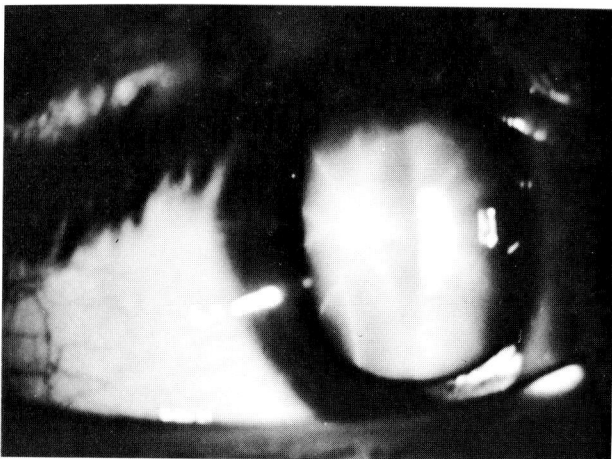

posit has been observed in about one-third of hemizygous males, but rarely in heterozygous females. Typically, these lenticular opacities are bilateral and inferior in position. They frequently appear in a "propellerlike" distribution, i.e., wedge-shaped with their bases near the lenticular equator and aligned radially with the apexes toward the center of the anterior capsule. A second, and possibly pathognomonic, lenticular opacity has been observed in both hemizygous and heterozygous individuals.[74,75] It may be the first ocular manifestation to appear. The opacity is posterior, linear, and appears as a whitish, almost translucent, spokelike deposit of fine granular material on or near the posterior lens capsule. These lines usually radiate from the central part of the posterior cortex. This unusual opacity has been termed the *Fabry cataract*[74] and is best seen by retroillumination.

Conjunctival and retinal vascular lesions are common and represent part of the diffuse systemic vascular involvement. These vascular lesions occur early in life in normotensive individuals and are characterized by mild to marked tortuosity of the conjunctival and retinal vessels. There is an aneurysmal dilatation of thin-walled venules as well as angulation and segmental, sausagelike dilatation of veins typically seen on the inferior bulbar conjunctiva. As the disease progresses, retinal changes associated with the development of hypertension and uremia may be superimposed. Vision is not impaired by the vascular lesions in the conjunctiva and retina or by the corneal dystrophy. However, acute visual loss has occurred in hemizygotes as a result of unilateral total central retinal artery occlusion.[74]

Other ocular findings have included lid edema in the absence of renal insufficiency, myelinated nerve fibers radiating from the optic disc, mild optic atrophy, papilledema, peripapillary edema, nystagmus, and internuclear ophthalmoplegia.[33,74–76]

Other Clinical Features. Because of the widespread visceral distribution of the glycosphingolipid deposits, signs and symptoms of this disorder arise in many other organs and systems. Minor changes in electroencephalogram (EEG) and electromyogram (EMG) as well as slowed and latent peripheral nerve conduction abnormalities may be observed.[79] Several patients have had chronic bronchitis, wheezing respiration,[10] or dyspnea with alveolar capillary block.[80] Pulmonary function studies in older hemizygotes may show significant airflow obstruction, reduced diffusing capacity, and a reduction in the V_{max25} values.[81] Roentgenographic studies may reveal hyperinflation and/or bullous disease. Smokers have greater airflow obstruction than expected from smoking alone.[81] In general, hemizygotes do not manifest significant clinical or functional primary pulmonary involvement.[82] Presumably the reported findings of pneumothorax, pleural effusions, and pulmonary edema were secondary to primary cardiac, vascular, and/or renal insufficiency. However, primary pulmonary involvement has been reported in the absence of cardiac or renal disease.[83]

Lymphedema of the legs may be present in adulthood without hypoproteinemia, varices, or any clinically manifest vascular disease.[84] This sign presumably reflects the progressive glycosphingolipid deposition in the lymphatic vessels and lymph nodes. Many patients have varicosities and hemorrhoids. Priapism also has been reported.[85,86]

Episodic diarrhea and, to a lesser extent, nausea, vomiting, and flank pain are the most common gastrointestinal complaints.[87] These symptoms may be related to the deposition of glycosphingolipid in intestinal small vessels and in the autonomic ganglia of the bowel.[88] Achalasia and jejunal diverticulosis, which may lead to perforation of the small bowel, have been described.[89,90] Although intestinal malabsorption has been reported, it is not a recognized feature of the disease. Radiologic studies may reveal thickened, edematous folds and mild dilatation of the small bowel, a granular-appearing ileum, and the loss of haustral markings throughout the colon, particularly in the distal segments.[87] The symptomatology and pathophysiology of the gastrointestinal involvement have been reviewed.[87,88,91]

Anemia is probably due to decreased erythrocyte survival.[92] A decreased serum iron concentration, normal erythrocyte fragility, and an elevated reticulocyte count have been reported.[33] Increased platelet aggregation and a high concentration of β-thromboglobulin have been described.[93] Lipid-laden, foamy-appearing macrophages are present in the bone marrow.[94] The spleen is not enlarged.

Many patients have evidence of musculoskeletal involvement. A characteristic permanent deformity arises from changes in the distal interphalangeal joint of the fingers, causing limited extension of the terminal joints.[10] The bony changes are characterized by multiple enthesopathic ossifications at the insertions of fibrous structures and by intra- and extra-articular erosions.[95] Avascular necrosis of the head of the femur or talus, multiple, small infarctlike opacities in the femoral heads, and involvement of the metacarpals, metatarsals, and temporomandibular joint have been described.[33]

Many hemizygous males appear to have retarded growth or delayed puberty and sparse, fine facial and body hair. In some kindreds, affected males have a characteristic acromegaliclike facies.[33] Affected individuals may complain of fatigue and weakness and may be incapacitated for prolonged periods of time.

Atypical Hemizygotes

Fabry hemizygotes have been described who were essentially asymptomatic at ages when classic hemizygotes would be severely affected by the disease.[46,96–99] Many of these variants were identified serendipitously during evaluation of other medical problems or of their family members. Biochemical studies revealed residual α-galactosidase activity compatible with their milder phenotype (see "Genetic Variants"). Bach et al. reported a totally asymptomatic 51-year-old male of Arab descent[97] who was identified after his daughter was found to have lupus nephritis and lesions characteristic of Fabry disease in a renal biopsy.[100] Two independent reports described males of Italian descent who were identified at ages 38 and 42 years during evaluations for hypercholesterolemia and rheumatoid arthritis,[96,99] respectively. The finding of proteinuria in each led to renal biopsies which revealed ultrastructural findings consistent with Fabry disease. Neither had acroparesthesias, angiokeratoma, hypohidrosis, or corneal opacities. The atypical hemizygote with poorly controlled hypercholesterolemia had normal renal function until his death at age 49 from a second myocardial infarction. The hemizygote with rheumatoid arthritis remains asymptomatic at 50 years of age with normal creatinine clearance and renal concentrating values. Kobayashi et al. described a 26-year-old Japanese male who experienced acroparesthesias but who did not have angiokeratoma, hypohidrosis, or the keratopathy.[98] Finally, a 54-year-old male of German descent with isolated myocardial involvement was identified following a diagnostic endocardial biopsy that revealed ultrastructural findings suggestive of Fabry disease.[101] He denied a history of acroparesthesias and did not have any other manifestations of Fabry disease. It is likely that additional mildly affected or asymptomatic variants will be identified in the future. Astute recognition of subtle clinical manifestations or the observation of abnormal ultrastructural findings usually will suggest the diagnosis of Fabry disease. Subsequent biochemical and molecular studies will definitively establish the diagnosis (see "Diagnosis").

The Heterozygote

The clinical course and prognosis of heterozygotes and hemizygotes differ significantly.[33] Heterozygotes experience little difficulty in adult life at ages when hemizygous males already have severe renal and/or cardiac involvement. Although most biochemically documented heterozygotes are asymptomatic throughout a normal life span, with increasing age some manifest minor symptoms of the disease (Table 70-2). Approximately 30 percent of heterozygotes have a few, isolated skin lesions, a smaller percentage have experienced the characteristic intermittent pain in the extremities, and about 70 percent have whorllike corneal dystrophy. Some heterozygotes will develop cardiac involvement with advanced age.[103] However, a few heterozygotes have been reported in whom the expression of the disease was comparable to that observed in severely affected hemizygous males.[48,104,105] In contrast, obligate heterozygotes (daughters of affected hemizygous males) without any clinical manifestations and with normal levels of leukocyte α-galactosidase and urinary sediment glycosphingolipids have been reported.[105,106] Such markedly variable expression is expected in females heterozygous for X-linked diseases due to random X inactivation.[107] At the cellular level, heterozygotes for most X-linked enzymatic defects have two populations of cells, one with mutant and the other with normal enzymatic activity due to the random inactivation of one X chromosome in each cell early in embryogenesis. Representatives of two such populations have been cloned from cultured skin fibroblasts from obligate heterozygotes, one with normal and the other with defective α-galactosidase activity.[108] Ultrastructural examination of renal tissue from heterozygotes also demonstrated two populations of glomerular, interstitial, and vascular cells: one normal, the other with observed glycosphingolipid deposition.[109]

Of more than 150 heterozygotes reported in the literature, corneal involvement is the most frequent and often the only manifestation.[74] Frequently, the corneal dystrophy is more prominent than in affected males in the same family. However, biochemically documented and/or obligate heterozygous females without corneal opacities have been described.[10,75,106]

The skin lesions are absent or much less prominent in carrier females than in affected males. Often they are not clinically manifest. The angiokeratoma may occur in the characteristic distribution. Isolated lesions may occasionally be observed on the breasts, lips, and trunk. The cutaneous involvement may be more prominent in heterozygotes who have blood group B substances. The lesions have been detected in heterozygotes during childhood. Skin biopsies of clinically uninvolved skin from obligate heterozygotes obtained in the first decade of life contain deposits of glycosphingolipid in the vascular endothelial and muscularis cells.

Other manifestations may include intermittent pain in the extremities, edema (particularly of the ankles), vascular lesions

Table 70-2 Clinical Manifestations in Heterozygotes for Fabry Disease

Manifestation	Estimated incidence,* %	Remarks
Corneal dystrophy	~70	Useful for heterozygote identification
Angiokeratoma	~30	Single or isolated lesions
Acroparesthesias	<10	Infrequent; hands, feet, and lower abdomen
Hypohidrosis	<1	Rare variants†
Cardiac involvement	<1	Rare variants†
CNS involvement	<1	Rare variants†
Renal failure	<1	Rare variants†

*Based on review of over 122 heterozygous females, 1–85 years old, evaluated by the authors.
†Rare female variants with 0–5% α-galactosidase activity.

in the conjunctiva and retina, and cardiovascular changes such as hypertension, electrocardiographic abnormalities, and left ventricular hypertrophy.[10,45,73] Basilar artery aneurysms have also been reported. Renal findings in heterozygotes include hyposthenuria; the occurrence of erythrocytes, leukocytes, and granular and hyaline casts in the urinary sediment; proteinuria; and other signs of renal impairment. Mucosal lesions, hypohidrosis, and diarrhea have been recorded less frequently. Heterozygotes may develop arthritis in the distal interphalangeal joints of the fingers.

PATHOLOGY

Morphologically, Fabry disease is characterized by widespread tissue deposits of crystalline glycosphingolipids which show birefringence with characteristic "Maltese crosses" under polarization microscopy. The glycosphingolipid is deposited in all areas of the body, occurring predominantly in the lysosomes of endothelial, perithelial, and smooth-muscle cells of blood vessels (Fig. 70-5) and, to a lesser degree, in histiocytic and reticular cells of connective tissue. Lipid deposits are also prominent in epithelial cells of the cornea and in glomeruli and tubules of the kidney, in muscle fibers of the heart, and

Fig. 70-5 Photomicrograph of a prostatic arteriole showing the hypertrophied, lipid-laden endothelial cells encroaching on the vascular lumen. H&E, × 600.

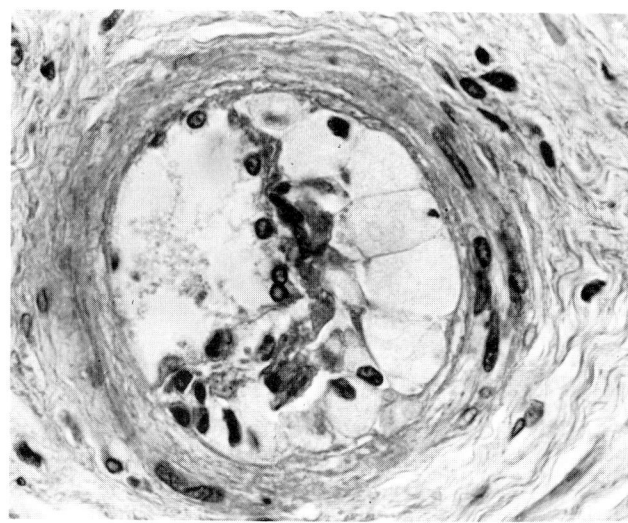

in ganglion cells of the autonomic system. Glycosphingolipid deposition does not occur in hepatocytes or in the liver sinus endothelium.[110]

Skin

The skin lesions are telangiectases or small superficial angiomas. After a silent period, cumulative vascular damage leads eventually to clinically apparent and progressive angiectases. This sequence is suggested by the biopsy finding of lipid deposits in areas of clinically normal skin[111,112] or in patients with no skin lesions,[113] and by recognition of patients who have visceral lesions but whose skin lesions were either of minimal consequence or delayed. The pathologic involvement was observed in the vascular endothelium and perithelium of clinically normal skin from a 1-year-old hemizygote.[112]

Capillaries, venules, and arterioles contain pathologic lipid storage in the endothelium, perithelium, and smooth muscle (Fig. 70-6). There is marked dilation of the capillaries of the dermal papillae. Deeper vessels show less dilatation and aneurysmal formation. Lipid stores have been noted in arrectores pilorum muscles, sweat gland epithelium, and perineural cells.[111–115] Similar findings have been observed in gingival tissues. Atrophic or scarce sweat and sebaceous glands have been reported.[80]

The fully developed classic lesions are usually located in the upper dermis, where they may produce elevation, flattening, or hypertrophy of the epithelium. The larger lesions may have a slight to moderate hyperkeratosis; hence the term *angioker-*

Fig. 70-6 Photomicrograph of the skin lesion reveals dilated vascular channels of varying size in the upper dermis. The vessels may contain thrombi, and the overlaying epithelium may be thinned, ulcerated, and/or keratotic. H&E, × 65.

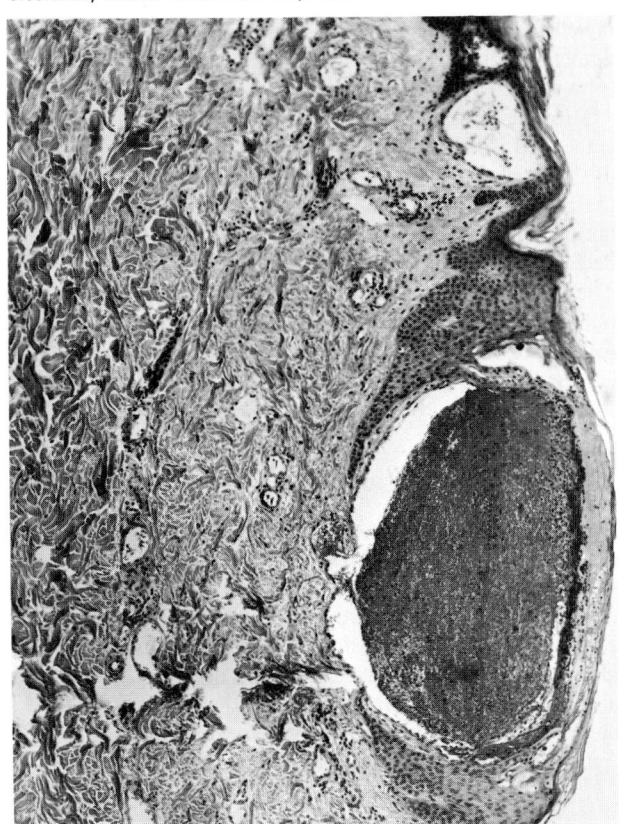

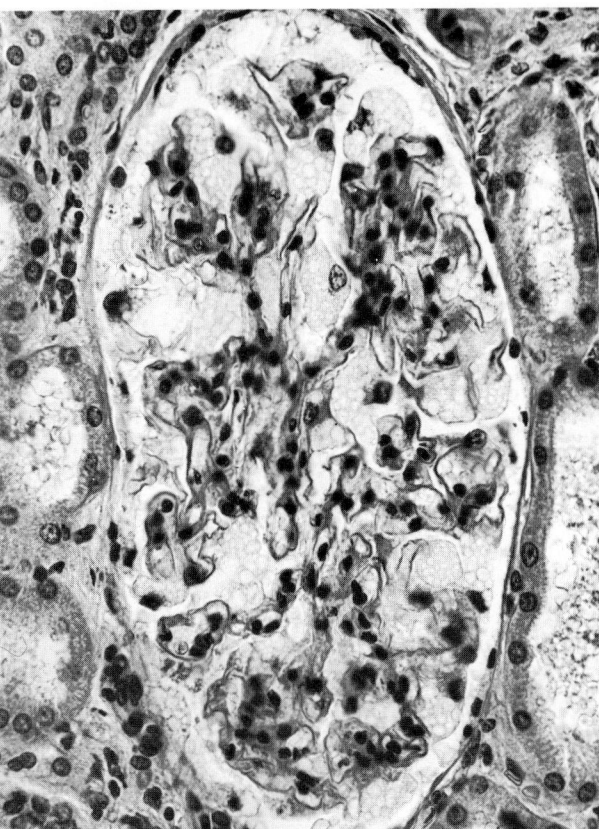

Fig. 70-7 Photomicrograph of a glomerulus from a 35-year-old hemizygote. The epithelial cells of the parietal and visceral layers of Bowman's capsule show multiple vacuoles from which the stored glycosphingolipids were extracted. Zenker's fixation, paraffin embedding; H&E, × 225.

atoma. As in all forms of angiokeratomas, the hypertrophy and hyperkeratosis may be secondary to pressure on the epithelium by the underlying dilated vessel.

Kidney

The earliest lesions are due to the accumulation of glycosphingolipid in endothelial and epithelial cells of the glomerulus and of Bowman's space (Fig 70-7) and in the epithelium of the loops of Henle and of distal tubules (Fig. 70-8). In later stages, and to a lesser degree, proximal tubules, interstitial histiocytes, and fibrocytes may show lipid accumulation. Lipid-laden distal tubular epithelial cells desquamate and may be detected in the urinary sediment.[14] These cells have been shown to account for about 75 percent of the urinary cells shed by an affected hemizygote.[116]

Concurrently, renal blood vessels are involved progressively and often extensively. An early finding is arterial fibrinoid deposits, which may result from the necrosis of severely involved muscular cells.[7,109] Other histologic changes in the kidney are the sequelae of nonspecific, end-stage renal disease with evidence of severe arteriolar sclerosis, glomerular atrophy and fibrosis, pseudotubular proliferation of residual glomerular epithelium, tubular atrophy, and diffuse interstitial fibrosis. Renal size increases during the third decade of life, followed by a decrease in the fourth and fifth decades. The renal involvement has been the subject of comprehensive reviews.[71,114,117,118]

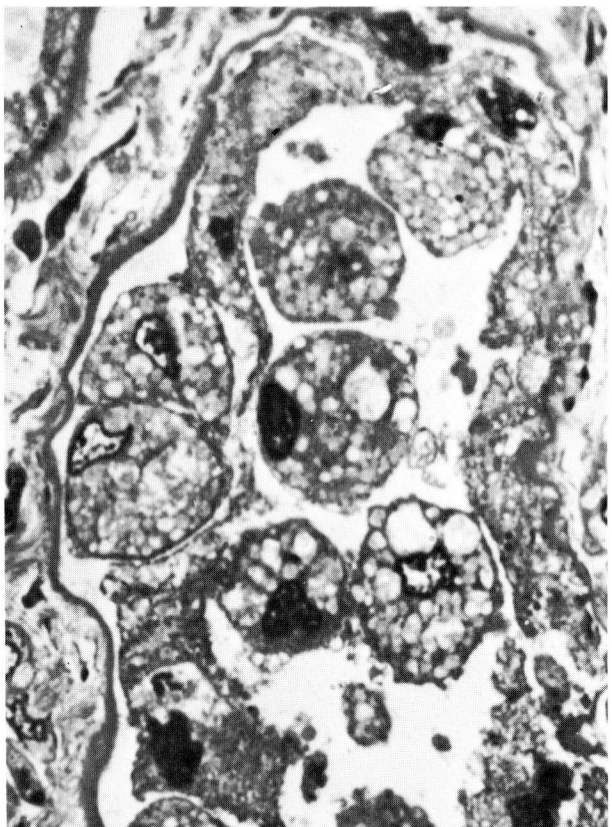

Fig. 70-8 Photomicrograph of the lipid-laden cells in the lining and in the lumen of a renal tubule. Formalin fixation, postfixation in osmium tetroxide, and embedding in Vestopal; 1-mm-thick section; ×1000.

Nervous System

Vascular involvement is also prominent in the nervous system[119–126] and presumably accounts for the observation of minor EEG and EMG abnormalities in these patients. In addition, vascular ischemia and lipid deposition in the perineurium may cause the peripheral nerve conduction abnormalities of slowed conduction velocities and distal latency, respectively.[79] In both heterozygotes and hemizygotes, glycosphingolipid deposition in nervous tissue appears to be limited to perineural sheath cells of peripheral nerves, neurons of the peripheral and central autonomic nervous system, and certain primary neurons of somatic afferent pathways.[8,120–124,127] Lipid deposition has been observed in Schwann cells by some, but not by other investigators.[123,124] Qualitative[120–123] and quantitative[122] studies of peripheral sensory neurons in sural nerves and spinal ganglia have shown preferential loss of small myelinated and unmyelinated fibers as well as small cell bodies of spinal ganglia.[122,128]

Brainstem centers in which lipid deposition has been observed include the nuclei gracilis and cuneatus, the dorsal autonomic vagal nuclei, salivary nuclei, nucleus ambiguus, thalamus, reticular substance, mesencephalic nucleus of the fifth nerve, and the substantia nigra.[122,123] Hemisphere involvement has been noted in the amygdaloid, hypothalamic, and hippocampal nuclei. Recent studies have revealed abnormal lipid deposits in the fifth and sixth cortical layers of the inferior temporal gyrus, the Edinger-Westphal nucleus, the parasym-

pathetic cell column, and the midline nucleus.[123] Lipid storage in neuronal cells of the anterior and posterior lobes of the pituitary has been described. Detailed reviews of the neurologic findings are available.[123,127]

Eye

Histologically, abnormal glycosphingolipid deposits are found in endothelial, perivascular, and smooth-muscle cells of all ocular and orbital vessels, in smooth muscle of the iris and ciliary body, in perineural cells, and in connective tissue of the lens and cornea.[129,130] Inclusions have been found in the epithelium of the conjunctiva, cornea, and lens, and, by electron microscopy, in the basal layer of conjunctival epithelial cells, in the surface epithelium, and in the conjunctival goblet cells.[131] There may be hyperplasia and edema of corneal epithelial cells. Bowman's membrane appears normal, and no deposits are observed in the stroma of endothelium by light or electron microscopy. It has been suggested that the whorllike corneal dystrophic pattern may result from the formation of a series of subepithelial ridges or from the reduplication of the basement membrane.[129,130]

Heart

The progressive deposition of glycosphingolipid in myocardial cells and valvular fibrocytes appears to be a primary cause of cardiac disease in hemizygotes and some heterozygotes.[16,48,49] Gross cardiomegaly involving all chambers has been observed. Most commonly, the left atrium and ventricle are enlarged and the ventricular walls and septum are markedly thickened; right atrial and ventricular dilatation and enlargement are variable findings. Within the myocardial cells, there is extensive glycosphingolipid deposition around the nucleus and between myofibrils. The vessels show marked hypertrophy of the endothelial cells and smooth-muscle cells secondary to lipid deposition.

Mitral and tricuspid valves have numerous lipid-laden cells embedded in fibrous tissue.[16] The most common valvular defect is thickening and interchordal hooding of the leaflets of the mitral valve, with normal chordae tendineae and either normal or thickened and shortened papillary muscles. This defect may lead to the high incidence of mitral valve prolapse. The tricuspid valve may be similarly involved; the aortic and pulmonary valves are usually normal. Clinical and pathologic features of cardiac involvement in both hemizygotes and heterozygotes have been reviewed.[16,48,49]

Other Tissues

Many other organs, including the liver, pancreas, testis, thyroid, prostate, urinary bladder, adrenal glands, and gastrointestinal tract, show involvement of the blood vessels, smooth muscle, ganglia, and nerves. In addition, vacuoles or lipid stores have been demonstrated in epithelial cells, mucous glands, synovial membrane, smooth muscle of the bronchus, alveolar ciliated epithelial cells and goblet cells, and type II alveolar epithelial pneumocytes. No inclusions have been found in alveolar macrophages. Involvement of reticuloendothelial cells has been noted in the bone marrow, liver, spleen, and lymph nodes.[33]

Histochemistry and Ultrastructure

The accumulated glycosphingolipids are birefringent and show a "Maltese cross" configuration in polarized light. They can be stained in frozen sections with lipid-soluble dyes, and may be removed from tissues by the process of dehydration and embedding in paraffin. If lipid-solubilizing procedures are used, empty vacuoles are observed by light microscopy. Most of the lipid crystals are retained through alcohol dehydration, but are lost on exposure to xylene or pyridine. Exposure of formalin-fixed tissue to 3% potassium chromate for 1 week helps to preserve the lipid; improved fixation of the lipid deposits can be achieved with 1% calcium formol. A comparison of various fixation and embedding techniques to preserve the storage material has been reported.[132] A modified periodic acid–Schiff (PAS) stain specific for neutral glycosphingolipids[133] and a positive test for sphingosine[134] have served to confirm the chemical identification of the accumulated glycosphingolipids. Peroxidase- or fluorescent-labeled *Bandeiraea simplicifolia* lectin, which is specific for α-D-galactosyl residues, and antiglobotriaosylceramide antibodies also have been used to stain the glycosphingolipid substrates selectively.[116,132,135] The ultrastructural characteristics of the lesions and of the lipid inclusions in various tissues from hemizygous males have been described extensively (e.g., Refs. 136–138). At high resolution, a typical pattern of concentric or lamellar inclusions with alternating light- and dark-staining bands is observed (Fig. 70-9). The periodicity of these bands has been reported variably as 40 to 50 Å, 50 to 60 Å, 60 to 65 Å, or as great as 98 Å. The electron-dense component is 20 to 30 Å in thickness, with coarser periods of 150 to 200 Å.

THE METABOLIC DEFECT IN FABRY DISEASE

Nature of the Accumulated Glycosphingolipids

The deficient activity of α-galactosidase in patients with Fabry disease leads to the progressive accumulation of glycosphingolipids with terminal α-galactosyl residues in the lysosomes of most nonneural tissues and in body fluids. These substances are members of a family of structurally and metabolically related glycosphingolipids that are widely distributed in human tissues as normal surface constituents of plasma membranes[139,140] and of some intracellular membranes including those of the Golgi and lysosomes.[141] In the plasma, they are associated with lipoproteins, with the highest concentration found in the low density lipoprotein fraction.[142–145] The concentrations of the individual neutral glycosphingolipids in the various lipoprotein fractions are presented in the previous edition of this text.[33]

Glycosphingolipid Structure. The lipoidal moiety of the amphipathic glycosphingolipids is a hydrophobic structure called *ceramide*, which consists of a mixture of 4-sphingenine (sphingosine) and related long-chain aliphatic amines joined by amide linkages to various fatty acids. In neutral glycosphingolipids, the fatty acid moieties are primarily saturated and monounsaturated compounds with chain lengths from C_{16} to C_{26}. Carbohydrate groups are covalently attached by a glycosidic linkage between the reducing end of the carbohydrate and the terminal hydroxyl group of the ceramide. The carbohydrate moiety may vary from a simple monosaccharide (cerebrosides) to large branched-chain oligosaccharides with 20 or more sugar residues.

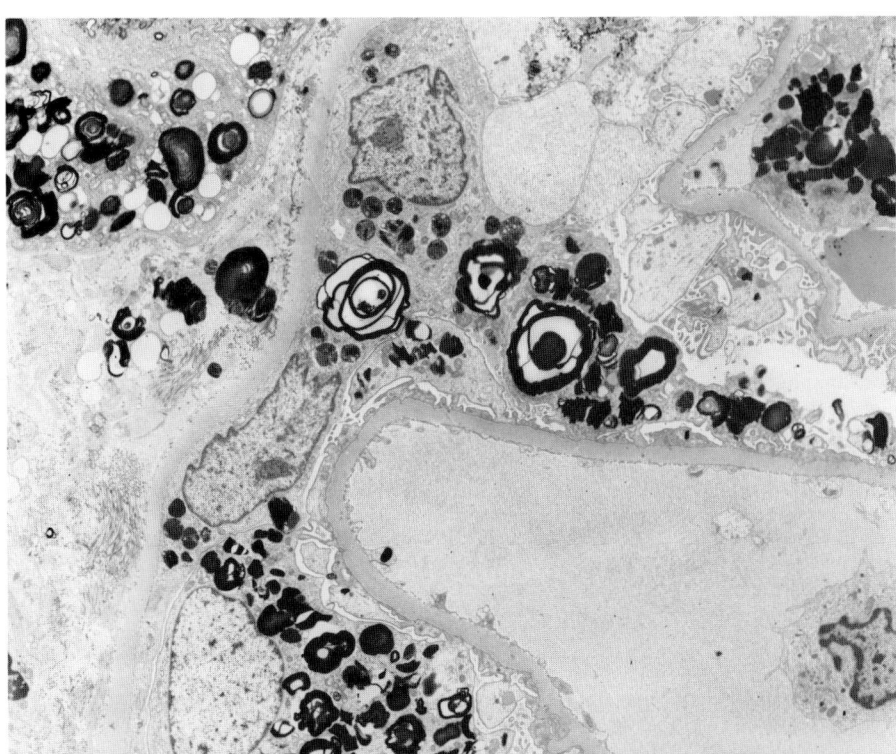

Fig. 70-9 Electron photomicrograph of a portion of a glomerulus, adjacent tubule, and an interstitial cell from a 32-year-old classic hemizygote. Note the numerous concentric lamellar inclusions in the lysosomes of the podocytes, Bowman's capsular epithelium, interstitial cells, and tubular epithelium. ×6200. (Courtesy of Dr. S.K. Lee and Ms. C.E. Sheehan, Albany Medical College.)

$$\text{Carbohydrate. . .O—CH}_2\text{CHCHC=C(CH}_2)_{12}\text{CH}_3$$

with HO and H above the CHCH carbons, NH and H below, and:

$$\text{O=C(CH}_2)_{14-24}\text{CH}_3$$

Ceramide

The glycosphingolipids that accumulate in Fabry disease are neutral glycosphingolipids, as contrasted with the negatively charged gangliosides and sulfoglycosphingolipids (sulfatides). The neutral glycosphingolipids have been grouped into families based on their structural or biosynthetic relationships, and these groups have provided the basis for their nomenclature.[146,147] The complete structural determination of individual neutral glycosphingolipids can be accomplished by proton resonance spectroscopy. Application of two-dimensional spin-echo J-correlated spectroscopy, nuclear Overhauser effect spectroscopy, and J-relayed coherence transfer spectroscopy has permitted the complete delineation of the molecular structure, anomeric-linkage, and linkage position of these glycosphingolipids.[148] Recently identified enzymes that specifically cleave the oligosaccharide moiety from ceramide[149,150] allow separate analyses of the carbohydrate and ceramide portions of various neutral and acidic glycosphingolipids. The structures and nomenclature for the neutral glycosphingolipids of human origin that have terminal α-galactosyl moieties are indicated in Table 70-3. More detailed information on glycosphingolipid structure, isolation, quantitation methods, and tissue distribution are available in the previous edition of this text[33] and in several reviews.[140,151–153]

Globotriaosylceramide. In Fabry disease, there is widespread accumulation of the glycosphingolipid, globotriaosylceramide [Gal ($\alpha1\rightarrow4$)Gal($\beta1\rightarrow4$)Glc($\beta1\rightarrow1'$)Cer], particularly in the lysosomes of vascular endothelial and smooth-muscle cells as well as in epithelial and perithelial cells of most organs. The positions of the glycosidic linkages, the anomeric configurations of these linkages, and the fatty acid compositions of globotriaosylceramides from normal and Fabry tissue have been rigorously established.[33] Such analyses have demonstrated that the accumulated glycosphingolipids isolated from tissues of patients with Fabry disease are identical to that of normal tissues.[28,46,154] Globotriaosylceramide is identical to the rare P^k blood group antigen on human erythrocytes[155–157] and has been used as a cell-specific marker for Burkitt lymphoma.[158–161] The complete structure of this glycosphingolipid is shown in Fig. 70-10A. Its stereoselective, total chemical synthesis has been accomplished.[162,163]

In normal individuals, the highest concentrations of globotriaosylceramide were found in the kidney, followed by aorta, spleen, and liver.[15,154,164–167] As a function of body mass, however, kidney, liver, lung, and erythrocytes contribute much of the normal glycolipid load. In classic hemizygotes with Fabry disease, increased concentrations of globotriaosylceramide were found in all sources analyzed except erythrocytes,[13,15,164–167] which indicates that most tissues are involved in the catabolism of these glycosphingolipids. The magnitude of accumulation of globotriaosylceramide in Fabry hemizygotes was thirty- to more than three hundred-fold higher than normal levels.[15,164,165] The highest concentrations were found in kidney, lymph nodes, heart, prostate, striated muscle, and autonomic ganglia.[12,15,164,165]

Galabiosylceramide. A second neutral glycosphingolipid, galabiosylceramide [Gal($\alpha1\rightarrow4$)Gal($\beta1\rightarrow1'$)Cer], also accumulates in Fabry hemizygotes to abnormally high concentrations. The deposition of galabiosylceramide is tissue-specific, since this substrate has been detected only in the kidney, pancreas, right heart, lung, and urinary sediment.[12,14–16,164] The complete chemical structure of galabiosylceramide obtained from normal and Fabry kidney has been established[33] and is shown in Fig. 70-10B.

Blood Group B and P Glycosphingolipids. Two additional accumulated glycosphingolipids were identified in the pancreas of a Fabry hemizygote who had the blood group B and B1 antigens.[17] In human erythrocytes, there are two neutral glycosphingolipids with terminal α-galactosyl residues that inhibit blood group B–specific hemagglutination, the blood group B glycosphingolipid [Gal($\alpha1\rightarrow3$)Gal($2\leftarrow1\alpha$Fuc)($\beta1\rightarrow3$)GlcNac($\beta1\rightarrow3$)Gal($\beta1\rightarrow4$)Glc($\beta1\rightarrow1'$)Cer] and the blood group B1 glycosphingolipid [Gal($\alpha1\rightarrow3$)Gal($2\leftarrow1\alpha$Fuc)($\beta1\rightarrow4$)GlcNAc($\beta1\rightarrow3$)Gal($\beta1\rightarrow4$)Glc($\beta1\rightarrow1'$)Cer].[17,33,168] The structures of the blood group B and B1 glycosphingolipids isolated from Fabry pancreas were established by biochemical, enzymatic, and immunologic methods and were identical to those of the B and B1 glycosphingolipids of normal human erythrocytes.[17,33] Their complete structures are shown in Fig. 70-10C and D. In general, glandular epithelial tissues such as stomach, pancreas, and intestine are rich sources of these fucose-containing neutral glycosphingolipids, whereas parenchymatous organs and erythrocytes contain lower quantities. The concentrations of the B and B1 antigens in the Fabry pancreas analyzed were approximately 50 percent of the level of the accumulated globotriaosylceramide.[17] Thus, Fabry hemizygotes and heterozygotes who have blood group B and AB accumulate four glycosphingolipid substrates, whereas patients with A or O blood groups accumulate only globotriaosylceramide and galabiosylceramide.

Table 70-3 Neutral Glycosphingolipids with Terminal α-Galactosyl Moieties of Human Origin

Chemical structure	Trivial name	Approved nomenclature	Suggested abbreviation
Gal($\alpha1\rightarrow4$)Gal($\beta1\rightarrow4$)Glc($\beta1\rightarrow1'$)Cer	Ceramide trihexoside; trihexosylceramide	Globotriaosylceramide	GbOse$_3$Cer
Gal($\alpha1\rightarrow4$)Gal($\beta1\rightarrow1'$)Cer	Digalactosylceramide	Galabiosylceramide	GaOse$_2$Cer
Gal($\alpha1\rightarrow3$)Gal($2\leftarrow1\alpha$Fuc)($\beta1\rightarrow3$)GlcNAc-($\beta1\rightarrow3$)Gal($\beta1\rightarrow4$)Glc($\beta1\rightarrow1'$)Cer	Blood group B glycolipid	IV^2-α-Fucosyl-IV^3-α-galactosyl-lactotetraosylceramide	IV^2-α-Fuc-IV^3-α-Gal-LcOse$_4$Cer
Gal($\alpha1\rightarrow3$)Gal($2\leftarrow1\alpha$Fuc)($\beta1\rightarrow4$)GlcNAc-($\beta1\rightarrow3$)Gal($\beta1\rightarrow4$)Glc($\beta1\rightarrow1'$)Cer	Blood group B1 glycolipid	IV^2-α-Fucosyl-IV^3-α-galactosyl-neolactotetraosylceramide	IV^2-α-Fuc-IV^3-α-Gal-LcnOse$_4$Cer
Gal($\alpha1\rightarrow4$)Gal($\beta1\rightarrow4$)GlcNAc($\beta1\rightarrow3$)Gal($\beta1\rightarrow4$)Glc($\beta1\rightarrow1'$)Cer	Blood group P$_1$ glycolipid	IV^4-α-Galactosyl-neolacto-tetraosylceramide	IV^4-α-Gal-LcnOse$_4$Cer

For more complete information on glycosphingolipid structure, see Macher and Sweeley.[147]

A.

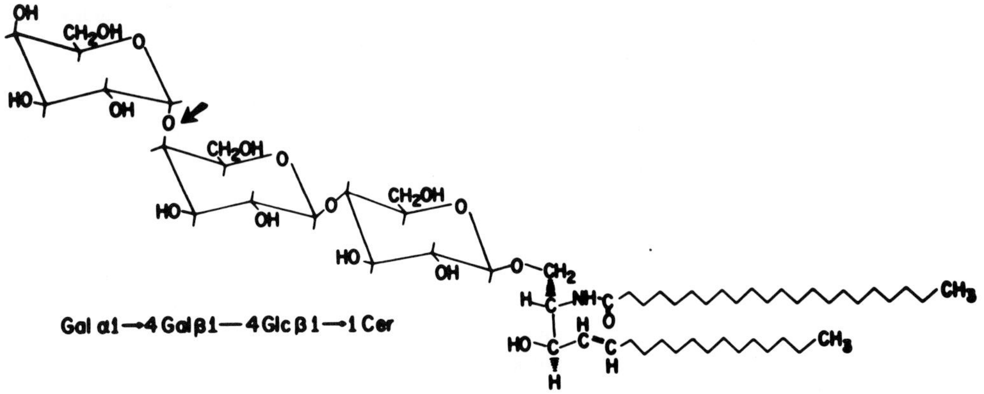

Gal α1→4 Galβ1—4 Glc β1→1 Cer

B.

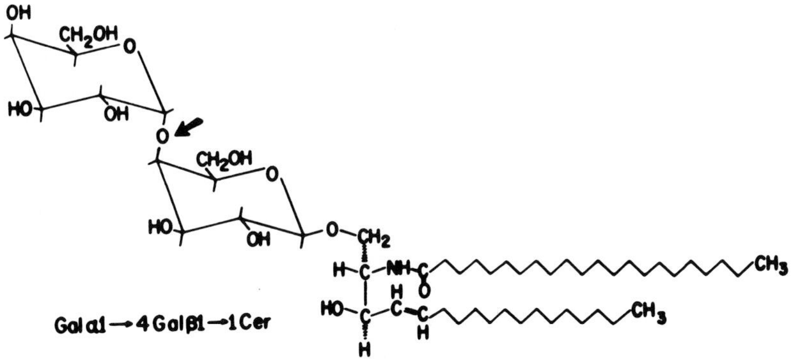

Gal α1→4 Galβ1→1Cer

C.

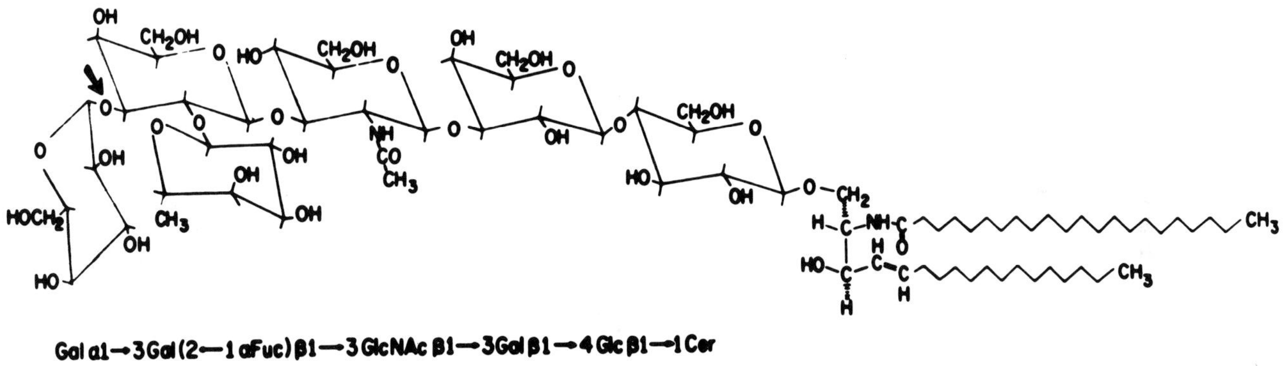

Gal α1→3Gal(2←1αFuc)β1→3GlcNAc β1→3Gal β1→4Glc β1→1Cer

D.

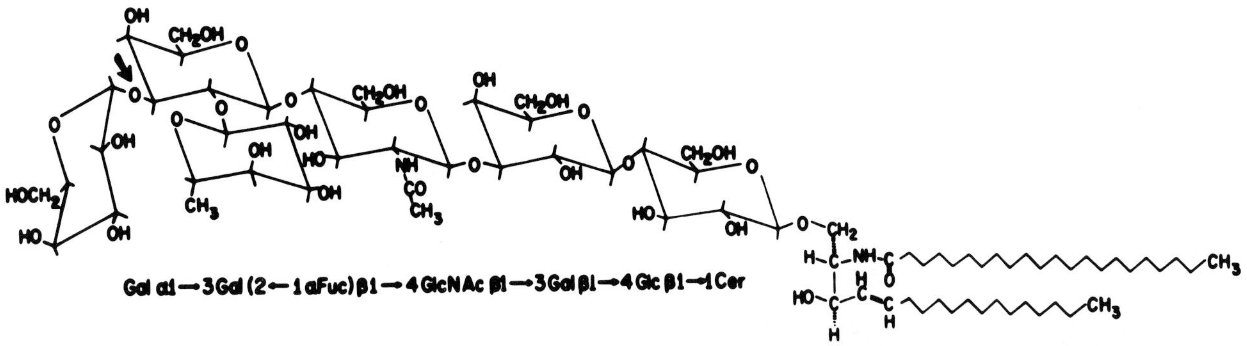

Gal α1→3Gal(2←1αFuc)β1→4GlcNAc β1→3Gal β1→4Glc β1→1Cer

Fig. 70-10 Complete chemical structures of the neutral glycosphingolipids that accumulate in Fabry disease. *A.* Globotriaosylceramide, the major accumulated substrate. *B.* Galabiosylceramide. *C* and *D.* The blood group B and B1 antigenic glycosphingolipids, respectively, which accumulate in blood group B and AB patients. The arrows indicate the α-galactosyl bonds which are normally cleaved by α-galactosidase.

A fifth neutral glycosphingolipid that can accumulate in Fabry disease is the P_1 blood group antigen. In the P blood group system, the P^k and P antigens have been shown to be globotriaosylceramide and globotetraosylceramide [GalNAc($\beta1\rightarrow3$)Gal($\alpha1\rightarrow4$)Gal($\beta1\rightarrow3$)Glc($\beta1\rightarrow1'$)Cer].[155-157] Although blood group P^k and P are rare, the P_1 antigen [Gal($\alpha1\rightarrow4$)Gal($\beta1\rightarrow4$)GlcNAc($\beta1\rightarrow3$)Gal($\beta1\rightarrow4$)Glc($\beta1\rightarrow1'$)-Cer] is present in about 75 percent of the population.[157] To date, the accumulation of the P_1 substance in Fabry disease has not been documented, nor has the possibility of increased disease severity due to the accumulation of this blood group substance been assessed.

Glycosphingolipid Biosynthesis. Neutral glycosphingolipids are synthesized by sequential enzymatic reactions involving the stepwise addition of monosaccharide units to acceptors which then become the appropriate substrates for subsequent enzymes in the pathway. This process, in which sugar nucleotides serve as donors of the carbohydrate residues, requires the concerted action of a group of glycosyltransferases that may be closely associated in a subcellular membrane as a multienzyme complex. A more extensive treatment of glycosphingolipid biosynthesis can be found in the previous edition of this chapter[33] and in the recent review by Basu et al.[169]

In the following section, discussion is limited to the biosynthetic steps involved in the addition of the terminal α-galactosyl residues to the glycosphingolipids that accumulate in Fabry disease. These biosynthetic reactions are mediated by different α-galactosyltransferases which attach the galactose moiety from the sugar nucleotide, UDPgalactose (UDPgal), to the glycosphingolipid acceptor by an α-anomeric linkage. The α-galactosyltransferases involved in glycosphingolipid biosynthesis are important because their specific activity and tissue-specific and/or regulated expression determine the cell and tissue distribution and the amount of the individual glycosphingolipids that accumulate in this disease. For example, lactosylceramide [Gal($\beta1\rightarrow4$)Glc($\beta1\rightarrow1$)Cer; Lac Cer] is found in all tissues and is the common precursor for the biosynthesis of certain neutral glycosphingolipids and gangliosides, whereas galactosylcerebroside [Gal($\beta1\rightarrow1'$)Cer], the precursor of galabiosylceramide, occurs primarily in the brain and kidney. Since the α-galactosyltransferase that recognizes galactosylcerebroside as an acceptor is present in kidney and not brain (see below), galabiosylceramide is not synthesized in the brain, consistent with the absence of neuronopathic involvement in Fabry disease.

UDPGal:LacCer($\alpha1\rightarrow4$)galactosyltransferase (GalT-6[169]) catalyzes the synthesis of globotriaosylceramide by addition of an α-galactosyl moiety to Lac-Cer. The transferase has been highly purified from rat liver and is composed of two nonidentical subunits with molecular weights of about 65 and 22 kDa.[170] This enzyme is highly specific for Lac-Cer and does not transfer α-galactosyl residues for the formation of galabiosylceramide or the blood group B or P_1 antigens. Recently, the GalT-6 gene has been isolated from a cosmid library constructed from a human Burkitt lymphoma cell, and the active enzyme has been expressed in mouse L5178 cells transfected with this clone.[171]

UDPGal:Gal($\beta1\rightarrow1'$)Cer($\alpha1\rightarrow4$)galactosyltransferase catalyzes the synthesis of galabiosylceramide and has been characterized in crude particulate fractions of rat kidney.[172] The activity was differentiated from GalT-6 by its greater sensitivity to heat denaturation. Notably, the activity was present in kidney, but not in brain, spleen, liver, or lung, consistent with

the observed tissue distribution of galabiosylceramide in Fabry patients.

UDPGal:Gal($\beta1\rightarrow4$)GlcNac[($\beta1\rightarrow3$)or($\beta1\rightarrow4$)]Gal($\beta1\rightarrow4$)Glc($\beta\rightarrow1'$)Cer($\alpha1\rightarrow3$)galactosyltransferase catalyzes the synthesis of the B and B1 blood group glycosphingolipids.[173] Interestingly, there are two alleles for this transferase, designated B^1 and B^2.[174] The B^1 allele produces the normal galactosyltransferse (B_1) found in whites while the B^2 allele encodes the B_2 enzyme which has a higher activity and a lower K_m for H substance. In fact, in AB blood type individuals, the B_2 enzyme converts H substance to blood group B and B1 glycosphingolipids so efficiently that little blood group A glycosphingolipid is synthesized.[174] In black and Oriental populations, the frequency of the B^2 allele in with blood group B with individuals is about 30 to 40 percent and 10 percent, respectively. The occurrence of the B^2 allele in hemizygotes with Fabry disease who are in blood group AB will result in the synthesis and subsequent accumulation of blood group B glycosphingolipids, at levels near those observed in blood group B hemizygotes.[17]

UDPGal:Gal($\beta1\rightarrow4$)GlcNAc($\beta1\rightarrow3$)Gal($\beta1\rightarrow4$)Glc($\beta1\rightarrow1'$)Cer($\alpha1\rightarrow4$)galactosyltransferase (GalT-5) catalyzes the synthesis of the P_1 blood group glycosphingolipid. The enzyme has been studied in crude preparations from rabbit bone marrow, bovine spleen, and human cultured lymphoblasts.[175-177] It is notable that the terminal α-anomeric linkage in the P_1 substance is $\alpha1\rightarrow4$, whereas the terminal galactosyl linkages in the B and B1 glycosphingolipids are $\alpha1\rightarrow3$. The $\alpha1\rightarrow4$ linkage on the P_1 glycosphingolipid apparently prevents the addition of fucose to the penultimate galactose in the P_1 glycosphingolipids.

Plasma neutral glycosphingolipids are synthesized primarily in the liver, where they are incorporated into lipoprotein particles.[178] This concept is supported by the kinetics of their turnover in plasma after incorporation in vivo of [^{14}C]glucose in pig[179] or [6,6-^{2}H$_2$]glucose in human beings;[180] these kinetics are comparable to those observed with triacyl-sn-glycerols and phospholipids after pulse labeling with fatty acids or inorganic phosphate.[181] The studies suggested that about 25 percent of the plasma glycosphingolipid pool was synthesized newly each day.[179] The reappearance of ^{14}C-glycosphingolipids in porcine plasma at 60 days after labeling indicated that a portion of the plasma glycosphingolipid pool is derived from senescent erythrocytes.[179] Thus, it appears that the liver and bone marrow are the primary synthetic sources of plasma glycosphingolipids. Since convincing evidence has been provided that erythrocyte glycosphingolipids, with carbohydrate moieties longer than that of glucosylceramide, do not exchange with lipoprotein glycosphingolipids in the circulation,[142,179] transfer must occur in tissues—presumably via specific transport proteins for glycosphingolipids which have been identified in spleen and liver.[182,183] The rate of exchange of plasma glycosphingolipids with those in plasma membranes has not been determined.

Catabolism

Glycosphingolipids are degraded in a stepwise fashion by a family of specific exoglycosidases, as illustrated by the pathway shown in Fig. 70-11 for the metabolism of globotetraosylceramide, galabiosylceramide, and the blood group B and P_1 active hexa- and pentaglycosylceramides. Reactions catalyzed by individual glycosidases involved in these pathways have

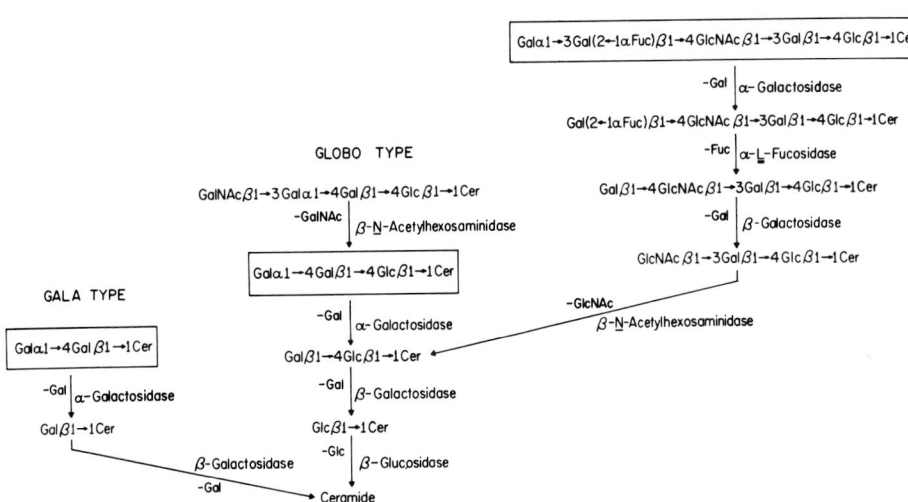

Fig. 70-11 Pathway for the catabolism of neutral glycosphingolipids involving the stepwise hydrolysis of individual sugar residues by specific glycosyl hydrolases. The accumulated substrates in Fabry disease—galabiosylceramide, globotriaosylceramide, and the blood group B glycosphingolipids—are indicated.

been extensively studied in cell-free extracts. Most of the enzymes have been obtained in relatively pure form and their kinetic properties and substrate specificities determined. Virtually all of these exoglycosidases are glycoproteins with optimal catalytic activity at acidic pH. They occur predominantly, but not exclusively, in lysosomes. There are multiple forms of many of these enzymes, which may be related to their subcellular distribution, differences in their substrate specificities, and chemical heterogeneity due to structurally different carbohydrate moieties or subunit peptides or both. In vivo, certain hydrophobic glycosphingolipid substrates are made available for hydrolysis by specific noncatalytic "activator" proteins which act as biologic detergents.[184,185] The resulting glycosphingolipid-glycoprotein complexes appear to be the true substrates for these glycosidases (with the notable exception of the glucocerebrosidase activator, which is an enzyme cofactor).[184,185] The lysosomal glycosidases involved in glycosphingolipid metabolism have been the subject of several reviews.[37,141,184–189]

α-Galactosidase: The Enzymatic Defect in Fabry Disease

The enzymatic defect in Fabry disease is the deficient activity of the lysosomal enzyme, α-galactosidase (previously designated α-galactosidase A).[33] Following the identification of globotriaosylceramide and galabiosylceramide as the accumulated substrates in Fabry disease,[12] Brady and coworkers synthesized globotriaosylceramide with a radiolabeled terminal galactosyl moiety and used the radiolabeled glycosphingolipid to demonstrate the presence of a galactosidase in normal intestinal tissue and its deficient activity in intestinal biopsy specimens from hemizygotes with Fabry disease.[18] The anomeric specificity of the deficient galactosidase activity was determined in 1970 by Kint, who demonstrated that leukocytes from hemizygotes with Fabry disease were deficient in an α-galactosidase assayed with either synthetic substrate, *p*-nitrophenyl-α-D-galactoside or 4-methylumbelliferyl-α-D-galactoside.[19] The identification of the anomeric linkage was confirmed in subsequent spectroscopic and enzymatic studies, which demonstrated that globotriaosylceramide from Fabry kidney has an α1→4 linkage in the terminal galactosyl moiety.[190–194]

Investigators documented the deficient activity of α-galac-

tosidase in affected hemizygotes and obligate heterozygotes using the radiolabeled natural substrate, globotriaosylceramide,[18] and/or synthetic chromogenic or fluorogenic substrates (e.g., Refs. 19, 23, 24). Early studies with the synthetic substrates revealed that classically affected hemizygotes had a level of α-galactosidase activity that was approximately 10 to 25 percent of that observed in the respective source from normal individuals.[23,24,195,196] The residual α-galactosidase activity in these Fabry hemizygotes was thermostable and was not inhibited by myoinositol, whereas 80 to 90 percent of the α-galactosidase activity in normal individuals was thermolabile and myoinositol-inhibitable.[23,24,195,197–200] Based on these studies with synthetic substrates, the two activities initially were thought to represent α-galactosidase isozymes and were designed *α-galactosidase A and B*.[195] Subsequently, α-galactosidase B has been shown to be a lysosomal α-N-acetylgalactosaminidase that differs from α-galactosidase A in substrate specificity as well as in its physical and immunologic properties.[20,21,201] Recent studies have shown that the two enzymes are distinct proteins though related by evolution (see "Schindler Disease"). Thus, it is no longer useful or appropriate to retain the A and B isozyme designations for human α-galactosidase and α-N-acetylgalactosaminidase, and future references should emphasize their appropriate catalytic specificities.

Purification. Because of its low abundance, purification of α-galactosidase from human tissues necessitates the careful application of multiple specific fractionation steps tailored to the unique properties of the enzyme. This glycoprotein enzyme typically can be isolated from crude tissue extracts in 80 percent yield by using conconavalin A Sepharose as an affinity ligand for mannose-containing glycoproteins. Since the enzyme is very unstable above pH 7 and below pH 5, most steps are conducted at pH 6.0. Diethylaminoethyl (DEAE)-cellulose chromatography provides another high-capacity separation step that affords about 80 percent separation from α-N-acetylgalactosaminidase. The α-galactosidase elutes as a broad peak due to charge heterogeneity resulting from differing amounts of sialic acid residues on its oligosaccharide side chains.[202] The remaining α-N-acetylgalactosaminidase in the α-galactosidase preparation can be completely removed by a two-stage hydroxyapatite chromatographic step in which α-N-acetylgalactosaminidase elutes with a low concentration of phosphate at pH 5.5 and the α-galactosidase elutes at higher phosphate concentrations at pH 6 to 7.[30] The most efficient chromatographic purification procedure uses the α-galactosidase affinity resin N-6-aminohexanoyl-α-D-galactosylamine coupled to Sepharose,[203] as modified for purification of the human enzyme.[202] A further improvement in purity can be obtained by a second affinity chromatographic step.[202] Although α-N-acetylgalactosaminidase also binds to this affinity resin, it can be preferentially eluted, or prevented from binding, with N-acetylgalactosamine. By such procedures, human α-galactosidase has been highly purified from liver,[204] spleen,[202] and placenta.[202,205] The most highly purified material has been isolated from human lung using high-performance liquid chromatography (HPLC) gel filtration to remove minor (<5 percent) contaminants.[30]

Physical Properties. The native α-galactosidase from human sources is a protein of approximately 101 kDa.[202,204,206,207] Polyacrylamide gel electrophoresis in the presence of sodium dodecylsulfate (SDS) has consistently shown a single diffuse subunit band of about 49 kDa,[30,202,206,208] indicating that the enzyme has a homodimeric structure. The enzyme is a glycoprotein containing 5 to 15 percent asparagine-linked complex and high mannose oligosaccharide chains.[30,202,207,208] Multiple forms are observed upon isoelectric focusing of purified preparations from plasma and various tissues (Fig. 70-12). The isoelectric points of the tissue forms a α-galactosidase range from 4.3 to as high as 5.1,[200,202,204,207] whereas the plasma form has a pI of 4.2.[202] The plasma and tissue forms of the enzyme are converted by neuraminidase to a single form with a sharp isoelectric focusing band of higher pI (5.1), suggesting that the heterogeneity results from variations in the amount of sialic acid on the carbohydrate chains. Such studies indicate that the plasma form may contain 10 to 12 sialic acid residues whereas the placental form of α-galactosidase has only one or two residues.[202] The negatively charged sialic acid residues presumably are responsible for the prolonged circulatory half-life of enzyme administered intravenously to patients with Fabry disease,[29] and may also be a factor determining which organs acquire enzyme activity after infusion.

Kinetic Properties. α-Galactosidase isolated from normal tissues and fluids is a relatively heat labile glycoprotein that catalyzes the hydrolysis of substrates possessing terminal α-galactosidic residues, including various synthetic water-soluble

Fig. 70-12 Isoelectric focusing of purified α-galactosidase. *Lane 1, plasma form; lanes 2 and 3, splenic forms (different preparations); lane 4, placental form; lane 5, placental α-N-acetylgalactosaminidase (From Bishop and Desnick.[202] Used by permission).*

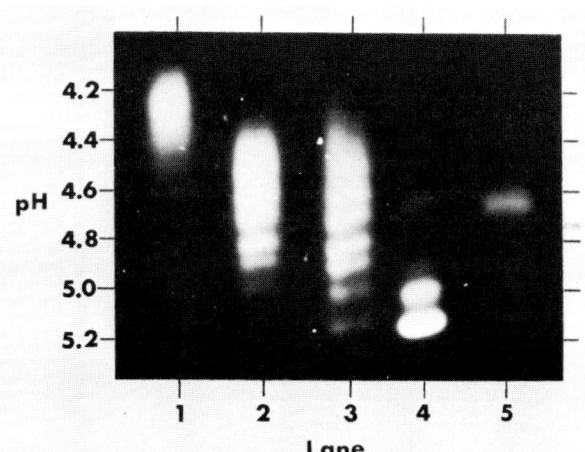

substrates and naturally occurring glycosphingolipids and glycoproteins. Maximal activity of α-galactosidase with the artificial substrate 4-methylumbelliferyl-α-D-galactopyranoside is obtained at pH 4.6. The Michaelis constant (K_m) of the reaction with this substrate is approximately 2 mM.[20,23,200,202,204,206,209] With the detergent-solubilized glycosphingolipid substrate globotriaosylceramide, the pH optimum is 3.8 to 4.0, and the K_m is 0.1 to 0.2 mM.[202,204,206,209] The turnover number[210] of the most highly purified human α-galactosidase is approximately 6×10^3 min^{-1}.[30,202]

Several substrate analogues of globotriaosylceramide have been described which could serve as useful tools for the study of α-galactosidase structure and function. Conduritol C trans-epoxide is a moderately effective inactivator and presumably forms a covalent bond with an active carboxyl group in the catalytic site.[211] The glucose analogue of this compound has been used to identify active site peptides in yeast[212] and almond[213] glucosidases as well as in human glucocerebrosidase.[214] Recently, potent competitive inhibitors of coffee bean α-galactosidase have been described; 1,4-dideoxy-1,4-imino-D-lyxitol and 1,5-dideoxyl-1,5-imino-D-galactitol had reported K_is of 0.2 and 0.4 μM, respectively.[215,216]

The in vitro cleavage of globotriaosylceramide by α-galactosidase requires the addition of an appropriate detergent, such as sodium taurocholate, to make the substrate available through the formation of mixed micelles. In vivo hydrolysis of globotriaosylceramide, as well as of certain other glycosphingolipids and gangliosides, is mediated by "activator" proteins [designated *sphingolipid activator proteins* (SAP)] that form complexes with specific glycosphingolipids (e.g., Refs. 189, 217). SAP-1 is a 22-kDa glycoprotein,[217–229] encoded by a gene localized to chromosome 10q21→q22,[230] which binds to sulfatide, G_{M1} ganglioside, and globotriaosylceramide and renders these glycosphingolipids available (i.e., soluble) for hydrolysis by their respective lysosomal enzymes. SAP-1 has been localized in the lysosomes of human liver and intestinal cells by immunoelectron microscopy.[231] The inherited deficiency of SAP-1 activity results in a recessive disorder which is phenotypically similar to metachromatic leukodystrophy,[232–235] a severe neurodegenerative disease (see Chap. 69). Similarly, SAP-2 is a 22-kDa glycoprotein[70,236] encoded by a gene recently mapped to chromosome 5[237] that is required for the hydrolysis of G_{M2} ganglioside and the neutral glycosphingolipid G_{A2} by β-hexosaminidases A and B.[237–239] The deficient activity of SAP-2 results in the AB variant of G_{M2} gangliosidosis, which is identical in phenotype to Sandhoff disease[238–240] (See Chap. 72). Comprehensive reviews concerning these activator proteins are available.[184,185,189] Investigators have purified the individual SAP-1 molecules required for the hydrolysis of sulphatide, G_{M1} ganglioside, and globotriaosylceramide from human kidney, brain, and urine, and have shown that the individually purified activator activities were chromatographically and immunologically identical.[223,228]

Human hepatic SAP-1 has been purified to homogeneity by several investigators.[219,220,223] The molecular size is approximately 22 kDa as determined by gel filtration.[219,220] Molecular weight estimates, determined under denaturing conditions, revealed multiple species ranging from 8 to 13 kDa.[224] These same species were observed in biosynthetic studies in cultured cells.[226] The activator is most likely a homodimeric glycoprotein[227] with size heterogeneity in its carbohydrate moiety. One Asn-linked carbohydrate acceptor site in the 12-kDa peptide is predicted by the cDNA sequence.[229] This small glycoprotein[220] has a remarkable resistance to proteolysis and heat denaturation. It is completely stable at pH 1.4 or 12 at 100°C for 4 min and is fully active after 6-h incubation with trypsin.[220] The substrate specificities and mode of interaction have been described in detail.[217,221,223,225,227,228]

In patients with SAP-1 deficiency, the α-galactosidase, β-galactosidase, and cerebroside sulfatase activities were not detectable in urine.[225] Kinetic and immunologic analysis in these patients have documented the absence of the SAP-1 protein.[225,233,235] Notably, the concentrations of globotriaosylceramide and galabiosylceramide in the urinary sediment of the SAP-1–deficient patients were markedly elevated,[225] similar to the pattern seen in urinary sediment from Fabry hemizygotes.[14] Thus, the SAP-1–deficient homozygotes have at least three enzyme deficiencies, and the disease phenotype results from the accumulation of their respective substrates.

Enzyme Biosynthesis and Processing. Biosynthetic studies in cultured human cells have shown that the α-galactosidase glycoprotein subunit is synthesized as a precursor peptide which is processed to the mature lysosomal subunit.[208,241] Metabolic labeling studies in cultured human fibroblasts[241] have identified a 50-kDa precursor which was processed via 47 to 50-kDa intermediates over several days to a mature lysosomal form of 46 kDa (Fig. 70-13). The transport to lysosomes is dependent on mannose-6-phosphate receptors, since the enzyme was secreted as a 52-kDa glycosylated precursor in mucolipidosis II cells or in the presence of NH_4Cl.[241] Studies of the carbohydrate chains of the enzyme synthesized in cultured cells revealed that the mature enzyme contained 48 percent complex and 52 percent high mannose oligosaccharides. The latter had identical chromatographic mobilities to Man_{8-9} GlcNAc. The complex oligosaccharides were resolved into two fractions containing 14 and 19 to 39 glucose units, suggesting a composition of tri- and/or tetra-antennary structures.[208]

Defective α-Galactosidase in Fabry Disease

Several categories of mutations in the α-galactosidase gene have been identified by biochemical and immunologic analyses. These include classic hemizygotes with no detectable α-galactosidase activity or enzyme protein, classic hemizygotes with no enzymatic activity but detectable levels of enzyme protein, and atypical variants with residual α-galactosidase activity. Immunologic techniques have been employed to determine the presence or absence of nonfunctional enzyme protein in classic hemizygotes with no detectable α-galactosidase activity. Using rabbit antihuman α-galactosidase A antibodies, Beutler and Kuhl,[200,242] Rietra et al.,[243] and Hamers et al.[244] were unable to detect cross-reacting immunologic material (CRIM) in fibroblasts, leukocytes, urine, or renal tissue from eight classically affected hemizygotes from seven unrelated Fabry families. Based on these findings, they independently concluded that the mutations in these families were CRIM-negative. Thus, the inability to detect any residual α-galactosidase activity in these Fabry sources was consistent with the absence of the enzyme protein.

Our laboratory also has evaluated the α-galactosidase CRIM status in hemizygotes with Fabry disease. Using a monospecific rabbit antibody to homogeneous placental α-galactosidase (which does not cross-react with α-N-acetylgalactosaminidase), the presence of CRIM has been evaluated by rocket immunoelectrophoresis in tissues from six unrelated classically affected hemizygotes who had no detectable α-galactosidase by

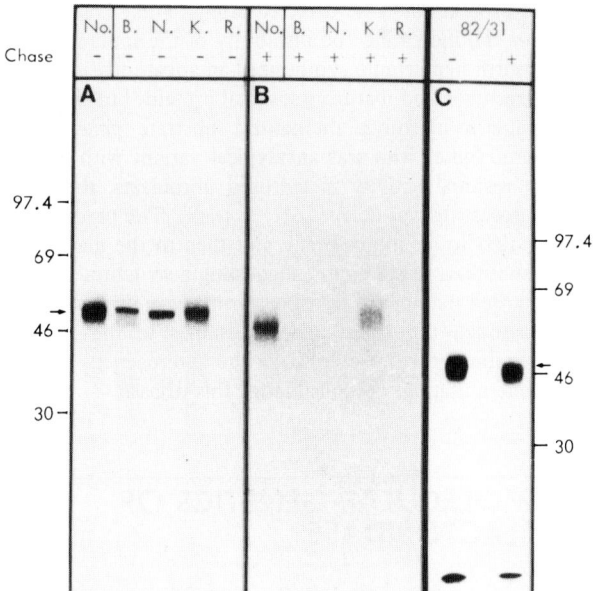

Fig. 70-13 Synthesis of α-galactosidase in fibroblasts from Fabry patients. Normal fibroblasts (Co) and cells from five Fabry hemizygotes (B, N, K, R, and 82/31) were labeled with [³⁵S]methionine for 4 h and harvested either immediately after labeling or after a chase for 2 days. α-Galactosidase *(arrows)* was immunoprecipitated from cell extracts. See text for details. *(From Lemansky et al.[241] Used by permission.)*

activity assay of the immunoprecipitated protein. Renal or splenic tissues from four hemizygotes were CRIM-negative, but CRIM corresponding to about 1 to 5 percent of normal enzyme protein levels was detected in the tissues of two other hemizygotes. The presence of enzyme protein in some classically affected hemizygotes demonstrates the heterogeneity in the structural gene mutations in this disease.

Romeo et al.[99] studied the residual α-galactosidase activity in cultured fibroblasts from five unrelated hemizygotes, including one patient previously reported to have about 20 percent residual activity.[46] The residual α-galactosidase activity was isolated and characterized using rabbit antihuman liver α-galactosidase and α-N-acetylgalactosaminidase antibodies (which were each absorbed with the other enzyme since they initially showed cross-reactivity) and purified by DEAE-cellulose chromatography.[99] Excluding the hemizygote who had about 20 percent of normal α-galactosidase activity (see "Genetic Variants"), the level of residual α-galactosidase activity in the fibroblasts from the four other hemizygotes was only about 3 percent of normal. This activity had an apparent K_m similar to that of normal α-galactosidase, but was thermostable and eluted more electronegatively on anion exchange chromatography. It has been suggested that the finding of residual α-galactosidase activity in these four hemizygotes was artifactual due to the fact that a portion of the thermostable α-N-acetylgalactosaminidase is rapidly converted, particularly during storage, to an "α-galactosidase-like" form which has some of the physical and kinetic properties of α-galactosidase (i.e., K_m toward artificial substrates, behavior on anion-exchange chromatography), but retains the thermostability and immunologic properties of α-N-acetylgalactosaminidase.[243]

More recent studies characterized the biosynthesis of α-galactosidase in several Fabry hemizygotes.[241] As shown in Fig. 70-13, four different patterns were observed in classically affected hemizygotes. One hemizygote synthesized no enzyme precursor (R, *panel A*): two synthesized the precursor, but no enzyme protein could be detected after a 4-day chase (B and N, *panel B*), indicating the instability of the mutant protein; and a fourth hemizygote synthesized an apparently normal enzyme precursor and mature lysosomal protein, but the protein was unable to hydrolyze the natural substrate (*panel C*). In a fifth hemizygote, who was an atypical variant with about 20 percent residual activity in cultured fibroblasts, the biosynthetic processing was delayed (K, *panel B*). The precursor was cleaved first to an intermediate and then to the mature lysosomal subunit at a slow rate, suggesting a structural mutation that retarded the normal transport from the endoplasmic reticulum through the Golgi and endosomes to the lysosome. These findings further emphasize the heterogeneity in structural gene mutations responsible for this disease.

THE MOLECULAR GENETICS OF α-GALACTOSIDASE

Our understanding of human α-galactosidase and Fabry disease has been advanced dramatically by the recent isolation of the cDNA and genomic sequences encoding this lysosomal enzyme.[30-32] The full-length cDNA sequence provided the primary structure of the enzyme precursor, including the signal peptide. The subsequent isolation of the entire chromosomal gene for α-galactosidase allowed characterization of the structural organization and regulatory elements of the gene. *In situ* hybridization and restriction fragment length polymorphism (RFLP) studies have narrowed the regional chromosomal assignment of the α-galactosidase gene on the long arm of the X chromosome. Initial analyses of the mutations in unrelated Fabry families have identified a variety of lesions underlying the molecular genetic heterogeneity of this disease (see "Molecular Pathology of Fabry Disease"). More accurate carrier diagnosis has become possible by identification of the specific lesions in families and by analysis of locus-specific or linked RFLPs (see "Diagnosis"). Expression of full-length cDNA and genomic sequences together with site-specific mutagenesis should provide information on the structure and function of the enzyme and enable the production of large amounts of active enzyme for therapeutic trials (see "Treatment") and structure-function studies.

Gene Assignment

The locus for human α-galactosidase was assigned to the X chromosome in 1970 when Kint convincingly demonstrated that the defective globotriaosylceramide hydrolysis in Fabry disease was due to the deficient activity of an α-galactosidase.[19] Somatic cell hybridization studies of human-hamster hybrid fibroblasts localized the α-galactosidase gene to a region on the long arm of the X chromosome, Xq21→q24.[245,246] Subsequently, the regional assignment was narrowed to Xq21→q22 using a series of somatic cell hybrids made from a human cell line with an X,2,15 translocation, 46X,t (X;2;15)(q22;p12;p12).[247] More recently, this localization was further refined to the region Xq22 by *in situ* hybridization using the radiolabeled cDNA as probe (Fig. 70-14; Ref. 248). In addition, the restriction fragments detected in genomic DNA by Southern hybridization using the full-length cDNA as probe exactly matched those identified by restriction mapping of genomic clones for α-galactosidase indicating the absence of

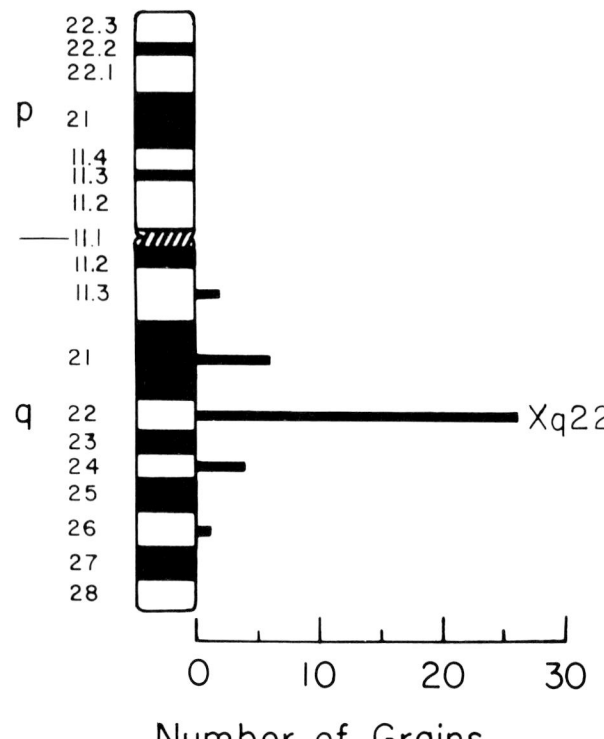

Fig. 70-14 Idiogram of the human G-banded X chromosome illustrating the distribution of sites of hybridization of radiolabeled α-galctosidase cDNA. Note that most of the grains on the chromosome were in the band Xq22, indicating the regional localization of the α-galactosidase gene.

closely related sequences or pseudogenes.[249,250] Thus, the *in situ* and Southern hybridization studies established the occurrence of a single X-chromosomal gene for α-galactosidase. The gene assignment was localized further by RFLP studies which indicated that the α-galactosidase locus was closely linked to the anonymous cloned X-chromosome sequence probes DXS17 and DXS87, but not to probes DXS11 or DXYS1.[251-253] Based on studies of informative Fabry families, it was estimated that the genetic distance between the α-galactosidase locus and DXS17 and DXS87 was about 2 to 4 centimorgans (see "Molecular Diagnosis"). Since DXS17 and DXS87 have been mapped independently to Xq21.33→q22,[254] the α-galactosidase locus also can be assigned to this narrow region.

The α-Galactosidase cDNA

Isolation of the Full-Length cDNA. A cDNA clone (designated λAG18) encoding α-galactosidase was isolated from a human liver cDNA library constructed in the expression vector λgt11.[30] The nucleotide sequence of the λAG18 cDNA insert contained an open reading frame of 1226 nucleotides that encoded five residues of the signal peptide and the entire mature form of the enzyme. This sequence was colinear with 86 amino acids determined by microsequencing the N terminus, and several tryptic and cyanogen bromide peptides from the purified enzyme. X-linkage was supported by X-dosage studies and gene mapping with a mouse-human somatic cell hybrid panel. The λAG18 cDNA insert was used as a probe to isolate a full-length 1362-base pair (bp) cDNA for human α-galactosidase (pcDAG126) from a human fibroblast cDNA library constructed in the pcD vector.[255] A full-length cDNA (pcDAG210) also was isolated from the pcD library using a specific oligonucleotide synthesized to 25 nucleotides of the most 5' region of λAG18.[256]

Characterization of the Full-Length cDNA. The pcDAG126 full-length cDNA insert contained 60 bp of 5' untranslated sequence, the initiation codon, and the entire open reading frame, which encoded a 31-amino acid signal peptide and the 398 residues of the mature enzyme subunit. The 1287-bp coding region predicted unglycosylated precursor and mature enzyme subunits of $M_r = 48,772$ and $45,356$, respectively. The signal peptide predicted for the precursor subunit is consistent in size with that predicted from maturation studies in which human α-galactosidase was synthesized as an ~50.5-kDa precursor glycoprotein and then was proteolytically cleaved to a mature ~46-kDa lysosomal glycoprotein.[241] As shown in Fig. 70-15, the predicted signal peptide had typical features (e.g., Refs. 257, 258) including a basic amino acid in the first five residues followed by a central hydrophobic core of 15 residues, two α-helix breakers (proline or glycine) −4 to −8 from the cleavage site, a more polar C-terminal region, and the most frequently observed C-terminal sequence, Ala-X-Ala. The weight-matrix method of von Heijne,[258] predicted cleavage after Ala-31 (score = 7.36). This site was consistent with Leu-32 being the amino-terminal residue, as established by microsequencing of the purified enzyme.[30] An identical signal peptide sequence for α-galactosidase was recently predicted from the cDNA sequence of the pcDAG210 insert.[256]

Analysis of the predicted amino acid sequence revealed four possible N-glycosylation sites. All four sites were located in β-turns within hydrophilic regions of the enzyme,[259] consistent with their probable surface localization. Of the four, only three sites are probably functional since the sequence of the most carboxy-terminal site, Asn-Pro-Thr, is rarely glycosylated.[259] Three oligosaccharide chains per subunit were suggested by previous studies of purified α-galactosidase from human plasma and spleen[202] and immunoprecipitated enzyme from cultured cells.[208] Thus, microsomal cleavage of the signal peptide appears to be the only amino-terminal processing step in the biosynthesis of α-galactosidase, as is the case with several other human lysosomal enzymes (e.g., see Ref. 260), though some enzymes contain pre and pro segments which require a second cleavage to form the mature polypeptide (e.g., see Refs. 261, 262).

An unusual feature of the first two α-galactosidase cDNAs[30] as well as of six additional cDNAs isolated from three different libraries[32] was the absence of a 3' untranslated sequence (Table 70-4). The polyadenylation signal sequence was in the coding region 12 bp from the termination codon, which was followed by the poly(A) tract. This finding is unique among human nuclear-encoded mRNAs. The only other known nuclear-encoded transcript lacking a 3' untranslated region in mammals is the mouse thymidylate synthase mRNA.[263] Interestingly, the human thymidylate synthase transcript does have a 3' untranslated region.[263] In two other α-galactosidase cDNAs, pcDAG7 and pcDAG41, the TAA termination codons were followed by the short 3' untranslated sequences AATGTTT and AATGTC, respectively, while a previously reported cDNA[256] had the sequence AATGTT. Thus, while the majority of the isolated α-galactosidase cDNAs lack a 3' untranslated sequence, alternative cleavage and polyadenylation can result in a short 6- or 7-bp untranslated sequence following the termination codon. These alternative, short 3' regions may indicate microheterogeneity of mRNAs due to alternate sites for the primary α-galactosidase cleavage reaction.[264] Additionally, a second upstream (−28 bp from the termination codon) polyadenylation signal, AATACA, may be involved in the variant cleavages. Whatever the mechanism responsible for these alternative 3' sequences, it is notable that the α-galactosidase transcript does not require a 3' untranslated region for expression in human cells.

Searches of amino acid and nucleotide sequence data bases identified a few sequences with very limited similarity to human α-galactosidase.[31] The predicted amino acid sequences of the yeast α-galactosidase cDNA and the *melA* gene of *E. coli* had only a few short regions of homology with the human enzyme.[265] Comparison of available data for the other human and mammalian lysosomal enzymes, including human cathepsin D, α-fucosidase, β-galacosidase, β-glucuronidase, β-hexosaminidase A α subunit and β subunit, as well as rat cathepsin B, revealed little nucleotide or amino acid sequence similarity.[31] One possible exception was α-fucosidase[266] in which bp 31 to 178 were 52 percent homologous to α-galac-

Fig. 70-15 The α-galactosidase signal peptide. The hydrophobicity profiles and the predicted secondary structure for the 31-amino acid residue signal peptide and the first nine residues of the mature N-terminus are shown. Amino acids are represented by their one letter code beginning with the initiation methionine at +1. Consensus sequences required for signal peptides are indicated, and the corresponding residues in the α-galactosidase signal peptide are underlined. Charged residues are indicated (+ or −). Deduced α-helical regions (α), β-pleated sheets (β), random coils (--), and turns (T) are indicated.

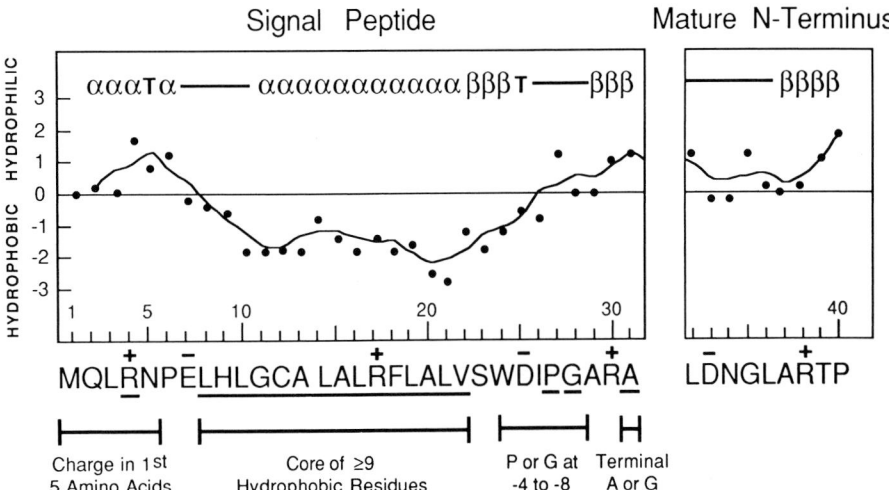

Table 70-4 3′ Sequences of α-Galactosidase cDNAs and Genomic Clone λB18

	Clone	3′ Sequence
cDNA:		
	λAG18	. . .TAA . . . .(A)^{12}
	λHLAG4	. . .TAA . . . .(A)^{122}
	pcDAG8	. . .TAA . . . .(A)^{33}
	pcDAG69	. . .TAA . . . .(A)^{92}
	pcDAG126	. . .TAA . . . .(A)^{43}
	pcDAG41	. . .TAA AATGTc . . . .(A)^{57}
	pcDAG7	. . .TAA AATGTTT. . . . .(A)^{91}
Genomic:		
	λB18	. . .TAA AATGTTTATTTTATTGCCAACT- -ACTACTTCCTGTCCACCTTTTTCTCC . . . .
	Downstream consensus:	YTGTTYY TTTTTTTT

NOTE: The α-Galactosidase cDNA and genomic clones were isolated and sequenced as described in the text. The 51-bp genomic 3′ sequence, beginning with the termination codon (TAA) and ending with CTCC, is aligned with the sequence in pcDAG7. The "GT-box" and "T-rich" element homologies each occur twice in the contiguous genomic sequence as indicated by underlines.

tosidase bp 34 to 168 when four gaps totaling 18 bases were introduced. Another notable exception was human α-N-acetylgalactosaminidase (see "Schindler Disease"), discussed below.

Expression of the Full-Length cDNA. The functional integrity of the full-length α-galactosidase cDNA was demonstrated by transient expression in COS-1 cells. The full-length pcD-AG126 cDNA insert was subcloned into the eukaryotic expression vector p91023(B),[267] and then the recombinant plasmid was transfected into COS-1 cells. As shown in Fig. 70-16, the construct in the sense orientation expressed active enzyme at three- to fourfold the endogenous level.

Fig. 70-16 Transient expression of α-galactosidase in COS-1 cells. Cells were transfected using a construct with the p91023(B) vector containing the pcDAG126 cDNA insert in the sense orientation (●), in the antisense orientation (♦), and with no DNA (■), (mock transfection).[269] The specific activities of α-galactosidase (*top panel*) and β-galactosidase (*lower panel*) were determined in extracts of transfected cells harvested at the indicated time points. At day 3 after transfection, human α-galactosidase activity was detected at a level of fourfold higher than the endogenous level.

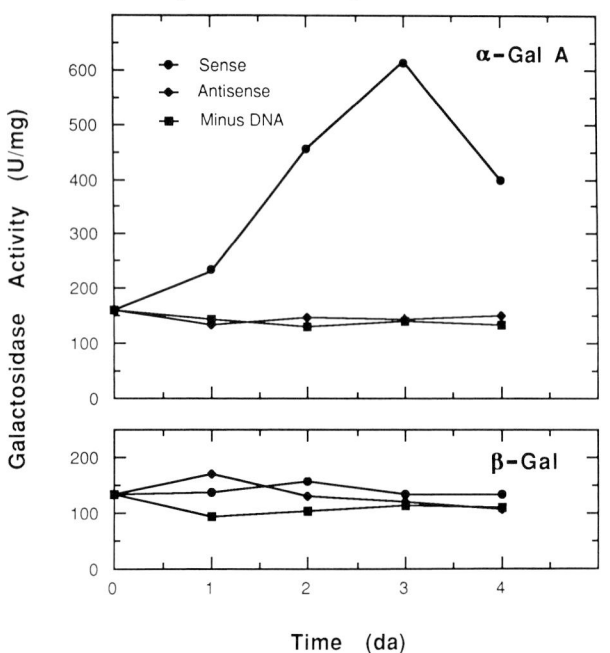

For expression in *E. coli*, the λAG18 cDNA that encodes the mature form of α-galactosidase and a derivative cDNA construct containing the signal peptide sequence were inserted into the ptrpL1 plasmid containing the regulatable trp promoter.[268] Low-level expression of the human enzyme was detected immunologically in maxicell experiments, but detection of activity using synthetic substrates was not possible. More recently, Ioannou et al.[269] inserted the full-length pcDAG126 cDNA into the prokaryotic secretion expression vector pin-III-*omp* A[270] and detected high levels of active human α-galactosidase in an *E. coli* K12 strain M2701,[271] in which the bacterial α-galactosidase gene, *melA*, is defective. If the unglycosylated forms of human α-galactosidase produced in *E. coli* are stable, the large-scale microbial production of the human enzyme, combined with site-directed mutagenesis techniques, could provide sufficient amounts of enzyme for structure-function studies as well as for evaluation of therapeutic replacement endeavors. Alternatively, the human enzyme can be produced in other expression systems such as those based on baculovirus,[272] yeast,[273] vaccinia virus,[274] and/or transgenic mice.[275]

The α-Galactosidase Gene

Structural Organization. Genomic clones containing the entire α-galactosidase gene and about 20 kb of flanking sequence have been isolated and characterized[32] (Fig. 70-17). The gene is approximately 12 kb and contains seven exons. The exons range in length from 92 to 291 bp, while the introns vary from 200 bp to 3.7 kb. All intron-exon splice junctions follow the "GT/AG" rule[276] and are consistent with the consensus sequences for splice junctions of RNA polymerase II–transcribed genes.[277] Exon 1 contains the entire 5′ untranslated region, the sequence encoding the signal peptide and the first 33 residues of the mature enzyme subunit. Intron 2 contains three *Alu*-repetitive sequences and is the only intron in which multiple *Alu* sequences have been identified.

Regulatory Elements. The α-galactosidase gene contains several possible regulatory elements in the 5′ flanking region including a TAATAA sequence, five CCAAT box sequences, and two GC box consensus sequences for the promoter–binding transcription factor Sp1.[32] Several potential enhancer binding sites are present, including the conserved recognition

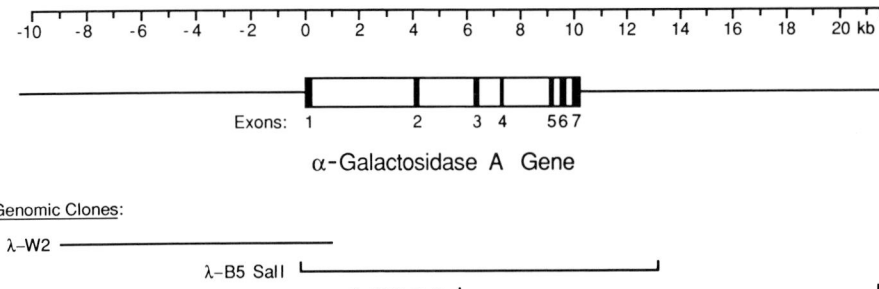

Fig. 70-17 Organization of the human α-galactosidase gene. Exons 1 to 7 are denoted by solid vertical lines and introns by open areas. The three overlapping genomic clones (λ-W2, λ-B5, λ-B18) used to characterize the gene are indicated.

motif (TGACTCA) of the AP1 enhancer–binding protein,[278] the immunoglobin "OCTA" enhancer element,[279] a reverse complement of the c-fos enhancer element GATGTCC,[280] and four direct repeats of the "chorion box" enhancer.[281] As yet, the functional significance of these putative promoter-enhancer elements in the regulation of α-galactosidase gene expression has not been defined.

The α-galactosidase gene contains a methylation-free island, or "HTF island," in the region upstream from the initiation ATG (bp −660 to +1) that includes the indicative SacII site.[282] These DNA islands are sequences of 500 to 2000 bp that are enriched in CpG dinucleotides (CpG/GpC > 1.0) in GC-rich regions (>50 percent) and are typically found in "housekeeping" genes.[283] The G + C content of this region in the α-galactosidase gene is 54 percent, and the CpG/GpC dinucleotide ratio is 1.4. HTF islands have been implicated in maintaining the inactivation of X-linked genes.[284,295] Analysis of the methylation patterns in this region in active versus inactive X chromosomes should be of interest.[286]

The 3′ Flanking Region. As noted above, the 3′ untranslated regions in the α-galactosidase cDNAs were absent or extremely short (i.e., 5 to 7 bp). Sequencing of the 3′ flanking region of the genomic clone indicated that this was not an artifact of cDNA library construction (Ref. 32; Table 70-4). The 3′ flanking region also contained sequences with similarities to the consensus downstream elements, YGTGTTYY ("GT-box") and T_n ("T-rich"), recently shown to be involved in polyadenylation.[287–289] Since two pairs of these downstream elements occur in the α-galactosidase gene, it is possible that the alternative cleavage sites may be due to the presence of these additional, more 3′, elements.

MOLECULAR PATHOLOGY OF FABRY DISEASE

The biosynthetic studies,[241] as well as previous biochemical and immunologic analyses of the defective α-galactosidase in unrelated hemizygotes with Fabry disease (see "Defective α-Galactosidase in Fabry Disease"), suggest at least three major categories of enzyme deficiency. (1) The first category comprises classic hemizygotes with no detectable enzymatic activity or enzyme protein (i.e., CRIM-negative).[200,242–244] Mutations underlying this category include: (a) partial or complete gene deletions as well as partial gene duplications, (b) point mutations which alter transcription, mRNA processing, or cause abnormal or premature termination of translation, or (c) point mutations which alter the enzyme's conformation, rendering it markedly unstable and subject to rapid degradation. The latter mutation has been documented by enzyme biosynthetic studies in which cultured cells from affected hemizy-

gotes synthesized the α-galactosidase precursor, but the mature form of the enzyme was not detected (Fig. 70-13).[241] (2) The second category includes classic hemizygotes with no detectable enzymatic activity, but with normal or decreased amounts of enzyme protein (i.e., CRIM-positive subjects). Presumably, the lesions in most of these hemizygotes resulted from point mutations in the structural gene which rendered the enzyme kinetically defective. The amount of CRIM detected would depend on the stability of the altered protein as well as the effect of the mutations on the major antigenic determinants, which might be altered by conformational changes (Fig. 70-13). (3) A third category would include the atypical hemizygotes with residual activity (see "Genetic Variants"). These variants could result from exonic point mutations that alter the kinetic and/or stability properties of the enzyme but retain sufficient in vivo catalytic activity to hydrolyze the glycosphingolipid substrates and modify the pathologic and clinical expression of the disease, or mutations which modify transcription or mRNA splicing to varying degrees.

The availability of the full-length cDNA and genomic sequences for α-galactosidase permits investigation of these possibilities at the molecular level. Techniques employed to analyze the nature of the molecular lesions include Southern and Northern hybridization analyses, RNase A studies, and enzymatic amplification of genomic DNA or reverse-transcribed mRNA sequences for subsequent sequencing. Southern hybridization analyses have identified gene rearrangements including partial gene deletions, a partial gene duplication, as well as a restriction endonuclease cleavage site obliteration in the α-galactosidase chromosomal gene.[249,250] Northern hybridization analyses and RNase A studies[250,280] have detected abnormalities in the size and amount of α-galactosidase mRNA including abnormalities in RNA processing and/or stability. The polymerase chain reaction has been used to amplify a selected α-galactosidase genomic region for sequencing and determination of a specific point mutation.[250,290] Such studies have demonstrated the variety of molecular lesions that cause Fabry disease, examples of which are discussed below. The characterization of specific lesions should provide understanding of the nature of the mutations causing this enzymatic defect as well as insight into the structure-function relationships for this lysosomal hydrolase. Moreover, the identification of the mutation in a given Fabry family will permit the precise diagnosis of other family members by the use of a mutation-specific restriction endonuclease or the use of oligonucleotide probes corresponding to the normal and mutant gene sequences.

Gene Rearrangements

DNA isolated from cultured fibroblasts or lymphoblasts from over 120 unrelated Fabry hemizygotes has been analyzed by

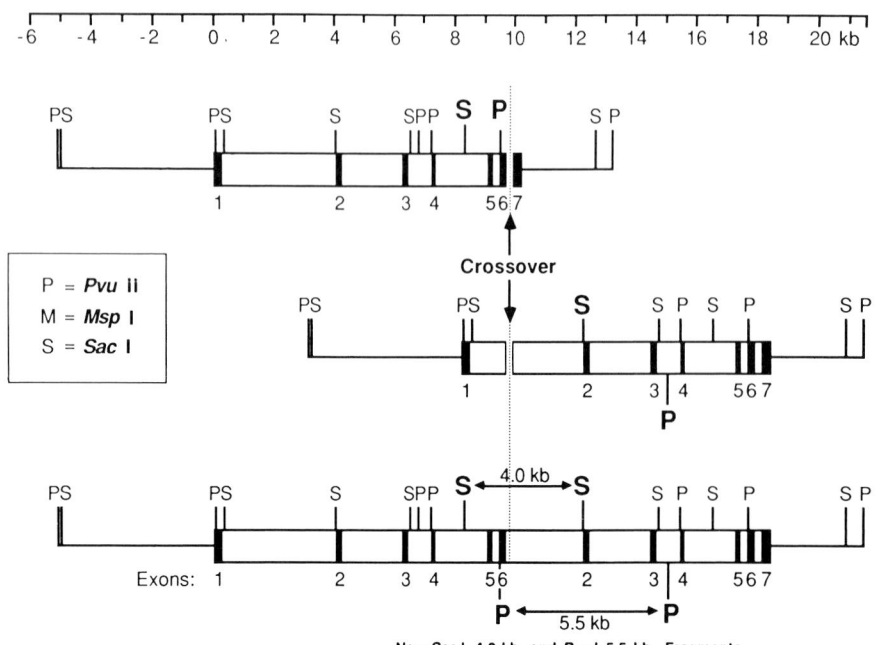

Crossover

P = *Pvu* II
M = *Msp* I
S = *Sac* I

Exons: 1   2   3   4   5 6   2   3 | 4   5 6 7

4.0 kb

5.5 kb

New *Sac* I 4.0 kb and *Pvu* I 5.5 kb Fragments

Duplication of Exons 2 Through 6 in Family D by
an Homologous but Unequal Crossover

Fig. 70-18 Schematic representation of the gene duplication in a classic hemizygote from family D. Restriction analysis of the gene rearrangement was consistent with an unequal crossover between introns 1 and 6 resulting in the duplication of α-galactosidase exons 2 through 6. The location of the crossover was based on the new SacI 4.0-kb and PvuII 5.5-kb restriction fragments observed in Southern hybridization analyses.

Southern hybridization. Six gene rearrangements have been detected.[249,250,290] These include a partial duplication and five partial gene deletions. The partial duplication, defined by restriction mapping, was a region of about 8 kb which included exons 2 through 6. This duplication presumably resulted from a homologous but unequal cross-over between introns 1 and 6, as illustrated in Fig. 70-18. Five partial gene deletions have been identified which range in size from about 400 bp to more than 5.5 kb (Fig. 70-19). Four of the five partial deletions had a breakpoint in intron 2, which contains three *Alu*-repetitive sequences. It has been proposed that *Alu* and *Alu*-like sequences are hot-spots for homologous but unequal cross-over events which generate deletions and duplications (e.g., Refs. 291, 292). The fifth partial gene deletion had a breakpoint in the middle of exon 5 and deleted the entire 3′ portion of the gene (family J; Fig. 70-19). This deletion was detected in a nonconsanguineous family in which two lysosomal diseases occurred in sibs.[293] The son had classic Fabry disease (no de-

tectable α-galactosidase activity), while the daughter was an affected homozygote with cystinosis and had a level of α-galactosidase activity consistent with heterozygosity for the Fabry gene. Heterozygosity for the cystinosis gene was demonstrated in both the mother and father as well as the maternal and paternal grandparents. In contrast, enzyme assays revealed the mother to be heterozygous for the Fabry gene, but her parents and other maternal and paternal relatives had normal α-galactosidase activities. These results suggested the occurrence of a new mutation in the α-galactosidase gene. Segregation of linked polymorphic DNA segments suggested that the mutation arose in the maternal grandfather (see "Diagno-

Fig. 70-19 Deletions in the α-galactosidase gene detected in unrelated families with Fabry disease. Restriction mapping of genomic and cloned genomic DNA from hemizygotes revealed five partial gene deletions ranging in size from 400 bp to at least 5.5 kb. Interestingly, four have breakpoints in intron 2, the only intron with multiple *Alu* repeat sequences. Exons are indicated by number. The three *Alu* sequences in intron 2 are indicated with diagonally striped boxes.

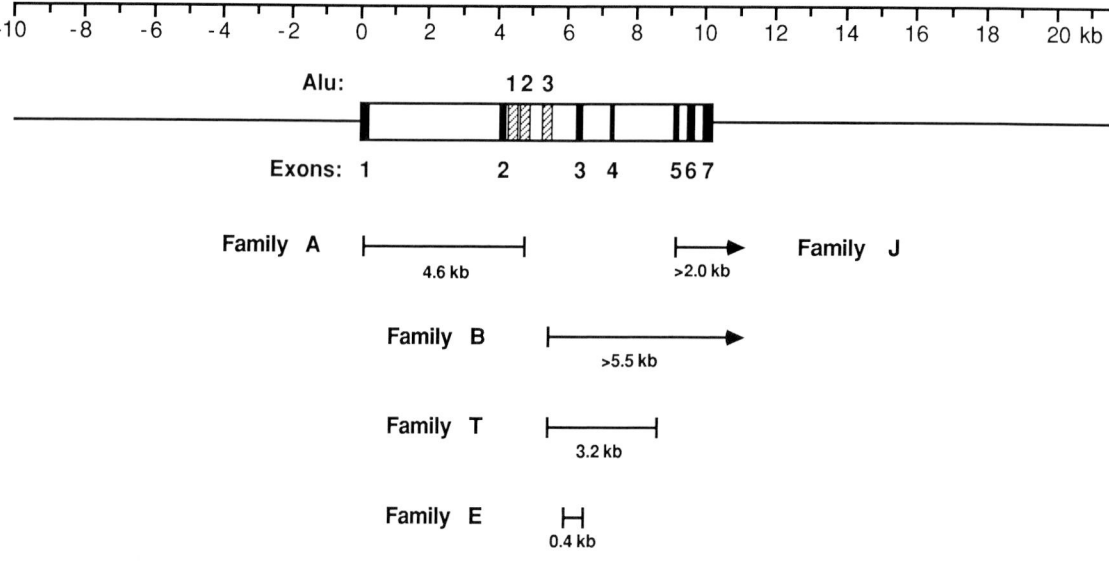

Alu: 1 2 3

Exons: 1   2   3   4   5 6 7

Family A   4.6 kb   >2.0 kb   Family J

Family B   >5.5 kb

Family T   3.2 kb

Family E   0.4 kb

sis"). Since the maternal grandmother's normal α-galactosidase activity could have been the result of random X inactivation (see "Diagnosis"), the existence and ancestry of a new mutation could not be proven. However, the DNA diagnostic studies in this family permitted the definitive demonstration that the deletion was a new mutation. Since HLA-typing established legitimacy, this partial gene deletion represents the first documented new mutation in Fabry disease.

Of the unrelated Fabry families studied to date, 5 percent had molecular lesions detectable by Southern hybridization, a frequency similar to that found in other X-linked disorders.[70] Presumably, the majority of mutations that cause Fabry disease result from small deletions or insertions not detectable by Southern hybridization or from single base substitutions.

Restriction Site Alteration

An alteration of a restriction endonuclease cleavage site was found in affected hemizygotes and heterozygotes from family C, in which the affected males had residual α-galactosidase activity.[8] In this variant family, the point mutation in the mutant allele was identified by Southern analysis using the restriction endonuclease *Msp*I, an enzyme that detects a high frequency of polymorphisms[5] as well as mutations (e.g., see Ref. 31) due to alterations of CpG dinucleotide sequences. In contrast to the five *Msp*I restriction fragments observed in DNA from normal individuals (2.4, 1.5, 0.97, 0.51, and 0.43 kb), affected family C hemizygotes had only four restriction fragments, three normal and a new 2.0-kb fragment (Fig. 70-20). The 2.0-kb fragment resulted from the loss of an *Msp*I cleavage site that normally produces the 1.5- and 0.51-kb fragments. The restriction patterns of heterozygotes in this family demonstrated one normal and one mutant allele. Since affected hemizygotes had residual α-galactosidase activity in their leukocytes (∼ 2 percent of normal), it was suspected that

the genetic lesion was a missense mutation. Since there is only one *Msp*I site in the α-galactosidase cDNA sequence (exon 7), it was likely that a base substitution in this cleavage site resulted in an amino acid substitution which altered the enzyme's stability and activity.[250] To demonstrate this mutation, a 288-bp genomic sequence including 78 bp of intron 6 and the exon 7 *Msp*I site was amplified by the polymerase chain reaction technique, cloned into M13 vectors, and then sequenced. The missense mutation was found to be a C→T transition in nucleotide 1066 of the full-length cDNA which caused an arginine to tryptophan substitution at residue 356. This substitution altered the charge, hydrophobicity, and size of the amino acid in this position.

Transcript Abnormalities and Other Lesions

Northern hybridization and RNase A studies have been performed to assess the quality and quantity of the α-galactosidase mRNA in hemizygotes from unrelated families. A single mRNA species of ∼1.4 kb was observed in cytoplasmic poly(A)+ RNA from HeLa cells and normal human lymphoblasts.[31] Of the 30 unrelated hemizygotes evaluated, 13 had α-galactosidase mRNAs of normal size and amount. No α-galactosidase mRNA was detected for hemizygotes with partial gene deletions and the partial duplication. The remaining hemizygotes had no detectable transcript, decreased amounts of normal-sized message, or decreased to normal amounts of short or abnormally large messages. These alterations suggest the existence of mutations which impair transcription and RNA processing. An interesting mRNA abnormality was ob-

Fig. 70-20 Detection of an *Msp*I restriction site obliteration in the α-galactosidase gene in family C by Southern hybridization analysis. Affected hemizygotes have a new 2.0-kb band, while the 1.5 and 0.51-kb bands are absent. Heterozygotes exhibit the normal bands plus the new 2.0-kb band. This difference is caused by a C→T transition at an *Msp*I site that creates an Arg→Trp substitution in the enzyme.

Fig. 70-21 An RNA processing defect in an affected hemizygote from family G detected by RNase A protection studies. Poly(A)+RNA from normal (N) and Fabry hemizygote (G) was hybridized to radiolabeled antisense α-galactosidase riboprobes of varying lengths (1, 2, and 3), and then the duplexes were digested with RNase A. The sizes of the protected fragments were determined by electrophoresis and autoradiography. As control, duplexes of each riboprobe with the full-length unlabeled sense strand riboprobe α-galactosidase RNA were analyzed as above (lane C). Based on the size of the protected fragments in hemizygote G, a 198-base deletion (exon 6) was detected.

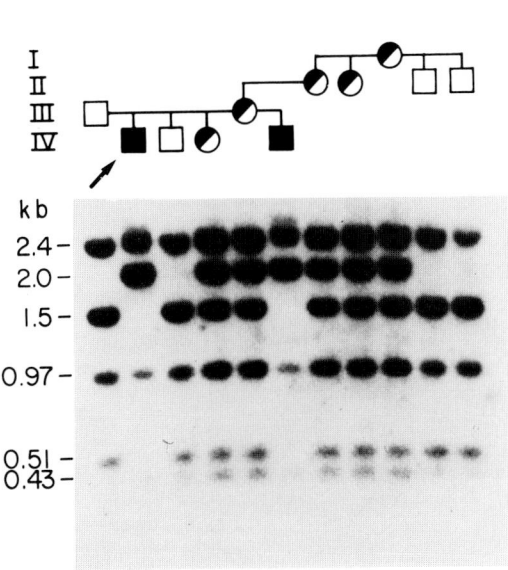

Family C

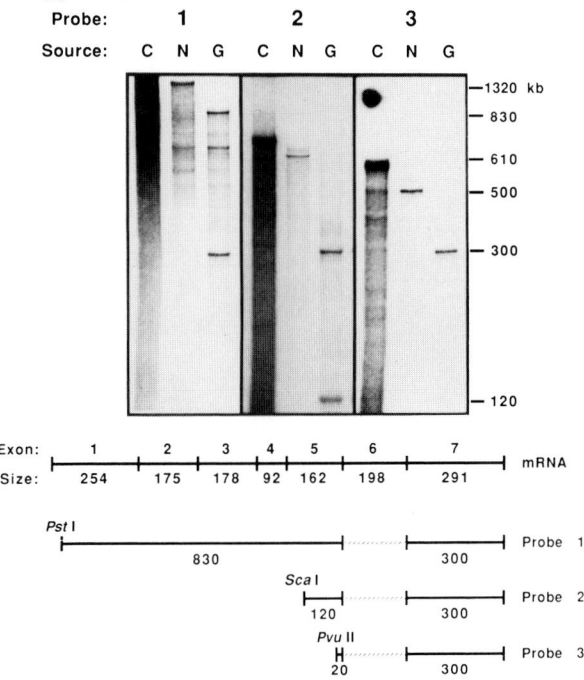

served in one family that had a normal gene profile on Southern hybridization analyses. Affected males from this family had essentially normal amounts of a shorter 1.2-kb message while heterozygotes had the short 1.2-kb mRNA as well as the normal 1.4-kb transcript. RNase A protection studies with a series of riboprobes containing different lengths of the α-galactosidase sequence permitted the localization of the lesion and the demonstration that the 198-bp exon 6 was deleted from the mature transcript in affected hemizygotes (Fig. 70-21).

PATHOPHYSIOLOGY

The pattern of glycosphingolipid deposition in Fabry disease, particularly its predilection for vascular endothelial and smooth-muscle cells, is different from that seen in other glycosphingolipidoses.[294] However, the origin of the accumulated glycosphingolipid substrates has not been fully clarified. A significant contribution comes from endogenous synthesis and subsequent lysosomal accumulation of terminal α-galactosyl–containing glycosphingolipids following autophagy of cellular membranous material containing these lipid substrates. Endogenous metabolism is a major source of substrate accumulation in avascular sites such as cornea and in neural cells, which presumably are protected from the increased circulating

levels of globotriaosylceramide by the blood-brain barrier. In addition, the turnover of globotriaosylceramide, and particularly its precursor, globotetraosylceramide (globoside), which are present in higher concentrations in normal renal tissue than in any other tissue, are presumably responsible for the endogenous renal deposition of the Fabry substrate.

The unique cellular and tissue distribution of accumulated globotriaosylceramide, particularly in the vascular endothelium (Fig. 70-22) and smooth muscle, suggests that a significant intracellular contribution may be derived by the endocytosis or diffusion of globotriaosylceramide from the circulation where the concentration is three- to tenfold higher than in normal individuals. In Fabry hemizygotes and normal individuals, the circulating globotriaosylceramide is primarily transported in the LDL and HDL lipoprotein fractions.[33,142–144,295] In plasma from hemizygotes, the accumulated globotriaosylceramide is distributed in the LDL and HDL fractions in proportions similar to those in normal plasma, approximately 60 and 30 percent, respectively. The finding that little, if any, substrate deposition occurs in Fabry hepatocytes (in contrast to the accumulation in Kupffer cells[110,132,296]) supports the contention that globotriaosylceramide synthesized in the hepatocyte is associated with lipoprotein and secreted as a complex.[297] In support of this concept is the fact that patients with hypercholesterolemia have proportional plasma elevations of both LDL and neutral glycosphingolipids including globotriaosylceramide.[142] The circulating globotriaosylceramide

Fig. 70-22 Electron micrograph of a section of an arteriole from a hemizygote, showing the marked accumulation of concentric lamellar inclusions in the lysosomes of the vascular endothelium. The progressive lysosomal deposition of the glycosphingolipid substrate leads to the narrowing and eventual occlusion of the vascular lumen. × 25,000. (*Courtesy of Dr. J.G. White, University of Minnesota.*)

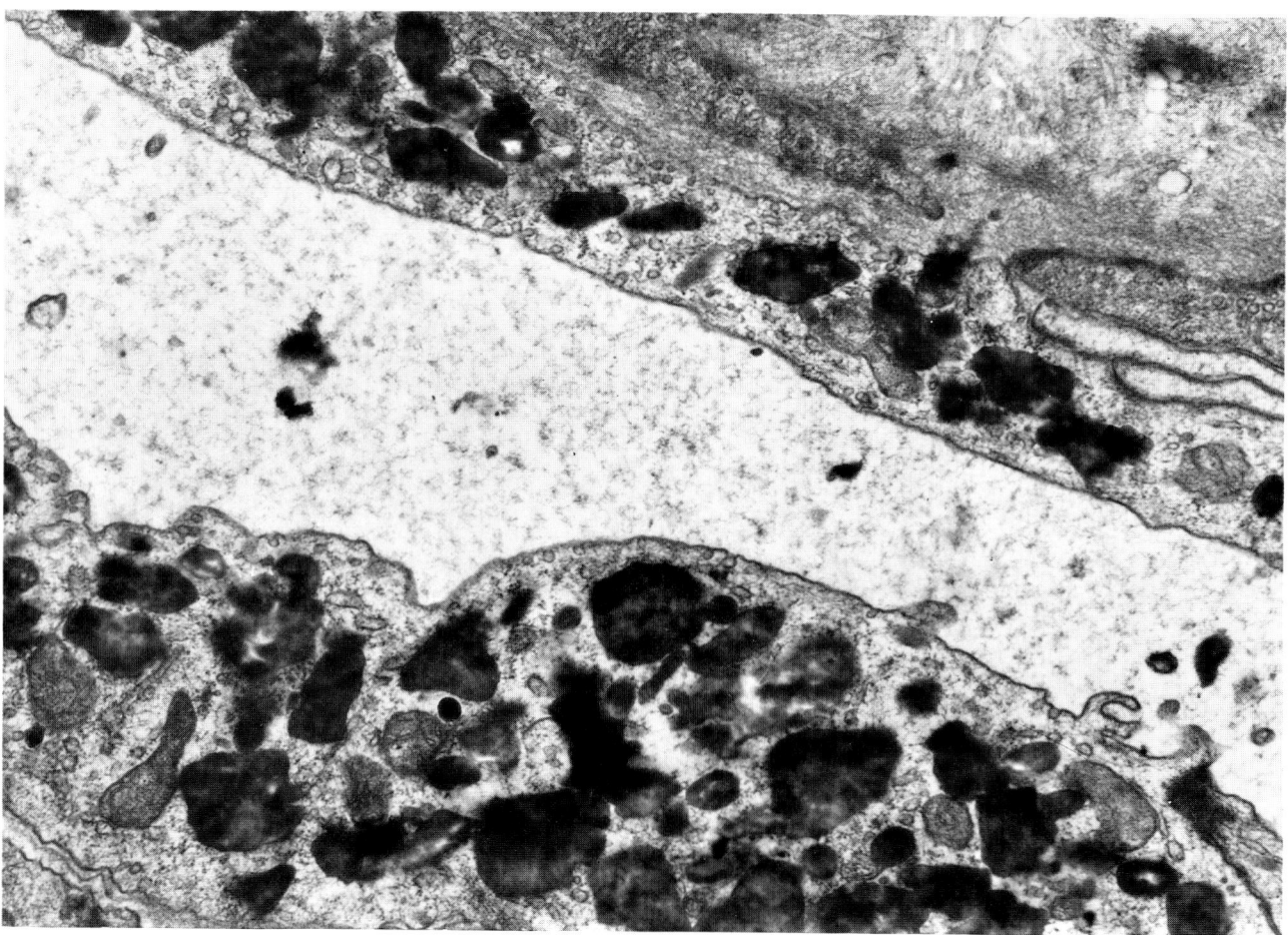

then presumably gains access to vascular endothelial and smooth-muscle cells throughout the body by the high affinity lipoprotein receptor–mediated uptake pathway.[298–300] Deposits in other tissues also may be derived to a lesser extent from receptor-independent diffusion or by nonabsorptive endocytosis of globoside- or globotriaosylceramide-lipoprotein complexes from the plasma. Since lysosomes in all cells are deficient in the α-galactosidase activity needed to degrade the deposited glycosphingolipids, the glycosphingolipids accumulate within extended multivesicular bodies or, in more advanced stages, as free intracytoplasmic masses which may lead to cellular dysfunction or degeneration.

In addition to biosynthesis in hepatocytes, glycosphingolipids are synthesized in the bone marrow, where they become incorporated into the membranes of the formed blood elements.[13,179,301] It has been postulated that erythrocyte globoside, the predominant glycosphingolipid of erythrocytes and the catabolic precursor of globotriaosylceramide (Fig. 70-11), may be another major metabolic source of the circulating pathogenic lipid. Globoside is presumably released into the circulation from senescent erythrocytes[179] and is subsequently catabolized (presumably in the spleen) to globotriaosylceramide. In Fabry disease, the globotriaosylceramide cannot be metabolized and may be partly released into the circulation where it can be incorporated into both HDL and LDL fractions[297] and/or rapidly cleared by the liver as has been shown for intravenously administered neutral glycosphingolipids.[302] Thus, the turnover of erythrocyte and other membrane glycosphingolipids may contribute significantly to the substrate load in Fabry disease. In addition, a minor amount of globotriaosylceramide may be "excreted" into the circulation from the secondary lysosomes of various cell types throughout the body. Since the glycosphingolipid cannot be catabolized in the circulation, it would slowly acccumulate at a rate reflecting the turnover of various cells, the contribution from exocytosis, and lipoprotein uptake and/or diffusion.

The metabolism of at least two other glycosphingolipids is also abnormal, as demonstrated by the accumulation of galabiosylceramide, and the blood group B substances. Hemizygous and heterozygous individuals who are blood group B or AB appear to be more severely affected, presumably due to the additional accumulation of B-specific glycosphingolipids.[35] Thus, the total amount of glycosphingolipid stored in a given tissue depends on time, the rate of accumulation from intracellular and circulatory sources, the possibilities for excretion, the individual's ABO blood type, and the presence or absence of residual α-galactosidase activity (see "Genetic Variants").

The pattern of glycosphingolipid accumulation—predominantly in the cardiovascular-renal system—best correlates pathophysiologically with the major clinical manifestations of the disease as selectively described below.

Vasculature

Narrowing, dilatation, motor unresponsiveness, and instability of blood vessels are major features of the altered physiology in Fabry disease. The swollen vascular endothelial cells, often accompanied by endothelial proliferation, encroach upon the lumen (Figs. 70-5 and 70-22), causing a focal increase of intraluminal pressure, dilatation, and angiectases as well as peripheral ischemia or frank infarction.[138] Such changes are frequently the precursors of thromboses and infarcts of the brain and other tissues. Muscle and peripheral nerve ischemia may contribute to the pain or fatigue.[125,303]

There may be progressive aneurysmal dilatation of the weakened vascular wall. This process is apparent in the progressive dilatation and microaneurysm formation of the retinal and conjunctival vessels and in the transition from normality to telangiectasia and frank angiokeratoma in the skin. Observed alterations of vasomotor control may reflect either the vascular lesions themselves or the extensive glycosphingolipid deposits in autonomic ganglia and perineural sheath cells (e.g., Refs. 126, 304, 305). Hemizygotes and heterozygotes with Fabry disease demonstrate an impaired ability for vasoconstriction, and the more severely involved hemizygotes show, in addition, an inability to vasodilate. Such a combined vascular and neural lesion may also explain the clinically observed temperature intolerance.

Nervous System

The involvement of peripheral and central autonomic nerve cells may be responsible for the paresthesias, pain, hypohidrosis, such gastrointestinal symptoms as nausea and diarrhea, and a variety of vague neurologic signs and symptoms. Fukuhara et al.[303] found marked degeneration of the secretory cells and myoepithelial cells of sweat glands by electron microscopy and proposed that the hypohidrosis was due to local lipid deposition rather than autonomic nervous system involvement. The episodic fevers may be related to lesions of the hypothalamus.[73] The observation of a selective decrease in the number of unmyelinated and small myelinated fibers in peripheral nerves[17,79,116,120,121,123,124,128,304,306,307] has led to the suggestion that the selective damage to these fibers may account for the production of pain and hypohidrosis in this disorder. Studies of autonomic function revealed sympathetic and parasympathetic dysfunction, particularly in distal cutaneous responses;[126,304] the diminished cutaneous flare responses are presumably due to the involvement and loss of peripheral unmyelinated fibers.[308] Alternatively, it has been suggested that the lipid deposition in the vasa nervorum may lead to the acroparesthesias rather than involvement of the autonomic nervous system.[303,304,306] Histochemical evidence of glycosphingolipid accumulation in neurons and nerve fibers of intestinal nerve plexuses and smooth muscle[89] may account for the uncoordinated intestinal smooth-muscle activity in Fabry hemizygotes which may lead to complaints of chronic diarrhea or constipation. Glycolipid deposition in the myenteric and submucosal plexuses and a marked decrease in argyrophilic neurons was observed in an involved segment of bowel from a Fabry hemizyote who had jejunal diverticulosis and perforation.

Kidney

The observed abnormalities in renal function have their basis in lesions of the nephron and of the renal vasculature, and possibly in disorders of the posterior pituitary and hypothalamus. Glycosphingolipid deposits antedate clinical signs and symptoms. During this early period, the lesions of the renal vasculature are less prominent than those of the nephron, and renal architecture is maintained. The observed mild proteinuria may be explained by alteration of the glomerular epithelial cells and their foot processes[117] and/or by increased desquamation of lipid-laden tubular epithelial cells.[116]

Loss of renal concentrating ability with polyuria and polydipsia may occur well in advance of a significant decrease in glomerular filtration or evidence of renal failure.[71] The defect in concentrating ability may be due to decreased water permeability of the distal tubules and collecting ducts secondary to lipid deposition. The diabetes insipidus–like syndrome, which is not related to faulty electrolyte transfer in distal tubules, may result from tubular insensitivity to antidiuretic hormone or to combined dysfunction of the renal tubular cells and lesions of the glycosphingolipid-laden supraoptic nucleus and antidiuretic center of the hypothalamus. The later and more severe renal changes are the result of vascular lesions and of systemic hypertension.

Heart

The progressive deposition of glycosphingolipids in the myocardial cells, the valvular fibrocytes, and the coronary vessels is the primary cause of cardiac disease in hemizygotes and some heterozygotes.[16,48,49] The frequent findings of left ventricular hypertrophy and mitral insufficiency are presumably related to the fact that the left ventricular myocardium and the mitral valve are the sites of the most marked lipid deposition in the heart.[16] The abnormally short PR interval and the finding of cardiomyopathy on ECG may be related to lipid deposition in the myocardium and/or conduction system.[50,55] The marked deposition of globotriaosylceramide in the coronary arteries leads to myocardial ischemia and frank infarction.[16,48,49]

Other Involvement

Pulmonary symptoms have been attributed to involvement of lung vasculature or bronchial and mucous gland epithelium.[82] The airflow obstruction may be due to the loss of elastic recoil secondary to lipid deposition in lung parenchyma. The lymphedema presumably results from lymphatic obstruction or venous insufficiency secondary to lipid-laden endothelial cells. Reports of growth retardation, delayed puberty, slow beard growth, or impaired fertility associated with a decrease of gonadotropins, may correlate with observations of testicular atrophy[309] or with glycosphingolipid storage in the interstitial cells of the testis or in anterior and posterior lobes of the pituitary gland.[132] No explanations have been offered for the frequently observed acromegaliclike appearance.

DIAGNOSIS

Genetic counseling should be made available to all families in which the diagnosis of Fabry disease is made[310] (see "Genetic and Family Counseling"). Inheritance of the Fabry gene from hemizygotes and heterozygotes should be considered, since both genotypes transmit the gene. In each family, all at-risk males should be diagnostically evaluated. All possible carriers should be examined clinically and biochemically for heterozygote identification. In addition, it may be necessary to carry out molecular studies in order to more accurately determine the genotype of women at risk for inheriting the disease gene (see "Molecular Diagnosis"). Fabry disease has been detected antenatally from cultured fetal cells and amniotic fluid obtained by amniocentesis as well as from chorionic villi (see "Prenatal Diagnosis," below).

Clinical Evaluation

The clinical diagnosis in hemizygous males is most readily made from the history and by observation of the characteristic skin lesions and corneal dystrophy. The most common childhood symptom before appearance of the cutaneous lesions is recurrent fever in association with pain of the hands and feet. The disorder has often been misdiagnosed as rheumatic fever, neurosis, erythromelalgia, or collagen vascular disease. Differential diagnosis of the cutaneous lesions must exclude the angiokeratoma of Fordyce,[311,312] angiokeratoma of Mibelli,[142,313] and angiokeratoma circumscriptum,[314,315] none of which have the typical histologic or ultrastructural pathology of the Fabry lesion (Fig. 70-6). The angiokeratoma of Fordyce are similar in appearance to those of Fabry disease, but are limited to the scrotum, and usually appear after age 30. The angiokeratoma of Mibelli are warty lesions on the extensor surfaces of extremities in young adults which are associated with chilblains. Angiokeratoma circumscriptum or naeviformus can occur anywhere on the body, are clinically and histologically similar to those of Fordyce, and are not associated with chilblains.

Angiokeratoma, reportedly similar to or indistinguishable from the clinical appearance and distribution of the cutaneous lesions in Fabry disease, have been described in patients with other lysosomal storage diseases, including fucosidosis,[316] sialidosis (α-neuraminidase deficiency with or without β-galactosidase deficiency),[317,318] adult-type β-galactosidase deficiency,[319] aspartylglucosaminuria,[320] and a recently reported lysosomal disorder which presents with mental retardation and some features of the mucopolysaccharidoses.[49,321] Ultrastructural examination of these lesions reveals lysosomal substrate deposition which differs in the fine structural appearance of the respective storage material. In addition, patients with classic-appearing angiokeratoma but no other clinical symptoms or morphologic evidence of lysosomal storage have been described;[322,323] these patients have had normal levels of α-galactosidase and other lysosomal enzymes. Clinical and pathologic details of the differential diagnosis of the skin lesions are available in reviews.[111,324,326]

Presumptive diagnosis of hemizygotes can be made by observation of the characteristic corneal dystrophy upon slit-lamp examination and by demonstration of the birefringent inclusions in the urinary sediment. Women suspected of being heterozygous carriers of the Fabry gene should be carefully examined for evidence of the corneal opacity and for isolated skin lesions, particularly on the breasts, back, trunk, and posterolateral thighs. Heterozygote detection also may be accomplished by the histologic finding of lipid-laden cells in biopsied skin and tissues or in the urinary sediment.

Genetic Variants

Although most affected hemizygotes present with the typical clinical features and disease progression, rare variants have been described with milder manifestations of disease (see "Atypical Hemizygotes").[46,96-99] In contrast to the typical patients, who have essentially no detectable α-galactosidase activity, biochemical investigation of these variants has revealed the presence of residual α-galactosidase activity, consistent with the attenuation or absence of the characteristic clinical manifestations.

Several of the reported variants have been the subjects of biochemical studies. The 51-year-old asymptomatic Arab male described by Bach and colleagues[97] had 10 percent of normal α-galactosidase activity in cultured skin fibroblasts and normal levels of globotriaosylceramide in his urinary sediment. Further enzymatic studies revealed that the residual enzymatic activity had a K_m value which was fourfold higher than normal and an increased stability. The 38-year-old Italian male described by Clark et al. had urinary sediment globotriaosylceramide levels in the heterozygote range and low levels of galabioasylceramide.[46] His total α-galactosidase activity (A and B) in cultured skin fibroblasts and leukocytes was about 30 percent of normal. Subsequently, his residual α-galactosidase activity in cultured fibroblasts was partially purified and shown to have kinetic and thermostability properties similar to those of α-galactosidase from normal fibroblasts. About 20 percent of normal α-galactosidase activity was detected in his fibroblasts, but the amount of cross-reactive immunologic material (CRIM) was not measured.[99] The 42-year-old asymptomatic Italian male with severe rheumatoid arthritis described by Bishop et al.[96] had levels of α-galactosidase activity that were about 1 percent of normal in plasma and urine. Immunoprecipitation with monospecific anti-α-galactosidase antibodies demonstrated residual activity in granulocytes, lymphocytes, platelets, liver, and cultured fibroblasts ranging from 9 to 37 percent of the respective normal levels. The immunoprecipitated residual α-galactosidase activity from fibroblasts had the same kinetic and physical properties as the immunoprecipitated enzyme from normal fibroblasts. Rocket immunoelectrophoresis studies demonstrated that the level of α-galactosidase activity corresponded to the amount of enzyme protein. However, compared to the normal enzyme, the residual fibroblast α-galactosidase was more thermolabile at pH 4.6 and 50°C and significantly less stable at pH 7.4 and 37°C. This finding was consistent with the extremely low enzyme levels in plasma and urine. Interestingly, the levels of globotriaosylceramide in plasma and urinary sediment were both in the low heterozygote range. No lysosomal inclusions were observed in hepatocytes or Kupffer cells in percutaneously biopsied liver. These findings are consistent with a stability mutation, resulting in an enzyme with normal kinetics. In this variant, it appears that 10 to 40 percent of normal intracellular activity is sufficient to prevent the clinical manifestations of the disease. In addition, the finding of only 1 percent of enzymatic activity in the plasma and low levels of plasma globotriaosylceramide suggests that circulating enzyme is not required to catabolize the plasma substrate.

The 26-year-old Japanese variant described by Kobayashi et al.[98] had no α-galactosidase activity in cultured fibroblasts when assayed with synthetic substrates. However, loading studies indicated that his cultured fibroblasts were able to hydrolyze some of the exogenously supplied substrate, suggesting the presence of residual activity toward the natural substrate.

An intriguing variant was recently identified with onset of myocardial disease only at 54 years of age.[101] No ultrastructural evidence of substrate deposition was observed in myocardial capillaries, but typical lysosomal inclusions were observed in myocytes from an endocardial biopsy. No histologic or ultrastructural evidence of lysosomal substrate deposition was observed in biopsied skeletal muscle, liver, rectum, and skin, including the small vessels and nerves in these tissues. The subject's plasma globotriaosylceramide concentration (4.2 nmol/ml) was only slightly higher than the levels in his normal brothers (3.6 and 4.0 nmol/ml), while his urinary sediment concentration was at the low end of the heterozygote range.

His α-galactosidase activities ranged from 2 to 22 percent of the respective normal mean values in granulocytes (lowest), urine, lymphocytes, cultured lymphoblasts and fibroblasts, and plasma (highest). Southern and Northern hybridization analyses revealed a normal gene structure and a normal quantity and quality of α-galactosidase mRNA. The fact that the manifestations of disease in this variant were limited to the myocardium in the sixth decade of life is of interest, particularly in the absence of histologic evidence of small vessel involvement or clinically manifest renal disease. Apparently the mutant enzyme in this variant was sufficiently active in vivo to limit substrate deposition.

Among lysosomal storage disorders, the rate of clinical progression in Fabry disease is among the slowest, reflecting the normally low rate of substrate metabolism. Therefore, it can be anticipated that other atypical variants who are asymptomatic or express subtle renal and/or cardiac manifestations of the disease will be discovered in the future.

Phenocopies

A phenocopy is a phenotypic mimic or simulation of a specific genetic trait. Since a phenocopy is usually the result of environmental factors, it is not inherited. There are two such phenocopies for Fabry disease, one that mimics the characteristic corneal opacity, and another that causes functional and ultrastructural renal changes resembling those in hemizygotes. Since the diagnosis of Fabry disease is often suspected from an eye examination or renal evaluation for proteinuria, these phenocopies have significant diagnostic import.

The whorllike keratopathy of Fabry disease is readily distinguished from the corneal opacities of other lysosomal storage disorders, but is clinically and ultrastructurally identical to the corneal dystrophy associated with long-term chloroquine therapy.[327,328] Chloroquine has been shown to concentrate rapidly in lysosomes, increase the intralysosomal pH, decrease the activity of specific lysosomal hydrolases, alter the rate of proteolysis, and cause the formation of lysosomal inclusions. Based on these findings, it has been proposed that the chloroquine-induced keratopathy results from the pH inactivation of lysosomal α-galactosidase and the subsequent accumulation of globotriaosylceramide.[328] In support of this concept is the finding that corneal α-galactosidase is more sensitive to increasing pH in vitro than other lysosomal hydrolases.[32,329] Similar studies have shown that chloroquine inactivated the α-galactosidase activity in cultured human skin fibroblasts.[330] These findings demonstrate the likely mechanism responsible for the phenocopy and represent the first biochemical elucidation of a human phenocopy. More recently, amiodarone has been shown to cause a phenocopy of the Fabry keratopathy. The mechanism underlying the amiodarone-induced pathology has not been characterized,[331] although it is presumed to act like chloroquine. Lipid-laden lysosomes have been observed in nerve and muscle biopsy specimens of amiodarone-treated patients who developed a neuromyopathy.[139a]

Another tissue-specific phenocopy of Fabry disease occurs in individuals who are environmentally exposed to silica dust. The pulmonary complications of silicolipoproteinosis have been described, but the renal manifestations of proteinuria and lipiduria have received little attention. Ultrastructural examination of renal tissue from these individuals has revealed the typical electron-dense lamellar inclusions in the lysosomes of glomerular epithelial and endothelial cells and proximal and distal tubular cells observed in Fabry disease.[33,333] The levels of α-galactosidase and urinary sediment glycosphingolipids were normal in one such patient.[333] Although the mechanism responsible for the silica-induced phenocopy is unknown, the finding of such lesions in biopsied renal tissue should include silicosis as well as Fabry disease in the differential diagnosis.

Biochemical Diagnosis of Affected Hemizygotes

All suspect hemizygotes should be confirmed biochemically by the demonstration of deficient α-galactosidase activities in plasma or serum, leukocytes, tears, biopsied tissues, or cultured skin fibroblasts (e.g., Refs. 23, 24, 195, 197, 334 335). Classically affected hemizygotes usually have no detectable α-galactosidase activity when the assay is performed with synthetic substrates for α-galactosidase with the addition of N-acetylgalactosamine in the reaction mixture to inhibit the α-N-acetylgalactosaminidase (formerly designated α-galactosidase B) activity.[335] This assay modification permits the reliable diagnosis of classically affected hemizygotes (Fig. 70-23).

Atypical hemizygotes may be detected by the presence of residual α-galactosidase activity ranging from less than 5 to 35 percent of normal. Variants have been detected with high levels of activity in plasma (~30 percent) and low levels (2 to 10 percent) in cellular sources; with absent or low levels in plasma and higher levels (5 to 25 percent) in cultured cells and tissues; as well as with low, but detectable residual activity in both plasma and cellular sources.[96,97,99,101] In most variants studied, the levels of residual activity have been highest (20 to 30 percent of normal) in cultured skin fibroblasts.[96–99,101] The kinetic and stability properties of the residual α-galactosidase should be determined as well as the levels of globotriaosylceramide in various fluid and cellular sources. Such studies are required to establish the biochemical diagnosis of atypical variants and to gain information on the structural and functional properties of these mutant enzymes.

Molecular Diagnosis of Fabry Heterozygotes

The biochemical identification of female carriers of the Fabry gene is less reliable due to random X-chromosomal inactivation.[107] Many heterozygous females can be detected by intermediate levels of α-galactosidase activity in various sources. However, due to random X-chromosomal inactivation, heterozygotes can express levels of enzymatic activity ranging from essentially zero to normal. Thus, reports of obligate heterozygotes with normal α-galactosidase activity and no keratopathy[75,106,336] are not unexpected and emphasize the need for precise carrier detection. In addition, recent evidence suggests that inactivated X-chromosomal genes may become reactivated as a result of aging and decreased levels of 5-methyldeoxycytidine.[337–339] Thus, the demethylation of X-chromosomal genes may explain the not infrequent observation that older obligate heterozygotes have levels of α-galactosidase activity at the high end of the heterozygote range or within the normal range. Clearly, this recently recognized aging phenomenon may further obscure precise enzymatic diagnosis of heterozygotes.

In the past, attempts to accurately establish heterozygosity have required the demonstration of both normal and mutant cell populations by α-galactosidase assays of single hair roots[60,340–342] or by the laborious and procedurally difficult cloning[108] or cell sorting[343] of individual fibroblasts. These studies are extremely time-consuming, require special expertise to perform, and may be difficult to interpret.[105] Therefore, molecular analyses using the α-galactosidase cDNA or closely linked X-chromosomal anonymous DNA sequences[344–346] may provide for more accurate heterozygote detection. The identification of a gene rearrangement, a restriction endonuclease cleavage site alteration, or a specific point mutation detectable by use of a specific restriction enzyme or synthetic oligonucleotide probe will permit the precise diagnosis of heterozygotes in families with those specific alterations. However, since only 5 percent of Fabry families have gene rearrange-

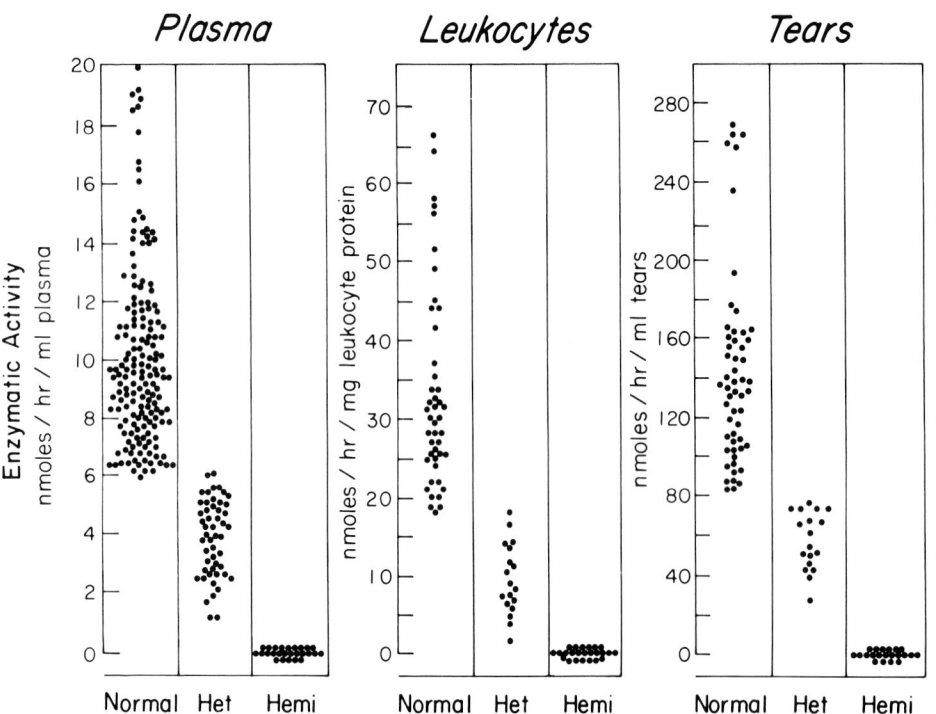

Fig. 70-23 Levels of α-galactosidase activity in plasma (or serum),[23] isolated leukocytes,[23] and tears[24] from normal individuals (N) and heterozygotes (Het) and hemizygotes (Hemi) with Fabry disease.

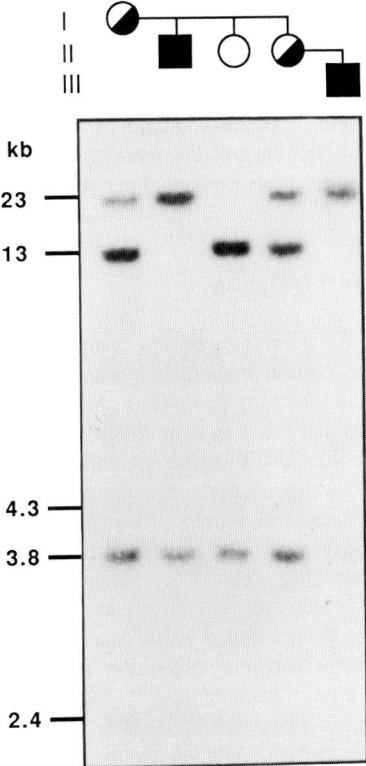

Fig. 70-24 Southern hybridization analysis of a Fabry family informative for the α-galactosidase-specific NcoI restriction fragment length polymorphism. Genomic DNA from each family member was digested with NcoI and hybridized to the radiolabeled α-galactosidase full-length cDNA. Note that the grandmother has both the common 13-kb fragment and the rarer 23-kb fragment. The mutant Fabry gene is inherited on the chromosome with the 23-kb fragment. Heterozygosity for Fabry disease can be excluded in the female who is homozygous for the 13-kb fragment.

using over 40 different restriction endonucleases. Only two RFLPs were identified using the full-length cDNA as probe.[253,347] Digestion of normal DNA with SacI and NcoI revealed RFLPs within and 3′ to the α-galactosidase gene, respectively. The rare form of the SacI polymorphism was observed in 8 percent of normal alleles and in only 2 percent of unrelated Fabry families studied. The rare form of the NcoI polymorphism was observed in 13 percent of normal alleles and in 12 percent of Fabry families. In each of these Fabry families, the locus-specific RFLPs were useful for precise carrier detection (Fig. 70-24). No linkage disequilibrium was observed between the Fabry allele and an RFLP, and no recombinants were observed in studies of affected hemizygotes, obligate heterozygotes, and their offspring. The finding of only two RFLPs in and adjacent to the α-galactosidase gene, whose coding region spans about 10 kb, is not unexpected for X-linked sequences.[348] Since the majority of polymorphisms are located in introns,[349] it may be useful to identify more frequent and, therefore, more informative locus-specific RFLPs using unique intronic sequences.

Linked Polymorphic Anonymous DNA Sequences. Another approach for heterozygote detection in Fabry families without readily detectable molecular lesions is the use of anonymous polymorphic DNA sequences that are closely linked to the Fabry locus (Xq21.33→q22). Several such RFLPs have been identified proximal (e.g., DXYS1 and DXS3), near (e.g., DXS17, DXS87, and DXS88), and distal (e.g., DXS11) to the locus for α-galactosidase.[251–253,344–346] Studies of the segregation of DXS17 and DXS87 in five informative Fabry families proved the usefulness of these probes.[251,252] No recombination was observed between the Fabry locus and DXS17 and DXS87, which gave lod$_{max}$ scores of 5.8 and 6.4, respectively, at θ = 0.0.[41,47] These findings suggested that these anonymous DNA sequences were close to the α-galactosidase locus and were informative in most families. More recent data[253] demonstrated that these probes were informative in only about 70 percent of the 42 families evaluated in our laboratory (Table 70-5). Several recombinants for both DXS17 and DXS87 were observed in the same individual, which suggests that both DNA fragments are on the same side of the α-galactosidase locus.[347] The calculated lod scores for these and previously reported data[41,47] indicated that these probes were about 1 to 2 centimorgans from the α-galactosidase locus.[253] Additional probes assigned to the region Xq21→q24 also have been evaluated including DXS94,[350] DXS72,[351] DXS106,[351] DXS287,[352] and a cDNA

ments or restriction site alterations, it may not be feasible or practical to attempt the identification of the specific molecular defect in each family. Alternatively, molecular diagnoses may be accomplished using indirect methods. These include the analysis of α-galactosidase–specific RFLPs[347] as well as RFLPs for anonymous X-chromosomal DNA probes that are closely linked to the α-galactosidase locus.[251–253,344–346]

Locus-Specific RFLPs. In order to identify α-galactosidase–specific RFLPs, genomic DNA obtained from normal females and males of various ethnic and racial groups was analyzed

Table 70-5 Informativeness and Segregation Analysis of Linked RFLPs and Fabry Disease

	DXS17	DXS87	DXS106	DXS287	DXS94	DXS72	PLP
Number of families studied	46	53	20	10	7	14	26
Percent informative	41	32	40	40	43	64	0
Number of informative meioses analyzed	82	67	28	23	21	9	—
Percent recombinants	8.0	9	14	9	10	0	—
(θ) Recombination fraction	0.01	0.01	0.05	0.1	0.1	—	—
Lod$_{max}$ these data	3.32	0.31	2.88	2.71	2.47	—	—
Lod$_{max}$ previous data[251,252]	5.55	6.31	—	—	—	—	—
Lod$_{max}$ total	8.87	6.62	2.88	2.71	2.47	—	—

sequence for proteolipid protein (PLP; Ref. 353) (Table 70-5). Of these, segregation analysis in informative Fabry families of DXS72, DXS94, and DXS106 revealed a sufficient number of recombinants to indicate that these RFLPs were not linked close enough to the Fabry locus to be useful diagnostically. Analysis of 25 unrelated Fabry heterozygotes for PLP did not reveal a single polymorphism. In contrast, DXS287 was informative in about 30 percent of the 12 families studied.[253] Although the lod score for DXS287 has not been determined, preliminary results suggest that it may be a useful RFLP for identification of Fabry heterozygotes.[253]

Prenatal Diagnosis

Prenatal diagnosis of Fabry disease can be accomplished by the assay of α-galactosidase activity in chorionic villi obtained at 9 to 10 weeks of pregnancy or in cultured amniotic cells obtained by amniocentesis at approximately 15 weeks of pregnancy.[25,26,354–356] The prenatal diagnosis of an affected hemizygous male fetus minimally requires the demonstration of deficient α-galactosidase activity and an XY karyotype.

Biochemical and ultrastructural studies of tissues from fetuses with Fabry disease have been reported.[25,354–356] Consistent with the prenatal diagnosis, the α-galactosidase activity was deficient in all tissues studied; slightly increased concentrations of globotriaosylceramide were found in all tissues analyzed with the exception of neural tissues.[354] Histologic and light-microscopic examination of various tissues were unremarkable, but ultrastructural examination revealed electron-dense concentric lamellar inclusions in the lysosomes of vascular endothelium, renal tubules, epithelial and endothelial cells of renal glomeruli, and epithelial cells of the cornea.[356]

TREATMENT

Medical Management

In Fabry disease, the chronicity of the clinical events causes severe debilitation and incapacity that extends over years. The single most debilitating and morbid aspect of Fabry disease is the excruciating pain. The pathophysiological events that cause the incapacitating episodes of pain or the chronic burning acroparesthesias have not been clarified. Numerous drugs have been tried for the relief of these agonizing pains.[10] The α-adrenergic blocking agent, phenoxybenzamine, which increases peripheral vascular flow, has been administered for pain relief; although this drug provided relief in a hemizygote on several occasions, priapism and epistaxis were early complications in two other hemizygotes.[86] With the exception of centrally acting narcotic analgesics, which have been only partially effective, conventional analgesic agents have not been helpful. However, prophylactic administration of low maintenance dosages of diphenylhydantoin have been found to provide relief from the periodic crises of excruciating pain and constant discomfort in hemizygotes and heterozygotes.[38] Lenoir et al.[357] noted that carbamazepine also provided pain relief. The combination of diphenylhydantoin and carbamazepine significantly reduced the pain in an affected hemizygote.[358] Subsequent reports have further documented the effectiveness of diphenylhydantoin and/or carbamazepine in the prevention and amelioration of these debilitating pains.[359]

Care of patients with regard to cardiac, pulmonary, and central nervous system manifestations remains nonspecific and symptomatic. Obstructive lung disease has been documented in older hemizygotes and heterozygotes, with more severe impairment in smokers; therefore, patients should be discouraged from smoking. Angiokeratoma can be removed for cosmetic appearance or other indications by argon laser treatment with little, if any, scarring.[360,361]

Dialysis and Renal Transplantation

Since renal insufficiency is the most frequent late complication in patients with this disease, chronic hemodialysis and/or renal transplantation have become lifesaving procedures. Successful transplantation will correct renal function. The α-galactosidase in the allograft will catabolize the turnover of endogenous renal glycosphingolipid substrates. Reports of substrate accumulation in transplanted cadaveric kidneys have identified rare, isolated deposits, observable only by electron microscopy, in infiltrating mononuclear cells[362] or nonglomerular capillary endothelial cells.[132] However, it is important to note that the transplantation of a kidney from a Fabry heterozygote was associated with significant substrate deposition and allograft dysfunction 5 years after transplantation.[363] Therefore, all potential related donors must be carefully evaluated so that only normal individuals are chosen. Also, the immune function in Fabry hemizygotes has been shown to be similar to that in other uremic patients, indicating that there is no immunologic contraindication to transplantation in this disease.[364]

In addition to treatment of the renal failure, kidney transplantation has been undertaken to determine if the allograft could provide normal α-galactosidase for substrate metabolism.[104,365] Hypothetically, the normal kidney might metabolize the accumulated substrate by uptake and catabolism within the allograft and/or by the release of the active enzyme into the circulation for uptake and metabolism in other tissues such as the vascular endothelium. Although biochemical and/or clinical improvement has been reported in several recipients (e.g., Refs. 104, 365–369). no biochemical effect could be demonstrated in other recipients.[362,370–372] Several patients with successful engraftment, who survived for 10 to 15 years, have expired from complications of cardiac disease.[373,374] Thus, the use of renal allografts to alter the rate of progressive substrate accumulation remains unclear, and further studies are required to document the long-term biochemical effects of this strategy. In view of these results, renal transplantation should be undertaken only in patients with clinically significant renal failure.

Genetic and Family Counseling

Fabry disease is inherited as an X-linked trait.[11] All sons of hemizygous males will be unaffected, but all daughters will be obligate carriers of the gene. On the average, half the sons of heterozygous females will have the disease and half the daughters will be carriers.

At present, the most practical and effective therapy is preventive. Biochemical and molecular screening of all suspect heterozygotes, genetic counseling, and prenatal diagnostic studies should be made available to all at-risk families (see "Diagnosis"). Family and vocational counseling should be provided, especially to families with affected children. Often, parents, teachers, and/or physicians misinterpret the excruciating pain experienced during childhood as psychosomatic, especially in the absence of any objective physical or laboratory findings. Since physical exertion, emotional stresses, and fatigue as well as rapid changes in the environmental temperature and humidity can trigger these painful episodes, appropriate arrangements must be made with physical education teachers, employers, and other individuals to minimize or eliminate stressful activities. In addition, young hemizygotes should be allowed to pursue selected activities and be permitted to stop these activities at their own discretion. Within this perspective, reasonable occupational and vocational objectives should be pursued. Vocational counseling should discourage occupations which require significant manual dexterity, physical exertion, emotional stress, or exposure to rapid changes in temperature or humidity.

Enzyme Replacement and Substrate Depletion Strategies

Enzyme Replacement. Attempts to replace the defective α-galactosidase activity with normal enzyme have been undertaken in vitro and in vivo. Studies using partially purified α-galactosidase from fig,[375] coffee bean,[376] and human sources[377–380] added to the media of cultured skin fibroblasts from Fabry hemizygotes demonstrated the ability of the exogenous enzyme to gain access to and catabolize the accumulated substrate, globotriaosylceramide. These in vitro studies indicated the feasibility of enzyme replacement and, in particular, demonstrated that low levels (<5 percent) of exogenous enzyme, particularly the high uptake form,[378,379] were capable of normalizing substrate metabolism.

Several in vivo exploratory studies of enzyme replacement have been undertaken to determine whether such endeavors can decrease the circulating accumulated substrate concentration. Normal plasma containing active enzyme has been administered to hemizygotes with Fabry disease.[27] Although active enzyme and decreased levels of globotriaosylceramide were demonstrated in the recipients' plasmas, the major limitation was the short half-life ($t_{1/2} \sim 95$ min) of the infused enzymatic activity. Subsequently, Brady and coworkers[28] partially purified a tissue form of α-galactosidase from human placenta and intravenously administered single doses to two patients (6000 and 11,000 units, respectively). The exogenous activity was rapidly cleared from the recipients' circulation, with half-lives of 10 and 12 min, respectively. The plasma substrate was decreased about 50 percent at 45 min with a return to the preinfusion level by 48 h. In addition, the administered activity was detected in percutaneously biopsied liver at 1 h.[28]

More recently, a clinical trial of enzyme replacement was performed involving multiple injections of purified splenic and plasma forms of α-galactosidase into two brothers with Fabry disease.[29] This trial confirmed the previously observed differences in clearance rates of enzyme from the circulation and demonstrated for the first time the differential substrate depletion and reaccumulation kinetics for enzyme purified from tissue versus plasma sources.[381] The differential plasma clearance of these enzyme forms was presumably related to differences in the posttranslational modifications of these glycoproteins. The splenic form, which was rapidly cleared from the circulation ($t_{1/2} \sim 10$ min), contained few sialic acid residues. The plasma form, however, was highly sialylated and was retained in the circulation ($t_{1/2} \sim 70$ min).[29] These results are in accor-

dance with the Ashwell model for the prolonged retention of sialylated glycoproteins in the circulation and the rapid clearance of desialylated glycoproteins.[387]

A marked difference in the clearance of circulating substrate was observed after the administration of these isozymes.[29,381,383] Administration of α-galactosidase isolated from human spleen effected a rapid decrease in the plasma concentration of accumulated substrate. The level of the circulating substrate decreased to approximately 50 percent of the preinfusion values 15 min after injection, followed by a rapid return to preinfusion levels by 2 to 3 h. In contrast, the administration of α-galactosidase from human plasma resulted in a prolonged depletion of the circulating substrate. At 2 h after injection, the levels of globotriaosylceramide were decreased by 50 to 70 percent of the preinfusion values. Significantly, low levels were retained up to 12 to 24 h, and the substrate levels slowly returned to preinfusion levels after 36 to 72 h. When the total amount of substrate cleared with time was calculated by integrating the mean concentrations of globotriaosylceramide, the plasma enzyme appeared to have cleared about 25 times more substrate over time than the splenic form. When two doses were administered on subsequent days, the plasma substrate level was reduced to normal range.[381] In addition, these clinical trials demonstrated that multiple doses of either partially purified enzyme, administered over a 117-day period, did not elicit an immune response in the recipients. Although the amounts of enzyme administered were small, these studies demonstrated the feasibility of enzyme therapy for Fabry disease. The current limitation of this approach is the unavailability of the purified human enzyme. The recent cloning of the full-length cDNA encoding α-galactosidase[32] already has stimulated efforts to use prokaryotic and eukaryotic systems for the expression of large amounts of enzyme for future trials of replacement therapy (see "Molecular Genetics of α-Galactosidase"). Only when large amounts of active enzyme are available will it be possible to properly evaluate the short- and long-term biochemical and clinical effects of enzyme replacement endeavors.

Fetal Liver Transplantation. Fetal liver has been transplanted in three hemizygotes with Fabry disease in an attempt to replace the deficient enzyme.[384] The rise and subsequent fall in the levels of serums α-fetoprotein evidenced the initial survival and subsequent maturation (or possible loss) of the fetal cells.[385] Following transplantation, the α-galactosidase levels in serums and leukocytes were unchanged and the substrate levels in urine and serums were slightly decreased. However, the recipients noted subjective clinical improvement (e.g., increased sweating, no acroparesthesias, slightly decreased angiokeratoma). The effectiveness of fetal liver transplantation must await the long-term evaluation of these recipients to document its efficacy.

Substrate Depletion. Another approach employed to deplete the accumulated circulating substrate has been chronic plasmapheresis.[386] This strategy was designed to deplete the accumulated substrate from the circulation prior to its deposition in the vascular wall and other cellular sites. Three plasmaphereses, performed at 2-day intervals, resulted in a 70 percent reduction of the level of circulating globotriaosylceramide to a value within the normal range. A total of 23 mg of substrate was removed. The plasma substrate levels slowly returned to preplasmapheresis levels in 5 days. Similar results have been observed with chronic plasmapheresis performed over a 6-month period.[387] A major question to be resolved with this approach is whether intervention by chronic plasmapheresis will deplete enough substrate in relation to the amount newly synthesized that the net result will be decreased substrate deposition in the target sites of pathology, particularly the vascular endothelium. Since most of the circulating globotriaosylceramide is transported by the LDL particle, the use of an anti-LDL-affinity column may permit the selective, more efficient, and safer removal of the accumulated plasma substrate. Thus, further evaluation is required to determine the value of this strategy in Fabry disease. Another therapeutic attempt to decrease the plasma substrate levels involved chronic phlebotomies, which were performed in an attempt to remove senescent erythrocytes, a source of the accumulated glycosphingolipid.[388] However, following chronic blood depletion for almost 6 months, the levels of plasma globotriaosylceramide unexpectedly increased, indicating that this approach was not therapeutic.

Recent reviews of the various approaches for the treatment of enzyme deficiency diseases are available.[389,390]

α-N-ACETYLGALACTOSAMINIDASE DEFICIENCY: SCHINDLER DISEASE

Schindler disease is a recently recognized neurodegenerative disease resulting from the deficient activity of the lysosomal hydrolase α-N-acetylgalactosaminidase.[391-393] The enzymatic defect, transmitted as an autosomal recessive trait, leads to the accumulation of glycoconjugates containing α-linked galactosaminyl residues. Eosinophilic lesions have been observed in terminal axons, primarily in gray matter and in the myenteric plexus. The precise nature of the storage material has not been determined. The disease was first recognized in two brothers, the offspring of a consanguineous couple of German descent. The affected infants developed normally until 9 to 12 months of life, then experienced a rapid regression of developmental milestones. By 3 to 4 years of age, the affected brothers were cortically blind and had spasticity, frequent myoclonic seizures, and profound psychomotor retardation. They functioned developmentally at the level of newborn infants.

HISTORICAL ASPECTS

Although this disorder is one of the most recently described, its history is both interesting and instructive. In the past, the delineation of lysosomal storage diseases with primary neurologic involvement was the domain of the astute neurologist-neuropathologist. Recognition of developmental regression in siblings was often the clue, but key to the identification and classification of these disorders was the expert neuropathologic examination. Such was the case for the original descriptions of neurodegenerative disorders with minimal, if any, visceral involvement including Tay-Sachs disease,[394,395] Krabbe disease,[396] and metachromatic leukodystrophy.[397] More recently, the application of modern ultrastructural, biochemical, and cell culture techniques has facilitated the identification of a variety of new metabolic disorders and disease variants. Of the recently described lysosomal disorders, e.g., galactosialidosis,[398] Salla disease,[399] and β-mannosidosis,[400,401] it is notable that each had prominent visceral manifestations similar to

those found in other lysosomal storage diseases which led to their elucidation (e.g., dysostosis multiplex, cherry-red maculae, and/or organomegaly). Key to the recognition of these disorders has been physician suspicion, phenotypic clues, and the diligent pursuit of the pathologic and biochemical defects.

Such was the brief historical trail that led Detlev Schindler, a human geneticist at the University of Wuerzburg in Germany, to identify this neurologic disease. He saw the index family in 1985 when the parents sought genetic counseling concerning the prognosis for their two affected sons and the possible reproductive risks for their normal son and other relatives. Although the affected brothers had been evaluated by many specialists, the absence of visceral manifestations did not provide diagnostic clues suggestive of a storage disease. No diagnosis had been made other than "psychomotor delay." Schindler suspected that the two affected brothers had an autosomal recessive metabolic disease since they experienced a remarkably similar regressive course and since the parents came from a small, inbred village. With parental consent, renewed efforts were undertaken to establish a diagnosis. Schindler began systematically; cultured lymphoblast and fibroblast lines were established, and urine and blood were collected for biochemical analyses. Initially, he had a variety of metabolic screening tests performed by various expert laboratories in Europe. The first positive finding was the abnormal urinary oligosaccharide profile observed by H. Christomanou in Munich. This pattern has not been previously seen in the known storage diseases with oligosacchariduria. This finding led Schindler to determine the activities of the lysosomal enzymes whose deficiencies result in oligosacchariduria. He arranged for his colleagues Christomanou, K. Harzer in Tuebingen, R. Sengers in Nijmegen, and A. Sewell in Mainz to assay various lysosomal enzyme activities in the leukocytes of the affected brothers. All the activities were normal. Subsequently, M. Cantz of Heidelberg determined that the neuraminidase activity, free and bound neuraminic acid content, and the mucopolysaccharide ^{35}S incorporation studies were normal in cultured fibroblasts from the propositi. He also repeated the urinary oligosaccharide screening studies and confirmed the original findings. Since Schindler was eager to characterize the nature of the abnormal oligosaccharides, he was referred to H. Egge, a glycoconjugate expert at the University of Bonn. Urines from the two brothers were analyzed, and the markedly increased amount of the blood group A trisaccharide GalNAcα(1→3)Gal(2←1)αFuc was detected in the older sib with blood group A.

Schindler also informed H. Galjaard of Rotterdam of the status of the diagnostic studies and requested additional suggestions. Another colleague, O. van Diggelen, responded with an offer to determine the α-N-acetylgalactosaminidase activity, one of the few lysosomal enzyme activities that had not been determined. Schindler sent blood and cultured fibroblasts from the affected brothers for assay, and van Diggelen found the marked deficiency of enzymatic activity, using p-nitrophenyl-α-N-acetylgalactosaminide (pNP-α-GalNAc) as substrate. Thus, Schindler's suspicion, pursuit, and persistence were rewarded in June of 1986 by the identification of the specific enzymatic defect, which documented the discovery of a new inborn error of metabolism. Word of this discovery reached our laboratory in May 1987. We already had microsequenced homogeneous human α-N-acetylgalactosaminidase, had produced monospecific antibodies against it, and were cloning the cDNA for this enzyme. Therefore, we contacted Schindler and established a collaboration. The affected brothers were evaluated at the General Clinical Research Center of the Mount Sinai School of Medicine in November 1987. The neurologic findings were documented, the enzymatic defect was characterized further,[402] and biopsies were performed for pathologic examination by D. E. Wolfe. A significant pathologic finding was the ultrastructural observation of "tubulovesicular" material in terminal axons in the myenteric plexus of a rectal biopsy.[403] In March 1988, a brain biopsy was performed in the older brother with informed parental consent. Histologic and ultrastructural examination revealed the presence of unique deposits in terminal axons, particularly in gray matter. These neuronal alterations resembled the spheroids seen in patients with Seitelberger disease[404–408] and in Hallervorden-Spatz disease,[409–411] the infantile and juvenile forms of neuronal axonal dystrophy, respectively. However, cultured fibroblasts from several patients with Seitelberger disease, who had been diagnosed definitively at autopsy, had normal levels of α-N-acetylgalactosaminidase activity.[402] Since the ultrastructural abnormalities are similar, it is possible that the neuroaxonal dystrophies and Schindler disease share common pathophysiological alterations, presumably in the fast axonal transport pathway.[411] It is likely that patients with α-N-acetylgalactosaminidase deficiency may have been diagnosed as having Seitelberger or Hallervorden-Spatz diseases in the past, consistent with the phenotypic heterogeneity observed in the neuroaxonal dystrophies.

Since it is cumbersome to refer to this disease as α-N-acetylgalactosaminidase deficiency, and since the parents of the propositi preferred not to name the disease after their village or by their surname, it seems only fitting to designate this disorder as *Schindler disease*, an appropriate eponym acknowledging the unusual persistence of a physician who successfully pursued a diagnosis in a family suffering from this previously unrecognized neurodegenerative disorder.

CLINICAL MANIFESTATIONS

The first cases of α-N-acetylgalactosaminidase deficiency were recognized in two German brothers, the consanguineous offspring of fifth cousins of German descent.[391–393] The clinical course experienced by these patients was characterized by three stages: (1) apparently normal development in the first 9

Fig. 70-25 The affected sibs with Schindler disease at 2.3 years (left) and at 1 year (right).

G.D. 2.3 yr B.D. 1.0 yr

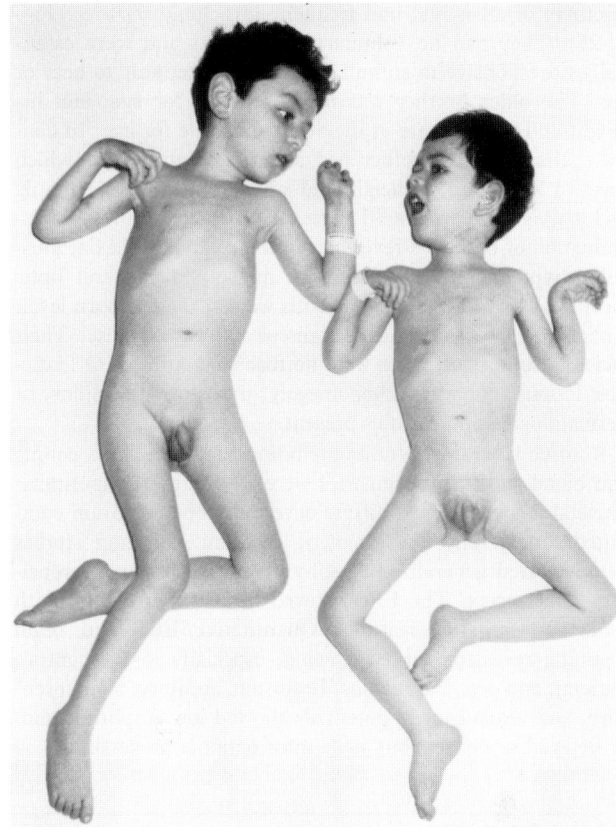

Fig. 70-26 The affected sibs at 5 years 3 months (left) and at 4 years (right).

to 12 months, (2) a period of developmental delay followed by rapid regression starting in the second year of life, and (3) increasing neurologic impairment resulting by 3 to 4 years of age in cortical blindness, myoclonic seizures, spasticity, decorticate posturing, and profound psychomotor retardation.

Normal pregnancies, labors, and deliveries had preceded the births of both affected brothers. Their early development was normal. They both sucked vigorously, had reactive smiles at 6 weeks, and began play activity in 2 to 3 months of life. They rolled over at 4 months, sat at 6½ months, and bottle-fed themselves by 6 and 9 months, respectively (Fig. 70-25). The older affected brother crawled at 9½ months and from 12 to 15 months of life developed the ability to walk independently for short distances, climb on chairs, use a spoon, and say up to 10 different words. The younger sib was more developmentally impaired. He was never able to stand from a sitting position, crawl, or learn any words.

Clinical onset of the disease in the older brother was signaled by sudden falling episodes and startle reactions at 12 months. In the younger sib, grand mal seizures began at 8 months and occurred five times over the next 6 months. Maximal development was achieved at 15 months in both brothers. Thereafter, each experienced rapid regression. The younger brother deteriorated at a faster rate. Both developed strabismus, optic atrophy, nystagmus, muscular hypotonia, and frequent myoclonic seizures. By 3 to 4 years of age, both brothers exhibited profound psychomotor retardation, were immobile, had decorticate postures and cortical blindness, and had little, if any, contact with the environment.

The physical findings of the affected brothers were essentially identical at ages 5 years, 3 months and 4 years, respectively. Both had decorticate posturing, marked flexion contractures of all joints, and frequent myoclonic seizures (Fig. 70-26). They had no voluntary movements and were essentially unresponsive to stimuli. They did not appear to hear or see. The older brother was normocephalic for age, and his height and weight were at the 50th percentile for age. In contrast, the younger brother had a head circumference which was −1 SD for age or height and a height at the 3d percentile and a weight below the 3d percentile for age. Neurologic examination of both sibs revealed symmetric hyperreflexia, muscular hypotonia, reduced muscle mass, and bilateral optic atrophy. Their developmental skills were at the newborn level. There were no other visceral signs of a storage disease. Their facies were normal, there were no macular, corneal, or lenticular lesions, nor were organomegaly, dysostosis multiplex, or dermatologic abnormalities present.

Routine laboratory studies including complete blood counts and blood and CSF chemistries were all within normal limits. Skeletal x-rays revealed diffuse severe osteopenia. Brain computed tomography and magnetic resonance imaging studies demonstrated generalized atrophy of the brain stem, cerebellum, and cortex. The EEG showed diffuse dysfunction with multifocal irritative features. Quantitative EEG and brain mapping revealed marked slowing, especially in the central, parietal, and occipital regions. Brainstem auditory, somatosensory, and visual evoked potentials showed low amplitude and/or delayed responses, but some informational processing.

PATHOLOGY

Ultrastructural alterations were observed in an autonomic axon of the myenteric plexus from a rectal biopsy. The abnormal material was "tubulovesicular" and appeared to be within membrane-bound structures in the cytoplasm of dystrophic axons (Fig. 70-27). These changes were not uniformly observed in other axons and were initially considered as possibly due to nonspecific axonal degeneration.

A brain biopsy revealed abundant storage material in the frontal cortex of the older sib.[403] On histologic examination, eosinophilic inclusions were present in all layers of the cortex and in the adjacent white matter. The inclusions were localized to the terminal axons of neurons; none was detected in

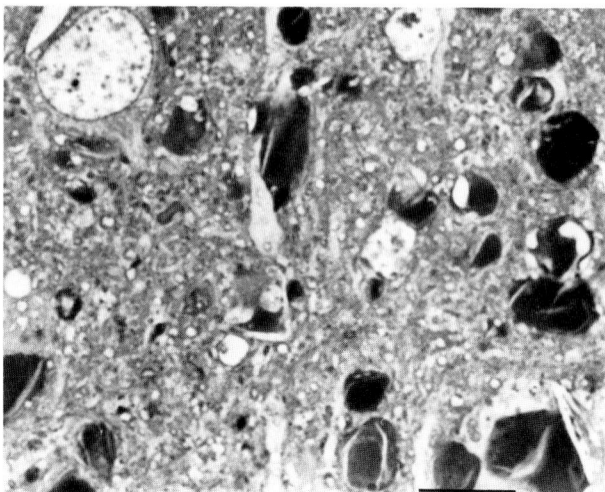

Fig. 70-28 Abundant discrete axonal spheroids throughout the cortical neuropil and in apposition to nerve cell bodies. Toludine blue–stained plastic section; bar = 10 μm. (*Courtesy of Dr. D.E. Wolfe.*)

dendrites or in nerve cell bodies (Fig. 70-28). Most interestingly, the inclusions appeared to be cytoplasmic aggregates of tubulovesicular structures and fine granular material. Occasionally, these aggregates contained membranous concentric lamellar bodies or had sharply demarcated empty clefts (Fig. 70-29). In addition, mitochondria and lysosomes were occasionally found within the abnormal aggregates. Notably, electron microscopy of blood leukocytes, secretory cells of eccrine sweat glands, myelinated axons of cutaneous nerves, and cultured fibroblasts from the affected brothers revealed the presence of inclusions with lamellar, fibrillar, vesicular, and granular material in single membrane, bound organelles. These latter observations clearly demonstrated that lysosomal storage occurs in this disease.

It is notable that similar ultrastructural findings have been observed in Seitelberger disease[404–408] and Hallervorden-Spatz disease,[409,410] the infantile and later-onset forms of neuroaxonal dystrophy. Fibroblasts from three unrelated patients with Seitelberger disease, diagnosed by ultrastructural examination, were not deficient in α-N-acetylgalactosaminidase activity.[393]

Fig. 70-27 Two dystrophic axons (*arrows*) showing abnormal tubulovesicular structures in the myenteric plexus of a rectal biopsy. Bar = 5 μm. (*Courtesy of Dr. D.E. Wolfe.*)

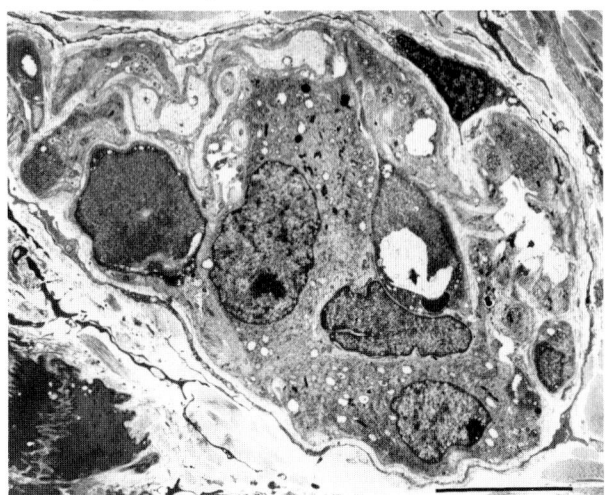

Fig. 70-29 Electron micrograph of a terminal axonal spheroid with dense membranous arrays in tubulovesicular and whorled configurations, electron-lucent clefts, and mitochondria. Bar = 1 μm. (*Courtesy of Dr. D.E. Wolfe.*)

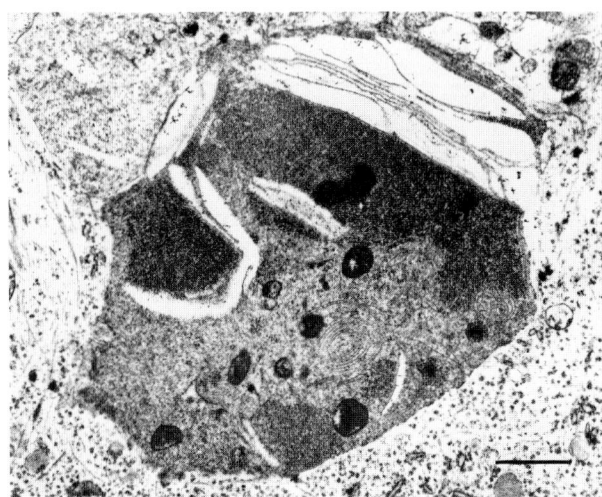

Table 70-6 α-*N*-Acetylgalactosaminidase Activities in Family D

Source	Plasma, nmol/(h · ml)	Lymphoblasts, nmol/(h · mg) protein	Fibroblasts, nmol/(h · mg) protein
G.D., affected homozygote	0.1	0.3	3.0
B.D., affected homozygote	0.2	0.2	1.7
C.D., heterozygote, mother	6.0	14.0	51.6
B.D., heterozygote, father	—	13.1	88.0
T.D., normal brother	—	32.6	148
Fabry hemizygote mean (n = 3,3,4)	12.7	32.2	153
Normal mean ± 1 SD and range (n = 53,36,33)	12.4 ± 3.1 7.8 – 25.7	43.1 ± 11.2 21.7 – 62.9	176 ± 41.1 94.3 – 260

NOTE: Assayed with 1.0 m*M* 4MU-α-*N*-acetylgalactosaminide.

Since the clinical and pathologic manifestations in Seitelberger disease and the ultrastructural findings in Hallervorden-Spatz disease are similar to those in Schindler disease, it is likely that some patients diagnosed as having neuroaxonal dystrophy actually had Schindler disease.

THE METABOLIC DEFECT IN SCHINDLER DISEASE

α-*N*-Acetylgalactosaminidase: The Enzymatic Defect

The deficient activity of lysosomal α-*N*-acetylgalactosaminidase (EC 3.2.1.49) has been identified as the specific enzymatic defect in Schindler disease.[391–393] Initially, the deficiency was detected by determining the pNP-α-GalNAc activity in plasma, leukocytes, and cultured fibroblasts from the affected sibs and other family members.[391] Using this assay, the affected sibs had apparent residual activities of 2 to 3 percent and their heterozygous parents had activities in or near the normal range. More recently, assays performed with the more sensitive, fluorogenic substrate 4-methylumbelliferyl-α-D-*N*-acetylgalactosaminide (4MU-α-GalNAc) also detected 0.5 to 2 percent residual activity in plasma, cultured fibroblasts, and cultured lymphoblasts from the affected homozygotes and provided significantly improved heterozygote discrimination (Refs. 392, 393, 402; Table 70-6).

Immunologic studies were conducted to further characterize the nature of the enzymatic defect. Using monospecific rabbit antihuman α-*N*-acetylgalactosaminidase antibodies raised against the homogeneous splenic enzyme (see "Purification," below), immunoblotting studies were performed with the purified enzyme and with cultured fibroblasts from normal individuals and members of the original family with Schindler disease.[387] Two bands of immunologically reactive material were detected in the purified enzyme preparation, and the same two bands were present in fibroblast extracts from normal individuals (Fig. 70-30). The bands were estimated to be 48 and 117 kDa. These findings suggested the presence of monomeric and homomultimeric forms of the normal enzyme, or the occurrence of two forms of human α-*N*-acetylgalactosaminidase in human tissues. Immunoblotting revealed the absence of detectable enzyme protein in cultured fibroblasts from the affected homozygotes (Fig. 70-30). It is notable that neither immunoreactive band was detectable in the affected homozygotes, suggesting that the two forms were encoded by a common gene (see "Physical Properties"). Thus, the enzymatic defect in this family was due to a mutation which resulted in the absence (or in an undetectable amount) of en-

zyme protein, consistent with the fact that only a small amount of α-*N*-acetylgalactosaminidase activity can be detected in cells from the affected homozygotes. Alternatively, it is possible that the residual activity results from an endo-α-*N*-acetylgalactosaminidase that can cleave the artificial substrates.

The nature of the accumulating glycoconjugate substrates in Schindler disease is the subject of current investigation. Presumably, glycoconjugates with terminal or internal α-*N*-acetylgalactosaminyl moieties are the natural substrates of this enzyme. α-*N*-Acetylgalactosaminyl residues are found in *O*-linked and *N*-linked glycopeptides and glycoproteins (e.g., mucins, blood group A substances), glycosphingolipids (e.g., Forssman hapten), and in proteoglycans (e.g., cartilage keratan sulfate II) (see "Nature of the Accumulated Glycoconjugates" below). To date, the only documented compound accumulating in Schindler disease is the blood group A trisaccharide. A fivefold increased urinary excretion of this trisaccharide was found in the older affected sib, who has blood type A.[391] Further characterization of the substrate specificities of human α-*N*-acetylgalactosaminidase, particularly with

Fig. 70-30 Immunoblot of human α-*N*-acetylgalactosaminidase. Fibroblast extracts from family members: mother *(lane 1)*, father *(lane 2)*, unaffected brother *(lane 3)*, and affected brothers *(lanes 4 and 5)*; a normal individual *(lane 6)*, and purified lung enzyme *(lane 7)*. Note that both bands are absent in the affected sibs.

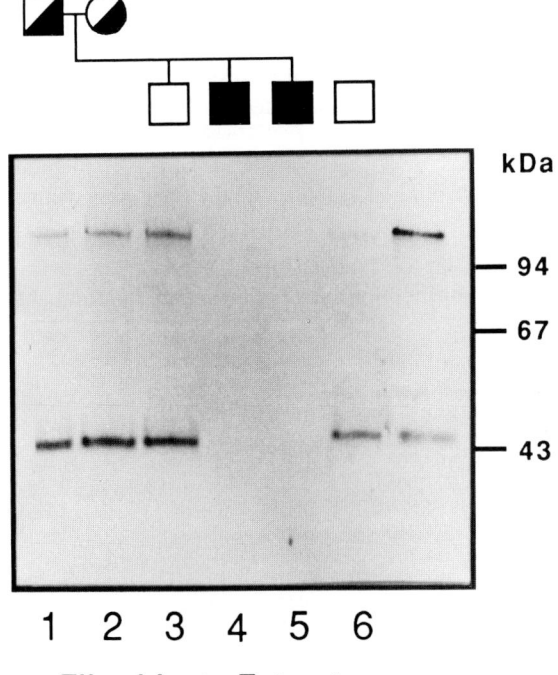

kDa

— 94

— 67

— 43

1 2 3 4 5 6

Fibroblast Extracts

reference to its function as an *exo-* or *endo*-glycosidase, will facilitate the identification and characterization of the substrates accumulating in this disease.

Human α-*N*-Acetylgalactosaminidase

α-Galactosidase B Is an α-*N*-Acetylgalactosaminidase. It is now recognized that human lysosomal α-galactosidase B is an α-*N*-acetylgalactosaminidase.[20,21,196,412–416] The confusion concerning the substrate specificity of this enzyme originally resulted from the use of artificial substrates in the identification and determination of the enzymatic defect in Fabry disease.[19,195,197,334,417] Kint[19] was the first to use *p*-nitrophenyl-α-D-galactoside (pNP-α-Gal) and 4MU-α-Gal to demonstrate the marked, but not total, deficiency of α-galactosidase activity in hemizygotes with Fabry disease (see "α-Galactosidase: The Enzymatic Defect," above). He[19,418,419] and others[23,195,197,200,334,417,420] subsequently demonstrated that two enzymes cleaved the synthetic, water-soluble pNP-α-Gal and 4MU-α-Gal substrates. One enzyme, designated α-galactosidase A, was thermolabile and inhibited by myoinositol, while the other, designated α-galactosidase B, was thermostable, had a higher K_m toward artificial galactosides, and was not inhibited by myoinositol. The A "isozyme" was deficient in Fabry disease.

Electrophoretic and isoelectric focusing studies revealed multiple forms of α-galactosidase A in various sources from normal individuals, the major components having pI values of 4.3 to 5.1.[200,202,204,207] In contrast, only a single form of α-galactosidase B was observed, with a pI value of about 4.5.[202,207,416,421] This enzyme was the residual activity in Fabry hemizygotes.[195,197,200,334,422,423] Neuraminidase treatment of normal α-galactosidases A and B in crude tissue extracts and in purified preparations converted the multiple α-galactosidase A forms to a single activity band at pI 5.1,[201,202,310] while the migration of α-galactosidase B was not altered by neuraminidase treatment.[201,202,207,416,424,425] These and other findings initially suggested that α-galactosidases A and B were isozymes with similar substrate specificities which could be interconverted by glycosylation.[197,334,418,419,426] In addition, partially purified human α-galactosidase B was shown to hydrolyze, albeit very inefficiently, the natural glycosphingolipid substrate globotriaosylceramide when incubated in the presence of the heat-stable glycoprotein activator.[201] However, further studies of these enzymes[196,198–201] demonstrated kinetic, structural, and immunologic differences indicating that they were distinct proteins.

In 1977, Dean and Sweeley[20,412] and Schram et al.[21] independently showed that α-galactosidase B actually functioned as an α-*N*-acetylgalactosaminidase which hydrolyzed natural substrates with terminal α-*N*-acetylgalactosaminyl moieties and was inhibited competitively by *N*-acetylgalactosamine. Purified α-galactosidase B was shown to have a higher affinity for α-*N*-acetylgalactosaminides (K_m ~1 m*M*) than for α-galactosides (K_m ~20 m*M*) and the same physical properties (i.e., thermostability and pH optimum, etc.) as human α-*N*-acetylgalactosaminidase purified previously.[427] Thus, it was concluded that α-galactosidase B was actually an α-*N*-acetylgalactosaminidase that did not hydrolyze the substrates accumulated in Fabry disease (see below, "Nature of the Accumulated Glycoconjugates").

Purification. Table 70-7 summarizes the purification and physical properties of human α-*N*-acetylgalactosaminidase isolated from various sources. The enzyme has been purified to homogeneity from placenta,[207] liver,[421] spleen,[387] and lung.[387] The purification strategy is similar to that for α-galactosidase (see "Purification," above). Concanavalin A Sepharose chromatography enriches the glycoprotein fraction from crude tissue extracts, and DEAE-cellulose chromatography affords additional purification and nearly complete separation from α-galactosidase, which elutes at a lower salt concentration than α-*N*-acetylgalactosaminidase.[200,202,416,428] Hydroxyapatite chromatography completely separates the two enzymes and provides a significant purification step.[30,202,421] Gel filtration,[207,421] or chromatography using ampholyte displacement,[421] SP-Sephadex,[207] or butyl agarose[207] have been used as final purification steps. However, affinity chromatography on α-galactosylamine coupled to Sepharose provides the most efficient step for the purification of both α-*N*-acetylgalactosaminidase and α-galactosidase. The former can be specifically eluted with *N*-acetylgalactosamine,[387,429] while both can be selectively eluted with D-galactose.[202]

Physical Properties. Human α-*N*-acetylgalactosaminidase has been estimated to have a native molecular weight of 90 to 117 kDa by gel filtration[207,334,387,415,416,430] (Table 70-7). The subunit molecular weights of the enzyme from human placenta and liver have been reported to be 47.7 and 46.8 kDa, respectively.[207,429] Consistent with these results, a 48-kDa subunit was detected following SDS polyacrylamide gel electrophoresis of homogeneous α-*N*-acetylgalactosaminidase from human lung.[387] However, a species of ~ 117 kDa was also present in this enzyme preparation. When the purified enzyme from human lung was subjected to native polyacrylamide gel electro-

Table 70-7 Purification and Properties of Human α-*N*-Acetylgalactosaminidase

Source	Specific activity, nmol/(h · mg)	Substrate	pI	Molecular weight		Reference
				Native, kDa	Subunit, kDa	
Placenta	67,000	4MU-α-Gal	4.4	150		198,200
Placenta	271,000	4MU-α-Gal	4.4	117	47.7	207
Liver	4,580	pNP-α-GalNAc			427	
Liver	4,740	pNP-α-GalNAc		110		21,415
Liver	14,800	4MU-α-Gal	4.9			201
Liver	394,000	4MU-α-Gal	4.5	90		416,421
Liver	2,900,000	oNP-α-GalNAc		90		416,421
Lung	370,000	4MU-α-Gal	4.6	117	45	387
Liver	7	4MU-α-Gal	4.3	90		334
Liver	251,000	4MU-α-Gal			46.8	429

Table 70-8 Kinetic Properties of Human α-N-Acetylgalactosaminidase

Source	Substrate	pH optimum	K_m, mM	V_{max}, nmol/(h · mg)	Reference
Liver	4MU-α-Gal	4.8	6.8	1.1×10^6	20, 421
Liver	oNP-α-GalNAc	4.3	1.3	3.6×10^6	20, 421
Liver	GbOse$_5$	4.4	3.7	5.5×10^5	20
Liver	GbOse$_5$Cer	3.9	0.59	1.6×10^5	20, 421
Liver	GbOse$_3$Cer	4.3	0.35	1.1×10^4	20, 421
Placenta	4MU-α-Gal	4.4	13.0		207
Lung	4MU-α-GalNAc	4.5	0.37		387
Liver	pNP-α-GalNAc	4.3	3.1		427

phoresis, only a single species of ~ 117 kDa was detected. Immunoblotting of the purified enzyme or crude human fibroblast extracts (after SDS gel electrophoresis) with rabbit anti-human splenic α-N-acetylgalactosaminidase demonstrated two immunoreactive species of 48 and 117 kDa, respectively. Notably, both species were present in immunoblots of normal human fibroblasts, but were absent in fibroblasts from the sibs with Schindler disease (Fig. 70-30). Microsequencing revealed identical N-terminal amino acids in both the 48- and 117-kDa species. These studies are consistent with a homodimeric structure for the human enzyme which appears to be highly resistant to denaturation or the existence of two enzyme forms with identical N-terminal amino acid sequences. Support for the homodimeric structure is based on biosynthetic studies of α-N-acetylgalactosaminidase in human fibroblasts which indicated that the enzyme was synthesized as a 65-kDa precursor which was processed to a 48-kDa mature lysosomal form.[431] For comparison, the porcine and bovine enzymes were tetramers with native and subunit molecular weights of 155 and 43 kDa, respectively.[432] Further studies of the purified human enzyme are required to definitively establish the normal structure and to determine the possible existence of two forms encoded by the same gene.

The composition of the oligosaccharide moieties present in the human enzyme has been reported.[217,431] The human placental enzyme contained 5 percent neutral sugars and 0.3 percent sialic acid.[207] Subsequent analysis of the radiolabeled oligosaccharides from immunoprecipitated human fibroblast α-N-acetylgalactosaminidase revealed high mannose–type oligosaccharide structures (Man$_{8-9}$GlcNAc) on both precursor and processed enzyme forms; only the precursor had phosphorylated mannose residues. The absence of complex type oligosaccharide moieties containing terminal sialic acid residues was supported by the previously mentioned neuraminidase studies which did not alter the pI of the enzyme.

Human α-N-acetylgalactosaminidase is a relatively thermostable enzyme.[195,200,420] At 50°C, the half-lives for the enzyme at pH 4.8 to 7.0 are greater than 2 h.[47,199,416,417,423,427]

Kinetic Properties. Since the natural substrates for human α-N-acetylgalactosaminidase are not presently known, most kinetic studies have been performed with synthetic chromogenic or fluorogenic substrates. Lysosomal α-N-acetylgalactosaminidase has an acidic pH optimum of about 4.6 for various synthetic substrates (Table 70-8). The apparent K_m values for the enzyme toward synthetic α-galactoside substrates are high, approximately 12 to 20 mM for 4MU-α-Gal[195,196,207] and 20 to 30 mM for pNP-α-Gal.[21,196] Reflecting its specificity, the enzyme's affinity for the N-acetylgalactosamine glycon is tenfold greater, with apparent K_m values for oNP-α-GalNAc ranging from 1 to 2 mM.[20,241] The apparent K_m for the purified human lung enzyme was 0.37 mM toward the fluorogenic substrate,

4MU-α-GalNAc.[402] Neither pNP-α-GalNAc nor 4MU-α-GalNAc was hydrolyzed by purified human α-galactosidase.[402] For purified human liver α-N-acetylgalactosaminidase, the turnover number using oNP-α-GalNAc as substrate was calculated to be 6600 min^{-1} using a molecular weight for the native enzyme of 110 kDa.[421] The apparent K_m of human liver α-N-acetylgalactosaminidase toward the glycosphingolipid Forssman hapten (globopentaosylceramide; GbOse$_5$Cer) was 0.59 mM with a V_{max} of 1.6×10^5 mmol/(h·mg) at the pH optimum, 3.9 (Table 70-8). Other possible natural substrates, including O-linked glycopeptides with terminal α-N-acetylgalactosaminyl residues, have not been used to characterize the kinetic properties of this enzyme. Moreover, kinetic studies of the human enzyme have been limited to characterization of its exo-glycosidase activity. Use of substrates with internal α-acetylgalactosaminyl moieties could definitively determine if the enzyme also can function as an endo-glycosidase.

α-N-Acetylgalactosaminidase hydrolysis of globotriaosylceramide (GbOse$_3$Cer), the primary glycosphingolipid substrate for human α-galactosidase, occurs at an extremely low rate, if at all, in vitro. α-N-Acetylgalactosaminidase did not cleave GbOse$_3$Cer in cultured fibroblasts or tissues from Fabry hemizygotes,[196,417] and minimal, if any, hydrolysis was detected using radiolabeled GbOse$_3$Cer and/or highly purified enzyme (see Table 70-8).[217,413,417,421]

Inhibitors can be used to discriminate α-N-acetylgalactosaminidase and α-galactosidase activities in assays with chromogenic or fluorogenic galactosides. α-N-Acetylgalactosaminidase activity, as measured with 4MU-α-Gal, is inhibited about 90 percent by 100 mM N-acetylgalactosamine (GalNAc), while it has no effect on α-galactosidase activity.[335] Conversely, 500 mM myoinositol inhibits about 50 percent of α-galactosidase activity without affecting the activity of α-N-acetylgalactosaminidase.[199,200] The K_i of α-N-acetylgalactosaminidase for GalNAc was 3.1 mM with pNP-α-GalNAc,[427] while 4MU-α-Gal hydrolysis was inhibited about 90 percent with 100 mM GalNAc.[335]

For comparison, purified α-N-acetylgalactosaminidase from porcine and bovine liver had a pH optimum of 4.3 to 4.7.[432,433] The bovine α-N-acetylgalactosaminidase specifically cleaved pNP-α-GalNAc with a K_m of 6.5 mM and had a K_i of 10 mM with GalNAc.[432] Additionally, partially purified α-N-acetylgalactosaminidases from bovine liver and ox spleen cleaved the terminal α-N-acetylgalactosaminyl residues that were O-linked to serine or threonine in desialylated ovine and bovine submaxillary mucins.[432,434]

Nature of the Accumulated Glycoconjugates

Table 70-9 lists the glycoconjugates found in human tissues which contain α-N-acetylgalactosamine residues. These in-

Table 70-9 Various Glycoconjugates Containing α-N-Acetylgalactosaminyl Residues

Structure	Trivial Name	References
Glycosphingolipids:		
GalNAcα(1→3)\ Galβ(1→3)GlcNAcβ(1→3) Galβ(1→4)Glcβ(1→1)Cer / Fucα(1→2)/	A^a Type 1 chain	438–440
GalNAcα(1→3)\ Galβ(1→4)GlcNAcβ(1→3) Galβ(1→4)Glcβ(1→1)Cer / Fucα(1→2)/	A^a Type 2 chain	438–440
GalNAcα(1→3)GalNAcβ(1→3) Galα(1→4)Galβ(1→4)Glcβ(1→1)Cer	Forssman antigen	441–444
Mucopolysaccharides:		
R — β(1→3)Galβ(1→4)GlcNAcβ(1→6)\ GalNAc(α1→) O-Ser/Thr / NeuAcα(2→3)Galβ(1→3)/	Keratan sulfate, type II	437
O - Linked glycopeptides:		
Galβ(1→3)GalNAc(α1→) O-Ser/Thr		435, 436
NeuAcα(2→6)GalNAc(α1→) O-Ser/Thr		436
NeuAcα(2→3)Galβ(1→3)GalNAc(α1→) O-Ser/Thr		436
Fucα(1→2)Galβ(1→3)GalNAc(α1→) O-Ser/Thr		435, 445
Fucα(1→2)Galβ(1→4) GlcNAcβ(2→6)\ GalNAc(α1→) O-Ser/Thr / Fucα(1→2)Galβ(1→3)/		445
Galβ(1→4)\ / Fucα(1→2)/ GlcNAcβ(2→6)\ GalNAc(α1→) O-Ser/Thr Galβ(1→3)/	SSEA-1 determinant	445
NeuAcα(2→6)\ GalNAcα(1→3)\ Galβ(1→3)/ GalNAc(α1→) O-Ser/Thr / Fucα(1→2)/	Blood group A mucin	435
N - Linked glycopeptides:		
GalNAcα(1→3)\ Galβ(1→4) [GlcNAcβ(1→3)Galβ(1→4)]$_n$ GlcNAcβ(1→2)Manα(1→6)\ Fucα(1→2)/ R→ Fucα(1→6)\ Manβ(1→4)GlcNAcβ(1→4)GlcNAc Asn R→ Fucα(1→2)Galβ(1→4) [GlcNAcβ(1→3)Galβ(1→4)]$_n$ GlcNAcβ(1→2)Manα(1→3)/ NeuACGalβ(1→4)GlcNAcβ(1→6)\ [GlcNAcβ(1→3)Galβ(1→4)]$_n$ GlcNAcβ(1→4)/	Blood group AHi glycopeptide	435

clude glycosphingolipids, mucins, asparagine-linked glycoproteins, and a keratan-sulfate mucopolysaccharide.[435–437] Potentially, each of these compounds can be the source of substrates which accumulate in this disease.

Glycosphingolipids with α-N-acetylgalactosaminyl residues include those with blood group A activity and the Forssman hapten. The blood group A glycosphingolipids are characterized by their terminal blood group A–specifying trisaccharide, GalNAcα(1→3)Gal(2←1)αFuc.[438] They contain varying numbers of internal Galβ(1→3)GlcNAcβ(1→3) (type 1) and/or Galβ(1→4)GlcNAcβ(1→3) (type 2) units and the core structure, Galβ(1→4)Glcβ(1→1)Cer.[435,439,440] In humans, Forssman antigen has been detected in low amounts in normal lung and was increased fivefold in lung carcinomas regardless of blood type.[441,442] In contrast, Forssman antigen was found in intestinal mucosal carcinoma, but not in normal mucosal cells.[443] The complete chemical synthesis of this neutral glycosphingolipid has been accomplished.[444] Quantitative glycosphingolipid analyses did not detect the Forssman hapten in plasma, erythrocytes, or urinary sediment of normal individuals or in the affected sibs with this disease.

A keratan sulfate type II mucopolysaccharide containing an O-linked α-GalNAc residue has been identified in human skeletal cartilage.[437] The O-linked mucins most commonly contain a Galβ(1→3)GalNAcα(1→)O-Ser/Thr core structure and additional N-acetylneuraminyl, fucosyl, N-acetylglucosaminyl and/or galactosyl residues.[435,445–448] Various structures are shown in Fig. 70-9. The predominant N-linked glycopeptide structure found in human erythrocytes is a complex-type triantennary oligosaccharide composed of 20 to 30 residues with a terminal A blood group trisaccharide.[435]

Significant accumulation was detected by histologic and ultrastructural examination of neuronal axons and cultured fibroblasts from the affected sibs. The occurrence of α-N-acetylgalactosaminyl residues in cortical neurons is supported by the selective cytochemical demonstration, using α-GalNAc–specific lectins, of terminal α-GalNAc residues on the surface of nonpyramidal multipolar neurons in the cerebral cortex of humans, consistent with their presence in synapses.[449] Ultrastructural evidence for only moderate accumulation and no glycosphingolipid substrate deposition in extraneuronal tissues suggests the possibility of alternative pathways for the hydrolysis of these compounds. There may be an endo-α-N-acetylgalactosaminidase, as in microorganisms[450,451] which can hydrolyze certain α-N-acetylgalactosaminyl linkages, thereby limiting the substrates that accumulate in this disease. Alternatively, α-N-acetylgalactosaminyl substrates may occur in relatively low abundance or only in certain cell types. To date, the only compounds known to accumulate in this disease is the blood group A trisaccharide, which was elevated fivefold in the urine of an affected homozygote with blood group A.[391] Further studies are required to characterize the nature of the storage material in axons and to understand the significance of the unusual concretions in the axonal cytosol of affected individuals.

MOLECULAR GENETICS OF α-N-ACETYLGALACTOSAMINIDASE

Gene Assignment

The gene encoding human α-N-acetylgalactosaminidase was originally assigned to chromosome 22 by somatic cell hybrid-

ization techniques.[452,453] The human enzyme, detected by the use of antihuman α-N-acetylgalactosaminidase antibodies,[452] segregated in human-mouse and human-Chinese hamster hybrid clones with human chromosome 22 and with human mitochondrial aconitase, an enzyme previously assigned to chromosome 22.[453] Subsequently, the locus for human α-N-acetylgalactosaminidase was localized further to the region 22q13→qter using somatic cell hybrids containing human X;22 and 1;22 reciprocal translocations.[454]

The α-N-Acetylgalactosaminidase cDNA

Recently, a cDNA encoding the entire mature human α-N-acetylgalactosaminidase subunit was isolated and characterized.[455] To facilitate molecular cloning, the human enzyme was purified to homogeneity and 129 nonoverlapping amino acids were determined by microsequencing the N-terminus and six internal peptides. A synthetic oligonucleotide, corresponding to a region of low codon redundancy in an internal peptide sequence, was constructed (26-mer; mixture of 576 species) and used to screen a fibroblast cDNA library in the pcD vector.[456,457] Ten putatively positive clones were identified and then screened with two different synthetic oligonucleotide mixtures (17-mers, mixtures of 64 species). Of the initially selected clones, two were positive with all three oligonucleotide probes. The longest, pcD-AGB72, had an insert of 2 kb which was subcloned into M13 mp18 and mp19 and sequenced in both orientations. The pcD-AGB72 cDNA encoded the entire mature enzyme subunit and a portion of the leader sequence. The cDNA had a 3′ untranslated region, in contrast to the cDNA for human α-galactosidase.[31]

Of particular interest was the finding of significant nucleotide and amino acid homology between human α-N-acetylgalactosaminidase and α-galactosidase, suggesting an evolutionary relationship. Since the structural organization of the α-galactosidase gene had been determined,[32] it was possible to compare the nucleotide homology in the α-N-acetylgalactosaminidase cDNA with the corresponding sequences in each of the α-galactosidase exons. Alignment of the two sequences required only four gaps and two insertions of three nucleotides each. The homology ranged from almost 70 percent in exon 1 to 44 percent in exon 7. Exons 1, 2, and 6 had over 60 percent nucleotide identity. The overall nucleotide and amino acid similarities of the two coding sequences were 57 and 48 percent, respectively.

The availability of the cDNA encoding α-N-acetylgalactosaminidase will permit the isolation of the chromosomal gene, characterization of the gene organization, investigation of the mutations which cause Schindler disease, structure-function studies of α-N-acetylgalactosaminidase, and studies of its evolutionary relationship to α-galactosidase. In addition, the cDNA can be used to further refine the regional localization of this gene on chromosome 22.

MOLECULAR PATHOLOGY OF SCHINDLER DISEASE

Southern hybridization analysis of genomic DNA from the affected homozygotes and their family members did not detect any abnormality after digestion with several different restriction endonucleases (Fig. 70-31). Northern hybridization anal-

Family D

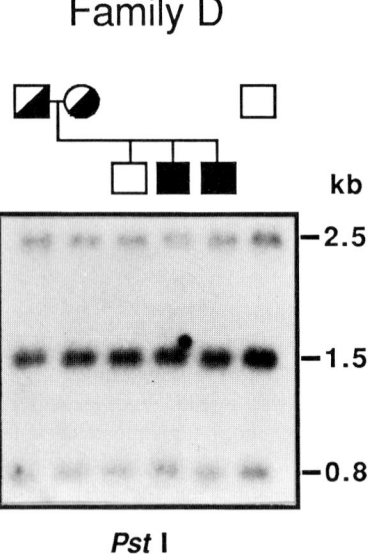

Fig. 70-31 A representative Southern blot for α-N-acetylgalactosaminidase showing identical bands of *Pst* I–digested genomic DNA from normal individuals and the affected sibs and other members of family D.

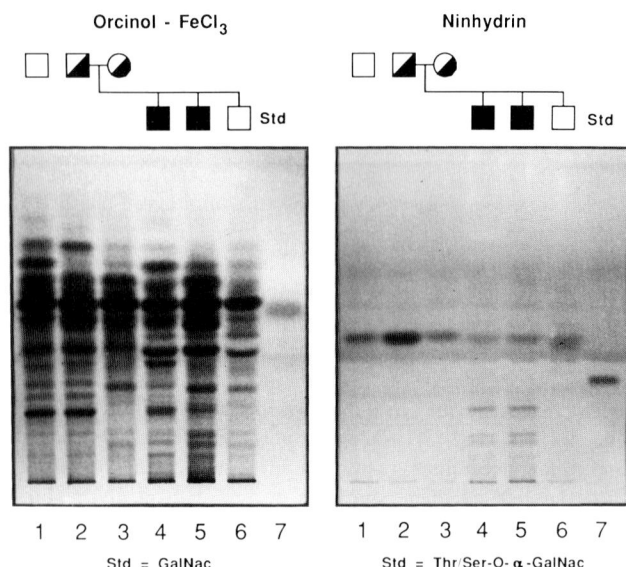

Fig. 70-32 Thin-layer chromatograms of urine from family D members stained for oligosaccharides with an orcinol–ferric chloride solution and for peptides with ninhydrin.[393] Family D members, *lanes 2 to 6;* a normal individual, *lane 1,* and the glycopeptide α-N-acetylgalactosaminidase-O-serine, *lane 7.*

ysis of poly(A)$^+$ RNA from the affected sibs revealed normal transcript size and amount. Since residual activity was detected by enzyme assay and since immunoblotting studies indicated that the amount of enzyme protein was markedly reduced, the mutation in this family presumably was due to a point mutation or small deletion or insertion that altered translation and/or the stability of the enzyme protein. Further biochemical and molecular studies will determine the precise genetic lesion.

DIAGNOSIS

Biochemical Evaluation

Children with developmental regression in the first or second years of life, clinical manifestations compatible with this disease, and no visceral evidence of a metabolic disorder should be evaluated. The ultrastructural demonstration of characteristic lysosomal alterations in dystrophic axons in the myenteric plexus of biopsied rectal tissue or skin should suggest this diagnosis.

Initial screening can be performed by analysis of the urinary oligosaccharide and glycopeptide profiles (Fig. 70-32). Abnormal urinary glycopeptiduria can be evaluated further by determining α-N-acetylgalactosaminidase activity in plasma, isolated leukocytes, and/or cultured lymphoblasts or fibroblasts, using the commercially available chromogenic substrate, pNP-α-GalNAc,[391–393] or the fluorogenic substrate, 4MU-α-GalNAc (Table 70-6). Prenatal diagnosis can be accomplished by determining the enzyme activity in chorionic villi obtained at 9 to 10 menstrual weeks or in cultured amniocytes obtained by amniocentesis at about 15 to 16 menstrual weeks.

Genetic Counseling

Genetic counseling should be provided to all families in which the diagnosis of an affected individual is made. The disease is inherited as an autosomal recessive trait. Therefore, the risk for each subsequent pregnancy of a carrier couple is 25 percent. Normal sibs of affected individuals have a 67 percent risk of being carriers. At-risk individuals in each family should have diagnostic enzyme determinations to identify all possible carriers. Identification of heterozygous carriers of the disease-causing gene is most reliably performed with the fluorogenic substrate (Table 70-6).

TREATMENT

There is no treatment for this disease. Supportive care should be implemented to optimize patient comfort.

This work was supported in part by a grant (1-578) from the March of Dimes Birth Defects Foundation, grants (DK 34045 and DK 12434) from the National Institutes of Health, and a grant (RR-71) from the Clinical Research Centers Program of the Division of Research Resources, National Institutes of Health. The authors are grateful to Ms. Jackie Bilski and Ms. Lorrie Guzzo for preparation of the manuscript.

REFERENCES

1. ANDERSON W: A case of angiokeratoma. *Br J Dermatol* 10:113, 1898.
2. FABRY J: Ein Beitrag Zur Kenntnis der Purpura haemorrhagica nodularis (Purpura papulosa hemorrhagica Hebrae). *Arch Dermatol Syph* 43:187, 1898.
3. FABRY J: Weiterer Beitrag zur Klinik des Angiokeratoma naeviforme (Naevus angiokeratosus). *Dermatol Wochenschr* 90:339, 1930.
4. STEINER L, VOERNER H: Angiomatosis miliaris: Eine ideiopathische Gefasserkrankung. *Dtsch Arch Klin Med* 96:105, 1909.
5. GUNTHER H: Anhidrosis und Diabetes insipidus. *Z Klin Med* 78:53, 1913.
6. WEICKSEL J: Angiomatosis, bzw. Angiokeratosis universalis (eine sehr seltene Haut- und Gafasskrankheit). *Dtsch Med Wochenschr* 51:898, 1925.
7. POMPEN AWM, RUITER M, WYERS JJG: Angiokeratoma corporis diffusum (universale) Fabry, as a sign of an unknown internal disease: Two autopsy reports. *Acta Med Scand* 128:234, 1947.

8. SCRIBA K: Zur Pathogenese des Angiokeratoma corporis diffusum Fabry mit cardio-vasorenalem Symptomenkomplex. *Verh Dtsch Ges Pathol* 34:221, 1950.

9. HORNBOSTEL H, SCRIBA K: Zur Diagnostik des Angiokeratoma Fabry mit kardiovasorenalem Symptomenkomplex als phosphatidspeicherungskrankheit durch Probeexcision der Haut. *Klin Wochenschr* 31:68, 1953.

10. WISE D, WALLACE HJ, JELLINCK EH: Angiokeratoma corporis diffusum: A clinical study of eight affected families. *Q J Med* 31:177, 1962.

11. OPITZ JM, STILES FC, WISE D, von GEMMINGEN G, RACE RR, SANDER R, CROSS EG, de GROOT WP: The genetics of angiokeratoma corporis diffusum (Fabry's disease), and its linkage with Xg(a) locus. *Am J Hum Genet* 17:325, 1965.

12. SWEELEY CC, KLIONSKY B: Fabry's disease: Classification as a sphingolipidosis and partial characterization of a novel glycolipid. *J Biol Chem* 238:3148, 1963.

13. VANCE DE, KRIVIT W, SWEELEY CC: Concentrations of glycosyl ceramides in plasma and red cells in Fabry's disease: A glycolipid lipidosis. *J Lipid Res* 10:188, 1969.

14. DESNICK RJ, DAWSON G, DESNICK SJ, SWEELEY CC, KRIVIT W: Diagnosis of glycosphingolipidoses by urinary sediment analysis. *N Engl J Med* 284:739, 1971.

15. SCHIBANOFF JM, KAMOSHITA S, O'BRIEN JS: Tissue distribution of glycosphingolipids in a case of Fabry's disease. *J Lipid Res* 10:515, 1969.

16. DESNICK RJ, BLEIDEN LD, SHARP HL, MOLLER JH: Cardiac valvular anomalies in Fabry's disease: Clinical, morphologic and biochemical studies. *Circulation* 54:818, 1976.

17. WHERRET JR, HAKOMORI S: Characterization of a blood group B glycolipid, accumulating in the pancreas of a patient with Fabry's disease. *J Biol Chem* 218:3046, 1973.

18. BRADY RO, GAL AE, BRADLEY RM, MARTENSSON E, WARSHAW AL, LASTER L: Enzymatic defect in Fabry's disease: Ceramide trihexosidase deficiency. *N Engl J Med* 276:1163, 1967.

19. KINT JA: Fabry's disease: Alpha-galactosidase deficiency. *Science* 167:1268, 1970.

20. DEAN KJ, SUNG S-SJ, SWEELEY CC: The identification of α-galactosidase B from human liver as an α-N-acetylgalactosaminidase. *Biochem Biophys Res Commun* 77:1411, 1977.

21. SCHRAM AW, HAMERS MN, TAGER JM: The identity of α-galactosidase B from human liver. *Biochim Biophys Acta* 482:138, 1977.

22. SCHINDLER D, BISHOP DF, WALLACE S, WOLFE DE, DESNICK RJ: Characterization of α-N-acetylgalactosaminidase deficiency: A new neurodegenerative lysosomal disease. *Pediatr Res* 23:333A, 1988.

23. DESNICK RJ, ALLEN KY, DESNICK SJ, RAMAN MK, BERNLOHR RW, KRIVIT W: Enzymatic diagnosis of hemizygotes and heterozygotes. Fabry's disease. *J Lab Clin Med* 81:157, 1973.

24. JOHNSON DL, del MONTE MA, COTLIER E, DESNICK RJ: Fabry disease: Diagnosis of hemizygotes and heterozygotes by α-galactosidase A activity in tears. *Clin Chim Acta* 63:81, 1975.

25. BRADY RO, UHLENDORF BW, JACOBSON CB: Fabry's disease: Antenatal diagnosis. *Science* 172:172, 1971.

26. DESNICK RJ, SWELLEY CC: Prenatal detection of Fabry's disease, in Dorfman A (ed): *Antenatal Diagnosis*. Chicago, IL, University of Chicago Press, 1971, p 185.

27. MAPES CA, ANDERSON RL, SWEELEY CC, DESNICK RJ, KRIVIT W: Enzyme replacement in Fabry's disease, an inborn error of metabolism. *Science* 169:987, 1970.

28. BRADY RO, TALLMAN JF, JOHNSON WG, GAL AE, LEAHY WR, QUIRK JM, DEKABAN AS: Replacement therapy for inherited enzyme deficiency: Use of purified ceramidetrihexosidase in Fabry's disease. *N Engl J Med* 289:9, 1973.

29. DESNICK RJ, DEAN KJ, GRABOWSKI GA, BISHOP DF, SWEELEY CC: Enzyme therapy XII: Enzyme therapy in Fabry's disease: Differential enzyme and substrate clearance kinetics of plasma and splenic α-galactosidase isozymes. *Proc Natl Acad Sci USA* 76:5326, 1979.

30. CALHOUN DH, BISHOP DF, BERNSTEIN HS, QUINN M, HANTZOPOULOS P, DESNICK RJ: Fabry disease: Isolation of a cDNA clone encoding human α-galactosidase A. *Proc Natl Acad Sci USA* 82:7364, 1985.

31. BISHOP DF, CALHOUN DH, BERNSTEIN HS, HANTZOPOULOS P, QUINN M, DESNICK RJ: Human α-galactosidase A: Nucleotide sequence of a cDNA clone encoding the mature enzyme. *Proc Natl Acad Sci USA* 83:4859, 1986.

32. BISHOP DF, KORNREICH R, DESNICK RJ: Structural organization of the α-galactosidase A gene: Further evidence for the absence of a 3' untranslated region. *Proc Natl Acad Sci USA*, 85:3903, 1988.

33. DESNICK RJ, SWEELEY CC: Fabry's disease: Defective α-galactosidase A, in Stanbury JB, Wyngaarden JB, Fredrickson DS, Goldstein JL, Brown MS (eds): *The Metabolic Basis of Inherited Disease*, 5th ed. New York, McGraw-Hill, 1983, p 906.

34. KAHLKE W: Angiokeratoma corporis diffusum (Fabry's disease), in Schettler G (ed): *Lipids and Lipidoses*. Berlin, Springer, 1967, p 332.

35. KINT JA, CARTON D: Fabry's disease, in Hers HF, Van Hoof F (eds): *Lysosomes and Storage Diseases*. New York, Academic, 1973, p 347.

36. DEAN K, SWEELEY C: Fabry disease, in Glew RH, Peters SP (eds): *Practical Enzymology of the Sphingolipidoses*, New York, AR Liss, 1977, p 173.

37. SALVAYRE R, NEGRE A, MARET A, DOUSTE-BLAZY L: α-Galactosidases et α-N-acetygalactosaminidase bases biochimiques de la maladie de Fabry. *Pathol Biol* 32:269, 1984.

38. LOCKMAN LA, HUNNINGHAKE DB, KRIVIT W, DESNICK RJ: Relief of pain of Fabry's disease by diphenylhydantoin. *Neurology* 23:871, 1973.

39. RAHMAN AN, SIMCONE FA, HACKEL DB, HALL PW III, HIRSCH EZ, HARRIS JW: Angiokeratoma corporis diffusum universale (hereditary dystopic lipidosis). *Trans Assoc Am Physicians* 74:366, 1961.

40. BURDA CD, WINDER PR: Angiokeratoma corporis diffusum universale (Fabry's disease) in female subjects. *Am J Med* 42:293, 1967.

41. BAGDALE JD, PARKER F, WAYS PO, MORGAN TE, LAGUNOFF D, EIDELMAN S: Fabry's disease: A correlative clinical, morphologic, and biochemical study. *Lab Invest* 18:681, 1968.

42. JOHNSTON AW, WELLER SD, WARLAND BJ: Angiokeratoma corporis diffusum. Some clinical aspects. *Arch Dis Child* 43:73, 1968.

43. SHETH KJ, BERNHARD GC: The arthropathy of Fabry disease. *Arthritis Rheum* 22:781, 1979.

44. URBAIN G, PEREMANS J, PHILIPPART M: Fabry's disease without skin lesions. *Lancet* 1:1111, 1967.

45. WALLACE RD, COOPER WJ: Angiokeratoma corporis diffusum universale (Fabry). *Am J Med* 39:656, 1965.

46. CLARKE JTR, KNAACK J, CRAWHALL JC, WOLFE LS: Ceramide trihexosidosis (Fabry's disease) without skin lesions. *N Engl J Med* 284:233, 1971.

47. AINSWORTH SK, SMITH RM: A case study of Fabry's disease occurring in a Black kindred without peripheral neuropathy or skin lesions. *Lab Invest* 38:373, 1978.

48. FERRANS VJ, HIBBS RB, BURDA CD: The heart in Fabry's disease: A historical, chemical and electron microscopic study. *Am J Cardiol* 24:95, 1969.

49. BECKER AE, SCHOORL R, BALK AG, van der HEIDE RM: Cardiac manifestations of Fabry's disease. Report of a case with mitral insufficiency and electrocardiographic evidence of myocardial infarction. *Am J Cardiol* 36:829, 1975.

50. MEHTA J, TUNA N, MOLLER JH, DESNICK RJ: Electrocardiographic and vector-cardiographic abnormalities in Fabry's disease. *Am Heart J* 93:699, 1977.

51. EFTHIMIOU J, McLELLAND J, BETTRIDGE DJ: Short P-R intervals and tachyarrhythmias in Fabry's disease. *Postgrad Med J* 62:285, 1986.

52. MATSUI S, MURAKAMI E, TAKEKOSHI N: Cardiac manifestations of Fabry's disease. *Nippon Junkankigaku Shi* 41:1023, 1977.

53. ROWE JW, CARALIS DG: Accelerated atrioventricular conduction in Fabry's disease: A case report. *Angiology* 29:562, 1978.

54. BASS JL, SHRIVASTAVA S, GRABOWSKI GA, DESNICK RJ, MOLLER JH: The M-mode echocardiogram in Fabry's disease. *Am Heart J* 100:807, 1980.

55. GOLDMAN M, CANTOR R, SCHWARTZ MF, BAKER M, DESNICK RJ: Echocardiographic abnormalities and disease severity in Fabry's disease. *J Am Coll Cardiol* 7:1157, 1986.

56. SAKURABA H, YANAGAWA Y, IGARASHI T, SUZUKI Y, SUZUKI T, WATANABE K, IEKI K, SHIMODA K, YAMANAKA T: Cardiovascular manifestations in Fabry's disease. A high incidence of mitral valve prolapse in hemizygotes and heterozygotes. *Clin Genet* 29:276, 1986.

57. COHEN IS, FLURI-LUNDEEN J, WHARTON TP: Two dimensional echocardiographic similarity of Fabry's disease to cardiac amyloidosis: A function of ultrastructural analogy? *J Clin Ultrasound* 11:437, 1983.

58. COLUCCI WS, LORELL BH, SCHOEN FJ, WARHOL MJ, GROSSMAN W: Hypertrophic obstructive cardiomyopathy due to Fabry's disease. *N Engl J Med* 2:926, 1982.

59. BETHUNE JE, LANDRIGAN PL, CHIPMAN CD: Angiokeratoma corporis diffusum (Fabry's disease in two brothers). *N Engl J Med* 264:1280, 1961.

60. BEAUDET AL, CASKEY CT: Detection of Fabry's disease heterozygotes by hair root analysis. *Clin Genet* 13:251, 1978.

61. MAISEY DN, COSH JA: Basilar artery aneurysm and Anderson-Fabry disease. *J Neurol Neurosurg Psychiatry* 43:85, 1980.

62. van ROEY A, WELLENS W: Angiokeratoma corporis diffusum van Fabry. *Arch Belg Dermatol Syph* 17:325, 1961.

63. DUPERRAT B: L'Angiokeratome diffus de Fabry (angiokeratoma corporis diffusum). *Presse Med* 67:1814, 1959.

64. CURRY HB, FLEISHER TL: Angiokeratoma corporis diffusum: A case report. *JAMA* 175:864, 1961.

65. STOUGHTON TB, CLENDENNING WE: Angiokeratoma corporis diffusum (Fabry). *Arch Dermatol* 79:601, 1959.

66. GUIN GH, SAINI N, BURNS WA, JONES WP: Diffuse angiokeratoma (Fabry's disease): Case report. *Milit Med* 141:259, 1976.

67. LISTON EH, LEVINE MD, PHILIPPART M: Psychosis in Fabry's disease and treatment with phenoxybenzamine. *Arch Gen Psychiatry* 29:402, 1973.

68. STEWARD VW, HITCHCOCK C: Fabry's disease (angiokeratoma corporis diffusum): A report of 5 cases with pain in extremities as the chief symptom. *Pathol Eur* 3:377, 1968.

69. BROWN A, MILNE JA: Diffuse angiokeratoma: Report of two cases with diffuse skin changes, one with neurological symptoms and splenomegaly. *Glasgow J Med* 33:361, 1952.

70. CONZELMANN E, BURG J, STEPHAN G, SANDHOFF K: Complexing of glycolipids and their transfer between membranes by the activator protein for degradation of lysosomal ganglioside G_{M2}. *Eur J Biochem* 123:455, 1982.

71. PABICO RC, ATANACIO BC, MCKENNA BA, PAMURCOGLU T, YODAIKEN R: Renal pathologic lesions and functional alterations in a man with Fabry's disease. *Am J Med* 55:415, 1973.

72. SHETH KJ, ROTH DA, ADAMS MB: Early renal failure in Fabry's disease. *Am J Kidney Dis* 2:651, 1983.

73. COLOMBI A, KOSTYAL A, BRACHER R, GLOOR F, MAZZI R, THOLEN H: Angiokeratoma corporis diffusum—Fabry's disease. *Helv Med Acta* 34:67, 1967.

74. SCHER NA, LETSON RD, DESNICK RJ: The ocular manifestations in Fabry's disease. *Arch Ophthalmol* 97:671, 1979.

75. SPAETH GL, FROST P: Fabry's disease: Its ocular manifestations. *Arch Ophthalmol* 74:760, 1965.

76. FRANCESCHETTI AT: La cornea verticillata (Gruber) et ses relations avec la maladie de Fabry (Angiokeratoma corporis diffusum). *Ophthalmologica* 156:232, 1968.

77. GRUBER H: Cornea verticillata. *Ophthalmologica* 111:120, 1946.

78. TERLINDE R, RICHARD G, LISCH W, ULLRICH K: Ruckbildung der Cornea verticillata bei Morbus-Fabry durch Kontaktlinsen. Erste beobachtungen. *Contactologia* 4:20, 1982.

79. SHETH KJ, SWICK HM: Peripheral nerve conduction in Fabry's disease. *Ann Neurol* 7:319, 1980.

80. PARKINSON JE, SUNSHINE A: Angiokeratoma corporis diffusum universale (Fabry) presenting as suspected myocardial infarction and pulmonary infarcts. *Am J Med* 31:951, 1961.

81. ROSENBERG DM, FERRANS VJ, FULMER JD, LINE BR, BARRANGER JA, BRADY RO, CRYSTAL RG: Chronic airflow obstruction in Fabry's disease. *Am J Med* 68:898, 1980.

82. BARTIMMON EE JR, GUSAN M, MOSER KA: Pulmonary involvement in Fabry's disease: A reappraisal. Follow up of a San Diego kindred and review of the literature. *Am J Med* 53:755, 1972.

83. KARIMAN K, SINGLETARY WV JR, SIEKER HO: Pulmonary involvement in Fabry's disease. *Am J Med* 64:911, 1978.

84. GEMIGNANI F, PIETRINI V, TAGLIAVINI F, LECHI A, NERI TM, ASINARI A, SAVI M: Fabry's disease with familial lymphedema of the lower limbs. *Eur Neurol* 18:84, 1979.

85. WILSON SK, KLIONSKY BL, RHAMY RK: A new etiology of priapism: Fabry's disease. *J Urol* 109:646, 1973.

86. FUNDERBURK SJ, PHILIPPART M, DALE G, CEDERBAUM SD, VYDEN JK: Priapism after phenoxybenzamine in a patient with Fabry's disease. *N Engl J Med* 290:630, 1974.

87. ROWE JW, GILLIAM JI, WARTHIN TA: Intestinal manifestations of Fabry's disease. *Ann Intern Med* 81:628, 1974.

88. SHETH KJ, WERLIN SL, FREEMAN ME, HODACH AE: Gastrointestinal structure and function in Fabry's disease. *Am J Gastroenterol* 76:246, 1981.

89. FRIEDMAN LS, KIRKHAM SE, THISTLETHWAITE JR, PLATIKA D, KOLODNY EH, SCHUFFLER MD: Jejunal diverticulosis with perforation as a complication of Fabry's disease. *Gasteroenterology* 86:558, 1984.

90. ROBERTS DH, GILMORE IT: Achalasia in Anderson-Fabry disease. *J R Soc Med* 77:430, 1984.

91. O'BRIEN BD, SHNITKA TK, MCDOUGALL R, WALKER K, COSTOPOULOS L, LENTLE B, ANHOLT L, FREEMAN H, THOMSON ABR: Pathophysiologic and ultrastructural basis for intestinal symptoms in Fabry's disease. *Gastroenterology* 82:957, 1982.

92. KRIVIT W, VANCE DE, DESNICK R, WHITECAR JP, SWEELEY CC: Red cell physiology in Fabry's disease. *J Lab Clin Med* 12:906, 1968.

93. IGARASHI T, SAKURABA H, SUZUKI Y: Activation of platelet function in Fabry's disease. *Am J Hematol* 22:63, 1986.

94. FESSAS P, WINTROBE MM, CARTWRIGHT GE: Angiokeratoma corporis diffusum universale (Fabry): First American report of a rare disorder. *Arch Intern Med* 95:469, 1955.

95. FISCHER E: Morbus Fabry, ein Erkrankung mit Rheumaaspekten: Radiologie der Weichsteil—und Knockenveranderungen an der Hand. *Z Rheumatol* 45:36, 1986.

96. BISHOP DF, GRABOWSKI GA, DESNICK RJ: Fabry disease: An asymptomatic hemizygote with significant residual α-galactosidase A activity. *Am J Hum Genet* 33:71A, 1981.

97. BACH G, ROSENMANN E, KARNI A, COHEN T: Pseudodeficiency of α-galactosidase A. *Clin Genet* 21:59, 1982.

98. KOBAYASHI T, KIRA J, SHINNOH N, GOTO I, KUROIWA Y: Fabry's disease with partially deficient hydrolysis of ceramide trihexoside. *J Neurol Sci* 67:179, 1985.

99. ROMEO G, URSO M, PISZCANE A, BLUM E, de FALCO A, RUFFILLI A: Residual activity of α-galactosidase A in Fabry's disease. *Biochem Genet* 13:615, 1975.

100. ROSENMANN E, KOBRIN I, COHEN T: Kidney involvement in systemic lupus erythematosus and Fabry's disease. *Nephron* 34:180, 1983.

101. von SCHEIDT W, KANDOLF R, ERDMANN E, HUBNER G, OLSEN EGJ, CHRISTOMANOU H, BISHOP DF, DESNICK RJ: Atypical Fabry disease: Onset of primary myocardial involvement in the sixth decade. *N Engl J Med*, in press.

102. FRANCESCHETTI ATH: Fabry disease. Ocular manifestations, in Bergsmu D, Bron AJ, Cotlier E (eds): *The Eye and Inborn Errors of Metabolism. Birth Defects.* New York, AR Liss, 1976, p 195.

103. BROADBENT JC, EDWARDS WD, GORDON H, HARTZLER GO, KRAWISZ JE: Fabry cardiomyopathy in the female confirmed by endomyocardial biopsy. *Mayo Clin Proc* 56:623, 1981.

104. DESNICK RJ, ALLEN KY, SIMMONS RL, WOODS JE, ANDERSON CF, NAJARIAN JS, KRIVIT W: Correction of enzymatic deficiencies by renal transplantation: Fabry's disease. *Surgery* 72:203, 1972.

105. RIETRA PJGM, BROUWER-KELDER EM, de GROOT WP, TAGER JM: The use of biochemical parameters for the detection of carriers of Fabry's disease. *J Mol Med* 1:237, 1976.

106. AVILA JL, CONVIT J, VELAZQUEZ-AVILA G: Fabry's disease: Normal α-galactosidase activity and urinary-sediment glycosphingolipid levels in two obligate heterozygotes. *Br J Dermatol* 89:149, 1973.

107. LYON M: Gene action in the X-chromosome of the mouse (*Mus musculus* L.). *Nature* 190:372, 1961.

108. ROMEO G, MIGEON BR: Genetic inactivation of the α-galactosidase locus in carriers of Fabry's disease. *Science* 170:180, 1970.

109. GUBLER MC, LENOIR G, GRUNFELD J-P, ULMANN A, DROZ D, HABIB R: Early renal changes in hemizygous and heterozygous patients with Fabry's disease. *Kidney Int* 13:223, 1978.

110. ELLEDER M: Fabry's disease: Absence of storage as a feature of liver sinus endothelium. *Acta Histochem* 77:33, 1985.

111. SAGEBIEL RW, PARKER F: Cutaneous lesions of Fabry's disease: Glycolipid lipidosis—Light and electron microscopic findings. *J Invest Dermatol* 50:208, 1968.

112. BREATHNACH SM, BLACK MM, WALLACE HJ: Anderson-Fabry disease: Characteristic ultrastructural features in cutaneous blood vessels in a 1 year old boy. *Br J Dermatol* 103:81, 1980.

113. TARNOWSKI WM, HASHIMOTO K: New light microscopic skin findings in Fabry's disease. *Acta Derm Venereol* 49:386, 1969.

114. MOREL-MAROGER L, GANTER P, ARDAILOU R, CATHELINEAU G, RICHET G: Des rapports avec l'angiokeratose de Fabry et la cytodystrophie renale familiale. *Bull Soc Med Hosp Paris* 117:49, 1966.

115. HASHIMOTO K, GROSS BG, LEVER WF: Angiokeratoma corporis diffusum (Fabry): Histochemical and electron microscopic studies of the skin. *J Invest Dermatol* 44:119, 1965.

116. CHATTERJEE S, GUPTA P, PYERITZ RE, KWITEROVICH PO: Immunohistochemical localization of glycosphingolipid in urinary renal tubular cells in Fabry's disease. *Am J Clin Pathol* 82:24, 1984.

117. MCNARY W, LOWENSTEIN LM: A morphological study of the renal lesion in angiokeratoma corporis diffusum universale (Fabry's disease). *J Urol* 93:641, 1965.

118. BURKHOLDER PM, UPDIKE SJ, WARE RA, REESE OG: Clinicopathologic, enzymatic and genetic features in a case of Fabry's disease. *Arch Pathol Lab Med* 104:17, 1980.

119. GRUNNET ML, SPILSBURY PR: The central nervous system in Fabry's disease. *Arch Neurol* 28:231, 1973.

120. KOCEN RS, THOMAS PK: Peripheral nerve involvement in Fabry's disease. *Arch Neurol* 22:81, 1970.

121. KAHN P: Anderson-Fabry disease: A histopathological study of three cases with observations on the mechanism of production of pain. *J Neurol Neurosurg Psychiatry* 36:1053, 1973.

122. OHNISHI A, DYCK PJ: Loss of small peripheral sensory neurons in Fabry disease. Histologic and morphometric evaluation of cutaneous nerves, spinal ganglia, and posterior columns. *Arch Neurol* 31:120, 1974.

123. SUNG JH, HAYANO M, MASTRI AR, DESNICK RJ: Neuropathology and neural glycosphingolipid deposition in Fabry's disease. *Excerpta Med Cong Ser* 1:267, 1975.

124. SUNG JH: Autonomic neurons affected by lipid storage in the spinal cord

of Fabry's disease: Distribution of autonomic neurons in the sacral cord. *J Neuropathol Exp Neurol* 38:87, 1979.

125. CABLE WJ, DVORAK AM, OSAGE JE, KOLODNY EH: Fabry disease: Significance of ultrastructural localization of lipid inclusions in dermal nerves. *Neurology* 32:347, 1982.

126. CABLE WJL, KOLODNY EH, ADAMS RD: Fabry disease: Impaired autonomic function. *Neurology* 32:498, 1982.

127. RAHMAN AN, LINDENBERG R: The neuropathology of hereditary dystopic lipidosis. *Arch Neurol* 9:373, 1963.

128. GEMIGNANI F, MARBINI A, BRAGAGLIA MM, GOVONI E: Pathological study of the sural nerve in Fabry's disease. *Eur Neurol* 23:173, 1984.

129. WITSCHEL H, MATHYL J: Morphological elements of the specific ocular changes in Morbus Fabry. *Klin Monatsbl Augenheilkd* 154:599, 1969.

130. FONT RL, FINE BS: Ocular pathology in Fabry's disease. Histochemical and electron microscopic observations. *Am J Ophthalmol* 73:419, 1972.

131. MacRAE WG, GHOSH M, McCULLOCH C: Corneal changes in Fabry disease: A clinico-pathologic case report of a heterozygote. *Ophthalmic Pediatr Genet* 5:185, 1985.

132. FARRAGINA T, CHURG J, GRISHAM E, STRAUSS L, PRADO A, BISHOP DF, SCHUCHMAN E, DESNICK RJ: Light and electron microscopic histochemistry of Fabry disease. *Am J Pathol* 103:247, 1981.

133. LEHNER T, ADAMS CWM: Lipid histochemistry of Fabry's disease. *J Pathol Bacteriol* 95:411, 1968.

134. van MULLEM PJ, RUITER M: Histochemical studies on lipid metabolism in so-called Fabry's disease (angiokeratoma corporis diffusum). *Arch Klin Exp Derm* 232:148, 1968.

135. ROBINSON D, KHALFAN HA: Fabry's disease. Identification of carrier status by fluorescent/electron binding. *Biochem Soc Trans* 12:1063, 1984.

136. van MULLEM PJ, RUITER M: Fine structure of the skin in angiokeratoma corporis diffusum (Fabry's disease). *J Pathol* 101:221, 1970.

137. HASHIMOTO K, LIEBERMAN P, LAMKIN N Jr: Angiokeratoma corporis diffusum (Fabry disease). *Arch Dermatol* 112:1416, 1976.

138. NAKAMURA T, KANEKO H, NISHINO I: Angiokeratoma corporis diffusum (Fabry disease): Ultrastructural studies of the skin. *Acta Dermatovener* 61:37, 1981.

139. STECK TL, DAWSON G: Topographical distribution of complex carbohydrates in the erythrocyte membrane. *J Biol Chem* 239:2135, 1974.

140. THOMPSON TE, TILLACK TW: Organization of glycosphingolipids in bilayers and plasma membranes of mammalian cells. *Annu Rev Biophys Chem* 14:361, 1985.

141. DAWSON G: Glycolipid catabolism, in Horowitz MI, Pigman W (eds): *The Glycoconjugate II*. New York, Academic, 1978, p 225.

142. DAWSON G, KRUSKI AW, SCANU AM: Distribution of glycosphingolipids in the serum lipoproteins of normal human subjects and patients with hypo- and hyperlipidemias. *J Lipid Res* 17:125, 1976.

143. CLARKE JTR, STOTLZ JM, MULCAHY MR: Neutral glycosphingolipids of serum lipoproteins in Fabry's disease. *Biochim Biophys Acta* 431:317, 1976.

144. CHATTERJEE S, KWITEROVICH PO Jr: Glycosphingolipids and plasma lipoproteins: A review. *Can J Biochem Cell Biol* 62:385, 1984.

145. KUNDU SK, DIEGO I, OSOVITZ S, MARCUS DM: Glycosphingolipids of human plasma. *Arch Biochem Biophys* 238:388, 1985.

146. SWEELEY CC, SIDDIQUI B: Chemistry of glycolipids, in Pigman W, Horowitz M (eds): *Biochemistry of Mammalian Glycoproteins and Glycolipids*. New York, Academic, in press.

147. MACHER BA, SWEELEY CC: Glycosphingolipids: Structure, biological source and nomenclature. *Methods Enzymol* 50C:236, 1978.

148. GASA S, NAKAMURA M, MAKITA A, IKURA M, HIKICHI K: Complete structural analysis of globoseries glycolipids by two-dimensional nuclear magnetic resonance. *Eur J Biochem* 155:603, 1986.

149. ITO M, YAMAGATA T: A novel glycosphingolipid-degrading enzyme cleaves the linkage between the ogliosaccharide and ceramide of neutral and acidic glycosphingolipids. *J Biol Chem* 261:14278, 1986.

150. LI S-C, DEGASPERI A, MULDREY JE, LI Y-T: A unique glycosphingolipid-splitting enzyme (ceramide-glycanase from leech) cleaves the linkage between the ogliosaccharide and the ceramide. *Biochem Biophys Res Commun* 141:346, 1986.

151. KANNAGI R, WATANABE K, HAKOMORI S-I: Isolation and purification of glycosphingolipids by high-performance liquid chromatography. *Methods Enzymol* 138:3, 1987.

152. ULLMAN MD, McCLUER RH: High-pressure chromotography analysis of neutral glycosphingolipids: perbenzoylated mono-, di-, tri- and tetraglycosylceramides. *Methods Enzymol* 138:117, 1987.

153. SUZUKI K: Enzymatic diagnosis of sphingolipidoses. *Methods Enzymol* 138:727, 1987.

154. MARTENSSON E: Neutral glycolipids of human kidney. Isolation, identification and fatty acid composition. *Biochim Biophys Acta* 116:296, 1966.

155. NAIKI M, MARCUS DM: Human erythrocyte P and P^k blood group antigens: Identification as glycosphingolipids. *Biochem Biophys Res Commun* 10:1105, 1974.

156. NAIKI M, MARCUS DM: An immunochemical study of the human blood group P$_1$, P, and P^k glycosphingolipid antigens. *Biochemistry* 14:4837, 1975.

157. MARCUS DM, NAIKI M, KUNDU SK: Abnormalities in the glycosphingolipid content of human P^k and P erythrocytes. *Proc Natl Acad Sci USA* 73:3263, 1976.

158. WIELS J, HOLMES EH, COCHRAN N, TURSZ T, HAKOMORI S: Enzymatic and organizational difference in expression of a Burkitt lymphoma-associated antigen (globotriaosylceramide) in Burkitt lymphoma and lymphoblastoid cell lines. *J Biol Chem* 259:14783, 1984.

159. NUDELMAN E, KANNAGI R, HAKOMORI S, PARSONS M: A glycolipid antigen associated with Burkitt Lymphoma defined by a monoclonal antibody. *Science* 220:509, 1983.

160. WILS P, JUNQUA S, LEPECQ JB: Determination of antibody-complement mediated cytotoxicity using ATP release induced by a monoclonal antibody against the Burkitt lymphoma associated globotriaosylceramide antigen. *J Immunol Methods* 87:217, 1986.

161. COHEN A, HANNIGAN GE, WILLIAMS BRG, LINGWOOD CA: Roles of globotriosyl- and galabiosylceramide in verotoxin binding and high affinity interferon receptor. *J Biol Chem* 162:17088, 1987.

162. SHAPIRO D, ACHER AJ: Total synthesis of ceramide trihexoside accumulating with Fabry's disease. *Chem Phys Lipids* 197:206, 1978.

163. KOIKE K, SUGIMOTO M, SATO S, ITO Y, NAKAHARA Y, OGAWA T: Total synthesis of globotriaosyl-*E* and *Z*-ceramides and isoglobotriaosyl-*E*-ceramide. *Carbohydr Res* 163:189, 1987.

164. MIYATAKE T: A study on glycolipids in Fabry's disease. *Jpn J Exp Med* 19:35, 1969.

165. LOU HOC: A biochemical investigation of angiokeratoma corporis diffusum. *Acta Pathol Microbiol Scand* 68:332, 1966.

166. SNYDER PD Jr, KRIVIT W, SWEELEY CC: Generalized accumulation of neutral glycosphingolipids with G$_{m2}$ ganglioside accumulation in the brain. *J Lipid Res* 13:128, 1972.

167. VANCE DE, SWEELEY CC: Quantitative determination of the neutral glycosyl ceramides in human blood. *J Lipid Res* 8:621, 1967.

168. KOSKIELAK J, PIASEK A, GORNIAK H, GARDAS A, GREGOR A: Structures of fucose-containing glycolipids with H and B blood group activity and of sialic acid and glucosamine-containing glycolipid of human-erythrocyte membrane. *Eur J Biochem* 37:214, 1973.

169. BASU M, DE T, DAS KK, KYLE JW, CHON H-C, SCHAEPER RJ, BASU S: Glycolipids. *Methods Enzymol* 138:575, 1987.

170. TANIGUCHI N, YANAGISAWA K, MAKITA A, NAIKI M: Purification and properties of rat liver globotriaosylceramide synthase, UDP-Galactose: Lactosyl-ceramide α1-4-galactosyltransferase. *J Biol Chem* 260:4908, 1985.

171. KOJIMA H, TSUCHIYA S, SEKIGUCHI K, GELINAS R, HAKOMORI S-I: Predefined gene transfer for expression of a glycosphingolipid antigen by transfection with a cosmid genomic library prepared from a cell line in which the specific glycosphingolipid is highly expressed. *Biochem Biophys Res Commun* 143:716, 1987.

172. MARTENSSON E, OHMAN R, GRAVES M, SVENNERHOLM L: Galactosyltransferases catalyzing the formation of the galactosyl-galactosyl linkage in glycosphingolipids. *J Biol Chem* 249:4132, 1974.

173. NAGAI M, DAVE V, MUENSCH H, YOSHIDA A: Human blood group glycosyltransferase II. Purification of galactosyltransferase. *J Biol Chem* 253:380, 1978.

174. YOSHIDA A: The existence of atypical blood group galactosyltransferase which causes an expression of A$_2$ character in A^{1}B red blood cells. *Am J Hum Genet* 35:1117, 1983.

175. BASU M, BASU S: Enzymatic synthesis of a blood group B-related pentaglycosylceramide by an α-galactosyltransferase from rabbit bone marrow. *J Biol Chem* 248:1700, 1973.

176. BASU S, BASU M, KYLE JW, DE T, DAS K, SCHAEPER RJ: in Freysz Z, Gatt S (eds): *Enzymes of Lipid Metabolism*. New York, Plenum, 1986, p 233.

177. IIZUKA S, CHEN S-H, YOSHIDA A: Studies on the human blood group P system: An existence of UDP-gal:lactosylceramide α1→4 galactosyltransferase in the small p type cells. *Biochem Biophys Res Commun* 137:1187, 1986.

178. BROWN MS, KOVANEN PT, GOLDSTEIN JL: Regulation of plasma cholesterol by lipoprotein receptors. *Science* 212:628, 1981.

179. DAWSON G, SWEELEY CC: In vivo studies on glycosphingolipid metabolism in porcine blood. *J Biol Chem* 245:410, 1970.

180. VANCE DE, KRIVIT W, SWEELEY CC: Metabolism of neutral glycosphingolipids in plasma of a normal human and a patient with Fabry's disease. *J Biol Chem* 250:8119, 1975.

181. ENTENMAN C, CHAIKOFF IL, ZILVERSMIT DB: Removal of plasma phospholipids as a function of the liver: The effect of exclusion of the liver on

the turnover rate of plasma phospholipids as measured with radioactive phosphorus. *J Biol Chem* 166:15, 1946.

182. METZ RJ, RADIN NS: Glucosylceramide uptake protein from spleen cytosol. *J Biol Chem* 255:4463, 1980.

183. BLOJ B, ZILVERSMIT DB: Accelerated transfer of neutral glycosphingolipids and ganglioside G_{M1} by a purified lipid transfer protein. *J Biol Chem* 256:5988, 1981.

184. CONZELMANN E, SANDHOFF K: Activator proteins for lysosomal glycolipid hydrolysis. *Methods Biochem Anal* 32:1, 1987.

185. CONZELMANN E, SANDHOFF K: Activator proteins for lysosomal glycolipid hydrolysis. *Methods Enzymol* 138:792, 1987.

186. GLEW RH, PETERS SP: *Practical Enzymology of the Sphingolipidoses.* New York, AR Liss, 1977.

187. KUSIAK JW, QUIRK JM, BRADY RO: Ceramide trihexoside from human placenta. *Methods Enzymol* 50:529, 1978.

188. DESNICK RJ (ed): *Enzyme Therapy in Genetic Diseases*, 2d ed. New York, AR Liss, 1980.

189. CONZELMANN E, SANDHOFF K: Glycolipid and glycoprotein degradation. *Adv Enzymol* 60:90, 1987.

190. BENSUADE I, CALLAHAN J, PHILIPPART M: Fabry's disease as an α-galactosidosis: Evidence for an α-configuration in trihexosyl ceramide. *Biochem Biophys Res Commun* 43:913, 1971.

191. CLARKE JTR, WOLFE LS, PERLIN AS: Evidence for a terminal α-D-galactopyranosyl residue in galactosyl-galactosyl-glucosyl-ceramide from human kidney. *J Biol Chem* 246:5563, 1971.

192. HAKOMORI SI, SIDDIQUI B, LI YT, LI SC, HELLERQVIST CB: Anomeric structures of globoside and ceramide trihexoside of human erythrocytes and hamster fibroblasts. *J Biol Chem* 246:2271, 1971.

193. HANDA S, ARIGA T, MIYATAKE T, YAMAKAWA T: Presence of α-anomeric glycosidic configurations in the glycolipids accumulated in kidney with Fabry's disease. *J Biochem (Tokyo)* 69:625, 1971.

194. LI YT, LI SC: Anomeric configuration of galactose residues in ceramide trihexosides. *J Biol Chem* 246:3769, 1971.

195. BEUTLER E, KUHL W: Biochemical and electrophoretic studies of α-galactosidase in normal man, in patients with Fabry's disease, and in Equidae. *Am J Hum Genet* 24:237, 1972.

196. RIETRA PJGM, van den BERGH FAJTM, TAGER JM: Properties of the residual α-galactosidase activity in the tissues of a Fabry hemizygote. *Clin Chim Acta* 62:401, 1975.

197. WOOD S, NADLER HL: Fabry's disease: Absence of an α-galactosidase isozyme. *Am J Hum Genet* 24:250, 1972.

198. BUTLER E, KUHL W: Relationship between human α-galactosidase isozymes. *Nature* 239:207, 1972.

199. CRAWHALL JC, BANFALVI M: Fabry's disease: Differentiation between two forms of α-galactosidase by myoinositol. *Science* 177:527, 1972.

200. BEUTLER E, KUHL W: Purification and properties of human α-galactosidases. *J Biol Chem* 247:7195, 1972.

201. ROMEO G, DIMATTEO G, d'URSO M, LI S-C, LI Y-T: Characterization of human α-galactosidase A and B before and after neuraminidase treatment. *Biochim Biophys Acta* 391:349, 1975.

202. BISHOP DF, DESNICK RJ: Affinity purification of α-galactosidase A from human spleen, placenta and plasma with elimination of pyrogen contamination. *J Biol Chem* 256:1307, 1981.

203. HARPAZ N, FLOWERS HM, SHARON N: Purification of coffee bean α-galactosidase by affinity chromatography. *Biochim Biophys Acta* 341:213, 1974.

204. DEAN KJ, SWEELEY CC: Studies on human liver α-galactosidases. I. Purification of α-galactosidase A and its enzymatic properties with glycolipid and oligosaccharide substrates. *J Biol Chem* 254:9994, 1979.

205. MAYES JS, BEUTLER E: Alpha-Galactosidase A from human placenta. Stability and subunit size. *Biochim Biophys Acta* 484:408, 1977.

206. BISHOP DF, SWEELEY CC: Plasma α-galactosidase A. Properties and comparisons with tissue α-galactosidases. *Biochim Biophys Acta* 525:399, 1978.

207. KUSIAK JW, QUIRK JM, BRADY RO, MOOK GE: Purification and properties of the two major isozymes of α-galactosidase from human placenta. *J Biol Chem* 253:184, 1978.

208. LEDONNE NC, FAIRLEY JL, SWEELEY CC: Biosynthesis of α-galactosidase A in cultured Chang liver cells. *Arch Biochem Biophys* 224:186, 1983.

209. HO MW: Hydrolysis of ceramide trihexoside by a specific α-galactosidase from human liver. *Biochem J* 133:1, 1973.

210. SEGAL IH: *Enzyme Kinetics: Behavior and Analysis of Rapid Equilibrium and Steady-State Enzyme Systems.* New York, Wiley, 1975, p 79.

211. LEGLER G, HERRCHEN M: Active site-directed inhibition of galactosidases by conduritol C epoxides (1,2 anhydro-*epi*-and *neo*-inositol). *FEBS Lett* 135:139, 1981.

212. BAUSE E, LEGLER G: Isolation and structure of a tryptic glycopeptide from the active site of β-glucosidase A_3 from *Aspergillus wentii. Biochim Biophys Acta* 626:459, 1980.

213. LEGLER G, HARDER A: Amino acid sequence at the active site of β-glucosidase A from bitter almonds. *Biochim Biophys Acta* 524:102, 1978.

214. GRABOWSKI GA, OSIECKI-NEWMAN K, DINUR T, FABBRO D, LEGLER G, GATT S, DESNICK RJ: Human acid β-glucosidase. Use of chonduritol B epoxide derivatives to investigate the catalytically active normal and Gaucher disease enzymes. *J Biol Chem* 261:8263, 1986.

215. FLEET GWJ, NICHOLAS SJ, SMITH PW, EVANS SV, FELLOWS LE, NASH RJ: Potent competitive inhibition of α-galactosidase and α-glucosidase activity by 1,4-dideoxy-1,4-iminopentitols: Synthesis of 1,4-dideoxy-1,4-imino-D-lyxitol and of both enantiomers of 1,4-dideoxy-1,4-iminoarabinitol. *Tet Lett* 26:3127, 1985.

216. BERNOTAS RC, PEZZONE MA, GANEM B: Synthesis of $(+)-1,5$-dideoxy-1,5-imino-D-galactitol, a potent α-D-galactosidase inhibitor. *Carbohydr Res* 167:305, 1987.

217. MEHL E, JATZKEWITZ H: Eine cerebrosidsulfatase aus schweineniere. *Hoppe-Seyler's Z Physiol Chem* 339:260, 1964.

218. LI S-C, WAN C-C, MAZZOTTA MY, LI Y-T: Requirement of an activator for the hydrolysis of sphingoglycolipids by glycosidases of human liver. *Carbohydr Res* 34:189, 1974.

219. FISCHER G, JATZKEWITZ H: The activator of cerebroside sulphatase. Purification from human liver and identification as a protein. *Hoppe-Seyler's Z Physiol Chem* 356:605, 1975.

220. LI S-C, LI Y-T: An activator stimulating the enzymic hydrolysis of sphingoglycolipids. *J Biol Chem* 251:1159, 1976.

221. FISCHER G, JATZKEWITZ H: The activator of cerebroside-sulphatase. A model of the activation. *Biochim Biophys Acta* 528:69, 1978.

222. LI S-C, NAKAMURA T, OGAMO A, LI Y-T: Evidence for the presence of two separate protein activators for the enzymatic hydrolysis of G_{M1} and G_{M2} gangliosides. *J Biol Chem* 254:10592, 1979.

223. GARTNER S, CONZELMANN E, SANDHOFF K: Activator protein for the degradation of globotriaosylceramide by human α-galactosidase. *J Biol Chem* 258:12378, 1983.

224. INUI K, WENGER DA: Biochemical, immunological and structural studies on a sphingolipid activator protein (SAP-1). *Arch Biochem Biophys* 233:556, 1984.

225. LI S-C, KIHARA H, SERIZAWA S, LI Y-T, FLUHARTY A, MAYES JS, SHAPIRO LJ: Activator protein required for the enzymatic hydrolysis of cerebroside sulfate. Deficiency in urine of patients affected with cerebroside sulfatase activator deficiency and identity with activators for the enzymatic hydrolysis of G_{M1} ganglioside and globotriaoslyceramide. *J Biol Chem* 260:1867, 1985.

226. FUJIBAYASHI S, WENGER DA: Biosynthesis of the sulfatide/G_{M1} activator protein (SAP-1) in control and mutant cultured skin fibroblasts. *Biochim Biophys Acta* 875:554, 1986.

227. WYNN CH: A triple-binding-domain model explains the specificity of the interaction of a sphingolipid activator protein (SAP-1) with sulphatide G_{M1}-ganglioside and globotriaosylceramide. *Biochem J* 240:921, 1986.

228. VOGEL A, FURST W, ABO-HASHISH MA, LE-VAUPEL M, CONZELMANN E, SANDHOFF K: Identity of the activator proteins for the enzymatic hydrolysis of sulfatide, ganglioside G_{M1} and globotriaosylceramide. *Arch Biochem Biophys* 259:627, 1987.

229. DEWJI NN, WENGER DA, O'BRIEN JS: Nucleotide sequence of cloned cDNA for human sphingolipid activator protein 1 precursor. *Proc Natl Acad Sci USA* 84:8652, 1987.

230. KAO FT, LAW ML, HARTZ J, JONES C, ZHANG X-L, DEWJI N, O'BRIEN JS, WENGER DA: Regional localization of the gene coding for sphingolipid activator protein SAP-1 on human chromosome 10. *Somatic Cell Mol Genet* 13:685, 1987.

231. TAMARU T, FUJIBAYASHI S, BROWN WR, WENGER DA: Immunocytochemical localization of sphingolipid activator protein-1, the sulfatide/G_{M1} ganglioside activator, to lysosomes, in human liver and colon. *Histochemistry* 86:195, 1985.

232. SHAPIRO LJ, ALECK KA, KABACK MM, ITABASHI H, DESNICK RJ, BRAND N, STEVENS RL, FLUHARTY AL, KIHARA H: Metachromatic leukodystrophy without arylsulfatase A deficiency. *Pediatr Res* 13:1179, 1979.

233. STEVENS RL, FLUHARTY AL, KIHARA H, KABACK MM, SHAPIRO LJ, MARSH B, SANDHOFF K, FISCHER G: Cerebroside sulfatase activator deficiency induced metachromatic leukodystrophy. *Am J Hum Genet* 33:900, 1981.

234. HAHN AF, GORDON BA, FELEKI V, HINTON CG, GILBERT JJ: A variant form of metachromatic leukodystrophy without arylsulfatase deficiency. *Ann Neurol* 12:33, 1982.

235. INUI K, EMMETT M, WENGER DA: Immunological evidence for deficiency of an activator protein for sulfatide sulfatase in a variant form of metachromatic leukodystrophy. *Proc Natl Acad Sci USA* 80:3074, 1983.

236. HIRABAYASHI Y, LI Y-T, LI S-C: The protein activator specific for the enzymic hydrolysis of G_{M2} ganglioside in normal human brain and brains of three types of G_{M2} gangliosidosis. *J Neurochem* 40:168, 1983.

237. BURG J, CONZELMANN E, SANDHOFF K, SOLOMON E, SWALLOW DM: Map-

ping of the gene coding for the human G_{M2} activator protein to chromosome 5. *Ann Hum Genet* 49:41, 1985.

238. SANDHOFF K, HARZER K, WASSLE W, JATZKEWITZ H: Enzyme alterations and lipid storage in three variants of Tay-Sachs disease. *J Neurochem* 18:2469, 1971.

239. CONZELMANN E, SANDHOFF K: AB variant of infantile G_{M2} gangliosidosis: Deficiency of a factor necessary for stimulation of hexosaminidase A-catalyzed degradation of ganglioside G_{M2} and glycolipid G_{A2}. *Proc Natl Acad Sci USA* 75:3979, 1978.

240. CONZELMANN E, SANDHOFF K, NEHRKORN H, GEIGER B, ARNON R: Purification and immunological characterization of hexosaminidases A from variant AB of infantile G_{M2} gangliosidosis. *Eur J Biochem* 84:27, 1978.

241. LEMANSKY P, BISHOP DF, DESNICK RJ, HASILIK A, von FIGURA K: Synthesis and processing of α-galactosidase A in human fibroblasts. Evidence for different mutations in Fabry disease. *J Biol Chem* 262:2062, 1987.

242. BEUTLER E, KUHL W: Absence of cross-reactive antigen in Fabry disease. *N Engl J Med* 289:694, 1973.

243. RIETRA PJGM, MOLENAAR JL, HAMERS MN, TAGER JM, BORST P: Investigation of the α-galactosidase deficiency in Fabry's disease using antibodies against the purified enzyme. *Eur J Biochem* 46:89, 1974.

244. HAMERS MN, WISE D, EJIOFOR A, STRIJLAND A, ROBINSON D, TAGER JM: Relationship between biochemical and clinical features in an English Anderson-Fabry Family. *Acta Med Scand* 206:5, 1979.

245. GRZESCHIK K, GRZESCHIK A, BANHOF S, ROMEO G, SINISCALCO M, van SOMEREN H, MEERA KHAN P, WESTERVELD A, BOOTSMA D: X-Linkage of human α-galactosidase. *Nature* 240:48, 1972.

246. MILLER OJ, SINISCALCO M: Report of the committee on the genetic constitution of the X and Y chromosomes. *Cytogenet Cell Genet* 32:121, 1982.

247. FOX MF, DUTOIT DL, WARNICH L, RETIEF AE: Regional localization of α-galactosidase (GLA) to Xpter→q22, hexosaminidase B (HEXB) to 5q13→qter, and arylsulfatase B (ARSB) to 5pter→q13. *Cytogenet Cell Genet* 38:45, 1984.

248. BISHOP DF, CALHOUN DH, BERNSTEIN HS, QUINN M, HANTZOPOULOS P, DESNICK RJ: Molecular cloning and nucleotide sequencing of a cDNA encoding human α-galactosidase A. *Am J Hum Genet* 37:A144, 1985.

249. BERNSTEIN HS, BISHOP DF, ASTRIN KH, KORNREICH R, DESNICK RJ: Fabry disease: Analysis of mutations in the human α-galactosidase A gene. *Am J Hum Genet* 39:A188, 1986.

250. BERNSTEIN HS, BISHOP DF, ASTRIN KH, SAKURABA H, ENG CM, DESNICK RJ: Fabry disease: Gene rearrangements and a coding region point mutation in the α-galactosidase A gene. *J Clin Invest*, in press.

251. MORGAN SH, CHESHIRE JK, WILSON TM, MACDERMOT K, CRAWFURD M: Anderson-Fabry disease—Family linkage studies using two polymorphic X-linked DNA probes. *Pediatr Nephrol* 1:536, 1987.

252. MACDERMOT KD, MORGAN SH, CHESHIRE JK, WILSON TM: Anderson Fabry Disease. Close linkage with highly polymorphic DNA markers DXS17, DXS87, and DXS88. *Hum Genet* 77:263, 1987.

253. DESNICK RJ, BERNSTEIN HS, ASTRIN KH, BISHOP DF: Molecular diagnosis of hemizygotes and heterozygotes. *Enzyme* 38:54, 1987.

254. YANG HM, NIEBUHR E, NORBY S, LUND T, SCHWARTZ M: Subregional localization of anonymous Xq DNA probe by deletion mapping. *Cytogenet Cell Genet* 46:722, 1988.

255. OKAYAMA H, BERG P: A cDNA cloning vector that permits expression of cDNA inserts in mammalian cells. *Mol Cell Biol* 3:280, 1983.

256. TSUJI S, MARTIN BM, KASLOW DC, MIGEON BR, CHOUDARY PV, STUBBLEFIELD BK, MAYOR JA, MURRAY GJ, BARRANGER JA, GINNS EI: Signal sequence and DNA-mediated expression of human lysosomal α-galactosidase A. *Eur J Biochem* 165:275, 1987.

257. WATSON MEE: Compilation of published signal sequences. *Nucleic Acids Res* 12:5145, 1984.

258. von HEIJNE G: A new method for predicting signal sequence cleavage sites. *Nucleic Acids Res* 14:4683, 1986.

259. AUBERT J-P, BISERTE G, LOUCHEUX-LEFEBVRE M-H: Carbohydrate-peptide linkage in glycoproteins. *Arch Biochem Biophys* 175:410, 1976.

260. SORGE J, WEST C, WESTWOOD B, BEUTLER E: Molecular cloning and nucleotide sequence of human glucocerebrosidase cDNA. *Proc Natl Acad Sci USA* 82:7289, 1985.

261. FAUST PL, KORNFELD S, CHIRGWIN JM: Cloning and sequence analysis of cDNA for human cathepsin D. *Proc Natl Acad Sci USA* 82:4910, 1985.

262. MYEROWITZ R, PIEKARZ R, NEUFELD EF, SHOWS TB, SUZUKI K: Human β-hexosaminidase α chain: Coding sequence and homology with the β chain. *Proc Natl Acad Sci USA* 82:7830, 1985.

263. JENH C-H, DENG T, LI D, DEWILLE J, JOHNSON LF: Mouse thymidylate synthase messenger RNA lacks a 3′ untranslated region. *Proc Natl Acad Sci USA* 83:8482, 1986.

264. BIRNSTIEL ML, BUSSLINGER M, STRUB K: Transcription termination and 3′ processing: The End Is In Site! *Cell* 41:349, 1985.

265. LILJESTROM PL, LILJESTROM P: Nucleotide sequence of the *melA* gene,

coding for α-galactosidase in *Escherichia coli* K-12. *Nucleic Acids Res* 156:2213, 1987.

266. FUKUSHIMA H, DEWET JR, O'BRIEN JS: Molecular cloning of a cDNA for human α-L-fucosidase. *Proc Natl Acad Sci USA* 82:1262, 1985.

267. WONG GG, WITEK JS, TEMPLE PA, WILKENS KM, LEARY AC, LUXENBERG DP, JONES SS, BROWN EL, KAY RM, ORR EC, SHOEMAKER C, GOLDE DW, KAUFMAN RJ, HEWICK RM, WANG EA, CLARK SC: Human GM-CSF: Molecular cloning of the complementary DNA and purification of the natural and recombinant proteins. *Science* 228:810, 1985.

268. HANTZOPOLOUS PA, CALHOUN DH: Expression of the human α-galactosidase A in Escherichia coli K-12. *Gene* 57:159, 1987.

269. IOANNOU Y, DESNICK RJ, BISHOP DB: Unpublished data.

270. GHRAYEB J, KIMURA H, TAKAHARA M, HSIUNG H, MASUI Y, INOUYE M: Secretion cloning vectors in *Escherichia coli*. *EMBO J* 3:2437, 1984.

271. SCHMITT R: Analysis of melibiose mutants deficient in α-galactosidase and thiomethylgalactoside permease II in *Escherichia coli* K-12. *J Bacteriol* 96:462, 1968.

272. MIYAMATO C, SMITH GE, FARREL-TAUT J, CHIZZONITE R, SUMMERS MD: Production of human c-myc protein in insect cells infected with a baculorius expression vector. *Mol Cell Biol* 5:2860, 1985.

273. BITTER GA, EGAN KM, KOSKI RA, JONES MO, ELLIOTT SG, GRIFFIN JC: Expression and secretion vectors for yeast. *Methods Enzymol* 153:516, 1987.

274. FUERST TR, NILES EG, STUDIER FW, MOSS B: Eukaryotic transient-expression system based on recombinant vaccina virus that synthesizes bacteriophage T7 RNA polymerase. *Proc Natl Acad Sci USA* 83:8122, 1986.

275. PALMITER RD, BRINSTER RL, HAMMER RE, TRUMBAUER ME, ROSENFELD MG, BIRNBERG NC, EVANS RN: Dramatic growth of mice that develop from eggs microinjected with metallothionein-growth hormone fusion genes. *Nature* 300:611, 1982.

276. BREATHNACH R, CHAMBON P: Organization and expression of eucaryotic split genes coding for proteins. *Annu Rev Biochem* 50:349, 1981.

277. MOUNT SM: A catalogue of splice junction sequences. *Nucleic Acids Res* 10:459, 1982.

278. LEE W, MITCHELL P, TJIAN R: Purified transcription factor AP-1 interacts with TPA-inducible enhancer elements. *Cell* 49:741, 1987.

279. LENARDO M, PIERCE JW, BALTIMORE D: Protein-binding sites in Ig gene enhancers determine transcriptional activity and inducibility. *Science* 236:1573, 1987.

280. PRYWES R, ROEDER RG: Inducible binding of a factor to the c-*fos* enhancer. *Cell* 47:777, 1986.

281. SPOEREL N, NGUYEN HT, KAFATOS FC: Gene regulation and evolution in the chorion locus of *Bombyx mori*: Structural and developmental characterization of four eggshell genes and their flanking DNA regions. *J Mol Biol* 190:23, 1986.

282. LINDSAY S, BIRD AP: Use of restriction enzymes to detect potential gene sequences in mammalian DNA. *Nature* 327:336, 1987.

283. BIRD AP: CpG-rich islands and the function of DNA methylation. *Nature* 321:209, 1986.

284. YANG TP, CASKEY TC: Nuclease sensitivity of the mouse *HPRT* gene promoter region: Differential sensitivity on the active and inactive X-chromosomes. *Mol Cell Biol* 7:2994, 1987.

285. KEITH DH, SINGER-SAM J, RIGGS AD: Active X chromosome DNA is unmethylated at eight CCGG sites clustered in a guanine-plus-cystosine-rich island at the 5′ end of the gene for phosphoglycerate kinase. *Mol Cell Biol* 6:4122, 1986.

286. MOHANDAS T, SPARKES RS, BISHOP DF, DESNICK RJ, SHAPIRO LJ: Frequency of reactivation and variability in expression of X-linked enzyme loci. *Am J Hum Genet* 36:916, 1984.

287. MCDEVITT MA, HART RP, WONG WW, NEVINS JR: Sequences capable of restoring poly (A) site function define two distinct downstream elements. *EMBO J* 5:2907, 1986.

288. GIL A, PROUDFOOT NJ: Position-dependent sequence elements downstream of AAUAAA are required for efficient rabbit β-Globin mRNA 3′ end formation. *Cell* 49:399, 1987.

289. MCLAUCHLAN J, GAFFNEY D, WHITTON JL, CLEMENTS JB: The consensus sequence YGTGTTYY located downstream from the AATAAA signal is required for efficient formation of mRNA 3′ termini. *Nucleic Acids Res* 13:1347, 1985.

290. DESNICK RJ, KORNREICH R, ASTRIN K, ENG CM, FITZMAURICE T, SAKURABA H, BISHOP DF: Fabry disease: Molecular genetics of α-galactosidase deficiency. *Clin Res* 36:612A, 1988.

291. HENTHORN PS, MAGER PL, HUISMAN THJ, SMITHIES O: A gene deletion ending within a complex array of repeated sequences 3′ to the human β-globin gene cluster. *Proc Natl Acad Sci USA* 83:5194, 1986.

292. LEHRMAN MA, RUSSELL DW, GOLDSTEIN JL, BROWN MS: Alu-Alu recombination deletes splice acceptor sites and produces secreted low density lipoprotein receptor in a subject with familial hypercholesterolemia. *J Biol Chem* 262:3354, 1987.

293. GAHL WA, ADAMSON M, KAISER-KUPFER I, LUDWIG IH, O'CONNELL HJ, COHEN W, BARRANGER J: Biochemical phenotyping of a single sibship with both cystinosis and Fabry disease. *J Inherited Metab Dis* 8:127, 1988.

294. JOHNSON DL, DESNICK RJ: Molecular pathology of Fabry's disease: Physical and kinetic properties of α-galactosidase A in cultured human endothelial cells. *Biochim Biophys Acta* 538:195, 1978.

295. VAN DEN BERGH FAJTM, TAGER JM: Localization of neutral glycosphingolipids in human plasma. *Biochim Biophys Acta* 441:391, 1976.

296. MEUWEISSEN SGM, DINGEMANS KP, STRIJLAND A, TAGER JM, OOMS BCH: Ultrastructural and biochemical liver analyses in Fabry's disease. *Hepatology* 2:263, 1982.

297. CLARKE JTR, STOLTZ JM: Uptake of radiolabeled galactosyl-(α1→4)-galactosyl-(β1→4)-glucosylceramide by human lipoproteins in vitro. *Biochim Biophys Acta* 441:165, 1976.

298. STEIN O, STEIN Y: High density lipoproteins reduce the uptake of low density lipoproteins by human endothelial cells in culture. *Biochim Biophys Acta* 431:363, 1976.

299. GOLDSTEIN JL, BROWN MS: The low density lipoprotein pathway and its relation to atherosclerosis. *Annu Rev Biochem* 46:897, 1977.

300. VLODAVSKY I, FEILDING PE, FIELDING CJ, GOSPODAROWICZ D: Role of contact inhibition in the regulation of receptor-mediated uptake of low density lipoprotein in cultured vascular endothelial cells. *Proc Natl Acad Sci USA* 75:356, 1979.

301. TAO RVP: Biochemistry and metabolism of mammalian blood glycosphingolipids. Ph.D. Thesis, Michigan State University, 1973.

302. BARKAI A, DICESARE JL: Influence of sialic acid groups on the retention of glycosphingolipids in blood plasma. *Biochim Biophys Acta* 398:287, 1975.

303. FUKUHARA N, SUZUKI M, FUJITA N, TSUBAKI T: Fabry's disease on the mechanism of the peripheral nerve involvement. *Acta Neuropathol (Berl)* 33:9, 1975.

304. DVORAK AM, CABLE WJL, OSAGE JE, KOLODNY EH: Diagnostic electron microscopy. II. Fabry's disease: Use of biopsies from uninvolved skin. Acute and chronic changes involving the microvasculature and small unmyelinated nerves. *Pathol Annu* 16:139, 1981.

305. SEINO Y, VYDEN JK, PHILIPPART M, ROSE HB, NAGASAWA K: Peripheral hemodynamics in patients with Fabry's disease. *Am Heart J* 105:783, 1983.

306. TOME FMS, FARDEAU M, LEOIR G: Ultrastructure of muscle and sensory nerve in Fabry disease. *Acta Neuropathol* 38:187, 1977.

307. PELISSIER JF, VAN HOOF F, BOURDET-BONERANDI D, MONIER-FAUGERE MC, TOGA M: Morphological and biochemical changes in muscle and peripheral nerve in Fabry's disease. *Muscle Nerve* 4:381, 1981.

308. WALKER F: Histamine flare in Fabry's disease. *Neurology* 33:387, 1983.

309. VOGELBERG KH, SOLBACH HG, GRIES FA: Lipoidchemische Untersuchungen beim Angiokeratoma corporis diffusum (Fabry-syndrome). *Klin Wochenschr* 47:916, 1969.

310. SORENSEN SA, HASHOLT L: Attitudes of persons at risk for Fabry's disease toward predictive and genetic counseling. *J Biol Soc Sci* 15:89, 1983.

311. FORDYCE JA: Angiokeratoma of the scrotum. *J Cutan Genitourin Dis* 14:81, 1986.

312. IMPERIAL R, HELIWIG EB: Angiokeratoma of the scrotum (Fordyce type). *J Urol* 98:379, 1967.

313. TRAUB EF, TOLMACH JA: Angiokeratoma. Comprehensive study of the literature and report of a case. *Arch Dermatol Syph* 24:39, 1931.

314. DAMMERT K: Angiokeratosis naeviformis—a form of naevus telangiectatieus lateralis (naevus flammeus). *Dermatologica* 130:17, 1965.

315. GOLDMAN L, GIBSON SH, RICHFIELD DF: Thrombotic angiokeratoma circumscriptum simulating melanoma. *Arch Dermatol* 117:138, 1981.

316. EPINETTE WW, NORINS AL, DREW AL, ZEMAN W, PATEL V: Angiokeratoma corporis diffusum with α-L-fucosidase deficiency. *Arch Dermatol* 107:755, 1973.

317. MIYATAKE T, ATSUMI T, OBAYASKI T, MIZUNO Y, ANDO S, ARIGA T, MATSUI-NAKAMURA K, YAMADA T: Adult type neuronal storage disease with neuraminidase deficiency. *Ann Neurol* 6:232, 1978.

318. ISHIBASHI A, TSUBOI R, SHINMEI M: β-Galactosidase and neuraminidase deficiency associated with angiokeratoma corporis diffusum. *Arch Dermatol* 120:1344, 1984.

319. WENGER DA, SATTLER M, MUELLER OT, MYERS GG, SCHNEIMAN RS, NIXON GW: Adult GM1 gangliosiodosis: Clinical and biochemical studies on two patients and comparison to other patients called variant or adult GM1 gangliosidosis. *Clin Genet* 17:323, 1980.

320. GEHLER J, SEWELL AC, BECKER C, HARTMANN J, SPRANGER J: Clinical and biochemical delineation of aspartylglycosaminuria as observed in two members of an Italian family. *Helv Paediatr Acta* 36:179, 1981.

321. MCCALLUM DI, MacADAM RF, JOHNSTON AW: Angiokeratoma corporis diffusum with features of a mucopolysaccharidosis. *J Med Genet* 17:21, 1980.

322. HOLMES RC, FENSOM AH, MCKEE P, CAIRNS RJ, BLACK MM: Angiokeratoma corporis diffusum in a patient with normal enzyme activities. *J Am Acad Dermatol* 10:384, 1984.

323. CROVATO F, REBORA A: Angiokeratoma corporis diffusum and normal enzyme activities. *J Am Acad Dermatol* 12:885, 1985.

324. FROST P, SPAETH GL, TANAKA Y: Fabry's disease: Glycolipidosis. Skin manifestations. *Arch Intern Med* 117:440, 1966.

325. IMPERIAL R, HELIWIG EB: Angiokeratoma: A clinicopathological study. *Arch Dermatol* 95:166, 1967.

326. van MULLEM PJ, RUITER M: Electron microscopic study of the skin in angiokeratoma corporis diffusum. *Arch Klin Exp Dermatol* 226:453, 1966.

327. FRANCOIS J, de BECKER L: Les manifestations oculaires de l'intoxication chloroquine. *Ann Oculist* 198:513, 1965.

328. DESNICK RJ, DOUGHMAN DJ, RILEY FC, WHITLEY CB: Fabry keratopathy: Molecular pathology of the chloroquine-induced phenocopy. *Am J Hum Genet* 26:A26, 1974.

329. WHITLEY CB: Studies of heritable and induced lysosomopathies. Ph.D. Thesis, University of Minnesota, 1977.

330. de GROOT PG, ELFERINK RO, HOLLEMANS M, STRIJLAND A, WESTERVELD A, MEERA KHAN P, TAGER JM: Inactivation by chloroquine of α-galactosidase in cultured human skin fibroblasts. *Exp Cell Res* 136:327, 1981.

331. WHITLEY CB, TSAI MY, HEGER JJ, PRYSTOWSKY EN, ZIPES DP: Amiodarone phenocopy of Fabry's keratopathy. *JAMA* 249:2177, 1983.

332. DUDOGNON P, HAUW JJ, de BAECQUE C, et al: Amiodarone neuropathy: Clinical and pathological study of a new drug induced lipidosis. *Rev Neurol* 135:527, 1979.

333. BANKS DE, MILUTINOVIC J, DESNICK RJ, GRABOWSKI GA, LAPP NL, BOEHLECKE BA: Silicon nephropathy mimicking Fabry's disease. *Am J Nephrol* 3:279, 1983.

334. HO MW, BEUTLER E, TENNANT L, O'BRIEN JS: Fabry's disease: Evidence for a physically altered α-galactosidase. *Am J Hum Genet* 24:256, 1972.

335. MAYES JS, SCHEERER JB, SIFERS RN, DONALDSON ML: Differential assay for lysosomal α-galactosidases in human tissues and its application to Fabry's disease. *Clin Chim Acta* 112:247, 1981.

336. FRANCOIS J: Heterozygotes for sex-linked traits and Mary Lyon's inactivation theory. XIV. Fabry's dystopic lipidosis, in *Proceedings of the III International Congress of Human Genetics.* Baltimore, MD, Johns Hopkins Press, 1967, p 423.

337. HOLLIDAY R: Strong effects of 5-azacytidine on the in vitro lifespan of human diploid fibroblasts. *Exp Cell Res* 166:543, 1986.

338. WAREHAM KA, LYON MF, GLENISLER PH, WILLIAMS ED: Age related reactivation of an X-linked gene. *Nature* 327:725, 1987.

339. WILSON VL, SMITH RA, MA S, CUTLER RG: Genomic 5-methyldeoxycytidine decreases with age. *J Biol Chem* 262:9948, 1987.

340. GRIMM T, WIENKER TF, ROPERS H-H: Fabry's disease: Heterozygote detection by hair root analysis. *Hum Genet* 32:329, 1976.

341. SPENSE MW, GOLDBLOOM AL, BURGESS JK, D'ENTREMONT D, RIPLEY BA, WELDON KL: Heterozygote detection in angiokeratoma corporis diffusum (Anderson-Fabry disease). *J Med Genet* 14:91, 1977.

342. VERMORKEN AJM, WETERINGS PJJM, SPIERENBURG GT, VAN BENNEKOM CA, WIRTZ P, de BRUYN CHMM, OEI TL: Fabry's disease: Biochemical and histochemical studies on hair roots for carrier detection. *Br J Dermatol* 98:191, 1978.

343. JONGKIND JF, VERKERK A, NIERMEIJER MF: Detection of Fabry's disease heterozygotes enzyme analysis in single fibroblasts after cell sorting. *Clin Genet* 23:261, 1983.

344. DAVIES KE: Molecular genetics of the human X chromosome. *J Med Genet* 22:243, 1985.

345. DRAYNA D, WHITE R: Genetic linkage map of the human X-chromosome. *Science* 230:753, 1985.

346. WILLIARD HF, SKOLNICK M, PEARSON PL, MANDEL J-L: Report of the committee on human gene mapping by recombinant DNA techniques, in Human Gene Mapping 8. *Cytogenet Cell Genet* 40:360, 1985.

347. ASTRIN K, BISHOP DB, DESNICK RJ: Unpublished data.

348. HOFKER MH, SKRAASTAD MI, BERGEN AAB, WAPENAAR MC, BAKKER E, MILLINGTON-WARD A, van OMMEN GJB, PEARSON PL: The X chromosome shows less genetic variation at restriction sites than the autosomes. *Am J Hum Genet* 39:438, 1986.

349. COOPER DN, SCHMIDTKE J: DNA restriction fragment length polymorphisms and heterozygosity in the human genome. *Hum Genet* 66:1, 1984.

350. DAVATELIS G, SINISCALCO M, SZABO P: An anonymous single copy X-chromosome clone DXS94 from xq11→q21 identifies a common RFLP. *Nucleic Acids Res* 15:4694, 1987.

351. SCHMECKPEPER BJ, DAVIS J, WILLARD HF, SMITH KD: An anonymous single-copy X-chromosome RFLP for DXS72 from Xq13-Xq22. *Nucleic Acids Res* 13:5724, 1985.

352. KEPPEN LD, LEPPERT MF, O'CONNELL P, YUSUKE N, STAUFFER D, LATHROP M, LALOUEL J-M, WHITE R: Etiological heterogeneity in X-linked spastic paraplegia. *Am J Hum Genet* 41:933, 1987.

353. WU J-S, RIORDAN JR, WILLARD HF, MILNER R, KIDD KK: MSP RFLP for X-linked proteolipid protein gene (PLP) identified with either rat or human PLP cDNA clone. *Nucleic Acids Res* 15:1882, 1987.

354. DESNICK RJ, RAMAN MK, BENDEL RP, KERSEY J, LEE JC, KRIVIT W: Prenatal diagnosis of glycosphingolipidoses: Sandhoff's (SD) and Fabry's diseases (FD). *J Pediatr* 83:149, 1973.

355. MALOUF M, KIRKMAN HN, BUCHANAN PD: Ultrastructural changes in antenatal Fabry's disease. *Am J Pathol* 82:132, 1976.

356. KLEIJER WJ, HUSSAARTS-ODIJK LM, SACKS ES, JAHODA MGJ, NIERMEIJER MF: Prenatal diagnosis of Fabry's disease by direct analysis of chorionic villi. *Prenat Diagn* 7:283, 1987.

357. LENOIR G, RIVRON M, GUBLER MC, DUFIER JL, TOME FSM, GUIVARARCH M: La maladie de Fabry. Traitement du syndrome acrodyniforme par la carbamazepine. *Arch Fr Pediatr* 34:704, 1977.

358. ATZPODIEN W, KREMER GJ, SCHNELLBACHER E, DENK R, HAFERKAMP G, BIERBACH H: Angiokeratoma corporis diffusum (Morbus Fabry). Biochemische Diagnostik im Blutplasma. *Dtsch Med Wochenschr* 100:423, 1975.

359. DUPERRAT B, PUISSANT A, SAURAT JH, DELANOE J, DOYARD PA, GRUNFELD JP: Maladie de Fabry. Angiokeratomes presents a la naissance. Action del la diphenylhydantoine sur les crises douloureuses. *Ann Dermatol Syph* 102:392, 1975.

360. NEWTON JA, McGIBBON DH: The treatment of multiple angiokeratoma with the argon laser. *Clin Exp Dermatol* 12:23, 1987.

361. HOBBS ER, RATZ JL: Argon laser treatment of angiokeratomas. *J Dermatol Surg Oncol* 13:1319, 1987.

362. CLARKE JTR, GUTTMANN RD, WOLFE LS, BEAUDOIN JG, MOREHOUSE DD: Enzyme replacement therapy by renal allotransplantation in Fabry's disease. *N Engl J Med* 287:1215, 1972.

363. POPLI S, MOLNAR AV, LEEHEY DJ, DAUGIRDAS JT, ROTH DA, ADAMS MB, CHENG J-C, ING TS: Involvement of renal allograft by Fabry's disease. *Am J Nephrol* 7:316, 1987.

364. DONATI D, SABBADINI MG, CAPSONI F, BARATELLI L, CASSANI D, de MAIO A, FRATINI G, MARTEGANI M, GASTALDI L: Immune function and renal transplantation in Fabry's disease. *Proc Eur Dialysis Transpl Assoc* 21:686, 1984.

365. PHILIPPART M, FRANKLIN SS, GORDON A: Reversal of an inborn sphingolipidosis (Fabry's disease) by kidney transplantation. *Ann Intern Med* 77:195, 1972.

366. DESNICK RJ, ALLEN KY, SIMMONS RL, WOODS JE, ANDERSON CF, NAJARIAN JS, KRIVIT W: Fabry disease: Correction of the enzymatic deficiency by renal transplantation, in Desnick RJ, Bernlohr RW, Krivit W (eds): *Enzyme Therapy in Genetic Diseases*. Baltimore, MD, Williams and Wilkins, 1973, p 88.

367. JACKY E: Fabrysche Erkrankung (Angiokeratoma corporis diffusum universale): Gunstiger Verlauf nach Nierentransplantation. *Schweiz Med Wochenschr* 106:703, 1976.

368. BUHLER FR, THIEL G, DUBACH VC, ENDERLIN F, GLOOR F, THOLEN H: Kidney transplantation in Fabry's disease. *Br Med J* 3:28, 1973.

369. CLEMENT M, MONKHOUSE PM, MARTEN RH, PARSONS V, McGONIGLE RJS, KEOGH AM, BEWICK M: Renal transplantation in Anderson-Fabry disease. *J R Soc Med* 75:557, 1982.

370. SPENCE MW, MacKINNON KE, BURGESS JK, d'ENTREMONT DM, BELITSKY P, LANNON SG, MacDONALD AS: Failure to correct the metabolic defect by renal allotransplantation in Fabry's disease. *Ann Intern Med* 84:13, 1976.

371. GRUNFELD JP, LEPORRIER M, DROZ D, BENSAUDE I, HINGLAIS N, CROSNIER J: Le transplantation renale chez les sujets atteints de maladie de Fabry. *Nouv Presse Med* 4:2081, 1975.

372. van den BERGH FAJTM, RIETRA PJGM, KOLK-VEGTER AJ, BOSCH E, TAGER JM: Therapeutic implications of renal transplantation in a patient with Fabry's disease. *Acta Med Scand* 200:249, 1976.

373. BANNWART F: Morbus Fabry. Licht- und elektronenmikroskopischer Herzbefund 12 Jahre nach erfolgreicher Nierentransplantation. *Schweiz Med Wochenschr* 112:1742, 1982.

374. KRAMER W, THORMANN J, MUELLER K, FRENZEL H: Progressive cardiac involvement by Fabry's disease despite successful renal allotransplantation. *Int J Cardiol* 7:72, 1984.

375. DAWSON G, MATALON R, LI YT: Correction of the enzymatic defect in cultured fibroblasts from patients with Fabry's disease: Treatment with purified α-galactosidase from Ficin. *Pediatr Res* 7:684, 1973.

376. OSADA T, KURODA Y, IKAI A: Endocytic internalization of α-2-macroglobulin: α-Galactosidase conjugate by cultured fibroblasts derived from Fabry hemizygote. *Biochem Biophys Res Commun* 142:100, 1987.

377. JOHNSON DL, DESNICK RJ: Unpublished results.

378. MAYES JS, CRAY EL, DELL VA, SCHEERER JB, SIFERS RN: Endocytosis of lysosomal α-galactosidase A by cultured fibroblasts from patients with Fabry disease. *Am J Hum Genet* 34:602, 1982.

379. HASHOLT L, SORENSON SA: Con A-mediated binding and uptake of purified α-galactosidase A in Fabry fibroblasts. *Exp Cell Res* 148:405, 1983.

380. HASHOLT L, SORENSEN SA: A microtechnique for quantitative measurements of acid hydrolases in fibroblasts. Its application in diagnosis of Fabry disease and enzyme replacement studies. *Clin Chim Acta* 142:257, 1984.

381. DESNICK RJ, DEAN KJ, GRABOWSKI GA, BISHOP DF, SWEELEY CC: Enzyme therapy XVII. Metabolic and immunologic evaluation of α-galactosidase A replacement in Fabry disease, in Desnick RJ (ed): *Enzyme Therapy in Genetic Diseases*, 2d ed. New York, AR Liss, 1980, p 393.

382. ASHWELL G, MORELL AG: The role of surface carbohydrates in the hepatic recognition and transport of circulating glycoproteins. *Adv Enzymol* 41:99, 1974.

383. BISHOP DF, KOVAC CR, DESNICK RJ: Enzyme therapy XX: Further evidence for the differential in vivo fate of human splenic and plasma forms of α-galactosidase A in Fabry disease. Recovery of exogenous activity from hepatic tissue, in Callahan JW, Lowden JA (eds): *Lysosomes and Lysosomal Storage Diseases*. New York, Raven, 1981, p 381.

384. TOURAINE JL, MALIK MC, PERROT H, MAIRE I, REVILLARD JP, GROSSHANS E, TRAEGER J: Maladie de Fabry: Deux maladies ameliores par la greffe de cellules de foie foetal. *Nouv Presse Med* 8:1499, 1979.

385. GROSSHANS E: A propos de la revue generale la maladie de Fabry. *Ann Dermatol Venereol* 113:277, 1986.

386. PYERITZ RE, ULLMAN MD, MOSER AB, BRAINE HG, MOSER HW: Plasma exchange removes glycosphingolipid in Fabry disease. *Am J Med Genet* 7:301, 1980.

387. BISHOP DF, DESNICK RJ: Unpublished data.

388. BUETLER E, WESTWOOD B, DALE GL: The effect of phlebotomy as a treatment of Fabry disease. *Biochem Med* 30:363, 1983.

389. DESNICK RJ, GRABOWSKI GA: Advances in the treatment of inherited metabolic diseases. *Adv Hum Genet* 11:281, 1981.

390. DESNICK RJ: Treatment of inherited metabolic diseases: Current status and prospects, in Deitz AA (ed): *Genetic Diseases: Diagnosis and Treatment*. Washington, DC, American Association for Clinical Chemistry, 1983, p 183.

391. van DIGGELEN OP, SCHINDLER D, KLEIJER WJ, HUIJMANS JMG, GALJAARD H, LINDEN HU, PETER-KATALINIC J, EGGE H, DABROWSKI U, CANTZ M: Lysosomal α-N-acetylgalactosaminidase deficiency: A new inherited metabolic disease. *Lancet* 2:804, 1987.

392. SCHINDLER D, BISHOP DF, WALLACE S, WOLFE DE, DESNICK RJ: Characterization of α-N-acetylgalactosaminidase deficiency: A new neurodegenerative lysosomal disease. *Pediatr Res* 23:333A, 1988.

393. SCHINDLER D, BISHOP DF, WOLFE DE, WANG AM, EGGE H, LEMIEUX RU, DESNICK RJ: α-N-acetylgalactosaminidase deficiency, a new neurodegenerative lysosomal disease with primary neurologic involvement. *N Engl J Med*, in review.

394. TAY W: Symmetrical changes in the region of the yellow spot in each eye of an infant. *Trans Ophthalmol Soc UK* 1:55, 1881.

395. SACHS B: On arrested cerebral development with special reference to its cortical pathology. *J Nerv Ment Dis* 14:541, 1887.

396. KRABBE K: A new familial, infantile form of diffuse brain sclerosis. *Brain* 39:74, 1916.

397. SCHOLZ W: Klinische, pathologisch-anatomische und erbbiologische Untersuchungen bei familiärer, diffuser Hirnsklerose im Kindesalter. *Z Ges Neurol Psychiat* 99:651, 1925.

398. WENGER DA, TARBY JF, WHARTON C: Macular cherry-red spots and a myoclonus with dementia: Co-existent neuraminidase and β-galactosidase deficiencies. *Biochem Biophys Res Commun* 82:589, 1978.

399. AULA P, AUTIO S, RAIVIO KO, RAPOLA J, THODEN CJ, KOSKELA SL, YAMASHINA I: "Salla disease": a new lysosomal storage disorder. *Arch Neurol* 36:88, 1979.

400. WENGER DA, SUJANSKY E, FENNESSEY PV, THOMPSON JN: Human β-mannosidase deficiency. *N Engl J Med* 315:1201, 1986.

401. COOPER A, SARDHARWALLA IB, ROBERTS MM: Human β-mannosidase deficiency. *N Engl J Med* 315:1231, 1986.

402. SCHINDLER D, BISHOP DF, LEMIEUX RU, DESNICK RJ: Schindler disease: Enzymatic diagnosis of homozygotes and heterozygotes. α-N-Acetylgalactosaminidase activity in plasma, leukocytes and cultured cells, in preparation.

403. WOLFE DE, PERL D, SCHINDLER D, DESNICK RJ: The histologic and ultrastructural pathology of Schindler disease, α-N-acetylgalactosaminidase deficiency, in preparation.

404. SEITELBERGER F: Eine unbekannte Form von infantiler Lipoid Speicher Krankheit des Gehirns, in *Proceedings of the First International Congress of Neuropathology* (Rome, Sept. 8–13, 1952), vol 3, Torino, Rosenberg, Sellier (eds), 1952, p 323.

405. SEITELBERGER F, JELLINGER K: Neuroaxonal dystrophy and Hallervorden-Spatz disease, in Goldensohn ES, Appel SH (eds): *Scientific Approaches to Clinical Neurology*. Philadelphia, PA, Lea & Febiger, 1977, p 1052.

406. COWEN D, OLMSTEAD EV: Infantile neuroaxonal dystrophy. *J Neuropathol Exp Neurol* 22:175, 1963.

407. HEDLEY-WHYTE ET, GILLES FH, UZMAN BG: Infantile neuroaxonal dystrophy. *Neurology* 18:891, 1968.

408. de LEON GA, MITCHELL MH: Histological and ultrastructural features of dystrophic isocortical axons in infantile neuroaxonal dystrophy (Seitelberger's disease). *Acta Neuropathol (Berl)* 66:89, 1985.

409. INDRAVASU S, DEXTER RA: Infantile neuroaxonal dystrophy and its relationship to Hallervorden-Spatz disease. *Neurology* 18:693, 1968.

410. PARK BE, NETSKY MG, BETSILL WL: Pathogenesis of pigment and spheroid formation in Hallervorden-Spatz syndrome and related disorders. *Neurology* 25:1172, 1975.

411. GRIFFEN JW, WATSON DF: Axonal transport in neurological disease. *Ann Neurol* 23:3, 1988.

412. DEAN KJ, SUNG S-SJ, SWEELEY CC: Purification and partial characterization of human liver α-galactosidases: Is α-galactosidase B an α-N-acetylgalactosaminidase? *Fed Proc* 36:731, 1977.

413. SCHRAM AW, HAMERS MN, BROUWER-KELDER B, DONKER-KOOPMAN WE, TAGER JM: Enzymological properties and immunological characterization of α-galactosidase isoenzymes from normal and Fabry human liver. *Biochim Biophys Acta* 482:125, 1977.

414. SCHRAM AW: Studies on human α-galactosidase, N-acetyl-α-galactosaminidase and α-glucosidase in relation to lysosomal storage diseases. Ph.D. Thesis, University of Amsterdam, 1978.

415. SCHRAM AW, deGROOT PG, HAMERS MN, BROUWER-KELDER B, DONKER-KOOPMAN WE, TAGER JM: Further characterization of two forms of N-acetyl-α-galactosaminidase from human liver. *Biochim Biophys Acta* 525:410, 1978.

416. BISHOP DF, DEAN KJ, SWEELEY CC, DESNICK RJ: Purification and characterization of human α-galactosidase isozymes: Comparison of tissue and plasma forms and evaluation of purification methods, in Desnick RJ (ed): *Enzyme Therapy in Genetic Diseases*, 2d ed. New York, AR Liss, 1980, p 17.

417. ROMEO G, CHILDS B, MIGEON B: Genetic heterogeneity of α-galactosidase in Fabry's disease. *FEBS Lett* 27:161, 1972.

418. KINT JA: On the existence and the enzymatic interconversion of α-galactosidase in human organs. *Arch Int Physiol Biochem* 79:633, 1971.

419. KINT JA, HUYS A: Effect of bacterial neuraminidase on the isoenzymes of acid hydrolases of human brain and liver, in Zambotti V, Tettamanti G, Arrigoni M (eds): *Proceedings of the International Symposium on Glycolipids, Glycoproteins and Mucopolysaccharides of the Nervous System*. New York, Plenum, 1972, p 273.

420. BEUTLER E, KUHL W: Fabry's disease: Structural or regulatory mutation? *J Lab Clin Med* 78:987a, 1971.

421. DEAN KJ, SWEELEY CC: Studies on human liver α-galactosidases II. Purification and enzymatic properties of α-galactosidase B (α-N-acetyl-galactosaminidase). *J Biol Chem* 254:10001, 1979.

422. KANO I, YAMAKAWA T: The properties of α-galactosidase remaining in kidney and liver of patients with Fabry's disease. *Chem Phys Lipids* 13:283, 1974.

423. SALVAYRE R, MARET A, NEGRE A, DOUSTE-BLAZY L: Properties of multiple molecular forms of α-galactosidase and α-N-acetylgalactosaminidase from normal and Fabry leukocytes. *Eur J Biochem* 100:377, 1979.

424. BEUTLER E, GUINTO E, KUHL W: Variability of α-galactosidase A and B in different tissues of man. *Am J Hum Genet* 25:42, 1973.

425. SORENSEN SA, HASHOLT L: α-Galactosidase isozymes in normal individuals, and in Fabry hemizygotes and heterozygotes. *Ann Hum Genet* 43:313, 1980.

426. MAPES CA, SWEELEY CC: Interconversion of the A and B forms of ceramide trihexosidase from human plasma. *Arch Biochem Biophys* 158:297, 1973.

427. CALLAHAN JW, LASSILA EL, den TANDT W, PHILIPPART M: Alpha-N-acetylgalactosaminidase: Isolation, properties and distribution of the human enzyme. *Biochem Med* 7:424, 1973.

428. ROMEO G, d'URSO M, PISACANE A, BLUM E, DeFALCO A, RUFFILLI A: Residual activity of α-galactosidase A in Fabry's disease. *Biochem Genet* 13:615, 1975.

429. WILKINSON F, SWEELEY CC: Unpublished data.

430. ANDREWS P: Estimation of the molecular weights of proteins by Sephadex gel filtration. *Biochem J* 91:222, 1964.

431. SWEELEY CC, LeDONNE NC Jr, ROBBINS PW: Post-translational processing reactions involved in the biosynthesis of lysosomal α-N-acetylgalactosaminidase in cultured human fibroblasts. *Arch Biochem Biophys* 223:158, 1983.

432. WEISSMANN B, HINRICHSEN DF: Mammalian α-acetylgalactosaminidase. Occurrence, partial purification, and action on linkages in submaxillary mucins. *Biochemistry* 8:2034, 1969.

433. WEISSMANN B, FRIEDERICI D: Occurrence of a mammalian α-N-acetyl-D-galactosaminidase. *Biochim Biophys Acta* 117:498, 1966.

434. WERRIES E, WOLLEK E, GOTTSCHALK A, BUDDECKE E: Separation of N-acetyl-α-glucosaminidase and N-acetyl-α-galactosaminidase from ox spleen. Cleavage of the O-glycosidic linkage between carbohydrate and polypeptide in ovine and bovine submaxillary glycoprotein by N-acetyl-α-galactosaminidase. *Eur J Biochem* 10:445, 1969.

435. HAKOMORI S: Blood group ABH and Ii antigens of human erythrocytes: Chemistry, polymorphism, and their developmental change. *Semin Hematol* 18:39, 1981.

436. BERGER EG, BUDDECKE E, KAMERLING JP, KOBATA A, PAULSON JC, VLIEGENTHART JFG: Structure, biosynthesis and functions of glycoprotein glycans. *Experientia* 38:1129, 1982.

437. POOLE AR Proteoglycans in health and disease: Structure and functions. *Biochem J* 236:1, 1986.

438. REGE VP, PAINTER TJ, WATKINS WM, MORGAN WTJ: Three new trisaccharides obtained from human blood-group A, B, H and Le^a substances: Possible sugar sequences in the carbohydrate chains. *Nature* 200:532, 1963.

439. MAKITA A, TANIGUCHI N: Glycosphingolipids, in Wiegandt H (ed): *Glycolipids*. New York, Elsevier, 1985, p 1.

440. BREIMER ME, JOVALL P-A: Structural characterization of a blood group A heptaglycosylceramide with globo-series structure. The major glycolipid based blood group A antigen of human kidney. *FEBS Lett* 179:165, 1985.

441. YODA Y, ISHIBASHI T, MAKITA A: Isolation, characterization, and biosynthesis of Forssman antigen in human lung and lung carcinoma. *J Biochem* 88:1887, 1980.

442. TANIGUCHI N, YOKOSAWA N, NARITA M, MITSUYAMA T, MAKITA A: Expression of Forssman antigen synthesis and degradation in human lung cancer. *J Natl Can Inst* 67:577, 1981.

443. HAKOMORI S, WANG S-M, YOUNG WW Jr: Isoantigenic expression of Forssman glycolipid in human gastric and colonic mucosa: Its possible identity with "A-like antigen" in human cancer. *Proc Natl Acad Sci USA* 74:3023, 1977.

444. PAULSEN H, BÜNSCH A: Synthese der Pentosaccharid-Kette des Forssman-Antigens. *Carbohydr Res* 100:143, 1982.

445. LAMBLIN G, LHERMITTE M, KLEIN A, ROUSSEL P, van HALBEEK H, VLIEGENTHART JFG: Carbohydrate chains from human bronchial mucus glycoproteins: A wide spectrum of oligosaccharide structures. *Biochem Soc Trans* 12:599, 1984.

446. FEIZI T, GOOI HC, CHILDS RA, PICAREL JK, UEMURA K, LOOMES LM, THORPE SJ, HOUNSELL EF: Tumor-associated and differentiation antigens on the carboydrate moieties of mucin-type glycoproteins. *Biochem Soc Trans* 12:591, 1984.

447. TAKASAKI S, YAMASHITA K, KOBATA A: The sugar chain structures of ABO blood group active glycoproteins obtained from human erythrocyte membrane. *J Biol Chem* 253:6086, 1978.

448. LLOYD KO, KABAT EA: Immunological studies on blood groups, XLI. Proposed structures for the carbohydrate portions of blood group A, B, H, Lewis^a, and Lewis^b substances. *Proc Natl Acad Sci USA* 61:1470, 1968.

449. NAKAGAWA F, SCHULTE BA, SPICER SS: Selective cytochemical demonstration of glycoconjugate-containing terminal N-acetylgalactosamine on some brain neurons. *J Comp Neurol* 243:280, 1986.

450. KOBATA A, TAKASAKI S: Endo-β-galactosidase and endo-α-N-acetyl-galactosaminidase from *Diplococcus pneumoniae*. *Methods Enzymol* 50:560, 1978.

451. UMEMOTO J, BHAVANANDAN VP, DAVIDSON EA: Purification and properties of an endo-α-N-acetyl-D-galactosaminidase from Diplococcus pneumoniae. *J Biol Chem* 252:8609, 1977.

452. de GROOT PG, HAMERS MN, WESTERVELD A, SCHRAM AW, MEERA KHAN P, TAGER JM: A new immunochemical method for the quantitative measurement of specific gene products in man-rodent somatic cell hybrids. *Hum Genet* 44:295, 1978.

453. de GROOT PG, WESTERVELD A, KHAN PM, TAGER JM: Localization of a gene for human α-galactosidase B (= N-acetyl-α-D-galactosidase) on chromosome 22. *Hum Genet* 44:305, 1978.

454. GEURTS van KESSEL AHM, WESTERVELD A, de GROOT PG, MEERA KHAN P, HAGEMEIJER A: Regional localization of the genes coding for human ACO2, ARSA, and NAGA on chromosome 22. *Cytogenet Cell Genet* 28:169, 1980.

455. WANG AM, BISHOP DF, DESNICK RJ: The full-length cDNa encoding α-N-acetyl-galactosaminidase has 50% sequence homology with the α-galactosidase cDNA, in preparation.

456. OKAYAMA H, BERG P: High-efficiency cloning of full-length cDNA. *Mol Cell Biol* 2:161, 1982.

457. OKAYAMA H, BERG P: A cDNA cloning vector that permits expression of cDNA inserts in mammalian cells. *Mol Cell Biol* 3:280, 1983.

β-GALACTOSIDASE DEFICIENCY (G$_{M1}$ Gangliosidosis, Galactosialidosis, and Morquio Syndrome Type B); GANGLIOSIDE SIALIDASE DEFICIENCY (Mucolipidosis IV)

JOHN S. O'BRIEN

1. *The G$_{M1}$ gangliosidoses produce at one end of the spectrum patients with acute infantile onset, rapid neurologic decline, and severe bony abnormalities, and at the other end patients with normal intelligence and survival to adulthood. At least three different subtypes are presently recognized: an infantile, a juvenile, and an adult subtype. All patients have severe deficiencies of acid β-galactosidase activity.*

2. *Patients with infantile G$_{M1}$ gangliosidosis present with somatic and bony changes and severe neurologic deterioration that leads to death in infancy. Patients with juvenile G$_{M1}$ gangliosidosis present with motor weakness, mild somatic and bony abnormalities, and slowly progressive psychomotor deterioration. Adults with G$_{M1}$ gangliosidosis present with dysarthria, choreoathetosis, and mild or absent bony abnormalities. Intellectual impairment, if present, is mild, and survival is prolonged.*

3. *Storage of G$_{M1}$ gangliosides in the nervous system and of galactosyl oligosaccharides and keratan-sulfate degradation products in somatic cells is prominent in the infantile type, but less so in juvenile and adult types. These compounds accumulate within lysosomes as a consequence of a deficiency of acid β-galactosidase, the primary enzymatic defect.*

4. *Cerebral dysfunction is primarily a consequence of G$_{M1}$ ganglioside accumulation in surface membranes, which gives rise to aberrant neuronal growth and morphology and interferes with neurotransmitter physiology.*

5. *Acid β-galactosidase exists in monomeric (A$_1$), dimeric (A$_2$), and multimeric (A$_3$) forms, composed of one or more 64-kDa subunits. The monomeric polypeptide A$_1$ is coded for by a single autosomal locus, located on the short arm of chromosome 3. Mutation at this locus leads to simultaneous loss of activity of all forms in patients with G$_{M1}$ gangliosidosis. β-Galactosidase A is heterocatalytic, cleaving β-D-galactose from ganglioside G$_{M1}$ galactose-containing oligosaccharides, and other galacto-conjugates. A single mutation producing β-galactosidase deficiency has pleiotropic effects leading to accumulation of its many substrates. Phenotypic variability among β-galactosidase A mutants results from greater residual activity of the mutant enzyme for some substrates than others. For example, patients with significantly higher residual activity for ganglioside G$_{M1}$ than for galactose-containing oligosaccharides or proteoglycans have severe bony involvement with minimal nervous system abnormalities, since these substrates vary in amounts and rates of turnover in brain and bones, respectively. Patients with this phenotype have recently been described, and their disease is called Morquio syndrome type B (MPS IV B).*

6. *Thus far, all human mutants for G$_{M1}$ β-galactosidase appear to be structural mutants, synthesizing nearly normal quantities of mutant enzyme. Several patients are proven K$_m$ mutants. The number of different mutations that lead to β-galactosidase deficiency is probably large. Some patients have an abnormality in processing the precursor.*

7. *Galactosialidosis is a disorder that is phenotypically similar to sialidosis but is due to a deficiency of a 34-kDa protein which prevents rapid degradation of β-galactosidase and perhaps neuraminidase. Accumulation of sialyloligosaccharides in lysosomes occurs in all patients. Severity of the disease varies from severe (infantile) to mild (juvenile). Although the deficiencies of β-galactosidase and neuraminidase can be severe, the primary defect appears to be a mutation at a locus on chromosome 22 that codes for the 34-kDa protective protein, and not in the structural genes for the enzymes. Galactosialidosis is transmitted as an autosomal recessive trait.*

8. *Mucolipidosis IV is a storage disease, primarily of gangliosides, due to deficiency of ganglioside sialidase. Psychomotor retardation and corneal clouding in the juvenile period are present in most patients. The disease is transmitted as an autosomal recessive trait.*

β-GALACTOSIDASE DEFICIENCY DISEASES; G$_{M1}$ GANGLIOSIDOSIS

G$_{M1}$ gangliosidosis was the second ganglioside storage disease to be described, the first being Tay-Sachs disease.[1] The clinical picture of infantile G$_{M1}$ gangliosidosis was recognized as a distinct entity and named *familial neurovisceral lipidosis* after a study of eight patients by Landing et al.[2] A striking accumulation of ganglioside G$_{M1}$ was documented by O'Brien et al.[3] in one of Landing's patients and by Gonatas and Gonatas in another patient.[4] The primary defect, a severe deficiency of acid β-galactosidase, was discovered by Okada and O'Brien.[5] The term *G$_{M1}$ gangliosidosis* was proposed by Suzuki and Chen[6] and is the commonly used name.

Although G$_{M1}$ gangliosidosis was originally recognized as an acute infantile neurovisceral disorder, the clinical spectrum of the disease has expanded to include a juvenile form affecting older children[7] and an adult form with milder symptoms and

Table 71-1 Major Clinical Features of G_{M1} Gangliosidoses

	Infantile	Juvenile	Adult	MPS IV B
Age at onset of symptom	Birth	6–20 mo	Teens	4–8 yr
Age at death	½–2 yr	3–10 yr	20+ yr	20+ yr
Mental-motor retardation	+	+	+	−
Facial appearance	Coarse	Normal	Normal	Normal
Edema	+	−	−	−
X-ray changes, long bones	+	Mild	Mild	Severe
X-ray changes, vertebrae	+	Mild	Mild	Severe
Vacuolated lymphocytes	+	+	±	+
Foam cells in marrow	+	+	±	?
Hepatomegaly	+	−	−	−
Splenomegaly	+	−	−	−
Cherry-red spot	50%	−	−	−
Retinitis pigmentosa	−	−	−	−
Startle response to sound	+	+	−	−
Macrocephaly	Rarely	−	−	−
Macroglossia	+	−	−	−
Seizures	+	+	−	−
Blindness	Early	Late	−	−
Neuronal lipidosis	+	+	+	?
Visceral histiocytosis	+	+	+	?
Glomerular epithelial ballooning	+	+	?	?
Mucopolysacchariduria	±	±	?	+
Dysarthria	+	+	+	−
Spasticity-ataxia	−	+	+	−
Hypotonia	+	−	−	−

survival through adulthood. Table 71-1 summarizes the major clinical features of the G_{M1} gangliosidoses.

Clinical Phenotypes[8]

Infantile G_{M1} Gangliosidosis (Type 1). The psychomotor development of the infant with G_{M1} gangliosidosis is retarded in the first year of life, often from birth. Appetite is usually poor, sucking is weak, and weight gain is subnormal. Many patients are hypoactive, hypotonic, and have facial and peripheral edema in the first few months of life. Other facial abnormalities include frontal bossing, and depressed nasal bridge, large, low-set ears, gum hypertrophy, and mild macroglossia (Figs. 71-1 and 71-2). Corneas are usually clear, but cherry-red spots in the macular region, identical to those in Tay-Sachs disease patients, are present in about 50 percent of the patients.

Mental and motor development are severely retarded. Patients may hold their heads up but usually do not achieve the ability to crawl or sit without support. Patients usually have poor grasp due to weakness and incoordination.

Hepatomegaly is usually present after 6 months of life, and splenomegaly occurs in the majority of patients. Lymphadenopathy is usually minor. Dorsolumbar kyphoscoliosis is often evident. Joints are stiff, and flexion contractures are often present at the elbows and knees. Generalized hyperreflexia is usually evident. Muscle strength is poor, and hypotonia is the rule. The skin is often thick, hirsute, and rough.

After 1 year of age, clonic-tonic convulsions occur. Tube feeding is necessary because of ineffective swallowing, and recurrent bronchopneumonia can be a major problem in medical management. Patients may expire suddenly. Several patients have been described with recurrent bouts of paroxysmal auricular tachycardia which led to their demise. An unusual complication is cardiopathy accompanied by cardiac failure and myopathy of skeletal muscles.[9,10] After 16 months of life the patient presents with a picture of decerebrate rigidity. Death occurs by 2 years of age, usually due to bronchopneumonia.

RADIOLOGY. Many newborn patients have exhibited generalized symmetric periosteal new bone formation (cloaking) around the shafts of the long bones and the ribs. Later, the periosteal lesions diminish and modeling abnormalities of the vertebral bodies and long bones predominate. After 6 months of age the most important radiologic signs are in the spine and upper extremity. These include rarefaction of the cortex of most bones, hypoplastic vertebral bodies with anterior beaking, midshaft widening of the long bones, wedge-shaped metacarpals, shoe-shaped sella turcica, spatulate ribs, and flared

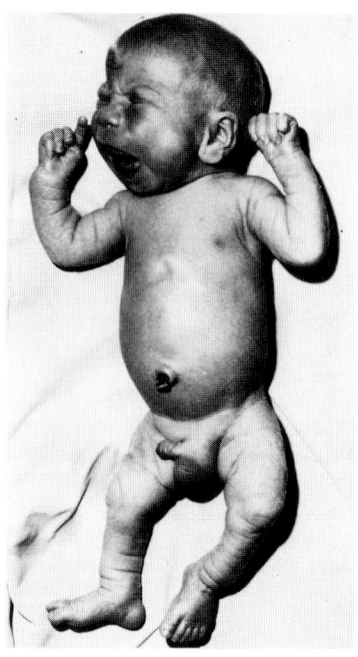

Fig. 71-1 Patient with generalized gangliosidosis at 2 weeks of age. Note the frontal bossing, low-set ears, depressed nasal bridge, wide upper lip, maxillary hyperplasia, and prominent wrist and ankle joints. *(From Scott et al.[92] By permission of authors and publishers.)*

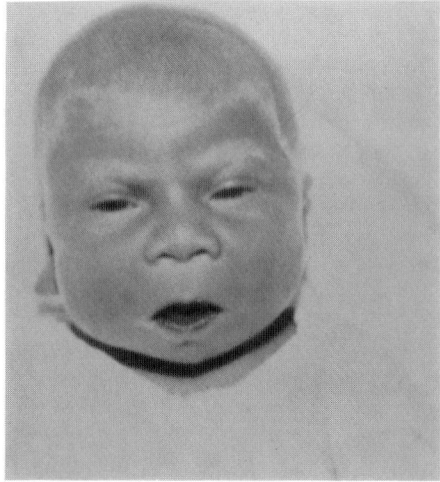
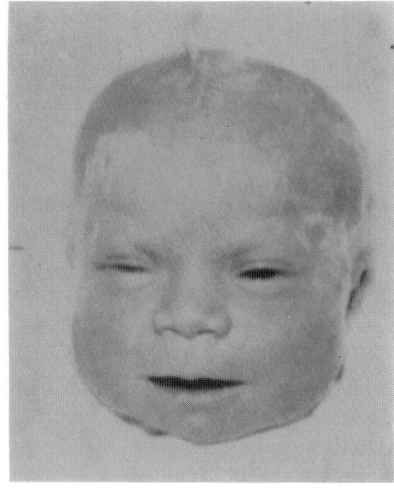

Fig. 71-2 Birth pictures of sibs with generalized gangliosidosis. Note the facial hirsutism, frontal bossing, depressed nasal bridge, and coarse facial features. *(Courtesy of Drs. Cynthia Barrett and C. Ronald Scott.)*

ilia. These modeling deformities are similar to those seen in the genetic mucopolysaccharidoses and are collectively referred to as *dysostosis multiplex*.

PATHOLOGY. The most striking pathologic changes are neuronal lipidosis and cytoplasmic vacuolation of cells outside the nervous system. Neuronal lipidosis occurs throughout the cortex, brainstem, and spinal cord as well as in the autonomic plexus. Rectal biopsy and ultrastructural examination have been useful in demonstrating neuronal lipidosis in such neurons. The neuronal cytoplasm is ballooned with storage material, displacing the nucleus to the periphery. Ultrastructurally, membranous bodies similar to those seen in Tay-Sachs disease are evident within neurons. The bodies are made up of spirally wound lamellar membranes enclosed within a limiting membrane.

In visceral organs, leukocytes, dermal fibroblasts, and epithelial cells, clear vacuoles accumulate within the cytoplasm. The vacuoles contain a finely fibrillar content on ultrastructural examination and are bounded by a limiting membrane. Enzyme histochemical staining has verified that both the neuronal cytoplasmic bodies and the visceral vacuoles are secondary lysosomes distended with storage material.

Juvenile G$_{M1}$ Gangliosidosis (Type 2). The clinical picture differs from that of the acute infantile disorder. Onset is later, the course is slower, and bony abnormalities are milder. Psychomotor development is often normal during the first year of life. Appetite is normal, weight gain is adequate, and developmental milestones are not significantly delayed. Locomotor ataxia beginning at about 1 year of age is usually the initial symptom. Internal strabismus, loss of coordinated manipulative hand movements, choreoathetoid movements, loss of speech, and generalized moderate muscular weakness of both upper and lower extremities are early signs. Mental and motor deterioration may progress rapidly thereafter, with dulling of sensorium, lack of socialization, and lethargy as prominent symptoms. Progressive spasticity of upper and lower extremities then develops, and, with time, a state of decerebrate rigidity is reached. Major motor siezures often appear after 16 months of life and may constitute a major problem in management. Recurrent infections, especially bronchopneumonia, are constant problems, and usually lead to the patients' demise. A survey of the patients reported thus far indicates an average life span of between 3 and 10 years.

Coarsening of facial features is usually not present. Corneas

are clear, and the retina and macula are normal. Blindness may occur late in the course of the disease. Hepatosplenomegaly is usually not present. Hyperreflexia, spasticity, and moderate to severe muscular weakness may be evident after 1 year of life.

RADIOLOGY. Radiographic examination may reveal mild inferior beaking of one or more lumbar vertebral bodies, proximal pointing of the metacarpal bones (especially the fifth), and moderate modeling deformities of the pelvic bones. Although these radiologic changes are mild, they are of considerable diagnostic value and have been noted prior to onset of neurologic symptoms.

PATHOLOGY. Pathologic changes include neuronal lipidosis similar to that seen in the infantile disorder. Cytoplasmic membranous bodies and pleomorphic lamellar bodies accumulate within neurons throughout the central nervous system. Visceral histiocytosis is also present. Ultrastructural examination reveals that clear vacuoles accumulate within visceral histiocytes, parenchymal cells, and epithelial cells. Generally, the lesions are less florid than those seen in the infantile type.

Adult G$_{M1}$ Gangliosidosis (Type 3). Over the last 5 years an increasing number of patients have been diagnosed with adult G$_{M1}$ gangliosidosis.[11-18] These patients usually presented to adult neurology clinics and were diagnosed as having juvenile parkinsonism, atypical spinal muscular atrophy, atypical spinocerebellar degeneration, or "cerebral palsy."

The clinical picture is usually that of gait disturbance and dysarthria beginning in the teenage period, although in some patients symptoms have appeared as early as at age 4. Accompanying these symptoms is a slowly progressive dystonia affecting the face and limbs, eventually becoming incapacitating. Intellectual impairment, when present, was mild. Seizures are uncommon, and vision remains unimpaired. Cerebellar ataxia, myoclonus, corneal opacity, cherry-red spot, dysmorphism, and organomegaly are absent.

RADIOLOGY. Radiologic changes in the bones such as flattening of the vertebral bodies are occasionally evident, but these may be minimal.

PATHOLOGY. Intraneuronal storage of cytoplasmic membranous material is localized primarily to neurons of the basal ganglia.[14] It has been proposed that the selective and prominent neuropathologic changes of the basal ganglia, especially the head of the caudate nucleus and anterior putamen, might be responsible for the majority of the extrapyramidal signs. In fact, CT scans may reveal atrophy of the basal ganglia, especially the head of the caudate nucleus. In addition to the neuronal changes in the central nervous system, the ganglion cells in the submucosal plexus obtained by rectal biopsy contain characteristic osmiophyllic lamellar inclusions.[18,19] Some of these are typical membranous cytoplasmic bodies. Others are pleomorphic in character. Ultrastructural changes in rectal neurons have been emphasized as important clues to the diagnosis in patients who have been screened in adult neurology clinics for adult forms of lysosomal storage diseases.

The lamellar inclusions and clear vacuoles also accumulate in visceral organs, skin, and rectal mucosal cells, but are less abundant than in the early onset forms of G_{M1} gangliosidosis.

Genetics

All types of G_{M1} gangliosidosis are transmitted as autosomal recessive traits with obligate heterozygotes having approximately one-half normal activities of β-galactosidase in fibroblasts and leukocytes. The autosomal locus coding for the human enzyme has been mapped to chromosome 3p21-cen. Prenatal diagnosis has been carried out in many at-risk pregnancies.

Structure of Storage Material

Throughout the nervous system the predominant compound stored is ganglioside G_{M1}, with the same sugar composition, fatty acid composition, sugar sequence, and glycosidic linkages of normal ganglioside G_{M1}. (For pathways of ganglioside synthesis and degradation, see Chap. 72.) The quantity of G_{M1} stored is massive and generalized in the infantile form, moderate in the juvenile form, and focal in the adult form. Biochemical analyses of brain tissue from patients with adult G_{M1} gangliosidosis reveal only slight to moderate elevations in the proportion of G_{M1} ganglioside in the cortex and white matter but significant accumulations in the basal ganglia.[20] To date no experimental information is available concerning the reason for this focal accumulation. One possibility is that ganglioside synthesis and degradation in the basal ganglia neurons proceed at a faster rate than elsewhere in the nervous system, making these cells more vulnerable to the partial block in G_{M1} ganglioside degradation.

POSSIBLE PATHOPHYSIOLOGICAL MECHANISMS CAUSING NEURONAL DYSFUNCTION

The precise mechanism giving rise to neuronal dysfunction in G_{M1} gangliosidosis is unclear. G_{M1} is a significant component of the neuronal surface membrane and is localized within the synaptic plasma membranes.[21-23] It has been proposed that abnormal accumulation of ganglioside G_{M1} could produce neuronal dysfunction by causing neuronal death, by alteration of intracellular organelle function, by induction of new abnormal growth processes, or by alteration of synaptic neurotransmis-

sion. Animal models of G_{M1} gangliosidosis, especially in cats, have been helpful in understanding the predominant pathogenic process.[24] These studies are discussed below.

Cytotoxicity

The accumulated ganglioside G_{M1} and its asialo derivative are relatively insoluble in water and aggregate within lamellated membranous bodies in lysosomes, distending the cell and displacing the nucleus to the periphery. The cytotoxic hypothesis suggests that the massive accumulation results in mechanical disruption and death of neurons. A related hypothesis suggests that excretion of lysosomal residual bodies in the cytoplasm impedes normal axoplasmic and intracellular flow of organelles.[25] Another proposal is that ganglioside storage interferes with protein and glycoprotein synthesizing functions of the endoplasmic reticulum and Golgi apparatus.[26] Other hypotheses suggest that cytotoxicity results from the leakage of intralysosomal products of enzymes into the cytoplasm,[25] the formation of a toxic product, especially lyso derivatives of glycosphingolipids which inhibit protein kinase C,[27] and the exhaustion of precursor pools required for the biosynthesis of cellular components.[28] Despite considerable experimentation, no substantive experimental evidence supports a cytotoxic hypothesis. In fact, electrophysiological and morphologic studies in the feline gangliosidosis model contradict this hypothesis. In cats with G_{M1} gangliosidosis, intercellular[29] recordings were carried out to evaluate the assumption that a toxic effect of ganglioside accumulation would be reflected in reduced capacity of neurons to generate membrane potentials and spontaneous and evoked spike discharges. Such recordings obtained in cats with G_{M1} gangliosidosis with advanced neurologic deterioration revealed no appreciable alteration of basic electrophysiological properties in nonpyramidal cells laden with storage bodies. In addition, morphologic studies revealed that neuronal loss did not become obvious until very late in the clinical course of the disease, well after neurologic symptoms appeared.[30,31] Similarly, in the same animal model, the capacity to biosynthesize neurotransmitters, especially the synthesizing activities of choline acetyltransferase, glutamate decarboxylase, and tyrosine hydroxylase, was unaffected even in advanced stages.[32]

Aberrant Growth

A second hypothesis for the pathogenesis of neurologic symptoms in G_{M1} gangliosidosis relates to abnormalities in neuronal membrane production and regulation. Morphologic analysis of neurons in the brains of patients with ganglioside storage disease revealed distortions of neuronal structure.[33] Subsequent studies in feline gangliosidosis have confirmed and extended the original observations.[30,31,34-36] The major abnormality is the proliferation of growth cone–associated neurites from the axon helix (secondary neurites) and the formation of bizarre swellings (meganeurites) interposed between the soma and the initial segment of the axon. Such meganeurites contain membranous cytoplasmic bodies, spines, and postsynaptic contacts with fibers of unknown origin. Unusual neurites resembling growth cones also are noted projecting from meganeurite areas. The distribution of these unusual structural changes is similar to the distribution of ganglioside G_{M1} storage. However, the significance of this finding to ganglioside accumulation is unknown, even though gangliosides do induce neurite growth. Since similar changes have been found in cats with mannosidosis in which ganglioside accumulation does not occur,[37] morphologic changes of this type can be induced by accumulating substrates other than gangliosides.

As a consequence of these findings, it has been proposed that such morphologic alterations lead to neuronal dysfunction. Additional support for this hypothesis is that these changes appear at about the same time as the clinical symptoms, and they progress slowly, coincident with neural behavioral deterioration.

Synaptic Dysfunction

A third hypothesis is that synaptic neurotransmission is disturbed. Neuronal membranes are unique in containing a high percentage of ganglioside G_{M1} distributed asymmetrically over a large portion of the surface membrane, with large concentrations within the synaptic plasma membrane.[21–23] Gangliosides are known to play a role in synaptic neurotransmission since they serve as receptors for serotonin,[38] are used in the release of neurotransmitters,[39] and provide a rapid transport mechanism for the input of signals into the cell.[21] Thus, excess accumulation has been proposed to affect synaptic membrane–related functions such as neurotransmitter release, reuptake, and receptor-mediated events.[32]

Direct measurement of deranged neurotransmitter biochemistry has been obtained from studies on cerebral samples taken from cats with G_{M1} gangliosidosis. A significant reduction in synaptosomal uptake of glutamate, γ-aminobutyric acid, and norepinephrine (24 to 77 percent of controls) was demonstrated in motor, occipital, and cerebellar brain regions of such animals. The transport abnormality was not associated with alterations in neural transmitter levels or in activity of the synthetic enzymes choline acetyltransferase, glutamate decarboxylase, or tyrosine hydroxylase.[32] Additional studies revealed that the number of GABA receptors measured by tritiated muscimol binding in feline G_{M1} gangliosidosis cerebellar tissue is reduced. A striking increase in G_{M1} concentration within isolated synaptic plasma membranes from the motor region was evident; the affected cat had 10 times higher concentrations of G_{M1} in such membranes than controls.[24] Similar synaptosomal plasma membrane analysis in feline G_{M1} gangliosidosis revealed that gangliosides were increased 24 times, cholesterol 2.3 times, and phospholipid content 1.4 times.[40] In this study fluorescence polarization measurements of the rotational mobility of a probe incorporated into the synaptosomal membrane revealed that membrane fluidity was reduced in feline G_{M1} gangliosidosis.

From these studies, the current prevailing belief is that distortions of neuron structure due to aberrant growth of neurites and distortions of neuronal morphology accompanied by synaptic neurotransmission abnormalities are very likely the principal underlying pathophysiological factors responsible for neuronal dysfunction in patients with G_{M1} gangliosidosis. Further studies in animal models over the course of the disease may provide even greater insight into which of these mechanisms predominate and when. Such an understanding is a necessary prerequisite for therapeutic intervention to correct the neurologic symptoms.

GALACTOSE-CONTAINING OLIGOSACCHARIDES

Galactose-containing oligosaccharides accumulate predominantly in the viscera and are excreted in the urine in G_{M1} gangliosidosis. A remarkable array of these compounds is found, with the most abundant storage compound being an octasaccharide. These oligosaccharides are derived from the incomplete degradation of glycoproteins in lysosomes (see Chap. 63). Normally, after removal of sialic acid and fucose residues and release of the oligosaccharide chain from the partially degraded polypeptide, further degradation of the oligosaccharide side chain occurs by the action of the lysosomal enzyme, acid β-galactosidase. Of the many carbohydrate side chains with differing structures that occur in glycoproteins, those containing a terminal galactose residue at the nonreducing end accumulate as a consequence of the β-galactosidase deficiency. It is generally believed that the accumulation of these water-soluble compounds is responsible for the cytoplasmic vacuolization of visceral cells (so-called clear or empty vacuoles), the visceromegaly, the foamy histiocytosis evident in bone marrow, and the vacuoles in circulating lymphocytes.

Using high performance liquid chromatography (HPLC), it is possible to delineate the pattern of these oligosaccharides and their relative urinary excretion in the subtypes of G_{M1} gangliosidosis. The concentration of the urinary oligosaccharides correlates with the severity of the disease. The major urinary oligosaccharide of infantile patients is the octasaccharide, OS1. Levels excreted by infantile patients are 3 to 10 times greater than those of juvenile G_{M1} patients and 130 to 180 times greater than those of adult G_{M1} gangliosidosis patients.[41] Generally, the qualitative oligosaccharide patterns of infantile and juvenile patients are very similar. Several Japanese patients[42,43] have been exceptions in that very highly branched galactosyl oligosaccharides were excreted by infantile patients that were not excreted by juvenile onset patients.

Oligosaccharide analysis has been used as an ancillary method for prenatal diagnosis of infantile G_{M1} gangliosidosis.[44]

KERATAN SULFATE DEGRADATION PRODUCTS

Storage of galactose-containing partially degraded derivatives of keratan sulfate has been demonstrated in infantile G_{M1} gangliosidosis. These compounds are glycopeptides containing N-acetyllactosamine units which are similar in structure to undersulfated keratan sulfate. Two major oligosaccharides linked to polypeptide and having the structures,

$$\text{GlcNAc}\beta1\rightarrow3\text{Gal}$$

$$\text{Gal}\beta1\rightarrow4\text{GlcNAc}\beta1\rightarrow3\text{Gal}$$

were found to accumulate in liver and brain in type I patients but not in type II.[45] Since keratan sulfate is a major cartilage mucopolysaccharide, storage of these molecules may be responsible for the modeling deformities of bone.

Enzyme Defect: Acid β-Galactosidase Deficiency

The primary defect in the G_{M1} gangliosidoses is the nearly complete absence of activity of the lysosomal hydrolase acid β-galactosidase. The mature enzyme is a monomeric polypeptide with a molecular weight of 64 kDa containing 7.5 percent carbohydrate.[46,47] The enzyme hydrolyzes the non-reducing terminal galactose from a variety of substrates including ganglioside G_{M1}, asialo G_{M1}, lactosylceramide, lactose, and the galactose-containing oligosaccharides. The enzyme does not cleave galactocerebroside, which is hydrolyzed by a different enzyme, galactocerebroside β-galactosidase, an enzyme deficient in Krabbe disease (see Chap. 68). Acid β-galactosidase hydrolyzes β-galactose from 4-methylumbelliferyl-β-D-galactopyranoside, a convenient and widely used assay substrate for diagnosis.

Acid β-galactosidase is present in all nucleated cells. The diagnosis of G_{M1} gangliosidosis can be confirmed by acid β-galactosidase assays of leukocytes, cultured skin fibroblasts, and amniotic cells. Since the enzyme is secondarily deficient in I-cell disease, mucolipidosis III, galactosialidosis, some of the genetic mucopolysaccharidoses, and in cystinosis cells in culture, verification of G_{M1} gangliosidosis in probands by demonstration of G_{M1} or galacto-oligosaccharide accumulation or half-normal enzyme levels in obligate heterozygotes is important in making the diagnosis.

Molecular Genetics of Acid β-Galactosidase

Human lysosomal β-galactosidase is synthesized as an 88-kDa precursor form which is processed by way of intermediate forms to the 64-kDa mature enzyme.[48] The 88-kDa precursor polypeptide is coded by a structural locus on chromosome 3 (3p21-cen).[48-51] After processing, the 64-kDa monomer aggregates to a homopolymer of approximately 700 kDa. Experiments indicate that this aggregation is promoted by association with a 32-kDa protein[52] coded by a separate locus on chromosome 22[51] that protects the multimer against the action of intralysosomal proteases. This interpretation is supported by the observations that the stability of β-galactosidase increases under conditions favoring its aggregation to the multimeric state[53,54] and that the monomeric form is much more sensitive to proteolytic degradation. D'Azzo et al.[48] have published evidence indicating that in galactosialidosis (discussed below), absence of the 32-kDa protective protein results in rapid degradation of β-galactosidase (half-life 1 day versus 20 days in normals[55]) and very low activity levels in cells.

Previous studies have indicated that all human G_{M1} gangliosidosis patients studied thus far (16 patients with types 1, 2, and 3) produce normal quantities of immunoreactive β-galactosidase as determined by immunoprecipitation experiments with monospecific antibody.[56,57] Hoogeveen et al.[58] have presented evidence that the mutation in most forms of G_{M1} gangliosidosis results in abnormal trafficking of the enzyme (for discussion see Chap. 62). In these studies G_{M1} gangliosidosis fibroblasts secreted normal quantities of 88-kDa β-galactosidase precursor, yet the quantity of the mature 64-kDa form was reduced to 5 to 15 percent of normal values. They propose that the mutation in the infantile and adult forms of G_{M1} gangliosidosis interferes with the phosphorylation of precursor β-galactosidase,[59] and as a result the precursor is secreted instead of being compartmentalized into the lysosomes and further processed. The impairment of phosphorylation

could be due to conformational changes of the precursor molecule. This finding is unexpected and is inconsistent with other studies indicating normal concentrations of immunoreactive β-galactosidase in most patients studied.[56,57]

One would predict genetic heterogeneity, i.e., that a variety of mutations altering not only the precursor polypeptide but the mature enzyme would be present.

Studies of a patient with juvenile onset G_{M1} gangliosidosis revealed an electrophoretic variant of β-galactosidase with a more positive charge than normal. The enzyme had a K_m that was five times normal using ganglioside G_{M1} as substrate but had the same molecular weight as normal mature enzyme (a K_m mutant and electrophoretic variant).[60] In the future, definition of the molecular genetics of G_{M1} gangliosidosis at the nucleic acid level should clarify the precise nature of the mutations that give rise to the subtypes of G_{M1} gangliosidosis.

Morquio Syndrome Type B (MPS IV B). This inherited disease, which is due to a primary defect in the gene encoding β-galactosidase,[61] has also been classified under the genetic mucopolysaccharidoses due to its clinical similarity to Morquio syndrome. Patients[61-66] have presented with progressive skeletal dysplasia without neurologic impairment, usually in the first decade of life. A characteristic clinical presentation is that of hip pain due to progressive dysplastic changes of the pelvis and femoral heads. Vertebral platyspondyly and unusual modeling deformities of the vertebral bodies similar to those seen in the hereditary spondyloepiphyseal dysplasias are evident. Some patients have been of short stature, and others have not. Corneal clouding has been present but is less dense than in Hurler syndrome or Sheie syndrome. All patients have had normal intelligence and no evidence of neurologic deterioration. Excessive excretion of galactose oligosaccharides has been evident in urine, as has the excessive excretion of degradation products of keratan sulfate. A striking deficiency of acid β-galactosidase is present in leukocytes and fibroblasts, and intermediate levels of enzyme activity have been evident in parents of affected patients, indicating that β-galactosidase deficiency is the primary enzyme defect.[61-66]

As discussed above, β-galactosidase is a heterocatalytic enzyme cleaving β-linked galactose from a variety of substrates including lipids, oligosaccharides, and mucopolysaccharides, particularly keratan sulfate. The author has previously suggested[56] that the multiplicity of phenotypes with β-galactosidase deficiency can be explained by different alterations in the catalytic activity of the mutant enzyme which differentially alter its activity against a variety of substrates. It was proposed that patients with Morquio type B syndrome retain more catalytic activity for ganglioside G_{M1} than for water-soluble substrates. This hypothesis was supported by studies of catalytic activities in cultured fibroblasts.[61] Turnover of ganglioside G_{M1} in fibroblasts from such patients has been found to be normal.[67]

Substrates cleaved by β-galactosidase differ in molecular size, ionic charge, solubility in water, and requirement for the presence of natural detergent activators. It is known, for example, that sphingolipid activator protein 1 (SAP-1) is required for the in vivo cleavage of ganglioside G_{M1} by β-galactosidase.[68-71] SAP-1, the cDNA for which has recently been cloned,[72] is a small molecular weight (78-amino acid) glycoprotein of 9 kDa. SAP-1 not only activates β-galactosidase to cleave ganglioside G_{M1}, but also activates the cleavage of sulfatide and globotriosylceramide by arylsulfatase A and α-galactosidase, respectively.[71] SAP-1 is known to be deficient in a newly described disease which is similar clinically to metachromatic leukodystrophy and has been called *activator-deficient metachromatic leukodystrophy* (Chap. 69).[73,74]

Wynn[75] has proposed that a triple-binding domain model explains the specificity of the interaction of SAP-1 with G_{M1} ganglioside. The hydrocarbon chains of the fatty acid and sphingosine moieties of G_{M1} form a hydrophobic domain interacting with a complementary hydrophobic domain in SAP-1. Secondly, electrostatic interaction occurs between the charged sialic acid and a positively charged group on the protein. Thirdly, hydrophilic interaction occurs, presumably mediated by hydrogen bond formation between a plane of hydroxyl groups in the carbohydrate portion of the ganglioside and a similar and complementary plane in the carbohydrate side chain of SAP-1. Analysis indicates that the SAP-1 monomer contains two or possibly three helical regions which could associate to form the cylindrical hydrophobic domain, a glycosylation site 21 residues from the amino terminus, and a positively charged region at its carboxy terminus. It is important to note that SAP-1 only activates hydrolysis of lipid substrates such as G_{M1} and not water-soluble galactosyl oligosaccharides.

In two patients with Morquio syndrome type B, Paschke and Kresse[76] reported that residual G_{M1} β-galactosidase activity in the fibroblasts increased from 4 to 20 percent of the respective normal value in the presence of purified SAP-1. No such activation was found in similar experiments using fibroblasts from a patient with infantile G_{M1} gangliosidosis. Hydrolysis of β-galactose from keratan sulfate was not influenced by SAP-1 in the Morquio type B cells, leading the authors to propose[76] that the absence of neurologic symptoms in Morquio type B is caused by a specific activation of the G_{M1} β-galactosidase in vivo by SAP-1. However, in two different patients with Morquio syndrome type B studied by Inui and Wenger[77] and one studied in the author's laboratory (Yamamoto and O'Brien, unpublished results), highly purified SAP-1 failed to activate β-galactosidase in fibroblast extracts more than in controls. It seems likely that more than one type of mutation can produce the clinical phenotype of Morquio syndrome type B.

GALACTOSIALIDOSIS

Over the past few years the lysosomal storage disorder galactosialidosis has been recognized as a distinct genetic and biochemical entity associated with a combined deficiency of β-galactosidase and neuraminidase.[78–80] The clinical picture has included patients with an early infantile form with edema, ascites, skeletal dysplasia, and cherry-red spots, a phenotype similar to infantile G_{M1} gangliosidosis. A late infantile form has been recognized in which patients exhibit symptoms after 6 to 12 months, with the main features being dysostosis multiplex, visceromegaly, macular cherry-red spots, and mild mental retardation. The largest number of patients (mainly of Japanese origin) have a late juvenile form in which symptoms appear between infancy and adulthood, with the major features being skeletal dysplasia, dysmorphism, corneal clouding, bilateral cherry-red spots, an angiokeratomatous rash in the bathing suit area, progressive neurologic deterioration, and mental retardation with survival into adulthood.[79]

Patients have previously been misdiagnosed as having G_{M1} gangliosidosis and/or sialidosis based upon measurements of enzyme activity of leukocytes and skin fibroblasts which demonstrate reduced activities of both enzymes. Despite the remarkably reduced activity levels of β-galactosidase, the storage compounds are predominantly sialylated oligosaccharides similar to those excreted in the urine of patients with sialidosis (Chap. 63), implicating neuraminidase deficiency as the underlying pathogenic defect.

Evidence that these patients differ from those with G_{M1} gangliosidosis came from complementation analysis, using somatic cell hybridization studies on cultured fibroblasts, which revealed that patients with galactosialidosis have a different gene mutation than patients with G_{M1} gangliosidosis.[81–83] Hybridization studies also indicated that they had a different genetic defect than patients with sialidosis, since restoration of sialidase activity in the heterokaryons occurred. Turnover studies of β-galactosidase in cultured fibroblasts from patients with galactosialidosis revealed exceedingly rapid degradation of the enzyme compared to turnover in normal fibroblasts.[55] D'Azzo et al.[48] demonstrated that patients with galactosialidosis have a severe deficiency of a 32-kDa protective protein that protects β-galactosidase and neuraminidase against intralysosomal proteolytic degradation. They proposed that β-galactosidase and neuraminidase exist in a multiple molecular aggregation complex along with the 32-kDa protective factor in normal individuals. This result is in keeping with purification studies of both enzymes which indicate that they copurify.[84,85] They suggested that the deficiency of the 32-kDa protective protein coded by a locus on chromosome 22[51] gives rise to a secondary deficiency of acid β-galactosidase and neuraminidase by destabilization of the complex which allows proteolytic degradation of β-galactosidase. The role of the protective factor in neuraminidase degradation has yet to be clarified. The bulk of neuraminidase activity (95 percent) is not associated with β-galactosidase. It is possible to physically separate the remaining neuraminidase activity from β-galactosidase activity by such mild procedures as sucrose gradient ultracentrifugation and isoelectric focussing.[84] Thus, the biologic importance of the "complex" in the pathogenesis of the combined deficiency requires further study.

Genetics

Galactosialidosis is transmitted as an autosomal recessive trait.

MUCOLIPIDOSIS IV

A recent summary of 20 patients with mucolipidosis IV (ML IV) has appeared.[86] This disease is characterized by severe visual impairment and psychomotor retardation. Corneal clouding is a characteristic clinical feature and is the initial diagnostic sign in most patients. The age of onset of corneal clouding varies from infancy to 5 years. However, retinal degeneration is also present and often produces visual impairment within the first year of life before corneal opacities are sufficient to impair vision. Psychomotor retardation is present in all patients, with psychomotor skills being retarded to approximately the 1-year level. After the initial retardation in motor and language function, little further psychomotor deterioration is apparent, even in patients with life spans beyond 10 years of age. In fact, some patients exhibit slow but continuous improvement in cognitive language and motor function with time. However, most patients remain severely retarded, exhibiting both mental and growth retardation.

Pathology

Ultrastructural examination reveals striking lysosomal storage inclusions in cells from almost every organ or tissue in the body. These inclusions resemble the membranous cytoplasmic bodies seen in the gangliosidoses, but differ in their localization. In the gangliosidoses, cytoplasmic membranous bodies are not found in liver, spleen, cultured fibroblasts, or dermal epithelial cells (Fig. 71-3). They are prominent in these locations in mucolipidosis IV. In addition to the cytoplasmic membranous bodies, granulofibrillar material also accumulates, often surrounded by cytoplasmic membranous lamellae with lamellar and granular components blending into one another.[87]

Biochemical analysis of cultured fibroblasts in tissue obtained from brain biopsy[87–89] reveals elevated ganglioside content. In fibroblasts, accumulation especially involves the poly-sialylated species (gangliosides G_{DIA} and G_T). In addition, phospholipids and acidic mucopolysaccharides accumulate within cultured fibroblasts. The fundamental enzyme defect in this disease that leads to accumulation of this diverse group of storage compounds is unknown. It had been proposed[88,90,91] that the fundamental defect was a deficiency of a ganglioside sialidase which is distinct from the sialidase which cleaves water-soluble oligosaccharides that is deficient in sialidosis (Chap. 63). The ganglioside sialidase cleaves sialic acid from a variety of gangliosides, including the monosialoganglioside G_{M3} and the disialoganglioside G_{DIA}. However, growing evidence indicates that ganglioside sialidase deficiency is not the primary defect in ML IV. It has also been proposed that an appropriate term for mucolipidosis type IV is *sialolipidosis*.[88] This was meant to distinguish this disorder eponymically from sialidosis, which is due to a defect in the sialidase that hydrolyzes sialo-oligosaccharide.[78] The disease is transmitted as an autosomal recessive trait. A higher frequency of patients of Ashkenazi Jewish origin has been noted, although several non-Jewish patients have also been described. Although the primary defect is still unknown, the ultrastructural findings are

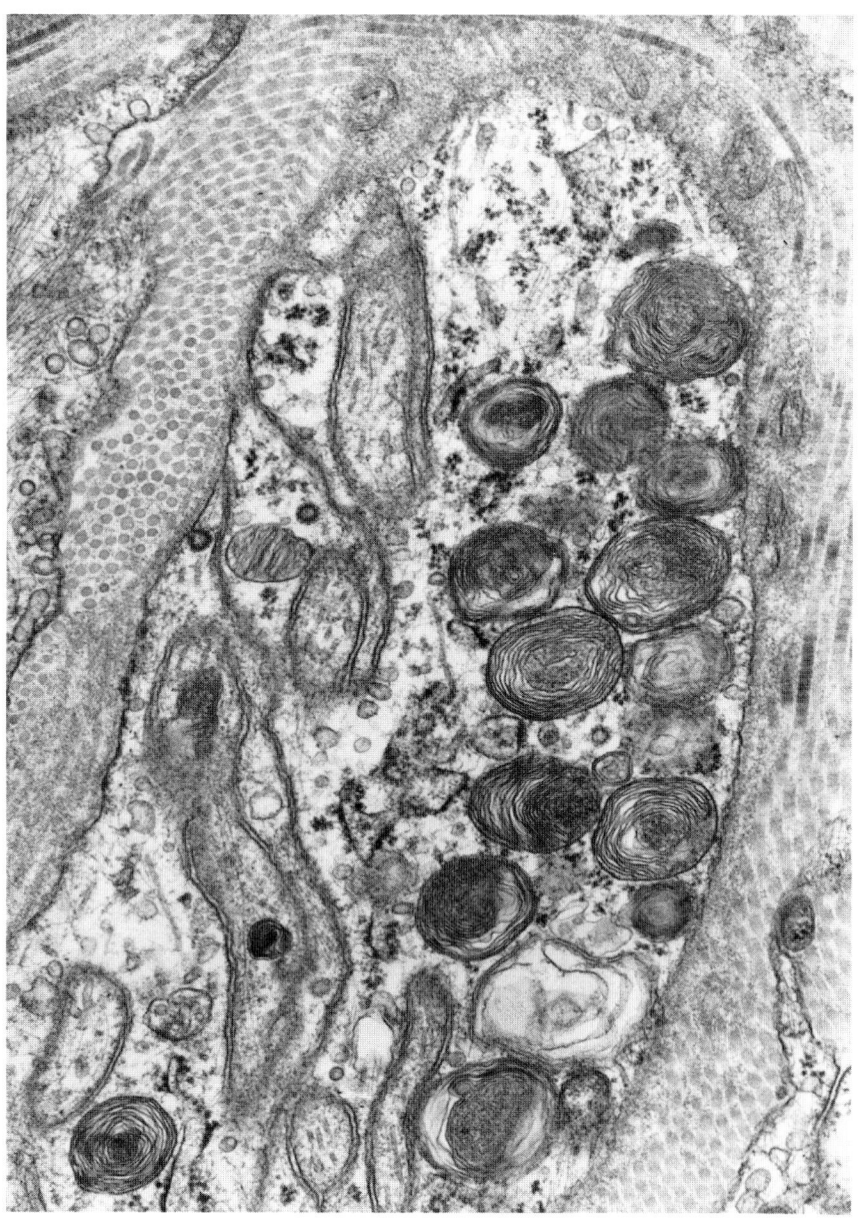

Fig. 71-3 Electron micrograph of dermal fibroblast in patient with mucolipidosis IV demonstrating cytoplasmic membranous inclusions, some of which contain a granular core. Magnification × 32,640.

characteristic and cultured amniotic cells have been used for the prenatal diagnosis of fetuses affected with ML type IV.[86]

REFERENCES

1. TAY W: Symmetrical changes in the region of the yellow spot in each eye of an infant. *Trans Ophthalmol Soc UK* 1:155, 1881.

2. LANDING BH, SILVERMAN FN, CRAIG JM, JACOBY MD, LAHEY ME, CHADWICK DF: Familial neurovisceral lipidosis. *Am J Dis Child* 108:503, 1964.

3. O'BRIEN JS, STERN MB, LANDING BH, O'BRIEN JK, DONNELL GN: Generalized gangliosidosis. *Am J Dis Child* 109:338, 1965.

4. GONATAS NK, GONATAS J: Ultrastructural and biochemical observations on a case of system late infantile lipidosis and its relationship to Tay-Sachs disease and gargoylism. *J Neuropathol Exp Neurol* 24:318, 1965.

5. OKADA S, O'BRIEN JS: Generalized gangliosidosis, β-galactosidase deficiency. *Science* 160:1002, 1968.

6. SUZUKI K, CHEN GC: Brain ceramide hexosides in Tay-Sachs disease and generalized gangliosidosis (GM$_1$-gangliosidosis). *J Lipid Res* 8:105, 1967.

7. DERRY DM, FAWCETT JS, ANDERMANN F, WOLFE LS: Late infantile systemic lipidosis—Major monosialogangliosidosis. Delineation of two types. *Neurology* 18:340, 1968.

8. STANBURY JB, WYNGAARDEN JB, FREDRICKSON DS (eds): *The Metabolic Basis of Inherited Disease*, 5th ed. New York, McGraw-Hill, 1983.

9. KOHLSCHUTTER A, SIEG K, SCHULTE FJ, HAYEK HW, GOEBEL HH: Infantile cardiomyopathy and neuromyopathy with β-galactosidase deficiency. *Eur J Pediatr* 139:75, 1982.

10. BENSON PF, BABARIK A, BROWN SP, MANN TP: GM$_1$-generalized gangliosidosis variant with cardiomegaly. *Postgrad Med J* 52:159, 1976.

11. SUZUKI Y, NAKAMURA N, FUKUOKA K, SHIMADA Y, UONO M: Beta-galactosidase deficiency in juvenile and adult patients—Report of six Japanese cases and review of literature. *Hum Genet* 36:219, 1977.

12. STEVENSON RE, TAYLOR HA, PARKS SE: Beta-galactosidase deficiency—Prolonged survival in three patients following early central nervous system deterioration. *Clin Genet* 13:305, 1978.

13. WENGER DA, SATTLER M, MUELLER OT, MYERS GG, SCHNEIMAN RS, NIXON GW: Adult GM$_1$-gangliosidosis—Clinical and biochemical studies on two patients and comparison to other patients called variant or adult GM$_1$-gangliosidosis. *Clin Genet* 17:323.

14. GOLDMAN JE, KATZ D, RAPIN I, PURPURA DP, SUZUKI K: Chronic GM$_1$-gangliosidosis presenting as dystonia, Part I (Clinical and pathological features). *Ann Neurol* 9:465, 1981.

15. KONDO K, OGUCHI K, YANAGISAWA N, MITSUI Z, ISSHII Z: Chronic GM$_1$-gangliosidosis—An adult case of localized neuronal storage in the basal ganglia, in *Abstracts of the 9th International Congress of Neuropathology*. Vienna, 1982, p 221.

16. OHTA K, TSUJI S, ATSUMI T, MIZUNO Y, MIYATAKE T: Biochemical and clinical studies on type 3 (adult type) GM$_1$-gangliosidosis. *Clin Neurol* 32:191, 1983.

17. NAKANO T, IKEDA S, KONDO K, YANAGISAWA N: Adult GM$_1$-gangliosidosis—Clinical patterns and rectal biopsy. *Neurology* 35:875, 1985.

18. USHIYAMA M, IKEDA S, NAKAYAMA J, YANAGISAWA N, HANYU N, KATSUYAMA T: Type III (Chronic) GM$_1$-gangliosidosis. Histochemical and ultrastructural studies of rectal biopsy. *J Neurol Sci* 71:209, 1985.

19. IKEDA S, USHIYAMA M, NAKANO T, KIKKAWA T, KONDO K, YANAGISAWA N: Ultrastructural findings of rectal and skin biopsies in adult GM$_1$ gangliosidosis. *Acta Pathol Jpn* 36:1823, 1986.

20. KOBAYASHI T, SUZUKI K: Chronic GM$_1$-gangliosidosis presenting as dystonia. II Biochemical Studies. *Ann Neurol* 9:476, 1980.

21. LEDEEN RW: Structure and distribution of gangliosides, in Margolis RU, Margolis RK (eds): *Complex Carbohydrates of Nervous Tissue*. New York, Plenum, 1979, pp 1–23.

22. HUNGUND BL, MAHADIK SP: Topographic studies of gangliosides of intact synaptosomes from rat brain cortex. *Neurochem Res* 6:183, 1981.

23. SKRIVANEK JA, LEDEEN RW, MARGOLIS RU, MARGOLIS RK: Gangliosides associated with microsomal subfractions of brain: Comparison with synaptaic plasma membranes. *J Neurobiol* 13:95, 1982.

24. SINGER HS: Animal models of ganglioside storage diseases in animal models of dementia, in V. Chan-Palay and S.L. Palay (eds): *Neurology and Neurobiology*, Vol. 33. New York, A.R. Liss, 1987, pp 199–222.

25. GOEBEL HH: Morphology of the gangliosidoses. *Neuropediatr Suppl* 15:97, 1984.

26. SCHULTE FJ: Clinical course of GM$_2$ gangliosidosis: A correlative attempt. *Neuropediatr Suppl* 15:66, 1984.

27. HANNUN YA, BELL RM: Lysosphingolipids inhibit protein kinase C: Implications for the sphingolipidoses. *Science* 235:670, 1987.

28. SANDHOFF K, CONZELMANN E: The biochemical basis of gangliosidoses. *Neuropediatr Suppl* 15:85, 1984.

29. PURPURA DP, HIGHSTEIN SM, KARABELAS AB, WALKLEY SU: Intracellular recording and HRP-staining of cortical neurons in feline ganglioside storage disease. *Brain Res* 181:446, 1980.

30. WALKLEY SU, BAKER HJ, PURPURA DP: Morphological changes in feline gangliosidosis: A Golgi study, in Rose FC, Behon PO (eds): *Animal Models of Neurological Diseases*. London, Pittmans Medical, 1980.

31. WALKLEY SU, WURZELMANN S, PURPURA DP: Ultrastructure of neurites and meganeurites of cortical pyramidal neurons in feline gangliosidosis as revealed by the combined Golgi-EM technique. *Brain Res* 211:393, 1981.

32. SINGER HS, COYLE JT, WEAVER DL, KAWAMURA N, BAKER HJ: Neurotransmitter chemistry in feline GM$_1$ gangliosidosis: A model for human ganglioside storage disease. *Ann Neurol* 12:37, 1982.

33. PURPURA DP, SUZUKI K: Distortion of neuronal geometry and formation of aberrant synapses in neuronal storage disease. *Brain Res* 116:1, 1976.

34. PURPURA DP, BAKER HJ: Neurite induction in mature cortical neurons in feline GM$_1$ gangliosidosis storage disease. *Nature* 266:553, 1977.

35. PURPURA DP, BAKER HJ: Meganeurites and other aberrant processes of neurons in feline GM$_1$ gangliosidosis: A Golgi study. *Brain Res* 143:13, 1978.

36. PURPURA DP, PAPPAS GD, BAKER HJ: Fine structure of meganeurites and secondary growth processes in feline GM$_1$ gangliosidosis. *Brain Res* 143:1, 1978.

37. WALKLEY SU, BLAKEMORE WF, PURPURA DP: Alterations in neuron morphology in feline mannosidosis. *Acta Neuropathol (Berl)* 53:75, 1981.

38. TAMIR H, BRUNNER W, CASPER D, RAPPORT MM: Enhancement by gangliosides of the binding of serotonin to serotonin binding protein. *J Neurochem* 34:1719, 1980.

39. CUMAR FA, MAGGIO B, CAPUTTO R: Dopamine release from nerve endings induced by polysialogangliosides. *Biochem Biophys Res Commun* 84:65, 1978.

40. WOOD PA, MCBRIDE MR, BAKER HJ, CHRISTIAN ST: Fluorescence polarization analysis, lipid composition, and Na$^+$, K$^+$-ATPase kinetics of synaptosomal membranes in feline GM$_1$ gangliosidosis. *J Neurochem* 44:947, 1985.

41. WARNER T, ROBERTSON AD, O'BRIEN JS: Diagnosis of GM$_1$ gangliosidosis based on detection of urinary oligosaccharides with high performance liquid chromatography. *Clin Chim Acta* 127:313, 1983.

42. YAMASHITA K, OHKURA T, OKADA S, YABUUCHI H, KOBATA A: Urinary oligosaccharides of GM$_1$ gangliosidosis. *J Biol Chem* 256:4789, 1981.

43. OHKURA T, YAMASHITA K, KOBATA A: Urinary oligosaccharides of GM1 gangliosidosis. *J Biol Chem* 256:8485, 1981.

44. WARNER TG, ROBERTSON AD, MOCK AK, JOHNSON WG, O'BRIEN JS: Prenatal diagnosis of GM$_1$ gangliosidosis by detection of galactosyl-oligosaccharides in amniotic fluid with high performance liquid chromatography. *Am J Hum Genet* 35:1034, 1983.

45. BERRA B, DE GASPERI R, RAPELLI S, OKADA S, LI S-C, LI Y-T: Presence of glycoproteins containing the polylactosamine structure in brain and liver of GM$_1$ gangliosidosis patients. *Neurochem Pathol* 4:107, 1986.

46. NORDEN AGW, TENNANT LL, O'BRIEN JS: GM$_1$ ganglioside β-galactosidase A. Purification and studies of the enzyme from human liver. *J Biol Chem* 249:7969, 1974.

47. FROST RG, HOLMES EW, NORDEN AGW, O'BRIEN JS: Characterization of purified human liver acid β-galactosidases A$_2$ and A$_3$. *Biochem J* 175:181, 1978.

48. D'AZZO A, HOOGEVEEN A, REUSER ADJ, ROBINSON D, GALJAARD H: Molecular defect in combined β-galactosidase and neuraminidase deficiency. *Proc Natl Acad Sci USA* 79:4535, 1982.

49. BRUNS GAP, LEARY AC, REGINA VM, GERALD PS: Lysosomal β-D-galactosidase in man-hamster somatic cell hybrids. *Cytogenet Cell Genet* 22:177, 1978.

50. SHOWS TB, SCRAFFORD-WOLFF L, BROWN JA, MEISLER M: Assignment of a β-galactosidase gene (β-gal A) to chromosome 3 in man. *Cytogenet Cell Genet* 22:219, 1978.

51. SIPS HJ, DEWIT-VERBEEK HA, DEWIT A, WESTERVELD A, GALJAARD H: The chromosomal localization of human β-galactosidase on human chromosome 3 and for its protective protein on human chromosome 22. *Hum Genet* 69:340, 1985.

52. HOOGEVEEN AT, VERHEIJEN FW, GALJAARD H: The relationship between human lysosomal β-galactosidase and its protective protein. *J Biol Chem* 258:12143, 1983.

53. HEYWORTH CM, NEUMANN EF, WYNN CH: The stability and aggregation properties of human acid β-D-galactosidase. *Biochem J* 193:773, 1981.

54. YAMAMOTO Y, NISHIMURA K: Aggregation-dissociation and stability of acid β-D-galactosidase purified from pork spleen. *Int J Biochem* 18:327, 1986.

55. VAN DIGGELEN OP, SCHRAM AW, SINNOTT ML, SMITH PJ, ROBINSON D, GALJAARD H: Turnover of β-galactosidase in fibroblasts from patients with genetically different types of β-galactosidase deficiency. *Biochem J* 200:143, 1981.

56. O'BRIEN JS: Molecular genetics of GM₁ β-galactosidase. *Clin Genet* 8:303, 1975.

57. O'BRIEN JS, NORDEN AGW: Nature of the mutation in adult β-galactosidase deficient patients. *Am J Hum Genet* 29:184, 1977.

58. HOOGEVEEN AT, GRAHAM-KAWASHIMA H, D'AZZO A, GALJAARD H: Processing of human β-galactosidase in GM₁ gangliosidosis and Morquio B syndrome. *J Biol Chem* 259:1974, 1984.

59. HOOGEVEEN AT, REUSER AJJ, KROOS M, GALJAARD H: GM1 gangliosidosis: Defective recognition site on β-galactosidase precursor. *J Biol Chem* 261:5702, 1986.

60. NORDEN AGW, O'BRIEN JS: An electrophoretic variant of β-galactosidase with altered catalytic properties in a patient with GM₁ gangliosidosis. *Proc Natl Acad Sci USA* 72:240, 1975.

61. O'BRIEN JS, GUGLER E, GIEDION A, WIESSMANN U, HERSHKOWITZ N, MEIER C, LEROY J: Spondyloepiphyseal dysplasia, corneal clouding, normal intelligence and acid β-galactosidase deficiency. *Clin Genet* 9:495, 1976.

62. ARBISSER AI, DONNELLY KA, SCOTT CI, DIFERRANTE N, SINGH J, STEVENSON RE, AYLSWORTH AS, HOWELL RR: Mild Morquio Syndrome (MPS IVB) with keratan sulfaturia but normal 6-sulfatase activity. *Am J Med Genet* 1:195, 1977.

63. GROEBE H, KRINS M, SCHMIDBERGER H, VON FIGURA K, HARZER K, KRESSE H, PASHKE E, SEWELL H, ULLRICH H: Morquio syndrome (mucopolysaccharidosis IVB) associated with β-galactosidase deficiency: Report of two cases. *Am J Hum Genet* 32:258, 1980.

64. TROJAK JE, CHEN-KUNG H, ROESEL RA, LEVIN LS, KOPITS SE, THOMAS GH, TOMA S: Morquio-like syndrome (MPS IVB) associated with a deficiency of β-galactosidase. *Johns Hopkins Med J* 146:75, 1980.

65. HOLZGREVE W, GROEBE H, VON FIGURA K, KRESSE H, BECK H, MATTAR JF: Morquio syndrome: Clinical findings in 11 patients with MPS IVA and 2 patients with MPS IVB. *Hum Genet* 57:360, 1981.

66. VAN GEMUND JJ, GEISBERTS MAH, EERDMANS RF, BLOM W, KLEIJER WJ: Morquio-B disease, spondyloepiphyseal dysplasia associated acid β-galactosidase deficiency. Report of three cases in one family. *Hum Genet* 64:50, 1983.

67. MANCINI GMS, HOOGEVEEN AT, GALJAARD H, MANSSON JE, SVENNERHOLM L: Ganglioside GM₁ metabolism in living human fibroblasts with β-galactosidase deficiency. *Hum Genet* 73:35, 1986.

68. LI S-C, WAN C-C, MAZZOTTA MY, LI Y-T: Requirement of an activator for the hydrolysis of sphingoglycolipids by glycosides of human liver. *Carbohydr Res* 34:189, 1974.

69. LI S-C, LI Y-T: An activator stimulating the enzymic hydrolysis of sphingoglycolipids. *J Biol Chem* 251:1159, 1976.

70. INUI K, WENGER DA: Concentrations of an activator protein for sphingolipid hydrolysis in liver and brain samples from patients with lysosomal storage disease. *J Clin Invest* 72:1622, 1983.

71. WENGER DA, INUI K: Studies on the sphingolipid activator protein for the enzymatic hydrolysis of GM₁ ganglioside and sulfatide, in Brady RO, Barranger JA (eds): *The Molecular Basis of Lysosomal Storage Diseases.* New York, Academic, 1984, p 61.

72. DEWJI N, WENGER D, FUJIBAYASHI S, DONOVIEL M, ESCH F, HILL F, O'BRIEN JS: Molecular cloning of the sphingolipid activator protein (SAP-1) the sulfatide sulfatase activator. *Biochem Biophys Res Commun* 134:989, 1986.

73. INUI K, EMMETT M, WENGER DA: Immunological evidence for deficiency in an activator protein for sulfatide sulfatase in a variant form of metachromatic leukodystrophy. *Proc Natl Acad Sci USA* 80, 3074, 1983.

74. LI S-C, KIHARA H, SENZAWA S, LI Y-T, FLUHARTY AL, MAYES JS, SHAPIRO LJ: Activator protein required for the enzymatic hydrolysis of cerebroside sulfate. *J Biol Chem* 260:1867, 1985.

75. WYNN C: A triple-binding domain model explains the specificity of the interaction of a sphingolipid activator protein (SAP-1) with sulfatide, GM1 ganglioside and globotriaosylceramide. *Biochem J* 240:921, 1986.

76. PASHKE E, KRESSE H: Morquio disease type B: Activation of GM₁ β-galactosidase by GM₁ activator protein. *Biochem Biophys Res Commun* 109:568, 1982.

77. INUI K, WENGER D: Biochemical, immunological and structural studies on a sphingolipid activator protein (SAP-1). *Arch Biochem* 233:556, 1984.

78. LOWDEN JA, O'BRIEN JS: Sialidosis: A review of human neuraminidase deficiency. *Am J Hum Genet* 31:1, 1979.

79. SUZUKI Y, SAKURABA H, YAMANAKA T: Galactosialidosis: A comparative study of clinical and biochemical data on 22 patients, in Arima M (ed): *The Developing Brain and Its Disorders.* Tokyo, University of Tokyo Press, 1984, p 161.

80. ADRIA G, STRISCIUGLIO P, PONTARELLI G, SLY WS, DODSON WE: Infantile neuraminidase and β-galactosidase deficiencies (galactosidase) with mild clinical course, in *Perspectives in Inherited Metabolic Diseases.* Milan, Ermes, 1981, vol 4, p 379.

81. GALJAARD H, REUSER AJJ: Genetic aspects of lysosomal storage diseases, in Dingle JT, Dean RT, Sly WS (eds): *Lysosomes in Biology and Pathology.* Amsterdam/New York, Elsevier, 1984, p 315.

82. STRISCIUGLIO P, CREEK K, SLY WS: Complementation, cross correction and drug correction studies of combined β-galactosidase neuraminidase deficiencies in human fibroblasts. *Pediatr Res* 18:167, 1984.

83. MUELLER OT, SHOWS TB: Human β-galactosidase and neuraminidase deficient mucolipidosis: Genetic complementation and analysis of the neuraminidase deficiency. *Hum Genet* 60:158, 1982.

84. VERHEIJEN T, PALMIERI S, GALJAARD H: Purification and partial characterization of lysosomal neuraminidase from human placenta. *Eur J Biochem* 162:63, 1986.

85. YAMAMOTO Y, NISHIMURA K: Copurification and separation of β-galactosidase and sialidase from porcine testis. *Int J Biochem* 19:435, 1987.

86. AMIR N, ZLOTOGORA J, BACH G: Mucolipidosis Type IV: Clinical spectrum and natural history. *Pediatrics* 79:953, 1987.

87. BACH G, COHEN M, KOHN G: Abnormal ganglioside accumulation in cultured fibroblasts from patients with mucolipidosis IV. *Biochem Biophys Res Commun* 66:1483, 1975.

88. CAIMI L, TETTAMANTI G, BERRA B, SALE FO, BORRONE C, GATTI R, DURAND P, MARTIN JJ: Mucolipidosis IV, a sialolipidosis due to ganglioside sialidase deficiency. *J Inherited Metab Dis* 5:218, 1982.

89. TELLEZ-NAGEL I, RAPIN I, IWAMOTO T, JOHNSON AB, NORTON WT, NITOWSKY H: Mucolipidosis IV: Clinical, ultrastructural, histochemical and chemical studies of a case including a brain biopsy. *Arch Neurol* 33:828, 1976.

90. BACH G, ZEIGLER M, SCHAPP T, KOHN G: Mucolipidosis type IV, ganglioside sialidase deficiency. *Biochem Biophys Res Commun* 90:1341, 1979.

91. BEN YOSEF Y, MOMOI T, HAHN LC, NADLER HL: Catalytically defective ganglioside neuraminidase in mucolipidosis IV. *Clin Genet* 21:374, 1982.

92. SCOTT CR, LANGUNOFF D, TRUMP BF: Familial neurovisceral lipidosis. *J Pediatr* 71:357, 1967.

CHAPTER 72

THE G_{M2} GANGLIOSIDOSES

KONRAD SANDHOFF
ERNST CONZELMANN
ELIZABETH F. NEUFELD
MICHAEL M. KABACK
KINUKO SUZUKI

1. The G_{M2} gangliosidoses are a group of heritable disorders caused by excessive accumulation of ganglioside G_{M2} and a few related glycolipids. Accumulation occurs mainly in the neurons of the patients and is due to defective lysosomal degradation of these compounds. The enzymatic hydrolysis of the lipids is accomplished by the action of two lysosomal glycoproteins, hexosaminidase A and the G_{M2} activator protein. Hexosaminidase A is, in turn, composed of two distinct subunits, α and β, which are encoded on different chromosomes. Defects in any one of the three gene loci are known to impair lysosomal catabolism of ganglioside G_{M2}. Hence, three nonallelic enzymatic variants of G_{M2} gangliosidosis can be distinguished: (a). Hexosaminidase α-subunit defect or deficiency (variant B, Tay-Sachs disease): Defects or absence of the α subunit (encoded on chromosome 15) affect the activity or formation of β-hexosaminidase A, while hexosaminidase B, a dimer of β subunits only, is unaffected. The eponym Tay-Sachs disease refers to the most severe infantile form of this variant. (b). Hexosaminidase β-subunit defect or deficiency (variant 0, Sandhoff disease): Patients with a defect or absence of the β subunit (encoded on chromosome 5) lack activity of both major hexosaminidase isoenzymes, A and B. As a consequence, they accumulate not only glycolipids but also water-soluble hexosaminidase substrates, primarily oligosaccharides derived from glycoproteins. (c). G_{M2} activator deficiency (variant AB): This variant is caused by a defective G_{M2} activator protein (encoded on chromosome 5). Both hexosaminidase isoenzymes, A and B, are unaffected and present in normal amounts, but the degradation of G_{M2} by hexosaminidase A does not occur in the absence of the activator protein.

2. Detailed molecular analysis has revealed considerable genetic heterogeneity among allelic variants, even among those with identical clinical presentation. For each of the two hexosaminidase subunit deficiency disorders, there is a wide range of clinical severity. The disorders are usually classified according to the age of onset as infantile, late infantile, juvenile, and adult cases. The later the disease is manifested, the slower its progression and the more variable its symptomatology. With appropriate test systems, a good correlation can be made between residual hexosaminidase A activity and the severity of the disease. Infantile patients have virtually no detectable enzyme activity. Juvenile and adult cases possess small but significant residual hexosaminidase A activity (up to 3 to 4 percent that of normal controls).

3. Heterozygotes for any one of the defects are asymptomatic; thus all G_{M2} gangliosidosis variants are inherited in an autosomal recessive fashion. The availability of rapid and inexpensive methods for the identification of heterozygotes for hexosaminidase A deficiencies has made possible large programs for family and population screening. In the general population, the heterozygote frequencies were estimated at 0.006 for α-subunit deficiencies and 0.0036 for β-subunit deficiencies. In some ethnic groups, much higher frequencies are observed. Among the Ash-kenazi Jewish people in North America and in Israel a heterozygote frequency of 0.032 was found for infantile Tay-Sachs disease (α-subunit deficiency). Extensive genetic counseling and monitoring of fetuses at risk has reduced the incidence of Tay-Sachs disease in the Ashkenazi Jewish population by almost 90 percent.

4. Specific therapy for G_{M2} gangliosidosis is not available to date. However, all hexosaminidase A deficiency variants can be diagnosed prenatally from amniotic fluid and amniotic fluid cells or chorionic villus biopsies.

HISTORICAL INTRODUCTION

In 1881 Warren Tay,[1] a British ophthalmologist, was the first to draw attention to the clinical characteristics of "infantile amaurotic idiocy" when he observed a cherry-red spot in the retina of a 1-year-old child with mental and physical retardation. The term *familial amaurotic idiocy* was coined by the American neurologist Bernhard Sachs.[2] Before the turn of the century he described the typical morphologic feature of the disease: distended cytoplasm of the neurons and ballooning of their dendrites.[3] There was little progress in the understanding of the disease, now known as *Tay-Sachs disease*, until the development of chemical, biochemical, and histochemical means of investigation. In the late 1930s the German biochemist Ernst Klenk[4,5] detected a new group of acidic glycosphingolipids as storage material in the brains of patients with amaurotic idiocy. Because of their high concentration in normal ganglion cells, he named these sialic acid–containing glycolipids *gangliosides*.[6] The main neuronal storage compound in Tay-Sachs disease, ganglioside G_{M2} (Fig. 72-1), was identified by Svennerholm[7] and its structure elucidated by Makita and Yamakawa[8] and Ledeen and Salsman.[9] The underlying metabolic defect, a deficiency of the catabolic enzyme hexosaminidase A, was discovered in 1969 by Okada and O'Brien[10] and Sandhoff,[11] and confirmed by Hultberg.[12] A combined deficiency of hexosaminidases A and B had been described a year earlier in a variant type of the disease.[13] These findings opened the way for biochemical diagnosis, prenatal diagnosis, and identification of carriers. A decade later, the deficiency of yet another protein, the G_{M2} activator protein, was reported to cause ganglioside G_{M2} accumulation in an "atypical case of Tay-Sachs disease" without hexosaminidase A deficiency.[14]

A useful and comprehensive term, G_{M2} *gangliosidosis*, was introduced by Suzuki and Chen[15] for disorders characterized by a primary accumulation of ganglioside G_{M2} caused by a defect in the hydrolytic degradation of this compound.

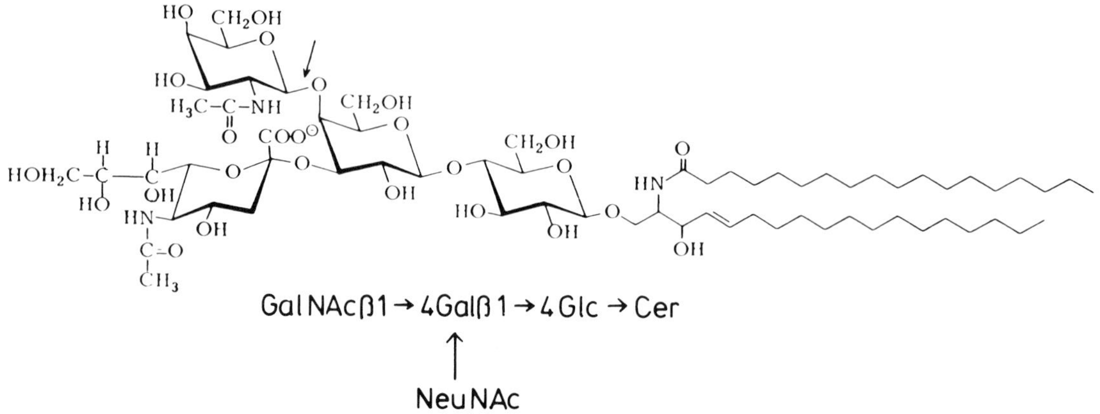

$$GalNAc\beta1 \rightarrow 4Gal\beta1 \rightarrow 4Glc \rightarrow Cer$$

$$\uparrow$$

$$NeuNAc$$

Fig. 72-1 Structure of ganglioside G_{M2}. The arrow indicates the bond to be cleaved by hexosaminidase A.

GANGLIOSIDES

Structure and Function

Gangliosides[16–18] are glycosphingolipids consisting of a hydrophobic ceramide (N-acylsphingosine) and a hydrophilic oligosaccharide chain bearing one or more N-acetylneuraminic acid (sialic acid, NeuAc) residues. The first ganglioside structure was established in 1963 by Kuhn and Wiegandt[19] for the monosialoganglioside G_{M1}. The ganglioside nomenclature used in this article is that of Svennerholm.[20] In adult human brain at least 12 different gangliosides have been identified, four of which, the gangliosides G_{M1}, G_{D1a}, G_{D1b}, and G_{T1b}, make up more than 90 percent of the total. They all contain the same tetrasaccharide chain, to which one (G_{M1}), two (G_{D1a} and G_{D1b}), or three (G_{T1b}) sialic acid residues are attached (Fig. 72-2). In gangliosides G_{M2} and G_{M3}, this oligosaccharide chain is incomplete and consists of a trisaccharide (gangliotriaose) or disaccharide (lactose), respectively.

Gangliosides, as well as other glycosphingolipids, are typical components of the outer leaflet of plasma membranes of animal cells. Here they are anchored by their hydrophobic ceramide moiety so that their hydrophilic oligosaccharide chains extend into the extracellular space.[21] They cover part of the cell surface, where they form cell-type-specific patterns that change with cell differentiation and cell transformation.[22] As specific cell surface markers, they are likely to be involved in cell differentiation and cell-cell interaction.[23] Though their physiological functions are still obscure, specific gangliosides have been implicated as binding sites on cell surfaces for viruses and bacterial toxins and as coreceptors for hormones, e.g., thyroid-stimulating hormone, growth factors, and interferons (for reviews, see Refs. 16, 24, 25).

The highest ganglioside content has been found in the gray matter of the brain.[26] Ganglioside content and pattern differ widely between different portions of the brain[27] and change significantly during ontogenesis.[28–32] Whereas the gangliosides of the central nervous system belong almost exclusively to the ganglio series, those of peripheral nerves (about 0.1 μmol NeuAc per gram wet weight[33]) and the extraneural tissues (in the range of 0.1 to 0.4 μmol NeuAc per gram wet weight[34]) contain high proportions of gangliosides of the lacto series,[35–38] Gal(β1→3)GlcNAc(β1→3)Gal(β1→4)Glc, or globo series,[39,40] GalNAc(β1→3)Gal(α1→4)Gal(β1→4)Glc. Major gangliosides of peripheral nerves are G_{M3} and G_{D3}; a major ganglioside of peripheral nerve myelin is NeuAc(α2→3)Gal(β1→4)GlcNAc(β1→3)Gal(β1→4)Glc(β1→1')Cer.[41]

Gangliosides are highly concentrated in neuronal plasma membranes,[26,42] especially in regions of nerve endings and

Fig. 72-2 Structure of a higher brain ganglioside (G_{Q1b}). Other major gangliosides may be derived by omission of one or several sialic acid (NeuNAc) residues: G_{M1} (-A,B,C), G_{D1a} (-B,C), G_{D1b} (-A,B), G_{T1a} (-C), G_{T1b} (-B).

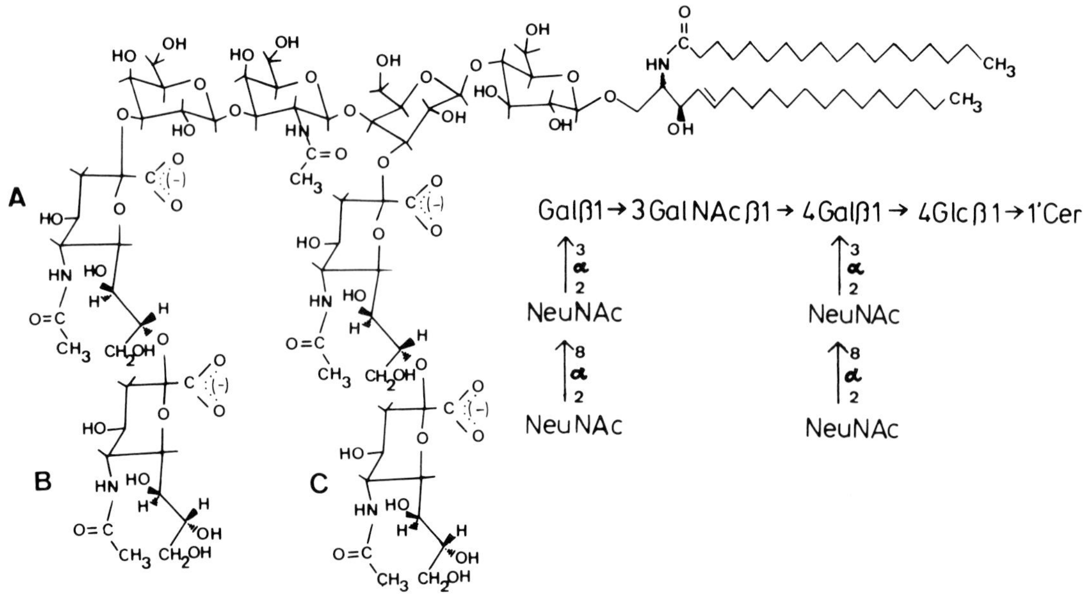

$$Gal\beta1 \rightarrow 3GalNAc\beta1 \rightarrow 4Gal\beta1 \rightarrow 4Glc\beta1 \rightarrow 1'Cer$$

dendrites.[43] The bulk of brain ganglioside is localized in neurons, but glial cells, such as oligodendrocytes and astrocytes, and other cell types also have their unique ganglioside composition. The function of gangliosides in neuronal plasma membranes is unknown. As Ca^{2+} binding sites, they have been implicated indirectly in neuronal transmission.[26,44] Recent experiments show that gangliosides have neuritogenic and neurotrophic properties: they can induce differentiation in some primary neuronal cultures and neuroblastoma cell lines. Exogenously added gangliosides also facilitate in vivo survival and repair of damaged neurons in both the central and peripheral nervous systems (for review, see Refs. 18, 45).

Biosynthesis and Intracellular Transport

Ganglioside biosynthesis starts from ceramide. The glycosyl chain of the lipid is formed in a stepwise manner by sequential addition of the individual sugar and sialyl residues to the growing glycolipid. The glycosyl residues are donated by the respective uridine-5'-diphosphate (UDP) derivatives, while the active species for the sialyl residue is cytidine-5'-monophosphate (CMP)–NeuAc. Each step is catalyzed by a specific glycosyltransferase (for review, see Refs. 46, 47). These enzymes are membrane-bound[48] and act at the luminal surface of the Golgi stacks.[49–52]

It is now believed that the gangliosides, after synthesis in the Golgi apparatus, are transported to the plasma membrane by vesicle flow.[53] Studies in vitro suggest that oligosialogangliosides can be partially degraded there to ganglioside G_{M1} by a membrane-based sialidase which is regulated by the organization and physical properties of the membranes.[54]

In neurons, synthesis and degradation of gangliosides apparently occur in the cell body but not in the axons or nerve terminals. The latter structures receive gangliosides by fast anterograde axonal transport and discharge them by retrograde axonal transport.[55,56]

Ganglioside Degradation

Catabolism of gangliosides and other sphingolipids has been studied intensively in many laboratories over the last 20 years, primarily to understand the molecular basis of the inherited lipidoses and their steadily increasing heterogeneity. Gangliosides are degraded by exohydrolases in the lysosomal compartment, in an acidic environment, in a stepwise manner starting at the hydrophilic end of the molecules. Almost any one of the degrading steps can be deficient in a lipid storage disease (for review, see Refs. 57, 58). All ganglioside storage diseases identified until now are due to defective lysosomal catabolism. The inherited deficiency of one catabolic reaction causes the lysosomal storage of its substrates. Nevertheless the diseases resulting from these defects are rather heterogeneous both biochemically and clinically. Though the lysosomal hydrolases as well as their inherited deficiencies are found in all organs, body fluids, and cells (with the exception of erythrocytes), lipids accumulate predominantly in the organs in which the respective lipid substrates are synthesized. Therefore, defects in ganglioside catabolism lead mainly to neuronal storage. These poorly water-soluble amphiphiles precipitate together with other membrane components within the cells in which they were synthesized. Only small amounts of the accumulating lipids leave the cells; they may be detected in cerebrospinal fluid and in urine.

In human tissues, ganglioside G_{M2} is degraded in the lysosomal compartment by hexosaminidase A, which removes the terminal *N*-acetylgalactosaminyl residue of ganglioside G_{M2}, provided the latter is complexed by the G_{M2} activator, a glycosphingolipid-binding protein. Sialidase has little activity on G_{M2} even though sialic acid is in a terminal position.

THE HEXOSAMINIDASE ISOENZYMES

Structure and Biosynthesis

The existence of an *N*-acetyl-β-D-glucosaminidase in mammalian tissues was reported as early as 1936.[59] Later it was found that the β-glycosides of the two amino sugars *N*-acetyl-D-glucosamine and *N*-acetyl-D-galactosamine are cleaved in the lysosomes by the same enzyme,[60–67] which was therefore called *β-hexosaminidase* or simply *hexosaminidase* (EC 3.2.1.52). The same enzyme is also listed as β-*N*-acetylglucosaminidase (EC 3.2.1.30) in *Enzyme Nomenclature*. The lysosomal location of this enzyme was demonstrated by subcellular fractionation.[65,68,69]

In 1968 Robinson and Stirling separated the hexosaminidase of human spleen into two isoenzymes, an acidic form, A, and a basic form, B.[65] This finding was confirmed by isoelectric focusing.[70] At first, the two isoenzymes were thought to be the same protein differing only in sialic acid content, because sialidase preparations appeared to "convert" hexosaminidase A to B.[65] This was, in fact, due to nonenzymatic action of the merthiolate that contaminated the sialidase preparations.[71,72] The relationship between the two isoenzymes was clarified by immunologic and biochemical analyses. Both isoenzymes were found to be oligomers with a subunit in common and a subunit unique to hexosaminidase A.[75–76] These were designated β and α, respectively. Subsequently, a third isoenzyme, with low catalytic activity, was discovered in tissues of patients with Sandhoff disease,[11,77,78] who lack both hexosaminidase A and B; this third isoenzyme (hexosaminidase S) was found to contain α subunits only.[78–80]

The two-subunit theory was confirmed by use of somatic cell genetics. Two distinct polypeptides require two genetic loci, one of which should be common to the A and B isoenzymes. By using human-mouse cell hybrids with a partial complement of human chromosomes, it was shown that expression of hexosaminidase B required only the presence of chromosome 5, whereas that of hexosaminidase A required the presence of chromosomes 5 and 15.[81–84]

Cloning and sequencing of the cDNAs has shown that the α and β subunits are quite similar.[85,86] There are long stretches of identical sequence in the two polypeptides, particularly in the central portions. The overall amino acid homology is 57 percent. There is also considerable similarity in the organization of the genomic DNAs.[87,88] It is tempting to speculate that the genes coding for the α and β chains diverged from a common ancestral gene, and that hexosaminidase polypeptides with properties intermediate between the mammalian α and β chains might be found in lower organisms.

Like other acid hydrolases of mammalian cells, the hexosaminidases are glycoproteins that undergo posttranslational modifications in order to be targeted to lysosomes (reviewed in Refs. 89, 90). The amino acid sequences deduced from cDNA show that both the α and the β chains have characteristic hydrophobic signal sequences at the NH_2 termini that facilitate entry into the lumen of the endoplasmic reticulum. The signals are removed, and the two chains undergo glycosylation of asparagine residues in the same manner as secreted or membrane glycoproteins. The oligosaccharide moieties are then modified to provide the mannose-6-phosphate recognition signal for targeting to lysosomes by way of a specific receptor. The phosphorylation occurs by the action of two enzymes, believed to be located in the cis and medial Golgi compartments, respectively.[90] Further processing of the carbohydrate groups can also occur in the Golgi apparatus; this gives rise to "complex" or "hybrid" structures that contain galactose and sialic acid.[91-93]

Where do the α and β chains associate to give hexosaminidase A? A priori, one might expect this event to occur soon after the nascent polypeptides have entered the lumen of the endoplasmic reticulum; but such is not the case. In cultured human fibroblasts the α chain remains in the monomeric form for many hours after the start of biosynthetic labeling and becomes associated with the β chain only after phosphorylation, i.e., after it has reached the Golgi apparatus.[94] We don't know what structural features on the polypeptides prevent their early association, nor what modifications subsequently make the association possible; nor do we know where β chains associate to give hexosaminidase B.

After association, some of the newly made enzyme may be secreted, appearing in cell culture medium and in body fluids. The bulk of the enzyme is transported to lysosomes, where it undergoes limited proteolysis as well as dephosphorylation and partial deglycosylation.

Thus, there are many molecular forms of the α and β chains: the "preprecursors" (the polypeptides corresponding to the cDNA reading frames), which are observed only in cell-free translation; the "precursors," which are transported through the organelles and which are also seen in extracellular enzyme; and the "mature" or smaller forms, which are found in lysosomes and are the most likely forms to be purified from tissues.[95] The preprecursors are always monomeric; the mature forms are associated into isoenzymes; while the precursor forms may be found free or associated depending on the location, intra- or extracellular, from which they have been obtained. Thus, the mature isoenzymes purified from tissues have somewhat different properties from the precursor hexosaminidases isolated from body fluids, which, in turn, differ from precursor α and β chains isolated at early times in biosynthetic labeling experiments.

The molecular heterogeneity of the hexosaminidase isoenzymes caused by their natural history in vivo and additional heterogeneity that can be introduced inadvertently during enzyme purification have led to some difficulties in the assignment of molecular structure. Though there has long been general agreement that the A and B isoenzymes have a molecular mass of about 120,000 ($\pm$ 20,000) Da, as measured by gel filtration or sedimentation,[75,96-100] the number of subunits has been variously reported as six, four, three, and two. It is now clear that there is but one α chain in hexosaminidase A (about 50,000 Da in the mature form[95,100]); previous findings of a larger number were the result of fragmentation of the α chain in vitro.

The situation is more complicated in the case of the β chain, which becomes nicked internally during maturation in many cells and tissues, including human fibroblasts and placenta.[95,101] The α chain and the two fragments of the β chain of mature placental hexosaminidases have been isolated and their amino termini sequenced.[102,102a] Similar experiments

have been performed with radiolabeled α and β chains synthesized by cultured fibroblasts.[103] With this information, it has been possible to identify the cleavage sites within the precursor sequences deduced from the cDNAs. The carboxy-terminal fragment of the β chain ("β_a," see below) from placental hexosaminidase A contained one less amino acid residue at the amino terminus than the C-terminal fragment from the B isoenzyme.[102] The fragments remain linked to each other by disulfide bridges. The nicking is not universal; it does not occur in human monocytes, because of a lack of the right protease,[104] nor in Chinese hamster ovary (CHO) cells, because the β chain itself is resistant to proteolytic clipping.[105] Mahuran et al.[101,106] take cognizance of the two fragments of the mature human β chain, referring to them as β_a and β_b (acidic and basic, as determined by isoelectric focusing), and refer to hexosaminidase A and B as $\alpha\beta_a\beta_b$ and $(\beta_a\beta_b)_2$, respectively. Our own preference is to consider the primary β subunit to be the unnicked precursor and to refer to the two isoenzymes as $\alpha\beta$ and $\beta\beta$. Hexosaminidase S has a molecular mass of 130,000 to 150,000 Da[80,107] and occurs as a dimer of the α chain.[94,106] The S isoenzyme is seen in biosynthetic labeling experiments primarily in precursor form;[94] whether it is not transported to lysosomes, where maturation would occur, or is rapidly degraded therein is not clear.

There exist several other hexosaminidase isoenzymes with intermediate isoelectric point and electrophoretic mobility, designated I[108-110] or P;[111] the latter is elevated in the serum of pregnant women.[112] The I and P forms in serum appear to be differently glycosylated forms of hexosaminidase B,[106,108-110] whereas the I forms isolated from liver and placenta appear related to hexosaminidase A.[106,109,110] An enzyme frequently referred to as *hexosaminidase C* is not a lysosomal hexosaminidase at all but rather a specific β-N-acetylglucosaminidase with a neutral pH optimum, located in the cytosol.[113-116] Its biologic role is not known.

The Catalytic Reaction—Substrate Specificity and Enzyme Kinetics

Hexosaminidases, like most lysosomal glycosidases, are specific for certain sugar residues (N-acetylglucosamine and N-acetylgalactosamine) in a certain anomeric linkage (in this case β anomers), while the nature of the aglycone is usually of little importance. In vivo, these enzymes are therefore active on a variety of glycoconjugates, including ganglioside G_{M2} and other glycolipids, such as G_{A2} and globoside (see "Storage Compounds"), glycosaminoglycans, and glycoprotein-derived oligosaccharides. In vitro, they are usually assayed with artificial substrates such as the chromogenic p-nitrophenyl and the fluorogenic 4-methylumbelliferyl glycosides.

Kresse and coworkers[117,118] discovered a most unusual reaction catalyzed by hexosaminidase A: this isoenzyme liberates intact N-acetylglucosamine-6-sulfate from the reducing end of keratan sulfate and from corresponding tetra- and (albeit more slowly) disaccharides, as well as from the artificial p-nitrophenyl and 4-methylumbelliferyl-6-sulfo-N-acetylglucosaminides (see Chap. 61).

Recent evidence suggests that both subunits, α and β, carry an active site but each has different substrate specificities.[119,120] Neutral water-soluble substrates are hydrolyzed much faster by the β than by the α subunit.[120] With such substrates generally used to assay hexosaminidases, the kinetic constants of hexosaminidases A and B have usually been found to be identical or very similar (except for the specific activity, which is almost twice as high for hexosaminidase B as for hexosaminidase A).[120-124] Likewise, the pH optimum for both isoenzymes with the N-acetyl glucosaminides as well as N-acetyl galactosaminides of p-nitrophenol and of 4-methylumbelliferone is the same, namely pH 4.4.[97,125-127] In contrast, hexosaminidase S, which consists entirely of α subunits, cleaves the 4-methylumbelliferyl-β-D-N-acetyl-glucosaminide (4-MU-GlcNAc) optimally at pH 4.8 to 5.0.[80,107]

The α subunit appears to be specific for negatively charged substrates such as oligosaccharides with a penultimate charged (uronic acid) residue, as might be derived from dermatan sulfate or chondroitin sulfates,[128,129] or with a negative charge on the terminal N-acetylglucosamine residue itself, as in keratan sulfate oligosaccharides[117,130] or in the artificial 6-sulfo-N-acetylglucosaminides. The latter, which are substrates for hexosaminidases A and S[117,131] but not for hexosaminidase B,[117] are cleaved by hexosaminidase A with a pH optimum of 3.8.[117,120]

The Michaelis constants for 4-methylumbelliferyl- and p-nitrophenyl-β-D-N-acetylglucosaminides are usually in the range of 0.3 to 1 mM for all three isoenzymes, A, B, and S, depending to some extent on the assay conditions.[66,80,96,97,107,122,127] With 4-MU-GlcNAc, turnover numbers of 300 per second and 790 per second were measured for hexosaminidases A and B, respectively. Identical K_m values for hexosaminidases A and B were also found with desulfated keratan sulfate (4 mM[118]) and the reduced disaccharide GlcNAc(β1→3)galactitol (0.1 mM[132]). For N-acetyl-β-D-galactosaminides both K_m and V_{max} values were approximately five to ten times lower than those for the corresponding glucosaminides.[66,122,127]

6-Sulfo-N-acetylglucosaminides are hydrolyzed by hexosaminidase A with lower K_m values (1.25 and 0.31 mM) and much higher maximal velocities [2.24 and 25 μmol/(min·mg) for the p-nitrophenyl and 4-methylumbelliferyl sulfated glycosides, respectively[117,120]] than those found for hexosaminidase B [K_m 3.4 mM, V_{max} 1.2 μmol/(min·mg) for the 4-MU substrate[120]].

Desulfated keratan sulfate was hydrolyzed by both isoenzymes,[118] whereas the B isoenzyme seems to be almost inactive or only poorly active with more negatively charged substrates such as chondroitin sulfates.[128,129] Hexosaminidase A liberated N-acetylglucosamine from polymeric hyaluronic acid some three times as fast as hexosaminidase B;[133] with a hyaluronic acid–derived trisaccharide the difference was even more pronounced, hexosaminidase A being 40 times as active as hexosaminidase B.[134]

Determination of kinetic constants for glycolipid substrates encounters some basic difficulties: neither purified micellar nor membrane-bound glycolipids can be attacked by the water-soluble hexosaminidases to a significant extent. For in vitro assays, this problem has been overcome by the addition of "suitable" detergents, usually bile salts. However, this creates an artificial system, and the results thus obtained do not necessarily reflect the physiological specificities of the enzymes. Glycolipid G_{A2} (GgOse$_3$Cer), for example, is hydrolyzed in vitro by both A and B hexosaminidases with comparable velocity,[123] whereas in vivo the B isoenzyme appears to be inactive toward this substrate as evidenced by the accumulation of G_{A2} in hexosaminidase A deficiency (α-subunit deficiency form of G_{M2} gangliosidosis).[77] Even the hydrolysis of the major storage compound, ganglioside G_{M2}, by hexosaminidase B has been the subject of some controversy[66,77,97,123,125,135,136] because of misleading results obtained with detergents.

The interaction in vivo between the water-soluble hexos-

aminidases and their glycolipid substrates is mediated by a specific nonenzymatic protein, the G_{M2} activator. In the presence of this activator protein, the substrate specificities of the A and B isoenzymes are entirely different from those found in the presence of detergents. These specificities and their relevance for the glycolipid storage processes in the different G_{M2} gangliosidosis variants will be discussed in the next section.

THE G_{M2} ACTIVATOR PROTEIN

In 1964 Mehl and Jatzkewitz[137] found that the degradation of sulfatide by arylsulfatase A depended in vitro on the presence of an enzymically inactive, heat-stable factor, which was later isolated[138] and identified as a small, lipid-binding, water-soluble protein.[139] In 1973 Li et al.[140] reported that the hydrolysis of ganglioside G_{M2} by hexosaminidase A required the presence of a similar nondialyzable cofactor. However, their attempt to purify this factor led to the isolation of a protein that stimulated the enzymatic degradation of ganglioside G_{M1} and globotriaosylceramide[141] and which was recently shown to be identical with the sulfatide activator.[142,143] The protein that specifically promotes the hydrolysis of lipid substrates by hexosaminidase A (particularly ganglioside G_{M2}, hence the name G_{M2} activator protein) has been shown to be different from the sulfatide activator.[144]

The activation of glycolipid hydrolysis by such ancillary proteins was generally viewed with great skepticism and was considered an in vitro artifact until the deficiency of the G_{M2} activator was shown to cause the same fatal glycolipid accumulation as the deficiency of the respective hydrolase.[14] The G_{M2} activator from normal kidney was purified to apparent homogeneity,[145] and its mechanism of action has been studied intensively.[146]

Properties of the G_{M2} Activator

The G_{M2} activator has been characterized as a small acidic protein which is heat-stable up to 60°C.[145] The amino acid composition recently reported for the liver protein by Li et al.[147] has shown a preponderance of acidic amino acids over basic ones. The similar molecular weights found with gel filtration and SDS electrophoresis indicate a monomeric structure of the protein.

After metabolic labeling of cultured skin fibroblasts with [³H]leucine, a precursor with an apparent molecular mass of 24,000 Da could be precipitated from culture medium, whereas only the mature 22,000-Da form could be detected intracellularly.[148] The glycoprotein nature of G_{M2} activator was demonstrated by metabolic labeling with [³H]mannose[148] and by direct analysis of the carbohydrate content of the protein (G. Stephan and K. Sandhoff, unpublished). These studies suggest that this activator carries not more than two, probably only one, N-linked oligosaccharide chains.

The subcellular locale of the G_{M2} activator has been studied in cultured human fibroblasts; it was clearly shown that the activator activity is associated with the lysosomal fractions.[149] The gene for G_{M2} activator was mapped to chromosome 5 in the human genome.[150] Using a sensitive enzyme-linked immunosorbent assay (ELISA), Banerjee et al.[149] determined the concentrations of G_{M2} activator in different biologic specimens (Table 72-1). Human kidney and urine appeared to be rich sources for the activator. Human liver and brain contained only about 7 and 11 percent, respectively, of the amount found in kidney tissue.

Role of the G_{M2} Activator in Ganglioside G_{M2} Degradation

The mechanism by which the G_{M2} activator stimulates the catabolism of glycolipids has been studied in some detail. The formation of water-soluble 1:1 complexes of the G_{M2} activator with gangliosides G_{D1a}, G_{M1}, G_{M2}, and G_{M3}, and glycolipid G_{A2} was demonstrated with isoelectric focusing, gel filtration, gel electrophoresis, and ultracentrifugation techniques.[146] The strength of the interaction between the activator and the glycolipids decreased in the order $G_{M2} > G_{M1} \approx G_{D1a} >> G_{M3} \approx G_{A2}$. This indicates some specificity of the carbohydrate recognition site for the glycolipid substrate. The contribution of the negative charge of sialic acid to the binding of ganglioside G_{M2} to the G_{M2} activator was also pointed out by Li et al.[151] They showed that the reduction of its carboxylate group to the alcohol or conversion to the methyl ester completely blocked the degradation of the ganglioside in the presence of the activator.

The water-soluble glycolipid-activator complexes are obviously formed by extracting single lipid molecules from membranes or micelles. This concept is supported by the finding that the G_{M2} activator, a glycolipid-binding protein, was able to act as a glycolipid transfer protein in the absence of hexosaminidase A. Under suitable in vitro conditions, the G_{M2} activator extracted ganglioside G_{M2} from G_{M2}-labeled liposomes and transferred it to acceptor liposomes.[146] These transfer studies also showed that only molecules of the outer leaflet of the liposomal membrane were accessible to the activator protein, indicating that it could not penetrate the liposomal membrane.[146]

Enzymatic studies performed with purified G_{M2} activator protein, hexosaminidase A, and ganglioside G_{M2} in the absence of detergents gave the first interpretable kinetics for the degradation of ganglioside G_{M2}.[145] The pH optimum for glycolipid degradation by hexosaminidase A in the presence of the G_{M2} activator was pH 4.2.[145] The kinetic constants were initially determined at high ionic strength (100 mM citrate buffer). Under these conditions, K_m values for the activator-lipid complexes (the true substrates of the reaction) of 4.6 and 0.9 μM and maximal velocities of 0.02 and 0.12 μmol/(min · mg) for ganglioside G_{M2} and glycolipid G_{A2}, respectively, were

Table 72-1 G_{M2} Activator in Normal and Pathologic Human Tissue Extracts and Body Fluids

Sample	Normal controls, n ≥ 4, ng/mg protein	Sandhoff disease, ng/mg protein	Tay-Sachs disease, ng/mg protein	Variant AB ng/mg protein
Kidney	804 (330–1120)	1600	—	1.2
Urine	600 (190–1430)	—	—	—
Placenta	121 (108– 135)	—	—	—
Brain	94 (36– 140)	1022	227	2.7, 4.9
Spleen	88 (40– 164)	—	223	1.8
Liver	54 (28– 70)	—	191	1.2, 1.5
Serum	48 (23– 75)*	—	—	—

*In ng/ml.
SOURCE: Data from Banerjee et al.[149] Used by permission.

determined for hexosaminidase A.[145] Measurement of the constants for ganglioside G_{M2} at lower ionic strength (10 mM citrate buffer) gave a slightly lower K_m value (1.9 μM) but a tenfold higher maximal velocity.[120]

Interestingly, the hydrolysis of a minor storage compound in hexosaminidase α-subunit deficiency (Tay-Sachs disease), G_{D1a}-GalNAc, by hexosaminidase is not accelerated by the G_{M2} activator. G_{D1a}-GalNAc, when presented as a component of liposomes, is directly attacked by hexosaminidases A and B (E. Meier and K. Sandhoff, unpublished). Nor is the hydrolysis of water-soluble substrates such as 4-methylumbelliferyl-N-acetyl-β-D-glucosaminides by hexosaminidase stimulated by the G_{M2} activator.[145] The G_{M2} activator acts primarily as a cosubstrate with G_{M2} ganglioside and does not really "activate" the enzyme.

This does not mean that the interaction of the activator with the enzyme is as nonspecific as that of a detergent. The G_{M2} activator shows a clear isoenzyme specificity for hexosaminidase A. It promotes the degradation of ganglioside G_{M2}, glycolipid G_{A2}, and kidney globoside by hexosaminidase A but not by hexosaminidase B (Table 72-2)[145] or S.[131] Precise analysis, however, revealed that β-hexosaminidase B possesses minute but still detectable activity (about 3 percent of that of hexosaminidase A) against glycolipid G_{A2} in the presence of the activator protein.[145]

Recently, a more detailed study on the interaction between the G_{M2} activator and hexosaminidase A[120] showed that hexosaminidase A has two different active sites, one on the β subunit and another on the α subunit (Fig. 72-3). The water-soluble p-nitrophenyl and 4-methylumbelliferyl derivatives of β-N-acetylglucosamine and β-N-acetylgalactosamine are cleaved by the β site much faster than by the α site, whereas the sulfated derivatives of these substrates (p-nitrophenyl- and 4-methylumbelliferyl-N-acetyl-β-D-glucosaminide-6-sulfate) and the glycolipids G_{M2} and G_{A2} in the form of their activator complexes are hydrolyzed exclusively by the α site. Since hexosaminidase B is composed of two β subunits, it only hydrolyzes the unsulfated water-soluble substrates (and glycolipid G_{A2} in the presence of detergent). On the other hand, hexosaminidase S, composed of two α subunits, hydrolyzes sulfated water-soluble substrates but is ineffective in hydrolyzing ganglioside G_{M2}.[131] Therefore it must be assumed that the β subunit is in some way needed for recognition and binding of the ganglioside G_{M2}–G_{M2} activator complex.

The G_{M2} activator, even in the absence of ganglioside G_{M2}, inhibited the degradation of the sulfated fluorogenic substrate by hexosaminidases A and S, indicating that the α subunit provides a binding site for the activator protein. When the activator was saturated with ganglioside G_{M2}, the activity of hexosaminidase A but not of hexosaminidase S was further decreased. This suggests that the β subunit may be necessary to bring the ganglioside G_{M2} molecule, delivered by the G_{M2} activator, into the right position for cleavage.

From our present knowledge, a model can be suggested for the mechanism by which G_{M2} activator stimulates glycolipid breakdown in lysosomes, which is schematically summarized in Fig. 72-3. The hydrophilic moiety of ganglioside G_{M2} on the membrane surface cannot be attacked directly by hexosaminidase A. It can, however, be recognized and bound by a specific region on the G_{M2} activator protein. In a second step, the ceramide residue of this lipid is pulled out of the membrane and instead folds into a hydrophobic groove of the ac-

Table 72-2 Glycolipid Specificity of Liver Hexosaminidases A and B in the Presence of Detergents or G_{M2} Activator

| Substrate | Hexosaminidase | Stimulating agent, degradation rate, $\mu mol/(h \cdot mg)$ | | |
		None	NaTDC,* 2 mM	Activator protein, 13.5 AU/assay†
Ganglioside G_{M2}	A	0.009	0.40	0.97
	B	0.001	0.07	0.005
Glycolipid G_{A2}	A	0.008	6.3	2.48
	B	0.001	30.7	0.072
Globoside	A	0.004	14.4	0.42
	B	0.005	24.0	0.005
4-Methylumbelliferyl GalNAc	A	675	350	680
	B	1300	850	1390

*NaTDC = Sodium taurodeoxycholate. Enzyme is inactivated during incubation. Values given were obtained with short incubation times (30 min).
†Glycolipid degradation rate depends on activator concentration, which was not saturating in this case. AU = activator unit as defined in source.
SOURCE: Data from Conzelmann and Sandhoff.[145] Used by permission.

tivator. The resulting activator-lipid complex is fully water-soluble, as is the free activator. This extraction process is, of course, reversible. The activator binds to a specific recognition site of hexosaminidase A, most probably in such a way that the terminal residue of the glycolipid is correctly positioned in the active center of the α subunit of the enzyme.[120] After hydrolysis is completed, the activator-product complex is released and diffuses away; the lipid product may be reinserted into the membrane or perhaps "handed over" to the next activator on the degradative pathway.

THE G_{M2} GANGLIOSIDOSIS VARIANTS

Classification and Nomenclature

From the preceding discussion it is evident that the lysosomal degradation of ganglioside G_{M2} and related glycolipids requires three genetically distinct polypeptides, namely the α and β subunits of the β-hexosaminidases and the G_{M2} activator protein. Defects or deficiencies of any of them are known to im-

Fig. 72-3 Model for the lysosomal catabolism of ganglioside G_{M2}.[152] Hexosaminidase A does not directly interact with the membrane-bound ganglioside. Instead, the activator protein extracts the glycolipid and the resulting (water-soluble) activator/lipid complex is the substrate for the enzymatic reaction. After the reaction, the product, ganglioside G_{M3}, is reinserted into the membrane and the activator is available for another round of catalysis.

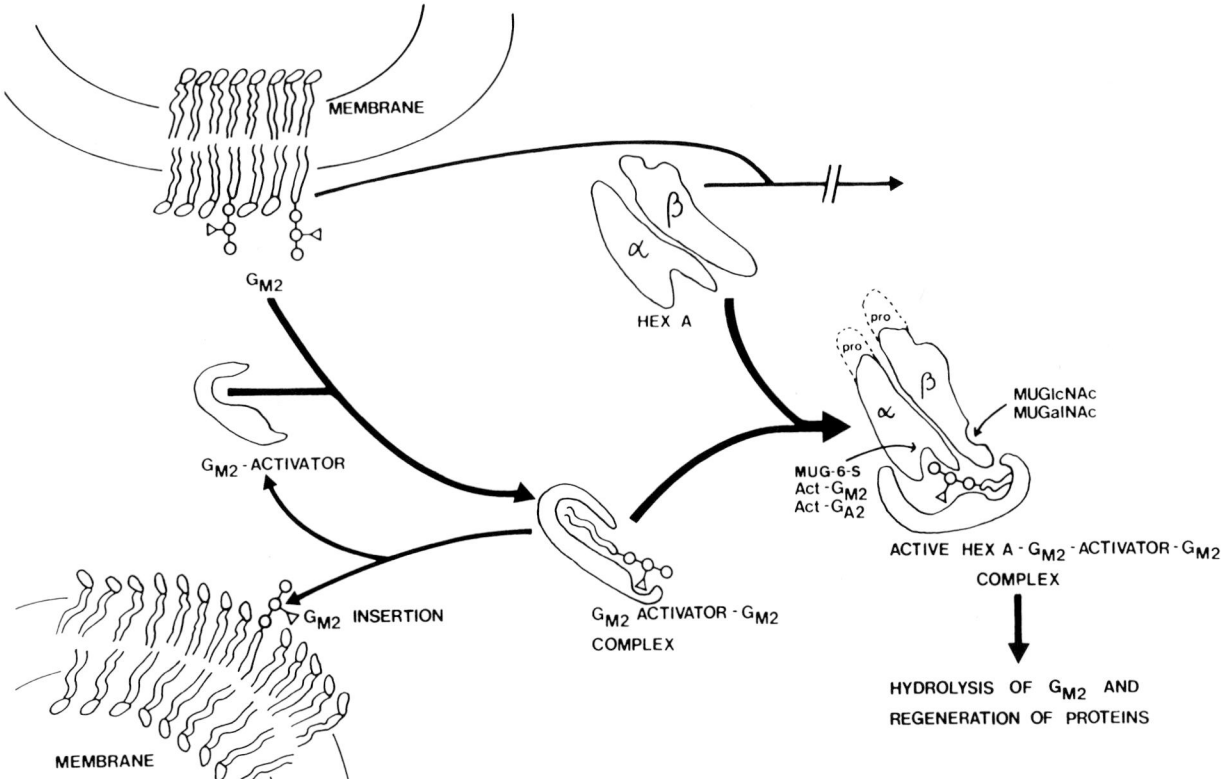

pair ganglioside catabolism. Accordingly, three nonallelic biochemical variants of G_{M2} gangliosidosis can be distinguished. These have been classified on the basis of the isoenzyme that is still to be found in the patient's tissues (i.e., the biochemical phenotype) as variants B, 0 (zero), and AB.[77] Now that the polypeptides and genes involved have been identified, it is possible and also desirable to establish a more logical nomenclature that refers to the defective component rather than to the unaffected ones. We would suggest denoting the three variants as hexosaminidase α-subunit defect (or deficiency), hexosaminidase β-subunit defect, and G_{M2} activator deficiency, respectively.

Hexosaminidase α-Subunit Defect or Deficiency (Variant B, Tay-Sachs Disease). A deficiency or defect of the α subunit of hexosaminidase A[153–156] blocks the formation of intact hexosaminidase A (and the minor isoenzyme hexosaminidase S, which is an α_2 dimer) while the unaffected β subunits can still associate to form hexosaminidase B, which is a homodimer of β subunits.[74–76] Biochemically, this disorder is characterized by the presence of normal or even elevated levels of hexosaminidase B[10,11,77] and has therefore been referred to as *variant B of G_{M2} gangliosidosis.*[77] The eponym *Tay-Sachs disease* usually refers to the infantile form of this enzymatic variant. (From the clinical descriptions it appears that the original patients described by Tay and Sachs were indeed of this variant.)

A few patients have been found to synthesize an α subunit that still associates almost normally with the β subunit but is devoid of catalytic activity. The resulting dimer, $\alpha\beta$, behaves like normal hexosaminidase A in various respects (isoelectric point, activity with several artificial substrates) but is inactive on the physiological substrate, ganglioside G_{M2}.[119,157] This variant was first thought to be related to G_{M2} activator deficiency[158] (see below) but was later shown to be allelic with other hexosaminidase α-subunit deficiencies[159] and was therefore referred to as variant B1.

Hexosaminidase β-Subunit Defect or Deficiency (Variant 0, Sandhoff Disease). Patients with a deficiency of the β subunit (encoded on chromosome 5[81,82,160]) that is common to both major hexosaminidase isoenzymes, A and B,[74–76] lack both activities.[13,77] This variant has therefore been designated as *variant 0* (for zero hexosaminidase activity). The eponym *Sandhoff disease* relates to the fact that this enzymatic variant was first distinguished from classic Tay-Sachs disease (variant B) by Sandhoff et al.[13] The small residual hexosaminidase activity still found in the tissues of infantile patients is due to the (physiologically probably irrelevant) dimer of α subunits, hexosaminidase S.[79]

G_{M2} Activator Deficiency (Variant AB). A third variant, so far rarely diagnosed, is caused by the deficiency of the G_{M2} activator protein[14,161,162] (encoded on chromosome 5[150]) needed for the degradation of ganglioside G_{M2} (and a few related glycolipids) by hexosaminidase A. The hexosaminidase isoenzymes are not affected in these patients[77,127] and are present in normal or elevated amounts, hence the name variant AB.

Clinical Phenotypes

Each of these biochemical variants comprises a series of allelic mutations with great variability in clinical expression. Complete deficiencies of enzymatic function are associated with early onset and the most fulminant clinical abnormalities. Infantile Tay-Sachs disease and Sandhoff disease have onset of symptoms in infancy, rapid progression, and death usually before the age of 4 years. In contrast, patients with less severe forms have a small amount of functional enzyme which suffices to retard the process of ganglioside accumulation and thus delays the onset of symptoms and the progression of the disease. Depending on the residual enzyme activity, onset of symptoms may occur anywhere between late infancy and adulthood. Accordingly, from a clinical point of view hexosaminidase α-subunit and β-subunit deficiencies are usually subclassified into infantile, late infantile, juvenile, and adult forms. Although the distinction between these forms cannot be as sharp as between the enzymatic variants, this classification is quite useful since the clinical appearance changes and the scope of clinical heterogeneity broadens considerably with increasing age of onset.

α-Subunit Defect or Deficiency Diseases (Variant B). The clinical phenotypes of this enzymatic variant are usually classified into four groups:

INFANTILE TAY-SACHS DISEASE. In all of the early infantile G_{M2} gangliosidoses—the prototype and most common of which is Tay-Sachs disease in Ashkenazi Jewish infants—the clinical picture is virtually identical. The earliest symptoms of mild motor weakness begin around 3 to 5 months of age, although this is often appreciated only retrospectively by the parents. An increased startle reaction to sharp, but not necessarily loud, sounds with extension of both upper and lower extremities and a myoclonic-like jerk is also frequently noted at about this time. This, too, is often not considered to be abnormal by parents until later, when more obvious symptoms have developed. Often parents will relate this abnormality in response to the question, How well do you think the baby hears?

Progressive weakness, hypotonia, poor head control, and decreasing attentiveness usually begin to cause parental concern between 6 and 10 months of age. Frequently, it is these symptoms which bring the infant to the attention of the physician. Although some motor skills may have been achieved earlier (e.g., crawling, sitting alone, or even pulling up to stand), these landmarks are usually not attained. If attained, they are nearly always lost by 10 to 12 months of age. Both motor and mental deterioration progress rapidly thereafter.

It is not uncommon for visual symptoms to lead to the initial diagnosis. Seeming inattentiveness, unusual eye movements, or apparent staring episodes may lead parents or primary physicians to request ophthalmologic consultation. On direct or indirect ophthalmoscopy, the finding of macular pallor with contrasted prominence of the macular fovea centralis (the so-called cherry-red spot) immediately raises the possibility of Tay-Sachs disease or one of the other neuronal storage disorders (Fig. 72-4). Though not pathognomonic of this disorder, this finding is seen in virtually all patients with Tay-Sachs disease where thorough efforts are made to visualize the maculae bilaterally. This finding in the absence of organomegaly, particularly in a child of Jewish ancestry with an early clinical course as described, strongly suggests the possibility of Tay-Sachs disease. A faint cherry-red spot has been observed at 2 days of age by indirect ophthalmoscopy in an affected infant born to a family with a previous offspring with Tay-Sachs disease (M. Kaback, unpublished observations).

After 8 to 10 months of age, the infant becomes progres-

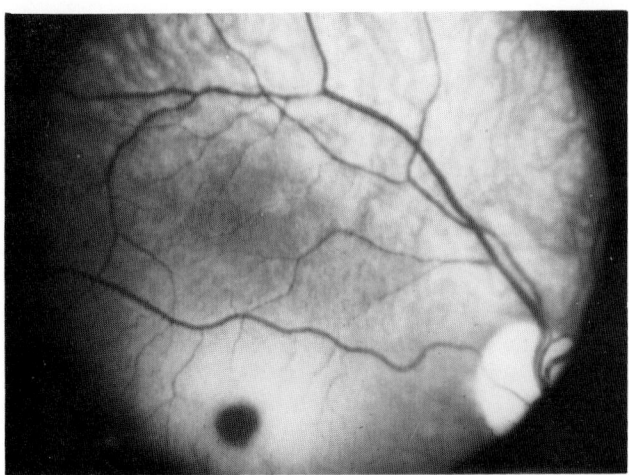

Fig. 72-4 "Cherry-red" spot in the fundus of an infantile Tay-Sachs patient (at bottom left).

sively less responsive to its parents and surroundings. Vision diminishes rapidly, although some distinction between light and dark may persist. Neurologic signs of both upper and lower motor neuron deterioration become increasingly more evident. Seizures commonly begin after the first year, are usually highly variable in character, and typically change in frequency and type with time. Reasonable seizure control can usually be achieved with standard antiepileptic medications. Progressive increase in head size (macrocephaly) is typical by 1½ to 2 years, the result of reactive cerebral gliosis rather than true hydrocephalus with ventricular enlargement.

Further deterioration in the second year of life invariably leads to decerebrate posturing, dyscoordinate swallowing, and eventually to a completely unresponsive, vegetative state. Bronchopneumonia, associated with aspiration and/or diminished capacity to cough, is frequently the antecedent to death. Although children with infantile G$_{M2}$ gangliosidosis usually do not survive beyond the second to fourth year of life, one child with Tay-Sachs disease is known to have survived to age 6 years.

Patients with complete hexosaminidase A deficiency of other than the Ashkenazi Jewish type exhibit an identical phenotype.

JUVENILE G$_{M2}$ GANGLIOSIDOSIS. Late onset G$_{M2}$ gangliosidosis was first described in 1968 by Bernheimer and Seitelberger[163] and is still occasionally referred to as *Bernheimer-Seitelberger disease*.

Symptoms of motor ataxia first become evident between 2 and 6 years of age. A progressive dementia ensues with loss of speech, increasing spasticity, and seizures by the end of the first decade.[164,165] Generally, loss of vision occurs much later than in Tay-Sachs disease,[166] and macular degeneration (cherry-red spot) is not a consistent finding. Rather, optic atrophy and retinitis pigmentosa may be seen late in the course of this condition. A vegetative state with decerebrate rigidity is reached by 10 to 12 years with death, usually the result of intercurrent infection, occurring by age 10 to 15 years. Less than 20 patients with this condition have been described.[165,167,168] Since most are Ashkenazi Jewish or of mixed Jewish/non-Jewish parentage, this condition most probably represents a compound heterozygous state with a rare allelic mutation in combination with the common Tay-Sachs disease gene.

CHRONIC G$_{M2}$ GANGLIOSIDOSIS. A more indolent form of G$_{M2}$ gangliosidosis has been described in which early abnormalities of gait and posture begin between 2 and 5 years of age.[169,170] Mentation and verbal intelligence remain intact, although emotional lability may become striking. Cerebellar symptoms are prominent, and a pattern suggestive of atypical spinocerebellar degeneration is manifested with spasticity, dysarthria, and mild to moderate ataxia of the limbs and trunk, along with progressive muscle wasting and weakness. As in all the G$_{M2}$ gangliosidoses, sensory modalities remain intact. Vision and funduscopic examination are normal throughout the course of this illness. Most of the patients with this condition, including several of those originally described, are still living in their third to fourth decade of life. Only a few families have been described, usually in Jewish or mixed Jewish/non-Jewish matings, again suggesting a compound heterozygous state with the Tay-Sachs disease gene. Parents of such patients appear as Tay-Sachs disease heterozygotes on synthetic substrate carrier detection testing.[170]

ADULT-ONSET G$_{M2}$ GANGLIOSIDOSIS. The most clinically variable type of the G$_{M2}$ gangliosidoses is the so-called adult-onset form(s). Thirty-five patients with this disorder have been reviewed recently,[171] and they reveal a wide range of symptoms and abnormal findings. Distinction between this and chronic G$_{M2}$ gangliosidosis may be difficult and even arbitrary, as many adult-onset patients at the time of diagnosis may relate subtle symptoms that go back to relatively early childhood. Extreme variability of symptoms and course can even be seen in the same family or sibship, with complete dementia in one member by age 20 years while other "affected" members of the same family function well in their sixth to seventh decade.

Clinically, symptoms of spinocerebellar and lower motor neuron dysfunction are most prominent. Psychosis, usually of the hebephrenic-schizophrenia type with slow personality disintegration, often with episodes of depression, is evident or develops in nearly one-third of cases reported, either with or without pyramidal, cerebellar, or lower neuron findings. Vision and intelligence, in most patients, remain unaffected. Early muscle symptoms (weakness, tremor, etc.) often lead to electromyography and/or muscle biopsy. Findings in both are consistent with anterior motor horn cell dropout and group atrophy. Nerve conduction time is normal. Premortem electron microscopy of myenteric neuronal cells (e.g., by rectal biopsy or appendectomy) reveals typical intralysosomal membranous cytoplasmic bodies.[172]

Because of the diversity in clinical symptoms associated with the adult-onset type of G$_{M2}$ gangliosidosis, patients not uncommonly have been diagnosed previously with an array of neurologic conditions. These include diagnoses such as Kugelberg-Welander disease, atypical spinocerebellar degeneration, spinal muscular atrophy, atypical Friedreich ataxia (with sensory modalities intact), and amyotrophic lateral sclerosis.[169,173–176] Clearly, hexosaminidase testing of individuals with such diagnoses is appropriate. Very low residual hexosaminidase A activities can be detected in most tissues (serum, leukocytes, and/or skin fibroblasts) from such patients. In cultured fibroblasts, low but measurable activity of G$_{M2}$ gangliosidase is detectable under optimal assay conditions.[177]

HEXOSAMINIDASE A DEFICIENCY WITH NORMAL PHENOTYPE. Through family testing, when infant probands with Tay-Sachs disease or other G$_{M2}$ gangliosidoses have been identified (or, on rare occasion, in population screening programs), individuals have been identified who, by serum and/or leukocyte hexosaminidase profile with synthethic substrates, are found to have very low hexosaminidase A levels.[178–183] Several of these individuals have been identified in their forties or fifties and have been completely asymptomatic. Although the residual activities of G_{M2} gangliosidase were not yet measured in such cases (at least not under appropriate assay conditions), it is very likely that those probands who remain healthy possess a higher activity than adult G_{M2} gangliosidosis patients, which is sufficient for normal ganglioside catabolism (see discussion of pathogenesis below). Where G_{M2} gangliosidase levels are measurable but severely decreased in cells from a hexosaminidase A–deficient asymptomatic individual, it is highly probable that they are in a presymptomatic phase of adult-onset G_{M2} gangliosidosis.[177,178,184,185]

β-Subunit Defect or Deficiency Diseases (Sandhoff Disease, Variant 0). This enzymatic variant shows as wide a spectrum of clinical phenotypes as the α-subunit deficiency.

INFANTILE SANDHOFF DISEASE. The classic infantile β-subunit-deficient G_{M2} gangliosidosis, Sandhoff disease, manifests a clinical picture nearly identical with that of Tay-Sachs disease. Distinguishing features of Sandhoff disease other than the ethnic background of the child and the obvious differences on biochemical determination of the hexosaminidase profiles (total deficiency of both hexosaminidase A and hexosaminidase B) include the presence of organomegaly and occasional bony deformities similar to those associated with infantile G_{M1} gangliosidosis. Otherwise the onset and progression of symptoms and the abnormal physical findings, including retinal abnormalities (cherry-red spot), psychomotor retardation, and neurologic signs are virtually identical with Tay-Sachs disease. Clinical laboratory findings that may distinguish the two disorders include occasional foamy histiocytes in the bone marrow as well as the presence of N-acetylglucosamine–containing oligosaccharides in the urine of infants with Sandhoff disease.

JUVENILE SANDHOFF DISEASE. This condition has been described in only a few patients and presents at 3 to 10 years of age with evidence of slurred speech, cerebellar ataxia, and progressive psychomotor retardation.[186,187] Vision is normal, and the fundi appear benign. Increasing spasticity, hypertonia, and mental deterioration ensue.

Hexosaminidase profiles in such children are characterized by a virtual absence of hexosaminidase B activity and a profound (but not total) reduction of hexosaminidase A.

HEXOSAMINIDASE A AND B DEFICIENCY WITH NORMAL PHENOTYPE. A normal adult male and his healthy 15-month-old daughter have been described in whom a marked deficiency of hexosaminidase A and virtually no hexosaminidase B were present in leukocytes and fibroblasts in synthetic substrate assays. Two prior children had died with "Tay-Sachs disease." Assays in skin fibroblasts, with ganglioside G_{M2} as substrate, revealed activities between 10 and 20 percent of normal, well above the range of activity found in G_{M2} gangliosidosis patients.[177] The mother of all of the children appeared as a typical Sandhoff disease heterozygote, suggesting strongly that the two dead children actually had succumbed to Sandhoff disease.[188,189] The father and daughter are most likely compound heterozygotes, with allelic mutations at the two subunit loci. One mutation is that associated with classic Sandhoff dis-

ease while the other results in impaired activity as well as inability to dimerize into hexosaminidase B. This variant phenotype, called *hexosaminidase Paris*, will be discussed below.

G_{M2} Activator Deficiency (Variant AB). Since the G_{M2} activator is an essential intralysosomal component for the hydrolysis of ganglioside G_{M2}, a severe deficiency of this factor leads to accumulation of the ganglioside substrate exactly as in the complete α- and β-subunit deficiency disorders. Accordingly, the phenotype is identical with Tay-Sachs disease and infantile Sandhoff disease. When hexosaminidase A and hexosaminidase B activities are assayed with synthetic substrates, however, they are found to be normal.[77] With ganglioside G_{M2} as substrate, in the absence of added activator or detergent, no activity is evident.[14]

Clearly, where any of the G_{M2} gangliosidoses are diagnostic considerations in a patient, and where synthetic substrate assays are within normal limits (or only moderately depressed), natural substrate assays with and without added G_{M2} activator should be performed.

PATHOLOGY

Hexosaminidase α-Subunit Defect or Deficiency (Variant B)

Infantile Form (Tay-Sachs Disease). Gross appearance of the brain varies considerably depending on the duration of the disease. The brain shows marked atrophy with widened sulci and narrowed gyri. The leptomeninges are somewhat thickened and fibrotic. The ventricular system is diffusely dilated. The white matter is shrunken and often shows gelatinous appearance. The cerebral cortex is thin, and the gray-white junction is blurred; laminar necrosis is often conspicuous in the cortex. The brain weight is increased considerably in patients who survived longer. The brain weight may reach as much as 2400 g, and the gyri may be diffusely widened. The consistency of the brain is firm and rubbery. However, the increase of the volume is limited to the cerebrum. Cerebellum and brainstem are atrophic.[190,191]

The most pronounced histopathological change is the presence of neurons swollen with storage material throughout the nervous system. The nuclei and Nissl substance are pushed to

Fig. 72-5 A ballooned neuron with storage material, Nissl stain. Magnification ×500.

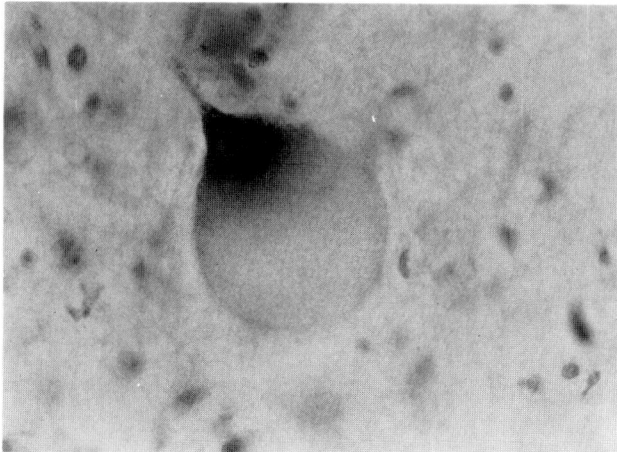

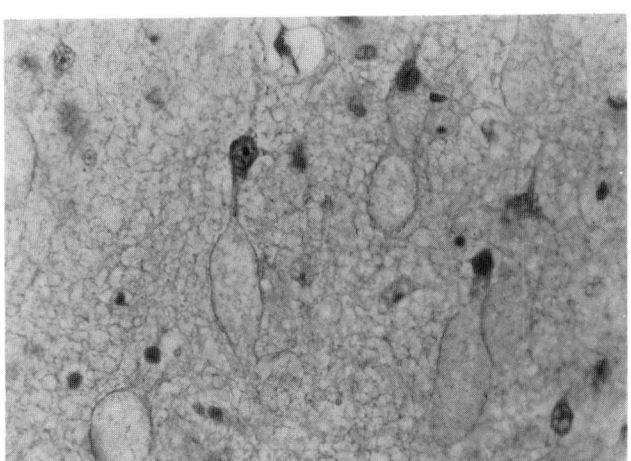

Fig. 72-6 Cerebral cortical neuron with prominent meganeurite formation. H & E stain. Magnification ×312.

the periphery (Fig. 72-5), and "meganeurites"[192] are very conspicuous in many of the cerebral cortical neurons (Fig. 72-6). Golgi preparation reveals atrophic dendrites and numerous fine neurites originating from the meganeurites (Fig. 72-7). The storage material shows strong acid phosphatase activity[193] and consists of numerous concentrically arranged lamellar structures (membranous cytoplasmic bodies, or MCBs) at the ultrastructural level (Fig. 72-8).[194] MCBs are also seen in astrocytes. In spite of the presence of numerous MCBs in the neuronal perikaryons, mitochondria and other cellular organelles are normal. The meganeurites also are packed with MCBs, and synaptic spines are often found in their cell membrane.[192]

Initially normal cytoarchitecture is well preserved, but in later stages, it is totally disturbed by the loss of neurons and by markedly distorted neuronal morphology. Numerous macrophages containing storage material are scattered throughout the affected cortex, and fibrillary gliosis is very pronounced in the later stage. The cerebral white matter shows degenerative changes with loss of myelin and axons.[195] Initially the cerebellar changes are limited to the focal swelling of the Purkinje cells, but in later stages both Purkinje and granular cells are diminished in number. The dendrites of the Purkinje cells often show focal expansions, and severe gliosis is noted in the

molecular laver of the cerebellum (Fig. 72-9). Swollen neurons are also noted in the spinal ganglia, autonomic ganglia, and neurons of the myenteric plexes (Fig. 72-10).[190,191,196,197] The ganglion cells and amacrine cells in the retina are swollen with storage material.[190,198] In later stages many of these cells have disappeared. Storage is also noted in pinealocytes and the cells in the anterior pituitary gland.[190,199]

In a series of electron-microscopic studies on the fetus (gestational age 12 to 22 weeks) with Tay-Sachs disease, Adachi et al.[200] found membranous inclusions (MCBs) in the anterior horn cells of the spinal cord as early as 12 weeks of gestation. MCBs were also noted in the spinal ganglion cells, retinal ganglion cells, the neurons in the myenteric plexus, and some cells in the pituitary gland in these fetuses. Light-microscopic examination showed fine vacuolation in the perikarya of these cells. Similar vacuolation was noted in some of the neurons in the deep cerebral nuclei, but cytoarchitecture and neuronal morphology in the cerebral cortex of these fetuses appeared normal.[200]

Inactive α-Subunit Variant (Variant B1). A single postmortem report of this variant is available in the literature. This case was originally thought to be an example of G~M2~ activator deficiency and included as Case 1 in the report by Goldman and coworkers.[201] The brain of this patient was small, and a mild degree of cerebral atrophy was present. There was a diffuse neuronal storage in the CNS, but storage appeared to be more pronounced in the deep cerebral nuclei and brainstem. The cerebral cortical cytoarchitecture was preserved, and neuronal loss and gliosis appeared minimal. In the cerebellum the dendrites of Purkinje cells were swollen, and there was a loss of Purkinje cells, but the somata of the remaining cells were not swollen. Electron-microscopic examination of the neurons revealed typical MCBs and many additional more pleomorphic inclusions.

Late Onset Forms of Hexosaminidase A Deficiency. Unlike infantile hexosaminidase A deficiency (Tay-Sachs disease), which shows rather stereotypic clinical manifestation and neuropathology, the late onset cases show varieties of clinicopathological features. Since many of these late onset cases have been diagnosed by rectal biopsy and/or enzyme assays and only a few cases were examined post-mortem, generalization of the neuropathologic findings is not appropriate. However,

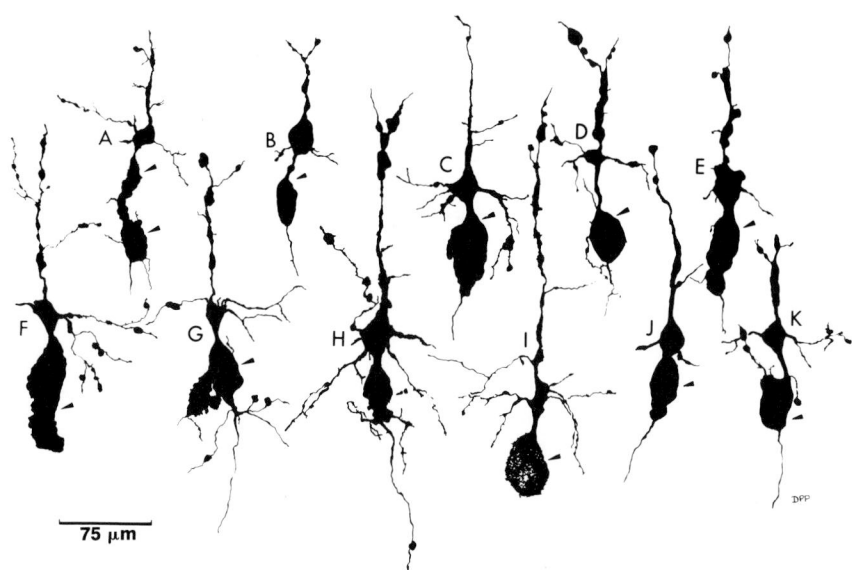

Fig. 72-7 Composite of camera lucida drawing of layer II and III small and medium pyramidal neurons. Arrowheads identify primary and secondary meganeurites. Dendrites are atrophic and devoid of spines. (From Purpura et al.,[192] with permission.)

75 μm

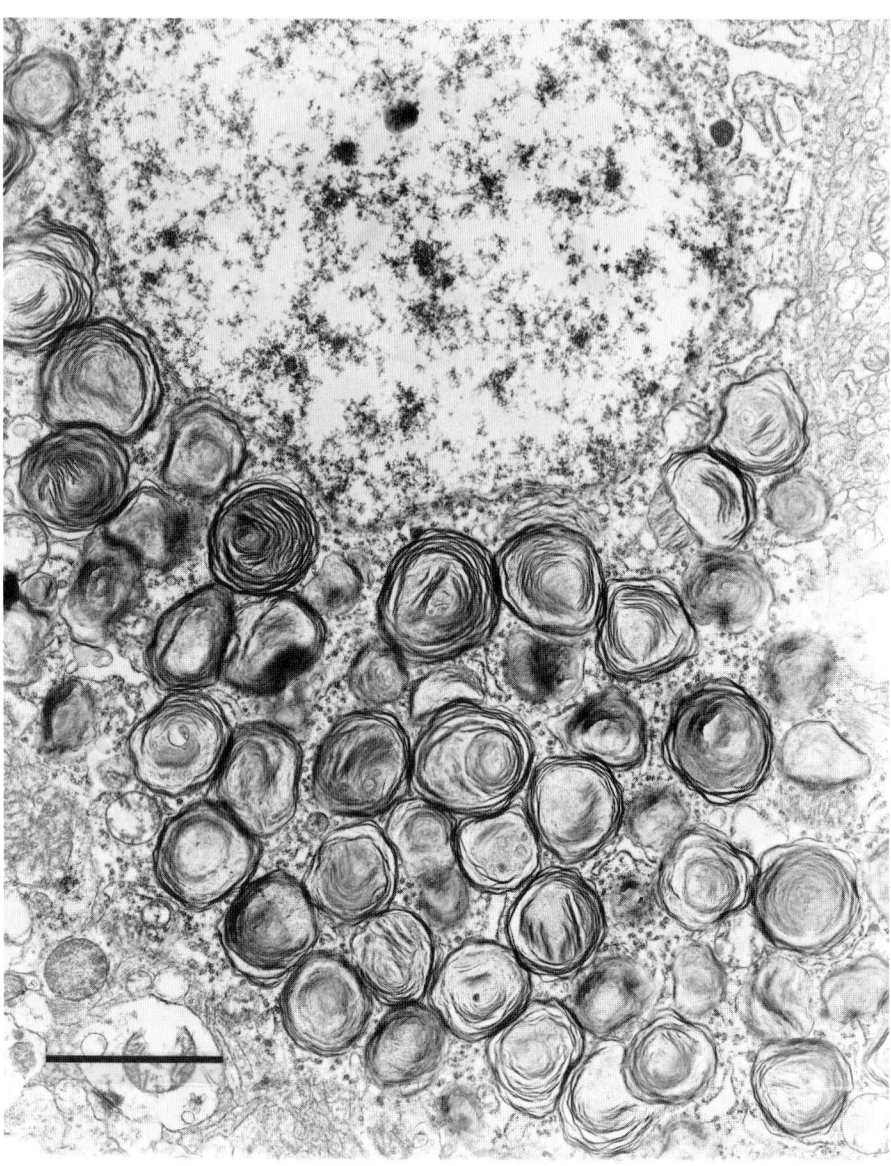

Fig. 72-8 Membranous cytoplasmic bodies (MCBs) occupy neuronal perikarya. Line indicates 1 μm.

the findings appear reasonably similar regardless of the various clinical expressions.[164,165,169,174,202] The brain weight is less than normal, and there is mild to moderate cerebral atrophy. As a general tendency, neuronal swelling (storage) is less marked in the cerebral cortex (Fig. 72-11) than in the cerebellum, brainstem, and spinal cord. The swollen neurons in the central nervous system (CNS) often contain storage material with staining characteristics similar to the storage material in ceroid lipofuscinosis (Fig. 72-11), in addition to or instead of typical storage material seen in the infantile form. Electron-microscopic studies also revealed neuronal inclusions to be combinations of typical MCBs, conglomerates of pleomorphic membranous structures, and electron-dense granular or amorphous material.[164,169,174] However, peripheral ganglion cells usually show marked cytoplasmic swelling and contain typical MCBs.[163,167,170,172,185,203]

Hexosaminidase β-Subunit Defect or Deficiency (Sandhoff Disease, Variant 0)

Published reports of postmortem examination of Sandhoff disease are limited to the infantile form. Gross pathology of the brain is very similar to that of the infantile form of hexosaminidase α-subunit deficiency (Tay-Sachs disease). In addition, however, Dolman and coworkers observed a bright-yellow discoloration of the dorsal root ganglia in one of the cases and yellowish discoloration of the cerebral cortex in another case.[204] Hadfield and coworkers also wrote: "The cortex and centrum ovale were *light butterscotch* in color" and "the deep nuclear structures were colored a darker golden tan, reminiscent of the yellow discoloration seen in kernicterus" and suggested that this color change could be related to the higher levels of asialoganglioside.[205] Unlike hexosaminidase A deficiency, there is gross pathology in the visceral organs, such as endocardial fibrosis and hepatosplenomegaly.[204–206]

Light-microscopic features of the central nervous system are very similar, if not identical, to those of Tay-Sachs disease. Cerebral cortical neurons are swollen with storage material. Macrophages containing PAS-positive and/or sudanophilic material are numerous, and various degrees of neuronal loss and gliosis are noted. White matter degeneration appears to be more pronounced in Sandhoff disease than in Tay-Sachs disease.[207,208] In the former, lipid inclusions are frequently noted in the vascular endothelial cells in the cerebral cortex. PAS-positive granules are noted in many cells in the visceral organs

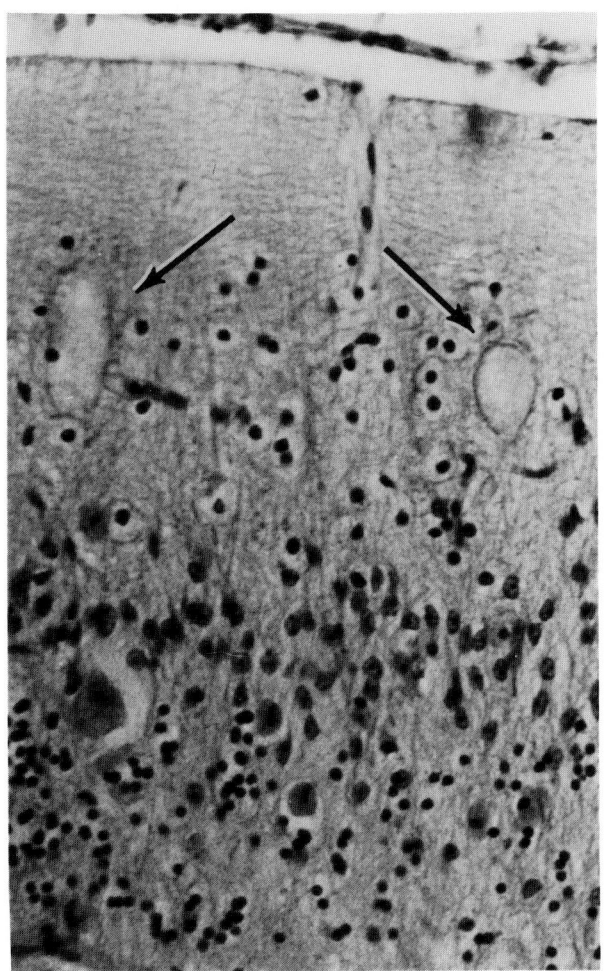

Fig. 72-9 Loss of Purkinje and granular cells is striking in the cerebellum. Arrows indicate focal swelling of Purkinje cell dendrites. Magnification × 380.

such as the hepatocytes, Kupffer cells, histiocytes in the spleen, the renal tubular epithelium, pancreatic acinar cells, and vascular endothelial cells. The neurons in the myenteric plexuses are swollen as well. Electron-microscopic examination reveals MCBs in the cortical neurons as well as similar but more pleomorphic membranous inclusions in many of the cells in the visceral organs (Fig. 72-10).[204–211]

In recent years clinical and biochemical findings in several late onset cases of Sandhoff disease have been reported,[187,212–215] but there has been no postmortem pathologic report on these cases to date.

G_{M2} Activator Deficiency (Variant AB)

This variant is very rare, and pathologic description is limited to two autopsy cases.[201,216,217] The brain weight was close to normal, and no significant abnormalities were described on gross examination of the brain. Microscopically, widespread neuronal storage was noted in the cerebral cortex, deep cerebral nuclei, brainstem, and spinal cord. Subcortical white matter reveals severe demyelination. Purkinje cells and granular cells were markedly depleted.[201] Comparison of Golgi preparations at 28 months ante mortem and at postmortem examination shows significant increase of volume and numbers of "meganeurites" and atrophy of the perisomatic dendritic system.[218]

Electron-microscopic study reveals MCBs in the neuronal soma (Fig. 72-8). In addition, some neurons contain Zebra body inclusions and other types of more pleomorphic inclusions. There are prominent inclusions in glial cells, including large conglomerates of lipid inclusions, which differ significantly from those of Tay-Sachs disease.[217]

STORAGE COMPOUNDS

Almost all storage compounds are either substrates of hexosaminidase A or of both A and B isoenzymes. They contain as the terminal nonreducing sugar moiety either β-*N*-acetylgalac-

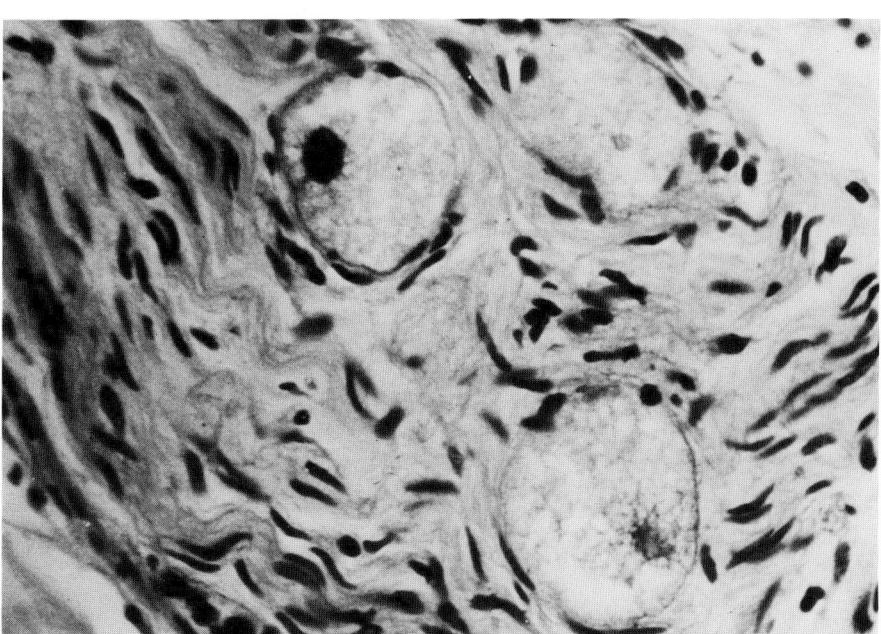

Fig. 72-10 Swollen ganglion cells in myenteric plexus in a late onset case. Hematoxylin-eosin stain. Magnification × 570.

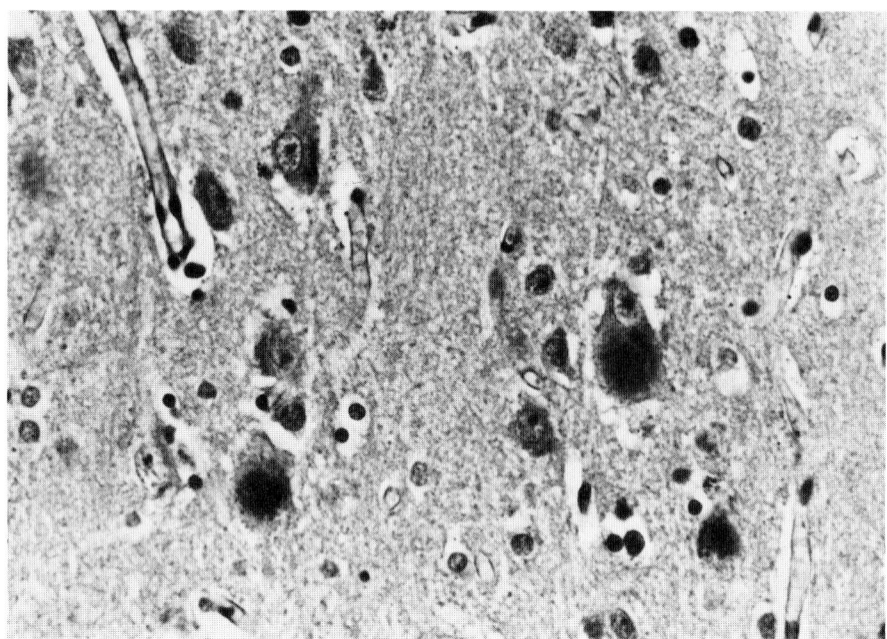

Fig. 72-11 Cerebral cortex of late onset case, showing moderate degree of storage in a few neurons. Periodic acid–Schiff (PAS) stain. Magnification ×468.

tosamine (on most of the accumulating glycolipids) or β-*N*-acetylglucosamine (on most of the accumulating oligosaccharides).

Glycolipids

The major neuronal storage compound of all variants of G_{M2} gangliosidosis is ganglioside G_{M2} (Fig. 72-1). Its accumulation starts at an early embryonic age and has been observed in the brain of 18- to 20-week-old Tay-Sachs fetuses (100 to 150 nmol G_{M2} per gram wet weight).[219,220] Other accumulating lipids are listed in Table 72-3.

Figures for the extent of lipid accumulation were recalculated from the literature and are given in Tables 72-4 and 72-5. The great variability for the content of individual compounds is probably due to the application of very different analytical procedures and variation in the preservation of the pathological samples analyzed. All accumulating lipids are amphiphilic membrane components which precipitate together with other membrane components, such as phospholipids, cholesterol, and proteins, mostly in multilamellar cytoplasmic bodies in the cells in which they have been synthesized.

At the storage level, infantile Sandhoff disease is distinguished from both Tay-Sachs disease and G_{M2} activator deficiency by a pronounced accumulation of globoside in visceral organs, and from Tay-Sachs disease by an increased storage of G_{A2} in the brain. The process of lipid accumulation affects primarily the gray matter (Table 72-4) and is accompanied by a decrease of major gangliosides (G_{M1}, G_{D1a}, G_{D1b}, G_{T1b}). In infantile Tay-Sachs disease these gangliosides are decreased to 20 to 50 percent of control levels.[77,227] This process is less pronounced in infantile Sandhoff disease and in infantile G_{M2} activator deficiency. A demyelination observed in all infantile variants seems to be secondary to nerve cell degeneration and is reflected at the biochemical level in a sharp decrease in the amount of lipids characteristic of myelin. Cerebrosides and sulfatides are usually decreased in infantile Tay-Sachs disease and Sandhoff disease to levels less than 30 percent of control values; in one case of infantile G_{M2} activator deficiency, the cerebroside level was 10 percent and sulfatide level 40 percent of control.[77]

The extent of lipid accumulation in juvenile and adult forms of G_{M2} gangliosidosis is much less pronounced than in infantile forms (see Table 72-4).[164,229] Lipid accumulation in infantile forms is excessive and ubiquitous throughout the nervous

Table 72-3 Lipids Accumulating in the G_{M2} Gangliosidoses

Substance	Structure	References
G_{A2}	GalNAc(β1→4)Gal(β1→4)Glc(β1→1')Cer	77,221
G_{D2}	GalNAc(β1→4)[NeuAc(α2→8)NeuAc(α2→3)]Gal(β1→4)Glc(β1→1')Cer	222
Globoside	GalNAc(β1→3)Gal(α1→4)Gal(β1→4)Glc(β1→1')Cer	13,77,221
Lyso-G_{M2}	GalNAc(β1→4)[NeuAc(α2→3)]Gal(β1→4)Glc(β1→1')sphingosine	223,224
G_{D1a}-GalNAc	GalNAc(β1→4)[NeuAc(α2→3)]Gal(β1→3)GalNAc(β1→4)[NeuAc(α2→3)]Gal(β1→4)Glc(β1→1')Cer	222
G_{M1b}-GalNAc	GalNAc(β1→4)[NeuAc(α2→3)]Gal(β1→3)GalNAc(β1→4)Gal(β1→4)Glc(β1→1')Cer	225
G_{M1a}-GalNAc	GalNAc(β1→4)Gal(β1→3)GalNAc(β1→4)[NeuAc(α2→3)]Gal(β1→4)Glc(β1→1')Cer	226
G_{M3}*	NeuAc(α2→3)Gal(β1→4)Glc(β1→1')Cer	227
G_{D3}*	NeuAc(α2→8)NeuAc(α2→3)Gal(β1→4)Glc(β1→1')Cer	227

*Gangliosides G_{M3} and G_{D3} are not substrates for hexosaminidases. Their storage is therefore probably secondary.

Table 72-4 Glycosphingolipids in Normal and G$_{M2}$ Gangliosidosis Brain*

Storage compounds (hexosaminidase substrates)

	Age, years	Ganglioside, nmol/g wet weight				Glycolipid G$_{A2}$, nmol/g wet weight
		G$_{M2}$	G$_{D2}$	G$_{D1a}$-GalNAc	Lyso-G$_{M2}$	
Controls						
Total brain	1–3[c]	19[c]	—	—	n.d.[d,h]	n.d.[c]
Gray matter	0.2–2[a]	84[a]	22[a]	6[m]	—	n.d.[h]
	5[h]	78[h]	67[h]	67[h]		
	5[m]		89[m]			
White matter	0.2–2[a]	60[a]	19[a]	5[m]	—	n.d.[h]
	5[m]	35[m]	15[m]			
Infantile Tay-Sachs disease:						
Total brain	1.3–2.3[c]	10,840[c]			15[d] 12–16[h]	1,042[c]
Gray matter	3[h]	7,868[e]	98[m]	106[m]	—	1,045[e]
		8,326[f]	102[h]	160[h]		1,381[h]
		12,200[h]				
		14,344[m]				
White matter	3[h]	4,192[e]	53[m]	53[m]	—	406[e]
		8,810[h]	64[h]	126[h]		811[h]
		7,726[m]				
Infantile variant B$_1$:						
Gray matter	4.7[k]	4,691[k]	178[k]	—	—	—
Infantile Sandhoff disease:						
Total brain	1.3–2.5[c]	9,285[c]	110[h]	73[h]	45[h]	5,126[c]
	5.5[h]	12,950[h]				6,410[h]
Gray matter	1.5[i]	6,913[n]	—	—	—	4,383[e]
	2.8[e]	8,295[e]				4,610[i]
		5,430[i]				6,694[n]
White matter	1.5[i]	2,213[n]	—	—	—	6,220[e]
	2.8[e]	6,595[e]				3,200[i]
		920[i]				2,491[n]
Infantile G$_{M2}$ activator deficiency:						
Total brain[c]	2.5[c]	18,390	—	—	—	4,436
Gray matter	3.5 (case 2)[k]	8,209	94	—	—	—
Juvenile Tay-Sachs disease:[f]						
Gray matter	14.5	1,880	167	—	—	—
White matter		151	34	—	—	—

Other gangliosides, nmol/g wet weight

	G$_{M3}$	G$_{D3}$	G$_{M1}$	G$_{D1a}$	G$_{D1b}$	G$_{T1b}$
Controls:						
Total brain				912[c]	156[c]	115[c]
Gray matter	30[a]	41[a]	438[a]	502[a]	106[a]	103[a]
	32[h]	101[h]	474[h]	1,010[h]	463[h]	563[h]
	84[m]	94[m]	497[m]	489[m]	245[m]	218[m]
White matter	22[a]	20[a]	373[a]	172[a]	35[a]	32[a]
	35[m]	38[m]	285[m]	154[m]	90[m]	54[m]
Infantile Tay-Sachs disease:						
Total brain			298[c]	385[c]	79[c]	41[c]
Gray matter	228[m]	188[m]	123[f]	212[f]	49[m]	41[f]
	211[h]	106[h]	750[h]	428[h]	169[h]	109[h]
			179[m]	196[m]		98[m]
White matter	123[m]	92[m]	144[m]	123[m]	27[m]	38[m]
	121[h]	100[h]	401[h]	345[h]	143[h]	171[h]
Infantile variant B$_1$:						
Gray matter[k]	—	184	564	423	44	52
Infantile Sandhoff disease:						
Total brain	241[h]	90[h]	920[h]	276[h]	138[h]	89[h]
	—	—	398[c]	525[c]	118[c]	47[c]
Gray matter[i]	70	—	300	330	140	110
White matter[i]	20	—	90	90	40	20

Continued.

Table 72-4 Glycosphingolipids in Normal and G_{M2} Gangliosidosis Brain* (continued)

Other gangliosides, nmol/g wet weight

	G_{M3}	G_{D3}	G_{M1}	G_{D1a}	G_{D1b}	G_{T1b}
Infantile G_{M2} activator deficiency:						
Total brain[c]	—	—	605	622	113	73
Gray Matter[k]	—	197	85	213	53	78
Juvenile Tay-Sachs disease[f]						
Gray matter	143	—	585	545	140	139
White matter	23	—	233	118	56	26

*Data were taken from the indicated references and recalculated if necessary. — = not determined; n.d. = not detected.
SOURCES: a, Ref. 228, b, Ref. 222, c, Ref. 77, d, Ref. 223, e, Ref. 208, f, Ref. 164, g, Ref. 225, h, Ref. 224, i, Ref. 221, k, Ref. 201, m, Ref. 227, n, Ref. 207.

system. In juvenile and adult forms the cortex is almost uninvolved. The hippocampus and the nuclei of the brainstem, the spinal cord, as well as the granular cells in the cerebellum and the retina are mostly affected.[194,229,230]

Glycoproteins, Glycopeptides, and Oligosaccharides

The crude glycoprotein preparation from gray matter of Tay-Sachs disease and Sandhoff disease contained three- to fourfold more N-acetylglucosamine and mannose than that of normal controls.[231] However, oligosaccharides which are derived from glycoproteins and contain terminal β-glycosidically linked N-acetylglucosaminyl residues are ubiquitous storage compounds in Sandhoff disease only.

In contrast to glycolipids, accumulating oligosaccharides are water-soluble and can be excreted in the urine. Oligosaccharides identified so far are degradation products of asparagine-linked glycoproteins. They originate by the combined action of proteases, β-endo-N-acetylglucosaminidase, sialidase, and β-galactosidase. The accumulation and excretion of N-acetylglucosaminyl oligosaccharides which are normally degraded by hexosaminidases A and B has been observed predominantly in Sandhoff disease. The structures of the compounds identified so far are listed in Table 72-6.

The amount of stored and excreted oligosaccharides is given in Table 72-7. According to Warner et al.,[232,236] the biantennary bisected oligosaccharide 6 (Table 72-6) is a predominant, water-soluble storage product in all tissues analyzed, including liver, spleen, kidney, lung, pancreas, and brain. In brain tissue it comprised 70 percent of the total water-soluble glycoconjugates. Oligosaccharide 5, a triantennary heptasaccharide, occurred in all visceral organs and was the major storage prod-

Table 72-5 Globoside in Visceral Organs

	Globoside, nmol/g wet weight		
	Liver	Kidney	Spleen
Control, 2.5–3 yr	—	156[c] 190[c]	—
Sandhoff disease, 1–2.5 yr	1656[c] 300[i]	1895[c] 2305[n] 670[i]	1781[c] 2040[i]
Tay-Sachs disease, 2–4.8 yr	—	365[c]	248[c]
G_{M2} activator deficiency, 2.5 yr	—	234[c]	—

NOTE: For lettered references, see legend to Table 72-4.

uct in pancreas but was at very low levels in the brain. The biantennary oligosaccharide 4 is the major storage product in liver tissue and together with oligosaccharide 6 is the most abundant oligosaccharide excreted into the urine (Table 72-7). Oligosaccharide excretion in urine was much more pronounced in infantile than in juvenile patients with Sandhoff disease. Analysis of N-acetylglucosaminyl oligosaccharides in the urine of patients and in amniotic fluid has been used by Warner et al. for postnatal and prenatal diagnosis of Sandhoff disease.[232,237]

Glycosaminoglycans

Little is known about the extent of glycosaminoglycan accumulation in tissues of G_{M2} gangliosidosis patients. Studies conducted in vitro with purified enzymes and substrates strongly suggest the participation of hexosaminidases in the degradation of these compounds,[118,128,129,132–134] but even in patients with both hexosaminidase A and B deficiency, glycosaminoglycans were neither found to be stored in tissues[208,238] nor to be excreted in urine.[239] On the other hand, Cantz and Kresse[240] demonstrated moderate accumulation of dermatan sulfate and chondroitin sulfates in cultured skin fibroblasts of Sandhoff disease patients. The turnover of these compounds in Tay-Sachs fibroblasts was only slightly retarded.

In some cases, e.g., with hyaluronic acid and chondroitin-4-sulfate, it is likely that endoglycosidases degrade the polymers to smaller oligosaccharides that escape detection by the methods used to measure glycosaminoglycans. Also, the small residual activity of hexosaminidase S may be sufficient to degrade some of these substrates in the absence of the other two isoenzymes. The role of hexosaminidase in glycosaminoglycan degradation is discussed in Chap. 61.

Physiological Significance of the Enzymatic Components Deduced from Storage Products

The roles played by the various hexosaminidase isoenzymes and by the G_{M2} activator in the catabolism of various classes of glycoconjugates can be deduced from the substances that accumulate in the different enzymatic variants of infantile G_{M2} gangliosidosis (see Tables 72-3 to 72-7).

Glycolipids. Patients who lack hexosaminidase A and the minor S isoenzyme but have the B isoenzyme in normal or even elevated amounts, accumulate glycolipids G_{M2} and G_{A2} (and a

Table 72-6 Structure of Oligosaccharides that Accumulate in Hexosaminidase β-Subunit Deficiency (Variant 0, Sandhoff Disease)

No.	Structure	References
1	GlcNAc(β1→2) Man(α1→3) Man(β1→4) GlcNAc	232–234
2	GlcNAc(β1→4) Man(α1→3) Man(β1→4) GlcNAc	232–234
3a	GlcNAc(β1→4) Man(α1→6) Man(β1→4) GlcNAc	232, 233
3b	GlcNAc(β1→2) Man(α1→3) Man(β1→4) GlcNAc GlcNAc(β1→4) ⎯↑	232
3c	GlcNAc(β1→2) Man(α1→6) Man(β1→4) GlcNAc	233
4	GlcNAc(β1→2) Man(α1→6) Man(β1→4) GlcNAc GlcNAc(β1→2) Man(α1→3) ⎯↑	233, 235, 236
5	GlcNAc(β1→2) Man(α1→6) Man(β1→4) GlcNAc GlcNAc(β1→2) Man(α1→3) ⎯↑ GlcNAc(β1→4) ⎯↑	233, 235, 236
6	GlcNAc(β1→2) Man(α1→6) ⎤ GlcNAc(β1→4) Man(β1→4)GlcNAc GlcNAc(β1→2) Man(α1→3) ⎯↑	233, 235, 236

few minor gangliosides, see Table 72-4) in neurons. This indicates that the two lipids cannot be degraded by hexosaminidase B. As outlined above, the glycolipids are not attacked directly by hexosaminidase but are first solubilized by the G_{M2} activator protein, and the resulting glycolipid-activator complex is the substrate of the enzymatic reaction. Studies in vitro showed that human hexosaminidase B does not interact with this complex.[14,145] In accordance with these results, patients with the rare deficiency of the G_{M2} activator protein also accumulate ganglioside G_{M2} and glycolipid G_{A2}.[14,77] The structural basis of this substrate specificity is discussed in the section on the G_{M2} activator protein. The lower accumulation of glycolipid G_{A2} in α-subunit deficiency as compared to β-subunit deficiency may be explained by a small but significant activity of hexosaminidase B (approximately 3 percent that of hexosaminidase A, measured in vitro) with this substrate in the presence of the G_{M2} activator.[145] The degradation of kidney globoside is still an open question. This glycolipid accumulates in Sandhoff disease but not in the other variants,[77] indicating that it also can be degraded by hexosaminidase B.

Glycoproteins and Oligosaccharides. Significant tissue accumulation and urinary excretion of glycoprotein-derived oligosaccharides have so far been found only when both hexosaminidases are deficient (Table 72-7).[237] It is therefore evident

that these water-soluble substrates can also be hydrolyzed by hexosaminidase B. The elevated level of glycoprotein-bound carbohydrate in the brains of patients with Tay-Sachs disease described by Brunngraber et al.[231] may therefore reflect a secondary disturbance of lysosomal function.

THE MOLECULAR DEFECTS

The three-loci, three-polypeptide system required for ganglioside G_{M2} degradation gives rise to three major classes of deficiency diseases (Fig. 72-12). Mutation may occur at the α-chain locus, giving rise to deficiency of hexosaminidase A, at the β-chain locus, giving rise to deficiency of both hexosaminidases A and B, and at the G_{M2} activator locus, resulting in a deficiency of the activator. Within each of these major groups, there exist a number of mutations that can either totally abolish ganglioside G_{M2} hydrolysis, resulting in an infantile G_{M2} gangliosidosis of utmost severity, or allow some residual activity, which results in a disease of later onset and milder course. The mutations can be further subdivided into those that do not permit the synthesis of an immunologically recognizable protein (cross-reactive-material-negative, or CRM-negative) and those in which immunologically recognizable protein is

Table 72-7 Oligosaccharide (OS) Accumulation in Sandhoff Disease

Source	N-Acetylglucosaminyl oligosaccharides					
	nmol/mg protein					
	OS 1	OS 2	OS 3	OS 4	OS 5	OS 6
Brain, infantile	0.8–0.9	1.2–2.1	1.4–1.6	1– 5.4	0 – 2.1	8–19.1
Liver, infantile	2.9–4.0	4.7–5.1	2.1–3.1	9–12	3 – 5	2– 7
Pancreas, infantile	—	—	—	10–19	17 –46	10–20
Kidney, infantile	—	—	—	1– 5	0.5– 2	3– 4
Spleen, infantile	—	—	—	1– 4	0.3– 0.5	2– 3
Lung, infantile	—	—	—	1– 3	0.4– 1	2
	nmol/mg creatinine					
Urine, infantile	69–265	62–205	46–226	122–507	31–109	152–829
Urine, juvenile	7–11	6	18–30	15– 17	5	12
Amniotic fluid, 16-wk gestation	—	—	—	282 ± 50	62 ± 2	395 ± 25
Amniotic fluid control	—	—	—	n.d.	n.d.	n.d.

NOTE: — = not determined; n.d. = not detectable. The structures of the oligosaccharides are listed in Table 72-6.
SOURCE: Warner et al.[232,236,237] Used by permission.

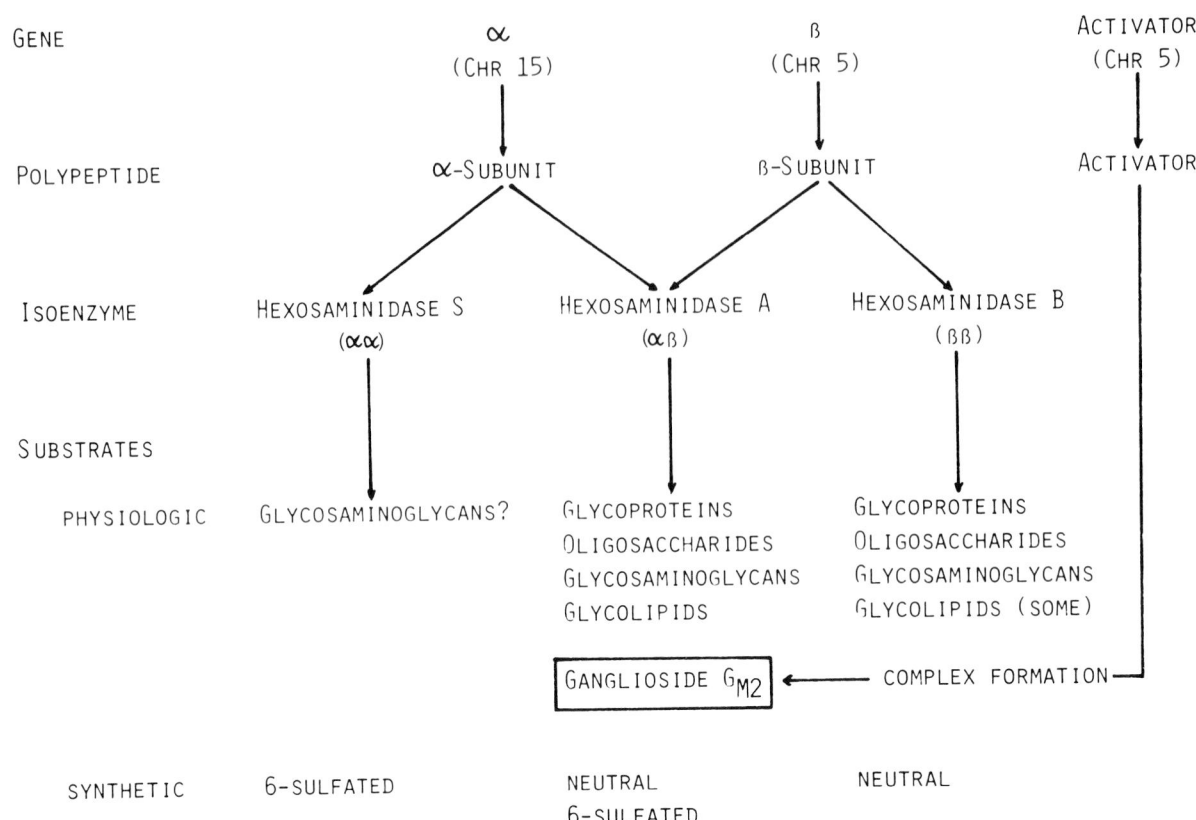

Fig. 72-12 The β-hexosaminidase system. Three polypeptides, each encoded in a different gene, are needed for the degradation of ganglioside G_{M2}: the α and β subunit of the A isozyme and the activator protein which binds the ganglioside and presents it to the enzyme. (For explanation of the various substrates, see text.)

synthesized (CRM-positive) but is defective in its posttranslational processing, transport, stability, or catalytic activity.

Mutations at the Hexosaminidase α-Subunit Locus (Variant B, Tay-Sachs Disease)

The most frequent, best known, and most studied of the G_{M2} gangliosidoses is the infantile Tay-Sachs disease, which prior to heterozygote screening programs occurred with high frequency in the Ashkenazi Jewish population (see "Clinical Phenotypes," "Incidence and Heredity," and "Diagnosis and Carrier Detection"). The primary defect is mutation in the α-chain gene that results in a CRM-negative phenotype. No α-polypeptide is observed in biosynthetic labeling of cells cultured from the patients' mRNA.[241] The gene itself appears grossly intact, as seen by Southern hybridization analysis after treatment with restriction enzymes.[86,242] Northern hybridization analysis shows a profound deficiency of mRNA encoding the α subunit,[85,86,243] but there is normal nuclear transcription of the α-chain gene.[244] The mutation is presumed to affect RNA nuclear-cytoplasmic transport, processing, or stability. Its precise location in the large and complex α-subunit gene, which is over 40 kb in length and is divided into 14 exons,[87] is under intensive scrutiny. A splice site mutation (G→C transversion at the 5′ end of intron 12) has been identified in several Ashkenazi Tay-Sachs patients.[244a,244b,244c] A surprising finding is that this mutation occurs in a minority of patients and carriers of Ashkenazi Jewish origin, indicating molecular heterogeneity within this population.

Infantile Tay-Sachs disease also occurs in a subgroup of the non-Jewish French-Canadian population at a frequency comparable to that among the Ashkenazi.[245] Recent findings[242,246] have identified a 7.6-kb deletion at the 5′ end of the α-subunit gene in this population. Therefore, the French-Canadian and the Ashkenazi mutations are different, but the resulting biochemical phenotype (absence of mRNA, of immunoprecipitable α chain, and of hexosaminidase A) and the clinical phenotype are identical.

A number of CRM-positive defects have been reported among infantile Tay-Sachs patients who are neither of Ashkenazi nor of French-Canadian origin. Two instances have been reported of an altered α-polypeptide that apparently failed to be transported from the endoplasmic reticulum to the Golgi, as judged by the pattern of posttranslational modifications.[241,247] The α-polypeptide was not phosphorylated, did not associate with β subunits, was not secreted, and did not convert to the mature form. Though both cases occurred in families of Italian origin, the different properties of the altered α subunits indicate two different mutations affecting intracellular transport.

A mutation that appears to affect the catalytic site of hexosaminidase A in some clinically classic (infantile) cases of Tay-Sachs disease has been designated variant B1 (discussed above). Because of the absence of ganglioside G_{M2} degradation in spite of substantial hexosaminidase A activity toward 4-methylumbelliferyl-N-acetylglucosaminide and a normal level of G_{M2} activator, the defect was at first ascribed to faulty binding of activator to the α chain.[157] Subsequently, the finding of defective hydrolysis of the sulfated N-acetylglucosaminide derivative of 4-methylumbelliferone in two further cases indicated defective catalytic activity.[119] Hybridization experiments with cultured fibroblasts also proved clearly that this variant was allelic with classic Tay-Sachs disease.[159] The mutation has been identified as a single base change, such that arginine 178 is changed to histidine; this results in substantial change in the secondary structure of the protein.[248] Some other reports have described instances in which a low level of hexosaminidase A activity (attributable to reduced synthesis, transport, and/or stability) was associated with altered catalytic properties.[249,250] Mutations that affect the catalytic site only are likely to be rare, perhaps because the site represents only a small part of the gene and therefore presents a small target for mutation.

Clinically nonclassic G$_{M2}$ gangliosidoses (juvenile, chronic, or adult forms) differ biochemically from infantile Tay-Sachs disease in retention of some residual hexosaminidase A activity toward the physiologically relevant substrate, ganglioside G$_{M2}$.[177] The higher the residual activity, the milder the disorder—the highest levels being found in asymptomatic (or presymptomatic) individuals who were identified as hexosaminidase A–deficient in screening programs or family studies.

In all of the clinically milder cases of hexosaminidase A deficiency examined, the defect has been found to be CRM-positive. In several patients with juvenile, chronic, and adult G$_{M2}$ gangliosidosis phenotypes, the defect was attributed to an altered α subunit that failed to associate with the β subunit.[251] A caveat is in order here: an altered β subunit that failed to associate with the α subunit though it associated with itself would produce a similar phenotype. Assignment of the defect to the α subunit must be rigorously demonstrated by complementation analysis; this has been done for one case of "chronic" G$_{M2}$ gangliosidosis and one case of the adult form.[251]

The absence of α-β association is not absolute; sensitive methods allow the detection of some α-β complexes that account for the residual hexosaminidase A and the attenuated clinical phenotype. It is likely, though not confirmed by use of the appropriate antibodies, that the "adult Tay-Sachs disease" patients extensively described by Navon et al.[171] belong to the association-defective group. Their fibroblasts produce precursor but not mature α-polypeptides, one of the signs of defective α-β association. The patients described by Navon et al.[171] and several of the demonstrated association-defective individuals[251] have been of Ashkenazi Jewish origin; it is likely that they have one allele for a CRM-negative Ashkenazi mutation and another for an altered, nonassociating α-polypeptide.

It is interesting to note that in this group of patients, there is considerable clinical variability not only between but within families.[171,251] Since sibs presumably carry the same α-subunit mutation, such variability implies that products of other genes or even environmental factors impinge on the effectiveness of the residual hexosaminidase A activity. To mention but a few possibilities, polymorphism at the β-subunit locus, or variations in the amount of G$_{M2}$ activator, the rate of synthesis of the mannose-6-phosphate recognition marker, the regulation of lysosomal pH, or the turnover of plasma membrane gangliosides may influence the levels or the consequences of a marginal level of hexosaminidase A activity.

Yet another defect of the α subunit that appears to have no untoward clinical consequences results in the specific absence of hexosaminidase A from serum.[183,252] The isoenzyme is found in leukocytes, fibroblasts, and presumably in tissues. Processing of the α subunit in fibroblasts was found to be normal. Whether the problem lies in the release of hexosaminidase A into serum or in subsequent clearance is not known.

O'Brien[166] has proposed a numerical classification for α-subunit alleles that includes a normal allele, a mutant allele for classic Tay-Sachs disease with hexosaminidase A deficiency, another mutant allele for classic Tay-Sachs disease with altered substrate specificity, and several additional alleles that would have clinically milder or asymptomatic consequences. The existence of genetic compounds with two different mutant alleles was correctly predicted. However, this classification underestimated the complexity of the system. We already know of several different mutations that can give rise to clinically classic Tay-Sachs disease, and the total number of mutant alleles that may result in hexosaminidase A deficiency or malfunction cannot be predicted at this time. But the information will surely come quickly, since all the tools and techniques are available to characterize the mutations at the level of DNA or protein sequences.

Mutations at the Hexosaminidase β-Subunit Locus (Variant 0, Sandhoff Disease)

Like the mutations of the α-polypeptide, those of the β-polypeptide are a heterogeneous group. Both CRM-positive and CRM-negative mutations are encountered, as is clinical variability that is correlated with residual activity of the A isoenzyme. O'Dowd et al.[168] have shown that mutations in patients with infantile Sandhoff disease may involve partial deletion of the gene and a normal or reduced level of mRNA, but always result in essentially undetectable hexosaminidase A activity; on the other hand, mutations in patients with juvenile Sandhoff disease allow hexosaminidase A activity to be expressed at a level of 1 to 3 percent of normal.[177]

A normal adult and his daughter, both with nearly complete deficiency of hexosaminidase B yet significant residual activity of hexosaminidase A were described by Dreyfus et al.[188,189] They named the mutation *hexosaminidase Paris*, after the city in which it was discovered. The biochemical phenotype of hexosaminidase Paris has since been encountered in another asymptomatic adult and in two patients, one previously described,[186] with juvenile Sandhoff disease.[252a] The altered β-polypeptide synthesized in each case was larger than normal and did not undergo many of the usual posttranslational processing reactions. A small fraction that was handled normally was incorporated into hexosaminidase A. It is possible that the β-subunit mutation described in an adult with progressive motor neuron disease is related to hexosaminidase Paris, since it gave rise to hexosaminidase A but not B; however, the β-polypeptide precursor in this instance was reported to be of normal size.[253] The hexosaminidase Paris mutation sheds some light on the role of hexosaminidase B. That isoenzyme may have no unique catalytic functions, since its absence has no adverse consequences provided sufficient hexosaminidase A activity remains. We suggest that the normal role of hexosaminidase B is to hydrolyze some portion of water-soluble substrates. Hexosaminidase A has the unique task of degrading ganglioside G$_{M2}$ and other glycolipids.

Mutations at the G$_{M2}$ Activator Locus (Variant AB)

Deficiency of the activator is rare; in one of the authors' laboratories (K.S., E.C.), five cases were identified by 1986. The usual phenotype is that of clinically classic infantile Tay-Sachs disease with normal activity of hexosaminidases A and B.

In the two cases examined, material cross-reactive with the G$_{M2}$ activator was depressed to approximately 3 percent of control values in cultured skin fibroblasts and to 2 to 5 percent in other tissues.[149] The little cross-reactive material detected in the fibroblasts had a significantly higher molecular weight

(24 to 26 kDa) than the normal G_{M2} activator (22 kDa) and resembled the precursor form rather than the mature activator protein.[148]

DIAGNOSIS AND CARRIER DETECTION

Biochemical Methods

Metabolite Assays. Since extraneural tissues possess only very low levels of gangliosides, lipid analyses for diagnostic purposes are usually limited to nervous tissue, and their applicability is restricted to postmortem examinations and, occasionally, to verification of a prenatal diagnosis after abortion. A four- to fivefold ganglioside G_{M2} accumulation was observed in G_{M2} gangliosidosis fetuses at as early as 18 to 20 weeks' gestation.[219,220]

In contrast, the N-acetylglucosaminyl oligosaccharides that accumulate in almost all tissues of patients with Sandhoff disease are also excreted in the urine in considerable amounts (see Table 72-7). Analysis of urinary oligosaccharides may therefore be used for the diagnosis of this G_{M2} gangliosidosis variant.[232] A much lower but still significant level of such oligosaccharides was also found in the amniotic fluid of fetuses affected with the disease, providing a basis for prenatal diagnosis.[237]

Enzyme Assays. The nature of the aglycone is usually of little importance for the action of hexosaminidase. Therefore these enzymes can be conveniently assayed with artificial chromogenic or fluorogenic substrates. Although, as the name hexosaminidase implies, the enzymes accept both N-acetylglucosaminides and N-acetylgalactosaminides, the glucosaminides are usually preferred because they are more sensitive (hydrolyzed faster) and less expensive.

With the few exceptions stated below, the enzymes can be assayed in any tissue sample or body fluid that can be obtained from the patient. Most convenient specimens are serum and leukocytes. Skin fibroblast cultures or organ biopsies are necessary only in some unclear cases.

HEXOSAMINIDASE α-SUBUNIT DEFECT OR DEFICIENCY (VARIANT B, TAY-SACHS DISEASE). Diagnosis of α-subunit deficiency requires the demonstration of the isolated deficiency of hexosaminidase A, in the presence of a normal or even elevated activity of the B isoenzyme. This can be done after separation of hexosaminidase A and B using artificial chromogenic or fluorogenic substrates which are hydrolyzed by both isoenzymes. Alternatively, substrates that are specifically hydrolyzed by hexosaminidase A can be used. Separation of the isoenzymes is usually achieved with ion-exchange chromatography,[108,254-257] isoelectric focusing,[70,258-260] or electrophoresis in starch gels[10,65,261] or on cellulose acetate.[262-264] While electrophoretic separation allows only for a qualitative assay, the other techniques permit the quantitative determination of each of the two isoenzymes.

Less accurate but more rapid methods frequently used for large-scale screening purposes are based on the lower thermal[254,265,266] or pH stability[267] of hexosaminidase A. At pH 4.4, hexosaminidase B is comparatively stable up to 55°C, whereas hexosaminidase A is inactivated with a half-life of some 10 min at 50°C[80,127] and 3 min at 55°C.[127] (At pH 6.0, 50°C, hexosaminidase A, especially in purified form, is largely

converted to hexosaminidase B,[97,268] due to rearrangement of subunits.) Total activity is measured before and after selective denaturation of hexosaminidase A and the activity of this isoenzyme is calculated from the difference. Problems may, however, arise with these methods in some unusual cases, e.g., in families that harbor an allele coding for a heat-labile, but functionally active, β chain of hexosaminidase.[269,270]

The discovery by Kresse and coworkers[117,118] that the hexosaminidase A but not the B isoenzyme releases intact N-acetylglucosamine-6-sulfate from keratan sulfate led to the development of the corresponding artificial substrates p-nitrophenyl- and 4-methylumbelliferyl-6-sulfo-N-acetyl-β-D-glucosaminide,[117,120,271,272] which are hydrolyzed almost exclusively by hexosaminidase A (and probably also by the minor S isoenzyme[131]) but only very poorly by hexosaminidase B. These substrates have already proved to be useful for diagnosis of Tay-Sachs disease.[220,273,274]

The most accurate method for the determination of the residual hexosaminidase A activity employs the natural substrate, ganglioside G_{M2}, in the presence of the activator protein to stimulate the reaction. The use of detergents for this purpose[135,275] should be discouraged since they are likely to change the substrate specificities of the isoenzymes and also to denature them,[276] and may thus lead to wrong results. With an improved assay system,[177] it has been possible to determine the residual ganglioside G_{M2} hydrolase activity in crude extracts of fibroblasts and to discriminate between different clinical variants of G_{M2} gangliosidosis (Table 72-8). This assay is too expensive and too time-consuming for routine applications. It also requires a certain minimal enzyme concentration so that it cannot be applied to serum or urine. Still, it may be very valuable for certain diagnostic applications. For example, it is useful for prenatal diagnosis of the B1 variant, which has high residual hexosaminidase A activity toward the usual synthetic substrates,[220] or for the discrimination between infantile and adult variants, which may occur in the same family.[185] The 6-sulfated N-acetylglucosaminide substrate may prove to be a suitable substitute for ganglioside G_{M2} in this assay.

Prenatal diagnosis may be performed with cultured amniotic fluid cells, which are similar to fibroblasts in their hexosaminidase content and pattern. Caution should be exercised in using amniotic fluid as the sole enzyme source because the

Table 72-8 Degradation of Ganglioside G_{M2} by Extracts of Fibroblasts from Patients with G_{M2} Gangliosidosis

Probands	Ganglioside G_{M2} degradation, pmol/(h·mg·AU)*	
	Mean	Range
Controls, $n = 9$	535	296–762
Heterozygotes, $n = 4$ (different genotypes)	285	121–395
Hexosaminidase α-subunit deficiency (variant B, Tay-Sachs disease):		
Infantile, $n = 5$	2.4	0.8– 3.8
Juvenile, $n = 5$	15.8	13.6–18.0
Adult, $n = 9$	19.1	13.1–32.8
Hexosaminidase β-subunit deficiency (variant 0, Sandhoff disease):		
Infantile, $n = 2$	6.6	3.6– 9.5
Juvenile, $n = 3$	23.3	9.5–39.4
Healthy adult, $n = 2$	105	75–143

*AU = activator unit as defined in Ref. 145.

presence of an acidic heat-stable enzyme, presumably hexos-aminidase B complexed with acidic mucopolysaccharides, may mimic the presence of hexosaminidase A.[277] Other pitfalls in prenatal diagnosis were summarized in the previous edition of this work.[166] Chorionic villus biopsies are beginning to replace amniotic fluid or cells as the material of choice for prenatal diagnosis of the G$_{M2}$ gangliosidoses.

HEXOSAMINIDASE β-SUBUNIT DEFECT OR DEFICIENCY (VARIANT 0, SANDHOFF DISEASE). The absence or near-absence of total β-hexosaminidase activity can in principle be demonstrated with any one of the substrates used for Tay-Sachs diagnosis, provided that the preservation of the specimen to be assayed is checked to rule out artifacts due to deterioration of the sample. In our experience, the ratio of total hexosaminidase to β-galactosidase is a fairly reliable indicator. If diagnostic material is to be stored for any period of time or to be sent to other laboratories, it should be kept frozen.

The simultaneous existence of infantile Sandhoff disease and pseudodeficiency (low total hexosaminidase in an apparently healthy adult proband) within the same family[188,189] may create problems, especially for prenatal diagnosis. Such a case would necessitate the use of specialized methods to determine the residual activity of the enzyme and should be referred to an experienced laboratory.

G$_{M2}$ ACTIVATOR DEFICIENCY (VARIANT AB). G$_{M2}$ activator deficiency gangliosidosis is the most difficult form of G$_{M2}$ gangliosidosis to diagnose. So far, biochemical diagnosis has only been made from cultured skin fibroblasts, and postmortem analyses of autopsy tissues. Three different methods have been used: (1) An assay system was developed to determine the G$_{M2}$ activator activity in fibroblast extracts on the basis of their ability to stimulate hydrolysis of ganglioside G$_{M2}$ by purified β-hexosaminidase A in vitro.[119] Although values are generally low, an accurate distinction can be made between G$_{M2}$ activator–deficient cells and others (Table 72-9). (2) The G$_{M2}$ activator protein was assayed immunochemically in fibroblast extracts with an ELISA.[149] (3) Radiolabeled ganglioside G$_{M2}$ was fed to skin fibroblasts in cell culture (see below). The deficit of variant AB cells in the degradation of this substrate could be corrected by the addition of purified G$_{M2}$ activator to the culture medium (Fig. 72–13).[278]

METABOLIC STUDIES IN CULTURED CELLS. Studies of the metabolism of exogenously added radiolabeled ganglioside G$_{M2}$ in cultured skin fibroblasts may provide a useful alternative for diagnosis of unusual G$_{M2}$ gangliosidosis variants,[279,280] particularly when enzyme assays are inconclusive, as in G$_{M2}$ activator deficiency. Gangliosides dissolved in culture medium (preferably with low content of fetal calf serum[278]) insert into the cell membrane[281] and are internalized and metabolized like endogenous glycolipids. If the radiolabel is in the sphingosine base, almost all labeled products are neutral lipids.[278,280] When, after a few days of feeding, the lipids are extracted from the cells and separated by ion-exchange chromatography, the percentage of radioactivity in the neutral lipids fraction is a reliable measure of the degradative capability of the cells.[278] Alternatively, the less polar products may be separated from unreacted ganglioside substrate by partitioning in a water-chloroform-methanol two-phase system.[280]

It should be pointed out that the catabolic capacity of the cells is not proportional to their residual enzyme activity; even small residual activities (e.g., as in adult G$_{M2}$ gangliosidosis

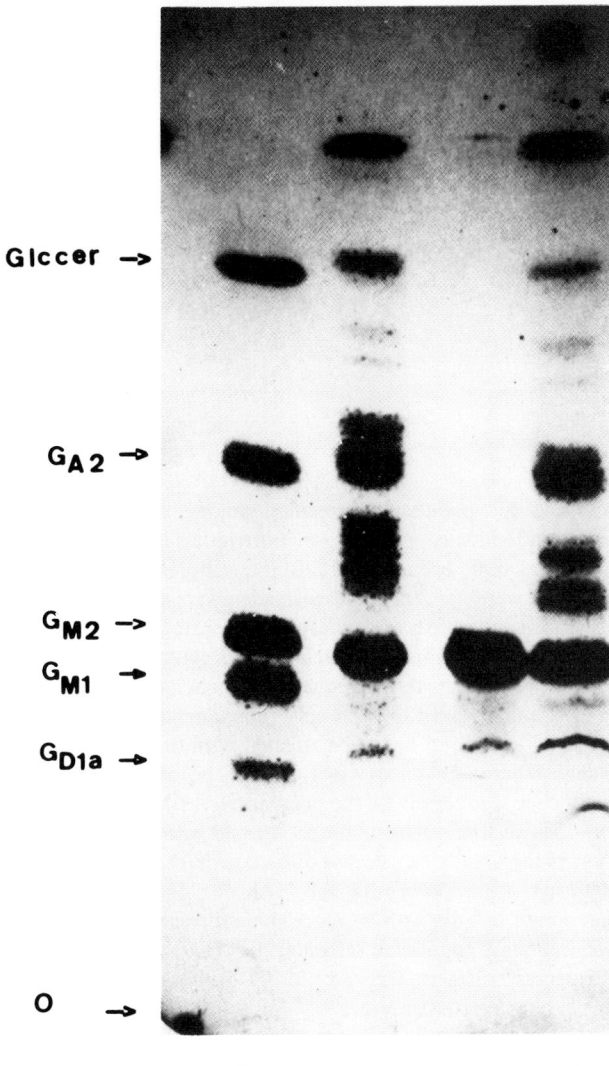

Fig. 72-13 Metabolism of ganglioside G$_{M2}$ in G$_{M2}$ activator deficient fibroblasts. [³H]Ganglioside G$_{M2}$ was added to the culture media of skin fibroblasts. After 70 h, the lipids were extracted, separated on thin-layer chromatography plates and the radioactive spots visualized with fluorography. Lane 1 = standards. Lane 2 = normal control cells. Lane 3 = G$_{M2}$ activator deficient cells. Lane 4 = G$_{M2}$ activator deficient cells, 30 μg of purified G$_{M2}$ activator protein added with the ganglioside substrate.

cases) may suffice to maintain an overall degradation rate close to normal values, depending on the amount of substrate fed to the cells and on its rate of uptake and intracellular transport. (For a theoretical discussion on the correlation between residual activity and overall turnover rate, see the section on pathogenesis.)

Population Screening for G$_{M2}$ Gangliosidosis Heterozygotes

Reduced hexosaminidase A was demonstrated (with synthetic hexosaminide substrates) in serum,[265] leukocytes,[282] fibroblasts,[283] and tears[284] of obligate heterozygotes for the Tay-Sachs disease mutation. These findings led to the development of simple, inexpensive, and sufficiently accurate methods for heterozygote identification.[266] In addition, because of the ethnic predilection for this disorder, and the availability of genetic counseling and of prenatal diagnosis, a rationale was es-

Table 72-9 G_{M2} Activator Activity in
Fibroblast Extracts

Cells	Stimulation of ganglioside G_{M2} degradation, pmol/(h·mg protein·mU hexosaminidase A)
Controls, $n = 3$	22.5 ± 8.3
Hexosaminidase α-subunit deficiency, late infantile	18.0
Variant B1:	
Case 1	26.0
Case 2	23.1
G_{M2} activator deficiency:	
Case 1	1.8
Case 2	1.7

SOURCE: Data from Kytzia et al.[119] Used by permission.

tablished for population screening among reproductive-age Jewish individuals.[285] In this way individuals identified as heterozygotes and, even more critically, couples in which both members were carriers could be made aware of their risk status prior to the birth of any affected offspring. With comprehensive genetic counseling, such families could choose, if they desired, to monitor all subsequent pregnancies by prenatal diagnosis and to carry to term only those pregnancies in which the fetus was found not to be affected with the deficiency disorder. Where the fetus was found to be affected, families could choose to terminate the pregnancies. Albeit an imperfect solution, such an interim approach could provide at-risk families, if they chose, a selective means to have only unaffected offspring, while preventing the birth of children destined to deteriorate and die with an untreatable disease.

Large-scale population screening for Tay-Sachs disease heterozygotes began in the early 1970s in Jewish communities throughout North America.[286,287] Subsequently such programs have been initiated in countries throughout the world.[288] As of mid-1985, more than 535,000 young adults had been screened voluntarily to determine their Tay-Sachs disease carrier status and more than 520 at-risk couples (both partners heterozygotes) identified. None of these couples previously had children afflicted with Tay-Sachs disease. These results are summarized in Table 72-10.

Such screening efforts, usually employing automated thermal or pH fractionation of serum hexosaminidase,[267,268] allow quantification of total hexosaminidase activity as well as the hexosaminidase A fraction (that fraction inactivated either by defined exposure to heat or low pH). Follow-up leukocyte hexosaminidase profiles are then employed for confirmation of carrier status or for clarification of status in individuals with

Table 72-10 Tay-Sachs Disease Heterozygote
Screening, 1969–1985

Country	No. tested	Carriers identified	At-risk couples identified
United States	431,851	16,369	412
Canada	43,448	2,286	36
Israel	49,242	1,629	52
South Africa	5,336	492	8
Europe (excluding UK)	1,933	67	15
United Kingdom	1,822	148	1
Brazil	943	60	3
Mexico	655	26	0
Australia	80	0	0
Total	535,310	21,077	527

inconclusive or "unusual" serum profiles or where confounding factors may be present, e.g., pregnancy, birth control medication, unusual drugs, selected current illnesses, etc. In this way nearly all of the mutations affecting α-subunit function can be identified in the heterozygous state. (A notable exception is variant B1. For this variant, carrier detection, like the homozygote diagnosis, requires the use of specific hexosaminidase A substrates.)

These routine screening methods do not permit a distinction to be made *between* the different α-subunit mutations. This can be achieved only by use of more complex and sophisticated biochemical and molecular methods. Accordingly, by these methods, carriers of the mutations for the variant α-subunit conditions (e.g., juvenile, chronic, adult-onset G_{M2} disorders) are indistinguishable from heterozygotes for classic Tay-Sachs disease. Estimates can be made, however, that such "variant" heterozygotes, in the aggregate, comprise only a small fraction (2 to 3 percent) of the total apparent Tay-Sachs disease carrier population identified through screening programs of Jewish adults.[290] Among non-Jews identified as Tay-Sachs disease carriers through such screening efforts, however, as many as 50 percent may actually be heterozygotes for a mutation leading to a milder disease than clinically classic Tay-Sachs disease.[291] Nevertheless, for population screening, the ability of the test to detect the great majority of mutant phenotypes is a major advantage as compared to DNA diagnosis for a specific allele.

Serum and leukocyte hexosaminidase profiles employed for Tay-Sachs disease carrier identification can also be utilized for the delineation of heterozygotes for β-subunit mutations.[292] Such heterozygotes are characterized by significantly *low total* β-hexosaminidase-specific activities with a relatively *increased* fraction of hexosaminidase A (thermal or acid-labile). In this way heterozygotes for Sandhoff disease and most other variant β-subunit mutations can be distinguished.

To date, heterozygote identification in the G_{M2} activator deficiency disorder has not been reported.

Prenatal Diagnosis

As described above, both hexosaminidases A and B are readily quantified in normal fetal tissues obtained in early to midgestation, including amniotic fluid, uncultured and cultured amniocytes, and direct or cultured material derived from chorionic villus samples. Such normative data provide the basis for the intrauterine detection of Tay-Sachs disease, Sandhoff disease, and most of the other G_{M2} gangliosidoses. For G_{M2} activator deficiency, prenatal diagnosis should be possible through direct assessment of cellular G_{M2} ganglioside degradation or quantitative (functional or immunologic) studies of the G_{M2} activator itself.

The prenatal diagnosis of Tay-Sachs disease was first accomplished in 1970.[261,293,294] This capability, as stated previously, provided a rationale for prospective population heterozygote screening. At first, prenatal testing was employed only in pregnancies in couples in which prior affected offspring had been born. More recently, the majority of pregnancies monitored for fetal Tay-Sachs disease, either by amniocentesis at 16 to 18 weeks of pregnancy or by chorionic villus sampling at 9 to 12 weeks[295,296] has been in couples identified to be at risk through heterozygote testing. Table 72-11 reflects the worldwide experience with prenatal diagnosis through mid-1985.

Table 72-11 Prenatal Diagnosis of Tay-Sachs Disease: Worldwide Experience, 1969–1985

	Fetuses known to be at risk because of		
	Previous child	Carrier screening	Total
No. pregnancies monitored	834	602	1,436
Tay-Sachs-disease fetuses identified	189	104	293
Electively aborted*	179	103	282
Diagnoses confirmed†	158	97	255
Fetal diagnosis missed	2	1	3

*Eleven identified fetuses not electively aborted: all affected as predicted.
†Tissue not obtained or available for confirmatory studies in 27 cases.

It should be noted in Table 72-11 that the frequency of fetuses affected with Tay-Sachs disease is significantly less than the expected 25 percent, both in families with prior affected offspring and in those identified to be at risk through screening. This is because the numbers include a substantial number of monitored pregnancies in which the actual risk was substantially less than 25 percent or even negligible (e.g., remarried parent of a prior child with Tay-Sachs disease requesting the procedure for reassurance, one parent identified as a carrier and the other unavailable or inconclusive through screening, etc.). In the 11 instances in which a prenatal diagnosis of Tay-Sachs disease was made but the pregnancies went to term, the diagnosis was made too late in pregnancy for legal termination to be performed, or there were parental moral or religious proscriptions against abortion. All 11 children manifested classic Tay-Sachs disease in infancy.

INCIDENCE AND HEREDITY

Gene Frequencies and Disease Incidence

Earlier estimates of the gene frequencies for the Tay-Sachs disease allele in Jewish and non-Jewish North American populations were based on disease incidence figures developed from death certificate information.[297,298] By Hardy-Weinberg analysis, a disease incidence of about 1 in 4000 Ashkenazi Jewish births predicted a carrier rate for Tay-Sachs disease of 1 in 30 to 1 in 40 among Jewish Americans of Central-Eastern European extraction. Among non-Jews and Sephardic Jews, the disease incidence was observed to be 100 times less frequent, corresponding to one-tenth the carrier frequency (about 1 in 300). Such figures can only be viewed as estimates because of ascertainment bias and possible misdiagnosis. Clearly, misdiagnosis of Sandhoff disease as Tay-Sachs disease (particularly prior to the introduction of biochemical methods for their differentiation) would result in an inflated Tay-Sachs disease carrier estimate, or conversely, missed diagnoses of Tay-Sachs disease would cause underestimates of the heterozygote frequency in either population.

More recently, carrier frequency estimates for Tay-Sachs disease have been made directly from data obtained in large-scale population screening programs in the United States and Canada.[299] In such programs, serum and leukocyte profiles of hexosaminidase A and B are made in order to identify individuals with the reduced hexosaminidase A phenotypes characteristic of heterozygosity for Tay-Sachs disease. Altered hexosaminidase profiles characteristic of β-subunit mutations, predominantly those of Sandhoff disease heterozygotes, are also identified, thereby allowing estimates to be made of the frequency of mutations at this gene locus as well.[300]

It is important to emphasize, however, that with current screening methods, heterozygotes for other α- and β-subunit mutations are indistinguishable from heterozygotes for Tay-Sachs or Sandhoff disease, respectively. Accordingly, unless appropriate adjustments are made, an inflation will result both in gene frequencies and projected disease incidences. From gene frequency estimates derived with these considerations in mind, a direct prediction of disease incidence can be developed for Tay-Sachs disease and Sandhoff disease in both Jewish and non-Jewish North American populations. These are provided in Table 72-12.

It should be noted from Table 72-12 that the carrier frequency for Tay-Sachs disease among non-Jewish individuals is approximately twice that predicted by death record–derived data. Also, the projected birth incidence for Tay-Sachs disease among non-Jews would indicate nearly 40 new cases each year in the United States in this population, nearly four times that previously estimated. Since recent annual surveillance throughout the United States and Canada identified between 6 and 12 new cases of Tay-Sachs disease among non-Jewish infants, the "apparent" carrier frequency among non-Jews in North America seems to represent an overestimate by a factor of approximately 2. As many as half of the "apparent" Tay-Sachs disease heterozygotes among screened non-Jews may be carriers of other mutant α-subunit alleles which, with current screening techniques, mimic the Tay-Sachs disease carrier state. Such individuals, however, could be at risk (depending on the genotype of their reproductive partners) for other significant neurologic disorders in their offspring. In the Jewish population of North America, such "variant" heterozygotes are estimated to comprise no more than 2 to 3 percent of the total population detected. The development and application of new biochemical and molecular methods should permit more specific elucidation of the nature and frequency of these mutations in the future.

The reported heterozygote frequencies for Sandhoff disease indicate a birth incidence for this disorder of about 1 in 1,000,000 among Jewish newborns in North America and

Table 72-12 Tay-Sachs Disease and Sandhoff Disease: Heterozygote Frequencies and Predicted Birth Incidence in North American Populations Based on Data from Population Screening Programs

	Jewish	Non-Jewish
Tay-Sachs disease:		
Individuals tested*	46,304	34,532
Heterozygote frequency	0.032†	0.006
	(1 in 31)	(1 in 167)
Predicted birth rate	1 in 3,900	1 in 112,000
Sandhoff disease:		
Individuals tested*	22,043	32,342
Heterozygote frequency†	0.0020	0.0036
	(1 in 500)	(1 in 278)
Predicted birth rate	1 in 1,000,000	1 in 309,000

*No known family history of Tay-Sachs disease, Sandhoff disease, or identified carriers for either disorder at the time of testing.
†Adjusted for estimated α-subunit "variant" heterozygote frequency of 0.001.

about 1 in 300,000 among non-Jewish infants. These projections are consistent with our annual worldwide surveillance data for newly diagnosed G_{M2} ganglioside disorders, initiated for Tay-Sachs disease in 1980 and for other G_{M2} storage disorders in 1982.[301] One would expect a Jewish infant to be born with Sandhoff disease in North America about once every 10 to 15 years. None have been reported since we began collecting such data. Similarly, about 15 to 20 births of non-Jewish infants with Sandhoff disease would be expected each year in North America. From 1982 to 1985, the diagnosis of classic Sandhoff disease was made in 41 such infants, consistent with the rate predicted.

Heredity and Population Genetics

All of the known mutations affecting α-subunit, β-subunit, and G_{M2} ganglioside activator synthesis and/or function are expressed, in terms of clinical phenotype, in a recessive fashion. Mapping of the respective gene loci for each of these components necessary for G_{M2} ganglioside degradation has been accomplished; the structural gene for the α-subunit production is on chromosome 15, while separate and independent loci have been identified, both on chromosome 5, for direction of synthesis of the β subunit and the G_{M2} activator protein, respectively.

Recent molecular studies provide evidence that two or more mutant alleles on chromosome 15 underlie Tay-Sachs disease in Ashkenazi Jewish infants (see "Molecular Defects"). Similar studies suggest that Tay-Sachs disease in non-Ashkenazi, as well as the juvenile, chronic, adult-onset, and other variant types of G_{M2} gangliosidosis associated with α-subunit deficiencies, represent either compound heterozygous states, involving an Ashkenazi allele with another allelic mutation, or homozygosity for other rare recessive mutations (particularly in offspring of consanguineous matings or in non-Ashkenazi, highly isolated, inbred populations).

Classic Tay-Sachs disease (clinically) has been observed throughout the world in "non-Jewish" infants of all racial groups.[302] An increased incidence of Tay-Sachs disease has been reported in at least four geographic isolates—in Switzerland,[303] in Japan,[304] in a Pennsylvania Dutch group in Pennsylvania,[305] and in a French-Canadian deme in Eastern Quebec.[245] Only in the latter two instances were hexosaminidase profiles employed to confirm diagnoses. The French-Canadian mutation has been mapped to a deletion at the 5′ end of the α-subunit gene.[242,246]

In a similar fashion, several small isolated populations in different areas of the world have been shown to have an increased incidence of Sandhoff disease. An increased frequency for this β-subunit disorder has been found in an inbred community of Metis Indians in northern Saskatchewan,[306] among Lebanese-Canadians[245] as well as in Lebanon,[307] and in a sizable geographic isolate of the Creole population in the northern part of Argentina.[308,309] Recent population screening data from California suggest a relatively increased Sandhoff disease gene frequency among Hispanics of Mexican or Central American origins as well.[300]

For the Ashkenazi Tay-Sachs disease mutation, population studies suggest that the initial mutation for this disorder occurred sometime after 70 A.D. (the second diaspora of the Jews from Palestine) and before the year 1100 A.D. in areas of Central-Eastern Europe now occupied by Austria, Czechoslovakia, and Hungary.[299] Previously, the mutation was believed

to have originated further north in regions which are now northeastern Poland and northwestern Russia.[310]

The impact of carrier detection programs and the provision of a mechanism for selective reproduction in at-risk couples (through the monitoring of all pregnancies and the termination of those in which the fetus is found to be affected) has raised questions as to the impact such efforts might have on the gene frequency for the Tay-Sachs disease allele in the Jewish and general populations. Since the vast majority of autosomal recessive genes are passed from one generation to the next through heterozygote-nonheterozygote matings, it is clear that the impact on overall gene frequency is minimal.

While the influence of applied technology on gene frequency is trivial, the impact on overall disease incidence can be profound. Unquestionably, the advent of prenatal diagnosis for Tay-Sachs disease and the concomitant development of wide-scale community education, carrier screening, and genetic counseling programs throughout North America have contributed greatly to the reduced incidence of Tay-Sachs disease in Jewish infants in the United States and Canada since 1970. These data are presented in Table 72-13. Note that as such programs have been targeted primarily (but not exclusively) to the higher risk Jewish population, the reduction in disease incidence in that group (approaching 90 percent) is not matched by a comparable reduction in incidence in the non-Jewish population. In fact, in the mid- to late-1980s, more cases of classic Tay-Sachs disease are identified annually in non-Jewish infants than in Jewish ones. This, of course, represents a relative increase only, since the number of new cases annually in non-Jewish children has remained unchanged or only slightly decreased while the number of cases in Jewish infants has dropped precipitously.

PATHOGENESIS

Possible Pathogenic Factors Involved in the Development of Gangliosidoses

The pathogenic mechanisms that lead to the malfunction of neuronal circuitry in ganglioside storage diseases are not yet understood. For some factors their involvement appears quite obvious (although their exact contribution remains unclear) while others are more speculative.

Monosialogangliosides are practically insoluble in water, with the critical micellar concentrations around 10^{-10} M.[312] They precipitate in the cells in which they are synthesized,[194] mainly within the lysosomal compartment,[313] together with phospholipids, cholesterol, and amphiphilic proteins and pep-

Table 72-13 Incidence of Tay-Sachs Disease in the United States and Canada, 1970–1985

	Jewish	Non-Jewish	Total
1970*	30–40*	6–10*	40–50*
1980	13	11	24
1982	9	7	16
1983	2	9	11
1984	3	12	15
1985	6	5	11

*Estimates based on Myrianthopoulos,[297] Aronson,[298] Aronson et al.,[302] and O'Brien.[317]

tides. In the severe infantile cases, the accumulation of ganglioside G$_{M2}$ alone may amount to 12 percent of dry brain weight (see "Storage Compounds"), and the resulting storage granules (MCBs) may fill the entire cytoplasm of a neuronal cell body (see "Pathology"). Although the storage compounds themselves are normal, nontoxic membrane components, this excessive accumulation is likely to interfere with intracellular transport and other activities, particularly since the total brain volume is limited by the skull and the volume occupied by the storage granules is at the expense of normal cellular metabolism.

In late onset forms glycolipid accumulation is much less pronounced than in infantile forms of the disease, suggesting that other mechanisms should also be discussed for the pathogenesis of gangliosidoses. Purpura and Suzuki[192] demonstrated formation of meganeurites and tremendous increase of synaptic spines on neurons in patients with ganglioside storage diseases. Similar findings have been reported for some animal models of mucopolysaccharide storage diseases[314,315] and suggest formation of misconnections in the nervous tissue.

Preliminary evidence suggests the possibility that in G$_{M2}$ gangliosidosis cells, the undegraded storage material is not confined to secondary lysosomes but can to some extent be recycled and reach other compartments such as Golgi and plasma membrane by normal membrane flow.[278] Such an effect might lead to changes in the content and pattern of gangliosides in the plasma membrane. Although convincing proof is still lacking, gangliosides are implicated in cell-cell recognition phenomena including synaptogenesis (see "Gangliosides"). An altered ganglioside pattern on neuronal surfaces might thus interfere with the establishment of proper connections.

Another possible mechanism in pathogenesis might be the formation of toxic compounds in analogy to the occurrence of glycosylsphingosine and galactosylsphingosine in Gaucher and Krabbe disease, respectively.[316–318] Indeed, lysoganglioside G$_{M2}$ (II^3-sialylgangliotriaosylsphingosine) was recently found in the brain of patients with Tay-Sachs disease (about 15 nmol per gram wet weight[223,224]) and in the brain of patients with Sandhoff disease (about 45 nmol per gram wet weight[224]) but not in normal human brain. Like other psychosine derivatives and lysolecithin, lysoganglioside G$_{M2}$ has lytic properties and is toxic in cell culture.[223] However, the concentration of lysoganglioside is some 300 to 600 times lower than that of the main storage compound, ganglioside G$_{M2}$. In view of this ratio and of the different lysoganglioside G$_{M2}$ levels reported so far for brains of patients with Tay-Sachs and Sandhoff disease, it appears unlikely that the toxicity of this compound is the immediate cause of cell death. Hannun and Bell[319] reported that lysosphingolipids are potent inhibitors of protein kinase C and thus may interfere with signal transduction in nerve cells. Other mechanisms that may possibly contribute to the overall clinical picture may relate to secondary effects of the primary storage compounds. In vitro, higher concentrations of gangliosides were shown to inhibit ganglioside sialidase.[54,320] Accumulating glycolipids may also inhibit enzymes of other pathways, causing a disturbance of cellular metabolism.

Finally, the tremendous accumulation observed in the ballooned neurons of patients with infantile gangliosidosis may deplete precursor pools for the biosynthesis of cellular components, e.g., the pools of sphingosine, leading to a severe imbalance of metabolism.

Degree of Enzyme Deficiency and Development of Different Clinical Diseases

Though all clinical forms (infantile, juvenile, and adult) of hexosaminidase α-subunit deficiency are caused by allelic mutations of the α subunit of hexosaminidase A, a tremendous clinical heterogeneity between them is evident. The same applies to the different clinical forms of β-subunit deficiency (Sandhoff disease).

On the biochemical level this heterogeneity is paralleled by a corresponding variation in the extent and pattern of glycolipid accumulation in different regions of the brain. Infantile forms have an excessive and ubiquitous neuronal glycolipid storage (up to 12 percent of the brain dry weight). Late onset forms show much less pronounced accumulation, which is restricted to specific brain regions, the cortex being almost unimpaired whereas the hippocampus, the nuclei of the brainstem, and spinal cord as well as the granular cells in the cerebellum and retina are markedly affected.[194,229,230] Thus, different allelic mutations in one gene locus lead to variable clinical and neuropathologic forms. A crucial difference between the various clinical manifestations (e.g., the infantile and adult forms) is different residual activity against the natural substrate of hexosaminidase A.

Unfortunately, the in vivo activity of mutant enzymes against their natural substrates cannot be determined directly. The experimental approaches that are so far considered to yield the best approximations are (1) feeding of natural substrate to cultivated fibroblasts and (2) in vitro determination of enzyme activity in fibroblast homogenates, using the natural substrate in the presence of the respective activator protein. Data obtained with the latter method indicate that adult and juvenile patients with hexosaminidase α-subunit deficiency have some residual activity, i.e., significantly higher than that of infantile forms of G$_{M2}$ gangliosidosis (Table 72-8).[177] Residual activities in the range of 10 to 20 percent of the mean control value appear to be compatible with normal life. These findings stress the importance of small variations of the low residual enzyme activity for the development of a different clinical course of the disease.

Observations that a moderate residual activity (e.g., 10 percent of normal) may still suffice to sustain normal catabolism of a substrate and that small variations within the range of low residual activities observed in patients (below 5 percent of normal) greatly influence the clinical course of the disease can easily be understood on the basis of a greatly simplified kinetic model (Fig. 72-14).[321] Assuming a constant influx rate of the substrate into the lysosomal compartment of an individual cell and a degradation rate proportional to the degree of saturation of the available enzyme, the steady state substrate concentration can be calculated as a function of the residual enzyme activity. For lysosomal enzymes, which are probably not regulated, this steady state concentration should usually be far below the K_m value. It is then evident that even substantial reduction of the amount or turnover number of the enzyme will only lead to a moderate increase in the steady state concentration of the substrate, but not to an accumulation, since the remaining activity would still be sufficient to cope with the influx rate of the substrates. Only when the residual activity falls below a critical threshold would the overall turnover rate be reduced. In this case the substrate accumulation would be proportional to the difference between threshold activity and the smaller actual residual activity in the lysosome. Since influx rate of the substrate as well as enzyme activity differ in

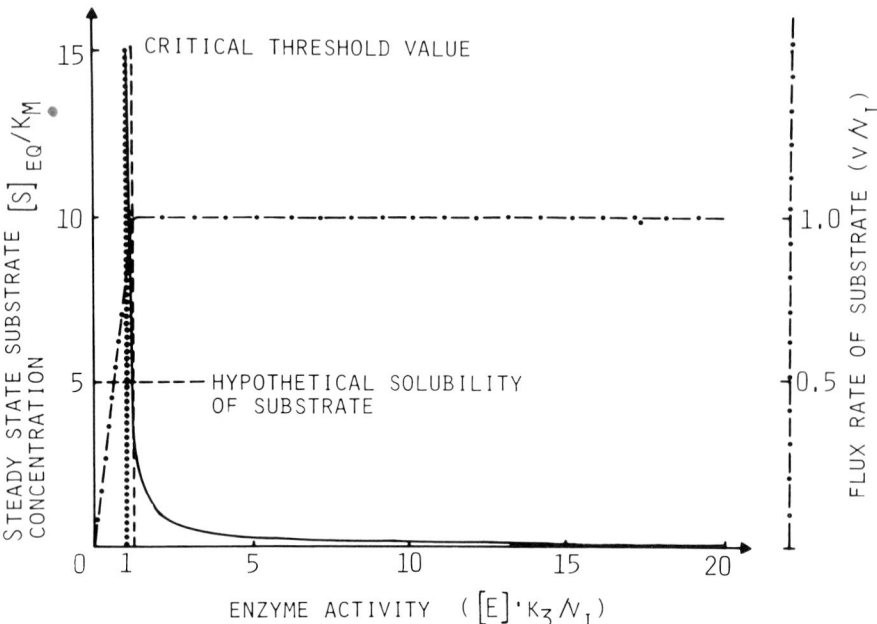

Fig. 72-14 Steady state concentration of a substrate as a function of residual enzyme activity.[321] The model assumes constant influx of a substrate into a compartment and its subsequent utilization by an enzyme.
———: $[S]_{eq}$ = steady state substrate concentration.
·······: theoretical critical threshold activity of enzyme.
------: critical threshold value, taking limited solubility of substrate into account.
-·-·-: v, turnover rate of substrate (flux rate).

different organs and cell types and may even vary between individual cells (e.g., neurons), the consequence of a mutation on different organs and cell types may be quite variable. For instance, in late onset forms of the disease with residual ganglioside G_{M2}-cleaving activity, neurons with a low rate of ganglioside biosynthesis (corresponding to a low influx rate, V_i, in Fig. 72-14) may avoid irreversible glycolipid accumulation if the influx rate V_i is lower than the residual degradation capacity (i.e., those cells would range above 1 on the abscissa in Fig. 72-14). Conversely, in cells with a high rate of ganglioside biosynthesis, the influx rate would exceed the maximal capacity (which might be as high as in the other cells), the ratio $[E] \times K_3/V_i$ would fall below the critical threshold (i.e., below 1 on the abscissa of Fig. 72-14), and the cells would suffer from irreversible glycolipid accumulation. Thus, in contrast to infantile forms in which all neurons are affected and the relative metabolic rates merely determine the temporal sequence of symptoms, in late onset forms the function and viability of some neurons are affected preferentially while others may remain unimpaired (see Fig. 72-11).

The calculations for Fig. 72-14 were performed as a first-order approximation on the basis of simple Michaelis-Menten kinetics without consideration of any complications which might arise, e.g., from regulatory properties of the enzyme considered or from the interaction of accumulating substrates with other components within the lysosomes. Still, they suggest how critical small variations of low residual enzyme activity (e.g., between 1 and 5 percent of normal) may be for the severity of a lysosomal storage disorder.

THERAPY

For the most part, treatment for any of the G_{M2} gangliosidoses is restricted to supportive care and appropriate management of intervening problems, e.g., maintenance of adequate nutrition and hydration, management of infectious disease, and control of seizures when and where they occur. In the most disabling conditions, bowel management frequently poses a

continuing problem. No specific therapy for any of these disorders has been identified.

Several attempts have been made in recent years at enzyme replacement therapy for patients with infantile G_{M2} gangliosidoses. Intravenous infusions with purified human hexosaminidase A (derived from urine) were administered to a child with Sandhoff disease.[322] This was followed by rapid clearance of enzyme activity from the circulation (half-life 10 to 20 min) with uptake of the enzyme primarily in the reticuloendothelial cells of the liver. No transfer of infused enzyme to the central nervous system was apparent. With a different approach, purified placental hexosaminidase A was administered intrathecally to two children with Tay-Sachs disease in an attempt to circumvent the blood-brain barrier. This also met with less than encouraging results.[323] Brain biopsies carried out before and after these therapeutic attempts showed no hexosaminidase A activity in brain tissue after infusion and no significant alterations in brain ganglioside content.

In yet another therapeutic attempt, multiple (6 units) HLA-matched mixed leukocyte infusions from normal individuals were given over 2 days to a child with Tay-Sachs disease. No evidence of hexosaminidase A activity was found in serial spinal fluid samples, nor was there any alteration of CSF G_{M2} ganglioside profiles over a 7-day period after transfusions.[324]

Most recently, suggestions have been made that bone marrow transplantation might offer a potentially successful therapeutic approach to lysosomal storage disorders, possibly including those with central nervous system macromolecular accumulation. While some measurable improvement has been detected in individuals with storage diseases involving peripheral organs after successful marrow transplant,[325] it remains unclear whether storage disorders involving the central nervous system can benefit significantly from this form of therapy with its high contingent mortality and morbidity. Again, the question of whether bone marrow–derived cells can enter the central nervous system and whether, in turn, once having entered, they can provide adequate enzyme replacement for neuronal cells engorged with undigested gangliosides or other macromolecules, remains to be answered. Whether the blood-brain barrier can be modified pharmacologically (or otherwise) in order to allow such a transfer of cellular or enzymatic material to occur is unresolved.

The availability of animal models for ganglioside storage disorders potentially makes such questions amenable to appropriate laboratory investigation before further human trials are initiated. Recent reports of bone marrow transplantations into α-L-iduronidase–deficient (MPS I) dogs,[326] α-L-fucosidase–deficient dogs,[327] and galactosylceramidase-deficient twitcher mice[328] have suggested transfer of some donor enzyme across the blood-brain barrier as well as infiltration of donor-derived macrophages.[328a]

ANIMAL MODELS

G$_{M2}$ gangliosidosis was identified in dogs almost 20 years ago,[329,330] but no breeding colony could be established at that time. Another animal model of the disease, in Yorkshire swine,[331,332] has been examined biochemically[333] and morphologically,[334] but the exact enzymatic variant could not be analyzed.

A deficiency of both hexosaminidases A and B corresponding to β-subunit deficiency in human has been characterized in cats,[335,336] and this model has been used for research on the possibilities of enzyme replacement therapy.[337] An apparently even more severe form of β-subunit deficiency with hepatomegaly in addition to the neurologic symptoms was recently described in Korat cats.[338]

A case of G$_{M2}$ gangliosidosis in a Japanese spaniel[339] was identified as an animal model of G$_{M2}$ activator deficiency,[340] whereas another canine G$_{M2}$ gangliosidosis detected by L. C. Cork and H. Singer (Johns Hopkins University, Baltimore) seems to correspond to human variant B1, i.e., an A isoenzyme with altered catalytic activity.[341]

REFERENCES

1. TAY W: Symmetrical changes in the region of the yellow spot in each eye of an infant. *Trans Ophthalmol Soc UK* 1:155, 1881.
2. SACHS B: A family form of idiocy, generally fatal associated with early blindness. *J Nerv Ment Dis* 21:475, 1896.
3. SACHS B: On arrested cerebral development with special reference to its cortical pathology. *J Nerv Ment Dis* 14:541, 1887.
4. KLENK E: Über die Natur der Phosphatide und anderer Lipoide des Gehirns und der Leber bei der Niemann-Pick'schen Krankheit. *Hoppe-Seyler's Z Physiol Chem* 235:24, 1935.
5. KLENK E: Beiträge zur Chemie der Lipidosen. I. Niemann-Pick'sche Krankheit und amaurotische Idiotie. *Hoppe-Seyler's Z Physiol Chem* 262:128, 1939/40.
6. KLENK E: Über die Ganglioside, eine neue Gruppe von zuckerhältigen Gehirnlipoiden. *Z Physiol Chem* 273:76, 1942.
7. SVENNERHOLM L: The chemical structure of normal human brain and Tay-Sachs gangliosides. *Biochem Biophys Res Commun* 9:436, 1962.
8. MAKITA A, YAMAKAWA T: The glycolipids of the brain of Tay-Sachs disease. The chemical structure of globoside and main ganglioside. *Jpn J Exp Med* 33:361, 1963.
9. LEDEEN R, SALSMAN K: Structure of the Tay-Sachs ganglioside. *Biochemistry* 4:2225, 1965.
10. OKADA S, O'BRIEN JS: Tay-Sachs disease: Generalized absence of a beta-D-N-acetylhexosaminidase component. *Science* 165:698, 1969.
11. SANDHOFF K: Variation of β-N-acetylhexosaminidase-pattern in Tay-Sachs disease. *FEBS Lett* 4:351, 1969.
12. HULTBERG B: N-Acetylhexosaminidase activities in Tay-Sachs disease. *Lancet* 2:1195, 1969.
13. SANDHOFF K, ANDREAE U, JATZKEWITZ H: Deficient hexosaminidase activity in an exceptional case of Tay-Sachs disease with additional storage of kidney globoside in visceral organs. *Pathol Eur* 3:278, 1968.
14. CONZELMANN E, SANDHOFF K: AB variant of infantile G$_{M2}$-gangliosidosis: Deficiency of a factor necessary for stimulation of hexosaminidase A-catalyzed degradation of ganglioside G$_{M2}$ and glycolipid G$_{A2}$. *Proc Natl Acad Sci USA* 75:3979, 1978.
15. SUZUKI K, CHEN GC: Brain ceramide hexosides in Tay-Sachs disease and generalized gangliosidosis. *J Lipid Res* 8:105, 1967.
16. WIEGANDT H: The Gangliosides, in Agranoff BW, Aprison MH (eds): *Advances in Neurochemistry*. New York, Plenum, 1982, p 149.
17. ANDO S: Gangliosides in the nervous system. *Neurochem Int* 5:507, 1983.
18. LEDEEN RW, YU RK, RAPPORT MM, SUZUKI K: *Ganglioside Structure, Function and Biomedical Potential*. New York, Plenum, 1984.
19. KUHN R, WIEGANDT H: Die Konstitution der Gangliotetraose und des Gangliosids G$_I$. *Chem Ber* 96:866, 1963.
20. SVENNERHOLM L: Chromatographic separation of human brain gangliosides. *J Neurochem* 10:613, 1963.
21. THOMPSON TE, TILLACK TW: Organization of glycosphingolipids in bilayers and plasma membranes of mammalian cells. *Annu Rev Biophys Biophys Chem* 14:361, 1985.
22. HAKOMORI S-I: Glycosphingolipids as differentiation-dependent, tumor-associated markers and as regulators of cell proliferation. *Trends Biochem Sci* 9:453, 1984.
23. ROSEMAN S: Studies on specific intercellular adhesion. *J Biochem* 97:709, 1985.
24. YAMAKAWA T, NAGAI Y: Glycolipids at the cell surface and their biological functions. *Trends Biochem Sci* 3:128, 1978.
25. SVENNERHOLM L: Biological significance of gangliosides. *Colloque INSERM/CNRS* 126:21, 1984.
26. SVENNERHOLM L: Gangliosides and synaptic transmission, in Svennerholm L, Mandel P, Dreyfus H, Urban P-F (eds): *Structure and Function of Gangliosides*. New York, Plenum, 1980, p 533.
27. KRACUN I, RÖSNER H, COSOVIC C, STAVLJENIC A: Topographical atlas of the gangliosides of the adult human brain. *J Neurochem* 43:979, 1984.
28. VANIER M-T, HOLM M, OHMANN R, SVENNERHOLM L: Developmental profiles of gangliosides in human and rat brain. *J Neurochem* 18:581, 1971.
29. SUZUKI K: The patterns of mammalian brain gangliosides. III. Regional and developmental differences. *J Neurochem* 12:969, 1965.
30. YUSUF HKM, MERAT A, DICKERSON JWT: Effect of development on the gangliosides of human brain. *J Neurochem* 28:1299, 1977.
31. MARTINEZ M, BALLABRIGA A: A chemical study on the development of the human forebrain and cerebellum during the growth spurt period. I. Gangliosides and plasmalogens. *Brain Res* 159:351, 1981.
32. SEYFRIED TN, MIYAZAWA N, YU RK: Cellular localization of gangliosides in the developing mouse cerebellum: Analysis using the weaver mutant. *J Neurochem* 41:491, 1983.
33. SVENNERHOLM L, BRUCE A, MANSSON JE, RAYSNARK BM, VANIER MT: Sphingolipids of human skeletal muscle. *Biochim Biophys Acta* 280:626, 1972.
34. SWEELEY CC, SIDDIQUI B: Chemistry of mammalian glycolipids, in Pigman W, Horowitz MF (eds): *The Glycoconjugates*. New York, Academic, 1977, p 459.
35. WIEGANDT H, BÜCKING W: Carbohydrate components of extraneural gangliosides from bovine and human spleen, and bovine kidney. *Eur J Biochem* 15:287, 1970.
36. CHIEN JL, HOGAN EL: Characterization of two gangliosides of the paragloboside series from chicken skeletal muscle. *Biochim Biophys Acta* 620:454, 1980.
37. GHIDONI R, SONNINO S, MASSERINI M, ORLANDO P, TETTAMANTI G: Specific tritium labeling of gangliosides at the 3-position of sphingosines. *J Lipid Res* 22:1286, 1981.
38. RÖSNER H: Isolation and preliminary characterization of novel polysialogangliosides from embryonic chick brain. *J Neurochem* 37:993, 1981.
39. CHIEN J-L, HOGAN EL: Glycosphingolipids of chicken skeletal muscle, in Yamakawa T, Osawa T, Handa S (eds): *Glycoconjugates*. Tokyo, Japan Scientific Societies Press, 1981, p 74.
40. BREIMER ME, HANSSON GC, KARLSSON KA, LEFFLER H: Glycosphingolipids of rat tissues. Different composition of epithelial and nonepithelial cells of small intestine. *J Biol Chem* 257:557, 1982.
41. CHOU KH, NOLAN CE, JUNGALWALA FB: Composition and metabolism of gangliosides in rat peripheral nervous system during development. *J Neurochem* 39:1547, 1982.
42. LEDEEN RW: Ganglioside structures and distribution: Are they localized at the nerve endings? *J Supramol Struct* 8:1, 1978.
43. HANSSON HA, HOLMGREN J, SVENNERHOLM L: Ultrastructural localization of cell membrane G$_{M1}$ ganglioside by cholera toxin. *Proc Natl Acad Sci USA* 74:3782, 1977.

44. RAHMANN H, RÖSNER H, BREER H: A functional model of sialoglycoma-cromolecules in synaptic transmission and memory formation. *J Theoret Biol* 57:231, 1976.

45. LEDEEN RW: Gangliosides of the neuron. *Trends Neurosci* 8:169, 1985.

46. SCHACHTER H, ROSEMAN S: Mammalian glycosyltransferases: Their role in the synthesis and function of complex carbohydrates and glycolipids, in Lennarz WJ (ed): *The Biochemistry of Glycoproteins and Proteoglycans.* New York, Plenum, 1980, p 85.

47. FISHMAN PH, BRADY RO: Biosynthesis and function of gangliosides. *Science* 194:906, 1976.

48. KEENAN TW, MORRÉ DJ, BASU S: Ganglioside biosynthesis. Concentration of glycosphingolipid glycosyltransferases in Golgi apparatus from rat liver. *J Biol Chem* 249:310, 1974.

49. CAREY DJ, HIRSCHBERG CB: Topography of sialoglycoproteins and sialyltransferases in mouse and rat liver Golgi. *J Biol Chem* 256:989, 1981.

50. CREEK KE, MORRÉ DJ: Translocation of cytidine-5'-monophosphosialic acid across Golgi apparatus membranes. *Biochim Biophys Acta* 643:292, 1981.

51. LANDA CA, DEFILPO SS, MACCIONI HJF, CAPUTTO R: Disposition of gangliosides and sialosylglycoproteins in neuronal membranes. *J Neurochem* 37:813, 1981.

52. YUSUF HKM, POHLENTZ G, SANDHOFF K: Ganglioside biosynthesis in Golgi apparatus: New perspectives on its mechanism. *J Neurosci Res* 12:161, 1984.

53. MILLER-PODRAZA H, FISHMAN PH: Effect of drugs and temperature on biosynthesis and transport of glycosphingolipids in cultured neurotumor cells. *Biochim Biophys Acta* 804:44, 1984.

54. SCHEEL G, ACEVEDO E, CONZELMANN E, NEHRKORN H, SANDHOFF K: Model for the interaction of membrane-bound substrates and enzymes. Hydrolysis of ganglioside G_{D1a} by sialidase of neuronal membranes isolated from calf brain. *Eur J Biochem* 127:245, 1982.

55. LANDA CA, MACCIONI HJF, CAPUTTO R: The site of synthesis of gangliosides in the chick optic system. *J Neurochem* 33:825, 1979.

56. LEDEEN RW, SKRIVANEK JA, NUNEZ J, SCLAFANI JR, NORTON WT, FAROOQ M: Implications of the distribution and transport of gangliosides in the nervous system, in Rapport MM, Gorio A (eds): *Gangliosides in Neurological and Neuromuscular Function, Development and Repair.* New York, Raven, 1981, p 211.

57. NEUFELD EF, LIM TW, SHAPIRO LJ: Inherited disorders of lysosomal metabolism. *Ann Rev Biochem* 44:357, 1975.

58. SANDHOFF K: The biochemistry of sphingolipid storage diseases. *Angew Chem (Int Ed)* 16:273, 1977.

59. WATANABE K: Biochemical studies on carbohydrates. XXII. Animal β-N-monoacetylglucosaminidase. *J Biochem (Tokyo)* 24:297, 1936.

60. WOOLLEN J, HEYWORTH R, WALKER P: Studies on glucosaminidase. 3. Testicular N-acetyl-β-glucosaminidase and N-acetyl-β-galactosaminidase. *Biochem J* 78:111, 1961.

61. WALKER P, WOOLLEN J, HEYWORTH R: Studies on glucosaminidase. 5. Kidney N-acetyl-β-glucosaminidase and N-acetyl-β-galactosaminidase. *Biochem J* 79:288, 1961.

62. WOOLLEN J, WALKER P, HEYWORTH R: Studies on glucosaminidase. 6. N-Acetyl-β-glucosaminidase and N-acetyl-β-galactosaminidase activities of a variety of enzyme preparations. *Biochem J* 79:294, 1961.

63. WEISSMANN B, HADJIIOANNOU S, TORNHEIM J: Oligosaccharase activity of β-N-acetyl-D-glucosaminidase of beef liver. *J Biol Chem* 239:59, 1964.

64. FROHWEIN YZ, GATT S: Isolation of β-N-acetylglucosaminidase and β-N-acetylgalactosaminidase from calf brain. *Biochemistry* 6:2775, 1967.

65. ROBINSON D, STIRLING JL: N-Acetyl-β-D-glucosaminidases in human spleen. *Biochem J* 107:321, 1968.

66. SANDHOFF K, WÄSSLE W: Anreicherung und Charakterisierung zweier Formen der menschlichen N-Acetyl-β-D-hexosaminidase. *Hoppe-Seyler's Z Physiol Chem* 352:1119, 1971.

67. ROBINSON D, JORDAN TW, HORSBURGH T: The N-acetyl-β-D-hexosaminidase of calf and human brain. *J Neurochem* 19:1975, 1972.

68. SELLINGER OZ, BEAUFAY H, JACQUES P, DOYEN A, DE DUVE C: Tissue fractionation studies. 15. Intracellular distribution and properties of β-N-acetylglucosaminidase and β-galactosidase in rat liver. *Biochem J* 74:450, 1960.

69. CONCHIE J, HAY A: Mammalian glycosidases. 4. The intracellular localization of β-galactosidase, α-mannosidase, β-N-acetylglucosaminidase and α-L-fucosidase in mammalian tissues. *Biochem J* 87:354, 1963.

70. SANDHOFF K: Auftrennung der Säuger-N-Acetyl-β-D-hexosaminidase in multiple Formen durch Elektrofokussierung. *Hoppe-Seyler's Z Physiol Chem* 349:1095, 1968.

71. CARMODY MH, RATTAZZI MC: Conversion of human hexosaminidase B by crude *Vibrio cholerae* neuraminidase preparations: Merthiolate is the active factor. *Biochim Biophys Acta* 371:117, 1974.

72. BEUTLER E, VILLACORTE D, KUHL W, SRIVASTAVA S: Non-enzymatic conversion of human hexosaminidase A. *J Lab Clin Med* 86:195, 1975.

73. SRIVASTAVA SK, BEUTLER E: Hexosaminidase-A and Hexosaminidase-B: Studies in Tay-Sachs and Sandhoff's Disease. *Nature* 241:463, 1973.

74. BEUTLER E, YOSHIDA A, KUHL W, LEE JES: The subunits of human hexosaminidase A. *Biochem J* 159:541, 1976.

75. GEIGER B, ARNON R: Chemical characterization and subunit structure of human N-acetylhexosaminidases A and B. *Biochemistry* 15:3484, 1976.

76. SRIVASTAVA SK, WIKTOROWICZ JE, AWASTHI YC: Interrelationship of hexosaminidase A and B: Confirmation of the common and the unique subunit theory. *Proc Natl Acad Sci USA* 73:2833, 1976.

77. SANDHOFF K, HARZER K, WÄSSLE W, JATZKEWITZ H: Enzyme alterations and lipid storage in three variants of Tay-Sachs disease. *J Neurochem* 18:2469, 1971.

78. IKONNE JU, RATTAZZI MC, DESNICK RJ: Characterization of hex-S, the major residual β-hexosaminidase activity in type O G_{M2}-gangliosidosis. *Am J Hum Genet* 27:639, 1975.

79. BEUTLER E, KUHL W, COMINGS D: Hexosaminidase isoenzyme in type O G_{M2}-gangliosidosis. *Am J Hum Genet* 27:628, 1975.

80. GEIGER B, ARNON R, SANDHOFF K: Immunochemical and biochemical investigation of hexosaminidase S. *Am J Hum Genet* 29:508, 1977.

81. LALLEY PA, RATTAZZI MC, SHOWS TB: Human β-D-N-acetylhexosaminidases A and B: Expression and linkage relationships in somatic cell hybrids. *Proc Natl Acad Sci USA* 71:1569, 1974.

82. BOEDECKER HJ, MELLMAN WJ, TEDESCO TA, CROCE CM: Assignment of the human gene for hex B to chromosome 5. *Exp Cell Res* 93:468, 1975.

83. CHERN CJ, BEUTLER E, KUHL W, GILBERT F, MELLMAN WJ, CROCE CM: Characterization of heteropolymeric hexosaminidase A in human X mouse hybrid cells. *Proc Natl Acad Sci USA* 73:3637, 1976.

84. CHERN CJ, KENNETH R, ENGEL E, MELLMAN WJ, CROCE CM: Assignment of the structural genes for the α subunit of hexosaminidase A, mannose phosphate isomerase and pyruvate kinase to the region of 22 qter of human chromosome 15. *Somatic Cell Genet* 3:533, 1977.

85. MYEROWITZ R, PIEKARZ R, NEUFELD EF, SHOWS TB, SUZUKI K: Human β-hexosaminidase α chain: Coding sequence and homology with the β chain. *Proc Natl Acad Sci USA* 82:7830, 1985.

86. KORNELUK RG, MAHURAN DJ, NEOTE K, KLAVINS MH, O'DOWD BF, TROPAK M, WILLARD HF, ANDERSON M-J, LOWDEN JA, GRAVEL RA: Isolation of cDNA clones coding for the α-subunit of human β-hexosaminidase. Extensive homology between the α- and β-subunits and studies on Tay-Sachs disease. *J Biol Chem* 261:8407, 1986.

87. PROIA RL, SORAVIA E: Organization of the gene encoding the human β-hexosaminidase α-chain. *J Biol Chem* 262:5677, 1987.

88. PROIA RL: Gene encoding the human β-hexosaminidase β-chain: Extensive homology of intron placement in the α- and β-chain genes. *Proc Natl Acad Sci USA* 85:1883, 1988.

89. KORNFELD S: Trafficking of lysosomal enzymes in normal and disease states. *J Clin Invest* 77:1, 1986.

90. VON FIGURA K, HASILIK A: Lysosomal enzymes and their receptors. *Annu Rev Biochem* 55:167, 1986.

91. FREEZE H, GEIGER B, MILLER AL: Carbohydrate composition of human placental N-acetylhexosaminidase A and B. *Biochem J* 177:749, 1979.

92. HASILIK A, VON FIGURA K: Oligosaccharides in lysosomal enzymes. *Eur J Biochem* 121:125, 1981.

93. O'DOWD BF, MAHURAN D, CUMMING D, LOWDEN JA: Characterization by nuclear magnetic resonance of the concanavalin A binding oligosaccharide on the $β_b$ chain of placental hexosaminidase B: Lectin binding to the separated polypeptide chains of hexosaminidases A and B. *Can J Cell Biol* 63:723, 1985.

94. PROIA RL, D'AZZO A, NEUFELD EF: Association of α- and β-subunits during the biosynthesis of β-hexosaminidase in cultured human fibroblasts. *J Biol Chem* 259:3350, 1984.

95. HASILIK A, NEUFELD EF: Biosynthesis of lysosomal enzymes in fibroblasts. Synthesis as precursors of higher molecular weight. *J Biol Chem* 255:4937, 1980.

96. SRIVASTAVA SK, YOSHIDA A, AWASTHI YC, BEUTLER E: Studies on human β-D-N-acetylhexosaminidases. II. Kinetic and structural properties. *J Biol Chem* 249:2049, 1974.

97. TALLMAN JF, BRADY RO, QUIRK JE, VILLALBA M, GAL AE: Isolation and relationship of human hexosaminidases. *J Biol Chem* 249:3489, 1974.

98. BEUTLER E, YOSHIDA A, KUHL W, LEE JE: The subunits of human hexosaminidase A. *Biochem J* 159:541, 1976.

99. LEE JES, YOSHIDA A: Purification and chemical characterization of human hexosaminidases A and B. *Biochem J* 159:535, 1976.

100. MAHURAN D, LOWDEN JA: The subunit and polypeptide structure of hexosaminidases from human placenta. *Can J Biochem* 58:287, 1980.

101. MAHURAN DJ, TSUI F, GRAVEL RA, LOWDEN JA: Evidence for two dissimilar polypeptide chains in the $β_2$ subunit of hexosaminidase. *Proc Natl Acad Sci USA* 79:1602, 1982.

102. MAHURAN DJ, NEOTE K, KLAVINS MH, LEUNG A, GRAVEL RA: Proteolytic

processing of pro-α and pro-β precursors from human hexosaminidase. Generation of the mature α and β_aβ_b subunits. *J Biol Chem* 263:4612, 1988.

102a. STIRLING J, LEUNG A, GRAVEL RA, MAHURAN D: Localization of the pro-sequence within the total deduced primary structure of human β-hexosaminidase B. *FEBS Lett* 231:47, 1988.

103. LITTLE LE, LAU MMH, QUON DVK, FOWLER AV, NEUFELD EF: Proteolytic processing of the α-chain of the lysosomal enzyme, β-hexosaminidase, in normal human fibroblasts. *J Biol Chem* 263:4288, 1988.

104. GUPTA DK, SCHMIDT A, VON FIGURA K, HASILIK A: Processing and transport of lysosomal enzymes in human monocyte line U937. *Hoppe-Seyler's Z Physiol Chem* 365:867, 1984.

105. ROBBINS AR, MYEROWITZ R: The mannose-6-phosphate receptor of Chinese hamster ovary cells. *J Biol Chem* 256:10623, 1981.

106. MAHURAN D, NOVAK A, LOWDEN JA: The lysosomal hexosaminidase isozymes. *Cur Top Biol Med Res* 12:229, 1985.

107. POTIER M, TEITELBAUM H, MELANCON SB, DALLAIRE L: Purification and some properties of liver and brain β-N-acetylhexosaminidase S. *Biochim Biophys Acta* 566:80, 1979.

108. PRICE RG, DANCE M: The demonstration of multiple heat-stable forms of N-acetyl-β-glycosaminidase in normal human serum. *Biochim Biophys Acta* 271:145, 1972.

109. LOWDEN JA, MAHURAN D, O'DOWD B, GRAVEL R, TSUI F: The intermediate hexosaminidases of placenta and their relationship to precursor processing, in Barranger JA, Brady RO (eds): *The Molecular Basis of Lysosomal Storage Disorders*. Orlando, Academic, 1984, p 257.

110. DEWJI NN, DE-KEYZER DR, STIRLING JL: Purification and characterization of β-N-acetylhexosaminidase I₂ from human liver. *Biochem J* 234:157, 1986.

111. GEIGER B, CALEF E, ARNON R: Biochemical and immunochemical characterization of hexosaminidase P. *Biochemistry* 17:1713, 1978.

112. STIRLING JL: Separation and characterization of N-acetyl-β-glucosaminidases A and P from maternal serum. *Biochim Biophys Acta* 271:154, 1972.

113. FROHWEIN YZ, GATT S: Separation of β-N-acetylglucosaminidase and β-N-acetylgalactosaminidase from calf brain cytoplasm. *Biochim Biophys Acta* 128:216, 1966.

114. BRAIDMAN I, CARROLL M, DANCE N, ROBINSON D, POENARU L, WEBER A, DREYFUS JC, OVERDIJK B, HOOGHWINKEL GJM: Characterization of human N-acetyl-β-hexosaminidase C. *FEBS Lett* 41:181, 1974.

115. PENTON E, POENARU L, DREYFUS JC: Hexosaminidase C in Tay-Sachs and Sandhoff disease. *Biochim Biophys Acta* 391:162, 1975.

116. IZUMI T, SUZUKI K: Neutral β-N-acetylhexosaminidase of rat brain. Purification and enzymatic and immunological characterization. *J Biol Chem* 258:6991, 1983.

117. KRESSE H, FUCHS W, GLÖSSL J, HOLTFRERICH D, GILBERG W: Liberation of N-acetylglucosamine-6-sulfate by human β-N-acetylhexosaminidase A. *J Biol Chem* 256:12926, 1981.

118. LUDOLPH T, PASCHKE E, GLÖSSL J, KRESSE H: Degradation of keratan sulphate by N-acetylhexosaminidases A and B. *Biochem J* 193:811, 1981.

119. KYTZIA H-J, HINRICHS U, MAIRE I, SUZUKI K, SANDHOFF K: Variant of G_{M2} gangliosidosis with hexosaminidase A having a severely changed substrate specificity. *EMBO J* 2, 1201, 1983.

120. KYTZIA H-J, SANDHOFF K: Evidence for two different active sites on human β-hexosaminidase A. Interaction of G_{M2} activator protein with β-hexosaminidase A. *J Biol Chem* 260:7568, 1985.

121. LEE JES, YOSHIDA A: Purification and chemical characterization of human hexosaminidases A and B. *Biochem J* 159:535, 1976.

122. MARINKOVIC DV, MARINKOVIC JN: Purification of two hexosaminidases from human kidney. *Biochem J* 163:133, 1977.

123. SANDHOFF K, CONZELMANN E, NEHRKORN H: Specificity of human liver hexosaminidases A and B against glycosphingolipids G_{M2} and G_{A2}. Purification of the enzymes by affinity chromatography employing specific elution. *Hoppe-Seyler's Z Physiol Chem* 358:779, 1977.

124. GEIGER B, ARNON R: Hexosaminidases A and B from human placenta. *Methods Enzymol* 50:547, 1978.

125. WENGER DA, OKADA S, O'BRIEN JS: Studies on the substrate specificity of hexosaminidase A and B from liver. *Arch Biochem Biophys* 153:116, 1972.

126. WIKTOROWICZ JE, AWASTHI YC, KUROSKY A, SRIVASTAVA SK: Purification and properties of human kidney-cortex hexosaminidases A and B. *Biochem J* 165:49, 1977.

127. CONZELMANN E, SANDHOFF K, NEHRKORN H, GEIGER B, ARNON R: Purification, biochemical and immunological characterization of hexosaminidase A from variant AB of infantile G_{M2} gangliosidosis. *Eur J Biochem* 84:27, 1978.

128. THOMPSON JN, STOOLMILLER AC, MATALON R, DORFMAN A: N-acetyl-β-hexosaminidase: Role in the degradation of glycosaminoglycans. *Science* 181:866, 1973.

129. BEARPARK TM, STIRLING J: A difference in the specificities of human liver

130. GLÖSSL J, KRESSE H: Impaired degradation of keratan sulphate by Morquio A fibroblasts. *Biochem J* 203:335, 1982.

131. KYTZIA H-J, HINRICHS U, SANDHOFF K: Diagnosis of infantile and juvenile forms of G_{M2} gangliosidosis variant O. Residual activities toward natural and different synthetic substrates. *Hum Genet* 67:414, 1984.

132. TOMA S, COPPA G, DONNELLY PV, RICCI R, DIFERRANTE N, SRIVASTAVA SK: Cleavage of the (1→3)-2-acetamido-2-deoxy-β-D-glucopyranosyl linkage present in keratan sulfate. The A and B isoenzymes of human liver hexosaminidase. *Carbohydr Res* 96:271, 1981.

133. BACH G, GEIGER B: Human placental N-acetyl-β-D-hexosaminidase isoenzymes. Activity toward native hyaluronic acid. *Arch Biochem Biophys* 189:37, 1978.

134. WERRIES E, NEUE I, BUDDECKE E: Evidence for different glycohydrolase and glycosyltransferase activities of β-N-acetylglucosaminidases A and B. *Hoppe-Seyler's Z Physiol Chem* 356:953, 1975.

135. O'BRIEN JS, NORDEN AGW, MILLER AL, FROST RG, KELLY TE: Ganglioside G_{M2} N-acetyl-β-D-galactosaminidase and asialo G_{M2} (G_{A2}) N-acetyl-β-D-galactosaminidase; studies in human skin fibroblasts. *Clin Genet* 11:171, 1977.

136. SANDHOFF K: The hydrolysis of Tay-Sachs ganglioside (TSG) by human N-acetyl-β-D-hexosaminidase A. *FEBS Lett* 11:342, 1970.

137. MEHL E, JATZKEWITZ H: Eine Cerebrosidsulfatase aus Schweineniere. *Hoppe-Seyler's Z Physiol Chem* 339:260, 1964.

138. FISCHER G, JATZKEWITZ H: The activator of cerebroside sulfatase: Purification from human liver and identification as a protein. *Hoppe-Seyler's Z Physiol Chem* 356:605, 1975.

139. FISCHER G, JATZKEWITZ H: The activator of cerebroside sulfatase: Binding studies with enzyme and substrate demonstrating the detergent function of the activator protein. *Biochim Biophys Acta* 481:561, 1977.

140. LI Y-T, MAZZOTTA MY, WAN CC, ORTH R, LI S-C: Hydrolysis of Tay-Sachs ganglioside of β-hexosaminidase A of human liver and urine. *J Biol Chem* 248:7512, 1973.

141. LI S-C, LI Y-T: An activator stimulating the enzymic hydrolysis of sphingoglycolipids. *J Biol Chem* 251:1159, 1976.

142. INUI K, EMMETT M, WENGER DA: Immunological evidence for the deficiency in an activator protein for sulfatide sulfatase in a variant form of metachromatic leukodystrophy. *Proc Natl Acad Sci USA* 80:3074, 1983.

143. LI S-C, KIHARA H, SERIZAWA S, LI Y-T, FLUHARTY AL, MAYES JS, SHAPIRO LJ: Activator protein required for the enzymatic hydrolysis of cerebroside sulfate. *J Biol Chem* 260:1867, 1985.

144. LI S-C, NAKAMURA T, OGAMO A, LI Y-T: Evidence for the presence of two separate protein activators for the enzymic hydrolysis of G_{M1} and G_{M2} ganglioside. *J Biol Chem* 254:10592, 1979.

145. CONZELMANN E, SANDHOFF K: Purification and characterization of an activator protein for the degradation of glycolipids G_{M2} and G_{A2} by hexosaminidase A. *Hoppe-Seyler's Z Physiol Chem* 360:1837, 1979.

146. CONZELMANN E, BURG J, STEPHAN G, SANDHOFF K: Complexing of glycolipids and their transfer between membranes by the activator protein for degradation of lysosomal ganglioside G_{M2}. *Eur J Biochem* 123:455, 1982.

147. LI S-C, HIRABAYASHI Y, LI Y-T: A protein activator for the enzymic hydrolysis of G_{M2} ganglioside. *J Biol Chem* 256:6234, 1981.

148. BURG J, BANERJEE A, SANDHOFF K: Molecular forms of G_{M2}-activator protein. A study on its biosynthesis in human skin fibroblasts. *Biol Chem Hoppe Seyler* 366:887, 1985.

149. BANERJEE A, BURG J, CONZELMANN E, CARROLL M, SANDHOFF K: Enzyme-linked immunosorbent assay for the ganglioside G_{M2}-activator protein. Screening of normal human tissues and body fluids, of tissues of G_{M2} gangliosidosis, and for its subcellular localization. *Hoppe-Seyler's Z Physiol Chem* 365:347, 1984.

150. BURG J, CONZELMANN E, SANDHOFF K, SOLOMON E, SWALLOW DM: Mapping of the gene coding for the human G_{M2} activator protein to chromosome 5. *Ann Hum Genet* 49:41, 1985.

151. LI S-C, SERIZAWA S, LI Y-T, NAKAMURA K, HANDA S: Effect of modification of sialic acid on enzymic hydrolysis of gangliosides G_{M1} and G_{M2}. *J Biol Chem* 259:5409, 1984.

152. SANDHOFF K, CONZELMANN E: The biochemical basis of gangliosidoses. *Neuropediatrics, Suppl* 15:85, 1984.

153. CARROLL M, ROBINSON D: Immunological properties of N-acetyl-β-D-glucosaminidase of normal human liver and of G_{M2} gangliosidosis liver. *Biochem J* 131:91, 1973.

154. SRIVASTAVA SK, BEUTLER E: Studies on human β-D-N-acetylhexosaminidases. III. Biochemical genetics of Tay-Sachs and Sandhoff's diseases. *J Biol Chem* 249:2054, 1974.

155. BARTHOLOMEW WR, RATTAZZI MC: Immunochemical characterization of

human β-D-N-acetylhexosaminidase from normal individuals and patients with Tay-Sachs disease. *Int Arch Allergy Appl Immunol* 46:512, 1974.

156. GEIGER B, NAVON R, BEN-YOSEPH Y, ARNON R: Specific determination of N-acetyl-β-D-hexosaminidase isoenzymes A and B by radioimmunoassay and radial immunodiffusion. *J Biochem* 56:311, 1975.

157. LI S-C, HIRABAYASHI Y, LI Y-T: A new variant of type-AB G$_{M2}$-gangliosidosis. *Biochem Biophys Res Commun* 101:479, 1981.

158. LI Y-T, HIRABAYASHI Y, LI S-C: Differentiation of two variants of type-AB G$_{M2}$-gangliosidosis using chromogenic substrates. *Am J Hum Genet* 35:520, 1983.

159. SONDERFELD S, BRENDLER S, SANDHOFF K, GALJAARD H, HOOGEVEEN AT: Genetic complementation in somatic cell hybrids of four variants of infantile G$_{M2}$ gangliosidosis. *Hum Genet* 71:196, 1985.

160. GILBERT F, KUCHERLAPATI RP, CREAGAN RP, MURNANE RJ, DARLINGTON GJ, RUDDLE FH: The assignment of genes for hexosaminidase A and B to individual chromosomes. *Proc Natl Acad Sci USA* 72:263, 1975.

161. HECHTMAN P, GORDON BA, NG YING KIN NMK: Deficiency of the hexosaminidase A activator protein in a case of G$_{M2}$ gangliosidosis; variant AB. *Pediatr Res* 16:217, 1982.

162. HIRABAYASHI Y, LI Y-T, LI S-C: The protein activator specific for the enzymic hydrolysis of G$_{M2}$ ganglioside in normal human brain and in brains of three types of G$_{M2}$ gangliosidosis. *J Neurochem* 40:168, 1983.

163. BERNHEIMER H, SEITELBERGER F: Über das Verhalten der Ganglioside im Gehirn bei 2 Fällen von spätinfantiler amaurotischer Idiotie. *Wiener klin Wochenschr* 80:163, 1968.

164. SUZUKI K, SUZUKI K, RAPIN I, SUZUKI Y, ISHII H: Juvenile G$_{M2}$ gangliosidosis. Clinical variant of Tay-Sachs disease or a new disease? *Neurology* 20:190, 1970.

165. BRETT EM, ELLIS RB, HAAS L, IKONNE JU, LAKE BD, PATRICK AD, STEPHENS R: Late onset G$_{M2}$ gangliosidosis: Clinical, pathological and biochemical studies on eight patients. *Arch Dis Child* 48:775, 1973.

166. O'BRIEN JS: The Gangliosidoses, in Stanbury JS, Wyngaarden JB, Fredrickson DS, Goldstein JL, Brown MS (eds): *The Metabolic Basis of Inherited Disease*, 5th ed. New York, McGraw-Hill, 1983, p 945.

167. PARNES S, KARPATI G, CARPENTER S, NG YING KIN NMK, WOLFE LS, SURANYI I: Hexosaminidase-A deficiency presenting as atypical juvenile-onset spinal muscular atrophy. *Arch Neurol* 42:1176, 1985.

168. O'DOWD BF, KLAVINS MH, WILLARD HF, GRAVEL R, LOWDEN JA, MAHURAN DJ: Molecular heterogeneity in the infantile and juvenile forms of Sandhoff disease (O-variant G$_{M2}$ gangliosidosis). *J Biol Chem* 261:12680, 1986.

169. RAPIN I, SUZUKI K, SUZUKI K, VALSAMIS MP: Adult (chronic) G$_{M2}$ gangliosidosis: Atypical spinocerebellar degeneration in a Jewish sibship. *Arch Neurol* 33:120, 1976.

170. WILLNER JP, GRABOWSKI GA, GORDON RE, BENDER AN, DESNICK RJ: Chronic G$_{M2}$ gangliosidosis masquerading as a typical Friedreich ataxia: Clinical, morphologic, and biochemical studies of nine cases. *Neruology* 31:787, 1981.

171. NAVON R, ARGOV Z, FRISCH A: Hexosaminidase A deficiency in adults. *Am J Med Genet* 24:179, 1986.

172. KABACK M, MILES J, YAFFE M, ITABASHI H, MCINTYRE H, GOLDBERG M, MOHANDAS T: Hexosaminidase-A (Hex-A) deficiency in early adulthood. A new type of G$_{M2}$ gangliosidosis. *Am J Hum Genet* 30:31A, 1978.

173. YAFFE M, KABACK MM, GOLDBERG M, MILES G, ITABASHI H, MCINTYRE H, MOHANDAS T: An amyotrophic lateral sclerosis-like syndrome with hexosaminidase A deficiency: A new type of G$_{M2}$ gangliosidosis. *Neurology* 29:611, 1979.

174. JELLINGER K, ANZIL AP, SEEMANN D, BERNHEIMER H: Adult G$_{M2}$ gangliosidosis masquerading as slowly progressive muscular atrophy: Motor neuron disease phenotype. *Clin Neuropath* 1:31, 1982.

175. JOHNSON W, WU P: Hexosaminidase deficiency with spinal muscular atrophy: Biochemical characterization of the residual enzyme. *Neurology* 34 (suppl 1):273, 1984.

176. ARGOV Z, NAVON R: Clinical and genetic variations in the syndrome of adult G$_{M2}$ gangliosidosis resulting from hexosaminidase A deficiency. *Ann Neurol* 16:14, 1984.

177. CONZELMANN E, KYTZIA H-J, NAVON R, SANDHOFF K: Ganglioside G$_{M2}$ N-acetyl-β-D-galactosaminidase activity in cultured fibroblasts of late-infantile and adult G$_{M2}$ gangliosidosis patients and of healthy probands with low hexosaminidase levels. *Am J Hum Genet* 35:900, 1983.

178. NAVON R, PADEH B, ADAM A: Apparent deficiency of hexosaminidase A in healthy members of a family with Tay-Sachs disease. *Am J Hum Genet* 25:287, 1973.

179. VIDGOFF J, BUIST N, O'BRIEN J: Absence of β-N-acetyl-D-hexosaminidase A activity in a healthy lyswoman. *Am J Hum Genet* 25:372, 1973.

180. KELLY T, REYNOLDS L, O'BRIEN J: Segregation within a family of two mutant alleles for hexosaminidase A. *Clin Genet* 9:540, 1976.

181. O'BRIEN J, GEIGER B: Normal adult with absent HEX A: Immunoreactive HEX A is present. *Am J Hum Genet* 31:642, 1979.

182. ZLOTOGORA J, BACH G: Deficiency of lysosomal hydrolases in apparently healthy individuals. *Am J Med Genet* 14:73, 1983.

183. GREBNER EE, MANSFIELD DA, RAGHAVAN SS, KOLODNY EH, D'AZZO A, NEUFELD EF, JACKSON LG: Two abnormalities of hexosaminidase A in clinically normal individuals. *Am J Hum Genet* 38:505, 1986.

184. NAVON R, GEIGER B, BEN-YOSEPH Y, RATTAZZI M: Low levels of β-hexosaminidase A in healthy individuals with apparent deficiency of this enzyme. *Am J Hum Genet* 28:339, 1976.

185. NAVON R, ARGOV Z, BRANDT N, SANDBANK U: Adult G$_{M2}$ gangliosidosis in association with Tay-Sachs disease: A new phenotype. *Neurology* 31:1397, 1981.

186. WOOD S, MACDOUGALL BG: Juvenile Sandhoff disease: Some properties of the residual hexosaminidase in cultured fibroblasts. *Am J Hum Genet* 28:489, 1976.

187. MACLEOD PM, WOOD S, JAN JE, APPLEGARTH DA, DOLMAN CL: Progressive cerebellar ataxia, spasticity, psychomotor retardation, and hexosaminidase deficiency in a 10-year-old child: Juvenile Sandhoff disease. *Neurology* 27:571, 1977.

188. DREYFUS JC, POENARU L, SVENNERHOLM L: Absence of hexosaminidase A and B in a normal adult. *N Engl J Med* 292:61, 1975.

189. DREYFUS JC, POENARU L, VIBERT M, RAVISE N, BOUE J: Characterization of a variant of β-hexosaminidase: "Hexosaminidase Paris." *Am J Hum Genet* 29:287, 1977.

190. VOLK BW, SCHNECK L, ADACHI M: Clinic, pathology and biochemistry of Tay-Sachs disease, in Vinken PJ, Bruyn GW (eds): *Textbook of Neurology*. Amsterdam, North-Holland, 1970, vol 10, p 385.

191. SUZUKI K: Neuronal storage disease: A review, in Zimmerman HM (ed): *Progress in Neuropathology*. New York, Grune & Stratton, 1976, vol III, p 173.

192. PURPURA DP, SUZUKI K: Distortion of neuronal geometry and formation of aberrant synapses in neuronal storage disease. *Brain Res* 116:1, 1976.

193. LAZARUS SS, WALLACE BJ, VOLK BW: Neuronal enzyme alterations in Tay-Sachs disease. *Am J Pathol* 41:579, 1962.

194. TERRY RD, WEISS M: Studies in Tay-Sachs disease: II. Ultrastructure of the cerebrum. *J Neuropathol Exp Neurol* 22:18, 1963.

195. HABERLAND C, BRUNNGRABER E, WITTING L, BROWN B: The white matter in G$_{M2}$ gangliosidosis: A comparative histopathological and biochemical study. *Acta Neuropathol (Berl)* 24:43, 1973.

196. SCHMITT HP, BERLET H, VOGT B: Peripheral intra-axonal storage in Tay-Sachs disease (G$_{M2}$ gangliosidosis type 1). *J Neurol Sci* 44:115, 1979.

197. ABE T, OGAWA K, FUZIWARA H, URAYAMA K, NAGASHIMA K: Spinal ganglia and peripheral nerves from a patient with Tay-Sachs disease. *Acta Neuropathol (Berl)* 66:239, 1985.

198. NAGASHIMA K, KIKUCHI F, SUZUKI Y, ABE T: Retinal Amacrine cell involvement in Tay-Sachs disease. *Acta Neuropathol (Berl)* 53:333, 1981.

199. ADACHI M, VOLK BW, SCHNECK L, RELKIN R: Ultrastructural alterations of endocrine glands in Tay-Sachs Disease. *J Clin Pathol* 57:557, 1972.

200. ADACHI M, SCHNECK L, VOLK BW: Ultrastructural studies of eight cases of fetal Tay-Sachs disease. *Lab Invest* 30:102, 1974.

201. GOLDMAN JE, YAMANAKA T, RAPIN I, ADACHI M, SUZUKI K, SUZUKI K: The AB-Variant of G$_{M2}$-gangliosidosis. Clinical, biochemical and pathological studies of two patients. *Acta Neuropathol (Berl)* 52:189, 1980.

202. BUXTON P, CUMINGS JN, ELLIS RB, LAKE BD, MAIR WGP, ROBERTS JR, YOUNG EP: A case of G$_{M2}$ gangliosidosis of late onset. *J Neurol Neurosurg Psychiatry* 35:685, 1972.

203. JOHNSON WG, WIGGER HJ, KARP HR, GLAUBIGER LM, ROWLAND LP: Juvenile spinal muscular atrophy: A new hexosaminidase deficiency phenotype. *Ann Neurol* 11:11, 1982.

204. DOLMAN CL, CHANG E, DUKE RJ: Pathologic findings in Sandhoff disease. *Arch Pathol* 96:272, 1973.

205. HADFIELD MG, MAMUNES P, DAVID RB: The pathology of Sandhoff's disease. *J Pathol* 123:137, 1977.

206. KRIVIT W, DESNICK RJ, LEE J, MOLLER J, WRIGHT F, SWEELEY CC, SNYDER PD JR, SHARP HL: Generalized accumulation of neutral glycosphingolipids with G$_{M2}$ ganglioside accumulation in the brain. *Am J Med* 52:763, 1972.

207. PILZ H, MÜLLER D, SANDHOFF K, TER MEULEN V: Tay-Sachssche Krankheit mit Hexosaminidase-Defekt. *Dtsch Med Wochenschr* 93:1833, 1968.

208. SUZUKI Y, JACOB JC, SUZUKI K, KUTTY KM, SUZUKI K: G$_{M2}$-gangliosidosis with total hexosaminidase deficiency. *Neurology* 21:313, 1971.

209. DESNICK RJ, SNYDER PD, DESNICK SJ, KRIVIT W: Sandhoff's disease: Ultrastructural and biochemical studies, in Volk BW, Aronson SM (eds): *Sphingolipids, Sphingolipidoses and Allied Disorders*. New York, Plenum, 1972, p 351.

210. JUIF JG, LUCKEL JC, NUSSBAUM JL, STOEBNER R, KAPPS R: La gangliosi-

dose G$_{M2}$ avec déficit complet en β-N-acétyl-hexosaminidase ou maladie de Sandhoff. *Arch Fr Pediatr* 30:29, 1973.

211. VIDAILHET M, NEIMANN N, GRIGNON G, HARTEMANN P, PHILIPPART M, PAYSANT P, NABET P, FLOQUET J: Maladie de Sandhoff (gangliosidose a G$_{M2}$, de type 2). *Arch Fr Pediatr* 30:45, 1973.

212. JOHNSON WG, CHUTORIAN A, MIRANDA A: A new juvenile hexosaminidase deficiency disease presenting as cerebellar ataxia. Clinical and biochemical studies. *Neurology* 27:1012, 1977.

213. GOLDIE WD, HOLTZMAN D, SUZUKI K: Chronic hexosaminidase A and B deficiency. *Ann Neurol* 2:156, 1977.

214. O'NEIL B, BUTLER AB, YOUNG E, MANN P, BASS NH: Adult-onset G$_{M2}$ gangliosidosis. Seizures, dementia, and normal pressure hydrocephalus associated with glycolipid storage in the brain and arachnoid granulation. *Neurology* 28:1117, 1978.

215. OONK HGW, VAN DER HELM HJ, MARTIN JJ: Spinocerebellar degeneration: Hexosaminidase A and B deficiency in two adult sisters. *Neurology* 29:380, 1979.

216. KOLODNY EH, PRUSZKOW IW, MOSER HW, COGAN DG, KUWABARA T: G$_{M2}$ gangliosidosis without deficiency in the artificial substrate cleaving activity of hexosaminidase A and B. *Neurology* 23:427, 1973.

217. DE BAEQUE CM, SUZUKI K, RAPIN I, JOHNSON AB, WHETHERS DL, SUZUKI K: G$_{M2}$ gangliosidosis, AB variant. Clinico-pathological study of a case. *Acta Neuropathol (Berl)* 33:207, 1975.

218. PURPURA DP: Ectopic dendritic growth in mature pyramidal neurons in human ganglioside storage disease. *Nature* 276:520, 1978.

219. HOFFMAN LM, AMSTERDAM D, BROOKS SE, SCHNECK L: Glycosphingolipids in fetal Tay-Sachs disease brain and lung cultures. *J Neurochem* 29:551, 1977.

220. CONZELMANN E, NEHRKORN H, KYTZIA H-J, SANDHOFF K, MACEK M, LEHOVSKY M, ELLEDER M, JIRASEK A, KOBILKOVA J: Prenatal diagnosis of G$_{M2}$ gangliosidosis with high residual hexosaminidase A activity (variant B^1; Pseudo AB variant). *Pediatr Res* 19:1220, 1985.

221. SNYDER PD, KRIVIT W, SWEELEY CC: Generalized accumulation of neutral glycosphingolipids with G$_{M2}$ ganglioside accumulation in the brain. *J Lipid Res* 13:128, 1972.

222. IWAMORI M, NAGAI Y: Ganglioside composition of brain in Tay-Sachs disease: Increased amounts of G$_{D2}$ and N-acetyl-β-D-galactosaminyl G$_{D1a}$ ganglioside. *J Neurochem* 32:767, 1979.

223. NEUENHOFER S, CONZELMANN E, SCHWARZMANN G, EGGE H, SANDHOFF K: Occurrence of lysoganglioside lyso-G$_{M2}$ (II^3-Neu-5-Ac-gangliotriaosyl-sphingosine) in G$_{M2}$ gangliosidosis brain. *Biol Chem Hoppe Seyler* 367:241, 1986.

224. ROSENGREN B, MANSSON J-E, SVENNERHOLM L: Composition of gangliosides and neutral glycosphingolipids of brain in classical Tay-Sachs and Sandhoff disease: More lyso-G$_{M2}$ in Sandhoff disease? *J Neurochem,* 49:834, 1987.

225. ITOH T, LI Y-T, LI S-C, YU RK: Isolation and chracterization of a novel monosialosylpentahexosyl ceramide from Tay-Sachs brain. *J Biol Chem* 256:165, 1981.

226. IWAMORI M, NAGAI Y: Isolation and characterization of a novel ganglioside monosialosyl pentahexosyl ceramide from human brain. *J Biochem* 84:1601, 1978.

227. YU RK, ITOH T, YOHE HC, MACALA LJ: Characterization of some minor gangliosides in Tay-Sachs brain. *Brain Res* 275:47, 1983.

228. VANIER M-T, HOLM M, MANSSON JE, SVENNERHOLM L: The distribution of lipids in the human nervous system. V. Gangliosides and allied neutral glycolipids of infant brain. *J Neurochem* 21:1375, 1973.

229. JATZKEWITZ H, PILZ H, SANDHOFF K: The quantitative determination of gangliosides and their derivatives in different forms of amaurotic idiocy. *J Neurochem* 12:135, 1965.

230. ESCOLA J: Über die Prozessausbreitung der amaurotischen Idiotie im Zentralnervensystem in verschiedenen Lebensaltern und Besonderheiten der Spätform gegenüber der Pigmentatrophie. *Arch Psychiatrie Nervenkr* 202:95, 1961.

231. BRUNNGRABER EG, BROWN BD, ARO A: Glycoproteins in brain tissue of the O-variant of G$_{M2}$ gangliosidosis. *J Neurochem* 22:125, 1974.

232. WARNER TG, DE KREMER RD, APPLEGARTH D, MOCK AK: Diagnosis and characterization of G$_{M2}$ gangliosidosis type II (Sandhoff disease) by analysis of the accumulating N-acetyl-glucosaminyl oligosaccharides with high performance liquid chromatography. *Clin Chim Acta* 154:151, 1986.

233. STRECKER G, HERLANT-PEERS MC, FOURNET B, MONTREUIL J, DORLAND L, HAVERKAMP J, VLIEGENTHART JFG: Structure of seven oligosaccharides excreted in the urine of a patient with Sandhoff's disease. *Eur J Biochem* 81:161, 1977.

234. NG YING KIN NMK, WOLFE LS: Structure of the minor oligosaccharides in the liver of a patient with G$_{M2}$ gangliosidosis variant O (Sandhoff-Jatzkewitz disease). *Carbohyd Res* 67:522, 1978.

235. NG YING KIN NMK, WOLFE LS: Oligosaccharides accumulating in the liver from a patient with G$_{M2}$-gangliosidosis variant O (Sandhoff-Jatzkewitz disease). *Biochem Biophys Res Commun* 59:837, 1974.

236. WARNER TG, DE KREMER RD, SJOBERG ER, MOCK AK: Characterization and analysis of branched-chain N-acetylglucosaminyl oligosaccharides accumulating in Sandhoff disease tissue. *J Biol Chem* 260:6194, 1985.

237. WARNER TG, TURNER MW, TOONE JR, APPLEGARTH D: Prenatal diagnosis of infantile G$_{M2}$ gangliosidosis type II (Sandhoff disease) by detection of N-acetylglucosaminyl-oligosaccharides in amniotic fluid with high-performance liquid chromatography. *Prenat Diagn* 6:393, 1986.

238. APPLEGARTH DG, BOZOIAN G: Mucopolysaccharide storage in organs of a patient with Sandhoff's disease. *Clin Chim Acta* 39:269, 1972.

239. STRECKER G, MONTREUIL J: Description d'une oligosaccharidosurie accompagnant une gangliosidose G$_{M2}$ à déficit total en N-acétyl-hexosaminidases. *Clin Chim Acta* 33:395, 1971.

240. CANTZ M, KRESSE H: Sandhoff disease: Defective glycosaminoglycan catabolism in cultured fibroblasts and its correction by β-N-acetylhexosaminidase. *Eur J Biochem* 47:581, 1974.

241. PROIA RL, NEUFELD EF: Synthesis of β-hexosaminidase in cell-free translation and in intact fibroblasts: An insoluble precursor α chain in a rare form of Tay-Sachs disease. *Proc Natl Acad Sci USA* 79:6360, 1982.

242. MYEROWITZ R, HOGIKYAN ND: Different mutations in Ashkenazi Jewish and non-Jewish French Canadians with Tay-Sachs disease. *Science* 232:1646, 1986.

243. MYEROWITZ R, PROIA RL: cDNA clone for the α-chain of human hexosaminidase: Deficiency of α-chain mRNA in Tay-Sachs fibroblasts. *Proc Natl Acad Sci USA* 81:5394, 1984.

244. PAW BH, NEUFELD EF: Normal transcription of the β-hexosaminidase α-chain gene in the Ashkenazi Tay-Sachs mutation. *J Biol Chem* 263:3012, 1988.

244a. MYEROWITZ R: A splice junction mutation in some Ashkenazi Jews with Tay-Sachs disease: Evidence against a single defect within this ethnic group. *Proc Natl Acad Sci USA* 85:3955, 1988.

244b. ARPAIA E, DUMBRILLE-ROSS A, MALER T, NEOTE K, TROPAK M, TROXEL C, STIRLING JL, PITTS JS, BAPAT P, LAMHONWAH AM, MAHURAN DJ, SCHUSTER SM, CLARKE JTR, LOWDEN JA, GRAVEL RA: Identification of an altered splice site in Ashkenazi Tay-Sachs disease. *Nature* 333:85, 1988.

244c. OHNO K, SUZUKI K: A splicing defect due to an exon-intron junctional mutation results in abnormal β-hexosaminidase α-chain mRNAs in Ashkenazi Jewish patients with Tay-Sachs disease. *Biochem Biophys Res Commun* 153:463, 1988.

245. ANDERMAN E, SCRIVER C, WOLFE L, DANSKY S, ANDERMAN F: Genetic variant of Tay-Sachs disease, in Kaback MM (ed): *Tay-Sachs Disease: Screening and Prevention.* New York, AR Liss, 1977.

246. MYEROWITZ R, HOGIKYAN ND: A deletion involving Alu sequences in the β-hexosaminidase α-chain gene of French Canadians with Tay-Sachs disease. *J Biol Chem* 262:15396, 1987.

247. ZOKAEEM G, BAYLERAN J, KAPLAN P, HECHTMAN P, NEUFELD EF: A shortened β-hexosaminidase α-chain in an Italian patient with infantile Tay-Sachs disease. *Am J Hum Genet* 40:537, 1987.

248. OHNO K, SUZUKI K: The mutation in G$_{M2}$ gangliosidosis B1 variant. *J Neurochem* 50:316, 1988.

249. KOLODNY EH, RAGHAVAN SS, LYERLA TA, PROIA RL, NEUFELD EF, GREBNER EE: Misdiagnosis in a fetus with an unstable hexosaminidase A catalytically inactive toward G$_{M2}$ ganglioside. *Am J Hum Genet* 35:47A, 1983.

250. BAYLERAN J, HECHTMAN P: Atypical Tay-Sachs disease; characterization of the defective hexosaminidase A. *Am J Hum Genet* 37:A6, 1985.

251. D'AZZO A, PROIA RL, KOLODNY EH, KABACK MM, NEUFELD EF: Faulty association of α- and β-subunits in some forms of β-hexosaminidase A deficiency. *J Biol Chem* 259:11070, 1984.

252. THOMAS GH, RAGHAVAN S, KOLODNY EH, FRISCH A, NEUFELD EF, O'BRIEN JS, REYNOLDS LW, MILLER CS, SHAPIRO J, KAZAZIAN JR. HH, HELLER RH: Nonuniform deficiency of hexosaminidase A in tissues and fluids of two unrelated individuals. *Pediatr Res* 16:232, 1982.

252a. DLOTT B, QUON D, D'AZZO A, NEUFELD EF: Characterization of the hexosaminidase Paris variant of β-hexosaminidase (abstract). *Am J Hum Genet,* in press.

253. HANCOCK LJ, HORWITZ AL, CASHMAN NR, ANTEL JP, DAWSON G: N-Acetyl-β-hexosaminidase B deficiency in cultured fibroblasts from a patient with progressive motor neuron disease. *Biochem Biophys Res Commun* 130:1185, 1985.

254. DANCE N, PRICE RG, ROBINSON D: Differential assay of human hexosaminidases A and B. *Biochim Biophys Acta* 222:662, 1970.

255. YOUNG EP, ELLIS RB, LAKE BD, PATRICK AD: Tay-Sachs disease and related disorders: Fractionation of brain N-acetyl-β-D-hexosaminidase on DEAE-cellulose. *FEBS Lett* 9:1, 1970.

256. KANFER JN, SPIELVOGEL C: Hexosaminidase activity of cultured human skin fibroblasts. *Biochim Biophys Acta* 293:203, 1973.

257. SUZUKI Y, KOIZUMI Y, TOGARI H, OGAWA Y: Sandhoff disease: Diagnosis of heterozygous carriers by serum hexosaminidase assay. *Clin Chim Acta* 48:153, 1973.

258. HARZER K: Analytische isoelektrische Fraktionierung der N-acetyl-β-D-hexosaminidasen. *Z Anal Chem* 252:170, 1970.

259. HAYASE K, KRITCHEVSKY D: Separation and comparison of isoenzymes of N-acetyl-β-D-hexosaminidase of pregnant serum by polyacrylamide gel electrofocusing. *Clin Chim Acta* 46:455, 1973.

260. CHRISTOMANOU H, CAP C, SANDHOFF K: Isoelectric focusing pattern of acid hydrolases in cultured fibroblasts, leukocytes and cell-free amniotic fluid. *Neuropädiatrie* 8:238, 1977.

261. O'BRIEN JS, OKADA S, FILLERUP DL, VEATH ML, ADORANTO B, BRENNER PH, LEROY J: Tay-Sachs disease—Prenatal diagnosis. *Science* 172:61, 1971.

262. SUZUKI Y, SUZUKI K: Partial deficiency of hexosaminidase component in a juvenile G$_{M2}$ gangliosidosis. *Neurology* 20:848, 1970.

263. KLIBANSKY C: Separation of N-acetyl-β-D-hexosaminidase isoenzymes from human brain and leukocytes by cellulose acetate paper electrophoresis. *Isr J Med Sci* 7:1086, 1971.

264. DAVIDSON RG, RATTAZZI MC: Prenatal diagnosis of genetic disorders. Trials and tribulations. *Clin Chem* 18:179, 1972.

265. O'BRIEN JS, OKADA S, CHEN A, FILLERUP DL: Tay-Sachs disease: Detection of heterozygotes and homozygotes by serum hexosaminidase assay. *N Engl J Med* 283:15, 1970.

266. KABACK MM: Thermal fractionation of serum hexosaminidases: Applications to heterozyote detection and diagnosis of Tay-Sachs disease. *Methods Enzymol* 28:862, 1972.

267. SAIFER A, PERLE G: Automated determination of serum hexosaminidase A by pH inactivation for detection of Tay-Sachs disease heterozygotes. *Clin Chem* 20:538, 1974.

268. SANDHOFF K: Multiple human hexosaminidases. *Birth Defects* 9(2):214, 1973.

269. NAVON R, NUTMAN J, KOPEL R, GABER L, GADOTH N, GOLDMAN B, NITZAN M: Hereditary heat-labile hexosaminidase B: Its implications for recognizing Tay-Sachs genotypes. *Am J Hum Genet* 33:907, 1981.

270. NAVON R, KOPEL R, NUTMAN J, FRISCH A, CONZELMANN E, SANDHOFF K, ADAM A: Hereditary heat-labile hexosaminidase B: A variant whose homozygotes synthesize a functional HEX A. *Am J Hum Genet* 37:138, 1985.

271. INUI K, WENGER DA: Usefulness of 4-methylumbelliferyl-6-sulfo-2-acetamido-2-deoxy-β-D-glucopyranoside for the diagnosis of G$_{M2}$ gangliosidoses in leukocytes. *Clin Genet* 26:318, 1984.

272. BAYLERAN J, HECHTMAN P, SARAY W: Synthesis of 4-methylumbelliferyl-β-D-N-acetylglucosamine-6-sulfate and its use in classification of G$_{M2}$ gangliosidosis genotypes. *Clin Chim Acta* 143:73, 1984.

273. FUCHS W, NAVON R, KABACK MM, KRESSE H: Tay-Sachs disease: One-step assay of β-N-acetylhexosaminidase in serum with a sulfated chromogenic substrate. *Clin Chim Acta* 133:253, 1983.

274. INUI K, WENGER DA, FURUKAWA M, SUEHARA N, YUTAKA Y, OKADA S, TANIZAWA O, YABUUCHI H: Prenatal diagnosis of G$_{M2}$ gangliosidoses using a fluorogenic sulfated substrate. *Clin Chim Acta* 154:145, 1986.

275. HARZER K: Assay of the G$_{M2}$-ganglioside cleaving hexosaminidase activity of skin fibroblasts for G$_{M2}$-gangliosidoses. *Clin Chim Acta* 135:89, 1983.

276. ERZBERGER A, CONZELMANN E, SANDHOFF K: Assay of ganglioside G$_{M2}$-N-acetyl-β-D-galactosaminidase activity in human fibroblasts employing the natural activator protein—Diagnosis of variant forms of G$_{M2}$ gangliosidosis. *Clin Chim Acta* 108:361, 1980.

277. CHRISTOMANOU H, CAP C, SANDHOFF K: Prenatal diagnosis of Tay-Sachs disease in cell-free amniotic fluid. *Klin Wochenschr* 56:1133, 1978.

278. SONDERFELD S, CONZELMANN E, SCHWARZMANN G, BURG J, HINRICHS U, SANDHOFF K: Incorporation and metabolism of ganglioside G$_{M2}$ in skin fibroblasts from normal and G$_{M2}$ gangliosidosis subjects. *Eur J Biochem* 149:247, 1985.

279. KOLODNY EH, RAGHAVAN SS: G$_{M2}$-gangliosidosis. Hexosaminidase mutations not of the Tay-Sachs type produce unusual clinical variants. *Trends Neurosci* 6:16, 1983.

280. RAGHAVAN SS, KRUSSEL A, LYERLA TA, BREMER EG, KOLODNY EH: G$_{M2}$-ganglioside metabolism in cultured human skin fibroblasts: Unambiguous diagnosis of G$_{M2}$ gangliosidosis. *Biochim Biophys Acta* 834:238, 1985.

281. SCHWARZMANN G, HOFFMANN-BLEIHAUER P, SCHUBERT J, SANDHOFF K, MARSH D: Incorporation of ganglioside analogues into fibroblast cell membranes. A spin label study. *Biochemistry* 22:5041, 1983.

282. SUZUKI Y, BERMAN P, SUZUKI K: Detection of Tay-Sachs disease heterozygotes by assay of hexosaminidase A in serum and leukocytes. *J Pediatr* 78:643, 1971.

283. OKADA S, VEATH M, LEROY J, O'BRIEN JS: Ganglioside G$_{M2}$ storage diseases: Hexosaminidase deficiencies in cultured fibroblasts. *Am J Hum Genet* 23:55, 1971.

284. CARMODY P, RATTAZZI M, DAVIDSON R: Tay-Sachs disease—The use of tears for the detection of heterozygotes. *N Engl J Med* 289:1072, 1973.

285. KABACK M, ZEIGER R: Heterozyote detection in Tay-Sachs disease: A prototype community screening program for the prevention of recessive genetic disorders, in Volk BW, Aronson SM (eds): *Sphingolipids, Sphingolipidoses, and Allied Disorders. Advances in Experimental Medicine and Biology.* New York, Plenum, 1972, vol 19, p 613.

286. KABACK M, ZEIGER R, REYNOLDS L, SONNEBORN M: Approaches to the control and prevention of Tay-Sachs disease, in Steinberg AG, Bearn A (eds): *Progress in Medical Genetics.* New York, Grune & Stratton, 1974, vol 10, p 103.

287. KABACK M, NATHAN T, GREENWALD S: Tay-Sachs heterozygotes screening and prenatal diagnosis, USA experience and world perspectives, in Kaback MM (ed): *Tay-Sachs Disease: Screening and Prevention.* New York, AR Liss, 1977.

288. KABACK M: Heterozygote screening and prenatal diagnosis in Tay-Sachs disease: A worldwide update, in Callahan J, Lowden J (eds): *Lysosomes and Lysosomal Storage Diseases.* New York: Raven Press, 1981, p 331.

289. LOWDEN JA, SKOMOROWSKI M, HENDERSON F, KABACK MM: The automated assay of hexosaminidases in serum. *Clin Chem* 19:1345, 1973.

290. GREENBERG D, KABACK MM: Estimation of the frequency of hexosaminidase A variant alleles in the American Jewish population. *Am J Hum Genet* 34:444, 1982.

291. PETERSEN G, CANTOR R, ROY C, LIN J, ROTTER J, KABACK MM: Partial hexosaminidase A deficiency in American Jewish and non-Jewish populations: Implications for genetic counseling in G$_{M2}$ gangliosidoses. In preparation, 1988.

292. CANTOR R, LIM J, ROY C, KABACK MM: Sandhoff disease heterozygote detection: A component of population screening for Tay-Sachs disease carriers: I. Statistical methods. *Am J Hum Genet* 37:912, 1985.

293. SCHNECK L, FRIEDLAND J, VALENTI C, ADACHI M, AMSTERDAM D, VOLK BW: Prenatal diagnosis of Tay-Sachs disease. *Lancet* 1:582, 1970.

294. NAVON R, PADEH B: Prenatal diagnosis of Tay-Sachs genotypes. *Br Med J* 4:17, 1971.

295. PERGAMENT E, GINSBERG N, VERLINSKY Y, CADKIN A, CHU L, TRUKA L, GREBNER EE, WAPNER RJ, BARR MA, JACKSON LG: Prenatal Tay-Sachs diagnosis by chorionic villi sampling. *Lancet* 2:286, 1983.

296. BESANÇON AM, BELON JP, CASTELNAU L, DUMEZ Y, POENARU L: Prenatal diagnosis of atypical Tay-Sachs disease by chorionic villi sampling. *Prenatal Diagn* 4:365, 1984.

297. MYRIANTHOPOULOS N: Some epidemiologic and genetic aspects of Tay-Sachs disease, in Aronson S, Volk BW (eds): *Cerebral Sphingolipidoses: A Symposium on Tay-Sachs Disease and Allied Disorders.* New York, Academic, 1962, p 375.

298. ARONSON S: Epidemiology, in Volk BW (ed): *Tay-Sachs Disease.* New York, Grune & Stratton, 1964, p 118.

299. PETERSEN G, ROTTER J, CANTOR R, FIELD L, GREENWALD S, LIM J, ROY C, SCHOENFELD J, LOWDEN A, KABACK M: The geographic variation and origin of the Tay-Sachs disease gene in North American Jewish populations. *Am J Hum Genet* 35:1258, 1983.

300. CANTOR RM, ROY C, LIM JST, KABACK MM: Sandhoff disease heterozyote detection: A component of population screening for Tay-Sachs disease carriers. II. Sandhoff disease gene frequencies in American Jewish and non-Jewish populations. *Am J Hum Genet* 41:16, 1987.

301. KABACK MM: International Tay-Sachs Disease Quality Control, and Data Collection Center, in preparation 1988.

302. ARONSON S, VALSAMIS M, VOLK B: Infantile amaurotic idiocy. Occurrence, genetic considerations and pathophysiology in the non-Jewish infant. *Pediatrics* 26:229, 1960.

303. HANHART E: Über 27 Sippen mit infantiler amaurotischer Idiotie (Tay-Sachs). *Acta Genet Med Gemellol* 3:331, 1954.

304. MURAKAMI U: Clinicogenetic study of hereditary diseases of the nervous system. *Folia Psychiatr Neurol Jpn (Suppl)* 1:1, 1957.

305. KELLY T, CHASE G, KABACK M, KUMOR K, MCKUSICK V: Tay-Sachs disease; high gene frequency in a non-Jewish population. *Am J Hum Genet* 27:287, 1975.

306. LOWDEN J, IVES E, KEENE D, BURTON A, SKOMOROWSKI M, HOWARD F: Carrier detection in Sandhoff disease. *Am J Hum Genet* 30:38, 1978.

307. DERKALOUSTIAN V, KHOURY M, HALLAL R, IDRISS Z, DEEB M ET AL: Sandhoff disease: A prevalent form of infantile G$_{M2}$ gangliosidosis in Lebanon. *Am J Hum Genet* 33:85, 1981.

308. DE KREMER R, DE LEVSTEIN I: Enfermedad de Sandhoff o gangliosidosis G$_{M2}$ tipo 2. Alta Frequencia del gen en una poblacion Criolla. *Medicina* 40:55, 1980.

309. WARNER T, O'BRIEN J: Genetic defects in glycoprotein metabolism. *Annu Rev Genet* 17:395, 1983.

310. MYRIANTHOPOULOS N, ARONSON S: Population dynamics of Tay-Sachs disease. I. Reproductive fitness and selection. *Am J Hum Genet* 18:313, 1966.

311. O'BRIEN J: Tay-Sachs disease: From enzyme to prevention. *Fed Proc* 32:191, 1973.

312. MRAZ W, SCHWARZMANN G, SATTLER J, MOMOI T, SEEMANN B, WIEGANDT H: Aggregate formation of gangliosides at low concentrations in aqueous media. *Hoppe-Seyler's Z Physiol Chem* 361:177, 1980.

313. WALLACE BJ, VOLK BW, LAZARUS SS: Fine structural localization of acid phosphatase activity in neurons of Tay-Sachs disease. *J Neuropathol Exp Neurol* 23:676, 1964.

314. WALKLEY SU, BLAKEMORE WF, PURPURA DP: Alterations in neuron morphology in feline mannosidosis: A Golgi study. *Acta Neuropathol* 53:75, 1981.

315. WALKLEY SU, HASKINS ME: Aberrant neurite and meganeurite development in a feline model of mucopolysaccharidosis (MPS) type 1 as revealed by the Golgi method. *Soc Neurosci Abstr* 8:1009, 1982.

316. SVENNERHOLM L, VANIER M-T, HANSSON J-E: Krabbe disease: A galactosylsphingosine (psychosine) lipidosis. *J Lipid Res* 21:53, 1980.

317. NILSSON O, MANSSON J-E, HAKANSSON G, SVENNERHOLM L: The occurrence of psychosine and other glycolipids in spleen and liver from the three major types of Gaucher's disease. *Biochim Biophys Acta* 712:453, 1982.

318. IGISU H, SUZUKI K: Progressive accumulation of toxic metabolite in a genetic leukodystrophy. *Science* 224:753, 1984.

319. HANNUN YA, BELL RM: Lysosphingolipids inhibit protein kinase C: Implications for the sphingolipidoses. *Science* 235:670, 1987.

320. ÖHMANN R, ROSENBERG A, SVENNERHOLM L: Human brain sialidase. *Biochemistry* 9:3774, 1970.

321. CONZELMANN E, SANDHOFF K: Partial enzyme deficiencies: Residual activities and the development of neurologic disorders. *Dev Neurosci* 6:58, 1983/84.

322. JOHNSON W, DESNICK R, LONG D, SHARP M, KRIVIT W, BRADY B, BRADY RO: Intravenous injection of purified hexosaminidase A into patients with Tay-Sachs disease, in Desnick R, Bernlohr R, Krivit W (eds): *Enzyme Therapy in Genetic Diseases.* New York, AR Liss, 1973, p 120.

323. VON SPECHT B, GEIGER B, ARNON R, PASSWELL J, KEREN G, GOLDMAN B, PADEH B: Enzyme replacement in Tay-Sachs disease. *Neurology* 29:858, 1979.

324. KABACK MM, unpublished observation.

325. KRIVIT W, PAUL NW: Bone marrow transplantation for treatment of lysosomal storage disorder. *Birth Defects* 22:1, 1986.

326. SHULL RM, HASTINGS NE, SELCER RR, JONES JB, SMITH JR, CULLEN WC, CONSTANTOPOULOS G: Bone marrow transplantation in canine mucopolysaccharidosis. Effects within the nervous system. *J Clin Invest* 79:435, 1987.

327. TAYLOR RM, FARROW BRH, STEWART GJ, HEALY PJ: Enzyme replacement in nervous tissue after allogenic bone-marrow transplantation for fucosidosis in dogs. *Lancet* 1:722, 1986.

328. SUZUKI K, HOOGERBRUGGE PM, POORTHUIS BJHM, VAN BEKKUM DW, SUZUKI K: The twitcher mouse. Central nervous system pathology after bone marrow transplantation. *Lab Invest* 58:302, 1988.

328a. HOOGERBRUGGE PM, SUZUKI K, SUZUKI K, POORTHUIS BJHM, KOBAYASHI T, WAGEMAKER G, VAN BEKKUM DW: Donor-derived cells in the central nervous system of twitcher mice after bone marrow transplantation. *Science* 239:1035, 1988.

329. KARBE E, SCHIEFER B: Familial amaurotic idiocy in male German short-hair pointers. *Vet Pathol* 4:223, 1967.

330. BERNHEIMER H, KARBE E: Morphologische und neurochemische Untersuchungen von zwei Formen der amaurotischen Idiotie des Hundes. Nachweis einer G$_{M2}$-Gangliosidose. *Acta Neuropathol (Berl)* 16:243, 1970.

331. READ WK, BRIDGES CH: Cerebrospinal lipodystrophy in swine. A new disease model in comparative pathology. *Vet Pathol* 5:67, 1968.

332. PIERCE KR, KOSANKE SD, BAY WW, BRIDGES CH: Animal model: Porcine cerebrospinal lipodystrophy (G$_{M2}$ gangliosidosis). *Am J Pathol* 83:419, 1976.

333. KOSANKE SD, PIERCE KR, BAY WW: Clinical and biochemical abnormalities in porcine G$_{M2}$-gangliosidosis. *Vet Pathol* 15:685, 1978.

334. KOSANKE SD, PIERCE KR, READ WK: Morphogenesis of light and electron microscopic lesions in porcine G$_{M2}$ gangliosidosis. *Vet Pathol* 16:6, 1979.

335. CORK LC, MUNNELL JF, LORENZ MD, MURPHY JV, BAKER JH, RATTAZZI MC: G$_{M2}$ ganglioside lysosomal storage disease in cats with β-hexosaminidase deficiency. *Science* 196:1014, 1977.

336. CORK LC, MUNNELL JF, LORENZ MD: The pathology of feline G$_{M2}$ gangliosidosis. *Am J Pathol* 90:723, 1978.

337. RATTAZZI MC, APPEL AM, BAKER HJ: Enzyme replacement in G$_{M2}$ gangliosidosis: Catabolic effects of human β-hexosaminidase A (Hex A). *Pediatr Res* 15:567, 1981.

338. NEUWELT EA, JOHNSON WG, BLANK NK, PAGEL MA, MASLEN-MCCLURE C, MCCLURE M, WU PM: Characterization of a new model of G$_{M2}$ gangliosidosis (Sandhoff's disease) in Korat cats. *J Clin Invest* 76:482, 1985.

339. CUMMINGS JF, WOOD PA, WALKLEY SU, DE LAHUNTA A, DEFOREST ME: G$_{M2}$ gangliosidosis in a Japanese Spaniel. *Acta Neuropathol (Berl)* 67:247, 1985.

340. ISHIKAWA Y, LI S-C, WOOD PA, LI Y-T: Biochemical basis of type AB G$_{M2}$ gangliosidosis in a Japanese Spaniel. *J Neurochem* 48:860, 1987.

341. MICHEL S, MEIER E, CONZELMANN E, SANDHOFF K: unpublished results.

PART 12

HORMONES: SYNTHESIS AND ACTION

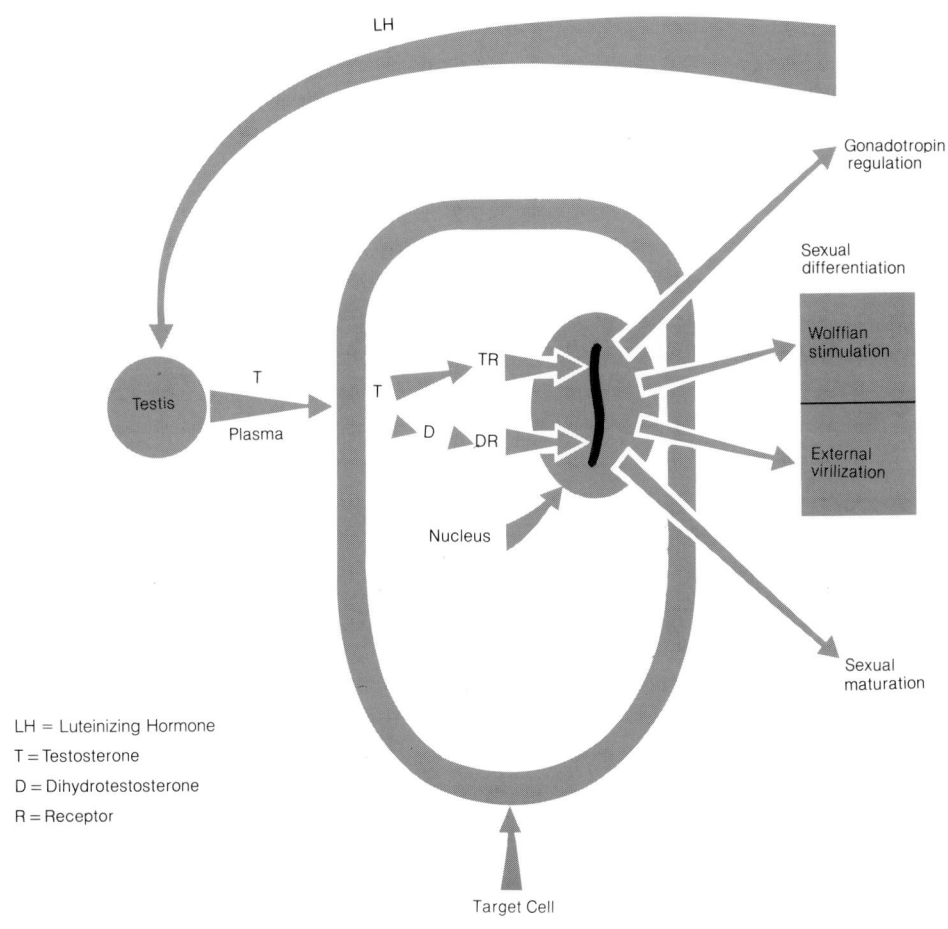

LH

Gonadotropin
regulation

Sexual
differentiation

Wolffian
stimulation

External
virilization

Sexual
maturation

Testis

T

Plasma

T

D

TR

DR

Nucleus

Target Cell

LH = Luteinizing Hormone

T = Testosterone

D = Dihydrotestosterone

R = Receptor

Testosterone

CHAPTER 73

THYROID DISORDERS

J. E. DUMONT
G. VASSART
S. REFETOFF

1. Synthesis, storage, secretion, delivery, and utilization of the thyroid hormones involve a complex sequence of metabolic events, many of which are dependent upon specific enzymes. Thyroid disease may result from impairments at many steps in this metabolic process. Congenital blocks are sometimes reproduced locally in discrete thyroid adenomas. The thyroid operates under hypothalamic-pituitary control; inherited disorders along this control pathway may also cause thyroid disease.

2. Inadequate response to thyrotropin causes a decrease in functional activity (synthesis and secretion of thyroid hormone) and in growth (hypotrophy) of the thyroid. When this results from a defect in the thyroid-stimulating hormone receptor, it is specific for the thyroid. Defects in the postreceptor complex would cause defects in multiple organs. For example, defects of the activating guanosine triphosphate–binding protein of adenylate cyclase produce pseudohypoparathyroidism. Constitutive hyperactivation of the thyroid causes hyperthyroidism.

3. Familial goiter and hypothyroidism may occur when there is failure of the thyroid cell to transport iodide and maintain a favorable concentration gradient inside the follicle (iodide transport defect). The salivary and gastric glands of such patients are also unable to concentrate iodide.

4. Familial goiter may also result from failure to convert iodide into organic iodine in the thyroid gland (organification defect). This may result from absence of thyroid peroxidase, abnormal peroxidase, or perhaps because of a diminished supply of peroxide. Accumulated iodide is precipitously discharged from the gland upon administration of perchlorate.

5. Several families of patients have been studied which have a defect in the coupling of iodotyrosines into iodothyronines (coupling defect). Different components of the enzymatic system (thyroperoxidase, H_2O_2-generating system) as well as the thyroglobulin substrate may be involved. The disease can be suspected when other inborn errors have been excluded and can be confirmed by the lack of iodothyronines despite a normal or nearly normal concentration of iodine in biopsy specimens of thyroid tissue.

6. Some families are known to be unable to deiodinate iodotyrosines (iodotyrosine deiodinase defect). Loss of hormone precursors from the gland into the urine accounts for hypothyroidism and compensatory goiter. Goitrous but euthyroid relatives of such patients may deiodinate diiodotyrosine (DIT) less well than normal individuals. The condition is diagnosed by the demonstration that intravenously administered, labeled DIT is excreted intact in the urine.

7. Familial goiter may occur in humans and animals because of impaired synthesis of thyroglobulin. In some instances, other proteins may be iodinated within the thyroid cell. In other patients, the thyroid may synthesize abnormal forms of thyroglobulin.

8. Impaired response to thyroid hormone has been described. The severity of the resistance and the degree of hyporesponsiveness among body tissues are variable. The diminished sensitivity may be confined to the thyrotroph cells.

9. Familial hypothyroidism may arise from several disorders of hypothalamic or pituitary control of the thyroid.

10. Abnormalities of serum proteins which transport thyroid hormone are recognized but usually are not accompanied by disturbances in hormone synthesis or action.

11. With the exception of hormone transport defects which are X-linked, most of the above conditions are inherited as autosomal recessive traits. Because of the rarity of the defects responsible for each disorder, a high proportion of cases occur in consanguineous matings.

Laboratory investigations of subjects with familial thyroid disease have resulted in classification of most patients according to their biochemical defect in specialized thyroid metabolism. In each of the categories reviewed here, the lesion affects one of the many proteins involved. However, the net effect of all defects is the same: reduced thyroid hormone action through defective synthesis, delivery, or action of hormone. Before considering each defect, it is appropriate to review relevant aspects of thyroid and iodine metabolism. A scheme of the metabolic pathway of iodine appears in Fig. 73-1. General reviews are available elsewhere.[1,2] For a relevant older bibliography, earlier editions of this chapter may be consulted.[3,4]

THYROID PHYSIOLOGY AND METABOLISM: AN OVERVIEW

Iodide* ion is absorbed through the gastrointestinal tract and is rapidly distributed throughout the extracellular fluid of the

---

*In this chapter, *iodine* is used in a generic sense to encompass all forms and oxidation states unless otherwise indicated; *iodide* designates the anion.

Nonstandard abbreviations used in this chapter are: C = catalytic subunit of cyclic AMP–dependent protein kinase; DIT = 3,5-diiodotyrosine; I-5′DI = type I 5′-deiodinase; II-5′DI = type II 5′-deiodinase; EGF = epidermal growth factor; G_i = inhibitory guanine nucleotide–binding protein; G_s = stimulatory guanine nucleotide–binding protein; G_p = guanine nucleotide–binding protein affecting phospholipase C; IP_3 = inositol (1,4,5)phosphate; MIT = 3-monoiodotyrosine; PBI = protein-bound iodine; PIP_2 = diphosphatidylinositol-4,5-phosphate; PTU = propylthiouracil; R = regulatory subunit of cyclic AMP–dependent protein kinase; rT_3 = 3,3′,5′-triiodothyronine, or reverse T_3; T_3 = 3,5,3′-triiodothyronine; T_4 = L-thyroxine, or 3,5,3′,5′-tetraiodothyronine; TBG = thyroxine-binding globulin; TBPA = thyroxine-binding prealbumin; TRH = thyrotropin-releasing hormone; TRIAC = 3,5,3′-triiodothyroacetic acid; TSH = thyroid-stimulating hormone; and TSI = thyroid-stimulating immunoglobulins.

Data Expressed as μg of Iodine

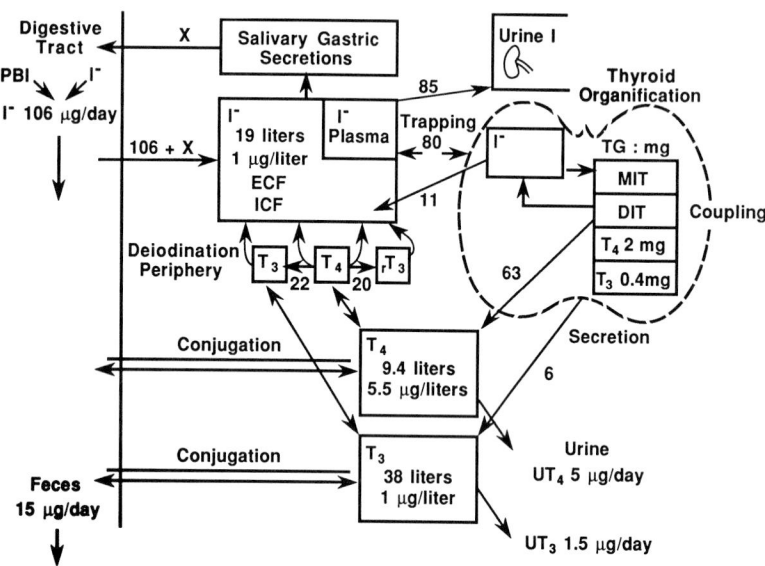

Fig. 73-1 Metabolism of iodine in humans. Compartments are identified with the concentration of iodine (in μg/liter) and distribution spaces (in liters). In the case of the thyroid, the total iodine content of each compartment is indicated in milligrams. Fluxes (arrows) of iodine are expressed in micrograms iodine per day. PBI = protein-bound iodine; ECF = extracellular fluid or space; ICF = intracellular fluid or space; Tg = thyroglobulin; UT_4 and UT_3 = urinary excretions of T_4 and T_3; X = flux of iodine through the digestive tract cycle.

body. The volume of distribution is approximately 30 percent of body weight. Iodinated thyronines and tyrosines (Fig. 73-2) may be absorbed intact but are partially (T_3 and T_4 less than 5 percent) or almost totally (iodotyrosines ≈ 95 percent) deiodinated prior to absorption. Upon absorption or secretion, thyroxine (T_4) and to some extent triiodothyronine (T_3) are first confined to the vascular compartment because of binding to carrier proteins in the plasma.

Except in the postprandial state, the iodide concentration in the plasma is less than 0.2 μg/dl. The iodide is removed from plasma almost entirely by the kidney and the thyroid gland. Renal clearance of iodide is normally about 35 ml/min and is independent of the iodine supply. Thyroid clearance varies widely, depending on the functional state of the gland, but is normally between 10 and 35 ml/min. The iodide taken by the salivary and gastric glands is returned to plasma after absorption in the small intestine. Small amounts of iodide are removed by the mammary glands during lactation, and some organic iodine is lost in the feces and urine.

The function of the thyroid follicle cell is to trap iodide from the blood and to use it for the synthesis of the thyroid hormones, T_4 and T_3. The thyroid cell synthesizes principally one exportable glycoprotein, thyroglobulin, which is secreted

by exocytosis into the follicular lumen. Iodide is trapped at the basal membrane of the cell and concentrated in the lumen; it is oxidized and bound to the tyrosyl residues of thyroglobulin by thyroperoxidase at the apical membrane of the cell (Fig. 73-3). The H_2O_2 required by the peroxidase is supplied by a still poorly defined H_2O_2-generating system. Thyroperoxidase also catalyzes the oxidative coupling of iodotyrosines into iodothyronines, T_4 and T_3, within the matrix of thyroglobulin. Thyroglobulin slowly diffuses within the follicular lumen to ensure the relative homogeneity of the luminal content, the colloid. Thyroid colloid thus constitutes a store of sequestered iodine, the iodotyrosyls, and thyroid hormones contained in thyroglobulin. In the secretory process, follicular cells internalize thyroglobulin by micropinocytosis or macropinocytosis and digest its constituent amino acids in secondary lysosomes. While the iodothyronines are released, presumably by diffusion, the iodotyrosines are deiodinated in the cell, thus allowing the reutilization of their iodine.

All the metabolic steps of the follicular cell, as well as its growth, are controlled by TSH (thyroid-stimulating hormone, or thyrotropin). The level of TSH in the plasma is the result of positive hypothalamic control exerted through TRH (thyrotropin-releasing hormone) and negative control

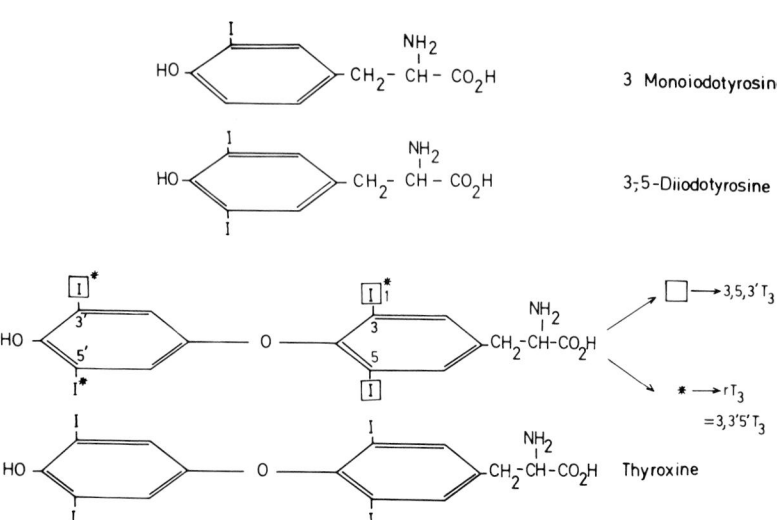

Fig. 73-2 Iodinated amino acids of the thyroid. rT_3 = reverse triiodothyronine.

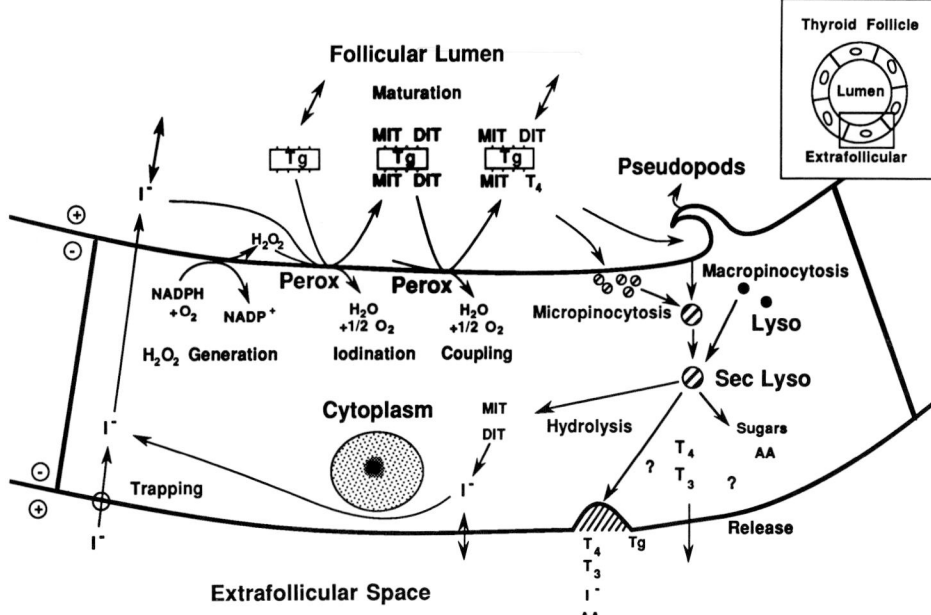

Fig. 73-3 Specialized metabolism of the thyroid follicular cell. AA = amino acids; LYSO = primary lysosome; PEROX = thyroperoxidase; SEC LYSO = secondary lysosome; Tg = thyroglobulin; MIT = monoiodotyrosine; DIT = diiodotyrosine.

on TSH synthesis and secretion by the pituitary thyrotrophs exerted by circulating iodothyronines. There are additional negative controls through hypothalamic somatostatin and dopamine.

Thyroid hormones are transported mostly bound to serum proteins: thyroxine-binding globulin (TBG), thyroxine-binding prealbumin (TBPA), and albumin. T_4, which must be considered a prohormone, is deiodinated to the active hormone, 3,5,3'-triiodothyronine (T_3), or to an inactive species, 3,3',5'-triiodothyronine, or reverse T_3 (rT_3), in peripheral tissues. The action of thyroid hormone on the peripheral cells, exerted mostly at the level of gene expression, is to enhance certain components of cellular intermediary metabolism and to sustain body and brain growth and development.

Most of the metabolic steps outlined here involve several different proteins. Structural or regulatory defects may be expected for any of the proteins involved in each metabolic step, but the phenotypic expression of such defects will be virtually identical. In this chapter, defects will be classified on the basis of the function involved, i.e., according to the phenotypic expression. It will be understood that each of these classes may encompass several different genetic defects.

THYROTROPIN AND THYROID FUNCTION

Metabolism

Thyroid function and growth are stimulated by TSH. Several accessory circuits involving neurotransmitters (acetylcholine, norepinephrine, and TRH), prostaglandins, and iodine are superimposed on this main regulation. Thus, overall control is exerted by a complex regulatory network[5] (Fig. 73-4). TSH acutely stimulates the binding of iodide to proteins, iodotyrosine oxidative coupling, thyroid hormone release, and many pathways of intermediary metabolism, such as the oxidation of glucose by the pentose phosphate pathway. With a delay of several hours, TSH enhances the trapping of iodide and the synthesis of RNA, proteins, and so on. Chronically adminis-

tered, it induces cell growth and multiplication, i.e., cell hypertrophy and thyroid hyperplasia.[6]

TSH interacts with the thyroid follicular cell at the level of the plasma membrane by binding to specific receptor(s) coupled to effectors or catalytic units. One such system, thyroid adenylate cyclase, has been well characterized. It represents for the thyroid cell and TSH the application of the Sutherland model of hormone action. TSH binds to a receptor and activates it; this, in turn, stimulates a nucleotide-binding protein (G_s), which releases guanosine diphosphate and binds guanosine triphosphate (GTP); the GTP-activated G protein stimulates the catalytic unit, i.e., the cyclase that catalyzes the generation of cyclic adenosine monophosphate (cAMP) from ATP (turn on). The action of the hormone is terminated by the hydrolysis of bound GTP to GDP by the GTPase activity of the G protein (turn off). The receptor, on the one hand, and the G_s protein and cyclase, on the other hand, freely float in the two-dimensional plane of the membrane and interact at the

Fig. 73-4 Human thyroid cell regulation. Demonstrated controls are represented by uninterrupted lines. Controls suggested by analogy with other systems or demonstrated in dog but not yet in humans are represented by interrupted lines; (+) and (−) indicate positive and negative controls. DAG = diacylglycerol; IP_3 = myoinositol 1,4,5-triphosphate; PIP_2 = phosphatidylinositol-4,5-biphosphate; Tg = thyroglobulin; TRH = thyrotropin-releasing hormone; TSI = thyroid-stimulating immunoglobulins; VIP = vasointestinal peptide; XI = unknown mediator of the inhibitory effect of iodide.

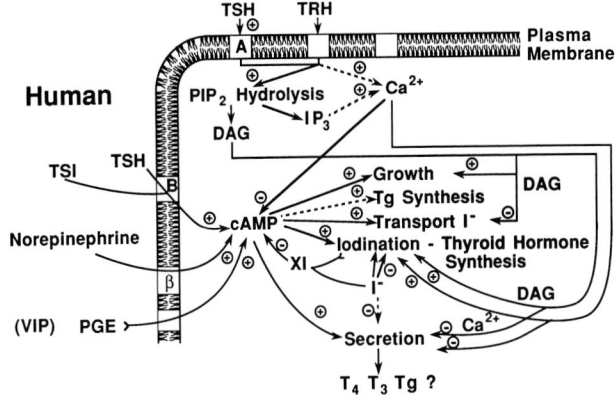

cytoplasmic side.[7,8] In the cytosol, cyclic AMP binds to cyclic AMP–dependent protein kinases by the reaction $R_2C_2 + 4$ cyclic AMP = R_2(cyclic AMP)$_4$ + 2 C. R, the regulatory subunit of the kinases, blocks enzyme activity, while the binding of cyclic AMP to R releases the active catalytic (C) subunits that phosphorylate specific protein substrates in the cell. In the dog thyroid, at least 12 such proteins are phosphorylated in response to TSH, but only two of these, the histone H_1 and high mobility group protein HMG_{14}, have been identified, and the relation of these phosphorylations to the physiological effects of the hormone are still unknown. It has been demonstrated that this pathway accounts for most of the effects of TSH on the dog thyroid, including promotion of growth.[5,9] In the human thyroid, so far as it has been studied, the same scheme applies (Fig. 73-4).

In the human thyroid, TSH also activates the release in the cell of inositol (1,4,5)phosphate (IP_3) and Ca^{2+}.[10] By analogy with better studied systems, it can be surmised that TSH activates, through another GTP-binding transducing protein (G_p), a phospholipase C that specifically hydrolyzes diphosphatidylinositol-4,5-phosphate (PIP_2) to inositol (1,4,5)-phosphate and diacylglycerol. Diacylglycerol stimulates a specific protein kinase C; IP_3 causes the release of Ca^{2+} from endoplasmic reticulum, generally accompanied by a Ca^{2+} influx from the extracellular medium. Calcium activates various intracellular enzymes including, through calmodulin, specific protein kinases. The specific pattern of protein phosphorylation induced by each intracellular signal molecule (cyclic AMP, diacylglycerol, calcium) explains their respective effects. By analogy with the adrenergic system, we call A the effects secondary to the activation of the PIP_2 cascade and B the effects mediated by cyclic AMP.[11,12] The dual action of TSH on the human thyroid gland could be explained, as in the case of neurotransmitters such as noradrenaline, histamine, and dopamine and of peptides such as secretin and vasopressin, by the existence of two different receptors for TSH, or less likely, of two effector systems coupled to one receptor.

In the human thyrocyte, the stimulations by TSH of secretion and iodination, which is rapid, and of iodide trapping and proliferation, which is delayed, are all mimicked by cyclic AMP enhancers and thus, presumably are mediated by cyclic AMP. On the other hand, evidence based on the use of pharmacologic probes (calcium ionophores and phorbol esters) suggests that calcium and diacylglycerol independently activate iodination and inhibit secretion. Diacylglycerol also inhibits iodide transport and induces growth.[5]

Chronic stimulation of the thyroid gland by TSH leads to a relative decrease in the secretory response (desensitization). Several mechanisms account for this: acute decrease in the stimulation of adenylate cyclase, exhaustion of the apical membranes available for macropinocytosis, and a later downregulation of the number of TSH receptors.[13,14]

Several other physiological agents activate thyroid adenylate cyclase, among these norepinephrine acting on β-adrenergic receptors and E prostaglandins. Compared to those of TSH, their effects are in general of lower amplitude, shorter duration, and unknown functional significance. The thyroid-stimulating immunoglobulins (TSI) found in the serum of patients with Graves disease reproduce the effects of TSH and bind to the same receptor(s). TSH receptor blocking antibodies, on the other hand, cause hypothyroidism.

The thyroid cyclic AMP system is negatively controlled by iodide at the level of adenylate cyclase. This effect is relieved by inhibitors of iodide trapping and iodide oxidation and presumably is mediated by a still unknown signal molecule termed *XI*, which may contain iodine. The same or a similar mechanism may also account for the inhibition by iodide of its own oxidation (Wolff-Chaikoff effect), the Ca^{2+}-PIP_2 cascade, several transports including that of iodide itself, and perhaps of growth and secretion.

Several neurotransmitters and local hormones modulate positively or negatively the cyclic AMP and the Ca^{2+} phosphatidylinositol cascade in the thyroid cell. These controls vary from one species to another. In the dog thyroid norepinephrine, through α_2-adrenergic receptors and inhibitory GTP-binding protein, G_i, inhibits adenylate cyclase. In the human thyroid cell, TRH, ATP, and $PGF_2\alpha$ activate phospholipase C and phosphatidylinositol-4,5-phosphate hydrolysis.[5]

TSH action on the human thyroid gland can be studied at different levels: in vivo, in vitro in intact cells, or in broken cell preparations. The best indices of stimulation may be the normal functional effects of the hormone in vivo, i.e., the acute stimulation of hormone and thyroglobulin release, as measured by plasma T_4 and T_3 and thyroglobulin, and the delayed enhancement of iodide trapping, as measured by sodium pertechnetate ^{99m}Tc uptake. However, such tests give no clue concerning the mechanisms involved. For example, an absent secretory response may reflect an already maximal stimulation, deficient hormone synthesis, iodine overexposure, etc. Moreover, each test provides only one result. With one piece of tissue, several in vitro results can be obtained, but it cannot be overemphasized that whatever the parameter measured, information must be obtained on the kinetics of the response and on concentration effects. Also, in order to validate a negative result, it is essential that a tissue with positive response be tested simultaneously with the same reagents. Studies on intact cells, in slices, or in culture give fewer artifacts, but the responses are more complex than in studies using broken cell systems. Responses to be measured include accumulations of cyclic AMP and inositol phosphates, iodination of protein, and oxidation of [^{14}C]glucose.[10,15,16] The latter two explore the whole sequence of events between hormone binding and terminal effects. The effect of TSH on iodination of protein in human thyroid slices is not constant, and the glucose oxidation response is biphasic[16] (decreased at low and increased at high TSH concentrations). The effect at low concentration is mediated by cyclic AMP (B-type effect) while the effect at high concentration is presumably an A type of TSH effect. In the absence of TSH action, the demonstration of cyclic AMP, Ca^{2+}, or diacylglycerol effects using pharmacologic probes would suggest a defect at the membrane receptor level. Conversely, a lack of effect with a probe would point out defects in the action of the intracellular signal.

The binding of TSH to thyroid membranes and TSH activation of adenylate cyclase in membranes can be studied with broken cell systems. For binding studies, it is essential that specificity and high affinity of binding be ensured by chase experiments.[16,17] For studies of adenylate cyclase activation, it should be noted that damaged preparations with normal basal activity, NaF activation, and TSH binding may show no effect of TSH on the enzyme. It is advisable to investigate the TSH response by several different methods to ensure demonstration of a defect in TSH response.

Related Clinical Disorders

Congenital Hypothyroidism with Impaired Response to Thyrotropin. A block at any step in TSH action would cause hypothyroidism. However, a specific thyroid defect could only result from a lesion in the specific part of the TSH stimulation pathway, i.e., on the receptor(s) or on the distally modulated proteins (e.g., those subject to effects of cyclic AMP, Ca^{2+}, calmodulin, or diacylglycerol-activated protein kinases). For example, in pseudohypoparathyroidism type Ia (Albright hereditary osteodystrophy) (see Chap. 79), the partial congenital defect in the expression of the α subunit of G_s, the GTP-binding protein activating adenylate cyclase, is observed in many cell types; mild hypothyroidism is therefore just a minor component of this disease.[18] On the other hand, a disorder in the control of one of the functions regulated by TSH (e.g., iodination) would have the same consequences as a defect in this function itself. The general consequences of a general defect in TSH action can be predicted from our knowledge of the action of this hormone as follows: hypothyroidism, with a smaller but normally positioned thyroid gland; low thyroid hormone but high TSH plasma levels; low thyroidal uptake of radioiodide or ^{99m}Tc pertechnetate with a slow iodine turnover; and reduced or absent response to TSH action in vivo and in vitro.

Crucial for the diagnosis is the combination of high TSH levels and low thyroidal response in vivo, as shown by low or normal iodide uptake and absence of goiter. An almost normal thyroid gland size is conceivable because TSH does not appear to be necessary for differentiation and early growth in utero. Of course, such a picture could result from inflammation followed by fibrosis at an early age. In this case, the thyroid gland would be fully activated but would not grow. One would expect a very fast turnover of a small thyroid iodine pool and follicular cell hypertrophy, as, for example, in Congolese myxedematous endemic cretinism or in ectopic (lingual) thyroid glands. Such a picture could also result from high levels of immunoreactive but biologically inactive TSH. Increased TSH levels should therefore be confirmed by bioassay. Four patients have been reported with a disease which appears to be consistent with this description.[19-22] In one case[20] radioiodide uptake was stimulated in vivo by dibutyryl cyclic AMP but not by TSH, which suggests a lesion before cyclic AMP. On the other hand, TSH binding to membranes as well as basal and NaF-stimulated, but not TSH-stimulated, adenylate cyclase activity were normal, which would imply that the interaction between receptor and the cyclase activating GTP-binding protein N_s was defective.

A suggested set of diagnostic criteria for this syndrome appears in Table 73-1. In addition, as opportunities arise, a detailed study of thyroid membrane preparations will provide useful information and refine the molecular diagnosis. Given the complexity of the receptor and the adenylate cyclase system, one may anticipate that there are several subsets of this syndrome of impaired response to TSH. Also, since goiter is not a feature of the syndrome, it is possible that some patients carrying a diagnosis of sporadic cretinism in fact belong to this group.

The observation that two of the patients were products of consanguineous matings suggests the possibility of autosomal recessive inheritance. A strain of mice with an apparently sim-

Table 73-1 Diagnostic Criteria for Thyrotropin Insensitivity*

In vivo
1. Hypothyroid: no goiter, thyroid in normal position
2. Low ^{131}I and pertechnetate ^{99m}Tc uptake
3. Slow iodine turnover and small iodine pool in the thyroid
4. No in vivo response to TSH (hormone release, iodide uptake)
5. Plasma TSH high, confirmed by bioassay

In vitro (thyroid tissue studies)
1. Little colloid; no thyroglobulin, no colloid droplet
2. Epithelial cells small, no cell division
3. No response of slices to TSH
   a. No cyclic AMP or inositol phosphate accumulation
   b. No functional effect; no appearance of colloid droplets, no decrease and no increase in glucose [1-^{14}C] oxidation, etc.

*If the defect involved adenylate cyclase, analogues of cAMP should elicit the functional effect of TSH. Studies of TSH binding by thyroid membranes should permit investigation of the receptor. Measurement of cyclase activity with Mn^{2+} ATP as substrate would assess the integrity of the catalytic unit of the enzyme, and measurement of cyclase activity in the presence of NaF or GPP-NHP would assess the activity of the GTP-binding protein activating cyclase, G_s. The whole operation of the receptor-cyclase complex can be assessed by measurement of cyclase activity in the presence of TSH and GTP.

ilar defect and an autosomal recessive mutation has been described.[23]

Hereditary Hyperthyroidism. Two studies have reported cases of a hereditary form of hyperthyroidism in the absence of ophthalmopathy or other signs of autoimmune Graves disease.[24,25] These patients were characterized by a diffuse painless goiter, the clinical symptoms of thyrotoxicosis, and acceleration of bone maturation. Serum T_4 and T_3 levels were high, with undetectable basal and TRH-stimulated TSH. The thyroidal uptake of radioiodide was high and diffuse; the basal metabolic rate was also high. There was no evidence of immunologic disturbance or signs of thyroid autoimmunity (microsomal or thyroglobulin antibodies in the serum). There was no indication of autoimmune TSH receptor stimulation, no TSH-binding, -inhibiting, or -stimulating immunoglobulins in the serum, and no histopathologic signs of lymphocytic infiltration of the thyroid gland. In one case, tissue grafted in nude mice similarly manifested an autonomous high rate of activity. This disease thus presents all the characteristics of the autonomous nodule except that it is congenital and it involves the entire thyroid. The pattern of transmission appears to be autosomal dominant.

IODIDE TRANSPORT

Metabolism

The first step of iodine metabolism in the thyroid is the trapping of iodide by the follicles. The uptake, which takes place even in the absence of any further metabolism of iodide, requires an active transport mechanism. At normal plasma iodide concentrations, trapping is generally the limiting step of iodine metabolism in the thyroid.

Iodide uptake, as measured by its clearance, depends upon blood flow through the thyroid gland and on the iodide extraction ratio, $(A - V)/A$, where A and V are the arterial and venous concentrations, respectively, of iodide. Since the blood transit time in the thyroid gland is shorter than the half-life of iodide in red cells, this extraction ratio cannot be greater than 0.55 to 0.60, even if 99 percent of the plasma iodide is eventually taken up. Such ratios are obtained in iodine-deficient dogs in which iodide trapping is limited by the thyroid blood flow. In normal humans, the extraction ratio is estimated at around 0.20.[26–28]

The iodide extraction ratio in the thyroid reflects the activity of an iodide transport mechanism commonly called the iodide pump. Pump efficiency is generally evaluated, in tissues in which iodide oxidation has been blocked, as the ratios T/M, T/S, or C/M, where T, C, M, and S are the radioactivities per unit volume of labeled iodide in the thyroid, in isolated cells, in the incubation medium, and in the serum, respectively. At equilibrium, and if the thyroid is considered as one compartment, these ratios are equal to $C/M \div KTB$, where C/M is the unidirectional iodide clearance per unit weight of tissue and KTB is the rate constant for unidirectional iodide efflux.[29]

Autoradiography, as well as compartmental analysis of uptake kinetics, shows that the thyroid follicle concentrates radioiodide in its lumen. This requires follicle integrity and implies a flux through both the basal and apical membranes of the cell. The potential difference across the membrane is about -50 mV with the interior negative. Iodide has to overcome an electrical gradient to enter the cell, but it may flow downhill with the gradient to accumulate in the lumen. This, and the fact that isolated cells also concentrate iodide, indicates the existence of an active transport mechanism in the basal membrane. Kinetic and autoradiographic experiments showing that under certain conditions perchlorate and radioiodide first accumulate in the cell suggest a permeability barrier and a transport at the apical membrane.[28–32]

The characteristics of the iodide transport system have been established in the thyroids of several species[29,32] and include the following:

1. It concentrates iodide as such against a chemical and electrical gradient.
2. It is saturable and obeys Michaelis-Menten kinetics with an apparent K_m of $3 \times 10^{-5} M$.
3. It depends on the availability of ATP derived from oxidative phosphorylation and/or glycolysis.
4. It concentrates other anions (ClO_4^-, BF_4^-, etc.) which compete with iodide, having a similar charge and ionic volume.
5. It is inhibited by thiocyanate and inhibitors of the Na^+, K^+-activated ATPase such as ouabain.

Iodide trapping with similar characteristics has been demonstrated in the salivary gland, gastric mucosa, the mammary gland, and the choroid plexus. The fact that these glands are unable to concentrate iodide in congenital cretins with a thyroidal defect of iodide trapping supports the hypothesis that the same mechanism is involved in other tissues. Iodide is, however, not oxidized or bound to proteins in tissue other than thyroid.

The biochemical mechanism of iodide transport is unknown. It is known that Na^+ is required in the extracellular medium and that there is a delay in the inhibitory action of metabolic inhibitors and ouabain. These data suggest that an ion gradient generated by the Na^+, K^+-activated ATPase rather than the enzyme itself is the motive force for the transport. There is good evidence in favor of a model in which Na^+

influx would be coupled to I^- influx by a mobile carrier. Such a model explains why thiocyanate and perchlorate not only block iodide uptake but also release iodide already trapped in the gland.[28–32]

Iodide trapping is decreased and then increased by TSH. The former effect reflects an accelerated efflux presumably caused by increased cell permeability; the latter effect reflects an increased influx by enhancement of the V_{max} of the pump. This TSH action is blocked by inhibitors of RNA and protein synthesis, which suggests an action at the level of transcription. Both effects of TSH are reproduced by cyclic AMP analogues. Chronic treatment with TSH considerably increases iodide trapping, while excess iodine depresses it, even in hypophysectomized animals.[4]

Iodide trapping can be evaluated in vivo by measurement of iodide clearance under the influence of methimazole or, more conveniently but qualitatively, by the uptake of $^{99m}TcO_4^-$, a nonmetabolizable analogue. The transport mechanism can also be studied in other glands with iodide-concentrating ability, such as the salivary gland, as the salivary to plasma (S/P) radioiodide or thiocyanate (SCN^-) ratios.[32]

Most studies of iodide transport in vitro utilize intact cells. Measurements can be made at equilibrium in the presence of peroxidase inhibitors (methimazole, propylthiouracil), by the thyroid/medium (T/M) ratio in thyroid slices, or by the cell/medium (C/M) ratio in isolated cells. T/M ratios in human thyroid slices are 8 to 15 at 1 μM iodide in the presence of 0.1 mM methimazole. They decrease to half this value around 10 μM iodide. T/M or C/M ratios can be measured in the absence of inhibitors with $^{99m}TcO_4^-$, which is not organified. However, the accumulation of this ion in an undefined bound form may lead to quantitative errors. It should be remembered that these ratios can be modified by factors other than changes in the transport mechanism itself. For instance, iodide uptake in slices will be much decreased if follicles are opened by the slicing procedure or by released proteolytic enzymes. The probability of damaging follicle integrity is greater with large follicles (e.g., in colloid goiter) and in thinner slices.[33] Iodide transport can also be measured in particulate preparations and in phospholipid vesicles loaded with microsomal proteins, provided a Na^+ gradient is set up.[34]

Related Clinical Disorders

Hypothyroidism from Failure to Transport Iodide (Iodide Transport Defect). Since iodide transport depends on the integrity of Na^+, K^+-activated ATPase, the supply of ATP, and the transport system itself, defects in the first two processes would affect a number of cell types, overshadowing the effect on the thyroid. Moreover, Na^+, K^+-activated ATPase has been found to be increased in thyroid tissue of two affected subjects.[32] The hyperplasia of thyroid tissue and normal gastric and salivary secretion in these patients are also incompatible with a defective energy supply. The transport system itself probably involves few steps and perhaps only one. Thus inherited defects in transport may involve only a single protein.

Twenty-two cases with iodide transport defects have been reported.[32] As is the case with other primary thyroid defects, the clinical picture is characterized by hypothyroidism and goiter (see Table 73-2). Hypothyroidism may vary in severity. Goiter may not be noticed in early life but is present in all adults. The size and nodularity of the gland and the severity

Table 73-2 Diagnostic Criteria for the Complete Iodide Transport Defect

Required	*Helpful and confirmatory*
1. Goiter: common in untreated cases	1. No concentration of iodide and thiocyanate by the gastric mucosa and salivary gland
2. Primary hypothyroidism (high TSH, low T_4 and T_3) or compensated hypothyroidism	2. High serum thyroglobulin
3. No history of high iodine intake	3. Low tissue/medium (T/M) radioiodide and ^{99m}Tc pertechnetate in thyroid slices
4. Little if any thyroidal uptake of radioiodide	4. Normal methimazole-inhibited radioiodide binding to proteins in thyroid slices with 100 μM iodide
5. Little if any uptake of ^{99m}Tc pertechnetate	
6. No concentration of iodide or $^{99m}TcO_4^-$ by the salivary gland	
7. Clinical and biologic response to iodine	

of hypothyroidism and of its consequences on physical and mental development are obviously influenced by the duration of the disease, by iodine supply, and perhaps by the completeness of the defect. There was family history of goiter in 10 out of 22 cases, consanguinity in 6 out of 21 cases, and affected sibs in 7 cases. The defect appears to be as frequent in males as in females. These findings are compatible with an autosomal recessive trait.

The laboratory findings also reflect primary hypothyroidism including decreased serum T_3 and T_4, increased TSH levels, and absence of thyroid autoantibodies. Thyroidal radioiodide and $^{99m}TcO_4^-$ uptakes are low. The iodide clearance by the thyroid gland (normal 8 to 40 ml/min) is low while the renal clearance is normal.

Histology of the thyroid gland shows signs of hyperplasia with multiple adenomas of the microfollicular or embryonal type. The iodine content of the gland is low. Special investigations in vivo allow the demonstration of the defect in other tissues. The saliva/serum radioiodide or $^{99m}TcO_4^-$ ratios are close to 1 (normal 20 or more). Similar results have been obtained for the gastric juice/serum radioiodide ratios. In one case the SCN^- saliva/serum ratio was also low. Proper measurement of these ratios requires comparison of unstimulated salivary secretion with serum obtained in the middle of the time that saliva is being collected.[32]

Slices of thyroid tissue studied in vitro exhibit low tissue-to-medium radioiodide ratios (T/M). However, ratios even slightly higher than 1, i.e., higher than in the presence of 100 μM NaClO$_4$ (T/M = 0.7), indicate some iodide concentration.

The reversible consequences of an iodide trapping defect should by definition be corrected by iodide therapy. At high enough concentrations, diffusion alone should be sufficient to supply enough iodide for organification. Indeed, in the cases in which this has been done, iodide supplementation has been sufficient to restore euthyroidism. The dosage recommended by Wolff is 14 mg of iodide per day.[32,35] Treatment with physiological doses of thyroid hormone is obviously also acceptable.

Other defects should be excluded. If an iodide organification defect is accompanied by low radioiodide uptake at 24 h, in vivo kinetic studies of radioiodide or pertechnetate uptake, and if possible in vitro studies, could clarify the diagnosis. High iodine intake could also lead to primary hypothyroidism with low radioiodide and pertechnetate uptake and therefore

should also be excluded. Finally, the fact that the hypothyroidism can be corrected by iodine treatment is not alone diagnostic, as other defects (e.g., dehalogenase defect and thyroglobulin deficiency, see below) could give a similar response.[36]

IODIDE OXIDATION AND BINDING TO PROTEINS; IODOTYROSINE COUPLING

Metabolism

Most of the iodine stored in the thyroid is covalently bound to amino acids within 19 S thyroglobulin in the form of thyroid hormones (T_3, T_4) and their iodotyrosine precursors (monoiodotyrosine, MIT, and diiodotyrosine, DIT). Thyroglobulin also contains small amounts of $3',3',5'$-iodothyronine (rT_3), $3',3'$-diiodothyronine (T'_2), and monoiodohistidine. A small percent of the thyroglobulin is in the form of a dimer of the 19 S form with a 27 S sedimentation coefficient. Other organic forms are found including particulate insoluble iodoproteins (a small percent of the iodine) and traces of iodinated lipids. The role of these forms is unknown. The concentrations of iodide (less than 0.25 percent) and of free hormones or iodotyrosines are very low.

The synthesis of thyroid hormones requires several elements, iodide and thyroglobulin as substrates, an H_2O_2-generating system, and thyroperoxidase. At least three steps are involved: generation of H_2O_2, oxidation of iodide and binding to the tyrosyl residues of thyroglobulin, and the oxidative coupling of these iodotyrosyls into iodothyronines. The last two steps take place in a sequential manner within the matrix of thyroglobulin; they are catalyzed by the same enzymes and will be considered together in this section. Iodination and oxidative coupling are posttranslational processes. They are independent of protein synthesis.[4,37]

When iodination is allowed to proceed, the normal thyroid gland accumulates little iodide. Iodide transport is therefore the limiting step in iodide uptake; the machinery of protein iodination is geared to lock any iodide trapped by the gland efficiently into covalent linkage.

Iodination in thyroid hemogenates occurs in the sedimenting particulate fractions, suggesting that it takes place in a sedimentable cellular organelle. On the other hand, autoradiography of glands exposed in vivo or in vitro to radioiodide always shows the protein-labeled material in the colloid lumen. In fact, iodination occurs at the interface between the follicular cells and the colloid lumen, i.e., at the level of the apical membrane and its microvilli. Rings of radioiodine-labeled proteins at the periphery of the colloid and on the apical cell membrane can be demonstrated by light and electron microscopy early after administration of radioiodide. Furthermore, iodinating activity is higher in preparations of apical cell membranes. Histochemical staining demonstrates peroxidase activity on the apical cell surface and also in other intracellular membranes. This apical localization fits the location of the substrates for protein iodination (iodide and thyroglobulin), which are concentrated in the lumen, and of the cytosol coenzyme NADPH of the H_2O_2-generating system. It explains the correlation between iodinating capacity and follicular structure during ontogenesis and in cell cultures. This arrangement serves to sequester H_2O_2 and possibly oxygen radicals and the iodinating system that might iodinate or oxidize cell lipids and proteins in the absence of the proper substrate, thyroglobulin. Under some circumstances, iodination can take place inside the follicular cells, e.g., in isolated cells and in some tumors.[38] In these cases, the major iodination sites are microfollicular spaces inside the cell or in a few cells. Although such a mechanism may be operative in some pathologic conditions, its physiological significance is questionable. On the other hand, whether iodination at the apex of the cell can also take place during exocytosis of vesicles remains an open question.[4,38]

All the peroxidases need H_2O_2 in order to oxidize I^- and to bind it to proteins. Protein iodination in broken cell thyroid particulate systems is inhibited by catalase. The nature of the H_2O_2-generating system is poorly understood. As in leukocytes, NADH and predominantly NADPH stimulate iodination in broken cell systems. Accordingly, it has been postulated that the system might be a NADPH (NADH) oxidase. NADPH cytochrome c reductase could be a part of the system, since antibodies against this enzyme inhibit iodination in vitro.[39] Since the enzyme is not thought to interact directly with O_2, other auto-oxidizable factor(s) must be involved. Vitamin K_3, cytochrome b, and flavin have been suggested. H_2O_2 could be formed from O_2^- as a precursor by superoxide dismutase, since thyroid cells, like all cells, contain such enzymes. However, thyroid NADPH cytochrome c reductase has not been found to produce O_2^-, and superoxide dismutase does not inhibit iodination in broken cell systems. Monoamine

oxidase and xanthine oxidase have also been proposed as thyroid H_2O_2-generating systems.[4]

In intact cells, as in broken cell systems, H_2O_2 greatly enhances iodination. Catalase inhibits iodination, and stimulation by TSH of iodination in dog thyroid slices is accompanied by a stimulation of H_2O_2 formation. These facts suggest that H_2O_2 generation may be the limiting step regulating iodination.[6] Iodination is stimulated by any agent which increases intracellular free Ca^{2+} and is inhibited by calcium influx blockers. This suggests that intracellular Ca^{2+} controls the rate-limiting step in iodination. Indeed, H_2O_2 formation depends of the presence of extracellular Ca^{2+}.[5,6,9] On the other hand, a NADPH-dependent H_2O_2-generating system solubilized from the thyroid particulate fraction also requires the presence of Ca^{2+}.[39]

Inorganic iodide must lose an electron before it can displace hydrogen from tyrosyl residues. This is accomplished in the presence of H_2O_2 by thyroid peroxidase. Most antithyroid drugs and goitrogens, which inhibit protein iodination in vivo or in intact cells, inhibit the peroxide-peroxidase system.

Thyroperoxidase is a glycosylated hemoprotein bound to the apical plasma membrane of thyroid follicular cells with its catalytic domain facing the colloid space.[37] The protein has been resistant to purification, which led to controversies regarding its size. Monoclonal antibodies allowed isolation of the undegraded protein by affinity chromatography.[40,41] It seems to exist in two molecular forms, 105 kDa and 110 kDa, and was identified as the major antigenic component of the thyroid "microsomal antigen" involved in thyroid autoimmunity.[40,42,43] The primary structure of human thyroperoxidase has been deduced from cloned cDNA.[43–45] Two cDNAs differing by 171 nucleotides were obtained resulting from alternative splicing,[44] which accounts most probably for the 105- and 110-kDa protein species observed on western blots. Analysis of hydropathy profiles of the encoded polypeptides indicates that the protein is anchored in the membrane by a segment close to its carboxy terminus (Fig. 73-5).[43] The extracellular domain has similarities with myeloperoxidase (42 percent)[43] over 745 residues, indicating a common evolutionary origin. However, these genes do not share a common chromosomal locus, as thyroperoxidase is located on the short arm of chromosome 2 and myeloperoxidase on chromosome 17.[43–46] A closer analysis of thyroperoxidase sequence reveals similarity with domains belonging to the epidermal growth factor (EGF) precursor, C_4b families, and, surprisingly, to subunit I of cytochrome oxidase, which is encoded in the mitochondrial genome[43] (Fig. 73-5). These findings raise specu-

Fig. 73-5 Modular homologies within human thyroperoxidase sequence. Schematic representation of the primary structure of human thyroperoxidase with reference to modular homologies shared with other proteins. MPO = myeloperoxidase; Cytox I = cytochrome oxidase, subunit I; C4b = module of the C4-binding protein; EGF = module of the EGF precursor protein. The relationship between the protein and the apical membrane of the thyrocyte is also indicated. The numbers refer to the position of residues in the preprotein. (*Adapted from Libert et al.[43] Used with permission of EMBO J.*)

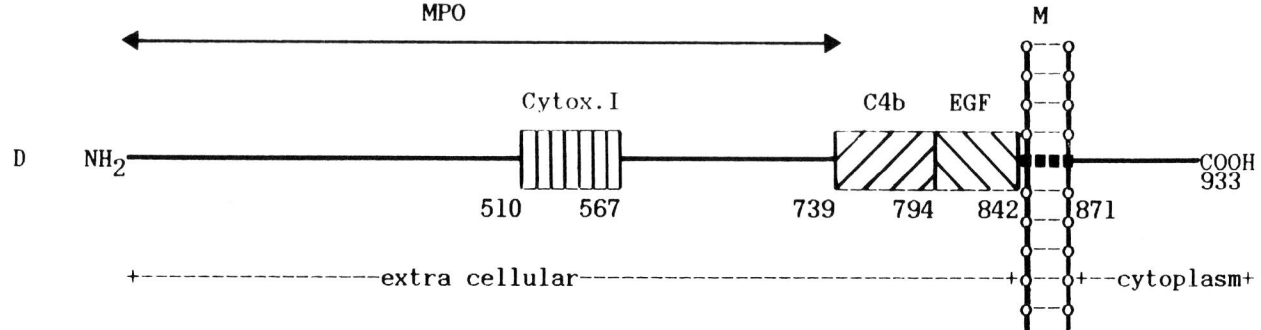

lations about the possible evolutionary contribution of a mitochondrial gene domain to a typical nuclear mosaic gene. Thyroid peroxidase exhibits a rather broad specificity. It is active only in the presence of H_2O_2, but excess H_2O_2 inhibits it. The enzyme catalyzes the iodination of free or bound tyrosines, and it also catalyzes the oxidation of I^- to I_2 and that of tyrosine to bityrosine. These reactions involve two closely related binding sites which bind either tyrosine or iodide and oxidize iodide to iodinium (I^+) or hypoiodous ion (OI^-).[37,47]

$$E \overset{1}{\underset{2}{\diagup\hspace{-0.3em}\diagdown}} + H_2O_2 + I^- + Tyr \longrightarrow E \overset{I°}{\underset{Tyr°}{\diagup\hspace{-0.3em}\diagdown}} \longrightarrow E + MIT \tag{1}$$

This explains why each time I_2 is formed in the reaction, iodination is inhibited, and thus why high levels of iodide inhibit iodination. Inhibition of iodination by thiourea and similar drugs is attributed to two reactions. In the absence of iodide, the drug inactivates the peroxidase irreversibly, and in the presence of iodide the enzyme catalyzes the oxidation of the drug, thus partially preventing enzyme inactivation. In the latter case, antithyroid drugs behave as competitors of iodination.[37]

Thyroid peroxidase, like other peroxidases, is also able to catalyze the intramolecular coupling of iodotyrosyl groups in thyroglobulin. The same antithyroid agents that inhibit iodination in intact cells and in broken cell systems also inhibit oxidative coupling. Iodothyronine synthesis by coupling of free 3,5-diiodo-4-hydroxyphenylpyruvic acid (DIHPPA) to iodotyrosines bound in thyroglobulin is possible, but there is little evidence that this mechanism operates in vivo. Recent results obtained with thyroperoxidase and lactoperoxidase support the idea that the iodination and the coupling reactions are catalyzed by two different peroxidase-H_2O_2 species. The formation of these different species would depend on the respective levels of H_2O_2 and iodide. The coupling results in the replacement of one iodotyrosine by an iodothyronine and the other by a dehydroalanine in the peptidic chains of thyroglobulin. Thyroid peroxidase is the only enzyme which catalyzes iodination and coupling at physiological pH. Other peroxidases catalyze the two reactions at different pHs. Coupling requires iodotyrosines and H_2O_2 and also iodide and free DIT. Thyroperoxidase may also oxidatively cleave peptides at the level of tyrosyl and tryptophan peptide bonds.[37]

The formation of iodotyrosines and iodothyronines in thyroglobulin does not follow a simple MIT, DIT, T_3, and T_4 precursor-product relationship. In fact, the kinetics suggest that iodination and coupling proceed in a rigid sequential manner, so that only four to eight tyrosyl groups, which are among the first to be iodinated, are coupled into iodothyronines. T_3 is preferentially formed at low levels of iodination but never exceeds 0.4 mol T_3 per mole of thyroglobulin. A large part of the 144 tyrosyl groups in thyroglobulin are not iodinated, while only part of the MIT can be transformed into DIT. There is a maximal number of iodothyronines synthesized in thyroglobulin (three to four). All these facts indicate that there are rigid structural and spatial requirements for tyrosyl iodination and coupling imposed by the thyroglobulin structure itself (see below).

Iodination of thyroglobulin is accompanied by important structural changes in the protein. There is an increase in the sedimentation coefficient (17 to 19 S), lower dissociability, etc. These changes reflect not only the effects of the addition of iodine but also those of cystine formation and structural changes in the protein.

The inhibitory effect of iodide on adenylate cyclase after its oxidation to an unknown intermediate certainly affects this system, but other effects of iodide are not excluded.[5,32] Thyroid peroxidase itself is also inhibited by excess iodide, which competes with tyrosine for the second substrate site of the enzyme. The latter effect, alone or in combination with the former, could explain the well-known Wolff-Chaikoff effect, in which excess iodide inhibits protein iodination in intact cells. No evidence has been found for an action of TSH or cyclic AMP on thyroid peroxidase activity. Two biochemical controls of the isolated peroxidase have been demonstrated: a requirement for iodide in the coupling reaction and an activation of the enzyme by very low levels ($10^{-7}M$) of DIT. The physiological relevance of these controls remains to be elucidated.[37]

In normal humans, radioiodide is organified immediately after trapping. The thyroidal radioactivity rises while that in plasma decreases, and no radioiodide can be chased from the thyroid gland by thiocyanate or perchlorate. In the case of a complete block of protein iodination, thyroidal radioactivity declines in parallel with plasma radioiodide, and this radioactivity is completely released within minutes after administration of anions such as SCN^- and ClO_4^-. It is thus easy to detect in vivo a complete block of protein iodination. With partial defects, the perchlorate discharge test is not very sensitive, and quantitative measurements in vivo of protein iodination capacity are needed. This requires a protocol in which this parameter could be measured (as radioiodide uptake or clearance) under conditions in which this step becomes rate-limiting, i.e., at relatively high ($\pm 10^{-5}M$) iodide concentrations.

Iodinating activity can be studied in thyroid slices, at various concentrations of iodide (10^{-7} to $10^{-4}M$). Stimulation of radioiodide binding to proteins by 1 μM of the calcium ionophore A23187 will demonstrate that iodide transport is not limiting. Under such conditions, variations in the affinity and capacity (V_{max}) of the whole iodinating system can be demonstrated. Activation of iodination by an exogenous H_2O_2-generating system (e.g., D-alanine and D-amino acid oxidase) would suggest that the H_2O_2 supply is limiting in the tissue and would be an argument for the normality of thyroperoxidase.[48]

The function of thyroperoxidase can be studied in particulate or solubilized preparations from fresh or frozen thyroid tissue supplemented with an exogenous H_2O_2-generating system. Guaiacol peroxidation measures the oxidation of the enzyme by H_2O_2; oxidation of iodide to I_2 or I_3^- measures the oxidation of iodide by the enzyme; binding of iodide to thyroglobulin or another exogenous protein such as albumin measures the whole iodination process. The latter reaction, carried out with normal and patients' thyroglobulin might demonstrate a defect at the level of this substrate. Coupling of iodotyrosines to form iodothyronines in a thyroglobulin preparation containing few iodothyronines (poorly iodinated thyroglobulin iodinated by horseradish peroxidase at pH 5.5) measures the oxidative coupling step. Those experiments can be carried out in the absence or the presence of various concentrations of hematin to identify defects in heme binding to the enzyme. The use of preparations completely solubilized by mild proteolysis or pseudosolubilized by nonproteolytic methods from particulate fractions may allow the demonstration of a "masking in membranes of a normal peroxidase."[37] H_2O_2 generation by particulate preparations can be measured by the scopoletin method.[39]

The availability of cDNA probes of human thyroperoxidase can now be used to measure and characterize thyroperoxidase mRNA in diseased thyroid tissue by Northern blotting. The presence of the gene can be demonstrated by Southern blotting of DNA extracted from any tissue after cleavage by restriction enzymes. Characterization of the defect in individual cases will require the cloning, restriction analysis, and sequencing of the patient's thyroperoxidase cDNA or genomic DNA. These methodologies have not yet been applied to this type of congenital defect.

Related Clinical Disorders

Iodination of thyroglobulin requires the generation of H_2O_2 and the oxidation of iodide and tyrosyl residues by the thyroid peroxidase. Oxidative coupling of the iodotyrosyls requires both a proper thyroglobulin structure and normal peroxidase activity. Defects at any of these levels will impair the synthesis of thyroid hormones (see Table 73-3). These patients are characterized by primary hypothyroidism and goiter of variable degree depending on the severity of the defect. Consanguinity and familial clustering are frequent. When accompanied by deafness, the disease is called Pendred syndrome. Patients have low thyroid hormone and high TSH levels in serum. However, there are cases where normal values are obtained.

In patients with a complete defect, high early thyroidal uptake of radioactive iodide is followed by a fast subsequent decline which parallels that in serum. Administration of KSCN (1 g orally) or $KClO_4$ (500 mg orally) at any time after radioiodide induces a precipitous fall in the thyroidal uptake. In normal individuals, these drugs only stabilize the uptake (Fig. 73-6).[4] A similar phenotypic defect can be observed in some cold nodules.[48] Analysis of the thyroid tissue shows a low iodine content (less than 100 μ/g). Incubation of thyroid tissue slices in vitro reveals normal radioiodide trapping but low protein iodination. Differential diagnosis should exclude chronic exposure to peroxidase-inhibiting antithyroid drugs or to similarly acting goitrogens. On the other hand, thyroglobulin deficiency in mice leads to similar findings, including perchlorate-induced iodide discharge.[49]

Biochemical investigation has demonstrated several different types of thyroperoxidase defects[37,50-55]:

1. Thyroperoxidase activity by all reactions tested (guaiacol peroxidation, iodide oxidation to I_2 or I_3^-, and thyroglobulin iodination in the presence or absence of hematin) may be absent, suggesting absence of the enzyme.

2. Reactivity may be low in all assays and may be restored by preincubation of the enzyme with hematin.[54] This suggests an anomaly in heme binding to the enzyme.

3. Enzyme activity may be normal by all criteria if solubilized but may be poorly active in particulate or in the pseudosolubilized form. This suggests a defect at the level of membrane structures to which the enzyme is normally bound.[37]

4. Enzyme may be present and active in iodide oxidation but not in iodination. This suggests an abnormal interaction with the protein substrate.

5. Thyroglobulin may be resistant to iodination. In this case, the patient's thyroperoxidase iodinates normally but the patient's thyroglobulin is not a normal substrate. The patient's thyroglobulin is poorly iodinated by horseradish or hog thyroid peroxidases. This suggests an abnormality in thyroglobulin. In one case, this resistance was removed by extensive dialysis and ascribed to a firmly attached inhibitor.

6. Subcellular localization may be abnormal.[37]

The nature of the defects suggested by such observations could now be studied at the level of thyroperoxidase gene structure using the newly available human cDNA probes.

Deficiency in H_2O_2 production has been suggested in one case. Iodination in the homogenate was low but could be restored to normal by supplementation with an exogenous H_2O_2-generating system of flavin-adenine dinucleotide (FAD).[56] A similar observation was made in slices of an isolated cold nodule.[48]

Obviously, the common denominator of such pathologies, defective thyroglobulin iodination and consequent accumulation of perchlorate-dischargeable iodide, covers several different genetic defects. This heterogeneity may explain the wide variations in the severity of the disease among cases and the discrepancies in the hypotheses on genetic transmission. The occurrence of goiter without hypothyroidism in family members of index patients[51] has suggested that thyroid disease may be a manifestation of the heterozygous state of a condition which, when homozygous, results in goiter, hypothyroidism, and consequent growth and mental retardation. Perchlorate discharge tests have failed to disclose significant iodide discharge in these patients as an indication of limited peroxidase activity. Perhaps a more stringent test of peroxidase activity in the thyroid glands of obligate heterozygotes would disclose a partial defect. On the other hand, Baschieri et al.[57] tested a large number of patients with thyroid disease and their relatives with ClO_4^- after administration of ^{131}I. A significant number of normal relatives of patients who had positive discharge test results also had positive test results, whereas no relatives of patients with negative results had positive results. The authors suggested that according to this method of ascertainment, the character has dominant transmission.

Table 73-3 Diagnostic Criteria for the Peroxidase Defect

Required	*Helpful and confirmatory*
1. Goiter; hypothyroid or compensated hypothyroidism	**1.** High serum thyroglobulin
2. Developmental retardation usually	**2.** Thyroid biopsy
3. Rapid thyroidal accumulation and turnover of radioiodine	**a.** Hyperplasia
4. Rapid discharge of radioiodine from the thyroid gland after administration of SCN^- or ClO_4^-	**b.** Low iodine content, little if any organic iodine.
5. Low T_4; elevated TSH or enhanced TSH response to TRH	**c.** Little iodinating activity in intact cells (slices or homogenate)

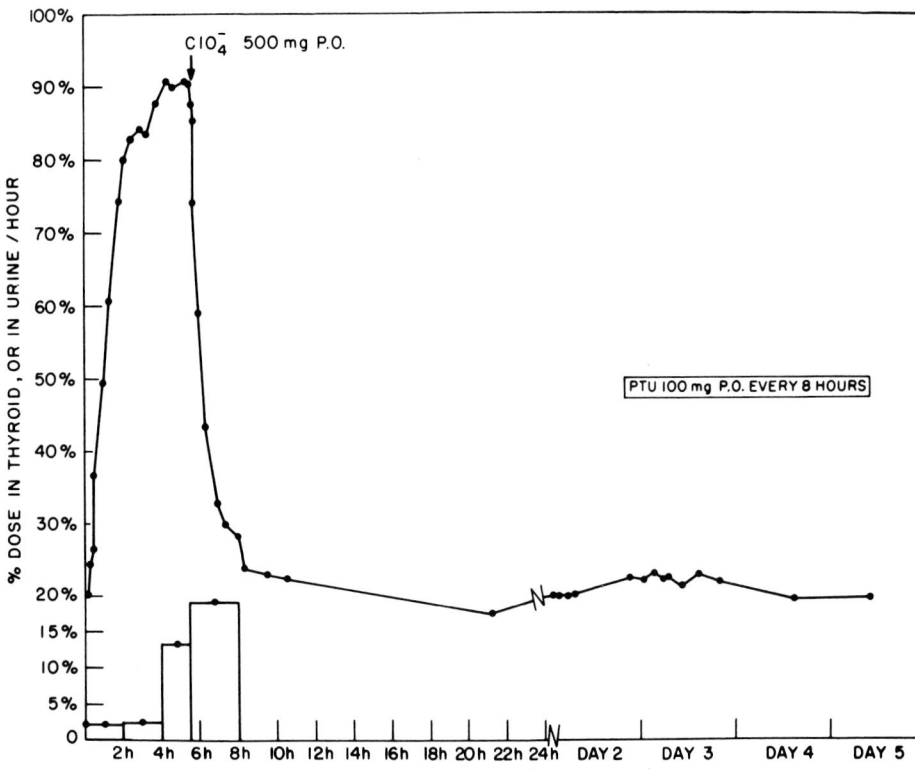

Fig. 73-6 Discharge of accumulated labeled iodide by perchlorate from the thyroid of a patient with incomplete peroxidase deficiency. Administration of propylthiouracil (PTU) occasioned no change in retention of iodine by the thyroid or increased renal excretion (bars).

The potential for malignancy in congenital goiters with organification defects has been noted by Salabe et al.[58] A similar observation has been made in some cold nodules.[48] It is tempting to speculate that the absence in these cells of the negative feedback of iodine derivatives contributes to chronic stimulation and tumorigenesis.

Familial Goiter and Deaf Mutism (Pendred Syndrome). Since a first report of five families with congenital goiter and deafness,[58a] many other families with this association have been described.[4] With few exceptions, the clinical pattern has been uniform. Goiter has been apparent either at birth or within the first decade or two of life, and nerve deafness has been present from birth or has developed during childhood. Intelligence and growth have usually, but not always, been normal. Vestibular function has been normal or somewhat impaired, and the tympanic membranes have been intact.

These patients usually have small goiters. Thyroid function, as assessed by the usual clinical and laboratory data, has been normal in most. The serum concentrations of protein-bound iodine (PBI) in most of the affected persons of Johnsen's kindreds were distinctly low,[59] and the mean value of the 15 patients of Thould and Scowen was 3.36 μg/dl.[60] Two of the four affected members of the sibship of Elman[61] developed invasive adenocarcinoma, and Roberts' patient[62] had a localized histologic change suggestive of malignant alteration. Two of the four patients in Thieme's sibship also had a local malignant change without evidence of distant extension.[63]

Morgans and Trotter[64] first showed that ClO_4^- causes an appreciable discharge of iodide from the thyroid glands of patients with Pendred syndrome, and this abnormality has become a hallmark of the disease. The fraction of the radioiodine which accumulates in the thyroid within the first hour or two and which is discharged with ClO_4^- is usually 25 to 50 percent. Discharge is not so complete as in the patients with the

complete organification defect described in the preceding sections. Similar findings were obtained later in other cases.[4]

A few in vitro studies showed a normal peroxidase activity suggesting a defect in H_2O_2 production.[65,66] The patients of the Pendred group appear to differ from those with the full organification defect in several particulars:

1. They are not myxedematous, and most, but not all, are clinically euthyroid. Nevertheless, an exaggerated response to TRH suggests a compensated or borderline hypothyroid state.

2. The patients with Pendred syndrome rarely have large goiters.

3. The discharge of radioiodide from the gland is not precipitous and is incomplete.

4. The pathogenetic relationship between the deafness and the thyroid defect is entirely obscure. There is no evidence for fetal hypothyrodism, which is a requirement for the induction of neuroacoustic pathology in the experimental animal.

5. The curious hypersensitivity to perchlorate also remains unexplained.[4]

GENETICS. Fraser et al.[67] summarized their genetic studies of Pendred syndrome up to 1960. They found 113 affected subjects in 72 families. Johnsen's two families included 24 members, 21 of whom were examined. Of these, 12 had goiter and deafness, 4 of which were the product of intermarriage between two affected members of two families, the syndrome being manifest in successive generations.[59] Fraser et al.[67] reported the Pendred syndrome in children of a marriage between two affected persons. The syndrome appeared in one generation in all other recorded instances. While in most instances the pattern is that of an autosomal recessive inheritance with tight concordance between goiter and deafness, there are reports of dissociation of deafness and goiter within kindreds.[68] Approximately one-half the sibs were found to be afflicted, but if a correction is applied for ascertainment bias, the ratio of affected to unaffected sibs is almost 1:3 in accordance with the pattern of autosomal recessive inheritance.[69]

Congenital Hypothyroidism with Failure of Coupling of Iodotyrosines. Defective coupling of iodotyrosines to form iodothyronines accounts for some cases of congenital goitrous hypothyroidism, but evidence is mostly indirect.[4,70] These patients present the usual characteristics of congenital primary hypothyroidism with goiter. They have a very high thyroidal uptake of radioiodine, with a fast release of the isotope which is also accelerated by antithyroperoxidase drugs. Some radioactive iodothyronines, and sometimes iodotyrosines, appear in serum. Chromatography of thyroid tissue digests reveals large amounts of iodotyrosines, but little iodothyronine is detected by in vivo labeling.

The diagnosis of this defect is reached by exclusion. In the presence of normal amounts of MIT and DIT in the gland, absence of iodothyronines suggests defective coupling. In the absence of efficient iodothyronine secretion to suppress pituitary TSH, the thyroid gland is overstimulated and secretes at a very high rate its main iodinated products, MIT and DIT, which are then deiodinated in the thyroid and in peripheral tissues. However, similar findings are observed in severe uncompensated endemic goiter. In this disease, it has been hypothesized that dilution of the iodine in an important thyroglobulin pool prevents sufficient iodination of each thyroglobulin to account for the formation of even one iodothyronine per monomer and to bring about the necessary conformational changes of the protein.[71]

In one case,[70] the amount of iodine leaving the thyroid gland was calculated to be at least 1 mg/day (normal, 0.50 to 0.150 mg). Only a small fraction of this iodine could have 3701been in the form of thyroid hormone, or the patient would have been thyrotoxic. Accordingly, the thyroid gland must have been releasing iodide or a readily metabolized iodinated substance which was quickly broken down, either by the gland itself or in peripheral tissues, to yield iodide.

The simplest formulation to account for these observations is that coupling of DIT to yield T_4 was limited, and the T_4 that was formed was rapidly secreted. The highly stimulated gland maintained an exceedingly rapid flux of some of its own iodine. Some iodine went on to form a small amount of hormone; some was retained for storage as MIT and DIT; and a large fraction—perhaps in the form of MIT—was released and deiodinated.

Defective iodination necessarily entails a reduced coupling but not a coupling defect per se (see above). The complexity of the coupling reaction creates several hypothetical causes for a specific defect. They could be grouped in two categories: defects at the peroxidase level and defects at the thyroglobulin level. These could be distinguished by the joint crossed study of oxidative coupling in patient and normal thyroglobulin as catalyzed by patient and normal thyroid peroxidase.[37] The patient thyroglobulin contains iodotyrosines but little iodothyronine; the normal thyroglobulin used must be poorly iodinated thyroglobulin (e.g., from endemic goiters) that has been iodinated in vitro under conditions in which no coupling takes place (during the lag period with thyroperoxidase or with lactoperoxidase at pH 5.5).[37]

Defects at the peroxidase level could involve failure of the peroxidase to recognize its thyroglobulin substrates or other, more subtle alterations. In the case of defects at the level of thyroglobulin, several possibilities should be considered: absence of thyroglobulin (see below), mutation at the donor or acceptor tyrosyls, or change in the presumably rigid structural arrangement of the tyrosyl groups or in their accessibility to peroxidase. A case of coupling defect has been reported in which thyroperoxidase iodinated thyroglobulin normally but was unable to catalyze the oxidative coupling reaction.[37]

Little can be said regarding the genetics of this poorly defined group, which is almost surely heterogeneous. Consanguinity and family clustering are found in those consigned to this category. Both sexes are represented. The most probable pattern of inheritance is autosomal recessive.[4]

THYROGLOBULIN

Introduction

The central role played by thyroglobulin in the production of thyroid hormones and the basic characteristics of its function as hormone precursor have been known for decades.[1,72] Thyroglobulin is secreted by the thyrocyte into the lumen of the thyroid follicle, where it becomes the substrate of a complex series of reactions catalyzed by thyroperoxidase and requiring iodide and H_2O_2. The result is iodination of up to 40 tyrosyl residues to form mono- or diiodotyrosine followed by coupling of a maximum of about 8 to 10 such residues to yield the thyroid hormones (with a normal iodine diet, an average of 2.3 mol T_4 and 0.3 mol T_3 per molecule of thyroglobulin). Thyroglobulin thus provides three things: a thyroid hormone precursor, storage of iodine, and storage of inactive thyroid hormones (covalently bonded within the protein structure). Strictly speaking, thyroglobulin is the homodimeric glycosylated iodoprotein of sedimentation coefficient 19 S that accumulates in the follicular lumen. Its abundance and degree of iodination vary greatly depending on the activity of the gland. It may constitute 75 percent of total protein and contribute up to 50 percent of protein synthesis in the gland. Dimers (27 S) or trimers (37 S) of 19 S thyroglobulin are formed in variable amounts during the oxidative iodination of the molecule by thyroperoxidase. As these molecular species result from the expression of the same gene, they will not be considered independently here. Immunoreactive thyroglobulin circulating in the plasma represents another distribution of the same gene product.[1] Its role, if any, remains mysterious, as do its route to the plasma and the mechanisms controlling its production. From a practical viewpoint, however, plasma thyroglobulin represents an important diagnostic tool, as it reflects the activity of the thyroid independently of iodine.[73]

Thyroglobulin protomers have a molecular weight of 330,000. A repeatedly quoted paradox is the disproportion between the size of thyroglobulin and the very low yield of thyroid hormones it produces. No definite explanation of this paradox has been provided by the analysis of thyroglobulin primary structure (see below), although the system may achieve an efficient use of iodide. When iodine is scarce, it is specifically targeted to the primary hormonogenic segment of the molecule, which is able to produce some T_4 even under these unfavorable conditions.[37] When iodine is more available, it is progressively directed to residues that are less and less efficient for hormone production and to the bulk of nonhormonogenic tyrosines. The hierarchy of tyrosines relative to iodination and coupling reactions ensures that thyroid hormone formation proceeds efficiently even with a very low or intermittent supply of iodine. This view of thyroglobulin function emerged from the kinetic analysis of the iodination and coupling reactions and from the identification of peptides containing T_4, T_3, DIT, or MIT within molecules iodinated to variable degrees.[37,73a–75]

Complete understanding of the hormonogenic reactions, their regulation, and their genetic alterations will require knowledge of the tertiary structure of both thyroglobulin and thyroperoxidase. While knowledge of the tertiary structures of such large molecules is still beyond reach, recombinant DNA methodology has provided detailed information on thyroglobulin primary structure, organization of the gene, and regulation of expression.

Primary Structure

Even before the cDNA for thyroglobulin was cloned, decisive arguments for its homodimeric structure (2 × 330,000 dalton)[76] were obtained from the translation of thyroglobulin 33 S mRNA in *Xenopus* oocyte[77] and from restriction mapping of the uncloned full-length double-stranded cDNA.[78] These results ended the controversies regarding the number, size and possible heterogeneity of thyroglobulin subunits.

The sequences of bovine and human thyroglobulin mRNA have been determined from cDNA clones.[79,80] They display a very similar structure, with a 41-nucleotide 5′-untranslated sequence preceding a 8307 (bovine)– or 8301 (human)– nucleotide open reading frame. The 3′-untranslated sequence is 83 (bovine) or 106 (human) bases long. Organization of the coding sequence and the amino acid content are virtually identical in both species. Following a 19-amino acid signal peptide, the polypeptide chains are composed of 2750 (bovine) and 2748 (human) residues. Overall similarity is 77 percent in terms of amino acid sequence. Analysis of the protein sequence for internal homology led to its subdivision into four regions from amino to carboxy terminus as follows: domain A is composed of 10 type I repeats containing about 60 amino acids including 24 highly conserved residues, six of which are cysteines. Domain A extends over 1200 residues. Sequences of variable length, unrelated to the motif, interrupt the repeats at fixed positions (see Fig. 73-7). Correlation of the polypeptide sequence in domain A with the intron-exon organization of the gene suggests that these "inserted sequences" might have an intronic origin, resulting from a partial "exonization" process during evolution.[81] Domain B (from position 1439 to 1486) contains three type II repeats of a shorter motif (17 residues). Domain C is composed of the repetition of a type III motif existing as two subtypes (IIIa, IIIb) sharing a similar pattern of cysteine residues. Both subtypes are repeated twice in tandem, between positions 1586 and 2111. A third copy of motif IIIa is found further downstream. Domain D, constituting the last 600 residues of thyroglobulin, shows no internal homology, is poor in cysteine compared to the other regions, and contains a cluster of tyrosine residues.

Comparison of the primary structure of thyroglobulin to available polypeptide sequences revealed a structural *analogy* with other large peptides containing repeats of cysteine-rich motifs (e.g., EGF precursor, EGF receptor, LDL receptor, and factor VIII). However, *no* sequence *similarity* was found with any of these proteins. However, a significant sequence similarity (28 percent) was found between domain D of thyroglobulin and the whole sequence of acetylcholinesterase from *Torpedo californica*.[82] The similarity suggests that these proteins share a common ancestor and that they exhibit conserved tridimensional characteristics.[83] The functional significance, if any, of this homology is unclear, as the residues involved in the enzymatic activity of acetylcholinesterase and in thyroid hormonogenesis (see below) are not conserved. The similarity could have pathophysiological implications in thyroid autoimmunity if immunologic cross-reactions between the two proteins could be demonstrated.[84] Sequence similarity between the type I motif of domain A and an exon found in certain transcripts of the invariant chain of class II antigens[85] has been reported. Again, the sequence similarity is suggestive of a common ancestor but does not reveal functional relationships. As the invariant chain is apparently involved in antigen processing and presentation on the surface of macrophages, it was proposed that this segment in thyroglobulin could play a role in addressing the molecule to specific subcellular compartments.[85] This homology also might have immunopathologic significance and explain why the thyroid gland is so frequently involved in autoimmune processes.

Four tryptic peptides containing thyroid hormones have been isolated from thyroglobulin of various species and sequenced.[73a–75] The corresponding tyrosine residues have been identified in the primary structure of the protein (Fig. 73-8).[79,80] Two of them map at subterminal positions (residues 5 and 2748 in the bovine sequence). They correspond to sites involved preferentially in the synthesis of T_4 and T_3, respectively. The two other sites are closely linked around position

Fig. 73-7 Internal repetition in the primary structure of thyroglobulin. The sequence is given in the one-letter code. The best alignment is shown defining the three types of repeats (I, II, $III_{A,B}$). The numbers in parenthesis refer to the position of residues in the bovine sequence.[79] The numbers within the sequence indicate the length of segments showing no similarity between individual repeats.

I.1	R P C E 12 Y V P Q C 3 G S F 2 V Q C 6 C W C V D 2 G R E 2 G S R 7	(13 - 72)
I.2.	C L S F C Q 18 Y L P Q C 3 G D Y 2 V Q C 6 C W C V D 2 G M E 2 G T R 7	(73 - 140)
I.3.	C P R S C E 13 S P P Q C 3 G A F 2 V Q C 40 C Y C A D 2 G R E 52	(141 - 277)
I.4.	C P T K C E 12 Y V P S C 3 G E Y 2 A Q C 5 C W C V D 2 G Q E 2 G T R 13	(278 - 344)
I.5.	C P S E R R 245 F V P A C 3 G S Y 2 V Q C 4 C W C V D 2 G R E 2 G S R 7	(345 - 637)
I.6.	C P T E C E 19 F V P A C 3 G N F 2 V Q C 4 C Y C V D 2 G Q P 2 G T R 8	(638 - 705)
I.7.	C P S P C Q 27 Y I P Q C 3 G Q W 2 V Q C 124 C W C V D 2 G Q K 2 G T R 8	(706 - 901)
I.8.	C P G S C E 100 Y L P Q C 3 G G W 2 V Q C 6 C W C V D 2 G E Y 14	(902 - 1053)
I.9.	C P T S C E 25 F I P T C 3 G E F 2 L Q A 4 T W C V D 2 S G E 2 P P G 6	(1054 - 1125)
I.10.	C P S L C E 14 Y S P A C 4 G G F 2 V Q C 6 C W C V L 2 G E E 2 G T R 7	(1126 - 1190)
II.1.	A L G C V K C P E G S Y F Q	(1439 - 1452)
II.2.	D E Q C I P C P A G F Y Q E Q A G	(1453 - 1469)
II.3.	S L A C V P C P E G R T T V Y A G	(1470 - 1486)
III.A.1.	C L A D C A L D E A C 3 T 2 T 4 V S C D F Y A 45 Y L K K 9 K R F 8 L S G 9 S 2 S 7	(1586 - 1706)
III.A.2.	C L S R C A 20 C T L Y P 2 Q V C 3 L 6 C R L I L 7 Y R K K 7 K N F 8 L T G 9 S 2 S 7	(1875 - 1977)
III.A.3.	C L W E C S R H Q D C 3 T 2 T 4 V R C M F Y A 2 Q S C 3 L 4 C R L L L 7 Y R K P	(2112 - 2169)
III.B.1.	C L L A C D H D S C C D G F 3 Q 2 G G 3 C 2 L S S 5 C 45 G 2 D T 9 W 13 C 5 P 22 V I V D 25	(1707 - 1874)
III.B.2.	C E R L C D M D P C C T G F 6 Q 2 G G 3 C 2 L N S 4 C 13 G 2 D T 8 W 13 C 5 P 18 V I V D 25	(1978 - 2111)

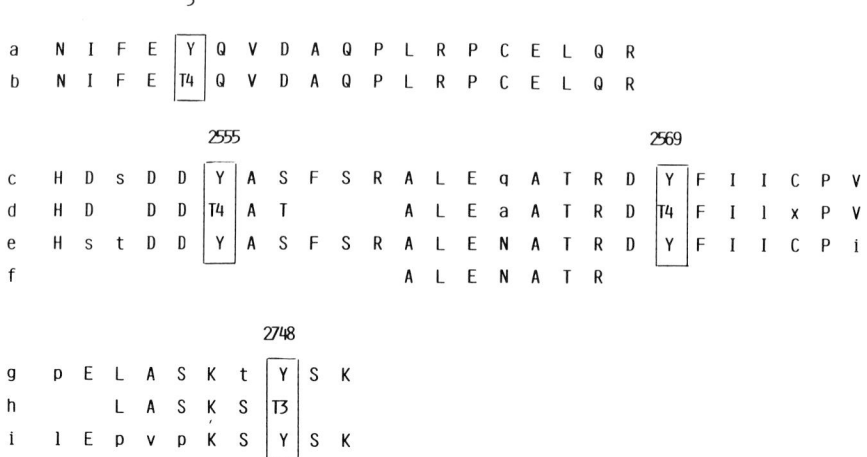

```
                  5
a   N  I  F  E  │Y│ Q  V  D  A  Q  P  L  R  P  C  E  L  Q  R
b   N  I  F  E  │T4│ Q  V  D  A  Q  P  L  R  P  C  E  L  Q  R

                  2555                                    2569
c   H  D  s  D  D │Y│ A  S  F  S  R  A  L  E  q  A  T  R  D │Y│ F  I  I  C  P  V
d   H  D     D  D │T4│ A  T           A  L  E  a  A  T  R  D │T4│ F  I  l  x  P  V
e   H  s  t  D  D │Y│ A  S  F  S  R  A  L  E  N  A  T  R  D │Y│ F  I  I  C  P  i
f                                    A  L  E  N  A  T  R

                  2748
g   p  E  L  A  S  K  t │Y│ S  K
h         L  A  S  K  S │T3│
i   l  E  p  v  p  K  S │Y│ S  K
```

Fig. 73-8 Hormonogenic domains in thyroglobulin. The hormone-containing domains identified in various species are represented by the one-letter code and are aligned for maximum homology. The capital letters correspond to amino acids occurring at least twice in different species. The four hormogenic tyrosines are boxed and their positions in the protein are indicated. Identifications are as follows: a, c, and g are the peptide sequences derived from the bovine cDNA sequence; b represents the four identical hormone-containing peptides determined from bovine, human ovine, and porcine thyroglobulin; d represents the sequences of three peptides obtained from porcine thyroglobulin; e and i are protein sequences derived from a partial rat cDNA sequence; f is a tryptic peptide, isolated from human thyroglobulin, containing a glycosidic chain attached to the asparagine residue; and h is the sequence of a hormone-containing peptide isolated from porcine thyroglobulin (for references, see text). *(Adapted from Merken et al.[79] Used by permission of Nature.)*

2560. The amino-terminal hormonogenic domain (around Tyr 5) occurs just before the first type I motif and may share sequence characteristics with it. The three other hormonogenic tyrosines map in the acetylcholinesterase-like segment, domain D. Comparison of the sequences surrounding the hormonogenic tyrosines reveals no striking similarities except for the presence of at least one charged amino acid on their amino side and the occurrence of a Ser or Thr residue at position −3 relative to the three hormonogenic tyrosines in domain D. The recent identification of donor tyrosines involved in the coupling reactions[86,87] opens the way to the understanding of structure-function relationships in thyroglobulin.

Compilation of the sequences of the hormonogenic segments available from various species shows a remarkable conservation of the amino-terminal domain (Fig. 73-8). Evidence for a major role of this domain in hormonogenesis has been presented; and this domain may contribute as much as 50 percent of T_4 in mature thyroglobulin.[73a–75] The other hormonogenic segments do not show the same degree of sequence conservation, suggesting that a less stringent evolutionary pressure was exerted on these less efficient sites. Unlike tyrosine 5, they have not been clearly identified as functional hormonogenic sites in more than one species. All this points to the tyrosine in position 5 as the major hormone-forming residue of thyroglobulin. In this context, it is noteworthy that a series of amino-terminal peptides containing T_4 (18 to 26 kDa) are cleaved from thyroglobulin during the hormonogenic reaction and can be released by reduction of disulfide bonds.[73a–75] The mechanism for this phenomenon and its possible role are unclear. It has been suggested that these peptides would in some way facilitate the proteolytic release of T_4 from thyroglobulin in lysosomes. Figure 73-9 summarizes some structural and functional data for the thyroglobulin molecule.

The Thyroglobulin Gene

Data are available on the structure of the thyroglobulin gene in three species, including human beings.[81,88–90] Although some details are missing due to the resistance of certain segments to gene cloning, a common picture emerges from these studies, and it can be used to infer the structure of the human gene. The coding information is scattered amongst 42 exons[89] of average size under 200 bp. Exons 9 and 10 are exceptions, with sizes of 1101 and 588 bp, respectively.[81] The 8448-nucleotide mature transcript is encoded in more than 250,000 bp of chromosomal DNA.[88–90] Introns vary in size from ± 100 bp to 64,000 bp. The gene may be subdivided into two regions on the basis of its proportion of intronic material. The 5' portion does not deviate significantly from the average (exons

Fig. 73-9 Schematic representation of the bovine thyroglobulin precursor. For clarity, a space has been introduced between the homologous domains even when they are contiguous in the protein. The tyrosine and thyroid hormone residues are represented by short and longer bars, respectively. Recent evidence indicates that tyrosine in position 5 also can exist as dehydroalanine.[86] *(Adapted from Merken et al.[79] Used by permission of Nature.)*

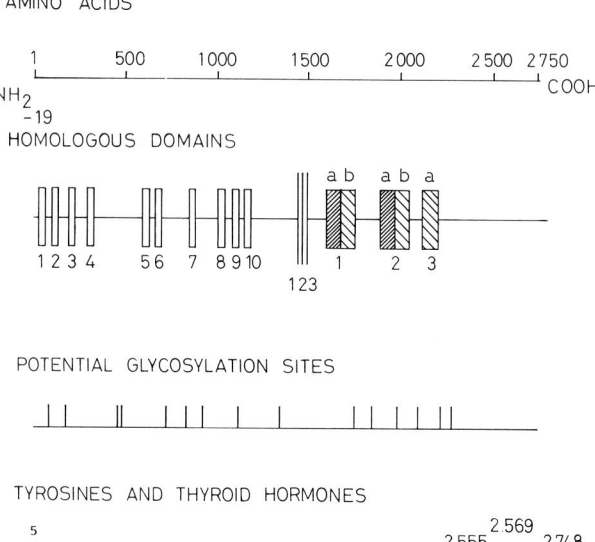

equal to 10 percent of total sequence), while the 3' portion with 2 percent exons is certainly uncommon in this respect. Whether this asymmetry reflects the different evolutionary origin of domains A (type I motif, homology with Ia protein) and D (homology with acetylcholinesterase) may become clear when knowledge of the gene organization for acetylcholinesterase is available. The gene has been mapped to chromosome 8q24, distal to the c-myc locus.[91–94] The synteny between c-myc and thyroglobulin is conserved in rat and mouse, on chromosomes 7 and 15, respectively.[95] Several restriction fragment length polymorphisms (RFLP) have been described using thyroglobulin probes (Table 73-4), which makes the Tg locus a useful marker for this region of chromosome 8.

The borders of the first 16 exons have been determined and their positions correlated with the repetitive organization of the corresponding protein segment (domain A, made of 10 type I motifs, see Fig. 73-7).[81] When related to the consensus sequence of the type I motif, intron positions fall either between the motifs or at places where the motifs are interrupted by unrelated sequences. This leads to the elaboration of a model for the evolution of the gene involving both the loss and the "exonization" of long segments of intronic sequences.[81]

The 5'-flanking sequence of the thyroglobulin gene containing the promoter has been determined for human,[96] bovine,[90] and rat[97] genes. In addition to a canonical TATA box sequence, the genes contain a distinctive repetitive sequence presenting a purine-pyrimidine asymmetry (Pu/Py box) centered around position −400 in human beings.[96] Such sequences, also present in the vicinity of other genes (see Ref. 96), may adopt a non-B DNA structure when subjected to torsional stress.[98] Their function is still unknown. The Pu/Py boxes in the human being and the rat are about 200 bp long.[96,97] In the bovine gene, where it is much smaller (38 bp),[90] it is flanked by another type of repetitive element about 200 bp long (BMF sequence), which is the bovine homologue of human Alu sequences.[99] The conservation of the Pu/Py boxes and of the approximate total length of repetitive sequences upstream of the gene in different species might be fortuitous. Alternatively, it might play some kind of punctuation role in the organization of the gene. The roles of 5'-gene segments in the control of gene expression by TSH or cAMP and of tissue-specific expression are just becoming clear from studies in animal models and cell cultures. Studies in two species identify a crucial regulatory element around position −160 from the cap site (see below).[100,101] Another segment identified by hypersensitivity to DNase I treatment of thyroid chromatin is located further upstream (between −2000 and −1600).[100]

Control of Thyroglobulin Gene Expression

TSH controls both the growth and the expression of the differentiated phenotype of the thyrocyte. Most of its effects are exerted through the cAMP and protein kinase system as discussed above. As will be seen from experiments in animal models or tissue culture, all the steps involved in the expression of the thyroglobulin gene that were amenable to experimental measurements were shown to be positively regulated by TSH and cAMP. The thyroglobulin gene in the thyrocyte chromatin is committed to expression. This committed state is consistent with the presence in the 5'-flanking region of the gene of a thyroid-specific site, which is hypersensitive to

Table 73-4 Restriction Fragment Length Polymorphisms Described at the Thyroglobulin Locus (Chromosome 8q24)

Probes (Ref.)	Enzymes	Alleles (frequency)
pCHT 16/3.2 (91)	EcoRV	14 kb (0.85)/8.5 kb (0.15)
pCHT 16/8.0 (91)	TaqI	5.8 kb (0.20)/5.2 kb (0.80)
HT 0.98 (150)	HindIII	6.5 kb (0.98)/6.0 kb (0.02)
phTg 1 (150a)	PvuII	13.2 kb (0.50)/4.4 kb (0.50)
phTg 1 (150a)	MspI	8.2 kb (0.80)/5.1 kb (0.20)

DNase irrespective of the transcription rate[100] and with the presence of unmethylated cytosines in CG pairs.[102] Direct measurements of the rate of thyroglobulin gene transcription have been performed on isolated nuclei from rat thyrocytes.[103] Under normal physiological conditions, the gene appears to be maximally transcribed as a proportion of total RNA polymerase II transcriptional activity. Chronic treatment of the animals with propylthiouracil, which results in hyperstimulation by endogenous TSH, does not lead to a significant increase of the transcription rate expressed as parts per million.[103] However, total transcription and cell proliferation are strongly stimulated, leading to a net increase in thyroglobulin transcription on a "per gland" basis.

Hypostimulation of thyrocytes by TSH, as achieved by hypophysectomy or thyroid hormone administration, causes a dramatic and specific decrease in thyroglobulin gene transcription relative to total transcriptional activity. This effect is counteracted both in vivo[103] and in vitro[104] by TSH administration and in vitro by stimulation of the incubated tissue with the cAMP agonist forskolin.[104] Quantitations of thyroglobulin mRNA accumulation in cultured thyrocytes stimulated by TSH, forskolin, choleratoxin, or dibutyryl cAMP all support the view that transcription of the thyroglobulin gene requires the continuous presence of a cAMP agonist.[105,106] The target of this cAMP-dependent regulation has been delineated in the 5'-flanking region of the gene by transfection of dog thyrocytes with chimeric gene constructs.[107] These constructs were made of variably deleted versions of the thyroglobulin gene promoter, ligated upstream of the bacterial chloramphenicol acetyltransferase gene, which was used as a reporter gene. The region between −1 and −250 relative to the transcription start was shown to contain a segment with characteristics of a cis-acting cAMP regulatory element. The molecular events between intracellular cAMP elevation and control of transcription are still unknown. Current hypotheses propose either a direct role for the regulatory (RII) subunit of protein kinase A[108] or a more classic pathway involving phosphorylated protein factors. Arguments are accumulating in other model systems that favor the latter mechanism.[109]

Although TSH is the main physiological agent regulating function and growth of the thyroid gland, other factors like EGF, insulin, or ill-defined constitutents of serum may play important roles. Contrary to the concomitant proliferating and differentiating effects of TSH, these agents, with the exception of insulin,[110] tend to repress expression of the differentiated thyrocyte phenotype, even when administered together with thyrotropin (see above).

In addition to the transcriptional regulation by TSH and cAMP, a variety of experimental results points to translation as another regulated step. Classic pulse-chase experiments and examination of polysome profiles have demonstrated a general effect of TSH on mRNA translation (see Ref. 11 and its bibliography). More sophisticated experiments directly addressing thyroglobulin synthesis have provided evidence for the specific recruitment by TSH of a pool of thyroglobulin messenger ribonucleoproteins into large functional polysomes.[111] The relative importance of transcription, translation, and possibly stabilization of mRNA in the overall regulation of thyroglobulin production is presently unknown. Similarly, whether splicing of the primary transcript is a regulated step has not been determined. Direct evidence for the existence of an alternative splicing pathway has been provided for the bovine transcript[112] (see below). There are arguments for a similar situation in human beings.[113] However, there is no evidence suggesting a role for these minor transcripts nor for regulation of their production.

The transfer of newly synthesized thyroglobulin from the rough endoplasmic reticulum to the follicular space is also stimulated by TSH and cAMP agonists. The last step, involving fusion of the exocytotic vesicles with the apical cell membrane, is under tight control, as was clearly shown by electron-microscopic autoradiographs.[114] Glycosylation of the thyroglobulin precursor seems to be controlled by TSH as well. In cultured porcine thyrocytes, TSH increases the galactose content of thyroglobulin and, to a smaller extent, the number of its sialic acid residues.[115]

A small fraction of thyroglobulin molecules (about 7 percent of total synthesis) is not found in the colloid but enters the blood plasma instead.[11] The mechanism responsible for this phenomenon is still much debated (discussed in Ref. 116). Is it due to intercellular leakage from the colloid, to fusion of misrouted exocytotic vesicles to the basolateral cell membrane, or to "trancytosis" from the follicular lumen, as suggested from experiments with inside-out follicles in tissue culture?[117] It has been reported that circulating thyroglobulin is poorly iodinated and glycosylated under normal conditions, which favors the second hypothesis. Whatever the mechanism and its physiological significance, release of thyroglobulin from the gland is also under the control of TSH.[11] In the absence of primary thyroid cell pathology, the level of plasma thyroglobulin may be considered an index of thyroid gland stimulation by TSH or stimulating immunoglobulins. Apart from its use as a marker for thyroid neoplasia,[118] it is an effective measure of thyroid gland stimulation in clinical practice.[73,119]

Posttranslational Modifications

The synthesis of thyroglobulin on the rough endoplasmic reticulum involves a 19-amino acid signal peptide that directs the newly synthesized subunits to the secretory pathway of the thyrocyte. From the site of its synthesis to the point where it is released in the follicular space, thyroglobulin undergoes a series of modifications including glycosylation, phosphorylation, and sulfation. It is then ready for the last and most important modifications leading to thyroid hormone formation, the peroxidase-catalyzed iodination and coupling reactions.

Thyroglobulin contains about 10 percent carbohydrate by weight.[120] The human protein contains two types of N(asparagine)-linked carbohydrate units. It also contains O(serine/threonine)-linked units which are not found in most animal thyroglobulins.[121] The N-linked units display considerable microheterogeneity (see Chap. 3). Type A units are of the high mannose type. They contain from nine to five mannose residues linked to an internal di-N-acetylglucosamine. Type B units, referred to as complex, contain a variable number of sialic acid-galactose-N-acetylglucosamine chains at-

tached to the mannose-N-acetylglucosamine core. Out of the 20 or so N-linked units, about six are of the high mannose (A) type. Addition of the carbohdrate chains to the asparagine of the acceptor signals in thyroglobulin (Asn-X-Ser/Thr) takes place cotranslationally during the transfer of the nascent peptide into the lumen of the rough endoplasmic reticulum.[121] It involves the transfer of preformed, glucose-containing oligosaccharides from a dolichol residue in the membrane to the nascent protein (see Chap. 3). Thereafter, excision of the glucose and of a variable amount of mannose residues occurs in the rough ER and in the Golgi.[122] This trimming results in the mature, high mannose (A) units, and allows for the addition of peripheral sugars to those oligosaccharide chains which will become the complex, sialic acid–containing B units. Sialic acid appears to be added immediately before or concomitant with delivery of thyroglobulin to the follicular space.

Less is known of the O-linked oligosaccharide units found in human thyroglobulin. They constitute a minor part of thyroglobulin carbohydrates and account for its galactosamine content. They seem to be composed of two types of units, one containing an additional glucuronic acid in a structure reminiscent of glycosaminoglycans.[121]

In the primary structures as deduced from cDNA sequencing, there are 20 and 15 potential acceptor sites for N-glycosylation in human and bovine thyroglobulin subunits, respectively.[79,80] About three-quarters of these must be effectively used to account for the carbohydrate content of thyroglobulin.[121] However, only one such site, which was sequenced 20 years ago,[123] has been positively identified in the human protein as bearing an oligosaccharide chain. It is located between two hormonogenic tyrosines in domain C of the molecule.[80]

The relationships between the addition and processing of carbohydrate units to thyroglobulin and its synthesis and secretion into the follicular space have been investigated. Complete inhibition of N-glycosylation by tunicamycin blocks thyroglobulin secretion,[124–126] while variable effects on thyroglobulin synthesis have been reported.[124,125] Addition of the terminal sialic acid residues was reported to be required for the release of the protein from the apical membrane.[127] However, inhibition of α-mannosidase II by swainsonine and of α-glucosidases by deoxynojirimycin, which results in profoundly altered oligosaccharide units, did not inhibit thyroglobulin secretion or synthesis.[128]

Conflicting results have been obtained regarding the presence of phosphate in thyroglobulin. Mannose 6-phosphate was detected in porcine thyroglobulin,[129] and the possible role of this lysosomal recognition marker in the targeting of the protein to the lysosomal compartment has been discussed.[130] However, in other studies, no mannose 6-phosphate could be found in thyroglobulin from calf, pig, sheep, and normal human thyroid glands[131]; small amounts of phosphate were only found on serine and threonine residues.[131] In still another study, mannose phosphate was found as characteristic of human thyroglobulin from malignant thyroid tissue.[132] Since technical problems are probably responsible for these differences, it seems premature to draw conclusions about the possible role of mannose 6-phosphate and its receptor in the normal cycle of thyroglobulin synthesis and degradation.

Sulfate groups have been found in thyroglobulin of various mammalian species.[133] A total of about 13 sulfates seems to be added to the high mannose chains and to tyrosine residues during the transit of thyroglobulin through the Golgi. It is suggested that this phenomenon, which contributes to the anionic character of the molecule, may play a role in its exceptionally high solubility, which is necessary to permit the high concentration of thyroglobulin in the colloid (100 to 400 mg/ml).

Iodination and coupling of iodotyrosines are the last post-translational modifications, and they produce thyroglobulin, also known as prothyroid hormone. Very extensive studies have been devoted to the understanding of the respective roles of thyroglobulin, thyroperoxidase, cofactors, and ultrastructure in the phenomenology of thyroid hormone formation.[37,134] As all of these studies were carried out before the primary structure of thyroglobulin was known, they were necessarily limited by the difficulty in handling a huge and heterogeneous substrate, and they could not define precise structure-function relationships. The precise description of thyroid hormone formation still awaits reconstruction and site-directed mutagenesis experiments using available cloned thyroglobulin cDNA. Nevertheless, a fairly good picture of what is happening may be drawn. The protagonists are thyroglobulin, thyroperoxidase, iodide, and hydrogen peroxide. Thyroperoxidase is membrane-bound and delivered to the apical membrane from the same exocytotic vesicles as those releasing thyroglobulin. H_2O_2 is provided by an enzymatic complex located at the apical membrane[135,136] and requiring NADPH. Iodination takes place on thyroglobulin molecules in contact with the apical membrane and proceeds in an ordered fashion.[37] The first tyrosine residues to be iodinated are those that are susceptible to coupling into thyroid hormones by the same enzymatic machinery. The tyrosine in position 5 holds a key role in the hierarchy of hormonogenic residues, as it is the first to be converted to T_4. There is no consensus, at present, as to the relative physiological importance of the three other hormonogenic tyrosines. While more hormonogenic tyrosines will be defined, it is likely that they play minor roles under conditions of normal or low iodine supply, as about 50 percent of all T_4 in thyroglobulin is accounted for by tyrosine 5 (see above). Apart from their differential susceptibility to overall iodination and coupling, individual tyrosine residues also present different potential for transformation into diiodotyrosine. This is exemplified by the tyrosine in position 2748 (the antepenultimate residue of thyroglobulin), which is mainly found as triiodothyronine in porcine thyroglobulin.[137] The donor iodotyrosine participating in this particular hormonogenic reaction must be more refractory to diiodination than other residues. The specificity and hierarchy displayed by the hormonogenic reaction is clearly determined by the thyroglobulin molecule itself and is not a property of thyroperoxidase. This was well demonstrated in experiments where thyroperoxidase was used with substrates other than thyroglobulin.[134]

The recent identification of tyrosine residues acting as donors in the hormonogenic reaction[86] led to the suggestion that the coupling reaction could be an intersubunit phenomenon, involving two homologous iodotyrosines in position 5.[86]

An interesting and puzzling posttranslational modification associated with thyroid hormone formation and/or iodination is the cleavage of the thyroglobulin polypeptide chain. Early observations, which were apparently specific for guinea pig thyroglobulin, reported that depending on the stimulation of the gland by TSH, thyroglobulin contained varying amounts of 300,000, 210,000, and 110,000 molecular species.[138] Probably unrelated to this observation is the finding in most species of peptides in the 28- to 16-kDa size range that can be released from iodinated thyroglobulin by reducing agents.[73a–75] All these peptides correspond to the amino-terminal portion of thyroglobulin and, thus, contain the major hormonogenic tyrosine in the form of a T_4 residue. The production of these

peptides seems to be related to the hormonogenic reaction or at least to exposure of thyroglobulin to a stimulated peroxidase activity.[139] Also, a progressive trimming of these peptides on their carboxyl side is observed when the degree of iodination of thyroglobulin increases.[73a,74] The mechanism of these cleavage reactions is unknown. The sequence at the carboxy end of one such peptide of bovine origin has been reported. When placed in the primary structure of the protein, it does not correspond to any signal recognized by known enzymatic activity, nor to bonds reported to be broken by peroxidase and halide action.[140] The putative function of these peptides remains hypothetical. They could facilitate the release of T_4 from thyroglobulin during proteolysis in lysosomes. However, in the absence of data suggesting the existence of a specific fate for these hormone-rich peptides, the significance of having one bond cleaved in advance of all the others is not obvious.

The structure of thyroglobulin is profoundly remodeled during the iodination-hormonogenic reactions. Disulfide bonds are broken and reestablished between different partners.[72] Noniodinated, newly synthesized thyroglobulin subunits are held together by noncovalent bonds and are readily separated by sodium dodecyl sulfate or urea. With increasing iodine content, the subunits are joined by disulfide bridges and, for a small proportion of them, by an ill-defined covalent bond resisting reducing agents. Contrary to an early suggestion which received much credence, the overall shape of thyroglobulin, as observed in electron microscopy, does not change with its iodine content.[141]

Genetic Defects of Thyroglobulin Production

Introduction. Defective production of thyroglobulin belongs to the group of dyshormonogenesis disorders. It is one of the rarest causes of congenital hypothyroidism with an estimated frequency of less than 1 in 80,000 births.[142] There are numerous reports of patients with convincing evidence of a qualitative or a quantitative defect of thyroglobulin production causing a congenital goiter associated with some degree of hypothyroidism.[4] However, not one of these cases has yet been defined in molecular terms with the mutation identified. The reasons for this situation are many-fold. Patients are scarce. The exceptional size of the thyroglobulin gene and mRNA have been limitations, and recombinant clones are only recently available. The amount of thyroid tissue available for study is limited, since patients correctly treated with hormone replacement usually escape surgery. The major reason, however, and the main characteristic of the genetic defects associated with thyroglobulin production, is heterogeneity. Reviewing the published cases, it is difficult to find two descriptions likely to correspond to a common mutation. In the absence of consanguinity, this genetic heterogeneity suggests that many of the investigated cases might be compound heterozygotes, i.e., bearing different mutations on their two thyroglobulin alleles. Nonallelic heterogeneity is less likely but possible.

The study of animal models has been more rewarding. The first mutation affecting the thyroglobulin gene was identified as a nonsense mutation in exon 9 of the Afrikander cattle.[112]

Human Cases. Up to now, there is not a unique criterion on which to base the diagnosis of defective thyroglobulin production. The diagnosis is reached by exclusion of other defects, and its confirmation requires direct study of goitrous tissue.[143]

The patient should be hypothyroid (or show a compensated hypothyroidism) with elevated TSH, should trap iodide excessively, should have a negative perchlorate discharge test, and should have no MIT or DIT in the urine. Determination of plasma thyroglobulin is helpful only when undetectable. Indeed, the presence of hyperstimulated thyroid tissue with concomitant absence of circulating thyroglobulin is indicative of defective thyroglobulin production (see above). However, normal or even high levels of immunoreactive thyroglobulin have been found in the blood of patients with demonstrated production of qualitatively abnormal thyroglobulin.[144] Findings of abnormal iodoprotein in the plasma (high PBI relative to circulating thyroid hormones with the major part of it as non-butanol-extractable iodine) and of abnormal low molecular weight iodinated compounds in the urine complete the picture.[145] Urinary iodohistidine,[146] which is an important component of the abnormal low molecular weight iodinated material, is diagnostic of iodination within the thyroid of protein material unrelated to thyroglobulin. Albumin is the most likely substrate for iodohistidine production as well as for the abnormal iodinated protein found in the blood. The mechanism leading to the iodination of albumin remains obscure. Suggestions that a "thyralbumin," acting as a substitute for thyroglobulin, could be synthesized within the thyroid have been neither confirmed nor clearly ruled out.[4] Iodination of albumin is a very nonspecific phenomenon which is observed in a series of situations leading to goiter formation.[4] However, it appears that iodohistidine is produced in significant amounts only in cases where very little, if any, thyroglobulin is present in the gland.[145]

Analysis of DNA from white blood cells by Southern blotting using thyroglobulin cDNA probes is the logical next step. While no deletion of the gene has been demonstrated yet, the number of cases investigated in this way is small. Southern blotting of DNA from affected sibs and analysis of the inheritance of RFLPs at the thyroglobulin locus may exclude the thyroglobulin gene as a responsible locus in some cases. If the family is informative and all affected individuals display identical alleles, the data may support the likelihood that the thyroglobulin gene is defective, without giving definite proof.

If tissue samples become available through surgery or biopsy, thyroglobulin and thyroglobulin mRNA may be directly measured by standard methods and their structure compared to normal. Examination of tissue structure and ultrastructure is sometimes helpful, but it usually simply displays the signs of hyperstimulation by TSH.

In the absence of new data on molecular genetics of the condition, it seems futile to list again all the cases reported in the literature in which defective production of thyroglobulin has been implicated in the development of human congenital goiter (see previous edition of this book for references). One of the conclusions common to such reports is that some thyroglobulin-related antigens are almost invariably found in the glands and that ultrastructural evidence for defective secretion of thyroglobulin is frequently present (overdistension of rough endoplasmic reticulum).[148] In some such cases where it has been measured, the concentration and size of thyroglobulin mRNA were normal.[149] Altogether, available evidence suggests that most cases correspond to the production of structurally abnormal thyroglobulin molecules. The problem of deciding whether a concomitant quantitative defect is present is a difficult one, as hyperstimulation of goitrous glands by TSH leads to a greatly accelerated turnover of the thyroglobulin-like material, and newly synthesized proteins have usually not

been analyzed. In one well-studied sibship, abnormal thyroglobulin was found associated with an apparent autosomal dominant mode of inheritance[150] as revealed by RFLP analysis. This case is of particular interest in keeping with the hypothesis that cooperation between thyroglobulin subunits would be required in order for efficient hormonogenesis to take place.[86] A mutation affecting the hormone-forming site in one allele would lead to 75 percent of defective thyroglobulin dimers, which might account for the dominant character of the disease in this sibship.

Animal Models. Genetic models for defective production of thyroglobulin are available in sheep,[151] mice,[152] goats,[153] and cattle.[154] Only the three last species have been analyzed in some detail. Contrary to the exceptional human case described above, all these disorders follow an autosomal recessive mode of transmission.

The hereditary goiter of the Dutch goat[153] is associated with a hypothyroid state which can be corrected by increasing the iodine supply in the diet. Small amounts of abnormal (7 S) thyroglobulin-related antigen are found in the glands which contain low levels of a normal-sized thyroglobulin mRNA. The fact that concentrations of thyroglobulin mRNA sequences were approximately normal in nuclei from the goiter[155] led to the suggestion that the mutation caused abnormal transfer of transcripts to the cytoplasm or accelerated cytoplasmic turnover of transcripts. A likely explanation is that the mutation would lead to the inefficient translation of a defective mRNA, resulting in both abnormal thyroglobulin molecules and mRNA destabilization.

The mouse model, called the cog mutation,[152] is associated with hypothyroidism in homozygotes. Thyroglobulin antigens are low in the goiter tissue (< 1 percent of normal littermates) and slightly elevated in the serum. The mutation maps within 1 centimorgan of the thyroglobulin gene, which makes it unlikely that some other gene would be responsible for the phenotype.[156] The data indicate the accumulation of normal amounts of an apparently normal-sized thyroglobulin mRNA. While identification of the mutation is still lacking, this model system combined with the power of the transgenic mouse technology should provide an invaluable tool for investigating structure-function relationships of the thyroglobulin transcription unit.

The hereditary goiter of the Afrikander cattle[154] is characterized clinically by a euthyroid state and biochemically by the production of thyroglobulin antigens with an abnormal size. Northern blotting experiments have revealed the coexistence of two classes of thyroglobulin mRNA in the goiter of homozygous animals: an 8.4-kb, normal-sized message and a 7.3-kb mRNA.[157] Both are present at a concentration much lower than normal (about 10 percent). Translation of this mRNA mixture in vitro yielded 75-kDa and 250-kDa thyroglobulin polypeptides.[158] Cloning of cDNA segments corresponding to the 7.3-kb message and of genomic DNA segments from the mutated gene provided an explanation for the phenotype of the animals.[112] The mutation responsible for the disease is a nonsense mutation in codon 697. Translation of the mutated 8.4-kb mRNA is expected to yield a 75-kDa protein. Surprisingly, the 7.3-kb mRNA corresponds to a misspliced transcript, lacking exon 9 in which the mutated codon is located. As removal of exon 9 does not alter the reading frame,[81] the 7.3-kb message would encode a peptide of 250 kDa. Further studies have shown that the 7.3-kb message is present within the thyroid of normal animals as well, though at such a low level that it could not be detected by standard Northern blotting.[112] The nonsense mutation in exon 9 would thus lead to the aborted translation of the 8.4-kb mRNA, resulting in both an abnormal thyroglobulin polypeptide (75 kDa) and perhaps in the destabilization of the ill-translated message. The 7.3-kb transcript, lacking the mutated exon, would escape destabilization and produce 250-kDa polypeptides. As they contain all the hormonogenic sites described to date, these thyroglobulin molecules are likely to be functional hormone precursors and probably account for the euthyroid state of the goitrous animals. Apart from being the first congenital goiter to be elucidated at the molecular level, this model indicates that minor thyroglobulin transcripts do exist and could be responsible for some microheterogeneity of the protein.

Conclusion. Analysis of the human cases and of the animal models leads to the conclusion that many different mutations are responsible for the various phenotypes associated with congenital goiter and thyroglobulin deficiency in human beings. The large size of the gene and the numerous steps required in the processing of its 42-exon transcript make this no surprise. The demonstration that severely altered molecules (like those of the Afrikander cattle) can still play their roles as hormone precursors raises the suggestion that mutated thyroglobulin genes could have a part in the development of euthyroid goiter with familial clustering.

SECRETION OF THYROID HORMONE AND IODINE RECYCLING

Metabolism

Secreted iodothyronines and iodide appear in the venous outflow and thyroglobulin appears mostly in the thyroid lymphatics. The turnover of the colloid in humans is normally about 1 percent per day, but this may be increased or decreased, depending on the level of activity of the gland. In the chronically stimulated gland, the colloid lumen virtually disappears, and the thyroglobulin pool is almost nonexistent. This suggests that the whole storage process is short-circuited and that thyroglobulin is iodinated and hydrolyzed within a very short time.[11,159]

The endocytosis of the colloid in the follicular cells takes place by macro- and micropinocytosis. Macropinocytosis accounts for thyroid secretion after an acute stimulation by TSH. Within minutes pseudopods develop, mostly at the margin of follicular cells. Their size and number depend on the level of TSH. The lateral and apical borders of the pseudopods progressively fuse, engulfing the colloid indiscriminately in a process similar to phagocytosis. Tubulin and actomyosin are involved in the process. The resulting colloid droplets are interiorized and later fuse with primary lysosomes to form secondary lysosomes in which hydrolysis can take place. In fully stimulated dog follicular cells, the lifetime of the colloid droplet may extend to 40 min. Although endocytosis is obviously the limiting step in secretion, lysis of thyroglobulin may become limiting during acute stimulation of cells filled with colloid droplets.[160,161] Thyroid secretion is not fully accounted for by macropinocytosis. For example, the very active secretion of chronically hyperstimulated follicular cells is not inhibited by inhibitors of macropinocytosis; moreover, it is not accompanied by morphologic evidence of this process (pseudopods,

colloid droplets, etc., as shown by transmission or scanning electron microscopy). On the other hand, micropinocytosis of proteins (ferritin, for example) has been demonstrated in follicular cells by electron microscopy. Micropinocytosis plays an important (probably the major) role in basal thyroid secretion. Experiments in vitro suggest some selectivity in this process, the mature and more iodinated molecules being taken up more rapidly. Thyroglobulin receptors and binding of desialated thyroglobulin could be involved. The fate of the vesicles depends upon their protein content. Thus, cationized ferritin reaches the Golgi cisternae, and this indicates that membrane patches involved in micropinocytosis could be recycled through the Golgi and secretory vesicles to the plasma membrane. This suggests an orderly traffic of vesicles and a sophisticated signal system.[6,11,12,38,159–163]

During endocytosis of colloid, a large surface of the apical membrane is interiorized. This is possible only because exocytosis of newly formed thyroglobulin by fusion of secretory microvesicles with the membrane supplies the necessary membranes. In fact, the two processes of exocytosis and endocytosis are coupled, exocytosis preceding endocytosis after TSH stimulation. Under several circumstances, such as after chronic thyroid hormone treatment, the supply of secretory vesicles becomes limiting for endocytosis. Thus, the secretory cycle is similar in the follicular cell to that in other protein-secreting cells if one considers that protein secretion is directed toward the follicular lumen. Endocytosis and iodination take place at the periphery of the colloid lumen. It is clear that more recently iodinated thyroglobulin molecules have more chance to be taken up and hydrolyzed than the others. Slow diffusion of the colloid enhances this phenomenon, which is referred to as the *last come, first served hypothesis*.[6,11,13,38,159]

The fact that excretory vesicles as well as apical membranes at the bases of microvilli, but not pseudopod or colloid droplet membranes, contain peroxidase shows that extensive membrane reshuffling takes place in both exocytosis and endocytosis.[164]

The hydrolysis of thyroglobulin droplets resulting from micropinocytosis as well as macropinocytosis takes place in the lysosomes. These organelles contain all the enzymes necessary to hydrolyze glycoproteins at acid pH, i.e., proteases, glycoside hydrolases, peptidyl amino acid hydrolases, dipeptide hydrolases, and so on. Lysis of thyroglobulin in intact lysosomes is activated by glutathione, suggesting that reduction of disulfide bonds in the protein could be a limiting step. The released amino acids are probably mixed with the cellular pools, causing a dilution of exogenous amino acids taken up by the cells. After intense stimulation a spillover of amino acids into venous blood is observed. The carbohydrate moieties of thyroglobulin are digested, as evidenced by the loss of PAS staining. The released carbohydrates are presumably recycled in the cells, although some sialic acid is released into the blood.[159]

Free iodotyrosines, but not iodothyronines, are rapidly deiodinated by a deiodinase constituted of a ferredoxin, NADPH ferredoxin reductase, and a flavin mononucleotide–containing deiodinase.[165] The same system operates in thyroid and in peripheral tissues (e.g., kidney, liver). It is inhibited competitively by dinitrotyrosine and blocked by any agent which oxidizes NADPH, such as menadione. The exact localization of this "microsomal" system has not been elucidated. The iodide released from iodotyrosines is largely reutilized in the thyroid, mixing with the trapped exogenous iodide. Part of this iodide leaks out of the gland. The importance of this leakage is related to the intrathyroidal iodine content. In cases of intense or acute TSH stimulation, some iodotyrosines escape the deiodinase and spill over into the venous effluent of the gland. The iodothyronines (T_4, T_3, and small amounts of rT_3) are excreted by an unknown mechanism. Since there is no evidence of lysosomal exocytosis at the basal membrane, it is believed that the iodothyronines are secreted by passive diffusion or, since they are charged amino acids, by passive mediated transport.[11,38,159] The T_4/T_3 ratio in the thyroid secretion is lower than in thyroglobulin, especially early after TSH stimulation. This reflects two mechanisms, an earlier release of T_3 during lysis of thyroglobulin and a partial deiodination of T_4 by an enzymatic system inhibited by propylthiouracil, similar to that in peripheral tissues.[166]

Thyroid secretion is controlled by TSH. In the dog, basal secretion, mostly involving micropinocytosis of thyroglobulin, may not require cyclic AMP, while secretion after acute TSH administration, involving macropinocytosis, is mediated by cyclic AMP.[6,161,162] Secretion is inhibited by iodide even in patients treated with antiperoxidase drugs.

Thyroid secretion can be best studied in vivo by the serum T_4, T_3, and thyroglobulin response to TSH administration.[167] In vitro methods may not be reliable. The presence of an active dehalogenating system can also be studied in vivo. In patients presenting a defect in dehalogenase activity, labeled iodotyrosines will be found in the plasma and urine after radioiodine administration. Moreover, a large proportion of injected radioiodine-labeled DIT or MIT will be recovered after 1 and 2 h in the urine as iodotyrosines and not as iodide. Deiodination of iodotyrosines can also be studied in vitro using slices or homogenates of thyroid tissue. Normal tissue incubated in the presence of dinitrotyrosine should also fail to deiodinate the labeled DIT.

In spite of the large number of steps and proteins involved in thyroid secretion, no true congenital defect has been observed for this process. This is perhaps due to the relative nonspecificity of the secretion machinery. Defects in actomyosin, tubulin, membrane, or lysosomal proteins would have very general consequences in all cells. It is therefore not surprising that the only well-defined defect involves the deiodinase system, which is important only for the metabolism of iodotyrosines. It may be hypothesized that specific defects involving thyroid secretion could exist. If such a defect involved endocytosis, it would lead to distension of the colloid lumen and colloid goiter; if localized beyond endocytosis, a defect would lead to a thyroid lysosomal disease with accumulation of precursors such as thyroglobulin upstream of the metabolic block. Under such circumstances, it would be of great interest to know whether increased thyroglobulin secretion could compensate for the defects.

Related Clinical Disorders

Congenital Hypothyroidism from Failure of Iodotyrosine Deiodinase Activity. Failure of iodotyrosine deiodinase activity does not interfere directly with thyroid hormone synthesis or secretion. However, it leads to leakage of iodotyrosines into the circulation, with a failure of iodine recirculation in the thyroid and loss of the iodotyrosines in the urine. The iodine in the serum iodotyrosines can of course not be recovered by the thyroid iodide trapping mechanism. The main consequence of this defect is, therefore, a great loss of iodine, which

sets up a vicious circle of thyroid stimulation, hyperplasia, goiter, and increased synthesis and leakage of hormone precursors. The severity of the defect is therefore inversely proportional to the iodine content of the diet.

The clinical picture of the patients affected by the deiodinase defect is that of congenital hypothyroidism with goiter. The severity of hypothyroidism and goiter and of their possible consequences depends on the severity of the defect and on the supply of iodine. The decrease in serum T_4 and T_3 levels and increase in serum TSH will vary accordingly. Radioiodide or $^{99m}TcO_4^-$ uptakes are high and fast, and radioiodide release is rapid. Trichloroacetic acid treatment of serum precipitates partially the iodotyrosines and thus part of the released radioiodine. Chromatography of extracts of the serum and the urine demonstrates radioiodine in the iodotyrosines. Demonstration of the defect is achieved by the in vivo diiodotyrosine test. Radioiodine-labeled DIT is injected intramuscularly or intravenously, and urine is collected at 1-h intervals for a few hours. Chromatography of the urine demonstrates less than 5 percent of the radioactivity in the iodotyrosines in normal controls, but up to 80 percent in patients.[4,168–173] Alternatively, urinary DIT may be measured by radioimmunoassay after its immunoprecipitation from urine. Its secretion is considerably increased in deficient patients (12 to 16 vs. 0.108 ± 48 nmol per millimeter of creatinine).[174] Thyroid slices from these patients will not deiodinate labeled DIT; to validate such a finding, positive deiodination by human and/or animal thyroid slices should be demonstrated at the same time. The latter activity should be inhibited by dinitrotyrosine (mM), an inhibitor of the enzyme. Finally, demonstration of the defect and of the proposed pathogenetic mechanism requires that iodine medication alone should be sufficient to reestablish euthyroidism.[171,175] An isolated defect in the deiodinating capacity of peripheral tissues but not of the thyroid should not cause the syndrome, as iodotyrosines as such are only released as traces by the thyroid.

An unusual opportunity to study the genetics of this kind of goitrous creatinism has been exploited by Hutchison and McGirr.[176,177] They have traced the complex family history of their Scottish parents through 160 years. The original male member came from Ireland and married his first cousin. There was subsequently little marriage outside the group; close intermarriage within the group has been extremely frequent. Ten goitrous cretins are known to have appeared among 31 persons in four sets of sibs.

A study of the pedigree shows that this form of cretinism with goiter behaves as a simple autosomal recessive trait. There is no sex predilection. The marriages which resulted in affected persons were all consanguineous, but in no case was a parent affected. The inheritance ratio was somewhat in excess of the expected 1:3 in that there were 10 affected sibs and 21 normal children in four sibships, but this is probably explained by ascertainment bias and Hutchison and McGirr point out that a number of unaffected sibs undoubtedly were lost to genetic study.[177] There have been no marriages of the affected members of this kindred, so that there has been no opportunity to test inheritance from phenotypes. On the other hand, relatives of some of these patients demonstrated defective DIT deiodinase activity and had evidence of thyroid disease but without mental or skeletal retardation. These relatives presumably were heterozygous. Rochiccioli and Dufau[172] have been able to identify carriers of the trait by giving stable DIT along with the labeled DIT. Carriers are less efficient in deiodinating the DIT. Similarly, Codaccioni et al.[178] studied relatives of patients with dehalogenase deficiency. They gave 20 to 25 mg stable DIT along with labeled DIT and found that the best discrimination was achieved when the first 2-h excretion of undeiodinated labeled DIT was measured. The relatives of patients excreted an average of 20.4 percent during this time, whereas normal subjects excreted 11.4 percent and the patients with dehalogenase deficiency excreted 52 to 79 percent.

TRANSPORT OF THYROID HORMONES IN BLOOD

Metabolism

The bulk of thyroid hormone is transported in blood bound to three serum proteins: thyroxine-binding globulin (TBG), thyroxine-binding prealbumin (TBPA, or transthyretin), and albumin. The normal distribution of T_4 among these proteins is 75 to 80 percent bound to TBG, 15 to 20 percent bound to TBPA, and 5 to 10 percent bound to ablumin. The proportion of T_3 bound to TBG is the same as that of T_4, but due to limited binding to TBPA, the remaining 20 to 25 percent of T_3 is carried by albumin. All circulating iodothyronines are associated in various proportions with the same carrier proteins. Several other serum proteins, such as α- and β-lipoptoteins, make a minor contribution to thyroid hormone transport.[179] Others, such as γ-globulins can, in pathologic conditions, bind various amounts of the circulating iodothyronines.[180]

The interactions of all iodothyronines with the binding proteins are noncovalent and reversible, and they obey the law of mass action. The concentration of free (unbound) iodothyronine (FTi) can be calculated from the total concentration of the iodothyronine (TTi), that of the binding protein (BPj), and their association constant (Ki,j). The concentration of free iodothyronine is very small relative to the total iodothyronine, being under normal circumstances 0.03 percent for T_4 and 0.3 percent for T_3.

Since only the minute fraction of free thyroid hormone is diffusible and thus immediately available to tissues, it has been speculated that the large extrathyroidal pool of dissociable protein-bound hormone serves as a reservoir readily available to tissues as well as a safeguard to protect the body from the effect of abrupt changes in hormonal secretion or metabolism. It can be estimated that in the absence of binding proteins, a small extrathyroidal pool of free hormone would be completely depleted in a matter of hours after a sudden cessation of hormone secretion. However, in the presence of a normally functioning hypothalamic-pituitary-thyroid axis, the free hormone concentration, and thus the metabolic status, can be maintained even with profound alternations in circulating thyroid hormone–binding proteins.[181]

All three thyroid hormone–binding proteins are synthesized in the liver. Their concentrations in serum can be measured by colorimetric, electrophoretic, radioimmunometric, and ligand-binding techniques.

TBG is an acidic glycoprotein composed of a single polypeptide chain and four heterosaccharide units with five to nine residues of sialic acid. The carbohydrate moiety is not required for hormone binding. Rather, it appears to be responsible for the posttranslational acquisition of the molecule's tertiary structure and for its multiple isoforms (microheterogeneity.)[182,183]

The molecule has a single iodothyronine-binding site with affinity of approximately $10^{10}\ M^{-1}$ for T_4 and $10^9\ M^{-1}$ for T_3. It is stable at room temperature and in dilute alkali but rapidly undergoes irreversible denaturation at temperatures above 55°C and pH below 4. The complete amino acid sequence of TBG has been recently deduced from analysis of cDNA clones.[184] The polypeptide core has a molecular mass of 44,180 daltons, with striking homology to the antiproteases, α_1-antitrypsin and antichymotrypsin. The single TBG gene is located on the long arm of the X chromosome.[185] In the normal euthyroid adult, about one-third of the TBG molecules carry thyroid hormone, mainly T_4. At full saturation, the 1.6 mg/dl TBG can carry 20 μg T_4 per deciliter of serum. The biologic half-life of TBG is about five days. A number of compounds may alter its concentration in serum. The most common, estrogens, elevated during pregnancy or when given for birth control, increase TBG concentration mainly through reduction of its rate of degradation as a result of an increase in complexity of the oligosaccharide residues.[186] Many compounds compete with T_4 at its binding site on TBG owing to their structural similarities to the iodothyronines.

TBPA is a stable tetramer composed of four identical subunits, each containing 127 amino acid residues encoded by a single copy gene located on chromosome 18.[187,188] The complete molecule has a molecular mass of 55,000 daltons, is highly acidic, but contains no carbohydrate. The four subunits form a symmetric, double-trumped-shaped channel that traverses the molecule, forming two T_4 binding sites. However, only a single T_4 is usually bound with a K_a of approximately $10^8\ M^{-1}$ because the binding affinity for the second, identical site is greatly reduced through negative cooperativity of the first ligand interaction.[189] TBPA complexes with retinol-binding protein and thus also plays a role in the transport of vitamin A. This interaction does not influence T_4 binding.[190]

Although on a molar basis the normal TBPA concentration is twentyfold that of TBG, it plays a minor role in thyroid hormone transport due to its lower association constant. Thus, despite its relatively short half-life of 2 days and high propensity for wide fluctuation in response to a variety of physiological and pathologic factors, its effect on the concentration of circulating thyroid hormones is of no practical consequence.

Albumin circulates in serum mainly as a monomer of approximately 69 kDa. It associates with a wide variety of natural and exogenous substances having a hydrophobic domain. In this sense, the association of iodothyronines with albumin can be viewed as nonspecific. Despite the high abundance of albumin and multiple thyroid hormone–binding sites, their relatively low affinities (less than $10^7\ M^{-1}$) are responsible for the negligible contribution of albumin as thyroid hormone transport protein.[191]

Related Clinical Disorders

Inherited abnormalities of thyroid hormone transport have been described for each of the three hormone carrier proteins. They generally result in alterations of variable degree in the concentration of total hormone in serum. However, free hormone concentrations, the activity of the thyroid gland, and the metabolic status of the patient remain unaltered.[192–194] Also, with the possible exception of familial dysalbuminemia,[195] the daily production and metabolism of thyroid hormones remain unaltered.[194,195] Nevertheless, inappropriate therapeutic interventions to correct the changes in total T_4 or T_3 concentration in serum are not uncommon.[196] Since TBPA and albumin serve other functions than thyroid hormone transport, some inherited defects of these proteins can cause specific illnesses, such as familial amyloidotic polyneuropathy, associated with mutations in the TBPA gene (Chap. 97).[197] In contrast, even extreme abnormalities of TBG, such as complete deficiency, do not affect the health or survival of affected individuals. This benign phenotype may explain why inherited TBG abnormalities are rather common in the population: 1 in 2800 newborn males have TBG deficiency, and approximately 1 in 25,000 have increased TBG.[198,199] In some populations, variant TBGs occur in over 50 percent of the population.[200] The associations of inherited TBG defects with thyrotoxicosis,[201] goiter,[202] and Turner syndrome[203,204] are most likely fortuitous.

Inherited TBG Abnormalities. Inherited defects of TBG in human beings are X-linked and are expressed in hemizygotes as complete TBG deficiency, partial TBG deficiency, or TBG excess.

In the complete deficiency, affected males have undetectable TBG levels, and heterozygous females have approximately half the normal concentration.[193,203–205] The inheritance follows a typical X-linked pattern with no male-to-male transmission, and all female offspring of affected fathers are heterozygotes. Recent analysis of DNA from six unrelated TBG-deficient families digested with 11 restriction endonucleases showed no fragment length differences.[206] Thus, large fragment deletions, insertions, or rearrangements are not common mechanisms for complete TBG deficiency.

In partial TBG deficiency, by definition, males have reduced but not absent TBG levels. Thus, separation of partial from complete TBG deficiency is dependent upon the sensitivity of the TBG assay, which is variable, with limits of detectability from 300 to 5 μg/dl, or 1.9 to 0.03 percent the mean normal level. In families where TBG levels in affected males are 15 percent above the mean average, those in heterozygous females often overlap the normal range, invalidating the assignment of genotype. Nevertheless, studies in subjects with partial TBG deficiency have uncovered a number of variant TBG molecules. In 1980, Dick and Watson[207] were first to describe an inherited variant TBG widely distributed in Australian aborigines (TBG-A). Affected individuals have reduced serum total T_4 and T_3 concentrations out of proportion to that of TBG measured by radioimmunoassay, but are euthyroid and have normal serum TSH levels. The abnormality appears

to be due to a structural gene defect, since TBG-A has a reduced affinity for T_4 and T_3 and increased lability to inactivation by heat and acid.[208] The same year, Daiger et al.[209] described another variant TBG with cathodal shift on isoelectric focusing (TBG-S). This variant TBG occurs in 5 to 10 percent of populations of African and Oceanian origin. A number of different inherited variant TBGs have since been described, all occurring in families with partial TBG deficiency and characterized by alterations in hormone-binding properties, thermal lability, and/or electrophoretic mobility (Table 73-5). The association with high levels of denatured TBG in serum of affected subjects supports the impression that the reduced TBG concentration is due to the more rapid in vivo degradation of the unstable TBG mutants.[210] The gene of one variant TBG, TBG-Gary,[204] has been recently cloned and sequenced. It has a single substitution of A for T in the codon for amino acid 96 of the mature protein leading to the replacement of the normal isoleucine with asparagine and providing a new potential glycosylation site.[211] This result explains the anodal shift on IEF of all TBG bands which is due to the addition of sialic acid on the glycosylated asparagine substitution.

Inherited TBG excess is associated with approximately fourfold elevation of the TBG level in serum of affected men. The level in heterozygous females is approximately 2.5 times above the normal mean.[193,205] The TBG molecule has been found to have normal physicochemical properties. The abnormalities are believed to reside at the promoter area of the gene.

Inherited TBPA Abnormalities. Moses et al.[213] described a family in which affected members had elevated serum total T_4 that was predominantly bound to TBPA. Tetraiodothyroacetic acid bound with even higher affinity than T_4. The subjects were clinically euthyroid and had normal free T_4 levels measured by equilibrium dialysis. In accordance with the thyroid hormone–binding properties of the molecule, serum T_3 concentration was normal. The inheritance appears to be autosomal dominant. A variant TBPA causing an increase in the concentration of total T_4 in serum in an unrelated subject has been studied in detail.[214] The clinical and laboratory features were similar to those described by Moses. Additional findings were increased affinity for rT_3, explaining its increased concentration in serum. Given the normal concentration of TBPA in serum, the defect appears to involve the structure of the

Table 73-5 Characteristics of Variant TBGs Associated with Partial Deficiency

| Variant | Serum levels, % of TBG-C | | | nTBG Properties | | |
	nTBG	dnTBG	TT_4	Heat lability, °C for $t_{1/2}$ 7 min*	K_a for T_4, % of TBG-C	IEF, pI shift†
TBG-C	100	100	100	60	100	—
TBG-S	88	100	84	59	100	−0.06
TBG-A	74	100	58	58	54	None
TBG-Quebec	16	260	41	50	70	−0.06
TBG-Montreal	14	390	38	48	73	−0.02
TBG-Gary	1.2	1000	24	45	<1	+0.02

*Temperature at which 50% of nTBG is denatured in 7 min.
†Shift compared to the IEF pattern of TBG-C, with "−" referring to cathodal and "+" to anodal shift.
NOTE: TBG-C = common type TBG; TBG-S = isoelectric focusing or slow variant TBG; TBG-A = aboriginal variant TBG; nTBG = native TBG; dnTBG = denatured TBG; and IEF = isoelectric focusing. Data represent mean values for hemizygous subjects (see Refs. 200, 204, 208, 210, 212).

molecule, resulting in altered thyroid hormone–binding properties.

Four types of structurally variant TBPAs have been described in association with familial amyloidotic polyneuropathy (Chap. 97).[197,215] All are due to single amino acid substitutions. The defects are autosomal dominant, and carriers have the variant TBPA in both serum and amyloid deposits. The amyloid deposits are responsible for the neuropathy and progressive organ failure. Two of the variant TBPAs, namely type I (methionine transposition for the valine at position 30) and type II (serine for isoleucine substitution at position 84) have also five- to sixfold reduced affinity for T_4.[215] The affinity constant of the Appalachian type of TBPA (alanine substitution for threonine at position 60) was, however, normal.[215] While these defects have no direct effects on thyroid function, information derived from these mutants has been valuable in understanding the structural requirements for protein-hormone interactions. Increased incidence of hypothyroidism in patients with familial amyloid polyneuropathy is probably due to destruction of the thyroid gland by amyloid deposits.[215]

Another genetic defect, giving rise to a striking polymorphism, has been found in monkeys but not in humans.[216] Its biologic significance has not been fully explored.[217]

Familial Dysalbuminemic Hyperthyroxinemia. A variant albumin with increased binding affinity for T_4 but not T_3 appears to occur as frequently as TBG deficiency. Patients are euthyroid, have normal basal serum TSH levels that respond normally to TRH, and have normal free T_4 concentration measured by equilibrium dialysis using appropriate buffer systems.[218,219] However, estimation of the free T_4 level using the T_3-uptake test or measurements employing labeled T_4 analogues give spuriously high values.

The variant albumin, with approximately a tenfold higher affinity for T_4, is inherited as an autosomal dominant trait. Affected subjects appear to be heterozygous, expressing two albumin genes; each is responsible for 50 percent of the total albumin, the concentration of which remains normal.[220]

Due to the minor contribution of normal albumin to thyroid hormone transport, congenital analbuminemia does not have an important effect on thyroid hormone concentration in serum.[221]

TRANSPORT OF THYROID HORMONE INTO CELLS AND METABOLISM

Metabolism

It is generally accepted that thyroid hormones enter the cell in an unbound or "free" form. This concept is in agreement with the observation that the concentration of free rather than total (protein-bound) hormone in serum best correlates with the thyroid hormone–dependent metabolic status of the organism. Because the amount of T_4 and T_3 metabolized each day represents 150 to 300 times that available in the circulation in free form, continuous dissociation of protein-bound hormone must occur in the capillary bed. While this mechanism of hormone supply to cells is realistic, both on analytical and theoretical grounds,[222,223] Pardridge has postulated that a major source of thyroid hormone for cellular uptake is protein-bound.[224] A more critical issue concerning thyroid hormone transfer into cells which has not been resolved is the requirement of a spe-

cific transport system at the level of the cell membrane. A saturable and energy-dependent system involving a plasma membrane protein and ATP has been described in rat hepatocytes.[225] A mechanism of hormone internalization through coated pits has also been suggested.[226] Finally, even less is known of the processes that determine the intracellular distribution of thyroid hormones. A stereospecific pump acting at the nuclear membrane has been suggested.[227]

While the principal secretory product of the thyroid gland is T_4, this "prohormone" needs to undergo "activation" by conversion to T_3 through a specific intracellular 5′ monodeiodination. As a matter of fact, 80 percent of T_4 is metabolized through a process of stepwise deiodination which eventually strips all four iodines from the molecule (Fig. 73-10). Minor pathways of iodothyronine metabolism include conjugation with glucuronic or sulfuric acid at the phenolic hydroxyl, deamination and decarboxylation of the alanine side chain, and cleavage of the ether bond.[228,229]

The only source of T_4 is the thyroid gland, which, in an average adult, secretes from 80 to 90 μg/day (approximately 110 nmol). The deiodination pathway of T_4 metabolism yields about equal amounts (45 nmol) of T_3 (3,5,3′-T_3) and rT3 (3,3′,5′-T_3, or reverse T_3) by 5′ and 5 monodeiodination, respectively. About 80 percent of the T_3 is derived from T_4, while the remaining 20 percent is secreted by the thyroid gland. T_4 has a large extrathyroidal pool which is predominantly extracellular. The smaller pool of T_3 is mainly localized in the intracellular compartment and is metabolized 20 times more rapidly than that of T_4 (Table 73-6).

The ability of peripheral tissues to generate either a metabolically active (T_3) or inactive (rT_3) hormone through T_4 monodeiodination provides target cells with a mechanism of autoregulation of thyroid hormone supply. Two enzymes are involved in 5′ monodeiodination: type I 5′-deiodinase (I-5′DI) and type II 5′-deiodinase (II-5′DI). I-5′DI has a high K_m for T_4 (0.5 μM), is inhibited by propylthiouracil (PTU), and is present in liver, kidney, muscle, and skin, thus providing T_3 for the whole body. In contrast, II-5′DI has a low K_m for T_4 (<5 nM), is not inhibited by PTU, and is present mainly in the anterior pituitary, cerebral cortex, and brown adipose tissue controlling the intracellular T_3 concentration locally.[228,229] Both enzymes are inhibited by iopanoic acid. While I-5′DI also mediates inner ring deiodination of T_4 and T_3 in liver and kidney, a third deiodinase (II-5′DI) catalyzes specifically 5′ deiodination in the central nervous system.[230] The subcellular localization of the enzymes varies somewhat from tissue to tissue and includes microsomes, endoplasmic reticulum, and plasma membrane. The deiodination reaction is reductive in nature, probably involving a sulfenyl iodide intermediate.

The autoregulation of hormonal activity is apparent in the selective effect on the enzymes. Hyperthyroidism is associated with reduced II-5′DI and increased I-5′DI activity. In contrast, reciprocal changes are observed in hypothyroidism. The net effect, mediated through actual changes in tissue enzyme content, is an apparent protection of the central nervous system by increasing T_3 supply when hormone supply is restricted and disposing of T_3 by increased metabolism in peripheral tissues when hormone is available in excess. During carbohydrate deprivation and in systemic illnesses, I-5′DI activity is greatly reduced through a decrease in tissue cofactors, which accounts for the diminished T_3 production and for both a decrease in T_3 and an increase in rT_3 levels in serum. This situation, referred to as the *low T_3 syndrome*,[231] is believed to safeguard the body from the catabolic effect of thyroid hor-

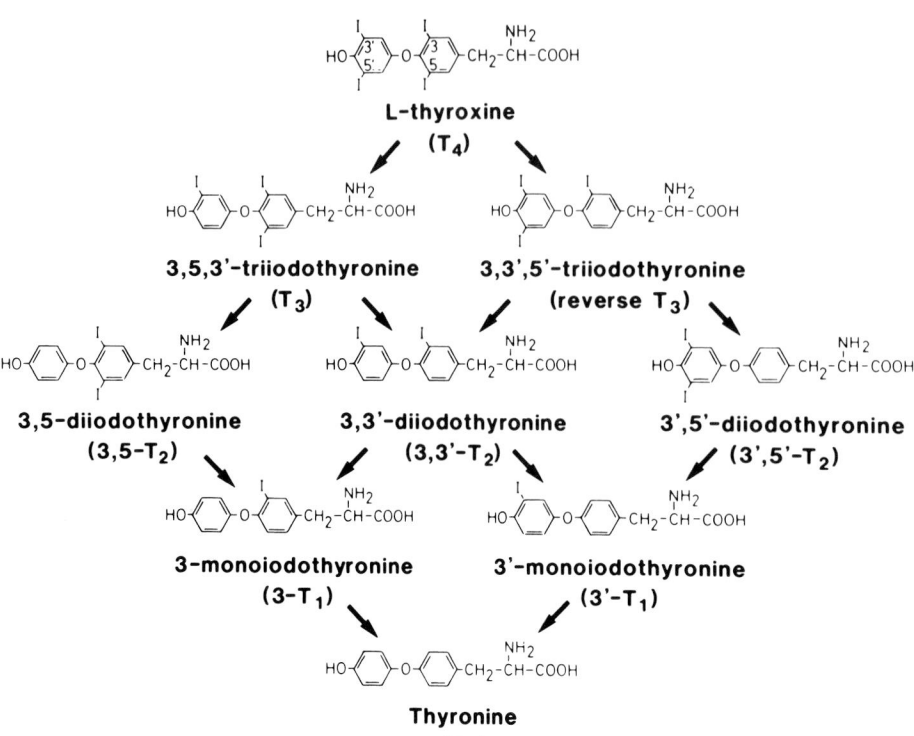

Fig. 73-10 The pathway of monodeiodination of iodothyronines. The process involves stepwise monodeiodination eventually stripping the molecule of all iodines. (From Engler and Burger.[229] Used with permission of Endocrinology Review.)

mone and thus serves the purpose of energy conservation in the face of decreased calorie supply or increased metabolic demands. 5'-Deiodinase activity is also very low in the fetus, producing low T_3 and high rT_3 levels at birth.

Related Clinical Disorders

A defect in the plasma membrane transport of T_4 has been suggested in a 74-year-old woman, based on an apparent reduction in the ratio of cytosol to total T_4 uptake in red blood cells.[232] This individual was a member of a family in which affected subjects were euthyroid despite high T_4 and T_3 concentrations and had no thyroid hormone–binding serum protein defect. However, the postulated plasma membrane defect of T_4 but not T_3 transport cannot explain the high serum T_3 and rT_3 levels and the severe hyporesponsiveness of the patient's fibroblasts to T_3.[233]

While reduced conversion of T_4 to T_3 is common in nonthyroidal illness and in response to a variety of drugs,[231] inherited defects in iodothyronine deiodination have not been clearly demonstrated. Maxon et al.[234] reported the occurrence of familial elevation of serum T_4 and rT_3 but not T_3 concentration

in subjects who were clinically euthyroid. Although this finding is compatible with a primary abnormality in the deiodination of T_4 in peripheral tissues, direct proof could not be obtained, owing to the refusal of the subjects to undergo turnover studies or ingest thyroid hormone. Ostensibly, the existence of such a defect has been suggested in very early publications.[235, 236] Two unrelated cases with elevated serum T_4 and rT_3 but not T_3 concentrations have been described and postulated to have either reduced transport of T_4 into cells or impaired intracellular 5'deiodination.[237] However, the possible presence of variant TBPA or albumin has not been fully examined.

ACTIONS OF THYROID HORMONES

Thyroid hormones play an important role in growth and development and act on peripheral tissues of the adult to regulate their level of metabolism. The effects of thyroid hormone are not confined to mammals and even extend to nonvertebrate species, such as the regulation of the life cycle of coelenterates.[238] Some of the most dramatic effects of thyroid hormone involve the metamorphosis of amphibians. In an extraordinary sequence of events which involves simultaneous inhibition and stimulation of synthesis of specific proteins, the tail of the larval tadpole is resorbed; together with budding of the limbs, this results in the acquisition of the adult form, freed from dependence on the aquatic environment. The biochemical changes of this metamorphosis are even more dramatic and include conversion from ammonotelism to ureotelism.[239]

The actions of thyroid hormone are not only determined by the species but also by the type of tissue, by the duration and time of exposure in relation to the developmental stage of the organism, by the level of thyroid hormone, and by the influence of other hormones.

Table 73-6 Metabolic Parameters of T_4, T_3, and rT_3*

		T_4	T_3	rT_3
Concentration in serum	μg/dl	8	0.125	0.025
	nmol/liter	103	0.19	0.038
Distribution volume, liters		10	42	90
Metabolic clearance rate, liters/day		1.1	24	110
Disposal (production)	μg/day	88	30	28
	nmol/day	113	46	43
Fraction derived from T_4, %			80	98
Fraction of T_4, %			40	38

*Mean values for a 70-kg man.

Physiological and Biochemical Effects

Although the impact of thyroid hormone is in comparison less dramatic in human beings, the hormone is necessary for the sustenance of normal body growth and maturation, including cerebral development. It is unclear whether the hormone is required at all before late intrauterine life.[240] However, thyroid hormone deficiency during early neonatal life leads not only to reversible growth retardation and delay in bone development but, more importantly, results in an irreversible failure of brain maturation. Supply of thyroid hormone during the perinatal period appears to be most important for mental development[241,242] with severe and more prolonged deficiency resulting in cretinism, the full-blown syndrome of congenital hypothyroidism.

The early observation of a relationship between thyroid hormone and oxygen consumption led to the conclusion that the hormone is a principal regulator of metabolic activity, and to the notion of thyroid hormone–responsive tissues based on measurements of oxygen consumption. Unfortunately, this same finding was the source of misconceptions, namely, that the hormonal effect is mediated through uncoupling of oxidative phosphorylation and that the brain is hormonally unresponsive.

The calorigenic sodium pump which operates through membrane-bound Na^+, K^+-ATPase accounts, at least in part, for the thyroid hormone–mediated thermogenesis.[243] The energy for the function of this pump is derived from the hydrolysis of ATP to ADP, a heat-producing process. Thyroid hormone increases the level of the pump enzyme as well as the activity of α-glycerophosphate dehydrogenase which catalyzes the shuttle of reducing equivalents from cytosol to the mitochondrial electron transport system. The parallel stimulation of Na^+, K^+-ATPase and α-glycerophosphate dehydrogenase by thyroid hormone results in thermogenesis with maintenance of coupled oxidative phosphorylation. Na^+, K^+-ATPase also mediates the thermogenic action of catecholamines and provides a means for synergistic interaction with thyroid hormone in brown adipose tissue.[244,245]

Thyroid hormone interacts not only with other hormones but also with a variety of physiological processes. For example, the effect of thyroid hormone on the induction of cytosolic malic dehydrogenase is greatly influenced by diet. High glucose diet shifts the dose response curve and increases the maximal effect of thyroid hormone. This effect known as "amplification" has been observed with other lipogenic and hexose monophosphate shunt enzymes.[246]

There is no question that thyroid hormone plays an important role in protein metabolism. The predominant effect is induction of specific protein synthesis. This is often true even when there is an apparent reduction in the concentration of a protein or the observed and more dramatic effect does not involve protein metabolism. In the first instance, another protein specifically induced by the hormone may have a net catabolic effect on a protein under study. Similarly, a thyroid hormone–induced protein with enzymatic properties could profoundly influence a process which does not directly involve protein metabolism.

Several observations are worth mentioning in order to provide an overview of the peculiarities and characteristics of thyroid hormone action:[247] (1) Cells may respond to thyroid hormone during a limited period in their life span, related or not to cell differentiation. (2) Not all cells respond to the hormone even if they share a common process; this difference in cell responsiveness is sometimes dependent on the anatomic position or conditions of the external environment. (3) The level of thyroid hormone affects not only the magnitude of the response but also its net outcome. Thus, in general, low concentrations are biosynthetic or anabolic, whereas degradative or catabolic pathways predominate at high hormone concentrations. This phenomenon confers a typical biphasic character to thyroid hormone action. (4) Opposite effects of thyroid hormone are not only dose-dependent but could be mediated through effects on different metabolic processes concerned with a similar function. (5) The rapidity with which the final effect of thyroid hormone is manifested or fully established may take minutes or may be preceded by a lag period lasting several days. (6) Thyroid hormone has no specific target tissue, and multiple cell processes occurring in a single cell are influenced by the hormone. (7) The hormone is probably essential for the life of the more complex vertebrate species. Thus, total unresponsiveness to thyroid hormone is unlikely to be compatible with long-term survival.

Mechanisms of Actions

Until recent years, the concepts of the mechanisms of thyroid hormone were by and large descriptive, based on observations made under conditions of hormone deprivation or excess. The rapid progress witnessed during the past 15 years was triggered by the demonstration of intranuclear localization of thyroid hormone[248] followed by the characterization of a nuclear protein that fulfills the criteria for a hormone receptor and thus, potentially, for a specific inducer of biologic activity.[249] These criteria include: (1) high affinity and limited capacity for the hormone; (2) correlation between receptor affinity for thyroid hormone analogues and their relative biologic potency; (3) concordance of receptor density with the hormone responsiveness of different tissues; (4) relationship between receptor occupancy and intensity of biologic responses; (5) partial saturability at physiological concentrations of thyroid hormone; (6) identity in hormone-binding characteristics of receptors in all tissues and species responsive to thyroid hormone; (7) receptor occupancy by the hormone preceding the initiation of hormone action; and (8) modification of thyroid hormone responses in the presence of receptor abnormalities.

The thyroid hormone receptor is present in cell nuclei in low concentrations and has so far resisted purification to homogeneity. However, based on studies carried out on nuclear extracts and partially purified preparations, the receptor has been characterized as a chromatin-associated nonhistone protein with molecular mass of 47,000 to 57,000 daltons. It has the highest binding affinity for 3,5,3′-triiodothyroacetic acid (TRIAC), followed closely by T_3 ($0.5 \times 10^9\ M^{-1}$) and lesser affinity for T_4. The relatively lower biologic potency of TRIAC, despite a high binding affinity to the receptor, can be explained by a more rapid fractional turnover rate of this analogue, reducing its time of nuclear residency.[250] The receptor concentration varies greatly among different tissues, ranging from 100 sites per cell, with virtually no responsiveness to the hormone, to 10,000 sites in the highly hormone sensitive pituitary cells. In the physiological range of hormone concentration, about 30 percent of the receptor is occupied by thyroid hormone, predominantly T_3.

Recent studies have provided further definition of the nuclear thyroid hormone receptor. Tryptic digestion and photoaffinity labeling of the receptor with T_3 identified two functional domains: a hormone-histone binding domain and a DNA-binding domain. All known properties of the receptor were preserved in a 38,000-dalton fragment, while a 26,000-dalton fragment lost the ability to bind to DNA but retained both hormone- and histone-binding domains.[251,252] Recently two groups of investigators[253,254] probed cDNA libraries from chicken, rat, and human beings with the avian viral oncogene (v-erb-A), which is related to the nuclear steroid receptors. The product of this cellular analogue (c-erb-A) encoded a protein with properties virtually indistinguishable from those of the native thyroid hormone receptor. Further studies have shown that thyroid hormone receptors constitute a family of related proteins likely to exhibit tissue-specific distribution. A receptor specific for brain tissue has been identified recently.[255]

The structural requirements for thyromimetic activity are rather loose and include a central lipophilic core, sterically constrained by bulky 3,5,3'-substituents, with two specific anionic groups located at the distal ends of the molecule. Extensive modifications of the alanine side chain, of the oxygen linkage between the phenolic groups, of the hydroxyl group, and even substitution of the iodines may not abolish the hormonal activity.[243,256] Important from a physiological point of view is the fact that trisubstituted analogues, leaving the 5' position of the phenolic ring free, are more active. This allows regulation of hormonal activity by removal of a single iodine, at either the 5 position, causing reduction, or the 5' position, producing enhanced potency.

The suggestion that thyroid hormone initiated synthesis of specific proteins by interaction with the cell nucleus was provided in early work which showed enhancement of growth hormone mRNA in rat pituitary tumor cells.[257,258] Of the various mechanisms that could lead to the accumulation of mature cytoplasmic mRNA, two have been shown to be operative in the hormonal induction of different proteins. These are stimulation of transcriptional activity and stabilization of the mRNA. The former mechanism is predominant in the thyroid hormone regulation of growth hormone synthesis.[259,260] Transcription appears to be induced by binding of the hormone receptor to the promoter, a specific portion of the 5'-untranslated region of the growth hormone gene.[261,262] Thyroid hormone–induced suppression of TSH synthesis is mediated through a down-regulation of gene transcription.[263] An example of thyroid hormone–regulated protein synthesis through stabilization of the pre-messenger RNA is that of the rat cytosolic protein, spot 14. While the nuclear level of spot 14–precursor RNA was increased five- to sixfold 10 to 20 min after administration of T_3, direct assays of transcriptional activity showed only a small stimulatory effect.[264] Evidence that thyroid hormone can transcriptionally regulate the same genes in opposite directions in different tissues has been provided in studies of the myosin heavy-chain genes.[265]

Several investigators have suggested that thyroid hormone can initiate cellular responses through interaction with extranuclear cell components. There is partial evidence for the involvement of plasma membrane hormone transport units and specific mitochondrial receptors which requires further investigation.[225,266]

Related Clinical Disorders

The first and most extensively studied family involved three of six sibs, products of a consanguineous marriage.[233,267-272]

Affected subjects were deaf-mute, had delayed bone age, stippled epiphyses, and small goiters. Despite these stigmata suggestive of hypothyroidism, their serum T_4 and T_3 concentrations were high, without abnormalities in hormone-binding serum proteins; thus, they had elevated levels of free T_4 and T_3. This discrepancy between the clinical state and laboratory tests was the most striking finding. The impression of target organ resistance to the action of thyroid hormone was confirmed by studies carried out both in vivo and in vitro.

The authenticity of the circulating thyroid hormones was established by their binding properties to the native serum transport protein, TBG, and to specific antibodies. Normal stereochemical structure of the hormone was confirmed by L-amino acid oxidase digestion.[268] In vivo iodide kinetic and thyroid hormone turnover studies indicated that thyroid hormone was synthesized and secreted from the thyroid gland in excessive amounts and that the hormone was metabolized in peripheral tissues through the normal pathways, generating high levels of the metabolically active T_3.[267,268] This was confirmed by T_4 to T_3 conversion studies carried out in cultured fibroblasts obtained from the affected sibs.[269] The fractional uptake of radioiodide and the absolute amount of iodide accumulated by the thyroid gland were clearly elevated. Normal iodide organification was confirmed by the perchlorate discharge test, and all other inborn errors of thyroid hormone synthesis were ruled out by specific studies. The possibility of a defective transport of the hormone from blood to tissues was not only examined in fibroblasts but was also evaluated in vivo from the early disappearance of simultaneously administered labeled T_4 or T_3 and albumin.[268] Such studies showed excessive penetration of T_4 and T_3 into the extra-albumin space, compatible with a normal transport into cells of the increased free fractions of the circulating hormones.

To confirm the clinical impression of apparent resistance to thyroid hormone, its impact on target tissues was assessed in the basal state and during the administration of graded doses of T_4 and T_3.[268,271] In addition to determination of the basal metabolic rate, a number of parameters were measured which, under normal circumstances, reflect the level of thyroid hormone activity. A partial list includes serum cholesterol, carotene, lipids, enzymes, tyrosine, sex hormone–binding globulin, ferritin, prolactin, and TSH, as well as its response to TRH; and urinary excretion of magnesium, hydroxyproline, creatine, carnitine, and cAMP. Their levels indicated normal or reduced thyroid hormone effect compatible with the clinical impression of euthyroidism or hypothyroidism, depending upon the target organ under evaluation. More importantly, a thyromimetic response was observed only with administration of supraphysiological doses of T_4 and T_3. For some of the parameters measured, doses of 1000 μg T_4 or 400 μg T_3, or 8 times the physiological amount of hormone, was required to elicit a response (Fig. 73-11).

Serum levels of TSH and its response to TRH paradoxically increased with the administration of physiological doses of T_3 but were ultimately suppressed at the highest T_3 dose given.[271] In contrast, glucocorticoids and L-dopa produced normal suppressive responses. Taking into account the exquisitely sensitive regulation of TSH by thyroid hormone, these results confirm the tissue resistance and its specificity to thyroid hormone. The ability to achieve complete TSH suppression, albeit with very large doses of T_3, indicates that the resistance to thyroid hormone is partial. Finally, reduction of thyroid hormone activity and endogenous hormone production during the administration of large doses of hormone, which sup-

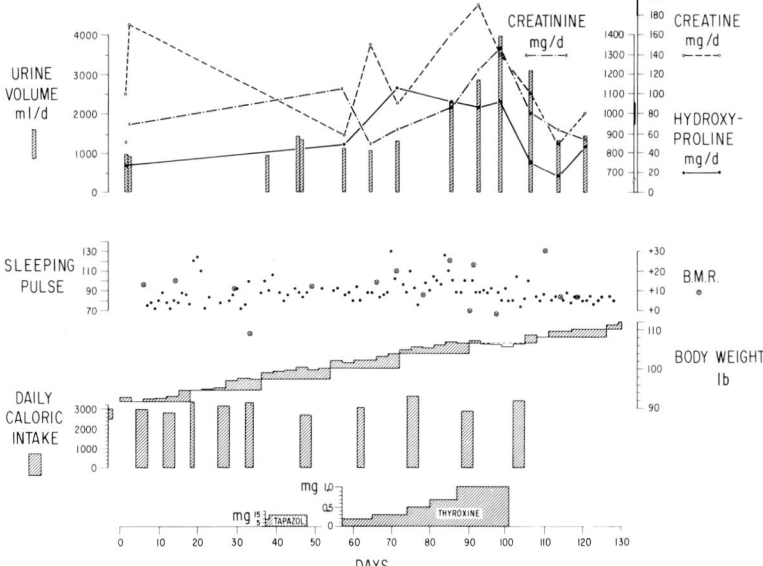

Fig. 73-11 Metabolic responses to the administration of exogenous thyroxine to a 14-year-old subject with apparent resistance to thyroid hormone. Hatched areas under the body weight plot represent incremental weight gains over periods of 18 days. Note the failure of thyroxine treatment to produce changes in the caloric intake, sleeping pulse rate, and basal metabolic rate. Urinary volume and creatine and hydroxyproline excretion increased, the latter rising from subnormal to normal values for the patient's chronological age. (From Refetoff et al.[268] Used by permission of Metabolism.)

pressed TSH, indicate that the thyroid gland hyperactivity and excessive thyroid hormone synthesis and secretion in these patients are mediated through pituitary TSH. The biologic activity of their TSH has been confirmed, and no abnormal thyroid stimulators or antibodies to TSH could be detected. No other significant endocrine abnormalities were found, and subtle, but uniform, features of body habitus of the affected sibs could not be explained on the basis of their defective response to thyroid hormone.

Quantitative or qualitative abnormalities of the nuclear thyroid receptor were sought. A tenfold reduction in the affinity of the receptor for T_3 could be demonstrated in circulating mononuclear cells but not in cultured skin fibroblasts.[270] Although these studies are far from conclusive, they support the hypothesis of defect in the mediation of thyroid hormone action.

Since the initial description of the syndrome, 149 patients fulfilling the criteria of generalized resistance to thyroid hormone have been described, most of whom were reviewed in detail[273,274]; 136 subjects belonged to 39 families with two or more affected members. Familial occurrence cannot be excluded in the remaining 13 cases classified as sporadic because of unknown family history due to adoption, failure to test family members, or small pedigrees. In different families, either autosomal dominant or recessive modes of inheritance have been proposed. The syndrome has no clear geographic, racial, or ethnic distribution, and the female-to-male ratio is close to 1.

Although the clinical presentation of generalized resistance to thyroid hormone is variable, the common features are: (1) elevated serum levels of free T_4 and T_3; (2) preserved TSH response to TRH; (3) absence of symptoms and metabolic consequences of thyroid hormone excess; and (4) in the majority of cases, goiter. Although the etiology of the defect remains unknown, there are reasons to believe that the syndrome may be caused by a number of defects involving various steps in the mediation of thyroid hormone action. The severity of the hormone resistance is variable among different families, as is the degree of hormone insensitivity in different tissues. This results in a mosaic of apparent hormonal deficiency, at times mixed with the suggestion of appropriate response. Clinical features such as delayed bone maturation, stunted growth, mental retardation, learning disabilities, emo-

tional disturbances, and hearing defects are clearly related to defects in hormonal action. Isolated somatic abnormalities and transient hyperactivity in children are difficult to explain on a hormonal basis.

Several attempts have been made to demonstrate a receptor defect or abnormal tissue responses by in vitro studies carried out on patients' tissues. T_3 binding to the putative nuclear receptor in mononuclear cells and skin fibroblasts have shown reduced affinity with reduced, increased, or normal maximal binding capacity. However, more than half of the subjects studied have shown normal parameters of T_3 binding. It is these inconsistencies that strengthen the impression that the syndrome represents different genetic defects with a common phenotype due to defective expression of the observed end effects of thyroid hormone action. Measurements of tissue responses to thyroid hormone in vitro have also been, in part, disappointing. They included the effects of thyroid hormone on degradation of low density lipoproteins[275] and on synthesis of glycosaminoglycans[233] and fibronectin[272] by skin fibroblasts. The latter test is most promising, with six of seven subjects tested showing clearly a subnormal response to thyroid hormone.

A sequence of diagnostic procedures is shown in Table 73-7. The combination of elevated serum levels of free T_4 and

Table 73-7 Suggested Sequence of Diagnostic Procedures for Evaluation of Generalized Resistance to Thyroid Hormone

1. Look for usual presentation: goiter and high serum T_4 without thyrotoxicosis ("compensated euthyroidism").
2. Confirm the elevated serum levels of free thyroid hormones (T_4 and T_3) and the absence of thyroid hormone serum transport defects.
3. Demonstrate the presence of TSH in serum and its response to TRH ("inappropriate secretion of TSH").
4. Exclude the presence of common thyroid diseases by a critical review of the case.
5. Exclude the presence of pituitary adenoma by radiographic procedures and measurement of the α subunit of TSH in serum.
6. Demonstrate the absence or inadequacy of metabolic responses to the administration of pharmacologic doses of thyroid hormone ("peripheral tissue resistance to thyroid hormone action").
7. Study thyroid hormone–receptor interaction and in vitro tissue responses to the hormone.
8. Study receptor mRNA in target tissues and genomic DNA using newly available DNA probes.

T_3 and lack of suppression of TSH narrows the differential diagnosis to a small number of relatively uncommon conditions known collectively as *inappropriate secretion of TSH*.[276] Possible causes include autonomous hypersecretion of TSH by a pituitary tumor, abnormal hypothalamic feedback control, and isolated pituitary resistance to thyroid hormone. Such patients exhibit some manifestations of thyrotoxicosis at the level of peripheral tissue. Almost all TSH-producing pituitary tumors have disproportionately high serum levels of the α subunit relative to whole TSH. The most vexing mistake made in the diagnosis of all syndromes of inappropriate secretion of TSH is the failure to differentiate them from ordinarily thyrotoxicosis. This common error results in inappropriate treatment, with the devastating consequences of hypothyroidism, especially severe in early life[277] (see above).

THYROID CONTROL

Metabolism

The thyroid system is controlled at five levels: the brain, hypothalamus, hypophysis, thyroid, and periphery by the conversion of prohormone T_4 to T_3.[278–281] Various controls are exerted on the TRH-secreting neurons largely through positive α-adrenergic and perhaps serotonin receptors. The pituitary thyrotrophs are stimulated by TRH and inhibited by somatostatin and dopamine. T_4 after transformation to T_3 also exerts an inhibition. Chronic administration of estrogens activates the thyrotrophs. TSH stimulates the thyroid, as described earlier in detail. The catabolism of TSH and TRH depends on thyroid hormone action (Fig. 73-12).

Effects at the level of the hypothalamus are of the neural type, i.e., immediate and of short duration. At the lower levels, effects are more delayed and of longer duration. For example, the first effects of T_3 take place hours after hormone administration and persist for days. Desensitization to TRH and TSH actions contributes to termination of their action. Control of the hypothalamohypophyseal thyroid system matures only at the end of fetal life and the beginning of neonatal life.[278]

Impulses from the brain influence the hypophysiotropic TRH secretory neurons through an ill-defined neural network. Adrenergic neurons probably constitute the final common pathway for diverse positive (e.g., cold), negative (e.g., stress, morphine), or periodic (e.g., nyctohemeral rhythms) stimuli. Norepinephrine acts on the TRH-secreting neurons through α-adrenergic receptors.[279] A negative feedback of thyroid hormones on these TRH neurons has been proposed.[280]

TRH is a tripeptide (pyroglutamylhistidylprolinamide). It results from the hydrolysis and posttranslational processing (cyclization) of a large protein prohormone containing five Gln-His-Pro-Gly sequences. TRH neurons are located in the thyrotropic area of the hypothalamus, i.e., in an area where electrical excitation causes TSH release. They extend from the paraventricular and supraoptic nuclei to the anterior border of the median eminence. TRH granules are transported down the axon by axoplasmic flow and are secreted at the level of the median eminence, where TRH penetrates fenestrated capillaries into the hypophyseal portal venous system, to be carried to the anterior lobe of the hypophysis.

Apart from its role in the hypothalamohypophyseal system, TRH is a general neurotransmitter found in various areas of

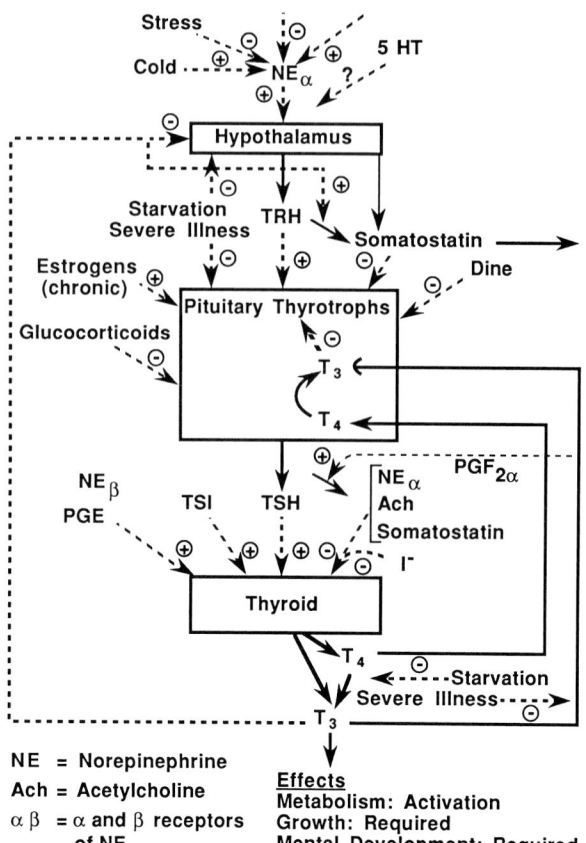

NE = Norepinephrine
Ach = Acetylcholine
α β = α and β receptors of NE

Effects
Metabolism: Activation
Growth: Required
Mental Development: Required

Fig. 73-12 *Control of thyroid hormone action. Uninterrupted arrows indicate chemical transformations or transports. Interrupted arrows indicate controls:* (+) = *positive control, or stimulation,* (−) = *negative control, or inhibition. The dominant elements of the system are indicated by heavy arrows.* NE = *norepinephrine acting through receptors* (α *or* β); 5HT = 5-hydroxytryptamine or serotonin; Dine = dopamine; Ach = acetylcholine; TSI = thyroid-stimulating immunoglobulins; PG = prostaglandins.

the brain and in the periphery (e.g., in the pancreas).[282] It is inactivated in the serum within minutes.

The action of TRH on the thyrotrophs is very rapid. Binding to its receptor triggers a depolarization and an influx of calcium into the cytosol and an activation of the Ca^{2+}-phosphatidylinositol cascade. Calcium and diacylglycerol by the classic stimulus-secretion coupling mechanism cause TSH secretion. TRH activates adenylate cyclase, which may complement the first mechanism. TRH also activates TSH synthesis and glycosylation. It activates prolactin secretion, but whether this effect has a physiological meaning remains controversial.[279]

There is a good evidence that hypothalamic somatostatin is a physiological inhibitor of TSH secretion. This tetradecapeptide and probably its natural analogues (of 28 amino acids and of about 100 amino acids) are released by somatostatinergic neurons in the hypophyseal portal system at the level of the median eminence. It acts as a tonic negative modulator in the pituitary thyrotrophs.

TSH is a glycoprotein of molecular weight 28,000. It is composed of two noncovalently linked subunits, α (M_r = 14,700, two oligosaccharide moieties) and β (M_r = 15,600, one oligosaccharide moiety). The α subunit is common to TSH, FSH, hCG, and LH, while the β subunit is specific for each of these hormones. This subunit confers on the hormone its biologic specificity and is the major determinant of immunologic specificity. Separate α and β subunits have no thyroid effect. The α and β subunits are coded on different genes, and there is no common precursor protein. Their biosynthesis is comparable to that of other glycoproteins, such as thyroglobulin. Thus, there is synthesis of a preprotein with a signal sequence in the endoplasmic reticulum, cleavage of the signal sequence in the lumen of the ER, core glycosylation of dolichol phosphate intermediates, transfer to asparagine residues in the proteins, removal of some glucoses, and further glycosylation in the reticulum and Golgi apparatus. The α subunits are synthesized in large excess compared to the β, but the β subunits have to be glycosylated in order to combine. In normal humans, TSH and its α and β subunits are secreted, but when the thyrotrophs are stimulated, as in hypothyroidism, both α- and β-subunit levels may increase. The final processed structure of secreted TSH carbohydrates varies depending on the physiological conditions and it is important in determining the intrinsic biologic activity, i.e., the biologic vs. the immunologic activity ratio, as well as the clearance rate of the hormone.[281]

The thyrotrophs are mainly controlled by the antagonistic control of TRH and thyroid hormones. Hypothalamic control accounts for the TSH nyctohemeral rhythm, with its nocturnal maximum, and for the cold-induced TSH, T_4, and T_3 secretion immediately after birth.[278] TRH has only a small effect on transcription of the TSH gene, but stimulates the processing and glycosylation of the subunits and selectively increases the bioactivity of the secreted TSH.

TSH secretion is tightly controlled by the level of free thyroid hormone.[280] Small relative changes result in altered TSH secretion over the entire physiological range. The inhibiting effect of thyroid hormone is exerted both acutely and chronically on the number of TRH receptors, the relative bioactivity of circulating TSH, TSH secretion, transcription of the TSH subunit genes, TSH synthesis, and even the growth and multiplication of thyrotrophs.[279,281] The inhibition of secretion is faster and will induce TSH accumulation in a first phase.[283]

T_3 inhibits the thyrotrophs directly, but at the physiological level the main external agent of control is T_4, which, through deiodination in the thyrotrophs themselves, provides the inhibiting cellular T_3. Chronic primary hypothyroidism leads not only to increased TSH levels but also to hypertrophy and multiplication of the thyrotrophs (which normally represent about 2 percent of the cell population of the anterior lobe) and to enlargement of the sella turcica.[280]

Estrogens enhance the responsiveness of the thyrotrophs to TRH in animals and possibly in humans. Dopamine exerts negative control on TSH secretion in humans, probably at the level of the thyrotrophs. The metabolism of TSH is rapid (half-life about 1 h). It is accelerated by hyperthyroidism and decreased in hypothyroidism. TSH is principally metabolized in the kidney.[279]

Investigation of the thyroid system can be carried out in vivo. Plasma levels of TRH, TSH, and thyroid hormones can be measured. TRH levels reflect largely the secretion of TRH from organs other than the hypothalamus.[282] The introduction of ultrasensitive assays for TSH now permits distinction of the very low TSH levels encountered in hyperthyroidism from low normal levels. Activity is usually measured on human thyroid cells in culture or on the rat FRTL5 cell line using the cyclic AMP response or the inhibition of iodide transport. For determination of low levels, TSH may first be concentrated by immunopurification.[284] These tests only measure the cyclic AMP branch of TSH action. The effect of TRH on TSH secretion is routinely measured. The action of TSH on T_4, T_3,

and thyroglobulin secretion, and on thyroid uptake of radioiodide or pertechnetate after 24 h can also be measured. However, since only bovine TSH is available, such tests should only be used if absolutely necessary and then only once. The feedback of thyroid hormones on the pituitary can be evaluated by measuring TSH or thyroid uptake of radioiodide or pertechnetate after administration of 75 μg T_3 for 3 to 7 days. Pharmacologic testing of the hypothalamus itself is not yet developed.

Related Clinical Disorders

Nonneoplastic Central Hyperthyroidism. Inappropriate hypersecretion of thyrotropin causes hyperthyroidism and goiter with no exophthalmopathy or other characteristics of thyroid autoimmune disease. This could result from any suppression of a negative control or enhancement of a positive control at the level of the hypothalamus or pituitary. Such a syndrome may result from TSH hypersecreting pituitary adenomas. In this case, the ratio of α subunit to TSH will be high, and TSH levels will not be modified by TRH or T_3.[285] A congenital form of this disease has been demonstrated, presumably due to pituitary resistance to thyroid hormones. It is characterized by clinical and biologic hyperthyroidism with high serum levels of TSH. The TSH and thyroid hormone levels were restored to normal by treatment with T_3 but not T_4, suggesting a deficiency of pituitary T_4 deiodinase.[286,287] On the other hand, a high TRH secretion was not excluded.

Hypothalamic Hypothyroidism. While it seems probable that there are inherited defects in the synthesis or secretion of TRH, these have not yet been described. Hypothyroidism arising from TRH deficiency has been described in isolated cases[288] and is presumed if the pituitary of a hypothyroid subject with low TSH responds to TRH with a rise in TSH.[289]

Familial Pituitary Hypothyroidism. Hypothetically, familial TSH deficiency would be caused by failure of the TSH-secreting cells to bind or respond to TRH, impaired synthesis or secretion of TSH, or abnormal sensitivity to inhibition by circulating thyroid hormone. TSH deficiency could arise from a failure of the cells specifically concerned with TSH supply or because the pituitary as a whole is functioning poorly.

Six syndromes of familial pituitary hypothyroidism are recognized. These are only briefly described here because so little is known about the exact biochemical disturbance which is responsible for each.

ISOLATED TSH DEFICIENCY. One family has been reported.[290] Two of three sibs from a consanguineous mating were hypothyroid and had no detectable TSH. The third sib had died at age 3 years of pneumonia. The thyroids of both children responded to TSH, but the pituitary did not respond to TRH. Other indicators of pituitary function were normal. The precise cause of the TSH deficiency in these two patients is unknown. The defect appears to involve the gene of the subunit of TSH.

FAMILIAL PANHYPOPITUITARISM. These patients have evidence, usually obvious, of deficiencies of other anterior pituitary hormones, and the clinical impression of hypothyroidism may not be striking. There is almost invariably a deficiency of human growth hormone, and gonadotropic hormones are often lacking.[291,292] Stress may elicit evidence of adrenocorticotropic hormone deficiency. It is possible that some of these patients have congenital lack of multiple releasing factors. The failure of the patients of Adler-Bier et al.[292] to respond to TRH or to luteinizing hormone releasing factor tends to place the defect in the pituitary.

There are two forms of familial panhypopituitarism. The more common form has been reported in approximately 20 families from Canada, Switzerland, Morocco, and Yugoslavia.[291,292] It is inherited as an autosomal recessive trait. Another variant affects only males.[293–295] Available information is consistent with X-linked inheritance, but sex-limited autosomal inheritance has not been ruled out.

FAMILIAL ABSENCE OF THE PITUITARY. A number of patients in several families have been reported with a syndrome of pituitary agenesis.[296–298] Although weight and length at birth were usually normal, the subjects developed a uniform clinical presentation, with early lethargy, cyanosis, hypoglycemia, convulsions, and collapse. Prolonged jaundice is present in those who survive beyond the first days of life. Administration of TRH causes no increase in the low TSH levels. Most have died within the first days or weeks of life. Two sibs who survived into their teens showed extreme physical and mental retardation.[297] Two affected sibs, younger children of an affected sibship, were developing normally on replacement therapy.[298] Earlier reports have been reviewed.[296] Radiologically, the sella turcica is small but normally shaped. Autopsy findings include absent anterior pituitary tissue, absent posterior pituitary, atrophic gonads in 50 to 60 percent, and atrophic thyroids in about 90 percent of the patients. The occurrence of the syndrome in a consanguineous mating suggests autosomal recessive inheritance.[297]

FAMILIAL ABSENCE OF THE SELLA TURCICA. Two pairs of sisters have been described with a virtual absence of the sella turcica, growth failure, hypoglycemia, and hypothyroidism.[299,300] One pair died in infancy.[300] The others were mentally retarded. Response tests indicated that some pituitary tissue was present.

FAMILIAL ENLARGEMENT OF THE SELLA TURCICA. Three sibs, one male and two females, with short stature and hypothyroidism have been described who had enlarged sella turcica.[301] The TSH response to TRH was impaired, and there was evidence of growth hormone deficiency. The parents were not consanguineous.

DIAGNOSIS OF FAMILIAL THYROID DISEASE

The prevalence of permanent congenital hypothyroidism in Western populations is about 1 in 4000 births. The disease has numerous causes:

1. Embryogenic defects can lead to agenesis (50 to 55 percent) or dysgenesis (30 to 35 percent) of the thyroid. These defects thus account for more than 85 percent of the cases.
2. Inborn errors of metabolism account for 10 to 15 percent of the cases.
3. Embryogenic defects or inborn errors at the level of the

pituitary or hypothalamus represent less than 4 percent of this population.

Untreated, this syndrome inevitably causes developmental and mental retardation, the latter irreversible. As the results of treatment depend critically on an early start, the diagnosis must be established as soon as possible after birth. This is imperative and thus human, social, and even economic reasons have led to programs of systematic screening of newborns in North America, Europe, Japan, and Canada in the late seventies. To avoid interference by the early postdelivery stimulation of pituitary thyrotrophs and thyroid, measurements are carried out 5 days after birth on blood collected on filter paper.[278,302]

Two strategies for newborn screening have been adopted:

1. Serum thyroxine is measured in the United States; theoretically it will allow the diagnosis of all forms of congenital hypothyroidism, except the resistance to thyroid hormones,
2. Serum TSH is measured in Europe. An increase in this value will signal all cases of congenital hypothyroidism, except for the few cases due to pituitary or hypothalamic defects. This test is more discriminating and far more sensitive than the first. The application of the new ultrasensitive TSH assays should even allow detection of the great decreases resulting from pituitary and hypothalamic defects. Best results would be obtained by combining both thyroxine and TSH measurements. A high serum thyroglobulin will demonstrate thyroid activation while a very low value may suggest thyroglobulin defects.[303] In cases where family history suggests the possibility of congenital hypothyroidism, measurement of TSH in amniotic fluid could demonstrate the disorder in the fetus.[304]

Preferably all positive tests should be confirmed by other types of measurements. Congenital hypothyroidism should be distinguished from a transient hypothyroidism, which appears with variable frequencies in different countries. This syndrome results from the conjunction of thyroid immaturity in premature babies and other factors such as iodide deficiency, iodide excess (from amniofetography or iodine tincture applications, etc.), or an acute disease. An interesting false high TSH test has been observed: Antibodies against rabbit immunoglobulins were found in the serum of the mother and in the newborn serum. These antibodies bound anti-TSH rabbit antibodies, thus making the latter unavailable to bind labeled TSH in the assay. In such cases, false high positive serum TSH titers are also found in the mother. Transient hypothyroidism due to maternal TSH receptor blocking antibodies has also been observed. In such cases, the mother is hypothyroid.[305]

In countries in which no systematic screening is carried out, patients may be detected early in the postnatal period because of failure to thrive and some of the other manifestations of hypothyroidism, or they may go undetected until much later.

If hypothyroidism is established in the postnatal period or during the first important developmental months, then in general it is probably unwise to undertake extensive investigation. Rather, the child should be vigorously treated. If started within the first month after birth, very good results are obtained.[306] Some years later, medication can be withdrawn and an effort made to ascertain the precise type of hypothyroidism.

At the time of critical evaluation, a TSH measurement is invaluable in indicating whether the origin of the hypothyroidism is in the pituitary or elsewhere. If elsewhere, a radioiodide or technetium scan will indicate the size and position of the functional thyroid, if present. For this purpose, especially in the young, technetium is preferred.

The most useful observation thereafter is the uptake and retention of labeled iodine by the thyroid. Characteristically, these patients, except those with the transport defect and TSH unresponsiveness, have an unusually rapid uptake curve, which reaches high levels within the first hour or two following administration. Measurements of turnover and of the effects of ClO_4^- and methimazole may give further clues to diagnosis. Analysis of the pattern of metabolism of the iodoamino acids in the peripheral blood also may be helpful. Most important is histological and biochemical analysis of the thyroid itself. Study of one of these patients may rapidly become a major research project.

The discussion thus far has centered largely on the diagnosis in patients who have a complete defect, i.e., homozygous expression. An important problem, and a more difficult one from many points of view, is the diagnosis of a specific genetic defect in a patient who may be heterozygous for the defect. Thus in the deiodinase-defect group, the heterozygous state may cause disease. There is also evidence that heterozygotes for the transport and organification defects may also have goiter. Clearly, much further research is needed so that heterozygotes may be detected and the contribution of the heterozygous state of these defects to mild thyroid disease determined.

TREATMENT

Satisfactory treatment depends on the stage of development of the local disease and the degree to which irreversible changes have occurred in the skeleton and central nervous system. Remarkable shrinkage of the goiter (if present) may be expected from treatment with thyroid hormone in usual maintenance doses, provided irreversible changes of degeneration, cyst formation, and fibrous replacement have not taken place. Iodine can replace thyroid hormones in cases of iodide trapping or iodotyrosine dehalogenase defect. The goiter will inevitably recur if medication is discontinued.

Care should be exercised in managing a patient with a familial goiter in view of the tendency of some goiters to undergo malignant change. In general, it would be wise to remove any nodule which fails to shrink after several weeks of replacement therapy. Unfortunately, this is often the case with well-established goiters, so that more often than not these patients eventually require surgery. Thyroid hormone is required after thyroidectomy, unless it is desirable to maintain the patient in a hypothyroid state.

Unless treatment is begun early, within the first few weeks of life, there is risk of permanent retardation of intellectual development or skeletal growth. Even then, damage may have occurred in utero.

REFERENCES

1. DE VISSCHER M (ed): *The Thyroid Gland*. New York, Raven, 1980.
2. GREER MA, SOLOMON DH: *Handbook of Physiology*, Sec 7, *Endocrinology*. Washington, DC, American Physiological Society, 1974, vol 3.
3. STANBURY JB: Familial goiter, in Stanbury JB, Wyngaarden JB, Frederickson DS (eds): *The Metabolic Basis of Inherited Disease*, 4th ed. New York, McGraw-Hill, 1978, p. 206.
4. STANBURY JB, DUMONT JE: Familial goiter and related disorders, in Stanbury JB, Wyngaarden JB, Frederickson DS, Goldstein JL, Brown MB (eds): *Inborn Errors of Metabolic Diseases*, 5th ed. New York, McGraw-Hill, 1983, p 231.
5. LAMY F, ROGER P, CONTOUR S, REUSE S, RASPE E, VAN SANDE J, DUMONT JE: Control of thyroid cell proliferation: The example of the dog thyrocyte. *Horm Cell Regul* 153:168, 1987.
6. DUMONT JE: The action of thyrotropin on thyroid metabolism. *Vitam Horm* 29:287, 1971.
7. ROSS EM, HAGA T, HOWLETT AC, SCHWARZMEIER J, SCHLEIFER LS, GILMAN AG: Hormone-sensitive adenylate cyclase: Resolution and reconstitution of some components necessary for regulation of the enzyme, *Adv Cyclic Nucleotide Res* 9:53, 1978.
8. SWILLENS S, DUMONT JE: A unifying model of current concepts and data on adenylate cyclase activation by α-adrenergic agonists. *Life Sci* 27:1013, 1980.
9. DUMONT JE, BOEYNAEMS JM, DE COSTER C, ERNEUX C, LAMY F, LECOCQ R, MOCKEL J, UNGER J, VAN SANDE J: Biochemical mechanisms in the control of thyroid function and growth. *Adv Cyclic Nucleotide Res* 9:723, 1978.
10. LAURENT E, MOCKEL J, VAN SANDE J, GRAFF I, DUMONT JE: Dual activation by thyrotropin of the phospholipase C and cyclic AMP cascades in human thyroid. *Mol Cell Endocrinol* 52:273, 1987.
11. VAN HERLE AJ, VASSART G, DUMONT JE: Control of thyroglobulin synthesis and secretion. *N Engl J Med* 301:239, 1979.
12. DUMONT JE, MIOT F, ERNEUX C, COUCHIE D, COCHAUX P, GERVY-DECOSTER C, VAN SANDE J, WELLS JN: Negative regulation of cyclic AMP levels by activation of cyclic nucleotide phosphodiesterases: The example of the dog thyroid. *Adv Cyclic Nucleotide Protein Phosphorylation Res* 16:325, 1984.
13. EKHOLM R: Thyroid hormone secretion. *Horm Cell Regul* 1:51, 1977.
14. FIELD JB, MUTO H, CHOU MCY: The adenylate cyclase-cyclic AMP system in Graves' disease. *Adv Cyclic Nucleotide Res* 12:359, 1980.
15. VAN SANDE J, MOCKEL J, BOEYNAEMS JM, DOR P, ANDRY G, DUMONT JE: Regulation of cyclic nucleotide and prostaglandin formation in normal human thyroid tissues and in autonomous nodules. *J Clin Endocrinol Metab* 50:776, 1980.
16. OTTEN J, DUMONT JE: Glucose metabolism in normal human thyroid tissue in vitro. *Eur J Clin Invest* 2:213, 1972.
17. PEKONEN F, WEINTRAUB BD: Thyrotropin receptors on bovine thyroid membranes: Two types with different affinities and specificities. *Endocrinology* 105:352, 1979.
18. CARTER A, BARDIN C, COLLINS R, SIMONS C, BRAY P, SPIEGEL A: Reduced expression of multiple forms of the α subunit of the stimulatory GTP-binding protein in pseudohypoparathyroidism type Ia. *Proc Natl Acad Sci USA* 84:7266, 1987.
19. STANBURY JB, ROCMANS P, BUHLER UK, OCHI Y: Congenital hypothyroidism with impaired thyroid response to thyrotropin. *N Engl J Med* 279:1132, 1968.
20. CODACCIONI JL, CARAYON P, MICHEL-BECHET M, FOUCAULT F, LEFORT G, PIERRON H: Congenital hypothyroidism associated with thyrotropin unresponsiveness and thyroid cell membrane alterations. *J Clin Endocrinol Metab* 50:932, 1980.
21. MEDEIROS-NETO GA, KNOBEL M, BRONSTEIN MD, SIMONETTI J, FILHO FF, MATTAR E: Impaired cyclic-AMP response to thyrotropin in congenital hypothyroidism with thyroglobulin deficiency. *Acta Endocrinol (Copenh)* 92:62, 1972.
22. JOB JC, CANLORBE P, THOMASSIN N, VASSAL J: L'hypothyroïdie infantile à début précoce avec glande en place, fixation fiable de radioiode et défaut de réponse à la thyrostimuline. *Ann Endocrinol (Paris)* 30:696, 1979.
23. BEAMER WG, EICHER EM, MALTAIS LJ, SOUTHARD JL: Inherited primary hypothyroidism in mice. *Science* 212:61, 1981.
24. THOMAS JL, LECLERC J, HARTEMANN P, DUBEILLE J, ORGIAZZI J, PETERSEN M, JANOT C, GUEDENET C: Familial hyperthyroidism without evidence of autoimmunity. *Acta Endocrinol (Copenh)* 100:512, 1982.
25. HORTON GL, SCAZZIGA BR: Hereditary hyperthyroidism with diffuse non autoimmune hyperreactivity due to autonomy of function and growth. *Ann Endocrinol (Paris)* 48:92, 1987.
26. MERIN RM, WOLLMAN SH: Transparent-chamber studies of vessels, circulation, and follicles in thyroid grafts in unanesthetized mice. *JNCI* 34:415, 1965.
27. SODERBERG U: Temporal characteristics of thyroid activity. *Physiol Rev* 39:777, 1959.
28. ROCMANS P, PENEL JC, CANTRAINE FR, DUMONT JE: Kinetic analysis of iodide transport in dog thyroid slices: Perchlorate-induced discharge. *Am J Physiol* 232:E343, 1977.
29. WOLFF J: Transport of iodide and other anions in the thyroid gland. *Physiol Rev* 44:45, 1964.

30. ANDROS G, WOLLMAN SH: Autoradiographs localization of radioiodide in the thyroid gland of the mouse. *Am J Physiol* 213:198, 1967.

31. CHOW SY, WOODBURY DM: Kinetics of distribution of radioactive perchlorate in rat and guinea pig thyroid glands. *J Endocrinol* 47:207, 1970.

32. WOLFF J: Congenital goiter with defective iodide transport. *Endocrinol Rev* 4:240, 1983.

33. JORTAY AM, CANTRAINE FRL, DUMONT JE: Iodide trapping by thyroid slices in vitro. *Horm Metab Res* 6:309, 1974.

34. SAITO K, YAMAMOTO K, TAKAI T, YOSHIDA S: Inhibition of iodide accumulation by perchlorate and thiocyanate in a model of the thyroid iodide transport system. *Acta Endocrinol (Copenh)* 104:456, 1983.

35. LEGER FA, DOUMITH R, COURPOTIN C, HELAL OB, DAVOUS N, AURENGO A, SAVOIE JC: Complete iodide trapping defect in two cases with congenital hypothyroidism: Adaptation of thyroid to huge iodide supplementation. *Eur J Clin Invest* 17:249, 1987.

36. VAN VOORTHUIZEN WF, DE VIJLDER JJM, VAN DIJK JE, TEGELAERS WHH: Euthyroidism via iodide supplementation in hereditary congenital goiter with thyroglobulin deficiency. *Endocrinology* 103:2105, 1978.

37. NUNEZ J, POMMIMER J: Formation of thyroid hormones. *Vitam Horm* 39:175, 1982.

38. ERICSON LE: Exocytosis and endocytosis in the thyroid follicle cell. *Mol Cell Endocrinol* 22:1, 1981.

39. DEME D, VIRION A, HAMMOU NA, POMMIER J: NADPH-dependent generation of H_2O_2 in a thyroid particulate fraction requires Ca^{2+}. *FEBS Lett* 186:107, 1985.

40. CZARNOCKA B, RUF J, FERRAND M, CARAYON P, LISSITZKY S: Purification of the human thyroid peroxidase and its identification as the microsomal antigen involved in autoimmune thyroid diseases. *FEBS Lett* 190:147, 1985.

41. OHTAKI S, KOTANI T, NAKAMURA Y: Characterization of human thyroid peroxidase purified by monoclonal antibody-assisted chromatography. *J Clin Endocrinol Metab* 63:570, 1986.

42. PORTMAN L, HAMADA N, HEINRICH G, DE GROOT LJ: Anti-thyroid peroxidase antibody in patients with autoimmune thyroid disease: Possible identity with anti-microsomal antibody. *J Clin Endocrinol Metab* 61:1001, 1985.

43. LIBERT F, RUEL J, LUDGATE M, SWILLENS S, ALEXANDER N, VASSART G, DINSART C: Thyroperoxidase: An autoantigen with a mosaic structure made of nuclear and mitochondrial gene modules. *EMBO J* 6:4193, 1987.

44. KIMURA S, KOTANI T, BRIDE OW, UMEKI K, HIRAI K, NAKAYAMA T, OHTAKI S: Human thyroid peroxidase: Complete cDNA and protein sequence, chromosome mapping and identification of two alternatively spliced mRNAs. *Proc Natl Acad Sci USA* 86:5555, 1987.

45. LIBERT F, RUEL J, LUDGATE M, SWILLENS S, ALEXANDER N, VASSART G: Complete nucleotide sequence of the human thyroperoxidase-microsomal antigen cDNA. *Nucleic Acids Res* 15:6735, 1987.

46. WEIL SC, ROSNER GL, REID MS, CHISHOLM RL, FARBER NM, SPITZNAGEL JK, SWANSON M: cDNA cloning of human myeloperoxidase: Decrease in myeloperoxidase mRNA upon induction of HL-60 cells. *Proc Natl Acad Sci USA* 84:2057, 1987.

47. VIRION A, COURTIN F, DEME D, MICHOT JL, KANIEWSKI J, POMMIER J: Spectral characteristics and catalytic properties of thyroid peroxidase-H_2O_2 compounds in the iodination and coupling reactions. *Arch Biochem Biophys* 242:41, 1985.

48. DEMEESTER-MIRKINE N, VAN SANDE J, CORVILAIN J, DUMONT JE: Benign thyroid nodule with normal iodide trap and defective organification. *J Clin Endocrinol Metab* 41:1169, 1975.

49. BEAMER WG, MALTAIS LJ, DEBAETS MH, EICHER EM: Inherited congenital goiter in mice. *Endocrinology* 120:838, 1987.

50. STANBURY JB, HEDGE AN: A study of a family of goitrous cretins. *J Clin Endocrinol Metab* 10:1471, 1950.

51. PEREZ-CUVIT E, CRIGLER JF, STANBURY JB: Partial and total iodide organification defect in different sibships in a kindred. *Am J Hum Genet* 29:142, 1977.

52. POMMIER J, TOURNIAIRE J, RAHMOUN B, DEME D, PALLO D, BORNET H, NUNEZ J: Thyroid iodine organification defects: A case with lack of thyroglobulin iodination and a case without any peroxidase activity. *J Clin Endocrinol Metab* 42:319, 1976.

53. EGGO MC, BURROW GN, ALEXANDER NM, GORDON JH: Iodination and the structure of human thyroglobulin. *J Clin Endocrinol Metab* 51:7, 1980.

54. MEDEIROS-NETO GA, KNOBEL M, YAMAMOTO K, CAVALIERE H, KALLAS W: Deficient thyroid peroxidase causing organification defect and goitrous hypothyroidism. *J Endocrinol Invest* 2:353, 1979.

55. MEDEIROS-NETO GA, NAKASHIMA T, TAUROG A, KNOBEL M, SIMONETTI JP, MATTAR E: Congenital goitre and hypothyroidism with impaired iodide organification and high thyroid peroxidase concentration. *Clin Endocrinol* 11:123, 1979.

56. KUSAKABE T: Deficient cytochrome b_5 reductase activity in nontoxic goiter with iodide organification defect. *Metabolism* 24:1103, 1975.

57. BASCHIERI L, BENEDETTI G, DELUGA F, NEGRI M: Evaluation and limitations of the perchlorate test in the study of thyroid function. *J Clin Endocrinol Metab* 23:786, 1963.

58. SALABE BG, PINCHERA A, BACHIERI L, MONACO F: The potential malignancy of thyroid nodules with organification defect. Report of a case. *Folia Endocrinol* 22:23, 1969.

58a. BRAIN WR: Heredity in simple goiter. *Q J Med* 20:303, 1927.

59. JOHNSEN S: Familial deafness and goitre in persons with a low level of protein bound iodide. *Acta Otolaryngol (Stockh) (Suppl)* 140:168, 1958.

60. THOULD AK, SCOWEN EF: The syndrome of congenital deafness and simple goiter, in Pitt-Rivers (ed): *Advances in Thyroid Research.* Elmsford, NY, Pergamon, 1961.

61. ELMAN DS: Familial association of nerve deafness with nodular goiter and thyroid carcinoma. *N Engl J Med* 259:219, 1958.

62. ROBERTS KD: Thyroid carcinoma in childhood in Great Britain. *Arch Dis Child* 32:58, 1957.

63. THIEME ET: A report of the occurrence of deaf-mutism and goiter in four of six siblings of a North American family. *Ann Surg* 146:941, 1957.

64. MORGANS ME, TROTTER WR: Association of congenital deafness with goitre. *Lancet* 1:607, 1958.

65. LJUNGREN JG, LINDSTROM H, HJERN B: The concentration of peroxidase in normal and adenomatous human thyroid tissue with special reference to patients with Pendred's syndrome. *Acta Endocrinol (Copenh)* 72:272, 1973.

66. BURROW GN, SPAULDING SW, ALEXANDER NM, BOWER BF: Normal peroxidase activity in Pendred's syndrome. *J Clin Endocrinol Metab* 36:522, 1973.

67. FRASER GR, MORGANS ME, TROTTER WR: The syndrome of sporadic goitre and congenital deafness. *Q J Med* 29:279, 1960.

68. PAPASOV VG: Intersuchungen über das wesen des Pendred-syndromes. *Z Gesamte Inn Med* 24:766, 1969.

69. TROTTER WR: The association of deafness with thyroid dysfunction. *Br Med Bull* 16:92, 1960.

70. STANBURY JB, OHELA K, PITT-RIVERS R: The metabolism of iodine in two goitrous cretins compared with that in two patients receiving methimazole. *J Clin Endocrinol Metab* 15:54, 1955.

71. ERMANS AM, KINTHAERT H, CAMUS M: Defective intrathyroidal iodine metabolism in nontoxic goiter: Inadequate iodination of thyroglobulin. *J Clin Endocrinol Metab* 28:1307, 1968.

72. EDELHOCH H: The structure of thyroglobulin and its role in iodination. *Recent Prog Horm Res* 21:1, 1965.

73. REFETOFF S, LEVER E: The value of serum thyroglobulin measurement in clinical practice. *JAMA* 250:2342, 1983.

73a. MARRICQ C, LEJEUNE PJ, ROLLAND M, LISSITZKY S: Structure of thyroid hormone-containing peptides in porcine and human thyroglobulins, in Eggo M, Burrow G (eds): *Thyroglobulin—The Prothyroid Hormone.* New York, Raven, 1985, p 21.

74. DUNN J, KIM PS, MOORE RC: Hormone-rich peptides of thyroglobulin: Studies on their structure and origin, in Eggo M, Burrow G (eds): *Thyroglobulin—The Prothyroid Hormone.* New York, Raven, 1985, p 33.

75. RAWITCH A, GREGG J, TURNER C: Nature and Location of hormonogenic sites within the structure of thyroglobulin, in Eggo M, Burrow G (eds): *Thyroglobulin—The Prothyroid Hormone.* New York, Ravne, 1985, p 43.

76. LISSITZKY S, MAUCHAMP J, REYNAUD J, ROLLAND M: The constituent polypeptide chain of porcine thyroglobulin. *FEBS Lett* 60:359, 1975.

77. VASSART G, REFETOFF S, BROCAS H, DINSART C, DUMONT JE: Translation of thyroglobulin 33S messenger RNA as a means of determining thyroglobulin quaternary structure. *Proc Natl Acad Sci USA* 72:3839, 1975.

78. VASSART G, BROCAS H: Restriction mapping of synthetic thyroglobulin structural gene as a means of investigation of thyroglobulin structure. *Biochim Biophys Acta* 610:189, 1980.

79. MERCKEN L, SIMONS MJ, SWILLENS S, MASSAER M, VASSART G: Primary structure of bovine thyroglobulin as deduced from the sequencing of its 8431 base cDNA. *Nature* 316:647, 1985.

80. MALTHIERRY Y, LISSITZKY S: Primary structure of human thyroglobulin deduced from the sequence of its 8448-base complementary DNA. *Eur J Biochem* 165:491, 1987.

81. PARMA J, CHRISTOPHE D, POHL V, VASSART G: Structural organization of the 5′region of the thyroglobulin gene: Evidence for intron loss and "exonization" during evolution. *J Mol Biol* 196:769, 1987.

82. SCHUMACHER M, CAMP S, MAULET Y, NEWTON M, MCPHEE-QUIGLEY K, TAYLOR S, FRIEDMAN T, TAYLOR P: Primary structure of *Torpedo californica* acetylcholinesterase deduced from its cDNA sequence. *Nature* 319:407, 1986.

83. SWILLENS S, LUDGATE M, MERCKEN L, DUMONT J, VASSART G: Analysis of sequence and structure homologies between thyroglobulin and acetylcho-

linesterase: Possible functional and clinical significance. *Biochem Biophys Res Commun* 137:142, 1986.

84. LUDGATE M, SWILLENS S, MERCKEN L, VASSART G: Homology between thyroglobulin and acetylcholinesterase: An explanation for the pathogenesis of Graves' ophthalmopathy? *Lancet* 2:219, 1986.

85. KOCH N, LAUER W, HABICHI J, DOBBERSTEIN B: Primary structure of the gene for the murine IA antigen associated invariant chain. An alternatively spliced exon encodes a cystein-rich domain homologous to a repetitive sequence of thyroglobulin. *EMBO J* 6:1677, 1987.

86. OHMYA Y, HAYASHI H, KONDO T, KONDO Y: Thyroglobulin structure necessary for hormone formation: Identification of a "donor" residue in the primary structure of bovine thyroglobulin subunit. *Ann Endocrinol (Paris)* 48:141, 1987.

87. PALUMBO G: Thyroid hormonogenesis. Identification of a sequence containing iodophenyl donor site(s) in calf thyroglobulin. *J Biol Chem* 262:17182, 1987.

88. BAAS F, VAN OMMEN GJ, BIKKER H, ARNBERG A, DE VILJDER J: The human thyroglobulin gene is over 300 kb long and contains introns up to 64 kb. *Nucleic Acids Res* 14:5171, 1986.

89. MUSTI AM, AVVEDIMENTO E, POLISTINA V, URSINI VM, OBICI S, NITSCH L, COCOZZA S, DI LAURO R: The complete structure of the rat thyroglobulin gene. *Proc Natl Acad Sci USA* 83:323, 1986.

90. DE MARTYNOFF G, POHL V, MERCKEN L, VAN OMMEN GJ, VASSART G: Structural organization of the bovine thyroglobulin gene and of its 5' flanking region. *Eur J Biochem* 164:591, 1987.

91. BAAS F, BIKKER H, GEURTS VAN KESSEL A, MELSERT R, PEARSON PL, DE VIJLDER JJM, VAN OMMEN GJ: The human thyroglobulin gene: A polymorphic marker localized distal to c-myc on chromosome 8 band q24. *Hum Genet* 69:138, 1985.

92. BERGE-LEFRANC JL, CARTOUZOU G, MATTEI MG, PASSAGE E, MALEZET C, LISSITZKY S: Localization of the thyroglobulin gene by in situ hybridization to human chromosomes. *Hum Genet* 69:28, 1985.

93. RABIN M, BARKER P, RUDDLE F, BROCAS H, TARGOVNIK H, VASSART G: Proximity of thyroglobulin and c-myc genes on human chromosome 8. *Somatic Cell Mol Genet* 11:397, 1985.

94. AVVEDIMENTO VE, DI LAURO R, MONTICELLI A, BERNARDI F, PATRACCHINI P, CALZOLARI E, MARTINI S, VARRONE S: Mapping of human thyroglobulin gene on the long arm of chromosome 8 by in situ hybridization. *Hum Genet* 71:163, 1985.

95. BROCAS H, SZPIRER J, LEBO RV, LEVAN G, SZPIRER C, CHEUNG MC, VASSART G: The thyroglobulin gene resides on chromosome 8 in man and on chromosome 7 in the rat. *Cytogenet Cell Genet* 39:150, 1985.

96. CHRISTOPHE D, CABRER B, BACOLLA A, TARGOVNIK H, POHL V, VASSART G: An unusually long poly(purine)-poly(pyrimidine) sequence is located upstream from the human thyroglobulin gene. *Nucleic Acids Res* 13:5127, 1985.

97. URSINI MV, MUSTI AM, DI LAURO R: Delimitation of a cis acting regulatory element of the rat thyroglobulin gene promoter. *Ann Endocrinol* 47:77, 1986.

98. CANTOR CR, EFSTRATIADIS A: Possible structures of homopurine-homopyrimidine S1 hypersensitive sites. *Nucleic Acids Res* 12:8059, 1984.

99. SKONROWSKY J, PLUCIENNICZAK A, BEONAREK A, JAWORSKY J: Bovine 1.709 satellite. Recombination hotspots and dispersed repeated sequences. *J Mol Biol* 177,399, 1984.

100. CHRISTOPHE D, HANSEN C, LIBERT F, BACOLLA A, GERARD C, VASSART G: Study of the control of prothyroid hormone (thyroglobulin) gene expression, in Black S, Lopez O, Melner MH, Scott W, Whelen WJ (eds): *Advances in Gene Technology: Molecular Biology of the Endocrine System.* Cambridge, Cambridge University Press, 1986.

101. GALLO A, MUSTI AM: DNA-protein interactions in the promoter region of rat thyroglobulin gene. *Ann Endocrinol (Paris)* 48:112, 1987.

102. LIBERT F, VASSART G, CHRISTOPHE D: Methylation and expression of the human thyroglobulin gene. *Biochem Biophys Res Commun* 134:1109, 1986.

103. VAN HEUVERSWYN B, STREYDIO C, BROCAS H, REFETOFF S, DUMONT J, VASSART G: Thyrotopin controls transcription of the thyroglobulin gene. *Proc Natl Acad Sci USA* 81:5941, 1984.

104. VAN HEUVERSWYN B, LERICHE A, VAN SANDE J, DUMONT JE, VASSART G: Transcriptional control of thyroglobulin gene expression by cyclic AMP. *FEBS Lett* 188:192, 1985.

105. ROGER PP, VAN HEUVERSWYN B, LAMBERT C, REUSE S, VASSART G, DUMONT JE: Antagonistic effects of thyrotropin and epidermal growth factor on thyroglobulin mRNA levels in a cultured thyroid cells. *Eur J Biochem* 122,239, 1985.

106. AVVEDIMENTO VE, TRAMONTANO D, URSINI MV, MONTICELLA A, DI LAURO R: The level of thyroglobulin mRNA is regulated by TSH both in vitro and in vivo. *Biochem Biophys Res Commun* 122:472, 1984.

107. CHRISTOPHE D, GERARD C, HANSEN C, CHRISTOPHE-HOBERTUS C, JU-

VENAL G, LIBERT F, ROGER P, DUMONT JE, VASSART G: Control of thyroglobulin gene expression. *Horm Cell Regul* 153:205, 1987.

108. CONSTANTINOU A, SQUINTO S, JUNGMANN A: The phosphoform of the regulatory subunit RII of cAMP-dependent protein kinase possesses intrinsic protein topoisomerase activity. *Cell* 42:429, 1985.

109. MONTMINY M, BILEZIKJIAN L: Binding of a nuclear protein to the cyclic-AMP response element of the somatostatin gene. *Nature* 328:175, 1987.

110. SANTISTEBAN P, KOHN LD, DI LAURO R: Thyroglobulin gene expression is regulated by insulin and insulin-like growth factor I, as well as thyrotropin, in FRTL-5 thyroid cells. *J Biol Chem* 262:4048, 1987.

111. CHABAUD O, CHEBATH J, GIRAUD A, MAUCHAMP J: Modulation by thyrotropin of thyroglobulin synthesis in cultured thyroid cells: Correlations with polysome profile and cytoplasmic thyroglobulin mRNA content. *Biochem Biophys Res Commun* 93:118, 1980.

112. RICKETTS MH, SIMONS MJ, PARMA J, MERCKEN L, DONG O, VASSART G: A non-sense mutation causes hereditary goitre in the afrikander cattle and unmasks alternative splicing of thyroglobulin transcripts. *Proc Natl Acad Sci USA* 84:3181, 1987.

113. MALTHIERY Y: Structure primaire de la thyroglobuline humaine. These d'Etat, Université d'Aix Marseille II, 1987.

114. BJORKMAN A, RING P, EKHOLM R: Intracellular transport and secretion of thyroglobulin in isolated thyroid follicles, in Eggo M, Burrow G (eds): *Thyroglobulin—The Prothyroid Hormone (Progress in Endocrine Research and Therapy,* vol 2). New York, Raven, 1985, p 127.

115. RONIN C, FENOUILLET E, HOVSEPIAN S, FAYET G: Biosynthesis of thyroglobulin carbohydrate chains, in Eggo M, Burrow G (eds): *Thyroglobulin—The Prothyroid Hormone (Progress in Endocrine Research and Therapy,* vol 2). New York, Raven, 1985, p 95.

116. SCHNEIDER A: Physical characterization of serum thyroglobulin implication for the mechanism of secretion into the circulation, in Eggo M, Burrow G (eds): *Thyroglobulin—The Prothyroid Hormone (Progress in Endocrine Research and Therapy,* vol 2). New York, Raven, 1985, p 297.

117. HERZOG V: Vesicular transport of thyroglobulin across the follicular wall, in Eggo M, Burrow G (eds): *Thyroglobulin—The Prothyroid Hormone (Progress in Endocrine Research and Therapy,* vol 2). New York, Raven, 1985, p 143.

118. VAN HERLE AJ: Circulating thyroglobulin in thyroid cancer, in Eggo M, Burrow G (eds): *Thyroglobulin—The Prothyroid Hormone (Progress in Endocrine Research and Therapy,* vol 2). New York, Raven, 1985, p 317.

119. PINCHERA A, PACINI F, MARIOTTI S, MARTINO E: Recent studies on the application of serum thyroglobulin measurement in thyroid disease, in Eggo M, Burrow G (eds): *Thyroglobulin—The Prothyroid Hormone (Progress in Endocrine Research and Therapy,* vol 2). New York, Raven, 1985, p 307.

120. SPIRO RG, SPIRO MJ: The carbohydrate composition of thyroglobulin from several species. *J Biol Chem* 240:997, 1965.

121. SPIRO MJ, SPIRO RG: Synthesis and processing of thyroglobulin carbohydrate units, in Eggo M, Burrow G (eds): *Thyroglobulin—The Prothyroid Hormone (Progress in Endocrine Research and Therapy,* vol 2). New York, Raven, 1985, p 103.

122. GODELAINE D, SPIRO MJ, SPIRO RG: Processing of the carbohydrate units of thyroglobulin. *J Biol Chem* 256:10161, 1981.

123. RAWITCH AB, LIAO T, PIERCE JG: The amino acid sequence of a tryptic glycopeptide from human thyroglobulin. *Biochim Biophys Acta* 160:360, 1968.

124. SEAGAR MJ, MIQUELIS RD, SIMON C: Inhibitory effects of tunicamycin and 2-deoxyglucose in thyroglobulin synthesis. *Eur J Biochem* 113:91, 1980.

125. EGGO MC, DRUCKER R, CHEIFETZ R, BURROW G: Posttranslational modification of prothyroid hormone. *Can J Biochem Cell Biol* 61:662, 1982.

126. BJORKMAN U, EKHOLM R: Effects of tunicamycin on thyroglobulin secretion. *Eur J Biochem* 125:585, 1982.

127. CONSIGLIO E, SALVATORE G, RALL J, KOHN L: Thyroglobulin interactions with thyroid plasma membrane. *J Biol Chem* 254:5065, 1979.

128. FRANC JL, HOVESPIAN S, FAYET G, BOUCHILLOUX S: Inhibition of N-linked oligosaccharide processing does not prevent secretion of thyroglobulin. *Eur J Biochem* 157:225, 1986.

129. HERZOG V, NEUMULLER W, HOLZMAN B: Thyroglobulin carries the lysosomal recognition marker mannose-6-phosphate. *EMBO J* 6:555, 1987.

130. KOHN LD, DE LUCAS M, SANTISTEBAN P, SHIFRIN S, YEH H, FORMISANO S, CONSIGLIO E: Thyroglobulin interactions with thyroid membranes: Implications for the regulation of thyroid hormone formation, in Eggo M, Burrow G (eds): *Thyroglobulin—The Prothyroid Hormone (Progress in Endocrine Research and Therapy,* vol 2). New York, Raven, 1985, p 171.

131. SPIRO MJ, GORSKI K: Studies on the posttranslational migration and processing of thyroglobulin: Use of inhibitors and evaluation of the role of phosphorylation. *Endocrinology* 119:1146, 1986.

132. YAMMAMOTO K, TSUJI I, TARUTANI O, OSAWA T: Phosphorylated high mannose type and hybrid type oligosaccharide chains of human thyro-

globulin isolated from malignant thyroid tissue. *Biochim Biophys Acta* 838:84, 1985.

133. HERZOG V: Secretion of sulfated thyroglobulin. *Eur J Cell Biol* 39:399, 1985.

134. TAUROG A: in Ingbar S, Braverman E (eds): *Werner's the Thyroid*, 59th ed. Philadelphia, Lippincott, 1986, p 53.

135. EKHOLM R, BJORKMAN U: Generation of hydrogen peroxide. A factor in thyroglobulin iodation, in Eggo M, Burrow G (eds): *Thyroglobulin—The Prothyroid Hormone (Progress in Endocrine Research and Therapy*, vol 2). New York, Raven, 1985, p 3.

136. DUPUY C, VIRION A, HAMMOU NA, KANIEWSKI J, DEME D, POMMIER J: Solubilization and characteristics of the thyroid NADPH-dependent H2O2 generating system. *Biochem Biophys Res Commun* 141:839, 1986.

137. MARRIQ CL, ROLLAND M, LISSITZKY S: Amino acid sequence of the unique 3,5,3′-triiodothyronine-containing sequence from porcine thyroglobulin. *Biochem Biophys Res Commun* 112:206, 1983.

138. HAEBERLI A, BILSTAD J, EDELHOCH H, RALL JE: Elementary chain composition of guinea pig thyroglobulin. *J Biol Chem* 250:7294, 1975.

139. VAN DEN HOVE MF, PATERNOSTER S, COUVREUR M: Hormonogenic peptides of thyroglobulin are released during the coupling of iodotyrosines. *Ann Endocrinol (Paris)* 47:39, 1986.

140. ALEXANDER NM: Oxidative cleavage of tryptophoryl peptide bands during chemical and peroxidase catalyzed iodinations. *J Biol Chem* 249:1946, 1974.

141. DELAIN E, AOUANI A, VIGNAL A, COUTURE-TOSI E, HOVESPIAN S, FAYET G: The structure of thyroglobulin is independent of its iodine content. *Mol Cell Endocrinol* 49:173, 1987.

142. DUSSAULT JH: in Ingbar S, Braverman E (eds): *Werner's the Thyroid*. Philadelphia, Lippincott, 1986, p 1396.

143. STANBURY JB: in Ingbar S, Braverman E (eds): *Werner's the Thyroid*. Philadelphia, Lippincott, 1986, p 687.

144. ENRIQUE J, SANTELICES R, KISHIHARA M, SCHNEIDER A: Low molecular weight thyroglobulin leading to a goiter in a 12-year-old girl. *J Clin Endocrinol Metab* 58:526, 1984.

145. GONS HH, KOK JH, TEGELAERS WH, DE VIJLDER JJM: Concentration of plasma thyroglobulin and urinary excretion of iodinated material in the diagnosis of thyroid disorders in congenital hypothyroidism. *Acta Endocrinol (Copenh)* 104:27, 1983.

146. SAVOIE JC, THOMOPOULOS C, SAVOIE F: Congenital goitrous hypothyroidism with thyroglobulin defect and iodohistidine-rich iodoalbumin production. *J Clin Invest* 52:126, 1973.

147. LISSITZKY S, BISMUTH J, CODACCIONI J, CARTOUZOU G: Congenital goitre with iodo-albumin replacing thyroglobulin. *J Clin Endocrinol Metab* 28:1797, 1968.

148. LISSITZKY S, TORRESANI J, BURROW GN, BOUCHILLOUX S, CHABAUD O: Defective thyroglobulin export as a cause of congenital goitre. *Clin Endocrinol* 4:363, 1975.

149. CABRER B, BROCAS H, PEREZ-CASTILLO A, POHL V, NAVAS JJ, TARGOVNIK H, VASSART G: Normal level of thyroglobulin mRNA in a human congenital goitre with thyroglobulin deficiency. *J Clin Endocrinol Metab* 63:931, 1986.

150. BAAS F, BIKKER H, VAN OMMEN GJB, DE VIJLDER JM: Unusual scarcity of restriction site polymorphism in the human thyroglobulin gene. A linkage study suggesting autosomal dominance of a defective thyroglobulin allele. *Hum Genet* 67:301, 1984.

150a. SIMON P, BROCAS H, RODESCH F, VASSART G: RFLP detected at the 8q24 locus by a thyroglobulin cDNA probe. *Nucleic Acids Res* 15:373, 1985.

151. DOLLING CE, GOOD BF: Congenital goitre in sheep: Isolation of the iodoproteins which replace thyroglobulin. *J Endocrinol* 71:179, 1976.

152. BEALER GW, MALTAIS LJ, DEBAETS MH, EICHER EM: Inherited congenital goiter in mice. *Endocrinology* 120:838, 1987.

153. DE VIJLDER JJM, VAN OMMEN GJB, VAN VOORTHUIZEN WF, KOCH CA, ARNBERG AC, VASSART G, DINSART CH, FLAVELL RA: Non functional thyroglobulin messenger RNA in goats with hereditary congenital goiter. *J Mol Appl Genet* 1:51, 1981.

154. RICKETTS MH, SCHULZ K, VAN ZYL A, BESTER AJ, BOYD CD, MEINHOLD H, VAN JAARSVELD PP: Autosomal recessive inheritance of congenital goiter in afrikander cattle. *J Hered* 76:12, 1985.

155. VAN VOORTHUIZEN FW, DINSART C, FLAVELL RA, DEVIJLDER JJM, VASSART G: Abnormal cellular localization of thyroglobulin mRNA associated with hereditary congenital goiter and thyroglobulin deficiency. *Proc Natl Acad Sci USA* 75:74, 1978.

156. TAYLOR BA, ROWLE L: The congenital goiter mutation is linked to the thyroglobulin gene in the mouse. *Proc Natl Acad Sci USA* 84:1986, 1987.

157. RICKETTS MH, POHL V, DE MARTYNOFF G, BOYD CD, BESTER AJ, VAN JAARSVELD PP, VASSART G: Defective splicing of thyroglobulin gene transcripts in the congenital goitre of the afrikander cattle. *EMBO J* 4:731, 1985.

158. TASSI VPN, DI LAURO R, VAN JAARSVELD P, ALVINO CG: Two abnormal thyroglobulin-like polypeptides are produced from afrikander cattle congenital goiter mRNA. *J Biol Chem* 259:10507, 1984.

159. VANDENHOVE E, VANDENBROUCKE MF: Secretion of thyroid hormones, in De Visscher M (ed): *The Thyroid Gland*, New York, Raven, 1980, p 61.

160. WOLLMAN SH: Secretion of thyroid hormones, in Dingle ZT, Fell MS (eds): *Lysosomes in Biology and Pathology*. Amsterdam, Elsevier North-Holland Biomedical Press, 1969, vol 2, p 483.

161. UNGER J, BOEYNAEMS JM, KETELBANT-BALASSE P, DUMONT JE, MOCKEL J: Kinetics of dog thyroid secretion in vitro. *Endocrinology* 103:1597, 1978.

162. DUMONT JE, WILLEMS C, VAN SANDE J, NEVE P: Regulation of the release of thyroid hormones: Role of cyclic AMP. *Ann NY Acad Sci* 185:291, 1971.

163. SELJELID R, REITH A, NAKKEN KF: The early phase of endocytosis in rat thyroid follicle cells. *Lab Invest* 23:595, 1970.

164. HERZOG V, MILLER F: Membrane retrieval in epithelial cells of isolated thyroid follicles. *Eur J Cell Biol* 19:203, 1979.

165. GOSWAMI A, ROSENBERG IN: Ferredoxin and ferredoxin reductase activities in bovine thyroid. Possible relationship to iodotyrosine deiodinase. *J Biol Chem* 256:893, 1981.

166. LAURBERG P: The effect of propylthiouracil on thyroid stimulating hormone-induced alterations in iodothyronine secretion from perfused dog thyroids. *Biochim Biophys Acta* 588:351, 1979.

167. UNGER J, VAN HEUVERSWYN B, DECOSTER C, CANTRAINE F, MOCKEL J, VAN HERLE AJ: Thyroglobulin and thyroid hormone release after intravenous administration of bovine thyrotropin in man. *J Clin Endocrinol Metab* 51:590, 1980.

168. STANBURY JB, KASSENAAR AAH, MEIJER JWA, TERPSTRA J: The occurrence of mono- and diiodotyrosine in the blood of a patient with congenital goiter. *J Clin Endocrinol Metab* 15:1216, 1955.

169. STANBURY JB, MEIJER JWA, KASSENAAR AAH: The metabolism of iodotyrosines. II. The metabolism of mono- and diiodotyrosine in certain patients with familial goitre. *J Clin Endocrinol Metab* 16:848, 1956.

170. STANBURY JB, KASSENAAR AAH, MEIJER JWA: The metabolism of iodotyrosines. I. The fate of mono- and diiodotyrosine in normal subjects and in patients with various diseases. *J Clin Endocrinol Metab* 16:735, 1956.

171. CHOUFOER JC, KASSENAAR AAH, QUERIDO A: The syndrome of congenital hypothyroidism with defective dehalogenation of iodotyrosines: Further observations and discussion of the pathophysiology. *J Clin Endocrinol Metab* 20:983, 1960.

172. ROCHICCIOLI P, DUFAU G: Trouble de l'hormonosynthése thyroïdienne par déficit en iodotyrosine-déshalogénase. *Arch Fr Pediatr* 31:25, 1974.

173. KUSAKABE T, MIYAKE T: Thyroidal deiodination defect in three sisters with simple goiter. *J Clin Endocrinol Metab* 24:456, 1964.

174. MEINHOLD H, OLBRICHT T, SCHWARTZ-PORSCHE D: Turnover and urinary excretion of circulating diiodotyrosine. *J Clin Endocrinol Metab* 64:794, 1987.

175. VAGUE J, CODACCIONI JL: Bilan de 7 ans de traitement par l'iode d'un premier cas d'hypothyroïdie infantile par défaut de désiodation des iodotyrosines. *Ann Endocrinol (Paris)* 31:1156, 1970.

176. MCGIRR EM, HUTCHISON JH, CLEMENT WE: Sporadic goitrous cretinism: Dehalogenase deficiency in the thyroid gland of a goitrous cretin and in heterozygous carriers. *Lancet* 2:823, 1959.

177. MURRAY P, THOMSON JA, MCGIRR EM, WALLACE TJ, MACDONALD EM, MACCABE HJ: Absent and defective iodotyrosine deiodination in a family some of whose members are goitrous cretins. *Lancet* 1:183, 1965.

178. CODACCIONI JL, RINALDI JP, BISMUTH J: The test of overloading of 1-diiodotyrosine (DIT) in the screening of iodotyrosine dehalogenase deficiency. *Acta Endocrinol (Copenh)* 87:95, 1978.

179. HOCH H, LEWALLEN CG: Low affinity binding of thyroxine to proteins of human serum. *J Clin Endocrinol Metab* 38:663, 1974.

180. IKEKUBO K, KONISHI J, ENDO K, NAKAJIMA K, OKUNO T, KASAGI K, MORI T, NAGATA I, TORIZUKA K: Anti-thyroxine and anti-triiodothyronine antibodies in three cases of Hashimoto's thyroiditis. *Acta Endocrinol (Copenh)* 89:557, 1978.

181. ROBBINS J, CHENG SY, GERSHENGORN MC, GLINOER D, CAHNMANN HJ, EDELNOCH H: Thyroxine transport proteins of plasma. Molecular properties and biosynthesis. *Recent Prog Horm Res* 34:477, 1978.

182. MURATA Y, MAGNER JA, REFETOFF S: The role of glycosylation in the molecular conformation and secretion of thyroxine-binding globulin. *Endocrinology* 118:1614, 1986.

183. GARTNER R, HENZE R, HORN K, PICKARDT CR, SCRIBA PC: Thyroxine-binding globulin: Investigation of microheterogeneity. *J Clin Endocrinol Metab* 52:657, 1981.

184. FLINK IL, BAILEY TJ, GUSTEFSON TA, MARKHAM BE, MORKIN E: Complete amino acid sequence of human thyroxine-binding globulin deduced from

cloned DNA: Close homology to the serine antiproteases. *Proc Natl Acad Sci USA* 83:7708, 1986.

185. TRENT JM, FLINK IL, MORKIN E, VAN TUINEN P, LEDBETTER DH: Localization of the human t hyroxine-binding globulin gene to the long arm of the X chromosome (Xq21-22). *Am J Hum Genet* 41:428, 1987.

186. AIN KB, MORI Y, REFETOFF S: Reduced clearance of thyroxine-binding globulin (TBG) with increased sialylation: A mechanism for estrogen induced elevation of serum TBG concentration. *J Clin Endocrinol Metab* 65:689, 1987.

187. TSUZUKI T, MITA S, MAEDA S, ARAKI S, SHIMADA K: Structure of human prealbumin gene. *J Biol Chem* 260:122224, 1985.

188. WALLACE MR, NAYLOR SL, KLUVE-BECKERMAN B, LONG GL, MCDONALD L, SHOWS TB, BENSON MD: Localization of the human prealbumin gene to chromosome 18. *Biochem Biophys Res Commun* 129:753, 1985.

189. IRACE G, EDELHOCH H: Thyroxine induced conformational changes in prealbumin. *Biochemistry* 17:5729, 1978.

190. VAN JAARSVELD PP, EDELHOCH H, GOODMAN DEW S, ROBBINS J: The interaction of human plasma retinol binding protein with prealbumin. *J Biol Chem* 248:4698, 1973.

191. TABACHNICK M, GIORGIO NA Jr: Thyroxine-protein interactions. II. The binding of thyroxine and its analogues to human serum albumin. *Arch Biochim Biophys* 105:563, 1964.

192. DUSSAULT JH, FISHER DA, NICOLOFF JT, ROW VV, VOLPE R: The effect of alterations of thyroxine binding capacity on the dialyzable and absolute fractions of triiodothyronine in circulation. *Acta Endocrinol (Copenh)* 72:265, 1973.

193. REFETOFF S, ROBIN NI, ALPER CA: Study of four new kindreds with inherited thyroxine-binding globulin abnormalities: Possible mutations of a single gene locus. *J Clin Invest* 51:848, 1972.

194. REFETOFF S, FANG VS, MARSHALL JS, ROBIN NI: Metabolism of thyroxine-binding globulin in man: Abnormal rate of synthesis in inherited thyroxine-binding globulin deficiency and excess. *J Clin Invest* 57:485, 1976.

195. BIANCHI R, IERVASI G, PILO A, VITEK F, FERDEGHINI M, CAZZUOLA F, GIRAUDI G: Role of serum carrier proteins in the peripheral metabolism and tissue distribution of thyroid hormones in familial dysalbuminemic hyperthyroxinemia and congenital elevation of thyroxine-binding globulin. *J Clin Invest* 80:522, 1987.

196. LEAHY BC, LAING I, DAVIS D, WALTON L: High serum thyroxine-binding globulin—An important cause of hyperthyroxinaemia. *Postgrad Med J* 60:324, 1984.

197. DWULET FE, BENSON MD: Primary structure of an amyloid prealbumin and its plasma precursor in a heredofamilial polyneuropathy of Swedish origin. *Proc Natl Acad Sci USA* 81:694, 1984.

198. JENKINS MB, STEFFES MW: Congenital thyroxine binding globulin deficiency: Incidence and inheritance. *Hum Genet* 77:80, 1987.

199. VIACARDI RM, SHEA M, SRIWANTANAKUR K, MCCORMICK K: Hyperthyroxinemia in newborns due to excess thyroxine-binding globulin. *N Engl J Med* 309:897, 1983.

200. REFETOFF S, MURATA Y: X-chromosome-linked inheritance of the variant thyroxine-binding globulin in Australian Aborigines. *J Clin Endocrinol Metab* 60:356, 1985.

201. HORWITZ DL, REFETOFF S: Graves' disease associated with familial deficiency of thyroxine-binding globulin. *J Clin Endocrinol Metab* 44:242, 1977.

202. SHANE SR, ULYSSES SS, JONES JE: X-chromosome-linked inheritance of elevated thyroxine-binding globulin in association with goiter. *J Clin Endocrinol Metab* 32:587, 1971.

203. REFETOFF S, SELENKOW HA: Familial thyroxine-binding globulin deficiency in a patient with Turner's syndrome (XO): Genetic study of a kindred. *N Engl J Med* 278:1081, 1968.

204. MURATA Y, TAKAMATSU J, REFETOFF S: Inherited abnormality of thyroxine-binding globulin with no demonstrable thyroxine-binding activity and high serum levels of denatured thyroxine binding globulin. *N Engl J Med* 314:694, 1986.

205. BURR WA, RAMSDEN DB, HOFFENBERG R: Hereditary abnormalities of thyroxine-binding globulin concentration. *Q J Med* 49:295, 1980.

206. MORI Y, REFETOFF S, FLINK IL, CHARBONEAU M, MURATA Y, SEO H, MORKIN E, DUSSAULT J: Detection of thyroxine-binding globulin (TBG) gene in six unrelated families with complete TBG deficiency. *J Clin Endocrinol Metab* 67:727, 1988.

207. DICK M, WATSON F: Prevalent low serum thyroxine-binding globulin level in Western Australian Aborigines. *Med J Aust* 1:115, 1980.

208. MURATA Y, REFETOFF S, SARNE DH, DICK M, WATSON F: Variant thyroxine-binding globulin in serum of Australian Aborigines: Its physical, chemical and biological properties. *J Endocrinol Invest* 8:225, 1985.

209. DAIGER SP, RUMMEL DP, WANG L, CAVALLI-SFORZA LL: Detection of genetic variation with radioactive ligands. IV. X-linked, polymorphic genetic variation of thyroxine-binding globulin (TBG). *Am J Hum Genet* 33:640, 1981.

210. TAKAMATSU J, REFETOFF S, CHARBONNEAU M, DUSSAULT JH: Two new inherited defects of the thyroxine-binding globulin (TBG) molecule presenting as partial TBG deficiency. *J Clin Invest* 79:833, 1987.

211. MORI Y, REFETOFF S, SEINO S, FLINK IL, MURATA Y: Asparagine for isoleucine substitution in position 96 of thyroxine-binding globulin (TBG) is the likely cause of severe impairment of T4-binding in the variant TBG-Gary. The Sixty-second Annual Meeting of the American Thyroid Association, Washington, DC, September 16–19, 1987. *Endocrinology (Suppl)* 120:T22, 1987.

212. TAKAMATSU J, ANDO M, WEINBERG M, REFETOFF S: Isoelectric focusing variant thyroxine-binding globulin (TBG-S) in American Blacks: Increased heat lability and reduced concentration in serum. *J Clin Endocrinol Metab* 63:80, 1986.

213. MOSES AC, LAWLOR J, HADDOW J, JACKSON IMD: Familial euthyroid hyperthyroxinemia resulting from increased thyroxine binding to thyroxine-binding prealbumin. *N Engl J Med* 306:966, 1982.

214. LALLOZ MRA, BYFIELD PGH, HIMSWORTH RL: A prealbumin variant with an increased affinity for T4 and reverse-T3. *Clin Endocrinol* 21:331, 1984.

215. REFETOFF S, DWULET FE, BENSON MD: Reduced affinity for thyroxine in two of three structural thyroxine-binding prealbumin variants associated with familial amyloidotic polyneuropathy. *J Clin Endocrinol Metab* 63:1432, 1986.

216. ALPER CA, ROBIN NI, REFETOFF S: Genetic polymorphism of rhesus thyroxine-binding prealbumin: Evidence for tetrameric structure in primates. *Proc Natl Acad Sci USA* 63:775, 1969.

217. VAN JAARSVELD PP, BANCH WT, EDELHOCH H, ROBBINS J: Polymorphism of Rhesus monkey serum prealbumin. Molecular properties and binding of thyroxine and retinol-binding protein. *J Biol Chem* 248:4706, 1973.

218. RUIZ M, RAJATANAVIN R, YOUNG RA, TAYLOR C, BROWN R, BRAVERMAN LE, INGBAR SH: Familial dysalbuminemic hyperthyroxinemia. A syndrome that can be confused with thyrotoxicosis. *N Engl J Med* 306:635, 1982.

219. BARLOW JW, CSICSMANN JM, WHITE EL, FUNDER JW, STOCKIGT JR: Familial euthyroid thyroxine excess: Characterization of abnormal intermediate affinity thyroxine binding to albumin. *J Clin Endocrinol Metab* 55:244, 1982.

220. LALLOZ MRA, BYFIELD PGH, HIMSWORTH RL: Hyperthyroxinaemia: Abnormal binding of T4 by an inherited albumin variant. *Clin Endocrinol* 18:11, 1983.

221. HOLLANDER CS, BERNSTEIN G, OPPENHEIMER JH: Abnormalities of thyroxine binding in analbuminemia. *J Clin Endocrinol Metab* 28:1064, 1968.

222. ROBBINS J, RALL JE: The iodine containing hormones, in Grey CH, James VHT (eds): *Hormones in Blood*, 3d ed. London, Academic, 1983, p 219.

223. EKINS R, EDWARDS P, NEWMAN B: The role of binding-proteins in hormone delivery, in Albertini A, Ekins RP (eds): *Free Hormones in Blood*. Amsterdam, Elsevier Biomedical, 1982, p 45.

224. PARDRIDGE WM: Transport of protein-bound hormones into tissues in vivo. *Endocrinol Rev* 2:103, 1981.

225. KRENNING E, DOCTER R, BERNARD B, VISSER T, HENNEMANN G: Characteristics of active transport of thyroid hormone into rat hepatocytes. *Biochim Biophys Acta* 676:314, 1981.

226. MAXFIELD ER, WILLINGHAM MC, PASTAN I, DRAGSTEN P, CHENG SY: Binding and mobility of the cell surface receptors for 3,3'5-triiodo-L-thyronine. *Science* 211:63, 1981.

227. OPPENHEIMER JH, SCHWARTZ HL: Stereospecific transport of triiodothyronine from plasma to cytosol and from cytosol to nucleus in rat liver, kidney, brain and heart. *J Clin Invest* 75:147, 1985.

228. LARSEN PR, SILVA JE, KAPLAN MM: Relationships between circulating and intracellular thyroid hormones. Physiological and clinical implications. *Endocrinol Rev* 87:102, 1981.

229. ENGLER D, BURGER AG: The deiodination of iodothyronines and of their derivatives in man. *Endocrinol Rev* 5:151, 1984.

230. KAPLAN MM, MCCANN UD, YASKOSKI KA, LARSEN PR, LEONARD JL: Anatomical distribution of phenolic and tyrosyl ring deiodinases in the nervous system of normal and hypothyroid rats. *Endocrinology* 109:397, 1981.

231. WARTOFSKY L, BURMAN KD: Alterations of thyroid function in patients with systemic illness: The "Euthyroid Sick Syndrome." *Endocrinol Rev* 3:164, 1982.

232. WORTSMAN J, PREMACHANDRA BN, WILLIAMS K, BURMAN KD, HAY ID, DAVIS PJ: Familial resistance to thyroid hormone associated with decreased transport across the plasma membrane. *Ann Intern Med* 98:904, 1983.

233. MURATA Y, REFETOFF S, HORWITZ AL, SMITH TJ: Hormonal regulation of

glycosaminoglycan accumulation in fibroblasts from patients with resistance to thyroid hormone. *J Clin Endocrinol Metab* 57:1233, 1983.

234. MAXON HR, BURMAN KD, PREMACHANDRA BN, CHEN IW, BURGER A, LEVY P, GEORGES LP: Familial elevation of total and free thyroxine in healthy, euthyroid subjects without detectable binding protein abnormalities. *Acta Endocrinol (Copenh)* 100:224, 1982.

235. HUTCHISON JH, ARNEIL GC, MCGERR EM: Deficiency of an extra-thyroid enzyme in sporadic cretinism. *Lancet* 2:314, 1957.

236. WIENER JD, LINDEBOOM GA: Observations on an unusual case of myxoedema. *Acta Endocrinol (Copenh)* 39:439, 1962.

237. JANSEN M, KRENNING EP, OOSTDIJK W, DOCTER R, KINGMA BE, VAN DER BRANDE JVL, HENNEMANN G: Hyperthyroxinemia due to decreased peripheral triiodothyronine production. *Lancet* 2:849, 1982.

238. SPANGENBERG DB: Thyroxine in early strobilation in Aurelia aurita. *Ann Zool* 14:825, 1974.

239. FRIEDEN E: Thyroid hormones and the biochemistry of amphibian metamorphosis. *Recent Prog Horm Res* 23:139, 1967.

240. SEO H, WUNDERLICH C, VASSART G, REFETOFF S: Growth hormone responses to thyroid hormone in the neonatal rat. Resistance and anamnestic response. *J Clin Invest* 67:569, 1981.

241. MCFAUL R, DORNER S, BRETT EM, GRANT DB: Neurological abnormalities in patients treated for hypothyroidism from early life. *Arch Dis Child* 53:611, 1978.

242. GLORIEUX J, DUSSAULT JH, LETARTE J, GUYDA H, MORISSETTE J: Preliminary results on the mental development of hypothyroid infants detected by the Quebec Screening Program. *J Pediatr* 102:19, 1982.

243. EDELMAN IS, ISMAIL-BEIGI F: Thyroid thermogenesis and active sodium transport. *Recent Prog Horm Res* 30:235, 1974.

244. SILVA JE, LARSEN PR: Adrenergic activation of triiodothyronine production in brown adipose tissue. *Nature* 305:712, 1983.

245. BIANCO AC, SILVA E: Intracellular conversion of thyroxine to triiodothyronine is required for the optimal thermogenic function of brown adipose tissue. *J Clin Invest* 79:295, 1987.

246. MARIASH CN, KAISER FE, SCHWARTZ HL, TOWLE HC, OPPENHEIMER JH: Synergism of thyroid hormone and high carbohydrate diet in the induction of lipogenic enzymes in the rat. Mechanisms and implications. *J Clin Invest* 65:1126, 1980.

247. BERNAL J, OBREGON MJ, RODRIQUEZ-PERA A, MALLOL J, HERNANDEZ P, ESCOBAR DEL RAY F, MORREALE DE ESCOBAR G: Metabolism and action of thyroid hormone. *Horm Cell Regul* 5:107, 1981.

248. OPPENHEIMER JH, KOERNER D, SCHWARTZ HL, SURKS MI: Specific-nuclear triiodothyronine binding sites in rat liver and kidney. *J Clin Endocrinol Metab* 35:330, 1972.

249. OPPENHEIMER JH: The nuclear receptor-triiodothyronine complex: Relationship to thyroid hormone distribution, metabolism and biological action, in Oppenheimer JH, Samuels HH (eds): *Molecular Basis of Thyroid Hormone Action.* New York, Academic, pp 1–35.

250. GOSLINGS B, SCHWARTZ HL, DILLMANN W, SURKS MI, OPPENHEIMER JH: Comparison of the metabolism and distribution of L-triiodothyronine and triiodothyroacetic acid in the rat: A possible explanation of differential hormonal activity. *Endocrinology* 98:666, 1976.

251. ICHIKAWA K, DEGROOT LJ: Separation of DNA binding domain from hormone and core histone binding domains by trypsin digestion of rat liver nuclear thyroid hormone receptor. *J Biol Chem* 261:16540, 1986.

252. ICHIKAWA K, DEGROOT LJ: Purification and characterization of rat liver nuclear thyroid hormone receptors. *Proc Natl Acad Sci USA* 84:3420, 1987.

253. SAP J, MUNOZ A, DAMM K, GOLDBERG Y, GHYSDAEL J, LENZ A, BENG H, VENNSTROM B: The c-erb-A protein is a high-affinity receptor for thyroid hormone. *Nature* 324:635, 1976.

254. WEINBERGER C, THOMPSON CC, ONG ES, LEBO R, GUOL DJ, EVANS RM: The c-erb-A gene encodes a thyroid hormone receptor. *Nature* 324:641, 1986.

255. THOMPSON CC, WEINBERG C, LEBO R, EVANS RM: Identificaiton of a novel thyroid hormone receptor expressed in the mammalian central nervous system. *Science* 237:1610, 1987.

256. JORGENSEN EC: Stereochemistry of thyroxine and analogues. *Mayo Clin Proc* 39:560, 1964.

257. SEO H, VASSART G, BROCAS H, REFETOFF S: Triiodothyronine stimulates specifically growth hormone mRNA in rat pituitary tumor cells. *Proc Natl Acad Sci USA* 74:2054, 1977.

258. MARTIAL JA, BAXTER JD, GOODMAN HM, SEEBURG PH: Regulation of growth hormone messenger RNA by thyroid and glucocorticoid hormones. *Proc Natl Acad Sci USA* 74:1816, 1977.

259. EVANS RM, BIRNBERG NC, ROSENFELD MG: Glucocorticoid and thyroid hormones transcriptionally regulate growth hormone gene expression. *Proc Natl Acad Sci USA* 79:7659, 1982.

260. YAFFE BM, SAMUELS HH: Hormonal regulation of the growth hormone gene. *J Biol Chem* 259:6284, 1984.

261. CASANOVA J, COPP RP, JANOCKO L, SAMUELS HH: 5'-Flanking DNA of the rat growth hormone gene mediates regulated expression of thyroid hormone. *J Biol Chem* 200:11744, 1985.

262. LARSEN PR, HARNEY JW, MOORE DD: Sequences required for cell-type specific thyroid hormone regulation of rat growth hormone promoter activity. *J Biol Chem* 261:14373, 1986.

263. SHUPNIK MA, CHIN WW, HABNER JF, RIDGWAY EC: Transcriptional regulation of the thyrotropin subunit genes by thyroid hormone. *J Biol Chem* 260:2900, 1985.

264. NARAYAN P, TOWLE HC: Stabilization of a specific nuclear mRNA precursor by thyroid hormone. *Mol Cell Biol* 5:2642, 1985.

265. ISUMO S, NADAL-GINARD B, MAHDAVI V: All members of the MHC multigene family respond to thyroid hormone in a highly tissue-specific manner. *Science* 231:597, 1986.

266. STERLING K, MILCH PO, BRENNER MA, LAZARUS JH: Thyroid hormone action: The mitochondrial pathway. *Science* 197:996, 1977.

267. REFETOFF S, DEWIND LT, DEGROOT LJ: Familial syndrome combining deaf-mutism, stippled epiphyses, goiter and abnormally high PBI: Possible target organ refractoriness to thyroid hormone. *J Clin Endocrinol* 27:279, 1967.

268. REFETOFF S, DEGROOT LJ, BENARD B, DEWIND LT: Studies of a sibship with apparent hereditary resistance to the intracellular action of thyroid hormone. *Metabolism* 21:723, 1972.

269. REFETOFF S, MATALON R, BIGAZZI M: Metabolism of L-thyroxine (T$_4$) and L-triiodothyronine (T$_3$) by human fibroblasts in tissue culture: Evidence for cellular binding proteins and conversion of T$_4$ to T$_3$. *Endocrinology* 91:934, 1972.

270. BERNAL J, REFETOFF S, DEGROOT LJ: Abnormalities of triiodothyronine binding to lymphocyte and fibroblast nuclei from a patient with peripheral resistance to thyroid hormone action. *J Clin Endocrinol Metab* 47:1266, 1978.

271. REFETOFF S, DEGROOT LJ, BARSANO CP: Defective thyroid hormone feedback regulation in the syndrome of peripheral resistance to thyroid hormone. *J Clin Endocrinol Metab* 51:41, 1980.

272. CECCARELLI P, REFETOFF S, MURATA Y: Resistance to thyroid hormone diagnosed by the reduced response of fibroblasts to the triiodothyronine-induced suppression of fibronectin synthesis. *J Clin Endocrinol Metab* 65:242, 1987.

273. REFETOFF S: Syndromes of thyroid hormone resistance. *Am J Physiol* 243:E88, 1982.

274. REFETOFF S: Thyroid hormone resistance syndromes, in Ingbar SH, Braverman LE (eds): *Werner's the Thyroid: A Functional and Clinical Text.* New York, Lippincott, 1986, pp 1292–1307.

275. CHAIT A, KANTER R, GREEN W, KENNY M: Defective thyroid hormone action in fibroblasts cultured from subjects with the syndrome of resistance to thyroid hormone. *J Clin Endocrinol Metab* 54:767, 1982.

276. WEINTRAUB BD, GERSHENGORN MC, KOURIDES IA, FEIN H: Inappropriate secretion of thyroid stimulating hormone. *Ann Intern Med* 95:339, 1981.

277. REFETOFF S, SALAZAR A, SMITH TJ, SCHERBERG NH: The consequences of inappropriate treatment due to failure to recognize the syndrome of pituitary and peripheral tissue resistance to thyroid hormone. *Metabolism* 32:822, 1983.

278. FISCHER DA, KLEIN AH: Thyroid development and disorders of thyroid function in the newborn. *N Engl J Med* 304:702, 1981.

279. DEMEESTER-MIRKINE N, DUMONT JE: The hypothalamo-pituitary thyroid, in De Visscher M (ed): *The Thyroid,* New York, Raven, 1980, p 145.

280. LARSEN PR: Feedback regulation of thyrotropin secretion by thyroid hormones. *N Engl J Med* 306:23, 1982.

281. WEINTRAUB BD, STANNARD BS, MAGNER JA, RONIN C, TAYLOR T, JOSHI L, CONSTANT RB, MENEZES-FERREIRA MM, PETRICK P, GESUNDHEIT N: Glycosylation and posttranslational processing of thyroid-stimulating hormone: Clinical implications, *Recent Prog Horm Res* 41:577, 1985.

282. ENGLER D, SCANLON MF, JACKSON IMD: Thyrotropin releasing hormone in the systemic circulation of the neonatal rat is derived from the pancreatic and other extraneural tissues. *J Clin Invest* 67:800, 1981.

283. SPIRA O, BIRKENFELD A, AVNI A, GROSS J, GORDON A: TSH synthesis and release in the thyroidectomized rat. *Acta Endocrinol (Copenh)* 92:502, 1979.

284. DAHLBERG PA, PETRICK PA, NISSIM M, MENEZES-FERREIRA M, WEINTRAUB BD: Intrinsic bioactivity of thyrotropin in human serum is inversely correlated with thyroid hormone concentrations. *J Clin Invest* 79:1388, 1987.

285. FAGLIA G, BECK-PECCOZ P, PISCITELLI G, MEDRI G: Inappropriate secretion of thyrotropin by the pituitary. *Horm Res* 26:79, 1987.

286. ROSLER A, LITVIN Y, HAGE C, GROSS J, CERASH E: Familial hyperthyroidism due to inappropriate thyrotropin secretion successfully treated with triiodothyronine. *J Clin Endocrinol Metab* 54:76, 1982.

287. GERSHENGORN MC, WEINTRAUB BD: Thyrotropin-induced hyperthyroid-

ism caused by selective pituitary resistance to thyroid hormone. *J Clin Invest* 56:633, 1975.

288. PITTMAN JA, HAIGLER ED, HERSHMAN JM, PITTMAN CS: Hypothalamic hypothyroidism. *N Engl J Med* 285:844, 1971.

289. GHARIB H, ABBOUD CF: Primary idiopathic hypothalamic hypothyroidism. *Am J Med* 83:171, 1987.

290. MIYAI K, AZIKIZAWA M, KUMUHARA Y: Familial isolated thyrotropin deficiency with cretinism. *N Engl J Med* 285:1043, 1971.

291. RIMOIN DL, SCHIMKE RN: *Genetic Disorders of the Endocrine Glands.* St Louis, CV Mosby, 1971, p 29.

292. ADLER-BIER M, PERTZELAND A, LARON Z, LIEBERMAN E, MOSES S: Multiple pituitary hormone deficiencies in eight siblings of one Jewish Moroccan family. *Acta Paediatr Scand* 68:401, 1979.

293. SCHIMKE RN, SPAULDING JJ, HOLLOWELL JG: X-linked congenital panhypopituitarism. *Birth Defects* 7:21, 1971.

294. PHELAN PD, CONELLY J, MARTIN FIR, WETTENHALL HNB: X-linked recessive hypopituitarism. *Birth Defects* 7:24, 1971.

295. ZIPF WB, KELCH RP, BACON GE: Variable X-linked recessive hypopituitarism with evidence of gonadotropin deficiency in two pre-pubertal males. *Clin Genet* 11:249, 1977.

296. SADEGHI-NEJAD A, SENIOR B: A familial syndrome of isolated "aplasia" of the anterior pituitary. *J Pediatr* 84:79, 1974.

297. STEINER MM, BOGGS JD: Absence of pituitary gland, hypothyroidism, hypoadrenalism and hypogonadism in a 17 year old dwarf. *J Clin Endocrinol* 25:1591, 1965.

298. STEINER MM: Rare dwarfism with chronic hypoglycemia and convulsions. *J Clin Endocrinol* 13:283, 1953.

299. FIERRIER PE, STONE EF JR: Familial pituitary dwarfism associated with an abnormal sella turcica. *Pediatrics* 43:858, 1969.

300. SIPPONEN P, SIMILA S, COLLAN Y, AUTERE T, HERVA R: Familial syndrome with panhypopituitarism, hypoplasia of the hypophysis, and poorly developed sella turcica. *S Arch Dis Child* 53:664, 1978.

301. PARKS JS, TENORE A, BONGIOVANNI AM, KIRKLAND RT: Familial hypopituitarism with large sella turcica. *N Engl J Med* 298:698, 1978.

302. MEDEIROS-NETO G, MACIEL RMB, HALPERN A: Iodine deficiency disorders and congenital hypothyroidism, in *Frontiers in Thyroidology*. São Paulo, Plenum, 1986.

303. CZERNICHOW P, SCHLUMBERGER M, POMAREDE R, FRAGU P: Plasma thyroglobulin measurements help determine the type of thyroid defect in congenital hypothyroidism. *J Clin Endocrinol Metab* 56:242, 1983.

304. YOSHIDA K, SAKURADA T, TAKAHASHI T, FURUHASHI N, KAISE K, YOSHINAGA K: Measurement of TSH in human amniotic fluid: Diagnosis of fetal thyroid abnormality in utero. *Clin Endocrinol* 25:313, 1986.

305. GENDREL D, FEINSTEIN MC, GRENIER J: Falsely elevated serum TSH in newborn infants: Transfer from mothers to infants of a factor interfering in the TSH radioimmunoassay. *J Clin Endocrinol Metab* 52:62, 1981.

306. GLORIEUX J, DUSSAULT JH, MORISSETTE J, DESJARDINS M, LETARTE J, GUYDA H: Follow-up at ages 5 and 7 years on mental development in children with hypothyroidism detected by Quebec Screening Program. *J Pediatr* 107:913, 1985.

CHAPTER 74

THE ADRENAL HYPERPLASIAS

MARIA I. NEW
PERRIN C. WHITE
SONGYA PANG
BO DUPONT
PHYLLIS W. SPEISER

1. Congenital adrenal hyperplasia (CAH) consists of a family of disorders arising from specific defects in the enzymes of the adrenal cortex required for cortisol biosynthesis; all are transmitted as autosomal recessive traits.

2. The adrenal cortex is divided histologically into three zones: the zona glomerulosa, zona fasciculata, and zona reticularis. The glucocorticoid hormone cortisol is synthesized in the zona fasciculata and is regulated by corticotropin (ACTH) secreted by the anterior pituitary. The mineralocorticoid hormone aldosterone is produced in the zona glomerulosa under the primary control of the renin-angiotensin system.

3. Cortisol is synthesized from cholesterol in five enzymatic steps: cleavage of the cholesterol side chain between carbons 20 and 22, dehydrogenation at the 3β position with Δ^5-Δ^4 isomerization, and successive hydroxylations at positions 17α, 21, and 11β. All steps except 3β dehydrogenation isomerization require specific cytochromes P450, which are heme-containing membrane-bound monooxygenases. Aldosterone synthesis requires the same enzymatic steps except for 17α hydroxylation. An additional hydroxyl is added at the 18 position and further oxidized to an aldehyde. These additional steps are mediated by the same P450 enzyme that performs 11β hydroxylation.

4. Although any of the enzymatic steps required for cortisol synthesis may be defective in CAH, steroid 21-hydroxylase deficiency accounts for more than 90 percent of all cases of CAH, while deficiencies of 11β-hydroxylase and 3β-hydroxysteroid dehydrogenase account for almost all remaining cases.

5. Clinical consequences of 21-hydroxylase deficiency arise primarily from overproduction and accumulation of precursors proximal to the blocked enzymatic step. These are shunted into the androgen biosynthesis pathway. Thus, affected females with classic 21-hydroxylase deficiency are born with ambiguous genitalia due to prenatal exposure to elevated levels of androgens. Postnatally, both sexes manifest rapid somatic growth with accelerated skeletal maturation, early closure of the epiphyses, and short adult stature, a problem that may not be completely prevented by current therapy. Other symptoms of androgen excess include abnormal patterns of body hair and decreased fertility due to disruption of the hypothalamic-pituitary-gonadal axis.

Patients with nonclassic disease are born without symptoms of prenatal androgen exposure but subsequently have a variable course; they may be asymptomatic or may develop signs of androgen excess.

6. Three-fourths of patients with classic 21-hydroxylase deficiency also have a defect in their ability to synthesize aldosterone. Such patients may die in the neonatal period from shock due to salt wasting, an inability to conserve sodium.

7. Deficiency of 21-hydroxylase is inherited as an autosomal recessive trait closely linked to the HLA major histocompatibility complex on the short arm of chromosome 6. In addition, there are specific associations between HLA antigens—or combinations of antigens called haplotypes—*and different forms of 21-hydroxylase deficiency. HLA-A3,Bw47,DR7, and Bw60 are associated with salt-wasting disease, HLA-B5 with simple virilizing disease, and HLA-B14,DR1 with nonclassic disease. HLA-A1,B8,DR3 is negatively associated with 21-hydroxylase deficiency.*

8. While classic 21-hydroxylase deficiency is found in about 1 in 12,500 births, nonclassic deficiency is far more frequent, occurring in up to 3 percent of persons among certain ethnic groups. This figure, derived from combined analysis of hormonal data and HLA associations in parents of patients with 21-hydroxylase deficiency, indicates that nonclassic 21-hydroxylase deficiency is one of the most common autosomal recessive disorders in human beings.

9. Molecular genetic analysis has demonstrated that there are two 21-hydroxylase genes, CYP21A and CYP21B, respectively adjacent to the C4A and C4B genes encoding the fourth component of serum complement. This cluster is located between HLA-Band DR. The CYP21B and C4B genes are deleted on the HLA-Bw47 haplotype associated with salt-wasting disease, while the CYP21A and C4A genes are deleted in hormonally normal individuals who carry HLA-A1,B8,DR3. This suggests that the CYP21B gene product is required for cortisol biosynthesis but the CYP21A gene is not.

DNA sequence analysis of the CYP21B genes has confirmed that the CYP21B gene encodes 21-hydroxylase (P450c21), whereas the CYP21A gene is a pseudogene, con-

---

Nonstandard abbreviations used in this chapter are: ACTH = corticotropin; AMH = antimüllerian hormone; Bf = properdin factor B; 3β-HSD = 3β-hydroxysteroid dehydrogenase; C2 = second component of serum complement; C4 = fourth component of serum complement; CAH = congenital adrenal hyperplasia; CMO I and II = corticosterone methyl oxidase type I and type II; CYP21A = the 21-hydroxylase pseudogene; CYP21B = the 21-hydroxylase functional gene; DHEA = dehydroepiandrosterone; DOC = 11-deoxycorticosterone; Δ^4-A = Δ^4-androstenedione; Δ^5-17P = Δ^5-17-hydroxypregnenolone; FSH = follicle-stimulating hormone; 17-KS = 17-oxo(keto)steroids; LH = luteinizing hormone; MHC = major histocompatibility complex; 18-OHB = 18-hydroxycorticosterone; 17-OHP = 17α-hydroxyprogesterone; 18OH-THA = 18-hydroxytetrahydroaldosterone; P450c11 = 11β-hydroxylase; P450c17 = 17α-hydroxylase; P450c21 = 21-hydroxylase; P450scc = cholesterol desmolase, or side-chain cleavage enzyme; PCO = polycystic ovary disease; PRA = plasma renin activity; SCP_2 = sterol carrier protein 2; SHIP = steroid hydroxylase inducer protein; SRP = sterol regulatory protein; THAldo = tetrahydroaldosterone; TNF = tumor necrosis factor.

taining several mutations that completely prevent synthesis of a functional enzyme.

About 25 percent of classic deficiency alleles are deletions of CYP21B. Many of the remaining mutant alleles result from transfers of deleterious mutations from the CYP21A pseudogene to CYP21B, a phenomenon termed gene conversion.

10. *Steroid 11β-hydroxylase deficiency produces symptoms of androgen excess that are similar to those observed in 21-hydroxylase deficiency. The blocked enzymatic step also results in accumulation of 11-deoxycorticosterone; this steroid and certain metabolites have mineralocorticoid activity. Thus, in contrast to 21-hydroxylase deficiency, untreated patients with 11β-hydroxylase deficiency retain sodium and suffer from hypertension.*

The structural gene (CYP11B) for the specific enzyme (P450c11) is located on the long arm of chromosome 8. Because 18-hydroxylase and corticosterone methyl oxidase II activities (the latter activity converts the 18-hydroxyl to an aldehyde) are mediated by P450c11, it is hypothesized that deficiencies of these activities may result from unusual mutant alleles of the P450c11 structural gene.

11. *Classic 3β-hydroxysteroid dehydrogenase deficiency causes incomplete prenatal genital development in genetic males due to impaired synthesis of bioactive androgens. Females may have relatively mild symptoms of androgen excess due to elevated levels of dehydroepiandrosterone, a weak androgen. Mineralocorticoid synthesis is usually affected in this disorder.*

A nonclassic form of 3β-hydroxysteroid dehydrogenase deficiency is a relatively common cause of symptoms of androgen excess in females.

12. *The rare deficiencies of 17α-hydroxylase and cholesterol desmolase also result in incomplete masculinization in genetic males. Cholesterol desmolase deficiency affects all classes of steroid synthesis and is often a lethal disorder. As with 11β-hydroxylase deficiency, 17α-hydroxylase deficiency causes accumulation of precursors with mineralocorticoid activity, resulting in hypertension.*

CYP11A and CYP17, the structural genes for cholesterol desmolase (P450scc) and 17α-hydroxylase (P450c17), have been cloned and mapped to chromosomes 15 and 10, respectively.

13. *Treatment of congenital adrenal hyperplasia consists of glucocorticoid (e.g., hydrocortisone) replacement and, if necessary, a mineralocorticoid hormone. Masculinized female genitalia are corrected surgically. Advances in prenatal diagnosis of 21-hydroxylase deficiency have made it possible to prevent prenatal virilization of affected females by treating the mother with dexamethasone, which crosses the placenta, suppressing production of androgens by the fetal adrenal gland.*

Congenital adrenal hyperplasia (CAH) consists of a family of disorders resulting from enzymatic defects of steroidogenesis inherited as autosomal recessive traits. Each enzyme deficiency produces characteristic hormonal abnormalities and associated clinical syndromes.

Since 1983, when the previous edition of this text was written,[1] significant advances in understanding the biochemical, genetic, and clinical forms of CAH have occurred.[2] The frequency of the disorder due to steroid 21-hydroxylase deficiency has been more precisely defined by screening large populations with a microfilter paper technique and using population genetic principles. Nonclassic clinical forms of several of the steroidogenic defects have been recognized and attributed to genetic allelism. Some of the nonclassic forms produce clinical symptoms and signs indistinguishable from other syndromes of androgen excess except by genetic and hormonal studies. Since the nonclassic 21-hydroxylase deficiency is the

most common autosomal recessive defect in humans and unlike other androgen-excess syndromes responds readily to treatment, correct diagnosis is important.

The elucidation of a molecular genetic basis for the disease due to 21-hydroxylase deficiency has suggested a basis for the clinical variants observed.

Prenatal diagnosis of 21-hydroxylase deficiency, utilizing the new molecular probes for HLA antigens combined with hormonal studies and serological HLA genotyping, is now possible early in gestation with tissue obtained by chorionic villus biopsy. Early diagnosis now permits prenatal treatment by administering oral dexamethasone to the mother in time to prevent masculinization of female genitalia. Genes for other steroidogenic enzymes have been cloned, but the mutation or mutations causing the disease have yet to be clarified. Despite these great advances, lifelong treatment with glucocorticoids remains necessary and is as yet imperfect in ensuring normal hormonal levels throughout the day, ultimate normal stature, and fertility.

GENERAL STEROIDOGENESIS

Morphology and Function of the Adrenal Cortex

The steroidogenic cells of the adrenal cortex are divided into three regions: the outer zona glomerulosa, which may not be continuous, cells of the glomerular type often appearing only focally in the subcapsular space; the zona fasciculata, named for the columnar structures of corded lipid-rich clear cells in the wide middle of the cortex; and the more compact cell population and interlaced pattern of blood vessels of the dense inner zona reticularis.[2a] Blood flow proceeds from the subcapsular region toward the medulla and the central portal vein.[2a] Local variations in the activity of certain steroidogenic enzymes correspond to this histological zonation.[2b] The three classes of steroids synthesized by the adrenal cortex are mineralocorticoids and glucocorticoids, both C_{21} steroids, and sex steroids, predominantly androgenic (C_{19}) steroids (Fig. 74-1). The final enzymatic step in aldosterone synthesis is limited to the zona glomerulosa, while synthesis of all other mineralocorticoids may occur also in the zona fasciculata and zona reticularis. In contrast, the enzyme activity necessary for formation of glucocorticoids and androgens is absent in the outer zone but present in the middle and inner zones, which thus together are capable of synthesis of all corticosteroids except aldosterone. Cortisol is the principal glucocorticoid and quantitatively the main secretory product of the adrenal cortex in humans and in most mammalian species.[2c] Cortisol production takes place in the zona fasciculata and zona reticularis, and it is here also that the androgenic steroids are produced in normal and abnormal amounts.[2b]

Biochemistry

The synthesis of cortisol in the zona fasciculata[3] is under the control of the peptide corticotropin (ACTH) secreted by the anterior pituitary (Fig. 74-2). Binding to an adrenocortical cell surface receptor, plasma ACTH activates adenylate cyclase and increases intracellular levels of 3',5'-cyclic adenosine monophosphate (cAMP); cAMP-dependent protein kinases in turn stimulate a number of cell processes. Both acute and

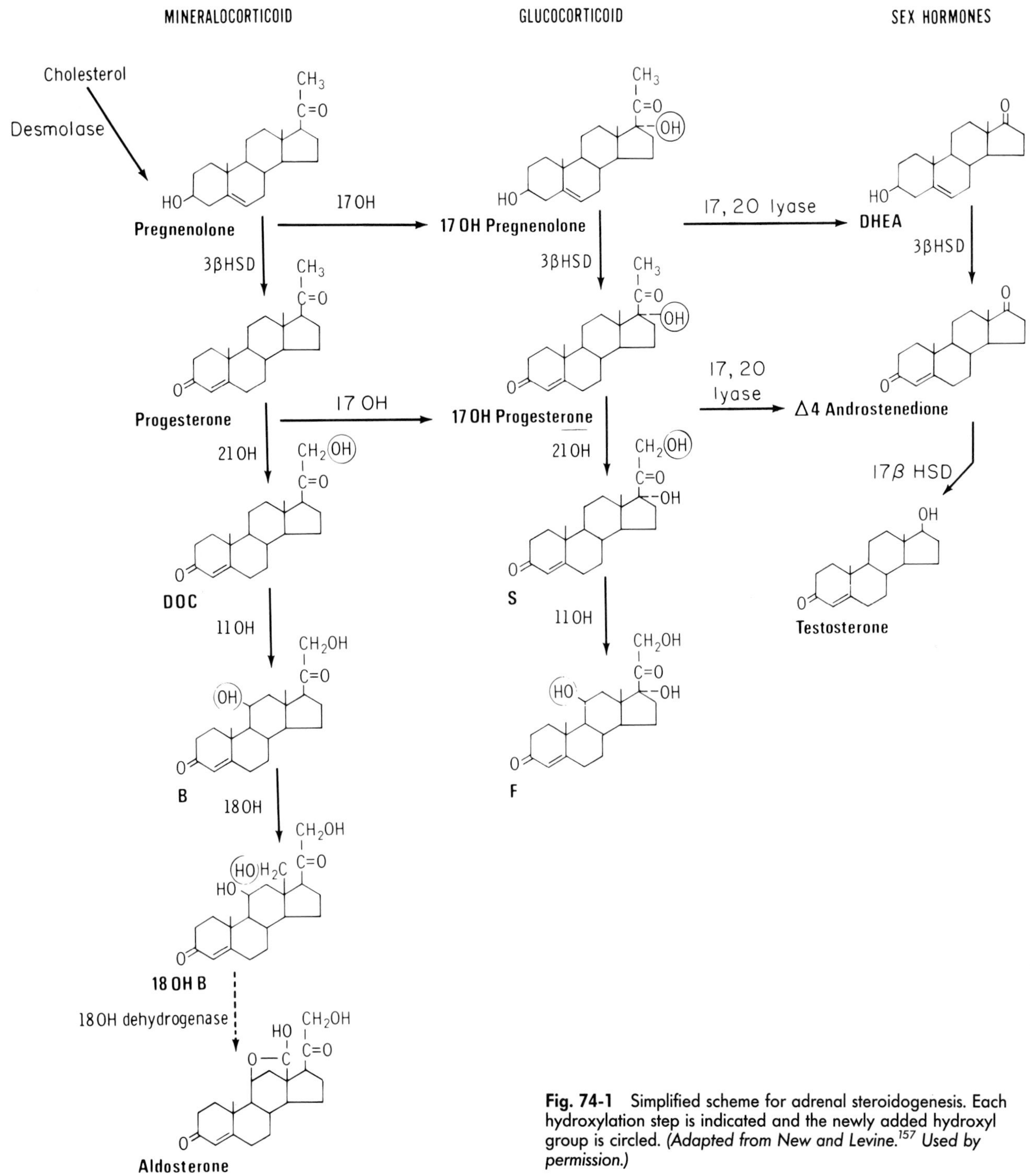

MINERALOCORTICOID   GLUCOCORTICOID   SEX HORMONES

Fig. 74-1 Simplified scheme for adrenal steroidogenesis. Each hydroxylation step is indicated and the newly added hydroxyl group is circled. (Adapted from New and Levine.[157] Used by permission.)

chronic effects result.[3a] Most directly, phosphorylation activates cholesteryl ester hydrolase, which mobilizes esterified cholesterol from storage in cytoplasmic lipid droplets.[3b] Free cholesterol is transported into the mitochondria by sterol carrier protein 2 (SCP$_2$),[4] this movement being facilitated by kinase-induced cytoskeletal changes,[4a] and is converted to the common steroid precursor pregnenolone by cholesterol desmolase, or side-chain cleavage enzyme. This first step of cortisol (and all steroid) biosynthesis is normally rate-limiting and is controlled by substrate availability to the enzyme system at the inner mitochondrial membrane.[4b] Maximum rates require the mediation of ACTH-sensitive protein factors affecting intramitochondrial transfer and binding of cholesterol.[5a] This is the immediate steroidogenic stimulus of ACTH. Continued

ACTH elevation increases transcription of mRNA for the steroidogenic enzymes[5b] and enzymes for cholesterol storage, transport, and synthesis.[5c]

Cholesterol 20,22-desmolase is a specific mitochondrial cytochrome P450, cytochrome P450scc, integrally bound to the inner membrane. Side-chain cleavage is actually three distinct reactions: cholesterol is hydroxylated at the 20S and then at the 22R position, and finally the 20,22 carbon-carbon bond is oxidatively cleaved. The enzyme functions as the terminal oxidase of an electron-transport chain that utilizes NADPH and includes an adrenodoxin reductase, which is a flavoprotein, and adrenodoxin, which is a protein containing a nonheme iron atom. Each cycle of the reaction uses one oxygen molecule and two reducing equivalents; thus, the complete side-

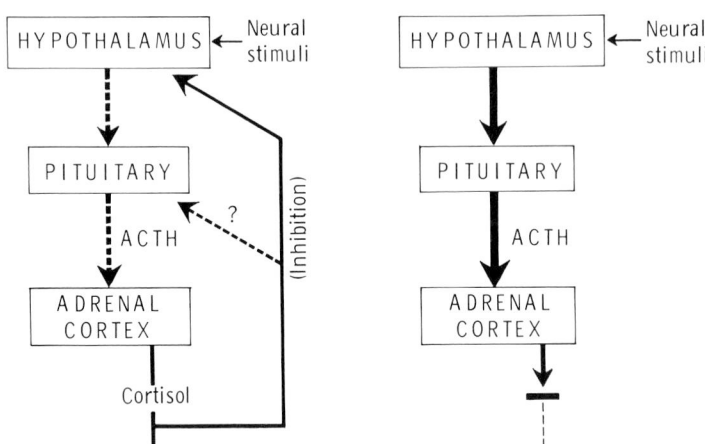

Fig. 74-2 Regulation of cortisol secretion in normal subjects and in patients with congenital adrenal hyperplasia. *(From New and Levine.[157] Used by permission.)*

chain cleavage reaction requires three molecules each of NADPH and O_2.[6]

Pregnenolone leaves the mitochondria and, in the endoplasmic reticulum, is dehydrogenated at the 3β position by 3β-hydroxysteroid dehydrogenase (3β-HSD) to yield progesterone. The enzyme 3β-HSD has a molecular weight of 46,000, is not a cytochrome P450, and requires NAD^+ as a cofactor.[7]

Most progesterone produced in the zona fasciculata is hydroxylated at the 17α position by another specific P450, P450c17, a microsomal enzyme (i.e., one located in the endoplasmic reticulum), to form 17α-hydroxyprogesterone. For each hydroxylation, this enzyme accepts two reducing equivalents directly from an NADPH-dependent cytochrome reductase. P450c17 also acts as a 17,20 lyase to cleave the 17,20 carbon-carbon bond, converting 17α-hydroxyprogesterone to the androgen Δ^4-androstenedione.[8] 17,20-Lyase activity is not normally important in the adrenal gland (the same pathway, however, is required for testosterone synthesis in the testis,[9] but when concentrations of substrate are excessive, as occurs in several of the forms of CAH, the resulting production of adrenal androgens can be physiologically significant.

Next, 17α-hydroxyprogesterone is hydroxylated at the 21 position by another microsomal cytochrome P450, P450c21, which utilizes the same reductase as P450c17, producing the steroid 11-deoxycortisol (compound S).[10] 11-Deoxycortisol is transported back to the mitochondrial inner membrane, where a fourth P450 enzyme (P450c11) hydroxylates it to finally yield cortisol. P450c11 utilizes adrenodoxin and adrenodoxin reductase as does P450scc.[11] (See the scheme of enzyme locations in Fig. 74-1.)

In addition to the short-term effects of ACTH (minutes to hours) on the activities of cholesteryl ester hydrolase and P450scc, longer stimulation with ACTH results in augmented synthesis of all four P450 enzymes involved in cortisol synthesis as well as in increases in adrenodoxin reductase and adrenodoxin.[5b] These changes result from increased transcription of the genes encoding these enzymes (i.e., elevated levels of the corresponding messenger RNAs),[12–14] an effect of ACTH that appears to be mediated by a labile protein factor (steroid hydroxylase inducer protein, SHIP) that has not as yet been isolated.

The mineralocorticoid hormone aldosterone is synthesized in the zona glomerulosa of the adrenal cortex under the control of the renin-angiotensin system.[15] Angiotensin II acts via a specific receptor which uses protein kinase C as a second messenger. Because they are regulated differently, it is useful to consider the zona glomerulosa and the zona fasciculata as distinct glands.[16] The biosynthetic pathway for aldosterone is similar to that for cortisol, except that 17α-hydroxylase is not active in the zona glomerulosa. Thus, cholesterol is cleaved to pregnenolone, which is dehydrogenated to progesterone, which is successively hydroxylated at the 21, 11β, and 18 positions to produce (respectively) deoxycorticosterone, corticosterone, and 18-hydroxycorticosterone. These reactions utilize the same enzymes as those involved in cortisol biosynthesis; in fact, this 17-deoxy pathway also exists in the zona fasciculata, although its magnitude is small compared with the 17-hydroxy pathway leading to cortisol. The 18-hydroxylation step (corticosterone methyl oxidase type I activity) occurs in mitochondria and utilizes P450c11; thus, this P450 enzyme is able to catalyze the production of both 11β- and 18-hydroxy steroids (18-hydroxycortisol is produced in limited amounts in normal individuals but is of questionable physiological significance).[17]

The final step in aldosterone synthesis is a further oxidation of the 18-hydroxyl group to an aldehyde. This activity, which has also been called corticosterone methyl oxidase II activity, again requires P450c11. Mitochondria isolated from the zona glomerulosa have this enzyme activity, while mitochondria from the zona fasciculata do not,[18] which is consistent with the ability of the zona fasciculata to synthesize deoxycorticosterone but not aldosterone. However, P450c11 purified from bovine zona fasciculata mitochondria *does* have corticosterone methyl oxidase II activity; this implies that an as yet unidentified inhibitor of corticosterone methyl oxidase II exists in zona fasciculata mitochondria and is lost during purification of P450c11. Perhaps these variations in activity can be explained by differences in lipid composition of mitochondria in the zona fasciculata and zona glomerulosa.

Structure and Function of Cytochromes P450

Molecular genetic analysis of adrenal steroidogenesis has centered on the P450 enzymes involved in four of the five conversions required for cortisol biosynthesis. Cytochromes P450 make up a superfamily of membrane-bound heme-containing monooxygenases (oxidases and peroxidases) which metabolize a wide variety of lipophilic compounds.[19] Many P450 enzymes are found in the liver and lung, where they are inducible to

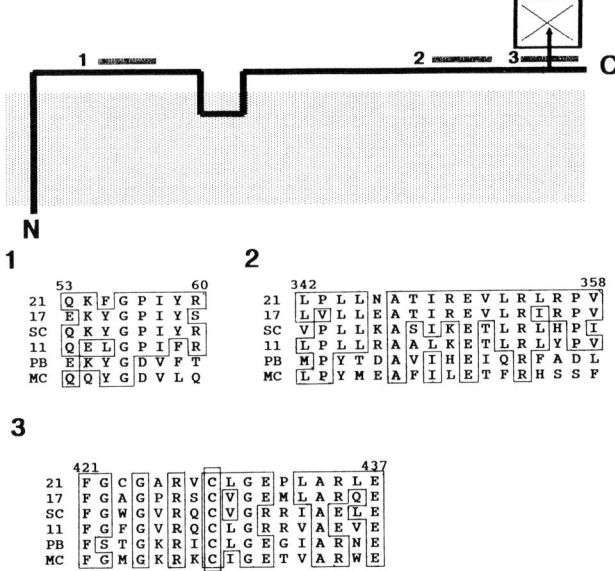

Fig. 74-3 Structural schematic of a cytochrome P450 enzyme. Amino (N) and carboxy (C) termini are marked. The heme prosthetic group is represented by the crossed square at the upper right of the figure. This protein is bound to the membrane of the endoplasmic reticulum, indicated by stippling. An amino acid terminal transmembrane segment, consisting of at least 16 hydrophobic and neutral residues, is predicted, as well as another intramembrane segment which is too short to span the membrane. Three areas of interest are marked by shaded bars and are numbered. Areas 1 and 2 are relatively well conserved among steroidogenic P450 enzymes and may be involved in substrate interactions. Area 3 interacts with the heme functional group. The amino acid sequences of these areas are shown for six cytochrome P450 enzymes: 21, human 21-hydroxylase (P450c21); 17, bovine 17α-hydroxylase (P450c17); sc, bovine cholesterol side-chain cleavage enzyme (P450scc); 11, bovine 11β-hydroxylase (P450c11); pb, a P450 induced in rat liver by phenobarbital; mc, a P450 induced in human liver by polycyclic hydrocarbons such as methylcholanthrene. Matching residues are boxed. The residues at the beginning and end of each conserved region (in P450c21) are numbered. It is proposed that the heavily boxed cysteine residue in the third conserved region coordinates with the heme iron atom. Sequences are displayed using the single-letter code for amino acids: A, alanine; C, cysteine; D, aspartic acid; E, glutamic acid; F, phenylalanine; G, glycine; H, histidine; I, isoleucine; K, lysine; L, leucine; M, methionine; N, asparagine; P, proline; Q, glutamine; R, arginine; S, serine; T, threonine; V, valine; W, tryptophan; Y, tyrosine.

high levels by xenobiotic substrates, including carcinogens and drugs such as phenobarbital. These drug-metabolizing P450s usually have broad and overlapping substrate specificities, in contrast to the adrenal P450s, which hydroxylate endogenous steroids in a relatively specific manner. In view of the lack of absolute specificity of most P450s, it is not surprising that P450scc (20S-hydroxylase/22R-hydroxylase/20,22-lyase), P450c17 (17α-hydroxylase/17,20-lyase), and P450c11 (11β-hydroxylase/18-hydroxylase/corticosterone methyl oxidase type II, or CMO II) all exhibit multiple enzymatic activities.

All P450s have molecular weights of about 50,000 and have certain structural features in common (Fig. 74-3). These include a relatively high degree of conservation of hydrophobic residues and a conserved "heme-binding" peptide near the carboxyl terminus containing a cysteine residue that coordinates with the iron atom of the heme prosthetic group. Microsomal P450s have a hydrophobic "tail" at the amino terminus that anchors the enzyme in the membrane of the endoplasmic reticulum. Mitochondrial P450s (which are encoded by nuclear genes) have a signal sequence at the amino terminus to direct transport of the newly synthesized protein to the mitochondrial inner membrane, after which the signal sequence is cleaved.

Otherwise, there is remarkably poor homology between different families of P450 enzymes, with about 25 percent overall amino acid sequence conservation. The genes encoding different P450 families are likewise so poorly conserved that cross-hybridization between different P450 genes is often not observed. This has increased considerably the effort required to isolate cDNA clones encoding the different adrenal P450 enzymes.

Nevertheless, bovine and human cDNA clones encoding all four adrenal P450s have been isolated.[14,20-25] Forty percent of the amino acid residues of P450scc[20,21] and P450c11[22] are identical, indicating a relatively close evolutionary relationship between these two mitochondrial enzymes. P450c21[26,27] and P450c17[14,25] are about 36 percent homologous, but less than 20 percent homologous with the mitochondrial P450s. P450c21 is about 28 percent homologous with several drug-metabolizing P450s, suggesting that during evolution the steroidogenic microsomal P450s diverged from drug-metabolizing P450s before diverging from each other.[28]

Further data on evolutionary relationships between P450 gene families has come from sequence analysis of genomic clones (prepared from chromosomal DNA instead of cDNA), which locates intervening sequences, or introns, in the genes. While the gene encoding P450c21 has nine introns,[26,27] genes encoding phenobarbital-inducible P450s have eight,[29] and genes encoding polycyclic hydrocarbon–inducible P450s have six introns (Fig. 74-4).[30] When the coding sequences of these genes are displayed in a way that optimizes the alignment of conserved amino acid residues, it is apparent that none of the introns is located in the same position in any two of the three P450 families of P450 genes. If P450 genes have descended from a common ancestor, introns must have been inserted into these genes or must have moved within them as they evolved. The mechanism by which this might have occurred is not known.

Despite the poor homology among steroidogenic P450s, two short regions in addition to the heme-binding peptide show relatively high conservation (Fig. 74-3), raising the possibility that they are involved in substrate interactions. Supporting this idea is the finding that one of these regions is well conserved among different P450 enzymes that metabolize phenobarbital. Functional studies to test this hypothesis have not yet been performed.

The genes encoding the steroidogenic P450 enzymes have been found to be located on different human chromosomes;

Fig. 74-4 Comparison of intron-exon organization of cytochrome P450 genes. The predicted amino acid sequence of human 21-hydroxylase (c21) was aligned using the program FASTP[30a] with sequences of P450 enzymes induced in rat liver by phenobarbital (pb)[29] and methylcholanthrene (mc).[30] Bars representing exons are drawn to scale (marked every 500 base pairs). The relative positions of introns are marked by vertical spaces that are not to scale. Untranslated sequences at the 5' and 3' ends of the mRNA are indicated by narrow bars and are also not to scale.

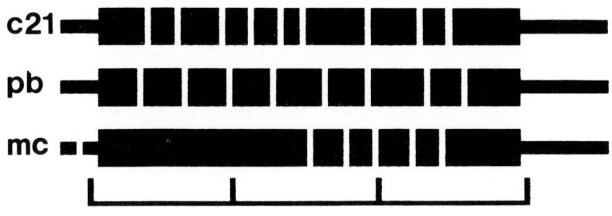

Table 74-1 The Forms of Adrenal Hyperplasia, with Clinical and Population and Molecular Genetic Aspects

Deficiency	Syndrome	Ambiguous genitalia	Postnatal virilization	Salt metabolism	Steroids increased	Steroids decreased	Enzyme
Cholesterol desmolase	Lipoid hyperplasia	Males	No	Salt wasting	None	All	P450scc
3β-OH-steroid dehydrogenase	Classic	Males	Yes	Salt wasting	DHEA, 17-OH-pregnenolone	Aldo, T, cortisol	3β-OH-steroid dehydrogenase
	Nonclassic	No	Yes	Normal	DHEA, 17-OH-pregnenolone	—	3β-OH-steroid dehydrogenase
17α-Hydroxylase	—	Males	No	Hypertension	DOC, corticosterone	Cortisol, T	P450c17
17,20-Lyase	—	Males	No	Normal	—	DHEA, T, Δ⁴-A	P450c17
21-Hydroxylase							
	Salt wasting	Females	Yes	Salt wasting	17-OHP, Δ⁴-A	Aldo, cortisol	P450c21
	Simple virilizing	Females	Yes	Normal	17-OHP, Δ⁴-A	Cortisol	P450c21
	Nonclassic	No	Yes	Normal	17-OHP, Δ⁴-A	—	P450c21
11-Hydroxylase	Classic	Females	Yes	Hypertension	DOC, 11-deoxycortisol (S)	Cortisol, ± aldo	P450c11
	Nonclassic	No	Yes	Normal	11-deoxycortisol ± DOC	—	P450c11
Corticosterone methyl oxidase type II	Salt wasting	No	No	Salt wasting	18-OH-corticosterone	Aldo	P450c11

NOTE: Aldo = aldosterone; T = testosterone; Δ⁴-A = Δ⁴-androstenedione; DHEA = dehydroepiandrosterone; DOC = (11-)deoxycorticosterone; 17-OHP = 17α-hydroxyprogesterone; ± = with or without increase (decrease) of

the gene for P450scc is on chromosome 15,[21] a gene encoding P450c17 is on chromosome 10,[25] the P450c21 genes are on chromosome 6p within the HLA major histocompatibility complex (see below),[24,31,32] and the P450c11 gene (genes?) is on chromosome 8q.[22] Thus, despite their common regulation by ACTH, there is no clustering of these genes.

It seems likely a priori that deficiencies of enzymatic activities resulting in congenital adrenal hyperplasia are caused by mutations in structural genes from the corresponding P450 enzymes. Cloned cDNAs encoding these enzymes have been used to examine patients with different enzymatic deficiencies; this hypothesis has been confirmed for 17α- and 21-hydroxylase deficiencies. The molecular genetic analysis of this disorder is discussed below.

ENZYME DEFECTS IN ADRENAL HYPERPLASIA

The following enzymatic defects of steroidogenesis and the clinical syndromes associated with each defect have been described:

Cholesterol desmolase deficiency (lipoid hyperplasia)
3β-hydroxysteroid dehydrogenase deficiency (classic and nonclassic CAH)
17α-hydroxylase deficiency
17,20-lyase deficiency
21-hydroxylase deficiency (salt-wasting, simple virilizing, and nonclassic)
11β-hydroxylase (classic CAH)
Corticosterone methyl oxidase type I and II (salt-wasting)

A summary of the clinical and biochemical features of these disorders appears in Table 74-1. It should be noted that sexual

ambiguity is not a feature of the 18-hydroxylase (corticosterone methyl oxidase type I) and the 18-dehydrogenase (corticosterone methyl oxidase type II) deficiencies, since in patients with these disorders, sex hormone secretion is normal.

Though the defects are listed above according to early or late synthesis, the more detailed description of each defect will be given in order of either frequency of the disease or new developments since the last edition of this text.

21-Hydroxylase Deficiency

Decreased cortisol synthesis owing to impaired 21 hydroxylation is the most common biochemical cause of CAH. The decreased plasma cortisol induces ACTH secretion into the blood,[33–35] causing elevated adrenal production both of cortisol and androgen precursors and of androgens, which do not require 21-hydroxylase for their biosynthesis.

Early clinical studies of patients with 21-hydroxylase deficiency showed an increased presence in the urine of pregnanetriol—the principal metabolite of 17α-hydroxyprogesterone (17α-OHP)[36]—and also of 17-oxo(keto)steroids (17-KS), which result from the metabolism of DHEA, Δ⁴-androstenedione, and testosterone.[37] More recently, radioimmunoassays for the determination of serum hormone levels have provided a simple and reliable laboratory method allowing more accurate diagnosis than could be provided by the assessment of urinary hormones.[38]

Clinical Features

CLASSIC 21-HYDROXYLASE DEFICIENCY (SIMPLE VIRILIZING). The prominent feature of 21-hydroxylase deficiency is progressive virilism with advanced somatic development. The classic disorder of the simple virilizing type is present in about one-fourth of cases. Developmental genital anomalies are manifest in females as varying degrees of genital ambiguity, which

Table 74-1 *(Continued)*

Chromosomal location	Frequency	Gene cloned
15	Rare	Yes
—	Rare	No
—	? frequent	—
10	Rare	Yes
10	Rare	Yes
6p (HLA-B40; HLA-Bw47,DR7)	1:12,000 75%	Yes —
6p (HLA-B5)	25%	—
6p (HLA-B14,DR1)	0.1-1% (3% in European Jews)	—
8q	1:100,000	Yes
8q	? frequent	—
8q	Rare (except in Iranian Jews)	—

should flag the diagnosis in the female. Because genital formation in males is normal, the syndrome often goes unrecognized in the male until signs of androgen excess such as accelerated height and precocious sexual hair appear later in childhood.

Adrenocortical cell differentiation occurs early in embryogenesis, with the formation of a provisional fetal zone, active for the remainder of gestation, that involutes after birth. Although the schedule of evolving steroid synthesis in the fetal and adult (permanent) zones has not been completely elucidated, it is clear that genital development in the fetus takes place under the influence of active adrenal steroid synthesis. Thus, in the female, the extent of masculinization of the external genitalia ranges from mild clitoral enlargement through varying degrees of fusion of the labioscrotal folds, to the profound morphological anomaly of a penile urethra (very rare).

Genetic sex and gonadal differentiation are normal in patients with CAH. Internal genital differentiation to the male pattern proceeds under the control of two hormonal factors produced in effective amounts only by the fetal testes: (1) testosterone, which directs formation of the male genital structures from the wolffian (mesonephric) ducts; and (2) a nonsteroidal factor, antimüllerian hormone (AMH),[38a] also termed müllerian-inhibiting substance or factor, which suppresses development of the müllerian ducts into the female internal structures. AMH is a glycoprotein first synthesized by differentiating Sertoli cells between weeks 6 and 7 of embryonic life,[38a] prior to the start of testosterone secretion by the Leydig cells (week 8). Since there is no anomalous secretion of AMH in females with CAH, the fallopian tubes, uterus, and upper vagina develop normally. Wolffian duct stabilization and differentiation requires the high intraluminal androgen levels provided by the male gonads; androgen elevations of adrenal origin appear not to affect this process, and there is no observable wolffian development in females suffering even the most extreme virilization from androgen excess. Thus internal genital morphogenesis is normal in both sexes.

CAH due to 21-hydroxylase deficiency is the most common

cause of ambiguous genitalia in the newborn female, and because affected females have the capacity for an entirely normal female sex role including childbearing, it is very important to recognize this disorder in newborns with ambiguous genitalia. Although the male is not jeopardized by inappropriate sex assignment, premature masculinization and accelerated physical development cause problems of adjustment. In addition, continued adrenal androgen excess in males may suppress the pituitary-gonadal axis, preventing maturation of the testes and resulting in infertility. In both sexes there is early fusion of the epiphyses with resulting short stature.

CLASSIC 21-HYDROXYLASE DEFICIENCY (SALT-LOSING). In three-fourths of patients with classic 21-hydroxylase deficiency, salt wasting occurs, as defined by hyponatremia, hyperkalemia, inappropriate natriuresis, and low serum and urinary aldosterone with concomitantly high plasma renin activity (PRA). The increase in the proportion of salt-wasting cases in recent years may be attributed in part to enhanced ascertainment because of advances in diagnostic capabilities, as well as increased survival due to the availability of exogenous mineralocorticoid supplements. Salt wasting results from inadequate secretion of salt-retaining steroids, especially aldosterone. In addition, hormonal precursors of 21-hydroxylase may act as mineralocorticoid antagonists in the marginally competent sodium-conserving mechanism of the immature newborn renal tubule.[39-42] It has been observed that a defect in aldosterone biosynthesis apparent in infancy may be ameliorated with age,[43,44] and therefore it is desirable to follow sodium and mineralocorticoid requirements carefully by measuring plasma renin activity in patients who have been labeled neonatally as salt wasters.

Although it has been claimed that salt wasting correlates with severe virilism,[45] it is important to recognize that the extent of virilism may be the same in simple virilizing and salt-wasting CAH. Thus even a mildly virilized newborn with 21-hydroxylase deficiency should be observed carefully for signs of a potentially life-threatening crisis within the first few weeks of life. In the publication most frequently quoted to demonstrate that severe 21-hydroxylase deficiency and hence salt wasting are correlated with the degree of masculinization, the patient described was no longer a salt waster by 4 years of age.[46]

With few exceptions,[47] the literature until recently has indicated that the type of 21-hydroxylase deficiency, i.e., simple virilizing versus salt wasting, breeds true within a family and subsequently affected offspring are predicted to have the same form of the disease as the proband. Recently, however, several families with HLA-identical sibs discordant for salt wasting have been reported.[43] Investigation of these families (in which separate HLA allelic and haplotypic associations were noted) revealed: (1) that under stress of a low sodium diet, no differences in sodium, aldosterone, or renin levels were noted between obligate heterozygote parents of salt-wasting patients and simple virilizing patients and (2) that HLA-identical siblings may exhibit discordance for salt wasting *and* for aldosterone synthesizing capability.

Screening. The incidence of classic CAH due to 21-hydroxylase deficiency based on retrospective case surveys has been reported by several investigators since the late 1950s and has varied from 1 in 490 to 1 in 67,000 live births (Table 74-2).[48-63] The reports of the last 2 decades based on case surveys from Switzerland,[52,53,59] Austria,[58] Germany,[55] Birmingham in En-

Table 74-2 Incidence of Classic CAH by Case Survey

Geographic area	Population	Incidence	Reference	Year
Alaska, U.S.A.	Yupik Eskimo	1:490	50	1969
Alaska, U.S.A.	Native Alaskan	1:1481	50	1969
Zurich, Switzerland	Caucasoid	1:5041	52	1958
Birmingham, U.K.	Caucasoid	1:7255	54	1966
Tyrol, Austria	Caucasoid	1:8991	58	1979
Munich, W.Ger	Caucasoid	1:9831	55	1977
Wisconsin, U.S.A.	Heterogeneous*	1:15,000	56	1966
Switzerland	Caucasoid	1:15,472	59	1980
Switzerland	Caucasoid	1:18,445	52	1958
Scotland	Caucasoid	1:20,907	60	1986
France	Caucasoid	1:23,000	57	1985
Toronto, Canada	Heterogeneous*	1:26,292	51	1972
U.S.A.	Heterogeneous	1:40,000	49, 63	1962, 1965
Japan	East Asian	1:43,764	61	1981
U.S.A.	Heterogeneous	1:67,000	48	1956

*Majority white.
NOTE: Average incidence worldwide (excluding Alaska): 1 in 23,147 live
births.

gland,[54] and Scotland[60] indicate that CAH due to 21-hydroxylase deficiency in these populations occurs in 1 out of 7215 to 1 out of 20,907 live births[52–55,58,59] while the incidence in two regions in North America was reported to be 1 out of 15,000 to 1 out of 26,292 live births.[49,51,56,63] The incidence of 21-hydroxylase deficiency by case survey in Japan was recently reported to be 1 in 43,674.[61] The highest incidence of 21-hydroxylase deficiency by case survey, however, was provisionally reported in the Alaskan Eskimos.[50]

A reliable and valid screening test for 21-hydroxylase deficiency, using a heel-prick capillary blood specimen spotted onto filter paper, first became available in 1977.[64] A pilot newborn screening program among the Alaskan Yupik Eskimos at high risk for 21-hydroxylase deficiency first demonstrated the feasibility of an effective newborn screening program. The direct benefit of this program—avoidance of adrenal crisis, shock and its sequelae, and death—prompted further development of newborn screening programs for 21-hydroxylase deficiency in various nations.[62,66–73]

During the period 1978–1988, 13 newborn screening programs for 21-hydroxylase deficiency were established in six countries worldwide.[80] These included two regional screening programs (Lyons and Lille; La Réunion) in France,[62] two regional screening programs (Emilia-Romagna and Rome) in Italy,[67,68] four regional screening programs (Sapporo, Tokyo, Kanagawa, and Shizuoka) in Japan,[69,73] national screening programs in New Zealand[71] and Scotland,[70] and in the United States the pilot program in Alaska and two regional screening programs (Washington state, Illinois).[65,66,72]

In all these screening programs for 21-hydroxylase deficiency, a blood specimen (spotted onto a ½″ filter paper disk) was obtained at the time of blood sample collection for phenylketonuria and congenital hypothyroidism screening. Blood sample collection (obtained by heel prick) for the majority of newborns was on the third day of life in all programs with the exception of the Scottish and French programs, in which collection was specified for the fifth day. In all screening programs, the newborns identified by the screening as being affected were assumed to have the salt-wasting form of 21-hydroxylase deficiency if there was clinical and biochemical evidence of salt wasting with serum $[Na^+] < 130$ meq/liter in association with hyperkalemia (serum $[K^+] > 6.5$ meq/liter) and acidosis (serum $[HCO_3^-] < 17$ meq/liter) or based on the reports. The affected newborns who had no clinical or biochemical evidence of salt wasting were presumed to have simple virilizing 21-hydroxylase deficiency.

INCIDENCE OF CLASSIC CAH DUE TO 21-HYDROXYLASE DEFICIENCY ACCORDING TO SCREENING COMPARED WITH THE INCIDENCE REPORTED BY CASE SURVEY. The highest incidences for 21-hydroxylase deficiency uncovered by screening were reported for two relatively isolated populations: the Yupik-speaking Eskimos of southwestern Alaska and the island inhabitants of La Réunion (France) in the Indian Ocean. The three next highest incidences were reported from the studies conducted in Rome, in France, and in Illinois. The incidences of 21-hydroxylase deficiency found by screening in the Emilia-Romagna region in Italy, in Japan, New Zealand, and Scot-

Table 74-3 Incidence of Classic CAH Found in Screening and Its Comparison with Incidence Reported by Case Survey

Geographic area	Population	Screening (1978–1986)			Case survey (1965–1985)	
		No. tested	Incidence	Reference	Incidence	Reference
Alaska, U.S.A.	Yupik Eskimo	1131	1:282*	65	1:490*	50
		2737	1:684	66		
La Réunion, France	Heterogeneous	9964	1:2141	62	—	—
Rome, Italy	Caucasoid	22,400	1:5580	68	—	—
Emilia-Romagna, Italy	Caucasoid	73,000	1:10,428†	67	—	—
France	Caucasoid	173,662	1:12,000†	62	1:23,000	57
Illinois, U.S.A.	Heterogeneous	120,000	1:13,333	80	—	—
Japan	East Asian	253,494	1:15,800	69	1:43,674	61
		89,291	1:12,756	73		
New Zealand	Heterogeneous	97,552	1:19,500	71	—	—
Scotland	Caucasoid	119,690	1:17,098	70	1:20,907	60
Washington State, U.S.A.	Heterogeneous	142,122	1:17,765	72a	—	—
Wisconsin, U.S.A.	Heterogeneous	—	—	—	1:15,000	56
Baltimore, Maryland, U.S.A.	Heterogeneous	—	—	—	1:40,000	63
Toronto, Canada	Heterogeneous	—	—	—	1:26,792	51

*Salt-wasting form only.
†Average incidence in Mediterranean Europeans 1 in 9000 live births.

Table 74-4 Worldwide Incidence of Classic 21-Hydroxylase Deficiency CAH Salt-Wasting and Simple Virilizing Forms, Excluding Alaska and La Réunion

Total number of newborns screened	Total number of affected newborns	Incidence		
		Ratio of homozygous affected to live births (based on screening)	Ratio of heterozygote live births	Gene frequency, $\times\ 10^{-3}$
			(Both calculated using Hardy-Weinberg equation)	
All populations: 1,135,232	78	1:14,554 (1:11,203–1:19,318)	1:61 (1:53–1:70)	8.3 (7.2–9.4)
Salt-wasting type	60	1:18,921 (1:14,565–1:25,114)	1:69 (1:61–1:80)	7.3 (6.3–8.3
Simple virilizing type	18	1:63,068 (1:39,903–1:106,395)	1:126 (1:100–1:164)	4.0 (3.1–5.0)
White populations only: 806,710	59	1:13,673 (1:10,526–1:18,148)	1:59 (1:52–1:68)	8.6 (7.4–9.7)

*Lower and upper 95% confidence limits.

land were next in frequency of occurrence, and the lowest incidence was reported from Washington state (Table 74-3). As predicted, results from screening yielded a higher frequency of disease than did case surveys (Table 74-3).

WORLDWIDE INCIDENCE OF BOTH SALT-WASTING AND SIMPLE VIRILIZING FORMS OF CLASSIC CAH DUE TO 21-HYDROXYLASE DEFICIENCY FOUND BY SCREENING, EXCLUDING ALASKA AND LA RÉUNION (TABLE 74-4). For the estimation of worldwide incidence of 21-hydroxylase deficiency, the data from the two high-frequency populations were excluded. A total of 1,135,232 newborns were screened in six countries during the period 1978–1988, and 78 newborns were proved to be affected with either the salt-wasting or the simple virilizing form of classic 21-hydroxylase deficiency after identification by screening test.[80] The worldwide incidence of 21-hydroxylase deficiency uncovered by screening was estimated to be 1 in 1:14,554 live births for the homozygote. Using the Hardy-Weinberg equation,[74] the corresponding heterozygote (carrier) frequency was calculated to be 1 in 61, and the gene frequency was calculated to be 0.0082.

In the white population, the worldwide incidence of homozygous patients with 21-hydroxylase deficiency found by screening was 1 in 13,673. Heterozygote frequency and gene frequency were calculated to be 1 in 59 and 0.0085 respectively.

The worldwide incidence of salt-wasting 21-hydroxylase deficiency according to screening of Caucasoid and East Asian populations was estimated to be 1 in 18,921 live births, while incidence of simple virilizing 21-hydroxylase deficiency was 1 in 63,068 live births.[80]

RATIO OF SALT-WASTING TO SIMPLE VIRILIZING 21-HYDROXYLASE DEFICIENCY FOUND WITH AND WITHOUT SCREENING. Of the newborns screened, 77 percent had CAH of the salt-wasting type and 23 percent, of the simple virilizing type.[80] The earliest reports (by case survey) of the relative frequency of the two forms indicated that salt wasting occurred either less commonly than or with a frequency equal to that of simple viril-

izing 21-hydroxylase deficiency.[53,75–78] A more recent case survey study by Fife and Rappaport[79] reported an increased relative frequency for salt wasting, 50 to 66 percent. The suggestion that this observed change is attributable to improved case detection and survival of salt wasters is supported by the most recent data reported here; screening programs for 21-hydroxylase deficiency indicate that the salt-wasting form is fully three times more common at birth than the simple virilizing form (Table 74-5).

CLINICAL PRESENTATION AND AGE OF AFFECTED NEWBORNS AT TIME OF DIAGNOSIS BY NEWBORN SCREENING PROGRAMS. In three screening programs for 21-hydroxylase deficiency, none of the affected newborns with either salt-wasting or simple virilizing CAH had clinical evidence of either mineralocorticoid or glucocorticoid hormone deficiency (such as vomiting, dehydration, poor feeding, or lethargy) at the time of medical evaluation for confirmation of the diagnosis by screening.[65,67,72] In two of these programs, the affected newborns were from 5 to 12 days of age at diagnosis.[65,72] In another screening program, affected newborns had mild symptoms,

Table 74-5 Prevalence of Salt-Wasting and Simple Virilizing Forms of CAH Found by Screening in Comparison with Determination by Case Survey

Report	Reference	Salt-wasting, %	Simple virilizing, %
Earlier reports (1962–1980)			
Prader et al.	53		
Raiti et al.	75	33	76
Kowarski	76		
Migeon	77		
Bondy	78	50	50
Later reports (1983)			
Fife and Rappaport	79	66	34
Newborn screening (1988)			
Pang et al.	80	77	23

giving evidence of glucocorticoid and mineralocorticoid deficiency in only one-third of identified cases.[69]

All affected genetic female newborns (43 of the 88 cases identified in total) were found to have some degree of sexual ambiguity at the time of medical evaluation after identification by the screening test. At least four female newborns were given a male sex assignment at birth, and thus screening resulted in immediate reversal and correction of the sex assignment.[65,72] Despite sexual ambiguity, one-third to one-half of the affected female newborns were not diagnosed to have CAH until identification of 21-hydroxylase deficiency by the screening test, thus clearly demonstrating the value of screening in females as well as males.[80]

HLA and 21-Hydroxylase Deficiency. The HLA genetic region is located on the short arm of chromosome 6 and contains the genes encoding the human major histocompatibility complex (MHC). The HLA antigens are the major barriers for allogenic transplantation, but the HLA genetic region also contains a number of additional genes with functions unrelated to histocompatibility and immune responses. Classical genetic analyses of pedigrees have demonstrated that the HLA complex spans a recombinative distance of approximately 3 cM (centimorgans).[81] Molecular genetic analysis of the HLA genetic region has resulted in the isolation and characterization of all of the prototype genes[82–84] and, more recently, further nonexpressed genes and genes encoding secondary products within this region. The entire HLA region is now estimated to contain about 50 genes within a physical length of 3500 kb.[84a]

The HLA class I region, a genetic segment about 1000 kb in length, contains approximately 20 class I genes, of which HLA-A, -B, and -C are the classic class I genes, the products of which are expressed by most somatic cell types. The other class I–like genes located within the HLA complex are still puzzling; some are pseudogenes, while recent evidence suggests that others may be expressed.[84b,84c]

The HLA-D region (class II) corresponds to a segment 800 to 1000 kb in length.[85] Genomic cloning has led to the identification of as many as 15 different class II genes per HLA haplotype. Cloning from cDNA libraries has identified seven expressed genes per haplotype: one DR-α and two DR-β genes, one DQ-α and one DQ-β gene, and one DP-α and one DP-β gene. RNA has also been found in some cell lines for the DO-β and DZ-α genes. Recent analysis with allele-specific oligonucleotides (oligotyping) for class II antigens indicates greater allelic variability than shown by standard serologic typing.[85a]

Between the class I and class II regions is the class III region, which contains the genes encoding the second and fourth components of serum complement (C2, and C4A and C4B) and properdin factor B (Bf), as well as the genes for adrenal steroid 21-hydroxylase.[84] The relative position of the C2, the Bf, and the tandemly duplicated C4 and 21-hydroxylase genes (see "Molecular Genetics," below) has been known for some time; the orientation of the class III segment on the chromosome is the opposite of that formerly supposed and has only recently been established in large-scale genomic maps for mouse[85b] and human[84a,85c] constructed using pulsed field gradient gel electrophoresis. Also recently, the two genes encoding tumor necrosis factor (TNF-α, or cachectin; and TNF-β, or lymphotoxin) have been mapped to the MHC class III region in both mouse[86] and human.[87]

21-Hydroxylase deficiency is inherited as a monogenic autosomal recessive trait closely linked to the HLA complex.[88,89] Thus, a proband sharing both HLA haplotypes with an index case (a living, affected sib) is predicted to be affected with 21-hydroxylase deficiency, one who shares a single haplotype is predicted to be a heterozygote, and one who shares no HLA haplotype is predicted to be unaffected.[88,89]

HLA LINKAGE WITH 21-HYDROXYLASE DEFICIENCY. Linkage between HLA and the 21-hydroxylase gene was first shown by Dupont et al.[88] in a study on six families; the total maximum Lod score was 3.394, obtained for the recombinant fraction θ = 0.00. In humans, linkage is considered to be established when the Lod score is greater than 3.00. Reports from other groups soon after confirmed 21-hydroxylase linkage with HLA (reviewed in Ref. 90).

A study of persons with intra-HLA recombinations suggested that the locus for 21-hydroxylase is situated between HLA-B and HLA-D, within the class III region (Fig. 74-5).[91]

Fig. 74-5 Schematic of gene organization within HLA, the human major histocompatibility complex. Order and spacing determined from restriction map prepared from results of pulsed field gel electrophoresis and Southern blot analysis using five different restriction endonucleases (*Not*I, *Nru*I, *Mlu*I, *Sal*I, and *Bss*HI) and seventeen DNA probes (eleven cDNA probes and six genomic DNA probes); sites not shown. (Pulse frequency 1/60 to 1/30 s^{-1}. Limit of resolution: 50-kb fragments.) (*After Carroll et al.*[84a])

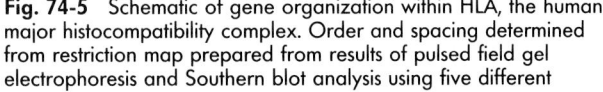
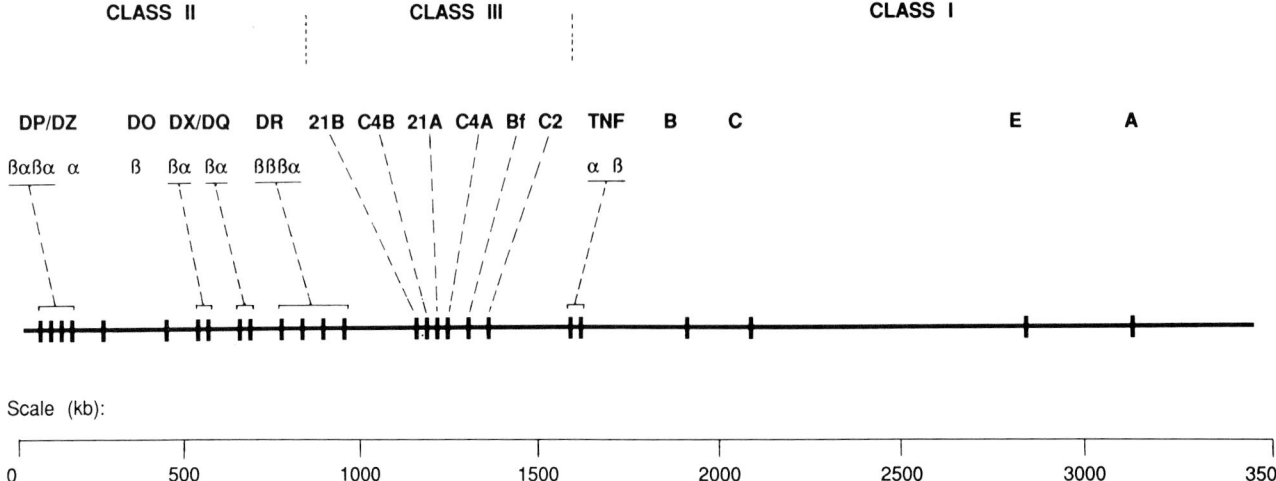

While this location has now been firmly established from the molecular genetic studies, a very recent classical genetic study has endeavored to determine the arrangement and relative proximity of the B, DR, and 21-hydroxylase loci on the basis of observed recombinations within this small genetic interval.[91a]

In addition to being linked to HLA, 21-hydroxylase deficiency is often found in association with specific HLA antigens or combinations of antigens, referred to as *haplotypes*. These haplotypes include specific alleles of the HLA-linked complement components.[92–96] Salt-wasting 21-hydroxylase deficiency is associated with HLA-Bw60 and with the extended haplotype HLA-A3,Bw47,DR7. This haplotype includes a null allele at the C4B locus encoding the fourth component of complement. Simple virilizing disease is associated with HLA-Bw51 in selected ethnic groups, and nonclassic disease with HLA-B14,DR1 in all ethnic groups examined except the Yugoslavs. This latter haplotype includes a duplicated C4 locus.[97] Figure 74-6 depicts two pedigrees exhibiting these haplotypic associations. Another extended haplotype, HLA-A1,B8,DR3, is negatively associated with 21-hydroxylase deficiency and carries a null allele at C4A.

Nonclassic Deficiency and Population Genetics

NONCLASSIC 21-HYDROXYLASE DEFICIENCY. An attenuated, late-onset form of adrenal hyperplasia was first suspected in the early 1950s by gynecologists in clinical practice who used glucocorticoids for the treatment of women with physical signs of hyperandrogenism, including infertility.[98,99] The first documentation of suppression of 21-hydroxylase precursors in the urine of such women after glucocorticoid therapy was by Baulieu and coworkers in 1957.[100] During the next 2 decades, the empirical use of glucocorticoids for the treatment of virilized women became commonplace, as it was assumed that adrenal androgens were often elevated in those patients. The diagnosis of a 21-hydroxylase defect by serum assay was made possible in the early 1970s, when a radioimmunoassay for 17-OHP, the direct precursor of the enzyme in the adrenal zona fasciculata, was developed.[101] The initial finding of family members with elevated serum concentrations of 17α-hydroxyprogesterone led to the speculation that these individuals were "expressing heterozygotes" of the gene for severe 21-hydroxylase deficiency.[102,103] Subsequently, with use of the 17-OHP radioimmunoassay, the autosomal recessive mode of genetic transmission of the nonclassic form of 21-hydroxylase deficiency became apparent through family studies of classic 21-hydroxylase deficiency.[104–106] The establishment of linkage to HLA[107–108] confirmed the existence of this disorder as an allele of classic 21-hydroxylase deficiency.[104,109] The HLA associations for nonclassic 21-hydroxylase deficiency[107,110,111] are distinct from those found in classic 21-hydroxylase deficiency and differ according to ethnicity.[108,112]

Clinical symptomatology of nonclassic 21-hydroxylase deficiency is variable, and symptoms may appear at any age. A subset of individuals with nonclassic 21-hydroxylase deficiency are overtly asymptomatic when the condition is detected (usually as part of a family study), but it is thought, on the basis of longitudinal follow-up of such patients, that symptoms of hyperandrogenism may wax and wane with time.

Nonclassic 21-hydroxylase deficiency can result in premature development of pubic hair in children; to our knowledge, the youngest such patient was noted to have pubic hair at 5 months of age.[105] In a review of 23 patients presenting to The New York Hospital–Cornell Medical Center for evaluation of premature pubarche, 7 children demonstrated a 17-OHP response to ACTH stimulation consistent with the diagnosis of nonclassic 21-hydroxylase deficiency, a prevalence of 30 percent in this preselected group of pediatric patients at high risk.[113] Other investigators found only 1 of 15 children with premature adrenarche demonstrating an ACTH-stimulated 17-OHP response greater than that of obligate heterozygote carriers of the 21-hydroxylase deficiency gene.[114] Elevated adrenal androgens promote the early fusion of epiphyseal growth plates, and it is commonly found that children with the disorder have advanced bone age and accelerated linear growth velocity and are ultimately shorter than the height which might be predicted on the basis of mid-parental height.

Severe cystic acne refractory to oral antibiotics and retinoic acid has been attributed to nonclassic 21-hydroxylase deficiency. In one study of 31 young female patients with acne and/or hirsutism tested with low-dose ACTH stimulation after overnight dexamethasone suppression, no cases of 21-hydroxylase deficiency were found.[115] In another study comparing the responses of 11 female patients with acne and 8 (female) control subjects to a 24-h infusion of ACTH, elevated urinary excretion of pregnanetriol in 6 patients was suggestive of a partial 21-hydroxylase deficiency.[116]

Additionally, male pattern baldness in young women with this disorder has been noted as the sole presenting symptom. Menarche may be normal or delayed, and secondary amenorrhea is a frequent occurrence. The syndrome of polycystic ovarian disease includes a subgroup of women with nonclassic 21-hydroxylase deficiency. The pathophysiology of this phenomenon probably relates to adrenal sex-steroid excess disrupting the usual cyclicity of gonadotropin release and/or the direct effects of adrenal androgens upon the ovary, leading ultimately to the formation of ovarian cysts, which may then autonomously produce androgens.

Retrospective analysis of the etiologies of hirsutism and oligomenorrhea revealed that 18 of 108 (14 percent) of women presenting to this institution for endocrinologic evaluation of these complaints had nonclassic 21-hydroxylase deficiency.[117] In other published series the prevalence of nonclassic 21-hydroxylase deficiency in hirsute, oligomenorrheic women ranges from 1.2 to 30 percent.[118–124] The disparity in frequency of nonclassic 21-hydroxylase deficiency reported by different authors may be attributed to differences in the ethnic groups studied, since the disease frequency is ethnospecific.

Although the androgen profile in serum and urine in both the basal and ACTH-stimulated states may not be markedly different from that demonstrated by women with the syndrome of polycystic ovaries, the response of 17-OHP to ACTH clearly differentiates the patients with an adrenal 21-hydroxylase defect.[117] In six women with nonclassic 21-hydroxylase deficiency who underwent sonographic or laparoscopic visualization of the ovaries, four had polycystic ovaries.[117] Thus even sonograms of the ovary do not distinguish women with excess androgens due to polycystic ovarian disease from those with nonclassic 21-hydroxylase deficiency. ACTH tests are required for the differential diagnosis (see below). The response of the hypothalamic-pituitary-gonadal axis to LHRH has been observed to be variably abnormal in virilized women with nonclassic 21-hydroxylase deficiency.[125,126] Similarly, ACTH tests are necessary to differentiate polycystic

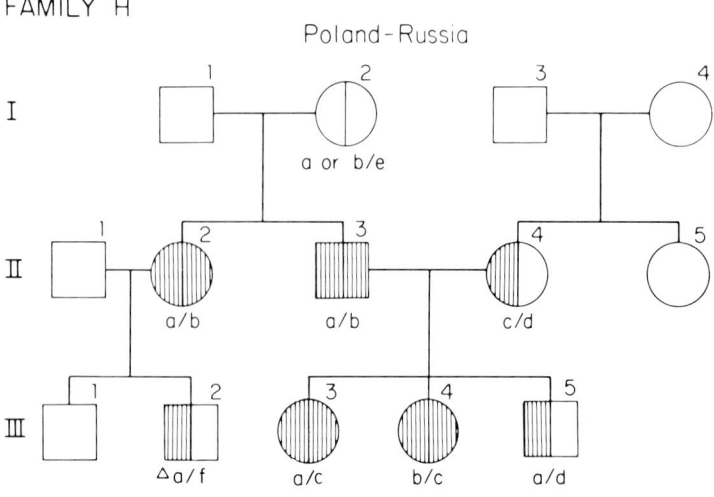

FAMILY H

a) Aw24, B14(w6), Cw2, DR1
b) Aw24, B14(w6), C-, DR1
c) A2, B14(w6), C-, DR1
d) A1, B37(w4), Cw6, DR5
e) Aw33, B14(w6), DR1
f) A1, Bw53(w4), Cw4, DR5

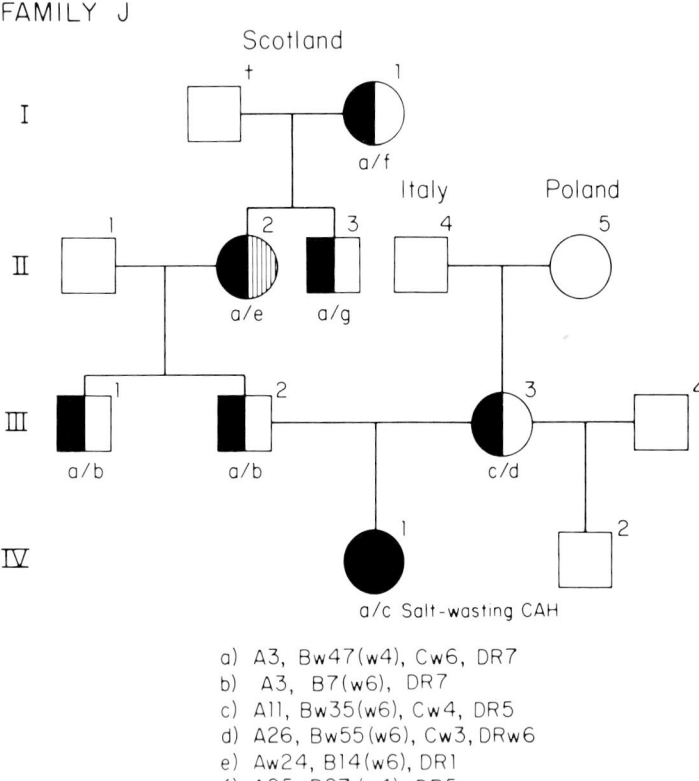

FAMILY J

a) A3, Bw47(w4), Cw6, DR7
b) A3, B7(w6), DR7
c) A11, Bw35(w6), Cw4, DR5
d) A26, Bw55(w6), Cw3, DRw6
e) Aw24, B14(w6), DR1
f) A25, B27 (w4), DR5
g) A2, B8(w6), DR3

Fig. 74-6 Pedigrees of families H and J with nonclassic symptomatic adrenal hyperplasia. ● = Infant with classic 21-hydroxylase deficiency; ◐◻ = heterozygous carriers of the severe deficiency gene for CAH; ◑ = patient with nonclassic adrenal hyperplasia having both a gene for severe 21-hydroxylase deficiency (classic) and a gene for mild deficiency (nonclassic). *(Adapted from Kohn et al.,[105] by permission.)*

ovarian disease from nonclassic 21-hydroxylase deficiency after LHRH testing of pituitary gonadotropin secretion.

Treatment with glucocorticoids is effective in suppressing adrenal androgen production, and with time, clinical signs of androgen excess show improvement. Given the 9-month life expectancy of established hair follicles, remission of hirsutism generally takes at least 1 to 2 years. Since the presumptive identification of the first nonclassic patients some 30 years ago,

it has been recognized that infertility in women may be reversed during glucocorticoid therapy.[98–100,127] An exact timetable to regression of each clinical sign has yet to be established, but Riddick and Hammond[128] reported that five patients with postmenarchal onset of 21-hydroxylase deficiency resumed regular menses and demonstrated adequate suppression of 17-ketosteroids and pregnanetriol within 2 months after beginning therapy with glucocorticoids alone.

Birnbaum and Rose[127] found that of 18 infertile women with acne and/or facial hirsutism and hormonal criteria consistent with 21-hydroxylase deficiency, five conceived after 2 months and one after 7 months of prednisone treatment alone; four more women conceived within 2 months of the addition of clomiphene to the therapeutic regimen. Hormonal profiles after initiation of therapy were not reported in this study.

In boys, early beard growth, acne, and growth spurt may be detected. A highly reliable constellation of physical signs of adrenal (as opposed to testicular) androgen excess in boys is the presence of pubic hair, enlarged phallus, and relatively small testes. In men, signs of androgen excess are difficult to appreciate, and may theoretically be manifest only by adrenal sex steroid–induced suppression of the hypothalamic-pituitary-gonadal axis, resulting in diminished fertility.

Oligospermia and subfertility have been reported in men with nonclassic 21-hydroxylase deficiency,[129,130] and reversal of infertility with glucocorticoid treatment in two men.[130,131] In the only published study of response to ACTH stimulation in a population of men with infertility and idiopathic oligospermia, none of the 50 subjects tested by Ojeifo and colleagues demonstrated a 17-OHP response consistent with the diagnosis of nonclassic 21-hydroxylase deficiency.[132] It is again conceivable that variations in reported disease frequency when small populations are studied are attributable to sampling error in this disorder which is more prevalent in selected ethnic groups.

HORMONAL STANDARDS FOR GENOTYPING 21-HYDROXYLASE DEFICIENCY. In our experience, an ACTH (Cortosyn, 0.25 mg) stimulation test measuring the serum concentration of 17-OHP at 0 and 60 min after intravenous bolus ACTH administration has proved to be the best test for genotyping for 21-hydroxylase deficiency.[136] The nomogram in Fig. 74-7 provides hormonal standards for assignment of the 21-hydroxylase genotype; i.e., patients whose hormonal values fall on the regression line within a defined group are assigned to that group. Because of diurnal variation of 17-OHP, an early-morning serum concentration of 17-OHP may be useful as a screening test for genotyping 21-hydroxylase deficiency; but ACTH stimulation is the most definitive diagnostic test.[124,133,134] A glossary of terms to describe allelic variants of 21-hydroxylase deficiency according to symptoms, hormonal findings, and predicted genotype has been reported (Table 74-6).

Pedigree analysis in families with classic 21-hydroxylase deficiency has permitted identification of members with nonclassic 21-hydroxylase deficiency who are compound heterozy-

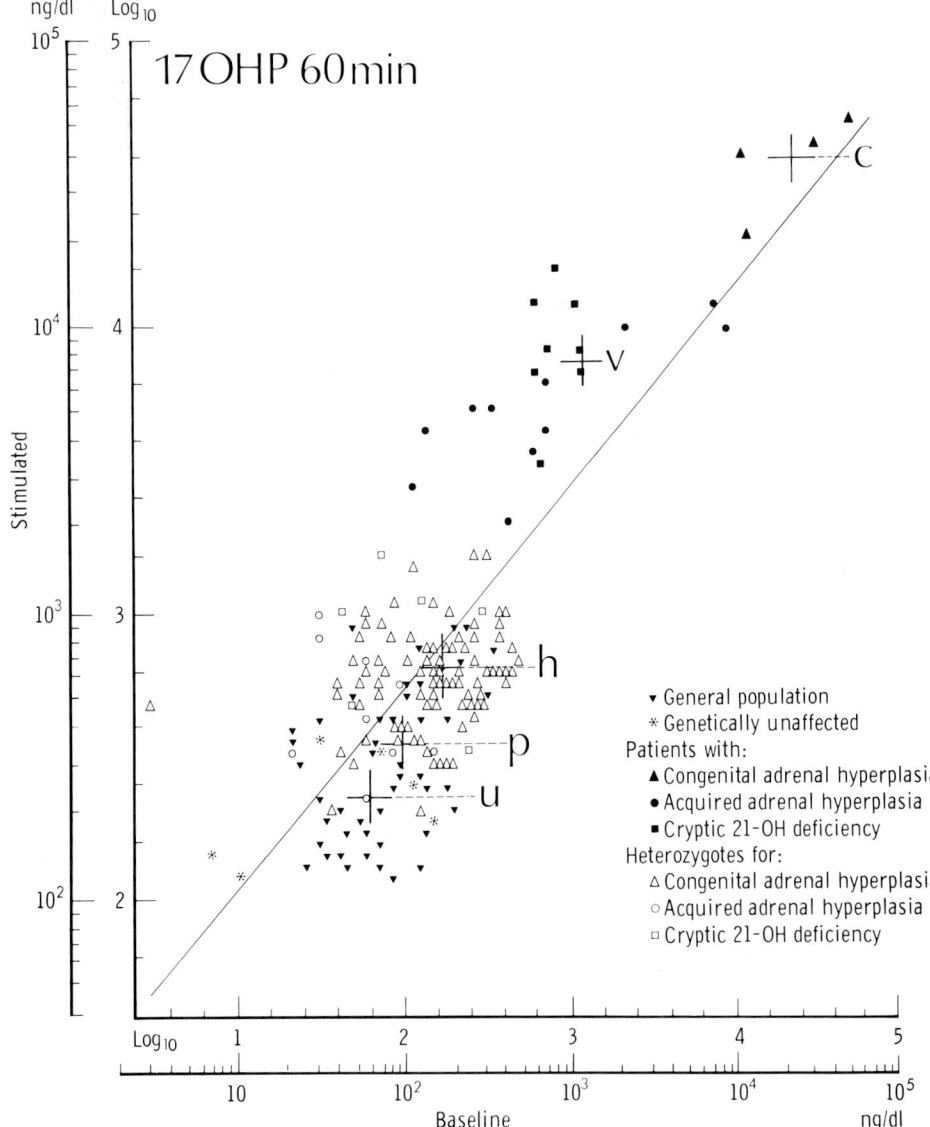

Fig. 74-7 Nomogram relating baseline to ACTH-stimulated serum concentrations of 17-OHP. Scales are logarithmic. A regression line for all data points is shown. The mean for each group is indicated by a large cross and adjacent letter: c = classic 21-hydroxylase deficiency; v = variant or nonclassic 21-hydroxylase deficiency (combined mean of values in patients with cryptic and late-onset disease); h = heterozygotes for all forms of 21-hydroxylase deficiency; p = general population; and u = unknown unaffected persons (e.g., siblings of patients with 21-hydroxylase deficiency who carry neither affected parental haplotype as determined by HLA typing); OH = hydroxyl. (*From New et al.*[136])

Table 74-6 Genotypic Characterization of the Forms of 21-Hydroxylase Deficiency

Form of 21-hydroxylase deficiency	Clinical phenotype	Hormonal phenotype (in response to ACTH)	Genotype
Classic	Prenatal virilization, fully symptomatic	Marked elevation of precursors (serum 17-OHP and Δ^4-A)	$\dfrac{\text{21-OH-def}^{\text{severe}}}{\text{21-OH-def}^{\text{severe}}}$
Nonclassic	Symptomatic: later development of virilization; milder symptoms Asymptomatic: no virilization or other symptoms	Moderate elevation of precursors	$\dfrac{\text{21-OH-def}^{\text{severe}}}{\text{21-OH-def}^{\text{mild}}}$ $\dfrac{\text{21-OH-def}^{\text{mild}}}{\text{21-OH-def}^{\text{mild}}}$
Carrier	Asymptomatic	Precursor level greater than normal	$\dfrac{\text{21-OH-def}^{\text{severe}}}{\text{21-OHase (normal)}}$ $\dfrac{\text{21-OH-def}^{\text{mild}}}{\text{21-OHase (normal)}}$
Normal	(Asymptomatic)	Lowest levels—some overlap seen with carriers	$\dfrac{\text{21-OHase (normal)}}{\text{21-OHase (normal)}}$

gotes. These individuals have inherited from one parent an allele for severe 21-hydroxylase deficiency (shared with the index case, 21-OH-def^{severe}) and from the other an allele for mild, nonclassic deficiency (haplotype, 21-OH-def^{mild}). Alternatively, nonclassic 21-hydroxylase deficiency may result from a homozygous mild enzyme deficiency. Identification of either the severe or the mild deficiency may be corroborated by the presence of the respective HLA marker. Although differences in the hormonal profiles of these two types of affected individuals are detectable, these hormonal differences are apparently not directly related to the degree of clinical manifestations of androgen excess. Among 62 patients with nonclassic 21-hydroxylase deficiency for whom unequivocal categorization of haplotypes as either classic or nonclassic was made possible by pedigree analysis and/or HLA linkage, compound heterozygotes demonstrated a significantly greater response after ACTH stimulation than did mild-deficiency-gene homozygotes for 17-OHP level, for 17-OHP/cortisol ratio, and for Δ^4-androstenedione level.[135] Thus, hormonal testing verified an HLA-based prediction of compound heterozygosity. No differences were detected between simple heterozygotes for a severe and for a mild 21-hydroxylase deficiency, implying that even in the case of a severe gene defect on the opposite haplotype and only 50 percent normal enzyme levels, activity is adequate to avoid precursor hormone accumulation. Possible explanations for the finding that compound heterozygotes were no more likely to exhibit overt signs of androgen excess than homozygotes for the mild deficiency might include the mode of subject ascertainment, or might concern physiological factors modifying androgen effect in target tissues.

Thus, the nonclassic form of 21-hydroxylase deficiency is an attenuated variant of the classic 21-hydroxylase deficiency that is clinically characterized by polymorphic presentation with signs of androgen excess. The underlying basis for phenotypic variability in the face of identical hormonal profiles is under investigation.

POPULATION GENETICS. The nonclassic form of 21-hydroxylase deficiency may go undetected by screening infants or children with the microfilter paper technique, since the random serum 17-OHP concentrations may be indistinct from normal values, especially if taken past the early morning, because of diurnal variations in 17-OHP. The frequency of the nonclassic

21-hydroxylase deficiency gene has been studied using ethnic group–specific associations between HLA-B and nonclassic 21-hydroxylase deficiency in conjunction with ACTH testing in obligate heterozygote parents.[112] Since the disease is transmitted by an autosomal recessive gene, parents of a classic or nonclassic proband are obligate heterozygotes. The haplotypes of these obligate heterozygotes which are not transmitted to the respective probands represent an a priori random sample of the haplotypes in the population.

If the proband has classic 21-hydroxylase deficiency, then the parents both must carry classic 21-hydroxylase deficiency allele(s) (Fig. 74-8A). If a parent manifests nonclassic 21-hydroxylase deficiency upon hormonal testing, then the parental allele not transmitted to the proband is, of necessity, a nonclassic allele (Fig. 74-8B). Thus these parents with nonclassic 21-hydroxylase deficiency are compound heterozygotes, whose genotype can be represented as (21-OH-def^{severe}/21-OH-def^{mild}). Compound heterozygotes are thus defined as individuals who are heterozygous for two different abnormal alleles at the same locus.

If the proband has nonclassic 21-hydroxylase deficiency,

Fig. 74-8 Two possibilities for the parental genotypes in the case of a child affected with classic 21-hydroxylase deficiency. A. Both parents are simple heterozygotes (carriers). B. One parent is a compound heterozygote and is thus affected with nonclassic 21-hydroxylase deficiency. Solid shading = classic (severe) deficiency haplotype; hatched shading = nonclassic (mild) deficiency haplotype; unshaded = normal 21-hydroxylase. *(From Speiser et al.[112] Used by permission.)*

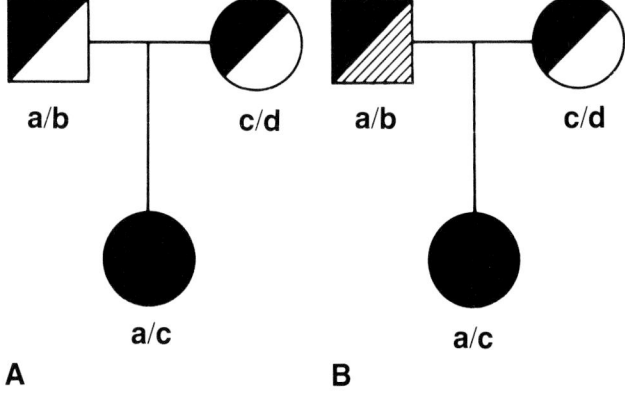

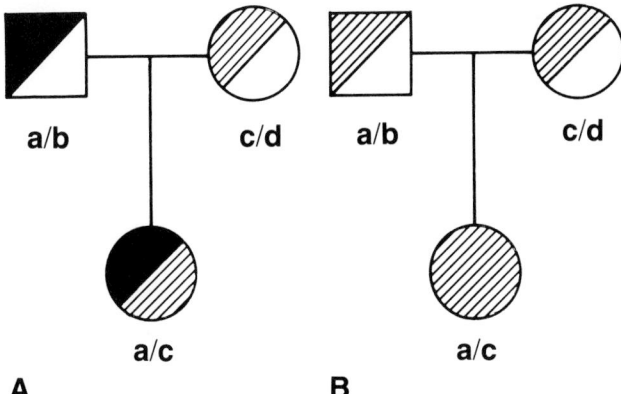

Fig. 74-9 Two possible pedigrees for a child with nonclassic 21-hydroxylase deficiency and neither parent affected (simple heterozygotes). A. One parent carries a classic deficiency allele, and the affected offspring is thus a compound heterozygote. B. Both parents are carriers of a nonclassic deficiency allele, and the offspring is homozygous affected (mild). Key as in Fig. 74-8. (From Speiser et al.[112] Used by permission.)

then the parents may be heterozygotes for either the classic or the nonclassic gene, since the child could be either a compound heterozygote (21-OH-def [severe]/21-OH-def [mild]) or a homozygote for the mild deficiency (21-OH-def [mild]/21-OH-def [mild]; Fig. 74-9). Results of the ACTH test do not clearly distinguish between parents who have the genotypes 21-OH-def [severe]/21-OH-def [mild] and 21-OH-def [mild]/21-OH-def [mild].

As indicated above, if the parent, on hormonal testing with ACTH, proves to be a patient with nonclassic 21-hydroxylase deficiency, then that parent could be a compound heterozygote or a homozygote for the mild deficiency.[112] Figure 74-10 demonstrates the possible 21-hydroxylase deficiency genotypes of parents and offspring in families in which both a child and a parent have been diagnosed as patients with nonclassic 21-hydroxylase deficiency upon hormonal testing. In these families there are no classic patients and so there can be no identification of a parental HLA haplotype linked to a classic genetic defect. Thus, while in Fig. 74-10A, B, and C the haplotype not transmitted to the proband from the affected parent *must* carry the nonclassic gene, the haplotype of the affected parent not transmitted to the proband in Fig. 74-10D and E *might* carry a classic gene. In order to avoid inclusion of classic genes in analyzing the nonclassic gene frequency, we excluded affected parents of offspring with nonclassic 21-hydroxylase deficiency from this analysis unless the haplotype not transmitted to the proband carried HLA-B14,DR1, which is in genetic linkage disequilibrium with the nonclassic 21-hydroxylase deficiency gene. In such cases the probability is high that the haplotype not transmitted to the affected offspring carries a nonclassic genetic defect. This exception applied to three Ashkenazic Jewish families. Two additional Ashkenazic Jewish families, in which the haplotype not transmitted to the affected offspring carried B40 or B8, were also included because these antigens have not been found in any Ashkenazic classic patients and are present in some nonclassic Ashkenazic patients.

The occurrence of nonclassic 21-hydroxylase deficiency in parents of affected offspring was detected by hormonal criteria using the nomograms referred to above.[136] By counting the incidence of nonclassic 21-hydroxylase deficiency in parents, we could estimate the frequency of the nonclassic deficiency gene relative to the presumed normal genes [Table 74-7 (Ref. 112)]. Thus for example:

1. There were 94 parental haplotypes in our Ashkenazic Jewish families.

2. Of these ninety-four, 47 are obligate carrier haplotypes and the other 47 haplotypes represent, a priori, a random sample of (normal and 21-hydroxylase-deficient) haplotypes in the population.

3. Among the parents, we found nine who were actually nonclassic patients, rather than heterozygotes, upon hormonal testing.

4. Therefore, the gene frequency q for the nonclassic 21-hydroxylase gene is estimated as:

$$\frac{9 \text{ nonclassic genes}}{47 \text{ random genes}} = 0.191 \qquad [74\text{-}1]$$

or 1 in 5 (95% confidence limits: 0.092 to 0.333).

5. Heterozygote frequency $2pq = 2(0.191)(0.809)$
$$= 0.309 \qquad [74\text{-}2]$$

or approximately 1 in 3.

6. Nonclassic disease frequency $q^2 = 0.037$ [74-3]

or 1 in 27 by the Hardy-Weinberg law for a population at equilibrium (95% confidence limits 0.008 to 0.111, or 1 in 125 to 1 in 9).[74]

Fig. 74-10 Possible 21-hydroxylase genotypic arrangements in the case of one nonclassically affected and one unaffected (carrier) parent producing a nonclassically affected child. In all cases, A to E, sibling offspring would be affected or carriers with 50 percent probability. Note that in case D the couple is at risk for producing a child affected with the classic disorder. Key as in Fig. 74-8. (From Speiser et al.[112] Used by permission.)

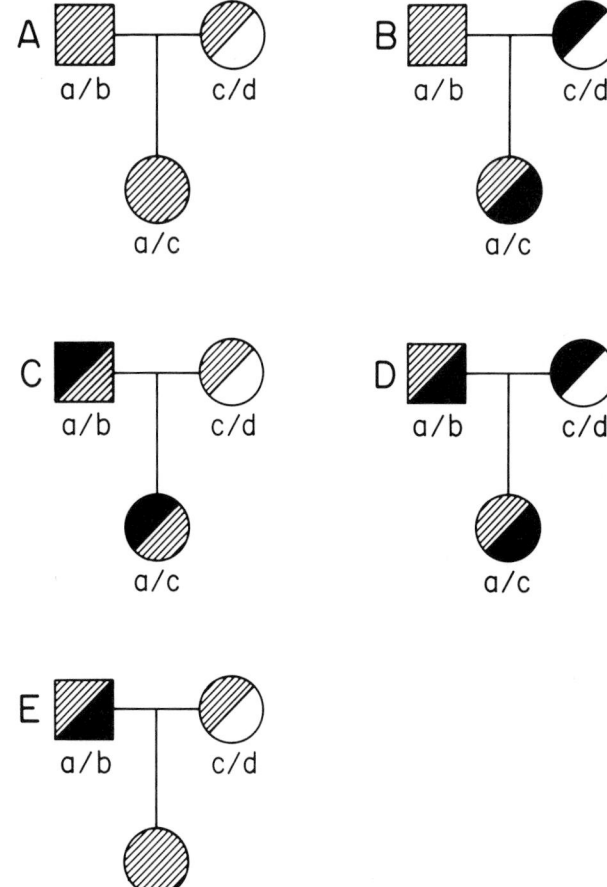

Table 74-7 Nonclassic 21-Hydroxylase Gene and Disease Frequencies

*Hormonal criteria**

Ethnic group†	Total	Parental haplotypes Random Total	Affected‡	Gene frequency q	Disease frequency q^2	Heterozygote frequency $2q(1-q)$
Ashkenazic Jewish	94	47	9	0.191 (0.089–0.308)	0.037 (0.0079–0.099)	0.309 (0.162–0.431)
Hispanic	44	22	3	0.136 (0.015–0.302)	0.019 (0.0002–0.091)	0.235 (0.085–0.421)
Yugoslav	80	40	5	0.125 (0.035–0.240)	0.016 (0.0001–0.058)	0.219 (0.061–0.366)
Italian	208	104	6	0.058 (0.018–0.108)	0.003 (0.0003–0.012)	0.109 (0.034–0.195)
Other whites†	112	56	2	0.036§ (<0.001–0.094)	0.001 (<0.0001–0.008)	0.069 (<0.001–0.163)
Black American	14	7	0	—§	—	—
American Indian	4	2	0	—§	—	—
Sum of all groups	556	278	25	0.090 (0.058–0.125)	0.009 (0.003–0.016)	0.164 (0.104–0.221)

Sib-pair analyses

Ethnic group†	Total haplotypes	Sib pairs sharing one HLA haplotype	Gene frequency q	Disease frequency q^2	Heterozygote frequency $2q(1-q)$
Mixed ethnic group¶	18	3 (0.401–6.601)	0.100 (0.050–0.300)	0.010 (0.0025–0.090)	0.180 (0.095–0.421)

*Only parents who had undergone ACTH testing were included.
†Ethnic background was homogeneous in each category except "other whites," which includes non-Jewish persons of German, French, Polish, Russian, Hungarian, Greek, Anglo-Saxon, and Nordic origin.
‡As revealed by ACTH testing.
§Because of low disease frequency in these ethnic groups, more families must be studied.
¶Including Ashkenazic Jews, Anglo-Saxons, Italians, Hispanics, Germans, and American Indians.

This analysis was carried out for each ethnic group studied. The gene frequency for nonclassic 21-hydroxylase deficiency was highest in Ashkenazic Jews (19.1 percent) and was also high in Hispanics (13.6 percent), Yugoslavs (12.5 percent), and Italians (5.8 percent). In other subjects, a heterogeneous mix of Caucasoid groups, 41 percent of whom had some Anglo-Saxon ancestry, the gene frequency was 3.2 percent. Corresponding heterozygote frequencies were 1 in 3 for Ashkenazic Jews, 1 in 4 for Hispanics, 1 in 5 for Yugoslavs, 1 in 9 for Italians, and 1 in 14 for other whites. Disease frequencies were 1 in 27 for Ashkenazic Jews, 1 in 53 for Hispanics, 1 in 63 for Yugoslavs, 1 in 333 for Italians, and 1 in 1000 for other whites (Fig. 74-11).

Confirmation of this approach was obtained by the affected sib pair method of Thomson and Bodmer.[137] HLA genotypes of sib pairs in families with two or more similarly affected members in one generation were analyzed. Among the families with nonclassic 21-hydroxylase deficiency, 14 of 18 sib pairs were HLA-identical. Among the four sib pairs who were not identical, one sib pair shared no HLA haplotype and three sib pairs shared one haplotype.

1. $$\frac{3 \text{ (affected sib pairs sharing only one haplotype)}}{18 \text{ (total number of sib pairs)}} = 0.167$$

[74-4]

2. By reference to Thomson and Bodmer's Table 2,[137] 0.167 yields a nonclassic gene frequency of 0.1, or 10 percent (95% confidence limits are approximately 0.009 to 0.324).

3. Heterozygote frequency $2pq = 2(0.1)(0.9) = 0.18$ [74-5] or 1 out of 5 to 6 people.

4. Expected nonclassic disease frequency $q^2 = 0.01$ [74-6] or 1 in 100 (95% confidence limits are 0.00008 to 0.105).

The overall gene and disease frequencies and ethnic specificities were independently confirmed in a study analyzing family data by the method of commingling distributions, using the computer program SKUMIX.[138]

Molecular Genetics. The initial molecular genetic analysis of 21-hydroxylase deficiency made use of the known associations between this disorder, specific HLA antigens, and alleles of HLA-linked complement loci. In particular, salt-wasting 21-hydroxylase deficiency is often (10 to 20 percent of all alleles) associated with an extended HLA haplotype, A3,Bw47,DR7; this haplotype carries a null allele at one of the C4 loci encoding the fourth component of serum complement.[95,96] Because 21-hydroxylase and C4 loci are both affected on this haplotype, it was hypothesized that a single major DNA deletion or rearrangement affected both loci. Therefore, to determine whether the HLA-linked defect in 21-hydroxylase deficiency involved a structural gene for P450c21, a bovine cDNA clone encoding part of this enzyme was hybridized with Southern blots of DNA samples obtained from normal individuals and from patients with 21-hydroxylase deficiency who carried the Bw47 haplotype.

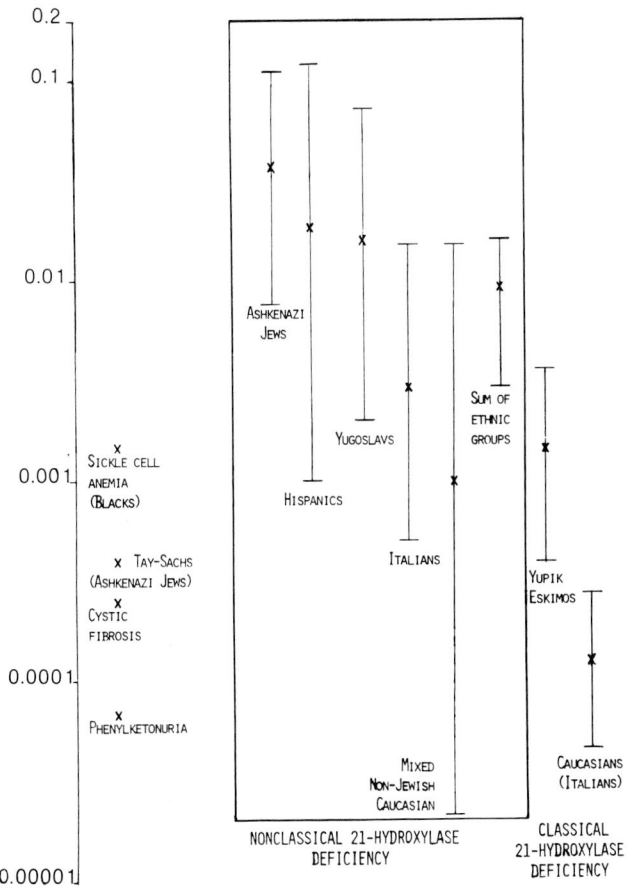

Fig. 74-11 Disease frequencies of nonclassic 21-hydroxylase deficiency and classic 21-hydroxylase deficiency relative to other common autosomal recessive disorders. The latter frequencies derived from Behrman and Vaughan.[267] Bars represent the 95% confidence levels. (*From Speiser et al.[112] Used by permission.*)

After analysis in this manner, normal DNA samples yielded two fragments that hybridized with the probe at equal intensity after digestion with any of several restriction endonucleases. One of these bands was absent in digests of DNA from an HLA-Bw47 homozygous patient, consistent with a deletion of one of two P450c21 (i.e., 21-hydroxylase) genes (Figs. 74-12 and 74-13).[31]

Because a 21-hydroxylase gene and a complement C4 gene were both affected on the HLA-Bw47 haplotype, it was likely that they were located very near each other on the sixth chromosome. The precise arrangement of these genes was determined by examination of long (40-kb) cosmid clones of human DNA that had originally been isolated because they carried the C4 gene.[24,32]

There are two steroid 21-hydroxylase genes, now termed CYP21A and CYP21B,[139] each immediately adjacent to the corresponding member of the C4 gene pair, C4A and C4B. The arrangement is thus C4A-CYP21A-C4B-CYP21B with all four genes oriented in the same direction (Fig. 74-12). (Other names found in the literature are: OH21A and OH21B,[2] P450C21A and P450C21B,[140] and CA21H-A and CA21H-B.[140a]) The functional roles of these genes were deduced by comparing Southern blots of cosmid DNA with blots of uncloned DNA from patients with 21-hydroxylase deficiency and from selected normal individuals.[24] After digestion with the restriction endonuclease *Taq*I, the CYP21A gene carries a 3.2-kb *Taq*I fragment while the CYP21B gene carries a 3.7-kb fragment. These correspond to the two fragments seen when uncloned human DNA is hybridized with a 21-hydroxylase cDNA probe. The 3.7-kb fragment associated with the CYP21B gene is deleted when 21-hydroxylase deficiency is associated with the HLA-Bw47 haplotype, suggesting that the CYP21B gene product is required for 21-hydroxylase activity. In contrast, hormonally normal individuals who are homozygous for the HLA haplotype A1,B8,DR3 (which is negatively associated with 21-hydroxylase deficiency) have a homozygous deletion of the 3.2-kb *Taq*I fragment associated with the

Fig. 74-12 Map of CYP21 genes (21A and 21B) encoding P450c21. These genes alternate with the C4A and C4B genes encoding the fourth component of serum complement. Arrows represent direction of transcription. Fragments produced by four restriction enzymes that hybridize with a full-length 21-hydroxylase cDNA probe are shown; fragment sizes are indicated in kilobase (kb). One *Eco*RI site detected in cloned genes is not cut well in uncloned genomic DNA and is indicated by parentheses. *Top.* Normal chromosome. *Middle.* Chromosome with a deletion of C4A and CYP21A, as found on the HLA-A1,B8,DR3 haplotype. *Bottom.* Chromosome with a deletion of C4B and CYP21B, as found on the HLA-A3,Bw7,DR7 haplotype. The region normally located to the right by the CYP21B gene (thick line) is spliced onto the CYP21A gene. Thus, deletions of C4A-CYP21A and C4B-CYP21B produce indistinguishable restriction patterns when DNA is digested *Eco*RI or *Bgl*II.

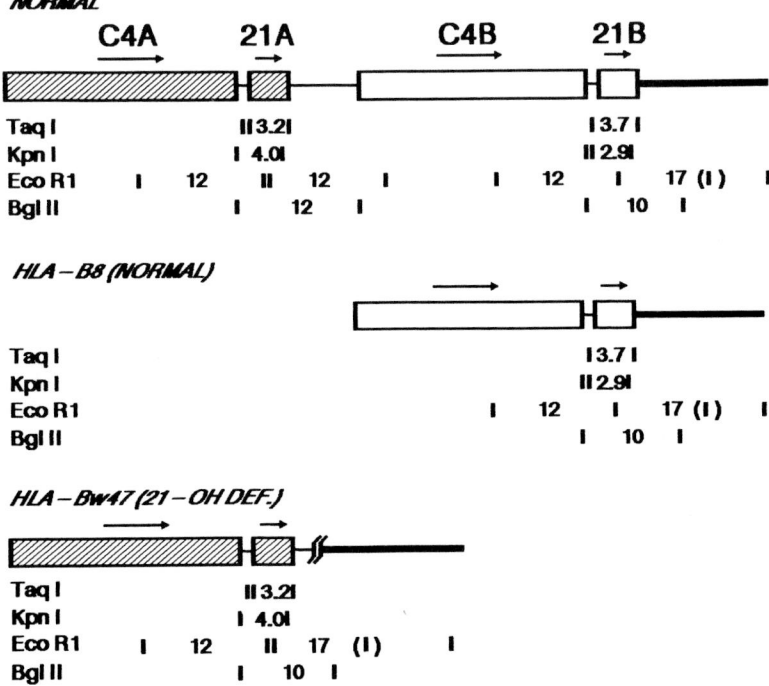

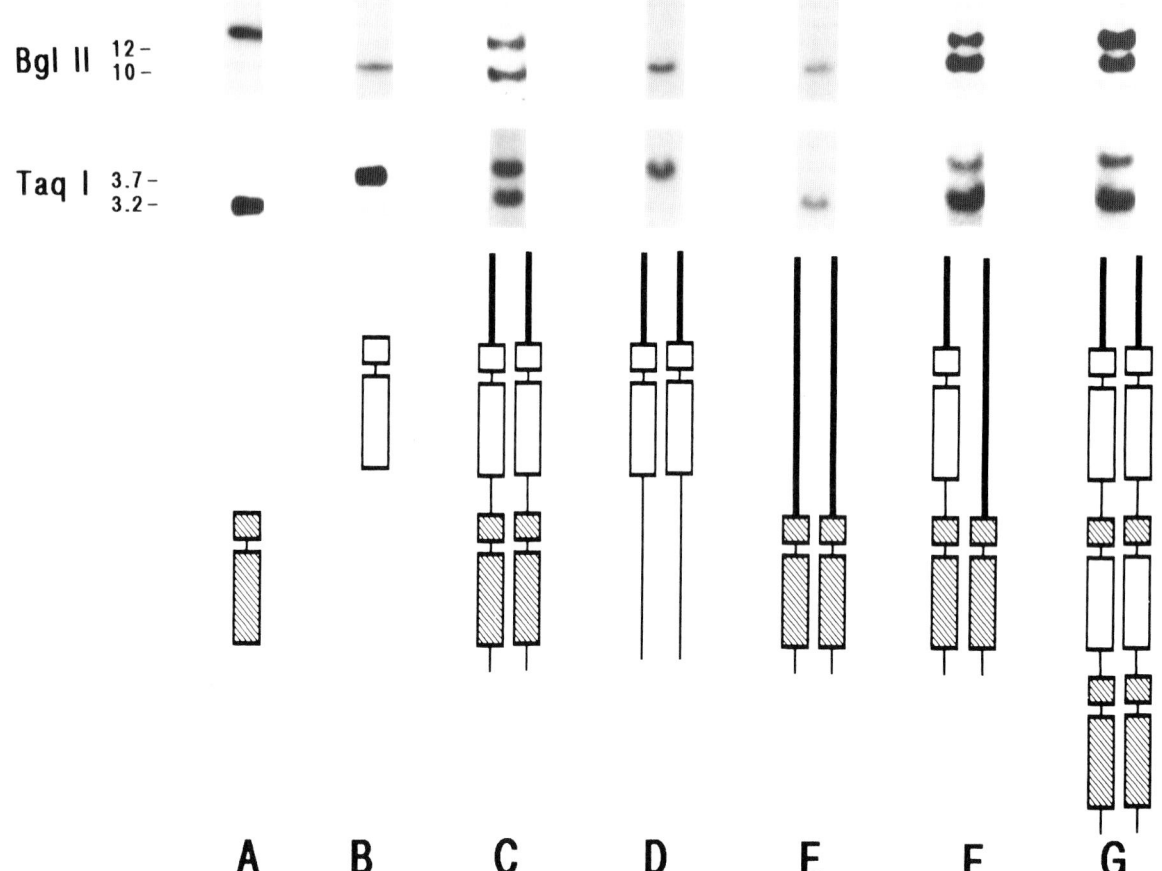

Fig. 74-13 Analysis of 21-hydroxylase deficiency by genomic blot hybridization. Samples of cloned and uncloned human DNA were digested with restriction endonucleases *Taq*I or *Bgl*II, subjected to agarose gel electrophoresis, blotted to nitrocellulose, and hybridized with a radioactive probe encoding 21-hydroxylase (P450c21). Hybridizing fragments of 3.7 or 3.2 kb (*Taq*I) or 10 or 12 kb (*Bgl*II) were observed. These respectively correspond to the CYP21B (unfilled bar) and CYP21A (hatched bar) genes in normal DNA (see Fig. 74-12). The C4A and C4B genes are also shown. *A.* Cloned CYP21A gene. *B.* Cloned CYP21B gene. *C.* DNA from a normal individual. Each of the subject's two chromosomes 6 has an A and a B gene, yielding a pattern with two fragments of equal intensity for both digests. *D.* Hormonally normal individual homozygous for the HLA haplotype A1,B8,DR3. The absence of the CYP21A pseudogene has no apparent clinical effect. *E.* Patient with 21-hydroxylase

deficiency, homozygous for HLA-A3,Bw47,DR7. The CYP21B gene is deleted. Note that *Bgl*II digests for this and *D,* above (deletion of CYP21A), are identical. *F.* Patient with 21-hydroxylase deficiency, heterozygous for HLA-A3,Bw47,DR7. Such a patient has a total of two A genes and one B gene, and so the 3.7-kb *Taq*I band is less intense than the 3.2-kb band, and the 12 kb *Bgl*II band is also decreased in intensity. The nondeleted CYP21B gene presumably has a small mutation not detectable with these techniques. *G.* Patient with nonclassic 21-hydroxylase deficiency, homozygous for HLA-B14,DR1. This patient has a total of four A genes and two B genes, so that the hybridization pattern after *Taq*I digestion is indistinguishable from that of the patient with a heterozygous deletion (i.e., a 2:1 ratio of intensity of the 3.2 and 3.7-kb *Taq*I bands). However, the *Bgl*II pattern has increased intensity of the 12-kb band, reflecting the extra CYP21A genes.

CYP21A gene.[24,141] Thus, absence of the CYP21A gene is not deleterious, suggesting that the putative product of this gene is not active in steroidogenesis (Fig. 74-13).

The boundaries of these deletions have been determined by detailed mapping of restriction endonuclease recognition sites and by hybridization analysis using cloned cDNA encoding C4. The HLA-A1,B8,DR3 haplotype carries a deletion of both C4A and CYP21A, consistent with the null allele for C4A which is known to occur on this haplotype.[141–143] This haplotype occurs in about 5 percent of all normal chromosomes.[92] In contrast, the A3,Bw47,DR7 haplotype has deleted C4B as well as CYP21B, explaining the null C4B allele on this haplotype. This latter deletion splices the chromosomal region 3′ of the CYP21B gene onto the CYP21A gene, causing the CYP21A gene to migrate electrophoretically like a CYP21B gene after DNA is digested with certain restriction endonucleases. Thus, deletions of CYP21A and CYP21B are difficult to distinguish after digestion with such enzymes,[144] and the difficulty in telling them apart may lead to errors of interpre-

tation of Southern blots (Figs. 74-12 and 74-13).[145] The apparent lack of function of the CYP21A gene has been explained by nucleotide sequence analysis.[26,27] The CYP21A and CYP21B genes are about 98 percent homologous in their coding regions. The DNA sequence of a nearly full-length cDNA clone derived from human fetal adrenal glands is identical to exons of the CYP21B gene sequence. There are several differences between these and the sequence of the CYP21A gene. The CYP21A gene contains an 8 base-pair deletion and a single base-pair insertion, each of which shifts the reading frame of translation. There is also a nonsense mutation as well as several nonconservative amino acid substitutions. Since the frameshift and nonsense mutations prevent an active protein from being synthesized, this means that the CYP21A gene is a pseudogene with no evident function (Fig. 74-14). The two sets of C4 and 21-hydroxylase genes probably arose by duplication of a single pair of genes at some time in the past. While both C4 genes have remained active in humans, only one 21-hydroxylase gene was necessary for normal steroidogenesis,

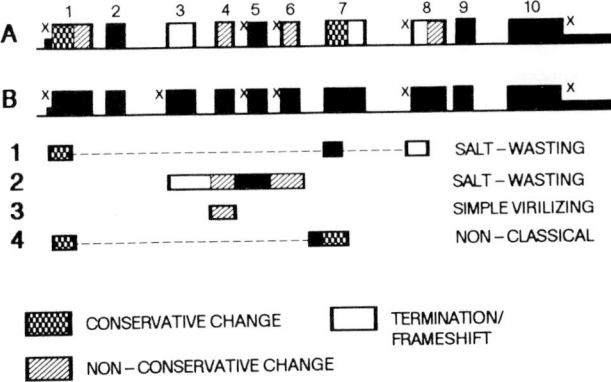

Fig. 74-14 Possible gene conversions causing 21-hydroxylase deficiency. The CYP21A and B genes are drawn schematically, with mutations in CYP21A indicated by different shadings of exons. X's in introns indicate the presence of *chi*-like sequences which are postulated to be sites for recombination between homologous regions of CYP21A and CYP21B. Boundaries of conversions are indicated by bars, and the resulting phenotype of each gene is listed.

and so the extra gene accumulated deleterious mutations with no apparent ill effects on the organism.

The tandemly duplicated C4 and 21-hydroxylase genes create the possibility of misalignment during meiotic metaphase and unequal crossing-over between sister chromatids, resulting in chromosomes containing one or three sets of C4 and 21-hydroxylase genes. This mechanism presumably created the rearrangements observed in the HLA-A1,B8,DR3 and A3,Bw47,DR7 haplotypes, which have respectively deleted the C4A-CYP21A and C4B-CYP21B pairs of genes.[32] The HLA-B14,DR1 haplotype associated with nonclassic 21-hydroxylase deficiency has a third C4 gene, as determined by electrophoretic analysis of C4 proteins;[97] and molecular genetic analysis of individuals carrying this haplotype has demonstrated that there is indeed a third set of genes, consisting of an extra C4B gene[146] and an extra CYP21A gene (based on the sizes of the extra restriction enzyme fragments; Fig. 74-13).[141,147] If the extra CYP21A gene is a pseudogene like the normally present CYP21A gene, then it presumably does not contribute to the development of the nonclassic 21-hydroxylase deficiency phenotype (which probably then results from a mutation in the CYP21B gene), but is merely an associated marker.

While the HLA-B14,DR1 haplotype and nonclassic 21-hydroxylase deficiency are very common, the HLA-A3,Bw47,DR7 haplotype is extremely rare in the normal population and comprises only perhaps 20 percent of classic 21-hydroxylase deficiency alleles. Additional patients with classic 21-hydroxylase deficiency who do not carry the HLA-Bw47 haplotype have been examined by hybridization analysis using 21-hydroxylase and/or C4 probes.[147,148] Approximately one-fourth of the alleles in these patients have deletions of the CYP21B gene; the majority of such alleles also have a deletion of C4B. In one family, on one chromosome a second CYP21A gene has been substituted for CYP21B.[149] All patients with homozygous deletions of the CYP21B gene have salt-wasting 21-hydroxylase deficiency.

The remaining three-fourths of classic alleles do not have associated restriction fragment polymorphisms and cannot be detected by Southern blot hybridization. Small exchanges of sequences between homologous genes, termed gene conversions, could cause many of these alleles by transferring one of

the deleterious mutations from the CYP21A pseudogene to the CYP21B gene. Gene conversions have been previously documented in other cytochrome P450 genes.[150] Thus far, four possible gene conversions have been observed in mutant CYP21B genes.[151–154] One of these transfers the nonsense mutation in codon 318 from the CYP21A gene into CYP21B,[151] while another changes isoleucine-172 to asparagine,[152] possibly affecting interactions between the P450 protein and the membrane of the endoplasmic reticulum (Figs. 74-14 and 74-15). Each of these mutations was noted in 3 of 20 patients with classic 21-hydroxylase deficiency. All patients with the nonsense mutation have salt-wasting disease, whereas all patients with the asparagine-172 mutation retain the ability to synthesize aldosterone (two have simple virilizing disease while one has an elevated plasma renin/aldosterone ratio without clinical salt wasting). One patient with salt-wasting disease carries a larger rearrangement involving exons 3 to 6 that transfers an 8 base-pair deletion from CYP21A to CYP21B, shifting the reading frame of translation and preventing synthesis of a functional protein.[152] Finally, the mutation associated with the nonclassic allele on the HLA-B14,DR1 haplotype is a conversion involving the sixth intron and part of exon 7, including a single-base mutation that changes Val-281 to leucine.[153] This valine residue is conserved in bovine, porcine, and murine P450c21, suggesting that it is functionally important; the change to leucine, a chemically similar amino acid, is consistent with the relatively mild degree of enzymatic impairment seen in nonclassic 21-hydroxylase deficiency.

These data[151–154] and other reports[154a] suggest that gene conversions are roughly as common as deletions as a cause of 21-hydroxylase deficiency alleles. In principle, gene conversions involving the restriction sites used to distinguish CYP21A and CYP21B might be confused with deletions of CYP21B.[145] This potential problem is avoided by Southern blot analysis of several different restriction digests, and such studies[147,148,154b,154c] demonstrate that this confusing type of gene conversion is rare compared with actual CYP21B gene deletions.

Other alleles may carry point mutations which affect transcription of the gene or processing of mRNA, or which result in amino acid substitutions altering enzymatic function. One mutant gene from an individual with salt-wasting 21-hydroxylase deficiency has two mutations: serine-269 is changed to threonine, and asparagine-494 is changed to serine.[154a] However, neither of these residues is conserved in P450c21 from other species, and so the functional significance of these mutations is unclear.

In general, the molecular genetic characterization of patients with different forms of 21-hydroxylase deficiency suggests that clinical severity is roughly correlated with the severity of each mutation. Thus, deletions, nonsense mutations, frameshifts, and presumably some amino acid substitutions result in salt-wasting alleles; one nonconservative substitution causes a simple virilizing allele, and a conservative substitution is associated with a nonclassic allele. It should be pointed out that the distinctions between these diagnostic categories are not absolute; some males diagnosed as having simple virilizing 21-hydroxylase deficiency by hormonal testing in fact carry the presumed nonclassic allele associated with HLA-B14,DR1. Conversely, some patients with documented episodes of salt wasting in infancy develop the ability to synthesize adequate amounts of aldosterone later in life, which might result from increased levels of a poorly active 21-hydroxylase enzyme (that is, P450c21) or from the presence in some individuals of an-

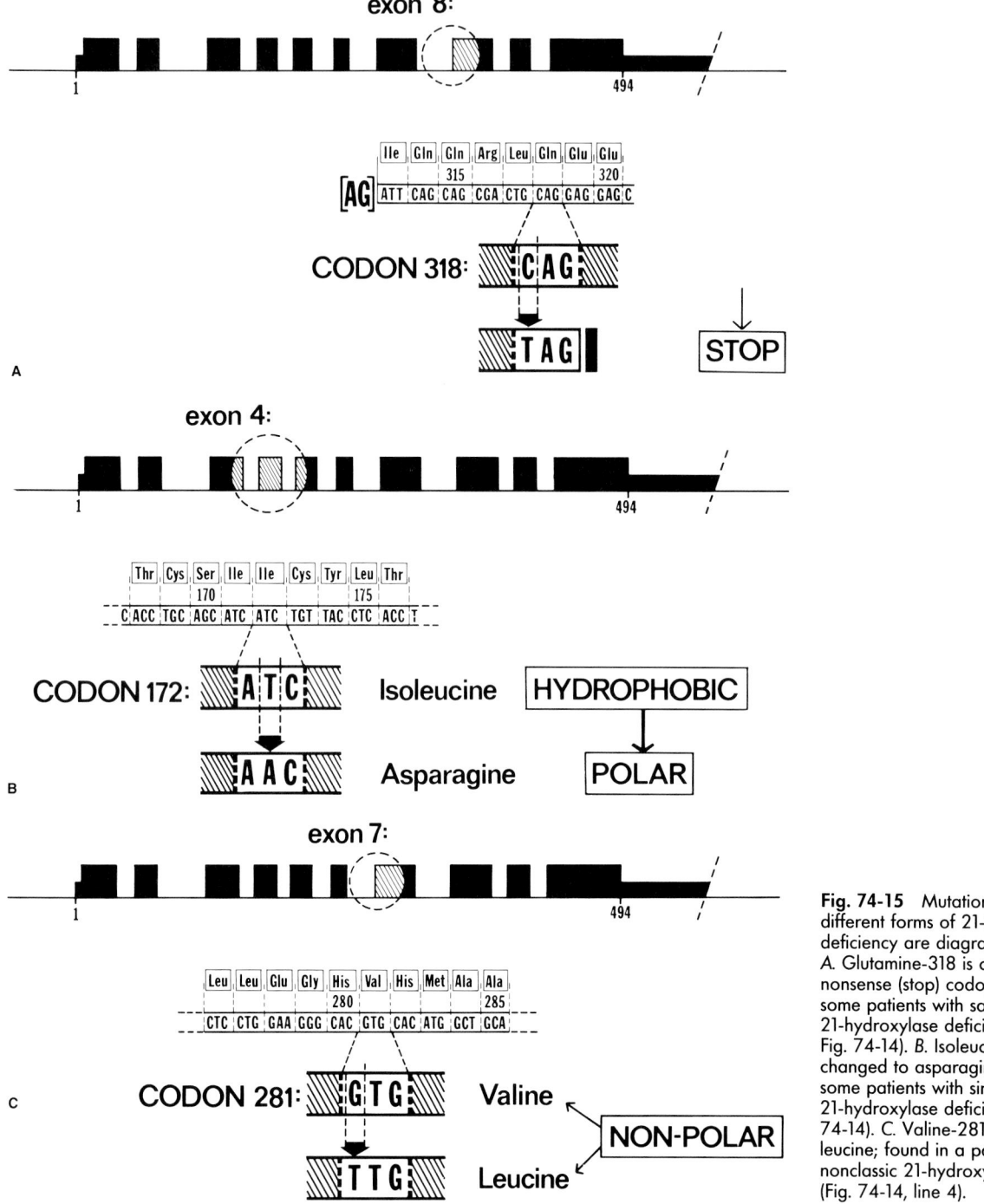

Fig. 74-15 Mutations causing different forms of 21-hydroxylase deficiency are diagramed. *A.* Glutamine-318 is changed to a nonsense (stop) codon; found in some patients with salt-wasting classic 21-hydroxylase deficiency (line 1 in Fig. 74-14). *B.* Isoleucine-172 is changed to asparagine; found in some patients with simple virilizing 21-hydroxylase deficiency (line 3, Fig. 74-14). *C.* Valine-281 is changed to leucine; found in a patient with nonclassic 21-hydroxylase deficiency (Fig. 74-14, line 4).

other P450 enzyme distinct from P450c21, with some steroid 21-hydroxylase activity.[155]

Prenatal Diagnosis and Prenatal Treatment

PRENATAL DIAGNOSIS. Since the report by Jeffcoate et al.[156] of the successful identification of an affected fetus by elevated concentrations of 17-ketosteroids and pregnanetriol in the amniotic fluid, several investigators have undertaken prenatal diagnosis for congenital adrenal hyperplasia by similar measurements of hormone levels in gestation.[157,158] The most specific hormonal diagnostic test for 21-hydroxylase deficiency is amniotic fluid 17-OHP;[159–163] Δ^4-androstenedione may be employed as an adjunctive diagnostic assay.[62] It has been sug-

gested that elevated amniotic fluid 21-deoxycortisol may also be a marker for 21-hydroxylase deficiency.[164] Amniotic fluid testosterone levels may be inside the normal range in the case of an affected male.[162,165]

HLA genotyping of fetal cells cultured from the amniotic fluid provides an additional method for prenatal diagnosis of 21-hydroxylase deficiency.[166,167] A fetus sharing both HLA haplotypes with the affected proband is predicted to be affected; one who shares one haplotype with the proband is expected to be a carrier of the defective gene; and if no HLA antigens are shared, the fetus should be genetically unaffected. Exceptions are found in cases of intra-HLA recombination. Because the class II (HLA-DR, -DQ, and -DP) antigens are not serologically detected, recombination between the maternal and/or paternal HLA-B and -DR loci, including the 21-hydroxylase locus, will not be identified. Possible homozygosity at the HLA-B locus in either of the parents or antigen sharing between parents are also factors which limit categorization of the fetal 21-hydroxylase genotype by this method. Amniotic fluid assay for 17-OHP should thus still be performed, since anomalous hormone levels may in some cases call into question the HLA result. Forest et al.[168] in evaluating 17 pregnancies at risk for CAH found in 2 cases that HLA-A and -B typing of amniocytes predicted an affected fetus, while hormonal results were normal. These pregnancies were terminated, and it was postulated by the authors that either there had been recombination between HLA-B and the HLA-D region or that the enzymatic defect was not expressed in midgestation. Pang et al.[169] reported normal amniotic fluid 17-OHP and Δ^4-A levels in two affected cases: In the first case, where the infant proved postnatally to have simple virilizing 21-hydroxylase deficiency, the fetus was haploidentical (maternal) with the affected older sib and was predicted to be a carrier. Because of a paternal recombination, HLA typing—hampered in addition in this case by antigen sharing between the parents—failed to identify inheritance of the second 21-hydroxylase deficiency allele prenatally. The recombination was revealed postnatally by peripheral blood leukocyte HLA typing (Figure 74-16). In the second case, normal amniotic fluid hormone levels did not contribute to the diagnosis for a nonclassically affected fetus and the HLA-identical index case, also affected with nonclassic deficiency, had been earlier miscategorized as a classic patient (Figure 74-16). These were the only two false negative results in 32 pregnancies at risk for 21-

hydroxylase deficiency evaluated by amniocentesis. A third diagnostic error in this series resulted from the HLA identity of a normal fetus (with normal hormonal values) with the index case, thought to be classically affected; the diagnosis of both sibs was later corrected to normal.

With the advent of chorionic villus biopsy, evaluation of the fetus at risk is now possible in the first trimester at 8 to 11 weeks of gestation. Since normative standards for hormonal levels measurable at this early stage remain to be established, chorionic villus biopsy diagnosis at present depends on HLA typing of the chorionic tissue. A new option is HLA typing by molecular genetic techniques, which identifies DNA polymorphisms in the genes for antigens of both class I (HLA-A, -B, -C) and class II (HLA-DR, -DQ, and -DP) with the aid of specific probes.[170] This technique is more exact (it has already begun to resolve subgroups of the standard serological specificities), and the availability of class II probes makes possible the identification of B,DR recombinations. It is interesting to note that in the French experience, amniotic fluid 17-OHP was clearly elevated even at 10 to 13 weeks of gestation in three affected pregnancies; there was no discordance between hormonal results and restriction fragment length polymorphism–based diagnostic prediction in seven families studied.[170] An algorithm for diagnostic management of potentially affected pregnancies is given in Fig. 74-17.

It is currently estimated that 25 percent of classic 21-hydroxylase deficiency alleles carry a deletion of the active 21-hydroxylase gene (CYP21B).[147] Identification of the presumed sequence aberrations occurring in the remaining 80 percent of cases will depend on the appearance of characteristic RFLPs

Fig. 74-16 Pitfalls in prenatal diagnosis of classic simple virilizing 21-hydroxylase deficiency. The fetus was prenatally predicted to be a carrier for 21-hydroxylase deficiency on the basis of HLA typing and a normal amniotic fluid 17-OHP concentration. Postnatally, the child was found to have a paternal HLA-A/B recombinant haplotype; he was affected with simple virilizing classic CAH and was identical to his affected brother for the HLA-Cw,B,DR haplotype of the father and the full HLA (i.e., A,Cw,B,DR) haplotype of the mother. (*From Pang et al.[169] Used by permission.*)

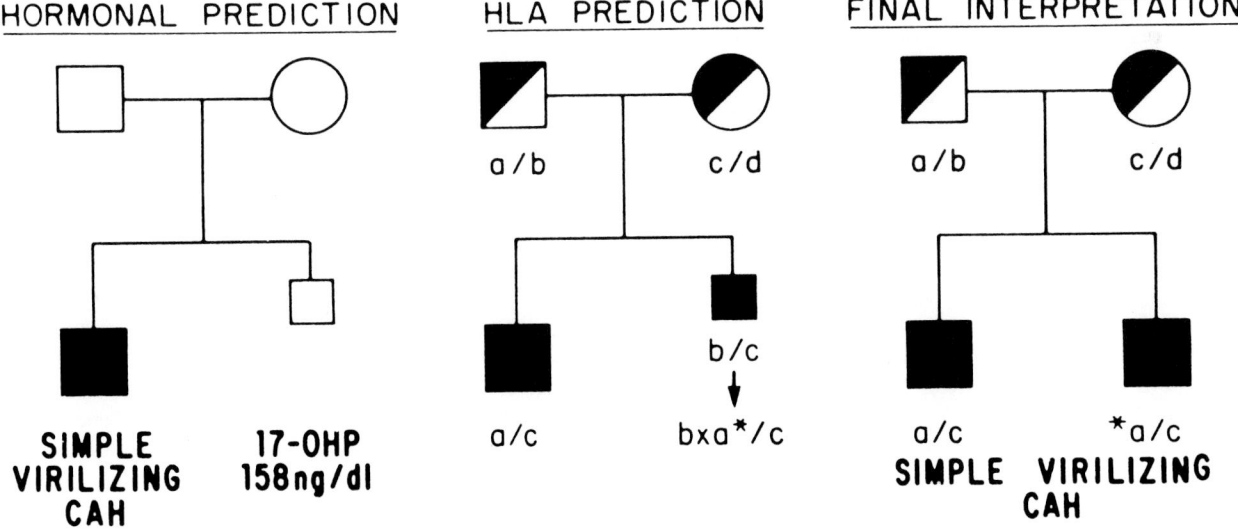

HORMONAL PREDICTION

SIMPLE VIRILIZING CAH   17-OHP 158ng/dl

HLA PREDICTION

a / b   c / d

a/c   b/c
↓
bxa*/c

FINAL INTERPRETATION

a / b   c / d

a/c   *a/c
SIMPLE VIRILIZING CAH

HLA demonstrated an A/B paternal recombination but was B/DR identical to the index case:
A2, Cw-, B18, DR4
A25, Cw-, B18, DR2

HLA:

a) A11, Cw-, B18, DR4
b) A2, Cw2, B27, DR5

c) A25, Cw-, B18, DR2
d) A25, Cw-, Bw38(39), DR7

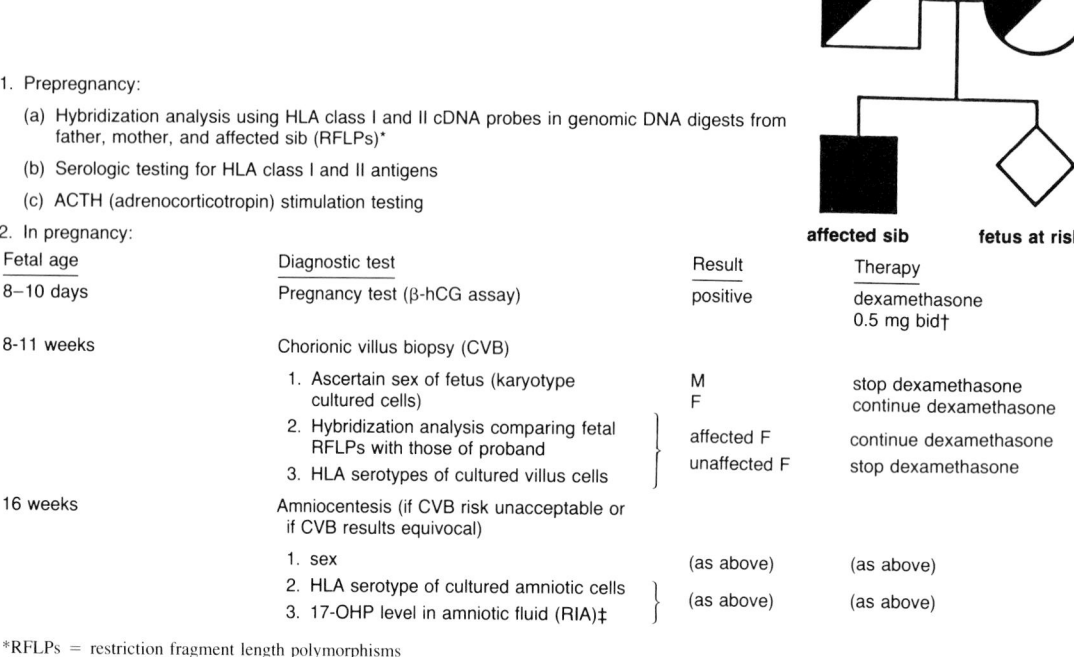

1. Prepregnancy:

   (a) Hybridization analysis using HLA class I and II cDNA probes in genomic DNA digests from
        father, mother, and affected sib (RFLPs)*

   (b) Serologic testing for HLA class I and II antigens

   (c) ACTH (adrenocorticotropin) stimulation testing

2. In pregnancy:

Fetal age	Diagnostic test	Result	Therapy
8–10 days	Pregnancy test (β-hCG assay)	positive	dexamethasone 0.5 mg bid†
8-11 weeks	Chorionic villus biopsy (CVB)		
	1. Ascertain sex of fetus (karyotype cultured cells)	M / F	stop dexamethasone / continue dexamethasone
	2. Hybridization analysis comparing fetal RFLPs with those of proband	affected F	continue dexamethasone
	3. HLA serotypes of cultured villus cells	unaffected F	stop dexamethasone
16 weeks	Amniocentesis (if CVB risk unacceptable or if CVB results equivocal)		
	1. sex	(as above)	(as above)
	2. HLA serotype of cultured amniotic cells		
	3. 17-OHP level in amniotic fluid (RIA)‡	(as above)	(as above)

*RFLPs = restriction fragment length polymorphisms
†bid = *bis in die* ("twice daily")
‡Not useful if mother is on dexamethasone

Fig. 74-17 Algorithm depicting prenatal management of pregnancy in families at risk for a fetus affected with 21-hydroxylase deficiency.

in digests of genomic DNA samples. It is hoped that with the characterization of specific nondeletional mutations a growing panel of oligonucleotide probes informative in the resolution of 21-hydroxylase genotypes may be used in prenatal diagnosis.

PRENATAL TREATMENT. Prenatal treatment with dexamethasone has recently been employed for fetuses at risk for 21-hydroxylase deficiency.[171–173] Where treatment was begun at 3 to 10 weeks of gestation (0.5 mg dexamethasone orally twice daily), all measurements at amniocentesis showed complete suppression of adrenocortical hormones. Only when dexamethasone therapy was discontinued before amniotic fluid sampling were the amniotic fluid hormone levels elevated. Masculinization of genitalia was completely prevented in one of three affected female fetuses and partially prevented in another female. In the third case, where treatment failed, the mother had begun dexamethasone at 10 weeks and terminated therapy at 28 weeks. In one multicenter study, no congenital malformations were found in any of 21 treated fetuses.[171] Another group of investigators failed to find evidence of suppression of the fetal pituitary-adrenal axis after acute administration of dexamethasone at midterm,[174] but this is not necessarily reflective of the situation in which chronic therapy is begun in the first trimester. German investigators[172] also found high amniotic fluid 17-OHP levels in two pregnancies at risk for CAH in which the mothers were treated with dexamethasone from the tenth to the seventeenth week, although therapy was stopped 5 days before the amniocentesis. The latter group postulated increased metabolic clearance of dexamethasone, or inadequate dosage.

Theoretically, institution of such therapy at 6 to 7 weeks of gestation, before onset of adrenal androgen secretion, should effectively suppress adrenal androgen production and allow normal separation of the vaginal and urethral orifices in addition to preventing clitoromegaly. Obviously, if dexamethasone is to be administered at such an early date, treatment is blind to the status of the fetus. Following HLA and/or hormonal diagnosis by either chorionic villus biopsy or amniocentesis, cessation of prenatal therapy may be considered if the fetus is male, or if it is an unaffected female.

To date, no fetus of a mother treated with dexamethasone in low doses has been found to have any congenital malformation. Specifically, no cases have been reported of cleft palate, or of placental degeneration, or fetal death, which have been observed in a rodent model of in utero exposure to high-dose glucocorticoids.[175] The current dosage recommendation is dexamethasone 20 µg/(kg · day) divided in 3 equal doses with the maximum daily dose being 1.5 mg.

3β-Hydroxysteroid Dehydrogenase Deficiency

A defect in 3β-hydroxysteroid dehydrogenase (3β-HSD) was first described by Bongiovanni in 1962.[176] On the basis of pedigree analysis, a monogenic autosomal recessive mode of inheritance seemed most likely.[176–178] This disorder affects the synthesis of all classes of adrenocortical steroids. Deficiency of 3β-HSD may be diagnosed by measuring elevated levels of the Δ^5-steroids: pregnenolone, 17α-hydroxypregnenolone, and dehydroepiandrosterone (DHEA) in serum, and pregnenetriol and 16-pregnenetriol in urine. An elevated ratio of Δ^5 to Δ^4 steroids characterizes the biochemical findings in patients with 3β-HSD deficiency. Unlike 21-hydroxylase, this enzyme is active in the gonads as well as in the adrenal glands. Androgen deficiency resulting from deficiency of the enzyme 3β-HSD causes ambiguous genitalia in genetic male newborns. Affected males will usually have some degree of hypospadias (often the severe perineal-scrotal form) and palpable testes. Affected females may have normal to enlarged clitoral dimensions due to very high levels of the weak androgen DHEA, which undergoes peripheral conversion to more potent androgens. The deficiency of aldosterone in classic cases of 3β-HSD deficiency results in salt wasting.[176-186] Several cases have been described in which the ability to conserve sodium was intact.[176,178,180,182,186]

Classic 3β-HSD Deficiency. In 3β-HSD deficiency, as in the other two common forms of CAH known to produce ambiguous genitalia in the newborn, there is a spectrum of clinical phenotypes, including both salt-wasting and non-salt-wasting forms.[178] It is not possible to judge the degree of severity of the enzyme defect on the basis of the appearance of the external genitalia at birth.

Nonclassic 3β-HSD Deficiency. Late-onset 3β-HSD deficiency is an entity which is usually identified in girls with premature adrenarche or in adolescent and young adult women with hirsutism and oligomenorrhea.[187] The latter groups were, until recently, largely classified as having polycystic ovarian syndrome. Careful scrutiny of ACTH-stimulated adrenal hormone profiles has allowed differentiation of this subgroup of women.[117] There is relatively little known about late-onset 3β-HSD deficiency in males, as all of the males reported at an older age had some degree of hypospadias, suggesting prenatal onset of the disorder.[188] It has been proposed that the congenital and late-onset forms of 3β-HSD deficiency are allelic variants at the same structural gene locus.

In a study of 116 hirsute women,[117] 15 percent, or 17, met the hormonal criteria for the diagnosis of mild 3β-HSD deficiency: the Δ^5-17α-hydroxypregnenolone (Δ^5-17P) and DHEA levels in response to ACTH stimulation did not overlap with the normal range and were more than 2 standard deviations above the normal mean. The Δ^5-17P and DHEA levels in these women were significantly ($p < .05$) higher than those of hirsute women with partial 21-hydroxylase deficiency, although some values overlapped between the two groups. ACTH-stimulated 17-OHP and cortisol levels in these hirsute women did not significantly differ from the same ACTH-stimulated levels in normal women. The ratios of ACTH-stimulated Δ^5-17P to 17-OHP and Δ^5-17P to cortisol in the 17 hirsute women were more than 2 standard deviations above the normal mean (Fig. 74-18).

The age range at the time of diagnosis of the 17 hirsute women defined to have adrenal 3β-HSD deficiency was 16.3 to 27 years with a mean age of 20 years. The heights of these women ranged from 154 to 177 cm (mean: 163 cm), while all the women weighed from 50.1 to 77.1 kg (mean: 63.6 kg) with the exception of one woman whose weight was 92 kg. The available long-term growth data in two women indicated that they had had growth acceleration between the ages of 4 and 8 years and growth arrest between the ages of 8 and 11 years, with their final height below their parents' heights. These two women had more severe hirsutism than three women with normal growth data. In total, 7 of the 17 women had final heights at least 2 to 5 in. below their parents' heights.

The history of pubertal changes was reliably determined in 11 of the 17 women. It was found that 5 of 11 women had pubarche between ages 5 and 8.5 years and 6 had pubarche between ages 10.5 and 12. In these women, in general, thelarche had occurred either by 0.6 to 5 years after pubarche or at the same time as pubarche. None had thelarche prior to pubarche. Menarche occurred in all women between ages 9.5 and 15 years (mean age: 11.8 years).

The onset of hirsutism or acne in all 17 women was between ages 12 and 20 years (mean: 15.3 years), occurring either at menarchal age or 0.5 to 5 years after menarche. Eight of the 17 women began to have menstrual abnormalities either simultaneously with onset of hirsutism or acne or 2 years after onset of hirsutism. Of note is the fact that two women who did not have menstrual abnormalities were found to have polycystic changes of the ovaries on pelvic ultrasonogram.

Baseline random serum LH and FSH concentrations (3-19 mIU/ml and 5-17 mIU/ml, respectively) in 13 of the 17 women were in the range of normal early to late follicular levels, irrespective of presence or absence of menstrual disorders or cystic changes of the ovaries on sonogram. However, random serum LH concentrations in 4 of the 17 women were elevated (>29 mIU/ml). These four women had menstrual abnormalities; of the four, three underwent pelvic sonography, with normal findings in one and abnormal findings in two. Serum prolactin levels in 16 women measured were in the normal range (4 to 22 ng/ml, where the normal range is less than 25 ng/ml).

Four of the 17 women underwent adrenal computerized tomography, which showed unequivocal mild to marked bilateral adrenal hyperplasia. One of the 17 women had abdominal ultrasonographic studies, which revealed clear-cut enlargement of the left adrenal gland; the right adrenal gland was not visualized.[117]

EPIDEMIOLOGY. Although it has been claimed that the 3β-HSD deficiency is the second most common steroidogenic defect,[189] no epidemiological studies to date have verified the true frequency. There have been no reports of geographic clusters of 3β-HSD deficiency, nor is there a recognized ethnic predominance. As in the case of 21-hydroxylase deficiency, an attenuated, or late-onset, form of the disease is more common than the severe deficiency form.

MOLECULAR GENETIC STUDIES. The 3β-HSD enzyme has a molecular weight of 46,000, is not a P450 cytochrome, and requires NAD^+ as a cofactor.[7] The gene encoding 3β-HSD has not yet been cloned. Deficiency of this enzyme is not linked to the HLA complex.[178]

A recent study showed in several strains of mouse that the enzyme 3β-HSD is encoded by the same structural gene in adrenal and gonadal tissue, and is under separate regulatory control genetically in the two tissues.[190]

11β-Hydroxylase Deficiency

An inborn error of steroid biosynthesis resulting in defective 11β-hydroxylase activity was first described by Eberlein and Bongiovanni[191] and accounts for approximately 5 percent of all cases of CAH.[59,63,157,192] The 11β-hydroxylase deficiency results in a rise of the 11-deoxysteroids, 11-deoxycortisol (compound S), and 11-deoxycorticosterone (DOC), a moderately potent salt-retaining steroid. The elevated DOC causes sodium retention, plasma volume expansion, and suppression of plasma renin activity (PRA). Indeed, the suppressed PRA is considered a hallmark of this defect, but recently exceptions have been noted.[193] Hypertension is the single clinical feature of this disorder which, if present, allows distinction from 21-hydroxylase deficiency. Hypokalemia and alkalosis resulting from mineralocorticoid hormone excess are inconstant features of this form of CAH. It is not entirely clear that DOC is the agent causing elevation of blood pressure,[157,191] since there are

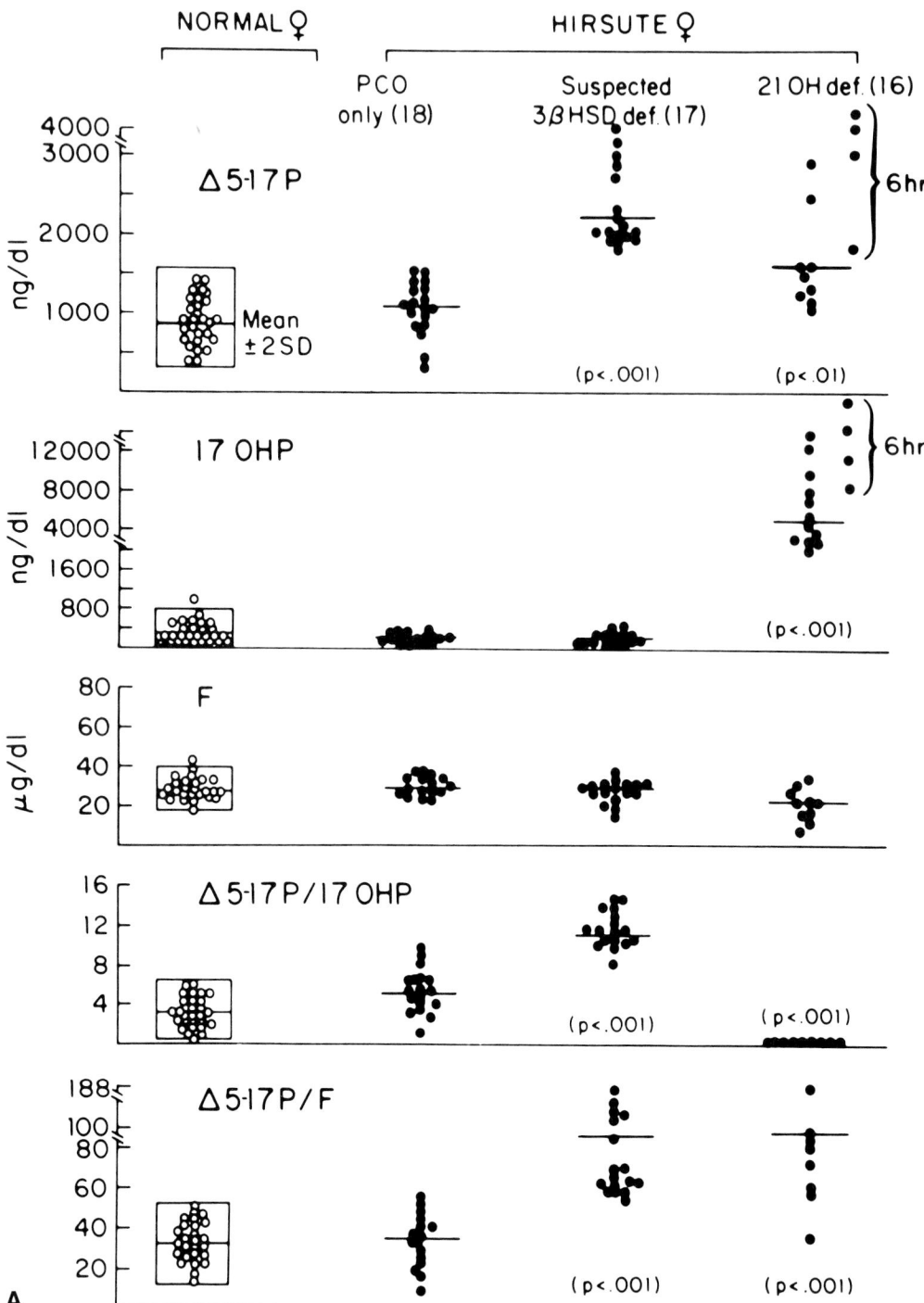

Fig. 74-18 *A.* Serum 17-hydroxysteroid responses to ACTH stimulation (1 h after 0.25-mg intravenous bolus dose) in normal women and women with hirsutism. *B.* Serum androgen levels after ACTH stimulation in normal women and women with hirsutism.

Numbers in parentheses represent the number of determinations.
F = cortisol; DS = dehydroepiandrosterone sulfate;
T = testosterone; DHEA = dehydroepiandrosterone.
(From Pang et al.[117] Used by permission.)

normotensive patients with 11β-hydroxylase deficiency and elevated DOC[194,195] and hypertensive patients with normal to mildly elevated DOC.[196,197] Furthermore, intravenous DOC infusion does not necessarily induce hypertension in control subjects.[198,199] Nor does suppression of DOC always cause remission of the hypertension in all patients.[200] In patients with 11β-hydroxylase deficiency who are in remission from hypertension while treated with dexamethasone, infusion of DOC should show recurrence of hypertension if DOC is indeed the hypertensive agent. Conclusive results from such an experiment have not yet been reported. It has been proposed that

DOC metabolite(s), perhaps 18-hydroxyl-11-deoxycorticosterone, may be partially responsible for the hypertension.[200,201] The presence of mineralocorticoid excess and hypertension is not necessarily proportional to the degree of hypokalemia, nor is there a direct correlation between the degree of virilization and hypertension.[200]

As in 21-hydroxylase deficiency, excess fetal androgen production causes prenatal virilization of females, resulting in ambiguous external genitalia with normal female internal reproductive organs. In newborn males with 11β-hydroxylase deficiency the external genitalia may be normal, but in either

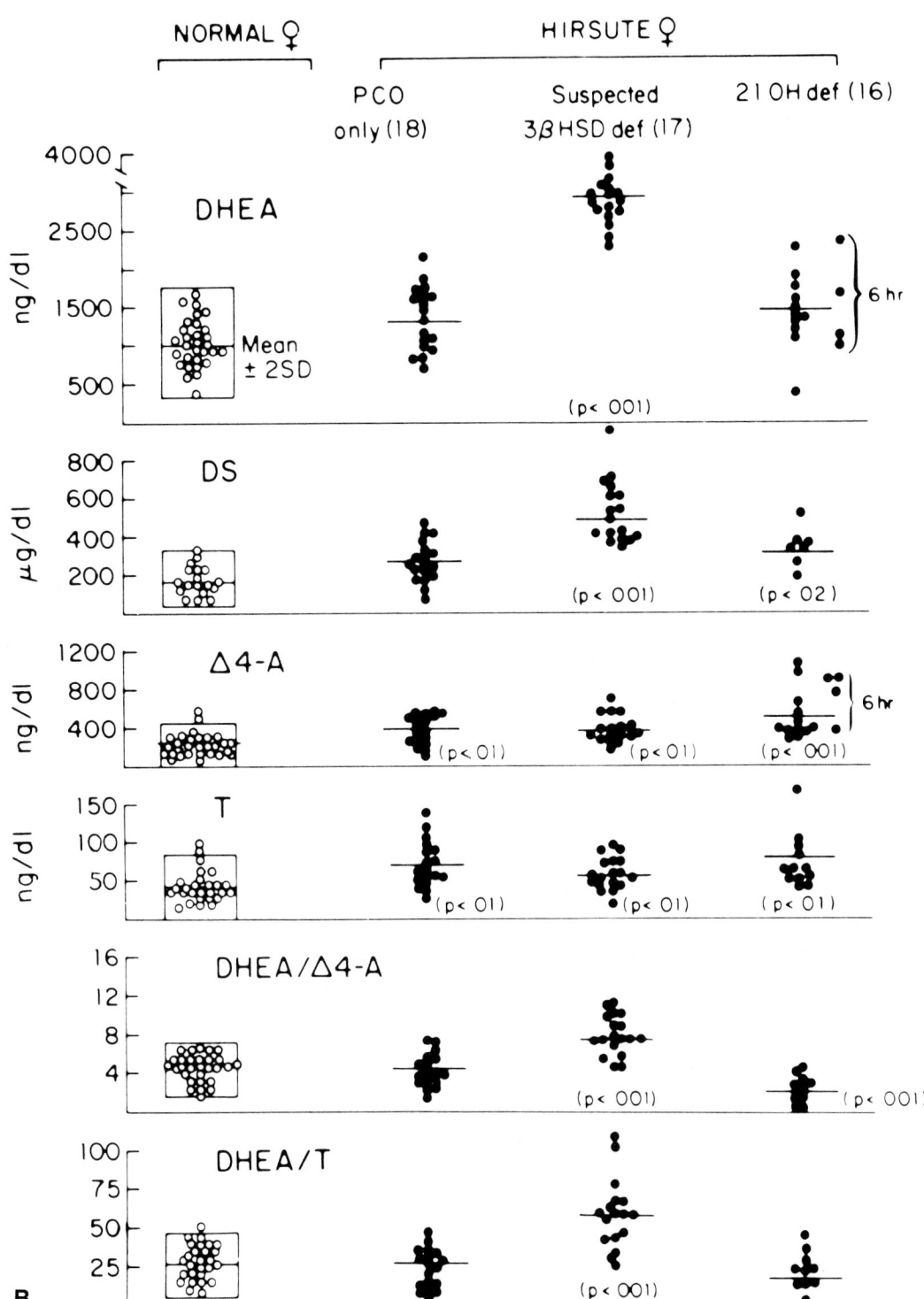

Fig. 74-18 *(continued)*

sex, virilization ensues postnatally if the disorder is untreated.

Mild, late-onset, and even cryptic forms of 11β-hydroxylase deficiency have been reported[202-207] and may represent allelic variants. Investigators have been unable to demonstrate a consistent biochemical defect in obligate heterozygote parents, either in the baseline state or with ACTH stimulation. Some, but not all, showed an elevated 17-OHP/cortisol or 11-deoxy-cortisol/cortisol ratio.[208] It is possible that in 11β-hydroxylase deficiency as in 21-hydroxylase deficiency the group with incomplete penetrance or late onset of the clinical symptoms may represent compound heterozygotes for one severe and one mild gene defect. Whereas in 21-hydroxylase deficiency het-

erozygotes for the severe and mild enzyme defects fall within the same range of values, it is conceivable that individuals who are heterozygotes for a mild 11β-hydroxylase deficiency gene may demonstrate no biochemical abnormality.

The mode of genetic transmission is autosomal recessive. Linkage studies showed that 11β-hydroxylase deficiency is not linked to the HLA complex.[208-210] More recently, the gene for 11β-hydroxylase has been assigned to chromosome 8 (see "Molecular Genetics," below).

EPIDEMIOLOGY. While 11β-hydroxylase deficiency accounts for approximately 5 percent of the worldwide cases of CAH, a retrospective survey in Israel (1957–1973) revealed that 20 percent of that country's CAH population was made up of 11β-hydroxylase deficiency patients.[211] There was one 11β-hydroxylase deficiency patient per 60,000 live births, with a corresponding heterozygote frequency of 1 in 150 persons. This unexpected clustering of cases was traced to families of North African origin, particularly Morocco and Tunisia, where Jews had settled before the destruction of the Second Temple in Jerusalem by the Romans in A.D. 70, and where little intermarriage had occurred until the mid-twentieth century. Turkish Jews have also been found to carry the 11β-hydroxylase deficiency gene in high frequency.[200,212,213]

CMO II DEFICIENCY. Since recent biochemical studies of Hall and his group indicate that the enzymatic activities of 11β-hydroxylase and corticosterone methyl oxidase types I (CMO I; 18-hydroxylase) and II (CMO II; 18-dehydrogenase) all reside in one protein (P450c11),[18] it is possible that patients with CMO II deficiency may represent allelic variants of 11β-hydroxylase deficiency. Previous studies have indicated that 18-hydroxylase activity is deficient in patients with 11β-hydroxylase deficiency.[202,214] It has recently been demonstrated that the mutation causing CMO II deficiency is indeed within or near the structural gene for P450c11.[214a]

Patients with CMO II deficiency present at birth with hyponatremic hyperkalemia and dehydration. The disorder was first described by Royer[215] and Russell[216] and is reviewed by Ulick.[217] Diagnosis is established by raised precursor/product ratios of 18-hydroxytetrahydrocorticosterone (18OH-THB) to tetrahydroaldosterone (THA) measured in urine or of 18-hydroxycorticosterone (18-OHB) to aldosterone in serum. A cluster of cases amongst Jews of Iranian origin was described by Rösler,[218] but American pedigrees have been described as well.[219,220]

MOLECULAR GENETICS. If this disorder follows the model of 21-hydroxylase deficiency (the only adrenal disorder in which a mutation in the structural gene has been correlated with the disease), then presumably mutations in the structural gene for P450c11 can produce a spectrum of clinical symptoms from hypertension and virilism (11β-hydroxylase deficiency) to salt wasting without virilism (CMO I/II). As no mutations causing any of the clinical syndromes of 11β-hydroxylase or CMO I or II deficiency have yet been identified, future studies will elucidate whether the clinical variability results from heterogeneity of mutant alleles.

A cDNA clone encoding human P450c11 has been isolated and used to locate the corresponding structural gene, CYP11B (formerly OH11 or P450C11), on the long arm of chromosome 8.[22] Mutually confirmatory results were obtained by hybridization *in situ* with metaphase spreads of human chromosomes, and hybridization with a panel of human-rodent somatic cell hybrids of known chromosomal composition.[22] Other genes of interest in this chromosomal region include the cellular oncogenes MYC and MOS and the thyroglobulin gene, TG.[220a] Further studies will be required to establish a linkage map of CYP11B in relation to these genes. While it appears that CYP11B is present in the haploid genome in a single copy, the possibility of two closely linked homologues, as occurs with 21-hydroxylase (genes CYP21A and CYP21B), has not been ruled out.

Thus far, hybridization studies of DNA samples from patients with 11β-hydroxylase deficiency have not shown gross

deletions or rearrangement of the CYP11 gene, and linkage of the disease to polymorphisms of this gene remains to be demonstrated.

Prenatal Diagnosis of 11β-Hydroxylase Deficiency. Levels of 11-deoxycortisol and tetrahydro-11-deoxycortisol (THS) in amniotic fluid and of tetrahydro-11-deoxycortisol in maternal urine have been found to be increased in pregnancies with fetuses affected with 11β-hydroxylase deficiency.[221,222] This suggests that prenatal diagnosis of this disorder by hormonal measurement is feasible. Now that the 11β-hydroxylase gene has been cloned (see "Molecular Genetics," above), it is possible that polymorphism may be found; if so, it would be useful in prenatal diagnosis.

17α-Hydroxylase Deficiency

A defect in 17α-hydroxylase results in diminished secretion of glucocorticoids and sex steroids and increased secretion of mineralocorticoids. Since the first description of 17α-hydroxylase deficiency by Biglieri in a female[223] and by New in a male,[224] additional cases in males and females have been reported.[225–228,228a] In all cases there has been an overproduction of 17-deoxysteroids, especially corticosterone. The hypertension and hypokalemia have been attributed to the excessive DOC secretion. Untreated females with 17α-hydroxylase deficiency have had sexual infantilism. The androgen deficiency results in pseudohermaphroditism in males. In males, also, there is suppression of the müllerian ducts and the uterus and fallopian tubes are absent, indicating the normal production of müllerian-inhibiting hormone; on the other hand, gynecomastia is a prominent feature of puberty. About 40 cases have been reported to date.[228a]

Laboratory tests show decreased serum androgen levels and decreased urinary excretion of 17-ketosteroids and 17-hydroxycorticosteroids, as expected as a consequence of the 17α-hydroxylase defect. Also reported in many cases are low aldosterone levels. As renin rises consequent to the fall in DOC resulting from dexamethasone treatment, the low aldosterone levels rise, giving evidence for the capacity of the zona glomerulosa to synthesize aldosterone.[228]

17,20-Lyase Deficiency. 17,20-Lyase activity resides in the same P450 enzyme (P450c17).[9] Deficiency of this activity causes an isolated defect in the synthesis of C_{19} sex steroids.[229] Urinary pregnanetriolone, a metabolite of 17α-hydroxyprogesterone, is increased and increases further after ACTH and human chorionic gonadotropin (hCG) stimulation, the latter observation indicating concordance for the gene defect in both adrenal and testicular tissue.[230]

Testosterone or DHEA excretion does not rise appreciably. Seven patients in a total of three different kindreds with this disorder have been reported. All seven patients were genetic males.[230–233] As has been noted for the 11β-hydroxylase deficiency, it has been reported for 17,20-lyase deficiency that the defect may be selective for one of the enzyme's two substrates[233] and may be of variable severity. Indeed, patients have been reported in whom the presenting clinical feature was hypospadias.[234] It is thus conceivable that mild forms of 17,20-lyase deficiency may be more common than generally suspected, and could potentially be detected in the course of human chorionic gonadotropin and/or ACTH stimulation of hypospadiac males.

Earlier, family studies showed no HLA association with this enzyme defect.[235,236] The structural gene for P450c17, CYP17, has now been located on chromosome 10,[25] but thus far a regional localization of this gene has not been performed. Apparently the same gene is expressed in both the adrenal gland and the testis.[237] Other genes have been reported but not mapped.[238]

Hybridization studies of DNA samples from patients with 17α-hydroxylase deficiency have not demonstrated gross deletions or rearrangements of this gene.[239] One mutation causing combined 17α-hydroxylase/17,20-lyase deficiency has now been described, a duplication near the carboxy terminus producing a slightly abbreviated alternate sequence in place of the final 28 amino acids of the P450c17 protein.[239a]

Cholesterol Desmolase Deficiency

Cholesterol desmolase deficiency involves the side-chain cleavage converting cholesterol to pregnenolone. At least three enzymes are involved in this conversion: 20S-hydroxylase, 22R-hydroxylase, and 20R,22R-desmolase.[240]

In 1955, Prader and Gurtner[241] described a male pseudohermaphrodite with severe salt wasting and impaired synthesis of all three classes of adrenal steroids: mineralocorticoids, glucocorticoids, and sex steroids. In this genetic male, female external genitalia with male internal genital ducts were found at autopsy. The severe ambiguity of the external genitalia in males suggests that the enzyme defect is also present in the testes. The enlarged adrenal glands seen in this first known case were remarkable in that the cortical cells were filled with lipoid material consisting of cholesterol and cholesterol esters, which prompted the name *lipoid adrenal hyperplasia*.

About 32 patients with this biosynthetic defect have since been described.[242,243] Recently reported, however, was the case of a patient diagnosed in the newborn period who was successfully treated for 18 years.[244] Most of the 32 reported cases were of patients who did not survive beyond infancy and died in adrenal crisis due to deficient mineralocorticoid and glucocorticoid production.

Degenhart[245] obtained biochemical evidence that the deficient enzyme in one patient was the cholesterol 20S-hydroxylase, but deficiency of any of the three enzymes would lead to profound adrenal insufficiency. As in the enzyme defects described above, attenuated forms of this enzyme deficiency may have gone unrecognized.

There appears to be geographic clustering of patients. Eighteen patients, or about 56 percent of those reported, are of Japanese origin; another group was reported from Switzerland and Germany, where five of the nine European patients resided. Thus these two groups account for 23 of the 32 cases reported.[244]

Bovine[20] and human cDNA clones that encode P450scc have been isolated; the corresponding human gene is located on chromosome 15.[21] As yet, it has not been demonstrated that this gene is affected in lipoid adrenal hyperplasia;[246] presumably, similar effects would result from mutations in cholesteryl ester hydrolase, sterol carrier protein 2 (SCP$_2$), any of the ACTH-sensitive labile protein factors, adrenodoxin, or adrenodoxin reductase.

THERAPY

Treatment

The fundamental aim of endocrine therapy for CAH is to provide replacement of the deficient hormones. Since 1949, when Wilkins et al.[247] and Bartter[248] discovered the efficacy of cortisone therapy for CAH due to 21-hydroxylase deficiency, glucocorticoid therapy has been the keystone of treatment for this disorder. Glucocorticoid administration both replaces the deficient cortisol and suppresses ACTH overproduction, resulting in cessation of overstimulation of the adrenal cortex and amelioration of the noxious effects of oversecreted adrenal steroids. Proper replacement therapy in 21- and 11β-hydroxylase deficiency suppresses excessive adrenal androgen production, averting further virilization, slowing accelerated growth and bone age advancement to a more normal rate, and allowing a normal onset of puberty (Fig. 74-19). Glucocorticoid treatment also leads to remission of hypertension in 11β- and 17α-hydroxylase deficiency, presumably by suppressing oversecretion of DOC. Excessive glucocorticoid administration should be avoided, since this produces cushingoid facies, growth retardation, and inhibition of epiphyseal maturation. For patients with the enzyme deficiencies impairing mineralocorticoid synthesis, the administration of salt-retaining steroid is required to maintain adequate sodium balance.

Hydrocortisone (cortisol) is most often used; it is the physiological hormone and does not introduce the complication of adjustment for potency, biologic half-life, or altered profile of steroid action. Oral administration is the preferred and usual mode of treatment; it has conventionally been believed that better suppression of adrenal androgen production is achieved with divided doses, although a recent study questions this;[249] 10 to 20 mg/m^2 hydrocortisone divided equallly in two daily doses by tablet is adequate for the otherwise healthy child. In non-life-threatening illness or stress, increased dosage of two to three times the maintenance regimen is indicted for a few days. Each family must be given injection kits of hydrocortisone (50 mg for young children, 100 mg for older patients) for emergency use. In the event of a surgical procedure, a total of 5 to 10 times the daily maintenance dose (depending on the nature of the operative procedure) may be required over the first 24 h; the dose can then be rapidly tapered.

If there is poor response to hydrocortisone at the standard dose, dosage may be increased to 20 to 30 mg/(m^2 · day), or the regimen may be changed to either one of the hormone analogues prednisone (17,21-dihydroxypregna-1,4-diene-3,11, 20-trione) or dexamethasone (9-fluoro-16α-methylprednisolone). These agents are more potent and are longer-acting, although their relative glucocorticoid and mineralocorticoid effects differ and the smaller amounts used make dosage adjustment more critical. Because of individual variations in hepatic capability in metabolizing 11-oxosteroids, and thus in plasma clearance and half-life, prednisolone (11β-hydroxyprednisone) is found in some patients to be more effective than prednisone in the replacement of cortisol function. Classic 21-hydroxylase patients with salt losing additionally require mineralocorticoid replacement. The cortisol analogue (21-acetyloxy)-9α-fluorohydrocortisone (Florinef;9α-FF) is used for its potent mineralocorticoid activity. In an adrenal crisis, if the patient is unable to ingest medications, liberal infusions of iso-

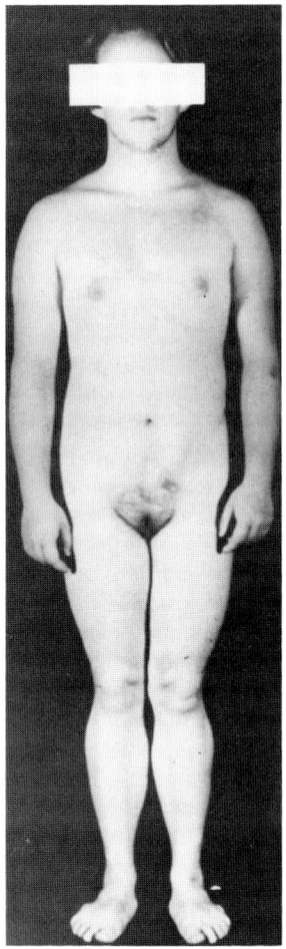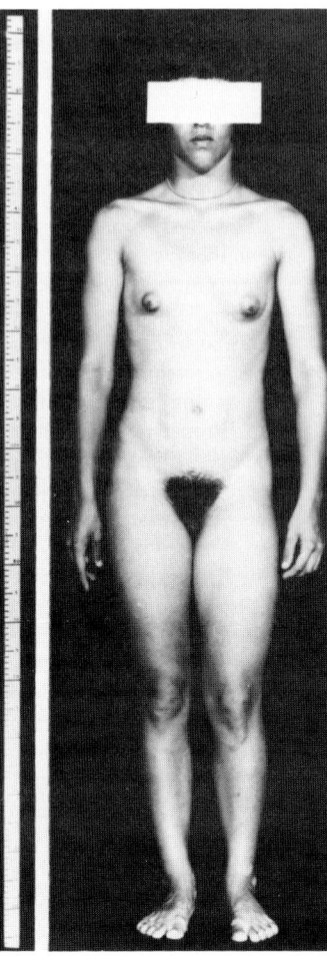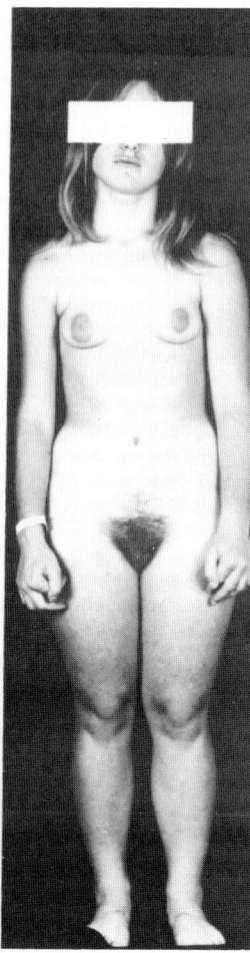

Fig. 74-19 Habitus of pubertal girls with CAH due to 21-hydroxylase deficiency. Patient on the left was untreated until age 16 years; patient in the center was treated from age 9 years; patient on the right was treated from age 4 years. Note the progressively more feminine habitus with earlier start of treatment. (From New and Levine.[157] Used by permission.)

tonic saline or parenteral DOCA (deoxycorticosterone acetate) should be used.

Increasing attention has been focused on the role of the renin-angiotensin system in the treatment of CAH. Although aldosterone levels are not deficient in the non-salt-wasting (simple virilizing) form of 21-hydroxylase deficiency, it has long been recognized that PRA is elevated in the non-salt-wasting as well as in the salt-wasting form.[250-256] Despite the observation of elevated PRA, it has not been customary to supplement conventional glucocorticoid replacement therapy with the administration of salt-retaining steroids in cases of non-salt-wasting 21-hydroxylase deficiency. Rösler and colleagues[255] demonstrated that the addition of salt-retaining hormone to glucocorticoid therapy in non-salt-wasting patients with elevated PRA does in fact improve the hormonal control of the disease.

Rösler showed that in patients with CAH due to 21-hydroxylase deficiency, the PRA was closely correlated with the ACTH level. Thus, when PRA was normalized by the added administration of 9α-fludrocortisone acetate, a steroid with salt-retaining activity, the ACTH level fell and excessive androgen stimulation by ACTH decreased. The addition of salt-retaining steroids to the therapeutic regimen often made a decrease in the glucocorticoid dose possible. Normalization of PRA also resulted in improved statural growth in these patients, a finding which has been corroborated in subsequent reports (Fig. 74-20).[255,256]

The newly developed steroid radioimmunoassays have been useful not only for the initial diagnosis of CAH, but also for improved monitoring of hormonal control once therapy has been instituted. Serum 17-OHP and Δ^4-androstenedione levels provide sensitive index of biochemical control in patients with 21-hydroxylase deficiency.[257-259] In females and prepubertal males, but not in newborn and pubertal males, the serum testosterone level is also a useful index.[258] The combined determinations of PRA, 17-OHP, and serum androgens, as well as the clinical assessment of growth and pubertal status, must all be considered in adjusting the dose of glucocorticoid and salt-retaining steroid for optimal therapeutic control. Both in our clinic and in others, combinations of hydrocortisone and 9α-FF have proved to be highly effective treatment modalities.[257]

Measurement of PRA can be used to monitor efficacy of treatment not only in 21-hydroxylase deficiency but also in other salt-losing forms of CAH (cholesterol desmolase and 3β-HSD deficiencies). It is also useful as a therapeutic index in those forms of CAH with mineralocorticoid excess and suppressed PRA (11β-hydroxylase deficiency and 17α-hydroxylase deficiencies). In poor control, PRA is elevated in the salt-losing forms and suppressed in the mineralocorticoid excess forms (Fig. 74-20).

Sex Assignment

Sexual ambiguity at birth characteristic of male or female pseudohermaphroditism is a common presenting sign of CAH (see Table 74-1). In such cases, a rational and judicious choice of sex assignment is a critical aspect of treatment, since the decision of sex assignment has obvious lifelong implications. Determination of genetic sex by karyotype and accurate diag-

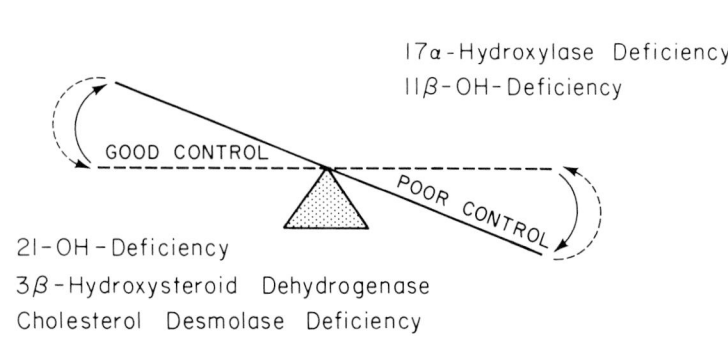

Fig. 74-20 The pivotal role of PRA monitoring in various forms of CAH. In poor control, renin is elevated in 21-hydroxylase (OH) deficiency, 3β-hydroxysteroid deficiency, and cholesterol desmolase deficiency and decreases with proper mineralocorticoid treatment. In 17α-hydroxylase deficiency and 11β-hydroxylase deficiency, in contrast, renin is suppressed in poor control and rises with proper treatment. *(From New et al.[1] Used by permission.)*

nosis of the specific underlying enzymatic defect are essential in assessing a patient's potential for future sexual activity and fertility.

In cases of female pseudohermaphroditism resulting from 21- or 11β-hydroxylase deficiency, a female sex assignment is appropriate. When medical treatment is begun early in life, the initially large and prominent clitoris shrinks slightly, and as the surrounding structures grow normally, it becomes much less prominent and surgical revision of the clitoris may not be required. When the clitoris is conspicuously enlarged or when the abnormal genitalia interfere with parent-child bonding, plastic surgery to correct the appearance of the clitoris should be carried out in infancy. Definitive vaginoplasty should, in general, be performed in early to mid adolescence by an experienced gynecologic surgeon.[260] Because of the normal internal genitalia and gonads in these patients, normal puberty, fertility, and childbearing are possible when there is early therapeutic intervention. In view of this potential for normal female sexual development, it is unfortunate when, as a result of a hasty delivery room examination of the virilized external genitalia, affected females are improperly assigned and reared as males.

In patients with male pseudohermaphroditism due to enzyme deficiencies impairing androgen synthesis, a sex assignment consistent with the genetic sex—i.e., a male sex assignment—is not always optimal. Virilization of the genitalia in these children is frequently so extremely and irrevocably incomplete that the anatomy precludes normal male functioning. There are certain physiologic capacities which we consider integral to "normal" male sexual development: a capacity for urinating in a standing position in prepuberty, and the capacity for sexual intercourse. The development of secondary sex characteristics adequate for the presentation of a male gender identity in society and a capacity for relatively normal sexual activity may be possible. However, because these capacities are often severely compromised in genetic males with congenital disorders of sex steroid synthesis, a female sex assignment may be advisable. If the male pseudohermaphrodite is to be raised as a female, surgical correction of the genitalia and gonadectomy are required; with appropriate therapeutic measures, sexual development as a female and relatively normal, albeit infertile, sexual activity are again possible. In cases of impaired androgen synthesis, administration of sex steroids is usually required to induce development of appropriate sex characteristics at puberty—either estrogens if the patient is to be reared as a female or androgens if reared as a male.

Society sees phenotype, not genotype. In assigning a sex of rearing to a male or female pseudohermaphrodite, the genetic sex is of less consideration than the physiologic and anatomic character of the genitalia and their potential for development

and function. Because of the wide individual variability in the presentation of ambiguous genitalia in these patients, there can be no all-inclusive rules for sex assignment based solely on genetic sex or type of enzyme deficiency.

Psychoendocrine Treatment. Psychologists and psychiatrists well acquainted with these endocrine disorders provide a vital component of the treatment regimen, since one of the major goals of therapy is to ensure that gender role, gender behavior, and gender identity are isosexual with the sex of assignment.[261]

PROBLEMS, SPECULATIONS, AND HISTORY

Despite a huge literature and a great number of investigations developed on congenital adrenal hyperplasia, there are still many unanswered questions:

1. The masculinization of the genitalia of the newborn female with congenital adrenal hyperplasia (CAH) is not accompanied by other signs of androgen excess such as wolffian duct development or advanced linear growth or bone age. It is presumed that the failure of wolffian duct development may be attributed to the absence of local testosterone, despite a circulating level of testosterone sufficient to masculinize genitalia. This is not proven. The absence of anabolic signs—advanced height, weight, or bone age—in the newborn remains unexplained, and puzzled Bongiovanni until his death.

2. The masculinizing signs of nonclassic 21-hydroxylase deficiency are extremely variable despite similar levels of androgen. Thus, some patients with nonclassic 21-hydroxylase deficiency develop acne, and others develop hirsutism, oligomenorrhea, or even reduced fertility, while some remain asymptomatic. The basis for the specific and idiosyncratic organ response to excess androgen remains unexplained. A suggestion is that receptor sensitivity may vary among individuals and thus among individual patients. Now that the androgen receptor has been cloned,[261a,261b] variability of organ response may be studied on a molecular basis. It is also possible that peripheral androgen metabolism in skin or hair follicles may vary among patients and within patients with time.

Sonography, which is now a much used diagnostic tool, frequently demonstrates cystic ovaries in patients with CAH due to 21-hydroxylase, 11β-hydroxylase, and 3β-hydroxysteroid dehydrogenase deficiency similar to the syndrome of polycystic ovary disease (PCO). Will the suppression of adrenal androgens, readily accomplished in treatment of CAH, cause reversal of the cystic changes in the ovary? Preliminary evidence indicates this is likely, suggesting that cystic changes of the ovary in humans can result from excess androgens from adrenal (or other extraovarian) sources. Further, it may be valuable to test all women with cystic ovaries seen on sonography for inborn errors of steroidogenesis—especially those women from ethnic groups at high risk for nonclassic 21-hydroxylase deficiency.

3. Though glucocorticoid treatment has been available since 1950, there is no agreement as to the regimen that gives the best outcome in terms of height. Recent studies suggest that even the most compliant patient may not achieve a final height compatible with parental stature. Is this due to overtreatment? Or is it due to the failure of oral glucocorticoid therapy given twice or even three times daily to keep excess androgen production suppressed? A simple system is necessary for home-monitoring the hormonal status of patients at sufficiently frequent intervals to ensure hormonal control. A recent report using salivary 17-OHP concentration may provide an easy means to monitor hormone levels on a daily basis. Similar considerations may apply to the preservation of fertility.[133]

4. That androgens influence aspects of central nervous system development and function is well recognized, but there are controversial data with regard to specific effects resulting from CAH. It has been proposed that a masculinized gender role in girls, with behavioral manifestations such as tomboyism, is a result of prenatal androgen excess in CAH. Similarly considered, behavior changes resulting from other alterations in the androgen milieu are seen in studies on male pseudohermaphrodites with 5α-reductase or 17-ketosteroid reductase deficiency, who often elect a male gender identity at puberty.[261a,261b] Yet there is a great body of careful psychological studies indicating that in humans, unlike other mammals, the sex of rearing overrides prenatal hormonal effects.[262]

An effect of androgens on handedness has recently been documented in a study showing increased prevalence of left-handedness in girls with CAH.[263] This indicates masculinization of the brain, since left-handedness is more frequent in males. However, studies of postnatal androgen effects on handedness would be necessary to prove that the increased sinistrality is a result of increased androgen effect prenatally. There is now recognition, apart from endocrine gland secretions, of endogenous steroid production within the brain;[263c,263d] the functions of such neurosteroids will clearly prove to be involved in central nervous system development.

Perhaps the most controversial of the effects of androgens on the brain is their effect on intelligence. Some studies indicate that IQ is higher in CAH patients than in the general population.[264,265] Is the effect on IQ the result of prenatal androgens, or is it linked to the genetic mutation for 21-hydroxylase deficiency? Heterozygotes might be expected to exhibit higher IQs than homozygotes for the normal gene even though both of these genotypes could have normal prenatal androgen levels. No conclusive study linking intelligence to the actual gene defect in families with CAH has yet been reported.

5. Another challenging question is whether synthesis of aldosterone in the zona glomerulosa is under different genetic control from the synthesis of corticosterone in the zona fasciculata; both require 21 hydroxylation. Only one gene for 21-hydroxylase has been shown to be active. Deletions of this gene or point mutations in the gene that completely prevent synthesis of active P450c21 cause aldosterone deficiency associated with salt-wasting symptoms in infants, and nonsynthesis of the P450c21 enzyme protein should indeed always

result in an aldosterone deficiency phenotype. Yet, one-fourth of patients never have aldosterone deficiency and some patients outgrow the aldosterone deficiency of infancy. The most difficult to explain is the case of a patient with a homozygous deletion of the active 21-hydroxylase gene who was a profound salt waster in infancy and who after age 12 recovered the capacity to make aldosterone.[266] Explanations for this recovery include the following:

a. An extraadrenal enzyme capable of 21 hydroxylation, e.g., renal 21-hydroxylase, peripherally converts the oversecreted precursor progesterone to DOC, which then circulates to the adrenal glands for conversion to aldosterone. This explanation seems unlikely, since aldosterone synthesis has been observed in a patient with homozygous deletion of the active 21-hydroxylase gene (CYP21B) while adrenal production of progesterone was suppressed by dexamethasone. The suppression of progesterone is especially relevant, since only 1 percent of the blood volume circulates through the adrenal glands. Thus, the DOC level would have to be very high in the adrenal artery for conversion in the adrenal glands to aldosterone in sufficient quantities to cause sodium conservation.

b. A cytochrome P450 nonhomologous with P450c21 is (aberrantly) expressed in the adrenal glands and assumes the 21-hydroxylation function. This is eminently plausible.

c. The recovery of aldosterone-synthesizing capacity in those patients with a mild 21-hydroxylase deficiency occurs because of increased synthesis of a partially deficient enzyme as the adrenal glands increase in size with age. This explanation would not apply to the patient with the homozygous deletion. Further, the degree of defect if judged by the degree of virilization is not correlated with salt wasting.

d. There may be other epigenetic phenomena promoting aldosterone synthesis in the presence of a mutation in the active 21-hydroxylase gene.

6. Another problem to be resolved is whether the risk to the fetus of chorionic villus biopsy (2 percent mortality) is too high for the benefit of early diagnosis. In only one-fourth of pregnancies in question will the fetus be affected, and one-half of these will be males who do not need prenatal treatment for prevention of virilization. Thus, only one-eighth of fetuses require treatment. Since prenatal treatment with dexamethasone is apparently without ill effect for the fetus, treatment could be initiated early in all pregnancies with a fetus at risk and continued until diagnosis could be made by amniocentesis at 16 weeks by HLA typing. Amniocentesis has a 0.5 percent mortality risk to the fetus, which is lower than the risk of chorionic villus biopsy. In circumstances where even the risk of amniocentesis is unacceptable, unnecessary continued treatment of the fetus to term may be an acceptable alternative. Further experience will help evaluate this risk/benefit ratio. Until then the pregnant woman must be given both options.

7. A very interesting problem to be investigated is the basis for the very high frequency of nonclassic 21-hydroxylase deficiency in Ashkenazic Jews (Jews tracing their origins to the communities that grew up in, mostly, Central and Eastern Europe).[268] Is it the result of genetic drift, sex transmission ratio distortion, or selective advantage to the heterozygote? The heterozygote advantage explanation gains support from the observation of the high frequency of the salt-wasting 21-hy-

droxylase deficiency in Yupik Eskimos. In that population, which has an incidence of classic CAH of 1 in 600 live births, there is also 10 times the world's incidence of *Haemophilus influenzae* meningitis. Resistance to *H. influenzae* may be an advantage enjoyed by the heterozygote, allowing for an increased population of heterozygotes, who then mate and produce progeny with CAH. The same mechanism applies to the high frequency of sickle-cell disease and malaria in the black population. Finally, the haplotype associated with autoimmune disease, HLA-A1,B8,DR3, is infrequent in both classic and nonclassic CAH patients, suggesting that resistance to autoimmune disease may be a heterozygote advantage (see Chap. 4).

8. Ashkenazic Jews, the group in which nonclassic 21-hydroxylase deficiency occurs with such high frequency, represent one of the three major divisions of the Jewish people, along with Sephardim (with roots in Jewish communities in the Mediterranean basin and parts of Western Europe) and Oriental Jews (comprising many subgroups scattered throughout the Near East including North Africa and extending to Arabia and parts of Asia).[268] Since the frequency of the disease is not as high in Sephardic or Oriental Jews, a stem mutation could be posited and dated after the dispersion of the Jews by the Romans in A.D. 70 (the second diaspora) and before the consolidation of the Ashkenazic communities of Eastern Europe, probably by the early second millenium of this era. The present-day Roman Jews are the oldest continuous Jewish community in Europe and first came to Rome two centuries before the second diaspora. A genetic anthropologic study of the Roman Jewish population might elucidate the relationship of this community to the other major branches of the world Jewish community. An international collaborative effort to study the molecular genetics of the Roman Jewish population should provide an insight into the history of this ancient Jewish community. The analysis of surnames of Roman Jewish families suggests a high degree of intermarriage among the Roman Jews, but the answer lies in the study of genetic polymorphism of the known linkage markers as well as the 21-hydroxylase gene.

Supported by grants from the National Institutes of Health, U.S. Public Health Service, HD00072 (MIN), AM07029, DK37867 (PCW), and CA22507 and CA08748 (BD), and by a grant (RR47) from the Division of Research Resources, General Clinical Research Centers Program, NIH. Support is also acknowledged from the Horace Goldsmith Foundation and the Harold and Juliet Kalikow Foundation. Dr. Pang's contribution is based on work conducted by her while a member of the faculty of Cornell Medical College.

We thank Susan Baker for critical reading of sections of the chapter. The authors wish to acknowledge the extraordinary efforts of Christopher Crawford and Vita Amendolagine, without whose industry, intelligence, and skills, this manuscript would never have been completed.

REFERENCES

1. NEW MI, DUPONT B, GRUMBACH K, LEVINE LS: Congenital adrenal hyperplasia and related conditions, in Stanbury JB, Wyngaarden JB, Fredrickson DS, Goldstein JL, Brown MS (eds): *The Metabolic Basis of Inherited Disease*, 5th ed. New York, McGraw-Hill, 1982, p 973.

2. WHITE PC, NEW MI, DUPONT B: Congenital adrenal hyperplasia. *N Engl J Med* 316:1519 and 316:1580, 1987.

2a. DOBBIE JW, MacKAY AM, SYMINGTON T: The structure and functional zon-ation of the human adrenal cortex, in James VHT, Landon J (eds): *The Investigation of Hypothalamic-Pituitary-Adrenal Function (Mem Soc Endocrinol*, vol 17). Cambridge, Cambridge University Press, 1968, p 103.

2b. HORNSBY PJ: Physiological and pathological effects of steroids on the function of the adrenal cortex. *J Steroid Biochem* 27:1161, 1987.

2c. NUSSDORFER GC: *Cytophysiology of the Adrenal Cortex (Int Rev Cytol*, vol 98). New York, Academic, 1986.

3. FINKELSTEIN M, SCHAEFER JM: Inborn errors of steroid biosynthesis. *Physiol Rev* 59:353, 1979.

3a. WATERMAN MR, SIMPSON ER: Cellular mechanisms involved in the acute and chronic actions of ACTH, in Anderson DC, Winter JSD (eds): *Adrenal Cortex*. London, Butterworths, 1985.

3b. VAHOUNY GV, CHANDERBHAN R, NOLAND BJ, SCALLON TJ: Cholesterol ester hydrolase and sterol carrier proteins. *Endocrine Res* 10:473, 1985.

4. CHANDERBHAN RF, KHARROUBI AT, NOLAND BJ, SCALLEN TJ, VAHOUNY GV: Sterol carrier protein: Further evidence for its role in steroidogenesis. *Endocrine Res* 12:351, 1986.

4a. HALL PF: On the mechanism of action of ACTH: The role of actin. *Endocrine Res* 10:431, 1985.

4b. LAMBETH JD, STEVENS VL: Cytochrome P-450$_{scc}$: Enzymology, and the regulation of intramitochondrial cholesterol delivery to the enzyme. *Endocrine Res* 10:283, 1985.

5a. PEDERSEN RC: Polypeptide activators of cholesterol side-chain cleavage. *Endocrine Res* 10:533, 1985.

5b. VOUTILAINEN R, MILLER WR: Hormonal regulation of genes for steroidogenic enzymes, in D'Agata R, Chrousos GP (eds): *Recent Advances in Adrenal Regulation and Function (Serono Symp*, vol 40). New York, Raven, 1987.

5c. BOGGARAM V, FUNKENSTEIN B, WATERMAN MR, SIMPSON ER: Lipoproteins and the regulation of adrenal steroidogenesis. *Endocrine Res* 10:387, 1985.

6. TAKIKAWA O, GOMI T, SUHARA K, ITAGAKI E, TAKEMORI S, KATAGIRI M: Properties of an adrenal cytochrome P450 (P450scc) for the side chain cleavage of cholesterol. *Arch Biochem Biophys* 190:300, 1978.

7. ISHII-OHBA H, SAIKI N, INANO H, TAMAOKI BI: Purification and characterization of rat adrenal 3β-hydroxysteroid dehydrogenase with steroid 5-ene-4-ene-isomerase. *J Steroid Biochem* 24:753, 1986.

8. KOMINAMI S, SHINZAWA K, TAKEMORI S: Purification and some properties of cytochrome P-450 specific for steroid 17α-hydroxylation and C17-C20 bond cleavage from guinea pig adrenal microsomes. *Biochem Biophys Res Commun* 109:916, 1982.

9. NAKAJIN S, SHINODA M, HANIU M, SHIVELY JE, HALL PF: C21 steroid side-chain cleavage enzyme from porcine adrenal microsomes. *J Biol Chem* 259:3971, 1984.

10. KOMINAMI S, OCHI H, KOBAYASHI Y, TAKEMORI S: Studies on the steroid hydroxylation system in adrenal cortex microsomes. *J Biol Chem* 255:3386, 1980.

11. SUHARA K, GOMI T, SATO H, ITAGAKI E, TAKEMORI S, KATAGIRI M: Purification and immunochemical characterization of the two adrenal cortex mitochondrial cytochrome P-450 proteins. *Arch Biochem Biophys* 190:290, 1978.

12. JOHN ME, JOHN MC, SIMPSON ER, WATERMAN MR: Regulation of cytochrome P-450$_{11}$β gene expression by adrenocorticotropin. *J Biol Chem* 260:5760, 1985.

13. JOHN ME, OKAMURA T, DEE A, ADLER B, JOHN MC, WHITE PC, SIMPSON ER, WATERMAN MR: Bovine steroid 21-hydroxylase: Regulation of biosynthesis. *Biochemistry* 25:2846, 1986.

14. ZUBER MX, JOHN ME, OKAMURA T, SIMPSON ER, WATERMAN MR: Bovine adrenocortical cytochrome P450$_{17}$α: Regulation of gene expression by ACTH and elucidation of primary sequence. *J Biol Chem* 261:2475, 1986.

15. AGUILERA G, CATT KJ: Regulation of aldosterone secretion by the renin-angiotensin system. *Proc Natl Acad Sci USA* 75:4057, 1978.

16. KUHNLE U, CHOW D, RAPAPORT R, PANG S, LEVINE LS, NEW MI: The 21-hydroxylase activity in the glomerulosa and fasciculata of the adrenal cortex in congenital adrenal hyperplasia. *J Clin Endocrinol Metab* 52:534, 1981.

17. GOMEZ-SANCHEZ CE, UPCAVAGE RJ, ZAGER PG, FOECKING MF, HOLLAND OB, GANGULY A: Urinary 18-hydroxycortisol and its relationship to the excretion of other adrenal steroids. *J Clin Endocrinol Metab* 65:310, 1987.

18. YANAGIBASHI K, HANIU M, SHIVELY JE, SHEN WH, HALL P: The synthesis of adosterone by the adrenal cortex. *J Biol Chem* 261:3556, 1986.

19. NEBERT DW, GONZALEZ FJ: P450 genes: Structure, evolution, and regulation. *Annu Rev Biochem* 56:945, 1987.

20. MOROHASHI K, FUJII-KURIYAMA Y, OKADA Y, SOGAWA K, HIROSE T, INAYAMA S, OMURA A: A molecular cloning and nucleotide sequence of cDNA for mRNA of mitochondrial cytochrome P-450(SCC) of bovine adrenal cortex. *Proc Natl Acad Sci USA* 81:4647, 1984.

21. CHUNG BC, MATTESON KJ, VOUTILAINEN R, MOHANDAS TK, MILLER WM:

Human cholesterol side-chain cleavage enzyme, P450scc: cDNA cloning assignment of the gene to chromosome 15, and expression in the placenta. *Proc Natl Acad Sci USA* 83:8962, 1986.

22. CHUA SC, SZABO P, VITEK A, GRZESCHIK K-H, JOHN M, WHITE PC: Cloning of cDNA encoding steroid 11β-hydroxylase (P450c11). *Proc Natl Acad Sci USA* 84:7193, 1987.

23. WHITE PC, NEW MI, DUPONT B: Cloning and expression of cDNA encoding a bovine adrenal cytochrome P-450 specific for steroid 21-hydroxylation. *Proc Natl Acad Sci USA* 81:1986, 1984.

24. WHITE PC, GROSSBERGER D, ONUFER BJ, CHAPLIN D, NEW MI, DUPONT B, STROMINGER JL: Two genes encoding steroid 21-hydroxylase are located near the genes encoding the fourth component of complement in man. *Proc Natl Acad Sci USA* 82:1089, 1985.

25. MATTESON KJ, PICADO-LEONARD J, CHUNG B-C, MOHANDAS TK, MILLER WM: Assignment of the gene for adrenal P450c17 (steroid 17α-hydroxylase/17,20-lyase) to human chromosome 10. *J Clin Endocrinol Metab* 63:789, 1986.

26. WHITE PC, NEW MI, DUPONT B: Structure of the human steroid 21-hydroxylase genes. *Proc Natl Acad Sci USA* 83:5111, 1986.

27. HIGASHI Y, YOSHIOKA H, YAMANE M, GOTOH O, Y FUJII-KURIYAMA: Complete nucleotide sequence of two steroid 21-hydroxylase genes tandemly arranged in human chromosome: A pseudogene and a genuine gene. *Proc Natl Acad Sci USA* 83:2841, 1986.

28. YOSHIOKA H, MOROHASHI KI, SOGAWA K, YAMANE M, KOMINAMI S, TAKEMORI S, OKADA Y, OMURA T, FUJII-KURIYAMA Y: Structural analysis of cloned cDNA for mRNA of microsomal cytochrome P-450(C21) which catalyzes steroid 21-hydroxylation in bovine adrenal cortex. *J Biol Chem* 261:4106, 1986.

29. MIZUKAMI Y, SOGAWA K, SUWA Y, MURAMATSU M, FUJII-KURIYAMA Y: Gene structure of a phenobarbital-inducible cytochrome P-450 in rat liver. *Proc Natl Acad Sci USA* 80:3958, 1983.

30. SOGAWA K, GOTOH O, KAWAJIRI K, FUJII-KURIYAMA Y: Distinct organization of methylcholanthrene- and phenobarbital-inducible cytochrome P-450 genes in the rat. *Proc Natl Acad Sci USA* 81:5066, 1984.

30a. LIPMAN DJ, PEARSON WR: Rapid and sensitive protein similarity searches. *Science* 227:1435, 1985.

31. WHITE PC, NEW MI, DUPONT B: HLA-linked congenital adrenal hyperplasia results from a defective gene encoding a cytochrome P-450 specific for steroid 21-hydroxylation. *Proc Natl Acad Sci USA* 81:7505, 1984.

32. CARROLL MC, CAMPBELL RD, PORTER RR: Mapping of steroid 21-hydroxylase genes adjacent to complement component C4 genes in HLA, the major histocompatibility complex in man. *Proc Natl Acad Sci USA* 82:521, 1985.

33. SYDNOR KL, KELLEY VC, RAILE RB, ELY RS, SAYERS G: Blood adrenocorticotrophin in children with congenital adrenal hyperplasia. *Proc Soc Exp Biol Med* 82:695, 1953.

34. BINOUX M, PHAM-HUU-TRUNG MT, GOURMELEN M, GIRARD F, CANLOBRE P: Plasma ACTH in adrenogenital syndrome. *Acta Paediatr Scand* 61:269, 1972.

35. GANONG WF, ALPERT LC, LEE TC: ACTH and the regulation of adrenocortical secretion. *N Engl J Med* 290:1006, 1974.

36. BUTLER GC, MARRIAN GF: The isolation of pregnane-3,17,20-triol from the urine of women showing the adrenogenital syndrome. *J Biol Chem* 119:565, 1937.

37. MASON HL, KEPLER EJ: Isolation of steroids from urine of patients with adrenal cortical tumors and adrenal cortical hyperplasia: A new 17-ketosteroid, androstane-3α,11-diol-17-one. *J Biol Chem* 161:235, 1945.

38. HUGHES IA, WINTER JSD: The application of a serum 17OH-progesterone radioimmunoassay to the diagnosis and management of congenital adrenal hyperplasia. *J Pediatr* 88:766, 1976.

38a. JOSSO N: Antimullerian hormone: New perspectives for a sexist molecule. *Endocrine Rev* 7:421, 1986.

39. PRADER A, SPAHR A, NEHER R: Erhöhte Aldosteronausscheidung beim kongenitalen adrenogenitalen Syndrom. *Schweiz Med Wochenschr* 85:45, 1955.

40. KLEIN R: Evidence for and evidence against the existence of a salt-losing hormone. *J Pediatr* 57:452, 1960.

41. KOWARSKI AA, FINKELSTEIN JW, SPAULDING JS, HOLMAN GS, MIGEON CJ: Aldosterone secretion rate in congenital adrenal hyperplasia. A discussion of the theories on the pathogenesis of the salt-losing form of the syndrome. *J Clin Invest* 44:1505, 1965.

42. KUHNLE U, LAND M, ULICK S: Evidence for the secretion of an antimineralocorticoid in congenital adrenal hyperplasia. *J Clin Endocrinol Metab* 62:934, 1986.

43. STONER E, DIMARTINO J, KUHNLE U, LEVINE LS, OBERFIELD SE, NEW MI: Is salt wasting in congenital adrenal hyerplasia genetic? *Clin Endocrinol* 24:9, 1986.

44. LUETSCHER JA: Studies of aldosterone in relation to water and electrolyte balance in man. *Recent Prog Horm Res* 12:175, 1956.

45. VERKAUF BS, JONES HW: Masculinization of the female genitalia in congenital adrenal hyperplasia: Relationship to the salt-losing variety of the disease. *South Med J* 63:634, 1970.

46. PRADER A: Vollkommen männliche äußere Genitalentwicklung und Salzverlustsyndrom bei Mädchen mit kongenitalem adrenogenitalem Syndrom. *Helv Paediatr Acta* 13:231, 1958.

47. ROSENBLOOM AL, SMITH DW: Varying expression for salt losing in related patients with congenital adrenal hyperplasia. *Pediatrics* 38:215, 1966.

48. CHILDS B, GRUMBACH MM, VAN WYK JJ: Virilizing adrenal hyperplasia: A genetic and hormonal study. *J Clin Invest* 35:213, 1956.

49. WILKINS L: Adrenal disorders. II. Congenital virilizing adrenal hyperplasia. *Arch Dis Child* 37:231, 1962.

50. HIRSCHFELD AJ, FLESHMAN JK: An unusually high incidence of salt-losing congenital adrenal hyperplasia in the Alaskan Eskimo. *J Pediatr* 75:492, 1969.

51. QAZI QH, THOMPSON MW: Incidence of salt-wasting form of congenital virilizing adrenal hyperplasia. *Arch Dis Child* 47:302, 1972.

52. PRADER A: Die Häufigkeit des kongenitalen adrenogenitalen Syndroms. *Helv Paediatr Acta* 13:426, 1958.

53. PRADER A, ANDERS GJPA, HABICH H: Zur Genetik des kongenitalen adrenogenitalen Syndroms (virilisierende Nebennierenhyperplasie). *Helv Paediatr Acta* 17:271, 1962.

54. HUBBLE D: Congenital adrenal hyperplasia, in Holt KS, Raine DN (eds): *Basic Concepts of Inborn Errors and Defects of Steroid Biosynthesis.* Edinburgh, Livingston, 1966, p 68.

55. MAUTHE I, LASPE H, KNORR D: Zur Häufigkeit des kongenitalen adrenogenitalen Syndroms (AGS): München 1963–1972. *Klin Padiatr* 189:172, 1977.

56. ROSENBLOOM AL, SMITH DW: Congenital adrenal hyperplasia. *Lancet* 1:660, 1966.

57. BOIS E, MORNET E, CHOMPRET A, FEINGOLD J, HOCHEZ J, GOULET V: L'hyperplasie congenitale des surrenales (21-OH) en France. *Arch Fr Ped* 42:175, 1985.

58. MULLER W, PRADER A, KOFLER J, GLATZL J, GEIR W: Frequency of congenital adrenal hyperplasia. *Padiatr Padol* 14:151, 1979.

59. WERDER EA, SIEBENMANN RE, KNORR-MURSET G, ZIMMERMAN A, SIZONENKO PC, THEINTE P, GIRARD J, ZACHMANN M, PRADER A: The incidence of congenital adrenal hyperplasia in Switzerland—A survey of patients in 1960 to 1974. *Helv Paediatr Acta* 35:5, 1980.

60. WALLACE AM, BEASTALL GH, COOK B, CURRIE AJ, ROSS AM, KENNEDY R, GIRDWOOD RWA: Neonatal screening for congenital adrenal hyperplasia: A programme based on a novel direct radioimmunoassay for 17-hydroxyprogesterone in blood spots. *J Endocrinol* 108:229, 1986.

61. SUWA SY, IGARASHI I, KATO K, KUSUNOKI T, TANAE A, NIMI K, YATA J: A case survey study for congenital adrenal hyperplasia in Japan. 1. Study for incidence. *Acta Paediatr Jap* 85:204, 1981.

62. DORCHE C, DHOUDT SL, BOZON D: Systematic neonatal screening for congenital adrenal hyperplasia. Report of a pilot study in two centers in France, in Therrell BL (ed): *Advances in Neonatal Screening (Excerpta Medica Intl Congr Series).* Amsterdam, Elsevier, 1987, p 289.

63. WILKINS L: *The Diagnosis and Treatment of Endocrine Disorders in Childhood and Adolescence,* 3d ed. Springfield, Charles C Thomas, 1965, pp 401–427.

64. PANG S, HOTCHKISS J, DRASH AL, LEVINE LS, NEW MI: Microfilter paper method for 17α-progesterone radioimmunoassay: Its application for rapid screening for congenital adrenal hyperplasia. *J Clin Endocrinol Metab* 45:1003, 1977.

65. PANG S, MURPHEY W, LEVINE LS, SPENCE D, LEON A, LAFRANCHI S, SURVE A, NEW MI: A pilot newborn screening for congenital adrenal hyperplasia (CAH) in Alaska. *Pediatr Res* 15:512, 1981.

66. PANG S, SPENCE DA, NEW MI: Newborn screening for congenital adrenal hyperplasia with special reference to screening in Alaska. *Ann NY Acad Sci* 458:90, 1985.

67. CACCIARI E, BALSAMO A, CASSIO A, PIAZZI S, BERNARDI F, SALARDI S, CIGOGNANI A, PIRAZOLLI P, ZAPPULLA F, CAPELLI M, PAOLINI M: Neonatal screening for congenital adrenal hyperplasia in a homogeneous Caucasian population. *Ann NY Acad Sci* 458:85, 1985.

68. NATOLI G, MOSCHINI L, ACCONCIA P, ALBINO G, COSTA P, PANSA G: Newborn screening for 21-hydroxylase deficiency. Radioimmunoassay (RIA) of 17α-hydroxyprogesterone by microfilter paper method, in *Second International Symposium in Recent Progress in Pediatric Endocrinology (Serono), Milan Oct 22–23, 1981.* New York, Raven, 1981, p 33.

69. SUWA SY, SHINOZAWA K, KITAGAWA K, FUJIEDA F, MATSU-URA N, TAKASUGI N, FUKUSHI M, IGARASHI Y, TAKAHASHI T: Collaborative study on regional neonatal screening for congenital adrenal hyperplasia in Japan,

in Therrell BL (ed): *Advances in Neonatal Screening, (Excerpta Medica Intl Congr Series*, vol 741). Amsterdam, Elsevier, 1987, p 279.

70. WALLACE AM, BEASTALL GH, KENNEDY R, GIRDWOOD RWA: Congenital adrenal hyperplasia in 120,000 Scottish neonates, in Therrell BL (ed): *Advances in Neonatal Screening (Excerpta Medica Intl Congr Series*, vol 741). Amsterdam, Elsevier, 1987, p 293.

71. LYON I, WEBSTER D, DANCE P: Newborn screening for congenital adrenal hyperplasia in New Zealand, in Therrell BL (ed): *Advances in Neonatal Screening (Excerpta Medica Intl Congr Series*, vol 741). Amsterdam, Elsevier, 1987, p 297.

72. HOFMAN LF: Screening infants for congenital adrenal hyperplasia: The Washington experience, in Therrell BL (ed): *Advances in Neonatal Screening (Excerpta Medica Intl Congr Series*, vol 741). Amsterdam, Elsevier, 1987, p 287.

72a. THULINE HC: Newborn screening for congenital adrenal hyperplasia (CAH), in Therrell BL (ed): *Advances in Neonatal Screening (Excerpta Medica Intl Congr Series*, vol 741). Amsterdam, Elsevier, 1987, p 301.

73. FUJIEDA K, MATSU-URA N, TAKASUGI N, FUKUSHI M, ARAI O, MIZUSHIMA Y: Five years' experience of newborn screening program for congenital adrenal hyperplasia in Sapporo, in Therrell BL (ed): *Advances in Neonatal Screening (Excerpta Medica Intl Congr Series*, vol 741). Amsterdam, Elsevier, 1987, p 281.

74. CAVALLI-SFORZA LL, BODMER WR: *The Genetics of Human Populations*. San Francisco, WH Freeman, 1971.

75. RAITI S, NEWNS GH: Congenital adrenal hyperplasia. *Arch Dis Child* 39:324, 1964.

76. KOWARSKI AA: Mechanism of salt loss in congenital virilizing adrenal hyperplasia, in *Lee PA, Plotnick LP, Kowarski AA, Migeon CJ (eds): Congenital Adrenal Hyperplasia*. Baltimore, University Park Press, 1977, p 114.

77. MIGEON CJ: Diagnosis and treatment of adrenogenital disorders, in DeGroot LJ, Cahill GF Jr, Odell WD, Martini L, Potts JT Jr, Nelson DH, Steinberger E, Winegrad AI (eds): *Endocrinology*. New York, Grune & Stratton, 1979, p 1204.

78. BONDY PK: The adrenal cortex, in Bondy PK, Rosenberg LE (eds): *Metabolic Control and Disease*, Philadelphia, Saunders, 1980, p 1482.

79. FIFE D, RAPPAPORT EB: Prevalence of salt losing among congenital adrenal hyperplasia patients. *Clin Endocrinol* 19:259, 1983.

80. PANG S, WALLACE MA, HOFMAN L, THULINE HC, DORCHE C, LYON ICT, DOBBINS RH, KLING S, FUJIEDA K, SUWA S: Worldwide experience in newborn screening for congenital adrenal hyperplasia due to 21-hydroxylase deficiency. *Pediatrics* 81:866, 1988.

81. BAUR MP, SIGMUND S, SIGMUND M, RITTNER C: Analysis of MHC recombinant families, in Albert ED, Baur MP, Mayr WR (eds): *Histocompatibility Testing 1984*. Berlin, Springer-Verlag, 1984, p 324.

82. MÖLLER G (ed): Molecular genetics of class I and II MHC antigens 1. *Immunol Rev* 84:1, 1985.

83. MÖLLER G (ed): Molecular genetics of Class I and II MHC antigen 2. *Immunol Rev* 85:1, 1985.

84. MÖLLER G (ed): Molecular genetics of Class III MHC antigens. *Immunol Rev* 87:1, 1985.

84a. CARROLL MC, KATZMAN P, ALICOT EM, KOLLER BH, GERAGHTY DE, ORR HT, STROMINGER JL, SPIES T: Linkage map of the human major histocompatibility complex including the tumor necrosis factor genes. *Proc Natl Acad Sci USA* 84:8534, 1987.

84b. GERAGHTY DEW, KOLLER BHL, ORR HT: A human major histocompatibility complex class I gene that encodes a protein with a shortened cytoplasmic segment. *Proc Natl Acad Sci USA* 84:9145, 1987.

84c. SHIMIZU Y, GERAGHTY DE, KOLLER BH, ORR HT, DEMARS R: Transfer and expression of three cloned human non-HLA-A,B,C class I major histocompatibility complex genes in mutant lymphoblastoid cells. *Proc Natl Acad Sci USA* 85:227, 1988.

85. HARDY DA, BELL JI, LONG EO, LINDSTEN T, MCDEVITT HO: Genomic organization of the HLA Class II region genes. *Nature* 323:453, 1986.

85a. TIERCY J-M, GORSKI J, JEANNET M, MACH B: Identification and distribution of three serologically undetected alleles of HLA-DR by oligonucleotide. DNA typing analysis. *Proc Natl Acad Sci USA* 85:198, 1988.

85b. MULLER U, STEPHAN D, PHILIPPSEN P, STEINMETZ M: Orientation and molecular map position of the complement genes in the mouse MHC. *EMBO J* 6:369, 1987.

85c. DUNHAM I, SARGENT CA, TROWSDALE J, CAMPBELL RD: Molecular mapping of the human major histocompatibility complex by pulsed-field gel electrophoresis. *Proc Natl Acad Sci USA* 84:7237, 1987.

86. SPIES T, MORTON CC, NEODOSPASOV SA, FIERS W, PIUS D, STROMINGER JL: Genes for the tumor necrosis factors alpha and beta are linked to the human major histocompatibility complex. *Proc Natl Acad Sci USA* 83:8699, 1986.

87. MULLER U, JONGENEEL CV, NEDOSPASOV SA, LINDAHL KF, STEINMETZ M: Tumor necrosis factor and lymphotoxin genes map close to H-2D in the mouse major histocompatibility complex. *Nature* 325, 265, 1987.

88. DUPONT B, OBERFIELD SE, SMITHWICK EM, LEE TD, LEVINE LS: Close genetic linkage between HLA and congenital adrenal hyperplasia (21-hydroxylase deficiency). *Lancet* 2:1309, 1977.

89. LEVINE LS, ZACHMANN M, NEW MI, PRADER A, POLLACK MS, O'NEILL GJ, YANG SY, OBERFIELD SE, DUPONT B: Genetic mapping of the 21-hydroxylase deficiency gene within the HLA linkage group. *N Engl J Med* 299:911, 1978.

90. NEW MI: HLA and adrenal disease, in Farid NR (ed): *Immunogenetics of Endocrine Disorders*, 2d ed. New York, Alan R. Liss, 1988, p 309.

91. DUPONT B, POLLACK MS, LEVINE LS, O'NEILL GH, HAWKINS BR, NEW MI: Congenital adrenal hyperplasia. Joint report from the Eighth International Histocompatibility Workshop, in Terasaki PI (ed): *Histocompatibility Testing 1980*. Los Angeles, UCLA Tissue Typing Laboratory, 1981, p 693.

91a. ASTON CE, SHERMAN SL, MORTON NE, SPEISER PW, NEW MI: Genetic mapping of the 21-hydroxylase locus: Estimation of small recombination frequencies. *Am J Hum Genet* 43:304, 1988.

92. AWDEH ZL, RAUM D, YUNIS EJ, ALPER CA: Extended HLA/complement allele haplotypes: Evidence for T/t-like complex in man. *Proc Natl Acad Sci USA* 80:259, 1983.

93. KLOUDA PT, HARRIS R, PRICE DA: Linkage and association between HLA and 21-hydroxylase deficiency. *J Med Genet* 17:337, 1980.

94. DUPONT B, VIRDIS R, LERNER AJ, NELSON C, POLLACK MS, NEW MI: Distinct HLA-B antigen associations for the salt-wasting and simple virilizing forms of congenital adrenal hyperplasia due to 21-hydroxylase deficiency, in Albert ED, Baur MP, Mayr WR (eds): *Histocompatibility Testing 1984*. Berlin, Springer-Verlag, 1984, p 660.

95. FLEISCHNICK E, RAUM D, ALOSCO SM, GERALD PS, YUNIS EJ, AWDEH ZL, GRANADOS J, CRIGLER JF, GILES CM, ALPER CA: Extended MHC haplotypes in 21-hydroxylase deficiency congenital adrenal hyperplasia. *Lancet* 1:152, 1983.

96. O'NEILL GJ, DUPONT B, POLLACK MS, LEVINE LS, MI NEW: Complement C4 allotypes in congenital adrenal hyperplasia due to 21-hydroxylase deficiency: Further evidence for different allelic variants at the 21-hydroxylase locus. *Clin Immunol Immunopathol* 23:312, 1982.

97. RAUM DW, AWDEH ZL, ANDERSON J, STRONG L, GRANADOS J, TERAN L, GIBLETT E, YUNIS EJ, ALPER CA: Human C4 haplotypes with duplicated C4A or C4B. *Am J Hum Genet* 36:72, 1984.

98. JONES HW, JONES GES: The gynecological aspects of adrenal hyperplasia and allied disorders. *Am J Obstet Gynecol* 68:1330, 1954.

99. JEFFERIES WM, WEIR WC, WEIR DR, PROUTY RL: The use of cortisone and related steroids in infertility. *Fertil Steril* 9:145, 1958.

100. DECOURT MJ, JAYLE MF, BAULIEU E: Virilisme cliniquement tardif avec excrétion de pregnanetriol et insuffisance de la production du cortisol. *Ann Endocrinol (Paris)* 18:416, 1957.

101. ABRAHAM GE, SWERDLOFF RS, TULCHINSKY D, HOPPER K, ODELL WD: Radioimmunoassay of plasma 17-hydroxyprogesterone. *J Clin Endocrinol Metab* 33:42, 1971.

102. ZACHMANN M, PRADER A: Unusual heterozygotes of congenital adrenal hyperplasia due to 21-hydroxylase deficiency. *Acta Endocrinol (Kbh)* 87:557, 1978.

103. ZACHMANN M, PRADER A: Unusual heterozygotes of congenital adrenal hyperplasia due to 21-hydroxylase deficiency confirmed by HLA tissue typing. *Acta Endocrinol (Kbh)* 92:542, 1979.

104. LEVINE LS, DUPONT B, LORENZEN F, PANG S, POLLACK M, OBERFIELD S, KOHN B, LERNER A, CACCIARI E, MANTERO F, CASSIO A, SCARONI C, CHIUMELLO G, RONDANINI GF, GARGANTINI L, GIOVANNELLI G, VIRDIS R, BARTOLOTTA E, MIGLIORI C, PINTOR C, TATO L, BARBONI F, NEW MI: Cryptic 21-hydroxylase deficiency in families of patients with classical congenital adrenal hyperplasia. *J Clin Endocrinol Metab* 51:1316, 1980.

105. KOHN B, LEVINE LS, POLLACK MS, PANG S, LORENZEN F, LEVY D, LERNER A, RONDANINI GF, DUPONT B, NEW MI: Late-onset steroid 21-hydroxylase deficiency: A variant of classical congenital adrenal hyperplasia. *J Clin Endocrinol Metab* 55:817, 1982.

106. ROSENWAKS Z, LEE PA, JONES GS, MIGEON CJ, WENTZ AC: An attenuated form of congenital virilizing adrenal hyperplasia. *J Clin Endocrinol Metab* 49:335, 1979.

107. POLLACK MS, LEVINE LS, O'NEILL GJ, PANG S, LORENZEN F, KOHN B, RONDANINI GF, CHIUMELLO G, NEW MI, DUPONT B: HLA linkage and B14,DR1,BfS haplotype association with the genes for late onset and cryptic 21-hydroxylase deficiency. *Am J Hum Genet* 33:540, 1981.

108. LARON Z, POLLACK MS, ZAMIR R, ROITMAN A, DICKERMAN Z, LEVINE LS, LORENZEN F, O'NEILL GJ, PANG S, NEW MI, DUPONT B: Late onset 21-

hydroxylase deficiency and HLA in the Ashkenazi population; a new allele at the 21-hydroxylase locus. *Hum Immunol* 1:55, 1980.

109. LEVINE LS, DUPONT B, LORENZEN F, PANG S, POLLACK MS, OBERFIELD SE, KOHN B, LERNER A, CACCIARI E, MANTERO F, CASSIO A, SCARONI C, CHIUMELLO G, RONDANINI GF, GARGANTINI L, GIOVANNELLI G, VIRDIS R, BARTOLOTTA E, MIGLIORI C, PINTOR C, TATO L, BARBONI F, NEW MI: Genetic and hormonal characterization of cryptic 21-hydroxylase deficiency. *J Clin Endocrinol Metab* 53:1193, 1981.

110. BLANKSTEIN J, FAIMAN C, REYES FI, SCHROEDER ML, WINTER JSD: Adult-onset familial adrenal 21-hydroxylase deficiency. *Am J Med* 68:441, 1980.

111. MIGEON CJ, ROSENWAKS Z, LEE PA, URBAN MD, BIAS WB: The attenuated form of congenital adrenal hyperplasia as an allelic form of 21-hydroxylase deficiency. *J Clin Endocrinol Metab* 51:647, 1980.

112. SPEISER PW, DUPONT B, RUBINSTEIN P, PIAZZA A, KASTELAN A, NEW MI: High frequency of nonclassical steroid 21-hydroxylase deficiency. *Am J Hum Genet* 37:650, 1985.

113. TEMECK JW, PANG S, NELSON C, NEW MI: Genetic defects of steroidogenesis in premature pubarche. *J Clin Endocrinol Metab* 64:609, 1987.

114. GRANOFF AB, CHASALOW FI, BLETHEN SL: 17-Hydroxyprogesterone responses to adrenocorticotropin in children with premature adrenarche. *J Clin Endocrinol Metab* 60:409, 1985.

115. LUCKY AW, ROSENFIELD RL, MCGUIRE J, RUDY S, HELKE J: Adrenal androgen hyperresponsiveness to adrenocorticotropin in women with acne and/or hirsutism: Adrenal enzyme defects and exaggerated adrenarche. *J Clin Endocrinol Metab* 62:840, 1986.

116. ROSE LI, NEWMARK SR, STRAUSS JS, POCHI PE: Adrenocortical hydroxylase deficiencies in acne vulgaris. *J Invest Dermatol* 66:324, 1976.

117. PANG S, LERNER AJ, STONER E, LEVINE LS, OBERFIELD SE, ENGEL I, NEW MI: Late-onset adrenal steroid 3β-hydroxysteroid dehydrogenase deficiency. A cause of hirsutism in pubertal and postpubertal women. *J Clin Endocrinol Metab* 60:428, 1985.

118. CHILD DF, BU'LOCK DE, ANDERSON DC: Adrenal steroidogenesis in hirsute women. *Clin Endocrinol* 12:595, 1980.

119. GIBSON M, LACKRITZ R, SCHIFF I, TULCHINSKY D: Abnormal adrenal responses to adrenocorticotropic hormone in hyperandrogenic women. *Fertil Steril* 33:43, 1980.

120. LOBO RA, GOEBELSMANN U: Adult manifestation of congenital adrenal hyperplasia due to incomplete 21-hydroxylase deficiency mimicking polycystic ovarian disease. *Am J Obstet Gynecol* 138:720, 1980.

121. CHROUSOS GP, LORIAUX DL, MANN DL, CUTLER GB: Late-onset 21-hydroxylase deficiency mimicking idiopathic hirsutism or polycystic ovarian disease. An allelic variant of congenital virilizing adrenal hyperplasia with a milder enzymatic defect. *Ann Intern Med* 96:143, 1982.

122. CHROUSOS GP, LORIAUX DL, MANN D, CUTLER GB: Late-onset 21-hydroxylase deficiency is an allelic variant of congenital adrenal hyperplasia characterized by attenuated clinical expression and different HLA haplotype association. *Horm Res* 16:193, 1982.

123. CHETKOWSKI R, DeFAZIO J, SHAMONKI I, JUDD HL, CHANG RJ: The incidence of late-onset congenital adrenal hyperplasia due to 21-hydroxylase deficiency among hirsute women. *J Clin Endocrinol Metab* 58:595, 1984.

124. KUTTENN F, COUILLIN P, GIRARD F, BILLAUD L, VINCENS M, BOUCEKKINE C, THALABARD J-C, MAUDELONDE T, SPRITZER P, MOWSZOWICZ I, BOUE A, MAUVAIS-JARVIS P: Late-onset adrenal hyperplasia in hirsutism. *N Engl J Med* 313:224, 1986.

125. GANGEMI M, BENATO M, GUACCI AM, MENGHETTI G: Stimulation tests in adrenogenital syndrome induced by 21-hydroxylase deficit. *Clin Exp Obstet Gynecol* 10:127, 1983.

126. SPEISER PW, DRUCKER S, NEW MI: Hypothalamic-pituitary-gonadal axis in nonclassical 21-hydroxylase deficiency. Program and Abstracts, 69th Annual Meeting of the Endocrine Society, Indianapolis, IN, June 1987.

127. BIRNBAUM MD, ROSE LI: The partial adrenocortical hydroxylase deficiency syndrome in infertile women. *Fertil Steril* 32:536, 1979.

128. RIDDICK DH, HAMMOND CB: Adrenal virilism due to 21-hydroxylase deficiency in the postmenarchial female. *Obstet Gynecol* 45:21, 1975.

129. CHROUSOS GP, LORIAUX DL, SHERINS RJ, CUTLER GB Jr: Unilateral testicular enlargement resulting from inapparent 21-hydroxylase deficiency. *J Urol* 126:127, 1981.

130. WISCHUSEN J, BAKER HWG, HUDSON B: Reversible male infertility due to congenital adrenal hyperplasia. *Clin Endocrinol* 14:571, 1981.

131. BONACCORSI AC, ADLER I, FIGUEIREDO JG: Male infertility due to congenital adrenal hyperplasia: Testicular biopsy findings, hormonal evaluation, and therapeutic results in three patients. *Fertil Steril* 47:664, 1987.

132. OJEIFO JO, WINTERS SJ, TROEN P: Basal and ACTH-stimulated serum 17α-hydroxyprogesterone in men with idiopathic infertility. *Fertil Steril* 42:97, 1984.

133. ZERAH M, PANG S, NEW MI: Morning salivary 17-hydroxyprogesterone is a useful screening test for nonclassical 21-hydroxylase deficiency. *J Clin Endocrinol Metab* 65:227, 1987.

134. KUTTENN F: Late-onset adrenal hyperplasia (letter). *N Engl J Med* 314:450, 1986.

135. SPEISER PW, NEW MI: Genotype and hormonal phenotype in nonclassical 21-hydroxylase deficiency. *J Clin Endocrinol Metab* 64:86, 1987.

136. NEW MI, LORENZEN F, LERNER AJ, KOHN B, OBERFIELD SE, POLLACK MS, DUPONT B, STONER E, LEVY DJ, PANG S, LEVINE LS: Genotyping steroid 21-hydroxylase deficiency: Hormonal reference data. *J Clin Endocrinol Metab* 57:320, 1983.

137. THOMSON G, BODMER W: The genetic analysis of HLA and disease associations, in Daussett J, Svejgaard A (eds): *HLA and Disease*. Baltimore, Williams and Wilkins, 1977, pp 84–93.

138. SHERMAN SL, ASTON CE, MORTON NE, SPEISER PW, DUPONT B, NEW MI: A segregation and linkage study of classical and nonclassical 21-hydroxylase deficiency. *Am J Hum Genet* 42:830, 1988.

139. SPENCE MA, TSUI LC: Report of the committee on the genetic constitution of chromosomes 7, 8, and 9, in *Human Gene Mapping 9*. Ninth International Workshop on Human Gene Mapping (*Cytogenet Cell Genet*, vol 46). Basel, Karger, 1987, p. 170.

140. NEBERT DW, ADESNIK M, COON MJ, ESTABROOK RW, GONZALEZ FJ, GUENGERICH FP, GUNSALUS IC, JOHNSON EF, KEMPER B, LEVIN W, PHILLIPS IR, SATO R, WATERMAN M: The P450 gene superfamily: Recommended nomenclature. *DNA* 6:1, 1987.

140a. MCKUSICK VA: The human gene map 15 April 1986. *Clin Genet* 29:545, 1986.

141. GARLEPP MJ, WILTON AN, DAWKINS RL, WHITE PC: Rearrangement of 21-hydroxylase genes in disease-associated MHC supratypes. *Immunogenetics* 23:100, 1986.

142. CARROLL MC, PALSDOTTIR A, BELT KT, PORTER RR: Deletion of complement C4 and steroid 21-hydroxylase genes in the HLA class III region. *EMBO J* 4:2547, 1985.

143. DONOHOUE PA, JOSPE N, MIGEON CJ, MCLEAN RH, BIAS WB, WHITE PC, VAN DOP C: Restriction maps and restriction fragment length polymorphisms of the human 21-hydroxylase genes. *Biochem Biophys Res Commun* 136:722, 1986.

144. MORNET E, COUILLIN P, KUTTENN F, RAUX MC, WHITE PC, COHEN D, BOUE A, DAUSSETT J: Associations between restriction fragment length polymorphisms detected with a probe for human 21-hydroxylase (21-OH) and two clinical forms of 21-hydroxylase deficiency. *Hum Genet* 74:402, 1986.

145. MATTESON KJ, PHILLIPS JA III, MILLER WL, CHUNG B-C, ORLANDO PJ, FRISCH H, FERRANDEZ A, BURR IM: P450XXI (steroid 21-hydroxylase) gene deletions are not found in family studies of congenital adrenal hyperplasia. *Proc Natl Acad Sci USA* 84:5858, 1987.

146. CARROLL MC, CAMPBELL RD, BENTLEY DR, PORTER RR: A molecular map of the major histocompatibility complex class III region linking the complement genes C4, C2 and factor B. *Nature* 307:237, 1984.

147. WERKMEISTER JW, NEW MI, DUPONT B, WHITE PC: Frequent deletion and duplication of the steroid 21-hydroxylase genes. *Am J Hum Genet* 39:461, 1986.

148. RUMSBY G, CARROLL MC, PORTER RR, GRANT DB, HJELM M: Deletion of the steroid 21-hydroxylase and complement C4 genes in congenital adrenal hyperplasia. *J Med Genet* 23:204, 1986.

149. DONOHOUE PA, VAN DOP C, MCLEAN RH, WHITE PC, JOSPE N, MIGEON CJ: Gene conversion in salt-losing congenital adrenal hyperplasia with absent complement C4 protein. *J Clin Endocrinol Metab* 62:995, 1986.

150. ATCHISON M, ADESNIK M: Gene conversion in a ctyochrome P-450 gene family. *Proc Natl Acad Sci USA* 83:2300, 1986.

151. GLOBERMAN H, AMOR M, NEW MI, WHITE PC: A nonsense mutation causing steroid 21-hydroxylase deficiency. Program and Abstracts, Bat-Sheva Seminar on Molecular Approaches to Hormone Action, Tiberias, Israel, October 1987.

152. AMOR M, PARKER KL, GLOBERMAN H, NEW MI, WHITE PC: Amino acid substitution in the CYP21B gene causing steroid 21-hydroxylase deficiency. *Proc Natl Acad Sci USA* 85:1600, 1988.

153. SPEISER PW, AMOR M, NEW MI, WHITE PC: Molecular genetic basis for nonclassical 21-hydroxylase deficiency. *N Engl J Med* 319:19,1988.

154. RODRIGUES NR, DUNHAM I, YU C-Y, CARROLL MC, PORTER RR, CAMPBELL RD: Molecular characterization of the HLA-linked steroid 21-hydroxylase B gene from an individual with congenital adrenal hyperplasia. *EMBO J* 6:1653, 1987.

154a. HARADA F, KIMURA A, IWANAGA T, SHIMOZAWA K, YATA J, SASAZUKI T: Gene conversion-like events cause steroid 21-hydroxylase deficiency in congenital adrenal hyperplasia. *Proc Natl Acad Sci USA* 84:8091, 1987.

154b. JOSPE N, DONOHOUE PA, VAN DOP C, MCLEAN RH, BIAS WB, MIGEON CJ: Prevalence of polymorphic 21-hydroxylase gene (CA21HB) mutations in salt-losing congenital adrenal hyperplasia. *Biochem Biophys Res Commun* 142:798, 1987.

154c. WHITE PL, VITEK A, DUPONT B, NEW MI: Characterization of frequent deletions causing steroid 21-hydroxylase deficiency. *Proc Natl Acad Sci USA* 85:4436, 1988.

155. TUKEY RH, OKINO S, BARNES H, GRIFFIN KJ, JOHNSON EF: Multiple gene-like sequences related to the rabbit hepatic progesterone 21-hydroxylase cytochrome P-450 1. *J Biol Chem* 260:13347, 1985.

156. JEFFCOATE TNA, FLEIGNER JRH, RUSSELL SH, DAVIS JC, WADE AP: Diagnosis of the adrenogenital syndrome before birth. *Lancet* 2:553, 1965.

157. NEW MI, LEVINE LS: Congenital adrenal hyperplasia, in Harris H, Hirschhorn K (eds): *Advances in Human Genetics*. New York, Plenum, 1973, p 326.

158. LEVINE LS: Prenatal detection of congenital adrenal hyperplasia, in Milunsky A (ed): *Genetic Disorders and the Fetus*. New York, Plenum, 1986, pp 369–385.

159. FRASIER SD, THORNEYCROFT IH, WEILL BA, HORTON R: Elevated amniotic fluid concentration of 17-hydroxyprogesterone in congenital adrenal hyperplasia. *J Pediatr* 86:310, 1975.

160. NAGAMANI M, MCDONOUGH PG, ELLEGOOD JO, MAHESH VB: Maternal and amniotic fluid 17-hydroxyprogesterone levels during pregnancy: Diagnosis of congenital adrenal hyperplasia *in utero*. *Am J Obstet Gynecol* 130:791, 1978.

161. HUGHES IA, LAURENCE KM: Antenatal diagnosis of congenital adrenal hyperplasia. *Lancet* 2:7, 1979.

162. PANG S, LEVINE LS, CEDERQVIST LL, FUENTES M, RICCARDI VM, HOLCOMBE JH, NITOWSKY HM, SACHS G, ANDERSON CE, DUCHON MA, OWENS R, MERKATZ I, NEW MI: Amniotic fluid concentration of Δ^5 and Δ^4 steroids in fetuses with congenital adrenal hyperplasia due to 21-hydroxylase deficiency and in anencephalic fetuses. *J Clin Endocrinol Metab* 51:223, 1980.

163. HUGHES IA, LAURENCE KM: Prenatal diagnosis of congenital adrenal hyperplasia due to 21-hydroxylase deficiency: Amniotic fluid steroid analysis. *Prenat Diagn* 2:97, 1982.

164. BLANKSTEIN J, FUJIEDA K, REYES FI, FAIMAN C, WINTER JSD: Cortisol, 11-deoxycortisol and 21-desoxycortisol concentrations in amniotic fluid during normal pregnancy. *Am J Obstet Gynecol* 137:781, 1980.

165. FRASIER SD, WEISS BA, HORTON R: Amniotic fluid testosterone: Implications for the prenatal diagnosis of congenital adrenal hyperplasia. *J Pediatr* 84:738, 1974.

166. COUILLIN P, NICOLAS H, BOUE J, BOUE A: HLA typing of amniotic-fluid cells applied to prenatal diagnosis of congenital adrenal hyperplasia. *Lancet* 1:1076, 1979.

167. POLLACK MS, LEVINE LS, PANG S, OWENS RP, NITOWSKY HM, MAURER D, NEW MI, DUCHON M, MERKATZ IR, SACHS G, DUPONT B: Prenatal diagnosis of congenital adrenal hyperplasia (21-hydroxylase deficiency) by HLA typing. *Lancet* 1:1107, 1979.

168. FOREST MG, BETUEL H, COUILLIN P, BOUE A, DAVID M, FLORET D, FRANCOIS R, GUIBAUD P, PLAUCHU H, RAPPAPORT R: Prenatal diagnosis of congenital adrenal hyperplasia (CAH) due to 21-hydroxylase deficiency by steroid analysis in the amniotic fluid of mid-pregnancy: Comparison with HLA typing in 17 pregnancies at risk for CAH. *Prenat Diagn* 1:197, 1981.

169. PANG S, POLLACK MS, LOO M, GREEN O, NUSSBAUM R, GLAYTON G, DUPONT B, NEW MI: Pitfalls of prenatal diagnosis of 21-hydroxylase deficiency congenital adrenal hyperplasia. *J Clin Endocrinol Metab* 61:89, 1985.

170. MORNET E, BOUE J, RAUX-DEMAY M, COUILLIN P, OURY JF, DUMEZ Y, DAUSSET J, COHEN D, BOUE A: First trimester prenatal diagnosis of 21-hydroxylase deficiency by linkage analysis of HLA-DNA probes and by 17-hydroxyprogesterone determination. *Hum Genet* 73:358, 1986.

171. FOREST MG, BETUEL H, DAVID M: Traitement antenatal de l'hyperplasie congenitale des surrenales par deficit en 21-hydroxylase: Étude multicentrique. *Ann Endocrinol (Paris)* 48:31, 1987.

172. DORR HG, SIPPELL WG, HAACK D, BIDLINGMAIER F, KNORR D: Pitfalls of prenatal treatment of congenital adrenal hyperplasia (CAH) due to 21-hydroxylase deficiency. Prog and Abstr, 25th Annual Meeting of the European Society for Paediatric Endocrinology, Zurich, August 1986.

173. EVANS MI, CHROUSOS GP, MANN DW, LARSEN JW, GREEN I, MCCLUSKEY J, LORIAUX DL, FLETCHER JC, KOONS G, OVERPECK J, SCHULMAN JD: Pharmacologic suppression of the fetal adrenal gland in utero. *JAMA* 253:1015, 1985.

174. CHARNVISES S, FENCL MdeM, OSATHANONDH R, ZHU M-G, UNDERWOOD R, TULCHINSKY D: Adrenal steroids in maternal and cord blood after dexamethasone administration at midterm. *J Clin Endocrinol Metab* 61:1220, 1985.

175. GOLDMAN AS, SHAPIOR BH, KATSUMATA M: Human foetal palatal corticoid receptors and teratogens for cleft palate. *Nature* 272:464, 1978.

176. BONGIOVANNI AM: The adrenogenital syndrome with deficiency of 3β-hydroxysteroid dehydrogenase. *J Clin Invest* 41:2086, 1962.

177. KENNY FM, REYNOLDS JW, GREEN OC: Partial 3β-hydroxysteroid dehydrogenase (3β-HSD) deficiency in a family with congenital adrenal hyperplasia: Evidence for increasing 3β-HSD activity with age. *Pediatrics* 48:756, 1971.

178. PANG S, LEVINE LS, STONER E, OPITZ JM, POLLACK MS, DUPONT B, NEW MI: Nonsalt-losing congenital adrenal hyperplasia due to 3β-hydroxysteroid dehydrogenase deficiency with normal glomerulosa function. *J Clin Endocrinol Metab* 56:808, 1983.

179. HAMILTON W, BRUSH MG: Four clinical variants of congenital adrenal hyperplasia. *Arch Dis Child* 39:66, 1964.

180. JÄNNE O, PERHEENTUPA J, VIHKO R: Plasma and urinary steroids in an eight year old boy with 3β-hydroxysteroid-dehydrogenase deficiency. *J Clin Endocrinol Metab* 31:162, 1970.

181. PARKS GA, BERMUDEZ JA, ANAST CS, BONGIOVANNI AM, NEW MI: Pubertal boy with the 3β-hydroxysteroid dehydrogenase defect. *J Clin Endocrinol Metab* 33:269, 1971.

182. SCHNEIDER G, GENEL M, BONGIOVANNI AM, GOLDMAN AS, ROSENFIELD RL: Persistent testicular Δ5-isomerase-3β-hydroxysteroid dehydrogenase (Δ5-3β-HSD) deficiency in the Δ5-3β-HSD form of congenital adrenal hyperplasia. *J Clin Invest* 55:681, 1975.

183. DEPERETTI E, FOREST MG, FEIT JP, DAVID M: Endocrine studies in two children with male pseudohermaphroditism due to 3β-hydroxysteroid dehydrogenase defect, in Genazzani AR, Thijssen JHH, Siiteri PK (eds): *Adrenal Androgens*. New York, Raven, 1980, p 141.

184. ZACHMANN M, VÖLLMIN JA, MÜRSET G, CURTIUS H-C, PRADER PA: Unusual type of congenital adrenal hyperplasia probably due to deficiency of 3β-hydroxysteroid dehydrogenase. Case report of a surviving girl and steroid studies. *J Clin Endocrinol Metab* 30:719, 1970.

185. CATHRO DM, BIRCHALL K, MITCHELL FL, FORSYTH CC: 3β:21-Dihydroxy-pregn-5-ene-20-one in urine of normal newborn infants and in third day urine of child with deficiency of 3β-hydroxysteroid-dehydrogenase. *Arch Dis Child* 40:251, 1965.

186. KOGUT MD: Adrenogenital syndrome. *Am J Dis Child* 110:562, 1965.

187. BONGIOVANNI AM: Congenital adrenal hyperplasia due to 3β-hydroxysteroid dehydrogenase deficiency, in New MI, Levine LS (eds): *Adrenal Diseases in Childhood (Pediatr Adolesc Endocrinol*, vol 13). Basel, Karger, 1984, p 72.

188. ROSENFIELD RL, RICH BH, WOLFSDORF JI, CASSORLA F, PARKS JS, BONGIOVANNI AM, WU CH, SHACKLETON CHL: Pubertal presentation of congenital Δ5-3β-hydroxysteroid dehydrogenase deficiency. J Clin Endocrinol Metab 51:345, 1980.

189. BONGIOVANNI AM: Late-onset adrenal hyperplasia (letter). *N Engl J Med* 314:450, 1986.

190. STALVEY JRD, MEISLER MH, PAYNE AH: Evidence that the same structural gene encodes testicular and adrenal 3β-hydroxysteroid dehydrogenase-isomerase. *Biochem Genet* 25:181, 1987.

191. EBERLEIN WR, BONGIOVANNI AM: Plasma and urinary corticosteroids in the hypertensive form of congenital adrenal hyperplasia. *J Biol Chem* 223:85, 1956.

192. BONGIOVANNI AM: Congenital adrenal hyperplasia and related conditions, in Stanbury JB, Wyngaarden JB, Fredrickson DS (eds): *The Metabolic Basis of Inherited Disease*, 4th ed. New York, McGraw-Hill, 1978, p 868.

193. NEW MI, NEMERY RL, CHOW DM, KAUFMAN ED, STONER E, ZERAH M, CRAWFORD C, SPEISER PW: Low-renin hypertension of childhood. *Symposium Kyoto July 17:23, 1988), The Adrenal and Hypertenaion: From Cloning to Clinic Serono, Mantero F et al., (eds): New York, Raven (in press, 1988)*.

194. GANDY HLM, KEUTMANN EH, ISSO AJ: Characterization of urinary steroids in adrenal hyperplasia: Isolation of metabolites of cortisol, compound S, and deoxycorticosterone from a normotensive patient with adrenogenital syndrome. *J Clin Invest* 39:364, 1960.

195. BLUNCK W: Die α-ketolischen Cortisol and Corticosteronmetaboliten sowie die 11-Oxy- and 11-Desoxy-17-ketosteroide im Urine von Kindern. *Acta Endocrinol* 134(suppl):9, 1968.

196. GREEN OC, MIGEON CJ, WILKINS L: Urinary steroids in the hypertensive form of congenital adrenal hyperplasia. *J Clin Endocrinol Metab* 20:929, 1960.

197. GLENTHOJ A, NIELSEN MD, STARUP J: Congenital adrenal hyperplasia due to 11β-hydroxylase deficiency: Final diagnosis in adult age in three patients. *Acta Endocrinol* 93:94, 1980.

198. FERREBEE JW, RAGAN C, ATCHLEY DW, LOEB RF: Deoxycorticosterone esters. Certain effects in the treatment of Addison's disease. *JAMA* 113:1725, 1939.

199. PERERA GA, KNOWLTON AI, LOWELL A, LOEB RF: Effect of deoxycorticosterone acetate on the blood pressure of man. *JAMA* 125:1030, 1944.

200. ROSLER A, LEIBERMAN E, SACK J, LANDAU H, BENDERLY A, MOSES SW, COHEN T: Clinical variability of congenital adrenal hyperplasia due to 11β-hydroxylase deficiency. *Hormone Res* 16:133, 1982.

201. ULICK S: Adrenocortical factors in hypertension. 1. Significance of 18-hydroxy-11-deoxycorticosterone. *Am J Cardiol* 38:814, 1976.

202. ROSLER A, LEIBERMAN E: Enzymatic defects of steroidogenesis: 11β-hydroxylase deficiency congenital adrenal hyperplasia, in New MI, Levine LS (eds): *Adrenal Diseases in Childhood (Pediatr Adolesc Endocrinol* vol 13). Basel, Karger, 1984, pp 47–71.

203. HURWITZ A, BRAUTBAR C, MILWIDSKY A, VECSEI P, MILEWICZ A, NAVOT D, ROSLER A: Combined 21- and 11β-hydroxylase deficiency in familial congenital adrenal hyperplasia. *J Clin Endocrinol Metab* 60:631, 1985.

204. NEWMARK S, DLUHY RG, WILLIAMS GH, POCHI P, ROSE LI: Partial 11- and 21-hydroxylase deficiencies in hirsute women. *Am J Obstet Gynecol* 127:594, 1977.

205. GABRILOVE JL, SHARMA DC, DORFMAN RI: Adrenocortical 11β-hydroxylase deficiency and virilism first manifest in the adult woman. *N Engl J Med* 272:1189, 1965.

206. CATHELINEAU G, BRERAULT JL, FIET J, JULIEN R, DREUX C, CANIVET J: Adrenocortical 11β-hydroxylation defect in adult women with postmenarchial onset of symptoms. *J Clin Endocrinol Metab* 51:287, 1980.

207. BIRNBAUM MD, ROSE LI: Late onset adrenocortical hydroxylase deficiencies associated with menstrual dysfunction. *Obstet Gynecol* 63:445, 1984.

208. PANG S, LEVINE LS, LORENZEN F, CHOW D, POLLACK MS, DUPONT B, GENEL M, NEW MI: Hormonal studies in obligate heterozygotes and siblings of patients with 11β-hydroxylase deficiency congenital adrenal hyperplasia. *J Clin Endocrinol Metab* 50:586, 1980.

209. GLENTHOJ A, NIELSEN MD, STARUP J, SVEJGAARD A: HLA and congenital adrenal hyperplasia due to 11-hydroxylase deficiency. *Tissue Antigens* 14:181, 1979.

210. BRAUTBAR C, ROSLER A, LANDAU H, COHEN I, NELKEN D, COHEN T, LEVINE C, SACK J, BENDERLI A, MOSES S, LEIBERMAN E, DUPONT B, LEVINE LS, NEW MI: No linkage between HLA and congenital adrenal hyperplasia due to 11β-hydroxylase deficiency. *N Engl J Med* 300:205, 1980.

211. PORTER B, FINZI M, LEIBERMAN E, MOSES S: The syndrome of congenital adrenal hyperplasia in Israel. *Pediatrician* 6:100, 1977.

212. ZACHMANN M, TASSINARI D, PRADER A: Clinical and biochemical variability of congenital adrenal hyperplasia due to 11β-OHD. A study of 25 patients. *J Clin Endocrinol Metab* 56:222, 1983.

213. BLUNCK W, BIERICH JR: CAH with 11β-hydroxylase deficiency. A case report and contribution to diagnosis. *Acta Paed Scand* 57:157, 1968.

214. LEVINE LS, RAUH W, GOTTESDIENER K, CHOW D, GUNCZLER P, RAPAPORT R, PANG S, SCHNEIDER B, NEW MI: New studies of the 11-hydroxylase and the 18-hydroxylase enzymes in the hypertensive form of congenital adrenal hyperplasia. *J Clin Endocrinol Metab* 51:223, 1980.

214a. GLOBERMAN RÖSLER A, THEODOR R, NEW MI, WHITE PC: An inherited defect in aldosterone biosynthesis is caused by a mutation in or near the gene for steroid 11-hydroxylase. *N Engl J Med* (in press, 1988).

215. ROYER P, LESTERADET H, DeMENIBUS CIH, VERMEIL G: Hypoaldosteronisme familial chronique a debut neo-natal. *Ann Pediatr (Paris)* 8:133, 1961.

216. RUSSELL A, LEVIN B, SINCLAIR L, OBERHOLZER VG: A reversible salt-wasting syndrome of the newborn and infant. Possible infantile hypoaldosteronism. *Arch Dis Child* 38:313, 1963.

217. ULICK S: Selective defects in the biosynthesis of aldosterone, in New MI, Levine LS (eds): *Adrenal Diseases in Childhood (Pediatr Adolesc Endocrinol*, vol 13). Basel, Karger, 1984, p 145.

218. RÖSLER A, RABINOWITZ D, THEODOR R, RAMIREZ L, ULICK S: The nature of the defect in a salt-wasting disorder in Jews of Iran. *J Clin Endocrinol Metab* 44:279, 1977.

219. LEE PDK, PATTERSON BD, HINTZ RL, ROSENFELD RG: Biochemical diagnosis and management of corticosterone methyl oxidase type II deficiency. *J Clin Endocrinol Metab* 62:225, 1986.

220. VELDHUIS JD, KULIN HK, SANTEN RJ, WILSON TE, MELBY JC: Inborn error in the terminal step of aldosterone biosynthesis. Corticosterone methyl oxidase type II deficiency in a North American pedigree. *N Engl J Med* 303:117, 1980.

220a. SMITH M, SPENCE MA: Report of the committee on the genetic constitution of chromosomes 7, 8 and 9. Eighth International Workshop on Human Gene Mapping (*Cytogenet Cell Genet* 40). Basel, Karger, 1985, p 156.

221. RÖSLER A, LEIBERMAN E, ROSENMANN A, BEN-UZILIO R, WEIDENFELD J: Prenatal diagnosis of 11β-hydroxylase deficiency congenital adrenal hyperplasia. *J Clin Endocrinol Metab* 49:546, 1979.

222. SCHUMERT Z, ROSENMANN A, LANDAU H, RÖSLER A: 11-Deoxycortisol in amniotic fluid: Prenatal diagnosis of congenital adrenal hyperplasia due to 11β-hydroxylase deficiency. *Clin Endocrinol* 12:257, 1980.

223. BIGLIERI EG, HERRON MA, BRUST N: 17α-Hydroxylation deficiency in man. *J Clin Invest* 45:1946, 1966.

224. NEW MI: Male pseudohermaphroditism due to 17α-hydroxylase deficiency. *J Clin Invest* 49:1930, 1970.

225. MANTERO F, BUSNARDO B, RIONDEL A, VAYRAT R, AUSTONI M: Hypertension arterielle, alcalose hypokaliemique et pseudohermaphoriditisme male par deficit en 17α-hydroxylase. *Schweiz Med Wochenschr* 101:38, 1971.

226. MADAN K, SCHOEMAKER J: XY females with enzyme deficiencies of steroid metabolism. A brief review. *Hum Genet* 53:291, 1980.

227. DEAN HJ, SHACKELTON CHL, WINTER JSD: Diagnosis and natural history of 17-hydroxylase deficiency in a newborn male. *J Clin Endocrinol Metab* 59:513, 1984.

228. SCARONI C, OPOCHER G, MANTERO F: Renin-angiotensin-aldosterone system: A long-term follow-up study in 17α-hydroxylase deficiency syndrome (17OHDS). *Hypertension (Clin Exp Theory Pract)* A8:773, 1986.

228a. MANTERO F, SCARONI C: Enzymatic defects of steroidogenesis: 17α-hydroxylase, in New MI, Levine LS (eds): *Adrenal Diseases in Childhood (Pediatr Adolesc Endocrinol*, vol 13). Basel, Karger, 1984, pp 83–94.

229. ZACHMANN M, VOLLMIN JA, HAMILTON W, PRADER A: Steroid 17,20-desmolase deficiency: A new cause of male pseudohermaphroditism. *Clin Endocrinol* 1:369, 1972.

230. FOREST MG, LECORNU M, DE PERETTI E: Familial male pseudohermaphroditism due to 17,20-desmolase deficiency. I. *In vivo* endocrine studies. *J Clin Endocrinol Metab* 50:826, 1980.

231. ZACHMANN M, PRADER A: 17,20-Desmolase deficiency, in New MI, Levine LS (eds): *Adrenal Diseases in Childhood (Pediatr Adolesc Endocrinol*, vol 13). Basel, Karger, 1984, p 95.

232. GOEBELSMANN U, ZACHMANN M, DAVAJAN V, ISRAEL R, MESTMAN JH, MISHELL DR: Male pseudohermaphroditism consistent with 17-20 desmolase deficiency. *Gynecol Invest* 7:138, 1976.

233. ZACHMANN M, WERDER EA, PRADER A: Two types of male pseudohermaphroditism due to 17,20-desmolase deficiency. *J Clin Endocrinol Metab* 55:487, 1982.

234. DAVID M, FOREST MG, ZACHMANN M, DePERETTI E: 17,20-Desmolase deficiency in two unrelated prepubertal and adolescent boys previously diagnosed as simple hypospadias. *Pediatr Res* 15:83, 1981.

235. MANTERO F, SCARONI C, PASINI CV, FAGIOLO U: No linkage between HLA and congenital adrenal hyperplasia due to 17α-hydroxylase deficiency. *N Engl J Med* 303:530, 1980.

236. D'ARMIENTO M, REDA G, BISIGNANI G, TABOLLI S, CAPPELLACI S, LULLI P: No linkage between HLA and congenital adrenal hyperplasia due to 17α-hydroxylase deficiency. *N Engl J Med* 308:970, 1983.

237. CHUNG BC, PICADO-LEONARD J, HANIU M, BIENKOWSKI M, HALL PF, SHIVELY JE, MILLER WM: Cytochrome P450c17 (steroid 17α-hydroxylase/17,20-lyase): Cloning of human adrenal and testis cDNAs indicates the same gene is expressed in both tissues. *Proc Natl Acad Sci USA* 84:407, 1987.

238. VOUTILANIEN R, MILLER WL: Developmental expression of genes for steroidogenic enzymes P450scc (20,22-desmolase), P450c17 (17α-hydroxylase/17,20-lyase), and P450c21 (21-hydroxylase) in the human fetus. *J Clin Endocrinol Metab* 63:1145, 1986.

239. BRADSHAW KD, WATERMAN MR, COUCH RT, SIMPSON ER, ZUBER MX: Characterization of complementary deoxyribonucleic acid for human adrenocortical 17α-hydroxylase: A probe for analysis of 17-hydroxylase deficiency. *Mol Endocrinol* 1:348, 1987.

239a. KAGIMOTO M, WINTER JSD, KAGIMOTO K, SIMPSON ER, WATERMAN MR: Structural characterization of normal and mutant human steroid 17α-hydroxylase genes: Molecular basis of one example of combined 17α-hydroxylase/17,20 Lyase deficiency. *Molec Endocrinol* 2:564, 1988.

240. HOCHBERG RB, McDONALD PD, FELDMAN M, LIEBERMAN S: Studies on the biosynthetic conversion of cholesterol into pregnenolone. *J Biol Chem* 249:1277, 1974.

241. PRADER A, GURTNER HP: Das Syndrom des Pseudohermaphroditismus masculinus bei kongenitaler Nebennierenrinden Hyperplasie ohne Androgenüberproduktion. *Helv Paediatr Acta* 10:397, 1955.

242. CAMACHO AM, KOWARSKI A, MIGEON CJ, BROUGH AJ: Congenital adrenal hyperplasia due to a deficiency of one of the enzymes involved in the biosynthesis of pregnenolone. *J Clin Endocrinol Metab* 28:153, 1968.

243. KIRKLAND RT, KIRKLAND JL, JOHNSON C, HORNING MH, LIBRICK L, CLAYTON GW: Congenital lipoid adrenal hyperplasia in an eight-year-old phenotypic female. *J Clin Endocrinol Metab* 36:488, 1973.

244. HAUFFA BP, MILLER WL, GRUMBACH MM, CONTE FA, KAPLAN SL: Congenital adrenal hyperplasia due to deficient cholesterol side-chain cleavage activity (20, 22 desmolase) in a patient treated for 18 years. *Clin Endocrinol* 23:481, 1985.

245. DEGENHART HJ, VISSER HKA, BOON H: A study of the cholesterol splitting enzyme system in normal adrenals and in adrenal lipoid hyperplasia. *Acta Paediatr Scand* 60:611, 1971.

246. MATTESON KJ, CHUNG B-C, URDEA MS, MILLER WL: Study of cholesterol side-chain cleavage (20,22-desmolase) deficiency causing congenital lipoid adrenal hyperplasia using bovine-sequence P450scc oligodeoxyribonucleotide probes. *Endocrinology* 118:1296, 1986.

247. WILKINS L, LEWIS RA, KLEIN R, ROSEMBERG E: The suppression of andro-

gen secretion by cortisone in a case of congenital adrenal hyperplasia. *Bull Johns Hopkins Hosp* 86:249, 1950.

248. BARTTER FC: Adrenogenital syndromes from physiology to chemistry (1950–1975), in Lee PA, Plotnick LP, Kowarski AA, Migeon CJ (eds): *Congenital Adrenal Hyperplasia*. Baltimore, University Park Press, 1977, p 9.

249. WINTERER J, CHROUSOS GP, LORIAUX DL, CUTLER GB: Effect of hydrocortisone dose schedule on adrenal steroid secretion in congenital adrenal hyperplasia. *J Pediatr* 106:137, 1985.

250. GODARD C, RIONDEL AM, VEYRAT R, MEGEVAND A, MULLER AF: Plasma renin activity and aldosterone secretion in congenital adrenal hyperplasia. *Pediatrics* 41:883, 1968.

251. SIMOPOULOS AP, MARSHALL JR, DELEA CS, BARTTER FC: Studies on the deficiency of 21-hydroxylation in patients with congenital adrenal hyperplasia. *J Clin Endocrinol Metab* 32:438, 1971.

252. STRICKLAND AL, KOTCHEN TA: A study of the renin-aldosterone system in congenital adrenal hyperplasia. *J Pediatr* 81:962, 1972.

253. DILLON MJ: Plasma renin activity and aldosterone concentrations in children: Results in salt-wasting states. *Arch Dis Child* 50:330, 1975.

254. EDWIN C, LANES R, MIGEON CJ, LEE PA, PLOTNICK LP, KOWARSKI AA: Persistence of the enzymatic block in adolescent patients with salt-losing congenital adrenal hyperplasia. *J Pediatr* 95:534, 1979.

255. RÖSLER A, LEVINE LS, SCHNEIDER B, NOVOGRODER M, NEW MI: The interrelationship of sodium balance, plasma renin activity and ACTH in congenital adrenal hyperplasia. *J Clin Endocrinol Metab* 45:500, 1977.

256. KUHNLE U, RÖSLER A, PAREIRA JA, GUNCZLER P, LEVINE LS, NEW MI: The effects of long term normalization of sodium balance on linear growth in disorders with aldosterone deficiency. *Acta Endocrinol* 102:577, 1983.

257. WINTER JSD: Maximal comment: Current approaches to the treatment of congenital adrenal hyperplasia. *J Pediatr* 97:81, 1980.

258. KORTH-SCHUTZ S, VIRDIS R, SAENGER P, CHOW DM, LEVINE LS, NEW MI: Serum androgens as a continuing index of adequacy of treatment of congenital adrenal hyperplasia. *J Clin Endocrinol Metab* 46:452, 1978.

259. GOLDEN MP, LIPPE BM, KAPLAN SA, LAVIN N, SLAVIN J: Management of congenital adrenal hyperplasia using serum dehydroepiandrosterone sulfate and 17-hydroxyprogesterone concentrations. *Pediatrics* 61:867, 1978.

260. NIHOUL-FEKETE C: Feminizing genitoplasty in the intersex child, in Josso N (ed): *The Intersex Child (Pediatr Adolesc Endocrinol*, vol 8). Basel, Karger, 1981, p 247.

261. BAKER SW: Psychological management of intersex children, in Josso N (ed): *The Intersex Child (Pediatr Adolesc Endocrinol*, vol 8). Basel, Karger, 1981, p 261.

261a. LUBAHN DB, JOSEPH DR, SULLIVAN PM, WILLARD HF, FRENCH FS, WILSON EM: Cloning of human androgen receptor complementary DNA and localization to the X chromosome. *Science* 240:327, 1988.

261b. CHANG CS, KOKONTIS J, LIAO ST: Molecular cloning of human and rat complementary DNA encoding androgen receptors. *Science* 240:324, 1988.

261c. HERDT GH, DAVIDSON J: The Sambia "Turnim-man": Sociocultural and clinical aspects of gender formation in male pseudohermaphrodites with 5α-reductase deficiency in Papua New Guinea. *Arch Sexual Behavior* 17:33, 1988.

261d. PRICE P, WASS JAH, GRIFFIN JE, LESHIN M, SAVAGE MO, LARGE DM, BU'LOCK DE, ANDERSON DC, WILSON JD, BESSER GM: High dose androgen therapy in male pseudohermaphroditism due to 5α-reductase deficiency and disorders of the androgen receptor. *J Clin Invest* 74:1596, 1984.

262. MONEY J, EHRHARDT AA: *Man and Woman, Boy and Girl. Differentiation and Dimorphism of Gender Identity*. Baltimore, Johns Hopkins University Press, 1972, p 89.

263. NASS R, BAKER S, SPEISER P, VIRDIS R, BALSAMO A, CACCIARI E, LOCHE A, DUMIC M, NEW MI: Hormones and handedness: Lefthand bias in female congenital adrenal hyperplasia patients. *Neurology* 37:711, 1987.

263a. HU ZY, BOURREAU E, JUNG-TESTAS I, ROBEL P, BAULIEU E-E: Neurosteroids: Oligodendrocyte mitochondria convert cholesterol to pregnenolone. *Proc Natl Acad Sci USA* 84:8215, 1987.

263b. LE GOASCOGNE C, ROBEL P, GOUEZOU M, SANANES N, BAULIEU E-E, WATERMAN M: Neurosteroids: Cytochrome P450scc in rat brain. *Science* 237:1212, 1988.

264. MONEY J, EHRHARDT AA: *Man and Woman, Boy and Girl. Differentiation and Dimorphism of Gender Identity*. Baltimore, Johns Hopkins University Press, 1972, p 102.

265. BAKER SW, EHRHARDT AA: Prenatal androgen, intelligence and cognitive sex differences, in Friedman RC, Richart RM, Vande Wiele RL (eds): *Sex Differences in Behavior*. New York, Wiley, 1974, p 53.

266. SPEISER PW, WHITE PC, NEW MI: Acquisition of aldosterone biosynthetic capacity in congenital adrenal hyperplasia with homozygous deletion of the gene encoding P450/c21. *Pediatr Res* 21:254A/486, 1987.

267. BEHRMAN RE, VAUGHAN VC (eds): Prenatal disturbances. Autosomal dominant inheritance, in *Nelson Textbook of Pediatrics*. Philadelphia, Saunders, 1983, p 284.

268. GOODMAN RM: Comments on the origin and size of the world's Jewish communities, in Goodman RM: *Genetic Disorders among the Jewish People*. Baltimore, Johns Hopkins University Press, 1979, p 1.

CHAPTER 75

THE ANDROGEN RESISTANCE SYNDROMES: 5α-Reductase Deficiency, Testicular Feminization, and Related Disorders

JAMES E. GRIFFIN
JEAN D. WILSON

1. The mechanism by which androgens act within target cells is similar to that of other steroid hormones: the hormone combines with a receptor protein and the receptor-hormone complex becomes anchored in the nucleus, attaches to chromatin, and promotes the formation of messenger RNA. Androgen action, however, differs from that of other steroids in two ways. First, testosterone, the major circulating androgen, must be converted to dihydrotestosterone before exerting certain of its actions. Second, androgens act during embryogenesis to convert the undifferentiated genital tract into the male phenotype. In this manner, androgens promote differentiation of those tissues that serve as the major androgen target tissues in later life.

2. Hereditary defects that impede androgen action frequently cause resistance to the hormone both during later life and during embryogenesis and hence cause developmental defects of the male urogenital tract. Such defects in genetic men result in a phenotypic spectrum ranging from infertile but otherwise normal men to individuals with ambiguous genitalia to phenotypic women. In molecular terms, these disorders can be classified on the basis of the step in androgen action that is impeded by the individual mutations.

3. 5α-Reductase deficiency is an autosomal recessive defect in which the conversion of testosterone to dihydrotestosterone is impaired. As a consequence, in affected males the internal urogenital tract virilizes normally, but the external genitalia are predominantly female in character. The syndrome is the result of any of several mutations that impair the function of the 5α-reductase enzyme.

4. A variety of disorders influence the androgen receptor that mediates the action of both testosterone and dihydrotestosterone. At least four phenotypic variants are known—complete testicular feminization, incomplete testicular feminization, the Reifenstein syndrome, and the infertile male syndrome, each of which is inherited as an X-linked trait. Absence of receptor function is usually associated with complete testicular feminization, but qualitative or quantitative defects in receptor function can be associated with all four variants.

5. A third type of disorder—termed receptor-positive resistance—also causes a spectrum of defects in male development and is associated with normal 5α-reductase activity and normal (or elevated) levels of androgen receptor. The underlying defect is presumed to lie at the intranuclear site or sites of action of the receptor-hormone complex.

6. Normal androgen action is essential for reproduction but not for the life of individuals. Because even slight abnormalities in androgen actions are usually manifested by anatomic or functional

abnormalities (and hence come to the attention of physicians frequently), the syndromes of androgen resistance provide a remarkable opportunity to study single-gene mutations for the simultaneous elucidation of the normal pathway of action of a hormone and of the pathogenesis of common abnormalities of human sexual development.

The fact that endocrine disease can result from resistance to hormonal action at the cellular level was first recognized by Albright and his colleagues, who deduced that pseudohypoparathyroidism is caused by peripheral resistance to the action of parathyroid hormone.[1] The second disorder shown to result from resistance to hormone action was the testicular feminization syndrome, a form of male pseudohermaphroditism in which genetic males with testes differentiate as phenotypic women as a result of a single-gene defect.[2] In 1957 Wilkins showed that the administration of androgen to a woman with testicular feminization did not induce virilization, and he deduced that this disorder is caused by resistance to the action of androgen during embryogenesis and postnatal life.[3] Additional syndromes of androgen resistance have subsequently been delineated; these include other types of male pseudohermaphroditism and infertility in otherwise normal men.[4]

Investigations of several types have provided insight into the underlying pathophysiology of these disorders: (1) The role of androgens in the development of the male phenotype during embryogenesis has been defined.[5] (2) Quantitative techniques for the assessment of androgen and estrogen metabolism in intact subjects have provided insight into the pathogenesis of the various phenotypes that occur in different forms of androgen resistance.[6,7] (3) Analysis of the patterns of inheritance has provided insight into the pathogenesis and has made it possible to define distinct subgroups of the disorders.[8,9] (4) The molecular processes by which androgens act within cells have been identified,[10,11] and techniques have been developed to assess these processes in biopsy material from affected subjects and in fibroblasts cultured from skin biopsies.[4] As a consequence, we now have considerable insight into the roles of the various genes involved in normal androgen action.

The principal focus of this chapter is to describe the mechanisms by which androgens promote virilization of the normal male during fetal development and in postnatal life and to summarize the current concepts of the pathogenesis of the syndromes of androgen resistance.

DYNAMICS OF ANDROGEN AND ESTROGEN METABOLISM IN NORMAL MEN

The principal androgen secreted by the testis and present in male plasma is testosterone. Testosterone also serves as the precursor (or prohormone) for two other active hormones—dihydrotestosterone and estradiol (Fig. 75-1).[6,7,10] Dihydrotestosterone is the intracellular mediator of many androgen actions and also circulates in blood; circulating dihydrotestosterone is derived primarily by conversion from testosterone in extraglandular tissues and to a lesser extent by direct secretion into the circulation by the testes. The plasma level of dihydrotestosterone is on the average about one-tenth that of testosterone.[10]

Whether estrogen performs an essential function in normal men is unclear.[12] Excess estrogen—either relative or absolute—causes feminization in men, particularly enlargement of the breasts (gynecomastia).[13] As a consequence, estradiol serves a major role in determining the final phenotype in several disorders of androgen action, and it is essential to understand the dynamics of estrogen and androgen production and metabolism (Fig. 75-2).[7] As determined by isotope dilution techniques, the production rates of estrone and estradiol, respectively, average about 65 and 45 μg/day in normal men, and plasma production rates of testosterone and the adrenal C_{19} steroid androstenedione, respectively, average about 5000 and 3000 μg/day.[7] Thus, the ratio of the production rate of testosterone to that of estradiol in normal men is about 100 to 1. All the estrone and about 85 percent of estradiol are formed by peripheral conversion of androstenedione and testosterone. Thus, in normal men an average of only 6 to 10 μg estradiol is secreted directly into the circulation by the testes.[6,7] Kelch et al.[14] and Weinstein et al.[15] reached a similar conclusion—that estrogen in men is synthesized predominantly in peripheral tissues—as the result of direct measurements of estrogen levels in testicular venous blood of normal men. However, when large amounts of human chorionic gonadotropin (hCG) are administered to normal men [or when plasma luteinizing hormone (LH) activity is elevated in pathologic states], direct secretion of estrogen by the stimulated testes increases in pro-

portion to the increase in the secretion of testosterone.[15] Thus, whereas most estrogen in men is normally formed by peripheral aromatization of circulating C_{19} steroids, the testes may secrete significant amounts of estrogen directly into the circulation when gonadotropin concentrations are elevated. Feminization of men results when the normal 100-fold excess of androgens to estrogens is disturbed either by an increase in estrogen production or by a decrease in testosterone formation (or action) under circumstances in which estrogen production remains appreciable.[13]

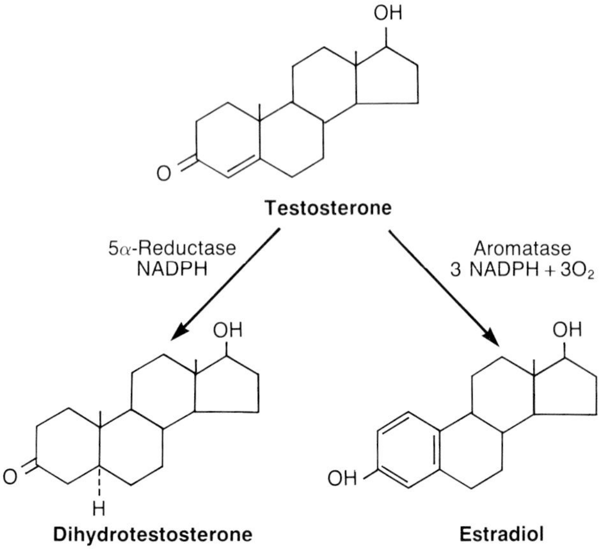

MECHANISMS OF ANDROGEN ACTION

The current concepts of the mechanisms by which androgens act are summarized schematically in Fig. 75-3. Testosterone, the principal androgen secreted by the testis and the major androgen in the plasma of men, circulates for the most part bound to two proteins, namely, testosterone-binding globulin (TeBG, also termed sex-hormone-binding globulin, or SHBG) and albumin.[16] The protein-bound steroid is in dynamic equilibrium with unbound or free hormone, the latter comprising 1 to 3 percent of the total.[16] The entry of unbound testosterone into cells is not energy-dependent and probably occurs by passive diffusion.[17] The fact that the concentration of testosterone in most androgen target tissues is lower than that in plasma is in keeping with this interpretation.[18,19]

Inside the cell, testosterone can be reduced to dihydrotestosterone by the 5α-reductase enzyme or aromatized to estradiol. Dihydrotestosterone and testosterone can bind to the same high-affinity receptor protein (R). The receptor-androgen complexes (TR and DR) then undergo a transformation reaction that promotes binding to DNA (the transformed complexes are denoted by TR$\star$ and DR$\star$). It is not clear whether the androgen receptors are formed in the cytosol or the nucleus, but the net consequence of their formation and transformation to the DNA-binding state is to anchor the complexes in the nuclear compartment, where they are attached to chromatin. The native receptor in the cell is large (8 S or greater), whereas the transformed form recoverable from the nuclear chromatin is smaller in size (4 S or less).[20,21] The cDNA that encodes a portion of the human androgen receptor has been cloned,[21a,21b,21c] and the predicted structure of the DNA binding domain of this protein resembles that of other steroid hormone receptor proteins. Receptor-androgen complexes are believed to influence the transcription of genes by binding to regulatory sites at the 5' end of the genes.[11]

Although dihydrotestosterone and testosterone bind to the same receptor protein, the two hormones perform different roles in androgen physiology. The receptor-testosterone complex is responsible for the regulation of the secretion of the gonadotropin LH by the hypothalamic-pituitary system and for the virilization of the Wolffian ducts during male phenotypic sex differentiation.[10,22] The receptor-dihydrotestosterone complex, in contrast, is responsible for the development of the male external genitalia and prostate during embryogenesis and for most of the androgen-mediated events of sexual maturation at the time of male puberty (growth of facial and body hair, temporal hair recession, maturation of external genitalia).[10,22] It is not clear which of the androgens mediates spermatogenesis. The reason that different species of one hormone perform different functions is twofold: testosterone binds less avidly to the receptor than does dihydrotestosterone,[20] and the

Fig. 75-1 Principal hormones formed from testosterone by the testes and in peripheral tissues.

Testosterone

5α-Reductase
NADPH

Aromatase
3 NADPH + 3O$_2$

Dihydrotestosterone

Estradiol

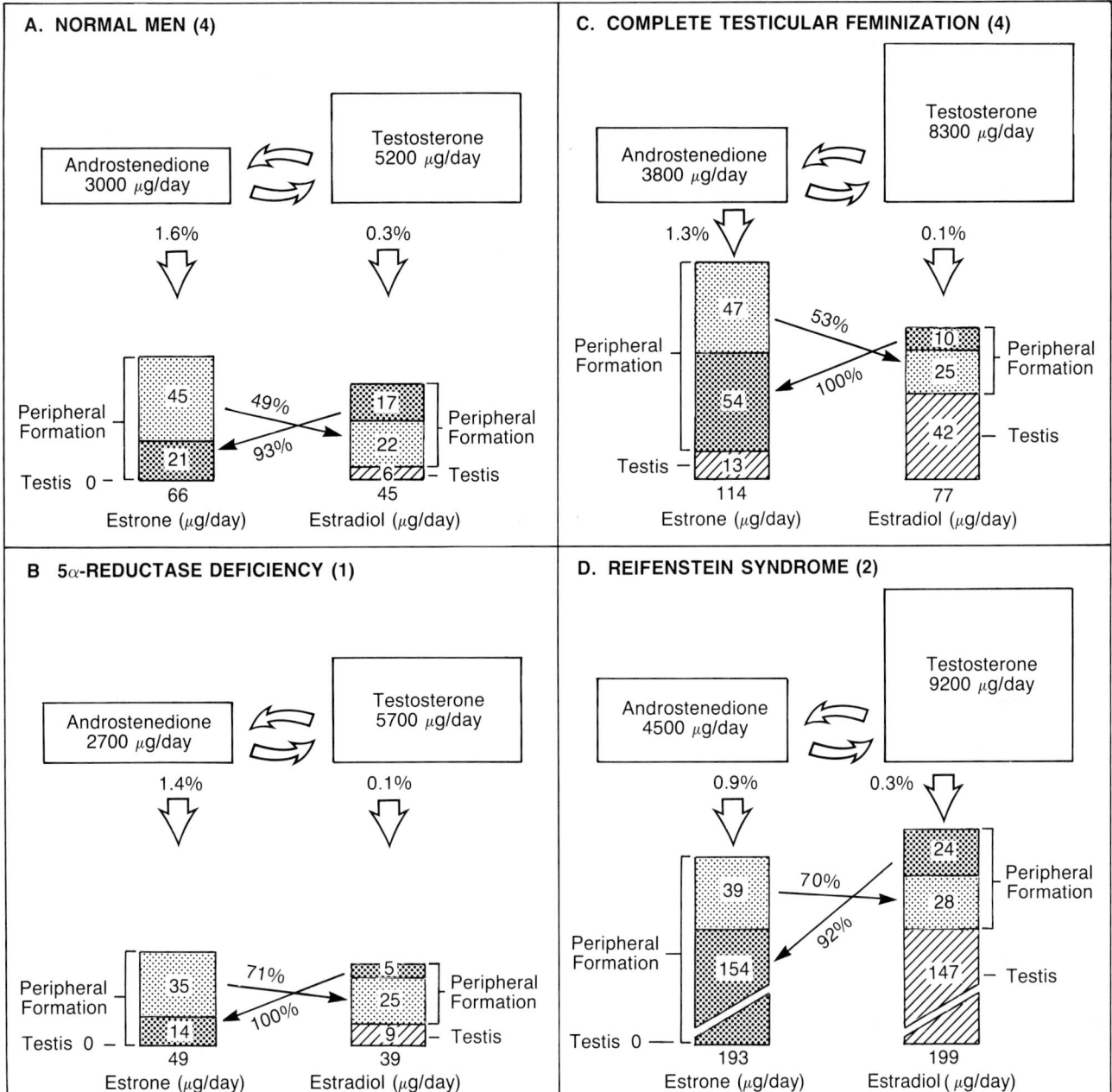

Fig. 75-2 Dynamics of androgen and estrogen production in normal men and in 46,XY subjects with androgen resistance. A. Four normal men. B. One subject with 5α-reductase deficiency. C. Four subjects with complete testicular feminization. D. Two men with Reifenstein syndrome. Average production rates of androgen are indicated in the upper boxes, and the production rates of estrogen are shown below the vertical bar. Extent of conversion of plasma testosterone and androstenedione to estradiol and estrone is indicated by the vertical arrows, and interconversion of estrone and estradiol and of testosterone and androstenedione are indicated by the horizontal arrows. The sources of estradiol and estrone are indicated in the vertical bars. Thus, estradiol arises from plasma testosterone, from estrone, and from direct secretion by the testis, and estrone arises from plasma androstenedione, from estradiol, and in some instances from direct secretion by the testis. (From Wilson et al.,[131] Walsh et al,[50] and MacDonald et al.[7] Used by permission.)

receptor-dihydrotestosterone complex is much more readily transformed to the DNA-binding state.[23] The net consequence of dihydrotestosterone formation is a major amplification of the androgenic signal.

In summary, the general process by which all steroid hormones act is believed to involve passive entry of the hormone into target tissue, binding of the hormone to a receptor protein, attachment of the protein-hormone complex to the nuclear chromatin, and promotion of the transcription of mRNA. Androgen action differs from that of other steroid hormones in at least two ways: (1) Many effects of testoster-

one, the major circulating androgen, are mediated by intracellular metabolites of testosterone: dihydrotestosterone and (possibly) estradiol. Thus, the sum of the physiologic effects of testosterone comprises the actions of testosterone itself and of its 5α-reduced and estrogenic metabolites. Since dihydrotestosterone cannot be converted to estrogen, its actions are purely androgenic. (2) During embryogenesis, androgen promotes differentiation of those tissues that will be major sites of action for the hormone in postnatal life. In exerting this critical role in normal male sexual development, androgens exert their most fundamental action.

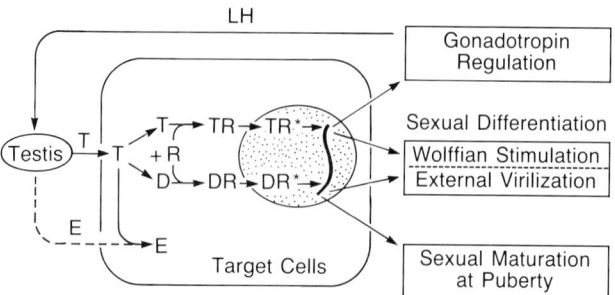

Fig. 75-3 Schematic diagram of normal androgen physiology. LH, luteinizing hormone; T, testosterone; D, dihydrotestosterone; E, estradiol; R, receptor, R*, transformed receptor.

NORMAL MALE SEXUAL DEVELOPMENT

Normal sexual development during embryogenesis consists of three sequential, ordered, and interrelated processes.[5] The first involves the establishment of *chromosomal sex* at the time of fertilization. In the mammal the heterogametic sex (XY) is male, and the homogametic sex (XX) is female. In the second phase, chromosomal sex is translated into *gonadal sex*. The exact mechanisms by which the genetic information determines that an indifferent gonad differentiates into a testis in the male or an ovary in the female and secretes the hormones characteristic of the testis or ovary are not understood entirely, but genetic determinants that induce the indifferent gonad to develop into a testis are present on the Y chromosome.[24] A 230-kilobase segment of the human Y chromosome that contains some or all the testis-determining genes has been cloned.[24a] The third phase, the translation of gonadal sex into *phenotypic sex*, is the direct consequence of the type of gonad formed and the resulting endocrine secretions of the fetal testis. In the formation of phenotypic sex, indifferent internal and external genital anlagen are converted to male or female forms, and the sexual, behavioral, and functional characteristics are ultimately determined.

The embryologic processes involved in the development of phenotypic sex are summarized in Fig. 75-4. The internal genitalia arise from the Wolffian and müllerian ducts, both of which are present in early embryos of both sexes.[22] The Wolffian ducts are the excretory ducts of the mesonephric kidney system and are connected anatomically with the indifferent gonad. The müllerian duct forms secondarily from the Wolffian duct and is not contiguous with the gonad.[25] In the male, the Wolffian ducts give rise to the epididymides, vasa deferentia, and seminal vesicles, and the müllerian ducts disappear. In the female, the müllerian ducts give rise to the fallopian tubes, uterus, and upper vagina, and the Wolffian ducts either disappear or persist in vestigial form as Gartner's ducts. Thus,

the internal genital tracts in males and females arise from different anlagen. In contrast, the external genitalia and urethra of both sexes develop from common anlagen, the genital tubercle, genital folds, and genital swellings. In the female the system elongates but changes very little; the genital tubercle becomes the clitoris, the genital folds become the labia minora, and the genital swellings become the labia majora. In the male, fusion and elongation of the genital folds cause formation of the urethra and shaft of the penis and ultimately bring the urethral orifice to the genital tubercle (glans penis). The fused genital swellings become the scrotum, and a prostate forms in the wall of the urogenital sinus.[22]

In the absence of the testes, as in the normal female or in male animal embryos castrated prior to the onset of phenotypic differentiation, the development of phenotypic sex proceeds along female lines.[5] Thus, masculinization of the fetus is the positive result of action by testicular hormones, whereas development of the female phenotype does not require hormone from the fetal ovary. Under ordinary conditions, development of the sexual phenotype conforms faithfully to the chromosomal sex, i.e., chromosomal sex determines gonadal sex, and gonadal sex in turn determines phenotypic sex.

Three hormones act to control the development of the male phenotype (Table 75-1).[22,26] Two of the hormones—müllerian inhibiting substance and testosterone—are secretory products of the fetal testes. Müllerian inhibiting substance is a large glycoprotein hormone formed by the Sertoli cells of the fetal and newborn testis.[27,28] The substance causes regression of the müllerian ducts, probably acting in concert with testosterone, and hence prevents development of the uterus and fallopian tubes in the male.

Testosterone is the principal androgen secreted by both the fetal testes and the adult testes.[29,30] The onset of testosterone secretion occurs just prior to the onset of virilization of the male embryo (at about the eighth week of development). The factors that regulate the initial secretion of testosterone have not been defined, but some evidence suggests that the initiation and early maintenance of Leydig cell function is autonomous and that gonadotropin control of testosterone formation is acquired later during embryogenesis.[31,32]

On the basis of studies of androgen metabolism in embryos of several species, including humans, it was deduced that testosterone promotes virilization of the urogenital tract in two different ways. Testosterone acts directly to stimulate the Wolffian ducts and to induce development of the epididymides, vasa deferentia, and seminal vesicles.[33,34] As illustrated in Fig. 75-5, differentiation of the Wolffian ducts into seminal vesicle and epididymis is completed in the human male embryo at about 13 weeks of development, before the capacity to form dihydrotestosterone is acquired by these tissues.[30] In contrast, in the urogenital sinus and external genitalia testos-

Table 75-1 Hormonal Control of Male Phenotypic Sex Differentiation

		Phase of phenotypic differentiation		
Gonadal hormone	*Intracellular hormone*	*Müllerian duct regression*	*Wolffian duct differentiation*	*Virilization of urogenital sinus and external genitalia*
Müllerian inhibiting substance	?	+		
Testosterone	Testosterone		+	
	Dihydrotestosterone			+

FEMALE INDIFFERENT STAGE MALE

INTERNAL DUCTS

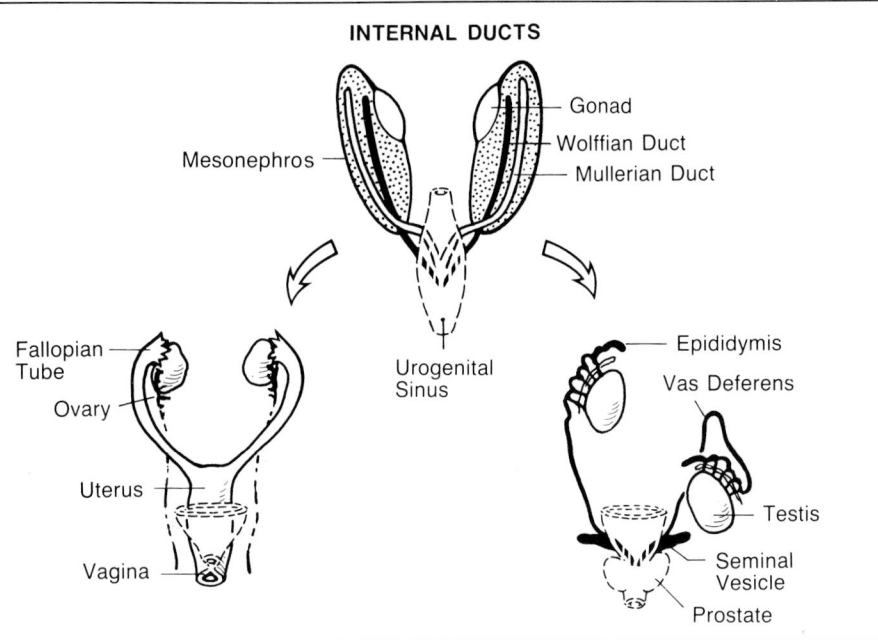

EXTERNAL GENITALIA

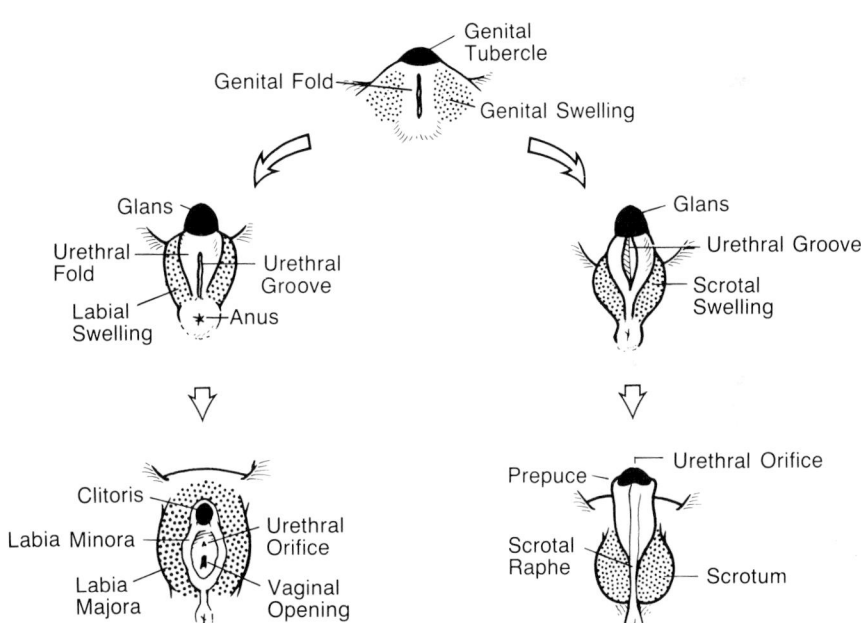

Fig. 75-4 Phenotypic differentiation of internal ducts and external genitalia in male and female embryos.

terone acts as a prohormone for dihydrotestosterone, the third hormone of fetal virilization.[33,34] Dihydrotestosterone is synthesized in small amounts by the human fetal testes at the time of male phenotypic development,[35] but the bulk of the hormone is formed by enzymatic reduction of testosterone within the urogenital sinus and external genitalia.[30,33–36] Dihydrotestosterone acts in the urogenital sinus to induce development of the male urethra and prostate, and it acts in the urogenital tubercle, swelling, and folds to cause the midline fusion, elongation, and enlargement that eventuate in the male external genitalia. The deduction that testosterone and dihydrotestosterone perform separate roles in male embryogenesis has been substantiated by studies of human mutations that impair the 5α-reductase enzyme (see below) and by studies of the effects of specific inhibitors of the 5α-reductase enzyme in rat embryos.[37]

Because of the small amounts of embryonic tissues available for study, the receptor machinery for androgen action in embryonic tissues was characterized after that for adult tissues. It is now clear, however, both from direct studies[38] and as a result of studies of single-gene defects that impede androgen action, that the schema shown in Fig. 75-3 is valid for the embryonic as well as for postnatal androgen action—namely, that a single high-affinity receptor protein is responsible for mediating the actions of both testosterone and dihydrotestosterone.[4] It is also established that the androgen-receptor mechanism is fundamentally the same in male and female embryos. Thus, when female embryos are exposed to androgens at the appropriate time in embryonic development, both the Wolffian ducts and the external genitalia virilize in characteristic male fashion[39] (also see Chap. 74). The differences in male and female phenotypic development, therefore, are due solely to

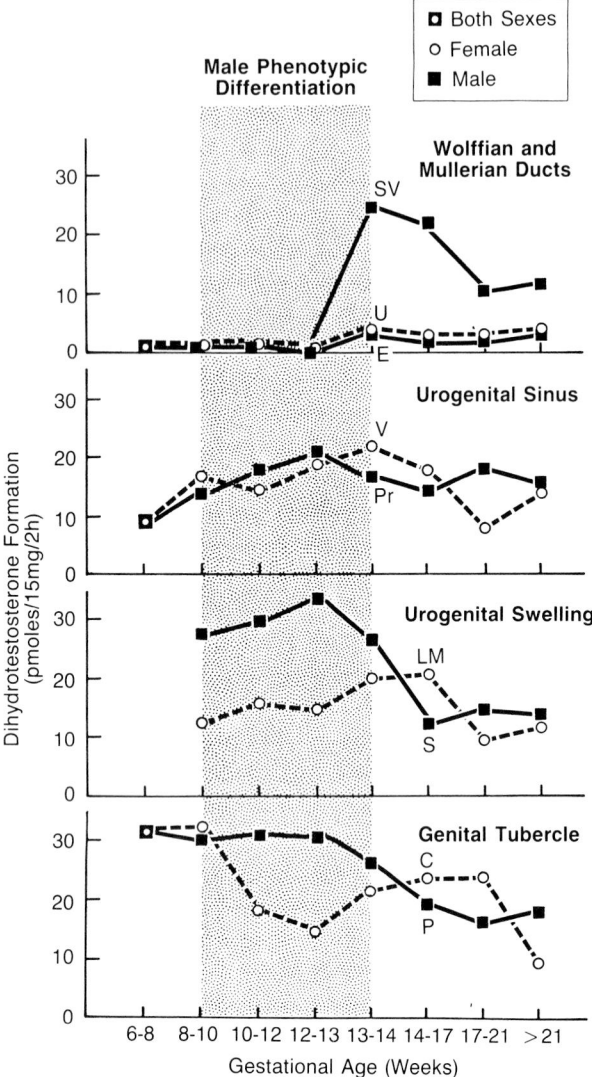

Fig. 75-5 Dihydrotestosterone formation during phenotypic differentiation of the human embryo by the urogenital tract as a function of age of the human embryo. SV, seminal vesicles; U, uterus; E, epididymides; V, vagina; Pr, prostate; LM, labia majora; S, scrotum; C, clitoris; P, penis. (*From Siiteri and Wilson.[30] Used by permission.*)

the hormones produced by the fetal testes at the critical period of embryonic development and not to differences in the receptors for the hormones.

DISORDERS OF SEXUAL DEVELOPMENT

A disturbance at any step of sexual differentiation during embryogenesis may give rise to a disorder of sexual development. Disorders so caused can be classified in terms of the initial developmental stage influenced by the mutant gene, e.g., errors in chromosomal sex, errors in gonadal sex, or errors in phenotypic sex.[8,9,40] Such abnormalities may arise by several mechanisms, such as environmental insult (as maternal ingestion of a virilizing drug during pregnancy), nonfamilial aberration in the sex chromosomes (as in 45,X gonadal dysgenesis), developmental birth defect of multifactorial etiology (as in most cases of hypospadias), or a hereditary disorder resulting from a single-gene mutation (as in the testicular feminiza-

tion syndrome). Indeed, at least 19 simply inherited disorders of sexual development are now recognized.[8,9]

Male pseudohermaphroditism is a disorder of phenotypic sex in which chromosomal and gonadal males do not develop as normal men. Three general categories of such disorders have been delineated: the persistent müllerian duct syndrome, deficiency of testosterone formation, and the androgen resistance syndromes.

The persistent müllerian duct syndrome is a rare disorder characterized by normal male virilization but failure of müllerian regression, so that affected men have a uterus and fallopian tube(s) in addition to normal Wolffian structures.[41] This syndrome results from an autosomal or X-linked gene defect. Some instances are due to failure to produce müllerian inhibiting substance, and others appear to be due to resistance at the target tissue level to the action of the hormone.[41a]

Disorders of testosterone formation result either from developmental abnormalities in the testis or from a deficiency in any of the five enzymes necessary for testosterone synthesis from cholesterol: 20,22-desmolase, 3β-hydroxysteroid dehydrogenase, 17α-hydroxylase, 17,20-desmolase, or 17β-hydroxysteroid dehydrogenase. The latter disorders result in a spectrum of defects in virilization of affected males and are discussed in Chap. 74.

The third type of disorder, and the focus of this chapter, androgen resistance, may be responsible for most cases of male pseudohermaphroditism.[42-44] Testosterone synthesis and müllerian duct regression are normal, but because of a defect in some aspect of androgen action, affected persons are resistant to the hormone during embryogenesis as well as in the postnatal state. These abnormalities were originally delineated by studying patients in whom defects in virilization were associated with normal male (or high) production rates of testosterone. Subsequently, it was recognized that partial defects in androgen action do not necessarily result in anatomic abnormalities but can be manifested only as failure of sperm production in otherwise normal men. Thus, the spectrum of androgen resistance syndromes is broader than envisioned originally. The molecular defects responsible for androgen resistance can occur at any of the three major sites in the pathway of androgen action: abnormalities in 5α-reductase, in the androgen receptor, or in the subsequent phases of androgen action (Fig. 75-6). This last category has been termed receptor-positive resistance. There is considerable genetic heterogeneity in these disorders, so that several mutations in the 5α-reductase enzyme and a variety of defects in the androgen receptor are now recognized.

Fig. 75-6 Classification of androgen resistance syndromes on basis of site of defect in androgen action. T, testosterone: D, dihydrotestosterone; R, receptor protein; R*, transformed receptor.

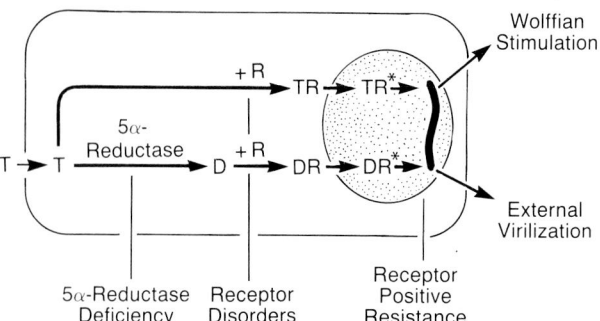

THE ANDROGEN RESISTANCE SYNDROMES

5α-Reductase Deficiency

Clinical Features. A specific form of hereditary male pseudohermaphroditism termed *pseudovaginal perineoscrotal hypospadias* was defined on clinical and genetic grounds in 1961 by Nowakowski and Lenz.[45–47] Other affected subjects were described by Simpson et al.[48] and Opitz and coworkers.[49] Affected persons are 46,XY males who have an autosomal recessive disorder characterized by an external female phenotype at birth, bilateral testes, and normally virilized Wolffian structures that terminate in or empty into the vagina. This entity (also called *familial incomplete male pseudohermaphroditism type 2*)[50] constitutes a distinct disorder on genetic, phenotypic, and endocrine grounds and is now recognized to result from deficient conversion of testosterone to dihydrotestosterone. Accordingly, the disorder is now termed 5α-reductase deficiency.

The clinical features are summarized in Table 75-2: (1) autosomal recessive inheritance; (2) severe perineoscrotal hypospadias with a dorsal, hooded prepuce and a ventral urethral groove that opens at the base of the phallus (illustrated in Fig. 75-7A); (3) a blind-ending vaginal pouch of variable length, opening either into a urogenital sinus or onto the perineum immediately behind the urethral orifice; (4) well-developed and histologically differentiated testes with normal epididymides, vasa deferentia, and seminal vesicles (Fig. 75-7B); (5) the absence of müllerian duct derivatives; and (6) variable masculinization and little or no breast enlargement at the time of expected puberty. Typically, affected individuals are raised as girls, despite the clitoromegaly that is usually present at birth.

Certain features deserve emphasis. First, the ejaculatory ducts usually terminate in the vagina. In some individuals no vaginal pouch is present, and the Wolffian duct derivatives terminate adjacent to the urethra on the perineum. Prostatic tissue is not palpable by rectal examination, and a prostatic utricle cannot be demonstrated by cystoscopy. Thus, Wolffian derivatives are male in character, whereas the urogenital sinus and external genitalia are predominantly female.[50] A radi-

Table 75-2 Features of 5α-Reductase Deficiency

External phenotype: Female genitalia with some clitoromegaly at birth and variable virilization at expected time of puberty; normal male breast development.
Urogenital tract: Testes; epididymides, vasa deferentia, and seminal vesicles empty into vagina; no müllerian duct derivatives.
Karyotype: 46,XY.
Inheritance: Autosomal recessive.
Endocrinology:
  Testosterone: Normal male plasma levels and production rates.
  Estrogen: Normal male plasma levels and production rates.
  Gonadotropin: Normal to slightly elevated plasma LH levels.
Pathogenesis: Inability to form dihydrotestosterone.

ogram of the lower Wolffian duct system from one such patient is shown in Fig. 75-7B.

Second, the degree of masculinization at the time of expected puberty can be striking, and in some subjects the habitus becomes masculine.[48,49,51–55] The reason why virilization at puberty is more extensive than that in utero is unclear. On the one hand, all subjects described to date have measurable, albeit low, levels of circulating dihydrotestosterone, and the late virilization may be mediated by the small amount of this metabolite. Alternatively, the virilization at the expected time of puberty could be mediated by testosterone itself over a period of several years (Fig. 75-8).[55] Despite the partial virilization, however, affected subjects are characteristically less virilized than their unaffected brothers.

Third, in some,[51–56] but not all,[50,57–61] subjects who are untreated until later in life a reversal of gender role occurs at the time of expected puberty so that individuals raised as girls begin to function as men. Whether this change in gender role behavior is due to a true reversal of gender identity or is instead the resolution of uncertain gender identity in children with partial masculinization is unclear. It is our impression that the change in gender role behavior is more likely to occur the greater the degree of virilization at expected puberty.

Fourth, spermatogenesis is either profoundly impaired or absent in all affected subjects studied to date,[60] but it is not known whether the spermatogenic arrest is due to a deficiency of dihydrotestosterone formation in the testis or is instead a consequence of testicular maldescent, which is a common feature. Indeed, the scrotum is almost never male in character,

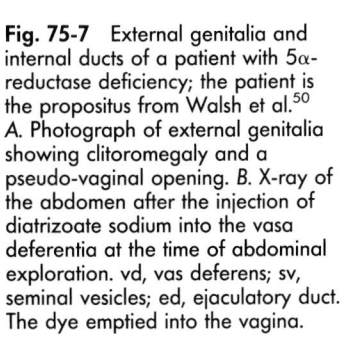
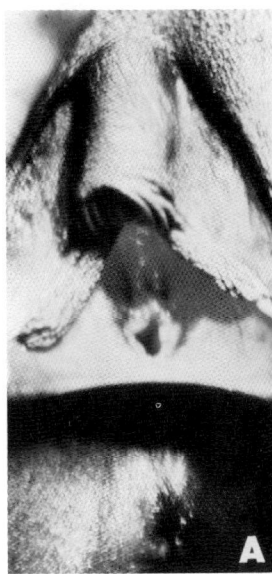
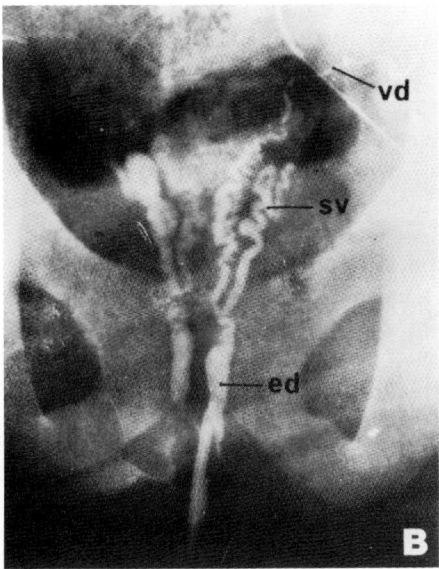

Fig. 75-7 External genitalia and internal ducts of a patient with 5α-reductase deficiency; the patient is the propositus from Walsh et al.[50] A. Photograph of external genitalia showing clitoromegaly and a pseudo-vaginal opening. B. X-ray of the abdomen after the injection of diatrizoate sodium into the vasa deferentia at the time of abdominal exploration. vd, vas deferens; sv, seminal vesicles; ed, ejaculatory duct. The dye emptied into the vagina.

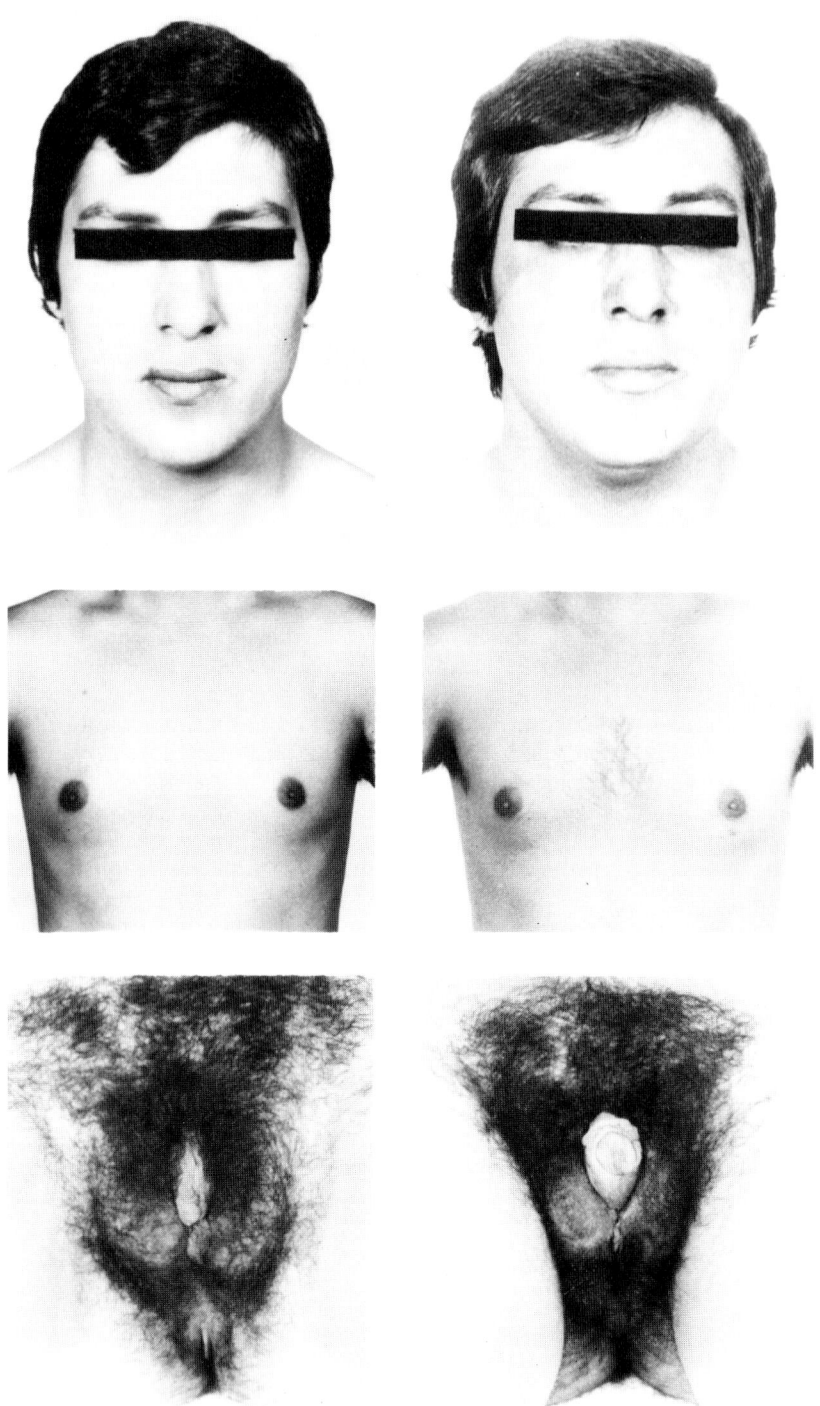

Fig. 75-8 Photographs of a patient with 5α-reductase deficiency before and after high-dose androgen therapy. *Left.* Before treatment (June 1976). *Right.* After treatment with a mixture of testosterone esters 500 mg IM weekly (March 1980). Correction of chordee was performed between these dates. (From Price et al.[55] Used by permission.)

so that even when testes descend into the labial folds their position is rarely truly normal.

Endocrinology. Simpson et al. observed that normal male levels of testosterone in one affected individual rose even higher after administration of human chorionic gonadotropin (hCG) and fell to the castrate range after removal of the testes.[48] They concluded that testosterone secretion in 5α-reductase deficiency is normal and is under normal feedback control. Subsequent studies have supported this interpretation.

The characteristic endocrine features are as follows: (1) normal male to high levels of plasma testosterone and low levels of plasma dihydrotestosterone,[50–52] (2) an elevation in the ratio of the concentration of plasma testosterone to dihydrotestos-

terone in adulthood and after stimulation with hCG in childhood,[52,53,59,62,63] (3) elevated ratios of urinary 5β- to 5α-metabolites of androgen,[52,53,63–67] (4) diminished conversion of testosterone to dihydrotestosterone in tissues of affected subjects,[52,53] (5) elevated ratios of urinary 5β- to 5α-metabolites of C_{21} steroids,[66–68] and (6) increased ratio of plasma testosterone to dihydrotestosterone after the administration of testosterone.[55,63] Levels of plasma LH are either normal[50,55,60,64] or slightly elevated (although never as high as in men with primary testicular failure or in subjects with male pseudohermaphroditism due to abnormalities of the androgen receptor[51–54,57,68,69]). Detailed studies of the origins and rates of production of androgen and estrogen have been conducted in one person (Fig. 75-2B);[50] plasma levels of androstenedione

(1.1 ng/ml) and testosterone (6.9 ng/ml) and the plasma production rates of androstenedione (2.7 mg/day) and testosterone (5.2 mg/day) were in the range for normal men. Estradiol production was also in the range for normal men in regard to the total production rate (45 μg/day), the amount secreted by the testes (9 μg/day), and the amount derived from the peripheral aromatization of plasma C_{19}-steroid precursors (36 μg/day). These quantitative studies demonstrating normal male androgen and estrogen production explain the failure of patients to undergo female breast development at the time of puberty and are in contrast to the situation in male pseudohermaphroditism caused by disorders of the androgen receptor; in the latter disorders the variable degree of feminization at the expected time of puberty is associated with increased production of estrogen by the testes.

Genetics. Simpson et al.[48] and Opitz and coworkers[49] provided evidence that 5α-reductase deficiency is due to the homozygous state of a rare autosomal recessive gene. Affected sibs are common, and consanguinity can be documented in approximately half of the cases. Many cases have occurred in geographic areas where the coefficient of inbreeding is high. Affected homozygous 46,XX sisters of affected males are phenotypically normal and have normal reproductive capacity.[53] Thus, the mutation appears to be silent in women. Heterozygous carriers for the mutation are also phenotypically normal but can frequently be identified by the measurement of 5α- and 5β-steroid metabolites in the urine.[66-68] The prevalence of the disorder is uncertain; it has been reported in individuals from Algeria,[65] France,[70] Mexico,[57] Cyprus,[64] the Dominican Republic,[51-53] Israel,[69] Italy,[54] Pakistan,[71] Turkey,[68] Egypt,[72] Austria,[60] and Vietnam,[60] as well as from the United States.[50,60,61] It is now established that more than one mutation of the enzyme causes functional impairment in enzyme activity.[54,60,73] Such genetic heterogeneity is similar to that in other hereditary enzyme deficiencies.

Pathogenesis. The fact that dihydrotestosterone formation is essential for virilization of the external genitalia and male urethra, whereas testosterone itself causes male differentiation of the Wolffian ducts, was deduced from studies of androgen metabolism in normal embryos.[30,33-36] Consequently, it was predicted that impairment of dihydrotestosterone formation in the male embryo with normal testosterone synthesis would re-

sult in the phenotype observed in subjects with pseudovaginal perineoscrotal hypospadias, namely, normal male Wolffian duct derivatives but defective masculinization of the urogenital sinus and external genitalia.[74] Substantiating evidence that this phenotype is the result of deficient production of dihydrotestosterone was obtained in 1974 by studies of two families with the disorder, one in Dallas[50] and the other in the Dominican Republic.[51]

The initial studies in Dallas were performed in a 13-year-old 46,XY phenotypic girl with primary amenorrhea. She was partially virilized, and plasma testosterone values were in the adult male range (Fig. 75-7). Because of the female phenotype a decision was made to remove the testes and to repair the virilization of the external genitalia. Documentation at surgery of normal male Wolffian duct structures—epididymides, vasa deferentia, seminal vesicles, and ejaculatory ducts—that terminated in a blind-ending vagina established the phenotype as that of pseudovaginal perineoscrotal hypospadias. Dihydrotestosterone formation was examined in tissue slices of foreskin, corpora cavernosa of the phallus, epididymis, and labia majora obtained from the subject at the time of surgery and compared with rates of formation in tissue slices from control subjects and from individuals with other forms of male pseudohermaphroditism. Dihydrotestosterone formation was virtually undetectable in tissues from the subject but clearly measurable in tissues from all control groups (Table 75-3),[50] suggesting that deficiency in dihydrotestosterone formation is the cause of this disorder.

A similar conclusion was reached by Imperato-McGinley and colleagues[51-53] from studies of a large family with the disorder in the Dominican Republic. The urinary excretion of 5α-androstanediol and androsterone (the end products of dihydrotestosterone metabolism) was low, as would be predicted if dihydrotestosterone formation were deficient.

The subsequent endocrine and enzymatic studies of this disorder have substantiated and expanded insight into the pathogenesis. It is of interest that to date no person has been described in whom there is total absence of plasma dihydrotestosterone, and it is not known to what extent the partial virilization that occurs at puberty is mediated by the small amounts of dihydrotestosterone present in the circulation.

The molecular features of 5α-reductase deficiency have been characterized in fibroblasts cultured from the skin of persons with the disorder. 5α-Reductase activity is high on average in

Table 75-3 Dihydrotestosterone Formation by Tissue Slices from Normal Subjects and from Patients with Various Forms of Androgen Resistance

Group	Age range, years	Dihydrotestosterone formation, pmol/(h · 100 mg tissue) ± SEM				
		Scrotum	Foreskin	Epididymis	Labia majora	Miscellaneous body skin
Miscellaneous control subjects	6–85	526 ± 60	211 ± 26	142 ± 32	183 ± 25	49 ± 6
5α-Reductase deficiency	13		8	3	0	
Complete testicular feminization	2–56			101 ± 15	72 ± 22	
Incomplete testicular feminization	26			71	319	19
Reifenstein syndrome	9	422	87			

NOTE: Tissue slices (40 to 100 mg) were incubated with 0.5 μM [³H]testosterone, 10 mM glucose, and Krebs-Ringer phosphate buffer, at pH 7.4 in a total volume of 2.5 ml. After incubation for 1 h (genital tissue) or 2 h (miscellaneous body sites) the steroids were extracted and analyzed. Samples from 5 to 20 subjects were pooled for each of the control tissues analyzed, and 6 patients with complete testicular feminization were studied. The other groups represent 1 subject each.
SOURCES: From Walsh et al.[50] and Madden et al.[125] Used by permission.

normal genital skin (foreskin, scrotum, labia majora)[75] and in fibroblasts cultured from normal genital skin.[73,76-79] The enzyme catalyzes the 5α-reduction of many C_{19} and C_{21} steroids including cortisol.[61] The pH optimum of enzyme activity in homogenates of normal genital skin fibroblasts is 5.5, with a broad shoulder of activity extending over a more alkaline range.[77] Measurement of the activity in fibroblast homogenates at pH 5.5 has proved to be the most sensitive means to detect the enzyme deficiency. Very low rates of enzyme activity were observed in cells grown from skin biopsies from subjects from the original Dallas family and from 15 other families that fulfill the endocrine, genetic, phenotypic, and enzymatic criteria for the diagnosis of 5α-reductase deficiency (data points labeled "deficient enzyme" in Fig. 75-9). These families with deficient enzyme include the Dominican Republic family studied by Imperato-McGinley and coworkers,[51-53] additional families reported in the literature,[54,55,60,64] and some families that have not been reported in detail as well. In approximately half of these families consanguinity has been documented or is probable. Thus, deficiency of enzyme activity is the most common cause of the syndrome and results in a fairly uniform phenotype.

The picture became more complex when an affected family from Los Angeles was evaluated. The two affected members had typical endocrine findings of 5α-reductase deficiency, a phenotype identical to that of previously characterized families, and deficiency of 5α-reductase in direct biopsy material.[61] However, activity of the enzyme in fibroblasts cultured from the genital skin of these subjects was within the normal range (labeled "abnormal enzyme" in Fig. 75-9).[73] Furthermore, in contrast to the situation in the previous cases, the enzyme from these patients had a normal pH optimum and a normal apparent K_m for testosterone. Affinity of the enzyme for reduced nicotin-

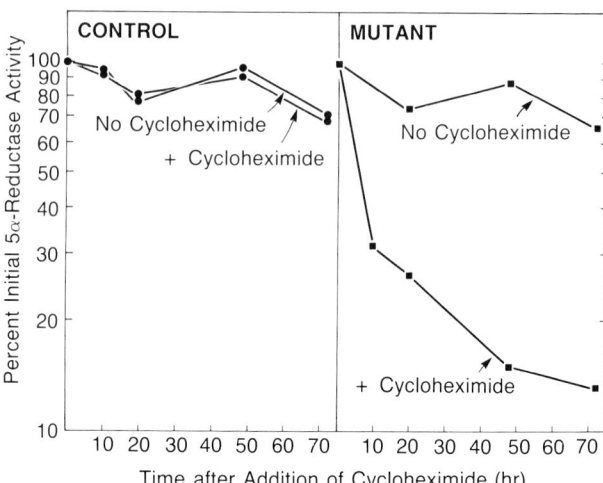

Fig. 75-10 Stability of 5α-reductase in intact fibroblasts from a control subject and a patient with the unstable variant of 5α-reductase deficiency. On day 7 after plating, 1 mM cycloheximide was added to half the samples of fibroblasts from a control and a mutant subject. 5α-Reductase was assayed in the whole cell at varying intervals. (*Redrawn from Leshin et al.[73] Used by permission.*)

amide adenine dinucleotide phosphate (NADPH), the cofactor for the reaction, was decreased, and as a consequence the enzyme was unstable and exhibited a rapid turnover (Fig. 75-10).[73] The enzymes in cells from subjects from three additional families have exhibited similar evidence of a qualitatively abnormal function (Fig. 75-9).[54,60] We believe that the qualitatively defective enzyme in these four families is synthesized at a normal rate but does not function normally within the cell and is degraded more rapidly than normal so that the steady state activity in intact cells is profoundly decreased. The phenotypic expression is thus identical to that in families with deficient enzyme.

In contrast to other androgen target tissues, 5α-reductase activity is normal in roots of most scalp hair from persons with 5α-reductase deficiency.[80] The reason for this dichotomy among androgen target tissues is unknown, but it may be due to the expression in hair roots of the residual 5α-reductase activity that can be demonstrated at around pH 7.5 in fibroblasts from normal extragenital tissues and in skin fibroblasts from some patients with 5α-reductase deficiency.[78]

Diagnosis. The diagnosis of 5α-reductase deficiency is commonly made either at the time of expected puberty or in infancy. In the adolescent or young adult, diagnosis is usually straightforward, namely a 46,XY male pseudohermaphrodite with the characteristic phenotype, male plasma testosterone levels, and abnormal ratios of plasma testosterone to dihydrotestosterone. In this group it is necessary to distinguish 5α-reductase deficiency from defects in testosterone biosynthesis on the one hand (Chap. 74) and partial defects of the androgen receptor on the other (see below). In all three disorders, virilization of the Wolffian ducts can be more complete than that of the external genitalia. Defects in testosterone biosynthesis are usually associated with low plasma testosterone for men, but in men with partial enzyme deficiency, testosterone can be normal at the expense of high LH values.[81,82] The most common hereditary defect in testosterone biosynthesis, 17β-hydroxysteroid dehydrogenase deficiency, can be recognized on the basis of elevated androstenedione levels,[81,82] and it is our practice to measure androstenedione routinely in suspected cases of 5α-reductase deficiency. The recognition of partial de-

Fig. 75-9 5α-Reductase activity in genital skin fibroblasts cultured from skin biopsies from 20 families with 5α-reductase deficiency. The range of pH 5.5 activity in 41 control subjects is illustrated in the black bar, and the activity in 20 patients from different families with 5α-reductase deficiency is shown in the individual points (■).

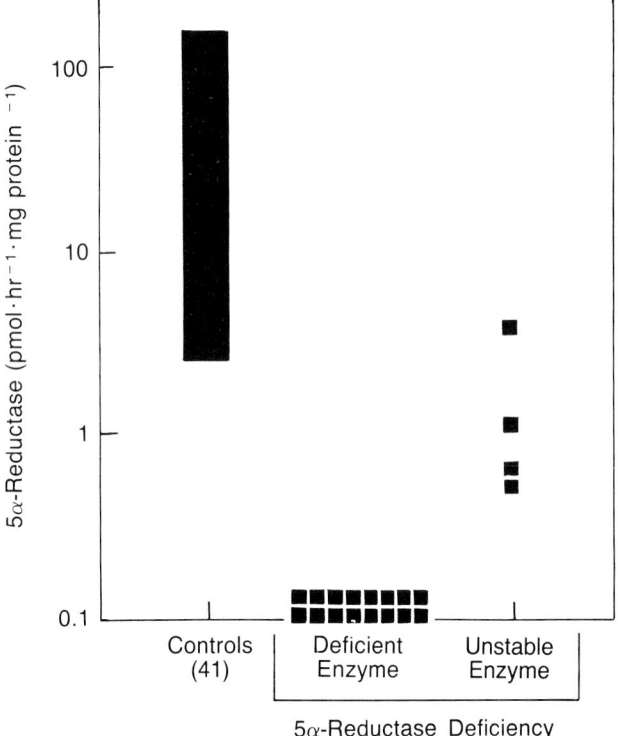

5α-Reductase Deficiency

fects in the androgen receptor can be more perplexing, since such defects can impair the development of organs that are the major sites of dihydrotestosterone biosynthesis and hence cause secondary forms of apparent 5α-reductase deficiency with abnormally high ratios of plasma testosterone to dihydrotestosterone.[83,84] In the latter cases, detailed family histories indicating the pattern of inheritance, careful phenotypic characterization to determine the presence or absence of gynecomastia, and measurements of the ratios of 5β- to 5α- urinary glucocorticosteroid metabolites (which reflect hepatic metabolism, predominantly) may provide insight into the true diagnosis (see below and Table 75-9).[84]

Recognition of 5α-reductase in infancy presents special problems, particularly when the family history is uninformative. In this situation, as in all prepubertal subjects, determination of the ratios of plasma testosterone to dihydrotestosterone before and after administration of hCG generally serves to establish the diagnosis.[85] In those situations in which the testes have previously been removed, the diagnosis can be established either by determining the ratio of urinary 5β- to 5α-glucocorticosteroid metabolites[52,85] or by determining the ratio of plasma testosterone to dihydrotestosterone after the administration of testosterone esters by injection.[59]

Management. For those individuals raised as males or who elect to function as males, several procedures are appropriate. First, urological consultation should be obtained regarding appropriate corrective surgery to repair chordees, correct hypospadias, and bring cryptorchid testes into the labioscrotal folds. Second, in view of the fact that the degree of virilization is generally unsatisfactory, supplemental androgen therapy is indicated in such patients. The ideal agent would be one that replaces the missing dihydrotestosterone; in experimental studies the administration of dihydrotestosterone enanthate by injection at 4- to 6-week intervals results in a sustained elevation of plasma dihydrotestosterone levels,[86] but at present the agent is not available for general use. A second technique has been to administer testosterone esters in quantities sufficient to elevate plasma testosterone to supraphysiological levels; when this has been done in patients with 5α-reductase deficiency, it is possible to bring dihydrotestosterone levels to the normal male range and to promote virilization in a satisfactory manner.[55] Unfortunately, it is not known whether the supraphysiological levels of testosterone will produce deleterious side effects over the long term. A third approach would be to administer androgen in a form that does not require 5α-reductase to be active. For example, 19-nortestosterone is active in the absence of 5α-reduction[87] and can be given by injection in an esterified form such as nandrolone decanoate.

In those subjects who elect to lead life as women, the management should be similar to that in the incomplete forms of testicular feminization. That is, the testes should be removed to preclude (or stop) the partial virilization at expected puberty, estrogen/progestogen therapy should be instituted at an appropriate age to promote feminization, and, when appropriate, vaginoplasty should be undertaken by either surgical or medical means.[40]

Disorders of the Androgen Receptor

Disorders of the androgen receptor can cause several distinct phenotypes. Despite differences in the clinical manifestation

and molecular pathology, these disorders are similar in regard to endocrinology, genetics, and basic pathophysiology.

Clinical Features.

COMPLETE TESTICULAR FEMINIZATION. The clinical features of complete testicular feminization are summarized in Table 75-4. The syndrome has been recognized for many years (the literature was reviewed by Hauser[88]). The initial insight into the pathogenesis of the disorder was provided by two pioneering studies. In 1937, Pettersson and Bonnier deduced from family studies that affected individuals are genetic males, that the pattern of inheritance is consistent either with X-linked or a sex-limited autosomal mode of transmission, and that the syndrome could best be explained by a failure of male development in an embryo in which the fundamental trend is toward the female phenotype.[89] In 1953, Morris reviewed 79 published cases that fulfilled the criteria for inclusion in the syndrome and added two new cases and introduced the term *testicular feminization*.[2] The disorder has been the subject of a number of reviews.[88,90,91] The typical subject is seen by a physician either because of primary amenorrhea (postpubertally) or an inguinal hernia (prepubertally). On occasion the diagnosis is not established until later in life. Breast development is that of a normal woman, and the general body habitus and distribution of body fat are female in character (Fig. 75-11A). Axillary and pubic hair are absent or scanty, but some vulvar hair (albeit diminished in amount) is usually present. Facial and scalp hair are those of normal women. The external genitalia are unambiguously female (Fig. 75-12A). The labia and clitoris are normal or somewhat underdeveloped. Although usually adequate for successful coitus, the vagina may be absent or shallow. The vagina, if present, is blind-ending, and the internal genitalia are absent except for gonads that have the histologic features of undescended testes (i.e., normal or increased Leydig cells and seminiferous tubules without spermatogenesis). The testes may be located in the abdomen, along the course of the inguinal canal, or in the labia majora. Occasionally, remnants of müllerian or Wolffian duct origin can be found in the paratesticular fascia or in fibrous bands extending from the testes,[88,92] and rarely uterine remnants are present.[93,94] Morris[2] also noted the occurrence of tumors in the cryptorchid testes of affected subjects.

Documentation that nuclear chromatin is male in character,[95,96] that the chromosomal complement is 46,XY, and that the chromosomes are of normal structure[97–99] confirmed the deductions from pedigree analysis and gonadal histology that

Table 75-4 Clinical Features of Complete Testicular Feminization

External phenotype: Female external genitalia with underdevelopment of the labia and a blind-ending vagina, female habitus and breast development, paucity of axillary and pubic hair
Urogenital tract: Testes that may be intraabdominal, along the course of the inguinal canal, or in the labia; absent Wolffian and müllerian derivatives
Karyotype: 46,XY
Inheritance: X-linked recessive
Endocrinology:
 Testosterone: Normal or high male plasma levels and production rates
 Estrogen: Plasma levels and production rates higher than in normal men
 Gonadotropin: Elevated plasma LH levels
Pathogenesis: Complete resistance to all actions of testosterone and dihydrotestosterone

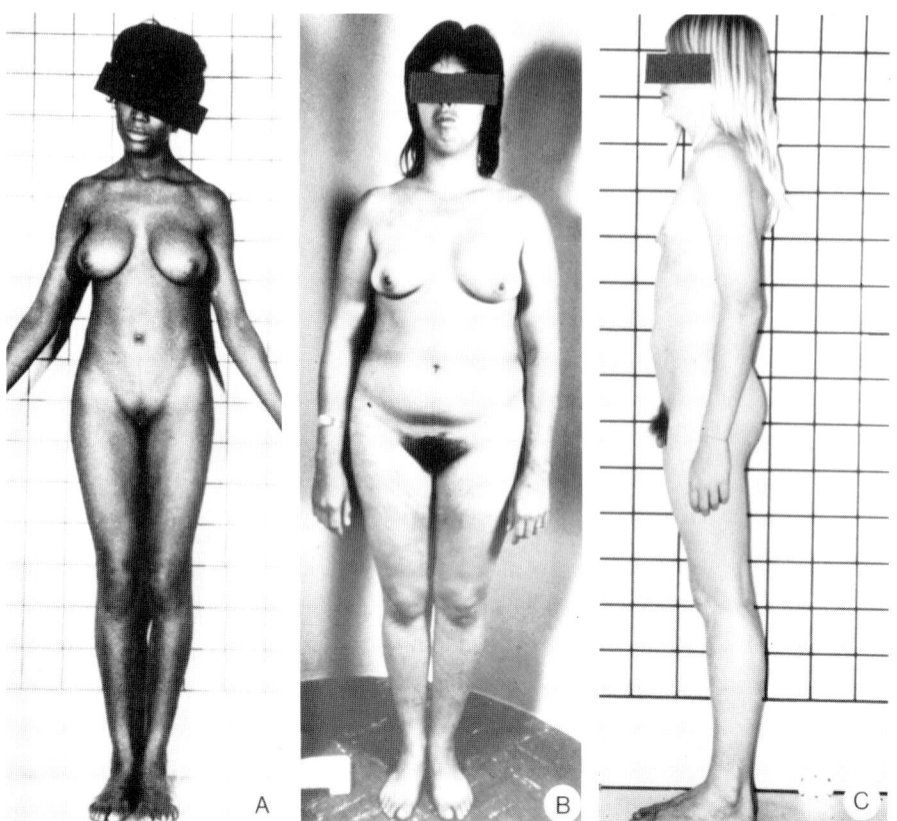

Fig. 75-11 Photographs of 3 patients with disorders of androgen receptor function. A. Complete testicular feminization. B. Incomplete testicular feminization. C. Reifenstein syndrome. (From Griffin and Wilson.[40] Used by permission.)

the affected individuals are genetic males. Affected subjects tend to be rather tall for women, averaging 171.5 cm in height in one series;[100] bone age corresponds to chronologic age;[88] body size is larger than average;[100] and tooth size is as large as in normal men (and larger than in normal women).[101] The fact that height and tooth size are greater than those of normal women suggests that the Y chromosome may have a direct affect on these parameters not mediated by androgens. A possible role of estrogens has been postulated to explain the acceleration of linear growth.[102] Adrenal and thyroid function are normal, and there are no commonly associated somatic anomalies.[89] Intelligence is normal,[103] and psychologic development is unmistakably feminine in regard to behavior, outlook, and maternal instincts.[104]

Estimates of incidence vary from 1 in 20,000 to 1 in 64,000 male births.[88,105] Through studies of buccal smears, it has been estimated that as many as 1 to 2 percent of girls with inguinal hernias may have the disorder.[105–106] In a nationwide survey in Japan, testicular feminization was the most common form of primary resistance to hormone action, some 390 patients having been ascertained in a 10-year period.[107] In some series this disorder is the third most frequent cause of primary amenorrhea in women after gonadal dysgenesis and congenital absence of the vagina.[108]

These women have a profound resistance to the action of both exogenous and endogenous androgens. Wilkins[3] gave methyltestosterone in large doses to women with testicular feminization after castration and showed that there was no growth of sexual hair (despite documentation of the presence of pubic hair follicles by biopsy), no enlargement of the clitoris, no change in the voice, and no other obvious clinical effect. Subsequent work confirmed the lack of response of pubic hair to androgen treatment[109,110] and demonstrated, in addition, resistance to androgen in regard to sebum production,[110] failure of the expected decrease in thyroxine-binding globulin

concentration in plasma,[111,112] diminished feedback on the secretion of LH by the pituitary,[113] and lack of effect on phosphorus and nitrogen balance.[114–116] Thus, resistance to the action of androgen appears to be virtually absolute in the complete form of testicular feminization.

The histologic characteristics of the testes are similar to those of testes in patients with cryptorchidism due to other causes but differ in that spermatogenesis is virtually always absent (present in half of age-matched cryptorchid testes), germinal elements are detected only rarely, and adenoma formation of the Sertoli cells is frequent.[117–118] Although the number of Leydig cells per high-power field is increased,[117] the total volume and number of Leydig cells are probably normal.[119]

INCOMPLETE TESTICULAR FEMINIZATION. The term *incomplete testicular feminization* was introduced by Prader[120] and by Morris and Mahesh[121] to characterize a phenotype somewhat similar to that of complete testicular feminization but associated with partial virilization of the external genitalia and partial virilization as well as feminization at the time of expected puberty. The term was utilized subsequently to characterize several types of incomplete male pseudohermaphroditism, including defects of testosterone synthesis, the Reifenstein syndrome, and some subjects for whom data are not available to determine the etiology of the underlying disorders. Nevertheless, certain of these subjects constitute a distinct phenotype that is associated with abnormalities of the androgen receptor.[122–125]

The clinical features are summarized in Table 75-5. Affected individuals have the habitus and general appearance of women and, as in the complete form of the disorder, most commonly present because of primary amenorrhea (Fig. 75-11*B*). The karyotype is 46,XY; the testes are in the abdomen or in the inguinal canals and are indistinguishable on histologic grounds from those in patients with complete testicular

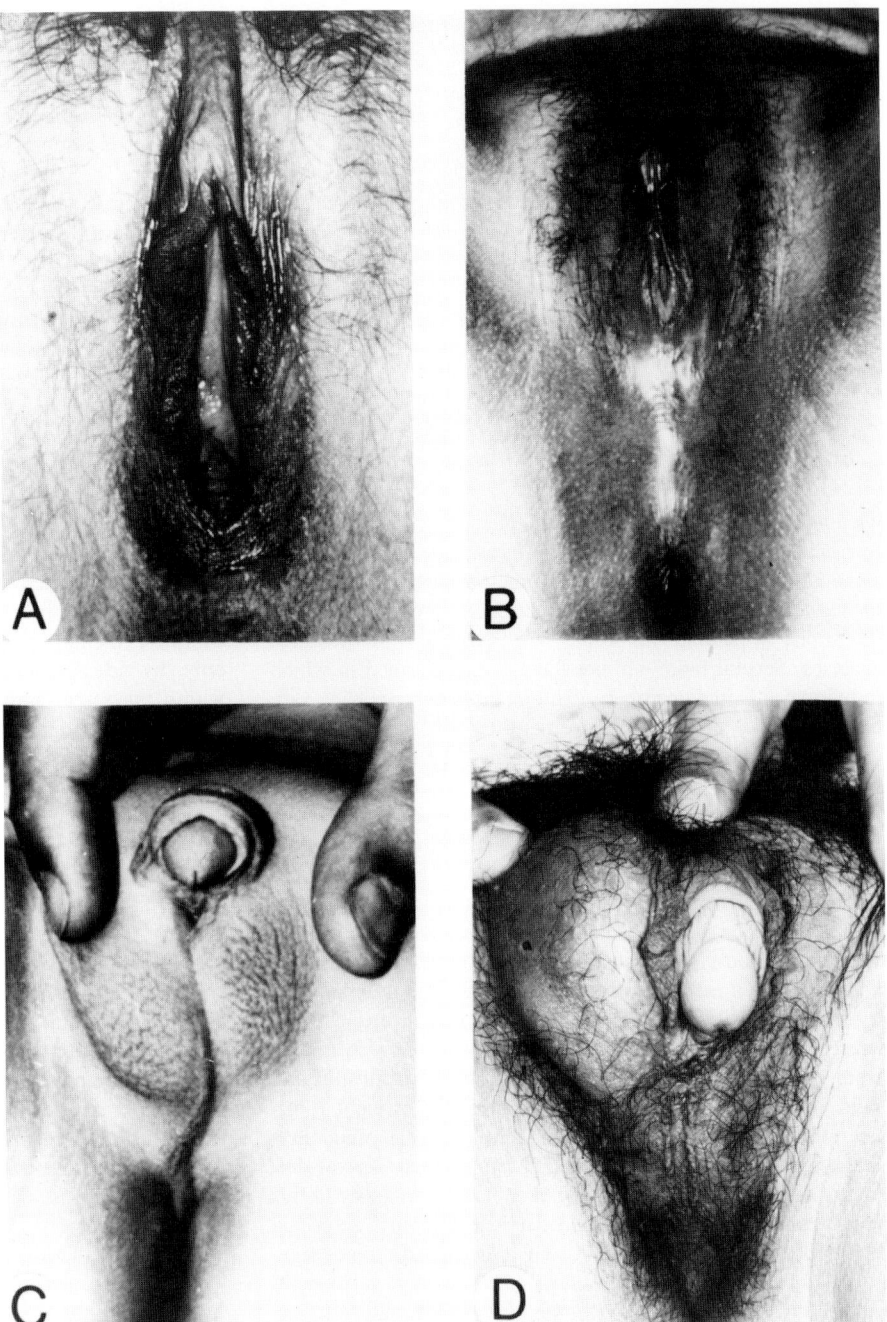

Fig. 75-12 Photographs of external genitalia of four subjects with disorders of androgen receptor function. *A.* Complete testicular feminization. *B.* Incomplete testicular feminization. *C.* Reifenstein syndrome (prepubertal). *D.* Reifenstein syndrome (adult). *(From Griffin and Wilson.[40] Used by permission.)*

feminization. The external genitalia are distinctive in that the labioscrotal folds are partially fused, and clitoromegaly is common (Fig. 75-12*B*). The vagina is short and ends blindly. At the expected time of puberty both variable feminization and partial virilization may take place. Müllerian duct derivatives are absent, but Wolffian duct structures are present; this latter feature, together with the partial virilization of the external genitalia, separates the phenotype from that of testicular feminization. Not only are upper Wolffian duct structures present (epididymides and vasa deferentia), but, in addition, the terminal derivatives of the Wolffian ducts, including the ampullae of the vasa deferentia, the seminal vesicles, and the ejaculatory ducts, are male in character (although underdeveloped in comparison with those of a normal man). The ejaculatory ducts empty into the vagina. Thus, certain features resemble testicular feminization (female breast development), some resemble 5α-reductase deficiency (presence of male Wolffian

duct derivatives and ambiguous external genitalia), and some resemble the Reifenstein syndrome (mixed virilization and feminization at the time of expected puberty).

The frequency of this disorder is uncertain, but in most series (including the personal experience of the authors) it is about one-tenth as common as complete testicular feminization.

REIFENSTEIN SYNDROME. In some families, individuals with hereditary male pseudohermaphroditism have a less severe failure of virilization than in incomplete testicular feminization. The disorder is inherited as an apparent X-linked recessive trait. Although the usual phenotype is male, affected individuals within a given family may have a spectrum of abnormalities ranging from almost complete failure of virilization to nearly complete masculinization. The disorder has been described under a variety of terms, including *Reifenstein*

Table 75-5 Clinical Features of Incomplete Testicular Feminization

External phenotype: Clitoromegaly and partial fusion of the labioscrotal folds, female habitus and breast development, normal axillary and pubic hair

Urogenital tract: Testes that may or may not be cryptorchid, Wolffian duct derivatives emptying into the vagina, no müllerian duct derivatives

Karyotype: 46,XY

Inheritance: X-linked recessive

Endocrinology:

  Testosterone: Normal or high male plasma levels and production rates

  Estrogen: Plasma levels and production rates higher than in normal men

  Gonadotropin: Elevated plasma LH level

Pathogenesis: Partial resistance to the actions of testosterone and dihydrotestosterone

syndrome,[126,127] *Lubs syndrome,*[128] *Gilbert-Dreyfus syndrome,*[129] *Rosewater syndrome,*[130] and *familial incomplete male pseudohermaphroditism, type 1,*[131] but the common appellation is *Reifenstein syndrome.* The fact that these disorders are variable manifestations of similar mutations was derived from pedigree analyses. Several large families have been described in which individual affected members exhibited phenotypes that vary from infertility in otherwise normal men to an extreme form of male pseudohermaphroditism in which the subjects have a vaginal orifice, no vas deferens, and severe hypospadias. The most extensive of these pedigrees is that reported originally by Ford[132] and subsequently by Walker et al.[133] In this family the manifestations in 12 affected men ranged from moderate abnormalities (microphallus and gynecomastia) to intermediate defects of virilization (hypospadias) to such severe defects of virilization (complete failure of scrotal fusion) that three affected family members were identified initially as females.[133] In another family reported originally by Bowen et al.[127] and subsequently by Wilson et al.,[131] the phenotype also ranged from a moderate defect in virilization in two (microphallus and bifid scrotum) to a more severe abnormality in eight (perineoscrotal hypospadias) to almost complete male pseudohermaphroditism in one (perineoscrotal hypospadias, no vas deferens, and a vaginal orifice). The phenotypic variability in this family is illustrated in Fig. 75-13. In a third family, described by Gardo and Papp,[134] three of four affected individuals were

phenotypic females, whereas the fourth had perineoscrotal hypospadias, bifid scrotum, and gynecomastia typical of the Reifenstein syndrome. Variability in phenotypic expression has been noted in other families with the disorder.[135,136] For this chapter, the assumption has been made that these various disorders are the consequence of X-linked defects in the androgen receptor, and we have chosen to use the eponymic term Reifenstein syndrome.

The characteristic clinical features are summarized in Table 75-6. The most common presentation is a 46,XY male with perineoscrotal hypospadias, azoospermia and infertility, incomplete virilization at the usual time of puberty, and gynecomastia that develops at the expected time of puberty (Fig. 75-11C). The external genitalia of an affected child and an affected adult are shown in Fig. 75-12C and D, respectively. Axillary and pubic hair are normal, but chest and facial hair tend to be absent or sparse. Temporal recession of the hairline is minimal, and the voice tends to be somewhat high-pitched. Less severely affected members may exhibit only a bifid scrotum, infertility, and incomplete virilization at puberty. More severely affected individuals can have incomplete Wolffian duct structures and formation of a vagina; only by identification of less severely affected members within the same family can the syndrome exhibited by such severely affected subjects be distinguished from incomplete testicular feminization. Incomplete virilization of the urogenital sinus results in a prostatic utricle but no true prostate. The lower ejaculatory duct system has never been characterized in detail.

Cryptorchidism is common, and the testes on average are small (although usually larger than in the Klinefelter syndrome). By histologic examination, Leydig cells are normal; spermatogenic tubules contain both Sertoli cells and germinal epithelium, but the germ cells are not matured beyond the primary spermatocyte stage. Hyaline degeneration of the tubules is often present.[127]

Certain features of the disorder are of particular interest. First, most affected individuals are raised as men. Although the number of reported subjects is small and no in-depth psychologic studies have been performed, gender in affected subjects raised as men seems to be unambiguously male in character, and some have had successful marriages. Second, infertility is the most consistent feature of the syndrome

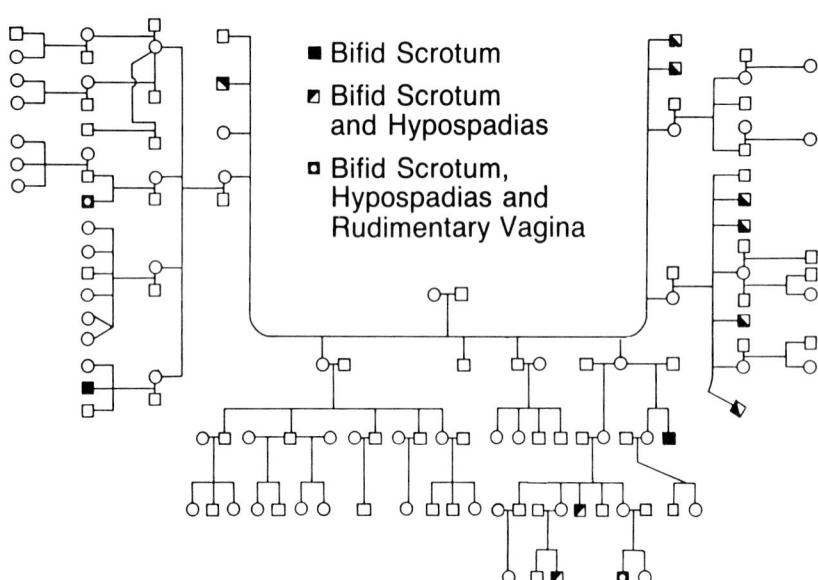

■ Bifid Scrotum

◧ Bifid Scrotum and Hypospadias

◻ Bifid Scrotum, Hypospadias and Rudimentary Vagina

Fig. 75-13 Pedigree of a family with Reifenstein syndrome. *(From Wilson et al.[131] Used by permission.)*

Table 75-6 Clinical Features of the Reifenstein
Syndrome

External phenotype: Usually a male with perineoscrotal hypospadias, normal axillary and pubic hair but scant beard and body hair; breast enlargement at time of expected puberty

Urogenital tract: Testes which are often cryptorchid, Wolffian duct structures varying in the degree of male development, no müllerian duct derivatives

Karyotype: 46,XY

Inheritance: X-linked recessive

Endocrinology:

   Testosterone: Normal or high male plasma levels and production rates

   Estrogen: Plasma levels and production rates higher than those in normal men

   Gonadotropin: Elevated plasma LH levels

Pathogenesis: Variable resistance to the action of testosterone and dihydrotestosterone

---

and appears to be the result of defective spermatogenesis and possibly of the anatomic abnormalities of the ejaculatory system.

INFERTILE MALE SYNDROME. In a study of a family with the Reifenstein syndrome, some affected men were identified who were infertile but otherwise phenotypically normal. They had the same apparent degree of androgen resistance, as assessed by endocrinologic criteria,[131] and the same abnormality of the androgen receptor in cultured skin fibroblasts as did the more severely affected relatives.[137] Gynecomastia was variable and late in appearance. Thus, it was clear that individuals with the Reifenstein syndrome may have only mild phenotypic evidence of androgen receptor deficiency. Subsequently, it was established that some infertile men without a family history of the Reifenstein syndrome have endocrine evidence of androgen resistance, and the androgen resistance is associated with an abnormality of the androgen receptor similar to the defect demonstrated in individuals with familial Reifenstein syndrome.[138] Similar subjects have subsequently been described by others.[139–143] The clinical features are summarized in Table 75-7. Such men have normal male external genitalia, apparently normal Wolffian duct structures, and infertility due to absence or extreme deficiency of sperm production. Some have gynecomastia. The prevalence of this form of androgen resistance as a cause of male infertility is not established, but in some series it appears to account for a significant fraction of male infertility associated with idiopathic azoospermia or severe oligospermia.[144–145] The infertile male syndrome may be the most common form of primary resistance to the action of any hormone.

Table 75-7 Clinical Features of the Infertile Male
Syndrome

External phenotype: Normal man, sometimes with minimal male beard and body hair, occasional gynecomastia

Urogenital tract: Testes, infertility associated with azoospermia or extreme oligospermia, Wolffian duct structures of normal men, no müllerian duct derivatives

Karyotype: 46,XY

Inheritance: Probably X-linked recessive

Endocrinology:

   Testosterone: Plasma levels and production rates of normal men or slightly higher

   Estrogen: Production rates usually higher than in normal men

   Gonadotropin: Plasma LH levels normal or elevated

Pathogenesis: Resistance to the action of androgen principally in the testes

---

Endocrinology. The endocrine pattern is similar in all forms of androgen receptor disorders but has been characterized best in subjects with complete testicular feminization. The early deductions by Morris[2] and by Wilkins[3] that androgen production is normal in patients with testicular feminization have been confirmed and extended. Plasma levels of testosterone are either in the normal male range or somewhat higher than those of normal men,[7,146–150] a phenomenon that is probably due to two factors: (1) the subjects have elevated estrogen production rates (see below) that result in an increase in the level of testosterone-binding globulin in plasma, and (2) blood production rates of testosterone tend to be somewhat higher than in normal men.[7] As in normal men, the major portion of testosterone production occurs in the testes.[14,147,151] In one study of six affected subjects, the daily production of testosterone averaged about 50 percent more than in normal men (8.3 versus 5.7 mg/day), but in individual subjects testosterone production was higher than normal only in those with inguinal testes and not in subjects with intraabdominal testes (Fig. 75-2C).[7]

The elevated testosterone production rate is presumably secondary to high levels of LH in plasma, which in turn are the consequence of defective feedback regulation because of resistance at the hypothalamic-pituitary level to the feedback effects of androgen on LH production.[113,149,150,152] The elevated plasma LH level is the result of two interlocking phenomena—more frequent secretory episodes and greater amplitude of the secretory spikes as compared with normal.[150] The increase in plasma LH levels after the administration of luteinizing hormone–releasing hormone (LHRH) is within the normal range.[150] Plasma levels of follicle-stimulating hormone (FSH) are usually normal.[150] Although there is failure of the negative feedback regulation of LH secretion by androgens in women with testicular feminization, the steady state control of LH secretion in these patients is regulated by estradiol. Namely, the administration of the antiestrogen clomiphene citrate causes a further increase in plasma LH, and plasma LH also rises after castration.[153]

The origin of estrogen in four women with testicular feminization is illustrated in Fig. 75-2C;[7] the mean production rates of estrone and estradiol, respectively, were 114 and 77 μg/day (as contrasted to 66 and 45 μg/day, respectively, in normal men). Testicular estradiol secretion in these women averaged 42 μg/day (in contrast to a mean of 6 μg/day by the testes of normal men). Thus, not only is the production rate of estradiol increased, but the major portion of the increased production is due to secretion by the testes. This finding is in keeping with the reports by Kelch and coworkers[14] and by Laatikainen et al.[151] that levels of estradiol in spermatic vein blood are high in women with testicular feminization.

To summarize, resistance to the feedback regulation of LH production by circulating androgen results in elevated plasma LH levels, and this in turn results in the enhanced secretion of both testosterone and estradiol by the testes. The fact that gonadotropin levels rise even higher (and that symptoms of menopausal flushing develop) when the testes are removed is consistent with the view that gonadotropin secretion is under some type of regulatory control; presumably, in the steady state and in the absence of an effect of androgen, estrogen regulates LH secretion in subjects with testicular feminization. This feedback control is accomplished at the expense of a higher plasma estrogen level than in normal men.[113,153]

Endocrine findings in patients with incomplete testicular feminization and the Reifenstein syndrome are similar to those in patients with complete testicular feminization (Fig. 75-2). In subjects with incomplete testicular feminization, plasma levels of testosterone are similar to those of normal men,[154,155] and in one such subject the daily production rate of testosterone was greater (12.0 mg/day)[125] than the average in normal men.[7] Plasma LH levels[125,154,155] and estrogen production rates and estrogen secretion by the testes[125] are also elevated. Interestingly, administration of a large amount of estradiol benzoate to a subject with incomplete testicular feminization (to simulate the preovulatory surge of estradiol in normally cycling women) resulted in an LH surge similar to that of normal women, again indicating an effect of estrogen at the hypothalamic-pituitary level.[156] The fact that gonadotropins are elevated in subjects with the Reifenstein syndrome was established through urinary assays by Bowen et al.[127] Plasma LH and testosterone levels are also high on average,[131] indicative of defective feedback control of LH secretion at the hypothalamic-pituitary level. When LHRH is administered to subjects with Reifenstein syndrome, the surge in plasma LH is either normal or somewhat greater than normal.[150,157] Furthermore, plasma LH does not decrease after the administration of medroxyprogesterone acetate,[131] testosterone,[158] or dihydrotestosterone.[150] These findings further substantiate the concept that the incomplete male differentiation during embryogenesis and the defective virilization at the expected time of puberty are the result of a defect in androgen action. Quantitative studies of the rates of androgen and estrogen formation have provided further insight into the phenotype of persons with this disorder (Fig. 75-2D).[131] The production rates for plasma testosterone (9.2 mg/day) and for estradiol (199 μg/day) were high; three-fourths of the estradiol (147 μg/day, 10 times the normal amount) was secreted directly into the circulation, presumably from the testes.[131]

The endocrine changes in men with infertility due to androgen resistance are similar to but less marked than those in subjects with other forms of androgen receptor defects. Specifically, plasma production rates of testosterone and plasma levels of LH are normal to high, and estradiol production rates are normal or slightly elevated.[138]

The mechanism by which feminization occurs in individuals with androgen resistance is now clear. In each disorder, androgen resistance usually results in a high mean level of plasma LH, elevated estradiol secretion by the testes, and the development of feminizing signs at puberty. There is, however, no direct relation between the absolute amount of estrogen secretion and the degree of feminization. Indeed, two phenotypic men with Reifenstein syndrome had higher estrogen secretion rates[131] than any that has been found to date in an individual with either complete or incomplete testicular feminization. We conclude that feminization after puberty in subjects with androgen resistance requires increased estradiol production but that the degree of feminization is influenced by the severity of the androgen resistance. It follows that the slight degree of feminization in some infertile men with androgen resistance is a function both of a less severe resistance to the action of androgen at the cellular level and of an inconsistent increase in estradiol formation.

The conversion of testosterone to dihydrotestosterone in tissues of persons with the various receptor abnormalities is listed in Table 75-3. Dihydrotestosterone formation is low on average in skin slices from patients with complete testicular feminization,[76,122,159] and in some testicular feminization patients the excretion of dihydrotestosterone metabolites in urine is also decreased.[160,161] This decrease in 5α-reductase activity

is believed to be secondary to the primary defect in androgen action that leads to a decrease in the mass of androgen target tissues (or organelles) that form dihydrotestosterone.[162] A defect in dihydrotestosterone formation is usually not manifested in fibroblasts cultured from skin biopsies from such individuals.[78] Furthermore, in genital skin biopsies from subjects with incomplete testicular feminization[125] and the Reifenstein syndrome[131] dihydrotestosterone formation is normal (Table 75-3), as it is in fibroblasts cultured from skin of such patients.[77–79] Thus, on endocrine, genetic, and phenotypic grounds these individuals are clearly distinct from subjects with 5α-reductase deficiency.

Genetics. Although familial occurrence of testicular feminization is the usual finding, approximately a third of women with typical complete testicular feminization have negative family histories. Since affected individuals cannot reproduce, the natural selection against persistence of the mutation is strong, and hence most instances with negative family histories are probably the result of new mutations. In 1937 Pettersson and Bonnier deduced on the basis of pedigree analysis that testicular feminization could be due either to an X-linked recessive trait or to an autosomal trait that is manifested only in genetic males.[89] Since affected individuals are infertile, these two possibilities could not be resolved by pedigree analysis. Furthermore, attempts to establish X linkage by evaluating the association between testicular feminization and other X-linked traits such as hemophilia and color blindness were uninformative.[163–166] However, on indirect grounds it was concluded that the disorder is in fact X-linked. Similar mutations have been described in the dog,[167] cow,[168] rat,[169] mouse,[170] horse,[171] and chimpanzee.[172] In the mouse, X linkage of the mutant gene was established by standard mapping techniques.[170] Because there are no known instances in which genes are X-linked in one species and autosomal in other species,[173] documentation of X linkage for the gene in the mouse suggested that the mutation is on the X chromosome in other species as well. More important, Meyer et al.[174] found that when skin fibroblasts from an obligate heterozygote for complete testicular feminization were cloned, some clones had deficient androgen binding and other clones exhibited normal binding. This finding is consistent with random inactivation of one X-linked allele in each cell, as would be predicted by the Lyon hypothesis,[175] and indicates X linkage for the mutant gene associated with the receptor-deficient form of testicular feminization. X linkage for this gene was formally established by Migeon and coworkers with the use of mouse-human hybrid cells; the gene is located near the centromere of the X chromosome between Xq13 and Xp11.[176]

Evidence for X linkage of a mutant gene that causes a qualitative abnormality (thermolability; see below) of the androgen receptor associated with testicular feminization was obtained by studying fibroblasts cloned from the skin of an obligate heterozygote for the disorder (Fig. 75-14).[177] This finding suggested that these two disorders of the androgen receptor are due to allelic mutations of the same gene. Indeed, all disorders involving the androgen receptor may be caused by allelic mutations of the gene that normally specifies the structure for the androgen receptor.

The family histories in most cases of incomplete testicular feminization have been uninformative, but in one family the pattern of inheritance is compatible with X linkage.[178] The fact that about half of instances of incomplete testicular feminization are due to qualitative abnormalities of the androgen

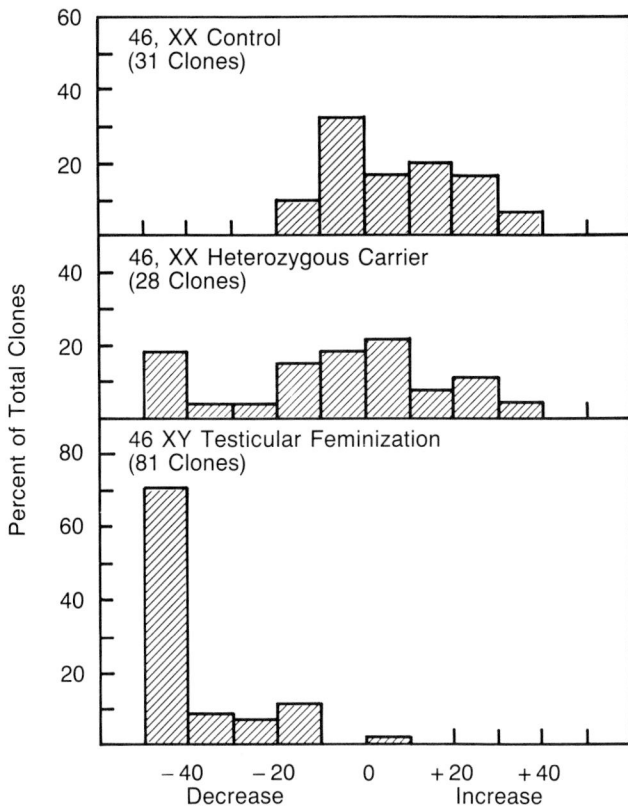

Fig. 75-14 Effect of elevated temperature on methyltrienolone binding in genital skin fibroblast clones from a control subject, a carrier for testicular feminization, and the carrier's affected offspring with testicular feminization. Cells were grown to confluence. On the day of assay, medium was replaced with medium prewarmed to either 30°C or 41°C for a 1-h preincubation of the appropriate temperature. Medium containing 1 nM [³H]methyltrienolone with or without 250 nM nonradioactive methyltrienolone that had also been prewarmed to 30°C or 41°C was then incubated with the monolayers for 1 h at the appropriate temperature. The monolayers (four for each clone) were rinsed and harvested with trypsin-EDTA, and the specific binding at each temperature was calculated. Specific binding at 41°C was compared with that at 30°C and expressed as a percent decrease or increase. Percentage of total clones for each cell strain exhibiting a given magnitude of increase or decrease in binding is plotted. Note that the heterozygous carrier for the disorder has some clones that express the thermolabile androgen receptor. (From Elawady et al.[177] Used by permission.)

receptor (see below) suggests involvement of the same gene as in the complete form of the disorder. The fact that no convincing pedigree has been reported in which the complete and incomplete forms of testicular feminization coexist in the same family,[121] however, indicates that the phenotypic expression in a given family is very consistent.

A number of pedigrees of the Reifenstein syndrome have been described in which the inheritance pattern, like that of testicular feminization, is consistent with either an X-linked recessive gene or an autosomal mutation that is manifested only in genetic males.[126,127,131–136] (One such pedigree is shown in Fig. 75-13.[131]) More important, this disorder can be due to qualitative abnormalities of the androgen receptor,[179,180] and linkage analysis indicates that the mutant genes for testicular feminization and the Reifenstein syndrome are either allelic or very closely linked on the X chromosome.[181]

The genetic basis for the infertile male syndrome is less well studied. In most affected men described to date, the family history is uninformative.[137,138] However, the disorder in some

is associated with qualitative abnormality of the androgen receptor,[142] again suggesting X linkage in such families.

To summarize, each of these disorders involves the same gene product, namely, the androgen receptor, and since X linkage has been established in two of the disorders—complete testicular feminization and the Reifenstein syndrome—the implication is that X linkage is common to all. The fact that all pedigrees in the various disorders (when informative) are consistent with X-linked inheritance and that X linkage is known to be conserved among species[173] further supports this interpretation. This is not to imply that a single mutation is common to the various disorders—only that different mutations of this gene influence the amount and function of the androgen receptor.

It would be useful for genetic counseling if a means were available for diagnosing the obligate heterozygote before pregnancy. Although some heterozygous carriers of complete testicular feminization have diminished body hair,[45] no clear-cut means have been established for identifying most carriers of the gene. The fact that approximately half of fibroblast clones derived from the skin of heterozygous carriers express the abnormal androgen receptor makes it theoretically possible to diagnose such individuals in some families.[174,177]

Pathogenesis. Androgen resistance in patients with testicular feminization is caused by abnormalities of the androgen receptor. The basic study that allowed the pathogenesis of these disorders to be unraveled was the observation by Keenan and coworkers that a specific dihydrotestosterone receptor protein is present in fibroblasts cultured from the skin of normal subjects.[182,183] Receptor content is greater in fibroblasts cultured from genital skin (foreskin, scrotum, labia majora) than from nongenital sites.[137] The receptor in fibroblasts has a dissociation constant of approximately 0.2 nM and is believed to be the same as the intracellular androgen receptor in androgen target tissues. Furthermore, Kennan et al. established that fibroblasts grown from some women with complete testicular feminization showed no detectable dihydrotestosterone binding,[183] a finding that has been confirmed in other laboratories.[137,184] The finding of absent binding in fibroblasts from some women with testicular feminization is illustrated in Fig. 75-15 and provides an explanation for the profound resistance to all androgen actions characteristic of this disorder (Fig. 75-6). Whether absent binding of dihydrotestosterone in such cases is due to absence of the androgen receptor protein or to the presence of a mutant protein that cannot bind the ligand is not known.

Other subjects with complete testicular feminization have a qualitatively abnormal receptor protein (Fig. 75-15). Identification of such a phenomenon came first from studies of thermolability of binding.[178] The initial studies involved two sisters with complete testicular feminization who had about half the normal levels of binding under the usual assay conditions at 37°C and normal binding at 26°C. When the assay was performed at an elevated temperature (42°C), dihydrotestosterone binding decreased to less than one-fifth that seen at 37°C (Fig. 75-15). The binding was restored by lowering the assay temperature to 37°C, suggesting that the alteration of binding at elevated temperatures is reversible.[178] Similar receptor thermolability has been observed in other laboratories.[142,186,187] Qualitative abnormalities of the receptor have subsequently been identified by a variety of tests of receptor function (Table 75-8). These include: examination of the ultracentrifugation characteristics of the cytosol receptor in the presence of mo-

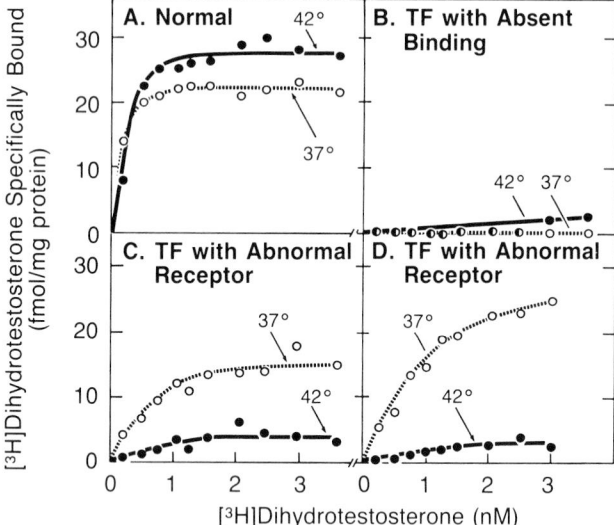

Fig. 75-15 Androgen receptor assay in fibroblasts from a normal control and from patients with testicular feminization due to absent binding or abnormal receptor. Specific dihydrotestosterone binding in intact fibroblast monolayers as a function of dihydrotestosterone concentration was assessed at two temperatures (37°C and 42°C) in cells grown from a normal control subject (A), a patient with complete testicular feminization associated with absent binding (B), and two unrelated patients with complete testicular feminization associated with intermediate levels of dihydrotestosterone binding (C and D). (From Griffin.[178] Used by permission.)

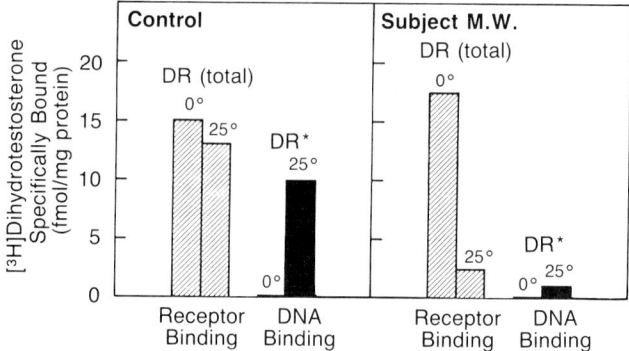

Fig. 75-16 Heat-induced transformation of normal and androgen-resistant fibroblast cytosolic [3H]dihydrotestosterone-receptor complexes. Cytosols from control fibroblasts and subject M.W.'s fibroblasts were incubated for 3 h at 0°C with 3 nM [3H]dihydrotestosterone. Parallel aliquots were incubated with a 500-fold excess of nonradioactive hormone to assess nonspecific binding. After the incubation, aliquots were assayed for specific [3H]dihydrotestosterone binding (DR) by the gel filtration method. The remaining samples were warmed at 25°C for 1 h. Aliquots were again taken for estimation of specific [3H]dihydrotestosterone binding (DR) by gel filtration. The amount of transformed receptor-hormone complexes (DR*) was assayed in aliquots of cytosol by the DNA-cellulose binding assay. Note that the cells from the affected subject with androgen resistance (M.W.) have receptor inactivation under the conditions that normally promote transformation to the DNA-binding state. (From Kovacs et al.[198] Used by permission.)

lybdate, a compound that stabilizes the normal 8-S androgen receptor but not the receptor from many subjects with androgen resistance;[142,180,185] demonstration of decreased affinity of ligand binding to the receptor;[140,186,188–190] documentation of impairment of nuclear retention of the binding ligand;[191] demonstration of failure of androgens to up-regulate the level of androgen receptor;[140,188,189,192–195] evidence for an increased rate of dissociation of ligand from receptor;[140,186–190,196,197] and demonstration of lability of the androgen receptor under transforming conditions (Fig. 75-16).[198] Presumably, each of these functional assays reflects structural abnormality of the receptor protein.

The characteristics of the androgen receptor in fibroblasts grown from biopsies of individuals from 95 families studied in our laboratory who fulfill the phenotypic and endocrine requirements to be designated androgen-resistant, including 28 families having cases of complete testicular feminization, are summarized in Fig. 75-17. Receptor has been designated as qualitatively abnormal when it is measurable in intact cells at 37°C and exhibits thermolability or inability to form an 8-S complex in the presence of molybdate, or both. In subjects

from 24 of the families, binding was virtually undetectable in fibroblast monolayers at any temperature and was designated as absent. These subjects are representative of the receptor-negative category of androgen resistance identified in the early studies of the disorder[137,182–184] and span the spectrum from testicular feminization to the Reifenstein syndrome. Presumably, in those subjects with Reifenstein syndrome and absent binding, some receptor function must be present in vivo although it was not detected in the in vitro assay. In subjects from 43 of the families, the receptor is qualitatively abnormal, and these subjects span an even wider spectrum, from complete testicular feminization to infertile men. Intuitively, the functional defects in the testicular feminization group must be more severe than in the phenotypic men with qualitative ab-

Table 75-8 Known Markers of Qualitative Abnormalities of the Human Androgen Receptor in Skin Fibroblasts

Marker	References
1. Thermolability in monolayers	142, 178, 180, 186, 187
2. Instability of cytosol receptor	142, 180, 185
3. Decreased affinity of ligand binding	140, 186, 188–190
4. Impaired nuclear retention of ligand	191
5. Failure of up-regulation of the androgen receptor by androgens	140, 188, 189, 192–195
6. Increased rate of dissociation of ligand from receptor	140, 186–190, 196, 197
7. Lability of the androgen receptor under transforming conditions	198

Fig. 75-17 Androgen receptor assays in subjects from 95 families with androgen resistance and putative defects in the androgen receptor. The 95 families include 80 families with established defects of the androgen receptor and 15 with no abnormality identified (receptor-positive resistance). Absent binding is more commonly associated with the phenotype of complete testicular feminization, but qualitative defects in the receptor can be associated with a spectrum of phenotypes from complete testicular feminization to infertile men.

Phenotypic Spectrum: Female ⟶ Male

Type of Receptor Defect / Diagnostic Category	Complete Testicular Feminization	Incomplete Testicular Feminization	Reifenstein Syndrome	Infertile Male
Absent Binding	●●●●● ●●●●● ●●●●●	●●●●	●●●	
Qualitatively Abnormal	●●●●● ●●●●●	●●●	●●●●● ●●●●●	●●●●
Decreased Amount		●●	●●● ●●●	●●●
Abnormality Unidentified	●	●●●	●●	●●●

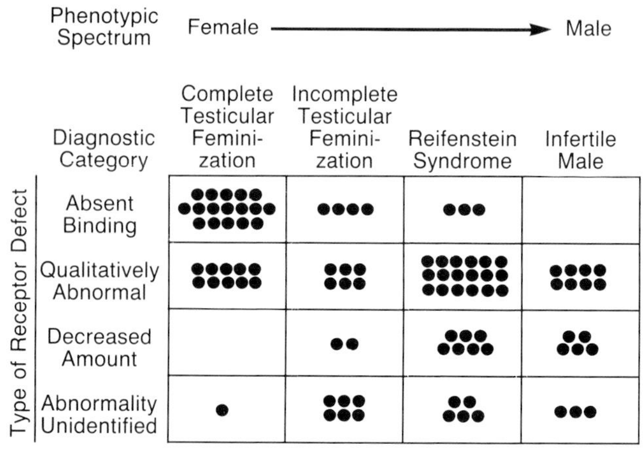

normalities of the androgen receptor. A decreased amount of apparently normal receptor was present in subjects in 14 families whose phenotypes spanned incomplete testicular feminization (two families), Reifenstein syndrome (seven families), and infertile men (five families). In affected subjects of 15 families (seven with the phenotype of testicular feminization, five with the Reifenstein syndrome, and three infertile men), no abnormality of the androgen receptor was demonstrable, in spite of endocrine evidence of profound androgen resistance (see "Receptor-Positive Androgen Resistance," below).

The deduction that the receptor in fibroblasts grown from biopsies of these subjects reflects the in vivo situation is supported by the findings that the androgen receptor was missing from the testis of a woman with complete testicular feminization[199] and that the androgen receptor defect can be demonstrated in fibroblasts cultured from the testes of patients with testicular feminization.[200] The pathogenesis of androgen resistance in humans with the disorder is similar to that in the mouse with testicular feminization; indeed, deficiency of the high-affinity cytosol androgen receptor protein in the mouse had been reported in several laboratories.[201,202]

Before more specific correlations can be drawn between specific abnormalities of the androgen receptor and the nature of the functional defect in androgen action, it will be necessary to have more precise insight into the various structural defects responsible for these receptor abnormalities.

Receptor-Positive Androgen Resistance

A category of androgen resistance that does not appear to involve either the 5α-reductase enzyme or the androgen receptor was postulated by Amrhein et al.[203] from studies in three affected members of one family with the phenotype of testicular feminization and with normal 5α-reductase, normal amounts of androgen receptor, and normal nuclear localization of dihydrotestosterone. The subjects are 46,XY and have bilateral testes and normal or high levels of testosterone and LH in plasma. Other subjects have been described with a variety of phenotypes ranging from complete testicular feminization to the infertile male syndrome.[143,204-212] The site of the molecular abnormality in these individuals is unclear. In some the receptor may be qualitatively abnormal, but the defect is too subtle to be detected by present methods. In fact, the initial family reported to have receptor-positive androgen resistance[203] was later shown to have a qualitatively abnormal receptor.[186] In the 15 families that we have assessed—labeled "abnormality unidentified" in Fig. 75-17—all parameters of receptor function evaluated to date are normal, including affinity of binding, nuclear localization of the receptor-hormone complex,[204] and stability of binding when subjected both to elevated temperature[178] and to ultracentrifugation.[185] Alternatively, the defect may reside at some step in androgen action distal to the receptor, such as the binding of the receptor-hormone complex to the nuclear acceptor sites.[211] Indeed, it is unlikely that a uniform defect is present; the disorder may comprise a heterogeneous group of molecular abnormalities.

Diagnosis and Management of Disorders of the Androgen Receptor and Receptor-Positive Androgen Resistance

Diagnosis. Suspicion of the existence of an androgen receptor disorder is based upon genital ambiguity at birth, abnormal sexual development, primary amenorrhea, or unexplained male infertility. It is necessary to separate these disorders from 5α-reductase deficiency (see above) and from defects in testosterone biosynthesis (see Chap. 74). In the adolescent or adult the diagnosis of complete testicular feminization on the one hand or the male infertility syndrome on the other is most straightforward. In the one case, a phenotypic woman with primary amenorrhea, a 46,XY karyotype, male levels of testosterone, and bilateral testes (abdominal or inguinal) is found to have absence of müllerian derivatives, by ultrasound[213] or by computed tomography of the abdomen.[214] In the case of the infertile male syndrome, the initial diagnosis is one of exclusion in a man with unexplained azoospermia or severe oligospermia and can be confirmed by measurement of androgen receptors in genital skin fibroblasts.[138,144] The real diagnostic problem in the adult or adolescent is the separation of incomplete testicular feminization from 5α-reductase deficiency (see above) and from defects in testosterone formation including single-gene defects in testosterone biosynthesis (Chap. 74), the testicular regression syndrome,[215] and both pure gonadal dysgenesis and mixed gonadal dysgenesis.[40] In all three types of disorders, defects in virilization of the external genitalia may be more severe than in that of the Wolffian ducts. The gonadal dysgenesis syndromes are usually diagnosed by chromosomal analysis. Defects in testosterone biosynthesis can usually be excluded by the presence of normal male testosterone levels. On occasion, patients have partial deficiency in one of the enzymes of testosterone biosynthesis and, as a consequence, plasma testosterone levels in the steady state may approach the normal male range; such partial defects, however, are accompanied by elevations in the plasma levels of androgen precursors.[81,82] The diagnosis of 5α-reductase deficiency in this age group is usually confirmed on the basis of measurement of plasma or urinary 5α-reduced steroids (see above). In resolving these issues, careful analysis of the family history, the phenotype, the endocrine profile, and androgen metabolism in cultured fibroblasts may be required (Table 75-9).

The diagnosis is a special problem in the neonate and young infant, particularly in the situation when the family history is uninformative. A presumptive diagnosis of androgen resistance can be made on those neonates in whom plasma LH and/or testosterone are elevated.[216,217] In most circumstances a more extensive evaluation is necessary, including evaluation of karyotype, measurement of plasma steroids after stimulation with chorionic gonadotropin, evaluation of the genitourinary tract by radiographic or endoscopic procedures, and on occasion assessment of androgen metabolism in cultured skin fibroblasts.[40,218] It is of particular importance to establish the correct diagnosis of incomplete testicular feminization as early as possible so that castration can be performed early enough in life to prevent the partial virilization at puberty.

Once the diagnosis of an androgen receptor defect is established in a specific subject, it is not possible to make the diagnosis in subsequent fetuses at risk early in gestation, because the expression of androgen receptor in normal amniotic cells is too variable.[219] However, the diagnosis has been made at 20 weeks of gestation by documenting absence of male external genitalia in a 46,XY fetus.[220] In families in which the mutant receptor has distinct qualitative abnormality, it is theoretically possible to diagnose heterozygous carriers for this X-linked defect by cloning skin fibroblasts,[177] but such studies are rarely practical.

Table 75-9 Current Classification of the Androgen Resistance Syndromes According to Genetic, Anatomic, and Endocrine Characteristics

		Phenotype							Endocrine profile relative to normal men		
Category	Inheritance	General	Wolffian ducts	Spermatogenesis	Urogenital sinus	External genitalia	Breast	Testosterone production	Estrogen production	Plasma LH
5α-Reductase deficiency	Autosomal recessive	F	M	N or ↓	F	C	M	N	N	N or ↑
Receptor disorders										
Complete testicular feminization	X-linked recessive	F	A	A	F	F	F	↑	↑	↑
Incomplete testicular feminization	X-linked recessive	F	IMD	A	F	C; PF	F	↑	↑	↑
Reifenstein syndrome	X-linked recessive	M	IMD	A	V from M to F	IMD	F	↑	↑	↑
Infertile male syndrome	X-linked recessive	M	M	A or ↓	M	M	M to F	N or ↑	N or ↑	N or ↑
Receptor-positive resistance	Uncertain	M or F	V	A	V	F to IMD	V	N or ↑	↑	↑

NOTE: A = absent; C = clitoromegaly; F = female; IMD = incomplete male development; M = male; N = normal; PF = posterior fusion; V = variable; ↓ = decreased; ↑ = increased.

Management. Since no specific therapy is available to circumvent or reverse the abnormal development that takes place during embryogenesis, treatment is directed toward prevention of complications and adverse secondary effects of the mutations, appropriate hormone replacement or supplementation when necessary, and suitable psychological support.

THE PSYCHOLOGICAL PROBLEMS. Subjects with the infertile male syndrome and complete testicular feminization, respectively, have unambiguous male and female phenotypes at birth and are raised in accordance. Individuals with incomplete testicular feminization and the Reifenstein syndrome have varying degrees of abnormal external genitalia, and the correct diagnosis can usually be made in the newborn or quite early in life. Because gender identity is critical to psychological development and normal mental health, it is mandatory that gender assignment be made as early as possible, preferably at the time of birth in newborns with ambiguous external genitalia. A detailed discussion of the diagnostic procedures and of the various problems encountered in reaching a decision about gender assignment in infants with ambiguous genitalia is given elsewhere.[40,218] Once gender assignment is made, the central obligation is to perform any indicated surgery as early as feasible, to provide the appropriate hormonal environment at the time of expected puberty, and to assist affected individuals to adjust to their inevitable infertility. Vaginal agenesis can be corrected after the time of expected puberty by surgical or nonsurgical means.[221]

At all ages in life it is rarely wise to inform patients that their genetic sex and phenotypic sex do not coincide. When castration is indicated it should be explained that as a result of hereditary defect the gonads are abnormal, that the resulting infertility is not treatable, and that because of the potential for tumor development the gonads should be removed at a suitable time. With appropriate counseling and reassurance, most persons with male pseudohermaphroditism that we have managed have made adequate adjustment, especially in the case of phenotypic women.

THE CRYPTORCHID TESTIS. The most serious complication of the undescended testis in complete testicular feminization is the development of tumors.[2,88,222,223] It is not known whether tumor incidence is more common in patients with this disorder than in those with cryptorchidism of other causes. Approximately 1 in 64 undescended testes becomes malignant, and the frequency of tumor is about four times greater in abdominal than in inguinal testes.[224] The natural history of the tumors in women with testicular feminization is not entirely clear, but some behave as true malignancies.[223] Therefore, it is generally accepted that the testes should be removed in women with complete testicular feminization. Since these patients undergo a normal pubertal growth spurt and feminize successfully at the time of expected puberty[2,88] and since tumors rarely develop in cryptorchid testes until after this time, it is customary to delay castration until after secondary sexual maturation is completed. Carcinoma *in situ* of the testes has been described in prepubertal children with testicular feminization, but the functional significance of these lesions is unclear.[225,226] If, however, hernia repair is indicated in the prepubertal years or if the testes are in the inguinal region or the labia majora and cause discomfort, some physicians prefer to remove the testes at the time of herniorrhaphy. If the testes are removed prepubertally, estrogen therapy is required at the appropriate age to ensure normal growth and breast development. If castration is performed after pubescence, menopausal symptoms and other evidences of estrogen withdrawal supervene,[2,88] and suitable estrogen replacement is indicated.

Whether tumors develop in intraabdominal testes in women with incomplete testicular feminization is uncertain, but presumably the same considerations would apply as in women with complete testicular feminization. To prevent disfiguring virilization that may take place in incomplete testicular feminization, the testes should be removed prior to the expected time of puberty if possible, and feminization should be induced with estrogens. Cryptorchidism is also frequent in the Reifenstein syndrome[131] and should be corrected surgically. The Reifenstein case material is small, but in other forms of cryptorchidism development of tumors is rare following successful repair.[224]

GYNECOMASTIA IN MEN WITH DEFECTS OF THE ANDROGEN RECEPTOR. In the instances in which gynecomastia has been studied histologically, it is indistinguishable from other forms of estrogen-induced gynecomastia.[127] In men with the Reifenstein syndrome[131] and in some infertile men,[138] gynecomastia develops as the result of increased estrogen production and androgen resistance, as in testicular feminization.[7,125] Because most Reifenstein subjects have male gender assignment and male gender identity, the gynecomastia may be disfiguring as well as disturbing. The appropriate therapy is surgical removal. As in normal men who are castrated,[13] gynecomastia can occasionally develop following castration of individuals with androgen resistance.[227] This is presumably due to the fact that estrogen formation from adrenal precursors continues unabated following removal of the testes.[13] Carcinoma of the breast has not been described in men with androgen resistance. Presumably the risk of cancer is small, since it is an infrequent complication of other forms of gynecomastia.[228]

HORMONE TREATMENT. Appropriate estrogen treatment is indicated in all phenotypic women after removal of the testes.[2,88,91] Supplemental androgen has been administered with success in some[55] but not all[150,158] men with Reifenstein syndrome. The precise role of androgen treatment in this disorder is not clear.

THE NATURE OF ANDROGEN RESISTANCE

Hormone resistance was originally defined as a lack of response to endogenous and exogenous hormone.[229] In the case of androgen resistance, it was assumed that the degree of resistance to the hormone is equal in all tissues at all times of life and that the inevitable phenotypic expression of such a disorder was male pseudohermaphroditism. As the complexity of androgen action has been elucidated further, the spectrum of the manifestations of androgen resistance has expanded beyond the original formulation. Not only do different androgen metabolites have different effects, but any one androgen may have different actions during different phases of life—from embryogenesis to old age. Furthermore, at the clinical level androgen resistance can be documented in some but not all tissues of the same affected subject. Therefore, we have adopted a more complex classification of androgen resistance that is dependent on a combination of molecular, genetic, phenotypic, and endocrine characteristics.

Subjects with 5α-reductase deficiency have a special type of androgen resistance—in these individuals certain target tissues that are resistant to the action of endogenous androgen (testosterone) would have responded normally to the missing end product (dihydrotestosterone) if it had been administered at the appropriate time during embryogenesis. This condition is analogous to hereditary resistance to the action of vitamin D; in one form of this disorder, so-called vitamin D–dependent rickets type I, the subject is unable to synthesize the 1,25-dihydroxyvitamin D.[230] In contrast, persons with androgen receptor abnormalities and those with receptor-positive resis-

tance appear to be equally unresponsive to all androgens.

Fibroblasts cultured from genital skin have proved to be useful in defining the defects that underlie these various disorders and in the classification of specific entities. In disorders such as 5α-reductase deficiency and testicular feminization, the cultured fibroblast symbolizes the whole body in that the molecular defect present in vivo in all androgen target tissues is also expressed in fibroblasts cultured from genital skin. The clinical manifestations of these disorders tend to be consistent within families, and the molecular defects are uniform among tissues. The identification of qualitative abnormalities in the 5α-reductase and in the androgen receptor in fibroblasts cultured from some affected families provides additional support for the concept that the defect expressed in the fibroblast is, indeed, the primary genetic defect in the disorders.

For other conditions (e.g., the Reifenstein syndrome and the infertile male syndrome), the reconstruction of the pathogenesis is less certain. Even within the same family the phenotypic expression of androgen resistance in these disorders varies from subject to subject and from tissue to tissue. Disorders of the androgen receptor are almost always associated with defective spermatogenesis and abnormal gonadotropin regulation, whereas the phenotypic abnormalities and degree of sexual maturation at puberty are variable. This phenomenon could be explained in at least two ways. First, different factors may regulate the activity of the androgen receptor in different tissues in the intact organism. For example, phenotypic expression of the Reifenstein syndrome among individuals within the same family can vary from male infertility to women with pseudovagina formation even though the receptor defects appear to be identical in preparations in vitro. This finding indicates that unidentified factors must modify hormone action in vivo. Second, different amounts of androgen receptor may be required for different actions of the hormone in vivo. Accordingly, a partial defect (either qualitative or quantitative) in the production of the androgen receptor could cause more complete manifestations of androgen resistance in some tissues than in others. The fact that qualitative defects in the androgen receptor have been identified in some families with Reifenstein syndrome and male infertility indicates that the fundamental mutation in these disorders involves the androgen receptor primarily. Thus, the receptor abnormality and the resulting androgen resistance probably cause the disorders, regardless of the mechanism of the incomplete expression of the hormone resistance among tissues and among individuals.

Androgen resistance associated with male pseudohermaphroditism is relatively common, and if androgen resistance is the cause of a significant fraction of male infertility, it may prove to be more frequent than all other forms of primary hormone resistance combined.[107,229] There are several possible reasons for this frequency. First, expression of androgen activity is required for reproduction but not for the life of the individual. As a consequence, those with even the most complete forms of androgen resistance have a normal life span. In contrast, severe mutations affecting the action of hormones essential for life (such as cortisol) probably result in fetal wastage.[229] Second, defects in androgen action result either in abnormal sexual development or in reproductive failure. As a consequence there is a high probability that even subtle defects in the cellular processes required for normal androgen action eventually come to the attention of physicians. Third, since the gene that specifies the androgen receptor is X-linked, defects in the androgen receptor become clinically manifested in the hemizygous (XY) state. As a consequence, there is a high probability that a new mutation in the androgen receptor will be clinically evident. If the gene were autosomal, most mutations would probably be manifested only in the homozygous state.

As in other forms of hormone resistance, elucidation of the pathophysiology of the androgen resistance syndromes has been important in providing insight into the normal pathway of androgen action. Each new type of androgen resistance that is recognized provides an opportunity for defining the nature of a specific reaction essential for the action of the hormone.

REFERENCES

1. ALBRIGHT F, BURNETT CH, SMITH PH, PARSON W: Pseudohypoparathyroidism—An example of "Seabright-Bantam syndrome." *Endocrinology* 30:922, 1942.
2. MORRIS JM: The syndrome of testicular feminization in male pseudohermaphrodites. *Am J Obstet Gynecol* 65:1192, 1953.
3. WILKINS L: Abnormal sex differentiation: Hermaphroditism and gonadal dysgenesis, in *The Diagnosis and Treatment of Endocrine Disorders in Childhood and Adolescence*, 2d ed. Springfield, IL, Charles C Thomas, 1975, p 258.
4. GRIFFIN JE, WILSON JD: The syndromes of androgen resistance. *N Engl J Med* 302:198, 1980.
5. JOST A: Hormonal factors in the sex differentiation of the mammalian foetus. *Philos Trans R Soc Lond*, Ser B, 259:119, 1970.
6. SIITERI PK, MacDONALD PC: Role of extraglandular estrogen in human endocrinology, in Greep RO, Astwood EB (eds): *Handbook of Physiology. Endocrinology*. vol II, *Endocrinology*. Washington, American Physiological Society, 1973, Sec 7, p 615.
7. MacDONALD PC, MADDEN JD, BRENNER PF, WILSON JD, SIITERI PK: Origin of estrogen in normal men and in women with testicular feminization. *J Clin Endocrinol Metab* 49:905, 1979.
8. GOLDSTEIN JL, WILSON JD: Hereditary disorders of sexual development in man, in Motulsky AG, Lentz W (eds): *Birth Defects*. International Congress Series 310, Amsterdam, Excerpta Medica, 1974, p 165.
9. WILSON JD, GOLDSTEIN JL: Classification of hereditary disorders of sexual development, in Bergsma D (ed): *Genetic Forms of Hypogonadism*. New York, Birth Defects: Original Article Series, Stratton Corp, 1975, vol 11, p 1.
10. WILSON JD: Metabolism of testicular androgens, in Greep RO, Astwood EB, (eds): *Handbook of Physiology. Endocrinology, Male Reproductive System*. vol V, Washington, American Physiological Society, 1975, Sec 7, p 491.
11. CLARK JH, SCHRADER WT, O'MALLEY BW: Mechanisms of steroid hormone action, in Wilson JD, Foster DW (eds): *Williams Textbook of Endocrinology*, 7th ed. Philadelphia, Saunders, 1985, p 33.
12. MARCUS R, KORENMAN SG: Estrogens and the human male. *Annu Rev Med* 27:357, 1976.
13. WILSON JD, AIMAN J, MacDONALD PC: The pathogenesis of gynecomastia. *Adv Intern Med* 25:1, 1980.
14. KELCH RP, JENNER MR, WEINSTEIN R, KAPLAN SL, GRUMBACH MM: Estradiol and testosterone secretion by human, simian, and canine testes, in males with hypogonadism and in male pseudohermaphrodites with the feminizing testes syndrome. *J Clin Invest* 51:824, 1972.
15. WEINSTEIN RL, KELCH RP, JENNER MR, KAPLAN SL, GRUMBACH MM: Secretion of unconjugated androgens and estrogens by the normal and abnormal human testis before and after human chorionic gonadotropin. *J Clin Invest* 53:1, 1974.
16. PARDRIDGE WM: Serum bioavailability of sex steroid hormones. *Clin Endocrinol Metab* 15:259, 1986.
17. LASZNITZKI I, FRANKLIN HR, WILSON JD: The mechanism of androgen uptake and concentration by rat ventral prostate in organ culture. *J Endocrinol* 60:81, 1974.
18. SIITERI PK, WILSON JD: Dihydrotestosterone in prostatic hypertrophy. I. The formation and content of dihydrotestosterone in the hypertrophic prostate of man. *J Clin Invest* 49:1737, 1970.
19. MOORE RJ, GAZAK JM, QUEBBEMAN JF, WILSON JD: Concentration of dihydrotestosterone and 3α-androstanediol in naturally occurring and androgen-induced prostatic hyperplasia in the dog. *J Clin Invest* 64:1003, 1979.
20. WILBERT DM, GRIFFIN JE, WILSON JD: Characterization of the cytosol androgen receptor of the human prostate. *J Clin Endocrinol Metab* 56:113, 1983.
21. GRINO PB, GRIFFIN JE, WILSON JD: Transformation of the androgen receptor to the deoxyribonucleic acid-binding state: Studies in homogenates and intact cells. *Endocrinology*, 120:1914, 1987.
21a. LUBAHN DB, JOSEPH DR, SULLIVAN PM, WILLARD HF, FRENCH FS, WILSON EM: Cloning of human androgen receptor complementary DNA and localization to the X chromosome. *Science* 240:327, 1988.
21b. CHANG C, KOKONTIS J, LIAO S: Molecular cloning of human and rat complementary DNA encoding androgen receptors. *Science* 240:324, 1988.
21c. TRAPMAN J, KLAASSEN P, KUIPER GGJM, VAN DER KORPUT JAGM, FABER PW, VAN ROOIJ HCJ, VAN KESSEL AG, VOORHORST MM, MULDER E, BRINKMANN AO: Cloning, structure, and expression of a cDNA encoding the human androgen receptor. *Biochem Biophys Res Commun* 153:241, 1988.
22. GEORGE FW, WILSON JD: Embryology of the genital tract, in Walsh PC, Gittes RF, Perlmutter AD, Stamey TA (eds): *Campbell's Urology*, Philadelphia, Saunders, 1986, p 1804.
23. KOVACS WJ, GRIFFIN JE, WEAVER DD, CARLSON BR, WILSON JD: A mutation that causes lability of the androgen receptor under conditions that normally promote transformation to the DNA-binding state. *J Clin Invest* 73:1095, 1984.
24. GEORGE FW, WILSON JD: Sexual differentiation, in Beard RW, Nathanielsz PW (eds): *Fetal Physiology and Medicine: The Basis of Perinatology*, New York, Marcel Dekker, 1984, p 57.
24a. PAGE DC, MOSHER R, SIMPSON EM, FISHER EMC, MARDON G, POLLACK J, MCGILLIVRAY B, DE LA CHAPELLE A, BROWN LG: The sex-determining region of the human Y chromosome encodes a finger protein. *Cell* 51:1091, 1987.
25. GRUENWALD P: The relation of the growing mullerian duct to the wolffian duct and its importance for the genesis of malformations. *Anat Rec* 81:1, 1941.
26. GOLDSTEIN JL, WILSON JD: Genetic and hormonal control of male sexual differentiation. *J Cell Physiol* 85:365, 1975.
27. JOSSO N: Antimüllerian hormone: New perspectives for a sexist molecule. *Endocrinol Rev* 7:421, 1986.
28. DONAHOE PK, CATE RL, MacLAUGHLIN DT, EPSTEIN J, FULLER AF, TAKAHASHI M, COUGHLIN JP, NINFA EG, TAYLOR LA: Müllerian inhibiting substance: Gene structure and mechanism of action of a fetal regressor. *Recent Prog Horm Res* 43:431, 1987.
29. WILSON JD, SIITERI PK: Developmental pattern of testosterone synthesis in the fetal gonad of the rabbit. *Endocrinology* 92:1182, 1973.
30. SIITERI PK, WILSON JD: Testosterone formation and metabolism during male sexual differentiation in the human embryo. *J Clin Endocrinol Metab* 38:113, 1974.
31. CATT KJ, DUFAU ML, NEAVES WB, WALSH PC, WILSON JD: LH-hCG receptors and testosterone content during differentiation of the testis in the rabbit embryo. *Endocrinology* 97:1157, 1975.
32. GEORGE FW, SIMPSON ER, MILEWICH L, WILSON JD: Studies on the regulation of the onset of steroid hormone biosynthesis in fetal rabbit gonads. *Endocrinology* 105:1100, 1979.
33. WILSON JD, LASNITZKI I: Dihydrotestosterone formation in fetal tissues of the rabbit and rat. *Endocrinology* 89:659, 1971.
34. WILSON JD: Testosterone uptake by the urogenital tract of the rabbit embryo. *Endocrinology* 92:1192, 1973.
35. GEORGE FW, CARR BR, NOBLE JF, WILSON JD: 5α-reduced androgens in the human fetal testis. *J Clin Endocrinol Metab* 64:628, 1987.
36. WILSON JD: Testosterone metabolism in skin. *Symp Dtsch Ges Endokrin* 17:11, 1971.
37. GEORGE FW, PETERSON K: 5α-Dihydrotestosterone formation is necessary for embryogenesis of the rat prostate. *Endocrinology* 122:1159, 1988.
38. GEORGE FW, NOBLE JF: Androgen receptors are similar in fetal and adult rabbits. *Endocrinology* 115:1451, 1984.
39. SCHULTZ FM, WILSON JD: Virilization of the wolffian duct in the rat fetus by various androgens. *Endocrinology* 94:979, 1979.
40. GRIFFIN JE, WILSON JD. Disorders of sexual differentiation, in Walsh PC, Gittes RF, Perlmutter AD, Stamey TA (eds): *Campbell's Urology*. Philadelphia, Saunders, 1986, p 1819.
41. SLOAN WR, WALSH PC: Familial persistent mullerian duct syndrome. *J Urol* 115:459, 1976.
41a. GUERRIER D, TRAN D, VAN DER WINDEN JM, HIDEUX S, VAN OUTRYVE L, LEGEAI L, BOUCHARD M, VAN VLIET G, DE LAET MH, PICARD JY, KAHN A, JOSSO N: The persistent müllerian duct syndrome: A molecular approach. *J Clin Endocrinol Metab*, in press.
42. SAVAGE MO, CHAUSSAIN JL, EVAIN D, ROGER M, CANLORBE P, JOB JC: En-

docrine studies in male pseudohermaphroditism in childhood and adolescence. *Clin Endocrinol* 8:219, 1978.

43. CAMPO S, STIVEL M, NICOLAU G, MONTEAGUDO C, RIVAROLA M: Testicular function in postpubertal male pseudohermaphroditism. *Clin Endocrinol* 11:481, 1979.

44. CAMPO S, MONTEAGUDO C, NICOLAU G, PELLIZZARI E, BELGOROSKY A, STIVEL M, RIVAROLA M: Testicular function in prepubertal male pseudohermaphroditism. *Clin Endocrinol* 14:11, 1981.

45. NOWAKOWSKI H, LENZ W: Genetic aspects in male hypogonadism. *Recent Prog Horm Res* 17:53, 1961.

46. LENZ W: Genetisch bedingte Storungen der weiblichen Fortpflanzungsfunktionen. *Med Welt* 1:16, 1962.

47. LENZ W: Pseudohermaphroditismus masculinus externus mit Sckundarbehaarung und ohne Brustentwicklung (pseudovaginale, perineoskrotalehypospadie), in Becker PE (ed): *Humangenetik*. Stuttgart, Verlag, 1964, p 385.

48. SIMPSON JL, NEW M, PETERSON RE, GERMAN J: Pseudovaginal perineoscrotal hypospadias (PPSH) in sibs, in Bergsma D (ed): *Birth Defects*. Original Article Series, Baltimore, Williams and Wilkins, vol 7, no 6, p 140, May 1971.

49. OPITZ JM, SIMPSON JL, SARTO GE, SUMMITT RL, NEW M, GERMAN J: Pseudovaginal perineoscrotal hypospadias. *Clin Genet* 3:1, 1972.

50. WALSH PC, MADDEN JD, HARROD MJ, GOLDSTEIN JL, MacDONALD PC, WILSON JD: Familial incomplete male pseudohermaphroditism, type 2. Decreased dihydrotestosterone formation in pseudovaginal perineoscrotal hypospadias. *N Engl J Med* 291:944, 1974.

51. IMPERATO-McGINLEY J, GUERRERO L, GAUTIER T, PETERSON RE: Steroid 5α-reductase deficiency in man: An inherited form of male pseudohermaphroditism. *Science* 186:1213, 1974.

52. PETERSON RE, IMPERATO-McGINLEY J, GAUTIER T, STURLA E: Male pseudohermaphroditism due to steroid 5α-reductase deficiency. *Am J Med* 62:170, 1977.

53. IMPERATO-McGINLEY J, PETERSON RE, GAUTIER T, STURLA E: Male pseudohermaphroditism secondary to 5α-reductase deficiency—A model for the role of androgens in both the development of the male phenotype and the evolution of a male gender identity. *J Steroid Biochem* 11:637, 1979.

54. IMPERATO-McGINLEY J, PETERSON RE, LESHIN M, GRIFFIN JE, COOPER G, DRAGHI S, BERENYI M, WILSON JD: Steroid 5α-reductase deficiency in a 65 year old male pseudohermaphrodite: The natural history, ultrastructure of the testes and evidence for inherited enzyme heterogeneity. *J Clin Endocrinol Metab* 50:15, 1980.

55. PRICE P, WASS JAH, GRIFFIN JE, LESHIN M, SAVAGE MO, LARGE DM, Bu'LOCK DE, ANDERSON DC, WILSON JD, BESSER GM: High dose androgen therapy in male pseudohermaphroditism due to 5α-reductase deficiency and disorders of the androgen receptor. *J Clin Invest* 74:1496, 1984.

56. IMPERATO-McGINLEY J, PETERSON RE, GAUTIER T, STURLA E: Androgens and the evolution of male-gender identity among male pseudohermaphrodites with 5α-reductase deficiency. *N Engl J Med* 300:1233, 1979.

57. CANTÚ JM, CORONA-RIVERA E, DÍAZ M, MEDINA C, ESQUINCA E, CORTÉS-GALLEGOS V, VACA G, HERNÁNDEZ A: Post-pubertal female psychosexual orientation in incomplete male pseudohermaphroditism type 2 (5α-reductase deficiency). *Acta Endocrinol* 94:273, 1980.

58. MAUVAIS-JARVIS P, KUTTENN F, MOWSZOWICZI, WRIGHT F: Different aspects of 5α-reductase deficiency in male pseudohermaphroditism and hypothyroidism. *Clin Endocrinol* 14:459, 1981.

59. CORRALL RJM, WAKELIN K, O'HARE JP, O'BRIEN IAD, ISHMAIL AAA, HONOUR J: 5α-reductase deficiency: Diagnosis via abnormal plasma levels of reduced testosterone derivatives. *Acta Endocrinol* 107:538, 1984.

60. JOHNSON L, GEORGE FW, NEAVES WB, ROSENTHAL IM, CHRISTENSEN RA, DECRISTOFORO A, SCHWEIKERT H-U, SAUER MV, LESHIN M, GRIFFIN JE, WILSON JD: Characterization of the testicular abnormality in 5α-reductase deficiency. *J Clin Endocrinol Metab* 63:1091, 1986.

61. FISHER LK, KOGUT MD, MOORE RJ, GOEBELSMANN U, WEITMAN JJ, ISAACS H Jr, GRIFFIN JE, WILSON JD: Clinical, endocrinological, and enzymatic characterization of two patients with 5α-reductase deficiency: Evidence that a single enzyme is responsible for the 5α-reduction of cortisol and testosterone. *J Clin Endocrinol Metab* 47:653, 1978.

62. SAENGER P, GOLDMAN AS, LEVINE LS, KORTHSCHUTZ S, MUECKE EC, KATSUMATA M, DOBERNE Y, NEW MI: Prepubertal diagnosis of steroid 5α-reductase deficiency. *J Clin Endocrinol Metab* 46:627, 1978.

63. GREENE S, ZACHMANN M, MANELLA B, HESSE V, HOEPFFNER W, WILLGERODT H, PRADER A: Comparison of two tests to recognize or exclude 5α-reductase deficiency in prepubertal children. *Acta Endocrinol* 114;113, 1987.

64. SAVAGE MO, PREECE MA, JEFFCOATE SL, RANSLEY PG, RUMSBY G, MANSFIELD MD, WILLIAMS DI: Familial male pseudohermaphroditism due to deficiency of 5α-reductase. *Clin Endocrinol* 12:397, 1980.

65. KUTTENN F, MOWSZOWICZ I, WRIGHT F, BAUDOT N, JAFFIOL C, ROBIN M, MAUVAIS-JARVIS P: Male pseudohermaphroditism: A comparative study of one patient with 5α-reductase deficiency and three patients with the complete form of testicular feminization. *J Clin Endocrinol Metab* 49:861, 1979.

66. IMPERATO-McGINLEY J, PETERSON RE, GAUTIER T, ARTHUR A, SHACKLETON C: Decreased urinary C_{19} and C_{21} steroid 5α-metabolites in parents of male pseudohermaphrodites with 5α-reductase deficiency: Detection of carriers. *J Clin Endocrinol Metab* 60:553, 1985.

67. PETERSON RE, IMPERATO-McGINLEY J, GAUTIER T, SHACKLETON C: Urinary steroid metabolites in subjects with male pseudohermaphroditism due to 5α-reductase deficiency. *Clin Endocrinol* 23:43, 1985.

68. AKGUN S, ERTEL NH, IMPERATO-McGINLEY J, SAYLI BS, SHACKLETON C: Familial male pseudohermaphroditism due to 5α-reductase deficiency in a Turkish village. *Am J Med* 81:267, 1986.

69. OKON E, LIVNI N, RÖSLER A, YORKONI S, SEGAL S, KOHN G, SCHENKER JG: Male pseudohermaphroditism due to 5α-reductase deficiency: Ultrastructure of the gonads. *Arch Pathol Lab Med* 104:363, 1980.

70. JAFFIOL C, ROBIN M, CORRATGE P, MIROUZE J: Société française d'endocrinologie. *Ann Endocrinol (Paris)* 39:47, 1978.

71. GREENE SA, SYMES E, BROOK CGD: 5α-reductase deficiency causing male pseudohermaphroditism. *Arch Dis Child* 53:751, 1978.

72. ELAWADY MK, SALAM MA, TEMTAMY SA: Deficient 5α-reductase due to mutant enzyme with reduced affinity to steroid substrate. *Enzyme* 32:116, 1984.

73. LESHIN M, GRIFFIN JE, WILSON JD: Hereditary male pseudohermaphroditism associated with an unstable form of 5α-reductase. *J Clin Invest* 62:685, 1978.

74. WILSON JD: Recent studies on the mechanism of action of testosterone. *N Engl J Med* 287:1284, 1972.

75. WILSON JD, WALKER JD: The conversion of testosterone to 5α-androstan-17β-ol-3-one (dihydrotestosterone) by skin slices of man. *J Clin Invest* 48:371, 1969.

76. WILSON JD: Dihydrotestosterone formation in cultured human fibroblasts: Comparison of cells from normal subjects and patients with familial incomplete male pseudohermaphroditism, type 2. *J Biol Chem* 250:3498, 1975.

77. MOORE RJ, GRIFFIN JE, WILSON JD: Diminished 5α-reductase activity in extracts of fibroblasts cultured from patients with familial incomplete male pseudohermaphroditism, type 2. *J Biol Chem* 250:7168, 1975.

78. MOORE RJ, WILSON JD: Steroid 5α-reductase in cultured human fibroblasts: Biochemical and genetic evidence for two distinct enzyme activities. *J Biol Chem* 251:5895, 1976.

79. PINSKY L, KAUFMAN M, STAISFELD C, ZILAHI B, HALL C ST-G: 5α-reductase activity of genital and nongenital skin fibroblasts from patients with 5α-reductase deficiency, androgen insensitivity, or unknown forms of male pseudohermaphroditism. *Am J Med Genet* 1:407, 1978.

80. SCHMIDT JA, SCHWEIKERT H-U: Testosterone and epitestosterone metabolism of single hairs in 5 patients with 5α-reductase deficiency. *Acta Endocrinol* 113:588, 1986.

81. GIVENS JR, WISER WL, SUMMITT RL, KERBER IJ, ANDERSEN RN, PITTAWAY DE, FICH SA: Familial male pseudohermaphroditism without gynecomastia due to deficient testicular 17-ketosteroid reductase activity. *N Engl J Med* 291:938, 1974.

82. LANES R, BROWN TR, DE BUSTOS EG, VALVERDE B, PIERETTI RB, BIANCO N, ORTEGA G, MIGEON CJ: Sibship with 17-ketosteroid reductase (17-KSR) deficiency and hypothyroidism. Lack of linkage of histocompatibility leucocyte antigen and 17-KSR loci. *J Clin Endocrinol Metab* 57:190, 1983.

83. IMPERATO-McGINLEY J, PETERSON RE, GAUTIER T, COOPER G, DANNER R, ARTHUR A, MORRIS PL, SWEENEY WJ, SHACKLETON C: Hormonal evaluation of a large kindred with complete androgen insensitivity: Evidence for secondary 5α-reductase deficiency. *J Clin Endocrinol Metab* 54:931, 1982.

84. JUKIER L, KAUFMAN M, PINKSY L, PETERSON RE: Partial androgen resistance associated with secondary 5α-reductase deficiency: Identification of a novel qualitative androgen receptor defect and clinical implications. *J Clin Endocrinol Metab* 59:679, 1984.

85. IMPERATO-McGINLEY J, GAUTIER T, PICHARDO M, SHACKLETON C: The diagnosis of 5α-reductase deficiency in infancy. *J Clin Endocrinol Metab* 63:1313, 1986.

86. KEENAN BS, EBERLE AJ, SPARROW JT, GREGER NG, PANKO WB: Dihydrotestosterone heptanoate: Synthesis, pharmacokinetics, and effects on hypothalamic-pituitary-testicular function. *J Clin Endocrinol Metab* 64:557, 1987.

87. LIAO S, LIANG T, FANG S, CASTANEDA E, SHAO T-C: Steroid structure and androgenic activity: Specificities involved in the receptor binding and nuclear retention of various androgens. *J Biol Chem* 248:6154, 1973.

88. HAUSER GA: Testicular feminization, in Overzier C (ed): *Intersexuality.* London, Academic, 1963, p 255.

89. PETTERSSON G, BONNIER G: Inherited sex-mosaic in man. *Hereditas* 23:49, 1937.

90. SOUTHREN AL: The syndrome of testicular feminization, in Levine R, Luft R (eds): *Advances in Metabolic Disorders.* New York, Academic, 1965, vol 2, p 277.

91. SIMMER HH, PION RJ, DIGNAM WJ: In Selle WA (ed): *Testicular Feminization: Endocrine Function of Feminizing Testes, Comparison with Normal Testes.* Springfield, IL, Charles C Thomas, 1965, pp 1–100.

92. ULLOA-AGUIRRE A, MÉNDEZ JP, ANGELES A, DEL CASTILLO CE, CHÁVEZ B, PÉREZ-PALACIOS G: The presence of Mullerian remnants in the complete androgen insensitivity syndrome: A steroid hormone-mediated defect? *Fertil Steril* 45:302, 1986.

93. OKA M, KATABUCHI H, MUNEMURA M, MIZUMOTO J, MAEYAMA M: An unusual case of male pseudohermaphroditism: Complete testicular feminization associated with incomplete differention of the Mullerian duct. *Fertil Steril* 41:154, 1984.

94. DODGE ST, FINKELSTON MS, MIYAZAWA K: Testicular feminization with incomplete Mullerian regression. *Fertil Steril* 43:937, 1985.

95. STERN ON, VANDERVORT WJ: Testicular feminization in the male pseudohermaphrodite: Report of a case. *N Engl J Med* 254:787, 1956.

96. GRUMBACH MM, BARR ML: Cytologic tests of chromosomal sex in relation to sexual anomalies in man. *Recent Prog Horm Res* 14:255, 1958.

97. JACOBS PA, BAIKIE AG, COURT BROWN WM, FORREST H, ROY JR, STEARD JSS, LENNOX B: Chromosomal sex in the syndrome of testicular feminisation. *Lancet* 2:591, 1959.

98. PUCK TT, ROBINSON A, TJIO JH: Familial primary amenorrhea due to testicular feminization: A human gene affecting sex differentiation. *Proc Soc Exp Biol Med* 103:192, 1960.

99. CHU EHY, GRUMBACH MM, MORISHIMA A: Karyotypic analysis of a male pseudohermaphrodite with the syndrome of feminizing testes. *J Clin Endocrinol Metab* 20:1608, 1960.

100. VARRELA J, ALVESALO L, VINKKA H: Body size and shape in 46,XY females with complete testicular feminization. *Ann Hum Biol* 2:291, 1984.

101. ALVESALO L, VARRELA J: Permanent tooth sizes in 46,XY females. *Am J Hum Genet* 32:736, 1980.

102. ZACHMANN M, PRADER A, SOBEL EH, CRIGLER JF Jr, RITZÉN EM, ATARÉS M, FERRANDEZ A: Pubertal growth in patients with androgen insensitivity: Indirect evidence for the importance of estrogens in pubertal growth of girls. *J Pediatr* 108:694, 1986.

103. MASICA DN, MONEY J, EHRHARDT AA, LEWIS VG: IQ, fetal sex hormones and cognitive patterns: Studies in the testicular feminizing syndrome of androgen insensitivity. *Johns Hopkins Med J* 124:34, 1969.

104. MONEY J, EHRHARDT AA, MASICA DN: Fetal feminization induced by androgen insensitivity in the testicular feminizing syndrome: Effect on marriage and maternalism. *Johns Hopkins Med J* 123:105, 1968.

105. GERMAN J, SIMPSON JL, MORILLO-CUCCI G, PASSARGE E, DEMAYO AP: Testicular feminisation and inguinal hernia. *Lancet* 1:891, 1973.

106. PERGAMENT E, HEIMLER A, SHAH P: Testicular feminisation and inguinal hernia. *Lancet* 2:740, 1973.

107. IMURA H, MATSUMOTO K, OGATA E, YOSHIDA S, IGARASHI Y, KONO T, MATSUKURA S: "Hormone receptor diseases" in Japan: A nation-wide survey for testicular feminization syndrome, pseudohypoparathyroidism, nephrogenic diabetes insipidus, Bartter's syndrome and congenital adrenocortical unresponsiveness to ACTH. *Folia Endocrinol Jap* 56:1031, 1980.

108. ROSS GT: Disorders of the ovary and female reproductive tract, in Wilson JD, Foster DW (eds): *Williams Textbook of Endocrinology.* Philadelphia, Saunders, 1985, chap 9, p 206.

109. SCHREINER WE: On a hereditary form of male pseudohermaphroditism ("testicular feminization"). *Geburtshilfe Frauenheikd* 19:1110, 1959.

110. GWINUP G, WIELAND RG, BESCH PK, HAMWI GJ: Studies on the mechanism of the production of the testicular feminization syndrome. *Am J Med* 41:448, 1966.

111. VAGENAKIS AG, HAMILTON C, MALOOF F, BRAVERMAN LE, INGBAR SH: The concentration and binding of thyroxine in the serum of patients with the testicular feminization syndrome: Observations on the effects of ethinyl estradiol and norethandrolone. *J Clin Endocrinol Metab* 34:327, 1972.

112. TREMBLAY RR, SCHLAEDER G, DUSSAULT JH: Effects de l'ethynil estradiol et des androgènes sur les parametres de la fonction throidienne dans le syndrome de pseudohermaprodisme male avec feminisation testiculaire. *Union Med Can* 103:421, 1974.

113. FAIMAN C, WINTER JSD: The control of gonadotropin secretion in complete testicular feminization. *J Clin Endocrinol Metab* 39:631, 1974.

114. FRENCH FR, VAN WYK JJ, BAGGETT V, ESTERLING WE, TALBERT LM, JOHNSTON FR, FORCHIELLI E, DEY AC: Further evidence of a target organ defect in the syndrome of testicular feminization. *J Clin Endocrinol Metab* 26:493, 1966.

115. VOLPE R, KNOWLTON TG, FOSTER AD, CONEN PE: Testicular feminization: A study of two cases, one with a seminoma. *Can Med Assoc J* 98:438, 1968.

116. CASTANEDA E, PEREZ AE, GUILLEN MA, RAMIERZ-ROBLES S, GUAL C, PEREZ-PALACIOS G: Metabolic studies in a patient with testicular feminization syndrome. *Am J Obstet Gynecol* 110:1002, 1971.

117. O'LEARY JA: Comparative studies of the gonad in testicular feminization and cryptorchidism. *Fertil Steril* 16:813, 1965.

118. JUSTRABO E, CABANNE F, MICHIELS R, BASTIEN H, DUSSERRE P, PANSIOT F, CAYOT F: A complete form of testicular feminisation syndrome: A light and electron microscopy study. *J Pathol* 126:165, 1978.

119. FAULDS JS, LENNOX B: Leydig-cell hyperplasia in testicular feminisation. *Lancet* 1:344, 1971.

120. PRADER A: Gonadendysgenesie und testikuläre feminisierung. *Schweiz Med Wochenschr* 87:178, 1957.

121. MORRIS JM, MAHESH VB: Further observations on the syndrome, "testicular feminization." *Am J Obset Gynecol* 87:731, 1963.

122. ROSENFIELD RL, LAWRENCE AM, LIAO S, LANDAU RL: Androgens and androgen responsiveness in the feminizing testis syndrome: Comparison of complete and "incomplete" forms. *J Clin Endocrinol Metab* 32:625, 1971.

123. CRAWFORD JD, ADAMS RD, KLIMAN B, FEDERMAN DD, ULFELDER HS, HOLMES LH: Syndromes of testicular feminization. *Clin Pediatr* 9:165, 1970.

124. WINTERBORN MH, FRANCE NE, RAITI S: Incomplete testicular feminization. *Arch Dis Child* 45:811, 1970.

125. MADDEN JD, WALSH PC, MacDONALD PC, WILSON JD: Clinical and endocrinological characterization of a patient with the syndrome of incomplete testicular feminization. *J Clin Endocrinol Metab* 40:751, 1975.

126. REIFENSTEIN EC JR: Hereditary familial hypogonadism. *Clin Res* 3:86, 1947.

127. BOWEN P, LEE CSN, MIGEON CJ, KAPLAN NM, WHALLEY PJ, McKUSICK VA, REIFENSTEIN EC JR: Hereditary male pseudohermaphroditism with hypogonadism, hypospadias, and gynecomastia (Reifenstein's syndrome). *Ann Intern Med* 62:252, 1965.

128. LUBS HA JR, VILAR O, BERGENSTAL DM: Familial male pseudohermaphroditism, hypospadias, and gynecomastia (Reifenstein's syndrome). *Ann Intern Med* 62:252, 1965.

129. GILBERT-DREYFUS S, SEBAOUN CA, BELAISCH J: Étude d'un cas familial d'androgynoidisme avec hypospadias grave, gynécomastie et hyperoestrogénie. *Ann Endocrinol (Paris)* 18:93, 1957.

130. ROSEWATER S, GWINUP G, HAMWI GJ: Familial gynecomastia. *Ann Intern Med* 63:377, 1965.

131. WILSON JD, HARROD MG, GOLDSTEIN JL, HEMSELL DL, MacDONALD PC: Familial incomplete male pseudohermaphroditism, Type I. Evidence for androgen resistance and variable clinical manifestations in a family with the Reifenstein syndrome. *N Engl J Med* 290:1097, 1974.

132. FORD E: Congenital abnormalities of the genitalia in related Bathurst Island natives. *Med J Aust* 1:450, 1941.

133. WALKER AC, STACK EM, HORSFALL WA: Familial male pseudohermaphroditism. *Med J Aust* 1:156, 1970.

134. GARDO S, PAPP Z: Clinical variations of testicular intersexuality in a family. *J Med Genet* 11:267, 1974.

135. PEREZ-PALACIOS G, ORTIZ S, LÓPEZ-AMOR E, MORATO T, FEBRES F, LISKER R, SCAGLIA H: Familial incomplete virilization due to partial end organ insensitivity to androgens. *J Clin Endocrinol Metab* 41:946, 1975.

136. PITTAWAY DE, STAGE AH: Familial male pseudohermaphroditism with incomplete virilization. *Obstet Gynecol* 51:82s, 1978.

137. GRIFFIN JE, PUNYASHTHITI K, WILSON JD: Dihydrotestosterone binding by cultured human fibroblasts: Comparison of cells from control subjects and from patients with hereditary male pseudohermaphroditism due to androgen resistance. *J Clin Invest* 57:1342, 1976.

138. AIMAN J, GRIFFIN JE, GAZAK JM, WILSON JD, MacDONALD PC: Androgen insensitivity as a cause of infertility in otherwise normal men. *N Engl J Med* 300:223, 1979.

139. WARNE GL, KHALID BAK, GYORKI S, FUNDER JW, RISBRIDGER GP: Correlations between fibroblast androgen receptor levels and clinical features in abnormal male sexual differentiation and infertility. *Aust NZ J Med* 13:335, 1983.

140. PINSKY L, KAUFMAN M, KILLINGER DW, BURKO B, SHATZ D, VOLPÉ RP: Human minimal androgen insensitivity with normal dihydrotestosterone-binding capacity in cultured genital skin fibroblasts: Evidence for an androgen-selective qualitative abnormality of the receptor. *Am J Hum Genet* 36:965, 1984.

141. MIGEON CJ, BROWN TR, LANES R, PALCIOS A, AMRHEIN JA, SCHJOEN EJ: A clinical syndrome of mild androgen insensitivity. *J Clin Endocrinol Metab* 59:672, 1984.

142. SMALLRIDGE RC, VIGERSKY R, GLASS AR, GRIFFIN JE, WHITE BJ, EIL C:

Androgen receptor abnormalities in identical twins with oligospermia. *Am J Med* 77:1049, 1984.

143. CUNDY TF, REES M, EVANS BAJ, HUGHES IA, BUTLER J, WHEELER MJ: Mild androgen insensitivity presenting with sexual dysfunction. *Fertil Steril* 46:721, 1986.

144. AIMAN J, GRIFFIN JE: The frequency of androgen receptor deficiency in infertile men. *J Clin Endocrinol Metab* 54:725, 1982.

145. MORROW AF, GYORKI S, WARNE GL, BURGER HG, BANGAH ML, OUTCH KH, MIROVICS A, BAKER HWG: Variable androgen receptor levels in infertile men. *J Clin Endocrinol Metab,* 64:1115, 1987.

146. SOUTHREN AL, ROSS H, SHARMA DC, GORDON G, WEINGOLD AB, DORFMAN RI: Plasma concentration and biosynthesis of testosterone in the syndrome of feminizing testes. *J Clin Endocrinol Metab* 23:1044, 1963.

147. JEFFCOATE SL, BROOKS RV, PRUNTY FTG: Secretion of androgens and oestrogens in testicular feminization: Studies *in vivo* and *in vitro* in two cases. *Br Med J* 1:208, 1968.

148. TREMBLAY RR, FOLEY TP JR, CORVOL P, PARK IJ, KOWARSKI A, BLIZZARD RM, JONES HW JR, MIGEON CJ: Plasma concentration of testosterone, dihydrotestosterone, testosterone-oestradiol binding globulin, and pituitary gonadotropins in the syndrome of male pseudohermaphroditism with testicular feminization. *Acta Endocrinol* 70:331, 1972.

149. TREMBLAY RR, KOWARSKI A, PARK IJ, MIGEON CJ: Blood production rate of dihydrotestosterone in the syndrome of male pseudohermaphroditism with testicular feminization. *J Clin Endocrinol Metab* 35:101, 1972.

150. BOYAR RM, MOORE RJ, ROSNER W, AIMAN J, CHIPMAN J, MADDEN JD, MARKS JF, GRIFFIN JE: Studies of gonadotropin-gonadal dynamics in patients with androgen insensitivity. *J Clin Endocrinol Metab* 47:1116, 1978.

151. LAATIKAINEN T, APTER D, WAHLSTRÖM T: Steroids in spermatic and peripheral vein blood in testicular feminization. *Fertil Steril* 34:461, 1980.

152. ZARATE A, CANALES ES, SORIA J, CARBALLO O: Studies on the luteinizing hormone- and follicle-stimulating hormone-releasing mechanism in the testicular feminization syndrome. *Am J Obstet Gynecol* 119:971, 1974.

153. MEDINA M, ULLOA-AGUIRRE A, FERNÁNDEZ MA, PÉREZ-PALACIOS G: The role of oestrogens on gonadotropin secretion in the testicular feminization syndrome. *Acta Endocrinol* 95:314, 1980.

154. GUNASEGARAM R, LOGANATH A, PEH KL, SINNIAH R, KOTTEGODA SR, RATNAM SS: Altered hypothalamic-pituitary-testicular function in incomplete testicular feminization syndrome. *Aust NZ J Obstet Gynaecol* 24:288, 1984.

155. FREDRICSSON B, CARLSTRÖM K, KJESSLER B, LINDSTEDT J, PLÖEN L, RITZÉN M, DE LA TORRE B: Incomplete androgen insensitivity: Asymmetry in morphology and steroid profile and metabolism of the gonads. An analysis of a case. *Acta Endocrinol* 110:564, 1985.

156. HOCHMAN J, GANGULY M, WEISS G: Induction of an LH surge with estradiol benzoate in a patient with incomplete testicular feminization syndrome. *Obstet Gynecol* 49:17s, 1977.

157. FLATAU E, JOSEFSBERG Z, PRAGER-LEWIN R, MARKMAN-HALABE E, KAUFMAN H, LARON Z: Response to LH-RH and HCG in two brothers with the Reifenstein syndrome. *Helv Paediatr Acta* 30:377, 1975.

158. LEONARD JM, BREMNER WJ, CAPELL PT, PAULSEN CA: Male hypogonadism: Klinefelter and Reifenstein syndrome, in Vergama D (ed): *Genetic Forms of Hypogonadism. Birth Defects:* Original Article Series, New York, Stratton Corp, 1975, vol XI, no 4, p 17.

159. NORTHCUTT RC, ISLAND DP, LIDDLE GW: An explanation for the target organ unresponsiveness to testosterone in the testicular feminization syndrome. *J Clin Endocrinol Metab* 29:422, 1969.

160. MAUVAIS-JARVIS P, FLOCH HH, BERCOVICI J-P: Studies on testosterone metabolism in human subjects with normal and pathological sexual differentiation. *J Clin Endocrinol Metab* 29:422, 1969.

161. MAUVAIS-JARVIS P, VERCOVICI JP, CREPY O, GAUTHIER F: Studies on testosterone metabolism in subjects with testicular feminization syndrome. *J Clin Invest* 49:31, 1970.

162. IMPERATO-MCGINLEY J, PETERSON RE, GAUTIER T, COOPER G, DANNER R, ARTHUR A, MORRIS PL, SWEENEY WJ, SHACKLETON C: Hormonal evaluation of a large kindred with complete androgen insensitivity: Evidence for a secondary 5α-reductase deficiency. *J Clin Endocrinol Metab* 54:931, 1982.

163. STEWARD JSS: Testicular feminisation and colour-blindness. *Lancet* 2:592, 1959.

164. NILSSON IM, BERGMAN S, REITALU J, WALDENSTRÖM J: Haemophilia A in a "girl" with male sex-chromatin pattern. *Lancet* 2:264, 1959.

165. SANGER R, TIPPETT P, GAVIN J, GOOCH A, RACE RR: Inheritance of testicular feminization syndrome: Some negative linkage findings. *J Med Genet* 6:26, 1969.

166. HOLMBERG L: Genetic studies in a family with testicular feminization, haemophilia and colour blindness. *Clin Genet* 3:253, 1972.

167. SCHULTZ MG: Male pseudohermaphroditism diagnosed with aid of sex chromatin technique. *J Am Vet Med Assoc* 140:241, 1962.

168. NEW N: Testikulaer feminisering hos storfe. *Nord Vet Med* 18:19, 1966.

169. BARDIN CW, BULLOCK L, SCHNEIDER G, ALLISON JE, STANLEY AJ: Pseudohermaphrodite rat: End organ insensitivity to testosterone. *Science* 167:1136, 1970.

170. LYON MF, HAWKES SG: X-linked gene for testicular feminization in the mouse. *Nature* 227:1217, 1970.

171. KIEFFER NM, BURNS SJ, JUDGE NG: Male pseudohermaphrodite of the testicular feminizing type in a horse. *Equine Vet J* 8:38, 1976.

172. EIL C, MERRIAM GR, BOWEN J, EBERT J, TABOR E, WHITE B, DOUGLASS EC, LORIAUX DL: Testicular feminization in the chimpanzee. *Clin Res* 28:624A, 1980.

173. OHNO S: *Major Sex-Determining Genes.* New York, Springer-Verlag, 1979.

174. MEYER WJ III, MIGEON BR, MIGEON CJ: Locus on human X chromosome for dihydrotestosterone receptor and androgen insensitivity. *Proc Natl Acad Sci USA* 72:1469, 1975.

175. LYON MF: X-chromosome inactivation and developmental patterns in mammals. *Biol Rev* 14:1, 1972.

176. MIGEON BR, BROWN TR, AXELMAN J, MIGEON CJ: Studies of the locus for androgen receptor: Localization on the human X chromosome and evidence for homology with the *Tfm* locus in the mouse. *Proc Natl Acad Sci USA* 78:6339, 1981.

177. ELAWADY MK, ALLMAN DR, GRIFFIN JE, WILSON JD: Expression of a mutant androgen receptor in cloned fibroblasts derived from a heterozygous carrier for the syndrome of testicular feminization. *Am J Hum Genet* 35:376, 1983.

178. GRIFFIN JE: Testicular feminization associated with a thermolabile androgen receptor in cultured human fibroblasts. *J Clin Invest* 64:1624, 1979.

179. WILSON JD, CARLSON BR, WEAVER DD, KOVACS WJ, GRIFFIN JE: Endocrine and genetic characterization of cousins with male pseudohermaphroditism: Evidence that the Lubs phenotype can result from a mutation that alters the structure of the androgen receptor. *Clin Genet* 26:363, 1984.

180. SCHWEIKERT H-U, WEISSBACH L, STANGENBERG C, LEYENDECKER G, KLEY H-K, GRIFFIN JE, WILSON JD: Clinical and endocrinological characterization of two subjects with Reifenstein syndrome associated with qualitative abnormalities of the androgen receptor. *Hormone Res* 25:72, 1987.

181. WIEACKER P, GRIFFIN JE, WIENKER T, BRECKWOLD M, LOPEZ JM, WILSON JD: Linkage analysis with RFLPs in families with androgen resistance syndromes: Evidence for close linkage between the androgen receptor locus and the DXS1 segment. *Hum Genet* 76:248, 1987.

182. KEENAN BS, MEYER WJ III, HADJIAN AJ, JONES HW, MIGEON CJ: Syndrome of androgen insensitivity in man: Absence of 5α-dihydrotestosterone binding protein in skin fibroblasts. *J Clin Endocrinol Metab* 38:1143, 1974.

183. KEENAN BS, MEYER WJ III, HADJIAN AJ, MIGEON CJ: Androgen receptor in human skin fibroblasts: Characterization of a specific 17β-hydroxy-5α-androstan-3-one-protein complex in cell sonicates and nuclei. *Steroids* 25:535, 1975.

184. KAUFMAN M, STRAISFELD C, PINSKY L: Male pseudohermaphroditism presumably due to target organ unresponsiveness to androgens: Deficient 5α-dihydrotestosterone binding in cultured skin fibroblasts. *J Clin Invest* 58:345, 1976.

185. GRIFFIN JE, DURRANT JL: Qualitative receptor defects in families with androgen resistance: Failure of stabilization of the fibroblast cytosol androgen receptor. *J Clin Endocrinol Metab* 55:465, 1982.

186. BROWN TR, MAES M, ROTHWELL SW, MIGEON CJ: Human complete androgen insensitivity with normal dihydrotestosterone receptor binding capacity in cultured genital skin fibroblasts: Evidence for a qualitative abnormality of the receptor. *J Clin Endocrinol Metab* 55:61, 1982.

187. EVANS BAJ, JONES TR, HUGHES IA: Studies of the androgen receptor in dispersed fibroblasts: Investigation of patients with androgen insensitivity. *Clin Endocrinol* 20:93, 1984.

188. KAUFMAN M, PINSKY L, BOWIN A, AU MWS: Familial external genital ambiguity due to a transformation defect of androgen-receptor complexes that is expressed with 5α-dihydrotestosterone and the synthetic androgen methyltrienolone. *Am J Med Genet* 18:493, 1984.

189. PINSKY L, KAUFMAN M, CHUDLEY AE: Reduced affinity of the androgen receptor for 5α-dihydrotestosterone but not methyltrienolone in a form of partial androgen resistance. *J Clin Invest* 75:1291, 1985.

190. JUKIER L, KAUFMAN M, PINSKY L, PETERSON RE: Partial androgen resistance associated with secondary 5α-reductase deficiency: Identification of a novel qualitative androgen receptor defect and clinical implications. *J Clin Endocrinol Metab* 59:679, 1984.

191. EIL C: Familial incomplete male pseudohermaphroditism associated with impaired nuclear androgen retention. *J Clin Invest* 71:850, 1983.

192. KAUFMAN M, PINSKY L, FEDER-HOLLANDER R: Defective up-regulation of the androgen receptor in human androgen insensitivity. *Nature* 293:735, 1981.

193. KAUFMAN M, PINSKY L, HOLLANDER R, BAILEY JD: Regulation of the androgen receptor by androgen in normal and androgen-resistant genital skin fibroblasts. *J Steroid Biochem* 18:383, 1983.

194. KAUFMAN M, PINSKY L, KILLINGER DW: Ligand-specific thermal misbehavior of synthetic androgen-receptor complexes in genital skin fibroblasts of subjects with familial ligand-sensitive androgen resistance. *J Steroid Biochem* 25:323, 1986.

195. EVANS BAJ, HUGHES IA: Augmentation of androgen-receptor binding *in vitro*: Studies in normals and patients with androgen insensitivity. *Clin Endocrinol* 23:567, 1985.

196. KAUFMAN M, PINSKY L, SIMARD L, WONG SC: Defective activation of androgen-receptor complexes. A marker of androgen insensitivity. *Mol Cell Endocrinol* 25:151, 1982.

197. PINSKY L, KAUFMAN M, SUMMITT RL: Congenital androgen insensitivity due to a qualitatively abnormal androgen receptor. *Am J Med Genet* 10:91, 1981.

198. KOVACS WJ, GRIFFIN JE, WEAVER DD, CARLSON BR, WILSON JD: A mutation that causes lability of the androgen receptor under conditions that normally promote transformation to the DNA-binding state. *J Clin Invest* 73:1095, 1984.

199. TAMAYA T, NIOKA S, FURUTA N, BOKU S, MOTOYAMA T, OHONO Y, OKASA H: Preliminary studies on steroid-binding proteins in human testes of testicular feminization syndrome. *Fertil Steril* 30:170, 1978.

200. BROWN TR, SPINOLA-CASTRO A, BERKOVITZ GD, MIGEON CJ: Androgen receptor in cultured human testicular fibroblasts. *J Clin Endocrinol Metab* 61:134, 1985.

201. GEHRING U, TOMKINS GM, OHNO S: Effect of the androgen-insensitivity mutation on a cytoplasmic receptor for dihydrotestosterone. *Nature* 232:106, 1971.

202. VERHOEVEN G, WILSON JD: Cytosol androgen receptor in submandibular gland and kidney of the normal mouse and the mouse with testicular feminization. *Endocrinology* 99:79, 1976.

203. AMRHEIN JA, MEYER WJ III, JONES HW JR, MIDGEON JC: Androgen insensitivity in man: Evidence for genetic heterogeneity. *Proc Natl Acad Sci USA* 73:891, 1976.

204. COLLIER ME, GRIFFIN JE, WILSON JD: Intranuclear binding of [³H]dihydrotestosterone by cultured human fibroblasts. *Endocrinology* 103:1499, 1978.

205. KEENAN BS, KIRKLAND JL, KIRKLAND RT, CLAYTON GW: Male pseudohermaphroditism with partial androgen insensitivity. *Pediatrics* 59:224, 1977.

206. MAES M, LEE PA, JEFFS RD, SULTAN C, MIGEON CJ: Phenotypic variation in a family with partial androgen insensitivity syndrome. *Am J Dis Child* 134:470, 1980.

207. KAUFMAN M, PINSKY L, BAIRD PA, MCGILLIVRAY BC: Complete androgen insensitivity with a normal amount of 5α-dihydrotestosterone-binding activity in labium majus skin fibroblasts. *Am J Med Genet* 4:401, 1979.

208. BROWN TR, ROTHWELL SW, MIGEON CJ: Human androgen insensitivity mutation does not alter oligonucleotide recognition by the androgen receptor-DHT complex. *Mol Cell Endocrinol* 32:215, 1983.

209. GRUNSTEIN HS, WARNE GL, GYORKI S, CLIFTON-GLIGH P, POSEN S: "Receptorpositive" androgen insensitivity: Report of a case with brief review of the literature. *Aust NZ J Med* 12:289, 1982.

210. BROWN TR, MIGEON CJ: Androgen binding in nuclear matrix of human genital skin fibroblasts from patients with androgen insensitivity syndrome. *J Clin Endocrinol Metab* 62:542, 1986.

211. GYORKI S, WARNE GL, KHALID BAK, FUNDER JW: Defective nuclear accumulation of androgen receptors in disorders of sexual differentiation. *J Clin Invest* 72:819, 1983.

212. HUGHES IA, EVANS BAJ, ISMAIL R, MATTHEWS J: Complete androgen insensitivity syndrome characterized by increased concentration of a normal androgen receptor in genital skin fibroblasts. *J Clin Endocrinol Metab* 63:309, 1986.

213. GRIFFIN JE, EDWARDS C, MADDEN JD, HARROLD MJ, WILSON JD: Congenital absence of the vagina. The Mayer Rokitansky-Kuster-Hauser syndrome. *Ann Intern Med* 85:224, 1976.

214. HALES ED, ROSSER SB: Computed tomography of testicular feminization. *J Comput Tomogr* 8:772, 1984.

215. EDMAN CD, WINTERS AJ, PORTER JC, WILSON JD, MACDONALD PC: Embryonic testicular regression. A clinical spectrum of XY agonadal individuals. *Obstet Gynecol* 49:208, 1977.

216. NAGEL BA, LIPPE BM, GRIFFIN JE: Androgen resistance in the neonate: Use of hormones of hypothalamic-pituitary-gonadal axis for diagnosis. *J Pediatr* 109:486, 1986.

217. LEE PA, BROWN TR, LATORRE HA: Diagnosis of the partial androgen insensitivity syndrome during infancy. *JAMA* 255:2207, 1986.

218. BERKOVITZ GD, LEE PA, BROWN TR, MIGEON CJ: Etiologic evaluation of male pseudohermaphroditism in infancy and childhood. *Am J Dis Child* 138:755, 1984.

219. SULTAN C, EMBERGER J-M, DEVILLIER C, CHAVIS C, TERRAZA A, DESCOMPS B, JEAN R: Specific 5α-dihydrotestosterone receptor and 5α-reductase activity in human amniotic fluid cells. *Am J Obstet Gynecol* 150:956, 1984.

220. STEPHENS JD: Prenatal diagnosis of testicular feminisation. *Lancet* 2:1038, 1984.

221. WABREK AJ, MILLARD PR, WILSON WB JR, PION RJ: Creation of a neovagina by the Frank nonoperative method. *Obstet Gynecol* 37:408, 1971.

222. DEWHURST CJ, FERREIRA HP, GILLETT PG: Gonadal malignancy in XY females. *J Obstet Gynaecol Br Commonw* 78:1077, 1971.

223. O'CONNELL MJ, RAMSEY HE, WHANG-PENG J, WIERNIK PH: Testicular feminization syndrome in three sibs: Emphasis on gonadal neoplasia. *Am J Med Sci* 265:321, 1973.

224. MacNAB GH: Maldescent of the testicle. *J R Coll Surg Edinb* 1:126, 1955.

225. MÜLLER J: Morphometry and histology of gonads from twelve children and adolescents with the androgen insensitivity (testicular feminization) syndrome. *J Clin Endocrinol Metab* 59:785, 1984.

226. MÜLLER J, SKAKKEBAEK NE: Testicular carcinoma in situ in children with the androgen insensitivity (testicular feminisation) syndrome. *Br Med J* 288:1419, 1984.

227. ANDLER W, ZACHMANN M: Spontaneous breast development in an adolescent girl with testicular feminization after castration in early childhood. *J Pediatr* 94:304, 1979.

228. HALL PF: *Gynecomastia*. Monographs of Federal Council of British Medical Association in Australia No 2. Glebe, New South Wales, Australasian Medical Publishing Co, 1959.

229. VERHOEVEN GFM, WILSON JD: The syndromes of primary hormone resistance. *Metabolism* 28:253, 1979.

230. FRASER D, KOOH SW, KIND HP, HOLICK MF, TANAKA Y, DELUCA HF: Pathogenesis of hereditary vitamin-D-dependent rickets: An inborn error of vitamin D metabolism involving defective conversion of 25-hydroxyvitamin D to 1α-25-dihydroxyvitamin D. *N Engl J Med* 289:817, 1973.

CHAPTER 76

STEROID SULFATASE DEFICIENCY AND X-LINKED ICHTHYOSIS

LARRY J. SHAPIRO

1. Steroid sulfatase deficiency is an inborn error of metabolism inherited as an X-linked recessive trait. It affects between 1 in 2000 and 1 in 6000 males in many different populations coming from a range of geographic locations and racial and ethnic backgrounds. Most patients with steroid sulfatase deficiency have deletions of the X-encoded gene for this enzyme.

2. Steroid sulfatase deficiency produces ichthyosis and mild corneal opacities postnatally. In fetal life, placental deficiency of the enzyme results in diminished estrogen biosynthesis by the maternal-fetal-placental pregnancy unit. Dehydroepiandrosterone sulfate and 16 OH-dehydroepiandrosterone sulfate accumulate in amniotic fluid and maternal urine before birth. After delivery cholesterol sulfate is increased in plasma, stratum corneum, and perhaps in other tissues.

3. Some patients with steroid sulfatase deficiency have additional phenotypic abnormalities, such as hypogonadotropic hypogonadism with anosmia, or chondrodysplasia punctata. These individuals probably have deletions of contiguous genes. Some have normal karyotypes, as do patients with simple X-linked ichthyosis, but others have visible cytogenetic rearrangements involving Xp22.3→pter.

4. The steroid sulfatase gene is not subject to X-chromosome inactivation in either the human or the mouse. In humans, there is a dosage inequity between females and males. A steroid sulfatase pseudogene is located on the long arm of the Y chromosome.

5. Steroid sulfatase deficiency may be readily diagnosed either prenatally or postnatally by a combination of enzymatic, endocrinologic, and molecular methods.

In 1969 France and Liggins described a novel inborn error of metabolism characterized by absence of neutral steroid sulfatase (STS) activity from the placenta of a pregnancy associated with very low estrogen production. Following the recognition of additional cases in ensuing years, further attention has been focused on this condition, on the steroid sulfatase enzyme protein, and on the gene which encodes it. These studies, carried out by geneticists, endocrinologists, and dermatologists, have provided a rich collection of data with implications that extend far beyond what was originally anticipated. The findings have yielded insight into the mechanism of steroid hormone metabolism and estrogen biosynthesis, into the interconversion and role of sterols in the skin, and into the evolution of and regulation of gene expression on the mammalian X chromosome.

SULFATED STEROIDS

Sulfated steroids are ubiquitously distributed compounds found in abundance in mammalian tissues and body fluids.[1] They have unique biologic and chemical properties that are conferred by their relative solubility in water (as compared to the parent steroids) and their capacity for lipophilic interactions due to their cyclopentenophenanthrene ring structure. These molecules have in common a 3β-hydroxysteroid sulfate ester linkage. The first sulfated steroid to be isolated and structurally characterized was estrone sulfate, which was found in pregnant mare's urine.[2] Shortly afterward, androsterone sulfate and dehydroepiandrosterone sulfate (DHEAS) were identified in human urine.[3,4] Relatively little further work was done with these compounds until the 1950s and 1960s when adequate chemical methods for separating and quantitating these steroids were developed. In addition to methodologic constraints, a general feeling prevailed that steroid sulfates were merely water-soluble storage or excretory forms of active hormones and thus were uninteresting. With the development of chromatographic separation methods and the availability of isotopically labeled steroid sulfates, this view has gradually changed. A comprehensive summary of the chemistry, distribution, and physiology of the steroid sulfates is beyond the scope of this chapter, but several excellent reviews are available.[1,5]

3β-Hydroxysteroid sulfates are formed from free steroids by the action of the sulfotransferase activity present in the adrenal glands, liver, skin, testis, ovary, and placenta (Fig. 76-1). The high energy sulfate donor is 3′-phosphoadenosine-5′-phosphosulfate (PAPS). Phosphoadenosine phosphosulfate is formed by the sequential action of ATP-sulfurylase and adenosine phosphosulfate phosphokinase. Whether all sulfotransferase reactions are mediated by a single enzyme or gene product is not known. 3β-hydroxysteroid sulfates can be interconverted along pathways analogous to those used for the unconjugated steroids. This was elegantly verified by infusion into experimental subjects of sulfated steroids labeled with tritium in the sterol nucleus and ^{35}S in the sulfate moiety. When doubly labeled substrates were given, a variety of metabolites could be isolated with the same ^{35}S/^{3}H ratio as the starting material.[6] This would be indicative of the metabolism of these compounds without prior desulfation. In spite of the conclusive

Nonstandard abbreviations used in this chapter include: CS = cholesterol sulfate; DHEA = dehydroepiandrosterone; DHEAS = dehydroepiandrosterone sulfate; MSD = multiple sulfatase deficiency; RFLP = restriction fragment length polymorphism; STS = steroid sulfatase; Sxr = sex-reversed; and TDF = testis determining factor.

demonstration of the existence of these pathways of biotransformation, their relative importance in normal steroid hormone economy is still largely unknown (Fig. 76-1).

For a number of years, several investigators have endeavored to explain why there are such large quantities of circulating sulfated steroids, given their relative biologic inactivity. Pregnenolone sulfate is not active per se. DHEAS fails to cause changes in the activities of several enzymes that are modulated by free dehydroepiandrosterone (DHEA) and large doses of DHEAS given to human subjects are generally without effect. Estrogen sulfates apparently cannot interact with the estrogen receptor without prior hydrolysis.[7,8] It has been suggested that sulfated steroids are a reservoir or a source of precursors for the production of active hormones, and this point of view may have some merit. It has been shown that

the circulating half-life of most plasma steroid sulfates is longer than that of the corresponding free steroids, so that the sulfates must be more slowly metabolized or excreted. In addition, sulfated steroids may be hydrolyzed in situ by the ubiquitously distributed steroid sulfatase enzyme to yield free active hormones in target tissues (Fig. 76-1). This has been demonstrated for estrogen sulfate in breast cancer cells[8] and in the fetal ovine hypothalamus, where possible physiologic significance has been proposed.[9]

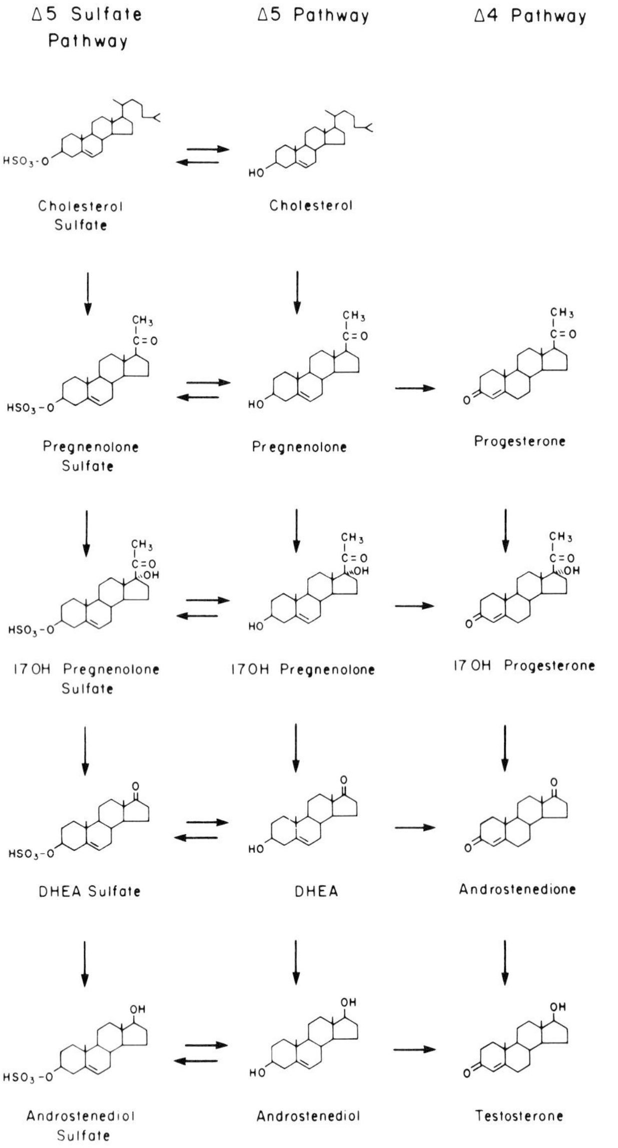

Cholesterol Sulfate

Cholesterol sulfate (CS) has been identified in considerable abundance in plasma, urine, seminal fluid, feces, gallstones, aortic plaques, and cell membranes.[10–12] CS is among the least soluble of the 3β-hydroxysteroid sulfates and can by virtue of its amphiphilic nature act as a detergent and form micelles or mixed micelles in aqueous solution. Normal plasma contains 150 to 350 μg/dl CS, most of which is associated with low density lipoprotein (LDL).[14] Very large amounts of CS in plasma can alter the electrophoretic charge of plasma LDL, but there is no evidence that this affects the interaction of LDL with its receptor. However, Williams et al. have shown that cholesterol sulfate is a very potent inhibitor of HMG-CoA reductase activity, the rate-limiting step in the de novo sterol biosynthetic pathway.[15,16] It is possible that this inhibition is important in the pathogenesis of the ichthyosis associated with steroid sulfatase deficiency and might account for the somewhat reduced level of total plasma cholesterol seen in these individuals.

Red blood cells and spermatozoa both have relatively high concentrations of cholesterol sulfate in their cell membranes under basal conditions and tend to absorb or concentrate exogenous cholesterol sulfate from the surrounding medium. It is thought that CS may stabilize membrane structure. Canine red cells incubated with CS become increasingly stable to osmotic lysis,[17–19] and patients with elevated levels of plasma and red cell cholesterol sulfate due to steroid sulfatase deficiency have modest increases in red cell osmotic stability.[13] Roberts and coworkers have shown that spermatozoa concentrate CS in the region of the acrosome.[20–22] They speculate that this CS must be removed from sperm during the process of capacitation. There is a relatively high activity of steroid sulfatase in the female genital tract which could theoretically carry out this function. However, it is of note that steroid sulfatase activity is largely, if not exclusively, intracellular (it is an integral endoplasmic reticulum protein) and is not known to be secreted into the extracellular compartment.

Cholesterol sulfate is also an important component of the stratum corneum of the epidermis.[23,24] Most of the CS found in this location is synthesized locally rather than being taken up from the plasma. As mentioned above, CS has the potential to regulate de novo sterologenesis. CS increases in concentration as a function of proximity to the epidermal surface. Most of the epidermal sterols are located in the intercellular space, where roles for them in epidermal cohesion and in water barrier function are postulated.[25,26] Solvent extraction of the epidermis modifies epidermal cohesion, stimulates transepidermal water loss, and activates de novo lipid biosynthesis.[27] The precise role of CS in mediating either cohesion or barrier function has not yet been fully clarified. However, the abnormalities in epidermal shedding and water loss seen in patients with steroid sulfatase deficiency and consequent elevation of stratum

Fig. 76-1 Interrelationships of sulfated steroids with other metabolic pathways. Δ^5 steroid sulfates are interconverted exactly as their parent Δ^5 free steroids are metabolized. For each compound, the sulfate can be converted to the free steroid by STS, and the sulfate esters can be regenerated by the sulfotransferase reaction. Δ^5 steroids can be transformed to Δ^4 steroids in some tissues by the action of 3β-hydroxysteroid dehydrogenase. Testosterone can potentially be derived either via the Δ^5 or the Δ^4 pathway.

corneum CS levels suggest that CS may be an important physiological regulator in vivo. A variety of models have been put forth to explain the ichthyosis that is invariably associated with steroid sulfatase deficiency. It has been suggested that the accumulation of CS in steroid sulfatase–deficient patients alters epidermal cohesion through changes in ionic properties or in thermal transition properties of the stratum corneum. Additional studies are needed to clarify the precise relationship between sterol metabolism and epidermal development and function.

Dehydroepiandrosterone Sulfate

Dehydroepiandrosterone sulfate (DHEAS) is another quantitatively important sulfated steroid. It has a clear role as a precursor for estrogen production during human pregnancies, and may be important in the overall metabolism of androgen by the testis as well. It is the most abundant secretory product of the human adrenal gland. DHEAS is present at relatively high levels in cord blood but rapidly diminishes in concentration during the first few months of life. Plasma levels begin to rise again 1 to 2 years prior to the onset of puberty.[28–30] Adult production rates of DHEAS are on the order of 6 to 10 mg/day. Although an arteriovenous difference in DHEAS concentration across the testis can be demonstrated,[31] studies of surgically adrenalectomized patients and subjects with exogenously induced adrenal suppression confirm that most of the circulating plasma DHEAS is derived from adrenal secretion. Paralleling the age-related decline in adrenal function in general, DHEAS levels are reduced in aged patients. In addition to a number of more clearly defined roles, DHEAS may be important in the regulation of caloric expenditure and in longevity. This proposal has attracted considerable attention for DHEAS, both in the lay press and in the scientific literature.

DHEAS secreted by the maternal adrenal glands early in pregnancy and by the fetal adrenal glands later in gestation appears to be the precursor for the very large amounts of estrogen produced in normal human pregnancies (Fig. 76-2).[32,33]

When pregnant women are given ACTH, augmentation of estrogen production is observed, and when maternal adrenal glands are suppressed by dexamethasone, estrogen production diminishes.[34] Isolated fetal adrenal hypoplasia or fetal adrenal hypoplasia associated with anencephaly impairs DHEAS availability and leads to diminished estrogen production. Administration of exogenous DHEAS loads to pregnant women stimulates estrogen biosynthesis.[35] DHEAS which traverses the fetal compartment is subject to 16 hydroxylation by the fetal liver and can ultimately be converted to estriol.

The principal site of conversion of DHEAS to estrogen is probably the placenta and, specifically, the syncytiotrophoblast.[36–38] This metabolic transformation requires desulfation of DHEAS prior to aromatization to estrogen. The placenta contains very high levels of both steroid sulfatase and aromatase activities, and both seem to localize to the endoplasmic reticulum of the outer syncytiotrophoblast layer (Salido and Shapiro, unpublished). Perfused placentas can efficiently carry out desulfation and aromatization whether the DHEAS is supplied to the maternal surface (intervillous space) or via the umbilical circulation. The mechanism and kinetics of steroid transport across the placenta still require further investigation. However, the nearly complete inability of placentas which are genetically deficient in STS to support estrogen production is one of the strongest pieces of evidence regarding the importance of steroid sulfatase in estrogen production.

DHEAS may also play a significant role in androgen metabolism. Since the half-life of DHEAS in plasma is considerably greater than the half-life of DHEA, and as DHEAS is present at about 1000 times the concentration of DHEA, continual desulfation of DHEAS may ensure a basal level of DHEA in plasma in between the episodic bursts that characterize DHEA secretion.[39] Circulating DHEAS could also be a potential precursor of testosterone via the sequence DHEAS→DHEA→androstenedione→testosterone (Fig. 76-1). Several investigators have attempted to assess the hormone flux through this pathway. MacDonald and Chapdelaine found that 3 to 12 percent of an administered dose of [³H]DHEAS was converted to urinary testosterone glucuronide.[40,41] However, it is possible that metabolism of DHEAS→testosterone

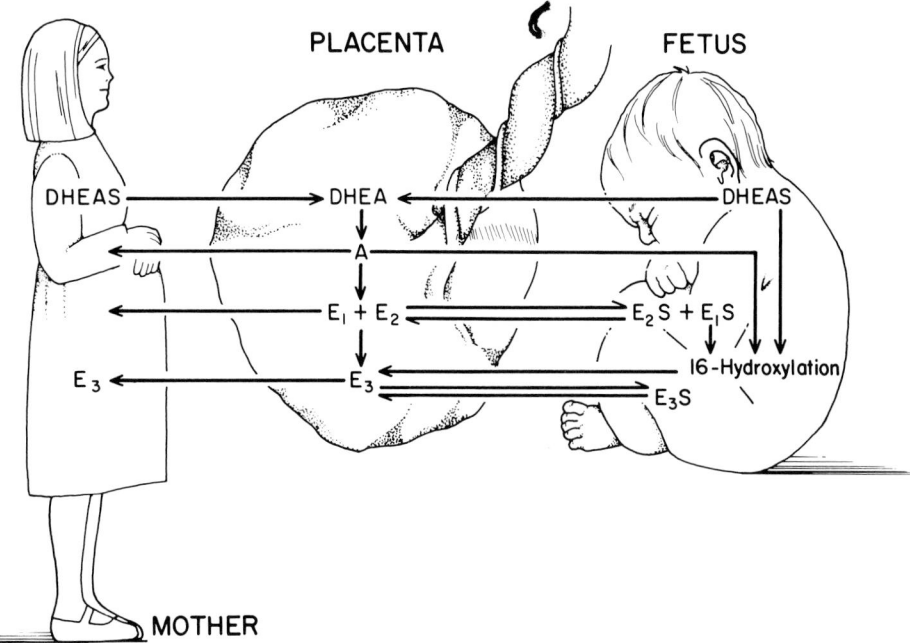

Fig. 76-2 Schematic outline of fetal-maternal-placental estrogen biosynthesis. Total estrogen production increases several-hundred fold during the course of a normal pregnancy. The primary substrates for this biosynthetic activity are C_{19} steroids, particularly DHEA, 16 OH-DHEA, and their sulfates. Earlier in pregnancy, DHEAS supplied by the maternal adrenals is important; later in gestation, fetally derived DHEAS and 16 OH-DHEAS are most significant. These precursors are supplied to the placenta, where they are hydrolyzed by steroid sulfatase and metabolized by 3β-hydroxysteroid dehydrogenase, Δ^5-isomerase, and aromatase enzyme systems to give rise to estrogens. The estrogen present in largest quantities in normal pregnancies is estriol. E_1 = estrone, E_2 = estriol.

glucuronide occurs entirely within the liver, and thus no net flux of DHEAS into circulating, biologically active, free testosterone would exist. Horton and Tait administered labeled DHEA to experimental subjects and found that less than 1 percent of circulating testosterone was derived from DHEA in males and less than 15 percent in females.[42] The results of these studies plus determinations of testosterone levels in adrenalectomized patients make it unlikely that adrenally secreted, circulating DHEAS is a quantitatively important precursor for testosterone biosynthesis.

The possibility that DHEAS and other sulfated steroids are entirely intratesticular intermediaries in the testosterone biosynthetic pathway has also been considered (Fig. 76-1).[43-52] Testicular homogenates contain substantial amounts of a number of C_{19} and C_{21} sulfated steroids. In addition, these homogenates can convert labeled DHEAS to testosterone. Furthermore, administration of human chorionic gonadatropin stimulates secretion by the testis of some sulfated steroids and increases the activity of several of the enzymes involved in these pathways. For these reasons, the Δ^5-3β-hydroxysteroid sulfates have been thought to be important intermediates in testosterone synthesis. On the other hand, to the extent to which the Δ^4 pathway of progesterone→17-hydroxyprogesterone→androstenedione→testosterone predominates, sulfated steroids may not be of significant quantitative importance. Supporting this latter model is the finding that patients with inherited steroid sulfatase deficiency have normal testosterone, FSH, and LH values; are normally virilized; and have normal fertility (to be discussed below).[52-55] Detailed understanding of the role of steroid sulfates in steroidogenesis will ultimately require knowledge of the anatomic compartments in which these reactions take place. Hormone levels in these endocrine glands and target tissues are difficult to sample, and plasma steady state levels and the metabolism of labeled tracers given intravenously may not reflect what is taking place at a tissue level. Furthermore, species differences and possible ontogenetic differences in hormone metabolism may further confound work in this area.

STEROID SULFATASE

Most mammalian tissues have a 3β-hydroxysteroid sulfate sulfatase activity which has a neutral pH optimum, and is capable of hydrolyzing the sulfate ester bonds of a variety of sulfated sterols.[5,56] In addition, sulfate ester hydrolase activity against a variety of artificial chromogenic and fluorogenic compounds can be observed. The latter are conventionally referred to as *arylsulfatases*. Steroid sulfatase is one of the arylsulfatases. Several arylsulfatases are clearly distinct from one another since they can be independently purified, they have unique pH optima, they have different susceptibilities to inhibitors, and they are genetically separable, as they map to different chromosomes and have their function disrupted by distinct genetic disorders. Arylsulfatases A and B are lysosomal in their subcellular localization, have acidic pH optima, are inhibited by SO_4^{2-}, PO_4^{3-}, and Ba^{2+}, and are deficient in metachromatic leukodystrophy and mucopolysaccharidosis VI (Maroteaux-Lamy syndrome), respectively (see Chaps. 69 and 61). Both hydrolyze nitrocatechol sulfate and 4-methylumbelliferyl sulfate. The natural substrate for arylsulfatase A is galactosyl sulfatide and that for arylsulfatase B is the *N*-acetylgalacto-

samine-4-sulfate linkage in dermatan sulfate. In contrast, arylsulfatase C is microsomal in location, has a neutral-to-alkaline pH optimum, is inhibited preferentially by CN^-, and is deficient in X-linked ichthyosis (steroid sulfatase deficiency). Arylsulfatase C will hydrolyze *p*-nitrophenylsulfate and 4-methylumbelliferyl sulfate at the appropriate pH and ionic conditions.

Steroid sulfatase is an integral endoplasmic reticulum protein as shown by differential centrifugation and by immunoelectron microscopy (Salido and Shapiro, unpublished). STS can be solubilized and released from the microsomal fraction by a variety of detergents. Detergents have proved necessary to maintain solubility during all purification procedures. Several groups have reported the partial purification[57-60] or the preparation of apparently homogeneous STS from human placentas.[61,62] The active enzyme is a multimer of identical subunits, each with a molecular weight of approximately 63 kDa. The minimum size aggregate that has activity appears to be a 126-kDa dimer (by gel-filtration analysis). A variety of other molecular weights for the native enzyme have been suggested including an estimate of 533 kDa achieved by neutron inactivation analysis[59] and 1000 kDa, by chromatography.[59a] The enzyme appears to be a glycoprotein since it binds to concanavalin A–sepharose and can be specifically eluted.[62] Furthermore, the purified enzyme protein shows a reduction in subunit molecular weight of about 4 kDa following endoglycosidase treatment. Finally, the amino acid sequence of the protein predicted from the cDNA sequence includes three potential *N*-linked glycosylation sites as well as a number of possible *O*-linked glycosylation sites.[62] The enzyme is remarkably stable to heat, alterations of pH, and exposure to urea. SDS-PAGE experiments indicate that there are no intermolecular disulfide bonds. The enzyme has no apparent cofactor requirements and is unaffected by divalent cation concentration.

Using antibodies prepared against the purified enzyme and partial amino acid sequence data, cDNA clones for STS have been obtained from expression libraries.[62,64,65] Sequencing studies predict a mature protein of 492 amino acids.[62] There is a 22-amino-acid hydrophobic signal sequence which is probably cleaved after translocation across the endoplasmic reticulum membrane. There is a relatively long core hydrophobic region as well as some potential membrane-spanning domains. Northern blot analysis revealed mRNA transcripts of 2.7, 5.2, and 7.2 kilobases (kb) in different tissues, and the size differences seem to be the result of alternate poly(A) addition site usage with consequent variation in the length of the 3' untranslated message.[62] Whether or not these various transcripts have functionally different properties remains to be established. The STS cDNA is encoded in 10 genomic exons separated by 9 introns, which together span approximately 146 kb of X-chromosome DNA (Yen and Shapiro, unpublished).

Several investigators have questioned the number of discrete steroid sulfatases which might exist and which could be necessary to hydrolyze the full range of structurally disparate steroid sulfates.[56,57,66-70] Kinetic data have indicated that many sulfated steroids inhibit each other's hydrolysis but they do so noncompetitively, as assessed from Lineweaver-Burk plots. In addition, the relative activities toward different substrates are not always concomitantly enriched during enzyme purification, and the pH optima and thermal stabilities of enzyme activity differ for various substrates.[57] These data should be viewed with some caution. First, most of these studies were conducted using relatively crude microsomal preparations or partially purified enzyme. In such impure systems, there may be a variety of other factors which affect apparent activities. Furthermore, a number of the substrates used have limited solubility and may in fact exist as micelles in aqueous media. There are a number of compelling reasons to believe that all of the steroid sulfatase activities are associated with a single gene product. First, all of the activities copurify to homogeneity and have never been physically separated (Shapiro, unpublished). Second, antibodies (including several monoclonal antibodies) raised against STS precipitate all of the enzyme activities (Ref. 62, and Shapiro, unpublished). Third, all of the STS activities map to the same region of the X-chromosome short arm in somatic cell genetic experiments. Fourth, an entirely intrageneic deletion of the STS gene in a patient (see below) and all other mutations described for STS are associated with a loss of all of the various enzyme activities. Fifth, and finally, transfection of a mammalian expression plasmid containing a full-length STS cDNA construct confers all of the 3β-hydroxysteroid sulfatase activities upon recipient cells.[62] Thus, it is highly probable that this single enzyme has a fairly broad substrate specificity with regard to the steroid sulfates it will hydrolyze. On the other hand, there is some degree of specificity in that 3α-hydroxysteroid sulfates, vitamin D sulfate, and tyrosine sulfate cannot serve as substrates (Ref. 71, and Bergner and Shapiro, unpublished).

GENETICS OF STEROID SULFATASE

In addition to the interest focused on steroid sulfatase due to its role in steroid metabolism and the inborn errors of metabolism characterized by STS deficiency, much excitement has been engendered by the elucidation of some unique aspects of the genetics of the STS system. With the recognition that mutations at the human STS locus could be ascertained by the readily visible phenotype of ichthyosis (to be described below), it became possible to easily identify families segregating inherited STS deficiency.[72,73] The pattern of transmission of this phenotype was typical of an X-linked condition. This inherited disorder is relatively frequent in most populations and is not associated with any significant reduction in genetic fitness.[74,75] Therefore, several large, multigenerational families with this genodermatosis were already well known and had been the object of extensive linkage investigations.[76,77] In addition to clear X-linked inheritance of STS deficiency, strong evidence for linkage with the polymorphic blood group antigen Xg was obtained. The aggregate lod score at a $\Theta_{max} = 0.10$ is in excess of 17.[78-83] Thus, from this formal genetic analysis, it seemed clear that the gene *responsible for STS deficiency* is located on the human X chromosome. For a time, however, it remained a possibility that the structural gene for STS mapped elsewhere in the genome. This was of particular concern since an autosomal gene mutation had been described which produces multiple sulfatase deficiency (MSD) with marked reduction in activity of STS and a number of other sulfatases.[84-86]

Mapping the STS Gene

A variety of approaches have been utilized to map the STS gene to the distal tip of the X-chromosome short arm (Fig.

76-3). Linkage of the putative STS structural gene to Xg had already been established, and the latter locus was thought to reside near the distal end of Xp. Somatic cell genetic studies provided extensive verification of this assignment. STS activity can be visualized in agarose/acrylamide gels by reaction under appropriate conditions with the fluorogenic substrate 4-methylumbelliferyl sulfate.[87] In preparation for the mapping studies, methods were established which distinguish rodent and human steroid sulfatases electrophoretically. However, it was soon observed that several permanent rodent cell lines, most notably murine A9 cells, were completely deficient in endogenous STS activity. In the case of A9 cells, this could be the result of their derivation from STS-deficient mice of the C3H/An strain (see below). In any event, standard somatic cell fusion studies with hybrids segregating intact human X chromosomes or portions of the human X chromosome derived from X/autosome translocation chromosomes permitted the assignment of the STS structural gene to Xp22.3→pter.[87,88] This conclusion has been verified by more refined mapping using X/Y translocation chromosomes with very distal X rearrangements[89,90] and by deletion mapping studies of patients who were found to be nullisomic for portions of distal Xp.[91] All of these observations have been confirmed by analysis of genomic DNA from the relevant cell lines and hybrids with STS molecular probes.[62] The human STS gene is flanked distally on Xp by at least one functional gene (MIC2) and by loci revealed by several cloned anonymous DNA segments.[90] Finally, the chromosomal assignment of the STS gene is further verified by mapping data for the STS gene in the mouse and by gene dosage studies which indicate a sex-specific difference (XX>XY) in gene expression.

Fig. 76-3 Diagrammatic representation of the genetic organization of the human Y chromosome and the X-chromosome short arm. There are X-unique and Y-unique areas as well as the segments of homology at the telomeres referred to as the *pseudoautosomal region* (stippled). The pseudoautosomal region contains sequences referred to as 29C1, 113D, 601, and MIC2. The first three of these are detected by hybridization with "anonymous" DNA probes which can recognize restriction fragment length polymorphisms at each of these sites. MIC2 is a functional locus that encodes a cell surface antigen. The MIC2 gene on the X chromosome escapes inactivation. Xg and STS lie outside (hatched area) the true pseudoautosomal regions but also appear to escape regulation by X inactivation. There is an STS pseudogene on the long arm of the Y chromosome. This may have arisen by a pericentric inversion of an ancestral Y chromosome. TDF is the putative testis determining factor.

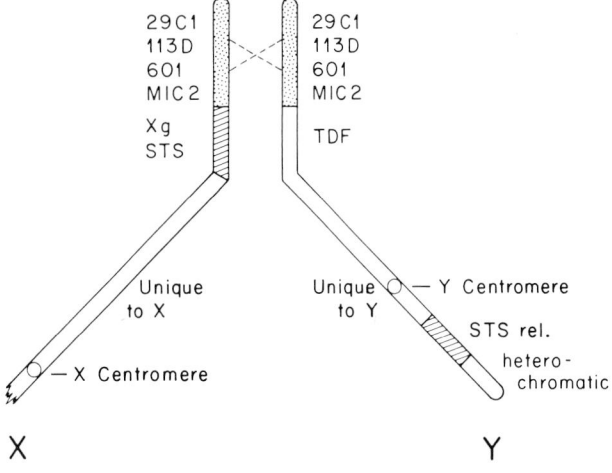

STS Escapes X-Chromosome Inactivation

X-chromosome inactivation is an example of a developmentally programmed pattern of regulation of early embryonic gene expression.[92] This phenomenon has been extensively documented and studied and occurs in all somatic cells of female mammals. The inactivation of one of the two X chromosomes in normal females results in dosage compensation (as compared to XY males) for the expression of X-linked gene products, and females who are detectably heterozygous for any X-linked locus are rendered mosaic at a cellular level. This mechanism is significant when considering the range of phenotypic expression in females who are heterozygous for deleterious human mutations. X inactivation has been used to establish the clonal or multicellular origins of a number of human tumors.

In X-aneuploid individuals, all Xs seem to be inactivated except one. Studies of human triploid conceptions suggest that the X/autosome ratio may be important in establishing the number of Xs to remain active, as two Xs are often observed to be transcriptionally active and early replicating in such embryos.[93,94] Normally, the X that is inactivated in any given embryonic cell is random, but once established, it is stably inherited by all mitotic descendants throughout the life of the organism.[92] Furthermore, the inactive X seems to replicate its DNA late in the S phase of the cell cycle; it is relatively heterochromatic; and it can be seen condensed in the interphase nucleus as the familiar Barr body. Genetic and cytologic evidence suggests that X inactivation is a chromosomal event which may be initiated from a unique site. After propagation of the inactivation signal along the X chromosome, inactivation seems to be rigidly maintained through many cell doublings by a process that acts at a local gene level and involves DNA methylation (reviewed in Ref. 95). There are probably no unique structural features that distinguish X-encoded genes and render them "inactivatable," as it is clear that autosomal genes translocated to an inactive X chromosome can be inactivated as well by spreading from contiguous regions.[96] The biology and molecular genetics of X-chromosome inactivation have recently been extensively reviewed.[92]

It has long been suspected that there might be portions of the X chromosome that are not inactivated. If it were the case that some X-encoded genes normally escape inactivation, then it might be possible to explain some of the abnormalities observed clinically in X-chromosome-aneuploid states.[97] If one of the two X chromosomes in normal female somatic cells was completely inactivated, then one would anticipate that there would be no genetic difference between XY males with one copy of X-chromosome material, 45,X Turner syndrome individuals with one copy of X-chromosome material, and normal XX females who have two copies of X-chromosome material with one set of X-encoded genes inactivated. Similarly, if the second X in Klinefelter (47,XXY) individuals were completely inactivated, then one would not anticipate the clinical abnormalities characteristic of this condition. Finally, based on genetic and evolutionary considerations, it seems likely that there is a small group of genes which have functional counterparts on both the X and Y chromosomes.[70,97,98] Such genes may well have evolved in such a way as not to require X inactivation for dosage compensation. Genes that are equally expressed from the X and from the Y would result in equivalent dosage between males and females only if the X-encoded locus escaped X inactivation in XX female somatic cells.

There are now reasonably good data supporting the lack of inactivation of three distinct human X-encoded loci, the Xg blood locus, the STS locus, and a gene called MIC2 (Fig. 76-3). The functional Xg and STS genes in human beings are strictly X-linked, while MIC2, in fact, does have transcriptionally active homologues on both the X and Y chromosomes.[95]

Xg antigen (Xg^a) is present exclusively on the surface of erythrocytes, and so its expression cannot be manipulated in somatic cell systems. Neither the biochemical nature of the antigen nor the function of the encoded gene product (e.g., glycosyl transferase versus protein antigen) is known. Nonetheless, a good deal of data suggest that the gene is not subject to X inactivation.[95] The presence or absence of Xg^a is a highly polymorphic trait that clearly segregates as an X-linked marker in pedigree studies.[99] As mentioned before, in most females heterozygous for discernible alleles at an X-linked locus, it is possible to demonstrate a mosaic cellular population. Therefore, it was anticipated that female Xg^a/Xg heterozygotes would have two discernible populations of erythrocytes, one $Xg^a(+)$ and the other $Xg^a(-)$. However, no such heterogeneity in cell phenotype was found in spite of the fact that artificial mixtures of $Xg^a(+)$ and $Xg^a(-)$ red cells can be readily separated by immunologic techniques.[100] One potential explanation for these findings is that Xg^a is added to erythrocytes at some late stage in development and is not the direct result of gene expression in erythroid progenitors. However, it appears that Xg^a *is* expressed in a cell-autonomous manner. Evidence in support of this statement comes from a human blood chimeric twin pair in which each twin had circulating cells which were blood type O and others which were AB. This permitted easy separation of these genetically distinct cell populations. The O cells were found to be $Xg^a(+)$ and the AB cells were $Xg^a(-)$. Thus $Xg^a(+)$ and $Xg^a(-)$ cells can coexist in the same circulation.[101]

Further evidence for failure of inactivation of the Xg locus comes from studying several women who were doubly heterozygous for Xg^a expression and other X-linked genes. One individual, who was a carrier of X-linked sideroblastic anemia, had two populations of erythrocytes which could be physically separated on the basis of size.[102] This made possible the identification of red cells derived from progenitors in some of which the paternal X was active and in others of which the maternally derived X chromosome was active. Since the subject's father was $Xg^a(-)$, it might have been expected that those erythroid progenitors with the maternal X inactivated would have produced $Xg^a(-)$ cells. However, it was observed that both populations of red blood cells were positive for Xg^a expression. Similar and convincing data come from the work of Fialkow et al., who studied three women heterozygous for hypoxanthine guanine phosphoribosyl transferase deficiency (they were mothers of Lesch-Nyhan patients) and for Xg^a positivity.[103] By examination of the pedigrees and knowledge of the distribution of enzyme-positive red cells, it was possible to provide strong evidence that the Xg locus was not subject to inactivation. In spite of this rather compelling evidence, some doubt has remained about the status of Xg inactivation. This is because Xg^a expression cannot be readily quantitated, because the agglutination assay is somewhat subjective, and because the antiserums available for use as reagents are of low titer and in short supply. Furthermore, it has been suggested that Xg may in fact be inactivated when it is positioned on a structurally abnormal X chromosome.[104] Once again, these questions could not be resolved using more rigorous somatic cell genetic approaches due to lack of expression of Xg^a in hybrid cells.

The linkage of STS and Xg and the ability to detect STS expression in interspecific hybrids made it appropriate to study the inactivation of the STS locus. At least three lines of evidence support the conclusion that STS does not undergo full X inactivation. These include fibroblast cloning studies, somatic cell genetic experiments, and gene dosage determinations. When fibroblast cultures from females who were obligate heterozygotes for STS null alleles were diluted and single-cell-derived clones were isolated, all clones expressed significant amounts of STS activity.[105,106] This is in contrast to the anticipated recovery of fully STS deficient clones expected if the STS locus did undergo inactivation. A number of the women studied were also heterozygous for glucose-6-phosphate dehydrogenase electrophoretic or activity variants. This permitted the distinction of clones in which the paternal X was active from those in which the maternal X was the active chromosome. Furthermore, it was possible through pedigree analysis to assign the phase relationship between the two X chromosomes in each subject and the STS(+) and STS(−) alleles. Carefully controlled measurements indicated that there was slight repression of expression of the intact STS allele when on an inactive X compared to its expression when on the active X chromosome.[106] These studies provided the first indication that STS genes could continue to be expressed from an otherwise inactive X chromosome.

Further support for this model comes from studies in which inactive human X chromosomes were segregated from any active X genetic material in murine × human hybrid cell lines. This can be accomplished through appropriate selective culture conditions. It is interesting to note that the inactive X chromosome in such hybrids continues to demonstrate the properties of late DNA replication and extinction of gene expression even with this unusual heterologous background and even when the inactive X is separated from most of the human genetic complement.[107]

The preparation of somatic cell hybrid lines retaining only the inactive human X chromosome has facilitated other studies regarding X inactivation.[108] These cell lines have been used to isolate inactive X-chromosome DNA for molecular comparisons with active X DNA. Such studies have supported the role of DNA methylation in the maintenance of X inactivation. Comparison of digestion patterns of genes on active and inactive Xs generated by methylation-sensitive restriction enzymes has revealed clear differences.[109] Furthermore, DNA purified from such cell lines and separated from any associated chromosomal proteins is not competent in a gene transfer assay, which verifies that a fundamental modification of DNA structure has occurred during X inactivation.[110–114] Cell hybrids with inactive X chromosomes also provide a system that can be experimentally perturbed in efforts to reveal the mechanism of X inactivation. Agents that impair DNA methylation can efficiently reactivate gene expression from an otherwise quiescent X.[112,115] This reactivation seems to occur at the level of individual genes rather than of larger transcription units and results in the reestablishment of competence of the demethylated gene in the gene transfer assay. All of these results support the role of DNA methylation in the maintenance of X inactivation and argue against any irreversible gene rearrangement in the genesis of this process. These experiments have been made possible by the isolation of somatic cell hybrids

retaining inactive X chromosomes which are conveniently recognized and monitored by STS expression. The persistent expression of human STS in cell lines that contain only an "inactive" X chromosome provides the second major piece of evidence indicating that STS escapes inactivation. These cell lines also provide a tool for testing any other X-chromosome genes of interest to see whether or not they are subject to inactivation. In this way it has been shown that the MIC2 gene on the X also escapes X inactivation.[116]

A final line of evidence supporting the lack of inactivation of the human STS locus derives from gene dosage studies. Although data from X-aneuploid individuals have not provided consistent results, there is a clear difference in STS activity between normal males and females that has been documented in a variety of tissues and by a number of laboratories. The ratio of female to male activities ranges from 1.6 to 1.8 in fibroblasts, leukocytes, and placenta. More careful quantitation of STS levels in fibroblasts from obligate heterozygotes is consistent with the view that some partial repression of STS expression may in fact occur on the inactive X chromosome.[14,70,117–122]

Genes on the X chromosome that escape inactivation might conceivably do so through one of two general mechanisms. Either the position of these genes at the distal X short arm in some way protects them from being inactivated, or there are some intrinsic aspects of the individual gene structure (e.g., promoter, etc.) which render them resistant to X inactivation. Current data would seem to favor the latter, gene-specific model. This conclusion derives from studies of patients with X-chromosome translocations and inversions. When autosomal segments are positioned at the distal end of Xp, they may be inactivated if the X chromosome to which they are attached undergoes such regulation.[96] Thus, other genes translocated to a position comparable to that of STS may be inactivated. Conversely, when the STS and MIC2 loci are relocated to a site wihin the long arm of the X and are flanked by other DNA sequences that are inactivated, the STS and MIC2 genes continue to be expressed.[123] Thus, these two genes appear to escape inactivation by a mechanism independent of their chromosomal location.

The Pseudoautosomal Region of the X and Y Chromosomes

It is generally believed that the X and Y chromosomes evolved from an ancestral homologous chromosome pair.[97,98] Some differential functions related to sex determination then became localized to the X, the Y, or both. Over evolutionary time, there has probably been very efficient selection for alterations that would suppress recombination between the X and the Y so that the sex-determining and associated genes would not "inadvertently" be transposed to the wrong sex chromosome by crossing over or other genetic exchange. The mechanism of this recombination suppression has probably involved a number of inversions, deletions, and other gross chromosomal alterations that had the end effect of isolating the X and Y. When these two chromosomes ceased exchanging DNA during meiosis, they were free to rapidly diverge from one another. There appear to be few functional genes on the mammalian Y chromosome. Because X inactivation equalizes gene expression of X-encoded genes in XX and XY individuals and since any mutations of the Y-encoded copy of genes shared by the X would be "covered" functionally, the Y has been freed of selective constraints and has developed extensive deletions and other mutations.

For more than 50 years, however, it has been predicted that the X and Y chromosomes would retain a segment of persistent homology.[124] In some way, the two sex chromosomes must recognize one another in order to pair during meiotic division in spermatogenesis. It is believed that actual chiasma formation is required to ensure proper segregation of chromosome pairs and to avoid nondisjunction. Such a region of the X and Y has been identified in both the human[125–128] and the mouse[129–134] sex chromosomes and is referred to as the *pseudoautosomal region*. The pseudoautosomal regions of the human X and Y are located at the distal ends of their respective short arms (Fig. 76-3). In the mouse, this area corresponds to the telomeres of the single chromosome arms of the X and Y chromosomes. Cytogenetic demonstration of chiasmata and synaptonemal complexes in these regions complements the more recently obtained genetic and molecular evidence for a pseudoautosomal region. By definition, pseudoautosomal DNA sequences should be identical at the corresponding loci of the X and Y because of the relatively frequent recombination which would transfer sequences between these two chromosomes in succeeding generations. Since a given allele at a pseudoautosomal locus might be on the X in one generation and on the Y in another, such markers would demonstrate either partial sex linkage or no sex linkage at all upon pedigree analysis depending on how telomeric the marker is and therefore how frequently recombination is observed relative to the X-unique and Y-unique portions of the chromosomes. Such frequently recombining genes could readily be confused with autosomally inherited loci; hence the derivation of the term *pseudoautosomal*.[98]

A number of noncoding DNA segments have been used to identify pseudoautosomal loci in human beings. These sequences are identical in males and females, map to the distal tip of Xp and Yp, and can be used to detect restriction fragment length polymorphisms (RFLP). Study of the segregation of RFLPs in families documents a gradient of recombination increasing from proximal to distal sites such that the most telomeric loci show no sex linkage whatsoever.[128] Comparison of recombination frequencies using these RFLPs in XX and XY individuals indicates a tenfold increased recombination in the latter as compared to the former and a very high rate of recombination relative to physical distance between markers in the XY subjects. It seems that there must be an obligatory recombination event in any functional male meiotic division, and the recombination is constrained to occur within a relatively small region of homology between the X and the Y. In contrast, recombination events between the two Xs in female meiosis can occur anywhere along the length of the X chromosomes. The identification of functional genes which are transcriptionally active in the pseudoautosomal region has been more difficult. In humans, the only known example is the previously described MIC2 locus.[127,135] An identical MIC2 gene is present on X and Y and encodes a ubiquitously detectable cell surface antigen called 12E7. 12E7 is identified by reaction with a monoclonal antibody.[136] The function of the 12E7 protein is not known, but it is species-specific and is found on all cells that have been surveyed in humans except for spermatozoa. STS is presumed to be located relatively close to MIC2, but proximal to it, on a segment of the X chromosome that is not homologous to Yp. No other functional pseudoautosomal genes have been identified in human

beings, but one might speculate that some of the genes that are responsible for the Turner syndrome phenotype might be located there. This conclusion is supported by the finding of short stature and other abnormalities in patients monosomic for the pseudoautosomal region as the result of terminal X deletions or unbalanced X/Y translocations.[137] In the mouse, three pseudoautosomal loci have been identified. These include the site of a retroviral insertion in a transgenic mouse strain,[133,134] the sex-reversed (Sxr) gene that is involved in aberrant sex determination,[129,130] and the murine STS gene.[131–133] The mouse pseudoautosomal region will be considered in more detail below.

From the above discussion, it would seem that there may be particularly frequent recombination occurring in the pseudoautosomal region, giving rise to a far greater frequency of crossing over per unit physical length than is the case for most of the rest of the genome. While these exchange events are supposed to be confined to the homologous segments of the X and Y chromosomes, there is growing evidence that occasional recombination can be initiated in nearby regions. The most dramatic clinical consequence of aberrant X-Y exchange is seen in XX males. A large number of such patients have now been examined and found to have sustained transfer of some Y-chromosome-unique material, including the so-called testis determining factor gene (TDF), to their paternally derived X chromosome.[138–145] The breakpoint in the Y chromosome in these individuals must, by definition, be proximal to the TDF locus in the Y-unique region. Detailed study of a number of XX males suggests that TDF is very close to the boundary with the pseudoautosomal region. The corresponding breakpoint on the X chromosome creating the molecular Y-to-X translocation can occur within the X pseudoautosomal region or more proximally on the X. In one case, it has been proposed that the X-chromosome breakpoint was located proximal to the STS locus and resulted in the loss of the STS gene from the TDF-bearing X chromosome.[146] In a larger sample of XX males studied by genomic blotting rather than activity measurements, it seems that such proximal breakpoints must not be very common in XX males (Stern and Shapiro, unpublished).

Genetics of STS in Mice and Other Mammals

A number of investigators have endeavored to further clarify the genetics of STS in other mammals, and several of these studies may well shed light on the organization and regulation of the human STS gene. An insightful observation was made by Balazs et al., who noted that the murine A9 cell line that had been so useful for somatic cell genetic studies because it was deficient in STS activity was derived from the C_3H/An inbred mouse strain. When tissues of these animals were examined, they were found to be essentially devoid of STS activity as well.[147] Subsequently, other investigators documented interstrain variation in STS activity in several other inbred mouse lines, although none of them were nearly as deficient in STS as the C_3H/An.[148–152] In contrast to human patients with genetic defects of STS, the C_3H/An mice are healthy, have normal skin and reproductive capacity, and have only twofold increases in plasma cholesterol sulfate levels compared to other mice (Bergner and Shapiro, unpublished). In initial test crosses and backcrosses, these STS variations behaved like single gene Mendelian traits, but showed no sex linkage and so were assumed to represent autosomal genes affecting STS activity. However, further experiments suggest that the mouse STS gene in fact is a true pseudoautosomal gene with frequent recombination between functional X and Y loci. Keitges et al. crossed C₃H/An STS(−) males with XO (fertile in the mouse), STS(+) females.[131] All of the XX and all of the XY progeny that resulted had STS activity. These animals would have received the maternal STS(+) X chromosome. However, one-third of the animals obtained were karyotypically XO, and all of these were STS-deficient. Their X was paternally derived. Thus, the STS gene must be on the mouse X chromosome. This conclusion is further supported by the earlier finding of a 2:1 ratio of STS enzyme activity in oocytes of XX as compared to XO mice.[153] The fact that heterozygous X/Y, STS(+)/STS(−) or X/Y, STS(−)/STS(+) mice when backcrossed to X/X, STS(−)/STS(−) females produced both STS(+) and STS(−) males and both STS(+) and STS(−) females strongly suggests the presence of a functional STS gene on the Y chromosome which is frequently mobilized to the X and vice versa. More recently, formal segregation analysis of STS with the other murine pseudoautosomal markers, MOV-15, and Sxr, demonstrates linkage with both. Repeated comparison of STS activity in several tissues of XX and XY mice shows there to be no sex difference, so STS must not be subject to X inactivation in the female mouse.[152,154]

Additional comparative research on STS expression has been carried out in the wood lemming,[155] the root vole,[156] and several marsupials.[151–159] In the wood lemming, STS activity parallels the number of X chromosomes present, providing indirect evidence for X linkage and escape from inactivation in this species. In the root vole, STS activity is higher in the male than in the female for reasons that are not clear. Somatic cell genetic methods have been applied in attempts to map STS in kangaroos and in dasyurid marsupials. The investigators failed to demonstrate X linkage. However, there are two possible explanations for such results. The first is technical, in that marsupial chromosomes when placed in a rodent cell background frequently undergo fragmentation and rearrangement. Thus, the apparent loss of STS could be artifactual, as the locus was not specifically assigned to any of the autosomes. The second possibility is that in these most distantly related mammals, the STS gene locus is truly autosomal. There should not be any significant selective advantage for a locus to be situated on an autosomal pair as opposed to the pseudoautosomal region of the sex chromosomes, where the genes would escape X inactivation and be free to recombine. In summary, there is a clear contrast in the organization of the STS gene(s) in mice and humans (Table 76-1). The mouse has functional loci on X and Y and equivalent dosage in males and females, indicating a lack of X inactivation at this locus. Humans have only an X-encoded functional locus that does not normally undergo recombination with the Y chromosome, and humans have a female/male activity ratio greater than 1 due to

lack of a functional Y gene and escape from X inactivation in females. Recent molecular studies of human STS sequences help to clarify this apparent disparity.

Structure and Organization of the Human STS Gene

The availability of human STS cDNA clones has made it possible to characterize the genomic organization of the STS gene. A representation of the X-encoded gene has been obtained in overlapping phage genomic clones and spans approximately 146 kb (Yen and Shapiro, unpublished). Sequences corresponding to the cDNA have been localized to 10 individual exons, with the longest intron being about 37 kb in length. Surprisingly, sequences that cross-hybridize to the STS cDNA were found on the human Y chromosome as well.[62] Much of this Y region has also been cloned, and the locus has been mapped to the long arm (Fig. 76-3) by both somatic cell genetic and deletion mapping methods (Y deletion interval 6). The Y locus is a pseudogene, as a number of single nucleotide changes and small deletions have created many nonsense codons. However, intron-exon boundaries have been conserved (from the X gene), and there is approximately 90 percent sequence similarity between the X and Y genes within both intron-like and exon-like areas.[160] This finding suggests that about the time the X and Y genes began to diverge from one another, the Y locus became nonfunctional, and thus the exons were freed from selective constraints and mutations could occur at an equal rate in exons and in introns. The most parsimonious explanation for all of these observations is that at an earlier point in evolution (as currently exemplified by the mouse) STS was present as a functional gene on both X and Y and that these loci exchanged readily so as to maintain sequence similarity. Due to the presence of two functional genes in both males and females, dosage compensation was not required, and so there was selection for regulatory sequences that resisted X inactivation. Later in evolution, a pericentric inversion may have relocated the Yp gene to Yq and abruptly halted pseudoautosomal exchange. The Y locus is currently in the process of degenerating in the absence of selective pressure, and the functional X gene (which is no longer pseudoautosomal) still has its ancestral regulatory sequences, which protect it from X inactivation. Further functional and phylogenetic studies will be needed to confirm or refute this scenario. Preliminary analysis of the putative STS promoter does suggest that it is similarly methylated on otherwise active or inactive X chromosomes.[160]

STEROID SULFATASE DEFICIENCY

Steroid Deficiency and Estrogen Metabolism

In 1969 France and Liggins reported studies of a single pregnancy in which estriol production was strikingly impaired despite normal growth and viability of the fetus.[161] Labor was prolonged, and after delivery placental extracts were assayed for activities of several enzymes thought to be important in estrogen biosynthesis. A specific and virtually complete absence of steroid sulfatase was found. These investigators were subsequently able to study another pregnancy in vivo by loading techniques.[162] Intravenously administered DHEAS could not be converted to estrogen in a normal fashion, while exog-

Table 76-1 Comparison of Human and Mouse Steroid Sulfatase Genetics

	Human	Mouse
X-encoded functional gene	Yes	Yes
Y-encoded functional gene	No	Yes
Exchange between X and Y homologues	No	Yes
Y-encoded pseudogene	Yes	?
Subject to X inactivation	No	No
Ratio of female/male enzyme activity	1.8:1	1:1

enous free DHEA could serve as an effective substrate. This suggested a metabolic block in the conversion of DHEAS to DHEA which was again confirmed by biochemical studies of the placenta.

During the ensuing years a number of similar cases were described in the obstetrical literature (reviewed in Refs. 163, 164). This was in part due to the growing use of radioimmunoassay determination of maternal urinary and serum estriol levels as an index of fetal-placental-maternal integrity and well-being during pregnancy. In many of these earlier cases, there was an ascertainment bias since estriol measurements were done routinely only in complicated obstetrical situations. However, with the advent of large-scale estriol screening programs, many more cases of apparent "placental" steroid sulfatase deficiency were identified, and this was a well-established clinical entity by the mid-1970s. The total 24-h urinary estrogen excretion of women carrying affected fetuses is generally less than 3 mg, and serum estriol levels are reduced to less than 10 percent of normal values controlled for gestational age.

In the initial reports of the clinical features of steroid sulfatase deficiency, a relative refractoriness to the onset of labor was noted, particularly in primigravidas (Table 76-2). Further evaluation suggests that this may be due to some difficulty in cervical effacement with concomitant prolongation of labor. In spite of the fact that many women carrying affected fetuses have required cesarian section, many have delivered vaginally as well.[165] Some women have had a history of prior pregnancy losses with death of full-term or postmature infants. A single pregnancy in which steroid sulfatase deficiency was present in a fetus due to autosomal recessive multiple sulfatase deficiency disease also involved marked impairment of estriol production.[166] Diminished maternal-fetal-placental estrogen production is also seen in substrate deficiency conditions such as fetal adrenal hypoplasia (with or without anencephaly). Infants born of pregnancies complicated by STS deficiency are usually clinically normal at birth, and their placentas lack any anatomic defects. Maternal urinary excretion of a number of sulfated steroids is abnormally elevated during the latter half of pregnancy with the 16OH-DHEAS level averaging twenty times normal.[167] DHEAS levels in amniotic fluid from affected fetuses are also strikingly increased.[168,169] In contrast, levels of DHEAS and 16OH-DHEAS are usually normal in the cord blood and urine of affected infants.[161,164,167,170]

Most of the earlier studies of STS deficiency focused on obstetrical aspects. Since cord blood and neonatal urinary steroid levels were normal in infants born of affected pregnancies, and since these children looked well clinically, it was speculated that STS deficiency was an enzymopathy that was confined to the placenta. This view changed with the development of sensitive enzyme assays that could be applied to cultured skin fibroblasts, leukocytes, and hair follicles.[171] It then became clear that STS is a generalized metabolic disturbance that affects essentially all tissues in the fetus and newborn. Furthermore, ichthyosis provided a visible phenotypic manifestation that made it clear that there was at least some postnatal impact from this inborn error of metabolism. The availability of the fibroblast assay has facilitated widespread case finding and made possible family studies that would not have been feasible if it were necessary to have placental tissue in order to recognize affected individuals. The first reports of steroid sulfatase deficiency noted both recurrence within families and the fact that all affected fetuses were males. Application of the cell culture assay to postnatally derived samples permitted the rigorous confirmation of X-linked inheritance in several families.[72]

STS Deficiency as the Cause of X-Linked Ichthyosis

Ichthyosis is a term used to describe a number of genetic and acquired skin disorders.[172] The clinical hallmark is hyperker-

Table 76-2 Clinical Abnormalities Associated with Steroid Sulfate Deficiency

Prenatally:	*Postnatally:*
Consistent features	
1. Low maternal urinary and serum estriol 2. Male fetus 3. Elevated DHEAS and 16OH-DHEAS in maternal urine and amniotic fluid 4. Absent placental 3β-hydroxysteroid sulfatase activity	1. Ichthyosis with onset from birth to 4 months 2. Corneal opacities 3. Pedigree evidence of X-linked defect 4. Increased cholesterol sulfate in plasma, red blood cells, and skin with rapidly migrating LDL 5. Absent steroid sulfatase enzyme activity
Variable features	
1. Delayed onset of labor 2. Relative refractoriness of cervical dilatation	1. Undescended testis 2. Testicular tumors? 3. Hypogonadotropic hypogonadism and anosmia 4. Mental retardation 5. Short stature 6. Chondrodysplasia punctata 7. STS gene deletion (90 percent) 8. Visible chromosome deletion or rearrangement 9. Multiple sulfatase deficiency

atosis or increased thickness of the stratum corneum (Fig. 76-4). A number of complex syndromes have been described of which ichthyosis is one component. In addition, there are distinct hereditary disorders that have been delineated in which ichthyosis is the sole feature. These include a relatively severe autosomal recessive condition known as *lamellar ichthyosis*, the somewhat milder disorder of autosomal dominant *ichthyosis vulgaris*, and *X-linked ichthyosis*. It had been known for over a hundred years that ichthyosis can segregate in some families as an X-linked trait.[173] The work of Wells, Kerr, and Jennings in the early and middle 1960s provided clear-cut genetic and clinical delineation of these various forms of ichthyosis.[174–178] These workers were able to demonstrate that autosomal dominant and X-linked ichthyosis were relatively common disorders, with the latter condition being present in approximately 1 in 6,000 males studied in their population. They had reason to believe that they had achieved complete ascertainment within the geographic area under consideration. They were able to show that X-linked ichthyosis differed from autosomal dominant ichthyosis vulgaris in age of onset, relative distribution of disease, severity, and a variety of histopathologic features.

Aside from the obvious differences in inheritance patterns, X-linked ichthyosis is characterized by onset between birth and 4 months of age and involvement of the upper and lower limbs and trunk. There is frequent involvement of the scalp and neck, but sparing of the palms and soles. The nails and hair are normal. The scales are large, dark, and prominent. Histologically there is hyperkeratosis, with a normal or increased granular layer. Finally, characteristic corneal opacities may be observed on slit-lamp examination. These opacities have no effect on visual acuity.[179] Female heterozygotes are generally asymptomatic.

Two groups independently observed that patients with steroid sulfatase deficiency as ascertained by low estrogen production had clinically apparent ichthyosis.[72,73] Furthermore, in the extended families of a number of probands, a clear history of X-linked ichthyosis could be obtained. When family studies of steroid sulfatase activity in cultured fibroblasts were conducted, complete concordance between enzyme deficiency and ichthyosis was demonstrated. Finally, many studies of families ascertained solely on the basis of the X-linked inheritance of ichthyosis showed them all to be associated with ste-

roid sulfatase deficiency, while enzyme assays done on patients with other types of ichthyosis revealed normal activity levels.[76,77]

It has been suggested that STS deficiency might not be causally related to ichthyosis, but that the STS gene and the "ichthyosis" gene might be contiguous and included in deletion events. Although it does turn out that STS deficiency is often the result of a gene deletion (see below), it seems exceedingly likely that STS deficiency per se does cause the ichthyosis. There are several reasons for coming to this conclusion. First, there is an invariant association between ichthyosis and STS deficiency. All patients lacking STS activity have this phenotypic finding. Second, there is good pathophysiologic reason to suspect that disordered sulfated sterol metabolism might interfere with epidermal function. The distribution of STS within skin and the role of sulfated steroids in epidermal cohesion, regulation of cholesterol biosynthesis, etc., have already been described. The observation that topical application of cholesterol sulfate to hairless mice can induce ichthyosis adds further credence to this proposal.[180] This conclusion is also supported by the finding of ichthyosis in other disorders of lipid metabolism (Table 76-3).[181] Refsum syndrome, in which ichthyosis is a prominent feature, is the result of a defect in phytanic acid oxidation with the accumulation of phytanic acid cholesteryl esters (see Chap. 59). Abnormal fatty alcohol metabolism has recently been reported in the Sjögren-Larsson syndrome, in which ichthyosis also occurs.[183] Fetuses with harlequin ichthyosis have been found to have various abnormalities of their epidermal lipids (184), and exogenous hypocholesterolemic drugs such as triparanol or nicotinic acid may also result in ichthyosis.[185–188] Finally, essential fatty acid deficiency in experimental animals produces epidermal changes that include ichthyosis.[189,190]

The third line of evidence supporting the causal relationship of X-linked ichthyosis and steroid sulfatase deficiency is genetic. At least two patients with apparent point mutations in the STS gene and an additional subject with an entirely intragenic deletion at the steroid sulfatase locus have ichthyosis (Shapiro, unpublished). Finally, patients with the rare autosomal recessive disorder of multiple sulfatase deficiency have reduced steroid sulfatase activity as the result of a non-X-linked mutation, and still have clinically apparent ichthyosis.

STS Deficiency and Androgen Metabolism

Following the demonstration that STS deficiency is, in fact, a systemic disorder affecting all tissues and organs, a systematic search for phenotypic and biochemical abnormalities has been undertaken in several centers. In addition to the ichthyosis and corneal opacities already mentioned, several other features have been noted in occasional patients. Several families have been reported in which a variety of neurologic abnormalities, hypogonadotropic hypogonadism, and anosmia have segregated along with ichthyosis and STS deficiency. For reasons that will be discussed below, it is likely that such individuals have a discernible syndrome that is the result of deletion of other genes in proximity to the STS locus (Table 76-3). Patients with cytogenetic abnormalities involving the distal X chromosome also probably represent entities that should be considered separately. However, there have been several gonadal abnormalities identified in patients who appear to have the common type of STS deficiency and X-linked ichthyosis. At least four such patients with testicular neoplasms have been

Fig. 76-4 Photograph of the arm of a 45-year-old adult with X-linked ichthyosis due to steroid sulfatase deficiency. The scales are thick and dark and were present on the neck, trunk, and lower extremities. There was sparing of the face and of the palms and soles. This individual had two affected grandsons and an affected brother and uncle.

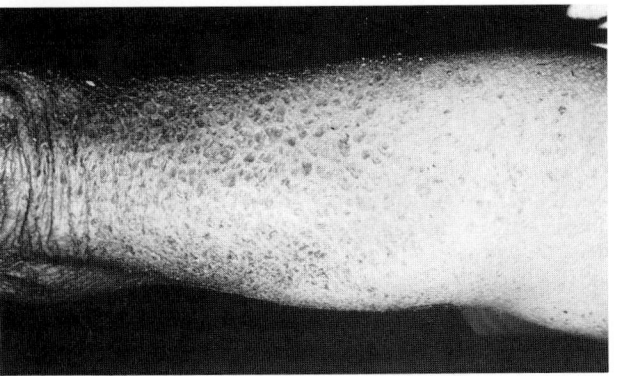

Table 76-3 Disturbances of Lipid Metabolism Producing Ichthyosis

Disorder	Enzyme defect	Pathogenesis	Inheritance	Other features
X-linked ichthyosis	Steroid sulfatase deficiency	Elevated cholesterol sulfate in stratum corneum	X-linked recessive	See text
Refsum syndrome	Phytanic acid oxidase deficiency	Accumulation of phytanic acid and phytanic acid–cholesteryl esters	Autosomal recessive	Retinitis pigmentosa, polyneuritis, ataxia, deafness
Sjögren-Larsson syndrome	Fatty alcohol oxidoreductase deficiency	Accumulation of long-chain fatty alcohols	Autosomal recessive	Spasticity, mental retardation, short stature, brittle hair, hypoplasia of teeth, metaphyseal dysplasia
Neutral lipid storage disease	Unknown	Triglyceride storage of unknown cause	Autosomal recessive	Cataracts, deafness, ataxia, droplets in many cells
Multiple sulfatase	Specific defect not known	STS deficiency (along with other sulfatase deficiencies)	Autosomal recessive	Neurodegeneration, hepatosplenomegaly, and skeletal disorders
Harlequin ichthyosis	Unknown	Increased cholesterol and triglycerides in stratum corneum	Uncertain	Ectropion, malformations, absent eyebrows and lashes, ? developmental delay

seen, including one unfortunate man with an embryonal-cell carcinoma and seminoma discovered 5 years apart.[191] What the precise relationship between these tumors and STS deficiency might be is presently unknown.[191,192]

Traupe and Happle have called attention to the possible association of cryptorchidism and STS deficiency.[193] They observed unilateral or bilateral testicular maldescent in 7 of 25 patients examined and found a total of 30 cases of cryptorchidism with STS deficiency described in the literature. One other series of patients has also shown this association.[194] There is a group of patients with STS deficiency and ichthyosis who have clear features of hypogonadotropic hypogonadism with anosmia (the Kallmann syndrome), which breeds true in affected families.[195–200] Some of these individuals also have mental retardation and neurologic abnormalities. Such patients most likely have a deletion involving the STS locus and some adjacent gene(s). Microphallus and undescended testes may be the result of the hypothalamic-pituitary dysfunction characteristic of this syndrome. It is not clear how carefully Traupe and Happle evaluated pituitary function and gonadotropin levels in their patients with ichthyosis and cryptorchidism, so some of their cases may have represented examples of this latter entity. Furthermore, a significant number of cases of individuals with cytogenetically visible rearrangements of Xp (usually X/Y translocations) have been reported to have cryptorchidism. In summary, two general mechanisms may be operative in producing the cryptorchidism seen in some STS-deficient patients. Small Xp deletions might result in the loss of some genes necessary for gonadal development, function, and descent quite apart from the STS locus per se. It can also be speculated that Xp deletions or rearrangements could lead to disordered X-Y meiotic pairing in spermatogenesis and thus predispose to abnormal germ-cell development. The second category of theories would hold that abnormal STS function per se is responsible in some cases for hypogonadism and cryptorchidism. The relative importance of STS in testicular testosterone biosynthesis has not been definitively established (see below) and could conceivably be implicated. It is possible that some degree of polymorphism exists regarding the flux through various potential steroidogenic pathways, and while testosterone biosynthesis appears to be

normal in *most* STS-deficient subjects studied, there may be a subset in whom it is not, with consequent testicular abnormality. Alternatively, at different stages of ontogeny, the relative importance of various steroidogenic pathways might change.

There is probably no gross alteration of testosterone biosynthesis or secretion in STS deficiency.[52–54] Several groups have measured serum testosterone, FSH, and LH values in adults with STS deficiency and have found these parameters to be normal. Furthermore, several subjects who received hCG stimulation responded with a normal augmentation of testosterone levels. DHEA sulfate, 17-hydroxypregnenolone sulfate, and androstenediol sulfate have been found to be moderately increased in the circulation of STS-deficient individuals, and their corresponding free steroids are slightly reduced on average (Bergner and Shapiro, unpublished). These data suggest that STS has some physiological role in the desulfation of these steroids, but quantitatively, the production of the free steroids must not be terribly dependent on sulfated intermediates. Conversely, there must be active systemic pathways capable of disposing of or metabolizing the sulfated compounds without the necessity for hydrolysis.

Although the quantitative importance of desulfation in the metabolism of DHEAS cannot be great, the question can be raised as to whether any desulfation of this major adrenal secretory product can be demonstrated in vivo. We have administered [³H]DHEAS and [¹⁴C]DHEA to a series of STS-deficient subjects and controls.[201] The conversion of [¹⁴C]DHEA to either DHEAS or DHEA glucuronide occurred normally in STS-deficient patients, indicating no impairment of conjugation. Furthermore, the plasma half-life of [³H]DHEAS infused into STS-deficient patients was essentially normal. However, when the conversion of DHEAS to DHEA glucuronide was examined, an unexpected result was obtained. A significant amount of labeled DHEAS was converted to the glucuronide in two of three STS-deficient individuals. Presumably, the exchange of sulfate for glucuronide at the 3β-OH position requires desulfation to the free intermediate and reconjugation, although it is possible that a "transconjugase" activity might exist which could carry out this exchange without hydrolysis. The observation that some STS-deficient subjects can apparently hydrolyze some DHEA in vivo can be explained in only one other way; i.e., that there might be some cryptic steroid sulfatase activity situated in an anatomical site not previously anticipated. Since most patients with STS deficiency have gene deletions, it is not likely that there are tissue differences in the expression of the authentic STS gene product. However, it is possible that there are separately encoded enzymes capable of hydrolyzing DHEAS that are expressed in a tissue-specific fashion. There is no evidence to support a second STS gene or enzyme, but a detailed autopsy survey of STS activity in organs and tissues of STS-deficient subjects has not been undertaken. The most likely explanation for the observed desulfation of DHEAS in STS deficiency is enterohepatic circulation of this compound with intraluminal intestinal metabolism of DHEAS by gut microflora. There is precedent for the role of such physiological interactions in other species and in human beings for several steroid hormones.[202–208] In support of this suggestion, we have observed loss of the ability to desulfate intravenously administered DHEAS by alteration of gut microflora following oral antibiotic therapy in an STS-deficient patient. However, the number of patients studied to date has been small.

To date, cholesterol sulfate is the only sulfated 3β-hydroxysteroid observed to accumulate in STS-deficient patients in amounts comparable to the increases of substrates seen in other inborn errors of metabolism. Cholesterol sulfate is strikingly elevated in plasma, red blood cell membranes, and stratum corneum of STS-deficient individuals.[13,209] The amounts may be as much as 20 times the normal levels. As is the case in normal individuals, most of the cholesterol sulfate in the plasma is physically associated with the low density lipoprotein plasma fraction, and the increased cholesterol sulfate gives the LDL an abnormal electronegativity. Some groups have attempted to use lipoprotein electrophoresis as a simple, readily available screening test for X-linked ichthyosis, but the validity of this approach has not been systematically studied. Determination of plasma cholesterol sulfate content also may be useful for diagnostic purposes. The striking buildup of cholesterol sulfate in STS deficiency as compared to the much more modest increases in DHEAS suggests that cholesterol sulfate is much more dependent on hydrolysis for its metabolism or elimination. For reasons that were discussed previously, it is likely the cholesterol sulfate accumulation within the epidermis is causally related to the development of ichthyosis in STS-deficient patients.

The Molecular Basis of STS Deficiency

The cloning of cDNA for human STS and the characterization of the STS gene have provided the basis for elucidating the molecular defects in STS deficiency. Some patients with STS deficiency have detectable cytogenetic abnormalities. More than 40 patients with X/Y translocations involving breaks in Xp22.3→pter have been described (Fig. 76-5) (reviewed in Ref. 137). Most of these subjects are males who have no normal X chromosome, but do have an additional intact Y chromosome. The STS locus appears to be deleted along with a number of adjacent genes, producing a variety of additional phenotypic features including short stature, mild mental retardation, and hypogonadism even in the presence of a normal, free-standing Y chromosome. This would suggest that there is a gene or genes on the X chromosome (for which these individuals are nullisomic) that is important for gonadal differentiation or maintenance. Some clues regarding this locus may be obtained from the study of patients with the Kallmann syndrome and STS deletions (see above). This putative gonadal maintenance factor could reside in the X-unique or in the pseudoautosomal region of the X chromosome. In most of these X/Y translocation chromosomes, the TDF (testis determining factor) region of the Y appears to have been lost as well. Thus, these 46,X, t(X;Y) individuals are phenotypically female. Although short [implying the presence of a gene(s) involved in stature in the pseudoautosomal region], these translocation carrier females are otherwise normal and can transmit the X/Y translocation chromosome to their progeny. Some multigenerational families segregating X/Y translocations have been reported. A few rare individuals have been found in whom a very distal breakpoint on the Y chromosome is likely, resulting in a male phenotype with a 46,X, t(X;Y) karyotypic constitution. Thus, there is some heterogeneity in the location of the Y-chromosome breakpoints in these X/Y translocations. Similarly, there is evidence for variability of X-chromosome breakpoints in that some of the involved chromosomes retain expression of both STS and MIC2, others lack both the MIC2 and STS, and a third class of X/Y translocation chromosomes retains the STS gene, but have lost the MIC2 gene.[90] This latter observation has verified the physical location of STS proximal to MIC2 on the X-chromosome short arm.

An additional group of patients with visible Xp cytogenetic abnormalities was reported by Curry et al.[91] Two families seg-

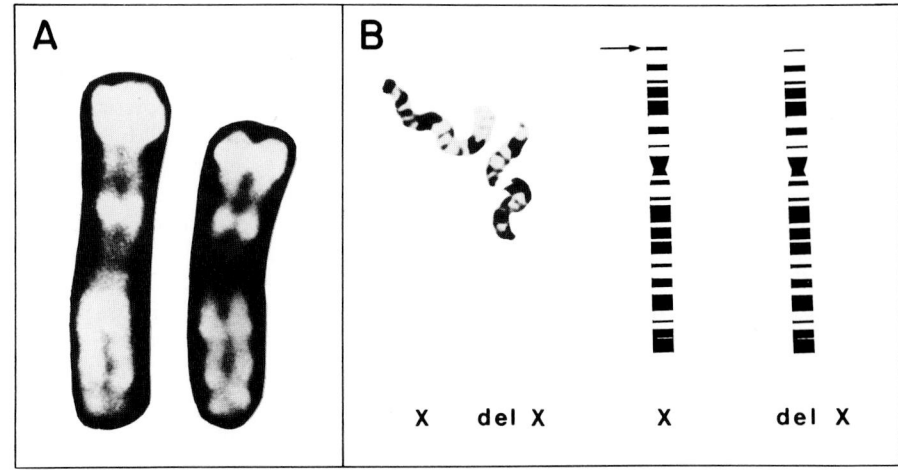

Fig. 76-5 Cytogenetic abnormalities seen in some patients with STS deficiency. *A* includes two different X/Y translocation chromosomes identified in two unrelated STS-deficient individuals. Both appear to have small deletions of the Xp telomere. A brightly fluorescent region of the Y chromosome is seen at the top of both. *B* shows an Xp22.3→pter deletion seen on prophase banding of a heterozygous carrier.

A   B

X   del X   X   del X

regating an X chromosome with a very distal Xp deletion visible only with careful prophase banding studies were described (Fig. 76-5). The deletion appears to include the STS gene as well as the pseudoautosomal region in both families. Females heterozygous for this deletion are short, while hemizygous males have short stature, chondrodysplasia punctata with epiphyseal stippling in early childhood, and ichthyosis with STS deficiency. These patients have been useful for a number of gene mapping studies, and further investigation may indicate what functional consequences might result from the loss of Xp telomeric sequences. There is also a well-described X-linked dominant form of chondrodysplasia punctata thought to be lethal in hemizygous males.[210] It will be of interest to see whether this clinically distinct disorder shows any abnormalities of steroid sulfatase activity or whether linkage with steroid sulfatase RFLPs might be demonstrable.

A second group of patients with STS deficiency includes those that have more complex syndromes with a possible deletion of contiguous genes, but in whom no visible cytogenetic abnormalities can be detected. Patients with the Kallmann syndrome and ichthyosis discussed above typify this class of STS deficiency. In addition to hypogonadotropic hypogonadism and anosmia, some of these patients have suffered from short stature and neurologic deficits. When genomic DNA from such patients is examined with STS probes, a complete STS deletion of more than 146 kb is seen.[62,65] Since the same abnormality can be seen in simple STS deficiency (see below), the deletion end points are presumably located farther away from the STS gene in these patients than in subjects with isolated X-linked ichthyosis. At least one other complex syndrome including STS deficiency (due to a submicroscopic deletion) has been found. This is a family in which X-linked ocular albinism cosegregates with an STS deletion (R. Nussbaum, personal communication). It is possible that this association in only a single family is fortuitous and that the ocular albinism gene and the STS gene could be a considerable distance apart. This is not a likely explanation for the association of Kallmann syndrome and STS deficiency, since these two features have been found together in several families of different ethnic and racial backgrounds. If mental retardation, short stature, chondrodysplasia punctata, neurologic abnormalities, hypogonadotropic hypogonadism, anosmia, cryptorchidism, and ocular albinism are all phenotypic features associated at some time with STS deletions or rearrangements, it should be possible by physical mapping of the region, and ordering of a nested series of phenotypic findings in patients, to construct a deletion map of the distal short arm of the X chromosome. This map may then eventually be further refined through linkage analysis in families segregating only one of these traits or features.

Molecular probes have enabled the characterization of patients with a simple phenotype and isolated STS deficiency as well. Using full-length cDNA probes, genomic probes, partial cDNA clones, and anonymous cloned DNA segments from Xp, at least 45 independently ascertained patients have been scrutinized.[62,64,65,211,212] The great majority, 41 of 45, of these subjects appear to have sustained major deletions (Fig. 76-6). Of 25 individuals studied with probes that permit analysis of the entire gene, 22 had deletions spanning at least 146 kg (the entire STS gene) with breakpoints not yet more finely mapped. One additional patient had an intragenic deletion of about 40 kb including exons II to V. This subject's cells made reduced amounts of shortened RNA transcripts. They con-

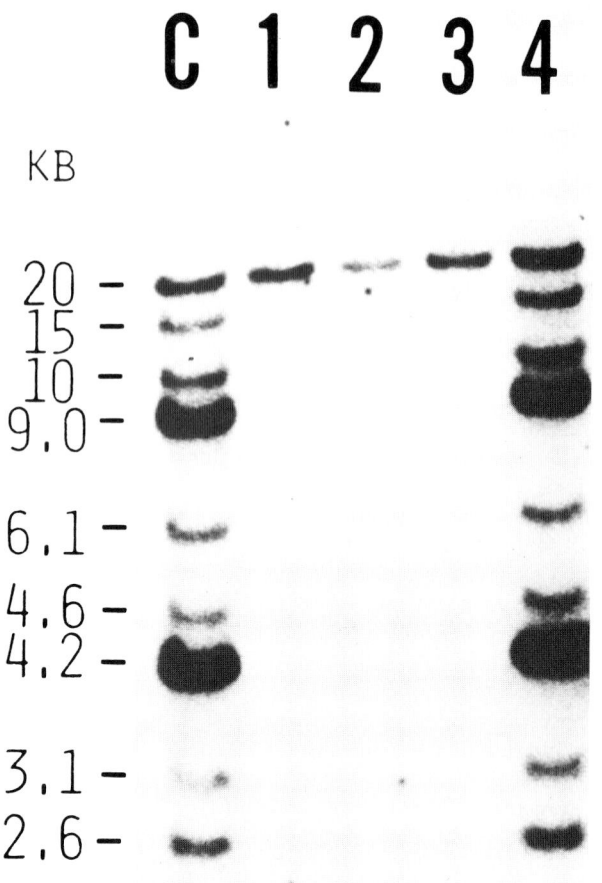

Fig. 76-6 Southern blot of genomic DNA from four patients with X-linked ichthyosis due to steroid sulfatase deficiency. A control subject (C) is included as well. The DNA was digested with *Eco*RI and hybridized with a full-length STS cDNA probe. The normal pattern includes bands of approximately 15, 10, 9, 6.1, 4.9, 4.2, 3.1, and 2.6 kb corresponding to the X locus and bands of approximately 20 and 1.5 kb derived from the Y-encoded pseudogene. Patients 1, 2, and 3 are missing all X-derived bands but still have Y sequences. Patient 4 has a normal pattern of hybridizing fragments and most likely has a point mutation.

tained neither functional nor immunologically recognizable STS protein. Two final patients were ascertained with grossly intact Southern blot patterns, normal transcripts by Northern analysis, but absent immunoreactive protein and enzyme activity. They presumably represent point mutations which disrupt function. One patient with alleged partial deficiency of STS activity has been reported,[213] and a pedigree in which X-linked ichthyosis appears to be segregating without detectable alteration in STS expression has been described (M. Siniscalco, personal communication). Whether either of these situations represent bona fide STS mutation is not clear. Further study will be needed to characterize the full spectrum of STS mutations.

STS deficiency is unusual, since large deletions represent the most frequent type of mutation at the disease locus. Deletions account for a larger fraction of the mutations observed in the STS gene as compared to any other locus, except for the α thalassemias. In the case of the α thalassemias, it is likely that the original mutations occurred only a relatively small number of times but were expanded in frequency within certain populations by selection. We do not yet have detailed information about the heterogeneity of the deletions in STS deficiency. However, STS deficiency appears to be quite common and equally frequent in many racial and ethnic groups, and geographic areas. Furthermore, no obvious selective advantage for hemizygosity or heterozygosity has been suggested. It is tempting to speculate that the lesions involving the STS locus are fairly frequent *de novo* events, perhaps facilitated by the novel position of the gene with respect to the pseudoautosomal region. Further analysis involving RFLP assessment and precise mapping of deletion end points, will be required in order to substantiate or to refute this hypothesis.

If deletions, either intragenic, involving all 146 kb of the STS gene, or even extending to neighboring genes, are so common, what are the possible mechanisms by which these deletions arise? Unequal X-X recombination is certainly possible and might be facilitated if there were any moderately repetitive sequences in the vicinity of STS. X-Y recombination is a tempting hypothesis. The visible X/Y translocations described previously might represent an extreme example of such aberrant recombination. Since recombination is very active within the adjacent pseudoautosomal region in males, one could speculate that nonhomologous rearrangements might occur occasionally (instead of homologous exchanges) in such a way as to cause the loss of STS sequences from the X by translocation, gene conversion, etc. The corresponding Y chromosome breakpoints could occur within the pseudoautosomal region or within the Y-unique region. In the latter case, one would predict the occurrence of Y-unique DNA on some X chromosomes bearing STS deletions. Using a number of Y-specific probes, we have not yet found evidence for such rearrangments (Shapiro and Page, unpublished). Further support for an X-Y interchange model for generating STS deletions might be obtained in the future by studying "new mutations" at the STS locus in families. RFLP analysis could be used to determine if the deletions arose during gametogenesis in the proband's maternal grandfather and to show that the grandfather's Y telomeric sequences have been translocated to the deletion-bearing X.

STS deletions could also result from intrachromosomal events with loops forming via direct repeats or inverted repeats. In male gametogenesis, the X-unique portion of the chromosome has nothing with which to pair during meiosis, so that such intrachromosomal loops may be favored. Given that the distal X short arm is close to the hyper-recombinogenic pseudoautosomal region, such loops could become substrates for this kind of reaction giving rise to deletions of material within the loops. Future studies should help to clarify the mechanisms of these deletions. Mapping of deletion end points by pulsed field gel electrophoresis, chromosome walking, and other methods should indicate whether the deletion end points are clustered or are heterogeneous. Observations in families with new mutations will clarify whether these deletions arise preferentially during male or female meiosis. RFLP analysis of flanking markers should indicate whether the recombinational events are intra- or interchromosomal.

Multiple Sulfatase Deficiency Disease

As mentioned above, a relatively rare group of patients has been identified who are deficient in STS activity, but who also lack arylsulfatases A and B, iduronate sulfatase, heparan-*N*-sulfatase, and galactosamine-6-sulfatase activities. These unfortunate individuals have symptoms referrable to several of these deficits. They store cerebroside sulfatide (the natural substrate for arylsulfatase A) and have neurologic symptoms reminiscent of metachromatic leukodystrophy. They also have osseous and systemic features that resemble the mucopolysaccharidoses. In addition, affected subjects have ichthyosis and diminished fetal estrogen production, as do patients with isolated steroid sulfatase deficiency.

Although at present obscure, the mechanism of the multiple sulfatase deficiency is of great interest. The various sulfatases involved all appear to be distinct enzymes, and there is evidence that their structural genes are dispersed throughout the genome. Only STS and iduronate sulfatase are X-linked, and the latter has been mapped to the long arm of the X chromosome. To the extent that immunologic reagents have been prepared, there is no evidence for cross-reactivity. At this point, STS is the only sulfatase gene that has been cloned so that its primary structure can be determined. STS is found in the endoplasmic reticulum (ER), while all of the other sulfatases are localized to the lysosome. STS is composed of a single subunit. There is no evidence that these sulfatases require any common cofactor or modulating subunit, although this has not been rigorously excluded. Several somatic cell hybridization-complementation studies have been performed in which MSD cells have been fused with cells genetically deficient in a single sulfatase activity.[214–216] In each instance, complementation has been observed, suggesting that the MSD locus is unique and that the mutation is recessive at a cellular level as it is at the phenotypic level.

Several experiments indicate that various manipulations of tissue culture conditions, most notably the pH, can result in some degree of restoration of enzyme activity to fibroblasts from MSD patients.[217,218] More recently, pulse-chase experiments utilizing immunoprecipitation of metabolically labeled cells have demonstrated a strikingly decreased half-life of newly synthesized arylsulfatase A and steroid sulfatase following normal initial rates of synthesis.[63,218] Taken together, these data are best explained by a defect in some common posttranslational modification which is shared by all of the relevant sulfatase enzymes and is required for stability. Since all of the enzymes are apparently glycoproteins, some aberration of carbohydrate addition or modification is a possible candidate for the defect in MSD. Proteolytic processing, phosphorylation, or other covalent modification must be considered as well. Since STS is probably only partially translocated across the ER membrane into the lumen while the other sulfatases must traverse the ER, Golgi, endosomes, and the lysosomal compartment, the defect must occur fairly early in this pathway. It is unclear what structural similarity or evolutionary relationship the various sulfatases have to one another. They appear merely to effect similar reactions on very diverse substrates. Immunologic data fail to indicate any structural similarity, and genomic hybridization experiments in patients with simple STS deletions do not identify any cross-hybridizing sequences elsewhere in the genome. Therefore, if there is some common posttranslation step shared by these sulfatase enzymes, the signal for the modification is not likely to be encoded in the primary structure per se. This may be analogous to the mechanism by which most lysosomal enzymes are recognized as being unique as they traverse the Golgi and receive a mannose-6-phosphate recognition marker to target their segregation into the lysosomal compartment (see Chap. 62). It has not yet been possible to discern the structural features that are important for recognition in the mannose-6-phosphate system either.

Incidence, Clinical Diagnosis, Carrier Identification, Prenatal Diagnosis, and Therapy

STS deficiency appears to be among the more common inborn errors of metabolism. It has been described in all racial backgrounds and in a diversity of ethnic populations. Frequency estimates reported by Wells and Kerr, who ascertained patients on the basis of x-linked ichthyosis, were about 1 in 6,000 (175) males. There may have been some bias in ascertainment of the families in this and in other studies that use ichthyosis as the discriminant, which could lead to underreporting. First, in cases where there is not extensive pedigree information available to support a diagnosis of an X-linked disorder, dermatologists who are consulted might be less inclined to consider this diagnostic possibility. Secondly, because of the non-life-threatening nature of the condition, its variation of severity, the seasonal fluctuations, and the lack of responsiveness (until recently) to therapy, many affected individuals have probably not sought medical care. Lykkesfeldt et al. have suggested that when patients are ascertained through maternal estriol screening, the incidence may be as high as 1 in 2000 males, at least in Western Europe.[219] The true population incidence will need to be determined through suitable large-scale prospective studies. Similarly, the relative homogeneity or heterogeneity of mutations at this locus will require prospective assessment by molecular studies to see whether mutations have arisen on a common RFLP haplotype background and whether deletion end points are unique or recurrent.

Confirmation of diagnosis of suspected cases is now relatively straightforward. Affected males can have STS activity assayed using one of a variety of substrates in fibroblasts, leukocytes, hair follicles, etc. Since 90 percent of patients appear to have gene deletions, genomic DNA blots can also be used to establish a diagnosis in many instances, although one obviously cannot exclude STS deficiency based on a normal Southern blot pattern in a patient who lacks other affected family members. Assessment of substrate levels may also be useful in that elevated plasma cholesterol sulfate levels appear to be diagnostic of STS deficiency. The corollary finding of abnormal lipoprotein electrophoresis due to CS incorporation into LDL could be of great value because of the wide availability of this test in clinical laboratories, but its validity has not been systematically assessed over a range of patients' ages.

Heterozygote identification is somewhat more problematic. While it is clear that there is normally a gene dosage effect on STS enzyme activity between subjects bearing one X-encoded copy of STS (XY, XO, or XX heterozygotes for STS mutations) and those bearing two copies (XX), there is considerable overlap between these two groups. This is largely the result of poorly understood variations in enzyme activity measurements. Thus, it may be difficult to be certain about heterozygote status in any single individual. Somewhat better results are likely if DNA analysis is used. RFLP analysis may be informative in families at risk for deletion or nondeletion forms of STS deficiency. In deletion patients, dosage blot, carefully normalized to compensate for differences in DNA content by hybridization with a control probe, should give accurate carrier information. However, these methods have not yet been used extensively.

There are many methods potentially applicable to the prenatal diagnosis of STS deficiency. In those forms of STS defects associated with visible cytogenetic abnormalities, karyotypic assessment should provide a useful adjunct to measurements of STS activity. The syncytiotrophoblast is normally very rich in STS activity, and this is particularly true in the first trimester, when STS-specific activity is higher than later in gestation. Thus, chorionic villus biopsy should be a reliable means of early prenatal assessment. These determinations can, of course, be supplemented by suitable studies of fetal genomic DNA with STS probes. Midtrimester diagnosis is also readily made by careful assessment of serum estriol levels (with gestational-age-appropriate standards) and by measurement of amniotic fluid DHEAS concentrations. Cultured amniocytes normally express STS and can be used for either DNA or enzymatic analysis. Finally, in the third trimester, maternal urinary estriol and sulfated steroid excretion can be monitored in addition to the other studies already described. The purpose of establishing a third trimester diagnosis of STS deficiency might be to exclude a more serious cause of incidentally detected low estriol levels. In addition, it might be argued that such diagnostic information would be useful in obstetrical management so that prolonged labor might be anticipated and suitable intervention planned if needed. The rationale for prenatal diagnosis in simple uncomplicated X-linked ichthyosis due to STS deficiency should be carefully considered with at-risk families from a medical and ethical standpoint. The overall severity and impact on quality of life is usually minimal and can now be quite effectively managed. It is therefore important to be sure that parents have an adequate understanding of the nature of this dermatologic disorder before preceding with prenatal studies.

Treatment of X-linked ichthyosis is now quite satisfactory. Lac-Hydrin (12% ammonium lactate) is a well-tolerated and effective keratolytic agent that gives good cosmetic results. Older preparations seemed to be associated with unacceptable stinging and itching. Use of cis-retinoic acid is probably contraindicated, although it is useful in the treatment of some other forms of ichthyosis. The risks of teratogenesis are not of direct concern in the male patients under treatment, but reports of hypertriglyceridemia are of concern. Furthermore, patients with X-linked ichthyosis seem not to respond to cis-retinoic acid and may even become somewhat worse. In any event, the simple application of a topical keratolytic is quite effective and without apparent side effects. The only other point worth mentioning is the possible increased risk of testicular neoplasms in STS-deficient patients. Although the data supporting this association are not compelling at present, it may be appropriate to instruct patients in testicular self-examination and to employ other efforts at prospective diagnosis without unduly alarming these subjects. Since the general health of STS-deficient patients is otherwise good, no other specific management is indicated.

REFERENCES

1. ROBERTS DR, LIEBERMAN S: The biochemistry of the 3β-hydroxy-Δ⁵-steroid sulfates, in Bernstein S, Solomon S (eds): *Chemical and Biological Aspects of Steroid Conjugation.* New York, Springer-Verlag, 1970, p 219.
2. SCHACHTER B, MARRIAN GF: The isolation of estrone sulfate from the urine of pregnant mares. *J Biol Chem* 126:663, 1938.
3. VENNING EH, HOFFMAN MM, BROWNE JSL: Isolation of androsterone sulfate. *J Biol Chem* 146:369, 1942.
4. MUNSON PL, GALLAGHER TF, KOCK FC: Isolation of dehydroisoandrosterone sulfate from normal male urine. *J Biol Chem* 152:67, 1944.
5. ROY AB: Enzymological aspects of steroid conjugation, in Bernstein S, Solomon S (eds): *Chemical and Biological Aspects of Steroid Conjugation.* New York, Springer-Verlag, 1970, p 74.
6. ROBERTS KD, BANDI L, CALVIN HI, DRUCKER WD, LIEBERMAN S: Evi-

dence that steroid sulfates serve as biosynthetic intermediates. IV. Conversion of cholesterol sulfate *in vivo* to urinary C$_{19}$ and C$_{21}$ steroidal sulfates. *Biochemistry* 3:1983, 1964.

7. PAYNE AH, LAWRENCE CC, FOSTER DL, JAFFEE RB: Intranuclear binding of 17-estradiol and estrone in female ovine pituitaries following incubation with estrone sulfate. *J Biol Chem* 248:1598, 1973.

8. VIGNON F, TERQUI M, WESTLEY B, DEROCQ D, ROCHEFORT H: Effects of plasma estrogen sulfates in mammary cancer cells. *Endocrinology* 6:1079, 1980.

9. JENKIN G, HEAP RB: Formation of oestradiol-17 from oestrone sulphate by sheep foetal pituitary in vitro. *Nature* 259:330, 1976.

10. DRAYER NM, LIEBERMAN S: Isolation of cholesterol sulfate from human blood and gallstones. *Biochem Biophys Res Commun* 18:126, 1965.

11. DRAYER NM, LIEBERMAN S: Isolation of cholesterol sulfate from human aortas and adrenal tumors. *J Clin Endocrinol Metab* 27:136, 1967.

12. MOSER HW, MOSER AB, ORR JC: Preliminary observations on the occurrence of cholesterol sulfate in man. *Arch Biochem Biophys* 116:146, 1966.

13. BERGNER E, SHAPIRO LJ: Increased cholesterol sulfate in plasma and red blood cell membranes of steroid sulfatase deficient patients. *J Clin Endocrinol Metab* 53:221, 1981.

14. EPSTEIN EH, KRAUSS RN, SHACKELTON CHL: X-linked ichthyosis: Increased blood cholesterol sulfate and electrophoretic mobility of low-density lipoprotein. *Science* 214:659, 1981.

15. WILLIAMS ML, WILEY M, ELIAS PM: Inhibition of 3-hydroxymethyl-glutaryl coenzyme A reductase activity and sterol synthesis by cholesterol sulfate in cultured fibroblasts. *Biochim Biophys Acta* 845:349, 1985.

16. WILLIAMS ML, RUTHERFORD SA, FEINGOLD KR: Effects of cholesterol sulfate on lipid metabolism in cultured human keratinocytes and fibroblasts. *J Lipid Res* 28:955, 1987.

17. BLEAU G, BODLEY FH, LONGPRE J, CHAPDELAINE A, ROBERTS KD: Cholesterol sulfate I. Occurrence and possible biological function as an amphipathic lipid in the membrane of the human erythrocyte. *Biochim Biophys Acta* 352:1, 1974.

18. LALUMIERE G, LONGPRE J, TRUDEL J, CHAPDELAINE A, ROBERTS KD: Cholesterol sulfate II. Studies on its metabolism and possible function in canine blood. *Biochim Biophys Acta* 394:120, 1975.

19. BLEAU G, LALUMIERE G, CHAPDELAINE A, ROBERTS KD: Red cell surface structure. Stabilization by cholesterol sulfate as evidenced by scanning electron microscopy. *Biochim Biophys Acta* 375:220, 1975.

20. BLEAU G, VANDENHEUVEL WJA: Demosteryl sulfate and desmosterol in hamster epididymal spermatozoa. *Steroids* 24:549, 1974.

21. LALUMIERE G, BLEAU G, CHAPDELAINE A, ROBERTS KD: Cholesteryl sulfate and sterol sulfatase in the human reproductive tract. *Steroids* 27:247, 1976.

22. LEGAULT Y, BLEAU G, CHAPDELAINE A, ROBERTS KD: The binding of sterol sulfates to hamster spermatozoa. *Steroids* 34:89, 1979.

23. WILLIAMS ML, ELIAS PM: Stratum corneum lipids in disorders of cornification. I. Increased cholesterol sulfate content of stratum corneum in recessive X-linked ichthyosis. *JClin Invest* 68:1404, 1981.

24. ELIAS PM, WILLIAMS ML, MALONEY MB, BONIFAS JA, BROWN BE, GRAYSON S, EPSTEIN EH: Stratum corneum lipids in disorders of cornification.II. Steroid sulfatase and cholesterol sulfate in normal desquamation and the pathogenesis of recessive of X-linked ichthyosis epidermis. *J Clin Invest* 74:1414, 1984.

25. ELIAS PM: Epidermal lipids, membranes, and keratinization. *J Dermatol (Tokyo)* 20:1, 1981.

26. EPSTEIN EH, WILLIAMS ML, ELIAS PM: Steroid sulfatase, X-linked ichthyosis, and stratus corneum cell cohesion. *Arch Dermatol* 117:761, 1981.

27. GRUBAUER G, FEINGOLD KR, ELIAS PM: Relationship of epidermal lipogenesis to cutaneous barrier function. *J Lipid Res* 28:746, 1987.

28. KORTH SCHULTZ S, LEVINE LS, NEW I, CHOW DM: Dehydroepiandrosterone sulfate (DS) levels, a rapid test for abnormal adrenal androgen secretion. *J Clin Endocrinol Metab* 42:1005, 1976.

29. RIITER EO, FULDAUER VG, ROOT AW: Secretion of the adrenal androgen, dehydroepiandrosterone sulfate during normal infancy, childhood, and adolescence, in sick infants, and in children with endocrinologic abnormalities. *J Pediatr* 90:766, 1977.

30. DE PERETTI E, FOREST MG: Patterns of plasma dehydroepiandrosterone sulfate levels in humans from birth to adulthood: Evidence for testicular production. *J Clin Endocrinol Metab* 47:572, 1978.

31. VIHKO R, RUOKONEN A: Regulation of steroidogenesis in testis. *J Steroid Biochem* 5:843, 1974.

32. FRANDSEN VA, STAKEMAN G: The site of production of oestrogenic hormones in human pregnancy. Hormone excretion in pregnancy with anencephalic fetus. *Acta Endocrinol* 38:383, 1961.

33. FRANDSEN VA, STAKEMAN G: The site of production of oestrogenic hormones in human pregnancy II. Experimental investigations on the role of the fetal adrenal. *Acta Endocrinol* 43:184, 1963.

34. SIITERI PK, MacDONALD PC: Placental estrogen biosynthesis during human pregnancy. *J Clin Endocrinol Metab* 26:751, 1966.

35. SIITERI PK, MacDONALD PC: The utilization of circulating dehydroisoandrosterone sulfate for estrogen synthesis during human pregnancy. *Steroids* 2:713, 1963.

36. WARREN JC, TIMBERLAKE CE: Steroid sulfatase in the human placenta. *J Clin Endocrinol Metab* 22:1148, 1962.

37. WARREN JC, TIMBERLAKE CE: Biosynthesis of estrogens in pregnancy: Precursor role of plasma dehydroisoandrosterone. *Obstet Gynecol* 23:689, 1964.

38. RYAN KJ: Biological aromatization of steroids. *J Biol Chem* 234:268, 1959.

39. ROSENFELD RS, HELLMAN L, GALLAGHER TF: Metabolism and interconversion of dehydroisoandrosterone and dehydroisoandrosterone sulfate. *J Clin Endocrinol Metab* 35:187, 1972.

40. MacDONALD PC, CHAPDELAINE A, GONZALEZ O, GURPIDE E, VAN DeWIELE RL, LIEBERMAN S: Studies on the secretion and interconversion of the androgens. III. Results obtained after the injection of several radioactive C$_{19}$ steroids, singly or as mixtures. *J Clin Endocrinol* 25:1557, 1965.

41. CHAPDELAINE A, MacDONALD PC, GONZALEZ O, GURPIDE E, VAN DeWIELE RL, LIEBERMAN S: Studies on the secretion and interconversion of the androgens. IV. Quantitative results in a normal man whose gonadal and adrenal function were altered experimentally. *J Clin Endocrinol* 25:1569, 1965.

42. HORTON R, TAIT JF: *In vivo* conversion of dehydroisoandrosterone to plasma androstenedione and testosterone in man. *J Clin Endocrinol* 27:79, 1967.

43. DOMINGUEZ OV, VALENCIA SA, LOZA AC: On the role of steroid sulfates in hormone biosynthesis. *J Steroid Biochem* 6:301, 1975.

44. HUHTANIEMI I: Studies on steroidogenesis and its regulation in human fetal adrenal and testis. *J Steroid Biochem* 8:491, 1977.

45. NOTATION AD: Regulatory interactions for the control of steroid sulfate metabolism. *J Steroid Biochem* 6:311, 1975.

46. PAYNE AH: Testicular steroid sulfotransferases: Comparison to liver and adrenal steroid sulfotransferases of the mature rat. *Endocrinol* 106:1365, 1980.

47. SIITERI PK, WILSON JD: Testosterone formation and metabolism during male sexual differentiation in the human embryo. *J Clin Endocrinol Metab* 38:113, 1974.

48. VIHKO R, RUOKONEN A: Regulation of steroidogenesis in testis. *J Steroid Biochem* 5:843, 1974.

49. VIHKO R, RUOKONEN A: Steroid sulphates in human adult testicular steroid synthesis. *J Steroid Biochem* 6:353, 1975.

50. RUOKONEN A, LUKKARINEN O, VIHKO R: Secretion of steroid sulfates from human testis and their response to a single intramuscular injection of 5000 IU hCG. *J Steroid Biochem* 14:1357, 1981.

51. RUOKONEN A, VIHKO R: Quantitative changes of endogenous unconjugated and sulfated steroids in human testis in relation to synthesis of testosterone in vitro. *J Androl* 4:104, 1983.

52. RUOKONEN A, OIKARINEN A, VIHKO R: Regulation of serum testosterone in men with steroid sulfatase deficiency: Response to human chorionic gonadotropin. *J Steroid Biochem* 25:113, 1986.

53. SHAPIRO LJ: Steroid sulfatase deficiency, in Stanbury JB, Wyngaarden JB, Fredrickson DS, Goldstein JL, Brown MS (eds): *The Metabolic Basis of Inherited Disease*, 5th ed. New York, McGraw-Hill, 1983, p 1027.

54. LYKESFELDT G, BENNET P, LYKKESFELDT AE, NICIC S, MULLER S, SVENSTRUP B: Abnormal androgen and oestrogen metabolism in men with steroid sulfatase deficiency and recessive X-linked ichthyosis. *Clin Endocrinol* 23:385, 1985.

55. BERGNER EA, SHAPIRO LJ: Metabolism of dehydroepiandrosterone sulfate in subjects with steroid sulfatase deficiency. *J Inherited Metab Dis*, in press, 1988.

56. ROSE FA: The mammalian sulphatases and placental sulfatase deficiency in man. *J Inherited Metab Dis* 5:145, 1982.

57. IWAMORI M, MOSER HW, KISHIMOTO Y: Solubilization and partial purification of steroid sulfatase from rat liver: Characterization of estrone sulfatase. *Arch Biochem Biophys* 174:199, 1976.

58. GAUTHIER R, VIGNEAULT N, BLEAU G, CHAPDELAINE A, ROBERTS KD: Solubilization and partial purification of steroid sulfatase of human placenta. *Steroids* 31:783, 1978.

59. NOEL H, BEAUREGARD G, POTIER M, BLEAU G, CHAPEDELAINE A, ROBERTS KD: The target sizes of the *in situ* and solubilized forms of human placental steroid sulfatase as measured by radiation inactivation. *Biochim Biophys Acta* 758:88, 1982.

59a. McNAUGHT RW, FRANCE JT: Studies of the biochemical basis of steroid sulphatase deficiency: Preliminary evidence suggesting a defect in membrane-enzyme structure. *J Steroid Biochem* 13:363, 1980.

60. EPSTEIN EH, BONIFAS JM: Recessive X-linked ichthyosis: Lack of immu-

nologically detectable steroid sulfatase enzyme protein. *Hum Genet* 71:201, 1985.

61. BURNS GRJ: Purification and partial characterization of arylsulphatase C from human placental microsomes. *Biochim Biophys Acta* 759:199, 1983.

62. YEN PH, ALLEN E, MARSH B, MOHANDAS T, WANG N, TAGGART T, SHAPIRO LJ: Cloning and expression of steroid sulfatase cDNA and the frequent occurrence of deletions in STS deficiency: Implications for X-Y interchange. *Cell* 49:443, 1987.

63. HORWITZ AL, WARSHAWSKY L, KING J, BURNS G: Rapid degradation of steroid sulfatase in multiple sulfatase deficiency. *Biochem Biophys Res Commun* 135:389, 1986.

64. CONARY JT, LOYKOWSKI G, SCHMIDT B, POHLMANN R, NAGEL G, MEYER HE, von FIGURA K: Genetic heterogeneity of steroid sulfatase deficiency revealed with cDNA for human steroid sulfatase. *Biochem Biophys Res Commun* 144:1010, 1987.

65. BALLABIO A, PARENTI G, CARROZZO R, SEBASTIO G, ANDRIA G, BUCKLE V, FRASER N, CRAIG I, ROCCHI M, ROMEO G, JOBSIS AC, PERSICO G: Isolation and characterization of a steroid sulfatase cDNA clone: Genomic deletions in patients with X-chromosome-linked ichthyosis. *Proc Natl Acad Sci USA* 84:4519, 1987.

66. ZUCKERMAN NA, HAGERMAN DD: The hydrolysis of estrone sulfate by rat kidney microsomal sulfatase. *Arch Biochem Biophys* 135:410, 1966.

67. FRENCH AP, WARREN JC: Properties of steroid sulphatase and arylsulphatase activities of human placenta. *Biochem J* 105:233, 1967.

68. BLEAU G, CHAPDELAINE A, ROBERTS KD: Studies on mammalian and moluscan steroid sulfatase. Solubilization and properties. *Can J Biochem* 49:234, 1971.

69. HAMEISTER H, WOLFF G, LAURITZEN CH, LEHMANN WO, HAUSER A, ROPERS HH: Clinical and biochemical investigations on patients with partial deficiency of placental steroid sulfatase. *Hum Genet* 46:199, 1979.

70. CRAIG IW, TOLLEY E: Steroid sulphatase and the conservation of mammalian X chromosomes. *Trends Genet* 2:201, 1986.

71. EPSTEIN EH, ALLEN A, SHACKLETON HL: Failure of steroid sulfatase to desulfate vitamin D₃ sulfate. *J Invest Dermatol* 80:514, 1983.

72. SHAPIRO LJ, WEISS R, WEBSTER D, FRANCE JT: X-linked ichthyosis due to steroid sulfatase deficiency. *Lancet 1:70, 1978.*

73. KOPPE JG, MARINKOVIC-ILSEN A, RIJKEN Y, De GROOT WP, JOBSIS AC: X-linked ichthyosis. A sulphatase deficiency. *Arch Dis Child* 53:803, 1978.

74. De GROOT WP, JOBSIS AC, MARINKOVIC-ILSEN A, KOPPE JG, De BRUIJN HWA: Sex-linked ichthyosis and placental sulphatase C deficiency. *Br J Dermatol* 103:73, 1980.

75. JOBSIS AC, De GROOT WP, TIGGES AJ, De BRUIJN HWA, RIJKEN Y, MEIJER AEFH, MARKINOKOVIC-ILSEN A: X-linked ichthyosis and X-linked placental sulfatase deficiency: A disease entity. *Am J Pathol* 99:279, 1980.

76. SHAPIRO LJ, BUXMAN MM, WEISS R, VIDGOFF J, DIMOND RL, ROLLER JA, WELLS RS: Enzymatic basis of typical X-linked ichthyosis. *Lancet* 2:756, 1978.

77. SHAPIRO LJ: X-linked ichthyosis. *Int J Dermatol* 20:26, 1981.

78. KERR CB, WELLS RS, SANGER R: X-linked ichthyosis and the Xg groups. *Lancet* 2:1369, 1964.

79. ADAM A, ZIPRKOWSKI L, FEINSTEIN A, SANGER R, RACE RR: Ichthyosis, Xg blood groups, and protan. *Lancet* 1:877, 1966.

80. WELLS RS, JENNINGS MC, SANGER R, RACE RR: Xg blood groups and ichthyosis. *Lancet* ii:493, 1966.

81. FILIPPI G, MEERA KHAN P: Linkage studies on X-linked ichthyosis in Sardinia. *Am J Hum Genet* 20:564, 1968.

82. ADAM A, ZIPROKOWKI L, FEINSTEIN A, SANGER R, TIPPET P, GAVIN J, RACE RR: Linkage relations of X-borne ichthyosis to Xg blood groups and to other markers of the X in Israelis. *Ann Hum Genet* 32:323, 1969.

83. WENT LN, De GROOT WP, SANGER R, TIPPET P, GAVIN J: X-linked ichthyosis: Linkage relationship with the Xg blood groups and other studies in a large Dutch kindred. *Ann Hum Genet* 32:333, 1969.

84. AUSTIN J: Studies in metachromatic leukodystrophy XII. Multiple sulfatase deficiency. *Arch Neurol* 15:13, 1966.

85. MURPHY JV, WOLFE HJ, BALAZS I, MOSER HW: A patient with deficiency of arylsulfatases A, B, C, and steroid sulfatase associated with storage of sulfatide, cholesterol sulfate, and glycosaminoglycans, in Bernsohn J, Grossman H (eds): *Lipid Storage Diseases: Enzymatic Defects and Clinical Implications.*New York, Academic, p 67, 1971.

86. KOLODNY EH, MOSER HW: Sulfatide lipidosis: Metachromatic leukodystrophy, in Stanbury JB, Wyngaarden JB, Fredrickson DS, Goldstein JL, Brown MS (eds): *The Metabolic Basis of Inherited Disease*, 5th ed. New York, McGraw-Hill, 1983, p 881.

87. MOHANDAS T, SHAPIRO LJ, SPARKES RS, SPARKES MC: Regional assignment of the steroid sulfatase-X-linked ichthyosis locus: Implications for a non-inactivated region on the short arm of human X chromosome. *Proc Natl Acad Sci USA* 76:5779, 1979.

88. MULLER CR, WESTERVELD A, MIGL B, FRANKE W, ROPERS HH: Regional

assignment of the gene locus for steroid sulfatase. *Hum Genet* 54:01, 1980.

89. TIEPOLO L, ZUFFARDI O, FRACCARO M, di NATALE D, GARGANTINI L, MULLER CR, ROPERS HH: Assignment by deletion mapping of the steroid sulfatase X-linked ichthyosis locus to Xp223. *Hum Genet* 54:205, 1980.

90. GELLER RL, SHAPIRO LJ, MOHANDAS TK: Fine mapping of the distal short arm of the human X chromosome using X/Y translocations. *Am J Hum Genet* 38:884, 1986.

91. CURRY CJR, LANMAN JT, TASAI J, O'LAUGE P, MAGENIS RE, BROWN M, GOODFELLOW P, MOHANDAS T, BERGNER EA, SHAPIRO LJ: Chondrodysplasia punctata due to a deletion of the short arm of the X chromosome. *N Engl J Med* 311:1010, 1984.

92. GARTLER SM, RIGGS AD: Mammalian X-chromosome inactivation. *Annu Rev Genet* 17:155, 1983.

93. WEAVER DD, GARTLER SM, BOUE A, BOUE JG: Evidence for two active X chromosomes in a human XXY triploid. *Humangenetik* 28:39, 1975.

94. MIGEON BR, SPRENKLE JA, DO T: Stability of the "two active X phenotype" in triploid somatic cells. *Cell* 18:637, 1981.

95. SHAPIRO LJ: Steroid sulfatase deficiency and the genetics of the short arm of the human X chromosome. *Adv Hum Genet* 14:331, 1985.

96. MOHANDAS T, SPARKES RS, SHAPIRO LJ: Genetic evidence for the inactivation of a human autosomal locus attached to an inactive X chromosome. *Am J Hum Genet* 34:811, 1982.

97. POLANI PE: Pairing of X and Y chromosomes, non-inactivation of X-linked genes, and the maleness factor. *Hum Genet* 60:207, 1982.

98. BURGOYNE PS: Genetic homology and crossing over in the X and Y chromosomes of mammals. *Hum Genet* 61:87, 1982.

99. RACE RR, SANGER R: *Blood Groups in Man*, 6th ed. Oxford, Blackwell, 1975.

100. GORMAN JG, DIRE J, TREACY AM, CAHAN A: The application of −Xgᵃ antiserum to the question of red cell mosaicism in female heterozygotes. *J Lab Clin Med* 61:642, 1963.

101. DUCOS J, MARTY Y, SANGER R, RACE RR: Xg and X chromosome inactivation. *Lancet* 2:219, 1971.

102. WEATHERALL DJ, PEMBREY ME, HALL EG, SANGER R, TIPPET P, GAVIN J: Familial sideroblastic anaemia: Problem of Xg and X chromosome inactivation. *Lancet* 2:744, 1970.

103. FIALKOW PJ: X-chromosome inactivation and the Xg locus. *Am J Hum Genet* 22:460, 1970.

104. POLANI PE, ANGELL R, GIANNELLI F, De La CHAPELLE A, RACE RR, SANGER R: Evidence that the Xg locus is inactivated in structurally abnormal X chromosomes. *Nature* 227:613, 1970.

105. SHAPIRO LJ, MOHANDAS T, WEISS R, ROMEO G: Non-inactivation of an X-chromosome in man. *Science* 204:1224, 1979.

106. MIGEON BR, SHAPIRO LJ, NORUM RA, MOHANDAS T, AXELMAN J, DABORA RC: Differential expression of the steroid sulfatase locus on the active and inactive human X chromosome. *Nature* 299:838, 1982.

107. SHAPIRO LJ, MOHANDAS T: DNA methylation and the control of gene expression on the human X chromosome. *Cold Spring Harbor Symp Quant Biol* 47:631, 1983.

108. MOHANDAS T, SPARKES RS, HELLKUHL B, GRZESCHIK KH, SHAPIRO LJ: Expression of an X-linked gene from an inactive human X chromosome in mouse-human hybrid cells: Further evidence for the noninactivation of the steroid sulfatase locus in man. *Proc Natl Acad Sci USA* 77:6759, 1980.

109. YEN PH, PATEL P, CHINAULT C, SHAPIRO LJ: Methylation of HPRT genes on active and inactive human X chromosomes. *Proc Natl Acad Sci USA* 81:1759, 1984.

110. LISKAY RM, EVANS RJ: Inactive X chromosome DNA-mediated cell transformation for the hypoxanthine phosphoribosyl transferase gene. *Proc Natl Acad Sci USA* 77:4895, 1980.

111. VENOLIA L, GARTLER SM, WASSMAN ER, YEN P, MOHANDAS T, SHAPIRO LJ: Transformation with DNA from 5 azacytidine reactivated X chromosomes. *Proc Natl Acad Sci USA* 79:2352, 1982.

112. LESTER SC, KORN NK, DeMARS R: Derepression of genes on the human inactive X chromosome: Evidence for differences in locus-specific rates of derepression and rates of transfer of active and inactive genes after DNA-mediated transformation. *Somatic Cell Genet* 8:265, 1982.

113. CHAPMAN VM, KRATZER PG, SIRACUSA LD, QUARANTILLO BA, EVANS R, LISKAY RM: Evidence for DNA modification in the maintenance of X chromosome inactivation in adult mouse tissue. *Proc Natl Acad Sci USA* 79:5357, 1982.

114. KRATZER PG, CHAPMAN VM, LAMBERT H, EVANS RE, LISKAY RM: Differences in the DNA of the inactive X chromosome of fetal and extraembryonic tissues of mice. *Cell* 33:38, 1983.

115. MOHANDAS T, SPARKES RS, SHAPIRO LJ: Reactivation of an inactive human X chromosome: Evidence for X-inactivation by DNA methylation. *Science* 211:393, 1981.

116. GOODFELLOW P, PYM B, MOHANDAS T, SHAPIRO LJ: The *MIC2X* locus escapes X inactivation. *Am J Hum Genet* 36:777, 1984.

117. MULLER CR, MIGL B, ROPERS HH, HAPPLE R: Heterozygote detection in steroid sulfatase deficiency. *Lancet* 2:546, 1980.

118. MULLER CR, MIGL B, TRAUPE H, ROPERS HH: X-linked steroid sulfatase: Evidence for different gene dosage in males and females. *Hum Genet* 54:197, 1980.

119. BEDIN M, WEIL D, FOURNIER T, CEDAR L, FREZAL J: Biochemical evidence for the non-inactivation of the steroid sulfatase locus in human placenta and fibroblasts. *Hum Genet* 59:256, 1981.

120. LYKKESFELDT G, BOCK E, LYKKESFELDT AE: Sex specific difference in placental steroid sulphatase activity. *Lancet* 2:255, 1981.

121. CHANCE PF, GARTLER SM: Evidence for a dosage effect at the X-linked steroid sulfatase locus in human tissues. *Am J Hum Genet* 35:234, 1983.

122. DANCIS J, JANSEN V, HUTZLER J: Hair root analysis in X-linked ichthyosis. *J Inherited Metab Dis* 6:173, 1983.

123. MOHANDAS T, YEN P, GELLER R, YOSHIDA A, BERNSTEIN R, SHAPIRO LJ: Cytogenetic and molecular studies on a recombinant human X chromosome: Implications for the spreading of X chromosome inactivation. *Proc Natl Acad Sci USA* 84:4954, 1987.

124. KOLLER PD, DARLINGTON CD: The genetical and mechanical properties of the sex chromosomes of *Rattus norvegicus*. *J Genet* 29:159, 1934.

125. COOKE HJ, BROWN WRA, RAPPOLD GA: Hypervariable telomeric sequences from the human sex chromosomes are pseudoautosomal. *Nature* 317:687, 1985.

126. SIMMLER MC, ROUYER F, VERGNAUD G, NYSTROM-LAHTI M, NGO KY, de la CHAPELLE A, WEISSENBACH J: Pseudoautosomal DNA sequence in the pairing region of the human sex chromosomes. *Nature* 317:692, 1985.

127. BUCKLE V, MONDELLO C, DARLING S, CRAIG IW, GOODFELLOW PN: Homologous expressed genes in the human sex chromosome pairing region. *Nature* 317:739, 1985.

128. ROUYER F, SIMMLER MC, JOHNSSON C, VERGNAUD G, COOKE HJ, WEISSENBACH J: A gradient of sex linkage in the pseudoautosomal region of the human sex chromosomes. *Nature* 319:291, 1986.

129. SINGH L, JONES KW: Sex reversal in the mouse (Mus musculus) is caused by a recurrent non-reciprocal crossover involving the X and an aberrant Y chromosome. *Cell* 28:205, 1982.

130. EVANS EP, BURTENSHAW MD, CATTANACH BM: Meiotic crossover between the X and Y chromosomes of male mice carrying the sex-reversing (Sxr) factor. *Nature* 300:443, 1982.

131. KEITGES E, RIVEST M, SINISCALCO M, GARTLER SM: X-linkage of steroid sulphatase in the mouse is evidence for a functional Y-linked allele. *Nature* 315:226, 1985.

132. KEITGES EA, SCHORDERET DF, GARTLER SM: Linkage of the steroid sulfatase gene to the sex-reversed mutation in the mouse. *Genetics* 116:465, 1987.

133. SORIANO P, KEITGES EA, SCHORDERET DF, HARBERS K, GARTLER SM, JAENISCH R: High rate of recombination and double crossovers in the mouse pseudoautosomal region during male meiosis. *Proc Natl Acad Sci USA* 84:7218, 1987.

134. HARBERS K, SORIANO P, MULLER U, JAENISCH R: High frequency of unequal recombination in pseudoautosomal region shown by proviral insertion in transgenic mouse. *Nature* 324:682, 1986.

135. GOODFELLOW PJ, DARLING SM, THOMAS NS, GOODFELLOW PN: A pseudoautosomal gene in man. *Science* 234:740, 1986.

136. GOODFELLOW P, BANTING G, LEVY R, POVEY S, MCMICHAEL A: A human X-linked antigen defined by a monoclonal antibody. *Somatic Cell Genet* 6:777, 1980.

137. BERNSTEIN R: X, Y chromosome translocations and their manifestations, in Sandberg AA (ed): *Progress and Topics in Cytogenetics, The Y Chromosome*. New York, AR Liss, vol 6B, 1985, p 171.

138. GUELLAEN G, CASANOVA M, BISHOP C, GELDWERTH D, ANDRE G, FELLOUS M, WEISSENBACH J: Human XX males with Y single-copy DNA fragments. *Nature* 307:172, 1984.

139. VERGNAUD G, PAGE DC, SIMMLER M-C, BROWN L, ROUYER F, NOEL B, BOTSTEIN D, de la CHAPELLE A, WEISSENBACH J: A deletion map of the human Y chromosome based on DNA hybridization. *Am J Hum Genet* 38:109, 1986.

140. PAGE DC: Sex reversal: Deletion mapping the male-determining function of the human Y chromosome, *Cold Spring Harbor Symp Quant Biol* 51:229, 1986.

141. AFFARA NA, FERGUSON-SMITH MA, TOLMIE J, KWOK K, MITCHELL M, JAMIESON D, COOKE A, FLORENTIN L: Variable transfer of Y specific sequences in XX males. *Nucleic Acids Res* 14:5375, 1986.

142. MAGENIS RE, CASANOVA M, FELLOUS M, OLSON S, SHEEHY R: Further cytologic evidence for Xp-Yp translocation in XX males using in situ hybridization with Y-derived probe. *Hum Genet* 75:228, 1987.

143. PAGE DC, BROWN LG, de la CHAPELLE A: Exchange of terminal portions of X- and Y-chromosomal short arms in human XX males. *Nature* 328:437, 1987.

144. PETIT C, de la CHAPELLE A, LEVILLIERS J, CASTILLO S, NOEL B, WEISSENBACH J: An abnormal X-Y interchange accounts for most but not all cases of human XX maleness. *Cell* 49:595, 1987.

145. PAGE DC, MOSHER R, SIMPSON EM, FISHER EMC, MARDON G, POLLACK J, MCGILLIVARY B, de la CHAPELLE A, BROWN LG: The sex determining region of the human Y chromosome encodes a finger protein. *Cell* 51:1091, 1987.

146. ROPERS HH, MIGL B, ZIMMER J, MULLER CR: Steroid sulfatase activity in cultured fibroblasts of XX males. *Cytogenet Cell Genet* 30:168, 1981.

147. BALAZS I, PURRELLO M, ROCCHI M, SINISCALCO M: Is the gene for steroid sulfatase X-linked? An appraisal of data from humans, mice, and their hybrids. *Cytogenet Cell Genet* 32:251, 1982.

148. NELSON K, DANIEL WL: Interstrain variation of murine arylsulfatase C[1]. *Experientia* 35:309, 1979.

149. ERICKSON RP, HARPER K, KRAMER JM: Identification of an autosomal locus affecting steroid sulfatase activity among inbred strains of mice. *Genetics* 105:181, 1983.

150. KEINANAN BM, NELSON K, DANIEL WL, ROQUE JM: Genetic analysis of murine arylsulfatase C and steroid sulfatase. *Genetics* 105:191, 1983.

151. NELSON K, KEINANEN BM, DANIEL WL: Murine arylsulfatase C: Evidence for two isozymes. *Experientia* 39:740, 1983.

152. CROCKER M, CRAIG I: Variation in regulation of steroid sulphatase locus in mammals. *Nature* 303:721, 1983.

153. GARTLER SM, RIVEST M: Evidence for X-linkage of steroid sulfatase in the mouse: Steroid sulfatase levels in oocytes of XX and XO mice. *Genetics* 103:137, 1983.

154. KEITGES E, GARTLER SM: Dosage of the STS gene in the mouse. *Am J Hum Genet* 30:470, 1986.

155. ROPERS HH, WIBERG U: Evidence for X-linkage and non-inactivation of steroid sulphatase locus in wood lemmings. *Nature* 296:766, 1982.

156. WIBERG UH, FREDGE K: Steroid sulphatase levels are higher in males than in females of the root vale (Microtus oeconomus). *Hum Genet* 77:6, 1987.

157. COOPER DW, MCALLAN BM, DONALD JA, DAWSON G, DOBROVIC A, GRAVES JAM: Steroid sulphatase is not detected on the X chromosome of Australian marsupials. *Cytogenet Cell Genet* 37:439, 1984.

158. DOBROVIC A, GRAVES JAM: Gene mapping in marsupials and monotremes II. Assignments to the X chromosome of dasyurid marsupials. *Cytogenet Cell Genet* 41:9, 1980.

159. GRAVES JAM: The evolution of mammalian sex chromosomes and dosage compensation: Clues from marsupials and monotremes. *Trends Genet* 3:252, 1987.

160. YEN PH, MARSH B, ALLEN E, MOHANDAS T, SHAPIRO LJ: Organization of the human steroid sulfatase gene and sequence homology between the X and the Y chromosomes. *Am J Hum Genet* 41:A248, 1987.

161. FRANCE JT, LIGGINS GC: Placental sulfatase deficiency. *J Clin Endocrinol Metab* 29:138, 1969.

162. FRANCE JT, SEDDON RJ, LIGGINS GC: A study of a pregnancy with low estrogen production due to placental sulfatase deficiency. *J Clin Endocrinol Metab* 36:1, 1973.

163. CRAWFURD Md'A: Review: Genetics of steroid sulfatase deficiency and X-linked ichthyosis. *J Inherited Metab Dis* 5:153, 1982.

164. TAYLOR NF: Review: Placental sulphatase deficiency. *J Inherited Metab Dis* 5:164, 1982.

165. HARKNESS RA: Current clinical problems in placental steroid or arylsulphatase C deficiency and the related "cervical dystocia" and X-linked ichthyosis. *J Inherited Metab Dis* 5:142, 1982.

166. STEINMANN B, MIETH D, GITZELMANN R: A newly recognized cause of low urinary estriol in pregnancy: Multiple sulfatase deficiency of the fetus. *Gynecol Obstet Invest* 12:107, 1981.

167. TAYLOR NF, SHACKLETON CHL: Gas chromatographic steroid analysis for diagnosis of placental sulfatase deficiency: A study of nine patients. *J Clin Endocrinol Metab* 49:78, 1979.

168. OSATHANONDH R, CANICK J, RYAN KJ, TULCHINSKY D: Placental sulfatase deficiency: A case study. *J Clin Endocrol Metab* 43:208, 1976.

169. BRAUNSTEIN GD, ZIEL FH, ALLEN A, van De VELDE R, WADE M: Prenatal diagnosis of placental steroid sulfatase deficiency. *Am J Obstet Gynecol* 126:716, 1976.

170. TABEI T, HEINRICHS WL: Diagnosis of placental sulfatase deficiency. *Am J Obstet Gynecol* 124:409, 1976.

171. SHAPIRO LJ, COUSINS L, FLUHARTY AL, STEVENS RL, KIHARA H: Steroid sulfatase deficiency. *Pediatr Res* 11:894, 1976.

172. MARKS R, DYKES PJ: *The Ichthyoses*. New York, SP Medical Books, 1978.

173. SEDGWICK W: On the influence of sex in hereditary disease. *Br Foreign Med-Churg Rev* 31:445, 1863.

174. KERR CB, WELLS RS: Sex-linked ichthyosis. *Ann Hum Genet* 29:33, 1965.

175. WELLS RS, KERR CB: Clinical features of autosomal dominant and sex-linked ichthyosis in an English population. *Br Med J* 1:947, 1966.

176. WELLS RS, KERR CB: The histology of ichthyosis. *J Invest Dermatol* 46:530, 1966.

177. MERRETT JD, WELLS RS, KERR CB, BARR A: Discriminant function analysis of phenotype variates in ichthyosis. *Am J Hum Genet* 19:575, 1967.

178. WELLS RS, JENNINGS MC: X-linked ichthyosis and ichthyosis vulgaris. *JAMA* 202:485, 1967.

179. SEVER RJ, FROST P, WEINSTEIN G: Eye changes in ichthyosis. *JAMA* 206:2283, 1968.

180. MAHONEY ME, WILLIAMS ML, EPSTEIN EH, JAY MYL, FRITSCH PO, ELIAS PM: Lipids in the pathogenesis of ichthyosis: Topical cholesterol sulfate-induced scaling in hairless mice. *J Invest Dermatol* 82:235, 1984.

181. WILLIAMS ML, KOCK TK, O'DONNELL JJ, FROST PN, EPSTEIN LB, GRIZZARD WS, EPSTEIN CJ: Ichthyosis and neurallipid storage disease. *Am J Med Genet* 20:711, 1985.

183. RIZZO WB, DAMMANN AL, CRAFT DA: Sjögren-Larsson syndrome: Impaired fatty alcohol oxidation in cultured fibroblasts due to deficient fatty alcohol: NAD$^+$ oxidoreductase activity. *J Clin Invest* 81:738, 1988.

184. BUXMAN MM, GOODKIN PE, FAHRENBACH WH, DIMOND RL: Harlequin ichthyosis with epidermal lipid abnormality. *Arch Dermatol* 115:189, 1979.

185. WINKLEMANN RK, PERRY HO, ACHOR RU, KIRBY JJ: Cutaneous syndromes produced as side effects of triparanol therapy. *Arch Dermatol* 87:372, 1963.

186. FLESCH P: Inhibition of keratinizing structures by systemic drugs. *Pharmacol Rev* 15:653, 1963.

187. ELIAS PM, LAMPE MA, CHUNG J-C, WILLIAMS ML: Diazacholesterol-induced ichthyosis in the hairless mouse: Morphological, histochemical, and lipid biochemical characterization of a new animal model. *Lab Invest* 48:565, 1983.

188. WILLIAMS ML, FEINGOLD KR, GRUBAUER G, ELIAS PM: Ichthyosis induced by cholesterol-lowering drugs: Implications for epidermal cholesterol homeostasis. *Arch Dermatol* 123:1535, 1987.

189. LOWE NJ, STOUGHTON RB: Essential fatty acid deficient hairless mouse: A model of chronic epidermal hyperproliferation. *Br J Dermatol* 96:155, 1977.

190. FEINGOLD KR, BROWN BE, LEAR SR, MOSER AH, ELIAS PM: Effect of essential fatty acid deficiency on cutaneous sterol synthesis. *J Invest Dermatol* 87:588, 1986.

191. LYKKESFELDT G, HOYER H, LYKKESFELDT AE, SKAKKEBAER NE: Steroid sulphatase deficiency associated with testis cancer. *Lancet* 2:1456, 1983.

192. TOLLEY E, CRAIG IW, JONASSON J, CARTWRIGHT RA, JONES WG: Steroid sulphatase deficiency and testicular cancer. *Lancet* 1:563, 1985.

193. TRAUPE H, HAPPLE R: Clinical spectrum of steroid sulfatase deficiency: X-linked recessive ichthyosis, birth complications and cryptorchidism. *Eur J Pediatr* 140:19, 1983.

194. LYKKESFELDT G, HOYER H, IBSEN HH, BRANDRUP F: Steroid sulphatase deficiency disease. *Clin Genet* 28:231, 1985.

195. LYNCH HT, OZER F, McNUTT CW, JOHNSON JE, JAMPOLSKY NA: Secondary male hypogonadism and congenital ichthyosis: Association of two rare genetic diseases. *Am J Hum Genet* 12:440, 1960.

196. TRAUPE H, MULLER-MIGL CR, KOLDE G, HAPPLE R, KOVARY PM, HAMEISTER H, ROPERS HH: Ichthyosis vulgaris with hypogenitalism and hypogonadism: Evidence for different genotypes by lipoprotein electrophoresis and steroid sulfatase testing. *Clin Genet* 25:42, 1984.

197. ANDRIA G, BALLABIO A, PARENTI G, Di MAIO S, PICCIRILLO A: Steroid sulphatase deficiency is present in patients with the syndrome "ichthyosis and male hypogonadism" and with "Rud syndrome." *J Inherited Metab Dis* 7:158, 1984.

198. ABE K, MATSUDA I, MATSUURA N, MURAYAMA T, UZUKI K, ENDO M, MIYAKOSHI M, OKUNG A: X-linked ichthyosis, bilateral cryptorchidism, hypogenitalism and mental retardation in two siblings. *Clin Genet* 9:341, 1976.

199. BALLABIO A, PARENTI G, TIPPETT P, MONDELLO C, Di MAIO S, TENORE A, ANDRIA G: X-linked ichthyosis, due to steroid sulfatase deficiency, associated with Kallmann syndrome (hypogonadism and anosmia): Linkage relationships with Xg and cloned DNA sequences from the distal short arm of the X chromosome. *Hum Genet* 72:237, 1986.

200. SUNOHARA N, SAKURAGANA N, SATOYOSHI E, TANAE A, SHAPIRO LJ: A new syndrome of anosmia, ichthyosis, hypogonadism, and various neurological manifestations with deficiency of steroid sulfatase and arylsulfatase C. *Ann Neurol* 14:174, 1986.

201. BERGNER EA, SHAPIRO LJ: Metabolism of dehydroepiandrosterone sulfate (DHEAS) by subjects with steroid sulfatase deficiency. *Am J Hum Genet* 36:75, 1984.

202. TIKKANEN MJ, PULKKINEN MO, ADLERCREUTZ H: Effect of ampicillin treatment on the urinary excretion of estriol conjugates in pregnancy. *J Steroid Biochem* 4:439, 1973.

203. ADLERCREUTZ H, MARTIN F, TIKKANEN MJ, PULKKINEN M: Effect of ampicillin administration on the excretion of twelve oestrogens in pregnancy urine. *Acta Endocrinol (Copenh)* 80:551, 1975.

204. WILLIAM K, PULKKINEN MO: Reduced maternal plasma and urinary estriol during ampicillin treatment. *Am J Obstet Gynecol* 109:893, 1971.

205. ADLERCREUTZ H, MARTIN F, PULKKINEN M, DENCKER H, RIMER U, SJOBERT N-O, TIKKANEN MJ: Intestinal metabolism of estrogens. *J Clin Endocrinol Metab* 43:497, 1976.

206. MARTIN F, PELTONEN J, LAATIKAINEN T, PULKKINEN M, ADLERCREUTZ H: Excretion of progesterone metabolites and estriol in faeces from pregnant women during ampicillin treatment. *J Steroid Biochem* 6:1339, 1975.

207. JANNE OA, LAATIKAINEN TJ, VIHKO RK: Effect of reduction of the intestinal microflora on the excretion of neutral steroids in human faeces and urine. *Eur J Biochem* 20:120, 1971.

208. CASEY ML, MacDONALD PC: Metabolism of deoxycorticosterone and deoxycorticosterone sulfate in men and women. *J Clin Invest* 70:312, 1982.

209. EPSTEIN EH, KRAUSS RM, SHACKLETON CHL: X-linked ichthyosis: Increased blood cholesterol sulfate and electrophoretic mobility of low-density lipoprotein. *Science* 214:659, 1981.

210. HAPPLE R: X-linked dominant chondrodysplasia punctata. Review of literature and report of a case. *Hum Genet* 53:65, 1979.

211. GILLARD EF, AFFARA NA, YATES JRW, GOUDIE DR, LAMBERT J, AIKEN DA, FERGUSON-SMITH MA: Deletion of a DNA sequence in eight of nine families with X-linked ichthyosis (steroid sulphatase deficiency). *Nucleic Acids Res* 15:3977, 1987.

212. SHAPIRO LJ, YEN PH, MARSH B, MOHANDAS T: Frequent deletions at the steroid sulfatase (STS) locus. *Am J Hum Genet* 41:A238, 1987.

213. HAMEISTER H, WOLFF G, LAURITZEN CH, LEHMANN WO, HAUSER A, ROPERS HH: Clinical and biochemical investigations on patients with partial deficiency of placental steroid sulfatase. *Hum Genet* 46:199, 1979.

214. HORWITZ AL: Genetic complementation studies of multiple sulfatase deficiency. *Proc Natl Acad Sci USA* 76:6496, 1979.

215. EISENBERG LR, MIGEON BR: Enrichment of human heterokaryons by Ficoll gradient for complementation analysis of iduronate sulfatase deficiency. *Somatic Cell Genet* 5:1079, 1979.

216. FEDDE K, HORWITZ AL: Complementation of multiple sulfatase deficiency in somatic cell hybrids. *Am J Hum Genet* 36:623, 1984.

217. FLUHARTY AL, STEVENS RL, DAVIS LL, SHAPRIO LJ, KIHARA H: Presence of arylsulfatase A in multiple sulfatase deficiency disorder fibroblasts. *Am J Hum Genet* 30:249, 1978.

218. KRESSE H, HOLTFERICH D: Thiosulfate-mediated increase of arylsulfatase activities in multiple sulfatase deficiency disorder fibroblasts. *Biochem Biophys Res Commun* 97:41, 1980.

219. LYKKESFELDT G, NIELSEN MD, LYKKESFELDT AE: Placental steroid sulfatase deficiency: Biochemical diagnosis and clinical review. *Obstet Gynecol* 64:49, 1984.

CHAPTER 77

INHERITED DEFECTS IN GROWTH HORMONE SYNTHESIS AND ACTION

JOHN A. PHILLIPS, III

1. Human growth hormone (hGH, or somatotropin) is essential for normal postnatal growth. It is a 191-amino acid protein which is released from the anterior pituitary gland upon stimulation by growth hormone releasing hormone (GHRH, or somatocrinin), a factor produced by the hypothalamic region of the brain. Like other pituitary hormones, hGH acts on target tissues, in this case primarily the liver, to cause synthesis and release of a second hormone mediator, insulinlike growth factor (IGF) I, also called somatomedin C, into the systemic circulation. IGF-I is a growth-accelerating peptide that acts directly on cartilage to promote bone growth.

2. Deficiency of hGH production causes metabolic alterations and growth failure. While most cases of hGH deficiency are idiopathic, 13 known single gene disorders as well as a variety of other genetic disorders and syndromes are associated with deficiency of hGH or defective action. These genetic disorders are caused by (a) alterations in the hGH gene, (b) alterations of distant loci that cause hGH deficiency through epistatic effects, or (c) alterations of genes that affect the response to hGH.

3. Deficiency of hGH has in the past been treated by replacement with exogenous hGH isolated from cadaver pituitaries. Because of the accompanying danger of transmission of infectious neurodegenerative disease (Creutzfeldt-Jakob disease), alternative methods of treatment are now used. These include replacement with biosynthetic hGH or in some cases treatment with GHRH. The potential for hGH gene therapy has been demonstrated in animals.

4. Human chorionic somatomammotropin (hCS, or human placental lactogen) has similar biologic activities, but it is much less potent than hGH. During pregnancy maternal hCS levels are very high and approximately 300 times greater than fetal levels. While hCS is thought to be important in maternal carbohydrate and fat metabolism, normal fetal growth occurs in pregnancies in which it is absent.

5. Two genetic disorders of the hCS loci have been described. While these alterations lead to deficiency or absent hCS production, affected individuals are thought to be asymptomatic.

HUMAN GROWTH AND CHORIONIC SOMATOMAMMOTROPIN HORMONES

Structure of Human Growth Hormone

Human growth hormone (hGH, or somatotropin) is a globular protein with a molecular mass of 22,000 daltons. It consists of a single polypeptide chain of 191 amino acid residues, with two disulfide bridges and no carbohydrate moieties (Fig. 77-1).[1-3] Growth hormones from cattle, sheep, and pigs are very similar though not identical in structure to hGH, but all are sufficiently different to render them inactive in humans.[4] The hGH molecule is predominantly α-helical in its secondary structure. While most of the hGH contained in the pituitary gland is the 22 kDa form shown in Fig. 77-1, four other variants (one 45 kDa, two 24 kDa, and one 20 kDa) have been identified.[4] The 45 kDa variant is an aggregate or dimer that probably arises during synthesis of the 22 kDa form in the anterior pituitary.[4-8] It can be converted to the 22 kDa form by treatment with mercaptoethanol and constitutes about 1 percent of the hGH isolated from pituitary glands.[9-10] One 24 kDa variant results from proteolytic cleavage of the 22 kDa molecule between residues 139 and 140. Removal of this peptide bond converts the hGH molecule to a two-chain form, thereby altering its secondary and tertiary structure and increasing its apparent molecular mass.[4,11] A second 24 kDa variant of GH represents pre-hGH which retains the amino-terminal signal peptide sequence of 26 amino acids (molecular mass about 2000 daltons). This signal or leader sequence is important in directing the transport of the nascent protein molecule across the membrane of the rough endoplasmic reticulum into its cisternae for packaging.[12] The final hGH variant found in the anterior pituitary is the 20 kDa form (see Fig. 77-2). This variant, unlike the others, represents a direct gene product rather than posttranslational modification. The 20 kDa variant has a single chain and differs from the 22 kDa form by its deletion of amino acid residues 32 to 46.[13] The 20 kDa variant constitutes 5 to 10 percent of the total pituitary hGH and arises from alternative splicing of one of the intervening sequences during processing of hGH pre-mRNA.[13,14]

hGH is synthesized by the somatotropic cells of the anterior pituitary (see Fig. 77-2). It is the most abundant hormone in the pituitary, and the content of a single pituitary gland ranges from 5 to 15 mg, which corresponds to 1 to 3 percent of the weight of the gland.[15]

Structure of Human Chorionic Somatomammotropin and Prolactin

Two other known hormones are similar in structure to hGH. The first, chorionic somatomammotropin (hCS, or human pla-

---

Nonstandard abbreviations used in this chapter are: ACTH = adrenocorticotropic hormone; EEC = ectrodactyly-ectodermal dysplasia-clefting syndrome; FSH = follicle-stimulating hormone; GH = growth hormone; GHRH = human growth hormone releasing hormone, or somatocrinin; hCS = human chorionic somatomammotropin, or human placental lactogen; hGH = human growth hormone, or somatotropin; hPRL = human prolactin; IGF = insulinlike growth factor; IGHD = isolated growth hormone deficiency; LH = luteinizing hormone; TRH = thyroid-releasing hormone; TSH = thyroid-stimulating hormone.

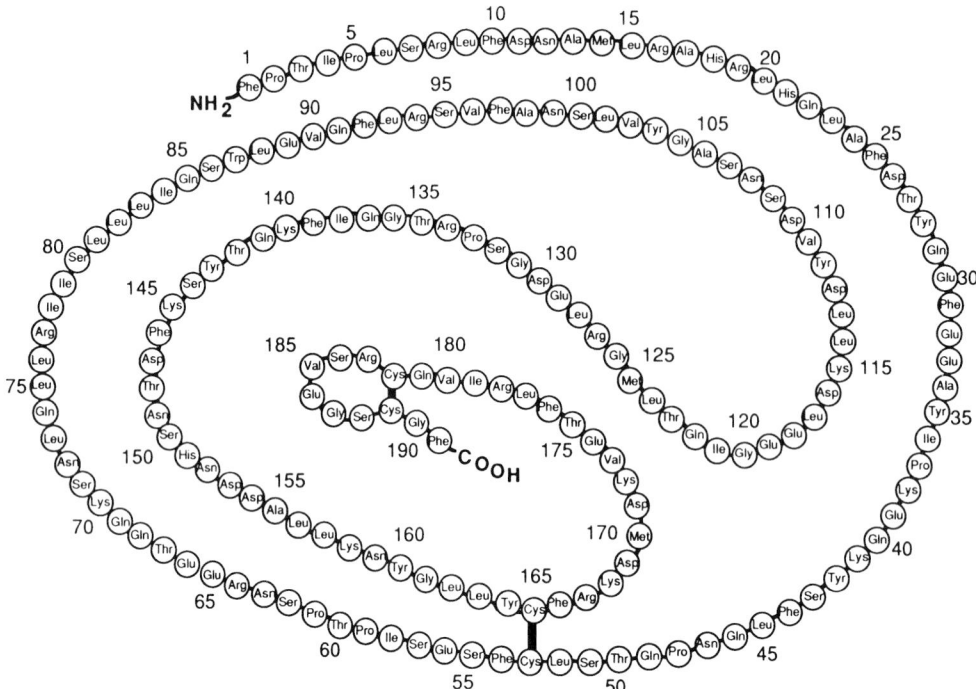

Fig. 77-1 Amino acid sequence of 22 kDa hGH.

cental lactogen), also contains 191 amino acids, of which 85 percent are identical to hGH, and it also has two disulfide bonds that occur at the same positions as in hGH.[16,17] hCS is synthesized by the syncytiotrophoblastic cells of the fetal placenta, and it is secreted into the maternal circulation. The second hormone that is structurally similar to hGH is prolactin (hPRL), which contains 199 amino acids of which 35 percent are identical to hGH and 13 percent are identical to hCS.[18,19] hPRL like hGH is produced and secreted by the anterior pituitary gland but differs in that hPRL acts to initiate and maintain lactation. hGH, hCS, and hPRL are thought to share sequence homologies because of their evolution from a common ancestral gene through duplication events followed by sequence divergence.[18-20]

Functional Properties of hGH and hCS

hGH promotes postnatal growth of skeletal and soft tissues through a variety of effects. Controversy remains about the contribution of direct and indirect actions of hGH in this process. On one hand, direct effects of hGH have been demonstrated in a variety of tissues and organs and the presence of hGH receptors has been documented on a variety of cell types.[4,21-23] On the other hand, a large amount of data indicate that at least a major portion of the effects of hGH are mediated by hGH-dependent insulinlike growth factors (IGF) called *somatomedins*.[21,24,25] IGF-I, also called somatomedin C, is highly dependent on the circulating level of hGH.[26] It is a 7649-dalton peptide containing 70 amino acid residues and three disulfide bonds.[27] Traditionally, the liver was thought to be the primary site of IGF-I synthesis, but recent evidence suggests that IGF-I is synthesized in many organs and tissues.[28] IGF-II is less dependent upon the level of hGH.[27] The protein sequences of both IGF-I and IGF-II have a homology with proinsulin.[29] Preparations of IGF devoid of hGH, insulin, testosterone, or thyroxine have been shown to have somatic and cartilage growth-stimulating potential equivalent to that of

hGH.[24,30] Regulation of IGF-I levels is a complex process that is influenced by hGH, hCS, hPRL, steroid hormones (including glucocorticoids, estrogens, and androgens), thyroid hormones, and insulin, as well as the nutritional status and certain disease states.[24,25]

While the biologic functions of hCS and hGH are similar,

Fig. 77-2 Schematic representation of hGH biosynthesis. The GH1 gene is transcribed to produce pre-mRNA containing intron sequences. Processing of the pre-mRNA includes removal of introns I to V and the addition of a poly-A tail. In 90 percent of the GH1 pre-mRNA molecules, intron II is removed. Alternative splicing of 10 percent of the pre-mRNA molecules also removes the first 15 codons of exon III. The translation products of the major and minor species of pre-mRNA yield 22 kDa and 20 kDa hGH, respectively. Solid and open rectangles represent exons and introns, and AAA = poly-A tail. k = kDa.

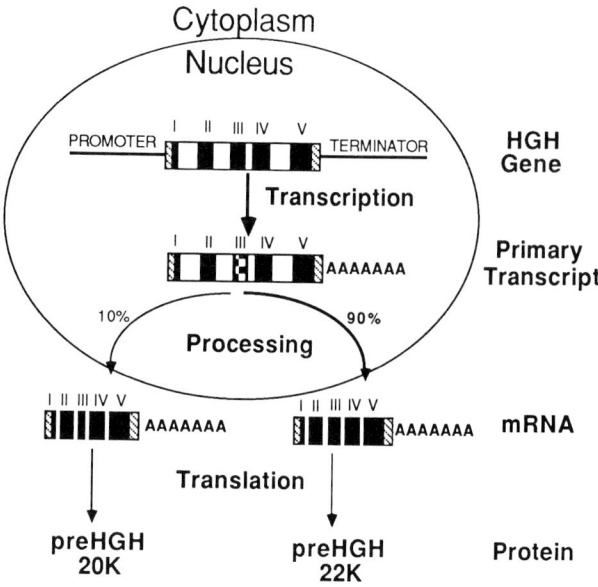

Pituitary Somatotroph

hCS is a much less potent hormone. Interestingly, hCS is present in very high concentrations in maternal serum and is thought to be partially responsible for the rise in maternal IGF-I levels that occur during pregnancy.[31] hCS shares an anti-insulin effect with hGH, and it is probably important in maternal carbohydrate and fat metabolism during pregnancy.[32-33] Interestingly, studies of two pregnancies associated with an absence of hCS indicate that the hormone is not essential for either fetal growth, maintenance of pregnancy, or postpartum lactation.[34,35]

hGH AND hCS BIOSYNTHESIS

Genetics

Chromosomal Localizations of hGH and hCS Genes. The genes for hGH and hCS lie within a 50-kb portion of human chromosome 17 (see Fig. 77-3). The hGH gene cluster has been assigned to the 17q22-q24 region, while the hPRL gene has been mapped to 6p23-q12.[36-39]

hGH Gene Cluster. Past estimates of the number of hGH-related loci within the 50-kb limits of the hGH gene cluster have ranged from 5 to 7.[4,40-47] Studies of the nucleotide sequences of isolated genomic DNA fragments containing hGH or hCS alleles as well as studies of large genomic fragments cloned into cosmid vectors currently indicate that only five loci (two hGH, two hCS, and one hCS-like) residue within the hGH gene cluster (see Fig. 77-3).[45-47] In the case of the hGH genes, one locus (GH1) encodes the known protein sequence, while the other locus (GH2) encodes a protein that differs from the primary sequence of hGH (see Fig. 77-4) at 13 amino acid residues.[41-48] In the case of the hCS genes there are three loci. The CHS1 and CSH2 loci encode proteins of identi-

cal sequence, while the CSHP1 locus encodes a protein that differs by 13 amino acids.[47] Unusual features of the hGH gene cluster include the very high degree of sequence homology retained between its component loci and their flanking regions and the large number ($\geq$ 27) of *Alu*-type middle repetitive sequences that occur throughout the cluster.[47]

Gene Structure. The nucleotide sequences of the GH1, CSHP1, CSH1, GH2, and CSH2 genes as well as allelic variants of CSH1 and CSH2 have been reported.[41,47,48] Cloned *Eco*RI-derived genomic DNA fragments of 2.6 kb contain the 2 nonallelic GH1 and GH2 genes. The 2.9-kb *Eco*RI-derived fragments contain the nonallelic CSH1 and CSH2 genes, while the 9.5-kb fragment contains the CSHP1 gene. All five genes are very similar in organization (see Figs. 77-3 and 77-4), with each having five exons interrupted at identical positions by small introns. These genes retain 92 to 98 percent homology in their immediate flanking, intervening, and coding sequences.[18] An important exception to the conserved intron/exon organizational homology is CSHP1, which contains 25 nucleotide substitutions within its exons, of which 13 give rise to amino acid substitutions.[47] Another important feature of CSHP1 is the presence of a G to A transition in the 5' or donor splice site of its second intron.[47] This substitution would prevent pre-mRNA processing at the same donor splice site utilized by the GH1, CSH1, GH2, and CSH2 loci.[49] While CSHP1 has a cryptic splice site located 45 nucleotides downstream that would yield a protein having 15 additional amino acids, this alternative splice site does not appear to be utilized, since CSHP1-specific oligonucleotides do not detect cDNA clones in libraries derived from human pituitary or placental mRNAs.[47] These data suggest that either CSHP1 is a pseudogene (an inactive gene), hence the designation CSHP1, or that it is only expressed in human tissues other than pituitary or placenta.

The GH1, GH2, CSH1, CSH2, and CSHP1 genes all have CATAAA and TATAAA promoter sequences located 85 and

Fig. 77-3 Schematic representation of the GH gene cluster and its localization on human chromosome 17. Exons, introns, and nontranslated sequences are depicted by solid, open, and shaded rectangles. GH1 encodes hGH; GH2 encodes a variant protein that differs from hGH by 13 amino acids; CSH1 and CSH2 both encode hCS. While CSHP1 has homology, no functional status has been shown.

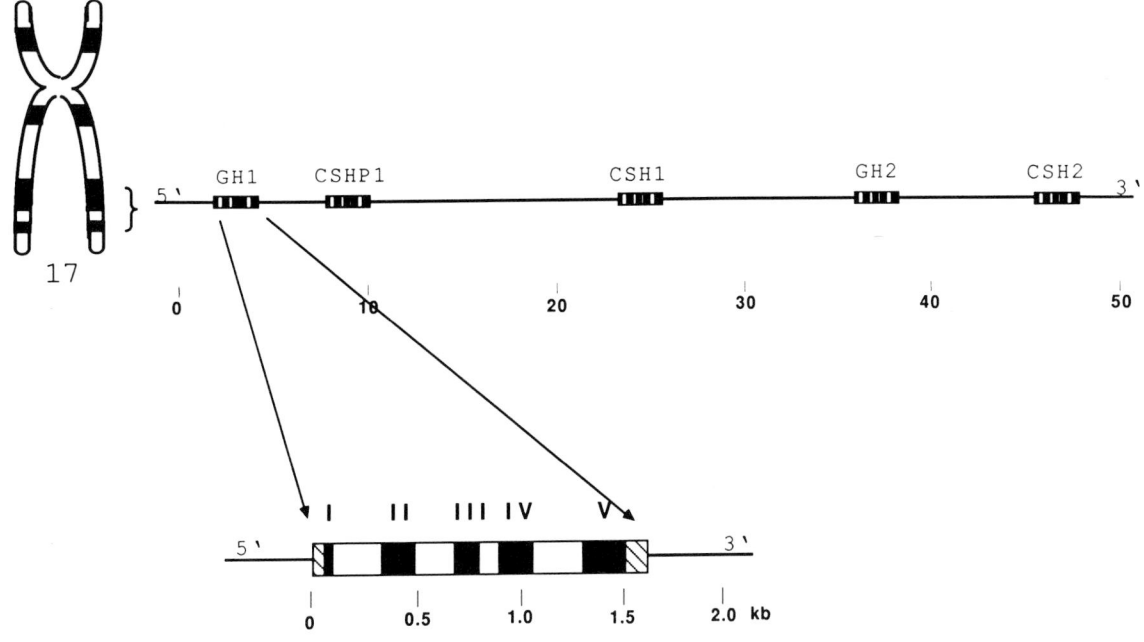

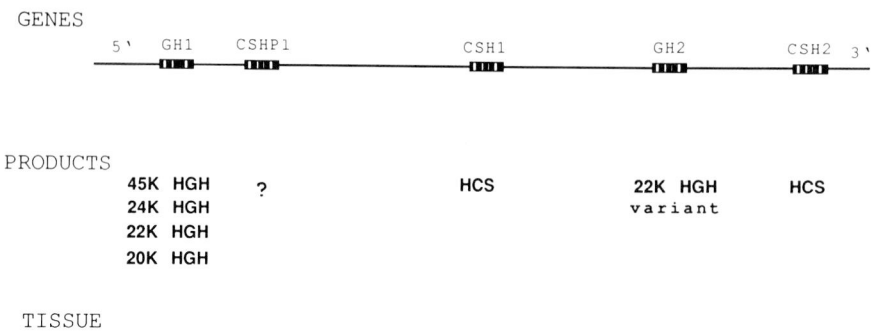

Fig. 77-4 The hGH gene cluster is shown above and the corresponding protein products and the sites of expression are shown below. k = kDa.

30 bp, respectively, upstream from their 5'-transcription initiation sites (see Fig. 77-2). In addition, all have the AATAAA sequence in their 3'-flanking regions 20 bp upstream from their polyadenylate (poly-A) addition sites.[41,47] The first four genes encode protein products of 217 amino acids (see Fig. 77-4). The length of any possible protein encoded by CSHP1 remains in question because of the gene's possible alternative splice sites and the lack of identified transcripts.[47] The 26 additional amino acids at the amino terminal of each 217 amino acid product constitute signal peptides, or leader sequences, that are important in directing transport through the membrane of the rough endoplasmic reticulum.[12] Following transport to this compartment, the signal peptides are cleaved from the 24 kDa prehormones to yield the 191 amino acid (20 kDa) mature hormones.

Introns I, II, III, and IV of GH1 are 256, 209, 93, and 253 bp in length (see Figs. 77-2 and 77-3).[4] Each intron has a 5'-GT and a 3'-AG dinucleotide as seen in other eukaryotic intervening sequences. Exon I contains 60 bp of 5'-untranslated sequences, codons −26 to −24 and the first nucleotide of codon −23 (codons −26 to −1 encode the 26 amino acids of the leader sequence with codon −26 encoding the initial methionine residue). Exon II encodes the remainder of the signal peptide sequence and amino acids 1 to 31 of mature hGH (see Fig. 77-1). Exons III, IV, and V encode amino acids 32–71, 72–126, and 127–191, respectively.[4,47] The last exon includes 112 bp of 3'-flanking sequence that extends to the poly-A addition site. An ATAAA sequence lies 20 bp upstream from the poly-A addition site. The hGH and hCS genes diverge in

their 3'-nontranscribed regions, where the genes for GH1 and GH2 contain complete members of an *Alu* family repeat, while the hCS genes all contain a truncated *Alu* sequence of 25-bp length.[41,47]

Evolution of the hGH Gene Cluster. The extensive homology between the various loci within the hGH gene cluster suggests that this multigene family arose through a series of gene duplication events. The finding of a middle-dispersed *Alu* repeat 100 bp downstream from the poly-A site of GH1 and GH2 but only a truncated *Alu* repeat in the corresponding region of CS1 and CS2 and CSHP1 suggests that the truncated *Alu* repeat represents the 3' end point of homology.[46,47] The presence of an *Alu* repeat at the breakpoint also suggests that the mechanism of duplication involved unequal recombination between two nonallelic *Alu* repeats as has been reported for nonreciprocal recombination events in the globin and low density lipoprotein receptor genes.[50,51] Interestingly, sequences extending at least 500 bp upstream from the hGH and hCS genes show very high homology. This homology includes a 5'-*Eco*RI-derived fragment of 4.7 to 5.3 kb flanking each of the hGH and hCS loci. These *Eco*RI-derived fragments contain three *Alu* repeats located in analogous positions.[46,47] The hGH gene cluster is hypothesized to have arisen by serial unequal crossover events involving copies of these repeated segments.[18,20,46,47] *Alu-Alu* recombination probably constituted the first duplication event that yielded a GH-CS unit (see Fig. 77-5). The second hypothesized duplication event created a 5'-GH1-CSHP1-GH2-CSH2-3' cluster. Subsequently the CSH1

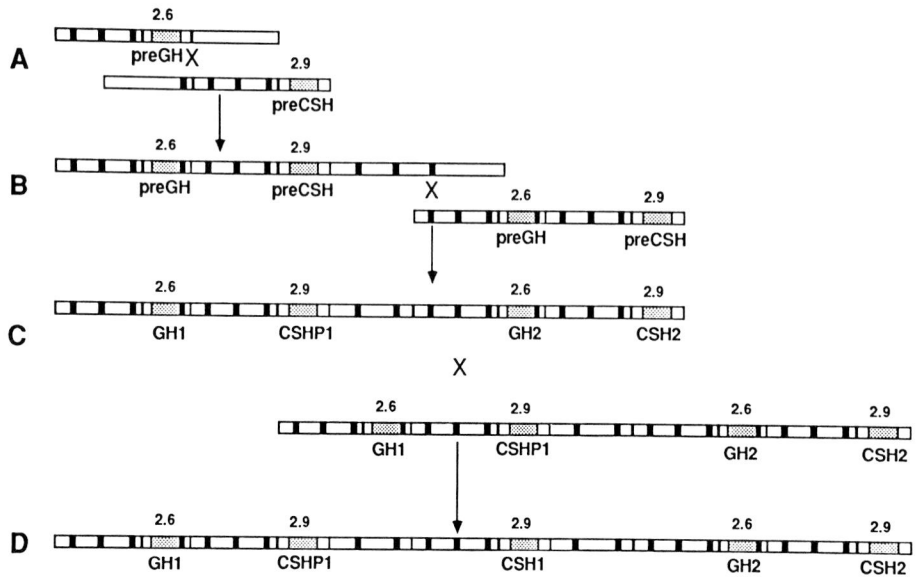

Fig. 77-5 Schematic diagram of the evolution of the hGH gene cluster. The GH/CS precursor gene contained in a 2.6-kb *Eco*RI fragment is shown in A. The product of the first duplication event and the resulting GH and CS genes are shown in B. The GH1-CSHP1-GH2-CSH2 products of the second duplication event are shown in C. Mechanism of the final duplication event which yielded the complete GH gene cluster is shown in D with the partial *Eco*RI restriction map noted above the cluster.

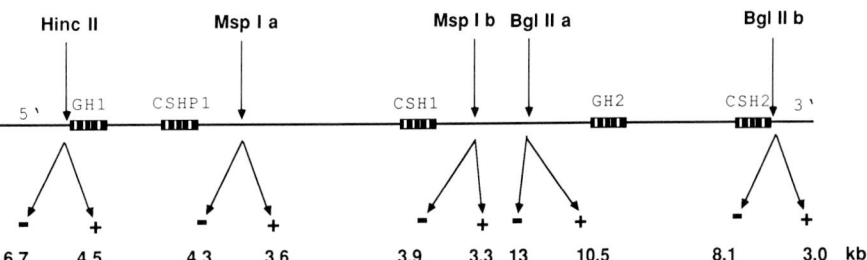

Fig. 77-6 Locations of 5 polymorphic restriction endonuclease cleavage sites in the hGH gene cluster detected with GH1 cDNA as a probe. The size (kb) of the alternative alleles is shown below.

locus probably arose by another unequal crossover between *Alu* repeats to give the final 5'-GH1-CSHP1-CSH1-GH2-CSH2-3' cluster (see Fig. 77-5).[18,20,46,47]

DNA Polymorphisms. Six restriction fragment length polymorphisms (RFLPs) have been reported in the hGH gene cluster (see Fig. 77-6).[20] Of these 6 RFLPs, 5 (two *Bgl*II, two *Msp*I, and one *Hinc*II) occur in blacks, Mediterraneans, and Northern Europeans.[20,45] The sixth, a *Bam*HI-derived RFLP, occurs predominantly in blacks. Haplotypes constructed for these RFLPs display strong nonrandom associations. Interestingly, the strongest associations are found between the RFLPs closely related by evolution rather than between those that are in closest physical proximity.[20] The observations of strong linkage disequilibrium between GH1 and GH2 and between CSHP1 and CSH1 and CSH2 support the idea of an evolution of the hGH gene cluster through the serial duplications described above (see Fig. 77-5).

Ontogeny and Disease Manifestation

The hGH and hCS genes are expressed in different tissues in different relative amounts and at different times during human development (see Fig. 77-4). Fetal production of hCS is roughly proportional to the syncytiotrophoblastic cell mass.[52] The amount synthesized at 34 to 37 weeks of gestation is four- to fivefold higher than at the end of the first trimester. At term, 15 to 20 percent of poly-A+ placental RNA is hCS mRNA, and 1 g/day hCS is produced.[53,54] Maternal serum hCS levels reach 3 to 8 μg/ml, about 300 times fetal levels. The CSH1 and CSH2 genes are expressed in an approximately 1:1 ratio at term.[55] Since production of hCS is normally limited to placental tissue, none is produced after birth. Complete deficiency of hCS production has been detected during pregnancy by monitoring maternal serum levels.[34,35] The presence of a normal growth pattern during fetal life and infancy in these cases suggests that hCS is not required for fetal or extrauterine growth.[56]

Synthesis of hGH in the fetal pituitary occurs by 7–9 weeks' gestation.[57–58] Human GH appears in fetal serum at the end of the first trimester, and its level increases rapidly to reach a peak of 100 to 150 ng/ml at about 20 weeks' gestation.[58] Mean fetal plasma levels then decline to about 30 ng/ml at term. Levels of hGH continue to decline for the first several months after birth, and in childhood the basal levels of hGH are similar to those of adults. Secretion of hGH occurs in pulses, and the frequency and amplitude of these increase during puberty. Secretion continues throughout life, declining in old age.

While hGH production occurs in the fetus, its presence seems to be less important to fetal growth than maternal and nutritional factors.[57–59] For example, anencephalic fetuses and those with aplasia of the pituitary gland as well as those with absent hGH production due to genetic defects are of relatively normal size at birth. Growth between birth and puberty is affected by hormonal and familial factors as well as nutrition. Growth retardation may occur due to deficiencies in hGH or other hormonal deficiencies, as well as chronic illness. The combined actions of hGH, sex steroids, and IGF-I are required for the pubertal growth spurt.[60] Human growth hormone production continues throughout life and is limited to the anterior pituitary.[61]

The onset of growth retardation due to hGH deficiency usually occurs after birth. Fetuses who are homozygous for GH1 gene deletions have relatively normal fetal growth suggesting that other gene products are primarily responsible for stimulation of embryonic and fetal growth.[62] Infants with severe congenital hGH deficiency manifest growth retardation by 4 to 6 months of age. Children with acquired or progressive hGH deficiency may appear to have had relatively normal growth until several months or years of age, but their growth data often reveals a decreased growth velocity in infancy. Finally, certain growth disorders may not present until puberty. The short stature of African pygmies, for example, is due to absence of the normal pubertal increase in IGF-I levels with resultant lack of a pubertal growth spurt.[63]

hGH and hCS Biosynthesis

Normal and Alternative Transcription Initiation. The primary transcripts of GH1 and GH2 and CSH1 and CSH2 genes are about 1650 nucleotides in length (see Figs. 77-2 and 77-3). In the case of the CSH1 and CSH2 genes, two different initiation sites for transcription have been demonstrated.[64] While the majority of transcripts initiate 30 bp downstream from the TATAAA sequence, about 5 percent of the transcripts initiate 30 bp downstream from a CATAAA sequence that is located 55 bp upstream of the TATAAA sequence.

Normal and Alternative Splicing. Processing of the transcripts, including excision of intervening sequences and splicing of the five exons, yields mRNAs that encode the prehormones of 217 amino acids. The mRNA sizes expected to correspond to unprocessed and processed hCS RNA have been documented in Northern blot analysis of term placental RNA.[54] Placental total RNA contained a predominance of hCS mRNA that was about 860 nucleotides in length, while nuclear RNA also contained species that were 990, 1200, 1460, and 1760 nucleotides in length. These higher molecular weight nuclear RNA species represent intermediate and unspliced transcripts of hCS mRNA.

Alternative splicing of the primary GH1 transcripts is the basis of the 20 kDa hGH variant peptide (see Figs. 77-2 and 77-4)[11,13] in contrast to the 22 kDa standard hGH. The 20 kDa variant constitutes between 5 and 10 percent of the total hGH in pituitary extracts, and it differs from the major 22 kDa hGH polypeptide by having an internal deletion of 15 amino acids (residues 32–46).[13,14] The triplets that encode these 15 amino acids begin precisely at the 5′ end of exon III (see Fig. 77-2). In addition, 45 bp downstream from this point the sequence preceding the codon for amino acid 47 corresponds to consensus sequences for splice acceptor sites.[44,65–67] Thus, the 45 nucleotides contained in the 5′ end of exon III are deleted by alternative splicing at the cryptic splice acceptor site that precedes codon 47, and this results in the deletion of codons 32 through 46.

Variant Peptides. Multiple size and charge variants of hGH in addition to the 20 kDa alternative splice product have been described (see Fig. 77-4). These include the 45 kDa dimers and two 24 kDa variants that result from posttranslational modifications of hGH. One 24 kDa variant results from retention of the 26-amino acid signal peptide sequence of pre-hGH. The other 24 kDa variant results from cleavage between amino acids residues 139 and 140 of the normal 22 kDa form of hGH.[4] While each may represent a unique hormone with specific receptors and physiological functions, only in the case of the latter, 24 kDa variant is a specialized function reported. This variant may be responsible for the lactogenic activity of hGH.[68] While none of these variants are thought to represent products of the CSHP1 or GH2 genes, specific radioimmune assays to detect these products in serum are not available. An alternative method of detection of expression of these gene products is to screen cDNA libraries derived from various tissues. Using this approach, GH2-specific mRNA has been detected in placental tissue.[44,47]

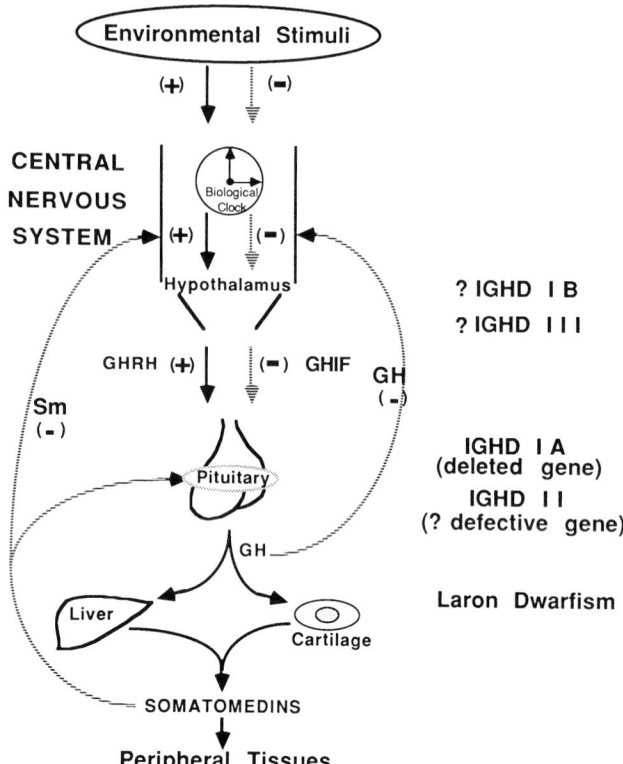

Fig. 77-7 Regulation of hGH secretion by various tissues and organs. The probable sites of derangements responsible for various familial types of hGH deficiency are indicated on right.

Physiological Regulation

Gene Structure. Human GH production and secretion by the anterior pituitary gland is under complex regulatory control (see Figs. 77-2 and 77-7). At the level of transcription hGH production is increased by thyroid hormone, glucocorticoids, and growth hormone releasing hormone (GHRH).[69,70] The DNA sequences required for the effects of thyroid and glucocorticoid hormone induction appear to be different. The thyroid hormone receptor complex binds to GH1 flanking sequences −290 to −129 bp upstream from the transcription initiation site.[71] Additional studies of the local effects of thyroid hormone on GH1 chromatin indicate that four sites may function in transcription: one is located over 1000 bp upstream from the GH1 promoter; a second within the first 200 bp upstream from the origin of transcription; a third at the position of the TATA sequence; and the fourth is within the first intron.[72] Sequences of hGH that preferentially bind to glucocorticoid receptor complexes also include immediate 5′-flanking sequences as well as a portion of the first intron.[73] The effects of thyroid and glucocorticoid hormones appear to be independent and additive.[69] In addition to inducing GH1 transcription glucocorticoids may also enhance its expression through stabilization of the mRNA.[74]

In contrast to hGH relatively little is known about the regulation of hCS secretion. Synthesis of hCS is normally limited to the syncytiotrophoblastic cells of the placenta. Thyroid hormone may also enhance hCS transcription, since the thyroid hormone–receptor complex binds to analogous promoter regions of the CSH genes.[71]

Hormonal Modulators and Interactions. Secretion of hGH into the peripheral circulation is controlled by at least two hy-

pothalamic factors, growth hormone releasing hormone (GHRH or somatocrinin) and somatostatin (GHIF) (see Fig. 77-7).[75,76] Secretion of hGH into the general circulation is promoted by the 44 amino acid GHRH, and pulsatile release of hypothalamic GHRH is the principal cause of the pulsatile pattern of hGH secretion.[77] Somatostatin is a 14 amino acid neuropeptide that inhibits release of hGH.[76,78,79] In turn, GHRH and GHIF are modulated by the effects of various environmental and biologic factors including stress, sleep, hypoglycemia, chemicals (L-dopa, chlorpromazine), and hormones (androgens, estrogens, hGH, and vasopressin) on the central nervous system and hypothalamus.[75] Apart from sleep, most physiologic stimuli of hGH release are inhibited by α-adrenergic blocking agents such as phentolamine, and release is stimulated by α-adrenergic agonists such as clonidine. β-Adrenergic blockade increases hGH secretion and propranolol is used to stimulate hGH secretion in provocative tests. Stimulation of hGH release by L-dopa is mainly through its conversion to norepinephrine. Estrogens enhance hGH secretion, and hGH responses in males increase with the onset of puberty due to androgens.[75] High hGH levels are thought to inhibit hGH release by negative feedback. In conditions in which the level of IGF-I is low, such as severe malnutrition, these low levels may function to increase hGH release.[25,27]

The complex interactions of various factors that modulate hGH synthesis and secretion result in its pulsatile secretion pattern. After the neonatal period, basal plasma levels of hGH are low throughout most of the 24-h daily cycle. Intermittent pulses of secretion occur in response to physiological stimuli, and a consistent surge lasting about 2 h occurs 1 to 2 h after sleep begins. Additional pulses of secretion occur with exercise, stress, or high protein meals, while hyperglycemia suppresses hGH release. The mean concentration of hGH in plasma calculated from continuous 24-h monitoring is 2 to 4 ng/ml in young adults and 5 to 8 ng/ml in children and adolescents. Based on mean hGH plasma levels and calculated clearance of hGH, the 24-h secretion rate in young men is about 1 to 2 mg/day.[80]

GENETIC DISORDERS OF hGH OR hCS SYNTHESIS AND ACTION

Background

Since neither hGH or hCS is essential for fetal growth, newborns with complete deficiency are usually of normal length and weight. The presence of micropenis or fasting hypoglycemia in some affected infants may be early diagnostic clues.[81] Linear growth of affected individuals continues at a low rate, falling into the subnormal range by 6 to 12 months of age, and the height becomes progressively retarded with advancing age. In isolated hGH deficiency (IGHD) the skeletal maturation or bone development age usually exhibits a delay that is proportional to the retardation in height. The presence of a fine, wrinkled skin similar to that of premature aging often occurs in adult patients.[82] Puberty may be delayed until the late teens, but IGHD is quite compatible with fertility in both sexes. Concomitant deficiency of luteinizing hormone (LH), follicle-stimulating hormone (FSH), thyrotropin (TSH), and/or adrenocorticotropic hormone (ACTH) along with hGH deficiency is called panhypopituitarism. With these additional hormone deficiencies, the retardation of growth and skeletal maturation tends to be more severe, and spontaneous puberty may not occur.

Diagnosis of hGH Deficiency

Basal levels of hGH are high in normal newborns. Very low or undetectable levels during the neonatal period are significant, and hypoglycemia in the neonatal period without abnormalities in insulin or cortisol levels should be evaluated by determining an hGH level. Serum hGH levels of < 10 ng/ml in the presence of hypoglycemia and low insulin concentrations should be considered highly suggestive of hGH deficiency. In such cases thyroxine and TSH should be measured, since primary hypothyroidism can impair the response to hGH. The small genitalia of males with hGH deficiency may or may not be associated with gonadotropin deficiency. If an infant does not have hypoglycemia or other signs that make IGHD likely, provocative tests may be delayed to permit observations of the growth velocity over several months.

During early childhood the presence of short stature and decreased growth velocity provide easy clues to hGH deficiency. Most children with hGH deficiency have truncal obesity in addition to significant short stature, and their facial appearance often suggests that they are younger than their chronological age. Secondary dentition is often delayed, and the voice is usually high-pitched. Small genitalia in males and features associated with deficiencies of other pituitary hormones may also be present.

In the school-age child with IGHD the height is usually 2.5 to 3 SD below the mean.[83,84] This may not be true for those with deficiency of recent onset such as that caused by craniopharyngioma or other CNS tumors, head trauma, histiocytosis

X, meningitis, or head irradiation.[75,80] The parental heights should be used to calculate a target range for the child's height appropriate for the genetic background. Also the weight-for-height percentile should be determined, because IGHD children, in contrast to those with short stature due to nonendocrine causes, tend to be obese. Finally, determinations of upper/lower segment body ratios and skeletal radiographs are helpful in detecting the various skeletal dysplasias. While most school-age children with IGHD will have bone ages that are 2 or more SD below the mean for their age, untreated patients with panhypopituitarism may have even greater retardation of the bone age with epiphyseal closure delayed beyond the third decade.

Confirmatory Tests of hGH Deficiency

There is no single laboratory test or procedure that will establish with 100 percent accuracy the presence or absence or hGH deficiency. Most tests require the measurement of stimulated serum levels of hGH by radioimmunoassay. Since levels of hGH are low throughout most of the 24-h period, results of single random blood samples usually are not helpful. For this reason provocative tests of hGH secretory reserve are utilized. Those most frequently used include stimulation of hGH release by exercise, L-dopa, insulin, arginine, clonidine, glucagon, or combinations of exercise plus L-dopa or insulin plus arginine.[80,85,86] An inadequate hGH response (peak plasma levels < 7 ng/ml) following two or more of the provocative tests suggests hGH deficiency. Peak levels between 7 and 15 ng/ml are compatible with partial deficiency, and levels over 15 ng/ml exclude deficiency.[86]

Patients should be carefully evaluated for other systemic diseases prior to testing for hGH deficiency. The usual screening tests for evaluation of a child with significant short stature include determination of levels of serum electrolytes, creatinine, thyroid hormone/thyroid-stimulating hormone, chromosome analysis in females, lateral skull films, and bone age determinations. Disorders that should be considered include: Bartter syndrome, craniopharyngioma, hypothyroidism, renal tubular acidosis or chronic renal failure, Turner syndrome, and systemic diseases such as congenital heart disease, cystic fibrosis, etc.[86] Selected testing procedures for hGH status include the following:

Postexercise Test. A blood sample for hGH is taken 25 min after strenuous exercise—for example, after 15 min on a bicycle ergometer or after climbing stairs. About 80 percent of healthy children will have normal hGH levels.[87]

L-Dopa Tests. Following administration of an oral dose of L-dopa (125 mg for subjects under 10 kg, 250 mg for those weighing 10 to 30 kg, and 500 mg for those over 30 kg or 50 mg/1.75 m^2 to a maximum of 500 mg), about 80 percent of normal children will respond.[85,88]

Insulin Tolerance Test. Blood samples for hGH levels are taken at 0, 20, 30, 45, 60, 90, 120, and 150 min after administration of intravenous insulin (0.1 u/kg.)[85,86] About 90 percent of normal children will respond.[89] For a valid test the blood glucose level must fall to less than one-half the fasting level. Precautions must be taken to prevent severe hypoglycemia. The insulin dose should be decreased to 0.05 u/kg in those with suspected panhypopituitary dwarfism.

Table 77-1 Genetic Disorders of hGH or hCS Biosynthesis or Action

Disorder	Inheritance*	Endogenous hGH	Response to hGH
Isolated hGH deficiency:			
IA	AR	Absent	Often temporary
IB	AR	Decreased	Present
II	AD	Decreased	Present
III	X-linked	Decreased	Present
"Bioinactive" hGH	? AR	? Inactive	? Present
Laron dwarfism	AR	Normal or increased	Absent
Panhypopituitary dwarfism:			
I	AR	Decreased†	Present
II	X-linked	Decreased†	Present
EEC syndrome	AR	Deficient†	Present
Fanconi pancytopenia	AR	Deficient	Present
Holoprosencephaly	AD or AR	Absent or deficient†	NA‡
Pituitary aplasia	? AR	Absent†	Present
Rieger syndrome	AD	Deficient†	? Present
Isolated hCS deficiency:			
IA	AR	Absent	NA
IB	AR	Decreased	NA

*AR = autosomal recessive; AD = autosomal dominant.
†Conditions in which deficiencies of hGH and other anterior pituitary hormones (ACTH, FSH, LH, TSH) occur.
‡NA = nonapplicable.

Intravenous Arginine Test. Blood samples for hGH are taken at 0, 30, 60, 90, 120, and 150 min after administration of intravenous arginine (0.5 g/kg; maximum dose 40 g) over 30 min.[90] Between 80 and 90 percent of normal children respond.[85,86,90] This test is contraindicated in children with diabetes insipidus or severe renal disease.

Oral Clonidine Test. Blood samples for hGH are taken at 0, 30, 60, 90, 120, and 150 min after oral administration of clonidine (0.15 mg/m²).[86,91–94] This test has a comparable reliability (about 90 percent) to the insulin tolerance test but may be safer.[94] Side effects include hypotension and drowsiness.

Intramuscular Glucagon Test. Blood samples for hGH are taken 0, 30, 60, 90, 120, and 150 min after the administration of glucagon (30 to 100 μg/kg; maximum dose 1 mg) intramuscularly.[86,93] About 55 percent of normal adults respond, and the reliability is improved with oral administration of propranolol prior to glucagon administration (note: this increases the danger of hypoglycemia).[94]

Exercise and L-Dopa Test. Following 20 min of climbing stairs, blood samples are drawn 0, 30, 60, 90, and 120 min after administration of 10 mg/kg L-dopa orally.[95] This test is reported to increase the sensitivity of either component test.

Insulin Plus Arginine Test. Blood samples for hGH are taken at 0, 20, 30, 45, 60, and 90 min after the administration of intravenous insulin (0.1 or 0.05 u/kg, see above). Immediately after obtaining the 90-min sample, intravenous arginine (0.5 g/kg) is given over 30 min, and samples are taken at 30, 45, 60, 90, and 120 min.[86] The combination of these two tests provokes response in about 95 percent of normal children.[96]

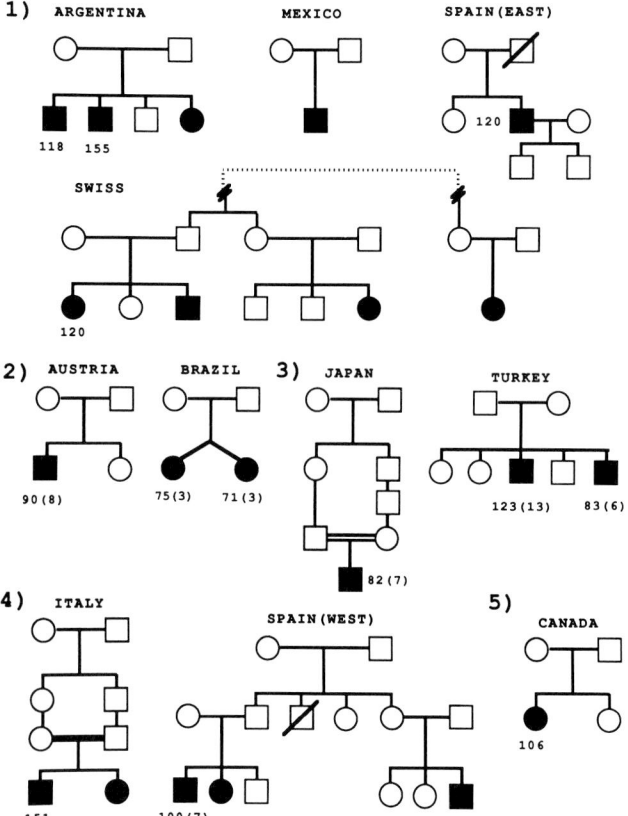

Fig. 77-8 Pedigrees of families each having one or more individuals affected (solid symbols) with IGHD-IA. The country of origin and adult heights are given above and below the pedigree symbols.

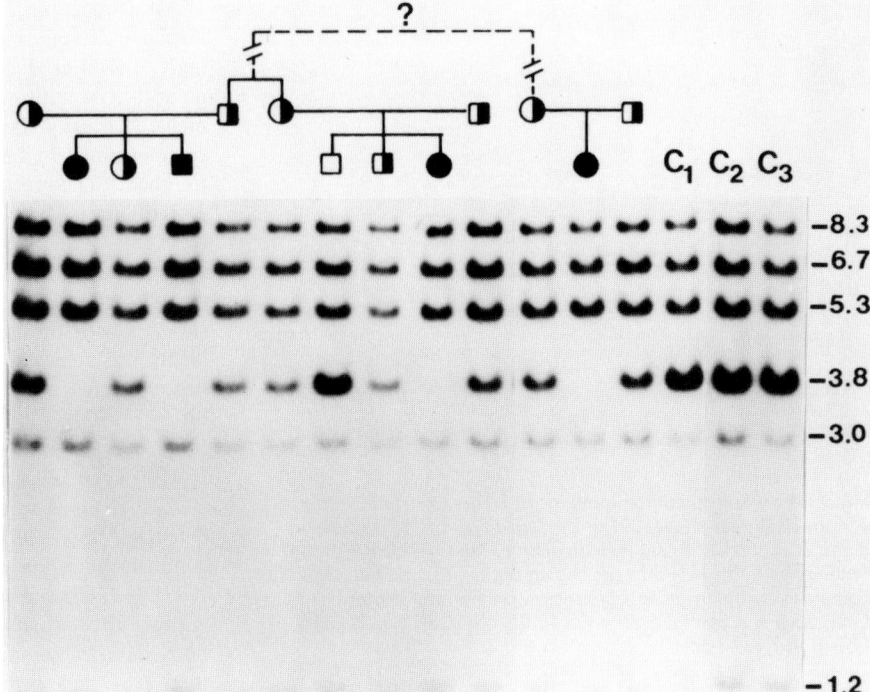

Fig. 77-9 Autoradiogram patterns of DNA from three Swiss families and three controls (C₁₋₃) following digestion with *BamHI* and hybridization to the GH1 cDNA probe. The multiple bands seen correspond to DNA fragments containing the various genes that comprise the GH gene cluster (see Figs. 77-3 to 77-6). In decreasing order of size the fragments and genes included are 8.3 kb CSHP1, 6.7-kb CSC2, 5.3-kb CSH1, 3.8-kb GH1, and 3.0- plus 1.2-kb GH2.[46,117] Note that the affected individuals lack and their parents have decreased amounts of the 3.8-kb fragment as compared to the controls (C₁₋₃).[117]

Etiology of hGH Deficiency

Estimates of the frequency of hGH deficiency range from 1 in 4000 to 1 in 10,000 births in the British Isles.[97–99] Most cases are sporadic and are presumed to be secondary to a wide variety of etiologies including CNS insults or defects such as septo-optic dysplasia, head trauma, meningitis, cerebral edema, congenital infections, histiocytosis X, chromosome anomalies, cranial tumors, or cranial radiation.[75,80,100–107] In families in which there is consanguinity or a second case occurs, a genetic etiology should be suspected. Estimates of the number of cases having an affected first-degree relative (parent or sib) range from 3 to 30 percent in different series.[98,108,109] There are 15 recognized Mendelian disorders involving the GHRH-hGH–IGF-I axis that can lead to decreased hGH or hCS production or action (Table 77-1). These disorders differ in their phenotypes (degree of hGH or other hormonal deficiencies) as well as their modes of inheritance.

Isolated hGH Deficiency (IGHD). There are four known Mendelian types of IGHD (see Table 77-1). These disorders differ in their degree of hGH deficiency, mode of inheritance, or responsiveness to hGH replacement. Of the Mendelian types of IGHD, type IA (originally referred to as type A) is the most severe. Subjects with IGHD type IA occasionally

have short body length at birth and hypoglycemia, but severe dwarfism by 6 months of age is a consistent finding. In response to exogenous hGH, they have a strong initial anabolic response which is frequently followed by the development of anti-hGH antibodies in sufficient titer to cause an arrest of response to hGH replacement.[110–112] These features led Illig et al. to hypothesize that individuals affected with IGHD-IA had prenatal deficiency of endogenous hGH secretion causing a lack of immune tolerance to exogenous hGH.[112]

The pedigrees of 11 unrelated families each having one or more individuals with several of these clinical features are shown in Fig. 77-8. The affected individuals are indicated by solid symbols, and the numbers below the symbols indicate their adult heights. To determine if the GH1 genes were altered in these subjects, genomic DNA was isolated from the leukocytes and each subject's GH1 gene complement was determined by Southern blotting and hybridization with ³²P-labeled GH1 cDNA (see Chap. 2).[114–116] The affected individuals were found to be homozygous for GH1 gene deletions (see Fig. 77-9).[46,117] Additional studies of DNA from affected individuals in pedigrees from other countries (Fig. 77-8) also revealed homozygous deletions of their GH1 genes.[118–121] Additional patients from Israel and France have been described,[122,123] so that over 25 cases are known.

Fig. 77-10 Schematic representation of the hGH gene cluster showing the location of *HindIII* (arrows) and selected *BamHI* (vertical lines) restriction sites below. The locations of four known deletions of various loci in the hGH gene cluster are shown at the bottom with dark and open rectangles indicating obligatory deletions and ranges of end points, respectively.

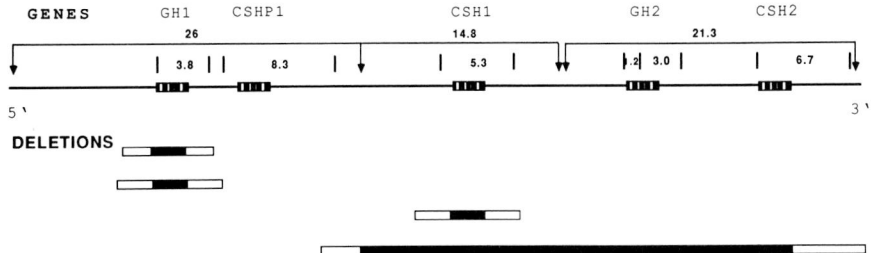

GH GENE DELETIONS

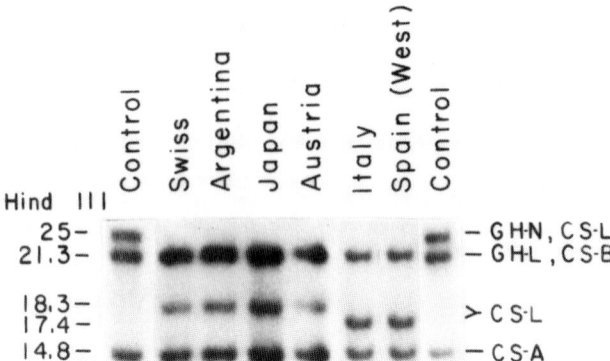

Fig. 77-11 *Autoradiogram patterns of DNAs from individuals of various pedigrees shown in Fig. 77-8 and two controls following digestion with* HindIII *and hybridization to the GH1 cDNA probe. Fragment sizes in kilobases are shown on the left and the gene(s) contained by the fragments are shown on the right. Note: GH-N = GH1; CS-L = CSHP1; CS-A = CSH1; CS-B = CSH2; and GH-V = GH₂ (see Fig. 77-10).*

To determine if the deletions were heterogeneous in affected individuals whose pedigrees are shown in Fig. 77-8, aliquots of DNA were digested with *Hind*III. Since both GH1 and CSHP1 reside in the same 25-kb fragment (Fig. 77-10), deletions of GH1 should decrease the size of the fragment accordingly.[46,117] The results of these studies are shown in Fig. 77-11.[119] Note that the Swiss, Argentinean, Japanese, and Austrian subjects all have 18.3-kb fragments replacing their normal 25-kb fragments. This indicates that individuals in these four nonrelated families all have deletions of approximately 6.7 kb, that include their GH1 genes. The Italian and Western Spanish subjects have an overlapping but larger deletion of 7.6 kb, confirming heterogeneity of the deletions.[121,124] The majority (14 of 19, or ~75 percent) of deletions identified by me in this way are those of approximately 6.7 kb depicted just below GH1 in Fig. 77-10. A minority (5 of 19, or ~25 percent) of deletions are 7.6 kb in size (depicted immediately beneath the 6.7-kb deletions in Fig. 77-10).[124] Further evidence for heterogeneity of these deletions is seen when RFLPs containing components of the remaining loci within the GH gene clusters are studied (Figs. 77-6 and 77-12).[124] Interestingly, the affected individuals from four different families (Argentina, Austria, Japan, and Switzerland) yield three different patterns, or haplotypes, when all the RFLP sites are examined (see Fig. 77-12 and Table 77-2). The explanation for the observed heterogeneity in deletion size and RFLP haplotypes is that the deletions from different families represent recurring events, and thus each is potentially different.[125]

The peak hGH levels obtained after various stimulation tests and the IGF-I levels obtained prior to provocative testing for a subject with each of the four deletion types is shown in Table 77-2.[124] The levels of hGH indicated are extremely low and represent the basal levels determined by the radioimmunoassay. Also, of the patients studied by me, 14 of 17, or 82 percent, developed high titers of anti-hGH antibodies during replacement which blocked the growth response to exogenous hGH.[117–120,124–126] Interestingly, 1 of the 14 who developed blocking antibodies to pituitary-derived hGH has subsequently shown a good initial response when treated with recombinant DNA–derived methionyl-hGH.[127] In addition 3 of

17, or 18 percent, have shown fair to good long-term growth responses despite high titers of anti-hGH antibodies. Interestingly, Laron et al. have reported cases of IGHD-IA in which no anti-hGH antibodies were detected following hGH replacement.[122] Finally the clinical response to treatment with hGH as determined by height increments ranged widely from poor to good. The growth responses are shown on composite growth charts (Figs. 77-13 and 77-14) in which the solid lines represent growth without and the dotted lines represent growth during hGH replacement therapy.[118–122,124] It is of interest to note that better growth responses occurred in the subjects with the larger, 7.6-kb deletion.[119,120] Normal adult height was achieved in one subject with this deletion who was begun on hGH replacement within the first 3 months after birth (Fig. 77-14).[121]

IGHD Type IB. A second autosomal recessive type of IGHD (IGHD-IB) is characterized by the production of deficient but detectable amounts of hGH after provocative stimuli. This contrasts with the absence of hGH secretion that occurs in IGHD-IA. Criteria used to identify IGHD-IB subjects include (1) two affected sibs whose parents are of normal height; (2) no demonstrable anatomic cause for IGHD; (3) stature more than 2 SD below the mean for age and sex; (4) significantly delayed bone age; (5) peak hGH levels less than 7 ng/ml after provocative tests; (6) deficient growth velocity that responded to exogenous hGH; (7) normal thyroid function; (8) spontaneous pubertal changes at an appropriate bone age; and

Fig. 77-12 *Autoradiogram patterns of genomic DNA from affected individuals of four pedigrees shown in Fig. 77-8 and one control following digestion with* BglII *(top) or* MspI *(bottom) and hybridization to the GH1 cDNA probe. Fragment sizes in kilobases are shown on the right (note the* MspI *fragments < 3.3 kb are not shown).*

GH GENE DELETIONS

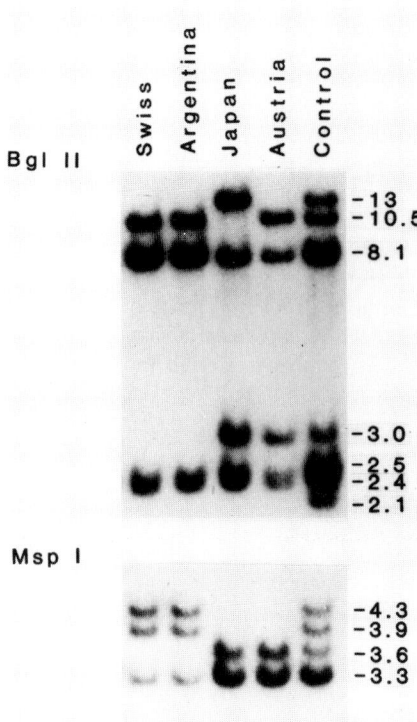

Table 77-2 GH1 Gene Deletions

Origin	Size, kb	BglII MspI haplotype	Peak GH, ng/ml	IGF-I, U/ml	Growth hormone antibodies	Response
Argentina	6.7	+ – – –	?	0.21*	+	Poor-fair
China					?	Not treated
Mexico					+	Poor
Spain (East)					?	Poor
Switzerland			2.0	0.20*	+	Poor
Austria	6.7	+ + + +	1.0	0.34†	+	Poor
Brazil‡					+	Poor-good
Japan	6.7	– + + +	1.0	0.38†	+	Poor
Brazil‡					+	Poor-good
Turkey§		– + ??			+	Good
Italy	7.6	– + + +	0.81	0.20*	+	Fair-good
Spain (West)					–	Fair
United States¶		?? + +			+	Poor
Canada**	~7.0	+ – – –	?	?	+	Poor

*Normal range for IGF-I is 0l46–1.5 U/ml.
†Normal range for IGF-I is 0.5–2 U/ml.
‡Affected sibs have two different RFLP haplotypes. In addition, one is not responding and the other is responding well to hGH replacement.
§Patient was refractory to hGH replacement but is responding well to Met-GH treatment.
¶Parents of the patients are Armenian.
**Patient also has osteogenesis imperfecta.

(9) absence of immunodeficiency or history of recurrent infections in patients from pedigrees having only affected males.[45]

In contrast to IGHD-IA subjects, those with IGHD-IB have no detectable GH1 gene deletions.[45] To determine if subtle GH1 gene alterations were responsible that did not cause detectable alterations in fragment sizes on Southern blots, the *Bgl* II, *Msp* I, and an additional *Hinc* II RFLP were used as markers for the GH1 gene in linkage analysis of family members. Among the 12 pairs of sibs affected with IGHD-IB whose pedigrees are shown in Fig. 77-15, those in families 1 to 7 were discordant in the RFLPs and hence GH1 genes that were inherited from one or both parents (Fig. 77-16). Thus, we conclude that in these families a majority (at least 7 of 12) of the mutation(s) causing the IGHD-IB phenotype segregate independently of the GH1 gene cluster and that the mutation(s) causing IGHD-IB involves a nonlinked locus or loci (possibly important for GHRH production or release, or alternatively important for development of somatotropic cell function).[45] In the remaining five families (families 8 to 12, Fig. 77-16) the affected sib pairs were shown to have the same two GH1 alleles only in the case of families 9 and 11. The RFLPs were not sufficiently informative in families 8, 10, and 12 to determine if the affected sibs did or did not share identical GH1 alleles.

The clinical criteria used to classify the IGHD-IB phenotype includes an accelerated growth response to exogenous hGH replacement.[45,126] This observation and lack of anti-hGH antibodies in those studied suggests that sufficient endogenous hGH secretion occurs to prevent the anti-hGH antibody production that characterizes IGHD-IA. Interestingly, some subjects with IGHD-IB have been shown to have intact secretory granules in their somatotropes and to exhibit normal hGH responses to GHRH infusions.[128,129] This observation indicates that the GH1 allele(s) are capable of expression and suggests that defects in GHRH synthesis or secretion may underlie this disorder.

IGHD-II. A third type of IGHD (IGHD-II) has an autosomal dominant mode of inheritance. Affected individuals from different kindreds differ in the severity of hGH deficiency, their propensity to develop hypoglycemia, as well as their response to exogenous hGH.[130–133] The same criteria used to diagnose IGHD-IB apply to IGHD-II with the exception that a parent and one or more children are affected in IGHD-II and, if possible, X-linked inheritance is excluded by the presence of male-to-male transmission.

The pedigree of a large family having multiple individuals affected with IGHD, good response to exogenous hGH, and

Fig. 77-13 Composite growth charts of males homozygous for GH1 gene deletions whose pedigrees are shown in Fig. 77-8. Solid lines indicate growth without and dotted lines growth during treatment with exogenous hGH.

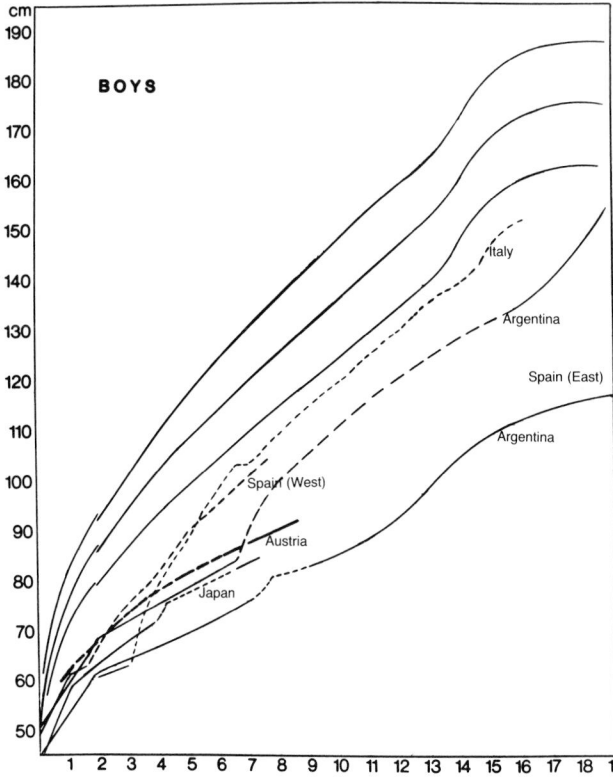

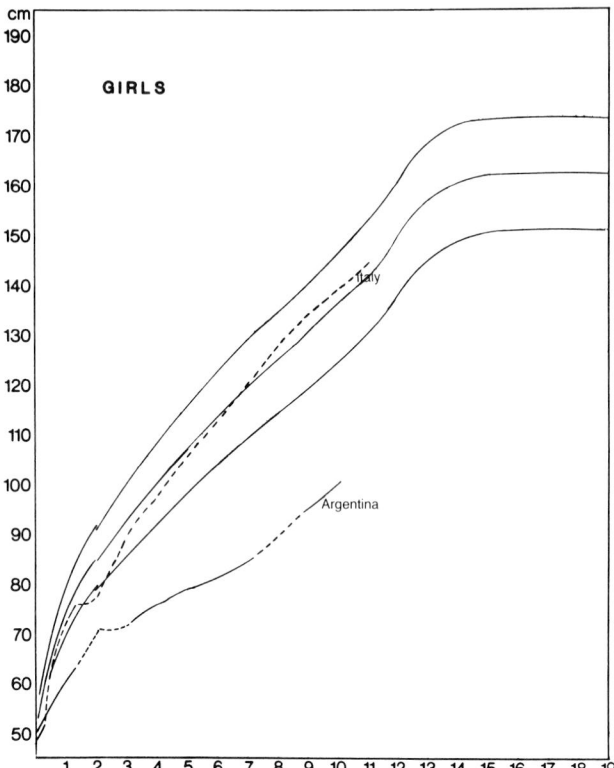

Fig. 77-14 Subjects are females; otherwise see legend to Fig. 77-13.

an apparent autosomal dominant mode of inheritance is shown in Fig. 77-17. Since the GH1 genes are retained, the various RFLPs within the hGH gene cluster can be used as markers in segregation analysis.[20,45,124] In the pedigree shown an affected female is heterozygous for the *Msp*I a (4.3/3.6 kb) and *Msp*I b (3.9/3.3) RFLP alleles (see Figs. 77-6 and 77-17). Note that her nonaffected son inherited her 4.3- and 3.9-kb alleles, while both affected sons inherited her 3.6- and 3.3-kb alleles. While these results suggest that the GH1 gene in coupling with her 3.6- and 3.3-kb RFLPs may be defective, the number of informative matings is far short of that needed to statistically prove linkage.

Interestingly, multiple related individuals with IGHD-II have been tested for hGH response to GHRH infusions.[128] Four related subjects all failed to show significant hGH secretion, suggesting that the defect was distal to GHRH in the kindred tested (see Fig. 17-7).

IGHD-III. A fourth reported type of IGHD (IGHD-III) has an X-linked recessive mode of inheritance (see Table 77-1). In the reported kindred all four affected males had hypogammaglobulinemia (deficient IgG, IgA, IgM, and IgE) and peak hGH responses of ≤ 5 ng/ml hGH to various provocative tests.[134] Interestingly, one of these subjects was treated with exogenous hGH and developed detectable circulating B lymphocytes as well as higher levels of IgA, IgM, and IgE than his affected relatives. Since hGH replacement in other hGH-deficient children who do not have IGHD-III is associated with a decrease in B lymphocytes, it seems plausible that IGHD-III is caused by a mutation (perhaps a deletion) of a portion of the X chromosome that contains two loci, one necessary for normal immunoglobulin production and the other for hGH expression.[134,135]

Bioinactive hGH. Some children with short stature comparable to that seen in hGH deficiency have low levels of IGF-I but normal levels of hGH assayed by radioimmunoassay (RIA).[136–140] In such cases the administration of exogenous hGH is reported to produce an increase in IGF-I levels and a growth response. In some, the concentration of hGH as measured by radioimmunoassay greatly exceeds the concentration measured by radioreceptor assay. These results suggest that the primary defect could be production of an abnormal hGH polypeptide whose alteration causes a reduced somatogenic activity but enables it to react with anti-hGH antibodies. This remains a hypothesis because alterations in the primary sequence of hGH have not been documented in subjects with this syndrome.[4] In addition there is no clear evidence of familial aggregations of "bioinactive" hGH to support Mendelian inheritance.

Laron Dwarfism. Laron dwarfism is an autosomal recessive disorder charcterized by low IGF-I levels but normal to high levels of hGH by RIA.[141] While the majority of reported patients are Jewish, the disorder has been described in other ethnic groups.[130,142] Laron dwarfs have the clinical appearance of severe IGHD with very delayed growth, abnormal facial appearance, high-pitched voice, and small male genitalia.[141–144] Length at birth may be short in relation to the birth weight, and tooth eruption and fontanelle closure are delayed. Laron dwarfs have the truncal obesity and the increased upper/lower segment body ratios typical of pituitary dwarfs. While spontaneous hypoglycemia can occur, the production of other anterior pituitary hormones (ACTH, TSH, and gonadotropins) remains intact. Fasting hGH levels are usually increased and range from normal to greater than 100 ng/ml. Plasma IGF-I levels are low and, in contrast to those of hGH-deficient subjects, do not respond to exogenous hGH.[143,144]

Studies indicate that hGH produced by Laron dwarfs reacts normally in radioreceptor assays with the hGH receptors of normal hepatic cells.[143] This, along with their lack of response to exogenous hGH, suggests the primary defect may be an abnormality of membrane receptors for hGH. Proof of this awaits characterization of the genes encoding hGH receptors in such subjects.

Panhypopituitary Dwarfism. Panhypopituitary dwarfism is characterized by the presence of a deficiency of one or more of the other pituitary trophic hormones (ACTH, FSH, LH, or TSH) in addition to hGH deficiency. While the great ma-

Fig. 77-15 Pedigrees of 12 families each having two sibs (solid symbols) affected with IGHD-IB.

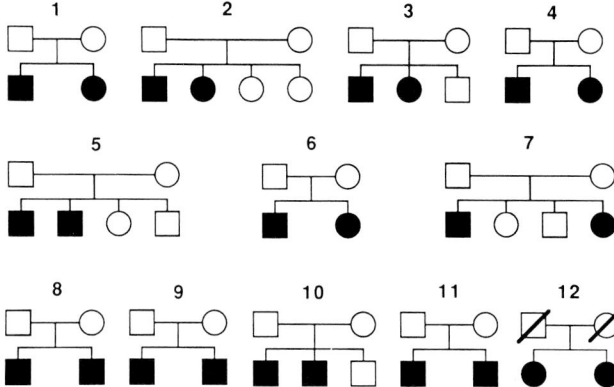

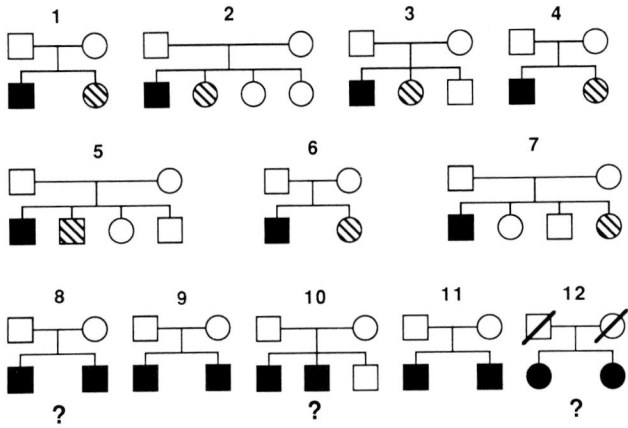

Fig. 77-16 Pedigrees of IGHD-IB families shown in Fig. 77-15 with results of segregation analysis of RFLPs shown in Fig. 77-6. Sibs are concordant (solid symbols), uninformative (? symbols), or discordant (hatched symbols) for inheritance of identical parental RFLPs, and hence GH1 alleles as indicated.

jority of cases are sporadic, at least two Mendelian forms are known (Table 77-1). These two types differ in their modes of inheritance, type I having an autosomal recessive and type II an X-linked recessive mode of inheritance.[124,132,134]

The clinical features of familial panhypopituitary dwarfism are identical to those of cases of nongenetic etiology. The phenotype varies with the specific trophic hormone deficiencies, which occur in decreasing order: gonadotropins (FSH, LH) > ACTH > TSH.[134] Associated gonadotropin deficiency causes sexual immaturity and primary amenorrhea in females and small external genitalia and lack of beard growth in males. While TSH deficiency is usually not severe, ACTH deficiency may contribute to recurrent hypoglycemia. The severity of deficiencies of various trophic hormones exhibit inter- and intrafamilial variability in both types of panhypopituitary dwarfism. Furthermore, the hGH secretory responses to GHRH infusions vary from deficient to normal in different related individuals from the same families.[128] The locus responsible for type I familial panhypopituitarism in a Hutterite family is not linked to the GH1 locus or the HLA region.[145] These results, along with the secretory responses discussed above, suggest that the hypothalamus is the probable site of the basic defect, but a primary pituitary defect with varying degrees of severity of damage is also possible.

African Pygmies. Peripheral unresponsiveness to exogenous hGH and normal levels of hGH have been documented in African pygmies. These individuals resemble pituitary dwarfs in size and proportions, but they lack the truncal obesity, typical facies, and skin findings of pituitary dwarfs.[130]

Serum concentrations of IGF-I are decreased in African pygmies.[146] Since levels of hGH and IGF-II were normal, an isolated deficiency of IGF-I was hypothesized. Recently, examinations of children as well as adult pygmies indicate that the short stature of adult pygmies is due mainly to a failure of growth acceleration during puberty due to the absence of an increase in the level of IGF-I during puberty.[63]

Developmental Anomalies and Genetic Syndromes. A variety of complex genetic syndromes associated with hypothalamic or pituitary defects that result in hGH and/or trophic hormone deficiencies have been described.[130] Those that are best characterized or that are reported to have genetic etiologies are briefly discussed.

Congenital Absence of the Pituitary. Complete absence of the pituitary causes adrenal insufficiency, hGH deficiency, hypothyroidism, and hypoglycemia. The thyroid and adrenal glands are usually hypoplastic, and the penis is small.[130] Occurrence of the disorder in multiple sib pairs suggests that it can be inherited as an autosomal recessive trait.

Anencephaly. Anencephaly is associated with absence of the hypothalamus and hypoplasia of the pituitary. Often the adrenals are hypoplastic, and plasma hGH levels may be absent to low normal.[130] Anencephaly is due to multifactorial inheritance, and the recurrence risk for a subsequent sib of an affected proband is 2 to 4 percent.[147]

Holoprosencephaly. Holoprosencephaly is characterized by the presence of median cleft lip and palate. Cases are usually sporadic but can be familial with either autosomal dominant or recessive modes of inheritance in different families.[147] Those due to chromosome anomalies (trisomy 13, 13q−, 18p−, and triploidy) usually have a variety of additional congenital anomalies.[130,147] Associated abnormalities of the hypothalamus can cause IGHD or panhypopituitary dwarfism.

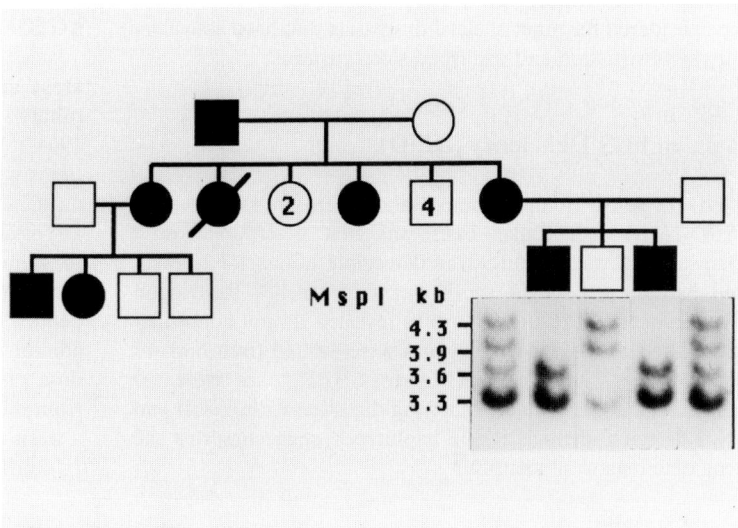

Fig. 77-17 Pedigree of a family having multiple individuals affected with IGHD-II. Autoradiogram patterns of DNAs from five family members following digestion with MspI and hybridization to the GH1 cDNA probe. Fragment sizes are shown on the right (note that the MspI fragments < 3.3 kb are not shown).

Septo-optic Dysplasia. This disorder, also referred to as de Morsier syndrome, is characterized by hypoplastic optic disks, absent septum pellucidum, and hGH deficiency.[147] There is no evidence for Mendelian etiology as all cases have been isolated.

Cleft Lip and Palate. While over 200 syndromes, including many that are either chromosomal or Mendelian in etiology, have cleft lip and/or palate as components, the great majority of cases with isolated cleft lip and/or cleft palate are due to multifactorial inheritance.[130,147] Associated developmental defects of the pituitary causing IGHD or panhypopituitary dwarfism occur in about 4 percent of cases.[148]

Rieger Syndrome. Rieger syndrome is characterized by iris dysplasia, hypodontia, and occasional optic atrophy and pituitary insufficiency.[130,147] It has an autosomal dominant mode of inheritance and variable expression.

Panhypopituitary Dwarfism with Abnormal Sella Turcica. Familial cases of pituitary insufficiency with hGH, TSH, and ACTH deficiency associated with an abnormally small or large sella turcica have been reported.[130,147] Both disorders have an apparently autosomal recessive mode of inheritance.

Fanconi Pancytopenia Syndrome. This syndrome is inherited as an autosomal recessive trait, and it is characterized by short stature, anomalies of the thumbs, hyperpigmentation, pancytopenia, and occasional hGH deficiency.[130,147] Complementation studies indicate that genetic defects at least two different loci may be responsible.

Ectrodactyly–Ectodermal Dysplasia–Clefting (EEC) Syndrome. The features of the EEC syndrome include defects in the hands and feet varying from syndactly to ectrodactly, ectodermal dysplasia causing fair, thin skin and partial anodontia, and cleft lip and/or palate. The disorder has an autosomal recessive mode of inheritance. Patients with EEC and hGH deficiency associated with absent septum pellucidum have been reported.[149]

Achondroplasia with Obstructive Sleep Apnea. Obstructive sleep apnea due to upper airway obstruction is a common complication of achondroplasia. When the obstructive sleep apnea is severe, it can cause secondary hGH deficiency due to deficient hGH release during sleep.[150] This mechanism should be considered for other skeletal dysplasias that have associated airway obstruction and disturbed sleep patterns.

Isolated hCS Deficiency (ICSD)

ICSD Type IA. Complete antenatal deficiency of hCS is called ICSD-IA. Its molecular basis was first determined in a Danish child who produced no detectable hCS prior to birth and had normal height at 4½ years of age.[34,56] Restriction analysis of his CSH and GH genes revealed several abnormalities. The CSH1-GH2-CSH2 genes were deleted from both 17 chromosomes, and the GH1 and CSHP1 genes were retained.[56] Analysis of DNA following digestion with *Hinc*II and *Msp*I detected identical RFLP haplotypes, suggesting that the gene deletions were identical.

ICSD Type IB. Partial deficiency of hCS is termed ICSD-IB. A normal Danish child born following a pregnancy associated with peak maternal hCS levels of 1.1 μg/ml (normal, 3 to 9.2 μg/ml).[151] Analysis of DNA from the child revealed heterozygosity for the CSH1-GH2-CSH2 deletion described above and a chromosome having only the CSH1 gene deleted. Thus, the child retained only one of the four normal CSH alleles in agreement with the roughly one-quarter normal levels of hCS that were observed. Interestingly, Orlando et al.[152] recently found that 3 of 66 CSH1 alleles were deleted in a Spanish cohort of patients with IGHD. This finding suggests either that CSH1 deletions are relatively frequent or that the reports that CSH1 deletions are not associated with hGH deficiency in childhood warrant further study.

Mouse Models of hGH Deficiency

In the mouse, three nonallelic recessive mutant genes have been identified that cause dwarfism as a result of decreased GH production. These mutant genes, referred to as Little (*lit*), Snell dwarf (*dw*), and Ames dwarf (*df*), have been assigned to three different chromosomes.[153] The GH deficiency is isolated in the case of Little mice, while Snell and Ames dwarfs have deficiencies of additional anterior pituitary hormones. Restriction analysis studies suggest that the GH genes are grossly intact in all three types of dwarfs. Ultrastructural studies of the anterior pituitary gland of Little mice showed a deficiency of secretory granules within somatotropes, while Snell and Ames dwarf pituitaries lacked identifiable somatotropes. Furthermore, GH precursor RNA and mRNA were decreased in the total RNA from Little pituitaries, while GH transcripts appeared to be absent in the total RNA from Snell or Ames dwarf pituitaries.[154] These results suggest that the basic defect in Little mice may involve the production or stability of GH transcripts, while GH deficiency in Snell and Ames dwarfs is probably secondary to defective somatotrope formation. Subsequent studies of the effect of GHRH on GH release from pituitary cells of *lit/lit* dwarf mice suggest tht defective GHRH receptor binding or dysfunction of the hormone-receptor complex may result in GH deficiency.[155]

TREATMENT OF hGH DEFICIENCY

hGH Replacement

Dose and Route of Administration. hGH extracted from pituitary glands was first administered to humans in 1958.[156] By 1964 it was clear that hGH stimulated linear growth in patients with hGH deficiency. The amount of response depended on the chronological age, height, weight, and bone age as well as possibly the pretreatment growth rate, peak hGH response to stimuli, and degree of obesity.[157] The linear growth response to hGH treatment during the first year of therapy depended on both the dose of hGH used and the schedule of its administration. Frazier et al.[158] demonstrated a significant dose response increment as the dose of hGH was increased from 0.03 IU/kg three times a week to 0.05 IU/kg three times a week to 0.10 IU/kg three times a week. A recent trial of 0.3 IU/kg three times a week suggests that a dose-response relationship continues with higher amounts.[159] The conventional route of administration is intramuscular, although subcutaneous injection is reported to achieve the same growth rate without detected differences in antibody production or lipodystrophy.[160] If glucocorticoid replacement is indicated because of panhypopituitary dwarfism, the dose should be limited to 10 to 15 mg/m²/day to avoid blunting the growth response to exogenous hGH.[157]

Results of Long-Term Treatment. The effectiveness of long-term treatment with hGH for children with short stature due to hGH deficiency has been well documented.[105,151,155–157,161,162] While the average final height improved from 6 SD below the mean in untreated subjects to 2.3 SD below the mean in treated subjects, only half the males and 15 percent of the females had final heights above the third percentile.[162] The subjects studied had relatively severe growth retardation and were 9 to 14 years old before treatment was begun. While better outcomes occur when treatment is begun earlier, before the growth retardation becomes severe, it remains unclear if optimal replacement therapy can consistently ameliorate the growth deficit.

Side Effects of hGH Therapy. The development of hypothyroidism during hGH therapy occurs in a small percentage of euthyroid children treated with hGH.[157] The decreased thyroxine concentrations observed reflect the inhibition by hGH of TSH responsiveness to TRH as well as the natural history of panhypopituitary dwarfism.[157,163]

Antibodies to hGH. The development of anti-hGH antibodies following hGH replacement occurs in 30 to 60 percent of treated patients.[157,164] However antibodies of sufficient titer to inhibit responsiveness to hGH treatment occur in no more than 5 percent of treated cases and in less than 15 percent of those who develop antibodies.[157] While some patients who become refractory to hGH therapy due to antibody production may respond to higher doses of hGH,[165] most with IGHD-IA develop antibody titers that preclude response to even very high dose hGH treatment.[110–112,117–127]

Creutzfeldt-Jakob Disease. hGH purified from cadaver pituitaries was used in treatment for 27 years before the first recipient to contract with degenerative neurologic disease was detected.[166] The first patient was a 22-year-old who died of Creutzfeldt-Jacob disease, a brain infection caused by a "slow virus." The patient's death occurred 6 years after completion of a 13-year course of treatment with hGH supplied by the National Hormone and Pituitary Program.[166] The discovery of additional cases suggested that the infections arose by contamination of one or more hGH preparation lots with the Creutzfeldt-Jacob disease agent.[166–168] Because of this discovery the National Institutes of Health halted distribution of hGH derived from cadaver pituitaries in 1985. Due to the potential for a long latency period and contamination of multiple batches of hGH, it is doubtful that distribution of this material will be resumed.

Biosynthetic hGH

Following withdrawal of hGH derived from cadaver pituitaries in 1985, about 3500 hGH-deficient children and adolescents were left without treatment.[167–169] This problem was solved by approval of the Food and Drug Administration to Genentech, Inc., and subsequently to other companies to market genetically engineered versions of hGH.[169]

The original report of successful expression of hGH in bacteria was in 1979.[170] *Escherichia coli* containing the recombinant vector produced an altered hGH (methionyl-hGH or met-hGH) which contained an additional amino-terminal methionine encoded by the AUG or start codon of the cloned hGH segment.[171] Treatment with this product resulted in production of antibodies that were later found to be induced by small amounts of contaminating *E. coli* proteins rather than the recombinant hGH itself. These antibodies were demonstrated in 21 of 22 treated subjects.[172] Subsequent refinements were successful in lowering this contamination so that met-hGH was equivalent to pituitary hGH in potency and had a much lower incidence of antibody formation. These improvements and subsequent production of recombinant hGH, which lacks the extra methionine residue, now provide a plentiful supply of hGH that has the full biologic activity of pituitary hGH. The availability of recombinant hGH in large amounts has raised concern that it will be misused to make normal children taller and for other "cosmetic endocrinology" applications.[169,172]

Somatocrinin (GHRH)

Treatment of hGH deficiency with GHRH can provide an alternative to hGH replacement for some hGH-deficient children. In two different studies about 40 percent of hGH-deficient subjects had increases of over 5 ng/ml in plasma hGH after intravenous injection of GHRH preparations.[173,174] Subsequent trials of intermittent or constant infusions of GHRH have demonstrated restoration of endogenous hGH secretion and growth in hGH-deficient children.[175,176] The utility of this approach is limited by the need for frequent doses and the lack of response by a majority of hGH-deficient subjects.

Gene Therapy

The successes in attaining integration and expression of GH and GHRH genes in animals have provided dramatic models for studies of the biologic effects of these genes products and the potential for correcting genetic diseases.[177–179] The method utilized is microinjection of DNA fragments encoding GH or GHRH into pronuclei of fertilized mouse, rabbit, pig, or sheep eggs and reimplantation of these eggs into appropriate females. Many of the resulting offspring produce high levels of GH or GHRH and manifest enhanced growth. While this approach has potential for producing transgenic livestock, applications to humans have three major limitations: First, the levels of plasma or GHRH that result vary from animal to animal. Furthermore, since synthesis does not occur in the appropriate tissue (anterior pituitary or hypothalamus), the resulting high levels are not under normal regulatory control (see Fig. 77-7). Second, the mutagenic potential of integration of recombinant DNA into the host genome can result in disruption of mature genes and cause lethal mutations in the homozygous state.[180] Finally, infertility is frequently found in transgenic animals, especially among females.[179] While potential applications of gene therapy to somatic cells of humans are feasible, the potential for achieving appropriate hormonal regulation less dangerously than with exogenous hormone replacement seems remote.

The author thanks Drs. P.H. Seeburg, J.S. Parks, M. Zachmann, B.L. Hjelle, Y. Nishi, M.A. Rivarola, R.G. McArthur, S. Braga, K. Zuppinger, A. Ferrandez, H. Frisch, J.J. Heinrich, D-f. Wang, and R. Illig for their collaboration in portions of these studies. The author also thanks Mrs. Judith Copeland for expert preparation of the manuscript. This work was supported in part by National Institutes of Health grants AM35592 and RCDA AM01434.

REFERENCES

1. LI CH, DIXON JS: Human pituitary growth hormone XXXII. The primary structure of the hormone: *Rev Arch Biochem Biophys* 146:233, 1971.
2. NIALL HD: Revised primary structure for human growth hormone. *Nature* 23:90, 1971.
3. LI CH: Human growth hormone: 1974–1981. *Mol Cell Biochem* 46:31, 1982.
4. CHAWLA RK, PARKS JS, RUDMAN D: Structural variants of human growth hormone: Biochemical, genetic, and clinical aspects. *Annu Rev Med* 34:519, 1983.
5. FERGUSON KA, WALLACE ALC: Prolactin activity of human growth hormone. *Nature* 190:632, 1961.
6. CHEEVER EV, LEWIS UJ: Estimation of the molecular weights of the multiple components of growth hormone and prolactin. *Endocrinology* 85:465, 1969.
7. CHRAMBACH A, YARDLEY RA, BEN-DAVID M, RODBARD D: Isohormones of human growth hormone. *Endocrinology* 93:848, 1973.
8. HUMMEL BCW, BROWN GM, HWANG P, FRIESEN HG: Human and monkey prolactin and growth hormone: Separation of polymorphic forms by isoelectric focusing. *Endocrinology* 97:855, 1975.
9. FROHMAN LA, BUREK L, STACHURA ME: Characterization of growth hormone different molecular weights in rat, dog, and human pituitaries. *Endocrinology* 91:262, 1972.
10. LEWIS UJ, PETERSON SM, BONEWALD LF, SEAVEY BK, VANDERLAAN WP: An interchain disulfide dimer of human growth hormone. *J Biol Chem* 252:3697, 1977.
11. LEWIS UJ, SINGH RNP, TUTWILER GF, SIGEL MB, VANDERLAAN EF, VANDERLAAN WP: Human growth hormone: A complex of proteins. *Recent Prog Horm Res* 36:477, 1980.
12. LINGAPPA VR, BLOBEL G: Early events in the biosynthesis of secretory and membrane proteins: The signal hypothesis. *Recent Prog Horm Res* 36:451, 1980.
13. LEWIS UJ, BONEWALD LF, LEWIS LJ: The 20,000-dalton variant of human growth hormone: Location of the amino acid deletions. *Biochem Biophys Res Commun* 92:511, 1980.
14. DENOTO F, MOORE DD, GOODMAN HM: Human growth hormone DNA sequence and mRNA structures: Possible alternative splicing. *Nucleic Acids Res* 9:3719, 1981.
15. WILHELMI AE: Fractionation of human pituitary glands. *Can J Biochem Physiol* 39:1659, 1961.
16. LI CH, DIXON JS, CHUNG D: Primary structure of the human chorionic somatomammotropin (HCS) molecule. *Science* 173:56, 1971.
17. SHERWOOD LM, HANDWEGER S, MCLAURIN WD: Amino-acid sequence of human placental lactogen. *Nature* 233:59, 1971.
18. MILLER WL, EBERHARDT NL: Structure and evolution of the growth hormone gene family. *Endocr Rev* 4:97, 1983.
19. COOKE NE, COIT D, SHINE J, BAXTER JD, MARTIAL JA: Human prolactin cDNA structural analysis and evolutionary comparisons. *J Biol Chem* 255:4007, 1981.
20. CHAKRAVARTI A, PHILLIPS JA III, MELLITS KH, BUETOW KH, SEEBURG PH: Patterns of polymorphism and linkage disequilibrium suggest independent origins of the human growth hormone gene cluster. *Proc Natl Acad Sci USA* 81:6085, 1984.
21. VAN BUUL-OFFERS S, DUMOLEIJN L, HACKING W, et al: The Snell dwarf mouse: Interrelationship of growth in length and weight, serum somatomedin activity and sulfate incorporation in costal cartilage during growth hormone, thyroxine and somatomedin treatment, in Giordano G, Van Wyk JJ, Minuto F (eds): *Somatomedins and Growth: Proceedings of the Serono Symposia.* New York, Academic, 1979, vol 23, pp 281–283.
22. ISAKSSON OGP, JANSSON J-O, GAUSE IAM: Growth hormone stimulates longitudinal bone growth directly. *Science* 216:1237, 1982.
23. GRICHTING G, LEVY LK, GOODMAN HM: Relationship between binding and biological effects of human growth hormone in rat adipocytes. *Endocrinology* 113:1111, 1983.
24. PHILLIPS LS, VASSILOPOULOU-SELLIN R: Somatomedins (first of two parts). *N Engl J Med* 302:371, 1980.
25. PHILLIPS LS, VASSILOPOULOU-SELLIN R: Somatomedins (second of two parts). *N Engl J Med* 302:438, 1980.
26. D'ERCOLE AJ, UNDERWOOD LE, VAN WYK JJ: Serum somatomedin-C in hypopituitarism and in other disorders of growth. *J Pediatr* 90:375, 1977.
27. D'ERCOLE AJ: Somatomedins/insulin-like growth factors: Relationship to insulin and diabetes, in *Infants of the Diabetic Mother,* Report of the 93rd Ross Conference on Pediatric Research, W Oh, SG Gabbe (eds): Ross Laboratories, Columbus, Ohio, pp 50–65.
28. HAN VKM, D'ERCOLE AJ, LUND PK: Cellular localization of somatomedin (insulin-like growth factor) messenger RNA in the human fetus. *Science* 236:193, 1987.
29. RINDERNECHT E, HUMBEL RE: The amino acid sequence of human insulin-like growth factor 1 and its structural homology with proinsulin. *J Biol Chem* 253:2769, 1978.
30. UNDERWOOD LE, D'ERCOLE AJ: Insulin and insulin-like growth factors/somatomedins in fetal and neonatal development. *Clin Endocrinol Metab* 13:69, 1984.
31. MERIMEE TJ, ZAPF J, FROESCH ER: Insulin-like growth factor in pregnancy: Studies in a growth hormone-deficient dwarf. *J Clin Endocrinol Metab* 54:1101, 1982.
32. GRUMBACH MM, KAPLAN SL, VINIK A: *Peptide Hormones.* New York, North Holland, 1974.
33. ROSENFELD RG, WILSON DM, DOLLAR LA, BENNETT A, HINTZ RL: Both human pituitary growth hormone and recombinant DNA-derived human growth hormone cause insulin resistance at a postreceptor site. *J Clin Endocrin Metab* 54:1033, 1982.
34. NIELSEN PV, PEDERSEN H, KAMPMANN EM: Absence of human placental lactogen in an otherwise uneventful pregnancy. *Am J Obstet Gynecol* 135:322, 1979.
35. BORODY IB, CARLTON MA: Isolated defect in human placental lactogen synthesis in a normal pregnancy. *Br J Obstet Gynecol* 88:44, 1981.
36. OWERBACH D, RUTTER WJ, MARTIAL JA, BAXTER JD, SHOWS TB: Genes for growth hormone, chorionic somatomammotropin, and growth hormone-like gene on chromosome 17 in humans. *Science* 209:289, 1980.
37. GEORGE DL, PHILLIPS JA III, FRANCKE U, SEEBURG PH: The genes for growth hormone and chorionic somatomammotropin are on the long arm of human chromosome 17 in region q21 to qter. *Hum Genet* 57:138, 1981.
38. HARPER ME, BARRERA-SALDANA HA, SAUNDERS GF: Chromosomal localization of the human placental lactogen-growth hormone gene cluster to 17q22-24. *Am J Hum Genet* 34:227, 1982.
39. OWERBACH D, RUTTER WJ, COOKE NE, MARTIAL JA, SHOWS TB: The prolactin gene is located on chromosome 6 in humans. *Science* 212:815, 1981.
40. FIDDES JC, SEEBURG PH, DENOTO FM, HALLEWELL RA, BAXTER JD, GOODMAN HM: Structure of genes for human growth hormone and chorionic somatomammotropin. *Proc Natl Acad Sci USA* 76:4294, 1979.
41. SEEBURG PH: The human growth hormone gene family: Nucleotide sequences show recent divergence and predict a new polypeptide hormone. *DNA* 1:239, 1982.
42. MOORE DD, CONKLING MA, GOODMAN HM: Human growth hormone: A multigene family. *Cell* 29:285, 1982.
43. KIDD VJ, SAUNDERS GJ: Linkage arrangement of human placental lactogen and growth hormone genes. *J Biol Chem* 157:10673, 1982.
44. MOORE DD, WALKER MD, DIAMOND DJ, CONKLING MA, GOODMAN HM: Structure, expression, and evolution of growth hormone genes. *Recent Prog Horm Res* 38:197, 1982.
45. PHILLIPS JA III, PARKS JS, HJELLE BL, HERD JE, PLOTNICK LD, MIGEON CJ, SEEBURG PH: Genetic basis of familial isolated growth hormone deficiency type I. *J Clin Invest* 70:489, 1982.
46. BARSH GS, SEEBURG PH, GELINAS RE: The human growth hormone gene family: Sturcture and evolution of the chromosomal locus. *Nucleic Acids Res* 11:3939, 1983.
47. HIRT K, KIMELMAN J, BIRNBAUM MJ, CHEN EY, SEEBURG PH, EBERHARDT NL, BARTA A: The human growth hormone gene locus: Structure, evolution, and allelic variations. *DNA* 6:59, 1987.
48. PAVLAKIS GN, HIZUKA N, GORDEN P, SEEBURG P, HAMER DH: Expression of two human growth hormone genes in monkey cells infected by simian virus 40 recombinants. *Proc Natl Acad Sci USA* 78:7398, 1981.
49. WIERINGA B, MEYER F, REISER J, WEISSMAN C: Unusual splice sites revealed by mutagenic inactivation of an authentic splice site of the rabbit, β-globin gene. *Nature* 301:38, 1983.
50. VANIN EF, HENTHON PS, KIOUSSI D, GROSVELD I, SMITHIES O: Unex-

pected relationships between four large deletions in the human β-globin cluster. *Cell* 35:701, 1983.

51. LEHRMAN MA, SCHNEIDER WJ, SUDHOF TC, BROWN MS, GOLDSTEIN JL, RUSSELL DW: Mutation in LDL receptor: Alu-Alu recombination deletes exons encoding transmembrane and cytoplasmic domains. *Science* 227:140, 1985.

52. McWILLIAMS D, BOIME I: Cytological localization of placental lactogen messenger ribonucleic acid in syncytiotrophoblast layers of human placenta. *Endocrinology* 107:761, 1980.

53. McWILLIAMS D, CALLAHAN RC, BOIME I: Human placental lactogen mRNA and its structural genes during pregnancy: Quantitation with a complementary DNA. *Proc Natl Acad Sci USA* 71:1024, 1977.

54. BARRERA-SALDANA HA, ROBBERSON DL, SAUNCERS GF: Transcriptional products of the human placental lactogen gene. *J Biol Chem* 257:12399, 1982.

55. BARRERA-SALDANA HA, SEEBURG PH, SAUNDERS GF: Two structurally different genes produce the same placental lactogen hormone. *J Biol Chem* 258:3787, 1983.

56. WURZEL JM, PARKS JS, HERD JE, NIELSEN PV: A gene deletion is responsible for absence of human chorionic somatomammotropin. *DNA* 1:251, 1982.

57. SILER-KHODR TM, MORGENSTERN LL, GREENWOOD FC: Hormone synthesis and release from human fetal adenohypophyses in vitro. *J Clin Endocrinol Metab* 39:891, 1974.

58. GLUCKMAN PD, GRUMBACH MM, KAPLAN SL: The neuroendocrine regulation and function for growth hormone and prolactin in the mammalian fetus. *Endocr Rev* 2:363, 1981.

59. RECHLER MM, NISSLEY SP, ROTH J: Hormonal regulation of human growth. *N Engl J Med* 316:941, 1987.

60. HALL K, SARA VR: Somatomedin levels in childhood, adolescence and adult life. *Clin Endocrinol Metab* 13:91, 1984.

61. MEITES J: Changes in neuroendocrine control of anterior pituitary function during aging. *Neuroendocrinology* 34:151, 1982.

62. SARA VR, HALL K, RODECK CH, WETTERBERG L: Human embryonic somatomedin. *Proc Natl Acad Sci USA* 78:3175, 1981.

63. MERIMEE TJ, ZAPF J, HEWLETT B, CAVALLI-SFORZA LL: Insulin-like growth factors in pygmies: The role of puberty in determining final stature. *N Engl J Med* 316:906, 1987.

64. SELBY MJ, BARTA A, BAXTER JD, BELL GI, EBERHARDT NL: Analysis of a major human chorionic somatomammotropin gene. Evidence for two-functional promoter elements. *J Biol Chem* 259:13131, 1984.

65. SEIF I, KHOURY G, DHAR R: BKV splice sequences based on analysis of preferred donor and acceptor sites. *Nucleic Acids Res* 6:3387, 1979.

66. LERNER M, BOYLE J, MOUNT S, WOLIN S, STEITZ J: Are snRNPs involved in splicing? *Nature* 283:220, 1980.

67. RODGERS J, WALL R: A mechanism for RNA splicing. *Proc Natl Acad Sci USA* 77:1877, 1980.

68. LEWIS UJ, SINGH RNP, TUTWILER GF, SIGEL MB, VANDERLAAN EF, VANDERLAAN WP: Human growth hormone: A complex of proteins. *Recent Prog Horm Res* 36:477, 1980.

69. EVANS RM, BIRNBERG NC, ROSENFELD MG: Glucocorticoid and thyroid hormones transcriptionally regulate growth hormone gene expression. *Proc Natl Acad Sci USA* 79:7659, 1982.

70. BARINAGA M, YAMONOTO G, RIVIER C, VALE W, EVANS E, ROSENFELD MG: Transcriptional regulation of growth hormone gene expression by growth hormone-releasing factor. *Nature* 306:84, 1983.

71. BARLOW JW, VOZ MLJ, ELIARD PH, MATHY-HARTERT M, DENAYER P, ECONOMIDIS JV, BELAYEW A, MARTIAL JA, ROUSSEAU GG: Thyroid hormone receptors bind to defined regions of the growth hormone and placental lactogen genes. *Proc Natl Acad Sci USA* 83:9021, 1986.

72. NYBORG JK, SPINDLER SR: Alterations in local chromatin structure accompany thyroid hormone induction of growth hormone gene transcription. *J Biol Chem* 261:5685, 1986.

73. SLATER EP, RABENAU O, KARIN M, BAXTER JD, BEATO M: Glucocorticoid receptor binding and activation of a heterologous promoter by dexamethasone by the first intron of the human growth hormone gene. *Mol Cell Biol* 5:2984, 1985.

74. PAEK I, AXEL R: Glucocorticoids enhance stability of human growth hormone mRNA. *Mol Cell Biol* 7:1496, 1987.

75. MARTIN JB: Neural regulation of growth hormone secretion. *N Engl J Med* 288:1384, 1973.

76. WEHRENBERG WB, LING N, BOHLEN P, ESCH F, BRAZEAU P, GUILLEMIN R: Physiological roles of somatocrinin and somatostatin in the regulation of growth hormone secretion. *Biochem Biophys Res Commun* 109:562, 1982.

77. GROSSMAN A, SAVAGE MO, BESSER GM: Growth hormone releasing hormone. *Clin Endocrinol Metab* 15:607, 1986.

78. BRAZEAU P, EPELBAUM J, TANNENBAUM GS, et al: Somatostatin: Isolation,

characterization, distribution, and blood determination. *Metabolism* 27:1133, 1978.

79. KASTING NW, MARTIN JB, ARNOLD MA: Pulsatile somatostatin release from the median eminence of the unanesthetized rat and its relationship to plasma growth hormone levels. *Endocrinology* 109:1739, 1981.

80. DAUGHADAY WH: The anterior pituitary, in Wilson JD, Foster DW (eds): *Textbook of Endocrinology*, 7th ed. Philadelphia, Saunders, 1985, pp 568–613.

81. WOLFSDORF JI, SADEGHI-NEJAD A, SENIOR B: Hypoketonemia and age-related fasting hypoglycemia in growth hormone deficiency. *Metabolism* 32:457, 1983.

82. ABRAMOVICI A, JOSEFSBERG Z, MIMOUNI M, LIBAN E, LARON Z: Histopathological features of the skin in hypopituitarism and laron-type dwarfism. *Isr J Med Sci* 19:515, 1983.

83. NATIONAL CENTRE FOR HEALTH STATISTICS: *NCHS Growth Curves for Children, Birth to 18 Years.* United States Vital and Health Statistics, Series 11, No 165. November 1977.

84. TANNER JM, WHITEHOUSE RH: Clinical longitudinal standards for height, weight, height velocity, weight velocity and stages of puberty. *Arch Dis Child* 51:170, 1976.

85. EDDY RL, GILLILAND PF, IBARRA JD JR, McMURRY JF JR, THOMPSON JQ: Human growth hormone release: Comparison of provocative tests procedures. *Am J Med* 56:179, 1974.

86. MILNER RDG, BURNS EC: Investigation of suspected growth hormone deficiency. *Arch Dis Child* 57:944, 1982.

87. LACEY KA, HEWISON A, PARKIN JM: Exercise as a screening test for growth hormone deficiency in children. *Arch Dis Child* 48:508, 1973.

88. COLLU R, BRUN G, MILSANT F, et al: Reevaluation of levodopapropranolol as a test of growth hormone reserve in children. *Pediatrics* 61:242, 1978.

89. ROTH J, GLICK SM, YALOW RS, et al: Hypoglycemia: A potent stimulus to secretion of growth hormone. *Science* 140:987, 1963.

90. PARKER ML, HAMMOND JM, DAUGHADAY WH: The arginine provocative test: An aid to the diagnosis of hyposomatotropism. *J Clin Endocrinol* 27:1129, 1967.

91. GIL-AD I, TOPPER E, LARON Z: Oral clonidine as a growth hormone stimulation test. *Lancet* 2:278, 1979.

92. THE HEALTH SERVICES HUMAN GROWTH HORMONE COMMITTEE: Comparison of the intravenous insulin and oral clonidine tolerance tests for growth hormone secretion. *Arch Dis Child* 56:852, 1981.

93. VANDERSHUERIN-LODEWEYCKX WR, MALVAUX P, EGGERMONT E, et al: The glucagon stimulation test: Effect on plasma growth hormone and on immunoreactive insulin, cortisol and glucose in children. *J Pediatr* 85:182, 1974.

94. PARKS JS, AMRHEIN JA, VAIDYA V, et al: Growth hormone response to proponal-glucagon stimulation: A comparison with other tests of growth hormone reserve. *J Clin Endocrinol* 37:85, 1973.

95. LIBERMAN B, CESAR FP, WAJCHENBERG BL: Human growth hormone (hGH) stimulation tests: The sequential exercise and L-dopa procedure. *Clin Endocrinol* 10:649, 1979.

96. PENNY R, BLIZZARD RM, DAVIS WT: Sequential study of arginine and insulin tolerance tests on the same day. *J Clin Endocrinol Metab* 29:1499, 1969.

97. VIMPANI GV, VIMPANI AF, LIDGARD GP, CAMERON EHD, FARQUHAR JW: Prevalence of severe growth hormone deficiency. *Br Med J* 2:427, 1977.

98. RONA RJ, TANNER JM: Aetiology of idiopathic growth hormone deficiency in England and Wales. *Arch Dis Child* 52:197, 1977.

99. LACEY KA, PARKIN JM: Causes of short stature—A community study of children in New Castle upon Tyne. *Lancet* 1:42, 1974.

100. ISHIHARA M: Optic hypoplasia with pituitary dwarfism (Kaplan-Grumbach-Hoyt Syndrome, or DeMorsier Syndrome). *Endocrinol Jap* 30:7, 1983.

101. KELLER RJ, WOLFSDORF JI: Isolated growth hormone deficiency alters cerebral edema complicating diabetic ketoacidosis. *N Engl J Med* 316:857, 1987.

102. PREECE MA, KEARNEY PJ, MARSHALL WC: Growth-hormone deficiency in congenital rubella. *Lancet* 2:842, 1977.

103. BUTENANDT O: Growth hormone deficiency and growth hormone therapy in Ullrich-Turner-Syndrome. *Klin Wochenschr* 58:99, 1980.

104. SHALET SM, BEARDWELL CG, MORRIS JONES PH, PEARSON D: Growth hormone deficiency after treatment of acute leukemia in children. *Arch Dis Child* 51:489, 1976.

105. BURNS EC, TANNER JM, PREECE MA, CAMERON N: Growth hormone treatment in children with craniopharyngioma: Final growth status. *Clin Endocrinol* 14:587, 1981.

106. RICHARDS GE, WARA WM, GRUMBACH MM, KAPLAN SL, SHELINE GE, CONTE FA: Delayed onset of hypopituitarism: Sequelae of therapeutic irradiation of central nervous system, eye, and middle ear tumors. *J Pediatr* 89:553, 1976.

107. ROMSHE CA, ZIPF WB, MISER A, MISER J, SOTOS JF, NEWTON WA: Evaluation of growth hormone release and human growth hormone treatment in children with cranial irradiation-associated short stature. *J Pediatr* 104:177, 1984.

108. TANNER JM: Human growth hormone. *Nature* 237:433, 1972.

109. SEIP M, TRYGSTAD O, AARSKOG D: Comment on pituitary dwarfism in Norway, 1961–1970. *Birth Defects* 7:33, 1971.

110. ILLIG R: Growth hormone antibodies in patients treated with different preparations of human growth hormone (HGH). *J Clin Endocrinol Metab* 31:679, 1970.

111. ILLIG R, PRADER A, FERRANDEZ A, ZACHMANN M: Hereditary prenatal growth hormone deficiency with increased tendency to growth hormone antibody formation in Kracht J (ed): *Endokrinologie der Entwicklung und Reifung*, Berlin, Springer-Verlag, 1970, p 246.

112. ILLIG R, PRADER A, FERRANDEZ A, ZACHMANN M: Hereditary prenatal growth hormone deficiency with increased tendency to growth hormone antibody formation ("A-type" isolated growth hormone deficiency). *Acta Pediatr Scand Suppl* 60:607, 1971.

113. KUNKEL LM, SMITH KD, BOYER SH, BORGAONKOR DS, WACHTEL SS, MILLER OJ, BREG WR, JONES HW, RARY JM: Analysis of human Y-chromosome specific reiterated DNA in chromosome variants. *Proc Natl Acad Sci USA* 74:1245, 1977.

114. MARTIAL JA, HALLEWELL RA, BAXTER JD, GOODMAN HM: Human growth hormone: Complementary DNA cloning and expression in bacteria. *Science* 205:602, 1979.

115. SOUTHERN EM: Detection of specific sequences among DNA fragments separated by gel electrophoresis. *J Mol Biol* 98:503, 1975.

116. JEFFREYS AJ, FLAVELL RA: A physical map of the DNA regions flanking the rabbit β-globin gene. *Cell* 12:429, 1977.

117. PHILLIPS JA III, HJELLE BL, SEEBURG PH, ZACHMANN M: Molecular basis for familial isolated growth hormone deficiency. *Proc Natl Acad Sci USA* 78:6372, 1981.

118. RIVAROLA MA, PHILLIPS JA III, MIGEON CJ, HEINRICH JJ, HJELLE BJ: Phenotypic heterogeneity in familial isolated growth hormone deficiency (IGHD) type A. *J Clin Endocr Metab* 59:34, 1984.

119. NISHI Y, AIHARA K, USUI T, PHILLIPS JA III, MALLONEE RL, MIGEON CJ: Isolated growth hormone deficiency type 1A in a Japanese family. *J Pediatr* 104:885, 1984.

120. FRISCH H, PHILLIPS JA III: Growth hormone deficiency due to GH-N gene deletion in an Austrian family. *Acta Endocrinol* 113:107, 1986.

121. BRAGA S, PHILLIPS JA III, JOSS E, SCHWARZ H, ZUPPINGER K: Familial growth hormone deficiency resulting from a 7.6 kb deletion within the growth hormone gene cluster. *Am J Med Genet* 25:443, 1986.

122. LARON Z, KELIJMAN M, PERTZELAN A, KERET R, SHOFFNER JM, PARKS JS: Human growth hormone gene deletion without antibody formation or growth arrest during treatment—A new disease entity? *Isr J Med Sci* 21:999, 1985.

123. GOOSSENS M, BRAUNER R, CZERNICHOW P, DUQUESNOY P, RAPPAPORT R: Isolated growth hormone (GH) deficiency type 1A associated with a double deletion in the human GH gene cluster. *J Clin Endocrinol Metab* 62:712, 1986.

124. PHILLIPS JA III, FERRANDEZ A, FRISCH H, ILLIG R, ZUPPINGER K: Defects of GH genes: Clinical syndromes, in Raiti S (ed): *Human Growth Hormone*. New York, Plenum, 1986, pp 211–226.

125. PHILLIPS JA III: Genetic diagnosis: Differentiating growth disorders. *Hosp Pract* 20:85, 1985.

126. SCHWARZ S, BERGER P, FRISCH H, MONCAYO R, PHILLIPS JA III, WICK G: Growth hormone blocking antibodies in a patient with deletion of the GH-N gene. *Clin Endocrinol* 27:213, 1987.

127. BERTHOLD P, HAUFFA B: Personal communication.

128. ROGOL AD, BLIZZARD RM, FOLEY TP JR, FURLANETTO R, SELDEN R, MAYO K, THORNER MO: Growth hormone releasing hormone and growth hormone: Genetic studies in familial growth hormone deficiency. *Pediatr Res* 19:489, 1985.

129. RIMOIN DL, SCHECHTER JE: Histological and ultrastructural studies of isolated growth hormone deficiency. *J Clin Endocrinol Metab* 37:725, 1973.

130. RIMOIN DL: Genetic disorders of the pituitary gland, in Emery AEH, Rimoin DL (eds): *Principles and Practice of Medical Genetics*. Edinburgh, Churchill Livingstone, 1983, pp 1134–1151.

131. SHEIKHOLISLAM BM, STEMPFEL RS JR: Hereditary isolated somatotropin deficiency: Effects of human growth hormone administration. *Pediatrics* 49:362, 1972.

132. POSKITT EME, RAYNER PHW: Isolated growth hormone deficiency: Two families with autosomal dominant inheritance. *Arch Dis Child* 49:55, 1974.

133. VAN GELDEREN HH, VAN DER HOOG CE: Familial isolated growth hormone deficiency. *Clin Genet* 20:173, 1981.

134. FLEISHER TA, WHITE RM, BRODER S, NISSLEY SP, BLAESE RM, MULVIHILL

JJ, OLIVE G, WALDMANN TA: X-linked hypogammaglobulinemia and isolated growth hormone deficiency. *N Engl J Med* 302:1429, 1980.

135. RAPAPORT R, OLESKE J, AHDIEH H, SOLOMON S, DELFAUS D, DENNY T: Suppression of immune function in growth hormone-deficient children during treatment with human growth hormone. *J Pediatr* 109:434, 1986.

136. KOWARSKI AA, SCHNEIDER J, BEN-GALIM E, WELDON VV, DAUGHADAY WH: Growth failure with normal serum RIA-GH and low somatomedin activity: Somatomedin restoration and growth acceleration after exongeous GH. *J Clin Endocrinol Metab* 47:461, 1978.

137. RUDMAN D, KUTNER MH, GOLDSMITH MA, KENNY J, JENNINGS H, BAIN RP: Further observations on four subgroups of normal variant short stature. *J Clin Endocrinol Metab* 51:1378, 1980.

138. RUDMAN D, KUTNER MH, BLACKSTON RD, CUSHMAN RA, BAIN RP, PATTERSON JH: Children with normal-variant short stature: Treatment with human growth hormone for six months. *N Engl J Med* 305:123, 1981.

139. HAYEK A, PEAKE GT: Growth and somatomedin-C responses to growth hormone in dwarfed children. *J Pediatr* 99:868, 1981.

140. FRAZER T, GAVIN JR, DAUGHADAY WH, HILLMAN RE, WELDON V: Growth hormone-dependent growth failure. *J Pediatr* 101:12, 1982.

141. PERTZELAN A, ADAM A, LARON Z: Genetic aspects of pituitary dwarfism due to absence or biological inactivity of growth hormone. *Isr J Med Sci* 4:895, 1968.

142. ADAM A, JOSEFSBERG Z, PERTZELAN A, ZADIK Z, CHEMKE JM, LARON Z: Occurrence of four types of growth hormone-related dwarfism in Israeli communities. *J Pediatr* 137:35, 1981.

143. JACOBS LS, SNEID SD, GARLAND JT, LARON Z, DAUGHADAY WH: Receptor-active growth hormone in laron dwarfism. *J Clin Endocrinol Metab* 42:403, 1976.

144. LARON Z, PERTZELAN A, KARP M, KOWADLO-SILBERGELD A, DAUGHADAY WH: Administration of growth hormone to patients with familial dwarfism with high plasma immunoreactive growth hormone: Measurement of sulfation factor, metabolic and linear growth response. *J Clin Endocrinol Metab* 33:332, 1971.

145. MCARTHUR RG, MORGAN K, PHILLIPS JA III, BALA M, KLASSEN J: The natural history of familial hypopituitarism. *Am J Med Genet* 22:553, 1985.

146. MERIMEE TJ, ZAPF J, FROESCH ER: Dwarfism in the pygmy: An isolated deficiency of insulin-like growth factor I. *N Engl J Med* 305:965, 1981.

147. MCKUSICK VA: *Mendelian Inheritance in Man*, 7th ed. Baltimore, The Johns Hopkins University Press, 1986.

148. RUDMAN D, DAVIS GT, PRIEST JH, PATTERSON JH, KUTNER MH, HEYMSFIELD SB, BETHEL RA: Prevalence of growth hormone deficiency with cleft lip or palate. *J Pediatr* 93:378, 1978.

149. KNUDTZON J, AARSKOG D: Growth hormone deficiency associated with the ectrodactyly-ectodermal dysplasia-clefting syndrome and isolated absent septum pellucidum. *Pediatrics* 79:410, 1987.

150. GOLDSTEIN SJ, SPHRINTZEN RJ, WU RHK, THORPY MJ, HAHM SY, MARION R, SHER AE, SAENGER P: Achondroplasia and obstructive sleep apnea: Correction of apnea and abnormal sleep-entrained growth hormone release by tracheostomy. *Birth Defects* 21(2):83, 1985.

151. PARKS JS, NIELSEN PV, SEXTON LA, JORGENSEN EH: An effect of gene dosage on production of human chorionic sommatomammotropin. *J Clin Endocrinol Metab* 60:994, 1986.

152. ORLANDO PJ, PHILLIPS JA III, FERRANDEZ AN, ARNAL JM, WOODARD MJ, BUENO M: Frequency and types of deletions in the growth hormone (GH) gene clusters of Spanish subjects with GH deficiency. *Am J Hum Genet* 41:A105, 1987.

153. PHILLIPS JA III, BEAMER WG, BARTKE A: Analysis of growth hormone genes in mice with genetic defects of growth hormone expression. *J Endocrinol* 92:405, 1982.

154. CHENG TC, BEAMER WG, PHILLIPS JA III, BARTKE A, MALLONEE RL, DOWLING C: Etiology of growth hormone deficiency in Little, Ames, and Snell dwarf mice. *Endocrinology* 113:1669, 1983.

155. JANSSON J-O, DOWNS TR, BEAMER WG, FROHMAN LA: Receptor-associated resistance to growth hormone releasing factor in dwarf "Little" mice. *Science* 232:511, 1986.

156. RABEN MS: Treatment of pituitary dwarf with human growth hormone. *J Clin Endocrinol Metab* 18:901, 1958.

157. FRAZIER SD: Human pituitary growth hormone (hGH) therapy in growth hormone deficiency. *Endocr Rev* 4:155, 1983.

158. FRASIER SD, COSTIN G, LIPPE BM, ACETO T, BUNGER PF: A dose-response curve for human growth hormone. *J Clin Endocrinol Metab* 53:1213, 1981.

159. GERTNER JM, TAMBORLANE WV, GIANFREDI SP, GENEL M: Renewed catch-up growth with increased replacement doses of human growth hormone. *Clin Lab Obs* 110:425, 1987.

160. RUSSO L, MOORE WV: A comparison of subcutaneous and intramuscular administration of human growth hormone in the therapy of growth hormone deficiency. *J Clin Endocrinol Metab* 55:1003, 1982.

161. SOYKA LF, BODE HH, CRAWFORD JD, FLYNN FJ: Effectiveness of long-term human growth hormone therapy for short stature in children with growth hormone deficiency. *Growth Horm Ther Short Stature* 30:1, 1970.

162. BURNS EC, TANNER JM, PREECE MA, CAMERON N: Final height and pubertal development in 55 children with idiopathic growth hormone deficiency, treated for between 2 and 15 years with human growth hormone. *Eur J Pediatr* 137:155, 1981.

163. LIPPE BM, VAN HERLE AJ, LaFRANCHI SH, ULLER RP, LAVIN N, KAPLAN SA: Reversible hypothyroidism in growth hormone-deficient children treated with human growth hormone. *J Clin Endocrinol Metab* 40:612, 1975.

164. FRASIER SD, ACETO T, HAYLES AB, PARKER ML, MEYER-BAHLBURG HFL: Collaborative study of the effects of human growth hormone in growth hormone deficiency. II. Development and significance of antibodies to human growth hormone during the first year of therapy. *J Clin Endocrinol Metab* 38:14, 1974.

165. WINTERER J, CHOUSOS G, CASSORLA F, LORIAUX DL: Acquired refractoriness to growth hormone in a patient with isolated growth hormone deficiency: Growth and plasma somatomedin-C response to high-dose growth hormone therapy. *J Pediatr* 104:908, 1984.

166. REPORT OF THE COMMITTEE ON GROWTH HORMONE USE OF THE LAWSON WILKINS PEDIATRIC ENDOCRINE SOCIETY, MAY 1985: Degenerative neurologic disease in patients formerly treated with human growth hormone. Special article. *J Pediatr* 107:10, 1985.

167. Virus scare halts hormone research. Three deaths attributed to a brain virus have halted distribution of human growth hormone and other products of the pituitary gland. *Science* 228:1176, 1985.

168. PREECE MA: Creutzfeldt-Jakob disease: Implications for growth hormone deficient children. *Neuropathol Appl Neurobiol* 12:509, 1986.

169. NEW GROWTH INDUSTRY IN HUMAN GROWTH HORMONE? *Science* 234:22, 1986.

170. GOEDDEL DV, HEYNECKER HL, HOZUMI T, ARENTZEN R, ITAKURA K, YANSURA DG, ROSS MJ, MIOZZARI G, CREA R, SEEBURG PH: Direct expression in *Escherichia coli* of a DNA sequence coding for human growth hormone. *Nature* 281:544, 1979.

171. OLSON KC, FENNO J, LIN N, HARKINS RN, SNIDER C, KOHR WH, ROSS MJ, FODGE D, PRENDER G, STEBBING N: Purified human growth hormone from *E. coli* is biologically active. *Nature* 293:408, 1981.

172. KAPLAN SL, AUGUST GP, BLETHEN SL, BROWN DR, HINTZ RL, JOHANSEN A, PLOTNICK LP, UNDERWOOD LE, BELL JJ, BLIZZARD RM, FOLEY TP, HOPWOOD NJ, KIRKLAND RT, ROSENFELD RG, VAN WYK JJ: Clinical studies with recombinant-DNA derived methionyl human growth hormone in growth hormone deficient children. *Lancet* 1:697, 1986.

173. ROGOL AD, BLIZZARD RM, JOHANSON AJ, FURLANETTO RW, EVANS WS, RIVIER J, VALE WW, THORNER MO: Growth hormone release in response to human pancreatic tumor growth hormone-releasing hormone-40 in children with short stature. *J Clin Endocrinol Metab* 59:580, 1984.

174. TAKANO K, HIZUKA N, SHIZUME K, ASAKAWA K, MIYOKAWA M, HEROSE N, SHIBASAKI T, LING NC: Plasma growth hormone (GH) response to GH-releasing factor in normal children with short stature and patients with pituitary dwarfism. *J Clin Endocrinol Metab* 58:236, 1984.

175. THORNER MO, RESCHKE J, CHITWOOD J, ROGOL AD, FURLANETTO R, RIVIER J, VALE W, BLIZZARD RM: Acceleration of growth in two children treated with human growth hormone-releasing factor. *N Engl J Med* 312:4, 1985.

176. ROCHICCIOLI PE, TAUBER M-T, UBOLDI F, COUDE F-X, MORRE M: Effect of over night constant infusion of human growth hormone (GH)-releasing hormone-(1-44) on 24-hour GH secretion in children with partial GH deficiency. *J Clin Endocrinol Metab* 63:1100, 1986.

177. PALMITER RD, BRINSTER RL, HAMMER RE, TRUMBAUER ME, ROSENFELD MG, BIRNBERG NC, EVANS RM: Dramatic growth of mice that develop from eggs microinjected with metallothionein-growth hormone fusion genes. *Nature* 300:611, 1982.

178. HAMMER RE, PURSEL VG, REXROAD CE Jr, WALL RJ, BOLT DJ, EBERT KM, PALMITER RD, BRINSTER RL: Production of transgenic rabbits, sheep and pigs by microinjection. *Nature* 315:680, 1985.

179. HAMMER RE, BRINSTER RL, ROSENFELD MG, EVANS RM, MAYO KE: Expression of human growth hormone-releasing factor in transgenic mice results in increased somatic growth. *Nature* 315:413, 1985.

180. WAGNER EF, COVARRUBIAS L, STEWART TA, MINTZ B: Prenatal lethalities in mice homozygous for human growth hormone gene sequences integrated in the germ line. *Cell* 35:647, 1983.

CHAPTER 78

NEPHROGENIC DIABETES INSIPIDUS

W. BRIAN REEVES
THOMAS E. ANDREOLI

1. Nephrogenic diabetes insipidus is a disorder, familial or acquired, characterized by renal tubular insensitivity to antidiuretic hormone (ADH). Polydipsia, polyuria, and hyposthenuria are the cardinal clinical manifestations of this disease. Nephrogenic diabetes insipidus is distinguished from pituitary diabetes insipidus by a lack of response to exogenous vasopressin and by serum levels of arginine vasopressin that rise appropriately with increases in serum osmolality.

2. The familial disorder exhibits a hereditary pattern consistent with X-linked transmission with variable degrees of manifestation in females. Acquired nephrogenic diabetes insipidus may occur as a consequence of drug therapy with lithium, demethylchlorotetracycline, or volatile anesthetics such as methoxyflurane, or in association with systemic disorders such as amyloidosis, Sjögren syndrome, or sarcoidosis.

3. The causes for vasopressin unresponsiveness in either the familial or acquired forms of the disorder are not certain. In normal individuals, ADH enhances cAMP accumulation in collecting duct cells; in turn, cAMP enhances the rate of water transport by increasing the number of water-specific channels in urinary (luminal) membranes. Inferential but not conclusive data in patients and experimental animals suggest that, in the familial disease, there is an inability of renal tubular cells to accumulate cAMP in response to vasopressin. Demethylchlorotetracycline may also produce a defect in vasopressin-stimulated cAMP accumulation by renal tubular cells. In lithium-induced nephrogenic diabetes insipidus, there may be defects both in vasopressin-stimulated cAMP formation and in cAMP enhancement of water transport through urinary (luminal) membranes.

4. Morbidity is related to the development of hypertonic encephalopathy. This complication may be avoided by the ingestion of adequate amounts of water. When the amount of water required is inconveniently large, this can be reduced by restriction of dietary solute intake and by the administration of thiazide diuretics, amiloride, or nonsteroidal anti-inflammatory agents. Life expectancy is normal if episodes of dehydration are prevented.

Nephrogenic diabetes insipidus is a familial or acquired disorder in which renal tubular cells are unresponsive to antidiuretic hormone (ADH). The clinical hallmarks of the syndrome, polyuria and polydipsia, are the direct consequence of this tubular unresponsiveness to ADH, since patients with nephrogenic diabetes insipidus are unable to concentrate urine effectively, even with extreme degrees of volume contraction.

In normal individuals, the plasma osmolality is maintained remarkably constant, in the range 285 to 295 mosmol/kg H_2O, despite wide variations in water or solute intake. The cardinal factors regulating water homeostasis are illustrated in Fig. 78-1. The positive limbs of the water repletion reaction include two elements: the solid lines indicate processes activated by osmotic stimuli, while the dashed lines denote those processes referable to nonosmotic stimuli. The dotted lines refer to the negative feedback for water repletion. The osmoreceptors, both for ADH release and for thirst, respond to small changes in effective extracellular fluid (ECF) osmolality, while baroreceptors respond to changes in effective circulating volume (ECV). As little as a two percent increase in effective ECF osmolality causes shrinkage of osmoreceptor cells. In turn, ADH is released from storage sites in the posterior pituitary gland, and water ingestion occurs, probably because of local angiotensin II release. A second way of stimulating both ADH release and thirst involves volume-mediated stimuli. Activation of extrarenal baroreceptors by blood volume depletion produces afferent signals, carried by cranial nerves IX and X, which result in nonosmotic ADH release and thirst. Volume contraction also stimulates thirst by way of local angiotensin II release. Thus water acquisition involves two distinct mechanisms, osmotic and nonosmotic, each of which operates at a different sensitivity. Moreover, both osmotic as well as nonosmotic stimuli evoke two distinct responses, water conservation by antidiuresis and water acquisition via thirst.

The negative feedback limb of the water repletion reaction involves suppression of both osmotic and nonosmotic stimuli to ADH release and to thirst. Current evidence indicates that this suppression is referable to central release of atrial natriuretic peptide.

The cardinal cellular elements of the antidiuretic response are illustrated in Fig. 78-2. Both in cells of the medullary thick ascending limb of Henle (mTALH) and in the collecting tubule (CT), ADH binding to contraluminal membranes results in activation of adenylate cyclase (EC 4.6.1.1.), which catalyzes the formation of cyclic adenosine monophosphate (cAMP) from ATP. In turn, cAMP-dependent processes exert an admittance effect on luminal membranes of mTALH and CT cells. In the mTALH, there is a hormone-dependent increase, by mechanisms as yet unknown, in the functional number of apical membrane K^+ channels and $Na^+:K^+:2Cl^-$

Nonstandard abbreviations used in this chapter are: ADH = antidiuretic hormone; ANP = atrial natriuretic peptide; AII = angiotensin II; AVP = arginine vasopressin; cAMP = cyclic adenosine monophosphate; CRF = corticotropin releasing factor; CT = collecting tubule; cTALH = cortical thick ascending limb of Henle; dAVP = 1-deamino-arginine vasopressin; dVAVP = 1-deamino-8-D-arginine vasopressin; ECF = extracellular fluid; ECV = effective circulating volume; GFR = glomerular filtration rate; LAP = left atrial pressure; mTALH = medullary thick ascending limb of Henle; NTS = nucleus of the tractus solitarius; OVLT = organum vasculosum laminae terminalis; P_{D_w} = permeability coefficient for water diffusion across a membrane; P_f = permeability coefficient for osmotic water flow across a membrane; PVN = paraventricular nucleus; SFO = subfornical organ; SON = supraoptic nucleus; THO = tracer water.

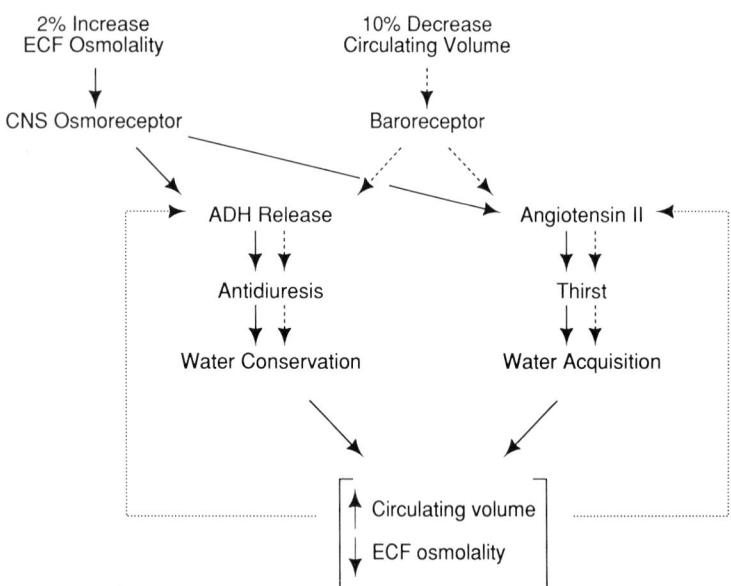

Fig. 78-1 A schematic illustration of the water repletion reaction. Solid lines indicate osmotically stimulated pathways, and dashed lines indicate volume-mediated pathways. The dotted lines represent negative-feedback mediated by atrial natriuretic peptide.

cotransport units. This results in an increase in the net rate of mTALH salt absorption and consequently in an enrichment of medullary interstitial osmolality. In the CT, there is an increase in the number of apical membrane water channels produced by a hormone-dependent increase in intramembranous aggregates of clathrin-coated pits containing these water channels. Consequently, the water permeability of the CT rises, thus permitting osmotic transfer of tubular fluid to the hypertonic renal medullary interstitium. Thus with circulating ADH, normal individuals elaborate a urine hypertonic to plasma.

On the other hand, an individual having nephrogenic diabetes insipidus excretes urine which is consistently hypotonic to plasma, even when plasma osmolality and plasma ADH concentrations are significantly increased, because the epithelial cells of collecting ducts are insensitive to ADH. Virtually all the clinical manifestations of the disease, including the obligatory requirement for ingesting large volumes of solute-free water, the effects of polyuria on the hydrodynamics of the urinary tract, and the hypertonic dehydration which inevitably attends water restriction, are directly referable to this deficient renal mechanism for water homeostasis.

The first modern descriptions of nephrogenic diabetes insipidus focused on a relatively rare X-linked hereditary disorder.[1-5] But it is not apparent that polyuric disorders due to failure of the renal tubule to respond to ADH may also occur as a complication either of drug therapy or, in rare instances, of systemic diseases. Because the clinical and pathophysiological findings in these conditions resemble closely those occurring in familial nephrogenic diabetes insipidus, this chapter considers both the familial and acquired forms of nephrogenic diabetes insipidus.

FAMILIAL NEPHROGENIC DIABETES INSIPIDUS: CLINICAL CONSIDERATIONS

History

In 1892, McIlraith[2] described (Fig. 78-3) three generations of individuals with diabetes insipidus: males were affected with "extreme thirst"; females were "slightly affected"; and male offsprings of "slightly affected" females suffered from "extreme thirst." He concluded that this form of diabetes insipidus involved "a heredity occurring chiefly in males on the female side of the house." de Lange,[3] in a report of a family with hereditary diabetes insipidus involving four generations, observed no male-to-male transmission, and noted that injections of posterior pituitary lobe extracts did not reduce urine volume or increase urine specific gravity in affected patients.

In 1945, Forssman[4] published an analysis of the existing literature on hereditary diabetes insipidus together with data acquired on five different kindreds having 32 possible male patients with the disorder; 16 of these patients were studied personally by him. He established that male-to-male transmission did not occur, that descendants of phenotypically normal males were healthy, that polyuria invariably had its onset in infancy, that daily urine volumes in adults exceeded 4 liters, that urinary specific gravities after water deprivation were in the range 1.003 to 1.008, and that female carriers frequently had unusual thirst, nocturnal water consumption, and impaired urinary concentrating ability following water deprivation. In three affected males from one kindred, water deprivation combined with injections of posterior pituitary lobe extracts failed to reduce urine volume or to increase urine specific gravity. In 1947, Williams and Henry[5] applied the term *nephrogenic diabetes insipidus* to the disease, stressing the fact that renal tubular insensitivity to ADH was the primary pathophysiological disturbance in the disorder.

Clinical Manifestations

Little can be added to the descriptions provided by Forssman,[4,6] Williams and Henry,[5] and Waring et al.[7] The following narrative by Waring et al.[7] summarizes eloquently and succinctly the main clinical and pathophysiological features of the disease:

The syndrome is characterized by onset shortly after birth . . . polydipsia and polyuria which do not respond to pitressin . . . high values for serum sodium and chloride . . . rapid dehydration if fluids are reduced or withheld . . . inability to excrete urine of high specific gravity . . . familial incidence and occurrence in boys only (?).

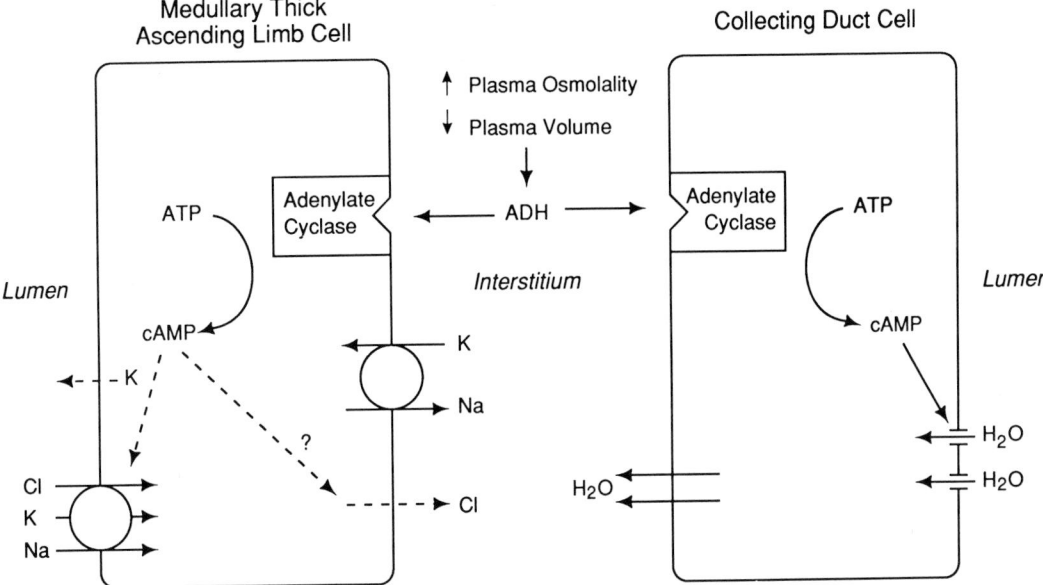

Fig. 78-2 A schematic illustration of the major effects of ADH in the kidney.

The presenting complaints were unexplained fever, failure to gain weight and constipation. . . . The bouts of dehydration are usually not associated with acidosis.

The thirst of one of the patients studied was satisfied only when five to six times the normal requirement of fluid was offered. The levels of serum sodium and chloride decreased to normal, and the infant remained afebrile on this high fluid intake. . . . With total restriction of fluids the infant became severely dehydrated within twelve hours; the flow of urine virtually ceased in ten hours; the temperature rose, and the serum sodium and chloride increased greatly. . . . The dehydration could be corrected rapidly by giving water.

Pitressin was given until toxic reactions were seen without any alteration in fluid intake or output.

Renal clearances done under good conditions of hydration showed normal values for mannitol, urea, phosphates and paraaminohippuric acid at high and low levels. . . . Only 70 to 80% of filtered water, as against 99.5 per cent of the filtered sodium and 98.8 per cent of the chloride, was reabsorbed in the renal tubules. Administration of ammonium chloride . . . revealed that the children could excrete acid urine.

In short, the clinical picture in dehydrated patients with nephrogenic diabetes insipidus is one of volume contraction, hypernatremia, hyperthermia, polyuria, vomiting, constipation, and failure to thrive. Because of the relatively nonspecific nature of symptoms in early stages of the disease, the disorder may be difficult to identify in the first few months of life. Polyuria, in particular, may frequently be absent in infancy,[8] due presumably to dehydration, hypovolemia, and a reduced glomerular filtration rate.

The following considerations illustrate the extreme degree of volume contraction which may occur in affected infants. During the first 6 months of life, body water content is approximately 12 liters per square meter of body surface area[9] and the glomerular filtration rate ranges between 25 and 40 ml/min per square meter of body surface area[10]; thus a 5-kg male infant with body surface area of 0.3 m[2] has a body water content of approximately 4.0 liters and a glomerular filtration rate of 7.5 to 12 ml/min. If he were affected with severe familial nephrogenic diabetes insipidus where 20 percent of filtered water was excreted, his obligatory urine loss would be 2.0 to 3.5 liters daily, or about 50 to 85 percent of total body

water. Small wonder, then, that infants suffering from the disease are markedly susceptible to volume depletion, hyperthermia, and hyernatremia, particularly since they are unable to regulate their own fluid intake.

Mental and physical retardation may accompany hereditary

Fig. 78-3 McIlraith's pedigree [2] for hereditary diabetes insipidus affecting three generations of a family.

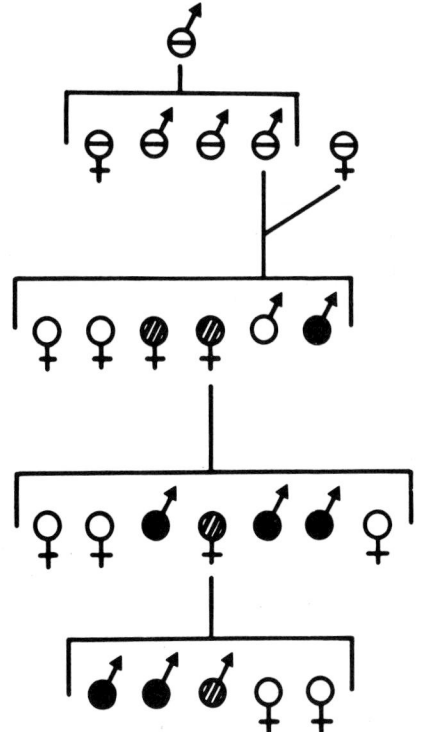

● "affected with extreme thirst"
◑ "slightly affected"
○ "not affected"
⊖ "not affected so far as known"

nephrogenic diabetes insipidus, but children with the disorder may also have normal intelligence and physical maturation. Current evidence indicates that inadequate caloric ingestion associated with incessant water intake accounts for growth retardation.

Hypertonic Encephalopathy

Hypertonic encephalopathy, particularly during infancy, is the most lethal complication of nephrogenic diabetes insipidus. Furthermore, the sequelae of repeated bouts of hypernatremia lead to mental impairment in familial nephrogenic diabetes insipidus. In one series of 50 hypernatremic children the acute mortality was 20 percent, and 37 percent of the survivors had abnormalities on neurologic examination, intelligence testing, or electroencephalography.[11] Similarly, in 100 infants who developed hypernatremic encephalopathy, brain damage developed in 16 patients, eight of whom subsequently died.[12]

These encephalopathic effects relate directly to changes in brain volume during hypernatremia. Since virtually all cells in the body are rather permeable to water, hypernatremia inevitably results in an increase in intracellular osmolality. This equilibration may occur in at least two ways: in acute hypernatremia, water is lost from cells and the acute shrinkage in brain volume results in hypertonic encephalopathy; in chronic hypernatremia, CNS cells accumulate solutes and brain shrinkage is minimized so that CNS symptoms are also minimized. In other words, the relations between increases in effective ECF osmolality, changes in brain volume, and the occurrence of hypertonic encephalopathy depend on the magnitude of the ECF osmolality increase, the duration of the increase, and the solute responsible for the osmolality increase.

A dramatic example of hypertonic encephalopathy referable to brain shrinkage occurred in 1962 when infants, inadvertently given a nursery formula containing salt rather than sugar, developed hypernatremic encephalopathy with more than a 50 percent fatality rate.[13] In experiments with rabbits subjected to hypernatremia, early neurologic symptoms occur when the serum osmolality reaches 350 to 375 mosmol/kg water; nystagmus and ataxia occur at 375 to 400 mosmol/kg water; and coma, stupor, and death occur when serum osmolality is in the range of 400 to 435 mosmol/kg water.[14]

Experimental hypernatremic encephalopathy and death occur in the absence of any central nervous system pathologic changes other than brain shrinkage and a marked rise in brain NaCl content.[15] In other words, the combination of hyperosmolality and cellular shrinkage are the major factors responsible for hypertonic encephalopathy.[16] This hypothesis coincides with the well-known clinical observation that, for a given elevation of serum osmolality, cerebral symptoms are severe in patients with hypernatremia, diabetic ketoacidosis, or nonketotic hyperglycemic coma and negligible in azotemia.

Cell Volume Adjustments to ECF Hypertonicity. The adjustments in brain cell water and in cell content of osmotically active solutes that occur during acute (1–2 h) and chronic (2 h to 2 weeks) increases in osmolality produced by a variety of solutes are shown in Table 78-1. Although these data derive from animal experiments,[16–18] similar changes probably occur in humans. The term *idiogenic* osmoles refers to osmotically active solutes measured as the difference between total cell osmolality and the sum of the osmolalities of Na^+, K^+, and Cl^-.

During acute increases in osmolality by any of these endogenous or exogenous solutes, osmotic equilibrium between intracellular and extracellular water is achieved almost completely by cell water loss (Table 78-1). In this case, increases in cell Na^+, K^+, and Cl^- concentrations account for the increase in cell osmolality, and idiogenic osmoles are therefore absent. It is this rapid change in brain cell volume that appears to account for the severity of CNS symptoms and the high mortality referable to acute increases in serum Na^+ concentrations.

In chronic hypertonic states, brain cell volume returns toward normal (volume regulatory increase) when the increase in osmolality is produced by endogenous solutes such as Na^+, glucose, and urea, but not with exogenous solutes such as glycerol, mannitol, or sucrose (Table 78-1).[16] Why the exogenous solutes do not produce a brain cell volume regulatory increase is not understood, but this result provided a rationale for the use of these solutes to reduce brain volume during episodes of cerebral edema.

The extent to which brain cell volume regulation occurs by solute or electrolyte uptake, or by accumulation of organic idiogenic osmoles, is different for each of the endogenous solutes. About 50 to 60 percent of the increase in brain osmoles responsible for brain cell volume regulation during chronic hypernatremia is due to amino acids.[16,19] The remaining 40 to 50 percent of cell volume regulation during hypernatremia results from the cellular accumulation of Na^+, K^+, and Cl^-. The transport mechanism mediating intracellular accumulation of the latter ions has not been explicitly defined but may be similar to the coupled (Na^+,K^+,$2Cl^-$) transport process responsible for hypertonic volume regulation in several other cell types.[20] Finally, it should be recognized that dissipation of the hypernatremia-induced organic osmoles after returning to the isotonic state is not rapid but takes several hours to a day.

During hyperglycemia, brain volume regulation is due not only to insulin-independent cellular uptake of glucose (20 percent) but also to electrolyte uptake and to accumulation of idiogenic osmoles. The latter, however, are not amino acids, and their nature remains unknown. In contrast to the hypernatremia-induced amino acids, the idiogenic osmoles that are accumulated during hyperglycemia dissipate rapidly with decreasing plasma glucose.[16] This difference may account for the well-established clinical axiom that rapid reduction in serum sodium concentrations in nephrogenic diabetes insipidus may elicit seizures, while relatively rapid reductions in plasma glucose concentrations in nonketotic hyperglycemic coma generally improve CNS function.

Renal Function

The cardinal abnormality in familial nephrogenic diabetes insipidus is the failure of collecting ducts to increase their water permeability in response to ADH, resulting in the excretion of urine which is hypotonic to plasma. Williams and Henry[5] showed clearly that the concentrating defect was due to end-organ refractoriness to ADH, since doses of pitressin sufficient to cause abdominal cramps and cutaneous blanching had no effect on urine volume and concentration.

In Brattleboro strain rats having hereditary hypothalamic diabetes insipidus, urinary hypertonicity in the absence of ADH occurs when the glomerular filtration rate (GFR) is severely reduced,[21] but it can occur with very little or no reduc-

Table 78-1 Brain Volume Adjustment during Hyperosmolality

Solute	Endogenous			Exogenous
	Na⁺	Glucose	Urea	Mannitol, glycerol, sucrose
Acute (1–2 h)				
Brain water	↓↓	↓↓	↓↓	↓↓
Electrolyte content	Normal	Normal	Normal	Normal
"Idiogenic" osmoles	Absent	Absent	Absent	Absent
Chronic (2 h–2 wk)				
Brain water	Normal	Normal	Normal	↓↓
Electrolyte content	↑	↑	Normal	Normal
"Idiogenic" osmoles	↑↑↑	↑↑	↑	Absent

SOURCE: Reference 20.

tion in GFR if renal blood flow is reduced.[22] The suggested mechanism[22] for the formation of hypertonic urine under these conditions involves a striking reduction in the volume of fluid delivered to distal tubules and collecting ducts, so that, in the absence of ADH, the removal of even small amounts of water from collecting ducts results in at least partial equilibration of collecting duct fluid with the renal medullary interstitium and hence the generation of urine which is hypertonic to plasma. In one patient with familial nephrogenic diabetes insipidus,[23] in whom severe reductions in glomerular filtration rate and virtual cessation of urine flow were produced by induced hypotension, the urine became isotonic but not hypertonic to plasma. Other patients with this disease, however, are able to produce urine hypertonic to plasma with reductions in GFR of approximately 50 percent.[24]

Other disturbances in renal structure or function, or in other epithelial transport processes, have been noted in familial nephrogenic diabetes insipidus. Renal plasma flow may be reduced in the presence of a normal glomerular filtration rate, resulting in an elevated filtration fraction. It has been proposed[25] that the rise in filtration fraction is the consequence of renal vasoconstriction produced by high concentrations of circulating ADH.

Hyperuricemia and clinical gout have been observed in some adults with familial nephrogenic diabetes insipidus.[23,25] Urinary clearances of uric acid are reduced while glomerular filtration rates are normal, suggesting that, in adult patients, the disease may be accompanied by a renal tubular defect in uric acid excretion. Since children with familial nephrogenic diabetes insipidus had normal serum uric acid concentrations, Gorden et al.[25] proposed that such a defect is acquired rather than congenital, and possibly related to an elevated filtration fraction or to urinary tract dilatation.

Also, microdissection of autopsy specimens from children with the disease reveal shortening of proximal convoluted tubule segments.[26] It is difficult to reconcile these anatomic findings with the concentrating defect occurring in more terminal nephron segments.

Finally, infants and children with the disorder have increased NaCl concentrations in sweat.[27,28] The excess salt concentrations in sweat are not reduced by administration of 9-α-fluorohydrocortisone.[28]

In all other respects, renal function in the disease appears to be normal. In the absence of dehydration or hydronephrosis, plasma electrolytes and plasma acid-base balance are normal, as are the glomerular filtration rate, glucose and amino acid reabsorptive rates, phosphate excretion, and urinary acidifying ability.[1]

Radiographic Manifestations

Striking dilatation of the urinary tract may occur in familial nephrogenic diabetes insipidus.[29–32] The dilatation progresses in some instances to massive hydroureter, hydronephrosis, and a urinary bladder capacity of 1000 ml. Lacking evidence of anatomic obstruction, these patients may develop hydronephrosis when urinary flow rates exceed the normal emptying capacity of the bladder.[31]

Serum Vasopressin Concentration

Robertson and his associates, using a specific radioimmunoassay for the antidiuretic hormone arginine vasopressin (AVP), have shown that (Fig. 78-4A), both in normal subjects and in patients with nephrogenic diabetes insipidus, serum osmolalities greater than 280 mosmol/kg result in near-linear increments in serum AVP concentrations, while in pituitary diabetes insipidus plasma AVP concentrations change negligibly or not at all in response to an osmotic challenge.[33] Second, as shown in Fig. 78-4B,[33,34] normal subjects and patients with either primary polydipsia or pituitary diabetes insipidus exhibit a near-linear relationship between urine osmolality and plasma AVP concentrations, while patients with nephrogenic diabetes insipidus excrete a consistently hypotonic urine despite fifteenfold variations in plasma AVP levels. These observations confirm the hypothesis that familial nephrogenic diabetes insipidus is characterized by end-organ unresponsiveness to ADH.

Heredity

Familial nephrogenic diabetes insipidus is transmitted as a sex-linked recessive characteristic. Consistent with this view are the observations that male patients with the disorder exhibit complete unresponsiveness to vasopressin and that male-to-male transmission does not occur. However, incomplete forms of the disease may occur in female relatives of affected males.[1] And, in families having no evidence of paternal involvement, several females have been reported in whom the disease was as severe as that observed in males.[35–37] Based on these observations, it appears that familial nephrogenic diabetes insipidus is an X-linked disorder with variable degrees of manifestation, or expression, in heterozygous females. In families evaluated with this question in mind, approximately two-thirds of the female relatives of males having the complete disorder failed to concentrate urine normally following dehy-

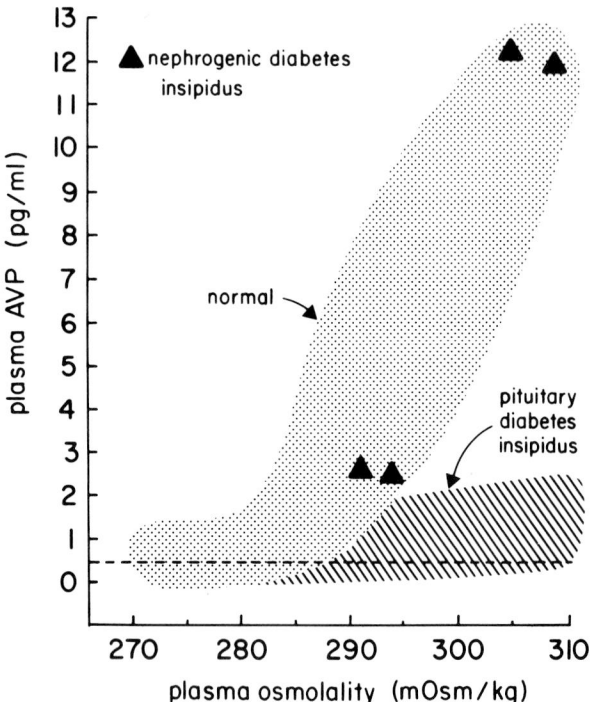

A.

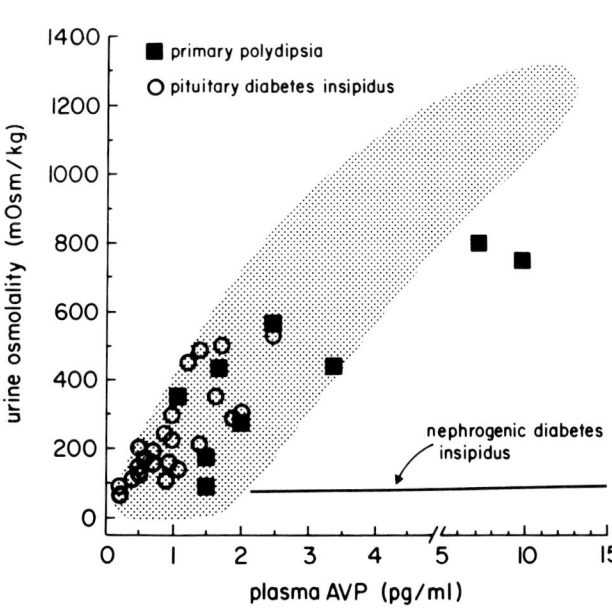

B.

Fig. 78-4 *A. The relations between plasma arginine vasopressin (AVP) concentrations and plasma osmolality. Patients with nephrogenic diabetes insipidus (triangles) respond normally to increases in plasma osmolality. B. The relations between urine osmolality and plasma AVP concentration. Patients with nephrogenic diabetes insipidus fail to respond to AVP with appropriate increases in urine osmolality. (Adapted from Robertson et al.[33,34])*

dration.[1,38] Female carriers may also demonstrate a reduced factor VIII response to ADH analogues as compared with that of normal females.[39]

Bode and Crawford[40] deduced that most North American patients with the disease are descendants of the Ulster Scot clan who reached Nova Scotia in 1761 on the ship Hopewell. Among these people, there is a long tradition of "water drinkers" which conforms to the inheritance pattern of an X-linked recessive trait. Indeed, these early settlers in Nova Scotia re-

corded, two centuries before the first report in the medical literature, quite detailed descriptions of the clinical manifestations and deduced the mode of inheritance of nephrogenic diabetes insipidus. Bode and Crawford[40] recounted the legend of the "water drinker's curse" which, handed down over many generations, illustrates this point delightfully.

A gypsy woman and her son were traveling the road and became thirsty. Pausing at a well in front of the next house, the gypsy requested water for her son; the housewife refused, whereupon, the gypsy woman cast upon her a curse. Henceforth, the story goes, the woman's sons would be afflicted with a craving for water. The curse would be passed on by her daughters and revisited upon their sons for generations to come.

However, it is clear that nephrogenic diabetes insipidus is ethnically heterogenous. Nakano,[41] for example, described the occurrence of nephrogenic diabetes insipidus in a Samoan Caucasian family residing in Hawaii; the family history was traced back to a heterozygous Samoan woman carrier. Familial nephrogenic diabetes insipidus has also been described in an Australian aboriginal kindred having no Caucasian ancestry.[42]

PHYSIOLOGY OF WATER METABOLISM

In normal individuals having widely disparate salt and water intakes, plasma osmolality is virtually constant. Although the range of normal values in the population is 285 to 295 mosmol/kg H_2O, the value of plasma osmolality in an individual varies by only 1 to 2 percent. Because plasma osmolality expresses the ratio of aqueous solutes to total body water, it is evident that invariance of plasma osmolality in the presence of nonisotonic solute and water ingestion depends on the ability of the kidney to dissociate solute and water excretion: a patient excretes urine which is either hypotonic to plasma, in the case of relative water excess, or hypertonic to plasma, in the case of selective water deficit.

Since proximal tubular absorption of glomerular ultrafiltrate is an isotonic process, the independent modulation of solute and water excretion is effected by transport phenomena occurring in more distal nephron sites. Stated briefly, the ability to excrete urine as dilute as 50 mosmol/kg H_2O or as concentrated as 1400 mosmol/kg H_2O depends on the following processes. Solute (NaCl) absorption in the water-impermeable medullary thick ascending limb of Henle results in dilution of luminal fluid and enrichment of the hypertonic medullary interstitium. In the absence of ADH, the dilute fluid passes unchanged water-impermeable distal convoluted tubules and collecting ducts, yielding a dilute urine. In the presence of ADH, the water permeability of collecting ducts increases by at least tenfold, thus allowing equilibration of luminal fluid with the hypertonic interstitium and the production of concentrated urine. Glomerular filtration rate and the rate of proximal tubular absorption of glomerular filtrate also influence the final osmolality of urine by varying the magnitude of solute and water delivered to more distal nephron segments.[20]

Antidiuretic Hormone

Chemistry. The hormones elaborated by most mammalian neurohypophyses include oxytocin and ADH or arginine vasopressin. Figure 78-5 shows the structure of AVP and that of a commonly used analogue, 1-deamino-8-D-arginine vasopres-

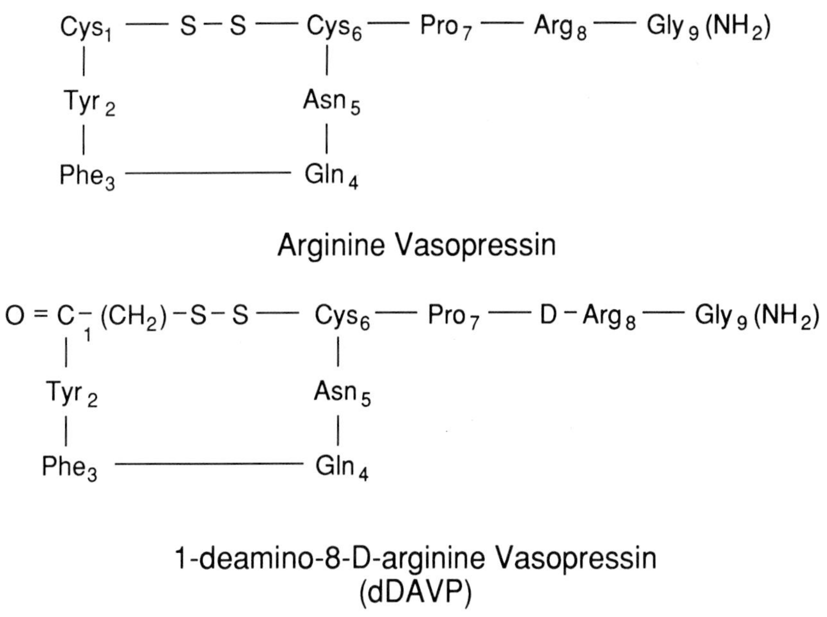

Cys$_1$ —— S – S —— Cys$_6$ —— Pro$_7$ —— Arg$_8$ —— Gly$_9$ (NH$_2$)

Tyr$_2$ Asn$_5$

Phe$_3$ ——————— Gln$_4$

Arginine Vasopressin

O = C –$_1$ (CH$_2$) – S – S —— Cys$_6$ —— Pro$_7$ —— D – Arg$_8$ —— Gly$_9$ (NH$_2$)

Tyr$_2$ Asn$_5$

Phe$_3$ ——————— Gln$_4$

Fig. 78-5 The structures of arginine vasopressin (antidiuretic hormone) and a commonly used synthetic analogue (1-deamino-8-D-arginine vasopressin).

1-deamino-8-D-arginine Vasopressin (dDAVP)

sin (dDAVP). There are many synthetic analogues of AVP. The vast majority of these agents possess varying degrees of antidiuretic, vasopressin, and uterotonic activities.[43] There are also structural analogues which function as competitive antagonists of both the vasopressor and antidiuretic action of the hormone. In this section, we consider some of the structural features of neurohypophyseal peptides, with particular emphasis on those which determine antidiuretic activity and specificity.

Vasopressin acts via tissue receptors classified as V_1 receptors in smooth muscle and V_2 receptors in renal epithelia; only the latter receptors activate adenylate cyclase.[44] Antidiuretic activity in the intact animal depends on the ability of a peptide to bind to the renal receptor, to stimulate the adenylate cyclase system, and to resist metabolic degradation. Thus, peptides that activate adenylate cyclase very poorly may still produce a maximal antidiuretic response in the whole animal.[45,46] In many cases, synthetic analogues of ADH which have reduced receptor affinity and reduced ability to activate adenylate cyclase in vitro exhibit potent and specific antidiuretic activity in the whole animal.[47-49] Given these apparent discrepancies between in vitro and in vivo observations, it is clear that metabolic stability plays an important role in determining in vivo antidiuretic activity.

Deamination of position 1 reduces receptor affinity but also renders the compound more resistant to metabolic degradation. As a result, 1-deamino-arginine vasopressin (dAVP) possesses antidiuretic activity fourfold greater than ADH. Substitution of D-arginine for L-arginine at position 8 decreases the pressor activity so that the product, DAVP, has an antidiuretic/pressor activity ratio of 28.[49] Deamination at position 1 combined with substitution of D- for L-arginine at position 8 yields a compound, dDAVP, which has a long duration of action and an antidiuretic/pressor ratio of approximately 3000.[49] dDAVP is one of the most widely used synthetic ADH analogues. Further substitution of the hydrophobic amino acid valine for glutamine at position 4 (1-deamino-4-valine-[8-D-arginine]-vasopressin, dDVAVP) prolongs the duration of action and abolishes the pressor effects, making it the most specific antidiuretic agonist reported.[49]

There are also selective antagonists to the antidiuretic effects of vasopressin. The first such compound, discovered in 1981, contained a pentamethylene ring at position 1, an O-ethyl-tyrosine at position 2, and a valine substitution for glutamine at position 4.[50] This compound, d(CH$_2$)$_5$Tyr(ET)VAVP, is a potent antidiuretic antagonist as well as a potent vasopressor antagonist; that is, it is a vasopressin antagonist for both V_1 and V_2 receptors. Manning and Sawyer[51] have determined that selective modification of d(CH$_2$)$_5$Tyr(ET)VAVP can yield compounds with enhanced antidiuretic antagonist activity and increased selectivity for antidiuretic over antivasopressor activity. The substitution of the L-Tyr(ET) at position 2 of d(CH$_2$)$_5$Tyr(ET)VAVP by aliphatic D-amino acids, such as D-Ile, D-Leu, or D-Val, results in increased antidiuretic/antivasopressor selectivity.[52] Further substitution of position 4 with aminobutyric acid, isoleucine, or alanine leads to even greater antidiuretic/antivasopressor selectivity.[53] Finally, the C-terminal glycine-NH$_2$ may be deleted or substituted by a variety of amino acid amides with full retention of antagonist activity.[54] While causing an initial, brief antidiuresis, these analogues competitively inhibit the antidiuretic response to exogenous and endogenous ADH, and result in a water diuresis in normally hydrated rats that is equal in intensity to that seen in vasopressin-deficient Brattleboro rats.[50] These antagonists have also been shown to inhibit competitively lysine vasopressin binding and adenylate cyclase activation in renal medullary membrane preparations.[55]

In isolated segments of collecting ducts and medullary thick ascending limbs, these antagonists inhibit the ADH-induced increase in adenylate cyclase activity but do not affect the response to other agonists such as glucagon or parathyroid hormone.[56] In isolated perfused collecting duct segments, d(CH$_2$)$_5$Tyr(ET)VAVP completely prevents the ADH-induced increase in water permeability but has no effect on the response to forskolin, an agent which activates directly the catalytic subunit of adenylate cyclase.[56] In other words, these agents antagonize the effect of ADH by preventing the binding of ADH to its receptor and thus preventing the subsequent activation of adenylate cyclase.

Biosynthesis, Storage, and Release. The relations between the hypothalamus, the posterior pituitary gland, and ADH production derive largely from the work of Scharrer and Scharrer,[57] who showed that nerve endings in the posterior pituitary gland had their origin in cell bodies located in the supra-optic (SON) and paraventricular nuclei (PVN) of the hypothalamus and that these nerve cells contained dense neurosecretory granules. Because these neurosecretory granules accumulate on the hypothalamic rather than pituitary side of axons following transection of the neurohypophyseal tract, the Scharrers[57] proposed that ADH, or a precursor, is synthesized in the SON and PVN, packaged into neurosecretory granules, and carried by axoplasmic streaming to nerve endings in the posterior pituitary gland. Supporting this hypothesis is the observation that, following the injection of [^{35}S]cysteine into the hypothalamus, this amino acid is rapidly incorporated into proteins of the SON, whereas appearance of the label in the posterior pituitary is delayed by several hours. Moreover, treatment with colchicine, which disrupts axonal transport, completely prevents the appearance of labeled cysteine in the posterior pituitary.[58]

The biosynthesis of vasopressin is a paradigm for the way small peptide hormones are produced, namely, by posttranslational cleavage of a larger protein precursor molecule.[59] Neurosecretory granules contain vasopressin along with a specific carrier protein, neurophysin II, in a 1:1 stoichiometry.[60–62] The neurosecretory granules of oxytocin-secreting neurohypophyseal cells contain oxytocin complexed to a similar but distinct carrier protein, neurophysin I.[61] The first evidence that vasopressin and neurophysin were derived from a common precursor came from studies of the incorporation of [^{35}S]cysteine into proteins of the SON and PVN.[63,64] Further proof has come from the recent identification and sequencing of the vasopressin gene.[65,66] The organization of the vasopressin precursor peptide and the vasopressin gene of the rat are illustrated in Fig. 78-6. The hormone precursor contains three peptide regions: a signal peptide and ADH at the N terminal, a neurophysin II region, and a C-terminal glycoprotein region of unknown significance.[59] Each of these three principal regions of the precursor protein is, in turn, coded for by one of three different exons of the vasopressin precursor gene. The vasopressin gene is located on human chromosome 20.[67]

Thus the main steps in the biosynthesis of ADH are: transcription of the vasopressin precursor mRNA; translation of the mRNA to a 166–amino acid preprohormone; removal of the signal peptide sequence while the peptide is still attached to the ribosome, yielding the prohormone; and conversion of the prohormone peptide into ADH and neurophysin II. This final step occurs within the neurosecretory granule during its transport to the neurohypophysis.[64]

Using cDNA probes for the vasopressin mRNA, expression of the vasopressin precursor mRNA has been detected in a variety of tissues outside the hypothalamus such as ovary, adrenal, testis, and cerebellum.[68] The extrahypothalamic mRNA is shorter than the hypothalamic mRNA owing to differences in the length of the poly A tail. These types of studies have yielded an interesting insight into the possible pathogenesis of hereditary central diabetes insipidus. The Brattleboro rat lacks the ability to produce hypothalamic ADH and therefore is a useful model for the study of central diabetes insipidus. In the Brattleboro rat, this defect has been shown to be due to a single base deletion in the exon encoding neurophysin II.[69] While the vasopressin-containing region of the precursor is translated normally, the frame shift which results from the nucleotide deletion causes misreading of the C-terminal codons, including the step codon, so that translation proceeds to the extreme 3′ end of the poly A tail of the mRNA (Fig. 78-6). The resulting protein is unable to be processed nor-

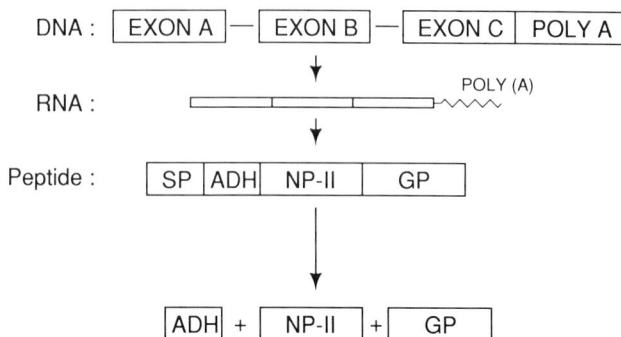

Fig. 78-6 A schematic illustration of the structure of the ADH gene, mRNA, and peptide. SP = signal peptide; ADH = arginine vasopressin; NP-II = neurophysin II; GP = C-terminal glycoprotein.

mally into ADH and neurophysin II so that no hormone is detectable in the pituitary, even though relatively normal amounts of vasopressin mRNA are present in the hypothalamus nuclei.[69]

VASOPRESSIN RELEASE. Current evidence indicates that neurohypophyseal secretion occurs by exocytosis, a quantal process.[62] The exocytotic events involve fusion of membranes from neurosecretory granules with plasma membranes, granule opening at the site of fusion, and release of granule material, including ADH and neurophysin II, into the extracellular space.[62] Since all the ADH-neurophysin complexes within the posterior pituitary gland are not readily available for release, ADH and neurophysin II may be segregated into two pools, a readily released pool and a storage pool.[70] The readily released pool constitutes ADH-neurophysin complexes within neurosecretory granules located adjacent to plasma membranes, while the storage pool contains ADH-neurophysin complexes in granules remote from plasma membranes.

Exocytosis of the neurosecretory granules is triggered by neurotransmitter-induced depolarization of the ADH-producing hypothalamic magnocellular neurons. The control of ADH neuron electrical activity by various neurotransmitters and afferent pathways is discussed below. The partial depolarization caused by these neurotransmitters, however, results in the generation and propogation of a sodium-dependent tetrodotoxin-sensitive[71] action potential. The latter results in a rapid calcium influx into nerve endings due to an increase in the permeability of axonal membranes to calcium attendant to depolarization.[72,62,73] The calcium entry in turn activates, by an as yet unidentified mechanism, exocytosis of neurosecretory granules and release of ADH and neurophysin II into the circulation. The rate of ADH secretion depends on both the rate and the pattern of neuron firing. For example, stimulation of ADH-producing neurons in rapid, intermittent bursts results in greater ADH secretion than does the same degree of stimulation delivered at a regular interval.[74]

Distribution and Metabolism. Lysine- or arginine-vasopressin entering the circulation is distributed in a volume approximating that of the extracellular space.[75] Nearly all the hormone in the plasma of dogs and humans exists in an unbound form[75] which, because of its relatively low molecular weight, permeates peripheral and glomerular capillaries readily. In humans the total clearance of ADH, which represents both metabolic degradation and renal excretion, is in the range of 2 to 4 ml/min per kilogram of body weight, yielding biologic half-lives in the range of 30 to 40 min.[76,77] These observations[75,77,78] indicate that, in humans, suppression of endogenous ADH release will result in a detectable change from the antidiuretic to water diuretic state after approximately 30 min.

Metabolic degradation of ADH appears to be mediated through binding of biologically active ADH to specific hormone receptors.[76,79] At least four sites of proteolytic cleavage for the hormone have been identified. With reference to Fig. 78-5, arginine vasopressin may undergo cleavage: within the liver, by rupture of 1,6-disulfide bond[80,81]; within the brain, by cleavage at the 6,7 position and subsequent hydrolysis of 9-glycinamide from the tripeptide[82]; in a variety of tissues, by hydrolysis of the peptide bond between the hemicystine residue in position 1 and tyrosine in position 2[82,83]; and within the kidney, by proteolysis of the peptide bond between residues 8 and 9, resulting in glycinamide release.[84] A peptidase of molecular weight 442,000 which cleaves glycinamide and results in biologic inactivation has been isolated from renal plasma membranes.[85] Renal excretion of ADH is the second method for elimination of circulating hormone and is estimated to account for about one-fourth of total metabolic clearance.[75,76]

Physiological Control of ADH Release

In order to maintain plasma osmolality at a constant level, ADH secretion from the posterior pituitary gland must vary directly with small changes in plasma osmolality. However, ADH may also be released when the plasma osmolality is less than normal. The latter occurs in at least two clinical settings: when extracellular fluid volume is either normal or increased with no disturbance in its distribution; and when extracellular fluid, primarily blood volume, is either reduced or abnormally distributed.

Disorders in which antidiuresis and body fluid hypotonicity occur in combination with a normal or an expanded extracellular fluid volume include: the syndrome of inappropriate ADH production[86] which occurs with pulmonary neoplasms, other pulmonary disorders, cranial lesions, and possibly acute intermittent porphyria[87]; the administration of drugs which either stimulate ADH release, such as morphine, barbiturates, and clofibrate,[88] or enhance hormone activity, such as chlorpropamide[89] and carbamapezine[90]; and endocrinopathies such as myxedema, where the factors responsible for an inability to excrete an appropriately dilute urine are uncertain.[91]

The combination of plasma hypotonicity and excretion of urine which is either isosmotic or hypertonic to plasma also occurs when blood volume is either reduced absolutely or abnormally distributed. This class of conditions includes: contraction of the extracellular fluid space, particularly when coupled to the administration of electrolyte-free solutions[92]; reductions in left atrial pressure following mitral commissurotomy[93]; prolonged mechanical ventilation[94]; and, severe congestive heart failure of hepatic cirrhosis. Thus, nonosmotic factors which relate to changes either in total blood volume or in the distribution of extracellular fluid also elicit ADH release.

Organization of the Hypothalamic-Neurohypophyseal System. Since stimulation of ADH-producing neurons is required for ADH secretion, it is pertinent to consider the organization of these neurons and the afferent neural pathways which affect them. The neurohypophysis consists of a set of hypothalamic nuclei, the supraoptic and paraventricular nuclei, which house the perikarya of the magnocellular neurons responsible for

synthesis of oxytocin and vasopressin; the axonal processes of these neurons, which form the supraopticohypophyseal tract, and the termini of these neurons within the posterior lobe of the pituitary. Thus, nerve endings of the posterior pituitary derive from magnocellular neurons of the SON and PVN.[20]

The locations of the neurohypophyseal nuclei, first identified by their Gomori positive staining characteristics, are shown schematically in Fig. 78-7. The SON is situated along the proximal half of the optic tract, while the PVN lies vertically within the anterolateral wall of the third ventricle; scattered neurons bridge the two principal nuclei in some species, thus forming the internuclear group. The SON consists almost entirely of magnocellular neurons, all of which project to the posterior pituitary,[95] while the PVN contains magnocellular neurons, projecting to the posterior pituitary, as well as parvocellular neurons, which project to the median eminence or to autonomic centers in the brain stem.[96] Using specific antibodies to vasopressin, immunocytochemical staining has indicated the presence of cells containing vasopressin in both nuclei. Vasopressin-containing neurons are concentrated in the posterior magnocellular division of the PVN[97] and the posteroventral portion of the SON.[96] Vasopressin-containing cells are also found in the parvocellular division of the PVN, particularly the medial division.[97] Vasopressin secretion by these cells, which terminate in the hypophyseal-portal capillary bed, accounts for the high concentration of vasopressin in portal blood.[98] These parvocellular neurons also secrete corticotropin releasing factor (CRF) into the portal blood. Following adrenalectomy, the number of neurons which stain for both CRF and vasopressin increase dramatically.[99,100]

The axons of magnocellular neurons are unmyelinated fibers slightly less than 1 μm in diameter, containing clusters of Gomori-positive granules.[101] Microtubules can be traced down the length of the axons but do not appear to radiate into the granule-filled dilations. These axons terminate in the posterior lobe (pars nervosa) of the pituitary gland, where they constitute about 40 percent of the bulk of the gland.

In order to respond to hemodynamic changes or changes in

Fig. 78-7 A schematic illustration of the neurohypophysis showing hypothalamic magnocellular nuclei, the supraopticohypophyseal tract with Herring bodies, and nerve endings on capillaries of the posterior pituitary.[20]

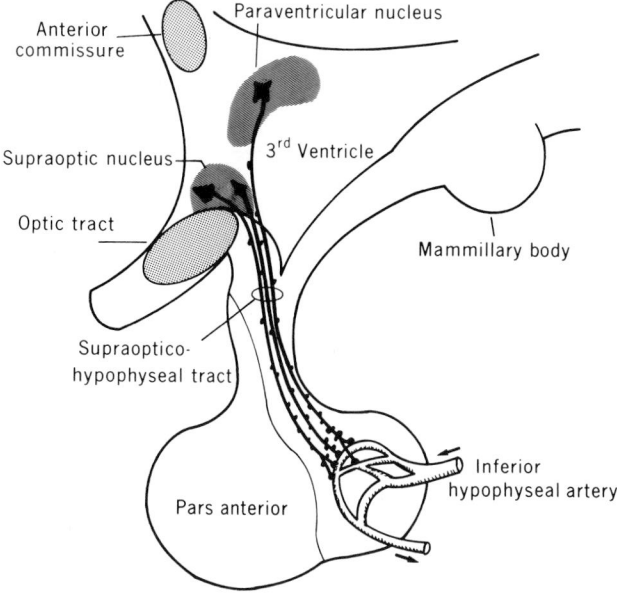

the composition of body fluids, the ADH-producing cells in the PVN and SON must receive information from various sensor elements. For example, information from low pressure baroreceptors is carried to the brain stem by cranial nerves IX and X. These afferents relay in the nucleus of the tractus solitarius (NTS), and then a noradrenergic nucleus (A1) before ultimately projecting to the magnocellular region of the PVN and SON.[102] Additional noradrenergic afferents arise from the locus coeruleus (A6) and solitary tract and project to the ADH/CRF parvocellular neurons of the medial PVN.[103] Cholinergic innervation of the SON is provided by cholinergic neurons situated immediately adjacent to the SON.[104,105] Nicotinic and muscarinic receptors are present in the SON and PVN, respectively, and stimulation of these receptors increases ADH secretion.[106]

Two circumventricular organs, the subfornical organ (SFO) and the organum vasculosum laminae terminalis (OVLT), also innervate the ADH neurons of the SON and PVN. These organs lie outside the blood-brain barrier and therefore may be important for osmoreception and interaction with blood-borne hormones, such as angiotensin II (see below).

Osmotic Regulation of ADH Release. Verney's classical studies[107] delineated the relationship between changes in plasma osmolality and ADH release. His meticulous observations on urine flow and composition in dogs showed clearly that: (1) following water loading, there was a lag period of approximately 15 min before the onset of water diuresis; (2) short duration (5 to 20 s) injections of hypertonic NaCl or sucrose, but not urea solutions, provoked a prompt antidiuresis which was abolished by removal of the posterior pituitary gland; and (3) reductions in urine volume during a maximal water diuresis required as little as a 2 percent increase (produced by NaCl or sucrose but not urea) in the osmolality of blood perfusing the internal carotid arteries.

Verney[107] deduced that osmoreceptors, located in the distribution of the internal carotid arteries, stimulated ADH release when plasma osmolality was raised by solutes to which osmoreceptors were impermeable; the failure of hypertonic urea injections to provoke antidiuresis was interpreted as indicating that these osmoreceptors were freely permeable to urea. McKinley et al.[108] confirmed Verney's results and showed that carotid infusion of hypertonic urea solutions led to a higher CSF sodium concentration than either hypertonic saline or sucrose, yet produced only minor antidiuresis compared with the latter two solutions. They postulated that the osmoreceptors must be located in an area of the brain lacking an effective blood-brain barrier.[108]

The precise location of the osmoreceptors is still debated. Leng has shown that the neurons of the SON are themselves osmosensitive,[109] in that microinjections of hypertonic saline into the SON produced a depolarization of the membrane potential and increased frequency of action potentials. He has argued that the SON itself is the most important site of osmoreception.[110] There is considerable evidence, though, that the osmoreceptor is separate from the SON. First, the study of McKinley et al.[108] and a similar one by Thrasher et al.[111] indicate that the osmoreceptor lies outside the blood-brain barrier. Second, the observation that neurotransmitter antagonists block osmotically induced ADH release[112] suggests a need for neural afferents in the process. Third, lesions of the OVLT, which resides outside the blood-brain barrier (v.s.), impair vasopressin secretion.[112] Finally, interruption of the pathways between the AV3V region and the SON produced

hypernatremia in rats.[113] Thus, it seems clear that afferent fibers, probably from the OVLT, play an important role in the osmotic stimulation of ADH secretion. There is also evidence for peripheral osmoreceptors in the hepatic portal vascular bed.[102]

Nonosmotic Regulation of ADH Release. In 1935, Peters[114] recognized the role of ADH in volume regulation by commenting that "In subjects who have become dehydrated . . . volume of body fluids seems to become more important than . . . osmotic pressure as a determinant of renal activity." Leaf and Mamby[115] provided early evidence for an ADH release mechanism not regulated by extracellular fluid tonicity by showing that dehydrated individuals permitted access to solute-free water developed hyponatremia concomitant with urinary hypertonicity. Subsequently, there has accumulated a large body of evidence indicating that volume-mediated release of ADH may occur as a consequence of stimuli arising from "volume receptors," or baroreceptors. Gauer and Henry[116] termed loci in the venous bed of the systemic circulation, the right side of the heart, and the left atrium the "low" pressure baroreceptors and loci within the systemic arterial system "high" pressure baroreceptors.

With regard to the relationship between ADH release and low pressure regions of the vascular bed, positive pressure breathing and the upright position produce antidiuresis, while negative pressure breathing produces a water diuresis. The water diuresis produced by negative pressure breathing can be abolished by administering exogenous ADH,[117] thereby providing indirect evidence that the diuresis is mediated by suppression of ADH release. Gauer and Henry[116] found that balloon distension of the left atrium produced increases in urine volume and concluded that stimulation of left atrial stretch receptors resulted in suppression of ADH release. The afferent pathway was presumed to be the vagus nerve, which affected ADH production in hypothalamic nuclei by pathways traversing the reticular formation in the brain stem. Corroborative evidence for this relation comes from electrophysiological studies[118] of the neurohypophysis in which balloon distension of the left atrium inhibited electrical activity in cells of the supraoptic nucleus, and section of the vagus nerve abolished the inhibitory influence of atrial distension.

Considering the role of the arterial bed in regulating ADH release, hemorrhage in experimental animals resulted in increases in vasopressin.[119,120] Stimulation of arterial baroreceptors, either by balloon distension at the carotid bifurcation or by an increase in systemic blood pressure, inhibits electrical activity of supraoptic neurons; local anesthesia of the carotid bifurcation abolishes the reflex.[118]

Specific radioimmunoassays for vasopressin have provided a measure of the sensitivity for nonosmotic release of ADH. In the rat, isosmotic volume contraction produced by intraperitoneal glycerol stimulated vasopressin release at a "threshold" of about 8 percent plasma volume contraction.[119] Acute plasma volume contraction in humans, produced by hemofiltration, resulted in detectable rises in plasma vasopressin concentrations at as little as 3 percent plasma volume reduction.[121]

The major effect of hemodynamic stimuli on ADH secretion is to alter the set point, or threshold, for ADH secretion. Volume depletion, for example, shifts the set point to the left (Fig. 78-8) so that, for any given plasma osmolality, vasopressin secretion is increased relative to normal. This change in set point has been confirmed by the demonstration that adequate water loading can suppress ADH secretion even in the pres-

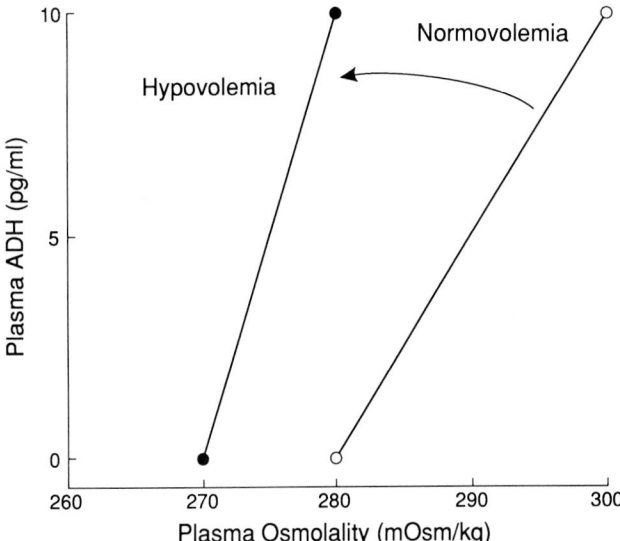

Fig. 78-8 The effect of hypovolemia on the relationship between plasma osmolality and plasma AVP concentrations. Hypovolemia shifts the "set-point" for the osmotic release of ADH to the left.[122]

ence of a hypovolemic stimulus.[122,123] The resetting of the osmotic threshold in response to osmotic stimuli may involve opioid-secreting neurons and can be abolished by opioid antagonists.[122]

Quantitative Aspects of Osmotic and Nonosmotic Stimuli to ADH Release. It is evident from the preceding discussion that the regulation of plasma ADH concentrations depends on both osmotic and volume-mediated, nonosmotic stimuli. Dunn et al.[119] have provided a quantitative analysis of the interplay between these two sets of stimuli and plasma ADH levels estimated by radioimmunoassay. Figure 78-9, adapted from their work in the rat,[119] shows that osmotic stimuli produce linear increases in ADH release, but with blood volume

Fig. 78-9 The relationship between blood volume, plasma osmolality, and plasma AVP concentration. (*Adapted from Dunn et al.[119]*)

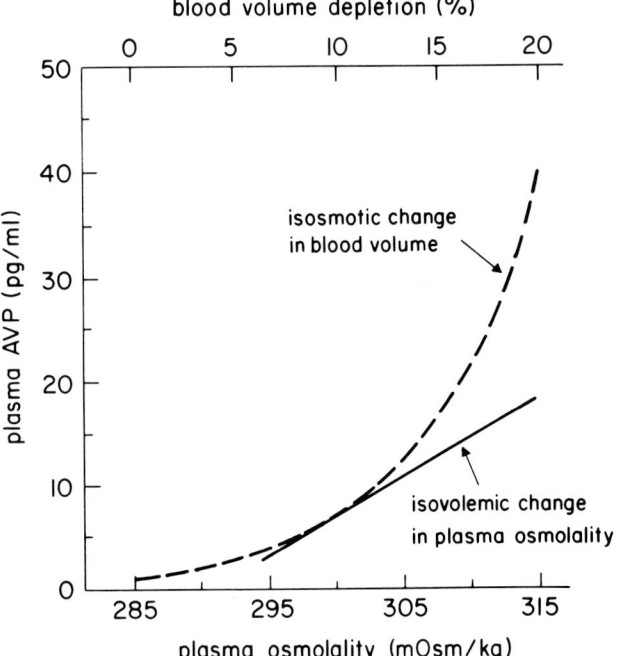

depletion of greater than 10 percent, plasma ADH concentrations rise in a near-exponential fashion. With modest degrees of volume contraction, such as that induced by several days of water deprivation; hemodynamic stimuli have virtually no effect on the ADH-plasma osmolality relation.[124] Further interplay between osmotic and nonosmotic stimuli for ADH release has been demonstrated by Quillen and Cowley[125] through studies in conscious dogs in whom left atrial pressure (LAP) was manipulated and the response in plasma AVP to osmotic stimulation was measured. They found that decreases in LAP reduced the osmotic threshold and increased sensitivity for osmotic ADH release, while increases in LAP elevated the threshold and dampened the sensitivity for osmotic ADH release.

Chemical Mediators of ADH Release. Yet another dimension of complexity to understanding nonosmotic mechanisms for ADH release has been added by the possibility that the latter may also be modulated by agents which have either systemic hemodynamic effects or central nervous system actions. Table 78-2 lists the drugs, neurotransmitters, and other chemical agents that have been implicated in the regulation of ADH release either via peripheral or central nervous system effects.

CATECHOLAMINES. Schrier et al.[126] have summarized the results of studies that provide evidence for a hemodynamic role of α- and β-adrenergic agents in mediating vasopressin release. The β-agonist isoproterenol caused antidiuresis in normal rats, while the α agonist norepinephrine reduced the urine osmolality. Neither agent, however, has an effect on Brattleboro rats lacking ADH or animals receiving exogenous ADH. These results indicate that the effects on water excretion were secondary to stimulation (β-agonists) or suppression (α-agonists) of endogenous ADH release.[127]

Adrenergic agents also stimulate central release of ADH through a neurotransmitter function. An abundance of nerve terminals containing norepinephrine has been demonstrated in both the SON and PVN by histochemical and immunocytochemical fluorescence.[128] Recent studies using a variety of techniques have confirmed that central adrenergic fibers, primarily norepinephrine fibers, exert a stimulatory effect on ADH secretion.[129]

ANGIOTENSIN II. The renin-angiotensin system may also participate in the physiological regulation of ADH release. Angiotensin II (AII)–containing nerve cells and fibers have been detected in the SFO and the magnocellular divisions of the PVN and SON.[130] The SFO lies outside the blood-brain barrier and may be responsible for conveying blood-borne signals to the hypothalamic nuclei. Peripherally or centrally administered AII, for instance, increases ADH secretion in the rat.[131,132] This response can be abolished by lesions of the SFO[131] or transection of the SFO efferents.[132] There is also electrophysiological evidence that circulating AII may modulate ADH release. In one study, neurons in the SFO with efferent projections to the PVN were identified by antidromic stimulation, and then intravenous AII was administered. The electrical activity of these neurons was increased by AII.[133]

In humans, intravenous infusion of AII stimulates ADH release,[134] and reduction of AII by the converting enzyme inhibitor captopril inhibits ADH release.[135] In one study, however, in which plasma AII levels were increased fivefold by sodium depletion, no change in plasma ADH levels was detected.[136]

Table 78-2 Agents That Alter Antidiuretic Hormone Release

Enhance release	Suppress release
Prostaglandin E_2	Diphenylhydantoin-phenytoin
Morphine and narcotic analogues	Alcohol
Nicotine	α-Adrenergic agents
β-Adrenergic agents	Atrial natriuretic peptide
Angiotensin II	
Anesthetic agents	
Hypoxia	
Hypercapnia	
Vincristine	
Cyclophosphamide	
Clofibrate	
Carbamazepine	
Barbiturates	

OPIATES. It has long been known that morphine induces antidiuresis. The recent demonstrations of endogenous opiates within the neurohypophysis and the frequent association of Leu-enkephalin with vasopressin-containing nerve terminals[137] have led to a reinvestigation of the relation between opiates and ADH release. Thus far no clear picture has emerged. Studies using various opioid agonists and antagonists have demonstrated both inhibitory and stimulatory effects on either osmotic, or volume-mediated, or electrically evoked ADH secretion (for review see Refs. 138 and 139).

PROSTAGLANDINS. Endogenous CNS prostaglandins may modulate the response of ADH release to osmotic stimulation. Intraventricular infusions of E prostaglandins[140] have been shown to raise plasma AVP levels in the absence of changes of systemic hemodynamics. In close agreement, Hoffman et al.[141] found that intraventricular prostaglandin synthesis inhibition by indomethacin attenuated the osmotic response for ADH release, although release could be effected by exogenous PGE_2 even with indomethacin present.

Negative Feedback Control of Water Repletion

It now seems probable that suppression of ADH release and of thirst, that is, the negative feedback limbs of the water repletion reaction (Fig. 78-1), may be mediated via intracerebral atrial natriuretic peptide (ANP). The latter, a recently discovered peptide hormone with potent natriuretic and diuretic activities, alters intrarenal hemodynamics and increases the glomerular filtration rate. Because of its diuretic and vasodilating properties, ANP of cardiac origin serves as a counter regulatory hormone for the peripheral effects of ADH and angiotensin II. There is also evidence that ADH, principally through its vasopressor action, may stimulate the release of ANP.[142] ANP, in turn, may inhibit the effect of ADH on the water permeability of renal collecting duct.[143]

ANP of central origin appears to provide negative feedback control to both limbs of the water repletion reaction (Fig. 78-1). ANP-containing nerve cell bodies have recently been detected in the AV3V region of the brain.[104,144] This region, which surrounds the third ventricle and is involved in cardiovascular regulation,[104] receives innervation from the subfornical organ, and plays an important role in the regulation of thirst.[105]

It appears that intracerebral ANP can suppress thirst stimulated by intracerebral angiotensin II.[145] Further, the injection

of ANP into the cerebral ventricles of rats in vivo[146,147] or superfusion of hypothalamopituitary explants with ANP in vitro,[146,148,149] inhibits the secretion of ADH. These data thus indicate a key contribution by intracerebral ANP to the negative feedback control of the water repletion reaction illustrated in Fig. 78-1.

The Antidiuretic Response

The Countercurrent Multiplication Mechanism. Modern views of renal concentrating and diluting mechanisms have their origin in the work of Kuhn and Ryffel,[150] who considered the descending and ascending limbs of Henle as parallel tubes joined by a hairpin turn; oppositely directed flows in the two tubes permitted small differences in osmolality between fluid in the descending and ascending limbs at any level of the renal medulla to be amplified many-fold along the length of the loop of Henle, thus producing "single effect" countercurrent multiplication. Wirz, Hargitay, and Kuhn[151] then showed conclusively that renal medullary fluid became progressively hypertonic in going from renal cortex to papillary tip, and Hargitay and Kuhn[152] recognized that the loop of Henle might function as a countercurrent multiplier (i.e., the loop itself would provide the driving force for generating both loop and medullary hypertonicity) either by abstracting water in excess of solute from descending limbs and/or by abstracting solute in excess of water from ascending limbs.

Gottschalk and his colleagues provided a clear mechanism for countercurrent multiplication: urine in the loop of Henle at the papillary tip was as concentrated as that in the collecting duct during antidiuresis[153]; fluid entering the early distal convolution was hypotonic to plasma both in the absence and presence of ADH,[153,154] and approximately 20 percent of glomerular filtrate was absorbed in the loop of Henle.[154,155] Since proximal tubular fluid absorption is an isotonic process, Gottschalk reasoned that the combination of net fluid absorption in loop of Henle and early distal tubular fluid hypotonicity meant that, during transit through the loop, more solute than water was removed from tubular fluid, and therefore that the single effect driving countercurrent multiplication was solute abstraction from ascending limbs.[154,155]

While this scheme was adequate to explain concentration in the outer medulla, where active salt transport by the thick ascending limb of Henle provided the single effect[156,157] it could not account for the progressive concentration in the inner medulla and papilla. Only the thin ascending and descending limbs are found in these regions, and these segments are not thought to participate in active transepithelial transport.[158,159] In 1972, Stephenson[160] and Kokko and Rector[161] proposed models to address this issue of a concentrated inner medulla in the absence of active transport.[162] Their model calls for two spatially distinct sites for countercurrent multiplication: an active step in the outer medulla and a passive step in the inner medulla. The salient features of the model, illustrated schematically in Fig. 78-10, may be qualitatively described in the following way. The first multiplication step depends on active transport producing NaCl efflux from water-impermeable thick ascending limbs; thus, fluid entering the distal tubule is both hypotonic and salt-poor. During antidiuresis, ADH-enhanced water abstraction from urea-impermeant cortical and outer medullary collecting ducts results in accumulation of urea in fluid entering papillary collecting ducts. Since the latter are urea-permeable, passive urea trans-

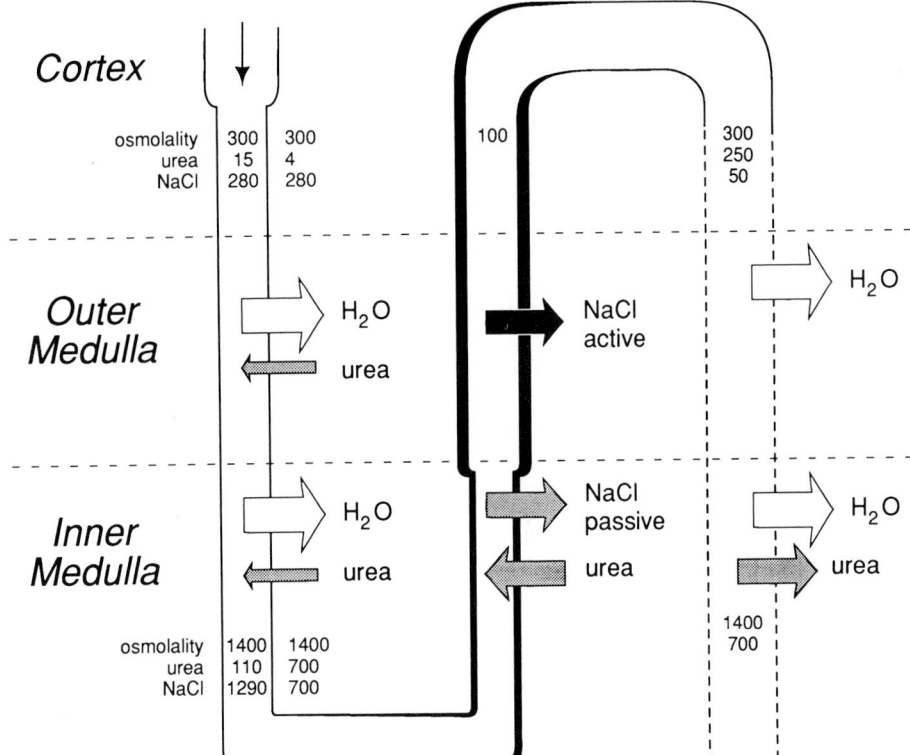

Fig. 78-10 A schematic illustration of the countercurrent multiplication model for the renal concentrating mechanism. The arrows indicate the relative magnitudes of solute and water fluxes in the various segments. Hatched and open arrows represent the passive movement of solutes and water, respectively. The solid arrow represents the active transport of salt.

port down a chemical gradient from tubular fluid to medullary interstitium contributes to medullary hypertonicity, thereby providing a second, but in this case passive, multiplication step. Simultaneously, osmotic equilibration of papillary collecting duct fluid with the medullary interstitium results in the formation of hypertonic urine.

The progressive concentration and dilution of tubular fluid in, respectively, descending and ascending thin limbs, can be reconciled in terms of passive flows. Consider, for example, a medulla whose osmolality ranges from 300 mosmol/kg at the corticomedullary junction to 1400 mosmol/kg at the papillary tip (Fig. 78-10). In keeping with tissue analyses,[163] approximately half of the medullary hypertonicity is assigned to NaCl and the remainder to urea. Isotonic fluid containing 280 mosmol/kg NaCl entering the highly water-permeable but urea- and Na+-impermeable descending thin limb is concentrated almost entirely by water abstraction, so that fluid entering the ascending thin limb has a higher NaCl concentration and a lower urea concentration than the medullary interstitium. These passive driving forces between lumen and interstitium, coupled with the fact that the thin ascending limb is more permeable to NaCl than to urea, poise the system for fluid dilution. As fluid moves up the water-impermeable ascending thin limb, passive NaCl efflux from lumen to interstitium exceeds passive urea influx from interstitium to tubular fluid resulting in tubular fluid dilution. Finally, in the thick ascending limb, tubular fluid is diluted further by the active transport of NaCl from lumen to interstitium.

Not all workers agree with such models for countercurrent multiplication. Kokko and Rector[161] have proposed that 96 percent of osmotic equilibration of descending thin limb fluid is due to water abstraction and only 4 percent to urea entry; thus, NaCl contributes more than 90 percent to the osmolality of fluid reaching the papillary bend of the loop of Henle. In contrast, Pennel et al.[164] have found that, in the rat, urea addition contributes 40 percent to the osmolality increase in as-

cending thin limb fluid. Moreover, recent microperfusion studies of the descending limbs from rabbits, hamsters, and rats show them to have a high permeability to sodium chloride.[165] Thus, concentration in the descending thin limb may occur by solute addition rather than water extraction. Solute influx, in turn, limits the extent to which passive mechanisms can contribute to inner medullary concentration.[162] Finally, computer simulations of the concentrating mechanism based upon the models of Kokko and Rector[161] and Stephenson[160] agree qualitatively, but not quantitatively, with experimental observations. That is, the steep inner medullary concentration gradients observed experimentally cannot be generated, at least in computer simulations, without allowance for active transport in the inner as well as outer medulla.[166]

It should be evident from the preceding discussion that two conditions must be met for the production of a concentrated urine: the medullary interstitium must be hypertonic, and ADH must interact with an ADH-responsive collecting tubule. The former is determined in large part by the rate of solute absorption by the mTALH, while the latter depends on both the secretion of ADH and the ability of the collecting tubule to increase its permeability to water upon stimulation by ADH. We next consider the role of ADH in regulating transport processes in these two nephron segments.

The Medullary Thick Ascending Limb of Henle. Early in the transition from a water diuresis to antidiuresis, the NaCl content of the renal medulla increases. Wirz[167] first suggested that ADH might regulate concentrating ability by augmenting the rate of NaCl abstracted from the ascending limb of the loop of Henle. This hypothesis was supported by the demonstration that ADH stimulated adenylate cyclase activity and cAMP-dependent protein kinase activity in medullary thick ascending limbs of rat and mouse.[168]

The effects of ADH on salt transport in the in vitro microperfused medullary thick ascending limb of Henle (mTALH) of different mammalian species are summarized in Table 78-3. In both the rat and the mouse, ADH increases the rate of net salt absorption $[\mathcal{J}_{NaCl}, pm/(s\cdot cm^2)]$ and the spontaneous transepithelial voltage (V_e, mV).[169] In the mouse, this effect occurs in medullary but not cortical TALH segments and requires concentrations of ADH similar to those found during in vivo antidiuresis.[170] Likewise, ADH increases the rate of mTALH NaCl absorption in Brattleboro rats when assessed by in vitro or in vivo microperfusion of the loop of Henle. In contrast, no effect of pharmacologic concentrations of ADH or cAMP on salt transport could be demonstrated in the rabbit mTALH.[171]

Figure 78-11 presents a model for net NaCl absorption in the mTALH. Net transepithelial Cl^- absorption in the mTALH is a secondary active transport process in which the movement of Cl^- across the luminal membrane of mTALH cells is mediated by an electroneutral $Na^+:K^+:2Cl^-$ cotransport mechanism.[169,172] The intracellular Cl^- activity in the rabbit cTALH is above its electrochemical equilibrium,[173] as is the calculated intracellular Cl^- activity in the mouse mTALH.[174] After inhibition of $Na^+:K^+:2Cl^-$ cotransport activity with furosemide, the cell Cl^- activity falls to its equilibrium value and net Cl^- transport ceases.[173] Likewise, the stimulation of Cl^- transport is accompanied by a rise in cell Cl^- activity.[174] Therefore, the entry of Cl^- must be coupled to the energetically favorable movement of another solute, in this case Na^+. Accordingly, removal of sodium from the luminal fluid abolishes Cl^- transport.[175] The coupled nature of Na^+, K^+, and Cl^- transport has also been demonstrated in studies of tracer Na^+ uptake into membrane vesicles[176,177] and cells[178] derived from the mTALH.

The apical membranes of the mTALH also contain a Ba^{2+}-sensitive K^+ conductance which accounts almost entirely for the electrical conductance of this membrane.[172,179] These K^+ channels constitute the route for K^+ secretion in this segment. However, 90 percent of secreted K^+ is recycled back into cells via the $Na^+:K^+:2Cl^-$ cotransporter, so that the rate of net K^+ secretion is less than 10 percent of the rate of net Cl^- absorption.[180,181]

Cl^- exit across basolateral membranes of the mTALH proceeds primarily via conductive Cl^- channels.[169] This notion derives both from the fact that net Cl^- absorption accounts for about 90 percent of the equivalent short circuit current in the mouse mTALH[181] and the rabbit cTALH[182] and from the observation that agents which block Cl^- channels reduce the short circuit current in the TALH.[183] Cl^- efflux is dissipative; that is, Cl^- moves down its electrochemical gradient as it crosses basolateral membrane.

Table 78-3 Effect of ADH on NaCl Transport in the Medullary Thick Ascending Limb of Henle

Species	ADH	$\mathcal{J}_{NaCl}$* (pM s^{-1} cm^{-2})	V_e, mV
Mouse	−	2,600	5
	+	10,800	11
Rabbit	−	6,400	3–7
	+	6,400	3–7
Rat	−	3,450	2.5
	+	9,070	3.6

*$\mathcal{J}_{NaCl}$ is the measured maximal net rate of salt absorption for each of the observed conditions; V_e is the spontaneous transmembrane voltage accompanying $\mathcal{J}_{NaCl}$ for the given condition.
SOURCE: Modified from Ref. 169.

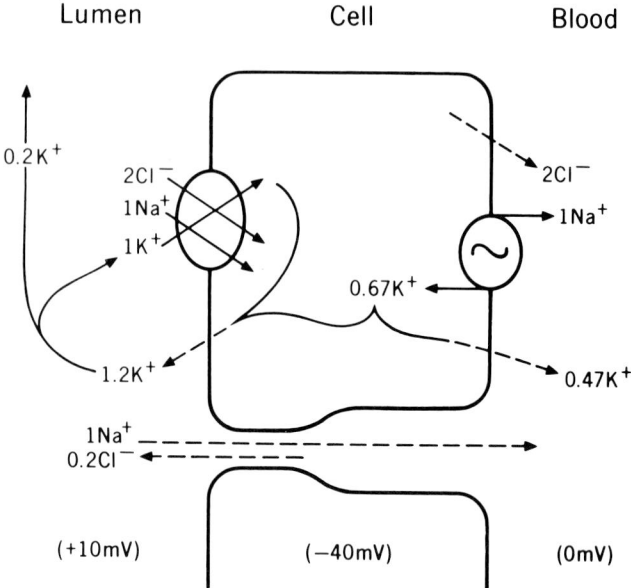

Fig. 78-11 A model for salt absorption in the thick ascending limb of Henle. The solid lines denote conservative processes; the dashed lines denote dissipative processes.[169]

The electrophysiological properties of the isolated mouse mTALH in basal and ADH-stimulated states are summarized in Table 78-4. Coincident with ADH-mediated stimulation of salt absorption ($\mathcal{J}_{NaCl}^{net}$) and transepithelial voltage (V_e), the transepithelial electrical conductance $(G_e, mS\ cm^2)$ increases approximately 20 percent. The increase in transepithelial conductance is due entirely to an increase in the cellular electrical conductance G_c; ADH has no effect on the paracellular electrical conductance, G_s. Finally, ADH results in a depolarization of the basolateral membrane voltage, V_{bl} (mV). It is generally agreed[174,184] that, since ADH depolarizes basolateral membranes while increasing transcellular conductance (Table 78-4), the ADH-dependent increase in transcellular conductance is referable mainly to an increase in basolateral Cl^- conductance.

At least two classes of explanations could account for this ADH-dependent increase in basolateral membrane Cl^- conductance. It has been proposed, for example, that the hormone might increase directly the Cl^- conductance of basolateral membranes.[184] Alternatively, basolateral Cl^- channels of mTALH cells have rectification characteristics similar to those of Goldman rectifiers.[174] Accordingly, if ADH increased the functional number of apical membrane $Na^+:K^+:2Cl^-$ cotransport units, the attendant rise in intracellular Cl^- activity could result in a secondary rise in basolateral membrane Cl^- conductance.[174] According to this view, an admittance effect of ADH on an electroneutral apical membrane transport process, that is, $Na^+:K^+:2Cl^-$ entry, is the prime factor producing an increase in basolateral Cl^- conductance.

The data presented in Table 78-5 indicate, in this connection, that when apical $Na^+:K^+:2Cl^-$ entry into mTALH cells is blocked by luminal application of the diuretic furosemide, ADH fails to produce an increase in transcellular electrical conductance. These results are consistent with the view that the primary effect of ADH in mTALH segments is to increase the entry of Cl^- into the cell via the $Na^+:K^+:2Cl^-$ cotransporter, and that the increase in cell Cl^- activity produces both a depolarization of basolateral membranes and an increase in basolateral electrical conductance.[174] The hormone-dependent increase in the $Na^+:K^+:2Cl^-$ cotransport activity could be a

Table 78-4 Effects of ADH on Electrophysiological Properties of the mTALH

ADH	G_e	G_s, mS/cm^2	G_c	V_e, mV	V_{bl}, mV
−	103.7	45.1	58.6	5.6	−50.7
+	121.3	60.2	61.0	9.9	−38.9

NOTE: G_e, the total transepithelial conductance, was measured with 5 mM K$^+$ in the luminal solution. G_s is the residual conductance measured in the presence of zero K, 20 mM Ba^{2+} in the lumen. G_c, the cellular conductance, was calculated as $(G_e − G_s)$. V_e and V_{bl} are the transepithelial and basolateral membrane voltages, respectively.
SOURCE: Modified from Ref. 174.

result of an increased number of cotransporters, e.g., insertion of new proteins into the membrane, or an increase in the activity of the cotransporters already present in the membrane.[174]

The Collecting Tubule. The second major site at which ADH modulates renal concentrating power is the collecting tubule, where the hormone increases strikingly the permeability to water. In the presence of ADH, the increase in water permeability of the collecting tubule augments osmotic water flow from tubular lumen into a hypertonic medullary interstitium, thus increasing the final urine osmolality.[20] Morphologic studies of water flow in the collecting tubule have confirmed that, in the absence of ADH, the apical plasma membrane is the rate limiting site for osmotic water flow[185–187] and that ADH increases the water permeability of this membrane.[187,188] Several approaches have been used to assess this ADH-mediated increase in water permeability.

The analysis of water transport through epithelia requires understanding two kinetic methods used for evaluating water transport through membranes. In one instance, net water flux is measured when either a hydrostatic or an osmotic pressure gradient exists across the membrane. In accord with the Starling hypothesis, net water flow across the membrane is linearly related to the driving force by P_f (cm/s), the permeability coefficient for net water flow; thus, P_f may be computed from the relation between net water flux and hydrostatic or osmotic pressure.

In the second method, the flux of tracer water, e.g., THO, is measured at zero net volume flow: both solutions bathing a membrane are at the same hydrostatic pressure and are identical in composition. Tracer water molecules in one solution exchange by random diffusion across the membrane with unlabeled water molecules in the other solution, but there is no net water flux. From Fick's first law of diffusion and the tracer appearance rate in the nonlabeled solution, one may

Table 78-5 Interaction of Furosemide and ADH on Cellular Conductance

Furosemide	G_c, mS/cm^2		
	−ADH	+ADH	ΔG_c
−	44.5 ± 5.6	58.9 ± 8.9	14.3 ± 5.5 ($p < 0.02$)
+	36.5 ± 4.4	41.5 ± 6.4	5.0 ± 4.3 (NS)

NOTE: The effect of furosemide on cellular conductance, G_c, was measured in isolated perfused tubules. In the absence of furosemide (top line), ADH caused a significant increase in G_c. When active transport was blocked by furosemide however (bottom line), ADH no longer produced a significant increase in G_c. From Ref. 174.

compute P_{D_w} (cm/s), the permeability coefficient for water diffusion across the membrane. P_{DW} may be defined as

$$P_{D_w} = \frac{\beta D_m}{\Delta x} \qquad [78\text{-}1]$$

where β is the partition coefficient for water between aqueous and membrane phases, D_m (cm^2/s) is the diffusion coefficient of water within the membrane, and the Δx (cm) is the membrane thickness.

Table 78-5 shows the effects of ADH on P_f, P_{D_w}, and the permeability coefficient for urea in the in vitro rabbit cortical collecting tubule.[189] The data in Table 78-6 indicate that the ratio of P_f to P_{D_w} (P_f/P_{D_w}) in the absence of ADH is 4 and in the presence of ADH is 13. This hormone-associated increase in P_f/P_{D_w} occurs because of a greater stimulation of osmotic than diffusional water movement. Although dramatic increases in both the diffusional and osmotic water permeability coefficients are observed with ADH, the permeability of small nonelectrolytes, such as urea, remains low. In qualitative terms, nearly the same conclusions obtain in the case of the effects of ADH on water and nonelectrolyte transport in anuran epithelia such as frog skin or the toad urinary bladder.[190–193]

In order to evaluate the data in Table 78-5, we note that, in quantitative terms, the relation between P_f and P_{D_w} can be expressed as

$$\frac{1}{P_{D_w}} = \frac{N_w}{P_f} + \frac{\beta \Delta x}{D_w^\circ} \qquad [78\text{-}2]$$

where $1/P_{D_w}$ is the resistance to THO diffusion at zero volume flow, $1/P_f$ is the apical membrane resistance to net water movement during osmosis, and N_w is the number of water molecules in apical water channels, if the latter are sufficiently narrow to permit single-file, rather than side-by-side water flux. The term $\beta \Delta x/D_w^\circ$ refers to a postapical membrane resistance to water diffusion, where Δx is epithelial thickness, D_w° is the free diffusion coefficient for water, and β is equivalent to a tortuosity factor for postapical membrane diffusion resistances. Thus, from equation [78-2], a disparity between P_f and P_{D_w} might be due either to an inherent P_f/P_{D_w} discrepancy in apical membranes and/or to an appreciable postapical membrane diffusion resistance. It now appears that both factors are operative both in cortical collecting tubules and in amphibian epithelia. The following considerations are pertinent in this regard.

If the apical plasma membrane contained aqueous channels sufficiently narrow to preclude side-by-side passage of water molecules, water transport would follow single-file kinetics such that $P_f/P_{D_w} = N$, where N is the number of water molecules in a channel.[194] Analysis of the temperature dependence of P_f and P_{D_w} in the rabbit collecting tubule indicates that both ADH-independent and ADH-dependent water transport occurs via narrow aqueous channels containing, on an average, four to seven water molecules per channel.[189,195] It may also be deduced that, given the failure of ADH to increase urea permeability in collecting ducts (Table 78-5), these channels are sufficiently narrow to preclude significant urea entry.

Moreover, in rabbit cortical collecting tubules, there is clear evidence that cellular constraints to diffusion impede cytosolic THO diffusion about tenfold more than in free solution.[187,194,195] Similar considerations apply to the cytosolic

Table 78-6 The Effect of ADH on Transport Coefficients in the Rabbit Cortical Collecting Tubule

ADH	P_f	P_{D_w}, cm/s $\times 10^4$	$P_{D_{urea}}$	P_f/P_{D_w}
−	20	5	0.03	4
+	186	14	0.02	13

NOTE: P_f = osmotic water permeability; P_D = diffusional permeability for water measured from ^{3}H-tracer fluxes at zero volume flow; $P_{D_{urea}}$ = diffusional permeability coefficient for urea also measured from tracer fluxes at zero volume flow.
SOURCE: See Ref. 189 for original sources of data.

layer of toad urinary bladder.[196] In short, it appears that, for cortical collecting tubules, an N_w of 4 to 7 and a β of approximately 10 (see equation [78-2]) account quantitatively, when taken together, for the ADH-dependent disparity between P_f and P_{D_w} shown in Table 78-6.

THE AGGREPHORE MECHANISM. There is now a compelling body of information consistent with the view that, both in toad urinary bladder and in the collecting tubule, ADH increases the water permeability of apical membranes by increasing the number of intramembranous particles, or aggregates, containing water channels within apical membranes. In the toad urinary bladder, and in frog skin, vacuoles containing these aggregates are situated beneath the apical membranes of granular cells.[197,198] In the presence of ADH, the number of aggregate-containing vacuoles, or aggrephores, decreases markedly while the number of aggregates in the apical membrane increases. These aggrephores can also be noted to fuse with apical membranes, and the frequency of these fusion events correlates with the accumulation of aggregates in the apical membrane.[199] These observations have led to the hypothesis that the water permeation sites are "shuttled" from the membranes of these aggrephores to the apical membrane under the influence of ADH.[198,200]

This general scheme of ADH action in anuran epithelia, namely, insertion of water channels into the apical membrane and their subsequent retrieval, also occurs in mammalian collecting ducts. Thus, apical intramembranous particle aggregates have been identified in medullary collecting ducts from rat[201–203] and in outer medullary and cortical collecting tubules of rabbits where the aggregates are confined to the apical membranes of principal cells.[204] The particle aggregates in these mammalian tubules are similar to, but not identical with, those of anuran epithelia. Further, cytoplasmic aggrephores or fused tubulovesicular structures typical of the anuran bladder have not been found in mammalian collecting ducts. Rather, the movement of aggregates, i.e., water channels, into and out of the apical membrane of collecting duct cells may be mediated by the exocytosis and endocytosis of clathrin-coated vesicles.[201]

Homology of Hormone Action. The observations presented in the preceding sections lead to a general statement about the mechanism of action of ADH. In the mTALH, ADH increases the functional number of apical membrane $Na^+:K^+:2Cl^-$ cotransporter units (Fig. 78-11).[174] In the collecting duct, ADH increases the functional number of narrow aqueous channels[194] in apical plasma membranes. It has also been noted that ADH can activate directly the K^+ conductance of cultured chick kidney cells[205] and the apical Na^+ con-

ductance of rabbit cortical collecting tubule,[206] although the mechanism for ADH activation of these conductances, or of apical $Na^+:K^+:2Cl^-$ cotransport in apical membranes of the mTALH, is obscure. Moreover, in apical membranes of amphibian epithelia, ADH increases both the functional number of small channels for water transport and the functional number of Na^+−conductive channels.[207] Accordingly, there may exist a general mode of action of ADH in hormone-sensitive epithelia, that is, to increase the functional number of transport units in apical membranes for those molecular species whose flux is augmented by ADH. It should be emphasized, however, that ADH may increase ionic conductances and/or $Na^+:K^+:2Cl^-$ activity by mechanisms different from the aggrephore effect of the hormone on collecting duct water permeability.

Intracellular Mediators of ADH Action. The effects of ADH on transport processes in renal epithelia are mediated primarily by the intracellular second messenger cAMP.[208] As illustrated in Fig. 78-2, ADH binds to specific receptors on basolateral membrane surfaces of hormone-responsive epithelial cells and activates membrane-associated adenylate cyclase to catalyze cAMP generation from ATP. Adenylate cyclase is a multicomponent enzyme system (Fig. 78-12) in which the catalytic subunit is under regulation by two GTP binding proteins, G_s and G_i.[209] G_s and G_i require GTP binding for activity and, when activated, stimulate or inhibit the activity of catalytic subunit, respectively.[210] Consequently, these proteins, sometimes referred to as guanine nucleotide-binding proteins or G proteins, are responsible for the transduction of hormone-receptor interactions into changes in cAMP formation.[211] In tissues in which hormone action is mediated by cAMP, the hormone-receptor complex activates the G_s subunit of the adenylate cyclase enzyme; this G_s subunit may also be activated by cholera toxin.[210] The activated, GTP-bound G_s then stimulates the catalytic subunit of adenylate cyclase to produce more cAMP. Hormones which antagonize the tissue effects of cAMP bind to receptors which are coupled to the G_i subunit. Activation of G_i by these hormone-receptor complexes inhibits the activity of the catalytic subunit of adenylate cyclase; the G_i subunit may be inactivated by pertussis toxin.[210] Since the effects of ADH on epithelia are mediated by cAMP, it is believed that the ADH receptor is associated with the G_s regulatory subunit.

Evidence for this chain of events in ADH-responsive epithelia was first provided by Orloff, Handler et al.,[212,213] who observed that, in toad bladder, cAMP or theophylline, an inhibitor cyclic nucleotide phosphodiesterase, brought about changes in Na^+ and water transport identical to those observed with ADH. This finding has been documented by subsequent work in a number of intact tissues, including isolated rabbit cortical collecting tubules[188,214] and mouse medullary thick ascending limbs.[215,171,169] In accord with this view, ADH raises adenyl cylase activity in tissue slices, cell homogenates, and membrane fractions of mammalian renal medulla[216–219] but not in comparable preparations from mammalian renal cortex.[220] The receptor-ADH interaction is both tissue- and hormone-specific,[45,221] and localized to basolateral rather than apical membranes.[222]

Elegant studies with individual nephron segments have also identified vasopressin-stimulated adenylate cyclase in the medullary thick ascending limb of Henle and along the entire collecting duct. The intimate relationship between hormone

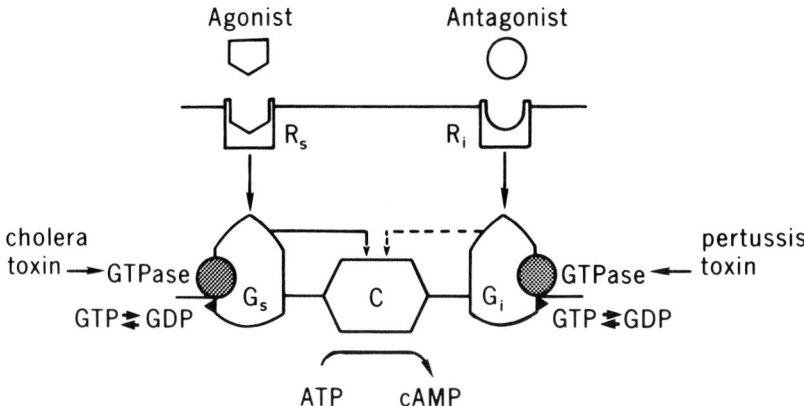

Fig. 78-12 A schematic illustration of the hormone-receptor-adenylate cyclase system. The abbreviations are explained in the text. (*From Hebert et al.[20]*)

binding and adenylate cyclase activation was firmly established by Jard and co-workers,[223,224] who described a close correlation between binding of analogues of lysine vasopressin and adenylate cyclase activation as well as comparable halftimes of lysine vasopressin binding and adenylate cyclase activation. Their work[224] and that of others[225] has led to the suggestion that binding of neurohypophyseal hormones to only a small fraction of receptors is necessary to activate sufficient adenylate cyclase for a maximal physiological response.

The role of G_s and G_i units in ADH-responsive renal epithelia has been demonstrated through stimulation of ADH-dependent transport processes in the mouse mTALH with cholera toxin, a G_s-specific agent, or with forskolin, an agent specific for the catalytic subunit, adenylate cyclase, [226] in the absence of ADH.[227] Likewise, in the rabbit cortical collecting tubule, either cholera toxin or forskolin increases hydraulic water permeability in the absence of ADH.[228] The presence of G_s and G_i proteins has also been demonstrated directly in microdissected segments of the mouse and rabbit thick ascending limb[229] and the rabbit cortical collecting tubule.[230] Intracellular cAMP, probably acting via a cell-specific protein kinase, effects an alteration in transport processes located at the luminal membrane of renal epithelia to augment water transport in the collecting duct cell and sodium chloride transport in the medullary thick ascending limb cell. Finally, the level of cAMP within the cell may be reduced through enzymatic cleavage to 5'-AMP by cytosolic phosphodiesterase, a process which serves to terminate hormone action.

The finding that the bovine renal medulla contains a cAMP-dependent protein kinase which phosphorylates membrane proteins from that tissue has led to the conclusion that cAMP-dependent protein phosphorylation is the next step in the sequence of intracellular events mediating the effects of ADH on renal epithelial transport.[231] Studies in intact renal medullary tissue have shown the activation of protein kinase to be proportional to the concentration of ADH bathing the tissue and to the concentration of cAMP achieved within the tissue.[232]

The molecular details explaining how ADH regulates apical membrane transport processes are uncertain. As noted above, stimulation of amphibian urinary bladder or mammalian collecting ducts with ADH leads to the insertion of patches of membrane which contain water channels into the apical membrane.[201,233] The insertion of these membrane units appears to depend on the integrity of the cytoskeleton.[234] Treatment of amphibian bladders with agents which disrupt microtubules and microfilaments decreases the number of fusion events between aggrephores and the apical membrane, the number of aggregates appearing on the cell surface, and the hydroosmotic response to ADH.[234,235]

These studies, considered together, suggest that ADH, working via cAMP and protein kinase, alters water transport in hormone-responsive epithelia by causing the microtubule-dependent insertion of specialized membrane units within the apical plasma membranes of these cells. It should be recognized, however, that ADH may act by entirely different mechanisms to increase the functional number of $Na^+:K^+:2Cl^-$ cotransport units and K^+ channels in apical membranes of the mTALH.

Modulation of ADH Action. α-ADRENERGIC AGENTS. In addition to their effects on ADH secretion, α-adrenergic agents also modulate water excretion at the level of the collecting duct. In isolated collecting ducts stimulated with ADH, the α-adrenergic agonist phenylephrine decreased water permeability.[236] This effect was blocked by α-adrenergic antagonists and was also not observed in tubules stimulated with cAMP,[236] indicating that the point of modulation of α agonists is at the generation of cAMP. Moreover, the inhibitory effect of the $α_2$-adrenergic agonist clonidine was attended by preincubation of collecting ducts with pertussis toxin,[230] an agent which inactivates the inhibitory guanine regulatory protein, G_i. Thus, α-adrenergic agonists inhibit ADH action in the collecting duct by activating the G_i subunit and decreasing cAMP formation.

ATRIAL NATRIURETIC PEPTIDE. This agent inhibits the hydroosmotic effect of ADH in isolated rabbit cortical collecting tubules. This inhibition apparently occurs at a site proximal to the catalytic subunit of adenylate cyclase since ANP had no effect on cAMP and forskolin stimulated water flow.[143]

PROSTAGLANDINS. Considerable evidence also points to the importance of locally generated renal prostaglandins in modulating the actions of ADH on renal epithelial transport processes. In the mammalian cortical collecting tubule, in the medullary interstitial cell, and in the toad urinary bladder, ADH stimulates the production of prostaglandin E_2.[237,238] In these tissues, inhibition of endogenous prostaglandin E_2 production with prostaglandin synthetase inhibitors such as indomethacin or meclofenamate increases the rate of sodium transport or the rate of osmotic water permeation.[239] In both the rabbit cortical collecting tubule and the toad urinary bladder, prostaglandins inhibit the ADH-stimulated accumulation of cAMP within the cell, and exert little or no inhibitory action on transport events beyond the accumulation of cAMP within the cell.[240,241,228] Thus the ADH effects on transport in these tissues are modulated by an inhibitor which is synthesized *in situ*, whose production is stimulated by ADH, and whose action is to reduce the ability of ADH to elevate cellular levels of cAMP.

Prostaglandin E_2 also participates in a local negative feedback system in the renal medulla that modulates the rate of net NaCl absorption by the mTALH. Studies using micropuncture techniques[242] and using the isolated, perfused mTALH segments[243,244] have also been consistent with the notion that prostaglandin E_2 inhibits NaCl absorption by the mTALH. Thus in the in vitro mouse mTALH, prostaglandin E_2 reduces the ADH-dependent values for transepithelial voltage and net NaCl absorption to ADH-independent values. In other words, prostaglandin E_2 blocks only the ADH-stimulated components of net NaCl absorption. Moreover, the prostaglandin E_2-mediated reduction in ADH-dependent NaCl transport can be reversed either by cAMP or by supramaximal concentrations of ADH. Likewise, in the mTALH, prostaglandin E_2 has no effect on cellular cAMP concentrations in the absence of ADH but markedly inhibits the ADH-dependent stimulation of cytosolic cAMP concentrations.[245]

The locus for this prostaglandin E_2–mediated inhibition of cAMP formation has been defined. Prostaglandin E_2 does not inhibit the component of NaCl transport in the mouse mTALH stimulated by the nonhormonal catalytic subunit activator forskolin, but does inhibit transport stimulation by cholera toxin, which activates adenylate cyclase by irreversible binding for G_s, the stimulatory guanine nucleotide-binding subunit of adenylate cyclase. Thus it is likely that prostaglandin E_2 inhibits the ADH-stimulated generation of cAMP in the mTALH by interacting with G_i, the inhibitory guanine nucleotide-binding subunit of adenylate cyclase.[227] An identical pattern of interactions has been reported for prostaglandin-mediated inhibition of hydraulic permeability in isolated collecting ducts.[228]

It is noteworthy in this connection that ADH appears to stimulate prostaglandin E_2 synthesis in medullary interstitial cells[246,238] and in medullary collecting duct cells,[247] although some studies have failed to show this effect.[248–250] Moreover, increases in osmolality produced by NaCl stimulate medullary prostaglandin E_2 production, while hypertonic urea suppresses prostaglandin E_2 production.[246,247] Thus, the increase in osmolality in the renal medulla produced by an ADH-mediated increase in NaCl absorption might be expected to play a major role in prostaglandin E_2 synthesis in vivo.

PROTEIN KINASE C. The action of ADH in the collecting duct and thick ascending limb is, as detailed in the previous section, mediated by intracellular cAMP. In other tissues, such as hepatocytes and vascular smooth muscle cells, ADH activates a V_1 receptor leading to phosphoinositide turnover. Recent studies indicate that the phosphoinositide-protein kinase C pathway may modulate ADH action in the kidney. In the toad bladder,[251] frog skin,[252] and rabbit cortical collecting tubule,[253] compounds such as phorbol esters, which activate protein kinase C, inhibit the hydroosmotic effect of ADH. The studies in the toad[251] and frog[252] indicate an effect on the generation of cAMP, since the phorbol esters do not inhibit the response to exogenous cAMP, whereas in the rabbit collecting duct a "post-cAMP" effect has been proposed.[253]

PERITUBULAR HYPERTONICITY. In isolated mouse mTALH segments, peritubular hypertonicity, produced either with per-

meant solutes such as urea, or with impermeant solutes such as mannitol or NaCl, inhibits the ADH-stimulated rate of net Cl^- absorption.[254] This inhibition of transcellular salt absorption occurs at a locus beyond the generation of cAMP, since supramaximal concentrations of cAMP are unable to reverse the hypertonicity-mediated reduction in NaCl absorption. Electrophysiological analysis of isolated TALH segments indicates that peritubular hypertonicity decreases the chloride conductance of the basolateral membrane, thereby decreasing the dissipative movement of chloride from the cell into the peritubular space.[255]

Studies using membrane vesicles prepared from the renal medulla also show an effect of osmolality on NaCl entry across the luminal cell membrane of the mTALH. Decreasing external osmolality diminishes the transport of NaCl via the $Na^+:K^+2Cl^-$ cotransporter located in the luminal membrane of the mTALH cell.[256] Thus peritubular hypertonicity and luminal hypotonicity may act in concert to suppress the ADH-dependent rate of salt absorption by the mTALH.

A scheme depicting the complementary interactions of interstitial osmolality, prostaglandins, and ADH on the urinary concentrating mechanism is presented in Fig. 78-13. According to this model, ADH-stimulated salt absorption by the mTALH is regulated by two negative-feedback loops. During early antidiuresis, the ADH-stimulated increase in NaCl absorption by the mTALH leads to an increase in the interstitial NaCl concentration. This increase in NaCl concentration stimulates prostaglandin E_2 production by the medullary interstitial cells; ADH may also stimulate directly prostaglandin E_2 production by the latter. In turn prostaglandin E_2 release decreases the rate of ADH-stimulated NaCl absorption by the TALH and the ADH-stimulated increase in water permeability in the collecting tubule. During sustained antidiuresis, a rise in the interstitial urea concentration inhibits prostaglandin E_2 release from interstitial cells but also inhibits directly the rate of NaCl absorption by the mTALH.[169]

Fig. 78-13 Model for the feedback regulation of urinary concentrating mechanisms.[169] PGE_2 = prostaglandin E_2.

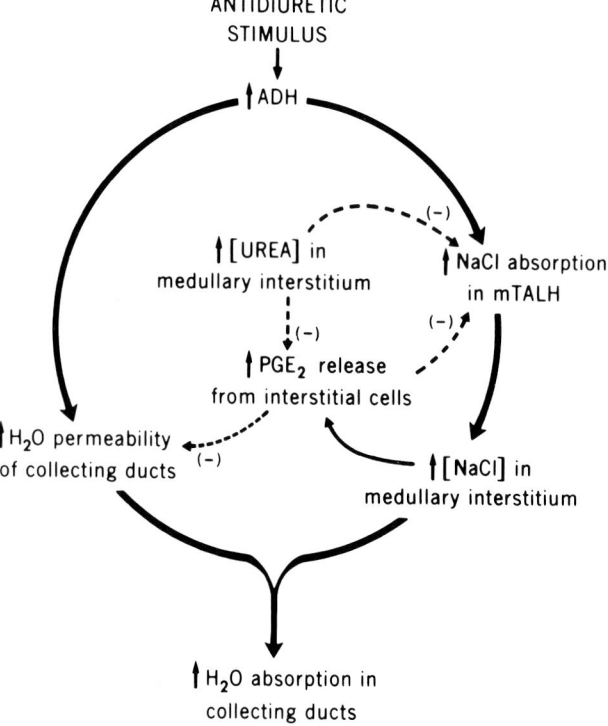

The Countercurrent Exchange System. The maintenance of a hypertonic medullary interstitium requires that the rate of solute removal by medullary blood flow be reduced sufficiently to prevent equilibration of medullary interstitial fluid with isotonic plasma. These requirements are satisfied by countercurrent exchange processes within medullary capillary loops.

The efferent arterioles of juxtamedullary glomeruli branch into peritubular capillary networks. These networks form long loops which descend into the medulla in parallel with descending and ascending limbs of the loop of Henle, have hairpin turns at the same medullary level as the associated loop of Henle, and are connected at several levels of the medulla by branches of the capillary plexus.

Thus the vasa recta are a counterflow system. In descending vasa recta, water leaves the blood and solute enters, so that the osmolality at the bend of the vasa recta is the same as that of the tip of the loop of Henle, and presumably also of the medullary interstitium, at the same point.[153] As blood flows from the tip of the vasa recta back to venules in the inner cortex, it gains water and loses salt to the progressively less hypertonic medullary interstitium. The water lost and solute gained by the descending vasa recta results in water gain and solute loss in the ascending vasa recta, a process requiring no energy input other than the hydrostatic pressure of the blood. The net effect of this countercurrent exchange in the vasa recta is to reduce both the rate of solute loss from the medulla, with respect to a linear blood flow system, and the energy expenditure required to maintain a hypertonic medulla.

The Effects of Filtration Rate and Solute Excretion. Factors other than antidiuretic hormone and counterflow processes within the renal medulla also affect urinary concentration and dilution. The water permeability of the collecting duct, even in the absence of ADH, is clearly finite. Thus by varying the rate of fluid delivery to collecting ducts, the rate of GFR can influence directly the final osmolality of urine. For example, in hypophysectomized dogs,[257] severe reductions in GFR result in the formation of hypertonic urine in the absence of ADH. Moreover, Brattleboro rats with hypothalamic diabetes insipidus increase urinary osmolality two- to threefold consequent to partial aortic clamping that produced minimal or no decreases in GFR.[22] Conversely, increased GFR produced by sustained expansion of the extracellular fluid volume can result in a hypoosmotic urine even when high levels of vasopressin are maintained by infusion.[258]

In clinical terms, the nature and rate of solute excretion have a greater influence on urinary osmolality than GFR. A filtered but nonabsorbed solute like mannitol acts as an osmotic diuretic and reduces fluid absorption within the proximal tubule, so that a progressively greater amount of isosmotic fluid containing nonabsorbed solute enters the loop of Henle. As a consequence, the capacity of the loop of Henle and collecting duct to modify the osmolality of urine is reduced. In hydropenic individuals receiving ADH, urine osmolality falls during osmotic diuresis.[259] Alternatively, both in patients with nephrogenic diabetes insipidus[36] and in normal subjects undergoing water diuresis,[260] urine osmolality rises during progressive osmotic diuresis.

The effect of osmotic diuresis on urine composition may be viewed by considering solute excretion in terms of the osmolar clearance (C_{osm},ml/min), which can be regarded as the urinary flow rate required to produce a urine isotonic to plasma. In antidiuresis, a volume of solute-free water, termed negative free-water clearance, is removed from urine, and the urinary flow rate $\dot{V}$ is less than C_{osm}. In water diuresis, the urinary flow rate $\dot{V}$ exceeds C_{osm}; the difference between $\dot{V}$ and C_{osm}, termed positive free-water clearance, is the amount of solute-free water excreted. During progressive osmotic diuresis, an increasingly greater volume of isotonic fluid containing nonabsorbed solute escapes proximal tubular absorption and is delivered to the loop of Henle. As a consequence, C_{osm} becomes sufficiently large that, even if the magnitude of either positive (during water diuresis) or negative (during antidiuresis) free water clearance stays unchanged, urine osmolality approaches isotonicity.

PATHOGENESIS OF NEPHROGENIC DIABETES INSIPIDUS

Vasopressin-resistant hyposthenuria or isosthenuria may be due to three types of disturbances:

1. The renal tubules may be ADH-responsive and negative free water formation may be normal, but the urine osmolality approaches isotonicity because the volume of isotonic fluid entering the loop of Henle is increased. This mechanism may account for the isosthenuria of chronic renal disease.

2. The renal tubule may be ADH-responsive, but the renal countercurrent multiplication and exchange systems fail to generate an appropriately hypertonic medullary interstitium; thus, the osmotic driving force for negative free water formation is either reduced or abolished. Such a disturbance may contribute to the ADH-unresponsive concentrating defect in a number of instances, including individuals with sickle cell disease[261]; normal individuals subjected to prolonged water ingestion[262]; patients with pituitary diabetes insipidus, who exhibit a transient inability to concentrate urine maximally following exogenous vasopressin administration; subjects with hypokalemia and hypercalcemia, where renal papillary Na^+ and total solute concentrations are reduced[263]; and those with obstructive uropathy associated with hydronephrosis which produces significant reductions in papillary and medullary solute concentrations.[264]

3. The volume of isotonic fluid entering the loop of Henle and the countercurrent multiplication and exchange systems are normal, but the renal tubule is unresponsive to ADH.

Following Williams and Henry,[5] the term *nephrogenic diabetes insipidus* should be applied to disorders where renal tubular unresponsiveness to ADH, without disturbances either in solute delivery to the loop of Henle or in countercurrent multiplication or exchange processes, is responsible for polyuria and hyposthenuria. Thus, with regard to Fig. 78-2, nephrogenic diabetes insipidus may be due to an inability of ADH to raise cellular cAMP concentrations, to an inability of cAMP to increase the water permeability of luminal membranes, or to a combination of these two disorders.

Familial Nephrogenic Diabetes Insipidus

Hereditary vasopressin-unresponsive diabetes insipidus occurs in a genotypic strain of mice, termed DI +/+ severe, some of which exhibit vasopressin-unresponsiveness.[265] Stimulation of medullary adenylate cyclase activity by vasopressin is markedly reduced in these mice. Since the basal level of renal medullary adenylate cyclase activity is normal, as is the stimulation of renal cortical adenylate cyclase activity by parathyroid hormone, the defect seems specific.[266] Further studies in these mice indicate that vasopressin-stimulated adenylate cyclase activity is modestly reduced in medullary collecting duct segments and severely reduced in medullary ascending limb segments.[267] Medullary collecting duct cAMP phosphodiesterase activity was markedly higher in DI +/+ mice than in normal mice.

The net result of these findings is failure of vasopressin-stimulated cellular cAMP accumulation in cells of either the medullary collecting duct or medullary ascending limbs of the nephrogenic diabetes insipidus mice.[267] This defect in the vasopressin-stimulated accumulation of cAMP in collecting duct segments is only partially corrected by the addition of a phosphodiesterase inhibitor. However, in the presence of a phosphodiesterase inhibitor, stimulation of the nephron segments by the combination of vasopressin and forskolin, a direct activator of the catalytic subunit of adenylate kinase, results in normal cAMP accumulation.[268] These data indicate that elevated phosphodiesterase activity, and a defect in the coupling of the vasopressin receptor to the catalytic subunit of adenylate cyclase, may contribute to the concentrating defect in the DI +/+ mice.

It is unclear how these studies may relate to the pathogenesis of familial diabetes insipidus of humans. In normal individuals or patients with pituitary diabetes insipidus, exogenous ADH increases the rate of urinary cAMP excretion.[269] Studies of the responsiveness of urinary cAMP excretion to ADH stimulation in patients with familial nephrogenic diabetes insipidus have yielded conflicting results. It appears that in the majority of patients, ADH has little or no effect on the cAMP excretion.[270–272] Occasional patients, however, may respond to ADH with a rise in cAMP excretion.[272,273]

It is important to note that, while urinary cAMP has been studied, the effect of ADH on renal tubular cellular accumulation of cAMP in familial nephrogenic diabetes insipidus is totally unknown. It is tempting to speculate that the pathogenesis of nephrogenic diabetes insipidus may differ in some families. In the majority the defect could be the failure to accumulate cAMP in response to ADH, due to either decreased formation or increased catabolism. In others, the defect may reside at a post-cAMP step.

Acquired Nephrogenic Diabetes Insipidus

Vasopressin-resistant hyposthenuria associated with otherwise normal or nearly normal renal function may occur as a complication of drug therapy or in association with systemic diseases. Appropriately termed *acquired nephrogenic diabetes insipidus*, this condition is to be distinguished from the rare familial disorder described earlier.

Drug-Induced Nephrogenic Diabetes Insipidus. Vasopressin-unresponsive hyposthenuria occurs in patients receiving demethylchlortetracycline; both the concentrating defect and vasopressin unresponsiveness are reversible and disappear shortly after discontinuing antibiotic therapy.[274–276] The glomerular filtration rate in these patients is generally normal, as is the ability for maximal urinary dilution (positive free water formation), indicating that solute abstraction from the loop of Henle is probably unimpaired.[276]

In toad urinary bladder, contraluminal (serosal) demethylchlortetracycline inhibited the water permeability increase produced by either vasopressin or cAMP.[276] Although other tetracyclines can inhibit ADH or cAMP enhancement of water permeation in toad bladder,[277] only demethylchlortetracycline has caused clinical nephrogenic diabetes insipidus in humans. Likewise, in human renal medulla, demethylchlortetracycline inhibits basal adenyl cyclase activity, ADH-stimulated adenyl cyclase activity, and cAMP-dependent protein kinase activity but not cyclic nucleotide phosphodiesterase activity.[278] These in vitro observations[276–278] suggest that demethylchlortetracycline-induced nephrogenic diabetes insipidus may be due to inhibition of both cAMP accumulation and the action of cAMP on urinary membranes by that antibiotic.

Nephrogenic diabetes insipidus may also be produced by volatile fluorocarbon anesthetics. Methoxyflurane anesthesia is complicated by a full spectrum of renal injury, ranging from vasopressin-resistant polyuria and hyposthenuria to acute tubular necrosis.[279] The polyuric state is related to the markedly increased serum concentration and urinary excretion of inorganic fluoride, which is a metabolic product of methoxyflurane.[280] Sodium fluoride causes a vasopressin-resistant polyuria in dogs.[281] In rats, inorganic fluoride seems to reduce collecting duct water permeability without affecting salt transport in the ascending limb.[282]

Finally, it is now widely recognized that serum lithium concentrations of 0.5 to 1.5 meq/liter, which are generally regarded as being in the therapeutic range for affective disorders, produce vasopressin-resistant diabetes insipidus.[283–285] Nephrogenic diabetes insipidus has been observed in 12 to 30 percent of patients receiving lithium therapy[285]; the defect is usually reversible, and urinary concentrating ability returns toward normal when lithium is discontinued.[285] Patients on chronic lithium therapy tend to have higher levels of plasma antidiuretic hormone for a given plasma osmolality.[286]

In toad urinary bladder, 11 meq/liter lithium in mucosal (urinary) solutions inhibits the stimulation of water transport produced by vasopressin but not that produced by cAMP.[284] Furthermore, lithium specifically inhibits ADH-activated adenylate cyclase in mammalian renal medulla.[287,288] This inhibition is seen in both medullary thick ascending limbs and collecting ducts with acute introduction of lithium, but only in medullary collecting ducts in animals chronically treated with lithium.[289] Likewise, in isolated perfused cortical collecting tubules, lithium inhibits the hydroosmotic action of ADH[290] but not of the adenylate cyclase catalytic subunit-specific agent forskolin[291] or dibutyryl cAMP.[290] These data indicate that lithium interferes with ADH action at a site proximal to the generation of cAMP, probably by interacting with G_s.[291]

Lithium-induced polyuria may also depend on other factors. In the rat, chronic lithium administration produces a polyuria which was unresponsive to either vasopressin or dibutyryl cAMP, while both agents enhanced urinary concentrating ability in rats with hereditary hypothalamic diabetes insipidus.[285] Finally, lithium has been thought to cause primary polydipsia because it stimulates water ingestion and increases polyuria in normal rats[292] and in rats with hereditary hypothalamic diabetes insipidus.[293] So it appears that the lithium-induced polyuria observed clinically may be the consequence of three effects of the cation: inhibition of vasopressin-stimulated cAMP formation[287–289]; interference with the action of cAMP on water transport in collecting ducts[285]; and primary polydipsia.[292,293]

Nephrogenic Diabetes Insipidus in Systemic Diseases. In rare instances, vasopressin-resistant polyuria may occur in association with amyloidosis.[294,295] In one such patient, amyloid deposits were localized primarily to the basement membranes of medullary collecting ducts, without involvement of the loops of Henle.[294] In eight patients with Sjögren syndrome, four had persistent hyposthenuria out of proportion to mild reductions in glomerular filtration rate; in one patient tested, maximal urinary concentration following vasopressin administration was impaired.[296] The factors responsible for the renal concentrating defect observed in these conditions are not understood.

DIAGNOSIS AND TREATMENT

Diagnosis

The diagnostic characteristics of familial nephrogenic diabetes insipidus include onset during infancy, a positive family history, persistent thirst, polyuria and hyposthenuria which are unresponsive to vasopressin, and serum arginine vasopressin levels which vary appropriately with changes in serum osmolality (Fig. 78-4). In the absence of dehydration, renal function is normal. Likewise, acquired nephrogenic diabetes insipidus, either drug-induced or accompanying systemic disorders, is characterized by vasopressin-resistant polyuria.

As indicated previously, renal concentrating defects and apparent vasopressin resistance may occur in a number of other settings. For convenience, these may be classified into three major groups: disorders where the concentrating defect is largely due to relatively high rates of solute excretion, including primarily chronic renal failure; disorders where impairment of the renal countercurrent and exchange systems is a major factor contributing to the concentrating defect, including sickle cell disease,[261] prolonged water ingestion,[262] hypokalemia,[263] hypercalcemia,[263] and obstructive uropathy[264]; and disorders having a renal concentrating defect of uncertain cause, including juvenile nephronopthosis, medullary cystic disease, cystic disease of the kidney, cystinosis, and pyelonephritis. In most of these conditions, the characteristic findings of the underlying disorder generally preclude error in diagnosis.

A condition associated with vasopressin-resistant polyuria which can be confused with nephrogenic diabetes insipidus is osmotic diuresis. This syndrome is commonly iatrogenic and is typically seen in patients in the setting of the intensive care unit or in the postoperative state who are infused with large volumes of colloid or saline. The polyuria which results is often perceived as being inappropriate and prompts the administration of even more fluid and hence further propagation of the diuresis. A careful analysis of the fluid therapy and measurement of the urine solute excretion rate generally is sufficient to diagnose this problem. Treatment is achieved by gradual reduction in the rate of solute administration.

Treatment

There is no specific therapy for the disorder. Adequate hydration, easily achieved by oral intake in children and adults, but sometimes requiring parenteral supplementation in infants, is essential to prevent the damaging effects of hypernatremia and circulatory collapse, particularly in children. Although polyuria may be minimized by reducing solute intake, this is rarely necessary except in children.

Neither arginine vasopressin nor any of its analogues has any effect in the disease. Obviously, drugs that stimulate endogenous ADH release, such as clofibrate,[88] or that enhance the tubular activity of ADH,[89] such as chlorpropamide,[89] are also ineffective.

Nonsteroidal anti-inflammatory drugs reduce the urine volume and the free water clearance in children with nephrogenic diabetes insipidus.[271,297,298] Indomethacin is the agent which has been used most frequently. An agent such as sulindac, which does not inhibit renal prostaglandin synthesis, would not be expected to be effective. In one comparison, ibuprofen was not as effective as indomethacin in reducing urine volume and free water clearance in patients with nephrogenic diabetes insipidus.[298] Nonsteroidal anti-inflammatory drugs appear to work by reducing the delivery of solute to the distal tubule rather than by alleviating the prostaglandin antagonism of the tubular action of ADH.

Diuretics such as chlorothiazide are useful therapeutic agents. Crawford and Kennedy[299] first noted that chronic administration of these derivatives to patients with diabetes insipidus resulted in a marked reduction in urine flow and a moderate increase in urine concentration. The observed increase in urine concentration provided by chlorothiazide is in accord with its effect in normal animals and humans during water diuresis where the drug interferes with sodium chloride absorption in distal portions of the nephron, thereby reducing the formation of solute-free water. However, this effect alone cannot account for the reduction in urine flow. Instead, chlorothiazide-induced reductions in urine volume are also referable to an increased proximal fractional absorption of glomerular filtrate. Enhanced absorption of isosmotic fluid in the proximal nephron may be related to the mild degree of sodium depletion induced by the drug.

This increase in isosmotic proximal tubular fluid absorption results in a decrease in the volume of fluid delivered to the distal nephron, the site of defective water absorption, and therefore, to a reduction in urine volume. Furthermore, once a sodium deficiency is achieved by the diuretic agent, antidiuresis persists without further drug administration as long as the sodium deficiency is maintained by salt restriction. When salt losses are restored, polyuria rapidly returns.

Treatment of nephrogenic diabetes insipidus with thiazide diuretics commonly causes hypokalemia, which may aggravate further the renal concentrating defect. Amiloride, a potassium-sparing diuretic, when used in combination with thiazide diuretics may limit potassium losses and have an additive effect to the thiazide in terms of reducing urine volume.[300] Amiloride has also been effective as a single agent for the treatment of polyuria in patients receiving lithium therapy.[301]

Treatment of Hypertonic Encephalopathy. Patients with nephrogenic diabetes insipidus may require emergency therapy for hypertonic encephalopathy, generally associated with impending or actual circulatory collapse, if they are not able, for whatever cause, to ingest free water. The obvious therapeutic goal is the administration of sufficient free water to expand body water, thereby expanding the effective circulating volume and, at the same time, restoring osmotic homeostasis. If it is assumed that the primary deficit is in free water, that is, that negligible Na^+ loss has occurred, the free water deficit in nephrogenic diabetes insipidus complicated by hypernatremia may be expressed as

$$\text{Water deficit} = (0.6)(\text{body weight})(1 - 140/[Na^+])$$

where body weight is expressed in kilograms and 140 is the normal serum Na^+ concentration.

As noted in connection with Table 78-1, the brain adjusts to hypernatremia by accumulating intracellular solute, which is dissipated relatively slowly during the correction of hypernatremia. Consequently, a rapid expansion of body water with dilute solutions may cause water translocation into the central nervous system, cerebral edema, and seizures. Indeed, seizures have been reported to occur in up to 40 percent of severely hypernatremic patients with rapid infusion of dilute salt solutions.[302] It is therefore appropriate to administer fluids at a rate sufficient to reduce the serum Na^+ concentration by about 0.5 meq/liter every hour.

Hypotonic NaCl solutions (e.g., 0.45% NaCl) may be used in patients who have mild volume contraction and serum Na^+ concentrations less than 160 meq/liter. In more advanced hypernatremia complicated by signs of circulatory collapse, normal saline solutions are probably the more prudent therapeutic choice. Normal saline is dilute relative to body water osmolality and consequently will decrease serum osmolality and expand effective circulating volume while minimizing the risk of cerebral edema. The use of 5% glucose solutions should be restricted to instances of acute hypernatremia without significant circulatory collapse. The urine should be monitored carefully for glycosuria, since the latter, acting as an osmotic diuretic, will aggravate urinary free water loss.

REFERENCES

1. CULPEPPER RM, HEBERT SC, ANDREOLI TE: Nephrogenic diabetes insipidus, in Stanbury JB, Wyngaarden JB, Frederickson DJ, Goldstein JF, Brown MS (eds): *The Metabolic Basis of Inherited Disease.* New York, McGraw-Hill, 1983.
2. MCILRAITH CH: Notes on some cases of diabetes insipidus with marked family and hereditary tendencies. *Lancet* 2:767, 1892.
3. de LANGE C: Über erblichen Diabetes insipidus. *Jahrbuch Kinderheilk* 145:1, 1935.
4. FORSSMAN H: On hereditary diabetes insipidus. *Acta Med Scand* 121:suppl. 159:9, 1945.
5. WILLIAMS RH, HENRY C: Nephrogenic diabetes insipidus: Transmitted by females and appearing during infancy in males. *Ann Intern Med* 27:84, 1947.
6. FORSSMAN HH: Om Ärftlighetsgångsen vid diabetes insipidus. *Nord Med* 16:3211, 1942.
7. WARING AJ, KAJDI L, TAPPAN V: A congenital defect of water metabolism. *Am J Dis Child* 69:323, 1945.
8. SPRENGER KJ, WINSHIP WS, WITTENBERG DF: Nephrogenic diabetes insipidus presenting with infantile hypotonia. A report of 2 cases. *S Afr Med J* 70:228, 1986.
9. FRIIS-HANSEN B: Body water compartments in children: Changes during growth and related changes on body composition. *Pediatrics* 28:169, 1961.
10. EDELMAN CM JR, BARNETT HL: Pediatric nephrology, in Strauss MB, Welt LG (eds): *Diseases of the Kidney,* 2d ed. Boston, Little, Brown, 1971, p 1349.
11. MORRIS-JONES PH, HOUSTON IB, EVANS RC: Prognosis of the neurological complications of acute hypernatremia. *Lancet* 2:1385, 1967.
12. MACAULAY D, WATSON M: Hypernatraemia in infants as a cause of brain damage. *Arch Dis Child* 42:485, 1967.
13. FINBERG L, KILEY S, LETTRELL CN: Mass accidental salt poisoning in infancy. *JAMA* 184:187, 1963.
14. DODGE PR, SOTOS JF, GAMSTORP I, DeVITO D, LEVY M, RABE T: Neurophysiologic disturbances in hypertonic dehydration. *Trans Am Neurol Assoc* 87:33, 1962.
15. SOTOS JF, DODGE PR, MEARA P, TALBOT NB: Studies in experimental hypertonicity: Pathogenesis of the clinical syndrome, biochemical abnormalities and cause of death. *Pediatrics* 26:925, 1960.
16. ARIEFF AI, GUISADO R, LAZAROWITZ VC: The pathophysiology of hyperosmolar states, in Andreoli TE, Grantham JJ, Rector FC (eds): *Disturbances in Body Fluid Osmolality.* Bethesda, American Physiological Society, 1977, p 227.
17. HOLLIDAY MA, KALAYCI MN, HARRAH J: Factors that limit brain volume changes in response to acute and sustained hyper- and hyponatremia. *J Clin Invest* 47:1916, 1968.
18. ARIEFF AI, GUISADO R: Effects on the central nervous system of hypernatremic and hyponatremic states. *Kidney Int* 10:104, 1976.
19. CHAN PH, FISHMAN RA: Elevation of rat brain amino acids and idiogenic osmoles induced by hyperosmolality. *Brain Res* 161:293, 1979.
20. HEBERT SC, CULPEPPER RM, ANDREOLI TE: The posterior pituitary and water metabolism, in Foster DW, Wilson JD (eds): *Textbook of Endocrinology,* 7th ed. Philadelphia, Saunders, 1985, p 614.
21. GELLAI M, EDWARDS BR, VALTIN H: Urinary concentrating ability during dehydration in the absence of vasopressin. *Am J Physiol* 237:F100, 1979.
22. EDWARDS BR, GELLAI M, VALTIN H: Concentration of urine in the absence of ADH with minimal or no decrease in GFR. *Am J Physiol* 239:F84, 1980.
23. CUTLER RE, KLEEMAN CR, MAXWELL MH, DOWLING JT: Physiologic studies in nephrogenic diabetes insipidus. *J Clin Endocrinol Metab* 22:827, 1962.
24. MCCONNELL RF, LORENTZ WB, BERGER M, SMITH EH, CARVAJAL HF, TRAVIS LB: The mechanism of urinary concentration in nephrogenic diabetes insipidus. *Pediatr Res* W:33, 1977.
25. GORDEN P, ROBERTSON GL, SEEGMILLER JE: Hyperuricemia, a concomitant of congenital vasopressin-resistant diabetes insipidus in the adult. Studies of uric acid metabolism and plasma vasopressin. *N Engl J Med* 284:1057, 1971.
26. DARMADY E, OFFER J, PRINCE J, STRANACK F: The proximal convoluted tubule in the renal handling of water. *Lancet* 2:1254, 1964.
27. WEBER JW, GAUTIER E: Pitressinresistenter Diabetes insipidus. Therapie mit Silidiuretica. *Helv Paedr Acta* 16:565, 1961.
28. LOBECK CC, BARTA RA, MANGOS JA: Study of sweat in pitressin-resistant diabetes insipidus. *J Pediatrics* 62:868, 1963.
29. TEN BENSEL RW, PETERS ER: Progressive hydronephrosis, hydroureter, and dilatation of the bladder in siblings with congenital nephrogenic diabetes insipidus. *J Pediatr* 77:439, 1970.
30. MANSON AD, YALOWITZ PA, RANDALL RV, GREENE LF: Dilatation of the urinary tract associated with pituitary and nephrogenic diabetes insipidus. *J Urol* 103:327, 1970.
31. SHAPIRO SR, WOERNER S, ADELMAN RD, PALMER JM: Diabetes insipidus and hydronephrosis. *J Urol* 119:715, 1978.
32. HARTENBERG MA, CORY M, CHAN IC: Nephrogenic diabetes insipidus. Radiological and clinical features. *Int J Pediatr Nephrol* 6:281, 1985.
33. ROBERTSON GL, MAHR EA, ATHAR S, SINHA T: Development and clinical application of a new method for the radioimmunoassay of arginine vasopressin in human plasma. *J Clin Invest* 52:2340, 1973.
34. ROBERTSON GL: Vasopressin in osmotic regulation in man. *Annu Rev Med* 25:315, 1974.
35. DANCIS J, BIRMINGHAM JR, LESLIE SH: Congenital diabetes insipidus resistant to treatment with pitressin. *Am J Dis Child* 75:316, 1949.
36. ORLOFF J, WALSER M: Water and solute excretion in pitressin-resistant diabetes insipidus. *Clin Res Proc* 4:136, 1956.
37. CRAWFORD JD, KENNEDY GC: Chlorothiazide in diabetes insipidus. *Nature* 183:891, 1959.
38. SCHOEN EJ: Renal diabetes insipidus. *Pediatrics* 26:808, 1960.
39. KOBRINSKY NL, DOYLE JJ, ISRAELS ED, WINTER JJ, CHEANG MS, WALKER RD, BISHOP AJ: Absent factor VIII response to synthetic vasopressin analogue (DDAVP) in nephrogenic diabetes insipidus. *Lancet* 8441:1293, 1985.
40. BODE HH, CRAWFORD JD: Nephrogenic diabetes insipidus in North America—The Hopewell hypothesis. *N Engl J Med* 280:750, 1969.
41. NAKANO KK: Familial nephrogenic diabetes insipidus. *Hawaii Med J* 28:205, 1969.
42. SCHULTZ P, LINES DR: Nephrogenic diabetes insipidus in the Australian aboriginal kindred. *Humangenetik* 26:79, 1975.
43. du VIGNEAUD V: Hormones of the mammalian posterior pituitary gland and their naturally occurring analogues. *Johns Hopkins Med J* 124:53, 1969.
44. SAWYER WH: Evolution of neurohypophyseal hormones and their receptors. *Fed Proc* 36:1842, 1977.
45. BUTLEN D, GUILLON G, RAJERISON RM, JARD S, SAWYER WH, MANNING M: Structural requirements for activation of vasopressin-sensitive adenylate cyclase, hormone binding, and antidiuretic actions: Effects of highly

potent analogues and competitive inhibitors. *Mol Pharmacol* 14:1006, 1978.

46. BARTH T, RAJERISON RM, ROY C, JARD S: Activation of rat kidney adenylate cyclase by vasopressin analogues: Lack of correlation with antidiuretic activity. *Mol Cell Endocrinol* 2:81, 1975.

47. HECHTER O, TERADA S, NAKAHARA T, FLOURET G, BERGMAN RN: Neurohypophyseal hormone-responsive renal adenylate cyclase. II. Relationship between hormonal occupancy of neurohypophyseal hormone receptor sites and adenylate cyclase activation. *J Biol Chem* 253:3219, 1978.

48. ROY C, BARTH T, JARD S: Vasopressin-sensitive kidney adenylate cyclase. Structural requirements for attachment to the receptor and enzyme activation: Studies with vasopressin analogues. *J Biol Chem* 250:3149, 1975.

49. SAWYER WH, ACOSTA M, BALASPIRI L, JUDD J, MANNING M: Structural changes in the arginine vasopressin molecule that enhance antidiuretic activity and specificity. *Endocrinology* 94:1106, 1974.

50. SAWYER WA, PANG PKT, SETO J, MCENROE M, LAMMEK B, MANNING M: Vasopressin analogs that antagonize antidiuretic responses by rats to the antidiuretic hormone. *Science* 212:49, 1981.

51. MANNING M, SAWYER WH: Synthesis and receptor specificities of vasopressin antagonists. *J Cardiovasc Pharmacol* 8:S29, 1986.

52. MANNING M, KLIS WA, OLMA A, SETO J, SAWYER WH: Design of more potent and selective antagonists of the antidiuretic responses to arginine vasopressin. *J Med Chem* 25:414, 1982.

53. MANNING M, NAWROCKA E, MISICKA A, OLMA A, KLIS WA: Potent and selective antagonists of the antidiuretic responses to arginine vasopressin based on modification of [1-(β-mercapto-β, β-cyclopentamethylenepropionic acid) 2-D-isoleucine, 4-valine] arginine-vasopressin at position 4. *J Med Chem* 27:423, 1984.

54. MANNING M, SAWYER WA: Development of selective agonists and antagonists of vasopressin and oxytocin, in Schrier RW (ed): *Vasopressin*. New York, Raven, 1985.

55. STASSEN FL, HECKMAN GD, SCHMIDT DB, STEFANKIEWICZ J, SULAT L, HUFFMAN WF, MOORE MM, KINTER LB: Actions of vasopressin antagonists: Molecular mechanisms, in Schrier RW (ed): *Vasopressin*. New York, Raven, 1985.

56. KIM JK, SCHRIER RW: Cellular effect of arginine vasopressin antagonist on the isolated renal tubule, in Schrier RW (ed): *Vasopressin*. New York, Raven, 1985.

57. SCHARRER E, SCHARRER B: Hormones produced by neurosecretory cells. *Recent Prog Horm Res* 10:183, 1954.

58. BROWNSTEIN MJ, RUSSELL JT, GAINER H: Synthesis, transport and release of posterior pituitary hormones. *Science* 207:373, 1980.

59. SCHMALE H, FEHR S, RICHTER D: Vasopressin biosynthesis—From gene to peptide hormone. *Kidney Int* 32:S8, 1987.

60. SACHS H, FAWCETT CP, TAKABATAKE Y, PORTANOVA R: Biosynthesis and release of vasopressin and neurophysin. *Recent Prog Horm Res* 25:447, 1969.

61. PICKERING BT, JONES CW: The neurophysins, in Li CH (ed): *Hormonal Protein and Peptides*. New York, Academic, 1978, vol V, p 103.

62. DREIFUSS JJ: A review on neurosecretory granules: Their contents and mechanisms of release. *Ann NY Acad Sci* 248:184, 1975.

63. SACHS H, TAKABATAKE Y: Evidence for a precursor in vasopressin biosynthesis. *Endocrinology* 75:943, 1964.

64. GAINER H, SARNE Y, BROWNSTEIN MJ: Neurophysin biosynthesis: Conversion of a putative precursor during axonal transport. *Science* 195:1354, 1977.

65. LAND H, SCHUETZ G, SCHMALE H, RICHTER D: Nucleotide sequence of cloned cDNA encoding bovine arginine vasopressin-neurophysin II precursor. *Nature* 295:299, 1982.

66. SCHMALE H, HEINSOHN S, RICHTER D: Structural organization of the rat gene for the arginine vasopressin-neurophysin precursor. *EMBO J* 2:763, 1983.

67. RIDDELL DC, MALLONEE R, PHILLIPS JA, PARKS JS, SEXTOR LA, HAMERTON JL: Chromosomal assignment of human sequences encoding arginine vasopressin-neurophysin II and growth hormone releasing factor. *Somatic Cell Mol Genet* 11:189, 1985.

68. IVELL R, SCHMALE H, KRISCH B, NAHKE P, RICHTER D: Expression of a mutant vasopressin gene: Differential polyadenylation and read-through of the mRNA 3' end in a frame-shift mutant. *EMBO J* 5:971, 1986.

69. SCHMALE H, RICHTER D: Single base deletion in the vasopressin gene is the cause of diabetes insipidus in Brattleboro rats. *Nature* 308:705, 1984.

70. SACHS H, HALLER EW: Further studies on the capacity of the neurohypophysis to release vasopressin. *Endocrinology* 83:251, 1968.

71. DREIFUSS JJ, KALNINS I, KELLY JS, RUF KB: Action potentials and release of neurohypophysial hormones in vitro. *J Physiol (Lond)* 215:805, 1971.

72. NORDMANN JJ: Stimulus-secretion coupling. *Prog Brain Res* 60:281, 1983.

73. NORDMANN JJ, DYBALL REJ: Effects of veratridine on Ca fluxes and the release of oxytocin and vasopressin from the isolated rat neurohypophysis. *J Gen Physiol* 72:297, 1978.

74. NORDMANN JJ, DIAYANITHI G, CAZALIS M: Coupling between the bioelectrical activity of a neurosecretory cell and the release at its terminals of neuropeptides, in Schrier RW (ed): *Vasopressin*. New York, Raven, 1985.

75. BAUMAN G, DINGMAN JF: Distribution, blood transport and degradation of antidiuretic hormone in man. *J Clin Invest* 57:1109, 1976.

76. WEITZMAN RE, FISHER DA: Arginine vasopressin metabolism in dogs. I. Evidence for a receptor-mediated mechanism. *Am J Physiol* 235:E591, 1978.

77. CZACZKES JW, KLEEMAN CR, KOENIG M: Physiologic studies of antidiuretic hormone by its direct measurement in human plasma. *J Clin Invest* 43:1625, 1964.

78. NITSCHKE U, BALZAR H: Die Inaktivierung von infundiertem Vasopressin bei Diabetes insipidus-Probanden. *Acta Endocrinol* 62:270, 1969.

79. WILSON KC, WEITZMAN RE, FISHER DA: Arginine vasopressin metabolism in dogs. II. Modeling and systems analysis. *Am J Physiol* 235:E598, 1978.

80. BARTH T, KREJČI I, KUPKOVÁ B, JOŠT D: Pharmacology of cyclic analogues of deamino-oxytocin not containing a disulphide bond (carba analogues). *Eur J Pharmacol* 24:183, 1973.

81. KOIDA M, GLASS JD, SCHWARTZ IL, WALTER R: Mechanism of inactivation of oxytocin by rat kidney enzymes. *Endocrinology* 88:633, 1971.

82. MARKS N, ABRASH L, WALTER R: Degradation of neurohypophyseal hormones by brain extracts and purified brain enzymes. *Proc Soc Exp Biol Med* 142:455, 1973.

83. CORT JH, SCHÜCK O, STŘIBRNÁ J, ŠKOPKOVÁ J, JOŠT K, MULDER JL: Role of the disulfide bridge and the C-terminal tripeptide in the antidiuretic action of vasopressin in man and the rat. *Kidney Int* 8:292, 1975.

84. WALTER R, BOWMAN RH: Mechanism of inactivation of vasopressin and oxytocin by the isolated perfused rat kidney. *Endocrinology* 92:189, 1973.

85. NARDACCI NJ, MUKHOPADHYAY S, CAMPBELL BJ: Partial purification and characterization of the antidiuretic hormone-inactivating enzyme from renal plasma membranes. *Biochim Biophys Acta* 377:146, 1975.

86. BARTTER FC, SCHWARTZ WB: The syndrome of inappropriate secretion of antidiuretic hormone. *Am J Med* 42:790, 1967.

87. NIELSEN B, THORN NA: Transient excess urinary excretion of antidiuretic material in acute intermittent porphyria with hyponatremia and hypomagnesemia. *Am J Med* 38:345, 1965.

88. MOSES AM, HOWANTIZ J, VAN GEMERT M, MILLER M: Clofibrate-induced antidiuresis. *J Clin Invest* 53:535, 1973.

89. WEISSMAN PN, SHENKMAN L, GREGERMAN RI: Chlorpropamide hyponatremia: Drug-induced inappropriate antidiuretic-hormone activity. *N Engl J Med* 284:65, 1971.

90. MEINDERS AE, CEJKA V, ROBERTSON GL: The antidiuretic action of carbamazepine in man. *Clin Sci Mol Med* 47:289, 1974.

91. DISCALA VA, KINNEY MJ: Effects of myxedema on the renal diluting and concentrating mechanism. *Am J Med* 50:325, 1971.

92. SHARE L: Vasopressin, its bioassay and the physiological control of its release. *Am J Med* 42:701, 1967.

93. SHU'AYB WA, MORGAN WH, ZIMMERMANN B: Studies of the mechanism of antidiuretic hormone secretion and the post-commissurotomy dilutional syndrome. *Ann Surg* 162:690, 1965.

94. SLADEN A, LAVER MB, PONTOPPIDAN H: Pulmonary complications and water retention in prolonged mechanical ventilation. *N Engl J Med* 279:448, 1968.

95. MORRIS JF: Organization of neural inputs to the supraoptic and paraventricular nuclei: Anatomical aspects, in Cross BA, Leng G (eds): *Prog Brain Res*. New York, Elsevier, vol 60, 1983.

96. SAWCHENKO PE, SWANSON LW: The organization and biochemical specificity of afferent projections to the paraventricular and supraoptic nuclei, in Cross BA, Leng G (eds): *Prog Brain Res*. New York, Elsevier, vol 60, 1983.

97. SAWCHENKO PE, SWANSON LW: Immunohistochemical identification of neurons in the paraventricular nucleus of the hypothalamus that project to the medulla or to the spinal cord in the rat. *J Comp Neurol* 205:260, 1982.

98. ZIMMERMAN EA, SILVERMAN A-J: Vasopressin and adrenal cortical interactions, in Cross BA, Leng G (eds): *Prog Brain Res*. New York, Elsevier, vol 60, 1983.

99. SAWCHENKO PE, SWANSON LW, VALE WW: Co-expression of corticotropin-releasing factor and vasopressin immunoreactivity in parvocellular neurosecretory neurons of the adrenalectomized rat. *Proc Natl Acad Sci USA* 81:1883, 1984.

100. KISS JZ, MEZEY E, SKIRBOLL L: Corticotropin-releasing factor—Immuno-

reactive neurons of the paraventricular nucleus become vasopressin-positive after adrenalectomy. *Proc Natl Acad Sci USA* 81:1854, 1984.

101. CROSS BA, DYBALL REJ, DYER RG, JONES CW, LINCOLN DW, MORRIS JF, PICKERING BT: Endocrine neurons. *Recent Prog Horm Res* 31:243, 1975.

102. CARTER DA, LIGHTMAN SL: Neuroendocrine control of vasopressin secretion, in Baylis PH, Padfield PL (eds): *The Posterior Pituitary. Hormone Secretion in Health and Disease.* New York, Marcel Dekker, 1985.

103. SAWCHENKO PE, SWANSON LW: Central noradrenergic pathways for the integration of hypothalamic neuroendocrine and autonomic responses. *Science* 214:685, 1981.

104. SAPER CB, STANDAERT DG, CURRIE MG, SCHWARTZ D, GELLER DM, NEEDLEMAN P: Atriopeptin-immunoreactive neurons in the brain: Presence in cardiovascular regulatory areas. *Science* 227:1047, 1985.

105. JOHNSON AK, CUNNINGHAM JT: Brain mechanisms and drinking: The role of lamina terminalis-associated systems in extracellular thirst. *Kidney Int* 32:S35, 1987.

106. IITAKE K, SHARE L, OUCHI Y, CROFTON JT, BROOKS DP: Central cholinergic control of vasopressin release in conscious rats. *Am J Physiol* 251:E146, 1986.

107. VERNEY EB: The antidiuretic hormone and the factors which determine its release. *Proc R Soc Lond Ser B* 135:25, 1947.

108. MCKINLEY MJ, DENTON DA, WEISINGER RS: Sensors for antidiuresis and thirst-osmoreceptors or CSF sodium detectors? *Brain Res* 141:89, 1978.

109. LENG G: Rat supraoptic neurones: The effects of locally applied hypertonic saline. *Am J Physiol* 304:405, 1980.

110. LENG G, DYBALL REJ, MASON WT: Electrophysiology of osmoreceptors, in Schrier RW (ed): *Vasopressin.* New York, Raven, 1985.

111. THRASHER TN, BROWN CJ, KEIL LC, RAMSAY DJ: Thirst and vasopressin release in the dog: An osmoreceptor or sodium receptor mechanism? *Am J Physiol* 238:R333, 1980.

112. THRASHER TN, KEIL LC, RAMSAY DJ: Lesions of the organism vasculosim of the lamina terminalis (OVLT) attenuate osmotically induced drinking and vasopressin secretion in the dog. *Endocrinology* 110:1837, 1982.

113. BEALER SL, CROFTON JT, SHARE L: Hypothalamic knife cuts alter fluid regulation, vasopressin secretion and natriuresis during water deprivation. *Neuroendocrinology* 36:364, 1983.

114. PETERS JP: *Body Water. The Exchange of Fluids in Man.* Springfield, Charles C Thomas, 1935, p 284.

115. LEAF A, MAMBY AR: An antidiuretic mechanism not regulated by extracellular fluid tonicity. *J Clin Invest* 31:60, 1952.

116. GAUER OH, HENRY JP: Circulatory basis of fluid volume control. *Physiol Rev* 43:423, 1963.

117. MURDAUGH HV, SIEKER HO, MANFREDI F: Effect of altered intrathoracic pressure on renal hemodynamics, electrolyte excretion and water clearance. *J Clin Invest* 38:834, 1959.

118. POULAIN DA, WAKERLEY JB: Electrophysiology of hypothalamic magnocellular neurones secreting oxytocin and vasopressin. *Neuroscience* 7:773, 1982.

119. DUNN FL, BRENNAN TJ, NELSON AE, ROBERTSON GL: The role of blood osmolality and volume in regulating vasopressin secretion in the rat. *J Clin Invest* 52:3212, 1973.

120. WEINSTEIN H, BERNE RM, SACHS H: Vasopressin in blood: Effect of hemorrhage. *Endocrinology* 66:712, 1960.

121. CAILLENS H, PRUSZCZYNSKI W, MEYRIER A, ANG K-S, ROUSSELET F, ARDAILLOU R: Relationship between change in volemia at constant osmolality and plasma antidiuretic hormone. *Miner Electrolyte Metab* 4:161, 1980.

122. ROBERTSON GL: Physiology of ADH secretion. *Kidney Int* 32:S20, 1987.

123. STRICKER EM, VERBALIS JG: Interaction of osmotic and volume stimuli in regulation of neurohypophyseal secretion in rats. *Am J Physiol* 250:R267, 1986.

124. WANG BC, GOETZ KL: Volume influence on the plasma osmolality-plasma vasopressin relationship mediated by cardiac receptor, in Schrier RW (ed): *Vasopressin.* New York, Raven, 1985.

125. QUILLEN EW, COWLEY AW: Influence of volume changes on osmolality-vasopressin relationships in conscious dogs. *Am J Physiol* 244:H73, 1983.

126. SCHRIER RW, BERL T, ANDERSON RJ: Osmotic and nonosmotic control of vasopressin release. *Am J Physiol* 236:F321, 1979.

127. MCDONALD KM, KURUVILA KC, AISENBREY GA, SCHRIER RW: Effect of alpha and beta adrenergic stimulation on renal water excretion and medullary cyclic AMP in intact and diabetes insipidus rats. *Kidney Int* 12:96, 1977.

128. SLADEK JR JR, MCNEILL TH: Simultaneous monoamine histofluorescence and neuropeptide immunocytochemistry. IV. Verification of catecholamine-neurophysin interactions through single section analysis. *Cell Tissue Res* 210:181, 1980.

129. SCHRIER RW, KIM JK: Water metabolism in historical perspectives: Its research in the past and present. *Kidney Int* 32:S113, 1987.

130. LIND RW, SWANSON LW, GANTEN D: Organization of angiotensin II immunoreactive cells and fibers in the rat central nervous system. *Neuroendocrinology* 40:2, 1985.

131. IOVINO M, STEARDO L: Vasopressin release to central and peripheral angiotensin II in rats with lesion of the subfornical organ. *Brain Res* 322:365, 1984.

132. KNEPEL W, NUTTO D, MEYER DK: Effects of transection of subfornical organ efferent projections on vasopressin release induced by angiotensin or isoprendaline in the rat. *Brain Res* 248:180, 1982.

133. TANAKA J, KABA H, SAITO H, SETO K: Electrophysiological evidence that circulating angiotensin II sensitive neurons on the subfornical organ alter the activity of hypothalamic paraventricular neurohypophyseal neurons in the rat. *Brain Res* 342:361, 1985.

134. USBERTI M, FEDERICO S, CIANCIARUSO B, DiMINNO G, UNGARO B, CERBONE AM, ARDILLO G, PECORARO C, GARGIULO A, ANDREUCCI VE: Effects of angiotensin II on plasma ADH, PGE_2 synthesis and water excretion in normal man. *Am J Physiol* 248:F254, 1985.

135. USBERTI M, DiMINNO G, UNGANO B, CIANCIARUSO B, FEDERICO S, ARDILLO G, GARGIULO A, MARTUCCI F, PANNAIN M, CERBONE AM, CONTE G, PECORARO C, ANDREUCCI VE: Angiotensin II inhibition with captopril on plasma ADH, PG synthesis, and renal function in humans. *Am J Physiol* 250:F986, 1986.

136. MORTON JJ, CONNELL JM, HUGHES MJ, INGLIS GC, WALLACE EC: The role of plasma osmolality, angiotensin II and dopamine in vasopressin release in man. *Clin Endocrinol* 23:129, 1985.

137. BLOOM FE: The endorphins: A growing family of pharmacologically pertinent peptides. *Annu Rev Pharmacol Toxicol* 23:151, 1983.

138. FORSLING ML: Opioid peptides and vasopressin release, in Schrier RW (ed): *Vasopressin.* New York, Raven, 1985.

139. NORDMANN JJ, DAYANITHI G, CAZALIS M: Do opioid peptides modulate, at the level of the nerve endings, the release of neurohypophyseal hormones? *Exp Brain Res* 61:560, 1986.

140. SKLAR AH, SCHRIER RW: Central nervous system mediators of vasopressin release. *Physiol Rev* 63:1243, 1983.

141. HOFFMAN PK, SHARE L, CROFTON JT, SHADE RE: The effect of intracerebroventricular indomethacin on osmotically stimulated vasopressin release. *Neuroendocrinology* 34:132, 1982.

142. MANNING PT, SCHWARTZ D, KATSUBE NC, HOLMBERG SW, NEEDLEMAN P: Vasopressin-stimulated release of atriopeptin: Endocrine antagonists in fluid homeostasis. *Science* 229:395, 1985.

143. DILLINGHAM MA, ANDERSON RJ: Inhibition of vasopressin action by atrial natriuretic factor. *Science* 231:1572, 1986.

144. ZIMMERMAN EA, MA L-Y, NILAVER G: Anatomical basis of thirst and vasopressin secretion. *Kidney Int* 32:S14, 1987.

145. ANTUNES-RODRIGUES J, McCANN SM, ROGERS LC, SAMSON WK: Atrial natriuretic factor inhibits dehydration and angiotensin II induced fluid intake in the conscious, unrestrained rat. *Proc Natl Acad Sci USA* 82:8720, 1985.

146. POOLE CJM, CARTER DA, VALLEJO M, LIGHTMAN SL: Atrial natriuretic factor inhibits the stimulated in vivo and in vitro release of vasopressin and oxytocin in the rat. *J Endocrinol* 112:97, 1987.

147. IITAKE K, SHARE L, CROFTON JT, BROOKS DP, OUCHI Y, BLAIRE EH: Central atrial natriuretic factor reduces vasopressin secretion in the rat. *Endocrinology* 9:438, 1986.

148. OBANA K, NATUSE M, INAGAMI T, BROWN AB, NARUSE K, KURIMOTO F, SAKURAI H, DEMURA H, SHIZUME K: Atrial natriuretic factor inhibits vasopressin secretion from rat posterior pituitary. *Biochem Biophys Res Commun* 132:1088, 1985.

149. CRANDALL ME, GREGG CM: In vitro evidence for an inhibitory effect of atrial natriuretic peptide on vasopressin release. *Neuroendocrinology* 44:439, 1986.

150. KUHN W, RYFFEL K: Herstellung konzentrierter Lösungen aus verdünnten durch blosse Membranwirkung. Ein Modellversuch zur Funktion der Niere. *Z Physiol Chem* 276:145, 1942.

151. WIRZ VH, HARGITAY B, KUGN W: Lokalisation des Konzentrierungsprozesses in der Niere durch direkte Kryoskopie. *Helv Physiol Acta* 9:196, 1951.

152. HARGITAY B, KUHN W: Das Multiplikationsprinzip als Grundlage der Harnkonzentrierung in der Niere. *Z Elektrochem* 55:539, 1951.

153. GOTTSCHALK CW, MYLLE M: Micropuncture study of the mammalian urinary concentrating mechanism: Evidence for the countercurrent hypothesis. *Am J Physiol* 4:927, 1959.

154. GOTTSCHALK CW: Micropuncture studies of tubular function in the mammalian kidney. *Physiologist* 4:35, 1961.

155. GOTTSCHALK CW: Osmotic concentration and dilution of the urine. *Am J Med* 36:670, 1964.

156. ROCHA AS, KOKKO JP: Sodium chloride and water transport in the medullary thick ascending limb of Henle. Evidence for active chloride transport. *J Clin Invest* 52:612, 1973.

157. BURG M, GREEN N: Function of the thick ascending limb of Henle's loop. *Am J Physiol* 224:659, 1973.

158. KOKKO JP: Sodium chloride and water transport in the descending limb of Henle. *J Clin Invest* 49:1838, 1970.

159. IMAI M, KOKKO JP: Sodium chloride, urea and water transport in the thin ascending limb of Henle. Generation of osmotic gradients by passive diffusion of solutes. *J Clin Invest* 53:393, 1974.

160. STEPHENSON JL: Concentration of urine in a central core model of the renal counterflow system. *Kidney Int* 2:85, 1972.

161. KOKKO JP, RECTOR FC JR: Countercurrent multiplication system without active transport in inner medulla. *Kidney Int* 2:214, 1972.

162. JAMISON RJ: The renal concentrating mechanism. *Kidney Int* 32:S43, 1987.

163. VALTIN H: Sequestration of urea and nonurea solutes in renal tissues of rats with hereditary hypothalamic diabetes insipidus: Effect of vasopressin and dehydration on the countercurrent mechanism. *J Clin Invest* 45:337, 1966.

164. PENNELL JP, LACY FB, JAMISON RL: An in vivo study of the concentrating process in the descending limb of Henle's loop. *Kidney Int* 5:337, 1974.

165. IMAI M: Functional heterogeneity of the descending limbs of Henle's loop: II. Interspecies difference among rabbits, rats and hamsters. *Pflugers Arch* 402:393, 1984.

166. STEPHENSON JL: Models of the urinary concentrating mechanism. *Kidney Int* 31:648, 1987.

167. WIRZ H: The location of antidiuretic action in the mammalian kidney, in Heller H (ed): *The Neurohypophysis. Proc 8th Sympos Colston Res Soc.* New York, Academic, 1957, p 157.

168. EDWARDS RM, JACKSON BA, DOUSA TP: Protein kinase activity in isolated tubules of rat renal medulla. *Am J Physiol* 238:F269, 1980.

169. HEBERT SC, ANDREOLI TE: Control of NaCl transport in the thick ascending limb. *Am J Physiol* 246:F745, 1984.

170. HEBERT SC, CULPEPPER RM, ANDREOLI TE: NaCl transport in mouse medullary thick ascending limbs. I. Functional nephron heterogeneity and ADH-stimulated NaCl cotransport. *Am J Physiol* 241:F412, 1981.

171. SASAKI S, IMAI M: Effects of vasopressin on water and NaCl transport across the in vitro perfused medullary thick ascending limbs of Henle's loop of mouse, rat and rabbit kidneys. *Pflugers Arch* 383:215, 1980.

172. GREGER R, SCHLATTER E: Properties of the lumen membrane of the cortical thick ascending limb of Henle's loop of rabbit kidney. *Pflugers Arch* 396:315, 1983.

173. GREGER R, OBERLEITHNER H, SCHLATTER E, CASSOLA AC, WEIDTKE C: Chloride activity in cells of isolated thick ascending limb of rabbit kidney. *Pflugers Arch* 399:29, 1983.

174. MOLONY DA, REEVES WB, HEBERT SC, ANDREOLI TE: ADH increases apical Na^+, K^+, $2Cl^-$ entry in mouse medullary thick ascending limbs of Henle. *Am J Physiol* 252:F177, 1987.

175. GREGER R: Chloride reabsorption in the rabbit cortical thick ascending limb of the loop of Henle. A sodium dependent process. *Pflugers Arch* 390:38, 1981.

176. KOENIG B, RICAPITO S, KINNE R: Chloride transport in the thick ascending limb of Henle's loop: Potassium dependence and stoichiometry of the NaCl cotransport system in plasma membrane vesicles. *Pflugers Arch* 399:173, 1983.

177. KINNE R, KINNE-SAFFRAN E, SCHOLERMANN B, SCHULTZ H: The anion specificity of the sodium, potassium, chloride cotransporter in rabbit kidney outer medulla: Studies on medullary plasma membranes. *Pflugers Arch* 407:S168, 1986.

178. EVELOFF JL, CALAMIA J: Effect of osmolarity on cation fluxes in medullary thick ascending limb cells. *Am J Physiol* 250:F176, 1986.

179. HEBERT SC, ANDREOLI TE: Effects of antidiuretic hormone on cellular conductive pathways in mouse medullary thick ascending limb of Henle. II. Determinants of the ADH-mediated increases in transepithelial voltage in net Cl^- absorption. *J Membr Biol* 80:221, 1984.

180. STOKES JB: Consequences of potassium recycling in the renal medulla. Effects of ion transport by the medullary thick ascending limb of Henle's loop. *J Clin Invest* 70:219, 1982.

181. HEBERT SC, FRIEDMAN PA, ANDREOLI TE: The effects of antidiuretic hormone on cellular conductive pathways in mouse medullary thick ascending limbs of Henle. I. ADH increases transcellular conductance pathways. *J Membr Biol* 80:201, 1984.

182. GREGER R, SCHLATTER E: Properties of the basolateral membrane of the cortical thick ascending limb of Henle's loop of rabbit kidney—A model for secondary active chloride transport. *Pflugers Arch* 396:325, 1983.

183. WANGEMANN P, WITTNER M, DISTEFANO A, ENGLERT HC, LANG HJ, SCHLATTER E, GREGER R: Cl^- channel blockers in the thick ascending limb of the loop of Henle. Structure activity relationship. *Pflugers Arch* 407:S128, 1986.

184. SCHLATTER E, GREGER R: cAMP increases the basolateral Cl^- conduct-

185. GANOTE CE, GRANTHAM JJ, MOSES HL, BURG MB, ORLOFF J: Ultrastructural studies of vasopressin effect on isolated perfused renal collecting tubules of the rabbit. *J Cell Biol* 36:355, 1968.

186. GRANTHAM JJ, GANOTE CE, BURG MB, ORLOFF J: Paths of transtubular water flow in isolated renal collecting tubules. *J Cell Biol* 41:562, 1968.

187. SCHAFER JA, ANDREOLI TE: Cellular constraints to diffusion: The effect of antidiuretic hormone on water flows in isolated mammalian collecting tubules. *J Clin Invest* 51:1264, 1972.

188. GRANTHAM JJ, BURG MB: Effect of vasopressin and cyclic AMP on permeability of isolated collecting tubules. *Am J Physiol* 211:255, 1966.

189. HEBERT SC, ANDREOLI TE: Interactions of temperature and ADH on transport processes in cortical collecting tubules. *Am J Physiol* 7:F470, 1980.

190. ANDREOLI TE, SCHAFER JA: Mass transport across cell membranes: The effects of antidiuretic hormone on water and solute flow in epithelia. *Annu Rev Physiol* 39:451, 1976.

191. MAFFLY RH, HAYS RM, LAMDIN E, LEAF A: The effect of neurohypophyseal hormones on the permeability of the toad bladder to urea. *J Gen Physiol* 39:630, 1960.

192. HAYS RM, LEAF A: Studies on the movement of water through the isolated toad bladder and its modification by vasopressin. *J Gen Physiol* 45:904, 1962.

193. LEVINE S, FRANKL N, HAYS RM: Effect of phloretin on water and solute movement in the toad bladder. *J Clin Invest* 52:1435, 1973.

194. HEBERT SC, ANDREOLI TE: Water movement across the mammalian cortical collecting duct. *Kidney Int* 22:526, 1982.

195. AL-ZAHID G, SCHAFER JA, TROUTMAN SL, ANDREOLI TE: The effect of antidiuretic hormone on water and solute permeation and the activation energies for these processes, in mammalian cortical collecting tubules: Evidence for parallel ADH-sensitive pathways for water and solute diffusion in luminal plasma membranes. *J Membr Biol* 31:103, 1977.

196. LEVINE SD, JACOBY M, FINKELSTEIN A: The water permeability of toad urinary bladder. II. The value of Pf/P_{D_w} for the antidiuretic hormone-induced water pathway. *J Gen Physiol* 85:543, 1984.

197. SCHWARTZ IL, HUANG CJ, FISCHMAN AJ, MASUR SK, WYSSBROD HR: Current ideas on the sequence of events involved in the hydroosmotic action of antidiuretic hormones, in Schlessinger DH (ed): *Neurohypophyseal Peptide Hormones and Other Biologically Active Peptides.* New York, Elsevier, 1981, p 101.

198. WADE JB, STETSON DL, LEWIS SA: ADH action: Evidence for a membrane shuttle mechanism. *Ann NY Acad Sci* 372:106, 1981.

199. MULLER J, KACHADORIAN WA, DISCALA VA: Evidence that ADH-stimulated intramembrane particle aggregates are transferred from cytoplasmic to luminal membranes in toad bladder epithelial cells. *J Cell Biol* 85:83, 1980.

200. WADE JB: Membrane structural studies of the action of vasopressin. *Fed Proc* 44:2687, 1985.

201. BROWN D, ORCI L: Vasopressin stimulates formation of coated pits in rat kidney collecting ducts. *Nature* 302:253, 1983.

202. HARMANCI MC, KACHADORIAN WA, VALTIN H, DISCALA VA: Antidiuretic hormone-induced intramembranous alteration in mammalian collecting ducts. *Am J Physiol* 235:F440, 1978.

203. HARMANCI MC, STERN P, KACHADORIAN WA, VALTIN H, DISCALA VA: Vasopressin and collecting duct intramembranous particle clusters: A dose-response relationship. *Am J Physiol* 239:F560, 1980.

204. HARMANCI MC, LORENZEN M, KACHADORIAN WA: Vasopressin-induced intramembranous particle aggregates in isolated rabbit collecting duct. *Kidney Int* 21:275A, 1982.

205. GUGGINO SE, SUAREZ-ISLA BA, GUGGINO WB, SACKTOR B: Forskolin and antidiuretic hormone stimulate a Ca^{2+}-activated K^+ channel in cultured kidney cells. *Am J Physiol* 249:F448, 1985.

206. SCHLATTER E, SCHAFER JA: Electrophysiological studies in principal cells of rat cortical collecting tubules. ADH increases the apical membrane Na^+-conductance. *Pflugers Arch* 409:81, 1987.

207. LI JH-Y, PALMER LG, EDELMAN IS, LINDEMANN B: The role of sodium-channel density in the natriferic response of the toad urinary bladder to an antidiuretic hormone. *J Membr Biol* 64:77, 1982.

208. DOUSA TP: Cyclic nucleotides in the cellular action of neurohypophyseal hormones. *Fed Proc* 36:1867, 1977.

209. HILDEBRANDT J, SEKURA R, CODINA J, IYENGAR R, MANCLARK C, BIRNBAUMER L: Stimulation and inhibition of adenyl cyclases mediated by distinct regulatory proteins. *Nature* 302:706, 1983.

210. GILMAN AG: Guanine nucleotide-binding regulatory proteins and dual control of adenylate cyclase. *J Clin Invest* 73:1, 1984.

211. RODBRELL M: The role of hormone receptors and GTP-regulatory proteins in membrane transduction. *Nature* 284:17, 1980.

212. ORLOFF J, HANDLER JS: The similarity of effects of vasopressin adenosine-3′, 5′-monophosphate (cyclic AMP) and theophylline on the toad bladder. *J Clin Invest* 41:702, 1962.

213. MENDOZA SA, HANDLER JS, ORLOFF J: Effect of inhibitors of sodium transport on response of toad bladder to ADH and cyclic AMP. *Am J Physiol* 219:1440, 1970.

214. GRANTHAM JJ, ORLOFF J: Effect of prostaglandin E₁ on the permeability response of the isolated collecting tubule to vasopressin, adenosine 3′,5′-monophosphate and theophylline. *J Clin Invest* 47:1154, 1968.

215. MOREL F: Sites of hormone action in the mammalian nephron. *Am J Physiol* 9:F159, 1981.

216. CAMPBELL BJ, WOODWARD G, BORBERG V: Calcium-mediated interactions between antidiuretic hormone and renal plasma membranes. *J Biol Chem* 247:6167, 1972.

217. DOUSA TP: Effect of renal medullary solutes on vasopressin-sensitive adenyl cyclase. *Am J Physiol* 222:657, 1972.

218. DOUSA TP, WALTER R, SCHWARTZ IL, SANDS H, HECHTER O: Role of cyclic AMP in the action of neurohypophyseal hormones on kidney. *Adv Cyclic Nucleotide Res* 1:121, 1972.

219. ANDERSON WA, BROWN E: The influence of arginine-vasopressin upon the production of adenosine-3′,5′-monophosphate by adenyl cyclase from the kidney. *Biochim Biophys Acta* 67:674, 1963.

220. CHASE IR, AURBACH GD: Renal adenyl cyclase: Anatomically separate sites for parathyroid hormone and vasopressin. *Science* 159:545, 1968.

221. BOCKAERT J, ROY C, RAJERISON R, JARD S: Specific binding of (³H) lysine-vasopressin to pig kidney plasma membranes. Relationship of receptor occupancy to adenylate cyclase activation. *J Biol Chem* 248:5922, 1973.

222. SCHWARTZ IL, SHLATZ LJ, KINNE-SAFFRAN E, KINNE R: Target cell polarity and membrane phosphorylation in relation to the mechanism of action of antidiuretic hormone. *Proc Natl Acad Sci USA* 71:2595, 1974.

223. RAJERISON R, MARCHETTI J, ROY C, BOCKAERT J, JARD S: The vasopressin-sensitive adenylate cyclase of the rat kidney. *J Biol Chem* 249:6390, 1974.

224. JARD S, ROY C, BARTH T, RAJERISON R, BOCKAERT J: Antidiuretic hormone-sensitive kidney adenylate cyclase. *Adv Cyclic Nucleotide Res* 5:31, 1975.

225. EGGENA P, SCHWARTZ IL, WALTER R: Threshold and receptor reserve in the action of neurohypophyseal peptides. A study of synergists and antagonists in the hydroosmotic response on the toad urinary bladder. *J Gen Physiol* 56:250, 1970.

226. SEAMON KB, DALY JW: Forskolin, cyclic AMP and cellular physiology. *Trends Pharmacol Sci* 4:120, 1983.

227. CULPEPPER RM, ANDREOLI TE: PGE₂, forskolin and cholera toxin interactions in modulating NaCl transport in mouse mTALH. *Am J Physiol* 247:F784, 1984.

228. NADLER SP, HEBERT SC, BRENNER BM: PGE₂, forskolin and cholera toxin interaction in rabbit cortical collecting tubule. *Am J Physiol* 250:F127, 1986.

229. CULPEPPER RM, SMITH W, CODINA J, BIRNBAUMER L: Guanine nucleotide regulatory proteins in pars recta and thick ascending limb of rabbit and mouse kidney. *Kidney Int* 29:33A, 1986.

230. RIBEIRO CP, RIBEIRO-NETO F, FIELD JB, SUKI WN: Prevention of α2-adrenergic inhibition on ADH action by pertussis toxin in rabbit CCT. *Am J Physiol* 253:C105, 1987.

231. DOUSA TP, VALTIN H: Cellular actions of vasopressin in the mammalian kidney. *Kidney Int* 10:46, 1976.

232. DOUSA TP, BARNES LD, KIM JK: The role of cyclic AMP-dependent protein phosphorylations and microtubules in the cellular action of vasopressin in mammalian kidney, in Moses AM, Share L (eds): *Neuropophysis.* Basel, Karger, 1977, p 220.

233. KACHADORIAN WA, WADE JB, UITERWYK CC, DiSCALA VA: Membrane structural and functional responses to vasopressin in toad urinary bladder. *J Membr Biol* 30:381, 1977.

234. PEARL M, TAYLOR A: Actin filaments and vasopressin-stimulated water flow in toad urinary bladder. *Am J Physiol* 245:C28, 1983.

235. KACHADORIAN WA, ELLIS SJ, MULLER J: Possible roles for microtubules and microfilaments in ADH action on toad urinary bladder. *Am J Physiol* 236:F14, 1979.

236. KROTHAPALLI RK, DUFFY WB, SENEKJIAN HO, SUKI WN: Modulation of the hydro-osmotic effect of vasopressin on the rabbit cortical collecting tubule by adrenergic agents. *J Clin Invest* 72:287, 1983.

237. HANDLER JS: Vasopressin-prostaglandin interaction in the regulation of epithelial cell permeability to water. *Kidney Int* 19:831, 1981.

238. BECK TR, DUNN MJ: The relationship of antidiuretic hormone and renal prostaglandins. *Miner Electrolyte Metab* 6:46, 1981.

239. HANDLER JS: Vasopressin-prostaglandin interactions in the regulation of epithelial cell permeability to water. *Kidney Int* 19:931, 1981.

240. ORLOFF J, HANDLER JS, BERGSTROM S: Effect of prostaglandin (PGE) on the permeability response of the toad bladder to vasopressin, theophylline and adenosine 3′-5′-monophosphate. *Nature* 205:397, 1965.

241. GRANTHAM JJ, ORLOFF J: Effect of prostaglandin E₁ on the permeability response of the isolated collecting tubule to vasopressin, adenosine 3′-5′-monophosphate and theophylline. *J Clin Invest* 47:1154, 1968.

242. HIGASHIHARA E, STOKES JB, KOKKO JP, CAMPBELL WB, DuBOSE TD: Cortical and papillary micropuncture examination of chloride transport in segments of the rat kidney during inhibition of prostaglandin production. *J Clin Invest* 64:1277, 1979.

243. STOKES JB: Effect of prostaglandin E₂ on chloride transport across the rabbit thick ascending limb of Henle. *J Clin Invest* 64:495, 1979.

244. CULPEPPER RM, ANDREOLI TE: Interaction among prostaglandin E₂, antidiuretic hormone and cyclic adenosine monophosphate in modulating Cl⁻ absorption in single mouse medullary thick ascending limbs of Henle. *J Clin Invest* 71:1588, 1983.

245. TORIKAI S, KUROKAWA K: Effect of PGE₂ on vasopressin dependent cell cAMP in isolated single segments. *Am J Physiol* 245:F58, 1983.

246. CRAVEN PA, DeRUBERTIS FR: Effects of vasopressin and urea on Ca²⁺-calmodulin dependent renal prostaglandin E. *Am J Physiol* 241:F649, 1981.

247. WUTHRICH RP, LOUP R, FAVRE L, VALLOLTON MB: Dynamic response of PG synthesis to peptide hormones and osmolality in renal tubular cells. *Am J Physiol* 250:F790, 1986.

248. SCHLONDORFF D, SATRIANO JA, SCHWARTZ GJ: Synthesis of prostaglandin E₂ in different segments of isolated collecting tubules from adult and neonatal rabbits. *Am J Physiol* 248:F134, 1985.

249. SATO M, DUNN MJ: Interaction of vasopressin, prostaglandins and cAMP in rat papillary collecting tubule cells in culture. *Am J Physiol* 247:F423, 1984.

250. PORTILLA D, SHAYMAN JA, MORRISON AR: Vasopressin does not hydrolyze polyphosphoinositides in rabbit papillary collecting tubule cells. *Biochim Biophys Acta* 928:305, 1987.

251. SCHLONDORFF D, LEVINE SD: Inhibition of vasopressin-stimulated water flow in toad bladder by phorbol myristate acetate, dioctanoylglycerol and RHC-80267. *J Clin Invest* 76:1071, 1985.

252. CASAVOLA V, IACOVELLI L, SVELTO M: Phorbol ester effect on the hydroosmotic response to vasopressin in frog skin. *Pflugers Arch* 408:318, 1987.

253. ANDO Y, JACOBSON MR, BREYER MD: Phorbol myristate acetate, dioctanoylglycerol and phosphatidic acid inhibit the hydroosmotic effect of vasopressin on rabbit cortical collecting tubule. *J Clin Invest* 80:590, 1987.

254. HEBERT SC, CULPEPPER RM, ANDREOLI TE: NaCl transport in mouse medullary thick ascending limbs. III. Modulation of the ADH effect by peritubular osmolality. *Am J Physiol* 241:F443, 1981.

255. MOLONY DA, ANDREOLI TE: Diluting power of isolated thick ascending limbs of Henle. I. Peritubular hypertonicity blocks basolateral Cl⁻ channels. *Am J Physiol.* In press, 1988.

256. REEVES WB, DUDLEY MA, MEHTA P, ANDREOLI TE: Diluting power of isolated thick ascending limbs of Henle. II. Osmotic gradients modulate bumetanide-sensitive ²²Na⁺ influx in medullary vesicles. *Am J Physiol.* In press, 1988.

257. BERLINER RW, DAVIDSON DG: Production of hypertonic urine in the absence of pituitary antidiuretic hormone. *J Clin Invest* 36:1416, 1957.

258. WESSON LG JR, ANSLOW WP JR, RAISZ LG, BOLOMEY AA, LADD M: Effect of sustained expansion of extracellular fluid volume upon filtration rate, renal plasma flow and electrolyte and water excretion in the dog. *Am J Physiol* 162:677, 1950.

259. MCCANCE RA: The excretion of urea, salt and water during periods of hydropenia in man. *J Physiol* 104:196, 1945.

260. KLEEMAN CR, EPSTEIN FH, WHITE C: The effect of variations in solute excretion and glomerular filtration on water diuresis. *J Clin Invest* 35:749, 1956.

261. van EPS LWS, PINEDO-VEELS C, De VRIES GH, De KONING J: Nature of concentrating defect in sickle-cell nephropathy. *Lancet* 1:450, 1970.

262. deWARDENER HE, HERXHEIMER A: The effect of a high water intake on the kidney's ability to concentrate the urine in man. *J Physiol* 139:42, 1957.

263. BENNETT CM: Urine concentration and dilution in hypokalemic and hypercalcemic dogs. *J Clin Invest* 49:1447, 1970.

264. EKNOYAN G, SUKI WN, MARTINEZ-MALDONADO M, ANHALT MA: Chronic hydronephrosis: Observations on the mechanism of the defect in urine concentration. *Proc Soc Exp Biol Med* 134:634, 1970.

265. VIRGO NS, MILLER, JR: Hereditary vasopressin-resistant diabetes insipidus in SWV mice. *Can J Physiol Pharmacol* 52:995, 1974.

266. DOUSA TP, VALTIN H: Cellular action of antidiuretic hormone in mice with inherited vasopressin-resistant urinary concentrating defects. *J Clin Invest* 54:753, 1974.

267. JACKSON BA, EDWARDS RM, VALTIN H, DOUSA TP: Cellular action of vasopressin in medullary tubules of mice with hereditary nephrogenic diabetes insipidus. *J Clin Invest* 66:110, 1980.

268. KUSANO E, YUSUFI ANK, MURAYAMA N, BRAUN-WERNESS J, DOUSA TP: Dynamics of nucleotides in distal nephron of mice with nephrogenic diabetes insipidus. *Am J Physiol* 250:F151, 1986.

269. FICHMAN MP, BROOKER G: Deficient renal cyclic adenosine 3'-5'-monophosphate production in nephrogenic diabetes insipidus. *J Clin Endocrinol Metab* 35:35, 1972.

270. BELL NH, CLARK CM JR, AVERY S, SINHA T, TRYGSTAD CW, ALLEN DO: Demonstration of a defect in the formation of adenosine 3',5'-monophosphate in vasopressin-resistant diabetes insipidus. *Pediatr Res* 8:223, 1974.

271. USBERTI M, DECHAUX M, GUILLOT M, SELIGMANN R, PAULOVITCH H, LOIRAT C, SACHS C, BROYER M: Renal prostaglandin E₂ in nephrogenic diabetes insipidus: Effects of inhibition of prostaglandin synthesis by indomethacin. *J Pediatr* 97:476, 1980.

272. OHZEKI T: Urinary adenosine 3',5'-monophosphate (cAMP) response to antidiuretic hormone in diabetes insipidus (DI): comparison between congenital nephrogenic DI type 1 and 2, and vasopressin-sensitive DI. *Acta Endocrinol* 108:485, 1985.

273. ZIMMERMAN D, GREEN OC: Nephrogenic diabetes insipidus—Type II: Defect distal to the adenylate cyclase step. *Pediatr Res* 9:381a, 1975.

274. HAYEK A, RAMIREZ J: Demeclocycline-induced diabetes insipidus. *JAMA* 229:676, 1974.

275. WILSON DM, PERRY HO, SAMS WM JR, DOUSA TP: Selective inhibition of human distal tubular function by demeclocycline. *Curr Ther Res* 15:734, 1973.

276. SINGER I, ROTENBERG D: Demeclocycline-induced nephrogenic diabetes insipidus. *Ann Intern Med* 79:679, 1973.

277. FELDMAN HA, SINGER I: Comparative effects of tetracyclines on water flow across toad urinary bladders. *J Pharmacol Exp Ther* 190:358, 1974.

278. DOUSA TP, WILSON DM: Effects of demethylchlortetracycline on cellular action of antidiuretic hormone in vitro. *Kidney Int* 5:279, 1974.

279. COUSINS MJ, MAZZE RI: Methoxyflurane nephrotoxicity. *JAMA* 225:1611, 1973.

280. COUSINS MJ, MAZZE RI, KOSEK JC, HITT BA, LOVE FV: The etiology of methoxyflurane nephrotoxicity. *J Pharmacol Exp Ther* 190:530, 1974.

281. FRASCINE JA, O'FLAHERTY J, OLMO C, RIVERA S: Effect of inorganic fluoride on the renal concentrating mechanism. Possible nephrotoxicity in man. *J Lab Clin Med* 79:192, 1972.

282. WALLIN JD, KAPLAN RA: Effect of sodium fluoride on concentrating and diluting ability in the rat. *Am J Physiol* 232:F335, 1977.

283. LEE RV, JAMPOL LM, BROWN WV: Nephrogenic diabetes insipidus and lithium intoxication—Complications of lithium carbonate therapy. *N Engl J Med* 284:93, 1971.

284. SINGER I, ROTENBERG D, PUSCHETT JB: Lithium-induced nephrogenic diabetes insipidus: in vivo and in vitro studies. *J Clin Invest* 51:1081, 1972.

285. FORREST JN JR, COHEN AD, TORETTI J, HIMMELHOCH JM, EPSTEIN FH: On the mechanism of lithium-induced diabetes insipidus in man and the rat. *J Clin Invest* 53:1115, 1974.

286. PADFIELD PL, PARK SJ, MORTON JJ, BRAIDWOOD AE: Plasma levels of antidiuretic hormone in patients receiving prolonged lithium therapy. *Br J Psychiatry* 130:144, 1977.

287. DOUSA TP: Interaction of lithium with vasopressin-sensitive cyclic AMP system of human renal medulla. *Endocrinology* 95:1359, 1974.

288. GEISLER A, WRAAE O, OLESEN OV: Adenyl cyclase activity in kidneys of rats with lithium-induced polyuria. *Acta Pharmacol Toxicol* 31:203, 1972.

289. JACKSON BA, EDWARDS EM, DOUSA TP: Lithium-induced polyuria: Effect of lithium on adenylate cyclase and adenosine 3',5'-monophosphate phosphodiesterase in medullary ascending limb of Henle's loop and in medullary collecting tubules. *Endocrinology* 107:1693, 1980.

290. COGAN E, ABRAMOW M: Inhibition of lithium of the hydroosmotic action of vasopressin in the isolated perfused collecting tubule of the rabbit. *J Clin Invest* 77:1507, 1986.

291. COGAN E, SVOBODA M, ABRAMOW M: Mechanisms of lithium-vasopressin interaction in rabbit cortical collecting tubule. *Am J Physiol* 252:F1080, 1987.

292. GALLA JN, FORREST JN, HECHT B, KASHGARIAN M, HAYSLETT JP: Effect of lithium on water and electrolyte metabolism. *Yale J Biol Med* 48:305, 1975.

293. HOCHMAN S, GUTMAN Y: Lithium: ADH antagonism and ADH independent action in rats with diabetes insipidus. *Eur J Pharmacol* 28:100, 1974.

294. CARONE FA, EPSTEIN FH: Nephrogenic diabetes insipidus caused by amyloid disease: Evidence in man of the role of the collecting ducts in concentrating urine. *Am J Med* 29:539, 1960.

295. DORHOUT-MEES EJ, DePLANQUE BA, HELDERS J, KOOIKER CJ: Renal amyloidosis presenting as water losing syndrome. *Nephron* 5:31, 1968.

296. KAHN M, MERRITT AD, WOHL MJ, ORLOFF J: Renal concentrating defect in Sjögren's syndrome. *Ann Intern Med* 56:883, 1962.

297. BLACHAR Y, ZADIK Z, SHEMESH M, KAPLAN BS, LEVIN S: The effect of inhibition of prostaglandin synthesis on free water and osmolar clearances in patients with hereditary nephrogenic diabetes insipidus. *Int J Pediatr Nephrol* 1:48, 1980.

298. LIBBER S, HARRISON H, SPECTOR D: Treatment of nephrogenic diabetes insipidus with prostaglandin synthesis inhibitors. *J Pediatr* 108:305, 1986.

299. CRAWFORD JD, KENNEDY GC: Chlorothiazide in diabetes insipidus. *Nature* 183:891, 1959.

300. ALON U, CHAN JC: Hydrochlorothiazide-amiloride in the treatment of congenital nephrogenic diabetes insipidus. *Am J Nephrol* 5:9, 1985.

301. BATTLE DC, von RIOTTE AB, GAVIRIA M, GRUPP M: Amelioration of polyuria by amiloride in patients receiving long-term lithium therapy. *N Engl J Med* 312:408, 1985.

302. MORRIS-JONES PH, HOUSTON IB, EVANS RC: Prognosis of the neurological complications of acute hypernatremia. *Lancet* 2:1385, 1967.

CHAPTER 79

PSEUDOHYPOPARATHYROIDISM

ALLEN M. SPIEGEL

1. Pseudohypoparathyroidism *is a term applied to a heterogeneous group of disorders whose common feature is resistance to parathyroid hormone.*

2. *Most patients with pseudohypoparathyroidism are hypocalcemic and hyperphosphatemic despite elevated concentrations of parathyroid hormone in plasma. Hypocalcemia and hyperphosphatemia are due to loss of the anticalciuric and phosphaturic actions of parathyroid hormone, and reduced formation of 1,25-dihydroxyvitamin D with resultant defective mobilization of calcium from bone and reduced gastrointestinal absorption of calcium.*

3. *Clinical features and location of the putative defect causing hormone resistance permit separation of pseudohypoparathyroidism into distinct subtypes.*

4. Pseudohypoparathyroidism type Ia *is associated with resistance to multiple hormones in addition to parathyroid hormone and with a constellation of physical abnormalities collectively termed* Albright osteodystrophy. *Relatives of patients with pseudohypoparathyroidism may show features of Albright osteodystrophy without overt hormone resistance, a condition termed* pseudopseudohypoparathyroidism. *The molecular defect causing hormone resistance in most, but not all, patients with pseudohypoparathyroidism Ia is a deficiency in a guanine nucleotide–binding protein (Gs) that couples hormone receptors to stimulation of adenylate cyclase. Patients with pseudohypoparathyroidism Ia may show clinical signs, or even present with, endocrinopathies other than hypoparathyroidism, presumably due to generalized hormone resistance. This defect appears to be inherited in autosomal dominant fashion in most families with pseudohypoparathyroidism Ia. Gs deficiency occurs in family members with either pseudohypoparathyroidism or pseudopseudohypoparathyroidism. This suggests that overt hormone resistance may be a polygenic trait, with the consequences of Gs deficiency conditioned by allelic variation at other loci coding for components of the cAMP cascade. A defect in some other general component of the receptor-Gs–adenylate cyclase complex is postulated in patients with the identical phenotype of pseudohypoparathyroidism Ia but normal Gs activity.*

5. *In* pseudohypoparathyroidism type Ib, *physical appearance is normal, and resistance is limited to parathyroid hormone. As in pseudohypoparathyroidism Ia, the defect is located proximal to cAMP formation, but unlike in pseudohypoparathyroidism Ia, the defect is likely to involve a specific signal transduction component such as the parathyroid hormone receptor. The disease may be both sporadic and familial, and in the latter case the mode of inheritance has not been defined.*

6. Pseudohypoparathyroidism type II *is rarely if ever familial. Resistance is limited to parathyroid hormone and is due to a defect distal to cAMP formation.*

HISTORICAL BACKGROUND

In 1942 Albright and colleagues[1] described three patients with hypocalcemia, hyperphosphatemia, and normal renal function,

characteristic findings in hypoparathyroidism. All three subjects showed reduced calcemic and phosphaturic responses (by comparison with other hypoparathyroid subjects) to injected bovine parathyroid extract. This led Albright to postulate that hypoparathyroidism in the three reported subjects was due to resistance to parathyroid hormone action rather than to parathyroid hormone deficiency and to term the disorder *pseudohypoparathyroidism.* Albright's formulation of the pathogenesis of the disorder in these subjects is notable as perhaps the first description of the concept of hormone resistance as a basis for reduced hormone action.

In the original report,[1] Albright noted certain abnormal physical features in the patients with pseudohypoparathyroidism. These included short stature, obesity, rounded face and short neck, and shortened metacarpals. No obvious connection between these features and the abnormality in calcium metabolism was apparent, nor was familial occurrence noted. In a subsequent report,[2] Albright and colleagues described a 29-year-old woman with physical features similar to those of the subjects with pseudohypoparathyroidism but with no evident abnormality in calcium metabolism. Albright considered this a distinct syndrome, which he termed *pseudopseudohypoparathyroidism.*

Albright's postulate of end-organ resistance to parathyroid hormone action as the basis for pseudohypoparathyroidism was confirmed by subsequent studies. Parathyroid hyperplasia was found on biopsy of untreated subjects with pseudohypoparathyroidism,[3] and biologically active parathyroid hormone was found in gland extracts.[4] Elevation in immunoreactive parathyroid hormone in plasma of untreated subjects with pseudohypoparathyroidism has been found in numerous studies. The locus of the defect in most patients with pseudohypoparathyroidism was defined by Chase, Melson, and Aurbach.[5] These authors showed in the normal subject that parathyroid hormone stimulates formation of the second messenger, cAMP, in bone and kidney. The latter action is reflected in urinary excretion of cAMP. Subjects with pseudohypoparathyroidism showed a markedly reduced rise in urinary cAMP excretion in response to infused bovine parathyroid hormone compared with normal subjects and subjects with other forms of hypoparathyroidism. Subsequently,[6] a 22-month-old child was described in whom resistance to parathyroid hormone was associated with a normal urinary cAMP response to parathyroid hormone. This, and other observations, emphasized the heterogeneity of pseudohypoparathyroidism. More recent efforts have been aimed at elucidating the biochemical and genetic basis for this heterogeneity. In one subtype of pseudohypoparathyroidism, deficient activity was found[7,8] of a guanine nucleotide–binding protein, Gs, that couples hormone receptors to stimulation of cAMP formation. This defect could explain resistance to parathyroid hormone and to other agents that act by stimulating production of cAMP in subjects with this form of pseudohypoparathyroidism.

CONTROL OF CALCIUM AND PHOSPHORUS METABOLISM BY PARATHYROID HORMONE AND VITAMIN D

A brief review of the actions of parathyroid hormone and vitamin D in regulating calcium and phosphorus metabolism is necessary before a discussion of the pathophysiology of pseudohypoparathyroidism. Together, parathyroid hormone and vitamin D control the flux of calcium and phosphate into and out of the kidney, the gastrointestinal tract, and bone. The concerted actions of these two hormones maintain the serum ionized calcium concentration within narrow limits and permit normal skeletal growth and remodeling.

Parathyroid Hormone Synthesis and Secretion

Parathyroid hormone is synthesized in the parathyroid glands as a 115-amino acid polypeptide, preproparathyroid hormone. The hydrophobic 25-amino acid *pre*, "leader," sequence, and the basic hexapeptide *pro* sequence are cleaved before secretion of the native amino acids 1–84 hormone.[9] The intact hormone is rapidly cleaved in the peripheral circulation into biologically inactive fragments. There is an inverse relationship between parathyroid hormone secretion and the extracellular fluid concentration of ionized calcium.[10] A decrease in the latter provokes secretion of parathyroid hormone, which, through direct actions on kidney and bone and indirect actions on the gastrointestinal tract, raises extracellular fluid calcium concentration (Fig. 79-1).

Parathyroid Hormone Actions on Kidney

Effect on Phosphate Clearance. Parathyroid hormone acts on sites in the proximal and probably also the distal nephron to increase phosphate clearance.[10] The phosphaturic action of parathyroid hormone counteracts the hormone-induced release of phosphate from bone into extracellular fluid. The net effect of the hormone in subjects with normal renal function is to lower serum phosphate concentration. Elevations in serum phosphate concentration depress serum calcium by reducing bone resorption and by decreasing synthesis of 1,25-dihydroxyvitamin D, the active metabolite of vitamin D. The phosphaturic action of parathyroid hormone thus serves indirectly to maintain normal serum calcium concentration.

Effect on Calcium Clearance. Parathyroid hormone enhances calcium reabsorption by the kidney through an action on sites beyond the proximal tubule.[10] Increased parathyroid hormone secretion releases calcium from bone into extracellular fluid, thereby increasing the filtered load of calcium, but for any filtered load, parathyroid hormone reduces net calcium excretion.

Increased Formation of 1,25-Dihydroxyvitamin D. Vitamin D (cholecalciferol) is formed by the action of ultraviolet light on skin or is ingested as the plant sterol, ergocalciferol. These precursor forms of the active hormone are hydroxylated in the 25 position in the liver to form 25-hydroxyvitamin D, the major circulating form. The active metabolite, 1,25-dihydroxyvitamin D, is formed by hydroxylation in the 1α position by a microsomal enzyme in the kidney. The 1-hydroxylation reaction is under the direct (or indirect, through lowering of the serum phosphate level) control of parathyroid hormone. By increasing formation of 1,25-dihydroxyvitamin D, parathyroid hormone acts indirectly on the gastrointestinal tract to increase calcium absorption. 1,25-dihydroxyvitamin D is also required for parathyroid hormone to release calcium from bone. Loss of parathyroid hormone action on the kidney impairs normal calcium homeostasis both through loss of the direct effects (phosphaturic and anticalciuric) of parathyroid hormone and through the indirect effects mediated by 1,25-dihydroxyvitamin D.

Parathyroid Hormone Actions on Bone. Parathyroid hormone has dual actions on bone. The hormone acutely mobilizes calcium from bone to the extracellular fluid. Osteocytes are the presumed target cells for the acute effect of parathyroid hormone, which serves to maintain normal serum calcium concentration.[10] Parathyroid hormone also stimulates bone resorption. Available evidence suggests that parathyroid hormone acts directly on osteoblasts to alter their shape and function.[11] There is no cogent evidence for a direct action of parathyroid hormone on osteoclasts.[12] Instead, parathyroid hormone may stimulate osteoclastic resorption indirectly by causing osteoblasts to release factors that activate osteoclasts.[11,12] Coupling of bone formation to bone resorption

Fig. 79-1 Control of calcium and phosphorus metabolism by parathyroid hormone (PTH). A fall in the concentration of extracellular fluid ionized calcium (ECF Ca^{2+}) provokes parathyroid hormone secretion from the parathyroid glands. The actions of parathyroid hormone (discussed in the text) on its principal targets, bone and kidney, lead to an increase in ECF Ca^{2+}.

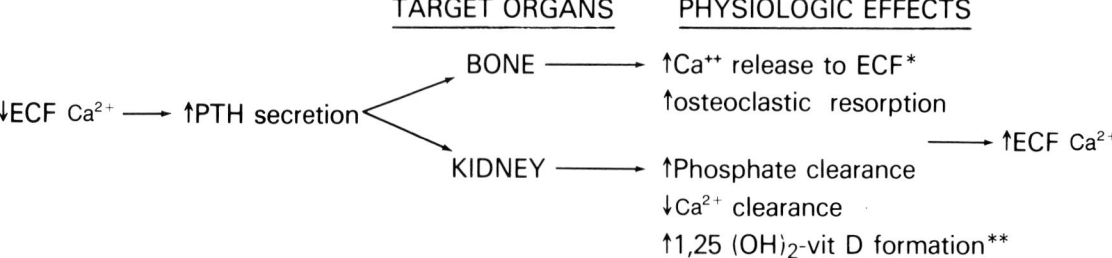

TARGET ORGANS   PHYSIOLOGIC EFFECTS

$\downarrow$ECF Ca^{2+} ⟶ $\uparrow$PTH secretion ⟨ BONE ⟶ $\uparrow$Ca^{++} release to ECF*
$\uparrow$osteoclastic resorption
⟶ $\uparrow$ECF Ca^{2+}
KIDNEY ⟶ $\uparrow$Phosphate clearance
$\downarrow$Ca^{2+} clearance
$\uparrow$1,25 (OH)$_2$-vit D formation**

* 1,25 (OH)$_2$-vit D has permissive effect

** 1,25 (OH)$_2$-vit D acts on intestine to increase Ca^{2+} absorption (possibly through release of paracrine factors) is reflected in increased bone formation that follows parathyroid hormone–stimulated resorption.[13] The long-term effects of excess parathyroid hormone action on bone are increased resorption (osteitis fibrosa cystica in the most extreme form) and a secondary increase in bone formation by osteoblasts reflected by increased serum alkaline phosphatase activity. The dual effects of parathyroid hormone on bone, the calcemic effect and the skeletal remodeling effect, can be dissociated. 1,25-Dihydroxyvitamin D is required for the normal calcemic response to parathyroid hormone but is not essential for the skeletal remodeling effect.[14] In states of parathyroid hormone excess and 1,25-dihydroxyvitamin D deficiency (e.g., chronic renal failure), osteitis fibrosa cystica and hypocalcemia may coexist.

MECHANISM OF PARATHYROID HORMONE ACTION

Understanding resistance to parathyroid hormone action requires an understanding of the mechanism of action of the hormone. Several steps in the pathway of parathyroid hormone action are now defined in considerable detail, but major gaps remain. Parathyroid hormone is assumed to act by binding to specific receptors on the surface of its target cells in bone and kidney.[10] Receptor activation triggers formation of intracellular second messengers.

Second Messengers of Parathyroid Hormone Action in Kidney and Bone

Parathyroid hormone stimulates formation of the second messenger, cAMP, in kidney and bone.[15] Whether cAMP is the exclusive, or even the most important, mediator of all parathyroid hormone actions in kidney and bone is unclear. Urinary cAMP excretion reflects parathyroid hormone action on the kidney.[5,15] Administration of parathyroid hormone increases urinary excretion of cAMP and increases the concentration of cAMP in plasma.[16] Both effects result from parathyroid hormone action on the kidney and are useful clinically as tests of renal responsiveness to parathyroid hormone.[5,16]

cAMP appears to mediate the phosphaturic action of parathyroid hormone,[17] and is probably the second messenger for parathyroid hormone action on the renal 25-hydroxycholecalciferol-1α-hydroxylase as well.[18] There is no convincing evidence that cAMP mediates the anticalciuric effect of parathyroid hormone.[19] In bone, because of the heterogeneity of cell types and the likelihood of important cell-cell interactions via local mediators,[11] identification of second messengers for parathyroid hormone actions is particularly difficult. Parathyroid hormone binds to and stimulates cAMP formation in osteoblasts.[11] It is not clear, however, that cAMP mediates parathyroid hormone–stimulated bone resorption.[20] cAMP itself has complex effects on bone resorption in organ culture studies.[20] Parathyroid hormone may also utilize a signal transduction pathway involving changes in cytosolic calcium concentration in bone cells.[21] Many polypeptide hormones, in addition to stimulating cAMP formation, stimulate breakdown of phosphoinositides.[22] The latter leads to release of two second messengers, diacylglycerol, which activates protein kinase C, and inositol trisphosphate, which increases cytosolic calcium.[23]

The precise relationship between the cAMP and phosphoinositide signal transduction pathways and the actions of parathyroid hormone on skeletal calcium mobilization and remodeling remains to be elucidated.

Components of Signal Transduction Pathway for Parathyroid Hormone

The first step in the action of parathyroid hormone, as for many other polypeptide hormones and amine neurotransmitters, is binding to specific cell surface receptors. Activated receptors interact with one or more members of a family of guanine nucleotide–binding proteins to facilitate exchange of GDP for GTP.[24,25] GTP-bound guanine nucleotide–binding proteins in turn interact with specific effectors, often enzymes that catalyze formation of second messengers. The latter mediate the effects of first messengers on cell function, generally by causing specific protein kinases to phosphorylate key proteins within the cell.

As discussed above, parathyroid hormone action is mediated by cAMP and possibly also by products of phosphoinositide breakdown. Since cAMP mediates some, if not all, of the actions of parathyroid hormone, I discuss the components of the cAMP pathway in greater detail. Adenylate cyclase catalyzes the formation of cAMP from ATP and Mg^{2+} and is under dual regulation by distinct guanine nucleotide–binding proteins, Gs and Gi.[24] Gs couples receptors for many agonists, including parathyroid hormone, that stimulate cAMP formation, and Gi couples receptors for agonists that inhibit cAMP formation to adenylate cyclase (Fig. 79-2). cAMP is degraded by cyclic nucleotide phosphodiesterase activity. The concentration of cAMP within the cell controls the activity of a specific cAMP-dependent protein kinase that in turn regulates the function of key substrates through phosphorylation.

The components of the cAMP cascade may be divided into those unique to a given hormone and cell and those common to all cells and hormones. Receptors and substrates for cAMP-dependent protein kinase are in the first category. Gs, adenylate cyclase, cAMP phosphodiesterase, and cAMP-dependent protein kinase are in the latter category. Specificity in hormone action resides in the first (receptor binding) and last (cAMP-dependent phosphorylation of specific cellular substrates) steps of the cAMP cascade.[26]

Structure of Components of the cAMP Transduction Pathway

Receptors. The structures of several receptors coupled to guanine nucleotide–binding proteins have been defined, but as yet not that of the parathyroid hormone receptor. The β-adrenergic receptor, which like the parathyroid hormone receptor couples to Gs, and the muscarinic cholinergic receptor and rhodopsin, which couple to other guanine nucleotide–binding proteins, share certain structural features.[27] Each receptor comprises a single polypeptide chain with two asparagine-linked glycosylation sites near the amino terminal. Hydrophobicity plots suggest that the receptor protein has seven distinct membrane-spanning domains with three loops and the amino terminal on the extracellular surface, and three loops and the carboxy terminal on the cytoplasmic side of the plasma membrane. Since the parathyroid hormone receptor

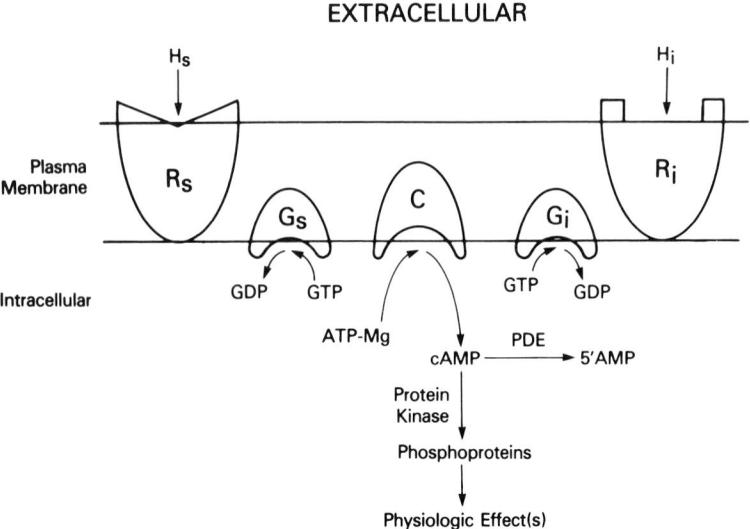

Fig. 79-2 Schematic outline of the signal transduction system using cAMP as second messenger. Hs and Hi denote stimulatory and inhibitory agonists, respectively; Rs and Ri, stimulatory and inhibitory receptors; Gs and Gi, the stimulatory and inhibitory guanine nucleotide–binding proteins. C denotes the catalytic unit of adenylate cyclase, and PDE refers to phosphodiesterase. Details of the interactions between these components are discussed in the text. (From Spiegel et al.[26] Used by permission of the New England Journal of Medicine.)

interacts with Gs,[28] it is likely that the overall structure of the parathyroid hormone receptor will be similar to that of other receptors coupled to guanine nucleotide–binding proteins, and in particular to that of the β-adrenergic receptor.

Heterogeneity of parathyroid hormone receptors is possible. A parathyroid hormone receptor capable of coupling to the phosphoinositide breakdown pathway could differ from the receptor that couples to Gs and the cAMP pathway. Receptor heterogeneity occurs for glucagon, vasopressin, and other polypeptide hormones that modulate both signal transduction pathways.[22] Distinct forms of receptor could also occur in bone and kidney. Photoaffinity labeling of parathyroid hormone receptors in bone- and kidney-derived cells identifies a single protein with identical molecular size (70 kDa) in bone and kidney.[29] Nonetheless, differences in the binding and activity[30,31] of certain analogues of parathyroid hormone in kidney and bone suggest that renal and skeletal parathyroid hormone receptors differ. The 3–34 analogue of parathyroid hormone is an antagonist of parathyroid hormone–stimulated cAMP formation in the kidney but shows agonist activity in bone in vitro[30] and when administered in vivo.[32] Precise definition of the structure of the parathyroid hormone receptor and the extent, if any, of heterogeneity, awaits receptor purification and cloning of cDNAs.

Gs. Gs couples receptors for the many agents that stimulate cAMP formation, including parathyroid hormone, to adenylate cyclase.[24,25] Like other guanine nucleotide–binding proteins, Gs consists of three subunits, α, β, and γ, each the product of a separate gene. The α subunit binds guanine nucleotides with high affinity, and shows intrinsic GTPase activity that serves to terminate Gs activation. Activation of Gs by GTP binding is dependent on interaction with agonist-bound receptor. Interaction of Gs with receptor confers upon the receptor a higher affinity for agonist binding. The β and γ subunits, which behave as a tightly bound complex under native conditions, facilitate Gs interaction with receptors and dissociate from the α subunit upon Gs activation. The activated Gs-α subunit alone can bind to and activate adenylate cyclase. The β subunit of Gs may be identical to that of Gi and other guanine nucleotide–binding proteins[24,25]; the γ subunit has not yet been fully characterized.

Gs is ubiquitously distributed. The stoichiometry between Gs and the other components of the receptor–adenylate cy-

clase complex has not been defined. In several tissues, Gs is about one-tenth as abundant as Gi. The α subunit of Gs is a substrate for ADP-ribosylation by cholera toxin. This covalent modification has profound effects on Gs function. By lowering the activity of the "turn-off" GTPase reaction, cholera toxin activates Gs and provokes constitutively increased cAMP formation. With radioactive NAD as cofactor, the cholera toxin–catalyzed reaction can also be used to identify and quantitate Gs-α in cell membranes. At least two forms of Gs-α (approximate sizes 45 and 52 kDa) have been identified in most cells by this method.

cDNAs for Gs-α from several species, including human,[33] have been cloned. The amino acid and nucleotide sequences show extremely high (>94 percent) conservation. Multiple forms of Gs-α mRNA, corresponding to the multiple forms of Gs-α protein, have been identified.[33] mRNA heterogeneity is thought to arise via alternative splicing of a single gene.[33] Definition of the number, structure, and chromosomal localization of Gs-α gene(s) in human and other species is not yet available.

Adenylate Cyclase. The purified enzyme is an approximately 150-kDa glycoprotein.[34] The Gs-stimulated form of the enzyme is similar if not identical in all mammalian cells. A calmodulin-sensitive adenylate cyclase is found in brain, but detailed comparisons of its structure with that of the Gs-sensitive enzyme have not yet been done.

cAMP-Phosphodiesterase. Multiple forms of cyclic nucleotide phosphodiesterase, differing in substrate specificity and affinity, are found in different tissues, and even within the same cell.[35] Amino acid sequencing and sequencing of the cDNA clones identify conserved domains among the different forms of phosphodiesterase, but differences between at least two of the forms make it likely that these are products of separate genes. The number and identity of forms responsible for physiological regulation of intracellular cAMP concentration have not been unequivocally established.

cAMP-Dependent Protein Kinase and Kinase Substrates. cAMP-dependent protein kinase is a tetramer, consisting of two regulatory (cAMP-binding) and two catalytic subunits. Binding of cAMP promotes regulatory subunit dissociation and activation of catalytic subunits. At least two forms of regulatory subunits, differing in tissue distribution, have been identified, and recent evidence[36] suggests that there are two closely related forms of catalytic subunit. In very few cases have specific substrates for cAMP-dependent protein kinase been identified and functionally characterized. Parathyroid hormone can be shown to modulate cAMP-dependent protein kinase activity in its target organs,[37] but the structure and function of substrates for phosphorylation in kidney and bone cells have not been elucidated.

PATHOPHYSIOLOGY OF PSEUDOHYPOPARATHYROIDISM

As originally proposed by Albright,[1] defective target organ response to parathyroid hormone should lead to the same consequences, hypocalcemia and hyperphosphatemia, as deficiency of the hormone (Fig. 79-1). In theory, resistance could involve either of the target organs of the hormone (kidney and bone) or both. Renal resistance to parathyroid hormone would cause loss of the phosphaturic response and lead to hyperphosphatemia. The latter and/or primary resistance to parathyroid hormone would lead to diminished renal formation of 1,25-dihydroxyvitamin D. 1,25-Dihydroxyvitamin D deficiency by reducing gastrointestinal absorption of calcium also contributes to hypocalcemia. Loss of the anticalciuric effect of parathyroid hormone further accentuates the tendency to hypocalcemia. Since the skeletal calcium-mobilizing effect of parathyroid hormone is dependent upon 1,25-dihydroxyvitamin D,[14] a blunted calcemic response to parathyroid hormone could be caused by renal resistance to parathyroid hormone with resultant reduction in 1,25-dihydroxyvitamin D formation, without invoking primary skeletal resistance to parathyroid hormone. Primary skeletal resistance to parathyroid hormone should cause loss of both the calcemic and bone remodeling responses to the hormone.

Resistance to parathyroid hormone action could in theory be due to defects at any of the multiple steps in the pathway of hormone action. If parathyroid hormone actions are mediated through second messenger pathways other than, or in addition to, stimulation of cAMP formation (Fig. 79-2), selective lesions causing incomplete forms of parathyroid hormone resistance are possible. Heterogeneity of parathyroid hormone receptors, e.g., between kidney and bone, could provide another theoretical basis for selectivity in target organ resistance.

Within the cAMP pathway (Fig. 79-2), certain lesions (e.g., specific parathyroid hormone receptor antagonists, abnormal receptor, abnormal substrate(s) for cAMP-dependent protein kinase) would be expected to cause isolated resistance to parathyroid hormone. In contrast, defects in Gs, adenylate cyclase, cAMP phosphodiesterase, or cAMP-dependent protein kinase could cause generalized resistance to agonists acting through the cAMP pathway.[26] Genetic defects in several components of the cAMP transduction pathway have been identified in eukaryotic cells. Discrete mutations in the α subunit of Gs in mouse S49 lymphoma cells can lead to partial or total deficiency of Gs activity, to receptor uncoupling, or to uncoupling from adenylate cyclase.[38] Mutations in cAMP phosphodiesterase causing excessive activity in S49 cells[39] or deficient activity in *Drosophila*[40] have also been described. Mutants deficient in adenylate cyclase activity or showing constitutive activation of cAMP-dependent protein kinase due to a regulatory subunit defect have been described in yeast,[41] whereas a catalytic subunit mutation abolishes kinase activity in S49 cells.[38] Each of these mutations causes generalized abnormalities in cellular response to extracellular signals.

Available evidence suggests that defects at different sites in the parathyroid hormone response pathway are responsible for distinct forms of pseudohypoparathyroidism. The majority of patients with pseudohypoparathyroidism tested show a markedly lower increase in urinary cAMP excretion in response to parathyroid hormone infusion than do normal controls or patients with parathyroid hormone–deficient forms of hypoparathyroidism (Fig. 79-3). These data indicate that a defect (or defects) proximal to cAMP generation on the pathway is responsible for the majority of cases of pseudohypoparathyroidism. Certain patients with pseudohypoparathyroidism[6] show a normal rise in urinary cAMP excretion in response to parathyroid hormone. Their defect is presumptively located distal to cAMP generation.

In the sections that follow, pseudohypoparathyroidism is tentatively classified according to the presumed locus of the defect causing parathyroid hormone resistance. Pseudohypoparathyroidism is divided into type I (defect proximal to cAMP production) and type II (defect distal to cAMP generation). Pseudohypoparathyroidism type I may be further subdivided into Ia (generalized hormone resistance due to a defect in a common component of the receptor-cyclase complex, such

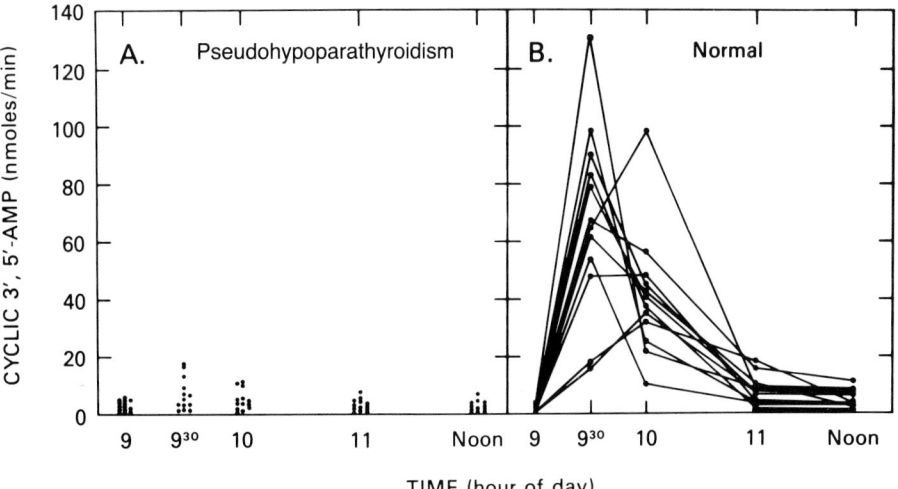

Fig. 79-3 Deficient urinary cAMP excretion in response to parathyroid hormone infusion in pseudohypoparathyroidism. Two hundred USP units of purified bovine parathyroid hormone were infused intravenously between 9:00 and 9:15 A.M. Urine was collected hourly (one-half-hourly immediately after infusion) before and after infusion for measurement of cAMP. The individual responses in a group of 13 subjects with pseudohypoparathyroidism and a group of normal controls is shown. (*From Chase et al.[5] Used by permission of the Journal of Clinical Investigation.*)

as Gs) and Ib (resistance limited to parathyroid hormone). *Pseudopseudohypoparathyroidism* is the term applied to individuals who are first-degree relatives of subjects with pseudohypoparathyroidism type Ia and show Gs deficiency, but are not overtly resistant to hormones.

Pseudohypoparathyroidism Type Ia

This is a familial form of pseudohypoparathyroidism characterized by generalized resistance to agents that stimulate adenylate cyclase and by the phenotypic features of Albright osteodystrophy. Patients with pseudohypoparathyroidism Ia show a blunted rise in urinary cAMP excretion in response to parathyroid hormone.[5,42] This implicates a defect in the receptor–guanine nucleotide binding protein–adenylate cyclase complex. Clinical observations compatible with resistance to hormones other than parathyroid hormone suggested the possibility of a defect in a general (e.g., Gs) rather than a specific (e.g., parathyroid hormone receptor) component of the complex.[26] Thus, primary hypothyroidism, particularly a subtle form detectable by thyrotropin-releasing factor stimulation of thyrotropin, is extremely common *in this form* of pseudohypoparathyroidism.[43] Primary hypothyroidism in these patients is not associated with thyroid enlargement, nor are thyroid antibodies detectable.[43] These results could be explained by primary thyroid resistance to thyrotropin. Similarly, a patient with pseudohypoparathyroidism and phenotypic features of Albright osteodystrophy was reported to show resistance to gonadotropins and to glucagon.[44]

Renal tissue obtained at autopsy from a woman with a familial form of pseudohypoparathyroidism associated with Albright osteodystrophy showed qualitatively normal stimulation of adenylate cyclase activity by parathyroid hormone.[45] Studies of renal biopsy material from a similar patient confirmed that the parathyroid hormone receptor and adenylate cyclase

were qualitatively normal, but revealed a subtle abnormality compatible with a defect in Gs.[46] Since Gs is ubiquitously distributed,[24,25] the hypothesis that Gs deficiency causes generalized hormone resistance in certain patients with pseudohypoparathyroidism could be tested by assays of accessible tissues rather than of relatively inaccessible parathyroid hormone target organs, bone and kidney.

Two groups,[7,8] using a functional assay based on stimulation of adenylate cyclase activity by Gs in membrane extracts and an assay based on cholera toxin–catalyzed incorporation of radioactive ADP-ribose into Gs-α, measured Gs in membranes from patients with pseudohypoparathyroidism and normal controls. An approximately 50 percent reduction in Gs activity was found in red cell membranes from almost all patients with pseudohypoparathyroidism and Albright osteodystrophy (Fig. 79-4), and normal activity was seen in membranes from patients with pseudohypoparathyroidism lacking the physical features of Albright osteodystrophy.[7,8] Platelet,[47] fibroblast,[48,49] and lymphoblast[50] membranes from subjects with pseudohypoparathyroidism and Albright osteodystrophy are also deficient in Gs activity. Renal membranes from the patient with pseudohypoparathyroidism that showed a subtle defect in adenylate cyclase stimulation[46] were also found to contain about half the Gs activity of renal membranes taken from three normal controls.[51]

Reduced Gs activity in membranes from patients with pseudohypoparathyroidism, in particular those showing phenotypic features of Albright osteodystrophy, has been confirmed in studies of patients in Japan[52] and Europe.[53] Gi, the G protein associated with inhibition of adenylate cyclase (Fig. 79-2), is a gene product distinct from Gs[25] and a substrate for ADP-ribosylation by pertussis toxin. Two studies, using cholera and pertussis toxin–catalyzed ADP-ribosylation, indicate that Gs is deficient in red cell membranes from patients with pseudohypoparathyroidism and Albright osteodystrophy but that Gi concentration is normal.[54,55] Deficient Gs activity is also re-

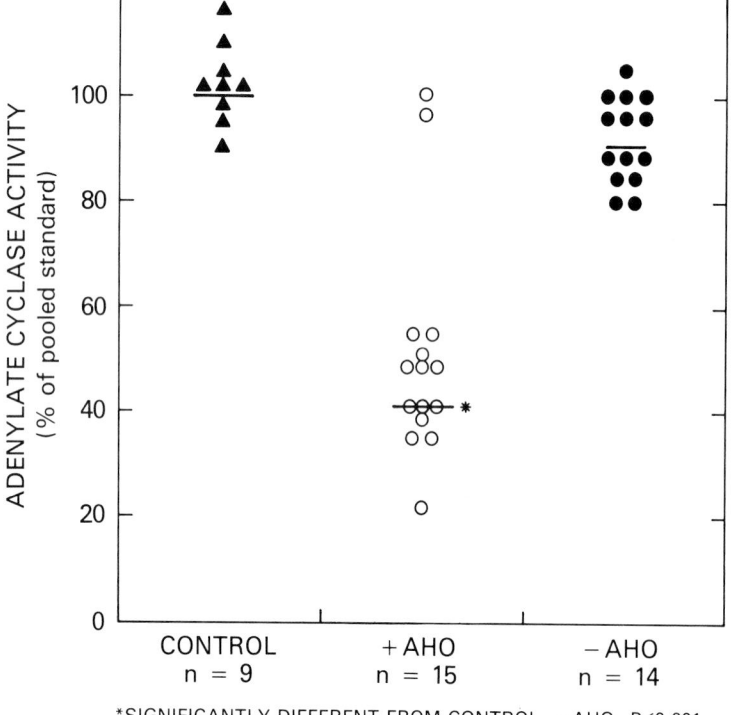

Fig. 79-4 Gs activity in erythrocyte membranes of control subjects and subjects with pseudohypoparathyroidism with (+AHO) or without (−AHO) the phenotypic features of Albright osteodystrophy. Membrane extracts to be assayed for Gs activity were added to a preparation of avian erythrocyte membranes containing the catalytic unit of adenylate cyclase. Resultant adenylate cyclase activity is a function of Gs activity in the added extract of human erythrocyte membranes. Activity is expressed as percent of the activity (defined as 100 percent) of a pooled membrane standard from normal subjects. *(From Levine et al.[59] Used by permission of the American Journal of Medicine.)*

flected in reduced formation of the high affinity ternary complex between agonist, receptor, and Gs in membranes from patients with pseudohypoparathyroidism Ia.[56]

Deficient Gs activity in membranes from patients with pseudohypoparathyroidism Ia could be due to reduced synthesis of Gs protein or to synthesis of a defective form of one of the subunits of Gs. Blot hybridization analysis of RNA from cultured skin fibroblasts shows a significant reduction (to about 25 percent of normal) in steady state content of Gs-α mRNA in patients with pseudohypoparathyroidism Ia (Fig. 79-5).[57] No abnormality in mRNA size was observed; also, S-1 nuclease analysis showed that all forms of Gs-α mRNA (see above) are proportionately reduced in patients with pseudohypoparathyroidism Ia.[57] Preliminary data from genomic blots show no gross deletions or rearrangements of the Gs-α gene in affected subjects. The data are compatible with a subtle lesion (e.g., point mutation in promoter region) in the Gs-α gene that reduces transcription and thereby synthesis of the protein. Further molecular genetic studies are needed to define the specific lesion(s) in pseudohypoparathyroidism Ia.

Deficient Gs activity might be expected to reduce adenylate cyclase responsiveness to stimulation by a wide variety of agonists. Indeed, the S49 mouse lymphoma mutant, CYC⁻, which is totally deficient in Gs activity[38] and in Gs-α mRNA,[33] fails to respond to prostaglandins and β-adrenergic agonists,

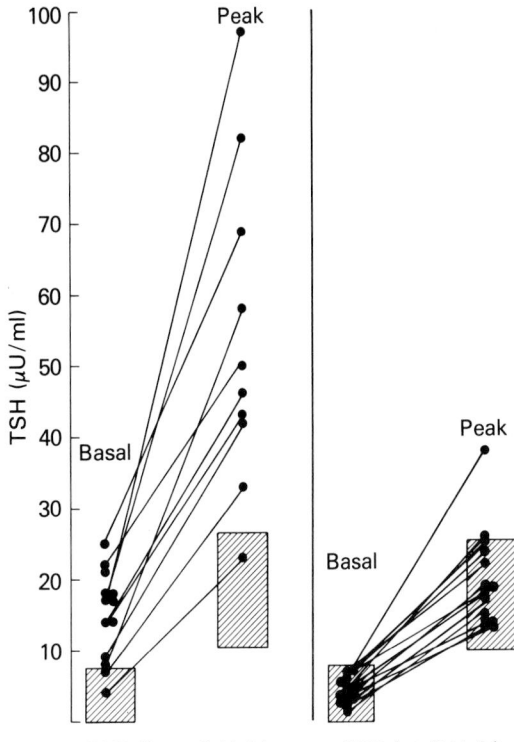

Fig. 79-6 Basal and peak serum thyrotropin (TSH) concentrations following intravenous administration of 500 μg thyrotropin releasing factor (TRF) to subjects with pseudohypoparathyroidism (PHP). The normal range for basal and peak TSH is shown in the hatched boxes. Most subjects with deficient Gs activity (low G unit) show hyperresponsiveness to TRF, indicative of primary hypothyroidism. Subjects with pseudohypoparthyroidism and normal Gs activity (with one exception) show normal responses. (*From Levine et al.[59] Used by permission of the American Journal of Medicine.*)

Fig. 79-5 Reduced expression of mRNA for the α subunit of Gs in subjects with pseudohypoparathyroidism type Ia: 10 μg of total RNA from the cultured skin fibroblasts of three normal subjects (N8, N9, N3) and from three unrelated subjects with pseudohypoparathyroidism type Ia (P1, P4, P5) was size-fractionated by formaldehyde–agarose gel electrophoresis and blotted onto nitrocellulose. Blots were probed with a Gs-α cDNA probe. After autoradiography, the probe was stripped and the blot was reprobed with a β-actin cDNA probe. (*From Carter et al.[57]*)

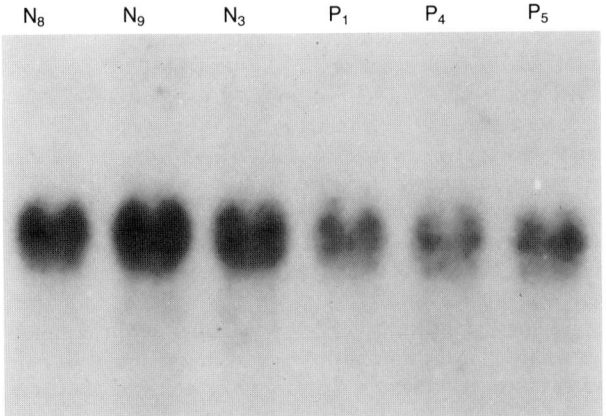

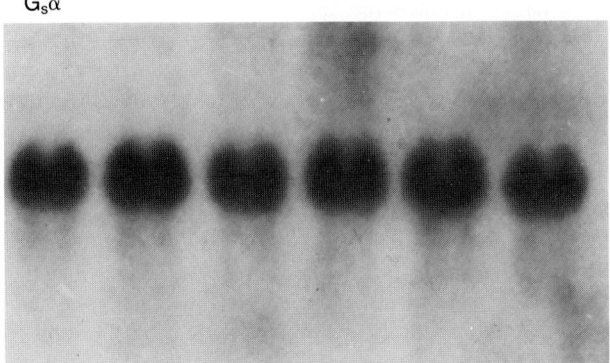

potent stimulators of adenylate cyclase in wild type cells. An S49 cell mutant with partial deficiency of Gs shows reduced adenylate cyclase stimulation by agonists.[38] Fibroblasts and platelets from patients with pseudohypoparathyroidism Ia have shown reduction in agonist-stimulated cAMP formation in some[48,58] but not all studies.[47,49]

Impaired adenylate cyclase stimulation due to Gs deficiency should lead to generalized resistance to agents acting via cAMP. Clinical studies of patients with pseudohypoparathyroidism Ia provide evidence for resistance to hormones other than parathyroid hormone. Primary thyroid resistance to thyrotropin appears to be extremely common, if not universal, in patients with pseudohypoparathyroidism Ia (Fig. 79-6).[43,59] Defective adenylate cyclase stimulation by GTP and thyrotropin in thyroid membranes obtained from a patient with pseudohypoparathyroidism Ia provides direct evidence for thyroid resistance to thyrotropin, presumably secondary to Gs deficiency, in this disease.[60] Gonadotropin,[44,59,61] glucagon,[44,59,62] and isoproterenol[63] resistance have also been documented in patients with pseudohypoparathyroidism Ia, particularly when proximal responses such as plasma cAMP concentration are measured. Distal responses to hormones, e.g., glycemic response to glucagon,[59,62] free fatty acid response to isoproterenol,[64] and antidiuretic response to arginine vasopressin,[65] however, are often normal in patients with pseudohypoparathyroidism Ia.

The basis for variability in clinical expression of hormone

resistance in pseudohypoparathyroidism Ia is unclear. Clinically overt hypoparathyroidism, hypothyroidism, and hypogonadism are common but not universal. Olfactory dysfunction is evident upon objective testing in patients with pseudohypoparathyroidism Ia but not pseudohypoparathyroidism Ib (normal Gs). This is consistent with evidence for transduction of odorant stimuli by Gs and adenylate cyclase.[66] One may speculate that the degree of clinically evident hormone resistance is a function of tissue- and hormone-specific variations in the components of the cAMP signal transduction pathway. Differences in the absolute concentrations of cAMP needed to achieve physiological responses to agonists could also influence the impact of Gs deficiency. Renal resistance to parathyroid hormone might be especially likely to cause clinically evident disease, since it simultaneously compromises two important calcium homeostatic factors, parathyroid hormone and 1,25-dihydroxyvitamin D.[67]

The phenotypic features of Albright osteodystrophy (Fig. 79-7) are an important component of pseudohypoparathyroidism Ia, but their underlying basis is no more evident today than when Albright first described them. One possibility is that Gs deficiency, perhaps through limitation in cAMP formation, is the proximate cause of Albright osteodystrophy. This is a plausible, but unproven, mechanism for the obesity and mental retardation often seen in patients with pseudohypoparathyroidism Ia, since lipolytic factors act by stimulating cAMP formation, and abnormalities in cAMP metabolism are associated with learning defects in invertebrate model systems.[68] Short stature and metacarpal and metatarsal shorten-

Fig. 79-7 Mother (*left*) and daughter with pseudohypoparathyroidism type Ia. Several features of Albright osteodystrophy are evident. These include obesity, short stature, round face, and short neck. Short fourth and fifth fingers (particularly on the right hands of both subjects), and short fourth toes on the left feet of both subjects are due to short metacarpal and metatarsal bones, respectively.

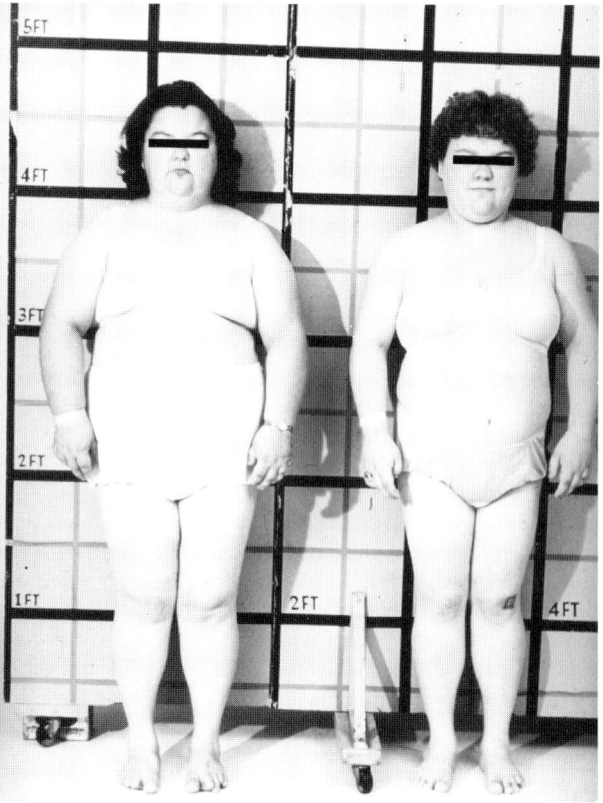

ing are typical of patients with pseudohypoparathyroidism Ia and may be due to premature skeletal maturation and closure of epiphyses.[69] The relationship between these features, as well as the soft tissue ossification of Albright osteodystrophy, and Gs deficiency is unclear. Limited data suggest normal growth hormone secretion in pseudohypoparathyroidism Ia,[70] but this requires further study with newer methods, including serum insulinlike growth factor measurements.

Pseudopseudohypoparathyroidism. Since its initial description by Albright,[2] the entity pseudopseudohypoparathyroidism has generated much confusion. In part, this stems from the relative lack of objective specificity of certain features of the Albright phenotype including short stature, obesity, "round face," and even shortening of fourth metacarpals. Diagnosis of normocalcemic individuals with some or all of these features as having pseudopseudohypoparathyroidism is almost certain to lead to inaccuracy, e.g., patients with Turner syndrome may be included. Genetic linkage between pseudohypoparathyroidism and pseudopseudohypoparathyroidism was recognized early,[3] and reemphasized more recently.[71] The term pseudopseudohypoparathyroidism is best restricted to relatives of patients with pseudohypoparathyroidism Ia who show phenotypic features of Albright osteodystrophy and a normal rise in urinary cAMP excretion in response to parathyroid hormone infusion.[5]

Diagnosis of pseudohypoparathyroidism or pseudopseudohypoparathyroidism on the basis of serum calcium concentration (Albright's original criterion) may be misleading. Patients with clear-cut resistance to parathyroid hormone (elevated serum parathyroid hormone, blunted urinary cAMP response to parathyroid hormone) may be normocalcemic.[72,73] Hypocalcemia is not present from birth in patients with pseudohypoparathyroidism Ia; instead, it may develop during the first decade, and be preceded by other signs of parathyroid hormone resistance, including hyperphosphatemia and elevated serum parathyroid hormone.[42,74] Serum calcium, moreover, may fluctuate between low and normal concentrations in patients with pseudohypoparathyroidism.[75] Since Gs deficiency is likely present from birth, and unlikely to fluctuate during life, variations in serum calcium must reflect other factors such as 1,25-dihydroxyvitamin D synthesis. Estrogens and placental synthesis of 1,25-dihydroxyvitamin D in pregnancy are among the factors that can alter serum calcium in pseudohypoparathyroidism.[76]

Within a family with pseudohypoparathyroidism Ia, multiple members may show features of Albright osteodystrophy and yet show wide variation in degree of hormone resistance. The biochemical basis for this variability is unknown. Unaffected family members (no hormone resistance, no features of Albright osteodystrophy) show normal Gs activity,[77] but subjects with Albright osteodystrophy show similar reduction in Gs activity whether (with pseudohypoparathyroidism) or not (with pseudopseudohypoparathyroidism) they are overtly resistant to hormones.[52,78,79] This suggests that Gs deficiency alone cannot explain hormone resistance in pseudohypoparathyroidism Ia. One possibility is that overt hormone resistance is a polygenic trait, i.e., the consequences of Gs deficiency are conditioned by allelic variation at other loci coding for other components of the cAMP cascade. Variations in cAMP phosphodiesterase activity,[39] for example, could exert powerful effects on hormone response when combined with Gs deficiency. Subtle signs of hormone resistance such as elevated serum parathyroid hormone and hyperresponse of thyrotropin to thyrotropin-releasing factor may be detected in patients with pseudopseudohypoparathyroidism,[78,79] consistent with a partial defect in hormone response. Further studies are needed to elucidate the relationship between Gs deficiency and hormone resistance, and the basis for phenotypic differences between subjects with pseudohypoparathyroidism and pseudopseudohypoparathyroidism.

Pseudohypoparathyroidism with Albright Osteodystrophy, Generalized Hormone Resistance, and Normal Gs Activity

This form of pseudohypoparathyroidism could be termed Ia or Ib depending upon whether phenotype or Gs activity is used for classification. Although most patients with generalized resistance and Albright osteodystrophy are deficient in Gs, several groups have reported normal Gs activity in a small number of patients with this phenotype.[53,59,77] It is possible that subtle defects in Gs in such individuals have not been detected by available assays, but in at least two families, such a Gs defect (receptor uncoupling) was specifically excluded.[77] Elevation in Gi, another theoretical explanation for this phenotype, has not been observed using pertussis toxin–catalyzed ADP-ribosylation.[54] Additional functional assays of Gi are necessary to evaluate this possible defect. Defects in other general components of the cAMP pathway, e.g., adenylate cyclase and cAMP phosphodiesterase, also should be sought as these could lead to a similar phenotype. The occurrence of Albright osteodystrophy in this form of pseudohypoparathyroidism suggests the possibility that different defects in the cAMP signal transduction pathway could cause this phenotype, with impaired cAMP synthesis or action as the underlying mechanism.

Pseudohypoparathyroidism Type Ib

In this form of pseudohypoparathyroidism, physical appearance is normal, resistance is limited to parathyroid hormone, and Gs activity is normal.[59,67] The presumed site of the defect on the pathway is proximal to cAMP generation, as in pseudohypoparathyroidism Ia, since urinary cAMP excretion in response to parathyroid hormone infusion is abnormally low.[59] The specificity of hormone resistance suggests a defect involving a unique component of the transduction mechanism, e.g., the parathyroid hormone receptor. This form of pseudohypoparathyroidism may itself be heterogeneous, with reports of both familial[80,81] and apparently sporadic[82] cases. In one study,[82] cultured skin fibroblasts from 7 of 10 patients with pseudohypoparathyroidism Ib showed selective resistance to parathyroid hormone in terms of cAMP formation. The persistence of abnormal parathyroid hormone response in cells cultured in vitro is consistent with an intrinsic abnormality in the parathyroid hormone receptor, but more direct analyses of the parathyroid hormone receptor, including use of cDNA probes when available, will be necessary to evaluate the status of the receptor in patients with pseudohypoparathyroidism.

In addition to hypoparathyroidism, prolactin deficiency has been reported in pseudohypoparathyroidism.[81,83,84] Defective prolactin response to various stimuli occurs in some, but not all, patients with both pseudohypoparathyroidism Ia and Ib.[59,83] The cause of this abnormality is not known. Primary hypothyroidism in a family with pseudohypoparathyroidism Ib[81] was associated with antithyroid antibodies, in distinction

to the form of hypothyroidism associated with pseudohypoparathyroidism Ia, in which antithyroid antibodies are generally not found.

Pseudohypoparathyroidism Type II

This form of pseudohypoparathyroidism involves a defect distal to parathyroid hormone–stimulated cAMP production. It was originally described in a child of normal appearance who was hypocalcemic and hyperphosphatemic, showed elevated serum parathyroid hormone concentration, and had normal renal function, all consistent with parathyroid hormone–resistant hypoparathyroidism.[6] Urinary cAMP response to parathyroid hormone infusion, however, was completely normal, and the phosphaturic response was equivocal. Such a phenotype could be caused by a defect in a parathyroid hormone and cAMP-sensitive renal phosphate transport mechanism, but this hypothesis has not been directly tested. Since the phosphaturic response to parathyroid hormone is often equivocal even in normal subjects,[6] the diagnosis rests on finding clear elevations in serum parathyroid hormone in association with hypocalcemia, normal renal function, and a normal urinary cAMP response to parathyroid hormone infusion.

Pseudohypoparathyroidism type II may be an acquired disease[85]; only a single instance of familial pseudohypoparathyroidism II (in two brothers) has been reported.[85] Calcium infusion may normalize the phosphaturic response to parathyroid hormone in patients with pseudohypoparathyroidism type II.[86] This effect is not due to suppression of endogenous parathyroid hormone secretion, and may reflect calcium dependence of parathyroid hormone–stimulated phosphaturia.[86] Findings compatible with pseudohypoparathyroidism type II also occur in some patients with vitamin D deficiency.[85,87] Urinary cAMP excretion in response to parathyroid hormone is normal in such patients, but the phosphaturic response is defective. Treatment with vitamin D restores a normal phosphaturic response.[85,87] The mechanism of vitamin D action involves more than restoration of normocalcemia, since hypocalcemic patients with parathyroid hormone–deficient hypoparathyroidism show a normal phosphaturic response to parathyroid hormone.

Pseudohypoparathyroidism type II in association with Sjögren syndrome has been reported in a patient with antirenal tubular plasma membrane autoantibodies.[88] Whether such antibodies were relevant to the pathogenesis of the phosphate transport defect is not clear, but this case emphasizes that pseudohypoparathyroidism type II may be an acquired defect caused by diverse mechanisms.

Parathyroid Hormone Inhibitors as a Cause of Pseudohypoparathyroidism

Potent antagonists to parathyroid hormone action on its target organs could, in theory, cause pseudohypoparathyroidism. Inhibitors could be abnormal forms of parathyroid hormone itself or unrelated molecules such as antibodies to parathyroid hormone receptors. An abnormal form of parathyroid hormone, lacking biologic activity, could not by itself account for the resistance to exogenous parathyroid hormone characteristic of pseudohypoparathyroidism. Thus, in two cases[89,90] with secretion of a putatively ineffective form of parathyroid hormone, renal responsiveness to exogenous parathyroid hormone was normal. As yet, there is no definitive evidence for secretion of an abnormal form of parathyroid hormone in human beings. Studies of patients with familial isolated hypoparathyroidism failed to detect deletions or gross rearrangements in the parathyroid hormone gene.[91]

Using an ultrasensitive renal cytochemical assay for parathyroid hormone, one group has reported a dissociation between parathyroid hormone biologic activity and immunoreactivity in patients with pseudohypoparathyroidism type I.[92] Whereas immunoreactivity was supranormal, biologic activity was in the normal range. Another group, using the same assay, reported similar findings in treated patients with pseudohypoparathyroidism but observed that patients treated for nutritional vitamin D deficiency showed a similar discrepancy between immunoreactive parathyroid hormone and biologic activity.[93] Reports of improved parathyroid hormone responsiveness after correction of hypocalcemia with vitamin D treatment[94] or after parathyroidectomy (in one of Albright's original patients[95]) have prompted speculation that secretion of an abnormal form of parathyroid hormone could lead to parathyroid hormone resistance in pseudohypoparathyroidism. Plasma from four patients with pseudohypoparathyroidism was found to inhibit parathyroid hormone activity in the renal cytochemical assay; plasma from a fifth patient with pseudohypoparathyroidism who had been parathyroidectomized lacked inhibitory activity.[95] The relevance of the latter observation is unclear, since this patient showed a deficient urinary cAMP response to parathyroid hormone infusion even after parathyroidectomy.[5] Two additional studies offer conflicting data on the relationship between parathyroid hormone inhibitory activity and parathyroid hormone itself in plasma of patients with pseudohypoparathyroidism. Intravenous calcium infusion was found to suppress parathyroid hormone inhibitory activity in plasma of three patients with pseudohypoparathyroidism.[96] This suggests, but does not prove, that inhibitory activity is being secreted by the parathyroid glands, and is subject to feedback regulation by serum calcium. Gel filtration of plasma from patients with pseudohypoparathyroidism, however, separates immunoreactive and biologically active parathyroid hormone from inhibitory activity.[97] The latter fails to react with various parathyroid hormone antiserums. Indeed, given the difficulty in synthesizing parathyroid hormone analogues that function as potent antagonists,[32] it seems unlikely that secretion of an altered form of parathyroid hormone could explain resistance to pharmacologic doses of exogenous parathyroid extract in patients with pseudohypoparathyroidism. With a different assay, renal adenylate cyclase activation, one group has found inhibitory activity in plasma of patients with pseudohypoparathyroidism,[98] but no inhibitory activity was observed in two other studies.[99,100] Parathyroid hormone inhibitors in any event could not explain the resistance to other hormones commonly seen in pseudohypoparathyroidism Ia.

Skeletal Resistance to Parathyroid Hormone in Pseudohypoparathyroidism

Studies of vitamin D metabolites in patients with pseudohypoparathyroidism suggest that the deficient calcemic response to parathyroid hormone reflects 1,25-dihydroxyvitamin D deficiency rather than primary skeletal resistance to parathyroid hormone. Serum 1,25-dihydroxyvitamin D concentration is often low in untreated patients with pseudohypoparathyroidism type I, and treatment with vitamin D restores calcemic

responsiveness to parathyroid hormone without changing the deficient urinary cAMP response.[14,101–104] Selective deficiency of 1,25-dihydroxyvitamin D was invoked as the cause of isolated skeletal resistance to parathyroid hormone in an unusual variant of pseudohypoparathyroidism.[105] Deficient 1,25-dihydroxyvitamin D formation in response to parathyroid hormone has been directly demonstrated in patients with pseudohypoparathyroidism,[106,107] and reflects renal resistance to parathyroid hormone. Dibutyryl cAMP, a metabolically stable analogue, can bypass the site of resistance in pseudohypoparathyroidism type I, increase 1,25-dihydroxyvitamin D formation, and correct other abnormalities secondary to renal resistance to parathyroid hormone.[108,109]

The bone remodeling response to parathyroid hormone is relatively intact in many patients with pseudohypoparathyroidism. Decreased bone density, increased urinary hydroxyproline excretion, and increased resorption on bone biopsy have been reported.[14,110] These findings reflect the difference in requirement for normal 1,25-dihydroxyvitamin D concentration of the remodeling as opposed to calcemic response to parathyroid hormone. Patients with pseudohypoparathyroidism may actually show signs of rickets[111,112] or osteomalacia[103] that improve upon treatment with vitamin D.

Overt osteitis fibrosa cystica is rare in pseudohypoparathyroidism, but some patients with hypocalcemia, hyperphosphatemia, renal resistance to parathyroid hormone, and skeletal findings of excessive parathyroid hormone secretion have been reported.[113,114] These have virtually all been patients with pseudohypoparathyroidism type Ib. Although subtle findings compatible with bony demineralization can be seen in patients with pseudohypoparathyroidism Ia,[110] radiographically visible parathyroid bone disease is rare.[114] One group has postulated that there is a spectrum of skeletal responsiveness to parathyroid hormone in pseudohypoparathyroidism.[114] It is possible, though, that patients with pseudohypoparathyroidism and signs of osteitis fibrosa cystica (so-called pseudohypo-hyperparathyroidism) represent a unique variant of the disease with a distinctive pathogenesis. Potential differences in the transduction mechanisms of the skeletal calcemic and remodeling responses to parathyroid hormone and in the parathyroid hormone receptors of kidney and bone provide a theoretical basis for lesions that spare the bone remodeling response to parathyroid hormone. Parathyroid hormone hypersecretion secondary to renal resistance could then lead to the characteristic finding of osteitis fibrosa cystica.

GENETICS

Most reports on the mode of inheritance of pseudohypoparathyroidism have not taken into account the heterogeneity of the disease. Pseudohypoparathyroidism type II is rarely if ever familial, and many cases of pseudohypoparathyroidism type Ib appear to be sporadic. Small kindred size and lack of a definitive genetic marker preclude clear-cut identification of the mode of inheritance in the few reported kindreds with pseudohypoparathyroidism Ib.[80,81]

The pattern of inheritance of pseudohypoparathyroidism type Ia was initially considered to be X-linked dominant[3] on the basis of a 2:1 ratio of female-to-male cases and a presumed lack of well-documented cases of male-to-male transmission. More recent evidence argues in favor of autosomal dominant transmission as the most common pattern.[71,77,115] Male-to-male transmission does occur in pseudohypoparathyroidism Ia[116]; in one family, father-to-son transmission of Gs deficiency was observed.[117] Gs deficiency segregates with phenotypic features of Albright osteodystrophy in families with pseudohypoparathyroidism Ia.[77] Kindreds with pseudohypoparathyroidism Ia tend to be relatively small, perhaps in part due to impaired fertility in patients expressing the full defect, Albright osteodystrophy and generalized hormone resistance. Gs-deficient patients expressing the full phenotypic defect and patients with Gs deficiency, Albright osteodystrophy, but no overt hormone resistance (pseudohypoparathyroidism) often occur in the same family.[78,79]

There may be genetic heterogeneity within the pseudohypoparathyroidism Ia subtype. A family originally reported to show autosomal recessive inheritance of Albright osteodystrophy and hormone resistance[118] has been restudied and found to inherit Gs deficiency in the same manner.[77] In another family,[119] four affected sisters show Gs deficiency, Albright osteodystrophy, and generalized hormone resistance.[59] Two sisters are normal. The father was said to show pseudohypoparathyroidism on the basis of a single short fifth metacarpal bone.[119] If the defect is transmitted by the father (HLA and blood typing showed no evidence of parental exclusion), the two normal daughters exclude an X-linked pattern of inheritance. Unfortunately, identification of the father, on the basis of a single short metacarpal, as transmitter of the defect must be considered tentative. Gs activity appears to be normal in the father and has not been measured in the mother.[73] Occurrence of pseudohypoparathyroidism Ia in four sibs with possibly normal parents may not represent either simple dominant or recessive inheritance. A hypothetical form of simple inheritance, neither recessive nor dominant, involving allelic genes coding for different subunits of a protein or nonallelic genes coding for proteins that interact in other ways, has been postulated to account for the pattern of inheritance in certain unusual kindreds.[120] Until the defect in pseudohypoparathyroidism Ia is defined precisely at the molecular genetic level, any statement about the inheritance of the disorder must be considered tentative.

CLINICAL FEATURES

The clinical features of pseudohypoparathyroidism may be divided into those common to all patients with hypoparathyroidism and those unique to different subtypes of pseudohypoparathyroidism. The former include the characteristic chemical findings of hypoparathyroidism, hypocalcemia, and hyperphosphatemia with normal renal function; symptoms of neuromuscular irritability secondary to hypocalcemia such as paresthesias, tetany, seizures, and prolonged QT interval on electrocardiogram; dental defects, such as enamel hypoplasia and failure of teeth to erupt, particularly in patients with onset of disease in childhood; cataracts; and basal ganglion calcification.[121] As noted earlier, hypocalcemia may not be evident immediately after birth in pseudohypoparathyroidism Ia but may develop later in the first decade.[74] Patients with pseudohypoparathyroidism type Ib may show unique clinical features such as overt skeletal demineralization, even osteitis fibrosa cystica, not found in patients with hormone-deficient hypoparathyroidism.[114]

In addition to the findings common to all forms of hypoparathyroidism, patients with pseudohypoparathyroidism type Ia show clinical features of Albright osteodystrophy (Fig. 79-8) and generalized hormone resistance. The features of Albright osteodystrophy include short stature (usually first evident late in childhood[69]), obesity, mental retardation,[69] subcutaneous ossification,[122] and a number of bony abnormalities, most commonly metacarpal and metatarsal shortening.[123,124] The

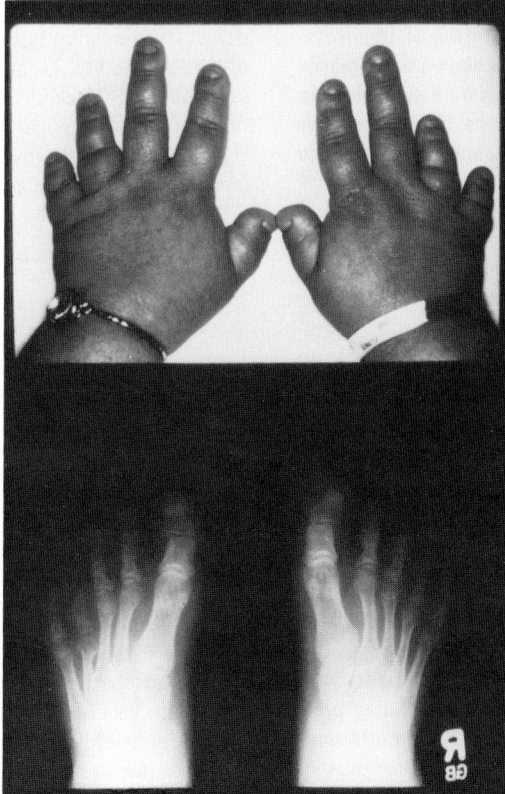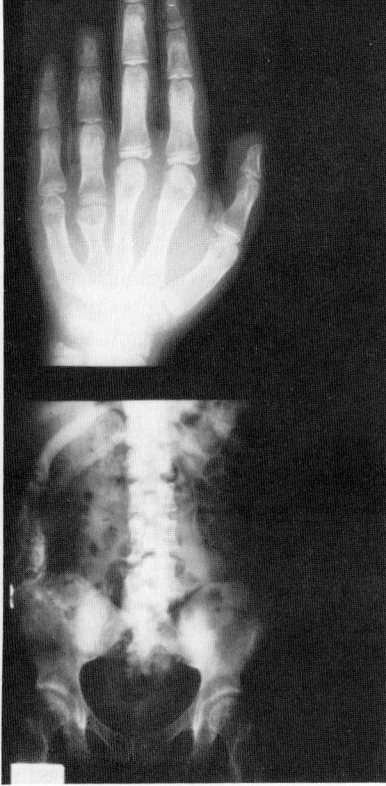

Fig. 79-8 Features of Albright osteodystrophy (clockwise from upper left) include: (1) short stubby fingers, particularly the fourth and fifth and the distal phalanx of the thumb; (2) shortening of the fourth metacarpal; (3) subcutaneous calcification, shown here in the abdominal wall (right lower quadrant); and (4) shortening of the left fourth metatarsal.

expression of the bony abnormalities is often asymmetric, and variable even within the same family. The fourth and fifth metacarpals are most commonly short; the second, least commonly. Shortening of distal phalanges, particularly relative to increased width, is another common finding.[124] Patients without hypocalcemia and hyperphosphatemia may show all these features, including subcutaneous ossification. This suggests that the features are not directly caused by abnormal calcium homeostasis.

Clinical features of generalized hormone resistance are also unique to pseudohypoparathyroidism Ia. These include primary hypogonadism and chemical or overt hypothyroidism. Screening for congenital hypothyroidism has led to the diagnosis of pseudohypoparathyroidism Ia in at least four cases.[73,125,126] These cases are interesting in that they emphasize that resistance to thyrotropin may be clinically evident before resistance to parathyroid hormone in patients with pseudohypoparathyroidism Ia. Hypocalcemia developed only after clinically apparent hypothyroidism in several of these cases. These cases also raise the question of whether mental retardation in pseudohypoparathyroidism Ia is due to hypothyroidism. This appears unlikely, since patients may show mental retardation unassociated with overt hypothyroidism (or hypocalcemia), but further studies of this question are needed.

Refer to Chap. 69 in the fifth edition of this text for a detailed tabulation of the frequency of various clinical findings in pseudohypoparathyroidism.

DIAGNOSIS

Hypocalcemia, hyperphosphatemia, and normal renal function establish the diagnosis of hypoparathyroidism. Other causes of hypocalcemia are generally associated with low or normal serum phosphorus with the exception of renal failure, where renal function is obviously abnormal.[10] Distinction between hormone-deficient and hormone-resistant forms of hypoparathyroidism in patients with hypocalcemia depends primarily upon radioimmunoassay of parathyroid hormone in plasma. In theory, patients could show elevated plasma immunoreactive parathyroid hormone without being resistant to parathyroid hormone, e.g., biologically inactive parathyroid hormone,[89,90] but this is rare. Increased plasma immunoreactive parathyroid hormone in a patient with hypocalcemia, hyperphosphatemia, and normal renal function is generally diagnostic for pseudohypoparathyroidism. Testing responsiveness to exogenous parathyroid hormone can confirm this diagnosis and distinguish between pseudohypoparathyroidism types I and II. In the former, the urinary cAMP response to parathyroid hormone is deficient; in the latter, it is normal. The phosphaturic response to parathyroid hormone may be deficient in both pseudohypoparathyroidism type I and type II, but this response may be equivocal even in normal subjects.

The features of Albright osteodystrophy and evidence of resistance to hormones other than parathyroid hormone help distinguish pseudohypoparathyroidism Ia from pseudohypoparathyroidism Ib. Gs measurement also distinguishes between these two subtypes of pseudohypoparathyroidism I, but this test is performed in only a few laboratories. Patients with pseudohypoparathyroidism Ia, as discussed earlier, may present with signs of other endocrinopathies, e.g., hypothyroidism,[125,126] rather than hypocalcemia. Phenotypic features of Albright osteodystrophy and blunted urinary cAMP response

to parathyroid hormone infusion (even when patients are normocalcemic) may still permit diagnosis of pseudohypoparathyroidism Ia in patients presenting with other endocrinopathies.

Relatives of patients with pseudohypoparathyroidism Ia may also show features of Albright osteodystrophy without overt signs of hormone resistance and with relatively normal urinary cAMP response to parathyroid hormone infusion (pseudopseudohypoparathyroidism). The diagnosis of pseudopseudohypoparathyroidism should not be made indiscriminately. Isolated shortening of the fourth metacarpal is a relatively nonspecific finding, insufficient by itself for a diagnosis of Albright osteodystrophy.[127] A variety of familial disorders share certain features in common with pseudohypoparathyroidism Ia but in general are readily distinguished from it. Soft tissue ossification is present in myositis ossificans but differs in location (muscle) from that in pseudohypoparathyroidism Ia (subcutaneous). The pattern of metacarpal shortening differs in pseudohypoparathyroidism Ia and in Turner syndrome,[124] and the latter is not associated with resistance to parathyroid hormone. Acrodysostosis is an apparently sporadic syndrome with metacarpal abnormalities similar to those of Albright osteodystrophy.[124] Nasal hypoplasia may be a distinctive feature of acrodysostosis, but this finding was present in at least one patient with other features characteristic of pseudohypoparathyroidism Ia.[128] Thus, the distinction between acrodysostosis and pseudohypoparathyroidism Ia may not be clear-cut. The Kenney-Caffey syndrome is associated with short stature, hypocalcemia, and bony anomalies, but unlike pseudohypoparathyroidism Ia, hypocalcemia in the Kenney-Caffey syndrome is of the parathyroid hormone–deficient type, skeletal involvement consists of medullary stenosis of the long bones, and there are distinctive ophthalmologic abnormalities.[129] Several types of familial brachydactyly show metacarpal abnormalities said to be similar, and in some instances identical, to those in Albright osteodystrophy.[124,130] The suggestion that familial brachydactyly and pseudohypoparathyroidism Ia represent variable expressions of the same genetic defect is interesting but unproven. A report of the coexistence of brachydactyly D and pseudohypoparathyroidism in the same family[130] lacked conclusive evidence to support a diagnosis of pseudohypoparathyroidism. Definition of the relationship between these familial disorders awaits analysis of the defects at the molecular genetic level.

TREATMENT

Treatment of hypocalcemia associated with pseudohypoparathyroidism is in general similar to treatment of other forms of hypoparathyroidism.[10] Chronic therapy with vitamin D, ergocalciferol, or one of its more active metabolites such as 1,25-dihydroxyvitamin D should be given in an effort to maintain the patient free of symptoms of tetany and to prevent cataract formation. The serum calcium should be maintained in the low normal range. Oral calcium supplements may be useful but, depending upon dietary calcium intake, may not be essential. Vitamin D therapy and correction of hypocalcemia generally cause lowering of serum phosphorus. Acetazolamide causes phosphaturia and lowering of serum phosphorus in patients with pseudohypoparathyroidism.[131] Treatment with acetazolamide could lessen requirements for vitamin D, but this probably does not justify adding this agent to the treatment regimen. Patients receiving vitamin D treatment must be closely monitored to avoid under- or overtreatment. The latter can lead to hypercalcemia and renal damage. Compliance, particularly in patients with subnormal intelligence, must be ensured. Treatment with vitamin D is less expensive than with 1,25-dihydroxyvitamin D, and for this reason may be preferred for chronic use. 1,25-Dihydroxyvitamin D has the theoretical advantage of more rapid onset of action (and more rapid offset in the event of intoxication), but treatment with vitamin D can achieve control of serum calcium at least as adequate as that with 1,25-dihydroxyvitamin D. With vitamin D treatment, serum 25-hydroxyvitamin D can be used to monitor compliance, whereas with 1,25-dihydroxyvitamin D treatment, serum 1,25-dihydroxyvitamin D must be measured.

In patients with pseudohypoparathyroidism Ia, treatment of associated endocrinopathies, in particular hypothyroidism, may be needed. Sex steroid treatment of patients with hypogonadism may be appropriate in some patients.

REFERENCES

1. ALBRIGHT F, BURNETT CH, SMITH PH, PARSON W: Pseudohypoparathyroidism—An example of Seabright-Bantam syndrome. *Endocrinology* 30:922, 1942.

2. ALBRIGHT F, FORBES AP, HENNEMAN PH: Pseudopseudohypoparathyroidism. *Trans Assoc Am Physicians* 65:337, 1952.

3. MANN JB, ALTERMAN S, HILLS AG: Albright's hereditary osteodystrophy comprising pseudohypoparathyroidism and pseudopseudohypoparathyroidism. *Ann Intern Med* 56:315, 1962.

4. TASHJIAN JR, FRANTZ AG, LEE JB: Pseudohypoparathyroidism: Assays of parathyroid hormone and thyrocalcitonin. *Proc Natl Acad Sci USA* 56:1138, 1966.

5. CHASE LR, MELSON GL, AURBACH GD: Pseudohypoparathyroidism: Defective excretion of 3',5'-AMP in response to parathyroid hormone. *J Clin Invest* 48:1832, 1969.

6. DREZNER M, NEELON FA, LEBOVITZ HE: Pseudohypoparathyroidism type II. A possible defect in the reception of the cyclic AMP signal. *N Engl J Med* 289:1056, 1973.

7. LEVINE MA, DOWNS RW JR, SINGER M, MARX SJ, AURBACH GD, SPIEGEL AM: Deficient activity of guanine nucleotide regulatory protein in erythrocytes from patients with pseudohypoparathyroidism. *Biochem Biophys Res Commun* 94:1319, 1980.

8. FARFEL Z, BRICKMAN AS, KASLOW HR, BROTHERS VM, BOURNE HR: Defect of receptor-cyclase coupling protein in pseudohypoparathyroidism. *N Engl J Med* 303:237, 1980.

9. HABENER JF, POTTS JT: Biosynthesis of parathyroid hormone. *N Engl J Med* 299:580,635, 1978.

10. AURBACH GD, MARX SJ, SPIEGEL AM: Parathyroid hormone, calcitonin, and the calciferols, in Wilson J, Foster D (eds): *Williams Textbook of Endocrinology*, 7th ed. Philadelphia, Saunders, 1985, p 1137.

11. RODAN GA, RODAN SB: Expression of the osteoblastic phenotype, in Peck WA (ed): *Bone and Mineral Research, Annual 2*. Amsterdam, Elsevier, 1983, p 244.

12. JILKA RA: Are osteoblastic cells required for the control of osteoclast activity by parathyroid hormone? *Bone Mineral* 1:261, 1986.

13. HOWARD GA, BOTTEMILLER BL, BAYLINK DJ: Evidence for the coupling of bone formation to bone resorption in vitro. *Metab Bone Dis Relat Res* 2:131, 1980.

14. DREZNER MK, NEELON FA, HAUSSLER M, MCPHERSON HT, LEBOVITZ HE: 1,25-dihydroxycholecalciferol deficiency: The probable cause of hypocalcemia and metabolic bone disease in pseudohypoparathyroidism. *J Clin Endocrinol Metab* 42:621, 1976.

15. AURBACH GD, CHASE LR: Cyclic nucleotides and biochemical actions of parathyroid hormone and calcitonin, in Aurbach GD (ed): *Parathyroid Gland*. Washington, DC, American Physiological Society, 1976, p 353 [Greep RO, Astwood EB (eds): *Handbook of Physiology, Endocrinology Section*, Section 7, vol VII].

16. LEWIN IG, PAPAPOULOS SE, TOMLINSON S, HENDY GN, O'RIORDAN JLH: Studies of hypoparathyroidism and pseudohypoparathyroidism. *Q J Med* 47:533, 1978.

17. CAVERZASIO J, RIZZOLI R, BONJOUR JP: Sodium-dependent phosphate transport inhibited by parathyroid hormone and cyclic AMP stimulation in an opossum kidney cell line. *J Biol Chem* 261:3233, 1986.

18. HORIUCHI N, SUDA T, TAKAHASHI H, SHIMAZAWA E, OGATA E: In vivo evidence for the intermediary role of 3',5'-cyclic AMP in parathyroid hormone-induced stimulation of 1 alpha, 25-dihydroxyvitamin D3 synthesis in rats. *Endocrinology* 101:969, 1977.

19. PUSCHETT JB: Are all of the renal tubular actions of parathyroid hormone mediated by the adenylate cyclase system? *Miner Electrolyte Metab* 7:281, 1982.

20. PECK WA: Cyclic AMP as a second messenger in the skeletal actions of parathyroid hormone: A decade old hypothesis. *Calcif Tissue Int* 29:1, 1979.

21. LOWIK CWGM, VAN LEEUWEN JPTM, VAN DER MEER JM, VAN ZEELAND JK, SCHEVEN BAA, HERMANN-ERLEE MPM: A two receptor model for the action of parathyroid hormone on osteoblasts: A role for intracellular free calcium and cAMP. *Cell Calcium* 6:311, 1985.

22. WAKELAM MJO, MURPHY GJ, HRUBY VJ, HOUSLAY MD: Activation of two signal transduction systems in hepatocytes by glucagon. *Nature* 323:68, 1986.

23. BERRIDGE MJ, IRVINE RF: Inositol triphosphate, a novel second messenger in cellular signal transduction. *Nature* 312:315, 1984.

24. GILMAN AG: Guanine nucleotide regulatory proteins and dual control of adenylate cyclase. *J Clin Invest* 73:1, 1983.

25. SPIEGEL AM: Signal transduction by guanine nucleotide binding proteins. *Mol Cell Endocrinol* 49:1, 1987.

26. SPIEGEL AM, GIERSCHIK P, LEVINE MA, DOWNS RW JR: Clinical implications of guanine nucleotide binding proteins as receptor-effector couplers. *N Engl J Med* 312:26, 1985.

27. KOBILKA BK, DIXON RAF, FRIELLE T, DOHLMAN HG, BOLANOWSKI MA, SIGAL IS, YANG-FENG TL, FRANCKE U, CARON MG, LEFKOWITZ RJ: cDNA for the human Beta2-adrenergic receptor: A protein with multiple membrane-spanning domains and encoded by a gene whose chromosomal location is shared with that of the receptor for platelet-derived growth factor. *Proc Natl Acad Sci USA* 84:46, 1987.

28. NISSENSON RA: Functional properties of parathyroid hormone receptors. *Miner Electrolyte Metab* 8:151, 1982.

29. GOLDRING SR, TYLER GA, KRANE SM, POTTS JT JR, ROSENBLATT M: Photoaffinity labeling of parathyroid hormone receptors: Comparison of receptors across species and target tissues and after desensitization to hormone. *Biochemistry* 23:495, 1984.

30. DEMAY M, MITCHELL J, GOLTZMAN D: Comparison of renal and osseous binding of parathyroid hormone and hormonal fragments. *Am J Physiol* 249:E437, 1985.

31. MARTIN KJ, BELLORIN-FONT E, MORRISSEY JJ, JILKA RL, MACREGOR RR, COHN DV: Relative sensitivity of kidney and bone to the amino-terminal fragment b-parathyroid hormone (1-30) of native bovine parathyroid hormone. *Calcif Tissue Int* 35:520, 1983.

32. HORIUCHI N, ROSENBLATT M, KEUTMANN HT, POTTS JT JR, HOLICK MF: A multiresponse parathyroid hormone assay: An inhibitor has agonist properties in vivo. *Am J Physiol* 244:E589, 1983.

33. BRAY P, CARTER A, SIMONS C, GUO V, PUCKETT C, KAMHOLTZ J, SPIEGEL A, NIRENBERG M: Human cDNA clones for four species of Gs-alpha signal transduction protein. *Proc Natl Acad Sci USA* 83:8893, 1986.

34. PFEUFFER E, DREHER RM, METZGER H, PFEUFFER T: Catalytic unit of adenylate cyclase: Purification and identification by affinity crosslinking. *Proc Natl Acad Sci USA* 82:3086, 1985.

35. CHARBONNEAU H, BEIER N, WALSH KA, BEAVO JA: Identification of a conserved domain among cyclic nucleotide phosphodiesterases from diverse species. *Proc Natl Acad Sci USA* 83:9308, 1986.

36. SHOWERS MO, MAURER RA: A cloned bovine cDNA encodes an alternate form of the catalytic subunit of cAMP-dependent protein kinase. *J Biol Chem* 261:16288, 1986.

37. AUSIELLO DA, ROSENBLATT M, DAYER JM: Parathyroid hormone modulates protein kinase in giant cell tumors of human bone. *Am J Physiol* 239:E144, 1980.

38. FARFEL Z, SALOMON MR, BOURNE HR: Genetic investigation of adenylate cyclase: Mutations in mouse and man. *Annu Rev Pharmacol Toxicol* 21:251, 1981.

39. BROTHERS VM, WALKER N, BOURNE HR: Increased cyclic nucleotide phosphodiesterase activity in a mutant S49 lymphoma cell. *J Biol Chem* 257:9349, 1982.

40. CHEN CN, DENOME S, DAVIS RL: Molecular analysis of cDNA clones and the corresponding genomic sequences of the *Drosophila* dunce + gene, the structural gene for cAMP phosphodiesterase. *Proc Natl Acad Sci USA* 83:9313, 1986.

41. MATSUMOTO K, UNO I, OSHIMA Y, ISHIKAWA T: Isolation and characterization of yeast mutants deficient in adenylate cyclase and cAMP-dependent protein kinase. *Proc Natl Acad Sci USA* 79:2355, 1982.

42. WERDER EA, FISCHER JA, ILLIG R, KIND HP, BERNASCONI S, FANCONI A, PRADER A: Pseudohypoparathyroidism and idiopathic hypoparathyroidism: Relationship between serum calcium and parathyroid hormone levels and urinary cyclic adenosine 3′,5′-monophosphate response to parathyroid extract. *J Clin Endocrinol Metab* 46:872, 1978.

43. WERDER EA, ILLIG R, BERNASCONI S, KIND HP, PRADER A, FISCHER JA, FANCONI A: Excessive thyrotropin response to thyrotropin-releasing hormone in pseudohypoparathyroidism. *Pediatr Res* 9:12, 1975.

44. WOLFSDORF JI, ROSENFELD RL, FANG VS, KOBAYASHI R, RAZDAN AK, KIM MH: Partial gonadotrophin-resistance in pseudohypoparathyroidism. *Acta Endocrinol* 88:321, 1978.

45. MARCUS R, WILBER JF, AURBACH GD: Parathyroid hormone-sensitive adenyl cyclase from the renal cortex of a patient with pseudohypoparathyroidism. *J Clin Endocrinol Metab* 33:537, 1971.

46. DREZNER MK, BURCH WM JR: Altered activity of the nucleotide regulatory site in the parathyroid hormone-sensitive adenylate cyclase from the renal cortex of a patient with pseudohypoparathyroidism. *J Clin Invest* 62:1222, 1978.

47. FARFEL Z, BOURNE HR: Deficient activity of receptor-cyclase coupling protein in platelets of patients with pseudohypoparathyroidism. *J Clin Endocrinol Metab* 51:1202, 1980.

48. LEVINE MA, EIL C, DOWNS RW JR, SPIEGEL AM: Deficient guanine nucleotide regulatory unit activity in cultured fibroblast membranes from patients with pseudohypoparathyroidism type I. *J Clin Invest* 72:316, 1983.

49. BOURNE HR, KASLOW HR, BRICKMAN AS, FARFEL Z: Fibroblast defect in pseudohypoparathyroidism, type I: Reduced activity of receptor-cyclase coupling protein. *J Clin Endocrinol Metab* 53:636, 1981.

50. FARFEL Z, ABOOD ME, BRICKMAN AS, BOURNE HR: Deficient activity of receptor-cyclase coupling protein in transformed lymphoblasts of patients with pseudohypoparathyroidism type I. *J Clin Endocrinol Metab* 55:113, 1982.

51. DOWNS RW JR, LEVINE MA, DREZNER MK, BURCH WM JR, SPIEGEL AM: Deficient adenylate cyclase regulatory protein in renal membranes from a patient with pseudohypoparathyroidism. *J Clin Invest* 71:231, 1983.

52. SAITO T, AKITA Y, FUJITA H, FURUKAWA Y, TSUCHIYA Y, YASUDA T, YAMAMOTO M, KITAGAWA T, NAKAGAWA Y, TAKEHIRO A, FUJITA T, KODAMA S, KUZUYA T: Stimulatory guanine nucleotide binding protein activity in the erythrocyte membrane of patients with pseudohypoparathyroidism type I and related disorders. *Acta Endocrinol* 111:507, 1986.

53. RADEKE HH, AUFMKOLK B, JUPPNER H, KROHN HP, KECK E, HESCH RD: Multiple pre- and postreceptor defects in pseudohypoparathyroidism (a multicenter study with twenty four patients). *J Clin Endocrinol Metab* 162:393, 1986.

54. DOWNS RW JR, SEKURA RD, LEVINE MA, SPIEGEL AM: The inhibitory adenylate cyclase coupling protein in pseudohypoparathyroidism. *J Clin Endocrinol Metab* 61:351, 1985.

55. AKITA Y, SAITO T, YAJIMA Y, SAKUMA S: The stimulatory and inhibitory guanine nucleotide-binding proteins of adenylate cyclase in erythrocytes from patients with pseudohypoparathyroidism type I. *J Clin Endocrinol Metab* 61:1012, 1985.

56. HEINSIMER JA, DAVIES AO, DOWNS RW JR, LEVINE MA, SPIEGEL AM, DREZNER MK, DELEAN A, WREGGET KA, CARON MG, LEFKOWITZ RJ: Impaired formation of beta-adrenergic receptor-nucleotide regulatory protein complexes in pseudohypoparathyroidism. *J Clin Invest* 73:1335, 1984.

57. CARTER A, BARDIN C, COLLINS R, SIMONS C, BRAY P, SPIEGEL A: Reduced expression of multiple forms of Gs-alpha in pseudohypoparathyroidism type Ia. *Proc Natl Acad Sci USA* 84:7266, 1987.

58. MOTULSKY HJ, HUGHES RJ, BRICKMAN AS, FARFEL Z, BOURNE HR, INSEL PA: Platelets of pseudohypoparathyroidism patients: Evidence that distinct receptor-cyclase coupling proteins mediate stimulation and inhibition of adenylate cyclase. *Proc Natl Acad Sci USA* 79:4193, 1982.

59. LEVINE MA, DOWNS RW JR, MOSES AM, BRESLAU NA, MARX SJ, LASKER RD, RIZZOLI RE, AURBACH GD, SPIEGEL AM: Resistance to multiple hormones in patients with pseudohypoparathyroidism. *Am J Med* 74:545, 1983.

60. MALLET E, CARAYON P, AMR S, BRUNELLE P, DUCASTELLE T, BASUYAU JP, HELLOUIN DE MENIBUS C: Coupling defect of thyrotropin receptor and adenylate cyclase in a pseudohypoparathyroidism patient. *J Clin Endocrinol Metab* 54:1028, 1982.

61. SHAPIRO MS, BERNHEIM J, GUTMAN A, ARBER I, SPITZ IM: Multiple abnormalities of anterior pituitary hormone secretion in association with pseudohypoparathyroidism. *J Clin Endocrinol Metab* 51:483, 1980.

62. BRICKMAN AS, CARLSON HE, LEVIN SR: Responses to glucagon infusion in pseudohypoparathyroidism. *J Clin Endocrinol Metab* 63:1354, 1986.

63. CARLSON HE, BRICKMAN AS, WILLIAMS A: Blunted plasma cyclic adenosine monophosphate response to isoproterenol in pseudohypoparathyroidism. *J Clin Endocrinol Metab* 56:1323, 1983.

64. CARLSON HE, BRICKMAN AS, BURNS TW, LANGLEY PE: Normal fatty acid

65. MOSES AM, WEINSTOCK RS, LEVINE MA, BRESLAU NA: Evidence for normal antidiuretic responses to endogenous and exogenous arginine vasopressin in patients with guanine nucleotide-binding stimulatory protein-deficient pseudohypoparathyroidism. *J Clin Endocrinol Metab* 62:221, 1986.

66. WEINSTOCK RS, WRIGHT HN, SPIEGEL AM, LEVINE MA, MOSES AM: Olfactory dysfunction in humans with deficient guanine nucleotide-binding protein. *Nature* 322:635, 1986.

67. FARFEL Z, BOURNE HR: Pseudohypoparathyroidism: Mutation affecting adenylate cyclase. *Miner Electrolyte Metab* 8:227, 1982.

68. FARFEL Z, FRIEDMAN E: Mental deficiency in pseudohypoparathyroidism type I is associated with Ns-protein deficiency. *Ann Intern Med* 105:197, 1986.

69. DE WIJN EM, STEENDIJK R: Growth and maturation in pseudohypoparathyroidism; a longitudinal study in five patients. *Acta Endocrinol* 101:223, 1982.

70. URDANIVIA E, MATAVERDE A, COHEN MP: Growth hormone secretion and sulfation factor activity in pseudohypoparathyroidism. *J Lab Clin Med* 86:772, 1975.

71. FITCH N: Albright's hereditary osteodystrophy: A review. *Am J Med Genet* 11:11, 1982.

72. BALACHANDAR V, PAHUJA J, MADDAIAH VT, COLLIPP PJ: Pseudohypoparathyroidism with normal serum calcium level. *Am J Dis Child* 129:1092, 1975.

73. SPIEGEL A: Unpublished observations.

74. TSANG RC, VENKATARAMAN P, HO M, STEICHEN JJ, WHITSETT J, GREER F: The development of pseudohypoparathyroidism. *Am J Dis Child* 138:654, 1984.

75. BRESLAU NA, NOTMAN DD, CANTERBURY JM, MOSES AM: Studies on the attainment of normocalcemia in patients with pseudohypoparathyroidism. *Am J Med* 68:856, 1980.

76. BRESLAU NA, ZERWEKH JE: Relationship of estrogen and pregnancy to calcium homeostasis in pseudohypoparathyroidism. *J Clin Endocrinol Metab* 62:45, 1986.

77. FARFEL Z, BROTHERS VM, BRICKMAN AS, CONTE F, NEER R, BOURNE HR: Pseudohypoparathyroidism: Inheritance of deficient receptor-cyclase coupling activity. *Proc Natl Acad Sci USA* 78:3098, 1981.

78. LEVINE MA, JAP TS, MAUSETH RS, DOWNS RW JR, SPIEGEL AM: Activity of the stimulatory guanine nucleotide-binding protein is reduced in erythrocytes from patients with pseudohypoparathyroidism and pseudopseudohypoparathyroidism: Biochemical, endocrine, and genetic analysis of Albright's hereditary osteodystrophy in six kindreds. *J Clin Endocrinol Metab* 62:497, 1986.

79. FISCHER JA, BOURNE HR, DAMBACHER MA, TSCHOPP F, DE MEYER R, DEVOGALAER JP, WERDER EA, NAGANT DE DEUXCHAISNES C: Pseudohypoparathyroidism: Inheritance and expression of deficient receptor-cyclase coupling protein activity. *Clin Endocrinol* 19:747, 1983.

80. WINTER JSD, HUGHES JA: Familial pseudohypoparathyroidism without somatic anomalies. *Can Med Assoc J* 123:26, 1980.

81. CARLSON HE, BRICKMAN AS, BOTTAZZO GF: Prolactin deficiency in pseudohypoparathyroidism. *N Engl J Med* 296:140, 1977.

82. SILVE C, SANTORA A, BRESLAU N, MOSES A, SPIEGEL A: Selective resistance to parathyroid hormone in cultured skin fibroblasts from patients with pseudohypoparathyroidism type Ib. *J Clin Endocrinol Metab* 62:640, 1986.

83. BRICKMAN AS, CARLSON HE, DEFTOS LJ: Prolactin and calcitonin responses to parathyroid hormone infusion in hypoparathyroid, pseudohypoparathyroid, and normal subjects. *J Clin Endocrinol Metab* 53:661, 1981.

84. KRUSE K, GUTEKUNST B, KRACHT U, SCHWERDA K: Deficient prolactin response to parathyroid hormone in hypocalcemic and normocalcemic pseudohypoparathyroidism. *J Clin Endocrinol Metab* 52:1099, 1981.

85. RAO DS, PARFITT AM, KLEEREKOPER M, PUMO BS, FRAME B: Dissociation between the effects of endogenous parathyroid hormone on adenosine 3′,5′-monophosphate generation and phosphate reabsorption in hypocalcemia due to vitamin D depletion: An acquired disorder resembling pseudohypoparathyroidism type II. *J Clin Endocrinol Metab* 61:285, 1985.

86. RODRIGUEZ HJ, VILLAREAL H, KLAHR S, SLATOPOLSKY E: Pseudohypoparathyroidism type II. Restoration of normal renal responsiveness to parathyroid hormone by calcium administration. *J Clin Endocrinol Metab* 39:693, 1974.

87. MATSUDA I, TAKEKOSHI Y, TANAKA M, MATSUURA N, NAGAI B, SEINO Y: Pseudohypoparathyroidism type II and anticonvulsant rickets. *Eur J Pediatr* 132:303, 1979.

88. YAMADA K, TAMURA Y, TOMIOKA H, KUMAGAI A, YOSHIDA S: Possible existence of anti-renal tubular plasma membrane autoantibody which

blocked parathyroid hormone-induced phosphaturia in a patient with pseudohypoparathyroidism type II and Sjogren's syndrome. *J Clin Endocrinol Metab* 58:339, 1984.

89. NUSYNOWITZ ML, KLEIN MH: Pseudoidiopathic hypoparathyroidism: Hypoparathyroidism with ineffective parathyroid hormone. *Am J Med* 55:677, 1973.

90. CONNORS MH, IRIAS JJ, GOLABI M: Hypohyperparathyroidism: Evidence for a defective parathyroid hormone. *Pediatrics* 60:343, 1977.

91. AHN TG, ANTONIARAKIS SE, KRONENBERG HM, IGARASHI T, LEVINE MA: Familial isolated hypoparathyroidism: A molecular genetic analysis of 8 families with 23 affected persons. *Medicine* 65:73, 1986.

92. NAGANT DE DEUXCHAISNES C, FISCHER JA, DAMBACHER MA, DEVOGELAER JP, ARBER CE, ZANELLI JM, PARSONS JA, LOVERIDGE N, BITENSKY L, CHAYEN J: Dissociation of parathyroid hormone bioactivity and immunoreactivity in pseudohypoparathyroidism type I. *J Clin Endocrinol Metab* 53:1105, 1981.

93. ALLGROVE J, CHAYEN J, JAYAWEERA P, O'RIORDAN JLH: An investigation of the biological activity of parathyroid hormone in pseudohypoparathyroidism: Comparison with vitamin D deficiency. *Clin Endocrinol* 20:503, 1984.

94. STOGMANN W, FISCHER JA: Pseudohypoparathyroidism: Disappearance of the resistance to parathyroid extract during treatment with vitamin D. *Am J Med* 59:140, 1975.

95. LOVERIDGE N, FISCHER JA, NAGANT DE DEUXCHAISNES C, DAMBACHER MA, TSCHOPP F, WERDER E, DEVOGALAER JP, DE MEYER R, BITENSKY L, CHAYEN J: Inhibition of cytochemical bioactivity of parathyroid hormone by plasma in pseudohypoparathyroidism type I. *J Clin Endocrinol Metab* 54:1274, 1982.

96. LOVERIDGE N, FISCHER JA, DEVOGELAER JP, NAGANT DE DEUXCHAISNES C: Suppression of parathyroid hormone inhibitory activity of plasma in pseudohypoparathyroidism type I by IV calcium. *Clin Endocrinol* 24:549, 1986.

97. LOVERIDGE N, TSCHOPP F, BORN W, DEVOGELAER JP, NAGANT DE DEUXCHAISNES C, FISCHER JA: Separation of inhibitory activity from biologically active parathyroid hormone in patients with pseudohypoparathyroidism type I. *Biochim Biophys Acta* 889:117, 1986.

98. MITCHELL J, GOLTZMAN D: Examination of circulating parathyroid hormone in pseudohypoparathyroidism. *J Clin Endocrinol Metab* 61:328, 1985.

99. AUFMKOLK B, HESCH RD: Renal adenylate cyclase assay for biologically active parathyroid hormone: Clinical utility and physiological significance. *J Endocrinol* 108:9, 1986.

100. SESHADRI MS, CHAN YL, WILKINSON MR, MASON RS, POSEN S: An adenylate cyclase bioassay for parathyroid hormone: Some clinical experiences. *Clin Sci* 68:321, 1985.

101. SUH SM, FRASER D, KOOH SW: Pseudohypoparathyroidism: Responsiveness to parathyroid extract induced by vitamin D2 therapy. *J Clin Endocrinol Metab* 30:609, 1970.

102. DREZNER MK, HAUSSLER MR: Normocalcemic pseudohypoparathyroidism: Association with normal vitamin D3 metabolism. *Am J Med* 66:503, 1979.

103. EPSTEIN S, MEUNIER PJ, LAMBERT PW, STERN PH, BELL NH: 1,25-dihydroxyvitamin D corrects osteomalacia in hypoparathyroidism and pseudohypoparathyroidism. *Acta Endocrinol* 103:241, 1983.

104. SINHA TK, DELUCA HF, BELL NH: Evidence for a defect in the formation of 1,25-dihydroxyvitamin D in pseudohypoparathyroidism. *Metabolism* 26:731, 1977.

105. METZ SA, BAYLINK DJ, HUGHES MR, HAUSSLER MR, ROBERTSON RP: Selective deficiency of 1,25-dihydroxyvitamin D: A cause of isolated skeletal resistance to parathyroid hormone. *N Engl J Med* 297:1084, 1977.

106. LAMBERT PW, HOLLIS BW, BELL NH, EPSTEIN S: Demonstration of a lack of change in serum 1,25-dihydroxyvitamin D in response to parathyroid extract in pseudohypoparathyroidism. *J Clin Invest* 66:782, 1980.

107. BRAUN JJ, BIRKENHAGER JC, VISSER TJ, JUTTMANN JR: Lack of response of 1,25-dihydroxyvitamin D to exogenous parathyroid hormone in a patient with treated pseudohypoparathyroidism. *Clin Endocrinol* 14:403, 1981.

108. BELL NH, AVERY S, SINHA T, CLARK CM JR, ALLEN DO, JOHNSTON C JR: Effects of dibutyryl cyclic adenosine 3',5'-monophosphate and parathyroid extract on calcium and phosphorus metabolism in hypoparathyroidism and pseudohypoparathyroidism. *J Clin Invest* 51:816, 1972.

109. YAMAOKA K, SEINO Y, ISHIDA M, ISHII T, SHIMOTSUJI T, TANAKA Y, KUROSE H, MATSUDA S, SATOMURA K, YABUUCHI H: Effect of dibutyryl adenosine 3',5'-monophosphate administration on plasma concentrations of 1,25-dihydroxyvitamin D in pseudohypoparathyroidism type I. *J Clin Endocrinol Metab* 53:1096, 1981.

110. BRESLAU NA, MOSES AM, PAK CYC: Evidence for bone remodeling but lack of calcium mobilization response to parathyroid hormone in pseudohypoparathyroidism. *J Clin Endocrinol Metab* 57:638, 1983.

111. WILSON JD, HADDEN DR: Pseudohypoparathyroidism presenting with rickets. *J Clin Endocrinol Metab* 51:1184, 1980.

112. DABBAGH S, CHESNEY RW, LANGER LO, DELUCA HF, GILBERT EF, DEWEERD JH JR: Renal-nonresponsive, bone-responsive pseudohypoparathyroidism. *Am J Dis Child* 138:1030, 1984.

113. FRAME B, HANSON CA, FROST HM, BLOCK M, ARNSTEIN AR: Renal resistance to parathyroid hormone with osteitis fibrosa. *Am J Med* 52:311, 1972.

114. KIDD GS, SCHAAF M, ADLER RA, LASSMAN MN, WRAY HL: Skeletal responsiveness in pseudohypoparathyroidism. *Am J Med* 68:772, 1980.

115. VAN DOP C, BOURNE HR: Pseudohypoparathyroidism. *Annu Rev Med* 34:259, 1983.

116. WEINBERG AG, STONE RT: Autosomal dominant inheritance in Albright's hereditary osteodystrophy. *J Pediatr* 79:996, 1971.

117. VAN DOP C, BOURNE HR, NEER RM: Father to son transmission of decreased Ns activity in pseudohypoparathyroidism type Ia. *J Clin Endocrinol Metab* 59:825, 1984.

118. CEDERBAUM SD, LIPPE BM: Probable autosomal recessive inheritance in a family with Albright's hereditary osteodystrophy and an evaluation of the genetics of the disorder. *Am J Hum Genet* 25:638, 1973.

119. KINARD RE, WALTON JE, BUCKWALTER JA: Pseudohypoparathyroidism: Report on a family with four affected sisters. *Arch Intern Med* 139:204, 1979.

120. JOHNSON WG: Metabolic interference and the + − heterozygote: A hypothetical form of simple inheritance which is neither dominant nor recessive. *Am J Hum Genet* 32:374, 1980.

121. ILLUM F, DUPONT E: Prevalences of CT-detected calcification in the basal ganglia in idiopathic hypoparathyroidism and pseudohypoparathyroidism. *Neuroradiology* 27:32, 1985.

122. EYRE WG, REED WB: Albright's hereditary osteodystrophy with cutaneous bone formation. *Arch Dermatol* 104:635, 1971.

123. POZNANSKI AK, WERDER EA, GIEDION A, MARTIN A, SHAW H: The pattern of shortening of the bones of the hand in pseudohypoparathyroidism and pseudopseudohypoparathyroidism—A comparison with brachydactyly E, Turner syndrome, and acrodysostosis. *Radiology* 123:707, 1977.

124. STEINBACH HL, YOUNG DA: The roentgen appearance of pseudohypoparathyroidism and pseudopseudohypoparathyroidism. *Am J Roentgenol* 97:49, 1966.

125. LEVINE MA, JAP TS, HUNG W: Infantile hypothyroidism in two sibs: An unusual presentation of pseudohypoparathyroidism type Ia. *J Pediatr* 107:919, 1985.

126. WEISMAN Y, GOLANDER A, SPIRER Z, FARFEL Z: Pseudohypoparathyroidism type Ia presenting as congenital hypothyroidism. *J Pediatr* 107:413, 1985.

127. SLATER S: An evaluation of the metacarpal sign. *Pediatrics* 46:468, 1970.

128. ABLOW RC, HSIA YE, BRANDT IK: Acrodysostosis coinciding with pseudohypoparathyroidism and pseudopseudohypoparathyroidism. *Am J Roentgenol* 128:95, 1977.

129. LARSEN JL, KIVLIN J, ODELL WD: Unusual cause of short stature. *Am J Med* 78:1025, 1985.

130. GRAUDAL N, MILMAN N, NIELSEN LS, NIEBUHR E, BONDE J: Coexistent pseudohypoparathyroidism and D brachydactyly in a family. *Clin Genet* 30:449, 1986.

131. BARAN DT, KLAHR S, SLATOPOLSKY E, AVIOLI LV: Effect of acetazolamide on calcium and phosphate metabolism in type I pseudohypoparathyroidism: Interaction with parathyroid hormone. *J Clin Endocrinol Metab* 48:766, 1979.

CHAPTER 80

VITAMIN D AND OTHER CALCIFEROLS

STEPHEN J. MARX

1. *Normal calciferol physiology includes activation through 25 hydroxylation in the liver and 1α hydroxylation in the renal proximal tubule: the most active metabolite is 1α,25-dihydroxy vitamin D_3 [1α,25$(OH)_2D_3$], which acts on target tissues by a mechanism analogous to that of the true steroid hormones. Two distinct hereditary defects have been recognized: selective (selective deficiency implies normal concentrations of the immediate precursor) and simple (simple deficiency implies that other metabolic pathways are not abnormal) deficiency of 1α,25$(OH)_2D$ and generalized (generalized means that all target tissues are affected) resistance to 1α,25$(OH)_2D$. Hereditary defects in calciferol metabolism or action show all the features of the calciferol deficiency states beginning early in life. These features are intestinal malabsorption of calcium, hypocalcemia, secondary hyperparathyroidism, hyperphosphaturia, and hypophosphatemia. The combination of hypocalcemia and hypophosphatemia results in impaired mineralization of bone (rickets and osteomalacia).*

2. *Hereditary selective and simple deficiency of 1α,25$(OH)_2D$ is an autosomal recessive trait. Patients respond to any doses of calciferol analogues that maintain normal circulating bioactivity of equivalents of 1α,25$(OH)_2D$. The cellular basis is presumed to be a deficiency of the renal 25$(OH)D$ 1α-hydroxylase. Because of inaccessibility of renal tissue, the specific deficiency has been confirmed so far only in an animal model for this disorder.*

3. *Hereditary selective deficiency of 1α,25$(OH)_2D$ can also occur as part of complex disorders that affect additional metabolic pathways not related to calciferols. Examples include X-linked hypophosphatemia, pseudohypoparathyroidism, and Fanconi syndrome.*

4. *Hereditary generalized resistance to 1α,25$(OH)_2D$ is an autosomal recessive trait. The cellular basis is presumed to be abnormality in the receptor for 1α,25$(OH)_2D$. At least five types of receptor defect have been identified in cells cultured from these patients. The type of defect has not correlated with the clinical features, and it seems likely that each defect could produce varying severity of clinical dysfunction. Approximately half of cases show alopecia; these are all among the more severely affected patients. The alopecia probably reflects dysfunction in 1,25$(OH)_2D$ target cells in the hair follicle. The most severely affected cases show no calcemic response to the highest available doses of calciferols. Depending upon the severity of the defect patients may respond to treatment with (1) calciferol analogues that allow for endogenous regulation of 1α,25-$(OH)_2D$ production, (2) calcium plus calciferol analogues that bypass 25$(OH)D$ 1α-hydroxylase, or (3) extremely high doses of calcium orally or intravenously (for patients unresponsive to maximal doses of all calciferols).*

HISTORY

Rickets and osteomalacia were widespread problems until the discovery of the calciferols in 1919.[1] This discovery resulted in the use of calciferols for prevention and treatment of rickets and osteomalacia. Some cases of rickets or osteomalacia did not respond to the usual doses of calciferols, and multiple causes of vitamin D resistance were subsequently recognized. In 1937 Albright reported detailed studies of a child with this problem and suggested a hereditary resistance to the actions of calciferols.[2] Rickets resistant to calciferols was subsequently recognized as a common cause of hereditary dwarfism. Most cases showed biochemical features different from those of nutritional deficiency of calciferols and are now classified as phosphate diabetes or X-linked hypophosphatemia (see Chap. 105).

In 1961 Prader et al. characterized a distinctive form of hereditary rickets which they called *pseudodeficiency rickets*.[3] Features which clearly distinguished pseudodeficiency rickets from X-linked hypophosphatemia were hypocalcemia, the potential for complete remission with high doses of calciferols, and a different transmission pattern. In 1970 it was shown that untreated patients with pseudodeficiency rickets had intestinal malabsorption of calcium[4] and secondary hyperparathyroidism[5] and that both of these abnormalities could be corrected by high doses of calciferols.

In 1971 three groups identified 1α,25$(OH)_2D_3$ as the active metabolite of vitamin D_3 that accumulated in the nuclei of vitamin D_3 target tissues.[6–8] This discovery accelerated further exploration of calciferol metabolism, including the development of methods to measure active metabolites in blood, characterization of defects in 1α,25$(OH)_2D$ synthesis and action, and understanding the roles of 1α-hydroxylated and other analogues for therapy. In 1973 Fraser and associates showed that a patient with pseudodeficiency rickets could be treated with a physiological dose of 1α,25$(OH)_2D_3$; they suggested that this disorder represented a defect in the 25$(OH)D$ 1α-hydroxylase enzyme.[9] In 1978 Brooks described a patient with similar clinical features but high serum levels of 1α,25$(OH)_2D$ before and during treatment and suggested that pseudodeficiency rickets be subclassified as type I [deficient production of 1α,25$(OH)_2D$] or type II [impaired end-organ response to 1α,25$(OH)_2D$].[10]

NORMAL PHYSIOLOGY OF CALCIFEROLS

Normal Metabolism

Vitamin D Sources. Cholecalciferol (vitamin D_3)[11] is a secosteroid that is formed by opening the B ring of 7-dehydrocholesterol (Fig. 80–1). In human beings, this reaction occurs in the basal layers of the epidermis[12] and is driven by ultraviolet radiation (from sunlight). Skin pigment in blacks can decrease

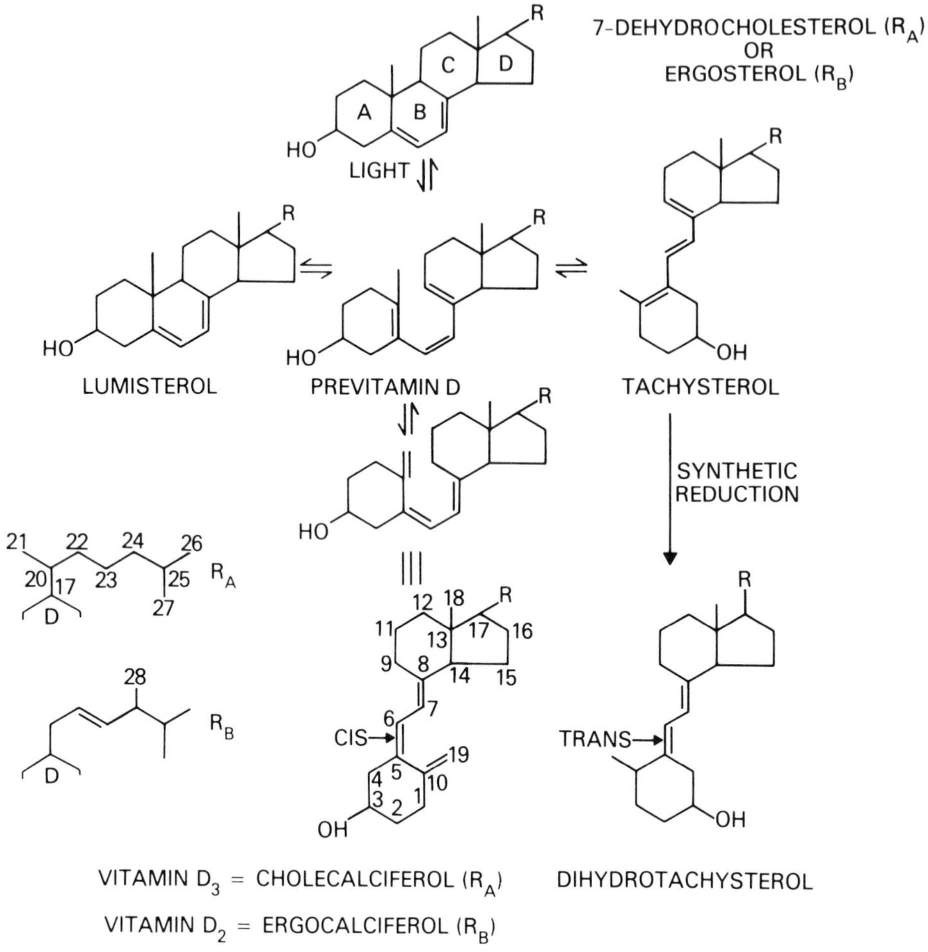

VITAMIN D$_3$ = CHOLECALCIFEROL (R$_A$)

VITAMIN D$_2$ = ERGOCALCIFEROL (R$_B$)

DIHYDROTACHYSTEROL

Fig. 80-1 Synthesis of cholecalciferol, ergocalciferol, and dihydrotachysterol.

the amount of cholecalciferol synthesized in response to a submaximal dose of UV radiation.[13] Ergocalciferol (vitamin D$_2$) is a secosteroid formed by opening the B ring of ergosterol, a sterol found in plants and fungi. Plants do not contain important amounts of ergocalciferol, but this chemical is synthesized in bulk for use as a nutritional supplement. Human beings obtain calciferols either as an endogenous metabolite in skin, as a natural dietary component, or as a dietary supplement. The metabolism and actions of D$_3$ and D$_2$ are similar in human beings.

Vitamin D 25 Hydroxylation. Cholecalciferol and ergocalciferol are inert when exposed directly to calciferol target tissues. They must be hydroxylated at positions 25 and 1α to become maximally active (Fig. 80-2). The initial hydroxylation at carbon 25 is carried out only in the liver by a mitochondrial cytochrome P$_{450}$ mono-oxygenase.[14] A different 25-hydroxylase system has been purified from rat liver microsomes, but absence of this system in microsomes from females makes its physiological significance doubtful.[15] 25 Hydroxylation of vitamin D is not highly regulated; the principal determinant of its rate is the circulating level of vitamin D.

1α Hydroxylation. 25(OH)D is 1α-hydroxylated to 1α,25(OH)$_2$D[16] or 24-hydroxylated to 24,25(OH)$_2$D by enzyme systems in the kidney. 25(OH)D 1α-hydroxylase activity is also found in placenta, in certain cultured cells of diverse origin, and in certain pathologic tissues (such as granulomas and activated T cells). Virtually all 1α,25(OH)$_2$D in blood normally comes from renal secretion.[17] The renal 1α-hydrox-

ylase enzyme is stringently regulated. Parathyroid hormone activates it in the renal proximal tubule through a cyclic AMP–mediated pathway;[18] calcitonin activates it in a more distal region of the proximal tubule apparently without a rise in cyclic AMP.[19] 1α,25(OH)$_2$D (perhaps through its receptor) and phosphate inhibit it by unknown mechanisms. Hypocalcemia may activate it to a modest degree. The 25(OH)D 1α-hydroxylase enzyme has been partially purified from renal mitochondria.[20,21] It contains a cytochrome P$_{450}$ and renoredoxin; dephosphorylation of the renoredoxin component may mediate activation of the 1α-hydroxylase by parathyroid hormone.[22]

24 Hydroxylation. 25(OH)D, 1α,25(OH)$_2$D, and other metabolites are substrates for 24 hydroxylation. The 24-hydroxylase enzyme shares many properties with the 25(OH)D 1α-hydroxylase enzymes. Both are mitochondrial enzymes containing cytochrome P$_{450}$.[23] Both are modulated (though in opposing directions) by cyclic AMP and probably by the receptor for 1α,25(OH)$_2$D.[24] Their anatomic distributions, however, are different, with the 1α-hydroxylase confined to the proximal renal tubule, but the 24-hydroxylase located in a wide range of normal tissues. Their many similarities have raised the possibilities that they might share certain components. The importance of 24-hydroxylase has not been fully determined; it may be the only route to a group of calciferols with unique actions not obtainable with 1α,25(OH)$_2$D (see "Specific Role of 24,25(OH)$_2$D"), and it might be the most important step in 1α,25(OH)$_2$D removal. Induction of 24-hydroxylase by 1α,25(OH)$_2$D in target tissues[23] and preference

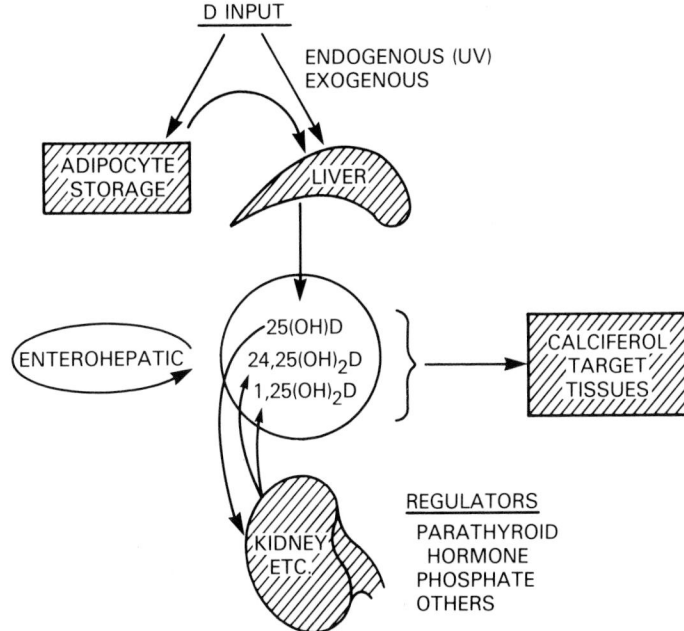

Fig. 80-2 Metabolic pathways for activation of cholecalciferol or ergocalciferol.

of this enzyme for $1\alpha,25(OH)_2D$ rather than $25(OH)D$ as substrate suggest an important role in ending the action of $1\alpha,25(OH)_2D$.

5,6-*Cis-Trans* Isomerization. $25(OH)D$ may also be converted to $5,6$-*trans*-$25(OH)D$. This pathway has so far been documented only with rat plasma after the animals were treated with pharmacologic amounts of vitamin D_3.[25] However, the pathway is of interest because it produces a metabolite analogous to $25(OH)$-dihydrotachysterol (Fig. 80-3) (dihydrotachysterol is a synthetic calciferol analogue used in therapy). These metabolites have an A ring rotated 180°, bringing the 3β-hydroxyl group into a pseudo-1α-hydroxyl position. This rotation increases the agonist potency of the parent metabolite on the $1\alpha,25(OH)_2D$ receptor. And 5,6-trans metabolites might have important roles in states where the renal 1α-hydroxylase enzyme is severely deficient.

Other Calciferol Metabolites. A series of hydroxylations and other oxidations of the C-17 side chain has been characterized by studies in vivo and in vitro. The 24-hydroxyl group can be oxidized to a ketone. 23 Hydroxylation[26] is the initial step in

Fig. 80-3 Steric conformation of two activated calciferol analogues. $1\alpha,25(OH)_2D_3$ has the 5–6 double bond in cis configuration. $25(OH)$dihydrotachysterol$_3$ has the 5–6 double bond in trans configuration; the 180° rotation of the A ring (lowest ring in figure) brings the 3-β-hydroxyl group into a pseudo-1α configuration.

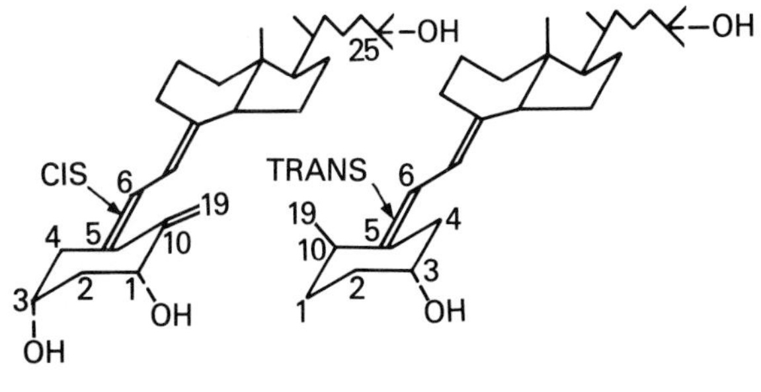

$1\alpha, 25\text{-}(OH)_2\text{-}D_3$ $25\text{-}(OH)\text{-}DHT_3$

conversion of $25(OH)D_3$ to $25(OH)D_3$-23-26-lactone, the principal circulating metabolite. $1\alpha,25(OH)_2D_3$ can also be metabolized to the analogous lactone. Multiple oxidations can be followed by cleavage of the C-17 side chain.

Transcalciferin as a Calciferol Binder. All calciferols are fat-soluble and circulate principally bound to transcalciferin, an α-globulin of 58 kDa.[27] Transcalciferin, also known as group-specific component, or Gc, is structurally homologous to albumin and α-fetoprotein.[28] It has one high affinity sterol binding site with preferential affinity for $25(OH)D$. Detailed affinity testing shows the following series: $25(OH)D_3$-26,23-lactone > $25(OH)D = 24,25(OH)_2D > 1\alpha,25(OH)_2D >>$ vitamin D. It is a major component of plasma protein (normal concentration 10^{-5} M) that has multiple isoforms[29] that had been extensively studied for their genetic diversity long before a function in calciferol transport was recognized.

Calciferol Turnover and Requirements. Most of the body pool of vitamin D is in body fat, while only a small fraction of the pools of $25(OH)D$ or $1\alpha,25(OH)_2D$ are in fat.[30] In the circulation greater than 99 percent of each metabolite is bound to transcalciferin. Normal daily turnover of vitamin D is approximately 30 μg/day; most of this is cleared through catabolic pathways with only 1 μg/day contributing to daily turnover of $1\alpha,25(OH)_2D$ (Table 80-1). In the vitamin D–deficient

Table 80-1 Serum Levels and Body Pools of Calciferol Metabolites in Adults

Metabolite	Concentration in serum, ng/ml	Half-time in serum, days	Pool size in body, μg	Turnover in body, μg/day
D_3	10*	30	1000	30
$25(OH)D$	25	15	500	15
$1\alpha,25(OH)_2D$	0.03	0.2	0.5	1
$24,25(OH)_2D$	1	2	10	10

NOTE: With the exception of serum concentrations, these numbers are based on limited data.
*Typical summer mean in temperate climate; normal winter mean is below 0.5 ng/ml. D_2 concentration (not tabulated) depends largely on diet supplements.

state, the fractional conversion of D to $1\alpha,25(OH)_2$ is far higher. The recommended daily allowance for vitamin D in the United States is 400 international units (10 µg).

Normal Actions

$1\alpha,25(OH)_2D$ Receptors. $1\alpha,25(OH)_2D$ is the most potent natural calciferol metabolite with a median effective dose (ED_{50}) of approximately one-thousandth that of $25(OH)D$ in most test systems. $1\alpha,25(OH)_2D$ acts by binding to a high affinity receptor, analogous to the receptors for true steroid hormones.[31] Structure-function studies with a series of calciferol analogues[32] indicate that in vivo the receptor may be activated by a mixture of agonists including $1\alpha,25(OH)_2D$, $25(OH)D$, and $5,6$-*trans*-$25(OH)D$. The $1\alpha,25(OH)_2D$ receptor is a 50- to 60-kDa peptide structurally homologous to a family of DNA-binding[33,33a] proteins that includes the receptors for true steroid hormones, the receptor for triiodothyronine, the retinoic acid receptor, and the product of the viral ERB-A oncogene. The structural information concerning the $1,25(OH)_2D$ receptor is derived from cDNA clones for the messenger RNA. The $1\alpha,25(OH)_2D$ receptor is found in many tissues[34] and can be induced by increased cell proliferation, by exposure to $1\alpha,25(OH)_2D$, and by the ontogenetic state. In particular, the receptor first appears in the rat intestine 14 days postnatally and correlates with the onset of $1\alpha,25(OH)_2D$-dependent calcium transport.[35] Hormone binding to the $1\alpha,25(OH)_2D$ receptor causes a receptor change that is analogous to the activation process of steroid hormone receptors.

Transcriptional Effects of $1\alpha,25(OH)_2D$. The specific genes with which the $1\alpha,25(OH)_2D$ receptor interacts have not yet been identified, but $1\alpha,25(OH)_2D$ directly or indirectly regulates mRNA levels for many different proteins. For example, cholecalcin mRNA levels in duodenal mucosa (and in many other tissues) are increased,[36] osteocalcin (also termed *bone γ-carboxyglutamic acid protein*) mRNA rises in osteoblasts,[37] preprocollagen type I mRNA levels rise or fall in bone cultures,[38] and preproparathyroid hormone mRNA levels fall in parathyroid cells[39] (see below for more details concerning the proteins encoded by each of these mRNAs).

Nongenomic Effects of $1\alpha,25(OH)_2D$. $1\alpha,25(OH)_2D$ may have some cellular effects not mediated by the genomic pathway. Evidence for these mechanisms includes very rapid effects in certain studies[40–41a] and effects that persist with high concentrations of blockers of protein synthesis.

Cholecalcin and Intestinal Transport of Calcium. The most important physiological action of $1\alpha,25(OH)_2D$ is stimulation of active calcium transport across the duodenum from lumen to bloodstream. Surprisingly few details are known about the molecular details of this process.[42] In particular the roles of cholecalcin (also called *calbindin*, or vitamin D–dependent calcium-binding protein) are not known; this is despite the fact that it binds calcium with high affinity (the calcium-binding regions are homologous to those of the calmodulin family), it constitutes approximately 2 percent of duodenal mucosal cell protein in the D-replete state, and it is undetectable in duodenum in the D-deficient state. Proposed roles of cholecalcin in duodenum include a buffer of intracellular calcium[43] or a regulator of calcium ATPase.[44] There are at least two cholecalcin genes in the rat; one codes for a 9-kDa protein concentrated in the duodenum, while the other codes for a homologous 28-kDa protein concentrated in kidney, brain, and many other tissues.

A widespread tissue distribution of $1\alpha,25(OH)_2D$ receptors and of a family of cholecalcin proteins indicates that $1\alpha,25(OH)_2D$ might have direct actions in many tissues. Several potential targets outside the intestine will be discussed here.

$1\alpha,25(OH)_2D$ Actions on Bone. Most of the antirachitic actions of calciferols are secondary to maintenance of adequate calcium and phosphate concentrations in extracellular fluid to allow mineralization.[45–47] The direct actions of 1α-$25(OH)_2D$ in bone seem to be mostly catabolic. For example, $1\alpha,25(OH)_2D_3$ inhibits proliferation and collagen synthesis in fetal bone and in fetal osteoblasts.[37] In osteoblast-like cells from adult humans, $1\alpha,25(OH)_2D_3$ stimulates collagen synthesis.[48] Differing effects on alkaline phosphatase have been reported in several systems; however, there is general agreement that in rapidly growing osteoblast-like cells alkaline phosphatase levels are low and will rise in response to $1\alpha,25(OH)_2D_3$.[49] $1\alpha,25(OH)_2D_3$ stimulates synthesis and secretion of osteocalcin by osteoblast-like cells.[37] Osteocalcin is a major component of bone matrix with unknown function, and its blood levels may be an index of osteoblastic activity and of $1\alpha,25(OH)_2D$ bioeffect.

$1\alpha,25(OH)_2D_3$ is a potent activator of osteoclasts in vivo and in organ culture. However, isolated osteoclasts have shown no response to $1\alpha,25(OH)_2D_3$;[50] this results from the absence of receptors for $1\alpha,25(OH)_2D$ in these cells.[51] At least three mechanisms have been suggested for $1\alpha,25(OH)_2D_3$ activation of osteoclasts: first, $1\alpha,25(OH)_2D_3$ may stimulate differentiation of osteoclast precursors, related to monocytes and macrophages[52,53]; second, $1\alpha,25(OH)_2D_3$ may stimulate fusion and metabolism of the immediate precursor of the multinucleated osteoclast[54]; and, third, $1\alpha,25(OH)_2D_3$ might stimulate adjacent cells such as osteoblasts to activate osteoclasts (adjacent cells could help make bone surface more accessible to osteoclasts or could release mediators to activate osteoclasts).[55]

$1\alpha,25(OH)_2D$ Actions on Skin and Hair. Receptors for $1\alpha,25(OH)_2D$ have been directly documented by in vivo autoradiography in basal layers of epidermis and in the outer root sheath cells of the rat hair follicle.[56] Furthermore, $1\alpha,25(OH)_2D_3$ stimulates differentiation of epidermal keratinocytes in tissue culture.[57]

$1\alpha,25(OH)_2D$ Actions on the Parathyroid Gland. $1\alpha,25(OH)_2D_3$ shows inhibitory effects on the parathyroid gland in vitro. $1\alpha,25(OH)_2D_3$ decreases transcription of mRNA for preproparathyroid hormone.[39]

$1\alpha,25(OH)_2D$ Actions on Calciferol Metabolism. $1\alpha,25(OH)_2D$ has shown potential to regulate calciferol metabolism at several steps. $1\alpha,25(OH)_2D_3$ can increase the levels of 7,8-didehydrocholesterol in skin.[58] $1\alpha,25(OH)_2D_3$ is a potent inhibitor of the renal $25(OH)D$ 1α-hydroxylase enzyme[16] (see above). $1\alpha,25(OH)_2D$ activates the 24-hydroxylase enzyme in kidney and in many other tissues.[24] $1\alpha,25(OH)_2D_3$

stimulates the clearance of 25(OH)D and 1α,25(OH)$_2$D; this regulated clearance is a combination of 24 hydroxylation, 23 hydroxylation, and less well defined processes.[59]

Specific Role of 24,25(OH)$_2$D. It has been reported that 24,25(OH)$_2$D$_3$ shows unique actions on cartilage from fetal or newborn animals, not reproduced by any dosage of 1α,25(OH)$_2$D$_3$.[60,61] These actions include stimulation of proliferation and stimulation of creatine kinase BB isoenzyme. However, extensive efforts have failed to show an important role for 24,25(OH)$_2$D$_3$ in vivo.[62] For example, rats can be raised through two generations without this metabolite. This has been accomplished by raising them on a vitamin D–free diet supplemented with 24,25(Fl)$_2$-25(OH)D$_3$, a metabolite that precludes the formation of the 24-hydroxylated metabolite [though it might not preclude formation of other metabolites that might activate a putative receptor for 24,25(OH)$_2$D].

NOMENCLATURE IN CALCIFEROL DEFICIENCY STATES

Hormones or Vitamins

The calciferols traverse a metabolic pathway that could justify their being described as normal metabolites, vitamins (a metabolic component required in trace amounts in states of limited skin exposure to ultraviolet light), or hormones [1α,25(OH)$_2$D is a secosteroid secreted by a "gland" at a regulated rate and acting on distant targets]. The term *calciferol* refers to the entire family of secosteroid metabolites in this pathway. The term *D*, as in 25(OH)D, refers to the sum of D$_2$ and D$_3$ forms.

Deficiency States

Prior terminology applied to the calciferol deficiency states has led to much confusion; this is principally because the terms were first used prior to our detailed understanding of calciferol pathophysiology. Since widely used terms to characterize calciferol pathophysiology are ambiguous and likely to remain in use, it is important to understand the limitations of these terms.

It is important to specify the location of a defect as precisely as possible. Thus the description of a deficiency state should indicate the most proximal metabolite in the biosynthetic pathway that is deficient. Deficiency of 1α,25(OH)$_2$D could result from deficiency of D or 25(OH)D. I use the term *selective deficiency* to emphasize that a deficiency is associated with normal levels of the immediate precursor of the metabolite specified.

Several terms related to the term *deficiency* have been used, including pseudodeficiency, dependency, and resistance. The term *vitamin D deficiency* should be reserved for states where blood and tissue levels of vitamin D (D$_3$ plus D$_2$) are abnormally low. Because of difficulty in measuring vitamin D in blood, the diagnosis is usually established by measuring 25(OH)D. Vitamin D deficiency can be associated with normal or even high circulating levels of 1α,25(OH)$_2$D (see below).

The term *pseudo vitamin D deficiency* refers to a state with biochemical and tissue features of vitamin D deficiency (i.e., calcium deficiency, secondary hyperparathyroidism, impaired skeletal mineralization) but no presumed deficiency in vitamin D levels or diet calcium. Pseudo vitamin D deficiency has been subdivided into type I [deficient 1α,25(OH)$_2$D] and type II [resistance to 1α,25(OH)$_2$D].

The term *vitamin D dependency* has been used interchangeably with pseudo vitamin D deficiency. However, it should be reserved for cases capable of responding to (i.e., dependent upon) supraphysiologic doses of vitamin D. It has been applied to but does not accurately describe patients responding to high doses of 1α,25(OH)$_2$D but not to vitamin D or patients completely unresponsive to vitamin D or 1α,25(OH)$_2$D but responsive to high doses of calcium.

The term *resistance* specifies a metabolite proximal to a defect while deficiency characterizes a metabolite distal to the defect (assuming the latter defect is in production, not clearance). The term resistance should only be used with the most distal metabolite to which there is resistance.

Some descriptions (of deficiency or resistance) include a bioeffect, such as rickets or osteomalacia.[63] This can be particularly confusing because not all causes of rickets or osteomalacia involve primary problems in calciferol metabolism or action. For example, rickets resistant to 1α,25(OH)$_2$D could include primary bone defects such as hypophosphatasia.[64] The most helpful bioeffect to include in a description is the most proximal one(s) known to be abnormal; thus calcium malabsorption is more useful than osteomalacia to characterize defects in calciferol metabolism or action. The term *vitamin D–resistant rickets* combines all the problems addressed above. It could be applied to a defect (associated with normal vitamin D intake) anywhere in the bone mineralization pathway (Fig. 80-4).

Since defects in calciferol metabolism or action can be associated with or even secondary to defects in other pathways, disease categories should also indicate if dysfunction extends to other pathways. I use the term *simple* to specify that a calciferol defect is not associated with defects in other pathways and *complex* to specify the converse. Other important qualifying terms can indicate if a defect is hereditary or acquired or if a defect is anatomically localized (tissue-selective) or generalized (tissue-nonselective).[64a] In this chapter, I will use precise terms (Table 80-2), consistent with our current understanding of calciferol metabolism. As our understanding increases, these terms will need to be replaced.

Two hereditary defects, limited to the calciferol pathway (i.e., simple defects), have been recognized. The first is selective* and simple† deficiency of 1α,25(OH)$_2$D 1α-hydroxylase. The second is generalized simple resistance to 1α,25(OH)$_2$D. It seems likely that all cases in the first category result from defects of 25(OH)D 1α hydroxylase and that all in the second category reflect simple deficiency of 1α,25(OH)$_2$D receptor function.

---

*By *selective deficiency* of a metabolite, I mean deficiency of this metabolite without deficiency of its immediate precursor.

†By *simple deficiency*, I mean a defect that involves only the calciferol metabolic pathway. The alternative is a complex deficiency involving other pathways as well. Most acquired disturbances in calciferol metabolism are complex as they involve multiple processes (for example, malabsorption or chronic renal disease). Some hereditary disturbances are also complex. For example, hereditary 25(OH)D 1α-hydroxylase deficiency can occur as a part of Fanconi syndrome, pseudohypoparathyroidism, or X-linked hypophosphatemia.

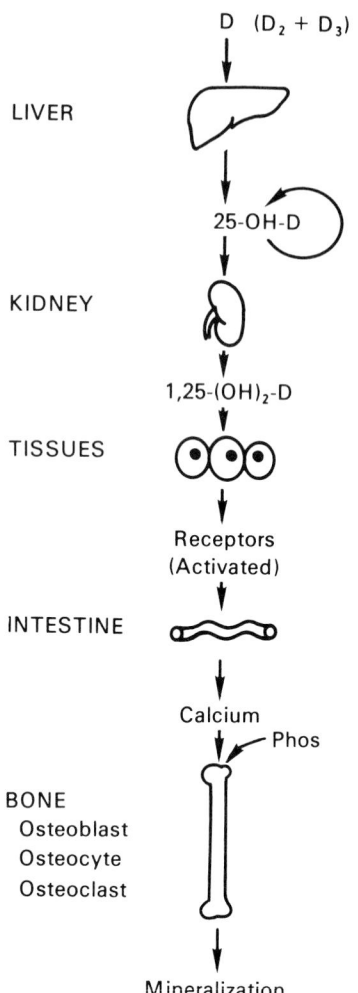

D (D$_2$ + D$_3$)

LIVER

25-OH-D

KIDNEY

1,25-(OH)$_2$-D

TISSUES

Receptors
(Activated)

INTESTINE

Calcium
— Phos

BONE
Osteoblast
Osteocyte
Osteoclast

Mineralization

Fig. 80-4 Calciferol activation as a component of the bone mineralization pathway.

GENERAL FEATURES OF CALCIFEROL DEFICIENCY

Clinical Presentation

The general features of vitamin D deficiency will be reviewed[65] because almost all are shown in patients with hereditary defects in calciferol metabolism [selective deficiency of 1α,25(OH)$_2$D or generalized resistance to 1α,25(OH)$_2$D].

The clinical features of calciferol deficiency are weakness, bone pain, bone deformity, and fracture. The most rapidly growing bones show the most striking abnormalities. In the first year of life the most rapidly growing bones are in the cranium, ribs, and wrists. Calciferol deficiency at this time leads to widened cranial sutures, frontal bossing, posterior flattening of the skull, bulging of costochondral junctions, and enlargement of the wrists. The rib cage may be so deformed that it contributes to respiratory failure. Dental eruption is delayed, and teeth show enamel hypoplasia. Muscular weakness and hypotonia are severe and result in a protuberant abdomen. Muscular weakness contributes to respiratory failure. Linear growth may be adequate, but the child may be unable to walk without support. Tetany is unusual, as the degree of hypocalcemia is mild and its onset is slow. After age 1, de-

Table 80-2 Classification of Calciferol Deficiency States by Theoretically Possible Etiology

Vitamin D deficiency
  Deficient input
    Deficient diet
    Deficient synthesis
  Increased clearance
Selective* 25(OH)D deficiency
  Deficient vitamin D 25-hydroxylase
  Increased clearance
Selective 1α,25(OH)$_2$D deficiency
  Deficient 25(OH)D 1α-hydroxylase
  Increased clearance
Resistance to 1α,25(OH)$_2$D
  Local
  Generalized
    Deficient 1α,25(OH)$_2$D receptor function
    Defects proximal or distal to 1α,25(OH)$_2$D
    receptor

NOTE: In theory, each category except deficient diet could have an hereditary or acquired etiology and each subcategory could be further partitioned into *simple* (implying that the defect is localized only to the step in calciferol metabolism) or *complex* (implying that the fundamental defect also involves other metabolic pathways). At present, the only recognized hereditary and simple defects are selective deficiency of 1α,25(OH)$_2$D and generalized resistance to 1α,25(OH)$_2$D.
Selective means that the immediate precursor of the metabolite is not deficient.

formities are most prominent in the legs because of their weight-bearing function.

The clinical features of calciferol deficiency states depend principally on age of onset. Calcium and phosphate levels in fetal plasma are sustained by placental transport from maternal plasma, and this transport is not regulated by calciferols.[66] A fetus with a hereditary abnormality in calciferol metabolism that develops in a mother with normal calciferol metabolism is presumed to have normal calcium and phosphate levels in plasma and bone until birth. In children, mineralization defects result in abnormalities of diaphyses, metaphyses, and epiphyses. In particular, deficient mineralization of the epiphyseal growth plate results in distorted (bulging) epiphyses and bone deformity.

Calciferol deficiency that begins after epiphyseal fusion causes less deformity. Calciferol deficiency in adults causes less severe features. In the mature, remodeling skeleton less than 5 percent of the calcium is newly deposited per year. Thus, a mineralization defect must be present for several years to be manifested. The earliest symptom is bone pain, particularly low in the back. Proximal muscle weakness may be so prominent as to suggest a primary neurologic disturbance.

Radiographs

The radiographic features of calciferol deficiency states in children are quite uniform. Delayed opacification of epiphyses causes widening and distortion of growth plates; the usually straight ends of the mineralizing metaphyses are irregular (frayed). The bone cortex is abnormally thin, and bone trabeculae are sparse. Pseudofractures are uncommon in children. Secondary hyperparathyroidism may cause subperiosteal erosions, but bone cysts are unusual in children.

Response to Therapy

During the first 1 to 4 months of treatment, endogenous production of $1\alpha,25(OH)_2D$ is regulated to rates above normal.[67-70] The minimal vitamin D requirement for treatment of D deficiency is 2 to 5 $\mu g/day$, but much larger amounts are usually given (100 to 200 $\mu g/day$) both to accelerate repletion of body vitamin D pools and because the excess vitamin D is not converted to excess $1\alpha,25(OH)_2D$. Successful initiation of therapy is evidenced by diminution of secondary hyperparathyroidism; that is to say, PTH and urinary cyclic AMP levels fall, serum phosphate level rises, and serum alkaline phosphatase level falls.

Pathophysiology

Virtually all the features of calciferol deficiency can be understood as direct or remote consequences of deficient calciferol effect on duodenal transport of calcium. Malabsorption of calcium results in hypocalcemia. Hypocalcemia (and perhaps also deficient calciferol effect on the parathyroid gland[71]) results in increased secretion of parathyroid hormone (i.e., secondary hyperparathyroidism). If this process continues for many months, the parathyroid glands develop hypertrophy and hyperplasia. Parathyroid hormone (PTH) acts on the proximal renal tubule to decrease reabsorption of phosphate and bicarbonate, resulting in hypophosphatemia and hyperchloremic acidosis. However, the phosphaturic effect of PTH is not uniform; hypocalcemia that is severe and long-standing can paradoxically inhibit the phosphaturic effect of PTH. This can result in a confusing picture of secondary hyperparathyroidism with high urinary cyclic AMP but not hypophosphatemia[72] (so-called pseudohypoparathyroidism type II). In children secondary hyperparathyroidism also causes generalized aminoaciduria. The combination of hypocalcemia and hypophosphatemia results in a slowed rate of mineralization of bone matrix. Parathyroid hormone also has direct actions on bone. It increases osteoclastic resorption (but the release of calcium and phosphate from bone does not fully compensate for the hypocalcemia or hypophosphatemia), and osteoblastic activity rises since it is "coupled" to osteoclast activity.

Patients with calciferol deficiency have many reasons for "resistance" to parathyroid hormone. These include failure of PTH to activate the $1\alpha,25(OH)_2D$ response pathway, downregulation of PTH receptors, and abnormally small PTH-responsive calcium pool in bone.

The response to therapy in calciferol deficiency states can be clearly understood by considering the changes in calcium homeostasis. The principal goal of therapy is provision of enough calcium and calciferol in plasma to allow normalization of bone mineralization and suppression of secondary hyperparathyroidism. A chronic deficiency of calciferol is associated with skeletal calcium deficiency that can withdraw calcium from plasma for many months after treatment begins. In children normal bone mass may be produced after recovery from calciferol deficiency, but in adults bone mass may remain low after "recovery".[73] In simple nutritional deficiency of vitamin D, therapy with vitamin D allows the PTH–1α-hydroxylase axis to generate high and appropriate amounts of $1\alpha,25(OH)_2D$ during this remineralization phase. Remineralization entails large fluxes of calcium and phosphate from blood into undermineralized bone; during this phase serum contains low calcium, high PTH, low phosphate, and normal or high 25(OH)D levels, all of which promote synthesis of $1\alpha,25(OH)_2D$. In cases with deficiency of the 1α-hydroxylase or with target resistance to $1\alpha,25(OH)_2D$, therapy should be designed to compensate for the defect and manage the phase of "hungry bones."

HEREDITARY DEFECTS IN CALCIFEROL METABOLISM

Hereditary Selective Deficiency of $1\alpha,25(OH)_2D$

Clinical Features. Deficiency of $1\alpha,25(OH)_2D$ occurs as a component of several hereditary disorders (X-linked hypophosphatemia, Fanconi syndrome), but selective and simple (as defined above) deficiency of $1\alpha,25(OH)_2D$ is a distinctive state to be described below. This disorder (formerly called hereditary vitamin D dependency type I or hereditary pseudo vitamin D deficiency type I) is an unusual cause of hereditary rickets.[74-76] Patients appear normal at birth but have recognizable dysfunction between ages 2 and 24 months, suggesting lack of calciferol effect (see above) that began at the time of birth. Muscle weakness is prominent, radiographic features are striking, and responsivity to calciferols is complete (see below).

Serum shows low calcium, high PTH, but low or even undetectable $1\alpha,25(OH)_2D$.[77,78] The latter can be associated with normal or even modestly increased 25(OH)D [reflecting vitamin D supplementation and/or diminished clearance of 25(OH)D]. During therapy with vitamin D or 25(OH)D, serum $1\alpha,25(OH)_2D$ continues to be low or undetectable. During successful maintenance therapy with $1\alpha(OH)D_3$, serum $1\alpha,25(OH)_2D$ is normal; random serum levels may be hard to interpret during therapy with $1\alpha,25(OH)_2D_3$ because of the rapid turnover of this drug. Serum calcium and phosphate in the partially treated patient can also be difficult to interpret. With partial treatment or early after discontinuation of treatment, mild secondary hyperparathyroidism can be associated with hypophosphatemia and normal serum calcium;[79] this can cause confusion with X-linked hypophosphatemia, particularly because some patients with that disorder can also show secondary hyperparathyroidism.

Inheritance. Several sibships show features highly suggestive of autosomal recessive inheritance. And there is a widespread assumption that this is the transmission mechanism in all cases. However, very few families have been evaluated in any detail since analysis of $1\alpha,25(OH)_2D$ in serum has been available. The homozygous state is relatively common in the Saguenay region of Quebec (estimated gene frequency 0.02), and this has been attributed to a founder effect rather than to a high rate of consanguinity.[80] Tests to recognize the heterozygous state have not yet been developed.

Therapy. Patients with this disorder have been treated successfully with all widely available calciferol analogues.[79,81-84] During the early phases of therapy (initial 3 to 6 months) they respond best to therapy with two to five times the expected long-term maintenance dose (Table 80-3) because of the high calcium requirements of the undermineralized skeleton. Long-term maintenance therapy is accomplished with any regimen that establishes normal circulating activity of metabolites that will activate receptors for $1\alpha,25(OH)_2D$ (Table 80-3). During

Table 80-3 Daily Calciferol Doses for Maintenance Treatment of Patients with Hereditary Defects in Calciferol Metabolism

Calciferol analogue	In deficient 25(OH)D-1α-hydroxylase, μg/day	In generalized resistance to 1α,25(OH)₂D, μg/day
D₃ or D₂	500–3000	500–?*
25(OH)D₃	30–200	30–?*
1α,25(OH)₂D₃	0.3–2	5–60†
1α-(OH)D₃	0.5–3	5–60†
Dihydrotachysterol	150–1000	2000–20,000†

NOTE: Dose requirements as μg/day (i.e., uncorrected for body size) are similar in children and adults.
*Patients with milder grades of resistance to 1α,25(OH)₂D (usually with normal hair) can respond to analogues requiring 1 hydroxylation. Maximal useful doses have not been defined. Serum 1α-25(OH)₂D must be maintained in the range of 200 to 10,000 pg/ml.
†Maximal doses are limited only by cost and patient acceptance; some patients have shown no response to maximal doses tested.

successful treatment with vitamin D or 25(OH)D, serum 25(OH)D levels are in the range of 250 ng/ml, but serum 1α,25(OH)₂D may remain low or undetectable.[77,78] This has several important implications. First, the degree of 1α-hydroxylase deficiency in these cases is severe; second, the indicated concentration of 25(OH)D is sufficient to be associated with normal activation of the 1α,25(OH)₂D receptor. The second implication does not establish whether 25(OH)D is acting directly or through other metabolites [such as 5,6-*trans*-25(OH)D]. During long-term maintenance therapy, the serum total 1α,25(OH)₂D bioactivity is presumed to be constant, determined by calciferol dosage. Regulation of calciferol activation is prevented by the deficiency of 1α-hydroxylase. Thus the patient must adapt to fluctuations in calcium availability through direct actions of PTH alone. Since intestinal fractional absorption of calcium cannot be regulated by endogenous mechanisms, all of external calcium balance must be regulated at the renal level. Thus, these patients might show more rapid fall of urine calcium or rise of urine calcium at times of calcium deficiency or excess, respectively. The best way to minimize such fluctuations is to include a fixed calcium supplement (1000 mg/day as elemental calcium).

Treatment must be continued indefinitely. Though relapses may be slow to develop after withdrawing treatment in an adult, relapses are inevitable and should be prevented.

Cellular Defect. The presumption is that hereditary selective deficiency of 1α,25(OH)₂D results, in all cases, from defects in 25(OH)D 1α-hydroxylase. It seems inconceivable that accelerated clearance of 1α,25(OH)₂D could produce this state. It is likely that the causes of 25(OH)D 1α-hydroxylase deficiency will be heterogeneous and that the degree of the deficiency will also prove variable.

Animal Models for Hereditary Selective Deficiency of 1α,25(OH)₂D. Ploniat reported an autosomal recessive rachitic disorder in pigs.[85] More recent studies showed that the animals had hypocalcemic rickets responsive to "physiological" doses of 1α,25(OH)₂D or 1α-(OH)D₃.[86] A similar trait was transferred to miniature pigs for detailed study. Direct assay of renal homogenates of homozygotes from both strains of pig established undetectable 25(OH)D₃ 1α-hydroxylase activity.[87,88] Both strains also exhibited low circulating

24,25(OH)₂D and undetectable renal 25(OH)D₃ 24-hydroxylase activity. This raised the possibility of associated hereditary deficiency of 24-hydroxylase or of low 24-hydroxylase activity secondary to hypocalcemia, hypophosphatemia, and secondary hyperparathyroidism.

States Resembling Hereditary Selective Deficiency of 1α,25(OH)₂D. In several hereditary or acquired disorders, 25(OH)D 1α-hydroxylase deficiency is one component of a more complex disturbance. These disorders affecting the proximal renal tubule include X-linked hypophosphatemia,[89–91] renal tubular acidosis,[92–94] Fanconi syndrome[95–97] (refer to Chaps 103 and 104), and tumor-associated osteomalacia (in which a humoral factor seems to cause impairment of 1α-hydroxylase and renal wasting of phosphate).[98] Replacement of 1α,25(OH)₂D is often an important component in therapy of these disorders.

Hereditary Generalized Resistance to 1α,25(OH)₂D

Clinical Features. Hereditary generalized resistance to 1α,25(OH)₂D (also called *vitamin D dependency type II or pseudo vitamin D deficiency type II*) is a rare disorder first recognized in 1977. The clinical features are almost identical to those in hereditary selective deficiency of 1α,25(OH)₂D with the exception that hereditary generalized resistance to 1α,25(OH)₂D has been associated with alopecia in about half of the kindreds.[99–101] Cases with hereditary generalized resistance to 1α,25(OH)₂D appear normal at birth but develop the clinical and biochemical features of calciferol deficiency (see above) with hypocalcemia and rickets over the first 2 to 8 months of life. In many cases, hair loss occurs between ages 2 and 12 months. The hair loss may be complete (Fig. 80-5) or incomplete; sometimes there is selective sparing of the eyelashes. Light-microscopic examination of a scalp biopsy showed normal numbers and morphology of hair follicles in a patient with total alopecia.[102] Alopecia occurs in patients with the most severe resistance to 1α,25(OH)₂D (see below). Without therapy, this disorder leads to inanition, severe skeletal deformity, recurrent respiratory infections, and death by age 8. Though therapy with calciferols can sustain complete biochemical remission, the alopecia does not improve. Other ectodermal defects have been reported in small numbers of cases and have an uncertain relation to the syndrome; these include oligodentia[103] and papular skin rash.[103,104] All patients suffer from the consequences of intestinal malabsorption of calcium. Attempts to show 1α,25(OH)₂D receptor-mediated dysfunctions outside the intestine in vivo have so far been inconclusive. Basal and stimulated concentrations of insulin, thyrotropin, prolactin, growth hormone, and testosterone have been normal (aside from deficiencies in insulin stimulation attributable to hypocalcemia).[105] Bone biopsies have shown normal or increased numbers of osteoclasts (suggesting that the 1α,25(OH)₂D receptor is not essential for osteoclast formation), but their resorptive activity was suggested to be impaired.[106]

In several cases, early postnatal development was apparently normal, and dysfunction was not evident until late in childhood[107] or even in adulthood[108] [in the latter case, serum 1α,25(OH)₂D was not measured, so alternate etiologies such as noncompliance were not excluded]. These patients did not show alopecia and responded to high doses of calciferols, indicating a mild variant of the syndrome. None showed clear features of a genetic etiology (that is to say, there was no parental consanguinity and no affected sibling; unfortunately, cultured cells were not evaluated in any).

Several patients have shown unexplained fluctuations in disease severity. Two patients without any clear calcemic response to calciferols experienced lessening of secondary hyperparathyroidism and improved bone mineralization around age 7 to 9.[109] These fluctuations may have resulted from subtle calciferol effect on the intestine and/or parathyroid gland.[109a] One patient showed a prolonged remission of biochemical and radiographic abnormalities that subsequently seemed completely unresponsive to much higher doses of calciferols.[110] Another patient showed amelioration of resistance to $1\alpha,25(OH)_2D$ in association with a brief trial of $24,25(OH)_2D$.[103]

Measurement of calciferol metabolites in plasma usually provides the most useful information for diagnosis. Serum concentrations of $1\alpha,25(OH)_2D$ are 50 to 1000 pg/ml (normal in children is 30 to 100 pg/ml) before treatment. During treatment typical concentrations are 200 to 10,000 pg/ml (Fig. 80-6).[111]

Inheritance. Approximately 30 kindreds had been reported as of 1986.[111] There have usually been strong suggestions of autosomal recessive transmission (parental consanguinity, etc.). Most cases have been recognized in a broad region centered on the Mediterranean shores, and this may relate to a high consanguinity rate in the receptor-disease source population.[112] No clinical abnormalities have been reported in obligate heterozygotes.

Fig. 80-5 Sisters (ages 7 and 3) with alopecia and rickets from hereditary generalized resistance to $1\alpha,25(OH)_2D$. *(From Rosen[100] et al.[100] Used with permission.)*

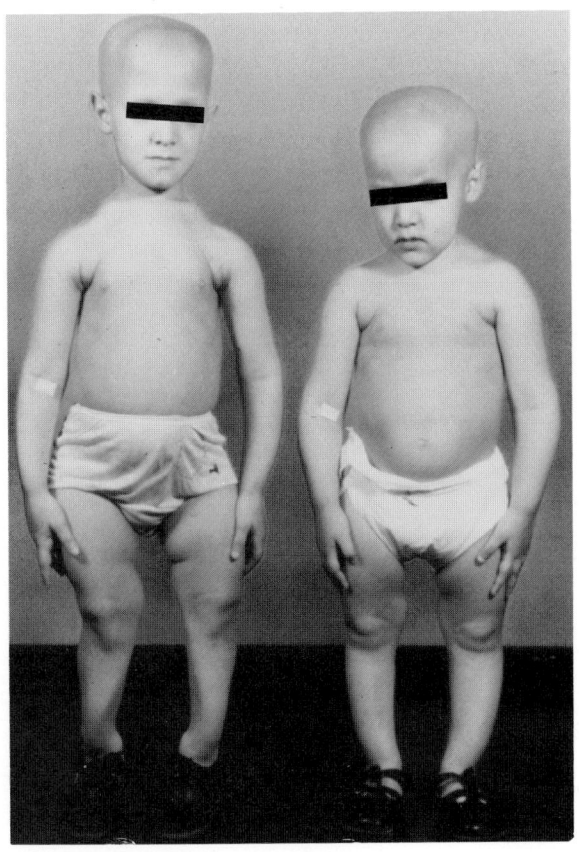

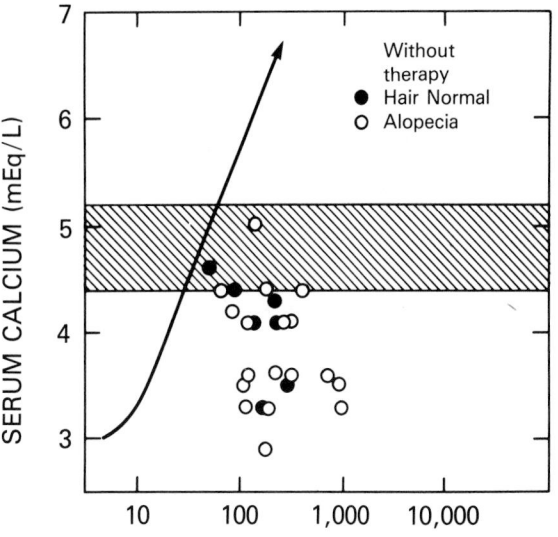

A.

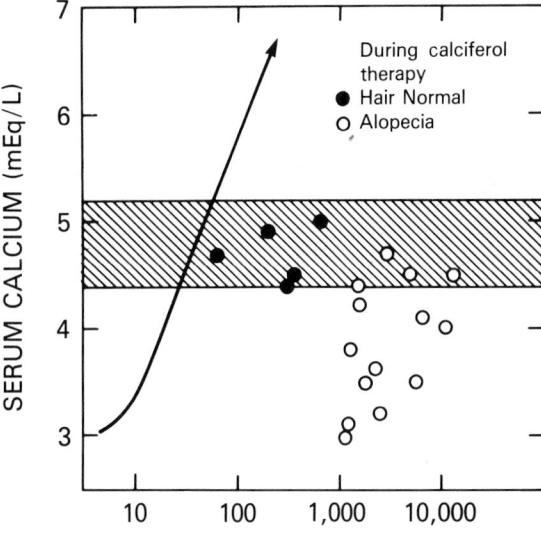

B.

Fig. 80-6 Relations between serum concentrations of calcium and $1\alpha,25(OH)_2D$. Stippled area is normal range for calcium. Solid curve is theoretical normal relation between calcium and $1\alpha,25(OH)_2D$. *A.* Without calciferol therapy. *B.* During calciferol therapy. Solid circle = hair normal. Open circle = alopecia. *(From Marx et al.[111])*

Treatment. Many patients show complete remission while receiving extraordinarily high doses of calciferols[101] (Table 80-3). The presence or absence of alopecia is one simple predictor of potential for response to therapy.[111] Virtually all patients with normal hair can sustain remission when given high doses of analogues not requiring 1 hydroxylation. Among patients with alopecia, approximately one-half have not responded to the highest doses of calciferols available; half have shown satisfactory calcemic response, but the dose requirement [deduced from serum $1,25(OH)_2D$ during therapy] is typically tenfold higher than in patients with normal hair (Fig. 80-6). Maintenance treatment is based upon four considerations: (1) the most mildly affected patients can be treated with calciferols [D_3, D_2, $25(OH)D_3$] that provide substrate for a high renal secretion of $1\alpha,25(OH)_2D$, (2) more severely affected patients may respond only to high doses of analogues [$1\alpha,25(OH)_2D$,

1α-(OH)D$_3$, dihydrotachysterol] that do not require 1 hydroxylation, (3) some patients may not respond to maximal doses of any calciferols, and (4) the role of calcium supplements is different in each of the prior three therapy categories.

Several patients have shown remissions while receiving high doses of D$_2$ or 25(OH)D$_3$;[10,99] they respond to this because their tissue resistance is only moderate and they can produce sufficient $1\alpha,25$(OH)$_2$D endogenously if presented with a high level of substrate for 1 hydroxylation. It is uncertain if this mechanism of therapy requires pathologic elevations of parathyroid hormone; it seems possible that near-normal parathyroid function may be sufficient because of deficient feedback suppression of 1 hydroxylation (Fig. 80-7) [resulting from the defect of $1\alpha,25$(OH)$_2$D receptors in the proximal renal tubule]. In this group calcium supplements may have little or no role, as serum concentrations of both PTH and $1\alpha,25$(OH)$_2$D can compensate for fluctuations in calcium availability. High levels of $1\alpha,25$(OH)$_2$D in an affected female can permit a normal pregnancy;[113] this is important because of concern that a high level of $1\alpha,25$(OH)$_2$D might disturb fetal tissues (see "Calciferol Excess States," below).

Patients unable to produce sufficient $1\alpha,25$(OH)$_2$D endogenously [because of a requirement for particularly high $1\alpha,25$(OH)$_2$D concentrations] may still respond to extraordinarily high doses of analogues not requiring 1 hydroxylation [i.e., $1\alpha,25$(OH)$_2$D$_3$, 1α-(OH)D$_3$, dihydrotachysterol]. Patients in this group requiring therapy that bypasses 1 hydroxylation should receive fixed calcium supplements (1000 mg/ day elemental calcium) for the same reasons as patients with hereditary selective deficiency of $1\alpha,25$(OH)$_2$D [see "Hereditary Selective Deficiency of 1,25(OH)$_2$D: Therapy"].

Some patients may have little or no response to maximal calciferol doses.[106,109,110] But it is difficult to identify these cases. There are no widely available indexes of intestinal responsivity to calciferols; fractional calcium absorption is the most relevant index, but this may be unavailable because of the inconvenience of balance studies or because of radiation exposure from calcium-47. It is possible to measure this parameter with stable calcium isotopes.[114] Most studies have relied upon the calcemic response to a therapeutic trial (Fig. 80-8). These trials may be unsatisfactory, first, because of the time required for repletion of undermineralized bones (i.e., as long as the bones retain the increased calcium input, this will not result in normalization of serum calcium). Second, therapeutic trials with high calciferol doses are limited by available drug formulations and drug cost. Patients with undetectable response to calciferols can receive substantial benefit if large amounts of calcium can be delivered to the bloodstream. The most rapid way to accomplish this is by intravenous infusions;[106,114] high calcium doses (1000 mg elemental calcium per day infused over 12 h) can be tolerated even by young children with this disorder. Since normal positive calcium balance during childhood growth is approximately 300 mg/day and since the total deficit may be several hundred grams of elemental calcium, such infusions must be given repeatedly over many months to accomplish significant results. This form of therapy requires methods similar to those used in hyperalimentation programs. Another way to increase calcium input to the bloodstream is to increase net absorption independent of calciferols. This can be accomplished by increasing calcium intake to the point of intolerance.[104] Unfortunately the upper limit of oral intake is around 6000 mg/day and requires great

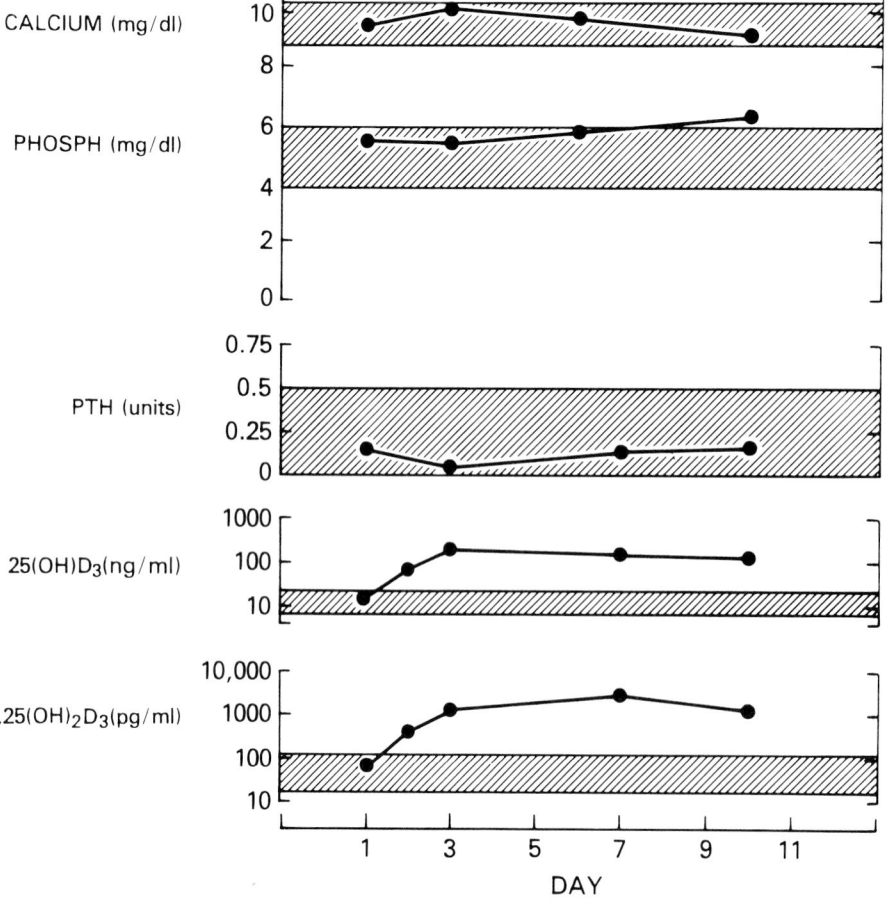

Fig. 80-7 Abnormal regulation of $1\alpha,25$(OH)$_2$D in serum. The patient has hereditary generalized resistance to $1\alpha,25$(OH)$_2$D. Serum calcium, phosphate, and parathyroid hormone have been normalized by treatment with 1α(OH)D$_3$. 1α(OH)D$_3$ was stopped for 2 days, and then the patient received 25(OH)D$_3$ as sole therapy. Stippled zones indicate normal ranges. Note logarithmic scales for calciferols. Serum $1\alpha,25$(OH)$_2$D reaches extremely high concentrations without the usual stimuli (low calcium, high PTH, low phosphate) for its production. *(From Marx et al.[101])* PHOSPH = phosphorus.

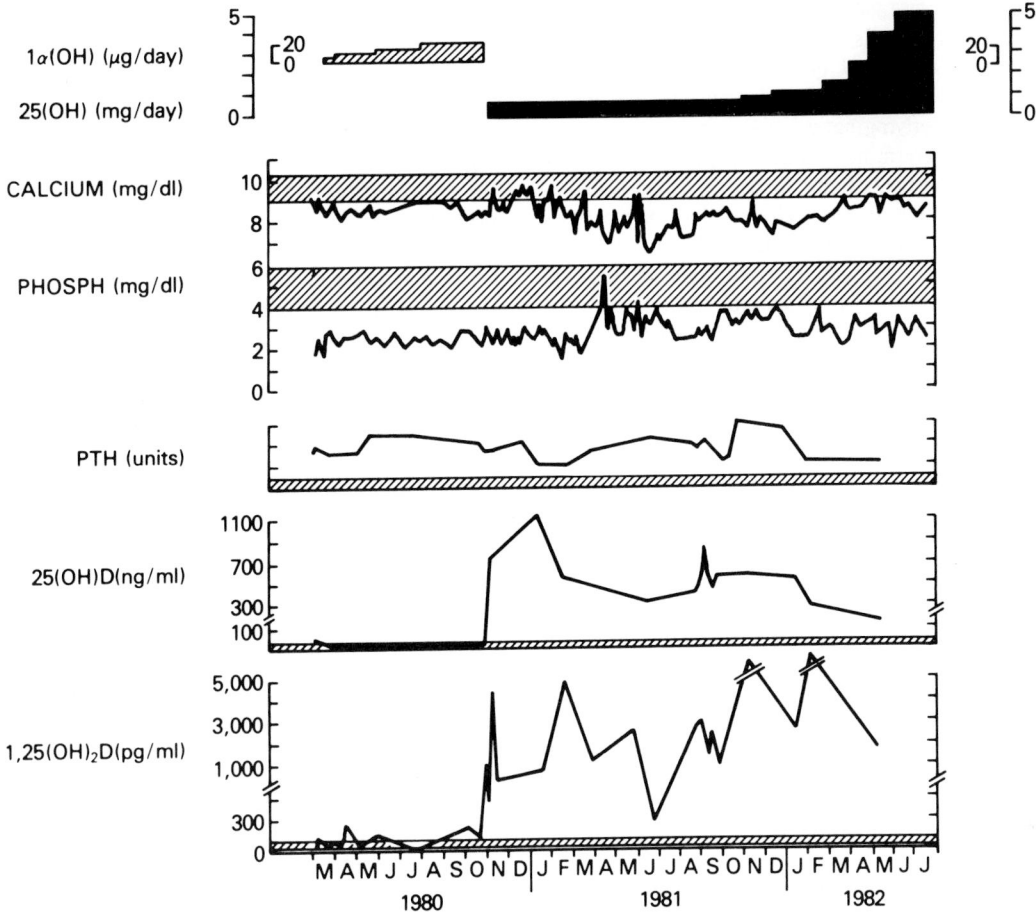

Fig. 80-8 Absent calcemic response during a long therapeutic trial with calciferols. Calciferol therapy is in upper panel: 1α(OH) refers to 1α(OH)D₃ or 1α,25(OH)₂D₃, and 25(OH) refers to 25(OH)D₃. Stippled zones indicate normal ranges. Not only is hypocalcemia persistent, but also secondary hyperparathyroidism persists (high parathyroid hormone and low phosphate), and very high serum levels of 1α,25(OH)₂D are documented. *(From Marx et al.[101]) PHOSPH = phosphorous.*

cooperation; in the absence of calciferol bioeffect, the fractional calcium absorption (virtually all of which is retained) is approximately 10 percent, implying that up to 600 mg/day can be delivered to the bloodstream by oral supplements. With high doses of calcium intravenously or orally, the serum phosphate level may decrease further; oral phosphate supplements should then be added. The utility of therapy with intravenous or oral calcium confirms the centrality of the intestine as a target tissue for 1α,25(OH)₂D.

Detailed studies of the interactions of calciferol dose with calcium dose have not been done. However, it seems likely that some patients (for example, those with 90 percent deficiency in hormone-binding capacity[101,110]) would have a diminished maximal response to calciferols; such patients with partial responses might obtain unique benefits from combinations of calciferols and calcium, both at high doses.

As in the calciferol deficiency states, total-body calcium requirements are highest at the onset of treatment. Thus, the doses of calcium, the doses of calciferols, and the type of approach judged necessary to initiate therapy (for example, intravenous calcium) may not prove the same as those used for maintenance therapy.

Cellular Defects. Cells from patients with hereditary generalized resistance to 1α,25(OH)₂D have been used to characterize the defect presumed to be present in all target tissues. Because of the widespread expression of the 1α-25(OH)₂D effector system in many tissues, these studies have been possible with skin fibroblasts,[115,116] keratinocytes,[117] bone cells,[118,119] and peripheral lymphocytes.[120] Five general categories of defect have been identified in these cells, as presented below.

HORMONE BINDING—NEGATIVE. The commonest defect has been undetectable high affinity binding of 1α,25(OH)₂D.[116,121] Cell extracts from four hormone binding–negative kindreds were tested with a monoclonal antibody against the receptor for 1α,25(OH)₂D; cross-reacting material was present in each, suggesting that this phenotype usually results not from absence of receptor protein but from mutations in the hormone-binding region.[122]

DECREASED MAXIMAL CAPACITY OF HORMONE BINDING. This abnormality has been reported in only one kindred.[110] Cell extracts showed a hormone-binding capacity only 10 percent of normal, but a hormone-binding affinity that was normal.

DECREASED AFFINITY OF HORMONE BINDING. A selective abnormality in hormone-binding affinity with normal hormone-binding capacity has been suggested but not proven conclusively in one kindred.[123] By standard criteria, the patient's cells were hormone binding–negative. However, using methods to increase the sensitivity of the assay, there was a suggestion of receptors normal in maximal capacity but severely deficient in hormone-binding affinity. A similar type of affinity defect has been suggested in a cell line from monkey kidney.[124]

NORMAL HORMONE BINDING BUT UNDETECTABLE NUCLEAR LOCALIZATION. Extracts of cells from two kindreds have shown normal capacity and affinity of hormone binding; however, high affinity uptake of hormone into the nucleus was undetectable.[115,116] The underlying nature of this interesting defect has not been fully determined. The receptors from both kindreds showed a normal affinity for nonspecific DNA.[125] Possible etiologies of these defects include failure of receptors to localize normally in the nucleus or instability of receptors [i.e., receptors may be stable under conditions of the hormone-binding assays (molybdate-containing buffers at 4°C) but labile under the conditions of the nuclear localization assay (dispersed cells at 37°C)].

NUCLEAR LOCALIZATION–POSITIVE. Cells from four kindreds have shown nearly normal nuclear uptake of hormone;[125–127] hormone binding to receptors was normal in capacity and affinity. With three kindreds the $1\alpha,25(OH)_2D$ receptor showed abnormal elution from nonspecific DNA;[125,126] in each the receptor eluted from the DNA at lower salt concentration than normal (Fig. 80-9).

To summarize, no case has met strict criteria for a possible pre- or post-receptor defect. Wherever detailed testing of $1\alpha,25(OH)_2D$ receptor properties has been done, abnormalities have been found. Only one case has so far showed no receptor defect,[127] but DNA-binding studies with that receptor have not been reported.

The class of cellular defect has shown no correlation with clinical features. Rather these cases seem to fit along one continuous spectrum of severity of disease.

$1\alpha,25(OH)_2D_3$ BIOEFFECT IN PATIENTS' CELLS. Several assays have tested posttranscriptional actions of $1\alpha,25(OH)_2D_3$ in cells from these patients. In all assays each patient's cells have

shown severely deficient actions. The most extensively tested response is $1,25(OH)_2D_3$ induction of $25(OH)D_3$ 24-hydroxylase activity.[127,128] In general, patients with milder disease (normal hair, calcemic response to high doses of calciferols) show inducible 24-hydroxylase with supraphysiological concentrations of $1\alpha,25(OH)_2D_3$ (Fig. 80-10), but patients with the severest disease (alopecia, no calcemic response to maximal doses of calciferols) show no 24-hydroxylase response to maximal concentrations of $1\alpha,25(OH)_2D_3$. Five of six obligate heterozygotes showed no abnormality;[121] the sixth showed a 50 percent decrease in hormone binding capacity and a similar decrease in maximal induction of 24-hydroxylase. Similar severe defects have been identified with other bioassays, including inhibition of cell growth by $1\alpha,25(OH)_2D$ (cultured skin fibroblasts or keratinocytes;[117] peripheral mononuclear cells[121]) and $1,25(OH)_2D_3$ mediated stimulation of 24-hydroxylase and of osteocalcin secretion in osteoblast-like bone cells.[115]

Animal Model for Hereditary Generalized Resistance to $1\alpha,25(OH)_2D$. A state resembling hereditary generalized resistance to $1\alpha,25(OH)_2D$ is present in new world primates (marmosets and tamarins). These animals sometimes develop osteomalacia in captivity and are known to have high nutritional requirements for calciferols.[129] New world primates have high circulating concentrations of $1\alpha,25(OH)_2D$.[130] Intestinal and other cells from these animals have shown deficient hormone-binding capacity (in comparison to cells from old world primates)[131–133] and deficient hormone-binding affinity.[133] These new world primates also exhibit hereditary generalized resistance to the true steroid hormones, including glucocorticoids, estrogens, and progestogens.[134] Thus, their special metabolic features appear to involve elements shared by many of the nuclear-active steroids and secosteroids.

States Resembling Hereditary Generalized Resistance to $1\alpha,25(OH)_2D$. There are multiple causes of rickets or osteomalacia in which calciferol metabolism is normal or is abnormal only as an appropriate response to a primary disturbance in mineral flux (Fig. 80-4). These include hereditary and acquired causes. Rickets or osteomalacia with high circulating $1\alpha,25(OH)_2D$ is found in generalized resistance to $1\alpha,25(OH)_2D$ and in two additional states (calcium deficiency or phosphate deficiency).

CALCIUM DEFICIENCY. Severe deficiency of calcium has been recognized as a common dysfunction in Bantu adolescents, who consume a diet severely deficient in calcium.[135] Of course, calcium repletion cures all abnormalities. Osteopetrosis (marble-bones disease) results from a spectrum of defects in osteoclast function. Both in humans and in animal models of this disease, serum $1\alpha,25(OH)_2D$ is increased and subtle histologic changes of osteomalacia have been noted.[135a] At least one patient has been treated with low calcium diet plus high doses of $1\alpha,25(OH)_2D$ with apparent improvement in osteoclast function.[136] Other cases of osteopetrosis have not responded to similar treatment, and at least one cellular defect (carbonic anhydrase II deficiency) unlikely to be overcome by $1\alpha,25(OH)_2D$ has been discovered.[137]

PHOSPHATE DEFICIENCY. Severe deficiency of phosphate can also cause rickets with high $1\alpha,25(OH)_2D$. In hereditary hypophosphatemic rickets with hypercalciuria, the primary renal loss of phosphate causes osteomalacia and activation of the renal 1α-hydroxylase.[138] High $1\alpha,25(OH)_2D$ results in absorp-

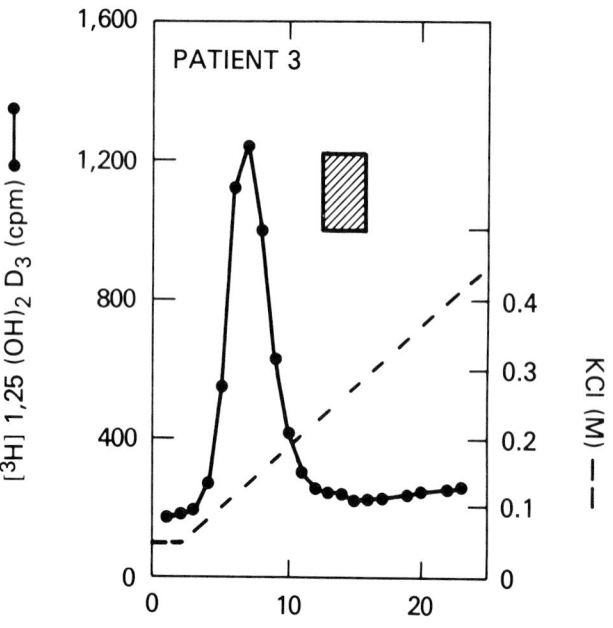

Fig. 80-9 Elution of $1\alpha,25(OH)_2D$ receptor from a column of DNA-cellulose. Shaded area shows location of elution peak for normal receptors. Solid circle = elution profile for receptors from patient with hereditary resistance to $1\alpha,25(OH)_2D$ and normal hormone binding to receptors in cell extracts (From Liberman et al.[125])

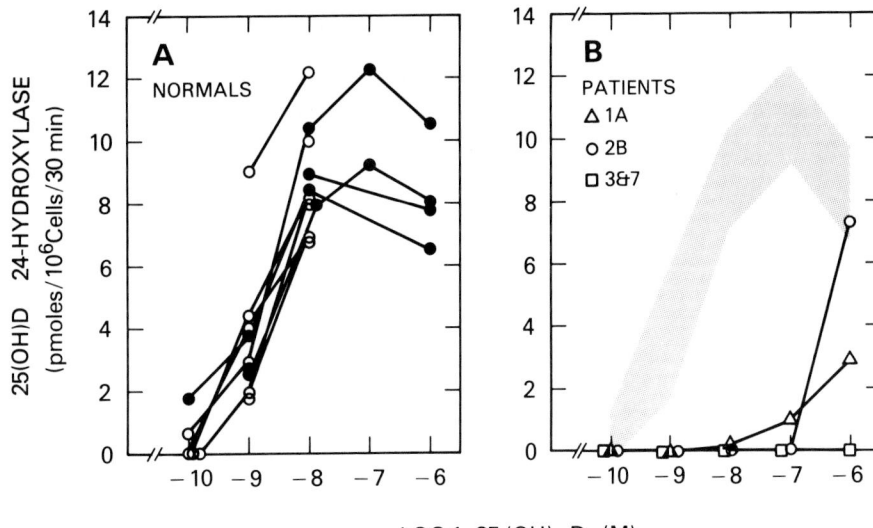

Fig. 80-10 25(OH)D$_3$ 24-hydroxylase in skin fibroblasts preincubated with indicated concentrations of 1α,25(OH)$_2$D$_3$. A. Normal subjects. B. Patients with hereditary generalized resistance to 1α,25(OH)$_2$D. Patients 1A and 2B each showed a satisfactory calcemic response to high doses of 1α,25(OH)$_2$D$_3$, but patients 3 and 7 showed no calcemic response. Shaded area in B shows normal response. (Modified from Gamblin et al.[128])

tive hypercalciuria; therefore, parathyroid function is suppressed in this condition, unlike in hereditary generalized resistance to 1α,25(OH)$_2$D.

Survivors of extreme prematurity can pass through a phase when their growing bones (deprived of the placental pump) are severely deficient in both calcium and phosphate, resulting in neonatal rickets with high serum 1α,25(OH)$_2$D.[139,140] In this group immaturity of the intestinal response to 1α,25(OH)$_2$D may contribute to the disturbance.[35]

DEFICIENT BONE MINERALIZATION WITH NORMAL CALCIUM AND PHOSPHATE IN SERUM. There are several causes of deficient bone mineralization with otherwise normal calcium and phosphate fluxes. These include hypophosphatasia,[64] the chondrodystrophies (which can disturb epiphyseal function), and skeletal accumulation of aluminum, diphosphonates, or fluoride.[65]

OTHER HEREDITARY DEFECTS IN CALCIFEROL METABOLISM

Calciferol Deficiency States

The only hereditary defects in calciferol metabolism proven to date are selective deficiency of and generalized resistance to 1α,25(OH)$_2$D. Though antigenic variation in transcalciferin is common, no differences in its function for calciferol transport have been identified in human beings.[141] However, in the chicken this protein shows tenfold higher affinity for D$_3$ metabolites than for D$_2$ metabolites, and this seems to account for a higher requirement for D$_2$ than D$_3$ in this species.[142]

Deficient 25 hydroxylation of vitamin D was suggested as an additional defect in one patient with hereditary generalized resistance to 1α,25(OH)$_2$D.[143] Increased clearance of 25(OH)D is an alternative explanation for these observations.

Deficient 24 hydroxylation of 25(OH)D was suggested in another patient with hereditary generalized resistance to 1α,25(OH)$_2$D.[103] That patient had low concentrations of 24,25(OH)$_2$D and showed partial remission of resistance to 1α,25(OH)$_2$D when given a therapeutic trial of 24,25(OH)$_2$D. Those observations remain unexplained, but a persistent abnormality in DNA binding of the 1α,25(OH)$_2$D receptors has

been documented in this patient, suggesting that any deficiency of 24,25(OH)$_2$D was a secondary feature.[125] Decreased production of 24,25(OH)$_2$D could be secondary to the abnormality in 1α,25(OH)$_2$D action, as one of its actions is induction of 25(OH)D 24-hydroxylase.

CALCIFEROL EXCESS STATES

Lightwood,[144] Williams et al.,[145] and Beuren et al.[146] described a syndrome of infantile hypercalcemia, elfin facies, mental retardation, and supravalvular aortic stenosis (also termed idiopathic hypercalcemia of infancy). The characteristic dysmorphology includes the following: wide, slack mouth, malocclusion, prominent upper lip, underdeveloped mandible, depressed nasal bridge, hypertelorism, epicanthic folds, low-set ears, increased bone density, craniostenosis, and osteosclerosis, especially of the base of the skull. Cases showing portions of the phenotype have sometimes been collected within this syndrome without implying identical pathophysiology for all cases.[147] Most cases have been sporadic, but several patients have had similarly affected siblings.[148] Autosomal dominant transmission was suggested in one kindred.[149] The hypercalcemia has many features suggesting excess vitamin D effect; there is increased calcium absorption, hypercalciuria, and nephrocalcinosis. In some cases glucocorticoids have lessened the hypercalcemia. Early studies suggested that calciferol bioactivity was increased in plasma,[150] but recent assays of specific calciferol metabolites have not provided a consistent explanation for these findings. Taylor et al. found that these patients and their phenotypically normal relatives show an abnormal accumulation of 25(OH)D when given a test dose of vitamin D$_2$.[151] However, serum 25(OH)D$_2$ and 25(OH)D$_3$ have been normal in most other cases during the normocalcemic or hypercalcemic phase.[152] Serum 24,25(OH)$_2$D and 25,26(OH)$_2$D have also been normal.[152] Garabedian et al. evaluated serum 1α,25(OH)$_2$D in four cases and found inappropriate increases.[153] However, other cases have shown clear suppression of 1α,25(OH)$_2$D,[152,154,155] suggesting more than one mechanism for the hypercalcemia.[156] The implication of factors related to calciferols is strengthened by an animal model for this disorder. The offspring of rabbits with vitamin D intoxication show similar skeletal features (mandibular hypoplasia and characteristic dental abnormalities)[157] and typical supravalvular aortic lesions.[158]

To summarize, it is unclear if the syndrome of idiopathic hypercalcemia with its associated abnormalities can result from a defect in calciferol metabolism or action.

REFERENCES

1. MELLANBY E: An experimental investigation on rickets. _Lancet_ I:407, 1919.
2. ALBRIGHT F, BUTLER AM, BLOOMBERG E: Rickets resistant to vitamin D therapy. _Am J Dis Child_ 54:531, 1937.
3. PRADER VA, ILLIG R, HEIDI E: Eine besondere form der primaren vitamin-D-resintenten rachitis mit hypocalcamie und autosomal-dominantem erbgang: Der hereditare pseudomangelrachitis. _Helv Paediatr Acta_ 5/6:452, 1961.
4. HAMILTON R, HARRISON J, FRASER D, RADDE I, MORECKI R, PAUNIER L: The small intestine in vitamin D dependent rickets. _Pediatrics_ 45:364, 1970.
5. ARNAUD C, MAIJER R, READE T, SCRIVER CR, WHELAN DT: Vitamin D dependency: An inherited postnatal syndrome with secondary hyperparathyroidism. _Pediatrics_ 46:871, 1970.
6. HOLICK MF, SCHNOES HK, DELUCA HF: Identification of 1,25-dihydroxycholecalciferol, a form of vitamin D3 metabolically active in the intestine. _Proc Natl Acad Sci USA_ 68:803, 1971.
7. LAWSON DEM, FRASER DR, KODICEK E, MORRIS HR, WILLIAMS DH: Identification of 1,25-dihydroxycholecalciferol, a new kidney hormone controlling calcium metabolism. _Nature_ 230:228, 1971.
8. NORMAN AW, MIDGETT RJ, MYRTLE JF, NOWICKI HG, WILLIAMS W, POPJACK G: 1,25-Dihydroxycholecalciferol: Identification of the proposed active form of vitamin D3 in the intestine. _Science_ 173:51, 1971.
9. FRASER D, KOOH SW, KIND HP, HOLICK MF, TANAKA Y, DELUCA HF: Pathogenesis of hereditary vitamin-D-dependent rickets: An inborn error of vitamin D metabolism involving defective conversion of 25-hydroxyvitamin D to 1α,25-dihydroxyvitamin D. _N Engl J Med_ 289:817, 1973.
10. BROOKS MH, BELL NH, LOVE L, STERN PH, ORFEI E, QUEENER SF, HAMSTRA AJ, DeLUCA HF: Vitamin-D-dependent rickets type II: Resistance of target organs to 1,25-dihydroxyvitamin D. _N Engl J Med_ 298:996, 1978.
11. AURBACH GD, MARX SJ, SPIEGEL AM: Parathyroid hormone, calcitonin, and the calciferols, in Wilson JD, Foster DW (eds): _Williams Textbook of Endocrinology_, 7th ed. Philadelphia, Saunders, 1985, pp 1137–1217.
12. HOLICK MF, MacLAUGHLIN JA, CLARK MB, HOLICK SA, POTTS JT JR, ANDERSON RR, BLANK IH, PARRISH JA: Photosynthesis of previtamin D3 in human skin and the physiological consequences. _Science_ 210:203, 1980.
13. CLEMENS TL, ADAMS JS, HENDERSON SL, HOLICK MF: Increased skin pigment reduces the capacity of skin to synthesise vitamin D3. _Lancet_ I:74, 1982.
14. SAAREM K, BERGSETH S, OFTEBRO H, PEDERSEN JR: Subcellular localization of vitamin D3 25-hydroxylase in human liver. _J Biol Chem_ 259:10936, 1984.
15. DAHLBACK H, WIKVALL K: 25-Hydroxylation of vitamin D3 in rat liver: Roles of mitochondrial and microsomal cytochrome P-450. _Biochem Biophys Res Comm_ 142:999, 1987.
16. TURNER RT: Mammalian 25-hydroxyvitamin D-1α-hydroxylase: Measurement and regulation, in Kumar R (ed): _Vitamin D: Basic and Clinical Aspects._ Boston, Mass: Martinus Nijhoff Publishing, 1984, pp 175–196.
17. REEVE L, TANAKA Y, DeLUCA HF: Studies on the site of 1,25-dihydroxyvitamin D3 synthesis in vivo. _J Biol Chem_ 258:3615, 1983.
18. TRECHSEL U, BONJOUR JP, FLEISCH H: Regulation of the metabolism of 25-hydroxyvitamin D3 in primary cultures of chick kidney cells. _J Clin Invest_ 64:206, 1979.
19. KAWASHIMA H, TORIKAI S, KUROKAWA K: Calcitonin selectively stimulates 25-hydroxyvitamin D3-1α-hydroxylase in proximal straight tubule of rat kidney. _Nature_ 291:327, 1981.
20. HIWATASHI A, NISHII Y, ICHIKAWA Y: Purification of cytochrome P-450D1α (25-hydroxyvitamin D3-1α-hydroxylase) of bovine kidney mitochondria. _Biochem Biophys Res Comm_ 105:320, 1982.
21. PAULSON SK, DELUCA HF: Subcellular location and properties of rat renal 25-hydroxyvitamin D3-1α-hydroxylase. _J Biol Chem_ 260:11488, 1985.
22. SIEGEL N, WONGSURAWAT N, ARMBRECHT HJ: Parathyroid hormone stimulates dephosphorylation of the renoredoxin component of the 25-hydroxyvitamin D3-1α-hydroxylase from rat renal cortex. _J Biol Chem_ 261:16998, 1986.
23. BURGOS-TRINIDAD M, BROWN AJ, DELUCA HF: Solubilization and reconstitution of chick renal mitochondrial 25-hydroxyvitamin D3 24-hydroxylase. _Biochemistry_ 25:2692, 1985.
24. COLSTON K, FELDMAN D: 1,25-Dihydroxyvitamin D3 receptors and functions in cultured pig kidney cells (LLCPK1): regulation of 24,25-dihydroxyvitamin D3 production. _J Biol Chem_ 257:2504, 1982.
25. KUMAR R, NAGUBANDI S, JARDINE I, LONDOWSKI JM, BOLLMAN S: The isolation and identification of 5,6-trans-25-hydroxyvitamin D3 from the plasma of rats dosed with vitamin D3. _J Biol Chem_ 256:9389,1981.
26. ENGSTRON GW, REINHART TA, HORST RL: 25-Hydroxyvitamin D3-23-hydroxylase, a renal enzyme in several animal species. _Arch Biochem Biophys_ 250:86, 1986.
27. HADDAD JG: Nature and functions of the plasma binding protein for vitamin D and its metabolites, in Kumar R (ed): _Vitamin D: Basic and Clinical Aspects._ Boston, Mass: Martinus Nijhoff Publishing, 1984, pp 383–395.
28. COOKE NE: Rat vitamin D binding protein: Determination of the full-length primary structure from cloned cDNA. _J Biol Chem_ 261:3441, 1985.
29. COPPENHAVER DH, SOLLENNE NP, BOWMAN BH: Posttranslational heterogeneity of the human vitamin D-binding protein (group-specific component). _Arch Biochem Biophys_ 226:218, 1983.
30. LAWSON DEM, DOUGLAS J, LEAN M, SEDRANI S: Estimation of vitamin D3 and 25-hydroxyvitamin D3 in muscle and adipose tissue of rats and man. _Clin Chim Acta_ 157:175, 1986.
31. HAUSSLER MR: Vitamin D receptors: Nature and function. _Ann Rev Nutr_ 6:527, 1986.
32. PROCSAL DA, OKAMURA WH, NORMAN AW: Structural requirements for the interaction of 1α,25-(OH)2-vitamin D3 with its chick intestinal receptor system. _J Biol Chem_ 250:8382, 1975.
33. BAKER AR, McDONNELL DP, HUGHES M, CRISP TM, MANGELSDORF DJ, HAUSSLER MR, PIKE JW, SHINE J, O'MALLEY BW: Cloning and expression of full-length cDNA encoding human vitamin D receptor. _Proc Nat Acad Sci USA_ 85:3294, 1988.
33a. EVANS RM: The steroid and thyroid hormone receptor super family. _Science_ 240:889, 1988.
34. STUMPF WE, SAR M, REID FA, TANAKA Y, DELUCA HF: Target cells for 1,25-dihydroxyvitamin D3 in intestinal tract, stomach, kidney, skin, pituitary, and parathyroid. _Science_ 206:1188, 1979.
35. HALLORAN BP, DELUCA HF: Appearance of the intestinal cytosolic receptor for 1,25-dihydroxyvitamin D3 during neonatal development in the rat. _J Biol Chem_ 256:7338, 1981.
36. PERRET C, DESPLAN C, BREHIER A, THOMASSET M: Characterisation of rat 9-kDa cholecalcin (CaBP) messenger RNA using a complimentary DNA. Absence of homology with 28-kDa cholecalcin mRNA. _Eur J Biochem_ 148:61, 1985.
37. LIAN JB, COUTTS M, CANALIS E: Studies of hormonal regulation of osteocalcin synthesis in cultured fetal rat calvariae. _J Biol Chem_ 260:8706, 1985.
38. ROWE DW, KREAM BE: Regulation of collagen synthesis in fetal rat calvaria by 1,25-dihydroxyvitamin D3. _J Biol Chem_ 257:8009,1982.
39. CANTLEY LK, RUSSEL J, LETTIERI, SHERWOOD LM: 1,25-Dihydroxyvitamin D3 suppresses parathyroid hormone secretion from bovine parathyroid cells in tissue culture. _Endocrinol_ 117:2114, 1985.
40. NEMERE I, YOSHIMOTO Y, NORMAN AW: Calcium transport in perfused duodena from normal chicks: Enhancement within fourteen minutes of exposure to 1,25-dihydroxyvitamin D3. _Endocrinology_ 115:1476, 1984.
41. BARAN DT, MILNE ML: 1,25-Dihydroxyvitamin D increases hepatocyte cytosolic calcium levels: A potential regulator of vitamin D-25-hydroxylase. _J Clin Invest_ 77:1622, 1986.
41a. BARSONY J, MARX SJ: Receptor-mediated rapid action of 1α,25-dihydroxycholecalciferol: Increase of intracellular cGMP in human skin fibroblasts. _Proc Nat Acad Sci USA_ 85:1223, 1988.
42. WASSERMAN RH, FULLMER CS, SHIMURA F: Calcium absorption and the molecular effects of vitamin D3, in Kumar R (ed): _Vitamin D: Basic and Clinical Aspects._ Boston, Mass: Martinus Nijhoff Publishing, 1984, pp 223–257.
43. FEHER JJ: Facilitated calcium diffusion by intestinal calcium-binding protein. _Am J Physiol_ 224:C303, 1983.
44. MORGAN DW, WELTON AF, HEICK AE, CHRISTAKOS S: Specific in vitro activation of Ca,Mg-ATPase by vitamin D-dependent rat renal calcium binding protein (calbindin D28K). _Biochem Biophys Res Comm_ 138:547, 1986.
45. UNDERWOOD JL, DELUCA HF: Vitamin D is not directly necessary for bone growth and mineralization. _Am J Physiol_ 246:E493, 1984.
46. WEINSTEIN RS, UNDERWOOD JL, HUTSON MS, DELUCA HF: Bone histomor-

phometry in vitamin D-deficient rats infused with calcium and phosphate. *Am J Physiol* 246:E499, 1984.

47. HOLTROP ME, COX KA, CARNES DL, HOLICK MF: Effects of serum calcium and phosphate on skeletal mineralization in vitamin D-deficient rats. *Am J Physiol* 251:E234, 1986.

48. BERESFORD JN, GALLAGHER JA, RUSSEL RGG: 1,25-Dihydroxyvitamin D₃ and human bone-derived cells in vitro: Effects on alkaline phosphatase, type I collagen, and proliferation. *Endocrinology* 119:1776, 1986.

49. MAJESKA RJ, RODAN GA: The effect of 1,25(OH)₂D₃ on alkaline phosphatase in osteoblastic osteosarcoma cells. *J Biol Chem* 257:3362, 1982.

50. CHAMBERS TJ, MCSHEEHY PMJ, THOMSON BM, FULLER K: The effect of calcium-regulating hormones and prostaglandins on bone resorption by osteoclasts disaggregated from neonatal rabbit bones. *Endocrinology* 60:234, 1985.

51. MERKE J, HUGEL U, WALDHERR R, RITZ E: No 1,25-dihydroxyvitamin D₃ receptors on osteoclasts of calcium-deficient chickens despite demonstrable receptors on circulating monocytes. *J Clin Invest* 77:312, 1986.

52. BAR-SHAVIT Z, KAHN AJ, STONE KR, TRIAL J, HILLIARD T, REITSMA PH, TEITELBAUM SL: Reversibility of vitamin D-induced human leukemia cell-line maturation. *Endocrinology* 118:679, 1986.

53. ROODMAN GD, IBBOTSON KJ, MACDONALD BR, KUEHL TJ, MUNDY GR: 1,25-Dihydroxyvitamin D₃ causes formation of multinucleated cells with several osteoclast characteristics in cultures of primate marrow. *Proc Natl Acad Sci USA* 82:8213, 1985.

54. ABE E, SHIINA Y, MIYAURA C, TANAKA H, HAYASHI T, KANEGASAKI S, SAITO M, NISHII Y, DELUCA HF, SUDA T: Activation and fusion induced by 1α,25-dihydroxyvitamin D₃ and their relation in alveolar macrophages. *Proc Natl Acad Sci USA* 81:7112, 1984.

55. CHAMBERS TJ: The pathobiology of the osteoclast. *J Clin Pathol* 38:241, 1985.

56. STUMPF WE, CLARK SA, SAR M, DELUCA HJ: Topographical and developmental studies on target sites of 1,25(OH)₂ vitamin D₃ in skin. *Cell Tissue Res* 238:489, 1984.

57. SMITH EL, WALWORTH NC, HOLICK MF: Effect of 1α,25-dihydroxyvitamin D₃ on the morphologic and biochemical differentiation of cultured human epidermal keratinocytes grown in serum-free conditions. *J Invest Dermatol* 86:709, 1986.

58. ESVELT RP, DELUCA HF, WICHMAN JK, YOSHIZAWA S, ZURCHER J, SAR M, STUMPF WE: 1,25-Dihydroxyvitamin D₃ stimulated increase of 7,8-didehydrocholesterol levels in rat skin. *Biochemistry* 19:6158, 1980.

59. CLEMENTS MR, JOHNSON L, FRASER DR: A new mechanism for induced vitamin D deficiency in calcium deprivation. *Nature* 325:62, 1987.

60. BINDERMAN I, SOMJEN D: 24,25-Dihydroxycholecalciferol induces the growth of chick cartilage in vitro. *Endocrinology* 115:430, 1984.

61. SOMJEN D, KAYE AM, BINDERMAN I: 24R,25-Dihydroxyvitamin D stimulates creatine kinase BB activity in chick cartilage cells in culture. *FEBS Lett* 167:281, 1984.

62. BROMMAGE R, DELUCA HF: Evidence that 1,25-dihydroxyvitamin D₃ is the physiologically active metabolite of vitamin D₃. *Endocrinol Rev* 6:491, 1985.

63. MAREL GM, MCKENNA MJ, FRAME B: Osteomalacia, in *Bone and Mineral Research*/4, New York, Elsevier, 1986, pp 335–412.

64. OPSHAUG O, MAURSETH K, HOWLID H, AKSNES L, AARSKOG D: Vitamin D metabolism in hypophosphatasia. *Acta Pediatr Scand* 71:517, 1982.

64a. MARX SJ, BARSONY J: Tissue selective 1,25-dihydroxyvitamin D₃ resistance: Novel applications of calciferols. *J Bone Min Res*, 3:481, 1988.

65. AURBACH GD, MARX SJ, SPIEGEL AM: Metabolic bone disease, in Wilson JD, Foster DW (eds): *Williams Textbook of Endocrinology*, 7th ed. Philadelphia, Saunders, 1985, pp 1218–1255.

66. BROMMAGE R, DELUCA HF: Placental transport of calcium and phosphate is not regulated by vitamin D. *Am J Physiol* 246:F526, 1984.

67. PAPAPOULOS SE, CLEMENS TL, FRAHER LJ, GLEED J, O'RIORDAN JLH: Metabolites of vitamin D in human vitamin D deficiency: Effect of vitamin D₃ or 1,25-dihydroxycholecalciferol. *Lancet* II:612, 1980.

68. STANBURY SW, TAYLOR CM, LUMB GA, MAWER BA, BERRY J, HANN J, WALLACE J: Formation of vitamin D metabolites following correction of human vitamin D deficiency. *Miner Electrolyte Metab* 5:212, 1981.

69. VENKATARAMAN PS, TSANG RC, BUCKLEY DB, HO M, STEICHEN JJ: Elevation of serum 1,25-dihydroxyvitamin D in response to physiologic doses of vitamin D in vitamin D-deficient infants. *J Pediatr* 103:416, 1983.

70. GARABEDIAN M, VAINSEL M, MALLET E, GUILLOZO H, TOPPET M, GRIMBERG R, NGUYEN TM, BALSAN S: Circulating vitamin D metabolite concentrations in children with nutritional rickets. *J Pediatr* 103:381, 1983.

71. LOPEZ-HILKER S, GALCEREN T, CHAN YL, RAPP N, MARTIN KJ, SLATOPOLSKY E: Hypocalcemia may not be essential for the development of hyperparathyroidism in chromic renal failure. *J Clin Invest* 78:1097, 1986.

72. RAO DS, PARFITT AM, KLEEREKOPER M, PUMO BS, FRAME B: Dissociation between the effects of endogenous parathyroid hormone on adenosine 3',5'-monophosphate generation and phosphate reabsorption in hypocalcemia due to vitamin D depletion: An acquired disorder resembling pseudohypoparathyroidism type II. *J Clin Endocrinol Metab* 61:285, 1985.

73. PARFITT AM, RAO DS, STANCIU J, VILLANUEVA AR, KLEEREKOPER M, FRAME B: Irreversible bone loss in osteomalacia: Comparison of radial photon absorptiometry with iliac bone histomorphometry during treatment. *J Clin Invest* 76:2403, 1985.

74. DOMMERGUES J-P, GARABEDIAN M, GUERIS J, LEDEUNFF M-J, CREIGNOU L, COURTECUISSE V, BALSAN S: Effets des principaux derives de la vitamine D: Chez trois enfants d'une fratrie atteints de rachitisme "pseudo-carentiel." *Arch Fr Pediatr* 35:1050, 1978.

75. KARPOUZAS J, PAPATHANASIOU-KLONTZA D, XIPOLITA-ZACHARIADU A, BENETOS S, MATSANIOTIS N: Pseudo-vitamin D deficiency rickets: Report of a case. *Helv Paediatr Acta* 34:461, 1979.

76. BRAVO H, ALMEIDA A, TATO IG, BUSTILLO JM, TOJO R: Early pseudo-deficiency or Prader's hypocalcemia familial type I rickets. *An Esp Pediatr* 25:121, 1986.

77. SCRIVER CR, READE TM, DELUCA HF, HAMSTRA AJ: Serum 1,25-dihydroxyvitamin D levels in normal subjects and in patients with hereditary rickets or bone disease. *N Engl J Med* 299:976, 1978.

78. GARABEDIAN M, N'GUYEN TM, GUILLOZO H, GRIMBERG R, BALSAN S: Mesure des taux circulants des metabolites actifs de la vitamine D chez l'enfant; interet et limites. *Arch Fr Pediatr* 38:857, 1981.

79. DELVIN EE, GLORIEUX FH, MARIE PJ, PETTIFOR JM: Vitamin D dependency: Replacement therapy with calcitriol. *J Pediatr* 99:26, 1981.

80. BOUCHARD G, LABERGE C, SCRIVER CR: La tyrosinémie héréditaire et le rachitisme vitamino-dépendant au Saguenay. *Union Med Can* 114:633, 1985.

81. BALSAN S, GARABEDIAN M: 25-Hydroxycholecalciferol: A comparative study in deficiency rickets and different types of resistant rickets. *J Clin Invest* 51:749, 1972.

82. BALSAN S, GARABEDIAN M, SORGNIARD R, HOLICK MF, DELUCA HF: 1,25-Dihydroxyvitamin D₃ and 1,α-hydroxyvitamin D₃ in children: Biologic and therapeutic effects in nutritional rickets and different types of vitamin D resistance. *Pediatr Res* 9:586, 1975.

83. READE TM, SCRIVER CR, GLORIEUX FH, NOGRADY B, DELVIN E, POIRIER R, HOLICK MF, DELUCA HF: Response to crystalline 1α-hydroxyvitamin D₃ in vitamin D dependency. *Pediatr Res* 9:593, 1975.

84. MARX SJ: Rickets and osteomalacia, in Conn HF et al. (eds): *Current Therapy*. Philadelphia, Saunders, 1983, p 451.

85. PLONIAT H: Klinsche fragen der calciumstoff wechselstorungen beim schwein. *Dtsch Tierarztl Wochenschr* 69:198, 1962.

86. HARMEYER J, GRABE V, WINKLER I: Pseudo vitamin D deficiency rickets in pigs. An animal model for the study of familial vitamin D dependency. *Exp Biol Med* 7:117, 1981.

87. FOX J, MAUNDER FMW, RANDALL VR, CARE AD: Vitamin D-dependent rickets type I in pigs. *Clin Sci* 69:541, 1985.

88. WINKLER I, SCHREINER F, HARMEYER J: Absence of 25-hydroxycholecalciferol-1-hydroxylase activity in a pig strain with vitamin D-dependent rickets. *Calcif Tissue Int* 38:87, 1986.

89. LYLES KW, CLARK AG, DREZNER MK: Serum 1,25-dihydroxyvitamin D levels in subjects with X-linked hypophosphatemic rickets and osteomalacia. *Calcif Tissue Int* 34:125, 1982.

90. HARRELL RM, LYLES KW, HARRELSON JM, FRIEDMAN NE, DREZNER MK: Healing of bone disease in X-linked hypophosphatemic rickets/osteomalacia: Induction and maintenance with phosphate and calcitriol. *J Clin Invest* 75:1858, 1985.

91. NESBITT T, LOBAUGH B, DREZNER M: Calcitonin stimulation of renal 25-hydroxyvitamin D-1α-hydroxylase activity in hypophosphatemic mice: Evidence that regulation of calcitriol production is not universally abnormal in X-linked hypophosphatemia. *J Clin Invest* 79:15, 1987.

92. BRENNER RJ, SPRING DB, SEBASTIAN A, MCSHERRY EM, GENANT HK, PALUBINSKAS AJ, MORRIS PC JR: Incidence of radiographically evident bone disease, nephrocalcinosis, and nephrolithiasis in various types of renal tubular acidosis. *N Engl J Med* 307:217, 1982.

93. KAWASHIMA H, KRAUT JA, KUROKAWA K: Metabolic acidosis suppresses 25-hydroxyvitamin D₃-1α-hydroxylase in the rat kidney: Distinct site and mechanism of action. *J Clin Invest* 70:135, 1982.

94. CHESNEY RW, KAPLAN BS, PHELPS M, DELUCA HF: Renal tubular acidosis does not alter circulating values of calcitriol. *J Pediatr* 104:51, 1984.

95. STEINHERZ R, CHESNEY RW, SCHULMAN JD, DELUCA HF, PHELPS M: Circulating vitamin D metabolites in nephropathic cystinosis. *J Pediatr* 102:592,1983.

96. BARAN DT, MARCY TW: Evidence for a defect in vitamin D metabolism in

a patient with incomplete Fanconi syndrome. *J Clin Endocrinol Metab* 59:998, 1984.

97. KITAGAWA T, AKATSUKA A, OWADA M, MANO T: Biologic and therapeutic effects of 1α-hydroxycholecalciferol in different types of Fanconi syndrome. *Contrib Nephrol* 22:107, 1980.

98. RYAN EQ, REISS E: Oncogenous osteomalacia: A review of the world literature of 42 cases and report of two new cases. *Am J Med* 77:501, 1984.

99. MARX SJ, SPIEGEL AM, BROWN EM, GARDNER DG, DOWNS RW JR, ATTIE M, HAMSTRA AJ, DELUCA HF: A familial syndrome of decrease in sensitivity to 1,25-dihydroxyvitamin D. *J Clin Endocrinol Metab* 47:1303, 1978.

100. ROSEN JF, FLEISCHMAN AR, FINBERG L, HAMSTRA A, DELUCA HF: Rickets with alopecia: An inborn error of vitamin D metabolism. *J Pediatr* 94:729, 1979.

101. MARX SJ, LIBERMAN UA, EIL C, GAMBLIN GT, DEGRANGE DA, BALSAN S: Hereditary resistance to 1,25-dihydroxyvitamin D. *Recent Prog Horm Res* 40:589, 1984.

102. HOCHBERG Z, GILHAR A, HAIM S, FRIEDMAN-BIRNBAUM R, LEVY J, BENDERLY A: Calcitriol-resistant rickets with alopecia. *Arch Dermatol* 121:646, 1985.

103. LIBERMAN UA, SAMUEL R, HALABE A, KAULI R, EDELSTEIN S, WEISMAN Y, PAPAPOULOS SE, CLEMENS TL, FRAHER LJ, O'RIORDAN JLH: End-organ resistance to 1,25-dihydroxycholecalciferol. *Lancet* I:504, 1980.

104. SAKATI N, WOODHOUSE NJY, NILES N, HARFI H, DE GRANGE DA, MARX S: Hereditary resistance to 1,25-dihydroxyvitamin D: Clinical and radiological improvement during high-dose oral calcium therapy. *Horm Res* 24:280, 1986.

105. HOCHBERG Z, BOROCHOWITZ Z, BENDERLI A, VARDI P, OREN S, SPIRER Z, HEYMAN I, WEISMAN Y: Does 1,25-dihydroxyvitamin D participate in the regulation of hormone release from endocrine glands? *J Clin Endocrinol Metab* 60:57, 1985.

106. BALSAN S, GARABEDIAN M, LARCHET M, GORSKI AM, COURNOT G, TAU C, BOURDEAU A, SILVE C, RICOUR C: Long-term nocturnal calcium infusions can cure rickets and promote normal mineralization in hereditary resistance to 1,25-dihydroxyvitamin D. *J Clin Invest* 77:1661, 1986.

107. KUDOH T, KUMAGAI T, UETSUJI N, TSUGAWA S, OYANAGI K, CHIBA Y, MINAMI R, NAKAO T: Vitamin D dependent rickets: Decreased sensitivity to 1,25-dihydroxyvitamin D. *Eur J Pediatr* 137:307, 1981.

108. FUJITA T, NOMURA M, OKAJIMA S, FURUYA H: Adult-onset vitamin D-resistant osteomalacia with the unresponsiveness to parathyroid hormone. *J Clin Endocrinol Metab* 50:927, 1980.

109. HOCHBERG Z, BENDERLI A, LEVY J, VARDI P, WEISMAN Y, CHEN T, FELDMAN D: 1,25-Dihydroxyvitamin D resistance, rickets, and alopecia. *Am J Med* 77:805, 1984.

109a. KRUSE K, FELDMAN E, BARTELS H: Hypoparathyroidism in hereditary resistance to 1,25(OH)₂D during long-term treatment with excessive doses of vitamin D₃, in Norman AW, Schaefer K, Grigoleit HG (eds): *Vitamin D: Molecular, Cellular, and Clinical Endocrinology.* Berlin, Walter De Gruyter, 1988, p 456.

110. BALSAN S, GARABEDIAN M, LIBERMAN UA, EIL C, BOURDEAU A, GUILLOZO H, GRIMBERG R, LE DEUNFF MJ, LIEBERHERR M, GUIMBAUD P, TROYER M, MARX SJ: Rickets and alopecia with resistance to 1,25-dihydroxyvitamin D: Two different clinical courses with two different cellular defects. *J Clin Endocrinol Metab* 57:803, 1983.

111. MARX SJ, BLIZIOTES MM, NANES M: Analysis of the relation between alopecia and resistance to 1,25-dihydroxyvitamin D. *Clin Endocrinol* 25:373, 1986.

112. AL-AWADI SA, MOUSSA MA, NAGUIB KK, FARAG TI, TEEBI AS, EL-KHALIFA M, EL-DOSSARY L: Consanguinity among the Kuwaiti population. *Clin Genet* 27:483, 1985.

113. MARX SJ, SWART EJ JR, HAMSTRA AJ, DELUCA HF: Normal intrauterine development of the fetus of a woman receiving extraordinarily high doses of 1,25-dihydroxyvitamin D₃. *J Clin Endocrinol Metab* 51:1138, 1980.

114. BLIZIOTES M, YERGEY A, NANES MS, MUENZER J, VIERA N, BEGLEY MG, KHER KK, BRANDI ML, MARX SJ: Absent intestinal response to calciferols in hereditary resistance to 1,25-dihydroxyvitamin D: Documentation and effective therapy with high dose intravenous calcium infusions. *J Clin Endocrinol Metab* 66:294, 1988.

115. EIL C, LIBERMAN UA, ROSEN JF, MARX SJ: A cellular defect in hereditary vitamin-D-dependent rickets type II: Defective nuclear uptake of 1,25-dihydroxyvitamin D in cultured skin fibroblasts. *N Engl J Med* 304:1588, 1981.

116. LIBERMAN UA, EIL C, MARX SJ: Resistance to 1,25(OH)₂D: Association with heterogeneous defects in cultured skin fibroblasts. *J Clin Invest* 71:192, 1983.

117. CLEMENS TL, ADAMS JS, HORIUCHI N, GILCHREST BA, CHO H, TSUCHIYA Y, MATSUO N, SUDA T, HOLICK MF: Interaction of 1,25-dihydroxyvitamin-D₃ with keratinocytes and fibroblasts from skin of normal subjects and a subject with vitamin-D-dependent rickets, type II: A model for study of

the mode of action of 1,25-dihydroxyvitamin D₃. *J Clin Endocrinol Metab* 56:824, 1983.

118. LIBERMAN UA, EIL C, HOLST P, ROSEN JF, MARX SJ: Hereditary resistance to 1,25-dihydroxyvitamin D: Defective function of receptors for 1,25-dihydroxyvitamin D in cells cultured from bone. *J Clin Endocrinol Metab* 57:958, 1983.

119. SILVE C, GROSSE B, TAU C, GARABEDIAN M, FRITSCH J, DELMAS PD, COURNOT-WITMER G, BALSAN S: Response to parathyroid hormone and 1,25-dihydroxyvitamin D₃ of bone-derived cells isolated from normal children and children with abnormalities in skeletal development. *J Clin Endocrinol Metab* 62:583, 1986.

120. KOREN R, RAVID A, LIBERMAN UA, HOCHBERG Z, WEISMAN Y, NOVOGRODSKY A: Defective binding and function of 1,25-dihydroxyvitamin D₃ receptors in peripheral mononuclear cells of patients with end-organ resistance to 1,25-dihydroxyvitamin D. *J Clin Invest* 76:2012, 1985.

121. CHEN TL, HIRST MA, CONE CM, HOCHBERG Z, TIETZE H-U, FELDMAN D: 1,25-Dihydroxyvitamin D resistance, rickets, and alopecia: Analysis of receptors and bioresponse in cultured fibroblasts from patients and parents. *J Clin Endocrinol Metab* 59:383, 1984.

122. PIKE JW, DOKOH S, HAUSSLER MR, LIBERMAN UA, MARX SJ, EIL C: Vitamin D₃-resistant fibroblasts have immunoassayable 1,25-dihydroxyvitamin D₃ receptors. *Science* 224:879, 1984.

123. CASTELLS S, GREIG F, FUSI M, FINBERG L, YASUMURA S, LIBERMAN UA, EIL C, MARX S: Severely deficient binding of 1,25-dihydroxyvitamin D to its receptors in a patient responsive to high doses of this hormone. *J Clin Endocrinol Metab* 63:252, 1986.

124. KELLY MA, MARION SL, DONALDSON CA, PIKE JW, HAUSSLER MR: A variant form of the 1,25-dihydroxyvitamin D₃ receptor with low apparent hormone affinity in cultured monkey kidney cells (LLC-MK2). *J Biol Chem* 259:2214, 1984.

125. LIBERMAN UA, EIL C, MARX SJ: Receptor positive hereditary resistance to 1,25-dihydroxyvitamin D: chromatography of hormone-receptor complexes on deoxyribonucleic acid-cellulose shows two classes of mutation. *J Clin Endocrinol Metab* 62:122, 1986.

126. HIRST M, HOCHMAN H, FELDMAN D: Vitamin D resistance and alopecia: A kindred with normal 1,25-dihydroxyvitamin D binding, but decreased receptor affinity for deoxyribonucleic acid. *J Clin Endocrinol Metab* 60:490, 1985.

127. GRIFFIN JE, CHANDLER JS, HAUSSLER MR, ZERWEKH JE: Receptor-positive resistance to 1,25-dihydroxyvitamin D: A new cause of osteomalacia associated with impaired induction of 24-hydroxylase in fibroblasts. *J Clin Invest* 72:1190, 1983.

128. GAMBLIN GT, LIBERMAN UA, EIL C, DOWNS RW JR, DEGRANGE DA, MARX SJ: Vitamin D dependent rickets type II: Defective induction of 25-hydroxyvitamin D₃-24-hydroxylase by 1,25-dihydroxyvitamin D₃ in cultured skin fibroblasts. *J Clin Invest* 75:954, 1985.

129. YAMAGUCHI A, KOHNO Y, YAMAZAKI T, TAKAHASHI N, SHINKI T, HORIUCHI N, SUDA T, KOIZUMI H, TANIOKA Y, YOSHIKI S: Bone in the marmoset: A resemblance to vitamin D-dependent rickets, type II. *Calcif Tissue Int* 39:22, 1986.

130. ADAMS JS, GACAD MA, BAKER AJ, GONZALES B, RUDE RK: Serum concentrations of 1,25-dihydroxyvitamin D₃ in platyrrhini and catarrhini: A phylogenetic appraisal. *Am J Primatol* 9:219, 1985.

131. TAKAHASHI N, SUDA S, SHINKI T, HORIUCHI N, SHIINA Y, TANIOKA Y, KOIZUMI H, SUDA T: The mechanism of end-organ resistance to 1α,25-dihydroxycholecalciferol in the common marmoset. *Biochem J* 227:555, 1985.

132. ADAMS JS, GACAD MA: Phenotypic diversity of the cellular 1,25-dihydroxyvitamin D₃-receptor interaction among different genera of new world primates. *J Clin Endocrinol Metab* 66:224, 1988.

133. LIBERMAN UA, DEGRANGE D, MARX SJ: Low affinity of the receptor for 1α,25-dihydroxyvitamin D₃ in the marmoset, a new world monkey. *FEBS Lett* 182:385, 1985.

134. LIPSETT MB, CHROUSOS GP, TOMITA M, BRANDON DD, LORIAUX DL: The defective glucocorticoid receptor in man and nonhuman primates. *Recent Prog Horm Res* 41:199, 1985.

135. PETTIFOR JM, ROSS FP, TRAVERS R, GLORIEUX FH, DELUCA HF: Dietary calcium deficiency: A syndrome associated with bone deformities and elevated serum 1,25-dihydroxyvitamin D concentrations. *Metab Bone Dis Relat Res* 2:301, 1981.

135a. MARKS SC JR: Osteopetrosis—Multiple pathways for the interruption of osteoclast functions. *Appl Pathol* 5:172, 1987.

136. KEY L, CARNES D, COLE S, HOLTROP M, BARSHAVIT Z, SHAPIRO F, ARCECI R, STEINBERG J, GUNDBERG C, KAHN A, ANAST CS: Treatment of congenital osteopetrosis with high-dose calcitriol. *N Engl J Med* 310:409, 1984.

137. SLY WS, WHYTE MP, SUNDARAM V, TASHIAN RE, HEWETT-EMMETT D, GUIBAUD P, VAINSEL M, BALUARTE HJ, GRUSKIN A, AL-MOSAWI M, SAKATI N, OHLSSON A: Carbonic anhydrase II deficiency in 12 families with the au-

tosomal recessive syndrome of osteopetrosis with renal tubular acidosis and cerebral calcification. *N Engl J Med* 313:139, 1985.

138. TIEDER M, MODAI D, SAMUEL R, ARIE R, HALABE A, BAB I, GABIZON D, LIBERMAN UA: Hereditary hypophosphatemic rickets with hypercalciuria. *N Engl J Med* 312:611, 1985.

139. CHESNEY RW, HAMSTRA AJ, DELUCA HF: Rickets of prematurity: Supranormal levels of serum 1,25-dihydroxyvitamin D. *Am J Dis Child* 135:34, 1981.

140. STEICHEN JJ, TSANG RC, GREER FR, HO M, HUG G: Elevated serum 1,25-dihydroxyvitamin D concentrations in rickets of very low-birth-weight infants. *J Pediatr* 99:293, 1981.

141. KAWAKAMI M, IMAWARI M, GOODMAN DS: Quantitative studies of the interaction of cholecalciferol (Vitamin D$_3$) and its metabolites with different genetic variants of the serum binding protein for these sterols. *Biochem J* 179:413, 1979.

142. BELSEY R, DELUCA HF, POTTS JT JR: Selective binding properties of the vitamin D transport protein in chick plasma in vitro. *Nature* 247:208, 1974.

143. ZERWEKH JE, GLASS K, JOWSEY J, PAK CYC: An unique form of osteomalacia associated with end organ refractoriness to 1,25-dihydroxyvitamin D and apparent defective synthesis of 25-hydroxyvitamin D. *J Clin Endocrinol Metab* 49:171, 1979.

144. LIGHTWOOD R: Idiopathic hypercalcemia with failure to thrive. *Proc R Soc Med* 45:401, 1952.

145. WILLIAMS JCP, BARRATT-BOYES BG, LOWE JB: Supravalvular aortic stenosis. *Circulation* 24:1311, 1961.

146. BEUREN AJ, APITZ J, HARMJANZ D: Supravalvular aortic stenosis in association with mental retardation and a certain facial appearance. *Circulation* 26:1235, 1962.

147. JONES KL, SMITH DW: The Williams elfin facies syndrome: A new perspective. *J Pediatr* 86:718,1975.

148. WILTSE HE, GOLDBLOOM RB, ANTIA AU, OTTESEN OE, TOWE RD, COOKE RE: Infantile hypercalcemia syndrome in twins. *N Engl J Med* 275:1157, 1966.

149. MEHES K, SZELID Z, TOTH P: Possible dominant inheritance of the idiopathic hypercalcemic syndrome. *Hum Hered* 25:30, 1975.

150. FELLERS FX, SCHWARTZ R: Etiology of the severe form of idiopathic hypercalcemia of infancy. *N Engl J Med* 259:1050, 1958.

151. TAYLOR AB, STERN PH, BELL NH: Abnormal regulation of circulating 25-hydroxyvitamin D in the Williams syndrome. *N Engl J Med* 306:972, 1982.

152. MARTIN NDT, SNODGRASS GJAI, COHEN RD, PORTEOUS CE, COLDWELL RD, TRAFFORD DJH, MAKIN HLJ: Vitamin D metabolites in idiopathic infantile hypercalcemia. *Arch Dis Child* 60:1140, 1985.

153. GARABEDIAN M, JACQZ E, GUILLOZO H, GRIMBERG R, GUILLOT M, GAGNADOUX M-F, BROYER M, LENOIR G, BALSAN S: Elevated plasma 1,25-dihydroxyvitamin D concentrations in infants with hypercalcemia and an elfin facies. *N Engl J Med* 312:948, 1985.

154. AARSKOG D, AKSNES L, MARKESTAD T: Vitamin D metabolism in idiopathic infantile hypercalcemia. *Am J Dis Child* 135:1021, 1981.

155. CHESNEY RW, DELUCA HF, GERTNER JM, GENEL M: Increased plasma 1,25-dihydroxyvitamin D in infants with hypercalcemia and elfin facies. Letter to the editor. *N Engl J Med* 313:889, 1985.

156. CULLER FL, JONES KL, DEFTOS LJ: Impaired calcitonin secretion in patients with Williams syndrome. *J Pediatr* 107:720, 1985.

157. FRIEDMAN WF, MILLS LF: The relationship between vitamin D and the craniofacial and dental anomalies of the supravalvular aortic stenosis syndrome. *Pediatrics* 43:12, 1969.

158. FRIEDMAN WF, ROBERTS WC: Vitamin D and the supravalvular aortic stenosis syndrome. The transplacental effects of vitamin D on the aorta of the rabbit. *Circulation* 34:77, 1966.

PART 13

VITAMINS

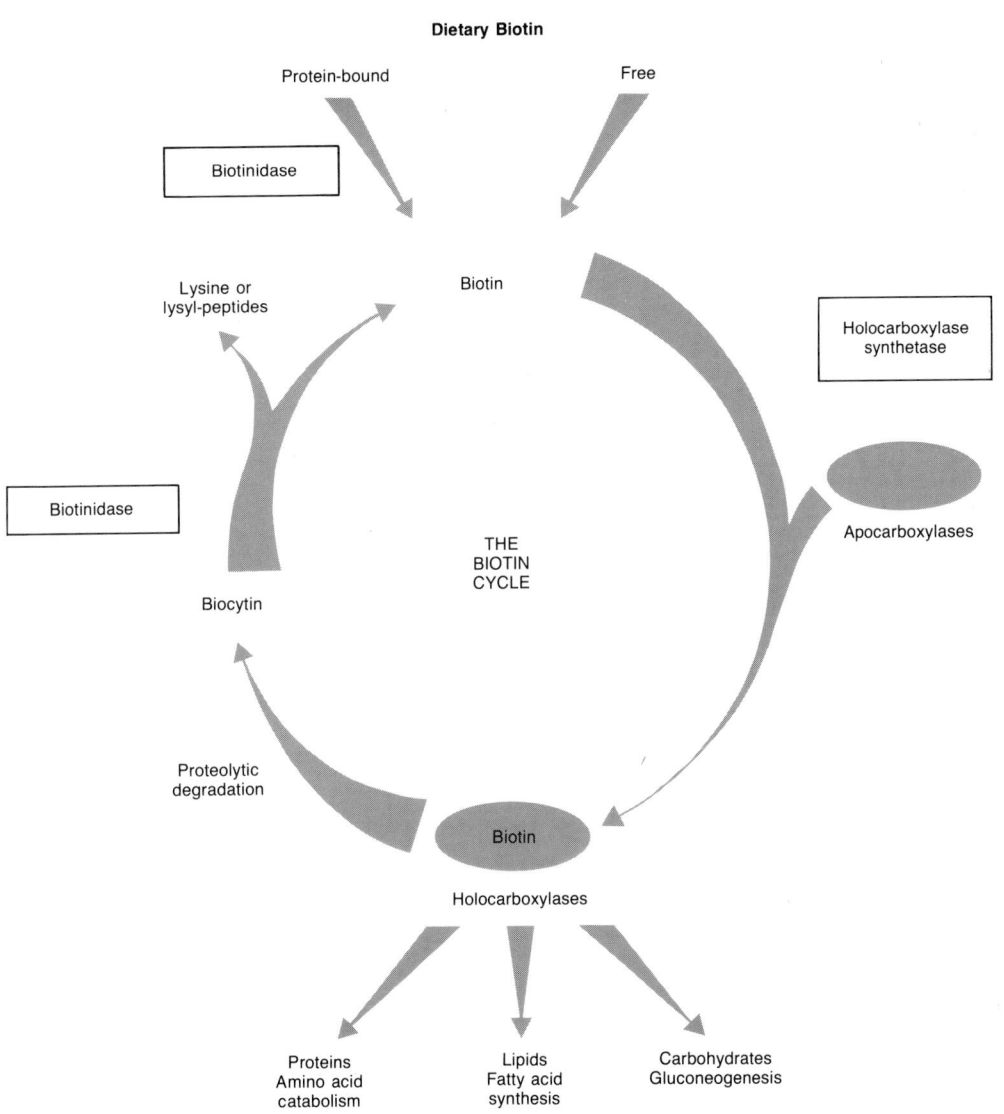

Dietary Biotin

Protein-bound   Free

Biotinidase

Lysine or
lysyl-peptides

Biotin

Holocarboxylase
synthetase

Biotinidase

Apocarboxylases

THE
BIOTIN
CYCLE

Biocytin

Proteolytic
degradation

Biotin

Holocarboxylases

Proteins
Amino acid
catabolism

Lipids
Fatty acid
synthesis

Carbohydrates
Gluconeogenesis

CHAPTER 81

INHERITED DISORDERS OF FOLATE TRANSPORT AND METABOLISM

DAVID S. ROSENBLATT

1. *Folate coenzymes participate in a number of critical single-carbon transfer reactions including those involved in the biosynthesis of pyrimidines, purines, serine, and methionine and in the degradation of histidine and purines.*

2. *Five inherited disorders of folate transport and metabolism have been well-substantiated: methylenetetrahydrofolate reductase deficiency; functional methyltetrahydrofolate:homocysteine methyltransferase (methionine synthase) deficiency due to cobalamin E (cblE) or cblG disease (see also Chap. 82); glutamate formiminotransferase deficiency; and hereditary folate malabsorption.*

3. *Four putative inherited disorders in the literature cannot yet be considered to be well-substantiated: dihydrofolate reductase deficiency; methenyltetrahydrofolate cyclohydrolase deficiency; cellular uptake defects; primary methyltetrahydrofolate:homocysteine methyltransferase deficiency.*

4. Methylenetetrahydrofolate reductase deficiency, *the most widely studied of the inherited disorders of folate metabolism, is a condition in which clinical severity correlates with the degree of enzyme deficiency. The clinical symptoms vary, with developmental delay accompanied by motor and gait abnormalities, seizures, and psychiatric manifestations being described. The age of onset has ranged from the neonatal period to adolescence. The major biochemical findings are moderate homocystinuria and homocystinemia with low or relatively normal levels of plasma methionine. Most severely affected patients have died. Pathologic findings have included vascular changes similar to those seen in classic homocystinuria and demyelination presumably due to low levels of neurotransmitters or methionine in the central nervous system. Methylenetetrahydrofolate reductase deficiency has been resistant to treatment; folates, methionine, pyridoxine, cobalamin, and carnitine have all been used. Betaine has the theoretical advantage of both lowering homocysteine levels and supplementing methionine levels, and has been the most promising therapeutic agent to date. Nevertheless the prognosis has been generally poor (see also Chap. 82).*

5. Functional methionine synthase deficiency, *due to the cblE and cblG mutations, is characterized by homocystinuria and defective biosynthesis of methionine. The patients have presented in the first few months of life with megaloblastic anemia and developmental delay. The distribution of vitamin B_{12} derivatives was altered in cultured cells, with decreased levels of methyl-B_{12} as compared to normal fibroblasts. The cblE mutation is associated with low methionine synthase activity when the assay is performed with low levels of thiol, whereas the* cblG *mutation is associated with low activity under all assay conditions. cblE and cblG represent distinct complementation classes. Both diseases respond to treatment with vitamin B_{12}.*

6. Glutamate formiminotransferase deficiency *is a heterogeneous condition associated with elevated excretion of formiminoglutamic acid, 4-amino-5-imidazole-carboxamide, and hydantoin-5-propionate. Clinical findings have varied from mental and physical retardation to massive excretion of formiminoglutamate in the absence of retardation. Therapy with folates and methionine has been described, but given that the correlation between symptoms and formiminoglutamate excretion remains uncertain, the basis for treating these patients is unclear.*

7. Hereditary folate malabsorption *is characterized by the early onset of failure to thrive and severe folate-responsive megaloblastic anemia. All patients have been severely restricted in their ability to absorb oral folic acid or oral reduced folates. Severe mental retardation may be a prominent feature if therapy does not succeed in maintaining adequate levels of folate in the cerebrospinal fluid. Two patients have shown increased susceptibility to infection. This disorder provides the best evidence for the existence of a specific carrier for folate both at the level of the intestine and at the choroid plexus. All but one of the dozen patients have been girls. Therapy has been attempted with large doses of oral or systemic folates.*

8. *All of the clearly delineated disorders of folate metabolism appear to be inherited as autosomal recessive traits. To date all patients with cblE disease have been boys. Heterozygotes for methylenetetrahydrofolate reductase deficiency show decreased enzymes levels in somatic cells. A difference in folate absorption in the heterozygote has been suggested in at least one family with hereditary folate malabsorption.*

9. *Prenatal diagnosis has been reported for methylenetetrahydrofolate reductase deficiency and for cblE disease using cultured amniotic cells.*

BACKGROUND

The chemistry, biochemistry, and physiology of folic acid and its derivatives have been extensively reviewed in the last edition of this text.[1] In addition, several excellent monographs[2,3] extensively bring up-to-date all of the current literature. A recent review gives a case by case analysis in tabular form of

---

Nonstandard abbreviations used in this chapter include: AdoMet = adenosylmethionine; AICAR = 5-phosphoribosyl-5-aminoimidazole-4-carboxamide; cbl = cobalamin; dTMP = 2′-deoxythymidine-5′-monophosphate; FAD = flavin-adenine dinucleotide; FGAR = α-*N*-formyl-glycinamide ribonucleotide; FIGLU = formiminoglutamate; GAR = 5-phophoribosylglycineamide; H_2PteGlu or H_2folate = dihydrofolate; H_4PteGlu, H_4folate, or THF = tetrahydrofolate; Ig = immunoglobulin; methyl-B_{12} or CH_3-B_{12} = methylcobalamin; NAD = nicotinamide adenine dinucleotide, NADP = nicotinamide adenine dinucleotide phosphate; OH-B_{12} = hydroxocobalamin.

each patient who has been reported up to 1986 with verified methylenetetrahydrofolate reductase deficiency or glutamate formiminotransferase deficiency.[4] Other reviews on this subject are also available.[5–11]

The pteridine compounds referred to as "folates" are involved as coenzymes in a number of critical 1-carbon transfer reactions, including those involved in the biosynthesis of purines, pyrimidines (dTMP), serine, and methionine and in the degradation of histidine. The biologically active folates are substituted derivatives of 5,6,7,8-tetrahydrofolic acid (Fig. 81-1). Wills and her colleagues determined that the absence of folate from the diet resulted in a macrocytic megaloblastic anemia[12,13] at about the same time that pteridine pigments of butterfly wings were being isolated and characterized. The synthesis of the parent compound was accomplished in the subsequent decade.[14] *Folic acid* and *folate* are the preferred synonyms for pteroylglutamic acid (PteGlu) and pteroylglutamate, respectively (Fig. 81-2). The term *folate* is used in the generic sense to designate members of the family of pteroylglutamates having various levels of reduction of the pteridine ring, 1-carbon substitutions, and numbers of glutamate residues. In the folate compounds, pteroic acid is conjugated with one or more molecules of L-glutamate, each linked by amide bonds to the preceding molecule of glutamate through the γ-carboxyl group. The terms *pteroylpolyglutamate* or *folate polyglutamate* apply to folate compounds with more than one glutamate residue.

As summarized in Fig. 81-2, there are at least three stages of reduction of the pyrazine ring of the pteridine moiety; at least six different 1-carbon groups substituted at positions N^5, N^{10}, or both; and γ-glutamyl-peptide chains of varying length linked to the γ-carboxyl group of the glutamic acid residue. 5-Methyltetrahydrofolate is the predominant form of folate in serum and in many tissues. 5-Formyltetrahydrofolate, also known as *folinic acid*, *leucovorin*, or *citrovorum factor*, is a reduced folate that has been used therapeutically because of its chemical stability.

Folate Transport. Folate transport across cell membranes is mediated by a single major transport system.[15] In the intestine all monoglutamate folates are transported with the same efficiency. In some other cells the concentration of folic acid needed to generate adequate concentrations of intracellular folates is much greater than that of reduced folates such as 5-methyltetrahydrofolate or 5-formyltetrahydrofolate.

Studies have employed brush border membrane vesicles to study the effects of pH and ionic gradients on the transport of folates. A pH gradient in these vesicle experiments, with a low outside pH, results in changes in the ionization and diffusibility of folates, changes in the K_m for transport, and changes in the ionization and diffusibility of folates, changes in the K_m for transport, and changes in folate-H⁺–coupled transport.[16] Studies using rat intestinal basolateral membrane vesicles sug-

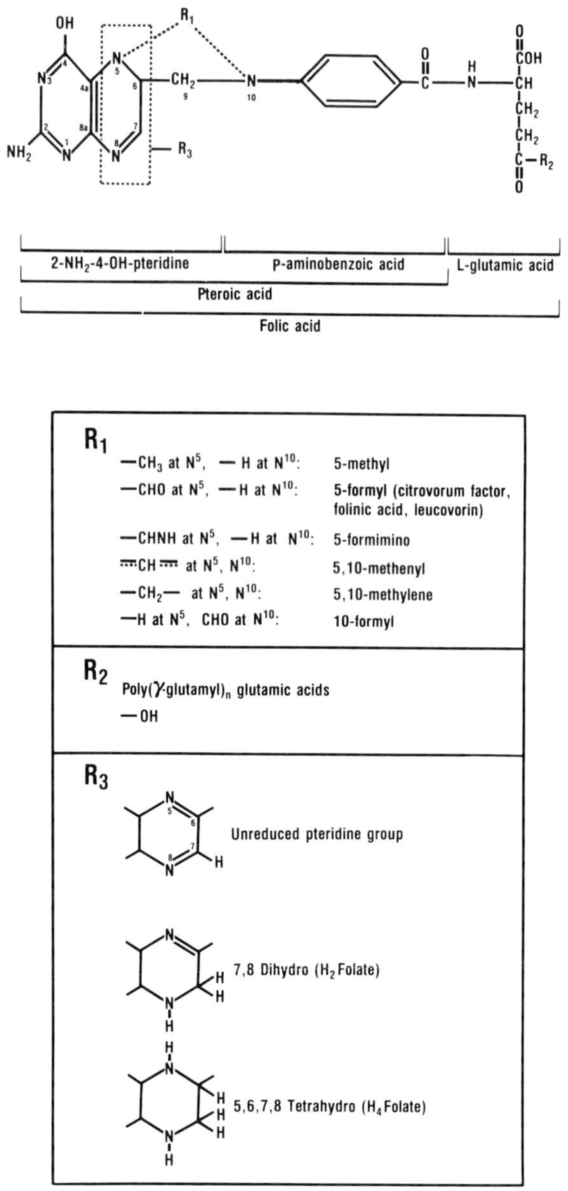

Fig. 81-2 The structure of folic acid and its derivatives. (Modified from Rowe.[1])

gest that a specific efflux transport mechanism exists for folates.

Recent evidence suggests that folate-binding proteins may play a role in transport. The folate-binding protein of rat kidney proximal tubule is involved in renal transport, and endocytosis has been proposed as a mechanism of uptake. Using a monkey kidney cell line, evidence has been provided for the receptor-mediated endocytosis of folate.[17] Whether this mechanism is involved in any of the postulated hereditary disorders of cellular folate uptake in human beings remains to be elucidated.

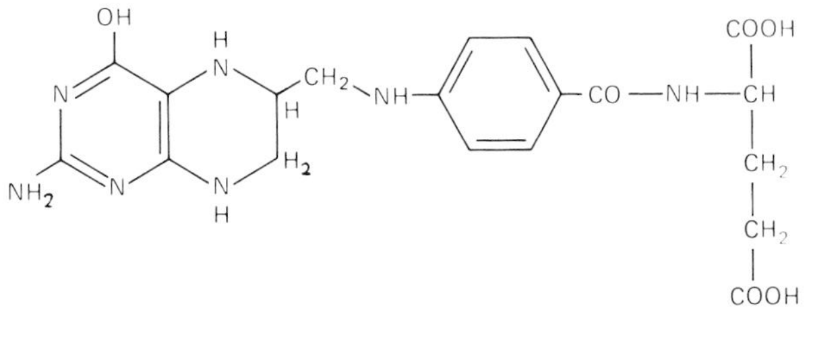

Folate Polyglutamates. Human cells need a critical concentration of intracellular folate to allow activity of folate-dependent enzymes. The amount required to maintain an optimal rate of growth varies from about 50 nM in human fibroblasts to about 1 μM in human lymphocytes and certain tumor cells.[18] The K_m for monoglutamate folate of many of the folate-dependent coenzymes is greater than 1 μM so that the folate-dependent enzyme reactions cannot progress in cells in

Fig. 81-1 The structure of 5,6,7,8-tetrahydrofolic acid (THF). (Reproduced from Rowe.[1])

the absence of the conversion of folate to polyglutamate forms. A cytoplasmic enzyme adds glutamate residues to selected folate molecules. This enzyme forms a peptide bond between the γ-carboxyl of the glutamate already on the molecule and the α amino group of the additional glutamate to be added. This γ-glutamyl chain is resistant to digestion by the common proteolytic enzymes and is hydrolyzed by specific "conjugase" enzymes. Folylpolyglutamate synthetase adds glutamate residues one at a time, requires ATP for its reaction, utilizes tetrahydrofolate folate and other folates as well as antifolates as substrates with different affinities, and reacts poorly with folic acid and 5-methyltetrahydrofolate. Polyglutamate folates of appropriate chain length have much lower K_ms for some of the folate-dependent reactions, allowing folate metabolism to progress at the concentration of those folates present in the cells. The K_m values of dihydrofolate reductase and methionine synthase for folic acid and 5-methyltetrahydrofolate are in the same general range as those of the polyglutamate forms of these folates. These reactions can utilize monoglutamate folates at cellular concentrations. Specific instances of channeling of polyglutamate intermediates between active sites of multifunctional proteins have been demonstrated. Thus, they may play a role in maintaining specific protein-protein interactions.[19] Several cell lines defective in folate polyglutamate formation have been reported. A mutant Chinese hamster cell line is auxotrophic for glycine, adenosine, and thymidine, apparently because reactions generating these within the cell require folate polyglutamate.[20,21] A human breast carcinoma cell line is defective in the synthesis of methotrexate polyglutamates and is resistant to methotrexate.

In addition there are changes in the distribution of polyglutamates in response to folate deprivation, partial hepatectomy, starvation, infection, and hormonal status. Since the response of polyglutamate chain length to changes in environment is relatively slow, it has been proposed[22] that the regulation of folate metabolism by means of polyglutamate chain length is secondary to the classic alterations in folate metabolism characterized by the activation and inhibition of the folate-dependent 1-carbon transfers which are described below. The response mediated by polyglutamates results from stimuli lasting hours or days, and results in the maintenance of a new steady state for single carbon metabolism.

It has been known for almost two decades that the folate polyglutamates must be hydrolyzed in the intestine prior to absorption and that monoglutamates are released into the circulation.[16,23] Two distinct forms of human pteroylpolyglutamate hydrolase ("conjugase") have been described in the intestine, one in the brush border, and the other with less clear function within the intestinal cell. There seems to be considerable species differences in the intestinal conjugases with only the pig and human being as yet showing the intrinsic intestinal brush border enzyme activity.

FOLATE ENZYMES

The major metabolic pathways of the folates are shown in Fig. 81-3. In most cells, because serine and glycine are the major sources of 1-carbon units, entry to the active 1-carbon pool of intermediates is by way of 5,10-methylenetetrahydrofolate (5,10-methylene-H4PteGlu). This compound is used unchanged for the synthesis of thymidylate (Fig. 81-3, 4). 5,10-Methylene-H4PteGlu is reduced to 5-methyl-H4PteGlu for the biosynthesis of methionine (Fig. 81-3, 1), or is oxidized to 10-formyl-H4PteGlu for use in purine synthesis[24] (Fig. 81-3, 6 and 7). All of the interconversions of folates involve exchange of side chains among tetrahydrofolates except for the formation of thymidylate using 5,10-methylene-H4PteGlu, catalyzed by thymidylate synthase (Fig. 81-3, 4), which also results in the oxidation of tetrahydrofolate (H4PteGlu) to dihydrofolate (H2PteGlu).

Fig. 81-3 Scheme of folate-mediated 1-carbon transfer reactions: 1, methionine synthase (methyltetrahydrofolate:homocysteine methyltransferase); 2, methylene-H4PteGlu reductase; 3, serine hydroxymethyltransferase; 4, thymidylate synthase; 5, dihydrofolate reductase; 6, methylene-H4PteGlu dehydrogenase (NAD- and NADP-dependent forms have been described); 7, methenyl-H4PteGlu cyclohydrolase; 8, 10-formyl-H4PteGlu synthase; 9, GAR (5-phosphoribosylglycineamide) transformylase; 10, AICAR (5-phosphoribosyl-5-aminoimidazole-4-carboxamide) transformylase; 11, glutamate formiminotransferase; 12, formimino-H4PteGlu cyclodeaminase; 13, 5,10-methenyl-H4PteGlu synthetase; 14, 10-formyl-H4PteGlu dehydrogenase; 15, glycine cleavage pathway.

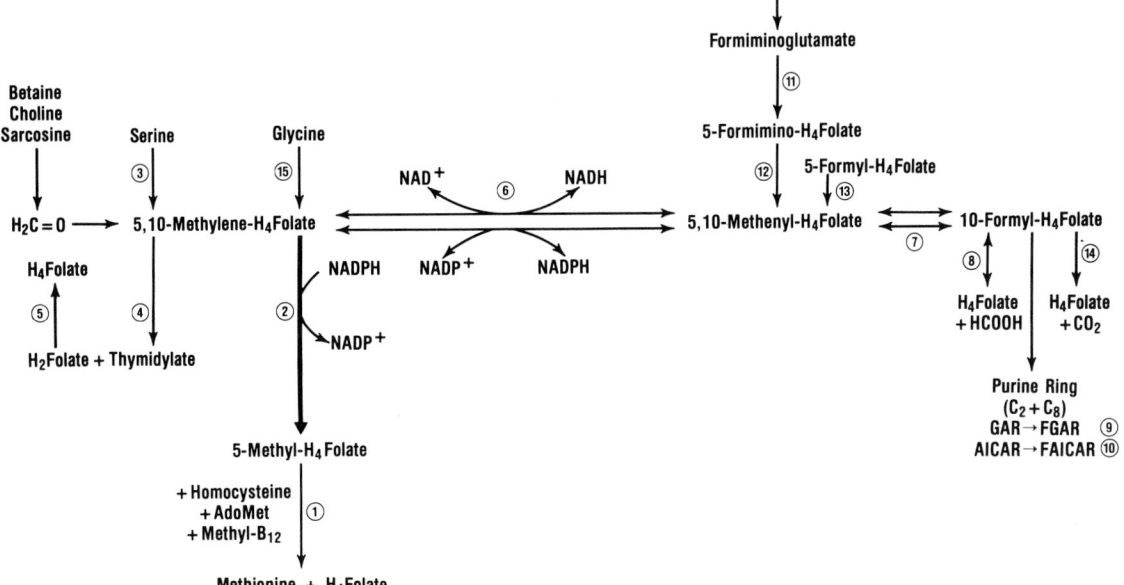

Folic acid, a synthetic vitamin which is not found in nature, and $H_2PteGlu$ are reduced by dihydrofolate reductase (Fig. 81-3, 5) to $H_4PteGlu$. Dihydrofolate reductase has long been thought to be the primary site of action of the chemotherapeutic drug methotrexate. Unstable gene amplification resulting in resistance to methotrexate is associated with cells with double, minute chromosomes, while in stably amplified cells that are resistant to methotrexate, the amplified genes are associated with elongated chromosomes.[25] The gene for dihydrofolate reductase has been assigned to 5 q11.1-q13.2.[25a,25b] In addition to the functional gene there are at least four intronless genes which are probably pseudogenes.[26] Dihydrofolate reductase was originally thought to be absent from brain[26a] but was subsequently found to be present.[26b,26c,26d] It has recently been shown that, despite the high levels of activity in cultured cell lines, fresh human tissue has only low levels of this enzyme.[27]

A trifunctional peptide bears activity for NADP-dependent methylene-$H_4PteGlu$ dehydrogenase, methenyl-$H_4PteGlu$ cyclohydrolase, and 10-formyl-$H_4PteGlu$ synthetase (Fig. 81-3, 6 to 8, 28). These enzyme activities mediate the interconversion of 5,10-methylene-$H_4PteGlu$, 5,10-methenyl-$H_4PteGlu$, and 10-formyl-$H_4PteGlu$. This interconversion of folates links the major source of single-carbon units (from serine via serine hydroxymethyltransferase (Fig. 81-3, 3) to form methylene-$H_4PteGlu$) with synthesis of thymidylate (thymidylate synthase, Fig. 81-3, 4) or purine (GAR and AICAR transformylase, Fig. 81-3, 9 and 10), and in the liver with the enzyme system that discards excess single carbons (Fig. 81-3, 14). The trifunctional peptide also permits either the release of single carbon from folate as formate or, more probably, the scavenging of potentially toxic formate (Fig. 81-3, 8).

Both NAD- and NADP-dependent methylenetetrahydrofolate dehydrogenases have been identified, with the former being active in transformed and embryonic cell lines.[29] The NAD-dependent dehydrogenase and the cyclohydrolase also exist as a bifunctional peptide that does not contain the synthetase activity.

The major sources of single-carbon units available for utilization in folate metabolism appear to be serine, entering the serine hydroxymethyltransferase reaction in the cytoplasm to form glycine, and glycine cleavage, which uses a four-enzyme sequence including a mitochondrial serine hydroxymethyltransferase. The direction of the glycine-serine interconversion appears determined by the supply of each amino acid.[30] Serine hydroxymethyltransferase requires pyridoxal phosphate as a cofactor. A mutant Chinese hamster ovary cell line deficient in the mitochondrial serine hydroxymethyltransferase is auxotrophic for glycine[31], indicating that the cytoplasmic enzyme cannot take over all of the functions of the mitochondrial enzyme.

Formyl-$H_4PteGlu$ dehydrogenase (Fig. 81-3, 14) releases excess active single-carbon fragments from folate and generates CO_2. Activity is restricted to the liver[32] and serves to maintain sufficient $H_4PteGlu$ to permit acceptance of single carbons in folate-dependent reactions.

5,10-Methenyltetrahydrofolate synthetase (Fig. 81-3, 13)[33] is an ATP-dependent enzyme which converts 5-formyl-$H_4PteGlu$ to 5,10-methenyl-$H_4PteGlu$. 5-Formyl-$H_4PteGlu$ appears to be a normal constituent of cells, perhaps formed nonenzymatically from unbound 10-formyl-$H_4PteGlu$ and methenyl-$H_4PteGlu$.

Methylene-$H_4PteGlu$ reductase (Fig. 81-3, 2)[34–37] mediates the conversion of 5,10-methylene-$H_4PteGlu$ to 5-methyl-$H_4PteGlu$ and probably utilizes only polyglutamates as sub-strates within the cell. The enzyme binds FAD and utilizes NADPH as electron donor.[34] The enzyme is inhibited by adenosylmethionine. In vitro the reaction is bidirectional, but in vivo it is essentially unidirectional in the direction of 5-methyl-$H_4PteGlu$. In vitro it is usually assayed in the reverse direction using menadione as electron acceptor, but it can be assayed in the physiological direction.[36] Under the latter conditions the concentration of adenosylmethionine required for inhibition of the reaction is considerably smaller than that required for inhibition of the reverse reaction.[37] The enzyme reaction is inhibited in vitro by dihydrofolate and by dihydrobiopterin,[38] providing a possible site of interaction between folate and pterin metabolic pathways.

Methionine is actively demethylated in the form of adenosylmethionine to form adenosylhomocysteine, which is hydrolyzed to homocysteine. Failure to regenerate methionine causes depletion of methionine and adenosylmethionine and exposes the organism to the toxicity of homocysteine. Methionine synthase (Fig. 81-3, 1) requires a reduced cobalamin as a prosthetic group, the cobalamin accepting a methyl group from adenosylmethionine or from methyl-$H_4PteGlu$ to convert homocysteine to methionine.[39] In vitamin B_{12} deficiency or when vitamin B_{12} is irreversibly oxidized by nitrous oxide,[40] methionine synthesis decreases. The resultant deficiency of adenosylmethionine shunts folates into the 5-methyl-$H_4PteGlu$ form, which requires the methionine synthase reaction for the regeneration of $H_4PteGlu$. In addition to the folate being "trapped" as methyl-$H_4PteGlu$ in vitamin B_{12} deficiency because of an inability to regenerate $H_4PteGlu$, the rate of folate polyglutamate synthesis is decreased in cells because methyl-$H_4PteGlu$ is a poor substrate for the folylpolyglutamate synthetase enzyme. Patients deficient in methionine synthase are expected to have homocystinuria, deficient plasma methionine levels, megaloblastic anemia, and possibly neurologic defects caused either by the vascular obstruction due to homocystine or to methionine deficiency in the brain. The level of intracellular methionine synthase enzyme activity decreases if cells are deficient in vitamin B_{12} probably because the enzyme is stabilized by its cofactor.

During the catabolism of histidine a formimino group is transferred to $H_4PteGlu$ followed by the release of ammonia and generation of 5,10-methenyl-$H_4PteGlu$. The two enzyme activities, glutamate formiminotransferase (Fig. 81-3, 11), and formimino-$H_4PteGlu$ cyclodeaminase (Fig. 81-3, 12), share a single octameric enzyme which channels polyglutamate folate molecules from one reaction to the next.[41,42] The pathway represents only a minor source of single carbon, and may exist only in liver and kidney. The enzymes seem to be absent from fibroblasts and blood cells. Defects in the pathway cause excretion of formiminoglutamate (FIGLU). FIGLU is also excreted in folate deficiency and by patients deficient in vitamin B_{12}.

INBORN ERRORS

The processes and reactions affected by inherited disorders of folate transport and metabolism are shown in Fig. 81-4. Those disorders involving folate transport are indicated by a broken line, whereas those involved in folate metabolism are indicated by a solid line. The numbered steps show the sites of well-characterized inherited disorders of folate transport or metabolism. Steps at which diseases have been described in the lit-

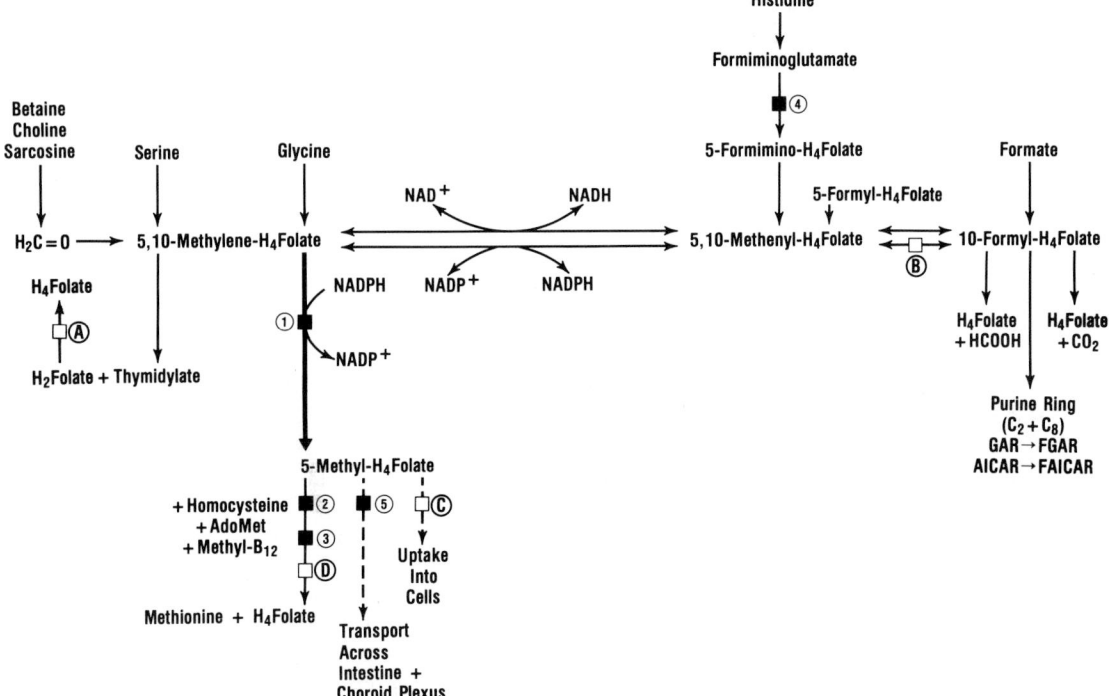

Fig. 81-4 Processes and reactions affected by inherited disorders of folate transport and metabolism: 1, methylene-H_4PteGlu reductase deficiency; 2 and 3, functional methionine synthase deficiency (cblE, cblG); see text and Chap. 82; 4, glutamate formiminotransferase deficiency; 5, hereditary folate malabsorption; A, dihydrofolate reductase deficiency; B, methenyltetrahydrofolate cyclohydrolase deficiency; C, cellular uptake defect of folates; D, methyltetrahydrofolate:homocysteine methyltransferase deficiency (primary defect). Those disorders involving folate transport are indicated by a broken line, whereas those involved in folate metabolism are indicated by a solid line. The numbered steps show the sites of well-characterized inherited disorders of folate transport or metabolism. Steps at which diseases have been presented in the literature but which remain in dispute are indicated by letters. AdoMet = adenosylmethionine; H_2folate = dihydrofolate; H_4folate = tetrahydrofolate; methyl-B_{12} = methylcobalamin; GAR = 5-phosphoribosylglycinamide; FGAR = α-N-Formyl-glycinamide ribonucleotide; AICAR = 5-phosphoribosyl-5-aminoimadazole-4-carboxamide; C_2, C_8 = carbons number 2 and 8 of purine ring.

erature but which remain in dispute are indicated with letters.

The well-characterized disorders that will be dealt with in some detail include: (1) methylenetetrahydrofolate reductase deficiency; (2 and 3) methyltetrahydrofolate-homocysteine methyltransferase (methionine synthase) deficiencies (cblE and cblG); (4) glutamate formiminotransferase deficiency; and (5) hereditary folate malabsorption.

CONFIRMED HEREDITARY DISORDERS

Methylenetetrahydrofolate Reductase Deficiency

Methylenetetrahydrofolate reductase (EC 1.1.1.68) is a cytoplasmic enzyme that catalyzes the NADPH-linked reduction of methylenetetrahydrofolate to form methyltetrahydrofolate (Fig. 81-3, 2). Methyltetrahydrofolate serves as the methyl donor for the methylation of homocysteine in the reaction catalyzed by 5-methyltetrahydrofolate:homocysteine methyltransferase (methionine synthase, Fig. 81-3, 1). The combined action of methylenetetrahydrofolate reductase and methionine synthase supplies single-carbon units for methylation reactions that use adenosylmethionine. The reaction catalyzed by methylenetetrahydrofolate reductase is essentially irreversible under physiological conditions, and the enzyme activity is regulated by levels of adenosylmethionine, which is an inhibitor.[37,43,44]

Clinical and Laboratory Findings. Since the first report of methylenetetrahydrofolate reductase deficiency in 1972[45,46]

(Fig. 81-4, 1), studies on more than 25 cases have been reported;[45–78] two-thirds of the patients have been female. The major biochemical findings are moderate homocystinuria and homocystinemia with low or relatively normal levels of plasma methionine. The clinical severity of this disorder varies greatly from case to case, and the age of diagnosis has ranged from before birth[68] to adolescence.[45] The most common clinical manifestation is developmental delay. Motor and gait abnormalities, seizures, and psychiatric manifestations have been reported. Of the patients with psychomotor retardation for whom clinical data have been reported, about half were microcephalic; EEG abnormalities were present in most patients; some abnormalities of gait were described in almost all patients who were old enough to walk.[4] Homocystinuria is present in all patients with a reported range of 15 to 667 μmol/24 h[4] and a mean of 130 μmol/24 h. Homocysteine was also found in the plasma with a mean value of 57 μM (range 12 to 233 μM). Usually homocysteine is not detected in control urine or plasma. Plasma methionine levels were low in all patients ranging from 0 to 18 μM with a mean of 12 μM. The fasting methionine concentration in plasma is usually 23 to 35 μM,[4] although values vary among laboratories.

Although homocystinuria is consistently seen in all patients, and indeed is the clinical clue by which the diagnosis of methylenetetrahydrofolate reductase deficiency is made, the excretion of homocysteine is much less than is found in homocystinuria due to cystathionine synthase deficiency, and indeed may not be detected on spot testing. The methionine levels in methylenetetrahydrofolate reductase deficiency are always low-normal or low. This again distinguishes these patients from those with cystathionine synthase deficiency. In contrast to patients who are functionally deficient in methionine biosynthesis because of abnormalities in methylcobalamin formation (cblC, cblD, cblE, cblF, and cblG) patients with methylenetetrahydrofolate reductase deficiency never have megaloblastic anemia. In addition, in contrast to patients with the cblC, cblD, and cblF disorders, these patients have no methylmalonic aciduria. Although serum folate levels were not always low, many of the patients with methylenetetrahydrofolate reductase deficiency had serum folate levels that were low on at least one determination. In contrast, serum cobalamin levels were almost always normal.

Patients have presented with clinical manifestations from the first week of life until adolescence. More than half of the patients have had presentations in the first year of life. Several patients came to medical attention after the first year but before adolescence, and only a few had onsets after age 12. One case was diagnosed prenatally.[68]

Although the levels of neurotransmitters in the cerebrospinal fluid have been measured in only a minority of patients, they have usually been low.[4]

Studies on Cultured Cells. A deficiency of methylenetetrahydrofolate reductase has been confirmed in studies of liver, leukocytes, cultured fibroblasts, and lymphoblasts. The enzyme assay that is routinely used for these studies measures the activity in the nonphysiological direction, using radioactive methyltetrahydrofolate as substrate and menadione as the electron acceptor. Full activity depends on the presence of FAD. The activity of methylenetetrahydrofolate reductase is extremely sensitive to the stage of the culture cycle of fibroblasts with the specific activity in control cells being highest in confluent cultures.[44] This variability is sufficiently great to allow for the misclassification of controls and heterozygotes if not taken into account. In general, there is rough correlation between residual enzyme activity and the clinical severity. Both the measurement of the proportion of folate present in cultured cells as methyltetrahydrofolate[57] and the synthesis of methionine from labeled formate[64] provide a better correlation with clinical severity. Studies on cultured fibroblasts[50,57] and liver[63,72] determined the levels and distribution of folate derivatives. In both control and mutant fibroblasts, most of the folates present were polyglutamates and the proportion of polyglutamates relative to folate monoglutamate was similar; a direct relationship was found in cultured fibroblasts between the proportion of cellular folate that was methyltetrahydrofolate and both the clinical severity and the residual enzyme activity, indicating that the distribution of the different folates may be an important control of intracellular folate metabolism.[57]

The differential microbiologic assay, which makes use of the fact that *Lactobacillus casei* can utilize methyltetrahydrofolate for growth but *Pediococcus cerevisiae* cannot, is a useful screening test for methylenetetrahydrofolate deficiency, as analysis requires only small numbers of cultured fibroblasts.[50]

Genetic heterogeneity in this disorder was suggested by the fact that fibroblast extracts from two of the original families showed differential heat inactivation.[51]

Control cultured fibroblasts can grow when homocysteine is substituted in the culture medium for methionine, an essential amino acid for these cells. In contrast, fibroblasts from patients with methylenetetrahydrofolate deficiency do not grow on homocysteine.[46,51] This inability to grow on homocysteine is shared by fibroblasts from patients who are functionally deficient in methionine synthase (cblC, cblD, cblE, cblF, and cblG).

Pathophysiology. The prominent biochemical manifestations of methylenetetrahydrofolate reductase deficiency include (1) homocystinuria and homocystinemia, (2) hypomethioninemia, (3) decreased proportion of intracellular folate as methyltetrahydrofolate, and (4) decreased neurotransmitter levels. None of the patients with this disease have had megaloblastic anemia, suggesting that there is not a folate-related defect in purine and pyrimidine biosynthesis. The relative importance of homocysteine excess and methionine deficiency in these patients remains a matter of conjecture.

The neurologic findings in monkeys treated with nitrous oxide, an agent which inactivates methionine synthase, are reported to be similar to those caused by vitamin B_{12} deficiency;[79–81] the effects are reversed by methionine therapy. Patients with disorders of vitamin B_{12} metabolism[82] who also have a block in methionine biosynthesis may have neurologic deterioration, but they also have hematologic abnormalities which are absent in methylenetetrahydrofolate reductase deficiency. The pathologic changes[4,49,52,54,70,71,72,75,78] in the patients with methylenetetrahydrofolate reductase deficiency who have been examined at autopsy include dilated cerebral ventricles, internal hydrocephalus, microgyria, and low brain weight. Also seen in the brain were perivascular changes, demyelination, macrophage infiltration, gliosis, and astrocytosis. Other major pathologic findings were thromboses of both arteries and cerebral veins; these appear to have been major factors in the death of these patients. These thromboses were the only pathologic findings shared with cystathionine synthase deficiency. Of the approximately 25 patients described, one patient had a fibrosarcoma.[78]

It has been pointed out[78] that the neuropathologic vascular findings in methylenetetrahydrofolate reductase deficiency are similar to those seen in classic homocystinuria due to cystathionine synthase deficiency. However, in methylenetetrahydrofolate reductase deficiency, it is necessary to explain the demyelination, astrogliosis, and lipid-filled macrophages which are associated in many patients with a progressive course of seizures, microcephaly, and severe psychomotor retardation.

Two reports[75,78] have described classic findings of subacute combined degeneration of the cord similar to that observed in patients with untreated vitamin B_{12} deficiency in patients dying with methylenetetrahydrofolate reductase deficiency. It has been proposed that methionine deficiency causes demyelination, presumably by interfering with methylation. As yet there have been no reports of subacute combined degeneration of the cord in patients with functional methionine synthase deficiency (cblE or cblG), (although one patient with adult-onset cblG had evidence of a peripheral neuropathy[83]), or in patients with combined methylmalonic aciduria and homocystinuria due to cblC disease. The latter patients do, however, have a distinct retinopathy[84,85] that is not seen in patients with methylenetetrahydrofolate reductase deficiency. It is logical to suppose that deficiency of methylenetetrahydrofolate reductase should lead to similar neurologic damage as a deficiency of methionine synthase or in the formation of methyl-B_{12} because all three function in the transfer of methyl groups from methyltetrahydrofolate to homocysteine to form methionine.

Methylenetetrahydrofolate reductase is present in mammalian brain.[86,87] Since several authors have suggested that only methyltetrahydrofolate can cross the blood-brain barrier,[58,88] methylenetetrahydrofolate reductase deficiency may result in functionally low folate levels in the brain. It has been suggested[89] that, since neurologic symptoms may be observed in patients without very low methionine levels, the neurologic dysfunction may occur as a result of impaired purine and pyrimidine synthesis as opposed to low levels of adenosylmethionine in the brain.

It has also been shown that methylenetetrahydrofolate reductase demonstrates dihydropteridine reductase activity,[90] leaving open the possibility that the enzyme may have a direct role in neurotransmitter biosynthesis.

The relative importance of low folate levels, low methionine levels, and low levels of neurotransmitters in the pathology of methylenetetrahydrofolate reductase deficiency is in the process of being investigated.[91] Differences seen between functional methionine synthase deficiency[82] (cblC, cblD, cblE, cblF, and cblG) and methylenetetrahydrofolate reductase deficiency should be useful in sorting out the relative importance of low levels of reduced folates other than methylenetetrahydrofolate, and low levels of methionine. These comparisons have the potential of being made more difficult by developmental and tissue differences in the distribution of these enzyme activities.[92,93] Certainly, the most important finding in the clinical differential diagnosis is the absence of megaloblastic anemia in patients with methylenetetrahydrofolate reductase deficiency as compared to patients with cblC, cblD, cblE, cblF (one patient), and cblG, and the absence of methylmalonic aciduria as compared to patients with cblC, cblD, and cblF disease (see also Chap. 82).

Treatment. Methylenetetrahydrofolate reductase deficiency has been very resistant to treatment.[4,11] The rationale for therapy has included (1) folates such as folic acid or folinic acid in an attempt to maximize any residual enzyme activity; (2) methyltetrahydrofolate to replace the missing product; (3) methionine to correct the cellular methionine deficiency; (4) pyridoxine to lower homocysteine levels because of its role as a cofactor for cystathionine synthase; (5) vitamin B_{12} because of its role as a cofactor for methionine synthase; (6) carnitine because of its requirement for *S*-adenosylmethionine; and (7) betaine[62] because it is a substrate for betaine methyltransferase,[93] an enzyme which is active primarily in the liver. Betaine has the theoretical advantage of both lowering homocysteine levels and supplementing methionine levels, although betaine should have no direct effect outside of those effects mediated through the liver.

Criteria for the success of treatment[4] have included reduction of the plasma homocysteine levels with elevation of plasma methionine levels to normal, along with improvement in the clinical picture. In most cases, several of the agents mentioned above have been used in combination and it is somewhat difficult to assess the efficiency of a single agent.

Successes at therapy have included a patient who was treated with a combination of methionine, oral 5-formyltetrahydrofolic acid (folinic acid), and vitamins B_6 and B_{12}[65,66] and several patients in whom betaine has been included in the regimen.[4,67,68,76] One of the patients who responded to betaine at doses of 20 g/day had not responded to other treatments including folates and methionine. Vitamin B_{12} had not been used in this patient.

Cooper[11] has suggested a therapeutic regimen consisting of oral betaine, folinic acid, and methionine, with additional vitamins B_6 and B_{12}. He recommended vitamin B_{12} because of the observations of subacute combined degeneration of the

cord[75] in a child treated with 5-methyltetrahydrofolate alone.

Betaine[67,76] has appeared to be the most promising agent for therapy of methylenetetrahydrofolate reductase deficiency, although, as mentioned above, some of the other therapies have been partially successful. Interestingly, therapy with methionine alone or with methyltetrahydrofolate has not been particularly effective in most cases, even though adenosylmethionine deficiency in the central nervous system appears to be playing a major role in the pathogenesis of this disease.[91]

Several authors[4,8] have stressed the importance of early diagnosis and therapy because of the poor prognosis in this disorder once there is evidence of neurologic involvement. Even with early diagnosis it is not clear that any of the therapeutic regimens are universally successful, and it is possible that genetic heterogeneity in the disease itself is responsible for some of the variability in clinical response to therapy.

Genetics. Autosomal recessive inheritance of methylenetetrahydrofolate reductase deficiency has been suggested by the occurrence of more than one case in several families, by the presence of both males and females with the disease within the same family, and by the decreased activity of the enzyme in the fibroblasts[51] and lymphocytes[53] of obligate heterozygotes. Consanguinity has been reported.[4,55]

Because of the heterogeneity of the biochemical and clinical phenotype among families, more than one mutant allele may be involved at this locus.

The diagnosis of methylenetetrahydrofolate reductase deficiency has been excluded prenatally in one pregnancy at risk.[94] Again, using amniocytes, prenatal diagnosis was successfully performed in another case,[68] allowing for early therapy with folic acid and betaine.[76] Enzyme activity of methylenetetrahydrofolate reductase has been detected in normal chorionic villi[68,74] which should allow for even earlier prenatal diagnosis.

Functional Methionine Synthase Deficiency

Methionine synthase [5-methyltetrahydrofolate: L-homocysteine methyltransferase (EC 2.1.1.13)] is a cytoplasmic enzyme that catalyzes the transfer of a methyl group from methyltetrahydrofolate or from adenosylmethionine to homocysteine to form methionine (Fig. 81-3, 1). Since the circulating form of folate in human beings is methyltetrahydrofolate monoglutamate, folate entering the cells must go through this reaction in order to generate tetrahydrofolate and the other folate cofactors.[79–81,95,96] Therapy with folic acid or folinic acid can bypass this reaction until methyltetrahydrofolate is again formed as a result of activity of methylenetetrahydrofolate reductase, which is irreversible in the cell. In the vitamin B_{12} (cobalamin)–dependent methionine synthase reactions studied in bacteria, the methyl group transferred from methyltetrahydrofolate converts enzyme-bound cob(I)alamin (vitamin B_{12} with a cobalt valence of 1^+) to methylcobalamin. The methyl group is then transferred to homocysteine, regenerating cob(I)alamin. After a number of cycles, the enzyme-bound cob(I)alamin oxidizes spontaneously to enzyme-cob(II)alamin [or perhaps cob(III)alamin] and requires a reducing system and adenosylmethionine to regenerate methylcobalamin (Chap. 82).[39,89,97,98]

Matthews and her colleagues partially purified methionine synthase from pig liver and suggest that the enzyme contains thiol oxidase activity,[89] and that thiols may serve as the physiological reductants for the mammalian enzyme. The question remains as to whether mammalian methionine synthase has an independent activation system analogous to the R and F proteins in *E. coli*[99,100] or whether the activation system is an integral part of the mammalian enzyme.[89] The answer to this question bears directly on human inborn errors of methionine biosynthesis.[101–103]

Matthews et al.[89] have provided evidence that the inhibition of methionine synthase by nitrous oxide involves the oxidation of cob(I)alamin to cob(II)alamin to cob(II)alamin with the production of nitrogen and a hydroxyl radical. They postulated that the formation of the hydroxyl radical at the active site is responsible for the irreversible loss of activity and for the partial loss of the cobalamin prosthetic group.

Using the binding of vitamin B_{12} as a marker and human-hamster hybrids, methionine synthase has been assigned to chromosome 1.[104,105] Given the fact that more than one locus appears to be involved in this activity,[102,103] refinement of this assignment may be required in the future.

Defect in Methionine Biosynthesis (clbE and cblG) Associated with Low Levels of Methyl-B_{12}

Because of the close interaction of folate and vitamin B_{12} metabolism and because of the low levels of methyl-B_{12} found in cultured cells from a group of patients with homocystinuria and megaloblastic anemia, the resulting disorders have been given names corresponding to defects in vitamin B_{12} (cobalamin) metabolism (Fig. 81-4, 2 and 3). However, since methylation of vitamin B_{12} occurs on methionine synthase[39,97] and since these disorders result in functional disorders of methionine biosynthesis, they will be discussed among the disorders of folate metabolism (see also Chap. 82).

Clinical and Laboratory Findings. cblE disease is characterized by homocystinuria without methylmalonic aciduria and by defective biosynthesis of methionine.[106] Activity of methionine synthase is normal in cell extracts under standard assay conditions when the assay is performed in the presence of high levels of thiols but is much less than that of controls in the presence of low thiol levels.[101] The defect appears to be related to maintaining vitamin B_{12} bound to methionine synthase in the reduced state.[101] As mentioned above, it is not known if this reducing activity is a function of a separate enzyme in human beings.

The original patient[106] had vomiting and poor feeding beginning at 9 weeks of age, associated with homocystinuria, hypomethioninemia, pancytopenia, and megaloblastic anemia. Diagnosis was based on homocystinuria that was responsive to vitamin B_{12} in the absence of methylmalonic aciduria. Diagnosis was confirmed by studies of cobalamin forms and the direct measurement of methionine synthase in extracts of cultured fibroblasts under different reducing conditions. Accumulation of labled vitamin B_{12} by cultured cells was normal, but the distribution of cobalamin cofactors was altered, with decreased levels of methylcobalamin as compared to normal fibroblasts. Methionine synthase from patients with cblE is insensitive to nitrous oxide inhibition,[101] suggesting that the enzyme in these patients is inactive and thus not producing the nitrous oxide–sensitive cob(I)alamin.

Treatment has been with hydroxocobalamin (OH-B_{12}) titrated to maintain normal levels of methionine in the plasma and the absence of homocystinuria. In some patients persistent macrocytic anemia has responded to therapy with folinic acid.

A sibling of the proband with cblE was diagnosed prenatally, and treatment of the mother with systemic hydroxocobalamin was begun before birth. The baby has been maintained on intramuscular OH-B_{12} twice weekly since birth and has never developed the severe clinical manifestations that his older brother showed.[107]

Subsequently, several additional patients have been described.[108–111] Although the children have all shown megaloblastic anemia and homocystinuria early in life and although all patients responded to vitamin B_{12} supplementation, sometimes response has been slow. In general the homocystinuria, hypomethioninemia, and megaloblastosis have resolved, and neurologic symptoms have been diminished if not eliminated. However, at least one patient has severe developmental delay despite commencing cobalamin therapy in the first year of life.[112] Activity of methionine synthase in cblG patients is low even under optimal assay conditions. It appears that these patients have a genetically different abnormality from those with clbE.[103]

Comparison of Methyl-B_{12} Deficiency Due to cblE and cblG. The original patient with methyl-B_{12} deficiency due to cblE presented at 9 weeks of age with severe megaloblastic anemia and homocystinuria that was responsive to therapy with hydroxocobalamin.[106] Fibroblasts from the patient were found to be deficient in the incorporation of label from methyltetrahydrofolate into protein, and methionine synthase activity in fibroblast extracts was decreased only if the assay was performed with low levels of thiols.[101] The total uptake of labeled cyanocobalamin by fibroblasts from this patient was normal, but the amount converted to methylcobalamin was severely depressed. As mentioned above, when the mother of this patient subsequently became pregnant, prenatal diagnosis determined that the fetus was affected;[107] the mother was successfully treated during her pregnancy, and the baby continued on therapy from birth. The baby never showed any clinical symptoms, presumably a result of early therapy rather than variability of clinical expression within the same family.

Since the description of this original family, additional patients with megaloblastic anemia and homocystinuria without methylmalonic aciduria have been found. All nontreated patients have shown developmental delay, although in one case it was mild enough not to be diagnosed until adulthood.[83] Most of the additional patients have shown low levels of methionine synthase activity in cultured fibroblasts even under optimal reducing conditions. In all cases intact cell methionine biosynthesis, as measured by the incorporation of methyltetrahydrofolate into cellular macromolecules, and methylcobalamin synthesis were impaired. Complementation analysis revealed the presence of two distinct classes, which were designated cblE and cblG.[102,103] The existence of two complementation groups giving rise to methylcobalamin deficiency and a functional deficiency of methionine biosynthesis suggest that the products of more than one locus may be necessary for methionine biosynthesis in human cells. The identities of the gene products affected by the cblE and cblG mutations are not yet known. As described above, in *E. coli* synthesis of enzyme-bound methylcobalamin occurs as a part of the catalytic cycle of methionine synthase. In addition, a reducing system consisting of two flavoproteins has been described. The mammalian enzyme contains iron and may contain its own reducing system.[98]

Further purification of the mammalian enzyme and elucidation of the nature of the reducing system with eventual cloning of the genes for the respective functions will determine whether either cblE, cblG, or both represent primary abnormalities of methionine synthase.

Genetics. All five patients with cblE disease have been male and two were brothers. Both males and females have been seen among the six patients with cblG disease. Parents have been unaffected. The inheritance of these disorders is presumed to be autosomal recessive. There is as yet no test for heterozygosity.

Therapy. All patients have responded well to therapy with vitamin B_{12} although reversal of early neurologic damage is not complete. On occasion, therapy has not been immediately successful, but the patient has responded to sustained therapy.

Differential Diagnosis. Disorders of cobalamin metabolism, in particular of cblC, cblD,[94] and cblF,[113–115] can be expected to show abnormalities of methionine biosynthesis and in some cases megaloblastic anemia. They can be distinguished by the presence of methylmalonic aciduria in patients with cblC, cblD, and cblF diseases. We have found that at least one patient who was described as having glutamate formiminotransferase deficiency in the literature[116] had an abnormality of methyl-B_{12} biosynthesis, probably cblG.

Glutamate Formiminotransferase Deficiency

As a result of the catabolism of histidine, a formimino group is transferred to tetrahydrofolate, followed by the release of ammonia and the formation of 5,10-methenyltetrahydrofolate. The two enzyme activities involved in these steps, glutamate formiminotransferase (EC 2.1.2.5) (Fig. 81-3, 11) and formiminotetrahydrofolate cyclodeaminase (EC 4.3.1.4) (Fig. 81-3, 12), share a single octameric enzyme[41,42] that channels polyglutamate folates from one reaction to the next. This pathway represents a minor source of single-carbon units and may be present only in liver and kidney. Defects in this pathway result in the excretion of formiminoglutamic acid (FIGLU). FIGLU excretion is also seen in patients deficient in folate or vitamin B_{12}.

Clinical and Laboratory Presentations. It is not at all clear whether this enzyme deficiency is associated with a disease state or whether the association of clinical findings with FIGLU excretion is a result of bias of ascertainment. Individuals with glutamate formiminotransferase deficiency (Fig. 81-4, 4) present with two distinct phenotypes. In one type there is mental and physical retardation, cortical atrophy with dilatation of cerebral ventricles, and abnormal electroencephalograms. The second type shows no mental retardation but massive excretion of FIGLU. It has been postulated that the severe form is associated with a major block in the cyclodeaminase enzyme and the mild form with a block in the formiminotransferase enzyme,[1] but no direct enzyme measurements have been presented to support this theory. Diagnosis of these diseases is hampered by the fact that the enzyme activity is absent in cultured human cells[8], and it is still disputed whether the deficiency can be diagnosed using red blood cells.[4,116] Indeed, in most cases in which the liver has been looked at, enzyme activities were higher than would have been expected for a complete block resulting in disease.[5] Erbe[4] has recently summarized and tabulated all patients with glutamate

formiminotransferase deficiency.[117–131] The patients have come to medical attention from age 3 months to 42 years. Three patients presented with delayed speech; two had mental retardation; and two presented with seizures. Two were studied because they were siblings of known cases. Mental retardation was described in most of the original Japanese patients,[5] whereas only three of the eight remaining patients were reported to show evidence of mental retardation.[124,126,127,130] Abnormal electroencephalograms and hypotonia have been frequently described. Several patients showed hematologic findings including hypersegmentation of neutrophils and macrocytosis.

The biochemical findings that have been reported include increased urinary FIGLU as well as increased formiminoglutamic acidemia, especially after a histidine load; normal to high serum folate levels with normal vitamin B_{12} levels; hyperhistidinemia; hypomethioninemia; and histidinuria.

In several of the Japanese patients FIGLU excretion was elevated only after histidine loading. Amino acid levels in plasma, including histidine, were usually normal, but occasionally low methionine levels were seen.[128,130] Urinary excretion of 4-amino-5-imidazolecarboxamide,[124,132] an intermediate metabolite in purine synthesis, has been reported, as has excretion of hydantoin-5-propionate, the stable oxidation product of the FIGLU precursor, 4-imidazolone-5-propionate.[11,130,131]

ENZYME ACTIVITY. Enzyme activity was measured in the livers of five patients and ranged from 14 to 54 percent of controls. In three families, the level of enzyme activity was said to be low in erythrocytes; yet several laboratories have been unable to detect enzyme activity in erythrocytes even in controls.[4]

Treatment. Response to therapy has been judged on the basis of decreased urinary excretion of FIGLU. Two patients in one family responded to treatment with folates;[125] six others did not.[4] One out of two patients[127,130] responded to methionine supplementation. Given that the correlation between clinical phenotype and FIGLU excretion remains uncertain, the basis for treating these patients is unclear.

Genetics. Glutamate formiminotransferase deficiency has been found in both male and female offspring of unaffected parents. No consanguinity has been described. The deficiency has been presumed to be inherited as an autosomal recessive. In the absence of detectable enzyme activity in cultured cells, definitive resolution of the inheritance of this disorder awaits the cloning of the mammalian gene and the localization of the primary defect, since it is likely that the primary defect could then be detected in DNA from patients. As the mammalian enzyme has been extensively purified,[41] DNA from putative patients should be put aside awaiting molecular diagnosis.

Differential Diagnosis. The major difficulty in the diagnosis of this disorder lies in the lack of expression of enzyme activity outside of the liver. Aside from FIGLU excretion in the urine and assay of enzyme activity in liver biopsy, which in reported cases has shown unusually high residual activities in patients,[5] definitive diagnosis is difficult. In addition, FIGLU excretion may be caused by other defects in folate or vitamin B_{12} metabolism. Indeed, we have had the opportunity to examine the fibroblasts of the last reported putative patient with this disease.[116] This patient had megaloblastic anemia and folate-responsive homocystinuria. We have been able to show that this patient has a low level of methionine biosynthesis and low levels of methionine synthase and methyl-B_{12} and is presumably a case of the newly described cblG mutation. Thus, it would be appropriate to study fibroblasts from all patients who show evidence of hypomethioninemia for evidence of functional methionine synthase deficiency.

INBORN ERRORS OF FOLATE TRANSPORT

Hereditary Folate Malabsorption

Clinical and Laboratory Findings. This disorder (Fig. 81-4, 5), which has also been called congenital malabsorption of folate because of its early clinical presentation, has been described in only a dozen patients, all but one of them girls.[133–146] The disease is characterized by severe megaloblastic anemia. Diarrhea, mouth ulcers, and failure to thrive are common, and most patients showed progressive neurologic deterioration. Among the patients were two pairs of sisters,[128,135] and there may have been additional unrecognized affected patients since one patient had a sibling who died at age 3 months[143] whose sex was not reported. Another patient who was one of nine children, had sisters who died shortly after birth, at age 2 years, and at age 13 years; in addition, she had a brother who died at the age of 13 years, but no further clinical details are provided.[144] A report from Israel[145] describes the only boy with this disorder, an infant who presented at age 4 months with severe bilateral pneumonia. He was one of seven siblings, two of whom had died in the first year of life without definitive diagnosis. In contrast to other cases, there was no sign of mental retardation, and correction of the serum folate levels did result in correction of the levels of folate in the cerebrospinal fluid. There is evidence for parental consanguinity in four families.[136,138,140,145]

The common clinical presentation in hereditary folate malabsorption is megaloblastic anemia in the first few months of life with low serum folate levels. Laboratory findings may include urinary excretion of FIGLU and orotic acid.[8,144] All patients were severely restricted in their ability to absorb oral folic acid or oral reduced folates. Large doses of oral folates did cause a hematologic response in some patients.[135,136,144] Parenteral therapy with folates has been effective in correcting anemia but has been of limited effectiveness in correcting the levels of folate in the cerebrospinal fluid. Other studies have suggested that folinic acid,[142,143] or methyltetrahydrofolate, is more effective in increasing the level of cerebrospinal fluid folate. There is significant clinical heterogeneity among patients. In some patients seizures were ameliorated, and in others they were exacerbated by folate therapy. It has been noted[147] that the presence of seizures, with or without cerebral calcifications, is coincident with the ability to respond hematologically to large doses of oral folinic or folic acid; the reason for this is unexplained.

These patients with hereditary folate malabsorption provide the best evidence for the existence of a specific carrier for folate at the level of both the intestine and the choroid plexus. Oxidized and reduced folates must share this system since the absorption of both is effectively blocked in these patients. The same gene product must mediate both intestinal transport and transport of folates into the brain, since except in the one affected male,[145] even when blood folate levels were raised sufficiently to correct the anemia, levels in the cerebrospinal fluid remained low. It is likely that uptake of folates into other cells of the body is normal in these patients since a hematologic response occurs in the presence of relatively low blood folate levels. In addition, the content and distribution of folates was normal in cultured fibroblasts from the one patient studied.[144]

One of the patients[144] had several additional interesting findings, including a relative inability to retain plasma folate after parenteral folate administration, a finding also seen in another patient;[138] high levels of folate in the red blood cells following folate therapy; low normal plasma levels of methionine; the presence of cystathionine in the cerebrospinal fluid and a response by the patient to methionine therapy; and increased susceptibility to infections associated with low levels of serum IgM and IgA. The affected boy[145] had a partial deficiency in both humoral (surface Ig and response to pokeweed mitogen) and cellular (E-rosette forming and response to hemagglutinin and concanavalin A) immunity.

Treatment. Cooper has stressed[11] that it is essential to maintain folate levels in the serum, red blood cells, and cerebrospinal fluid above levels associated with folate deficiency (4, 150, and 15 ng/ml, respectively). As mentioned above, some patients may respond to large oral doses of folic acid, folinic acid, or methyltetrahydrofolic acid. Oral doses may be increased to 100 mg or more daily if necessary.[11] If oral therapy does not work, systemic therapy must be instituted with daily injections (SC, IM, or IV) of folinic acid. If cerebrospinal fluid folate levels cannot be normalized, periodic intrathecal injections should be considered.[11]

Genetics. The occurrence of at least one sibship with hereditary folate malabsorption and the documented cases of consanguinity all suggest inheritance as an autosomal recessive disorder. In one of the families, other than the case from Israel, there is a suggestion of a possibly affected male,[144] and all but one of the documented cases[145] have been females. In the father of one of the patients the absorption of oral folate was seen to be intermediate,[138] again suggestive of autosomal recessive inheritance. The possibility of some pattern of sex-limited expression formally remains.

SUSPECT DISORDERS

Dihydrofolate Reductase Deficiency

Dihydrofolate reductase converts dihydrofolate to tetrahydrofolate (Fig. 81-3, 5); one mole of dihydrofolate is generated for each mole of thymidylate formed from deoxyuridylate by the thymidylate synthase reaction (Fig. 81-3, 4). Since thymidylate synthase uses methylenetetrahydrofolate polyglutamates, the dihydrofolate formed as a product of the reaction exists as polyglutamates.

There have been two published reports describing three cases of putative dihydrofolate reductase deficiency[148,149] (Fig. 81-4, A). These patients developed megaloblastic anemia soon after birth and showed a better clinical response to 5-formyltetrahydrofolate, a reduced folate, than to folic acid, an oxidized folate. In all three patients, dihydrofolate reductase activity was decreased in liver biopsies.

The original patient[148] had a reduction in dihydrofolate reductase activity in the liver to 35 percent of control values (more than 2 SD lower than autopsy liver samples in seven control subjects). This boy had anemia at 6 weeks of age that subsequently became megaloblastic. Oral doses of 50 to 500 μg/day of folic acid did not produce a clinical response; 5 mg/day of oral folic acid resulted in a sustained 3-year remission. When folate therapy was discontinued, the patient relapsed. Small doses of 5-formyl-H$_4$PteGlu (folinic acid, citrovorum factor) were effective in producing a remission. At age 19 years[4] the patient was not grossly mentally retarded but had manifested "sociopathic and frankly criminal behavior that resulted in repeated incarcerations."[4] Although he was still folate-dependent, extracts of cultured fibroblasts showed normal total activity, kinetics, and heat stability.

Two unrelated patients were later reported with neonatal megaloblastic anemia that was attributed to dihydrofolate reductase deficiency.[149] Activity in a liver biopsy was not detectable in the rouinte assay in the first case, but normal levels (1.0 to 1.7 nmol dihydrofolate reduced per minute per milligram of protein) were found in the presence of 0.6 M KCl. At age 3 years her bone marrow showed dihydrofolate reductase activity that was reduced to 10 percent of control levels, and a heat-labile enzyme with a molecular weight of 58,000 which was different from that of the normal enzyme.[150] At age 9 years[1] the child was severely mentally retarded and still showed folate-dependent macrocytic anemia.

The second child was first seen at age 26 days because of oral and anal moniliasis and poor feeding. Low neutrophil and platelet counts were seen, and over the next 2 weeks he developed a megaloblastic anemia. The serum folate level at 9.5 ng/ml was borderline normal for his age,[1] and the serum cobalamin level was normal. Dihydrofolate reductase activity in a liver biopsy specimen was 20 percent of the normal median value and was activated about two-fold by 0.6 M KCl, as was seen in the control liver samples.

Subsequent study revealed that the patient was deficient in functional transcobalamin II.[151] There was absent serum vitamin B$_{12}$–binding capacity although immunoassay did show transcobalamin II protein levels at 39 percent of the normal mean. There was no vitamin B$_{12}$–binding protein corresponding to transcobalamin II on Sephadex-gel chromatography. The patient was reinvestigated because of the development of mental retardation and severe neuropathy after 2 years of treatment.[152] It was concluded that this patient had functionally inactive transcobalamin II (see Chap. 82) of the type described by Seligman.[153]

No additional patients have been described in the past decade. It is possible that these children had other inborn errors of vitamin B$_{12}$ metabolism that were not identified, but the low liver values of dihydrofolate reductase remain difficult to explain. Of interest, urinary amino acids were reported to show a normal pattern, and no FIGLU was detected in the urine of the two patients who were reported in the most detail.[149] Thus, although the possibility of dihydrofolate reductase deficiency in an infant with severe megaloblastic anemia must be considered, all other known causes must be ruled out before this diagnosis can be confirmed.

Methenyltetrahydrofolate Cyclohydrolase Deficiency

As previously discussed, methenyltetrahydrofolate cyclohydrolase (Fig. 81-3, 7) exists as part of a trifunctional peptide in which resides the activities of methylenetetrahydrofolate dehydrogenase, methenyltetrahydrofolate cyclohydrolase, and 10-formyltetrahydrofolate synthase.[154,155] This peptide mediates the interconversion of 5,10-methylenetetrahydrofolate, 5,10-methenyltetrahydrofolate, and 10-formyltetrahydrofolate. This interconversion of folates links the major source of single-carbon units (serine) with those pathways that utilize these carbon units for purine and pyrimidine biosynthesis or, in the liver, with an enzyme that discards excess single carbons. This trifunctional peptide will also permit either the release of the single carbon from folate as formate or the scavenging of potentially toxic formate.[11]

Methenyltetrahydrofolate cyclohydrolase deficiency (Fig. 81-4, B) was proposed in three children who had 44 percent of control enzyme activity on liver biopsy and levels of 58, 36, and 43 percent of control values in erythrocytes.[156] Clinically, the patients showed mental retardation, microcephaly, ventricular dilatation, and abnormal electroencephalograms. A later report from the same laboratory[5] essentially retracted the diagnosis, and no additional cases have been reported.

Cellular Uptake Defects

This heading (Fig. 81-4, C) groups patients with varied clinical findings, some of which were associated with serious hematologic disease. Although the individual abnormalities of folate uptake have been well-characterized, it remains unclear whether these disorders represent primary inherited abnormalities.

Branda reported a patient with severe aplastic anemia that responded to high doses of folate therapy.[157] The patient was part of a large kindred in which there was a high incidence of severe hematologic disease including anemia, pancytopenia, and leukemia. These diseases were found in 34 individuals in four generations resulting in the death of 18. The proband showed a marked reduction of the uptake of methyltetrahydrofolate in stimulated lymphocytes despite a normal uptake of folic acid. Among eight healthy family members including three of the proband's children, four were found to have a similar abnormality. In addition, there was a less marked reduction in the uptake of methyltetrahydrofolate by bone marrow cells from the proband and his son. Of particular interest, however, was the finding that one son showed initially normal folate uptake, but subsequently developed neutropenia, and then exhibited the abnormality. This observation has been taken to suggest that this disorder may not be a primary defect in folate uptake.[147] Folate uptake by erythrocytes and the intestinal absorption of folate were found to be normal. Since the original report, the patient died at age 41 due to respiratory failure secondary to pleural effusion and ascites.[158] Three children in the family had an increased incidence of sister chromatid exchange.

An additional family was described with a transport defect which affected red cells and bone marrow but not lymphocytes.[159] The proband and his daughter had dyserythropoiesis without anemia; three brothers were normal. Erythrocytes from the patient showed abnormalities in the V_{max} and total uptake of methyltetrahydrofolate, whereas folic acid uptake was normal; the daughter showed only a possible elevation in the K_m for methyltetrahydrofolate, while the three clinically normal brothers resembled the proband kinetically. The status of both of these disorders of cellular uptake remains to be clarified.

Primary Methyltetrahydrofolate:Homocysteine Methyltransferase (Methionine Synthase) Deficiency (See Fig. 81-4, D).

One 6-month-old girl has been described with methionine synthase activity in liver that was 36 percent of normal.[160] She had megaloblastic anemia, seizures, dilated cerebral ventricles, and an elevated serum folate level. Significantly, she had no homocystinuria. Methionine synthase activity was not reduced in cultured fibroblasts from this patient.[8] Because of this finding and the absence of homocystinuria, it is uncertain whether the decreased hepatic methionine synthase activity was the primary cause of the clinical manifestations of the patient. For further discussion of deficiency in methionine biosynthesis, please see descriptions of the cblE and cblG disorders earlier in the chapter, and also Chap. 82.

CONCLUSIONS AND DIFFERENTIAL DIAGNOSIS

Although a number of children born to mothers with a diet deficiency in vitamin B_{12} have shown evidence of vitamin B_{12} deficiency, folate deficiency in the infant secondary to deficiency in the mother is unusual.[11] In nutritional folate deficiency in adults as described in Herbert's classic self-study,[161] the peripheral blood and bone marrow changes that occurred after 4 months were preceded much earlier by a fall in serum folate and a rise in urinary formiminoglutamic acid levels. Psychological and mental changes followed but were rapidly reversed by folic acid supplementation. Red blood cell folate levels fall in folate deficiency significantly later than do serum folate levels.

There are examples of some situations in which there are no defects in folate metabolism per se but in which folate therapy has been suggested as useful. For instance, supplements of folic acid in pregnant women produce an increase in the mean birth weight of infants;[162] the frequency of neural tube disorders in susceptible mothers is reduced when folate is given prior to conception;[163] folate reduces the frequency of the fragile site on the X chromosome in cultured cells.[164]

A guide to the differential diagnosis of the well-characterized disorders of folate metabolism is shown in Table 81-1. Most of these disorders are associated with normal serum and red blood cell folate levels. Hereditary folate malabsorption is always, and methylene-H_4PteGlu reductase deficiency is usually, associated with low serum folate levels. Serum folate levels were reported as elevated in most of the original Japanese patients but none of the subsequent ones with glutamate formiminotransferase deficiency. Homocystinuria has been described in methylene-H_4PteGlu reductase deficiency and cblE

Table 81-1 Inherited Defects of Folate Metabolism*

	Hereditary folate malabsorption	Methylenetetrahydrofolate reductase deficiency	Glutamate formiminotransferase deficiency	Functional methionine synthase deficiency cblE	cblG
Clinical sign:					
Prevalence	12 cases	>25 cases	13 cases	5 cases	6 cases
Megaloblastic anemia	A	N	N†	A	A
Developmental delay	A	A	N†	A	A
Seizures	A	A	N†	A	A
Speech abnormalities	N	N	A†	N	N
Gait abnormalities	N	A	N†	N	A†
Peripheral neuropathy	N	A	N†	N	A†
Apnea	N	A	N†	N†	N
Biochemical findings:					
Homocystinuria (-emia)	N	A	N	A	A
Hypomethioninemia	N	A	N	A	A
Formiminoglutamic aciduria	A†	N	A	N	N†
Folate absorption	A	N	N	N	N
Serum B_{12}	N	N	N†	N	N
Serum folate	A	A	N†	N	N
RBC folate	A	A†	N†	N	N
Defects detectable in cultured fibroblasts					
Whole cells:					
CH_3-H_4PteGlu uptake	N	N	N	A	A
CH_3-H_4PteGlu content	N	A	N	N	N
CH_3-B_{12} content	N	N	N	A	A
Extracts:					
Activity of holoenzyme of methionine synthase	N	N	N	N‡	A
Glutamate formiminotransferase	Activity undetectable in cultured cells		?Abnormal in liver and erythrocytes		
Methylene-H_4PteGlu reductase	N	A	N	N	N
Treatment	Folic acid or reduced folates in pharmacologic doses	Folates, betaine, methionine	?Folates		OH-B_{12}, folinic acid, betaine

*N = normal; A = abnormal (i.e., clinical findings or laboratory findings present).
†Exceptions described in some cases.
‡Abnormal activity with low concentrations of reducing agent in assay.

and cblG disorders. Megaloblastic anemia is seen in hereditary folate malabsorption and cblE and cblG diseases, but not in glutamate formiminotransferase deficiency except in the original Japanese patients, and notably never in methylene-$H_4PteGlu$ reductase deficiency.

Defects detectable in cultured cells include a decreased incorporation of label from methyl-$H_4PteGlu$ into protein in cblE and cblG disease and a decreased content of methyl-$H_4PteGlu$ in fibroblasts from patients with methylene-$H_4PteGlu$ reductase deficiency. Cells from patients with cblE and cblG diseases show decreased levels of methyl-B_{12}.

In cell extracts from cultured fibroblasts, activity of methylene-$H_4PteGlu$ reductase is decreased in methylene-$H_4PteGlu$ reductase deficiency. In extracts of cblE and cblG, disease fibroblast abnormalities in methionine synthase activity can be detected. Abnormalities of glutamate formiminotransferase have not been detected in any cultured cell system.

With respect to treatment, reduced folates have been of benefit in hereditary folate malabsorption. Methylene-$H_4PteGlu$ reductase deficiency is very refractory to therapy, but some response has been seen with folates, betaine, and methionine. Glutamate formiminotransferase deficiency is probably not a disease and does not need therapy, although many patients have received treatment with folates. Both cblE and cblG diseases respond to OH-B_{12}, and both folates and betaine have been used in some patients.

The author's original work cited in this chapter was supported by a Medical Research Council of Canada Group Grant in Genetics. I thank the following investigators who provided me with unpublished information on their patients or copies of publications which were in press: Stanley Berlow, MD; Bernard A. Cooper, MD; Dr. M. Duran; Richard W. Erbe, MD; Keith Hyland, PhD; Kuniaki Narisawa, MD; and Prof. Dr. U. Wendel. Thanks to Yasmin Karim and Maria Materniak for help in preparation of the text and to David Watkins, PhD; Angela Hosack; Nora Matiaszuk; Bernard A. Cooper, MD; Harvey Levy, MD; and Richard W. Erbe for helpful discussions. This is a publication of the Hess B. and Diane Finestone Laboratory in Memory of Jacob and Jenny Finestone.

REFERENCES

1. ROWE PB: Inherited disorders of folate metabolism, in Stanbury JB, Wyngaarden JB, Fredrickson DS, Goldstein JL, Brown MS (eds): *The Metabolic Basis of Inherited Diseases*, 5th ed. New York, McGraw-Hill, 1983, p 498.

2. BLAKLEY RL: *The Biochemistry of Folic Acid and Related Pteridines.* New York, Wiley, 1970.

3. BLAKLEY RL (ed): *Folates and Pterins.* vols 1,2, Blakley RL, Benkovic SJ (eds), vol 3, Blakley RL, Whitehead VM (eds). New York, Wiley, 1984–1986.

4. ERBE RW: Inborn errors of folate metabolism in folates and pterins, in Blakley RL, Whitehead VM (eds): *Nutritional, Pharmacological and Physiological Aspects.* New York, Wiley, 1986, vol 3, p 413.

5. ARAKAWA TS: Congenital defects in folate utilization. *Am J Med* 48:594, 1970.

6. ERBE RW: Inborn errors of folate metabolism. *N Engl J Med* 293:754, 1975.

7. COOPER BA: Megaloblastic anemia and disorders affecting utilization of vitamin B_{12} and folate in childhood. *Clin Haematol* 5:631, 1976.

8. ERBE RW: Genetic aspects of folate metabolism. *Adv Hum Gen* 9:293, 1979.

9. NIEDERWEISER A: Inborn errors of pterin metabolism, in Botez MI, Reynolds EH (eds): *Folic Acid in Neurology, Psychiatry and Internal Medicine.* New York, Raven, 1979, p 349.

10. ROSENBLATT DS: Inborn errors of folate and cobalamin metabolism, in Milunsky A (ed): *Genetic Disorders and the Fetus*, 2d ed. New York, Plenum, 1986, p 411.

11. COOPER BA: Anomalies congénitales du métabolisme des folates, in Zittoun J, Cooper BA (eds): *Folates et cobalamines.* Paris, Doin, 1987, chap 16.

12. WILLS L: Treatment of "pernicious anaemia of pregnancy" and "tropical anaemia." *Br Med J* 1:1059, 1931.

13. WILLS L, STEWART A: Experimental anemia in monkeys with special reference to macrocytic nutritional anemia. *Br J Exp Pathol* 16:444, 1935.

14. ANGIER RB, BOOTH JH, MOWAT JH, SEMB J, STOCKSTAD ELR, SUBBAROW Y, WALLER CW, COSULICH DB, FAHRENBACH MJ, HULTQUIST ME, KUN E, NORTHEY EH, SEEGER DR, SICKELS JP, SMITH JM JR: The structure and synthesis of the liver L. casei factor. *Science* 103:667, 1946.

15. HENDERSON GB: Transport of folate compounds by hemopoietic cells, in Zittoun J, Cooper BA (eds): *Folates et cobalamines.* Paris, Doin, 1987, chap 16.

16. ROSENBERG IH: Folate absorption and transport in chemistry and biology of pteridines, in Cooper BA, Whitehead VM (eds): *Pteridines and Folic Acid Derivatives.* Berlin, de Gruyter, 1986, p 587.

17. KAMEN BA, CAPDEVILA A: Receptor-mediated folate accumulation is regulated by the cellular folate content. *Proc Natl Acad Sci USA* 83:5983, 1986.

18. WATKINS D, COOPER BA: A critical intracellular concentration of fully reduced non-methylated folate polyglutamate prevents macrocytosis and diminished growth rate in human cell K562 in culture. *Biochem J* 214:456, 1983.

19. MacKENZIE RE: Summary. Pteroylpolyglutamate metabolism in chemistry and biology of pteridines, in Cooper BA, Whitehead VM (eds): *Pteridines and Folic Acid Derivatives.* Berlin, de Gruyter, 1986, p 767.

20. McBURNEY MW, WHITMORE FG: Isolation and biochemical characterization of folate deficient mutants of Chinese hamster cells. *Cell* 2:173, 1974.

21. TAYLOR RT, HANNA ML: Folate-dependent enzymes in cultured Chinese hamster cells. *Arch Biochem Biophys* 181:331, 1977.

22. PRIEST DE: Folates in tissues and cells in chemistry and biology of pteridines, in Cooper BA, Whitehead VM (eds): *Pteridines and Folic Acid Derivatives.* Berlin, de Gruyter, 1986, p 479.

23. HALSTED CM: Intestinal absorption and malabsorption of folates. *Annu Rev Med* 31:79, 1980.

24. SMITH GK, BENKOVIC PA, BENKOVIC SJ: L(−)10-formyltetrahydrofolate is the cofactor for glycinamide ribonucleotide transformylase from chicken liver. *Biochemistry* 20:4036, 1981.

25. KAUFMAN RJ, BROWN PC, SCHIMKE PT: Amplified dihydrofolate reductase genes in unstable methotrexate resistant cells are associated with double minute chromosomes. *Proc Natl Acad Sci USA* 76:5669, 1979.

25a. ANAGNOU NP, O'BRIEN SJ, SHIMADA T, NASH WG, CHEN M-J, NIENHUIS AW: Chromosomal organization of the human dihydrofolate reductase genes: Dispersion, selective amplification and a novel form of polymorphism. *Proc Natl Acad Sci USA* 81:5170, 1984.

25b. FUNANAGE VL, MYODA TT, MOSES PA, COWELL HR: Assignment of the human dihydrofolate reductase gene to the q11-q22 region of chromosome 5. *Mol Cell Biol* 4:2010, 1984.

26. McKUSICK VA: The human gene map. *Clin Genet* 29:545, 1987.

26a. MUKULU DR, SMITH EF, BERTINO JR: Lack of dihydrofolate reductase activity in brain tissues of mammalian species: Possible implications. *J Neurochem* 21:241, 1973.

26b. SPECTOR R, LEVY R, ABELSON HT: Identification of dihydrofolate reductase in rabbit brain. *Biochem Pharmacol* 26:1507, 1977.

26c. SPECTOR R, LEVY R, ABELSON HT: The development and regional distribution of dihydrofolate reductase in rabbit brain. *J Neurochem* 29:919, 1977.

26d. LYNN R, RUETER ME, GUYNN RW: Mammalian brain dihydrofolate reductase. *J Neurochem* 29:1147, 1977.

27. KAMEN BA, NYLEN PA, WHITEHEAD VM, ABELSON HT, DOLNIK BJ, PETERSON DW: Lack of dihydrofolate reductase in human tumor and leukemia cells *in vivo. Cancer Drug Deliv* 2:133, 1985.

28. TAN LUL, DRURY EJ, MACKENZIE RE: Methylenetetrahydrofolate dehydrogenase-methenyl-tetrahydrofolate cyclohydrolase-formyl-tetrahydrofolate synthetase; a multifunctional protein from porcine liver. *J Biol Chem* 234:1830, 1977.

29. MEJIA NR, MACKENZIE RE: NAD-dependent methylenetetrahydrofolate dehydrogenase is expressed by immortal cells. *J Biol Chem* 260:14616, 1986.

30. SCHIRCH L: Folates in serine and glycine metabolism, in Blakley R, Benkovic SK (eds): *Folates and Pterins. Chemistry and Biochemistry of Folates.* New York, Wiley, 1984, vol I, p 135.

31. CHASIN LA, FELDMAN A, KONSTAM M, URLAUB G: Reversion of a Chinese hamster cell auxotrophic mutant. *Proc Natl Acad Sci* 71:718, 1974.

32. KREBS HA, HEMS R, TYLER B: The regulation of folate and methionine metabolism. *Biochemistry* 158:341, 1976.
33. HOPKINS S, SCHIRCH L: 5,10-methenyltetrahydrofolate synthetase. *J Biol Chem* 259:5618, 1984.
34. MATTHEWS RG: Are the redox properties of tetrahydrofolate cofactors utilized in folate-dependent reactions? *Fed Proc* 41:2600, 1982.
35. MATTHEWS RG, BAUGH CM: Interactions of pig liver methylenetetrahydrofolate reductase with methylenetetrahydropteroyl polyglutamate substrates and with dihydropteroylpolyglutamate inhibitors. *Biochemistry* 19:2040, 1980.
36. LEWIS GP, ROWE PB: Methylene tetrahydrofolate reductase: Studies in a human mutant and mammalian liver, in Blair JA (ed): *Chemistry and Biology of Pteridines.* Berlin, de Gruyter, 1983, p 229.
37. KUTZBACH C, STOKSTAD ELR: Feedback inhibition of methylene tetrahydrofolate reductase in rat liver by S-adenosylmethionine. *Biochim Biophys Acta* 139:217, 1971.
38. SMITH I, HYLAND K, KENDALL B: Clinical role of pteridine therapy in tetrahydrobiopterin deficiency. *J Inherited Metab Dis* 8:(suppl I)39, 1985.
39. TAYLOR RT: B12-dependent methionine biosynthesis, in Dolphin D (ed): *Vitamin B12.* New York, Wiley, 1982, p 307.
40. CHANARIN I: Cobalamin folate interrelationships, in Zittoun J, Cooper BA (eds): *Folates et cobalamines.* Paris, Doin, 1987, chap 3.
41. BEAUDET R, MACKENZIE RE: Formiminotransferase-cyclohydrolase from porcine liver. An octameric enzyme containing bifunctional polypeptide. *Biochim Biophys Acta* 453:151, 1976.
42. MACKENZIE RE: Formiminotransferase-cyclodeaminase, a bifunctional protein from pig liver, in Kisliuk RL, Brown GM (eds): *Chemistry and Biology of Pteridines.* New York, Elsevier, 1979, p 443.
43. JENCKS DA, MATTHEWS RG: Allosteric inhibition of methylenetetrahydrofolate reductase by adenosylmethionine. *J Biol Chem* 262:2485, 1987.
44. ROSENBLATT DS, ERBE RW: Methylenetetrahydrofolate reductase in cultured human cells. I. Growth and metabolic studies. *Pediatr Res* 11:114, 1977.
45. SHIH VE, SALAM MZ, MUDD SH, UHLENDORF BV, ADAMS RD: A new form of homocystinuria due to N^5, N^{10}-methylenetetrahydrofolate reductase deficiency. *Pediatr Res* 6:135, 1972.
46. MUDD SH, UHLENDORF BW, FREEMAN JM, FINKELSTEIN JD, SHIH VE: Homocystinuria associated with decreased methylenetetrahydrofolate reductase activity. *Biochem Biophys Res Commun* 46:905, 1972.
47. FREEMAN JM, FINKELSTEIN JD, MUDD SH, UHLENDORF BW: Homocystinuria presenting as reversible "schizophrenia": A new defect in methionine metabolism with reduced 5,10-methylenetetrahydrofolate reductase activity. *Pediatr Res* 6:423, 1972.
48. FREEMAN JM, FINKELSTEIN JD, MUDD SH: Folate-responsive homocystinuria and "schizophrenia." A defect in methylation due to deficient 5,10-methylenetetrahydrofolate reductase activity. *N Engl J Med* 292:491, 1975.
49. KANWAR YS, MANALIGOD JR, WONG PWK: Morphologic studies in a patient with homocystinuria due to 5,10-methylenetetrahydrofolate reductase deficiency. *Pediatr Res* 10:598, 1976.
50. COOPER BA, ROSENBLATT DS: Folate coenzyme forms in fibroblasts from patients deficient in 5,10-methylenetetrahydrofolate reductase. *Biochem Soc Trans* 4:921, 1976.
51. ROSENBLATT DS, ERBE RW: Methylenetetrahydrofolate reductase in cultured human cells. II. Studies of methylenetetrahydrofolate reductase deficiency. *Pediatr Res* 11:1141, 1977.
52. WONG PWK, JUSTICE P, HRUBY M, WEISS EB, DIAMOND E: Folic acid nonresponsive homocystinuria due to methylenetetrahydrofolate reductase deficiency. *Pediatrics* 59:749, 1977.
53. WONG PWK, JUSTICE P, BERLOW S: Detection of homozygotes and heterozygotes with methylenetetrahydrofolate reductase deficiency. *J Lab Clin Med* 90:283, 1977.
54. BAUMGARTNER ER, SCHWEIZER K, WICK H: Different congenital forms of defective remethylation in homocystinuria. Clinical, biochemical and morphologic studies. *Pediatr Res* 11:1015, 1977.
55. NARISAWA K, WADA Y, SAITO T, SUZUKI K, KUDO M, ARAKAWA TS, KATSUSHIMA NA, TSUBOI R: Infantile type of homocystinuria with N^5,^{10}-methylenetetrahydrofolate reductase defect. *Tohoku J Exp Med* 121:185, 1977.
56. ROSENBLATT DS, COOPER BA: Methylenetetrahydrofolate reductase deficiency: Clinical and biochemical correlations, in Botez MI, Reynolds EH (eds): *Folic Acid in Neurology, Psychiatry and Internal Medicine.* New York, Raven, 1979.
57. ROSENBLATT DS, COOPER BA, LUE-SHING S, WONG PWK, BERLOW S, NARISAWA K, BAUMGARTNER R: Folate distribution in cultured human cells. Studies on 5,10-CH2-H4-PteGlu reductase deficiency. *J Clin Invest* 63:1019, 1979.
58. NARISAWA K: Brain damage in the infantile type of 5,10-methylenetetrahydrofolate reductase deficiency, in Botez MI, Reynolds EH (eds): *Folic Acid in Neurology, Psychiatry, and Internal Medicine.* New York, Raven, 1979, p 391.
59. SINGER HS, BUTLER I, ROTHENBERG S, VALLE D, FREEMAN J: Interrelationships among serum folate, CSF folate, neurotransmitters, and neuropsychiatric symptoms. *Neurology* 30:419, 1980.
60. BAUMGARTNER R, WICK H, OHNACKER H, PROBST A, MAURER R: Vascular lesions in two patients with congenital homocystinuria due to different defects of remethylation. *J Inherited Metab Dis* 3:101, 1980.
61. CEDERBAUM SD, SHAW KNF, COX DR, ERBE RW, BOSS GR, CARREL RE: Homocystinuria due to methylenetetrahydrofolate reductase (MTHFR) deficiency: Response to a high-protein diet. *Pediatr Res* 15:560, 1981.
62. ALLEN RJ, WONG PWK, ROTHENBERG SP, DIMAURO S, HEADINGTON JT: Progressive neonatal leukoencephalomyopathy due to absent methylenetetrahydrofolate reductase, responsive to treatment. *Ann Neurol* 8:211, 1980.
63. NARISAWA K: Folate metabolism infantile type of 5,10-methylenetetrahydrofolate reductase deficiency. *Acta Paediatr Jap* 23:82, 1981.
64. BOSS GR, ERBE RW: Decreased rates of methionine synthesis by methylenetetrahydrofolate reductase-deficient fibroblasts and lymphoblasts. *J Clin Invest* 67:1659, 1981.
65. HARPEY J-P, ROSENBLATT DS, COOPER BA, LEMOEL G, ROY C, LAFOURCADE J: Homocystinuria caused by 5,10-methylenetetrahydrofolate reductase deficiency. A case in an infant responding to methionine, folinic acid, and pyridoxine and vitamin B12 therapy. *J Pediatr* 98:275, 1981.
66. HARPEY J-P, LEMOEL G, ZITTOUN J: Follow-up in a child with 5,10-methylenetetrahydrofolate reductase deficiency. *J Pediatr* 103:1007, 1983.
67. WENDEL U, BREMER HJ: Betaine in the treatment of homocystinuria due to 5,10-methylene THF reductase deficiency. *Eur J Pediatr* 142:147, 1984.
68. CHRISTENSEN E, BRANDT NJ: Prenatal diagnosis of 5,10-methylenetetrahydrofolate reductase deficiency. *N Engl J Med* 313:50, 1985.
69. NISHIMURA M, YOSHINO K, TOMITA Y, TAKASHINA S, TANAKA J, NARISAWA K, KUROBANE I: Central and peripheral nervous system pathology of homocystinuria due to 5,10-methylenetetrahydrofolate reductase deficiency. *Pediatr Neurol* 1:375, 1985.
70. HAAN EA, ROGERS JG, LEWIS GP, ROWE PB: 5,10-methylenetetrahydrofolate reductase deficiency. Clinical and biochemical features of a further case. *J Inherited Metab Dis* 8:53, 1985.
71. HYLAND K, SMITH I, HOWELL DW, CLAYTON PT, LEONARD JV: The determination of pterins, biogenic amino metabolites, and aromatic amino acids in cerebrospinal fluid using isocratic reverse phase liquid chromatography within series dual cell coulometric electrochemical and fluorescence determinations—Use in the study of inborn errors of dihydropteridine reductase and 5,10-methylenetetrahydrofolate reductase, in Wachter H, Curtius H, Pfleiderer W (eds): *Biochemical and Clinical Aspects of Pteridines.* Berlin, de Gruyter, 1985, vol 4, p 85.
72. BAUMGARTNER ER, STOKSTAD ELR, WICK H, WATSON JE, KUSANO G: Comparison of folic acid coenzyme distribution patterns in patients with methylenetetrahydrofolate reductase and methionine synthetase deficiencies. *Pediatr Res* 19:1288, 1985.
73. BERLOW S: (letter) *Blood* 67:1526, 1986.
74. SHIN YS, PILZ G, ENDERS W: Methylenetetrahydrofolate reductase and methylenetetrahydrofolate methyltransferase in human fetal tissues and chorionic villi. *J Inherited Metab Dis* 9:275, 1986.
75. CLAYTON PT, SMITH I, HARDING B, HYLAND K, LEONARD JV, LEEMING RJ: Subacute combined degeneration of the cord, dementia, and Parkinsonism due to an inborn error of folate metabolism. *J Neurol Neurosurg Psychiatry* 49:920, 1986.
76. BRANDT NJ, CHRISTENSEN E, SKOVBY F, DJERNES B: Treatment of methylenetetrahydrofolate reductase deficiency from the neonatal period. Amersfoort, The Netherlands, The Society for the Study of Inborn Errors of Metabolism, 1986, p 23.
77. FOWLER B: Homocystinuria, remethylation defects. Methionine synthesis and cofactor response in cultured fibroblasts. Amersfoort, The Netherlands, The Society for the Study of Inborn Errors of Metabolism, 24th Annual Symposium, Sept 9–12, 1986, p 22.
78. BECKMAN DR, HOGANSON G, BERLOW S, GILBERT EF: Pathological findings in 5,10-methylenetetrahydrofolate reductase deficiency. *Birth Defects* 23:47, 1987.
79. SCOTT JM, WILSON P, DINN JJ, WEIR DG: Pathogenesis of subacute combined degeneration as a result of methyl group deficiency. *Lancet* 2:334, 1981.
80. SCOTT JM, WEIR DG: The methyl folate trap. A physiological response in man to prevent methyl group deficiency in kwashiorkor (methionine deficiency) and an explanation for folic-acid-induced exacerbation of subacute combined degeneration in pernicious anemia. *Lancet* 2:337, 1981.
81. CHANARIN I, DEACON R, LUMB M, MUIR M, PERRY J: Cobalamin-folate interrelations: A critical review. *Blood* 66:479, 1985.

82. COOPER BA, ROSENBLATT DS: Inherited disorders of vitamin B_{12} metabolism. *Annu Rev Nutr* 7:291, 1987.

83. CARMEL R, WATKINS D, GOODMAN SI, ROSENBLATT DS: A hereditary defect of cobalamin metabolism (cblG Mutation) presenting as a neurologic disorder in adulthood. *N Engl J Med* 318:1738, 1988.

84. ROBB RM, DOWTON SB, FULTON AB, LEVY HL: Retinal degeneration in vitamin B_{12} disorder associated with methylmalonic aciduria and sulfur amino acid abnormalities. *Am J Ophthalmol* 97:691, 1984.

85. MITCHELL GA, WATKINS D, MELANCON SB, ROSENBLATT DS, GEOFFROY G, ORQUIN J, HOMSEY MB, DALLAIRE L: Clinical heterogeneity in cobalamin C variant of combined homocystinuria and methylmalonic aciduria. *J Pediatr* 108:410, 1986.

86. BRODERICK DS, NORTH JA, MANGUM JH: Isolation of N^5, N^{10}-methylene tetrahydrofolate reductase from bovine brain. *Prep Biochem* 2(3):207, 1972.

87. BURTON EG, SALLACH HJ: Methylenetetrahydrofolate reductase in the rat central nervous system: Intracellular and regional distribution. *Arch Biochem Biophys* 166:483, 1975.

88. LEVITT M, NIXON PF, PINCUS JH, BERTINO JR: Transport of folates in cerebrospinal fluid: A study using doubly-labelled 5-methyltetrahydrofolate and 5-formyltetrahydrofolate. *J Clin Invest* 50:1301, 1971.

89. MATTHEWS RG, JENCKS DA, FRASCA V, MATTHEWS KD: Methionine biosynthesis in chemistry and biology of pteridines, in Cooper BA, Whitehead VM (eds): *Pteridines and Folic Acid Derivatives*. New York, de Gruyter, 1986, p 698.

90. MATTHEWS RG, KAUFMAN S: Characterization of dihydropteridine reductase activity of pig liver methylenetetrahydrofolate reductase. *J Biol Chem* 255:6014, 1980.

91. HYLAND K, SMITH I, BOTTIGLIERI T, PERRY J, WENDEL U, CLAYTON PT, LEONARD JV: Demyelination and decreased S-adenosylmethionine in 5,10-methylenetetrahydrofolate reductase deficiency. *Neurology* 38:459, 1988.

92. KALNITSKY A, ROSENBLATT DS, ZLOTKIN S: Differences in liver folate enzyme patterns in premature and full term infants. *Pediatr Res* 16:628, 1982.

93. GAULL GE, VON BERG W, RAIHA NCR, STURMAN JA: Development of methyltransferase activities of human fetal tissues. *Pediatr Res* 7:527, 1973.

94. WENDEL U, CLAUSSEN U, DICKMANN E: Prenatal diagnosis for methylenetetrahydrofolate deficiency. *J Pediatr* 102:938, 1983.

95. HERBERT V, ZALUSKY R: Interrelationship of vitamin B_{12} and folic acid metabolism: Folic acid clearance studies. *J Clin Invest* 41:1263, 1962.

96. NOROHNA JM, SILVERMAN MJ: On folic acid, vitamin B_{12}, methionine and formiminoglutamic acid metabolism, Henrich HC (ed): in *Vitamin B_{12} and Intrinsic Factor*. Stuttgart, Enke Verlag, 1962, p 728.

97. MATTHEWS RG: Methionine biosynthesis, in Blakley RL, Benkovic SJ (eds): *Folates and Pterins*. New York, Wiley, 1984, p 497.

98. UTLEY CS, MARCELL PD, ALLEN RH, ANTHONY AC, KOLHOUSE JF: Isolation and characterization of methionine synthase from human placenta. *J Biol Chem* 260:13656, 1985.

99. FUJII K, HUENNEKENS FM: Activation of methionine synthase by a reduced triphosphopyridine nucleotide-dependent flavoprotein system. *J Biol Chem* 249:6745, 1974.

100. FUJII K, GALIVAN JH, HUENNEKENS FM: Activation of methionine synthase: Further characterization of the flavoprotein system. *Arch Biochem Biophys* 178:662, 1977.

101. ROSENBLATT DS, COOPER BA, POTTIER A, LUE-SHING H, MATIASZUK N, GRAUER K: Altered vitamin B_{12} metabolism in fibroblasts from a patient with megaloblastic anemia and homocystinuria due to a new defect in methionine biosynthesis. *J Clin Invest* 74:2149, 1984.

102. WATKINS D, ROSENBLATT DS: Complementation studies in functional methionine synthase deficiency: Evidence for heterogeneity in cblE. *Am J Hum Genet* 39:A22, 1986.

103. WATKINS D, ROSENBLATT DS: Genetic heterogeneity among patients with methylcobalamin deficiency: Definition of two complementation groups, cblE and cblG. *J Clin Invest* 81(6):1690, 1988.

104. ROSENBERG LE: Disorders of propionate and methylmalonate metabolism, in Stanbury JB, Wyngaarden JB, Fredrickson DS, Goldstein JL, Brown MS (eds): *The Metabolic Basis of Inherited Disease*, 5th ed. New York, McGraw-Hill, 1983, p 474.

105. MELLMAN IS, LIN P-F, RUDDLE FH, ROSENBERG LE: Genetic control of cobalamin binding in normal and mutant cells: Assignment of the gene for 5-methyltetrahydrofolate: L-homocysteine S-methyltransferase to human chromosome 1. *Proc Natl Acad Sci USA* 76:405, 1979.

106. SCHUH S, ROSENBLATT DS, COOPER BA, SCHROEDER ML, BISHOP AJ, SEARGEANT LE, HAWORTH JA: Homocystinuria and megaloblastic anemia responsive to vitamin B_{12} therapy. An inborn error of metabolism due to a defect in cobalamin metabolism. *N Engl J Med* 310:686, 1984.

107. ROSENBLATT DS, COOPER BA, SCHMUTZ SM, ZALESKI WA, CASEY RE: Pre-natal vitamin B_{12} therapy of a fetus with methylcobalamin deficiency (cobalamin E disease). *Lancet* 1:1127, 1985.

108. WATKINS D, ROSENBLATT DS: Heterogeneity in functional methionine synthase deficiency, in Cooper BA, Whitehead VM (eds): *Chemistry and Biology of Pteridines 1986. Pteridines and Folic Acid-Derivatives*. Berlin, Walter de Gruyter, 1986, p 713.

109. ROSENBLATT DS, THOMAS IT, WATKINS D, COOPER BA, ERBE RW: Vitamin B_{12}-responsive homocystinuria and megaloblastic anemia: Heterogeneity in methylcobalamin deficiency (cblE). *Am J Med Genet* 26:377, 1987.

110. HALLAM R, CLARK AL, VAN DER WEYDEN MA: Neonatal megaloblastic anemia and homocystinuria associated with reduced levels of methionine synthase. *Blood* 66:44a, 1985.

111. MCKIE VC, ROESAL RA, HOMMES FA, WATKINS D, ROSENBLATT DS, FLANNERY DB: Clinical findings in an infant with methylcobalamin deficiency (cblE variant). *Am J Hum Genet* 39:A71, 1986.

112. MORTON DH, LEVY HL, BRESNAN MI, HALL CA, WATKINS D, ROSENBLATT DS: Cobalamin (cbl) E mutation with developmental delay, myoclonic seizures and hypsarrhythmia. Therapy with methylcobalamin. *Am J Hum Genet* 39:A16, 1986.

113. ROSENBLATT DS, POTTIER A, MATIASZUK NV, COOPER BA, LAFRAMBOISE R: Defect in vitamin B_{12} release from lysosomes: Newly described inborn error of vitamin B_{12} metabolism. *Science* 228:1319, 1985.

114. ROSENBLATT DS, LAFRAMBOISE R, PICHETTE J, LANGEVIN P, COOPER BA, COSTA T: New disorder of vitamin B_{12} metabolism (cobalamin F) presenting as methylmalonic aciduria. *Pediatrics* 78:51, 1986.

115. WATKINS D, ROSENBLATT DS: Failure of lysosomal release of vitamin B_{12}: A new complementation group causing methylmalonic aciduria (cblF). *Am J Hum Genet* 39:404, 1986.

116. SHIN YS, REITER S, ZELGER O, BRUNSTLER I, VRUCKER A: Orotic aciduria, homocystinuria, formiminoglutamic aciduria and megaloblastosis associated with the formiminotransferase/cyclodeaminase deficiency, in Nyhan WL, Thompson LF, Watts RWE (eds): *Purine and Pyrimidine Metabolism in Man*. New York, Plenum, 1986, p 71.

117. ARAKAWA T, OHARA K, KUDO Z, TADA K, HAYASHI T, MIZUNO T: Hyper-folic-acidemia with formiminoglutamic-aciduria following histidine loading: Suggested for a case of congenital deficiency in formiminotransferase. *Tohoku J Exp Med* 80:370, 1963.

118. ARAKAWA T, OHARA K, TAKAHASHI Y, OGASAWARA J, HAYASHI T, CHIBA R, WADA Y, TADA K, MIZUNO T, OHAMURA T, YOSHIDA T: Formiminotransferase-deficiency syndrome: A new inborn error of folic acid metabolism. *Ann Pediatr* 205:1, 1965.

119. ARAKAWA T, FUJII M, HIRONO H: Tetrahydrofolate-dependent enzyme activity in formiminotransferase deficiency syndrome. *Tohoku J Exp Med* 88:305, 1966.

120. ARAKAWA T, FUJII M, OHARA K: Erythrocyte formiminotransferase activity in formiminotransferase deficiency syndrome. *Tohoku J Exp Med* 88:195, 1966.

121. ARAKAWA T, TAMURA T, OHARA K, NARISAWA K, TANNO K, HONDA Y, HIGASHI O: Familial occurrence of formiminotransferase deficiency syndrome. *Tohoku J Exp Med* 96:211, 1968.

122. HERMAN RH, ROSENSWEIG NS, STIFEL FB, HERMAN YF: Adult formiminotransferase deficiency: A new entity. *Clin Res* 17:304, 1969.

123. ARAKAWA T, YOSHIDA T, KONNA T, HONDA Y: Defect of incorporation of glycine-1-^{14}C into urinary uric acid in formiminotransferase deficiency syndrome. *Tohoku J Exp Med* 106:213, 1972.

124. NIEDERWIESER A, GILIBERTI P, MATASOVIC A, PLUZNIK S, STEINMANN B, BAERLOCHER K: Folic acid non-dependent formiminoglutamic aciduria in two siblings. *Clin Chim Acta* 54:293, 1974.

125. PERRY TL, APPLEGARTH DA, EVANS ME, HANSEN S: Metabolic studies of a family with massive formiminoglutamic aciduria. *Pediatr Res* 9:117, 1975.

126. NIEDERWIESER A, MATASOVIC A, STEINMANN B, BAERLOCHER K, KEMPEN B: Hydantoin -5-propionic aciduria in folic acid non-dependent formiminoglutamic aciduria observed in two siblings. *Pediatr Res* 10:215, 1976.

127. RUSSEL A, STATTER M, ABZUG S: Methionine-dependent formiminoglutamic acid transferase deficiency: Human and experimental studies in its therapy. *Hum Hered* 27:205, 1977.

128. RUSSEL A, STATTER M, ABZUG-HOROWITZ S: Methionine-dependent glutamic acid formiminotransferase deficiency, in Sperling O, de Vries H (eds): *Inborn Errors of Metabolism in Man*. Basel, Karger, 1978, p 65.

129. BECK B, CHRISTENSEN E, BRANDT NJ, PEDERSON M: Formiminoglutamic aciduria in a slightly retarded boy with chronic obstructive lung disease. *J Inherited Metab Dis* 14:225, 1981.

130. DURAN M, KETTING D, deBREE PK, van SPRANG FJ, WADMAN SK, PENDERS TJ, WILMS RHH: A case of formiminoglutamic aciduria. *Eur J Pediatr* 136:319, 1981.

131. DURAN M, BRUINVIS L, WADMAN SK: Quantitative gas chromatographic determination of urinary hydantoin-5-propionic acid in patients with disorders of folate/vitamin B_{12} metabolism. *J Chromatography* 381:401, 1986.

132. ARAKAWA T, WADA Y: Urinary AICA (4-amino-5-imidazole-carboxamide) following an oral dose of AICA in formiminotransferase deficiency syndrome. *Tohoku J Exp Med* 96:211, 1968.

133. LUHBY AL, EAGLE FJ, ROTH E, COOPERMAN JM: Relapsing megaloblastic anemia in an infant due to a specific defect in gastrointestinal absorption of folic acid. *Am J Dis Child* 102:482, 1961.

134. LUHBY AL, COOPERMAN JM: Folic acid deficiency in man and its interrelationship with vitamin B$_{12}$ metabolism. *Adv Metab Disorders* 1:263, 1964.

135. LUHBY AL, COOPERMAN JM: Congenital megaloblastic anemia and progressive central nervous system degeneration. Further clinical and physiological characterization and therapy of syndrome due to inborn error of folate transport. *Proceedings of the American Pediatric Society Philadelphia*, Atlantic City, April 26–29, 1967.

136. LANKOWSKY P, ERLANDSON ME, BEZAN AI: Isolated defect of folic acid absorption associated with mental retardation and cerebral calcification. *Blood* 34:452, 1969.

137. LANKOWSKY P: Congenital malabsorption of folate. *Am J Med* 48:580, 1970.

138. SANTIAGO-BORRERA PJ, SANTINI R Jr, PEREZ-SANTIAGO E, MALDONADO N, MILLAN S, COLL-CAMALEZ G: Congenital isolated defect of folic acid absorption. *J Pediatr* 82:450, 1973.

139. SU PC: Congenital folate deficiency. *N Engl J Med* 294:1128, 1976.

140. NARISAWA K: Personal communication describing siblings reported in the Japanese literature: Kobayashi K, Hoshino M: *Jpn J Pediatr* 29:1788, 1976.

141. KONOMI H, KUWAJIMA K, YANAGISAWA M, KAMOSHITA S, NARISAWA K: A case of congenital folic acid malabsorption with infantile spasms. *Brain Dev* 3:234, 1978.

142. PONCZ M, COLMAN N, HERBERT V, SCHWARTZ E, COHEN AR: Congenital folate malabsorption. *J Pediatr* 99:828, 1981.

143. PONCZ M, COLMAN N, HERBERT V, SCHWARTZ E, COHEN AR: Therapy of congenital folate malabsorption. *J Pediatr* 98:76, 1981.

144. CORBEEL L, VAN DEN BERGHE G, JAEKEN J, VANTORNOUT J, EECKELS R: Congenital folate malabsorption. *Eur J Pediatr* 143:284, 1985.

145. URBACH J, ABRAHAMOV A, GROSSOWICZ N: Congenital isolated folic acid malabsorption. *Arch Dis Child* 62:78, 1987.

146. SAKIYAMA T, TSUDA M, NAKABAYASHI H, SHIMIZU H, OWAKA M, KITAGAWA T: Clinical and biochemical observations in a case with congenital defect of folate absorption. Annual Meeting of the SIEM, Newcastle upon Tyne 5-8 Sept, 1984.

147. BUCHANAN JA: Fibroblast plasma membrane vesicles to study inborn errors of transport. PhD Thesis. McGill University, 1984, p 23.

148. WALTERS TR: Congenital megaloblastic anemia responsive to N^5-formyl tetrahydrofolic acid administration. *J Pediatr* 70:686, 1987.

149. TAURO GP, DANKS DM, ROWE PB, VAN DER WEYDEN MB, SCHWARTZ MA, COLLINS VL, NEAL BW: Dihydrofolate reductase deficiency causing megaloblastic anemia in two families. *N Engl J Med* 294:466, 1976.

150. MCGREADY RK, TAURO GP, VAN DER WEYDEN M: Physical and kinetic characteristics of a mutant dihydrofolate reductase. *Proc Aust Biol Soc* 9:9, 1976.

151. HOFFBRAND AV, TRIPP E, JACKSON BFA, LUCK WE, FRATER-SCHRODER M: Hereditary abnormal transcobalamin II previously diagnosed as congenital dihydrofolate reductase deficiency. *N Engl J Med* (letter) 310:789, 1984.

152. THOMAS RK, HOFFBRAND AV, SMITH IS: Neurological involvement in hereditary transcobalamin II deficiency. *J Neurol Neurosurg Psychiatry* 45:74, 1982.

153. SELIGMAN PA, STEINER LL, ALLEN RH: Studies of a patient with megaloblastic anemia and an abnormal transcobalamin II. *N Engl J Med* 303:1209, 1980.

154. PAUKERT JL, D'ARI-STRAUSS L, RABINOWITZ JC: Formyl-methenyl-methylenetetrahydrofolate synthase (combined). An ovine protein with multiple catalytic activities. *J Biol Chem* 251:5104, 1976.

155. TAN LU, DRURY EJ, MACKENZIE RE: Methylenetetrahydrofolate dehydrogenase-methenyltetrahydrofolate cyclohydrolase-formyltetrahydrofolate synthetase. A functional protein from porcine liver. *J Biol Chem* 252:1117, 1977.

156. ARAKAWA T, FUJI M, OHARA K, WATANABE S, KARAHASHI M, KOBAYASHI M, HIRONO H: Mental retardation with hyperfolicacidemia not associated with formiminoglutamic aciduria; cyclohydrolase deficiency syndrome. *Tohoku J Exp Med* 88:341, 1966.

157. BRANDA RF, MOLDOW CF, MacARTHUR JR, WINTROBE MM, ANTHONY BK, JACOB HS: Folate-induced remission in aplastic anemia with familial defect of cellular folate uptake. *N Engl J Med* 298:469, 1978.

158. ARTHUR DC, DANZYL TJ, BRANDA FR: Cytogenetic studies of a family with a hereditary defect of cellular folate uptake and high incidence of hematologic disease, in *Nutritional Factors in the Induction and Maintenance of Malignancy*. New York, Academic, 1983, p 101.

159. HOWE RB, BRANDA RF, DOUGLAS SD, BRUNNING RD: Hereditary dyserythropoiesis with abnormal membrane folate transport. *Blood* 54:1080, 1979.

160. ARAKAWA T, NARISAWA K, TANNO K, OHARA K, HUGASHI O, ET AL: Megaloblastic anemia and mental retardation with hyperfolic acidemia. Probably due to N^5-methyltetrahydrofolate transferase deficiency. *Tohoku J Exp Med* 93:1, 1967.

161. HERBERT V: Experimental nutritional folate deficiency in man. *Trans Assoc Am Physicians* 75:307, 1962.

162. ROSCHAU J, DATE J, KRISTOFFERSEN K: Folic acid supplements and intrauterine growth. *Acta Obstet Gynecol Scand* 58:343, 1979.

163. LAURENCE KM, MILLER JN, TENNANT GB, CAMPBELL H: Double blind randomized controlled trial of folate treatment before conception to prevent recurrence of neural-tube detects. *Br Med J* 282:11509, 1981.

164. HECHT F, JACKY PB, SUTHERLAND GR: The fragile X syndrome: Current methods. *Am J Hum Genet* 11:489, 1982.

CHAPTER 82

INHERITED DISORDERS OF COBALAMIN TRANSPORT AND METABOLISM

WAYNE A. FENTON
LEON E. ROSENBERG

1. *Cobalamins (Cbls) are complex organometallic substances consisting of a corrin ring, a central cobalt atom, and various axial ligands. The basic structure, known as vitamin B_{12}, is synthesized exclusively by microorganisms, but most higher animals are capable of converting the vitamin into the two required coenzyme forms, adenosylcobalamin (AdoCbl) and methylcobalamin (MeCbl).*

2. *Dietary Cbl is acquired mostly from animal sources, including meat and milk, and is absorbed in a series of steps which includes release from its associated proteins, binding to a gastric secretory protein known as intrinsic factor (IF), recognition of the IF-Cbl complex by receptors on ileal mucosal cells, transport across those cells, and release into the portal circulation bound to transcobalamin II (TC II), the serum protein which carries newly absorbed Cbl throughout the body.*

3. *The cellular metabolism by which the coenzymes are formed involves receptor-mediated binding of the TC II–Cbl complex to the cell surface, adsorptive endocytosis of the complex, intralysosomal degradation of the TC II with concomitant release of Cbl into the cytoplasm, enzyme-mediated reduction of the central cobalt atom, and cytosolic methylation to form MeCbl or mitochondrial adenosylation to form AdoCbl.*

4. *Only two enzymes in mammalian cells are known to depend on cobalamin coenzymes: methylmalonyl-CoA mutase, which requires AdoCbl; and N^5-methyltetrahydrofolate:homocysteine methyltransferase, which requires MeCbl.*

5. *Ten different inherited defects are known which impair the pathways of Cbl transport and metabolism in humans (Fig. 82-4). Three affect absorption and transport; the other seven alter cellular utilization and coenzyme production.*

6. *The defects affecting Cbl absorption and transport generally manifest themselves in infancy or early childhood as developmental delay with megaloblastic anemia. Serum cobalamin levels may be reduced (IF or IF-receptor deficiency) or near normal (TC II deficiency). Treatment with periodic injections of Cbl, with or without folate therapy, has been generally effective in controlling these problems.*

7. *The clinical manifestations of deficiencies in cellular Cbl utilization and metabolism vary depending on whether one or both coenzymes are affected. Two abnormalities in adenosylcobalamin synthesis only (designated cblA and cblB) lead to impaired methylmalonyl-CoA mutase activity and result in methylmalonic acidemia. In most but not all patients with these defects, pharmacologic supplements of Cbl (cyanocobalamin or hydroxocobalamin) produce distinct reductions in methylmalonate accumulation and offer a valu-*

able therapeutic adjunct to dietary protein limitation. The defect in cblA is unknown, while the defect in cblB patients is in cob(I)alamin adenosyltransferase, the final step of AdoCbl biosynthesis.

8. *Two abnormalities in MeCbl synthesis only, designated cblE and cblG, result in reduced activity of the N^5-methyltetrahydrofolate:homocysteine methyltransferase and, consequently, lead to homocystinuria with hypomethioninemia. Children with these defects have developmental delay, failure to thrive, and megaloblastic anemia. Pharmacologic doses of Cbl resolve the clinical abnormalities. The defects involved are not known, but appear to involve the reducing systems necessary to maintain the MeCbl-methyltransferase complex in its active state.*

9. *Three other distinct mutations, designated cblC, cblD, and cblF, lead to impaired synthesis of both AdoCbl and MeCbl and, accordingly, to deficient activity of both methylmalonyl-CoA mutase and N^5-methyltetrahydrofolate:homocysteine methyltransferase. Children from the cblC and cblD groups have methylmalonic aciduria and homocystinuria; the single cblF patient had only mild methylmalonic acidemia. Those children with the cblC mutation appear to be more severely affected clinically than the two known sibs in the cblD group or the one cblF patient. Major clinical problems in cblC patients include failure to thrive, developmental retardation, and such hematologic abnormalities as megaloblastic anemia and macrocytosis. The precise defect in the cblC and cblD patients is not yet known, but it involves an early step in the intracellular metabolism of cobalamins. The defect in cblF appears to be in the transport mechanism by which Cbl is released from lysosomes.*

10. *The discriminating biochemical features of the inherited defects in Cbl transport and metabolism are shown in Table 82-3.*

11. *All of the disorders of Cbl metabolism for which there are adequate data are inherited as autosomal recessive traits. Heterozygotes can be detected only for cblB. Genetic complementation analyses with somatic cell heterokaryons have been particularly useful in demonstrating genetic heterogeneity and in confirming the existence of autosomal recessive inheritance among defects in cellular Cbl utilization and metabolism (cblA-cblF).*

12. *Prenatal detection of fetuses with defects in the complementation groups cblA, cblB, cblC, and cblE has been accomplished using cultured amniotic cells and chemical determinations on amniotic fluid or maternal urine. In several cases, in utero treatment has been attempted with apparent success.*

Nonstandard abbreviations used in this chapter include: AdoCbl = adenosylcobalamin; Cbl = cobalamin; cbl = cobalamin locus (*cblA, cblB*, etc.); CN-Cbl = cyanocobalamin; H_4folate = tetrahydrofolate; IF = intrinsic factor; MeCbl = methylcobalamin; Me-H_4folate = N^5-methyltetrahydrofolate; OH-Cbl = hydroxocobalamin; and TC (I, II, or III) = transcobalamin (I, II, or III).

The structure and function of cobalamins have intrigued students of human biology since 1926, when Minot and Murphy demonstrated that oral administration of crude liver extract was effective in the treatment of pernicious anemia.[1] In 1948 this "anti-pernicious anemia factor" was isolated from liver and kidney[2,3] and was named *vitamin B12*. Deficiency of the vitamin leads to an alteration of function or morphology of several organ systems: megaloblastic anemia and defective granulocyte and immune system function; abnormal intestinal function; and neurologic disease, including neurologic degeneration and dementia. Administration of as little as 1 μg of the vitamin daily was shown to prevent relapse of pernicious anemia. Although the vitamin is widely distributed in animal tissues, there is strong evidence that it is synthesized only by microorganisms found in soil, water, or in the rumen and intestine of animals. The reader is referred to Ref. 4 for comprehensive reviews of cobalamin structure, biosynthesis, and chemistry.

BIOCHEMISTRY

Structural Features

The isolation of vitamin B12 culminated in the elucidation of its three-dimensional structure by Hodgkin and coworkers using x-ray crystallographic techniques.[5] *Cobalamin* (Cbl), as it is officially designated, is composed of a central cobalt atom (Co) surrounded by a planar corrin ring which has a complex side chain extending down from the corrin plane consisting of a phosphoribo-5,6-dimethylbenzimidazolyl group (Fig. 82-1). One of the nitrogens of the benzimidazolyl is linked to the cobalt atom by coordination in the "bottom" axial position. The molecule is completed by coordination in the upper axial position of several different radicals. Thus, cyanocobalamin (CN-Cbl) [more strictly α-(5,6-dimethylbenzimidazolyl)-cobamide cyanide] is formed by the complexing of a cyanide ion to the cobalt atom. Although this compound is the most common commercial form of the vitamin, it is an artifact of isolation and does not occur naturally in microorganisms, plants, or animal tissues. Many other Cbls have been formed with other ligands, but only three have been routinely isolated from mammalian tissue: hydroxocobalamin (OH-Cbl), the "natural" form of the vitamin, methylcobalamin (MeCbl), and adenosylcobalamin (AdoCbl). Complexes of Cbl with glutathione and other sulfhydryl compounds have also been reported. MeCbl and AdoCbl are unique for two reasons. They are the only two compounds in nature known to have a direct covalent carbon-cobalt bond, and they are the only two forms of Cbl known to act as specific coenzymes in mammalian systems.

The structure and nomenclature of the Cbls are further complicated by oxidation and reduction of the cobalt atom. In OH-Cbl, the cobalt atom is trivalent [cob(III)alamin], and this compound has been called *vitamin B12a*. When the cobalt is reduced to a divalent state [cob(II)alamin], the molecule is called *vitamin B12r*, and in the monovalent state [cob(I)alamin] it is called *vitamin B12s*. These oxidation-reduction states are important because the cobalt atom must be reduced to its monovalent state prior to formation of MeCbl or AdoCbl, apparently by specific reductase enzymes that sequentially convert cob(III)alamin to cob(I)alamin, with cob(II)alamin acting as an intermediate.[6]

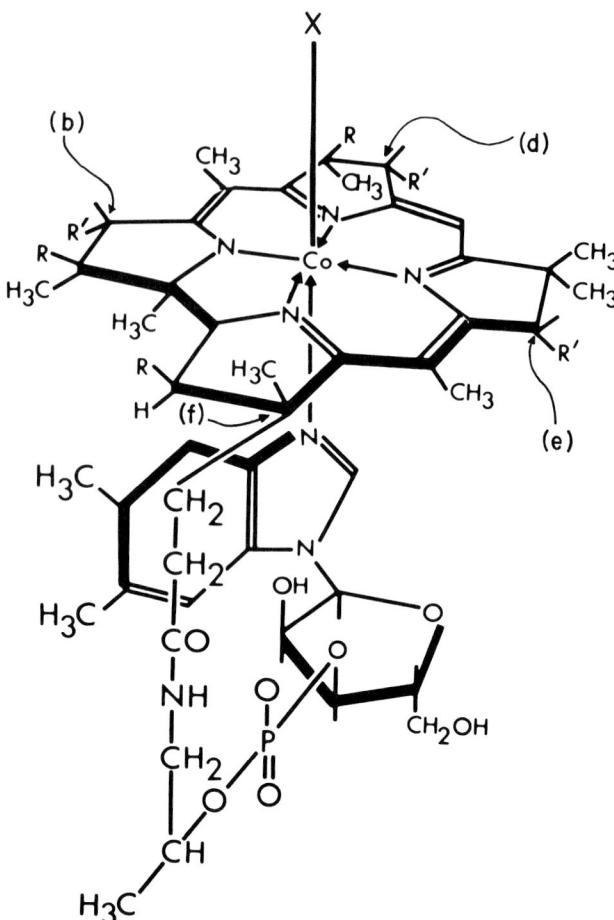

Fig. 82-1 The structure of cobalamin. R = –CH₂CONH₂; R′ = –CH₂CH₂CONH₂; X = –OH (hydroxocobalamin), –CN (cyanocobalamin), –CH₃ (methylcobalamin), or 5′-deoxy-5′-adenosyl (adenosylcobalamin). *(Reproduced from Fenton and Rosenberg.[61] Used with permission of the publisher.)*

Cobalamin Coenzymes

In 1958 Barker and his colleagues demonstrated that the glutamate mutase reaction in *Clostridium tetanomorphum* required vitamin B12[7] and, more specifically, that the active coenzyme form of the vitamin was AdoCbl.[8,9] One year later, Smith and Monty reported that the analogous isomerization of methylmalonyl-CoA to succinyl-CoA was defective in the liver of Cbl-deficient rats.[10] They suggested that Cbl is a cofactor for the latter isomerization system, a thesis born out by Gurnani et al.[11] and Stern and Friedmann,[12] who showed in vitro that the activity of methylmalonyl-CoA mutase in liver from Cbl-deficient animals could be restored to normal by addition of AdoCbl, but not by CN-Cbl or other vitamin B12 analogues. For several years, because AdoCbl was the only known coenzyme form of vitamin B12, it was designated as *coenzyme B12*.

In 1966 Weissbach and his colleagues[13] demonstrated that MeCbl is a cofactor in the complex series of reactions by which homocysteine is remethylated to methionine (Fig. 82-2). This reaction requires *S*-adenosylmethionine and *N*⁵-methyltetrahydrofolate (Me-H₄folate), as well as the methyltransferase apoenzyme and MeCbl. The exact mechanism of homocysteine remethylation remains obscure but probably involves the following sequence: Me-H₄folate is converted to tetrahydrofolate (H₄folate) by transferring its methyl group to a

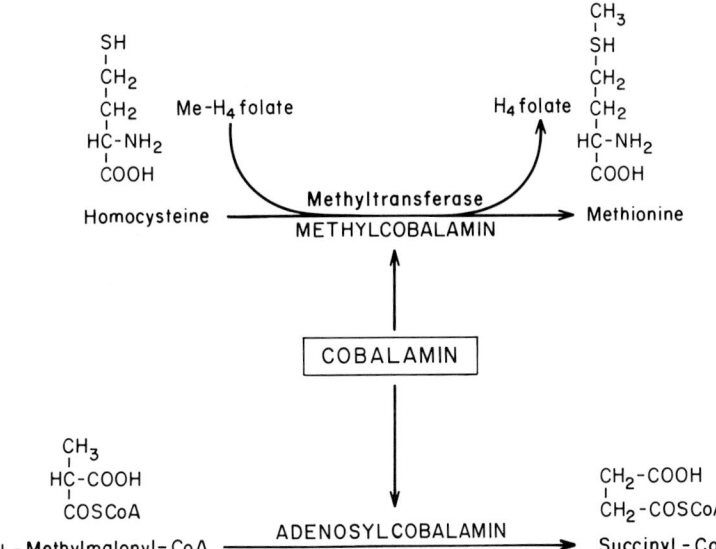

Fig. 82-2 Reactions catalyzed by cobalamin coenzymes in mammalian tissues. Note the specificity of adenosylcobalamin for the isomerization of methylmalonyl-CoA and of methylcobalamin for the methylation of homocysteine. Me-H_4folate = N^5-methyltetrahydrofolate; H_4folate = tetrahydrofolate.

Cbl prosthetic group [probably existing as enzyme-sequestered cob(I)alamin] on the methyltransferase apoenzyme; in turn, the methyl group is transferred from MeCbl to homocysteine, leading to the formation of methionine, with regeneration of the active Cbl species.[14,15] This sequence of reactions, which is relevant to the manifestations of Cbl deficiency and to the interrelationships between folate and Cbls, is discussed in more detail below and in Chap. 81.

The conversion of methylmalonyl-CoA to succinyl-CoA and the methylation of homocysteine to methionine are the only Cbl-dependent reactions that have been demonstrated conclusively in mammalian systems. Poston has reported that AdoCbl acts as a cofactor in the enzymatic reaction by which α-leucine is isomerized to β-leucine,[16] but this has not been confirmed in other laboratories. In microorganisms, several other apoenzymes require AdoCbl:[17,18] glutamate mutase; diol dehydrase; glycerol dehydrase; ethanolamine ammonia-lyase; and oligonucleotide reductase. In addition, MeCbl participates in the formation of methane and acetic acid and the fermentation of lysine in bacteria.

Cobalamin Absorption and Distribution

Cbls have a unique and highly specialized mechanism of intestinal absorption that has been reviewed in detail.[19–21] The ability to transport physiological quantities of vitamin depends on the combined action of gastric, ileal, and pancreatic components. The gastric substance, called *intrinsic factor* (IF) by Castle, who first demonstrated its existence, is a glycoprotein that binds Cbls in the intestinal lumen. IF, which has been isolated and characterized extensively[19] and for which a cDNA has recently been cloned,[22] is synthesized by gastric parietal cells. Evidence obtained in vitro[23,24] and in vivo[25] suggests that three events precede the formation of IF-Cbl in the gut lumen. First, Cbls are released from dietary protein in the acid environment of the stomach. Second, Cbls bind to "R" proteins of salivary and gastric origin; these R proteins are members of a family of glycoproteins with high affinity for Cbls. Third, pancreatic proteases digest the R proteins, thereby liberating Cbls in the upper small intestine, where they are complexed to IF. Subsequently, the IF-Cbl complex interacts through its protein moiety with specific ileal receptor sites in the presence

of calcium ions. The IF-Cbl complex is transported into the enterocyte by an endocytic mechanism, the complex is dissociated, and the vitamin is transported across the basal membrane into the portal blood, bound to transcobalamin II (TC II), the transport protein for newly absorbed vitamin.[20]

When labeled Cbl is administered intravenously or orally, most of the labeled vitamin is immediately bound to TC II and disappears from the plasma in a few hours.[26,27] Only a small fraction binds to transcobalamin I (TC I) or transcobalamin III (TC III), serum glycoproteins of the R-protein family, even though they carry the majority of the steady-state serum Cbl.[28] The Cbl bound to these components turns over very slowly, and its physiological role is still unclear. Surprisingly, MeCbl is the major circulating Cbl species, accounting for 60 to 80 percent of total plasma Cbl; OH-Cbl and AdoCbl make up the remainder.[29] Since >90 percent of total plasma Cbl is bound to TC I, it is clear that most of the circulating MeCbl travels with this R binder. This unusual Cbl distribution pattern is puzzling, particularly in the face of evidence indicating that AdoCbl accounts for ~70 percent of total hepatic Cbls, whereas MeCbl constitutes a mere 1 to 3 percent.[29] This preponderance of AdoCbl is also present in such other tissues as erythrocytes, kidney, and brain. The physiological significance of these widely different fractional Cbl distributions in extracellular and intracellular compartments remains obscure.

TC II also facilitates Cbl uptake by mammalian tissues. Finkler and Hall[30] showed that CN-Cbl bound to TC II was accumulated by HeLa cells much more rapidly than free CN-Cbl or CN-Cbl bound to TC I, IF, or other binding proteins. Such TC II–mediated uptake was subsequently confirmed in a variety of cell types, both in vivo and in culture (liver, kidney, heart, spleen, lung, small intestine, cultured fibroblasts, Chinese hamster ovary cells, mouse L cells, lymphoma cells, and phytohemagglutinin-stimulated lymphocytes) (see Ref. 20 for review). These findings, coupled with the observations in vivo that TC II disappeared from plasma as TC II–Cbl was absorbed[31] and appeared in lysosomal fractions of hepatic[32] and kidney cells,[33] led to the proposal that the circulating TC II–Cbl complex is recognized by a specific, widely distributed plasma membrane receptor. This notion has been supported by considerable experimental evidence. Using ^{125}I-labeled TC II–Cbl complexes, Youngdahl-Turner and associates[34] showed that the complex binds to a specific, high-affinity ($K_a \sim 10^{10}$ M^{-1}) cell surface receptor on cultured skin fibroblasts through a membrane site which recognizes TC II, and by a mechanism dependent on Ca^{2+}. They showed further that the TC II–Cbl complex is then internalized intact via adsorptive endocytosis[35] and that the degradation of TC II and release of Cbl from the complex occur as a result of lysosomal protease activity.[34,35] Cbl then exits from the lysosome by processes poorly understood, and is either converted to MeCbl and bound to the methyltransferase in the cytosol or enters the mitochondrion, where, after reduction and adenosylation to AdoCbl, it is bound to methylmalonyl-CoA mutase.[36,37]

The intricate process just described is surely the most widely distributed physiological means by which mammalian cells obtain Cbls, but it is not the only means. Hepatocytes, for instance, contain a surface receptor for asialoglycoproteins, and this receptor interacts with TC I–Cbl (and perhaps TC III–Cbl) complexes, thereby providing a second potential means by which this particular tissue obtaines Cbls.[38] Finally, there is evidence that at least some tissues are capable of taking up free (unbound) Cbl if the concentration of unbound vitamin is raised to sufficiently high concentrations. In cultured fibroblasts, this uptake process for free Cbl is saturable, Ca^{2+}-independent, and sensitive to inhibitors of protein synthesis and sulfhydryl reagents.[39] Its functional role, under most circumstances, is probably negligible.

Coenzyme Biosynthesis and Compartmentation

Because methylmalonyl-CoA mutase, the mammalian enzyme dependent on AdoCbl, is a mitochondrial protein,[40] whereas the MeCbl-dependent methyltransferase is cytoplasmic,[41] it becomes important to relate the cellular biology of the vitamin to its cellular and molecular chemistry. The chemical pathway of AdoCbl synthesis was defined initially in bacteria.[6,42] Three enzymes are required for coenzyme synthesis, two reductases and an adenosyltransferase. The reductases are flavoproteins which require NAD as a cofactor. The first (EC 1.6.99.8) is responsible for converting cob(III)alamin, e.g., OH-Cbl, to cob(II)alamin and the second (EC 1.6.99.9) for catalyzing the further reduction to cob(I)alamin. The latter compound and ATP are substrates for an adenosyltransferase (EC 2.5.1.17) which completes the synthesis of AdoCbl. Neither of the reductases has been purified extensively, but the adenosyltransferase has. It has a pH optimum of 8, requires Mn^{2+}, and has a K_m of 1×10^{-5} M for cob(I)alamin and 1.6×10^{-5} M for ATP.[42] The biosynthetic steps leading to MeCbl formation are not as clear. They likely involve a reduction-methylation sequence on the methyltransferase apoenzyme.[43,44]

Evidence has accumulated which indicates that mammalian cell metabolism of Cbl may proceed by a very similar set of reactions (see Fig. 82-3). In 1964, Pawalkiewicz et al.[45] showed that human liver and kidney homogenates could convert CN-Cbl to AdoCbl. Several years later, AdoCbl synthesis from OH-Cbl was observed in HeLa cell extracts incubated with ATP and a reducing system which presumably bypassed the enzymatic reduction of OH-Cbl [cob(III)alamin] to cob(II)alamin.[46] Subsequently, Mahoney and Rosenberg[47] demonstrated the synthesis of both AdoCbl and MeCbl by intact human fibroblasts growing in a tissue culture medium containing OH-[^{57}Co]Cbl. This system was subsequently char-

acterized in cell extracts.[48,49] As with the HeLa cell system, chemical reductants were employed to bypass both cobalamin reductases.[49] Such extracts synthesized AdoCbl, thereby demonstrating that the adenosyltransferase found in bacteria also exists in normal human cells. These experiments also revealed that the adenosyltransferase was mitochondrial in location, implying that both the synthesis and cofactor activity of AdoCbl take place in this organelle. It seems almost certain, as shown in Fig. 82-3, that MeCbl synthesis takes place in the cytosol.

Metabolic Abnormalities in Cobalamin Deficiency

The biochemical abnormalities in plasma and urine of patients with Cbl deficiency reflect the dysfunction of the enzymes dependent on Cbl coenzymes. The first relevant observation in this context was the demonstration by Cox and White[50] and by Barness and his colleagues[51] that methylmalonic acid excretion in the urine was distinctly increased in Cbl-deficient patients with classic pernicious anemia. The methylmalonic aciduria in these patients was reversed rapidly by administration of physiological doses of Cbl, indicating that repletion of Cbl stores restored the methylmalonyl-CoA mutase reaction to normal. Later, Cox et al. reported that patients with Cbl deficiency also have distinctly increased amounts of propionic acid in the urine, this abnormality again being reversed by treatment.[52] Interestingly, they also found excessive amounts of acetic acid in the urine of Cbl-deficient subjects. The mechanism of this abnormality is not clear, since acetate does not participate in the major pathway of propionate catabolism. The finding could, of course, reflect increased utilization of the alternative pathways of propionate metabolism in the face of a block in the major pathway, since each of the alternative routes leads eventually to the formation of acetyl-CoA (see Chap. 29). Excessive excretion of homocystine has also been documented in Cbl-deficient patients,[53,54] as has combined methylmalonic aciduria and homocystinuria.[55] The latter report is particularly interesting since it documents congenital but not hereditary Cbl deficiency due, in this instance, to acquired Cbl deficiency in the offspring of a strict vegetarian mother also deficient in the vitamin.

Biochemical studies in an animal model, the Cbl-deficient pig, have yielded other significant biochemical findings. Cardinale and his colleagues[56] noted that, as expected, the concentrations of total Cbl and AdoCbl were markedly reduced in the liver, kidney, and brain of Cbl-deficient pigs. They also observed that the methylmalonyl-CoA mutase apoenzyme content appeared to be increased. The latter finding suggests the possibility of a feedback control system between apoenzyme and coenzyme that must be explored further.

Cobalamins and Folic Acid

An interesting, important, and still puzzling aspect of Cbl function concerns its relationship to folic acid.[57] Several lines of evidence bear out this relationship: the appearance of megaloblastic anemia in either Cbl or folate deficiency; the reversal of megaloblastic anemia in Cbl deficiency by large doses of folate; the amelioration of megaloblastic changes in folic acid deficiency by pharmacologic doses of CN-Cbl; the increased plasma concentrations of N^5-methyltetrahydrofolate in pa-

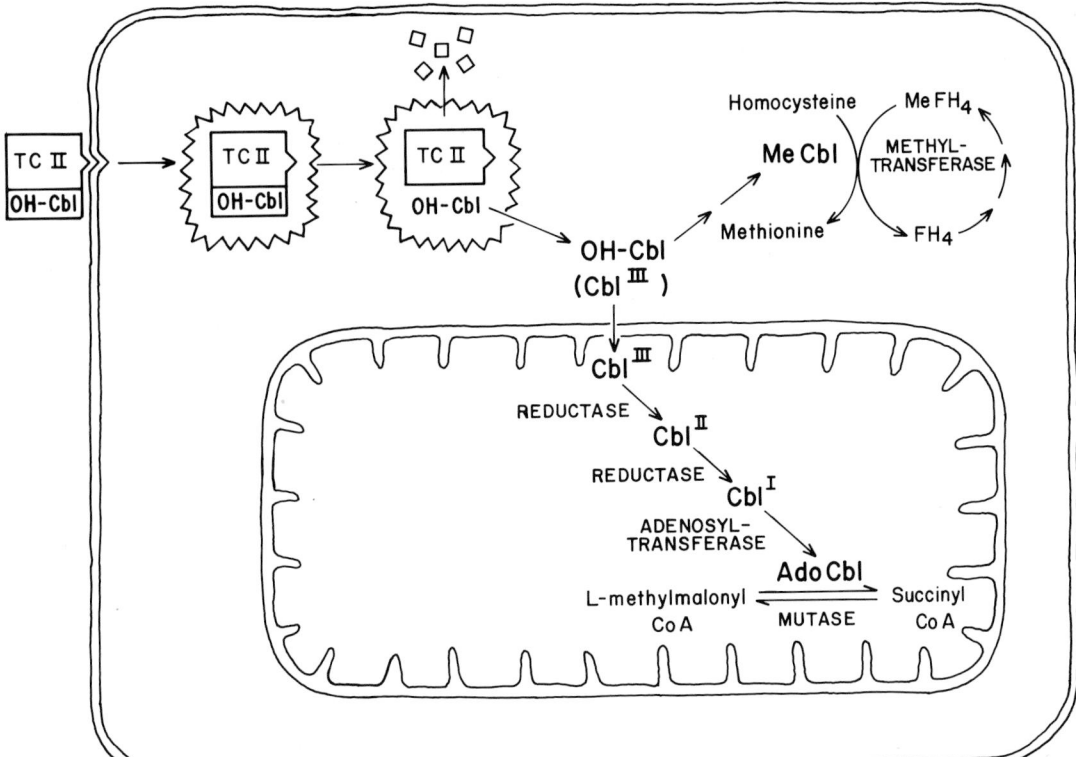

Fig. 82-3 General pathway of the cellular uptake and subcellular compartmentation of cobalamins, and of the intracellular distribution and enzymatic synthesis of cobalamin coenzymes. TC II = transcobalamin II; OH-Cbl = hydroxocobalamin; MeCbl = methylcobalamin; AdoCbl = adenosylcobalamin; Cbl^{III}, Cbl^{II}, Cbl^{I} = cobalamins with cobalt valence of 3$^+$, 2$^+$, and 1$^+$, respectively.

tients with cobalamin deficiency; the excretion of excessive amounts of formiminoglutamic acid (FIGLU) after histidine loading in patients with either Cbl or folate deficiency; and the reduced amounts of total Cbl in the liver of patients with folate deficiency. A plausible explanation for most of these effects was proposed independently by Herbert,[58] Noronha,[59] Larrabee,[60] and their colleagues and has been referred to as the *folate trap hypothesis*. This thesis rests on the evidence that the conversion of N^5-methyltetrahydrofolate to tetrahydrofolate depends on the MeCbl-dependent reaction, in which homocysteine is methylated to methionine. If methionine biosynthesis is the only quantitatively significant reaction using N^5-methyltetrahydrofolate, Cbl deficiency will interfere with the folate cycle and, barring other control mechanisms, will lead to the accumulation of N^5-methyltetrahydrofolate and the depletion of other folate derivatives. This depletion could become severe enough to interfere with other reactions requiring tetrahydrofolate, such as the synthesis of purines or pyrimidines and the conversion of formiminoglutamate to glutamate. Under these circumstances tetrahydrofolate deficiency could be relieved by administration of either folate or Cbl, but only the latter would complete the folate cycle. This scheme, if totally correct, would obviate the need for additional Cbl-dependent mechanisms to explain the megaloblastic changes observed in Cbl deficiency and would account for the specific disorders of folate metabolism observed in Cbl-deficient human beings. It does not explain the low Cbl content of livers from folate-deficient subjects or the hematologic response of folate-deficient patients to Cbl. These relationships between folate and Cbl are discussed further in Chap. 81.

DISEASE STATES

Inherited disorders in the transport and metabolism of Cbl manifest themselves clinically in ways that reflect the underlying defect and, in particular, that depend on which coenzyme is deficient and, hence, which of the two Cbl-dependent enzymes is reduced in activity (Fig. 82-2). Defects that affect only AdoCbl biosynthesis generally lead to metabolic ketoacidosis in the newborn or infant period, and regularly result in methylmalonic acidemia and methylmalonic aciduria. MeCbl deficiencies present as failure to thrive, megaloblastic changes, and neurologic signs, usually with homocystinuria and hypomethioninemia. Deficiencies of both coenzymes produce a variable combination of these signs and symptoms.

In the discussion below, the disorders have been grouped according to the coenzyme affected, with the transport deficiencies included with the cellular defects that affect both coenzymes.

Combined AdoCbl and MeCbl Deficiency

Cbl was first described as "extrinsic factor," an anti-pernicious anemia factor found in aqueous extracts of raw liver, which combined with "intrinsic factor," a component of normal gastric secretions, to cure pernicious anemia, an acquired disease resulting from gastric insufficiency. It has been recognized, however, that there are several inborn errors of metabolism with presentations similar to pernicious anemia that result from abnormal Cbl transport or from altered cellular Cbl metabolism. Although these diseases share the general clinical phenotype of failure to thrive, developmental delay, and megaloblastic anemia, the details of their presentations allow them to be differentiated. (For reviews, see Refs. 20, 21, 28, 61).

Transport Defects: Clinical and Laboratory Findings.

INTRINSIC FACTOR DEFICIENCY. A number of children have been described with a juvenile form of pernicious anemia (see Ref. 62 for references to case reports). The clinical symptoms, which usually appear after the first year and before the fifth, include developmental delay and the megaloblastic anemia characteristic of pernicious anemia.[21,62] Serum levels of Cbl are markedly deficient, but, in contrast to the adult disease, gastric function and morphology are normal and serum autoantibodies to IF are absent. Cbl absorption is abnormal in these children, but is restored when the vitamin is mixed with normal human gastric juice as a source of IF. Further investigations of the gastric secretions of these patients have shown that there are, as expected, several different classes of functional IF deficiency. One results in failure to produce or secrete any immunologically recognizable IF,[63,64] while another causes production of immunologically reactive protein which is inactive physiologically.[62,65–67] The latter group includes patients whose IF has reduced affinity for the ileal IF receptor,[66] or reduced affinity for Cbl,[68] or increased susceptibility to proteolysis.[62] In a few cases with partial deficiency, presentation has been delayed into the second decade or later.[65,69]

ENTEROCYTE Cbl MALABSORPTION (IMERSLUND-GRASBECK SYNDROME). At least 60 cases of a related disorder have been described with the clinical signs of juvenile pernicious anemia, but with normal IF and normal gastrointestinal function, except for specific intestinal Cbl malabsorption.[70–72] In addition to megaloblastic anemia and serum Cbl deficiency, many of these patients have proteinuria. In contrast to IF deficiency patients, these childrens' Cbl absorption defect is not corrected by providing normal human IF with the vitamin.[21] In at least some of these patients, the ileal receptor for IF-Cbl appears to be normal as measured by IF-Cbl binding to homogenates of ileal biopsy specimens.[72] In others, a functional receptor appears to be absent.[73] Because the mechanism for Cbl transport across the enterocyte is complex and not well understood, it seems likely that this syndrome encompasses defects at several points in this overall pathway, including the receptor itself, receptor internalization, and Cbl transfer to TC II. As in the case of IF deficiency, these patients usually present between years 1 and 5, although some have been diagnosed much later.[74]

TRANSCOBALAMIN II DEFICIENCY. A number of cases have now been described of deficiency of TC II, including both twins and siblings (see Ref. 21 and its references). In contrast to the previous two disorders, TC II deficiency has generally presented within the first or second month of life as failure to thrive, with such nonspecific signs as vomiting and weakness, accompanied by megaloblastic anemia and, eventually, immunologic deficiency, and neurologic disease.[21] Interestingly, serum Cbl levels are normal or nearly so in these patients, reflecting the fact that most serum Cbl is carried by TC I and other R-binders.[28] Intestinal Cbl absorption has been abnormal in some patients, but not in others.[21] Most patients have had no immunologically detectable TC II in plasma,[21] al-

though a few have detectable protein[75,76] and at least one produces a TC II which is able to bind Cbl, although apparently without function.[75]

R-BINDER DEFICIENCY. Several individuals are now known with deficient or absent R-binder (TC I) in plasma, saliva, and blood cells.[21] Although these patients have serum Cbl values in the deficient range, they show no signs of Cbl deficiency, probably because their TC II–Cbl levels are normal. The fact that these patients have no apparent clinical disease attributable to their lack of R-binder serves to emphasize our lack of understanding of the role of this protein in normal metabolism and homeostasis.

Chemical Abnormalities and Pathophysiology. While megaloblastic anemia has been the hallmark of the Cbl transport disorders, the chemical abnormalities expected to accompany functional Cbl deficiency have also been found in at least some cases. In theory, Cbl deficiency should lead to deficient synthesis of both AdoCbl and MeCbl and, thus, to decreased activities of their respective enzymes resulting in methylmalonic acidemia(-uria) and homocystinuria. When examined carefully, some patients with each of the transport deficiencies have been shown to have these chemical symptoms, although the quantities of both methylmalonate and homocystine excreted have been much lower than in patients with abnormalities in cellular Cbl metabolism (see below). On the other hand, some other patients do not have one or either of these chemical abnormalities.[21] To a certain extent, these variable findings, which do not appear to correlate well with the nature of the defect or the severity of the general symptoms and hematologic aberrations, may result from the fact that alternate pathways of Cbl transport exist which, although minor in normal individuals, may contribute significantly in patients with these transport defects. For example, receptors for free Cbl have been found on HeLa cells[77] and human fibroblasts[78] and may exist elsewhere as well to permit some Cbl transport even in the absence of one of the transport proteins. In addition, hepatocytes may be able to recover some Cbl from asialo–TC I–Cbl by means of the asialo glycoprotein receptor system.[79] This could be particularly important in TC II deficiency.

One major clinical difference between the two intestinal transport defects and TC II deficiency lies in the different age of onset of these conditions. While neither intestinal Cbl transport deficiency manifests itself before 1 year of age, many TC II–deficient patients are symptomatic within 1 or 2 months of birth, with some exceptions (see above). This appears to be due to two factors. First, the IF-dependent pathway for intestinal Cbl absorption may not become important until later in infancy when the gastrointestinal tract switches from pinocytotic mechanisms of transport to receptor-mediated ones. IF-Cbl transport falls into the latter category. Interestingly, a recent report[80] demonstrates that, in the rat, expression of IF by the gastric mucosa increases abruptly from the low levels found in the newborn animal to adult levels at about the time of weaning (13 to 20 days), consistent with this hypothesis. Second, the body stores considerable amounts of Cbl in blood, liver, and other tissues beyond daily requirements. Thus, IF-deficient patients and those with Imerslund-Grasbeck syndrome likely show no signs of deficiency early in infancy both because the IF-dependent mechanism for Cbl transport is not yet operating and because they acquire sufficient Cbl through other mechanisms to sustain themselves for a period of time after the developmental switch in intestinal absorption has occurred. Conversely, because TC II is presumably necessary for efficient Cbl transport into cells regardless of the mechanism by which it is acquired, TC II–deficient patients have no symptom-free period and become ill as soon as their maternally derived stores of Cbl are exhausted. The fact that most TC II–deficient patients have been normal at birth may reflect the fact that fetal tissues concentrate Cbl relative to the maternal serum.[81]

The megaloblastic anemia characteristic of these disorders likely reflects a deficiency in the activity of N^5-methyltetrahydrofolate:homocysteine methyltransferase brought about by the absence of its cofactor, MeCbl. Because patients with isolated deficiency of AdoCbl (see below) or its partner enzyme, methylmalonyl-CoA mutase (see Chap. 29), are usually hematologically normal, this conclusion seems to be solid. Likewise, the severe neurologic manifestations, particularly in patients who are diagnosed long after the onset of their disease, appear more likely to be due to deficient methyltransferase activity. Although isolated mutase deficiency can produce central nervous system dysfunction (see Chap. 29), this is believed to be a consequence of the severe metabolic ketoacidosis experienced by these patients, a condition not generally present in patients with Cbl transport defects.

The specific etiology of the hematologic and neurologic disturbances in these individuals is not completely understood, but clearly it must derive from the central role of the methyltransferase in cellular 1-carbon metabolic pathways, in terms of folate metabolism and homocysteine-methionine balance. Because the folate cycle in mammalian cells requires that N^5-methyltetrahydrofolate transfer its methyl group to homocysteine, via MeCbl, in order to regenerate tetrahydrofolate (see Chap. 81), it has been suggested that the accumulation of methyl folate in the absence of the Cbl coenzyme serves as a folate trap which produces functional folate deficiency intracellularly.[58–60] The effects of this deficiency on the important roles which folate metabolism plays in the synthesis of nucleotides and, hence, of RNA and DNA could easily account for the general disruptions in cellular homeostasis in rapidly dividing tissues such as the hematopoetic system. Whether this folate trap hypothesis is equally applicable to explaining the neurologic dysfunction in these patients is not clear. An alternative explanation might involve disruption of the interconversion of homocysteine and methionine and S-adenosylhomocysteine and S-adenosylmethionine and interference with the role these compounds play in methylation and enzyme regulation in the central nervous system. Until more is known about these pathways, however, any hypothesis will be difficult to establish.

Genetics and Molecular Biology. Each of these genetic lesions in Cbl transport appears to be inherited as an autosomal recessive trait on the basis of classical genetic criteria.[21] Because the Imerslund-Grasbeck syndrome may actually encompass deficiencies in more than one protein (receptor) or enzyme (see above), it remains possible that other modes of inheritance exist for a subset of families with this disorder.

TC II has electrophoretic isoforms in normal individuals whose inheritance is consistent with an autosomal localization of its structural gene.[82] It has been suggested that some cases of TC II deficiency manifest themselves as abnormal iso-

forms.[83] The structural locus for TC II has recently been linked to the P blood group system locus on the long arm of chromosome 22,[84] confirming its autosomal inheritance.

The intrinsic factor gene has not yet been localized, although a cDNA for the rat homologue has recently been reported.[22] There is suggestive evidence from biochemical analysis of some presumptive heterozygotes for IF deficiency that they express both a normal and an abnormal allele for IF and for the idea that some patients with IF deficiency express two different mutant alleles.[62] The rat IF cDNA has been used to establish that only one cell type, the chief cell of the rat gastric mucosa, expresses IF in the adult animal,[80] in keeping with immunochemical studies which indicate that the parietal cell is the only source of IF in human beings and other mammals.[19] Interestingly, these workers[80] have also shown that IF expression is developmentally controlled, with a major increase after postnatal day 12, corresponding with the onset of weaning (days 13 to 20) in the rat, and is possibly under glucocorticoid control. A similar developmental delay in IF expression in human beings may help to explain why IF deficiency and the Imerslund-Grasbeck syndrome do not manifest themselves until after the age of 1 year (see above).

Diagnosis and Treatment. All of these Cbl transport deficiencies are usually diagnosed initially by the observation of a combination of macrocytic anemia with developmental delay or failure to thrive.[21] Neurologic symptoms may also be present. Serum Cbl levels are low in IF deficiency and Imerslund-Grasbeck syndrome, but usually normal in TC II deficiency. Schilling tests are abnormal in the first two diseases and may also be abnormal in some cases of TC II deficiency.[21] The first two disorders can be differentiated by determining whether the Schilling test becomes normal when the test Cbl is incubated with normal human IF before it is administered. Only IF deficiency patients show correction. Confirmation of either of the intestinal malabsorption defects entails demonstration of normal gastric and ileal function other than the specific Cbl absorption deficiency, the absence of antibodies to IF, and, in some cases of IF deficiency, the absence of functional (i.e., Cbl-binding) or immunologically cross-reacting IF in the patient's gastric secretions.[21,62] TC II deficiency can sometimes be differentiated from the other two by an age of onset within the first months (as opposed to years) of life. The diagnosis can often be established by measuring the unsaturated Cbl-binding capacity of the patient's serum; in normals, this largely reflects the amount of TC II present. Gel filtration chromatography can be used to separate TC II from serum R-binders and thus to provide a more accurate assessment of Cbl-binding capacity. Unfortunately, both of these tests can be compromised by previous Cbl therapy, possibly even by previous Schilling tests.[85] Because TC II is synthesized by many cell types, including fibroblasts, and because fibroblasts from TC II–deficient patients synthesize a defective protein or none at all,[39] a more satisfactory approach is to grow patient fibroblasts in medium without TC II and to determine whether any functional TC II has been synthesized by incubating with radiolabeled Cbl and measuring the extent to which TC II–Cbl accumulates in the medium or in the cells.[39,86]

In the case of siblings or other relatives in families in which one of these defects has been diagnosed, hematologic changes can provide an early sign of the presence of the disease. In the two intestinal transport disorders, Schilling tests may prove abnormal before the onset of clinical symptoms. In TC II deficiency, because cord blood contains fetal, not maternal, TC II,[87] it is possible to test immediately for the presence of functional TC II. Prenatal diagnosis, based on the ability of normal amniocytes to synthesize functional TC II, is at present possible only for TC II deficiency.[86] Because no fetus at risk for TC II deficiency has yet been tested by this method and predicted to be affected, its applicability remains hypothetical. The two intestinal malabsorption syndromes are not expressed in accessible fetal tissues (if, in fact, those proteins are expressed at all during fetal life) and, thus, cannot be diagnosed prenatally. The recent cDNA cloning of IF[22] may make a DNA-based diagnostic procedure, such as RFLP analysis, possible in at least some cases of IF deficiency.

The major treatment regimen for each of these disorders has been pharmacologic doses of Cbl, either CN-Cbl or OH-Cbl, usually administered by injection.[21,85] Titration of the dosage used and frequency of therapy should be carried out to ensure resolution of all clinical abnormalities, particularly in TC II–deficient patients with defective immune system function.[88,89] The serum Cbl concentration at which patients become asymptomatic has varied widely, especially in TC II deficiency, and should be used as a guide only after the patient has stabilized. Folate has been administered to some TC II–deficient patients with effective correction of the hematologic signs of the disease.[21] At least one of these patients suffered a relapse, however, and the ability of folate to resolve other symptoms has not been determined. Consequently, folate therapy should accompany effective doses of Cbl.

The prognosis in these diseases appears to be generally very good as long as serum Cbl levels are maintained appropriately, although few patients have been followed for extended periods. For example, one woman with TC II deficiency has borne two normal children.[76] It remains unclear whether complete reversal of the neurologic damage and developmental delay that occur if patients remain undiagnosed for an extended period can be achieved or whether some residual deficit may persist in these cases.

Defects in Cellular AdoCbl and MeCbl Synthesis

Clinical and Laboratory Findings. In comparison to the Cbl transport defects described above, defects in the cellular metabolism of Cbl result generally in clinically more severe metabolic disease. As a consequence, patients with these disorders show the metabolic disturbances that result from deficient synthesis of both AdoCbl and MeCbl, namely methylmalonic acidemia and homocystinuria (Fig. 82-2). Because the amounts of these metabolites detected in these patients generally greatly exceed those occasionally found in patients with Cbl transport defects or Cbl deficiency, their measurement has served to distinguish these groups of individuals clinically. More than a dozen children with inherited methylmalonic acidemia and homocystinuria have been reported. Most of these patients have been the subjects of individual case reports.[90–104] Cells from these children comprise three biochemically and genetically distinct complementation groups, designated *cblC*, *cblD*, and *cblF*.[48,105–107,191,192,218] The *cblC* group is by far the largest, with the *cblD* represented by two siblings[90] and the *cblF* group by a single, recently reported individual.[104]

As noted in Table 82-1, detailed clinical information is available on 17 children (nine males; eight females) in the *cblC*

Table 82-1 Clinical and Laboratory Features of Patients with Methylmalonic Acidemia and Homocystinuria

Finding	Mutant class* cblC	cblD	cblF
Clinical:			
Sex (male/female)	9/8	2/0	0/1
Neonatal onset	10/17	0/2	1/1
Failure to thrive	9/17	0/2	1/1
Developmental retardation	9/17	1/2	1/1
Seizures	4/17	0/2	1/1
Feeding difficulties	5/17	0/2	1/1
Laboratory:			
Normal serum cobalamin	17/17	2/2	1/1
Anemia	11/17	0/2	0/1
Megaloblastic marrow	8/17	0/2	0/1
Hypersegmented PMNs	2/17	0/2	0/1
Thrombocytopenia	2/17	0/2	0/1
Complications:			
Hemolytic episodes	4/17	0/2	0/1
Congestive failure	3/17	0/2	0/1
Thromboemboli	0/17	1/2	0/1
Current status:			
Living and well	2/17	1/2	0/1
Living and impaired	11/17	1/2	1/1
Deceased	4/17	0/2	0/1

*Numerical ratios denote patients showing particular finding/total number of patients in each mutant class.
SOURCE: Information obtained from published case reports[90–104] and personal communications.

group. Clinical findings have varied widely among patients in this group. Most of the early described patients presented in the first 2 months of life because of failure to thrive, poor feeding, or lethargy. Subsequent reports have emphasized that some patients have a much delayed onset of symptoms: a 4-year-old with fatigue, delirium, and spasticity;[97] a 14-year-old with the rather sudden onset of dementia and myelopathy.[96] Thus, regardless of age, neurologic manifestations are prominent. Most, but not all, of these patients have had hematologic abnormalities characterized by megaloblastosis and macrocytic anemia; hypersegmented polymorphonuclear leukocytes and thrombopenia have been observed less often. A few patients have also had retinal degeneration and other ophthalmologic changes.[95,97,100,103] In addition to the methylmalonic aciduria and homocystinuria that characterize this group of patients, some have shown hypomethioninemia and cystathioninuria. The methylmalonic aciduria in these children is distinctly less severe than that encountered in children with isolated mutase deficiency (see Chap. 29), although much more severe than that occasionally reported for patients with Cbl transport defects. Moreover, neither hyperglycinemia nor hyperammonemia has been reported in any of the *cblC* (or *cblD* or *cblF*) patients. Serum cobalamin and folate concentrations have been normal in each child.

In sharp contrast, neither of the brothers in the *cblD* group[90] had any clinically significant problems until much later in life. The older brother came to medical attention because of severe behavioral pathology and moderate mental retardation at 14 years of age. He had, as well, a poorly defined neuromuscular problem involving his lower extremities. His then 2-year-old brother was asymptomatic, although biochemically affected. No hematologic abnormalities have been noted in either sib.

The single reported patient in the *cblF* group (a female)

presented during the first 2 weeks of life with stomatitis, seizures, and hypotonia. She developed poorly and was clearly delayed when diagnosed at 8 months of age.[104] No hematologic abnormalities were found. Further, the patient had no detectable homocystinuria despite cellular deficits in methyltetrahydrofolate:homocysteine methyltransferase activity and in MeCbl synthesis. Because only one patient has been studied, it remains unclear whether the absence of homocystinuria is an anomalous finding or whether it may be clinically or biochemically significant.

Localization of Cellular Metabolism Defects. It is clear that patients in the *cblC* and *cblD* groups have a defect in cellular metabolism of Cbls, based on the following data: Total Cbl content of liver, kidney, and cultured fibroblasts is markedly reduced;[92,108–110,205,219,220] the ability of cultured cells to retain [57]Co-labeled CN-Cbl[111] or to convert [57]Co-labeled CN-Cbl or OH-Cbl to AdoCbl and MeCbl is markedly impaired;[106,112] activity of methylmalonyl-CoA mutase and of N^5-methyltetrahydrofolate:homocysteine methyltransferase in cultured cells is deficient, such deficiency being improved by supplementation of the growth medium with OH-Cbl;[106,113,114] and the mutase and the methyltransferase apoenzymes in cells from affected patients appear to be normal.[90,106,108,113,115] The precise nature of the metabolic defect in the *cblC* and *cblD* classes remains elusive, but considerable progress has been made. Because these mutant cells demonstrate normal receptor-mediated adsorptive endocytosis of the TC II–Cbl complex and normal intralysosomal hydrolysis of TC II,[3,35,106,116] perusal of Fig. 82-3 makes it clear that the defects in the *cblC* and *cblD* cells must affect some step or steps subsequent to cellular uptake, common to the synthesis of both coenzymes, and prior to the binding of the Cbl coenzymes to their respective apoproteins. Significantly, *cblC* (and, to a lesser extent, *cblD*) cells use CN-Cbl less well than OH-Cbl[114,117] and are unable to convert CN-Cbl to OH-Cbl, a step shown in normal cells to be a metabolic prerequisite for the synthesis of both AdoCbl and MeCbl.[117] The latter results have been interpreted as evidence for a defect in a cytosolic cob(III)alamin reductase, which is required for reducing Cbl's trivalent cobalt prior to alkylation.[117] More direct assays of such a putative reductase in extracts of *cblC* and *cblD* cells will be necessary to confirm or deny this thesis. Finally, it should be mentioned that the distinction between the *cblC* and *cblD* classes is based first and foremost on complementation studies which define the two classes as unique.[106] Their biochemical differences appear to be quantitative rather than qualitative, with the *cblC* group having more severe metabolic derangements (and, *pari passu*, more severe clinical involvement) than the sibs designated *cblD*.

Studies using cultured fibroblasts from the single reported patient in the *cblF*[104,107,217,218] group are of particular interest.[118,225] As with cells from *cblC* and *cblD* patients, both mutase and methyltransferase activities were impaired, and AdoCbl and MeCbl content were reduced. In contrast to the *cblC* and *cblD* mutants, however, the *cblF* cells accumulate unmetabolized, non-protein-bound CN-Cbl in lysosomes. These findings indicate that *cblF* cells are deficient in the mediated process by which cobalamin vitamers exit from lysosomes after being taken up by receptor-mediated endocytosis.

Pathophysiology. The megaloblastic anemia so commonly observed in the *cblC* patients almost surely reflects the enzymatic disturbance of the N^5-methyltetrahydrofolate:homocysteine

methyltransferase. This can be stated with some assurance since patients with isolated methylmalonyl-CoA mutase deficiency (see Chap. 29) more severe than that encountered in the *cblC* patients exhibit no such hematologic dysfunction. The early and severe CNS abnormalities encountered in the *cblC* group probably reflect the methyltransferase abnormality as well, in that such patients do not have the severe metabolic ketoacidosis that probably accounts for the CNS problems in patients with mutase deficiency only. Thus, patients with severe, inherited dysfunction in the synthesis of both Cbl coenzymes resemble closely patients with exogenous Cbl deficiency—both groups having prominent hematologic and neurological manifestations resulting from the blocked methyltransferase system.

Genetic Considerations. Because equal numbers of affected males and affected females exist in the *cblC* group (Table 82-1), because females have been as seriously affected as males, and because cells from affected patients behave as recessives in complementation studies,[105] it seems safe to predict that this disorder is inherited as an autosomal recessive trait. The mode of inheritance of the *cblD* and the *cblF* mutations cannot yet be defined, because of the paucity of known patients and because both affected *cblD* patients in the only family yet described are males. Identification of heterozygotes for the *cblC*, *cblD*, or *cblF* group has not yet been accomplished.

Diagnosis, Treatment, and Prognosis. The combination of methylmalonic aciduria and homocystinuria with normal serum cobalamin concentrations and normal TC II is the set of biochemical parameters needed to distinguish patients in the *cblC*, *cblD*, and, probably, *cblF* groups from those with methylmalonic acidemia caused by isolated methylmalonyl-CoA mutase deficiency (see Chap. 29); from those with homocystinuria due to cystathionine synthase deficiency (see Chap. 23) or $N^{5,10}$-methylenetetrahydrofolate reductase deficiency (see Chap. 81) or isolated methyltetrahydrofolate methyltransferase deficiency (see Chap. 81 and below); and from those with Cbl transport defects or exogenous Cbl deficiency (see above). Because each of these defects is expressed in cultured cells from affected individuals, the diagnosis should be confirmed by genetic complementation analysis between patient fibroblasts and fibroblasts from patients whose complementation groups have been determined previously. This technique also allows the *cblC*, *cblD*, and *cblF* groups to be distinguished from each other. Biochemical studies on cultured cells, such as Cbl uptake, lysosomal Cbl efflux, or AdoCbl and MeCbl synthesis, and direct measurement of mutase and methyltransferase activities in cell extracts can be performed to provide further confirmation. Because normal amniotic fluid cells appear to carry out all of the steps of Cbl metabolism normally observed in cultured fibroblasts, it should be possible to detect each of these defects prenatally by assaying any of these parameters in cultured amniocytes. So far, this has been carried out successfully only in the *cblC* group (unpublished results).

The distinctions between these cellular metabolic defects and other related conditions are critically important, because appropriate therapy and prognosis depend on them. Whereas exogenous Cbl deficiency responds dramatically to physiologic amounts of Cbl and transport defects to somewhat larger dosages (above), successful management of *cblC*, *cblD*, and *cblF* patients probably demands, particularly in the first case, the administration of very large amounts of OH-Cbl, up to 1 mg daily, by intramuscular injection.[90,93,95–97] Such treatment has resulted in dramatic decreases in urinary methylmalonate and in less dramatic, but significant, decreases in urinary homocystine in many of those patients who have received it. The form of Cbl administered is probably important, because studies on cultured cells from *cblC* patients have shown that supplementation in culture with CN-Cbl is much less efficient than with OH-Cbl in eliciting an increase in the activity of the affected enzymes.[118] A number of adjunctive therapies have been employed for *cblC* patients with variable success, including: moderate protein restriction to reduce the load of metabolic end products and, hence, the amount of methylmalonate produced; carnitine supplementation, to improve organic acid excretion and relieve a postulated functional carnitine deficiency (see Chap. 29); folic and folinic acid administration, to bypass the so-called methylfolate trap and restore hematologic function (see Chap. 81); and betaine administration, to provide substrate for betaine:homocysteine methyltransferase, which is not dependent on a Cbl coenzyme, and thus return the serum methionine:homocysteine ratio toward normal. Few investigators have evaluated the efficacy of these treatments critically, however. In a recent report, Bartholomew and his colleagues have attempted to determine the effects of OH-Cbl dosage schedule and of treatment with carnitine, folinic acid, and betaine on the clinical and biochemical status of two patients with the *cblC* defect.[119] In each case, the OH-Cbl injection schedule could be titrated to control the patient's methylmalonic acidemia and homocystinuria. In addition, betaine administration [250 mg/(kg/day)] appeared to act synergistically with the OH-Cbl to produce a further reduction in plasma homocystine. No specific clinical improvement accompanied the betaine therapy, however. Neither patient responded clinically or biochemically to folinic acid or carnitine treatment. The overall result in both patients was good metabolic control, as measured by reduced methylmalonic acidemia and normal serum homocysteine and methionine concentrations, and resolution of most of their clinical symptoms, such as lethargy, irritability, vomiting, and failure to thrive, with a treatment regimen of daily betaine administration and biweekly injections of OH-Cbl. Significantly, both patients remained somewhat delayed developmentally, even after a year or more of therapy. In addition, the retinal degeneration present in these patients was not reversed by the therapy, although some improvement in cone response was noted in one of them.

This report serves also to emphasize the fact that early diagnosis and prompt institution of therapy with OH-Cbl (and possibly betaine) may be the only way to change the outcome of these patients, which at least in the case of the *cblC* group, has been dismal thus far. Four of the six earliest reported *cblC* patients died at ages 7 weeks,[91] 3 months (personal communication), 4 months,[94] and 7 years,[92] respectively. Severe hemolytic anemia has been a major complication in the deceased *cblC* patients, as has congestive heart failure. Thromboemboli, so often encountered in patients with homocystinuria due to cystathionine synthase deficiency, have, thus far, been documented only in the older of the two *cblD* brothers, and this complication was not noted until he reached 18 years of age. Moreover, the surviving patients, even those under apparently good metabolic control, continue to show signs of neurologic dysfunction, including mild to moderate mental retardation and delayed development of motor skills,[21] and, in some cases, the continued presence of abnormal ophthalmologic findings.[119] These problems could be the result of irreversible

damage which occurred prior to diagnosis and therapeutic intervention, or could reflect the impossibility of completely correcting the cellular lesion in Cbl metabolism in certain cells whose function is critical in neurologic development. Until patients with these defects are diagnosed before birth or soon thereafter, and treated immediately, or even prenatally, with Cbl supplements, we will not know whether the poor outcome in this group can be modified significantly. Documentation of such experience will be particularly important in assessing the clinician's ability to modify the natural history of these disorders.

Defects in AdoCbl Synthesis

In 1968, Rosenberg,[120,121] Linblad,[122,123] and their colleagues described infants with severe metabolic ketoacidosis and developmental delay who accumulated very large amounts of methylmalonate in blood and urine, similar to patients reported earlier by Oberholzer,[124] Stokke,[125] and their coworkers. In contrast to the earlier patients, however, these infants responded dramatically to pharmacologic doses of CN-Cbl or AdoCbl with resolution of their clinical symptoms and major reductions in their excretion of methylmalonate. Further studies indicated that the methylmalonyl-CoA mutase enzyme was normal in these patients, but that synthesis of AdoCbl was impaired.[112,126] Somewhat later, Kaye et al.[127] reported two patients with methylmalonic acidemia who were unresponsive in vivo to high doses of CN-Cbl but who also had apparently normal mutase enzyme and defective AdoCbl synthesis. Subsequent biochemical and genetic complementation analysis established that lesions at two genetically distinct loci can be responsible for defective AdoCbl synthesis; they are designated *cblA* and *cblB*.[48,105] Because both groups of patients with deficient AdoCbl synthesis share many clinical features with those with primary defects in the methylmalonyl-CoA mutase enzyme, the reader is referred to Chap. 29 for a discussion of the latter group.

Clinical and Laboratory Presentation. As mentioned above, the clinical findings in patients with methylmalonic acidemia due either to defective mutase enzyme (*mut*) or defective AdoCbl synthesis (*cblA*, *cblB*) are remarkable more for their similarities than for their differences. We have surveyed[128] the natural history in 45 such patients; 20 were *mut*; 14 were *cblA*, and 11 were *cblB* (see Chap. 29). There were approximately equal numbers of males and females in each group. Information was obtained from questionnaires completed by the patients' physicians, published reports, unpublished communications, and personal experience. The most common signs and symptoms at the onset of clinical difficulty were lethargy, failure to thrive, recurrent vomiting, dehydration, respiratory distress, and muscular hypotonia. Little interclass difference was observed for these major clinical manifestations or for such less common ones as developmental retardation, hepatomegaly, or coma. The only major clinical distinction between the *mut* group and the groups with defective AdoCbl synthesis was that most of the former group presented very early in life (<1 to 4 weeks) while 60 percent of the *cblA* group and 45 percent of the *cblB* group presented between 1 month and 1 year.[128]

The laboratory findings in affected patients at the same time that methylmalonic acidemia (with or without aciduria) was first documented are shown in Table 82-2. As expected, serum cobalamin concentrations were routinely normal. Metabolic acidosis, with blood pH values as low as 6.9 and serum bicarbonate concentrations as low as 5 meq/liter, was observed in the majority of patients. Ketonemia or ketonuria, hyperammonemia and hyperglycinemia or hyperglycinuria were also observed in many affected patients. Leukopenia, thrombocytopenia, and anemia were the only other manifestations that were noted. Earlier case reports (reviewed in Ref. 129) found that hypoglycemia occurs in about 40 percent of affected patients. Inadvertently, this parameter was not assessed in the survey. Significantly, the megaloblastic anemia characteristic of functional Cbl deficiency or the inherited disorders of MeCbl synthesis (cblC and cblD, above, cblE and cblG, below) was not present in these patients.

Chemical Abnormalities in Vivo. Large amounts of methylmalonic acid have appeared in the urine or blood of all reported patients. Whereas normal children and adults excrete less than 5 mg methylmalonate daily, children with isolated methylmalonic acidemia have excreted from 240 to 5700 mg in a 24-h period. Their plasma concentrations of methylmalonate, which is undetectable in normal subjects, have ranged from 2.6 to 34 mg/dl (0.22 to 2.88 mM). In those few patients in whom it was measured, the cerebrospinal fluid concentrations of methylmalonate equaled that of plasma (see Ref. 129 for references to early case reports). No relationship between the quantities of methylmalonate accumulated in body fluids and the etiology of mutase deficiency (i.e., apoenzyme versus coenzyme deficiency) has been reported. Methylmalonate is surely the major, but not the only, abnormal metabolite found in body fluids of these patients. Because propionyl-CoA carboxylation is reversible, propionate and some of its precursors (butanone) or metabolites (β-hydroxypropionate and methylcitrate) also accumulate in blood and urine,[120,130,131] their amounts being small compared to that of methylmalonate.

Several groups have studied the relationship between protein or amino acid loading and methylmalonate accumulation in these patients. Without exception, administration of protein or those amino acids known to be precursors of propionate and methylmalonate, such as methionine, threonine, valine, or isoleucine, has resulted in augmented methylmalonate accumulation and, in some instances, ketosis or acidosis.[120,122,124,125] When Cbl-responsive patients are given supplements of this vitamin, such augmentation by methylmalonate precursors is lessened considerably.[132] All these find-

ings suggest that patients with discrete defects at the mutase step have a major block in the utilization of methylmalonyl-CoA which is expressed as methylmalonate accumulation.

Localization of Enzymatic Defects. Because the conversion of propionate to succinate is blocked in each of the methylmalonic acidemias, whether due to mutase defects or AdoCbl synthesis deficiencies, an early screening test for these disorders measured the ability of intact peripheral blood leukocytes or cultured fibroblasts to oxidize [^{14}C]propionate or [^{14}C]methylmalonate to $^{14}CO_2$ and compared this with the oxidation of [^{14}C]succinate to $^{14}CO_2$.[121] More recently, incorporation of [^{14}C]propionate into trichloroacetic acid–precipitable material by intact cultured cells has replaced the more cumbersome $^{14}CO_2$ evolution technique.[133,134] Further discrimination among the methylmalonic acidemias has depended on studies of cobalamin uptake and AdoCbl formation by intact cultured fibroblasts, on assays of mutase activity in cell extracts, and on genetic complementation studies with cultured cells.

cblA. A series of observations by Rosenberg,[126] Mahoney,[112] and their colleagues on the fibroblasts of the index patient with Cbl-responsive methylmalonic acidemia led to the demonstration of a primary defect in AdoCbl synthesis: (1) Such cells were unable to oxidize propionate or methylmalonate in a medium containing 25 to 50 pg/ml Cbl and under these conditions, the cell content of AdoCbl was only 10 percent of normal.[126] (2) Supplementation of the medium to 250,000 pg/ml raised the AdoCbl content to that of controls and led to a distinct increase in propionate oxidation.[126] (3) Such intact cells were unable to convert OH-[^{57}Co]Cbl to Ado[^{57}Co]Cbl, although they took up the labeled vitamin normally and had no abnormality in synthesizing the other cobalamin coenzyme, MeCbl.[112] (4) Mutase activity in cell-free extracts supplemented with AdoCbl was normal.[126] (5) Cell-free extracts from this line synthesized AdoCbl normally when incubated with OH-[^{57}Co]Cbl, ATP, and a reducing system designed to bypass cob(III)alamin reductase and cob(II)alamin reductase and to measure only cob(I)alamin adenosyltransferase.[48] Fibroblasts from other patients in this clinically defined group had identical findings in similar studies.[48] Genetic complementation analysis established unequivocally that all of these patients belonged to a single complementation group, designated cblA, and thus presumably had defects in the same enzyme or protein.[105] Because it has been shown that mammalian mitochondria can synthesize AdoCbl from OH-Cbl without prior reduction,[135] and because Cbl adenosyltransferase activity is normal in this group,[48] it is presumed that the defect must lie in one of the early steps of mitochondrial Cbl metabolism, possibly in a mitochondrial Cbl reductase (Fig. 82-3). So far, the lack of a specific assay for the reductive step(s) in AdoCbl synthesis has prevented a more precise localization of the defect in the cblA group.

cblB. Another group of patients with defective AdoCbl synthesis was uncovered when Cbl metabolism was examined in a number of cell lines from patients with methylmalonic acidemia.[48,136] Detailed investigation of some of these fibroblasts showed a primary defect in AdoCbl synthesis similar to that described for the cblA class (above), except in one aspect. When cell-free extracts from these lines were incubated with OH-[^{57}Co]Cbl, a reducing system, and ATP, no AdoCbl syn-

Table 82-2 Laboratory Findings in 45 Patients with Methylmalonic Acidemia

Finding at clinical onset	Mutant class*		
	cblA	cblB	mut
Normal serum cobalamin	100	100	100
Metabolic acidosis	100	88	89
Ketonemia and/or ketonuria	78	67	88
Hyperammonemia	50	83	76
Hyperglycinemia and/or -glycinuria	70	83	60
Leukopenia	70	45	69
Anemia	10	45	44
Thrombocytopenia	75	45	40

*Numerical values represent percentages of patients in each group.
SOURCE: From Matsui et al.[128]

thesis was detected,[48] in contrast to the *cblA* cell lines. Because the assay is specific for ATP:cob(I)alamin adenosyltransferase, the patients in this group have defects in this enzyme.[49] Complementation analysis has indicated that a single locus, *cblB*, is involved in all of these patients, and that it is distinct from the *cblA* locus.[105]

Pathophysiology. All studies in vivo and in vitro in patients with methylmalonic acidemia due to methylmalonyl-CoA mutase deficiency, either primary or secondary to AdoCbl synthesis defects, indicate that the block in the conversion of methylmalonyl-CoA to succinyl-CoA explains admirably the accumulation of methylmalonate in blood and urine, the augmentation of methylmalonate excretion and the precipitation of ketosis by protein, amino acids, or propionate, and the excretion of long-chain ketones formed in the catabolism of branched chain amino acids. The primary block does not explain several important physiologic disturbances: the acidosis, hypoglycemia, hyperglycinemia, and hyperammonemia. Oberholzer et al.[124] pointed out that the concentration of methylmalonate in the blood (no more than 3 mM) could not alone explain the acidosis, and suggested other possibilities. They proposed that an accumulation of coenzyme A "trapped" intracellularly as methylmalonyl-CoA could lead to an insufficiency of this widely utilized coenzyme and secondarily to impaired carbohydrate metabolism and subsequent acidosis. Alternatively, they suggested that methylmalonyl-CoA, a known inhibitor of pyruvate carboxylase,[137] could interfere with gluconeogenesis and lead directly to hypoglycemia and indirectly to excessive catabolism of lipid, with ketosis and acidosis. Halperin et al.[138] showed that methylmalonate inhibited the transmitochondrial shuttle of malate and argued that impairment of this key step in gluconeogenesis could lead to hypoglycemia. As discussed earlier for deficiencies of β-ketothiolase (see Chap. 18) and propionyl-CoA carboxylase (see Chap. 29), the mechanism of the hyperglycinemia and hyperammonemia so often observed in children with any one of these disorders probably reflects inhibition of the intramitochondrial glycine cleavage enzyme and of carbamyl phosphate synthetase I, respectively, by the accumulated organic acids or their CoA esters. Thus, each of the major secondary abnormalities in the propionic and methylmalonic acidemias can be explained satisfactorily by inhibition of specific intramitochondrial processes by the accumulated organic acids and esters.

As mentioned earlier, about half of the reported patients with these defects show pancytopenia.[128] One report suggests that methylmalonate inhibited growth of marrow stem cells in a concentration-dependent fashion.[139] Further studies of this sort will be of interest.

By comparing and contrasting the findings in patients with isolated mutase deficiency, whether due to defects in mutase or in AdoCbl synthesis, with those in patients with functional Cbl deficiency (as in classic pernicious anemia, or the Cbl transport defects discussed above), it should be possible to shed some light on the mechanism responsible for the hematologic and neurologic abnormalities in the latter disorders. Thus, the absence of megaloblastic anemia in any patient with isolated mutase deficiency militates against any involvement of this enzyme in the typical megaloblastosis seen in Cbl deficiency. Similarly, the cerebellar and posterior column abnormalities so often encountered in Cbl-deficient patients have never been observed in patients with methylmalonic acidemia due to specific mutase dysfunction. Therefore, the notion that

neurologic dysfunction in pernicious anemia reflects aberrant incorporation of odd-chain or branched chain fatty acids into myelin because of a block in the propionate pathway has little to recommend it. It appears likely, then, that abnormalities in the Cbl-dependent methyltransferase account for the hematologic and neurologic abnormalities in Cbl-deficient patients (also see the discussion below of isolated MeCbl synthesis defects).

Genetic Considerations. Each of the bases for defective AdoCbl synthesis (*cblA* and *cblB*) is almost certainly inherited as an autosomal recessive trait. This conclusion is based on the following findings: First, approximately equal numbers of affected males and females are encountered in each group.[128] Second, no instance of vertical transmission from affected parent to affected child has been reported. Third, each mutant class behaves as a recessive in culture in complementation experiments.[105,106,113] And fourth, cell lines from heterozygotes for the *cblB* mutation show partial adenosyltransferase deficiency.[149]

Diagnosis, Treatment, and Prognosis. Because simple colorimetric assays for urinary methylmalonate and more complex gas-liquid chromatographic assays for serum and urinary methylmalonate are now available, it should no longer be difficult to make a diagnosis of methylmalonic acidemia, once this condition is considered. Other sources of neonatal or infantile ketoacidosis must be ruled out (see chapters in Part V, for example). The quantity of methylmalonate excreted, the absence of megaloblastic changes, and the normal amounts of serum homocysteine, methionine, and Cbl all serve to differentiate this set of diseases from others that may lead to methylmalonic aciduria. Distinguishing between primary mutase deficiency and primary AdoCbl synthesis defects and between the two causes of the latter ultimately depends on studies with cultured cells; routinely, genetic complementation analysis.[106] Prenatal detection of methylmalonic acidemia has been accomplished on several occasions in two different ways: by measurement of methylmalonate in amniotic fluid and maternal urine at midtrimester;[140,141] and by studies of mutase activity and Cbl metabolism in cultured amniotic fluid cells.[133,141,142] AdoCbl synthesis defects of both complementation groups[141,142] have been identified in these ways.

Two treatment regimens for children with methylmalonic acidemia exist and should be employed in tandem for patients with AdoCbl synthesis deficiencies. A diet restricted in protein (or a special formula restricted in amino acid precursors of methylmalonate) should be instituted as soon as such life-threatening problems of ketoacidosis, hypoglycemia, or hyperammonemia have been addressed; and supplementary Cbl (1 to 2 mg OH-Cbl intramuscularly daily for several days) should be given as soon as the diagnosis of methylmalonic acidemia is made (or even seriously considered). Such measures should decrease the circulating concentrations of methylmalonate and propionate. Even Cbl-unresponsive children with delayed development have been shown to improve markedly when treated with careful dietary protein restriction.[143,144] In Cbl-responsive patients, titration of Cbl dosage schedules against methylmalonate excretion and clinical status is probably worthwhile. It should be noted that the methylmalonic aciduria is not completely eliminated in even the most responsive patients, even though clinical symptoms such as ketosis and acidosis are completely resolved. As discussed earlier for patients with propionyl-CoA carboxylase deficiency (Chap. 29), Roe and associates[145–147] have pointed out that L-carnitine supplements may be a useful therapeutic adjunct in patients with methylmalonic acidemia, presumably by repleting intracellular and extracellular stores of free carnitine which are depleted in affected patients because of complexing with methylmalonyl-CoA and propionyl-CoA. No trial of this compound has been reported in *cblA* or *cblB* patients.

Our previously mentioned survey[128] suggests that both the response to Cbl supplements and the long-term outcome in affected patients depends considerably on the nature of the biochemical lesion. Whereas >90 percent of the *cblA* patients responded to Cbl supplements with a distinct fall in blood or urinary methylmalonate, only ~40 percent of the *cblB* patients showed such a response. Presumably, the ~60 percent of *cblB* patients unresponsive to Cbl supplements have such complete adenosyltransferase deficiency that AdoCbl synthesis cannot be augmented by Cbl supplements, in distinction to the *cblB* patients with apparently "leaky" mutations that permit responsiveness in vivo. The uniform responsiveness of patients in the *cblA* group suggests either that the responsible mutations are "leaky," thereby allowing mass action considerations to result in more AdoCbl synthesis, or that alternative pathways of Cbl reduction which require high substrate concentrations exist in cells. As in the case of primary mutase deficiency, it should be emphasized that responsiveness in vivo does not require complete correction of the functional mutase deficiency (see Chap. 29). Some patients unresponsive to CN-Cbl or OH-Cbl in vivo might be expected to respond to AdoCbl itself, but no published reports documenting the efficacy of this alternative exist at present. In fact, unpublished experiments in our laboratory suggest that AdoCbl is largely converted back to OH-Cbl during transport into cells in culture.

The long-term outlook for affected patients is revealing. The *cblA* patients (i.e., that group biochemically most responsive to Cbl supplements) had the best outcome according to our survey—~70 percent were alive and well at ages up to 14 years and presumably continue to be so 6 years later. The *cblB* group had about equal fractions in the alive and well, the alive and impaired, and the deceased category. It is interesting, albeit anecdotal, that the index patient in the *cblA* group (now 20 years old) discontinued Cbl supplements at age 9 years in spite of our advice to the contrary. In the ensuing 11 years, his development and general health have remained excellent despite accumulation of very large amounts of methylmalonate in the blood and urine. Perhaps, as in some other inherited metabolic disorders, treatment of methylmalonic acidemia is most critical during the early years of life. If this experience is borne out by others, it makes expert clinical management in the early weeks or months of life most important. Finally, the feasibility of prenatal therapy with Cbl supplements has also been demonstrated. Ampola et al.[141] showed that administration of Cbl supplements to a woman carrying an affected fetus of the *cblA* group resulted in significant reduction in maternal excretion of methylmalonate and the presence of only moderate methylmalonic acidemia(uria) in the newborn child. She was doing well at the time of the report (20 months) with moderate protein restriction and occasional Cbl therapy, whereas an undiagnosed affected sibling had died at 3 months of age.[141] The utility of this provocative observation must await the demonstration that prenatal damage occurs if therapy is withheld.

Defects in MeCbl Synthesis

While combined deficiency of AdoCbl and MeCbl synthesis and isolated deficiency of AdoCbl synthesis were described 15 to 20 years ago, it is only recently that a few patients with isolated defects in MeCbl synthesis have been reported. Two complementation groups appear to exist, *cblE* and *cblG*, which are very similar both clinically and biochemically (also see Chap. 81).

Clinical and Laboratory Findings. The patients so far reported with these disorders (six are known;[21] only three have been described in detail[148–150] have presented in the first few months of life with vomiting, poor feeding, lethargy, and hypotonia. Further evaluation has revealed developmental delay and a severe visual defect in one patient.[150] Laboratory findings have included macrocytic anemia, pancytopenia, megaloblastic bone marrow, normal serum Cbl and folate, homocystinuria, and hypomethioninemia. Methylmalonic aciduria has not been observed. One patient, a sibling of the index case, was diagnosed prenatally[151] and treated with Cbl supplements prospectively. He has remained asymptomatic, both clinically and biochemically, with continued Cbl therapy.

Localization of Defects. The constellation of homocystinuria and hypomethioninemia without methylmalonic aciduria suggested strongly that these patients had isolated deficiencies in the activity of N^5-methyltetrahydrofolate:homocysteine methyltransferase, either primary or secondary to abnormal synthesis or utilization of MeCbl, its cofactor (Fig. 82-3). Studies of fibroblasts derived from several of these patients have confirmed this hypothesis. Incorporation of [^{14}C]propionate into macromolecules was normal, while incorporation of [^{14}C]methyltetrahydrofolate was reduced to about 10 percent of control,[148] a value similar to that reported for patients from the *cblC* group. Genetic complementation analysis based on [^{14}C]methyltetrahydrofolate incorporation has recently been reported to distinguish two complementation groups:[152] *cblE* (index patient reported in Ref. 148) and *cblG* (index patient reported in Ref. 150). Accumulation of Cbl by fibroblasts was normal in these groups, as was the fraction recovered as AdoCbl. In contrast, the fraction identified as MeCbl was much reduced. When methyltransferase activities were determined under standard conditions in extracts of fibroblasts from the index *cblE* patient, both holoenzyme and total enzyme were normal.[148] Under suboptimal assay conditions, namely in the presence of lower concentrations of reducing agents, however, methyltransferase activities were less than those in controls.[153] In the other complementation group, methyltransferase activities have been reported to be reduced even under optimal assay conditions.[149,150]

These findings have led to the hypothesis that the *cblE* group has defects in an enzyme required either to reduce Cbl so that it can participate in the methyltransferase reaction or to maintain it in its active reduced form [probably cob(I)alamin] on the methyltransferase.[153] The bacterial enzyme has accessory proteins which appear to be reductases,[154] and the purified mammalian enzyme has multiple, dissimilar subunits,[155] one of which could perform a similar function. Because the *cblG* group has reduced methyltransferase activities even under optimal conditions, the possibility must be considered that it represents primary defects in the catalytic subunit of methyltransferase itself.[152] Until the purified mam-

Table 82-3 Salient Biochemical Features of Cultured Fibroblasts from Patients with Various Defects in Cellular Cbl Metabolism

	*Mutant class**						
	cblA	*cblB*	*cblC*	*cblD*	*cblE*	*cblF*	*cblG*
Studies with intact cells:							
[^{14}C]propionate oxidation	−	−	−	−	+	−	+
[^{14}C]MeTHF fixation	+	+	−	−	−	−	−
MeCbl synthesis	+	+	−	−	−	−	−
AdoCbl synthesis	−	−	−	−	+	−	+
Conversion of CN-Cbl to OH-Cbl	+	+	−	±	+	−	+
Lysosomal efflux of free Cbl	+	+	+	+	+	−	+
Enzyme activities in cell extracts:†							
Mutase holoenzyme	−	−	−	−	NT	NT	NT
Mutase total enzyme	+	+	+	+	NT	NT	NT
Methyltransferase holoenzyme	+	+	−	−	+	−	±
Methyltransferase total enzyme	+	+	±	±	+	±	±
Cob(I)alamin adenosyltransferase	+	−	+	+	NT	NT	NT

*+ = normal; − = markedly deficient or undetectable; ± = partially deficient; NT = not tested.
†*Holoenzyme* is defined as that enzyme activity measured in the absence of added cofactor; *total enzyme* is that activity measured in the presence of saturating concentrations of cofactor.
NOTE: MeTHF = N^5-methyltetrahydrofolate; MeCbl = methylcobalamin; AdoCbl = adenosylcobalamin; CN-Cbl = cyanocobalamin; OH-Cbl = hydroxocobalamin.

malian enzyme is studied further and more comparisons are made between it and the methyltransferase proteins present in cells from these groups of patients, these questions will remain unresolved.

Pathophysiology and Genetics. The association of isolated functional methyltransferase deficiency with megaloblastic anemia and neurologic defects in these patients provides strong evidence for the hypothesis outlined above and in Chap. 29 that these clinical signs are sequelae of defects in the MeCbl-methyltransferase branch of Cbl metabolism rather than the AdoCbl–methylmalonyl-CoA mutase one. A more complete understanding of the role of this system in hemato-

logic and neurologic development will require further study of both the enzymes involved and the patients with these disorders.

Each of these disorders is presumed to be inherited as an autosomal recessive trait, although the limited number of patients makes such a conclusion tentative. The three *cblE* patients are male (two are sibs); both male and female *cblG* patients have been reported. Both defects act as recessives in complementation analysis in culture.[152]

Diagnosis, Treatment, and Prognosis. The clinical hallmarks of these disorders appear to be developmental delay and megaloblastic anemia, with homocystinuria and without meth-

Fig. 82-4 Summary scheme of inherited defects of cobalamin metabolism. The circled numbers and their key signify the general sites at which abnormalities have been identified and the affected protein or process at each site. Cbl^{III} = cob(III)alamin (e.g., OH-Cbl); Cbl^{I} = cob(I)alamin; AdoCbl = adenosylcobalamin; MeCbl = methylcobalamin.

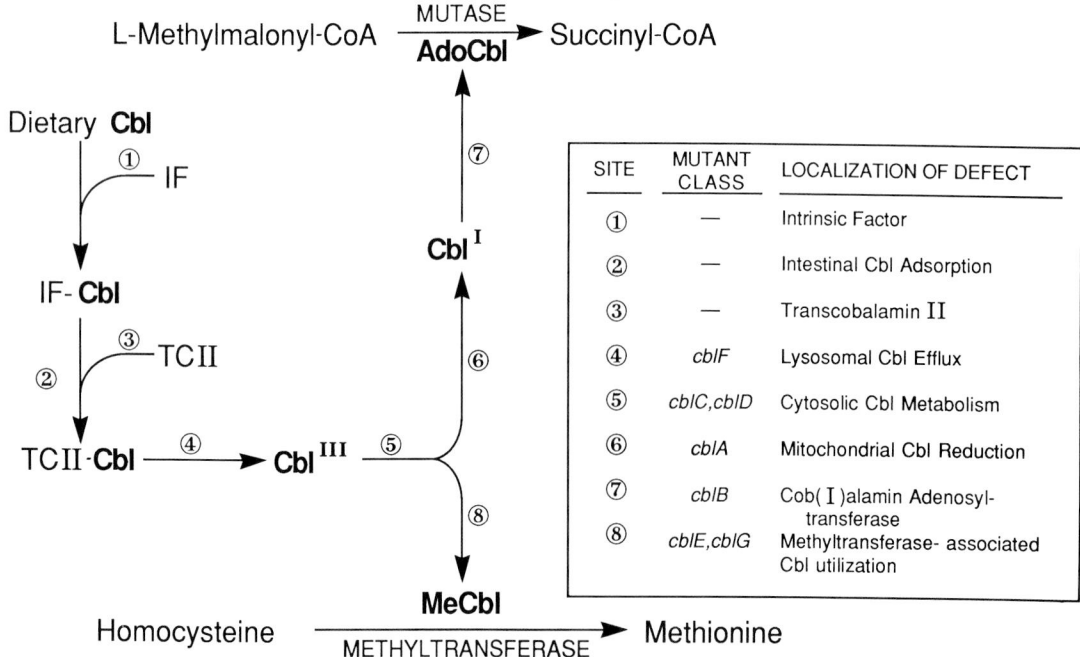

ylmalonic aciduria. Differentiation from other possible diagnoses such as TC II deficiency (see above), folate transport or metabolism defects (Chap. 81), or cystathionine β-synthase deficiency (Chap. 23) can be easily accomplished by studies of cultured cells, as can assignment to the appropriate complementation group. Prenatal diagnosis using amniotic fluid cells is possible and has been performed for the *cblE* defect.[151]

Because the patients reported to date have responded to OH-Cbl therapy with resolution of their clinical symptoms and normalization of their biochemical parameters,[21,148-150] and because it seems possible, as in the *cblC* patients (above), that delays in treatment may result in incompletely reversible developmental delays or neurologic deficits,[150] institution of OH-Cbl administration should occur as soon as the diagnosis is made. Dosages of 1 mg OH-Cbl per day (intramuscular injection) have been used initially, then tapered to 1 mg twice or three times a week. Biochemical improvement has been rapid on this regimen, and most clinical symptoms have resolved in a few weeks, although the index *cblG* patient was somewhat slower to improve.[150] On the other hand, the *cblE* patient diagnosed prenatally and treated with OH-Cbl prospectively (1 mg OH-Cbl twice a week) has developed normally without any clinical symptoms.[151] Whether prenatal therapy is warranted remains an open question, however.

Because the patients with these disorders have been described only recently, the long-term prognosis in these conditions remains unknown. The index *cblE* patient is thriving, although mildly developmentally delayed,[21] while his prenatally diagnosed and treated brother appears completely normal. In contrast, the index *cblG* patient, although clinically well, remains significantly retarded with major visual defects.[150] It seems likely that patients in the *cblE* and *cblG* groups will show a range of clinical outcomes similar to those of patients in the *cblC* group (above), because the majority of the symptoms of all of these patients arises from the same cause, i.e., functional methyltransferase deficiency. Likewise, early diagnosis and treatment may be the only way to avoid permanent neurologic damage and its consequences.

Table 82-3 summarizes the salient biochemical features of patients and cultured cells from patients with defects in various aspects of Cbl transport and metabolism. Figure 82-4 summarizes the localization of these defects.

REFERENCES

1. MINOT GR, MURPHY LP: Treatment of pernicious anemia by a special diet. *JAMA* 87:470, 1926.
2. SMITH EL: Purification of anti-pernicious anemia factors from liver. *Nature* 161:638, 1948.
3. RICKES EL, BRINK NG, KONIUSZY FR, WOOD TR, FOLKERS K: Crystalline vitamin B_{12}. *Science* 107:396, 1948.
4. DOLPHIN D (ed): B_{12}. New York/Toronto, Wiley, 1982.
5. HODGKIN DC, KAMPER J, MACKAY M, PICKWORTH J, TRUEBLOOD KN, WHITE JG: Structure of vitamin B_{12}. *Nature* 178:64, 1956.
6. WALKER GA, MURPHY S, HEUNNEKENS FH: Enzymatic conversion of vitamin B_{12} to adenosyl-B_{12}: Evidence for the existence of two separate reducing systems. *Arch Biochem Biophys* 134:95, 1969.
7. BARKER HA, SMYTH RD, WAWSZKIEWICZ EJ, LEE MN, WILSON RM: Enzymatic preparation and characterization of an α-L-β-methylaspartic acid. *Arch Biochem Biophys* 78:468, 1958.
8. BARKER HA, WEISSBACH H, SMYTH RD: A coenzyme containing pseudovitamin B_{12}. *Proc Natl Acad Sci USA* 44:1093, 1958.
9. WEISSBACH H, TOOHEY J, BARKER HA: Isolation and properties of B_{12} coenzymes containing benzimidazole or dimethylbenzimidazole. *Proc Natl Acad Sci USA* 45:521, 1959.
10. SMITH RM, MONTY KJ: Vitamin B_{12} and propionate metabolism. *Biochem Biophys Res Commun* 1:105, 1959.
11. GURNANI S, MISTRY SP, JOHNSON BC: Function of vitamin B_{12} in methylmalonate metabolism. I. Effect of a cofactor form of B_{12} on the activity of methylmalonyl-CoA isomerase. *Biochem Biophys Acta* 38:187, 1960.
12. STERN JR, FRIEDMANN DC: Vitamin B_{12} and methylmalonyl-CoA isomerase I. Vitamin B_{12} and propionate metabolism. *Biochem Biophys Res Commun* 2:82, 1960.
13. WEISSBACH H, TAYLOR R: Role of vitamin B_{12} in methionine biosynthesis. *Fed Proc* 25:1649, 1966.
14. TAYLOR RT, WEISSBACH H: Enzymatic synthesis of methionine: Formation of a radioactive cobamide enzyme with N^5methyl-^{14}C-tetrahydrofolate. *Arch Biochem Biophys* 119:572, 1967.
15. TAYLOR RT, WEISSBACH H: *Escherichia coli* B N^5-methyltetrahydrofolate-homocysteine vitamin-B_{12} transmethylase: Formation and photolability of a methylcobalamin enzyme. *Arch Biochem Biophys* 123:109, 1968.
16. POSTON JM: Leucine 2,3-aminomutase, an enzyme of leucine catabolism. *J Biol Chem* 251:1859, 1976.
17. BABIOR BM: Cobamides as cofactors: Adenosylcobamide dependent reactions, in Babior BM (ed): *Cobalamin Biochemistry and Pathophysiology*. New York, Wiley, 1975, p 141.
18. POSTON JM, STADTMAN TC: Cobamides as cofactors: Methylcobamides and the synthesis of methionine, methane and acetate, in Babior BM (ed): *Cobalamin Biochemistry and Pathophysiology*. New York, Wiley, 1975, p 111.
19. DONALDSON RM JR: Intrinsic factor and the transport of cobalamin, in Johnson LR (ed): *Physiology of the Gastrointestinal Tract*. New York, Raven, 1981, p 641.
20. SENNETT C, ROSENBERG LE, MELLMAN IS: Transmembrane transport of cobalamin in prokaryotic and eukaryotic cells. *Annu Rev Biochem* 50:1053, 1981.
21. COOPER BA, ROSENBLATT DS: Inherited defects of vitamin B_{12} metabolism. *Annu Rev Nutr* 7:291, 1987.
22. DIECKGRAEFE BK, SEETHARAM B, BANASZAK L, LEYKAM JF, APLERS DH: Isolation and structural characterization of a cDNA clone encoding rat gastric intrinsic factor, *Proc Natl Acad Sci USA* 85:46, 1988.
23. ALLEN RH, SEETHARAM B, PODELL E, ALPERS DH: Effect of proteolytic enzymes on the binding of cobalamin to R protein and intrinsic factor. In vitro evidence that a failure to partially degrade R protein is responsible for cobalamin malabsorption in pancreatic insufficiency. *J Clin Invest* 61:47, 1978.
24. ALLEN RH, SEETHARAM B, ALLEN NC, PODELL ER, ALPERS DH: Correction of cobalamin malabsorption in pancreatic insufficiency with a cobalamin analogue that binds with high affinity to R protein but not to intrinsic factor. In vivo evidence that a failure to partially degrade R protein is responsible for cobalamin malabsorption in pancreatic insufficiency. *J Clin Invest* 61:1628, 1978.
25. MARCOULLIS G, PARMENTIER Y, NICOLAS J-P, JIMENEZ M, GERARD P: Cobalamin malabsorption due to nondegradation of R proteins in the human intestine: Inhibited cobalamin absorption in exocrine pancreatic dysfunction. *J Clin Invest* 66:430, 1980.
26. HALL CA, FINKLER AE: The dynamics of transcobalamin. II. A vitamin B_{12} binding substance in plasma. *J Lab Clin Med* 65:459, 1965.
27. HOM BL: Plasma turnover of ^{57}cobalt-vitamin B_{12} bound to transcobalamin I and II. *Scand J Haematol* 4:321, 1967.
28. FERNANDEZ-COSTA F, METZ J: Vitamine B_{12} binders. *CRC Crit Rev Clin Lab Sci* 18:1, 1982.
29. LINNELL JC: The fate of cobalamins in vivo, in Babior BM (ed): *Cobalamin: Biochemistry and Pathophysiology*. New York, Wiley, 1975, p 287.
30. FINKLER AE, HALL CA: Nature of the relationship between vitamin B_{12} binding and cell uptake. *Arch Biochem Biophys* 120:79, 1967.
31. TAN CH, HANSEN HJ: Studies on the site of synthesis of transcobalamin II. *Proc Soc Exp Biol Med* 127:740, 1968.
32. PLETSCH QA, COFFEY JW: Properties of the proteins that bind vitamin B_{12} in subcellular fractions of rat liver. *Arch Biochem Biophys* 151:157, 1972.
33. NEWMARK P, NEWMAN GE, O'BRIEN JRP: Vitamin B_{12} in the rat kidney: Evidence of an association with lysosomes. *Arch Biochem Biophys* 141:121, 1970.
34. YOUNGDAHL-TURNER P, ROSENBERG LE, ALLEN RH: Binding and uptake of transcobalamin II by human fibroblasts. *J Clin Invest* 61:133, 1978.
35. YOUNGDAHL-TURNER P, MELLMAN IS, ALLEN RH, ROSENBERG LE: Protein mediated vitamin uptake: Adsorptive endocytosis of the transcobalamin II-cobalamin complex by cultured human fibroblasts. *Exp Cell Res* 118:127, 1979.
36. MELLMAN IS, YOUNGDAHL-TURNER P, WILLARD HF, ROSENBERG LE: Intracellular binding of radioactive hydroxocobalamin to cobalamin-dependent apoenzymes in rat liver. *Proc Natl Acad Sci USA* 74:916, 1977.
37. KOLHOUSE JF, ALLEN RH: Recognition of two intracellular cobalamin binding proteins and their identification as methylmalonyl-CoA mutase and methionine synthetase. *Proc Natl Acad Sci USA* 74:921, 1977.

38. BURGER RL, SCHNEIDER RJ, MEHLMAN CS, ALLEN RH: Human plasma R-type vitamin B_{12} binding protein. II. The role of transcobalamin I, transcobalamin III and the normal granulocyte vitamin B_{12}-binding protein in the plasma transport of vitamin B_{12}. *J Biol Chem* 250:7707, 1975.

39. BERLINER N, ROSENBERG LE: Uptake and metabolism of free cyancobalamin by cultured human fibroblasts from controls and a patient with transcobalamin II deficiency. *Metabolism* 30:230, 1981.

40. FRENKEL EP, KITCHENS RL: Intracellular localization of hepatic propionyl-CoA carboxylase and methylmalonyl-CoA mutase in humans and normal and vitamin B_{12} deficient rats. *Br J Haematol* 31:501, 1975.

41. WANG FK, KOCH J, STOKSTAD EL: Folate coenzyme pattern, folate linked enzymes and methionine biosynthesis in rat liver mitochondria. *Biochem Z* 246:458, 1967.

42. VITOLS E, WALKER GA, HUENNEKENS FM: Enzymatic conversion of vitamin B_{12} to a cobamide coenzyme, $\alpha(5,6$-dimethylbenzimidazolyl) deoxyadenosylcobamide (adenosyl-B_{12}). *J Biol Chem* 241:1455, 1966.

43. ERTEL R, BROT N, TAYLOR R, WEISSBACH H: Studies on the nature of the bound cobamide in *E. coli* N^5-methyltetrahydrofolate-homocysteine transmethylase. *Arch Biochem Biophys* 126:353, 1968.

44. TAYLOR RT, WEISSBACH H: *E. coli* B N^5-methyltetrahydrofolate-homocysteine methyltransferase: Sequential formation of bound methylcobalamin with S-adenosyl-L-methionine and N^5-methyltetrahydrofolate. *Arch Biochem Biophys* 129:728, 1969.

45. PAWALKIEWICZ J, GORNA M, FENRYCH W, MAGAS S: Conversion of cyanocobalamin in vivo and in vitro into its coenzyme form in humans and animals. *Ann NY Acad Sci* 112:641, 1964.

46. KERWAR SS, SPEARS C, MCAUSLAN B, WEISSBACH H: Studies on vitamin B_{12} metabolism in HeLa cells. *Arch Biochem Biophys* 142:231, 1971.

47. MAHONEY MJ, ROSENBERG LE: Synthesis of cobalamin coenzymes by human cells in tissue culture. *J Lab Clin Med* 78:302, 1971.

48. MAHONEY MJ, HART AC, STEEN VD, ROSENBERG LE: Methylmalonicacidemia: Biochemical heterogeneity in defects of 5'-deoxyadenosylcobalamin synthesis. *Proc Natl Acad Sci USA* 72:2799, 1975.

49. FENTON WA, ROSENBERG LE: The defect in the *cbl* B class of human methylmalonic acidemia: Deficiency of cob(I)alamin adenosyltransferase activity in extracts of cultured fibroblasts. *Biochem Biophys Res Commun* 98:283, 1981.

50. COX EV, WHITE AM: Methylmalonic acid excretion: Index of vitamin-B_{12} deficiency. *Lancet* 2:853, 1962.

51. BARNESS LA, YOUNG D, MELLMAN WJ, KAHN SB, WILLIAMS WJ: Methylmalonate excretion in patient with pernicious anemia. *N Engl J Med* 268:144, 1963.

52. COX EV, ROBERTSON-SMITH D, SMALL M, WHITE AM: The excretion of propionate and acetate in vitamin B_{12} deficiency. *Clin Sci* 35:123, 1968.

53. SHIPMAN RT, TOWNLEY RRW, DANKS DM: Homocystinuria, Addisonian pernicious anaemia, and partial deletion of a G chromosome. *Lancet* 2:693, 1969.

54. HOLLOWELL JG JR, HALL WK, CORYELL ME, MCPHERSON J JR, HAHN DA: Homocystinuria and organic aciduria in a patient with vitamin-B_{12} deficiency. *Lancet* 2:1428, 1969.

55. HIGGINBOTTOM MC, SWEETMAN L, NYHAN WL: A syndrome of methylmalonic aciduria, homocystinuria, megaloblastic anemia and neurologic abnormalities in a vitamin B_{12}-deficient breast-fed infant of a strict vegetarian. *N Engl J Med* 299:317, 1978.

56. CARDINALE GJ, DREYFUS PM, AULD P, ABELES RH: Experimental vitamin B_{12} deficiency: Its effect on tissue vitamin B_{12}-coenzyme levels and on the metabolism of methylmalonyl-CoA. *Arch Biochem Biophys* 131:92, 1969.

57. BECK WS: Metabolic features of cobalamin deficiency in man, in Babior BM (ed): *Cobalamin: Biochemistry and Pathophysiology.* New York, Wiley, 1975, p 403.

58. HERBERT V, ZALUSKY R: Interrelations of vitamin B_{12} and folic acid metabolism: Folic acid clearance studies. *J Clin Invest* 41:1263, 1962.

59. NORONHA JM, SILVERMAN M: On folic acid, vitamin B_{12}, methionine and formiminoglutamic acid metabolism, in Heinrich HC (ed): *Vitamin B_{12} and Intrinsic Factor.* Stuttgart, Verlag, 1962.

60. LARRABEE AR, ROSENTHAL S, CATHOW RE, BUCHANAN JM: Enzymatic synthesis of the methyl group of methionine. IV. Isolation, characterization, and role of 5-methyl tetrahydrofolate. *J Biol Chem* 238:1025, 1963.

61. FENTON WA, ROSENBERG LE: Genetic and biochemical analysis of human cobalamin mutants in cell culture. *Ann Rev Genet* 12:223, 1978.

62. LEVINE JS, PODELL ER, ALLEN RH: Cobalamin malabsorption in three siblings due to an abnormal intrinsic factor that is markedly susceptible to acid and proteolysis. *J Clin Invest* 76:2057, 1985.

63. SPURLING CL, SACKS MS, JIJI RM: Juvenile pernicious anemia. *N Engl J Med* 271:995, 1964.

64. MCINTYRE OR, SULLIVAN LW, JEFFRIES GH, SILVER RH: Pernicious anemia in childhood. *N Engl J Med* 272:981, 1965.

65. KATZ M, LEE SK, COOPER BA: Vitamin B_{12} malabsorption due to a biologically inert intrinsic factor. *N Engl J Med* 287:425, 1972.

66. KATZ M, MEHLMAN CS, ALLEN RH: Isolation and characterization of an abnormal human intrinsic factor. *J Clin Invest* 53:1274, 1974.

67. LEVINE JS, ALLEN RH: Intrinsic factor within parietal cells of patients with juvenile pernicious anemia: A retrospective immunohistochemical study. *Gastroenterology* 88:1132, 1985.

68. ROTHENBERG SP, QUADROS EV, STRAUS EW, KAPELNER S: An abnormal intrinsic factor (IF) molecule: A new cause of "pernicious anemia" (PA). *Blood* 64:41a, 1984.

69. CARMEL R: Gastric juice in congenital pernicious anemia contains no immunoreactive intrinsic factor molecule: Study of three kindreds with variable ages at presentation including a patient first diagnosed in adulthood. *Am J Hum Genet* 35:67, 1983.

70. CHANARIN I: *The Megaloblastic Anaemias.* Oxford, Blackwell Scientific, 1979.

71. GRASBECK R: Familial selective vitamin B_{12} malabsorption. *N Engl J Med* 287:358, 1972.

72. MACKENZIE IL, DONALDSON RM JR, TRIER JS, MATHAN VI: Ileal mucosa in familial selective B_{12} malabsorption. *N Engl J Med* 286:1021, 1972.

73. BURMAN JF, WALER WF, SMITH JA, PHILLIPS AD, SOURIAL NA, ET AL: Absent ileal uptake of IF-bound-vitamin B_{12} in the Imerslund-Grasbeck syndrome (familial vitamin B_{12} malabsorption with proteinuria). *Gut* 26:311, 1985.

74. CHISOLM JC: Selective malabsorption of vitamin B_{12} and vitamin B_{12}-intrinsic factor complex with megaloblastic anemia in an adult. *JAMA* 77:835, 1985.

75. HAURANI FI, HALL CA, RUBIN R: Megaloblastic anemia as a result of an abnormal transcobalamin II. *J Clin Invest* 64:1253, 1979.

76. SELIGMAN PA, STEINER LL, ALLEN RH: Studies of a patient with megaloblastic anemia and an abnormal transcobalamin II. *N Engl J Med* 303:1209, 1980.

77. HALL CA, HITZIG WH, GREEN PD, BEGLEY JA: Transport of therapeutic cyanocobalamin in the congenital deficiency of transcobalamin II (TCII). *Blood* 53:251, 1979.

78. BERLINER N, ROSENBERG LE: Uptake and metabolism of free cyanocobalamin by cultured human fibroblasts from controls and a patient with transcobalamin II deficiency. *Metabolism* 30:230, 1981.

79. LINDEMANS EJM, DEJONGH FCM, BRAND M, SCHOESTER M, VAN KAPEL J, ABELS J: The uptake of R-type binding protein by isolated rat liver. *Biochim Biophys Acta* 720:203, 1983.

80. DIECKGRAEFE BK, SEETHARAM B, ALPERS DH: Developmental regulation of rat intrinsic factor mRNA, *Am J Physiol* 254:G913, 1988.

81. GIUGLIANI ERJ, JORGE SM, GONCALVES AL: Serum vitamin B_{12} levels in parturients, in the intervillous space of the placenta, and in full-term newborns and their interrelationships with folate levels. *Am J Clin Nutr* 41:330, 1985.

82. DAIGER SP, LABOWE ML, PARSONS M, WANG L, CAVALLI-SFORZA LL: Detection of genetic variation with radioactive ligands. III. Genetic polymorphism of transcobalamin II in human plasma. *Am J Hum Genet* 30:202, 1978.

83. FRATER-SCHRODER M: Genetic patterns of transcobalamin II and the relationships with congenital defects. *Mol Cell Biochem* 56:5, 1983.

84. EIBERG H, MOLLER N, MOHR J, NIELSEN LS: Linkage of transcobalamin II (TC2) to the P blood group system and assignment to chromosome 22. *Clin Genet* 29:354, 1986.

85. ROSENBLATT DS, COOPER BA: Inherited disorders of vitamin B_{12} metabolism. *Blood Rev* 1:177, 1987.

86. ROSENBLATT DS, HOSACK A, MATIASZUK N: Expression of transcobalamin II by amniocytes. *Prenat Diagn* 7:35, 1987.

87. BEGLEY JA, HALL CA, SCOTT CR: Absence of transcobalamin II from cord blood. *Blood* 63:490, 1984.

88. HITZIG WH, DOHMANN U, PLUSS HJ, VISCHER D: Hereditary transcobalamin II deficiency: Clinical findings in a new family. *J Pediatr* 85:622, 1974.

89. RANA SR, COLMAN N, GOH K-O, HERBERT V, KLEMPERER MR: Transcobalamin II deficiency associated with unusual bone marrow findings and chromosomal abnormalities. *Am J Hematol* 14:89, 1983.

90. GOODMAN SI, MOE PG, HAMMOND KB, MUDD SH, UHLENDORF BW: Homocystinuria with methylmalonic aciduria: Two cases in a sibship. *Biochem Med* 4:500, 1970.

91. LEVY HL, MUDD SH, SCHULMAN JD, DREYFUSS PM, ABELES RH: A derangement in B_{12} metabolism associated with homocystinemia, cystathioninemia, hypomethioninemia and methylmalonic aciduria. *Am J Med* 48:390, 1970.

92. DILLON MJ, ENGLAND JM, GOMPERTZ D, GOODEY PA, GRANT DB, HUSSEIN HA, LINNELL JC, MATHEWS DM, MUDD SH, NEWNS GH, SEAKINS JWT, UHL-

ENDORF BW, WISE IJ: Mental retardation, megaloblastic anemia, methylmalonic aciduria and abnormal homocysteine metabolism due to an error in vitamin B$_{12}$ metabolism. *Clin Sci Mol Med* 47:43, 1974.

93. ANTHONY M, MCLEAY AC: A unique case of derangement of vitamin B$_{12}$ metabolism. *Proc Aust Assoc Neurol* 13:61, 1976.

94. BAUMGARTNER ER, WICK H, MAURER R, EGLI N, STEINMANN B: Congenital defect in intracellular cobalamin metabolism resulting in homocystinuria and methylmalonic aciduria. *Helv Paediatr Acta* 34:465, 1979.

95. CARMEL R, BEDROS AA, MACE JW, GOODMAN SI: Congenital methylmalonic aciduria-homocystinuria with megaloblastic anemia: Observations on response to hydroxocobalamin and on the effect of homocysteine and methionine on the deoxyuridine suppression test. *Blood* 55:570, 1980.

96. SHINNAR S, SINGER HS: Cobalamin C mutation (methylmalonic aciduria and homocystinuria) in adolescence. *N Engl J Med* 311:451, 1984.

97. MITCHELL GA, WATKINS D, MELANCON SB, ROSENBLATT DS, GEOFFROY G, ORQUIN J, HOMSY MB, DALLAIRE L: Clinical heterogeneity in cobalamin C variant of combined homocystinuria and methylmalonic aciduria. *J Pediatr* 108:410, 1986.

98. COGAN DG, SCHULMAN J, PORTER RJ, MUDD SH: Epileptiform ocular movements with methylmalonic aciduria and homocystinuria. *Am J Ophthalmol* 90:251, 1980.

99. LINNELL JC, MIRANDA B, BHATT HR, DOWTON SB, LEVY HL: Abnormal cobalamin metabolism in a megaloblastic child with homocystinuria, cystathioninuria and methylmalonic aciduria. *J Inherited Metab Dis [Suppl]* 6:127, 1980.

100. MAMLOCK RJ, ISENBERG JN, RASSIN DN: A cobalamin metabolic defect with homocystinuria, methylmalonic aciduria and macrocytic anemia. *Neuropediatrics* 17:94, 1986.

101. RAVINDRANATH Y, KRIEGER I: Vitamin-B$_{12}$ (Cbl) and folate interrelationship in a case of homocystinuria-methylmalonic (HC-MMA)-uria due to genetic deficiency. *Pediatr Res* 18:247a, 1984.

102. RIBES A, VILASECA A, BRIONES P: Methylmalonic aciduria with homocystinuria. *J Inherited Metab Dis [Suppl]* 7:129, 1984.

103. ROBB RM, DOWTON SB, FULTON AB, LEVY HL: Retinal degeneration in vitamin B$_{12}$ disorder associated with methylmalonic aciduria and sulfur amino acid abnormalities. *Am J Ophthalmol* 97:691, 1984.

104. ROSENBLATT DS, LAFRAMBOISE R, PICHETTE J, LANGEVIN P, COOPER BA, COSTA T: New disorder of vitamin B$_{12}$ metabolism (cobalamin F) presenting as methylmalonic aciduria. *Pediatrics* 78:51, 1986.

105. GRAVEL RA, MAHONEY MJ, RUDDLE FH, ROSENBERG LE: Genetic complementation in heterokaryons of human fibroblasts defective in cobalamin metabolism. *Proc Natl Acad Sci USA* 72:3181, 1975.

106. WILLARD HF, MELLMAN IS, ROSENBERG LE: Genetic complementation among inherited deficiencies of methylmalonyl-CoA mutase activity: Evidence for a new class of human cobalamin mutant. *Am J Hum Genet* 30:1, 1978.

107. WATKINS D, ROSENBLATT DS: Failure of lysosomal release of vitamin B$_{12}$: A new complementation group causing methylmalonic aciduria (cblF). *Am J Hum Genet* 39:404, 1986.

108. MUDD SH, LEVY HL, ABELES RH: A derangement in B$_{12}$ metabolism leading to homocystinemia, cystathioninemia and methylmalonicaciduria. *Biochem Biophys Res Commun* 35:121, 1969.

109. LINNEL JC, MATHEWS DM, MUDD SH, UHLENDORF BW, WISE IJ: Cobalamins in fibroblasts cultured from normal control subjects and patients with methylmalonic aciduria. *Pediatr Res* 10:179, 1976.

110. BAUMGARTNER ER, WICK H, LINNELL JC, GAULL GE, BACHMANN C, STEINMANN B: Congenital defect in intracellular cobalamin metabolism resulting in homocystinuria and methylmalonic aciduria. *Helv Paediatr Acta* 34:483, 1979.

111. ROSENBERG LE, PATEL L, LILLJEQVIST A: Absence of an intracellular cobalamin binding protein in cultured fibroblasts from patients with defective synthesis of 5′-deoxyadenosylcobalamin and methylcobalamin. *Proc Natl Acad Sci USA* 72:4617, 1975.

112. MAHONEY MJ, ROSENBERG LE, MUDD SH, UHLENDORF BW: Defective metabolism of vitamin B$_{12}$ in fibroblasts from patients with methylmalonicaciduria. *Biochem Biophys Res Commun* 44:375, 1971.

113. WILLARD HF, ROSENBERG LE: Inborn errors of cobalamin metabolism: Effect of cobalamin supplementation in culture on methylmalonyl CoA mutase activity in normal and mutant human fibroblasts. *Biochem Genet* 17:57, 1979.

114. MUDD SH, UHLENDORF BW, HINDS KR, LEVY HL: Deranged B$_{12}$ metabolism: Studies of fibroblasts grown in tissue culture. *Biochem Med* 4:215, 1970.

115. MELLMAN IS, LIN P-F, RUDDLE FH, ROSENBERG LE: Genetic control of cobalamin binding in normal and mutant cells. Assignment of the gene for 5-methyltetrahydrofolate:L-homocysteine S-methyltransferase to human chromosome 1. *Proc Natl Acad Sci USA* 76:405, 1979.

116. WILLARD HF, ROSENBERG LE: Inherited deficiencies of methylmalonyl CoA mutase activity: Biochemical and genetic studies in cultured skin fibroblasts, in Hommes FA (ed): *Models for the Study of Inborn Errors of Metabolism*. Amsterdam, Elsevier North-Holland Biomedical Press, 1979, p 297.

117. MELLMAN I, WILLARD HF, YOUNGDAHL-TURNER P, ROSENBERG LE: Cobalamin coenzyme synthesis in normal and mutant human fibroblasts: Evidence for a processing enzyme activity deficient in *cbl C* cells. *J Biol Chem* 254:11847, 1979.

118. ROSENBLATT DS, HOSACK A, MATIASZUK NV: Defect in vitamin B$_{12}$ release from lysosomes: Newly described inborn error of vitamin B$_{12}$ metabolism. *Science* 228:1319, 1985.

119. BARTHOLOMEW DW, ALLEN RH, ROE CR, ROSENBLATT D, VALLE DL, FRANCOMANO CA, BATSHAW ML: Therapeutic approaches to Cbl-C methylmalonic acidemia and homocystinuria. *J Pediatr* 112:32, 1988.

120. ROSENBERG LE, LILLJEQVIST A-C, HSIA YE: Methylmalonic aciduria: An inborn error leading to metabolic acidosis, long-chain ketonuria and intermittent hyperglycinemia. *N Engl J Med* 278:1319, 1968.

121. ROSENBERG LE, LILLJEQVIST A, HSIA YE: Methylmalonicaciduria: Metabolic block localization and vitamin B$_{12}$ dependency. *Science* 162:805, 1968.

122. LINDBLAD B, OLIN P, SVANBERG B, ZETTERSTRÖM R: Methylmalonic acidemia. *Acta Paediatr Scand* 57:417, 1968.

123. LINDBLAD B, LINDSTRAND K, SVANBERG B, ZETTERSTRÖM R: The effect of cobamide coenzyme in methylmalonic acidemia. *Acta Paediatr Scand* 58:178, 1969.

124. OBERHOLZER VC, LEVIN B, BURGESS EA, YOUNG WF: Methylmalonic aciduria: An inborn error of metabolism leading to chronic metabolic acidosis. *Arch Dis Child* 42:492, 1967.

125. STOKKE O, ELDJARN L, NORUM KR, STEEN-JOHNSEN J, HALVORSEN S: Methylmalonic aciduria: A new inborn error of metabolism which may cause fatal acidosis in the neonatal period. *Scand J Clin Lab Invest* 20:313, 1967.

126. ROSENBERG LE, LILLJEQVIST A-C, HSIA YE, ROSENBLOOM FM: Vitamin B$_{12}$ dependent methylmalonicaciduria: Defective B$_{12}$ metabolism in cultured fibroblasts. *Biochem Biophys Res Commun* 37:607, 1969.

127. KAYE CI, MORROW G, NADLER HL: In vitro "responsive" methylmalonic acidemia: A new variant. *J Pediatr* 85:55, 1974.

128. MATSUI SM, MAHONEY MJ, ROSENBERG LE: The natural history of the inherited methylmalonic acidemias. *N Engl J Med* 308:1857, 1983.

129. ROSENBERG LE: Disorders of propionate, methylmalonate and cobalamin metabolism, in Stanbury JB, Wyngaarden JB, Fredrickson DS (eds): *The Metabolic Basis of Inherited Disease*, 4th ed. New York, McGraw-Hill, 1978, p 411.

130. ANDO T, RASMUSSEN K, WRIGHT JM, NYMAN WL: Isolation and identification of methylcitrate, a major metabolic product of propionate in patients with propionic acidemia. *J Biol Chem* 247:2200, 1972.

131. STOKKE O, JELLUM E, ELDJARN L, SCHNITLER R: The occurrence of β-hydroxy-n-valeric acid in a patient with propionic and methylmalonic acidemia. *Clin Chim Acta* 45:391, 1973.

132. HSIA YE, SCULLY K, LILLJEQVIST A-C, ROSENBERG LE: Vitamin B$_{12}$ dependent methylmalonicaciduria. *Pediatrics* 46:497, 1970.

133. WILLARD HF, AMBANI LM, HART AC, MAHONEY MJ, ROSENBERG LE: Rapid prenatal and postnatal detection of inborn errors of propionate, methylmalonate, and cobalamin metabolism: A sensitive assay using cultured cells. *Hum Genet* 34:277, 1976.

134. MORROW G, REVSIN B, MATHEWS C, GILES H: A simple rapid method for prenatal detection of defects in propionate metabolism. *Clin Genet* 10:218, 1976.

135. FENTON WA, ROSENBERG LE: Mitochondrial metabolism of hydroxocobalamin: Synthesis of adenosylcobalamin by intact rat liver mitochondria. *Arch Biochem Biophys* 189:441, 1978.

136. MORROW G, MAHONEY MJ, MATHEWS C, LEBOWITZ J: Studies of methylmalonyl conenzyme A carbonylmutase activity in methylmalonic acidemia. I. Correlation of clinical, hepatic and fibroblast data. *Pediatr Res* 9:641, 1975.

137. UTTER MF, KEECH DB, SCRUTTEN ML: A possible role for acetyl-CoA in the control of gluconeogenesis, in Webber G (ed): *Advances in Enzyme Regulation*. New York, Pergamon, 1964, vol 2, p 49.

138. HALPERIN ML, SCHILLER CM, FRITZ IB: The inhibition by methylmalonic acid of malate transport by the dicarboxylate carrier in rat liver mitochondria. *J Clin Invest* 50:2276, 1971.

139. INQUE S, KRIEGER I, SARNAIK A, RAVINDRANATH Y, FRACASSA M, OTTENBREIT MJ: Inhibition of bone marrow stem cell growth *in vitro* by methylmalonic acid: A mechanism for pancytopenia in a patient with methylmalonic acidemia. *Pediatr Res* 15:95, 1981.

140. MORROW G, SCHWARTZ RH, HALLOCK JA, BARNESS LA: Prenatal detection

of methylmalonic acidemia. *J Pediatr* 77:120, 1970.

141. AMPOLA MG, MAHONEY MJ, NAKAMURA E, TANAKA K: Prenatal therapy of a patient with vitamin B$_{12}$ responsive methylmalonic acidemia. *N Engl J Med* 293:313, 1975.

142. MAHONEY MJ, ROSENBERG LE, LINDBLAD B, WALDENSTROM J, ZETTER-STROM R: Prenatal diagnosis of methylmalonic aciduria. *Acta Paediatr Scand* 64:44, 1975.

143. NYHAN WL, FAWCETT N, ANDO T, RENNERT OM, JULIUS RL: Response to dietary therapy in B$_{12}$ unresponsive methylmalonic acidemia. *Pediatrics* 51:539, 1973.

144. SATOH T, NARISAWA K, IGARASHI Y, SAITOH T, HAYASAKA K, ICHINOHA-ZAMA Y, ONODERA H, TADA K, OOHARA K: Dietary therapy in two patients with vitamin B$_{12}$-unresponsive methylmalonic acidemia. *Eur J Pediatr* 135:305, 1981.

145. ROE CR, BOHAN TP: L-carnitine therapy in propionic acidemia. *Lancet* 1:1411, 1982.

146. ROE CR, MILLINGTON DS, MALTBY DA, BOHAN TP: L-carnitine enhances excretion of propionyl *coenzyme A* as propionylcarnitine in propionic acidemia. *J Clin Invest* 73:1785, 1984.

147. ROE CR, HOPPEL CL, STACEY TE, CHALMERS RA, TRACEY BM, MILLINGTON DS: Metabolic response to carnitine in methylmalonic aciduria. *Arch Dis Child* 58:916, 1983.

148. SCHUH S, ROSENBLATT DS, COPPER BA, SCHROEDER M-L, BISHOP AJ, SEAR-GEANT LE, HAWORTH JC: Homocystinuria and megaloblastic anemia re-sponsive to vitamin B$_{12}$ therapy: An inborn error of metabolism due to a defect in cobalamin metabolism. *N Engl J Med* 31:686, 1984.

149. HALLAM LJ, SAWYER M, CLARK AC, VAN DER WEYDEN MB: Vitamin B$_{12}$-responsive neonatal megaloblastic anemia and homocystinuria with asso-ciated reduced methionine synthase activity. *Blood* 69:1128, 1987.

150. ROSENBLATT DS, THOMAS IT, WATKINS D, COOPER BA, ERBE RW: Vitamin B$_{12}$ responsive homocystinuria and megaloblastic anemia: Heterogeneity in methylcobalamin deficiency. *Am J Med Genet* 26:377, 1987.

151. ROSENBLATT DS, COOPER BA, SCHMUTZ SM, ZALESKI WA, CASEY RE: Pre-natal vitamin B$_{12}$ therapy of a fetus with methylcobalamin deficiency (co-balamin E disease). *Lancet* 1:1127, 1985.

152. WATKINS D, ROSENBLATT DS: Genetic heterogeneity among patients with methylcobalamin deficiency: Definition of two complementation groups, cblE and cblG. *J Clin Invest* 81:1690, 1988.

153. ROSENBLATT DS, COOPER BA, POTTIER A, LUE-SHING H, MATIASZUK N, GRAUER K: Altered vitamin B$_{12}$ metabolism in fibroblasts from a patient with megaloblastic anemia and homocystinuria due to a new defect in methionine biosynthesis. *J Clin Invest* 74:2149, 1984.

154. HUENNEKEUS FM, DIGIROLAMO PM, FUJII K, JACOBSEN DW, VITOLS KS: B$_{12}$-dependent methionine synthetase as a potential target for cancer chemotherapy. *Adv Enzyme Regul* 14:187, 1976.

155. UTLEY CS, MARCELL PD, ALLEN RH, ANTONY AC, KOLHOUSE JF: Isolation and characterization of methionine synthetase from human placenta. *J Biol Chem* 260:13656, 1985.

CHAPTER 83

DISORDERS OF BIOTIN METABOLISM

BARRY WOLF
GREGORY S. HEARD

1. Biotin, a water-soluble vitamin belonging to the B complex, acts as a prosthetic group in each of four carboxylases in humans: pyruvate carboxylase, propionyl-CoA carboxylase, β-methylcrotonyl-CoA carboxylase, and acetyl-CoA carboxylase. An adequate supply of biotin is vital because these enzymes participate in gluconeogenesis, fatty acid synthesis, and amino acid catabolism. Biotin is derived from the diet and possibly also from the synthetic activity of the gastrointestinal microflora.

2. Each of the carboxylases is synthesized as an inactive apoenzyme that is subsequently biotinylated through two partial reactions, each of which is catalyzed by the enzyme holocarboxylase synthetase. Acetyl-CoA carboxylase functions in the cytosol, whereas the other three holoenzymes function in the mitochondria. Ultimately these enzymes are degraded proteolytically, at least in part, in the lysosomal autophagic system. The biotin-containing products of degradation, biocytin (ε-N-biotinyl-L-lysine) and biotinyl peptides, are acted upon by biotinidase, which cleaves the amide bond between lysine and biotin. Some of this biotin is recycled.

3. There are two defects in the cycle of biotin utilization in humans. Both disorders result in multiple carboxylase deficiency. Holocarboxylase synthetase deficiency, also known as early onset (neonatal) multiple carboxylase deficiency based on the usual age of onset of symptoms, is a disorder of biotinylation. Biotinidase deficiency, also known as late onset (juvenile) multiple carboxylase deficiency, is a disorder of biotin recycling.

4. Holocarboxylase synthetase deficiency has been described in 11 children. The clinical symptoms include difficulties in feeding and breathing, hypotonia, seizures, and lethargy and sometimes progress to developmental delay or coma. Some children exhibit skin rash and alopecia. Affected children exhibit metabolic acidosis, organic aciduria, and mild to moderate hyperammonemia. The organic aciduria includes elevated concentrations of β-hydroxyisovalerate, β-methylcrotonylglycine, β-hydroxypropionate, methylcitrate, lactate, and tiglylglycine.

5. The enzyme defect has been demonstrated in lymphocytes, cultured fibroblasts, and cultured lymphoblasts from affected children. Holocarboxylase synthetase in tissues from all the patients examined had increased K_m values for biotin.

6. Holocarboxylase synthetase deficiency appears to be inherited as an autosomal recessive trait. Preliminary attempts to demonstrate heterozygosity have been unsuccessful.

7. Children with holocarboxylase synthetase deficiency usually improve clinically following the administration of 10 mg oral biotin per day. One child, whose enzyme had the highest K_m for biotin, continued to have a skin rash and excrete abnormal organic acids even while receiving 60 to 80 mg biotin per day.

8. Holocarboxylase synthetase deficiency can be diagnosed prenatally by measuring the concentration of abnormal organic acids in the amniotic fluid and/or by measuring and comparing the various mitochondrial carboxylase activities in the amniocytes cultured with and without biotin. Prenatal treatment has been performed during two pregnancies. The children were clinically normal at birth and did not have organic aciduria. It is not clear whether treatment of at-risk children with biotin immediately after birth is necessary.

9. Biotinidase deficiency has been described in 38 children. The clinical features commonly include seizures, hypotonia, ataxia, breathing problems, hearing loss, optic atrophy, developmental delay, skin rash, and alopecia. Other symptoms include conjunctivitis and fungal infections which are probably due to abnormalities in immunoregulation. The clinical expression of the disorder is highly variable. The age of onset of symptoms ranges from several weeks to several years of age; median and mean age of onset are 3 months and 5½ months, respectively. Most, but not all, symptomatic children exhibit metabolic ketolactic acidosis and organic aciduria. The organic aciduria commonly manifests as elevated concentrations of β-hydroxyisovalerate, lactate, β-methylcrotonylglycine, β-hydroxypropionate, and methylcitrate.

10. Biotinidase deficiency is diagnosed by demonstrating deficient enzyme activity in serum. Other tissues from these children also have deficient enzyme activity. Antiserum prepared against human biotinidase cross-reacts with two separate proteins in serums from normal individuals on immunoelectrophoresis; neither of these proteins is detectable in serums from individuals with less than 5 percent of normal activity in their serum. Only one of these proteins corresponds to the active enzyme in serum from individuals with normal biotinidase activity.

11. Individuals with biotinidase deficiency cannot recycle endogenous biotin and cannot release dietary protein-bound biotin. The brain may be unable to recycle biotin and may depend on biotin transferred across the blood-brain barrier. This may result in decreased pyruvate carboxylase activity in the brain and in the accumulation of lactate. The localized lactic acidosis may cause the early appearance of neurologic symptoms.

12. Biotinidase deficiency is inherited as an autosomal recessive trait. Heterozygotes can be determined in 95 percent of the cases by demonstrating that enzyme activity in serum is intermediate between that of normal and deficient individuals. Prenatal diagnosis of biotinidase deficiency is feasible but has not yet been performed.

13. Biotinidase activity can be determined in the same blood-soaked filter paper used in most newborn screening programs. A pilot screening program in Virginia demonstrated the feasibility of newborn screening for biotinidase deficiency. Children with enzyme deficiency identified by screening have been treated with biotin and have remained asymptomatic. Based on these studies, other states and countries have initiated similar screening programs. The screening method also offers a

simple, rapid means for the physician to evaluate biotinidase activity in individuals suspected of having the disorder.

14. *Children with biotinidase deficiency have been treated successfully with between 5 and 20 mg oral biotin (in the free, unbound form) per day. All patients with the deficiency should respond to biotin therapy. If a child remains undiagnosed for a long period of time or experiences severe metabolic compromise, some of the neurologic problems, such as hearing loss, optic atrophy, or developmental delay, may not resolve. Doses of biotin only slightly above physiological amounts may eventually be shown to suffice for treatment.*

15. *The multiple carboxylase deficiencies must be differentiated from other acute onset metabolic disorders and nutritional deficiencies that result from dietary indiscretion or hyperalimentation with solutions lacking biotin. Because both holocarboxylase synthetase deficiency and biotinidase deficiency are so amenable to biotin therapy, these disorders should be considered in any child with nonspecific neurologic symptoms, especially when cutaneous abnormalities are present. Newborn screening for biotinidase deficiency followed by prompt initiation of therapy in deficient children should prevent the clinical consequences of this disorder.*

Biotin is a member of the water-soluble B-complex group of vitamins and, as such, must be provided in the diet of mammals and birds. It was first recognized as an essential factor in living systems in 1936.[1] The biotin molecule consists of a heterocyclic ring attached to an aliphatic side chain terminating in a carboxylic acid group.[2,3] In human beings, biotin is directly involved in the vitally important metabolic processes of gluconeogenesis, fatty acid synthesis, and amino acid catabo-

lism via its role as a prosthetic group in each of four carboxylase enzymes (Fig. 83-1).

Three of the enzymes, pyruvate carboxylase (EC 6.4.1.1), propionyl-coenzyme A (CoA) carboxylase (EC 6.4.1.3), and β-methylcrotonyl-CoA carboxylase (EC 6.4.1.4), are mitochondrial and the fourth, acetyl-CoA carboxylase (EC 6.4.1.2), is cytosolic.[4] Pyruvate carboxylase catalyzes the conversion of pyruvate to oxaloacetate, an intermediate in the biosynthesis of phosphoenolpyruvate and, ultimately, glucose. Acetyl-CoA carboxylase catalyzes the formation of malonyl-CoA from acetyl-CoA, the first committed step in the biosynthesis of fatty acids. Propionyl-CoA carboxylase is involved in the catabolism of several branched-chain amino acids and fatty acids of odd-carbon chain lengths by converting propionyl-CoA to methylmalonyl-CoA which ultimately enters the tricarboxylic acid cycle. β-Methylcrotonyl-CoA carboxylase is involved in leucine catabolism by the conversion of β-methylcrotonyl-CoA to β-methylglutaconyl-CoA. Deficiencies of the carboxylases and the consequent accumulation of abnormally high concentrations of metabolic intermediates can have profound effects on other pathways.

The final step in the synthesis and activation of biotin-containing carboxylases is the formation of the active holocarboxylases by means of the covalent attachment of biotin to the various apoenzymes. The biotinyl moiety is attached via an amide linkage through the carboxyl group in its side chain to a lysyl ε-amino group of the apoenzyme. This attachment is catalyzed by holocarboxylase synthetase.[1,5,6] The terminal step in the degradation of the carboxylases, cleavage of the biotinyl moiety from the ε-amino group of lysine, is catalyzed by bio-

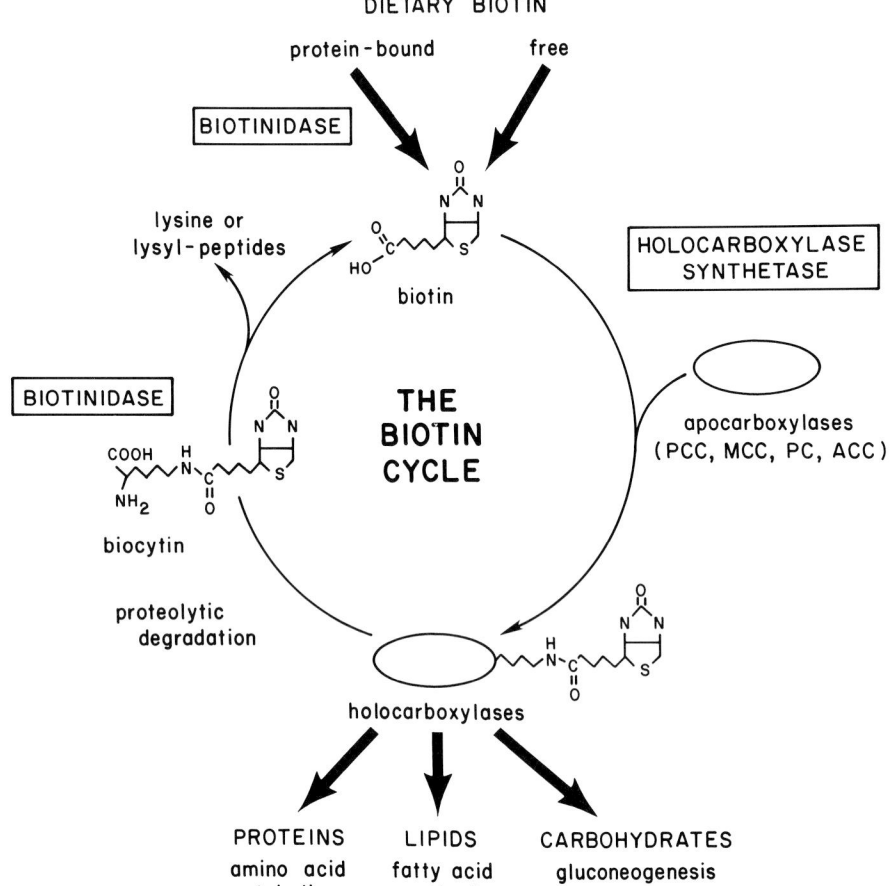

Fig. 83-1 The biotin cycle demonstrates the metabolic recycling of biotin. The two major enzymes involved in this cycle are holocarboxylase synthetase, which covalently attaches biotin to the various apocarboxylases to form holocarboxylases, and biotinidase, the hydrolase that cleaves biotin from biocytin or short biotinyl peptides which are formed from the proteolytic degradation of holocarboxylases and possibly from dietary protein-bound sources. Deficiencies of both of these enzymes have been described. *(From Wolf et al.[232] Used by permission of Alan R. Liss, Inc.)*

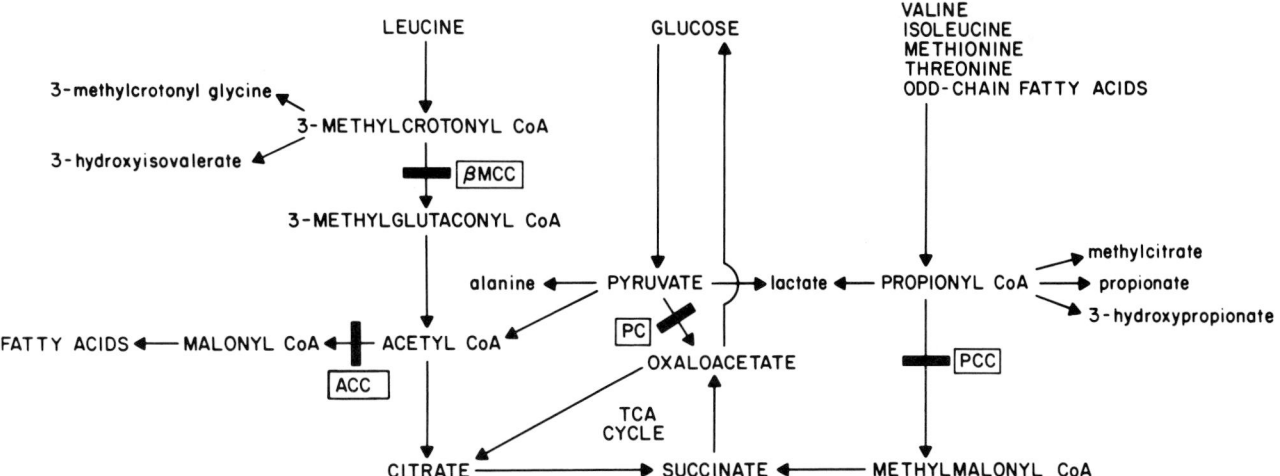

Fig. 83-2 Metabolic pathways in which biotin-dependent enzymes are involved. The solid rectangular blocks indicate the location of the enzymes. PCC = propionyl-CoA carboxylase; PC = pyruvate carboxylase; β-MCC = β-methylcrotonyl-CoA carboxylase; and ACC = acetyl-CoA carboxylase. Isolated deficiencies of the first three carboxylases have been established, whereas a deficiency in acetyl-CoA carboxylase activity has been reported in only a single case. All four of these enzymes appear to be deficient in holocarboxylase synthetase deficiency and possibly in biotinidase deficiency. Metabolites that are frequently found at elevated concentrations in urine of children with the various isolated and multiple carboxylase deficiencies are indicated by lowercase characters. *(From Wolf et al.[164] Used by permission of Pediatrics.)*

tinidase (EC 3.5.1.12) and results in the release of free biotin, some of which is recycled.

Disorders that result from deficient activity of each of the three mitochondrial, biotin-dependent carboxylases have been documented[8] (see Chaps. 28, 29, and 32). Each is characterized by an abnormal profile of organic acids in the urine, which is attributable to the accumulation of one or more intermediate compounds in the blood (see Fig. 83-2). A single case of acetyl-CoA carboxylase deficiency has been reported.[9] Children with the disorders of isolated carboxylases do not respond to treatment with biotin, and the information available indicates that structural alterations of the individual enzymes are responsible for the deficient activity.

Another group of disorders involving deficient activities of the carboxylases was found to be responsive to treatment with biotin. The first patient with such a disorder, reported originally in 1971, was described as having biotin-responsive β-methylcrotonylglycinuria.[10] From birth the child experienced episodic vomiting; at 6 weeks of age he developed an erythematous rash, and at 5 months he exhibited rapid respiration, persistent vomiting, and unresponsiveness. He also had metabolic acidosis and ketosis, and the concentrations of β-methylcrotonic acid and β-methylcrotonylglycine in his urine were greatly elevated. Several days after the commencement of treatment with oral biotin the symptoms resolved and the urinary metabolites normalized.[11] Later the excretion of tiglylglycine and β-hydroxyisovaleric acid in the urine was demonstrated.[12] Subsequently the patient was found to have deficient activity of all three biotin-dependent mitochondrial carboxylases in peripheral blood leukocytes and skin fibroblasts,[13–15] as well as deficient activity of acetyl-CoA carboxylase in fibroblasts.[16] These findings prompted the eventual diagnosis of "multiple carboxylase deficiency."

By 1980, several more patients with multiple or combined carboxylase deficiency were reported.[8] Based on the finding of deficient activities of more than one carboxylase in peripheral blood leukocytes and skin fibroblasts, it was suggested that a defect in holocarboxylase synthetase was the probable cause of the disorder.[17] However, the relatively late onset of symptoms

in some children prompted the proposal that the absorption and/or transport of biotin was defective.[18]

For several years, patients with multiple carboxylase deficiency were classified as having either the early onset (also referred to as neonatal) form or the late onset (or juvenile) form of multiple carboxylase deficiency, depending on the age of onset of symptoms.[19] Initially, most of the reported patients with the early onset form of the disorder were shown to have altered holocarboxylase synthetase activity, the K_m of biotin for the enzyme being markedly elevated.[20] Two patients with the late onset form were reported as having transport defects, because of their abnormal responses to oral loading tests with biotin,[21,22] but in 1983 it was shown that the primary biochemical defect in most patients with the late onset multiple carboxylase deficiency was deficient activity of biotinidase.[23] One of these patients who was initially described as having had a transport defect was shown subsequently to be able to absorb biotin normally if loading tests were performed when tissue biotin concentrations were normal.[24] Biotinidase deficiency has since been confirmed in both of these patients (Ref. 24; J.M. Saudubray, personal communication).

Most patients with holocarboxylase synthetase deficiency have become symptomatic soon after birth,[25] whereas most patients with biotinidase deficiency have shown no obvious clinical manifestations prior to 3 months of age.[26] Nevertheless, there is an overlap in the ranges of age of onset. The existence of this overlap raises some intriguing, and as yet unanswered, questions about the role of recycling of biotin.

We begin this chapter with a discussion of the biotin economy in human beings. Where it is appropriate, the results of studies on other species are presented; in some cases these studies provide our only insight into the utilization of this essential nutrient. We then describe the cyclical nature of the biochemical pathways involved in the metabolism of biotin and the reaction pathways involving the biotin-dependent carboxylases. The disease states involving the enzymes of biotin metabolism, holocarboxylase synthetase and biotinidase, are described, and their differential diagnosis is discussed. We conclude with a brief consideration of biotin-responsive disorders of unknown etiology and the likely developments in our understanding of these conditions.

ACQUISITION AND LOSS OF BIOTIN

In 1916, toxic effects were observed in rats receiving diets that contained a high concentration of dried, raw egg white,[27] and when raw egg white was the sole source of protein, rats developed a syndrome characterized by neuromuscular disorders, severe dermatitis, and loss of hair.[28] The condition was termed *egg white injury* and was shown to be preventable by heating the protein, by administering additional foods such as yeast, liver, or a compound from egg yolk that promoted the growth of yeast.[29] This compound was later shown to be biotin.[1,30] The antagonist for biotin which caused the observed egg white injury was the glycoprotein avidin.[31]

Sources

Foods. Although biotin occurs widely in natural foodstuffs, the absolute concentration even in the richest sources is very low. Liver, kidney, egg yolk, and some vegetables are good sources of biotin containing 20 to 120 μg per 100 edible portion, whereas lean meat, fruit, cereals, and bread products contain 1 to 10 μg/100 g.[32]

Intestinal Microflora. For perhaps 40 years it was assumed that the intestinal microflora either synthesized all of the biotin required in human beings or supplemented the biotin in the diet so that biotin was available in more than adequate quantities.[33] Few attempts have been made to estimate the actual contribution of the microflora. There is now evidence available from several sources to suggest that neither the diet nor the microflora alone satisfies the true demand for biotin, even in clinically normal members of the population.[33–36] Debate about the relative importance of the contribution of microflora continues, unfortunately with the almost complete absence of attempts to quantify this contribution. The strongest evidence in favor of a significant contribution by the microflora is the observation that the combined daily output of biotin in urine and stool exceeds the dietary intake.[33,37,38]

Biosynthesis. Mammals cannot synthesize biotin. More than 30 species of bacteria are known to be able to synthesize biotin,[39] and some of these biotin-synthesizing bacteria have been identified in the human gut.[40] Most microorganisms capable of biotin synthesis use a pathway from pimelic acid through 7,8-substituted pelargonic acid and dethiobiotin with subsequent incorporation of sulfur to form biotin.[41] The mechanism of introduction of sulfur into biotin is yet to be determined.

Antibiotics and sulfa drugs alter the intestinal flora and lead to a reduction in the fecal output of biotin.[42–45] The effects of these treatments on the urinary excretion of biotin are unclear. Several of these studies were conducted with very high concentrations of antibiotics or with avidin used in conjunction with the antibiotics, with the result that the urinary output of biotin was reduced.[44,45]

Bioavailability

Quantifying Biotin. Knowledge of the concentration of total biotin in a foodstuff is informative, but gives little indication of how efficiently biotin may be used for metabolic processes. The concept of bioavailability encompasses this notion of efficiency of utilization of nutrients. Several components affect bioavailability: digestibility, absorption, and availability of the nutrient in an appropriate form in target organs.

The biotin concentrations of foods, tissues, and biologic fluids have been measured using chick and rat growth assays, microbiologic growth assays,[46] and competitive binding assays that involve the use of avidin and radioactively labeled biotin.[47–51] Of these, the methods currently used are the microbiologic and avidin-binding assays. *Lactobacillus plantarum*[52] and the protozoan *Ochromonas danica*[53] are the two microorganisms that are used most frequently to measure biotin in biologic extracts, and several variations of the avidin-binding procedure are published.[47–51] Each procedure has its limitations, and it is important to know the method by which a quoted concentration was obtained.

The biotin in foods and biologic materials occurs in different chemical forms,[7,54,55] and selection of the appropriate extraction condition can be as important as selection of an assay technique for obtaining an accurate estimate of true biotin concentration. Vegetables, green plant materials, and fruits contain water-extractable forms of biotin. The biotin in yeast and animal products is abundant, but occurs in firmly bound complexes that are insoluble in water. Seeds and nuts also contain large amounts of bound biotin.[55] It is not known if this biotin is covalently bound.

Bound biotin may be freed either by acid hydrolysis or with enzymes such as trypsin, but it is also subject to degradation if the conditions of hydrolysis are severe. For example, treatment with 4 N sulfuric acid destroys some of the biotin in yeast, corn, and soybeans, and hydrolysis with hydrochloric acid also destroys biotin. The optimum conditions for hydrolysis of animal and plant products appear to be autoclaving for 2 h at 121°C with 6 N and 2 N sulfuric acid, respectively.[55,56]

Selection of the appropriate analytical method depends on the form of biotin in the material to be assayed. The methods based on the avidin-binding reaction are not specific for free biotin. Thus, any compounds that have a ureido ring in their structure will react in this assay system,[57] although not necessarily stoichiometrically. Therefore, these methods may overestimate the biotin concentration.

L. plantarum responds to free biotin and not to biocytin, but oleic acid can replace biotin if it is present at sufficiently high concentrations in the growth medium.[58] *O. danica* responds to free biotin as well as to biocytin.[59] These differences in specificity have led to some confusion about "normal" concentrations, and we stress the importance of establishing how biotin concentrations were obtained.

Release from Biotin-Containing Foods in vivo. The extent of predigestion required for the uptake of biotin-containing sources in human beings remains to be determined, but it has been shown in vitro that human plasma biotinidase acts on its natural substrate biocytin much more efficiently than on natural or synthetic biotinylated peptides.[60] The efficiency of release is negatively correlated with the number of amino acid residues in a biotinylated polypeptide. Biotinidase is present in the intestinal mucosa of several species[61] and in pancreatic juice and zymogen granules from rats.[62,63] It may play an important role in the digestion and uptake of dietary biotin in human beings.[62,64] Extensive proteolysis is probably required before biotinidase in the gut can be useful in making biotin from biotinylated peptides available for uptake.

Intestinal Absorption. Early studies using everted sacs prepared from the small intestine of rats indicated that free biotin was absorbed by passive diffusion.[65] This finding was confirmed and extended in a study using everted intestinal sacs prepared from rats and several other species.[66] Biotin failed to accumulate against a concentration gradient in the rat, rabbit, guinea pig, ferret, or carp, but did accumulate against a concentration gradient in the hamster, white mouse, chipmunk, gerbil, and squirrel. These studies employed pharmacologic concentrations of biotin (10 μM), whereas the physiological concentration in rat intestine has been estimated at 0.6 μM.[67] Further studies of intestinal uptake in the hamster indicated that biotin uptake is a saturable sodium-dependent process.[68,69] The uptake of biotin by isolated rat intestinal cells has been shown to be nonsaturable (from 0.01 to 2 μM), independent of temperature, and not inhibitable by antimycin C.[70] However, two recent studies, one using ligated loops of rat intestine in situ and the other with everted sacs, indicated that biotin absorption involved both saturable and nonsaturable components.[71,71a] Almost certainly some of these inconsistencies can be attributed to methodological differences, but apparently there are species differences in biotin uptake.

Biotin uptake in human beings has not been well studied, and the mechanism has not been determined. In humans, the vitamin is rapidly absorbed after oral loading, and peak plasma concentrations of biotin are attained 30 to 60 min after administration.[22,24,72] There is one preliminary communication describing experiments in which intracellular concentrations of biotin were measured after jejunal biopsy samples were incubated in medium containing [14C]biotin. The uptake of biotin proceeded against a concentration gradient. The intracellular/extracellular concentration ratio was 2.5, and the uptake was sodium-dependent, but few data were presented, and these results were difficult to interpret.[73]

The specificity of site of uptake of biotin has been studied in the rat, hamster, chicken, and to a limited extent in human beings. In rats and hamsters biotin is absorbed more rapidly in the upper half of the intestine than in the lower portion,[66,71a] but in the chicken there appears to be no site specificity in the small intestine.[74] Biotin introduced at high concentrations in vivo can be absorbed from the large intestine as well as the small intestine in human beings.[75]

Transport and Cellular Uptake. Biotin binds nonspecifically to plasma proteins,[76] and several specific biotin-binding proteins including biotinidase have been proposed, but not well studied.[77–79] Confirmation of the existence of specific biotin-binding proteins and elucidation of their role(s) in regulating biotin concentrations in blood and other tissues await further investigation.

In addition to the studies of isolated rat enterocytes already described, the transport of biotin has been studied in cultured HeLa cells, human fibroblasts, mouse fibroblasts, isolated and cultured rat hepatocytes, brush border and basolateral membrane vesicles prepared from rabbit kidney cortex, perfused rat brain, and isolated rabbit choroid plexus. HeLa cells and human fibroblasts take up protein-bound biotin in the form of an avidin–[3H]biotin complex, by a process that is time-dependent, saturable, and energy-dependent. HeLa cells take up free biotin more slowly than bound biotin; the rate of uptake is linear with respect to extracellular concentration of biotin and is temperature-dependent.[80,81]

Biotin uptake by mouse fibroblasts is temperature-sensitive, shows a nonlinear dependence on external biotin concentration, and demonstrates some substrate specificity. The transport is apparently controlled by two processes: a saturable process, probably carrier-mediated, and a second nonsaturable component that is linear above 75 μM and represents a diffusion-driven process.[82]

Based on the inhibition of transport by ouabain and/or sodium replacement, the uptake of biotin into isolated rat hepatocytes may involve a process that is dependent on sodium and ATP.[83] The uptake from cultured rat hepatocytes, however, was nonsaturable and was not affected by the extracellular sodium concentration, pH, biotin analogues, or metabolic inhibitors.[84] At least two factors could explain the apparent contradictions in these studies. First, isolated hepatocytes, adipocytes, and fibroblasts are prepared using enzymatic isolation methods that involve potential proteolytic damage to the external receptors. Second, there is evidence from other systems involving biotin and other nutrients to suggest that the gradient of sodium is more important than simply the presence or absence of the cation in the incubation medium.[85]

In brush border membrane vesicles from the rabbit kidney cortex, biotin uptake is stimulated by an inwardly directed sodium gradient. This gradient-dependent uptake of [3H]biotin is saturable with an apparent K_m of 28 μM and is inhibitible by unlabeled biotin and its structural analogues. Biotin is apparently reabsorbed by the Na$^+$/biotin$^-$ cotransporter in luminal brush border membranes. The mechanism does not operate in the basolateral membranes of the kidney cortex.[85]

In the rat brain, biotin is transported through cerebral capillaries by a low affinity saturable process that depends on the presence of the free carboxylic acid group of the biotin side chain.[86] The choroid plexus appears not to be involved in active transfer of biotin in the brain.[86]

Requirement

Recommended Safe Intake. Uncertainty about the contribution of the intestinal microflora has prevented the establishment of a recommended dietary allowance of biotin for humans, although safe daily intakes that are assumed to prevent the development of symptoms of biotin deficiency have been suggested in the United States. For infants, the safe daily intake has been set at 35 μg biotin; that for adults is from 150 to 300 μg.[87] The biotin pool in adults has been estimated to be 675 μg and that in a child to be about 120 μg.[53]

Biotin appears to be relatively nontoxic.[88] Over 200 infants and adults with various disorders have received doses of up to 10 mg daily either orally or intramuscularly for periods exceeding 6 months, and no toxic effects were reported.[33] An adverse effect of biotin on the development of fetuses and placentas in rats was reported.[88] The dose administered was 50 to 100 times greater than the therapeutic dose for infants, and the results could not be reproduced.[89]

Irreversible Loss. Balance studies with adults on "normal" diets[37,38,90–92] have shown that the total output of biotin in urine and feces is always greater than the dietary intake, suggesting that the excess is due to microbial synthesis. Changes in dietary biotin intake are reflected in urinary excretion.[38,93] The total amount of biotin excreted in urine is usually less than the total intake, but at very low intakes, e.g., less than one-tenth of the normal, the quantity excreted may exceed that ingested.[38] The quantity of biotin excreted under these conditions is probably an indication of endogenous loss due to normal turnover of the biotin-containing enzymes.[44,45]

Newborn infants excrete biotin in their urine (30 μg/liter), but by the seventh day after birth, it is undetectable.[94] Urinary output of biotin increases subsequently, such that by the age of 2 to 4 weeks it averages 6.5 μg/liter, and by 24 weeks it reaches 31 μg/liter,[95] which is within the range of normal adults. No information is available about the fecal biotin levels in infants.

Catabolism. Degradation of the heterocyclic ureido ring system of biotin does not occur in mammals, but small amounts of biotin sulfoxides are produced through the action of mixed function oxidase activity in liver.[96] Biotin is also degraded in the mitochondria to bisnorbiotin, which results from β oxidation of the side chain.[97] Decarboxylation of the intermediate β-keto acids leading to the production of methylketones also occurs, and these products are excreted in the urine. These findings are based on studies with rats; the quantitative significance of this catabolic activity in human beings is uncertain, but probably is small. Human urine contains no D-biotin sulfoxide or biotin sulfone,[98] which suggests that very little modification occurs.

Microbial Degradation. Although nothing is known about the catabolism of biotin by the gastrointestinal microflora as an ecological unit in any mammal, the microbial degradative pathways for biotin have been elucidated.[96] There is a *Pseudomonad* which can use biotin as its sole source of carbon, nitrogen, sulfur, and energy.[96] Degradation of dietary biotin and biotin synthesized in microorganisms could conceivably be important in conditions in which biotin metabolism is altered.

Deficiency. The most overt clinical symptoms of biotin deficiency in humans are alopecia and cutaneous abnormalities such as dermatitis, erythematous periorificial rash, dryness, and fungal infection. Neurologic signs noted in adults include mild depression progressing to extreme lassitude, somnolence, muscular pain, hyperesthesia, and parasthesia.[99–102] In the absence of dietary biotin and/or the presence in the diet of biotin-binding compounds such as avidin, the time required for the onset of symptoms depends on the quantity of accessible biotin stored in the body. Even when diets contain large amounts of egg white, symptoms do not appear in adults for 3 or 4 weeks. Although the relatively long interval required to induce deficiencies in human beings and other animals[99,103] has been cited as evidence for a contribution by the intestinal microflora, this also might be the result of biotin recycling in the body and of the relatively long biologic half-life of biotin.

Spontaneous biotin deficiency in human beings is practically unknown, although several reports have appeared in the last decade of biotin-responsive syndromes in intensively reared farm livestock, particularly poultry, swine, and calves.[104–106] The most notable of these describes the fatty liver and kidney syndrome, a biotin-responsive condition that occurs in young chickens fed diets based on wheat and meat meal without supplementary biotin.[107–109] Many of the birds die when they are subjected to mild stress such as hypothermia or short-term fasting. The syndrome is associated with a marginal deficiency of biotin. Affected chicks have abnormal plasma fatty acid profiles, low concentrations of biotin in the liver, fatty kidneys, and reduced activity of hepatic pyruvate carboxylase, but the classic symptoms of biotin deficiency are not observed.

The involvement of marginal biotin deficiency in the etiology of the sudden infant death syndrome (SIDS) in human infants has been proposed,[34] and SIDS victims have had significantly less biotin in their livers than infants who died of known causes.[34,35]

The consumption of raw eggs, which contain avidin, has led to biotin deficiency in several children and adults.[99–101,110] Patients receiving chronic total parenteral alimentation without biotin have also developed the clinical manifestations of biotin deficiency.[102,111,112] The prolonged use of anticonvulsants also may lead to biotin deficiency. Phenytoin, primidone, and carbamazepine, but not valproic acid, resulted in decreased serum biotin concentrations relative to control values.[113,114] The mechanism for this effect is unknown.

BIOCHEMICAL PATHWAYS

Biotinylation of Apocarboxylases

In active carboxylases, biotin is attached covalently to the ε-amino group of a lysine residue in the active sites.[4] Biotinylation of several apoenzymes has been studied in prokaryotes and eukaryotes;[5,20,115–127] it is catalyzed by holocarboxylase synthetase (Fig. 83-1). The sequence of amino acids in the region of the biotinylated lysyl residue of the carboxylases (Ala-Met-biocytin-Met) is conserved in different species.[128] This region may function as a recognition site for the synthetase.

The mammalian apocarboxylases pyruvate carboxylase and acetyl-CoA carboxylase are homopolymeric enzymes, whereas propionyl-CoA carboxylase and β-methylcrotonyl-CoA carboxylase are heteropolymeric.[4,129,130] The heteropolymeric enzymes are composed of α and β subunits; biotin is attached to each α subunit. The two nonidentical subunits that comprise the octomer of propionyl-CoA carboxylase are synthesized in the cytosol with leader peptides that facilitate their transport into the mitochondria,[131,132] a feature that they share with other mitochondrial enzymes. Assembly of the subunits occurs after transport and can take place without prior biotinylation. Biotinylation of assembled subunits of the enzyme can occur.[133]

Partial Reactions. Biotinylation of the apocarboxylase requires activation of biotin by ATP (Partial Reaction 1), which results in the formation of a biotinyl adenylate intermediate.[118,120,121,123] The biotinyl group is then transferred to the apoenzyme to form active carboxylase (Partial Reaction 2). These two partial reactions are catalyzed by the same enzyme, holocarboxylase synthetase.

Partial Reaction 1

Biotin + ATP $\rightleftharpoons$ biotinyl 5-AMP + PP$_i$

Partial Reaction 2

Biotinyl 5-AMP + apocarboxylase $\rightleftharpoons$

holocarboxylase + AMP

Total Reaction

Biotin + ATP + apocarboxylase $\rightleftharpoons$

holocarboxylase + AMP + PP_i

Holocarboxylase Synthetase. Bacterial and animal holocarboxylase synthetases are highly specific for biotin, but there is lower specificity for the high energy phosphate donor and the apoenzyme acceptor.[5,6,116,121,122] Analogues and compounds structurally related to biotin, such as biocytin, homobiotin, norbiotin, and dethiobiotin fail to substitute for biotin in the biotinylation reaction.[5,116] Holocarboxylase synthetases for propionyl-CoA carboxylase from rabbit and rat liver and from various bacteria specifically require ATP and cannot effectively use other nucleoside triphosphates,[5,124] whereas the synthetase for propionyl-CoA, pyruvate, and acetyl-CoA carboxylases from chicken liver can use nucleoside triphosphates other than ATP.[6,134–136] Holocarboxylase synthetase from one species can effectively biotinylate apocarboxylases from other species.[20,122]

FORMS. Is there a single synthetase that activates all four apocarboxylases? Holocarboxylase synthetase that has been partially purified from the cytosolic fraction of chicken liver biotinylates mitochondrial apopyruvate carboxylase, as well as the cytosolic enzyme apoacetyl-CoA carboxylase.[6] These findings suggest that, at least in the chicken, a single synthetase activates all of the apocarboxylases. However, because there are differences in pH optima and nucleotide requirements for the cytosolic and mitochondrial extracts from chicken liver, the existence of two distinct synthetases cannot be excluded.[137] The cytosol and mitochondria contain different apoenzymes, and the differences in the properties of activation may simply reflect differences in the apoenzyme acceptors and not the existence of two separate synthetases. Since holocarboxylase synthetase has not been sufficiently purified from any source, the molecular weight and subunit structure of the enzyme have not been determined.

In 3T3-L1 mouse cells which were fully differentiated into adipocytes and contained high concentrations of pyruvate carboxylase and acetyl-CoA carboxylase, 70 percent of holocarboxylase synthetase activity was localized in the cytosolic fraction. The remaining 30 percent of activity was associated with the particulate fraction which contains the mitochondria.[137] Studies of preparations of rat liver yielded similar results.[138]

The best evidence for the existence of a single holocarboxylase synthetase in human beings is the demonstration of deficient acetyl-CoA carboxylase activity in addition to deficient activities of the three mitochondrial carboxylases in fibroblasts from children with holocarboxylase synthetase deficiency.[139,140]

Reactions Involving Biotin-Dependent Carboxylases

The major biochemical pathways and intermediates involving the four biotin-containing carboxylases in humans are depicted in Fig. 83-2. Acetyl-CoA carboxylase catalyzes the formation of malonyl-CoA from acetyl-CoA. Malonyl-CoA is, the principal substrate in the synthesis and chain elongation of fatty acids. The synthesis of oxaloacetic acid from pyruvate is catalyzed by pyruvate carboxylase. This reaction provides a primary intermediate for the tricarboxylic acid cycle, and it provides a source of carbon skeletons for the synthesis of aspartate and glutamate. Oxaloacetic acid is used in the liver and kidney for gluconeogenesis. Propionyl-CoA carboxylase catalyzes the carboxylation of propionyl-CoA to form methylmalonyl-CoA, which undergoes isomerization to succinyl-CoA, and subsequently enters the tricarboxylic acid cycle. β-Methylcrotonyl-CoA carboxylase forms β-methylglutaconyl-CoA from β-methylcrotonyl-CoA in the catabolic pathway of leucine. Clearly, altered activity of one or more of the carboxylases would have profound metabolic consequences.

Regulation of Carboxylase Activities. Acetyl-CoA carboxylase and pyruvate carboxylase are subject to allosteric regulation; pyruvate carboxylase is activated by catalytic amounts of acetyl-CoA.[4,141,142] As carbohydrate is converted to pyruvate during glycolysis, it enters the mitochondria, where it is decarboxylated to form acetyl-CoA or carboxylated to form oxaloacetic acid. The increasing concentrations of acetyl-CoA and oxaloacetic acid, both derived from pyruvate, lead to increased production of citrate. The fraction of mitochondrial citrate exceeding that which can be catabolized in the tricarboxylic acid cycle can diffuse back into the cytoplasm and activate acetyl-CoA carboxylase,[4,143] to produce malonyl-CoA and, eventually, more fatty acids. Malonyl-CoA and derivatives of long-chain fatty acyl-CoA are feedback inhibitors because they are negative effectors of acetyl-CoA carboxylase.[144]

Removal of Biotin from Partially Degraded Carboxylases

Most cytosolic and membrane-associated proteins are continuously sequestered and digested by lysosomes. Degradation plays an important role in enzyme regulation and cytoplasmic regrowth, facilitates the correction of synthetic errors, and provides a source of free amino acids that can be used for biosynthetic purposes or for essential metabolic reactions, when the exogenous supply is limited. The lysosomal system functions as a general pathway for degrading most enzymes and structural proteins to the level of amino acids or dipeptides.[145] Whole mitochondria are degraded in lysosomes, but additional catabolic pathways must be invoked to account for the breakdown of mitochondrial proteins with short half-lives.[146,147]

Degradation of pyruvate carboxylase, and probably also the other mitochondrial carboxylases, is carried out by the autophagic lysosomal system of the cell.[146–148] The biotin-containing products, biocytin and/or biotinyl peptides, probably then leave the lysosome and perhaps even enter the plasma, before being acted on by biotinidase.[146–148]

Biotinidase. Biotinidase catalyzes the cleavage of biotin from biocytin or biotinyl peptides (Fig. 83-1), but not from intact holocarboxylases.[7,149] In 1954, enzymes in hog liver and kidney and in chicken pancreas were described that released free biotin from the proteolytic digests of hog liver. Biotinidase was partially purified from various bacteria, hog kidney, and hog plasma,[61,150,151] and most recently it has been purified to homogeneity from human serum and plasma by several groups.[60,152,153]

BIOCHEMICAL CHARACTERIZATION. The mammalian enzyme is detectable in most tissues, but the highest activities are present in liver, kidney, serum, and adrenal gland.[61] Human biotinidase is a glycoprotein composed of a single polypeptide having a molecular weight of between 67,000 and 76,000.[60,152,153] It contains an essential thiol, and possibly a serine residue in or near the active site,[60,152] and migrates to the α_1 region during the electrophoresis of serum on agarose gel.[153] The K_ms of the artificial substrate, biotinyl p-aminobenzoate, and the natural substrate, biocytin, for biotinidase range from 5 to 10 μM.[60,152] Biotin is one of the end products of the reaction and a competitive inhibitor of the enzyme, the K_i being between 225 and 1300 μM.[60,152] The enzyme in human serum has a broad pH optimum, pH 5 to 7, using biotinyl p-aminobenzoate as the substrate, and a slightly shifted optimum, pH 4 to 6, when biocytin is used.[60] Biotinidase is specific for the biotinyl moiety of various substrates; it cleaves at either amide or ester linkages.[150,152] The enzyme hydrolyzes biocytin much more readily than larger biotin-containing peptides comprised of from 5 to 13 amino acid residues. Biocytin is hydrolyzed 83 times faster than such residues derived from bacterial transcarboxylases.[60] Very large biotin-containing peptides (65 to 123 residues) are cleaved at a much lower rate (1200-fold slower) than biocytin. It has been suggested that biocytin or very short biotinyl peptides are the primary substrate of biotinidase in vivo.

FORMS, ORIGIN, AND SITES OF ACTION. Preliminary studies have shown that serum biotinidase activity correlates positively with the concentration of serum albumin;[154] the concentrations of albumin and the activities of biotinidase in serums of patients with cirrhosis were lowered. This suggests that biotinidase in human serum originates principally from the liver.

Studies in which hepatotoxic compounds were administered to rats showed that the liver is also the likely source of serum biotinidase in this species.[61] Other tissues with secretory function, such as fibroblasts, leukocytes, and pancreas, as well as the secretory products in pancreatic juice and isolated zymogen granules have biotinidase activity.[62,155] Biotinidase may be a secretory enzyme that hydrolyzes the products of carboxylase degradation reaching the blood. Because the pH optimum for biotinidase activity is mildly acidic and pyruvate carboxylase is known to be degraded in lysosomes, it is attractive to assume that biotinidase is localized in the lysosome, where it can hydrolyze biotinyl substrates. However, subcellular fractionation studies have revealed that biotinidase activity is enriched in the microsomal fraction rather than in the lysosomal fraction.[61,155]

The enzyme is sialylated in serum and is desialylated in tissues.[152,154] The relatively high specific activity of biotinidase in the serum (about 120 pmol/min per milligram of protein compared to 10 to 50 pmol/min per milligram of protein in other tissues) is consistent with the extracellular space being the primary site of action. There is evidence that biotin from degraded carboxylases is not recycled within the cells, but in the extracellular compartment.[146,148] Much remains to be determined about the functioning of biotinidase.

DISEASE STATES

Isolated deficiencies of each of the mitochondrial carboxylases have been reported. All three isolated mitochondrial carboxylase deficiencies appear to be inherited as autosomal recessive traits.[129] Detailed discussions of these disorders are presented

for β-methylcrotonyl-CoA carboxylase deficiency in Chap. 28, for propionyl-CoA carboxylase deficiency in Chap. 29, and for pyruvate carboxylase deficiency in Chap. 32. A single case involving an isolated deficiency of the cytosolic enzyme acetyl-CoA carboxylase has been reported[9] but not substantiated further. Our purpose here is to introduce the clinical and biochemical features that may be observed in individuals with isolated carboxylase deficiencies, because they may occur in combination in individuals with either of the multiple carboxylase deficiencies caused by holocarboxylase synthetase deficiency or biotinidase deficiency.

Individuals with any one of the isolated mitochondrial carboxylase deficiencies can exhibit vomiting, lethargy, or hypotonia. Some of these children may exhibit seizures and developmental delay. Children with propionyl-CoA carboxylase deficiency or pyruvate carboxylase deficiency may become comatose and die. All three disorders are characterized by metabolic ketolactic acidosis. Moderate to severe hyperammonemia may be seen in propionyl-CoA carboxylase deficiency, and mild hyperammonemia and hypoglycemia may occur in pyruvate carboxylase deficiency.

All three disorders are characterized by distinctive organic aciduria. Propionyl-CoA carboxylase deficiency is characterized by the accumulation of propionic acid in the blood and by the urinary excretion of β-hydroxypropionate, methylcitrate, tiglylglycine, and several other compounds characteristic of ketosis. In pyruvate carboxylase deficiency the excretion of lactate, alanine, and ketone bodies is elevated. In β-methylcrotonyl-CoA carboxylase deficiency increased amounts of β-hydroxyisovalerate, β-methylcrotonate, and β-methylcrotonylglycine are excreted.

Children with isolated carboxylase deficiencies do not respond to treatment with biotin.[129,156] Patients with propionyl-CoA carboxylase deficiency who were reported to have improved with biotin treatment were shown subsequently to be unresponsive. Most of the children who were reported with biotin-responsive, isolated β-methylcrotonyl-CoA carboxylase deficiency have been shown to have one of the forms of multiple carboxylase deficiency. The biochemical defect in each of the isolated carboxylase deficiencies appears to be an alteration in the structure of the respective carboxylase.[157,158]

The most successful means of treating these children is to restrict their dietary intake of protein and/or the various essential amino acids or odd-chain fatty acids that cannot be adequately catabolized, while increasing their caloric intake with carbohydrate and even-chain fatty acids.

There are two biotin-responsive disorders which, because they involve deficient activities of more than one carboxylase, have been known as multiple carboxylase deficiencies. For several years, patients were classified as having either the early onset (also referred to as neonatal) or the late onset (or juvenile) multiple carboxylase deficiency depending on the age of onset of symptoms.[19] Although there is overlap in the age of onset of the two disorders, most individuals with early onset multiple carboxylase deficiency have altered activity of holocarboxylase synthetase,[20] whereas most individuals with late onset multiple carboxylase deficiency have deficient activity of biotinidase.[23]

Holocarboxylase Synthetase Deficiency

Clinical Manifestations and Biochemical Abnormalities. The clinical and biochemical features of patients with holo-

Table 83-1 Clinical and Biochemical Features of Holocarboxylase Synthetase Deficiency

Feature	Initial symptom, incidence	Symptom occurred at any time,* incidence
Feeding difficulties, vomiting	2/11	3/11
Tachypnea, apnea, breathing problems	6/11	8/11
Hypotonia	2/11	4/11
Seizures	2/11	4/11
Ataxia	0/11	1/11
Lethargy	3/11	3/11
Coma	1/11	3/11
Developmental delay	1/11	4/11
Skin rash	3/11	5/11
Alopecia	0/11	2/11
Metabolic acidosis	11/11	11/11
Ketolactic acidosis	11/11	11/11
Hyperammonemia	6/6	6/6
Organic aciduria	10/10	10/10

*Feature may have been present but not reported in some of the affected children described in the literature.

carboxylase synthetase deficiency are summarized in Table 83-1.[10,11,13,14,159–166] Seven males and four females with the disorder have been reported. The age of onset of symptoms varied from a few hours after birth to 15 months of age; 9 of these 11 children presented with symptoms before reaching 3 months of age. One child had a skin rash at 2 months but did not exhibit metabolic ketoacidosis until 8 months of age.[140]

The most common initial clinical feature was tachypnea or another breathing difficulty. Other common symptoms, which are also observed in children with isolated carboxylase deficiencies, included feeding difficulties, hypotonia, seizures, lethargy, coma, and developmental delay. Many of the children exhibited metabolic acidosis, hyperammonemia, and organic aciduria when they first became symptomatic. Other symptoms that occurred at some time prior to diagnosis included seizures, skin rash, and developmental delay.

For a time, the absence of a skin rash was thought to distinguish individuals with early onset multiple carboxylase deficiency from those with the late onset form, but three of the children with holocarboxylase synthetase deficiency exhibited rashes and two others had alopecia. Several infants and sibs who were probably also affected became comatose and died before they could be diagnosed and treated. All of the children had metabolic ketoacidosis and organic aciduria at some time during the course of their illness.

One affected child had a history of bacteremia. Immunologic studies prior to biotin treatment revealed the absence of lymphocytic response to phytohemagglutinin in vitro.[163] The response was restored following the addition of biotin to the culture medium. Abnormalities in immunologic function were attributed to the effects of abnormal accumulations of the metabolites also observed in other organic acidemias.

The gas-liquid chromatographic profiles of organic acids in the urine from these children were characterized by the presence of relatively high concentrations of many of the same metabolites that are elevated in the urine of children with isolated carboxylase deficiencies.[167] These include β-hydroxyisovalerate, β-methylcrotonylglycine, β-hydroxypropionate, methylcitrate, lactate, and tiglylglycine.

Enzyme Defect. In 1971 a child was described with β-methylcrotonylglycinuria.[10] Based on the finding of β-methylcro-

tonylglycine in the child's urine, it was suspected and later confirmed that the patient had a deficiency of β-methylcrotonyl-CoA carboxylase.[13] Other metabolites, including β-hydroxypropionate and methylcitrate, that were identified subsequently in the urine of this patient were consistent with propionyl-CoA carboxylase deficiency. It was found that the activities of both of these carboxylases were deficient in the child's fibroblasts.[15] The final concentration of biotin in the medium (minimal essential medium supplemented with 10 percent fetal calf serum) was 6 nM. Eventually, the third mitochondrial carboxylase, pyruvate carboxylase, was shown to be deficient in this fibroblast line,[168] and the disorder was termed *neonatal or early onset multiple carboxylase deficiency.*[19]

Fibroblasts of patients with this disorder that are incubated in medium containing a low concentration of biotin have deficient activities of the three mitochondrial carboxylases,[15,17,168–171] but when the medium is supplemented with a higher concentration of biotin (>100 nM), the carboxylase activities increase to within the normal range. The restoration of carboxylase activity is demonstrable even in the presence of cycloheximide (an inhibitor of protein synthesis), which suggests that activation of preexisting apocarboxylases rather than *de novo* protein synthesis is responsible for the increased activity.[17]

Fibroblasts from patients with early onset multiple carboxylase deficiency complement fibroblasts from children with isolated propionyl-CoA carboxylase deficiency.[168,172,173] The propionyl-CoA carboxylase activities in the heterokaryons produced in cell fusions of the two enzyme-deficient fibroblast lines increased significantly above those in cultures of mixed, unfused cells. The fibroblasts from the early onset disorder also complement fibroblasts from patients with isolated pyruvate carboxylase deficiency; pyruvate carboxylase activity in the heterokaryons increases.[168,174] Cultured cells from children with early onset biotin-responsive multiple carboxylase deficiency do not complement one another, and they have been designated the *bio,* for *biotin-responsive holocarboxylase synthetase deficiency,* genetic complementation group.[168,172,173] Each of the lines belonging to this *bio* complementation group appears, therefore, to have a defect in the same enzyme. Several of the fibroblast lines that have been assigned to the *bio* group also have deficiency of the fourth biotin-dependent enzyme, acetyl-CoA carboxylase.[16,139,140] These studies suggest that the enzymatic defect in this disorder is an inability to effectively biotinylate the various apocarboxylases.

The primary defect in early onset multiple carboxylase deficiency was confirmed in experiments using the apoenzyme substrate, apopropionyl-CoA carboxylase, purified two hundredfold from the livers of rats made biotin-deficient through a diet containing avidin.[20] This apoenzyme preparation was then incubated with fibroblast extracts containing holocarboxylase synthetase, in the presence of biotin, ATP, and Mg^{2+}. In normal fibroblast extracts the holocarboxylase synthetase catalyzed the formation of holopropionyl-CoA carboxylase. The activity of the holopropionyl-CoA carboxylase was then determined by measuring the fixation of radioactive bicarbonate to propionyl-CoA to form labeled methylmalonyl-CoA. When extracts of fibroblasts from a patient with early onset multiple carboxylase deficiency were used, the formation of the methylmalonyl-CoA was decreased. The K_m of biotin for holocarboxylase synthetase in the normal fibroblast line was 8.2 nM, whereas the K_m for biotin in cells from the patient was 516 nM (a 63-fold elevation). The V_{max} was only 30 to 40 percent of normal. These findings indicated that the primary defect in early onset multiple carboxylase deficiency was in holocarboxylase synthetase.

These results were further substantiated by other studies of fibroblasts from patients with early onset multiple carboxylase deficiency.[175] Cells from a normal and an affected child were made biotin-deficient by maintaining them in medium supplemented with biotin-depleted fetal calf serum. Mitochondria prepared from these cells were incubated with ATP, biotin, and propionyl-CoA, and the incorporation of radioactive bicarbonate into methylmalonyl-CoA was measured. These studies revealed a K_m of biotin for holocarboxylase synthetase in normal cells of 0.1 mM and a greatly increased K_m of 554 mM in the cells of an affected child. The discrepancy between the K_m values in these two studies may be due to the difference in the species used and/or the sources of apoenzyme.

In a third study, holocarboxylase synthetase activity was determined in extracts of lymphoblasts that had been cultured in biotin-deficient medium.[176] Cell extracts from a normal individual and from a child with early onset multiple carboxylase deficiency were incubated with ATP and Mg^{2+} in the presence and absence of biotin and then evaluated for propionyl-CoA carboxylase activity. Extracts from normal cells, incubated with biotin, showed increased propionyl-CoA carboxylase activity above that in extracts from cells that were not incubated with biotin, whereas extracts from the patient showed no change in activity. Moreover, when an extract of normal cells from which the apocarboxylase had been removed by immunoprecipitation was incubated with the patient's cell extract, the propionyl-CoA carboxylase activity increased about twentyfold.

Holocarboxylase synthetase was characterized in peripheral blood leukocytes and skin fibroblasts from seven deficient children.[25] The activities of the mitochondrial carboxylases varied from 0 to 30 percent of normal in fibroblasts incubated in low biotin (6 nM) medium. The carboxylase activities increased when the cells were incubated with 220 nM biotin in the medium, but failed to increase above 30 percent of normal even when the cells of patient 1 (Table 83-2), who had the highest K_m for biotin, were incubated in medium containing 8000 nM biotin.

The K_m of biotin for holocarboxylase synthetase in these patients ranged from 3 to 70 times the normal concentration. The K_m and the age at onset of symptoms in affected children are strongly negatively correlated. All but two patients (1 and 7) had a V_{max} of propionyl-CoA carboxylase activity in fibroblasts that was below the normal range. Similar results were found in the leukocytes of these two patients. The K_m of ATP for the synthetase in controls ranged from 0.13 to 0.35 mM, whereas the K_m was normal for two patients with holocarboxylase synthetase deficiency and was elevated at 1.32 mM for patient 1.

Preliminary studies indicated that the apopropionyl-CoA carboxylase concentration that resulted in maximal activity for holocarboxylase synthetase in fibroblast homogenates from two control subjects did not result in maximal activity in cell homogenates from two of the patients. The instability of the apoenzyme in the preparation did not permit quantitation of the K_m for this substrate.

The percentage of mean normal maximum velocity of holocarboxylase synthetase was calculated from the data in Fig. 83-3 using the Michaelis-Menten equation, for low (6 nM) and high (220 nM) biotin concentrations. The resultant propionyl-CoA carboxylase activity was determined in the patients' fibroblasts that were cultured in one or the other medium. There was a linear relationship between the percentage of mean normal propionyl-CoA carboxylase activity and both the calculated velocity of holocarboxylase synthetase activity and the percent of mean normal maximal velocity (Fig. 83-3). Thus, the kinetic properties of the synthetase in vitro appear to be highly positively correlated with the functional activity of its product, holopropionyl-CoA carboxylase.

Although the optimum pH of holocarboxylase synthetase in two of the enzyme-deficient fibroblast lines (patients 4 and 5) was the same as in normal lines, the heat stabilities differed. Of the five patients studied, the synthetase was less stable than normal in two (patients 2 and 7) and more stable in three (patients 1, 4, and 5). These findings demonstrate the biochemical heterogeneity of the defect.

All of the patients with holocarboxylase synthetase deficiency have responded to vitamin therapy. Moreover, there is detectable residual synthetase activity in tissues of all affected children. These results indicate that complete deficiency of the enzyme may be lethal in utero.

Genetics. Holocarboxylase synthetase deficiency has been reported in males and females. Several families have had more than one affected child, but consanguinity has not been demonstrated in any family. These findings are consistent with an

Table 83-2 Kinetic Properties of Holocarboxylase Synthetase in Human Fibroblasts

Source of fibroblasts	K_m biotin, nmol/liter	V_{max} of propionyl-CoA carboxylase, pmol bicarbonate incorporated per min per mg protein
Holocarboxylase synthetase deficiency:*		
Patient 1	1062	42
Patient 2	718	102
Patient 3	394	124
Patient 4	346	119
Patient 5	322	70
Patient 6	281	95
Patient 7	48	96
Biotinidase deficiency:		
Mean ± 1 SD ($n=6$)	15 ± 6	210 ± 196
Normal:		
Mean ± 1 SD ($n=5$)	15 ± 3	345 ± 145

*The data for K_m and V_{max} for each patient are single determinations.
SOURCE: Data from Burri et al.[25]

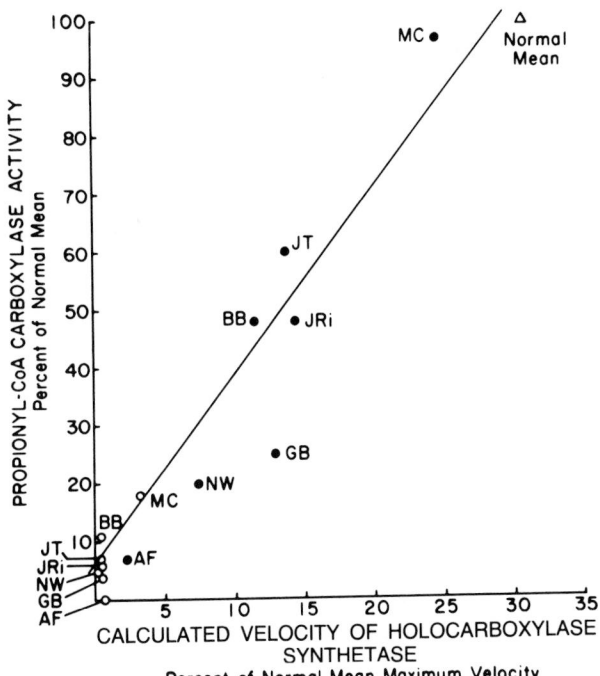

Fig. 83-3 Relationship between propionyl-CoA carboxylase activity and holocarboxylase synthetase velocity in fibroblast extracts from patients with holocarboxylase synthetase deficiency. The holocarboxylase synthetase velocities, expressed as the percent of mean normal maximum activity, were calculated from K_m values determined for biotin and the concentrations of biotin in the culture medium, using the Michaelis-Menten equation. The open circles represent cells cultured in a low concentration of biotin (6 nM), and the closed circles represent cells cultured in a higher concentration of biotin (220 nM). *(From Burri, Sweetman, and Nyhan.[25] Used by permission of* American Journal of Human Genetics.)

autosomal recessive pattern of inheritance. An attempt to demonstrate heterozygosity for the condition in the mother of one patient by studying the activity or kinetic properties of her holocarboxylase synthetase was unsuccessful.[25] Therefore, heterozygotes for holocarboxylase synthetase deficiency may not be identified using the enzyme assays that are available currently.

Treatment. Patients with holocarboxylase synthetase deficiency usually improve with oral administration of 10 mg biotin per day. Children treated before irreversible neurologic damage had occurred generally have shown resolution of the clinical symptoms and biochemical abnormalities. However, the child whose holocarboxylase synthetase in fibroblasts had the highest K_m for biotin continued to excrete abnormal organic acids and to have a mild skin rash even when treated with 60 to 80 mg biotin per day.[25] Another infant, who had disseminating intravascular coagulopathy and congestive heart failure, died a few days after biotin therapy was begun.[159,160]

Biotin that is approved for human use is available from Hoffmann–La Roche Company in Nutley, New Jersey.

Prenatal Diagnosis. Prenatal diagnosis of holocarboxylase synthetase deficiency has been performed by demonstrating deficient carboxylase activities in cultured amniocytes. The activities increased toward normal values after the cells had been incubated in the presence of biotin.[177] Demonstration of elevated concentrations of β-hydroxyisovalerate and/or methylcitrate in the amniotic fluid by stable isotope dilution techniques appears to be a simpler and more rapid method of prenatal

diagnosis.[177,178] The diagnosis can be confirmed by performing both diagnostic procedures on the same sample of amniotic fluid.

Prenatal Therapy. Prenatal treatment of holocarboxylase synthetase deficiency has been performed in two pregnancies in which sibs had been previously diagnosed with the disorder. In the first pregnancy, prenatal diagnosis was not performed.[179] The mother took 10 mg biotin orally, beginning at 34 weeks gestation. The pregnancy resulted in the birth of nonidentical twins. At birth, both twins were clinically normal, both had elevated concentrations of serum biotin, and neither child had organic aciduria. Skin fibroblasts from these infants were cultured and treatment with biotin was withheld pending the outcome of confirmatory enzyme analyses. At 3 months of age one of the twins became clinically and biochemically symptomatic.[161] Fortunately, treatment with 10 mg biotin rapidly reversed the clinical course. This twin was subsequently confirmed to have synthetase deficiency by enzyme analysis, and the other twin was shown to be unaffected.

In the second pregnancy, the fetus was diagnosed prenatally as having holocarboxylase synthetase deficiency.[177] The mother received 10 mg biotin daily beginning at 23½ weeks gestation. The infant was clinically normal at birth and the profile of urinary organic acids was normal. Both synthetase-deficient children have remained asymptomatic and are developing normally while continuing to be treated with biotin. Although the symptoms of holocarboxylase synthetase deficiency can appear soon after birth, it is not clear whether prenatal treatment with biotin is essential. Treatment of at-risk children with biotin immediately after birth until their enzyme status has been determined may be sufficient in this disorder.

Biotinidase Deficiency

Clinical Manifestations and Biochemical Abnormalities. The clinical features of 38 patients with biotinidase deficiency are summarized in Table 83-3.[18,26,64,180–197] There were 21 females and 16 males (the sex of one child was not reported) from 33 families. All of the children exhibited at least some of

Table 83-3 Clinical and Biochemical Features of Biotinidase Deficiency

Feature	Initial symptom, incidence	Symptom occurred at any time,* incidence
Seizures	24/36	28/38
Ataxia	5/36	21/38
Hypotonia	11/36	33/38
Hyperventilation, stridor, apnea	4/36	8/38
Developmental delay	5/36	22/38
Hearing loss	0/36	15/38
Visual problems (including optic atrophy)	1/36	19/38
Skin rash	7/36	22/38
Alopecia	8/36	27/38
Conjunctivitis	4/36	19/38
Fungal infection	0/36	9/38
Metabolic acidosis	—	30/38
Lactic acidosis	—	25/33
Hyperammonemia	—	12/35
Organic acidemia	—	31/36

*Symptom may have been present, but not reported in some of the affected children described in the literature.
SOURCE: Data taken in part from Wolf et al.[26]

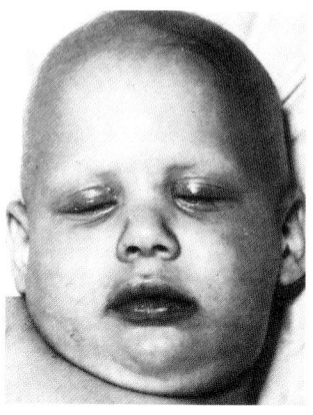
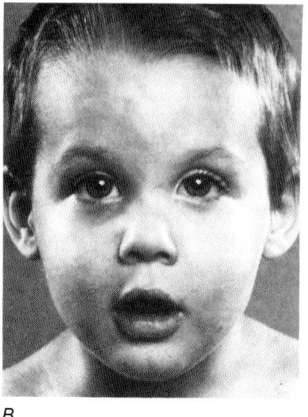
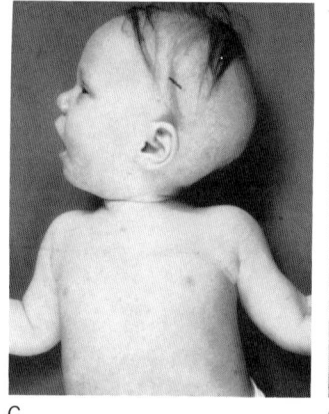

A.   B.   C.   D.

Fig. 83-4 Two children with biotinidase deficiency shown before and after biotin treatment. *A.* Child with biotinidase deficiency at 2 years and 9 months of age with alopecia and periorbital and perioral rash, before biotin therapy. *B.* Same child after 4 months of biotin therapy. (From Thoene, Baker, Yoshino, and Sweetman.[182]

Used by permission of New England Journal of Medicine.) *C.* Child with biotinidase deficiency at 10 months of age, before biotin therapy. *D.* Same child at 30 months of age, after 20 months of biotin therapy.

the symptoms usually seen in patients with late onset multiple carboxylase deficiency. The age of onset of symptoms varied from 1 week to 2 years, with median and mean ages of 3 months and 5½ months, respectively. The most common initial neurologic symptoms were myoclonic seizures and hypotonia. Several patients exhibited ataxia, hyperventilation, stridor, apnea or other breathing problems, and developmental delay. Other common initial symptoms included seborrheic or atopic dermatitis, partial or complete alopecia, and conjunctivitis. Many affected individuals initially showed combinations of these neurologic and cutaneous findings. The two children depicted in Fig. 83-4*A* and *C* exhibit several of the symptoms typical of biotinidase deficiency.

More than 70 percent of the patients had seizures or hypotonia or alopecia at some time prior to diagnosis and treatment. About half of the children had ataxia, developmental delay, conjunctivitis, and visual problems, including optic atrophy. Hearing loss, which was usually sensorineural in nature, was diagnosed in about 40 percent of the patients. Four of the affected children died while in metabolic coma. In addition, several sibs of biotinidase-deficient children reported in the literature have also died and were probably also affected.

Over 80 percent of the patients had organic aciduria, and 75 percent of the patients had metabolic ketoacidosis at some time. The most frequently observed abnormal urinary metabolite was β-hydroxyisovaleric acid. Other commonly observed metabolites included lactate, β-methylcrotonylglycine, β-hydroxypropionate, and methylcitrate. When examined, mild hyperammonemia was often found to be present. There is clinical variability among affected individuals from different families, and there is also considerable variability in expression of the disorder among affected individuals within a sibship.[187]

Recently, among 100 Japanese children with intractable seborrheic dermatitis, two children were found with serum biotinidase activities of 15 and 30 percent of mean normal activity.[198] These children had no neurologic symptoms. The dermatitis resolved after biotin therapy. Because all of the biotinidase-deficient patients who developed neurologic symptoms in addition to cutaneous symptoms have had less than 5 percent of normal activity, this study may provide further insight into the clinical variability and spectrum of the disorder.

Individuals with partial enzyme deficiency may be at risk for developing only the cutaneous symptoms.

Prior to the elucidation of the primary enzyme defect of late onset multiple carboxylase deficiency, diagnosis depended in part upon the presence of demonstrable organic aciduria. The absence of this finding would have excluded about 17 percent of our cases of biotinidase deficiency. Although the biochemical abnormalities attributed to biotinidase deficiency are often life-threatening, they appear to represent relatively late effects of the disorder. The cutaneous symptoms and some of the neurologic features are similar to those seen in biotin deficiency states, and they usually occur early in the course of the disease. The skin findings may be associated with fatty acid abnormalities, possibly attributable to deficient activity of acetyl-CoA carboxylase.[199]

Immunoregulatory dysfunction has been reported in several children with biotinidase deficiency. Three affected children from one family exhibited *Candida* dermatitis.[180] Two were evaluated and showed absence of delayed hypersensitivity by skin test and by in vitro lymphocyte responses to *Candida* challenge.[180,181] The responses to phytohemagglutinin in mixed lymphocyte cultures were normal. One of these children had IgA deficiency and failed to respond to pneumococcal immunization, whereas the other had subnormal amounts of T lymphocytes in peripheral blood. A third affected child, who was studied prior to biotin treatment, had normal B and T lymphocyte counts and responded normally to a *Candida* skin test.[182] A fourth patient had normal immunoglobulins and B lymphocyte counts but had only 50 percent of the normal number of T lymphocytes. Leukocyte killing activity against *Candida* was reduced in this patient, and the neutrophils lacked myeloperoxidase activity. The immunologic functions became normal after the child was treated with biotin. A fifth child was shown to have impaired lymphocyte suppressor activity and prostaglandin E_2 production in vitro in addition to low linoleic acid concentrations in plasma.[200,201] Incubation of the T lymphocytes with biotin restored the suppressor activity. Since prostaglandin E_2 is synthesized from linoleic acid, it was suggested that a deficiency of acetyl-CoA carboxylase resulted in deficient malonyl-CoA formation, which in turn affected prostaglandin E_2 synthesis. Biotin treatment corrected these abnormalities. The findings in these reports are inconsistent, and further systematic immunologic evaluation of biotinidase-deficient children before and after therapy is needed to better characterize the immunologic dysfunction in this disorder.

Loading tests performed on patients whose tissues are severely biotin-depleted apparently result in the rapid entry of the vitamin into these tissues with the result that biotin concentrations in plasma are misleadingly low. In one of two patients who were described initially as having impaired intestinal transport of biotin,[22] it was shown later that the response to oral biotin was normal when the loading test was conducted when the tissues were not depleted of biotin.[24] We would expect the other patient to respond similarly if the appropriate loading study were performed.[21] Therefore, to date no patient has been confirmed to have abnormal intestinal absorption of biotin.

Pathology. The postmortem findings in the brains of two children with presumptive biotinidase deficiency were similar. In the first patient, aged 3 years at the time of death, there was chronic cerebellar degeneration and atrophy characterized by the absence of the Purkinje cell layer, rarefaction of the granular layer, and proliferation of the Bergmann layer.[181] There was gliosis in the white matter and dentate nucleus. The cerebellar peduncles and brainstem were normal. Focal necrosis with vascular proliferation and infiltration by macrophages characterized the subacute necrotizing myelopathy. There was also acute meningoencephalitis of the entire central nervous system.

The second child died at 3 months of age.[202] Pathologic examination of the brain revealed defective myelination, focal areas of vacuolization, and gliosis in the white matter of the cerebrum and cerebellum. There was mild gliosis in the pyramidal cell layer of the hippocampus, and there were characteristic changes of viral encephalopathy in the putamen and, to a lesser extent, in the caudate nucleus.

Pathophysiology. Biotin deficiency does not alter biotinidase activity in vitro. The activities in the serums of several patients who became biotin-deficient while receiving parenteral hyperalimentation were normal.[23,203] Biotin-deficient rats and rats receiving adequate dietary biotin have similar biotinidase activities,[204] and it seems likely that the cutaneous and neurologic symptoms observed early in biotinidase-deficient patients may result from a mild to moderate depletion of biotin.

Biotinidase may play a critical role in the processing of dietary, protein-bound biotin.[62] We do not know whether biocytin and biotinyl peptides can be absorbed without first being hydrolyzed in the mucosa or in the intestinal lumen by biotinidase originating from bacteria, pancreatic juice, the intestinal mucosa, or all of these sources. If the action of biotinidase is a prerequisite, and if the production of biotin and biotinidase by intestinal microorganisms is quantitatively unimportant, then patients with biotinidase deficiency would lack a mechanism for liberating protein-bound biotin from food and would depend entirely on dietary free biotin to meet their requirements for the vitamin.

Biotinidase activity in human brain and cerebrospinal fluid is very low.[205] The brain may therefore be unable to recycle biotin and may depend on biotin transferred across the blood-brain barrier. The early stages of biotin deficiency that occur in biotinidase deficiency may cause a moderate decrease in pyruvate carboxylase activity and result in preferential accumulation of lactate in the brain.[194,206,207] This localized lactic acidosis may cause the appearance of neurologic symptoms before many of the other symptoms develop. Ketoacidosis and organic aciduria probably only appear after protracted biotin deficiency occurs.

Usually the hearing loss in biotinidase-deficient patients has been observed before the initiation of biotin treatment. The deficit does not appear to improve after biotin therapy.[208–210] It is possible that the hearing loss is caused by the accumulation of organic acids or by the accumulation of biocytin or larger biotinyl peptides. Either or both of these events may alter the metabolic pathways involved in the development and/or function of the auditory system. The metabolism of organic acids normalizes after biotin treatment is begun, but biocytin and biotinyl peptides would be expected to accumulate. Although there is no evidence suggesting that hearing loss worsens after treatment is begun, reports of follow-up evaluations are scarce, and it is possible that hearing loss may be progressive. Conversely, it is conceivable that the adverse effects of biocytin and biotinyl peptides on hearing would be prevented in the presence of adequate free biotin.

Although the abnormally high urinary output of biotin by several biotinidase-deficient patients has been attributed to defective reabsorption by the kidney tubules,[72,211,212] this finding could also be caused by the absence of biotinidase functioning as a plasma biotin-binding protein.[62,211] If biotinidase normally acts as a biotin-binding protein in serum, as some have suggested, and if it is absent from the serums of biotinidase-deficient patients or so altered structurally as to be unable to interact with biotin, then the increased excretion of biotin by these patients could be explained by the following mechanism:[62] Assuming that in the biotin-replete state normal individuals and biotinidase-deficient patients have similar concentrations of biotin in their serums, then the gradient between the serum and the lumen of renal tubules for free biotin would be greater in the patients, and, hence, they would excrete more biotin.

Enzyme Defect. In 1983, Wolf and colleagues[23] demonstrated that the primary biochemical defect in patients with late onset multiple carboxylase deficiency was deficient activity of biotinidase. Biotinidase activity has been determined by measuring the release of biotin from biocytin, using several microbiologic assays[7,149] and by the release of chromophoric or fluorescent amino compounds from biotinylated substrates. Enzyme activity was determined using a method in which p-aminobenzoate released from the artificial substrate, N-biotinyl p-aminobenzoate, is diazotized, coupled to a naphthol derivative to form an azo dye, and measured colorimetrically.[150] The liberation of p-aminobenzoate can also be monitored fluorometrically after the product has been separated from the substrate by high performance liquid chromatography.[213] Another fluorometric method has been developed which measures the liberation of 6-aminoquinoline from a different artificial substrate, N-biotinyl 6-aminoquinoline.[214]

Several assay methods have been recently developed which use the natural substrate biocytin to measure biotinidase activity. The first, a bioassay, measures the increase in propionyl-CoA carboxylase activity in holocarboxylase synthetase–deficient fibroblasts in response to the liberation of biotin from biocytin by biotinidase from serum.[215] This method was used to confirm that serums from children shown to be biotinidase-deficient using the artificial substrate were also deficient using the natural substrate.

Other methods available include a radioassay that measures the liberation of [^{14}C]biotin from [^{14}C]biocytin, after their separation by ion-exchange chromatography,[216] and a fluorometric assay in which the lysine released from biocytin is conjugated to a chromophore after the lysine initially in the sample is removed by dialysis.[217]

The mean biotinidase activity measured by the colorimetric method in the serum of 521 healthy, normal children and adults was 7.1 nmol p-aminobenzoate/(min·ml) with a range of 3.5 to 12.0 nmol (Fig. 83-5). Biotinidase activity in the serums of 26 children with the clinical features of late onset multiple carboxylase deficiency was deficient with a mean of 0.15 nmol p-aminobenzoate/min per milliliter of serum, or about 2 percent of mean normal activity, with a range of 0 to 9 percent. The activities in the serums of 43 obligate heterozygotes were intermediate between those of the affected children and normal controls with a mean of 49 percent of mean normal activity. We have shown that heterozygosity can be determined with about 95 percent accuracy by this method.[218]

Extracts of fibroblasts from normal individuals have very low detectable activity using the colorimetric assay.[23] Using a more sensitive radioassay based on the liberation of [^{14}C-carboxyl]p-aminobenzoate from N-biotinyl p-amino[^{14}C]benzoate, biotinidase activity was demonstrated to extracts of peripheral blood leukocytes and fibroblasts of normal individuals.[219] Extracts of peripheral blood leukocytes and fibroblasts of patients with biotinidase-deficient serum were found to have less than 1 percent of the mean normal activities for these cells (Table 83-4). These studies, and a report of deficient activity in the liver of an affected child,[220] demonstrate that the deficiency of biotinidase activity in patients is not confined to serum. The results also substantiate further that biotinidase deficiency is the primary defect in most patients with late onset multiple carboxylase deficiency.

Using a specific antiserum prepared against human biotinidase, two immunologically cross-reacting proteins were observed.[153] Neither of the proteins was detected by the antiserum in serums from 18 individuals with less than 5 percent of normal enzyme activity in their serum. Only one of these proteins corresponds to the active enzyme in serum from individuals with normal biotinidase activity.

Genetics. Both males and females have been reported with biotinidase deficiency. Several families had more than one affected child, and consanguinity was found in 8 of 33 families. These observations, together with the findings that parents of affected children have serum biotinidase activities intermediate between those of normal individuals and biotinidase-deficient children, are consistent with the view that biotinidase deficiency is inherited as an autosomal recessive trait.

Prenatal Diagnosis. Biotinidase activity is measurable in both amniotic fluid and cultured amniotic fluid cells obtained by amniocentesis of normal pregnancies.[221] Because the enzymes in amniotic fluid may be of maternal or fetal origin, the definitive diagnosis of biotinidase deficiency in the fetus probably depends on the determination of enzyme activity in extracts of amniotic fluid cells. Prenatal diagnosis of biotinidase deficiency has not yet been reported.

Although the serums of heterozygous mothers have half-normal biotinidase activity, neonates with biotinidase deficiency are asymptomatic. This indicates that these mothers can supply the developing infant with adequate free biotin.

Neonatal Screening. A method of neonatal screening for biotinidase deficiency is available. Semiquantitative colorimetric assessment of biotinidase activity is made on the same samples of whole blood spotted on filter paper that are used in phenylketonuria screening.[222] Samples with biotinidase activity show a characteristic purple color upon the addition of developing reagents after incubation with biotinyl p-aminobenzoate,

Table 83-4 Biotinidase Activity in Tissues of Individuals with Normal and Deficient Activity in Serum

Tissue	Normal or serum enzyme-deficient individuals	Biotinidase activity, pmol p-aminobenzoate per min per ml or mg protein		
		Mean	SD*	Range
Serum, ml	Normal (n = 8)	6000	800	4400–7600
	Deficient (n = 3)	0		0
Leukocytes,† mg protein	Normal (n = 8)	51	21	29–85
	Deficient (n = 2)	0		0
Fibroblasts, mg protein	Normal (n = 6)	29	5	23–36
	Deficient (n = 5)	0.1		0–0.3

*Standard deviation.
†Prepared from peripheral blood.
SOURCE: Data from Wolf et al.[203]

Fig. 83-5 Biotinidase activity in the serums of normal controls, children with biotinidase deficiency, and their parents are compared. The longer horizontal lines represent the mean activities of each group. The range of activities for the normal controls is indicated.

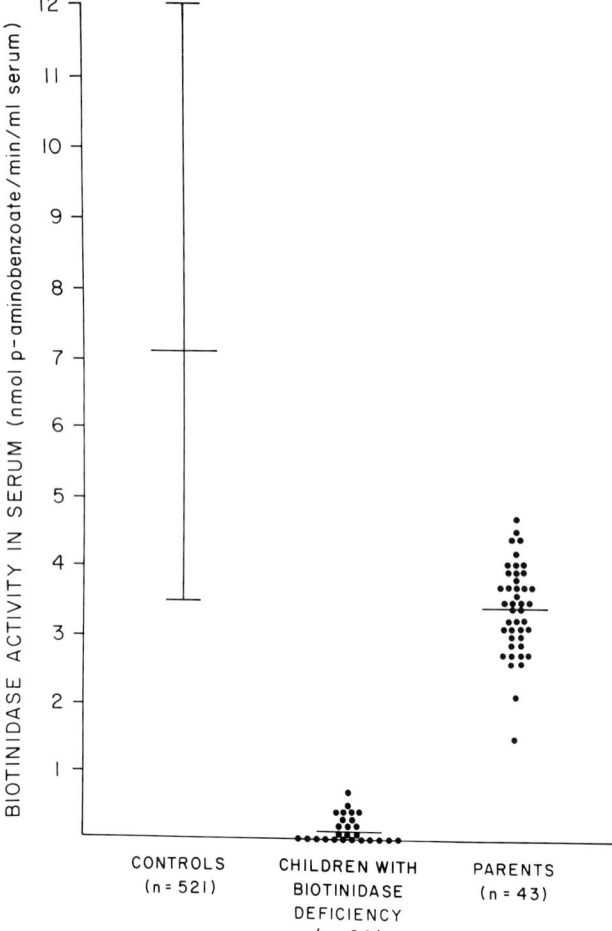

CONTROLS (n = 521) CHILDREN WITH BIOTINIDASE DEFICIENCY (n = 26) PARENTS (n = 43)

BIOTINIDASE ACTIVITY IN SERUM (nmol p-aminobenzoate/min/ml serum)

whereas those with little or no activity remain straw-colored. Positive screening tests can be confirmed by a quantitative assay of enzyme activity using additional samples of dried blood or fresh serum.

In 1984, we initiated a pilot study to estimate the incidence of the disorder using samples obtained in the Commonwealth of Virginia for screening for inborn errors of metabolism.[223,224] During the ensuing 2½-year period, we detected three infants and two sibs of one of these children with biotinidase deficiency.[225] Based on these results, other pilot programs have been initiated within the United States and in several other countries.[226,227] The results of testing for biotinidase deficiency in newborn infants up until November 1986 are summarized in Table 83-5. Of slightly more than 1 million newborns screened, 14 infants with less than 9 percent of mean normal serum biotinidase activity and 8 infants with 15 to 30 percent of mean normal activity have been identified.

Without biotin treatment the children with the lower range of enzyme activity are likely to develop some or most of the symptoms of the disorder; the clinical implications of the higher partial enzyme deficiency are still unknown. The preliminary studies from Japan may indicate that these children are at risk of developing seborrheic dermatitis.[198]

The screening technique also offers a simple, rapid means for the physician to evaluate biotinidase activity in children or adults suspected of having biotinidase deficiency.[26] Because the enzyme activity in the blood spots is stable for at least 18 months at room temperature, the cards may be sent to an appropriate reference laboratory without loss of activity.

Treatment. Children with biotinidase deficiency have been treated successfully with pharmacologic doses of between 5 and 20 mg biotin per day, an empirically determined dose. All patients have improved following treatment with pharmacologic doses of biotin.[26,64] The two children depicted in Fig. 83-4B and D illustrate the dramatic improvements that occur shortly after the commencement of biotin therapy. The cutaneous manifestations have usually resolved quickly, and the seizures and ataxia have usually stopped. However, the hearing loss and optic atrophy appear to be less reversible than the other symptoms. Depending on the severity and frequency of episodes of metabolic and neurologic compromise, many children with developmental delay have rapidly achieved new milestones or regained those that had been lost.

It should be stressed that the biotin used in treatment must be in the free form; one patient who was treated with yeast extracts containing large quantities of bound biotin did not improve clinically. However, he improved markedly after treatment with free biotin (B. Wolf, unpublished results).

A biotinidase-deficient child who had been treated with biotin from birth because a sib had the disorder became ataxic at 1 year of age.[228] This occurrence has been interpreted to indicate that not all children with biotinidase deficiency respond to biotin therapy.[229] However, there is strong evidence of noncompliance with the prescribed therapeutic regimen in this case (R. Kennedy, personal communication).

Patients with biotinidase deficiency can metabolize carboxylase enzymes to biocytin or biotinyl peptides, but no further. Although biocytin or biotinyl peptides are readily excreted in the urine of affected individuals[98,230] and there is no evidence of their accumulation, it is possible that they are toxic. Pharmacologic doses of biotin appear to result in increased concentrations of biocytin or biotinyl peptides in plasma and urine of biotinidase-deficient children.[98,230] It may prove necessary to

Table 83-5 Worldwide Experience of Neonatal Screening for Biotinidase Deficiency*

Country: state or province	Incidence
Australia:	
Queensland, N. Territory	0/5,000
Austria	1/86,700 (1)
Canada:	
British Columbia	1/45,000
Quebec	4/75,000 (5)
Italy	0/15,000
Japan:	
Tokyo	0/40,000
Sapporo City	0/20,000
Mexico	0/2,000
New Zealand	4/50,000
Scotland	0/56,000
Spain	0/37,000 (1)
United States:	
Ala.	0/30,500
Ill.	0/87,500
Md., Del.	0/90,000
Mass., Conn., N.H., R.I., Me.. Vt.	1/20,000
N.Y.	0/80,000
Pa. (Pittsburgh)	0/2,000
Ore., Idaho, Nev.	0/83,000
Va.	2/215,000 (1)
West Germany:	
Lower Saxony	1/140,000
Heidelberg	0/55,000

*Prior to November 1986. Numerator indicates number of infants detected with less than 7 percent of mean normal adult activity. The number in parentheses refers to additional infants detected with 15 to 30 percent of mean normal adult activity.
SOURCE: Data from Wolf and Heard.[227]

reduce the therapeutic doses of biotin to limit the production of biocytin. Further evaluation of this possibility is required.

The daily dose of 5 to 20 mg probably supplies more biotin than is actually required to meet the metabolic needs of these patients; one patient remained asymptomatic for 8 years while receiving only 150 μg of biotin daily.[194] An important modifying factor that should be considered in the treatment of this disorder is the amount of free biotin in the diet. It is conceivable that individuals consuming diets containing biotin predominantly in its free form may require less supplemental biotin than those whose diets contain biotin in the bound form. Titration of the doses of biotin necessary to treat these children may reveal that doses only slightly above physiological amounts will be sufficient for treatment.

Differential Diagnosis

Nonspecific clinical symptoms including vomiting, hypotonia, and seizures often characterize treatable disorders such as sepsis, gastrointestinal obstruction, and cardiorespiratory problems. After exclusion of these conditions, or when these findings are accompanied by metabolic ketoacidosis and/or hyperammonemia, the presence of an inborn error of metabolism should be considered. The prompt diagnosis and appropriate treatment of an inherited metabolic disorder may be lifesaving. Both holocarboxylase synthetase deficiency and biotinidase deficiency may present initially with these clinical features (Table 83-6).

Other symptoms characteristic of these biotin-responsive multiple carboxylase deficiencies, such as skin rash or alopecia

Table 83-6 Comparison of Holocarboxylase Synthetase and Biotinidase Deficiencies

Characteristic	Holocarboxylase synthetase deficiency	Biotinidase deficiency
Clinical features	See Table 83-1	See Table 83-3
Biochemical features	Ketolactic acidosis, hyperammonemia, organic aciduria	Ketolactic acidosis, hyperammonemia, organic aciduria
Biotin concentration in serum	Normal	Low to normal
Carboxylase activities in leukocytes:		
Before biotin therapy	Deficient	Deficient
After biotin therapy	Near-normal to normal	Normal
Carboxylase activities in fibroblasts cultured in:		
Low biotin medium (6 nM)	Deficient	Normal
High biotin medium (>100 nM)	Near-normal to normal	Normal

can occur in children with zinc deficiency or essential fatty acid deficiency. Frequent viral, bacterial, or fungal infections, due to abnormal immunologic function, may occur in holocarboxylase synthetase deficiency and biotinidase deficiency. Children with both deficiencies may have metabolic acidosis and large anion gaps, with elevated concentrations of lactate in the serum and urine. An amino acid analysis may reveal hyperglycinemia, which is also found in other organic acidemias.

The most useful screening technique for determining the type of organic acidemia, and for differentiating isolated carboxylase deficiencies from the biotin-responsive multiple carboxylase deficiencies, is the analysis of urine for abnormal organic acids. Isolated carboxylase deficiency can be confirmed by demonstrating deficient activity of one enzyme and normal activity for the other carboxylases in peripheral blood leukocytes or in cultured fibroblasts. β-Hydroxyisovalerate is the most common urinary metabolite observed in holocarboxylase synthetase deficiency and biotinidase deficiency, but it is also seen in isolated β-methylcrotonyl CoA carboxylase deficiency and biotin deficiency. Elevated urinary concentrations of lactate, methylcitrate, and β-hydroxypropionate, in addition to β-hydroxyisovalerate, are indicative of multiple carboxylase deficiency.

Biotin deficiency usually can be excluded unless there is a history of dietary indiscretion, such as the consumption of a diet containing raw eggs and/or few biotin-containing foods, or a history of protracted parenteral hyperalimentation without biotin supplementation. Low serum biotin concentrations can be useful in differentiating biotin and biotinidase deficiencies from holocarboxylase synthetase deficiency, but it is important to know the method used for the biotin determinations. Only those methods that discriminate biotin from biocytin or bound biotin yield reliable estimates of free biotin concentrations.

The symptoms of holocarboxylase synthetase deficiency and biotinidase deficiency are similar, and thus clinical differentiation may be difficult. However, the age of onset of symptoms can be useful in discriminating between these two disorders. Holocarboxylase synthetase deficiency usually manifests before 3 months of age, whereas biotinidase deficiency usually manifests after 3 months of age. Clearly, though, there are exceptions for both disorders, and age of onset alone is not completely reliable. A comparison of the major features of these two disorders is presented in Table 83-6.

Both disorders are characterized by deficient activities of carboxylases in peripheral blood leukocytes prior to biotin administration; the activities of these enzymes increase to near-normal or normal values after biotin treatment.[231] The disorders can be discriminated by determining the activities of the carboxylases in fibroblasts incubated in minimal essential medium containing only the biotin contributed by fetal calf serum (the final concentration is about 6 nM). Fibroblasts from patients with holocarboxylase synthetase deficiency have deficient carboxylase activities when cultured under these conditions, whereas fibroblasts from patients with biotinidase deficiency have activities within the normal range. The activities of the carboxylases are near to or within the normal range of activities when cells from patients having either disorder are cultured in medium supplemented with biotin (final concentration of greater than 200 nM). Definitive diagnosis of holocarboxylase synthetase deficiency is achieved by using one of the several methods detailed previously to measure enzyme activity. Biotinidase deficiency can easily be determined by measuring enzyme activity in the serum of suspected patients. The biotinidase activity in patients with isolated carboxylase deficiency or holocarboxylase synthetase deficiency is normal.

CONCLUSION

Several symptomatic children who have had neither holocarboxylase synthetase deficiency nor biotinidase deficiency have improved clinically after biotin therapy. The nature of the biochemical defect(s) in these patients is unknown. Biotin responsiveness need not be limited to frank biotin deficiency or to the two conditions discussed in this chapter, and failure to demonstrate deficiency of one of these two enzymes need not preclude the existence of a condition that is potentially responsive to treatment with biotin.

In the 4-year period since the identification of biotinidase deficiency as the primary defect of late onset multiple carboxylase deficiency, the number of known and documented symptomatic patients with the disorder has trebled. These numbers may be due, in part, to children now known to be biotinidase-deficient who had previously been classified as having idiopathic neurologic disorders. Fortuitously, the first patients to be diagnosed all had near-zero activity, and their parents had half-normal activity. Recently, seven children with between 15 and 30 percent of normal activity have been identified through screening programs. Biochemical characterization of these childrens' enzymes and those of the children with near-zero activity will no doubt provide valuable insight into the molecular changes underlying the variability in activity and in the age of onset of symptoms. The discovery of biotinidase deficiency demonstrates the importance of vitamin recycling in normal nutrition.

Few patients with holocarboxylase synthetase deficiency are available for study. The major advances in our understanding of the molecular basis for the immense range in the K_ms of biotin for holocarboxylase synthetase and, therefore, the variation in the therapeutic dose of biotin required for treatment, will come from further biochemical characterization of the enzyme in cultured fibroblasts.

REFERENCES

1. KOGL F, TONIS B: Über das Bios-Problem. Darstellung und Krystallisiertem biotin aus Eigelb. *Z Physiol Chem* 242:43, 1936.
2. DU VIGNEAUD V, HOFFMANN K, MELVILLE DB: On the structure of biotin. *J Am Chem Soc* 64:188, 1942.
3. MELVILLE D, MOYER AW, HOFMANN K, DU VIGNEAUD V: The structure of biotin: The formation of thiophenevaleric acid from biotin. *J Biol Chem* 146:487, 1942.
4. MOSS J, LANE MD: The biotin-dependent enzymes. Adv Enzymol 35:321, 1971.
5. LAND MD, YOUNG DL, LYNEN F: The enzymatic synthesis of holotranscarboxylase from apotranscarboxylase and (+)-biotin. I. Purification of apoenzyme and synthetase; characteristics of the reaction. *J Biol Chem* 239:2858, 1964.
6. ACHUTA MURTHY PN, MISTRY SP: Synthesis of biotin-dependent carboxylases from their apoproteins and biotin. *Biochem Rev* 4:247, 1972.
7. THOMA RW, PETERSON WH: The enzymatic degradation of soluble bound biotin. *J Biol Chem* 210:569, 1954.
8. BONJOUR JP: Biotin-dependent enzymes in inborn errors of metabolism in humans. *World Rev Nutr Diet* 38:1, 1981.
9. BLOM W, SCHOLTE HR: Acetyl-CoA carboxylase deficiency: An inborn error of de novo fatty acid synthesis. *N Engl J Med* 305:465, 1981.
10. GOMPERTZ D, DRAFFAN GH, WATTS JL, HULL D: Biotin-responsive beta-methylcrotonylglycinuria. *Lancet* 2:22, 1971.
11. GOMPERTZ D, BARTLETT K, BLAIR D, STERN CMM: Child with a defect in leucine metabolism associated with beta-hydroxyisovaleric aciduria and beta-methylcrotonylglycinuria. *Arch Dis Child* 48:975, 1973.
12. GOMPERTZ D, DRAFFAN GH: The identification of tiglylglycine in the urine of a child with beta-methylcrotonylglycinuria. *Clin Chim Acta* 37:405, 1972.
13. GOMPERTZ D, GOODEY PA, BARTLETT K: Evidence for the enzymatic defect in beta-methylcrotonylglycinuria. *FEBS Lett* 32:13, 1973.
14. SWEETMAN L, BATES SP, HULL D, NYHAN WL: Propionyl-CoA carboxylase deficiency in a patient with biotin-responsive 3-methylcrotonyl-glycinuria. *Pediatr Res* 11:1144, 1977.
15. WEYLER W, SWEETMAN L, MAGGIO DC, NYHAN WL: Deficiency of propionyl-CoA carboxylase and methylcrotonyl-CoA carboxylase in a patient with methylcrotonylglycinuria. *Clin Chim Acta* 76:321, 1977.
16. BARTLETT K, GHNIEM HK, STIRK JH, WASTELL HJ, SHERRAH HSA, LEONARD JV: Enzyme studies in combined carboxylase deficiency. *Ann NY Acad Sci* 447:235, 1985.
17. BARTLETT K, GOMPERTZ D: Combined carboxylase defect: Biotin-responsiveness in cultured fibroblasts. *Lancet* 2:804, 1976.
18. CHARLES B, HOSKING G, GREEN A, POLLIT R, BARTLETT K, TAITZ LS: Biotin-responsive alopecia and developmental regression. *Lancet* 2:118, 1979.
19. SWEETMAN L: Two forms of biotin-responsive multiple carboxylase deficiency. *J Inherited Metab Dis* 4:53, 1981.
20. BURRI BJ, SWEETMAN L, NYHAN WL: Mutant holocarboxylase synthetase: Evidence for the enzyme defect in early infantile biotin-responsive multiple carboxylase deficiency. *J Clin Invest* 68:1491, 1981.
21. MUNNICH A, SAUDUBRAY JM, CARRE G, GOODE FX, OGIER H, CHARPENTIER C, FREZAL J: Defective biotin absorption in multiple carboxylase deficiency. *Lancet* 2:263, 1981.
22. THOENE JG, LEMONS RM, BAKER H: Impaired intestinal absorption of biotin in juvenile multiple carboxylase deficiency. *N Engl J Med* 308:639, 1983.
23. WOLF B, GRIER RE, ALLEN RJ, GOODMAN SI, KIEN CL: Biotinidase deficiency: The enzymatic defect in late-onset multiple carboxylase deficiency. *Clin Chim Acta* 131:272, 1983.
24. THOENE J, WOLF B: Biotinidase deficiency in juvenile multiple carboxylase deficiency. *Lancet* 2:398, 1983.
25. BURRI BJ, SWEETMAN L, NYHAN WL: Heterogeneity of holocarboxylase synthetase in patients with biotin-responsive multiple carboxylase deficiency. *Am J Hum Genet* 37:326, 1985.
26. WOLF B, HEARD GS, WEISSBECKER KA, SECOR MCVOY JR, GRIER RE, LESHNER RT: Biotinidase deficiency: Initial clinical features and rapid diagnosis. *Ann Neurol* 18:614, 1985.
27. BATEMAN WG: The digestibility and utilization of egg protein. *J Biol Chem* 26:263, 1916.
28. PARSONS HT, LEASE JG, KELLY E: LIX. The interrelationship between dietary egg white and requirement for a protective factor in the cure of the nutritive disorder due to egg white. *Biochem J* 31:424, 1937.
29. GYORGY P: The curative factor (vitamin H) for egg white injury, with particular reference to its presence in different foodstuffs and in yeast. *J Biol Chem* 131:733, 1939.
30. GYORGY P: Rachitis and andere avitaminosen. *Z Arztl Fortbild* 28:377, 1931.
31. EAKIN RE, SNELL EE, WILLIAMS RJ: Concentration and assay of avidin, injury-producing agents in raw egg white. *J Biol Chem* 136:801, 1940.
32. HARDING MG, CROOKS H: Lesser known vitamins in foods. *J Am Diet Assoc* 38:204, 1961.
33. BONJOUR J-P: Biotin in man's nutrition and therapy—A review. *Int J Vitam Nutr Res* 47:107, 1977.
34. JOHNSON AR, HOOD RL, EMERY JL: Biotin and the sudden infant death syndrome. *Nature* 285:159, 1980.
35. HEARD GS, HOOD RL, JOHNSON AR: Hepatic biotin and the sudden infant death syndrome. *Med J Aust* 2:305, 1983.
36. DOSTALOVA L: Vitamin status during puerperium and lactation. *Ann Nutr Metab* 28:385, 1984.
37. GARDNER J, PARSONS HT, PETERSON WH: Human utilization of biotin from various diets. *Am J Med Sci* 211:198, 1946.
38. GARDNER J, PARSONS HT, PETERSON WH: Human biotin metabolism on various levels of biotin intake. *Arch Biochem* 8:339, 1945.
39. GYORGY P, LANGER BW JR: Biotin VII. Biogenesis, in Sebrell WH Jr, Harris RS (eds): *The Vitamins—Chemistry, Physiology, Pathology, Methods.* New York, Academic, 1968, p 292.
40. DONALDSON RM: *Handbook of Physiology, Alimentary Canal V.* Washington, American Physiological Society, 1968, p 2807.
41. EISENBERG MA: Biotin: biogenesis, transport, and their regulation. *Adv Enzymol* 38:317, 1973.
42. GRUNDY WE, FREED M, JOHNSON HC, HENDERSON CH, BERRYMAN GH, FRIEDEMANN TE: The effect of phthalylsulfathiozole (sulfathalidine) on the excretion of B vitamins by normal adults. *Arch Biochem* 15:187, 1947.
43. MARKKANEN T: Studies on the urinary excretion of thiamine, riboflavin, nicotinic acid, pantothenic acid and biotin in achlorhydria and after partial gastrectomy. *Acta Med Scand* 169 (Suppl):360, 1960.
44. OPPEL TW: Studies of biotin metabolism in man IV. Studies of the mechanism of absorption of biotin and the effect of biotin administration on a few cases of seborrhea and other conditions. *Am J Med Sci* 215:76, 1948.
45. SARETT HP: Effect of oral administration of streptomycin on urinary excretion of B vitamins in man. *J Nutr* 47:275, 1952.
46. GYORGY P, LANGER JR BW: Biotin IV. Estimation in foods and food supplements, in Sebrell WH Jr, Harris RS (eds): *The Vitamins—Chemistry, Physiology, Pathology, Methods.* New York, Academic, 1968.
47. DAKSHINAMURTI K, LANDMAN AD, RAMAMURTI L, CONSTABLE RJ: Isotope dilution assay for biotin. *Anal Biochem* 61:225, 1974.
48. HOOD RL: A radiochemical assay for biotin in biological materials. *J Sci Food Agric* 26:1847, 1975.
49. HORSBURCH T, GOMPERTZ D: A protein-binding assay for measurement of biotin in physiological fluids. *Clin Chim Acta* 82:215, 1978.
50. RETTENMAIER R: Biotin-bestimmung in lebergewebe nach dem prinzip der isopen-verdunnugsanalyse. *Anal Chim Acta* 113:107, 1980.
51. SANGHVI RS, LEMONS RM, BAKER H, THOENE JG: A simple method for determination of plasma and urinary biotin. *Clin Chim Acta* 124:85, 1982.
52. WRIGHT LD, SKEGGS HR: Determination of biotin with *Lactobacillus arabinosis*. *Proc Soc Exp Biol Med* 56:95, 1944.
53. BAKER H, FRANK O, MATOVITCH VB, PASHER I, AARONSON S, HUNTER SH, SOBOTKA H: A new method for biotin in blood, serum urine and tissues. *Anal Biochem* 3:31, 1962.
54. THOMPSON RC, EAKIN RE, WILLIAMS RJ: The extraction of biotin from tissues. *Science* 94:589, 1941.
55. LAMPEN JO, BAHLER GP, PETERSON WH: The occurrence of free and bound biotin. *J Nutr* 23:11, 1942.
56. SCHEINER J, DERITTER E: Biotin content of feedstuffs. *J Agric Food Chem* 23:1157, 1975.

57. GREEN NM: Avidin. *Biochem J* 89:585, 1963.
58. WILLIAMS VR, FIEGER EA: Oleic acid as a growth stimulant for Lactobacillus casei. *J Biol Chem* 166:335, 1946.
59. BAKER H: Assessment of biotin status: Clinical implications. *Ann NY Acad Sci* 447:129, 1985.
60. CRAFT DV, GOSS NH, CHANDRAMOULI N, WOOD HG: Purification of biotinidase from human plasma and its activity on biotinyl peptides. *Biochemistry* 24:2471, 1985.
61. PISPA J: Animal biotinidase. *Ann Med Exp Biol Fenn* 43 (Suppl 5):1, 1965.
62. WOLF B, HEARD GS, MCVOY JS, RAETZ HM: Biotinidase deficiency: The possible role of biotinidase in the processing of dietary protein-bound biotin. *J Inherited Metab Dis* 7 (Suppl 2):121, 1984.
63. HEARD GS, WOLF B, REDDY JK: Pancreatic biotinidase activity: The potential for intestinal processing of dietary protein-bound biotin. *Pediatr Res* 18:198A, 1984.
64. WOLF B, GRIER RE, SECOR MCVOY JR, HEARD GS: Biotinidase deficiency: A novel vitamin recycling defect. *J Inherited Metab Dis* 8 (Suppl 1):53. 1985.
65. TURNER JB, HUGHES DE: The absorption of some B-group vitamins by surviving rat intestine preparations. *Q J Exp Physiol* 47:107, 1962.
66. SPENCER RP, BRODY KR: Biotin transport by small intestine of rat, hamster and other species. *Am J Physiol* 206:653, 1964.
67. SPENCER RP, BOW TH: In vitro transport of radiolabeled vitamins by the small intestine. *J Nucl Med* 5:251, 1964.
68. BERGER E, LANG E, SEMENZA G: The sodium activation of biotin absorption in hamster small intestine in vitro. *Biochim Biophys Acta* 255:873, 1972.
69. URBAN E, MITCHELL AM, MCKEE CR, HOYUMPA A: Biotin transport in rat and hamster small intestine. *Clin Res* 32:866A, 1984.
70. GORÉ J, HOINARD C, MAINGAULT P: Biotin uptake by isolated rat intestinal cells. *Biochim Biophys Acta* 856:357, 1986.
71. BOWMAN BB, SELHUB J, ROSENBERG IH: Intestinal absorption of biotin in the rat. *J Nutr* 116:1266, 1986.
71a. SAID HM, REDHA R: A carrier-mediated system for transport of biotin in rat intestine *in vitro*. *Am J Physiol* 252:G52, 1987.
72. BAUMGARTNER R, SUORMALA T, WICK H, GEISERT J, LEHNERT W: Infantile multiple carboxylase deficiency: Evidence for normal intestinal absorption but renal loss of biotin. *Helv Paediatr Acta* 37:499, 1982.
73. MUNNICH A, GRASSET E, GAUDRY M, CRAIN AM, DESJEUX JF, SAUDUBRAY JM: Transport characteristics of biotin by the small intestine in man: Preliminary evidence for defective *in vitro* absorption of biotin in biotinidase deficiency, in *Proc 22nd Annu Symp of the Society for the Study of Inborn Errors of Metabolism*. Newcastle-Upon-Tyne, England, 1984, p O-7.
74. HEARD GS, BRYDEN WL, ANNISON EF: Uptake from the gut of pyridoxine, biotin, and their transfer to the egg. *Proc Australas Poult Stock Feed Conv* 2nd:100, 1978.
75. SORRELL MF, FRANK O, THOMSON A, AQUINO H, BAKER H: Absorption of vitamins from the large intestine *in vivo*. *Nutr Rep Int* 3:143, 1971.
76. FRANK O, LUISADA-OPPER AV, FEINGOLD S, BAKER H: Vitamin binding by humans and some animal plasma proteins. *Nutr Rep Int* 1:161, 1970.
77. VALLOTTON M, HESS-SANDER V, LEUTHARDT F: Fixation spontanée de la biotin a une proteine dans le serum humaine. *Helv Chim Acta* 48:126, 1965.
78. GEHRIG D, LEUTHARDT F: A biotin-binding glycoprotein from human plasma: Isolation and characterization. *10th Int Congr Biochem, Hamburg*. Frankfurt, Bronners Druckerei Breidenstein, 1976, p 209.
79. DAKSHINAMURTI K, CHALIFOUR L, BHULLAR RP: Requirement for biotin and the function of biotin in cells in culture. *Ann NY Acad Sci* 447:38, 1985.
80. DAKSHINAMURTI K, CHALIFOUR LE: The biotin requirement of HeLa cells. *J Cell Physiol* 107:427, 1981.
81. CHALIFOUR LE, DAKSHINAMURTI K: The biotin requirement of human fibroblasts in culture. *Biochem Biophys Res Comm* 104:1047, 1982.
82. COHEN ND, THOMAS M: Biotin transport into fully differentiated 3T3-L1 cells. *Biochem Biophys Res Commun* 108:1508, 1982.
83. BOWERS-KOMROW DM, MCCORMICK DB: Biotin uptake by isolated rat liver hepatocytes. *Ann NY Acad Sci* 447:350, 1985.
84. WEINER DA, WOLF B: Biotin uptake and efflux in cultured rat hepatocytes: Implications for the treatment of biotinidase deficiency. *Ann NY Acad Sci* 447:435, 1985.
85. PODEVIN RA, BARBARAT B: Biotin uptake mechanisms in brush-border and basolateral membrane vesicles isolated from rabbit kidney cortex. *Biochim Biophys Acta* 856:471, 1986.
86. SPECTOR R, MOCK D: Biotin transport through the blood-brain barrier. *J Neurochem* 48:400, 1987.
87. *Recommended Dietary Allowances*, 8th ed. Washington, DC, National Research Council, National Academy of Science, 1980.
88. PAUL PK: Effects of nutrient toxicities in animals and man: Biotin, in Rechcigle M Jr (ed): *Handbook in Nutrition and Food*. Boca Raton, FL, CRC Press, 1978, p 47.
89. MITTELHOLZER E: Absence of influence of high doses of biotin on reproductive performance in female rats. *Int J Vitam Nutr Res* 46:33, 1976.
90. DENKO CW, GRUNDY WE, PORTER JW, BERRYMAN GH, FRIEDEMANN TE, YOUMANS JB: The excretion of B-complex vitamins in the urine and feces of several normal adults. *Arch Biochem* 10:33, 1946.
91. DENKO CW, GRUNDY WE, WHEELER NC, HENDERSON CR, BERRYMAN GH, FRIEDEMANN TE, YOUMANS JB: The excretion of B-complex vitamins by normal adults on a restricted intake. *Arch Biochem* 11:109, 1946.
92. OPPEL TW: Studies on biotin metabolism in man. *Am J Med Sci* 204:856, 1942.
93. HOOD RL, JOHNSON AR: Supplementation of infant formulations with biotin. *Nutr Rep Int* 21:727, 1980.
94. HAMIL BM, CORYELL MN, RODERUCK C: Thiamine, riboflavin, nicotinic acid, pantothenic acid and biotin in urine of newborn infants. *Am J Dis Child* 74:434, 1947.
95. BERGER H: Die Biotinausscheidung im harn bei hautgesunden und hautkranken kindern. *Int Z Vitaminforsch* 22:190, 1950.
96. MCCORMICK DB: Biotin. *Nutr Rev* 33:97, 1975.
97. MCCORMICK DB, WRIGHT LD: The metabolism of biotin and analogues, in Florkin M, Stotz EH (eds): *Comprehensive Biochemistry: Metabolism of Vitamins and Trace Elements*. Amsterdam, Elsevier, 1971, p 81.
98. BONJOUR JP, BAUSCH J, SUORMALA T, BAUMGARTNER ER: Detection of biocytin in urine of children with congenital biotinidase deficiency. *Int J Vitam Nutr Res* 54:223, 1984.
99. SYDENSTRICKER VP, SINGAL SA, BRIGGS AP, DEVAUGHN NM, ISBELL H: Observations on the "egg white injury" in man and its cure with biotin concentrate. *JAMA* 118:1199, 1942.
100. WILLIAMS RH: Clinical biotin deficiency. *N Engl J Med* 228:247, 1943.
101. SWEETMAN L, SURH L, BAKER H, PETERSON RM, NYHAN WL: Clinical and metabolic abnormalities in a boy with dietary deficiency of biotin. *Pediatrics* 68:553, 1981.
102. MOCK DM, BASWELL DL, BAKER H, HOLMAN RT, SWEETMAN L: Biotin deficiency complicating parenteral alimentation: Diagnosis, metabolic repercussions and treatment. *Ann NY Acad Sci* 447:314, 1985.
103. ACHUTA MURTHY PN, MISTRY SP: Biotin. *Prog Food Nutr Sci* 2:405, 1977.
104. WHITEHEAD CC: The assessment of biotin status in man and animals. *Proc Nutr Soc* 40:165, 1981.
105. PAYNE CG: Nutritional syndromes of poultry in relation to wheat-based diets, in Haresign W, Swan H, Lewis D (eds): *Nutrition and the Climatic Environment*. London, Butterworths, 1977, p 155.
106. BALNAVE D: Clinical symptoms of biotin deficiency in animals. *Am J Clin Nutr* 30:1408, 1977.
107. PAYNE CG, GILCHRIST P, PEARSON JA: Involvement of biotin in the fatty liver and kidney syndrome of broilers. *Br Poult Sci* 15:489, 1974.
108. HOOD RL, JOHNSON AR, FOGARTY AC, PEARSON JA: Fatty liver and kidney syndrome in chicks. II. Biochemical role of biotin. *Aust J Biol Sci* 29:429, 1976.
109. PEARSON J, JOHNSON AR, HOOD RL, FOGARTY AC: Fatty liver and kidney syndrome in chicks. I. Effects of biotin in diet. *Aust J Biol Sci* 29:419, 1976.
110. SCOTT D: Clinical biotin deficiency (egg white injury). Report of a case with some remarks on serum cholesterol. *Acta Med Scand* 162:69, 1951.
111. INNES SM, ALLARDYA DB: Possible biotin deficiency in adults receiving long-term total parenteral nutrition. *Am J Clin Nutr* 37:185, 1983.
112. MCCLAIN CJ, BAKER H, ONSTAD GR: Biotin deficiency in an adult during home parenteral nutrition. *JAMA* 247:3116, 1982.
113. KRAUSE KH, BERLIT P, BONJOUR J-P: Impaired biotin status in anticonvulsant therapy. *Ann Neurol* 12:485, 1982.
114. KRAUSE KH, BONJOUR J-P, BERLIT P, KOCHEN W: Biotin status of epileptics. *Ann NY Acad Sci* 447:297, 1985.
115. KOSOW DP, LANE MD: Restoration of biotin-deficiency-induced depression of propionyl CoA carboxylase activity *in vivo* and *in vitro*. *Biochem Biophys Res Commun* 4:92, 1961.
116. KOSOW DP, HUANG SC, LANE MD: Propionyl holocarboxylase synthesis. *J Biol Chem* 12:3633, 1962.
117. FOOTE JL, CHRISTNER JE, COON MJ: Biotin and adenosine triphosphate-dependent activation of propionyl apocarboxylase. *Biochim Biophys Acta* 67:676, 1963.
118. SIEGEL L, FOOTE JL, CHRISTNER JE, COON MJ: Propionyl-CoA holocarboxylase synthesis from biotinyl adenylate and the apocarboxylase in the presence of an activating enzyme. *Biochem Biophys Res Commun* 3:307, 1963.
119. LANE MD, ROMINGER KL, YOUNG DL, LYNEN F: The enzymatic synthesis of holotranscarboxylase from apotranscarboxylase and (+)-biotin. II. Investigation of the reaction mechanism. *J Biol Chem* 239:2865, 1964.

120. CHRISTNER JE, SCHLESINGER MJ, COON MJ: Enzymatic activation of biotin: Biotinyl adenylate formation. *J Biol Chem* 239:3997, 1964.

121. SIEGEL L., FOOTE JL, COON MJ: The enzymatic synthesis of propionyl coenzyme A holocarboxylase from d-biotinyl 5-adenylate and the apocarboxylase. *J Biol Chem* 240:1025, 1965.

122. MCALLISTER HC, COON MJ: Further studies on the properties of liver propionyl coenzyme A holocarboxylase synthetase and the specificity of holocarboxylase formation. *J Biol Chem* 241:2855, 1966.

123. CAZZULO JJ, GUNDARAM TK, DILKS SN, KORNBERG HL: Synthesis of pyruvate carboxylase from its apoenzyme and (+)-biotin in Bacillus stearothermophilus: Purification and properties of the apoenzyme and the holoenzyme synthetase. *Biochem J* 122:653, 1971.

124. SUNDARAM TK, CAZZULO JJ, KORNBERG HL: Synthesis of pyruvate carboxylase from its apoenzyme and (+)-biotin in Bacillus stearothermophilus: Mechanism. *Biochem J* 122:663, 1971.

125. CHIANG GS, MISTRY SP: A comparative study of pyruvate holocarboxylase synthesis in rat liver and kidney preparations. *J Biochem* 6:527, 1975.

126. WOOD HG, HARMON FR, WUHR B, HUBNER K, LYNEN F: Comparison of the biotination of apotranscarboxylase and its aposubunits. *J Biol Chem* 255:7397, 1980.

127. BARKER DF, CAMPBELL AM: Genetic and biochemical characterization of the bio gene and its product: Evidence for a direct role of biotin holoenzyme synthetase in repression of the biotin operon in Escherichia coli. *J Mol Biol* 146:469, 1981.

128. RYLATT DB, KEECH DB, WALLACE JC: Pyruvate carboxylase: Isolation of the biotin-containing peptide and the determination of its primary structure. *Arch Biochem Biophys* 183:113, 1977.

129. WOLF B, FELDMAN GL: The biotin-dependent carboxylase deficiencies. *Am J Hum Genet* 34:699, 1982.

130. HOMMES FA: Biotin. *World Rev Nutr Diet* 48:34, 1986.

131. KRAUS JP, KALOUSEK F, ROSENBERG LE: Biosynthesis and mitochondrial processing of the beta subunit of propionyl CoA carboxylase from rat liver. *J Biol Chem* 258:7245, 1983.

132. KRAUS JP, FIRGAIRA F, NOROTNY J, KALOUSEK F, WILLIAMS KR, WILLIAMSON C, OHURA T, ROSENBERG LE: Coding sequence of the precursor of the beta subunit of rat propionyl-CoA carboxylase. *Proc Natl Acad Sci USA* 83:8049, 1986.

133. LANDMAN AD: Activation of biotin-enzymes: A possible biochemical rationale. *Life Sci* 19:1377, 1976.

134. MADAPPALLY MM, MISTRY SP: Synthesis of chicken liver pyruvate holocarboxylase in vivo and in vitro. *Biochim Biophys Acta* 215:316, 1970.

135. ACHUTA MURTHY PN, MISTRY SP: In vitro synthesis of propionyl-CoA holocarboxylase by a partially purified mitochondrial preparation from biotin-deficient chicken liver. *Can J Biochem* 52:800, 1974.

136. ACHUTA MURTHY PN, MISTRY SP: Synthesis of acetyl coenzyme A holocarboxylase in vitro by a cytosolic preparation from chicken liver. *Proc Soc Exp Biol Med* 147:114, 1974.

137. CHANG HI, COHEN ND: Regulation and intracellular regulation of the biotin holocarboxylase synthetase of 3T3-L1 cells. *Arch Biochem Biophys* 225:237, 1983.

138. COHEN ND, THOMAS M, STACK M: The subcellular distribution of the holocarboxylase synthetase of rat liver. *Ann NY Acad Sci* 447:393, 1985.

139. FELDMAN GL, WOLF B: Deficient acetyl-CoA carboxylase activity in multiple carboxylase deficiency. *Clin Chim Acta* 111:147, 1981.

140. PACKMAN S, CASWELL N, GONZALEZ-RIOS MC, KADLECEK T, CANN H, RASSIN D, MCKAY C: Acetyl CoA carboxylase in cultured fibroblasts: Differential biotin dependence in the two types of biotin-responsive multiple carboxylase deficiency. *Am J Hum Genet* 36:80, 1984.

141. SOLS A, GRISOLIA S (eds): *Metabolic Regulation and Enzyme Action.* New York, Academic, 1970, vol 19, p 53.

142. SCRUTTON MC: Pyruvate carboxylase. Studies of activator-independent catalysis and of the specificity of activation by acyl derivatives of coenzyme A for the enzyme from rat liver. *J Biol Chem* 249:7057, 1974.

143. WAKIL SJ (ed): *Lipid Metabolism.* New York, Academic, 1970, p 9.

144. NUMA S, BORTZ WM, LYNEN F: Regulation of fatty acid synthesis at the acetyl-CoA carboxylation step. *Adv Enzyme Regul* 3:407, 1965.

145. MORTIMORE GE: Regulation of intracellular proteolysis: Introductory remarks. *Fed Proc* 43:1281, 1984.

146. CHANDLER CS, BALLARD FJ: Inhibition of pyruvate carboxylase degradation and total protein breakdown by lysosomotropic agents in 3T3-1 cells. *Biochem J* 210:845, 1983.

147. CHANDLER CS, BALLARD FJ: Distribution and degradation of biotin-containing carboxylases in human cell lines. *Biochem J* 232:385, 1985.

148. FREYTAG SO, UTTER MF: Regulation of the synthesis and degradation of pyruvate carboxylase in 3T3-L1 cells. *J Biol Chem* 258:6307, 1983.

149. WRIGHT LD, DRISCOLL CA, BOGER WP: Biocytinase, an enzyme concerned with hydrolytic cleavage of biocytin. *Proc Soc Exp Biol Med* 86:335, 1954.

150. KNAPPE J, BROMMER W, BIEDERBICK K: Reinigung und Eigenschaften der Biotinidase aus Schweinenieren und Lactobacillus casei. *Biochem Z* 338:599, 1963.

151. KOIVUSALO M, PISPA J: Biotinidase activity in animal tissue. *Acta Physiol Scand* 58:13, 1963.

152. CHAUHAN J, DAKSHINAMURTI K: Purification and characterization of human serum biotinidase. *J Biol Chem* 261:4268, 1986.

153. WOLF B, MILLER JB, HYMES J, SECOR MCVOY J, ISHIKANA Y, SHAPIRA E. Immunological comparison of biotinidase in serum from normal and biotinidase-deficient individuals. *Clin Chim Acta* 164:27, 1987.

154. WEINER DL, GRIER RE, WATKINS P, HEARD GS, WOLF B: Tissue origin of serum biotinidase: Implication in biotinidase deficiency. *Am J Hum Genet* 34:56A, 1983.

155. HEARD GS, GRIER RE, WEINER DL, SECOR MCVOY JR, WOLF B: Biotinidase: A possible mechanism for the recycling of biotin. *Ann NY Acad Sci* 447:259, 1985.

156. SWEETMAN L, NYHAN WL: Inheritable biotin-treatable disorders and associated phenomena. *Ann Rev Nutr* 6:317, 1986.

157. ROBINSON BH, OCI J, SAUNDERS M, GRAVEL R: [^{3}H]Biotin-labelled proteins in cultured human skin fibroblasts from patients with pyruvate carboxylate deficiency. *J Biol Chem* 258:6660, 1983.

158. LAMHONWAH AM, LAM KF, TSUI F, ROBINSON B, SAUNDERS ME, GRAVEL RA: Assignment of the alpha and beta chains of human propionyl-CoA carboxylase to genetic complementation groups. *Am J Hum Genet* 35:889, 1983.

159. ROTH K, COHN R, YANDRASITZ J, PRETI G, DODD P, SEGAL S: Beta-methylcrotonic aciduria associated with lactic acidosis. *J Pediatr* 88:229, 1976.

160. ROTH KS, YANG W, FOREMAN JW, ROTHMAN R, SEGAL S: Holocarboxylase synthetase deficiency: A biotin-responsive organic acidemia. *J Pediatr* 96:845, 1980.

161. ROTH KS, ALLAN L, YANG W, FOREMAN JW, DAKSHINAMURTI K: Serum and urinary biotin levels during treatment of holocarboxylase synthetase deficiency. *Clin Chim Acta* 109:337, 1981.

162. LEONARD JV, SEAKINS JWT, BARTLETT K, HYDE J, WILSON J, CLAYTON B: Inherited disorders of 3-methylcrotonyl CoA carboxylation. *Arch Dis Child* 56:53, 1981.

163. PACKMAN S, SWEETMAN L, BAKER H, WALL S: The neonatal form of biotin responsive multiple carboxylase deficiency. *J Pediatr* 99:418, 1981.

164. WOLF B, HSIA YE, SWEETMAN L, FELDMAN G, BOYCHUK RB, BART RD, CROWELL DH, DI MAURO RM, NYHAN WL: Multiple carboxylase deficiency: Clinical and biochemical improvement following neonatal biotin treatment. *Pediarics* 68:113, 1981.

165. NARISAWA K, ARAI N, IGARASHI Y, SATOH T, TADA K: Clinical and biochemical findings on a child with multiple biotin-responsive carboxylase deficiencies. *J Inherited Metab Dis* 5:67, 1982.

166. SHERWOOD WG, SAUNDERS M, ROBINSON BH, BREWSTER T, GRAVEL RA: Lactic acidosis in biotin-responsive multiple carboxylase deficiency caused by holocarboxylase synthetase deficiency of early and late onset. *J Pediatr* 101:546, 1982.

167. SWEETMAN L, NYHAN WL: Organic aciduria in neonatal multiple carboxylase deficiency. *J Inherited Metab Dis* 5:49, 1982.

168. SAUNDERS M, SWEETMAN L, ROBINSON B, ROTH K, COHN R, GRAVEL RA: Biotin responsive organicaciduria. Multiple carboxylase defects and complementation studies with propionicacidemia in cultured fibroblasts. *J Clin Invest* 64:1695, 1979.

169. BARTLETT K, NG H, DALE G, GREEN A, LEONARD JV: Studies on cultured fibroblasts from patients with defects of biotin-dependent carboxylation. *J Inherited Metab Dis* 4:183, 1981.

170. FELDMAN GL, HSIA YE, WOLF B: Biochemical characterization of biotin responsive multiple carboxylase deficiency: Heterogeneity within the bio genetic complementation group. *Am J Hum Genet* 33, 692, 1981.

171. SAMBONI M, GAUDRY M, MARQUET A, MUNNICH A, SAUDUBRAY JM, MARSAC C: Search for the biochemical basis of biotin dependent multiple carboxylase deficiencies: Determination of biotin activation in cultured fibroblasts. *Clin Chim Acta* 122:241, 1981.

172. WOLF B, WILLARD HF, ROSENBERG LE: Kinetic analysis of complementation in heterokaryons of propionyl CoA carboxylase-deficient human fibroblasts. *Am J Hum Genet* 32:16, 1980.

173. WOLF B: Molecular basis for genetic complementation in propionyl CoA carboxylase deficiency. *Exp Cell Res* 125:502, 1980.

174. FELDMAN GL, WOLF B: Evidence for two genetic complementation groups in pyruvate carboxylase-deficient human fibroblast cell lines. *Biochem Genet* 18:617, 1980.

175. GHNEIM HK, BARTLETT K: Mechanism of biotin-responsive combined carboxylase deficiency. *Lancet* 1:1187, 1982.

176. SAUNDERS ME, SHERWOOD WG, DUTHIE M, SURH L, GRAVEL RA: Evidence for a defect of holocarboxylase synthetase activity in cultured lympho-

blasts from a patient with biotin-responsive multiple carboxylase deficiency. *Am J Hum Genet* 34:590, 1982.

177. PACKMAN S, COWAN MJ, GOLBUS MS, CASWELL NM, SWEETMAN L, BURRI BJ, NYHAN WL, BAKER H: Prenatal treatment of biotin-responsive multiple carboxylase deficiency. *Lancet* 1:1435, 1982.

178. JAKOBS C, SWEETMAN L, NYHAN WL: Stable isotope dilution analysis of 3-hydroxyisovaleric acid in amniotic fluid: Contribution to the prenatal diagnosis of inherited disorders of leucine catabolism. *J Inherited Metab Dis* 7:15, 1984.

179. ROTH KS, YANG W, ALLEN L, SAUNDERS M, GRAVEL RA, DAKSHINAMURTI K: Prenatal administration of biotin in biotin-responsive multiple carboxylase deficiency. *Pediatr Res* 16:126, 1982.

180. COWAN MJ, WANA DW, PACKMAN S, AMMANN AJ, YOSHINO M, SWEETMAN L, NYHAN WL: Multiple biotin-dependent carboxylase deficiencies associated with defects in T-cell and B-cell immunity. *Lancet* 2:115, 1979.

181. SANDER JE, MALAMUD N, COWAN MJ, PACKMAN S, AMMAN AJ, WARA DW: Intermittent ataxia and immunodeficiency with multiple carboxylase deficiencies: A biotin-responsive disorder. *Ann Neurol* 8:544, 1980.

182. THOENE J, BAKER H, YOSHINO M, SWEETMAN L: Biotin responsive carboxylase deficiency associated with subnormal plasma and urinary biotin. *N Engl J Med* 304:817, 1981.

183. MUNNICH A, SAUDUBRAY JM, OGIER H, COUDE F-X, MARSAC C, ROCCI-CHIOLI F, LABARTHE JC, CUZNAVE C, LAUGIER J, HARPENTIER C, FREZAL J: Deficit multiple des carboxylases. *Arch Fr Pediatr* 38:83, 1981.

184. MUNNICH A, SAUDUBRAY JM, COTJSSON A, COUDE FX, OGIER H, CHARPENTIER C, MARSAC C, GARRE G, BOURGEAY-CAUSSE M, FREZAL J: Biotin dependent multiple carboxylase deficiency presenting as a congenital lactic acidosis. *Eur J Pediatr* 137:203, 1981.

185. KIEN CL, KOHLER E, GOODMAN SI, BERLOW S, HONG R, HOROWITZ SP, BAKER H: Biotin-responsive in vivo carboxylase deficiency in two siblings with secretory diarrhea receiving total parenteral nutrition. *J Pediatr* 99:546, 1981.

186. PACKMAN S, SWEETMAN L, YOSHINO M, BAKER H, COWAN M: Biotin-responsive multiple carboxylase deficiency of infantile onset. *J Pediatr* 90:421, 1981.

187. WOLF B, GRIER RE, ALLEN RJ, GOODMAN SI, KIEN CL, PARKER WD, HOWELL DM, HURST DL: Phenotypic variation in biotinidase deficiency. *J Pediatr* 103:233, 1983.

188. SWICK HM, KEIN CL: Biotin deficiency with neurological and cutaneous manifestations but without organic aciduria. *J Pediatr* 103:265, 1983.

189. WILLIAMS ML, PACKMAN S, COWAN MJ: Alopecia and periorificial dermatitis in biotin responsive multiple carboxylase deficiency. *J Am Acad Dermatol* 9:97, 1983.

190. SCHUBIGER G, CAFLISCH U, BAUMGARTNER R, SUORMALA T, BACHMANN C: Biotinidase deficiency: Clinical course and biochemical findings. *J Inherited Metab Dis* 7:129, 1984.

191. MIENIE LJ, REINECK CJ: Organic aciduria in neonatal biotin-responsive multiple carboxylase deficiency, in *Proc 22nd Annu Symp of the Society for the Study of Inborn Errors of Metabolism.* Newcastle-Upon-Tyne, England, 1984, p 9.

192. GRETER J, HOLME E, KOIVIKKO M, LINDSTEDT S: Biotin-responsive 3-methyl-crotonylglycinuria with biotinidase deficiency, in *Proc 22nd Annu Symp of the Society for the Study of Inborn Errors of Metabolism.* Newcastle-Upon-Tyne, England, 1984, p 8.

193. KING M: Biotin-responsive stridor etcetera, in *Proc 22nd Annu Symp of the Society for the Study of Inborn Errors of Metabolism.* Newcastle-Upon-Tyne, England, 1984, p 22.

194. DIAMANTOPOULOS N, PAINTER MJ, WOLF B, HEARD GS, ROE C: Biotinidase deficiency: Accumulation of lactate in the brain and response to physiologic doses of biotin. *Neurology* 36:1107, 1986.

195. BAUMGARTNER R, SUORMALA T, WICK H, PROBST A, VEST M, BACHMANN C: Biotinidase deficiency with lethal outcome, in *Proc 24th Annu Symp of the Society for the Study of Inborn Errors of Metabolism.* Amersfoort, Netherlands, 1986, p 45.

196. MITCHELL G, OGIER H, MUNNICH A, SAUDUBRAY JM, SCHIRRER J, CHARPENTIER C, ROCCICCIOLI F: Neurological deterioration and lactic acidemia in biotinidase deficiency: A treatable condition mimicking Leigh's disease. *Neuropediatrics* 17:129, 1986.

197. BURTON B, ROACH ES, WOLF B, WEISSBECKER KA: Sudden death associated with biotinidase deficiency. *Pediatrics* 79:482, 1987.

198. OIZUMI J, HAYAKAWA K, IINUMA K, ODAJIMA Y, IIKURA Y: Partial deficiency of biotinidase activity. *J Pediatr* 110:818, 1987.

199. MUNNICH A, SAUDUBRAY JM, COUDE FX, CHARPENTIER C, SAURAT JH, FREZAL J: Fatty acid responsive alopecia in multiple deficiency. *Lancet* 1:1080, 1980.

200. MUNNICH A, FISCHER A, SAUDUBRAY JM, GRISCELLI C, COUDE FX, OGIER H, CHARPENTIER C, FREZAL J: Biotin-responsive immunoregulatory dys-

function in multiple carboxylase deficiency. *J Inherited Metab Dis* 4:113, 1981.

201. FISCHER A, MUNNICH A, SAUDUBRAY JM: Biotin-responsive immunoregulatory dysfunction in multiple carboxylase deficiency. *J Clin Immunol* 2:35, 1982.

202. ALLEN RJ, WOLF B, GRIER RE: Infantile seizures in biotinidase deficiency. *Ann Neurol* 14:386, 1983.

203. WOLF B, HEARD GS, SECOR MCVOY JR, GRIER RE: Biotinidase deficiency. *Ann NY Acad Sci* 447:252, 1985.

204. SUCHY SF, RIZZO WB, WOLF B: Fatty acids in biotin deficiency. *Ann NY Acad Sci* 447:429, 1985.

205. SUCHY SF, SECOR MCVOY JR, WOLF B: Neurologic symptoms of biotinidase deficiency: Possible explanation. *Neurology* 35:1510, 1985.

206. SANDER JE, PACKMAN S, TOWNSEND JJ: Brain pyruvate carboxylase and the pathophysiology of biotin-dependent diseases. *Neurology* 32:878, 1982.

207. DIROCCO M, SUPERTI-FURGA A, DURAND P, CERONE R, ROMANO C: Different organic acid patterns in urine and in cerebrospinal fluid in a patient with biotinidase deficiency. *J Inherited Metab Dis* 7 (Suppl 2):119, 1984.

208. TAITZ LS, GREEN A, STRACHAN I, BARTLETT K, BENNET M: Biotinidase deficiency and the eye and ear. *Lancet* 2:918, 1983.

209. WOLF B, GRIER RE, HEARD GS: Hearing loss in biotinidase deficiency. *Lancet* 2:1365, 1983.

210. TAITZ LS, LEONARD JV, BARTLETT K: Long-term auditory and visual complications of biotinidase deficiency. *Early Hum Dev* 11:325, 1985.

211. SUORMALA T, WICK H, BONJOUR JP, BAUMGARTNER ER: Intestinal absorption and renal excretion of biotin in patients with biotinidase deficiency. *Eur J Pediatr* 144:21, 1985.

212. BAUMGARTNER ER, SOURMALA T, WICK H, BONJOUR JP: Biotin-responsive multiple carboxylase deficiency (MCD): Deficient biotinidase activity associated with renal loss of biotin. *J Inherited Metab Dis* 7 (Suppl 2):123, 1984.

213. HAYAKAWA K, OIZUMI J: Determination of biotinidase activity by liquid chromatography with fluorimetric detection. *J Chromat* 383:148, 1986.

214. WASTELL H, DALE G, BARTLETT K: A sensitive fluorimetric rate assay for biotinidase using a new derivative of biotin, biotinyl-6-aminoquinoline. *Anal Biochem* 140:69, 1984.

215. WEINER DL, GRIER RE, WOLF B: A bioassay for determining biotinidase activity and for discriminating biocytin from biotin using holocarboxylase synthetase-deficient cultured fibroblasts. *J Inherited Metab Dis* 8:101, 1985.

216. THUY LE, ZIELINSKA B, SWEETMAN L, NYHAN WL: Determination of biotinidase activity in human plasma using [14C]biocytin as substrate. *Ann NY Acad Sci* 447:434, 1985.

217. EBRAHIM H, DAKSHINAMURTI K: A fluorometric assay for biotinidase. *Anal Biochem* 154:282, 1986.

218. WEISSBECKER KA, WOLF B, PUISSAN C, NANCE WE: Detection of heterozygotes for biotinidase deficiency. *Am J Hum Genet* 37:A81, 1985.

219. WOLF B, SECOR MCVOY JR: A sensitive radioassay for biotinidase activity: Deficient activity in tissues of serum biotinidase-deficient individuals. *Clin Chim Acta* 135:275, 1984.

220. GAUDRY M, MUNNICH A, OGIER H, MARSAC C, MARQUET A, SAUDUBRAY JM, MITCHELL G, CAUSSE M, FREZAL J: Deficient liver biotinidase activity in multiple carboxylase deficiency. *Lancet* 2:397, 1983.

221. SECOR MCVOY JR, HEARD GS, WOLF B: The potential for the prenatal diagnosis of biotinidase deficiency. *Prenat Diagn* 4:317, 1984.

222. HEARD GS, SECOR MCVOY JR, WOLF B: A screening method for biotinidase deficiency in newborns. *Clin Chem* 30:125, 1984.

223. HEARD GS, WOLF B, JEFFERSON LG, WEISSBECKER KA, NANCE WE, SECOR MCVOY JR, NAPOLITANO A, MITCHELL PL, LAMBERT FW, LINYEAR AS: Neonatal screening for biotinidase deficiency: Results of a 1-year pilot study. *J Pediatr* 108:40, 1986.

224. WOLF B, HEARD GS, JEFFERSON LG, PROUD VK, NANCE WE, WEISSBECKER KA: Clinical findings in four children with biotinidase deficiency detected through a statewise neonatal screening program. *N Engl J Med* 313:16, 1985.

225. WOLF B, HEARD GS, JEFFERSON LG, WEISSBECKER KA, SECOR MCVOY JR, NANCE WE, MITCHELL PL, LAMBERT FW, LINYEAR AS: Neonatal screening for biotinidase deficiency: An update. *J Inherited Metab Dis* 9 (Suppl 2):303, 1986.

226. WOLF B, HEARD GS, JEFFERSON LG, MITCHELL PL, BENNETT G, LAMBERT FW, LINYEAR AS: Neonatal screening of biotinidase deficiency, in Therrell B (ed): *Proceedings of the International Symposium for Neonatal Screening.* Amsterdam, Elsevier, 1987, p 311.

227. WOLF B, HEARD GS: Survey of results of neonatal screening programs for biotinidase deficiency, in Therrell B (ed): *Proceedings of the International Symposium for Neonatal Screening.* Amsterdam, Elsevier, 1987, p 321.

228. WALLACE SJ: Biotinidase deficiency: Presymptomatic treatment. *Arch Dis Child* 60:574, 1985.

229. WALLACE SJ: Biotinidase deficiency: Pre-symptomatic treatment, later cerebellar ataxia, in *Proceedings of the 24th Annu Symp of the Society for the Study of Inborn Errors of Metabolism.* Amerfoort, Netherlands, 1986, p 44.

230. CHAN PW, BARTLETT K: A new solid-phase assay for biotin and biocytin and its application to the study of patients with biotinidase deficiency. *Clin Chim Acta* 159:185, 1986.

231. SUORMALA T, WICK H, BONJOUR JP, BAUMGARTNER ER: Rapid differential diagnosis of carboxylase deficiencies and evaluation for biotin responsiveness in a single blood sample. *Clin Chim Acta* 145:151, 1985.

232. WOLF B, HEARD GS, JEFFERSON LG, WEISSBECKER KA, SECOR MCVOY JR, NANCE WE, MITCHELL PL, LAMBERT FW, LINYEAR AS: Newborn screening for biotinidase deficiency, in TP Carter, Willey AM (eds): *Birth Defect Symposium XVI Genetic Disease: Screening and Management.* New York, AR Liss, 1986, p 175.

PART 14

BLOOD AND BLOOD-FORMING TISSUE

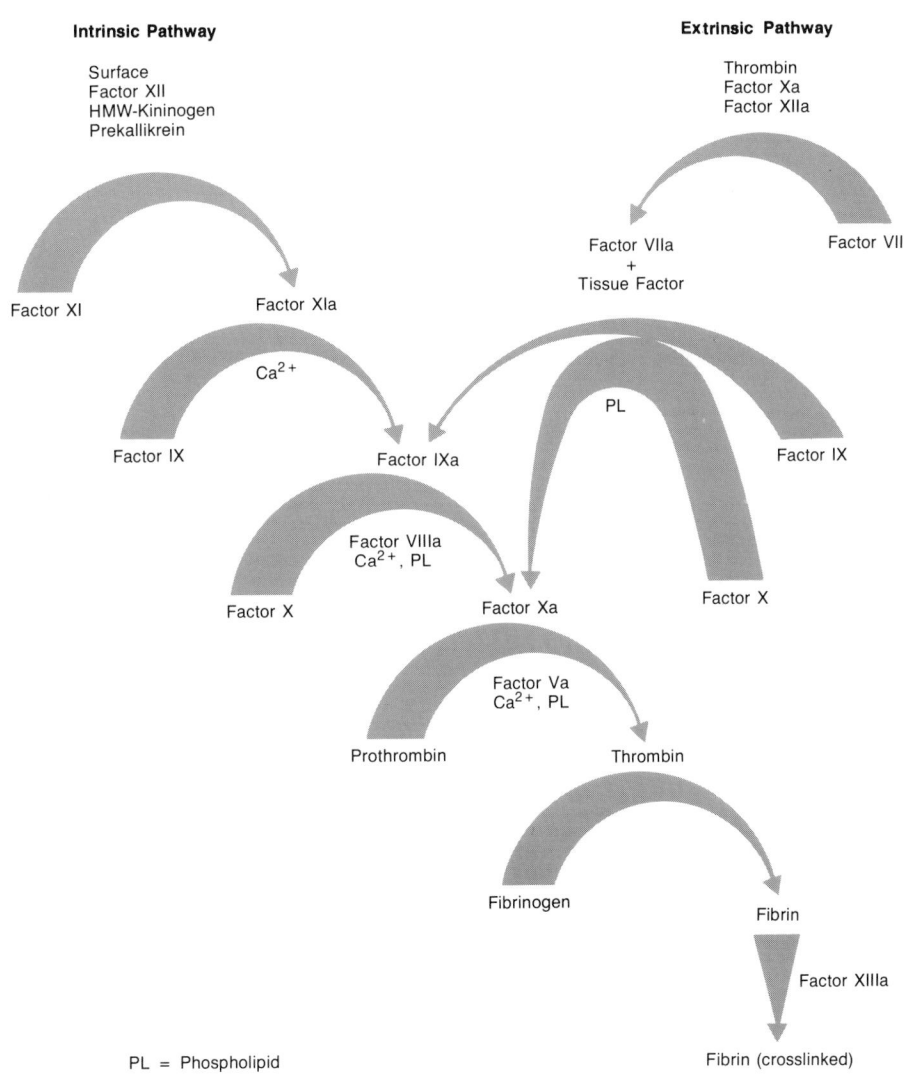

Intrinsic Pathway

Surface
Factor XII
HMW-Kininogen
Prekallikrein

Factor XI

Factor XIa

Ca^{2+}

Factor IX

Factor IXa

Factor VIIIa
Ca^{2+}, PL

Factor X

Factor Xa

Factor Va
Ca^{2+}, PL

Prothrombin

Thrombin

Fibrinogen

Fibrin

Extrinsic Pathway

Thrombin
Factor Xa
Factor XIIa

Factor VIIa
+
Tissue Factor

Factor VII

PL

Factor IX

Factor X

Factor XIIIa

Fibrin (crosslinked)

PL = Phospholipid

CHAPTER 84

INTRODUCTION TO HEMOSTASIS AND THE VITAMIN K–DEPENDENT COAGULATION FACTORS

ULLA HEDNER
EARL W. DAVIE

1. Six plasma proteins including prothrombin, factor VII, factor IX, factor X, protein C, and protein S require vitamin K for their biosynthesis in the liver. Each contains 9 to 12 γ-carboxyglutamic acid residues in the amino-terminal portion of their molecule, and these residues are formed by a vitamin K-dependent carboxylation of specific glutamic acid residues. The γ-carboxyglutamic acid residues are required for the calcium-dependent binding of the vitamin K-dependent proteins to phospholipid surfaces.

2. Prothrombin, factor VII, factor IX, factor X, and protein C circulate in blood as precursor molecules to serine proteases. When the blood coagulation cascade is initiated, prothrombin, factor VII, factor IX, and factor X are converted to serine proteases by minor proteolysis. Each protease in turn then cleaves a specific protein substrate(s). These reactions eventually lead to the generation of thrombin and fibrin at the site of vascular injury. Protein C is also converted to a serine protease by minor proteolysis during the coagulation cascade. This enzyme, however, plays a regulatory role in blood coagulation in that it inactivates factor Va and factor VIIIa in the presence of protein S. This helps to bring the coagulation process to a halt.

3. Reduced blood levels of prothrombin, factor VII, factor IX, or factor X result in bleeding complications in patients with these deficiencies. Reduced blood levels of protein C or protein S, however, may be associated with thrombotic disease since the regulation of the coagulation pathway is impaired.

4. The genes for prothrombin, factor VII, factor IX, factor X, and protein C have been well characterized and their chromosomal locations established. Abnormalities in the genes for most of the vitamin K-dependent proteins have been shown and range from partial gene deletions to single nucleotide changes or deletions. These abnormalities have been observed in the exons coding for the mature protein and the leader sequence as well as in the intron-exon boundaries in the genes for these proteins.

GENERAL INTRODUCTION TO HEMOSTASIS

Hemostasis in humans involves a number of plasma proteins and platelets, and their interaction with the vascular endothelium. Initially, a platelet plug is formed followed by a fibrin clot at the site of vascular injury. Platelet plug formation requires von Willebrand factor, a plasma protein that forms a bridge between the activated platelet and the subendothelium. This reaction, which is called *platelet adhesion*, involves a specific platelet membrane receptor (glycoprotein Ib) that binds to von Willebrand factor. Platelet adhesion is immediately fol-

lowed by platelet aggregation. In this reaction, fibrinogen forms a bridge between platelets by binding one platelet to another. Another platelet membrane receptor, called glycoprotein IIb/IIIa, is involved in this reaction. During platelet plug formation, phospholipid is made available and the blood coagulation cascade is initiated. The precise events that trigger the coagulation cascade are not known, but it appears that tissue factor, a subendothelial cell surface glycoprotein, plays an important role in the process.

The plasma proteins that participate in the coagulation cascade circulate in blood in precursor or inactive forms. When blood coagulation is initiated, these proteins are converted to active enzymes or cofactors which eventually leads to the generation of thrombin and fibrin. The plasma and cellular proteins and their cofactors have been assigned Roman numerals and are listed in Table 84-1 along with their common names. The terms fibrinogen, prothrombin, tissue factor, and calcium are employed by most investigators working in the field, while the remaining proteins (factors V through XIII) are usually referred to by their Roman numerals. No protein has been assigned as factor VI.

In recent years, the amino acid sequences for all of the proteins shown in Table 84-1 have been established by a combi-

Table 84-1 Nomenclature and Chapter Assignment for the Blood Coagulation Factors, Associated Proteins, and Platelets

Roman numeral designation	Common name	Chapter
Factor I	Fibrinogen	85
Factor II	Prothrombin	84
Factor III	Tissue factor	84
Factor IV	Calcium ions	—
Factor V	Proaccelerin	86
Factor VII	Proconvertin	84
Factor VIII	Antihemophilic factor	86
Factor IX	Christmas factor	84
Factor X	Stuart factor	84
Factor XI	Plasma thromboplastin antecedent	88
Factor XII	Hageman factor	88
Factor XIII	Fibrin-stabilizing factor	85
—	Prekallikrein (Fletcher factor)	88
—	HMW kininogen (high molecular weight kininogen)	88
—	Protein C	84
—	Protein S	84
—	Antithrombin III	89
—	Heparin cofactor II	89
—	von Willebrand factor	87
—	Platelets	90

nation of protein sequence analysis and cDNA cloning. Furthermore, the gene organization and DNA sequence have been determined for most of these proteins. These data have shown that the plasma proteins involved in fibrin formation and its regulation often share considerable amino acid sequence identity, physiological function, and mechanism of action. For instance, the vitamin K-dependent proteins (prothrombin; factors VII, IX, and X; protein C; and protein S) all share common domains and all but protein S are converted to serine proteases by minor proteolysis. Likewise, factors V and VIII are large single-chain glycoproteins with considerable sequence homology. These two proteins also participate in the coagulation cascade as cofactors in the presence of calcium and phospholipid following their activation by minor proteolysis. Similarly, factor XI and plasma prekallikrein are highly homologous molecules that share common domains and are converted to serine proteases by minor proteolysis.

In the following chapters (84 to 90), the plasma proteins and the platelet surface glycoproteins that are involved in hemostasis are discussed, and their gene structures are described.

INTRODUCTION TO VITAMIN K-DEPENDENT COAGULATION PROTEINS

The vitamin K-dependent proteins that participate in blood coagulation and its regulation include prothrombin, factor VII, factor IX, factor X, protein C, and protein S. These glycoproteins are synthesized in the liver and secreted into the blood. They circulate in blood as trace proteins with plasma concentrations that range from 0.47 μg/ml for factor VII to 80 to 90 μg/ml for prothrombin (Table 84-2). Their half-life in blood also varies considerably, with that for factor VII and protein C being the shortest.

Prothrombin, factor VII, factor IX, factor X, and protein C circulate in blood as precursor or zymogen molecules and are converted to active serine proteases during the coagulation cascade (Fig. 84-1). Protein S, however, participates as a cofactor to activated protein C,[1,2] and these two proteins are involved in the regulation of the coagulation pathway by the inactivation of factor Va[3–5] and factor VIIIa[6–9] in the presence of phospholipid (Fig. 84-2). The six vitamin K-dependent coagulation factors from human plasma each contain from 9 to 12 γ-carboxyglutamic acid (Gla) residues in the amino-terminal region of their molecule (Table 84-2). These residues are formed by a carboxylation of glutamic acid residues located within the first 40 to 45 amino acids in the amino-terminal region of each protein.[10–12] The carboxylation reaction is carried out by a membrane-bound enzyme complex requiring CO_2, O_2, polypeptide substrate, NADH, and vitamin K.[13–19] The reaction does not require ATP or biotin.[20] The carboxylation of the vitamin K-dependent proteins is inhibited by coumarin drugs, such as dicumarol or warfarin.[21] The γ-carboxyglutamic acid residues constitute the Gla domains in each of the vitamin K-dependent proteins and are required for the calcium-dependent binding of these proteins to phospholipid surfaces.[22] This binding localizes the vitamin K-dependent coagulation factors at the site of vascular injury where platelet plug formation has occurred and an active phospholipid surface has been made available.

The Gla domain in prothrombin is followed by two kringle domains.[23] The kringle domains are composed of approximately 80 amino acids with disulfide bonds linking the six Cys residues in a pattern of 1→6, 2→4, and 3→5. The kringle structures are also present in factor XII,[24] plasminogen,[25] tissue plasminogen activator,[26] and urokinase.[27] In factor VII,[28] factor IX,[29–31] factor X,[32–34] and protein C,[35,36] the kringle domains are replaced by two growth factor domains.[37] These domains are composed of 40 to 50 amino acids with disulfide bonds linking the six Cys residues in a characteristic pattern of 1→3, 2→4, and 5→6. These structures show considerable sequence similarity to epidermal growth factor and epidermal growth factor precursor.[38–40] Protein S contains four growth factor domains present as tandem repeats following the amino-terminal Gla domain.[41,42] The carboxyl-terminal region of prothrombin, factor VII, factor IX, factor X, and protein C contains the catalytic or serine protease domain. The amino acid sequence in this domain shows considerable sequence similarity to pancreatic trypsin and is responsible for hydrolysis of specific Arg-containing peptide bonds. The serine proteases that are generated during blood coagulation have a high degree of substrate specificity and cleave only one or two peptide bonds in their protein substrates. Thus, they are far more substrate-specific than the pancreatic serine proteases that are involved in protein digestion.

PROTHROMBIN

Prothrombin participates in the final stages of the blood coagulation cascade where it is converted to thrombin in the presence of factor Xa, factor Va, calcium ions, and phospholipid[43] (Fig. 84-1). Thrombin then cleaves fibrinopeptides A and B from the amino-terminal end of the α and β chains of fibrinogen leading to the formation of the fibrin clot. Thrombin also activates factor V,[44–47] factor VIII,[7,8,48,49] factor XIII,[50,51] and protein C[52–54] by limited proteolysis. Another important function of thrombin is the activation of platelets resulting in a shape change, aggregation, and release of intracellular components.

Table 84-2 Properties of the Vitamin K-Dependent Proteins*

Protein	Molecular weight	Number of chains	Number of Gla residues	Plasma conc., μg/ml	Plasma half-life
Prothrombin	71,600	One	10	80–90	2–5 days
Factor VII	50,000	One	10	0.47	2–5 h
Factor IX	56,800	One	12	4	20–24 h
Factor X	58,800	Two	11	6.4	32–48 h
Protein C	62,000	Two	9	3.9–5.9	6–8 h
Protein S	70,700	One	11	25–35	—

*Taken in part from Refs. 345 and 390 to 394.

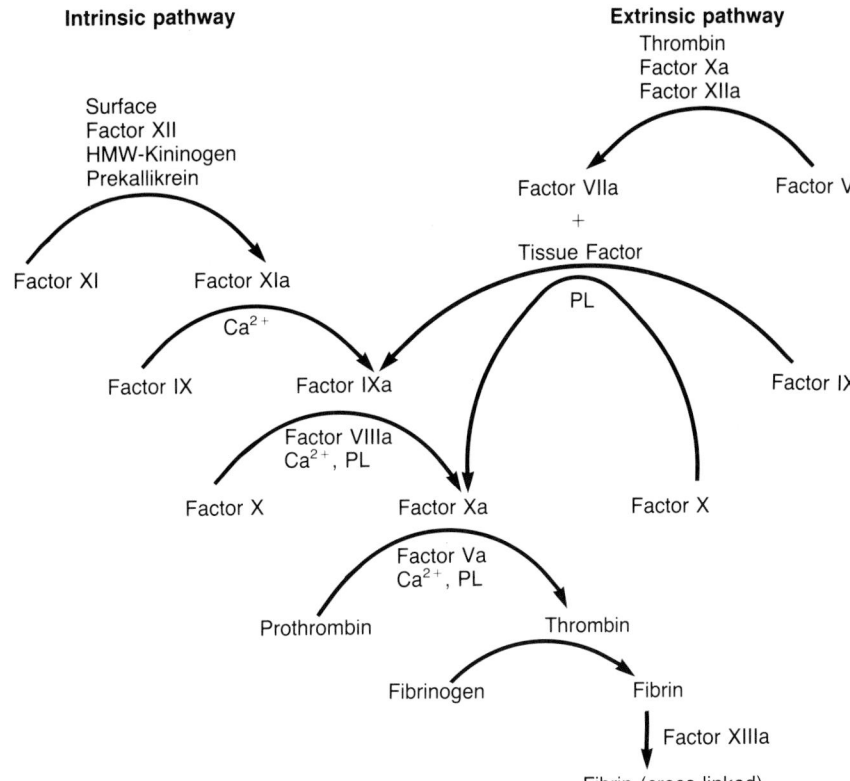

Fig. 84-1 Abbreviated scheme for fibrin formation in the intrinsic and extrinsic pathways of blood coagulation. PL = phospholipid; HMW-kininogen = high molecular weight kininogen. The factor VIIa-tissue factor complex is capable of activating factor IX and/or factor X as shown. (*Modified from Davie et al.*[389])

Human prothrombin is a single-chain glycoprotein with a molecular weight of 71,600 and an amino-terminal sequence of Ala-Asn-Thr-Phe-Leu[55,56] (Fig. 84-3). The mature protein circulating in human plasma contains 579 amino acids, including 10 residues of γ-carboxyglutamic acid that constitute the Gla domain. The two kringle structures in prothrombin are located between the Gla domain and the serine protease portion of the molecule. Prothrombin also contains 8.2% carbohydrate, which is probably attached to asparagine residues 78 and 100 located in kringle 1 and asparagine 53 in the catalytic domain of the molecule. The catalytic domain also contains the three active site residues, including His_{43}, Asp_{99}, and Ser_{205} (Fig. 84-3).

The activation of human prothrombin involves the cleavage of an internal Arg_{271}-Thr peptide bond and an Arg_{49}-Ile peptide bond by factor Xa^{57} (Fig. 84-4). The reaction requires calcium ions and is accelerated about 30,000-fold by the addition of phospholipid and factor Va.[58] The principal effect of the phospholipid is to decrease the K_m for the substrate about 1000-fold, while factor Va, complexed with factor Xa in a 1:1 molar ratio, produces a dramatic increase in the V_{max} of the reaction. In the presence of factor Va, the activation of human prothrombin proceeds by the initial cleavage of the Arg_{49}-Ile bond generating a meizothrombin intermediate[59] (Fig. 84-4). Meizothrombin has peptidase activity toward small synthetic substrates, incorporates di-isopropylfluoridate into its active site serine, but is unable to convert fibrinogen to fibrin. A second cleavage occurs in meizothrombin at the Arg_{271}-Thr bond generating thrombin with the liberation of fragment 1.2 containing amino acids 1 to 271, including the Gla and kringle domains (Fig. 84-4). The thrombin generated is composed of a light chain of 49 amino acids and a heavy chain of 259 amino acids, and these two chains are held together by a disulfide bond. This molecule undergoes further cleavage at Arg_{13}-Thr in the light chain to form a thrombin with a light chain of 36 amino acids. These reactions reduce the molecular weight of the precursor from 71,600 to about 34,500.

In the absence of factor Va, the activation of human prothrombin proceeds by a prethrombin-2 intermediate generated by the initial cleavage at the Arg_{271}-Thr bond[59] (Fig. 84-4). In whole plasma, the cleavage in prothrombin occurs primarily at Arg_{13}-Thr in the light chain as well as the Arg_{49}-Ile bond.[60] This latter pathway generates a thrombin molecule with an initial light chain of 36 amino acids rather than 49 amino acids and a Gla-kringle fragment of 284 amino acids (fragment 1.2.3). This latter pathway may well represent a major pathway for thrombin generation under physiological conditions.

Activation of prothrombin occurs on the surface of the phospholipid vesicles where the protein substrate is concentrated. The binding of the substrate as well as the enzyme to the phospholipid involves the Gla region in each of the vitamin K-dependent proteins.[22] When the newly generated thrombin is formed, it is released from the phospholipid surface and is then free to interact with its various substrates, such as fibrinogen and factor XIII.

Fig. 84-2 Activation of protein C and the inactivation of factors Va and VIIIa. PL = phospholipid.

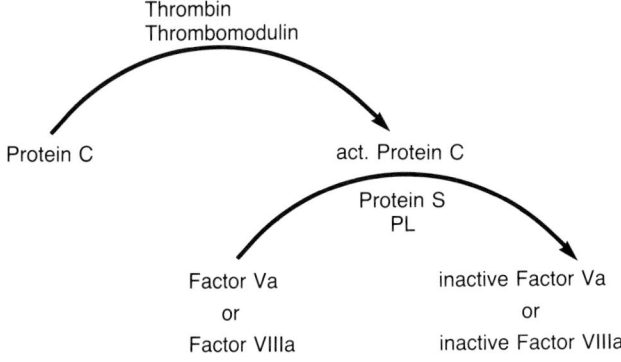

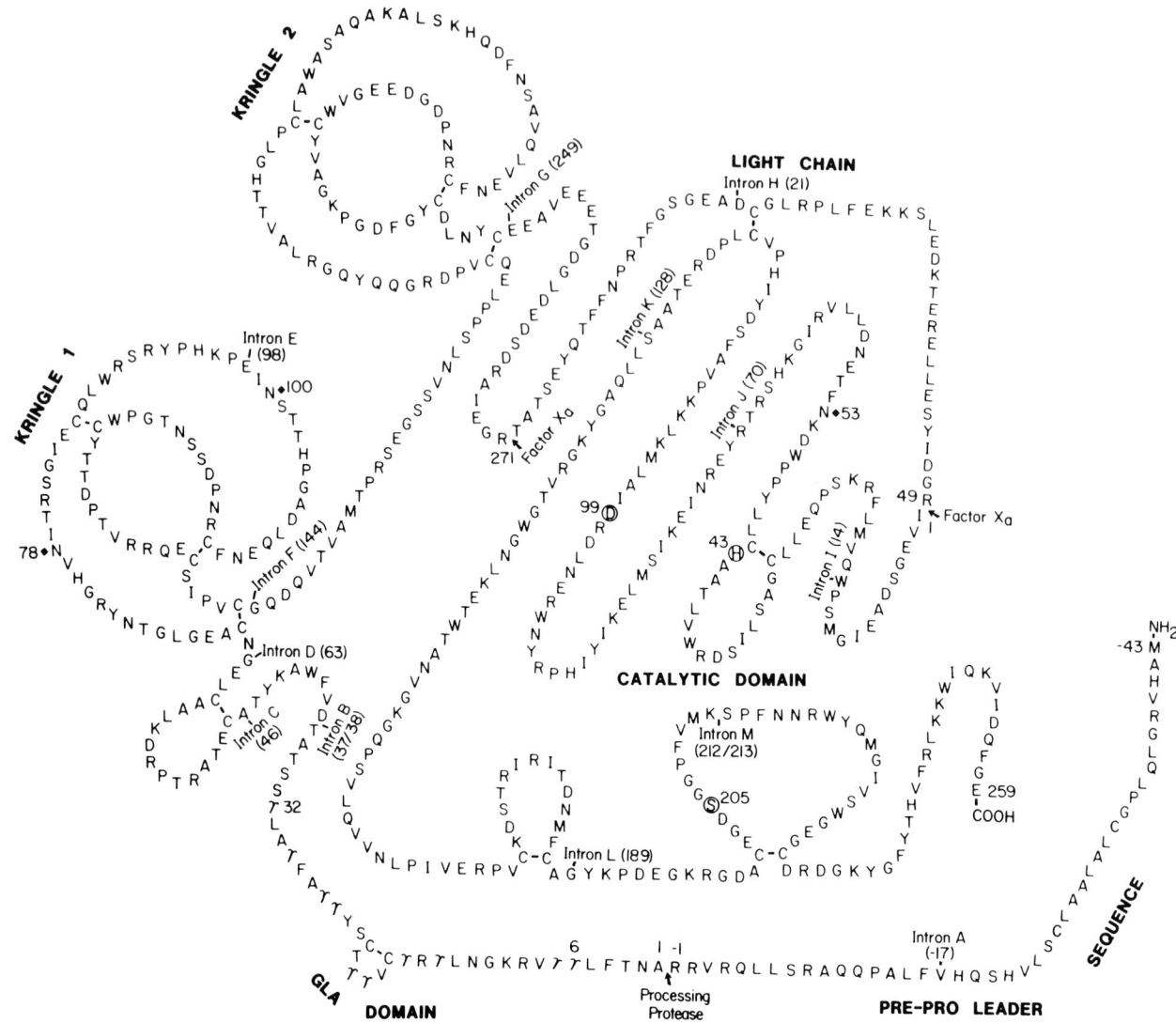

Fig. 84-3 Amino acid sequence and tentative structure of human prepro prothrombin. The locations of the 13 introns (A to M) are shown in the various regions of the protein. The prepro leader sequence is cleaved during protein biosynthesis to give rise to the mature protein with an amino-terminal sequence of A-N-T-F-. The two peptide bonds cleaved by factor Xa during the activation reaction are shown with small arrows. The three amino acids in the catalytic domain (H₄₃, D₉₉, S₂₀₅) that participate in catalysis are circled, while the three carbohydrate attachment sites are shown with solid diamonds. The amino acids are numbered as follows starting with the amino-terminal end of the protein: −43 to −1, prepro leader sequence; +1 to 271, prothrombin fragment 1.2; 1 to 49, light chain of thrombin; 1 to 259, catalytic chain of thrombin. The single-letter code for amino acids is as follows: A = Ala; R = Arg; N = Asn; D = Asp; C = Cys; Q = Gln; E = Glu; G = Gly; H = His; I = Ile; L = Leu; K = Lys; M = Met; F = Phe; P = Pro; S = Ser; T = Thr; W = Trp; Y = Tyr; V = Val; γ = γ-carboxyglutamic acid. *(From Degen et al.[55,56] Used by permission.)*

Genetic Aspects

Prothrombin deficiency is a rare abnormality, with fewer than 50 reported cases. Patients with the abnormality have been placed in two broad categories, including those with normal plasma levels of an abnormal protein that has decreased biologic activity (dysprothrombinemia)[61,62] and those with decreased biosynthesis and depressed plasma levels (hypoprothrombinemia).[63–66] Hypoprothrombinemia has been described as an autosomal recessive disorder.[61,67] Patients who are homozygous have bleeding complications and prothrombin coagulant activity ranging from 2 to 25 percent of normal. Individuals who are heterozygous have prothrombin activities of 50 percent or greater and are asymptomatic.

The gene for human prothrombin is located on chromosome 11 at p11-q12.[68] It contains about 21 kb of DNA, and its complete sequence has been established.[55,56] The gene is composed of 14 exons separated by 13 introns. The introns (A to M) range in size from 84 to 9447 nucleotides, while the exons range in size from 25 to 315 nucleotides (Table 84-3). The intron-exon splice junction sequences follow the GT-AG rule[69] and the typical splice junction consensus sequence,[70] except for the splice site at the 5′ end of intron L (Table 84-4). The exons in the gene for human prothrombin code for 579 amino acids constituting the mature protein that circulates in plasma, in addition to a prepro leader sequence of 43 amino acids. The first intron (intron A) is located in the prepro leader sequence (Val₋₁₇), while the second intron is located just after the Gla domain (between Thr₃₇ and Asp₃₈). The third intron is present nine residues later (Ala₄₆), while the fourth intron is present just prior to the first kringle (Gly₆₃). The fifth intron is located within the first kringle (Glu₉₈), and the sixth intron is present between kringles 1 and 2 (Gly₁₄₄). The second kringle in prothrombin, in contrast to the first kringle, is coded by a single

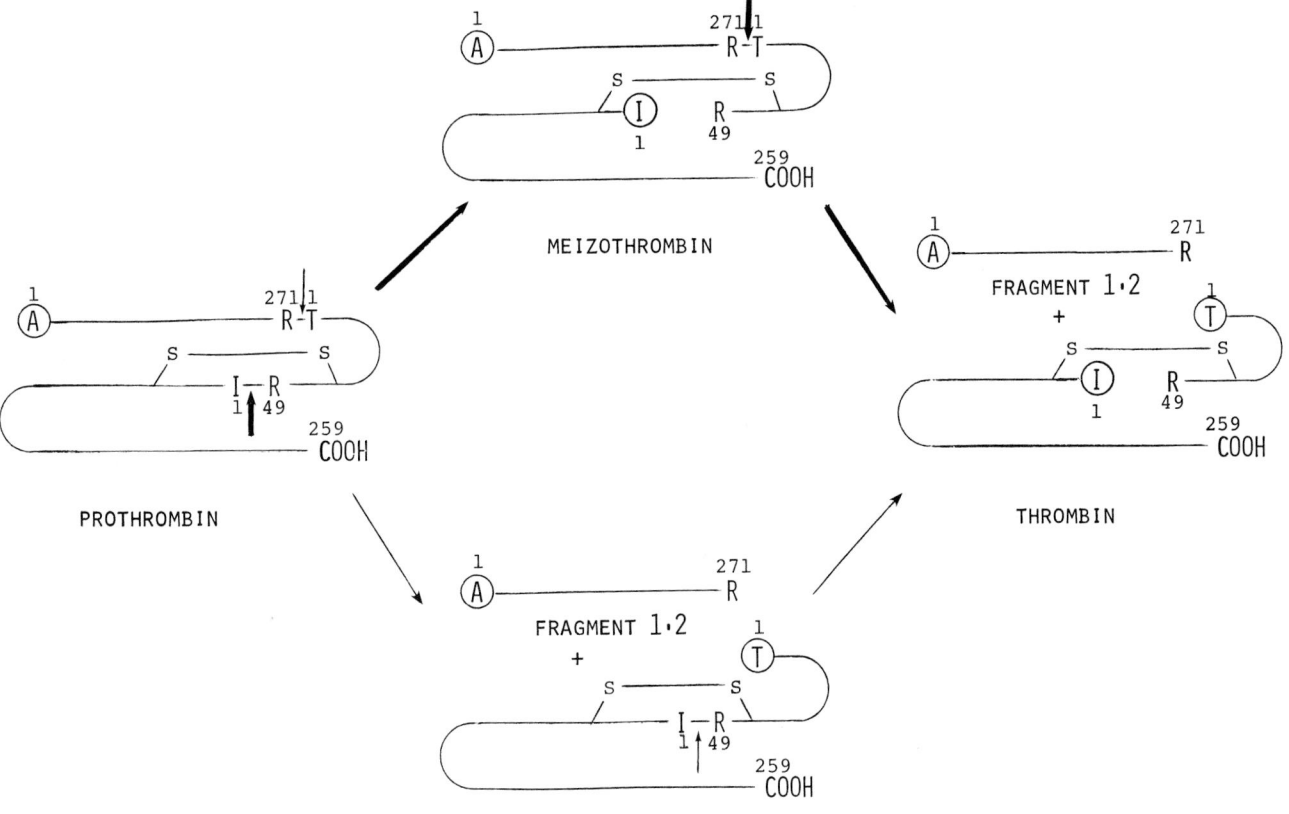

Fig. 84-4 Activation scheme for human prothrombin. In the presence of factor Va, the initial cleavage by factor Xa occurs at R_{49}-I_1 (heavy vertical arrow) generating the meizothrombin intermediate. The second cleavage by factor Xa then occurs at R_{271}-T_1 (heavy vertical arrow) generating thrombin and fragment 1.2. In the absence of factor Va, the initial cleavage by factor Xa occurs at R_{271}-T_1 (thin vertical arrow), generating prethrombin 2 and fragment 1.2. The second cleavage then occurs at R_{49}-I_1 (thin vertical arrow) generating thrombin. Amino-terminal amino acids are circled.

exon. Accordingly, the seventh intron is present immediately following kringle 2 (Glu_{249}). The remaining introns in the gene for prothrombin occur throughout the molecule, including five within the catalytic domain (Fig. 84-3).

The gene for human prothrombin contains 30 copies of *Alu* repetitive DNA and two copies of partial *Kpn*I repeats. These repeats constitute approximately 40 percent of the human gene for prothrombin. The *Alu* sequences occur in the gene for prothrombin in clusters, with 20 being present in the 12th intron (intron L). The human haploid genome contains about 300,000 copies of the *Alu* repetitive sequences that are about 300 nucleotides in length and show about 80 percent nucleo-

Table 84-3 Location and Size of Exons and Introns in the Gene for Human Prothrombin

Exon	Nucleotide positions	Length, bp	Amino acids	Intervening sequence	Nucleotide positions	Length, bp	Number of Alu repeats
I	+1–79	79 + *	−43 to −17	A	80–465	386	
II	466–626	161	−17 to 37	B	627–1285	659	
III	1286–1310	25	38–46	C	1311–1552	242	
IV	1553–1603	51	46–63	D	1604–3929	2326	4
V	3930–4035	106	63–98	E	4036–4131	96	
VI	4132–4268	137	98–144	F	4269–6606	2338	3
VII	6607–6921	315	144–249	G	6922–7245	324	
VIII	7246–7374	129	249–292	H	7375–7458	84	
IX	7459–7585	127	292–334	I	7586–8742	1157	2
X	8743–8910	168	334–390	J	8911–9407	497	
XI	9408–9581	174	390–448	K	9582–10123	542	1
XII	10124–10305	182	448–509	L	10306–19752	9447	20†
XIII	19753–19823	71	509–532	M	19824–19969	146	
XIV	19970–20210	241	533-polyA site				

*The length of the 5′ noncoding region of the mRNA for human prothrombin is unknown; therefore, the length of exon I is measured from the initiator methionine.
†This intervening sequence also has two copies of partial *Kpn* repeats.
SOURCE: Ref. 56.

Table 84-4 Intron-Exon Splice Junction Sequences in the Gene for Human Prothrombin

Intron	Exon	Splice junction sequences			Exon
		5′	Intron	3′	
A	ATG	GTAAGG	————	CCACCGCCTTTACAG	T
B	ACG	GTGAGC	————	GCCCTTGTTTTTCAG	G
C	CAG	GTGAGC	————	CTGGGTCTTTTCCAG	C
D	AAG	GTGAGC	————	GTGGGGTCTCCGCAG	G
E	TGA	GTGAGT	————	AATTTCCTCTTCCAG	A
F	GTG	GTAGGC	————	CCCCTCACCCACCAG	G
G	GTG	GTGAGC	————	CCTGGGTCCCAACAG	A
H	CAG	GTGAGG	————	TGGCTTGCTCTGCAG	A
I	TTG	GTGTGT	————	TGCTGCCCCTCCCAG	G
J	AAG	GTACAG	————	TTGGGGTCTCTGCAG	G
K	CAG	GTGGGC	————	CTTCCTTCCCCAAAG	C
L	CTG	GCAAGT	————	CTGTTCTCTTTCAAG	G
M	AAG	GTAAGC	————	ATCTTTCTTCTTCAG	A
Consensus sequence*	^C_AAG	GT^A_GAGT	————	$^T_C$$^T_C$$^T_C$$^T_C$$^T_C$$^T_C$$^T_C$$^T_C$$^T_C$$^T_C$$^T_C$$^T_CN^T_C$AG	G

*From Ref. 70.
SOURCE: Ref. 56.

tide sequence identity.[71,72] This is equivalent to about one *Alu* repetitive sequence in every 6 kb of human DNA. Thus, the prothrombin gene has an unusually high concentration of these repetitive sequences whose function is presently unknown.

Biosynthesis of Prothrombin

A number of steps are required for the biosynthesis of prothrombin as well as the other vitamin K-dependent proteins in liver. Initially, large mRNAs are synthesized in the nucleus of the hepatocyte for each of these proteins and processed by a capping reaction at the 5′ end, removal of the RNA corresponding to the introns, and polyadenylation at the 3′ end of the mRNA. For prothrombin, this results in a mature mRNA of approximately 2000 nucleotides that is transported from the nucleus into the cytoplasm of the cell. Translation of the mature mRNA for prothrombin on the ribosomal machinery results in an immature polypeptide chain that contains a prepro leader sequence of 43 amino acids[56] (Figs. 84-3 and 84-5). Removal of the prepro leader sequence by proteolytic processing gives rise to the mature protein of 579 amino acids that circulates in plasma.

The prepro leader sequence of human prothrombin and the other vitamin K-dependent proteins show considerable amino acid sequence similarity[28,29,33–36,41,42,56,73] (Fig. 84-5). Each contains an initiator methionine followed by a very hydropho-

bic region of 13 to 17 residues that is required for transport of these proteins into the lumen of the rough endoplasmic reticulum prior to their passage into the Golgi apparatus. The hydrophobic sequence is followed by a signal peptidase recognition site where cleavage of the pre or signal sequence occurs. Cleavage of the pre sequence occurs as a cotranslational event on the lumen side of the rough endoplasmic reticulum during polypeptide elongation. The pre sequences are 28, 23, and 18 amino acids in factor IX,[73] factor X,[74,75] and protein C,[76] respectively. The length of the pre sequence for prothrombin, factor VII, and protein S has not been established. The pre sequence in the vitamin K-dependent proteins is followed by a pro sequence ranging from 17 to 24 residues in length. This region is important for the carboxylation of the vitamin K-dependent proteins and appears to serve as a recognition site for the carboxylase complex.[73,76] The carboxyl end of the pro leader sequence serves as a recognition site for a processing protease(s) that preferentially cleaves peptide bonds following two basic amino acid residues, such as Lys-Arg or Arg-Arg. Cleavage of the pro leader sequence gives rise to an amino-terminal Ala in the mature polypeptide chain of prothrombin, factor VII, factor X, protein C, and protein S and to a Tyr in factor IX.

The vitamin K-dependent carboxylation reaction occurs on the first 10 glutamic acid residues in prothrombin. The stop signal preventing carboxylation of Glu residues beyond the first 10 is not known. Additional processing occurs in prothrombin by the addition of several carbohydrate chains.

Fig. 84-5 Prepro leader sequences of the vitamin K-dependent proteins present in human plasma. The apparent hydrophobic core of each signal or pre sequence is boxed. The known signal peptidase cleavage sites are indicated by arrowheads. Identical or homologous amino acid residues within the propeptide regions of each protein are also boxed. Numbering of the residues is relative to the amino terminus of the mature proteins circulating in plasma. (Modified from Foster et al.[76])

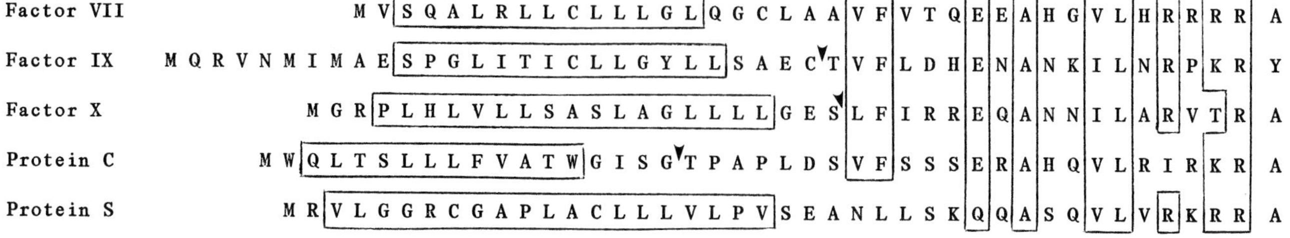

Variants of Prothrombin

Thus far, more than 15 abnormal prothrombins have been reported and nine have been isolated and characterized. Prothrombin Barcelona was originally reported by Josso and coworkers[77] as a dysprothrombinemia with an abnormal molecule that generated low thrombin activity. This abnormality has been shown to be due to a replacement of an Arg by a Cys residue at position 271.[78,*]

The peptide bond between Arg_{271}-Thr is one of two sites that must be cleaved by factor Xa during the conversion of prothrombin to thrombin, and the replacement of an Arg by a Cys residue prevents this cleavage (Fig. 84-4). The Cys residue in prothrombin Barcelona apparently results from a single base change of C to T in the CGT triplet originally coding for arginine in the gene for human prothrombin. This type of nucleotide transition probably occurs in this mutation since CG is a major site of methylation in genomic DNA and the deamination of methyl cytosine to thymidine would give rise to this base change.

Prothrombin Tokushima is an abnormal protein that is readily converted to thrombin by factor Xa in the presence of factor Va, phospholipid, and calcium ions.[80] The newly generated thrombin, however, shows only 21 percent clotting activity relative to normal thrombin. The abnormal thrombin also exhibits reduced platelet aggregating activity. Amino acid sequence analysis indicates that the reduced clotting activity in this protein is due to the replacement of Arg_{98} by Trp in the catalytic chain of the abnormal molecule. This mutation can also be explained by a single base change of C to T in the triplet of CGG coding for arginine in the normal molecule. The reduced fibrinogen clotting activity for thrombin Tokushima also suggests that Arg_{98} located adjacent to the essential Asp_{99} (Fig. 84-3) is important for the binding of fibrinogen to the enzyme. This is consistent with the increased K_m and decreased catalytic rate constant for the abnormal enzyme.

Prothrombin Madrid,[81,82] prothrombin Cardeza,[83] and prothrombin Clamart[84] appear to be due to defects similar to prothrombin Barcelona in that the zymogen is not converted to thrombin by factor Xa. In contrast, prothrombin Metz,[85–87] prothrombin Salakta,[88] and prothrombin Molise[89] apparently have abnormalities in the thrombin portion of the molecule. Recently, prothrombin Quick[62] has been separated into two components designated thrombin Quick I and thrombin Quick II.[90] Thrombin Quick I appears to be an abnormality in the fibrinogen binding site, while thrombin Quick II is an abnormality resulting in the complete loss of catalytic activity.

DEFICIENCY OF PROTHROMBIN IN ADDITION TO FACTORS VII, IX, AND X

A number of patients have been described who have a deficiency of prothrombin as well as factor VII, factor IX, and factor X.[91–95] The first patient identified was a 3-month-old girl with a history of hemorrhagic episodes and undetectable plasma levels of prothrombin, factor VII, factor IX, and factor X.[91,92] Administration of large doses of vitamin K to the patient dramatically increased the coagulant and antigen level for each of the four coagulation factors. In the case of prothrombin, the plasma coagulant activity increased to 7 percent of normal, while the antigen level increased to 57 percent of normal. Crossed immunoelectrophoresis of the patient's plasma indicated the presence of more than one form of prothrombin, including a minor form that corresponded to normal prothrombin and a major form that contained little or no γ-carboxyglutamic acid. These data suggest an abnormality in the vitamin K-dependent carboxylation complex in this patient, resulting in little or no carboxylation of prothrombin and the other vitamin K-dependent proteins. Furthermore, these data suggest that liver disease, malabsorption, or abnormal transport of vitamin K was not responsible for the combined deficiency of the vitamin K-dependent proteins.

FACTOR VII

Factor VII participates in the middle phase of the blood coagulation cascade where it is converted to factor VIIa in the presence of either thrombin, factor Xa, factor IXa, or factor XIIa[96–100] (Fig. 84-1). Factor VIIa in turn converts factor IX to factor IXa[101] and/or factor X to factor Xa.[102] Factor VIIa requires a cell-surface glycoprotein cofactor called tissue factor for the activation of either factor IX or factor X. Tissue factor is present in the plasma membrane of endothelial cells and binds to factor VIIa or factor VII following vascular injury. Tissue factor, however, is not accessible to factor VII without prior tissue damage. Generation of the factor VII-tissue factor complex may represent the major pathway for initiating the blood coagulation cascade leading to fibrin formation.

Human factor VII is a single-chain glycoprotein with a molecular weight of 50,000 and an amino-terminal sequence of Ala-Asn-Ala-Phe-Leu[28,103] (Fig. 84-6). The protein is initially synthesized with a prepro leader sequence of 38 amino acids, and this peptide is removed by signal peptidase and a processing protease. This results in a mature protein circulating in plasma composed of 406 amino acids. The Gla-containing region contains 10 γ-carboxyglutamic acid residues and is followed by two growth factor domains, the first of which probably contains β-hydroxyaspartic acid at position 63. β-Hydroxyaspartic acid (or β-hydroxyasparagine) is present in the growth factor domains of bovine factor VII as well as factor IX, factor X, protein C, and protein S.[104–109] Factor VII also contains carbohydrate, a portion of which is probably attached to Asn_{145} in the light chain and Asn_{170} in the heavy chain of the activated molecule.

The activation of human factor VII involves the cleavage of an internal Arg_{152}-Ile peptide bond[28] (Fig. 84-6). This generates factor VIIa, which is composed of a light chain of 152 amino acids and a heavy chain of 254 amino acids. These two chains are held together by a single disulfide bond. The heavy chain of the molecule contains the catalytic domain, including the active site residues of His_{41}, Asp_{90}, and Ser_{192}. No activation peptide is liberated during the activation reaction, and, thus, factor VII and factor VIIa have essentially the same molecular weight.

Human tissue factor ($M_r \approx 44,000$) is a single-chain glycoprotein composed of 263 amino acids.[110–113] It is initially synthesized with a signal peptide of 32 amino acids that is cleaved from the growing polypeptide chain by signal peptidase. This generates the mature membrane-bound glycoprotein with an

---

*This residue was originally assigned to position 273 according to the early protein sequence analysis of prothrombin.[79] In these studies, a Glu-Glu peptide was reported at positions 266 and 267. Subsequent amino acid sequence analysis and sequence analysis of the cDNA and the gene coding for human prothrombin indicated the absence of this peptide in the normal molecule.

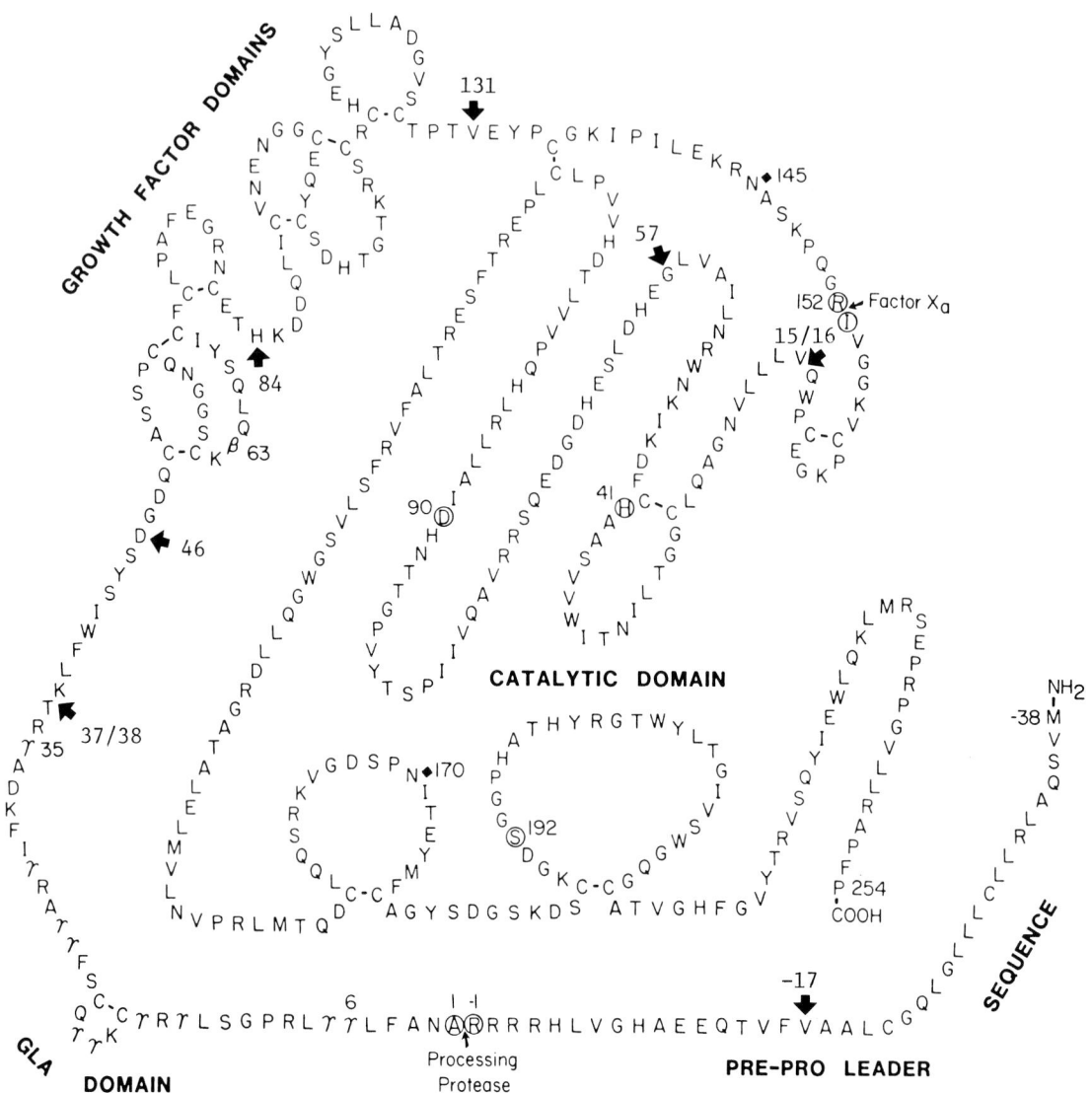

Fig. 84-6 Amino acid sequence and tentative structure of human prepro factor VII. The locations of the seven introns are shown by heavy arrows. The prepro leader sequence is cleaved during protein biosynthesis to give rise to the mature protein with an amino-terminal sequence of A-N-A-F-. The single peptide bond cleaved by factor Xa during the activation reaction is shown with a small arrow. The three amino acids in the catalytic domain (H₄₁, D₉₀, S₁₉₂) that participate in catalysis are circled, while the tentative carbohydrate attachment sites are shown with solid diamonds. The amino acids are numbered as follows, starting with the amino-terminal end of the protein: −38 to −1 = prepro leader sequence; +1 to 152 = light chain of factor VIIa; 1 to 254 = catalytic chain of factor VIIa. The single-letter code for amino acids is shown in the legend to Fig. 84-3. β = β-hydroxyaspartic acid. (*Modified from Hagen et al.*[28] *and O'Hara et al.*[124])

amino-terminal sequence of Ser-Gly-Thr-Thr (Fig. 84-7). The apparent extracellular domain at the amino-terminal end of the protein is about 219 residues in length and presumably contains the potential factor VII or factor VIIa binding site. This region is followed by a membrane-spanning region of 23 hydrophobic residues and a cytoplasmic region of 21 residues at the carboxyl end of the molecule.

Genetic Aspects

Congenital factor VII deficiency is a very rare condition. It is inherited as an autosomal recessive disorder with variable expression and high penetrance.[114–117] There is not an absolute correlation between a decreased plasma level of factor VII and bleeding symptoms. Cerebral hemorrhage has been reported to occur in 16 percent of the factor VII-deficient patients.[118] Patients with a coagulant activity (factor VII:C) of <0.03 U/

ml as measured in a clotting assay and a factor VII antigen level (factor VII:Ag) down to 20 percent of normal showed no bleeding problems.[119] [A unit (U) is defined as the amount of factor VII coagulant activity in 1 ml of normal pooled plasma.]

The gene for factor VII is located on chromosome 13 in the region q34-qter, which is very close to the gene for factor X.[120–123] The complete sequence for the gene for factor VII has been determined and found to span about 12.8 kb of DNA.[124] The mRNA for factor VII can undergo alternative splicing, forming a major transcript from eight exons and a very minor transcript utilizing nine exons.[28] The additional exon located in the 5' end of the gene results in a prepro leader sequence of 60 amino acids rather than the usual 38 amino acids (Fig. 84-5). The smallest exon in the gene for factor VII codes for nine amino acids (residues 38 to 46 in the light chain), while the largest exon codes for 198 amino acids (residues 57 to 254 in the heavy chain). The introns range in size from 68 nucleotides (intron C) to 2574 nucleotides (intron

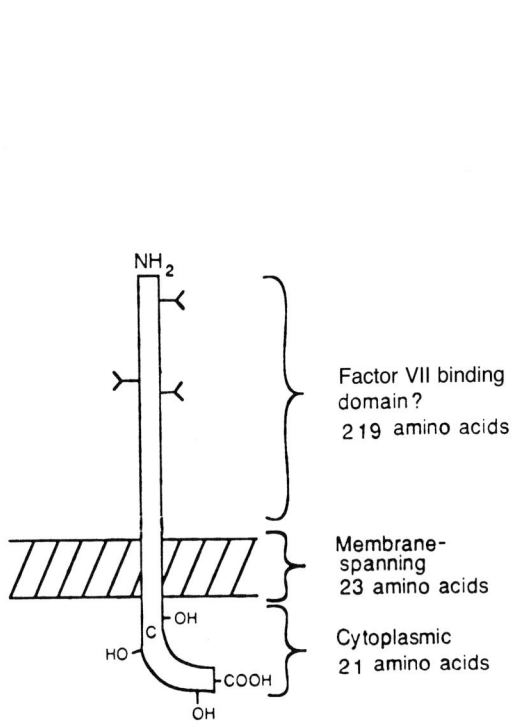

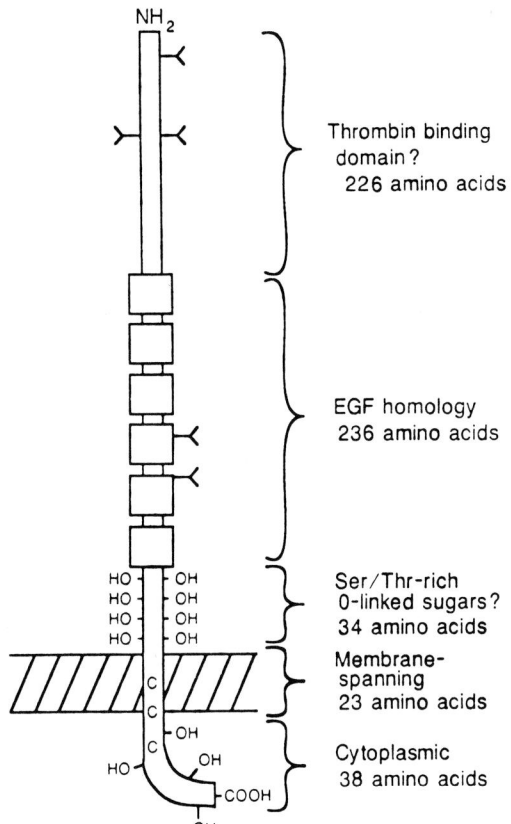

Fig. 84-7 *Structural domains of human tissue factor (left panel) and human thrombomodulin (right panel). The extracellular amino-terminal region of each portion is shown above the membrane (diagonal bar) and the cytoplasmic carboxyl-terminal region is shown below the membrane. Epidermal growth factor domains (EGF) are shown by open squares. Potential N-glycosylation sites are indicated by Y, while the hydroxy amino acids in the Ser/Thr-rich region and the cytoplasmic region are indicated by —OH. Cysteine residues in the transmembrane region and cytoplasmic regions are also indicated by C. (Modified from Scarpati et al.,[110] Spicer et al.,[111] Morrissey et al.,[112] Fisher et al.,[113] and Wen et al.[323])*

A). All the intron-exon splice junctions follow the GT-AG rule.[69] The gene for factor VII is free of *Alu* repetitive sequences.[124] It does contain, however, five regions of similar tandem repeats that are also similar to hypervariable minisatellite DNA. Minisatellite tandem repeats can result in polymorphism in the human genome due to allelic variation in the copy number of the repeats.

Five of the seven introns in the gene for factor VII are located in the regions coding for the amino terminal half of the protein (Fig. 84-6). The first intron occurs in the prepro leader sequence (Val$_{-17}$), while the second follows the Gla domain (between Thr$_{37}$ and Lys$_{38}$). The third intron is located just prior to the first growth factor domain (Asp$_{46}$). The fourth intron is located between the two growth factor domains (His$_{84}$), while the fifth intron is present just after the second growth factor domain (Val$_{131}$). The last two introns are present within the catalytic domain (between Gln$_{15}$ and Val$_{16}$ and Gly$_{57}$). The remaining portion of the protein (from Gly$_{57}$ to Pro$_{254}$) is coded by a single exon. These seven introns in the gene for factor VII are located in the same position as the seven introns in factor IX, factor X, and protein C and in the same position as the first three introns in prothrombin relative to the amino acid sequence of each of these proteins[30,33,56,124–126] (Table 84-5). The introns in the genes of this family of vitamin K-dependent proteins differ greatly, however, in their size and DNA sequence, with the exception of intron C in factor VII and protein C. The similarity of the amino acid sequence and the organization of the genes in this family of proteins have led to the proposal that the vitamin K-dependent proteins have evolved from a common ancestry through gene duplication and exon shuffling.[30,33,56,124–127]

Variants of Factor VII

Several families with factor VII deficiency have been described.[128–131] Some patients with a decrease in factor VII coagulant activity (factor VII:C) are reported to suffer from thromboembolism.[128,129,131,132] Several molecular variants of factor VII also exist showing variable patterns with regard to the level of factor VII antigen (factor VII:Ag) and factor VII coagulant activity (factor VII:C).[133–136] Furthermore, the factor VII activity may vary depending on what thromboplastin is used in the coagulation assay. One variant has been called factor VII$_{PADUA}$.[137,138] Several other variants have also been described.[139,140]

Factor VII has been found to be increased during pregnancy, delivery and puerperium most likely occurring in a phospholipid-factor VII complex.[141,142] In case of bleeding, factor VII-deficient patients can be given plasma which will be sufficient in most cases. Factor VII concentrates have also been prepared.[143,144]

Human factor VIIa has been successfully used to treat hemophilia A patients with antibodies against factor VIII.[145] By administration of factor VIIa, a direct activation of factor X may occur after complex formation between VIIa and tissue factor has occurred at the site of injury (Fig. 84-1). These reactions can occur in the absence of factor VIII.

Table 84-5 Comparison of the Location, Splice Junction Type, and Size of the Introns in the Genes for Human Factors VII, IX, and X, Protein C, and Prothrombin

Intron	Protein	Location* (amino acid)	Splice junction type	Size, bp
A	Factor VII	−17	I	2574
	Factor IX	−17	I	6206
	Factor X	−17	I	≈5000
	Protein C	−19	I	1263
	Prothrombin	−17	I	386
B	Factor VII	37/38	0	1919
	Factor IX	38/39	0	188
	Factor X	37/38	0	≈7400
	Protein C	37/38	0	1462
	Prothrombin	37/38	0	659
C	Factor VII	46	I	68
	Factor IX	47	I	3689
	Factor X	46	I	≈950
	Protein C	46	I	92
	Prothrombin	46	I	242
D	Factor VII	84	I	1908
	Factor IX	85	I	7163
	Factor X	84	I	≈1800
	Protein C	92	I	102
E	Factor VII	131	I	971
	Factor IX	128	I	2565
	Factor X	128	I	≈2900
	Protein C	137	I	2668
F	Factor VII	15/16	0	595
	Factor IX	15/16	0	9473
	Factor X	15/16	0	≈3400
	Protein C	15/16	0	873
G	Factor VII	57	I	816
	Factor IX	54	I	668
	Factor X	55	I	≈1700
	Protein C	55	I	1129

NOTE: Type 0 splice junctions have introns between the triplets coding for two amino acids; type I splice junctions have introns between the first and second nucleotides of the triplet coding for one amino acid. From Ref. 125.
*Numbering for introns A through E refers to light chain and for introns F and G refers to heavy chain.

FACTOR IX

Like most coagulation factors, factor IX was first recognized as a special entity by the observation that hemophilia could be caused by a deficiency of two different plasma proteins. In 1947, Pavlovsky found that the prolonged coagulation time of plasma from one hemophilia patient normalized the clotting time of another hemophilia plasma. Further studies[146,147] clearly showed two types of hemophilia, and both were inherited as X-linked disorders that were clinically indistinguishable from each other. One was already called hemophilia A and was caused by a deficiency of factor VIII. The other was designated hemophilia B and was defined as being caused by a deficiency of factor IX (Christmas factor, plasma thromboplastin component, β-prothromboplastin).

Factor IX participates in the middle stages of the blood coagulation cascade and is converted to factor IXa in the presence of either factor XIa and calcium ions[148,149] or factor VIIa, tissue factor, and calcium ions.[101,150] (Fig. 84-1). Factor IXa then activates factor X in the presence of factor VIIIa, calcium ions, and phospholipid.[151,152]

Human factor IX is a single-chain glycoprotein with a molecular weight of 56,800 and an amino-terminal sequence of Tyr-Asn-Ser-Gly-Lys[29] (Fig. 84-8). The mature protein circulating in plasma contains 415 amino acids, including 12 residues of γ-carboxyglutamic acid. The human protein also contains 0.3 equivalents of β-hydroxyaspartic acid at position 64 in the first of the two growth factor domains.[106–108] The function of β-hydroxyaspartic acid in factor IX has not been established. Equilibrium dialysis experiments have shown that it does not participate in the high affinity calcium binding sites present in factor IX.[153] Factor IX also contains 17% carbohydrate,[154] a portion of which is attached to asparagine residues 12 and 22 in the activation peptide.[29]

Human factor IX is converted to a serine protease during the coagulation process by the cleavage of two internal peptide bonds[148,149] (Figs. 84-8 and 84-9). These cleavages occur initially at the Arg_{145}-Ala bond with the formation of factor IXα followed by the cleavage of the Arg_{35}-Val bond leading to the generation of factor IXαβ. The second cleavage releases an activation glycopeptide of 35 amino acids. The light chain of factor IXaβ contains the Gla domain and the two growth factor domains, while the heavy chain contains the catalytic domain that includes the active site residues of His_{41}, Asp_{89}, and Ser_{185}. The light chain and the heavy chain of factor IXaβ are linked together by a single disulfide bond involving Cys_{132} in the light chain and Cys_{109} in the heavy (Figs. 84-8 and 84-9). The cleavage of the two internal arginine peptide bonds is catalyzed by either factor XIa in the presence of calcium ions or by factor VIIa in the presence of tissue factor, phospholipid, and calcium ions. Cleavage of only the Arg_{35}-Val bond gives rise to factor IXaα, an enzyme with a marked reduction in biologic activity (Fig. 84-9). This activation reaction occurs in the presence of a protease from Russell's viper venom (RVV-X).[155]

Genetic Aspects

Hemophilia B (factor IX deficiency) as well as hemophilia A (factor VIII deficiency) are X-linked bleeding disorders. The incidence of hemophilia is about one in every 10,000 individuals, being similar in different parts of the world and in different races. Hemophilialike symptoms have been described in ancient history, both in the Talmud and Egyptian history. Accordingly, the mutations causing a defect in factor IX or factor VIII are probably rather common. About 20 percent of the total hemophiliac population is deficient in factor IX (hemophilia B). Hemophilia in females is extremely rare but has been described.[156–160] In most cases, hemophilia B in females is associated with a chromosomal disorder, such as Turner syndrome or mosaicism.[156–158] Some reported cases may represent symptoms in heterozygotes.[161–165]

The genes for human factor IX and factor VIII are close to each other on the tip of the long arm of the X chromosome at q26-q27.[166,167] The gene for factor IX is about 34 kb in size, and its complete nucleotide sequence has been established.[30,31] The gene contains seven introns and eight exons within the coding and 3′ noncoding regions of the gene (Table 84-6). The eight exons code for 415 amino acids constituting the mature protein that circulates in plasma. The first two exons also code for a prepro leader sequence of 46 amino acids (Figs. 84-5 and 84-8), and the intron-exon splice junction sequences follow the GT-AG rule.[69] The introns contain four *Alu* repetitive sequences and range in size from 188 nucleotides (intron B) to 9473 nucleotides (intron F).

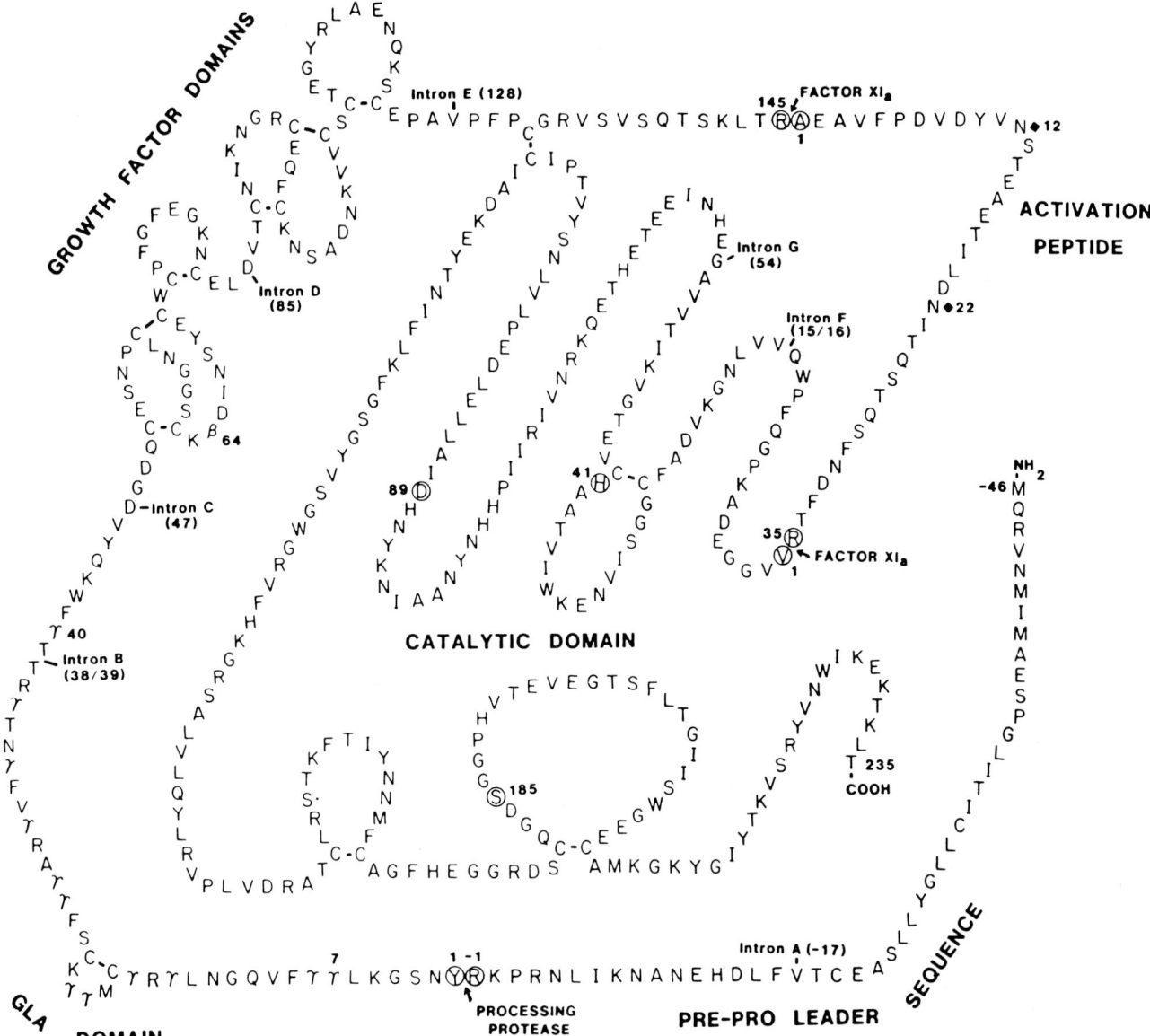

Fig. 84-8 Amino acid sequence and tentative structure for human prepro factor IX. The locations of the seven introns (A to G) are shown in the various regions of the protein. The prepro leader sequence is cleaved during protein biosynthesis to give rise to the mature protein with an amino-terminal sequence of Y-N-S-G-. The two peptide bonds cleaved by factor XIa during the activation reaction are shown with small arrows. The three amino acids in the catalytic domain (H_{41}, D_{89}, S_{185}) that participate in catalysis are circled, while the two potential carbohydrate attachment sites in the activation peptide are shown with solid diamonds. The amino acids are numbered as follows starting with the amino-terminal end of the protein: −46 to −1 = prepro leader sequence; +1 to 145 = light chain of factor IXa; 1 to 35 = activation peptide; 1 to 235 = catalytic chain of factor IXa. The single-letter code for amino acids is shown in the legend to Fig. 84-3. β = β-hydroxyaspartic acid. *(From Yoshitake et al.[30] Used by permission.)*

Normal Variants of Factor IX

McGraw et al.[168] found that either alanine or threonine may occur at position 148 in factor IX with no effect on biologic activity. Also, a fraction of the normal population seems to have a variant in the factor IX molecule detected by a special monoclonal antibody.[169] Monoclonal antibodies against factor IX have been used for determinations of factor IX:Ag[170,171] and also for preparing factor IX-deficient plasma.[172] The epitope structure of factor IX was also studied with a monoclonal antibody.[173] By using monoclonal antibodies, more sensitive methods for estimating factor IX:Ag can be employed. Such methods facilitate the measurement of factor IX:Ag in patients with moderate or severe factor IX deficiency. Furthermore, the monoclonal antibodies may provide additional valuable information to help identify carrier status. Women who are heterozygous for factor IX deficiency have been found to have factor IX:Ag in excess of factor IX coagulant activity (factor IX:C). This also occurred in cases from kindred classed as hemophilia B⁺ or Bᴿ.[174]

Abnormal Variants of Factor IX

All patients with hemophilia B have a prolonged coagulation time and a decreased factor IX:C in their plasma. However, in 1956 two genetic types of hemophilia B were described. In one case, plasma from one patient's blood after barium sulfate adsorption blocked a specific inhibitor against factor IX in the assay plasma, whereas in a second case, a similar fraction from

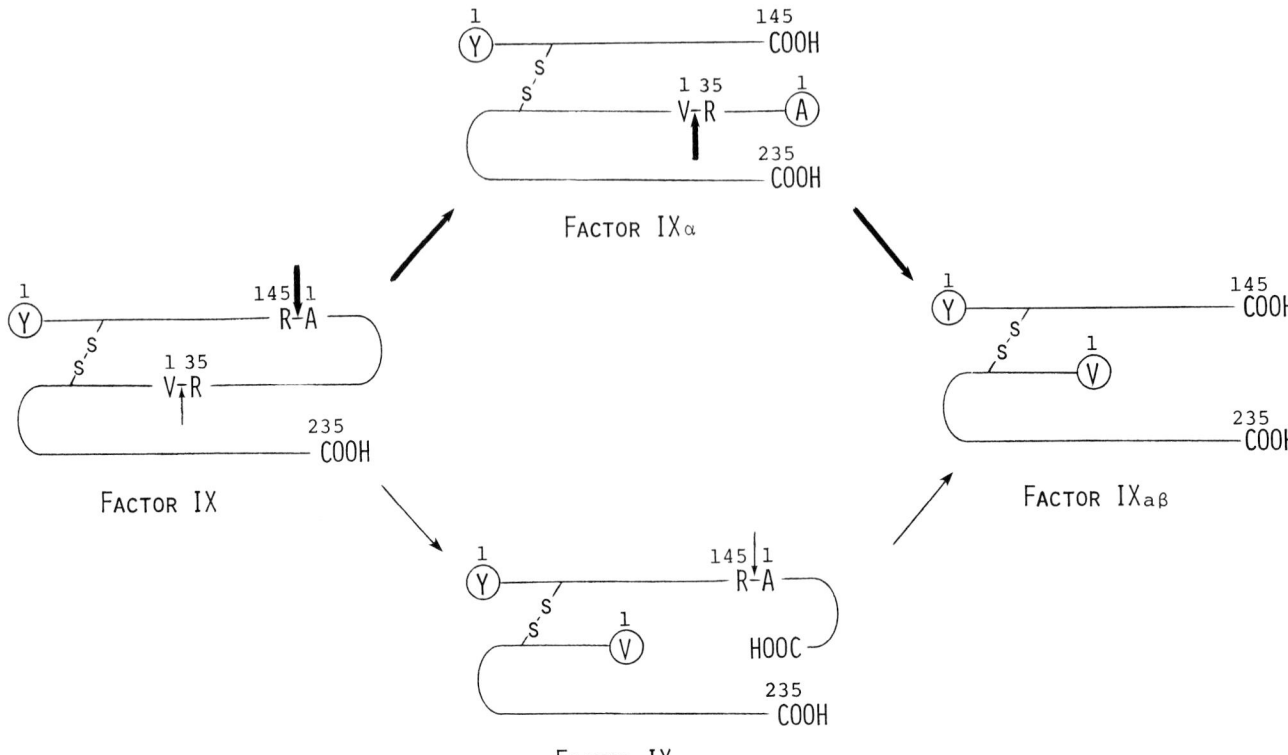

Fig. 84-9 Activation scheme for human factor IX. In the presence of factor XIa, the principal cleavage occurs initially at R_{145}-A_1 (heavy vertical arrow) generating the factor IXα intermediate. The second cleavage then occurs at R_{35}-V_1 (heavy vertical arrow) generating factor IXaβ and an activation peptide. Factor IX can also be cleaved initially at R_{35}-V_1 (thin vertical arrow) by factor XIa generating factor IXaα. The second cleavage then occurs at R_{145}-A_1 (thin vertical arrow) generating factor IXaβ and an activation peptide. Amino-terminal amino acids are circled.

another patient had no effect.[175] Later[176–179] it was shown that approximately 10 percent of all factor IX-deficient patients have factor IX:Ag or cross-reacting material (CRM$^+$) in their plasma. The remaining 90 percent of the factor IX-deficient patients either lack cross-reacting material (CRM$^-$) or have reduced amounts (CRM^R). Patients with severe factor IX deficiency have lower factor IX:Ag levels, while patients with mild defects are within the low, intermediate, or normal range.[180,181] A variant of CRM$^+$ was described by Hougie and Twomey,[182] who found a prolonged one-stage prothrombin time in some patients employing ox brain thromboplastin. Several more variants, called hemophilia BM (or factor IX BM where M refers to the family name of the original patient), were described later.[179,183–185] Patients with hemophilia BM synthesize a factor IX devoid of clotting activity but capable

of inhibiting coagulation in the ox brain prothrombin time assay. Later studies have identified several different abnormal factor IX molecules in patients with hemophilia BM. One was described by Bertina and van der Linden[186] and was called factor IXDEVENTER. In this patient, no cleavage occurs in the Arg_{35}-Val bond which releases the activation peptide (Fig. 84-9). Only the cleavage between the Arg_{145}-Ala bond occurs normally, resulting in factor IXα (Fig. 84-9). A second hemophilia BM variant was described by Osterud et al. in which the factor IX was cleaved normally to factor IXaβ.[187] The defect in this molecule was postulated to be localized somewhere in the heavy chain of the protein. This hemophilia BM molecule was found to inhibit factor X activation by factor VIIa and bovine tissue factor.

Recently, another factor IX BM variant called factor IX

Table 84-6 Location and Size of the Exons and Introns in the Gene for Human Factor IX

Exon	Nucleotide position*	Nucleotide length*	Amino acids†	Intron	Nucleotide position	Nucleotide length
I	1–117	117	−46 to −17	A	118–6325	6206‡
II	6326–6489	164	−17 to 37	B	6490–6677	188
III	6678–6702	25	38–47	C	6703–10391	3689
IV	10392–10505	114	47–85	D	10506–17668	7163
V	17669–17797	129	85–128	E	17798–20362	2565
VI	20363–20565	203	128–195	F	20566–30038	9473
VII	30039–30153	115	196–234	G	30154–30821	668
VIII	30822–32757	1935	234–415			

*Includes 30 nucleotides at the 5′ end and 1390 nucleotides at the 3′ end that are not translated.
†Amino acids coded for by each exon; negative numbers refer to amino acids in the prepro leader sequence.
‡Includes 50 extra nucleotides present in some polymorphic forms of the gene.
SOURCE: Ref. 30.

BMLAKE ELSINORE (factor IX BMLE) was described.[188] Factor IX BMLE was cleaved by either factor XIa or factor VIIa-tissue factor, but the factor IXa had virtually no detectable clotting activity. Another factor IX variant, factor IX BMLONG BEACH (factor IX BMLB), was identified by the same authors in three hemophiliac brothers who also had a moderately prolonged ox brain prothrombin time.[188] Factor IX BMLB was also cleaved by factor XIa and the factor VIIa-tissue factor complex. Three more factor IX BM variants have been described from Japan.[189] Two of these had a factor IX:C of <1%, while the other had a factor IX:C of 1 to 4 percent. All three variants were CRM+. One had a moderately prolonged ox brain prothrombin time, and the other two had substantially prolonged prothrombin time. Factor IX BMNAGOYA (IX:C of <1 percent, with a prolonged prothrombin time) was not cleaved by either factor XIa or RVV-X. Factor IX BMKASHIHARA (IX:C of <1 percent, moderately prolonged prothrombin time) was cleaved only at one site forming factor IXaα. It was not cleaved by the protease from Russell's viper venom (RVV-X). Factor IX BMKASHIHARA behaves similarly to factor IX BMDEVENTER[186] with regard to its activation pattern. However, factor IX BMKASHIHARA has a distinctly shorter ox brain prothrombin time than factor IX BMDEVENTER.[189] The third factor IX BM variant, called factor IX BMNIIGATA (IX:C of 1 to 4 percent, with a prolonged prothrombin time), was cleaved by both factor XIa and RVV-X at a rate similar to normal factor IX.

The first factor IX variants that were described in patients with mild or moderate hemophilia B had substantial amounts of factor IX antigen in their plasmas. Factor IXCHAPEL HILL (IXCH) was reported in 1978[190,191] in a patient with mild bleeding (100 percent factor IX:Ag, 20 percent factor IX:C). The molecular defect was later shown to be a substitution of a histidine for arginine in position 145.[191,192] Arg_{145} is located at the first cleavage site for factor XIa when factor IX is converted to factor IXa (Fig. 84-9). Factor IXCH is cleaved by factor XIa, however, at the second cleavage site (Arg_{35}-Val), giving rise to factor IXaα. In this molecule, the activation peptide remains attached to the light chain. Factor IXaαCH has only about 20 percent of the clotting activity of normal factor IXaβ, but it is essentially the same as normal factor IXaα.[193] By activating factor IXCH with trypsin, it was possible to obtain a factor IXaβ form with a coagulant activity similar to that of normal factor IXaβ. Trypsin cleaves at a lysine bond, giving rise to an activation peptide that contains three additional amino acid residues.[194] This means that the release of an activation peptide is vital for a normal factor IX activity. Also, a defective hydrolysis at the second cleavage site (Arg_{35}-Val) as found in the BM variant factor IXDEVENTER gives rise to a factor IX molecule with low coagulant activity.

Another factor IX variant, factor IXALABAMA, has been isolated from a patient with moderate hemophilia B. This factor IX molecule is activated normally by factor XIa, but the factor IXaβ formed has only about 10 percent of the clotting activity of normal factor IXaβ. Southern analysis of the factor IX gene from the patient with factor IXALABAMA failed to show any gross deletions or rearrangement of the factor IX gene. DNA sequencing, however, revealed a point mutation responsible for the defect of the protein.[195] These experiments demonstrated that an adenine was converted to a guanine in the first nucleotide of exon D, resulting in the conversion of Asp_{47} (GAT) to glycine (GGT). The interactions between factor IXALABAMA and factor VIIIa and phospholipid appear to be abnormal.[196]

Characterization of the genes from other patients has also provided significant information regarding the various abnormalities resulting in factor IX deficiency. In two patients who were CRM−, one had a point mutation in the GT donor splice junction in exon F which was changed to TT.[197] This prevented normal splicing of the mRNA and resulted in no antigen being detectable in the patient's plasma. In another CRM− patient (factor IXSEATTLE 2), a deletion of a single adenine in exon V was observed.[198] This caused a frameshift in the gene resulting in Asp_{85} in the protein being converted to Val and the formation of a stop signal at position 86. Thus, the gene for factor IXSEATTLE 2 codes for a polypeptide of 85 amino acids that terminates after the first growth factor domain. In another group of CRM− patients, significant portions of the gene for factor IX have been deleted.[199–201] In some of these patients, infusion of normal factor IX resulted in antibodies directed against the normal protein.

Two other patients who were CRM+ had abnormalities in their propeptide.[202,203] In one case, the arginine at position −4 was changed to glutamine resulting in the expression of a protein with an amino-terminal extension of 18 additional amino acids. In the second patient (factor IXCAMBRIDGE), the arginine at position −1 was converted to a serine, which prevented the removal of the pro piece from the amino-terminal end of the molecule. In the last two cases, presence of the propeptide on the protein resulted in a defective molecule.

A factor IX variant, factor IXZUTPHEN, with an abnormally high molecular weight of 90,000, has been isolated from a severely affected hemophilia B patient.[184] Factor IXZUTPHEN is thought to have a 33,000-dalton peptide linked to the factor IX protein by disulfide bonds. This abnormal molecule has a reduced affinity for calcium and is not cleaved normally by factor XIa.

Factor IXEINDHOVEN has been isolated from another severely affected hemophilia B patient.[204] This abnormal molecule is cleaved normally to the factor IXaβ form by both factor XIa and the factor VIIa tissue factor complex, but the factor IXaβ formed is unable to convert factor X to factor Xa. This factor IX molecule has very little coagulant activity, and the basic abnormality has been suggested to be a defective interaction with factor VIII.

Recently, another abnormal CRM+ factor IX variant, factor IXLOS ANGELES, was identified.[188] The factor IXLA was activated normally by factor XIa or the factor VIIa-tissue factor complex and exhibited clotting activity of about 5 to 6 percent of normal when activated. It resembles factor IXALABAMA, but the defect is postulated to be related to an important histidine and/or aspartic acid residue.

A rather unusual hemophilia B variant called hemophilia BLEYDEN has been described.[205,206] These patients are severely affected hemophiliacs at birth, being CRM−. However, at about the age of puberty, the factor IX:C as well as the factor IX:Ag begin to increase, and levels around 50 percent are observed in later life. The factor IX in these patients seems to be normal, and the abnormality does not seem to involve the structural portion of the gene.

Clinical Applications of the DNA Technology

DNA sequencing has made it possible to demonstrate polymorphisms in the gene as well as abnormalities in the factor IX in patients with hemophilia B. The Southern blotting method employs a radiolabeled DNA fragment or probe prepared from factor IX cDNA or genomic DNA (Chap. 2).[207] This can be used to identify individuals with hemophilia as well as carriers of hemophilia in prenatal diagnosis.

The Southern method for carrier detection of factor IX deficiency was first described by Peake et al.,[200] who identified a specific 4.8-kb *Eco*RI restriction fragment representative of the normal factor IX gene in a hemophilia B family. This band was absent in the DNA from the affected individual but was present in the father. The DNA from the mother yielded the corresponding fragment at a concentration of about half of that found in normal females, indicating that she was a carrier of the abnormal X chromosome. Using the same technique, prenatal diagnosis can be carried out with various members of the same family. Fetal DNA can be obtained either by culture of the cells from amniotic fluid or by biopsy of the chorionic villi. The usefulness of this approach depends on the ability to demonstrate the presence of the abnormal DNA of the affected mother in the DNA of the child.

Carrier detection and prenatal diagnosis may also be carried out by using restriction fragment length polymorphisms (RFLPs), as described by Botstein et al. (Chaps. 1 and 2).[208] Natural variations occur within restriction enzyme recognition sequences, and multiple alleles may be identified for the normal gene. The presence of a particular restriction site determines the size of the restriction fragment detected by a hybridization probe. Polymorphism within the factor IX gene has been described for the restriction enzymes *Taq*I, *Xmn*I, and *Hin*fI/*Dde*I. Using the factor IX cDNA as a probe and the restriction enzyme *Taq*I, a band of either 1.3 or 1.8 kb was detected in males and in females homozygous for one allele. In heterozygous females, both bands could be seen.[209,210] Recently, a *Bam*HI polymorphism in the factor IX gene was used to determine the carrier status of a female in a hemophilia B family that was uninformative for the other polymorphisms in the factor IX gene.[211] In general, the approach using RFLPs requires an affected male in order to establish which allele is present on the mutant chromosome. Also, carrier detection depends on the ability to demonstrate maternal heterozygosity. The frequency of the polymorphisms detected thus far in the general population is such that carrier diagnosis is possible on an average of only 68 percent of known hemophilia B pedigrees.

Clinical Aspects

Hemophilia B (Christmas disease) like hemophilia A occurs in a severe, moderate, or mild form according to the level of factor IX:C in plasma.[212,213] The clinical symptoms reflect the factor IX:C in plasma irrespective of the level of factor IX:Ag. Severe factor IX deficiency (factor IX:C of <0.01 U/ml) is characterized by spontaneous bleeding, especially in the joints. A unit (U) is defined as the amount of factor IX coagulant activity in 1 ml of normal pooled plasma. The disease is usually diagnosed when the affected male starts crawling or walking. A typical symptom at this stage is the development of large hematomas on the forehead. These hematomas may become the size of a golf ball and cause a dangerous strain on the skin. These hematomas must be watched carefully to avoid skin necrosis or any trauma to the skin. A typical feature for the superficial, subcutaneous hematomas that are often seen in hemophilia patients is the easily palpable subcutaneous infiltrate which never occurs in normal individuals. These characteristics are shared only by very severely thrombocytopenic patients. When the afflicted youngster begins to stand and

walk, recurrent joint bleeding is the most obvious clinical characteristic, appearing as swollen, very painful joint regions. The joints most often affected are the large joints, such as knees and ankles. Muscle bleeding may occur both spontaneously and after trauma in severely affected patients.[214,215] Large volumes of blood may be extravasated in the muscle tissue, resulting in compression of blood vessels and nerves. Muscle necrosis occurs rapidly due to ischemia. Bleeding into the ileopsoas muscle is rather common and presents with pain in the groin associated with local swelling. The patient is unable to stretch in the hip joint. Retroperitoneal bleeding is also rather common and may be difficult to diagnose. Ultrasound studies and computed tomography are both of great help in these situations. Muscle and tissue hematomas should never be aspirated or surgically treated. A serious sequela to deep tissue bleeding is the development of pseudotumors (hemophilic blood cysts). The incidence of such cysts has been reported to be 0.5 to 2 percent.[215-217] Further bleeding will occur with gradual increase in size, resulting in pressure on surrounding structures. These formations may assume enormous dimensions and erode the bone and even destroy adjacent joints and muscles. Finally, they may perforate into the abdomen or intestines. Infections may then supervene.[218,219] Treatment should be aimed at prevention, and all deep hematomas should be treated vigorously with plasma factor IX concentrates. Established pseudotumors may have to be removed surgically under the protection of adequate substitution therapy.[220-222] Intracranial bleeding is still the most common cause of death in hemophilia.[223,224] Any trauma to the head should be treated with prophylactic substitution therapy. Intracranial bleeding may give special problems in patients with mild hemophilia in whom there may be a tendency to underestimate the risks. Gastrointestinal bleeding and bleeding from the urinary tract are also rather common.[225-228] With the development of better plasma concentrates, surgical intervention in the case of peptic ulcers has often been recommended.[222]

It should be kept in mind that bleeding may imitate any disease in hemophiliacs. Thus, a hematoma in the wall of the bowel mimicked an acute appendicitis in a patient, and similar bleeding caused an acute hepatic stasis in another patient.[222] A rule of thumb is to regard any symptom in a hemophiliac as caused by bleeding, and substitution therapy should be started immediately as the diagnostic work proceeds.

Patients with a moderate form of hemophilia (factor IX:C 0.01 to 0.05 U/ml) most often have less severe bleeding, and massive joint bleeding appears less frequently. However, patients having a level of factor IX:C of 0.01 to 0.03 U/ml need substitution treatment to almost the same extent as severe hemophiliacs.[229]

Mild hemophiliacs (factor IX:C 0.05 to 0.50 U/ml) usually do not develop spontaneous joint bleeding. However, they present some special problems. Mild hemophilia often is not diagnosed until adulthood and is then detected at times of surgery or trauma. Such patients may be difficult to manage since they might have unexpected heavy bleeding, and mild hemophilia should be kept in mind as a diagnostic possibility. It should be stressed that gastrointestinal bleeding and hematuria are almost as common in mild hemophilia as in the severe form. After trauma, mild hemophiliacs may develop life-threatening bleeding such as intracranial bleeding and muscle bleeding. Both the patients and their doctors may tend to underestimate the risk resulting in an unnecessary delay in starting treatment.[224,230]

Joint Disease. The typical joint disease is seen mainly in severely affected hemophiliacs. Its clinical pattern is the same in hemophilia A and B. Acute hemarthrosis is most frequent in the knee joints, followed by the elbow, ankle, and wrist.[215] The hip is most often spared, probably because it is protected by the large muscle cuff.[231] Repeated joint bleeding leads to chronic changes of hyperplasia and hyperemia of the synovium, which makes the joint more susceptible to recurrent bleeding.[232] This stresses the need for adequate substitution treatment for each joint bleed to minimize the development of chronic synovitis.

Chronic Arthritis. The chronic degenerative lesions of the joints in hemophilia are characterized by the presence of gross deformity with fixed flexion contractures. The muscle cuffs around the joint are often severely atrophied. Often there are also chronic effusions and pain.[233] Microscopically, the synovium is greatly hypertrophied and heavily infiltrated with inflammatory cells and deposits of iron. Extensive fibrosis and bone cysts are seen. The radiologic findings have been described in detail.[233-235] Osteoporosis is invariable. Loss of cartilage results in loss of joint space, and underlying bone is resorbed with formation of subchondral cysts. Later osteophytic outgrowth may be marked. Resorption of bone occurs especially in the knee joint with production of an enlarged intercondylar fossa, which may lead to differential overgrowth of one of the femoral condyles. Such deformity may result in posterior subluxation of the tibia and lateral shift of the tibia on the femur.[233,236]

Treatment. Care of the patient with hemophilia B includes treatment of acute bleeding episodes, rehabilitation, and management of the chronic musculoskeletal complications, as well as prophylaxis. Since hemophilia care involves many different special requirements, centralization to hemophilia centers has been recommended.[230,237] Such centers should be capable of taking care of the psychological and social problems of the hemophilia family and should provide orthopedic, dental, and surgical treatment. The centers also should provide the laboratory facilities for diagnosis and for monitoring substitution therapy.[238]

Acute Bleeding Episodes Including Surgery. The goal for management of acute episodes is to normalize the hemostatic function by substitution of the missing coagulation protein, factor IX. Factor IX is relatively stable, and the in vivo half-life of 18 to 40 h[239] makes it possible to administer factor IX at longer intervals than those used in hemophilia A. Most often, infusion one to two times daily is enough. However, the in vivo yield is low and is only 20 to 40 percent of the factor IX activity administered as plasma or factor IX concentrate. This has been ascribed to the fact that factor IX is distributed both intra- and extravascularly.[240,241]

To achieve hemostasis, the patient's plasma level of factor IX should be increased to 0.6 to 1.0 U/ml (60 U/kg body weight). In minor bleeding situations, it may be enough to reach a plasma level of 0.2 to 0.4 U/ml. Minor bleeding is often managed by treatment for 1 to 3 days. Major hemorrhages, including muscle hematomas, most often require treatment for 7 to 14 days (50 to 60 U/kg the first day, followed by 20 to 30 U/kg on the following 2 to 4 days, and 10 to 20 U/kg for another 4 to 10 days). At major surgery, a plasma level of 0.6 to 1.0 U/ml plasma is desirable during the operation and for the first one to four postoperative days depending on the

operation. This corresponds to a dose of about 60 U/kg body weight. The dose is then slowly decreased to 30 to 40 U/kg for days 2 to 4 postoperatively (a plasma level of 0.3 to 0.4 U/ml) and later to 10 to 20 U/kg (plasma level of 0.1 to 0.2 U/ml) for another 10 to 15 days.[230,242]

Management of the Chronic Musculoskeletal Complications. Surgical correction of the chronic musculoskeletal defects in hemophilia has become possible with the availability of plasma factor concentrates.[222,233] Successful total arthroplasty of the knee and hip joints has been performed recently in hemophiliacs.[243-245] The chronic synovitis has increasingly been subjected to synovectomy.[246] Although there is some uncertainty about whether the joint function deteriorates after surgical synovectomy,[247] good long-term results have been reported.[248] Chemical synovectomy using radioactive isotopes like colloid ^{198}Au and ^{90}Y[249] has also been reported to be valuable. In chronic hemophilia, physiotherapy for the arthritis is of major importance.

Prophylaxis has been applied in severe hemophilia since the 1960s.[250] The idea was to prevent the development of heavy bleeding in patients with severe hemophilia by raising the factor IX concentration in plasma to a level at which severe spontaneous joint bleeding is rare, i.e., about 0.04 U/ml. This was based on earlier observations[233] where substantially less severe musculoskeletal complications were noted in patients with moderate or mild hemophilia. The prophylactic treatment means that factor IX concentrate (25 to 30 U/kg) is administered regularly about two times weekly.[229,250] Such treatment has decreased the chronic musculoskeletal complications substantially.[229,250] Similar long-term results have recently been reported in patients treated only at times of bleeding.[251,252] The most important point is an increase in the frequency of the treatment, whether this is given regularly without regard to ongoing bleeding or immediately when symptoms are first noted.[253,254]

Home treatment of hemophiliacs is now widely accepted. The patients achieve greater personal freedom, and the delay in receiving treatment is clearly reduced. Also, financial costs are lowered.[252,255]

Factor IX Concentrates. Factor IX is rather stable and retains about 80 percent of its activity in plasma stored at 4°C for up to 3 months.[215] Plasma therefore can be used in the replacement therapy of hemophilia B, but this method does not permit normalization of the plasma level of factor IX in patients with severe hemophilia B.

Factor IX concentrates are prepared by adsorption of the vitamin K-dependent coagulation factors (prothrombin and factors VII, X, and IX) on tricalcium phosphate,[256,257] DEAE-cellulose,[258,259] or DEAE-Sephadex.[260] The method of Tullis et al. has been used for most of the commercially available factor IX concentrates.[260] The starting material most commonly used is the supernatant from the production of cryoprecipitate for treatment of hemophilia A. The adsorbed vitamin K-dependent factors are eluted with phosphate or citrate buffers, and the final product is lyophilized. Such concentrates contain approximately equal amounts of prothrombin and factors 2X and IX. The content of factor VII varies substantially in different batches. The clinical experience with such factor IX concentrates has been reported by several groups.[222,242,259-261]

SIDE EFFECTS OF FACTOR IX CONCENTRATES. Thromboembolic complications following the administration of factor IX concentrates were reported.[128,262-266] The thrombogenic potential was found to vary between different preparations[267] and was ascribed to the presence of activated coagulation factors.[268] Also, the content of phospholipids probably derived from platelets remaining in the plasma used for the preparation was found to be important.[269] By improving the preparation methods with the focus on preventing activation of the coagulation zymogens, these side effects have become rarer. However, after administration of high doses of factor IX concentrates, as is necessary for treating hemophilia B patients with an inhibitor against factor IX, signs of a systemic activation of the coagulation system do occur.[270]

The factor IX concentrates are prepared from large plasma pools and are therefore associated with a high frequency of hepatitis. The risk of transmission of hepatitis B virus has decreased since screening of all plasma used for preparation of blood factor concentrates was introduced in the late 1970s. However, increased liver transaminases have been found in most of the severely affected hemophilia B patients, indicating a high incidence of hepatitis, especially non-A, non-B types.[271,272]

Acquired immunodeficiency syndrome (AIDS) has recently been recognized as one of the serious hazards of blood transfusion and especially of administration of plasma-derived products. Factor IX concentrates are most often prepared from plasma pooled from more than 2000 blood donors. As pointed out above, the risk of transmitting virus-borne disease increases substantially with the number of plasma donors involved. Hemophiliacs have been found to have antibodies against human immunodeficiency virus (HIV) in a rather high percentage (64 to 85 percent).[273,274] In hemophilia B, a somewhat lower incidence (39 percent) of antibodies to HIV has been reported.[273] The cumulative incidence of AIDS in hemophiliacs was reported to be about 3 percent in North America and about 2 percent in the United Kingdom in 1985.[273] The number of hemophilia-associated AIDS cases has increased each year since 1981, but not at an exponential rate. The relevance of AIDS-related complex and lymphadenopathy syndrome is, however, still not fully understood. The HIV is heat-labile[275,276] and can therefore be destroyed in coagulation factor concentrates subjected to heat treatment. The most effective heat treatment is the one performed in liquid stage.[275]

Other Forms of Treatment. Danazol has been reported to increase both factor IX and factor VII in the plasma,[277] but this has not been confirmed in other studies.[278,279] In fact, the two latter reports[278,279] pointed out that an increased bleeding frequency and increased fibrinolytic activity occurred during danazol treatment. Protein C and plasminogen showed the most significant increase during administration of danazol.

Antibodies against factor IX develop in about 10 percent of patients with severe hemophilia B. In some patients with antibodies, major gene deletions were demonstrated.[199] In patients with antibodies against factor IX:C, infused factor IX as part of factor IX complexes or plasma is rapidly neutralized and does not induce hemostasis until the patient's total amount of anti-IX:C has been neutralized. Furthermore, an anamnestic response will follow administration of any factor IX-containing product. *High responding* hemophilia patients are those with a substantial anamnestic response following infusion of factor IX.[280] In some patients, the stimulating effect on the antibody formation is not as striking. These patients

are called *low responders*. Both types of patients occur in hemophilia B. Treatment of patients with antibodies against IX:C includes treatment of acute bleeding episodes as well as attempts to induce tolerance, thus making them more like ordinary hemophiliacs. An acute bleeding episode can be handled by administering factor IX concentrate in amounts high enough to neutralize all inhibitors and also to give a hemostatic effect. This is possible, provided the antibody titer is not too high in relation to the activity of factor IX in the factor IX concentrates available. Concomitantly, immunosuppressive treatment has to be given to diminish the anamnestic response. Such treatment has been used successfully in a substantial number of patients.[281,282] In patients with extremely high antibody titers, this sort of treatment is impossible, and the antibodies can be removed by extracorporeal adsorption on protein A-Sepharose[283] or by specific immunoadsorption[284,285] before the administration of factor IX.

Tolerance has been claimed to develop after long-term administration of high amounts of coagulation factor concentrates in hemophilia A patients.[286] Repeated treatment episodes using the combination of high amounts of factor IX and cyclophosphamide seemed to result in a similar conversion of high responders to low responders.[287] Another hemophilia B patient became a low responder after two treatment episodes, including extracorporeal adsorption of his anti IX:C on protein A-Sepharose followed by administration of factor IX and cyclophosphamide.[285] The second treatment also included administration of intravenous gamma globulin to compensate for the nonspecific loss of IgG on the protein A-Sepharose.[288]

FACTOR X

Factor X (M_r = 59,000) participates in the middle stage of the blood coagulation cascade where it is converted to factor Xa by factor IXa in the presence of factor VIIIa, phospholipid, and calcium ions[151,152] or by factor VIIa in the presence of tissue factor and calcium ions[102] (Fig. 84-1). Human factor X is a glycoprotein that circulates in blood as a two-chain molecule[152,153] (Fig. 84-10). It contains a light chain (M_r = 16,900) and a heavy chain (M_r = 42,100), and these two chains are held together by a disulfide bond. The light chain contains 11 residues of γ-carboxyglutamic acid and two epidermal growth factor domains[32-34,37] (Fig. 84-10). It also contains β-hydroxyaspartic acid at position 63 in the first epidermal growth factor domain.[105-108] The total length of the light chain of human factor X is 139 residues, while the heavy chain is composed of 306 residues. The heavy chain also includes the catalytic domain and the active site serine. Human factor X contains 15 percent carbohydrate that includes N-linked chains attached to Asn-39 and Asn-49 in the activation peptide.[152,153] The presence of O-linked carbohydrate has also been demonstrated in the carboxyl end of the heavy chain of bovine factor X.[289]

The activation of human factor X results from the cleavage of an Arg_{52}-Ile bond in the amino-terminal end of the heavy chain by factor IXa[151] (Fig. 84-10). This releases an activation peptide of 52 amino acids and generates factor Xa, a serine protease. The V_{max} for the activation reaction is accelerated approximately 200,000-fold by the addition of factor VIIIa, while the phospholipid decreases the K_m of the reaction about 3000-fold.[290] The participation of factor VIII as a cofactor in

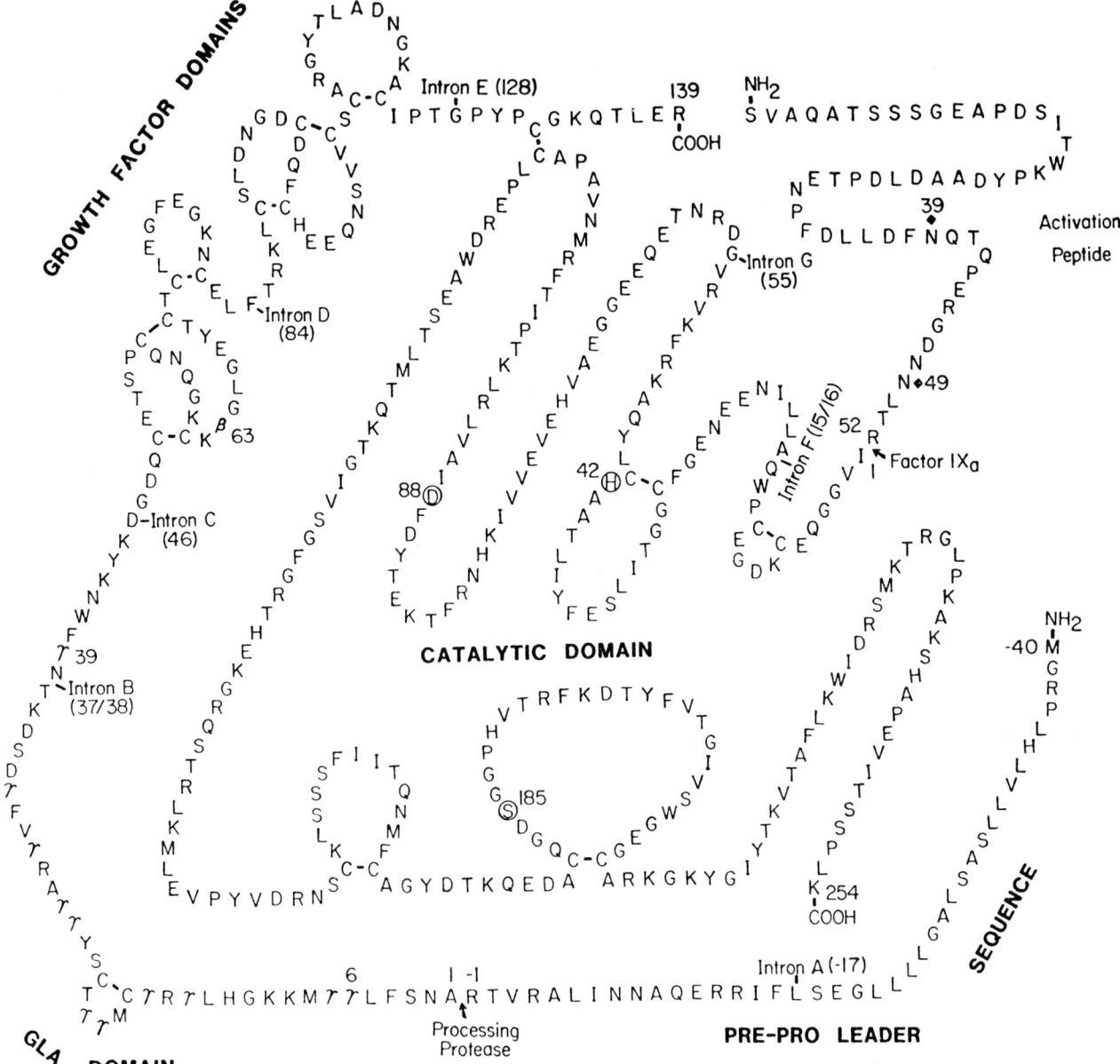

Fig. 84-10 Amino acid sequence and tentative structure of human prepro factor X. The locations of the seven introns (A to G) are shown in the various regions of the protein. The prepro leader sequence (−40 to −1) is cleaved during protein biosynthesis to give rise to the mature protein with an amino-terminal sequence of A-N-S-F- for the light chain. The Arg-Lys-Arg tripeptide that connects the light and heavy chains during biosynthesis is not shown. The peptide bond cleaved by factor IXa during the activation reaction is shown with a small arrow. The three amino acids in the catalytic domain (H_{42}, D_{88}, S_{185}) that participate in catalysis are circled, while the two potential carbohydrate attachment sites in the activation peptide are shown with solid diamonds. The amino acids are numbered as follows starting with the amino-terminal end of the protein: −40 to −1 = prepro leader sequence; +1 to 139 = light chain; 1 to 52 = activation peptide; 1 to 254 = catalytic chain. The single-letter code for amino acids is shown in the legend to Fig. 84-3. β = β-hydroxyaspartic acid. (From Leytus et al.[33] Used by permission.)

the reaction requires its prior activation by thrombin. Present evidence suggests that factor VIIIa forms a complex with the enzyme, factor IXa, in the presence of phospholipid and calcium ions, and this complex functions as the activator of factor X. This is analogous to the complex formed by factor Xa, factor Va, phospholipid, and calcium ions that carries out the activation of prothrombin.[58]

Biosynthesis of Factor X

Factor X is synthesized in the liver with a prepro leader sequence of 40 amino acids[33,34] (Figs. 84-5 and 84-10). Removal of the pre sequence (23 amino acids) by signal peptidase and

the pro sequence (17 amino acids) by a processing protease yields a single-chain polypeptide of 448 amino acids with an amino-terminal sequence of Ala-Asn-Ser-Phe-.[74,75] The single-chain polypeptide undergoes further proteolytic processing by cleavage of the peptide bond following Arg_{141} and removal of a basic tripeptide of Arg-Lys-Arg from the carboxyl end of the newly generated light chain.[32–34] The resulting light and heavy chains of the zymogen are held together by a disulfide bond. Further processing of the factor X precursor involves the vitamin K-dependent carboxylation of the first 11 glutamic acid residues in the light chain to form γ-carboxyglutamic acid and hydroxylation of Asp_{63} generating hydroxyaspartic acid.[105–108] Carbohydrate addition to the molecule also occurs prior to its secretion into the blood.

Genetic Aspects

In 1955, Duckert and coworkers reported the presence of a serum factor, called factor X, that was depressed by coumarin anticoagulants.[291] Inherited deficiencies were identified shortly thereafter, and the plasma protein was called *Prower factor*[292] and *Stuart factor*.[293] Factor X deficiency is characterized by a prolonged prothrombin time and partial thromboplastin time and a prolonged Russell viper venom clotting time.[293]

The gene for human factor X is located on chromosome 13 in the region of q34-qter.[120–123] It contains approximately 25 kb of DNA and includes seven introns and eight exons (Fig. 84-10). As previously mentioned, the seven introns in the gene for factor X interrupt the coding sequence at essentially identical locations in the amino acid sequence as the introns in the genes for human factor VII, factor IX, and protein C.

Thus far, more than 50 families have been reported with factor X deficiency.[294] The complete deficiency is inherited as an autosomal recessive disorder, although a subtle bleeding tendency occurs in heterozygotes.[295,296] Factor X deficiency has been divided into three principal groups, including those that are CRM$^+$ and CRM$^-$, as well as those that are CRM^R who have a reduced plasma level as determined by antibody neutralization.[297] Eleven out of twenty factor X-deficient plasmas studied by Fair and Edgington had plasma levels of factor X that were less than 10 percent of normal, while another five ranged from 13 to 65 percent of normal.[298] Four of the twenty factor X-deficient patients were from Northern Italy (factor X Friuli) and had severe coagulation disorders. Their factor X antigen levels, however, were higher than normal. The factor X Friuli defect was initially described in 1969,[299] and 15 different patients have now been identified.[300] These patients have an abnormal factor X that is not activated by tissue thromboplastins but is readily activated by a protease from Russell viper venom (RVV-X). Preliminary studies indicate that the abnormality in factor X Friuli may be associated with the activation peptide.[301] Thus, it appears likely that hereditary factor X deficiency is caused by mutations throughout the gene for factor X, and these mutations result in reduced or absent synthesis and secretion of the clotting factor or in the synthesis of an abnormal molecule with reduced biologic activity.

An acquired deficiency of factor X associated with amyloidosis has also been described (see Chap. 97).[302] Nine of ten of these patients recently described had factor X antigen levels ranging from 15 to 73 percent of normal, while the factor X activity was consistently below normal.[298]

PROTEIN C, PROTEIN S, AND THROMBOMODULIN

Protein C is a vitamin K-dependent protein that was described in 1976[303] and was later identified as an important regulator of the coagulation cascade.[304] Protein C is converted to activated protein C, a serine protease, by thrombin[9,305] in a reaction enhanced by an endothelial cell cofactor[52] (Fig. 84-2). The cofactor, called *thrombomodulin*, forms a complex with thrombin, resulting in a potent activator of protein C and a marked decrease in the procoagulant function of the enzyme.[306] The activated protein C then in turn inactivates the coagulation pathway[3] by inactivating factor Va and factor VIIIa in the presence of phospholipid.[3–9] The anticoagulant activity of activated protein C requires the presence of protein S,[1,2] another vitamin K-dependent coagulation factor[152,307] that enhances the activity of activated protein C about 14-fold.[308] Protein S functions as a cofactor in the binding of activated protein C to phospholipid and increases the affinity of activated protein C to membrane surfaces.[309,310] The complex of activated protein C and protein S is also readily formed on the endothelial cell surface.[311,312] Furthermore, the presence of activated protein C decreases the internalization and degradation of protein S by endothelial cells.[313] In addition to its anticoagulant activity, protein C also has a profibrinolytic effect, which was first demonstrated in animal studies.[314] The apparent mechanism of protein C as a profibrinolytic agent may involve in part the inactivation of a major inhibitor of tissue plasminogen activator.[315–317] This inactivation is also dependent on the presence of protein S.[317,318] Thus, activated protein C is regulated by a specific plasma protein inhibitor that binds to activated protein C to form a 1:1 stoichiometric complex.[319]

Human protein C ($M_r = 62,000$) is a glycoprotein that circulates in blood as a two-chain molecule held together by a single disulfide bond[9,305,320] (Fig. 84-11). The light chain ($M_r \approx 22,000$) is composed of 155 amino acids and contains nine residues of γ-carboxyglutamic acid and one residue of β-hydroxyaspartic acid at position 71.[104,106,107] The heavy chain ($M_r \approx 40,000$) is composed of 262 amino acids and contains the catalytic domain. Human protein C also contains 23% carbohydrate[305] including N-linked chains that are probably attached to Asn$_{97}$ in the light chain and Asn$_{79}$ and Asn$_{160}$ in the heavy chain of the activated protein.

The activation of human protein C by thrombin is due to the cleavage of an Arg$_{12}$-Ile bond in the amino-terminal region of the heavy chain. This releases an activation peptide of 12 amino acids and gives rise to an active serine protease. The rate of activation of protein C by thrombin is accelerated approximately 1000-fold by the presence of thrombomodulin, an endothelial cell surface glycoprotein.[54] The formation of the 1:1 molecular complex of thrombin and thrombomodulin changes the activity of the enzyme from a procoagulant in the coagulation cascade to an anticoagulant involved in the regulation of the coagulation cascade. Thus, the thrombin bound to thrombomodulin no longer converts fibrinogen to fibrin or factor V to factor Va, or activates platelets,[306,321] but instead it becomes a specific activator of protein C.

Thrombomodulin ($M_r \approx 75,000$ to $100,000$) is a single-chain surface glycoprotein containing 557 amino acids[322–324] (Fig. 84-7). The amino-terminal portion of the molecule contains an extracellular region (226 amino acids) followed by six growth factor domains present in tandem repeats (236 amino acids), a potential carbohydrate-rich region (34 amino acids including eight serine and threonine residues), a transmembrane domain (23 residues), and an intracellular domain (38 amino acids) located at the carboxyl-terminal end of the protein. The extracellular domain at the amino-terminal portion of the molecule has been proposed as the thrombin-binding region for the surface glycoprotein.[323]

Human protein S ($M_r \approx 70,000$) is a single-chain glycoprotein containing 11 γ-carboxyglutamic acid residues.[154,307] It also contains three residues of β-hydroxyaspartic acid and one β-hydroxyasparagine.[109,325] Approximately 60 percent of protein S circulates in plasma as a complex with complement C4 binding protien.[326–328] The binding to C4 binding protein significantly reduces the stimulating effect of protein S on activated protein C.[329,330] Human protein S is composed of 635 amino acids including four growth factor domains following

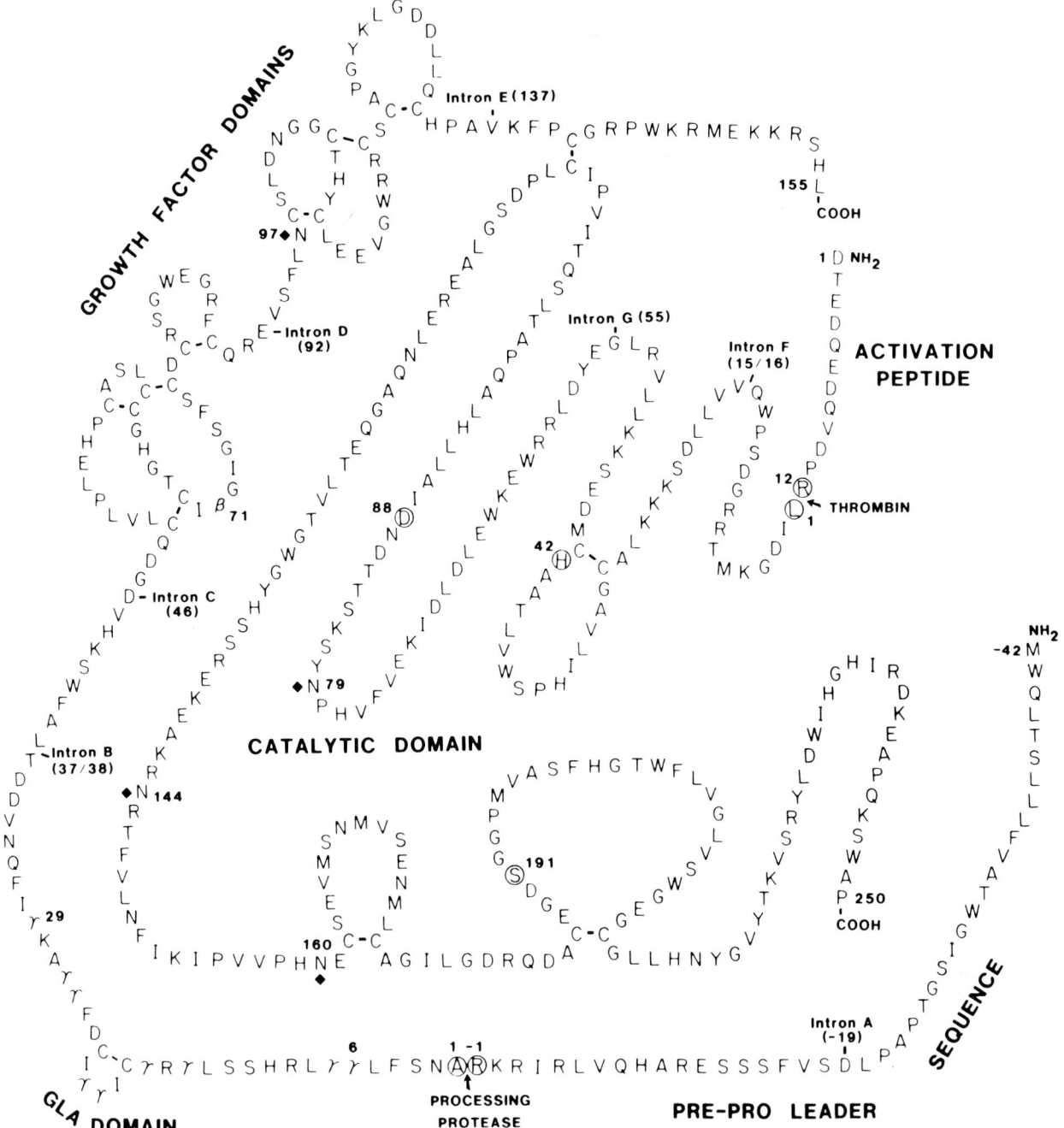

Fig. 84-11 Amino acid sequence and tentative structure for human prepro protein C. The locations of the seven introns (A to G) are shown in the various regions of the protein. An eighth intron located in the 5' noncoding region of the gene is not shown. The prepro leader sequence (−42 to −1) is cleaved during protein biosynthesis to give rise to the mature protein with an amino-terminal sequence of A-N-S-F- for the light chain. The Lys-Arg dipeptide that connects the light and heavy chains during biosynthesis is not shown. The peptide bond cleaved by the thrombin-thrombomodulin complex during the activation reaction is shown with a small arrow. The

three amino acids in the catalytic domain (H_{42}, D_{88}, S_{191}) that participate in catalysis are circled, while the four potential carbohydrate attachment sites are shown with solid diamonds. The amino acids are numbered as follows starting with the amino-terminal end of the protein: −42 to −1 = prepro leader sequence; +1 to 155 = light chain; 1 to 12 = activation peptide; 1 to 250 = catalytic chain. The single-letter code for amino acids is shown in the legend to Fig. 84-3. β = β-hydroxyaspartic acid. (*From Foster et al.*[125] *and Plutzky et al.*[126] *Used by permission.*)

the Gla domain.[41,42] The carboxyl-terminal region in protein S, in contrast to the carboxyl-terminal regions in the other vitamin K-dependent proteins, does not resemble a serine protease. This portion of the molecule, however, contains sequences that are similar to rat androgen-binding protein.[331] Human protein S also contains ≈7.8% carbohydrate with potential N-linked attachment sites at Asn residues 458, 468, and 489.[41,42] Protein S is inactivated by thrombin by minor proteolysis,[332] and this decreases its activity about sevenfold.[308]

Biosynthesis of Protein C, Protein S, and Thrombomodulin

Human protein C[35,36] and protein S[41,42] are synthesized in the liver with a prepro leader sequence of 42 and 41 amino acids, respectively (Fig. 84-5). In protein C, the pre sequence is 18 amino acids in length, while the pro piece is 24 amino acids.[76] Removal of the prepro leader sequence by proteolytic processing results in an amino-terminal sequence of Ala-Asn-Ser-Phe for protein C and an amino-terminal sequence of Ala-Asn-Ser-Leu for protein S. The single-chain protein C undergoes further proteolytic processing by cleavage and removal of a Lys-Arg dipeptide following Leu_{150}.[35,36] This gives rise to a two-chain molecule held together by a single disulfide bond. A small portion (5 to 15 percent) of protein C, however, circulates in plasma as a single-chain molecule.[333] Protein S also circulates in plasma as a single-chain molecule. Further processing of protein S as well as protein C involves the formation of γ-carboxyglutamic acid from glutamic acid and hydroxylation of aspartic acid or asparagine to generate β-hydroxyaspartic acid or β-hydroxyasparagine. Carbohydrate chains are also added to each protein during their biosynthesis.

Thrombomodulin is synthesized in endothelial cells and is found in arteries, veins, and lymphatics.[334,335] It is not present in the endothelium of human brain and hepatic sinusoids.[334,336] Thrombomodulin activity is decreased by endotoxin,[337] interleukin,[338] and tumor necrosis factor.[338]

Thrombomodulin is synthesized with a signal peptide of 18 amino acids.[322–324] This generates an amino-terminal sequence of Ala-Pro-Ala-Glu for the mature protein.[322] The addition of N- and O-linked carbohydrate chains also occurs at a number of sites within the molecule (Fig. 84-7).

Genetic Aspects

The phenotype due to deficiency of protein C is transmitted as an autosomal dominant disorder with variable expression.[339] Homozygotes are more severely affected (see below). The gene for the protein is located on chromosome 2[340] and contains approximately 11 kb of DNA.[125,126] It is composed of nine exons and eight introns. As previously mentioned, the seven introns in the gene for protein C that are located within the coding region are present in essentially the same positions in the amino acid sequence as the seven introns in the genes for human factor VII, factor IX, and factor X. The gene for protein C also contains two *Alu* sequences and two homologous repeats of about 160 nucleotides that are located in intron E.

Abnormalities in the gene for protein C have been established for two unrelated patients with protein C deficiency.[341] In one patient, the triplet of CGA coding for Arg_{137} in the last exon (Fig. 84-11) was converted to a stop codon of TGA. In the other patient, the highly conserved Trp_{233} (TGG) coded by the last exon was converted to Cys (TGC).

Deficiency of human protein S is also inherited as an autosomal dominant trait.[342] The structure of the gene and its chromosomal location, however, have not been established.

The gene for human thrombomodulin is located on chromosome 20.[323] Surprisingly, it contains no introns.[324] Accordingly, it represents an unusual example of a gene containing growth factor domains that are not separated by introns as is the case in the genes for factor VII, factor IX, factor X, and protein C.

Clinical Aspects of Protein C Deficiency

Protein C in plasma is determined immunochemically[343,344] or with a functional assay.[345] The plasma concentration has been found to be about 4 μg/ml (Table 84-2) and varies between 0.7 and 1.4 U/ml, where 1 U is the amount of protein C found in 1 ml of normal pooled plasma. No significant difference was seen with various ages or between males and females. Like the other vitamin K-dependent coagulation factors, protein C is

low in infants. This probably reflects a decreased synthesis relative to that in an older child or an adult.[346,347]

During anticoagulant treatment with coumarin drugs, the level of γ carboxylation of each of the vitamin K-dependent coagulation factors is reduced, and nonfunctional proteins are produced. Depending on their different half-lives, the activity of these proteins in plasma decreases with time, with protein C and factor VII showing an activity of only 10 to 20 percent of normal after 1 to 2 days. Factor X, prothrombin, and factor IX, however, have a much longer half-life and require 5 to 6 days to decrease to the same level.[348] It has been proposed that the rapid decrease in protein C in patients following administration of oral anticoagulants causes a transient hypercoagulable state. This question has specifically been raised with regard to the warfarin-induced skin necrosis associated with a congenital deficiency of protein C and with warfarin treatment in some patients.[349,350] Like other vitamin K-dependent coagulation factors, protein C is decreased in liver disease.[344,351–353] Low levels of protein C have been described in disseminated intravascular coagulation.[343,344,351,354] In this situation, liver disease may contribute to the low levels observed.[344,353,355] In thrombotic thrombocytopenic purpura, a decreased fibrinolytic potential was found and was tentatively attributed to impaired protein C function.[356]

A decrease in protein C activity has been found to be associated with thrombotic disease. Activity decreases postoperatively with a minimum on day 1 and a persistent depression for 7 days. Stanozolol used to increase defective vessel wall fibrinolysis[357] was shown to increase protein C significantly.[336,337] However, no difference was observed between patients who developed deep vein thrombosis postoperatively and those who did not.[358] Congenital protein C deficiency as well as congenital protein S deficiency have also been found to be associated with thrombotic disease.[359–363] Heterozygous protein C deficiency is complicated by development of deep vein thrombosis, pulmonary embolism, and superficial phlebitis[364,365] manifesting itself at an early age (<40 years).[349,361,364,366,367] Hereditary protein C deficiency should also be considered in young patients with acute or subacute cerebral symptoms associated with cerebral thrombosis.[368] Skin necrosis developing soon after the start of anticoagulant treatment has been found to be associated with a deficiency of protein C.[349,350,366] In this context, the rapid decrease in protein C compared to most other vitamin K-dependent coagulation factors after initiation of coumarin treatment has been stressed. It has been proposed that this may create a situation with a hypercoagulability and formation of thrombi in the small skin vessels. Patients with a decreased protein C may be at risk.[349] The protein C level in these patients is between 40 and 50 percent of normal. Although the protein C deficiency seems to be an autosomal dominant trait with variable expression,[339,349] thrombotic symptoms may be absent in patients with a hereditary protein C deficiency.[369] Also, a protein C deficiency characterized by normal antigen but reduced amidolytic levels of protein C has been reported.[345,362,363] If long-term oral anticoagulants are used in patients with a protein C deficiency, large initial doses of coumarin should be avoided because of the risk of developing skin necrosis.[350,370]

The homozygous form of protein C deficiency seems to manifest itself by massive venous thrombosis in the neonatal period or by purpura fulminans in newborns.[369,371–373] Treatment with heparin or a platelet aggregation inhibitor has been unsuccessful. These patients can, however, be treated during acute episodes with plasma or factor IX concentrate that provides protein C.[374] Long-term treatment with oral anticoagulant was used successfully in one patient.[375] Homozygous patients with moderate symptoms are also described.[376,377] Two other patients with a protein C level of about 5 percent with thromboembolic disease from early childhood but no life-threatening episodes of purpura fulminans or disseminated intravascular coagulation were described recently.[377] Also, some families obviously having a dysfunctional protein C are reported, among them one called protein C Bergamo.[362,363,378]

Clinical Aspects of Protein S Deficiency

Inherited protein S deficiency has also been found to be associated with a thrombotic tendency.[328,379–384] Thrombotic complications occurred in these patients at a relatively young age and were found in about 70 percent of the patients with a protein S deficiency. In 50 percent of the patients, the thromboembolism was recurrent. The incidence of protein S deficiency among patients with thromboembolism below age 40 years has been estimated at about 10 percent.[384] Two types of protein S deficiency have been identified. These include individuals who have little or no free protein S but a normal (or almost normal) amount of protein S complexed to complement C4 binding protein (type I) and individuals with little or no protein S either bound or free (type II).[328] Individuals with type I seem to be the most common, and their inheritance is autosomal dominant. The type II individuals who have been identified thus far are sons of two type I individuals.[328]

It is interesting to note that a decreased level of protein S has been reported at a fairly high frequency in patients with anticoagulants due to lupus erythematosus.[385] The presence of lupus anticoagulants is strongly associated with both arterial and venous thrombosis.[386]

Protein S has been found to decrease during pregnancy and in the postpartum period, the total protein S being reduced. The reduced protein S results in a larger decrease in the free functional protein S activity due to redistribution into a complex with complement C4 binding protein.[328] Furthermore, oral contraceptives have been found to lower both total and free protein S.[387]

Protein S has been found to occur also in platelets and seems to be colocalized with fibrinogen in the α granules. Released protein S seems to be necessary for the degradation of factor Va by activated protein C on the platelet surface.[388] The treatment in protein S deficiency should be oral anticoagulant therapy.

REFERENCES

1. WALKER FJ: Regulation of activated protein C by a new protein: A possible function for bovine protein S. *J Biol Chem* 255:5221, 1980.
2. WALKER FJ: Regulation of activated protein C by protein S: The role of phospholipid in factor Va inactivation. *J Biol Chem* 256:1128, 1981.
3. KISIEL W, CANFIELD WM, ERICSSON LH, DAVIE EW: Anticoagulant properties of bovine protein C following activation by thrombin. *Biochemistry* 16:5824, 1977.
4. WALKER FJ, SEXTON PW, ESMON CT: The inhibition of blood coagulation by activated protein C through the selective inactivation of activated factor V. *Biochim Biophys Acta* 571:333, 1979.
5. SUZUKI K, STENFLO J, DAHLBACK B, THEODORSSON B: Inactivation of human coagulation factor V by activated protein C. *J Biol Chem* 258:1914, 1983.
6. FULCHER CA, GARDINER JE, GRIFFIN JH, ZIMMERMAN TS: Proteolytic inactivation of human factor VIII procoagulant protein by activated human protein C and its analogy with factor V. *Blood* 63:486, 1984.
7. VEHAR GA, DAVIE EW: Preparation and properties of bovine factor VIII (antihemophilic factor). *Biochemistry* 19:401, 1980.
8. EATON D, RODRIGUEZ H, VEHAR GA: Proteolytic processing of human factor VIII. Correlation of specific cleavages by thrombin, factor Xa and activated protein C with activation and inactivation of factor VIII coagulant activity. *Biochemistry* 25:505, 1986.
9. MARLAR RA, KLEISS AJ, GRIFFIN JH: Mechanism of action of human activated protein C, a thrombin dependent anticoagulant enzyme. *Blood* 59:1067, 1982.
10. STENFLO J, FERNLUND P, EGAN W, ROEPSTORFF P: Vitamin K dependent modifications of glutamic acid residues in prothrombin. *Proc Natl Acad Sci USA* 71:2730, 1974.
11. NELSESTUEN GL, ZYTKOVICZ TH, HOWARD JB: The mode of action of vitamin K isolation of a peptide containing the vitamin K-dependent portion of prothrombin. *J Biol Chem* 249:6347, 1974.
12. MAGNUSSON S, SOTTRUP-JENSEN L, PETERSEN TE, MORRIS HR, DELL A: Primary structure of the vitamin K-dependent part of prothrombin. *FEBS Lett* 44:189, 1974.
13. ESMON CT, SADOWSKI JA, SUTTIE JW: A new carboxylation reaction: The vitamin K-dependent incorporation of $H^{14}CO_3^-$ into prothrombin. *J Biol Chem* 250:4744, 1975.
14. ESMON CT, SUTTIE JW: Vitamin K-dependent carboxylase: Solubilization and properties. *J Biol Chem* 251:6238, 1976.
15. MACK DO, SUEN ET, GIRARDOT JM, MILLER JA, DELANEY R, JOHNSON BC: Soluble enzyme system for vitamin K-dependent carboxylation. *J Biol Chem* 251:3269, 1976.
16. HOUSER RM, CAREY DJ, DUS KM, MARSHALL GR, OLSON RE: Partial sequence of rat prothrombin and the activity of two related pentapeptides as substrates for the vitamin K-dependent carboxylase system. *FEBS Lett* 75:226, 1977.
17. SUTTIE JW, HAGEMAN JM, LEHRMAN SR, RICH DH: Vitamin K-dependent carboxylase: Development of a peptide substrate. *J Biol Chem* 251:5827, 1976.
18. FRIEDMAN PA, SHIA M: Some characteristics of a vitamin K-dependent carboxylating system from rat liver microsomes. *Biochem Biophys Res Commun* 70:647, 1976.
19. JONES JP, GARDNER EJ, COOPER TG, OLSON RE: Vitamin K-dependent carboxylation of peptide-bound glutamate: The active species of CO_2 utilized by the membrane-bound preprothrombin carboxylase. *J Biol Chem* 252:7738, 1977.
20. FRIEDMAN PA, SHIA MA: The apparent absence of involvement of biotin in the vitamin K-dependent carboxylation of glutamic acid residues of proteins. *Biochem J* 163:39, 1977.
21. FRIEDMAN PA, GRIEP AE: In vitro inhibition of vitamin K-dependent carboxylation by tetrachloropyridinol and the imidazopyridines. *Biochemistry* 19:3381, 1980.
22. ESMON CT, SUTTIE JW, JACKSON CM: The functional significance of vitamin K action: Differences in phospholipid binding between normal and abnormal prothrombin. *J Biol Chem* 250:4095, 1975.
23. MAGNUSSON S, PETERSEN TE, SOTTRUP-JENSEN L, CLAEYS H: Complete primary structure of prothrombin: Isolation, structure and reactivity of ten carboxylated glutamic acid residues and regulation of prothrombin activation by thrombin, in Reich E, Rifkin DB, Shaw E (eds): *Proteases and Biological Control*. Cold Spring Harbor, NY, Cold Spring Harbor Laboratory, 1982, p 123.
24. MCMULLEN BA, FUJIKAWA K: Amino acid sequence of the heavy chain of human α-factor XIIa. *J Biol Chem* 260:5328, 1985.
25. SOTTRUP-JENSEN L, CLAEYS H, ZAJDEL M, PETERSEN TE, MAGNUSSON S: The primary structure of human plasminogen: Isolation of two lysine-binding fragments and one "mini"-plasminogen (MW, 38,000) by elastase-catalyzed-specific limited proteolysis, in Davidson JF, Rowan RM, Samama MM, Desnoyers PC (eds): *Progress in Chemical Fibrinolysis and Thrombolysis*. New York, Raven, 1978, vol 3, p 191.
26. PENNICA D, HOLMES WE, KOHR WJ, HARKINS RN, VEHAR GA, WARD CA, BENNETT WF, YELVERTON E, SEEBURG PH, HEYNEKER HL, GOEDDEL DV: Cloning and expression of human tissue-type plasminogen activator cDNA in E. coli. *Nature* 301:214, 1983.
27. GUNZLER WA, STEFFENS GJ, OTTING F, KIM S-MA, FRANKUS E, FLOHE L: The primary structure of high molecular mass urokinase from human urine: The complete amino acid sequence of the A chain. *Hoppe-Seyler's Z Physiol Chem* 363:1155, 1982.
28. HAGEN FS, GRAY CL, O'HARA P, GRANT FJ, SAARI GC, WOODBURY RG, HART CE, INSLEY M, KISIEL W, KURACHI K, DAVIE EW: Characterization of a cDNA coding for human factor VII. *Proc Natl Acad Sci USA* 83:2412, 1986.
29. KURACHI K, DAVIE EW: Isolation and characterization of a cDNA coding for human factor IX. *Proc Natl Acad Sci USA* 79:6461, 1982.
30. YOSHITAKE S, SCHACH BG, FOSTER DC, DAVIE EW, KURACHI K: Nucleotide

sequence of the gene for human factor IX (antihemophilic factor B). *Biochemistry* 24:3736, 1985.

31. ANSON DS, CHOO KH, REES DJG, GIANNELLI F, GOULD K, HUDDLESTON JA, BROWNLEE GG: The gene structure of human anti-haemophilic factor IX. *EMBO J* 3:1053, 1984.

32. LEYTUS SP, CHUNG DW, KISIEL W, KURACHI K, DAVIE EW: Characterization of a cDNA coding for human factor X. *Proc Natl Acad Sci USA* 81:3699, 1984.

33. LEYTUS SP, FOSTER DC, KURACHI K, DAVIE EW: Gene for human factor X, a blood coagulation factor whose gene organization is essentially identical to that of factor IX and protein C. *Biochemistry* 25:5098, 1986.

34. FUNG MR, HAY CS, MacGILLIVRAY RTA: Characterization of an almost full-length cDNA coding for human blood coagulation factor X. *Proc Natl Acad Sci USA* 82:3591, 1985.

35. FOSTER D, DAVIE EW: Characterization of a cDNA coding for human protein C. *Proc Natl Acad Sci USA* 81:4766, 1984.

36. BECKMANN RJ, SCHMIDT M, SANTERRE RF, PLUTZKY J, CRABTREE GR, LONG GL: The structure and evolution of a 461 amino acid human protein C precursor and its messenger RNA, based upon the DNA sequence of cloned human liver cDNAs. *Nucleic Acids Res* 13:5233, 1985.

37. DOOLITTLE RF, FENG DF, JOHNSON MS: Computer-based characterization of epidermal growth factor precursor. *Nature* 307:558, 1984.

38. CARPENTER G, ZENDEGUI JG: Epidermal growth factor, its receptor, and related proteins. *Exp Cell Res* 164:1, 1986.

39. GRAY A, DULL TJ, ULLRICH A: Nucleotide sequence of epidermal growth factor cDNA predicts a 128,000-molecular weight protein precursor. *Nature* 303:722, 1983.

40. SCOTT J, URDEA M, QUIROGA M, SANCHEZ-PESCADOR R, FONG N, SELBY M, RUTTER WJ, BELL GI: Structure of a mouse submaxillary messenger RNA encoding epidermal growth factor and seven related proteins. *Science* 221:236, 1983.

41. LUNDWALL A, DACKOWSKI W, COHEN E, SHAFFER M, MAHR A, DAHLBACK B, STENFLO J, WYDRO R: Isolation and sequence of the cDNA for human protein S, a regulator of blood coagulation. *Proc Natl Acad Sci USA* 83:6716, 1986.

42. HOSKINS J, NORMAN DK, BECKMANN RJ, LONG GL: Cloning and characterization of human liver cDNA encoding a protein S precursor. *Proc Natl Acad Sci USA* 84:349, 1987.

43. SUTTIE JW, JACKSON CM: Prothrombin structure, activation and biosynthesis. *Physiol Rev* 57:1, 1977.

44. NESHEIM ME, MYRMEL KH, HIBBARD L, MANN KG: Isolation and characterization of single chain bovine factor V. *J Biol Chem* 254:508, 1979.

45. SUZUKI K, DAHLBACK B, STENFLO J: Thrombin-catalyzed activation of human coagulation factor V. *J Biol Chem* 257:6556, 1982.

46. NESHEIM ME, MANN KG: Thrombin-catalyzed activation of single chain bovine factor V. *J Biol Chem* 254:1326, 1979.

47. NESHEIM ME, FOSTER WB, MANN KG: Characterization of factor V intermediates. *J Biol Chem* 259:3187, 1984.

48. FULCHER CA, ROBERTS JR, ZIMMERMAN TS: Thrombin proteolysis of purified factor VIII procoagulant protein: Correlation of activation with generation of specific polypeptide. *Blood* 61:807, 1983.

49. FAY PJ, ANDERSON MT, CHAVIN SI, MARDER VJ: The size of human factor VIII heterodimers and the effects produced by thrombin. *Biochim Biophys Acta* 871:268, 1986.

50. SCHWARTZ ML, PIZZO SV, HILL RL, MCKEE PA: Human factor XIII from plasma and platelets. Molecular weights, subunit structures, proteolytic activation, and cross-linking of fibrinogen and fibrin. *J Biol Chem* 248:1395, 1973.

51. TAKAGI T, DOOLITTLE RF: Amino acid sequence studies on factor XIII and the peptide released during its activation by thrombin. *Biochemistry* 13:750, 1974.

52. ESMON CT, OWEN WG: Identification of an endothelial cell cofactor for thrombin-catalyzed activation of protein C. *Proc Natl Acad Sci USA* 78:2249, 1981.

53. OWEN WG, ESMON CT: Functional properties of an endothelial cell cofactor for thrombin-catalyzed activation of protein C. *J Biol Chem* 256:5532, 1981.

54. ESMON NL, OWEN WG, ESMON CT: Isolation of a membrane-bound cofactor for thrombin-catalyzed activation of protein C. *J Biol Chem* 257:859, 1982.

55. DEGEN SJF, MacGILLIVRAY RTA, DAVIE EW: Characterization of the cDNA and gene coding for human prothrombin. *Biochemistry* 22:2087, 1983.

56. DEGEN SJF, DAVIE EW: Nucleotide sequence of the gene for human prothrombin. *Biochemistry* 26:6165, 1987.

57. DOWNING MR, BUTKOWSKI RJ, CLARK MM, MANN KG: Human prothrombin activation. *J Biol Chem* 250:8897, 1975.

58. ROSING J, TANS G, GROVERS-RIEMSLAG JWP, ZWAAL RFA, HEMKER HC:

The role of phospholipids and factor V_a in the prothrombinase complex. *J Biol Chem* 255:274, 1980.

59. KRISHNASWAMY S, CHURCH WR, NESHEIM ME, MANN KG: Activation of human prothrombin by human prothrombinase: Influence of factor Va on the reaction mechanism. *J Biol Chem* 262:3291, 1987.

60. RABIET MJ, BLASHILL A, FURIE B, FURIE BC: Prothrombin fragment 1.2.3, a major product of prothrombin activation in human plasma. *J Biol Chem* 261:13210, 1986.

61. SHAPIRO SS, MCCORD IS: Prothrombin, in Spaet TH (ed): *Hemostasis and Thrombosis.* New York, Grune & Stratton, 1978, vol 4, p 177.

62. OWEN CA, HENRIKSEN RA, MCDUFFIE FC, MANN KG: Prothrombin Quick: A new identified dysprothrombinemia. *Mayo Clin Proc* 53:29, 1978.

63. LANDWEHR G, LANG H, ALEXANDER B: Congenital hypoprothrombinemia: A case study with particular reference to the role of non-prothrombin factors in the conversion of prothrombin. *Am J Med* 8:255, 1950.

64. VAN CREVELD S: Congenital idiopathic hypoprothrombinemia. *Acta Pediatr Scand [suppl]* 100:245, 1954.

65. BIGGS R, DOUGLAS AS: The measurement of prothrombin in plasma: A case of prothrombin deficiency. *J Clin Pathol* 6:15, 1953.

66. QUICK AJ, PISCIOTTA AV, HUSSEY CV: Congenital hypoprothrombinemic states. *Arch Intern Med* 95:2, 1955.

67. KATTLOVE HE, SHAPIRO SS, SPIVACK M: Hereditary prothrombin deficiency. *N Engl J Med* 282:57, 1970.

68. ROYLE NJ, IRWIN DM, KOSCHINSKY ML, MacGILLIVRAY RTA, HAMERTON JL: Human genes encoding prothrombin and ceruloplasmin map to 11p11-q12 and 3q21-24, respectively. *Somatic Cell Mol Genet* 13:285, 1987.

69. BREATHNACH R, BENOIST C, O'HARE K, GANNON F, CHAMBON P: Ovalbumin gene: Evidence for a leader sequence in mRNA and DNA sequences at the exon-intron boundaries. *Proc Natl Acad Sci USA* 75:4853, 1978.

70. MOUNT SM: A catalogue of splice junction sequences. *Nucleic Acids Res* 10:459, 1982.

71. RINEHART FP, RITCH TG, DEININGER PL, SCHMID CW: Renaturation rate studies of a single family of interspersed repeated sequences in human deoxyribonucleic acid. *Biochemistry* 20:3003, 1981.

72. SCHMID CW, JELINEK WR: The alu family of dispersed repetitive sequences. *Science* 216:1065, 1982.

73. JORGENSEN MJ, CANTOR AB, CHANGE BG, BERKNER KL, KUMAR AA, HAGEN FS, SPRECHER CA, INSLEY MY, DAVIE EW: Recognition site directed vitamin K-dependent γ-carboxylation resides on the propeptide of factor IX. *Cell* 48:185, 1987.

74. BLANCHARD RA, FAYE KLK, BARNETT JM, WILLIAM B: Isolation and characterization of profactor X from the liver of a steer treated with sodium warfarin. *Blood [Suppl]* 66:331a, 1985.

75. SCHACH BG: Personal communication.

76. FOSTER DC, RUDINSKI MS, SCHACH BG, BERKNER KL, KUMAR AA, HAGEN FS, SPRECHER CA, INSLEY MY, DAVIE EW: Propeptide of human protein C is necessary for γ-carboxylation. *Biochemistry* 26:7003, 1987.

77. JOSSO F, MONASTERIO de SANCHEZ J, LAVERGNE JM, MENACHE D, SOULIER JP: Congenital abnormality of the prothrombin molecule (factor II) in four siblings: Prothrombin Barcelona. *Blood* 38:9, 1971.

78. RABIET M-J, FURIE BC, FURIE B: Molecular defect of prothrombin Barcelona. *J Biol Chem* 261:15045, 1986.

79. WALZ DA, HEWETT-EMMETT D, SEEGERS WH: Amino acid sequence of human prothrombin fragments 1 and 2. *Proc Natl Acad Sci USA* 74:1969, 1977.

80. MIYATA T, MORITA T, INOMOTO T, KAWUCHI S, SHIRAKAMI A, IWANAGA S: Prothrombin Tokushima, a replacement of arginine-418 by tryptophan that impairs the fibrinogen clotting activity of derived thrombin Tokushima. *Biochemistry* 26:1117, 1987.

81. BEZEAUD A, GUILLIN M-C, OLMEDA F, QUINTANA M, GOMEZ N: Prothrombin Madrid: A new familial abnormality of prothrombin. *Thromb Res* 16:47, 1979.

82. GUILLIN M-C, BEZEAUD A: Characterization of a variant of human prothrombin: Prothrombin Madrid. *Ann NY Acad Sci* 320:414, 1981.

83. SHAPIRO SS, MARTINEZ J, HOLBURN RR: Congenital dysprothrombinemia: An inherited structural disorder of human prothrombin. *J Clin Invest* 48:2251, 1969.

84. HUISSE MG, DREYFUS M, GUILLIN M-C: Prothrombin Clamart: Prothrombin variant with defective Arg 320-Ile cleavage by factor X_a. *Thromb Res* 44:11, 1986.

85. JOSSO F, RIO Y, BEGUIN S: Prothrombin Metz: A new variant of human prothrombin: Double heterozygosity for congenital hypoprothrombinemia and dysprothrombinemia. *Abstracts of XVII Congr Int Soc Hematol* (Paris) II:860, 1978.

86. RABIET M-J, ELION J, LABIE D, JOSSO F: Prothrombin Metz: Purification and characterization of a variant of human prothrombin. *Thromb Haemost* 42:57, 1979.

87. JOSSO F, RIO Y, BEGUIN S: A new variant of human prothrombin: Prothrombin Metz, demonstration in a family showing double heterozygosity for congenital hypoprothrombinemia and dysprothrombinemia. *Haemostasis* 12:309, 1982.

88. BEZEAUD A, SORIA C, DROUET L, GUILLIN M-C: Prothrombin Salakta: Prothrombin variant with abnormal thrombin activity. *Thromb Haemost* 50:250, 1983.

89. GIROLAMI A, COCCHERI S, PALARETI G, POGGI M, BURUL A, CAPPELLATO G: Prothrombin Molise: A "new" congenital dysprothrombinemia, double heterozygosis with an abnormal prothrombin and true prothrombin deficiency. *Blood* 52:115, 1978.

90. HENRIKSEN RA, OWEN WG: Characterization of the catalytic defect in the dysthrombin, thrombin Quick. *J Biol Chem* 262:4664, 1987.

91. MCMILLAN CW, ROBERTS HR: Congenital combined deficiency of coagulation factors II, VII, IX and X. *N Engl J Med* 274:1313, 1966.

92. CHUNG K-S, BEZEAUD A, GOLDSMITH JC, MCMILLAN CW, MENACHE D, ROBERTS HR: Congenital deficiency of blood clotting factors II, VII, IX and X. *Blood* 53:776, 1979.

93. JOHNSON CA, CHUNG KS, MCGRATH KM, BEAN PE, ROBERTS HR: Characterization of a variant prothrombin in a patient congenitally deficient in factors II, VII, IX and X. *Br J Haematol* 44:461, 1980.

94. GOLDSMITH GH, PENCE RE, RATNOFF OD, ADELSTEIN DJ, FURIE B: Studies on a family with combined functional deficiencies of vitamin K dependent coagulation factor. *J Clin Invest* 69:1253, 1982.

95. SOFF GA, LEVIN J: Familial multiple coagulation deficiencies: Combined factor II, VII, IX and X deficiency. *Semin Thromb Hemost* 7:133, 1981.

96. RADCLIFFE R, NEMERSON Y: Activation and control of factor VII by activated factor X and thrombin. Isolation and characterization of a single chain form of factor VII. *J Biol Chem* 250:388, 1975.

97. RADCLIFFE R, NEMERSON Y: Mechanism of activation of bovine factor VII. Products of cleavage by factor X_a. *J Biol Chem* 251:4797, 1976.

98. SELIGSOHN U, OSTERUD B, BROWN SF, GRIFFIN JH, RAPAPORT SI: Activation of human factor VII in plasma and in purified systems: Roles of activated factor IX, kallikrein, and activated factor XII. *J Clin Invest* 64:1056, 1979.

99. KISIEL W, FUJIKAWA K, DAVIE EW: Activation of bovine factor VII (proconvertin) by factor XII_a (activated Hageman factor). *Biochemistry* 16:4189, 1977.

100. BROZE GJ JR, MAJERUS PW: Purification and properties of human coagulation factor VII. *J Biol Chem* 255:1242, 1980.

101. OSTERUD B, RAPAPORT SI: Activation of factor IX by the reaction product of tissue factor and factor VII: Additional pathway for initiating blood coagulation. *Proc Natl Acad Sci USA* 74:5260, 1977.

102. NEMERSON Y, BACH R: Tissue factor revisited. *Prog Hemost Thromb* 6:237, 1982.

103. KISIEL W, MCMULLEN BA: Isolation and characterization of human factor VIIa. *Thromb Res* 22:375, 1981.

104. DRAKENBERG T, FERNLUND P, ROEPSTORFF P, STENFLO J: β-Hydroxyaspartic acid in vitamin K-dependent proteins. *Proc Natl Acad Sci USA* 80:1802, 1983.

105. MCMULLEN BA, FUJIKAWA K, KISIEL W, SASAGAWA T, HOWALD WN, KWA EY, WEINSTEIN B: Complete amino acid sequence of the light chain of human blood coagulation factor X: Evidence for identification of residue 63 as β-hydroxyaspartic acid. *Biochemistry* 22:2875, 1983.

106. MCMULLEN BA, FUJIKAWA K, KISIEL W: The occurrence of β-hydroxyaspartic acid in the vitamin K-dependent blood coagulation zymogens. *Biochem Biophys Res Commun* 115:8, 1983.

107. FERNLUND P, STENFLO J: β-Hydroxyaspartic acid in vitamin K-dependent proteins. *J Biol Chem* 258:12509, 1983.

108. SUGO T, FERNLUND P, STENFLO J: Erythro-β-hydroxyaspartic acid in bovine factor IX and factor X. *FEBS Lett* 165:102, 1984.

109. STENFLO J, LUNDWALL A, DAHLBACK B: β-Hydroxyasparagine in domains homologous to the epidermal growth factor precursor in vitamin K-dependent protein S. *Proc Natl Acad Sci USA* 84:368, 1987.

110. SCARPATI EM, WEN D, BROZE GJ JR, MILETICH JP, FLANDERMEYER RR, SIEGEL NR, SADLER JE: Human tissue factor: cDNA sequence and chromosome localization of the gene. *Biochemistry* 26:5234, 1987.

111. SPICER EK, HORTON R, BLOEM L, BACH R, WILLIAMS KR, GUHA A, KRAUS J, LIN T-C, NEMERSON Y, KONIGSBERG WH: Isolation of cDNA clones coding for human tissue factor: Primary structure of the protein and cDNA. *Proc Natl Acad Sci USA* 84:5148, 1987.

112. MORRISSEY JH, FAKHRAI H, EDGINGTON TS: Molecular cloning of the cDNA for tissue factor, the cellular receptor for the initiation of the coagulation protease cascade. *Cell* 50:129, 1987.

113. FISHER KL, GORMAN CM, VEHAR GA, O'BRIEN DP, LAWN RM: Cloning and expression of human tissue factor cDNA. *Thromb Res* 48:89, 1987.

114. HALL CA, RAPAPORT SI, AMES SB, De GROOT JA: A clinical and family study of hereditary proconvertin (factor VII deficiency). *Am J Med* 37:172, 1964.

115. DISCHE FE, BENFIELD V: Congenital factor VII deficiency: Haematological and genetic aspects. *Acta Haematol (Basel)* 21:257, 1959.

116. KUPFER HG, HANNA BL, KINNE DR: Congenital factor VII deficiency with normal Stuart activity: Clinical, genetic and experimental observations. *Blood* 15:146, 1960.

117. CLETON FJ, LOELIGER EA: Two typical hereditary charts of congenital factor VII deficiency. *Thromb Diath Haemorrh* 5:87, 1980.

118. RAGNI MV, LEWIS JH, SPERO JA, HASIBA U: Factor VII deficiency. *Am J Haematol* 10:79, 1981.

119. TRIPLETT DA, BRANDT JT, MCGANN BATARD MA, SCHAEFFER DIXON JL, FAIR DA: Hereditary factor VII deficiency. Heterogeneity defined by combined functional and immunochemical analysis. *Blood* 66:1284, 1985.

120. PFEIFFER RA, OTT R, GILGENKRANTZ S, ALEXANDRE P: Deficiency of coagulation factors VII and X associated with deletion of a chromosome 13 (q34). *Hum Genet* 62:358, 1982.

121. de GROUCHY J, DAUTZENBERG MD, TURLEAU C, BEGUIN S, CHAVIN-COLIN F: Regional mapping of clotting factors VII and X to 13q34. Expression of factor VII through chromosome 8. *Hum Genet* 66:230, 1984.

122. OTT R, PFEIFFER RA: Evidence that activities of coagulation factors VII and X are linked to chromosome 13 (q34). *Hum Hered* 34:123, 1984.

123. GILGENKRANTZ S, BRIQUEL ME, ALEXANDRE P, JALBERT P, Le MAREC B, POUZOL P, POMMEREUIL M: Structural genes of coagulation factors VII and X located on 13q34. *Ann Genet* 29:32, 1986.

124. O'HARA PJ, GRANT FJ, HALDEMAN BA, GRAY CL, INSLEY MY, HAGEN FS, MURRAY MJ: Nucleotide sequence of the gene coding for human factor VII, a vitamin K-dependent protein participating in blood coagulation. *Proc Natl Acad Sci USA* 84:5158, 1987.

125. FOSTER DC, YOSHITAKE S, DAVIE EW: The nucleotide sequence of the gene for human protein C. *Proc Natl Acad Sci USA* 82:4673, 1985.

126. PLUTZKY J, HOSKINS JA, LONG GL, CRABTREE GR: Evolution and organization of the human protein C gene. *Proc Natl Acad Sci USA* 83:546, 1986.

127. PATTHY L: Evolution of the proteases of blood coagulation and fibrinolysis by assembly from modules. *Cell* 41:657, 1985.

128. GERSHWIN ME, GUDE JK: Deep vein thrombosis and pulmonary embolism in congenital factor VII deficiency. *N Engl J Med* 288:141, 1973.

129. HASSAN HJ, CASALBORE P, De LAURENZI A, PETTI N, SINIBALDI L, ORLANDO M: Hereditary factor VII deficiency: Report of a case of intracranial hemorrhage. *Haemostasis* 14:244, 1984.

130. SHIH L-Y, HUNG I-J: Hereditary factor VII deficiency in a Chinese family. *Scand J Haematol* 30:97, 1983.

131. SHIFTER T, MACHTEY I, CRETER D: Thromboembolism in congenital factor VII deficiency. *Acta Haematol (Basel)* 71:60, 1984.

132. GODAL HC, MADSEN K, NISSEN-MEYER R: Thromboembolism in a patient with total proconvertin (factor VII) deficiency. *Acta Med Scand* 171:325, 1962.

133. GOODNIGHT SH, FEINSTEIN DI, OSTERUD B, RAPAPORT SI: Factor VII antibody-neutralizing material in hereditary and acquired factor VII deficiency. *Blood* 38:1, 1971.

134. DENSON KWE, CONARD J, SAMAMA M: Genetic variants of factor VII. *Lancet* 1:1234, 1972.

135. GIROLAMI A, FALEZZA G, PATRASSI G, STENICO M, VETTORE L: Factor VII Verona coagulation disorder: Double heterozygosis with an abnormal factor VII and heterozygous factor VII deficiency. *Blood* 50:603, 1977.

136. MARIANI G, MAZZUCCONI MG, HERMANS J, CIAVARELLA N, FAIELLA A, HASSAN HJ, MANNUCCI PM, NENCI GG, ORLANDO M, ROMOLI D, MANDELLI F: Factor VII deficiency: Immunological characterization of genetic variants and detection of carriers. *Br J Haematol* 48:7, 1981.

137. GIROLAMI A, FABRIS F, ZANON RDB, GHIOTTO G, BURUL A: Factor VII Padua: A congenital coagulation disorder due to an abnormal factor VII with a peculiar activation pattern. *J Lab Clin Med* 91:387, 1978.

138. GIROLAMI A, COTTAROZZI G, DAL BO ZANON R, CELLA G, TOFFANIN F: Factor VII Padua 2: Another factor VII abnormality with defective oxbrain thromboplastin activation and a complex hereditary pattern. *Blood* 54:46, 1979.

139. NENCI GC, AGNELLI G, De REGIS FM: Factor-VII_{coag} kinetics in factor-VII-CRM^+ and factor-VII-CRM^- deficiencies. *Br J Haematol* 46:307, 1980.

140. BRIET E, LOELIGER EA, VAN TILBURG NH, VELTKAMP JJ: Molecular variant of factor VII. *Thromb Haemost* 35:289, 1976.

141. DALAKER K, PRYDZ H: The coagulation factor VII in pregnancy. *Br J Haematol* 56:233, 1984.

142. DALAKER K: Clotting factor VII during pregnancy, delivery and puerperium. *Br J Obstet Gynaecol* 93:17, 1986.

143. DIKE GWR, GRIFFITHS D, BIDWELL E, SNAPE TJ, RIZZA CR: A factor VII concentrate for therapeutic use. *Br J Haematol* 45:107, 1980.

144. MARIANI G, MANNUCCI PM, MAZZUCCONI MG, CAPITANIO A: Treatment of congenital factor VII deficiency with a new concentrate. *Thromb Haemost* 39:675, 1978.

145. HEDNER U, KISIEL W: Use of human factor VIIa in the treatment of two hemophilia A patients with high-titer inhibitors. *J Clin Invest* 71:1836, 1983.

146. AGGELER PM, WHITE SG, GLENDENING MG, PAGE EW, LEAKE TB, BATES G: Plasma thromboplastin component (PTC) deficiency: A new disease resembling hemophilia. *Proc Soc Exp Biol Med* 79:692, 1952.

147. BIGGS R, DOUGLAS AS, MACFARLANE RG, DACIE JV, PITNEY WR, MERSKEY C, O'BRIEN JR: Christmas disease: A condition previously mistaken for haemophilia. *Br Med J* 2:1378, 1952.

148. FUJIKAWA K, LEGAZ ME, KATO H, DAVIE EW: The mechanism of activation of bovine factor IX (Christmas factor) by bovine factor XIₐ (activated plasma thromboplastin antecedent). *Biochemistry* 13:4508, 1974.

149. DISCIPIO RG, KURACHI K, DAVIE EW: Activation of human factor IX (Christmas factor). *J Clin Invest* 61:1528, 1978.

150. JESTY J, SILVERBERG SA: Kinetics of the tissue factor-dependent activation of coagulation factors IX and X in a bovine plasma system. *J Biol Chem* 254:12337, 1979.

151. FUJIKAWA K, COAN MH, LEGAZ ME, DAVIE EW: The mechanism of activation of bovine factor X (Stuart factor) by intrinsic and extrinsic pathways. *Biochemistry* 13:5290, 1974.

152. DISCIPIO RG, HERMODSON MA, DAVIE EW: Activation of human factor X (Stuart factor) by a protease from Russell's viper venom. *Biochemistry* 16:5253, 1977.

153. MORITA T, KISIEL W: Calcium binding to a human factor IXa derivative lacking γ-carboxyglutamic acid: Evidence for two high-affinity sites that do not involve β-hydroxyaspartic acid. *Biochem Biophys Res Commun* 130:841, 1985.

154. DISCIPIO RG, HERMODSON MA, YATES SG, DAVIE EW: A comparison of human prothrombin, factor IX (Christmas factor), factor X (Stuart factor), and protein S. *Biochemistry* 16:698, 1977.

155. LINDQUIST PA, FUJIKAWA K, DAVIE EW: The activation of bovine factor IX (Christmas factor) by factor XIₐ (activated plasma thromboplastin antecedent) and a protease from Russell's viper venom. *J Biol Chem* 253:1902, 1978.

156. BITHELL TC, PIZARRO A, MACDIARMID WD: Variant of factor IX deficiency in female with 45, X Turner's syndrome. *Blood* 36:169, 1970.

157. NEUSCHATZ J, NECHELES TF: Hemophilia B in a phenotypically normal girl with XX (ring)/XI mosaicism. *Acta Haematol (Basel)* 49:108, 1973.

158. SPINELLI A, SCHMID W, STRAUB PW: Christmas disease (haemophilia B) in a girl with deletion of the short arm of one X-chromosome (functional Turner syndrome). *Br J Haematol* 34:129, 1976.

159. ROZMAN C, CASTILLO R, RIBAS-MUNDO M, SUROUS J: Christmas disease in a girl with female karyotype. *Acta Haematol (Basel)* 37:217, 1967.

160. NISEN P, STAMBERG J, EHRENPREIS R, VELASCOS S, SHENDE A, ENGELBERG J, KARAYALCIN G, WABER L: The molecular basis of severe hemophilia B in a girl. *N Engl J Med* 315:1139, 1986.

161. LASCARI AD, TAYLOR JC: Christmas disease in a girl. *Am J Dis Child* 117:585, 1969.

162. NILEHN J-E, NILSSON IM: Haemophilia B in a girl. *Thromb Diath Haemorrh* 7:552, 1962.

163. REVESZ R, SCHULER D, GOLDSCHMIDT B, ELODI S: Christmas disease in one of a pair of monozygotic twin girls, possibly the effect of lyonization. *J Med Genet* 9:396, 1972.

164. RUST LA, GOODNIGHT SH, FREEMAN RK, JOHNSON CS: Pregnancy and delivery in a woman with hemophilia B. *Obstet Gynecol* 46:483, 1975.

165. HOLMBERG L, NILSSON IM, HENRIKSSON P, ORSTAVIK KH: Homozygous expression of haemophilia B in a heterozygote. *Acta Med Scand* 204:231, 1978.

166. CAMERINO G, GRZESCHIK KH, JAYE M, DE LA SALLE H, TOLSTOSHEV P, LECOCQ JP, HEILIG R, MANDEL JL: Regional localization on the human X chromosome and polymorphism of the coagulation factor IX gene (hemophilia B locus). *Proc Natl Acad Sci USA* 81:498, 1984.

167. CHANCE PF, DYER KA, KURACHI K, YOSHITAKE S, ROPERS H, WIEACKER P, GARTLER SM: Regional localization of human factor IX gene by molecular hybridization. *Hum Genet* 65:207, 1983.

168. MCGRAW RA, DAVIS LM, NOYES CM, LUNDBLAD RL, ROBERTS HR, GRAHAM JB, STAFFORD DW: Evidence for a prevalent dimorphism in the activation peptide of human coagulation factor IX. *Proc Natl Acad Sci USA* 82:2847, 1985.

169. WALLMARK A, LJUNG R, NILSSON IM, HOLMBERG L, HEDNER U, LINDVALL M, SJOGREN H-O: Polymorphism of normal factor IX detected by mouse monoclonal antibodies. *Proc Natl Acad Sci USA* 82:3839, 1985.

170. BAJAJ SP, RAPAPORT SI: Characterization of a monoclonal antibody to human factor IX. *Clin Res* 30:558A, 1982.

171. BERTINA RM, VAN DER LINDEN IK, MULLER HP, DERKS J, KLEIN-BRETELE E: A monoclonal anti-human factor IX produced by a mouse hybridoma. *Thromb Haemost* 46:165, 1981.

172. GOODALL AH, KEMBLE G, O'BRIEN DP, RAWLINGS E, ROTBLAT F, RUSSELL GC, JANOSSY G, TUDDENHAM EGD: Preparation of factor IX deficient human plasma by immunoaffinity chromatography using a monoclonal antibody. *Blood* 598:664, 1982.

173. THOMPSON AR: Monoclonal antibody to an epitope on the heavy chain of factor IX missing in three hemophilia-B patients. *Blood* 62:1027, 1983.

174. YOSHIOKA A, GIDDINGS JC, THOMAS JE, FUJIMURA J, BLOOM AL: Immunoassays of factor IX antigen using monoclonal antibodies. *Br J Haematol* 59:265, 1985.

175. FANTL P, SAWERS RJ, MARR AG: Investigation of a haemorrhagic disease due to beta-prothromboplastin deficiency complicated by a specific inhibitor of thromboplastin formation. *Aust Ann Med* 5:163, 1956.

176. ROBERTS HR, GROSS GP, WEBSTER WP, DEJANOV II, PENICK GD: Acquired inhibitors of plasma factor IX. A study of their induction, properties, and neutralization. *Am J Med Sci* 251:43, 1966.

177. ROBERTS HR, GRIZZLE JE, MCLESTER WD, PENICK GO: Genetic variants of hemophilia B. Detection by means of a specific PTC inhibitor. *J Clin Invest* 47:360, 1968.

178. PFUELLER S, SOMER JB, CASTALDI PA: Hemophilia B due to an abnormal factor IX. *Coagulation* 2:213, 1969.

179. DENSON KWE, BIGGS R, MANNUCCI PM: An investigation of three patients with Christmas disease due to an abnormal type of factor IX. *J Clin Pathol* 21:160, 1968.

180. THOMPSON AR: Factor IX antigen by radioimmunoassay. Abnormal factor IX protein in patients on warfarin therapy and with hemophilia B. *J Clin Invest* 59:900, 1977.

181. LEWIS RM, REISNER HM, CHUNG KS, ROBERTS HR: Detection of factor IX antibodies by radioimmunoassay. Effects of calcium on antibody-factor IX interaction. *Blood* 56:608, 1980.

182. HOUGIE C, TWOMEY JJ: Hemophilia Bm: A new type of factor IX deficiency. *Lancet* 1:698, 1967.

183. KASPER CK, OSTERUD B, MINAMI JY, SHONIK W, RAPAPORT SI: Hemophilia B: Characterization of genetic variants and detection of carriers. *Blood* 50:351, 1977.

184. BERTINA RM, VAN DER LINDEN IK: Factor IX Zutphen. A genetic variant of blood coagulation factor IX with an abnormally high molecular weight. *J Lab Clin Med* 100:695, 1982.

185. BROWN PE, HOUGIE C, ROBERTS HR: The genetic heterogeneity of hemophilia B. *N Engl J Med* 283:61, 1970.

186. BERTINA RM, VAN DER LINDEN IK: Factor IX Deventer—Evidence for the heterogeneity of hemophilia Bₘ. *Thromb Haemost* 47:351, 1977.

187. OSTERUD B, KASPER CK, LAVINE KK, PRODANOS C, RAPAPORT SI: Purification and properties of an abnormal coagulation factor IX (factor IX Bₘ): Kinetics of its inhibition of factor X activation by factor VII and bovine tissue factor. *Thromb Haemost* 45:55, 1981.

188. USHARANI P, WARN-CRAMER BJ, KASPER CK, BAJAJ SP: Characterization of three abnormal factor IX variants (Bm Lake Elsinore, Long Beach, and Los Angeles) of hemophilia-B. Evidence for defects affecting the latent catalytic site. *J Clin Invest* 75:76, 1985.

189. YOSHIOKA A, OHKUBO I, NISHIMURA T, TANAKA I, FUKUI H, OGATA K, KAMIYA T, TAKAHASHI H: Heterogeneity of factor IX BM difference of cleavage sites by factor XIa and Ca²⁺ in factor IX Kashihara, factor IX Nagoya and factor IX Niigata. *Thromb Res* 42:595, 1986.

190. CHUNG K-S, MADAR DA, GOLDSMITH JC, KINGDON HS, ROBERTS HR: Purification and characterization of an abnormal factor IX (Christmas factor) molecule. *J Clin Invest* 62:1078, 1978.

191. BRAUNSTEIN KM, NOYES CM, GRIFFITH MG, LUNDBLAD RL, ROBERTS HR: Characterization of the defect in activation of factor IX_Chapel Hill by human factor XIa. *J Clin Invest* 68:1420, 1981.

192. NOYES CM, GRIFFITH MJ, ROBERTS HR, LUNDBLAD RL: Identification of the molecular defect in factor IX_Chapel Hill: Substitution of histidine for arginine at position 145. *Proc Natl Acad Sci USA* 80:4200, 1983.

193. GRIFFITH MJ, BREITKREUTZ L, TRAPP H, BRIET E, NOYES CM, LUNDBLAD RL, ROBERTS HR: Characterization of the clotting activities of structurally different forms of activated factor IX. Enzymatic properties of normal human factor IXa, factor IXa, and activated factor IX_Chapel Hill. *J Clin Invest* 75:4, 1985.

194. MONROE DM, NOYES CM, STRAIGHT DL, ROBERTS HR, GRIFFITH MJ: Activation of normal and abnormal factor IX with trypsin. *Arch Biochem Biophys* 238:490, 1985.

195. DAVIS LM, MCGRAW RA, WARE JL, ROBERTS HR, STAFFORD DW: Factor IX_Alabama: A point mutation in a clotting protein results in hemophilia B. *Blood* 69:140, 1987.

196. JONES ME, GRIFFITH MJ, MONROE DM, ROBERTS HR, LENTZ BR: Compar-

ison of lipid binding and kinetic properties of normal, variant, and γ-carboxyglutamic acid modified human factor IX and factor IX$_a$. *Biochemistry* 24:8064, 1985.

197. REES DJG, RIZZA CR, BROWNLEE GG: Haemophilia B caused by a point mutation in a donor splice junction of the human factor IX gene. *Nature* 316:643, 1985.

198. SCHACH BG, YOSHITAKE S, DAVIE EW: Hemophilia B (Factor IX$_{Seattle\ 2}$) due to a single nucleotide deletion in the gene for factor IX. *J Clin Invest* 80:1023, 1987.

199. GIANNELLI F, CHOO KH, REES DJG, BOYD Y, RIZZA CR, BROWNLEE GG: Gene deletions in patients with haemophilia B and anti-factor IX antibodies. *Nature* 303:181, 1983.

200. PEAKE IR, FURLONG BL, BLOOM AL: Carrier detection by direct gene analysis in a family with haemophilia B (factor IX deficiency). *Lancet* 1:242, 1984.

201. CHEN S-H, YOSHITAKE S, CHANCE PF, BRAY GL, THOMPSON AR, SCOTT CR, KURACHI K: An intragenic deletion of the factor IX gene in a family with hemophilia B. *J Clin Invest* 76:2161, 1985.

202. DIGUID DL, RABIET MJ, FURIE BC, LIEBMAN HA, FURIE B: Molecular basis of hemophilia B: A defective enzyme due to an unprocessed propeptide is caused by a point mutation in the factor IX precursor. *Proc Natl Acad Sci USA* 83:5803, 1986.

203. BENTLEY AK, REES DJG, RIZZA C, BROWNLEE GG: Defective propeptide processing of blood clotting factor IX caused by mutation of arginine to glutamine at position -4. *Cell* 45:343, 1986.

204. MERTENS K, CUPERS R, VAN DER LINDEN IK, BERTINA RM: The functional defect of factor IX Eindhoven, a genetic variant of factor IX. *Thromb Haemost* 50:249, 1983.

205. VELTKAMP JJ, MEILOF J, REMMELTS HG, VAN DER VLERK D, LOELIGER EA: Another genetic variant of haemophilia B: haemophilia B Leyden. *Scand J Haematol* 7:82, 1970.

206. BRIET E, BERTINA RM, VAN TILBURG NH, VELTKAMP JJ: Hemophilia B Leyden. A sex-linked hereditary disorder that improves after puberty. *N Engl J Med* 306:788, 1982.

207. SOUTHERN EM: Detection of specific sequences among DNA fragments separated by gel electrophoresis. *J Mol Biol* 98:503, 1975.

208. BOTSTEIN D, WHITE RL, SKOLNICK M, DAVIS RW: Construction of a genetic linkage map in man using restriction fragment length polymorphisms. *Am J Hum Genet* 32:214, 1980.

209. GIANNELLI F, CHOO KH, WINSHIP PR, ANSON DS, REES DJG, FERRARI N, RIZZA CR, BROWNLEE GG: Characterization and use of an intragenic polymorphic marker for detection of carriers of haemophilia B (factor IX deficiency). *Lancet* 1:239, 1984.

210. WINSHIP PR, ANSON DS, RIZZA CR, BROWNLEE GG: Carrier detection in haemophilia B using two further intragenic fragment length polymorphisms. *Nucleic Acids Res* 12:8861, 1984.

211. HAY CW, ROBERTSON KA, YONG S-L, THOMPSON AR, GROWE GH, MacGILLIVRAY RTA: Use of a Bam HI polymorphism in the factor IX gene for the determination of hemophilia B carrier status. *Blood* 67:1508, 1986.

212. NILSSON IM, BLOMBACK M, RAMGREN O: Haemophilia in Sweden. I. Coagulation studies. *Acta Med Scand* 170:665, 1961.

213. HARTMANN JR, DIAMOND LK: Haemophilia and related haemorrhagic disorders. *Practitioner* 178:178, 1957.

214. FORBES CD: Clinical aspects of the hemophilias and their treatment, in Ratnoff OD, Forbes CD (eds): *Disorders of Hemostasis.* Orlando, FL, Grune & Stratton, 1984, p 177.

215. DUTHIE RB, MATTHEWS JM, RIZZA CR, STEEL WM, WOODS CG: The management of musculo-skeletal problems in the haemophiliacs. Oxford, Blackwell, 1972.

216. WENZL DJ, TULLY RJ, GIANGIACOMO J: Intraosseous hemophilic pseudotumor of the orbit. *J Pediatr Ophthalmol Strabismus* 20:109, 1983.

217. DE VALDERRAMA JAF, MATTHEWS JM: The haemophilic pseudotumour of haemophilic subperiosteal haematoma. *J Bone Joint Surg* 47B:256, 1965.

218. GILBERT MS: Hemophilic pseudotumour, in Brinkhous KM, Hemker HC (eds): *Handbook of Hemophilia.* Amsterdam, Excerpta Medica, 1975, p 435.

219. KERR CB: *Management of Haemophilia.* Glebe, NSW, Australian Medical Publication Co, 1963.

220. STEEL WM, DUTHIE RB, O'CONNOR BT: Hemophilic cysts. Report of five cases. *J Bone Joint Surg* 51B:614, 1969.

221. NILSSON IM, HEDNER U, AHLBERG A, LARSSON SA, BERGENTZ S-E: Surgery of haemophiliacs—20 years' experience. *World J Surg* I:55, 1977.

222. FORBES CD, PRENTICE CRM: Mortality in haemophilia—A United Kingdom survey, in Fratantoni JC, Aronson DL (eds): *Unsolved Therapeutic Problems in Hemophilia.* Washington, DC: DHEW Publication No (NIH) 77-10899, 1977, p 15.

223. LARSSON SA, WIECHEL B: Deaths in Swedish hemophiliacs, 1957–1980. *Acta Med Scand* 214:199, 1983.

224. STUART J, DAVIES SH, CUMMING RA, GIRDWOOD RH, DARG A: Haemorrhagic episodes in haemophilia: a 5-year prospective study. *Br Med J* 2:1624, 1966.

225. CARRON DB, BOON TH, WALKER FC: Peptic ulcer in the haemophiliac and its relation to gastrointestinal bleeding. *Lancet* 2:1036, 1965.

226. FORBES CD, DAVIDSON JF: Management of coagulation defects. *Clin Haematol* 2:101, 1973.

227. IKKALA E: Haemophilia. A study of its laboratory, clinical, genetic and social aspects based on known haemophiliacs in Finland. *Scand J Clin Lab Invest* 12[suppl 46]:1, 1960.

228. PETERSSON H, NILSSON IM, HEDNER U, NOREHN K, AHLBERG A: Radiologic evaluation of prophylaxis in severe haemophilia. *Acta Pediatr Scand* 70:565, 1981.

229. NILSSON IM: *Haemorrhagic and Thrombotic Diseases.* London, Wiley, 1974.

230. DUTHIE RB, RIZZA CR: Rheumatological manifestations of the haemophiliacs. *Clin Rheum Dis* 1:53, 1975.

231. BIGGS R, MATTHEWS JM: In Biggs R, Macfarlane RG (eds): *Treatment of Haemophilia and Other Coagulation Disorders.* Oxford, Blackwell, 1966, p 129.

232. AHLBERG A: Haemophilia in Sweden. VII. Incidence, treatment and prophylaxis of arthropathy and other musculo-skeletal manifestations of haemophilia A and B. *Acta Orthop Scand [suppl]* 77:3, 1965.

233. PETERSSON H, AHLBERG A, NILSSON IM: A radiologic classification of hemophilic arthropathy. *Clin Orthopaed* 149:153, 1980.

234. BOLDERO JL, KEMP HS: The early bone and joint changes in haemophilia and similar blood dyscrasias. *Br J Radiol* 39:172, 1966.

235. DePALMA AF, COTLER JM: Hemophilic arthropathy. *Arch Surg* 72:247, 1956.

236. BIGGS R: The detection of defects in blood coagulation. *Br J Haematol* 15:115, 1968.

237. KASPER CK, DIETRICH SL: Comprehensive management of haemophilia, in Ruggeri ZM (ed): *Clinics in Hematology Coagulation Disorders.* London, Saunders, 1985, vol 14/No 2, p 489.

238. BIGGS R, DENSON KWE: The fate of prothrombin and factors VII, IX, and X transfused to patients deficient in these factors. *Br J Haematol* 9:532, 1963.

239. LOELIGER EA, HENSEN A, MATTERN MJ, VELTKAMP JJ, BRUNING PF, HEMKER HC: Treatment of haemophilia B with purified factor IX (PPSB). *Folia Med Neerl* 10:112, 1967.

240. BIGGS R: Clinical experience with factor IX concentrate of Bidwell, in Brinkhous KM (ed): *Hemophilia and New Hemorrhagic States.* International Symposium, New York. Chapel Hill, NC, The University of North Carolina Press, 1970, p 31.

241. NILSSON IM, AHLBERG A, BJORLIN G: Clinical experience with a Swedish factor IX concentrate. *Acta Med Scand* 190:257, 1974.

242. LACHIEWICZ PF, INGLIS AE, INSALL JN, SCULCO TP, HILGARTNER MW, BUSSEL JB: Total knee arthroplasty in hemophilia. *J Bone Joint Surg* 67A:1361, 1985.

243. GOLDBERG VM, HEIPLE KG, RATNOFF OD, KURCZYNSKI E, ARVAN G: Total knee arthroplasty in classic hemophilia. *J Bone Joint Surg* 63:695, 1981.

244. INSALL JN, HOOD RW, FLAWN LB, SULLIVAN DJ: The total condylar knee prosthesis on gonarthrosis. A five to nine-year followup of the first one hundred consecutive replacements. *J Bone Joint Surg* 65:619, 1983.

245. STORTI E, ASCARI E: Surgical and chemical synovectomy. *Ann NY Acad Sci* 240:316, 1975.

246. STORTI E, ASCARI E, GAMBA G: Postoperative complications and joint function after knee synovectomy in haemophiliacs. *Br J Haematol* 50:544, 1982.

247. SCARPONI R, SILVELLO L, LANDONIO G, BAUDO F, DE CATALDO F: Long-term evaluation of knee-joint function after synovectomy in haemophilia. *Br J Haematol* 52:337, 1982.

248. LOFQVIST T, PETTERSSON C: Experience with colloid ^{198}Au synoviorthesis in hemophiliacs. *Ric Clin Lab* 16:97, 1986.

249. ESPINOSA C, CABALLERO O, AZNAR JA, QUEROL F: Synoviorthesis with ^{90}Y in hemophilic chronic synovitis. *Ric Clin Lab* 16:97, 1986.

250. NILSSON IM, BLOMBACK M, AHLBERG A: Our experience in Sweden with prophylaxis on haemophilia. The hemophilic and his world: Proc 5th Congr World Fed Hemophilia. Montreal, 1968, *Bibl Haematol* 34:111, 1970.

251. BRETTLER DB, FORSBERG AD, O'CONELL FD, CEDERBAUM AI, CHAITMAN AK, LEVINE PH: A long-term study of hemophilic arthropathy of the knee joint on a program of factor VIII replacement given at time of each hemarthrosis. *Am J Hematol* 18:13, 1985.

252. RIZZA CR, SPOONER RJD: Treatment of haemophilia and related disorders

in Britain and Northern Ireland during 1976–80: Report on behalf of the directors of haemophilia centres in the United Kingdom. *Br Med J (Clin Res)* 286:929, 1983.

253. STEVEN MM, YOGARAJAH S, MADHOK R, FORBES CD, STURROCK RD: Haemophilic arthritis. *Q J Med* 226:181, 1986.

254. GUENTHNER EE, HILGARTNER MW, MILLER CH, VIENNE G: Hemophilic arthropathy: Effect of home care on treatment patterns and joint disease. *J Pediatr* 97:378, 1980.

255. INGRAM GIC, DYKES SR, CREESE AL, MELLOR P, SWAN AV, KAUFERT J, RIZZA CR, SPOONER RJD, BIGGS R: Home treatment in haemophilia: Clinical, social and economic advantages. *Clin Lab Haematol* 1:13, 1979.

256. SOULIER JP, BLATRIX C, STEINBACH M: Fractions "coagulants" contenant les facteurs de coagulation absorbables par le phosphate tricalcique. *Presse Med* 72:1223, 1964.

257. JOSSO F, STEINBACH M, MENOCHE D, BLATRIX C, SOULIER JP: Preparation of factor IX concentrates with special reference to the PPSB fraction, in Brinkhous KM (ed): *Hemophilia and New Hemorrhagic States.* Int Symp New York. Chapel Hill, NC, The University of North Carolina Press, 1970, p 14.

258. DIKE GWR, BIDWELL E, RIZZA CR: The preparation and clinical use of a new concentrate containing factor IX, prothrombin and factor X and a separate concentrate containing factor VII. *Br J Haematol* 22:469, 1972.

259. BIDWELL E, BOOTH JM, DIKE GWR: The preparation for therapeutic use of a concentrate of factor IX containing also factors II, VII, and X. *Br J Haematol* 13:568, 1967.

260. TULLIS JL, MELIN M, JURGIAN P: Clinical use of human prothrombin complexes. *N Engl J Med* 273:667, 1965.

261. ZAUBER NP, LEVIN J: Factor IX levels in patients with hemophilia B (Christmas disease) following transfusion with concentrates of factor IX or fresh frozen plasma (FFP). *Medicine (Baltimore)* 56:213, 1977.

262. KASPER CK: Post-operative thromboses in hemophilia B. *N Engl J Med* 289:160, 1973.

263. MACHIN SJ, MILLER BR: Thrombosis and factor-IX concentrates. *Lancet* 1:136, 1978.

264. FUERTH JH, MAHRER P: Myocardial infarction after factor IX therapy. *JAMA* 245:1455, 1981.

265. SMALL M, LOWE GDO, DOUGLAS JI: Factor IX thrombogenicity: *in vivo* effects on coagulation activation and a case report of disseminated intravascular coagulation. *Thromb Haemost* 48:76, 1982.

266. KINGDON HS, LUNDBLAD RL, VELTKAMP JJ, ARONSON DL: Potentially thrombogenic materials in factor IX concentrates. *Thromb Diath Haemorrh* 33:617, 1975.

267. HEDNER U, NILSSON IM, BERGENTZ SE: Various prothrombin complex concentrates and their effect on coagulation and fibrinolysis *in vivo.* *Thromb Haemost* 35:386, 1976.

268. HULTIN MB: Activated clotting factors in prothrombin complex concentrates. *Blood* 54:1028, 1979.

269. GILES AR, NESHEIM ME, HOOGENDOORN H, TRACY PB, MANN KG: The coagulant-active phospholipid content is a major determinant of *in vivo* thrombogenicity of prothrombin complex (factor IX) concentrates in rabbits. *Blood* 59:401, 1982.

270. PRESTON FE, WINFIELD D, MALIA R: Serial changes in the coagulation system following clotting factor concentrate infusion. *Thromb Diath Haemorrh* 34:475, 1975.

271. HOOFNAGLE JH, ARONSON D, ROBERTS HR: Serologic evidence of hepatitis B infection in patients with hemophilia B. *Thromb Diath Haemorrh* 33:606, 1975.

272. CRASKE J: The epidemiology of factor VIII and IX associated hepatitis in the UK, in Forbes CD, Lowe GDO (eds): *Unresolved Problems in Haemophilia.* Lancaster, UK, MTP Press Limited, 1981, pp 5–14.

273. BLOOM AL: Aids and haemophilia. *Biomed Pharmacother* 39:355, 1985.

274. MCGRATH KM, SPELMAN D, BARNETT M, KELLNER S: Spectrum of HTLV-III infection in a hemophilic cohort treated with blood products from a single manufacturer. *Am J Hematol* 23:239, 1986.

275. LEVY JA, MITRA G, WONG MF, MOZEN MM: Inactivation by wet and dry heat of AIDS-associated retroviruses during factor VIII purification from plasma. *Lancet* 2:1456, 1985.

276. SPIRE B, BARRE-SINOUSSI F, CHERMAN JC, DORMONT D, MONTAGNIER L: Inactivation of lymphoadenopathy-associated virus by heat gamma rays, and ultraviolet light. *Lancet* 1:188, 1985.

277. GRALNICK HR, RICK ME: Danazol increases factor VIII and factor IX in classic hemophilia and Christmas disease. *N Engl J Med* 308:1353, 1983.

278. NUGENT DJ, BRAY GL, COUNTS RB, CLEMENTS MJ, THOMPSON AR: Danazol fails to increase factor VIII or IX levels in a double-blind crossover study of patients with haemophilia A and B. *Br J Haematol* 64:493, 1986.

279. SAIDI P, LEGA BZ, KIM HC, RASKA K: Effect of Danazol on clotting factor levels, bleeding incidence, factor infusion requirements, and immune parameters in hemophilia. *Blood* 68:673, 1986.

280. MEYER D: Specificity and structure of factor VIII and factor IX antibodies in haemophiliacs, in Seligsohn U, Rimon A, Horoszowski H (eds): *Haemophilia.* Tunbridge Wells, Kent, UK, Castle House Publications Ltd, 1981, pp 69–77.

281. NILSSON IM, HEDNER U: Immunosuppressive treatment in hemophiliacs with inhibitors to factor VIII and factor IX. *Scand J Haematol* 16:269, 1976.

282. HEDNER U, SUNDQVIST SB, NILSSON IM: Immunosuppressive treatment in haemophiliacs with inhibitors, in *The State of Art of Managing Hemophilia with FVIII Inhibitors, Proc Int Meeting on Activated Prothrombin Complex Concentrates.* New York, Praeger, 1982.

283. NILSSON IM, JONSSON S, SUNDQVIST S-B, AHLBERG A, BERGENTZ S-E: A procedure for removing high titer antibodies by extracorporeal protein-A-Sepharose adsorption in hemophilia: Substitution therapy and surgery in a patient with hemophilia B and antibodies. *Blood* 58:38, 1981.

284. THEODORSSON B, HEDNER U, NILSSON IM, KISIEL W: A technique for specific removal of factor IX alloantibodies from human plasma: Partial characterization of the alloantibodies. *Blood* 61:973, 1983.

285. NILSSON IM, SUNDQVIST S-B, LJUNG R, HOLMBERG L, FREIBURGHAUS C, BJORLIN G: Suppression of secondary antibody response by intravenous immunoglobulin in a patient with haemophilia B and antibodies. *Scand J Haematol* 30:458, 1983.

286. BRACKMANN HH, EGLI H: Treatment of haemophilia patients with inhibitors, in Seligsohn U, Rimon A, Horoszowski H (eds): *Haemophilia.* Tunbridge Wells, Kent, UK, Castle House Publications Ltd, 1981, pp 113–119.

287. HEDNER U, NILSSON IM: Induced tolerance in hemophilia patients with antibodies against IX:C. *Acta Med Scand* 214:191, 1983.

288. NILSSON IM, FREIBURGHAUS C, SUNDQVIST S-B, SANDBERG H: Removal of specific antibodies from whole blood in a continuous extracorporeal system. *Plasma Ther Transfus Technol* 5:127, 1984.

289. TITANI K, FUJIKAWA K, ENFIELD DL, ERICSSON LH, WALSH KA, NEURATH H: Bovine factor X_1 (Stuart factor): Amino acid sequence of heavy chain. *Proc Natl Acad Sci USA* 72:3082, 1975.

290. van DIEIJEN G, TANS G, ROSING J, HEMKER HC: The role of phospholipid and factor VIII$_a$ in the activation of bovine factor X. *J Biol Chem* 256:3433, 1981.

291. DUCKERT F, FLUCKIGER P, MATTER M, KOLLER F: Clotting factor X: Physiologic and physico-chemical properties. *Proc Soc Exp Biol Med* 90:17, 1955.

292. TELFER TP, DENSON KW, WRIGHT DR: A "new" coagulation defect. *Br J Haematol* 2:308, 1956.

293. HOUGIE C, BARROW EM, GRAHAM JB: Stuart clotting defect. I. Segregation of an hereditary hemorrhagic state from the heterogeneous group heretofore called "stable factor" (SPCA, proconvertin, factor VII) deficiency. *J Clin Invest* 36:485, 1957.

294. MAMMEN EF: Factor X abnormalities. *Semin Thromb Hemost* 9:31, 1983.

295. GRAHAM JB, BARROW EM, HOUGIE C: Stuart clotting defect II: Genetic aspects of a "new" hemorrhagic state. *J Clin Invest* 36:497, 1957.

296. LECHLER E, WEBSTER WP, ROBERTS HR, PENICK GD: The inheritance of Stuart disease: Investigation of a family with factor X deficiency. *Am J Med Sci* 249:191, 1965.

297. DENSON KWE, LURIE A, DeCATALDO F, MANNUCCI PM: The factor X defect: Recognition of abnormal forms of factor X. *Br J Haematol* 18:317, 1968.

298. FAIR DS, EDGINGTON TS: Heterogeneity of hereditary and acquired factor X deficiencies by combined immunochemical and functional analyses. *Br J Haematol* 59:235, 1985.

299. GIROLAMI A, MOLARO G, LAZZARIN M, SCARPA R: Una nuova coagulopatia emorragica congenita probabilmente dovuta alla presenza di un fattore X abnorme. Studio preliminare. *Minerva Med* 60:4939, 1969.

300. GIROLAMI A, LAZZARIN M, PROCIDANO M, LUZZATTO G: A family with heterozygous factor X Friuli defect outside Friuli. *Blut* 46:149, 1983.

301. FAIR D, REVAK D, EDGINGTON T, GIROLAMI A: Structural studies on the factor X Friuli variant. *Thromb Haemost* 50:279, 1983.

302. KORSAN-BENGSTEN L, HJORT PF, YGGE J: Acquired factor X deficiency in a patient with amyloidosis. *Thromb Diath Haemorrh* 7:558, 1962.

303. STENFLO J: A new vitamin K dependent protein: Purification from bovine plasma and preliminary characterization. *J Biol Chem* 251:355, 1976.

304. ESMON CT: Protein C: Biochemistry, physiology and clinical implications. *Blood* 62:1155, 1983.

305. KISIEL W: Human plasma protein C: Isolation, characterization and mechanism of activation by α-thrombin. *J Clin Invest* 64:761, 1979.

306. ESMON CT, ESMON NL, HARRIS KW: Complex formation between thrombin and thrombomodulin inhibits both thrombin catalyzed fibrin formation and factor V activation. *J Biol Chem* 257:7944, 1982.

307. DiSCIPIO RG, DAVIE EW: Characterization of protein S, a γ-carboxyglu-

tamic acid containing protein from bovine and human plasma. *Biochemistry* 18:899, 1979.

308. MITCHELL CA, HAU L, SALEM HH: Control of thrombin-mediated cleavage of protein S. *Thromb Haemost* 56:151, 1986.

309. WALKER FJ: Protein S and the regulation of activated protein C. *Semin Thromb Hemost* 10:131, 1984.

310. HARRIS K, ESMON C: Protein S is required for platelets to support activated protein C binding and activity. *J Biol Chem* 260:2007, 1985.

311. STERN DM, NAWROTH PP, HANDLEY D, KISIEL W: An endothelial cell-dependent pathway of coagulation. *Proc Natl Acad Sci USA* 82:2523, 1985.

312. NAWROTH PP, HANDLEY D, STERN DM: The multiple levels of endothelial cell-coagulation factor interactions, in Chesterman CN (ed): *Clinics in Haematology. Thrombosis and the Vessel Wall*. London, UK, Saunders, 1986, vol 15/no 2, pp 293–321.

313. STERN DM, NAWROTH PP, HARRIS K: Activated protein C regulates cellular processing of protein S. *Thromb Haemost* 54:707, 1985.

314. COMP PC, ESMON CT: Generation of fibrinolytic activity by infusion of activated protein C into dogs. *J Clin Invest* 68:1221, 1981.

315. SAKATA Y, CURRIDEN S, LAWRENCE D, GRIFFIN JH, LOSKUTOFF DJ: Activated protein C stimulates the fibrinolytic activity of cultured endothelial cells and decreases antiactivator activity. *Proc Natl Acad Sci USA* 82:1121, 1985.

316. TAYLOR FB, LOCKHART MS: A new function for activated protein C: Activated protein C prevents inhibition of plasminogen activators by releasate from mononuclear leukocytes - platelet suspensions stimulated by phorbol diester. *Thromb Res* 37:155, 1985.

317. van HINSBERGH VWM, BERTINA RM, VAN WIJNGAARDEN A, VAN TILBURG NH, EMEIS JJ, HAVERKATE F: Activated protein C decreases plasminogen activator inhibitor activity in endothelial cell conditioned medium. *Blood* 65:444, 1985.

318. D'ANGELO A, LOCKHART MS, D'ANGELO SV, TAYLOR FB: Protein S is a cofactor for activated protein C neutralization of an inhibitor of plasminogen activation released from platelets. *Blood* 69:231, 1987.

319. SUZUKI K: Activated protein C inhibitor. *Semin Thromb Hemost* 10:154, 1984.

320. KISIEL W, DAVIE EW: Protein C. *Methods Enzymol* 80:320, 1981.

321. ESMON NL, CARROLL RC, ESMON CT: Thrombomodulin blocks the ability of thrombin to activate platelets. *J Biol Chem* 258:12238, 1983.

322. SUZUKI K, KUSUMOTO H, DEYASHIKI Y, NISHIOKA J, MARUYAMA I, ZUSHI M, KAWAHARA S, HONDA G, YAMAMOTO S, HORIGUCHI S: Structure and expression of human thrombomodulin, a thrombin receptor on endothelium acting as a cofactor for protein C activation. *EMBO J* 6:1891, 1987.

323. WEN D, DITTMAN WA, YE RD, DEAVEN LL, MAJERUS PW, SADLER JE: Human thrombomodulin: Complete cDNA sequence and chromosome location of the gene. *Biochemistry* 26:4350, 1987.

324. JACKSON RW, BEELER DL, FRITZE L, SOFF G, ROSENBERG RD: Human thrombomodulin gene is intron depleted: Nucleic acid sequences of the cDNA and gene predict protein structure and suggest sites of regulatory control. *Proc Natl Acad Sci USA* 84:6425, 1987.

325. STENFLO J, JONSSON M: Protein S, a new vitamin K-dependent protein from bovine plasma. *FEBS Lett* 101:377, 1979.

326. DAHLBACK B, STENFLO J: High molecular weight complex in human plasma between vitamin K-dependent protein C and complement component C4b-binding protein. *Proc Natl Acad Sci USA* 78:2512, 1981.

327. DAHLBACK B: Interaction between vitamin K-dependent protein S and the complement protein, C4b-binding protein. A link between coagulation and the complement system. *Semin Thromb Hemost* 10:139, 1984.

328. COMP PC, DORAY D, PATTON D, ESMON CT: An abnormal plasma distribution of protein S occurs in functional protein S deficiency. *Blood* 67:504, 1986.

329. BERTINA RM, VAN WIJNGAARDEN A, REINALDA-POOT J, POORT SR, BOM VJJ: Determination of plasma protein S—The protein cofactor of activated protein C. *Thromb Haemost* 53:268, 1985.

330. DAHLBACK B: Inhibition of protein Ca cofactor function of human and bovine protein S by C4b-binding protein. *J Biol Chem* 261:12022, 1986.

331. BAKER ME, FRENCH FS, JOSEPH DR: Vitamin K-dependent protein S is similar to rat androgen-binding protein. *Biochem J* 243:293, 1987.

332. DAHLBACK B, LUNDWALL A, STENFLO J: Localization of thrombin cleavage sites in the amino-terminal region of bovine protein S. *J Biol Chem* 261:5111, 1986.

333. MILETICH JP, LEYKAM JF, BROZE GJ Jr: Detection of single chain protein C in human plasma. *Blood [suppl]* 62:306a, 1983.

334. MARUYAMA I, BELL CE, MAJERUS PW: Thrombomodulin is found on endothelium of arteries, veins, capillaries, and lymphatics, and on syncytiotrophoblast of human placenta. *J Cell Biol* 101:363, 1985.

335. DeBAULT LE, ESMON NL, OLSON JR, ESMON CT: Distribution of the thrombomodulin antigen in the rabbit vasculature. *Lab Invest* 54:172, 1986.

336. ISHII H, SALEM HH, BELL CE, LAPOSATA EA, MAJERUS PW: Thrombomodulin, an endothelial anticoagulant protein, is absent from the human brain. *Blood* 67:362, 1986.

337. MOORE KL, ANDREOLI SP, ESMON NL, ESMON CT, BANG NU: Endotoxin enhances tissue factor and suppresses thrombomodulin expression of human vascular endothelium in vitro. *J Clin Invest* 79:124, 1987.

338. NAWROTH PP, HANDLEY DA, ESMON CT, STERN DM: Interleukin 1 induces endothelial cell procoagulant while suppressing cell-surface anticoagulant activity. *Proc Natl Acad Sci USA* 83:3460, 1986.

339. HORELLOU MH, CONRAD J, van DREDEN P, SAMAMA M: Constitutional protein C deficiency in 57 patients from 22 non-related families. *Ann Med Interne (Paris)* 137:465, 1986.

340. ROCCHI M, RONCUZZI L, SANTAMARIA R, ARCHIDIACONO N, DENTE L, ROMEO G: Mapping through somatic cell hybrids and cDNA probes of protein C to chromosome 2, factor X to chromosome 13, and alpha 1-acid glycoprotein to chromosome 9. *Hum Genet* 74:30, 1986.

341. ROMEO G, HASSAN HJ, STAEMPFLI S, RONCUZZI L, CIANETTI L, LEONARDI A, VICENTE V, MANNUCCI PM, BERTINA R, PESCHLE C, CORTESE R: Hereditary thrombophilia: Identification of nonsense and missense mutations in the protein C gene. *Proc Natl Acad Sci USA* 84:2829, 1987.

342. ENGESSER L, BROEKMANS AW, BRIET E, BROMMER EJ, BERTINA RM: Hereditary protein S deficiency: Clinical manifestations. *Ann Intern Med* 106:677, 1987.

343. MARLAR RA, ENDRES-BROOKS J, MILLER C: Serial studies of protein C and its plasma inhibitor in patients with disseminated intravascular coagulation. *Blood* 66:59, 1985.

344. MANNUCCI PM, VIGANO S: Deficiencies of protein C, an inhibitor of blood coagulation. *Lancet* 2:463, 1982.

345. COMP PC, NIXON RR, ESMON CT: Determination of functional levels of protein C, an antithrombotic protein using thrombin-thrombomodulin complex. *Blood* 63:15, 1984.

346. KARPATKIN M, MANNUCCI PM, BHOGAL M, VIAGNO S, NARDI M: Low protein C in the neonatal period. *Br J Haematol* 62:137,1986.

347. SCHETTINI F, DE MATTIA D, ALTOMARE M, MONTAGNA O, CIAVARELLA G, MANZIONNA MM: Post-natal development of protein C in full-term newborns. *Acta Paediatr Scand* 74:226, 1985.

348. D'ANGELO SV, COMP PC, ESMON CT, D'ANGELO A: Relationship between protein C antigen and anticoagulant activity during oral anticoagulation and in selected disease states. *J Clin Invest* 77:416, 1986.

349. BROEKMANS AW, BERTINA RM, LOELIGER EA, HOFMANN V, KLINGEMANN HG: Protein C and the development of skin necrosis during anticoagulant therapy. *Thromb Haemost* 49:251, 1983.

350. MCGEHEE WG, KLOTZ TA, EPSTEIN DJ, RAPAPORT SI: Coumarin necrosis associated with hereditary protein C deficiency. *Ann Intern Med* 101:59, 1984.

351. BROEKMANS AW, VELTKAMP JJ, BERTINA RM: Congenital protein C deficiency and venous thromboembolism. A study of three Dutch families. *N Engl J Med* 309:340, 1983.

352. FRANCIS RC, PATCH MJ: A functional assay for protein C in human plasma. *Thromb Res* 32:605, 1983.

353. SALA N, OWEN WG, COLLEN D: Functional assay for protein C in human plasma. *Blood* 63:671, 1984.

354. VIGANO S, MANNUCCI PM, RUMI MG, VIGANO P, DELNINNO E, COLOMBO M, PODDA M: The significance of protein C antigen in acute and chronic liver and biliary disease. *Am J Clin Pathol* 89:454, 1985.

355. RODEGHIERO F, MANNUCCI PM, VIGANO S, BARBUI T, GUGLIOTTA L, CORTELLARO M, DINI E: Liver dysfunction rather than intravascular coagulation as the main cause of low protein C and antithrombin III in acute leukemia. *Blood* 63:965, 1984.

356. GRIFFIN JH, MOSHER DF, ZIMMERMAN TS, KLEISS AJ: Protein C, an antithrombotic protein is reduced in hospitalized patients with intravascular coagulation. *Blood* 60:261, 1982.

357. GLAS-GREENWALT P, HALL JM, PANKE TW, KANT KS, ALLEN CM, POLLAK VE: Fibrinolysis in health and disease: Abnormal levels of plasminogen activator, plasminogen activator inhibitor, and protein C in thrombotic thrombocytopenic purpura. *J Lab Clin Med* 108:415, 1986.

358. BLAMEY SL, MCARDLE BM, BURNS P, CARTER DC, LOWE GDO, FORBES CD: A double blind trial of intramuscular stanozolol in the prevention of postoperative deep vein thrombosis following elective abdominal surgery. *Thromb Haemost* 51:71, 1984.

359. BLAMEY SL, LOWE GDO, BERTINA RM, KLUFT C, SUE-LING HM, DAVIES JD, FORBES CD: Protein C antigen levels in major abdominal surgery: Relationships to deep vein thrombosis, malignancy and treatment with stanozolol. *Thromb Haemost* 54:622, 2985.

360. KLUFT C, BERTINA RM, PRESTON FE, MALIA RG, BLAMEY SL, LOWE GDO, FORBES CF: Protein C, an anticoagulant protein, is increased in healthy

volunteers and surgical patients after treatment with stanozolol. *Thromb Res* 33:297, 1984.

361. GRIFFIN JH, EVATT B, ZIMMERMAN TS, KLEISS AJ, WIDEMAN C: Deficiency of protein C in congenital thrombotic disease. *J Clin Invest* 68:1370, 1981.

362. BERTINA RM, BROEKMANS AW, KROMMERHOED VAN ES C, van WIJNGAARDEN A: The use of a functional and immunologic assay for plasma protein C in the study of the heterogeneity of congenital protein C deficiency. *Thromb Haemost* 51:1, 1984.

363. BARBUI T, FINAZZI G, MUSSONI L, RIGANTI M, DONATI MB, COLUCCI M, COLLEN D: Hereditary dysfunctional protein C (protein C Bergamo) and thrombosis. *Lancet* 2:819, 1984.

364. BERTINA RM, BROEKMANS AW, van der LINDEN IK, MERTENS K: Protein C deficiency in a Dutch family with thrombotic disease. *Thromb Haemost* 48:1, 1982.

365. MARLAR RA: Protein C in thromboembolic disease. *Semin Thromb Hemost* 11:387, 1985.

366. HORELLOU MH, CONRAD J, BERTINA RM, SAMAMA M: Congenital protein C deficiency and thrombotic disease in nine French families. *Br Med J* 289:1285, 1984.

367. PABINGER-FASCHING I, BERTINA RM, LECHNER K, NIESSNER H, KORNINGER C: Protein C deficiency in two Austrian families. *Thromb Haemost* 50:810, 1983.

368. WINTZEN AR, BROEKMANS AW, BERTINA RM, BRIET E, BRIET PE, ZECHA A, VIELVOYE GJ, BOTS GTAM: Cerebral hemorrhagic infarction in young patients with hereditary protein C deficiency: Evidence for "spontaneous" cerebral venous thrombosis. *Br Med J* 290:350, 1985.

369. SELIGSOHN U, BERGER A, ABEND M, RUBIN L, ATTIAS D, ZIVELIN A, RAPAPORT SI: Homozygous protein C deficiency manifested by massive venous thrombosis in the newborn. *N Engl J Med* 310:559, 1984.

370. ZAUBER NP, STARK MW: Successful warfarin anticoagulation despite protein C deficiency and a history of warfarin necrosis. *Ann Intern Med* 104:659, 1986.

371. MARCINIAK E, WILSON HD, MARLAR RA: Neonatal purpura fulminans as expression of homozygosity for protein C deficiency. *Blood [suppl]* 62:303a, 1983.

372. SILLS RH, MARLAR RA, MONTGOMERY RR, DESHPANDE GN, HUMBERT JR: Severe homozygous protein C deficiency. *J Pediatr* 105:409, 1983.

373. ESTELLES A, GARCIA-PLAZA I, DASI A, AZNAR J, DUART M, SANZ G, PEREZ-REQUEJO J, ESPANA F, JIMENEZ C, ABELEDO G: Severe inherited "homozygous" protein C deficiency in a newborn infant. *Thromb Haemost* 52:53, 1984.

374. MARLAR RA, SILLS RH, MONTGOMERY RR: Protein C in commercial factor IX concentrates and its use in the treatment of "homozygous" protein C deficiency. *Blood [suppl]* 62:303a, 1983.

375. GARCIA-PLAZA I, JIMENEZ-ASTORGA C, BORREGO D, MARTY ML: Syndrome due to homozygous protein C deficiency. *Lancet* 1:634, 1985.

376. MANABE S, MATSUDA M: Homozygous protein C deficiency combined with heterozygous dysplasminogenemia found in a 21-year-old thrombophilic male. *Thromb Res* 39:333, 1985.

377. SHARON C, TIRINDELLI MC, MANNUCCI PM, TRIPODI A, MARIANI G: Homozygous protein C deficiency with moderately severe clinical symptoms. *Thromb Res* 41:483, 1986.

378. TIRINDELLI MC, FRANCHI F, TRIPODI A, MARIANI G, MANNUCCI PM: Familial dysfunctional protein C. *Thromb Res* 44:893, 1986.

379. COMP PC, ESMON CT: Recurrent venous thromboembolism in patients with a partial deficiency of protein S. *N Engl J Med* 311:1525, 1984.

380. SCHWARZ HP, FISHER M, HOPMEIER P, BATARD MA, GRIFFIN JH: Plasma protein S deficiency in familial thrombotic disease. *Blood* 64:1297, 1984.

381. COMP PC, NIXON RR, COOPER MR, ESMON CT: Familial protein S deficiency is associated with recurrent thrombosis. *J Clin Invest* 74:2082, 1984.

382. SZATKOWSKI NS, MILLER CM, ENDRES-BROOKS JL, MADDEN RM, MARLAR RA: Clinical studies of human protein S and identification of a patient with protein S deficiency and thrombotic complication. *Circulation* 70:II:204, 1984.

383. KAMIYA T, SUGIHARA T, OGATA K, SAITO H, SUZUKI K, NISHIOKA J, HASHIMOTO S, YAMAGATA K: Inherited deficiency of protein S in a Japanese family with recurrent venous thrombosis: A study of three generations. *Blood* 67:406, 1986.

384. SALEM HH: The natural anticoagulants. *Clin Haematol* 15:371, 1986.

385. FRIEDMAN KD, MARLAR RA, GILL JC, ENDRES-BROOKS J, MONTGOMERY RR: Protein S deficiency in patients with the lupus anticoagulant. *Blood [suppl]* 68:333a, 1986.

386. ELIAS M, ELDOR A: Thromboembolism in patients with the "lupus"-type circulating anticoagulant. *Arch Intern Med* 144:510, 1984.

387. BOERGER LM, COMP PC: Oral contraceptives and gender influence on protein S status. *Blood [suppl]* 68:330a, 1986.

388. SCHWARZ HP, HEEB MJ, WENCEL-DRAKE JD, GRIFFIN JH: Identification and quantitation of protein S in human platelets. *Blood* 66:1452, 1985.

389. DAVIE EW, FUJIKAWA K, KURACHI K, KISIEL W: The role of serine proteases in the blood coagulation cascade. *Adv Enzymol* 48:277, 1979.

390. MARDER VJ, SHULMAN NR: Clinical aspects of congenital factor VII deficiency. *Am J Med* 37:182, 1964.

391. EPSTEIN DJ, BERGUM PW, RAPAPORT SI: Kinetics of protein C depression after coumadin administration. *Circulation [suppl]* 68:III:316, 1983.

392. VIGANO S, MANNUCCI PM, SOLINAS S, BOTTASSO B, D'ANGELO A, MARANI G: Early fall of protein C during short-term anticoagulant therapy. *Thromb Haemost* 50:310, 1983.

393. SCHWARTZ HP, HEEB MJ, WENCEL-DRAKE JD, GRIFFIN JH: Identification and quantitation of protein S in human platelets. *Blood* 66:1452, 1985.

394. DAHLBACK B: Purification of human vitamin K-dependent protein S and its limited proteolysis by thrombin. *Biochem J* 209:837, 1983.

CHAPTER 85

HEREDITARY DISORDERS RELATED TO FIBRINOGEN AND FACTOR XIII

DOMINIC CHUNG
AKITADA ICHINOSE

1. Fibrinogen is a dimeric protein consisting of six polypeptide chains ($A\alpha_2B\beta_2\gamma_2$) held together by disulfide bonds and folded in a trinodular structure where the nodules are connected by triple-stranded α-helices. Fibrinogen is converted to fibrin by thrombin, which removes fibrinopeptides from the amino terminals of the Aα and Bβ chains. Fibrin monomers polymerize into protofibrils through reciprocal half-staggered interactions. Other fibrin-fibrin interactions lead to lateral association of protofibrils and branch point formation. Fibrinogen and fibrin interact with a number of proteins including thrombin, plasminogen, fibronectin, thrombospondin, and the platelet surface receptor glycoprotein complex IIb-IIIa. The genes for the constituent chains of fibrinogen are present in single copies in the haploid genome and are located on chromosome 4. They are clustered in a region ~45 kb in length. Differential processing of the γ-chain transcript gives rise to two species of mRNA that direct the synthesis of two types of γ chains, γ and γ'.

2. Genetic abnormalities of fibrinogen are rare and include afibrinogenemia, hypofibrinogenemia, and dysfibrinogenemia, which refer to the complete absence of fibrinogen, reduced amounts of plasma fibrinogen, or the presence of dysfunctional fibrinogen molecules, respectively. Afibrinogenemia is characerized by neonatal umbilical cord bleeding, large ecchymoses, mucosal hemorrhage, gastrointestinal hemorrhage, and autosomal recessive inheritance. Hypofibrinogenemia is characterized by fibrinogen levels below 100 mg per deciliter of plasma (normal 250 to 350 mg/dl). The symptoms in hypofibrinogenemia are similar but milder than for afibrinogenemia, and there is evidence for both dominant and recessive inheritance. Dysfibrinogenemia is highly heterogeneous and may affect any one of the functional properties of fibrinogen. These functional abnormalities are associated with various disease manifestations that include hemorrhage, spontaneous abortion, and thromboembolism. Most patients with dysfibrinogenemia are heterozygous for amino acid substitutions, but homozygous occurrence is known.

3. Factor XIII is a proenzyme for a plasma transglutaminase. It is converted to the active form, factor XIIIa, by thrombin. It catalyzes the formation of intermolecular γ-glutamyl–ε-lysine bonds between fibrin monomers and between fibrin and α_2-plasmin inhibitor. Factor XIII in plasma is a tetramer (a_2b_2) held together by noncovalent bonds. The a subunit contains the active site. The sequence around the active site is identical to those of tissue transglutaminases. The b subunit contains 10 tandem repeats, which have been designated as GP-I structures. Homologous GP-I structures have been found in 15 other proteins. The site of synthesis of the a subunit is unclear. The a subunit is present in platelet, macrophage, placenta, and uterus. The b subunit is synthesized in the liver. The gene for the a subunit is located at the distal end of the short arm of chromosome 6 and is in excess of 160 kb in length. The gene for the b subunit is 30 kb in length and is located on the long arm of chromosome 1.

4. Factor XIII deficiency is inherited as an autosomal recessive trait and is caused by virtual absence of the a subunit. The condition is characterized by delayed bleeding while primary hemostasis is normal. Manifestations include neonatal bleeding from the umbilical cord, intracranial hemorrhage, and soft tissue hematomas. In addition, delayed wound healing and habitual abortion are common findings.

FIBRINOGEN

The central event in blood coagulation is the formation of an insoluble fibrin clot from soluble circulating fibrinogen. This conversion is catalyzed by thrombin generated on the surface of platelets that adhere to and become activated at the site of vascular damage. The fibrin clot is further cross-linked by factor XIIIa (fibrin-stabilizing factor), which introduces a small number of covalent bonds between adjacent fibrin monomers giving rise to a tough, insoluble clot. Congenital deficiency in fibrinogen which results in the complete absence of fibrinogen in the circulation, *afibrinogenemia*, is rare and usually fatal. Individuals with reduced circulating levels, *hypofibrinogenemia*, may exhibit a predisposition to bleeding. Individuals with inherited structural defects in the fibrinogen molecule, *dysfibrinogenemia*, may be asymptomatic or exhibit hemorrhagic episodes, abnormal wound healing, or even thrombosis. Congenital factor XIII deficiency exhibits symptoms of recurrent hemorrhage and delayed wound healing that can be attributed to unstable clot formation.

Structure of Fibrinogen

Fibrinogen is a plasma glycoprotein of 340,000 daltons.[1,2] It is a dimeric protein and is composed of three pairs of nonidentical but homologous polypeptide chains held together by disulfide bonds. The polypeptide chains, initially designated as the α, β, and γ chains, are 63,500, 56,000 and 47,000 daltons as determined by sedimentation equilibrium in the presence of 6 *M* guanidine.[3] These chains have also been designated as the Aα and Bβ and γ chains, and fibrinogen can be represented by the formula $A\alpha_2B\beta_2\gamma_2$. *N*-Linked carbohydrate is present on the Bβ and γ chains, but the contribution of carbohydrate to the function of fibrinogen is unknown.[6,7] The Aα chain of human fibrinogen contains an *O*-phosphoserine residue,[8,9] and the Bβ chains of bovine, fish, and frog fibrogen contain a sulfated tyrosine residue.[10–12] At the final stage of blood coagulation, thrombin proteolytically removes fibrinopeptides A and

B from the amino terminals of the Aα and Bβ chains.[13] The resultant molecule, a fibrin monomer ($\alpha_2\beta_2\gamma_2$), possesses new amino terminals on the α and β chains, while the γ chains remain unchanged. The removal of the fibrinopeptides exposes polymerization sites which make it possible for the monomers to polymerize into an insoluble fibrin gel composed of networks of fibers.

Tertiary Structures. Early studies on the structure of fibrinogen established that it possesses properties characteristic of a fibrous protein. X-ray diffraction studies show that fibrinogen and fibrin exhibit identical diffraction patterns that are also identical to those of other fibrous proteins, including keratin and myosin.[14] This characteristic diffraction pattern is attributed to the presence of triple-stranded α helices or "coiled coils." Since both fibrinogen and fibrin exhibit this diffraction pattern, it has been inferred that the coiled-coil structures remain unaltered in the conversion of fibrinogen to fibrin. Electron-microscopic studies[15] suggest that fibrinogen is folded into a trinodular structure. Additional evidence derived from alternative approaches, including electron-microscopic studies,[16-18] enzymatic fragmentation,[19,20] primary sequence,[21-23] immunologic studies,[24] and differential calorimetry,[25] provide results that are consistent with a trinodular structure linked by connecting coiled coils (Fig. 85-1). The overall length of fibrinogen is approximately 450 Å, and the diameter is approximately 90 Å. The central nodule (E domain) is approximately 50 Å in diameter and contains the "amino-terminal disulfide knot" (N-DSK) that is made up of the amino terminals of all six polypeptide chains.[26] The two outer nodules (D domains) are approximately 60 Å in diameter and are made up of the carboxy-terminal two-thirds of the Bβ and γ chains.[27,28] Recent results derived from more refined low resolution x-ray diffraction studies on microcrystals suggest that the D domain itself may consist of two subdomains which are formed by the independent folding of the Bβ and γ chains and are situated diagonally from the long axis of the molecule.[27] X-ray crystallographic studies also show that the fibrinogen molecule has a twofold axis of symmetry through the central E domain perpendicular to the long axis of the molecule.[29] The three domains are linked by triple-stranded α-helices or coiled coils, which contain stretches of 111 or 112 amino acids from each of the three polypeptide chains.[30] The coiled coils are flanked on both sides by a characteristic arrangement of disulfide bonds called the *disulfide rings* that hold the three strands in

optimal register for the formation of triple-stranded helices. The amino acid sequences of the coiled-coil region consist of alternating polar and nonpolar stretches of amino acids and are extremely low in proline content. This property favors the formation of helices. The coiled-coil region is briefly interrupted in the middle by a short region of nonhelical structure which has been implicated to be a region sensitive to proteolytic cleavages. Based on electron-microscopic measurements and calculations, the coiled coils are approximately 150 to 160 Å in length. The carboxy-terminal half of the Aα chain, which was previously believed to assume random coil conformation, is now believed to exist as a folded domain.[31-33] The disulfide rings and the coiled coil impart rigidity and contribute to the overall mechanical strength of the molecule.

Plasmin Degradation. The folding of fibrinogen into an extended trinodular structure predisposes the molecule to proteolytic cleavages in selected regions. Digestion of fibrinogen by plasmin and trypsin results in the formation of a set of core fragments that can be easily purified by ion-exchange chromatography.[34,35] Plasmin degradation proceeds in a sequential manner and involves the formation of a number of intermediates[35,36] (Fig. 85-2). Plasmin first removes the hydrophilic carboxy-terminal two-thirds of the Aα chains and the first 42 amino acids of the Bβ chains and converts fibrinogen to a clottable intermediate, fragment X [molecular weight (MW) 240,000 to 260,000]. Fragment X is further digested at one of the two coiled-coil regions to give rise to a fragment D (MW 100,000) and a fragment Y (MW 150,000). Fragment Y is subsequently cleaved at the remaining coiled-coil region to give a second fragment D and a fragment E (MW 45,000). The total mass of fragments D and E amounts to 50 and 15 percent of the starting material, respectively. Fragments D and E bear distinctly different antigenic determinants. Immunoelectron-microscopic studies using immunoglobulin fragments bound to specific regions of fibrinogen confirm the spatial arrangement of the D and E domains in the trinodular structure.[17,18] Furthermore, fragment E cross-reacts antigenically with the amino-terminal disulfide knot (N-DSK),[24,37,38] and the data indicate that the amino terminals of all six polypeptide chains are situated in the central domain. The trinodular structure is further supported by differential calorimetry studies[25] which show that fibrinogen has two clearly defined melting points, corresponding to those of purified fragment D (60°C) and fragment E (100°C). These observations

Fig. 85-1 Schematic representation of fibrinogen. The molecule is depicted in a trinodular structure containing a central nodule, the E domain, connected to two outer nodules, the D domains, by α-helices designated as coiled coils. Disulfide rings present on either sides of the coiled coils are represented by rings. N-Linked carbohydrate chains are represented by open hexagons.

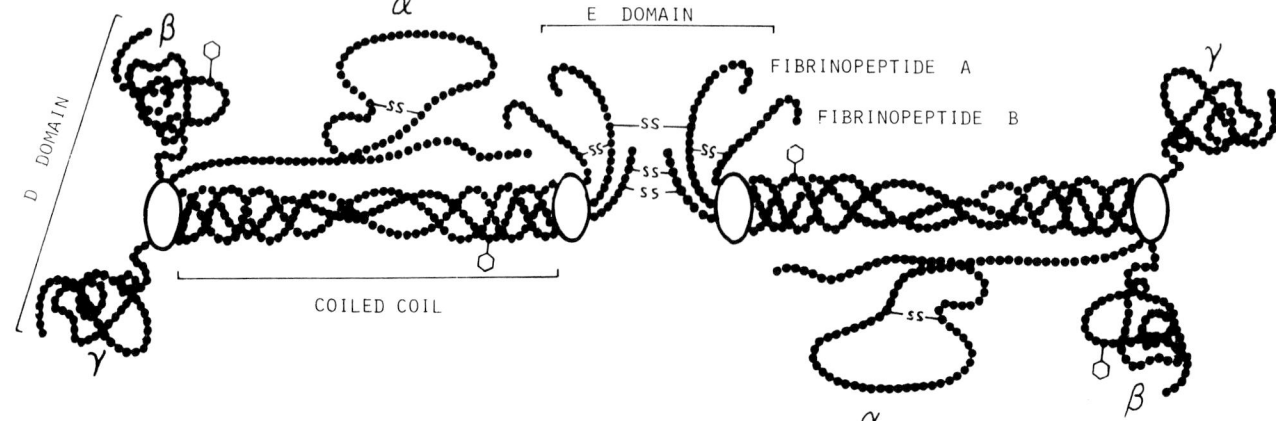

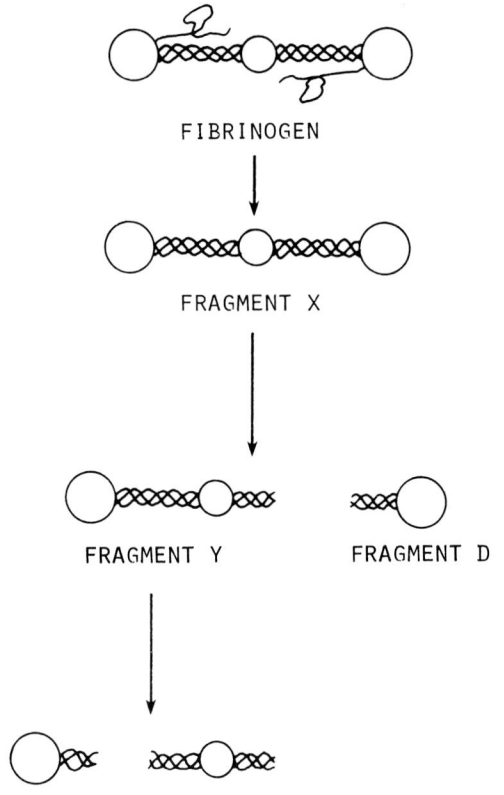

Fig. 85-2 Degradation of fibrinogen by plasmin according to Marder and coworkers.[35,36] The process involves the initial removal of the Aα chain protuberances, followed by cleavages at the coiled coils to generate degradation fragments D and E.

are inconsistent with a structure in which fragments D and E are in close contact.

Primary Structure. The amino acid sequence of the three chains of fibrinogen have been determined.[21–23] The Aα chain consists of 610, the Bβ chain, 461, and the γ chain 411 amino acids. The three chains, although nonidentical, are homologous and are derived from a common ancestor. The homology is evident from the conserved placement of half-cystinyl residues that form the disulfide rings in each of the three chains. In addition, the carboxy-terminal halves of the Bβ and γ chains are approximately 35 percent identical.

The Aα chain contains 610 amino acids and can be roughly divided into three zones of approximately equal size. The amino-terminal third (residues 1–194) is linked to the Bβ and γ chains by the unique disulfide rings. This segment is followed by a short interzonal sequence (residues 195–239). This region contains a high proline content, which suggests that it is folded into an exposed and vulnerable conformation, accessible to many proteases. Plasmin has been shown to cleave at four sites within this region.[39,40] The middle third of the molecule (240–424) is exceptionally rich in glycine, serine, threonine, proline, and tryptophan residues. The sequence of this section is predominantly nonpolar in nature and consists of eight tandem repeats, each 13 residues in length. This region probably assumes random coil conformation. The carboxy-terminal third of the Aα chain is mainly hydrophilic in character and contains sequences that vary greatly from species to species.[41] Sequences at the carboxy-terminal two-thirds of the Aα chain mediate the interaction of fibrinogen with fibronectin,[42] platelets,[43] and *Staphylococcus aureus* cells.[44,45] The Aα chains

are involved in the formation of intermolecular γ-glutamyl–ε-lysine bonds catalyzed by the transglutaminase factor XIIIa. In addition, the solubility of fibrionogen is affected by the presence of the Aα carboxy "protuberance." Fibrinogen with high solubility seems to have the carboxy terminal removed by proteolytic cleavages.[46]

The Bβ chain of human fibrinogen contains 461 amino acid residues. Similar to the Aα chain, the Bβ chain can be divided into three sections. The first 80 residues at the amino terminal show ≈15 percent identity to the corresponding region of the Aα chain and, together with the N terminals of the other chains, form the globular central E domain. The second section consists of 112 residues (81–192) and includes two sets of disulfide rings that delineate the coiled-coil region. The third section consists of the remaining 269 amino acids (193–461) which form a part of the terminal globular domain D.

The γ chain contains 41 amino acid residues. It can also be roughly divided into three sections. The first section (1–18) is significantly shorter than those of the Aα and Bβ chains, does not contain amino-terminal sequences that are susceptible to thrombin cleavage, and appears to have arisen through a gene deletion event that removes the cleavable fibrinopeptide domain. The second section (19–129) contains the disulfide rings and the 111 residues that form the coiled-coil region. The third section (130–411), which consists of the remaining 272 amino acids together with the third section of the Bβ chain, forms the globular terminal domain D. The third sections of the γ and Bβ chains share a high percent of sequence identity (35 percent). In an optimized alignment with the Bβ chain, the γ chain appears to have gained a carboxy-terminal extension of 18 amino acids that participates in intermolecular cross-linking. The Bβ chain is devoid of such sequences and does not participate in the cross-linking process.

Polymerization of Fibrinogen

Removal of Fibrinopeptides. The conversion of soluble fibrinogen into an insoluble gel can be divided into several stages. The process is initiated by thrombin which specifically cleaves at Arg—Gly bonds close to the amino terminals of the Aα and Bβ chains to release two molecules of fibrinopeptide A (Aα 1–16) and two molecules of fibrinopeptide B (Bβ 1–14) per molecule of fibrinogen. These peptides constitute ≈2 percent of the mass of the fibrinogen molecule, and their removal unmasks polymerization sites on the fibrin monomer. The release of fibrinopeptide A proceeds more rapidly than that of fibrinopeptide B,[47] but the release of fibrinopeptide A is not a prerequisite for the removal of fibrinopeptide B. Removal of fibrinopeptide A alone is sufficient to initiate polymerization, and assembly into a polymeric form induces conformational changes in the molecule which enhance the rate of fibrinopeptide B release.[48,49] In addition to thrombin, several snake venom enzymes have been shown to remove fibrionopeptides from fibrinogen. Batroxobin (reptilase), isolated from the venom of *Bothrops atrox*, and ancrod (arvin), from *Agkistrodon rhodostoma*, exclusively remove fibrinopeptide A from fibrinogen.[50,51] A different enzyme from the venom of *Agkistrodon contortrix* preferentially release fibrinopeptide B but also releases fibrinopeptide A slowly.[51–53]

Protofibril Assembly. The removal of fibrinopeptide A generates new amino terminals on the α chains with the sequence of Gly-Pro-Arg, and these terminals interact with complementary sites on the D domain of another fibrin molecule. The amino terminal of the α chain of the second molecule binds in a reciprocal manner to the D domain of the first molecule (Fig. 85-3). This reciprocal binding positions the two molecules in a half-staggered overlap structure through contacts that are designated as *DE-stag contacts*.[54,55] The addition of a third molecule and subsequent linear elongation align the D domains of adjacent fibrin monomers next to each other and bring together "end-to-end" contacts between adjacent fibrin monomers. The two-stranded linear polymer structure, which is composed of two rows of end-to-end monomers, is called a protofibril and has been shown to be an obligatory intermediate in fibrin assembly under physiological conditions.[56,57] A tripeptide with a sequence identical to the amino terminal of the α chain (Gly-Pro-Arg) can bind to the carboxyl terminal of the γ chain in the D domains of fibrinogen and fibrin and is an effective inhibitor of fibrin polymerization and protofibril elongation.[58] Present evidence indicates that the polymerization sites in the D domain are composed of the carboxy terminal of the γ chain. The removal of fibrinopeptide B allows lateral involvement and branch point formation and allows

protofibrils to laterally associate into thick fibrin strands.[47-59] The regions that are involved in this process are not defined and are thought to include DD-lateral as well as DE-lateral interactions.[55,60] A tripeptide with sequence identical to the amino terminal of the β chain (Gly-His-Pro) binds to the D domain but does not inhibit fibrin polymerization.[58,61]

The interactions among fibrin monomers in a fibrin gel are noncovalent, and the polymerization process is reversible and exothermic. The exothermicity can be accounted for by the formation of hydrogen bonds during the polymerization process.[62] The observed pH range of polymerization (5 to 10) is consistent with the involvement of a histidine and a tyrosine[63] in hydrogen bond formation. Photo-oxidation studies indicated that His-16 of the Bβ chain is essential for polymerization.[64]

Cross-linking. Because the interactions among the individual fibrin monomers are noncovalent, a fibrin gel can be resolubilized by chemical agents such as 6 *M* urea. The fibrin clot is stabilized by the introduction of covalent bonds which cross-link individual fibrin molecules. The cross-linking reac-

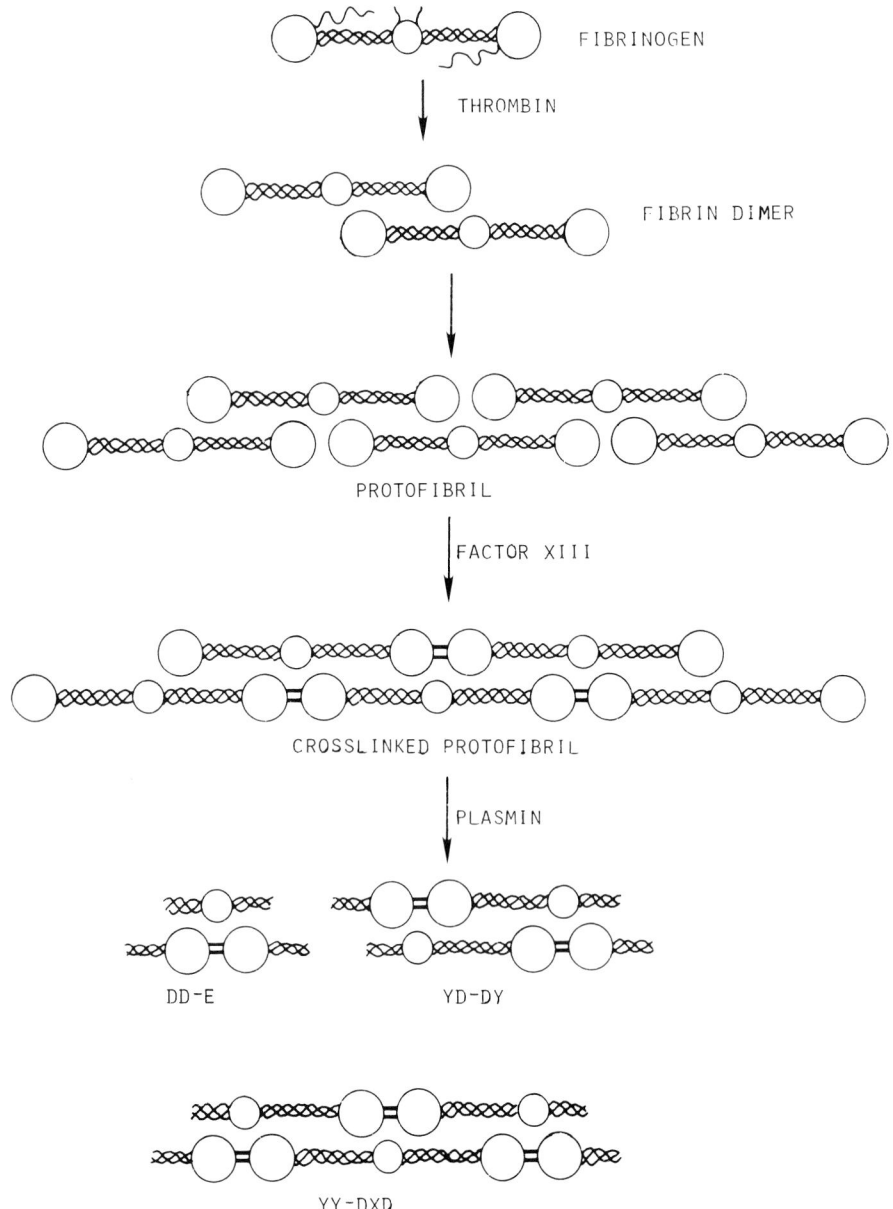

Fig. 85-3 Polymerization and degradation of fibrin. Removal of fibrinopeptides A and B by thrombin allows fibrin monomers to polymerize into protofibrils by half-staggered interactions. Covalent cross-links betwen γ chains of adjacent fibrin molecules are introduced by factor XIIIa. Plasmin digestion of cross-linked protofibrils at the coiled coils leads to the formation of DD-E complexes and other intermediates including YD-DY, and YY-DXD complexes. See Fig. 85-2 for structure of D, E, X, and Y.

tion is catalyzed by a plasma transglutaminase, factor XIIIa. These covalent linkages, in the form of isopeptide bonds between glutamine and lysine residues, impart mechanical strength to the clot and render the clot more resistant to proteolytic attack. The cross-linking reaction initially involves adjacent γ chains where Lys-406 of the γ chain from one fibrin molecule is cross-linked to the Gln-398 of the γ chain of a second adjacent fibrin molecule, and the Lys-406 of the second molecule is reciprocally cross-linked to Gln-398 of the first molecule.[65,66] This cross-linking leads to the formation of covalent γ-chain dimers. In a considerably slower process, cross-links between α chains are also introduced. The cross-linking sites have not been identified but include the participation of Gln-328, Gln-366, Lys-508, Lys-556, and Lys-562 in the Aα chain.[67–69] The presence of multiple acceptor and donor sites on each Aα chain leads to the formation of highly intricate α-chain multimers. Cross-linked α chains, which act as a "wrap-around" of the coiled-coil region, protect the fibrin network, especially the coiled-coil region, from proteolytic attack.[70]

Degradation of Fibrin. Cross-linked fibrin is degraded by plasmin to give products that are different from those generated from fibrinogen. Initially, the multiple cross-linked α chains are removed, exposing the connecting coiled-coil regions between D and E domains. Cleavage between the D and E domains liberates DD-E (or D dimer E) complexes which consist of covalently linked D domains because of the γ-γ cross-links and an E domain noncovalently bound[71,72] (Fig. 85-3). A series of intermediates in the digestion process have also been isolated and characterized. The derivation of these high molecular weight complexes, consisting of DY-YD, DXD-XY, and YXD-DXY moieties (see above, "Plasmin Degradation," and Fig. 85-2 for structure of D, E, X, and Y), is consistent with the two-stranded, half-staggered overlap protofibril structure in fibrin (Fig. 85-3).

Interaction with Other Molecules

Role of Calcium. Calcium ions play a significant role in the structure and function of fibrinogen. Three calcium-binding sites have been identified in fibrinogen, two of which are in the D domains and are localized to residues 311–336 of the γ chain. The sequence of this region bears resemblance in the calcium-binding regions of pavalbumin and calmodulin.[73] Binding of calcium ion to this site protects the γ chain from proteolysis by plasmin. The third binding site is tentatively localized to the E domain.[74] The K_d for calcium binding is 1.9 $\times$ 10^{-5} M and is below the concentration of free calcium in plasma (1.5 mM). Under physiological conditions, all three sites are occupied. The presence of calcium enhances the rate and extent of lateral association of protofibrils to fibrin strands.[75] The molecular basis for these effects is still unclear.

Interaction with Thrombin. In addition to the removal of fibrinopeptides from fibrinogen, thrombin specifically binds to the fibrin network, and this binding may serve to limit the amount of active thrombin in circulation.[76] Bound thrombin retains its enzymatic activity and is protected from inactivation by circulating inhibitors.[77] Bound thrombin can be released in an active form following fibrinolysis. The exact physiological role of bound thrombin is unclear. However, individuals whose fibrin is defective in thrombin binding are predisposed to thromboembolic disease.[78]

Interaction with Plasminogen. The specific binding of plasminogen to fibrin is essential to restrict the fibrinolytic agent to the site of a clot. Plasminogen binds to fibrin ($K_d \approx 1 \times 10^{-6}$ M), and weakly to fibrinogen ($K_d \approx 1 \times 10^{-3}$ M).[79] The rate of activation of plasminogen by tissue plasminogen activator is greatly enhanced by fibrin. Binding sites for plasminogen have been located on fragments D and E in regions which are not exposed in intact fibrinogen.[80] An additional binding site has also been located in the coiled-coil region, and plasmin digestion of the coiled-coil region is crucial to clot lysis.[81]

Interaction with Fibronectin. Fibronectin is a plasma glycoprotein with MW ≈ 440,000. It binds to fibrinogen and coprecipitates as a complex with fibrinogen in the cold (cold-insoluble globulin).[82,83] Fibronectin binds to both fibrinogen and fibrin, and the binding is mediated through sites located on the α chain of fibrinogen. Proteolytic removal of the α-chain protuberances in fibrinogen or fibrin results in a loss of affinity for fibronectin.[84] The fibrin binding site on fibronectin contains a repeated structure called "finger domain"[85] which is also present in tissue plasminogen activator. Under physiological conditions, fibronectin is incorporated into the fibrin clot and can be cross-linked to fibrin by factor XIIIa. The cross-linking sites involve donor lysine residues on the α chain of fibrinogen[86] and acceptor glutamine residues present at the amino-terminal third or fourth amino acid of fibronectin.[87] The physiological significance of fibronectin in fibrin clots is not clearly understood. Cross-linking of fibronectin to fibrin greatly enhances the attachment and spreading of cells on a fibrin-coated surface, and may be important for the adhesion and migration of fibroblasts, endothelial cells, and monocytes at the site of a fibrin clot.

Interaction with Thrombospondin. Thrombospondin is a glycoprotein that is released from the α granules of stimulated platelets and forms a stable complex with fibrinogen.[88] It is incorporated in fibrin clot but is not covalently cross-linked with fibrin. The incorporation of thrombospondin into fibrin is considered to be a copolymerization process, and its presence reduces the thickness of the fibrin fibrils. Since during platelet activation, thrombospondin is secreted and becomes partially bound to the platelet surface, its presence may influence the interaction of platelets with fibrin.

Interaction with Platelets. Platelet attachment, aggregation, and release depend on the interaction of platelet surface glycoproteins with a group of adhesive proteins which include fibrinogen, fibronectin, and von Willebrand factor. Fibrinogen acts as a cofactor for platelet aggregation[89] through a specific binding to a receptor on the platelet surface. Although binding to quiescent platelets is low, reversible saturable binding to stimulated platelets can be demonstrated.[90–93] The binding is dependent on divalent cations and is greatly reduced in patients with Glanzmann thrombasthenia. Several lines of evidence indicate that this receptor is the glycoprotein IIb-IIIa complex (see Chap. 90). First, platelets from patients with Glanzmann thrombasthenia lack glycoprotein IIb-IIIa and do not bind fibrinogen. Second, monoclonal antibodies directed against glycoprotein IIb-IIIa prevented fibrinogen binding and platelet aggregation. Third, direct binding of fibrinogen with purified glycoprotein IIb-IIIa has been demonstrated.[94,95] The binding involves the carboxy terminal of the γ chain[96–98] and can be inhibited by a decapeptide from the carboxy terminal of the γ chain.[95] In addition, fibrinogen binding to stimulated platelets is also inhibited by peptides containing the sequence Arg-Gly-Asp[99] which suggests that the two Arg-Gly-Asp sequences in the Aα chain (residues 95–97 and 572–574) may be involved in these interactions.

Biosynthesis of Fibrinogen

Structural Genes. Fibrinogen is synthesized in the liver by hepatic parenchymal cells and is secreted into the circulation.[100,101] The amount of fibrinogen synthesized ranges from 1.7 to 5 g/day, and the half-life in plasma is approximately 3 to 5 days.[102,103] The three chains of fibrinogen are encoded by distinct species of mRNA that are derived from the expression of three single copy genes.[104,105] Cosegregation and linkage analysis of an abnormal γ-chain variant show that the gene for the γ chain is linked to the MNSs blood group antigens,[106] which are located on chromosome 4. Analyses by *in situ* hybridization and with a panel of human × rodent somatic cell hybrids containing selectively rearranged chromosomes show that the human fibrinogen genes are located at chromosome 4q23-q32.[107,108] The three genes of human fibrinogen have been isolated and characterized (Fig. 85-4). They are linked and are located in a region that extends approximately 45 kb. The genes are arranged in the order of γ-Aα-Bβ, and the genes for the γ and Aα chains are transcribed in the same direction while the gene for the Bβ chain is transcribed in the opposite direction (Fig. 85-4).[108]

Analysis of cDNA sequences for the three chains of human fibrinogen indicates that they are synthesized in precursor forms with signal peptides at their amino terminals.[109–112] These signal sequences serve to direct the vectorial discharge of nascent chains from the cytosolic to the cisternal side of the rough endoplasmic reticulum. They share common characteristics of other signal peptides in having a hydrophobic core sequence flanked on either side by hydrophilic residues and a small uncharged amino acid at the site of cleavage by the signal peptidase. The Aα chain is also predicted to have a C-terminal extension of 15 amino acids,[109,113] which is presumably removed during secretion or assembly or in the circulation.

Assembly. Analysis of the kinetics of the incorporation of radioactive amino acids into fibrinogen in whole animals[114] and in cultured hepatocytes[115,116] shows that the Bβ chain is preferentially labeled prior to the Aα and γ chains by approximately 10 min. The data suggest the presence of an existing pool of Aα and γ chains in the cell. Intermediates with the composition of γ₂Aα and (γ₂Aα)₂ have been observed. It has been noted by Doolittle that the driving force for the assembly of the fibrinogen molecule is in the formation of the triple-stranded helices and the flanking disulfide rings.[30] The presence of excess γ and Aα chains suggests that the γ chains may first assemble into a trimer (γ₃) by assembly of triple-stranded coiled coil. One of the γ chains may be subsequently displaced by an Aα chain to form γ₂Aα, which dimerizes to (γ₂Aα)₂. Subsequently, replacement of two γ chains by two Bβ chains gives rise to the final six-chain structure.[116]

Alternative Processing. Two forms of γ chains have been found in human fibrinogen, and these have been referred to

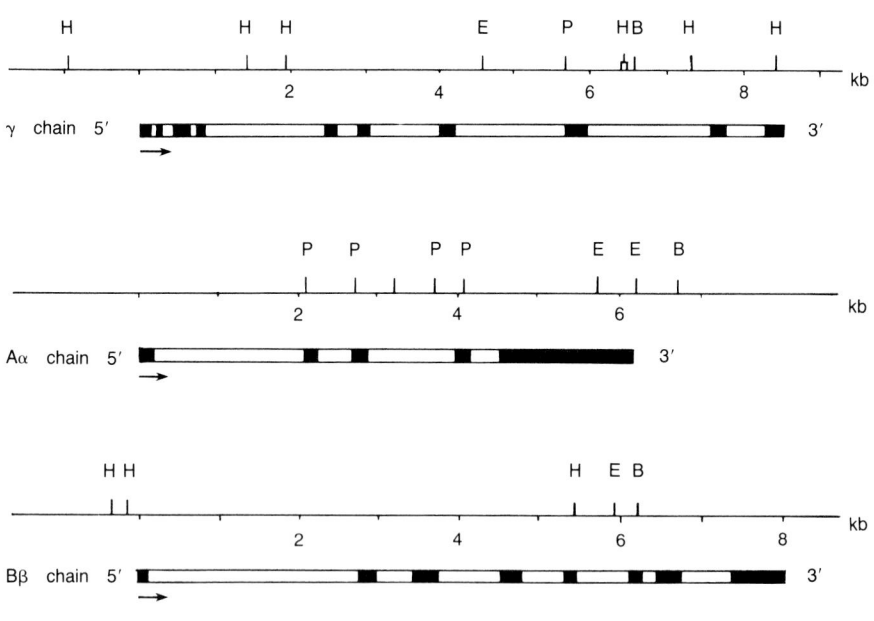

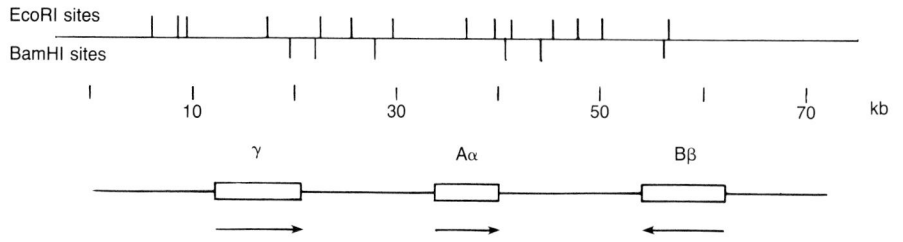

Fig. 85-4 Structural organization and restriction map of the three genes for human fibrinogen. Exons are represented by solid bars and introns by open bars. Arrows indicate the direction of transcription. Restriction enzyme cleavage sites are abbreviated as follows: B = *Bam*HI; E = *Eco*RI; H = *Hind*III; P = *Pst*I.

as γ and γ' or γ_A and γ_B.[117] The γ' variant has a higher molecular weight than γ. Peptide mapping and sequencing studies[118,119] indicate that in the γ' variant form, the carboxy-terminal four amino acids are replaced by a peptide of 20 amino acids. Hence the longer form, γ', is not a precursor to the γ form. Studies on the cDNA and gene structure of the γ chain show that the two forms of γ chain arise by alternative polyadenylation of the γ-chain transcript.[120–122] The choice of a less prevalently used polyadenylation site in the last intron (ninth intron) removes the 3' acceptor site of this intron as well as the following tenth exon sequences, enabling the immediate 5' end of the ninth intron to serve as an extension of the preceding exon. Translation of this mRNA leads to the replacement of the last four amino acids of the γ chain by a peptide of 20 amino acids. In humans, the γ' form amounts to approximately 10 percent of the total γ-chain population.[123] In rats, the γ' form constitutes ≈ 30 percent of the total γ chain.[124] Both of these polypeptides are incorporated into the fibrinogen molecule and are functionally normal in fibrin polymerization and in γ-chain cross-linking. Multiple polyadenylation sites in the Bβ-chain mRNA have also been observed.[110] However, these sites are located in the 3'-noncoding region, and the choice of these polyadenylation sites does not affect the splicing of the mRNA and does not result in changes in the encoded amino acid sequence.

Fibrinogen is present in the α granules of platelets where it constitutes ≈ 15 percent of the protein content.[125,126] Megakaryocytes from guinea pig synthesize fibrinogen in culture,[127] indicating that platelet fibrinogen is not derived from plasma. Although there are only single copy genes for fibrinogen chains, the synthesis of platelet fibrinogen may be under different control since the γ' variant form is either absent or present in markedly reduced amounts in platelets.[128,129]

The addition of core N-linked carbohydrate to the γ chain occurs early as a cotranslational event and precedes that of the Bβ chain, which occurs about the time of polypeptide termination or subsequent to the release of the polypeptide from ribosome.[104]

Regulation

Hepatic synthesis of fibrinogen is constitutive, but the rate can be modulated by a number of physiological and nonphysiological factors. First, massive defibrination by the injection of Malayan pit viper venom potentiates the synthesis of fibrinogen approximately tenfold in rats, and this increase correlates with a coordinated increase in the mRNA levels for all three chains.[130] These observations imply that fibrin or fibrinogen degradation products, fragments D and E, may be involved in a feedback process by fibrinogen regulation. Second, the rate of fibrinogen synthesis in chick hepatocytes cultured in serum-free conditions, can be stimulated approximately threefold by the addition of dexamethasone.[131] Third, as an acute phase reactant, the level of fibrinogen in circulation is elevated in response to trauma, inflammation, the injection of growth hormone, endotoxin, and prostaglandins. A possible mechanism for the acute phase response has been proposed.[132,133] According to this proposal, the exposure of peripheral blood leukocytes (including monocytes and macrophages) to fibrinogen degradation products fragments D and E causes these cells to release a protein factor, "hepatocyte-stimulating factor." This factor, when added to hepatocytes in culture, causes a four- to sixfold increase in fibrinogen synthesis. Hepatocyte-stimulat-

ing factor is distinctly different from interleukin 1.[134] The increased synthesis of fibrinogen in response to the addition of hepatocyte-stimulating factor correlates with a ten- to twelvefold increase in mRNA for each of the three chains. In addition, this response is not inhibited by cycloheximide, and therefore does not involve *do novo* protein synthesis.[135] Hepatocyte stimulating factor appears to exert its control directly at the level of transcription.

Genetic Abnormalities of Fibrinogen

Congenital abnormalities of fibrinogen are rare and can be categorized as afibrinogenemia, hypofibrinogenemia, and dysfibrinogenemia, which refer to conditions that are characterized by the complete absence of fibrinogen, reduced amounts of fibrinogen, or the presence of dysfunctional fibrinogen molecules. A nomenclature similar to that for abnormal hemoglobins has been adopted, and fibrinogen abnormalities are designated according to the city of origin of the patients, e.g., fibrinogen Detroit, fibrinogen Paris I, fibrinogen Bethesda II, etc.

Afibrinogenemia. Afibrinogenemia is rare, with about 150 cases reported thus far. The first case was reported in 1920 when the existence of other coagulation factors had not been discovered. The patient was anemic and suffered from repeated hemorrhagic episodes, severe epistaxis, and gingival bleeding. It was thought of as a peculiar case of hemophilia due to a lack of "fibrin" in the patient's blood.[136–138] Subsequently, reconstruction of a pedigree by Werder[139] showed that afibrinogenemia corresponded to the homozygous state of an autosomal recessive disorder of variable penetrance. This disorder was distinctly different from the hemophilias which were X-linked disorders. From the study of over 150 reported cases, a pattern of clinical symptoms can be compiled for this disorder. Neonatal umbilical cord bleeding is a cardinal symptom (72 out of 108 cases). Intracranial bleeding following minor head injury is usually a fatal complication, because internal hemorrhage may not be immediately recognized.[140] Large ecchymoses, mucosal hemorrhage (especially epistaxis), and sudden gastrointestinal hemorrhage are common symptoms. However, menorrhagia is uncommon in women with afibrinogenemia.[141] Afibrinogenemia is usually accompanied by mild thrombocytopenia,[142,143] and platelets from afibrinogenemic patients show normal adhesion and spreading properties but defective aggregation. Afibrinogenemic platelets contain trace amounts of fibrinogen,[144] and afibrinogenemic blood has an indefinitely prolonged clotting time which can be corrected only by the addition of fibrinogen. The levels of all other coagulation factors are within the normal range. Because of the early onset and severity of the hemorrhages, few affected individuals survive beyond the age of 20. Replacement therapy is required to restore and maintain an adequate level of fibrinogen in circulation for normal hemostasis. Replacement therapy by infusion of whole blood, plasma, fibrinogen, and cryoprecipitate have been effective. In two cases, replacement therapy led to the development of antibodies to fibrinogen and to severe intolerance reactions which resulted in death.[145,146]

Hypofibrinogenemia. Hypofibrinogenemia was first reported in 1935[147] and was much less frequent in occurrence than afibrinogenemia. Hypofibrinogenemia appears to be heterogeneous, and patients can roughly be categorized into two groups: those with fibrinogen levels below 50 mg per deciliter of plasma and those with levels between 50 and 100 mg per deciliter of plasma (normal range, 250 to 350 mg per deciliter of plasma). Patients with fibrinogen levels below 50 mg per deciliter of plasma exhibit hemorrhagic symptoms resembling those of afibrinogenemia but occurring less frequently and less severely. Umbilical cord bleeding occurs frequently (15 percent), and hemorrhage (especially cerebral hemorrhage) is a major cause of death.[148] In patients with fibrinogen levels between 50 and 100 mg per deciliter of plasma, symptoms are much milder. Among these patients, symptoms of massive postpartum bleeding and bleeding following laparotomy have been reported. Interestingly, multiple thromboses and pulmonary embolism have been described in four patients.[149,150] The mode of transmission is unclear and appears to be dominant in several families because of absence of consanguinity and low fibrinogen levels in only one of the patients. However, in other affected families, the presence of consanguinity and the lack of symptoms in both parents suggest a recessive mode of transmission. Both are possible (see Chap. 1). Replacement therapy is usually not needed except when acute bleeding occurs.

Dysfibrinogenemia. Functionally abnormal fibrinogen molecules are caused by mutations that usually result in single amino acid changes in one of the three chains. Over 130 cases have been described, and several detailed reviews have been published.[151,152] Dysfibrinogenemia is highly heterogeneous and may affect any one of the functional properties of fibrinogen, including absence or delayed release of fibrinopeptides A and B, delayed polymerization, enhanced polymerization, defective cross-linking, decreased thrombin binding, delayed plasmin digestion, and defective secretion from hepatocytes. These functional abnormalities are associated with varied disease manifestations that include hemorrhage, spontaneous abortion, thromboembolism, and thrombosis. A diagnosis of dysfibrinogenemia necessitates the application of a series of tests for the evaluation of each of the fibrinogen functions. A prolonged thrombin clotting time which cannot be eliminated by the addition of protamine or calcium is a good indication of dysfibrinogenemia. The release of fibrinopeptides is evaluated by digestion with thrombin, reptilase, and other venom enzymes, followed by quantitative analysis of the released fibrinopeptides. Immunoelectrophoresis of dysfibrinogenemic plasma is used to reveal charge differences in fibrinogen and to eliminate the presence of gammaglobulins that may interfere with fibrin polymerization. SDS-polyacrylamide gel electrophoresis is used to evaluate the molecular weight of each of the polypeptide chains and to evaluate the formation of cross-linked γ-chain dimers and α-chain polymers. The polymerization of fibrin monomers is monitored by following turbidity changes at 350 nm. Fibrin monomers are generated at pH 5.5 by digestion with thrombin or venom enzymes, and the polymerization process is initiated by adjusting the pH above 6.0. The cross-linking function can be evaluated by the incorporation of dansyl-cadaverine in the presence of factor XIIIa.

Based on these tests, dysfibrinogenemia has been divided into three main groups. Group I is characterized by the absence of fibrinopeptide release, and group II by the release of fibrinopeptides with abnormal sequences. Group III includes those that have normal fibrinopeptide release, but the defects are located in other parts of the molecule. To date, the precise amino acid changes in over 32 of the 130 cases of dysfibrino-

genemia have been elucidated, mainly from the work of Henschen and coworkers.[152] The elucidation of these changes has been useful in the study of the structure and function relationships in fibrinogen. A frequent amino acid substitution at the cleavage site of the fibrinopeptide A ($A\alpha$ Arg-16→Cys, fibrinogen Metz) abolishes fibrinopeptide A release. In the homozygous state, for example, with fibrinogen Metz,[153] removal of fibrinopeptide B alone will permit clotting. Other amino acid substitutions in the $A\alpha$ chain include $A\alpha$ Arg-16→His (fibrinogen Petoskey), which is cleaved quantitatively and selectively by thrombin, although at a much slower rate. Other structurally identified variants include $A\alpha$ Asp-7→Asn (fibrinogen Lille), Gly-12→Val (fibrinogen Rouen), Arg-19→Asn (fibrinogen Munchen I), and Arg-19→Ser (fibrinogen Detroit).[154]

A single case of fibrinopeptide B defect has been reported, fibrinogen New York I. This disorder is characterized by the presence of a shortened $B\beta$ chain which has the second exon (amino acids 9–72) deleted. This exon contains the thrombin cleavage site for fibrinopeptide B as well as a plasmin cleavage site (residue 42). The deletion also removes a putative thrombin-binding site in fibrin, the absence of which apparently causes recurrent thrombosis.[78]

Many abnormal fibrinogens defective in polymerization have been described. However, in only three cases have the molecular defects been elucidated. These mutations are located at the carboxy terminals of the $B\beta$ and γ chains. A change of Ala-335→Thr in the $B\beta$ chain creates a new N-linked glycosylation site on the $B\beta$ chain (Asn-333), and this residue is in fact glycosylated.[155] It is proposed that the introduction of a carbohydrate at this location interferes with polymerization. Fibrinogen Milano I is characterized by a substitution of γ Asp-330→Val,[156] which results in impaired calcium binding. Amino acid substitution in the γ chain Arg-275→His has been observed in three unrelated cases (fibrinogens Bergamo II, Essen, and Perugia). This substitution does not cause bleeding symptoms, but predisposes affected individuals to thrombosis.[157]

Fibrinogen Oslo I is a dysfibrinogen in which the defect is associated with the $B\beta$ chain, but the nature of the amino acid change(s) is not known. It is characterized by enhanced fibrin monomer polymerization compared to normal fibrin. It binds more strongly to stimulated platelets than normal fibrinogen and causes increased cofactor function in platelet aggregation.[158]

Fibrinogen Paris I is characterized by delayed fibrin aggregation and reduced γ-chain cross-linking. The abnormality has been located in the γ chain. The abnormal γ chain is longer than the normal γ chain and has a molecular weight of 51,000. Present evidence indicates that the structural abnormality involves a region near the carboxy terminal of the γ chain and probably includes the region involved in the normal γ-chain cross-linking.[159,160]

Most cases of dysfibrinogenemia are asymptomatic, and no treatment is necessary. In cases when the dysfunctional molecules cause clinical manifestations, therapy is mainly directed to alleviate the particular symptoms. Replacement therapy has been effective in some cases.

Acquired Abnormalities. Acquired fibrinogen abnormalities are usually associated with diseases of the liver, e.g., cirrhosis, hepatitis, and hepatocarcinoma. The most common way in which fibrinogen is affected is delayed polymerization, which is caused by an increase in carbohydrate content, particularly sialic acid. The additional carbohydrate probably is located at additional branch points in the existing carbohydrate side chains on the Bβ and γ chains. Treatment with neuraminidase in vitro restores the polymerization to normal.

Fetal Fibrinogen. Fetal fibrinogen isolated from cord blood shows delayed fibrin aggregation and has long been recognized to be different from adult plasma fibrinogen. Since the three chains are encoded by single copy genes in the haploid genome, it is unlikely that this difference is caused by differences in the amino acid sequences. The functional difference of fetal fibrinogen resembles that observed in acquired fibrinogen abnormalities and has been attributed, in part, to a high degree of phosphorylation and a high content of sialic acid compared to normal adult fibrinogen. The delayed polymerization of fetal fibrinogen has also been attributed to the presence of trace amounts of fibrinogen degradation product, fragment X, in fetal fibrinogen preparations.[161]

FACTOR XIII

Factor XIII (fibrin-stabilizing factor, or fibrinoligase) is a plasma glycoprotein that plays an important role in the final stages of blood coagulation and the regulation of fibrinolysis.

Thrombin that is generated during blood coagulation converts the proenzyme (factor XIII) to an active enzyme (factor XIIIa). Factor XIIIa is a transglutaminase that catalyzes the cross-linking of fibrin monomers and the cross-linking of fibrin and α_2-plasmin inhibitor through the formation of intermolecular γ-glutamyl–ε-lysine bonds. These reactions occur in the presence of calcium ions and result in a fibrin with considerable mechanical strength and increased resistance to proteolytic degradation by plasmin. The cross-linking of fibronectin to fibrin or to collagen is also catalyzed by factor XIIIa, and this reaction appears to be related to wound healing.

A deficiency of factor XIII results in a severe lifelong bleeding tendency, defective wound healing, and habitual abortion. Congenital factor XIII deficiency is inherited in an autosomal recessive manner.

Structure of Factor XIII

Physical Properties. Factor XIII (see Fig. 85-5) circulates in blood as a tetramer, a_2b_2 (about 320 kDa), consisting of two a subunits (75 kDa each), and two b subunits (80 kDa each).[162,163] The molecular complex of four polypeptide chains is held together by noncovalent bonds.[162] The carbohydrate content has been reported to be 1.5 and 8.5 percent for the a and b subunits, respectively.[164,165] The a subunit has six free sulfhydryl groups, while the b subunit has no free sulfhydryl groups.[163] The three-dimensional structure of factor XIII has not been established.

Primary Structure. The a subunit of plasma factor XIII consists of 731 amino acid residues.[166,167] Accordingly, the molecular weight of the polypeptide portion of the molecule was calculated to be 83,150. The addition of 1.5 percent carbohydrate[164] gives a molecular weight of approximately 84,400 for each of the a subunits.

The b subunit is composed of 641 amino acid residues[168] with a calculated molecular weight of 73,183. The addition of 8.5 percent carbohydrate[165] gives a molecular weight of about 79,700 for each of the b subunits of human factor XIII. These molecular weights are in agreement with those estimated by SDS-polyacrylamide gel electrophoresis.[162,163]

The amino terminal of the a subunit is acetylated,[169] while that of the b subunit is a free Glu residue.[168,169] The a subunit contains several functional regions including an activation peptide (37 amino acids), an active site, putative calcium-binding site(s), and a thrombin inactivation site (Fig. 85-6). The amino acid sequence around the active site (Tyr-Gly-Gln-Cys-Trp, YGQCW in Fig. 85-6) is identical with that of tissue transglutaminase.[170] The locations of other functional units, such as the binding site for fibrin or regions that are involved in the formation of dimers and tetramers, have not been determined.

The a subunit of factor XIII is also found in other tissues such as platelets, megakaryocytes, placenta, uterus, and macrophages (see "Synthesis for Factor XIII" below). The a subunits found in plasma and in these other tissues seem to be identical, because the amino acid sequences of the corresponding regions of the a subunits from plasma,[166,169] platelet,[169] and placenta[166,167,171] are indistinguishable. The carboxy terminal

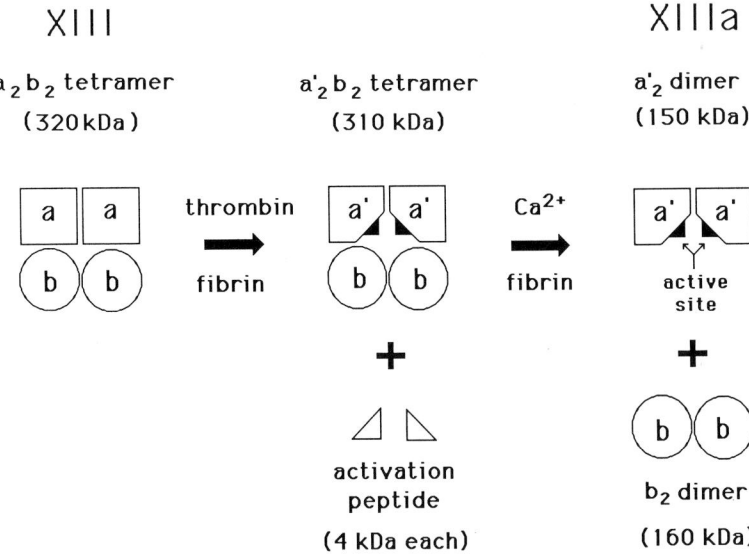

Fig. 85-5 Activation of factor XIII. Factor XIII is composed of two a and two b subunits and is converted to an active form (factor XIIIa) by thrombin releasing an activation peptide from each a subunit. In the presence of calcium ions, the a dimer dissociates from the b dimer and catalyzes an γ-glutamyl–ε-lysine cross-linking reaction.

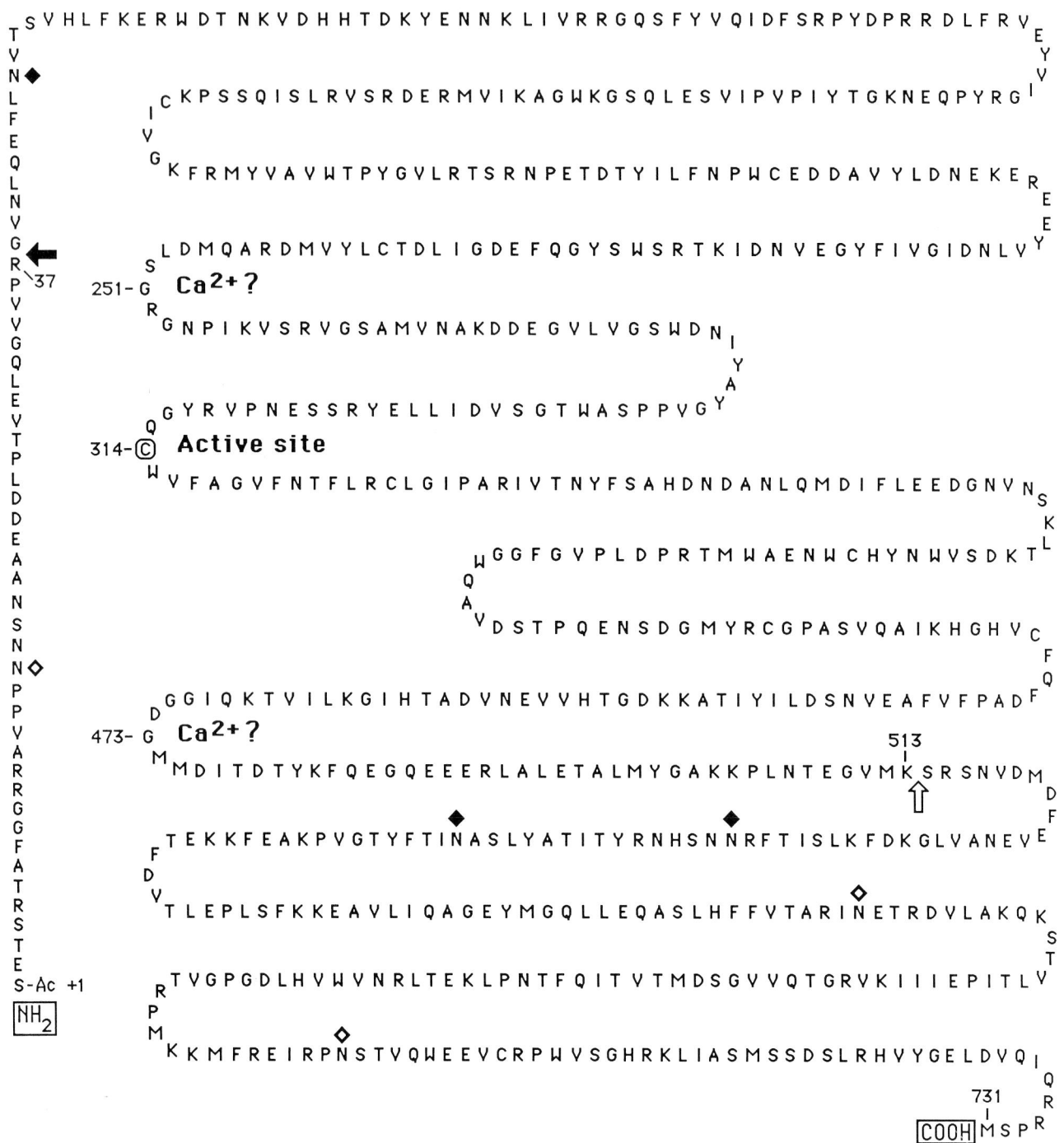

Fig. 85-6 Amino acid sequence and tentative structure for the a subunit of human coagulation factor XIII. The Ser residue at position 1 of the mature protein is acetylated. The cleavage sites by thrombin, one for activation and the other for inactivation, are indicated by the closed and open arrows, respectively. Residues marked with diamonds are potential Asn-linked glycosylation sites. (The residues with open diamonds seem to be not glycosylated because these residues were identified semiquantitatively by amino acid sequence analysis.) The active site Cys at residue 314 is circled.

of the purified a subunit from human placenta is reported to be heterogeneous in length.[171]

The a subunit of factor XIII is highly homologous to tissue transglutaminase (Titani, Zenita, Ando, and Kannagi, personal communication). As shown in Table 85-1, amino acid sequences from several regions of both enzymes are aligned. The degree of identity ranges from 33 percent (residues 365–373) to 76 percent (residues 311–339). This provides strong evidence that both enzymes are derived from a common ancestor.

The b subunit contains 10 tandem repeats (Fig. 85-7).

These repeats each consist of about 60 amino acids, two disulfide bonds, and highly conserved Pro, Gly, Tyr, and Trp residues.[168] These 10 repeats are subclassified into four groups according to the difference in degree of identity to each other. These repeats have been called GP-I structures,[172] because the disulfide bond pairing was first established in β$_2$-glycoprotein I between the first and third, and the second and fourth Cys residues in each repeat.[173] Therefore, it is likely that a similar pairing occurs with the disulfide bonds in the GP-I structures present in other proteins. At least 15 other proteins including β$_2$-glycoprotein I, various complement-related proteins (C1r,

Table 85-1 Homology Between the Partial Amino Acid Sequences of Human Tissue Transglutaminase (hTG) and the a Subunit of Human Factor XIII (XIIIa)

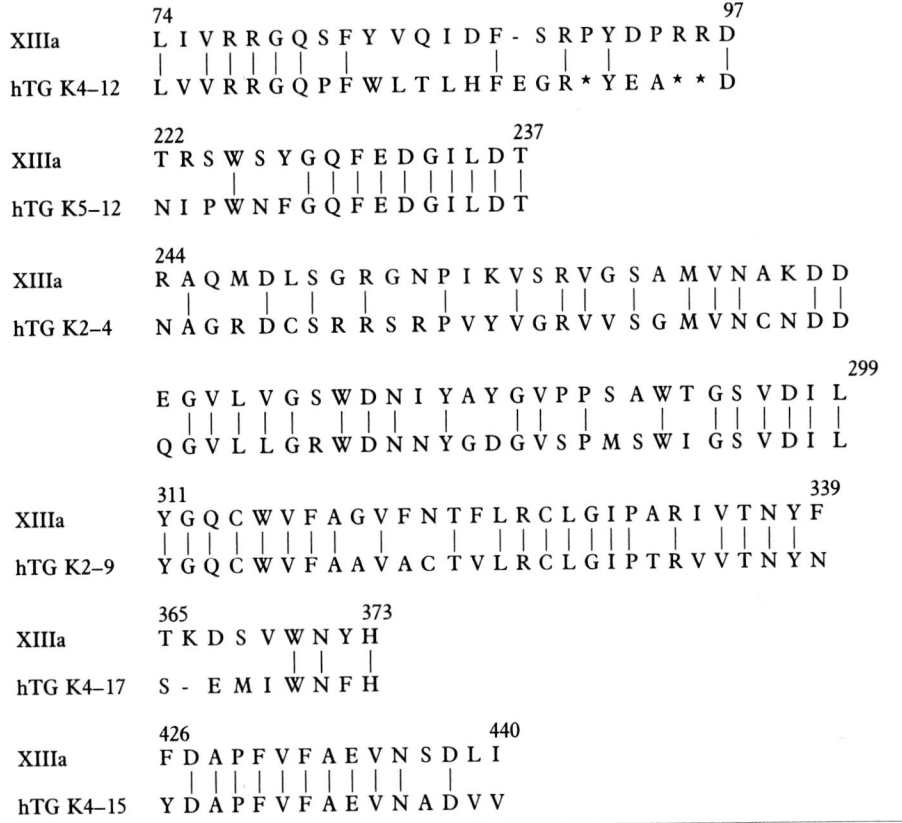

```
            74                               97
XIIIa     L I V R R G Q S F Y V Q I D F - S R P Y D P R R D
          | | | | |   |   |       |     | |       | |   |
hTG K4-12 L V V R R G Q P F W L T L H F E G R ★ Y E A ★ ★ D

            222                     237
XIIIa     T R S W S Y G Q F E D G I L D T
              |     |   | | | | | | | | |
hTG K5-12 N I P W N F G Q F E D G I L D T

            244
XIIIa     R A Q M D L S G R G N P I K V S R V G S A M V N A K D D
          |           |     |       | |     | |   | | |     | |
hTG K2-4  N A G R D C S R R S R P V Y V G R V V S G M V N C N D D

                                                         299
          E G V L V G S W D N I Y A Y G V P P S A W T G S V D I L
          |   | | |   | | |     |   | |       |   | | | | | | |
          Q G V L L G R W D N N Y G D G V S P M S W I G S V D I L

            311                                       339
XIIIa     Y G Q C W V F A G V F N T F L R C L G I P A R I V T N Y F
          | | | | | | | |       | | | | | | | |   |     | | | |
hTG K2-9  Y G Q C W V F A A V A C T V L R C L G I P T R V V T N Y N

            365       373
XIIIa     T K D S V W N Y H
                    |   | |
hTG K4-17 S - E M I W N F H

            426               440
XIIIa     F D A P F V F A E V N S D L I
            | | | | | | | | | |   | |
hTG K4-15 Y D A P F V F A E V N A D V V
```

NOTE: Gaps (-) are introduced to obtain maximal alignment. Asterisks (★) indicate residues not identified, and vertical lines (|) indicate identical amino acid residues. Numbers refer to the positions of amino acid residues in the a subunit of factor XIII, and K numbers denote proteolytic fragments of hTG.

SOURCE: Data from factor XIIIa from Ichinose et al.[166] and for hTG from Titani, Zenita, Ando, and Kannagi, personal communication.

Cls, C2, factor B, C4b-binding protein, protein H, factor I, C7, decay-accelerating factor, complement receptor type 1 and type 2), interleukin-2 receptor, haptoglobin, and horseshoe crab factor C are found to contain similar GP-I structure.[172] Eleven out of the 16 proteins are involved in the complement system, and five are involved in diverse systems such as blood coagulation, lymphocyte activation, or oxygen transport.

Near the carboxy terminal of the b subunit of factor XIII, there is an Arg-Gly-Asp (RGD) sequence which is reported to be responsible for the cell attachment of various proteins.[174] However, it remains to be determined whether or not this RGD sequence of the b subunit is related to its function.

Function of Factor XIII

The a subunit of factor XIII contains the catalytic site,[163] while the b subunit is thought to protect or stabilize the a subunit[175-177] or regulate the activation of the zymogen.[178,179]

Factor XIIIa catalyzes a γ-glutamyl–ε-lysine cross-linking reaction between several proteins. Fibrin acts as both an amino donor and acceptor,[66] while α_2-plasmin inhibitor and fibronectin preferentially serve as amino acceptors.[87,180]

Cross-linking of Fibrin Monomers. The cross-linking reaction catalyzed by factor XIIIa leads to a dimerization of the γ chains of fibrin followed by a polymerization of the α chains of fibrin.[162,181] The cross-linking sites between the γ chains are

Gln-398 and Lys-406[66] near the carboxy-terminal ends of the polypeptide chain. Gln-328 and Gln-366 are involved in α-chain polymerization.[67]

The γ-dimerization and α-polymerization reactions result in a fibrin with considerable mechanical strength and elasticity.[182-184] These polymerization reactions aid in primary hemostasis.

Cross-linking of α_2-Plasmin Inhibitor. The cross-linking reaction of α_2-plasmin inhibitor to the α chain of fibrin[185] or fibrinogen[186] in the presence of factor XIIIa occurs at a faster rate than with other proteins. Accordingly, in plasma, α_2-plasmin inhibitor and fibrin are considered to be the best substrates of factor XIIIa.[187] The cross-linking site in each substrate has been identified as Gln-2 in α_2-plasmin inhibitor[180,188] and Lys-303 in the α chain of fibrinogen.[189]

The cross-linking of α_2-plasmin inhibitor to fibrin renders the fibrin clot resistant to digestion by plasmin.[190,191] Consequently, the cross-linked α_2-plasmin inhibitor protects the hemostatic fibrin clot from premature lysis by plasmin.

Cross-linking of Fibronectin. Factor XIIIa catalyzes the cross-linking of fibronectin to the α chain of fibrin[185,192] and to collagen.[193] The cross-linking site of fibronectin is reported to be Gln-3 at its amino terminal.[87]

The cross-linking between fibronectin and fibrin or collagen may result in the anchorage of fibrin clots to cells or the structural matrix in vessel walls at the site of vascular injury. Fac-

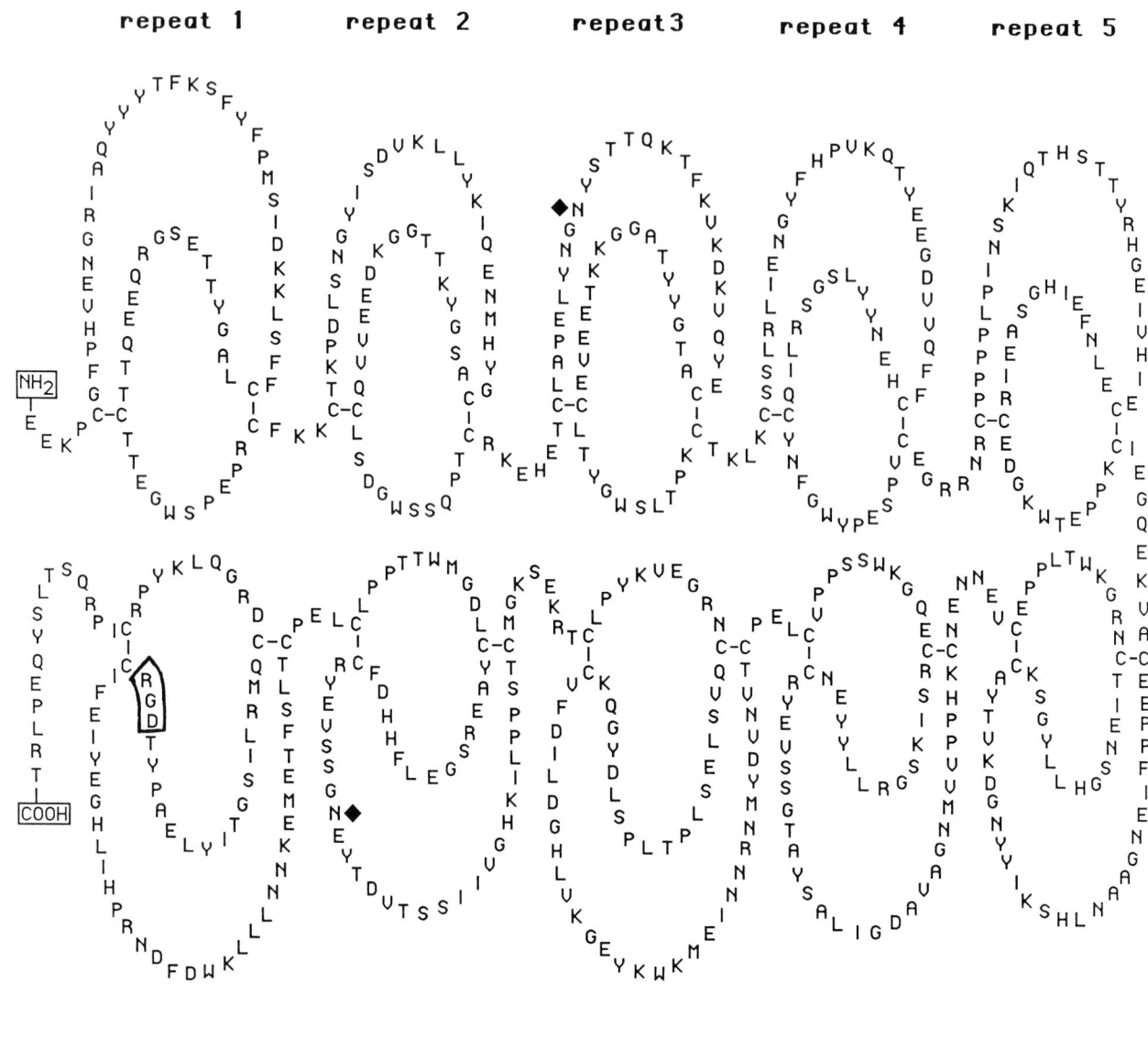

Fig. 85-7 Amino acid sequence and tentative structure for the b subunit of human plasma factor XIII. The disulfide bridges between the first and third Cys, and the second and fourth Cys are based on the homology between the b subunit of factor XIII and β₂-glycoprotein I, in which disulfide pairing has been established. The RGD (Arg-Gly-Asp) sequence is in the tenth repeat.

tor XIII is also reported to enhance fibroblast proliferation.[194] These reactions appear to be related to wound healing.[176,177,195]

Other Protein Substrates. The contractile proteins actin and myosin have also been shown to be substrates of factor XIIIa.[196–198] Since these three proteins exist in platelets, they might be involved in the cross-linking of structural proteins under certain conditions.[198]

Several other plasma proteins such as von Willebrand factor,[199,200] thrombospondin,[201] and factor V[202] have recently been reported to be cross-linked to themselves or other substrates by factor XIIIa. However, the precise functions of these reactions have not been established.

Synthesis of Factor XIII

Concentrations of the a and b subunits of factor XIII in normal plasma have been reported by a radioimmunoassay to be 15 μg/ml and 14 μg/ml, respectively.[203,204] This suggests that essentially all of the a and b subunits in plasma circulate in the form of an equimolar proenzyme complex.[204] This is, however, in contrast to previous reports that "free" b subunits exist in plasma.[205–207] The b subunit complexed with the a subunit and "free" b subunit have to be measured separately to settle this discrepancy.

Although it is not clear where or how the molecular assembly of the a and b subunits takes place, some information on the biosynthesis of factor XIII has been obtained in recent years.

Site of Synthesis for Factor XIII. Although conflicting results with immunologic techniques have led to some controversy regarding the site of biosynthesis for the a subunit,[208,209] the liver has long been thought to be a major site of synthesis for both the a and b subunits of plasma factor XIII.[210,211] In addition, the biosynthesis and secretion of both subunits of factor XIII by the human hepatoma cell line Hep G-2 have been reported.[212] However, a tumor cell does not always represent the features of a normal cell.

The a subunit of factor XIII is also found in other tissues such as human platelets, megakaryocytes, placenta, uterus, and macrophages.[208,213–216] The function of these intracellular forms of factor XIII is, however, not clear.

The contributory role of platelets in the production of the a subunit of the plasma enzyme is controversial.[214,217] Platelets and plasma contain equal amounts of the a subunit,[218,219] but the a subunit of platelets is present in the cytoplasm[219,220] and is not secreted from platelets.[218,219]

Northern blotting analyses of mRNA samples from placenta, macrophage, and osteosarcoma U-2 cells showed a single mRNA species (about 4.0 kb) for the a subunit of factor XIII, while little or no detectable hybridization signal was obtained from the mRNA samples of normal liver, Hep G-2 cells, and fibroblasts (Ichinose and Sakariassen, unpublished data; Refs. 167, 221). These results suggest that placenta and macrophage synthesize the a subunit. It is unlikely, however, that they are major sources of the a subunit of plasma factor XIII that is present at a concentration of 15 μg/ml.[204] These results do not exclude the possibility of the existence of a trace amount of mRNA in liver. The mRNA from megakaryocytes has not been examined because of the difficulty in obtaining sufficient material.

The site of synthesis for the b subunit has been reported to be the liver.[210,211] Accordingly, cDNAs for the b subunit have been isolated from a normal human liver library.[168]

Recently, Wolpl and coworkers[222] reported that after bone marrow transplantation the phenotype (see below) of the a subunit of the recipients was replaced by that of the donors, while the phenotype of the b subunit remained as that of the recipient. Conversely, after liver transplantation, the phenotype of the b subunit of the recipients was changed to the donor's, but the phenotype of the a subunit remained unchanged.

Mechanism for Secretion of the a Subunit of Factor XIII. The 5′ end of the cDNA for the placental a subunit does not encode a typical hydrophobic leader sequence for secretion.[166,167] Because the a subunit of factor XIII is known to remain in the cytoplasm of placenta,[208] macrophage,[215,216] megakaryocyte,[214] and platelets,[219,220] the Met at position −1 may function as the initiator for biosynthesis. The removal of the Met would then be followed by acetylation of the amino-terminal Ser residue.[169]

Alternatively, if the a subunit of factor XIII from placenta or other tissue is secreted into plasma, it is likely that it is synthesized with a prepro-leader sequence. The search for a possible prepro-leader sequence has been unsuccessful.

There are several proteins that lack typical hydrophobic leader sequences and distinct internal hydrophobic signals but are present and function in extracellular spaces.[223–227] This raises the possibility that they are released by "leakage" from damaged cells.[223]

The 5′ end of the cDNA for the b subunit of factor XIII codes for a typical hydrophobic leader sequence that aids in its secretion from the liver into circulation.[168]

Regulation of Production of the b Subunit. Patients with congenital factor XIII deficiency lack an immunologically detectable a subunit (less than 1 percent of normal) but have a reduced amount (about 50 percent of normal) of the b subunit.[205,228] Heterozygotes have about 50 and 80 percent of the a and b subunits, respectively.[229] Furthermore, the administration of a subunits obtained from placenta increased not only

the a subunit level in plasma but also the level of the b subunit, which reached a maximum after several days.[211,230] These findings suggest that the level of the b subunit in plasma is regulated, at least in part, by the amount of the a subunit.[211,230]

Metabolism of Factor XIII

The half-life for the a and b subunits of factor XIII has been reported to be about 8 to 10 days.[211,231] In rabbit, factor XIIIa (the activated form) is removed from circulation faster than factor XIII (the zymogen form)[210] probably through the reticuloendothelial system in liver. The uptake of factor XIIIa into fibrin clots[179] could be an additional mechanism for its clearance from plasma.

Activation of the Zymogen. During the final stage of blood coagulation, thrombin converts the proenzyme (factor XIII) to an active form (factor XIIIa) by releasing an activation peptide (4 kDa) from the amino terminal of each of the a subunits[162,169] (Fig. 85-5). The site of cleavage by thrombin is between Arg-37 and Gly-38 (Fig. 85-6). This reaction is stimulated by fibrin monomers.[232]

In the presence of calcium ions, the activated a_2 dimer dissociated from the b_2 dimer[163,164,175,178] and binds to fibrin more tightly. The binding of factor XIIIa to fibrin may be the mechanism by which enzyme activity is located at the site of vascular injury and by which general intravascular covalent cross-linking is averted.[179] Fibrin also lowers the calcium concentration required for the release of the b_2 dimer.[233] Calcium ions bind to the a subunit and unmask its active site.[175,234,235]

Several other enzymes, including trypsin, factor Xa, elastase, etc., are reported to activate factor XIII,[162,215,236,237] although the physiologic significance has not been established.

Degradation of the Enzyme. The loss of biologic activity of factor XIIIa during prolonged incubation with thrombin occurs in parallel with the generation of fragments of 56 kDa and 24 kDa from the a subunit.[162,238] The cleavage site for thrombin is reported to be between Lys-513 and Ser-514.[171] In general, however, Lys is not a good substrate for thrombin. Degradation of factor XIII or factor XIIIa has also been reported to occur by digestion with elastase and trypsin.[162,237]

Acquired Deficiencies in Factor XIII. The plasma level of factor XIII is decreased in disseminated intravascular coagulation,[239] in some cases of acute leukemia with disseminated intravascular coagulation,[240] and in Henoch-Schönlein purpura.[241] These conditions probably involve consumption of the enzyme, since factor XIII, in plasma, can be readily activated (and inactivated) by thrombin during coagulation.[242,243]

The level of factor XIII is also reduced in liver cirrhosis,[240,244,245] in leukemia without disseminated intravascular coagulation,[240] and in thrombocytopenia.[211] These effects may also be related to a decrease in production. A few patients have been described with inhibitors of factor XIII.[182,246]

Elevated Levels of Factor XIII. The concentration of the a subunit and, to a lesser extent, the b subunit were highly elevated in some cases of multiple myeloma.[247] Both the a and b subunits of factor XIII were reported to increase with age and in cases of hyperlipidemia,[245] diabetes,[248] and nephrosis.[245,249]

The precise reasons for these elevated levels of factor XIII in plasma are not clear.

Genetics of Factor XIII

Chromosomal Localization and Gene Structures. The gene for the a subunit of factor XIII is located at the distal end of the short arm of chromosome 6 and is linked to the HLA region.[250,251] This has recently been confirmed using a cDNA probe.[221] The gene for the b subunit is localized to the long arm of chromosome 1 (1q31) (Webb et al., personal communication). The genes for several complement proteins containing GP-I structures are also clustered on chromosome 1.[252]

Genomic DNA for both the a and b subunits has been characterized (Ref. 253, 253a; Bottenus et al., unpublished data). The gene for the a subunit spans more than 160 kb, and each functional region is encoded by a separate exon. The gene for the b subunit of factor XIII is about 30 kb in length, and each GP-I structure is encoded by a single exon. This is also true in the genes for several other proteins containing GP-I structures except for haptoglobin, where an additional intron interrupts the middle of the GP-I structure.

Genetic Polymorphism. Using agarose gel electrophoresis, several different allelic forms of the a subunit of factor XIII have been identified in the normal population.[254,255] The heterogeneity in the a subunit has been confirmed by both amino acid and DNA sequencing as shown in Table 85-2.[166,167,171] All amino acid substitutions can be explained by point mutations. Detection of numerous restriction fragments length polymorphisms indicates that extensive DNA polymorphism exists at the a subunit locus.[253a,255a]

Microheterogeneity of the b subunit[234] was also classified into several alleles.[256] However, differences in amino acid or DNA sequence have not been identified.[168]

Disorders of Factor XIII

Congenital Deficiency. The incidence of congenital factor XIII deficiency (with less than 1 percent of normal levels of the a subunit) occurs in about 1 in 5 million in the United Kingdom[177] and in Japan.[257] The mode of inheritance of this deficiency is autosomal recessive.[177,229]

In affected individuals, the first manifestation of bleeding is usually from the umbilical cord after birth, and this occurs in approximately 90 percent of the cases.[195] Intracranial hemorrhage occurs in one-fourth of the patients and is the leading cause of death. Superficial bruising, and hematomas in subcutaneous tissue and muscle are common, and sites can rebleed if not treated. Patients also have joint bleeding after trauma, but have much less spontaneous hemarthrosis than hemophiliacs.

Deficiencies of either factor XIII[176,177] or α_2-plasmin inhibitor[258] result in "delayed bleeding" after trauma, while primary hemostasis in individuals with these traits is normal.

In addition to a lifelong bleeding tendency, abnormal wound healing and habitual abortion are not uncommon.[177,195] Noteworthy is that recurrent abortion has also been described in patients with congenital hypofibrinogenemia or afibrinogenemia.[259,260] Moreover, abnormal wound healing and repetitive abortion are reported in patients with congenital dysfibrinogenemia (for review, see Ref. 261). These facts suggest the real functions of factor XIII and fibrin and their importance in vivo.

Platelets obtained from a patient with congenital factor XIII deficiency also showed little or no factor XIII activity, indicating that a single gene for the a subunit codes both the plasma and platelet enzymes.[218] The level of factor XIII activity in the placenta of factor XIII–deficient patients has not been reported yet. A search for the defect(s) in the gene for the a subunit of these patients is now underway.

Patients with a deficiency of the b subunit of factor XIII have not been described thus far.

Diagnosis for Factor XIII Deficiency and Factor XIII Assay. The diagnosis for a homozygote with a congenital deficiency is based on the pattern of inheritance, clinical symptoms, and laboratory tests. In addition to the typical umbilical cord bleeding, the characteristic delayed bleeding after trauma strongly suggests this disorder.

The screening tests for factor XIII deficiency are thromboelastogram, and more specifically, urea or monochloroacetic acid solubility of the recalcified plasma clot. Visualization of a γ-dimer or α-polymer of fibrin by SDS-polyacrylamide gel electrophoresis is useful to roughly estimate the functional level of factor XIII in plasma. The transglutaminase activity of factor XIII is quantitatively measured by the amine incorporation assays.[239,262] Quantitation of the a or b subunits of factor XIII is also measured immunologically by the Laurell rocket electrophoresis method[205,228] or by a radioimmunoassay.[203,204] Other laboratory coagulation tests are within normal range.

The diagnosis for a heterozygote, who usually lacks symptoms of factor XIII deficiency, can be made by the specific quantitative measurements of factor XIII.

Molecular Abnormality. A rare case of a congenital deficiency of factor XIII was reported which may have resulted from the presence of "unstable" a subunits.[263] Ukita and coworkers[264] and Forman and coworkers[265] have also reported patients with normal levels of the a subunit antigen in plasma but without

Table 85-2 Polymorphisms in the Amino Acid and DNA Sequences for the a Subunit of Human Factor XIII

					Residues					
	77		78		88		650		651	
Ichinose et al.[166]	R	CGC	R	AGA	F	TTC	I	ATT	Q	CAG
							V	GTT	E	GAG
Grundmann et al.[167]	R	CGC	R	AGA	L	CTC	V	GTT	Q	CAG
Takahashi et al.[171]	R	(CGC)*	R	(AGA)	F	(TTC)	V	(GTT)	E	(GAG)
	G	(GGC)	K	(AAA)						

*DNA sequences in parentheses indicate codons assumed from the amino acid residues.

biologic activity. The molecular defect underlying these functionally abnormal factor XIII molecules has not been determined.

Therapy for Factor XIII Deficiency. Both congenital and acquired factor XIII deficiencies have been treated successfully with fresh frozen plasma, cryoprecipitate, and crude factor XIII concentrate from placenta.[266,267] Maintaining the level of plasma factor XIII at 10 to 20 percent of normal is sufficient, since bleeding occurs frequently only in patients with less than 1 percent of normal plasma, and levels of 1 and 10 percent of normal are required for in vitro γ dimerization and α polymerization, respectively. The long half-life of factor XIII in plasma and minimum requirement of factor XIII for hemostasis are beneficial both for the treatment of acute bleeding and for prophylaxis. Prophylactic therapy by factor XIII concentrates would be desirable for the patients with severe deficiency (less than 1 percent). Although development of inhibitors to factor XIII following multiple infusions is rare, it must be considered when bleeding is not controlled by therapeutic preparations of factor XIII.

Thus far, no cases of hepatitis B have been associated with the administration of placental factor XIII concentrates.[177] Thus, the risk is probably low but not zero. The cloning of human factor XIII[166–168] and the possibility of its preparation by recombinant DNA techniques offer a potential therapeutic source of this protein that would be free of viral contamination.

REFERENCES

1. SCHERAGA HA, LASKOWSKI M JR: The fibrinogen-fibrin conversion. *Adv Protein Chem* 12:1, 1957.
2. DOOLITTLE RF: Structural aspects of the fibrinogen-fibrin conversion. *Adv Protein Chem* 27:1, 1973.
3. MCKEE PA, ROGERS LA, MARLER E, HILL RL: The subunit polypeptides of human fibrinogen. *Arch Biochem Biophys* 116:271, 1966.
4. TOPFER-PETERSEN E, LOTTSPEICH F, HENSCHEN A: Carbohydrate linkage site in the β-chain of human fibrin. *Hoppe-Seyler's Z Physiol Chem* 357:1509, 1976.
5. BLOMBACK B, GRONDAHL NJ, HESSEL B, IWANAGA S, WALLEN P: Primary structure of human fibrinogen and fibrin. II. Structural studies on NH₂-terminal part of γ chain. *J Biol Chem* 248:5806, 1973.
6. COLLER BS: Asialofibrinogen supports platelet aggregation and adhesion to glass. *Blood* 53:325, 1979.
7. HARFENIST EJ, PACKHAM MA, MUSTARD JF: Identical behavior of fibrinogen and asialofibrinogen in reactions with platelets during ADP-induced aggregation. *Thromb Res* 20:353, 1980.
8. BLOMBACK B, BLOMBACK M, EDMAN P, HESSEL B: Amino-acid sequence and the occurrence of phosphorus in human fibrinopeptides. *Nature* 193:883, 1962.
9. DOOLITTLE RF, WOODING GL, LIN Y, RILEY M: Hominoid evolution as judged by fibrinopeptide structures. *J Mol Evol* 1:74, 1971.
10. BETTELHEIM IR: Tyrosine-O-sulfate in a peptide from fibrinogen. *J Am Chem Soc* 76:2838, 1954.
11. DOOLITTLE RF: Characterization of lamprey fibrinopeptides. *Biochem J* 94:742, 1965.
12. GLADNER JA: The action of thrombin on fibrinogen. In Laki K (ed): *Fibrinogen.* New York, Dekker, 1968, pp 87–116.
13. BAILEY K, BETTELHEIM FR, LORAND L, MIDDLEBROOK WR: Action of thrombin in the clotting of fibrinogen. *Nature* 167:233, 1951.
14. BAILEY K, ASTBURY WT, RUDALL KM: Fibrinogen and fibrin as members of the keratin-myosin group. *Nature* 151:716, 1943.
15. HALL CE, SLAYTER HS: The fibrinogen molecule: Its size, shape and mode of polymerization. *J Biophys Biochem Cytol* 5:11, 1959.
16. FOWLER WE, ERICKSON HP: Trinodular structure of fibrinogen. *J Mol Biol* 134:241, 1979.
17. FOWLER WE, FRETTO LJ, ERICKSON HP, MCKEE PA: Electron microscopy of plasmic fragments of human fibrinogen as related to trinodular structure of the intact molecule. *J Clin Invest* 66:50, 1980.
18. WEISEL JW, PHILLIPS GN JR, COHEN C: A model from electron microscopy for the molecular structure of fibrinogen and fibrin. *Nature* 289:263, 1981.
19. MARDER VJ, SHULMAN NR, CARROLL WR: High molecular weight derivatives of human fibrinogen produced by plasmin. *J Biol Chem* 244:2111, 1969.
20. TAKAGI T, DOOLITTLE RF: Amino acid sequence studies on plasmin-derived fragments of human fibrinogen: Amino-terminal sequences of intermediate and terminal fragments. *Biochemistry* 14:940, 1975.
21. DOOLITTLE RF, WATT KWK, COTTRELL BA, STRONG DD, RILEY M: The amino acid sequence of the α-chain of human fibrinogen. *Nature* 280:464, 1979.
22. HENSCHEN A, LOTTSPEICH F: Amino acid sequence of human fibrin. Preliminary note on the completion of the β chain sequence. *Hoppe-Seyler's Z Physiol Chem* 358:1643, 1977.
23. HENSCHEN A, LOTTSPEICH F: Amino acid sequence of human fibrin: Preliminary note on the γ chain sequence. *Hoppe-Seyler's Z Physiol Chem* 358:935, 1977.
24. PRICE TM, STRONG DD, RUDEE ML, DOOLITTLE RF: Shadow-cast electron microscopy of fibrinogen with antibody fragments bound to specific regions. *Proc Natl Acad Sci USA* 78:200, 1981.
25. DONOVAN JW, MIHALYI E: Conformation of fibrinogen. Calorimetric evidence for a three-nodule structure. *Proc Natl Acad Sci USA* 71:4125, 1974.
26. BLOMBACK B: *Symp Zool Soc London* 27:167, 1970.
27. WEISEL JW, STAUFFACHER CV, BULLIT E, COHEN C: A model for fibrinogen: Domains and sequence. *Science* 230:1388, 1985.
28. MEDVED LV, LITVINOVICH SV, PRIVALOV PL: Domain organization of the terminal parts in the fibrinogen molecule. *FEBS Lett* 202:298, 1986.
29. COHEN C, WEISEL JW, PHILLIPS GN, STAUFFACHER CV, FILLERS JP, DAUB E: The structure of fibrinogen and fibrin. *Ann NY Acad Sci* 408:194, 1983.
30. DOOLITTLE RF, GOLDBAUM DM, DOOLITTLE LR: Designation of sequences involved in the "coiled coil" interdomainal connector in fibrinogen: Construction of an atomic scale model. *J Mol Biol* 120:311, 1978.
31. MOSESSON MW, HAINFIELD J, HASCHEMEYER RH, WALL J: Identification and mass analysis of human fibrinogen molecules and their domains by scanning transmission electron microscopy. *J Mol Biol* 153:695, 1981.
32. ERICKSON HP, FOWLER WE: Electron microscopy of fibrinogen and its plasmic fragments and small polymers. *Ann NY Acad Sci* 408:146, 1983.
33. MEDVED LV, GORKUN OV, PRIVALOV PL: Structural organization of C-terminal parts of fibrinogen Aα-chains. *FEBS Lett* 160:291, 1983.
34. MIHALYI E, GODFREY JE: Digestion of fibrinogen by trypsin. II. Characterization of the large fragment obtained. *Biochim Biophys Acta* 67:90, 1963.
35. MARDER VJ, SHULMAN NR, CARROLL WR: The importance of intermediate degradation products of fibrinogen in fibrinolytic hemorrhage. *Trans Assoc Am Physicians* 80:156, 1967.
36. MARDER VJ, SHULMAN NR, CARROLL WR: High molecular weight derivatives of human fibrinogen produced by plasmin. I. Physiochemical and immunological characterization. *J Biol Chem* 204:2111, 1969.
37. TELFORD NJ, NAGY JA, HATCHER PA, SCHERAGA HA: Location of peptide fragments in the fibrinogen molecule by immunoelectron microscopy. *Proc Natl Acad Sci USA* 77:2372, 1980.
38. NORTON PA, SLAYTER HS: Immune labeling of the D and E regions of human fibrinogen by electron microscopy. *Proc Natl Acad Sci USA* 78:1661, 1981.
39. TAGAKI T, DOOLITTLE RF: Amino acid sequence studies on the α chain of human fibrinogen. Location of four plasmin attack points and a covalent cross-linking site. *Biochemistry* 14:5149, 1975.
40. TAKAGI T, DOOLITTLE RF: The amino acid sequences of those portions of human fibrinogen fragment E which are not included in the amino-terminal disulfide knot. *Thromb Res* 7:813, 1975.
41. HENSCHEN A, LOTTSPEICH F, TOPFER-PETERSEN E, MEHL M, TIMPL R: Intra and inter-species comparisons. In Peeters H (ed): *Protides of Biological Fluids.* New York, Pergamon Press, 1980, vol 28, p 47.
42. MOSHER DF: Cross-linking of cold-insoluble globulin by fibrin-stabilizing factor. *J Biol Chem* 250:6614, 1975.
43. HAWIGER J, TIMMONS S, KLOCZEWIAK M, STRONG DD, DOOLITTLE RF: γ and α chains of human fibrinogen possess sites reactive with human platelet receptors. *Proc Natl Acad Sci USA* 79:2068, 1982.
44. HAWIGER J, TIMMONS S, STRONG DD, COTTRELL BA, RILEY M, DOOLITTLE RF: Identification of a region of human fibrinogen interacting with staphylococcal clumping factor. *Biochemistry* 21:1407, 1982.
45. STRONG DD, LAUDANO AP, HAWIGER J, DOOLITTLE RF: Isolation, characterization, and synthesis of peptides from human fibrinogen that block the staphylococcal clumping reaction and construction of a synthetic clumping particle. *Biochemistry* 21:1414, 1982.

46. MOSESSON MW, FINLAYSON JS, UMFLEET RA, et al: Human fibrinogen heterogeneity. I. Structural and related studies of plasma fibrinogens which are high solubility catabolic intermediates. *J Biol Chem* 247:5210, 1972.

47. BLOMBACK B, VESTERMARK A: Isolation of fibrinopeptides by chromatography. *Ark Kemi* 12:173, 1958.

48. MARTINELLI RA, SCHERAGA HA: Steady state kinetic study of the bovine thrombin-fibrinogen interaction. *Biochemistry* 19:2343, 1980.

49. LEWIS SD, SHIELDS PP, SHAFER JA: Characterization of the kinetic pathway for liberation of fibrinopeptides during assembly of fibrin. *J Biol Chem* 260:10192, 1985.

50. BILEZIKIAN SB, NOSSEL HL, BUTLER VP Jr, CANFIELD RE: Radioimmunoassay of human fibrinopeptide B and kinetics of fibrinopeptide cleavage by different enzymes. *J Clin Invest* 56:438, 1975.

51. STOCKER K, FISCHER H, MEIER J: Thrombin-like snake venom proteinases. *Toxicon* 20:265, 1982.

52. SHAINOFF JR, DARDIK BN: Fibrinopeptide B and aggregation of fibrinogen. *Science* 204:200, 1979.

53. DYR JE, BLOMBACK B, KORNALIK F: The fibrinogenolytic and procoagulant activity of southern copperhead venom enzymes. *Thromb Res* 30:185, 1983.

54. KRAKOW W, ENDRES GF, SIEGEL BM, SCHERAGA HA: An electron microscopic investigation of the polymerization of bovine fibrin monomer. *J Mol Biol* 71:95, 1972.

55. FOWLER WE, HANTGAN RR, HERMANS J, ERICKSON HP: Structure of the fibrin protofibril. *Proc Natl Acad Sci USA* 78:4872, 1981.

56. HANTGAN RR, HERMANS J: Assembly of fibrin: A light scattering study. *J Biol Chem* 254:11272, 1979.

57. HANTGAN RR, FOWLER RW, ERICKSON HP, HERMANS J: Fibrin assembly: A comparison of electron microscopic and light scattering results. *Thromb Haemost* 44:119, 1980.

58. LAUDANO AP, DOOLITTLE RF: Studies on synthetic peptides that bind to fibrinogen and prevent fibrin polymerization. *Proc Natl Acad Sci USA* 75:3085, 1978.

59. SHAINOFF JR, PAGE IH: Cofibrins and fibrin-intermediates as indicators of thrombin activity in vivo. *Circ Res* 8:1013, 1960.

60. HERMANS J, MCDONAGH J: Fibrin: Structure and interactions. *Semin Thromb Hemost* 8:11, 1982.

61. LAUDANO AP, DOOLITTLE RF: Studies on synthetic peptides that bind to fibrinogen and prevent fibrin polymerization. Structural requirements, number of binding sites, and species differences. *Biochemistry* 19:1013, 1980.

62. STURTEVANT JM, LASKOWSKI M, DONNELLY TH, SCHERAGA HA: Equilibria in the fibrinogen-fibrin conversion. III. Heats of polymerization and clotting of fibrin monomer. *J Am Chem Soc* 77:6168, 1955.

63. SCHERAGA HA: Interaction of thrombin and fibrinogen and the polymerization of fibrin monomer. *Ann NY Acad Sci* 408:330, 1983.

64. SHIMIZU A, SAITO Y, MATSUSHIMA A, INADA Y : Identification of an essential histidine residue for fibrin polymerization. *J Biol Chem* 258:7915, 1983.

65. CHEN R, DOOLITTLE RF: Identification of the polypeptide chains involved in the cross-linking of fibrin. *Proc Natl Acad Sci USA* 63:420, 1969.

66. CHEN R, DOOLITTLE RF: γ-γ cross-linking sites in human and bovine fibrin. *Biochemistry* 10:4486, 1971.

67. COTTRELL BA, STRONG DD, WATT KWK, DOOLITTLE RF: Amino acid sequence studies on the α chain of human fibrinogen. Exact location of cross-linking acceptor sites. *Biochemistry* 18:5405, 1979.

68. FRETTO LJ, FERGUSON EW, STEINMAN HM, MCKEE PA: Localization of the α-chain cross-link acceptor sites of human fibrin. *J Biol Chem* 253:2184, 1978.

69. CORCORAN DH, FERGUSON EW, FRETTO LJ, MCKEE PA: Localization of a cross-link donor site in the alpha-chain of human fibrin. *Thromb Res* 19:883, 1980.

70. GAFFNEY PJ, WHITAKER AN: Fibrin crosslinks and lysis rates. *Thromb Res* 14:85, 1979.

71. GAFFNEY PJ, JOE F: The lysis of crosslinked human fibrin by plasmin yields initially a single molecular complex, D dimer-E. *Thromb Res* 15:673, 1979.

72. FRANCIS CW, MARDER VJ, BARLOW GH: Plasmic degradation of cross-linked fibrin. Characterization of new macromolecular soluble complexes and a model of their structure. *J Clin Invest* 66:1033, 1980.

73. DANG CV, EBERT RF, BELL WR: Localization of a fibrinogen calcium binding site between γ subunit positions 311 and 336 by terbium fluorescence. *J Biol Chem* 260:9713, 1985.

74. NIEUWENHUIZEN W, HAVERKATE F: Calcium binding regions in fibrinogen. *Ann NY Acad Sci* 408:92, 1983.

75. HARDY JJ, CARRELL NA, MCDONAGH J: Calcium ion functions in fibrinogen conversion to fibrin. *Ann NY Acad Sci* 408:279, 1983.

76. LIU CY, NOSSEL HL, KAPLAN KL: The Binding of thrombin by fibrin. *J Biol Chem* 254:10421, 1979.

77. FRANCIS CW, MARKHAM RE Jr, BARLOW GH, FLORACK TM, DOBRZYNSKI DM, MARDER VJ: Thrombin activity of fibrin thrombi and soluble plasmic derivatives. *J Lab Clin Med* 102:220, 1983.

78. LIU CY, KOEHN JA, MORGAN FJ: Characterization of fibrinogen New York 1. A dysfunctional fibrinogen with a deletion of Bβ (9-72) corresponding exactly to exon 2 of the gene. *J Biol Chem* 260:4390, 1985.

79. LUCAS MA, FRETTO LJ, MCKEE PA: The binding of human plasminogen to fibrin and fibrinogen. *J Biol Chem* 258:4249, 1983.

80. VARADI A, PATTHY L: Location of plasminogen-binding sites in human fibrin(ogen). *Biochemistry* 22:2440, 1983.

81. VARADI A, PATTHY L: β(Leu 121-Lys 122) Segment of fibrinogen is in a region essential for plasminogen binding by fibrin fragment E. *Biochemistry* 23:2108, 1984.

82. EDSALL JT, GILBERT GA, SCHERAGA HA: The non-clotting component of the human plasma fraction I-1 ("cold insoluble globulin"). *J Am Chem Soc* 77:157, 1955.

83. MOSESSON MW, UMFLEET RA: The cold-insoluble globulin of human plasma. I. Purification, primary characterization, and relationship to fibrinogen and other cold-insoluble fraction components. *J Biol Chem* 245:5728, 1970.

84. STATHAKIS NE, MOSESSON MW, CHEN AB, GALANAKIS DK: Cryoprecipitation of fibrin-fibrinogen complexes induced by the cold-insoluble globulin of plasma. *Blood* 51:1211, 1978.

85. PETERSEN TE, THORGERSEN HC, SKORSTENGAARD K, VIBE-PEDERSEN K, SAHL P, SOTTRUP-JENSEN L, MAGNUSSON S: Partial primary structure of bovine plasma fibronectin: Three types of internal homology. *Proc Natl Acad Sci USA* 80:137, 1983.

86. MOSHER DF, JOHNSON RB: Specificity of fibronectin-fibrin cross-linking. *Ann NY Acad Sci* 408:583, 1983.

87. MCDONAGH RP, MCDONAGH J, PETERSEN TE, THORGERSEN HC, SKORSTENGAARD K, SOTTRUP-JENSEN L, MAGNUSSON S: Amino acid sequence of the factor XIIIa acceptor site in bovine plasma fibronectin. *FEBS Lett* 127:174, 1981.

88. LEUNG LL, NACHMAN RL: Complex formation of platelet thrombospondin with fibrinogen. *J Clin Invest* 70:542, 1982.

89. MCLEAN JR, MAXWELL RE, HERTLER D: Fibrinogen and adenosine diphosphate-induced aggregation of platelets. *Nature* 202:605, 1964.

90. MARGUERIE GA, EDGINGTON TS, PLOW EF: Human platelets possess an inducible and saturable receptor specific for fibrinogen. *J Biol Chem* 254:5357, 1979.

91. BENNETT JS, VILAIRE G: Exposure of platelet fibrinogen receptors by ADP and epinephrine. *J Clin Invest* 64:1393, 1979.

92. HAWIGER J, PARKINSON S, TIMMONS S: Prostacyclin inhibits mobilization of fibrinogen-binding sites on human ADP- and thrombin-treated platelets. *Nature* 283:195, 1980.

93. FUJIMOTO T, OHARA S, HAWIGER J: Thrombin-induced exposure and prostacyclin inhibition of the receptor for factor VIII/von Willebrand factor on human platelets. *J Clin Invest* 69:1212, 1982.

94. JENNINGS LK, PHILLIPS DR: Purification of glycoproteins IIb and III from human platelet plasma membranes and characterization of a calcium-dependent glycoprotein IIb-III complex. *J Biol Chem* 257:10458, 1982.

95. PARISE LV, PHILLIPS DR: Reconstitution of the purified platelet fibrinogen receptor. *J Biol Chem* 260:10698, 1985.

96. KLOCZEWIAK M, TIMMONS S, HAWIGER J: Recognition site for the platelet receptor is present on the 15-residue carboxy-terminal fragment of the γ chain of human fibrinogen and is not involved in the fibrin polymerization reaction. *Thromb Res* 29:249, 1983.

97. KLOCZEWIAK M, TIMMONS S, LUKAS TJ, HAWIGER J: Platelet receptor recognition site on human fibrinogen: Synthesis and structure-function relationship of peptides corresponding to the carboxyl-terminal segment of the γ chain. *Biochemistry* 23:1767, 1984.

98. PLOW EF, SROUJI AH, MEYER D, MARGUERIE G, GINSBERG MH: Evidence that three adhesive proteins interact with a common recognition site on activated platelets. *J Biol Chem* 259:5388, 1984.

99. PLOW EF, PIERSCHBACHER MD, ROUSLAHTI E, MARGUERIE GA, GINSBERG MH: The effect of Arg-Gly-Asp-containing peptides on fibrinogen and von Willebrand factor binding to platelets. *Proc Natl Acad Sci USA* 82:8057, 1985.

100. STRAUB PW: A study of fibrinogen production by human liver slices in vitro by immunoprecipitin method. *J Clin Invest* 42:130, 1963.

101. TAKEDA Y: Studies of the metabolism and distribution of fibrinogen in healthy men with autologous 125I-labeled fibrinogen. *J Clin Invest* 45:103, 1966.

102. COLLEN D, TYGAT GN, CLAEYS H, PIESSENS R: Metabolism and distribution of fibrinogen. I. Fibrinogen turnover in physiological conditions in humans. *Br J Haematol* 22:681, 1972.

103. RAUSEN AA, CRUCHAUD A, MCMILLAN CW, GITLIN D: A study of fibrinogen turnover in classical hemophilia and congenital afibrinogenemia. *Blood* 18:710, 1961.

104. NICKERSON JM, FULLER GM: In vitro synthesis of rat fibrinogen: Identification of preAα, preBβ, and preγ polypeptides. *Proc Natl Acad Sci USA* 78:303, 1981.

105. CRABTREE GR, KENT JA: Molecular cloning of cDNA for the alpha, beta, and gamma chains of rat fibrinogen. A family of coordinately regulated genes. *J Biol Chem* 256:9718, 1981.

106. OLAISEN B, TEISBERG P, GEDDE-DAHL T Jr: Fibrinogen gamma chain locus is on chromosome 4 in man. *Hum Genet* 61:24, 1982.

107. HENRY I, UZAN G, WEIL D, NICOLAS H, KAPLAN JC, MARGUERIE C, KAHN A, JUNIEN C: The genes coding for A alpha-, B beta-, and gamma-chains of fibrinogen map to 4q2. *Am J Hum Genet* 36:760, 1984.

108. KANT JA, FORNACE AJ Jr, SAXE D, SIMON MI, MCBRIDE OW, CRABTREE GR: Organization and evolution of the human fibrinogen locus on chromosome four. *Proc Natl Acad Sci USA* 82:2344, 1985.

109. RIXON MW, CHAN WY, DAVIE EW, CHUNG DW: Characterization of a complementary deoxynucleic acid coding for the α chain of human fibrinogen. *Biochemistry* 22:3237, 1983.

110. CHUNG DW, QUE BG, RIXON MW, MACE M, DAVIE EW: Characterization of complementary deoxyribonucleic acid and genomic deoxyribonucleic acid for the β chain of human fibrinogen. *Biochemistry* 22:3244, 1983.

111. CHUNG DW, CHAN WY, DAVIE EW: Characterization of a complementary deoxyribonucleic acid coding for the γ chain of human fibrinogen. *Biochemistry* 22:3250, 1983.

112. KANT JA, LORD ST, CRABTREE GR: Partial mRNA sequences for human Aα, Bβ and γ fibrinogen chains: Evolutionary and functional implications. *Proc Natl Acad Sci USA* 80:3953, 1983.

113. CHUNG DW, RIXON MW, DAVIE EW: In Bradshaw RA, et al (eds): *Proteins in Biology and Medicine.* New York, Academic, 1982, p 309.

114. ALVING BM, CHUNG SI, MURANO G, TANG DB, FINLAYSON JS: Rabbit fibrinogen: Time course of constituent chain production in vivo. *Arch Biochem Biophys* 217:1, 1982.

115. YU S, SHER B, KUDRYK B, REDMAN CM: Intracellular assembly of human fibrinogen. *J Biol Chem* 258:13407, 1983.

116. DOOLITTLE RF: Fibrinogen and fibrin. *Annu Rev Biochem* 53:195, 1984.

117. FRANCIS CW, KRAUS DH, MARDER VJ: Structural and chromatographic heterogeneity of normal plasma fibrinogen associated with the presence of three gamma-chain types with distinct molecular weights. *Biochim Biophys Acta* 744:155, 1983.

118. WOLFENSTEIN-TODEL C, MOSESSON MW: Human plasma fibrinogen heterogeneity: Evidence for an extended carboxyl-terminal sequence in a normal gamma chain variant (gamma'). *Proc Natl Acad Sci USA* 77:5069, 1980.

119. WOLFENSTEIN-TODEL C, MOSESSON MW: Carboxyl-terminal amino acid sequence of a human fibrinogen gamma-chain variant (gamma'). *Biochemistry* 20:6146, 1981.

120. CHUNG DW, DAVIE EW: γ and γ' chains of human fibrinogen are produced by alternative mRNA processing. *Biochemistry* 23:4232, 1984.

121. RIXON MW, CHUNG DW, DAVIE EW: Nucleotide sequence of the gene for the γ chain of human fibrinogen. *Biochemistry* 24:207, 1985.

122. FORNACE AJ, CUMMINGS D, COMEAU CM, KANT JA, CRABTREE GR: The γ_B chain of human fibrinogen is produced by alternate splice patterns of mRNA from a single gene. *J Biol Chem* 259:12826, 1984.

123. MOSESSON MW, FINLAYSON JS, UMFLEET RA: Human fibrinogen heterogeneities. III. Identification of chain variants. *J Biol Chem* 247:5223, 1972.

124. LEGRELE CD, WOLFENSTEIN-TODEL C, HURBOURG Y, MOSESSON MW: Evidence for two classes of rat plasma fibrinogen gamma chains differing by their COOH-terminal amino acid sequences. *Biochem Biophys Res Commun* 105:521, 1982.

125. NACHMAN RL: Immunologic studies of platelet protein. *Blood* 25:703, 1965.

126. CASTALDI PA, CAEN J: Platelet fibrinogen. *J Clin Pathol* 18:579, 1965.

127. LEVEN RM, SCHICK PK, BUDZYNSKI AZ: Fibrinogen biosynthesis in isolated guinea pig megakaryocytes. *Blood* 65:501, 1985.

128. FRANCIS CW, NACHMAN RL, MARDER VJ: Plasma and platelet fibrinogen differ in γ chain content. *Thromb Haemost* 51:84, 1984.

129. MOSESSON MW, HOMANDBERG GA, AMRANI DL: Human platelet fibrinogen gamma chain structure. *Blood* 63:990, 1984.

130. CRABTREE GR, KANT JA: Coordinate accumulation of the mRNAs for the α, β and γ chains of rat fibrinogen following defibrination. *J Biol Chem* 257:7277, 1982.

131. AMRANI DL, PLANT PW, PINDYCK J, MOSESSON MW, GRIENINGER G: Structural analysis of fibrinogen synthesized by cultured chicken hepatocytes in the presence or absence of dexamethasone. *Biochim Biophys Acta* 743:394, 1983.

132. RITCHIE DG, LEVY BA, ADAMS MA, FULLER GM: Regulation of fibrinogen synthesis by plasmin-derived fragments of fibrinogen and fibrin: An indirect feedback pathway. *Proc Natl Acad Sci USA* 79:1530, 1982.

133. RITCHIE DG, FULLER GM: Hepatocyte-stimulating factor: a monocyte-derived acute-phase regulatory protein. *Ann NY Acad Sci* 408:490, 1983.

134. WOLOSKI BM, FULLER GM: Identification and partial characterization of hepatocyte stimulating factor from leukemia cell lines: Comparison with interleukin 1. *Proc Natl Acad Sci USA* 82:1443, 1985.

135. FULLER GM, OTTO JM, WOLOSKI M, MCGARY CT, ADAMS MA: The effects of hepatocyte-stimulating factor on fibrinogen biosynthesis in hepatocyte monolayers. *J Cell Biol* 101:1481, 1985.

136. RABE F, SALOMON E: Über Faserstoffmangel im Blute bei einem Falle von Hämophilie. *Dtsch Arch Klin Med* 132:240, 1920.

137. MORAWIRZ P: Die Chemie der Blutgerinnung. *Ergeb Physiol* 4:307, 1905.

138. HOWELL WH: The condition of the blood in hemophilia, thrombosis and purpura. *Arch Intern Med* 13:76, 1914.

139. WERDER E: Kongenitale Afibrinogenamie. *Helv Paediatr Acta* 118:208, 1963.

140. IMPERATO C, DETTORI AG: *Le Malattie da Difetto di Fibrinogeno nel Bambino.* Naples (Italy), Edizione Scientifiche Italiane, Collana di Studi Pediatrici, 1960.

141. EGBRING R, ANDRASSY K, EGLI H, MEYER-LINDENBERG J: Diagnostische und therapeutische Probleme bei congenitaler Afibrinogenamie. *Blut* 22:175, 1971.

142. MAMMEN EF: Congenital abnormalities of the fibrinogen molecule. *Semin Thromb Hemost* 1:184, 1974.

143. FLUTE PT: Disorders of plasma fibrinogen synthesis. *Br Med Bull* 33:253, 1977.

144. GROSS R, SCHWICK G, LANG N, NIES D, RAHN B, BECKER M, HENGSTMANN H: Untersuchungen an einer angeborenen Afibrinogenamie. (Zur Rolle der Blutgerinnung bei der Blutstillung.) *Klin Wochenschr* 41:695, 1963.

146. DE VRIES A, ROSENBERG T, KOCHWA S, BOSS JH: Precipitating antifibrinogen antibody appearing after fibrinogen infusions in a patient with congenital afibrinogenemia. *Am J Med* 30:486, 1961.

147. RISAK E: Die Fibrinopenie. *Z Klin Med* 128:605, 1935.

148. FRIED K, KAUFMAN S: Congenital afibrinogenemia in 10 offspring of uncle-niece marriages. *Clin Genet* 17:223, 1980.

149. INGRAM GIC, MCBRIEN DJ, SPENCER H: Fatal pulmonary embolus in congenital fibrinopenia. *Acta Haematol (Basel)* 35:56, 1966.

150. NILSSON IM, NILEHN JE, CRONBERG S, NOVDEN G: Hypofibrinogenemia and massive thrombosis. *Acta Med Scand* 180:65, 1966.

151. BECK EA: in Colman RW, Hirsch J, Marder VJ, Salzman EW (eds): *Hemostasis and Thrombosis, Basic Principles and Clinical Practice.* New York, Lippincott, 1982, pp 152–209.

152. HENSCHEN A, MCDONAGH J: Fibrinogen, fibrin and factor XIII, in Zwaal RFA, Hemker HC (eds): *Blood Coagulation.* Amsterdam, Elsevier, 1986, pp 171–241.

153. SORIA J, SORIA C, SAMAMA M, HENSCHEN A, SOUTHAN C: Detection of fibrinogen abnormality in dysfibrinogenemia: Special report on Fibrinogen Metz characterized by an amino acid substitution located at the peptide bond cleaved by thrombin. In Henschen A, Graeff H, Lottspeich F (eds): *Fibrinogen—Recent Biochemical and Medical Aspects.* Berlin, De Gruyter, 1982, pp 129–143.

154. HENSCHEN A, LOTTSPEICH F, KEHL M, SOUTHAN C: Covalent structure of fibrinogen. *Ann NY Acad Sci* 408:28, 1983.

155. KAUDEWITZ H, HENSCHEN A, SORIA J, SORIA C: in Lane DA, Henschen A, Jasami MK (eds): *Fibrinogen.* Berlin, de Gruyter, 1986, vol 4, pp 91–96.

156. REBER P, FURLAN M, RUPP C, KEHL M, HENSCHEN A, MANUCCI PM, BECK EA: Characterization of Fibrinogen Milano I: Amino acid exchange γ330Asp→Val impairs fibrin polymerization. *Blood* 67:1751, 1986.

157. REBER P, FURLAN M, HENSCHEN A, KAUDEWITZ H, BARBUI T, HILGARD P, NENCI GG, BERRETTINI M, BECK EA: Three abnormal fibrinogen variants with the same amino acid substitution (γ 275 Arg→His): fibrinogens Bergamo II, Essen and Perugia. *Thromb Haemost* 56:401, 1986.

158. THORSEN LI, BROSSTAD F, SOLUM NO, STORMORKEN H: Increased binding to ADP-stimulated platelets and aggregation effect of the dysfibrinogen Oslo I as compared with normal fibrinogen. *Scand J Haematol* 36:203, 1986.

159. BUDZYNSKI AZ, MARDER VJ: Plasmic degradation of fibrinogen Paris I. *J Lab Clin Med* 88:817, 1976.

160. MOSESSON MW, FELDMANN G, MENACHE D: Electron microscopy of fibrin Paris I. *Blood* 56:80, 1980.

161. HAMULYAK K, NIEUWENHUIZEN W, DEVILEE PP, HEMKER HC: Reevaluation of some properties of fibrinogen, purified from cord blood of normal newborns. *Thromb Res* 32:301, 1983.

162. SCHWARTZ ML, PIZZO SV, HILL RL, MCKEE PA: Human factor XIII from plasma and platelets. *J Biol Chem* 248:1395, 1973.

163. CHUNG SI, LEWIS MS, FOLK JE: Relationships of the catalytic properties of human plasma and platelet transglutaminases (activated blood coagulation factor XIII) to their subunit structures. *J Biol Chem* 249:940, 1974.

164. BOHN H: Isolierung und Charakterisierung des fibrinstabilisierenden Faktors aus menschlichen Thrombozyten. *Thromb Diath Haemorrh* 23:455, 1970.

165. BOHN H, HAUPT H, KRANTZ T: Die molekulare Struktur der fibrinstabilisierenden Faktoren des Menschen. *Blut* 25:235, 1972.

166. ICHINOSE A, HENDRICKSON LE, FUJIKAWA K, DAVIE EW: Amino acid sequence of the a subunit of human factor XIII. *Biochemistry* 25:6900, 1986.

167. GRUNDMANN U, AMANN E, ZETTLMEISSL G, KUPPER HA: Characterization of cDNA coding for human factor XIIIa. *Proc Natl Acad Sci USA* 83:8024, 1986.

168. ICHINOSE A, MCMULLEN BA, FUJIKAWA K, DAVIE EW: Amino acid sequence of the b subunit of human factor XIII, a protein composed of ten repetitive segments. *Biochemistry* 25:4633, 1986.

169. TAKAGI T, DOOLITTLE RF: Amino acid sequence studies on factor XIII and the peptide released during its activation by thrombin. *Biochemistry* 13:750, 1974.

170. CONNELLAN JM, CHUNG SI, WHETZEL NK, BRADLEY LM, FOLK JE: Structural properties of guinea pig liver transglutaminase. *J Biol Chem* 246:1093, 1971.

171. TAKAHASHI N, TAKAHASHI Y, PUTNAM FW: Primary structure of blood coagulation factor XIIIa (fibrinoligase, transglutaminase) from human placenta. *Proc Natl Acad Sci USA* 83:8019, 1986.

172. DAVIE EW, ICHINOSE A, LEYTUS SP: Structural features of the proteins participating in blood coagulation and fibrinolysis. *Cold Spring Harbor Symp Quant Biol* 51:509, 1986.

173. LOZIER J, TAKAHASHI N, PUTNAM FW: Complete amino acid sequence of human plasma β2-glycoprotein I. *Proc Natl Acad Sci USA* 81:3640, 1984.

174. PIERSCHBACHER MD, RUOSLAHTI E: Cell attachment activity of fibronectin can be duplicated by small synthetic fragments of the molecule. *Nature* 309:30, 1984.

175. COOKE RD: Calcium-induced dissociation of human plasma factor XIII and the appearance of catalytic activity. *Biochem J* 141:683, 1974.

176. FOLK JE, FINLAYSON JS: The ε-(γ-glutamyl)lysine crosslink and the catalytic role of transglutaminases. *Adv Prot Chem* 31:1, 1977.

177. LORAND L, LOSOWSKY MS, MILOSZEWSKI KJM: Human factor XIII: Fibrin-stabilizing factor. *Prog Hemost Thromb* 5:245, 1980.

178. LORAND L, GRAY AJ, BROWN K, CREDO RB, CURTIS CG, DOMANIK RA, STERNBERG P: Dissociation of the subunit structure of fibrin stabilizing factor during activation of the zymogen. *Biochem Biophys Res Commun* 56:914, 1974.

179. FOLK JE, CHUNG SI: Blood coagulation factor XIII: Relationship of some biological properties to subunit structure, in Reich E, Rifkin DB, Show E (eds): *Proteases and Biological Control*. Cold Spring Harbor Lab, 1975, p 157.

180. TAMAKI T, AOKI N: Cross-linking of α2-plasmin inhibitor to fibrin catalyzed by activated fibrin-stabilizing factor. *J Biol Chem* 257:14767, 1982.

181. PISANO JJ, BRONZERT TJ, PEYTON MP, FINLAYSON JS: ε-(γ-glutamyl)lysine cross-link: Determination in fibrin from normal and factor XIII deficient individuals. *Ann NY Acad Sci* 202:98, 1972.

182. LORAND L: Fibrinoligase: The fibrin-stabilizing factor system of blood plasma. *Ann NY Acad Sci* 202:6, 1972.

183. SHEN LL, HERMANS J, MCDONAGH J, MCDONAGH RP, CARR M: Effects of calcium ion and covalent crosslinking on formation and elasticity of fibrin gels. *Thromb Res* 6:255, 1975.

184. SHEN L, LORAND L: Contribution of fibrin stabilization to clot strength. *J Clin Invest* 71:1336, 1983.

185. TAMAKI T, AOKI N: Cross-linking of α2-plasmin inhibitor and fibronectin to fibrin by fibrin-stabilizing factor. *Biochim Biophys Acta* 661:280, 1981.

186. ICHINOSE A, AOKI N: Reversible cross-linking of α2-plasmin inhibitor to fibrinogen by fibrin-stabilizing factor. *Biochim Biophys Acta* 706:158, 1982.

187. CARMASSI F, CHUNG SI: Regulation of fibrinolysis by factor XIII. *Prog Fibrinolysis* 6:281, 1983.

188. ICHINOSE A, TAMAKI T, AOKI N: Factor XIII-mediated cross-linking of NH2-terminal peptide of α2-plasmin inhibitor to fibrin. *FEBS Lett* 153:369, 1983.

189. KIMURA S, AOKI N: Cross-linking site in fibrinogen for α2-plasmin inhibitor. *J Biol Chem* 261:15591, 1986.

190. SAKATA Y, AOKI N: Cross-linking of α2-plasmin inhibitor to fibrin by fibrin-stabilizing factor. *J Clin Invest* 65:290, 1980.

191. SAKATA Y, AOKI N: Significance of cross-linking of α2-plasmin inhibitor to fibrin in inhibition of fibrinolysis and in hemostasis. *J Clin Invest* 69:536, 1982.

192. MOSHER DF: Cross-linking of cold-insoluble globulin by fibrin-stabilizing factor. *J Biol Chem* 250:6614, 1975.

193. MOSHER DF, SCHAD PE, KLEINMAN HK: Cross-linking of fibronectin to collagen by blood coagulation factor XIIIa. *J Clin Invest* 64:781, 1979.

194. GRINNELL F, FELD M, MINTER D: Fibroblast adhesion to fibrinogen and fibrin substrata: Requirement for cold-insoluble globulin (plasma fibronectin). *Cell* 19:517, 1980.

195. DUCKERT F: Documentation of the plasma factor XIII deficiency in man. *Ann NY Acad Sci* 202:190, 1972.

196. MUI PTK, GANGULY P: Cross-linking of actin and fibrin by fibrin-stabilizing factor. *Am J Physiol* 233:H346, 1977.

197. COHEN I, YOUNG-BANDALA L, BLANKENBERG TA, SIEFRING GE, BRUNER-LORAND J: Fibrinoligase-catalyzed cross-linking of myosin from platelet and skeletal muscle. *Arch Biochem Biophys* 192:100, 1979.

198. COHEN I, GLASER T, VEIS A, BRUNER-LORAND J: Ca2+-dependent cross-linking processes in human platelets. *Biochim Biophys Acta* 676:137, 1981.

199. HADA M, KAMINSKI M, BOCKENSTEDT P, MCDONAGH J: Covalent cross-linking of von Willebrand factor to fibrin. *Blood* 68:95, 1986.

200. BOCKENSTEDT P, MCDONAGH J, HANDIN RI: Binding and covalent cross-linking of purified von Willebrand factor to native monomeric collagen. *J Clin Invest* 78:551, 1986.

201. BALE MD, MOSHER DF: Thrombospondin is a substrate for blood coagulation factor XIIIa. *Biochemistry* 25:5667, 1986.

202. FRANCIS RT, MCDONAGH J, MANN KG: Factor V is a substrate for the transamidase factor XIIIa. *J Biol Chem* 261:9787, 1986.

203. IKEMATSU S, MCDONAGH RP, REISNER HM, SKRZYNIA C, MCDONAGH J: Immunochemical studies of human factor XIII. *J Lab Clin Med* 97:662, 1981.

204. SKRZYNIA C, REISNER HM, MCDONAGH J: Characterization of the catalytic subunit of factor XIII by radioimmunoassay. *Blood* 60:1089, 1982.

205. BOHN H, BECKER W, TROBISCH H: Die molekulare Struktur der fibrinstabilisierenden Faktoren des Menschen. *Blut* 26:303, 1973.

206. COOKE RD, HOLBROOK JJ: The calcium-induced dissociation of human plasma clotting factor XIII. *Biochem J* 141:79, 1974.

207. BANNERJEE D, MOSESSON MW: Characteristics of platelet protransglutaminase (factor XIII)-binding activity in human plasma. *Thromb Res* 7:323, 1975.

208. FEAR JD, JACKSON P, GRAY C, MILOSZEWSKI KJA, LOSOWSKY MS: Localization of factor XIII in human tissues using an immunoperioxidase technique. *J Clin Pathol* 37:560, 1984.

209. ADANY R, KISS A, THOMAZY V, MUSZBEK L: Origin of human factor XIII. *Thromb Haemost* [suppl] 54:147, 1985.

210. LEE SY, CHUNG SI: Biosynthesis and degradation of plasma protransglutaminase (factor XIII). *Fed Proc* 35:1486, 1976.

211. IKEMATSU S: An approach to the metabolism of factor XIII. *Acta Haematol Jap* 44:1499, 1981.

212. NAGY JA, HENRIKSSON P, MCDONAGH J: Biosynthesis of factor XIII b subunit by human hepatoma cell lines. *Blood* 68:1272, 1986.

213. CHUNG SI: Comparative studies on tissue transaminase and factor XIII. *Ann NY Acad Sci* 202:240, 1972.

214. KIESSELBACH TH, WAGNER RH: Demonstration of factor XIII in human megakaryocytes by a fluorescent antibody technique. *Ann NY Acad Sci* 202:318, 1972.

215. HENRIKSSON P, BECKER S, LYNCH G, MCDONAGH J: Identification of intracellular factor XIII in human monocytes and macrophages. *J Clin Invest* 76:528, 1985.

216. MUSZBEK L, ADANY R, SZEGEDI G, PLOGAR J, KAVAI M: Factor XIII of blood coagulation in human monocytes. *Thromb Res* 37:401, 1985.

217. RIDER DM, MCDONAGH RP, MCDONAGH J: A possible contributory role of the platelet in the formation of plasma factor XIII. *Br J Haematol* 39:579, 1978.

218. MCDONAGH J, MCDONAGH RP, DELAGE JM, WAGNER RH: Factor XIII in human plasma and platelets. *J Clin Invest* 48:940, 1969.

219. LOPACIUK S, LOVETTE KM, MCDONAGH J, CHUANG HYK, MCDONAGH RP: Subcellular distribution of fibrinogen and factor XIII in human blood platelets. *Thromb Res* 8:453, 1976.

220. SIXMA JJ, VAN DEN BERG A, SCHIPHORST M, GUEZE HJ, MCDONAGH J: Immunocytochemical localization of albumin and factor XIII in thin cryo sections of human blood platelets. *Thromb Haemost* 51:388, 1984.

221. WEISBERG LJ, SHIU DT, GREENBERG CS, KAN YW, SHUMAN MA: Localization of the gene for coagulation factor XIII a-chain to chromosome 6 and identification of sites of synthesis. *J Clin Invest* 79:649, 1987.

222. WOLPL A, LATTKE H, BOARD PG, ARNOLD R, SCHMEISER T, KUBANEK B, ROBIN-WINN M, PICHELMAYR R, GOLDMANN SF: Coagulation factor XIII a and b subunits in bone marrow and liver transplantation. *Transplantation* 43:151, 1987.

223. AURON PE, WEBB AC, ROSENWASSER LJ, MUCCI SF, RICH A, WOLFF SM, DINARELLO CA: Nucleotide sequence of human monocyte interleukin 1 precursor cDNA. *Proc Natl Acad Sci USA* 81:7907, 1984.

224. WALLNER BP, MATTALIANO RJ, HESSION C, CATE RL, TIZARD R, SINCLAIR LK, FOELLER C, CHOW EP, BROWNING JL, RAMACHANDRAN KL, PEPINSKY RB: Cloning and expression of human lipocortin, a phospholipase A2 inhibitor with potential anti-inflammatory activity. *Nature* 320:77, 1986.

225. JAYE M, HOWK R, BURGESS W, RICCA GA, CHIU IM, RAVERA MW, O'BRIEN SJ, MODI WS, MACIAG T, DROHAN WN: Human endothelial cell growth factor: Cloning, nucleotide sequence, and chromosome localization. *Science* 233:541, 1986.

226. KUROKAWA T, SASADA R, IWANE M, IGARASHI K: Cloning and expression of cDNA encoding human basic fibroblast growth factor. *FEBS Lett* 213:189, 1987.

227. YE RD, WUN TC, SADLER JE: cDNA cloning and expression in Escherichia coli of a plasminogen activator inhibitor from human placenta. *J Biol Chem* 262:3718, 1987.

228. BARBUI T, CARTEI G, CHISESI T, DINI E: Electroimmunoassay of plasma subunits-A and -S in a case of congenital fibrin stabilizing factor deficiency. *Thromb Diath Haemorrh* 32:124, 1974.

229. BARBUI T, RODEGHIERO F, DINI E, MARIANI G, PAPA ML, DE BIASI R, MURILLO RC, UMANA CM: Subunits A and S inheritance in four families with congenital factor XIII deficiency. *Br J Haematol* 38:267, 1978.

230. RODEGHIERO F, MORBIN M, BARBUI T: Subunit a of factor XIII regulates subunit b plasma concentration. *Thromb Haemost* 46:621, 1981.

231. FEAR JD, MILOSZEWSKI KJA, LOSOWSKY MS: The half life of factor XIII in the management of inherited deficiency. *Thromb Haemost* 49:102, 1983.

232. LEWIS SD, JANUS TJ, LORAND L, SHAFER JA: Regulation of formation of factor XIIIa by its fibrin substrates. *Biochemistry* 24:6772, 1985.

233. CREDO RB, CURTIS CG, LORAND L: α-chain domain of fibrinogen controls generation of fibrinoligase (coagulation factor XIIIa). *Biochemistry* 20:3770, 1981.

234. CURTIS CG, BROWN KL, CREDO RB, DOMANIK RA, GRAY A, STENBERG P, LORAND L: Calcium-dependent unmasking of active center cysteine during activation of fibrin stabilizing factor. *Biochemistry* 13:3774, 1974.

235. LEWIS BA, FREYSSINET J-M, HOLBROOK JJ: An equilibrium study of metal ion binding to human plasma coagulation factor XIII. *Biochem J* 169:397, 1978.

236. MCDONAGH J, MCDONAGH RP: Alternative pathways for the activation of factor XIII. *Br J Haematol* 30:465, 1975.

237. HENRIKSSON P, NILSSON IM, OHLSSON K, STENBERG P: Granulocyte elastase activation and degradation of factor XIII. *Thromb Res* 18:343, 1980.

238. SCHRODE J, CHUNG SI, FOLK JE: Thrombin cleavage products of human placental transglutaminase. *Fed Proc* 35:1487, 1976.

239. NISHIDA Y, IKEMATSU S, FUKUTAKE K, FUJIMAKI M, FUKUTAKE K, KAKISHITA E: A new rapid and simple assay for factor XIII activity using dancylcadaverine incorporation and gel filtration. *Thromb Res* 36:123, 1984.

240. BALLERINI G, GUERRA S, RODEGHIERO F, CASTAMAN G: A contribution of the pathology of acquired plasma factor XIII deficiency. *Semin Thromb Hemost* 11:357, 1985.

241. HENRIKSSON P, HEDNER U, NILSSON IM: Factor XIII (fibrin stabilizing factor) in Henoch-Schönlein's purpura. *Acta Paediatr Scand* 66:273, 1977.

242. TRIANTAPHYLLOPOULOS DC: Factor XIII consumption as an indicator of thrombin generation. *J Lab Clin Med* 84:74, 1974.

243. GREENBERG CS, MIRAGLIA CC, RICKLES FR, SHUMAN MA: Cleavage of blood coagulation factor XIII and fibrinogen by thrombin during in vitro clotting. *J Clin Invest* 75:1463, 1985.

244. BILAND L, DUCKERT F, PRISENDER S, NYMAN D: Quantitative estimation of coagulation factors in liver disease. *Thromb Haemost* 39:646, 1978.

245. CUCUIANU M, RUS HG, CRISTEA A, NICULESCU F, BEDELEANU D, PORUTIU D, ROMAN S: Clinical studies on plasma fibronectin and factor XIII; with special reference to hyperlipoproteinemia. *Clin Chim Acta* 147:273, 1985.

246. LEWIS JH: Hemorrhagic disease associated with inhibitors of fibrin crosslinkage. *Ann NY Acad Sci* 202:213, 1972.

247. KLINGEMANN HG, EGBRING R, HAVEMANN K: Incomplete fibrin formation and highly elevated factor XIII activity in multiple myeloma. *Scand J Haematol* 27:253, 1981.

248. KLOCZKO J, WOJTUKIEWICZ M, BIELAWIEC M, ZARZYCKA B, KINALSKA I: Plasma factor XIII and some other haemostasis parameters in patients with diabetic angiopathy. *Acta Haematol (Basel)* 76:81, 1986.

249. YOSHIOKA K, MIYATA H, URAOKA Y, MAKI S: Plasma factor XIII levels in children with renal disease. *Nephron* 27:19, 1981.

250. BOARD PG, REID M, SERJEANTSON S: The gene for coagulation factor XIII a subunit (F13A) is distal to HLA on chromosome 6. *Hum Genet* 67:406, 1984.

251. OLAISEN B, GEDDE-DAHL T, TEISBERG P, THORSBY E, SIVERTS A, JONASSEN R, WILHELMY MC: A structural locus for coagulation factor XIII A (F13A) is located distal to the HLA region on chromosome 6p in man. *Am J Hum Genet* 37:215, 1985.

252. REID KBM, BENTLEY DR, CAMPBELL RD, CHUNG LP, SIM RB, KRISTENSEN T, TACK BF: Complement system proteins which interact with C3b or C4b. *Immunol Today* 7:230, 1986.

253. ICHINOSE A, BOTTENUS RE, LEOB KR, DAVIE EW: Isolation and characterization of the genes for the a and b subunits of factor XIII. *Thromb Haemost* 58:500, 1987.

253a. ICHINOSE A, DAVIE EW: Characterization of the gene for the a subunit of human factor XIII (plasma transglutaminase), a blood coagulation factor. *Proc Natl Acad Sci USA*, 85:5829, 1988.

254. BOARD PG: Genetic polymorphism of the a subunit of human coagulation factor XIII. *Am J Hum Genet* 31:116, 1979.

255. CASTLE SL, BOARD PG: An extended survey of the genetic polymorphism at the human coagulation factor XIII: A subunit structural locus. *Hum Hered* 35:101, 1985.

255a. ZOGHBI HY, DAIGER SP, MCCALL AE, O'BRIEN WE, BEAUDET AL: Extensive DNA polymorphism at the Factor XIIIa (F13A) locus and linkage to HLA. *Am J Hum Genet* 42:877, 1988.

256. BOARD PG: Genetic polymorphism of the b subunit of human coagulation factor XIII. *Am J Hum Genet* 32:348, 1980.

257. FUKUI H: Hemophilia and the related diseases. *Nihon Rinsho* 41:704, 1983.

258. AOKI N, SAITO H, KAMIYA T, KOIE K, SAKATA Y, KOBAKURA M: Congenital deficiency of α₂-plasmin inhibitor associated with severe hemorrhagic tendency. *J Clin Invest* 63:877, 1979.

259. HAHN L, LUNDBERG PA, TEGER-NILSSON AC: Congenital hypofibrinogenemia and recurrent abortion. *Br J Obstet Gynaecol* 85:790, 1978.

260. EVRON S, ANTEBY SO, BRZEZINSKY A, SAMUELOFF A, ELDOR A: Congenital afibrinogenemia and recurrent early abortion: A case report. *Eur J Obstet Gynecol Reprod Biol* 19:307, 1985.

261. MCDONAGH J, CARRELL N: Disorders of fibrinogen structure and function, in Colman RW, Hirsh J, Marder VJ, Salzman EW (eds): *Hemostasis and Thrombosis.* Philadelphia, Lippincott, 1987, p 301.

262. LORAND L, CAMPBELL-WILKES LK, COOPERSTEIN L: A filter paper assay for transamidating enzymes using radioactive amine substrates. *Anal Biochem* 50:623, 1972.

263. CASTLE S, BOARD PG, ANDERSON RAM: Genetic heterogeneity of factor XIII deficiency: First description of unstable a subunits. *Br J Haematol* 48:337, 1981.

264. UKITA M, MIKAMI T, MIKAMI K, KITAHARA T, KATO M, KANI T: Studies on abnormal protein in seven patients with congenital factor XIII deficiency. *Rinsho Byori* 24:281, 1976.

265. FORMAN WB, BYER R, HADADY M, KRILL C, LUBIN A: Congenital fibrin stabilizing factor deficiency (FSF, XIII): Evidence for Dys-FSF. *Blood* 50 (Suppl 1):266, 1977.

266. TROBISCH H, EGBRING R: Substitution treatment of factor XIII deficiency with a new factor XIII concentrate. *Dtsch Med Wochenschr* 97:499, 1972.

267. KURATSUJI T, OIKAWA T, FUKUMOTO T, SHIMIZU S, IWASAKI Y, TOMITA Y, MEGURO T, YAMADA K: Factor XIII deficiency in antibiotic-associated pseudomembranous colitis and its treatment with factor XIII concentrate. *Haemostasis* 11:229, 1982.

CHAPTER 86

FACTOR VIII AND FACTOR V:
Biochemistry and Pathophysiology

GORDON A. VEHAR
RICHARD M. LAWN
EDWARD G. D. TUDDENHAM
WILLIAM I. WOOD

1. Hemophilia A (classic hemophilia) is a bleeding disorder characterized by a deficiency in the activity of a key component of the coagulation cascade, factor VIII. The disease, with rare exception, is confined to males, whose sons will be normal and whose daughters will be obligate carriers.

2. Factor VIII functions in the middle of the coagulation cascade. It appears to function as a cofactor in the activation of factor X to factor Xa in a reaction catalyzed by factor IXa on a phospholipid surface. The activity of factor VIII is greatly enhanced by limited proteolytic cleavage by thrombin and factor Xa. This activation results in an effective amplification of the coagulation signal through this step of the cascade. Factor VIII is inactivated by limited proteolysis catalyzed by factor Xa or by activated protein C, thereby limiting the coagulation response.

3. As a result of defective fibrin formation, afflicted individuals suffer joint and muscle hemorrhage, easy bruising, and prolonged bleeding from wounds. Notably, platelet function is not affected, resulting in normal blood loss from minor cuts and abrasions.

4. The defect arises from a variety of mutations within the factor VIII gene, which is located in the q28 region of the human X chromosome. The gene comprises 26 exons and spans 186,000 base pairs. The cause of hemophilia A in a number of individuals has been associated with a variety of deletion and point mutations that appear to result, in large part, in truncated molecules. A number of restriction fragment length polymorphisms have been identified that allow for improved methods of prenatal diagnosis and carrier detection.

5. The cDNA sequence has revealed that factor VIII is synthesized as a large precursor molecule (2332 amino acids). The sequence of the protein has shown that it has considerable sequence similarity with ceruloplasmin and coagulation factor V. The portions of factor VIII that are involved in the function are located in the amino-terminal and carboxy-terminal segments of the precursor and remain noncovalently associated following proteolysis in the central highly glycosylated region. Limited proteolysis associated with activation and inactivation occurs within these functional domains of the protein.

6. Treatment of hemophilia A is accomplished by infusions of concentrates prepared from human plasma. The half-life of such preparations is approximately 12 h. While such therapy is effective in most cases, approximately 15 percent of afflicted individuals eventually develop neutralizing antibodies that complicate further therapy.

7. Factor V is a coagulant protein that is very similar in structure and function to factor VIII. It functions as a cofactor in the reaction following factor VIII in the coagulation cascade. Factor V functions as a cofactor in the activation of prothrombin in a reaction catalyzed by factor Xa on a phospholipid surface. Factor V is subject to proteolytic activation and inactivation similar to that seen for factor VIII. Individuals afflicted with a deficiency in functional factor V are extremely rare and are subject to severe bleeding episodes that can be treated with infusions of fresh frozen plasma.

INTRODUCTION AND HISTORICAL PERSPECTIVES

Hemophilia is one of the first human genetic diseases to have been reported. The writers of the Talmud noted an affliction in certain families whose male children died after circumcision.[1] Circumcision was therefore waived for boys whose older brothers or cousins had died after the procedure. A sixteenth century report noted the existence of lifelong bleeding disorders and their familial occurrence.[2] An anonymous report attributed to G. W. Connsbruck published in 1793 has the distinction of being the first in the modern medical literature to clearly describe a hemophilic disorder with an X-linked pattern of inheritance.[3] A man and two sons of his sister were affected with a severe bleeding tendency, the older son dying of the disease.

The report by John Otto in 1803[4] is generally accepted as the first in the medical literature to arouse general interest. He noted the pattern of transmission of the disorder to males through unaffected females, and described the bleeding symptoms and potential treatment regimens. Otto's paper attracted interest on both sides of the Atlantic, giving rise to several reviews and many individual case reports and family studies.

The first major review of this subject was compiled by Nasse in 1820.[5] He asserted that the bleeding tendency occurred only in males and was transmitted to them by normal females through their marriage with normal males. No mention was made of the possibility that a bleeder male could pass the disease to ostensibly normal daughters and thence to bleeder grandsons.

Nonstandard abbreviations used in this chapter include: AHG = antihemophilic globulin; DDAVP = l-desamino-8-D-arginine vasopressin; VIIIR:Ag = factor VIII–related antigen; and VIIIC:Ag = factor VIII coagulant antigen; vWF = von Willebrand factor; and vWF:Ag-von Willebrand factor antigen.

The first recorded usage and therefore presumably the invention of the term *Haemophilie* (sic) was by Hopff in 1828.[6] The cases referred to in this dissertation were four brothers who variously bled to death following trivial injury, or in the last case, a ruptured tumor of the thigh.

In 1893 Almroth Wright discovered the prolonged clotting time of hemophilic blood.[7] Whereas normal blood took 5½ to 6 min to clot in a capillary tube, blood from a boy with severe hemophilia took over 10 min to clot. Thomas Addis[8,9] showed that the prolonged clotting time of hemophilic blood could be corrected by a fraction from normal blood. This fraction was studied by Patek and Taylor in 1937 and termed *antihemophilic globulin* (AHG).[10]

A further advance came when quantitative assays were devised for measuring the correcting fraction.[11,12] Hemophilia came to be defined as the condition resulting from deficiency of AHG, inherited in an X-linked manner, although occurring in sporadic cases due to new mutation.

In 1952 three groups simultaneously reported that classic X-linked hemophilia itself could be due to a deficiency of more than one factor.[13-15] This was based on finding cross-correction of the clotting defect in some hemophiliac's blood by that from other clinically identical cases. The vast majority of hemophilias are now known to be caused by a deficiency of one of two X-linked factors: factor VIII deficiency (hemophilia A) is responsible for approximately 85 percent of all hereditary bleeding disorders, while factor IX deficiency (hemophilia B) accounts for most of the remainder.

Hemophilia has had a major impact on world history, stemming from the occurrence of the disorder in the offspring of Queen Victoria.[16] Her daughters' marriages disseminated hemophilia throughout the royal families of Europe. Unfortunately, we may never know whether the deficiency was of factor VIII or factor IX since all of her hemophilic descendants had died by 1945.

In 1953 Larrieu and Soulier[17] discovered that patients with the autosomal dominant bleeding disorder first described by E. von Willebrand in 1926[18] also had low factor VIII levels in their blood. It was subsequently shown that an antigen detected by antiserums against partially purified factor VIII was reduced in the blood of patients with von Willebrand disease (vWD) but present in that of hemophilia A patients.[19] This antigen was termed *factor VIII–related antigen* (VIIIR:Ag) and gave rise to the idea that factor VIII and its related antigen are a single entity with multiple functions. This hypothesis, however, conflicted with the genetic evidence and also with a growing body of biochemical data showing that the factor VIII coagulant activity could be separated from the "related antigen."[20-23]

A full understanding of the pathophysiology and genetics of these various disorders was long delayed by the difficulty of purifying factor VIII to homogeneity. Eventually this problem was surmounted in conjunction with the cloning of the gene for factor VIII.[24-27] It is now clear that hemophilia A is due to any one of a series of possible defects in the factor VIII gene which is located near the tip of the long arm of the X chromosome; whereas von Willebrand disease is caused by defects in a gene coding for von Willebrand factor (formerly factor VIII–related antigen) located on the short arm of chromosome 12.[28] The low factor VIII levels in vWD are explained by the observation that vWF acts as a protective carrier for factor VIII, so that depressed levels of vWF in some manner lead to lower levels of factor VIII. Recent advances in protein chem-

istry and recombinant DNA technology have produced a comprehensive account both of normal coagulation and of the molecular genetics of hemophilia. In this chapter we describe the clinical features of hemophilia A and what is known of the underlying molecular genetics. A similar summary is presented on factor V, a coagulation protein very similar to factor VIII both structurally and functionally.

FACTOR VIII

Structure of Factor VIII

The structure of human factor VIII was determined by a combination of direct protein sequence data and nucleotide sequence information. The cloned cDNA sequence[25-27,29] contains an open reading frame that codes for a 2332–amino acid protein preceded by a 19-residue hydrophobic secretion signal peptide. This sequence gives a translated molecular weight of 265,000 which, with added carbohydrate, is large enough to code for the 330,000–molecular weight form of the molecule reported by one group.[30]

The protein is composed of distinct domains termed A, B, and C, with three homologous copies of the A domain and two copies of the C domain.[25,29] These domains occur within the factor VIII molecule in the order A1-A2-B-A3-C1-C2 beginning from the amino terminus of the protein (Fig. 86-1). Each of the triplicated A domains of factor VIII contains about 350 amino acids of approximately 30 percent sequence identity. Unexpectedly, these domains have approximately 35 percent sequence homology to the plasma protein ceruloplasmin,[29] a copper-binding protein of molecular weight 130,000.[31,32] Ceruloplasmin itself contains the triplicated A domain structure that differs from factor VIII in that the domains are contiguous whereas these segments of factor VIII are separated by either a short acidic peptide (between A1 and A2) or the B domain (between A2 and A3) (see Fig. 86-1).[29,31,32] The significance of sequence homology of a coagulation protein with a copper-binding protein is not known at present. An interesting proposal has come from the detection of a tightly bound iron atom in factor IX preparations,[33] raising the possibility of shared metal ion chelation as part of the mechanism of interaction of factor VIII with factor IX.

Ceruloplasmin is known to bind six copper atoms and possesses iron-oxidizing activity. Although neither factor VIII nor the closely related factor V have oxidase activity, factor V is known to bind a single copper atom.[34] Similar studies using purified factor VIII have not been reported. The role of such metal ions in factor VIII will be the subject of future experimentation.

The C1 and C2 domains are located carboxy-terminal to the A3 domain (Fig. 86-1). C1 and C2 each contain approximately 150 amino acids and share approximately 40 percent sequence homology.[24] The C domains also show weak homology with the first 150 amino acids of the discoidin lectins of *Dictyostelium* (proteins with a total of approximately 250 amino acids).[29] The functional significance of this lectin homology is not clear at present.

The A2 and A3 domains are separated by the B domain, consisting of 908 amino acids. This region of the factor VIII molecule is not homologous with any other known protein and contains 19 of the 25 potential asparagine-linked glycosylation

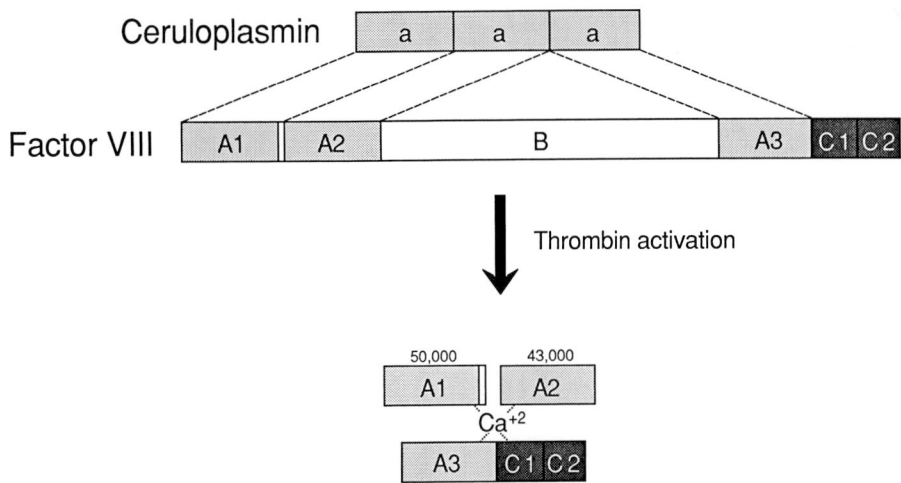

Fig 86-1 Single chain factor VIII, its thrombin-activated form, and the relationship to ceruloplasmin. The central bar represents the 2332-amino acid single chain form predicted from the cDNA sequence.[21-27,29] The positioning of the various domains is as indicated (see text for description). The upper bar depicts the triplicated domain structure of ceruloplasmin. The bottom figure represents the thrombin-activated form of the molecule. The subunits are probably held together by calcium ions.

sites of the molecule.[25-27,29] This large segment of factor VIII has no known function other than to the proteolytically removed during activation (see below).

The Factor VIII Protein

Factor VIII functions by accelerating the proteolytic activation of factor X by factor IXa.[35,36] This reaction requires calcium ions and a phospholipid surface, with factor VIII functioning as a cofactor.[37-39] This cofactor activity is dramatically increased by the proteolytic activation of factor VIII itself.[38,40-42] The exact mechanism whereby factor VIII exerts its role on this reaction is currently under investigation in a number of laboratories.

The low concentration of factor VIII in plasma (200 ng/ml), its instability, its association with von Willebrand factor (vWF), and the sensitivity of the protein to proteolytic cleavage have all combined to stymie its purification until recently. The interaction of factor VIII with vWF was not appreciated until the mid-1970s, a fact that must be borne in mine when reading the older literature. Materials that were termed factor VIII were, in fact, the factor VIII/vWF complex. Since the bulk of protein in such preparations is vWF, immunologic assays to detect this "factor VIII antigen" (also referred to as "factor VIII–related antigen") have no bearing upon factor VIII levels. Assays specific for factor VIII protein are usually denoted by the term *factor VIII coagulant antigen* (VIIIC:Ag).[43] More detailed discussions of this subject can be obtained in recent reviews.[44,45]

The extensive proteolytic processing of factor VIII complicates the identification of the circulating form(s). Immunologic procedures have failed to detect factor VIII species greater than M_r 240,000 in fresh plasma.[46,47] Attempts to isolate a single chain form of factor VIII from bovine, porcine, and human plasmas have therefore been unsuccessful, although a small amount of the single chain form was detected in one preparation from fresh cryoprecipitate.[30] These observations suggest that factor VIII is also secreted as a full-length precursor like factor V (see below), but that factor VIII is rapidly fragmented to forms of lower molecular weight either in vivo or during in vitro sample handling.

The proteolytic processing of factor VIII from bovine, porchine, and human plasmas results in a heterogeneous series of polypeptides.[27,28,30,48-56] The multiple fragments associated

with these factor VIII preparations can be divided into two groupings: One region of variable molecular weight, comprised of the A1-A2-B domains; and a second made up of the A3-C1-C2 domains. The cleavage freeing the A3-C1-C2 subunit occurs very rapidly. A number of secondary cleavages occur within the B domain, generating a series of A1-A2-B polypeptides that include different extents of the B domain. Since the B domain has yet to be associated with any role in coagulation,[52,54,57-59] all of the A1-A2-B polypeptides ranging in molecular weight from 90,000 to 210,000 appear to be functionally equivalent.

Purified preparations of factor VIII have specific activities that range between 4500 and 10,000 units per milligram of protein. A unit of factor VIII activity has been defined as that amount of activity present in one milliliter of pooled human plasma. The coagulant activity of factor VIII (and factor V) is dramatically increased by catalytic amounts of thrombin.[40] This proteolytic activation is the result of several cleavages within both of the factor VIII regions and is summarized in Fig. 86-1. The A3-C1-C2 subunit is cleaved at arginine-1689,[26,29,52,53] releasing an acidic peptide and decreasing its molecular weight from 80,000 to 73,000. In addition, thrombin rapidly removes the remaining B domain from the A1-A2-B region by cleavage at arginine-740,[26] resulting in the transient appearance of a polypeptide chain of M_r 90,000 (composed of A1-A2 domains). The generation of this subunit of human factor VIII was originally proposed to be associated with the maximal thrombin-generated activity;[30,60] subsequent work has indicated that an additional cleavage at arginine-372 results in the most active form.[52-54,61] This cleavage between the A1 and A2 domains generates fragments of M_r 50,000 and 43,000 from the M_r 90,000 polypeptide.[52,53]

Factor VIII is inactivated by activated protein C.[48,62,63] Protein C is a vitamin K–dependent serine protease that circulates in plasma in a zymogen form and is activated by the thrombin/thrombomodulin complex.[64-72] The potent anticoagulant properties in plasma of activated protein C are due to its proteolysis of factors V and VIII.[48,62,63,65] This reaction requires the presence of an additional vitamin K–dependent protein, protein S.[73,74] The inactivation of factor VIII is due to cleavage at arginine-336,[53] resulting in the generation of a fragment of molecular weight 45,000[53,63] representing the first 336 amino acids of factor VIII.

The expression of cloned factor VIII in mammalian tissue culture cells has led to direct tests of the function of various domains of the protein. Thrombin activation studies had previously implied that the B domain is not required for coagulant activity. This has now been demonstrated directly by recombinant DNA expression of a factor VIII cDNA with the ~1000-amino acid B domain removed.[57-59] Even though the central one-third of the protein is absent, these truncated forms of factor VIII retain apparently normal coagulation activity and thrombin activation. These proteins also bind von Willebrand factor.[59] Thus, the role, if any, of the B domain remains unclear.

The Factor VIII Gene

By obtaining overlapping cDNA and genomic clones, both the 9000 base pairs of factor VIII cDNA[25-27] and the 186,000 base pairs of the gene[24] have been isolated. When the full-length factor VIII cDNA is spliced to viral promoters and transfected into mammalian tissue culture cells, it directs the synthesis and secretion of biologically active factor VIII that can correct the clotting deficiency of hemophilic plasma. Purified, recombinant DNA–derived factor VIII appears, by all available criteria, to be equivalent to the plasma-derived protein. These criteria include electrophoretic mobility, specific cleavages by the proteases thrombin, factor Xa, and activated protein C, binding to von Willebrand factor, and neutralization by specific antibodies.[25-27,56] Recombinant DNA–derived factor VIII corrects the bleeding time in hemophilic dogs[75] and should provide a safer and more highly purified therapeutic alternative to currently available plasma concentrates.

The large size of the protein is reflected in the size of the gene. The factor VIII gene consists of 26 exons separated by 25 noncoding introns, and spans 186,000 base pairs (Fig. 86-2).[24] This represents about 0.1 percent of the human X chromosome. The human factor VIII gene has two notable features. It contains one unusually large exon of 3106 bp (average size for an exon is 75 to 200 bp). Also, an extremely large intron of 32,000 bp is present between exons 22 and 23. Only about 5 percent of the gene is made up of protein-encoding exons, which is typical for the genes of vertebrates. Although it might take hours to transcribe such a large gene into RNA, there apparently has been no effective selective pressure to reduce the relative intron size of this gene. The structure of the normal factor VIII gene and the DNA sequence of its exons form the basis of comparison

for the factor VIII genes of hemophiliacs, which will be the subject of a later section.

As discussed previously, the translated DNA sequence showed that factor VIII contains three types of internal domains: a triplicated A domain, a duplicated C domain, and the unique B domain. Presumably, the repeated domains arose from intragenic duplication and subsequent DNA divergence. The sequence homology of factor VIII, factor V, and ceruloplasmin suggests that these genes arose from a common ancestor, which itself was a product of intragenic triplication. Limited homology exists to small, copper-binding proteins of bacteria, fungae, and plants, allowing the construction of an evolutionary scenario of duplication and divergence from a single metal-binding domain.[76] Since the entire B domain of factor VIII is encoded by the unusually long 3106–base pair exon,[24] one could speculate that part of a processed gene may have interrupted two of the A domains of a common protogene.

Site of Synthesis

The cellular site of synthesis of factor VIII had been ambiguous.[77] Early studies suggested the liver as a major site of synthesis, but extrahepatic sources such as spleen and lung had been implicated and it had long been obvious that liver disease did not lead to hemophilia. The cloning of the factor VIII gene provided hybridization probes for the detection of factor VIII messenger RNA in cells. This procedure avoids misinterpretation due to the entrapment of plasma factor VIII in tissues and ambiguities about sites of synthesis and storage that affect antigen-based studies. Despite the low levels of circulating factor VIII, the mRNA is synthesized in a variety of tissues including liver, spleen, lymph nodes, pancreas, kidney, muscle, placenta, and separated hepatocyte cells.[78] No factor VIII mRNA could be detected in either hepatic sinusoidal endothelial cells or umbilical vein endothelial cells. Thus, the sites of factor VIII synthesis are surprisingly diverse, although the hepatocyte is a major source of plasma factor VIII.[78,79] The failure of factor VIII levels to decrease during chronic liver disease may reflect the many abnormalities associated with liver failure, such as clearance, acute-phase response and synthesis of protein C, an inactivator of factor VIII. It should also be noted that while endothelial cells are a major site of synthesis of vWF, they appear to produce little or no factor VIII.

Fig 86-2 The human factor VIII gene and its encoded protein. The human factor VIII gene, spanning 186,000 nucleotides, is shown with exons numbered from the 5' to the 3' end. Below the gene is shown the single chain primary translation product (minus the prepeptide), divided into the A, B, and C regions discussed in the text. The entire intermediate B domain, which is eliminated during activation, is encoded by the 3-kb exon 14. The locations of the 50,000-, 43,000-, and 73,000-dalton subunits of the thrombin-activated protein are shown at the bottom. (From Lawn et al.[154] Used by permission.)

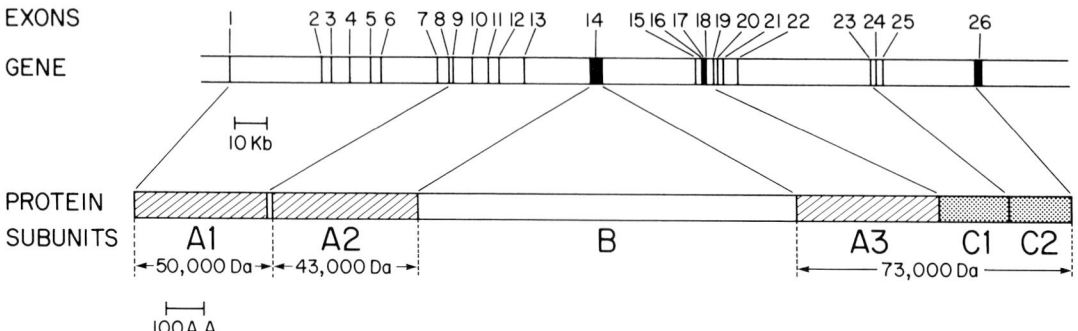

MOLECULAR PATHOLOGY OF HEMOPHILIA

Hemophilia A is a classic example of X-linked inheritance. Population genetic considerations lead to the conclusion that new mutations must account for the observed incidence of X-linked hemophilia. Haldane observed in 1935 that in an equilibrium population, one-third of affected X chromosomes will be found in males and two-thirds in females.[80] Due to the low reproductive fitness associated with the disease before modern forms of treatment, almost one-third of the mutant alleles will be lost per generation. Therefore, to maintain a constant frequency in the population, new mutations are required, and Haldane deduced that about one-third of cases will be due to recent mutation events. Haldane also demonstrated linkage between color blindness and hemophilia.[81] Later work showed that hemophilia A is also linked to the glucose-6-phosphate dehydrogenase locus.[82] Current linkage analysis places the factor VIII locus at the distal end of the long arm of the X chromosome at Xq28→Xqter.[83] With the cloning of the factor VIII gene, it has become possible to determine the precise nature of many hemophilia-causing mutations. This work has directly demonstrated the heterogeneity of mutant factor VIII alleles and has allowed for the unequivocal documentation of *de novo* mutations in a number of affected families. The heterogeneous nature of mutations partially accounts for the variable expression of the disease.

At this writing, the factor VIII gene of about 300 hemophiliacs has been examined. Southern blot hybridization of genomic DNA with the cloned factor VIII cDNA probe is used to compare the pattern of hybridizing restriction fragments of a hemophiliac's DNA with that from a normal individual. This method readily detects partial gene deletions of greater than 100 base pairs, but can only detect those base substitution (point) mutations that happen to occur in the recognition sequence of the restriction enzyme employed. Hence, the current survey of factor VIII mutations is biased toward detecting deletions. When an aberrant hybridization pattern is observed, the altered part of the gene is localized and ultimately subjected to direct DNA sequencing or hybridization analysis with synthetic oligonucleotide probes to determine the nucleotide change that constitutes the factor VIII mutation.

To date, 11 distinct deletions and six point mutations have been detected in the factor VIII gene of hemophiliacs. All of the point mutations occur in the DNA sequence, TCGA, the recognition sequence for the restriction enzyme *Taq*I. This restriction enzyme was used in these studies because its recognition sequence includes the dinucleotide CG, which may be a site of increased mutation in human DNA. This dinucleotide is the major site of DNA methylation, and deamination of methyl cytosine can lead to C → T transitions.[84] Five of the 7 *Taq*I sites in the factor VIII gene are in a translation reading frame such that a TCGA to TTGA mutation would produce a termination codon that would lead to the production of a truncated factor VIII protein.

In the first survey of hemophilic DNAs, two such nonsense mutations were found.[85] Blot hybridization analysis of DNA from the family of one case conclusively demonstrated that the hemophilia-causing mutation first arose in the X chromosome of the affected individual. The hybridization data from this family are shown as an example of the procedure in Figure 86-3. Examples of point mutations associated with hemophilia A have now been found in five of the *Taq*I sites in the factor VIII gene. The data are summarized in Table 86-1. Some of the results are noteworthy. The mutation in exon 26[85] occurs in a severe hemophiliac, even though it predicts a truncated factor VIII missing only the 26 carboxy-terminal amino acids

Table 86-1 Factor VIII Mutations

Independent Point Mutations

Location	Codon change	Severity	Inhibitors	Reference
Exon 24, amino acid 2209	Arg → stop	Severe	Yes	85
Exon 26, amino acid 2307	Arg → stop	Severe	No	85
Exon 18, amino acid 1941	Arg → stop	Severe	No	86
Exon 18, amino acid 1941	Arg → stop	Severe	Yes	86
Exon 22, amino acid 2116	Arg → stop	Severe	No	86
Exon 22, amino acid 2116	Arg → stop	Severe	No	86
Exon 23, amino acid 2147	Arg → stop	Severe	Yes	87
Exon 26, amino acid 2307	Arg → Gln	Mild	No	88

Deletions

Exons deleted	Size of deletion	Severity	Inhibitors	Reference
Exons 23–25	39 kb	Severe	Yes	85
Exon 26	22 kb	Severe	No	85
Exons 11–22	75–100 kb	Severe	Yes	89
Exons 1–22	>127 kb	Severe	Yes	90
Exon 6	7 kb	Severe	No	91
Exon 14	2.5 kb	Severe	No	91
Exons 24–25	>7 kb	Severe	No	91
Exons 23–25	>16 kb	Severe	No	91
Exon 22	5.5 kb	Moderate	No	91
Exons 1–26	>186 kb	Severe	No	92
Exons 15–18	15 kb	Severe	Yes	93

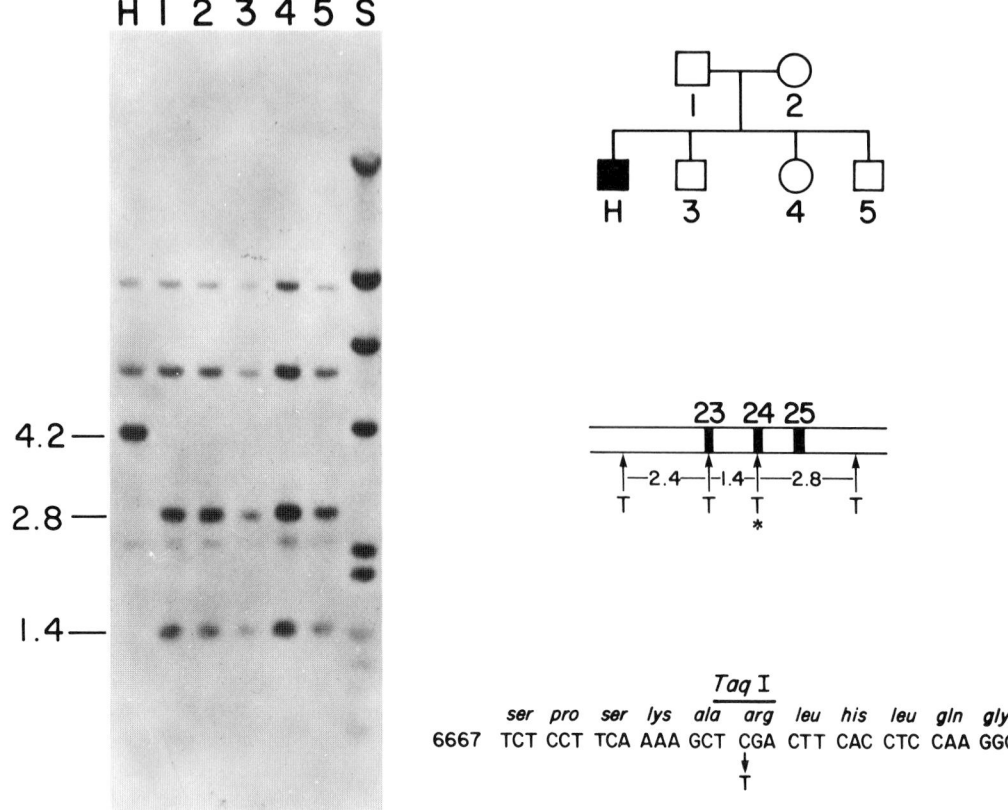

Fig. 86-3 Analysis of the factor VIII gene of a severe hemophiliac and his family. A Southern blot of DNA from patient H and his family members was probed with a radioactively labeled fragment of the factor VIII gene that includes all of exons 22–25 and parts of exons 21 and 26. Lanes H (hemophiliac), 1, 2, 3, 4, and 5 correspond to family members in the accompanying pedigree (□ = normal male; ■ = male hemophiliac; ○ = normal female). Lane S contains DNA size standards. The diagram below the pedigree indicates with an asterisk the location of the missing TaqI site in exon 24. Below this is shown the sequence of normal DNA and the changed base in H DNA that results in the loss of TaqI site and the occurrence of an in-frame stop codon TGA. (From Gitschier et al.[85] Used by permission.)

of the 2332-amino acid protein. It is not known whether such a truncated protein is inactive, unstable, or both.

Most of the above mutations occur in the factor VIII genes of severe hemophiliacs. One additional example of a hemophilia-related mutation is an amino acid substitution in the factor VIII gene of a mild hemophiliac.[88] Digestion of DNA from this individual produced the same hybridization pattern in the exon 26 point mutant discussed above. Oligonucleotide hybridization has confirmed that the TaqI site in exon 26 of the mild hemophiliac was destroyed by a CG→TG transition in the noncoding DNA strand, resulting in the replacement of an arginine codon with a glutamine codon CAA.[88] Although this amino acid replacement might be expected to yield a protein of diminished activity, both clotting activity and antigen levels in the patient are roughly equivalent (about 10 percent of normal). This suggests that the altered protein is relatively unstable or poorly synthesized but of normal specific activity when present. When factor VIII was partially purified from this individual, it was found to clot factor VIII–deficient plasma and to respond to activation by thrombin in a normal fashion.

The deletion mutations that have been characterized in hemophilic DNAs range in size from 2.5 kb to deletion of the entire gene. They are summarized in Table 86-1. All but one of the deletions causes severe hemophilia. In one patient, a deletion of about 6 kb eliminates exon 22 of the factor VIII gene. Despite this, the patient suffers only moderate hemo-

philia with factor VIII:C levels of 2 to 5 units/dl and no inhibitors.[91] The probable explanation of the moderate phenotype is that exon 22 encodes precisely 52 amino acids of the C1 domain, leaving an in-frame junction between exons 21 and 23. Therefore, the remainder of the molecule could be correctly translated, resulting in a protein with a 52-amino acid deletion that retains partial activity.

Although 4 of the 11 deletions are associated with the presence of antibodies against factor VIII, no definitive associations can be drawn between antibody formation and the presence of deletions or their size or position in the gene. In fact, gene deletions have only been detected in roughly 10 percent of the inhibitor patients examined. Thus, a simple blot analysis of hemophilic DNA would appear to be of little value in predicting the susceptibility of a patient to the development of inhibitor antibodies. Finally, only about 4 percent of all hemophilia A patients screened to date have detectable deletions to the factor VIII gene. Most of the remainder are presumably due either to nucleotide substitution (point) mutations or very small deletions, which have little effect on the gel mobility of restriction fragments. Advances in molecular technology will eventually allow the detection of point mutations that do not affect restriction enzyme sites[94,95] and speed DNA sequencing. It will then become practical to examine a larger set of factor VIII mutations and free the survey from the effects of ascertainment bias from which it now suffers.

At this stage in the study of mutant factor VIII genes, it is clear that Haldane was correct when he predicted that a substantial percentage of hemophiliacs represent new mutations.[80] Indeed, when DNA is available from three or more generations, blot hybridization analysis has frequently led to detection of the *de novo* mutation. For example, 6 of the 18 mutations listed in Table 86-1 were shown by DNA analysis to have arisen in the germline of the parent or grandparents of the hemophiliac. It also appears that most of these mutations are different, so that most families affected with hemophilia carry their own "private mutant allele." However, *Taq*I site mutations are encountered at a frequency much higher than expected by random occurrence, in support of the contention that CG dinucleotides represent mutation hot spots in humans.[84] In fact, the same independent point mutations have arisen twice in unrelated families (Table 86-1, exons 18 and 22).

DIAGNOSIS

Antigen- and/or Activity-Based Diagnosis

Carriers of hemophilia A have an average 50 percent of the normal mean level of the clotting factor (or its antigen VIII:Ag). However, owing to the wide scatter of normal values (50 to 150 percent), a carrier will often be within the normal range. By measuring the level of von Willebrand factor antigen (vWF:Ag), the autosomally coded carrier protein for factor VIII, it is possible to improve discrimination, since carriers will tend to have lower levels of VIII than of vWF.[96] Even so, there is still some overlap (about 15 percent) between normals and carriers who have the normal ratio (Fig. 86-4). This is due to the Lyon mechanism effect, whereby random X inactivation can cause predominantly the X chromosome bearing the mutant allele to be inactivated. Hence, one can

obtain strong evidence for heterozygote status by this method, but the results are not definitive.

Molecular Diagnosis

Prenatal diagnosis of hemophilia based on clotting activity of blood samples (phenotypic assay) suffers from the limitation that fetal blood sampling is not possible until about 18 to 20 weeks of pregnancy and involves significant risk to the fetus. This situation has been radically improved by the introduction of gene-specific DNA markers. In contrast to phenotypic assays, results from DNA-based diagnosis are definitive, and prenatal diagnosis is possible as early as at 8 to 12 weeks of gestation with the acquisition of fetal DNA by the technique of chorionic villus sampling.[97] Blot hybridization analysis of the factor VIII genes can be used to directly detect the presence of a mutant allele. However, because hemophilia A is caused by a myriad of different mutations (unlike sickle cell anemia, for example), direct detection of such mutations is rarely possible. Fortunately, DNA sequence polymorphisms in or near the factor VIII gene allow the tracking of alleles in affected families. These polymorphisms are detected as restriction fragment length polymorphisms (RFLPs) in Southern blot hybridizations using DNA probes either from the factor VIII gene or from nearby "anonymous" genomic fragments that are shown by linkage analysis to lie within several recombination units of the factor VIII gene. These polymorphisms do not involve DNA sequence change(s) that result in hemophilia but are instead markers that track an affected chromosome in families. The analysis requires that the mother be heterozygous (informative) for the RFLP and that DNA be available from sufficient family members to assign one of the two RFLP alleles to the affected X chromosome.

The first common RFLP discovered within the factor VIII gene utilizes a *Bcl*I recognition site in the eighteenth intron of

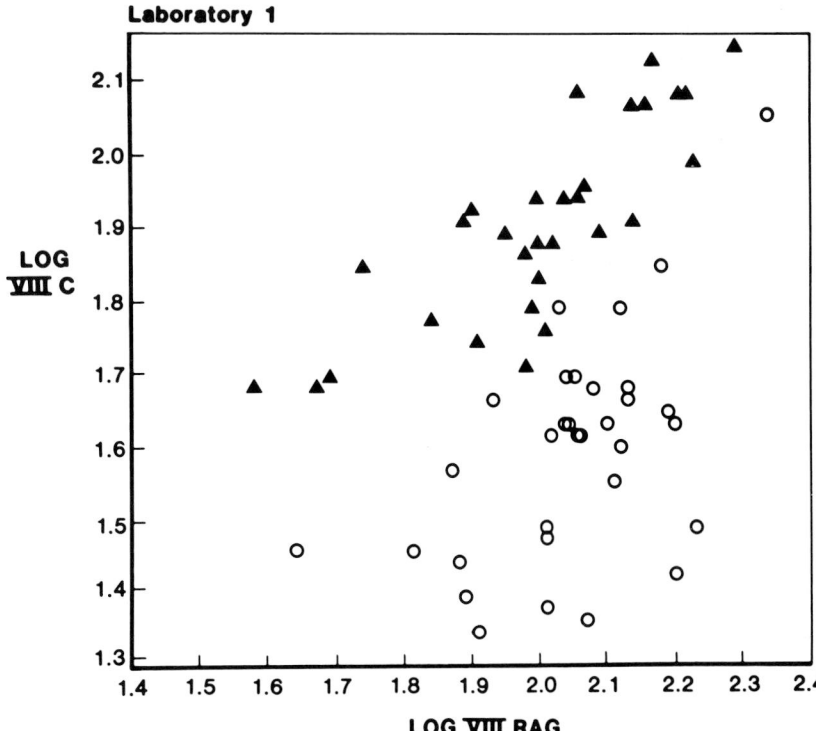

Fig. 86-4 Phenotypic assays used for carrier detection. Symbols are as follows: ▲ = normal females; ○ = obligate carriers. LOG VIII C indicates the natural log of factor VIII antigen measured with human antibody, while LOG VIII RAG indicates the von Willebrand factor antigen measured with heteroantibody assay.

the factor VIII gene.[98] The presence or absence of this site results in restriction fragments of either 879 or 1165 bp that hybridize to factor VIII cDNA. In the initial study, the frequency of the two alleles was 71 percent and 29 percent, predicting that 42 percent of females tested would be heterozygous for this marker. Further experience has indicated slightly different allele frequencies in different populations. To illustrate this technique, Fig. 86-5 shows the first prenatal diagnosis for hemophilia A performed with a factor VIII gene RFLP.[99] The Southern blot hybridization pattern is shown above the pedigree of the family in question. (For simplicity a small fragment of the factor VIII gene is used as a radiolabeled hybridization probe that detects only the polymorphic *Bcl*I fragment.) The woman seeking counseling (II-2) is heterozygous for the RFLP, while fetal DNA obtained at 8 weeks of gestation contained the 1165-bp allele. The hemophilic uncle (II-1) contained the 879-bp fragment, as did the maternal grandmother. Hence the mutant factor VIII gene in this family exists on an X chromosome harboring the 879-bp allele. The fetus, predicted to be free from hemophilia, can be seen to have inherited the X chromosome deriving from the normal maternal grandfather. Note that this diagnosis would not have been possible if the mother was homozygous for the RFLP.

To increase the percentage of females for whom such analysis will be informative, additional RFLPs have been identified in the factor VIII gene. Two have been reported. A *Bgl*I site polymorphism flanking exon 26 forms a two-allele system with allele frequencies of 0.9/0.1 in white communities and 0.75/0.25 in American blacks.[89] A polymorphic *Xba*I site in intron 22 has a more useful allele frequency of about 0.6/

0.4.[100] Fortunately, there is only partial linkage disequilibrium between these markers, so that approximately 25 percent of females who are homozygous for the *Bcl*I site are heterozygous for the *Xba*I polymorphism.[100]

The ideal RFLP for diagnosis would contain multiple alleles so that virtually all females were informative. Although no such RFLPs in the factor VIII gene have been found, there is one highly polymorphic marker, detected by an anonymous genomic fragment, that is tightly linked to the factor VIII gene.[101,102] The probe designated ST14 (or DXS52) detects at least 10 alleles. Obviously this is not due to the simple polymorphism of a nucleotide in a restriction enzyme recognition site and may be caused by a small repetitive DNA element that is present at various multiplicites. Although there were initially no recombinants reported between ST14 and factor VIII, there have now been several reported cases which suggest that a recombinational distance of about 4 percent may exist.[103–105] DX13 is another anonymous probe that detects a two-allele RFLP[106] within a 4 percent recombination distance from factor VIII.[103–106] The use of these linked markers entails an unavoidable error rate in diagnosis of up to 4 percent. However, the fact that well over 90 percent of all females are informative for ST14 suggests that an effective diagnostic strategy is the use of ST14 in combination with the intragenic *Bcl*I and *Xba*I RFLPs.[107,108]

In conclusion, DNA-based diagnosis of hemophilia A offers some distinct advantages over conventional phenotypic bioassays: they are relatively definitive, allow first trimester testing, and are not affected by the phenomenon of lyonization. It has been suggested, however, that a clinical unit planning to use these methods should also maintain the conventional procedures to offer diagnosis when family samples are incomplete or when key individuals are uninformative for available RFLPs.

Fig. 86-5 DNA-based prenatal diagnosis. At the top, DNA from family members was digested with *Bcl*I, electrophoresed, blotted onto filter paper, and hybridized with a radioactively labeled fragment of the factor VIII gene.[99] The two polymorphic restriction fragments measure 1165 and 879 bp. Each DNA track is aligned vertically with the corresponding family member on the kindred diagram. DNA was obtained from the fetus, III-1, at 8 weeks by chorion biopsy. As discussed in the text, the procedure predicts the birth of a hemophilia-free boy who has inherited the 1165-bp allele from the unaffected maternal grandfather, I-2. In this family, the 879-bp allele segregates with a hemophilia-causing mutation in the factor VIII gene carried by individuals I-1, II-1, and II-2. (From Gitschier et al.[99] Used by permission.)

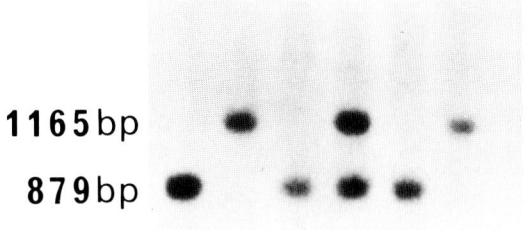

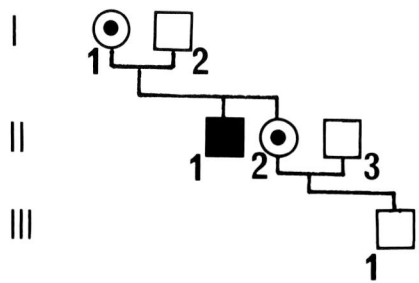

HEMOPHILIA A

Clinical Features

Classic hemophilia, or hemophilia A, is caused by a deficiency of factor VIII (antihemophilic factor). This disorder afflicts 1 out of every 10,000 males and is the most frequently encountered bleeding disorder. Nearly all patients are male (see 'Hemophilia A in Females," below). The severity and frequency of bleeding in hemophiliacs is inversely correlated with the residual factor VIII level. Table 86-2 summarizes this relationship and gives relative frequency of categories.[109] The joints

Table 86-2 Hemophilia A Clinical Severity

Factor VIII, units/dl	Bleeding tendency	Relative incidence of cases, percent
<2	Severe; frequent spontaneous* bleeding into joints, muscles, and internal organs	48
2–10	Moderately severe; some spontaneous bleeds; bleeding after minor trauma	31
>10–30	Mild; bleeding only after significant trauma, surgery	21

*Spontaneous bleeding refers to those episodes in which no obvious precipitating event preceded the bleed. No doubt minor tissue damage consequent on everyday activities actually initiates bleeding.

most affected are the main load- or strain-bearing articulations, ankles, knees, hips, and elbows, but any joint can be the site of bleeding. Untreated, this intracapsular bleeding causes severe swelling, pain, stiffness, and inflammation, which gradually resolves over days or weeks (for a vivid account of a case, see Ref. 110). Blood is highly irritant to the synovium and causes synovial overgrowth with a tendency to rebleed from friable vascular tissue, setting up a vicious circle. Probably through accumulation of iron in chondrocytes, a rapid degenerative arthritis occurs leading to irregularity of articular contour, thinning of the cartilage, bony overgrowth, and eventual ankylosis. A particular joint or joints tend to be the target for this destructive process in a given patient, while other joints may be relatively spared.

Muscle bleeding can be seen in any anatomic site but most often presents in the large load-bearing groups of the thigh, calf, posterior abdominal wall, and buttocks. Local pressure effects often cause entrapment neuropathy, particularly of the femoral nerve with iliopsoas bleeding. The latter causes a common symptom triad of groin pain, hip flexure, and cutaneous sensory loss over the femoral nerve distribution. Bleeding into the calf, forearm, or peroneal muscles can lead to ischemic necrosis and contracture.

Hematuria is less common than joint or muscle bleeding in hemophiliacs, but most severely affected cases have one or two episodes per decade. These may be painless and resolve spontaneously, but if bleeding is heavy, the hematuria can produce clot colic. Usually no anatomic abnormality is found to account for the hematuria on radiologic investigation.

Central nervous system bleeding is uncommon but can occur after slight head injury and was formerly the most common cause of death in hemophilia A. Intestinal tract bleeding usually presents as obstruction due to intramural hemorrhage, but hematemesis and melena also occur occasionally and should be routinely investigated, since they may be due to peptic ulcer or malignancy.

Oropharyngeal bleeding, although uncommon, is clinically dangerous since extension through the soft tissues of the floor of the mouth can lead to respiratory obstruction. Bleeding from the tongue after laceration can be very persistent and troublesome due to fibrinolytic substances in saliva and the impossibility of immobilizing the part.

Surgery and open trauma invariably lead to dangerous hemorrhage in the untreated hemophiliac. The most impressive feature is not the rate of hemorrhage but its persistence, often after an initial short-lived period of hemostasis. Clots, if formed, are bulky and friable and break off, causing renewed hemorrhage occurring intermittently over days and weeks. This is seen today only in patients who are resistant to conventional replacement therapy due to the presence of inhibitors (see below).

Bruising is a feature of hemophilia A, but is usually only of cosmetic significance since it remains superficial and self-limiting. Large, extending ecchymoses may occasionally require treatment.

Presentation

Where a woman is known to be a carrier or at high risk, cord blood factor VIII level will establish the diagnosis in her infant. One-third of cases are sporadic, however, and in these, the hemophilic condition may come to light in the neonatal period with cephalohematoma or prolonged bleeding from the

cord. In cultures in which early circumcision is the rule, this will cause prolonged hemorrhage. Quite often the diagnosis is delayed until it is noticed that the infant has many large bruises. These sometimes cause diagnostic confusion and the erroneous suspicion of child abuse with needless psychological trauma to the parents. Bleeding episodes, especially into the large joints, become more frequent as the infant starts to crawl actively. Without treatment, the ends of the long bones can become eroded, resulting in pain and necrosis. Intraosseous hemorrhage or intramuscular hemorrhage adjacent to long bones can develop into fibrous masses (termed *pseudotumors*) that may require surgical removal.[111] Excessive bleeding from eruption of primary dentition or from lacerations leads to performance of diagnostic tests in other children. Mild cases may present only in later life when severe trauma or surgery provokes unusual bleeding.

Pathophysiology

All the clinical features of hemophilia A are due directly or indirectly to lack of the clotting factor VIII. Lack of the cofactor drastically slows the rate of generation of factor Xa despite the presence of all other coagulation factors and platelets in normal amounts. Replacement by intravenous infusion of factor VIII can normalize the hemophiliac's hemostatic mechanism for the interval that infused factor residues in the circulation at physiological concentrations.

Laboratory Diagnosis

Of the standard laboratory coagulation tests, only the partial thromboplastin time is consistently abnormal. Specific assays show factor VIII clotting activity below 35 units/dl with all other factors normal and normal vWF antigen and ristocetin cofactor. The bleeding time as performed by the standardized template method is normal (see the discussion of van Willebrand disease in Chap. 87). A test for antibodies to factor VIII should also be performed.

Treatment

The mainstay of treatment is replacement therapy by means of intravenous infusion with factor VIII. At the present writing, all factor VIII used is blood-derived (Table 86-3). Ideally, all severely affected patients would be maintained on long-term prophylaxis with daily or alternate-day infusions to keep spontaneous hemorrhages to a minimum. This is impossible due to limitations of supply and finance. Since the half-life of factor VIII is 8 to 10 h, twice daily infusions are needed to maintain a normal level at all times. However, for prophylactic purposes, a fairly wide fluctuation is still very effective. In practice most patients are treated on demand. They receive an infusion of factor at the earliest symptoms of bleeding. Patients become skilled at recognizing very early joint bleeding, and provided that an infusion of factor VIII is given within a few minutes to 1 h of onset, the bleeding will be halted before a significant amount of blood has leaked into the joint. Normal activities can then be continued or resumed almost immediately.

It was realized in the 1960s that such prompt treatment could only be achieved if the patient or his relatives gave the

Table 86-3 Therapeutic Materials for Treatment of Hemophilia

Material	Factor VIII, units/ml	Advantages	Disadvantages
Fresh frozen plasma (FFP)	1	Low infection hazard	Storage at −20°C; high volume/low potency; allergic reactions
Cryoprecipitate	5–10	Low infection hazard (unless many units used)	Storage at −20°C; allergic reactions; potency not assayed
Heat-treated factor VIII concentrate	20–50	Assayed high potency, low or absent HIV and hepatitis B infectivity; storage at 4°C; few allergic reactions	Infective for non-A, non-B; high cost; heavy load of non-factor VIII proteins including iso anti-A, anti-B, β₂-microglobulin, fibrinogen, etc.
DDAVP	—	No infection risk; totally synthetic	Only effective in mild cases
Porcine* factor VIII (Hyate C)	20–50	No infection risk; high purity	Animal protein, allergic reactions; alloantibody to porcine factor VIII
Recombinant factor VIII	5000 units/mg	No infectious risk; totally pure	Not yet available
Recombinant von Willebrand factor	0	No infectious risk; totally pure	Not yet available

*Generally reserved for treatment of inhibitor cases.

injection. Therefore, home therapy programs were instituted. The results of these programs were a dramatic fall in time lost from work or school and a marked reduction in the onset of new, and the progression of old, joint damage. Severely affected patients who have grown up under this regime are now reaching their twenties with little or no arthritis, in marked contrast to the older patients or patients from developing countries who nearly all have severe damage in several joints, increasing relentlessly with age and number of bleeds.

Dosage of factor VIII is adjusted approximately to obtain a desired level in the circulation (Table 86-4). Formulas based on plasma volume and expected recovery give a rough guide to dosage, but where the level is critical, as for surgery or in the case of serious bleeding, it should always be checked by assay after infusion. On the average, factor VIII infusion produces a plasma increment of 2 units/dl per unit infused per kilogram of body weight. From this, a simple formula can be derived as follows:

$$\text{Dose to be infused (units)} = \frac{\text{weight (kg)} \times \text{increment needed (units/dl)}}{2.0}$$

Assessing the period of treatment required is a matter of clinical judgment regarding the individual episode or lesion. An early joint bleed will often resolve with a single infusion. Treatment for surgery other than very minor procedures will

Table 86-4 Plasma Levels of Factor VIII Required for Hemostasis

Clinical indication	Plasma factor VIII, units/dl	Dosage, units/kg
Early hemarthrosis or muscle bleed	15–20	8–10
More severe bleeding; minor trauma	30–50	15–25
Surgery; major trauma; head injury	80–120	40–60

need to be continued at full dosage twice daily, adjusted according to pre- and posttreatment assays, for a week or more, followed by a period at reduced dosage during convalescence.

Detailed discussion of the orthopedic management of hemophilic arthropathy is beyond the scope of this chapter, and the reader is referred to the texts on comprehensive care.[112–114] Suffice it to say that large numbers of patients have had total hip or knee joint replacements with good results and that arthrodesis of the knee or ankle can provide pain relief and improved locomotor function where arthroplasty is impractical. Physiotherapy plays a very important role in maintaining and improving the function of joints and muscles damaged or weakened by bleeding and enforced periods of immobilization.

Factor VIII concentrate has the advantages of convenient storage and assayed potency, and it is the material of choice for treatment of major bleeding in severe hemophilia where it is essential to maintain high circulating levels of the factor. The realization of its infective hazards (see "Complications" below) has given prominence to the use of a non-blood-derived alternative, DDAVP (1-desamino-8-D-arginine vasopressin). This synthetic analogue of vasopressin was noted to cause a rise in factor VIII and vWF levels without pressor effects. DDAVP retains the antidiuretic action of the natural hormone and also stimulates the release of vascular plasminogen activator. In practice, these effects can be used to elevate the plasma factor VIII level two- to fourfold above baseline, presumably by release from a storage site or sites.

Given together with a fibrinolytic inhibitor such as tranexamic acid to neutralize the fibrinolytic stimulus, DDAVP can correct the homeostatic defect sufficiently in mild hemophilia A to cover minor surgery or to treat a minor bleeding episode. A typical regimen would be to give 4 μg per kilogram body weight by slow intravenous infusion over 20 min together with 1 g tranexamic acid. The effect reaches a maximum at 1 h, when the factor VIII level may have risen, for example, in a mild hemophiliac from 10 units/dl to 40 units/dl. The half-life of the endogenously released factor VIII is about 8 h, and a repeat dose can be given, but with progressively diminishing response. The maximum useful number of doses is three in 24 h, after which a rest period is needed to allow stores to reaccumulate. Fibrinolytic inhibition is also useful for management of oral and intestinal tract bleeding. It must be strictly avoided where there is upper urinary tract bleeding, since it can cause obstructive nephropathy and acute renal failure due to mechanical outflow occlusion by blood clot.

The availability of factor VIII concentrates has resulted in dramatic improvements in the lifestyles of hemophiliacs. Afflicted individuals have been able to lead normal and productive lives without the fear of crippling or life-threatening bleeding episodes. The hepatitis contamination of concentrates has been considered an unfortunate but unavoidable side effect. However, the recent contamination of the blood supplies with the AIDS virus has focused efforts on improved plasma-based products (heat-treated or higher-purity) and on recombinant production systems.

Complications of Therapy

Inhibitors. The development of antibodies to factor VIII (often termed *inhibitors*) is a critical complication that occurs in about 5 percent of all patients with hemophilia A (but in up to 10 to 15 percent of severely affected individuals) after exposure to factor VIII.[115] These antibodies are predominantly of IgG_4,[116] a subclass that does not fix complement. Western blot epitope mapping using the antibodies from 14 patients demonstrated that the epitopes were directed against the A2 and A3-C1-C2 polypeptide chains of factor VIII.[117] The time of appearance of such antibodies is unpredictable and can occur after the first exposure, or many years later after thousands of treatments. Routine testing for factor VIII antibodies is therefore always performed prior to elective surgery and regularly at follow-up of severe case. Laboratory tests for antibody rely on neutralization of clotting activity in mixtures of normal and patient plasma. Since the plasma concentration of factor VIII is very low (200 ng/ml), it is necessary to prolong the incubation of the mixture to 1 to 4 h to attain equilibrium binding of antibody to antigen. Several tests have been devised with different periods of incubation and different units that are not strictly interconvertible. This is important when one considers therapeutic alternatives (see below). Thus Old Oxford units are based on 1-h incubation, Bethesda units on 2-h incubation, and New Oxford units on 4-h incubation. The most widely used at present are Bethesda units. Lack of interconvertibility is due to differing kinetics of inactivation of different antibodies.

Three aspects of the individual patient's antibody are of clinical importance: level in units at time of treatment, type of immune response to infusion of factor VIII (low or high), and cross-reaction with procine factor VIII. When the antibody level is low (Table 86-5), an increased dose to neutralize the circulating inhibitor plus additional factor to attain a hemostatic level will be effective. In some patients the level of antibody remains low to moderate (low responders) but in others, treatment with factor VIII elicits a sharp anamnestic response (high responders). The low responders can be treated repeatedly, but high responders become refractory so that alternative therapies have been developed. Most often the antibody is species-specific to human factor VIII, having little or no cross-reactivity with porcine factor VIII. A new concentrate from pig plasma, Hyate C (Table 86-5), is available, which has greatly improved clinical characteristics compared to the earlier animal factor VIII. This material is effective on many occasions when the titer against human factor VIII is too high to be neutralized. About half of patients treated with Hyate C have become resistant due to development of antiporcine factor VIII antibodies, but the remainder can be treated repeatedly with good response.

When the factor VIII inhibitor titer rises strongly to hundreds or even thousands of units per milliliter, factor VIII therapy is ineffective. In this situation, an alternative strategy is to attempt to bypass factor VIII with partly activated mixtures of the vitamin K–dependent factors. Conventional factor IX concentrate contains activated species and is, in fact, liable to produce thrombosis, particularly in patients with liver damage. Controlled trials have shown it to be more effective than albumin solution in hastening recovery from a hemarthrosis. Somewhat more effective, but much more expensive, are the deliberately activated coagulation factor mixtures FEIBA and AUTOPLEX. It is not entirely clear what the active principle in these products consists of, nor how to monitor the response by blood tests. Empirical dosage regimens have been established, and the fact remains that these products have been

Table 86-5 Guidelines for Treatment of Patients with Factor VIII Inhibitors*

Inhibitor level, BU/ml†		Type of responder	Therapeutic strategies
Antihuman	Antiporcine		
1–5	1–5	Low	(1) Give human factor VIII at increased dosage
		High	(1) Give factor IX for minor bleeds; or
			(2) Institute immune tolerance–inducing regimen
5–13	1–5	Low	(1) Use Hyate C for all bleeds (could use plasmapheresis and human VIII)
		High developing antiporcine antibodies	(1) Use factor IX for minor bleeds, reserve Hyate C for major bleeds; or
			(2) Attempt to induce tolerance
>13	>13	High	(1) Treat acute bleeds with activated factor complex; or
			(2) Institute immune tolerance–inducing regimen

*These suggestions are the author's own practice; other clinicians may advocate alternatives.
†BU = 1 Bethesda unit inhibits 0.5 units factor activity after 1-h incubation at 37°C.

strikingly effective on some occasions but fail to control bleeding on others. Few clinicians would recommend undertaking elective surgical procedures under cover of these products.

Induction of immune tolerance has been attempted on many occasions. Immunosuppressive substances such as glucocorticoids and alkylating agents are of no benefit, although probably valuable for treatment of spontaneously acquired autoantibodies to factor VIII. Megadose regimen of factor VIII infusion continued over many months was shown to be effective in abolishing inhibitory antibodies in over 90 percent of cases in one study.[118] The cost of this regimen is prohibitive in most economies. A medium-dose intermittent regimen is also fairly effective in the long term in blunting or abolishing immune response to factor VIII.[119] Various schemes have been proposed for inducing specific immune tolerance, but no consistently successful protocol has been reported to date. Infusion of intravenous gammaglobulin has been successful in temporarily lowering inhibitor titers,[120] presumably through the action of anti-idiotype antibodies (see manufacturer's literature). New combinations of these modalities offer hope.[121]

The multiplicity of proposed therapies reflects the present lack of any one universally successful regimen. A recent review of the topic can be found in Ref. 115. A recent report of potentially increased rate of inhibitor generation associated with heat-treated concentrates[122] raises concern over the safety of the new "virus-free" concentrates being used to counteract AIDS (see below).

Blood-Transmitted Infections. Multiple donor concentrates were introduced in the late 1960s. Very soon it was noted that a high incidence of hepatitis occurred and the newly discovered Australia antigen was present in most attacks. At the present time most older patients test positive for hepatitis B antibody or are chronically antigen-positive. During the 1970s, despite screening of blood for hepatitis B antigen, both acute and chronic hepatitis continued to appear in hemophiliacs, and it was realized that this was mainly due to another virus or transmissible agent, non-A, non-B. This agent is relatively heat resistant and continues to contaminate all multiple donor concentrates with an 80 to 100 percent attack rate after a single dose. No screening test is available that directly detects the non-A, non-B virus or viruses, but some advocate rejection of blood with elevated liver enzymes. Up to half of hemophiliacs have chronically or intermittently elevated liver enzymes[123] following a first attack of non-A, non-B hepatitis, which may cause a severe episode before converting to chronicity. Liver biopsies show characteristic histologic features[124] with chronic active or chronic persistent hepatitis in a high proportion of cases.[123] The long-term effect of this process can only be guessed at, but already a few patients have entered end-stage liver failure mainly or partly due to this pathogen. Prevention of hepatitis B is now assured by vaccinating all nonimmune patients.

The first hemophilic patient to develop AIDS was reported in the United States in 1983. Retrospective survey of stored blood serum of hemophiliacs in the United Kingdom and the United States shows that seroconversion to HIV-antibody–positive began to occur from 1978 onward. A few well-documented instances of contamination of U.K. blood-derived factor VIII by HIV have occurred. Currently all factor concentrates are from HIV antibody–negative plasma and are heat-treated. HIV is quite heat-sensitive, so reasonable recovery of factor VIII is obtained if conditions for inactivation are carefully adjusted.[124a] Hepatitis B is also inactivated, but the agent causing non-A, non-B hepatitis is not reliably inactivated.

The attack rate for conversion of an HIV antibody–positive condition to clinical AIDS is apparently somewhat lower for hemophiliacs than for other high-risk groups but is rising with time. Nevertheless, AIDS has now become the most common cause of death in hemophilia A. The only clinical point of difference between AIDS in hemophiliacs and the syndrome seen in homosexuals is that Kaposi sarcoma is very uncommon in hemophilia. Surveys of the families of HIV antibody–positive hemophiliacs show up to 5 percent positive tests in wives and sexual partners but no positives in other household contacts. Several wives of hemophiliacs have died of AIDS. This devastating situation has thrown a great strain on patients, their families, and those who care for them. Counseling and palliative treatment of the condition once it develops are all that can be offered at present. Patients have been strongly advised if they test positive to use barrier contraception and delay starting a family whether their wives test positive or not.

In the search for better therapy, efforts are under way to apply recombinant DNA technology. To develop a recombinant factor VIII protein would yield a product far superior to the current concentrates. In addition, the prospects of gene therapy are hopeful. Hemophilia is a reasonable candidate for this, since close control of plasma levels are not required and even an increase from 0 to 5 percent of normal levels would markedly improve the clinical status.

Hemophilia A in Females

True homozygous hemophilia A is rare but well-described.[11,125–129] Severe menstrual hemorrhage occurs but responds to factor VIII infusion. About 5 percent of heterozygous carriers have a low enough factor VIII level due to unfortunate lyonization to be classified as mild hemophiliacs, requiring precautions to cover surgery and occasionally experiencing traumatic bleeding. Due to sperm mutation in the father, such a carrier can present de novo with no hemophilic relative. Hemophilia A has been described in a female with Turner syndrome. One family with apparently clear-cut dominant factor VIII deficiency affecting females has been described.[130] The genetic basis for this last disorder awaits clarification. The most common reason for finding low factor VIII level in a female if the above have been excluded is vWD. This should usually be evident from assays of vWF and a prolonged bleeding time. Of course, vWD and hemophilia can coexist in the same family, which makes carrier detection difficult.

Acquired autoantibodies to factor VIII arise in previously normal people, sometimes in association with rheumatoid arthritis or in the puerperium. This is called acquired hemophilia but has no genetic basis. Treatment resembles that described above under "Inhibitors."

COMBINED FACTOR V AND FACTOR VIII DEFICIENCY

About 30 families with this surprising combined defect, inherited as an autosomal recessive, have been described worldwide (for a review up to 1981, see Ref. 131).

Parental consanguinity is common, and homozygotes have factor V and factor VIII levels generally below 20 units/dl. Bleeding manifestations include excessive blood loss after dental extraction or other surgery, epistaxes, and large bruises. A few cases have had hemarthroses or muscle hematomas. Treatment with fresh frozen plasma is effective. Factor VIII concentrates do not contain enough factor V to be effective. The pathophysiology of this disorder remains mysterious.

The level of factor VIII antigen is reduced to a similar extent as the coagulant activity,[132] but the level of factor V antigen was reported to be normal in one study[133] and reduced in another.[134] A casual association of the two isolated deficiencies (parahemophilia and hemophilia A) is ruled out by inheritance pattern and the extreme unlikeliness of such a chance combination (although two such families have been reported).

The basis of combined factor V and factor VIII deficiency is unknown at present. Although it was originally claimed that the plasma level of a protein C inhibitor was reduced in those patients,[135] subsequent studies proved that the protein C inhibitor is labile and present in normal amounts in fresh plasma samples from combined deficiency cases.[136–138] A defect in the control of activated protein C function is therefore a more likely explanation for the cause of this bleeding disorder.

FACTOR V

Protein Structure

The functional and structural similarities of factor V and factor VIII have long been recognized. Both are cofactors required for optimal coagulant activity as a result of their interaction with vitamin K–dependent serine proteases. Both proteins are activated by thrombin and factor Xa and inactivated by activated protein C. Both proteins are initially synthesized as proteins of M_r greater than 300,000 (see above description of factor VIII; Refs. 139–144 for factor V). For both proteins, proteolytic activation is correlated with the amino-terminal and carboxy-terminal portions representing the functional regions of these cofactors.[26,29,139–145] These two functional subunits are separated in the primary sequence by a large and highly glycosylated peptide. Amino acid[146] and nucleic acid[147] sequence analysis has demonstrated a high degree of homology between factors V and VIII. These two cofactors of the coagulation cascade are therefore closely related in both their structure and their function.

Deficiency

This is a rare autosomal recessive bleeding disorder (less than one per million) first described by Owren,[148] who gave it the name *parahemophilia*. According to most reports, the disease is inherited in an autosomal recessive manner.[148–150a] A curious feature of the condition is that the plasma factor levels do not correlate at all closely with the bleeding tendency.[151] However, it has been shown that the platelet surface–associated factor V levels are the critical determinants of the bleeding tendency.[152] Thus, patients may have no detectable plasma factor V but little bleeding. These patients have normal or slightly reduced platelet factor Xa–binding capacity, a measure of surface-associated factor V. Other cases have no platelet or plasma factor

V, and these patients bleed readily, especially after trauma or surgery. Many such individuals have a prolonged bleeding time, emphasizing the close relationship between factor V and platelet function. Treatment with plasma is effective, and the hemostatic level may be sufficient at 20 units/dl. Some cases are reported to have nonfunctional factor V antigen in their plasma,[153] but there is no further information on the underlying genotype.

Laboratory diagnosis shows prolonged prothrombin and partial thromboplastin times, since factor V functions in both the intrinsic and extrinsic pathways.

None of the commercially available plasma concentrates have sufficient factor V to be useful in treating a hemorrhagic episode. Therefore, treatment of factor V deficiency involves the infusion of fresh frozen plasma. Levels of factor V between 10 and 25 percent of normal are felt necessary to achieve hemostasis.

REFERENCES

1. ROSNER F: Hemophilia in the Talmud and Rabbinic writings. *Ann Intern Med* 70:833, 1969.
2. ALSAHARAVIUS: Liber theoricae necnon practicae Alsaharavii…qui vulgo Acaravius dicitur; jam………depromptus in lucem. Translated from the original Arabic into Latin by Paul Ricius. Published by S Grim and M Vuirsung, Augsburg. Tractatus XXXI; Sectio II. Capitulum XV. Folio CXLV, 1519.
3. CONNSBRUCH FW: Medicinische Ephemeriden nebst einer Topographie der Grafschaft. Ravensberg XII. 268 pp, Chemnitz, S. 267, 1793.
4. OTTO JC: *An Account of a Hemorrhagic Disposition Existing in Certain Families.* New York, The Medical Repository, 1803, vol VI, no 1, p 1.
5. NASSE CF: Von einer erblichen Neigung zu todtlichen Blutungen. Archiv für medizinishce Erfahrung im Gebiete der praktischen Medizin staatsarzneikunde, hrsg. von Horn, Nasse und Henke. Berlin, Mai-June, S. 385, 1820.
6. HOPFF F: Ueber die haemophilie oder die erbliche Anlage zu todtlichen Blutungen. Inaug Diss Wurzburg, 1828, p 17.
7. WRIGHT AE: On a method of determining the condition of blood coagulability for clinical and experimental purposes, and on the effect of the administration of calcium salts in haemophilia and actual or threatened hemorrhage. *Br Med J* 2:223, 1893.
8. ADDIS T: Hereditary haemophilia: Deficiency in the coagulability of the blood the only immediate cause of the condition. *Q J Med* 4:14, 1910.
9. ADDIS T: The pathogenesis of hereditary hemophilia. *J Pathol Bacteriol* 15:427, 1911.
10. PATEK AJ, TAYLOR FHL: Hemophilia II: Some properties of a substance obtained from normal human plasma effective in accelerating the coagulation of hemophilic blood. *J Clin Invest* 16:113, 1937.
11. MERSKEY C: The occurrence of hemophilia in the human female. *Q J Med* 20:299, 1951.
12. MERSKEY C, MacFARLANE RG: The female carrier of hemophilia: A clinical and laboratory study. *Lancet* 1:487, 1951.
13. AGGELER PM, WHITE SG, GLENDENING MB, PAGE EW, LEAKE TB, BATES G: Plasma thromboplastin component (PTC) deficiency: A new disease resembling hemophilia. *Proc Soc Exp Biol Med* 79:692, 1952.
14. BIGGS R, DOUGLAS AS, MacFARLANE RG, DAVID JV, PITNEY WR, MERSKEY C, O'BRIEN JR: Christmas disease, a condition previously mistaken for hemophilia. *Br Med J* 2:1378, 1952.
15. SCHULMAN I, SMITH CH: Hemorrhagic disease in an infant due to deficiency of a previously undescribed clotting factor. *Blood* 7:794, 1952.
16. McKUSICK VA: The royal hemophilia. *Sci Am* 213:88, 1965.
17. LARRIEU MJ, SOULIER JP: Deficit en facteur antihemophilique a chez une fille, associe a un trouble de saignement. *Rev Hematol* 8:361, 1953.
18. VON WILLEBRAND EA: Hereditare pseudohamofilie. *Fin Laekaresaellsk Handl* 67:87, 1926.
19. ZIMMERMAN TS, RATNOFF OD, POWELL AE: Immunologic differentiation of classic hemophilia (factor VIII deficiency) and von Willebrand's disease. *J Clin Invest* 50:244, 1971.
20. THELIN GM, WAGNER RH: Sedimentation of plasma antihemophilic factor. *Arch Biochem* 95:70, 1961.
21. ZIMMERMAN TS, EDGINGTON TS: Factor VIII coagulant activity and factor

VIII like antigen: Independent molecular entities. *J Exp Med* 138:1015, 1973.

22. RICK ME, HOYER LW: Immunologic studies of antihemophilic factor (AHF, factor VIII). V. Immunologic properties of AHF subunits produced by salt dissociation. *Blood* 42:737, 1973.

23. BLOOM AL, PEAKE IR, GIDDINGS JC: The presence and reactions of high and lower molecular weight procoagulant factor VIII in the plasma of patients with von Willebrand's disease after treatment: Significance for a structural hypothesis for factor VIII. *Thromb Res* 3:389, 1973.

24. GITSCHIER J, WOOD WI, GORALKA TM, WION KL, CHEN EY, EATON DH, VEHAR GA, CAPON DJ, LAWN RM: Characterization of the human factor VIII gene. *Nature* 312:326, 1984.

25. WOOD WI, CAPON DJ, SIMONSEN CC, EATON DL, GITSCHIER J, KEYT B, SEEBURG PH, SMITH DH, HOLLINGSHEAD P, WION KL, TUDDENHAM EGD, VEHAR GA, LAWN RM: Expression of active human factor VIII from recombinant DNA clones. *Nature* 312:330, 1984.

26. TOOLE JJ, KNOPF JL, WOZNEY JM, SULTZMAN LA, BUECKER JL, PITTMAN DD, KAUFMAN RJ, BROWN E, SHOEMAKER C, ORR EC, AMPHLETT GW, FOSTER WB, COE ML, KNUTSON GJ, FASS DN, HEWICK RM: Molecular cloning of a cDNA encoding human antihemophilic factor. *Nature* 312:342, 1984.

27. TRUETT MA, BLACHER R, BURKE RL, CAPUT D, CHU C, DINA D, HARTOG K, KUO CH, MASIARZ FR, MERRYWEATHER JP, NAJARIAN R, PACHL C, POTTER SJ, PUMA J, QUIROGA M, RALL LB, RANDOLPH A, URDEA MS, VALENZUELA P, DAHL HH, FAVALORO J, HANSEN J, NORDFANG O, EZBAN M: Characterization of the polypeptide composition of human factor VIII:C and the nucleotide sequence and expression of the human kidney cDNA. *DNA* 4:333, 1985.

28. VERWEIJ CL, DE VRIES CJM, DISTEL B, VAN ZONNEVELD A-J, VAN KESSEL AG, MOURIK JA, PANNEKOEK H: Construction of cDNA coding for human von Willebrand factor using antibody probes for colony-screening and mapping of the chromosomal gene. *Nucleic Acids Res* 13:4699, 1985.

29. VEHAR GA, KEYT B, EATON D, RODRIGUEZ H, O'BRIEN DP, ROTBLAT F, OPPERMAN H, KECK R, WOOD WI, HARKINS RN, TUDDENHAM EGD, LAWN RM, CAPON DJL: Structure of human factor VIII. *Nature* 312:337, 1984.

30. ROTBLAT F, O'BRIEN DP, O'BRIEN FJ, GOODALL AH, TUDDENHAM EGD: Purification of human factor VIII:C and its characterization by western blotting using monoclonal antibodies. *Biochemistry* 24:4294, 1985.

31. TAKAHASHI N, BAUMAN RA, ORTEL TL, DWULET FE, WANG C-C, PUTNAM FW: Internal triplication in the structure of human ceruloplasmin. *Proc Natl Acad Sci USA* 80:115, 1983.

32. TAKAHASHI N, ORTEL TL, PUTNAM FW: Single-chain structure of human ceruloplasmin: The complete amino acid sequence of the whole molecule. *Proc Natl Acad Sci USA* 81:390, 1984.

33. FOWLER SA, PAULSON D, OWEN BA, OWEN WG: Binding of iron by factor IX. Possible role for beta-hydroxyaspartic acid. *J Biol Chem* 261:4371, 1986.

34. MANN KG, LAWLER CM, VEHAR GA, CHURCH WR: Coagulation factor V contains copper ion. *J Biol Chem* 259:12949, 1984.

35. JACKSON CM, NEMERSON Y: Blood coagulation. *Annu Rev Biochem* 49:765, 1980.

36. DAVID EW, FUJIKAWA K, KURACHI K, KISIEL W: The role of proteases in the blood coagulation cascade. *Adv Enzymol* 48:277, 1979.

37. OSTERUD B, RAPAPORT SI: Synthesis of intrinsic factor X activator. Inhibition of the function of formed activator by antibodies to factor VIII and to factor IX. *Biochem J* 9:1854, 1970.

38. HULTIN M, NEMERSON Y: Activation of factor X by factors IXa and VIII: A specific assay for factor IXa in the presence of thrombin-activated factor VIII. *Blood* 52:928, 1978.

39. SUOMELA H, BLOMBACK M, BLOMBACK B: The activation of factor X evaluated using synthetic substrates. *Thromb Res* 10:267, 1977.

40. RAPAPORT SI, SCHIFFMAN S, PATCH MJ, AMES SB: The importance of activation of anti-hemophilic globulin and proaccelerin by traces of thrombin in the generation of intrinsic prothrombinase activity. *Blood* 21:221, 1963.

41. SWITZER MEP, PIZZO SV, MCKEE PA: Is there a precursive relatively procoagulant-inactive form of normal antihemophilic factor (factor VIII)? *Blood* 54:916, 1979.

42. VAN DIEIJEN G, TANS G, ROSING J, HEMKER HC: The role of phospholipid and factor VIIIa in the activation of bovine factor X. *J Biol Chem* 256:3433, 1981.

43. LAZARCHICK J, HOYER LW: Immunoradiometric measurement of the factor VIII procoagulant antigen. *J Clin Invest* 62:1048, 1978.

44. HOYER LW: The factor VIII complex: Structure and function. *Blood* 58:1, 1981.

45. ZIMMERMAN RS, RUGGERI ZM, FULCHER CA: Factor VIII/von Willebrand factor. *Prog Hematol* 13:279, 1983.

46. WEINSTEIN M, CHUTE L, DEYKIN D: Analysis of factor VIII coagulant antigen in normal, thrombin-treated, and hemophilic plasma. *Proc Natl Acad Sci USA* 78:5137, 1981.

47. WEINSTEIN MJ, FULCHER CA, CHUTE LE, ZIMMERMAN TS: Apparent molecular weight of purified human factor VIII procoagulant protein compared with purified and plasma factor VIII procoagulant protein antigen. *Blood* 62:1114, 1983.

48. VEHAR GA, DAVIE EW: Preparation and properties of bovine factor VIII (antihemophilic factor). *Biochemistry* 19:401, 1980.

49. FASS DN, KNUTSON GJ, KATZMANN JA: Monoclonal antibodies to porcine factor VIII coagulant and their use in the isolation of active coagulant protein. *Blood* 59:594, 1982.

50. FULCHER CA, ZIMMERMAN TS: Characterization of the human factor VIII procoagulant protein with a heterologous precipitating antibody. *Proc Natl Acad Sci USA* 79:1648, 1982.

51. KNUTSON GJ, FASS DN: Porcine factor VIII:C prepared by affinity interaction with von Willebrand factor and heterologous antibodies: Sodium dodecyl sulfate polyacrylamide gel analysis. *Blood* 59:615, 1982.

52. ANDERSSON L-O, FORSMAN N, HUANG K, LARSEN K, LUNDIN A, PAVLU B, SANDBERG H, SEWERIN K, SMART J: Isolation and characterization of human factor VIII: Molecular forms in commercial factor VIII concentrate, cryoprecipitate, and plasma. *Proc Natl Acad Sci USA* 83:2979, 1986.

53. EATON D, RODRIGUEZ H, VEHAR GA: Proteolytic processing of human factor VIII. Correlation of specific cleavages by thrombin, factor Xa, and activated protein C with activation and inactivation of factor VIII coagulant activity. *Biochemistry* 25:505, 1986.

54. FAY PJ, ANDERSON MR, CHAVIN SI, MARDER VJ: The size of human factor VIII heterodimers and the effects produced by thrombin. *Biochim Biophys Acta* 871:268, 1986.

55. HAMER RJ, KOEDAMN JA, BESSER-VISSIER NH, SIXMA JJ: Human factor VIII: Purification from commercial factor VIII concentrate, characterization, identification and radiolabeling. *Biochim Biophys Acta* 873:356, 1986.

56. EATON D, HASS P, RIDDLE L, GREGORY T, VEHAR GA: Characterization of recombinant human factor VIII. *J Biol Chem* 262:3285, 1987.

57. BURKE RL, PACHL C, QUIROGA M, ROSENBERG S, HAIGWOOD N, NORDFANG O, EZBAN M: The functional domains of coagulation factor VIII:C. *J Biol Chem* 261:12574, 1986.

58. TOOLE JJ, PITTMAN DD, ORR EC, MURTHA P, WASLEY LC, KAUFMAN RJ: A large region (95 kDa) of human factor VIII is dispensable for *in vitro* procoagulant activity. *Proc Natl Acad Sci USA* 83:5939, 1986.

59. EATON D, WOOD WI, EATON D, HASS PE, HOLLINGSHEAD P, WION K, MATHER J, LAWN RM, VEHAR GA, GORMAN C: Construction and characterization of an active factor VIII variant lacking the central one-third of the molecule. *Biochemistry* 25:8343, 1986.

60. FULCHER CA, ROBERTS JR, ZIMMERMAN TS: Thrombin proteolysis of purified factor VIII procoagulant protein: Correlation of activation with generation of a specific polypeptide. *Blood* 61:807, 1983.

61. PITTMAN DD, KAUFMAN RJ: Identification of the cleavage site(s) requirement(s) for activation and inactivation of factor VIII. *Blood* 68:352a, 1986.

62. MARLAR RA, KLEISS AJ, GRIFFIN J: Mechanism of action of human activated protein C, a thrombin-dependent anticoagulant enzyme. *Blood* 59:1067, 1982.

63. FULCHER CA, GARDINER JE, GRIFFIN JH, ZIMMERMAN TS: Proteolytic inactivation of human factor VIII procoagulant protein by activated human protein C and its analogy with factor V. *Blood* 63:486, 1984.

64. SEEGERS WH, MCCOY LE, GROBEN HD, SAKURAGAWA N, AGRAWAL BBL: Purification and some properties of autoprothrombin II-A: An anticoagulant perhaps also related to fibrinolysis. *Thromb Res* 1:443, 1973.

65. STENFLO J: A new vitamin K-dependent protein: Purification from bovine plasma and preliminary characterization. *J Biol Chem* 251:355, 1976.

66. ESMON CT, STENFLO J, SUTTIE JW, JACKSON CM: A new vitamin K-dependent protein (a phospholipid-binding zymogen of a serine esterase). *J Biol Chem* 251:3052, 1976.

67. KISIEL W, CANFIELD WM, ERICSSON LH, DAVID EW: Anticoagulant properties of bovine protein C following activation by thrombin. *Biochemistry* 16:5824, 1977.

68. KISIEL W: Human plasma protein C: Isolation, characterization and mechanism of activation of alpha-thrombin. *J Clin Invest* 64:761, 1979.

69. ESMON CT, OWEN WG: Identification of an endothelial cell cofactor for thrombin-catalyzed activation of protein C. *Proc Natl Acad Sci USA* 78:2249, 1981.

70. OWEN WG, ESMON CT: Functional properties of an endothelial cell cofactor for thrombin-catalyzed activation of protein C. *J Biol Chem* 256:5532, 1981.

71. ESMON NL, OWEN WG, ESMON CT: Isolation of membrane-bound cofactor

for thrombin-catalyzed activation of protein C. *J Biol Chem* 257:859, 1982a.

72. ESMON CT, ESMON NL, HARRIS KW: Complex formation between thrombin and thrombomodulin inhibits both thrombin-catalyzed fibrin formation and factor V activation. *J Biol Chem* 257:7944, 1982.

73. WALKER FJ: Regulation of activated protein C by a new protein: A possible function for bovine protein S. *J Biol Chem* 255:5521, 1980.

74. WALKER FJ: Regulation of activated protein C by protein S: The role of phospholipid in factor Va inactivation. *J Biol Chem* 256:11128, 1981.

75. GILES AR, TINLIN S, HOOGENDOORN H, FOURNEL MA, NG P, PANCHAM N: In vivo characterization of recombinant factor VIII in a canine model of hemophilia A (factor VIII deficiency). *Blood* 72:335, 1988.

76. RYDEN A: Structure and evolution of the small blue proteins, in Lontie R (ed): *Copper Proteins and Copper Enzymes*, Boca Raton, FL, CRC Press, 1984, vol 1, p 157.

77. BLOOM AL: The biosynthesis of factor VIII, in Rizza CR (ed): *Clinics of Haematology*. London, Saunders, 1979, vol 8, pp 53–77.

78. WION KL, KELLY D, SUMMERFIELD JA, TUDDENHAM EGD, LAWN RM: Distribution of factor VIII mRNA and antigen in human liver and other tissues. *Nature* 317:726, 1985.

79. ZELECHOWSKA MG, VAN MOURIK JA, BRODNIEWICZ-PROBA T: Ultrastructural localization of factor VIII procoagulant antigen in human liver hepatocytes. *Nature* 317:729, 1985.

80. HALDANE JBS: The rate of spontaneous mutation of a human gene. *J Genet* 31:317, 1935.

81. HALDANE JBS, SMITH CAB: A new estimate of the linkage between the genes for hemophilia and color blindness in man. *Ann Eugen London* 14:10, 1947.

82. BOYER SH, GRAHAM JB: Linkage between the X chromosome loci for glucose-6-phosphate dehydrogenase electrophoretic variation and hemophilia A. *Am J Hum Genet* 17:320,1965.

83. DRAYNA D, WHITE R: The genetic linkage map of the human X chromosome. *Science* 230:753, 1985.

84. BARKER D, SCHAFER M, WHITE R: Restriction sites containing CpG show a higher frequency of polymorphism in human DNA. *Cell* 36:131, 1984.

85. GITSCHIER J, WOOD WI, TUDDENHAM EGD, SHUMAN MA, GORALKA TM, CHEN EY, LAWN RM: Detection and sequence of mutations in the factor VIII gene of haemophiliacs. *Nature* 315:427, 1985.

86. YOUSSOUFIAN H, KAZAZIAN HH JR, PHILLIPS DG, ARONIS S, TSIFTIS G, BROWN VA, ANTONARAKIS SE: Recurrent mutations in hemophilia A: Evidence for CpG dinucleotides as mutation hotspots. *Nature* 27:380, 1986.

87. YOUSSOUFIAN H, ANTONARAKIS SE, BELL W, GRIFFIN AM, KAZAZIAN HH JR: Nonsense and missense mutations in hemophilia A: Estimate of the relative mutation rate at CG dinucleotides. *Am J Hum Genet* 42:718, 1988.

88. GITSCHIER J, WOOD WI, SHUMAN MA, LAWN RM: Identification of a missense mutation in the factor VIII gene of a mild hemophiliac. *Science* 232:1415, 1986.

89. ANTONARAKIS SE, WABER PG, KITTUR SD, PATEL AS, KAZAZIAN HH JR, MELLIS MA, COUNTS RB, STAMATOYANNOPOULOS G, BOWIE EJW, FASS DN, PITTMAN DD, WOZNEY JM, TOOLE JJ: Hemophilia A: Molecular defects and carrier detection by DNA analysis. *N Engl J Med* 313:842, 1985.

90. LILLICRAP DP, TAYLOR SAM, GROVER H, TEITEL J, GILES AR, HOLDEN JJA, WHITE BN: Genetic analysis of hemophilia A: Identification of a large factor VIII gene deletion in a patient with high titre antibodies to human and porcine factor VIII. *Blood* 68:337a, 1986.

91. YOUSSOUFIAN H, ANTONARAKIS SE, ARONIS S, TSIFTIS G, PHILLIPS DG, KAZAZIAN HH JR: Characterization of five partial deletions of the factor VIII gene in hemophilia A. *Proc Natl Acad Sci USA* 84:3772, 1987.

92. CASARINO L, PECORARA M, MORI PG, MORFINI M, MANCUSO G, SCRIVANO L, MOLINARI AC, LANZA T, GIAVARELLA G, LOI A, PERSEU L, CAO A, PIRASTU M: Molecular basis for hemophilia A in Italians. *Res Clin Lab* 16:227, 1986.

93. CAMERINO G, BARDONI B, SAMPIETRO M, ROMANO M, CRAPANZANO C, MANNUCCI PM: Deletion of part of coagulation factor VIII in a hemophiliac with inhibitor. *Res Clin Lab* 16:227, 1986.

94. MYERS RM, LUMELOKY N, LERMAN LS, MANIATIS T: Detection of single base substitutions in total genomic DNA. *Nature* 313:495, 1985.

95. MYERS RM, LARIN Z, MANIATIS T: Detection of single base substitutions by ribonuclease cleavage at mismatches in RNA:DNA duplexes. *Science* 230:1242, 1985.

96. KLEIN HG, ALEDORT LM, BOUMA BN, HOYER LW, ZIMMERMAN TS, DEMETS DL: A cooperative study for the detection of the carrier state of classic hemophilia. *N Engl J Med* 296:959, 1977.

97. WILLIAMSON R, ESKDALE J, COLEMAN DV, NIAZI M, LOEFFLER FE, MODELL BM: Direct gene analysis of chorionic villi: A possible technique for first-trimester antenatal diagnosis of haemoglobinopathies. *Lancet* 2:1125, 1981.

98. GITSCHIER J, DRAYNA D, TUDDENHAM EGD, WHITE RL, LAWN RM: Genetic mapping and diagnosis of haemophilia A achieved through a BclI polymorphism in the factor VIII gene. *Nature* 314:738, 1985.

99. GITSCHIER J, LAWN RM, ROTBLAT F, GOLDMAN E, TUDDENHAM EGD: Antenatal diagnosis and carrier detection of hemophilia A using a factor VIII gene probe. *Lancet* 1:1093, 1985b.

100. WION KL, TUDDENHAM EGD, LAWN RM: A new polymorphism in the factor VIII gene for prenatal diagnosis of hemophilia A. *Nucleic Acids Res* 14:4535, 1986.

101. OBERLE I, CAMERINO G, HEILIG R, GRUNEBAUM L, CAZENAVE JP, CRAPANZANO C, MANNUCCI P, MANDEL JL: Genetic screening for hemophilia A with a polymorphic DNA probe. *N Engl J Med* 312:682, 1985.

102. OBERLE I, DRAYNA D, CAMERINO G, WHITE R, MANDEL JL: The telomeric region of the human X chromosome long arm: Presence of a highly polymorphic DNA marker and analysis of recombination frequency. *Proc Natl Acad Sci USA* 82:2824, 1985.

103. PEAKE IR: Personal communication.

104. BROCKER-VRIENDS A, BRIET E, QUADT R, DREESEN J, BAKKER D, CLAASSEN-TEGELAAR R, KANHAI H, VAN DE KAMP J, PEARSON P: Genotype assignment of haemophilia A by use of intragenic and extragenic restriction fragment length polymorphisms. *Thromb Haemost* 57:131, 1987.

105. PEMBREY MR, MIBASHAN RS: Prenatal diagnosis of haemophilia A, in Seghatchian and Savidge (eds): *Factor VIII-vWF*. Boca Raton, FL, vol II (in press).

106. HARPER K, WINTER RM, PEMBREY ME, HARTLEY D, DAVIES KE, TUDDENHAM EGD: A clinically useful DNA probe closely linked to haemophilia A. *Lancet* 2:6, 1984.

107. JANCO RL, PHILLIPS JA, ORLANDO P, DAVIES KE, OLD J, ANTONARAKIS SE: Carrier testing strategy in haemophilia A. *Lancet* 1:148, 1986.

108. JANCO RL, PHILLIPS JA, ORLANDO P, WOODARD MJ, WION KL, LAWN RM: Added utility of an XbaI polymorphism in intron 22 of the factor VIII:C gene for detection of carriers of hemophilia. *Blood* 69:1539, 1987.

109. RIZZA CR, SPOONER RJD: Treatment of hemophilia and related disorders in Britain and Northern Ireland during 1976–80: Report on behalf of the directors of Haemophilia Centers in the United Kingdom. *Br Med J* 286:929, 1983.

110. MASSEY M, MASSEY S: *Journey*. New York, Knopf, 1973.

111. ALEDORT LM: Recent advances in hemophilia. *Ann NY Acad Sci* 240:1975.

112. BIGGS R: The treatment of hemophilia A and B and von Willebrand's disease. Oxford, Blackwell, 1978.

113. BOONE DC: *Comprehensive Management of Hemophilia*. Philadelphia, FA Davis, 1976.

114. GILBERT MS, ALEDORT L: Comprehensive care in hemophilia: A team approach. *Mt Sinai J Med* 4(3):1977.

115. MOYER LW: *Factor VIII Inhibitors*. New York, AR Liss, 1984.

116. HOYER LW, GAWRYL MS, DE LA FUENTE B: Immunological characterization of factor VIII inhibitors, in Hoyer LW (ed): *Factor VIII Inhibitors*. New York, AR Liss, 1984, vol 150, p 73.

117. FULCHER CA, MAHONEY SDG, ROBERTS JR, KASPER CK, ZIMMERMAN TS: Localization of human factor VIII inhibitor epitopes to two polypeptide fragments. *Proc Natl Acad Sci USA* 82:7728, 1985.

118. BRACKMAN HH: The treatment of inhibitor against factor VIII by continuous treatment with factor VIII and activated prothrombin complex concentrate, in Mariani G, Russo MA, Mandelli F (eds): *Activated Prothrombin Complex Concentrates*. New York, Praeger, 1982.

119. RIZZA CR, MATTHEWS JM: Effect of frequent factor VIII replacement on the level of factor VIII antibodies in hemophiliacs. *Br J Haematol* 52:13, 1982.

120. SULTAN Y, KAZATCHKINE MD, MAISONNEUVE P, NYDEGGER UE: Anti-idiotypic suppression of autoantibodies to factor VIII (antihaemophilic factor) by high dose intravenous gammaglobin. *Lancet* (2):765, 1984.

121. NILSSON IM, BERNTORP E, ZETTERVALL O: Induction of split tolerance and clinical cure in high responding hemophiliacs with factor IX antibodies. *Proc Natl Acad Sci USA* 83:9169, 1986.

122. HASEGAWA DK, EDSON JR: Detection of factor VIII and IX inhibitors after first exposure to heat-treated concentrates. *Lancet* 1:449, 1987.

123. PRESTON FE, UNDERWOOD JCE, MITCHELL VE: Percutaneous liver biopsy and chronic liver disease in hemophiliacs. *Lancet* 2:292, 1978.

124. ALEDORT LM, LEVINE PH, HILGARTNER M, BLATT P, SPERO JA, GOLDBERG JD, BIANCHI L, DESMET V, SCHEUER P, POPPER H, BERK PD: A study of liver biopsies and liver disease among hemophiliacs. *Blood* 66:367, 1985.

124a. GOMPERTS ED: Procedures for the inactivation of viruses in clotting factor concentrates. *Am J Hematol* 23:925, 1986.

125. GILCHRIST GS, HAMMOND D, MELNYK J: Hemophilia A in a phenotypically normal female with XX/XO mosaicism. *N Engl J Med* 273:1402, 1965.

126. LUSHER JM, ZUELZER WW, EVANS RK: Hemophilia A in chromosomal female subjects. *J Pediatr* 74:265, 1969.

127. MORITA H: The occurrence of homozygous hemophilia in the female. *Acta Haematol* 45:112, 1971.

128. ULUTIN ON, MUFTOUGLU AV, PALAMAL S: Hemophilia A in a girl with female sex-chromatin pattern. *Thromb Diath Haemorrh* 14:65, 1965.

129. WHISSELL DY, HOAG MS, AGGELER PM, KROPATKIN M, GAMER E: Hemophilia in a woman. *Am J Med* 38:119, 1965.

130. GRAHAM JB, BARROW ES, ROBERTS HR, WEBSTER WP, BLATT PM, BUCHANAN P, CEDERBAUM AI, ALLAIN JP, BARRETT DA, GRALNICK HR: Dominant inheritance of hemophilia A in three generations of women. *Blood* 46:175, 1975.

131. SOFF GA, LEIN J: Familial multiple coagulation factor deficiencies. *Semin Thromb Hemost* 7:112, 1981.

132. SELIGSOHN V, ZIVELIN A, ZWANG E: Decreased factor VIII clotting antigen levels in the combined factor V and VIII deficiency. *Thromb Res* 33:95, 1983.

133. GIDDINGS JC, SUGRUE A, BLOOM AL: Quantitation of coagulant antigens and inhibition of activated protein C in combined factor V and VIII deficiency. *Br J Haematol* 52:495, 1982.

134. TRACY PB, EIDE LL, BOWIE EJW, MANN KG: Radioimmunoassay of factor V in human plasma and platelets. *Blood* 60:59, 1982.

135. MARLAR RA, GRIFFIN JH: Deficiency of protein C inhibitor in combined factor V/VIII deficiency disease. *J Clin Invest* 66:1186, 1980.

136. CANFIELD WM, KISIEL W: Evidence of normal functional levels of activated protein C inhibitor in combined factor V/VIII deficiency disease APL inhibitor. *J Clin Invest* 70:1260, 1982.

137. GARDINER JE, GRIFFIN JH: Studies on human protein C inhibitor in normal and factor V/VIII deficient plasmas. *Thromb Res* 36:197, 1984.

138. SUZUKI K, NISHIOKA J, HASHIMOTO S, KAMIYA T, SAITO H: Normal titer of functional and immunoreactive protein C-inhibitor in plasma of patients with congenital combined deficiency of factor V and factor VIII. *Blood* 62:1266, 1983.

139. ESMON CT: The subunit structure of thrombin-activated factor V. Isolation of activated factor V, separation of subunits, and reconstruction of biological activity. *J Biol Chem* 254:964, 1979.

140. NESHEIM ME, MANN K: Thrombin-catalyzed activation of single chain bovine factor V. *J Biol Chem* 254:1326, 1979.

141. NESHEIM ME, MYRMEL KH, HIBBARD L, MANN KG: Isolation and characterization of human coagulation factor V. *J Biol Chem* 254:508, 1979.

142. KANE WH, MAJERUS PW: Purification and characterization of human coagulation factor V. *J Biol Chem* 256:1002, 1981.

143. KATZMAN JA, NESHEIM ME, HIBBARD LS, MANN KG: Isolation of functional human coagulation factor V by using a hybridoma antibody. *Proc Natl Acad Sci USA* 78:162, 1981.

144. SUZUKI K, DAHLBACK B, STENFLO J: Thrombin-catalyzed activation of human coagulation factor V. *J Biol Chem* 257:6556, 1982.

145. FASS DN, HEWICK RM, KNUTSON GJ, NESHEIM ME, MANN KG: Internal duplication and sequence homology of factors V and VIII. *Proc Natl Acad Sci USA* 82:1688, 1985.

146. CHURCH WR, JERNIGAN RL, TOOLE J, HEWICK RM, KNOPF J, KNUTSON GJ, NESHEIM ME, MANN KG, FASS DN: Coagulation factors V and VIII and ceruloplasmin constitute a family of structurally related proteins. *Proc Natl Acad Sci USA* 81:6934, 1984.

147. KANE WH, DAVIE EW: Cloning of a cDNA coding for human factor V, a blood coagulation factor homologous to factor VIII and ceruloplasmin. *Proc Natl Acad Sci USA* 83:6800, 1986.

148. OWREN PA: Parahemophilia, hemorrhagic diothesis due to the absence of a previously unknown clotting factor. *Lancet* 1:446, 1947.

149. KINGSLEY CS: Familial factor V deficiency: The pattern of heredity. *J Med* 23:323, 1954.

150. OWEN CA JR: Parahemophilia. *Arch Intern Med* 95:194, 1955.

150a. SEELER RA: Parahemophilia: Factor V deficiency. *Med Clin North Am* 56:119, 1972.

151. SEELER RA: Parahemophilia factor V deficiency. *Med Clin North Am* 56:119, 1972.

152. MILETICH JP, KANE WH, HOFMANN SL, STANFORD N, MAJERUS PW: Deficiency of factor Xa-factor Va binding sites on the platelets of a patient with a bleeding disorder. *Blood* 54:1015, 1979.

153. TRACY PB, EIDE LL, BOWIE EJW, MANN KG: Radioimmunoassay of factor V in human plasma. *Blood* 60:59, 1982.

154. LAWN RM, WOOD WI, GITSCHIER J, WION KL, EATON D, BEHAR GA, TUDDENHAM EGD: Cloned factor VIII and the molecular genetics of hemophilia. *Cold Spring Harbor Symp Quant Biol* 51:365, 1986.

CHAPTER 87

VON WILLEBRAND DISEASE

J. EVAN SADLER

1. Von Willebrand factor (vWF) is a complex multimeric glyco-protein that is found in plasma, in platelet α granules, and in subendothelial connective tissue. vWF performs two biologic functions that are required for normal hemostasis. It binds to specific receptors on the platelet surface and in subendothelial connective tissue to form a bridge between the platelet and areas of vascular damage, and it binds to and stabilizes blood coagulation factor VIII. This interaction between vWF and factor VIII is necessary for normal factor VIII survival in the circulation. Deficiency of vWF results in defective platelet adhesion and also causes a secondary deficiency of factor VIII. Consequently, deficiency of vWF may cause bleeding that mimics either platelet dysfunction or hemophilia.

2. Inherited deficiency of vWF causes von Willebrand disease (vWD), the most common inherited bleeding disorder of human beings. If all degrees of severity are included, vWD appears to affect approximately 8000 per million. Clinically significant vWD affects approximately 125 people per million, a prevalence similar to that of hemophilia A.

3. vWD is a very heterogeneous disorder that has been classified into several major subtypes. The most common form (type I) is transmitted as an autosomal dominant trait and appears to be due to simple quantitative deficiency of all vWF multimers. A clinically severe variant (type III) is characterized by recessive inheritance and virtual absence of vWF. Most variants that are characterized by a dysfunctional protein are classified as type II. These usually exhibit a relative deficiency of the larger vWF multimers in plasma. Type II vWD is further subdivided according to whether the dysfunctional protein has decreased or paradoxically increased function in certain laboratory tests that reflect binding of vWF to platelets. Additional variants are characterized by specific structural abnormalities that are detected upon gel electrophoresis of the mutant vWF multimers.

4. Replacement with human plasma cryoprecipitate is the cornerstone of therapy for severe vWD. Clinically milder variants can often be treated without exposure to blood products through pharamacologic manipulation of plasma vWF levels. For many patients with vWD the intravenous or intranasal administration of the vasopressin analogue DDAVP causes a rise in plasma vWF that is sufficient to treat spontaneous and traumatic bleeding or to sustain normal hemostasis during surgery.

5. The vWF cDNA and portions of the genomic DNA have been cloned and sequenced. These data provide a framework for the investigation of the molecular basis of vWD. Total and partial gene deletions have been characterized as the cause of severe vWD (type III) in four unrelated affected pedigrees. These patients also have developed alloantibody inhibitors to transfused vWF, an unusual complication of therapy. Several restriction fragment length polymorphisms have been described for the vWF gene that can augment the use of biochemical testing for genetic counseling and prenatal diagnosis.

HISTORICAL ASPECTS

Von Willebrand factor (vWF) and the corresponding inherited deficiency state take their name from Erik von Willebrand, who in 1926 described a bleeding disease that affected several branches of a large family from Föglö on the Åland islands in the Gulf of Bothnia, Finland.[1,2] In contrast to classic hemophilia, the mode of inheritance was autosomal dominant rather than X-linked and the bleeding was usually from mucocutaneous sites rather than joints and deep tissues. The disorder was characterized by a prolonged bleeding time, with normal coagulation time, clot retraction, and platelet count. Von Willebrand named the condition *hereditary pseudohemophilia*, distinguishing it from thrombocytopenic purpura and Glanzmann thrombasthenia.

The pathogenesis of von Willebrand disease (vWD) remained controversial for over 30 years. Von Willebrand and subsequent investigators thought that the bleeding disorder was caused either by platelet dysfunction or by a lesion of the vasculature.[3,4] In 1953, several reports described patients with prolonged bleeding times who also had decreased plasma factor VIII activity, suggesting that an abnormality of the blood might be responsible for their apparent platelet or vascular dysfunction.[4-6] These patients were not immediately recognized to have von Willebrand disease, but later studies showed that the original patients described by von Willebrand were indistinguishable and also had reduced factor VIII activity.[7,8]

The concept of a plasma deficiency was confirmed when the prolonged bleeding time and factor VIII deficiency in von Willebrand disease were shown to be corrected by transfusion of a plasma factor VIII concentrate.[7,8] The same plasma fraction prepared from patients with severe hemophilia A was also effective,[9] indicating that the hemostatic defect in von Willebrand disease could be corrected by a "von Willebrand factor" that was found in normal or hemophilia A plasma. This factor was clearly not identical to factor VIII.

Despite this clinical evidence that vWF and factor VIII were different, recognition that they were distinct proteins was obscured by the fact that factor VIII is usually deficient in von Willebrand disease. Furthermore, the transfusion of vWF into patients with von Willebrand disease produces a sustained rise in plasma factor VIII levels that cannot be explained by the content of factor VIII transfused. Factor VIII may remain elevated for several days, and decays with a half-disappearance time much longer than that of factor VIII in normal subjects.[9-12]

Nonstandard abbreviations used in this chapter are: DDAVP = 1-desamino-8-D-arginine vasopressin; GPIb (GPIIb, GPIIIa) = platelet glycoprotein Ib (IIb, IIIa); GPIIb-IIIa = platelet glycoprotein IIb-IIIa complex; vWAg = von Willebrand antigen; vWD = von Willebrand disease; vWF = von Willebrand factor.

The relationship between factor VIII and vWF was further confused because early partial purifications of factor VIII activity yielded a protein that by immunochemical assays was clearly deficient in von Willebrand disease plasma but was present in normal antigenic amounts in hemophilia A plasma.[13–17] Conversely, the autoantiserums to factor VIII that developed in some patients with hemophilia A did not recognize this "factor VIII–related antigen."[18–20] To reconcile these data, some investigators proposed that vWF was a protein specified by an autosomal gene that served as a precursor to factor VIII, which was produced when a protein specified by an X-linked gene acted on vWF.[21–23] These observations gave rise to one of the most persistent confusions in the study of hemostasis, in which the term *factor VIII* referred either to (antihemophilic) factor VIII or to vWF, depending on the context.

The first evidence that vWF was specifically required for platelet adhesion in vivo was obtained in 1960 by Borchgrevink, who found that patients with vWD had higher platelet counts in blood from capillary lesions than did normal controls.[24] Subsequently, decreased platelet adhesion in vitro was demonstrated by the perfusion of blood from patients with vWD through a column of glass beads.[25,26] Transfusion of either normal plasma, hemophilia A plasma, or factor VIII concentrate was shown to correct both the bleeding time and the in vitro platelet adhesion defect in vWD.[7,8,25,27] This glass bead retention assay was used for the first documented purification of vWF.[15]

A more convenient assay for human vWF was developed in 1971 by Howard and Firkin, who discovered that the antibiotic ristocetin induced platelet aggregation in normal platelet-rich plasma but not in plasma from patients with vWD.[28] The defect was corrected by normal plasma, hemophilia A plasma, or partially purified vWF. A similar defect could be induced in normal plasma by heteroantiserums to vWF.

Factor VIII was known to behave as a very large macromolecule that could apparently be dissociated into a smaller active species by buffers of high ionic strength.[29] This salt-induced transition was shown to resolve factor VIII from the ristocetin-dependent platelet aggregating activity of vWF which did not decrease in apparent size.[30] Bovine plasma aggregates human platelets in the absence of ristocetin, and similar experiments demonstrated that bovine platelet aggregating activity, or vWF, could also be resolved from factor VIII.[31]

Conclusive proof that factor VIII and vWF were independent proteins was subsequently obtained by protein sequencing and cDNA cloning, as discussed below for the vWF and in Chap. 86 for factor VIII. Together, these methods demonstrated that the two proteins have unique primary sequences that are encoded by distinct genes. Furthermore, the product of each gene has the appropriate biologic activity in the absence of the other.

At one time, von Willebrand disease was thought to be a single entity that was characterized in part by deficiency of both vWF activity and the corresponding protein antigen. In 1972 Holmberg and Nilsson showed that a subgroup of patients with von Willebrand disease have a normal plasma concentration of vWF antigen.[32] By crossed immunoelectrophoresis, the vWF antigen in these patients was shown to have excessively rapid mobility, consistent with a structural abnormality.[33,34] Subsequent studies have revealed still more evidence of phenotypic heterogeneity in von Willebrand disease.

BIOCHEMISTRY OF VON WILLEBRAND FACTOR

Knowledge of the biochemistry of vWF provides a necessary framework for organizing and understanding the pathogenesis of the many variants of von Willebrand disease. vWF has a particularly complex structure that requires a correspondingly complicated biosynthesis. Accordingly, vWF deficiency could result from defects in biosynthetic processing or from the structural alteration of specific functional domains.

Biosynthesis and Localization of vWF

Von Willebrand factor is synthesized by endothelial cells,[35,36] megakaryocytes,[37,38] and perhaps by the syncytiotrophoblast of placenta.[39] The structure of vWF was determined by a combination of protein chemistry methods and cDNA cloning. The ~9 kb vWF mRNA encodes a primary translation product of 2813 amino acids (Fig. 87-1) that includes a conventional signal peptide of 22 residues, an unusually large propeptide of 741 residues, or ~100,000 Da and the mature subunit of 2050 residues, or ~270,000 Da.[40–44] The pro-vWF contains four distinct types of repeated domains that together make up over 90 percent of the sequence. The A domains contain from 193 to 200 amino acids and are found in three imperfect tandem copies. The triplicated B domains contain 25 to 35 residues, and the duplicated C domains contain 116 to 119 residues. Finally, the D domains contain 351 to 376 residues and are present in four copies. There is also a small D′ fragment that represents the carboxy-terminal one-fourth of a complete D domain. The first pair of D domains are tandemly arranged in the propeptide, but the remaining complete D domains are separated by over 700 amino acids that contain the triplicated A domains. The propeptide cleavage site lies between the second D domain and the D′ fragment that occurs at the amino-terminal end of the third complete D domain.

vWF contains a remarkable amount of cysteine. In fact, cysteine is the most abundant amino acid in the protein, comprising 234 of the total 2813 residues (8.3 percent). The cysteines are clustered at the amino-terminal and carboxy-terminal ends of the sequence, and the triplicated A domains correspond to a cysteine-poor region in the middle of the protein.

Shortly after removal of the signal peptide, the ~370,000-Da pro-vWF[45–47] dimerizes by disulfide bond formation between the carboxy-terminal region of the subunits (Fig. 87-2) to yield the basic repeating unit of mature vWF, the protomer.[45,48,49] The protomers undergo further polymerization by forming disulfide bonds between the amino-terminal ends of subunits to yield a series of homologous oligomers. This polymerization appears to occur at about the same time that the pro-vWF dimers arrive in the Golgi apparatus, and is associated with removal of the propeptide from all but ~1 percent of the subunits.[48] The oligomers in plasma range in size from ~500,000-Da dimers to species of over 10 million Da and 20 subunits.[50–53] Subunits that retain the propeptide are found in all of the multimers.[48]

The propeptide of vWF is identical to von Willebrand antigen II,[44,54] a ~100-kDa protein of unknown function that is found in blood plasma and platelet α granules.[55,56] Whether von Willebrand antigen II is essential for vWF biosynthesis or

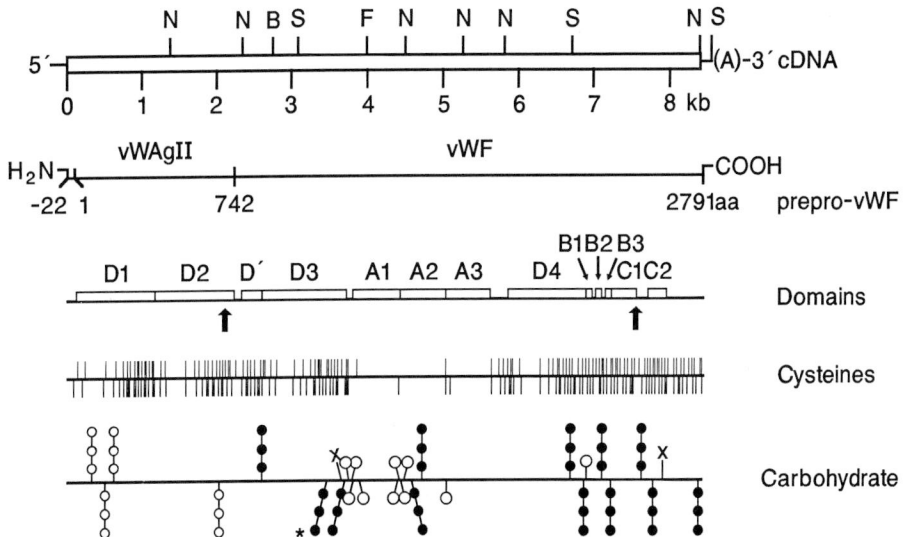

Fig. 87-1 Structural features of the prepro-vWF cDNA and protein sequences. cDNA: The restriction map of the cDNA indicates only sites for *Ncol*, N; *Bam*HI, B; *Sacl*, S; and *Fspl*, F. The open bar represents the open reading frame and the flanking thin lines the 5′- and 3′-noncoding sequences. The poly-A tail is represented by (A). The scale is in kilobases, kb. Prepro-vWF: The schematic structure of the primary translation product displays the amino acids (aa) of the signal peptide (−22 to −1), the von Willebrand antigen II (vWAgII) propeptide (1–741), and the mature vWF subunit (742–2791). Domains: The repeated domains are labeled A to D. The locations of two Arg-Gly-Asp sequences are indicated by arrows (↑). Cysteines: The sites of cysteine residues are indicated by vertical marks. In regions with a very high density of cysteine residues one mark may represent several cysteines. Carbohydrate: The sites of potential *N*-linked glycosylation are indicated by the open symbols (○-○-○). The filled symbols (●-●-●) indicate sites shown to be glycosylated by protein sequencing. The asterisk (*) marks a glycosylated asparagine residue in the unusual sequence Asn-Ser-Cys. The symbol X indicates potential *N*-linked glycosylation sites that are not glycosylated in mature vWF. The large open circles (○) mark sites of *O*-linked glycosylation.

has an independent biologic function is not known. One heterozygous individual was reported to have only partial propeptide removal with normal multimer distribution; therefore, vWAgII cleavage may not be required for multimer assembly.[57] By contrast, von Willebrand antigen II appears to form noncovalent dimers spontaneously,[58] and a recombinant cDNA construction that encoded a vWF precursor without the propeptide could only direct the formation of dimers and not higher multimers.[59] These observations suggest that the propeptide may be needed for vWF multimer assembly.

In addition to proteolytic processing and disulfide bond formation, vWF is subject to several other posttranslational modifications that may affect its function. There are a total of 17 potential *N*-linked glycosylation sites in prepro-vWF with the sequence Asn-X-Thr/Ser (Fig. 87-1). Plasma vWF contains ~19 percent carbohydrate by weight,[60] distributed among 12 asparagine-linked and 10 serine/threonine-linked oligosaccharides.[42] All but two of the 13 potential *N*-linked sites in the mature subunit are glycosylated, and one glycosylated asparagine residue occurs in the unusual sequence, Asn-Ser-Cys. Additional carbohydrate may be attached to the von Willebrand antigen II propeptide. The antibiotic tunicamycin inhibits the asparagine-linked glycosylation of nascent vWF. The resultant carbohydrate-deficient pro-vWF monomers do not dimerize and the propeptide is not removed, suggesting that this glycosylation is required for the normal assembly of vWF structure.[61] Also, inorganic sulfate is incorporated into

Fig. 87-2 Biosynthesis of vWF. The primary translation product of the mRNA for vWF is translocated into the lumen of the rough endoplasmic reticulum (ER), where the signal peptide is removed and *N*-linked glycosylation begins. The resultant pro-vWF rapidly dimerizes by the formation of number (x) of disulfide bonds in the carboxyl-terminal region of the protein sequence. Pro-vWF dimers are transported to the Golgi apparatus and then to Weibel-Palade bodies. In one or both of these locations, *O*-linked and *N*-linked glycosylation is completed, inorganic sulfate (Su) is incorporated, the vWAgII propeptide is cleaved from almost all of the subunits, and multimers are created by the formation of a number (y) of intersubunit disulfide bonds near the amino-terminal end of the subunits. The symbols for *N*-linked and *O*-linked oligosaccharides are as in Figure 87-1.

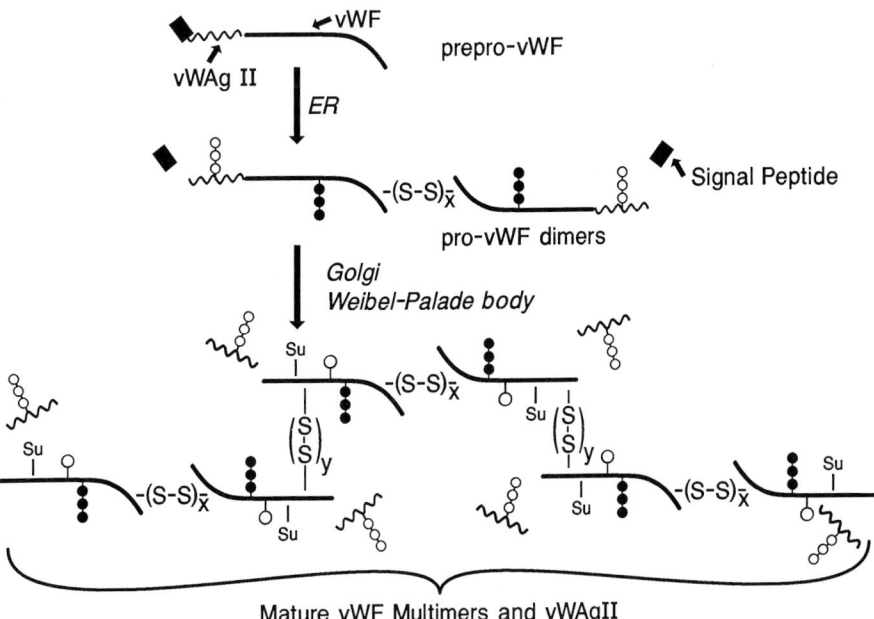

vWF by cultured endothelial cells (Fig. 87-2). Sulfate has been found in both the 270,000 Da and 370,000 Da subunits of all vWF multimers except the intracellular pro-vWF dimer.[62] The structure and function of the sulfated moiety is not known.

Mature vWF and von Willebrand antigen II are both stored in endothelial cells in a unique organelle, the Weibel-Palade body.[63] These are 0.1 × 2 to 3 μm vesicles containing regularly spaced longitudinal tubular structures[64] that may represent closely packed vWF molecules. Whether they participate in the assembly of vWF multimers or are simply storage organelles is not known. vWF is also found at the periphery of the α granules of platelets in tubular structures that resemble those of Weibel-Palade bodies,[65] as well as in subendothelial connective tissue[66,67] and the syncytiotrophoblast of placenta.[39] The vWF isolated from plasma, endothelial cells, subendothelium, and platelets displays similar multimeric structure, although the multimers and associated minor "satellite" bands of plasma and platelet vWF appear to have slightly different mobilities in high resolution gel electrophoresis systems.[68]

Metabolism

The plasma concentration of vWF is ~10 μg/ml, with a wide range of normal concentration from 40 to 200 percent of the mean.[69] Some of this variability may be due to an effect of blood type. Both vWF antigen levels[70,71] and ristocetin-cofactor activity[72] are lower in individuals of blood type O. Plasma vWF levels appear to increase slightly with increasing age.[71,72] Approximately 15 percent of circulating vWf is found in platelets.[73]

The plasma concentration of vWF increases in response to many physiological stimuli including adrenergic stress, vasopressin, growth hormone, and estrogens (reviewed in Ref. 74). Adrenergic agents and vasopressin act through independent pathways. The effect of adrenergic agonists is blocked by propranolol and is probably mediated by β-adrenoreceptors. Propranolol has no effect on the response to the vasopression analogue, 1-desamino-8-D-arginine vasopressin (DDAVP). Neither epinephrine nor vasopressin stimulates the secretion of vWF by cultured vascular endothelial cells.[75,76] In vivo, DDAVP may indirectly induce the secretion of vWF stored in Weibel-Palade bodies.

Estrogen stimulates vWF synthesis in cultured endothelial cells.[77] This in vitro response may explain the elevated vWF levels that occur during pregnancy and chronic estrogen therapy (reviewed in Ref. 74).

Certain products of blood coagulation act directly on endothelial cells to stimulate the secretion of vWF. Human α thrombin induces the rapid release of vWF that appears to be complete after 10 min of exposure to thrombin and does not require continued protein synthesis.[78-80] Release requires the presence of extracellular calcium, is associated with depletion of the Weibel-Palade bodies,[79] and appears to require the thrombin active site.[78] Fibrin also induces the release of vWF, and this effect is not duplicated by fibrinogen, fibrinopeptides A and B, factor XIII, or tissue plasminogen activator. Fibrin prepared by clotting with reptilase is not effective, indicating that a specific fibrin structure is required.[80] Thus, products of thrombosis may have localized effects on the adjacent vascular endothelium to recruit additional vWF to the clot environment. In addition, the vWF secreted by endothelial cells in

response to such stimuli appears to contain especially large and biologically potent vWF multimers.[81]

The metabolic fate of vWF is not known in much detail. Clearance from the circulation of ^{125}I-labeled vWF occurs in two phases. In both normal persons and patients with hemophilia A, an initial rapid phase with a half-disappearance time of 4.5 h is followed by a slower phase with a half-disappearance time of 20 h. The larger multimers seem to be cleared more rapidly than small multimers.[11] The catabolism of vWF probably involves proteolysis within the circulation. Specific proteolytic fragments of the basic subunit are present in plasma vWF.[60,82] These fragments are reduced or absent in the larger vWF multimers that are released into the circulation by the administration of DDAVP, and with time both the multimer pattern and subunit fragmentation pattern return to those present before DDAVP.[83] This proteolysis may contribute to the relatively rapid disappearance of larger multimers from the circulation, whether transfused or endogenous.

Biologic Activities and Structure-Function Relationships of vWF

vWF has two well-characterized biologic functions. It is necessary for the adhesions of platelets to regions of vascular damage, and it is necessary for the normal survival of factor VIII in circulation. These functions have been dissected in vitro into several distinct binding interactions that are dependent on specific domains of the protein sequence as well as higher orders of structure that include organization into multimers (Table 87-1). Abnormalities in any of these interactions might contribute to the phenotype of von Willebrand disease.

The Role of vWF in Platelet Adhesion to Subendothelial Connective Tissue. Several in vitro perfusion systems have been described for the study of vWF function in promoting platelet adhesion to damaged blood vessels and connective tissue constituents. When whole blood is perfused over everted blood vessel segments, platelets adhere to the surface if the endothelium has been removed.[84] Platelet adherence to the subendothelium is decreased in blood from patients with von Willebrand disease,[85-87] but can be corrected by the addition of purified vWF.[87,88] Conversely, platelet adherence using blood from patients with hemophilia A is normal[86,87] and that observed with normal blood is inhibited by antibodies to vWF.[89,90] This dependence on vWF is only seen at high wall shear rates that may occur in the microcirculation.[86,89] The

Table 87-1 Binding Activities of vWF

Ligand	_Biologic function_
Collagens	May mediate platelet adhesion to subendothelium
Other connective tissue elements	May mediate platelet adhesion to subendothelium
Platelet glycoprotein Ib	Required for platelet adhesion to subendothelium
Platelet glycoprotein IIb-IIIa	May mediate platelet adhesion to subendothelium and vWF-dependent platelet aggregation
Factor VIII	Stabilizes factor VIII in the circulation
Heparin	Unknown
Sulfated glycolipids	Unknown

NOTE: References can be found in the text.

platelet adhesion that is observed at lower shear rates is not increased by vWF and may depend on other proteins in the blood or subendothelium.

There are three principal sites of vWF localization that might contribute to vWF-dependent platelet adhesion: plasma, platelet α granule, and subendothelial connective tissue. The importance of plasma vWF for platelet adhesion is readily demonstrated in the perfusion systems just discussed and is evident from the successful treatment of bleeding in von Willebrand disease by transfusion of vWF. An independent contribution by the vWF already localized in the subendothelium is strongly supported by perfusion studies using rabbit[91] and human vessel segments.[92] The activation of platelets induces the release of additional vWF from platelet α granules that could augment vWF-dependent processes. Platelet vWF has been shown to promote adhesion to collagen in perfusates that lack vWF[93] and to correlate inversely with the bleeding time in some patients with vWD type I.[94] The relative role of vWF in these three pools in normal hemostasis is difficult to assess, but all of them may participate in vWF-mediated platelet adhesion in vivo.

Binding of vWF to Subendothelial Connective Tissue. The substances in the subendothelial connective tissue that support vWF-dependent platelet adhesion have not been completely characterized. The extracellular matrix elaborated by endothelial cells in culture contains many proteins besides vWF, including collagen, fibronectin, and thrombospondin. This extracellular matrix also supports vWF-dependent platelet adhesion, as does purified collagen.[95,96] vWF binds directly to a variety of native vertebrate collagens, but not to denatured collagen.[97–99] There may be targets other than collagen in the subendothelium or extracellular matrix, since vWF also binds to extracellular matrix that is apparently devoid of collagen.[100–102] A monoclonal antibody to vWF that inhibits the binding of vWF to purified collagens type I and III does not appear to inhibit vWF binding to the extracellular matrix, and conversely a different monoclonal antibody to vWF that inhibits binding to extracellular matrix does not appear to inhibit the binding of vWF to collagens.[103] Whether such a possible collagen-independent interaction will promote platelet adhesion is controversial. Plasma and matrix fibronectin may be able to support some platelet adhesion at high or low shear rates independent of vWF, while thrombospondin is apparently inactive in perfusion assays.[104,105] Thus, the best candidate for physiologically important vWF binding in the subendothelium is collagen, although other connective tissue elements may also be important.

Interaction of vWF with Specific Platelet Receptors. Two distinct receptors for vWF have been identified in the platelet plasma membrane. Platelet glycoprotein Ib (GPIb) appears to be the principal receptor responsible for vWF-dependent platelet adhesion to vascular subendothelium. Patients afflicted with the Bernard-Soulier syndrome, which is characterized by deficiency of platelet membrane glycoprotein Ib,[106,107] have a severe bleeding disorder associated with defective vWF-dependent platelet adhesion to subendothelium in vitro (see Chap. 90).[86,108] This phenomenon is mimicked by treatment of normal platelets with antibodies to GPIb.[109] This same receptor also mediates the ristocetin-dependent platelet-aggregating activity of vWF.[110,111] This interaction does not require platelet activation and can be demonstrated with formalin-fixed normal platelets.[112,113] Ristocetin-induced binding

of vWF to platelets is deficient in the Bernard-Soulier syndrome,[114] and binding to normal platelets is inhibited by monoclonal antibodies to GPIb.[115,116]

A second receptor for vWF is present on activated platelets. The platelet glycoprotein IIB-IIIa complex (GPIIb-IIIa) does not bind vWF in resting platelets. Upon activation with thrombin or other agonists, GPIIb-IIIa acquires the ability to bind several plasma proteins, including fibrinogen,[117–119] fibronectin,[120] and vWF.[121] These proteins appear to interact competitively with a common site on GPIIb-IIIa.[122] This may reflect the presence of similar short Arg-Gly-Asp–containing recognition sequences in all three proteins. Additional sequences may contribute to the binding of certain of these proteins to GPIIb-IIIa, particularly the carboxyl-terminal 12 amino acids of the γ chain of fibrinogen.[123] Binding of vWF to normal platelets is inhibited by antibodies to GPIIb-IIIa,[116] and does not occur at all in Glanzmann thrombasthenia, which is characterized by deficiency of GPIIb-IIIa (see Chap. 90).[124] The binding of vWF to GPIIb-IIIa requires calcium ions,[121] in contrast to the ristocetin-induced binding of vWF to GPIb, which is calcium-independent.[125]

The physiological importance of the interaction between vWF and GPIIb-IIIa is not known. Concentrations of fibrinogen found in plasma are sufficient to prevent the binding of soluble vWF to activated platelets,[126–128] and this suggests that vWF binding to GPIIb-IIIa should not occur, except perhaps in patients with afibrinogenemia.[129] However, vWF immobilized in the vessel wall may bind with higher affinity to activated platelets than does soluble vWF. Resting platelets do not adhere to surfaces coated with vWF, but thrombin-activated platelets bind avidly to such surfaces. This calcium-dependent interaction with surface-bound vWF is not inhibited by physiological concentrations of fibrinogen,[130] so that it might be significant in vivo.

The GPIb and GPIIb-IIIa sites may interact during vWF-mediated platelet adhesion. Human vWF treated with neuraminidase (asialo-vWF) will bind to normal platelets in the absence of ristocetin.[131–133] This binding is inhibited by antibodies to GPIb, so that asialo-vWF appears to bind to the same site as does native vWF in the presence of ristocetin.[134] The binding of asialo-vWF to platelets causes platelet granule release and stimulates the subsequent binding of fibrinogen to GPIIb-IIIa to cause platelet aggregation. Antibodies to GPIIb-IIIa do not inhibit the binding of asialo-vWF to platelets, but do prevent the subsequent binding of fibrinogen and platelet aggregation. Thus, vWF bound to GPIb appears to act as a platelet agonist, inducing platelet aggregation through a pathway dependent on GPIIb-IIIa.[134]

Stabilization of Factor VIII by vWF. Factor VIII is noncovalently bound to vWF in the blood and the two proteins can be resolved by chromatography in buffers of high ionic strength.[29,30] Activation of factor VIII by thrombin also appears to cause dissociation from vWF.[135] The vWF binding site is on the light chain of factor VIII.[136] Factor VIII is a minor constituent of this factor VIII–vWF complex, comprising only ~1 percent of the mass of circulating vWF. This interaction is necessary for the normal survival of factor VIII in the circulation. Pure factor VIII transfused into patients with hemophilia A or normal volunteers disappears from the circulation with a half-life of about 12 h, and this is similar to the half-life of the factor VIII–vWF complex.[11,12] In contrast, pure factor VIII transfused into patients with severe vWD has a half-life of only ~2.4 h.[12] As discussed under "Historical

Aspects," the transfusion of vWF in severe vWD produces a rise in plasma factor VIII that often persists for several days, while the bleeding time and ristocetin cofactor activity are only corrected for several hours.[9,10,12] This response to transfusion appears to be adequately explained by a model in which endogenously synthesized factor VIII binds to and is stabilized by the infused vWF. The larger multimers that can correct the bleeding time and ristocetin cofactor levels are more rapidly metabolized,[11] and the remaining smaller multimers continue to protect factor VIII. Thus, severe deficiency of vWF causes a secondary deficiency of factor VIII. In theory, defective interaction between vWF and factor VIII could give rise to a phenotype of autosomal dominant hemophilia A with normal vWF function. To date no such patients have been reported.

Other Binding Activities of vWF. Additional binding activities of vWF have been described that have no known physiological function at this time. vWF binds to immobilized heparin,[137] and this interaction was used for the purification of vWF by affinity chromatography on heparin agarose.[138] It is possible that binding to heparinlike glycosaminoglycans contributes to the interaction of vWF with the vascular subendothelium. vWF also binds specifically and with high affinity to certain sulfated glycolipids. This interaction is only weakly inhibited by heparin and may be mediated by an independent binding site.[139] Whether appropriate sulfated glycolipids are accessible to vWF in vivo is not known.

Structure-Function Relationships of vWF. The multimeric structure of vWF appears to be important for its function in promoting platelet adhesion. The larger multimers in plasma adhere selectively to resting platelets in the presence of ristocetin[140] and to collagen,[141] while the small multimers do not. The large multimers in cryoprecipitate support platelet adhesion to subendothelium in perfusion systems, while the small multimers found in cryosupernatant do not.[142] Accordingly, some degree of polymerization may be necessary for optimal vWF function. The apparent relationship between multimer size and function has been invoked to explain the functional defect in subtypes of von Willebrand disease that are characterized by a lack of large multimers. This correlation may instead reflect the greater proportion of degraded subunits in naturally occurring small multimers.[60,82] If small multimers are made in vitro by partial reduction of large multimers, they fully retain the ability to support platelet adhesion to subendothelium in perfusion assays, although ristocetin-dependent platelet aggregation is reduced.[142] Thus, the relationship between multimer formation, ristocetin cofactor activity, and hemostatic function of vWF remains poorly understood.

Binding sites for several ligands have been localized to specific segments of the vWF subunit (Fig. 87-3). The site of interaction with platelet glycoprotein Ib has been placed within a 48- to 52-kDa tryptic peptide that contains amino acid residues 448–729 of the mature subunit and correlates with repeated domain A1.[143] This same fragment also contains binding-sites for collagen[144] and heparin.[145] A second collagen-binding site appears to lie within domain A3.[146] A second heparin-binding site has been reported in the first ~300 amino acids of the mature subunit overlapping with domains D' and part of D3, although specificity and affinity for heparin were not determined.[147] This same region contains a binding site for factor VIII.[148] The tetrapeptide sequence, Arg-Gly-Asp-Ser, occurs near the carboxyl terminus of domain C1.[149] This sequence lies within a segment of the protein (residues 1366–2050 of the mature subunit) that interacts with the glycoprotein IIb-IIIa complex of thrombin-activated platelets.[150] Several other adhesive glycoproteins appear to interact with receptors through sites that contain Arg-Gly-Asp sequences (also known as RGD sequences in single letter code), including fibronectin, vitronectin, and fibrinogen (reviewed in Ref. 151). There is no direct evidence that this sequence in vWF is part of the ligand for the platelet glycoprotein IIb-IIIa complex, although short peptides containing Arg-Gly-Asp do inhibit vWF binding to activated platelets.[152] None of these proteins are known to be homologous, and the presence of similar functional binding sites may represent convergent evolution. A second Arg-Gly-Asp sequence occurs in the vWF propeptide;[43] whether it has any function is not known.

The glycosidically bound oligosaccharides of the vWF have been demonstrated to have nonspecific but nevertheless essential functions. The sialic acid and galactose residues appear to protect the native protein from degradation by proteases.[153] The sialic acid residues are necessary to prevent clearance of vWF from the circulation by the liver.[154] They also prevent spontaneous interaction of vWF with platelet GPIb in the absence of ristocetin, as discussed above under "Interaction of vWF with Specific Platelet Receptors."

MOLECULAR BIOLOGY OF VON WILLEBRAND FACTOR

Chromosome Localization of the vWF Gene and Related Sequences

The complete sequence of the ~9 kb vWF cDNA has been determined.[40,41,43,44,149,155–157] Hybridization probes from the extreme 3' end and 5' end of the ~9 kb vWF cDNA were used to localize the gene for vWF to the tip of the short arm of human chromosome 12.[156–158] The vWF locus has been ordered with 15 other loci into a continuous genetic map of chromosome 12, and is the most telomeric marker yet available on chromosome 12p (see Chap. 6). vWF lies within a region for which recombination is more frequent in males than in females, in contrast to the rest of chromosome 12, for which recombination is more frequent in females.[159]

Restriction fragments from the center of the cDNA sequence hybridize to the vWF locus on chromosome 12 and also to apparently homologous sequences on chromosome 22.[158] Whether the chromosome 22 sequences represent a pseudogene or a gene for a related protein is not known. These uncharacterized sequences on chromosome 22 interfere with the analysis of vWF gene structure by Southern blotting and cause some difficulty in the identification of restriction fragment length polymorphisms for the gene.

Structure of the Human vWF Gene

Overlapping λ-phage and cosmid clones that span over 170 kb of the vWF gene were isolated from human genomic DNA libraries by hybridization with vWF cDNA probes. Restriction mapping and Southern blotting studies indicate that there must be at least 30 exons. The sequence of six complete exons and the placement of 11 intron-exon boundaries are reported to date.[160–162] The transcription initiation site together with

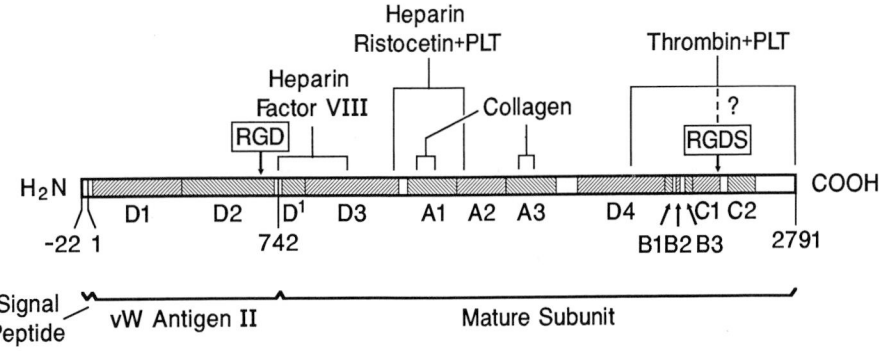

Fig. 87-3 Structure-function relationships of vWF. The repeated domains are shaded and labeled, and the positions of the signal peptide, vWAgII propeptide, and mature subunit sequences are indicated. The location of Arg-Gly-Asp (RGD) sequences and various binding sites of vWF are shown. Platelet is abbreviated PLT.

apparent promoter elements and the exon containing the extreme 3′ end of the gene were defined and sequenced.[162]

There is a rough correlation between the placement of certain intron-exon boundaries and the repeated domains defined by examination of the protein sequence, which lends further support to the hypothesis that these domains evolved by gene segment duplication. For example, intron-exon boundaries occur at the carboxyl-terminal boundary of domain A3, at the carboxyl-terminal boundary of domain C2, and at the amino-terminal boundary of domain D4.[160,161]

Nucleotide Sequence Polymorphisms for Human vWF

Several restriction fragment length polymorphisms (RFLPs) have been identified within the vWF gene using probes from the 3′ end of the cDNA[159,163–167] (Table 87-2). There is no published information concerning possible linkage disequilibrium between these RFLPs. Additional sequence polymorphisms that do not alter restriction endonuclease recognition sites have also been described.[41,44] Given the very large size of the vWF gene, many more such polymorphisms will certainly be discovered. These will find application in the study of the inheritance and mechanisms of vWD, and in genetic counseling.

Evolution of vWF and Possible Homology to Other Proteins

The highly repeated structure of vWF indicates that the gene has a complex evolutionary history including several gene segment duplications. Methods similar to those employed for detecting homology among different proteins have been used to compare the sequences of the vWF D domains and to develop a model for their evolution based upon the relative divergence of these homologues.[44]

Comparison of the amino acid sequence for the vWF precursor to other protein sequences has yielded five proteins that may be homologous to portions of vWF: complement factor B, complement component C2, thrombospondin, and α_1-procollagen types I and III. Complement factor B is a serine protease zymogen of the alternate complement pathway. A 225-amino acid segment of factor B between residues 230 and 454 can be aligned with each of the vWF A domains so that 20 to 24 percent of the amino acid residues are identical, and there is a rough correlation between the location of intron-exon boundaries in both genes.[41,160,161,168–171] This region of factor B contains the activation cleavage site but precedes the serine protease domain. Complement component C2 of the classic pathway plays a role analogous to that of factor B in the alternate pathway, and these two proteases are homologous along

their entire length. The sequence of complement component C2 between residues 219 and 444 also aligns well with the vWF A domains and the factor B sequence.[172,173] The corresponding region of other serine proteases is highly variable, and shows no resemblance to the A domains of vWF. No functional relationship between vWF and either complement component C2 or factor B has been demonstrated. The apparently significant alignment of these protein sequences and the similarities of vWF and factor B gene structure may prove to reflect descent from a common ancestor, but at present the significance of this potential relationship is not known.

Portions of the C domains of vWF appear to be homologous to cysteine-rich segments of thrombospondin[174] and α_1-procollagen types I[175] and III.[176,177] Among these proteins, the segments are similar in length (64–74 residues) and have nine or ten conserved cysteines. These segments are encoded by single exons of the procollagen genes[175,176] but by at least two exons of the vWF gene.[160] The functional significance of this potential homology is not known.

CLINICAL ASPECTS OF VON WILLEBRAND DISEASE

Diagnosis

Von Willebrand disease should be suspected in any patient with mucocutaneous bleeding despite a normal platelet count. The symptoms may be highly variable with time in a single patient, and all affected members of a given pedigree may not have the same difficulty with bleeding.[69,178–180] Even for se-

Table 87-2 RFLPs for the Human von Willebrand Factor Gene

Enzyme (reference)	Allele size, kb	Allele frequencies	Observed heterozygosity
BglII	9.7	0.64	0.40
(157,161)	7.1	0.36	
BamHI	7.2	0.82	NR*
(162)	7.8	0.18	
XbaI	6.9	0.87	NR
(163)	5.2	0.13	
TaqI	3.3	0.51	NR
(164)	2.6	0.49	
TaqI	4.5	0.95	NR
(164)	2.3	0.05	
RsaI	1.0	0.22	NR
(165)	0.66	0.78	

*NR = not reported.

verely affected patients with symptoms since birth and a clear family history, the pattern of bleeding is not specific for von Willebrand disease. Thus, final diagnosis depends on laboratory testing and may require repeated examinations of patients and family members.

Detailed reviews of the laboratory assessment of vWD can be found elsewhere.[181,182] Tests commonly applied to the diagnosis of vWD fall into four general categories: (1) *The template bleeding time.* This test assesses the formation of the platelet plug in vivo by determining the time required to stop bleeding from a standard skin laceration. A prolonged bleeding time is not at all specific for vWD because connective tissue and platelet disorders may also exhibit this abnormality. It is a sensitive test, since the bleeding time is prolonged at some time in essentially all patients with clinically significant vWD. Patients with mild vWD may have intermittently normal bleeding times.[69] (2) *Platelet aggregation stimulated by the antibiotic ristocetin.* This test measures vWF binding to platelet glycoprotein Ib. Two variations are used. One (ristocetin-induced platelet aggregation, or RIPA) employs patient platelets suspended in autologous plasma. The second (ristocetin cofactor activity) employs patient plasma and washed allogeneic platelets. In each assay platelet aggregation as a function of ristocetin concentration is compared to normal controls, and the concentration required to achieve a specific degree or rate of aggregation is noted. The snake venom factor botrocetin has effects similar but not identical to those of ristocetin and can also be used to measure the ability of vWF to bind to resting platelets.[183,184] (3) *Measurement of factor VIII antigen or activity in patient plasma.* Factor VIII binds to plasma vWF, so that factor VIII levels usually reflect vWF antigen concentration. Comparison of ristocetin cofactor activity with factor VIII level provides an estimate of the specific activity of the residual vWF protein in patient plasma. This ratio of ristocetin cofactor activity to factor VIII level is expected to be normal for quantitative deficiencies of vWF and reduced for variants of vWD with a qualitatively abnormal protein. (4) *Physical characterization of patient vWF.* Gel electrophoresis and immunochemical assays measure vWF concentration and also multimer distribution. This category of assays includes the quantitative immunoassay of vWF antigen and the qualitative assessment of multimer distribution by counterimmunoelectrophoresis. More precise assessment of multimer distribution is obtained by electrophoresis of plasma on agarose or agarose-acrylamide copolymer gels in the presence of sodium dodecyl sulfate (Fig. 87-4). In such systems, the vWF multimers are separated according to size and can be visualized by reaction with ^{125}I-labeled anti-human vWF antibody and autoradiography.[52,53]

Comparison of platelet and plasma vWF with these assays may be useful in the further characterization of specific variants of vWD.[185,186] In addition, the time course of response of plasma factor VIII, vWF antigen, ristocetin cofactor activity, and vWF multimer structure to a trial infusion of the vasopressin analogue DDAVP can distinguish still more phenotypic heterogeneity.[186-188] Finally, the detailed investigation of family members to show inheritance of vWD is useful to firmly exclude acquired conditions that may mimic vWD.

Prevalence

Von Willebrand disease appears to be the most common inherited bleeding disorder of human beings. If all cases that

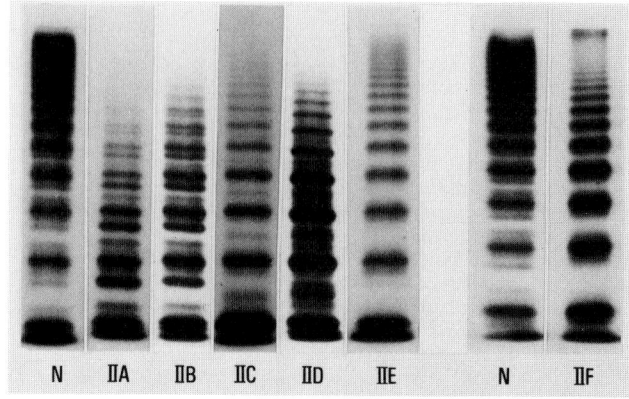

Fig. 87-4 Multimer patterns in variants of von Willebrand disease. The multimers and additional satellite bands that are present in vWD types IIA and IIB and have mobility like that of normal vWF (N) but the intensities are abnormal. Intrinsic structural abnormalities are present in the individual multimers in types IIC, IID, IIE, and IIF, which include the presence of abnormal bands or the absence of normal ones. (From Ruggeri and Zimmerman, Blood, 70:895, 1987. Used by permission.)

come to the attention of specialized referral centers are included, the prevalence of vWD is approximately 125 per million.[189] However, the screening of an unselected population of schoolchildren in Italy has suggested that the true prevalence is much higher and closer to ~8000 per million.[72] Severe vWD with essentially no detectable circulating vWF antigen is quite rare and affects 0.5 to 3 per million in Western Europe and Scandinavia,[190] and perhaps as many as 5.3 per million among selected Arab populations in the Middle East.[191]

The genetics of vWD emphasize some of the problems in the use of the terms *dominant* and *recessive* to describe human phenotypes (see Chap. 1). In many families, heterozygosity is consistently associated with obvious phenotypic effects and the dominant description is satisfactory. In other instances, heterozygosity is relatively or totally asymptomatic and may be associated with subtle laboratory abnormalities, thus blurring separation of dominant and recessive phenotypes. In addition, it is likely that the genotype at other loci and nongenetic factors influence the phenotype, particularly in individuals heterozygous for vWD. Recognizing these limitations, it is still useful to separate phenotypes generally as dominant or recessive disorders.

In most pedigrees, vWD is transmitted as an autosomal dominant trait. By contrast, many patients with severe vWD who appear to be homozygotes or compound heterozygotes for a mutant allele at the vWF locus are born to clinically normal parents. Sensitive testing may disclose mild functional abnormalities in such parents who are obligate heterozygotes, but these families are usually considered to be affected by a recessive disease. Selected pedigrees may exhibit both dominant and recessive patterns of inheritance.[179,180] This variability suggests that some interplay between specific mutant alleles and the genetic background of the host determines whether clinically significant bleeding may occur. Certain variants of type II vWD consistently exhibit recessive inheritance, although most are dominant.

One unlinked modifier of plasma vWF levels appears to be related to blood type. Both vWF antigen[70,71] and ristocetin cofactor activity[72] are lower in persons of blood type O compared to blood types A and B.

Classification

The most commonly employed scheme for the classification of vWD divides the disease into two broad categories based principally on the vWF multimer pattern observed in plasma. In type I disease all normal multimer species are present but reduced proportionally, suggesting a simple quantitative deficiency of vWF. In type II disease the larger multimers are absent (Fig. 87-4), indicating a qualitative structural abnormality of the mutant protein. Further subdivision of type II vWD is made based on the response of patient vWF to ristocetin. A third category, type III vWD, is distinguished by the virtual absence of vWF antigen and activity from plasma and by clinically recessive inheritance.

This scheme has the advantage that the major subdivisions correlate well with patient groups having distinctive biochemical and clinical characteristics. As more sensitive and discriminating tests have been devised, additional heterogeneity has been demonstrated in all types of vWD. In particular, certain patients with a type I multimer distribution clearly have structural and functional abnormalities of the vWF subunit. Thus, the distinction between quantitative (type I) and qualitative (type II) vWD has become more difficult. This chapter will emphasize the properties of the more common types of vWD (Table 87-3). A complete description of virtually all known variants of vWD has been compiled by Zaverio Ruggeri,[192] and that review can be consulted for references to case reports for rare or unclassified variants.

Type I vWD. This is the most common form of vWD and is the type originally identified by Erik von Willebrand. It accounts for approximately 70 percent of cases seen in specialized treatment centers.[189,193] Plasma vWF is reduced; ristocetin cofactor activity and factor VIII are reduced propor-

tionately, and multimer distribution is normal. This is compatible with a simple quantitative deficiency of vWF with no intrinsic functional abnormality. Inheritance is autosomal dominant.

vWD type I is a heterogeneous disorder. Some pedigrees have normal content of platelet vWF, while others have similar deficiencies of both plasma and platelet vWF.[185,186] These distinctions may correlate with the efficacy of therapy with DDAVP.[186] In addition, a normal-appearing multimer distribution does not correlate perfectly with normal function. Variants of type I have been described with normal multimers but with decreased ristocetin cofactor activity[194,195] or hyperresponsiveness to ristocetin.[196,197] Certain variants exhibit differences from normal multimer structure with characteristic abnormalities of "satellite" bands,[194] the presence of large amounts of uncleaved pro-vWF in multimers,[57] or larger than normal plasma multimers.[198] If type I vWD is constrained to include only quantitative disorders, then some of these variants that are currently designated as type I will require reclassification.

Type II vWD. The principal distinction between type I and type II vWD is that the larger multimers are missing from plasma of patients with type II vWD.[53] This structural difference from normal vWF is felt to reflect a qualitative abnormality. Further subdivision of type II vWD is made on the basis of ristocetin-dependent assays and analysis of multimer patterns by high-resolution gel electrophoresis (Fig. 87-4).

In type IIA vWD both ristocetin-induced platelet aggregation and ristocetin cofactor activity are disproportionately decreased relative to vWF antigen, indicating that the residual plasma vWF has reduced function.[53] This subgroup is structurally and immunochemically[199] heterogeneous. The plasma vWF levels may be normal or decreased. The distribution of

Table 87-3 Classification of von Willebrand Disease

von Willebrand disease	Genetics	Factor VIII	vWF antigen	Ristocetin cofactor activity	RIPA*	Multimer structure
Type I	Dominant	Decreased	Decreased	Decreased	Decreased or normal	Normal in plasma and platelets
Type IIA	Dominant	Decreased or normal	Decreased or normal	Markedly decreased	Absent or decreased	Large and intermediate multimers absent from plasma and platelets
Type IIB	Dominant usually	Decreased or normal	Decreased or normal	Decreased or normal	Increased	Large multimers absent from plasma; normal in platelets
Type IIC	Recessive	Decreased or normal	Decreased or normal	Decreased	Decreased	Large multimers absent from plasma and platelets; increased smallest multimer; characteristic abnormality of multimers and satellite bands
Type IID	Dominant	Normal	Normal	Decreased	Decreased	Large multimers absent from plasma and platelets; characteristic abnormality of multimers and satellite bands
Type IIE	Dominant	Normal	Decreased	Decreased	Decreased	Large multimers absent from plasma and platelets; characteristic abnormality of multimers and satellite bands
Type III	Recessive	Markedly decreased	Absent or markedly decreased	Absent	Absent	None visualized

*RIPA = Ristocetin-induced platelet aggregation in platelet-rich plasma.

multimers for platelet vWF is variable but usually resembles that of plasma.[53,185] The deficit of larger multimers suggests a defect in polymerization, but in some pedigrees increased sensitivity to proteolysis may contribute to the observed multimer distribution.[200,201] This is supported by the variable response to DDAVP in vWD type IIA. Many but not all patients show at least a partial correction of both bleeding time and multimer distribution after treatment with DDAVP.[188,201,202] The mode of inheritance is typically dominant.

In type IIB vWD, there is hyperresponsiveness of platelet-rich plasma to ristocetin,[203] although ristocetin cofactor activity is generally decreased. Plasma vWF multimers show a characteristic type II distribution, but platelets contain a normal multimer distribution.[53] Administration of DDAVP to patients with type IIB vWD causes the release of large multimers into the circulation, but the larger species are rapidly cleared, apparently through spontaneous binding to platelet glycoprotein Ib. This is accompanied by transient severe thrombocytopenia.[204] Thus, the small multimer pattern in this variant is at least partly due to enhanced clearance of large multimers rather than to a polymerization defect. The increased RIPA is due to the presence of large, abnormal, hyperresponsive vWF multimers adsorbed to patient platelets in platelet-rich plasma. The normal or decreased ristocetin cofactor activity is due to the absence of these same multimers from (platelet-poor) patient plasma, so that added allogeneic platelets are not agglutinated by them. Probable variants of this subtype have been reported with chronic thrombocytopenia, circulating platelet aggregates, and spontaneous platelet aggregation in vitro.[205,206] The disorder is usually transmitted as a dominant trait, but a few families that exhibit recessive inheritance of vWD type IIB have been reported.[207,208] The few cases described of vWD type I with hyperresponsiveness to ristocetin[196,197] probably represent a mild form of the type IIB defect.

Most type II vWD patients can be characterized as either type IIA or type IIB, but there are many additional rare type II variants. In general these have been defined by unique features of individual multimers upon gel electrophoresis (Fig. 87-4). Type IIC is an interesting variant that shows recessive inheritance.[209] There is some heterogeneity of the type IIC multimer pattern among affected pedigrees and even among patients within a single pedigree, suggesting that several different vWF alleles may interact to give a type IIC–like phenotype.[210–213] Type IID[214,215] and type IIE[82,216] are additional dominantly transmitted variants with characteristic structural abnormalities of individual multimers. In contrast to vWD type IIA and IIB, which exhibit increased proteolytic degradation of circulating vWF subunits, these rarer variants (types IIC, IID, and IIE) show less evidence of subunit degradation compared to normal vWF.[82]

Single case reports appear to define the additional variants called type IIF,[217] type IIG,[218] type IIH,[219] and type B.[220] The mode of transmission of vWD type IIF is not known. Type IIG is probably dominant, and type IIH appears to be recessive. Type B has a complex multimer distribution that is skewed toward smaller species and shows an interesting dissociation between ristocetin cofactor activity (absent) and botrocetin cofactor activity (normal). The mode of inheritance is autosomal dominant.

Type III vWD. Patients with type III, or "severe," vWD, also called "severe" type I, have essentially no detectable vWF antigen or activity in blood plasma, and usually have factor VIII

levels of $\leq$ 1 to 10 percent of normal.[27,221,222] Patients with undetectable factor VIII activity generally have low levels of detectable factor VIII antigen.[19,223] These patients appear to have received two defective vWF alleles, and many such patients have clinically unaffected parents. The traces of vWF detected in the plasma or platelets of some patients with type III vWD have exhibited several different structural abnormalities,[222] indicating that this subgroup is heterogeneous.

Some authors have separated type III patients occurring in clearly recessive pedigrees from the occasional severely deficient patient within type I pedigrees.[72] However, there is extensive variability in expression among heterozygotes within families that contain severe vWD patients, and deficiencies of vWF antigen and ristocetin cofactor activity can often be detected in the clinically normal relatives of type III patients.[179,180] Until the gene structure of type I and type III alleles can be compared, any distinction between "type III vWD" and "homozygous or compound heterozygous type I vWD" may be difficult to sustain.

Molecular Defect

In principle, deficiency of vWF activity could result from lesions within the vWF gene or indirectly as a consequence of mutations that affect biosynthesis or metabolism. No cause of vWD that is unlinked to the vWF locus has been described to date.

Southern blotting studies using vWF cDNA probes have been reported for 52 apparently unrelated vWD pedigrees so far. The mechanism of vWD was determined at the level of gene structure in a small number of these patients. Nineteen families with typical autosomal dominant vWD type I, and 27 families with vWD type III were shown to have hybridization patterns that were not distinguishable from normal controls.[157,158,224,225] This method of analysis cannot easily detect small gene deletions or point mutations, and more sensitive techniques will be necessary to determine the cause of vWD in these patients.

One patient with vWD type III was shown to have a heterozygous deletion of the entire vWF gene. An asymptomatic parent had the same abnormality by Southern blotting, so that the patient appeared to have inherited a second defective allele with a normal hybridization pattern from the other parent.[224] One patient with severe vWD type III was described who appeared to have a small deletion at the extreme 3' end of the vWF gene. The parents of this patient were second cousins, and it is likely that he was homozygous for the defective allele.[225] One patient from each of two unrelated Italian families[158] and four affected sibs from a third Italian family[224] with vWD type III were shown to have total deletions of both alleles of the vWF gene as the cause of their disease. The extent of deletion probably exceeded 160 kb of DNA in these patients.

All but one of these seven patients with detectable gene deletions in both alleles had developed alloantibody inhibitors to transfused vWF.[158,224,225] The one patient without this complication had three affected siblings who did have antibodies to vWF.[225] In contrast, none of the patients reported to date with vWD type III and normal Southern blotting patterns has had alloantibodies, which suggests that gene deletions may predispose to the development of inhibitors during therapy. A similar correlation has been noted for hemophilia B and the factor IX gene,[226] but as larger numbers of patients have been investigated, the concordance between the occurrence of antibodies to factor IX and the presence of gene deletions has been less consistent[227] (see Chap. 85). Such a simple correlation between gene deletion and alloantibody production seems unlikely to remain absolute for vWD as well.

A large pedigree for vWD type IIA was studied by Southern blotting with vWF cDNA probes to demonstrate that certain RFLPs cosegregate with the disease. The genetic defect causing the vWD type IIA phenotype in this family, therefore, is probably due to a mutation within or near the vWF gene and not to an abnormality at a locus that controls posttranslational processing.[228]

Clinical Course

For patients with a quantitative deficiency of vWF (vWD types I and III) the severity of disease generally correlates with the degree of vWF functional deficiency, and may vary from clinically insignificant to life-threatening. The severity of the disease in patients with qualitative disorders of vWF (vWD type II) may exceed what might be expected based on the functional deficiency ascertained by laboratory tests.[210,213,214,217] Symptoms are usually present from childhood and often from birth.[7,8,10,27] These commonly include easy bruisability, cutaneous hematomas, epistaxis, bleeding from gums, and prolonged bleeding from cuts. Persistent severe bleeding after minor oral trauma and after dental extraction is common. More than half of affected women have menorrhagia that may require blood transfusion. Bleeding from a ruptured ovarian follicle or corpus luteum may also be severe.[189,213] Gastrointestinal bleeding seems to be relatively rare but may be life-threatening. Patients with vWD type III and essentially undetectable vWF often have factor VIII levels low enough to predispose to spontaneous hemarthrosis, joint deformities, and soft tissue bleeding.[7,8,27] Milder forms of vWD are almost never associated with hemarthrosis. The bleeding tendency of vWD has been reported to decrease with advancing age,[7,27] although this is not a uniform feature of the disease.

During pregnancy the plasma vWF levels are increased in normal individuals and in patients with most forms of vWD other than vWD type III.[229–232] This increase is most marked in the third trimester, and reflects in part the influence of estrogens on vWF levels. If this increase represents functional vWF, then labor and delivery are usually uncomplicated. Plasma vWF levels return to baseline within a few days, and patients with vWD should be monitored closely during at least the first week after delivery for serious postpartum bleeding. Patients with dysfunctional vWF (most type II variants) frequently have severe difficulty with hemorrhage during labor and delivery.[196,210,214]

Type IIB vWD can present special problems during pregnancy. The increased plasma concentration of abnormal vWF that is a consequence of the physiologic stimulus of pregnancy can cause severe and prolonged thrombocytopenia, with marked blood loss during delivery.[233] Children born with vWD type IIB may present with congenital thrombocytopenia.[208]

The development of alloantibodies to vWF is distinctly uncommon in vWD (reviewed in Ref. 234). All of the reported cases have occurred in patients with vWD type III who produce no immunologically recognizable vWF-like protein. In the type III subgroup, the prevalence of alloantibodies to vWF is about 7.5 percent, this is similar to the prevalence of alloantibodies to factor VIII in hemophilia A. Not all severely affected patients develop antibodies, and there may be a familial predisposition to this complication of therapy. The apparent association between deletions within the vWF gene and the development of such antibodies was discussed above.

Differential Diagnosis

The symptoms that occur in vWD are not at all specific, and many conditions of quite different pathogenesis may be associated with a similar bleeding diathesis. These include primary platelet disorders such as Bernard-Soulier syndrome and the ingestion of antiplatelet drugs. In particular, the use of aspirin by patients with hemophilia A can produce a clinical picture quite like severe vWD.[235] In most cases, vWD can be excluded easily by appropriate laboratory testing.

vWD type IIB should be considered as a potential cause of congenital thrombocytopenia.[208] This subtype can also cause thrombocytopenia during pregnancy and may be confused with idiopathic thrombocytopenic purpura, leading to unnecessary therapy with prednisone and withholding of cryoprecipitate and platelet transfusions.[233] One man, who was ultimately found to have vWD type IIB, underwent splenectomy for presumed idiopathic thrombocytopenic purpura unresponsive to prednisone.[205]

Two conditions are especially difficult to distinguish from vWD because they may cause low vWF levels and even mimic vWD type II multimer distributions. These are the acquired von Willebrand syndrome and "platelet-type" or "pseudo" vWD. The *acquired von Willebrand syndrome* refers to a condition of spontaneous bleeding associated with decreased vWF occurring in adults without a prior personal or family history of vWD. Approximately 36 cases have been reported (reviewed in Ref. 234). Most have been associated with a recognized autoimmune or lymphoproliferative disorder that suggests an immunologic cause. Some patients have lacked such underlying diseases, and fewer than half of the afflicted patients were shown to possess autoantibodies to vWF. The multimer distribution in plasma may resemble type I or type II vWD. In the latter case, discrimination between vWD type IIB and the acquired von Willebrand syndrome may be difficult. Both conditions are characterized by relatively normal platelet vWF structure and concentration and by shortened survival in the circulation of the endogenous vWF released by DDAVP. In contrast to vWD type IIB, the ristocetin sensitivity of platelet vWF is normal in the acquired von Willebrand syndrome, and exogenous vWF administered by transfusion has shortened survival.

Platelet-type or pseudo-vWD is clinically very similar to vWD type IIB, but the abnormality lies with the platelet rather than with the vWF. Three unrelated affected families have been reported.[236–238] The condition is inherited as an autosomal dominant trait. Symptoms resemble those of moderately severe vWD, and laboratory abnormalities include a prolonged bleeding time, decreased plasma vWF and factor VIII levels, increased ristocetin-induced platelet aggregation, absence of larger multimers from plasma, and presence of all multimers in platelets. The response to DDAVP is like that of vWD type IIB, with transient thrombocytopenia and spontaneous platelet aggregation.[239] In contrast to vWD type IIB, the addition of normal plasma, hemophilic plasma, cryoprecipitate, or purified vWF to platelet-rich plasma in this disorder causes platelet aggregation without the addition of ristocetin.[237,238,240] The nature of the platelet defect causing this syndrome is not known, but it appears to include a defect in platelet glycoprotein Ib.[241]

Therapy

Patients with severe vWD may bleed either because they lack sufficient vWF to support normal platelet function or because they are factor VIII–deficient, and the response to therapy in vWD emphasizes the distinct functions of these molecules in hemostasis. Hemarthroses, soft tissue hematomas, and postoperative bleeding often respond to elevations of factor VIII, while mucocutaneous bleeding responds to infusions of functional vWF. Factor VIII levels are usually easy to support because even limited amounts of small vWF multimers can stabilize and cause a prolonged elevation of plasma factor VIII level. Correction of the platelet adhesion abnormality is more difficult. Fresh frozen plasma and cryoprecipitate consistently contain functional vWF multimers. The utility of fresh frozen plasma is limited by the large volume needed to infuse sufficient vWF. Frozen cryoprecipitate is widely available and will reliably shorten the bleeding time in most forms of vWD, but the possible transmission of disease by cryoprecipitate makes it less than an ideal therapy. Lyophilized cryoprecipitate may not be as effective.[242] The high potency factor VIII concentrates that are used for the treatment of hemophilia A often are ineffective in the treatment of vWD, probably because the larger vWF multimers in these preparations have been denatured or degraded.[243,244] It is possible to prepare heat-treated concentrates without destroying vWF function,[245] but such concentrates continue to transmit some form of non-A, non-B hepatitis virus,[246] although transmission of human immunodeficiency virus (HIV) is apparently greatly reduced.[247] Better formulations of vWF for replacement therapy would be welcome.

Many patients with mild vWD can avoid exposure to blood products through the pharmacological manipulation of plasma vWF levels. In many patients the vasopressin analogue DDAVP administered intravenously or intranasally causes a three- to sixfold elevation of vWF and factor VIII levels that is maximal in 30 to 90 min.[248–252] Levels decrease to baseline over several hours to several days. Repeated doses often elicit a diminished response,[250] but this is not consistently observed, and the efficacy of repeated doses should be evaluated in individual patients as indicated. For therapy with DDAVP to be effective, the patient must be able to synthesize at least a partially functional vWF. Consequently, DDAVP is expected to be most useful in vWD type I with a simple quantitative deficiency of vWF. The response to DDAVP in vWD type II variants is frequently unsatisfactory. However, there is a great deal of variability in response among these patients, and DDAVP has minimal side effects, so that a therapeutic trial should probably be evaluated in all variants with low ristocetin cofactor activity.[187,188] The drug is contraindicated in patients with enhanced sensitivity to ristocetin such as those who have vWD type IIB, in whom it causes thrombocytopenia and spontaneous platelet aggregation.[204,252] No adverse thrombotic complications have been described in vWD type IIB as a consequence of therapy with DDAVP, but no shortening of the bleeding time has been observed,[204,253] and the question of

whether DDAVP is safe or not in this variant seems moot. Patients with vWD type III generally do not have a useful response to DDAVP.

Fibrinolytic inhibitors may be useful adjuncts for the control of nasopharyngeal and oral bleeding. Menorrhagia in women with vWD can be treated successfully with oral contraceptives. Estrogens have also been used to control hemorrhage from other sites and as preparation for surgery in women with vWD type I.[254,255]

Genetic Counseling

Assessment of the risk of vWD is usually straightforward and requires only the determination of whether a family is affected by a dominant or a recessive variant. For families affected with severe forms of vWD (type III and some type II variants), genetic counseling is the same as for any severe recessive disorder. Prenatal diagnosis has been accomplished for vWD type III by assays of factor VIII and vWF in fetal blood samples.[256,257] The vWF multimer distribution in fetal blood may be diagnostic of type II vWD even if the levels of antigen are not depressed, provided there is no intercurrent disease that might consume large vWF multimers.[258] RFLPs for the vWF gene could be applied to prenatal diagnosis of severe vWD, but no example has yet been reported. Carriers of the defective allele in mildly affected pedigrees could identified with greater certainty by combining the currently employed vWF and factor VIII assays with RFLP analysis. Such families should receive counseling, but most families do not choose to alter reproductive plans because of the mild phenotype.

REFERENCES

1. VON WILLEBRAND EA: Hereditär pseudohemofili. *Fin Laekaresaellsk Handl* 68:87, 1926.
2. VON WILLEBRAND EA: Über hereditäre pseudohaemophilie. *Acta Med Scand* 76:521, 1931.
3. VON WILLEBRAND E, JÜRGENS R: Über eine neue Bluterkrankheit, die konstitutionelle Thrombopathie. *Klin Wochenschr* 12:414, 1933.
4. ALEXANDER B, GOLDSTEIN B: Dual hemostatic defect in pseudohemophilia. *J Clin Invest* 32:551, 1953.
5. LARRIEU MJ, SOULIER JP: Deficit en facteur antihemophilique A chez une fille associée à un trouble saignement. *Rev Hematol* 8:61, 1953.
6. QUICK AJ, HUSSEY VV: Hemophilic condition in the female. *J Lab Clin Med* 42:929, 1953.
7. NILSSON IM, BLOMBÄCK M, JORPES E, BLOMBÄCK B, JOHANSSON S-A: v. Willebrand's disease and its correction with human plasma fraction 1-0. *Acta Med Scand* 159:179, 1957.
8. NILSSON IM, BLOMBÄCK M, VON FRANCKEN I: On an inherited autosomal hemorrhagic diathesis with antihemophilic globulin (AHG) deficiency and prolonged bleeding time. *Acta Med Scand* 159:35, 1957.
9. NILSSON IM, BLOMBÄCK M, BLOMBÄCK B: von Willebrand's disease in Sweden. Its pathogenesis and treatment. *Acta Med Scand* 164:263, 1959.
10. CORNU P, LARRIEU MJ, CAEN J, BERNARD J: Transfusion studies on Willebrand's disease: Effect on bleeding time and factor VIII. *Br J Haematol* 9:189, 1963.
11. OVER J, SIXMA JJ, DOUCET-DE BRUÏNE MHM, TRIESCHNIGG AMC, VLOOSWIJK RAA, BEESER-VISSER NH, BOUMA BN: Survival of ^{125}iodine-labeled factor VIII in normals and patients with classic hemophilia. *J Clin Invest* 62:223, 1978.
12. TUDDENHAM EGD, LANE RS, ROTBLAT F, JOHNSON AJ, SNAPE TJ, MIDDLETON S, KERNOFF PBA: Response to infusions of polyelectrolyte fractionated human factor VIII concentrate in human haemophilia A and von Willebrand's disease. *Br J Haematol* 52:259, 1982.
13. STITES DP, HERSHGOLD EJ, PERLMAN JD, FUDENBERG HH: Factor VIII detection by hemagglutination inhibition: Hemophilia A and von Willebrand's disease. *Science* 171:196, 1971.
14. ZIMMERMAN TS, RATNOFF OD, POWELL AE: Immunologic differentiation

of classic hemophilia (factor VIII deficiency) and von Willebrand's disease. *J Clin Invest* 50:244, 1971.

15. BOUMA BN, WIEGERINCK Y, SIXMA JJ, VAN MOURIK JA, MOCHTAR IA: Immunological characterization of purified anti-haemophilic factor A (factor VIII) which corrects abnormal platelet retention in von Willebrand's disease. *Nature [New Biol]* 236:104, 1972.

16. LEGAZ ME, SCHMER G, COUNTS RB, DAVIE EW: Isolation and characterization of human factor VIII (antihemophilic factor). *J Biol Chem* 248:2946, 1973.

17. SHAPIRO GA, ANDERSEN JC, PIZZO SV, MCKEE PA: The subunit structure of normal and hemophilic factor VIII. *J Clin Invest* 52:2198, 1973.

18. ZIMMERMAN TS, EDGINGTON TS: Factor VIII coagulant activity and factor VIII-like antigen: Independent molecular entities. *J Exp Med* 138:1015, 1973.

19. LAZARCHICK J, HOYER LW: Immunoradiometric measurement of the factor VIII procoagulant antigen. *J Clin Invest* 62:1048, 1978.

20. PEAKE IR, BLOOM AL: Immunoradiometric assay of procoagulant factor VIII antigen in plasma and serum and its reduction in haemophilia. Preliminary studies on adult and fetal blood. *Lancet* 1:473, 1978.

21. BENNETT B, RATNOFF OD, LEVIN J: Immunologic studies in von Willebrand's disease. Evidence that the antihemophilic factor (AHF) produced after transfusions lacks an antigen associated with normal AHF and the inactive material produced by patients with classic hemophilia. *J Clin Invest* 51:2597, 1972.

22. GRALNICK HR, COLLER BS: Molecular defects in haemophilia A and von Willebrand's disease. *Lancet* 1:837, 1976.

23. GRAHAM JB: Genetic control of factor VIII. *Lancet* 1:340, 1980.

24. BORCHGREVINK CF: A method for measuring platelet adhesiveness in vivo. *Acta Med Scand* 162:361, 1960.

25. SALZMAN EW: Measurement of platelet adhesiveness: A simple in vitro technique demonstrating an abnormality in von Willebrand's disease. *J Lab Clin Med* 62:724, 1963.

26. ZUCKER MN: In vitro abnormality of the blood in von Willebrand's disease correctable by normal plasma. *Nature* 197:601, 1963.

27. LARRIEU MJ, CAEN JP, MEYER DO, VAINER H, SULTAN Y, BERNARD J: Congenital bleeding disorders with long bleeding time and normal platelet count. II. Von Willebrand's disease (report of thirty-seven patients). *Am J Med* 45:354, 1968.

28. HOWARD MA, FIRKIN BG: Ristocetin: A new tool in the investigation of platelet aggregation. *Thromb Diath Haemorrh* 26:362, 1971.

29. THELIN GM, WAGNER RH: Sedimentation of plasma antihemophilic factor. *Arch Biochem Biophys* 95:70, 1961.

30. WEISS HJ, HOYER LW: Von Willebrand factor: Dissociation from antihemophilic factor procoagulant activity. *Science* 182:1149, 1973.

31. GRIGGS TR, COOPER HA, WEBSTER WP, WAGNER RH, BRINKHOUS KM: Plasma aggregating factor (bovine) for human platelets: A marker for study of antihemophilic and von Willebrand factors. *Proc Natl Acad Sci USA* 70:2814, 1973.

32. HOLMBERG L, NILSSON IM: Genetic variants of von Willebrand's disease. *Br Med J* 3:317, 1972.

33. KERNOFF PBA, BRUSON R, RIZZA CR: A variant of factor VIII related antigen. *Br J Haematol* 26:435, 1974.

34. PEAKE IR, BLOOM AL, GIDDINGS JC: Inherited variants of factor VIII-related protein in von Willebrand's disease. *N Engl J Med* 291:113, 1974.

35. JAFFE EA, HOYER LW, NACHMAN RL: Synthesis of antihemophilic factor antigen by cultured human endothelial cells. *J Clin Invest* 52:2757, 1973.

36. JAFFE EA, HOYER LW, NACHMAN RL: Synthesis of von Willebrand factor by cultured human endothelial cells. *Proc Natl Acad Sci USA* 71:1906, 1974.

37. NACHMAN R, LEVINE R, JAFFE EA: Synthesis of factor VIII antigen by cultured guinea pig megakaryocytes. *J Clin Invest* 60:914, 1977.

38. SPORN LA, CHAVIN SI, MARDER VJ, WAGNER DD: Biosynthesis of von Willebrand protein by human megakaryocytes. *J Clin Invest* 76:1102, 1985.

39. MARUYAMA I, BELL CE, MAJERUS PW: Thrombomodulin is found on endothelium of arteries, veins, capillaries, and lymphatics, and on syncytiotrophoblast of human placenta. *J Cell Biol* 101:363, 1985.

40. BONTHRON DT, ORR EC, MITSOCK LM, GINSBURG D, HANDIN RI, ORKIN SH: Nucleotide sequence of pre-pro-von Willebrand factor cDNA. *Nucleic Acids Res* 14:7125, 1986.

41. SHELTON-INLOES BB, TITANI K, SADLER JE: cDNA sequences for human von Willebrand factor reveal five types of repeated domains and five possible protein sequence polymorphisms. *Biochemistry* 25:3164, 1986.

42. TITANI K, KUMAR S, TAKIO K, ERICSSON LH, WADE RD, ASHIDA K, WALSH KA, CHOPEK MW, SADLER JE, FUJIKAWA K: Amino acid sequence of human von Willebrand factor. *Biochemistry* 25:3171, 1986.

43. VERWEIJ CL, DIERGAARDE PJ, HART M, PANNEKOEK H: Full-length von Willebrand factor (vWF) cDNA encodes a highly repetitive protein considerably larger than the mature vWF subunit. *EMBO J* 5:1839, 1986.

44. SHELTON-INLOES BB, BROZE GJ JR, MILETICH JP, SADLER JE: Evolution of human von Willebrand factor: cDNA sequence polymorphisms, repeated domains, and relationship to von Willebrand antigen II. *Biochem Biophys Res Commun* 144:657, 1987.

45. WAGNER DD, MARDER VJ: Biosynthesis of von Willebrand protein by human endothelial cells. Identification of a larger precursor polypeptide chain. *J Biol Chem* 258:2065, 1983.

46. LYNCH DC, WILLIAMS R, ZIMMERMAN TS, KIRBY EP, LIVINGSTON DM: Biosynthesis of the subunits of factor VIIIR by bovine aortic endothelial cells. *Proc Natl Acad Sci USA* 80:2738, 1983.

47. LYNCH DC, ZIMMERMAN TS, KIRBY EP, LIVINGSTON DM: Subunit composition of oligomeric human von Willebrand factor. *J Biol Chem* 258:12757, 1983.

48. WAGNER DD, MARDER VJ: Biosynthesis of von Willebrand protein by human endothelial cells: Processing steps and their intracellular localization. *J Cell Biol* 99:2123, 1984.

49. WAGNER DD, LAWRENCE SO, OHLSSON-WILHELM BM, FAY PJ, MARDER VJ: Topology and order of formation of interchain disulfide bonds in von Willebrand factor. *Blood* 69:27, 1987.

50. VAN MOURIK JA, BOUMA BN, LABRUYERE WT, DE GRAF S, MOCHTAR IA: Factor VIII, a series of homologous oligomers and a complex of two proteins. *Thromb Res* 4:155, 1974.

51. COUNTS RB, PASKELL SL, ELGEE SK: Disulfide bonds and the quaternary structure of factor VIII/von Willebrand factor. *J Clin Invest* 62:702, 1978.

52. HOYER LW, SHAINOFF JR: Factor VIII-related protein circulates in normal plasma as high molecular weight multimers. *Blood* 55:1056, 1980.

53. RUGGERI ZM, ZIMMERMAN TS: Variant von Willebrand's disease. Characterization of two subtypes by analysis of multimeric composition of factor VIII/von Willebrand factor in plasma and platelets. *J Clin Invest* 65:1318, 1980.

54. FAY PJ, KAWAI Y, WAGNER DD, GINSBURG D, BONTHRON D, OHLSSON-WILHELM BM, CHAVIN SI, ABRAHAM GN, HANDIN RI, ORKIN SH, MONTGOMERY RR, MARDER VJ: Propolypeptide of von Willebrand factor circulates in blood and is identical to von Willebrand antigen II. *Science* 232:995, 1986.

55. MONTGOMERY RR, ZIMMERMAN TS: von Willebrand's disease antigen II. A new plasma and platelet antigen deficient in severe von Willebrand's disease. *J Clin Invest* 62:1498, 1978.

56. SCOTT JP, MONTGOMERY RR: Platelet von Willebrand's antigen II: Active release by aggregating agents and a marker of platelet release reaction in vivo. *Blood* 58:1075, 1981.

57. MONTGOMERY RR, DENT J, SCHMIDT W, KYRLE P, HIESSNER H, RUGGERI ZM, ZIMMERMAN TS: Hereditary persistence of circulating pro von Willebrand factor (pro-vWF). *Circulation* 74(II):406, 1986.

58. WAGNER DD, FAY PJ, SPORN LA, SHINA S, LAWRENCE SO, MARDER VJ: Divergent fates of von Willebrand factor and its propolypeptide (von Willebrand antigen II) after secretion from endothelial cells. *Proc Natl Acad Sci USA* 84:1955, 1987.

59. VERWEIJ CL, HART M, PANNEKOEK H: von Willebrand factor (vWF) propolypeptide is required for vWF multimer formation. *Thromb Haemost* 58:8, 1987.

60. CHOPEK MW, GIRMA J-P, FUJIKAWA K, DAVIE EW, TITANI K: Human von Willebrand factor: A multivalent protein composed of identical subunits. *Biochemistry* 25:3146, 1986.

61. WAGNER DD, MAYADAS T, MARDER VJ: Initial glycosylation and acidic pH in the Golgi apparatus are required for multimerization of von Willebrand factor. *J Cell Biol* 102:1320, 1986.

62. BROWNING PJ, LING EH, ZIMMERMAN TS, LYNCH DC: Sulfation of von Willebrand factor by human umbilical vein endothelial cells. *Blood* 65:218a, 1983.

63. WAGNER DD, OLMSTED JB, MARDER VJ: Immunolocalization of von Willebrand protein in Weibel-Palade bodies of human endothelial cells. *J Cell Biol* 95:355, 1982.

64. WEIBEL ER, PALADE GE: New cytoplasmic components in arterial endothelia. *J Cell Biol* 23:101, 1964.

65. CRAMER EM, MEYER D, LE MENN R, BRETON-GORIUS J: Eccentric localization of von Willebrand factor in an internal structure of platelet α-granule resembling that of Weibel-Palade bodies. *Blood* 66:710, 1985.

66. BLOOM AL, GIDDINGS JC, WILKS CJ: Factor VIII on the vascular intima: Possible importance in haemostasis and thrombosis. *Nature [New Biol]* 241:217, 1973.

67. HOYER LW, DE LOS SANTOS RP, HOYER JR: Antihemophilic factor antigen. Localization in endothelial cells by immunofluorescent microscopy. *J Clin Invest* 52:2737, 1973.

68. LÓPEZ-FERNANDEZ MF, LÓPEZ-BERGES C, NIETO J, MARTIN R, BATLLE J: Platelet and plasma von Willebrand factor: Structural differences. *Thromb Res* 44:125, 1986.

69. ABILDGAARD CF, SUZUKI Z, HARRISON J, JEFCOAT K, ZIMMERMAN TS: Se-

rial studies in von Willebrand's disease: Variability versus "variants." *Blood* 56:712, 1980.

70. WAHLBERG TB, BLOMBÄCK M, MAGNUSSON D: Influence of sex, blood group, secretor character, smoking habits, acetylsalicylic acid, oral contraceptives, fasting and general health state on blood coagulation variables in randomly selected young adults. *Haemostasis* 14:312, 1984.

71. GILL JC, ENDRES-BROOKS J, BAUER PJ, MARKS WJ JR, MONTGOMERY RR: The effect of ABO blood group on the diagnosis of von Willebrand disease. *Blood* 69:1691, 1987.

72. RODEGHIERO F, CASTAMAN G, DINI E: Epidemiological investigation of the prevalence of von Willebrand's disease. *Blood* 69:454, 1987.

73. NACHMAN RL, JAFFE EA: Subcellular platelet factor VIII antigen and von Willebrand factor. *J Exp Med* 141:1101, 1975.

74. BLOOM AL: The biosynthesis of factor VIII. *Clin Haematol* 8:53, 1979.

75. SHEARN SAM, PEAKE IR, GIDDINGS JC, HUMPHRYS J, BLOOM AL: The characterization and synthesis of antigens related to factor VIII in vascular endothelium. *Thromb Res* 11:43, 1977.

76. TUDDENHAM EGD, LAZARCHICK J, HOYER LW: Synthesis and release of factor VIII by cultured human endothelial cells. *Br J Haematol* 47:617, 1981.

77. HARRISON RL, MCKEE PA: Estrogen stimulates von Willebrand factor production by cultured endothelial cells. *Blood* 63:657, 1984.

78. LEVINE JE, HARLAN JM, HARKER LA, JOSEPH ML, COUNTS RB: Thrombin-mediated release of factor VIII antigen from human umbilical vein endothelial cells in culture. *Blood* 60:431, 1982.

79. LOESBERG C, GONSALVES MD, ZANDBERGEN J, WILLEMS C, VAN AKEN WG, STEL HV, VAN MOURICK JA, DE GROOT PG: The effect of calcium on the secretion of factor VIII-related antigen by cultured human endothelial cells. *Biochim Biophys Acta* 763:160, 1983.

80. RIBES JA, FRANCIS CW, WAGNER DD: Fibrin induces release of von Willebrand factor from endothelial cells. *J Clin Invest* 79:117, 1987.

81. SPORN LA, MARDER VJ, WAGNER DD: Inducible secretion of large, biologically potent von Willebrand factor multimers. *Cell* 46:185, 1986.

82. ZIMMERMAN TS, DENT JA, RUGGERI ZM, NANNINI LH: Subunit composition of plasma von Willebrand factor. Cleavage is present in normal individuals, increased in IIA and IIB von Willebrand disease, but minimal in variants with aberrant structure of individual oligomers (types IIC, IID, and IIE). *J Clin Invest* 77:947, 1986.

83. BATTLE J, LOPEZ-FERNANDEZ MF, LOPEZ-BORRASCA A, LOPEZ-BERGES C, DENT JA, BERKOWITZ SD, RUGGERI ZM, ZIMMERMAN TS: Proteolytic degradation of von Willebrand factor after DDAVP administration in normal individuals. *Blood* 70:173, 1987.

84. BAUMGARTNER HR: The role of blood flow in platelet adhesion, fibrin deposition and formation of mural thrombi. *Microvasc Res* 5:167, 1973.

85. TSCHOPP TB, WEISS HJ, BAUMGARTNER HR: Decreased adhesion of platelets to subendothelium in von Willebrand's disease. *J Lab Clin Med* 83:296, 1974.

86. WEISS HJ, TURITTO VT, BAUMGARTNER HR: Effect of shear rate on platelet interaction with subendothelium in citrated and native blood. I. Shear rate-dependent decrease of adhesion in von Willebrand's disease and the Bernard-Soulier syndrome. *J Lab Clin Med* 92:750, 1978.

87. SAKARIASSEN KS, BOLHUIS PA, SIXMA JJ: Human blood platelet adhesion to artery subendothelium is mediated by factor VIII-Von Willebrand factor bound to the subendothelium. *Nature* 279:636, 1979.

88. WEISS HJ, BAUMGARTNER HR, TSCHOPP TB, TURITTO VT, COHEN D: Correction by factor VIII of the impaired platelet adhesion to subendothelium in von Willebrand disease. *Blood* 51:267, 1978.

89. BAUMGARTNER HR, TSCHOPP TB, MEYER D: Shear rate dependent inhibition of platelet adhesion/aggregation on collagenous surfaces by antibodies to human factor VIII/von Willebrand factor. *Br J Haematol* 44:127, 1980.

90. MEYER D, BAUMGARTNER HR, EDGINGTON TS: Effect of hybridoma antibodies to human factor VIII/von Willebrand factor on the adhesion of platelets to the subendothelium. *Blood* 58:237, 1981.

91. TURITTO VT, WEISS HJ, ZIMMERMAN TS, SUSSMAN II: Factor VIII/von Willebrand factor in subendothelium mediates platelet adhesion. *Blood* 65:823, 1985.

92. STEL HV, SAKARIASSEN KS, DE GROOT PG, VAN MOURIK JA, SIXMA JJ: Von Willebrand factor in the vessel wall mediates platelet adherence. *Blood* 65:85, 1985.

93. FRESSINAUD E, BARUCH D, ROTHSCHILD C, BAUMGARTNER HR, MEYER D: Platelet von Willebrand factor: Evidence for its involvement in platelet adhesion to collagen. *Blood* 68 (Suppl):316a, 1986.

94. GRALNICK HR, RICK ME, MCKEOWN LP, WILLIAMS SB, PARKER RI, MAISON-NEUVE P, JENNEAU C, SULTAN Y: Platelet von Willebrand factor: An important determinant of the bleeding time in type I von Willebrand's disease. *Blood* 68:58, 1986.

95. MUGGLI R, BAUMGARTNER HR, TSCHOPP TB, KELLER H: Automated microdensitometry and protein assays as a measure for platelet adhesion and

aggregation on collagen-coated slides under controlled flow conditions. *J Lab Clin Med* 95:195, 1980.

96. SAKARIASSEN KS, AARTS PAMM, DE GROOT PG, HOUDIJK WPM, SIXMA JJ: A perfusion chamber developed to investigate platelet interaction in flowing blood with human vessel wall cells, their extracellular matrix, and purified components. *J Lab Clin Med* 102:522, 1983.

97. SANTORO SA: Adsorption of von Willebrand factor/factor VIII by the genetically distinct interstitial collagens. *Thromb Res* 21:689, 1981.

98. SANTORO SA, COWAN JF: Adsorption of von Willebrand factor by fibrillar collagen—Implications concerning the adhesion of platelets to collagen. *Coll Relat Res* 2:31, 1982.

99. MORTON LF, GRIFFIN B, PEPPER DS, BARNES MJ: The interaction between collagens and factor VIII/von Willebrand factor: Investigation of the structural requirements for interaction. *Thromb Res* 32:545, 1983.

100. FAUVELL F, GRANT ME, LEGRAND YJ, SOUCHON H, TOBELEM G, JACKSON DS, CAEN JP: Interaction of blood platelets with a microfibrillar extract from adult bovine aorta: Requirement for von Willebrand factor. *Proc Natl Acad Sci USA* 80:551, 1983.

101. HORMIA M, LEHTO V-P, VIRTANEN I: Factor VIII-related antigen. A pericellular matrix component of cultured human endothelial cells. *Exp Cell Res* 149:483, 1983.

102. WAGNER DD, URBAN-PICKERING M, MARDER VJ: von Willebrand protein binds to extracellular matrices independently of collagen. *Proc Natl Acad Sci USA* 81:471, 1984.

103. DE GROOT PG, VAN MOURIK JA, SIXMA JJ: Primary binding site of von Willebrand factor in the subendothelium which mediates platelet adhesion is not collagen. *Thromb Haemost* 58:213, 1987.

104. HOUDIJK WPM, SIXMA JJ: Fibronectin in artery subendothelium is important for platelet adhesion. *Blood* 65:598, 1985.

105. HOUDIJK WPM, DE GROOT PG, NIEVELSTEIN PFEM, SAKARIASSEN KS, SIXMA JJ: Subendothelial proteins and platelet adhesion. von Willebrand factor and fibronectin, not thrombospondin, are involved in platelet adhesion to extracellular matrix of human vascular endothelial cells. *Arteriosclerosis* 6:24, 1986.

106. NURDEN AT, CAEN JP: Specific roles for platelet surface glycoproteins in platelet function. *Nature* 255:720, 1975.

107. NURDEN AT, DUPUIS D, KUNICKI TJ, CAEN JP: Analysis of the glycoprotein and protein composition of Bernard-Soulier platelets by single and two-dimensional SDS-polyacrylamide gel electrophoresis. *J Clin Invest* 67:1431, 1981.

108. WEISS HJ, TSCHOPP TB, BAUMGARTNER HR, SUSSMAN II, JOHNSON MM, EGAN JJ: Decreased adhesion of giant (Bernard-Soulier) platelets to subendothelium: Further implication on the role of the von Willebrand factor in hemostasis. *Am J Med* 57:920, 1974.

109. SAKARIASSEN KS, NIEVELSTEIN PFEM, COLLER BS, SIXMA JJ: The role of platelet membrane glycoproteins Ib and IIb-IIIa in platelet adherence to human artery subendothelium. *Br J Haematol* 63:681, 1986.

110. CAEN JP, NURDEN AT, JEANNEAU C, MICHEL H, TOBELEM G, LEFY-TOLE-DANO S, SULTAN Y, VALENSI F, BERNARD J: Bernard-Soulier syndrome: A new platelet glycoprotein abnormality. Its relationship with platelet adhesion to subendothelium and with the factor VIII/von Willebrand protein. *J Lab Clin Med* 87:586, 1976.

111. JENKINS CSP, PHILLIPS DR, CLEMETSON KJ, MEYER D, LARRIEU MJ, LUSCHER EF: Platelet membrane glycoproteins implicated in ristocetin-induced aggregation. Studies on the proteins on platelets from patients with Bernard-Soulier syndrome and von Willebrand's disease. *J Clin Invest* 57:112, 1976.

112. MACFARLANE DE, ZUCKER MB: A method for assaying von Willebrand factor (ristocetin cofactor). *Thromb Diath Haemorrh* 34:306, 1975.

113. ALLAIN JP, COOPER HA, WAGNER RM, BRINKHOUS KM: Platelets fixed with paraformaldehyde: A new reagent for assay of von Willebrand factor and platelet aggregation factor. *J Lab Clin Med* 85:318, 1975.

114. MOAKE JL, OLSON JD, TROLL JH, TANG SS, FUNICELLA T, PETERSON DM: Binding of radioiodinated human von Willebrand factor to Bernard-Soulier, thrombasthenic and von Willebrand's disease platelets. *Thromb Res* 19:21, 1980.

115. COLLER BS, PEERSCHKE EI, SCUDDER LE, SULLIVAN CA: Studies with a murine monoclonal antibody that abolishes ristocetin-induced binding of von Willebrand factor to platelets: Additional evidence in support of GPIb as a platelet receptor for von Willebrand factor. *Blood* 61:99, 1983.

116. RUGGERI ZM, DE MARCO L, GATTI L, BADER R, MONTGOMERY RR: Platelets have more than one binding site for von Willebrand factor. *J Clin Invest* 72:1, 1983.

117. MARGUERIE GA, PLOW EF, EDGINGTON TS: Human platelets possess an inducible and saturable receptor specific for fibrinogen. *J Biol Chem* 254:5357, 1979.

118. COLLER BS, PEERSCHKE EI, SCUDDER LE, SULLIVAN CA: A murine monoclonal antibody that completely blocks the binding of fibrinogen to plate-

lets produces a thrombasthenic-like state in normal platelets and binds to glycoproteins IIb and/or IIIa. *J Clin Invest* 72:325, 1983.

119. BENNETT JS, HOXIE JA, LEITMAN SF, VILAIRE G, CINES DB: Inhibition of fibrinogen binding to stimulated human platelets by a monoclonal antibody. *Proc Natl Acad Sci USA* 80:2417, 1983.

120. PLOW EF, GINSBERG MH: Specific and saturable binding of plasma fibronectin to thrombin-stimulated human platelets. *J Biol Chem* 256:9477, 1981.

121. FUJIMOTO T, OHARA S, HAWIGER J: Thrombin-induced exposure and prostacyclin inhibition of the receptor for factor VIII/von Willebrand factor on human platelets. *J Clin Invest* 69:1212, 1982.

122. PLOW EF, SROUJI AH, MEYER D, MARGUERIE G, GINSBERG MH: Evidence that three adhesive proteins interact with a common recognition site on activated platelets. *J Biol Chem* 259:5388, 1984.

123. KLOCZEWIAK M, TIMONS S, LUKAS TJ, HAWIGER J: Platelet receptor recognition site on human fibrinogen. Synthesis and structure-function relationship of peptides corresponding to the carboxy-terminal segment of the γ-chain. *Biochemistry* 23:1767, 1984.

124. RUGGERI ZM, BADER R, DE MARCO L: Glanzmann thrombasthenia: Deficient binding of von Willebrand factor to thrombin-stimulated platelets. *Proc Natl Acad Sci USA* 79:6038, 1982.

125. KAO K-J, PIZZO SV, MCKEE PA: Demonstration and characterization of specific binding sites for factor VIII/von Willebrand factor on human platelets. *J Clin Invest* 63:656, 1979.

126. SCHULLEK J, JORDAN J, MONTGOMERY RR: Interaction of von Willebrand factor with human platelets in the plasma milieu. *J Clin Invest* 73:421, 1984.

127. GRALNICK HR, WILLIAMS SB, COLLER BS: Fibrinogen competes with von Willebrand factor for binding to the glycoprotein IIb/IIIa complex when platelets are stimulated with thrombin. *Blood* 64:797, 1984.

128. PIÉTU G, CHEREL G, MARGUERIE G, MEYER D: Inhibition of von Willebrand factor-platelet interaction by fibrinogen. *Nature* 308:648, 1984.

129. DE MARCO L, GIROLAMI A, ZIMMERMAN TS, RUGGERI ZM: von Willebrand factor interaction with the glycoprotein IIb/IIIa complex. Its role in platelet function as demonstrated in patients with congenital afibrinogenemia. *J Clin Invest* 77:1272, 1986.

130. SANTORO SA, COWAN JF: Thrombin enhanced adhesion of platelets to von Willebrand factor substrates. *Thromb Res* 43:57, 1986.

131. VERMYLEN J, DE GAETANO G, DONATI MB, VERSTRAETE M: Platelet-aggregating activity in neuraminidase-treated human cryoprecipitates: Its correlation with factor-VIII-related antigen. *Br J Haematol* 26:645, 1974.

132. VERMYLEN J, BOTTECCHIA D, SZPILMAN H: Factor VIII and human platelet aggregation. III. Further studies on aggregation of human platelets by neuraminidase-treated human factor VIII. *Br J Haematol* 34:321, 1976.

133. DE MARCO L, SHAPIRO SS: Properties of human asialo-factor VIII. A ristocetin-independent platelet-aggregating agent. *J Clin Invest* 68:321, 1981.

134. DE MARCO L, GIROLAMI A, RUSSELL S, RUGGERI ZM: Interaction of asialo von Willebrand factor with glycoprotein Ib induces fibrinogen binding to the glycoprotein IIb/IIIa complex and mediates platelet aggregation. *J Clin Invest* 75:1198, 1985.

135. COOPER HA, REISNER FF, HALL M, WAGNER RH: Effects of thrombin treatment on preparations of factor VIII and the Ca^{2+}-dissociated small active fragment. *J Clin Invest* 56:751, 1975.

136. HAMER RJ, KOEDAM JA, BEESER-VISSER NH, BERTINA RM, VAN MOURIK JA, SIXMA JJ: Factor VIII binds to von Willebrand factor via its Mr-80,000 light chain. *Eur J Biochem* 166:37, 1987.

137. MADARAS F, BELL WR, CASTALDI PA: Isolation and insolubilisation of human F VIII by affinity chromatography. *Haemostasis* 7:321, 1978.

138. FOWLER WE, FRETTO LJ, HAMILTON KK, ERICKSON HP, MCKEE PA: Substructure of human von Willebrand factor. *J Clin Invest* 76:1491, 1985.

139. ROBERTS DD, WILLIAMS SB, GRALNICK HR, GINSBURG V: von Willebrand factor binds specifically to sulfated glycolipids. *J Biol Chem* 261:3306, 1986.

140. MARTIN SE, MARDER VJ, FRANCIS CW, BARLOW GH: Structural studies on the functional heterogeneity of von Willebrand protein polymers. *Blood* 57:313, 1981.

141. AIHARA M, COOPER HA, WAGNER RH: Platelet-collagen interactions: Increase in rate of adhesion of fixed washed platelets by factor VIII-related antigen. *Blood* 63:495, 1984.

142. SIXMA JJ, SAKARIASSEN KS, BEESER-VISSER NH, OTTENHOF-ROVERS M, BOLHUIS PA: Adhesion of platelets to human artery subendothelium: Effect of factor VIII-von Willebrand factor of various multimeric composition. *Blood* 63:128, 1984.

143. FUJIMURA Y, TITANI K, HOLLAND LZ, RUSSELL SR, ROBERTS JR, ELDER JH, RUGGERI ZM, ZIMMERMAN TS: von Willebrand factor. A reduced and alkylated 52/48 kDa fragment beginning at amino acid residue 449 contains

the domain interacting with platelet glycoprotein Ib. *J Biol Chem* 261:381, 1986.

144. PARETI FI, FUJIMURA Y, DENT JA, HOLLAND LZ, ZIMMERMAN TS, RUGGERI ZM: Isolation and characterization of a collagen binding domain in human von Willebrand factor. *J Biol Chem* 261:15310, 1986.

145. FUJIMURA Y, TITANI K, HOLLAND LZ, ROBERTS JR, KOSTEL P, RUGGERI ZM, ZIMMERMAN TS: A heparin-binding domain in human von Willebrand factor. Characterization and localization to a tryptic fragment extending from amino acid residue Val-449 to Lys-728. *J Biol Chem* 262:1734, 1987.

146. ROTH GJ, TITANI K, HOYER LW, HICKEY MJ: Localization of binding sites within human von Willebrand factor for monomeric type III collagen. *Biochemistry* 25:8357, 1986.

147. FRETTO LJ, FOWLER WE, MCCASLIN DR, ERICKSON JP, MCKEE PA: Substructure of human von Willebrand factor. Proteolysis by V8 and characterization of two functional domains. *J Biol Chem* 261:15679, 1986.

148. FOSTER PA, FULCHER CA, MARTI T, TITANI K, ZIMMERMAN TS: A major factor VIII binding domain resides within the amino-terminal 272 amino acid residues of von Willebrand factor. *J Biol Chem* 262:8443, 1987.

149. SADLER JE, SHELTON-INLOES BB, SORACE JM, HARLAN JM, TITANI K, DAVIE EW: Cloning and characterization of two cDNAs coding for human von Willebrand factor. *Proc Natl Acad Sci USA* 82:6394, 1985.

150. GIRMA J-P, KALAFATIS M, PIETU G, LAVERGNE J-M, CHOPEK MW, EDGINGTON TS, MEYER D: Mapping of distinct von Willebrand factor domains interacting with platelet GPIb and GPIIb/IIIa and with collagen using monoclonal antibodies. *Blood* 67:1356, 1986.

151. RUOSLAHTI E, PIERSCHBACHER MD: Arg-Gly-Asp: A versatile cell recognition signal. *Cell* 44:517, 1986.

152. PLOW EF, PIERSCHBACHER MD, RUOSLAHTI E, MARGUERIE GA, GINSBERG MH: The effect of Arg-Gly-Asp-containing peptides on fibrinogen and von Willebrand factor binding to platelets. *Proc Natl Acad Sci USA* 82:8057, 1985.

153. FEDERICI AB, ELDER JH, DE MARCO L, RUGGERI ZM, ZIMMERMAN TS: Carbohydrate moiety of von Willebrand factor is not necessary for maintaining multimeric structure and ristocetin cofactor activity but protects from proteolytic degradation. *J Clin Invest* 74:2049, 1984.

154. SODETZ JM, PIZZO SV, MCKEE PA: Relationship of sialic acid to function and in vivo survival of human factor VIII/von Willebrand factor protein. *J Biol Chem* 252:5538, 1977.

155. LYNCH DC, ZIMMERMAN TS, COLLINS CJ, BROWN M, MORIN MJ, LING EH, LIVINGSTON DM: Molecular cloning of cDNA for human von Willebrand factor: Authentication by a new method. *Cell* 41:49, 1985.

156. VERWEIJ CL, DE VRIES CJM, DISTEL B, VAN ZONNEVELD A-J, VAN KESSEL AG, VAN MOURIK JA, PANNEKOEK H: Construction of cDNA coding for human von Willebrand factor using antibody probes for colony-screening and mapping of the chromosomal gene. *Nucleic Acids Res* 13:4699, 1985.

157. GINSBURG D, HANDIN RI, BONTHRON DT, DONLON TA, BRUNS GAP, LATT SA, ORKIN SH: Human von Willebrand factor (vWF): Isolation of complementary DNA (cDNA) clones and chromosome localization. *Science* 228:1401, 1985.

158. SHELTON-INLOES BB, CHEHAB FF, MANNUCCI PM, FEDERICI AB, SADLER JE: Gene deletions correlate with the development of alloantibodies in von Willebrand disease. *J Clin Invest* 79:1459, 1987.

159. O'CONNELL P, LATHROP GM, LAW M, LEPPERT M, NAKAMURA Y, HOFF M, KUMLIN E, THOMAS W, ELSNER T, BALLARD L, GOODMAN P, AZEN E, SADLER JE, LAI GY, LALOUEL J-M, WHITE R: A primary genetic linkage map for human chromosome 12. *Genomics* 1:93, 1987.

160. SORACE JM, SHELTON-INLOES BB, SADLER JE: Isolation and characterization of genomic clones for human von Willebrand factor (vWF). *Fed Proc* 45:1639, 1986.

161. SADLER JE, SHELTON-INLOES BB, SORACE JM, TITANI K: Cloning of cDNA and genomic DNA for human von Willebrand factor. *Cold Spring Harbor Symp Quant Biol* 51:515, 1986.

162. COLLINS CJ, UNDERDAHL JP, LEVENE RB, RAVERA CP, MORIN MJ, DOMBALAGIAN MJ, RICCA G, LIVINGSTON DM, LYNCH DC: Molecular cloning of the human gene for von Willebrand factor and identification of the transcription initiation site. *Proc Natl Acad Sci USA* 84:4393, 1987.

163. VERWEIJ CL, HOFKER M, QUADT R, BRIET E, PANNEKOEK H: RFLP for a human von Willebrand factor (vWF) cDNA clone, pvWF1100. *Nucleic Acids Res* 13:8289, 1985.

164. NISHINO K, LYNCH DC: A polymorphisms of the human von Willebrand factor (vWF) gene with BamHI. *Nucleic Acids Res* 14:4697, 1986.

165. QUADT R, VERWEIJ CL, DE VRIES CJM, BRIËT E, PANNEKOEK H: A polymorphic *Xba*I site within the human von Willebrand factor (vWF) gene identified by a vWF cDNA clone. *Nucleic Acids Res* 14:7139, 1986.

166. BERNARDI F, MARCHETTI G, BERTAGNOLO V, FAGGIOLI L, DEL SENNO L: Two TaqI RFLPs in the human von Willebrand factor gene. *Nucleic Acids Res* 15:1347, 1987.

167. IANNUZZI MC, KONKLE BA, GINSBURG D, COLLINS FS: RsaI RFLP in the human von Willebrand factor gene. *Nucleic Acids Res* 15:5909, 1987.

168. CHRISTIE DL, GAGNON J: Amino acid sequence of the Bb fragment from complement factor B. *Biochem J* 209:61, 1983.

169. CAMPBELL RD, PORTER RR: Molecular cloning and characterization of the gene coding for human complement protein factor B. *Proc Natl Acad Sci USA* 80:4464, 1983.

170. CAMPBELL RD, BENTLEY DR, MORLEY BJ: The factor B and C2 genes. *Philos Trans R Soc Lond B* 306:367, 1984.

171. MOLE JE, ANDERSON JK, DAVISON EA, WOODS DE: Complete primary structure for the zymogen of human complement factor B. *J Biol Chem* 259:3407, 1984.

172. PARKES C, GAGNON J, KERR MA: The reaction of iodine and thiol-blocking reagents with complement components C2 and factor B. *Biochem J* 213:201, 1983.

173. BENTLEY DR: Primary structure of human complement component C2. Homology to two unrelated protein families. *Biochem J* 239:339, 1986.

174. LAWLER J, HYNES RO: The structure of human thrombospondin, an adhesive glycoprotein with multiple calcium-binding sites and homologies with several different proteins. *J Cell Biol* 103:1635, 1986.

175. CHU M-L, DE WET W, BERNARD M, DING J-F, MORABITO M, MEYERS J, WILLIAMS C, RAMIREZ F: Human proα1(I) collagen gene structure reveals evolutionary conservation of a pattern of introns and exons. *Nature* 310:337, 1984.

176. YAMADA Y, LIAU G, MUDRYJ M, OBICI S, DE CROMBRUGGHE B: Conservation of the sizes for one but not another class of exons in two chick collagen genes. *Nature* 310:333, 1984.

177. HUNT LT, BARKER WC: von Willebrand factor shares a distinctive cysteine-rich domain with thrombospondin and procollagen. *Biochem Biophys Res Commun* 144:876, 1987.

178. SILWER J: von Willebrand's disease in Sweden. *Acta Paediatr Scand (suppl)* 238:5, 1973.

179. BLOOM AL, PEAKE IR: Apparent "dominant" and "recessive" inheritance of von Willebrand's disease within the same kindreds. Possible biochemical mechanisms. *Thromb Res* 15:505, 1979.

180. MILLER CH, GRAHAM JB, GOLDIN LR, ELSTON RC: Genetics of classic von Willebrand's disease. I. Phenotypic variation within families. *Blood* 54:117, 1979.

181. HOYER LW: The assessment of von Willebrand's disease, in Bloom AL (ed): *The Hemophilias*. Edinburgh, Churchill Livingstone, 1982, pp 106–121.

182. ZIMMERMAN TS, ROBERTS JR, RUGGERI ZM: Factor VIII-related antigen: Characterization by electrophoretic techniques, in Bloom AL (ed): *The Hemophilias*. Edinburgh, Churchill Livingstone, 1982, pp 81–91.

183. READ MS, SHERMER RW, BRINKHOUS KM: Venom coagglutinin: An activator of platelet aggregation dependent on von Willebrand factor. *Proc Natl Acad Sci USA* 75:4514, 1978.

184. BRINKHOUS KM, READ MS: Use of venom coagulation and lyophilized platelets in testing for platelet-aggregating von Willebrand factor. *Blood* 55:517, 1980.

185. WEISS HJ, PIETU G, RABINOWITZ R, GIRMA JP, ROGERS J, MEYER D: Heterogeneous abnormalities in the multimeric structure, antigenic properties, and plasma-platelet content of factor VIII/von Willebrand factor in subtypes of classic (type I) and variant (type IIA) von Willebrand's disease. *J Lab Clin Med* 101:411, 1983.

186. MANNUCCI PM, LOMBARDI R, BADER R, VIANELLO L, FEDERICI AB, SOLINAS S, MAZZUCCONI MG, MARIANI G: Heterogeneity of type I von Willebrand disease: Evidence for a subgroup with an abnormal von Willebrand factor. *Blood* 66:796, 1985.

187. HANNA WT, SLYWKA J, DENT J, RUGGERI ZM, ZIMMERMAN TS: Case report: 1-Deamino-8-D-arginine vasopressin and cryoprecipitate in variant von Willebrand disease. *Am J Hematol* 20:169, 1985.

188. GRALNICK HR, WILLIAMS SB, MCKEOWN LP, RICK ME, MAISONNEUVE P, JENNEAU C, SULTAN Y: DDAVP in type IIA von Willebrand's disease. *Blood* 67:465, 1986.

189. HOLMBERG L, NILSSON IM: von Willebrand disease. *Clin Haematol* 14:461, 1985.

190. MANNUCCI PM, BLOOM AL, LARRIEU MJ, NILSSON IM, WEST RR: Atherosclerosis and von Willebrand factor. I. Prevalence of severe von Willebrand's disease in western Europe and Israel. *Br J Haematol* 57:163, 1984.

191. BERLINER SA, SELIGSOHN U, ZIVELIN A, ZWANG E, SOFFERMAN G: A relatively high frequency of severe (type III) von Willebrand's disease in Israel. *Br J Haematol* 62:535, 1986.

192. RUGGERI ZM: Classification of von Willebrand disease, in Verstraete M, Vermylen J, Lijnen HR, Arnout J (eds): *Thrombosis and Haemostasis 1987*. Leuven, International Society on Thrombosis and Haemostasis and Leuven University Press, 1987, pp 419–445.

193. HOYER LW, RIZZA CR, TUDDENHAM EG, CARTA CA, ARMITAGE H, ROTBLAT F: von Willebrand factor multimer patterns in von Willebrand's disease. *Br J Haematol* 55:493, 1983.

194. CIAVARELLA G, CIAVARELLA N, ANTONCECCHI S, DE MATTIA D, RANIERI P, DENT J, ZIMMERMAN TS, RUGGERI ZM: High-resolution analysis of von Willebrand factor multimeric composition defines a new variant of type I von Willebrand disease with aberrant structure but presence of all size multimers (type IC). *Blood* 66:1423, 1985.

195. TAVORI S, TATARSKY I: Additional variant of type I von Willebrand disease. *Am J Hematol* 24:189, 1987.

196. WEISS HJ, SUSSMAN II: A new von Willebrand variant (Type I, New York): Increased ristocetin-induced platelet aggregation and plasma von Willebrand factor containing the full range of multimers. *Blood* 68:149, 1986.

197. HOLMBERG L, BERNTORP, DONNÉR M, NILSSON IM: von Willebrand's disease characterized by increased ristocetin sensitivity and the presence of all von Willebrand factor multimers in plasma. *Blood* 68:668, 1986.

198. MANNUCCI PM, LOMBARDI R, RODEGHIERO F, CASTMAN G, FEDERICI AB: A new variant of von Willebrand disease (vWD) with larger than normal high-molecular-weight (HMW) von Willebrand factor (vWF) multimers. *Blood* 68:338a, 1986.

199. GIRMA JP, PIETU G, LAVERGNE JM, MEYER D, LARRIEU MJ: Abnormal antigenic reactivity of factor VIII/von Willebrand factor subunit in variants of von Willebrand's disease. *J Lab Clin Med* 99:481, 1982.

200. GRALNICK HR, WILLIAMS SB, MCKEOWN LP, MAISONNEUVE P, JENNEAU C, SULTAN Y, RICK ME: In vitro correction of the abnormal multimeric structure of vWF in type IIA vWD. *Proc Natl Acad Sci USA* 82:5968, 1985.

201. BATTLE J, LOPEZ FERNANDEZ MF, CAMPOS M, JUSTICA B, BERGES C, NAVARRO JL, DIAZ CREMADES JM, KASPER CK, DENT JA, RUGGERI ZM, ZIMMERMAN TS: The heterogeneity of type IIA von Willebrand's disease: Studies with protease inhibitors. *Blood* 68:1207, 1986.

202. RUGGERI ZM, MANNUCCI PM, LOMBARDI R, FEDERICI AB, ZIMMERMAN TS: Multimeric composition of factor VIII/von Willebrand factor following administration of DDAVP: Implications for pathophysiology and therapy of von Willebrand's disease subtypes. *Blood* 59:1272, 1982.

203. RUGGERI ZM, PARETI FI, MANNUCCI PM, CIAVARELLA N, ZIMMERMAN TS: Heightened interaction between platelets and factor VIII/von Willebrand factor in a new subtype of von Willebrand's disease. *N Engl J Med* 302:1047, 1980.

204. HOLMBERG L, NILSSON IM, BORGE L, BUNNARSSON M, SJORIN E: Platelet aggregation induced by 1-desamino-8-D-arginine vasopressin (DDAVP) in type IIB von Willebrand's disease. *N Engl J Med* 309:816, 1983.

205. SABA HI, SABA SR, DENT J, RUGGERI ZM, ZIMMERMAN TS: Type IIB Tampa: A variant of von Willebrand disease with chronic thrombocytopenia, circulating platelet aggregates, and spontaneous platelet aggregation. *Blood* 66:282, 1985.

206. GRALNICK HR, WILLIAMS SB, MCKEOWN LP, RICK ME, MAISONNEUVE P, JENNEAU C, SULTAN Y: von Willebrand's disease with spontaneous platelet aggregation induced by an abnormal plasma von Willebrand factor. *J Clin Invest* 76:1522, 1985.

207. FEDERICI AB, MANNUCCI PM, BADER R, LOMBARDI R, LATTUADA A: Heterogeneity in type IIB von Willebrand disease: Two unrelated cases with no family history and mild abnormalities of ristocetin-induced interaction between von Willebrand factor and platelets. *Am J Hematol* 23:381, 1986.

208. DONNÉR M, HOLMBERG L, NILSSON IM: Type IIB von Willebrand's disease with probable autosomal recessive inheritance and presenting as thrombocytopenia in infancy. *Br J Haematol* 66:349, 1987.

209. RUGGERI ZM, NILSSON IM, LOMBARDI R, HOLMBERG L, ZIMMERMAN TS: Aberrant multimeric structure of von Willebrand factor in a new variant of von Willebrand's disease (type IIC). *J Clin Invest* 70:1124, 1982.

210. MANNUCCI PM, LOMBARDI R, PARETI FI, SOLINAS S, MAZZUCCONI MG, MARIANI G: A variant of von Willebrand's disease characterized by recessive inheritance and missing triplet structure of von Willebrand factor multimers. *Blood* 62:1000,1983.

211. BATTLE J, LOPEZ FERNANDEZ MF, LASIERRA J, FERNANDEZ VILLAMOR A, LOPEZ BERGES C, LOPEZ BORRASCA A, RUGGERI ZM, ZIMMERMAN TS: von Willebrand disease type IIC with different abnormalities of von Willebrand factor in the same sibship. *Am J Hematol* 21:177, 1986.

212. BATTLE J, LOPEZ FERNANDEZ MF, FERNANDEZ VILLAMOR A, LOPEZ BERGES C, ZIMMERMAN TS: Multimeric pattern discrepancy between platelet and plasma von Willebrand factor in type IIC von Willebrand disease. *Am J Hematol* 22:87, 1986.

213. MAZURIER C, MANNUCCI PM, PARQUET-GERNEZ A, GOUDEMAND M, MEYER D: Investigation of a case of subtype IIC von Willebrand disease: Characterization of the variability of this subtype. *Am J Hematol* 22:301, 1986.

214. KINOSHITA S, HARRISON J, LAZERSON J, ABILDGAARD CF: A new variant of dominant type II von Willebrand's disease with aberrant multimeric pattern of factor VIII-related antigen (type IID). *Blood* 63:1369, 1984.

215. HILL FGH, ENAYAT MS, GEORGE AJ: Investigation of a kindred with a new autosomal dominantly inherited variant type von Willebrand's disease (possible type IID). *J Clin Pathol* 38:665, 1985.

216. TRIPLETT D, MUSGRAVE K, DANIELS T, BOWIE EJW: Identification and further characterization of type IIE von Willebrand disease. *Thromb Haemostas* 58:360, 1987.

217. MANNUCCI PM, LOMBARDI R, FEDERICI AB, DENT JA, ZIMMERMAN TS, RUGGERI ZM: A new variant of type II von Willebrand disease with aberrant multimeric structure of plasma but not platelet von Willebrand factor (type IIF). *Blood* 68:269, 1986.

218. GRALNICK HR, WILLIAMS SB, MCKEOWN LP, MAISONNEUVE P, JENNEAU C, SULTAN Y: A variant of type II von Willebrand disease with an abnormal triplet structure and discordant effects of protease inhibitors on plasma and platelet von Willebrand factor structure. *Am H Hematol* 24:259, 1987.

219. MANNUCCI PM, LOMBARDI R, LATTUADA A, MULEO G, FEDERICI AB: High resolution and multimeric analysis identifies a new variant of type II von Willebrand's disease (type IIH) inherited in an autosomal recessive manner. *Ric Clin Lab* 16:237a, 1986.

220. HOWARD MA, SALEM HH, THOMAS KB, HAU L, PERKIN J, COGHLAN M, FIRKIN BG: Variant von Willebrand's disease type B—Revisited. *Blood* 60:1420, 1982.

221. ITALIAN WORKING GROUP: Spectrum of von Willebrand's disease: A study of 100 cases. *Br J Haematol* 35:101, 1977.

222. ZIMMERMAN TS, ABILDGAARD CF, MEYER D: The factor VIII abnormality in severe von Willebrand's disease. *N Engl J Med* 301:1307, 1979.

223. PEAKE IR, BLOOM AL, GIDDINGS JC, LUDLAM CA: An immunoradiometric assay for procoagulant factor VIII antigen: Results in haemophilia, von Willebrand's disease and fetal plasma and serum. *Br J Haematol* 42:269, 1979.

224. NGO KY, LYNCH D, GITSCHER J, CIAVARELLA N, RUGGERI Z, ZIMMERMAN T: Homozygous and heterozygous complete deletions of the von Willebrand factor gene coding region in severe von Willebrand disease and carriers. *Thromb Haemostas* 58:311, 1987.

225. STANDEN G, MOODIE P, PANNEKOEK H, VERWEIJ CL, PEAKE IR: Analysis of the von Willebrand factor (vWF) gene in 6 patients with severe type III von Willebrand's disease. *Thromb Haemostas* 58:498, 1987.

226. GIANNELLI F, CHOO KH, REESE DJG, BOYD Y, RIZZA CR, BROWNLEE GG: Gene deletions in patients with haemophilia B and anti-factor IX antibodies. *Nature* 303:181, 1983.

227. MATTHEWS RJ, ANSON DS, PEAKE IR, BLOOM AL: Heterogeneity of the factor IX locus in nine hemophilia B inhibitor patients. *J Clin Invest* 79:746, 1987.

228. VERWEIJ CL, QUADT R, BRIËT E, PANNEKOEK H: Two von Willebrand factor (vWF) gene polymorphisms segregate with von Willebrand's disease (vWD) type IIA: Assignment of the defective gene locus in vWD type IIA. *Thromb Haemostas* 58:499, 1987.

229. STRAUS HS, DIAMOND LK: Elevation of factor VIII (antihemophilic factor) during pregnancy in normal persons and in a patient with von Willebrand's disease. *N Engl J Med* 269:1251, 1963.

230. NOLLER KL, BOWIE EJW, KEMPERS RD, OWEN CA: von Willebrand's disease in pregnancy. *Obstet Gynecol* 41:865, 1973.

231. BENNETT B, OXNARD SC, DOUGLAS AS, RATNOFF OD: Studies on antihemophilic factor (AHF, factor VIII) during labor in normal women, in patients with premature separation of the placenta, and in a patient with von Willebrand's disease. *J Lab Clin Med* 84:851, 1974.

232. TELFER MC, CHEDIAK J: Factor-VIII-related disorders and their relationship to pregnancy. *J Reprod Med* 19:211, 1977.

233. RICK ME, WILLIAMS SB, SACHER RA, MCKEOWN LP: Thrombocytopenia associated with pregnancy in a patient with type IIB von Willebrand's disease. *Blood* 69:786, 1987.

234. MANNUCCI PM, MARI D: Antibodies to factor VIII-von Willebrand factor in congenital and acquired von Willebrand's disease, in Hoyer LW (ed): *Factor VIII Inhibitors.* New York, AR Liss, 1984, pp 109–122.

235. KANESHIRO MM, MIELKE CH JR, KASPER CK, RAPAPORT SI: Bleeding times after aspirin in disorders of intrinsic clotting. *N Engl J Med* 281:1039, 1969.

236. TAKAHASHI H: Studies on the pathophysiology and treatment of von Willebrand's disease. IV. Mechanism of increased ristocetin-induced platelet aggregation in von Willebrand's disease. *Thromb Res* 19:857, 1980.

237. MILLER JL, CASTELLA A: Platelet-type von Willebrand's disease: Characterization of a new bleeding disorder. *Blood* 60:790, 1982.

238. WEISS HJ, MEYER D, RABINOWITZ R, PIETY G, GIRMA J-P, VICIC WJ, ROGERS J: Pseudo-von Willebrand's disease. An intrinsic platelet defect with aggregation by unmodified human factor VIII/von Willebrand factor and enhanced adsorption of its high-molecular-weight multimers. *N Engl J Med* 306:326, 1982.

239. TAKAHASHI H, NAGAYAMA R, HATTORI A, SHIBATA A: Platelet aggregation induced by DDAVP in platelet-type von Willebrand's disease. *N Engl J Med* 310:722, 1984.

240. MILLER JL, KUPINSKI JM, CASTELLA A, RUGGERI ZM: von Willebrand factor binds to platelets and induces aggregation in platelet-type but not type IIB von Willebrand disease. *J Clin Invest* 72:1532, 1983.

241. BRYCKAERT MC, PIETY G, RUAN C, TOBELEM G, GIRMA JP, MEYER D, LARRIEU MJ, CAEN JP: Abnormality of glycoprotein Ib in two cases of "pseudo"-von Willebrand's disease. *J Lab Clin Med* 106:393, 1985.

242. MANNUCCI PM, MOIA M, REBULLA P, ALTIERI D, MONTEAGUDO J, CASTILLO R: Correction of the bleeding time in treated patients with severe von Willebrand disease is not solely dependent on the normal multimeric structure of plasma von Willebrand factor. *Am J Hematol* 25:55, 1987.

243. BLATT PM, BRINKHOUS KM, CULP HR, KRAUSS JS, ROBERTS HR: Antihemophilic factor concentrate therapy in von Willebrand's disease: Dissociation of bleeding time factor and ristocetin-cofactor activities. *JAMA* 236:2770, 1976.

244. GREEN D, POTTER EV: Failure of AHF concentrate to control bleeding in von Willebrand's disease. *Am J Med* 60:357, 1976.

245. KÖHLER M, HELLSTERN P, WENZEL E: The use of heat-treated factor VIII-concentrates in von Willebrand's disease. *Blut* 50:25, 1985.

246. MANNUCCI PM, COLOMBO M, RODEGHIERO F: Non-A, non-B hepatitis after factor VIII concentrate treated by heating and chloroform. *Lancet* 2:1013, 1985.

247. ROUZIOUX C, CHARMARET S, MONTAGNIER L, CARNELLI V, ROLLAND G, MANNUCCI PM: Absence of antibodies to AIDS virus in haemophiliacs treated wtih heat-treated factor VIII concentrate. *Lancet* 1:271, 1985.

248. MANNUCCI PM, RUGGERI ZM, PARETI FI, CAPITANO A: DDAVP, a new pharmacological approach to the management of haemophilia and von Willebrand's disease. *Lancet* 1:869, 1977.

249. MANNUCCI PM, CANCIANI MT, ROTA L, DONOVAN BS: Response of factor VIII/von Willebrand factor to DDAVP in healthy subjects and patients with haemophilia A and von Willebrand's disease. *Br J Haematol* 41:437, 1979.

250. THEISS W, SCHMIDT G: DDAVP in von Willebrand's disease: Repeated administration and the behaviour of the bleeding time. *Thromb Res* 13:1119, 1978.

251. WARRIER AI, LUSHER JM: DDAVP: A useful alternative to blood components in moderate hemophilia A and von Willebrand disease. *J Pediatr* 102:228, 1983.

252. DE LA FUENTE B, KASPER CK, RICKLES FR, HOYER LW: Response of patients with mild and moderate hemophilia A and von Willebrand's disease to treatment with desmopressin. *Ann Intern Med* 103:6, 1985.

253. SAKARIASSEN KS, CATTANEO M, V D BERG A, RUGGERI ZM, MANNUCCI PM, SIXMA JJ: DDAVP enhances platelet adherence and platelet aggregate growth on human artery subendothelium. *Blood* 64:229, 1984.

254. GLUECK HI, FLESSA HC: Control of hemorrhage in von Willebrand's disease and a hemophiliac carrier with norethynodrelmestranol. *Thromb Res* 1:253, 1972.

255. ALPERIN JB: Estrogens and surgery in women with von Willebrand's disease. *Am J Med* 73:367, 1982.

256. HOYER LW, LINDSTEN J, BLOMBÄCK M, HAGENFELDT L, CORDESIUS E, STRÖMBERG P, GUSTAVII B: Prenatal evaluation of fetus at risk for severe von Willebrand's disease. *Lancet* 2:191, 1979.

257. MIBASHAN RS, MILLAR DS: Fetal haemophilia and allied bleeding disorders. *Br Med Bull* 39:392, 1983.

258. MONTGOMERY RR, MARLAR RA, GILL JC: Newborn haemostasis. *Clin Haematol* 14:443.

CHAPTER 88

CONTACT ACTIVATION

KAZUO FUJIKAWA
HIDEHIKO SAITO

1. *Contact activation participates in several biologic cascade reactions, such as intrinsic coagulation, intrinsic fibrinolysis, and bradykinin release. Three serine proteases, factor XII, factor XI, and plasma prekallikrein, and one nonenzyme cofactor, high molecular weight kininogen, are involved in contact activation.*

2. *The reactions of contact activation proceed on a negatively charged surface. When blood comes in contact with surface materials, factor XII, prekallikrein, and factor XI are all activated on the surface. High molecular weight kininogen, which circulates in blood in complexes with prekallikrein and factor XI, accelerates these activations. Resultant factor XIa activates factor IX for intrinsic coagulation. Kallikrein activates prourokinase for intrinsic fibrinolysis and also releases bradykinin from high molecular weight kininogen. Factor XIIa activates the classic pathway of the complement system and also may participate in extrinsic coagulation by activating factor VII.*

3. *Acidic phospholipids, acidic glycolipids, acidic polysaccharides, heparin proteoglycan, glycosaminoglycan, and cholesterol sulfate have been identified as candidates for the biologic surface material which functions in contact activation.*

4. *The complete primary structures of all four contact factors have been established. The amino-terminal portion of factor XII contains structural domains similar to those of tissue-type plasminogen activator and prourokinase. Factor XI and prekallikrein are highly homologous proteins and contain four unique tandem repeats in their amino-terminal portions. The structures of the carboxy-terminal portions of these three factors are typical of those of trypsin-type serine proteases. The amino-terminal portion of high molecular weight kininogen contains two putative reactive sites of a cysteine protease inhibitor. The carboxy-terminal portion of high molecular weight kininogen contains two binding sites: one for a negatively charged surface and the other for factor XI and prekallikrein.*

5. *Deficiency in factor XI causes mild bleeding disorders, whereas deficiencies of factor XII, prekallikrein, and HMW-kininogen are asymptomatic. Thus, physiological roles of the latter three factors are not known.*

6. *The human genes of high molecular weight kininogen and factor XI have been isolated and characterized.*

INTRODUCTION

Contact activation participates in the early phase of the intrinsic pathways of blood coagulation, fibrinolysis, and kinin generation. When blood comes in contact with a foreign surface, the reaction of contact activation is triggered. The term *foreign surface* refers to any surface except for those of normal vascular lining and circulating blood cells. The mechanism by which blood clots upon surface contact has been a subject of extensive research since the beginning of this century, when Bordet and Gengou observed that blood clotted much more rapidly in a glass tube than in a paraffin-coated tube.[1] The clot-accelerating property of glass was considered to be exerted by an action on cell-poor plasma. Many attempts were then made to localize the effect of glass to one or another component of plasma, but the agent in plasma upon which glass exerts its clot-promoting effect remained unknown.

As in the cases of other coagulation factors, the clue was provided by the discovery of unique patients with abnormal blood clotting. In 1955 Ratnoff and Colopy[2] described three asymptomatic individuals with a markedly prolonged in vitro blood clotting time. The authors predicted the presence of a new agent, Hageman factor, which was named after the index patient, Mr. John Hageman. The defect in clotting was localized to an early phase of the intrinsic pathway. Hageman factor appeared to be the agent that was directly activated by glass. Subsequent studies showed that upon activation Hageman factor, in turn, activated another contact factor, plasma thromboplastin antecedent, described by Rosenthal et al.[3]

Soon after the clot-promoting role of Hageman factor was found, it was shown that Hageman factor, under certain conditions, could activate several other biologic systems of the host defense reaction such as fibrinolysis, kinin generation, and complement activation. Normal human plasma, when applied to the exposed base of a blister, was found to cause severe pain.[4] The pain-producing agent evolved only when the plasma had been exposed to glass surface, and it had properties resembling bradykinin. Hageman factor appeared to be required for the release of kinin, because no kinin generation was observed upon exposure of Hageman factor–deficient plasma to glass.[5] Similarly, the intrinsic fibrinolytic activity of normal plasma was greatly enhanced by contact with kaolin. This enhancement, however, was strikingly reduced in Hageman factor–deficient plasma, suggesting the critical role of Hageman factor in the generation of fibrinolytic activity.[6]

In the succeeding decades, two additional factors were incidentally found to participate in contact activation. In 1965, Hathaway et al.[7] described a new coagulation disorder and named an agent that was missing in the patient's plasma the *Fletcher factor*. Fletcher factor was assumed to have a role in intrinsic coagulation, but its nature was elusive until 1972, when Wuepper[8] identified Fletcher factor as plasma prekallikrein. The role of prekallikrein in blood coagulation was confirmed by the inhibition of clotting activity of normal plasma

Nonstandard abbreviations used in this chapter are: APTT = activated partial thromboplastin time; CRM = cross-reacting material; HMW-kininogen = high molecular weight kininogen; LMW-kininogen = low molecular weight kininogen; t-PA = tissue-type plasminogen activator.

with specific antikallikrein serum.[9] The study of Fletcher trait plasma also disclosed the function of prekallikrein in intrinsic fibrinolysis. In 1975, several individuals with another unrecognized clotting abnormality were reported, and the missing factor was called *Fitzgerald, Flaujeac,* or *Williams factor* after the names of the affected individuals.[10-12] The patients' plasmas were defective not only in clotting, but also in fibrinolysis and kinin generation. The missing factor was soon identified as high molecular weight (HMW) kininogen. The addition of purified HMW-kininogen to the patients' plasmas completely corrected abnormalities in clotting, fibrinolysis, and kinin generation.[11,13] These studies unexpectedly demonstrated that prekallikrein and HMW-kininogen, which were known as the components of the kinin-forming system, were also involved in intrinsic coagulation and fibrinolysis.

Four plasma factors, Hageman factor, plasma thromboplastin antecedent, plasma prekallikrein, and HMW-kininogen, are now recognized to participate in contact activation (Table 88-1). Roman numerals, factor XII and factor XI, were given to Hageman factor and plasma thromboplastin antecedent, respectively. Plasma prekallikrein and HMW-kininogen have not yet received a Roman numeral. In recent years, each of these proteins was isolated from human and bovine plasma. Their complex activation mechanisms were extensively studied.[14,15] Their complete amino acid sequences were also determined.[16-20] More recently, progress in recombinant DNA technology made it possible to clone cDNAs of all of these contact factors.[21-26] Furthermore, genomic DNAs for factor XI and HMW-kininogen were isolated, and their gross structures and restriction sites were established.[27-29] Hereditary deficiencies of the contact factors have not yet been characterized at the molecular level. It is expected in the near future that defective genes of the contact factors will be isolated and analyzed by using cloned cDNAs as hybridization probes.

This chapter will review the current information regarding the biochemistry and molecular biology of the contact factors as well as the clinical aspects of their deficiencies. The literature cited is by no means exhaustive, and reviews are cited in many places instead of the original articles to conserve space. Additional information is also available in earlier reviews.[14,15,30-32]

INTRINSIC COAGULATION–INITIATION OF CONTACT ACTIVATION

Three plasma serine proteases, factor XII, factor XI, and prekallikrein, participate in the early phase of intrinsic coagulation. HMW-kininogen, which is a nonenzyme cofactor and circulates in blood as complexes with prekallikrein and factor XI, stimulates the reactions involved in contact activation.

Table 88-1 Contact Factors

Factors	Synonyms	MW	Plasma concentration, $\mu g/ml$
Factor XII	Hageman factor	76,000	30
Factor XI	Plasma thromboplastin antecedent (TPA)	160,000	5
Prekallikrein	Fletcher factor	82,000	35–45
HMW-kininogen	Fitzgerald, Flaujeac, Williams factor	108,000	70–100

When normal plasma is incubated with negatively charged materials such as kaolin, ellagic acid, dextran sulfate, and sulfatide, the zymogens of the contact factors are activated. The activated contact factors, factor XIIa, factor XIa, and α-kallikrein, then promote several biologic reactions. Factor XIa activates factor IX for intrinsic coagulation.[33] α-Kallikrein cleaves HMW-kininogen to liberate a vasoactive peptide, bradykinin, and it also activates prourokinase for the initiation of intrinsic fibrinolysis (see "Intrinsic Fibrinolysis"). Besides these reactions, involvement of the contact factors in other systems has been reported. α-Kallikrein stimulates neutrophils to release elastase during in vitro blood coagulation.[34] Factor XIIa activates the classic pathway of the complement system,[35] and it is also a permeability factor.[36] Factor XIIa may function to accelerate extrinsic coagulation, because factor XIIa can convert the zymogen of factor VII to its active form.[37,38]

It was demonstrated in the bovine system that the first reaction of contact activation was the activation of prekallikrein by the zymogen of factor XII in the presence of a negatively charged surface and HMW-kininogen.[39,40] In this reaction, the zymogen of factor XII, which is incapable of hydrolyzing synthetic peptide substrates, can activate surface-bound prekallikrein. Although the zymogen of factor XIIa can activate prekallikrein at the same reaction rate as that obtained by α-factor XIIa in certain conditions, factor XIIa converts prekallikrein more efficiently than its zymogen under physiological conditions. The zymogen of bovine factor XII also activates factor XI in the same manner.[41] This activation probably does not occur in plasma, because this reaction bypasses prekallikrein, which is an essential factor for contact activation.

In the human system, reciprocal activations of factor XII and prekallikrein occur simultaneously when factor XII is incubated with prekallikrein and HMW-kininogen in the presence of a negatively charged surface. The activation of prekallikrein by the factor XII zymogen may also occur for the initiation of contact activation in the human system, but it has not been proved. Either the zymogen of factor XII or a trace of factor XIIa that may circulate in blood activates prekallikrein to initiate contact activation in the human system. Once α-kallikrein is formed, it activates factor XII to accelerate the reactions of contact activation. Resultant factor XIIa activates factor XI in the presence of HMW-kininogen and a negatively charged surface. Factor XIa then activates factor IX in the presence of Ca^{2+}, leading to activation of the remaining coagulation cascade[33] (Fig. 88-1).

Autoactivation of factor XII occurs in the presence of a negatively charged surface.[42-45] When purified human factor XII was incubated with sulfatide or dextran sulfate, the enzyme activity of factor XIIa was generated in a sigmoidal fashion typical of autoactivation of zymogens. The generation of the enzyme activity was in parallel with the formation of α-factor XIIa during the autoactivation.[43] The autoactivation of factor XII is initiated by a trace of factor XIIa inevitably contaminating factor XII preparations.[44] However, the mechanism involved in the initial generation of factor XIIa in factor XII preparations is not known. In plasma, the reciprocal activation of factor XII with prekallikrein is approximately two thousandfold more rapid than the autoactivation. Thus, reciprocal activation is the predominant mechanism for the initiation of contact activation of the human system.[44] Autoactivation is not observed with bovine factor XII.[40]

In the process of content activation, factor XII binds directly to negatively charged surfaces. The binding mechanism appears to be different depending on surface materials. Factor

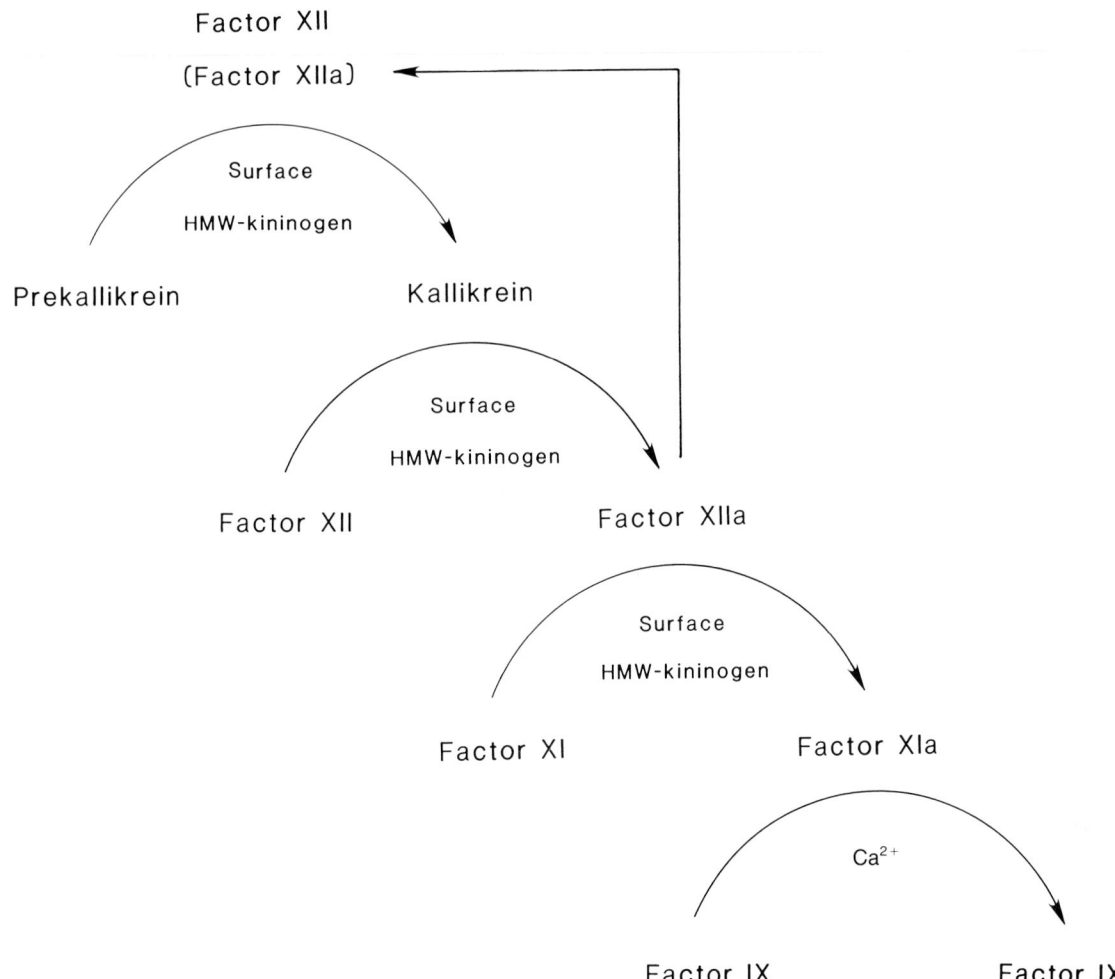

Fig. 88-1   A tentative pathway of intrinsic coagulation. *(Modified from Heimark et al.[39])*

XII binds to vesicles of sulfatide by an electrostatic interaction and dissociates from the vesicles at high salt concentrations.[45] However, high concentrations of salt do not inhibit the binding of factor XII to kaolin.[46] Thus, nonelectrostatic binding interactions are involved in the binding of factor XII to kaolin. Neither prekallikrein nor factor XI has been shown to bind directly to surface materials. The complexes of prekallikrein–HMW-kininogen and factor XI–HMW-kininogen bind to negatively charged surfaces through the HMW-kininogen molecule.[47] Thus, the role of HMW-kininogen is to facilitate enzyme-substrate interactions on the surfaces. Optimum binding of HMW-kininogen to a negatively charged surface requires proteolytic cleavages of the kininogen molecule (see "High Molecular Weight (HMW) Kininogen"). Binding of factor XII to the surface is also thought to increase its susceptibility to proteolytic cleavage by α-kallikrein.[48]

Where does contact activation take place, and what are the physiological surface materials? Membranes of activated or injured platelets, endothelial cells, and subendothelium are considered to be the sites of contact activation. Factor XI, factor XIa, and HMW-kininogen were shown to bind to thrombin-activated platelets in the presence of bivalent cations, Zn^{2+} and Ca^{2+} [see "High Molecular Weight (HMW) Kininogen" and "Factor XI Plasma Thromboplastin Antecedent"]. Factor XIa was also shown to activate factor IX that was bound on the surface of endothelial cells.[49]

As to surface materials, an early report showed that mixing of normal plasma with heated crude extract of human articular cartilage generated a kininlike activity. The development of this activity was not observed in factor XII–deficient plasma.[50] Chondroitin sulfate, which is one of the principal polysaccharides of cartilage, had the same effect as the crude extract at a concentration of 10 μg/ml. Heparin also caused the generation of bradykinin. These experiments indicate that acidic polysaccharides can serve as a negatively charged surface for contact activation. Sulfatide, sulfated cerebroside, was found to have a strong surface activity[51,52] and is currently used for studies of the mechanism of contact activation. A low concentration of sulfatide (40 μg/ml) shortens the clotting time of plasma and also provides an excellent surface for the activation of the contact factors. Although this compound is present in platelets and erythrocytes, its low concentration is probably insufficient to initiate contact activation. Cholesterol sulfate, not cholesterol, also shortens the factor XII–dependent clotting time of plasma.[53] This compound is distributed in erythrocytes, various organs, and body fluids. Recently, heparin proteoglycan and glycosaminoglycan from rat peritoneal mast cells were also shown to be active for contact activation.[54] Various phospholipids were tested for the surface activity at different salt concentrations and different temperatures. The results showed that almost every kind of acidic phospholipid, such as phosphatidylserine, phosphatidylglycerol, phosphatidic acid, and phosphatidylinositol-4-phosphate, was active to initiate contact activation if conditions were appropriately selected.[55] Consequently, one view is that the concentration of one kind of surface materials may not be sufficient to initiate contact activation, but the total concentration of all active materials probably provides an efficient surface for contact activation.

INTRINSIC FIBRINOLYSIS

The activity of intrinsic fibrinolysis is readily identified in the euglobulin fraction, which is a precipitate obtained from plasma by diluting with acidic buffer (e.g., twentyfold dilution with 10 mM sodium acetate, pH 5.0) in the presence of negatively charged surfaces such as kaolin and dextran sulfate. In this dilution, α_2-antiplasmin, a potent inhibitor of plasmin, denatures. After fibrinogen is supplemented to the euglobulin fraction, a fibrin clot is formed by thrombin. This fibrin clot will dissolve rapidly. In this process, plasminogen that is present in the euglobulin fraction converts to plasmin, which in turn hydrolyzes the fibrin clot. This fibrinolytic event is called *intrinsic fibrinolysis* or *factor XII–dependent fibrinolysis*. Intrinsic fibrinolysis is absent in plasmas deficient in factor XII and HMW-kininogen, and a delayed fibrinolytic activity is observed in prekallikrein-deficient plasma.[56]

For years, researchers looked for a plasminogen activator in the euglobulin fraction. When purified preparations of the contact factors became available, they were tested for the activity of plasminogen activator. All of the activated contact factors, α-kallikrein, factor XIIa, and factor XIa, were found to activate plasminogen, and α-kallikrein was once thought of as a plasminogen activator.[56] The physiological significance of these enzymes in the activation of plasminogen remained uncertain, because the activation rates of plasminogen by these enzymes are extremely low as compared with urokinase, which is one of the prime activators of plasminogen. Therefore, the participation of additional enzyme(s) appeared probable for the activation of plasminogen.[57] Recently, the involvement of urokinase in the intrinsic fibrinolytic system was reported,[57–59] and the activity of urokinase was also detected in the dextran sulfate–euglobulin fraction.[60]

Purified preparations of prourokinase (zymogen form of urokinase) became available from cultured media of human kidney cells. Accordingly, activation of prourokinase was tested by purified preparations of the activated contact factors as well as other coagulation factors. α-Kallikrein was found to convert a single chain molecule of prourokinase (MW 55,000) to a two-chain molecule of urokinase (MW 33,000 and 22,000) as fast as plasmin.[61] In this reaction, α-kallikrein and plasmin cleave the same Lys-Ile bond of prourokinase. α-Factor XIIa catalyzes this cleavage seven times more slowly than α-kallikrein. A pathway is now proposed for intrinsic fibrinolysis (Fig. 88-2). α-Kallikrein is first formed on a negatively charged surface in the presence of α-factor XIIa and HMW-kininogen (see "Intrinsic Coagulation—Initiation of Contact Activation," above). α-Kallikrein then activates prourokinase to urokinase, which in turn activates plasminogen to plasmin. Plasmin then hydrolyzes fibrin clots. Once plasmin is generated, it also converts prourokinase to urokinase to accelerate

Fig. 88-2 A proposed pathway of intrinsic fibrinolysis. *(Modified from Ichinose et al.[61])*

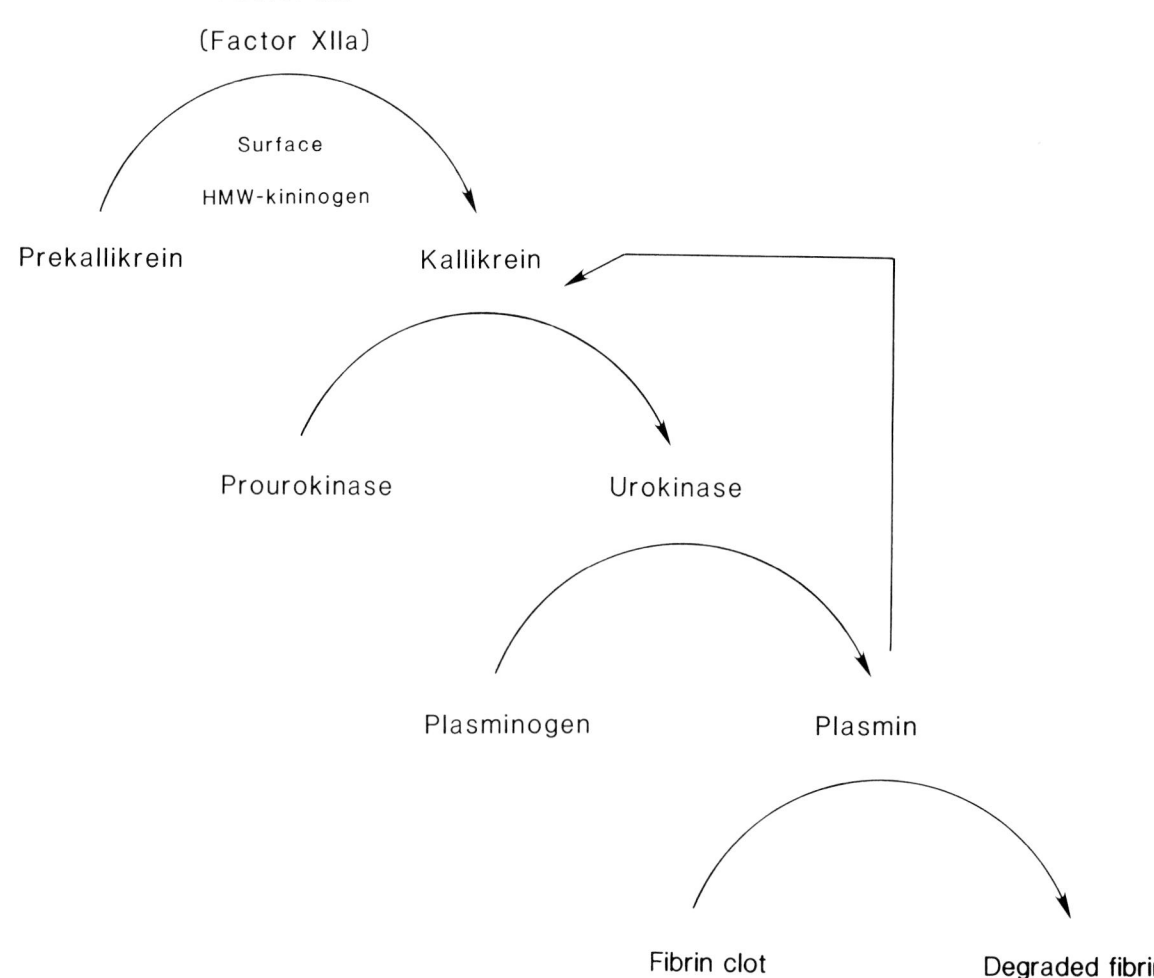

Factor XII

(Factor XIIa)

Surface

HMW-kininogen

Prekallikrein   Kallikrein

Prourokinase   Urokinase

Plasminogen   Plasmin

Fibrin clot   Degraded fibrin

fibrinolysis. The slow activation of plasminogen by factor XIIa may be involved in the delayed fibrinolytic activity in prekallikrein-deficient plasma. The physiological importance of intrinsic fibrinolysis is obscure at the present time because the activity of intrinsic fibrinolysis is detectable only in the euglobulin fraction and is negligible in plasma. In plasma, α_2-antiplasmin, a potent inhibitor of plasmin, quickly neutralizes plasmin to nullify the fibrinolytic activity.[62]

FACTOR XII (HAGEMAN FACTOR)

Factor XII is a glycoprotein that is present in normal plasma at a level of 30 μg/ml.[63] It was purified from human[64,65] and bovine plasmas,[66] and extensively characterized. Both human and bovine proteins have approximate molecular weights of 76,000 including 13 to 17 percent carbohydrate.

Factor XII is activated by α-kallikrein in the presence of a negatively charged surface and HMW-kininogen. It was reported that the bound form of factor XII was activated by α-kallikrein 500 times faster than the free form of factor XII.[48] During the activation, a peptide bond is cleaved to form α-factor XIIa, which is composed of an amino-terminal heavy chain (MW 50,000) and a carboxyl-terminal light chain (MW 28,000) held together by a disulfide bond.[63] The amino-terminal sequence analysis of the light chain by Edman degradation and the carboxy-terminal sequence analysis of the heavy chain by digestion with carboxypeptidase B showed that

an Arg-Val bond was cleaved by α-kallikrein. In an extended incubation with α-kallikrein, α-factor XIIa is converted to β-factor XIIa, which is composed of the light chain and a short peptide (nine amino acids) that originated from the heavy chain.[16] In this reaction, the heavy chain is first split into an amino-terminal fragment (MW 40,000) and a carboxy-terminal fragment with MW 12,000 called the *connecting region*.[63] The connecting region has several susceptible bonds to α-kallikrein and further degrades to the short peptide that is connected to the light chain by a disulfide bond.[16] A brief incubation of factor XII or α-factor XIIa with trypsin also produces β-factor XIIa.

The primary structure of human factor XII was determined by protein[16,17] and cDNA sequencing.[24] The heavy chain of factor XII comprises a total of 353 amino acid residues, including 27 half-cystinyl residues (Fig. 88-3). Although the disulfide bond pairings of these Cys residues of factor XII have not been determined, the heavy chain of factor XII was predicted to contain five folding domains by alignments of the conserved Cys residues. They are, in the order from the amino terminal, type II, a first growth factor, type I, a second growth factor, and a kringle structure. The type I and II structures were first identified in fibronectin.[67,68] The growth factor domain was found in rat epidermal growth factor[69] and later found in urokinase,[70–72] tissue-type plasminogen activator (t-PA),[73] and several vitamin K–dependent coagulation factors.[74] The kringle domain is present in prothrombin,[75] plasminogen,[76] t-PA,[73] and urokinase.[70–72] Besides the conserved Cys residues, the amino acid sequences in these five domains

Fig. 88-3 The complete amino acid sequence of human factor XII. The curved arrow shows the bond cleaved by α-kallikrein or trypsin for activation of factor XII. The solid diamonds indicate the *N*-glycosylation sites, and open diamonds represent the proposed *O*-glycosylation sites. The residues of the catalytic triad are circled (residues 40, 89, and 91). The disulfide bonds are arranged by the homology with those determined in other proteins (see the text).

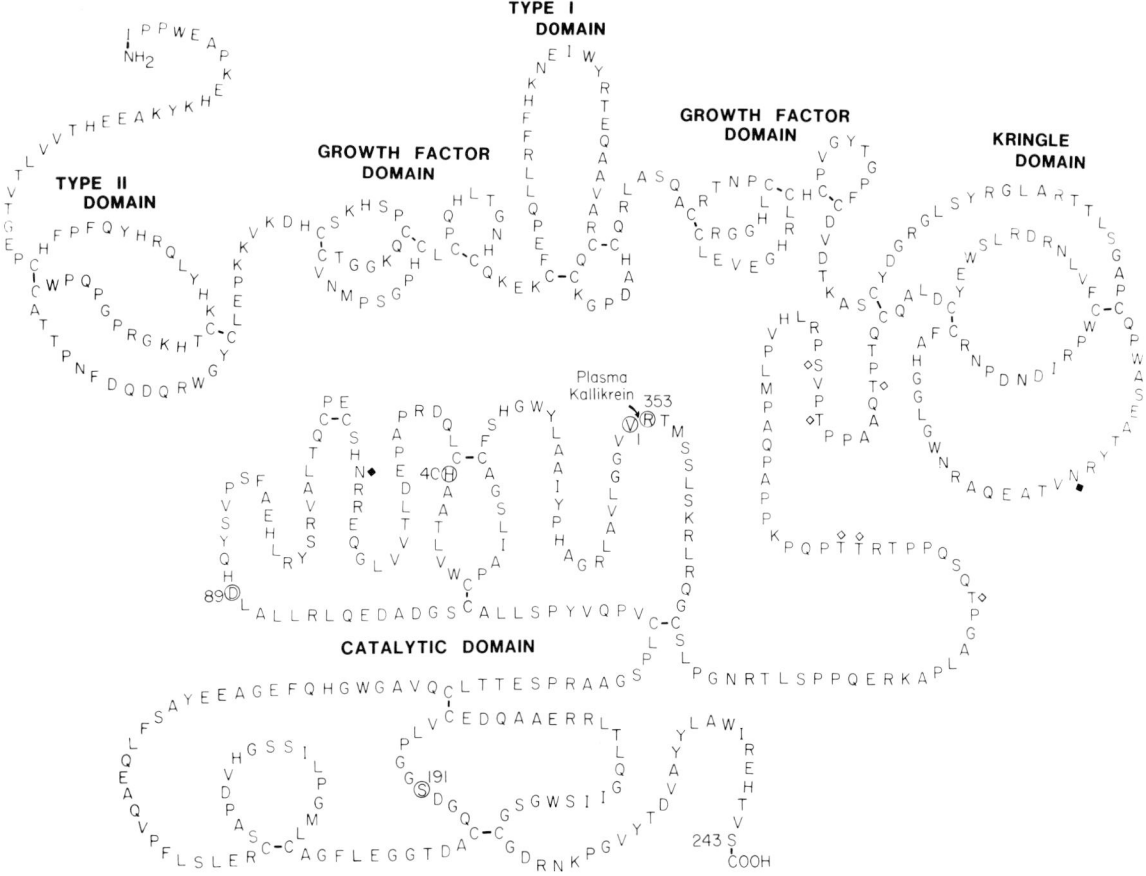

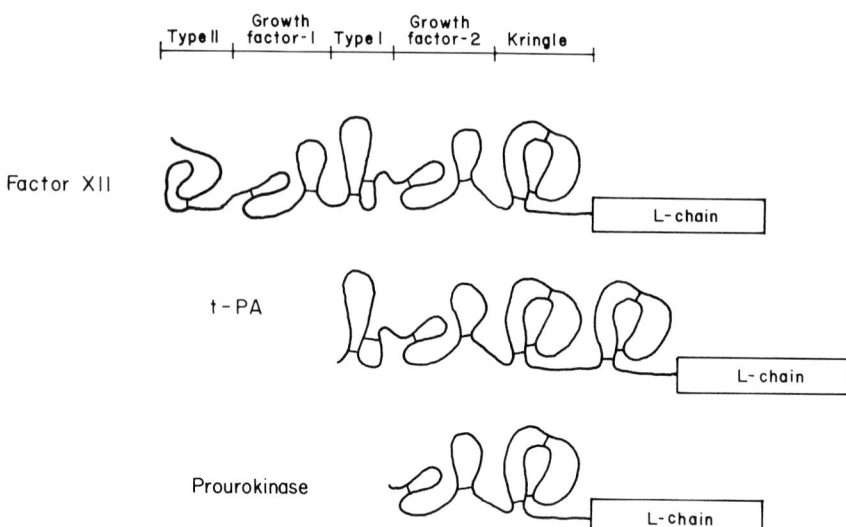

Fig. 88-4 Comparison of the domain alignment in factor XII with those in t-PA and prourokinase. (Modified from McMullen and Fujikawa.[17])

in factor XII are also homologous with the respective domains in the other proteins. The domain organization of factor XII is compared with those in t-PA and prourokinase (Fig. 88-4). t-PA has type I, growth factor, two kringles, and the catalytic domain. The heavy chain of prourokinase, which is shorter than factor XI and t-PA, contains one each of growth factor and kringle. The resemblance of the domain organization in the heavy chain of factor XII to t-PA and prourokinase suggests that factor XII belongs to the same family as these two fibrinolytic proteins.[17]

The light chain of factor XII contains 243 amino acid residues and the sequence is homologous to the corresponding regions of serine proteases such as trypsin, chymotrypsin, plasmin, and vitamin K–dependent coagulation factors.[16] The catalytic triad is located at His-40, Asp-89, and Ser-191. The presence of Asp-185 at the bottom of the binding pocket shows that factor XIIa is a trypsin-type enzyme, which cleaves arginyl and lysyl peptide bonds. Factor XIIa cleaves preferentially the arginyl peptide bond in the kallikrein molecule and synthetic substrates. A tertiary structure of β-factor XIIa is predicted, and the presence of Ala at position 186 in the light chain of factor XII instead of Ser in trypsin may explain why factor XIIa hydrolyzes arginyl peptide bonds but not lysyl peptide bonds.[24]

When the sequence of the light chain of factor XIIa was compared with the corresponding regions of other serine proteases, factor XIIa was found to have a higher degree of sequence identity with fibrinolytic enzymes than coagulation factors. The identities are 43 percent with t-PA, 41 percent with urokinase, 38 percent with plasminogen, 32 percent with factor IX, and 28 percent with factor X. This fact and the presence of similar domain organizations in the heavy chain and the fibrinolytic proteins suggest that factor XII plays a more important role in fibrinolysis than in coagulation (see "Factor XII (Hageman Factor) Deficiency").

The light chain of factor XIIa has a total of 13 half-cystinyl residues, indicating the presence of one interchain and six intrachain disulfide bonds. Six disulfide bonds is the highest number found in the serine protease families that have been sequenced to date. By analogy with the disulfide bond structures of plasmin[77] and t-PA,[73] the six interchain disulfide bonds can be aligned (Fig. 88-3). The remaining Cys residue at position 114 forms an interchain disulfide bond with Cys at 340 in the connecting region.

Two Asn-linked and six O-linked carbohydrate chains are present in the factor XII molecule.[16,17] All of the six O-linked carbohydrate chains are located in the connecting region. The heavy and light chains each possess one Asn-linked carbohydrate chain.

A nearly full length of cDNA cloned for human factor XII was isolated from a human liver cDNA library using synthetic oligonucleotides as a probe.[24] This clone contained the nucleotide sequence that includes an amino-terminal extension of six amino acids (probably a part of a leader peptide), the entire mature protein, a stop codon (TGA), a 3'-noncoding region, and a poly-A tail. The amino acid sequence deduced from the nucleotide sequence has one amino acid residue different from that established by protein sequence analysis (Pro is present in the protein at position 314, but Ser was predicted at this position by analysis of cDNA).

Proteinase inhibitors that circulate in blood regulate the enzyme activity of factor XIIa. Factor XIIa is inactivated by C1 esterase inhibitor,[78] antithrombin III, α_2-antiplasmin, and α_2-macroglobulin.[79] Factor XIIa forms 1:1 stoichiometric complexes with these inhibitors. Gel filtration of radiolabeled factor XIIa with plasma showed that a complex of factor XIIa and C1 esterase inhibitor was the major product.[79] These inhibitors do not inhibit surface bound factor XIIa. Thus, only β-factor XIIa that is released from the surface can be neutralized by these inhibitors.

α-Factor XIIa has both clotting and amidolytic activities, whereas β-factor XIIa retains only amidolytic activity.[80,81] The lack of clotting activity of β-factor XIIa is due to a loss of a binding site to negatively charged surfaces.[82] The binding site of factor XII for negatively charged surfaces is located in the amino-terminal MW-40,000 fragment.[63] Lysyl endopeptidase hydrolyzed a single peptide bond at Lys-73 or -74 of the MW-40,000 fragment to produce two fragments. This cleavage destroyed the ability of this fragment to bind to sulfatide (authors' unpublished result). This result suggests that the binding site of factor XII is located between the type II and the first growth factor domain. Interestingly, this region (residues 73–82) contains a fairly high content of basic amino acids (four Lys and two His in a total of 10 residues) and is somewhat similar to the histidine-rich region of HMW-kininogen, which has been shown to be the binding site for surfaces of HMW-kininogen.[47]

PLASMA PREKALLIKREIN (FLETCHER FACTOR)

Plasma prekallikrein is the zymogen to a serine protease that circulates in plasma at a level of 35 to 45 µg/ml as an equimolar complex with HMW-kininogen.[83] Purifications of prekallikrein and factor XI were difficult and required many steps of column chromatography.[84,85] Purifications of these proteins became easier with the use of HMW-kininogen–Sepharose column.[25,26,86] Recently, a synthetic peptide, the sequence for which was derived from the binding site of HMW-kininogen to prekallikrein, was found to be useful for affinity ligand purification of prekallikrein and factor XI.[87] Purified human prekallikrein migrates as a doublet on SDS-polyacrylamide gel with MWs 85,000 and 88,000.[88,89] Bovine prekallikrein also gives a doublet with MWs 86,000 and 89,000. Human and bovine prekallikrein contain 15.4 and 12.9 percent carbohydrate, respectively.[84]

Prekallikrein is converted to α-kallikrein by α-factor XIIa in the presence of HMW-kininogen and a negatively charged surface. Prekallikrein can also be activated in a fluid phase by α-factor XIIa or β-factor XIIa at a slow rate. Trypsin is also capable of activating preakallikrein. In the activation, a single peptide bond is cleaved by factor XIIa to produce a two-chain form of α-kallikrein.[84] α-Kallikrein is composed of an amino-terminal heavy chain and a carboxy-terminal light chain. The amino-terminal sequence of the light chain is Ile-Val-Gly-Gly. With the completion of the prekallikrein sequence, the cleavage site was found at an Arg-Ile bond. The heavy chain has a molecular weight of 52,000 and the light chain consists of two molecular species with MWs 44,000 and 40,000. The two forms of the light chain are probably produced by a different degree of glycosylation.

α-Kallikrein is converted to β-kallikrein by a prolonged incubation with β-factor XIIa.[80,90] During this conversion, the MW 52,000 heavy chain of α-kallikrein is cleaved into two fragments of MW 33,000 and MW 20,000. This cleavage is caused by an autolytic process, because Trasylol (kallikrein inhibitor) prevents this reaction.[90] The peptide bond that is cleaved during this conversion is not known. This cleavage decreases the functions of α-kallikrein.[80,90] Although α- and β-kallikrein have the same amidolytic activity, β-kallikrein has fivefold weaker clotting activity than α-kallikrein. β-Kallikrein also cleaves HMW-kininogen five times slower than α-kallikrein. α-Kallikrein induces aggregation of neutrophils, but β-kallikrein fails to elicit this response. We have obtained results indicating that the cleavage that occurred during the conversion of α-kallikrein to β-kallikrein in the heavy chain caused a loss of the binding affinity to HMW-kininogen. The inability of β-kallikrein to bind to HMW-kininogen is probably the reason for the weak activities of β-kallikrein for coagulation, kinin releasing, and neutrophil aggregation.

When prekallikrein was activated in plasma in the presence of a negatively charged surface, most of the kallikrein activity was found in the fluid phase.[91] This indicates that the activation of prekallikrein proceeds to the formation of β-kallikrein, which then liberates from the surface. β-Kallikrein is readily neutralized by circulating protease inhibitors. α-Kallikrein and α-factor XIIa have a similar susceptibility to circulating plasma protease inhibitors. Quantitative analysis shows that 52 percent of kallikrein is inactivated with C1 esterase inhibitor, 35 percent with α_2-macroglobulin, and 13 percent with antithrombin III.[92] The inactivation rate of α-kallikrein by these inhibitors is reduced when kallikrein is bound to HMW-kininogen.[93] HMW-kininogen competes with α_2-macroglobulin for binding to α-kallikrein.[94]

The functionally active heavy and light chains were separated by affinity column of HMW-kininogen after the selective reduction of one interchain disulfide bond of α-kallikrein. The reduction was performed in the presence of benzamidine, which seemed to protect the enzyme activity in the process of reduction and alkylation. It was demonstrated that the catalytic domain is associated with the light chain and the heavy chain contains the binding site to HMW-kininogen.[95] Complex formation of the isolated light chain with α_2-macroglobulin was demonstrated.

The primary structure of human prekallikrein was determined by a combination of protein and cDNA sequencing analysis.[25] In this study, a partial protein sequence was first obtained by analyzing peptide fragments produced by cyanogen bromide. Then, a cDNA expression library prepared from human liver mRNA was screened by an affinity-purified antibody to prekallikrein. Clones that contained inserts for prekallikrein were isolated and plaque-purified. The largest insert was a full-length cDNA coded for prekallikrein, which contained a 5′-noncoding region followed by the regions coding for a signal peptide of 19 amino acids and the mature prekallikrein of 619 amino acids. The 3′-noncoding region contained a stop codon and the AATAAA polyadenylation cleavage signal.

The amino acid sequence deduced from the nucleotide sequence is shown in Fig. 88-5A. Prekallikrein contains a signal sequence, and the presence of the signal peptide indicates that the gene product is synthesized in liver and secreted into blood. The sequence of the mature protein matched with the amino acid sequences determined from the cyanogen bromide peptides. The protein sequence analysis revealed dimorphism at position 124 in the heavy chain, where two amino acids, Asn and Ser, were found at a 7:3 ratio. The DNA sequence predicts Asn at this position. The site of cleavage by factor XIIa is a peptide bond between Arg-371 in the heavy chain and Ile-1 in the light chain. The heavy chain was found to contain four tandem repeats with an attachment of a small segment (363–371) at the carboxy-terminal end of the fourth repeat. Each repeat contains 90 or 91 residues including six half-cystinyl residues that likely form three intrarepeat disulfide bonds. The positions of these Cys residues are conserved in each repeat, indicating that each repeat has the same folding structure. The fourth repeat has two additional Cys (321 and 326) that are presumed to form one extra intrarepeat disulfide bond. The sequences of these repeats are unique and have no homology with any other proteins thus far sequenced.

The light chain has four internal disulfide bonds, which are aligned with the pairings of the four intrachain disulfide bonds determined in the B chain of plasmin.[77] Cys-113 in the light chain forms an interchain disulfide bond with Cys-364 in the connecting region. The light chain has a sequence typical of a trypsin-type protease, and the catalytic triad is located at His-44, Asp-93, and Ser-188.

Five sites for Asn-linked carbohydrate chains are placed by the protein sequencing at positions 108 and 289 in the heavy chain and 6, 63, and 104 in the light chain. Prekallikrein has no O-linked carbohydrate chain. The Asn residues were followed by the consensus sequence of -X-Thr or -X-Ser for N glycosylation.

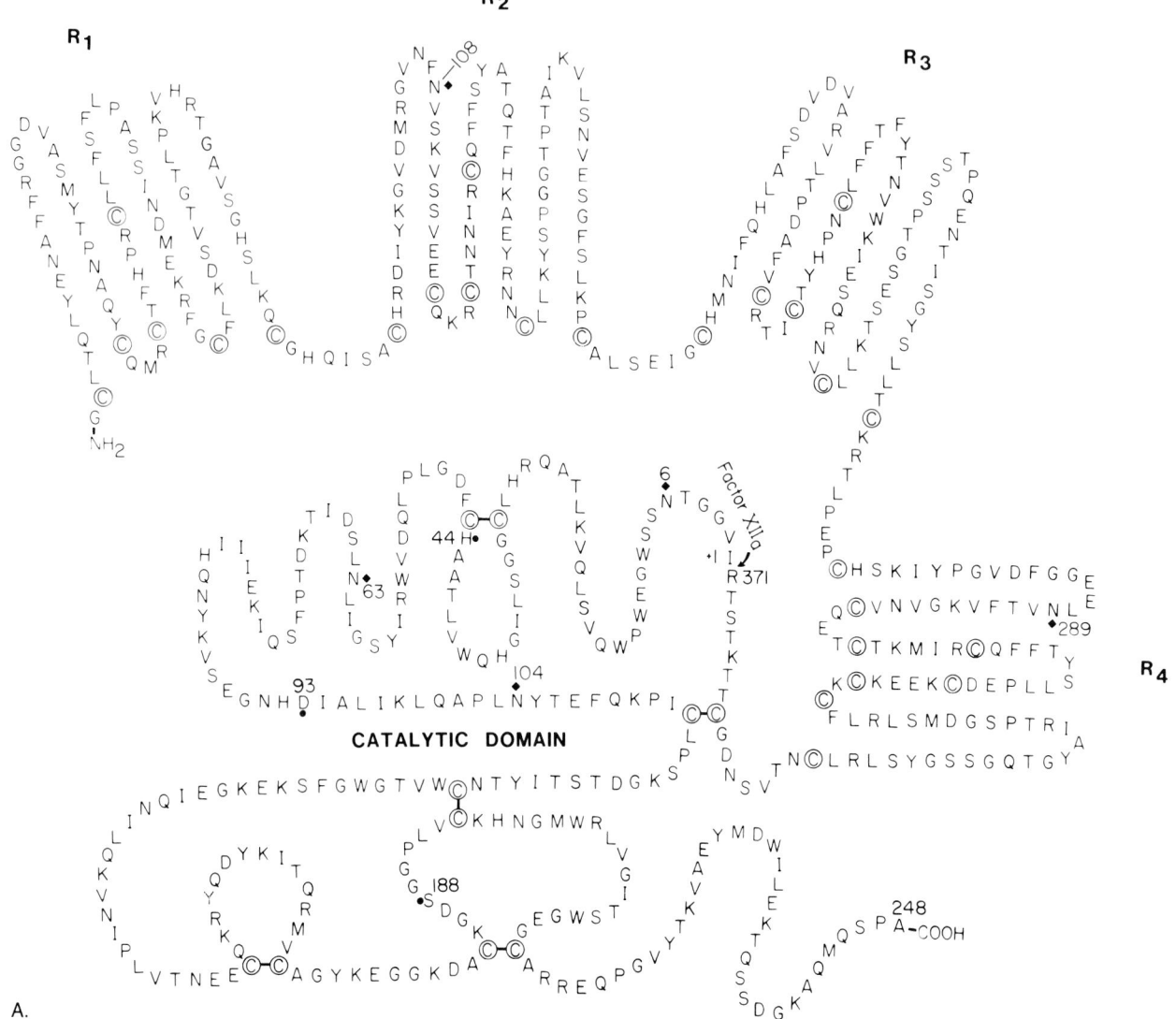

Fig. 88-5 The complete sequences of human plasma prekallikrein (A) and monomer of human factor XI (B). The sites activated by factor XIIa are shown by curved arrows. The heavy chains of both prekallikrein and factor XI are composed of four tandem repeats (R1 to R4). The residues of the catalytic triad are shown by closed circles (residues 44, 93, and 188). N-Linked glycosylation sites are shown by solid diamonds. Disulfide bridges in the heavy chain have not been determined. Disulfide bridges in the light chain are tentatively made by the alignment with those in the B chain of human plasmin. Cys residues at 11 and 321 in the light chain of factor XI probably form two disulfide bridges between the monomers. (Data are taken from Chung et al.[25] and Fujikawa et al.[26])

FACTOR XI (PLASMA THROMBOPLASTIN ANTECEDENT)

The Protein

Factor XI is a unique serine protease in that the protein is composed of two identical subunits held together by two disulfide bonds.[85,96,97] Human factor XI circulates in plasma at a level of 5 μg/ml as a complex with HMW-kininogen.[98] It has a molecular weight of 160,000 containing approximately 5 percent carbohydrate, and its monomer has a molecular weight of 83,000.[85,97] Bovine factor XI was also isolated and extensively characterized.[96]

Factor XI is activated by α-factor XIIa in the presence of a negatively charged surface and HMW-kininogen.[85,97] At a much slower rate, both α- and β-factor XIIa can activate factor XI in the absence of a negatively charged surface and HMW-kininogen. During the activation, a single peptide bond is cleaved on each subunit.[85,97] Thus, factor XIa is composed of two heavy and two light chains held together by four disulfide bonds. The molecular weight of the heavy chain is 50,000. As observed in α-kallikrein, the light chain of factor XIa also gives a doublet on SDS-gel with MWs 40,000 and

42,000. Factor XIa is inactivated primarily by α₁-protease inhibitor.[99]

The primary structure of human factor XI was predicted by cDNA sequencing.[26] The full-length cDNA was isolated from a human liver cDNA library. The nucleotide sequence included a leader peptide of 18 amino acids, the mature protein of 607 amino acids, a stop codon (TGA), a potential polyadenylation signal (AACAAA), and a poly-A tail at the 3' end. The amino acid sequence deduced from the cDNA sequence agreed with the previously published partial protein sequence except for a few residues. The DNA sequence of the coding region of the human factor XI gene agreed perfectly with the cDNA sequence.[29] Factor XI is 607 amino acids in length, and the sequence is extraordinarily homologous with prekallikrein

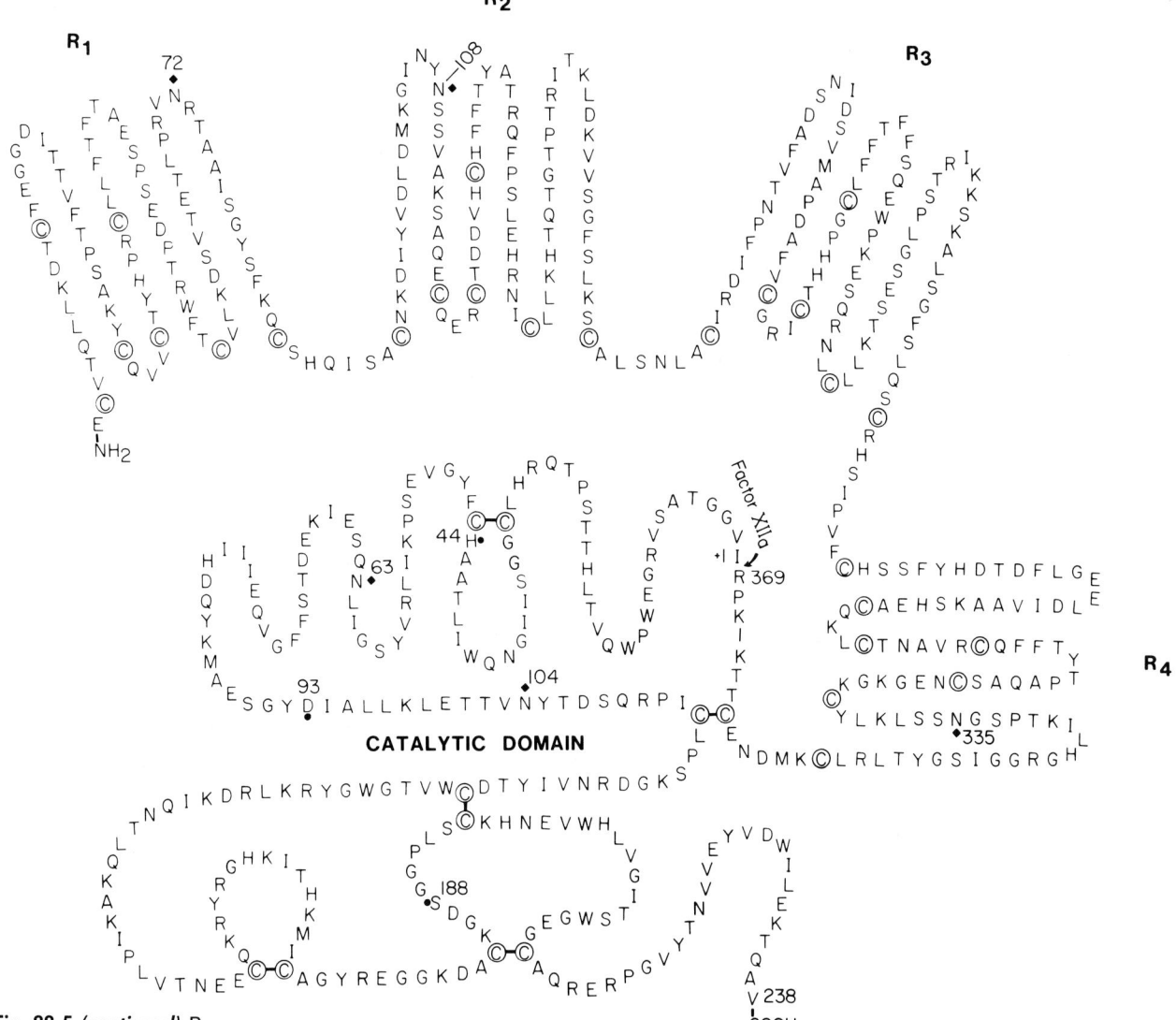

Fig. 88-5 *(continued)* B.

(Fig. 88-5*B*). The monomer of factor XI is 10 amino acid residues shorter than prekallikrein in the carboxy-terminal end of the light chain. Two amino acids are also deleted in the connecting region of factor XI. By placing only two gaps, these two proteins align with 58 percent identity.[26] The highly homologous sequences of these two proteins indicate that the genes of these two proteins diverged quite recently from a common ancestral gene. The time since the divergence of these two genes was calculated to be 280 million years.[25] In spite of the highly homologous structures, the substrate specificity and the function of these two proteins are clearly distinguished. α-Kallikrein cleaves HMW-kininogen to liberate bradykinin, and it also activates factor XII. Factor XIa does not activate factor XII, and its bradykinin-releasing activity is poor compared to kallikrein.[100] Only factor XIa can activate factor IX.

The site of factor XI cleaved by factor XIIa is located between Arg-369 in the heavy chain and Ile-1 in the light chain. A connecting region with eight amino acids (363–369) is attached to the carboxy-terminal end of the fourth repeat. The heavy chain of factor XI also contains four tandem repeats that are homologous to those found in prekallikrein. Each repeat has six half-cystinyl residues at the conserved positions. These Cys residues probably form three intrarepeat disulfide bonds in each repeat. In the first and fourth repeats, one each additional Cys residue is present at positions 11 and 321. These Cys residues are presumed to form two intersubunit disulfide bridges. Thus, two models, parallel and antiparallel, can be proposed for factor XI.[26] Four interchain disulfide bonds in the light chain of factor XIa are aligned with the known disulfide structure of the B chain of plasmin.[77] Cys-362 in the connecting region and Cys-113 in the light chain form an interchain disulfide bond. The light chain contains the catalytic triad, His-44, Asp-93, and Ser-188.

The subunit of factor XI contains five potential Asn-linked carbohydrate chains at 72, 108, and 335 in the heavy chain and 63 and 104 in the light chain. Three of these attachment sites (108, 63, and 104) are located at the same positions as in prekallikrein.

Two disulfide bonds between the heavy and light chains of factor XIa were selectively reduced and alkylated under mild conditions. The alkylated heavy chain was adsorbed to HMW-kininogen–Sepharose column, while the alkylated light chain did not bind to the column. The isolated light chain was as active as factor XIa toward synthetic peptide substrates, but only 1 percent of the factor XIa clotting activity was retained in the isolated light chain. These results demonstrate that the heavy chain contains a binding site for HMW-kininogen and the light chain has the catalytic domain.[101] These experiments also show that the binding of the heavy chain to HMW-kininogen is required for the clotting activity. The presence of one catalytic site per subunit was demonstrated by titration experiments with antithrombin III.[102] Each subunit of factor XI was also found to bind to one molecule of HMW-kininogen by titration of fluorescent-labeled factor XIa.[103]

Factor XIa activates factor IX in the presence of Ca^{2+}.[33] In this reaction, factor XIa cleaves Arg-Ala and Arg-Val bonds in factor IX molecule[104,105] and converts a single chain form of factor IX to a two-chain form, liberating an activation peptide. As mentioned above, the isolated light chain of factor XIa retains only 1 percent of the factor IX activating activity. This result indicates a possibility that the heavy chain of factor XIa has binding affinity to the factor IX molecule and is involved in the catalytic reaction. The direct involvement of the heavy chain of factor XIa in the activation of factor IX was shown by the experiments using monoclonal antibody specific to the heavy chain.[106]

Factor XI and factor XIa bind to thrombin-stimulated human platelets in the presence of HMW-kininogen, Zn^{2+}, and Ca^{2+}.[107,108] The zymogen and the active form of factor XI bind to independent sites on stimulated platelets.[108] The bound form of factor XIa can activate factor IX at the same reaction rate as is obtained with the free form of factor XIa.[109] HMW-kininogen binds directly to activated platelets in the presence of Zn^{2+} and Ca^{2+}.[110] Thus, a complex of HMW-kininogen–factor XI or factor XIa is presumably formed on the platelet surface. Scatchard analysis showed that platelets had approximately 24,000 HMW-kininogen binding sites per cell. The bound form of factor XIa, which can escape from neutralization by circulating plasma protease inhibitors, may serve to localize factor IX activation to the platelet plug.[109] Recently, a novel factor XIa inhibitor was found in platelets. This inhibitor is released from platelets upon activation by thrombin or collagen.[111] Binding of factor XIa to the platelet membrane may also be important to escape from this inhibitor.

Factor XI Gene

The gene of human factor XI was screened from two different human genomic libraries by using a full-length cDNA of human factor XI as a hybridization probe. Four overlapping re-

combinant λ phage containing the entire human factor XI gene were isolated and characterized.[29] The gene is 25 kb in length and consists of 15 exons and 14 introns (Fig. 88-6). Exon I codes for the 5′-noncoding region, and exon II codes for the signal peptide. The following eight exons (exon III to exon X) encode the four tandem repeats that are present in the heavy chain of factor XIa. These repeats are separated by introns located at the same positions. Each of these repeats contains one intron at essentially the same position. Exon XI codes for the connecting region, and the remaining four exons (exons XII to XV) encode the entire light chain of factor XIa. The locations of the introns in the light chain are identical with those in the human tissue plasminogen activator (t-PA) and the human urokinase genes. These results indicate that factor XI is derived from an ancestor that is more closely related to the t-PA subfamily.

HIGH MOLECULAR WEIGHT (HMW) KININOGEN

The Protein

Two different kininogens, HMW (Fitzgerald, Flaujeac, Williams factor)- and low molecular weight (LMW)-kininogen, circulate in plasma. These kininogens were purified from human[112,113] and bovine plasma,[113] and they were extensively characterized. Both kininogens are glycoproteins containing 13 to 16 percent carbohydrate.[113] Values of 70 to 100 μg/ml are reported for the plasma level of HMW-kininogen.[114] The concentration of HMW-kininogen exceeds the combined concentration (40 to 50 μg/ml) of prekallikrein and factor XI. Thus, approximately one-half of HMW-kininogen circulates as a complex with prekallikrein or factor XI, and the remaining molecules are free in blood. Kininogens are the precursors of a vasoactive peptide, bradykinin or kallidin, and they are also cysteine protease inhibitors.[115-117] HMW-kininogen, which circulates in blood as a complex with prekallikrein or factor XI, is a nonenzymatic cofactor for contact activation. LMW-kininogen, which does not have binding affinity to prekallikrein or factor XI, lacks procoagulant activity.[113] Recently,

Fig. 88-6 The gross structure of the human factor XI gene. The locations of 14 introns (A–I in the heavy chain and J–N in the light chain) are shown by arrows. These introns are located at the nucleotide sequences corresponding to the following amino acid residues: intron A(Met$_{-18}$), B(Glu$_1$), C(Trp$_{55}$), D(Ala$_{91}$), E(Arg$_{144}$), F(Ala$_{181}$), G(Arg$_{234}$), H(Val$_{271}$), I(Lys$_{135}$), J(Glu$_{361}$), K(Gly$_{48}$), L(Asp$_{107}$),

M(Asp$_{139}$), N(Lys$_{185}$/Gly$_{186}$) (see Fig. 88-5B for the locations of these amino acid residues. H, D, and S in circles represent the catalytic triad, and an arrowhead indicates the Arg—Ile peptide bond that is cleaved by factor XIIa for the activation. (Data are taken from Asakai et al.[29])

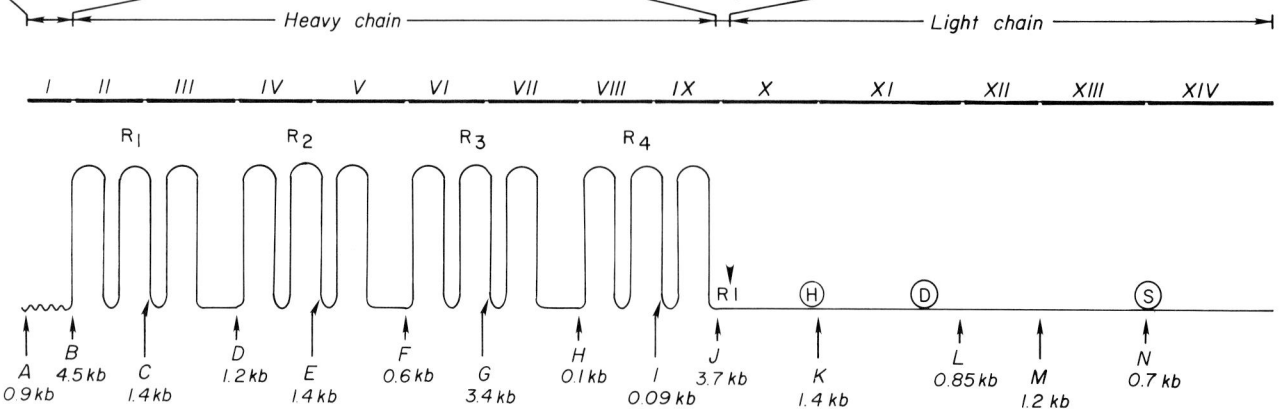

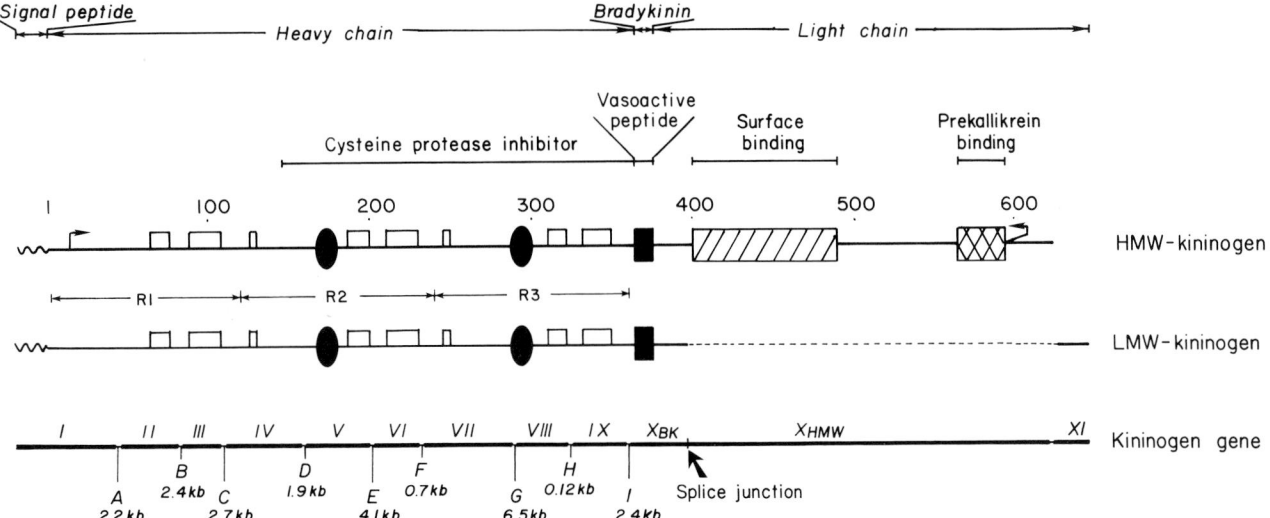

Fig. 88-7 The gross structure of human HMW- and LMW-kininogen. The bradykinin sequence is shown by a solid rectangle. The putative reactive sites of the cysteine protease inhibitor are shown by solid ovals. The binding region for negatively charged surfaces is shown by a slashed box, and the binding site for prekallikrein or factor XI is shown by a cross-slashed box. The bridges indicate eight intrachain disulfide bonds in the heavy chain. The horizontal arrows indicate an interchain disulfide bond. These disulfide bonds are placed by homology with bovine HMW-kininogen.[119] Three internal repeats are shown by R1–R3. Locations of introns and exons are shown in the bottom of the figure. The site of alternative mRNA splicing is shown by a curved arrow. A wavy line represents the leader sequence. (*Modified from Tait and Fujakawa.*[125])

the functions and the protein and gene structures of kininogens were reviewed.[118]

The complete primary structures of human and bovine HMW-kininogen were predicted by cDNA sequencing.[21–23] The structures of human[18,19] and bovine[119] HMW-kininogen were also established by protein sequence analysis. Human HMW-kininogen consists of 626 amino acid residues and has a 74 percent sequence identity with the bovine protein. The cleavage sites by α-kallikrein are at Lys-362—Arg-363 and Arg-371—Ser-372. These cleavages liberate a nonapeptide, bradykinin. The sequence of bradykinin is Arg-Pro-Pro-Gly-Phe-Ser-Pro-Phe-Arg. The remaining molecule consists of a heavy chain (362 residues) and a light chain (255 residues) linked by a disulfide bond. The heavy chain is composed of three internal repeats, each containing approximately 120 amino acids. There are three Asn-linked carbohydrate chains in the heavy chain and nine *O*-linked carbohydrate chains in the light chain. Pairings of eight interchain disulfide bonds in the heavy chain and one interchain disulfide bond between the heavy and light chains were determined in bovine HMW-kininogen.[119] It is likely that the human protein, which has 18 half-cystinyl residues at the same positions as the bovine protein, has the same disulfide bond structure (Fig. 88-7).

The heavy and the light chains of HMW-kininogen were separated after reduction and alkylation. The alkylated light chain retains the full coagulant activity of the intact HMW-kininogen.[120] Two distinct binding regions are required for the coagulant activity of the bovine light chain:[47] one for binding to a negatively charged surface, and the other for binding to prekallikrein or factor XI. A proteolytic fragment that originates from the amino-terminal region of the light chain of bovine protein binds to kaolin. This region, called the "His-rich region," is rich in basic amino acids containing 21 His, 13 Lys, and 3 Arg in a total of 110 residues. Human HMW-kininogen also has a His-rich region in the light chain, which is presumed to be a binding site to a negatively charged surface.[19] The human light chain was shown to bind to prekallikrein[121] and factor XI[86] with 1:1 stoichiometry.[53,121–123] The binding affinity of the light chain was reported to be sim-

ilar to intact HMW-kininogen.[124] The carboxy-terminal 123 amino acid residues of the bovine light chain[47] were shown to bind to prekallikrein. Recently, a carboxy-terminal 40-residue-long fragment that was isolated from a tryptic digest of the human light chain was found to retain full binding affinity for prekallikrein, with a K_d value of 20 nM.[125] Several shorter peptides covering this region were synthesized to define further the binding site, and a 31-residue peptide was found to be fully active for binding to prekallikrein. Over 80 percent of the residues of this region are conserved in bovine HMW-kininogen, indicating that the binding site of bovine HMW-kininogen to kallikrein is also located in this region. This peptide also bound to factor XI with a K_d value of 2 μM. Binding affinity of the light chain of HMW-kininogen for factor XI is weaker than for prekallikrein and requires a larger region for the maximum binding affinity.[87]

In normal plasma, HMW-kininogen is readily adsorbed to kaolin. This adsorption is less in factor XII– and prekallikrein-deficient plasmas, suggesting that alteration of the kininogen molecule is required for the optimum binding.[126] Indeed, several proteolytic fragments of bovine kininogen were tested for the coagulant activity. A kinin-free protein, which is composed of the heavy and the light chain linked by a disulfide bond, was five times more effective than intact HMW-kininogen for the activation of factor XII by α-kallikrein.[127]

LMW-kininogen differs from HMW-kininogen in molecular weight, and it also has different susceptibility to kallikreins. The primary structures of both human and bovine LMW-kininogen were determined by cDNA and protein sequencing.[20,22,23] Glandular kallikrein cleaves LMW-kininogen at a Met—Lys bond located one residue before the bradykinin sequence and liberates a decapeptide, kallidin (lysyl-bradykinin). The resultant protein consists of a heavy chain (MW 62,000) and a light chain (MW 4000) linked together by a disulfide bond.[20] The heavy chain of LMW-kininogen is identical with the heavy chain of HMW-kininogen except that it is one amino acid (Lys) shorter at the carboxy-terminal end. The light chain of human LMW-kininogen comprises only 38 amino acid residues, of which the first 12 residues are identical with the corresponding region of the light chain of HMW-kininogen. Beyond residue 13, no homology is observed between the light chains of HMW- and LMW-kininogens. Analysis of the gene and cDNA of human kininogen revealed that a single gene is transcribed to yield two different mRNAs for these two kininogens (see "Kininogen Gene").

At least two cysteine protease inhibitors, α_1- and α_2-types, circulate in blood and regulate the enzyme activity of cysteine proteases.[128] Sequence analysis of cDNA cloned for α_2-cysteine proteinase inhibitor revealed that this inhibitor was the same protein as LMW-kininogen.[129] Two sequences of Gln-Val-Val-Ala-Gly, which is a putative reactive site of cysteine protease inhibitors, are present in the second and third repeats in the heavy chain of both kininogens.[19,129] Subsequently, kininogens were found to inhibit cysteine proteases such as cathepsin B, cathepsin L, cathepsin H, and papain.[115–117] HMW- and LMW-kininogen inhibit cathepsins with K_i values of 10^{-8} to 10^{-9} M.[115] HMW-kininogen is thought to be the same as α_1-cysteine protease inhibitor.[118]

Kininogen Gene

The gene of human kininogen was isolated from a human genomic library and characterized. The gene comprises approximately 27-kb pairs and contains 11 exons. The exon-intron organization and a restriction map of human kininogen gene were established.[28] The 5'-end exon I covers the leader sequence, and the following eight exons (exon II–exon IX) cover most of the entire heavy chains of HMW- and LMW-kininogens. Exon X can be divided into two parts, exon X_{BK} and exon X_{HMW}. Exon X_{BK} encodes the remaining part of the heavy chain, bradykinin, and the first 12 amino-terminal amino acid residues of the light chain. The HMW- and LMW-kininogen mRNAs diverge at the first nucleotide of the codon for the thirteenth amino acid of the light chain by an alternative splicing mechanism. The HMW-kininogen mRNA continues through exon X_{HMW} for the remaining part of the light chain, whereas the transcription of LMW-kininogen mRNA is interrupted at this point. Exon XI, which is located downstream from exon X, encodes the remaining part of the light chain of LMW-kininogen (Fig. 88-7).

SYNTHESIS AND DISTRIBUTION OF CONTACT FACTORS

Synthesis of factor XII was studied in the perfusate of rat liver. In this experiment, radiolabeled lysine was incorporated into protein that was immunoprecipitated with antibody specific to factor XII, and the incorporation was inhibited by administration of cycloheximide in the perfusing buffer. The rate of factor XII synthesis was 3.5 μg/h per 100 g body weight, corresponding to approximately 0.2 percent of the rate of albumin synthesis.[130] A chemically synthesized bradykinin sequence was used as a hybridization probe to determine the level of kininogen message in various bovine tissues. Poly-A mRNAs were prepared from liver, kidney, spleen, mammary gland, and pancreas and used for dot hybridization to [^{32}P]DNA probe. The probe hybridized only to the liver mRNA. The kininogen message levels in other tissues were two orders of magnitude less than those of the liver.[131] These results showed that liver is the primary site of the synthesis of

factor XII and kininogens. Liver is also the sole site of factor XI synthesis. This was found by an accidental transfer of the factor XI–deficient trait to a recipient of a liver transplant.[132]

The distribution of factor XII and HMW-kininogen was studied immunohistochemically in liver, kidney, and skin in guinea pig. Antigens of factor XII and HMW-kininogen were detected in rough and smooth endoplasmic reticulum and Golgi apparatus in hepatocytes. The antigens were also distributed widely in the intercellular space of epidermis and in the interstitial tissue of capillary dermis, liver, and kidney. These results show that factor XII and HMW-kininogen are synthesized in liver, secreted into blood, and then distributed in tissues under normal conditions.[133]

FACTOR XII (HAGEMAN FACTOR) DEFICIENCY

Since the original description in 1955,[2] more than 200 cases of factor XII deficiency have been recognized. Individuals with this disorder usually do not bleed excessively either spontaneously or in response to trauma or surgery (Table 88-2). Most cases were incidentally found by a prolonged activated partial thromboplastin time (APTT) in a routine preoperative clotting test. The frequency of factor XII deficiency in the general population is difficult to estimate. One study suggested a minimal incidence of 1 in 800,000 persons.[30] This is probably an underestimate, since most patients are asymptomatic and are diagnosed only if routine coagulation tests are performed. There appears to be no particular ethnic predilection for factor XII deficiency. This disorder is usually transmitted in an autosomal recessive mode,[30] but in one exceptional family it appeared to be inherited in an autosomal dominant mode.[134] Among the patients with factor XII deficiency, a high frequency of parental consanguinity was reported.[30]

Laboratory tests show that plasma from factor XII–deficient individuals has a greatly prolonged APTT with a normal prothrombin time. The diagnosis is established by demonstrating that the addition of the patient's plasma to a known factor XII–deficient plasma does not readily correct the prolonged APTT. The plasma of homozygotes of factor XII deficiency contains less than 1 percent of normal factor XII coagulant activity, and that of heterozygotes has approximately 50 percent of the activity.

The physiological function of factor XII in hemostasis is puzzling because most factor XII–deficient patients have no bleeding symptoms. An alternative pathway(s), which bypasses factor XII, may exist for the activation of factor XI, leading to normal hemostasis. Paradoxically, some individuals with factor XII deficiency have suffered from thrombosis. Mr. Hageman, the index patient, died of pulmonary embolism,[135] and at least seven cases of myocardial infarction were reported among individuals with factor XII deficiency.[30] A review of 121 cases of factor XII deficiency showed a relatively high incidence (8.2 percent) of deep vein thrombosis or pulmonary thromboembolism.[136] Thus, it is possible that defective coagulation may be compensated for by defective fibrinolysis in this disorder. There is no indication that patients with factor XII deficiency have less susceptibility to thrombotic diseases.

Factor XII has been implicated in inflammatory or immunologic reactions. Using the skin window technique, in vivo leukocytic migration in response to antigenic stimulation was

Table 88-2 Hereditary Deficiencies of Contact Factors

	Factor XII	Factor XI	Prekallikrein	HMW-kininogen
Year described	1955	1953	1965	1975
Mode of transmission	Autosomal recessive	Autosomal recessive	Autosomal recessive	Autosomal recessive
Ethnic background	Variable	Predominantly in Jews	Variable	Variable
Bleeding symptoms	None	Mild	None	None
Prothrombin time	Normal	Normal	Normal	Normal
APTT	Prolonged	Prolonged	Prolonged	Prolonged
Intrinsic fibrinolysis	Impaired	Normal	Impaired	Impaired
Kinin formation	Impaired	Normal	Impaired	Impaired
CRM + case	Present	Unknown	Present	Unknown

markedly diminished in three factor XII–deficient persons.[137] Nonetheless, no significant clinical abnormality of inflammation has yet been observed in this disorder. Miscellaneous diseases, including peptic ulcer, gout, rheumatoid arthritis, systemic lupus erythematosus, scleroderma, and leukemia, have been reported in individuals with severe factor XII deficiency.[30,31] It is not known whether hereditary factor XII deficiency confers a predisposition to some disease or if it is only coincidentally related to these other disorders.

Some patients with coagulation disorders synthesize nonfunctional variant proteins. Such patients are called cross-reacting-material-positive (CRM +). When plasmas from 81 individuals with homozygous factor XII deficiency were tested for factor XII protein by an immunoassay, two unrelated CRM + cases were found.[31] Recently, a third CRM + case has been reported.[138] These results suggest that the occurrence of CRM + phenotype in factor XII deficiency is rare. A nonfunctional factor XII protein was isolated from one of the CRM + patients and characterized.[139] The abnormal factor XII was similar to the normal protein in molecular weight, isoelectric point, and amino acid composition. It was readily absorbed to a negatively charged surface. The abnormal protein also underwent cleavages identical with those of the normal protein when it was activated in plasma by contact activation or by trypsin. [³H]DFP was not incorporated into abnormal factor XIIa, suggesting that the defect in this protein is located at or near the catalytic triad His-40, Asp-89, and Ser-191 in the light chain (see Fig. 88-3). Studies on CRM + variants may lead to new information about the structure-function relationships of this plasma protein.

The gene of feline factor XII deficiency has recently been analyzed using human factor XII cDNA. Neither deletion of a large segment in the factor XII gene nor abnormalities in transcription or splicing were found.[140] Analysis of the gene for human factor XII deficiency has not been reported.

No treatment is required for hemostasis in individuals with factor XII deficiency.

FACTOR XI (PLASMA THROMBOPLASTIN ANTECEDENT) DEFICIENCY

Several hundred cases of this disorder have been detected since the first report in 1953. Factor XI deficiency appears to be inherited as an autosomal recessive trait and exists in two types. Major deficiency (homozygous) patients have factor XI activity below 20 percent of normal plasma, and there is po-

tential for serious surgical bleeding. Minor deficiency (heterozygous) patients have 30 to 65 percent of factor XI activity and do not have a significant risk of bleeding.[141] This disorder is mainly found in individuals of Jewish ancestry.[30] The incidence of homozygotes in the Ashkenazi Jewish community of Israel was 0.1 to 0.3 percent and of heterozygotes 5.5 to 11 percent.[142] Factor XI deficiency is not exclusively limited to those of Jewish extraction. In one study, 10 out of 80 kindreds were of non-Jewish origin, namely Japanese, Korean, black American, Arabian, Indian, and English American.[143] Interestingly, when factor XI activity of non-Jewish patients was compared with that of Jewish patients, the non-Jewish homozygotes (1.1 ± 0.9 percent, mean ± SD) and heterozygotes (43.0 ± 10.5 percent) had lower titers of factor XI activity than Jewish homozygotes (3.5 ± 3.3 percent) and heterozygotes (55.5 ± 17.4 percent).[143] In contrast to deficiencies of factor XII, prekallikrein, and HMW-kininogen, which are all characterized by an absence of abnormal bleeding, factor XI deficiency is often accompanied by a mild hemorrhagic tendency (Table 88-2). Affected individuals may have epistaxis, menorrhagia, bleeding after tonsillectomy or dental extractions, or prolonged posttraumatic hemorrhage. Bleeding symptoms in this disorder are milder than those seen in classic hemophiliacs, and hemarthroses and deep muscle hematomas rarely occur. Some patients are entirely asymptomatic and are discovered during coagulation tests prior to surgery or during a study of family members of a propositus. Surprisingly, there is no significant difference in factor XI activity between bleeders and nonbleeders.[144] The reason for the presence or absence of bleeding in this disorder is unknown. However, the bleeding tendency seems to be consistent within a given kindred.[144]

Factor XI deficiency may be suspected from a greatly prolonged APTT with normal prothrombin time in patients with a mild hemorrhagic tendency. The diagnosis can be established by demonstrating that the addition of the patient's plasma does not correct the prolonged APTT of a known factor XI–deficient plasma.

The deficiency of factor XI is probably due to decreased levels of the protein rather than to the presence of nonfunctional protein, because the factor XI coagulant activity is reduced in plasma in proportion to decreasing amounts of immunoreactive factor XI protein. When the levels of the factor XI coagulant activity and the immunoreactive factor XI antigen were examined in 38 homozygotes and 47 heterozygotes, a significant correlation between the coagulant activity and the antigen level of factor XI was found (r = 0.94, p < 0.001).[143] One study[144] reported two individuals who were suspected to be heterozygous for CRM + factor XI deficiency, but the absence of CRM + homozygotes makes it difficult to prove that they are definitely CRM + . Therefore, no evidence is available for the presence of CRM + variants in factor XI deficiency.

The patients with this disorder are not protected from thrombotic diseases. At least four patients with severe factor XI deficiency had myocardial infarctions, and one patient sustained pulmonary embolism.[31]

The management of hemorrhage following major surgery or serious accidents requires plasma infusion. The half-disappearance time of factor XI in plasma was reported to be 40 to 80 h. It was recommended that plasma levels of factor XI should be maintained above 50 percent of normal after severe bleeding. A 2 percent rise of factor XI activity in plasma results from infusion of 1 ml fresh frozen plasma per kilogram of body weight.[31]

PREKALLIKREIN (FLETCHER FACTOR) DEFICIENCY

Prekallikrein deficiency is a very rare disorder. Since the first description in 1965,[7] only 16 kindreds with prekallikrein deficiency have been reported.[31] This disorder appears to be more common in American blacks than in other races, but it has been reported in Spanish, Italian, Tunisian, and Japanese families.[31] The frequency of prekallikrein deficiency in the general population is not known because this disorder is asymptomatic.

The patients usually have no clinical symptoms. The majority of the patients with prekallikrein deficiency were discovered incidentally as a result of routine preoperative clotting tests, and they usually have no clinical symptoms or hemorrhagic tendency (Table 88-2). A few patients were reported to have some apparent bleeding symptoms such as prolonged epistaxis and hemarthrosis.[31] It is interesting to note that some individuals with this disorder had pulmonary embolism or acute myocardial infarction.[31] Various in vivo inflammatory reactions were examined in this disorder, but conflicting results were obtained. In one study, both immediate and delayed sensitivity of skin test reactions were within normal limits in two affected siblings.[145] Migration of the patients' leukocytes to attractants in a skin window was also normal. In contrast, other studies found prekallikrein-deficient patients defective in chemotaxis of leukocytes in skin windows.[137,146]

The APTT is a good screening test to detect prekallikrein deficiency. The correction of the abnormal APTT by a prolonged exposure of patients' plasma to surfaces is presumptive evidence for this disorder. APTT utilizing ellagic acid as a surface material is not sensitive to detect a deficiency of prekallikrein.[147] Definite diagnosis is dependent upon the observation that the addition of the patient's plasma does not readily correct the prolonged APTT of an established prekallikrein-deficient plasma. The plasma of the homozygotes contains less than 1 percent of the prekallikrein coagulant activity, while that of the heterozygotes has approximately 50 percent. Functional activity of prekallikrein in test plasmas can also be determined by measuring amidase activity with synthetic chromogenic peptide substrates (Pro-Phe-Arg-p-nitroanilide or Pro-Phe-Arg-4-methylcoumarin). Test samples should be activated by contact activation before assay.

CRM + variants were found in this disorder.[148] Neither prekallikrein activity nor prekallikrein antigen was detectable (CRM − cases) in 16 of 25 plasmas from the homozygous

prekallikrein deficiency.[31] In the remaining 9 plasmas, however, functionally defective prekallikrein antigen was detected (CRM + cases). Interestingly, all 16 of the CRM − subjects are black Americans, while 9 CRM + subjects are of Mediterranean or Japanese origin. A nonfunctional protein was isolated from plasma of a CRM + family and was compared to normal prekallikrein. The variant had a molecular weight of 80,000, which is similar to normal protein, and it was also immunologically indistinguishable from normal protein. The variant protein was readily complexed with HMW-kininogen. The variant protein was cleaved by α-factor XIIa 200 times more slowly than the normal molecule, and it had no enzymatic activity after activation.[149]

No therapy is required for hemostasis in this disorder.

HMW-KININOGEN (FITZGERALD, FLAUJEAC, OR WILLIAMS FACTOR) DEFICIENCY

HMW-kininogen deficiency is also a very rare disorder of blood coagulation, and less than 10 kindreds have been reported to date. The affected persons are asymptomatic and do not have any significant bleeding tendency (Table 88-2). Thus, the frequency in the general population is difficult to estimate. Because only a handful of cases of this disorder have been recognized, it is not known whether there is any particular ethnic predilection. This deficiency appears to be inherited in an autosomal recessive manner.[30,31]

Although all cases have a similar clotting abnormality due to the defect in the HMW-kininogen molecule, they exhibit variable defects in other components of the plasma kinin system. The plasma concentrations of prekallikrein and LMW-kininogen were quite variable in different cases. Mr. Fitzgerald's plasma was deficient only in HMW-kininogen,[10] whereas plasmas of some patients were deficient in both HMW- and LMW-kininogen (total kininogen deficiency).[11,150] The clotting activity of prekallikrein is low in some cases[11] and normal in others.[10] The application of genomic and cDNA probes of prekallikrein and kininogen to the study of this disorder may elucidate the pathophysiology at the molecular level. No definite evidence for CRM + variants was obtained in a study of seven HMW-kininogen deficient plasmas.[151]

Routine coagulation tests showed a markedly prolonged APTT with normal prothrombin time in HMW-kininogen–deficient individuals who have no hemorrhagic symptoms (Table 88-2). Differentiation of HMW-kininogen deficiency from factor XII or prekallikrein deficiency requires a cross-match test of patient plasma with plasma from a patient established by APTT.

HMW-kininogen is a precursor of bradykinin, which is one of the chemical mediators of inflammatory reactions. HMW- and LMW-kininogen have recently been shown to function as cysteine protease inhibitors.[115–117] In view of these findings, it will be interesting to see whether hereditary deficiency of kininogens predisposes to any disease states or provides resistance to some diseases. The inflammatory responses to various stimuli were studied in one patient with HMW-kininogen deficiency by the skin window technique.[137] Massive outpouring of neutrophils, four times more than are found in normal controls, was found following the induction of trauma. After challenge with diphtheria-tetanus toxoid, an unusually early increase in the number of eosinophils and a late increase in the number of basophils were observed. Another study reported that one individual with total kininogen deficiency had a very diminished response of plasma renin and angiotensin to salt restriction and postural changes.[152] The significance of these observations is not known at the present time. It is important to see if similar reactions occur in other kininogen deficiencies. No treatment is needed for this disorder.

REFERENCES

1. BORDET J, GENGOU O: Recherches sur la coagulation du sang et les serums anticoagulants. *Ann Inst Pasteur* 15:129, 1901.

2. RATNOFF OD, COLOPY JE: A familial hemorrhagic trait associated with a deficiency of a clot-promoting fraction of plasma. *J Clin Invest* 34:602, 1955.

3. ROSENTHAL RL, DRESKIN OH, ROSENTHAL N: New hemophilia like disease caused by deficiency of a third plasma thromboplastin factor. *Proc Soc Exp Biol Med* 82:171, 1953.

4. ARMSTRONG D, KEELE CA, JEPSON JB, STEWART JW: Development of pain-producing substance in human plasma. *Nature* 174:791, 1954.

5. MARGOLIS J: Activation of plasma by contact with glass: Evidence for a common reaction which releases plasma kinin and initiates coagulation. *J Physiol (London)* 144:1, 1958.

6. NIEWIAROWSKI S, PROU-WARTELLE O: Role du facteur contact (facteur Hageman) dans la fibrinolyse. *Thromb Diath Haemorrh* 3:593, 1959.

7. HATHAWAY WE, BELHASEN LP, HATHAWAY HS: Evidence for a new plasma thromboplastin factor. I. Case report, coagulation studies and physicochemical properties. *Blood* 26:521, 1965.

8. WUEPPER KD: Prekallikrein deficiency in man. *J Exp Med* 138:1345, 1973.

9. SAITO H, RATNOFF OD: Inhibition of normal clotting and Fletcher factor activity by rabbit anti-kallikrein antiserum. *Nature* 248:597, 1974.

10. SAITO H, RATNOFF OD, WALDMANN R, ABRAHAM JP: Fitzgerald trait. Deficiency of a hitherto unrecognized agent, Fitzgerald factor, participating in surface-mediated reactions of clotting, fibrinolysis, generation of kinins, and the property of diluted plasma enhancing vascular permeability (PF/Dil). *J Clin Invest* 55:1082, 1975.

11. WUEPPER KD, MILLER DR, LACOMBE MJ: Flaujeac trait. Deficiency of human plasma kininogen. *J Clin Invest* 56:1663, 1975.

12. COLMAN RW, BAGDASARIAN A, TALAMO RC, SCOTT CF, SEAVY M, GUIMARAES JA, PIERCE JV, KAPLAN AP: Williams trait: Human kininogen deficiency with diminished levels of plasminogen proactivator and prekallikrein associated with abnormalities of the Hageman factor-dependent pathways. *J Clin Invest* 56:1650, 1975.

13. DONALDSON VH, GLUECK HI, MILLER MA, MOVAT HZ, HABAL F: Kininogen deficiency in Fitzgerald trait: Role of high molecular weight kininogen in clotting and fibrinolysis. *J Lab Clin Med* 87:327, 1976.

14. COCHRANE CG, GRIFFIN JH: The biochemistry and pathophysiology of the contact system of plasma. *Adv Immunol* 33:241, 1982.

15. COLMAN RW: Surface-mediated defence reactions. The plasma contact activation system. *J Clin Invest* 73:1249, 1984.

16. FUJIKAWA K, MCMULLEN BA: Amino acid sequence of human β-factor XIIₐ. *J Biol Chem* 258:10924, 1983.

17. MCMULLEN BA, FUJIKAWA K: Amino acid sequence of the heavy chain of human α-factor XIIa (activated Hageman factor). *J Biol Chem* 260:5328, 1985.

18. LOTTSPEICH F, KELLERMAN J, HENSCHEN A, FOERTSCH B, MULLER-ESTERL W: The amino acid sequence of the light chain of human high-molecular-mass kininogen. *Eur J Biochem* 152:307, 1985.

19. KELLERMAN J, LOTTSPEICH F, HENSCHEN A, MULLER-ESTERL W: Completion of the primary structure of human high-molecular-mass kininogen. The amino acid sequence of the entire heavy chain and evidence for its evolution by gene triplication. *Eur J Biochem* 154:471, 1986.

20. LOTTSPEICH F, KELLERMANN J, HENSCHEN A, RAUTH G, MULLER-ESTERL W: Human low-molecular-mass kininogen: Amino-acid sequence of the light chain; homology with other protein sequences. *Eur J Biochem* 142:227, 1984.

21. TAKAGAKI Y, KITAMURA N, NAKANISHI S: Cloning and sequence analysis of cDNAs for human high molecular weight and low molecular weight prekininogens. *J Biol Chem* 260:8601, 1985.

22. NAWA H, KITAMURA N, HIROSE T, ASAI M, INAYAMA S, NAKANISHI S: Primary structures of bovine liver low molecular weight kininogen precursors and their two mRNAs. *Proc Natl Acad Sci USA* 80:90, 1983.

23. TAKAGAKI Y, KITAMURA N, NAKANISHI S: Cloning and sequence analysis of cDNAs for human high molecular weight and low molecular weight

24. COOL DE, EDGELL CJS, LOUIE GV, ZOLLER MJ, BRAYER GD, MacGILLIVRAY RTA: Characterization of human blood coagulation factor XII cDNA. *J Biol Chem* 260:13666, 1985.

25. CHUNG DW, FUJIKAWA K, MCMULLEN BA, DAVIE EW: Human plasma prekallikrein, a zymogen to a serine protease that contains four tandem repeats. *Biochemistry* 25:2410, 1986.

26. FUJIKAWA K, CHUNG DW, HENDRICKSON LE, DAVIE EW: Amino acid sequence of human factor XI, a blood coagulation factor with four tandem repeats that are highly homologous with plasma prekallikrein. *Biochemistry* 25:2417, 1986.

27. KITAMURA N, TAKAGAKI Y, FURUTO S, TANAKA T, NAWA H, NAKANISHI S: A single gene for bovine high molecular weight and low molecular weight kininogens. *Nature* 305:545, 1983.

28. KITAMURA N, KITAGAWA H, FUKUSHIMA D, TAKAGAKI Y, MIYATA T, NAKANISHI S: Structural organization of the human kininogen gene and a model for its evolution. *J Biol Chem* 260:8610, 1985.

29. ASAKAI R, DAVIE EW, CHUNG DW: Organization of the gene for human factor XI. *Biochemistry* 26:7221, 1987.

30. RATNOFF OD, SAITO H: Surface-mediated reactions. *Curr Top Hematol* 2:1, 1979.

31. SAITO H: Contact factors in health and disease. *Semin Thromb Hemost* 13:35, 1987.

32. KAPLAN AP: Initiation of the intrinsic coagulation and fibrinolytic pathways of man: The role of surfaces, Hageman factor, prekallikrein, high molecular weight kininogen, and factor XI. *Prog Hemost Thromb* 4:127, 1978.

33. DAVIE EW, FUJIKAWA K, KURACHI K, KISIEL W: The role of serine proteases in the blood coagulation cascade. *Adv Enzymol* 48:277, 1979.

34. WACHTFOGEL YT, KUCICH U, JAMES HL, SCOTT CF, SCHAPIRA M, ZIMMERMAN M, COHEN AB, COLMAN RW: Human plasma kallikrein releases neutrophil elastase during blood coagulation. *J Clin Invest* 72:1672, 1983.

35. GHEBREHIWET B, RANDAZZO BP, DUNN JT, SILVERBERG M, KAPLAN AP: Mechanisms of activation of the classical pathway of complement by Hageman factor fragment. *J Clin Invest* 71:1450, 1983.

36. YAMAMOTO T, COCHRANE CG: Guinea pig Hageman factor as a vascular permeability enhancement factor. *Am J Pathol* 105:164, 1981.

37. RADCLIFFE R, BAGDASARIAN A, COLMAN RW, NEMERSON Y: Activation of factor VII by Hageman factor fragment. *Blood* 59:611, 1977.

38. KISIEL W, FUJIKAWA K, DAVIE EW: Activation of bovine factor VII (Proconvertin) by factor XIIₐ (activated Hageman factor). *Biochemistry* 16:4189, 1977.

39. HEIMARK RL, KURACHI K, FUJIKAWA K, DAVIE EW: Surface activation of blood coagulation, fibrinolysis and kinin formation. *Nature* 286:456, 1980.

40. SUGO T, HAMAGUCHI A, SHIMADA T, KATO H, IWANAGA S: Mechanism of surface-mediated activation of bovine factor XII and plasma prekallikrein. *J Biochem* 92:689, 1982.

41. KURACHI K, FUJIKAWA K, DAVIE EW: Mechanism of activation of bovine factor XI by factor XII and factor XIIₐ. *Biochemistry* 19:1330, 1980.

42. SILVERBERG M, DUNN JT, GAREN L, KAPLAN AP: Autoactivation of human Hageman factor: Demonstration utilizing a synthetic substrate. *J Biol Chem* 255:7281, 1980.

43. TANS G, ROSING J, GRIFFIN JH: Sulfatide-dependent autoactivation of human blood coagulation factor XII (Hageman factor). *J Biol Chem* 258:8215, 1983.

44. TANKERSLEY DL, FINLAYSON JS: Kinetics of activation and autoactivation of human factor XII. *Biochemistry* 23:273, 1984.

45. GRIEP MA, FUJIKAWA K, NELSESTUEN GL: Binding and activation properties of human factor XII, prekallikrein, and derived peptides with acidic lipid vesicles. *Biochemistry* 24:4124, 1985.

46. KIRBY EP, MCDEVITT PJ: The binding of bovine factor XII to kaolin. *Blood* 61:652, 1983.

47. IKARI N, SUGO T, FUJII S, KATO H, IWANAGA S: The role of bovine high-molecular-weight (HMW) kininogen in contact-mediated activation of bovine factor XII: Interaction of HMW kininogen with kaolin and plasma prekallikrein. *J Biochem* 89:1699, 1981.

48. GRIFFIN JH: Role of surface-dependent activation of Hageman factor (blood coagulation factor XII). *Proc Natl Acad Sci USA* 75:1998, 1978.

49. STERN DM, DRILLINGS M, KISIEL W, NAWROTH P, NOSSEL HL, LaGAMMA KS: Activation of factor IX bound to cultured bovine aortic endothelial cells. *Proc Natl Acad Sci USA* 81:913, 1984.

50. MOSKOWITZ RW, SCHWARTZ HJ, MICHEL B, RATNOFF OD, ASTRUP T: Generation of kinin-like agents by chondroitin sulfate, heparin, chitin sulfate, and human articular cartilage: Possible pathophysiologic implications. *J Lab Clin Med* 76:790, 1970.

51. FUJIKAWA K, HEIMARK RL, KURACHI K, DAVIE EW: Activation of bovine

factor XII (Hageman factor) by plasma kallikrein. *Biochemistry* 19:1322, 1980.

52. TANS G, GRIFFIN JH: Properties of sulfatides in factor XII-dependent contact activation. *Blood* 59:69, 1982.

53. SHIMADA T, KATO H, IWANAGA S, IWAMORI M, NAGAI Y: Activation of factor XII and prekallikrein with cholesterol sulfate. *Thromb Res* 38:21, 1985.

54. HOJIMA Y, COCHRANE CG, WIGGINS RC, AUSTEN KF, STEVENS RL: In vitro activation of the contact (Hageman factor) system of plasma by heparin and chondroitin sulfate E. *Blood* 63:1453, 1984.

55. GRIEP MA, FUJIKAWA K, NELSESTUEN GL: Possible basis for the apparent surface selectivity of the contact activation of human blood coagulation factor XII. *Biochemistry* 25:6688, 1986.

56. KAPLAN AP, YECIES LD: Initiation of Hageman factor-dependent fibrinolysis, in Kline DL, Reddy KNN (eds): *Fibrinolysis*. Boca Raton, FL, CRC Press, 1980, p 43.

57. MILES LA, GREENGARD JS, GRIFFIN JH: A comparison of the abilities of plasma kallikrein, β-factor XIIa, factor XIa and urokinase to activate plasminogen. *Thromb Res* 29:407, 1983.

58. KLUFT C, WIJNGAARDS G, JIE AFH: Intrinsic plasma fibrinolysis: Involvement of urokinase-related activity in the factor XII-independent plasminogen proactivator pathway. *J Lab Clin Med* 103:408, 1984.

59. DOOIJEWAAD G, DE JONG YF, JIE AFH, KLUFT C: The role of kallikrein in the generation of factor XII-dependent plasminogen activator activity in human plasmas. *Thromb Haemost* 54:268, 1985.

60. BERGER H, TUTTLE PR: Comparative properties of six human plasminogen activators. *Prog Fibrinolysis* 6:29, 1983.

61. ICHINOSE A, FUJIKAWA K, SUYAMA T: The activation of pro-urokinase by plasma kallikrein and its inactivation by thrombin. *J Biol Chem* 261:3486, 1986.

62. AOKI N, HARPEL PC: Inhibitors of the fibrinolytic enzyme system. *Semin Thromb Hemost* 10:14, 1984.

63. REVAK SD, COCHRANE CG, GRIFFIN JH: Structural changes accompanying enzymatic activation of human Hageman factor. *J Clin Invest* 54:619, 1974.

64. GRIFFIN JH, COCHRANE CG: Human factor XII (Hageman factor). *Methods Enzymol* 45:56, 1976.

65. FUJIKAWA K, DAVIE EW: Human factor XII (Hageman factor). *Methods Enzymol* 80:198, 1981.

66. FUJIKAWA K, HEIMARK RL, KURACHI K, DAVIE EW: Activation of bovine factor XII (Hageman factor) by plasma kallikrein. *Biochemistry* 19:1322, 1980.

67. PETERSEN TE, THOGERSEN HC, SKORSTENGAARD K, VIBE-PEDERSEN K, SAHL P, SOTTRUP-JENSEN L, MAGNUSSON S: Partial primary structure of bovine plasma fibronectin: Three types of internal homology. *Proc Natl Acad Sci USA* 80:137, 1983.

68. SKORSTENGAARD K, THOGERSEN HC, PETERSEN TE: Complete primary structure of the collagen-binding domain of bovine fibronectin. *Eur J Biochem* 140:235, 1984.

69. GREGORY H, PRESTON BM: The primary structure of human urogastrone. *Int J Pept Protein Res* 9:107, 1977.

70. GUNZLER WA, STEFFENS GJ, OTTING F, KIM SM, FRANKUS E, FLOHE L: The primary structure of high molecular mass urokinase from human urine. The complete amino acid sequence of the A chain. *Hoppe-Seyler's Z Physiol Chem* 363:1155, 1982.

71. STEFFENS GJ, GUNZLER WA, OTTING F, FRANKUS E, FLOHE L: The complete amino acid sequence of low molecular mass urokinase from human urine. *Hoppe-Seyler's Z Physiol Chem* 363:1043, 1982.

72. VERDE P, STOPPELLI MP, GALEFFI P, Di NOCERA P, BLASI F: Identification and primary sequence of an unspliced human urokinase poly(A)+ RNA. *Proc Natl Acad Sci USA* 81:4727, 1984.

73. PENNICA D, HOLMES WE, KOHR WJ, HARKINS RN, VEHAR GA, WARD CA, BENNETT WF, YELVERTON E, SEEBURG PH, HEYNEKER HL, GOEDDEL DV, COLLEN D: Cloning and expression of human tissue-type plasminogen activator cDNA in *E. coli*. *Nature* 301:214, 1983.

74. DAVIE EW: The blood coagulation factors: Their cDNAs, genes, and expression, in Colman RW, Hirsh J, Marder VJ, Salzman EW (eds): *Hemostasis and Thrombosis*, 2d ed. Philadelphia, Lippincott, 1987, p 242.

75. MAGNUSSON S, PETERSEN TE, SOTTRUP-JENSEN L, CLAEYS H: Complete primary structure of prothrombin: Isolation, structure and reactivity of ten carboxylated glutamic acid residues and regulation of prothrombin activation by thrombin, in Reich E, Rifkin DB, Shaw E (eds): *Proteases and Biological Control*. Cold Spring Harbor, NY, Cold Spring Harbor Laboratory, 1975, vol 2, p 123.

76. MAGNUSSON S, SOTTRUP-JENSEN L, PETERSEN TE, DUDEK-WOJCIECHOWSKA G, CLAEYS H: Homologous "kringle" structures common to

77. WIMAN B: Primary structure of the B-chain of human plasmin. *Eur J Biochem* 76:129, 1977.

78. FORBES CD, PENSKY J, RATNOFF OD: Inactivation of activated Hageman factor and activated plasma thromboplastin antecedent by purified serum C1 inactivator. *J Lab Clin Med* 76:809, 1970.

79. PIXLEY RA, SCHAPIRA M, COLMAN RW: The regulation of human factor XIIa by plasma proteinase inhibitors. *J Biol Chem* 260:1723, 1985.

80. COLMAN RW, WACHTFOGEL YT, KUCICH U, WEINBAUM G, HAHN S, PIXLEY RA, SCOTT CF, de AGOSTINI A, BURGER D, SCHAPIRA M: Effect of cleavage of the heavy chain of human plasma kallikrein on its functional properties. *Blood* 65:311, 1985.

81. REVAK SD, COCHRANE CG: The relationship of structure and function in human Hageman factor. *J Clin Invest* 57:852, 1976.

82. REVAK SD, COCHRANE CG, GRIFFIN JH: The binding and cleavage characteristics of human Hageman factor during contact activation. A comparison of normal plasma with plasmas deficient in factor XI, prekallikrein, or high molecular weight kininogen. *J Clin Invest* 59:1167, 1977.

83. MANDLE RJ, COLMAN RW, KAPLAN AP: Identification of prekallikrein and high-molecular-weight kininogen as a complex in human plasma. *Proc Natl Acad Sci USA* 73:4179, 1976.

84. HEIMARK RL, DAVIE EW: Bovine and human plasma prekallikrein. *Methods Enzymol* 80:157, 1981.

85. KURACHI K, DAVIE EW: Human factor XI (plasma thromboplastin antecedent). *Methods Enzymol* 80:211, 1981.

86. BOUMA BN, VLOOSWIJK RA, GRIFFIN JH: Immunologic studies of human coagulation factor XI and its complex with high molecular weight kininogen. *Blood* 62:1123, 1983.

87. TAIT JF, FUJIKAWA K: Primary-structure requirements for the binding of human high molecular weight kininogen to plasma prekallikrein and factor XI. *J Biol Chem* 262:11651, 1987.

88. MANDLE R, Jr, KAPLAN AP: Hageman factor substrates. Human plasma prekallikrein: Mechanism of activation by Hageman factor and participation in Hageman factor-dependent fibrinolysis. *J Biol Chem* 252:6097, 1977.

89. BOUMA BN, MILES LA, BERETTA G, GRIFFIN JH: Human plasma prekallikrein. Studies of its activation by activated factor XII and of its inactivation by diisopropyl phosphofluoridate. *Biochemistry* 19:1151, 1980.

90. BURGER D, SCHLEUNING WD, SCHAPIRA M: Human plasma prekallikrein. Immunoaffinity purification and activation to α- and β-kallikrein. *J Biol Chem* 261:324, 1986.

91. WIGGINS RC, BOUMA BN, COCHRANE CG, GRIFFIN JH: Role of high-molecular-weight kininogen in surface-binding and activation of coagulation factor XI and prekallikrein. *Proc Natl Acad Sci USA* 74:4636, 1977.

92. van der GRAAF F, KOEDAM JA, BOUMA BN: Inactivation of kallikrein in human plasma. *J Clin Invest* 71:149, 1983.

93. SCHAPIRA M, SCOTT CF, COLMAN RW: Protection of human plasma kallikrein from inactivation by C1 inhibitor and other protease inhibitors. The role of high molecular weight kininogen. *Biochemistry* 20:2738, 1981.

94. van der GRAAF F, RIETVELD A, KEUS FJA, BOUMA BN: Interaction of human plasma kallikrein and its light chain with α2-macroglobulin. *Biochemistry* 23:1760, 1984.

95. van der GRAAF F, TANS G, BOUMA BN, GRIFFIN JH: Isolation and functional properties of the heavy and light chains of human plasma kallikrein. *J Biol Chem* 257:14300, 1982.

96. KOIDE T, KATO H, DAVIE EW: Bovine factor XI (plasma thromboplastin antecedent). *Methods Enzymol* 80:65, 1976.

97. BOUMA BN, GRIFFIN JH: Human blood coagulation factor XI. Purification, properties, and mechanism of activation by activated factor XII. *J Biol Chem* 252:6432, 1977.

98. THOMPSON RE, MANDLE R Jr, KAPLAN AP: Association of factor XI and high molecular weight kininogen in human plasma. *J Clin Invest* 60:1376, 1977.

99. SCOTT CF, SCHAPIRA M, JAMES HL, COHEN AB, COLMAN RW: Inactivation of factor XIa by plasma protease inhibitors. Predominant role of α1-protease inhibitor and protective effect of high molecular weight kininogen. *J Clin Invest* 69:844, 1982.

100. SCOTT CF, PURDON DA, SILVER LD, COLMAN RW: Cleavage of high molecular weight kininogen (HMWK) by plasma factor XIa. *J Biol Chem* 260:10856, 1985.

101. van der GRAAF F, GREENGARD JS, BOUMA BN, KERBIRIOU DM, GRIFFIN JH: Isolation and functional characterization of the active light chain of activated human blood coagulation factor XI. *J Biol Chem* 258:9669, 1983.

102. KURACHI K, DAVIE EW: Activation of human factor XI (plasma thrombo-

plastin antecedent) by factor XII$_a$ (activated Hageman factor). *Biochemistry* 16:5831, 1977.

103. WARN-CRAMER BJ, BAJAJ SP: Stoichiometry of binding of high molecular weight kininogen to factor XI/XIa. *Biochem Biophys Res Commun* 133:417, 1985.

104. FUJIKAWA K, LEGAZ ME, KATO H, DAVIE EW: The mechanism of activation of bovine factor IX (Christmas factor) by bovine factor XI$_a$ (activated plasma thromboplastin antecedent). *Biochemistry* 13:4508, 1974.

105. DISCIPIO RG, KURACHI K, DAVIE EW: Activation of human factor IX (Christmas factor). *J Clin Invest* 61:1528, 1978.

106. SINHA D, KOSHY A, SEAMAN FS, WALSH PN: Functional characterization of human blood coagulation factor XIa using hybridoma antibodies. *J Biol Chem* 260:10714, 1985.

107. GREENGARD JS, HEEB MJ, ERSDAL E, WALSH PN, GRIFFIN JH: Binding of coagulation factor XI to washed human platelets. *J Clin Invest* 25:3884, 1986.

108. SINHA D, SEAMAN FS, KOSHY A, KNIGHT LC, WALSH PN: Blood coagulation factor XIa binds specifically to a site on activated human platelets distinct from that for factor XI. *J Clin Invest* 73:1550, 1984.

109. WALSH PN, SINHA D, KOSHY A, SEAMAN FS, BRADFORD H: Functional characterization of platelet-bound factor XIa: Retention of factor XIa activity on the platelet surface. *Blood* 68:225, 1986.

110. GREENGARD JS, GRIFFIN JH: Receptors for high molecular weight kininogen on stimulated washed human platelets. *Biochemistry* 23:6863, 1984.

111. SOONS H, JANSSEN-CLAESSEN T, HEMKER HC, TANS G: The effect of platelets in the activation of human blood coagulation factor IX by factor XI. *Blood* 68:140, 1986.

112. KERBIRIOU DM, GRIFFIN JH: Human high molecular weight kininogen: Studies of structure-function relationships and of proteolysis of the molecule occurring during contact activation of plasma. *J Biol Chem* 254:12020, 1979.

113. KATO H, NAGAWAWA S, IWANAGA S: HMW and LMW kininogens. *Methods Enzymol* 80:172, 1981.

114. PROUD D, PIERCE JV, PISANO JJ: Radioimmunoassay of human high molecular weight kininogen in normal and deficient plasma. *J Lab Clin Med* 95:563, 1980.

115. SUEYOSHI T, ENJYOJI K, SHIMADA T, KATO H, IWANAGA S, BANDO Y, KOMINAMI E, KATUNUMA N: A new function of kininogens as thiol-proteinase inhibitors: Inhibition of papain and cathepsins B, H and L by bovine, rat and human plasma kininogens. *FEBS Lett* 182:193, 1985.

116. MULLER-ESTERL W, FRITZ H, MACHLEIDT W, RITONJA A, BRZIN J, KOTNIK M, TURK V, KELLERMAN J, LOTTSPEICH F: Human plasma kininogens are identical with α-cysteine proteinase inhibitors. *FEBS Lett* 182:310, 1985.

117. HIGASHIYAMA S, OHKUBO I, ISHIGURO H, KUNIMATSU M, SAWAKI K, SASAKI M: Human high molecular weight kininogen as a thiol proteinase inhibitor: Presence of the entire inhibition capacity in the native form of heavy chain. *Biochemistry* 25:1669, 1986.

118. MULLER-ESTERL W, IWANAGA S, NAKANISHI S: Kininogens revisited. *TIBS* 11:336, 1986.

119. SUEYOSHI T, MIYATA T, HASHIMOTO N, MIYATA T, KATO H, HAYASHIDA H, IWANAGA S: Bovine high molecular weight kininogen: The amino acid sequence, position of carbohydrate chains and disulfide bridge in the heavy chain portion. *J Biol Chem* 262:2768, 1987.

120. THOMPSON RE, MANDLE R Jr, KAPLAN AP: Characterization of human high molecular weight kininogen. Procoagulant activity assessed with the light chain of kinin-free high molecular weight kininogen. *J Exp Med* 147:488, 1978.

121. KERBIRIOU DM, BOUMA BN, GRIFFIN JH: Immunochemical studies of human high molecular weight kininogen and of its complexes with plasma prekallikrein or kallikrein. *J Biol Chem* 255:3952, 1980.

122. BOCK PE, SHORE JD: Protein-protein interactions in contact activation of blood coagulation. Characterization of fluorescein-labeled human high molecular weight kininogen-light chain as probe. *J Biol Chem* 258:15079, 1983.

123. SHIMADA T, KATO H, MAEDA H, IWANAGA S: Interaction of factor XII, high-molecular-weight (HMW) kininogen and prekallikrein with sulfatide: Analysis of fluorescence polarization. *J Biochem (Tokyo)* 97:1637, 1985.

124. BOCK PE, SHORE JD, TANS G, GRIFFIN JH: Protein-protein interactions in contact activation of blood coagulation. Binding of high molecular weight kininogen and the 5-(iodoacetamido)fluorescein-labeled kininogen light chain to prekallikrein, kallikrein, and the separated kallikrein heavy and light chains. *J Biol Chem* 260:12434, 1985.

125. TAIT JF, FUJIKAWA K: Identification of the binding site for plasma prekallikrein in human high-molecular-weight kininogen: A region from res-

idues 185 to 224 of the kininogen light chain retains full binding activity. *J Biol Chem* 261:15396, 1986.

126. SCOTT CF, SILVER LD, SCHAPIRA M, COLMAN RW: Cleavage of human high molecular weight kininogen markedly enhances its coagulant activity: Evidence that this molecule exists as a procofactor. *J Clin Invest* 73:954, 1984.

127. SUGO T, IKARI N, KATO H, IWANAGA S, FUJII S: Functional sites of bovine high molecular weight kininogen as a cofactor in kaolin-mediated activation of factor XII (Hageman factor). *Biochemistry* 19:3215, 1980.

128. SASAKI M, TANIGUCHI K, SUZUKI K, IMAHORI K: Human plasma α$_1$- and α$_2$-thiol proteinase inhibitors strongly inhibit Ca-activated neutral protease from muscle. *Biochem Biophys Res Commun* 110:256, 1983.

129. OHKUBO I, KURACHI K, TAKASAWA T, SHIOKAWA H, SASAKI M: Isolation of a human cDNA for α$_2$-thiol proteinase inhibitor and its identity with low molecular weight kininogen. *Biochemistry* 23:5691, 1984.

130. SAITO H, HAMILTON SM, TAVILL AS, GOODNOUGH LT, LOUIS L, ANGELL A: Synthesis and release of Hageman factor (factor XII) by the isolated perfused rat liver. *J Clin Invest* 72:948, 1983.

131. SULIMOVA GE, AKHUNDOVA AA, KAPELINSKAIA TV, GORODETSKII SI: mRNA localization and content in bovine kininogen. *Biokhimiia* 50:279, 1985.

132. DZIK WH, ARKIN CF, JENKINS RL: Transfer of congenital factor XI deficiency from a donor to a recipient by liver transplantation. *N Engl J Med* 316:1217, 1987.

133. TSURUTA J, YAMAMOTO T, KAMBARA T: Immunohistochemical studies on synthesis and distribution of Hageman factor and kininogen. *Adv Exp Med Biol* 198, part B:63, 1986.

134. BENNETT B, RATNOFF OD, HOLT JB, ROBERTS HR: Hageman trait (factor XII deficiency): A probable second genotype inherited as an autosomal dominant characteristic. *Blood* 40:412, 1972.

135. RATNOFF OD, BUSSE RJ, SHEON RP: The demise of John Hageman. *N Engl J Med* 279:760, 1968.

136. GOODNOUGH LT, SAITO H, RATNOFF OD: Thrombosis or myocardial infarction in congenital clotting factor abnormalities and chronic thrombocytopenias: A report of 21 patients and a review of 50 previously reported cases. *Medicine* 62:248, 1983.

137. REBUCK JW: The skin window as a monitor of leukocytic functions in contact activation factor deficiencies in man. *Am J Clin Pathol* 79:405, 1983.

138. BERRETTINI M, LAMMLE B, CIAVARELLA G, CIAVARELLA N: Functional and immunological studies of abnormal factor XII in a cross reacting material positive (CRM+) factor XII deficiency. *Thromb Haemost* 54:120, 1985.

139. SAITO H, SCIALLA SJ: Isolation and properties of an abnormal Hageman factor (factor XII) molecule in a cross-reacting material-positive Hageman trait plasma. *J Clin Invest* 68:1028, 1981.

140. JANIK J, KIER A, RATNOFF OD: Molecular analysis of Hageman factor deficiency in cats. *Blood* 68 (suppl):347a, 1986.

141. RAPAPORT SI, PROCTOR RR, PATCH MJ, YETTRA M: The mode of inheritance of PTA deficiency: Evidence for the existence of major PTA deficiency and minor PTA deficiency. *Blood* 18:149, 1961.

142. SELIGSOHN U: High gene frequency of factor XI (PTA) deficiency in Ashkenazi Jews. *Blood* 51:1223, 1978.

143. SAITO H, RATNOFF OD, BOUMA BN, SELIGSOHN U: Failure to detect variant (CRM+) plasma thromboplastin antecedent (PTA, factor XI) molecules in hereditary PTA deficiency: A study of 125 patients of several ethnic backgrounds. *J Lab Clin Med* 106:718, 1985.

144. RAGNI MV, SINHA D, SEAMAN F, LEWIS JH, SPERO JA, WALSH PW: Comparison of bleeding tendency, factor XI coagulant activity, and factor XI antigen in 25 factor XI-deficient kindreds. *Blood* 65:719, 1985.

145. HATHAWAY WE, WUEPPER KD, WESTON WL, HUMBERT JR, RIVERS RPA, GENTON E, AUGUST CS, MONTGOMERY RR, MASS MF: Clinical and physiologic studies of two siblings with prekallikrein (Fletcher factor) deficiency. *Am J Med* 60:654, 1976.

146. POON MC, MOORE MR, CASTLEBERRY RP, LURIE A, HUANG ST, LEHMEYER J: Combined deficiencies of Fletcher factor (plasma prekallikrein) and Hageman factor (factor XII). Report of a case with observation on in vivo and in vitro leukocyte chemotaxis. *Am J Hematol* 12:261, 1982.

147. ABILDGAARD CF, HARRISON J: Fletcher factor deficiency: Family study and detection. *Blood* 43:641, 1974.

148. SAITO H, GOODNOUGH LT, SORIA J, SORIA C, AZNAR J, ESPANA F: Heterogeneity of human prekallikrein deficiency (Fletcher trait). Evidence that five of 18 cases are positive for cross-reacting material. *N Engl J Med* 305:910, 1981.

149. BOUMA BN, KERBIRIOU DM, BAKER J, GRIFFIN JH: Characterization of a variant prekallikrein, prekallikrein Long Beach, from a family with

mixed cross-reacting material-positive and cross-reacting material-negative prekallikrein deficiency. *J Clin Invest* 78:170, 1986.

150. COLMAN RW, BAGDASARIAN A, TALAMO RC, SCOTT CF, SEAVY M, GUIMARAES JA, PIERCE JV, KAPLAN AP: Williams trait: Human kininogen deficiency with diminished levels of plasminogen proactivator and prekallikrein associated with abnormalities of the Hageman factor-dependent pathways. *J Clin Invest* 56:1650, 1975.

151. PROUD D, PIERCE JV, PISANO JJ: Radioimmunoassay of human high molecular weight kininogen in normal and deficient plasmas. *J Lab Clin Med* 95:563, 1980.

152. WONG PY, WILLIAMS GH, COLMAN RW: Studies on the renin-angiotensin system in a kininogen-deficient individual. *Clin Sci* 65:121, 1983.

CHAPTER 89

ANTITHROMBIN DEFICIENCY

DOUGLAS M. TOLLEFSEN

1. Antithrombin is a 58,000-dalton serine proteinase inhibitor in human plasma. It inhibits activated coagulation factors of the intrinsic pathway, including thrombin, factor IXa, and factor Xa. Inhibition occurs by formation of an apparently covalent, 1:1 complex between antithrombin and the proteinase.

2. Heparin increases the rate of the antithrombin-proteinase reaction at least 1000-fold by a catalytic mechanism. Binding of heparin to antithrombin (and perhaps also to the proteinase) is required for catalytic activity. The site on heparin which binds antithrombin is a specific pentasaccharide sequence that contains an unusual 3-O-sulfated glucosamine residue. This structure occurs in ≈30 percent of heparin molecules and less abundantly in heparan sulfate molecules on the surface of vascular endothelial cells. Other glycosaminoglycans (e.g., dermatan sulfate, chondroitin-4-sulfate, and chondroitin-6-sulfate) lack the antithrombin-binding structure. It is thought that heparan sulfate on the luminal surface of blood vessels binds a portion of the circulating antithrombin and thus inhibits thrombus formation.

3. Inherited antithrombin deficiency is estimated to occur with an incidence of ≈1 per 5000 and has been found in 1 to 2 percent of patients with venous thromboembolic disease. The deficiency is inherited as an autosomal dominant trait. Affected heterozygotes have ≈50 percent of the normal plasma antithrombin activity, which generally results from diminished biosynthesis of normal antithrombin. Variant forms of antithrombin with single amino acid substitutions that affect heparin and/or proteinase binding have also been reported.

4. There is evidence that prothrombin activation occurs continuously at a low rate in the circulation of normal individuals. Antithrombin deficiency results in a two- to threefold increase in the rate of this process. This biochemical abnormality may be indicative of a "prethrombotic" state in deficient patients.

5. Clinical manifestations of antithrombin deficiency include deep vein thrombosis and pulmonary embolism. Thrombosis may occur spontaneously or in association with pregnancy, trauma, or surgery. Arterial thrombosis is rare. Many patients experience recurrent thromboembolic disease beginning in early adulthood. It is estimated that by 50 years of age, ≈85 percent of patients with antithrombin deficiency will have had at least one thrombotic episode. Acute episodes are treated with a 7- to 10-day infusion of heparin followed by oral anticoagulant therapy for ≈3 months. Continuous prophylactic therapy of asymptomatic patients remains controversial.

6. Heparin cofactor II is a homologous serine proteinase inhibitor that inhibits thrombin in the presence of heparin or dermatan sulfate. The concentration of heparin cofactor II is normal in patients with inherited antithrombin deficiency. Two patients with inherited deficiency of heparin cofactor II and thrombosis have been reported. However, a causal relationship between these phenomena has not been established.

Blood coagulation results from activation of a series of proteinase zymogens in the presence of nonenzymatic protein cofactors, calcium, and negatively charged phospholipids or platelets (Fig. 89-1). Although the triggering mechanisms are poorly understood, a pivotal event in coagulation is the conversion of prothrombin (factor II) to thrombin (factor IIa), a serine proteinase that preferentially hydrolyzes substrates containing Arg-X peptide bonds. Thrombin has a variety of important biologic effects (see Chaps. 84 to 88). The *procoagulant* effects of thrombin include (1) stimulation of platelets to aggregate at the site of hemostasis; (2) conversion of fibrinogen to fibrin monomers, which then polymerize to form the clot; (3) activation of the nonenzymatic protein cofactors VIII and V, which accelerate the generation of factor Xa and thrombin, respectively; and (4) activation of factor XIII, which crosslinks polymerized fibrin to increase the mechanical stability of the clot. Thrombin also binds to thrombomodulin, an integral membrane protein of the endothelial cell; in this situation, thrombin activates protein C which then produces an *anticoagulant* effect by degrading factors Va and VIIIa. In addition, thrombin has mitogenic[1-3] and chemotactic[4] activities that may be important in wound healing and inflammation. Clearly, inhibition of thrombin at any of these sites of action could have profound physiological effects.

At the turn of the century, it was recognized that the procoagulant activity of thrombin decreases slowly ($t_{1/2} \approx 1$ to 2 min) when the proteinase is added to serum or to plasma from which the fibrinogen has been removed.[5] This slow inhibitory effect became known as the *progressive antithrombin* activity of plasma. Soon thereafter, heparin was isolated from the liver and was shown to exert an immediate anticoagulant effect when added to plasma.[6] Subsequent studies indicated that heparin dramatically accelerates the inhibition of thrombin and that this effect is mediated by an endogenous plasma component termed *heparin cofactor*.[7] In 1968, Abildgaard isolated a protein from plasma that possessed both progressive antithrombin and heparin cofactor activities.[8] This result was confirmed by Rosenberg and Damus, who purified a sufficient amount of the protein for biochemical characterization.[9] The protein is generally referred to as *antithrombin*, although the synonyms *antithrombin III* and *antithrombin/heparin cofactor* are also used.

In 1965, Egeberg reported the association between hereditary antithrombin deficiency and recurrent venous thromboembolic disease.[10] Independent reports of this association soon followed (reviewed in Refs. 11 and 12). The biochemical abnormality most often consists of a ≈50 percent decrease in the concentration of normal antithrombin. Some patients possess a variant form of the protein with an abnormal progressive antithrombin and/or heparin cofactor activity. In a few cases, single amino acid substitutions have been identified that have provided important information about the function of antithrombin.[13-16] Recently, evidence has been obtained that asymptomatic individuals with antithrombin deficiency continuously generate abnormally high amounts of factor Xa within the circulation,[17] a process that may be indicative of a "prethrombotic" state in these patients.

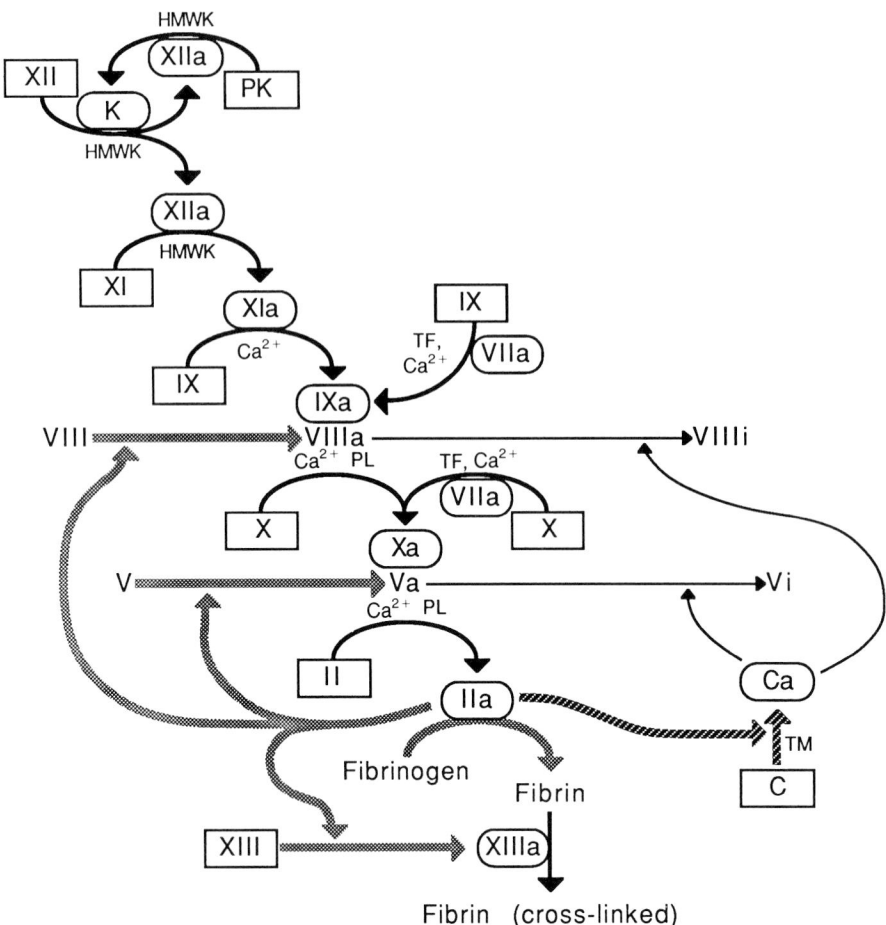

Fig. 89-1 Schematic diagram of the coagulation cascade. The procoagulant activities of thrombin (IIa) are indicated by stippled arrows. Activation of protein C by thrombin to produce an anticoagulant effect is indicated by the hatched arrows. Proteinase zymogens are indicated by boxes, active proteinases by ovals. The activated forms of the nonenzymatic protein cofactors VIII and V are designated VIIIa and Va, respectively. The inactive (degraded) forms of these cofactors are designated VIIIi and Vi. Other symbols include: PK = prekallikrein; K = kallikrein; HMWK = high molecular weight kininogen; TF = tissue factor; TM = thrombomodulin; Ca^{2+} = calcium ions; PL = negatively charged phospholipids or platelets.

BIOCHEMISTRY AND PHYSIOLOGY

Structure and Biosynthesis

Antithrombin is a 58,000-dalton glycoprotein that consists of a single polypeptide chain (Fig. 89-2). The protein contains ≈10 percent α helix and 10 to 40 percent β structure as determined by circular dichroism.[18,19] The amino acid sequence of antithrombin has been determined by Edman degradation[20] and by cDNA sequencing.[21–23] Antithrombin is homologous to α_1-antitrypsin, α_1-antichymotrypsin, and other members of the *serpin* (for *ser*ine *p*roteinase *in*hibitor) superfamily, to which it has approximately 30 percent amino acid sequence identity.[24] Antithrombin contains three disulfide bonds,[20] one of which (Cys_{247} to Cys_{430}) is required for heparin cofactor activity.[25] In addition, it contains four biantennary asparagine-linked oligosaccharides.[26] No other posttranslational modifications have been reported.

Two forms of antithrombin that differ in their carbohydrate content have been isolated from normal human plasma by heparin-agarose affinity chromatography.[27] The major form (α-antithrombin), constituting ≈90 percent of the total antithrombin, is eluted from the affinity matrix with 1 *M* NaCl and appears to be fully glycosylated. The minor form (β-antithrombin) is eluted at a higher salt concentration and contains 25 to 30 percent less carbohydrate than the α form. β-Antithrombin appears to lack the oligosaccharide unit linked to Asn_{135} in the putative heparin-binding domain of the inhibitor.[28] Both α- and β-antithrombin inhibit thrombin rapidly in the presence of heparin. However, β-antithrombin requires a

Fig. 89-2 Polypeptide structure of antithrombin. The positions of disulfide bonds, asparagine-linked oligosaccharides (circles) and certain amino acid residues thought to be involved in heparin and proteinase binding are indicated (see text).

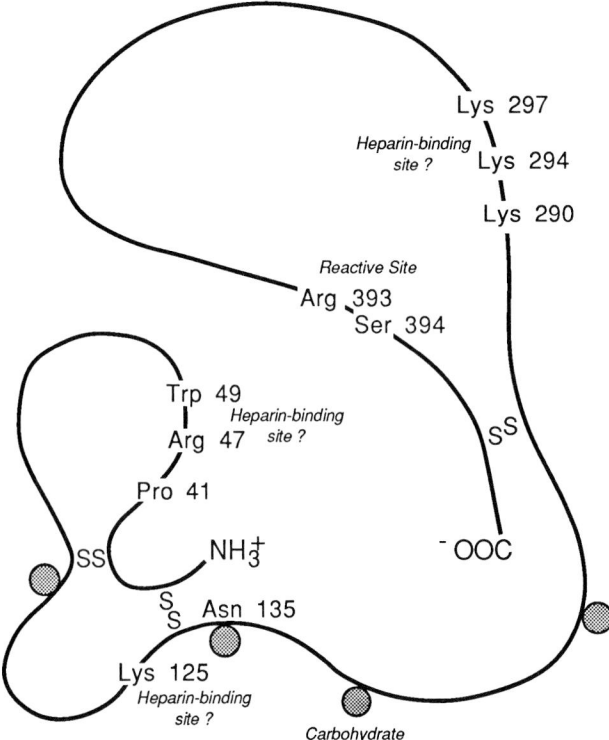

lower concentration of heparin for full activity, consistent with its higher heparin affinity.

Gene. The antithrombin gene is present as a single copy per haploid genome and is located on human chromosome 1q23-25.[29,30] The gene contains six exons and five introns distributed over $\approx$19 kb of DNA.[31] The positions of the introns within the homologous antithrombin and α_1-antitrypsin genes are not conserved.[31,32] The 5' flanking sequence of the antithrombin gene is unusual because it lacks a TATA-like sequence at the expected location 25 to 30 bases upstream from the transcription initiation site.[33] In addition, a DNA length polymorphism of unknown significance has been identified, resulting from insertion of either 32 or 108 base pairs of nonhomologous DNA at the position 345 bases upstream from the translation initiation codon.[34] Interestingly, the 5' flanking region of the antithrombin gene also contains short sequences that are similar to an enhancer element found in the immunoglobulin J_κ-C_κ gene.[35] When the antithrombin enhancer element was ligated to the chloramphenicol acetyltransferase gene and transfected into cells, expression of chloramphenicol acetyltransferase activity was increased preferentially in Alexander hepatoma (liver) and Cos-1 (kidney) cells. Thus, the enhancer may be involved in tissue-specific expression of the antithrombin gene.

Biosynthesis. The mRNA for antithrombin is approximately 1500 bases in length. It codes for a signal peptide of 32 residues followed by the mature protein of 432 residues.[21–23] Antithrombin mRNA is present in the liver, and synthesis of antithrombin has been demonstrated in cultured human hepatoma cells.[36] Alternative splicing of the antithrombin mRNA has been demonstrated in the liver.[33] The alternative splicing event introduces a 42-base segment between codons −19 and −18 of the signal peptide. This segment of mRNA contains an in-frame termination codon such that the predicted protein product encoded by the alternatively spliced mRNA would be only 19 amino acids long. Although the alternatively spliced mRNA accounts for 20 to 40 percent of the antithrombin mRNA in human liver, it is not known whether translation occurs. In the adult rat, antithrombin mRNA was detected in the kidney at a level $\approx$20 percent of that found in the liver.[37]

Little is known about the regulation of antithrombin biosynthesis. Biosynthesis of antithrombin by isolated rat hepatocytes is unaffected by the presence of proteinase-antithrombin complexes or by the supernatant medium of macrophages incubated with these complexes.[38] However, antithrombin biosynthesis is stimulated by the supernatant medium of macrophages incubated with endotoxin or fibrinogen fragment D. Under these conditions, fibrinogen and α_1-antitrypsin biosynthesis are stimulated concurrently.

Proteinase Inhibition

Antithrombin inhibits all the proteinases of the intrinsic coagulation pathway, including thrombin, factor Xa, factor IXa, factor XIa, factor XIIa, and kallikrein.[39] It also inhibits the fibrinolytic proteinase plasmin.[40] In contrast, antithrombin has very little activity toward factor VIIa of the extrinsic coagulation pathway[41] or activated protein C.[42]

In vitro experiments suggest that antithrombin is the major inhibitor of factors IXa, Xa, and thrombin in plasma.[43–45] In contrast, factor XIa is inhibited primarily by α_1-antitrypsin,[46] factor XIIa by C1-inhibitor,[47] and plasmin by α_2-antiplasmin.[48] Therefore, a major function of antithrombin appears to be regulation of proteinases in the later stages of the coagulation cascade (Fig. 89-1).

Mechanism of Proteinase Inhibition. Antithrombin inhibits a target proteinase by formation of an irreversible, equimolar complex.[9] The serine residue at the active site of the proteinase is required for complex formation but thereafter becomes inaccessible to substrates.[9] Furthermore, a small peptide is cleaved from the C terminus of antithrombin during complex formation.[49] Thrombin, factor Xa, and factor IXa cleave antithrombin at precisely the same location (Arg_{393}-Ser_{394}).[50] This peptide bond is termed the *reactive site* of the inhibitor. The antithrombin-proteinase complex resists dissociation in denaturing agents, suggesting that a covalent bond is formed between the two proteins. The complex can be dissociated by treatment with nucleophilic reagents, which release the proteinase along with the cleaved form of antithrombin from the complex.[49,51] This property is consistent with the presence of an ester linkage between the active center serine hydroxyl group of thrombin and the α-carbonyl group of Arg_{393} in the reactive site of antithrombin (Fig. 89-3). Alternatively, it is possible that the native complex is a noncovalent, tetrahedral adduct and that cleavage of the reactive site occurs during denaturation.

Kinetics. The concentration of antithrombin in plasma ($\approx$2.6 μM) greatly exceeds that of any of the target proteinases that are generated during coagulation. Under these conditions, proteinase inhibition follows pseudo-first-order kinetics. Thrombin and factor Xa are inhibited by antithrombin in plasma with $t_{1/2}$'s of $\approx$0.5 to 1.5 min, while factor IXa is inhibited $\approx$10 times more slowly.[52] The rates of inhibition of these proteinases are too slow to prevent coagulation in the absence of heparin.

Addition of heparin to plasma increases the rate of inhibition of thrombin, factor Xa, and factor IXa by antithrombin at least 1000-fold. As a result, inhibition of these proteinases becomes essentially instantaneous ($t_{1/2}$ = 10 to 60 ms).[52] Heparin also has a significant but lesser effect on inhibition of each of the other target proteinases.[39] Acceleration of antithrombin-proteinase reactions accounts for the anticoagulant effect produced by an intravenous infusion of heparin.

Heparin Catalysis

Heparin serves as a catalyst to accelerate formation of the antithrombin-proteinase complex.[9] Although the mechanism of action of heparin is incompletely understood, it is clear that binding of heparin to antithrombin is an essential part of the mechanism. Heparin can be fractionated according to its ability to bind to antithrombin. Thus, $\approx$30 percent of heparin extracted from porcine intestinal mucosa binds to antithrombin with high affinity.[53–55] The high affinity molecules account for virtually all the anticoagulant activity of the starting material, while the low affinity molecules are inactive.

Binding of Heparin to Antithrombin. Antithrombin binds to heparin with a dissociation constant of $\approx$2 × $10^{-8} M$.[56,57] The binding is disrupted at high ionic strength. Therefore, electrostatic interactions between basic amino acid residues on anti-

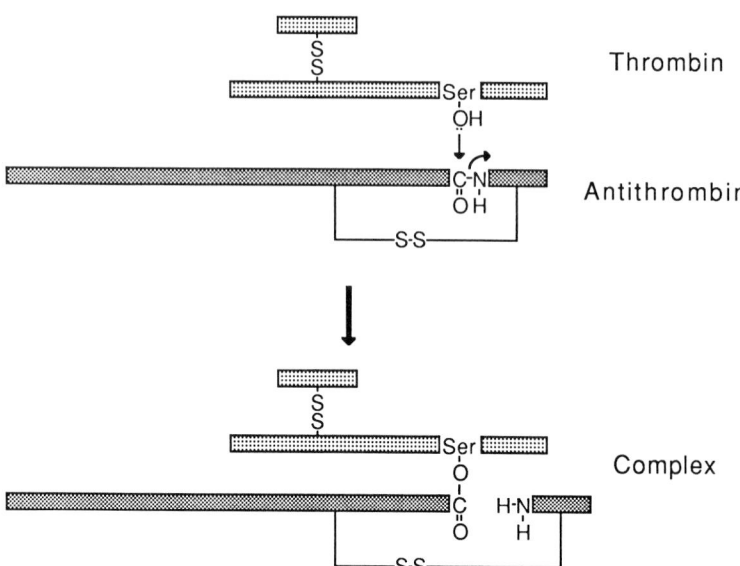

Fig. 89-3 Model for proteinase-antithrombin complex formation. The active center serine hydroxyl group of the proteinase attacks the reactive site peptide bond in antithrombin, becoming trapped in an acyl ester linkage.

thrombin and sulfate groups on the heparin molecule are thought to occur. The following observations have pointed to regions of antithrombin that may be involved in heparin binding:

1. Chemical modification of several lysine residues in antithrombin blocks heparin binding and heparin cofactor activity without affecting the thrombin inhibitory activity in the absence of heparin.[9,58] Recently, limited pyridoxylation of antithrombin has led to the identification of Lys_{125} as a critical residue for heparin binding.[59]

2. Chemical modification of a single tryptophan residue, identified as Trp_{49}, blocks heparin binding to antithrombin.[60] Furthermore, structural analyses of inherited antithrombin variants that react normally with thrombin but lack the ability to bind heparin have revealed mutations of Arg_{47}[13,15] and Pro_{41}.[16] These studies suggest that Pro_{41}, Arg_{47}, and Trp_{49} lie within or near the heparin-binding domain of antithrombin. When the sequence of antithrombin is superimposed upon the tertiary structure of the proteolytically cleaved form of α_1-antitrypsin, it appears that Arg_{47} and a cluster of basic amino acid residues surrounding Lys_{125} may occur in close proximity in the protein[24] (Fig. 89-4). If so, these residues could participate simultaneously in heparin binding.

3. An alternative model for the heparin binding site is based on the denaturation of an α-helical domain in antithrombin by exposure to guanidine-HCl.[61] This treatment is accompanied by loss of heparin binding activity, while the ability of antithrombin to react with thrombin is retained. The unstable α-helical domain of antithrombin has been tentatively identified as the segment containing Lys_{290}, Lys_{294}, and Lys_{297} based on secondary structure modeling.

Heparin Structure. Heparin is a complex linear polysaccharide of 60,000 to 100,000 daltons that is found in mast cell secretory granules covalently attached to a core protein. It is synthesized from UDP-sugar precursors as a polymer of alternating glucuronic acid and N-acetylglucosamine residues.[62] The polymer then undergoes a series of modification reactions that include (1) N-deacetylation and N-sulfation of glucosamine residues, (2) epimerization of glucuronic acid to iduronic acid, (3) O-sulfation of iduronic and glucuronic acid residues at the C-2 position, and (4) O-sulfation of glucosamine resi-

dues at the C-3 and C-6 positions. Each of these modification reactions is incomplete, yielding a large number of possible oligosaccharide structures within the glycosaminoglycan chain.[62] Heparan sulfate is a closely related glycosaminoglycan found on the surface of most eukaryotic cells and in the extracellular matrix. Heparan sulfate is synthesized from the same repeating disaccharide precursor (glucuronic acid linked to N-acetylglucosamine) as heparin. However, heparan sulfate undergoes less polymer modification than heparin and therefore contains higher proportions of glucuronic acid and N-acetylglucosamine and fewer sulfate groups.

The smallest fragment of heparin that binds to antithrombin with high affinity is the pentasaccharide shown in Fig. 89-5. Independent studies from several laboratories have confirmed

Fig. 89-4 Tertiary structure of the putative heparin-binding site of antithrombin. The polypeptide backbone shown in the diagram is that of the cleaved form of the homologous inhibitor α_1-antitrypsin. The positions of residues in antithrombin thought to be involved in heparin binding are superimposed on this backbone. Note that the amino acid residues of the reactive site (arrows) are separated by $\approx$70 Å after proteolytic cleavage. [*From Carrell, RW, Christey, PB, Boswell, DR: Serpins: antithrombin and other inhibitors of coagulation and fibrinolysis. Evidence from amino acid sequences. In* Thrombosis and Haemostasis 1987, M Verstraete, J Vermylen, R Lijnen, J Arnout (eds). Leuven: Leuven University Press, 1987, p. 1. Used by permission.]

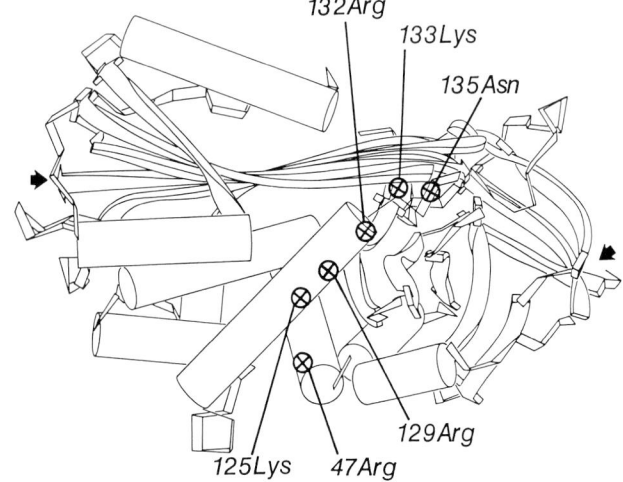

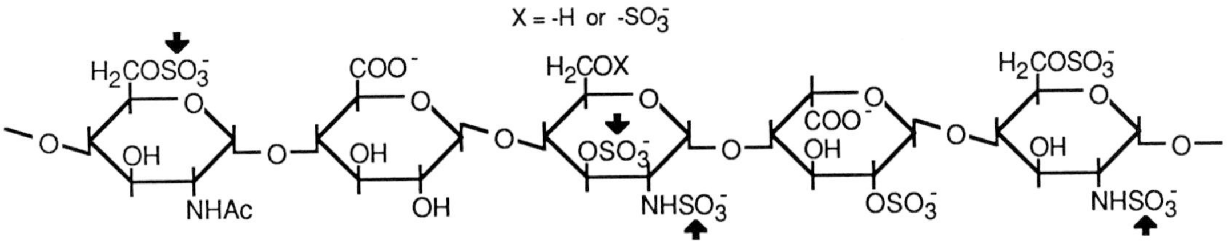

X = -H or -SO$_3^-$

Fig. 89-5 Antithrombin-binding structure of heparin. The pentasaccharide shown is the minimum structure required for binding to antithrombin with high affinity. Sulfate groups that are proposed to be essential for binding are indicated by arrows.

the details of this structure.[63–65] Lack of the 6-O-sulfate group of residue 1 or either of the two N-sulfate groups of residues 3 and 5 greatly reduces the affinity of binding to antithrombin. In addition, a unique 3-O-sulfate group at residue 3 is present only in high-affinity oligosaccharides and is considered to be essential for binding. The pentasaccharide shown in Fig. 89-5 has been chemically synthesized and shown to catalyze inhibition of factor Xa by antithrombin.[63] An identical antithrombin binding structure is thought to arise during the biosynthesis of heparan sulfate chains, although at a much lower frequency than during heparin biosynthesis. Other glycosaminoglycans that lack the specific pentasaccharide structure (e.g., dermatan sulfate, chondroitin-4-sulfate, chondroitin-6-sulfate) do not interact with antithrombin.[66]

Catalytic Mechanism. Rapid kinetic analyses indicate that heparin binding induces a conformational change in antithrombin that locks the heparin molecule into place on the surface of the inhibitor.[57] The heparin-antithrombin complex then reacts with a target proteinase. Proteinase binding reduces the affinity of antithrombin for heparin, allowing the antithrombin-proteinase complex to dissociate from the heparin molecule.[67] Thus, heparin is able to function in a catalytic manner in the reaction.

Two models have been proposed to explain the mechanism by which heparin catalyzes the inhibition of proteinases. In the first model, heparin binding induces a *conformational change* that affects the reactive site of antithrombin, allowing target proteinases to interact more rapidly with this site.[9] This model is supported by the fact that conformational changes in antithrombin can be detected spectroscopically as a consequence of heparin binding.[19,68–71] Furthermore, the initial rate of proteinase inhibition increases in proportion to the amount of heparin-antithrombin complex formed at low heparin concentrations ($< 1 \times 10^{-7}$ M).[52]

In the second model, heparin functions as a *template* to which both antithrombin and the target proteinase bind. Catalysis thus occurs mainly by an approximation effect. This model is supported by the fact that heparin molecules containing at least 18 sugar residues are required to catalyze the reaction of antithrombin with thrombin, even though smaller molecules bind with high affinity and induce a conformational change.[64,72] Formation of ternary complexes that contain antithrombin, heparin, and thrombin is supported also by physical evidence.[73,74] Kinetic analyses demonstrate that the rate of thrombin inhibition saturates at high proteinase concentrations; this finding has been interpreted to indicate that formation of a ternary complex is an obligate intermediate in the catalytic reaction.[75–77]

The relative importance of conformational and template phenomena in the inhibition of thrombin by antithrombin remains controversial (discussed further in Refs. 78 and 79). Nevertheless, the synthetic pentasaccharide that contains only the antithrombin binding site of heparin catalyzes inhibition of factor Xa.[63] Since an oligosaccharide of this size is unlikely to function as a template, induction of a conformational change in the reactive site of antithrombin may be sufficient to catalyze factor Xa inhibition.

Modulators of Heparin Catalysis. Several proteins interfere with catalysis of the thrombin-antithrombin reaction in vitro by competitively inhibiting antithrombin binding to heparin. These include (1) platelet factor 4, a 7800-dalton polypeptide secreted from platelets during hemostasis[80]; (2) histidine-rich glycoprotein, a 75,000-dalton protein present in plasma at a concentration of ≈ 135 µg/ml (1.8 µM)[80]; and (3) complement S-protein (also known as vitronectin), a 75,000-dalton protein present in plasma at a concentration of ≈ 300 µg/ml (4 µM).[81] Platelet factor 4 is likely to promote local clot formation at the site of platelet aggregation. Whether the latter two proteins serve as physiological modulators of hemostasis remains to be determined.

Activity of Antithrombin in Vivo

Proteinase Inhibition. When radiolabeled thrombin is injected intravenously into an experimental animal, the proteinase rapidly appears in the circulation as a complex with antithrombin.[82] Similarly, formation of factor IXa-antithrombin complexes occurs rapidly in vivo.[43] Although thrombomodulin has been shown to serve as a receptor for internalization of thrombin by endothelial cells in vitro,[83] the relative importance of this pathway in the clearance of thrombin in vivo remains to be clarified.

In contrast to thrombin and factor IXa, factor Xa has been reported to form complexes primarily with α_2-macroglobulin after intravenous injection.[84] Factor Xa is protected from inhibition by antithrombin in vitro when the proteinase is bound to platelets[85] or to the prothrombinase complex which contains factor Va, prothrombin, and phospholipids.[86] It is not known whether these mechanisms also protect factor Xa from inhibition by antithrombin in vivo.

Clearance. In experimental animals, antithrombin-proteinase complexes are removed from the circulation by hepatocytes with a $t_{1/2}$ of 2 to 3 min.[43,87] The hepatocyte uptake mechanism is saturable in vivo and recognizes the antithrombin-proteinase complex but not the free inhibitor. Complexes of proteinases with α_1-antitrypsin competitively inhibit uptake of the antithrombin-proteinase complex and, therefore, are thought to be taken up by the same hepatocyte mechanism.[88]

Uptake of antithrombin-proteinase complexes and degradation to low molecular weight peptides by rat hepatocytes in vitro have also been demonstrated.[89] Uptake by the hepatocyte receptor in vitro is saturable and is competitively inhibited by antithrombin-proteinase and α_1-antitrypsin-proteinase complexes, but not by free antithrombin, α_2-macroglobulin-methylamine, asialoorosomucoid, fucosyl-bovine serum albumin, N-acetylglucosaminyl-bovine serum albumin, or mannosyl-bovine serum albumin. Internalization of antithrombin-proteinase complexes by human hepatoma (HepG2) cells apparently does not occur.[90]

The in vivo distribution of ^{131}I-labeled antithrombin has been investigated in humans.[91] The data are compatible with a three-compartment model in which ≈40 percent of the antithrombin is distributed in the plasma, ≈10 percent in a noncirculating vascular pool, and ≈50 percent in an extravascular compartment. The fractional catabolic rates of the total intravascular pool and the extravascular pool are ≈0.5 per day and ≈0.2 per day, respectively. Thus, free antithrombin is cleared from the circulation much more slowly than its complexes with proteinases.

Endogenous Heparinlike Material. Under normal circumstances, heparin is not released from mast cells into the circulation and cannot be detected in plasma. However, a small amount of heparin may appear in the circulation of patients with systemic mastocytosis and produce mild prolongation of the activated partial thromboplastin time.[92] Circulating heparan sulfate, apparently released from damaged tissues, has been reported to cause marked prolongation of the activated partial thromboplastin time and bleeding in a few severely ill patients with hematologic malignancies.[93–95]

There is good evidence to suggest that heparan sulfate molecules possessing anticoagulant activity are located on the luminal surface of vascular endothelial cells. In this location, heparan sulfate could continuously bind a portion of the circulating antithrombin and thus inhibit thrombus formation.

Glycosaminoglycans extracted from cloned endothelial cells possess anticoagulant activity.[96] Treatment of the extracts with heparinase abolishes the activity, indicating that the active moiety is heparinlike. *De novo* biosynthesis of heparan sulfate proteoglycans has been demonstrated by culturing endothelial cells in the presence of [^{35}S]sulfate.[97] Approximately 1 to 10 percent of the labeled heparan sulfate from endothelial cells binds to immobilized antithrombin with high affinity, and this fraction possesses essentially all the anticoagulant activity of the cell extract. Structural analysis of the high-affinity heparan sulfate has revealed the presence of the 3-O-sulfated glucosamine residue that is characteristic of the antithrombin-binding structure of heparin.[97] One report suggests that the anticoagulant heparan sulfate chains are intimately associated with thrombomodulin on the endothelial cell surface.[98]

Direct binding of antithrombin to the surface of endothelial cells cloned from bovine aorta has also been demonstrated. The inhibitor binds to approximately 60,000 sites per cell with a dissociation constant of 12 nM.[97] Binding is diminished by pretreatment of the cells with heparinase. Similar results have been obtained with intact segments of bovine aorta.[99] However, one study suggests that binding of antithrombin to intact rabbit aortic endothelium is weak and is unaffected by heparinase, while antithrombin binds more avidly to heparinase-sensitive components beneath the endothelial cell layer.[100]

Evidence for the activation of antithrombin by heparan sulfate on the endothelial cell surface in vivo has been more difficult to obtain. Marcum et al.[101] perfused a rodent hind limb preparation with thrombin until a constant concentration of the proteinase was present in the venous effluent. They then perfused antithrombin through the preparation and determined the amount of thrombin-antithrombin complex that formed in comparison to the amount that formed during a similar time period in vitro. A fifteen- to nineteenfold increase in the rate of complex formation appeared to occur within the microvasculature as compared to in vitro incubations in the absence of heparin. The rate enhancement was diminished by prior perfusion of the hind limb preparation with heparinase or when Trp$_{49}$-modified antithrombin was used, suggesting that interaction of antithrombin with microvascular heparan sulfate was responsible for the effect.

A different process may occur when only a trace amount of thrombin is injected into the circulation. Under these circumstances, thrombin may become bound initially to thrombomodulin on the endothelial cell surface.[82] A modest (approximately threefold) increase in the rate of thrombin inhibition by circulating antithrombin may then occur because of the altered substrate specificity of thrombin when it is bound to thrombomodulin.[102] In comparison to free thrombin, thrombin bound to thrombomodulin in vitro reacts less rapidly with fibrinogen, more rapidly with protein C, and at about the same rate with antithrombin. The net effect of these changes in substrate specificity is postulated to be a small increase in the rate of the thrombin-antithrombin reaction because of diminished competition from other substrates. According to this hypothesis, only when thrombomodulin becomes saturated with thrombin will the excess thrombin interact with antithrombin in a heparan sulfate-catalyzed reaction.

ANTITHROMBIN DEFICIENCY

Diagnosis

Antithrombin deficiency was the first inherited abnormality to be linked to a thrombotic tendency.[10] The diagnosis is usually made in patients who experience the onset of recurrent thromboembolic disease at an early age or in whom a positive family history of thromboembolic disease is obtained. The diagnosis is established by determination of the antithrombin activity in the patient's plasma.

Assay Methods. Determination of the antithrombin concentration in plasma is best done using a functional assay that measures the capacity of a sample to inhibit thrombin or factor Xa over a short time period in the presence of heparin (i.e., heparin cofactor assay). Such assays are conveniently performed with a chromogenic substrate to detect the residual proteinase activity in the incubation.[103] Heparin cofactor assays that use thrombin as the target proteinase may overestimate the concentration of antithrombin to a modest degree due to the presence of heparin cofactor II in the sample.[104–106] Theoretically, the use of factor Xa would allow greater specificity, since heparin cofactor II does not react with this proteinase.[104] Assays that measure the progressive antithrombin activity (i.e., inhibition of thrombin over a longer period of time in the absence of heparin) give a rough indication of the antithrombin concentration but may also be influenced by α_1-antitrypsin and α_2-macroglobulin.[45] Immunologic assays are useful mainly in conjunction with functional assays to detect inactive variants of antithrombin.

Normal Levels. The concentration of antithrombin in adult plasma is approximately 150 μg/ml (2.6 μM).[107] The range of concentrations is narrow in normal individuals, who have heparin cofactor activities of 84 to 116 percent (mean ± 2 SD) and antithrombin antigen concentrations of 72 to 128 percent (mean ± 2 SD).[11] Healthy, full-term newborn infants have antithrombin antigen concentrations of 39 to 87 percent of adult values. The level gradually increases to the normal adult range by 3 months of age.[108]

Inherited Deficiencies

Quantitative. Antithrombin deficiency is inherited as an autosomal dominant trait. Affected heterozygotes have 25 to 60 percent of the antithrombin activity present in normal plasma.[11] Diminished antithrombin activity in the heterozygote classically results from a decreased concentration of normal antithrombin in the plasma. Total absence of antithrombin has not been reported and is presumed to be lethal in utero (see qualitative defects below). Oral anticoagulant therapy may increase the antithrombin level in some deficient patients,[109] making the diagnosis more difficult.

Classic antithrombin deficiency has been reported to result from deletion of one of the two antithrombin genes[110] or from a dysfunctional gene,[110,111] which is presumed to cause a decreased rate of synthesis of the protein. Diminished synthesis is supported by the finding that the catabolic rate of infused radiolabeled antithrombin is normal in patients with inherited deficiency.[112,113]

Qualitative. A number of families have been reported to have variant forms of antithrombin with abnormal functional properties. In contrast to classic antithrombin deficiency, the level of antithrombin antigen is normal in affected heterozygotes, while the antithrombin activity determined by heparin cofactor and/or progressive antithrombin assays is ≈50 percent of normal. In most instances, affected individuals have approximately an equimolar mixture of normal and variant antithrombin.

The variant forms of antithrombin have provided important insights into the mechanism of action of the inhibitor and can be grouped into several categories:

1. Variants in which the reactive site is intact but the heparin-binding site is altered include antithrombin$_{Toyama}$ ($Arg_{47} \rightarrow Cys$),[13] antithrombin$_{Rouen}$ ($Arg_{47} \rightarrow His$),[15] and antithrombin$_{Basel}$ ($Pro_{41} \rightarrow Leu$).[16] These variants have normal progressive antithrombin activity but bind weakly to heparin, which results in diminished heparin cofactor activity. Several other variants with similar properties have been reported.[114–117] One report includes a child born to consanguineous parents, both of whom had antithrombin deficiency (antithrombin$_{Fontainebleau}$).[117] The child was apparently homozygous, having undetectable heparin cofactor activity, and died at age 3 years of massive intracardiac thrombosis while receiving oral anticoagulant therapy. Two other kindreds included severely affected homozygous patients who had <10 percent heparin cofactor activity.[13,116]

2. Variants in which the heparin binding site is intact but the reactive site is abnormal include antithrombin$_{Denver}$ ($Ser_{394} \rightarrow Leu$).[14] This variant has a normal affinity for heparin but diminished heparin cofactor and progressive antithrombin activities. Several other variants of this type have been reported.[118–122] One variant (antithrombin$_{Aalborg}$) was reported to react normally with factor Xa but lack reactivity with thrombin.[122]

3. Variants having abnormalities that affect both the hepa-

rin binding site and the reactive site include antithrombin$_{Budapest}$[122] and antithrombin$_{Chicago}$.[123] Antithrombin$_{Chicago}$ is unusual because it has an abnormally high affinity for heparin, yet it lacks heparin cofactor activity. The molecular basis for these defects has not been reported.

Clinical Manifestations. The incidence of thromboembolism in patients with antithrombin deficiency has been estimated from retrospective reviews of published case reports (e.g., Refs. 11 and 12). Prospective studies of patients with antithrombin deficiency have not been done. An additional difficulty in assessing the clinical literature on antithrombin deficiency is that criteria for the diagnosis of thromboembolic disease are often not reported. Since the clinical manifestations of deep vein thrombosis and pulmonary embolism are nonspecific, definitive diagnosis usually requires a contrast angiographic study or postmortem examination. Therefore, the incidence of thromboembolism in individuals with antithrombin deficiency may be somewhat overestimated owing to selection bias or misdiagnosis.

Thromboembolic disease appears to occur equally in males and females with antithrombin deficiency and is most often reported as deep vein thrombosis of the legs or as pulmonary embolism.[11,12] Less frequently, thrombosis of the cerebral, renal, hepatic, or mesenteric veins occurs.[124,125] These complications may be life-threatening. Arterial thrombosis is rarely observed in patients with antithrombin deficiency. Thrombosis may occur spontaneously or after some predisposing event such as trauma, surgery, or pregnancy.

Typically, affected individuals present with thromboembolic disease after the age of 15. It is estimated that by 50 years of age, about 85 percent of the heterozygous individuals will have had at least one thromboembolic episode.[11] The median age of onset of symptoms is ≈24 years. A history of *recurrent* thrombosis occurs in ≈60 percent of patients and is the factor that usually prompts a search for antithrombin deficiency. There may be great variability in the severity of complications that arise in individuals within a single family. Therefore, it is presumed that antithrombin deficiency is but one of several risk factors that predispose to thrombosis in these patients.

Patients with variant forms of antithrombin are difficult to distinguish clinically from those with classic antithrombin deficiency. Nevertheless, it has been suggested that heterozygous patients with variant antithrombin molecules have fewer thromboembolic complications.[114,116,126]

Prevalence. The prevalence of antithrombin deficiency in the general population has been estimated to range from 1 per 2000[127] to 1 per 5000.[128] In a series of 752 patients with thromboembolic disease, inherited antithrombin deficiency was established in 13 (1.7 percent) by family studies.[129] An additional 14 patients had "probable" inherited antithrombin deficiency. Thus, it appears that antithrombin deficiency is significantly more common in patients with thromboembolic symptoms than in asymptomatic individuals, although this point has not been rigorously established.

Acquired Deficiencies. Acquired antithrombin deficiency can occur in liver disease,[130] in the nephrotic syndrome,[131] and during disseminated intravascular coagulation.[132] Whether antithrombin deficiency contributes to the thrombotic complications reported in these conditions is unclear.

Antithrombin is mildly decreased in patients taking estrogens.[133] Therefore, estrogen-containing medications should be avoided in patients with inherited antithrombin deficiency. A more profound decrease in antithrombin occurs in patients receiving L-asparaginase.[134] Despite the acquired antithrombin deficiency, there is no biochemical evidence of a hypercoagulable state in these patients,[135] perhaps due to the fact that the levels of procoagulant factors such as prothrombin are decreased concomitantly by L-asparaginase.

Physiological Consequences. The physiological consequences of antithrombin deficiency in humans have been studied using immunoassays for the prothrombin activation fragment 1.2 and for fibrinopeptides A and B.[17] Asymptomatic individuals with antithrombin deficiency have a two- to threefold increase in the steady state concentration of fragment 1.2 in their plasma (Fig. 89-6). Furthermore, the $t_{1/2}$ for clearance of fragment 1.2 from the plasma is normal, implying an increased rate of generation of the fragment. These results are interpreted to indicate a significantly elevated rate of intravascular prothrombin activation by factor Xa. The biochemical abnormality is corrected by intravenous infusion of purified antithrombin. Following an infusion of antithrombin in these subjects, the concentration of fragment 1.2 begins to increase when the total concentration of antithrombin declines to <70 percent of normal.

On the other hand, the concentrations of fibrinopeptides A and B are not elevated in the plasma of patients with antithrombin deficiency.[17] This finding suggests that the amount of thrombin generated in the circulation is insufficient to cause a significant increase in consumption of fibrinogen. The simplest interpretation of these observations is that small amounts of factors Xa and Va are generated within the blood vessels in normal individuals. Antithrombin deficiency allows the generation of increased amounts of these factors, which may predispose the patient to episodic thrombosis.

The complex interactions that have been shown to occur between antithrombin, heparan sulfate proteoglycans, and other proteins suggest that several types of molecular abnormalities, in addition to antithrombin deficiency, could lead to thrombosis. For example, abnormal heparan sulfate synthesis in the endothelium or abnormal release of platelet factor 4

Fig. 89-6 Plasma prothrombin fragment 1.2 (●) and fibrinopeptide A (○) in patients with inherited antithrombin deficiency and their unaffected siblings. Horizontal bars represent the mean values for each parameter. (*From Bauer, Goodman, Kass, and Rosenberg.*[17] *Used by permission of* The Journal of Clinical Investigation.)

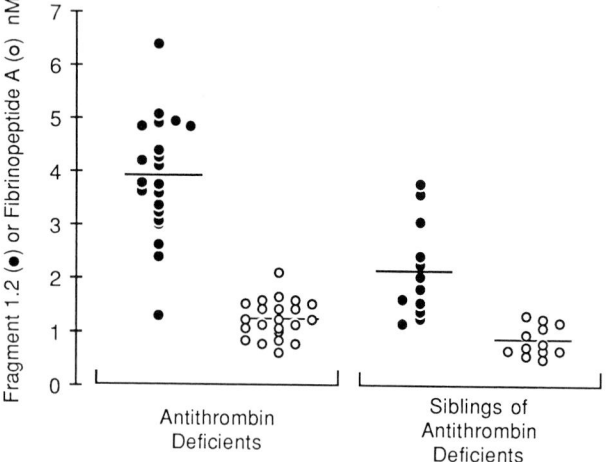

could have the same net effect on the antithrombin system. These abnormalities have not yet been discovered.

Treatment. Anticoagulant therapy is indicated for patients with antithrombin deficiency during acute episodes of deep vein thrombosis or pulmonary embolism. The approach to therapy of acute thromboembolism is similar to that in patients with normal amounts of antithrombin and usually consists of a 7- to 10-day course of heparin given by continuous intravenous infusion followed by ≈3 months of oral anticoagulant therapy.[136] Oral anticoagulant therapy with warfarin is initiated several days before discontinuation of the heparin infusion to allow time for depletion of the vitamin K–dependent coagulation factors from the circulation. Patients with antithrombin deficiency generally respond to standard doses of intravenous heparin as indicated by an increase in the activated partial thromboplastin time.[137] However, patients with severe acquired antithrombin deficiency (<10 percent of normal) and an occasional patient with inherited antithrombin deficiency may be resistant to heparin.[138] In theory, treatment with a concentrate of purified antithrombin in combination with intravenous heparin might benefit patients with heparin resistance, although early institution of oral anticoagulant therapy may suffice. Heparin itself can cause a modest (≈15 percent) decrease in the circulating antithrombin concentration, but this effect is unlikely to have clinical significance.[139]

The duration of therapy with warfarin remains controversial. Some physicians advocate lifelong treatment of antithrombin-deficient patients after their first thromboembolic episode. Others would treat asymptomatic family members with documented antithrombin deficiency who have never had a thromboembolic episode. These recommendations are based on anecdotal experience and may be unwarranted in view of the morbidity due to hemorrhage associated with chronic anticoagulant therapy.[140] However, patients with recurrent thromboembolism or those who develop complications such as pulmonary insufficiency may be candidates for long-term oral anticoagulant therapy. Newer, less intense, oral anticoagulant regimens that appear to prevent recurrence of idiopathic deep vein thrombosis may be preferable in patients with antithrombin deficiency because of the lower expected morbidity.[141]

The incidence of thrombotic complications in women with antithrombin deficiency during pregnancy has been estimated to be as high as 70 percent.[142] Therefore, it is reasonable to treat these patients prophylactically during gestation and delivery. Because warfarin has been associated with an increase in the incidence of fetal hemorrhage, stillbirth, and developmental abnormalities,[143] subcutaneous heparin regimens have been developed that appear to be effective in preventing thrombosis.[144] Because heparin may cause bleeding at the time of delivery, some physicians have used antithrombin concentrates and a lower dose of heparin in the peripartum period.[142,145–147] However, pregnancy has been managed successfully without the use of antithrombin concentrates in deficient patients.[137]

Antithrombin concentrates and androgens have been used in the treatment of deep vein thrombosis and to prevent thrombosis at the time of surgery.[148–153] Although these agents have been shown to increase the plasma concentration of antithrombin in deficient individuals, their clinical efficacy is unproven.

HEPARIN COFACTOR II

Originally, antithrombin was thought to account for all the heparin cofactor activity of plasma. However, an additional thrombin inhibitor in plasma with heparin cofactor activity was observed in 1974.[154] This inhibitor was later purified to homogeneity and termed *heparin cofactor II*.[104]

Heparin cofactor II is present in human plasma at a concentration (1.2 μM) about half that of antithrombin. It consists of a single polypeptide chain with a molecular weight of 66,000.[104] The complete amino acid sequence of the protein has been determined by cDNA cloning and is about 30 percent identical to that of antithrombin.[155–157] Thus, heparin cofactor II can be classified as a member of the serpin superfamily. The protein contains 480 amino acid residues preceded by a signal peptide 19 residues in length, three potential asparagine-linked glycosylation sites, and two tyrosine residues near the N terminus that become O-sulfated during biosynthesis.[158] A 2200-base mRNA for heparin cofactor II was isolated from human liver, and biosynthesis was demonstrated in cultured human hepatoma cells.[158,159] The gene for heparin cofactor II is located on human chromosome 22.[157]

Heparin cofactor II inhibits thrombin but has no activity with other proteinases generated during coagulation or fibrinolysis.[160] In this respect, heparin cofactor II differs significantly from antithrombin. The mechanism of inhibition of thrombin by heparin cofactor II is similar to that of antithrombin; i.e., thrombin attacks a peptide bond near the C terminus of heparin cofactor II and in so doing becomes trapped in a stable 1:1 complex. In contrast to the Arg-Ser reactive site of antithrombin, the reactive site of heparin cofactor II contains the sequence Leu_{444}-Ser_{445}.[155,156,161] This difference may explain the inability of most of the coagulation proteinases to react with heparin cofactor II. A proline residue occurs at position 443 in heparin cofactor II.[155,156] It may be significant that proline is found in a similar position (i.e., one residue N terminal to the cleavage site) in many thrombin substrates; this residue may, in part, enable thrombin to react with heparin cofactor II. It is interesting that both chymotrypsin and the chymotrypsinlike proteinase leukocyte cathepsin G are inhibited by heparin cofactor II.[160,162] Cleavage of the Leu_{444}-Ser_{445} bond has been demonstrated to occur during inhibition of chymotrypsin.[162]

Approximately tenfold higher concentrations of heparin and heparan sulfate are required to accelerate thrombin inhibition by heparin cofactor II compared to antithrombin.[66] The affinity of heparin cofactor II for heparin appears to be lower than that of antithrombin, and there is evidence that heparin cofactor II does not require the specific pentasaccharide structure shown in Fig. 89-5 in order to bind.[163] On the other hand, the activity of heparin cofactor II is stimulated approximately 1000-fold by *dermatan sulfate*, which has no effect on the activity of antithrombin.[66] Addition of dermatan sulfate to plasma in vitro causes prolongation of the thrombin time and the activated partial thromboplastin time.[164] These effects are mediated predominantly by heparin cofactor II.[66,165] Furthermore, intravenous infusion of dermatan sulfate into experimental animals produces an antithrombotic effect.[166]

Cultured fibroblasts and vascular smooth-muscle cells accelerate inhibition of thrombin by heparin cofactor II.[167] Dermatan sulfate proteoglycans isolated from fibroblasts have been shown to be responsible for this effect. These results suggest that heparin cofactor II might function as an inhibitor of thrombin in the connective tissues rather than within the blood vessels.

The concentration of heparin cofactor II in normal human plasma is $1.2 \pm 0.4 \mu M$ (mean $\pm$ 2 SD).[168] The level is markedly decreased in some patients with liver disease, disseminated intravascular coagulation, and obstetric complications.[168–171] In these situations, the heparin cofactor II and antithrombin levels are usually decreased to a similar degree. It is not known whether consumption, redistribution, or diminished synthesis is primarily responsible for the low levels observed. A normal concentration of heparin cofactor II is present in uncomplicated pregnancy, during oral anticoagulant use, and in the vast majority of patients with venous thromboembolic disease.[170,171] The heparin cofactor II level is also normal in symptomatic patients with inherited antithrombin deficiency.[169,170,172] Therefore, heparin cofactor II cannot substitute for antithrombin to prevent thrombosis.

Two patients have been described in whom hereditary deficiency of heparin cofactor II was associated with thrombosis.[173,174] The level of heparin cofactor II in these individuals was ≈40 to 60 percent of normal. The deficiency appears to have been inherited as an autosomal dominant trait. Some, but not all, of the family members with heparin cofactor II deficiency had histories of thromboembolism. However, a causal relationship between heparin cofactor II deficiency and thrombosis has not been proven. Further studies are needed to determine whether the incidence of heparin cofactor II deficiency is higher in patients with thrombosis than in the normal population. In this regard, one group found that 4 of 379 apparently healthy individuals had heparin cofactor II levels of <60 percent.[175]

REFERENCES

1. CHEN LB, BUCHANAN JM: Mitogenic activity of blood components. I. Thrombin and prothrombin. *Proc Natl Acad Sci USA* 72:131, 1975.
2. GLENN KC, CARNEY DH, FENTON JW, CUNNINGHAM DD: Thrombin active site regions required for fibroblast receptor binding and initiation of cell division. *J Biol Chem* 255:6609, 1980.
3. BAR-SHAVIT R, KAHN AJ, MANN KG, WILNER GD: Identification of a thrombin sequence with growth factor activity on macrophages. *Proc Natl Acad Sci USA* 83:976, 1986.
4. BAR-SHAVIT R, KAHN A, WILNER GD, FENTON JW: Monocyte chemotaxis: Stimulation by specific exosite region in thrombin. *Science* 220:728, 1983.
5. CONTEJEAN C: Rescherches sur les injections intraveineuses de peptone et leur influence sur la coagulabilité du sang chez le chien. *Arch Physiol Norm Pathol* 7:45, 1895.
6. MCLEAN J: The thromboplastic action of cephalin. *Am J Physiol* 41:250, 1916.
7. BRINKHOUS KM, SMITH HP, WARNER ED, SEEGERS WH: The inhibition of blood clotting: An unidentified substance which acts in conjunction with heparin to prevent the conversion of prothrombin to thrombin. *Am J Physiol* 125:683, 1939.
8. ABILDGAARD U: Highly purified antithrombin III with heparin cofactor activity prepared by disc electrophoresis. *Scand J Clin Lab Invest* 21:89, 1968.
9. ROSENBERG RD, DAMUS PS: The purification and mechanism of action of human antithrombin-heparin cofactor. *J Biol Chem* 248:6490, 1973.
10. EGEBERG O: Inherited antithrombin deficiency causing thrombophilia. *Thromb Diath Haemorrh* 13:516, 1965.
11. THALER E, LECHNER K: Antithrombin III deficiency and thromboembolism. *Clin Haematol* 10:369, 1981.
12. COSGRIFF TM, BISHOP DT, HERSHGOLD EJ, SKOLNICK MH, MARTIN BA, BATY BJ, CARLSON KS: Familial antithrombin III deficiency: Its natural history, genetics, diagnosis and treatment. *Medicine (Baltimore)* 62:209, 1983.
13. KOIDE T, ODANI S, TAKAHASHI K, ONO T, SAKURAGAWA N: Antithrombin

III Toyama: Replacement of arginine-47 by cysteine in hereditary abnormal antithrombin III that lacks heparin-binding ability. *Proc Natl Acad Sci USA* 81:289, 1984.

14. STEPHENS AW, THALLEY BS, HIRS CH: Antithrombin-III Denver, a reactive site variant. *J Biol Chem* 262:1044, 1987.

15. OWEN MC, BORG JY, SORIA C, SORIA J, CAEN J, CARRELL RW: Heparin binding defect in a new antithrombin III variant: Rouen, 47 Arg to His. *Blood* 69:1275, 1987.

16. CHANG JY, TRAN TH: Antithrombin III Basel. Identification of a Pro-Leu substitution in a hereditary abnormal antithrombin with impaired heparin cofactor activity. *J Biol Chem* 261:1174, 1986.

17. BAUER KA, GOODMAN TL, KASS BL, ROSENBERG RD: Elevated factor Xa activity in the blood of asymptomatic patients with congenital antithrombin deficiency. *J Clin Invest* 76:826, 1985.

18. NORDENMAN B, NYSTRÖM C, BJÖRK I: The size and shape of human and bovine antithrombin III. *Eur J Biochem* 78:195, 1977.

19. VILLANUEVA G, DANISHEFSKY I: Evidence for a heparin-induced conformational change on antithrombin III. *Biochem Biophys Res Commun* 74:803, 1977.

20. PETERSEN EE, DUDEK-WOJCIECHOWSKA G, SOTTRUP-JENSEN L, MAGNUSSON S: The primary structure of antithrombin III (heparin cofactor): Partial homology between alpha 1-antitrypsin and antithrombin III, in Collen D, Wiman B, Verstraete M (eds): *The Physiological Inhibitors of Coagulation and Fibrinolysis*. Amsterdam, Elsevier/North Holland, 1979, p 43.

21. BOCK SC, WION KL, VEHAR GA, LAWN RM: Cloning and expression of the cDNA for human antithrombin III. *Nucleic Acids Res* 10:8113, 1982.

22. STACKHOUSE R, CHANDRA T, ROBSON KJ, WOO SL: Purification of antithrombin III mRNA and cloning of its cDNA. *J Biol Chem* 258:703, 1983.

23. PROCHOWNIK EV, MARKHAM AF, ORKIN SH: Isolation of a cDNA clone for human antithrombin III. *J Biol Chem* 258:8389, 1983.

24. CARRELL RW, BOSWELL DR: Serpins: The superfamily of plasma serine proteinase inhibitors, in Barrett AJ, Salveson G (eds): *Proteinase Inhibitors*. Amsterdam, Elsevier, 1986, p 403.

25. FERGUSON WS, FINLAY TH: Localization of the disulfide bond in human antithrombin III required for heparin-accelerated thrombin inactivation. *Arch Biochem Biophys* 221:304, 1983.

26. FRANZÉN L-E, SVENSSON S, LARM O: Structural studies on the carbohydrate portion of human antithrombin III. *J Biol Chem* 255:5090, 1980.

27. PETERSON CB, BLACKBURN MN: Isolation and characterization of an antithrombin III variant with reduced carbohydrate content and enhanced heparin binding. *J Biol Chem* 260:610, 1985.

28. BRENNAN SO, GEORGE PM, CARRELL RW, JORDAN R: The physiological antithrombin (beta) variant with increased heparin affinity lacks carbohydrate at Asn 135. *Thromb Haemost* 58:238, 1987.

29. BOCK SC, HARRIS JF, BALAZS I, TRENT JM: Assignment of the human antithrombin III structural gene to chromosome 1q23-25. *Cytogenet Cell Genet* 39:67, 1985.

30. KAO FT, MORSE HG, LAW ML, LIDSKY A, CHANDRA T, WOO SL: Genetic mapping of the structural gene for antithrombin III to human chromosome 1. *Hum Genet* 67:34, 1984.

31. PROCHOWNIK EV, BOCK SC, ORKIN SH: Intron structure of the human antithrombin III gene differs from that of other members of the serine protease inhibitor superfamily. *J Biol Chem* 260:9608, 1985.

32. JAGD S, VIBE-PEDERSEN K, MAGNUSSON S: Location of two of the introns in the antithrombin-III gene. *FEBS Lett* 193:213, 1985.

33. PROCHOWNIK EV, ORKIN SH: In vivo transcription of a human antithrombin III "minigene." *J Biol Chem* 259:15386, 1984.

34. BOCK SC, LEVITAN DJ: Characterization of an unusual DNA length polymorphism 5' to the human antithrombin III gene. *Nucleic Acids Res* 11:8569, 1983.

35. PROCHOWNIK EV: Relationship between an enhancer element in the human antithrombin III gene and an immunoglobulin light-chain gene enhancer. *Nature* 316:845, 1985.

36. FAIR DS, BAHNAK BR: Human hepatoma cells secrete single chain factor X, prothrombin, and antithrombin III. *Blood* 64:194, 1984.

37. DSOUZA SE, MERCER JF: Antithrombin III mRNA in adult rat liver and kidney and in rat liver during development. *Biochem Biophys Res Commun* 142:417, 1987.

38. HOFFMAN M, FUCHS HE, PIZZO SV: The macrophage-mediated regulation of hepatocyte synthesis of antithrombin III and alpha 1-proteinase inhibitor. *Thromb Res* 41:707, 1986.

39. ROSENBERG RD: Biologic actions of heparin. *Semin Hematol* 14:427, 1977.

40. HIGHSMITH RF, ROSENBERG RD: The inhibition of human plasmin by human antithrombin-heparin cofactor. *J Biol Chem* 249:4335, 1974.

41. BROZE GJ, MAJERUS PW: Purification and properties of human coagulation factor VII. *J Biol Chem* 225:10073, 1980.

42. SUZUKI K, NISHIOKA J, HASHIMOTO S: Protein C inhibitor: Purification from human plasma and characterization. *J Biol Chem* 258:163, 1983.

43. FUCHS HE, TRAPP HG, GRIFFITH MJ, ROBERTS HR, PIZZO SV: Regulation of factor IXa in vitro in human and mouse plasma and in vivo in the mouse. Role of the endothelium and the plasma proteinase inhibitors. *J Clin Invest* 73:1696, 1984.

44. GITEL SN, MEDINA VM, WESSLER S: Inhibition of human activated factor X by antithrombin III and alpha 1-proteinase inhibitor in human plasma. *J Biol Chem* 259:6890, 1984.

45. DOWNING MR, BLOOM JW, MANN KG: Comparison of the inhibition of thrombin by three plasma protease inhibitors. *Biochemistry* 17:2649, 1978.

46. SCOTT CF, SCHAPIRA M, JAMES HL, COHEN AB, COLMAN RW: Inactivation of factor XIa by plasma protease inhibitors: Predominant role of alpha 1-protease inhibitor and protective effect of high molecular weight kininogen. *J Clin Invest* 69:844, 1982.

47. de AGOSTINI A, LIJNEN HR, PIXLEY RA, COLMAN RW, SCHAPIRA M: Inactivation of factor XII active fragment in normal plasma. Predominant role of C1-inhibitor. *J Clin Invest* 73:1542, 1984.

48. WIMAN B, COLLEN D: On the kinetics of the reaction between human antiplasmin and plasmin. *Eur J Biochem* 84:573, 1978.

49. FISH WW, BJÖRK I: Release of a two-chain form of antithrombin from the antithrombin-thrombin complex. *Eur J Biochem* 101:31, 1979.

50. BJÖRK I, JACKSON CM, JÖRNVALL H, LAVINE KK, NORDLING K, SALSGIVER WJ: The active site of antithrombin. Release of the same proteolytically cleaved form of the inhibitor from complexes with factor IXa, factor Xa, and thrombin. *J Biol Chem* 257:2406, 1982.

51. OWEN WG: Evidence for the formation of an ester between thrombin and heparin cofactor. *Biochim Biophys Acta* 405:380, 1975.

52. JORDAN RE, OOSTA GM, GARDNER WT, ROSENBERG RD: The kinetics of hemostatic enzyme-antithrombin interactions in the presence of low molecular weight heparin. *J Biol Chem* 255:10081, 1980.

53. HÖÖK M, BJÖRK I, HOPWOOD J, LINDAHL U: Anticoagulant activity of heparin: Separation of high-activity and low-activity species by affinity chromatography on immobilized antithrombin. *FEBS Lett* 66:90, 1976.

54. ANDERSSON L-O, BARROWCLIFFE TW, HOLMER E, JOHNSON EA, SIMS GEC: Anticoagulant properties of heparin fractionated by affinity chromatography on matrix-bound antithrombin III and by gel filtration. *Thromb Res* 9:575, 1976.

55. LAM LH, SILBERT JE, ROSENBERG RD: The separation of active and inactive forms of heparin. *Biochem Biophys Res Commun* 69:570, 1976.

56. JORDAN R, BEELER D, ROSENBERG R: Fractionation of low molecular weight heparin species and their interaction with antithrombin. *J Biol Chem* 254:2902, 1979.

57. OLSON ST, SRINIVASAN KR, BJÖRK I, SHORE JD: Binding of high affinity heparin to antithrombin III. Stopped flow kinetic studies of the binding interaction. *J Biol Chem* 256:11073, 1981.

58. PECON JM, BLACKBURN MN: Pyridoxylation of essential lysines in the heparin-binding site of antithrombin III. *J Biol Chem* 259:935, 1984.

59. PETERSON CB, NOYES CM, PECON JM, CHURCH FC, BLACKBURN MN: Identification of a lysyl residue in antithrombin which is essential for heparin binding. *J Biol Chem* 262:8061, 1987.

60. BLACKBURN MN, SMITH RL, CARSON J, SIBLEY CC: The heparin-binding site of antithrombin III. Identification of a critical tryptophan in the amino acid sequence. *J Biol Chem* 259:939, 1984.

61. VILLANUEVA GB: Predictions of the secondary structure of antithrombin III and the location of the heparin-binding site. *J Biol Chem* 259:2531, 1984.

62. LINDAHL U, FEINGOLD DS, RODÉN L: Biosynthesis of heparin. *TIBS* 11:221, 1986.

63. CHOAY J, PETITOU M, LORMEAU JC, SINAY P, CASU B, GATTI G: Structure-activity relationship in heparin: A synthetic pentasaccharide with high affinity for antithrombin III and eliciting high anti-factor Xa activity. *Biochem Biophys Res Commun* 116:492, 1983.

64. LINDAHL U, THUNBERG L, BÄCKSTRÖM G, RIESENFELD J, NORDLING K, BJÖRK I: Extension and structural variability of the antithrombin-binding sequence in heparin. *J Biol Chem* 259:12368, 1984.

65. ATHA DH, LORMEAU JC, PETITOU M, ROSENBERG RD, CHOAY J: Contribution of monosaccharide residues in heparin binding to antithrombin III. *Biochemistry* 24:6723, 1985.

66. TOLLEFSEN DM, PESTKA CA, MONAFO WJ: Activation of heparin cofactor II by dermatan sulfate. *J Biol Chem* 258:6713, 1983.

67. OLSON ST, SHORE JD: Transient kinetics of heparin-catalyzed protease inactivation by antithrombin III. The reaction step limiting heparin turnover in thrombin neutralization. *J Biol Chem* 261:13151, 1986.

68. EINARSSON R, ANDERSSON L-O: Binding of heparin to human antithrombin III as studied by measurements of tryptophan fluorescence. *Biochim Biophys Acta* 490:104, 1977.

69. NORDENMAN B, BJÖRK I: Binding of low-affinity and high-affinity heparin to antithrombin. Ultraviolet difference spectroscopy and circular dichroism studies. *Biochemistry* 17:3339, 1978.

70. OLSON ST, SHORE JD: Binding of high affinity heparin to antithrombin III. Characterization of the protein fluorescence enhancement. *J Biol Chem* 256:11065, 1981.

71. STONE AL, BEELER D, OOSTA G, ROSENBERG RD: Circular dichroism spectroscopy of heparin-antithrombin interactions. *Proc Natl Acad Sci USA* 79:7190, 1982.

72. OOSTA GM, GARDNER WT, BEELER DL, ROSENBERG RD: Multiple functional domains of the heparin molecule. *Proc Natl Acad Sci USA* 78:829, 1981.

73. POMERANTZ MW, OWEN WG: A catalytic role for heparin. Evidence for a ternary complex of heparin cofactor, thrombin and heparin. *Biochim Biophys Acta* 535:66, 1978.

74. DANIELSSON Å, RAUB E, LINDAHL U, BJÖRK I: Role of ternary complexes, in which heparin binds both antithrombin and proteinase, in the acceleration of the reactions between antithrombin and thrombin or factor Xa. *J Biol Chem* 261:15467, 1986.

75. GRIFFITH MJ: The heparin-enhanced antithrombin III/thrombin reaction is saturable with respect to both thrombin and antithrombin III. *J Biol Chem* 257:13899, 1982.

76. PLETCHER CH, NELSESTUEN GL: Two-substrate reaction model for the heparin-catalyzed bovine antithrombin/proteinase reaction. *J Biol Chem* 258:1086, 1983.

77. NESHEIM ME: A simple rate law that describes the kinetics of the heparin-catalyzed reaction between antithrombin III and thrombin. *J Biol Chem* 258:14708, 1983.

78. BJÖRK I, DANIELSSON Å: Antithrombin and related inhibitors of coagulation proteinases, in Barrett AJ, Salveson G (eds): *Proteinase Inhibitors.* Amsterdam, Elsevier, 1986, p 489.

79. ROSENBERG RD: Regulation of the hemostatic mechanism, in Stamatoyannopoulos G, Nienhuis AW, Leder P, Majerus PW (eds): *The Molecular Basis of Blood Diseases.* Philadelphia, Saunders, 1987, p 534.

80. LANE DA, PEJLER G, FLYNN AM, THOMPSON EA, LINDAHL U: Neutralization of heparin-related saccharides by histidine-rich glycoprotein and platelet factor 4. *J Biol Chem* 261:3980, 1986.

81. PREISSNER KT, MULLER-BERGHAUS G: S protein modulates the heparin-catalyzed inhibition of thrombin by antithrombin III. Evidence for a direct interaction of S protein with heparin. *Eur J Biochem* 156:645, 1986.

82. LOLLAR P, OWEN WG: Clearance of thrombin from the circulation in rabbits by high-affinity binding sites on the endothelium. Possible role in the inactivation of thrombin by antithrombin III. *J Clin Invest* 66:1222, 1980.

83. MARUYAMA I, MAJERUS PW: The turnover of thrombin-thrombomodulin complex in cultured human umbilical vein endothelial cells and A549 lung cancer cells. Endocytosis and degradation of thrombin. *J Biol Chem* 260:15432, 1985.

84. FUCHS HE, PIZZO SV: Regulation of factor Xa in vitro in human and mouse plasma and in vivo in mouse. *J Clin Invest* 72:2041, 1983.

85. MILETICH JP, JACKSON CM, MAJERUS PW: Properties of the factor Xa binding site on human platelets. *J Biol Chem* 253:6908, 1978.

86. LINDHOUT T, BARUCH D, SCHOEN P, FRANSSEN J, HEMKER HC: Thrombin generation and inactivation in the presence of antithrombin III and heparin. *Biochemistry* 25:5962, 1986.

87. SHIFMAN MA, PIZZO SV: The in vivo metabolism of antithrombin III and antithrombin III complexes. *J Biol Chem* 257:3243, 1982.

88. FUCHS HE, MICHALOPOULOS GK, PIZZO SV: Hepatocyte uptake of alpha 1-proteinase inhibitor-trypsin complexes in vitro: Evidence for a shared uptake mechanism for proteinase complexes of alpha 1-proteinase inhibitor and antithrombin III. *J Cell Biochem* 25:231, 1984.

89. FUCHS HE, SHIFMAN MA, MICHALOPOULOS G, PIZZO SV: Hepatocyte receptors for antithrombin III-proteinase complexes. *J Cell Biochem* 24:197, 1984.

90. FAIR DS, PLOW EF: Specific association of thrombin-antithrombin complexes with a human hepatoma cell line. *Thromb Res* 41:67, 1986.

91. CARLSON TH, SIMON TL, ATENCIO AC: In vivo behavior of human radioiodinated antithrombin III: Distribution among three physiologic pools. *Blood* 66:13, 1985.

92. NENCI GG, BERRETTINI M, PARISE P, AGNELLI G: Persistent spontaneous heparinaemia in systemic mastocytosis. *Folia Haematol (Leipzig)* 109:453, 1982.

93. KHOORY MS, NESHEIM ME, BOWIE EJW, MANN KG: Circulating heparan sulfate proteoglycan anticoagulant from a patient with a plasma cell disorder. *J Clin Invest* 65:666, 1980.

94. PALMER RN, RICK ME, RICK PD, ZELLER JA, GRALNICK HR: Circulating heparan sulfate anticoagulant in a patient with a fatal bleeding disorder. *N Engl J Med* 310:1696, 1984.

95. BUSSEL JB, STEINHERZ PG, MILLER DR, HILGARTNER MW: A heparin-like anticoagulant in an 8-month-old boy with acute monoblastic leukemia. *Am J Hematol* 16:83, 1984.

96. MARCUM JA, ROSENBERG RD: Heparin-like molecules with anticoagulant activity are synthesized by cultured endothelial cells. *Biochem Biophys Res Commun* 126:365, 1985.

97. MARCUM JA, ATHA DH, FRITZE LM, NAWROTH P, STERN D, ROSENBERG RD: Cloned bovine aortic endothelial cells synthesize anticoagulantly active heparan sulfate proteoglycan. *J Biol Chem* 261:7507, 1986.

98. BOURIN MC, BOFFA MC, BJÖRK I, LINDAHL U: Functional domains of rabbit thrombomodulin. *Proc Natl Acad Sci USA* 83:5924, 1986.

99. STERN D, NAWROTH P, MARCUM J, HANDLEY D, KISIEL W, ROSENBERG R, STERN K: Interaction of antithrombin III with bovine aortic segments. Role of heparin in binding and enhanced anticoagulant activity. *J Clin Invest* 75:272, 1985.

100. HATTON MW, MOAR SL, RICHARDSON M: On the interaction of rabbit antithrombin III with the luminal surface of the normal and deendothelialized rabbit thoracic aorta in vitro. *Blood* 67:878, 1986.

101. MARCUM JA, MCKENNEY JB, ROSENBERG RD: Acceleration of thrombin-antithrombin complex formation in rat hindquarters via heparinlike molecules bound to the endothelium. *J Clin Invest* 74:341, 1984.

102. JAKUBOWSKI HV, KLINE MD, OWEN WG: The effect of bovine thrombomodulin on the specificity of bovine thrombin. *J Biol Chem* 261:3876, 1986.

103. ABILDGAARD U, LIE M, ØDEGÅRD OR: Antithrombin (heparin cofactor) assay with "new" chromogenic substrates (S-2238 and Chromozym TH). *Thromb Res* 11:549, 1977.

104. TOLLEFSEN DM, MAJERUS DW, BLANK MK: Heparin cofactor II. Purification and properties of a heparin-dependent inhibitor of thrombin in human plasma. *J Biol Chem* 257:2162, 1982.

105. TRAN TH, DUCKERT F: Influence of heparin cofactor II (HCII) on the determination of antithrombin III (AT). *Thromb Res* 40:571, 1985.

106. CONARD J, BARA L, HORELLOU MH, SAMAMA MM: Bovine or human thrombin in amidolytic AT III assays. Influence of heparin cofactor II. *Thromb Res* 41:873, 1986.

107. CONARD J, BROSSTAD F, LIE-LARSEN M, SAMAMA M, ABILDGAARD U: Molar antithrombin concentration in normal human plasma. *Haemostasis* 13:363, 1983.

108. ANDREW M, PAES B, MILNER R, JOHNSTON M, MITCHELL L, TOLLEFSEN DM, POWERS P: Development of the human coagulation system in the fullterm infant. *Blood* 70:165, 1987.

109. MARCINIAK K, FARLEY CH, DESIMONE PA: Familial thrombosis due to antithrombin III deficiency. *Blood* 43:219, 1974.

110. PROCHOWNIK EV, ANTONARAKIS S, BAUER KA, ROSENBERG RD: Molecular heterogeneity of inherited antithrombin III deficiency. *N Engl J Med* 308:1549, 1983.

111. BOCK SC, HARRIS JF, SCHWARTZ CE, WARD JH, HERSHGOLD EJ, SKOLNICK MH: Hereditary thrombosis in a Utah kindred is caused by a dysfunctional antithrombin III gene. *Am J Hum Genet* 37:32, 1985.

112. AMBRUSO DR, LEONARD BD, BIES RD, JACOBSON L, HATHAWAY WE, REEVE EB: Antithrombin III deficiency: Decreased synthesis of a biochemically normal molecule. *Blood* 60:78, 1982.

113. KNOT EA, de-JONG E, ten-CATE JW, IBURG AH, HENNY CP, BRUIN T, STIBBE J: Purified radiolabeled antithrombin III metabolism in three families with hereditary AT III deficiency: Application of a three-compartment model. *Blood* 67:93, 1986.

114. CHASSE JF, ESNARD F, GUITTON JD, MOURAY H, PERIGOIS F, FAUCONNEAU G, GAUTHIER F: An abnormal plasma antithrombin with no apparent affinity for heparin. *Thromb Res* 34:297, 1984.

115. WOLF M, BOYER C, LAVERGNE JM, LARRIEU MJ: A new familial variant of antithrombin III: "Antithrombin III Paris." *Br J Haematol* 51:285, 1982.

116. FISCHER AM, CORNU P, STERNBERG C, MERIANE F, DAUTZENBERG MD, CHAFA O, BEGUIN S, DESNOS M: Antithrombin III Alger: A new homozygous AT III variant. *Thromb Haemost* 55:218, 1986.

117. BOYER C, WOLF M, VEDRENNE J, MEYER D, LARRIEU MJ: Homozygous variant of antithrombin III: AT III Fontainebleau. *Thromb Haemost* 56:18, 1986.

118. AIACH M, NORA M, FIESSINGER JN, RONCATO M, FRANCOIS D, GELAS MA: A functional abnormal antithrombin III (AT III) deficiency: AT III Charleville. *Thromb Res* 39:559, 1985.

119. HOWARTH DJ, SAMSON D, STIRLING Y, SEGHATCHIAN MJ: Antithrombin III "Northwick Park": A variant antithrombin with normal affinity for heparin but reduced heparin cofactor activity. *Thromb Haemost* 53:314, 1985.

120. FINAZZI G, TRAN TH, BARBUI T, DUCKERT F: Purification of antithrombin

"Vicenza": A molecule with normal heparin affinity and impaired reactivity to thrombin. *Br J Haematol* 59:259, 1985.

121. GIROLAMI A, MARAFIOTI F, RUBERTELLI M, VICARIOTO MA, CAPPELLATO G, MAZZUCCATO M: Antithrombin III Trento. A "new" congenital AT III abnormality with a peculiar crossed-immunoelectrophoretic pattern in the absence of heparin. *Acta Haematol (Basel)* 72:73, 1984.

122. SRENSEN PJ, SAS G, PETO I, BLASKO G, KREMMER T, SAMU A: Distinction of two pathologic antithrombin III molecules: Antithrombin III "Aalborg" and antithrombin III "Budapest". *Thromb Res* 26:211, 1982.

123. BAUER KA, ASHENHURST JB, CHEDIAK J, ROSENBERG RD: Antithrombin "Chicago": A functionally abnormal molecule with increased heparin affinity causing familial thrombophilia. *Blood* 62:1242, 1983.

124. GRUENBERG JC, SMALLRIDGE RC, ROSENBERG RD: Inherited antithrombin III deficiency causing mesenteric venous infarction: A new clinical entity. *Ann Surg* 181:791, 1975.

125. DAS M, CARROLL SF: Antithrombin III deficiency: An etiology of Budd-Chiari syndrome. *Surgery* 97:242, 1985.

126. GIROLAMI A, FABRIS F, CAPPELLATO G, SAINATI L, BOERI G: Antithrombin (ATIII) Padua2: A new congenital abnormality with defective heparin cofactor activities but no thrombotic disease. *Blut* 47:93, 1983.

127. ROSENBERG RD: Action and interaction of antithrombin and heparin. *N Engl J Med* 16:146, 1975.

128. ØDEGÅRD OR, ABILDGAARD U: Antithrombin III: Critical review of assay methods. Significance of variations in health and disease. *Haemostasis* 7:127, 1978.

129. VIKYDAL R, KORNINGER C, KYRLE PA, NIESSNER H, PABINGER I, THALER E, LECHNER K: The prevalence of hereditary antithrombin-III deficiency in patients with a history of venous thromboembolism. *Thromb Haemost* 54:744, 1985.

130. KNOT E, ten-CATE JW, DRIJFHOUT HR, KAHLE LH, TYTGAT GN: Antithrombin III metabolism in patients with liver disease. *J Clin Pathol* 37:523, 1984.

131. KAUFFMANN RH, VELTKAMP JJ, van TILBURG NH, van ES LA: Acquired antithrombin III deficiency and thrombosis in the nephrotic syndrome. *Am J Med* 65:607, 1978.

132. SPERO JA, LEWIS JH, HASIBA U: Disseminated intravascular coagulation. Findings in 346 patients. *Thromb Haemost* 43:28, 1980.

133. FAGERHOL MK, ABILDGAARD U, BERGSJØ P, JACOBSEN JH: Oral contraceptives and low antithrombin III concentration. *Lancet* 2:1175, 1970.

134. CONARD J, CAZENAVE B, MAURY J, HORELLOU MH: L-asparaginase, antithrombin III, and thrombosis. *Lancet* 1:1091, 1980.

135. BAUER KA, TEITEL JM, ROSENBERG RD: L-asparaginase induced antithrombin III deficiency: Evidence against the production of a hypercoagulable state. *Thromb Res* 29:437, 1983.

136. HIRSH J: Treatment of pulmonary embolism. *Annu Rev Med* 38:91, 1987.

137. LECLERC JR, GEERTS W, PANJU A, NGUYEN P, HIRSH J: Management of anti-thrombin III deficiency during pregnancy without administration of anti-thrombin III. *Thromb Res* 41:567, 1986.

138. NIELSEN LE, BELL WR, BORKON AM, NEILL CA: Extensive thrombus formation with heparin resistance during extracorporeal circulation. A new presentation of familial antithrombin III deficiency. *Arch Intern Med* 147:149, 1987.

139. HOLM HA, KALVENES S, ABILDGAARD U: Changes in plasma antithrombin (heparin cofactor activity) during intravenous heparin therapy: Observations in 198 patients with deep venous thrombosis. *Scand J Haematol* 35:564, 1985.

140. PETITTI DB, STROM BL, MELMON KL: Duration of warfarin anticoagulant therapy and the probabilities of recurrent thromboembolism and hemorrhage. *Am J Med* 81:255, 1986.

141. HULL R, HIRSH J, JAY R, CARTER C, ENGLAND C, GENT M, TURPIE AG, MCLOUGHLIN D, DODD P, THOMAS M, RASKOB G, OCKELFORD P: Different intensities of oral anticoagulant therapy in the treatment of proximal-vein thrombosis. *N Engl J Med* 307:1676, 1982.

142. HELLGREN M, TENGBORN L, ABILDGAARD U: Pregnancy in women with congenital antithrombin III deficiency: Experience of treatment with heparin and antithrombin. *Gynecol Obstet Invest* 14:127, 1982.

143. HALL JG, PAULI RM, WILSON KM: Maternal and fetal sequellae of anticoagulation during pregnancy. *Am J Med* 68:122, 1980.

144. HIRSH J, CADE JF, O'SULLIVAN EF: Clinical experience with anticoagulant therapy during pregnancy. *Br Med J* 1:270, 1970.

145. MICHIELS JJ, STIBBE J, VELLENGA E, van-VLIET HH: Prophylaxis of thrombosis in antithrombin III-deficient women during pregnancy and delivery. *Eur J Obstet Gynecol Reprod Biol* 18:149, 1984.

146. SAMSON D, STIRLING Y, WOOLF L, HOWARTH D, SEGHATCHIAN MJ, deCHAZAL R: Management of planned pregnancy in a patient with congenital antithrombin III deficiency. *Br J Haematol* 56:243, 1984.

147. TENGBORN L, BENGTSSON T: Antithrombin III concentrate. Thromboprophylaxis during pregnancy in a patient with congenital antithrombin III deficiency. *Acta Obstet Gynecol Scand* 65:375, 1986.

148. WINTER JH, FENECH A, BENNETT B, DOUGLAS AS: Prophylactic antithrombotic therapy with stanozolol in patients with familial antithrombin III deficiency. *Br J Haematol* 57:527, 1984.

149. WINTER JH, FENECH A, MACKIE M, BENNETT B, DOUGLAS AS: Treatment of venous thrombosis in antithrombin III deficient patients with concentrates of antithrombin III. *Clin Lab Haematol* 4:101, 1982.

150. MANNUCCI PM, BOYER C, WOLF M, TRIPODI A, LARRIEU MJ: Treatment of congenital antithrombin III deficiency with concentrates. *Br J Haematol* 50:531, 1982.

151. FAIRFAX AJ, IBBOTSON RM: Effect of danazol on the biochemical abnormality of inherited antithrombin III deficiency. *Thorax* 40:646, 1985.

152. EYSTER ME, PARKER ME: Treatment of familial antithrombin-III deficiency with danazol. *Haemostasis* 15:119, 1985.

153. TENGBORN L, FROHM B, NILSSON LE, NILSSON IM: Antithrombin III concentrate: Its catabolism in health and in antithrombin III deficiency. *Scand J Clin Lab Invest* 41:469, 1981.

154. BRIGINSHAW GF, SHANBERGE JN: Identification of two distinct heparin cofactors in human plasma. Separation and partial purification. *Arch Biochem Biophys* 161:683, 1974.

155. RAGG H: A new member of the plasma protease inhibitor gene family. *Nucleic Acids Res* 14:1073, 1986.

156. INHORN RC, TOLLEFSEN DM: Isolation and characterization of a partial cDNA clone for heparin cofactor II. *Biochem Biophys Res Commun* 137:431, 1986.

157. BLINDER MA, MARASA JC, REYNOLDS CH, DEAVEN LL, TOLLEFSEN DM: Heparin cofactor II: cDNA sequence, chromosome localization, restriction fragment length polymorphism, and expression in *Escherichia coli*. *Biochemistry* 27:752, 1988.

158. HORTIN G, TOLLEFSEN DM, STRAUSS AW: Identification of two sites of sulfation of human heparin cofactor II. *J Biol Chem* 261:15827, 1986.

159. JAFFE EA, ARMELLINO D, TOLLEFSEN DM: Biosynthesis of functionally active heparin cofactor II by a human hepatoma-derived cell line. *Biochem Biophys Res Commun* 132:368, 1985.

160. PARKER KA, TOLLEFSEN DM: The protease specificity of heparin cofactor II. Inhibition of thrombin generated during coagulation. *J Biol Chem* 260:3501, 1985.

161. GRIFFITH MJ, NOYES CM, TYNDALL JA, CHURCH FC: Structural evidence for leucine at the reactive site of heparin cofactor II. *Biochemistry* 24:6777, 1985.

162. CHURCH FC, NOYES CM, GRIFFITH MJ: Inhibition of chymotrypsin by heparin cofactor II. *Proc Natl Acad Sci USA* 82:6431, 1985.

163. HURST RE, POON MC, GRIFFITH MJ: Structure-activity relationships of heparin. Independence of heparin charge density and antithrombin-binding domains in thrombin inhibition by antithrombin and heparin cofactor II. *J Clin Invest* 72:1042, 1983.

164. TEIEN AN, ABILDGAARD U, HÖÖK M: The anticoagulant effect of heparan sulfate and dermatan sulfate. *Thromb Res* 8:859, 1976.

165. OFOSU FA, MODI GJ, SMITH LM, CERSKUS AL, HIRSH J, BLAJCHMAN MA: Heparan sulfate and dermatan sulfate inhibit the generation of thrombin activity in plasma by complementary pathways. *Blood* 64:742, 1984.

166. FERNANDEZ F, van RYN J, OFOSU FA, HIRSH J, BUCHANAN MR: The haemorrhagic and antithrombotic effects of dermatan sulfate. *Br J Haematol* 64:309, 1986.

167. MCGUIRE EA, TOLLEFSEN DM: Activation of heparin cofactor II by fibroblasts and vascular smooth muscle cells. *J Biol Chem* 262:169, 1987.

168. TOLLEFSEN DM, PESTKA CA: Heparin cofactor II activity in patients with disseminated intravascular coagulation and hepatic failure. *Blood* 66:769, 1985.

169. TRAN TH, DUCKERT F: Heparin cofactor II determination—Levels in normals and patients with hereditary antithrombin III deficiency and disseminated intravascular coagulation. *Thromb Haemost* 52:112, 1984.

170. ABILDGAARD U, LARSEN ML: Assay of dermatan sulfate cofactor (heparin cofactor II) activity in human plasma. *Thromb Res* 35:257, 1984.

171. EZENAGU LC, BRANDT JT: Laboratory determination of heparin cofactor II. *Arch Pathol Lab Med* 110:1149, 1986.

172. GRIFFITH MJ, CARRAWAY T, WHITE GC, DOMBROSE FA: Heparin cofactor activities in a family with hereditary antithrombin III deficiency: Evidence for a second heparin cofactor in human plasma. *Blood* 61:111, 1983.

173. SIÉ P, DUPOUY D, PICHON J, BONEU B: Constitutional heparin co-factor II deficiency associated with recurrent thrombosis. *Lancet* 2:414, 1985.

174. TRAN TH, MARBET GA, DUCKERT F: Association of hereditary heparin cofactor II deficiency with thrombosis. *Lancet* 2:413, 1985.

175. ANDERSSON TR, LARSEN ML, HANDELAND GF, ABILDGAARD U: Heparin cofactor II activity in plasma: Application of an automated assay method to the study of a normal adult population. *Scand J Haematol* 36:96, 1986.

CHAPTER 90

INHERITED DISORDERS OF PLATELETS

RODGER P. McEVER
PHILIP W. MAJERUS

1. Glanzmann thrombasthenia and Bernard-Soulier disease are inherited defects of the platelet membrane. Both diseases are characterized by autosomal recessive transmission. In both thrombasthenia and Bernard-Soulier disease, defects in a platelet membrane glycoprotein are associated with a serious impairment in platelet function which results in clinically significant bleeding.

2. Platelets from patients with Glanzmann thrombasthenia do not aggregate in response to physiological agonists such as ADP or thrombin, do not spread normally on subendothelial surfaces, and do not support clot retraction. The platelet membranes lack a glycoprotein complex known as IIb-IIIa. Current evidence suggests that abnormalities of this glycoprotein prevent the platelet membrane from interacting with extracellular "adhesive" proteins such as fibrinogen and fibronectin as well as with intracellular cytoskeletal proteins. These interactions are required for normal platelet aggregation, platelet spreading, and clot retraction.

3. Bernard-Soulier platelets (like platelets from patients with von Willebrand disease) do not adhere normally to exposed subendothelial surfaces of blood vessels. Membranes from Bernard-Soulier platelets are deficient in a glycoprotein complex called Ib-IX as well as another membrane protein called V, which may be loosely associated with the Ib-IX complex. Glycoprotein Ib is the receptor for von Willebrand factor (vWF). Lack of this receptor prevents platelets from binding vWF, which is required for platelet adhesion to subendothelium.

4. Inherited platelet abnormalities associated with defects in platelet secretion have also been described. Some of these appear to represent abnormalities in the synthesis of, or response to, prostaglandins. Others are associated with deficiencies in platelet storage granules. The inheritance patterns and the pathogenetic mechanisms of these disorders require further clarification.

The enormous progress that has been made in the investigation of disorders of hemostasis can be illustrated by a statement from the original chapter on blood clotting factors written for this book over 25 years ago: "The clotting factors are not known as specific chemical species (excepting Ca^{++}) and the reactions which they undergo or catalyze are known only phenomenologically."[1] There was no mention of platelet disorders in that chapter. With the recent isolation and cloning of the known plasma coagulation factors as well as several important platelet proteins, a much clearer picture is emerging. In this chapter we present in detail two genetic disorders of platelets and mention a few others that await clear definition. Future editions of this text will undoubtedly contain descriptions of other inherited disorders of platelet function.

ROLE OF PLATELETS IN NORMAL HEMOSTASIS

The initial response to injury of a vessel is the adherence of platelets to exposed subendothelial components, including collagen, von Willebrand factor, and fibronectin. Platelets do not adhere to intact endothelium because of unique properties of endothelial cell membranes[2] and also because endothelial cells produce the platelet inhibitory substance, prostacyclin.[3,4] The adherence of platelets to subendothelial surfaces depends on a protein found in plasma and subendothelial tissues known as *von Willebrand factor (vWF)*. Abnormalities of this protein produce a bleeding disorder, von Willebrand disease, which is described in Chap. 87. Following the initial adherence of platelets to the wound surface, the hemostatic plug enlarges as other platelets attach to the initial layer in a process known as *aggregation*. This process requires that fibrinogen bind to the platelet surface.[5–13]

As platelets aggregate, they also secrete the contents of two kinds of storage granules known as *dense granules* and α *granules*. Dense granules release calcium ions, adenosine diphosphate (ADP), and serotonin. α Granules release a variety of proteins involved in hemostasis and wound healing such as fibrinogen and platelet-derived growth factor.[14] In addition, arachidonic acid is released from phosphatidylinositol and phosphatidylcholine[15,16] and is metabolized to form thromboxane A_2, a labile compound that is a potent stimulus for further platelet aggregation and secretion.[17] Although thromboxane A_2 stimulates platelet aggregation and secretion, it is not required for these processes since thrombin can activate platelets that cannot synthesize thromboxane.[18] This was shown by treatment of platelets with aspirin, which covalently acetylates a serine residue in the active site of cyclooxygenase,[19] the first enzyme in the synthesis of thromboxane from arachidonic acid. Its inactivation results in the absence of thromboxane production.

It is likely that the most important physiological stimulant of platelets is thrombin. Early in hemostasis a minute amount of thrombin forms by an unknown pathway,[20] binds to specific receptors on the platelet surface, and triggers the events of platelet activation outlined above.[21] In addition, the interaction of platelets with coagulation factors is important in promoting reactions leading to fibrin formation. The best studied reaction is the conversion of prothrombin to thrombin. Platelets possess about 200 receptor sites for factor Va per cell, where factors Va and Xa and prothrombin interact efficiently to produce thrombin.[22,23] Finally, platelets are able to contract, and because they are bound to the fibrin network, they can consolidate the hemostatic plug into a tight mass.

Platelet function can be assessed by measurement of in vitro aggregation in response to various agonists, or by measurement of the secretion of granule contents. The products of arachidonate metabolism can also be measured. Clot retraction in vitro is a measure of the ability of platelets to contract. Perhaps the best in vivo test of platelet function is measurement of the bleeding time after a standard 1-mm cutaneous incision.[24]

GLANZMANN THROMBASTHENIA

In 1918 Glanzmann described a heterogeneous group of disorders, including some characterized by abnormal clot retraction, which were ascribed to a platelet defect.[25] Other early workers noted that the disease, designated *Glanzmann thrombasthenia*, was also characterized by a normal platelet count, a prolonged bleeding time, the lack of clumped platelets, and the appearance of isolated platelets on the peripheral blood smear.[26,27] In 1964 Hardisty et al. demonstrated decreased aggregation of thrombasthenic platelets in response to physiological agonists.[28] Since that report numerous patients with similar abnormalities have been described, and an autosomal recessive pattern of inheritance has been clearly documented.[29-36] The incidence of the disease has not been determined with precision, but it may be the most common inherited disorder of platelet function. The disorder is clustered with higher frequency in Iraqi-Jewish, Arab and other ethnic groups where consanguinity is prevalent.[36-38]

Diagnosis

A diagnosis of Glanzmann thrombasthenia can be made on the basis of the following criteria:

1. Mucocutaneous bleeding of variable severity which is usually present from birth
2. A family history of bleeding compatible with autosomal recessive transmission (helpful when present, but not required)
3. Normal platelet count and morphology in the presence of
   a. Prolonged bleeding time
   b. Absent or diminished clot retraction
   c. Absent platelet aggregation by ADP, epinephrine, collagen, and thrombin, but normal aggregation by ristocetin and human vWF
4. Normal coagulation factors (prothrombin time and partial thromboplastin time both normal)

The diagnosis can be confirmed specifically by demonstration of the decrease or absence of membrane glycoprotein IIb-IIIa (discussed under "Membrane Glycoprotein Defect," below). Other abnormalities include a decrease in total platelet fibrinogen, absence of the platelet alloantigens Lek, Pen, and Pl[A], and failure of activated platelets to bind fibrinogen, von Willebrand factor, and fibronectin.

Clinical Manifestations

The pattern of bleeding in thrombasthenia is characteristic of that in patients with thrombocytopenia or qualitative platelet disorders. Purpura, epistaxis, gingival bleeding, and menorrhagia are common. Gastrointestinal hemorrhages and hematuria are also seen. Unlike coagulation factor deficiencies, such as hemophilia A, hemarthroses are unusual. The severity of bleeding varies widely among patients but is frequently severe enough to require transfusion. Some patients die of hemorrhage during childhood, but most survive to adulthood and several have had unexplained amelioration as they grew older. Some virtually asymptomatic homozygous patients were discovered in the course of family studies undertaken after the diagnosis of a more severely affected proband. Heterozygotes for the disease are always asymptomatic.

Laboratory Studies

Plasma coagulation factors and platelet counts are normal. The appearance of platelets by light microscopy is normal, except for their occurrence as isolated elements, rather than aggregates on smear. The survival of ^{51}Cr-labeled platelets is unaffected, and platelet and megakaryocyte morphology is normal.[29] Total platelet fibrinogen is usually reduced.[29,30,32] The bleeding time is invariably prolonged. Clot retraction is absent in most patients but may be seen to a reduced extent.[29]

The most striking functional defect is the failure of thrombasthenic platelets to form large aggregates in response to any physiological agonist, including ADP, epinephrine, collagen, and thrombin.[28-36] The defect may not be absolute, since specialized assays indicate that small aggregates can form in whole blood in at least some patients with type II disease (see "Membrane Glyoprotein Defect," below).[39] Unlike Bernard-Soulier platelets, thrombasthenic platelets do aggregate when exposed to normal plasma and the antibiotic ristocetin.[14] Thrombasthenic platelets bind thrombin normally and respond with shape change and secretion.[40] This suggests that the aggregation defect is due to an abnormality occurring at a stage subsequent to platelet activation.

More recent studies suggest that thrombasthenic platelets also have a defect of spreading on subendothelial surfaces. In an experimental system in which blood is circulated through a perfusion chamber containing segments of rabbit aorta in which the subendothelium has been exposed, normal platelets first attach, then spread, then form larger platelet aggregates.[41] Thrombasthenic platelets attach normally, but fail to spread on the subendothelium as well as fail to form platelet aggregates.[42]

Human platelets washed free of plasma require exogenous fibrinogen in order to aggregate after stimulation with ADP, epinephrine, or collagen.[5-7] Thrombin causes release of intracellular fibrinogen, so that exogenous fibrinogen is not required for aggregation when thrombin is the stimulus. Several studies have clarified the role of fibrinogen in platelet aggregation with the demonstration that platelets possess specific, saturable receptors for fibrinogen.[8-13,43] Fibrinogen binding requires exposure of platelets to an agonist, and maximal binding occurs with the same concentrations of fibrinogen and calcium ions required for optimal platelet aggregation.[8-13,43] Activated platelets bind approximately 45,000 fibrinogen molecules per platelet under optimal conditions.[8-10,43] More recent studies indicate that activated platelets also bind von Willebrand factor and fibronectin, two other large "adhesive" macromolecules.[44-46] The conditions for binding of the three ligands are similar but not identical, since fibrinogen binds to platelets activated with thrombin, ADP, or epinephrine, von Willebrand factor binds to platelets activated with thrombin or ADP, but fibronectin binds only to platelets activated with thrombin.[44-47] One fascinating observation arising from these experiments is that activated thrombasthenic platelets are unable to bind fibrinogen,[8,13,43,48,49] von Willebrand factor,[50] or fibronectin.[51] These studies suggest that the interaction of activated platelets with large adhesive proteins may be essential for platelet aggregation and for spreading on subendothelial surfaces and that thrombasthenic platelets may lack a receptor for these proteins. The relationship of the fibrinogen binding defect to the deficiency in intracellular fibrinogen is not clear, but the data suggest that a surface fibrinogen receptor is involved in the process by which platelet granules acquire fibrinogen.

Membrane Glycoprotein Defect in Thrombasthenia

Nurden and Caen studied platelet membrane proteins by sodium dodecyl sulfate polyacrylamide gel electrophoresis and first noted a deficiency in a major glycoprotein in thrombasthenia.[52] Phillips and Agin, using two-dimensional sodium dodecyl sulfate gel electrophoresis of radioiodinated platelets, found that two membrane glycoproteins, now known as IIb and IIIa, are decreased in the disease.[53] This finding has been confirmed in other studies.[54-57]

The deficiency of two apparently discrete proteins in the same genetic disorder prompted numerous investigations into the structure of the proteins in normal platelets. Three different experimental approaches indicate that IIb and IIIa are associated as heterodimeric complexes in the platelet membrane. First, when normal membranes are solubilized in Triton X-100 and examined by crossed immunoelectrophoresis with antibodies raised against intact platelets, a number of immunoprecipitates are found, as shown in Fig. 90-1A.[58,59] One of these proteins, designated 16 in Fig. 90-1A, is absent in extracts from thrombasthenic platelets (Fig. 90-1B). This immunoprecipitate, eluted from agarose and further analyzed by sodium dodecyl sulfate polyacrylamide gel electrophoresis, contains both IIb and IIIa, suggesting that they are subunits of a single molecule designated glycoprotein IIb-IIIa. Second, monoclonal antibodies against either IIb or IIIa coisolate both IIb and IIIa from platelet lysates.[60-62] Third, standard chromatographic procedures result in the copurification of IIb and IIIa with 1:1 stoichiometry.[63,64] These IIb-IIIa complexes sediment on sucrose gradients with mobilities characteristic of a heterodimer consisting of one IIb and one IIIa subunit.[63-65] The association of IIb and IIIa requires micromolar quantities of calcium ions.[63,66-68] Exposure of IIb-IIIa heterodimers to EGTA at 37°C causes a time-dependent, irreversible dissociation of the individual subunits and the polymerization of both IIb and IIIa.[68-70] Calcium binding sites have been identified on IIb, but there is controversy as to whether IIIa also binds calcium ions.[71,72]

Glycoprotein IIb is a two-chain molecule[73] consisting of a disulfide linked heavy chain (IIbα, $M_r = 130,000$) and a light chain (IIbβ, $M_r = 23,000$), as shown in Fig. 90-2. Glycoprotein IIIa is a cysteine-rich, single-chain molecule with $M_r = 90,000$ under nonreducing conditions and 105,000 under reducing conditions.[73] The slower mobility of the reduced protein suggests that the native molecule has a compact structure stabilized by intrachain disulfide bridges. Both IIb and IIIa contain 15% carbohydrate by weight, but the proportion of individual sugars differs between the two glycoproteins.[74] The amino acid compositions of IIb and IIIa show some similarities,[63,74] but the proteins are immunologically distinct[75,76] and have dissimilar tryptic peptide maps.[74,75] Furthermore, messenger RNA from a leukemia cell line with properties of megakaryocytes (the bone marrow precursor cells of platelets) directs translation of distinct precursors for IIb and IIIa.[76] The IIb precursor is a single-chain polypeptide containing both the α and β chains,[76] which undergoes proteolytic cleavage during posttranslational processing to yield the mature two-chain protein.[77,78] Both IIb and IIIa undergo N-linked glycosylation and assemble into heterodimers prior to appearance at the cell surface.[77]

The above data suggest that IIb and IIIa are products of separate genes, an assumption further supported by recent cloning of distinct cDNAs encoding each protein.[79-83] The primary amino acid sequence deduced from the cDNAs has helped clarify several structural features of the IIb-IIIa complex (Fig. 90-3). The IIb cDNA predicts a molecule of 1039 amino acids, including a 31 amino-acid signal peptide. This is followed by the α (heavy) chain, then the β (light) chain separated by a putative cleavage site for an intracellular protease.[81,83] A single candidate hydrophobic transmembrane domain in the β chain is followed by a short cytoplasmic segment of 21 amino acids.[81,83] Four stretches of 12 amino acids present in the α chain are homologous with the calcium-binding regions of troponin C and calmodulin[83]; these may represent the domains for binding calcium previously noted with protein

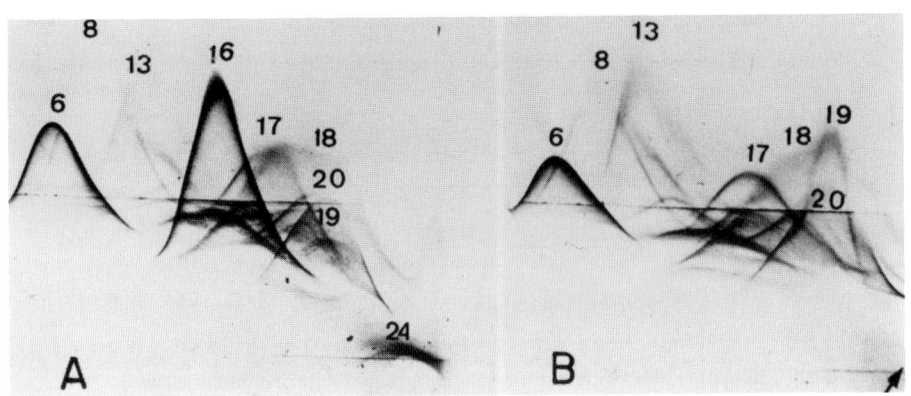

Fig. 90-1 Crossed immunoelectrophoresis of Triton X-100 solubilized proteins from (A) normal platelets and (B) thrombasthenic platelets. Electrophoresis in the vertical second dimension was performed in agarose gel containing rabbit antibodies to whole platelets. The thrombasthenic platelets lack two immunoprecipitates: peak 16, which represents membrane glycoprotein IIb-IIIa, and peak 24, which is platelet fibrinogen. (From Hagen et al.[58] Used by permission.)

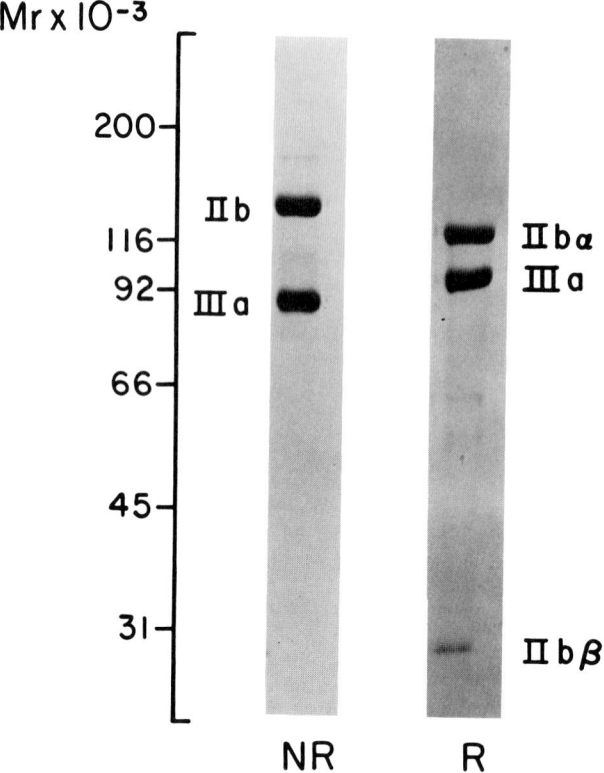

Fig. 90-2 Sodium dodecyl sulfate polyacrylamide gel electrophoresis of purified glycoprotein IIb-IIIa, isolated by immunoaffinity chromatography from platelet membrane proteins solubilized in Triton X-100. The affinity resin was made by cross-linking the monoclonal antibody, T10, to agarose. NR = nonreduced IIb-IIIa. R = IIb-IIIa treated with 2-mercaptoethanol to reduce disulfide bonds. In the reduced sample, the disulfide-linked heavy chain (IIbα) and light chain (IIbβ) are separated and migrate independently in the gel. The apparent molecular weight of reduced IIIa increases because of cleavage of intrachain disulfide bonds, which allows the molecule to unfold. (*Adapted from McEver and Martin.[251] Used by permission.*)

studies.[71,72] The IIIa cDNA encodes a protein of 762 amino acids, including a signal peptide of 26 residues.[79,80,82] A single transmembrane region is present along with a short cytoplasmic tail containing a tyrosine which may be phosphorylated under certain conditions. The most notable structural feature is the presence of four cysteine-rich tandem repeats. These cysteines all appear to be involved in intrachain disulfide bonding and are similar to cysteine-rich repeats found in

other membrane proteins such as the receptor for low density lipoprotein (Chap. 48) where they may represent ligand binding sites. Using the cDNAs as probes, the genes for IIb and IIIa have both been localized to chromosome 17[80–83]; the relative locations of the two genes on the chromosome have not yet been determined.

Glycoprotein IIb-IIIa is a major component of platelet membranes. Each platelet contains about 45,000 molecules as assessed by binding of radioiodinated monoclonal antibodies to IIb or IIIa.[61–63,84–86] An example of one such binding study with *Tab*, a monoclonal antibody to IIb,[60,61] is shown in Fig. 90-4. Antibody binding sites are decreased in platelets from patients with thrombasthenia, suggesting a decrease of IIb-IIIa.[60,85] Family members who are heterozygotes for the disease have intermediate levels of antibody binding, a finding consistent with the autosomal recessive pattern of inheritance. Studies employing crossed immunoelectrophoresis[37] and flow cytometry[87,88] also indicate that heterozygotes have intermediate levels of glycoprotein IIb-IIIa.

The degree of deficiency of glycoprotein IIb-IIIa may vary among patients. Caen originally noted that platelets from the majority of patients, designated type I, had absent clot retraction and undetectable platelet fibrinogen, while those of type II patients had some clot retraction and detectable, although reduced, platelet fibrinogen.[89] Crossed immunoelectrophoresis indicated that type I patients lacked the IIb-IIIa immunoprecipitate and an arc representing fibrinogen[58] (Fig. 90-1), while type II patients had detectable, although markedly decreased, arcs for IIb-IIIa and fibrinogen. However, a more recent study using a sensitive Western blot procedure suggests that most type I patients have detectable IIb and IIIa which comigrate on SDS gels with the normal proteins.[90] Flow cytometric analysis indicates that the IIb-IIIa deficiency is present in all platelets from affected individuals.[87,88] Recently, variant platelets with the thrombasthenic phenotype have been described in which the platelets contain quantitatively normal levels of IIb-IIIa.[91,92] In one of these patients, a subtle abnormality of IIb is suggested by the abnormal binding of a monoclonal antibody to a divalent cation-dependent epitope.[91] In another patient, IIb and IIIa appear to be associated as heterodimers in the membrane, but the complex may be unstable since it is abnormally sensitive to dissociation in solution by chelation of divalent cations with EDTA.[92]

The Pl^Al antigen is a platelet-specific alloantigen present in 98 percent of the normal population.[93] It is absent or reduced in all patients with thrombasthenia,[94] because the antigen is

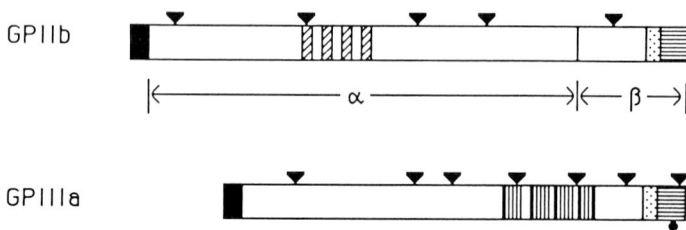

■, signal peptide; ▨, possible calcium binding site; ▦, transmembrane domain; ▤, cytoplasmic domain; ▥, cysteine-rich repeat; ▼, potential N-linked glycosylation site; ●, potential site for phosphorylation by tyrosine kinase.

Fig. 90-3 Schematic of the polypeptide precursors of glycoproteins (GP) IIb and IIIa. The domains marked are based on the amino acid sequence derived from cDNA clones encoding each protein. See text for details. (*Adapted from Poncz et al.[83] Used by permission.*)

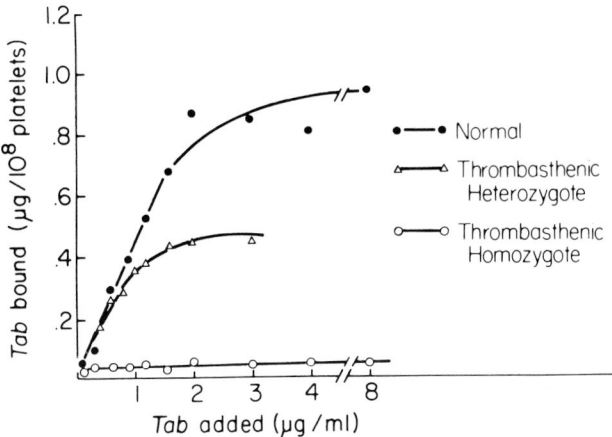

Fig. 90-4 Steady state binding of ^{125}I-*Tab* to normal and thrombasthenic platelets. With normal platelets, the *Tab* antibody, which recognizes membrane glycoprotein IIb, binds to 45,000 molecules per cell at saturation. *Tab* does not bind to platelets of thrombasthenic homozygotes and has reduced binding to platelets of thrombasthenic heterozygotes. *(From McEver et al.[60] Used by permission.)*

expressed by glycoprotein IIIa.[95] Individuals without thrombasthenia who lack Pl[A1] have normal levels of glycoprotein IIb-IIIa.[94] The Pl[A1] antigen is not required for normal function of the protein. A family study of thrombasthenic homozygotes and heterozygotes in which IIb-IIIa levels and Pl[A1] antigen levels were simultaneously measured indicates that the genes for inheritance of Pl[A1] and expression of glycoprotein IIb-IIIa segregate independently.[37] Recently, an alloantigen system on IIb, called *Lek*,[96] and a new alloantigen system on IIIa, called *Pen*,[97] have been described. These antigens are also missing in thrombasthenic platelets because the carrier proteins themselves are deficient.

Pathophysiology of Thrombasthenia

The deficiency of glycoprotein IIb-IIIa in thrombasthenic platelets strongly suggests that this membrane protein complex serves as the receptor in activated platelets for fibrinogen, von Willebrand factor, and fibronectin. Additional indirect evidence is the comparable estimate of 45,000 IIb-IIIa molecules per platelet as determined by monoclonal antibody measurements[60–62,84–86] and 45,000 fibrinogen binding sites per platelet determined by direct measurement of binding of radioiodinated fibrinogen to activated cells.[9,11,43] Three types of experiments provide direct evidence for the receptor role of IIb-IIIa in normal platelets. First, human alloantibodies and murine monoclonal antibodies to a variety of epitopes on IIb-IIIa inhibit platelet aggregation,[61,84–86,98,99] spreading on subendothelial surfaces,[42] and the binding of fibrinogen,[61,84–86,99] von Willebrand factor,[46,100,101] or fibronectin[100] to the activated platelet surface. Most antibodies inhibit the binding of all three ligands. However, one antibody has been described that inhibits the binding of von Willebrand factor but not fibrinogen, again suggesting that these ligands have related but not necessarily identical binding sites on the IIb-IIIa receptor.[102] Second, derivatized fibrinogen[103] or fibronectin[104] incubated with activated platelets can be chemically cross-linked to the IIIa subunit of IIb-IIIa. Third, purified IIb-IIIa in detergent solutions or reconstituted in phospholipid vesicles binds

fibrinogen[105–108] and fibronectin,[109] as well as another adhesive protein, vitronectin.[110] The kinetics of binding and the requirement for divalent cations in the reconstituted system are similar to those in intact platelets.[107,109]

Another large adhesive protein, thrombospondin, binds to activated platelets in a divalent cation-dependent manner and to unactivated platelets in a divalent cation-independent manner.[111–115] The calcium-dependent binding of thrombospondin has been reported to be deficient in thrombasthenic platelets.[116] In addition, certain monoclonal antibodies to IIb-IIIa which inhibit the binding of fibrinogen, fibronectin, and vWF to platelets also inhibit thrombospondin binding.[100] These data suggest that IIb-IIIa may also be a receptor for thrombospondin. However, purified IIb-IIIa in reconstituted vesicles does not bind thrombospondin.[110] Furthermore, in more quantitative binding studies, thrombospondin interacts normally with both the divalent cation-dependent and -independent sites on thrombasthenic platelets.[113] This binding is probably largely due to interaction with a recently described 72-kDa membrane receptor.[117,125] Nevertheless, thrombospondin bound to thrombasthenic platelets may not function normally, since interaction with fibrinogen bound to IIb-IIIa may be required for stabilization of platelet aggregates.[118]

It is noteworthy that IIb-IIIa on intact cells binds its adhesive ligands only after platelet activation,[8–13,43–46] although the molecule in detergent solutions or in reconstituted vesicles has binding activity.[105–110] This suggests that a conformational change occurs in IIb-IIIa when platelets are activated or when the lipid bilayer is disrupted. Support for such a conformational change comes from studies with certain monoclonal antibodies to IIb-IIIa which bind only to the molecule on activated platelets.[119,120]

Another activation-dependent property of IIb-IIIa is its interaction with cytoskeletal proteins. When platelets undergo thrombin-induced aggregation, IIb-IIIa becomes associated with a network of cytoskeletal filaments which are resistant to solubilization in nonionic detergents.[121–123] It is probable that this interaction occurs between cytoplasmic domains of IIb and/or IIIa and one or more cytoskeletal proteins. Ligand binding to extracellular domains induces clustering of IIb-IIIa molecules in the plane of the membrane.[124] It is conceivable that this clustering is one factor facilitating receptor interactions with the cytoskeleton, but the precise mechanisms remain unknown.

The evidence summarized above indicates that glycoprotein IIb-IIIa serves an essential role in mediating platelet aggregation. The binding of fibrinogen to the IIb-IIIa receptor on activated cells is most important probably because of the high concentration of this ligand in plasma. However, the binding to IIb-IIIa of fibronectin and vWF released in high local concentrations from α granules may also have a role in aggregation, as well as the indirect binding of thrombospondin to fibrinogen and to its own distinct platelet receptor.[125] Although the initial attachment of platelets to subendothelial surfaces requires the action of another membrane glycoprotein, Ib (see discussion under "Bernard-Soulier Disease," below), the subsequent spreading of activated platelets may depend on the interaction of fibronectin and vWF with IIb-IIIa. Finally, clot retraction is facilitated by the simultaneous interaction of IIb-IIIa with extracellular fibrinogen and cytoskeletal elements. Therefore, quantitative or qualitative abnormalities in glycoprotein IIb-IIIa result in a bleeding disorder in which platelet aggregation, platelet spreading, and clot retraction are all defective.

The physiological importance of platelet glycoprotein IIb-IIIa has been underscored by the recent discovery that it is part of a larger family of cell surface molecules involved in cell adhesion and cell-cell contacts. These molecules include receptors for fibronectin and vitronectin found in cells such as fibroblasts, osteosarcoma cells, placenta, and melanoma cells.[126,127] These receptors have in common an ability to recognize the arginine-glycine-aspartic acid (RGD) tripeptide sequence found in many adhesive proteins, including fibrinogen, fibronectin, von Willebrand factor, laminin, and vitronectin.[128] Synthetic peptides containing this sequence inhibit the binding of ligands to their receptors. Similarly, RGD peptides inhibit the binding of fibrinogen and fibronectin to activated platelets and inhibit agonist-induced platelet aggregation.[129–132] Related molecules in endothelium, smooth muscle, and other cells share immunologic reactivity with antibodies against platelet glycoprotein IIb-IIIa.[133–136] Like IIb-IIIa, these receptors have a heterodimeric structure with a larger, two-chain "α" subunit, similar to IIb, and a smaller, cysteine-rich "β" subunit, similar to IIIa.[126,137] A second group of related receptors are the LFA-1, Mac-1, and p150,95 surface molecules found in lymphocytes and macrophages (see Chap. 113 for disorders of these proteins).[138,139] These molecules, involved in cellular recognition in immune responses, also have a heterodimeric structure, but their known ligands do not contain the RGD sequence.[140] A third group of receptors are the group of five VLA (for "very late antigen") heterodimers initially described on T lymphocytes, at least some of which may also mediate cell adhesion and are also present on other cells.[141,142] Amino acid sequence information obtained either from the protein subunits or from cDNA clones encoding individual subunits indicates that there is sequence homology among the receptors.[79–82,137,139,143]

In terms of hemostasis, two points of interest have emerged from these studies of related receptors. The first is that the IIIa subunit of platelets is also found in endothelial cells, smooth muscle cells, and perhaps other tissues.[79,80,82,133–136] This common β subunit may assemble with distinct α subunits depending on the cell type. The second is that more than one of this class of receptors may be in the same cell. In platelets, a fibronectin receptor which does not require platelet activation for ligand binding has been identified.[144,145] This heterodimeric receptor has an α subunit distinct from IIb and a β subunit distinct from IIIa. The physiological role of this receptor in platelet function is unknown, but preliminary evidence suggests that it may also mediate the adherence and/or spreading of platelets on subendothelial surfaces.[144]

The genotypic defects in thrombasthenia are not yet known. As mentioned earlier, the precursors of IIb and IIIa undergo posttranslational processing and assembly into heterodimers during passage through the endoplasmic reticulum and Golgi apparatus.[77,78] Little if any free IIb or IIIa reaches the cell surface. In theory, mutations or deletions in the genes encoding either IIb or IIIa could result in improper processing and assembly of the heterodimeric complex. Unassembled subunits might then be degraded before reaching the plasma membrane. In the rare variant patients, mutations or small deletions might be compatible with processing, assembly, and delivery of the heterodimer to the cell surface, but nevertheless lead to abnormalities in ligand binding. Current biochemical techniques indicate that detectable amounts of IIb and IIIa are present in most patients. When examined in Western blots, the low levels of remaining protein have molecular weights identical with those in normal individuals.[90] This suggests that large gene deletions are uncommon in thrombasthenia. If the gene encoding IIb is transcribed only in megakaryocytes, then abnormalities in this gene would be expected to lead to receptor deficiencies only in megakaryocytes and platelets. As mentioned earlier, there is evidence that IIIa is expressed in other tissues such as vascular endothelium where it may associate with distinct IIb-like subunits.[133–136] Recently, a thrombasthenic patient with marked deficiencies in platelet IIb-IIIa was found to have normal levels of the related heterodimer in cultured endothelial cells.[145a] This suggests that this patient has a defect in the gene encoding the megakaryocyte/platelet IIb subunit; the endothelial molecule would be unaffected because it synthesizes a distinct α subunit which assembles with IIIa. In contrast, genetic abnormalities in IIIa might result in functionally abnormal cell-adhesion receptors in cells other than platelets. There have been isolated reports of abnormal clot retraction supported by fibroblasts from patients with thrombasthenia associated with clinically impaired wound healing.[146–148] In such cases the IIIa subunit may be affected, but precise biochemical studies of IIb-IIIa in the platelets of these patients are required. The availability of cDNAs encoding IIb and IIIa will provide tools to examine the genetic defects in patients with thrombasthenia. Such studies may be of particular interest in patients with quantitatively normal, but functionally defective, receptors, where clues to structure-function relationships in the normal IIb-IIIa molecule may be obtained.

Treatment

Treatment of this disease is limited to supportive measures. Chronic or acute hemorrhage may require blood transfusions or supplemental iron therapy. Platelet transfusions should be reserved for serious or life-threatening bleeding since patients may develop alloantibodies to normal platelets and become refractory to future transfusions.[34,149] Hormonal control of menses is usually effective in controlling menorrhagia, and good dental hygiene will prevent bleeding complications associated with gingival disease or tooth extractions.

BERNARD-SOULIER DISEASE

In 1948 Bernard and Soulier reported a 5-month-old infant with a history of spontaneous bleeding beginning shortly after birth.[150] The patient had a prolonged bleeding time, and his platelets appeared abnormally large on the peripheral blood smear. The parents and one sib had no history of abnormal bleeding, but a sister died of hemorrhage at age 3 years. In 1964 a review in the French literature described 14 symptomatic patients who had prolonged bleeding times, large platelets, and normal clot retraction.[151] Autosomal recessive inheritance was demonstrated. Since then, a number of other patients who meet these criteria have been reported in the English literature.[152–164] Most of them have been shown to have the platelet aggregation defect or membrane glycoprotein deficiency (described in the next three sections) considered specific for the disease. The incidence of the disorder, now known as Bernard-Soulier disease, is unknown, but probably occurs less frequently than thrombasthenia.

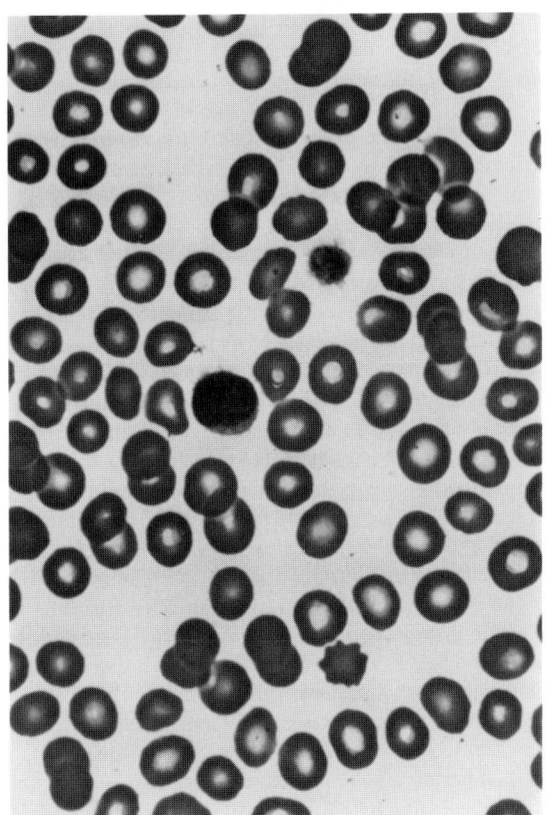
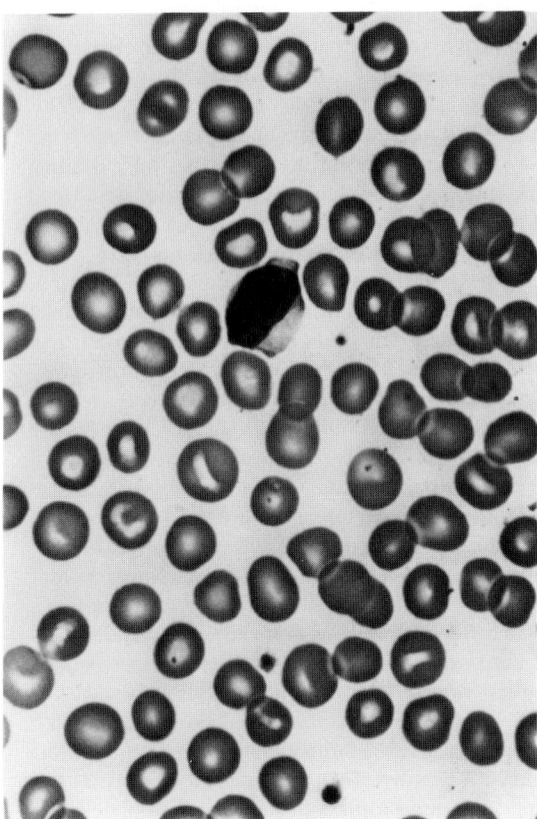

Fig. 90-5 *Left*, peripheral blood smear from a patient with Bernard-Soulier disease (Patient C.L. from Ref. 163), containing a characteristically enlarged platelet with a size similar to that of erythrocytes. *Right*, normal peripheral blood smear, showing several normal size platelets. *(Courtesy of Dr. James N. George and Dr. Charlotte N. Clare.)*

Diagnosis

Bernard-Soulier disease can be diagnosed by applying the following criteria:

1. Mucocutaneous bleeding
2. Family history of bleeding compatible with autosomal recessive transmission (helpful, but not required)
3. Normal or moderately decreased platelet count with
   a. Giant platelets on peripheral blood smear
   b. Normal clot retraction
   c. Absent platelet aggregation with human vWF plus ristocetin or with bovine vWF alone
   d. Normal platelet aggregation with ADP, epinephrine, collagen, but delayed rate of aggregation in response to thrombin
4. Normal coagulation factors (prothrombin time and partial thromboplastin time both normal)

An unequivocal diagnosis can be made by demonstrating deficiencies in membrane glycoproteins Ib, IX, and V. Other abnormalities are failure of unstimulated platelets to bind vWF in the presence of ristocetin, absence of receptors for drug-dependent antibodies, and an abnormal serum prothrombin time.

Clinical Manifestations

The degree of bleeding varies among patients, even within a family, but most patients experience episodes severe enough to require transfusion. The nature of the bleeding is similar to that seen in patients with thrombasthenia. Purpura, gingival bleeding, epistaxis, and menorrhagia are common. Gastrointestinal hemorrhage, hematuria, and cerebral hemorrhage have been reported. Unlike patients with coagulation factor abnormalities, these patients do not suffer from hemarthroses.

Laboratory Features

Morphology. On peripheral blood smear, Bernard-Soulier platelets appear large (Fig. 90-5). Electron micrographs also demonstrate large platelets but no other ultrastructural abnormalities.[158,159,161] The total protein content of Bernard-Soulier platelets is two to five times normal, consistent with the large size of the cells.[154,158,164] The platelets may spread abnormally because it has been shown that they are easily deformed in response to negative pressure from a micropipet.[165] Normal or increased numbers of megakaryocytes are found in the bone marrow, and their morphology appears normal.[152–154,158]

Aggregation and Adhesion Studies. Bernard-Soulier platelets aggregate normally in response to ADP, collagen, and epinephrine.[156–163] Aggregation in response to thrombin has been reported to be normal,[156,157,163] although some studies suggest that the rate of aggregation in response to low thrombin concentrations is reduced.[166] Bernard-Soulier platelets fail to aggregate in the presence of autologous plasma and the antibiotic ristocetin.[157,158,161–163,166–168] The same abnormality is seen in von Willebrand disease, which results from abnormalities of plasma vWF (Chap. 87). The aggregation defect in von Willebrand disease platelets is corrected by the addition of normal plasma or plasma from a Bernard-Soulier patient. However, Bernard-Soulier platelets fail to aggregate with ristocetin even in the presence of plasma from a normal subject.[157,168] This observation suggests that Bernard-Soulier platelets lack a receptor for a plasma component, most likely vWF. Binding studies with purified, radiolabeled vWF have confirmed the presence of receptors for human vWF on normal platelets[169,170] and their absence on Bernard-Soulier platelets.[171] The vWF binding, as does vWF-induced aggregation, requires the antibiotic ristocetin, and does not require platelet activation. The binding properties are therefore different than the activation-dependent binding of vWF to glycoprotein IIb-IIIa (see discussion of Glanzmann thrombasthenia). Abnormalities of either the vWF receptor in Bernard-Soulier disease or plasma vWF in von Willebrand disease result in failure of aggregation of platelet-rich plasma in the presence of ristocetin.

Although ristocetin-induced aggregation is an in vitro phenomenon, it is a manifestation of a physiological interaction of platelets at sites of vascular injury and clot formation. In a system in which blood is perfused over exposed subendothelial tissues, the initial attachment of platelets is defective both in Bernard-Soulier disease[42,162] and in von Willebrand disease.[172,173] In vivo, interactions of von Willebrand factor with other molecules in the subendothelium may change its conformation so that it can interact with the receptor found on unstimulated platelets and facilitate the adherence of platelets to the vessel wall. Polymerizing fibrin is another surface that binds vWF and converts it into a form which can interact with unstimulated platelets.[174] This may augment platelet adhesion at sites of vascular injury with clot formation. Circulating plasma vWF presumably does not bind to the receptor on resting platelets but could bind to the IIb-IIIa receptor on activated platelets. The latter binding may facilitate the spreading of platelets after initial attachment to the vessel wall.[42] Thus the functional defect in vivo in Bernard-Soulier disease is a failure of initial adherence of platelets to exposed subendothelium.

Membrane Glycoprotein Defect in Bernard-Soulier Disease

In 1969 Grottum and Solum reported that platelets from three patients with Bernard-Soulier disease had reduced electrophoretic mobility and reduced sialic acid, and suggested a membrane defect.[154] In 1975 Nurden and Caen fractionated platelet membrane proteins by electrophoresis in sodium dodecyl sulfate polyacrylamide gels and demonstrated a marked decrease in a major periodic acid-Schiff-stained glycoprotein of $M_r = 155,000$.[175] This protein has been designated glycoprotein Ib.[73,176] These findings have been confirmed in other studies using similar techniques.[55,163] Deficiencies in glycoprotein Ib have also been noted in studies using crossed immunoelectrophoresis,[58] modified polyacrylamide gel systems for increased resolution,[164,177,178] and binding of radiolabeled monoclonal anti-Ib antibodies to intact platelets.[87,179,180] Intermediate levels of glycoprotein Ib have been reported in obligate heterozygotes.[163,181]

Glycoprotein Ib is an abundant component of the platelet plasma membrane, with 25,000 copies per cell as estimated by binding of monoclonal antibodies.[179] Like glycoprotein IIb, it is a two-chain molecule consisting of a disulfide-linked heavy chain, Ibα, $M_r = 140,000$, and a light chain, Ibβ, $M_r = 22,000$.[73] Pulse-chase studies in a megakaryocytic cell line indicate that, unlike glycoprotein IIb, the α and β chains of Ib are synthesized from separate precursors are therefore probably different gene products.[182] Presumably the two chains are assembled by formation of interchain disulfide bonds during posttranslational processing. A large, water-soluble fragment of Ibα, termed *glycocalicin*, is liberated from platelet membranes by sonication or salt extraction.[183-185] Cleavage is prevented by incubating platelets with EDTA, suggesting that glycocalicin is produced by the action of an endogenous calcium-dependent protease.[185] Glycoprotein Ib is heavily glycosylated, particularly on the glycocalicin moiety which is 60% carbohydrate by weight.[183] Many of these sugars are of the O-linked variety,[183,186] although N-linked sugars are also present.[182] A cDNA encoding the α chain of Ib has recently been cloned and sequenced.[187] The deduced amino acid sequence (Fig. 90-6) predicts a mature protein of 610 amino acids preceded by a signal sequence of 16 amino acids. There is a single potential transmembrane domain of 29 amino acids followed by an intracellular domain of 95 amino acids. The extracytoplasmic domain contains a region of seven tandem repeats of 24 amino acids that are homologous with those present in leucine-rich α₂-glycoprotein; this region is located in the portion of the molecule that binds vWF and thrombin (discussed under "Pathophysiology of Bernard-Soulier Disease"). A region rich in serine and threonine residues just outside the plasma membrane contains the majority of the O-linked carbohydrate linkage sites.

It was initially thought that Bernard-Soulier platelets were deficient only in glycoprotein Ib. However, when platelet surface proteins were radiolabeled at carbohydrate residues by various procedures, then analyzed by sodium dodecyl sulfate polyacrylamide gel electrophoresis and fluorography, two

Fig. 90-6 Schematic of the domain structure of glycoprotein Ib, based on amino acid sequence data derived from a cDNA clone encoding the α chain as well as a number of studies employing protein chemistry. Not shown are glycoproteins IX and V, which may be noncovalently associated with Ib. See text for details. (*From Lopez et al.*[187] *Used by permission.*)

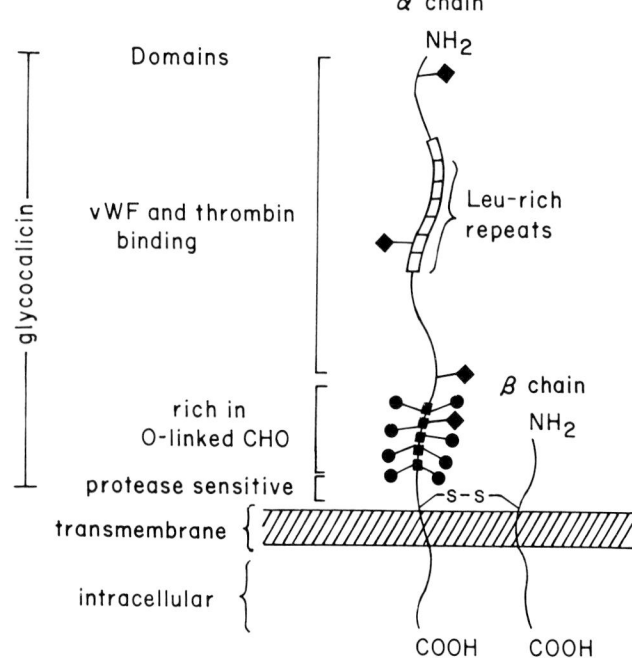

other membrane glycoproteins were noted to be missing or markedly decreased[178,181] (Fig. 90-7). These molecules are designated glycoprotein V (M_r = 82,000) and glycoprotein IX or 17 (M_r = 17,000). Both are difficult to detect by routine protein or carbohydrate staining procedures or by radioiodination, hence their failure to be detected in early studies. Glycoproteins Ib and IX can be coisolated from Triton X-100 lysates of normal platelets with monoclonal antibodies to either Ib[179,188,189] or IX,[190] suggesting that both are subunits of a single membrane complex. Glycoprotein V has not been coisolated by these procedures. This may indicate that V is not associated with Ib and IX in the membrane or that dissociation of V from the other glycoproteins occurs during the purification procedure. Glycoprotein V may be a peripheral membrane protein since it can be removed from the platelet surface by high salt buffers,[191] although others have suggested that V is an integral membrane protein.[192] Studies with thrombin and with drug-dependent antibodies (discussed in section on "Drug-Induced Purpura") suggest that V has some physical association with the Ib-IX complex in the platelet membrane.

Therefore Bernard-Soulier disease, like thrombasthenia, is a platelet membrane disorder in which a glycoprotein complex of more than one subunit is deficient. As in thrombasthenia, the degree of deficiency of the affected molecules is variable. Although some patients have undetectable Ib, IX, and V, others have low but detectable levels.[178,181,193] In recent studies with the more sensitive biochemical assays, all patients have been noted to have parallel deficiencies of all proteins.[194] The genetic defects responsible for these protein deficiencies are not known. A reasonable hypothesis is that separate genes encode glycoproteins V and IX and the α and β chains of Ib and that the subunits associate during synthesis and posttranslational processing. If so, then, theoretically, genetic defects in any of the four proteins could lead to instability of the complexes and/or altered function.

Pathophysiology of Bernard-Soulier Disease

The relationship between the deficiencies of glycoproteins Ib, IX, and V and the functional abnormalities in Bernard-Soulier platelets has been the subject of several reports. Most of the studies have employed alloantibodies,[195] polyclonal antibodies,[196] or monoclonal antibodies[46,179,181,197–199] to glycoprotein Ib. When preincubated with normal platelets, these antibodies inhibit ristocetin-induced platelet agglutination,[179,196,199] ristocetin-induced binding of vWF to platelets,[46,179,199] and the adherence of platelets to subendothelial surfaces.[195,200] These functional abnormalities mimic those seen in Bernard-Soulier disease and in von Willebrand disease and indicate that glycoprotein Ib constitutes at least one part of the receptor for vWF on normal unstimulated platelets. A recent study of purified proteolytic fragments of glycoprotein Ib indicates that the binding site for vWF resides in a fragment near the NH_2 terminus of the α chain at the outermost portion of the molecule[201] (Fig. 90-6). The binding site is distinct from the heavily glycosylated domain which lies nearer to the plasma membrane.[182–184,201] This work suggests that glycoproteins IX and V have no direct role in vWF binding but does not exclude their role in stability of a macromolecular complex or in other functions (see the following two sections).

These studies clearly indicate that glycoprotein Ib is a receptor for vWF when the latter is presented in a conformation suitable for binding such as that presumably found in suben-

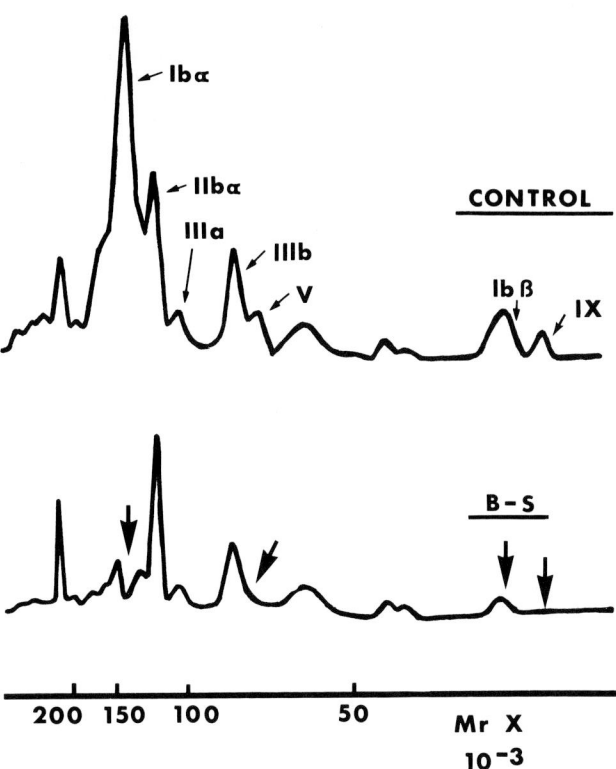

Fig. 90-7 Gel electrophoresis of the ^{3}H-labeled surface glycoproteins of normal *(top)* and Bernard-Soulier platelets. Electrophoresis in polyacrylamide gels which contain sodium dodecyl sulfate was performed after reduction of disulfide bonds. A fluorogram of the gel was prepared and scanned by densitometry. Bernard-Soulier platelets lack the peaks representing Ibα, Ibβ, V, and IX. *(From Nurden.[194] Used by permission.)*

dothelium or in developing fibrin clots.[174] In normal situations, the binding of vWF to glycoprotein Ib facilitates the initial attachment of platelet to injured blood vessel walls, where subsequent platelet spreading and aggregation (mediated by glycoprotein IIb-IIIa) takes place. Abnormalities of the receptor in Bernard-Soulier disease or of the ligand in von Willebrand disease result in defective adherence of platelets to vessel walls and a bleeding diathesis. Thus the pathogenesis of Bernard-Soulier disease and von Willebrand disease is related.

Role of Glycoprotein Ib, IX, and V in Drug-Induced Purpura

Certain drugs, such as quinine and quinidine, are capable of causing immune thrombocytopenia in susceptible individuals.[203,203] Platelet damage requires the presence of the drug as well as antibody. Recent studies indicate that antibody binding occurs through the *Fab* domain rather than through interaction of immune complexes with the platelet surface.[204] Bernard-Soulier platelets, unlike normal platelets, do not react with these drug-dependent antibodies,[205] suggesting that epitopes for the antibodies may be on glycoprotein Ib-IX and/or V. One quinidine-dependent antibody coprecipitated both Ib and IX from Triton X-100-solubilized platelets.[206] A monoclonal antibody to IX prevented binding of the quinidine-dependent antibody, while a monoclonal antibody to Ib had no effect.[207] This suggested that the responsible epitope might be on IX. However, Western blot assays of serum from six patients with quinidine-dependent antibodies indicated that all the antibodies reacted specifically with glycoprotein V.[208] If glycoprotein V is associated with the Ib-IX complex, the epitopes for the drug-dependent antibodies might be on a region of V in proximity to IX. However, it is not yet clear whether all quinidine-associated antibodies have specificity for glycoprotein V.

Other Reported Abnormalities

Glycoprotein Ib has been shown to have binding sites for thrombin on the glycocalicin portion of the molecule[209,210] (Fig. 90-6). In addition, glycoprotein V is the only known proteolytic substrate for thrombin on the platelet surface.[191,211,212] Platelets from two Bernard-Soulier patients were reported to have approximately one-third the normal number of thrombin receptors.[166] These platelets as well as those from other patients[194] have a decreased rate of aggregation in response to low levels of thrombin. These data are consistent with the hypothesis that thrombin binds to Ib and then proteolytically cleaves adjacent glycoprotein V; the proteolytic event would be required for platelet activation. However, Bernard-Soulier platelets will still aggregate normally in response to higher doses of thrombin.[156,157,163] Furthermore, the role of glycoprotein V in platelet activation has been questioned since thrombin-induced platelet aggregation does not correlate with the rate or extent of V hydrolysis,[213] and prior depletion of V by chymotrypsin[214] or by preventing hydrolysis of V by anti-V antibodies[215] does not prevent thrombin stimulation. Thus, although interactions of thrombin with both glycoproteins Ib and V do occur, the physiological role of these interactions and their relationship to the "thrombin receptor" remain unclear.

The shortened prothrombin time measured in serum from Bernard-Soulier patients[152,156,157,159,161] indicates decreased prothrombin consumption during the clotting of whole blood and therefore possibly defective conversion of prothrombin to thrombin at the platelet surface. Moreover, a monoclonal antibody to glycoprotein Ib has been shown to inhibit prothrombin consumption by normal platelets.[179] The reason for this phenomenon is not understood. It has been proposed that defective binding of vWF may result in failure to activate the coagulant activity of the associated coagulation protein factor VIII.[168] If so, deficiency of activated factor VIII might result in generation of less factor Xa, which in turn is required for prothrombin activation. It would be of interest to measure the binding of factors Xa and Va[22,23] to Bernard-Soulier platelets to determine if this binding is directly affected by the Bernard-Soulier defect. Decreased absorption of the clotting activities of factors V, VIII, and XI to washed Bernard-Soulier platelets have been described,[161] but the specificity of this adsorption and its physiological significance are unclear.

The mechanism for formation of large platelets in the disease is unknown. One important clue may be the recent finding that glycoprotein Ib interacts with the cytoskeleton in resting platelets. The cytoplasmic segment of glycoprotein Ib binds to actin binding protein.[216–218] This linkage may be important in maintaining the discoid shape and deformability properties of normal platelets. When platelets are activated, actin binding protein is hydrolyzed by an endogenous calcium-activated protease, thus leading to release of glycoprotein Ib from the cytoskeleton.[216,217] This event may be important for shape change during platelet activation. It seems likely that the increased deformability and spreading properties of Ber-

nard-Soulier platelets[165] are related to the loss of the linkage between the cytoskeleton and the plasma membrane. Perhaps cytoskeletal-membrane interactions are also important in demarcation of platelets from bone marrow megakaryocytes; loss of this linkage may lead to the large platelets seen in Bernard-Soulier disease. The survival of Bernard-Soulier platelets is decreased.[153,154,219] However, this is probably not the cause of thrombocytopenia, since adequate megakaryocytes are found in the bone marrow.[152,154,158] Since the platelets are enlarged, the total circulating platelet mass may be normal.

Treatment

As in Glanzmann thrombasthenia, treatment is supportive and consists of iron supplementation, good dental hygiene, hormonal control of menses, and transfusions for serious bleeding. Platelet transfusions should be reserved for severe hemorrhage. Although refractoriness to platelet transfusions has not been reported, the development of an alloantibody in one patient[195] suggests that this could become a clinical problem. Splenectomy has been attempted in some patients because of thrombocytopenia.[156,158,162] This may produce a transient increase in platelet count but no reduction in bleeding, because the basic platelet defect remains. Corticosteroids have been tried without benefit.[157]

SECRETION DEFECTS

In the past 20 years there have been many reports describing patients with congenital defects in agonist-induced platelet secretion. These patients represent an extremely heterogeneous group of disorders. In some cases hereditary transmission of the platelet defect is evident, but in others only isolated patients have been described.

Patients with secretion defects usually have less severe bleeding symptoms than those with thrombasthenia or Bernard-Soulier disease. The most frequent symptoms are easy bruising and excessive bleeding after operations such as tooth extractions or tonsillectomy, although epistaxis and menorrhagia have also been reported. The bleeding time is usually prolonged, but not to the extent seen in thrombasthenia or Bernard-Soulier disease, and it may be normal. In general these platelets aggregate reversibly with ADP or collagen, but fail to undergo "second-wave" aggregation and lack the concomitant release reaction, which includes thromboxane A_2 synthesis and the secretion of granule-bound substances.

Secretion defects are classified into two groups: (1) *primary release* defects related to abnormalities in the synthesis of, or response to, prostaglandins, and (2) *storage pool deficiency*, in which there is a decrease in platelet storage granules.

Primary Release Defects

Several patients have been reported with deficiencies in the platelet enzymes cyclooxygenase[220–222] and thromboxane synthetase.[223] The first enzyme catalyzes the conversion of arachidonic acid to cyclic endoperoxides; the second catalyzes the conversion of endoperoxides to thromboxane A_2. Thromboxane A_2, in turn, stimulates platelet aggregation and secretion,[17] although it is not required for thrombin activation. In these patients exogenous arachidonic acid fails to induce platelet aggregation and secretion. In many of these cases, there are insufficient genetic data to determine whether the enzymatic defect is inherited. The functional defect in cyclooxygenase deficiency is seen in individuals who ingest aspirin, which acetylates and inactivates cyclooxygenase.[224] Although the reported patients are said to have abstained from aspirin, it is difficult to prove this in view of the extremely low levels of aspirin required to inactivate the enzyme.[225] Measurement of cyclooxygenase levels by radioimmunoassay[226] may make it possible to detect patients who definitely lack the enzyme.

Other patients have been described in which platelets do not undergo secretion and second-wave aggregation in response to ADP and epinephrine.[227–229] Storage pools of secretable ADP are normal, and activated platelets are able to synthesize thromboxane A_2 normally. In some patients, rapid addition of arachidonate-stimulated normal platelet-rich plasma (which contains thromboxane A_2) fails to aggregate the patient's platelets. This defect has been attributed to a failure of the platelets to respond to thromboxane A_2,[228] although this conclusion has

been challenged.[230] The precise mechanism for the lack of responsiveness remains to be defined.

Storage Pool Deficiency

Patients in this heterogeneous group have diminished numbers of morphologically recognizable platelet secretory granules. These granules are of two types, as shown in Fig. 90-8. Dense granules contain calcium ions, ADP, and the vasoactive compound serotonin. α Granules contain a variety of hemostatically important proteins such as fibrinogen, thrombospondin, vWF, and platelet factor 4. Most of the reported patients lack recognizable dense granules (Fig. 90-8) and are biochemically deficient in their contents.[231] An occasional patient has been noted with partial deficiencies of the contents of both dense and α granules.[231] The relationship between the usually minor functional abnormalities of the platelets and the decrease in storage granules is not well understood but is thought to be related at least in part to defective release of ADP, one of the

Fig. 90-8 Electron micrographs of normal platelets and platelets from patients with gray platelet syndrome and storage pool deficiency. *A.* Normal discoid human platelet sectioned in the equatorial plane. A circumferential microtubule (MT) lies just under the surface membrane. Many α granules (G) and occasional mitochrondria (M) are randomly dispersed in the cytoplasm. $\times 14,740$. *B.* Large platelet from a patient with gray platelet syndrome. The cytoplasm is filled with large, clear vacuoles and narrow channels of the dense tubular system. A dense body (DB) is evident in this cell, along with occasional mitochondria, but there are no apparent α granules. $\times 11,323$. *C.* Whole mount preparation of normal human platelets. Rather than being fixed or stained, the cells were air-dried on the surface of a microscope grid. Several inherently electron opaque dense bodies are present in the cytoplasm of each cell. $\times 8,710$. *D.* Whole mount of platelets from a patient with Hermansky-Pudlak syndrome (tyrosinase-positive albinism, ceroid storage, and platelet storage pool deficiency). The platelets are virtually devoid of dense bodies. $\times 8,710$. (*Courtesy of Dr. James G. White.*)

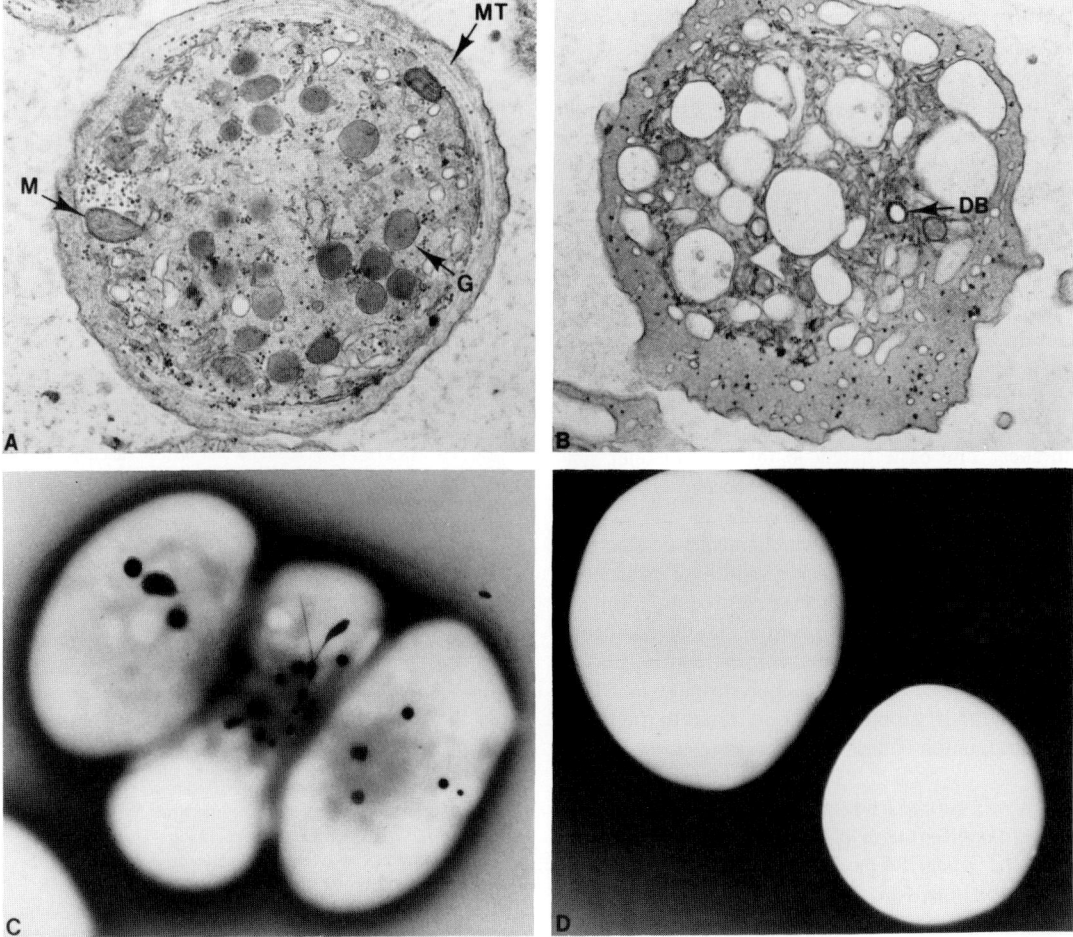

physiological platelet agonists. Two families with storage pool deficiency have been described in which the defect is transmitted in an autosomal dominant manner.[232,233] Morphologic abnormalities of platelet dense granules have been associated with other inherited disorders, including the Hermansky-Pudlak syndrome,[234,235] Wiskott-Aldrich syndrome,[236] syndrome of thrombocytopenia with absent radius,[237] and Chediak-Higashi syndrome.[238,239] The relationship of the platelet abnormalities to the other congenital defects is unknown.

Rare patients with an isolated deficiency in α granules have also been reported.[240–246] This disorder has been termed *the gray platelet syndrome*, because the platelets appear gray on routine stained blood smears.[247] Recognizable α granules are rare, but the platelets often appear highly vacuolated when examined by electron microscopy (Fig. 90-8). The levels of α-granule secretory proteins such as platelet factor 4, β-thromboglobulin, platelet-derived growth factor, and thrombospondin, which are thought to be synthesized by megakaryocytes, are very low.[242–244,248] However, several lines of evidence suggest that megakaryocytes from these patients synthesize α-granule proteins appropriately but then release them into the bone marrow by constitutive secretion: (1) the plasma concentrations of platelet factor 4 and β-thromboglobulin are normal or even increased in the patients,[241,243,244,248] and megakaryocytes are the only cells known to synthesize these proteins; (2) immunoreactive von Willebrand factor has been identified in the Golgi region of megakaryocytes from the patients;[249] and (3) increased numbers of reticulin fibers have been seen in the bone marrows of several of the patients, suggesting that megakaryocytes have inappropriately released platelet-derived growth factor.[194,243–245,250] Recently, an integral membrane protein of α granules has been identified.[251–255] This protein, termed *GMP-140* for *granule membrane protein* of $M_r = 140,000$, redistributes to the cell surface after platelet activation and fusion of α-granule membranes with the plasma membrane. Using antibodies to GMP-140 as a marker, the membranes of the intracellular vesicles in gray platelets have been identified as α-granule membranes.[246] These membranes fuse appropriately with the plasma membrane during platelet activation. Furthermore, certain α-granule secretory proteins such as albumin and IgG, which are thought to be derived from endocytosis of plasma proteins into megakaryocytes,[256,257] are present in substantial quantities and are secreted efficiently from gray platelets.[246] These studies suggest that α-granule membranes are synthesized normally in the gray platelet syndrome and that plasma proteins can be endocytosed and incorporated normally into the vesicles formed by these membranes. The basic defect in the gray platelet syndrome may be in the targeting of endogenously synthesized secretory proteins to developing α granules in megakaryocytes. The α granules do not have their characteristic electron-dense appearance because of the lack of the high concentrations of endogenously synthesized secretory proteins normally packaged within them. Thus, the disorder may be analogous to targeting abnormalities of lysosomal enzymes, such as occur in I-cell disease and pseudo-Hurler polydystrophy, in which the enzymes are synthesized but are not delivered to their normal lysosomal destination (Chap. 62).

We thank Dr. James George for helpful criticisms of this chapter and for providing the blood smear of the Bernard-Soulier patient. We also thank Dr. James White for providing the photomicrographs of the platelets from patients with storage pool disease and the gray platelet syndrome. This research was supported by NIH grants HLBI 34363, HLBI 33277, HLBI 14147, and HLBI 16634. Dr. McEver is the recipient of Research Career Development Award HLBI 01733 from the NIH.

REFERENCES

1. BIGGS R, GASTON LW: The blood clotting factors, in Stanbury JB, Wyngaarden JB, Fredrickson DS eds: *The Metabolic Basis of Inherited Disease.* New York, McGraw-Hill, 1960, p 1145.

2. CZERVIONKE RL, SMITH JB, FRY GL, HOAK JC, HAYCRAFT DL: Inhibition of prostacyclin by treatment of endothelium with aspirin. Correlation with platelet adherence. *J Clin Invest* 63:1089, 1979.

3. MONCADA S, HERMAN EA, VAN JR: Human arterial and venous tissues generate prostacyclin, a potent inhibitor of platelet aggregation. *Lancet* 1:18, 1977.

4. MONCADA A, HERMAN HG, HIGGS EA, VANE JR: Differential formation of prostacyclin by layers of the arterial wall. An explanation for the antithrombotic properties of vascular endothelium. *Thromb Res* 11:323, 1977.

5. SOLUM NO, STORMORKEN H: Influence on the aggregation of washed human blood platelets induced by adenosine diphosphate, thrombin, collagen, and adrenalin. *Scand J Clin Lab Invest* 17 (suppl 84):170, 1965.

6. BRINKHOUS KM, READ MS, MASON RG: Plasma thrombocyte-agglutinating activity and fibrinogen. Synergism with adenosine diphosphate. *Lab Invest* 14:335, 1965.

7. CROSS MF: Effect of fibrinogen on the aggregation of platelets by adenosine phosphate. *Thromb Diath Haemorrh* 12:524, 1964.

8. NIEWAROWSKI S, BUDZYNSKI AZ, MORINELLI TA, BUDZYNSKI TM, STEWART GJ: Exposure of fibrinogen receptor on human platelets by proteolytic enzymes. *J Biol Chem* 256:917, 1981.

9. MARGUERIE GA, PLOW EF, EDGINGTON TS: Human platelets possess an inducible and saturable receptor specific for fibrinogen. *J Biol Chem* 254:5357, 1979.

10. MARGUERIE GA, EDGINGTON TS, PLOW EF: Interaction of fibrinogen with its platelet receptor as part of a multistep reaction in ADP-induced platelet aggregation. *J Biol Chem* 255:154, 1980.

11. HAWIGER J, PARKINSON S, TIMMONS S: Prostacyclin inhibits mobilization of fibrinogen-binding sites on human ADP- and thrombin-treated platelets. *Nature* 283:195, 1980.

12. MUSTARD JF, PACKHAM MA, KINLOUGH-RATHBONE RL, PERRY JN, REGOECZI E: Fibrinogen and ADP-induced platelet aggregation. *Blood* 52:453, 1978.

13. PEERSCHKE EI, ZUCKER MB, GRANT RA, EGAN JJ, JOHNSON MM: Correlation between fibrinogen binding to human platelets and platelet aggregability. *Blood* 55:841, 1980.

14. WEISS HJ: Platelet physiology and abnormalities of platelet function. *N Engl J Med* 293:531, 1975.

15. BELL RL, KENNERLY DA, STANFORD N, MAJERUS PW: Diglyceride lipase: The pathway for arachidonate release from human platelets. *Proc Natl Acad Sci USA* 76:3238, 1979.

16. MAJERUS PW, CONNOLLY TM, DECKMYN H, ROSS TS, BROSS TE, ISHII H, BANSAL VS, WILSON DB: The metabolism of phosphoinositide-derived messenger molecules. *Science* 234:1519, 1986.

17. HAMBERG M, SVENSSON J, SAMUELSSON B: Thromboxanes: A new group of biologically active compounds derived from prostaglandin endoperoxides. *Proc Natl Acad Sci USA* 72:2994, 1975.

18. SALZMAN EW: Prostaglandins and platelet function, in Samuelsson B, Paoletti R (eds): *Advances in Prostaglandins and Thromboxane Research.* New York, Raven, 1976, vol 2.

19. ROTH GJ, STANFORD N, MAJERUS PW: Acetylation of prostaglandin synthase by aspirin. *Proc Natl Acad Sci USA* 72:3073, 1975.

20. SHUMAN MA, MAJERUS PW: The measurement of thrombin in clotting blood by radioimmunoassay. *J Clin Invest* 58:1249, 1976.

21. MAJERUS PW, MILETICH JP: Relationships between platelets and coagulation factors in hemostasis. *Annu Rev Med* 29:41, 1978.

22. MILETICH JP, JACKSON CM, MAJERUS PW: Interaction of coagulation factor X_a with human platelets. *Proc Natl Acad Sci USA* 74:4033, 1977.

23. KANE WH, LINDHOUT MJ, JACKSON CM, MAJERUS PW: Factor V_a-dependent binding of factor X_a to human platelets. *J Biol Chem* 255:1170, 1980.

24. MIELKE CH, KANESHIRO MM, MAHER IA, WEINER JM, RAPAPORT SI: The standardized normal Ivy bleeding time and its prolongation by aspirin. *Blood* 34:204, 1969.

25. GLANZMANN E: Hereditare hamorrhagische thrombasthenie: Ein beitrag zur pathologie der blutplattchen. *J Kinderheilk* 88:113, 1918.

26. NAEGELI D: *Blut Krankheiten and Blut Diagnostik.* Berlin, Springer-Verlag, 1931, vol 1.

27. FONIO A, SCHWENDENER J: *Die Thrombocyten des menschlichen Blutes.* Bern, HP Huber, 1942.

28. HARDISTY RM, DORMANDY KM, HUTTON RA: Thrombasthenia. Studies on three cases. *Br J Haematol* 10:371, 1964.

29. CAEN JP, CASTALDI PA, LECLERC JC, INCEMAN S, LARRIEU MJ, PROBST M, BERNARD J: Congenital bleeding disorders with long bleeding time and normal platelet count. I. Glanzmann's thrombasthenia (report of fifteen patients). *Am J Med* 41:4, 1966.

30. ZUCKER MB, PERT JH, HILGARTNER MW: Platelet function in a patient with thrombasthenia. *Blood* 28:524, 1966.

31. WALSH PN: Platelet coagulant activities in thrombasthenia. *Br J Haematol* 23:553, 1972.

32. WEISS HJ, KOCHWA S: Studies of platelet function and proteins in three patients with Glanzmann's thrombasthenia. *J Lab Clin Med* 71:153, 1968.

33. ROSSI EC, GREEN D: Disorders of platelet function. *Med Clin North Am* 56:35, 1972.

34. BROWN CH III, WEISBERG RJ, NATELSON EA, ALFREY CP Jr: Glanzmann's thrombasthenia: Assessment of the response to platelet transfusions. *Transfusion* 15:124, 1975.

35. LUSHER JM, BARNHARD MI: Congenital disorders affecting platelets. *Semin Thromb Haemostas* 4:123, 1977.

36. COLLER BS, SELIGSOHN U, ZIVELIN A, ZWANG E, LUSKY A, MODAN M: Immunologic and biochemical characterization of homozygous and heterozygous Glanzmann thrombasthenia in the Iraqi-Jewish and Arab populations of Israel: Comparison of techniques for carrier detection. *Br J Haematol* 62:723, 1986.

37. KUNICKI TJ, PIDARD D, CAZENAVE J-P, NURDEN AT, CAEN JP: Inheritance of the human platelet alloantigen, Pl^{A1}, in type I Glanzmann's thrombasthenia. *J Clin Invest* 67:717, 1981.

38. COLLER BS, SELIGSOHN U, LITTLE PA: Type I Glanzmann thrombasthenia patients from the Iraqi-Jewish and Arab populations in Israel can be differentiated by platelet glycoprotein IIIa immunoblot analysis. *Blood* 69:1696, 1987.

39. BURGESS-WILSON ME, COCKBILL SR, JOHNSTON GI, HEPTINSTALL S: Platelet aggregation in whole blood from patients with Glanzmann's thrombasthenia. *Blood* 69:38, 1987.

40. WHITE GC II, WORKMAN EF Jr, LUNDBLAD RL: Thrombin binding to thrombasthenic platelets. *J Lab Clin Med* 91:76, 1978.

41. BAUMGARTNER HR, MUGGLI R: Adhesion and aggregation: Morphological demonstration and quantitation in vivo and in vitro, in Gordon JL (ed): *Platelets in Biology and Pathology.* Amsterdam, Elsevier/North Holland, 1976, p 23.

42. WEISS HJ, TURITTO VT, BAUMGARTNER HR: Platelet adhesion and thrombus formation on subendothelium in platelets deficient in glycoproteins IIb-IIIa, Ib, and storage granules. *Blood* 67:322, 1986.

43. BENNETT JS, VILAIRE G: Exposure of platelet fibrinogen receptors by ADP and epinephrine. *J Clin Invest* 64:1393, 1979.

44. PLOW EF, GINSBERG MH: Specific and saturable binding of plasma fibronectin to thrombin-stimulated human platelets. *J Biol Chem* 256:9477, 1981.

45. FUJIMOTO T, OHARA S, HAWIGER J: Thrombin-induced exposure and prostacyclin inhibition of the receptor for factor VIII/von Willebrand factor on human platelets. *J Clin Invest* 69:1212, 1982.

46. RUGGERI ZM, De MARCO L, GATTI L, BADER R, MONTGOMERY RR: Platelets have more than one binding site for von Willebrand factor. *J Clin Invest* 72:1, 1983.

47. TIMMONS S, KLOCZEWIAK M, HAWIGER J: ADP-dependent common receptor mechanism for binding of von Willebrand factor and fibrinogen to human platelets. *Proc Natl Acad Sci USA* 81:4935, 1984.

48. MUSTARD JF, KINLOUGH-RATHBONE RL, PACKHAM MA, PERRY DW, HARFENIST EJ, PAI KRM: Comparison of fibrinogen association with normal and thrombasthenic platelets on exposure to ADP or chymotrypsin. *Blood* 54:987, 1979.

49. COLLER BS: Interaction of normal, thrombasthenic, and Bernard-Soulier platelets with immobilized fibrinogen: Defective platelet-fibrinogen interaction in thrombasthenia. *Blood* 55:169, 1980.

50. RUGGERI ZM, BADER R, De MARCO L: Glanzmann thrombasthenia: Deficient binding of von Willebrand factor to thrombin-stimulated platelets. *Proc Natl Acad Sci USA* 79:6038, 1982.

51. GINSBERG MH, FORSYTH J, LIGHTSEY A, CHEDIAK J, PLOW EF: Reduced surface expression and binding of fibronectin by thrombin-stimulated thrombasthenic platelets. *J Clin Invest* 71:619, 1983.

52. NURDEN AT, CAEN JP: An abnormal platelet glycoprotein pattern in three cases of Glanzmann's thrombasthenia. *Br J Haematol* 28:253, 1974.

53. PHILLIPS DR, AGIN PP: Platelet membrane defects in Glanzmann's thrombasthenia. *J Clin Invest* 60:535, 1977.

54. NURDEN AT, CAEN JP: The different glycoprotein abnormalities in thrombasthenic and Bernard-Soulier platelets. *Semin Hematol* 16:234, 1979.

55. JAMIESON GA, OKUMURA T, FISHBACK B, JOHNSON MM, EGAN JJ, WEISS HJ: Platelet membrane glycoproteins in thrombasthenia, Bernard-Soulier syndrome, and storage pool disease. *J Lab Clin Med* 93:652, 1979.

56. PETERSON DM, WEHRING B: Isoelectric characteristics and surface radioiodination of normal and thrombasthenic platelet membrane glycoproteins. *Thromb Res* 22:53, 1981.

57. HOLAHAN JR, WHITE GC II: Heterogeneity of membrane surface proteins in Glanzmann's thrombasthenia. *Blood* 57:174, 1981.

58. HAGEN I, NURDEN A, BJERRUM OJ, SOLUM NO, CAEN J: Immunochemical evidence for protein abnormalities in platelets from patients with Glanzmann's thrombasthenia and Bernard-Soulier syndrome. *J Clin Invest* 65:722, 1980.

59. HOWARD L, SHULMAN S, SADANANDEN S, KARPATKIN S: Crossed immunoelectrophoresis of human platelet membranes. The major antigen consists of a complex of glycoproteins, GPIIb and GPIIIa, held together by Ca^{2+} and missing in Glanzmann's thrombasthenia. *J Biol Chem* 257:8331, 1982.

60. MCEVER RP, BAENZIGER NL, MAJERUS PW: Isolation and quantitation of the platelet membrane glycoprotein deficient in thrombasthenia using a monoclonal hybridoma antibody. *J Clin Invest* 66:1311, 1980.

61. MCEVER RP, BENNETT EM, MARTIN MN: Identification of two structurally and functionally distinct sites on human platelet membrane glycoprotein IIb-IIIa using monoclonal antibodies. *J Biol Chem* 258:5269, 1983.

62. NEWMAN PJ, ALLEN RW, KAHN RA, KUNICKI TJ: Quantitation of membrane glycoprotein IIIa on intact human platelets using the monoclonal antibody, AP-3. *Blood* 65:227, 1985.

63. JENNINGS LK, PHILLIPS DR: Purification of glycoproteins IIb and III from human platelet plasma membranes and characterization of a calcium-dependent glycoprotein IIb-III complex. *J Biol Chem* 257:10458, 1982.

64. FITZGERALD LA, LEUNG B, PHILLIPS DR: A method for purifying the platelet membrane glycoprotein IIb-IIIa complex. *Anal Biochem* 151:169, 1985.

65. CARRELL NA, FITZGERALD LA, STEINER B, ERICKSON HP, PHILLIPS DR: Structure of human platelet membrane glycoproteins IIb and IIIa as determined by electron microscopy. *J Biol Chem* 260:1743, 1985.

66. KUNICKI TJ, PIDARD D, ROSA J-P, NURDEN AT: The formation of Ca^{++}-dependent complexes of platelet membrane glycoproteins IIb and IIIa in solution as determined by crossed immunoelectrophoresis. *Blood* 58:268, 1981.

67. FUJIMURA K, PHILLIPS DR: Calcium cation regulation of glycoprotein IIb-IIIa complex formation in platelet plasma membranes. *J Biol Chem* 258:10247, 1983.

68. FITZGERALD LA, PHILLIPS DR: Calcium regulation of the platelet membrane glycoprotein IIb-IIIa complex. *J Biol Chem* 260:11366, 1985.

69. BRASS LF, SHATTIL SJ, KUNICKI TJ, BENNETT JS: Effect of calcium on the stability of the platelet membrane glycoprotein IIb-IIIa complex. *J Biol Chem* 260:7875, 1985.

70. SHATTIL SJ, BRASS LF, BENNETT JS, PANDHI P: Biochemical and functional consequences of dissociation of the platelet membrane glycoprotein IIb-IIIa complex. *Blood* 66:92, 1985.

71. GOGSTAD GO, KRUTNES M-B, SOLUM NO: Calcium-binding proteins from human platelets. A study using crossed immunoelectrophoresis and ^{45}Ca^{2+}. *Eur J Biochem* 133:193, 1983.

72. FUJIMURA K, PHILLIPS DR: Binding of ^{45}Ca^{2+} to glycoprotein IIb from human platelet plasma membranes. *Thromb Haemostas* 50:251, 1983.

73. PHILLIPS DR, AGIN PP: Platelet plasma membrane glycoproteins. Evidence for the presence of nonequivalent disulfide bonds using nonreduced-reduced two-dimensional gel electrophoresis. *J Biol Chem* 252:2121, 1977.

74. MCEVER RP, BAENZIGER JU, MAJERUS PW: Isolation and structural characterization of the polypeptide subunits of membrane glycoprotein IIb-IIIa from human platelets. *Blood* 59:80, 1982.

75. LEUNG LLK, KINOSHITA T, NACHMAN RL: Isolation, purification, and partial characterization of platelet membrane glycoproteins IIb and IIIa. *J Biol Chem* 256:1994, 1981.

76. BRAY PF, ROSA J-P, LINGAPPA VR, KAN YW, MCEVER RP, SHUMAN MA: Biogenesis of the platelet receptor for fibrinogen: Evidence for separate precursors for glycoproteins IIb and IIIa. *Proc Natl Acad Sci USA* 83:1480, 1986.

77. ROSA J-P, CEVALLOS M, MCEVER RP: Fibrinogen receptor assembly in human erythroleukemia (HEL) cells. *Blood (suppl 1)* 68:325a, 1986.

78. DUPPERRAY A, BERTHIER R, CHAGNON E, RYCKEWAERT J-J, GINSBERG M, MARGUERIE G: Biosynthesis and processing of platelet GPIIb-IIIa in human megakaryocytes. *J Cell Biol* 104:1665, 1987.

79. FITZGERALD LA, STEINER B, RALL Jr SC, LO S-S, PHILLIPS DR: Protein sequence of endothelial glycoprotein IIIa derived from a cDNA clone.

Identity with platelet glycoprotein IIIa and similarity to "integrin." *J Biol Chem* 262:3936, 1987.

80. ZIMRIN AB, EISMAN R, VILAIRE G, SCHWARTZ E, BENNETT JS, PONCZ M: Structure of platelet glycoprotein IIIa. A common subunit for two different membrane receptors. *J Clin Invest* 81:1470, 1988.

81. BRAY PF, ROSA J-P, JOHNSTON GI, SHIU DT, COOK RG, LAU C, KAN YW, MCEVER RP, SHUMAN MA: Platelet glycoprotein IIb. Chromosomal localization and tissue expression. *J Clin Invest* 80:1812, 1987.

82. ROSA J-P, BRAY PF, GAYET O, JOHNSTON GI, COOK RG, JACKSON KW, SHUMAN MA, MCEVER RP: Cloning of glycoprotein IIIa cDNA from human erythroleukemia cells and localization of the gene to chromosome 17. *Blood*, in press.

83. PONCZ M, EISMAN R, HEIDENREICH R, SILVER SM, VILAIRE G, SURREY S, SCHWARTZ E, BENNETT JS: Structure of platelet membrane glycoprotein IIb. *J Biol Chem* 262:8476, 1987.

84. PIDARD D, MONTGOMERY RR, BENNETT JS, KUNICKI TJ: Interaction of AP-2, a monoclonal antibody specific for the human platelet glycoprotein IIb-IIIa complex, with intact platelets. *J Biol Chem* 258:12582, 1983.

85. COLLER BS, PEERSCHKE EI, SCUDDER LE, SULLIVAN CA: A murine monoclonal antibody that completely blocks the binding of fibrinogen to platelets produces a thrombasthenic-like state in normal platelets and binds to glycoproteins IIb and/or IIIa. *J Clin Invest* 72:325, 1983.

86. BENNETT JS, HOXIE JA, LEITMAN SF, VILAIRE G, CINES DB: Inhibition of fibrinogen binding to stimulated human platelets by a monoclonal antibody. *Proc Natl Acad Sci USA* 80:2417, 1983.

87. JOHNSTON GI, HEPTINSTALL S, ROBINS RA, PRICE MR: The expression of glycoproteins on single blood platelets from healthy individuals and from patients with congenital bleeding disorders. *Biochem Biophys Res Commun* 123:1091, 1984.

88. JENNINGS LK, ASHMUN RA, WANG WC, DOCKTER ME: Analysis of human platelet glycoproteins IIb-IIIa and Glanzmann's thrombasthenia in whole blood by flow cytometry. *Blood* 68:173, 1986.

89. CAEN J: Glanzmann thrombasthenia. *Clin Haematol* 1:383, 1972.

90. NURDEN AT, DIDRY D, KIEFFER N, MCEVER RP: Residual amounts of glycoproteins IIb and IIIa may be present in the platelets of most patients with Glanzmann's thrombasthenia. *Blood* 65:1021, 1985.

91. GINSBERG MH, LIGHTSEY A, KUNICKI TJ, KAUFMANN A, MARGUERIE G, PLOW EF: Divalent cation regulation of the surface orientation of platelet membrane glycoprotein IIb. Correlation with fibrinogen binding function and definition of a novel variant of Glanzmann's thrombasthenia. *J Clin Invest* 78:1103, 1986.

92. NURDEN AT, ROSA J-P, FOURNIER D, LEGRAND C, DIDRY D, PARQUET A, PIDARD D: A variant of Glanzmann's thrombasthenia with abnormal glycoprotein IIb-IIIa complexes in the platelet membrane. *J Clin Invest* 79:962, 1987.

93. van LOGHEM JJ Jr, DORFMEIJER H, van der HART M: Serological and genetical studies on a platelet antigen (ZW). *Vox Sang* 4:161, 1959.

94. KUNICKI TJ, ASTER RH: Deletion of the platelet-specific alloantigen Pl^{A1} from platelets in Glanzmann's thrombasthenia. *J Clin Invest* 61:1225, 1978.

95. KUNICKI TJ, ASTER RH: Isolation and immunologic characterization of the human platelet alloantigen, Pl^{A1}. *Mol Immunol* 16:353, 1979.

96. KIEFFER N, BOIZARD B, DIDRY D, WAUTIER J-L, NURDEN AT: Immunochemical characterization of the platelet-specific alloantigen Lek^a: A comparative study with the Pl^{A1} alloantigen. *Blood* 64:1212, 1984.

97. FURIHATA K, NUGENT DJ, BISSONETTE A, ASTER RH, KUNICKI TJ: On the association of the platelet-specific alloantigen, Pen^a, with glycoprotein IIIa. Evidence for the heterogeneity of glycoprotein IIIa. *J Clin Invest* 80:1624, 1987.

98. LEVY-TOLEDANO S, TOBELEM G, LEGRAND C, BREDOUX R, DEGOS L, NURDEN A, CAEN JP: Acquired IgG antibody occurring in a thrombasthenic patient: Its effect on human platelet function. *Blood* 51:1065, 1978.

99. DI MINNO G, THIAGARAJAN P, PERUSSIA B, MARTINEZ J, SHAPIRO S, TRINCHIERI G, MURPHY S: Exposure of platelet fibrinogen-binding sites by collagen, arachidonic acid, and ADP: Inhibition by a monoclonal antibody to the glycoprotein IIb-IIIa complex. *Blood* 61:140, 1983.

100. PLOW EF, MCEVER RP, COLLER BS, WOODS VL Jr, MARGUERIE GA, GINSBERG MH: Related binding mechanisms for fibrinogen, fibronectin, von Willebrand factor, and thrombospondin on thrombin-stimulated human platelets. *Blood* 66:724, 1985.

101. GRALNICK HR, WILLIAMS SB, COLLER BS: Fibrinogen competes with von Willebrand factor for binding to the glycoprotein IIb/IIIa complex when platelets are stimulated with thrombin. *Blood* 64:797, 1984.

102. LOMBARDO VT, HODSON E, ROBERTS JR, KUNICKI TJ, ZIMMERMAN TS, RUGGERI ZM: Independent modulation of von Willebrand factor and fibrinogen binding to the platelet membrane glycoprotein IIb/IIIa complex as demonstrated by monoclonal antibody. *J Clin Invest* 76:1950, 1985.

103. BENNETT JS, VILAIRE G, CINES DB: Identification of the fibrinogen receptor on human platelets by photoaffinity labeling. *J Biol Chem* 257:8049, 1982.

104. GARDNER JM, HYNES RO: Interaction of fibronectin with its receptor on platelets. *Cell* 42:439, 1985.

105. NACHMAN RL, LEUNG LLK, KLOCZEWIAK M, HAWIGER J: Complex formation of platelet membrane glycoproteins IIb and IIIa with the fibrinogen D domain. *J Biol Chem* 259:8584, 1984.

106. NACHMAN RL, LEUNG LLK: Complex formation of platelet membrane glycoproteins IIb and IIIa with fibrinogen. *J Clin Invest* 69:263, 1982.

107. PARISE LV, PHILLIPS DR: Reconstitution of the purified platelet fibrinogen receptor. Fibrinogen binding properties of the glycoprotein IIb-IIIa complex. *J Biol Chem* 260:10698, 1985.

108. BALDASSARE JJ, KAHN RA, KNIPP MA, NEWMAN PJ: Reconstitution of platelet proteins into phospholipid vesicles. Functional proteoliposomes. *J Clin Invest* 75:35, 1985.

109. PARISE LV, PHILLIPS DR: Fibronectin-binding properties of the purified platelet glycoprotein IIb-IIIa complex. *J Biol Chem* 261:14011, 1986.

110. PYTELA R, PIERSCHBACHER MD, GINSBERG MH, PLOW EF, RUOSLAHTI E: Platelet membrane glycoprotein IIb/IIIa: Member of a family of arg-gly-asp-specific adhesion receptors. *Science* 231:1559, 1986.

111. GEORGE JN, MORGAN RK, LEWIS PC: Studies on platelet plasma membranes. IV. Quantitative analysis of platelet membrane glycoproteins by (^{125}I)-diazotized diiodosulfanilic acid labeling and SDS-polyacrylamide gel electrophoresis. *J Lab Clin Med* 92:430, 1978.

112. PHILLIPS DR, JENNINGS LK, PRASSANA HR: Ca^{2+}-mediated association of glycoprotein G (thrombin-sensitive protein, thrombospondin) with human platelets. *J Biol Chem* 255:11629, 1980.

113. AIKEN ML, GINSBERG MH, PLOW EF: Identification of a new class of inducible receptors on platelets. Thrombospondin interacts with platelets via a GPIIb-IIIa-independent mechanism. *J Clin Invest* 78:1713, 1986.

114. AIKEN ML, GINSBERG MH, PLOW EF: Divalent cation-dependent and independent surface expression of thrombospondin on thrombin-stimulated human platelets. *Blood* 69:58, 1987.

115. WOLFF R, PLOW EF, GINSBERG MH: Interaction of thrombospondin with resting and stimulated human platelets. *J Biol Chem* 261:6840, 1986.

116. HOURDILLE P, HASITZ M, BELLOC F, NURDEN AT: Immunocytochemical study of the binding of fibrinogen and thrombospondin to ADP- and thrombin-stimulated human platelets. *Blood* 65:912, 1985.

117. MCGREGOR JL, CLEZARDIN P, JAMES E, MCGREGOR L, DECHAVANNE M, CLEMETSON KJ: Identification and characterization of fragments of major glycoproteins from platelet membrane after chymotrypsin treatment. *Eur J Biochem* 148:97, 1985.

118. LEUNG LLK: Role of thrombospondin in platelet aggregation. *J Clin Invest* 74:1764, 1984.

119. SHATTIL SJ, HOXIE JA, CUNNINGHAM M, BRASS LF: Changes in the platelet membrane glycoprotein IIb-IIIa complex during platelet activation. *J Biol Chem* 260:11107, 1985.

120. COLLER BS: Activation affects access to the platelet receptor for adhesive glycoproteins. *J Cell Biol* 103:451, 1986.

121. PHILLIPS DR, JENNINGS LK, EDWARDS HH: Identification of membrane proteins mediating the interaction of human platelets. *J Cell Biol* 86:77, 1980.

122. PAINTER RG, PRODOUZ KN, GAARDE W: Isolation of a subpopulation of glycoprotein IIb-III from platelet membranes that is bound to membrane actin. *J Cell Biol* 100:652, 1985.

123. PAINTER RG, GAARDE W, GINSBERG MH: Direct evidence for the interaction of platelet surface membrane proteins GPIIb and III with cytoskeletal components: Protein crosslinking studies. *J Cell Biochem* 27:277, 1985.

124. ISENBERG WM, MCEVER RP, PHILLIPS DR, SHUMAN MA, BAINTON DF: The platelet fibrinogen receptor: An immunogold-surface replica study of agonist-induced ligand binding and receptor clustering. *J Cell Biol* 104:1655, 1987.

125. ASCH AS, BARNWELL J, SILVERSTEIN RL, NACHMAN RL: Isolation of the thrombospondin membrane receptor. *J Clin Invest* 79:1054, 1987.

126. RUOSLAHTI E, PIERSCHBACHER MD: Arg-Gly-Asp: A versatile cell recognition signal. *Cell* 44:517, 1986.

127. HORWITZ A, DUGGAN K, GREGGS R, DECKER C, BUCK C: The cell substrate attachment (CSAT) antigen has properties of a receptor for laminin and fibronectin. *J Cell Biol* 101:2134, 1985.

128. PIERSCHBACHER MD, RUOSLAHTI E: Cell attachment activity of fibronectin can be duplicated by small synthetic fragments of the molecule. *Nature* 309:30, 1984.

129. GARTNER TK, BENNETT JS: The tetrapeptide analogue of the cell attachment site of fibronectin inhibits platelet aggregation and fibrinogen binding to activated platelets. *J Biol Chem* 260:11891, 1985.

130. PLOW EF, PIERSCHBACHER MD, RUOSLAHTI E, MARGUERIE GA, GINSBERG MH: The effect of Arg-Gly-Asp-containing peptides on fibrinogen and von

Willebrand factor binding to platelets. *Proc Natl Acad Sci USA* 82:8057, 1985.

131. GINSBERG M, PIERSCHBACHER MD, RUOSLAHTI E, MARGUERIE G, PLOW E: Inhibition of fibronectin binding to platelets by proteolytic fragments and synthetic peptides which support fibroblast adhesion. *J Biol Chem* 260:3931, 1985.

132. HAVERSTICK DM, COWN JF, YAMADA KM, SANTORO SA: Inhibition of platelet adhesion to fibronectin, fibrinogen, and von Willebrand factor substrates by a synthetic tetrapeptide derived from the cell-binding domain of fibronectin. *Blood* 66:946, 1985.

133. PLOW EF, LOFTUS JC, LEVIN EG, FAIR DS, DIXON D, FORSYTH J, GINSBERG MH: Immunologic relationship between platelet membrane glycoprotein GPIIb/IIIa and cell surface molecules expressed by a variety of cells. *Proc Natl Acad Sci USA* 83:6002, 1986.

134. CHARO IF, FITZGERALD LA, STEINER B, RALL SC Jr, BEKEART LS, PHILLIPS DR: Platelet glycoproteins IIb and IIIa: Evidence for a family of immunologically and structurally related glycoproteins in mammalian cells. *Proc Natl Acad Sci USA* 83:8351, 1986.

135. NEWMAN PJ, KAWAI Y, MONTGOMERY RR, KUNICKI TJ: Synthesis by cultured human umbilical vein endothelial cells of two proteins structurally and immunologically related to platelet membrane glycoproteins IIb and IIIa. *J Cell Biol* 103:81, 1986.

136. LEEKSMA OC, ZANDBERGEN-SPAARGAREN J, GILTAY JC, van MOURIK JA: Cultured human endothelial cells synthesize a plasma membrane protein complex immunologically related to the platelet glycoprotein IIb/IIIa complex. *Blood* 67:1176, 1986.

137. HYNES RO: Integrins: A family of cell surface receptors. *Cell* 48:549, 1987.

138. SPRINGER TA: The LFA-1, Mac-1 glycoprotein family and its deficiency in an inherited disease. *Fed Proc* 44:2660, 1985.

139. KISHIMOTO TK, O'CONNOR K, LEE A, ROBERTS TM, SPRINGER TA: Cloning of the beta subunit of the leukocyte adhesion proteins: Homology to a extracellular matrix receptor defines a novel supergene family. *Cell* 48:681, 1987.

140. WRIGHT SD, MEYER BC: Fibronectin receptor of human macrophages recognizes the sequence Arg-Gly-Asp-Ser. *J Exp Med* 162:762, 1985.

141. TAKADA Y, HUANG C, HEMLER ME: Fibronectin receptor structures in the VLA family of heterodimers. *Nature* 326:607, 1987.

142. HEMLER ME, HUANG C, SCHWARZ L: The VLA protein family: Characterization of five distinct cell surface heterodimers each with a common 130,000 molecular weight beta subunit. *J Biol Chem* 262:3300, 1987.

143. ROSA J-P, JOHNSTON GI, COOK RG, HARKINS RN, KERBACHER, KE, BRAY PF, SHUMAN MA, MCEVER RP: Amino acid sequence homologies between the platelet fibrinogen receptor and fibroblast fibronectin receptor. *Blood* (suppl 1) 68:325a.

144. PIOTROWICZ RS, ORCHEKOWSKI RP, NUGENT DJ, YAMADA KY, KUNICKI TJ: Glycoprotein Ic-IIa functions as an activation-dependent fibronectin receptor on human platelets. *J Cell Biol* 106:1359, 1988.

145. GIANCOTTI FG, LANGUINO LR, ZANETTI A, PERI G, TARONE G, DEJANA E: Platelets express a membrane protein complex immunologically related to the fibroblast fibronectin receptor and distinct from GPIIb/IIIa. *Blood* 69:1535, 1987.

145a. GILTAY JC, LEEKSMA OC, BREEDERVELD C, VAN MOURIK JA: Normal synthesis and expression of endothelial IIb/IIIa in Glanzmann's thrombasthenia. *Blood* 69:809, 1987.

146. DONATI MB, BALCONI G, REMUZZI G, BORGIA R, MORASCA L, de GAETANO G: Skin fibroblasts from a patient with Glanzmann's thrombasthenia do not induce fibrin clot retraction. *Thromb Res* 10:173, 1977.

147. REMUZZI G, MARCHESI E, de GAETANO G, DONATI MB: Abnormal tissue repair in Glanzmann's thrombasthenia. *Lancet* 1:374, 1977.

148. STEINBERG BM, SMITH K, COLOZZO M, POLLACK R: Establishment and transformation diminish the ability of fibroblasts to contract a native collagen gel. *J Cell Biol* 87:304, 1980.

149. DEGOS L, DAUTIGNY A, BROUET JC, COLOMBANI M, ARDAILLOU N, CAEN JP, COLOMBANI J: A molecular defect in thrombasthenic platelets. *J Clin Invest* 56:236, 1975.

150. BERNARD J, SOULIER JP: Sur une nouvelle variété de dystrophie thrombocytaire haemorragipare congenitale. *Semin Hop Paris* 24:3217, 1948.

151. ALAGILLE D, JOSSO F, BINET JL, BLIN ML: La dystrophie thrombocytaire hemorragipare. Discussion nosologique. *Nouv Rev Fr Hematol* 4:755, 1964.

152. KANSKA B, NIEWIAROWSKI S, OSTROWSKI L, POPLAWSKI A, PROKOPOWICZ J: Macrothrombocytic thrombopathia. Clinical, coagulation and hereditary aspects. *Thromb Diath Haemorrh* 10:88, 1963.

153. CULLUM C, COONEY DP, SCHRIER SL: Familial thrombocytopenic thrombocytopathy. *Br J Haematol* 13:147, 1967.

154. GROTTUM KA, SOLUM NO: Congenital thrombocytopenia with giant platelets: A defect in the platelet membrane. *Br J Haematol* 16:277, 1969.

155. JENKINS CSP, PHILLIPS DR, CLEMETSON KJ, MEYER D, LARRIEU M-J, LUSCHER EF: Platelet membrane glycoproteins implicated in ristocetin-induced aggregation. Studies of the proteins on platelets from patients with Bernard-Soulier syndrome and von Willebrand's disease. *J Clin Invest* 57:112, 1976.

156. BITHELL TC, PAREKH SJ, STRONG RR: Platelet-function studies in the Bernard-Soulier syndrome. *Ann NY Acad Sci* 201:145, 1972.

157. HOWARD MA, HUTTON RA, HARDISTY RM: Hereditary giant platelet syndrome: A disorder of a new aspect of platelet function. *Br Med J* 4:586, 1973.

158. EVENSEN SA, SOLUM NO, GROTTUM KA, HOVIG T: Familial bleeding disorder with a moderate thrombocytopenia and giant blood platelets. *Scand J Haematol* 13:203, 1974.

159. MALDONADO JE, GILCHRIST GS, BRIGDEN LP, BOWIE EJW: Ultrastructure of platelets in Bernard-Soulier syndrome. *Mayo Clin Proc* 50:402, 1975.

160. WEISS HJ, TSCHOPP TB, BAUMGARTNER HR, SUSSMAN II, JOHNSON MM, EGAN JJ: Decreased adhesion of giant (Bernard-Soulier) platelets to subendothelium. Further implications on the role of the von Willebrand factor in hemostasis. *Am J Med* 57:920, 1974.

161. WALSH PN, MILLS DCB, PARETI FI, STEWART GJ, MacFARLANE DE, JOHNSON MM, EGAN JJ: Hereditary giant platelet syndrome. Absence of collagen-induced coagulant activity and deficiency of factor-XI binding to platelets. *Br J Haematol* 29:639, 1975.

162. CAEN JP, NURDEN AT, JEANNEAU C, MICHEL H, TOBELEM G, LEVY-TOLEDANO S, SULTAN Y, VALENSI F, BERNARD J: Bernard-Soulier syndrome: A new platelet glycoprotein abnormality. Its relationship with platelet adhesion to subendothelium and with the Factor VIII von Willebrand protein. *J Lab Clin Med* 87:586, 1976.

163. GEORGE JN, REIMANN TA, MOAKE JL, MORGAN RK, CIMO PL, SEARS DA: Bernard-Soulier disease: A study of four patients and their parents. *Br J Haematol* 48:459, 1981.

164. NURDEN AT, DUPUIS D, KUNICKI TJ, CAEN JP: Analysis of the glycoprotein and protein composition of Bernard-Soulier platelets by single and two-dimensional sodium dodecyl sulfate-polyacrylamide gel electrophoresis. *J Clin Invest* 67:1431, 1981.

165. WHITE JG, BURRIS SM, HASEGAWA D, JOHNSON M: Micropipette aspiration of human blood platelets: A defect in Bernard-Soulier's syndrome. *Blood* 63:1249, 1984.

166. JAMIESON GA, OKUMURA T: Reduced thrombin binding and aggregation in Bernard-Soulier platelets. *J Clin Invest* 61:861, 1978.

167. FROJNOVIC MM, MILTON JG, CAEN JP, TOBELEM G: Platelets from "giant platelet syndrome (BBS)" are discocytes and normal sized. *J Lab Clin Med* 91:109, 1978.

168. CAEN JP, LEVY-TOLEDANO S: Interaction between platelets and von Willebrand factor provides a new scheme for primary haemostasis. *Nature* 244:159, 1973.

169. KAO K-J, PIZZO SV, MCKEE PA: Demonstration and characterization of specific binding sites for factor VIII/von Willebrand factor on human platelets. *J Clin Invest* 63:656, 1979.

170. MOAKE JL, OLSON JD, TROLL JH Jr, WEINGER RS, PETERSON DM, CIMO PL: Interaction of platelets, von Willebrand factor, and ristocetin during platelet agglutination. *J Lab Clin Med* 96:168, 1980.

171. MOAKE JL, OLSON JD, TROLL JH, TANG SS, FUNICELLA T, PETERSON DM: Binding of radioiodinated human von Willebrand factor to Bernard-Soulier, thrombasthenic and von Willebrand's disease platelets. *Thromb Res* 19:21, 1980.

172. TSCHOPP T, WEISS HJ, BAUMGARTNER H: Decreased adhesion of platelets to subendothelium in von Willebrand's disease. *J Lab Clin Med* 83:296, 1974.

173. WEISS HJ, BAUMGARTNER HR, TSCHOPP TB, TURITTO VT, COHEN D: Correction by factor VIII of the impaired platelet adhesion to subendothelium in von Willebrand disease. *Blood* 51:267, 1978.

174. LOSCALZO J, INBAL A, HANDIN RI: Von Willebrand protein facilitates platelet incorporation in polymerizing fibrin. *J Clin Invest* 78:1112, 1986.

175. NURDEN AT, CAEN JP: Specific roles for platelet surface glycoproteins in platelet function. *Nature* 255:720, 1975.

176. PHILLIPS DR: Effect of trypsin on the exposed polypeptides and glycoproteins in the human platelet membrane. *Biochemistry* 11:4582, 1972.

177. PETERSON DM, HIRST A, WEHRING B: Comparison of normal and Bernard-Soulier platelet membrane glycoproteins. Isoelectric characteristics and surface radiolabel. *J Lab Clin Med* 100:26, 1982.

178. CLEMETSON KJ, MCGREGOR JL, JAMES E, DECHAVANNE M, LUSCHER EF: Characterization of the platelet membrane glycoprotein abnormalities in Bernard-Soulier syndrome and comparison with normal by surface-labeling techniques and high-resolution two-dimensional gel electrophoresis. *J Clin Invest* 70:304, 1982.

179. COLLER BS, PEERSCHKE EI, SCUDDER LE, SULLIVAN CA: Studies with a murine monoclonal antibody that abolishes ristocetin-induced binding of

von Willebrand factor to platelets: Additional evidence in support of GPIb as a platelet receptor for von Willebrand factor. *Blood* 61:99, 1983.

180. MONTGOMERY RR, KUNICKI TJ, TAVES C, PIDARD D, CORCORAN M: Diagnosis of Bernard-Soulier syndrome and Glanzmann's thrombasthenia with a monoclonal assay on whole blood. *J Clin Invest* 71:385, 1983.

181. BERNDT MC, GREGORY C, CHONG BH, ZOLA H, CASTALDI PA: Additional glycoprotein defects in Bernard-Soulier's syndrome: Confirmation of genetic basis by parental analysis. *Blood* 62:800, 1983.

182. KIEFFER N, DEBILI N, WICKI A, TITEUX M, HENRI A, MISHAL Z, BRETON-GORIUS J, VAINCHENKER W, CLEMETSON KJ: Expression of platelet glycoprotein Ib alpha in HEL cells. *J Biol Chem* 261:15854, 1986.

183. OKUMURA T, LOMBART C, JAMIESON GA: Platelet glycocalicin. II. Purification and characterization. *J Biol Chem* 251:5950, 1976.

184. OKUMURA T, JAMIESON GA: Platelet glycocalicin. I. Orientation of glycoproteins of the human platelet surface. *J Biol Chem* 251:5944, 1976.

185. SOLUM NO, HAGEN I, FILION-MYKLEBUST C, STABACK T: Platelet glycocalicin. Its membrane association and solubilization in aqueous media. *Biochim Biophys Acta* 597:235, 1980.

186. TSUJI T, TSUNEHISA S, WATANABE Y, YAMAMOTO K, TOHYAMA H, OSAWA T: The carbohydrate moiety of human platelet glycocalicin. The structure of the major ser/thr-linked sugar chain. *J Biol Chem* 258:6335, 1983.

187. LOPEZ JA, CHUNG DW, FUJIKAWA K, HAGEN FS, PAPAYANNOPOULOU T, ROTH GJ: Cloning of the alpha chain of human platelet glycoprotein Ib: A transmembrane protein with homology to leucine rich alpha2-glycoprotein. *Proc Natl Acad Sci USA* 84:5615, 1987.

188. RUAN C, DU X, XI X, CASTALDI PA, BERNDT MC: A murine antiglycoprotein Ib complex monoclonal antibody, SZ 2, inhibits platelet aggregation induced by both ristocetin and collagen. *Blood* 69:570, 1987.

189. DU X, BEUTLER L, RUAN C, CASTALDI PA, BERNDT MC: Glycoprotein Ib and glycoprotein IX are fully complexed in the intact platelet membrane. *Blood* 69:1524, 1987.

190. BERNDT MC, GREGORY C, KABRAL A, ZOLA H, FOURNIER D, CASTALDI PA: Purification and preliminary characterization of the glycoprotein Ib complex of the human platelet membrane. *Eur J Biochem* 151:637, 1985.

191. BERNDT MC, PHILLIPS DR: Purification and preliminary physicochemical characterization of human platelet membrane glycoprotein V. *J Biol Chem* 256:59, 1981.

192. CLEMETSON KJ: Glycoproteins of the platelet plasma membrane, in George JN, Nurden AT, Phillips DR (eds): *Platelet Membrane Glycoproteins.* New York, Plenum, 1985, p 51.

193. NURDEN AT, DIDRY D, ROSA J-P: Molecular defects of platelets in the Bernard-Soulier syndrome. *Blood Cells* 9:333, 1983.

194. NURDEN AT: Disorders of platelets, in Gordon JL, MacIntyre DE (eds): *Platelets in Biology and Pathology*, 3d ed. Amsterdam, Elsevier, 1987, p 37.

195. TOBELEM G, LEVY-TOLEDANO S, BREDOUX R, MICHEL H, NURDEN A, CAEN JP, DEGOS L: New approach to determination of specific functions of platelet membrane sites. *Nature* 263:427, 1976.

196. NACHMAN RL, JAFFE EA, WEKSLER BB: Immunoinhibition of ristocetin-induced platelet aggregation. *J Clin Invest* 59:143, 1977.

197. KORNECKI E, LEE H, MERLIN F, HERSHOCK D, TUSZYNSKI GP, NIEWIAROWSKI S: Comparison of platelet fibrinogen receptors on intact and proteolytically-treated platelets by use of an anti-glycoprotein IIIa monoclonal antibody (MA 123). *Thromb Res* 34:35, 1984.

198. MCMICHAEL AJ, RUST NA, PILCH JR, SOCHYNSKY R, MORTON J, MASON DY, RUAN C, TOBELEM G, CAEN JP: Monoclonal antibody to human platelet glycoprotein I. Immunological studies. *Br J Haematol* 49:501, 1981.

199. RUAN C, TOBELEM G, MICHAEL AJ, DROUET L, LEGRAND Y, DEGOS L, KIEFFER N, LEE H, CAEN JP: Monoclonal antibody to human platelet glycoprotein I. Effects on human platelet function. *Br J Haematol* 49:511, 1981.

200. RUGGERI ZM, De MARCO L, GATTI L, BADER R, MONTGOMERY RR: Platelets have more than one binding site for von Willebrand factor. *J Clin Invest* 72:1, 1983.

201. HANDA M, TITANI K, HOLLAND LZ, ROBERTS JR, RUGGERI ZM: The von Willebrand factor-binding domain of platelet membrane glycoprotein Ib. Characterization by monoclonal antibodies and partial amino acid sequence analysis of proteolytic fragments. *J Biol Chem* 261:12579, 1986.

202. ACKROYD JF: Allergic purpura, including purpura due to food, drugs and infections. *Am J Med* 14:605, 1953.

203. BOLTON FG: Thrombocytopenic purpura due to quinidine. II. Serologic mechanisms. *Blood* 11:547, 1956.

204. CHRISTIE DJ, MULLER PC, ASTER RT: Fab-mediated binding of drug-dependent antibodies to platelets in quinidine- and quinine-dependent thrombocytopenia. *J Clin Invest* 75:310, 1985.

205. KUNICKI TJ, JOHNSON MM, ASTER RH: Absence of the platelet receptor for drug-dependent antibodies in the Bernard-Soulier syndrome. *J Clin Invest* 62:716, 1978.

206. CHONG BH, BERNDT MC, KOUTTS J, CASTALDI PA: Quinidine-induced thrombocytopenia and leukopenia: Demonstration and characterization of distinct antiplatelet and antileukocyte antibodies. *Blood* 62:1218, 1983.

207. BERNDT MC, CHONG BH, BULL HA, ZOLA H, CASTALDI PA: Molecular characterization of quinine-quinidine drug-dependent antibody platelet interactions using monoclonal antibodies. *Blood* 66:1291, 1985.

208. STRICKER RB, SHUMAN MA: Quinidine purpura: Evidence that glycoprotein V is a target platelet antigen. *Blood* 67:1377, 1986.

209. TAKAMATSU J, HORNE MKIII, GRALICK HR: Identification of the thrombin receptor on human platelets by chemical crosslinking. *J Clin Invest* 77:362, 1986.

210. HARMON JT, JAMIESON GA: The glycocalicin portion of platelet glycoprotein Ib expresses both high and moderate affinity receptor sites for thrombin. *J Biol Chem* 261:13224, 1986.

211. MOSHER DF, VAHERI A, CHOATE JJ, GAHMBERG CG: Action of thrombin on surface glycoproteins of human platelets. *Blood* 53:437, 1979.

212. OKUMURA T, HASITZ M, JAMIESON GA: Platelet glycocalicin. Interaction with thrombin and role as thrombin receptor of the platelet surface. *J Biol Chem* 253:3435, 1978.

213. KNUPP CL, WHITE GCII: Effect of active site-modified thrombin on the hydrolysis of platelet-associated glycoprotein V by native thrombin. *Blood* 65:578, 1985.

214. MCGOWAN EB, DING A, DETWILER TC: Correlation of thrombin-induced glycoprotein V hydrolysis and platelet activation. *J Biol Chem* 258:11243, 1983.

215. BIENZ D, SCHNIPPERING W, CLEMETSON KJ: Glycoprotein V is not the thrombin activation receptor on human blood platelets. *Blood* 68:720, 1986.

216. FOX JEB: Identification of actin-binding protein as the protein linking the membrane skeleton to glycoproteins on platelet plasma membranes. *J Biol Chem* 260:11970, 1985.

217. FOX JEB: Linkage of a membrane skeleton to integral membrane glycoproteins in human platelets. Identification of one of the glycoproteins as glycoprotein Ib. *J Clin Invest* 76:1673, 1985.

218. OKITA JR, PIDARD D, NEWMAN PJ, MONTGOMERY RR, KUNICKI TJ: On the association of glycoprotein Ib and actin-binding protein in human platelets. *J Cell Biol* 100:317, 1985.

219. NAJEAN Y, ARDAILLOU N, CAEN JP, LARRIEU MJ, BERNARD J: Survival of radiochromium-labeled platelets in thrombocytopenias. *Blood* 22:718, 1963.

220. MALMSTEN C, HAMBERG M, SVENSSON J, SAMUELSSON B: Physiological role of an endoperoxide in human platelets: Hemostatic defect due to platelet cyclo-oxygenase deficiency. *Proc Natl Acad Sci USA* 72:1446, 1975.

221. LAGARDE M, BYRON PA, VARGAFTIG BB, DECHAVANNE M: Impairment of platelet thromboxane A_2 generation of the platelet release reaction in two patients with congenital deficiency of platelet cyclo-oxygenase. *Br J Haematol* 38:251, 1978.

222. PARETI FI, MANNUCCI PM, D'ANGELO A, SMITH JB, SAUTEBIN L, GALLI G: Congenital deficiency of thromboxane and prostacyclin. *Lancet* 1:898, 1980.

223. WEISS HJ, LAGES BA: Possible congenital defect in platelet thromboxane synthetase. *Lancet* 1:760, 1977.

224. ROTH GJ, STANFORD N, JACOBS JW, MAJERUS PW: Acetylation of prostaglandin synthetase by aspirin. Purification and properties of the acetylated protein from sheep vesicular galnd. *Biochemistry* 16:4244, 1977.

225. BURCH JW, STANFORD N, MAJERUS PW: Inhibition of platelet prostaglandin synthetase by oral aspirin. *J Clin Invest* 61:314, 1978.

226. ROTH GJ, MACHUGA ET: Radioimmune assay of human platelet prostaglandin synthetase. *J Lab Clin Med* 99:187, 1982.

227. WU KK, MINKOFF IM, ROSSI EC, CHEN Y-C: Hereditary bleeding disorder due to a primary defect in platelet release reaction. *Br J Haematol* 47:241, 1981.

228. WU KK, LE BRETON GC, TAI H-H, CHEN Y-C: Primary release disorders due to an abnormal platelet response to thromboxane A2. *J Clin Invest* 67:1801, 1981.

229. LAGES B, MALMSTEN C, WEISS HJ, SAMUELSSON B: Impaired platelet response to thromboxane-A_2 and defective calcium mobilization in a patient with a bleeding disorder. *Blood* 57:545, 1981.

230. RAO AK, WILLIS J, HOLMSEN H: A major role of ADP in thromboxane transfer experiments: Studies in patients with platelet secretion defects. *J Lab Clin Med* 104:116, 1984.

231. WEISS HJ, WITTE LD, KAPLAN KL, LAGES BA, CHERNOFF A, NOSSEL HL, GOODMAN DS, BAUMGARTNER HR: Heterogeneity in storage pool deficiency: Studies on granule-bound substances in 18 patients including variants deficient in alpha-granules, platelet factor 4, beta-thromboglobulin, and platelet-derived growth factor. *Blood* 54:1296, 1979.

232. WEISS HJ, CHERVENICK PA, ZALUSKY R, FACTOR A: A familial defect in

platelet function associated with impaired release of adenosine diphosphate. *N Engl J Med* 281:1264, 1969.

233. INGERMAN CM, SMITH JB, SHAPIRO S, SEDAR A, SILVER MJ: Hereditary abnormality of platelet aggregation attributable to nucleotide storage pool deficiency. *Blood* 52:332, 1978.

234. WHITE JG, EDSON JR, DESNICK SJ, WITKOP CJ: Studies of platelets in a variant of the Hermansky-Pudlak syndrome. *Am J Pathol* 63:319, 1971.

235. HARDISTY RM, MILLS DCB, KETSA-ARD K: The platelet defect associated with albinism. *Br J Haematol* 23:679, 1972.

236. GROTTUM KA, HOVING T, HOLMSEN H: Wiskott-Aldrich syndrome: Qualitative platelet defects and short platelet survival. *Br J Haematol* 17:373, 1969.

237. DAY HJ, HOLMSEN H: Platelet adenine nucleotide "storage pool deficiency" in thrombocytopenic absent radius syndrome. *JAMA* 221:1053, 1972.

238. BUCHANAN GR, HANDIN RI: Platelet function in the Chediak-Higashi syndrome. *Blood* 47:941, 1976.

239. COSTA JL, FAUCI AS, WOLFF SM: A platelet abnormality in the Chediak-Higashi syndrome of man. *Blood* 48:517, 1976.

240. WHITE JG: Ultrastructural studies of the gray platelet syndrome. *Am J Pathol* 95:445, 1979.

241. GERRARD JM, PHILLIPS DR, RAO GHR, PLOW EF, WALZ DA, ROSS R, HARKER LA, WHITE JG: Biochemical studies of two patients with the gray platelet syndrome. Selective deficiency of platelet alpha granules. *J Clin Invest* 66:102, 1980.

242. NURDEN AT, KUNICKI TJ, DUPUIS D, SORIA C, CAEN JP: Specific protein and glycoprotein deficiencies in platelets isolated from two patients with the gray platelet syndrome. *Blood* 59:709, 1982.

243. BERNDT MC, HALLEY H, CASTALDI PA, MCPHERSON VJ, GORDON S: Morphological and biochemical confirmation of gray platelet syndrome in two siblings. *Aust NZ J Med* 13:387, 1983.

244. KOHLER M, HELLSTERN P, MORGENSTERN E, MUELLER-ECKHARDT C, BERBERICH R, MEISER RJ, SCHEFFLER P, WENZEL E: Gray platelet syndrome: Selective alpha-granule deficiency and thrombocytopenia due to increased platelet turnover. *Blut* 50:331, 1985.

245. BRETON-GORIUS J, VAINCHENKER W, NURDEN A, LEVY-TOLEDANO S, CAEN J: Defective alpha-granule production in megakaryocytes from gray platelet syndrome. Ultrastructural studies of bone marrow cells and megakaryocytes growing in culture from blood precursors. *Am J Pathol* 102:10, 1981.

246. ROSA J-P, GEORGE JN, BAINTON DF, NURDEN AT, CAEN JP, MCEVER RP: Gray platelet syndrome: Demonstration of alpha granule membranes that can fuse with the cell surface. *J Clin Invest* 80:1138, 1987.

247. RACCUGLIA G: Gray platelet syndrome: A variety of qualitative platelet disorder. *Am J Med* 51:818, 1971.

248. LEVY-TOLEDANO S, CAEN JP, BRETON-GORIUS J, RENDU F, CYWINER-GOLENZER C, DUPUY E, LEGRAND Y, MacLOUF J: Gray platelet syndrome: Alpha-granule deficiency. *J Lab Clin Med* 98:831, 1981.

249. CRAMER EM, VAINCHENKER W, VINCI G, GUICHARD J, BRETON-GORIUS J: Gray platelet syndrome: Immunoelectron microscopic localization of fibrinogen and von Willebrand factor in platelets and megakaryocytes. *Blood* 66:1309, 1985.

250. COLLER BS, HULTIN MB, NURDEN AT, ROSA J-P, LANE BP: Isolated alpha-granule deficiency (gray platelet syndrome) with slight increase in bone marrow reticulin and possible glycoprotein and/or protease defect. *Thromb Haemost* 50:211, 1983.

251. MCEVER RP, MARTIN MN: A monoclonal antibody to a membrane glycoprotein binds only to activated platelets. *J Biol Chem* 259:9799, 1984.

252. STENBERG PE, MCEVER RP, SHUMAN MA: A platelet alpha-granule membrane protein (GMP-140) is expressed on the plasma membrane after activation. *J Cell Biol* 101:880, 1985.

253. ISENBERG WM, MCEVER RP, SHUMAN MA, BAINTON DF: Topographic distribution of a granule membrane protein (GMP-140) that is expressed on the platelet surface after activation: An immunogold-surface replica study. *Blood Cells* 12:191, 1986.

254. HSU-LIN S-C, BERMAN CL, FURIE BC, AUGUST D, FURIE B: A platelet membrane protein expressed during platelet activation and secretion. Studies using a monoclonal antibody specific for thrombin-activated platelets. *J Biol Chem* 259:9121, 1984.

255. BERMAN CL, YEO EL, WENCEL-DRAKE JD, FURIE BC, GINSBERG MH, FURIE B: A platelet alpha granule membrane protein that is associated with the plasma membrane after activation. *J Clin Invest* 78:130, 1986.

256. HANDAGAMA PJ, GEORGE JN, SHUMAN MA, MCEVER RP, BAINTON DF: Incorporation of a circulating protein into megakaryocyte and platelet granules. *Proc Natl Acad Sci USA* 84:861, 1987.

257. GEORGE JN, SAUCERMAN S: Platelet IgG, IgA, IgM, and albumin: Correlation of platelet and plasma concentrations in normal subjects and in patients with ITP or dysproteinemia. *Blood* 72:362, 1988.

GLUCOSE-6-PHOSPHATE DEHYDROGENASE DEFICIENCY

LUCIO LUZZATTO
ATUL MEHTA

QUOD ALIIS CIBUS EST,
ALIIS FUAT ACRE VENENUM

What is food to some men
may be fierce poison to others

Lucretius Caro
De Rerum Natura 4:641, 65 B.C.

1. Glucose-6-phosphate dehydrogenase (G6PD) is a cytoplasmic enzyme that is distributed in all cells. G6PD catalyzes the first step in the hexose monophosphate pathway, and it produces NADPH required for reactions of various biosynthetic pathways as well as for the stability of catalase and the preservation and regeneration of the reduced form of glutathione (GSH). Since catalase and glutathione (via glutathione peroxidase) are essential for the detoxification of hydrogen peroxide, the defense of cells against this compound depends ultimately and heavily on G6PD. This is especially true in red cells, which are exquisitely sensitive to oxidative damage and in which other NADPH-producing enzymes are lacking.

2. G6PD in its active enzyme form is made up of either two or four identical subunits, each having a molecular mass of about 61 kDa. The complete primary sequence of 515 amino acids has been determined from the cDNA sequence and matches the previously known sequence of several peptides. The gene encoding G6PD maps to the telomeric region of the long arm of the X chromosome (band Xq28). Therefore, one of the two G6PD alleles is subject to inactivation in females. The structure of the gene, as determined from overlapping genomic phage clones, spans 18 kb and consists of 13 exons (the first of which is noncoding). The sequence of the DNA region upstream of the major transcription initiation site has features similar to those found in other housekeeping gene promoters.

3. G6PD deficiency is the most common known enzymopathy; it is estimated to affect 400 million people worldwide. The highest prevalence rates (with gene frequencies in the range of 5 to 25 percent) are found in tropical Africa, in the Middle East, in tropical and subtropical Asia, in some areas of the Mediterranean, and in Papua New Guinea. The commonest clinical manifestations are neonatal jaundice and acute hemolytic anemia. In some cases the neonatal jaundice is severe enough to entail the risk of death or permanent neurologic damage. The acute hemolytic anemia can be triggered by a number of drugs, by infections, or by the ingestion of fava beans. In a proportion of cases these manifestations may be life-threatening, especially favism in children. The detailed mechanism of hemolysis is not

fully known, but it undoutedly results from the inability of G6PD-deficient red cells to withstand the oxidative damage produced, directly or indirectly, by the triggering agents mentioned above. Red cell destruction is largely intravascular and therefore associated with hemoglobinuria. Fortunately, apart from these episodes of hemolytic anemia, most G6PD-deficient individuals are entirely asymptomatic. A very small proportion of G6PD-deficient individuals have a chronic hemolytic disorder, which may be quite severe.

4. G6PD deficiency is genetically heterogeneous. Over 300 different variants have been identified, and their biochemical characterization indicates that they result from as many allelic mutations in the G6PD gene. In addition, numerous structural mutants without enzyme deficiency have been characterized. Thus, the G6PD locus is the locus for which the largest number of alleles are known at present in the human species. Different mutants, each one having a polymorphic frequency, underlie G6PD deficiency in the various parts of the world where this abnormality is prevalent. Genetic heterogeneity also explains the diverse clinical manifestations. Different mutations are responsible for the sporadic patients who have chronic hemolytic anemia and for the frequent patients who are only at risk of developing episodic hemolysis. Recently, the molecular basis for G6PD deficiency has been determined by cloning and sequencing of mutant genes from numerous patients. Thus far, several different point mutations have been observed. No deletions have been demonstrated to date.

5. The high prevalence of independently arisen G6PD mutants suggests that the population genetics of this locus portrays a good example of converging evolution through balanced polymorphism. Epidemiologic data indicate strongly that G6PD deficiency can confer relative resistance against Plasmodium falciparum malaria, and clinical data indicate that this is confined to heterozygous females. In vitro culture studies have shown that the growth of malaria parasites is impaired upon first passage from normal to G6PD-deficient red cells, but that through subsequent passages they can adapt and grow normally, thus explaining clinical protection of heterozygotes but

---

Nonstandard abbreviations used in this chapter are: CNSHA = chronic nonspherocytic hemolytic anemia; EMP = Embden-Myerhof pathway; G6P = glucose-6-phosphate; G6PD = glucose -6-phosphate dehydrogenase; GSH = reduced glutathione; GSHPX = glutathione peroxidase; GSSG = oxidized glutathione; GSSGR = glutathione reductase; NNJ = neonatal jaundice; 6PGD = 6-phosphogluconate; RFLP = restriction fragment length polymorphism.

not in deficient hemizygotes. The adaptation phenomenon, and the failure of adaptation in heterozygotes, point to a novel type of interaction between the parasite and the host in the context of red cell mosaicism resulting from X-chromosome inactivation.

The recognition of human pathology associated with deficiency of glucose-6-phosphate dehydrogenase (G6PD) in red blood cells is quite ancient. It has gone through several stages. First came the anecdotal observation by the Greek philosopher and mathematician Pythagoras, who is said to have warned his disciples against the dangers of eating fava beans (*Vicia faba;* broad beans). Second was the clinical picture of favism drawn at the turn of the century by a number of physicians in Southern Italy and in Sardinia.[1-3] In contrast to some other inborn errors of metabolism, the mode of inheritance was not easy to establish, because exposure and response to fava beans is erratic; thus both a "toxic theory" and an "allergic theory" of the pathogenesis of favism were popular.[4] However, observant general practitioners had noticed that the condition did "run in families."[2] The third stage was the recognition of hemolytic anemia caused by drugs. It soon became clear that only some individuals were susceptible, and the term "primaquine sensitivity" was appropriately coined. For hematology, this syndrome was important because hemolytic anemia had been traditionally classified as being due to either intracorpuscular or extracorpuscular causes. Here was one that was caused by an exogenous agent, but only in people who presumably already had abnormal red cells.[5] The final stage was the discovery by Carson et al.[6] in Chicago that, indeed, primaquine-sensitive people had a very low level of G6PD activity in their red cells. Soon thereafter similar observations were made in Germany[7] and in Italy on the red cells of people with a past history of favism.[8] The genetic heterogeneity of this abnormality then became quickly apparent,[9,134] and the question arose as to whether G6PD deficiency was due mainly to qualitative or to quantitative changes in the enzyme. In other words, it was not clear whether it was more similar to a structural hemoglobinopathy or to a thalassemialike disorder. Over the last 30 years the biochemical basis and the clinical implications of G6PD deficiency have been largely established, and thus far all of G6PD deficiency appears to result from a multitude of different structural allelic mutants. More recently, the molecular structures of the normal gene and of some of its mutants have been elucidated. Since the previous edition of this book, several reviews dealing with G6PD have appeared.[484,589,590] The hematologic aspects of G6PD deficiency have also been covered in an authoritative and detailed way.[278,591,592]

STRUCTURE OF G6PD

G6PD in its active form is either a dimer or a tetramer consisting of identical subunits.[10,11] Both the dimer and the tetramer are active, and the two forms are in a pH-dependent equilibrium with each other, with about equal proportions present at neutral pH.[12,13] There are two molecules of tightly bound NADP per molecule of dimer,[14] but the relationship between this "structural" NADP and substrate NADP is not yet clear.

From the cDNA sequence (see below), the primary structure of the single subunit polypeptide chain has been determined. It consists of 515 amino acids (see Fig. 91-1), with a

molecular weight of 59,265 daltons. (These figures and the sequence itself are rather different from what were published in the previous edition of this book.[16]) It is not yet known whether the N-terminal methionine is still present in the mature protein, because the terminal amino group is blocked.[17] The C-terminal peptide predicted by the DNA sequence agrees with that determined by analysis of red cell G6PD,[18] in contrast to previous claims that this is different from leukocyte G6PD.[19] The sites for G6P and NADP binding have not yet been determined. However, a binding site for pyridoxal phosphate has been identified.[20] Its significance is unknown, but, interestingly, the region involved (amino acids 199 to 209 in Fig. 91-1) is highly conserved, since a peptide with an almost identical sequence has been found in yeast G6PD, and it contains a lysine residue that is essential for enzyme activity in this organism.[21] Evolutionary conservation is also apparent from recent data on G6PD from *Drosophila*[22] and from Leuconostoc mesenteroides.[23] There are 11 cysteine residues per subunit, and one or more of them must be important for enzyme activity, since sulfhydryl group inhibitors, such as hydroxymercuribenzoate and *N*-ethylmaleimide, cause marked inhibition.[24]

METABOLIC ROLE OF G6PD

G6PD is depicted classically in intermediary metabolism as a step in the conversion of glucose-6-phosphate to pentose phosphate. Indeed, it is the first enzyme in the so-called pentose phosphate pathway, also referred to as the oxidative "shunt" (by contrast to the "mainstream" glycolytic Embden-Myerhof pathway). However, pentose can be produced alternatively by the concerted action of transketolase and transaldolase, thus bypassing G6PD. There are limited data on what fraction of pentose is normally produced via G6PD, as opposed to the transketolase-transaldolase route, and this may vary in different cells and under different circumstances. However, Chinese hamster ovary cells[26] and human fibroblasts[27] with less than 5 percent of normal G6PD activity can grow normally, suggesting that G6PD does not need to contribute much to the large amount of pentose that is needed for nucleic acid synthesis. On the other hand, G6PD produces NADPH, the coenzyme that is the main hydrogen donor for numerous other enzymatic reactions. Some of these reactions are essential steps in biosynthetic pathways; another, catalyzed by glutathione reductase, is essential in protecting cells against oxidative damage (see Fig. 91-2). Glutathione converts H_2O_2 to H_2O stoichiometrically via glutathione peroxidase (GSHPX). Thus, the detoxification of each molecule of hydrogen peroxide requires one molecule of NADPH, ultimately provided by G6PD. An alternative pathway of H_2O_2 detoxification is catalase. Under normal circumstances this route is probably ineffective, because the affinity of catalase for H_2O_2 is much lower than that of GSHPX. In addition, the rare genetic defect, acatalasemia, is not associated with hemolytic anemia.[28] Recently, Kirkman and Gaetani[25,29] have discovered that catalase has four moles of tightly bound NADPH per mole of enzyme dimer, thereby bringing to light a further unexpected link between the G6PD coenzyme and H_2O_2 detoxification. Thus, it turns out that NADPH is essential for both pathways of H_2O_2 detoxification. Its role is stoichiometric when GSHPX is used, whereas it is catalytic when catalase is used. It has been postulated that when NADPH is in short supply, due to G6PD

```
                                                        10                                              20
Met Ala Glu Gln Val Ala Leu Ser Arg Thr Gln Val Cys Gly Ile Leu Arg Glu Glu Leu
                                                        30                                              40
Phe Gln Gly Asp Ala Phe His Gln Ser Asp Thr His Ile Phe Ile Ile Met Gly Ala Ser
                                                        50                                              60
Gly Asp Leu Ala Lys Lys Lys Ile Tyr Pro Thr Ile Trp Trp Leu Phe Arg Asp Gly Leu
                                                        70                                              80
Leu Pro Glu Asn Thr Phe Ile Val Gly Tyr Ala Arg Ser Arg Leu Thr Val Ala Asp Ile
                                                        90                                             100
Arg Lys Gln Ser Glu Pro Phe Phe Lys Ala Thr Pro Glu Glu Lys Leu Lys Leu Glu Asp
                                                       110                                             120
Phe Phe Ala Arg Asn Ser Tyr Val Ala Gly Gln Tyr Asp Asp Ala Ala Ser Tyr Gln Arg
                                                       130                                             140
Leu Asn Ser His Met Asn Ala Leu His Leu Gly Ser Gln Ala Asn Arg Leu Phe Tyr Leu
                                                       150                                             160
Ala Leu Pro Pro Thr Val Tyr Glu Ala Val Thr Lys Asn Ile His Glu Ser Cys Met Ser
                                                       170                                             180
Gln Ile Gly Trp Asn Arg Ile Ile Val Glu Lys Pro Phe Gly Arg Asp Leu Gln Ser Ser
                                                       190                                             200
Asp Arg Leu Ser Asn His Ile Ser Ser Leu Phe Arg Glu Asp Gln Ile Tyr Arg Ile Asp
                                                       210                                             220
His Tyr Leu Gly Lys Glu Met Val Gln Asn Leu Met Val Leu Arg Phe Ala Asn Arg Ile
                                                       230                                             240
Phe Gly Pro Ile Trp Asn Arg Asp Asn Ile Ala Cys Val Ile Leu Thr Phe Lys Glu Pro
                                                       250                                             260
Phe Gly Thr Glu Gly Arg Gly Gly Tyr Phe Asp Glu Phe Gly Ile Ile Arg Asp Val Met
                                                       270                                             280
Gln Asn His Leu Leu Gln Met Leu Cys Leu Val Ala Met Glu Lys Pro Ala Ser Thr Asn
                                                       290                                             300
Ser Asp Asp Val Arg Asp Glu Lys Val Lys Val Leu Lys Cys Ile Ser Glu Val Gln Ala
                                                       310                                             320
Asn Asn Val Val Leu Gly Gln Tyr Val Gly Asn Pro Asp Gly Glu Gly Glu Ala Thr Lys
                                                       330                                             340
Gly Tyr Leu Asp Asp Pro Thr Val Pro Arg Gly Ser Thr Thr Ala Thr Phe Ala Ala Val
                                                       350                                             360
Val Leu Tyr Val Glu Asn Glu Arg Trp Asp Gly Val Pro Phe Ile Leu Arg Cys Gly Lys
                                                       370                                             380
Ala Leu Asn Glu Arg Lys Ala Glu Val Arg Leu Gln Phe His Asp Val Ala Gly Asp Ile
                                                       390                                             400
Phe His Gln Gln Cys Lys Arg Asn Glu Leu Val Ile Arg Val Gln Pro Asn Glu Ala Val
                                                       410                                             420
Tyr Thr Lys Met Met Thr Lys Lys Pro Gly Met Phe Phe Asn Pro Glu Glu Ser Glu Leu
                                                       430                                             440
Asp Leu Thr Tyr Gly Asn Arg Tyr Lys Asn Val Lys Leu Pro Asp Ala Tyr Glu Arg Leu
                                                       450                                             460
Ile Leu Asp Val Phe Cys Gly Ser Gln Met His Phe Val Arg Ser Asp Glu Leu Arg Glu
                                                       470                                             480
Ala Trp Arg Ile Phe Thr Pro Leu Leu His Gln Ile Glu Leu Glu Lys Pro Lys Pro Ile
                                                       490                                             500
Pro Tyr Ile Tyr Gly Ser Arg Gly Pro Thr Glu Ala Asp Glu Leu Met Lys Arg Val Gly
                                                       510
Phe Gln Tyr Glu Gly Thr Tyr Lys Trp Val Asn Pro His Lys Leu
```

Fig. 91-1 Amino acid sequence of human G6PD, deduced from the cDNA sequence (see Ref. 15, p. 7822; except that amino acid 11 is Gln instead of His, due to a previous sequencing error). The sequence published by Takizawa et al.[38] agrees with this from amino acid 37 onward, except at positions 81, 435, and 436. The cDNA clone, the sequence of which is shown here, was transfected into cos cells, and human G6PD with normal electrophoretic mobility was expressed (P. Mason, in press). The underlined residue (Lys-205) is essential for activity in yeast G6PD and may be near the G6P-binding site.

deficiency, catalase may become much more important in H_2O_2 detoxification.[30]

Fig. 91-2 The main metabolic role of G6PD in red cells is defense against oxidizing agents, epitomized by hydrogen peroxide. NADPH, a product of the G6PD reaction, is both the hydrogen donor for regeneration of reduced glutathione and a ligand for catalase (see text). GSSGR = glutathione reductase; GSHPX = glutathione peroxidase; G6P = glucose-6-phosphate; 6PG = 6-phosphogluconate.

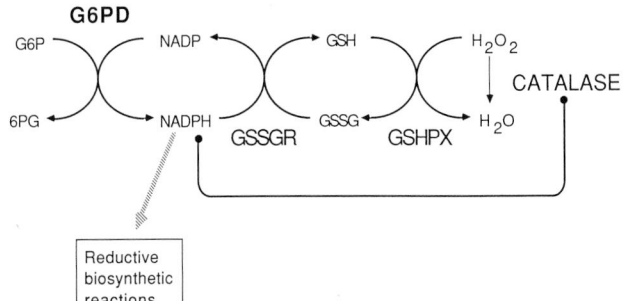

REGULATION OF G6PD ACTIVITY

As for all enzymes, the activity of G6PD in a cell could be changed by two general mechanisms, as discussed below:

Variation in the Number of G6PD Molecules. Enzyme activity measured in cell extracts under optimal conditions and with saturating substrate concentrations is assumed to be proportional to the number of molecules present. While G6PD is found in all cells, its level varies over a range of about two orders of magnitude in different tissues (see Table 91-1) regardless of whether the activity is expressed per cell or per milligram of protein. These tissue-specific differences may result from variations in the rate of transcription, postranscriptional processing, mRNA stability, or the rate of translation, or from posttranslational changes, especially proteolytic degradation. Each of these differences is likely to be important in selected circumstances. For instance, an increase in G6PD-specific mRNA has been observed in the liver of

Table 91-1 G6PD Activity in Selected Tissues

	In normal subjects, $IU \times 10^{-3}/mg$ protein[*]	In G6PD-deficient subjects, % of normal[†]
Erythrocytes	8.5	1–50
Granulocytes	851	1–90
Fibroblasts	174	2–90
Muscle	3.3	
Liver	7.2	15–50
Brain[‡]	85	

[*]From Battistuzzi et al.[32]
[†]From Luzzatto and Battistuzzi[484] and unpublished results. The range is very wide because the expression of G6PD deficiency, defined by assaying erythrocytes, varies widely with different *Gd*–alleles.
[‡]Fetal.

rats in which fatty acid synthesis is stimulated by a high carbohydrate diet after starvation,[33,34] and variation of mRNA is seen in various fetal and adult human organs.[32] Different rates of proteolysis are suggested by the widely different half-lives of normal G6PD in fibroblasts (about 2 days; see Ref. 35) and in red cells (about 60 days; see Ref. 36). Variation in the rate of transcription has not yet been conclusively proven, but it has been suggested by the finding of an empirical correlation between the extent of methylation of cytosine residues in a DNA region located 3′ to the G6PD gene and the level of G6PD activity in a variety of fetal and adult organs.[32]

Variation in Enzyme Activity of Existing G6PD Molecules. The actual intracellular activity of G6PD, like that of any other enzyme, may be very different from what is measured under optimal conditions in cell-free extracts. Many effectors, including pH,[12,13] divalent cations,[37] inorganic phosphate, phosphorylated intermediates, and other compounds,[39,40] have been found to affect G6PD activity. Among known metabolites, at least three must be major determinants of the intracellular G6PD activity: the two substrates, G6P and NADP, and one of the reaction products, NADPH, which is a potent, partially competitive inhibitor of G6PD.[41,42] In red cells the estimated concentration of G6P is about 32 μM (well below the K_m of G6P of 72 μM), the concentration of NADP is extremely low (probably less than 1 μM[43]), whereas the concentration of NADPH is high (the latter estimates are further complicated by the fact that a substantial fraction of NADP and NADPH are bound to catalase and NADPH diaphorase, respectively.[44]) Thus, it can be predicted that the intracellular

G6PD activity is only a small fraction of the maximum activity that would be available if substrate concentrations were saturating. It is practically impossible to faithfully simulate intracellular conditions, but in the case of G6PD the intracellular activity can be measured experimentally by the rate of production of $^{14}CO_2$ from [1-^{14}C]glucose. By using this technique, Kirkman and Gaetani[46] validated the above predictions. They estimated that, in normal red cells, G6PD operates at only about 1 to 2 percent of its maximal potential, even under the stimulatory action of methylene blue (which tends to continuously reoxidize NADPH produced by G6PD). This finding quantifies the vast reserve of reductive potential that is available to normal red cells, and which is substantially decreased in G6PD-deficient red cells, thus determining their pathophysiological features (see below).

GENETICS

Inheritance of G6PD shows a characteristic X-linked pattern, and the much higher incidence of favism in males compared to females had been recognized even before G6PD deficiency was discovered.[47] In contrast to several other X-linked conditions, however, there are many populations in which the frequency of G6PD deficiency is so high that homozygous females are not rare (see Ref. 48). In biochemical terms the inheritance of G6PD is typically codominant, as can be seen easily when electrophoretic variants segregate in a pedigree (see Fig. 91-3). In terms of clinical expression, G6PD deficiency is sometimes classified as X-linked recessive.[50] Although X-linked, it is not truly recessive since heterozygous females can develop hemolytic attacks, even severe ones (see below and Chap. 1). This is explained by the coexistence in heterozygotes of two cell populations [G6PD + and G6PD −], as a result of X-chromosome inactivation (see Fig. 91-6). This physiological mosaicism was first demonstrated in human red cells using G6PD as a marker by Beutler et al.[51] Soon afterward, Davidson, Nitowski, and Childs[52] obtained cellular clones expressing different G6PD alleles (Gd^B) and (Gd^A) from skin fibroblasts of heterozygotes, thus proving conclusively that mosaicism was genetically determined in somatic cells by faithful maintenance of the active state of either X chromosome in each cell and its progeny.

Formal genetic analysis had already established that Gd was closely linked to several other X-linked genes,[49,53] including those for hemophilia A, color blindness, and adrenoleukodys-

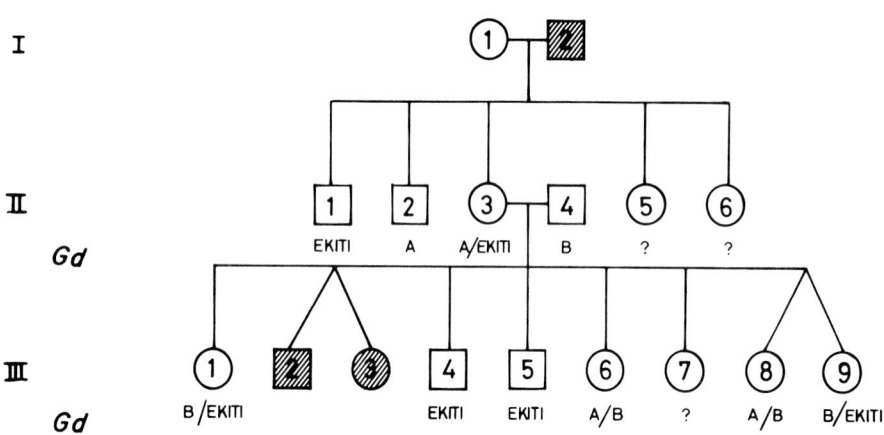

Fig. 91-3 X-linked inheritance of G6PD in a family segregating three different alleles (A, B, and EKITI) at the G6PD locus, *Gd*. Shaded symbols denote deceased subjects. *(From Usanga et al.[225])*

trophy (see Chaps. 58 and 86). The use of somatic cell hybrids[54] and of *in situ* hybridization with a G6PD-specific probe[55] has now firmly mapped Gd to the telomeric region of the long arm of the X chromosome (band Xq28), distal to the fragile site Xq27.3. Recently, physical linkage between Gd and the factor VIII gene has been established, within a length of about 400 kb, through analysis by pulse field gel electrophoresis of large DNA restriction fragments.[56] It is not yet known which of the two genes is telomeric with respect to the other. Although there have been several reports in the earlier literature of "complete" absence of G6PD,[57,58] complete G6PD deficiency has yet to be identified. All the human mutants are, in the language of classic microbial genetics, "leaky": therefore we must understand the pathophysiology of G6PD deficiency in terms of the quantity and quality of the residual mutant enzyme.

The G6PD Gene

Comparison of cDNA clones with genomic clones has revealed that the G6PD gene consists of 13 exons and 12 introns (Ref. 59; see Fig. 91-4). The coding exons vary in size from 38 to 236 bp. All introns are small (less than 1 kb), except for intron II, which is about 11 kb in size. The 5' untranslated portion of the mRNA corresponds to exon I and part of exon II: the initiation codon is in exon II, and the large intron, the significance of which is unknown, interrupts the coding sequence at codon 36. The size of the G6PD mRNA expected from the sequence is 2269 nucleotides. This is in good agreement with the size of about 2.4 kb [including the poly(A) tail] measured on Northern blots.[15] A sequence previously reported as the 3' end of the G6PD gene[60] turns out to belong to a separate gene, referred to provisionally as GdX,[59] located only 40 kb downstream from the G6PD gene itself, that encodes a protein having significant sequence homology to ubiquitin.[61] The relationship of this gene to G6PD is not yet known. It appears that a third gene exists between G6PD and GdX.[62]

The G6PD mRNA, like that of most genes, has a relatively short 5' untranslated region of 69 bp and a longer 3' untranslated region of 655 bp (see Table 91-2). Some 300 bases have been sequenced upstream of the transcription initiation site, and this region, or a portion thereof, can be regarded as the G6PD promoter.[59] This region is very GC-rich (more than 70 percent), and it contains several SP1-binding elements, GGCGGG and CCGCCC, reminiscent of the 21-bp repeats of the SV40 early promoter.[64] This region contains, therefore, a considerable number of CG dinucleotides, many of which are not methylated. They constitute an HTF (*Hpa*II tiny fragments) island, currently regarded as characteristic of DNA flanking a gene.[66] In this respect it is similar to other housekeeping gene promoters.[67,68] It also contains an ATTAAA element at position −30 to −25, which may play the role of a "TATA box" (present in some housekeeping genes but not in

others.[59]) We do not yet know whether and which of these features are required for the ubiquitous expression of G6PD, which is the property that operationally defines a housekeeping gene. It also remains to be defined what structural element, if any, determines the rate of transcription in different cells or under different physiological conditions, for instance, in response to changes in diet[69] or to hormones;[620] or in tissues with markedly increased G6PD activity, such as the lactating mammary gland[70] or tumors.[71]

Genetic Polymorphism of G6PD

It became apparent almost immediately after the discovery of G6PD deficiency that one was dealing not with a single mutation, but with a variety of genetic changes. The primary criteria for this inference were the level of residual activity and the electrophoretic mobility. Subsequently, the study of other physicochemical properties (thermostability, chromatographic behavior), and of kinetic properties (K_m of G6P, K_m of NADP, pH-dependence, utilization of substrate analogues) revealed that numerous different variants must exist, even within a set having the same or very similar residual activity and electrophoretic mobility. In 1967, a WHO study group[72] made recommendations on standardized methods of analysis, which have been followed by most investigators. Over 300 different variants are known to date (see Tables 91-3 and 91-4), and many others have never been published. For taxonomic purposes, it is convenient to classify G6PD variants according to the level of enzyme activity and the clinical manifestations (classes I to V); or according to whether they are sporadic or polymorphic. Not surprisingly, these classification criteria are

Table 91-2 Molecular Numerology of Human G6PD

DNA	
Size of gene, kb	17.5
Total number of exons	13
Coding exons	12
mRNA	
Size in nucleotides	2269
5' untranslated	69
Coding region	1545
3' untranslated region	655
Protein	
Amino acids, number	515
Molecular weight	59,265
Subunits per molecule of active enzyme	2 or 4
Molecules of tightly bound NADP per subunit	1

Fig. 91-4 Organization of the human G6PD gene (see Ref. 16). Exons are shown in black, introns in white (sizes approximate). The break in intron 2 indicates that it is much longer than shown (11.5 kb). The positions of point mutations found in different variants are indicated by the thin vertical arrows. (*From Vulliamy et al.*[598])

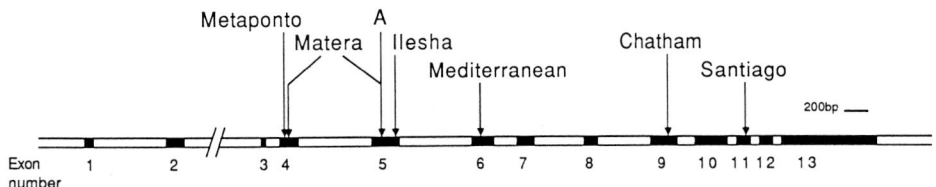

Table 91-3 List of G6PD Variants

Class I variants (associated with nonspherocytic hemolytic anemia)

Electrophoretically fast

	Refs.
AMMAN I	73
BARCELONA[b]	74
BAUDELOCQUE[b,d]	58
CHARLESTON[b,d]	75
EAST HARLEM[c]	76
GUADALAJARA[b]	77
HEIAN[c]	78
HOTEL DIEU[b]	79
JACKSON[b]	80
LAWNDALE[c]	81
LINCOLN PARK[b]	82
LINDA VISTA[b,d]	83
NAGANO[b]	84
OHIO[c,d]	85
PEA RIDGE[d]	86
SAN DIEGO[b]	87
ST LOUIS[c,d]	88
TORRANCE	89
VARADERO[b]	90
WAYNE[b]	263

Electrophoretically normal

AARAU[b,d]	91
AKITA[b]	92
ALBUQUERQUE[c,d]	93
BANGKOK[d]	94
BAT-YAM[b,d]	95
BOSTON[b]	96
CHINESE	97
CORNELL[d]	98
DOTHAN[d]	99
DUARTE[d]	93
DUBLIN	100
ENGLEWOOD	101
GALVESTON[b]	102
HAMBURG[c,d]	103
HAWAII[b,d]	104
HAYEM[b]	88
HELSINKI[b]	105
KALUGA[b]	107
KANAZAWA	108
KILGORE[b]	102
KREMENCHUG[b]	109
KYOTO[c]	110
MISSOULA[b]	111
NANCY[c]	112
NEW YORK	101
OGIKUBO[b,d]	92
OKLAHOMA[c]	113
REGENSBURG[b]	114
TOKUSHIMA[d]	115
YOKOHAMA	92

Electrophoretically slow

ALHAMBRA	438
AMMAN II[b]	73
ARLINGTON HEIGHTS[c,d]	82
ASHDOD[c]	95
ATLANTA[d]	116
CHICAGO[a,d,f]	117
FRIEBURG[c]	118
FUKUSHIMA[b]	119
GRAND PRAIRIE[b,d]	120
HURON[b,d]	263

HONG KONG POKFULAM	97
JOHANNESBURG[c]	121
KURUME[b,d]	119
LONG PRAIRIE[b,d]	122
MANCHESTER	123
MILWAUKEE[c]	124
MINNEAPOLIS[c,d]	125
PANAMA[b]	126
RENNES[c]	127
ROTTERDAM[b]	101
SAN FRANCISCO[c,d]	128
SANTA BARBARA[d]	129
SANTIAGO[d]	598
SENDAGI[b]	130
TOKYO[d]	115
TRIPLER[b,d]	131
WAKAYAMA[b,d]	119
WALTER REED[b]	132
WEST TOWN[d]	82
WORCESTER[b,d]	133
YAMAGUCHI[b,d]	119

Class II variants (severely deficient, less than 10% residual activity)

Electrophoretically fast

AMBOIN[a,b]	315
ANKARA	135
AZERBAIJAN[b]	136
BAKU	136
BETIKA[a]	137
BUKITU[a,c]	138
CASTILLA-LIKE[a,b]	315
FERRARA[b,d]	139
FERRARA III	140
FUKUOKA[c]	141
HAAD YAI[a,c]	142
HUALIEN[b,d]	143
HUALIEN-CHI[b]	143
LAGHOUAT[a,b]	144
LONG XUYEN[a,c]	145
LUBLIN[b]	146
MALI[a,b]	147
MARKHAM[a,b]	148
N-SAWAN[a,b,d]	142
PADREW[a,b]	142
PALMI[b]	140
SAN JOSE	149
TAIPEI-HAKKA[a,b]	150
TAIWAN-HAKKA[a,b]	150
TEHERAN[b]	143
TEPIC	151
UNION[a]	152
UNION-MARKHAM[a,b]	153
ZAEHRINGEN[b]	154

Electrophoretically normal

ABRAMI[b]	155
BAGHDAD	156
BIELEFELD[b]	157
BIRMINGHAM[b]	158
BLIDA[a,b]	144
BNEI-BRAK	159
BODENSEE	160
CAGLIARI[a,b]	260, 261
CAMPBELL PORE[a,b,d]	161
CHAINAT	142
COLUMBUS[a,c]	85, 163
CORINTH[a,b]	162

DAKAR[b]	147
DUSHANBA II	621
EL FAYOUM[a,b]	163
ESPOO[b]	164
FORT WORTH[b]	165
GIFU	141
GOODENOUGH[c]	315
GOTZE DELCHEV[a,b,d]	166
HAMM[b,d]	167
HONG KONG[a]	106
INDONESIA	168
ISERLOHN[b]	114
KIROVOGRAD[b]	169
MATAM[a,b]	170
MEDITERRANEAN[a,b]	171
MOSCOW[b]	172
N-PATHOM[a,c]	173
NUKUS[c]	174
OGORI[b]	175
PETRICH[a,b]	166
RUDOSEM[b]	176
SAPPORO	177
SASSARI[a,b]	178
SCHWABEN[b]	179
SELIM[b]	136
STRASBOURG[c]	180
TARSUS[b]	167

Electrophoretically slow

AACHEN[d]	181
ALGER[a,b,d]	144
ANGORAM[a,b]	315
ASAHIKAWA[c]	182
BOGIA[a]	138
BIDEIZ[b,d]	183
CALTANISSETTA[b]	140
CIUDAD DE LA HABANA[b]	184
COLOMIERS[b]	185
JAMMU	186
DUSHANBA I[b]	280
KALUAN[a,c,d]	138
KAR KAR[a,b]	315
LIFTA[b,d]	95
MADANG[a]	315
MAINOKI[a,b]	315
MANUS[a,c]	315
MENORCA	137
OKHUT I[b]	183
ONODA[b]	187
ORCHOMENOS[a,b]	153
PALAKAU	315
PANAY[a,b]	188
POPONDETTA[a,b]	618
PORT ELIZABETH[b,d]	189
POSILLIPO[d]	258
POZNAN[a,b]	190
RAMAT GAN[a,b,d]	95
SALATA[c]	138
SANTAMARIA[b]	191
SHEKII[b,d]	183
SHIRIN-BULAKH[b,d]	183
STELLA[d]	258
SWIT[a,b]	315
TITTERI[a,b]	144
TOULOUSE[d]	192
WEST BENGAL[a,b]	193
WEWAK[a,b]	618
WROCLAW[d]	264
ZAKATALY[b]	183
ZHITOMIR[b]	169

KEY: a = polymorphic; b = low K_m G6P; c = high K_m G6P; d = Very labile; e = see reference for details of electrophoretic mobility; f = G6PD. Chicago is the only Class I variant reported in several unrelated kindreds (see Ref. 86). We therefore regard it provisionally as polymorphic, although no gene frequency data are available.

Table 91-3 List of G6PD Variants (continued)

Class III (moderately deficient, 10–60% residual activity)

Electrophoretically fast

A–[a]	194, 195
ATTICA[b]	196
CANTON[a,b]	197
CASTILLA	175
CHIAPAS[b]	198
CHIBUTO[b]	199
DEBROUSSE[a]	200
DJYNET[b]	280
EAST AFRICA[c]	201
GALLIERA	140
GALLURA[b]	202
JALISCO[b]	203
JUNUT[c]	204
KABYLE[a]	205
KEPHALONIA[b]	196
KONAN[a,b]	206
LOZERE	207
MELISSA	208
MURET	185
PUERTO RICO[b]	209
SAN JUAN[b,d]	209
TAHTA[a,b]	163
TORONTO[b]	210
UBE[a]	199
VELLETRI[c,d]	211

Electrophoretically normal

AGRIGENTO[b]	202
CHATHAM[d]	598
COLUMBUS	85
EL KHARGA[a]	163
EL MORRO[b]	209
HILLBROW[b]	212
HOFU[b]	213
KAMIUBE[a,b]	206
MAHIDOL[a,b]	214
NEDELINO	176
SIRIRAJ[a,b]	215
TASHKENT[b]	174
TEL HASHOMER[a,b,c]	216
TRAPANI	140

Electrophoretically slow

ANANT[a,b]	217
ATHENS[a,b]	218
AVVOCATA	258
BENEVENTO[b]	209
CAMALDOLI	258
CAMPERDOWN[b]	162
CAPETOWN[b]	219
CARSWELL[b]	220
FERRARA II[b]	221
FRANKFURT	222
GABROVIZZA[b]	223
ILESHA[c]	225
INTANON	226
KALYAN[b]	227
KERALA[b]	193
KOBE[c,d]	177
KUANYAMA[b]	228
LIZU-BAISHA	229
LOS ANGELES[b]	230
METAPONTO	598
MEXICO[b]	231
NAPOLI[b]	221
OKHUT II[a,b]	183
PALEPOLI[a,d]	258
PALLONETTO[a,d]	258
PETILIA	232
PORDENONE[c]	232
REGAR[b]	233
SEATTLE[a,b]	234
SIWA[a,b]	163
TENGANAN[a,b]	235
THENIA[a]	144
TRINACRIA[b]	236
VIENTIANE[b]	237
WASHINGTON	143
YANGORU[a,b]	315

Class IV (normal activity, 60–150%)

Electrophoretically fast

A[a]	238
BALI[a]	235
BARBIERI[c]	240
INHAMBANE[a,b]	241
KING COUNTY[c]	162
KIWA[a]	206

LAURENZO MARQUEZ[a]	199
LEVADIA[b]	208
LUZ SAINT SAUVEUR[b]	242
MAMMOLA[b]	140
MISENO	258
PALMI II	140
S.DONA[c]	140
S-SAKORN[a,c]	243
STEILACOM	244

Electrophoretically normal

B[a]	72

Electrophoretically slow

ABEOKUTA[c]	225
ADAME[b]	225
ALESSANDRIA[b]	140
ALEXANDRA	162
AYUTTHAYA[a,c]	243
BALTIMORE-AUSTIN	245
EKITI	225
GAMBIA[a]	224
IBADAN-AUSTIN[a]	245
IJEBU-OOE	24
ITA-BALE[c]	24
KARDISTA[b]	208
LAGUNA[b]	246
LANLATE[b]	225
MADRONA	208, 247
MANJACASE[a,c]	241
MINAS GERAIS[b]	208, 248
MORELIA[b]	203
PINAR DEL RIO[b]	249
PORBANDER	250
PORT ALEGRE[b]	251
PORT ROYAL[b]	252
POZZALLO[c]	140
TACOMA[a,c]	253
THESSALY[b]	254
WESTERN[b]	253

Class V (increased activity)

Electrophoretically fast

HEKTOEN	255
VERONA[c]	257

Table 91-4 Summary of G6PD Variants

Class[*]	Polymorphic		Electrophoretic mobility			Altered electrophoretic mobility, %	Total
	Number	%	Fast	Normal	Slow		
I	1†	1	20	30	32	63	82
II	49	45	29	39	41	64	109
III	22	30	25	13	36	82	74
IV	14	32	15	2	26	95	43
V	—	—	2	—	—	100	2
Total	86	28	91	84	135	73	310

[*]See Table 91-3. Class I variants are associated with nonspherocytic hemolytic anemia. Class II variants are severely deficient, with less than 10% residual activity. Class III variants are moderately deficient, with 10–60% of normal residual activity. Class IV variants have nearly normal or normal activity (60–150% of normal). Class V variants have increased activity compared to normals.
†See footnote f in Table 91-3.
SOURCE: Data from Table 91-3.

not unrelated to each other. For instance, variants in class I (chronic nonspherocytic hemolytic anemia: CNSHD) are never polymorphic, presumably because their clinical expression is too severe to become balanced by malaria selection. Among variants in class IV (normal activity), nearly all are electrophoretically different from the wild type (B), because otherwise they would not be detected. A new approach to testing the identity of G6PD variants and the relationships among them by multivariate analysis has been proposed.[472]

From these data, the G6PD locus emerges as the locus in the human genome with the greatest apparent extent of genetic variability. Indeed, of the many loci covered in this book, none has nearly as many alleles identified (Chap. 3). Of course, many more mutants must exist, since roughly two out of three amino acid replacements are electrophoretically undetectable,[265] and additional mutations may be totally silent at the protein level because they do not entail any amino acid replacement (same sense mutations) or because they are located in introns. Therefore one might have surmised that analysis of the G6PD gene at the DNA level would reveal more genetic variation in the form of restriction fragment length polymorphisms (RFLPs). In fact, extensive tests carried out with numerous probes within the gene and flanking the gene, covering over 300 restriction sites, have revealed only one RFLP, and this only in the West African population.[266] This RFLP is indeed a same sense point mutation at amino acid position 372. The significance of this finding remains to be explained. As for the large number of structural alleles, we think it is cautious to assume for the time being that this may be explained simply by ease of ascertainment and by natural selection, before suggesting that the G6PD gene may have an intrinsically greater than average rate of mutation.

CLINICAL MANIFESTATIONS

The vast majority of individuals with glucose-6-phosphate dehydrogenase deficiency are usually asymptomatic and go through life without being aware of their genetic abnormality. The only common clinical manifestation is acute hemolysis, which may be rapidly compensated and often remains undetected. Clinical expression results from an interaction of the molecular properties of each individual G6PD variant with exogenous factors, and possibly additional genetic factors specific for a certain population. No significant adverse effects of G6PD deficiency were discernible on the health and military performance of young, enlisted U.S. black males.[267,582] However, G6PD deficiency can cause much human pathology, and the following clinical syndromes are recognized:

1. Drug-induced hemolysis
2. Infection-induced hemolysis
3. Favism
4. Neonatal jaundice (NNJ)
5. Chronic nonspherocytic hemolytic anemia (CNSHA)

Hemolysis has also been reported to occur in association with diabetic ketoacidosis[268–270] and hypoglycemia;[270] however, coexistent infection and/or oxidant drug exposure cannot always be excluded.[271] Pregnancy does not, of itself, precipitate hemolysis.[272]

Drug-Induced Hemolytic Anemia

As stated in the introductory paragraph, G6PD deficiency was discovered as a direct consequence of investigations into the development of hemolysis in some individuals, usually blacks, who had received primaquine (30 mg daily), which in other individuals causes no red cell destruction.[273–275] Thus, the acute hemolytic anemia associated with G6PD deficiency has become virtually a prototype of hemolytic episodes arising from a unique interaction between genetic and exogenous factors.[308] Clinical hemolysis and jaundice typically begin within 2 to 3 days of starting the drug.[276] The hemolysis is largely intravascular (although to what extent has been recently questioned[277]), and it is characteristically associated with hemoglobinuria. The anemia worsens until the seventh to eighth day. Heinz bodies (Fig. 91-5) are a characteristic finding in the peripheral blood.[278] A reticulocyte response then sets in, and the hemoglobin level begins to recover on the eighth to tenth day. A self-limited course is characteristic with some G6PD variants,[273–276] because newly produced red cells, having higher G6PD activity, are less susceptible than the older cells, which have been selectively destroyed. However, increased drug dosage or the presence of a severely deficient G6PD variant will cause more protracted hemolysis.[279]

A critical analysis of the data whereby individual drugs have been implicated in the causation of hemolysis in G6PD-deficient subjects has been conducted by Beutler,[253,281] who uncovered a discrepancy between the relatively small list of drugs for which there is strong evidence linking them to hemolytic anemia (Table 91-5) and a much larger list of agents for which the evidence is less secure. This discrepancy arises for two reasons.

First, clinical hemolysis is not always reproducible after administration of a particular drug, presumably because a number of factors influence both its interaction with the erythrocyte and the clinical consequences of such interaction (Table 91-6). Certain drugs are reported to cause oxidative hemolysis (but not necessarily anemia) in some population groups but not in others (e.g., chloramphenicol[290,291] and vitamin K[292,293]). Probably for the same reason, the same dose of primaquine given to G6PD-deficient subjects of different ethnic

Fig. 91-5 Heinz bodies in erythrocytes from a G6PD-deficient person. These particles of denatured protein, adhering to the red cell membrane and staining with basic dyes, are seen in large numbers in the red cells of G6PD-deficient individuals after drug exposure. They can also be produced in vitro in both G6PD-deficient and normal red cells after incubation with certain "oxidant" chemicals such as acetylphenylhydrazine. (*From Beutler.*[16])

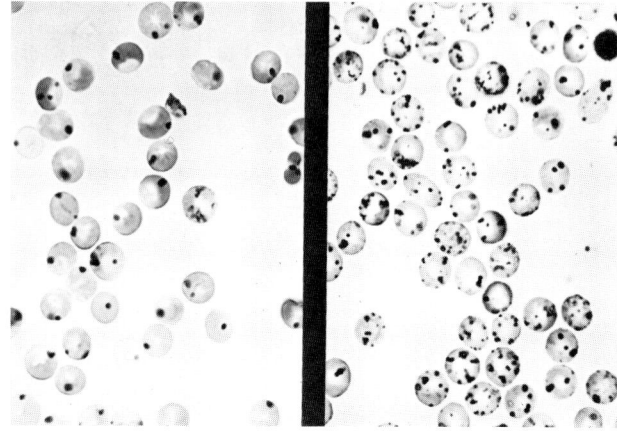

Table 91-5 Drugs and Chemicals Associated with Significant Hemolysis in Subjects with G6PD Deficiency

Drugs	Definite association	Possible association (Ref.)[*]	Doubtful association (Ref.)
Antimalarials	Primaquine, pamaquine	Chloroquine (276, 283–287)	Quinacrine (276)
	Pentaquine		Quinine (282)
Sulfonamides	Sulfanilamide	Sulfamethoxypyridazine	Sulfoxone (288)
	Sulfacetamide	Sulfadimidine	Sulfadiazine
	Sulfapyridine		Sulfamerizine
	Sulfamethoxazole		Sulfisoxazole (282)
Sulfones	Thiazolesulfone		
	Diaminodiaphenylsulphone (DDS, dapsone)		
Nitrofurans	Nitrofurantoin		
Antipyretic-analgesic	Acetanilid		Aminopyrine
			Acetominophen (289)
			Phenacetin (288)
			Aspirin (276)
Others	Nalidixic acid	Chloramphenicol (290, 291)	PAS (288)
	Naphthalone	Vitamin K analogues (292, 293)	L-Dopa
	Niridazole		Vitamin C
	Phenylhydrazine		Dimercaprol
	Toluidine blue		Doxorubicin (295)
	Trinitrotoluene (TNT)		Probenecid (282)
	Methylene blue		
	Phenazopyridine[294]		

[*]These agents will cause clinically significant hemolysis but only when given in larger than therapeutic doses or to subjects with severe variants or to neonates.

SOURCE: Based on data in Beutler,[253,256,281] Dacie,[278] Gordon-Smith,[296] Tarlov et al.,[297] and Wintrobe et al.[298]

origin gives rise to different degrees of hemolysis.[299] Genetic differences in drug metabolism[300,301] and in pharmacokinetics may also affect drug toxicity, while concomitant infection is an important source of additional oxidant stress, particularly in the neonate. Since the oldest red cells have the lowest enzyme activity, the preexisting hemoglobin and reticulocyte count will influence the severity of hemolysis.[302]

Second, clinical and hematologic assessment of hemolysis has notoriously low sensitivity, in that even a two- to threefold increase in red cell destruction may not produce a significant anemia or reticulocytosis. In addition, mere clinical association is not an ideal way of assessing the hemolytic potential of drugs in G6PD deficiency, because clinical situations are often complex. For instance, antibiotic, antipyretic, or analgesic drugs[303] are often administered to patients with infection, which may itself precipitate hemolysis. Similarly, it is unclear whether lead poisoning[253] or dimercaprol therapy[304] causes hemolysis in G6PD deficiency. Simultaneous administration of more than one drug makes it particularly difficult to assess the contribution of each. Thus, while the clinical association is very convincing for some agents (e.g., naphthalene,[305] nalidixic acid[306]), it is less so for others (e.g., sodium metasolphan noramidipyrine[307]). The most reliable technique to assess the hemolytic potential of a drug is to administer it to a normal volunteer and then to follow in this subject the survival of previously transfused ^{51}Cr-labeled G6PD-deficient cells.[275,309] However, the demonstration that a particular drug shortens red cell survival in an individual case[310] should still be interpreted cautiously,[289] since hemolysis may be dose-dependent. At any rate, it has been difficult to do this type of experiment in statistically valid numbers of cases, and it would be regarded today as unethical.

Because of these difficulties, in vitro tests (see Table 91-7) have been developed aiming to predict whether a drug will cause hemolysis in vivo.[285,316,317] Although these tests have been generally validated by analysis of drugs already known to cause hemolysis in vivo, they have not been widely used, less still made compulsory. In our view they should be carried out before a new drug is introduced to a population in which G6PD deficiency is prevalent.

Table 91-6 Factors Which Influence Individual Susceptibility to, and Severity of, Drug-Induced Oxidative Hemolysis

Inherited

Metabolic integrity of the erythrocyte
Precise nature of enzyme defect
Genetic differences in pharmacokinetics

Acquired

Age
Dose, absorption, metabolism, and excretion of drug
Presence of additional oxidative stress, e.g., infection
Effect of drug or metabolite on enzyme activity
Preexisting hemoglobin level
Age distribution of red blood cell population

Infection-Induced Hemolysis

Apart from those areas where favism is prevalent, infection is probably the most common cause of hemolysis in subjects with G6PD deficiency. It is true that in up to one-third of episodes the hemolysis might be attributed to coincidentally administered drugs;[318] but this is probably an overestimate,[319] and infection was, in fact, the true precipitant. The severity and clinical consequences of hemolysis are again influenced by

Table 91-7 Techniques Used to Evaluate the Hemolytic Potential of Drugs Administered to G6PD-Deficient Subjects

Clinical association

The occurrence of otherwise unexplained hemolysis in an individual known to be G6PD-deficient.

Clinical challenge

Administration of drugs in controlled studies to individuals known to be G6PD-deficient.[273]
Administration of drugs to normal volunteers transfused with ^{51}Cr-labeled G6PD-deficient erythrocytes.[282]
Administration of drugs to animals followed by in vitro studies of erythrocytes.[283]

In vitro studies

GSH stability test.[284]
Effect of drug metabolites on mechanical fragility of erythrocytes.[311,312]
Measurement of [14]CO_2 evolution and glucose utilization of normal erythrocytes suspended in homologous serum before and after drug ingestion.[285,313]
Measurement of hydrogen peroxide levels within erythrocytes after incubation with drugs.[314]

a number of factors, including concomitant administration of oxidant drugs, the preexisting level of hemoglobin, hepatic function, and age. Numerous bacterial, viral, and rickettsial infections have been reported as precipitants, but particularly important are infectious hepatitis,[318,320–326] pneumonia,[318,327–330] and typhoid fever.[290,291,332–337]

Viral infections affecting either the upper respiratory tract or the gastrointestinal tract are reported[319] to cause more severe hemolysis than bacterial infections in G6PD-deficient children. Hemolysis is nearly four times more frequent in children with G6PD deficiency who develop viral hepatitis than in normal children,[323] but the degree and duration of jaundice in such children[321] and in adults is frequently out of proportion to the degree of hemolysis,[338] suggesting that the jaundice is in part of hepatocellular origin. Indeed, hepatic dysfunction may contribute to the hyperbilirubinemia seen in G6PD deficiency complicated by viral hepatitis[321,338,339] and pneumonia.[328] On the other hand, erythrocyte G6PD activity is reported to be transiently depressed in individuals with normal G6PD and typhoid or paratyphoid fever.[340]

Renal failure is a well-recognized complication in adults,[318,324,327,331,341,342] whereas it is rare in children.[445] It may be particularly common after urinary tract infection[331] and in patients with preexisting renal disease,[341] while the concomitant administration of nephrotoxic drugs[342] and pathologic changes in the kidney directly attributable to the underlying infection[343] may contribute to its severity. Acute renal failure is a serious complication in patients with viral hepatitis and G6PD deficiency,[320,324,325,344] but it also occurs in subjects with normal G6PD.[345] The pathogenesis is likely to be multifactorial, but the pathologic lesion is probaby acute tubular necrosis,[325,331,342] and renal ischemia and tubular obstruction by hemoglobin casts[324,346] are important in pathogenesis. Most patients with infection-induced hemolysis make a complete recovery, even when the course has been complicated by renal failure, provided hemodialysis is instituted promptly when indicated.

The *mechanism* of infection-induced hemolysis is not well understood. Incubation of influenza A virus with normal red

cells leads to increased hexose monophosphate shunt activity; in contrast, this increase is not seen upon incubation of the virus with G6PD-deficient cells, which, instead, show increased autohemolysis with Heinz body formation.[347] Generation of hydrogen peroxide by activated polymorphonuclear neutrophils in close apposition to G6PD-deficient red cells in vitro can lead to a reduction in GSH content and diminished survival of red cells thus treated.[348] The phenomenon of "immune adherence,"[349] whereby opsonized bacteria adhere to red cells in a process mediated by complement, may be important in promoting close apposition of neutrophils to red cells.[350] Hepatic dysfunction may further aggravate the oxidant stress on red cells by permitting accumulation of metabolites capable of oxidizing red cell SH groups.[325] Activated neutrophils can also mediate lipid peroxidation of red cell membranes, but G6PD-deficient red cells seem no more susceptible than normal red cells.[351] A variable degree of marrow suppression frequently accompanies infection and may delay recovery of the hemoglobin level.

Favism

The occurrence of acute hemolysis after ingestion of broad beans (*Vicia faba*) has been noted since antiquity.[1,2,4] It has occurred on an epidemic scale particularly in Mediterranean countries (Italy,[4,352] Greece,[353] Spain, Portugal, and Turkey[354,355]), but also in the Middle East, the Far East, and North Africa.[355,356] Most,[357–359] but not all,[360,361] of the patients reported in North America and the United Kingdom have had direct Mediterranean ancestry. This geographic distribution correlates best with the endemic consumption of fava beans. Following observations on the similarity between favism and primaquine-induced hemolytic anemia,[362] it became clear that all patients with favism are G6PD-deficient.[8,363,364] However, not all G6PD-deficient subjects are sensitive to fava beans.[365,366] When ^{51}Cr-labeled G6PD-deficient cells from individuals with a clinical history of favism are infused into normal subjects, challenge with primaquine always leads to hemolysis of the deficient cells whereas challenge with fava beans leads to hemolysis only in some cases.[367,368] One or more factors in addition to G6PD deficiency are therefore required for the development of favism.[369] Factors accounting for intrapersonal variability in clinical expression must be environmental (e.g., the amount and form in which the bean is eaten and the season of consumption[355]). On the other hand, interpersonal variability may have a genetic component (inherited perhaps as an autosomal recessive gene[370] or as part of the genetic heterogeneity of G6PD deficiency itself[370–372]). Susceptible individuals probably do not differ in terms of digestion and absorption of fava beans,[278] and β-glucosidase levels in small intestinal biopsies of subjects with favism do not differ from those of normal and G6PD-deficient control subjects.[370] The activity of erythrocyte acid phosphatase has been suggested to be lower in G6PD-deficient males sensitive to fava beans than in the general population due to a higher frequency of the P^a and P^c alleles of the acid phosphatase gene.[373] Decreased urinary D-glutaric acid and defective hepatic glucuronide formation[374,375] have also been reported in these subjects. A reduction in the number of sheep red-cell rosetting lymphocytes[376] and inversion of the peripheral blood helper T cell (CD4) to suppressor T cell (CD8) ratio, due to a decrease of CD4+ and an increase of CD8+ cells,[377] have been described during the hemolytic crisis of favism. These changes may be the consequence of the hemolysis rather than an important pathogenic factor in favism, and similar changes have been reported in hypertransfused subjects with hemoglobinopathies.[378] Despite previous claims, there is no convincing evidence implicating immunologic mechanisms in the pathogenesis of favism.[278,355]

Clinical favism presents characteristically with sudden onset of acute hemolytic anemia within 24 to 48 h of ingestion of the beans. Pallor and hemoglobinuria are the hallmarks.[1] Jaundice is always present, but the bilirubin level is less than in hemolytic attacks triggered by drugs or infection, presumably because the hemoglobinuria is more massive and hemoglobin catabolism is therefore reduced. The anemia is often severe.[353] Acute renal failure may supervene,[379] and fatalities were not uncommon prior to the availability of transfusion therapy.[1] An increase in the proportion of young erythrocytes leads to a decrease in the level of glycosylated hemoglobin (HbA$_1$).[380] The highest incidence is in children aged 2 to 6 years. Boys are affected two to three times more frequently than girls[352] because of the greater number, in every population, of hemizygous males than homozygous females. However, it is well-documented that heterozygous girls are affected, although the condition is usually milder in these subjects.[361,381] Favism occurs after ingestion of fresh,[352] dried,[353] or frozen[352] beans, but fresh beans are by far the commonest offender, and therefore favism is commonest during the spring season. Hemolysis in breast-fed babies whose mothers have eaten fava beans is well-documented.[353,382,383] The mainstay of prevention is avoidance of fava beans, and the mainstay of treatment is blood transfusion in severe cases.[445] The single observation suggesting arrest of hemolysis by desferoxamine[384] has not been substantiated.[385] The injury to red cells in favism is likely to consist in oxidant damage due to a chemical agent. Based on studies of the effect of fractionated extracts on erythrocyte metabolism, the toxic components of fava beans have been suggested to be the pyrimidine aglycones, divicine and isouramil.[386–390] A possible basis for the erratic development of favism might then lie in the level of glucosidases that can release the aglycones. However, β-glucosidase levels in small intestinal biopsies of subjects with favism do not differ from those in normal and G6PD-deficient control subjects.[370] Oxidant damage causes cross-linking of erythrocyte membrane proteins, leading to the formation of distorted erythrocytes which are rapidly cleared from the circulation.[391] Disturbed erythrocyte calcium homeostasis (specifically, reduced activity of the membrane Ca^{2+}-ATPase, leading to increased intraerythrocytic calcium and decreased intraerythrocytic potassium) has been suggested to mediate activation of proteolytic activity within erythrocytes of favic subjects.[392–395] However, exactly similar electrolyte changes are seen on incubation of both G6PD-normal and G6PD-deficient erythrocytes with divicine in vitro,[392] suggesting that additional factors are involved in the hemolytic process.

Neonatal Jaundice

G6PD deficiency is the commonest red cell enzymopathy to cause neonatal hemolysis and jaundice.[396] It appeared from the earliest reports[397–400] that this complication occurs particularly in Greece, Sardinia, and the Far East, but it subsequently emerged as a major problem in Africa[401] and has been reported in North America.[402] Jaundice usually appears by 1 to 4 days of age, at about the same time or slightly earlier than so-called

physiological jaundice[292,396] and later than in blood group alloimmunization. There may be a slightly higher threshold for its clinical detection in black infants.[403]

The relative contributions of red cell destruction and of impaired hepatic function to the pathogenesis of unconjugated neonatal hyperbilirubinemia are disputed.[278] Reports of abnormal red cell morphology,[404] mild anemia,[405] or reticulocytosis[293] suggest an element of hemolysis, but impaired hepatic function, similar to that seen in normal premature infants, may well be a major cause.[406–408] Several distinctive features of neonatal erythrocytes may contribute to the degree of jaundice;[396,404] these include elevated levels of ascorbic acid[409] and depressed levels of vitamin E,[410] glutathione reductase,[411] and catalase.[412]

A striking feature of neonatal jaundice (NNJ) in association with G6PD deficiency is the wide variation in its frequency and severity in different populations (Table 91-8). Environmental or acquired factors are suggested as an explanation for this variation, since the incidence is higher among Africans in Africa than among subjects of African ancestry in America;[302] and among Greeks in Greece than among subjects of Greek ancestry in Australia.[443] Such factors might include administration of potentially hemolytic drugs[292,422,425] and herbal remedies,[405] exposure to naphthalene,[444] infection, gestational age and maturity, acidosis, hypoglycemia, the level of neonatal hemoglobin,[302] and the plasma levels of vitamin C, vitamin E, and riboflavin.[411] Genetic factors, however, are also likely to be important, and they would include the type of G6PD variant and the incidence of the possible superimposed effect of red cell incompatibility between mother and infant. Ethnic group differences in plasma bilirubin levels of full-term neonates may contribute to the severity of the clinical consequences of neonatal jaundice.[405,446]

With respect to treatment, general measures would include avoidance of oxidant drugs, and treatment of coexistent hypoxia, sepsis, and acidosis. Specific measures include prophylactic administration of phenobarbital for at-risk infants to improve hepatic conjugation of bilirubin[440] and exchange transfusion.[445] Although it has been suggested that phototherapy could worsen hemolysis by leading to riboflavin deficiency and loss of antioxidant activity,[447–449] several studies have shown conclusively that this treatment is effective in reducing hyperbilirubinemia.[445,450–452]

Chronic Nonspherocytic Hemolytic Anemia

Although a slight degree of chronic hemolysis invariably accompanies G6PD deficiency, the vast majority of individuals with G6PD deficiency experience significant hemolysis and anemia only under conditions of oxidant stress. Some G6PD variants (class I, Table 91-3), however, are characterized by overt chronic hemolytic anemia which is further exacerbated by oxidant stress. Such variants have been described (almost invariably in males) in many parts of the world, regardless of whether the common types of G6PD deficiency are endemic in the region. For instance, many cases have been reported from Japan.[141] Mostly a single kindred is known for each variant, but sometimes what is apparently the same variant (e.g., G6PD Chicago[86,117,163,209]) has been reported in unrelated individuals in different parts of the world.

That these variants represent structural and functional changes in the enzyme consequent upon mutations within the G6PD gene is suggested[302] by the similarity of the clinical phe-

Table 91-8 G6PD Deficiency and Neonatal Jaundice (NNJ)

Populations	Prevalence of G6PD deficiency (Ref.)	G6PD deficiency as a cause of NNJ (Ref.)
Africa		
West Africa (usually A− variant)	20.6%* (413) 10.7%† (413) 15.5–20%‡ (413, 414)	Well-recognized. Accounts for up to 80% cases of otherwise unexplained NNJ (421). Up to 33% of infants with NNJ have G6PD deficiency (413). Kernicterus is rare, but may occur after maternal exposure to oxidant drugs (422).
South Africa (Bantu)	1.3%* (415) 2–4%‡ (416)	3.1% of all Bantu infants (415) and 10% of full-term male infants (423) with NNJ have G6PD deficiency.
America		
Jamaica	9.4%‡ (417)	20.5% of neonatal jaundice is due to G6PD deficiency (417), and kernicterus occurs in approximately 10%.
USA	7.2%* (418) 5.2%‡ (418) 11.2%* (419) 11.5%* (420)	G6PD deficiency is not a major cause of NNJ among full-term black infants (293, 402, 418, 419) but is important among premature infants (404, 420), after maternal exposure to oxidant drugs (424, 426), and in the presence of unusual variants (75, 76).
Asia		
China/Hong Kong	3.6%* (427) 3.74%* (428)	G6PD deficiency is a very important cause of NNJ. Approximately 15% of all infants with NNJ are G6PD-deficient (427). While only 2–3% will develop kernicterus (429), 55% of infants with kernicterus are G6PD-deficient (427).
Thailand	7.5%* 15.6%† 11.5%‡ (430)	31-64% of infants with NNJ are G6PD-deficient, and up to 5% of hemizygous males and 2% heterozygous females will develop NNJ due to G6PD deficiency (430, 431).
Singapore		25% of NNJ is associated with G6PD deficiency (432); 19 (405) to 22% (433) of G6PD-deficient infants develop significant jaundice, and 2–8% (405) develop kernicterus. Up to 95% of cases of unexplained kernicterus have been reported to be due to G6PD deficiency in Chinese (397) and Malay (398) infants. G6PD deficiency is found in 20.9% of Chinese and 17.2% of Malay infants with NNJ (434).
Chinese	1.36% (405)	
Malay	1.34% (405)	
Indian	0.34% (405)	
M/F ratio for:		
Chinese	5:1 (405)	
Malay	6:1 (405)	
Chinese*	2.6% (397)	
Europe		
Greece (usually Mediterranean variant)	4.6% (435) 2.6–6.1%‡ (436) 2.9%‡ (437)	Approximately 15% of all infants with NNJ have G6PD deficiency (435), and up to 82% (399) of unexplained NNJ is due to G6PD deficiency. About 33% (292, 399) of infants with G6PD deficiency will develop NNJ, and in 5% it will be severe (437); about 50% of those with severe jaundice will develop kernicterus (437).
Italy/Sardinia (usually Mediterranean variant but others reported) (202)	8.8%* (439) 10.6%† (439) 8%* (440)	About 8.5% of unexplained NNJ is due to G6PD deficiency; 15.6% of females (439) and 30% of males (439) with G6PD deficiency will develop NNJ, and about 33% will require exchange transfusions (440).
Israel		The risk of NNJ is highest among Kurdistan Jews. Overall 14.3% of G6PD-deficient male infants develop NNJ (442) which is rarely severe.
Ashkenazi Jews	0.4%*	
Kurdistan	52%*	
Iraq	24.8%*	
Iran	15.1%* (441)	

*Male infants.
†Female infants.
‡Male and female infants.

notype when more than one member of a family is affected, and also when the same variant occurs among unrelated individuals. However, additional factors (genetic or environmental) may also operate to influence the clinical picture; and severely deficient variants can cause more severe hemolysis in some family members than in others.[73,453,454]

The causative link of a G6PD variant with chronic nonspherocytic hemolytic anemia (CNSHA) is usually based on clinical evidence. Often the degree of enzyme deficiency is very severe. Sometimes detailed biochemical characterization is lacking, partly due to the difficulty of purifying sufficient amounts of the (frequently unstable) enzyme for study. In rare cases with associated granulocyte dysfunction[74] hemolysis can be made worse by increased susceptibility to infection (see

Chap. 114). Sometimes chronic hemolysis may arise from an association of mild G6PD deficiency with an unrelated genetically transmitted erythrocyte abnormality, such as congenital dyserythropoietic anemia,[223] hereditary spherocytosis,[457,473] pyruvate kinase deficiency,[458] or 6-phosphogluconolactonase deficiency.[617]

Since the original descriptions,[459] a large number of detailed clinical observations have been reported. Presentation may be with severe neonatal jaundice, while many patients who present later in life give a history of neonatal jaundice often requiring exchange transfusion.[75,98,101,121,460–464] A history of infection or drug-induced hemolysis is also commonly obtained.[465,466] Gallstones may be a prominent feature.[131] Splenomegaly is usually (but not always)[465,467] present. While the hemoglobin concentration may occasionally be normal and the hemolysis well-compensated,[98,453,468] oxidant stress can lead to dramatic fall in the hemoglobin level.[122] The ^{51}Cr-labeled red cell half-life is shortened to 2 to 17 days, and all patients have a reticulocytosis (4 to 34 percent),[101] which may become extreme after splenectomy. Occasionally, the level of reticulocytosis is inappropriately low (3 percent) in relation to the shortening of the ^{51}Cr-labeled red cell half-life (12 days, Ref. 95); the cause is not clear, but folic acid deficiency[73] could be a factor. Increased red cell production at puberty can ameliorate the clinical findings.[470] Osmotic fragility is usually normal and moderately increased autohemolysis (with partial correction by added glucose) is reported.[121,463,465]

Female heterozygotes have been shown to have two populations of cells[471] which have normal and severely deficient G6PD; the severely deficient red cells disappear from the circulation rapidly, and these individuals therefore usually have normal G6PD levels in peripheral blood cells.

Hemolysis in CNSHA is only partly intravascular (as opposed to acute hemolysis due to G6PD deficiency), and studies with ^{51}Cr have usually indicated increased uptake in liver and spleen.[57,465] Splenic sequestration has occasionally been demonstrated,[473] although markedly increased osmotic fragility was also present in that patient and hereditary spherocytosis cannot be excluded as a coexistent abnormality.[253] Accelerated red cell aging also implies a role for the spleen in steady state hemolysis. In vitro deformability was unimpaired in some but not in other[474] severely G6PD-deficient erythrocytes. The presence of membrane polypeptide aggregates containing spectrin has been demonstrated in erythrocytes from patients with G6PD deficiency who had chronic hemolysis but not in those who did not.[475,476] Increased levels of membrane cholesterol and phospholipids are also reported.[477] There have been claims that high dose vitamin E, by acting as an antioxidant, may be useful in the management of chronic hemolysis due to G6PD deficiency,[478,479] and that oral selenium may have an additive beneficial effect.[480] The reported benefit has been only modest (e.g., an increase in red cell half-life from a mean of 15.6 days to 24.3 days, as measured by ^{51}Cr labeling), and such therapy may perhaps be useful in individuals who are vitamin E–deficient. Other studies have failed to show any benefit,[481,482] and no change in erythrocyte membrane polypeptide aggregates was observed after such treatment.[481] A therapeutic option, especially in severe cases, is splenectomy. On theoretical grounds one might question its advisability, since selective red cell destruction in the spleen is seldom documented. In fact, little or no benefit has been reported in some patients[89,101,128,453,468,483] but significant improvement in others[98,101,121,463,464] (also see the review in Ref. 302). We are personally aware of at least one patient who needed several blood transfusions before splenectomy but then only one transfusion in 30 years since splenectomy.

There is considerable variability of almost every manifestation of CNSHA associated with G6PD deficiency. This variability makes it somewhat problematic to give firm guidelines on management, but is in itself intriguing and may make one wonder why reports in the literature fail to give a comforting feeling of consensus. Unlike the G6PD variants without CNSHA, many of which are polymorphic, those associated with CNSHA are all sporadic, and most, if not all, result from independently arisen mutations, each of which is likely to be completely different. It is therefore not surprising that each

one may affect the pathophysiology of the red cell, and ultimately the clinical manifestations, in a subtly different way.

MECHANISM OF HEMOLYSIS

The mammalian red cell is notorious for having a very limited biochemical apparatus and therefore an equally limited range of responses to pathologic changes. Specifically, if any metabolic pathway fails, the predictable consequence is that the cell as a whole will fail: in other words, it will be destroyed prematurely. In essence, G6PD deficiency entails failure of the GSH pathway (Fig. 91-2), and the result is hemolysis. Since a large number of G6PD-deficient variants (classes II and III) are not associated with chronic hemolysis, we can infer that a small amount of residual G6PD activity is sufficient for the steady state requirements of the red cells. Below that level (class I variants), it is evident that NADPH production has become inadequate, although we do not yet know precisely how this leads to hemolysis. A reasonable model is that the GSH level becomes so low that critical sulfhydryl groups in some key proteins are not maintained in reduced form and intramolecular or intermolecular disulfides are formed. The most pertinent observation is probably that of membrane-cytoskeletal protein aggregates in red cells from patients with class I variants.[475,476] Such aggregates decrease red cell deformability,[474] and they may alter the cell surface sufficiently to make it recognizable by macrophages as abnormal (much like an aged red cell), thus leading to extravascular hemolysis. With class II and class III variants, hemolysis depends, by definition, on an exogenous trigger. Again, the exact sequence of events is incompletely known, but the following points are well-established:

1. Some of the agents that can cause hemolysis stimulate the hexose monophosphate shunt pathway in normal red cells, indicating that in their presence increased NADPH production is required.[313]

2. A fall in GSH is invariably associated with hemolytic events in G6PD-deficient individuals.

3. In some cases, particularly in favism, acute hemolysis is associated with massive formation of Heinz bodies (consisting of denatured hemoglobin), which by their very presence certainly mediate red cell destruction (Fig. 91-5).

4. Oxygen radicals generated by the autooxidation of hemoglobin and in other ways also cause formation of Heinz bodies,[45] intracellular proteolysis, and peroxidation of membrane lipids.[63,65]

These facts, taken together, indicate clearly that acute hemolysis in G6PD deficiency depends on a failure of the cell, when challenged, to supply enough NADPH for the detoxification of hydrogen peroxide and of oxygen radicals, thus justifying the popular phrase "oxidative hemolysis."[592]

The question of why some G6PD-deficient variants are associated with chronic nonspherocytic hemolytic anemia (CNSHA) (class I) and others are not (class II and III) is interesting, and not yet fully answered. Residual G6PD activity is certainly a factor, but the values in class I and II overlap extensively. Analysis of kinetic data has revealed that variants in class II often have abnormally high substrate affinities for

G6P, or NADP, or both; whereas variants in class I often have low substrate affinities and decreased affinity for the inhibitor, NADPH.[484] For reasons explained more fully elsewhere,[40] we think it is likely that residual enzyme activity and the K_m for G6P may be the most important determinants of whether a particular G6PD-deficient variant causes CNSHA or not.

MOLECULAR BASIS OF G6PD DEFICIENCY

As for any other genetically determined enzymopathy, deficiency of G6PD might be due to either a quantitative reduction in the number of enzyme molecules, or to a qualitative change in the structure of the enzyme molecule, or both. The findings reviewed in the previous sections support strongly the notion that the majority of subjects with G6PD deficiency have a qualitatively abnormal enzyme and that a wide range of different mutational changes have taken place in human populations. However, until recently this remained hypothetical. Very recently, some of the polymorphic G6PD variants[598,618,619] and some of the rare variants[598] have been cloned and sequenced (see Fig. 91-4). Thus far, the findings reported confirm our expectations, in that each variant is different and all but one differ from the normal G6PD (type B), by a single point mutation. The exception is G6PD A−, in which there are two mutations, one of which is the same as in G6PD A, supporting the notion that the former derives from the latter.[13]

OTHER CLINICAL STUDIES

Occasional patients have been described in whom deficiency of G6PD in tissues other than red cells contributes to the clinical picture (see Table 91-9). This is to be expected, since the same G6PD gene is expressed in all tissues. It is also not surprising that erythroid manifestations predominate, as the red cell is unable to renew its supply of G6PD, and is also uniquely dependent on the integrity of the hexose monophos-phate shunt for its ability to withstand oxidant stress. Other cells can replace G6PD molecules (if they are abnormally unstable) and may have alternative means of producing NADPH. Thus, for instance, the shortage of G6PD in G6PD-deficient leukocytes is much less than in erythrocytes (Ref. 484; and see Table 91-1). Moreover, a decreased leukocyte G6PD level has no clinical consequences in the majority of instances,[485,486] but it may be important in patients with very rare mutants[74,487–489] in whom less than 5 percent residual G6PD activity may be associated with defective neutrophil function. The functional defect is similar to that seen in chronic granulomatous disease, and it arises through disturbance of an NADPH-linked pathway required for killing ingested bacteria (see Chap. 114). Low levels of leukocyte G6PD in chronic granulomatous disease[490–492] are not due to a mutation at the G6PD locus, and they probably do not contribute to the neutrophil dysfunction. Low levels of G6PD activity in platelets are variably associated with in vitro abnormalities,[493,494] but with no demonstrable clinical consequences.

In well-designed population studies, there has been little or no evidence that any disorders other than hemolytic anemia arise more frequently in G6PD-deficient individuals than in nondeficient control subjects.[582] Nevertheless, a number of associations have been reported, some from population studies (Table 91-10). Reported genetic associations may in part arise because an ethnically heterogeneous population (American blacks) has been studied; an apparent association of a disorder with G6PD deficiency may simply reflect the presence of more than one gene of African origin within that population. However, the bulk of evidence from Africa[401,456,511,512] and from the United States[513,514,536] suggests that there is no true and independent association of G6PD deficiency and sickle-cell anemia. In some cases, the association is allegedly on the basis of coinheritance of linked X-chromosome loci (e.g., optic atrophy[133,472]), but in these, as with most other single case reports, there are no detailed family and molecular studies to support a genuine association. At a phenotypic level, the biochemical changes of G6PD deficiency in certain tissues (hematologic and nonhematologic) may predispose to the development of other conditions. In the presence of another abnormality, G6PD deficiency may act in an additive or even synergistic way to influence clinical expression. Thus, the coexistence of G6PD deficiency with another cause of hemolytic anemia may exacerbate the clinical picture. The clinical effects

Table 91-9 G6PD Deficiency in Nonerythroid Tissues

Tissue	Clinical effects	Refs.
Hematologic		
Leukocytes		
Granulocytes	Increased susceptibility to infection	74, 487–489, 484, 497
Lymphocytes	Probably none	376, 377
Platelets	Probably none	493, 494, 498, 569, 581
Nonhematologic		
Lens	Cataracts	499–502
Liver	Possible contributory factor in hyperbilirubinemia, e.g., of NNJ	339, 503
Renal, adrenal, myocardial, sperm, saliva	Probably none	503, 484, 504, 505

SOURCE: Valentine and Paglia,[495] Luzzatto and Battistuzzi,[484] and Marks et al.[496]

Table 91-10 Reported Clinical and Genetic Associations* of G6PD Deficiency

Hematologic (Refs.)	
Heterozygosity for sickle-cell anemia, β-thalassemia, and α-thalassemia	(506–513)
Nonhematologic (Refs.)	
Case reports	
Optic atrophy	(57, 133)
Malignant hyperthermia	(515)
Xeroderma pigmentosum	(516)
Cystic fibrosis	(517)
Population studies	
Schizophrenia	(518, 519)
Abnormal glucose tolerance	(520, 521)
Abnormal steroid metabolism	(522)
Pernicious anemia	(523)
Regional enteritis	(524)
Coronary artery disease	(525)
Hypertension	(526)

*None of these associations is proven.

of deficient G6PD levels in nonhematologic tissues are largely speculative, but may, for example, be important in the development of cataracts (Table 91-8).

G6PD activity in malignant cells from a variety of human tumors (breast,[527–529] prostate,[530] colon, and stomach[531]) is often increased in comparison to G6PD activity in benign cells, and this has formed the basis for cytochemical tests used in the characterization of these tumors.[531,532] The high G6PD activity of tumors has been known for 30 years,[71] and it is presumably related to a high rate of cell division. Perhaps this idea has led to studies in which the incidence of G6PD deficiency has been reported to be lower in cancer patients than in controls,[533–535] as though G6PD deficiency afforded a degree of protection against cancer. However, a recent study from Sardinia has failed to demonstrate a protective effect of G6PD deficiency against the development of hematologic neoplasm.[537]

DIAGNOSIS

The diagnosis of G6PD deficiency is easy. However, careful attention must be paid to the methodology and to the interpretation of the results. Important considerations include:

1. There is very wide geographical distribution of this defect and a high prevalence in developing countries, which makes a simple and inexpensive test important.

2. The actual enzyme activity of G6PD must be measured, rather than the amount of G6PD protein.

3. The level of activity in young erythrocytes is higher than in older ones. Thus, a reticulocytosis can lead to a false normal result. One way of circumventing this difficulty is to centrifuge the sample to be tested and to assay separately the enzyme activity in erythrocytes from the bottom (older cells) and from the top (younger cells) of the resulting column of cells, as well as the activity of the whole unfractionated sample.[538,539]

Alternatively, or additionally, one can determine the ratio of G6PD activity to the activity of another age-dependent enzyme, e.g., hexokinase.

4. Because of red cell mosaicism arising from random X-chromosome inactivation, heterozygotes have a mixture of normal and deficient erythrocytes, and the proportion between the two cell types (maternally and paternally derived) can vary enormously between the extremes of completely normal activity and complete deficiency. A cell lysate may therefore not reveal heterozygosity if the proportion of enzyme-deficient cells is small. Microscopic examination of individual cells on a blood film slide is preferable.

All the existing methods for measurement of G6PD activity depend essentially on the production of NADPH. The direct enzyme assay gives an accurate quantitative measurement. A number of other procedures provide convenient screening tests, aiming only to classify subjects as G6PD-normal or G6PD-deficient. Some of them are semiquantitative (Table 91-11).

ADDITIONAL NOTES ON MANAGEMENT

The vast majority of individuals with G6PD deficiency do not need treatment, as they suffer no ill effects in the steady state. Screening of all newborns except in areas where low risk populations predominate (e.g., in Northern Europe and among South American Indians) has been proposed,[396] and detection of male hemizygotes and most females heterozygotes has been shown to be feasible.[548,549] Such a program would obviously facilitate avoidance of potentially hemolytic agents (certain drugs and fava beans) or the use of such drugs in subhemolytic doses in individuals known to be susceptible. This is the single most important aspect of management.

Specific therapy (e.g., for neonatal jaundice) has been dis-

Table 91-11 Diagnosis of G6PD Deficiency

Method	Comments	References
Definitive assay	Spectrophotometer required. Measures 6PGD as well as G6PD (activities can be separated).	31, 253, 541–543 540
Screening Fluorescent spot test	Same principle as definitive assay, but special equipment not required. Cheap, simple, reliable. Stored blood usable. Semiquantitative results available.	544–550
Ascorbate cyanide test	Cheap and simple. Fresh blood required.	551, 552
MTT (tetrazolium) staining test	Highly reliable cytochemical technique for detecting heterozygotes.	553–557
Methemoglobin reduction methods	Cheap and simple, but prolonged incubation time required. Fresh blood required. False positives reported. Lends itself to cytochemical modification suitable for heterozygote detection.	558, 559 560
Dye decolorization	Cheap, simple, reliable, and extensively used, but prolonged incubation time required. Fresh blood required.	561, 562

cussed above with the relevant clinical syndromes. Patients with acute and chronic hemolysis may, in addition, require blood transfusion. Because the viability of G6PD-deficient erythrocytes after storage may not be as good as that of normal erythrocytes,[564] it has been suggested that blood from donors who are themselves G6PD-deficient should not be used for transfusion purposes.[567,568] There have been also occasional reports of hemolysis of transfused G6PD-deficient erythrocytes,[565,566] although it was not proven that hemolysis was the result of this enzyme defect. Indeed, G6PD-deficient erythrocytes have been shown to be perfectly satisfactory for transfusion purposes,[563] and proscribing deficient individuals from donating blood would severely deplete the number of available donors in parts of the world where the deficiency is common.[401] Thus, with the exception of exchange transfusion in severe neonatal jaundice and in the management of severe hemolytic anemia due to favism,[445] G6PD-deficient blood should be considered safe for transfusion purposes.

G6PD AS A CLONAL MARKER

Somatic cells in females heterozygous for the G6PD locus will be of two types, each type expressing only one or the other allele (Fig. 91-6; Ref. 52). If neoplastic transformation of a single cell were to lead to its proliferation, all the progeny cells of the resulting tumor would be expected to express a single G6PD allele. The product of this locus can therefore be used as a clonal marker. Since the original studies of uterine tumors using this approach,[570] a large number of other neoplasms have been studied,[571–573] and most have been revealed to be of clonal origin. In the case of hematologic malignancies[574–575] it has been shown that neoplastic cells that have differentiated along different pathways (e.g., erythrocytes, granulocytes, and platelets in chronic myeloid leukemia [576,577] and in polycythemia rubra vera[578]) nevertheless have a common stem-cell origin. Paroxysmal nocturnal hemoglobinuria is a nonmalignant hematologic disorder that has also been shown to be of clonal origin,[579] and clonal proliferation may be important in the pathogenesis of atheromatous plaques.[580]

There are several possible sources of error in the interpretation of G6PD phenotypes as clonal markers.[484,584] The admixture of normal cells (e.g., in a solid tumor biopsy) which will have both G6PD phenotypes may mask the presence of a single G6PD phenotype from the malignant cells. The relative activity of the two phenotypes in the normal tissue from which the neoplasm arises may vary from one tissue to another and at different sites within the same tissue. It is also possible that clonal proliferation of more than one cell has occurred (i.e., the tumor is of multicentric origin) but that each of the original cells has, by coincidence, the same G6PD phenotype. A further problem (Fig. 91-6) is somatic cell selection,[584–586] whereby X-linked genes other than that for G6PD may influence the proliferation of cells after the inactivation process has taken place.

G6PD DEFICIENCY AND MALARIA

The now classic notion that G6PD deficiency has become widespread as a result of malaria selection[587] can be visualized easily by simple inspection of the geographic distribution of

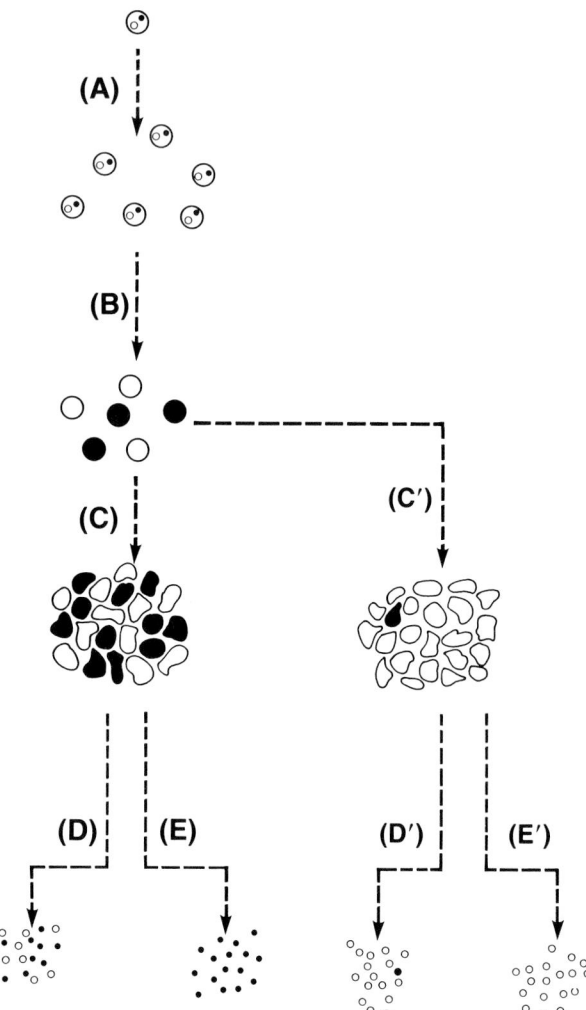

Fig. 91-6 The G6PD phenotype in heterozygotes can yield information on clonal proliferation and somatic cell selection. At the top embryonic cells (A) before X-chromosome inactivation: the two dots represent expression of two different alleles of G6PD. B. Inactivation of one X chromosome per cell produces two cell populations (empty and filled circles) distinguishable by their G6PD phenotype. C. Proliferation of cells at about even rates produces mosaicism in the adult. C'. Differential growth rate of the two cell types arising from X inactivation (somatic cell selection) may produce in the adult a (nearly) homogeneous population. This could apply to the whole body, or it may occur in one tissue and not in another, because a particular X-linked gene, for which the subject is heterozygous, may confer a growth advantage only in a tissue where the gene is expressed. D. Pathologic tissue (for instance, an inflammatory process or the healing of a wound) will still produce a mosaic. E. Pathologic proliferation arising from a single cell ("monoclonal") of an adult tissue (for instance, a tumor) will produce a homogeneous population. D' and E'. If pathologic proliferation arises in a tissue that is already homogeneous as a result of C', the resulting cell population will still be homogeneous, regardless of whether the proliferative process is monoclonal or polyclonal.

this red cell phenotype (Fig. 91-7) in comparison to an epidemiologic map of *P. falciparum* malaria (see, for instance, Ref. 588). Several discrepancies are easy to explain. In Southern Europe G6PD deficiency is common and there is no malaria, but the latter has been eradicated only over the last two generations. In North America there is no malaria, but the prevalence of G6PD deficiency in this continent is entirely accounted for by migrations that have taken place in relatively recent historical times. Geographic correlation alone is of course no proof of the "malaria hypothesis." The body of

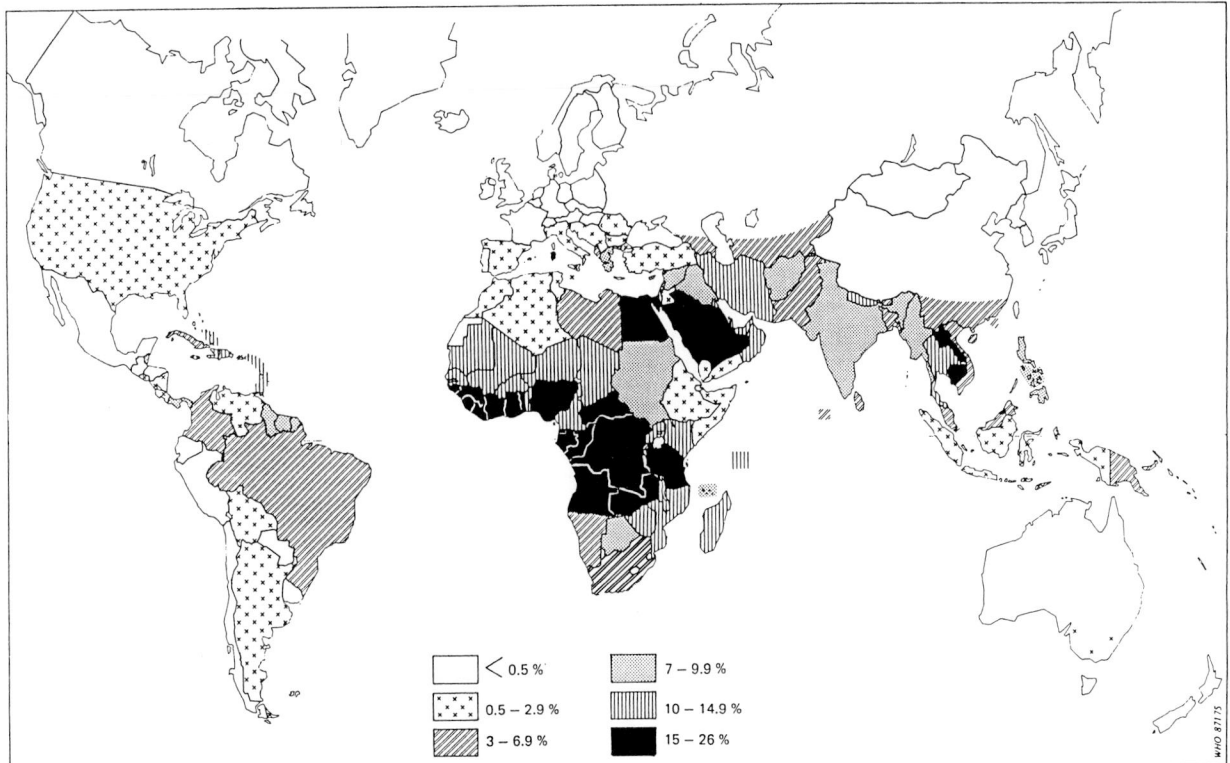

Fig. 91-7 World distribution of G6PD deficiency. The values shown by the different shadings are frequencies in the populations of the various countries of G6PD-deficient males (which are also gene frequencies, since the gene is X-linked). (The map has been assembled in collaboration with Bernadette Modell, based on Livingstone[455] and Luzzatto[469] and with the help of published and unpublished data provided by G.F. Gaetani, V. der Kaloustian, S. Miwa and V. Panich.)

more compelling evidence has been reviewed elsewhere,[593] and it can be only briefly summarized here (see related discussion about hemoglobin variation, Chap. 93).

Micromapping. Micromapping of relatively narrow geographic areas has consistently shown a good correlation between the frequency of G6PD deficiency and the intensity of malaria transmission, for instance, in East Africa,[594] Papua New Guinea,[595] Sardinia,[596] and Greece.[597] In the last two examples the evidence is strengthened by the fact that the population is genetically relatively homogeneous in these areas, and the variance of frequencies of other genes was shown to be significantly lower than that of G6PD deficiency.[583]

Genetic Heterogeneity of Polymorphic G6PD Variants. If G6PD deficiency had spread by genetic drift, the same mutant would be found everywhere. Instead, diverse point mutations (see above) must have arisen independently and then spread centrifugally to establish themselves at polymorphic frequencies: a good example of convergent microevolution in the human species. In this respect the G6PD deficiency polymorphism is more reminiscent of the highly heterogeneous thalassemia system than of the unique mutation of hemoglobin S (see Chap. 93).

Clinical Studies. Clinical studies in the field have yielded ambiguous data when prevalence of malaria or malaria parasitemia was compared between normal and G6PD-deficient males or in subjects of both sexes.[599–602] However, in the single study in which girls heterozygous for G6PD deficiency (Gd^B/Gd^{A-}) were rigorously classified, a significantly lower *P.falciparum* parasitemia was observed.[603,604] It would be highly desirable that this somewhat laborious test be repro-

duced independently in heterozygotes for this and other G6PD-deficient variants.

In Vitro Studies. Once a culture system for the intraerythrocytic cycle of *P.falciparum* was developed by Trager and Jensen,[605] it became possible to test in controlled experiments whether the G6PD genotype of red cells affected their ability to play host to the parasite. Several groups have independently reported that the growth of *P.falciparum* was impaired in G6PD-deficient red cells,[606–608] although in some studies the difference was apparent only when the cultures were subjected to oxidative stress.[609] The preferential development of parasites in G6PD-normal as opposed to G6PD-deficient red cells is in keeping with previous evidence obtained in vivo.[610]

Mechanism of Protection Against Malaria

The findings summarized above leave little doubt that the G6PD deficiency polymorphism is balanced by malaria selection. At the same time, the mechanism whereby this is effected is not yet fully explained. In our own view the most significant clue is that in vivo protection against malaria is a prerogative of heterozygotes. Therefore, two questions must be answered:

1. How does G6PD deficiency hinder the parasite cycle? In vitro culture experiments show clearly that the invasion stage is not affected, but intracellular schizogony is.[608] The most likely explanation is that the G6PD-deficient red cell environment causes oxidative injury to the parasite.[611–613]

2. Why are hemizygous or homozygous G6PD-deficient individuals not protected as well or better than heterozygotes?

This situation is paradoxical, since hemizygotes and homozygotes have only G6PD-deficient red cells in their blood, whereas heterozygotes, who are genetic mosaics, have on the average only 50 percent of them. Recent evidence suggests that it is the very coexistence of two different red cell populations in heterozygotes that may be responsible for their relative resistance to malaria.[614] Parasites that have survived passage through G6PD-deficient red cells become adapted to this type of host cell after several cycles,[615] thus explaining why hemizygotes and homozygotes are not protected. On the other hand, this process of adaptation is hindered when parasites cycle through G6PD-normal red cells, thus explaining the lower parasitemia in heterozygotes. The mechanism of adaptation is not yet known, but it is associated with expression of a parasite-specific G6PD,[615] and studies of this enzyme and of the gene encoding it in *P. falciparum* are in progress.[614,616]

ACKNOWLEDGMENTS

We are immensely indebted to Dr. Ernest Beutler who, having been a pioneer of research in this area, has authoritatively covered G6PD deficiency in all five previous editions of this textbook over a span of 23 years. We are grateful to him, to H.N. Kirkman, G.F. Gaetani, T. Meloni, G. Fiorelli, H. Marti, and others for communicating unpublished observations; to G.M. Persico, D. Toniolo, M. D'Urso, G. Battistuzzi, E.A. Usanga, G. Martini, D. Schlessinger, P.M. Mason, M. Town, and others for sharing in experimental work and many discussions; to T.M. Cox, L. Foroni, N. Foulkes, and T. Vulliamy for reviewing the manuscript; and to J. Garnet, S. Stanborough, and C. Gilham for preparing it. Work in the author's laboratory is supported by a Programme Grant from the Medical Research Council of Great Britain.

REFERENCES

1. LUISADA A: Favism: A singular disease chiefly affecting the red blood cells. *Medicine (Baltimore)* 20:229, 1941.
2. FERMI C, MARTINETTI P: Studio sul favismo. *Ann Ig Sper* 15:75, 1905.
3. GASBARRINI A: Il favismo. *Policlinico Sez Prat* 22:1505, 1915.
4. SANSONE G, PIGA AM, SEGNI G: Il favismo. *Minerva Med* 1958.
5. BEUTLER E: Glucose-6-phosphate dehydrogenase deficiency, in Stanbury JBB, Wyngaarden IB, Frederickson DS (eds): *The Metabolic Basis of Inherited Disease*, 1st ed. New York, McGraw-Hill, 1960.
6. CARSON PE, FLANAGAN CL, ICKES CE, ALVING AS: Enzymatic deficiency in primaquine-sensitive erythrocytes. *Science* 124:484, 1956.
7. WALLER HD, LOEHR GW, TABATABAI M: Haemolyse und Fehlen von Glucose-6-phosphate-dehydrogenase in roten Blutzellen (eine Fermentanomalie der Erythrocyten). *Klin Wochenschr* 35:1022, 1957.
8. SANSONE G, SEGNI G: Nuovi aspetti dell' alterato biochimismo degli eritrociti dei favici: Assenza pressoche' completa della glucosos-6-P deidrogenasi: *Boll Soc Ital Biol Sper* 34:327, 1958.
9. MARKS PA: *Glucose 6-Phosphate Dehydrogenase in the Red Cells*, 2d ed. Bishop C (ed). New York, Academic, 1965.
10. COHEN P, ROSEMEYER MA: Human glucose-6-phosphate dehydrogenase: Purification of the erythrocyte enzyme and the influence of ions on its activity. *Eur J Biochem* 8:1, 1969.
11. BONSIGNORE A, DE FLORA A: Regulatory properties of G6PD, in Horecker BC, Stadtman ER (eds): *Current Topics in Cellular Regulation*. New York, Academic, 1972, vol 6, p 21.
12. BONSIGNORE A, CANCEDDA R, NICOLINI A, DAMIANI G, DE FLORA A: Metabolism of human erythrocyte glucose-6-phosphate dehydrogenase. VI. Interconversion of multiple molecular forms. *Arch Biochem Biophys* 147:493, 1971.
13. BABALOLA AOG, BEETLESTONE JG, LUZZATTO L: Genetic variants of human erythrocyte glucose-6-phosphate dehydrogenase. *J Biol Chem* 251:2993, 1976.
14. DE FLORA, MORELLI A, BENATTI U, GIULIANO F, MOLINARI MP: Human erythrocyte G6PD. Interaction with oxidased and reduced coenzyme. *Biochem Biophys Res Commun* 60:999, 1974.
15. PERSICO MG, VIGLIETTO G, MARTINI G, TONIOLO D, PAONESSA G, MOSCATELLI C, DONO R, VULLIAMY T, LUZZATTO L, D'URSO M: Isolation of human glucose-6-phophate dehydrogenase (G6PD) cDNA clones: Primary structure of the protein and unusual 5' non-coding region. *Nucleic Acids Res* 14:2511 and 7822 (erratum), 1986.
16. BEUTLER E: Glucose-6-phosphate dehydrogenase deficiency, in Stanbury JB, Wyngaarden JB, Fredrickson DS (eds): *The Metabolic Basis of Inherited Disease*, 3d ed. New York, McGraw-Hill, 1972, p 1358.
17. CHUNG AE, LANGDON RC: Human erythrocyte glucose-6-phosphate dehydrogenase. II. Enzyme-coenzyme interrelationship. *J Biol Chem* 238:2317, 1963.
18. DESCALZI-CANCEDDA F, CARUSO C, ROMANO M, DI PRISCO G, CAMARDELLA L: Amino acid sequence of the carboxy-terminal end of human erythrocyte glucose-6-phosphate dehydrogenase. *Biochem Biophys Res Commun* 118:332, 1984.
19. KHAN A, BERTRAND O, COTTREAU D, BOIVIN P, DREYFUS JC: Evidence for structural differences between human glucose-6-phosphate dehydrogenase purified from leukocytes and erythrocytes. *Biochem Biophys Res Commun* 77:65, 1977.
20. CAMARDELLA L, CARUSO C, RUTIGLIANO B, ROMANO M, DI PRISCO G, DESCALZI F: Identification of a reactive lysine residue in human erythrocyte glucose-6-phosphate dehydrogenase, in Yoshida A, Beutler E (eds): *Glucose-6-Phosphate Dehydrogenase*. New York, Academic, 1986.
21. JEFFERY J, HOBBS L, JORNVALL H: Glucose-6-phosphate dehydrogenase from Saccharomyces cerevisiae: Characterization of a reactive lysine residue labeled with acetylsalicylic acid. *Biochemistry* 24:666, 1985.
22. MANNING JE: Personal communication.
23. BHADBHADE MM, ADAMS NJ, FLYNN TG, LEVY MR: Sequence identity between a lysine-containing peptide from leuconostoc mesenteroides glucose-6-phosphate dehydrogenase and an active site peptide from human erythrocyte glucose-6-phosphate dehydrogenase. *FEBS Lett* 211:243, 1987.
24. LUZZATTO L, AFOLAYAN A: Different types of human erythrocyte glucose-6-phosphate dehydrogenase, with characterization of two new genetic variants. *J Clin Invest* 47:1833, 1968.
25. KIRKMAN HN, GAETANI GF: Catalase: A tetrameric enzyme with four tightly bound molecules of NADPH. *Proc Natl Acad Sci USA* 81:4343, 1984.
26. ROSENSTRAUS M, CHASIN LA: Isolation of mammalian cell mutants deficient in glucose-6-phosphate dehydrogenase activity: Linkage to hypoxanthine phosphoribosyl transferase. *Proc Natl Acad Sci USA* 72:493, 1975.
27. TOWN M, LUZZATTO L: Unpublished results.
28. AEBI HE, WYSS SR: Acatalasemia, in Stanbury JB, Wyngaarden JB, Fredrickson DS (eds): *The Metabolic Basis of Inherited Disease*, 4th ed. New York, McGraw-Hill, 1978, p 1792.
29. KIRKMAN HN, GALIANO S, GAETANI GF: The function of catalase-bound NADPH. *J Biol Chem* 262:1, 1987.
30. GAETANI GF, FERRARIS AM: Recent developments on Mediterranean G6PD. *Br J Haematol* 68:1, 1988.
31. GLOCK GE, MCLEAN P: Further studies on the properties and assay of glucose-6-phosphate dehydrogenase of rat liver. *Biochem J* 55:400, 1953.
32. BATTISTUZZI G, D'URSO M, TONIOLO D, PERSICO GM, LUZZATTO L: Tissue-specific levels of human glucose-6-phosphate dehydrogenase correlate with methylation of specific sites at the 3' end of the gene. *Proc Natl Acad Sci USA* 82:1465, 1985.
33. TEPPERMAN HM, TEPPERMAN J: On the response of hepatic G6PD activity to changes in diet composition and food intake pattern, in Weber G (ed): *Advances in Enzyme Regulation*. New York, Pergamon, 1963, vol 1, p 121.
34. KLETZIEN RF, FRITZ RS, PROSTKO CR, JONES EA, DREHER KL: Hepatic glucose-6-phosphate dehydrogenase: Nutritional and hormonal regulation of mRNA levels, in Yoshida A, Beutler E (eds): *Glucose-6-phosphate Dehydrogenase*. New York, Academic, 1986, p 361.
35. PERSICO M, BATTISTUZZI G, MARENI C, NOBILE C, D'URSO M, TONIOLO D, LUZZATTO L: Genetic variants of human glucose-6-phosphate dehydrogenase (G6PD): Studies of turnover and of G6PD-specific mRNA, in Weatherall DJ et al (eds): *Advances in Red Cell Biology*. New York, Raven, 1982, p 309.
36. PIOMELLI S, CORASH LM, DAVENPORT DD, MIRAGLIA J, AMOROSI EL: In vivo liability of glucose-6-phosphate dehydrogenase in Gd^A and Gd^Mediterranean deficiency. *J Clin Invest* 47:940, 1968.
37. BONSIGNORE A, LORENZONI I, CANCEDDA R, CONSULICH ME, DE FLORA A: Effect of divalent cations on the structure of human erythrocyte G6PD. *Biochem Biophys Res Commun* 42:159, 1971.

38. TAKIZAWA T, HUANO I-Y, , IKUTA T, YOSHIDA A: Human glucose-6-phosphate dehydrogenase: Primary structure and cDNA cloning. *Proc Natl Acad Sci USA* 83:4157, 1986.

39. YOSHIDA A: Hemolytic anemia and G-6-PD deficiency. *Science* 179:532, 1973.

40. LUZZATTO L, TESTA U: Human erythrocyte glucose 6-phosphate dehydrogenase. Structure and function in normal and mutant subjects. *Curr Top Hematol* 1:1, 1978.

41. LUZZATTO L: Regulation of the activity of glucose-6-phosphate dehydrogenase by NADP+ and NADPH. *Biochim Biophys Acta* 146:18, 1967.

42. MORELLI A, BENATTI U, GIULIANO F, DE FLORA A: Human erythrocyte glucose-6-phosphate dehydrogenase. Evidence for competitive binding of NADP and NADPH. *Biochem Biophys Res Commun* 70:600, 1976.

43. KIRKMAN HN, GAETANI GD, CLEMONS EH, MARENI C: Red cell NADP and NADPH in glucose-6-phosphate dehydrogenase deficiency. *J Clin Invest* 55:875, 1975.

44. KIRMAN HN, GAETANI GF, CLEMONS EH: NADP-binding proteins causing reduced availability and sigmoid release of NADP in human erythrocytes. *J Biol Chem* 261:4039, 1986.

45. CARRELL RW, WINTERBOURN CC, RACHMILEWITZ EA: Activated oxygen and haemolysis. *Br J Haematol* 30:259, 1975.

46. GAETANI DG, PARKER JC, KIRKMAN HN: Intracellular restraint: A new basis for the limitation in response to oxidative stress in human erythrocytes containing low activity variants of glucose-6-phosphate dehydrogenase. *Proc Natl Acad Sci USA* 71:3584, 1974.

47. SARTORI E: Elementi per la genetica del favismo. *Studi Sassar* 35:I, 1957.

48. LUZZATTO L: Glucose-6-phosphate dehydrogenase deficiency. *Adv Med* 21:398, 1986.

49. ADAM A: Linkage between deficiency of glucose-6-phosphate dehydrogenase and colour blindness. *Nature* 189:686, 1961.

50. NORA JJ, FRAZER FC: *Medical Genetics.* Philadelphia, Lea & Febiger, 1974.

51. BEUTLER E, YEH M, FAIRBANKS VF: The normal human female as a mosaic of X-chromosome activity: Studies using the gene for G-6-PD deficiency as a marker. *Proc Natl Acad Sci USA* 48:9, 1962.

52. DAVIDSON RG, NITOWSKY HM, CHILDS B: Demonstration of two populations of cells in the human female heterozygous for glucose-6-phosphate dehydrogenase variants. *Proc Natl Acad Sci USA* 50:481, 1963.

53. KEATS B: Genetic mapping: X chromosome. *Hum Genet* 64:28, 1983.

54. PAI GS, SPRENKLE JA, DO TT, MARENI CE, MIGEON BR: Localisation of loci for hypoxanthine phosphoriboxyltransferase and glucose-6-phosphate dehydrogenase and biochemical evidence of non-random X-chromosome expression from studies of a human X-autosome translocation. *Proc Natl Acad Sci USA* 77:2810, 1980.

55. SZABO P, PURRELLO M, ROCCHI M, ARCHIDIACONO N, ALHADEFF B, FILIPPI G, TONIOLO D, MARTINI G, LUZZATTO L, SINISCALO M: Cytological mapping of the human glucose-6-phosphate dehydrogenase gene distal to the fragile-X site suggests a high rate of meiotic recombination across the site. *Proc Natl Acad Sci USA* 81:7855, 1984.

56. PATTERSON M, SCHWARTZ C, BELL M, SAUER S, HOFKER M, TRASK B, VAN DEN ENGH G, DAVIES KE: Physical mapping studies on the human X chromosome in the region Xq27-Zqter. *Genomics* 1:297, 1987.

57. ESCOBAR MA, HELLER P, TROBAUGH FE JR: "Complete" erythrocyte glucose 6-phosphate dehydrogenase deficiency. *Arch Intern Med* 113:428, 1964.

58. JUNIEN C, KAPLAN JC, HEIENHOFER HC, MALGRET P, SENDER A: G 6 PD Baudelocque: A new unstable variant characterized in cultured fibroblasts. *Enzyme* 18:48, 1974.

59. MARTINI G, TONIOLO D, VULLIAMY T, LUZZATTO L, DONO R, VIGLIETTO G, PAONESSA G, D'URSO M, PERSICO M: Structural analysis of the X-linked gene encoding human glucose 6-phosphate dehydrogenase. *EMBO J* 5:1849, 1986.

60. PERSICO MG, TONIOLO D, NOBILE C, D'URSO M, LUZZATTO L: cDNA sequences of human glucose-6-phosphate dehydrogenase cloned in pBR322. *Nature* 294:778, 1981.

61. TONIOLO D, PERSICO M, ALCALAY M: A new housekeeping gene of the X chromosome is similar to ubiquitin. *Proc Natl Acad Sci USA* 85:851, 1988.

62. TONIOLO D, MARTINI G, MIGEON BR, DONO R: Expression of the G6PD locus on the human X chromosome is associated with demethylation of three CpG clusters within 100 KB of DNA. *EMBO J* 7:401, 1988.

63. WINTERBOURN CC: Free radical production and oxidative reactions of hemoglobin. *Environ Health Perspect* 64:321, 1985.

64. DYNAN WS, TJIAN R: Control of eukaryotic messenger RNA synthesis by sequence-specific DNA-binding proteins. *Nature* 316:774, 1985.

65. DAVIES KJ, GOLDBERG AL: Oxygen radicals stimulate intracellular proteolysis and lipid peroxidation by independent mechanisms in erythrocytes. *J Biol Chem* 262:8220, 1987.

66. BIRD AP: CpE rich islands and the function of DNA methylation. *Nature* 321:209, 1986.

67. REYNOLDS GA, BAM SK, OSBORNE TF, CHU DJ, GIL G, BROWN MS, GOLDSTEIN JL, LUSKEY KL: HMG CoA reductase: A negatively regulated gene with unusual promoter and 5′ untranslated regions. *Cell* 38:275, 1984.

68. MELTON DW: HPRT gene organization and expression, in Maclean N (ed): *Oxford Surveys on Eukaryotic Genes.* Oxford, Oxford University Press, 1987, vol 4, p 34.

69. MORIKAWA N, NAKAYAWA R, HOLTEIN D: Dietary induction of glucose-6-phosphate dehydrogenase synthesis. *Biochem Biophys Res Commun* 120:1022, 1984.

70. RICHARDS AH, HILF R: Influence of pregnancy, lactation and involution on glucose 6-phosphate dehydrogenase and lactant dehydrogenase isoenzymes in the rat mammary gland. *Endocrinology* 91:287, 1972.

71. WEBER G, CANTERO A: Glucose-6-phosphate utilization in hepatoma, regenerating and newborn rat liver, and in the liver of fed and fasted normal rats. *Cancer Res* 17:995, 1957.

72. BETKE K, BEUTLER E, BREWER GJ, KIRKMAN HN, LUZZATTO L, MOTULSKY AG, RAMOT B, SINISCALCO M: Standardisation of procedures for the study of glucose-6-phosphate dehydrogenase. Report of a WHO Scientific Group. *WHO Tech Rep* Ser 366, 1967.

73. KARADSHEH NS, AWIBI AS, TARAWNEH MS: Two new glucose-6-phosphate dehydrogenase (G6PD) variants associated with hemolytic anemia. *Am J Hematol* 22:185, 1986.

74. VIVES-CORRONS JL, FELIU E, PUJADES MA, CARDELLACHE, ROZMAN C, CARRERAS A, JOU JM, VALLESPI MT, ZUAZU FJ: Severe glucose-6-phosphate dehydrogenase (G6PD) deficiency associated wtih chronic hemolytic anaemia, granulocyte dysfunction and increased susceptibility to infections. Description of a new molecular variant (G 6 PD Barcelona). *Blood* 59:428, 1982.

75. BEUTLER E, GROOMS AM, MORGAN SK, TRINIDAD F: Chronic severe hemolytic anemia due to G-6-PD Charleston: A new deficient variant. *J Pediatr* 80:1005, 1972.

76. FELDMAN R, GROMISCH DS, LUHBY AL, BEUTLER E: Congenital nonspherocytic hemolytic anemia due to glucose-6-phosphate dehydrogenase East Harlem: A new deficient variant. *J Pediatr* 90:89, 1977.

77. VACA G, IBARRA B, ROMERO F, OLIVARES N, CANTU JM, BEUTLER E: G-6-PD Guadalajara: A new mutant associated with chronic non-spherocytic hemolytic anemia. *Hum Genet* 61:175, 1982.

78. NAKAI T, YOSHIDA A: G6PD Heian, a glucose-6-phosphate dehydrogenase variant associated with hemolytic anemia found in Japan. *Clin Chim Acta* 51:199, 1974.

79. KAHN A, DAO G, COTTREAU D, BILSKI-PASQUIER G: "GD (-) Hotel Dieu": A new G-6PD variant with chronic hemolysis in a negro patient from Senegal. *Hum Genet* 39:353, 1977.

80. THIGPEN JT, STEINBERG MH, BEUTLER E, GILLESPIE GT JR, DREILING BJ, MORRISON FS: Glucose-6-phosphate dehydrogenase Jackson. A new variant associated with hemolytic anemia. *Acta Haematol* 51:310, 1974.

81. GROSSMAN A, RAMANATHAN K, JUSTICE P, GORDON J, SHAHIDI NT, HSIA D: Congenital nonspherocytic hemolytic anemia associated with erythrocyte G-6-PD deficiency in a negro family. *Pediatrics* 37:624, 1966.

82. HONIG GR, HABACON E, VIDA LN, MATSUMOTO F, BEUTLER E: Three new variants of glucose-6-phosphate dehydrogenase associated with chronic nonspherocytic hemolytic anemia: G-6-PD Lincoln Park, G-6-PD Arlington Heights, and G-6-PD West Town. *Am J Hematol* 6:353, 1979.

83. SMITH JW, BEUTLER E: Unpublished, 1981.

84. TAKAHASHI K, FUJII H, TAKEGAWA S, TANI K, HIRONO A, TAKIZAWA T, KAWAKATSU T, MIWA S: A new glucose-6-phosphate dehydrogenase variant (G6PD Nagano) associated with congenital hemolytic anemia. *Hum Genet* 62:368, 1982.

85. PINTO PVC, NEWTON WA JR, RICHARDSON KE: Evidence for four types of erythrocyte glucose-6-phosphate dehydrogenase from G-6-PD deficient human subjects. *J Clin Invest* 45:823, 1966.

86. FAIRBANKS VF, NEPO AG, BEUTLER E, DICKSON ER, HONIG G: Glucose-6-phosphate dehydrogenase variants: Reexamination of G6PD Chicago and Cornell and a new variant (G6PD Pea Ridge) resembling G6PD Chicago. *Blood* 55:216, 1980.

87. HOWELL EB, NELSON AJ, JONES OW: A new G-6-PD variant associated with chronic non-spherocytic haemolytic anaemia in a negro family. *J Med Genet* 9:160, 1972.

88. KAHN A, BOULARD M, HAKIM J, SCHAISON G, BOIVIN P, BERNARD J: Anemie hemolytique congenitale spherocytaire par deficit en glucose-6-phosphate-deshydrogenase erythrocytaire. Description de deux nouvelles variantes: GD (-) Saint Louis (Paris) et Gd (-) Hayem. *Nouv Rev Fr Hematol* 14:587, 1974.

89. TANAKA KR, BEUTLER E: Hereditary hemolytic anemia due to glucose-6-phosphate dehydrogenase Torrance: A new variant. *J Lab Clin Med* 73:657, 1969.

90. ESTRADA M, GARCIA M, GUTIERREZ A, QUINTERO I, GONZALEZ R: G6PD Varadero. *Vox Sang* 43:102, 1982.

91. GAHR M, SCHROETER W, STURZENEGGER M, BORNHALM D, MARTI HR: Glucose-6-phosphate dehydrogenase (G-6-PD) deficiency in Switzerland. *Helv Paediatr Acta* 31:159, 1976.

92. MIWA S, FUJII H, NAKASHIMA K, MIURA Y, YAAMADA K, HAGIWARA T, FUKUDA M: Three new electrophoretically normal glucose-6-phosphate dehydrogenase variants associated wtih congenital nonspherocytic hemolytic anemia found in Japan: G6PD Ogikubo, Yokohama, and Akita. *Hum Genet* 45:11, 1978.

93. BEUTLER E, MATHAI CK, SMITH JE: Biochemical variants of glucose-6-phosphate dehydrogenase giving rise to congenital nonspherocytic hemolytic disease. *Blood* 31:131, 1968.

94. TALALAK P, BEUTLER E: G-6-PD Bangkok: A new variant found in congenital nonspherocytic hemolytic disease (CNHD). *Blood* 33:772, 1969.

95. RAMOT B, BEN-BASSAT I, SHCHORY M: New glucose-6-phosphate dehydrogenase variants observed in Israel and their association with congenital nonspherocytic hemolytic disease. *J Lab Clin Med* 74:895, 1969.

96. NECHELES TF, SNYDER LM, STRAUSS W: Glucose-6-phosphate dehydrogenase Boston. A new variant associated with congenital nonspherocytic hemolytic disease. *Humangenetik* 13:218, 1971.

97. CHAN TK, LAI MCS: Glucose 6-phosphate dehydrogenase: Identity of erythrocyte and leukocyte enzyme with report of a new variant in Chinese. *Biochem Genet* 6:119, 1972.

98. MILLER DR, WOLLMAN MR: A new variant of glucose-6-phosphate dehydrogenase deficiency hereditary hemolytic anemia, G6PD Cornell: Erythrocyte, leukocyte, and platelet studies. *Blood* 44:323, 1974.

99. PRCHAL J, MORENO H, CONRAD M, VITEK A: G-6-PD Dothan: A new variant associated with chronic hemolytic anemia. *IRCS* 7:348, 1979.

100. MCCANN SR, SMITHWICK AM, TEMPERLEY IJ, TIPTON K: G6PD (Dublin): Chronic non-spherocytic haemolytic anaemia resulting from glucose-6-phosphate dehydrogenase deficiency in an Irish kindred. *J Med Genet* 17:191, 1980.

101. RATTAZZI MC, CORASH LM, VAN ZANEN GE, JAFFE ER, PIOMELLI S: G6PD deficiency and chronic hemolysis: Four new mutants—Relationships between clinical syndrome and enzyme kinetics. *Blood* 38:205, 1971.

102. ALPERIN JB, MILLS GC: New variants of glucose-6-phosphate dehydrogenase: G6PD Kilgore and G6PD Galveston. *Texas Rep Biol Med* 31:727, 1973.

103. GAHR M, SCHROETER W: Glucose-6-phosphate dehydrogenase (G-6-PD) Hamburg, a new variant with chronic nonspherocytic haemolytic anaemia. *Eur J Clin Invest* 4:187, 1974.

104. BEUTLER E, MATSUMOTO F: Unpublished, 1975.

105. VUOPIO P, HARKONEN R, JOHNSSON R, NUUTINEN M: Red cell glucose-6-phosphate dehydrogenase deficiency in Finland. *Ann Clin Res* 5:168, 1973.

106. WONG PWK, SHIH L-Y, HSIA DYY: Characterization of glucose-6-phosphate dehydrogenase among Chinese. *Nature* 208:1323, 1965.

107. SHATSKAYA TL, KRASNOPOLSKAYA KD, IDELSON LI: The new form of glucose-6-phosphate dehydrogenase (G6PD "Kaluga") from erythrocytes of a patient with chronic non-spherocytic hemolytic anemia. *Vopr Med Khim* 22:764, 1976.

108. KITAO T, ITO K, HATTORI K, MATSUKI T, YONEYAMA Y: G6PD Kanazama: A new variant of glucose-6-phosphate dehydrogenase associated with congenital nonspherocytic hemolytic anemia. *Acta Haematol* 68:131, 1982.

109. CHERNYAK NB, BATISCHEV AI, LAMZINA NV, TOKAREV YN, ALEXEEV GA: Electrophoretic and kinetic properties of glucose-6-phosphate dehydrogenase from erythrocytes or patients with hemolytic anemia, related to deficiency of the enzyme activity. *Vopr Med Khim* 23:166, 1977.

110. KOJIMA H: Congenital nonspherocytic hemolytic disease (cnhd) due to a G-6-PD variant: G-6-PD Kyoto. *Acta Haematol Jpn* 35:32, 1972.

111. WILSON WW: Congenital hemolytic anaemia due to deficiency of glucose-6-phosphate dehydrogenase. *Rocky Mt Med J* 73:160, 1976.

112. STREIFF F, VIGNERON C: Chronic haemolytic anemia due to a defect of glucose-6-phosphate dehydrogenase (G6PD) in a Lorraine family. Demonstration of a new type of the enzyme: Gd(-) Nancy. *Nouv Rev Fr Hematol* 11:279, 1971.

113. KIRKMAN HN, RILEY HD JR: Congenital nonspherocytic hemolytic anemia. *Am J Dis Child* 102:313, 1961.

114. EBER SW, GAHR M, SCHROTER W: Glucose-6-phosphate dehydrogenase (G6PD) Iserlohn and G6PD Regensburg: Two new severe enzyme defects in German families. *Blut* 51:109, 1985.

115. MIWA S, ONO J, NAKASHIMA K, ABE S, KAGEOKA T, SHINOHARA K, ISOBE J, YAMAGUCHI H: Two new glucose 6-phosphate dehydrogenase variants associated with congenital nonspherocytic hemolytic anemia found in Japan: Gd(-) Tokushima and gd(-) Tokyo. *Am J Hematol* 1:433, 1976.

116. BEUTLER E, KELLER JW, MATSUMOTO F: A new glucose-6-p dehydrogenase (G-6-PD) variant associated with nonspherocytic hemolytic anemia: G-6-PD Atlanta. *IRCS* 4:579, 1976.

117. KIRKMAN HN, ROSENTHAL IM, SIMON ER, CARSON PE, BRINSON AG: "Chicago I" variant of glucose-6-phosphate dehydrogenase in congenital hemolytic disease. *J Lab Clin Med* 63:715, 1964.

118. WEINREICH J, BUSCH D, GOTTSTEIN U, SCHAEFER J, ROHR J: Ueber zwei neue faelle von hereditaerer nichtsphaerocytaerer haemolytischer anaemie bei glucose-6-phosphat-dehydrogenase-defekt in einer nord deutschen familie. *Klin Wochenschr* 46:146, 1968.

119. MIWA S, FUJII H, NAKATSUJI T, ISHIDA Y, ODA E, KANETO A, MOTOKAWA M, ARIGA Y, FUKUCHI S, SASAI S, HIRAOKA K, KASHII H, KODAMA T: Four new electrophoretically slow-moving glucose 6-phosphate dehydrogenase variants associated with congenital nonspherocytic hemolytic anemia found in Japan: Gd(-) Kurume, Gd(-) Fukushima, Gd(-) Yamaguchi and Gd(-) Wakayama. *Am J Hematol* 5:131, 1978.

120. CEDERBAUM AI, BEUTLER E: Nonspherocytic hemolytic anemia due to G-6-PD Grand Prairie. *IRCS* 3:579, 1975.

121. BALINSKY D, GOMPERTS E, CAYANIS E, JENKINS T, BRYER D, BERSOHN I, METZ J: Glucose-6-phosphate dehydrogenase Johannesburg: A new variant with reduced activity in a patient with congenital non-spherocytic haemolytic anaemia. *Br J Haematol* 25:385, 1973.

122. JOHNSON GJ, KAPLAN ME, BEUTLER E: G6PD Long Prairie: A new mutant exhibiting normal sensitivity to inhibition by NADPH and accompanied by non-spherocytic hemolytic anaemia. *Blood* 49:247, 1977.

123. MILNER G, DELAMORE IW, YOSHIDA A: G-6-PD Manchester: A new variant associated with chronic nonspherocytic hemolytic anemia. *Blood* 43:271, 1974.

124. WESTRING DW, PISCIOTTA AV: Anemia, cataracts, and seizures in patient with glucose-6-phosphate dehydrogenase deficiency. *Arch Intern Med* 118:385, 1966.

125. JOHNSON GJ, BEUTLER E: Unpublished, 1980.

126. BEUTLER E, MATSUMOTO F, DAIBER A: Nonspherocytic hemolytic anemia due to G-6-PD Panama. *IRCS* 2:1389, 1974.

127. PICAT C, ETIEMBLE J, BOIVIN P, LE PRISE PY: Gd(-) Rennes: A new deficient variant of glucose-6-phosphate dehydrogenase associated with congenital nonspherocytic hemolytic anemia found in France. *Hum Genet* 55:125, 1980.

128. MENTZER WC JR, WARNER R, ADDIEGO J, SMITH B, WALTER T: G6PD San Francisco: A new variant of glucose-6-phosphate dehydrogenase associated with congenital nonspherocytic hemolytic anemia. *Blood* 55:195, 1980.

129. KIDDER WR, BEUTLER E: Unpublished, 1979.

130. MORISAKI T, FUJII H, TAKEGAWA S, TANI K, HIRONO A, TAKIZAWA T, TAKAHASHI K, SHINOGI M, TESHIROGI I, MIWA S: G6PD Sendagi: A new glucose-6-phosphate dehydrogenase variant associated with congenital hemolytic anemia. *Hum Genet* 65:214, 1983.

131. ENGSTROM PF, BEUTLER E: G-6-PD Tripler: A unique variant associated with chronic hemolytic disease. *Blood* 36:10, 1970.

132. BEUTLER E, HARTMAN K, GELBART T, FORMAN L: G-6-PD Walter Reed: Possible insight in "structural" NADP in G-6-PD. *Am J Hematol* 23:25, 1986.

133. SNYDER LM, NECHELES TF, REDDY WJ: G-6-PD Worcester: A new variant, associated with x-linked optic atrophy. *Am J Med* 49:125, 1970.

134. SHOWS TB, TASHIAN RE, BREWER GJ: Erythrocyte glucose-6-phosphate dehydrogenase in Caucasians: New inherited variant. *Science* 145:1056, 1064.

135. KAHN A, NORTH ML, MESSER J, BOIVIN P: G-6-PD "Ankara," a new G-6PD variant with deficiency found in a Turkish family. *Humangenetik* 27:247, 250, 1975.

136. SHATSKAYA TL, KRASNOPOLSKAYA KD, ANNENKOV GA: A description of new mutant forms of erythrocyte glucose-6-phosphate dehydrogenase isolated at the territory of the Soviet Union. *Genetika* 11:116, 1975.

137. VIVES-CORRONS JL, PUJADES A: Heterogeneity of Mediterranean type glucose-6-phosphate dehydrogenase (G-6-PD) deficiency in Spain and description of two new variants associated with Favism. *Hum Genet* 60:216, 1982.

138. CHOCKKALINGAM F, BOARD PG: Further evidence for heterogeneity of glucose-6-phosphate dehydrogenase deficiency in Papua New Guinea. *Hum Genet* 56:209, 1980.

139. CARANDINA G, MORETTO E, ZECCHI G, CONIGHI C: Glucose-6-phosphate dehydrogenase Ferrara. A new variant of G-6-PD identified in Northern Italy. *Acta Haematol* 56:116, 1976.

140. PERRONI L, TASSARA P, BALDI M, REALI R, SCARTEZZINI P: G 6 PD variants detected in Genoa area, in Weatherall DJ, Fiorelli G, Gorini S (eds): *Advances in Red Blood Cell Biology.* New York, Raven 1982, pp 409–416.

141. MIWA S, FUJII H: Glucose-6-phosphate dehydrogenase variants in Japan, in Yoshida A, Beutler E (eds): *Glucose-6-Phosphate Dehydrogenase.* New York, Academic, 1986, p 261.

142. PANICH V, NA-NAKORN S: G-6-PD variants in Thailand. *J Med Assoc Thai* 63:537, 1980.

143. MCCURDY PR: Unpublished, 1975.

144. BENABADJI M, MERAD F, BENMOUSSA M, TRABUCHET G, JUNIEN C, DREYFUS JC, KAPLAN JC: Heterogeneity of glucose-6-phosphate dehydrogenase deficiency in Algeria. *Hum Genet* 40:177, 1978.

145. PANICH V, BUMRUNGTRAKILL P, JITJAI C, KAMOLMATA YAKUL S, KHOPRASERT B, KLAISUVAN C, KONGMUANG U, MANAEECHAI P, PORNPATKUL M, RUENGRAIRATANAROJE P, SURAPRUK P, VIRIYAYUDHAKORN S: Glucose-6-phosphate dehydrogenase deficiency in South Vietnamese. *Hum Hered* 30:361, 1980.

146. PAWLAK AL, ZAGORSKI Z, ROZYNKOWA D, HORST A: Polish variant of glucose-6-phosphate dehydrogenase (G-6-PD Lublin). *Humangenetik* 10:340–343, 1970.

147. KAHN A, BOIVIN P, HAKIM J, LAGNEAU J: Heterogeneite des glucose-6-phosphate deshydrogenase erythrocytaire deficitaires dans la race noire. Étude cinetique et description de deux nouvelles variantes Gd (-) Dakar et Gd (-) Mali. *Nouv Rev Fr Hematol* 11:741, 1971.

148. KIRKMAN HN, KIDSON C, KENNEDY H: Variants of human glucose-6-phosphate dehydrogenase. Studies of samples from New Guinea, in Beutler E (ed): *Hereditary Disorders of Erythrocyte Metabolism. City of Hope Symp. Series.* New York, Grune & Stratton, 1968, pp 126–145.

149. CASTRO GAM, SNYDER LM: G6PD San Jose: A new variant characterized by NADPH inhibition studies. *Humangenetik* 21:361, 1974.

150. MCCURDY PR, BLACKWELL PQ, TODD D, TSO SC, TUCHINDA S: Further studies on glucose-6-phosphate dehydrogenase deficiency in Chinese subjects. *J Lab Clin Med* 75:788, 1970.

151. LISKER R, PEREZ-BRICENO R, BEUTLER E: A new glucose-6-phosphate dehydrogenase variant, Gd(-) Tepic, characterized by moderate enzyme deficiency and mild episodes of hemolytic anemia. *Hum Genet* 69:19, 1985.

152. YOSHIDA A, BAUR EW, MOTULSKY AG: A Philippino glucose-6-phosphate dehydrogenase variant (G6PD Union) with enzyme deficiency and altered substrate specificity. *Blood* 35:506, 1970.

153. STAMATOYANNOPOULOS G, VOIGTLANDER V, KOTSAKIS P, AKRIVAKIS A: Genetic diversity of the "Mediterranean" glucose-6-phosphate dehydrogenase deficiency phenotype. *J Clin Invest* 50:1253, 1971.

154. WITT I, YOSHIOKA S: Biochemical characterization of a glucose-6-phosphate dehydrogenase variant with favism: G-6-PD Zaehringen. *Klin Wochenschr* 50:205, 1972.

155. KAHN A, BERNARD J-F, COTTREAU D, MARIE J, BOLVIN P: Gd(-)Abrami. A deficient g-6pd variant with hemizygous expression in blood cells of a woman with primary myelofibrosis. *Humangenetik* 30:41, 1975.

156. GEERDINK RA, HORST R, STAAL GEJ: An Iraqi Jewish family with a new red cell glucose-6-phosphate dehydrogenase variant (Gd-Baghdad) and kernicterus. *Isr J Med Sci* 9:1040, 1973.

157. GAHR M, BORNHALM D, SCHROETER W: Biochemische Eigenschaften einer neuen Variante des glucose-6-phosphatdehydrogenase (G-6-PD)-Mangels mit Favismus: G-6-PD Bielefeld. *Klin Wochenschr* 55:379, 1977.

158. PRCHAL JT, CRIST WM, MALLUAH A, VITEK A, TAUXE WN, CARROLL AJ: A new glucose-6-phosphate dehydrogenase deficient variant in a patient with Chediak-Higahi syndrome. *Blood* 56:476, 1980.

159. SIDI Y, ADERKA D, BROK-SIMONI F, BENJAMIN D, RAMOT B, PINKHAS J: Viral hepatitis with extreme hyperbilirubinemia, massive hemolysis and encephalopathy in a patient with a new G 6 PD variant. *Isr J Med Sci* 16:130, 1980.

160. BENOEHR HC, WALLER HD, ARNOLD H, BLUME KG, LOEHR GW: Glucose-6-p-dehydrogenase Typ Bodensee (eine neue enzymvariante). *Klin Wochenschr* 49:1058, 1971.

161. MCCURDY PR, MAHMOOD L: Red cell glucose-6-phosphate dehydrogenase deficiency in Pakistan. *J Lab Clin Med* 76:943, 1970.

162. MOTULSKY AG, YOSHIDA A: Methods for the study of red cell glucose-6-phosphate dehydrogenase, in Yurvis JJ (ed): *Biochemical Methods in Red Cell Genetics.* New York, Academic, 1969.

163. MCCURDY PR, KAMEL K, SELIM O: Heterogeneity of red cell glucose-6-phosphate dehydrogenase (G-6-PD) deficiency in Egypt. *J Lab Clin Med* 84:673, 1974.

164. VUOPIO P, HARKONEN M, HELSKE T, NAEVERI H: Red cell glucose-6-phosphate dehydrogenase deficiency in Finland. Characterization of a new variant with severe enzyme deficiency. *Scand J Haematol* 15:145, 1975.

165. MILLS GC, ALPERIN JB, TRIMMER KB: Studies on variant-glucose-6-phosphate dehydrogenases: G6PD Fort Worth. *Biochem Med* 13:264, 1975.

166. SHATSKAYA TL, KRASNOPOLSKAYA KD, TZONEVA M, MAVRUDIEVA M, TONCHEVA D: Variants of erythrocyte glucose-6-phosphate dehydrogenase (G6PD) in Bulgarian populations. *Hum Genet* 54:115, 1980.

167. GAHR M, BORNHALM D, SCHROETER W: Haemolytic anaemia due to glucose-6-phosphate dehydrogenase (G6PD) deficiency: Demonstration of two new biochemical variants, G6PD Hamm and G6PD Tarsus. *Br J Haematol* 33:363, 1976.

168. KIRKMAN HN, LUAN-ENG L-I: Variants of glucose 6 phosphate dehydrogenase in Indonesia. *Nature* 221:959, 1969.

169. SHATSKAYA TL, KRASNOPOLSKAYA KD, IDELSON LJ: Mutant forms of erythrocyte glucose-6-phosphate dehydrogenase in Ashkenazi. Description of two new variants: G6PD Kirovograd and G6PD Zhitomir. *Hum Genet* 33:175, 1976.

170. KAHN A, HAKIM J, COTTREAU D, BOIVIN P: Gd (-) Matam, an African glucose-6-phosphate dehydrogenase variant with enzyme deficiency. Biochemical and immunological properties in various hemopoietic tissues. *Clin Chim Acta* 59:183, 1975.

171. KIRKMAN HN, SCHETTINI F, PICKARD BM: Mediterranean variant of glucose-6-phosphate dehydrogenase. *J Lab Clin Med* 63:726, 1964.

172. BATISCHEV AI, CHERNYAK NB, TOKAREV YN: Detection of a new abnormal variant of glucose-6-phosphate dehydrogenase in human red cells. *Bull Eksp Noi Bi* 84:728, 1977.

173. PANICH V, SUNGNATE T: Characterization of glucose-6-phosphate dehydrogenase in Thailand. The occurrence of 6 variants among 50 G6PD deficient Thai. *Humangenetik* 18:39, 1973.

174. YERMAKOV N, TOKAREV J, CHERNJAK N, SCHOENIAN G, GRIEGER M, GUCKLER G, JACOBASCH G, MAHMUDOVA M, BAHRAMOV S: New stable mutant Gd(-) variants: G6PD Tashkent and G6PD Nucus. Molecular basis of hereditary enzyme deficiency. *Acta Biol Med Ger* 40:559, 1981.

175. LISKER R, BRICENO RP, ZAVALA C, NAVARRETE JI, WESSELS M, YOSHIDA A: A glucose-6-phosphate dehydrogenase gd (-) Castilla variant characterized by mild deficiency associated with drug induced hemolytic anemia. *J Lab Clin Med* 90:754, 1977.

176. TONCHEVA D, TZONEVA M: Genetic polymorphism of G6PD in a Bulgarian population. *Hum Genet* 67:340, 1984.

177. FUJII H, MIWA S, TANI K, TAKEGAWA S, FUJINAMI N, TAKAHASHI K, NAKAYAMA S, KONNO M, SATO T: Glucose-6-phosphate dehydrogenase variants: A unique variant (G6PD Kobe) showed an extremely increased affinity for galactose 6-phosphate and a new variant (G6PD Sapporo) resembling G6PD Pea Ridge. *Hum Genet* 58:405, 1981.

178. TESTA U, MELONI T, LANIA A, BATTISTUZZI G, CUTILLO S, LUZZATTO L: Genetic heterogeneity of glucose-6-phosphate dehydrogenase deficiency in Sardinia. *Hum Genet* 56:99, 1980.

179. BENOEHR HC, KLUMPP F, WALLER HD: Glucose-6-phosphate dehydrogenase Typ Schwaben. *Dtsch Med Wochenschr* 96:1029, 1971.

180. WAITZ R, BOIVIN P, OBERLING F, CASENAVE JP, NORTH ML, MAYER S: Variante gd (-) Strasbourg de la glucose-6-phosphate-dehydrogenase. *Nouv Rev Fr Hematol* 10:312, 1970.

181. KAHN A, ESTERS A, HABEDANK M: Gd(-)Aachen, a new variant of deficient glucose-6-phosphate dehydrogenase. *Hum Genet* 32:171, 1976.

182. TAKIZAWA T, FUJII H, TAKAGAWA S, HIRONO A, MORISAKI T, KANNO H, OKA R, YOSHIOKA H, MIWA S, TAKAHASHI K: A unique electrophoretic slow-moving glucose 6-phosphate dehydrogenase variant (G6PD Asahikawa) with a markedly acidic pH optimum. *Hum Genet* 68:70, 1984.

183. KRASNOPOLSKAYA KD, SHATSKAYA TL, FILIPPOV IK, ANNENKOV GA, ZAKHAROVA TV, MEKHTIEV NK, MOVSUM-ZADE KH: Genetic heterogeneity of G 6 PD deficiency: Study of mutant alleles in Shekii district of Azerbaijan. *Genetika* 13:984, 1977.

184. GONZALEZ R, ESTRADA M, GARCIA M, GUTIERREZ A: A G6PD Ciudad de la Habana: A new slow variant with deficiency found in a Cuban family. *Hum Genet* 55:133, 1980.

185. VERGNES H, RIBER A, BOMMELAER G, AMADIEU J, BRUN H: Gd(-) Muret and Gd(-) Colomiers, two new variants of glucose-6-phosphate dehydrogenase associated with favism. *Hum Genet* 57:332, 1981.

186. BEUTLER E: Glucose-6-phosphate dehydrogenase deficiency: A new Indian variant, G 6 PD Jammu, in Sen NN, Basu AK (eds): *Trends in Haematology.* Calcutta, India, N N Sen, 1975, pp 279–283.

187. YOSHIDA A, BEUTLER E: Human glucose-6-phosphate dehydrogenase variants: A supplementary tabulation. *Ann Hum Genet* 41:347, 1978.

188. FERNANDEZ M, FAIRBANKS VF: Glucose-6-phosphate dehydrogenase deficiency in the Philippines: Report of a new variant—G 6 PD Panay. *Mayo Clin Proc* 43:645, 1968.

189. BALINSKY D, CAYANIS E, CARTER G, JENKINS T, BERSOHN I: A new variant of human erythrocyte glucose-6-phosphate dehydrogenase: G6PD Port Elizabeth. *Int J Biochem* 4:235, 1973.

190. PAWLAK AL, MAZURKIEWICZ CA, ORDYNSKI J, ROZYNKOWA D, HORST A: G-6-PD Poznan, variant with severe enzyme deficiency. *Humangenetik* 28:163, 1975.

191. SAENZ GF, CHAVES M, BERRANTES A, ELIZONDO J, MONTERO AG, YOSHIDA A: A glucose-6-phosphate dehydrogenase variant, Gd(-) Santamaria found in Costa Rica. *Acta Haematol* 72:37, 1984.

192. VERGNES H, YOSHIDA A, GOURDIN D, GHERARDI M, BIERME R, RUFFIE J: Glucose-6-phosphate dehydrogenase Toulouse. A new variant with marked instability and severe deficiency discovered in a family of Mediterranean ancestry. *Acta Haematol* 51:240, 1974.

193. AZEVEDO E, KIRKMAN HN, MORROW AC, MOTULSKY AG: Variants of red cell glucose-6-phosphate dehydrogenase among Asiatic Indians. *Ann Hum Genet* 31:373, 1968.

194. LUZZATTO L, ALLAN NC: Different properties of glucose-6-phosphate dehydrogenase from human erythrocytes with normal and abnormal enzyme levels. *Biochem Biophys Res Commun* 21:247, 1965.

195. YOSHIDA A, STAMATOYANNOPOULOS G, MOTULSKY A: Negro variant of glucose-6-phosphate dehydrogenase deficiency (A-) in man. *Science* 155:97, 1967.

196. RATTAZZI MC, LENZERINI L, KHAN PM, LUZZATTO L: Characterization of glucose-6-phosphate dehydrogenase variants. II. G6PD Kephalonia, G6PD Attica, and G6PD "Seattle-like" found in Greece. *Am J Hum Genet* 21:154, 1969.

197. MCCURDY PR, KIRKMAN HN, NAIMAN JL, JIM RTS, PICKARD BH: A Chinese variant of glucose-6-phosphate dehydrogenase. *J Lab Clin Med* 67:374, 1966.

198. LISKER R, BRICENO RP, AGRILAR L, YOSHIDA A: A variant glucose-6-phosphate dehydrogenase Gd (-) Chiapas. Associated with moderate enzyme deficiency and occasional hemolytic anemia. *Hum Genet* 43:81, 1978.

199. NAKASHIMA K, ONO J, ABE S, MIWA S, YOSHIDA A: G6PD Ube: a glucose-6-phosphate dehydrogenase variant found in four unrelated Japanese families. *Am J Hum Genet* 29:24, 1977.

200. KISSIN C, COTTE J: Étude d'un variant de glucose-6-phosphate deshydrogenase: Le type constantine. *Enzyme* 11:277, 1970.

201. OTHIENO-OBEL A: East African variant of glucose-6-phosphate dehydrogenase. *East Afr Med J* 49:230, 1972.

202. SANSONE G, PERRONI L, YOSHIDA A: Glucose-6-phosphate dehydrogenase variants from Italian subjects associated with severe neonatal jaundice. *Br J Haematol* 31:159, 1975.

203. VACA G, IBARRA B, GARCIA-CRUZ D, MEDINA C, ROMERO F, CANTU JM, BEUTLER E: G-6-PD Jalisco and G-6-PD Morelia: Two new Mexican variants. *Hum Genet* 71:82, 1985.

204. SHATSKAYA TL, KRASNOPOLSKAYA KD, ZAKHAROVA TV: Regularities of distribution of gd- alleles in Azerbaijan. III. Identification of G 6 PD mutant forms. *Genetika* 16:2217, 1980.

205. KAPLAN JC, ROSA R, SERINGE P, HOEFFEL JC: Le polymorphisme genetique de la glucose-6-phosphate dehydrogenase erythrocytaire chez l'homme. *Enzyme* 8:332, 1967.

206. NAKATSUJI T, MIWA S: Incidence and characteristics of glucose-6-phosphate dehydrogenase variants in Japan. *Hum Genet* 51:297, 1979.

207. VERGNES H, GHERARDI M, YOSHIDA A: G6PD Lozere and Trinacria-like. Segregation of two non hemolytic variants in a French family. *Hum Genet* 34:293, 1976.

208. STAMATOYANNOPOULOS G, KOTSAKIS P, VOIGTLANDER V, MOTULSKY AG: Electrophoretic diversity of glucose-6-phosphate dehydrogenase among Greeks. *Am J Hum Genet* 22:587, 1970.

209. MCCURDY PR, MALDONADO N, DILLON DE, CONRAD ME: Variants of glucose-6-phosphate dehydrogenase (G-6-PD) associated with G-6-PD deficiency in Puerto Ricans. *J Lab Clin Med* 82:432, 1973.

210. CROOKSTON JM, YOSHIDA A, LIN M, BOOSER DJ: G 6 PD Toronto. *Biochem J* 8:259, 1973.

211. MANDELLI F, AMADORI S, DE LAURENZI A, KAHN A, ISACCHI G, PAPA G: Glucose-6-phosphate dehydrogenase Velletri. *Acta Haematol* 57:121, 1977.

212. CAYANIS E, GOMPERTS ED, BALINSKY D, DISLER P, MYERS A: G6PD Hillbrow: A new variant of glucose-6-phosphate dehydrogenase associated with drug-induced haemolytic anaemia. *Br J Haematol* 30:343, 1975.

213. MIWA S, NAKASHIMA K, ONO J, FUJII H, SUZUKI E: Three glucose 6-phosphate dehydrogenase variants found in Japan. *Hum Genet* 36:327, 1977.

214. PANICH V, SUNGNATE T, WASI P, NA-NAKORN S: G-6-PD Mahidol. The most common glucose-6-phosphate dehydrogenase variant in Thailand. *J Med Assoc Thai* 55:576, 1972.

215. PANICH V, SUNGNATE T, NA-NAKORN S: Acute intravascular hemolysis and renal failure in a new glucose-6-phosphate dehydrogenase variant: G-6-PD Siriraj. *J Med Assoc Thai* 55:726, 1972.

216. KIRKMAN HN, RAMOT B, LEE JT: Altered aggregational properties in a genetic variant of human glucose-6-phosphate dehydrogenase. *Biochem Genet* 3:317, 1969.

217. PANICH V, SUNGNATE T: Characterization of glucose-6-phosphate dehydrogenase in Thailand. *Humangenetik* 18:39, 1973.

218. STAMATOYANNOPOULOS G, YOSHIDA A, BACOPOULOS C, MOTULSKY A: Athens variant of glucose-6-phosphate dehydrogenase. *Science* 157:831, 1967.

219. BOTHA MC, DERN RJ, MITCHELL M, WEST C, BEUTLER E: G6PD Capetown, A variant of glucose-6-phosphate dehydrogenase. *Am J Hum Genet* 21:547, 1969.

220. SIEGEL NH, BEUTLER E: Hemolytic anemia caused by G-6-PD Carswell, a new variant. *Ann Intern Med* 75:437, 1971.

221. DE FLORA A, MORELLI A, BENATTI U, GIUNTINI P, FERRARIS AM, GALIANO S, RAVAZZOLO R, GAETANI GF: G6PD Napoli and Ferrara II: Two new glucose-6-phosphate dehydrogenase variants having similar characteristics but different intracellular liability and specific activity. *Br J Haematol* 48:417, 1981.

222. NOWICKI L, STROBEL S, MARTIN H, KOSCHWITZ U: Über eine neue erythrocytare Glucose-6-phosphatdehydrogenase-Variante, Typ Frankfurt I. Charakterisierung der Variants durch enzymkinetische Parameter. *Klin Wochenschr* 52:478, 1974.

223. VENTURA A, PANIZON F, SORANZO MR, EVENEZIANO G, SANSONE G, TESTA U, LUZZATTO L: Congenital dyserythropoietic anaemia Type II associated with a new type of G6PD deficiency (G6PD Gabrovizza). *Acta Haematol* 71:227, 1984.

224. WELCH SG, MCGREGOR IA, WILLIAMS K: A new variant of human erythrocyte G6PD occurring at a high frequency amongst the population of two villages in the Gambia, West Africa. *Hum Genet* 40:305, 1978.

225. USANGA EA, BIENZLE U, CANCEDDA R, FASUAN FA, AJAYI O, LUZZATTO L: Genetic variants of human erythrocyte glucose 6-phosphate dehydrogenase: New variants in West Africa characterized by column chromatography. *Ann Hum Genet* 40:279, 1977.

226. PANICH V: G-6-PD Intanon. A new glucose-6-phosphate dehydrogenase variant. *Humangenetik* 21:203, 1974.

227. ISHWAD CS, NAIK SN: A new glucose-6-phosphate dehydrogenase variant (G-6-PD Kalyan) found in a Koli family. *Hum Genet* 66:171, 1984.

228. BALINSKY D, ROOT MAN AJ, NURSE GT, GAYANIS E, LANE A, JENKINS T, BERSOHN I: G6PD Kuanyama: A new variant of human erythrocyte glucose-6-phosphate dehydrogenase showing slower than normal electrophoretic mobility. *S Afr J Med Sci* 39:5, 1974.

229. CHUANSHU D, YANKANG X, LIN WQR, XIAOYUN II: Studies on erythrocyte glucose-6-phosphate dehydrogenase variants in Chinese. I. Gd(-) Lizu-Baisha. *Acta Acad Med Zhong* 2:649, 1981.

230. BEUTLER E, MATSUMOTO F: A new glucose-6-phosphate dehydrogenase variant: G-6-PD (-) Los Angeles. *IRGS* 5:89, 1977.

231. LISKER R, LINARES C, MOTULSKY AG: Glucose-6-phosphate dehydrogenase Mexico. A new variant with enzyme deficiency, abnormal mobility and absence of hemolysis. *J Lab Clin Med* 79:788, 1972.

232. SANSONE G, PERRONI L, TESTA U, MARENI C, LUZZATTO L: New genetic variants of glucose-6-phosphate dehydrogenase (G6PD) Italy. *Ann Hum Genet* 45:97, 1981.

233. ERMAKOV NV, CHERNYAK NB, TOKAREV YN: Properties of new variant of glucose-6-phosphate dehydrogenase (Regar variant). Glucose metabolism in erythrocytes containing abnormal enzyme. *Biokhimia* 48:577, 1983.

234. KIRKMAN HN, SIMON ER, PICKARD BM: Seattle variant of glucose-6-phosphate dehydrogenase. *J Lab Clin Med* 66:834, 1965.

235. CHOCKKALINGAM K, BOARD PG, BREGUET G: Glucose 6-phosphate dehydrogenase variants of Bali Island (Indonesia). *Hum Genet* 60:60, 1982.

236. SANSONE G, PERRONI L, YOSHIDA A, DAVE V: A new glucose-6-phosphate dehydrogenase variant (GD Trinacria) in two unrelated families of Sicilian ancestry. *Ital J Biochem* 26:44, 1977.

237. KAHN A, NORTH ML, GOTTREAU D, GIRON G, LANG JM: G6PD Vientiane: A new glucose-6-phosphate dehydrogenase variant with increased stability. *Hum Genet* 43:85, 1978.

238. BOYER SH, PORTER IH, WEILBACHER RG: Electrophoretic heterogeneity of glucose-6-phosphate dehydrogenase and its relationship to enzyme deficiency in man. *Proc Natl Acad Sci USA* 48:1868, 1962.

239. GANT FL, WINKS GF JR: Primaquine sensitive hemolytic anaemia complicating diabetic acidosis. *Clin Res* 9:27, 1961.

240. MARKS PA, BANKS J, GROSS R: Genetic heterogeneity of glucose-6-phosphate dehydrogenase deficiency. *Nature* 194:454, 1962.

241. REYS L, MANSO C, STAMATOYANNOPOULOS G: Genetic studies on Southeastern Bantu of Mozambique. I. Variants of glucose-6-phosphate dehydrogenase. *Am J Hum Genet* 22:203, 1970.

242. VERGNES H, GHERARDI M, QUILICI JG, YOSHIDA A, GIACARDY R: G6PD Luz-Saint-Sauveur: A new variant with abnormal electrophoretic mobility mild enzyme deficiency and absence of haematological disorders. *IRCS* (73-7) 3-1-14, 1973.

243. PANICH V: Glucose-6-phosphate dehydrogenase in Thailand. *Hum Genet* 53:227, 1980.

244. YOSHIDA A, BAUR E, VOIGTLANDER B: Unpublished, 1975.

245. LONG WK, KIRKMAN HN, SUTTON HE: Electrophoretically slow variants of glucose-6-phosphate dehydrogenase from red cells of negroes. *J Lab Clin Med* 65:81, 1965.

246. WEIMER TA, SCHUELER L, BEUTLER E, SALZANO FM: Gd (+) Laguna, a new rare glucose-6-phosphate dehydrogenase variant from Brazil. *Hum Genet* 65:402, 1984.

247. HOOK EB, STAMATOYANNOPOULOS G, YOSHIDA A, MOTULSKY AG: Glucose-6-phosphate dehydrogenase Madrona: A slow electrophoretic glucose-6-phosphate dehydrogenase variant with kinetic characteristics similar to those of normal type. *J Lab Clin Med* 72:404, 1968.

248. AZEVEDO ES, YOSHIDA A: Brazilian variant of glucose-6-phosphate dehydrogenase (Gd Minas Gerais). *Nature* 222:380, 1969.

249. GONZALEZ R, WADE M, ESTRADA M, SVARCH E, COLOMBO B: G6PD Pinar del Rio: A new variant discovered in a Cuban family. *Biochem Genet* 15:909, 1977.

250. CAYANIS E, LANE AB, JENKINS T, NURSE GT, BALINSKY D: Glucose-6-phosphate dehydrogenase Porbandar: A new slow variant with slightly reduced activity in a South African family of Indian descent. *Biochem Genet* 15:765, 1977.

251. HUTZ MH, YOSHIDA A, SALZANO FM: Three rare G-6-PD variants from Porto Alegre, Brazil. *Hum Genet* 39:191, 1977.

252. KAPLAN JG, HANLICKOVA-LEROUX A, NICHOLAS AM, ROSA R, WEILER G, LEPERCQ G: A new glucose-6-phosphate dehydrogenase variant (G6PD Port-Royal). *Enzyme* 12:25, 1970.

253. BEUTLER E: Glucose-6-phosphate dehydrogenase deficiency, in *Topics in Hematology—Hemolytic Anemia in Disorders of Red Cell Metabolism*. New York, Plenum, 1978.

254. STAMATOYANNOPOULOS G, VOIGTLAENDER V, AKRIVAKIS A: Thessaly variant of glucose-6-phosphate dehydrogenase. *Humangenetik* 9:23, 1970.

255. DERN RJ, MCGURDY PR, YOSHIDA A: A new structural variant of glucose-6-phosphate dehydrogenase with a high production rate (G6PD Hektoen). *J Lab Clin Med* 73:283, 1969.

256. BEUTLER E: Glucose 6-phosphate dehydrogenase deficiency, in Williams WJ, Beutler E, Erslev AJ (eds): *Hematology*. New York, McGraw-Hill, 1972, pp 391–399.

257. PERONA G, GUIDI GC, TUMMARELLO D, MARENI C, BATTISTUZZI G, LUZZATTO L: A new glucose-6-phosphate dehydrogenase variant (G6PD Verona) in a patient with myelodysplastic syndrome. *Scand J Haematol* 30:407, 1983.

258. COLONNA-ROMANO S, IOLASCON A, LIPPO S, PINTO L, CUTILLO S, BATTISTUZZI G: Genetic heterogeneity at the glucose-6-phosphate dehydrogenase locus in southern Italy: A study on the population of Naples. *Hum Genet* 69:228, 1985.

259. SHATSKAYA TL: New G6PD mutants in USSR. *Genetika* 11:12, 1975.

260. FENU MP, FINAZZI G, MANOUSSAKIS C, PALOMBA V, FIORELLI G: Glucose-6-phosphate dehydrogenase deficiency: Genetic heterogeneity in Sardinia. *Ann Hum Genet* 46:105, 1982.

261. DE FLORA A, MORELLI A, BENATTI U: Structural variants of human glucose 6-phosphate dehydrogenase (G6PD): Role of intracellular decay in the expression of deficiency. *Biomed Biochim Acta* 42:11, S247, 1983.

262. KRASNOPOLSKAYA KD: Genetic hetereogeneity. *Vestn Akad Med Nauk SSSR* 9:56, 1982.

263. RAVINDRANATH Y, BEUTLER E: Two new variants of glucose-6-phosphate dehydrogenase associated with hereditary non-spherocytic hemolytic anemia: G6PD Wayne and G6PD Huron. *Am J Hematol* 24:357, 1987.

264. KWIATKOWSKA J, KACPRZAK-BERGMAN: New erythrocyte glucose-6-phosphate dehydrogenase variant. *Acta Haematol (Basel)* 46:188, 1971.

265. HARRIS H: *The Principles of Human Biochemical Genetics*, 3d ed. Amsterdam, Elsevier North Holland, 1980.

266. D'URSO M, LUZZATTO L, PERRONI L, CICCODICOLA A, GENTILE G, PELUSO I, PERSICO MG, PIZZELLA T, TONIOLO D, VULLIAMY TJ: An extensive search for restriction fragment length polymorphism in the human glucose-6-phosphate dehydrogenase locus has revealed a silent mutation in the coding sequence. *Am J Hum Genet* 42:735, 1988.

267. HOIBERG A, ERNST J, UDDIN DE: Sickle cell trait and glucose-6-phosphate dehydrogenase deficiency. Effects on health and military performance in black naval enlistees. *Arch Intern Med* 141:1485, 1981.

268. GANT FL, WINKS GF JR: Primaquine sensitive hemolytic anaemia complicating diabetic acidosis. *Clin Res* 9:27, 1961.

269. GELLADY A, GREENWOOD RD: G6PD hemolytic anaemia complicating diabetic ketacidosis. *J Pediatr* 80:1037, 1972.

270. SHALEV O, ELIAKIM R, LUGASSY GZ, MENCZEL J: Hypoglycemia-induced hemolysis in glucose-6-phosphate dehydrogenase deficiency. *Acta Haematol (Basel)* 74:227, 1985.

271. SHALEV O, WOLLNER A, MENCZEL J: Diabetic ketoacidosis does not precipitate haemolysis in patients with the Mediterranean variant of glucose-6-phosphate dehydrogenase deficiency. *Br Med J* 288:179, 1984.

272. PERKINS RP: The significance of glucose-6-phosphate dehydrogenase deficiency in pregnancy. *Am J Obstet Gynecol* 125:215, 1976.

273. DERN RJ, BEUTLER E, ALVING AS: The hemolytic effect of primaquine II.

The natural course of the hemolytic anemia and the mechanism of its self-limiting character. *J Lab Clin Med* 44:171, 1954.

274. BEUTLER E, DERN RJ, ALVING AS: The hemolytic effect of primaquine III. A study of primaquine-sensitive erythrocytes. *J Lab Clin Med* 44:177, 1954.

275. BEUTLER E, DERN RJ, ALVING AS: The hemolytic effect of primaquine IV. The relationship of cell age to hemolysis. *J Lab Clin Med* 44:439, 1954.

276. KELLERMEYER RW, TARLOV AR, BREWER GJ, CARSON PE, ALVING AS: Hemolytic effect of therapeutic drugs. Clinical considerations of the primaquine-type hemolysis. *JAMA* 180:388, 1962.

277. ARESE P, MANNUZZO L, TURRINI F, FALIANOS, GAETANI GE: Etiological aspects of favism, in Yoshida A, Beutler E (eds): *Glucose-6-phosphate Dehydrogenase*. New York, Academic, 1986, p 45.

278. DACIE JV: Hereditary enzyme deficiency haemolytic anaemias III: Deficiency of glucose-6-phosphate dehydrogenase, in Dacie JV: *Haemolytic Anaemias. The Hereditary Haemolytic Anemias*, 3d ed. London, Churchill Livingstone, vol 1, part 1, pp 364–418, 1985.

279. PANNACCIULLI IM, TIZIANELLO A, AJMAR F, SALVIDIO E: The causes of experimentally induced haemolytic anaemia in a primaquine sensitive caucasian. *Blood* 25:92, 1965.

280. KRANSNOPOLSKAYA KD, BOCHKOV NP: Genetic heterogenecity g-hereditary enzymorphics. *Beth AMH CCCP* 9:56, 1972.

281. BEUTLER E: Sensitivity to drug-induced hemolytic anemia in glucose-6-phosphate dehydrogenase deficiency, in *Barnbury Report 16: Genetic Variability in Responses to Chemical Exposure*. Cold Spring Harbor, New York, Cold Spring Harbor Laboratory, 1984, pp 205–211.

282. ZAIL SS, CHARLTON RW, BOTHWELL TH: The haemolytic effect of certain drugs in Bantu subjects with a deficiency of glucose-6-phosphate dehydrogenase. *S Afr J Med Sci* 27:95, 1962.

283. HAM TH, GRAUEL JA, DUNN RF, MURPHY JR, WHITE JG, KELLERMEYER RW: Physical properties of red cells as related to effects in vivo. IV. Oxidant drugs producing abnormal intracellular concentration of hemoglobin (eccentrocytes) with a rigid-red-cell hemolytic syndrome. *J Lab Clin Med* 82:898, 1973.

284. BEUTLER E: The glutathione instability of drug-sensitive red cells. A new method for the in vitro detection of drug sensitivity. *J Lab Clin Med* 49:84, 1957.

285. GAETANI GD, MARENI C, RAVAZZOLD R, SALVIDIO E: Hemolytic effect of two sulphonamides evaluated by a new method. *Br J Haematol* 32:183, 1976.

286. CHAN TK, TODD D, TSO L: Drug induced haemolysis in glucose-6-phosphate dehydrogenase deficiency. *Br Med J* ii:1227, 1976.

287. SICARD D, KAPLAN JC, LABIE D: Haemoglobinopathies and G6PD deficiency in Laos. *Lancet* ii:571, 1978.

288. DERN RJ, BEUTLER E, ALVING AS: The haemolytic effect of primaquine V. Primaquine sensitivity as a manifestation of a multiple drug sensitivity. *J Lab Clin Med* 45:30, 1955.

289. BEUTLER E: Acetominophen and G6PD deficiency. *Acta Haematol (Basel)* 72:211, 1984.

290. MCCAFFREY RP, HALSTED CH, WAHAB MFA, ROBERTSON RP: Chloramphenicol-induced hemolysis in Caucasian glucose-6-phosphate dehydrogenase deficiency. *Ann Intern Med* 74:722, 1971.

291. CHAN TK, CHESTERMAN CN, MCFADZEAN AJS, TODD D: The survival of glucose-6-phosphate dehydrogenase deficient erythrocytes in patients with typhoid fever on chloramphenical therapy. *J Lab Clin Med* 77:177, 1971.

292. DOXIADIS SA, VALAES F: The clinical picture of glucose-6-phosphate dehydrogenase deficiency in early infancy. *Acad Dis Child* 39:545, 1964.

293. ZINKHAM WH: Peripheral blood and bilirubin values in normal full term primaquine-sensitive negro infants effects of vitamin K. *Pediatrics* 31:983, 1963.

294. MERCIECA JF, CLARKE MF, PHILLIPS ME, CURTIS JR: Acute hemolytic anemia due to phenazopyridine hydrochloride in a G6PD deficient subject. *Lancet* ii:564, 1982.

295. DOLL DC: Oxidative hemolysis after administration of doxorubicin. *Br Med J* 287:180, 1983.

296. GORDON-SMITH EC: Drug-induced oxidative hemolysis. *Clin Haematol* 9:557, 1980.

297. TARLOV AR, BREWER GJ, CARSON PE, ALVING AS: Primaquine sensitivity. Glucose-6-phosphate dehydrogenase deficiency: An inborn error of metabolism of medical and biological significance. *Arch Intern Med* 109:209, 1962.

298. WINTROBE MM, LEE GR, BOGGS DR, BITHELL TC, FOERSTER J, ATHENS JW, LUKENS JN (eds): *Clinical Haematology*, 8th ed. Philadelphia, Lea & Febiger, 1981, pp 786–802.

299. GEORGE JN, SEARS DA, MCCURDY PR, CONRAD ME: Primaquine sensitivity in Caucasians: Hemolytic reactions induced by primaquine in G6PD deficient subjects. *J Lab Clin Med* 70:80, 1967.

300. SHAHIDI NT: Acetophenetidin-induced methemoglobinemia. *Ann NY Acad Sci* 151:822, 1968.

301. VESELL ES: Drug therapy: Pharmacogenetics. *N Engl J Med* 287:904, 1972.

302. LUZZATTO L: Inherited hemolytic states: Glucose-6-phosphate dehydrogenase deficiency. *Clin Haematol* 4:83, 1975.

303. HERMAN J, BEN-MEIR S: Overt hemolysis in patients with glucose-6-phosphate dehydrogenase deficiency. A survey in general practice. *Isr J Med Sci* 11:340, 1975.

304. JANAKIRAMAN N, SEELER RA, ROYAL JE, CHEN ME: Hemolysis during BAL chelation therapy for high blood lead levels in two G6PD deficient children. *Clin Pediatr (Phila)* 17:485, 1978.

305. VALAES T, DOKIADIS S, FESSAS PH: Acute hemolysis due to naphthalene inhalation. *J Pediatr* 63:904, 1963.

306. MANDAL BK, STEVENSON J: Haemolytic crisis produced by nalidixic acid. *Lancet* i:614, 1970.

307. SANSONE G, REALI S, SANSONE R, ALLEGRANZA F: Acute hemolytic anemia induced by a pyrazolonic drug in a child with glucose-6-phosphate dehydrogenase deficiency. *Acta Haematol (Basel)* 72:285, 1984.

308. BEUTLER E: The hemolytic effect of primaquine and related compounds. A review. *Blood* 14:103, 1959.

309. CHAN TK, TODD D, TSO SC: Red cell survival studies in glucose-6-phosphate dehydrogenase deficiency. *Bull Hongkong Med Assoc* 26:41, 1974.

310. POOTRAKUL P, PANICH V: The effect of acetaminophen on glucose-6-phosphate dehydrogenase, Mahidol variant. *Acata Haematol (Basel)* 69:358, 1983.

311. FRASER IM, VESELL ES: Effects of drugs and drug metabolites on erythrocytes from normal and glucose-6-phosphate dehydrogenase deficient individuals. *Ann NY Acad Sci* 151:777, 1968.

312. FRASER IM, TILTON BE, VESELL ES: Effects of some metabolites of hemolytic drugs on young and old, normal and G6PD deficient human erythrocytes. *Ann NY Acad Sci* 179:644, 1971.

313. WELT SI, JACKSON EH, KIRKMAN HN, PARKER JC: The effects of certain drugs on the hexose monophosphate shunt of human red cells. *Ann NY Acad Sci* 179:625, 1971.

314. COHEN G, HOCHSTEIN P: Generation of hydrogen peroxide in erythrocytes by hemolytic agents. *Biochemistry* 3:895, 1964.

315. CHOCKKALINGHAM K, BOARD PG, NURSE GT: Glucose-6-phosphate dehydrogenase deficiency in Papua New Guinea. *Hum Genet* 60:189, 1982.

316. MAGON AM, LEIPZIG RM, ZANNONI VG, BREWER GJ: Interactions of glucose-6-phosphate dehydrogenase deficiency with drug acetylation and hydroxylation reactions. *J Lab Clin Med* 97:764, 1981.

317. LUZZATTO L: Glucose 6-phosphate dehydrogenase and other genetic factors interacting with drugs, in Kalow W, Goedde HW, and Agarwal DP (eds): *Ethnic Differences in Reactions to Drugs and Xenobiotics.* New York, AR Liss, 1986, p 385.

318. BURKA ER, WEAVER Z, MARKS PA: Clinical spectrum of hemolytic anemia associated with glucose-6-phosphate dehydrogenase deficiency. *Ann Intern Med* 64:817, 1966.

319. SHANNON K, BUCHANAN GR: Severe hemolytic anemia in black children with glucose-6-phosphate dehydrogenase deficiency. *Pediatrics* 70:364, 1982.

320. AGARWAL RK, MOUDGIL A, KISHORE K, SRIVASTAVA RN, TANDON RK: Acute viral hepatitis, intravascular haemolysis, severe hyperbilirubinaemia and renal failure in glucose-6-phosphate dehydrogenase deficient patients. *Postgrad Med J* 61:971, 1985.

321. CHOREMIS C, KATTAMIS CA, KYRIAZAKOU M, GAVRILLIDOU E: Viral hepatitis in G6PD deficiency. *Lancet* i:269, 1966.

322. BOON WH: Viral hepatitis in G6PD deficiency. *Lancet* i:882, 1966.

323. KATTAMIS CA, TJORTJATOU F: The hemolytic process of viral hepatitis in children with normal or deficient glucose-6-phosphate dehydrogenase activity. *J Pediatr* 77:422, 1970.

324. PHILLIPS SM, SILVERS NP: Glucose-6-phosphate dehydrogenase deficiency, infectious hepatitis, acute hemolysis and renal failure. *Ann Intern Med* 70:99, 1969.

325. SALEN G, GOLDSTEIN F, HAURANI F, WIRTS CW: Acute hemolytic anemia complicating viral hepatitis in patients with glucose-6-phosphate dehydrogenase deficiency. *Ann Intern Med* 65:1210, 1966.

326. CLEARFIELD HR, BRODY JI, TUMEN HJ: Acute viral hepatitis, glucose-6-phosphate dehydrogenase deficiency and hemolytic anemia. *Arch Intern Med* 123:6879, 1969.

327. MENGEL CE, METZ E, YANCEY WS: Anemia during acute infections. Role of glucose-6-phosphate dehydrogenase deficiency in Negroes. *Arch Intern Med* 119:287, 1967.

328. TUGWELL P: Glucose-6-phosphate dehydrogenase deficiency in Nigerians with jaundice associated with lobar pneumonia. *Lancet* i:968, 1973.

329. WILLIAMS AO, TUGWELL P, EDINGTON GM: Glucose-6-phosphate dehydrogenase deficiency and lobar pneumonia. *Arch Pathol Lab Med* 100:25, 1976.

330. OWUSU SK: G6PD deficiency in jaundice associated with lobar pneumonia. *Lancet* ii:325, 1973.

331. OWUSU SK, ADDY J, FOLI AK, JANOSI M, KONOTEY-AHULU FID, LARBI EB: Acute reversible renal failure associated with glucose-6-phosphate dehydrogenase deficiency. *Lancet* i:1255, 1972.

332. BAKSHI S, SINGH J: Acute hemolytic anemia in typhoid fever. *Indian J Pediatr* 39:270, 1972.

333. LAMPE RM, KIRDPON S, MANSUWAN P, BENENSON MW: Glucose-6-phosphate dehydrogenase deficiency in Thai children with typhoid fever. *J Pediatr* 87:576, 1975.

334. HERSKO C, VARDY PA: Hemolysis in typhoid fever in children with G6PD deficiency. *Br Med J* i:214, 1967.

335. CHAN TK: G6PD deficiency, typhoid and co-trimoxazole. *Lancet* ii:1258, 1972.

336. OWUSU SK: Acute haemolysis complicating co-trimoxazole therapy for typhoid fever in a patient with G6PD deficiency. *Lancet* ii:819, 1972.

337. OWUSU SK, FOLI AK, KONOTEY-AHULU FID, JANOSI M: Frequency of glucose-6-phosphate dehydrogenase deficiency in typhoid fever in Ghana. *Lancet* i:320, 1972.

338. MORROW RH, SMETANA HE, SAI FT, EDGCOMB JH: Unusual features of viral hepatitis in Accra, Ghana. *Ann Intern Med* 68:1250, 1968.

339. OLUBOYEDE OA, ESAN GJF, FRANCIS TI, LUZZATTO L: Genetically determined deficiency of glucose-6-phosphate dehydrogenase (type A−) is expressed in the liver. *J Lab Clin Med* 93:783, 1979.

340. CROWELL SB, CROWELL EB, MATHEW M: Depression of erythrocyte glucose-6-phosphate dehydrogenase (G6PD) activity in enteric fever. *Trans Soc Trop Med Hyg* 78:183, 1984.

341. SELROOS O: Reversible renal failure and G6PD deficiency. *Lancet* ii:284, 1972.

342. ANGLE CR: Glucose-6-phosphate dehydrogenase deficiency and acute renal failure. *Lancet* ii:134, 1972.

343. WALKER DH, HAWKINS HK, HUDSON P: Fulminant Rocky Mountain Spotted Fever. Its pathologic characteristics associated with glucose-6-phosphate dehydrogenase deficiency. *Arch Pathol Lab Med* 107:121, 1984.

344. CHAN TK, TODD D: Haemolysis complicating viral hepatitis in patients with glucose-6-phoshate dehydrogenase deficiency. *Br Med J* 1:131, 1975.

345. WILKINSON SP, DAVIS MH, PORTMAN B, WILLIAMS R: Renal failure in otherwise uncomplicated viral hepatitis. *Br Med J* 2:338, 1978.

346. GULATI PD, RIZVI SNA: Acute reversible renal failure in G6PD deficient siblings. *Postgrad Med J* 52:83, 1976.

347. NECHELES TF, GORSHEIN D: Virus-induced hemolysis in erythrocytes deficient in glucose-6 phosphate dehydrogenase. *Science* 160:535, 1968.

348. BAEHNER RL, NATHAN DG, CASTLE WB: Oxidant injury of Caucasian glucose-6-phosphate dehydrogenase-deficient red blood cells by phagocytosing leucocytes during infection. *J Clin Invest* 50:2466, 1971.

349. NELSON RA: The immune adherence phenomenon—An immunologically specific reaction between microorganisms and erythrocytes leading to phagocytosis. *Science* 118:733, 1953.

350. KASER ML, MILLER WJ, JACOB HS: G6PD deficiency infectious hemolysis: A complement dependent innocent bystander phenomenon. *Br J Haematol* 63:85, 1986.

351. CLASTER S, TSUN-YEE CHIU D, QUINTANILHA A, LUBIN B: Neutrophils mediate lipid peroxidation in human red cells. *Blood* 64:1079, 1984.

352. MELONI T, FORTELEONI G, DORE A, CUTILLO S: Favism and hemolytic anemia in glucose-6-phosphate dehydrogenase deficiency subjects in North Sardinia. *Acta Haematol (Basel)* 70:83, 1983.

353. KATTAMIS CA, KYRIAZAKOU M, CHAIDAS S: Favism: Clinical and biochemical data. *J Med Genet* 6:34, 1969.

354. KAHN A, MARIE J, DESBOIS JC, BOIVIN P: Favism in a Portuguese family due to a deficient glucose-6-phosphate dehydrogenase variant of Canton or Canton like type 1. *Acta Haematol (Basel)* 56:58, 1976.

355. BELSEY MA: The epidemiology of favism. *Bull WHO* 48:1, 1973.

356. PANICH V, NA NAKORN S: Acute hemolysis in G6PD Union (Thai) Report on four cases. *J Med Assoc Thai* 56:241, 1973.

357. DACIE JV: The hemolytic anemias: congenital and acquired, in *Drug-Induced Hemolytic Anemias, Paroxysmal Nocturnal Hemoglobinuria and Hemolytic Disease of the Newborn.* London, Churchill Livingstone, 1967, pp 1062–1063.

358. DISCOMBE G, MESLITZ W: Favism in an English-born child. *Br Med J* i:1023, 1956.

359. HOLT JM, SLADDEN RA: Favism in England. Two more cases. *Arch Dis Child* 40:271, 1965.

360. DAVIES P: Favism: a family study. *Q J Med* 122:157, 1962.

361. STOCKLEY R, DAWSON A, SLADE R: Favism in two British women. *Lancet* ii:1013, 1985.

362. CROSBY WH: Favism in Sardinia (Newletter). *Blood* 11:91, 1956.

363. SZEINBERG A, SHEBA C, HIRSCHORN N, BODONYI E: Studies on erythrocytes in cases with past history of favism and drug induced acute hemolytic anemia. *Blood* 12:603, 1957.

364. GROSS AT, HURWITZ RA, MARKS PA: An hereditary enzymatic defect in erythrocyte metabolism. Glucose-6-phosphate dehydrogenase deficiency. *J Clin Invest* 37:1176, 1958.

365. SINISCALCO M, BERNINI L, LATTE B, MOTULSKY AG: Favism and thalassaemia in Sardinia and their relationship to malaria. *Nature* 190:1179, 1961.

366. KATTAMIS CA, CHAIDAS A, CHAIDAS S: G6PD deficiency and favism in the island of Rhodes. *J Med Genet* 6:286, 1969.

367. VULLO C, PANIZON F: The mechanism of hemolysis in favism. Transfusion experiments with ^{51}CR tagged erythrocytes. *Acta Haematol (Basel)* 26:337, 1961.

368. PANIZON F, VULLO C: The mechanism of hemolysis in favism. Researches on the role of non corpuscular factors. *Acta Haematol (Basel)* 26:337, 1961.

369. SARTORI E: On the pathogenesis of favism. *J Med Genet* 8:462, 1971.

370. MARENI C, REPETTO, FORETELEONI G, MELONI T, GAETANI GF: Favism: Looking for an autosomal gene associated with glucose-6-phosphate dehydrogenase deficiency. *J Med Genet* 21:278, 1984.

371. STAMATOYANNOPOULOS G, FRASER GR, MOTULSKY AG, FESSAS PH, AKRIVAKIS A, PAPAYANNOPOULOU T: On the familial predisposition to favism. *Am J Hum Genet* 18:253, 1966.

372. BATTISTUZZI G, MORELLINI M, MELONI T, GANDINI E, LUZZATTO L: Genetic factors in favism, in Weatherall DJ, Fiorelli G, Gernin S (eds): *Advances in Red Cell Biology.* New York, Raven, 1982, pp 339–346.

373. BOTTINI E, LUCARELLI P, AGOSTINO R, PALMARINO R, BUSINCO L, ANTOGNONI G: Favism: Association with erythrocyte acid phosphatase phenotype. *Science* 171:409, 1971.

374. CASSIMOS CHR, MALAKA-ZAFIRIU K, TSIURES J: Urinary D-glucaric acid excretion in normal and G6PD deficient children with favism. *J Pediatr* 84:871, 1974.

375. CUTILLO S, COSTA S, VINTULEDOU MC, MELONI T: Salicylamide glucuronide formation in children with favism and their parents. *Acta Haematol (Basel)* 55:296, 1976.

376. SCHILIRO G, SCIOTTO A, RUSSO A, BOTTARD G, MINNITI C, MUSUMECI S, RUSSO G: Lymphocyte changes in favism: In vitro evidence of a modifying effect of bilirubin and hemoglobin on T-lymphocyte receptors. *Acta Haematol (Basel)* 69:230, 1983.

377. SCHILIRO G, NIMMITI C, SCIOTTO A, BELLINO A, RUSSO A: T lymphocyte subpopulation changes during haemolysis in glucose 6-phosphate dehydrogenase (G6PD) deficient children. *Am J Hematol* 21:73, 1986.

378. KAPLAN E, SARNAIK S, GITLIN J, LUSHER J: Diminished helper/suppressor ratios and natural killer activity in recipients of repeated blood transfusions. *Blood* 64:308, 1984.

379. SYMVOULIDIS A, VOUDICLARIS S, MOUNTOKALAKIS TH, POUGOUNIAS H: Acute renal failure in G6PD deficiency. *Lancet* ii:819, 1972.

380. BAULE GM, ONORATO D, TOLA G, FORTELEONI G, MELONI T: Hemoglobin A1 in subjects with G6PD deficiency during and after hemolytic crisis due to favism. *Acta Haematol (Basel)* 69:15, 1983.

381. RUGGO G, MOLLICA G, PAVONE L, SCHILIRO G: Hemolytic crisis of favism in Sicilian females heterozygous for G6PD deficiency. *Pediatrics* 49:854, 1972.

382. SCHILIRO G, RUSSO A, CURRERI R, MARINO S, SCIOTTO A, RUSSO G: Glucose-6-phosphate dehydrogenase deficiency in Sicily. Incidence biochemical characteristics and clinical implications. *Clin Genet* 15:183, 1979.

383. KATTAMIS C: Favism in breast-fed infants. *Arch Dis Child* 46:741, 1971.

384. EKERT U, RAWLINSON I: Desferrioxamine and favism. *N Engl J Med* 312:1260, 1985.

385. MELONI T, FORTELEONI G, GAETANI GF: Desferrioxamine and favism. *Br J Haematol* 63:394, 1986.

386. ARESE P: Favism. A natural model for the study of haemolytic mechanisms. *Rev Pure Appl Pharmacol Sci* 3:1234, 1982.

387. LIN JY, LING KH: Studies on favism. 1. Isolation of an active principle from fava beans (Vicia faba). *J Formosan Med Assoc* 61:484, 1962.

388. LIN JY, LING KH: Studies on favism. 2. Studies on the physiological activities of vicine in vivo. *J Formosan Med Assoc* 61:490, 1962.

389. ARESE P, BOSIA A, NAITANA A, GAETANI S, D'AQUINO M, GAETANI GF: Effect of divicine and isouramil on red cell metabolism in normal and G6PD deficient (Mediterranean variant) subjects. Possible role in the genesis of favism, in Brewer G (ed): *The Red Cell: Fifth Ann Arbor Conference.* New York, AR Liss, 1981, pp 725–744.

390. MAGER J, GLASER G, RAZIN A, IZAK G, BIEN S, NOAM M: Metabolic effects of pyrimidines derived from fava bean glycosides on human erythrocytes deficient in glucose 6-phosphate dehydrogenase. *Biochem Biophys Res Commun* 20:235, 1965.

391. FISCHER TM, PESCARMONA GP, BOSIA A, NAITANA A, TURRINI F, ARESE P: Membrane cross-banding in red cells in favic crisis—A missing link in the mechanism of extravascular haemolysis. *Br J Haematol* 59:159, 1985.

392. DE FLORA A, BENATTI U, GUIDA L, FORTELEONI G, MELONI T: Favism: Disordered erythrocyte calcium hemostatis. *Blood* 66:294, 1985.

393. TURRINI F, NAITANA A, MANUZZU L, PESCARMONA G, ARESE P: Increased red cell calcium, decreased calcium adenosine triphosphatase and altered membrane proteins during fava bean hemolysis in glucose-6-phosphate dehydrogenase-deficient (Mediterranean variant) individuals. *Blood* 66:302, 1985.

394. LORANO L, WEISSMAN LB, EPEL DL, BRUNER-LORAND J: Role of intrinsic transglutaminase in the Ca^{++} mediated crosslinking of erythrocyte proteins. *Proc Natl Acad Sci USA* 73:4479, 1976.

395. MORELLI A, GRASSO M, MELONI T, FORTELEONI G, ZOCCHI E, DeFLORA A: Favism: Impairment of proteolytic systems in red blood cells. *Blood* 69:1753, 1987.

396. MATTHAY KK, MENTZER WC: Erythrocyte enzymopathies in the newborn. *Clin Haematol* 10:31, 1981.

397. SMITH GD, VELLA F: Erythrocyte enzyme deficiency in unexplained kernicterus. *Lancet* 1:1133, 1960.

398. WEATHERALL DJ: Enzyme deficiency in hemolytic disease of the newborn. *Lancet* ii:835, 1960.

399. DOXIADIS SA, FESSAS PH, VALAES T: Erythrocyte enzyme deficiency in unexplained kernicterus. *Lancet* ii:44, 1960.

400. PANIZON F: Erythrocyte enzyme deficiency in unexplained kernicterus. *Lancet* ii:1093, 1960.

401. BIENZLE U: Glucose-6-phosphate dehydrogenase deficiency Part 1: Tropical Africa. *Clin Haematol* 10:785, 1981.

402. KARAYALCIN G, ACS H, LANZKOWSKY P: G6PD deficiency and hyperbilirubinaemia in black American full-term infants. *NY State J Med* 79:22, 1979.

403. TARNOW-MORDI WO, PICKERING D: Missed jaundice in black infants a hazard? *Br Med J* 286:463, 1983.

404. LOPEZ R, COOPERMAN JM: Glucose-6-phosphate dehydrogenase deficiency and hyperbilirubinaemia in the newborn. *Am J Dis Child* 122:66, 1971.

405. BROWN WR, BOON WH: Hyperbilirubinemia and kernicterus in glucose-6-phosphate dehydrogenase deficient infants in Singapore. *Pediatrics* 41:1055, 1968.

406. MELONI T, COSTA S, CUTILLO S: Haptoglobin, hemopexin, hemoglobin and hematocrit in newborns with erythrocyte glucose-6-phosphate dehydrogenase deficiency. *Acta Haematol (Basel)* 54:284, 1975.

407. MALAKA-ZAFIRIU K, TSIURES I, CASSIMOS C: D-Glucaric acid excretion in newborns with severe jaundice of unknown aetiology and due to glucose-6-phosphate dehydrogenase deficiency in Greece. *Helv Pediatr Acta* 30:201, 1975.

408. MALAKA-ZAFIRJU K, TSIURES I, DANIELIDES B, CASSIMOS C: Salicylamide glucuronide formation in newborns with severe jaundice of unknown aetiology and due to glucose-6-phosphate dehydrogenase deficiency in Greece. *Helv Paediatr Acta* 28:323, 1973.

409. HAMIL BM, MUNKS B, MOYER EZ, KAUCHER M, WILLIAMS HH: Vitamin C in the blood and urine of the newborn and in the cord and maternal blood. *Am J Dis Child* 74:417, 1947.

410. GROSS S: Hemolytic anemia in premature infants: Relationship to vitamin E, selenium, glutathione peroxidase and erythrocyte lipids. *Semin Hematol* 3:187, 1976.

411. BIENZLE U, EFFIONG CE, AIMAKU VE, LUZATTO L: Erythrocyte enzymes in neonatal jaundice. *Acta Haematol (Basel)* 55:10, 1976.

412. JONES PEH, MCCANCE RA: Enzyme activities in the blood of infants and adults. *Biochem J* 45:464, 1949.

413. CAPPS FPA, GILLES HM, JOLLY H, WORLLEDGE SM: Glucose-6-phosphate dehydrogenase deficiency and neonatal jaundice in Nigeria. Their relation to the prophylactic use of vitamin K. *Lancet* ii:379, 1963.

414. HARRIS R, GILLES HM: Glucose-6-phosphate dehydrogenase deficiency in the peoples of the Niger Delta. *Ann Hum Genet* 25:199, 1961.

415. LEVIN SE, CHARLTON RW, FREIMAN I: Glucose-6-phosphate dehydrogenase deficiency and neonatal jaundice in South African Bantu infants. *J Pediatr* 65:757, 1964.

416. BERNSTEIN RE: Occurrence and clinical implications of red cell glucose-6-phosphate dehydrogenase deficiency in South African racial groups. *S Afr Med J* 37:447, 1963.

417. GIBBS WN, GRAY R, LOWRY M: Glucose-6-phosphate dehydrogenase deficiency and neonatal jaundice in Jamaica. *Br J Haematol* 43:263, 1979.

418. WOLFF JA, GROSSMAN BH, PAYA K: Neonatal serum bilirubin and glucose-6-phosphate dehydrogenase. Relationship of various perinatal factors to hyperbilirubinemia. *Am J Dis Child* 113:251, 1967.

419. O'FLYNN MED, HSIA DY: Serum bilirubin levels and glucose-6-phosphate dehydrogenase deficiency in newborn American Negros. *J Pediatr* 63:160, 1963.

420. ESHAGHPOUR E, OSKI FA, WILLIAMS M: The relationship of erythrocyte glucose-6-phosphate dehydrogenase deficiency to hyperbilirubinemia in Negro premature infants. *J Pediatr* 70:595, 1967.

421. BIENZLE U, EFFIONG C, LUZZATTO L: Erythrocyte glucose-6-phosphate dehydrogenase deficiency (G6PD type A−) and neonatal jaundice. *Acta Paediatr Scand* 65:701, 1976.

422. IFEKWUNIGWE AE, LUZZATTO L: Kernicterus in G6PD deficiency. *Lancet* i:667, 1966.

423. ROUX P, KARABUS CD, HARTLEY PS: The effect of glucose-6-phosphate dehydrogenase deficiency on the severity of neonatal jaundice in Cape Town. *S Afr Med J* 22:781, 1982.

424. BROWN AK, CEVIK N: Hemolysis and jaundice in the newborn following maternal treatment with sulfamethoxpyridazine (Kynex). *Pediatrics* 36:742, 1965.

425. GLASS L, RAJEGOWDA BK, BOWEN E, EVANS HE: Exposure to quinine and jaundice in a glucose-6-phosphate dehydrogenase deficient newborn infant. *J Pediatr* 82:734, 1973.

426. PERKINS RP: Hydrops fetalis and stillbirth in a male glucose-6-phosphate dehydrogenase deficient fetus possibly due to maternal ingestion of sulfisoxazole. *Am J Obstet Gynecol* 11:379, 1971.

427. LAI HC, LAI MPY, LEUNG KS: Glucose-6-phosphate dehydrogenase deficiency in Chinese. *J Clin Pathol* 21:44, 1968.

428. YUE PCK, STRICKLAND M: Glucose-6-phosphate dehydrogenase deficiency and neonatal jaundice in Chinese male infants in Hongkong. *Lancet* i:350, 1965.

429. LU T-C, WEI H, BLACKWELL RQ: Increased incidence of severe hyperbilirubinemia among newborn Chinese infants with G6PD deficiency. *Pediatrics* 37:994, 1966.

430. FLATZ G, SRINGAM S, PREMYOTHIN C, PENBHARKKUL S, KETUSINGH R, CHULAJATA S: Glucose-6-phosphate dehydrogenase deficiency and neonatal jaundice. *Arch Dis Child* 38:566, 1963.

431. PHORNPHUTKUL C, WHITAKER JA, WORATHUMRONG N: Severe hyperbilirubinemia in Thai newborns in association with erythrocyte G6PD deficiency. *Clin Pediatr* 8:275, 1969.

432. VELLA F: The incidence of erythrocyte glucose-6-phosphate dehydrogenase deficiency in Singapore. *Experientia* 17:181, 1961.

433. TAN KL: Glucose-6-phosphate dehydrogenase status and neonatal jaundice. *Arch Dis Child* 56:874, 1981.

434. LIE-INJO LE, VIRJK HK, LIM PW, LIE AK, GANESAN J: Red cell metabolism and severe neonatal jaundice in West Malaysia. *Acta Haematol (Basel)* 58:152, 1977.

435. DOXIADIS SA, VALAES T, KARAKLIS A, STAVRAKAKIS D: Risk of severe jaundice in glucose-6-phosphate dehydrogenase deficiency of the newborn. Differences in population groups. *Lancet* ii:1210, 1964.

436. STAMATOYANNOPOULOS G, FESSAS PH: Thalassaemia, glucose 6-phosphate dehydrogenase deficiency, sickling and malarial endemicity in Greece. A study of five areas. *Br Med J* i:875, 1964.

437. FESSAS PH, DOXIADIS SA, VALAES T: Neonatal jaundice in glucose-6-phosphate dehydrogenase deficient infants. *Br Med J* ii:1359, 1962.

438. BEUTLER E, ROSEN R: Non-spherocytic congenital haemolytic anaemia due to a new G6PD variant, G6PD Alhambra. *Paediatrics* 45:230, 1970.

439. MELONI T, FORTELEONI G, DORE A, CUTILLO S: Neonatal hyperbilirubinaemia in heterozygous glucose-6-phosphate dehydrogenase deficient females. *Br J Haematol* 53:241, 1983.

440. MELONI T, CAGNAZZO G, DORE A, CUTILLO S: Phenobarbital for prevention of hyperbilirubinemia in glucose-6-phosphate dehydrogenase deficient newborn infants. *J Pediatr* 82:1048, 1973.

441. SZEINBERG A, OLIVER M, SCHMIDT R, ADAM A, SHEBA C: Glucose-6-phosphate dehydrogenase deficiency and hemolytic disease of the newborn in Israel. *Arch Dis Child* 38:23, 1963.

442. MILBAUER B, PELED N, SVIRSKY S: Neonatal hyperbilirubinemia and glucose-6-phosphate dehydrogenase deficiency. *Isr J Med Sci* 9:547, 1973.

443. DREW JH, SMITH MB, KITCHEN WH: Glucose-6-phosphate dehydrogenase in immigrant Greek infants. *J Pediatr* 90:659, 1977.

444. VALAES T, DOXIADIS SA, FESSAS PH: Acute hemolysis due to naphthalene inhalation. *J Pediatr* 63:904, 1963.

445. LUZZATTO L, MELONI T: Hemolytic anemia due to glucose-6-phosphate dehydrogenase deficiency, in Brain MC, Carbone PP (eds): *Current Therapy in Hematology/Oncology-2*. Phladelphia, Dekker, 1985, pp 21–24.

446. VALAES T, KARAKLIS A, STAVRAKAKIS D, BAVELA-STAVRAKAKIS D, PERAKIS A, DOXIADIS SA: Incidence and mechanism of neonatal jaundice related to glucose-6-phosphate dehydrogenase deficiency. *Pediatr Res* 3:448, 1969.

447. KOPELMAN AE, EY JL, LEE H: Phototherapy in newborn infants with glucose-6-phosphate dehydrogenase deficiency. *J Pediatr* 93:497, 1978.

448. GROMISCH DS, LOPEZ, COLE HS, COOPERMAN JM: Light (phototherapy)-induced riboflavin deficiency in the neonate. *J Pediatr* 90:118, 1977.

449. LOPEZ R, GROMISCH DS, COLE HS, COOPERMAN JM: Phototherapy in G6PD deficient infants. *J Pediatr* 102:326, 1983.

450. MELONI T, COSTA S, DORE A, CUTILLO S: Phototherapy for neonatal hyperbilirubinemia in mature newborn infants with G6PD deficiency. *J Pediatr* 85:560, 1974.

451. TAN KL: Phototherapy for neonatal jaundice in erythrocyte glucose-6-phosphatase dehydrogenase deficient infants. *Pediatrics (Neonatal Suppl)* 59:1023, 1977.

452. MELONI T, CORTI R, NAITANA AF, ARESE P: Lack of effect of phototherapy dehydrogenase activity in normal and G6PD deficient subjects with neonatal jaundice. *J Pediatr* 100:972, 1982.

453. BEUTLER E, MATHAI CK, SITH JE: Biochemical variants of glucose-6-phosphate giving rise to congenital non-spherocytic hemolytic disease. *Blood* 31:131, 1968.

454. BEN-ISHAY D, IZAK G: Chronic hemolysis associated with glucose-6-phosphate dehydrogenase deficiency. *J Lab Clin Med* 63:1002, 1964.

455. LIVINGSTONE FB: *Frequencies of Hemoglobin Variants*. Oxford, Oxford University Press, 1985.

456. BIENZLE U, SODEINDE O, EFFIONG CE, LUZZATTO L: Glucose-6-phosphate dehydrogenase deficiency and sickle cell anaemia: Frequency and features of the association in an African community. *Blood* 46:591, 1975.

457. ROTOLI B: Personal communication.

458. MELONI T, GAETANI GF: Personal communication.

459. NEWTON WA Jr, FRAJOLA WJ: Drug-sensitive chronic hemolytic anemia: Family studies. *Clin Res* 6:392, 1958.

460. SONNET J, LIEVENS M, VERPOORTEN C, KRIEKEMANS J, EECKELS R: Sporadic G6PD deficiency with haemolytic anemia in two children of West European ancestry. *Br J Haematol* 28:299, 1974.

461. SHAHIDI NT, DIAMOND LK: Enzyme deficiency in erythrocytes in congenital non-spherocytic hemolytic anemia. *Pediatrics* 24:245, 1959.

462. CLOUTIER MD, BURGERT EO Jr: Congenital non-spherocytic hemolytic disease secondary to glucose-6-phosphate dehydrogenase deficiency. Report of 3 cases. *Mayo Clin Proc* 41:316, 1966.

463. GREENBERG LH, TANAKA KR: Hereditary hemolytic anemia due to glucose-6-phosphate dehydrogenase deficiency. *Am J Dis Child* 110:206, 1965.

464. ZINKHAM WH, LENHARD RE: Metabolic abnormalities of erythrocytes from patients with congenital non-spherocytic hemolytic anemia. *J Pediatr* 55:319, 1959.

465. MOHLER DN, CROCKETT CL Jr: Hereditary hemolytic disease secondary to glucose-6-phosphate dehydrogenase deficiency. Report of 3 cases with special emphasis on ATP metabolism. *Blood* 23:427, 1964.

466. KIRKMAN HN, RILEY HD: Congenital non-sperocytic hemolytic anemia. Studies on a family with a qualitative defect in glucose-6-phosphate dehydrogenase. *Am J Dis Child* 102:313, 1961.

467. HUSKISSON EC, MURPHY B, WEST G: Glucose-6-phosphate dehydrogenase deficiency and chronic hemolysis in an English family. *J Clin Pathol* 23:135, 1970.

468. VUOPIO P, HARKONEN M, HELSKE T, NAVERI H: Red cell glucose-6-phosphate dehydrogenase deficiency in Finland. Characterisation of a new variant with severe enzyme deficiency. *Scand J Haematol* 15:145, 1975.

469. LUZZATTO L: New developments in glucose-6-phosphate dehydrogenase deficiency. *Isr J Med Sci* 9:1484, 1973.

470. SHAHIDI NT, CLATANOFF DV: The role of puberty in red cell production in hereditary hemolytic anemias. *Br J Haematol* 17:335, 1969.

471. DE MARS R: A temperature sensitive glucose-6-phosphate dehydrogenase in mutant cultured human cells. *Proc Natl Acad Sci USA* 61:562, 1968.

472. VERGNES HA, BONNET LG, GROZDEA JD: Genetic variants of human erythrocyte glucose-6-phosphate dehydrogenase: New characterization data obtained by multivariate analysis. *Ann Hum Genet* 49:1, 1985.

473. BEN-BASSAT J, BEN-ISHAY D: Hereditary hemolytic anemia associated with glucose-6-phosphate dehydrogenase deficiency Mediterranean type. *Isr J Med Sci* 5:1053, 1969.

474. TILLMAN W, GAHR M, LABITKE N, SCHROTER W: Membrane deformability of erythrocytes with glucose-6-phosphate dehydrogenase Hamburg. *Acta Haematol (Basel)* 57:162, 1977.

475. ALLEN DW, JOHNSON GJ, CADMAN S, KAPLAN ME: Membrane polypeptide aggregates in glucose-6-phosphate dehydrogenase deficient and in vitro aged red blood cells. *J Lab Clin Med* 91:321, 1978.

476. JOHNSON GJ, ALLEN DW, CADMAN S, FAIRBANKS VF, WHITE JG, LAMPKIN BC, KAPLAN ME: Red cell membrane polypeptide aggregates in glucose-6-phosphate dehydrogenase mutants with chronic hemolytic disease. A clue to the mechanism of hemolysis. *N Engl J Med* 301:522, 1979.

477. BAPAT JP, BAXI AJ: Mechanism of hemolysis of G6PD deficient red cells: Changes in membrane lipids and polypeptides. *Blut* 44:355, 1979.

478. CORASH L, SPIELBERG S, BARTSOCAS C, BOXER L, STEINHERTZ R, SHEETZ M, EGAN M, SCHLESSLEMAN J, SCHULMAN JD: Reduced chronic haemolysis during high dose vitamin E administration in Mediterranean-type

glucose-6-phosphate dehydrogenase deficiency. *N Engl J Med* 303:416, 1980.

479. SPIELBERG SP, BOXER LA, CORASH LM, SCHULMAN JD: Improved erythrocyte survival with high dose vitamin E in chronic haemolizing G6PD and glutathione synthetase deficiency. *Ann Intern Med* 90:53, 1979.

480. HAFEZ M, AMAR ES, ZEDAN M, HAMMAD H, SOROUR AH, ELDESOUKY ESA, GAMIL N: Improved erythrocyte survival with combined vitamin E and selenium therapy in children with glucose-6-phosphate dehydrogenase deficiency and mild chronic haemolysis. *J Pediatr* 108:558, 1986.

481. JOHNSON GJ, VATASSERY GR, FINKEL B, ALLEN DW: High dose vitamin E does not decrease the rate of chronic hemolysis in G6PD deficiency. *N Engl J Med* 303:432, 1983.

482. NEWMAN GJ, NEWMAN TB, BOWIE LJ, MENDLESOHN J: An examination of the role of vitamin E in G6PD deficiency. *Clin Biochem* 12:149, 1979.

483. BLACKBURN EK, LORBER J: Chronic hemolytic anemia due to glucose-6-phosphate dehydrogenase deficiency. *Proc R Soc Med* 56:505, 1963.

484. LUZZATTO L, BATTISTUZZI G: Glucose-6-phosphate dehydrogenase, in Harris H, Hirschorn K (eds): *Advance in Human Genetics*. New York, Plenum, 1985, pp 217–329.

485. SCHILIRO G, RUSSO A, MAURO L, PIZZARELLI G, MARINO S: Leucocyte function and characterisation of leukocyte glucose-6-phosphate dehydrogenase in Sicilian mutants. *Pediatr Res* 10:739, 1976.

486. COWAN JM, AMMANN AJ: Immunodeficiency syndromes associated with inherited metabolic disorders. *Clin Haematol* 10:139, 1981.

487. COOPER MR, De CHATELET LR, MCCALL CE, LA VIA MF, SPURR CL, BAEHNER RL: Complete deficiency of leucocyte glucose-6-phosphate dehydrogenase with defective bactericidal activity. *J Clin Invest* 51:769, 1972.

488. GRAY FR, KLEBANOFF SJ, STAMATOYANNOPOULOS G, AUSTIN T, NAIMAN SC, YOSHIDA A, KILMAN MR, ROBINSON GCF: Neutrophil dysfunction, chronic granulomatous disease, and non-spherocytic haemolytic anemia caused by complete deficiency of glucose-6-phosphate dehydrogenase. *Lancet* ii:530, 1973.

489. BAEHNER RL, JOHNSTON RB, NATHAN DG: Comparative study of the metabolic and bactericidal characteristics of severely glucose-6-phosphate dehydrogenase deficient polymorphonuclear leucocytes and leucocytes from children with chronic granulomatous disease. *J Reticuloendothelial Soc* 12:150, 1972.

490. BELLANTI JA, CANTZ BE, SCHLEGEL RJ: Accelerated decay of glucose-6-phosphate dehydrogenase activity in chronic granulomatous disease. *Pediatr Res* 4:405, 1970.

491. ERICKSON RP, STITES DP, FUDENBERG HH, EPSTEIN CJ: Altered levels of glucose-6-phosphate dehydrogenase stabilising factors in X-linked chronic granulomatous disease. *J Lab Clin Med* 80:644, 1972.

492. CORBERAND J, De LARRARD B, VERGNESH, CARRIERE JP: Chronic granulomatous disease with leukocyte glucose-6-phosphate dehydrogenase deficiency in a 28 month old girl. *Am J Clin Pathol* 70:296, 1978.

493. HOFFMANN J, BOSIA A, ARESE P, LOSCHE W, PESCARMONA GP, TAZARTES O, TILL U: Glucose-6-phosphate dehydrogenase deficiency in human platelets and its effect on platelet aggregation. *Acta Biol Med Ger* 40:1707, 1981.

494. SCHWARTZ JP, COOPERBERG AA, ROSENBERG A: Platelet function studies in patients with glucose-6-phosphate dehydrogenase deficiency. *Br J Haematol* 27:273, 1974.

495. VALENTINE WN, PAGLIA DE: Erythrocyte enzymopathies, hemolytic anemia and multi system disease: An annotated review. *Blood* 64:583, 1984.

496. MARKS PA, GROSS RT, HURWITZ RE: Gene action in erythrocyte deficiency of glucose-6-phosphate dehydrogenase: Tissue enzyme levels. *Nature* 183:1266, 1959.

497. CLARK M, ROOT RK: Glucose 6-phosphate dehydrogenase deficiency and infection: A study of hospitalized patients in Iran. *Yale J Biol Med* 52:169, 1979.

498. WURZEL H, MCGEARY T, BAKER L, GUMERMAN L: Glucose 6-phosphate dehydrogenase deficiency in platelets. *Blood* 17:314, 1961.

499. COHN J, CARTER N, WARBURG M: Glucose-6-phosphate dehydrogenase deficiency in a native Danish family. *Scand J Haematol* 23:403, 1979.

500. WESTRING DN, PISCIOTTA AV: Anemia, cataracts and seizures in a patient with glucose-6-phosphate dehydrogenase deficiency. *Arch Intern Med* 118:385, 1966.

501. MORO F, GORGONE G, LI-VOLTI S, CAVALLARO N, FARO S, CURRERI R, MOLLICA F: Glucose-6-phosphate dehydrogenase deficiency and incidence of cataract in Sicily. *Ophthalmic Paediatr Genet* 5:197, 1985.

502. ZINKHAM WH: A deficiency of glucose-6-phosphate dehydrogenase activity in lens from individuals with primaquine-sensitive erythrocytes. *Johns Hopkins Med J* 109:206, 1961.

503. CHAN TK, TODD D, WONG CC: Tissue enzyme levels in erythrocyte glucose-6-phosphate dehydrogenase deficiency. *J Lab Clin Med* 66:937, 1965.

504. SARKAR S, NELSON AJ, JONES OW: Glucose-6-phosphate dehydrogenase (G6PD) activity of human sperm. *J Med Genet* 14:250, 1977.

505. RAMOT B, SHEBA C, ADAM A, ASHKENASI I: Erythrocyte glucose-6-phosphate dehydrogenase deficient subjects: Enzyme-level in saliva. *Nature* 185:931, 1960.

506. WHITE JM, BYRNE M, RICHARDS R, BUCHANAN T, KATSOULIS E, WEERASINGH K: Red cell genetic abnormalities in Peninsular Arabs: Sickle hemoglobin, G6PD deficiency and alpha and beta thalassemia. *J Med Genet* 23:245, 1986.

507. SAMUEL AP, SAHA N, ACQUAYE JK, OMER A, GANESHAGURU K, HASSOUNH E: Association of red cell glucose-6-phosphate dehydrogenase with hemoglobinopathies. *Hum Hered* 36:107, 1986.

508. LEWIS RA, KAY RW, HATHORN M: Sickle cell disease and glucose-6-phosphate dehydrogenase phosphate dehydrogenase. *Acta Haematol (Basel)* 35:399, 1966.

509. BERNSTEIN SC, BOWMAN JE, NOCHE LK: Interaction of sickle cell trait and glucose-6-phosphate deficiency in Cameroon. *Hum Hered* 30:7, 1980.

510. OZSOYLU S: Sickle cell disease, G6PD deficiency and jaundice. *J Pediatr* 93:898, 1978.

511. LUZZATTO L, ALLAN NC: Relationship between the genes for glucose-6-phosphate dehydrogenase and for haemoglobin in a Nigerian population. *Nature* 219:1041, 1968.

512. NHONOLI AM, KUJWALILE JM, KIGONI EP, MASAWE AEJ: Correlation of glucose-6-phosphate dehydrogenase (G6PD) deficiency and sickle cell trait (Hb-AS). *Trop Geogr Med* 30:99, 1978.

513. STEINBERG MH, DREILING BJ: Glucose-6-phosphate dehydrogenase deficiency in sickle cell anemia. A study in adults. *Ann Intern Med* 80:217, 1974.

514. BEUTLER E, JOHNSON C, POWARS D, WEST C: Prevalence of glucose 6-phosphate dehydrogenase deficiency in sickle cell disease. *N Engl J Med* 280:826, 1974.

515. YOUNKER D, De VORE M, HARTZAGE PL: Malignant hyperthermia and glucose-6-phosphate dehydrogenase deficiency. *Anesthesiology* 60:601, 1984.

516. HARPER JI, COPEMAN PWM: A child with xeroderma pigmentosum and G6PD deficiency. *Clin Exp Dermatol* 7:213, 1982.

517. CONGDON PJ, LITTLEWOOD JM, AGGARWAL RK, SHAPIRO H: Glucose-6-phosphate dehydrogenase deficiency and cystic fibrosis. *Postgrad Med J* 57:453, 1981.

518. DERN RJ, GLYNN MF, BREWER GJ: Studies on the correlation of the genetically determined trait, glucose-6-phosphate dehydrogenase deficiency with behavioral manifestations in schizophrenia. *J Lab Clin Med* 62:319, 1963.

519. BOWMAN JE, BREWER GJ, FRISCHER H, CARTER JL, EISENTEIN RB, BAYRAKCI C: A re-evaluation of the relationship between glucose-6-phosphate dehydrogenase deficiency and behaviorial manifestations of schizophrenia. *J Lab Clin Med* 65:222, 1965.

520. CHANMUGAN D, FRUMIN AM: Abnormal oral glucose tolerance response in erythrocyte glucose-6-phosphate dehydrogenase deficiency. *N Engl J Med* 271:1202, 1964.

521. EPPES RB, BREWER GJ, DE GOWIN RL, MANAMARA JY, FLANAGAN CL, SCHRIER SL, TARLOV AR, POWELL RD, CARSON PE: Oral glucose tolerance in Negro men deficient in G6PD. *N Engl J Med* 275:855, 1966.

522. BORKOWSKI AJ, MARKS PA, KATZ FH, LIPMAN MM, CHRISTTY NP: An abnormal pathway of steroid metabolism in patients with glucose-6-phosphate dehydrogenase deficiency. *J Clin Invest* 41:1346, 1962.

523. MCCURDY PR: An apparent association between red cell glucose-6-phosphate dehydrogenase deficiency and pernicious anemia in negro males. *Clin Res* 14:91, 1966.

524. SHEEHAN RG, LINDEMAN RJ, MEYER J, PATTERSON JF, NECHELLES TF: The possible association of erythrocyte glucose-6-phosphate dehydrogenase deficiency and regional enteritis. *J Clin Invest* 44:1098, 1965.

525. LONG WK, WILSON SW, FRENKEL EP: Associations between red cell glucose-6-phosphate dehydrogenase variants and vascular diseases. *Am J Hum Genet* 19:35, 1967.

526. WIESENFELD SL, PETRAKIS NL, SAMS BJ, COLLEN MF, CUTLER JL: Elevated blood pressure, pulse rate and serum creatinine in Negro males deficient in glucose-6-phosphate dehydrogenase. *N Engl J Med* 282:1001, 1970.

527. PETERSEN OW, BRIAND P, van DEURS B: Identification of malignant cells in primary monolayer cultures of human breast tumours. *Acta Pathol Microbiol Immunol Scand* 92:103, 1984.

528. MESSERI G, TOZZI P, BODDI V, CIATTO S: Glucose-6-phosphate dehydrogenase activity and estrogen receptors in human breast cancer. *Oncology* 42:7, 1985.

529. BEZWODA WR, DERMAN DP, SEE N, MANSOOR N: Relative value of oestrogen receptor assay, lactoferrin content and glucose-6-phosphate dehydrogenase activity as prognostic indicators in primary breast cancer. *Oncology* 42:7, 1985.

530. ZAMPELLA EJ, BRADLEY EL, PRETLOW TG: Glucose-6-phosphate dehydrogenase: A possible indicator for prostatic carcinoma. *Cancer* 49:384, 1982.

531. IBRAHIM KS, HUSAIN OAN, BITENSKY L, CHAYEN J: A modified tetrazolium reaction for identifying malignant cells from gastric and colonic cancer. *J Clin Pathol* 36:133, 1983.

532. PETERSEN OW, HOYER PE, van DEURS B: Effect of oxygen on the tetrazolium reaction for glucose-6-phosphate dehydrogenase in cryosections of human breast carcinoma, fibrocystic disease and normal breast tissue. *Virchows Arch (B)* 50:13, 1985.

533. NAIK SN, ANDERSON DE: G6PD deficiency and cancer. *Lancet* i:1060, 1970.

534. NAIK SN, ANDERSON DE: The association between glucose-6-phosphate dehydrogenase deficiency and cancer in American Negroes. *Oncology* 25:356, 1971.

535. SULIS E: G6PD deficiency and cancer. *Lancet* i:1185, 1972.

536. STEINBERG MH, WEST MS, GALLAGHER D, MENTZER W: Cooperative Study of Sickle Cell Disease: Effects of glucose-6-phosphate dehydrogenase deficiency upon sickle cell anemia. *Blood* 71:748, 1988.

537. FERRARIS AM, BROCCIA G, MELONI T, FORTELEONI G, GAETANI GF: Glucose-6-phosphate dehydrogenase deficiency and incidence of haematological malignancy. *Am J Hum Genet* 42:516, 1988.

538. HERZ F, KAPLAN E, SCHEYE ES: Diagnosis of erythrocyte glucose-6-phosphate dehydrogenase deficiency in the Negro male despite hemolytic crisis. *Blood* 35:90, 1970.

539. RINGELHAHN B: A simple laboratory procedure for the recognition of the A−(African type) G6PS deficiency in acute haemolytic crisis. *Clin Chim Acta* 36:272, 1972.

540. DEUTSCH J: Maleimide as an inhibitor in measurement of erythrocyte glucose-6-phosphate dehydrogenase activity. *Clin Chem* 24:885, 1978.

541. BEUTLER E, BLUME KG, KAPLAN JC, LOHR GW, RAMOT B, VALENTINE WN: International Committee for Standardization in Hematology: Recommended methods for red cell enzyme analysis. *Br J Haematol* 35:331, 1977.

542. GLOCK GE, McLEAN P: Further studies on the properties and assay of glucose-6-phosphate dehydrogenase and 6-phosphogluconate dehydrogenase of rat liver. *Biochem J* 55:4000, 1953.

543. CATALANO EW, JOHNSON GF, SOLOMON HM: Measurement of erythrocyte glucose-6-phosphate dehydrogenase activity with a centrifugal analyzer. *Clin Chem* 21:134, 1975.

544. BEUTLER E: A series of new screening procedures for pyruvate kinase deficiency, glucose-6-phosphate dehydrogenase deficiency. *Blood* 32:816, 1968.

545. BEUTLER E, MITCHELL M: Special modifications for the fluorescent screening method for glucose-6-phosphate dehydrogenase deficiency. *Blood* 32:816, 1968.

546. BEUTLER E, BLUME KG, KAPLAN JC, LOHR GW, RAMOT B, VALENTINE WN: International Committee for Standardization in Haematology: Recommended screening test for glucose-6-phosphate dehydrogenase (G6PD) deficiency. *Br J Haematol* 43:465, 1979.

547. MISUMI H, WADA H, ICHIBA Y, SHORMORI T, KOSAKA M: Separate detection of glucose-6-phosphate dehydrogenase from 6-phosphogluconate dehydrogenase by DEAE-paper chromatography. *Blut* 45:33, 1982.

548. SOLEM E: Glucose-6-phosphate dehydrogenase deficiency: An easy and sensitive quantitative assay for the detection of female heterozygotes in red blood cells. *Clin Chim Acta* 142:153, 1984.

549. SOLEM E, PIRZER C, SIEGE M, KOLLMAN F, ROMERO-SARAVIA O, BARKTSCH-TREFS O, KORNHUBER B: Mass screening for glucose-6-phosphate dehydrogenase deficiency. Improved fluorescent spot test. *Clin Chim Acta* 152:135, 1985.

550. BENI A, FIORTINI G, SALVATI AM, TENTORI L, TORLONTANO G: Quantitation of the ultraviolet light test for erythrocyte glucose-6-phosphate dehydrogenase, pyruvate kinase and glutathione reductase. *Clin Chim Acta* 49:41, 1973.

551. JACOB H, JANDL JH: A simple visual screening test for glucose-6-phosphated dehydrogenase deficiency employing ascorbate and cyanide. *N Engl J Med* 274:1162, 1966.

552. FAIRBANKS VF, FERNADEZ MN: The identification of metabolic errors associated with hemolytic anemia. *JAMA* 208:316, 1969.

553. FAIRBANKS VF, LAMPE LT: A tetrazolium-linked cytochemical method for estimation of glucose-6-phosphate dehydrogenase activity in individual erythrocytes: Applications in the study of heterozygotes for glucose-6-phosphate dehydrogenase deficiency. *Blood* 31:589, 1968.

554. GORDON PA, STEWART J: Red cell cytochemistry in glucose-6-phosphate dehydrogenase deficiency. *Br J Haematol* 27:358, 1974.

555. van NOORDEN CJF, VOGELS IMC, JAMES J, TAS J: A sensitive cytochemical staining method for glucose-6-phosphate dehydrogenase activity in individual erythrocytes. *Histochemistry* 75:493, 1982.

556. van NOORDEN CJF, VOGELS IMC: A sensitive cytochemical staining method for glucose-6-phosphate dehydrogenase activity in individual erythrocytes. *Br J Haematol* 60:57, 1985.

557. VOGELS IMC, van NOORDEN CJF, WOLF BHM, SAELMAN DEM, TROMP A, SCHUTGENS RBH, WEENING RS: Cytochemical determination of heterozygous glucose-6-phosphate dehydrogenase deficiency in erythrocytes. *Br J Haematol* 63:402, 1986.

558. BREWER GJ, TARLOV AR, ALVING AS: The methemoglobin reduction test for primaquine-type sensitivity of erythrocytes. A simplified procedure for detecting a specific hypersusceptibility to drug hemolysis. *JAMA* 180:386, 1962.

559. BAPAT JP, BAXI AJ, BHATIA HM: Is methemoglobin reduction test a true index of G6PD deficiency? *Indian J Med Res* 64:1687, 1976.

560. GALL JC, BREWER GJ, DERN RJ: Studies of glucose-6-phosphate dehydrogenase activity of individual erythrocytes. The methemoglobin elution test for detection of females heterozygous for G6PD deficiency. *Am J Hum Genet* 17:359, 1965.

561. MOTULSKY AG, CAMPBELL-KRAUT JM: Population genetics of glucose-6-phosphate dehydrogenase deficiency of the red cell, in Blumberg BS (ed): *Proc Conf Genetic Polymorphisms and Geographic Variations in Disease.* New York, Grune & Stratton, 1961, pp 159-180.

562. BERNSTEIN RE: Brilliant cresyl blue screening test for demonstrating glucose-6-phosphate dehydrogenase deficiency in red cells. *Clin Chim Acta* 8:158, 1963.

563. MCCURDY PR, MORSE EE: Glucose-6-phosphate dehydrogenase deficiency and blood transfusion *Vox Sang* 28:230, 1975.

564. ORLINA AR, JOSEPHSON AM, MCDONALD BJ: The poststorage viability of glucose-6-phosphate dehydrogenase deficient erythrocytes. *J Lab Clin Med* 75:930, 1970.

565. VAN DER SAAR A, SCHOUTEN H, STRUYKER BOUDIER AM: Glucose-6-phosphate dehydrogenase deficiency in red cells. Incidence in the Curacao population, its clinical and genetic aspects. *Enzyme* 27:289, 1964.

566. MIMOUNI F, SHOHAT S, REISMER SH: G6PD-deficient donor blood as a cause of haemolysis in two pre-term infants. *Isr J Med Sci* 22:120, 1986.

567. TIZIANELLO A, PANNACCIULI I, SALVIDIO E, GAY E: Erythrocyte glucose-6-phosphate deficiency as problem in the selection of blood donors. *Vox Sang* 8:47, 1963.

568. STUCKEY WJ Jr: Hemolytic anemia and erythrocyte glucose-6-phosphate dehydrogenase deficiency. *Am J Med Sci* 251:104, 1966.

569. RAMOT B, SZEINBERG A, ADAM A, SHEBA C, GAFNI D: A study of subjects with glucose 6-phosphate dehydrogenase deficiency. I. Investigation of platelet enzyme. *J Clin Invest* 38:1659, 1959.

570. LINDER D, GARTLER SM: Glucose-6-phosphate dehydrogenase mosaicism: Utilization as a cell marker in the study of leiomyomas. *Science* 150:67, 1965.

571. BEUTLER E, COLLINS Z, IRWIN LE: Value of genetic variants of glucose-6-phosphate dehydrogenase in tracing the origin of malignant tumours. *N Engl J Med* 276:389, 1967.

572. FIALKOW PJ: The origin and development of human tumours studies with cell markers. *N Engl J Med* 291:26, 1974.

573. FIALKOW PJ: Clonal origin of human tumours. *Annu Rev Med* 30:135, 1979.

574. POVEY S, HOPKINSON DA: The use of polymorphic enzyme markers of human blood cells in genetics. *Clin Haematol* 10:161, 1981.

575. ADAMSON JW: Analysis of hemopoiesis: The use of cell markers and in vitro culture techniques in studies of cloncal hemopathies in man. *Clin Hematol* 13:489, 1984.

576. FIALKOW PJ, GARTLER SM, YOSHIDA A: Clonal origin of chronic myelocytic leukaemia in man. *Proc Natl Acad Sci USA* 58:1468, 1967.

577. FIALKOW PJ, JACOBSEN RJ, PAPYANNOPOULOU T: Chronic myelocytic leukaemia: Clonal origin in a stem cell common to the granulocyte, erythrocyte, platelet and monocyte/macrophage. *Am J Med* 63:125, 1977.

578. ADAMSON JW, FIALKOW PJ, MURPHY S, PRCHAL JF, STEINMAN L: Polycythaemia vera stem cell and probable clonal origin of the disease. *N Engl J Med* 295:913, 1976.

579. ONI SB, OSUNKOYA BO, LUZZATTO L: Paroxysmal nocturnal haemoglobinuria: Evidence for monoclonal origin of abnormal red cells. *Blood* 36:145, 1970.

580. PEARSON TA, DILLMAN J, HEPINSTALL RH: The clonal characteristics of human aortic intima. Comparison with fatty streaks and normal media. *Am J Pathol* 113:33, 1983.

581. GRAY GR, NAIMAN SC, FOBINSON GCF: Platelet function and G6PD deficiency. *Lancet* i:997, 1974.

582. HELLER P, BEST WR, NELSEN RB, BECKTEL J: Clinical implications of sickle cell trait and glucose 6-phosphate dehydrogenase deficiency in hospitalized Black male patients. *N Engl J Med* 300:1001, 1979.

583. PIAZZA A, MAYR WR, CONTU L, AMOROSO A, BORELLI I, CURTONI ES, MAR-

CELLO C, MORONI A, OLIVETTI E, RICHIARDI P, CEPPELLINI R: Genetic and population structure of four Sardinian villages. *Ann Hum Genet* 49:47, 1985.

584. FIALKOW PJ: Clonal origin of tumours. *Biochim Biophys Acta* 458:283, 1976.

585. WILLIAMS CKO, ESAN GJF, LUZZATTO L, TOWN MM, OGUNMOLA GB: X-linked somatic cell selection and polycythaemia rubra vera. *N Engl J Med* 310:1265. 1984.

586. LUZZATTO L, USANGA EA, BIENZLE U, ESAN GJF, FASUAN FA: Imbalance in X-chromosome expression: Evidence for a human X-linked gene affecting growth of hemopoietic cells. *Science* 205:1418, 1979.

587. MOTULSKY AG: Metabolic polymorphisms and the role of infectious diseases in human evolution. *Hum Biol* 32:28, 1960.

588. BRUCE-CHWATT LJ: *Essential Malariology*, 2d ed. London, Heinemann, 1985.

589. YOSHIDA A, BEUTLER E (eds): *Glucose 6-Phosphate Dehydrogenase*. New York, Academic, 1986.

590. ROSEMEYER MA: The biochemistry of glucose 6-phosphate dehydrogenase, 6-phospho-gluconate dehydrogenase and gluthathione reductase. *Cell Biochem Funct* 5:79, 1987.

591. PIOMELLI S: G6PD deficiency and related disorders of the pentose pathway, in Nathan DG, Oski FA (eds): *Haematology of Infancy and Childhood*, 3d ed. Philadelphia, Saunders, 1987, vol 1, pp 583–612.

592. JANDL JH: *Blood, Textbook of Haematology*. Boston, Little, Brown, 1987, pp 335–349.

593. LUZZATTO L: Genetics of red cells and susceptibility to malaria. *Blood* 54:961, 1979.

594. ALLISON AC: Glucose-6-phosphate dehydrogenase deficiency in red blood cells of East Africans. *Nature* 186:531, 1960.

595. YENCHITSOMANUS P, SUMMERS KM, BOARD PG, BHATIA KK, JONES GL, JOHNSTON K, NURSE GT: Alpha-thalassemia in Papua New Guinea. *Hum Genet* 74:432, 1986.

596. SINISCALCO M, BERNINI L, FILIPPI G, LATTE B, MEERA-KHAN P, PIOMELLI S, RATTAZZI M: Population genetics of hemoglobin variants, thalassemia and glucose-6-phosphate dehydrogenase deficiency, with particular reference to the malaria hypothesis. *Bull WHO* 34:379, 1966.

597. STAMATOYANNOPOULOS G, PANAYOTOPOULOS A, MOTULSKY AG: The distribution of glucose-6-phosphate dehydrogenase deficiency in Greece. *Am J Hum Genet* 18:296, 1966.

598. VULLIAMY TJ, D'URSO M, BATTISTUZZI G, ESTRADA M, FOULKES NS, MARTINI G, CALABRO V, POGGI V, GIORDANO R, TOWN M, LUZZATTO L, PERSICO MG: Diverse point mutations in the human glucose-6-phosphate dehydrogenase gene cause enzyme deficiency and mild or severe hemolytic anemia. *Proc Natl Acad Sci USA* in press, 1988.

599. MARTIN SK, MILLER LH, ALLING D, et al: Severe malaria and glucose-6-phosphate-dehydrogenase deficiency: A reappraisal of the malaria/G6PD hypothesis. *Lancet* 1:524, 1979.

600. LUZZATTO L, BIENZLE U: The malaria/G6PD hypothesis. *Lancet* 1:1183, 1979.

601. SEGAL HE, NOLL WW, THIEMANUN W: Glucose-6-phosphate-dehydrogenase deficiency and falciparum malaria in two Northeast Thai villages. *Proc Helminth Soc Wash* 39:79, 1972.

602. GILLES HM, FLETCHER KA, HENDRICKSE RG, LINDNER R, REDDU S, ALLAN N: Glucose-6-phosphate dehydrogenase deficiency, sickling, and malaria in African children in South Western Nigeria. *Lancet* 1:138, 1967.

603. BIENZLE U, AYENI O, LUCAS AO, LUZZATTO L: Glucose-6-phosphate-dehydrogenase and malaria; greater resistance of females heterozygous for enzyme deficiency and of males with non-deficient variant. *Lancet* 1:107, 1972.

604. GUGGENMOOS-HOLZMANN I, BIENZLE U, LUZZATTO I: Plasmodium Falciparum malaria and human red cells. II. Red cell genetic traits and resistance against malaria. *Int J Epidemiol* 10:1, 16, 1981.

605. TRAGER W, JENSEN JB: Human malaria parasites in continuous culture. *Science* 193:673, 1976.

606. LUZZATTO L: Genetics of human red cells and susceptibility to malaria, in Michal F (ed): *Modern Genetic Concepts and Techniques in the Study of Parasites*. Basel, Schwabe, 1981, p 257.

607. ROTH EF Jr, RAVENTOS-SUAREZ C, RINALDI A, NAGEL RL: Glucose-6-phosphate dehydrogenase deficiency inhibits in vitro growth of Plasmodium falciparum. *Proc Natl Acad Sci USA* 80:298, 1983.

608. MILLER J, GOLENSER J, SPIRA DT, KOSOWER NS: Plasmodium falciparum: Thiol status and growth in normal and glucose 6-phosphate dehydrogenase deficient human erythrocytes. *Exp Parasitol* 57:239, 1984.

609. FRIEDMAN MJ: Oxidant damage mediates variant red cell resistance to malaria. *Nature* 280:245, 1979.

610. LUZZATTO L, USANGA EA, REDDY S: Glucose-6-phosphate-dehydrogenase deficient red cells: Resistance to infection by malarial parasites. *Science* 164:839, 1969.

611. ECKMAN JR, EATON JW: Dependence of plasmodial glutathione metabolism on the host cells. *Nature* 278:754, 1979.

612. JANNEY SK, JOIST JJ, FITCH CD: Excess release of ferriheme in G6PD deficient erythrocytes: Possible cause of haemolysis and resistance to malaria. *Blood* 67:331, 1986.

613. CLARK IA, HUNT NH: Evidence for reactive oxygen intermediates causing hemolysis and parasite death in malaria. *Infect Immun* 39:1, 1983.

614. LUZZATTO L, O'BRIEN E, USANGA EA, WANACHIWANAWIN W: Origin of G6PD polymorphism: Malaria and G6PD deficiency, in Yoshida A, Beutler E (eds): *Glucose-6-phosphate Dehydrogenase*. New York, Academic, 1986, p 181.

615. USANGA EA, LUZZATTO L: Adaptation of *Plasmodium falciparum* to glucose 6-phosphate dehydrogenase deficient host red cells by production of parasite-encoded enzyme. *Nature* 313:793, 1985.

616. YOSHIDA A, ROTH EF: Glucose 6-phosphate dehydrogenase of malaria parasite Plasmodium falciparum. *Blood* 69:1528, 1987.

617. BEUTLER E, KUHL W, GILBART T: 6-phosphogluconolactonase deficiency, a hereditary erythrocyte enzyme deficiency: Possible interaction with glucose 6-phosphate dehydrogenase deficiency. *Proc Natl Acad Sci USA* 82:3876, 1985.

618. TAKIZAWA T, YONEYAMA V, MIWA S, VOSHIDA A: A single nucleotide base transition is the basis of the common human glucose-6-phosphate dehydrogenase variant A(+). *Genomics* 1:228, 1987.

619. HIRONO A, BEUTLER E: Molecular cloning and nucleotide sequence of cDNA for human glucose-6-phosphate dehydrogenase variant A(−). *Proc Natl Acad Sci USA* 85:3951, 1988.

620. MANOS P, HOLTEN D: Primary cultures of hepatocytes in serum and hormone-free medium: Identification of conditions which stimulate an in vivo-like induction of G6PD. *In Vitro Cell Dev Biol* 23:367, 1987.

621. KRANSNOPOLSKAYA KD, BOCHKOV NP: Genetic heterogeneity of hereditary enzymopathies. *Becth AMH CCCP* 9:56, 1982.

CHAPTER 92

CYTOCHROME b₅ REDUCTASE DEFICIENCY AND ENZYMOPENIC HEREDITARY METHEMOGLOBINEMIA

ERNST R. JAFFÉ
DONALD E. HULTQUIST

1. The major pathway for the reduction of methemoglobin to functional hemoglobin in human erythrocytes involves a NADH-dependent methemoglobin reductase system. In addition to NADH, this system requires the presence in the cytosol of both cytochrome b₅ reductase, a 32,000-dalton protein, and cytochrome b₅, a 12,000-dalton protein. These proteins are presumed to arise from larger parent molecules in the erythroid precursors by proteolytic cleavage of their hydrophobic tails.

2. Enzymopenic hereditary methemoglobinemia is a rare recessively inherited disorder due, in the majority of cases, to deficiency of cytochrome b₅ reductase only in erythrocytes (type I). Generalized cytochrome b₅ reductase deficiency, demonstrable in all tissues that have been examined, occurs in 10 to 15 percent of cases and is accompanied by methemoglobinemia and severe, progressive, lethal neurologic disability (type II). Cytochrome b₅ reductase deficiency limited to hematopoietic cells is also manifested by methemoglobinemia, but without neurologic effects (type III). Deficiency of cytochrome b₅ may also lead to methemoglobinemia (type IV).

3. The gene regulating the synthesis of cytochrome b₅ reductase has been assigned to chromosome 22. Deficiency of cytochrome b₅ reductase has a worldwide distribution, and electrophoretic variants of the enzyme with normal catalytic properties may have an incidence as high as 1:100. Heterozygotes for cytochrome b₅ reductase deficiency are asymptomatic, but have an increased propensity to develop toxic methemoglobinemia induced by drugs or other chemicals.

4. The diagnosis of enzymopenic hereditary methemoglobinemia may be made by relatively simple laboratory determinations, but definition of the specific defect requires more sophisticated studies.

5. Effective treatment may be provided by the administration of methylene blue, ascorbic acid, or riboflavin but is often not indicated, except for cosmetic reasons. Such therapy, however, has had no demonstrable effect on the neurologic aberrations in the generalized type II disorder.

HISTORY

Hereditary methemoglobinemia, an interesting albeit rare disorder, has a worldwide distribution and a century old history. In 1845, François[1] described a patient with long-standing congenital cyanosis without obvious cardiac or pulmonary disease. Although altered hemoglobin pigments and drug-induced cyanosis had been reported frequently, it was 1891 before

Dittrich[2] established that the methemoglobinemia that developed in dogs given *Blutgifte*, such as nitroglycerine and acetanilide, eventually disappeared without the occurrence of anemia. He also pointed out that the methemoglobinemic cyanosis that developed in patients receiving certain medicines tended to disappear and suggested that the methemoglobin was reduced to hemoglobin within the circulating erythrocytes. Subsequently, other authors described "enterogenous cyanosis" attributed to the absorption of toxic substances from the gastrointestinal tract.[3] Sulfhemoglobin present in some of these patients' erythrocytes was differentiated from methemoglobin in 1905.[4]

Hitzenberger[5] in 1932 was probably the first to describe a familial incidence of idiopathic cyanosis. He suggested the possibility of congenital, familial methemoglobinemia. Between 1943 and 1945, Gibson[6] and his associates[7] suggested that there was a decreased ability of the erythrocytes to reduce methemoglobin formed continuously at a normal rate in patients with familial, idiopathic methemoglobinemia. The classic investigations of Gibson[8] in 1948 provided substantial experimental evidence for a deficiency of a factor (a methemoglobin reductase) in the erythrocytes of patients with idiopathic methemoglobinemia. In 1959, Scott and Griffith[9] identified an enzyme in normal human erythrocytes that catalyzed the reduction of methemoglobin with NADH and called this enzyme a *diaphorase*. The enzyme was subsequently named and assayed as a NADH dehydrogenase, NADH-methemoglobin reductase, NADH-methemoglobin-ferrocyanide reductase, NADH-ferricyanide reductase, and, most recently, NADH-cytochrome b₅ reductase. Scott et al. described severe deficiency of this enzyme in the erythrocytes of native Alaskans with methemoglobinemia and intermediate levels of activity in the cells of their acyanotic parents and children.[10,11] To explain the typically recessive pattern of inheritance of idiopathic methemoglobinemia suggested by the family histories of many patients, they proposed that affected individuals inherited one abnormal gene from each parent. These observations have been extended and confirmed by other investigators.[12]

Hultquist and Passon[13] subsequently identified the NADH-dependent enzyme as a cytochrome b₅ reductase and demonstrated that the catalysis of methemoglobin reduction by this reductase involved the participation of a cytochrome b₅ present in normal human erythrocytes. This enzyme system is considered to be the most important one for the conversion of

---

Nonstandard abbreviations used in this chapter are: DPG = 2,3-diphosphoglycerate; DCIP = 2,6-dichlorophenolindophenol.

any methemoglobin formed in normal human erythrocytes to functional, oxygen-carrying hemoglobin. The activity of this system is markedly reduced in the erythrocytes of most patients with enzymopenic hereditary methemoglobinemia.

More than 500 cases of hereditary methemoglobinemia have been cited in the literature. Those patients with family histories suggesting dominant inheritance of the methemoglobinemia have usually been proved or presumed to have a hemoglobin M, the consequence of a mutation in the genetic code for hemoglobin which makes the hemoglobin more susceptible to oxidation and/or the resulting methemoglobin more resistant to reduction (see Chap. 93). More than half of the total reported cases, however, have had family histories or laboratory evidence consistent with inheritance of an autosomal recessive abnormality. With rare exceptions, these latter cases have been presumed or demonstrated to have an abnormality in the methemoglobin reductase activity of their erythrocytes. They have become known as instances of enzymopenic hereditary methemoglobinemia to differentiate them from those with one of the hemoglobin M disorders.

STRUCTURE AND PROPERTIES OF METHEMOGLOBIN

Fully Oxidized Hemoglobin

Methemoglobin is the derivative of hemoglobin obtained by oxidizing the iron of the heme group of deoxyhemoglobin or oxyhemoglobin from the ferrous (Fe^{2+}) state to the ferric (Fe^{3+}) state. For tetrameric hemoglobin, this transformation corresponds to a four-electron loss. Because methemoglobin is incapable of binding molecular oxygen, hemoglobin oxidation leads to loss of its biologic function and, when carried out to a sufficient extent, leads to pathologic consequences.

Structural and physical studies have established that in methemoglobin the sixth coordination position of the iron is occupied by a water molecule, whereas this axial position is empty in deoxyhemoglobin and occupied by O_2 in oxyhemoglobin. The coordinated water molecule of methemoglobin dissociates with a pK of approximately 8 to form a hydroxide ion which remains bound to the iron.[14] Thus, under physiological conditions, methemoglobin is present predominantly as the "aquo" form; the "hydroxy" form becomes more prevalent as the pH is raised.

The differences in valence and axial ligand between ferrous and ferric hemoglobin are the basis for the differences in the chemical, physical, and biologic properties of these forms of the protein. In contrast to ferrous forms of hemoglobin, methemoglobin has a *net* charge of +1 on the iron atom of each heme moiety, with the consequence that ferrous and ferric forms can be readily separated by electrophoretic techniques. Moreover, the net positive charge on the iron of methemoglobin leads to its binding of small anionic ligands such as CN^-, N_3^-, F^-, and Cl^-, but methemoglobin has little affinity for the classic hemoglobin ligands, O_2 and CO. The valence and ligand changes which accompany oxidation of hemoglobin also explain the dramatic change in color. In contrast to the bright red color of oxyhemoglobin, aquomethemoglobin appears chocolate brown and has absorbance maxima at 500 and 631 nm, and hydroxymethemoglobin appears dark red with absorbance maxima at 540 and 575 nm. These spectral differences are responsible for the observed differences between the

normal skin color of Caucasians and the slate-blue color of an individual with elevated methemoglobin levels.

X-ray diffraction studies carried out by Perutz and coworkers have established that the protein structure of the tetrameric methemoglobin molecule is very similar to that of the "R-state" conformation of oxyhemoglobin, but different from the "T-state" conformation of deoxyhemoglobin.[15] Methemoglobin, like deoxyhemoglobin, binds to polyanionic compounds such as 2,3-diphosphoglycerate (DPG), and the accompanying conformational shift has been termed an R-to-T-state shift.[16] This binding of polyanions results in changes in physical properties which have been interpreted by some as an increase in the spin state of the hemes.

Valence Hybrids of Hemoglobin

The conversion of tetrameric hemoglobin to tetrameric methemoglobin is a four-step oxidation. Both the oxidation of hemoglobin and the reduction of methemoglobin proceed in sequential one-electron steps, and thus there exist valence hybrids in which one, two, or three hemes are in the ferric form. It is primarily these valence hybrids, rather than fully oxidized hemoglobin, that are central participants in methemoglobin homeostasis. Because the hemoglobin molecule comprises two α chains and two β chains and because each of the two αβ dimers is relatively stable, eight different valence hybrids should exist (Fig. 92-1). This number of forms can be detected in a partially oxidized sample of hemoglobin under conditions which minimize the interconversion of hybrid forms.[17] However, under physiological conditions which allow for tetramer dissociation to αβ dimers, dimer dissociation, electron exchange, and heme exchange reactions, only two valence hybrids accumulate in appreciable amounts[18,19]; these are the two symmetric forms, $(\alpha^+\beta)_2$ and $(\alpha\beta^+)_2$, each of which comprises two identical half-oxidized dimers.

The stepwise *oxidation* of hemoglobin subunits, like the stepwise *oxygenation* of hemoglobin, shows cooperativity, has a Bohr (pH) effect, and is influenced by the binding of polyanions (see reviews in Refs. 20 and 21). Both the standard reduction potential (E'_0) and the degree of cooperativity (n,

Fig. 92-1 Valence hybrids of hemoglobin A.

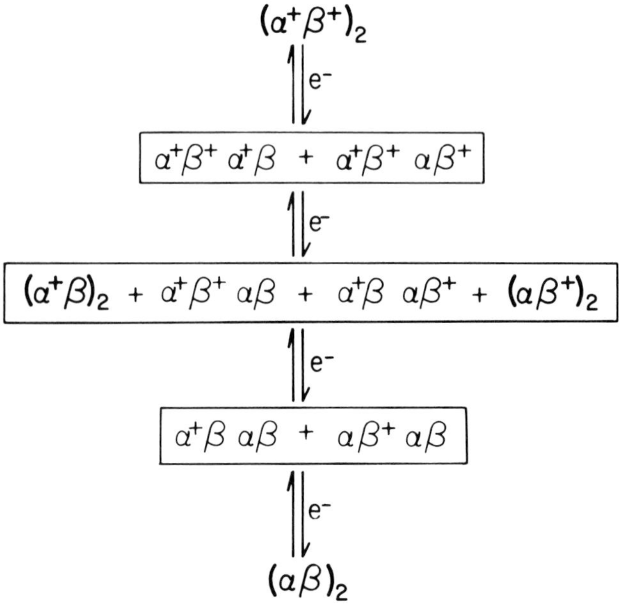

$$(\alpha^+\beta^+)_2$$

$$\Big\Updownarrow e^-$$

$$\boxed{\alpha^+\beta^+\ \alpha^+\beta\ +\ \alpha^+\beta^+\ \alpha\beta^+}$$

$$\Big\Updownarrow e^-$$

$$\boxed{(\alpha^+\beta)_2\ +\ \alpha^+\beta^+\ \alpha\beta\ +\ \alpha^+\beta\ \alpha\beta^+\ +\ (\alpha\beta^+)_2}$$

$$\Big\Updownarrow e^-$$

$$\boxed{\alpha^+\beta\ \alpha\beta\ +\ \alpha\beta^+\ \alpha\beta}$$

$$\Big\Updownarrow e^-$$

$$(\alpha\beta)_2$$

from a Hill plot) are dependent on pH. The reduction potential increases upon addition of polyanion or upon lowering the pH. Under physiological conditions, tetrameric hemoglobin A shows an $E'_0 = +0.14$ V. In the tetramer, α chains are slightly stronger reductants than the β chains ($E'_0 = +0.12$ and $+0.16$ V, respectively). Valence hybrids of hemoglobin show a greater affinity for oxygen than does hemoglobin.[20,22] This "left shift" of the oxygen saturation curve by ferric subunits has been interpreted as a shifting of the conformational equilibrium of the tetramer to its high oxygen affinity R state by the ferric subunits which themselves are present in an "R-type" conformation.

Throughout this chapter, *methemoglobin* is used in a general sense to include all forms of hemoglobin in which one or more of the subunits are in the ferric form and *methemoglobinemia* includes those states in which the valence hybrids are elevated in intact, circulating erythrocytes.

METHEMOGLOBIN HOMEOSTASIS

Observations from the nineteenth century demonstrated that methemoglobin can be generated within red blood cells either as a consequence of hereditary disorders or from the ingestion of toxic compounds and that normal red blood cells possess the capacity to restore methemoglobin to its functional ferrous form. Subsequent studies have demonstrated that methemoglobin is present at low concentrations in normal human erythrocytes and that both generation and reduction of methemoglobin are normal processes for the erythrocyte.[20,23] Moreover, the evidence that hemoglobin is synthesized in reticulocytes as the ferric form suggests that methemoglobin reduction may be a part of the normal biosynthesis of this heme-protein.[24]

The steady-state level of methemoglobin in normal erythrocytes is low, with most methods of measurement giving values of less than 1 percent of the total hemoglobin. This finding indicates that the capacity to reduce methemoglobin far exceeds the normal rate of hemoglobin oxidation. In isolated, intact erythrocytes methemoglobin reduction proceeds at a rate of about 5 percent total hemoglobin per hour (1 μmol hemoglobin subunit per hour per milliliter)[8]; the normal rate of hemoglobin oxidation is believed to be 0.02 to 0.12 percent total hemoglobin per hour.

The sustained reduction of methemoglobin in suspensions of intact erythrocytes proceeds only in the presence of a metabolite which can enter the cell and be utilized in a process leading to the generation of reduced pyridine nucleotide. Among the substrates which allow for rapid methemoglobin reduction are glucose and a variety of other sugars, lactate,

malate, and purine nucleosides such as inosine.[3,23] Studies of the stoichiometry of hemoglobin and pyruvate production in reactions with glucose or lactate as substrate, together with metabolic inhibitor studies, have demonstrated that electrons for methemoglobin reduction are generated primarily by glycolysis and primarily in the form of NADH (Fig. 92-2). However, the rapid methemoglobin reduction that is observed with xylitol and other nonglycolytic substrates[25] suggests that pathways other than glycolysis may be involved with the generation of the NADH used for methemoglobin reduction, at least under conditions where levels of methemoglobin are high.

The steady-state level of methemoglobin is a consequence of all the methemoglobin-reducing reactions (Fig. 92-2) and methemoglobin-generating reactions (Fig. 92-3) in erythrocytes. The major pathway of methemoglobin reduction is catalyzed by erythrocyte cytochrome b$_5$ reductase and cytochrome b$_5$; deficiencies of these proteins lead to methemoglobinemia. More difficult to evaluate is the possible role of an erythrocyte NADPH-reductase that requires flavin or a redox dye in order to reduce methemoglobin. Likewise, it has been difficult to assess the physiological significance of nonenzymatic reduction reactions which methemoglobin has been shown to undergo with a number of intracellular compounds. Since methemoglobin reduction proceeds to some extent in red cells severely deficient in cytochrome b$_5$ reductase activity, the minor pathways, collectively, may be of some importance to the erythrocyte.

A variety of reactions oxidize deoxyhemoglobin and oxyhemoglobin. Among the endogenous compounds which have been identified as reacting with hemoglobin to form methemoglobin are molecular oxygen, hydrogen peroxide (H_2O_2), and a number of free radicals including superoxide anion (O_2^-) and hydroxyl radical (HO$\cdot$). The rate of methemoglobin formation depends on the concentrations of these compounds. The steady-state concentrations of these oxidants, in turn, depend on the rates at which they are generated during metabolism, are consumed by reactions with other cellular components, and are destroyed by protective erythrocyte enzymes such as catalase, superoxide dismutase, and glutathione peroxidase.

Elevation of methemoglobin in erythrocytes results either from acceleration of an oxidation reaction or from diminution of a reduction reaction. Such alterations in reaction rates may arise from a hereditary defect or from an environmental stress. The most frequent cause of methemoglobinemia is rapid oxidation arising from ingestion of a toxic compound which either is an oxidant itself or gives rise to oxidants during its metabolism. Methemoglobinemia also arises from rapid autox-

Fig. 92-2 Erythrocyte pathways for the transfer of electrons from metabolites to methemoglobin.

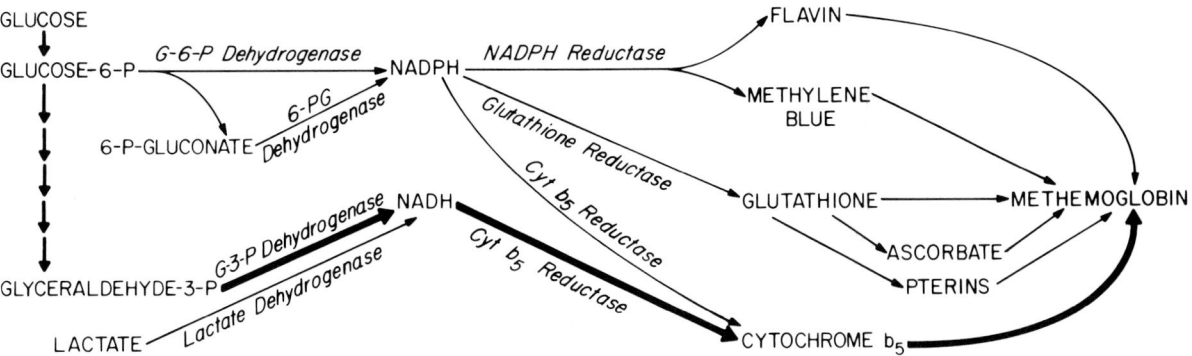

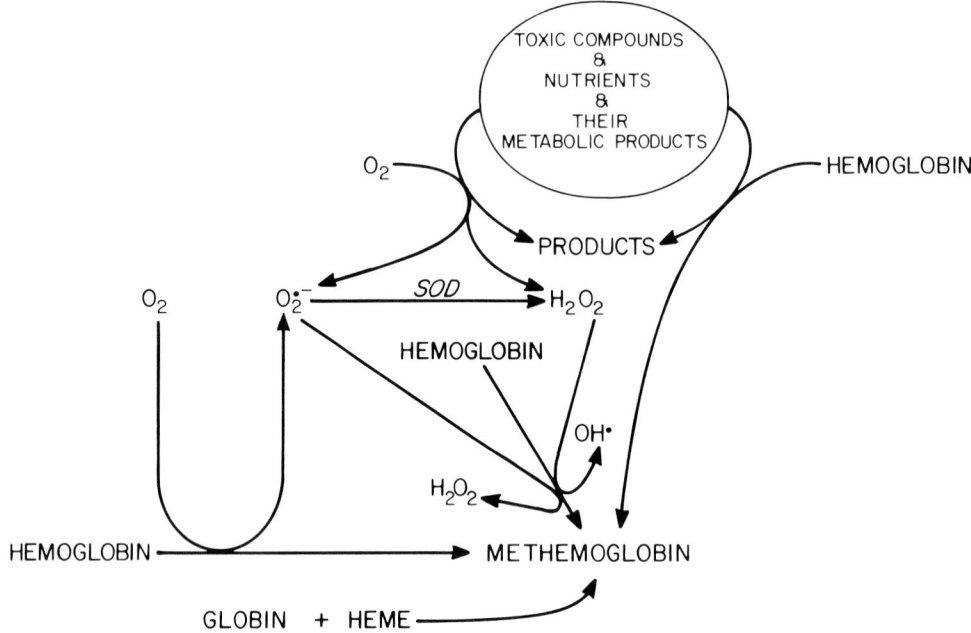

Fig. 92-3 *Generation of methemoglobin in erythrocytes.*

idation of a mutant hemoglobin belonging to the class of hemoglobin M. Methemoglobinemia due to depressed reduction usually results from deficiency of erythrocyte cytochrome b_5 reductase. A case of methemoglobinemia due to deficiency of cytochrome b_5 has recently been reported.[26] Diminished methemoglobin reduction rates and methemoglobinemia have been observed with hemoglobins N-Baltimore, I-Toulouse, and M-Milwaukee-1. These mutant hemoglobins presumably fail to interact efficiently with the cytochrome b_5 reductase/cytochrome b_5 system.[27,28] In contrast, methemoglobinemia has not been reported in cases of hereditary hemolytic disorders associated with severe deficiencies of glycolytic enzymes, although impaired ability to reduce NAD^+ might have been expected to lead to an impaired capacity to reduce methemoglobin, just as inhibition of glycolysis with iodoacetate diminishes methemoglobin reduction.[8]

Methemoglobinemia may also develop as the consequence of a modest decrease in the ability to reduce methemoglobin, coupled with an environmental stress. The erythrocytes of individuals who are heterozygous for cytochrome b_5 reductase deficiency reduce methemoglobin at approximately 50 percent of the normal rate[29] and are especially susceptible to the methemoglobin-inducing effects of exogenous oxidant agents.[30–32] Similarly, the erythrocytes of newborns have about half of the methemoglobin-reducing ability of adults' cells[33,34] and show an increased susceptibility to methemoglobin-producing drugs and chemicals.

OXIDATION OF HEMOGLOBIN

Although the conversion of a ferrous subunit of hemoglobin to the ferric subunit by the removal of an electron can be written as the simplest of chemical reactions, it actually involves a number of complex reactions. In the absence of foreign compounds, much of the oxidation of hemoglobin results from its interaction with O_2 or the partially reduced forms of oxygen, O_2^-, H_2O_2, and HO^-. Following ingestion of foreign compounds, methemoglobin is formed by mechanisms which in-

clude direct oxidation by the ingested compound, oxidation by a metabolite derived from the compound, and oxidation by O_2^- and H_2O_2 generated during the metabolism of the compound. The subject of hemoglobin oxidation has been reviewed comprehensively.[21,23,35]

Autoxidation of Hemoglobin

Hemoglobin reacts slowly with molecular oxygen to yield methemoglobin and superoxide anion. The reaction corresponds to the transfer of an electron from the iron of the ferrous heme to molecular oxygen. Since oxyhemoglobin apparently exists as a ferric-superoxide anion complex,[36] autoxidation may be visualized as the release of the O_2^- from this complex. Whereas autoxidation of free ferrous heme in aqueous solution proceeds very rapidly, the autoxidation of hemoglobin is slow. The hydrophobic environment provided by the globin is envisioned as a hindrance to the release of the superoxide anion, while allowing for the rapid release of molecular oxygen. This hypothesis is supported by the observations that mutant hemoglobins in which the heme environment is modified show altered rates of autoxidation. Autoxidation is accelerated by chloride and other small anions which may function by displacing the superoxide anion from the oxyhemoglobin. Polyanions and lower pH also accelerate the reaction. In tetrameric hemoglobin the α subunits autoxidize more rapidly than the β subunits with the result that the valence hybrid, $(\alpha^+\beta)_2$, is the predominant intermediate in autoxidation.[37,38]

The mechanism of autoxidation is more complex than the simple release of O_2^- described above. The rate of autoxidation increases as the oxygen tension is decreased. A maximum rate is achieved when approximately two molecules of oxygen are bound per tetramer.[39] This observation can be interpreted either as evidence that heme is more readily oxidized in deoxyhemoglobin than in oxyhemoglobin or as evidence that O_2^- is more readily released from oxyhemoglobin in the T conformation than in the R conformation. Regardless of the correct mechanism for autoxidation, it is clear that the O_2^- generated by autoxidation, together with the H_2O_2 and HO^- derived from the O_2^-, react with hemoglobin to generate additional methemoglobin.

Reactions of Hemoglobin with O_2^- and H_2O_2

O_2^- is generated in erythrocytes not only by the autoxidation of hemoglobin but by the autoxidation of a number of redox proteins including cytochrome b_5 and cytochrome b_5 reductase. H_2O_2 is derived from the O_2^- both by a rapid nonenzymatic dismutation reaction and by an even more rapid catalysis of this reaction by superoxide dismutase. H_2O_2 is also an expected end product of oxidase reactions in erythrocytes.

Both O_2^- and H_2O_2 oxidize oxyhemoglobin to methemoglobin. The reaction with O_2^- is a slow one in which the bound molecular oxygen of oxyhemoglobin receives one electron from O_2^- and a second electron from the heme iron:

$$HbFeO_2 + O_2^- + 2H^+ \longrightarrow HbFe^+ + H_2O_2 + O_2$$

The overall reaction of H_2O_2 with oxyhemoglobin and deoxyhemoglobin may be written as follows:

$$2HbFeO_2 + H_2O_2 \longrightarrow 2HbFe^+ + 2OH^- + 2O_2$$

$$HbFe + H_2O_2 \longrightarrow HbFe^+ + OH^- + HO^{\cdot}$$

The highly reactive $HO^{\cdot}$ generated in the latter reaction may react with additional ferrous hemoglobin to form methemoglobin.

The generation of O_2^-, H_2O_2, and $HO^{\cdot}$ not only leads to the formation of more methemoglobin but may also promote further oxidation of both the globin and the heme of methemoglobin. One intermediate in this pathway is *hemichrome*, a derivative of methemoglobin in which a functional group of the protein replaces the water molecule bound to the heme. The additional oxidative changes lead to denaturation of the hemoglobin, the formation of intracellular Heinz bodies, and ultimately cell lysis.

The concentrations of O_2^-, H_2O_2 and $HO^{\cdot}$ in erythrocytes are normally maintained at low levels by the actions of superoxide dismutase, catalase, and glutathione peroxidase. Superoxide dismutase catalyzes the dismutation of O_2^-, catalase the dismutation of H_2O_2, and glutathione peroxidase the reduction of H_2O_2 by reduced glutathione. Because of the relative affinity of catalase and glutathione peroxidase for the substrate, H_2O_2, glutathione peroxidase is presumed to be the major mechanism for the destruction of H_2O_2 under physiological conditions. The ingestion of toxic compounds can lead to rates of O_2^- and H_2O_2 production which overwhelm the protective enzymatic mechanisms.

Oxidation of Hemoglobin by Toxic Compounds

Many drugs, commercial products, other chemical compounds, and metabolic derivatives of such compounds react with hemoglobin to form methemoglobin. If such compounds gain entry into the human circulation, the rate of methemoglobin formation may be several orders of magnitude faster than the rate resulting from the reaction of hemoglobin with oxygen and oxidants generated by normal metabolism. Under such oxidative stress, the erythrocyte methemoglobin reduction systems may be unable to maintain hemoglobin in its functional ferrous form.

The direct reaction of ferrous hemoblobin with various oxidants proceeds with remarkably different reaction rates, reaction mechanisms, preference for α or β chains, and capacity to cause methemoglobinemia. Ferricyanide is an example of an oxidant which accepts one electron from a ferrous heme of hemoglobin. Although this reaction is very rapid, ferricyanide does not lead to methemoglobinemia because it cannot penetrate the red cell membrane. Ferricyanide oxidizes the β subunit somewhat faster than the α subunit, with the result that the $(\alpha\beta^+)_2$ valence hybrid predominates.[40] The reaction of ferricyanide contrasts with that of cupric ion which exclusively oxidizes the β subunit[41] and with that of O_2 which favors α-subunit oxidation.

While oxidation of hemoglobin by metal ions results in a valence change of the metal, direct reaction of hemoglobin with organic oxidants yields free radicals. Thus, a variety of oxidant drugs, dyes, and industrial products (including paraquat, menadione, doxorubicin, and methylene blue) react with hemoglobin to form methemoglobin and a free radical; for a quinone, the product is a semiquinone. Many of the free radicals are highly reactive reductants which react with O_2 to form O_2^-.

$$R + HbFe \longrightarrow HbFe^+ + R^{\cdot -}$$

$$R^{\cdot -} + O_2 \longrightarrow R + O_2^-$$

The resulting O_2^- leads to further oxidation of hemoglobin and cell damage. Cell damage may also result from direct reaction with the free radicals.

A number of methemoglobinemia-inducing compounds are not oxidizing agents but are instead reducing agents. Nitrites, hydrazines, hydrazides, thiols, phenylenediamines, and aminophenols are among the classes of compounds which oxidize hemoglobin indirectly by reducing O_2 to O_2^-, H_2O_2, or $HO^{\cdot}$. With several of these toxic compounds, reduction of O_2 to H_2O_2 proceeds with the bound O_2 of oxyhemoglobin in a reaction analogous to the reaction of oxyhemoglobin with O_2^-.

Methemoglobinemia also results from the ingestion of inorganic and organic compounds which are metabolized in vivo to oxidants or reductants which oxidize hemoglobin either directly or indirectly. Nitrate, aniline, and a number of drugs including primaquine, sulfanilamide, dapsone, phenacetin, acetanilide, benzocaine, and phenazopyridine are among the compounds which exert their toxic effects in this manner. Thus, the toxic effect of nitrate in infants arises from its transformation to nitrite in the digestive tract. Likewise, the methemoglobin-forming effect of aniline is dependent on its prior metabolic conversion to phenylhydroxylamine.

REDUCTION OF METHEMOGLOBIN BY MINOR PATHWAYS

Under normal conditions, most of the methemoglobin reduction carried out by the erythrocyte is catalyzed by the cytochrome b_5/cytochrome b_5 reductase system. Only a small fraction of methemoglobin reduction can be attributed to direct reduction of methemoglobin with endogenous reductants in the cell or to catalysis by another methemoglobin reductase system. In individuals with cytochrome b_5 reductase deficiency or in the presence of oxidant stress, these minor pathways may become more important (or even essential) to the cell. These minor pathways also provide the basis for the therapy of methemoglobinemia.

Direct Reaction with Endogenous and Ingested Reductants

Methemoglobin is reduced directly by ascorbic acid, reduced glutathione, reduced flavin, tetrahydropterin, cysteine, cysteamine, and the tryptophan metabolites, 3-hydroxyanthranilic acid and 3-hydroxykynurenine.[12,21,23] In order for these endogenous compounds to function in methemoglobin reduction, their reduced forms must be regenerated in the erythrocyte. Indeed, in erythrocytes, reduction of oxidized glutathione is catalyzed by a NADPH-dependent reductase, oxidized ascorbic acid by a glutathione-dependent reductase, and free flavin by a NADPH-dependent reductase, while dihydropterin reacts with reduced glutathione. Under normal conditions, these pathways contribute little to the overall reduction of methemoglobin. The reactions are slow at the concentrations of reductants present in the cell. Methemoglobinemia is not associated with ascorbic acid deficiency (scurvy)[12] or with glutathione deficiency.[42] An increase in the ascorbic acid concentration, however, leads to an increase in the rate of the nonenzymatic reaction between methemoglobin and ascorbic acid both in vitro and in vivo.[6,43] After ingestion of ascorbic acid, the rate of this reaction is sufficiently fast to allow this reductant to be used therapeutically in patients with hereditary methemoglobinemia due to cytochrome b_5 reductase deficiency. Ascorbic acid reduces the β subunit faster than the α subunit, with the result that partial reduction of methemoglobin yields predominantly the $(\alpha^+\beta)_2$ valence hybrid.[44] Polyanions markedly stimulate this reaction.

A number of foreign redox compounds also accelerate the rate of methemoglobin reduction in vitro and in vivo. Methylene blue, Nile blue, and divicine (2,6-diamino-4,5-dihydroxypyrimidine) are among the compounds which are reduced in the erythrocyte and whose reduced forms then reduce methemoglobin directly. Reductions of such foreign redox compounds involve glutathione, cytochrome b_5 reductase, cytochrome b_5, or the NADPH-reductase. The action of many of these reducing agents is complicated by side reactions which alter the amount of H_2O_2 generated.

Role of NADPH-Dependent Reductase of Erythrocytes

A NADPH-dependent reductase present in the cytoplasm of erythrocytes rapidly catalyzes the reduction of methemoglobin, but only in the presence of an electron transfer mediator such as methylene blue or free flavin. In analogy with the erythrocyte NADH-dependent enzyme, this NADPH-dependent enzyme has been variously referred to in the literature as an erythrocyte *dehydrogenase, reductase, diaphorase, methemoglobin reductase,* or *ferrihemoglobin reductase.* More recently, it has been called "NADPH-flavin reductase." Under normal conditions and in the absence of exogenous redox mediators, the role of this enzyme in methemoglobin reduction is minor, as evidenced by the fact that deficiency of the enzyme does not lead to methemoglobinemia.[45] The extent to which this enzyme catalyzes methemoglobin reduction in cytochrome b_5 reductase deficiency is debatable, but its central role in the treatment of methemoglobinemia is unequivocal.

The studies of Kiese,[23,46] Gibson,[8] and Warburg et al.[47] led to the conclusion that this reductase transferred electrons from NADPH to methylene blue and that the resulting leukomethylene blue then transferred electrons directly to methemo-

globin (see Fig. 92-2). Two forms of the NADPH-dependent enzyme with similar properties have been described. Purification procedures have led to increasingly pure enzyme preparations.[23] The enzyme appears to be present in the erythrocyte at nearly 10 μM concentration. The activity does not appear to decline with aging of the cell.

One form of the enzyme has been isolated as a homogeneous protein of 22,000 daltons.[48] The enzyme is unrelated to erythrocyte cytochrome b_5 reductase. Although the isolated protein contains no prosthetic group, it binds FMN or riboflavin and catalyzes the rapid reduction of these flavins with NADPH as electron donor, or a slower reduction with NADH.[49] The resulting reduced form of the flavin rapidly reduces methemoglobin. The β chain is reduced more rapidly than the α chain with the consequence that the $(\alpha^+\beta)_2$ hybrid is an intermediate form.[50] This NADPH-dependent, flavin-mediated pathway (Fig. 92-2) has been presented as a physiological pathway of methemoglobin reduction. The low concentration of flavin in the erythrocyte relative to the K_m values for flavin, however, relegates the pathway to a minor role under normal conditions. When methemoglobin concentration or flavin concentration is high, NADPH-flavin reductase might be expected to play a more significant role.

ERYTHROCYTE CYTOCHROME b_5 REDUCTASE

The early studies of Kiese[46] and Gibson[8] provided the insight that electrons for methemoglobin reduction were transferred from glyceraldehyde-3-phosphate or lactate to NADH by specific dehydrogenases of the glycolytic pathway, and then transferred from NADH to methemoglobin by a reductase (Fig. 92-2). Gibson demonstrated a deficiency of this "methemoglobin reductase" in the red blood cells of two families with idiopathic methemoglobinemia and correctly deduced that this was the basic defect of hereditary methemoglobinemia.

Scott and his colleagues isolated two forms of NADH-dependent reductase from the cytoplasm of normal human erythrocytes and demonstrated that one of these enzymes was absent in an individual with hereditary methemoglobinemia.[51,52] The normal reductase that was deficient in methemoglobinemic individuals rapidly catalyzed the reduction of 2,6-dichlorophenolindophenol (DCIP) and ferricyanide. Further purification of this human erythrocyte reductase has been achieved by Hegesh and Avron,[53] Niethammer and Huennekens,[54] Sugita et al.,[55] Passon and Hultquist,[56] Kuma and Inomata,[57] and Yubisui and Takeshita.[58]

The ability of the enzyme to catalyze the reduction of DCIP and ferricyanide has been used to detect, quantitate, and study the enzyme. These "diaphorase" activities are much faster with NADH than with NADPH as electron donor. In contrast to the very rapid electron transfer to the artificial acceptors, the reductase catalyzes the direct transfer of electrons from NADH to methemoglobin very slowly; the rate of methemoglobin reduction is approximately 0.01 percent of the rate of DCIP reduction. The catalysis of methemoglobin reduction is greatly facilitated by ferricyanide.[59] Ferricyanide is believed to act by transferring electrons between the reductase and methemoglobin.[60] DPG and other polyanionic effectors of hemoglobin stimulate the ferricyanide-facilitated reduction of methemoglobin,[61] suggesting that the T state of methemoglobin is more readily reduced by ferrocyanide than is the R state.

The purified reductase is a flavoprotein with a non-covalently bound FAD prosthetic group.[51,56,57] The flavoprotein shows absorbance maxima at 390 and 462 nm, and a shoulder at 488 nm. During isolation or storage of the protein, electrophoretic heterogeneity may arise from protein alteration or, in the absence of EDTA, from loss of the FAD prosthetic group.

Human erythrocyte cytochrome b₅ reductase is a protein of 32,000 daltons, comprising a single peptide chain and one FAD residue. Amino acid sequence analysis[62] has recently established that the structure of the enzyme corresponds to the sequence of 275 residues shown in Fig. 92-4. Notable structural features include four cysteine residues and a high content of proline. Although this slightly acidic protein is water soluble, several regions of its peptide chain are highly hydrophobic.

In normal adult human erythrocytes, cytochrome b₅ reductase is present at approximately a 0.1 μM concentration. The mean, standard deviation, and range of reported values vary considerably from laboratory to laboratory and by method of analysis. The more recent studies have shown a standard deviation from the mean of approximately ±15 percent. The reductase activity decreases slowly during aging of erythrocytes in the circulation, with a half-life of 240 days.[63] Modest changes in the kinetic parameters of the enzyme also occur during aging in vivo.[64] The activity in erythrocytes of cord blood and newborns is normally 50 to 60 percent of the activity in the adult, and activity in the premature infant is even lower. Within a few months of birth, the levels have risen to those of an adult. The reductase activity is very low in individuals homozygous for deficiency of erythrocyte cytochrome b₅ reductase. Individuals heterozygous for the deficiency generally have 50 to 60 percent of normal activity.

In addition to cytoplasmic cytochrome b₅ reductase, erythrocytes contain membrane-bound, NADH-dependent reductase activities.[65,66] One of these activities present in erythrocyte ghosts has been shown to be related to the cytoplasmic cytochrome b₅ reductase.[67-70] This membrane-bound reductase is an integral part of the red cell membrane, and detergent is required for its extraction. The detergent-solubilized reductase is a flavoprotein with enzymatic properties indistinguishable from the erythrocyte cytoplasmic cytochrome b₅ reductase. The two forms of the enzyme are immunologically cross-reactive. They appear to be encoded by the same gene since both enzymes have been reported to be deficient in six patients with enzymopenic hereditary methemoglobinemia.[68] The sol-

ubilized membrane reductase differs from the cytoplasmic reductase in that it has a measurably larger molecular weight and undergoes aggregation to form high molecular weight forms. Proteolytic digestion of erythrocyte ghosts releases the reductase from the membrane in a lower molecular weight form. This proteolyzed form has full enzymatic activity but does not aggregate.

The fraction of erythrocyte cytochrome b₅ reductase present in the membrane-bound form varies markedly among species. This form represents only 2 percent of the activity of rat erythrocytes, but nearly 100 percent of the activity of bird, reptile, and fish erythrocytes. In the erythrocytes of adult humans, 20 to 35 percent of the activity is bound to the membrane. The erythrocytes of human adults and newborns contain the same level of membrane-bound cytochrome b₅ reductase, but this form constitutes a larger fraction of the total activity in the newborn because of the lower levels of cytosolic enzyme in such erythrocytes.[69]

ERYTHROCYTE CYTOCHROME b₅

A hemeprotein with spectral properties of cytochrome b₅ and a flavoprotein that catalyzed the reduction of this hemeprotein were detected in the cytoplasm of human erythrocytes in 1969.[71] Erythrocyte cytochrome b₅ at physiological concentrations markedly enhanced the ability of the cytochrome b₅ reductase to catalyze the transfer of electrons from NADH to methemoglobin.[13,72] One major and two minor forms of human erythrocyte cytochrome b₅ have been isolated,[73] and the major form has been purified to homogeneity.[74] Cytochrome b₅ has also been isolated from the cytoplasm of rabbit, mouse, and steer erythrocytes.[73,75-77] Another "b-type" cytochrome was isolated from the membrane of human erythrocytes in relatively large amounts, but this "S-protein"[78] did not appear to be structurally or functionally related to erythrocyte cytochrome b₅.

Erythrocyte cytochrome b₅ is a small red protein of approximately 12,000 daltons. The protein is highly anionic with an isoelectric point of 4.9 and is readily water-soluble. It contains a single protoheme IX prosthetic group, present as a low-spin complex which does not bind carbon monoxide. The hemeprotein, isolated in its ferric state, shows a sharp absorbance maximum at 413 nm. The spectrum of the ferrous form shows sharp maxima at 423, 527, and 556 nm, and a prominent shoulder at 560 nm. The standard reduction potential at pH

Fig. 92-4 *Primary structure of human erythrocyte cytochrome b₅ reductase.*

```
                  5                    10                   15                   20                   25
Phe-Gln-Arg-Ser-Thr-Pro-Ala-Ile-Thr-Leu-Glu-Ser-Pro-Asp-Ile-Lys-Tyr-Pro-Leu-Arg-Leu-Ile-Asp-Arg-Glu-
                 30                   35                   40                   45                   50
Ile-Ile-Ser-His-Asp-Thr-Arg-Arg-Phe-Arg-Phe-Ala-Leu-Pro-Ser-Pro-Gln-His-Ile-Leu-Gly-Leu-Pro-Val-Gly-
                 55                   60                   65                   70                   75
Gln-His-Ile-Tyr-Leu-Ser-Ala-Arg-Ile-Asp-Gly-Asn-Leu-Val-Val-Arg-Pro-Tyr-Thr-Pro-Ile-Ser-Ser-Asp-Asp-
                 80                   85                   90                   95                  100
Asp-Lys-Gly-Phe-Val-Asp-Leu-Val-Ile-Lys-Val-Tyr-Phe-Lys-Asp-Thr-His-Pro-Lys-Phe-Pro-Ala-Gly-Gly-Lys-
                105                  110                  115                  120                  125
Met-Ser-Gln-Tyr-Leu-Glu-Ser-Met-Gln-Ile-Gly-Asp-Thr-Ile-Glu-Phe-Arg-Gly-Pro-Ser-Gly-Leu-Leu-Val-Tyr-
                130                  135                  140                  145                  150
Gln-Gly-Lys-Gly-Lys-Phe-Ala-Ile-Arg-Pro-Asp-Lys-Lys-Ser-Asn-Pro-Ile-Ile-Arg-Thr-Val-Lys-Ser-Val-Gly-
                155                  160                  165                  170                  175
Met-Ile-Ala-Gly-Gly-Thr-Gly-Ile-Thr-Pro-Met-Leu-Gln-Val-Ile-Arg-Ala-Ile-Met-Lys-Asp-Pro-Asp-Asp-His-
                180                  185                  190                  195                  200
Thr-Val-Cys-His-Leu-Leu-Phe-Ala-Asn-Gln-Thr-Glu-Lys-Asp-Ile-Leu-Leu-Arg-Pro-Glu-Leu-Glu-Glu-Leu-Arg-
                205                  210                  215                  220                  225
Asn-Lys-His-Ser-Ala-Arg-Phe-Lys-Leu-Trp-Tyr-Thr-Leu-Asp-Arg-Ala-Pro-Glu-Ala-Trp-Asp-Val-Gly-Gln-Gly-
                230                  235                  240                  245                  250
Phe-Val-Asn-Glu-Glu-Met-Ile-Arg-Asp-His-Leu-Pro-Pro-Pro-Glu-Glu-Glu-Pro-Leu-Val-Leu-Met-Cys-Gly-Pro-
                255                  260                  265                  270                  275
Pro-Pro-Met-Ile-Gln-Tyr-Ala-Cys-Leu-Pro-Asn-Leu-Asp-His-Val-Gly-His-Pro-Thr-Glu-Arg-Cys-Phe-Val-Phe
```

```
                                        10                                              20
Ac-Ala-Glu-Gln-Ser-Asp-Glu-Ala-Val-Lys-Tyr-Tyr-Thr-Leu-Glx-Glu-Ile-Glx-Lys-His-Asn-
                                        30                                              40
    His-Ser-Lys-Ser-Thr-Trp-Leu-Ile-Leu-His-His-Lys-Val-Tyr-Asp-Leu-Thr-Lys-Phe-Leu-
                                        50                                              60
    Glu-Glu-His-Pro-Gly-Gly-Glu-Glu-Val-Leu-Arg-Glu-Gln-Ala-Gly-Gly-Asp-Ala-Thr-Glu-
                                                    70                                  80
    Asx-Phe-Glu-Asp-Val-Gly-His-Ser-Thr-Asp-Ala-Arg-Glu-Met-Ser-Lys-Thr-Phe-Ile-Ile-
                                                    90
    Gly-Glu-Leu-His-Pro-Asp-Asp-Lys-Pro-Arg-Leu-Asn-Lys-Pro-Pro-Glu-Pro
```

Fig. 92-5 Primary structure of human erythrocyte cytochrome b_5.

7.0 is -2 mV.[79] The ferrous form autoxidizes at a moderate rate.

Erythrocyte cytochrome b_5 comprises 97 amino acid residues in a single peptide chain. No carbohydrate or other non-amino acid groups, other than the heme, are bound to the protein. The protein has a blocked N terminus, which recently has been identified as an *N*-acetylalanine residue.[80] Bovine erythrocyte cytochrome b_5 was the first of these proteins for which it was possible to deduce the amino acid sequence.[81] The sequences have now been deduced for the rabbit,[82] human,[80,83] and pig[80] erythrocyte proteins. The structure of human erythrocyte cytochrome b_5 is shown in Fig. 92-5.

Erythrocyte cytochrome b_5 can be quantitated on the basis of its distinct spectral properties or on the basis of its ability to stimulate the cytochrome b_5 reductase-catalyzed reduction of methemoglobin.[73,79,84–86] Mean values for cytochrome b_5 concentration in erythrocytes range from 0.2 to 0.6 μM. The protein is present in higher concentration in reticulocytes than in erythrocytes. Cytochrome b_5 concentrations decrease both during cell aging in the circulation and during cell storage under blood bank conditions. The apparent half-life in vivo is 44 days.[63]

RELATIONSHIP BETWEEN THE ERYTHROCYTIC AND MICROSOMAL PROTEINS

The erythrocyte cytochrome is named cytochrome b_5 on the basis of its similarity to microsomal cytochrome b_5. They have identical visible spectra, EPR spectra, prosthetic groups, chemical reactivity at the iron atom, and ability to serve as substrate for cytochrome b_5 reductase.[73] The erythrocyte reductase has been identified as a cytochrome b_5 reductase on the basis of its capacity to catalyze the reduction of cytochrome b_5 and its similarity to microsomal cytochrome b_5 reductase in terms of prosthetic group, substrate specificity, and effects of ionic strength, pH, and EDTA on catalytic activity.[56] The erythrocyte and microsomal proteins differ, however, in that the erythrocyte proteins are smaller, water soluble, and located in the cytoplasm, rather than in the endoplasmic reticulum. These comparisons have led to the suggestion that erythrocyte cytochrome b_5 and cytochrome b_5 reductase correspond to the microsomal proteins without their hydrophobic tails.[56] In liver and other tissues, it is the hydrophobic domains of these proteins that are embedded in the endoplasmic reticulum.

Erythrocyte cytochrome b_5 has been shown to be structurally related to the hydrophilic domain of liver microsomal cytochrome b_5. Trypsin degrades *human* cytochrome b_5 from liver and erythrocytes to electrophoretically identical heme peptides.[74] Likewise, trypsin degrades the 97-residue *bovine* erythrocyte cytochrome b_5 and the 133-residue bovine liver

cytochrome b_5 to the same 82-residue heme peptide.[76] The amino acid sequence of the bovine erythrocyte protein corresponds precisely to the sequence of 97 residues starting at the blocked N terminus of the liver protein,[87] with the possible exception that an asparagine residue in the liver is present as an aspartate residue in the erythrocyte. Like the bovine erythrocyte protein, *rabbit* erythrocyte cytochrome b_5 is a 97-residue protein with near identity to residues 1 to 97 of the 133-residue rabbit liver protein. Of the 97 residues, only the one at position 97 differs; it is C-terminal proline in rabbit erythrocyte cytochrome b_5 and threonine in the liver protein.[82] Likewise, *pig* and *human* cytochrome b_5 molecules comprise 97-residue erythrocyte proteins and 133-residue liver microsomal proteins in which there is identity between the first 96 residues but a difference at residue 97.[80] In pig, residue 97 is serine in erythrocytes and threonine in liver. In humans, residue 97 is proline in erythrocytes (Fig. 92-5) and threonine in liver.

Erythrocyte cytochrome b_5 reductase has been shown to be structurally related to microsomal cytochrome b_5 reductase. The two proteins are immunologically cross-reactive.[67,88,89] They are genetically related as evidenced by the finding that erythrocyte cytochrome b_5 reductase as well as the microsomal enzyme of other tissues are defective in the generalized cytochrome b_5 reductase deficiency of humans.[90] The reductases from bovine erythrocytes and liver are degraded by cathepsin D to electrophoretically identical flavopeptides.[91,92] Nucleotide sequencing of cDNA which codes for human liver cytochrome b_5 reductase has recently established that human erythrocyte cytochrome b_5 reductase is a piece of the liver microsomal cytochrome b_5 reductase.[93] These human liver cDNA sequence data, together with amino acid sequence data for bovine liver cytochrome b_5 reductase, establish that the 275-residue sequence of the human erythrocyte protein corresponds precisely to the 275 residues at the C terminus of the human liver protein. The erythrocyte reductase does not possess the membrane-binding, hydrophobic peptide of approximately 25 residues which is present at the N terminus of the liver reductase.

The structural relationship between the erythrocyte and microsomal proteins led to the proposition that erythrocyte cytochrome b_5 and cytochrome b_5 reductase were derived during erythroid maturation from microsomal precursor proteins.[74,94] This postulate was supported by the finding that an immature erythroid cell line contained only the amphipathic forms of cytochrome b_5 and cytochrome b_5 reductase, whereas mature erythrocytes contained the cytoplasmic forms of these proteins.[77] Moreover, a cathepsin D isolated from a membranous fraction of rabbit reticulocytes was shown to catalyze efficiently the proteolytic removal of the hydrophobic tails of microsomal cytochrome b_5 and cytochrome b_5 reductase without cleavage in their hydrophilic domains.[91,95,96] With rabbit liver cytochrome b_5 as substrate, the cathepsin removed peptides sequentially from the C terminus and generated a 98-residue limit heme peptide which was one residue longer than rabbit erythrocyte cytochrome b_5; the extra residue was leucine-98.[82] Similarly, an ATP-dependent protease of rabbit reticulocytes released cytochrome b_5 and cytochrome b_5 reductase as water-soluble proteins from rat liver microsomes.[97] The cytoplasmic form of erythrocyte cytochrome b_5 reductase was postulated by Kaplan and coworkers[70,98] to arise from proteolysis of the reductase which was bound to the erythrocyte membrane. Auto-incubation of erythrocyte membranes released a solubilized form of the reductase, a process stimulated by calcium ion.

Thus, acidic, ATP-dependent, and calcium-dependent proteases of reticulocytes are potential candidates for the putative enzyme responsible for converting microsomal proteins of immature erythroid cells to the cytoplasmic forms of the proteins found in mature erythrocytes. If indeed such a proteolytic event occurs, the processing would be responsible for the conversion of amphipathic, membrane-bound proteins which function in the desaturation of fatty acids to water-soluble proteins which function to reduce methemoglobin. However, the detection of the structural difference between the two forms of cytochrome b_5 at residue 97 brings into question whether such protein processing actually occurs during erythroid maturation. If it does occur, a form of microsomal cytochrome b_5 distinct from liver microsomal cytochrome b_5 (with a proline residue at position 97) must be present in immature erythroid cells.

THE MECHANISM OF METHEMOGLOBIN REDUCTION BY CYTOCHROME b_5 REDUCTASE AND CYTOCHROME b_5

The marked stimulation of the erythrocyte cytochrome b_5 reductase-catalyzed reduction of methemoglobin by physiological concentrations of erythrocyte cytochrome b_5 led to the postulate that methemoglobin is reduced in vivo by the following sequence of electron transfers:

NADH $\xrightarrow{e-}$ cytochrome b_5 reductase
$\xrightarrow{e-}$ cytochrome b_5 $\xrightarrow{e-}$ methemoglobin

These findings had been anticipated in 1959 by Petragnani and coworkers,[99] who demonstrated that solubilized forms of pig liver cytochrome b_5 reductase and cytochrome b_5 together catalyzed the reduction of methemoglobin. Unaware that cytochrome b_5 or cytochrome b_5 reductase was present in erythrocytes, these workers uncannily suggested that ". . . the erythrocyte methemoglobin reductase may be a similar multienzymatic system. . . ."

The mechanism of this major pathway of methemoglobin reduction has been deduced from studies in many laboratories.[13,51,55–57,79,91,100–105] The rate of methemoglobin reduction in intact cells can be reproduced in crude hemolysates or in systems reconstituted from purified NADH, cytochrome b_5 reductase, cytochrome b_5, and methemoglobin, demonstrating that no additional component plays an essential role in this pathway. Under close to physiological conditions, the rate of methemoglobin reduction is first-order with respect to methemoglobin and cytochrome b_5 reductase and second-order with respect to cytochrome b_5. Thus, methemoglobin reduction proceeds more rapidly when the concentration of methemoglobin is elevated and proceeds more slowly when either cytochrome b_5 reductase or cytochrome b_5 is present at less than normal concentration.

The results of the mechanistic studies are compatible with the scheme depicted in Fig. 92-6. After NADH binds to the oxidized flavoprotein (step 1), a pair of electrons is transferred from NADH to FAD (step 2). The reduced flavoprotein sequentially binds and reduces first one and then a second molecule of ferric cytochrome b_5, with the resulting formation of ferrous cytochrome b_5 and oxidized flavoprotein (steps 3 and 4). The generation of a complex between cytochrome b_5 reductase and cytochrome b_5 involves ionic interactions between anionic residues of cytochrome b_5 and cationic residues of cytochrome b_5 reductase. These first four steps are presumably identical with the extensively studied reduction of microsomal cytochrome b_5 catalyzed by microsomal cytochrome b_5 reductase.[106,107]

The reduction of methemoglobin is accomplished by the formation of an ionic complex between ferrous cytochrome b_5 and a ferric subunit of a hemoglobin tetramer (step 5) and the subsequent electron transfer in this complex between the hemes of these proteins (step 6). The cytochrome b_5-methemoglobin complex has been detected by isoelectric focusing[108] and by spectral perturbation of the absorbance spectra.[109,110] The formation of the complex and the transfer of electrons between the proteins of this complex have been separated kinetically.[91,101,103] Computer modeling studies by Poulos and Mauk[111] suggest that the complex is stabilized by ionic interactions between carboxylate anions on the face of a cytochrome b_5 molecule from which the heme group protrudes and lysyl cations on the face of methemoglobin subunits from which their heme groups protrude. Optimization of four such ionic bonds with the α subunit and five ionic bonds with the

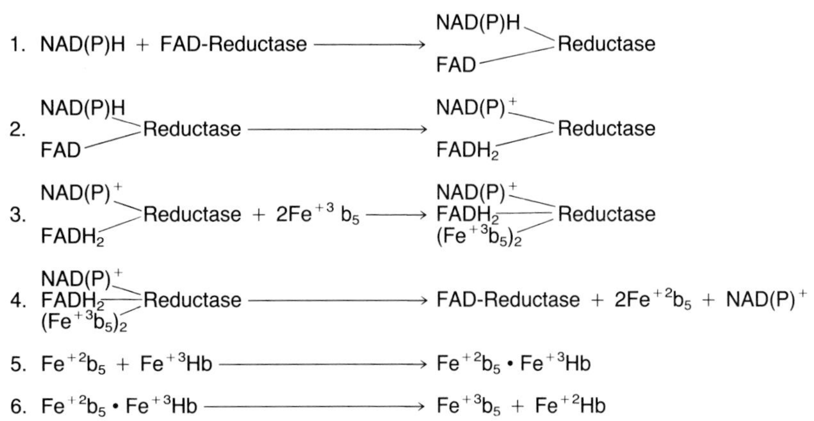

Fig. 92-6 Scheme for the reduction of methemoglobin by cytochrome b_5 reductase and cytochrome b_5.

1. NAD(P)H + FAD-Reductase $\longrightarrow$ $\overset{\displaystyle \text{NAD(P)H}}{\underset{\displaystyle \text{FAD}}{\diagdown}}$Reductase

2. $\overset{\displaystyle \text{NAD(P)H}}{\underset{\displaystyle \text{FAD}}{\diagup}}$Reductase $\longrightarrow$ $\overset{\displaystyle \text{NAD(P)}^+}{\underset{\displaystyle \text{FADH}_2}{\diagup}}$Reductase

3. $\overset{\displaystyle \text{NAD(P)}^+}{\underset{\displaystyle \text{FADH}_2}{\diagup}}$Reductase + $2Fe^{+3}b_5$ $\longrightarrow$ $\overset{\displaystyle \text{NAD(P)}^+}{\underset{\displaystyle (Fe^{+3}b_5)_2}{\diagup}}$FADH$_2$Reductase

4. $\underset{\displaystyle (Fe^{+3}b_5)_2}{\overset{\displaystyle \text{NAD(P)}^+}{\text{FADH}_2}}$Reductase $\longrightarrow$ FAD-Reductase + $2Fe^{+2}b_5$ + NAD(P)$^+$

5. $Fe^{+2}b_5$ + $Fe^{+3}Hb$ $\longrightarrow$ $Fe^{+2}b_5 \cdot Fe^{+3}Hb$

6. $Fe^{+2}b_5 \cdot Fe^{+3}Hb$ $\longrightarrow$ $Fe^{+3}b_5$ + $Fe^{+2}Hb$

β subunit places the interacting hemes in a coplanar orientation which presumably leads to facile electron transfer. Support for the validity of this model is provided by the observations that mutant hemoglobins in which one of these cationic residues is not present have decreased capacities to be reduced by the cytochrome b_5 reductase/cytochrome b_5 system.[27,28]

The overall rate of methemoglobin reduction in vivo depends on the concentration of the ferrous cytochrome b_5-ferric hemoglobin complex. The interaction between these proteins is weak, and under physiological conditions the concentration of complex depends on the concentrations of ferrous cytochrome b_5 and methemoglobin. The fraction of cytochrome b_5 present in the ferrous form, in turn, is determined by the concentration of cytochrome b_5 reductase. Complex formation between ferric hemoglobin and cytochrome b_5 appears to be inhibited by ferrous hemoglobin. Complexation proceeds more readily with the R state of methemoglobin than with the T state,[103] and the β subunit of methemoglobin is reduced preferentially in the presence of inositol hexaphosphate.[101] The concentrations of cytochrome b_5 reductase, cytochrome b_5, methemoglobin, and polyanionic effector determine the concentration of ferrous cytochrome b_5-methemoglobin complex and in this manner determine the rate of methemoglobin reduction in vivo.

The significance of NADPH as an electron donor for this system is debatable. The reduction of cytochrome b_5 reductase (steps 1 and 2) proceeds so much slower in vitro with NADPH than with NADH that the role of NADPH has been assumed to be insignificant. However, the transfer of electrons from reductase to methemoglobin (steps 3 through 6) is rate limiting as a consequence of the very low concentration of cytochrome b_5 in the erythrocyte (far below the K_m of the reductase). In a crude hemolysate or in a system reconstituted from purified cytochrome b_5 reductase and cytochrome b_5, methemoglobin reduction proceeds nearly as rapidly with a saturating level of NADPH as with a saturating level of NADH. Thus, it appears that in vivo steps 1 and 2 are the fast steps in the pathway, even with NADPH as electron donor. This conclusion in not compatible with other studies which indicate only a minor role for NADPH in methemoglobin reduction.

CLINICAL ASPECTS AND CLASSIFICATION

Subjects with enzymopenic hereditary methemoglobinemia present with persistent slate gray cyanosis, often dating from birth. A concentration of 1.5 to 2.0 g/dl of methemoglobin (10 to 15 percent of total hemoglobin) produces visible cyanosis, whereas 5 g/dl of deoxygenated hemoglobin is required to produce a comparable degree of cyanosis.[112] In most instances, the patients are really more blue than sick (see, however, type II, below). They lack evidence of cardiac or pulmonary disease. Significant erythrocytosis is observed only occasionally, and the oxygen dissociation curve is normal or shifted only slightly to the left.[3] The absence of manifestations of anoxia may be due to differences in the proportions of valence hybrids in the erythrocytes.[20,22] Hardly any systemic symptoms are reported when the methemoglobin level is 25 percent or less, except for the subjects' odd "cyanotic" appearance. Even with levels up to 40 percent, the only complaints may be those of headache, easy fatigue, and exertional dyspnea. Life expec-

tancy is normal, and pregnancies are not compromised. The methemoglobinemia is quite well tolerated, and may be readily controlled with appropriate therapy.

Recently, a clinical-biochemical classification of enzymopenic hereditary methemoglobinemia has been proposed on the basis of important differences in the pathophysiology of the disorder.[113]

Type I Enzymopenic Hereditary Methemoglobinemia (Erythrocyte Reductase Deficiency)

The majority of patients appear to have type I, the classic syndrome with the signs and symptoms described above, that has been extensively studied since the pioneering investigations of Gibson[8] and Scott and Griffith.[9] The subjects have methemoglobinemia alone because the deficiency of cytochrome b_5 reductase is limited to the erythrocytes. Their erythrocytes' metabolic machinery is otherwise intact, so there is no hemolysis.

Type II Enzymopenic Hereditary Methemoglobinemia (Generalized Reductase Deficiency)

A much more severe and lethal disorder occurs in perhaps 10 to 15 percent of patients with enzymopenic hereditary methemoglobinemia; it is referred to as type II. In addition to methemoglobinemia, signs of a progressive neurologic abnormality become apparent before age 1 year and may be observed even at birth. The association of these two aberrations was described in 1953.[114] The fully expressed syndrome is characterized by severe mental retardation, microcephaly, retarded growth, opisthotonus, attacks of bilateral athetoid movements, strabismus, and generalized hypertonia.[12,29] Death usually supervenes soon. Pathologic examinations of the brains of three sibs with this disorder have revealed only nonspecific alterations, including reduced numbers of nerve elements, and retarded myelinization.[29] Not only is the activity of cytochrome b_5 reductase markedly reduced in the patients' erythrocytes, but nearly total deficiency of microsomal cytochrome b_5 reductase is demonstrable in the leukocytes, muscle, liver, fibroblasts, and brain of such patients.[90,115,116] Because the microsomal cytochrome b_5/cytochrome b_5 reductase system participates in other tissues in the desaturation of fatty acids, it has been suggested that impairment of fatty acid desaturation, especially in the central nervous system, may account for the generalized systemic manifestations.[90] Lipid analyses of tissues from a child with the type II disorder have revealed decreased cerebroside (48 percent of normal) in the white matter of the brain,[117] decreased linoleic acid and increased palmitic acid in adipose tissue, decreased proportions of unsaturated fatty acids in the ethanolamine phosphoglycerides of the liver, and less than half of normal concentrations of linoleic acid in the ethanolamine phosphoglycerides of the liver, kidney, and spleen.[118] Cholesterol and lipid phosphorus concentrations, however, were normal in the liver, kidney, spleen, muscle, and adrenals. Thus, the effect of the generalized cytochrome b_5 reductase deficiency was unexpectedly slight, but the reduction in cerebroside content might have caused a decrease in myelination, leading to mental retardation.[118] The generalized deficiency of cytochrome b_5 reductase activity in patients with type II, as well as in their fetal amniotic cells, has made antenatal diagnosis feasible.[119]

Type III Enzymopenic Hereditary Methemoglobinemia (Hematopoietic Reductase Deficiency)

In addition to a German family reported only in an abstract,[120] a detailed study of a Japanese family has provided evidence for the occurrence of enzymopenic hereditary methemoglobinemia without neurologic involvement but with cytochrome b₅ reductase deficiency demonstrable in erythrocytes, platelets, lymphocytes, and granulocytes.[121] The enzyme stained normally in the two male sibs' hair root and buccal cells. The only clinical manifestations were their cyanotic appearance with methemoglobin concentrations of about 25 percent. These reports have made it necessary to exercise caution in drawing conclusions from assays of cytochrome b₅ reductase activities in detergent-treated leukocytes, the procedure advocated for making the diagnosis of the generalized type II disorder in infants younger than 1 year old or in newborns.

Type IV Enzymopenic Hereditary Methemoglobinemia (Cytochrome b₅ Deficiency)

The discovery of a patient with long-standing methemoglobinemic cyanosis (methemoglobin concentrations 12 to 19%) associated with an erythrocyte cytochrome b₅ concentration about 23 percent of normal has completed the current roster of pathophysiological mechanisms for this disorder.[26] This observation has provided direct evidence for the physiological role of cytochrome b₅ in the reduction of methemoglobin to hemoglobin in vivo in human erythrocytes. The precise nature of this presently unique abnormality remains to be defined.

THE GENETICS OF CYTOCHROME b₅ REDUCTASE

The gene coding for soluble NADH-cytochrome b₅ reductase has been assigned to chromosome 22. This assignment is based on studies of the electrophoretic mobility and isoelectric focusing patterns of soluble enzyme in the cytosol of rodent-human fibroblast hybrids and concurrent cytogenetic analyses.[122–123] The same gene is assumed to code for the full length of the microsomal enzyme polypeptide chain (i.e., polar plus membranous segments).

The diaphorase activity of cytochrome b₅ reductase has been exploited to permit its visualization after electrophoresis of hemolysates or tissue extracts on starch or polyacrylamide gels.[12,124] A survey of 2783 healthy subjects has revealed five electrophoretic phenotypes with normal staining intensity and suggests an incidence of variants of about 1 in 100.[125] Studies of patients with enzymopenic hereditary methemoglobinemia have disclosed at least 14 different phenotypes, based on electrophoretic mobility and/or kinetic aberrations.[12,126] Thus, the mutations causing reductase deficiency are heterogeneous, with several different mutant alleles occurring at the reductase locus. The molecular basis of these mutations is as yet unknown.

An unusually high incidence of enzymopenic hereditary methemoglobinemia is reported among Alaskan Eskimos and Indians, Navajo Indians, Puerto Ricans, people of Mediterra-

nean origins, and natives of the Yakutsk region of Siberia, 1000 miles west of the Bering Sea.[12]

Type I, uncomplicated, benign enzymopenic hereditary methemoglobinemia is attributable to mutations that affect the catalytic activity or stability of the enzyme in the erythrocytes. Clinically affected subjects are homozygous or genetic compounds for cytochrome b₅ reductase deficiency. Exaggerated lability characterizes at least five enzyme variants.[127,128] The role of altered proteolytic processes in erythrocyte precursors in enzymopenic hereditary methemoglobinemia remains to be defined.[129] The asymptomatic heterozygote may have an increased tendency to develop toxic methemoglobinemia on exposure to methemoglobin-inducing drugs or chemicals, such as malaria chemoprophylaxis,[30] phenazopyridine,[32] or the "recreational" sniffing of volatile nitrites.[130]

Type II, severe, lethal enzymopenic hereditary methemoglobinemia is a generalized disorder with defective cytochrome b₅ reductase in all tissues. This disorder is presumed to result from mutation(s) which affect the enzyme's activity, thermal stability, or resistance to proteolysis in all tissues.

The apparently rather benign type III disorder may simply be a variant of type II in that the enzyme is altered by selective activity of proteolytic enzymes only in the hematopoietic tissues.[121,129] On the other hand, it may represent a catalytically less significant mutation affecting cytochrome b₅ reductase, analogous to the variants observed in glucose-6-phosphate dehydrogenase deficiency.

The type IV disorder is a deficiency of cytochrome b₅ alone; the activity of cytochrome b₅ reductase is normal.[26] The concentration of cytochrome b₅ is normal in the erythrocytes of the parents and sibs of the only known patient with this form of hereditary methemoglobinemia. The genetics of cytochrome b₅ deficiency, therefore, remain to be determined.

DIAGNOSIS OF CYTOCHROME b₅ REDUCTASE DEFICIENCY

Blood with more than about 10% methemoglobin appears unusually dark red or even brown. It does not become bright red upon vigorous shaking with air, and it leaves a dark reddish brown stain on white filter paper or a white laboratory coat. The presence of methemoglobin may be established by the characteristic absorption spectrum of a clear, stroma-free hemolysate with peaks at 500 and 631 nm at an acid pH.[126] The latter peak should disappear promptly after the addition of a neutralized cyanide solution.

If the spectrum in the 600- to 640-nm region is atypical and the peak near 631 nm is shifted toward a lower wavelength and does not change significantly or quickly on the addition of cyanide, hemoglobin M should be suspected. A hemoglobin M should also be suspected if there is a family history of apparent parent-to-child transmission of long-standing, unexplained cyanosis. Electrophoresis of the methemoglobin form and amino acid analysis of the globin are required for the confirmation of the diagnosis of a hemoglobin M.

Congenital cyanosis in sibs, especially with a history of consanguinity, is suggestive of enzymopenic hereditary methemoglobinemia. Presumptive evidence for cytochrome b₅ reductase deficiency may be obtained by comparing the rate of reduction of methemoglobin in a patient's nitrite-treated, washed erythrocytes incubated with glucose or other substrates before and after the addition of methylene blue with the rate observed with cells from a normal subject.[12] Reductase deficiency may be confirmed by direct assay for NADH-diaphorase,[10] NADH-methemoglobin-ferrocyanide reductase,[131] cytochrome b_5 reductase,[56] or NADH-ferricyanide reductase[132] activity in hemolysates of the patient's erythrocytes. Assay of NADH-ferricyanide reductase activity has been advocated as the simplest because of the ready availability of the substrate, potassium ferricyanide. A rapid screening spot test for NADH-diaphorase deficiency has also been described.[133]

TREATMENT OF CYTOCHROME b_5 REDUCTASE DEFICIENCY

Because subjects with type I cytochrome b_5 reductase deficiency have only mild symptoms from the methemoglobinemia, therapy is mainly cosmetic. It may be indicated, however, for psychological reasons. A single dose of methylene blue, 1 mg/kg intravenously, will rapidly reduce the methemoglobin concentration to normal, provided that the subject is not glucose-6-phosphate dehydrogenase-deficient since the methylene blue-stimulated NADPH-methemoglobin reductase system requires the reduction of $NADP^+$. Methylene blue has been reported to cause urinary tract irritation and, of course, makes the urine blue or bright green. Oral ascorbic acid, 500 to 1000 mg daily, can maintain the methemoglobin concentration at acceptable levels, but its prolonged adminstration may be responsible for hyperoxaluria and renal stone formation. Oral riboflavin, 20 to 60 mg daily, has been reported to be as effective as ascorbic acid in keeping the methemoglobin level at about 5 percent.[134] These therapeutic agents would also be expected to be effective in patients with the type III and type IV disorders. Although methylene blue will control the methemoglobinemia in the type II disorder, it has had no effect on the progressive neurologic dysfunction.

REFERENCES

1. FRANÇOIS: Cas de cyanose congéniale sans cause apparente. *Bull Acad Roy Med Belg* 4:698, 1845.
2. DITTRICH P: Ueber methämoglobinbildende Gifte. *Naunyn-Schmiedeberg's Arch Exp Pathol Pharmacol* 29:247, 1891.
3. JAFFÉ ER: Hereditary methemoglobinemias associated with abnormalities in the metabolism of erythrocytes. *Am J Med* 41:786, 1966.
4. VAN DEN BERGH AAH: Enterogene Cyanose. *Dtsch Arch Klin Med* 83:86, 1905.
5. HITZENBERGER K: Autotoxische Zyanose (Intraglobuläre Methämoglobinamie). *Wien Arch Inn Med* 23:85, 1932.
6. GIBSON QH: The reduction of methaemoglobin by ascorbic acid. *Biochem J* 37:615, 1943.
7. BARCROFT H, GIBSON QH, HARRISON DC, MCMURRAY J: Familial idiopathic methaemoglobinaemia and its treatment with ascorbic acid. *Clin Sci* 5:145, 1945.
8. GIBSON QH: The reduction of methaemoglobin in red blood cells and studies on the cause of idiopathic methaemoglobinaemia. *Biochem J* 42:13, 1948.
9. SCOTT EM, GRIFFITH IV: The enzymic defect of hereditary methemoglobinemia: Diaphorase. *Biochim Biophys Acta* 34:584, 1959.
10. SCOTT EM: The relation of diaphorase of human erythrocytes to inheritance of methemoglobinemia. *J Clin Invest* 39:1176, 1960.
11. BALSAMO P, HARDY WR, SCOTT EM: Hereditary methemoglobinemia due to diaphorase deficiency in Navajo Indians. *J Pediatr* 65:928, 1964.
12. SCHWARTZ JM, REISS AL, JAFFÉ ER: Hereditary methemoglobinemia with deficiency of NADH cytochrome b_5 reductase, in Stanbury JB, Wyngaarden JB, Fredrickson DS, Goldstein JL, Brown MS (eds): *The Metabolic Basis of Inherited Disease*, 5th ed. New York, McGraw-Hill, 1983, p 1654.
13. HULTQUIST DE, PASSON PG: Catalysis of methaemoglobin reduction by erythrocyte cytochrome b_5 and cytochrome b_5 reductase. *Nature* 229:252, 1971.
14. HAUROWITZ F: Zur Chemie des Blutfarbstoffes; zur Kenntnis das Methämoglobins und seiner Derivative. *Z Physiol Chem* 138:68, 1924.
15. LADNER RC, HEIDNER EJ, PERUTZ MF: The structure of horse methaemoglobin at 2.0 Å resolution. *J Mol Biol* 114:385, 1977.
16. PERTUZ MF, FERSHT AR, SIMON SR, ROBERTS GCK: Influence of globin structure on the state of the heme. II. Allosteric transitions in methemoglobin. *Biochemistry* 13:2174, 1974.
17. PERRELLA M, CREMONESI L, BENAZZI L, ROSSI-BERNARDI L: Isolation of intermediate valence hybrids between ferrous and methemoglobin at subzero temperatures. *J Biol Chem* 256:11098, 1981.
18. ITANO HA, ROBINSON E: Electrophoretic separation of intermediate compounds in two reactions of ferrihemoglobin. *Biochim Biophys Acta* 29:545, 1958.
19. BUNN HF, DRYSDALE JW: The separation of partially oxidized hemoglobins. *Biochim Biophys Acta* 229:51, 1971.
20. BODANSKY O: Methemoglobinemia and methemoglobin-producing compounds. *Pharmacol Rev* 3:144, 1951.
21. BUNN HF, FORGET BG: *Hemoglobin: Molecular, Genetic, and Clinical Aspects*. Philadelphia, Saunders, 1986, p 638.
22. DARLING RC, ROUGHTON FJW: The effect of methemoglobin on the equilibrium between oxygen and hemoglobin. *Am J Physiol* 137:56, 1942.
23. KIESE M: *Methemoglobinemia: A Comprehensive Treatise*. Cleveland, CRC Press, 1974.
24. SCHULMAN HM, MARTINEZ-MEDELLIN J, SIDLOI R: The oxidation state of newly synthesized hemoglobin. *Biochem Biophys Res Commun* 56:220, 1974.
25. ASAKURA T, ADACHI K, MINAKAMI S, YOSHIKAWA H: Non-glycolytic sugar metabolism in human erythrocytes. I. Xylitol metabolism. *J Biochem (Tokyo)* 62:184, 1967.
26. HEGESH E, HEGESH J, KAFTORY A: Congenital methemoglobinemia with a deficiency of cytochrome b_5. *N Engl J Med* 314:757, 1986.
27. NAGAI M, YUBISUI T, YONEYAMA Y: Enzymatic reduction of Hemoglobins M Milwaukee-1 and M Saskatoon by NADH-cytochrome b_5 reductase and NADPH-flavin reductase purified from human erythrocytes. *J Biol Chem* 255:4599, 1980.
28. GACON G, LOSTANLEN D, LABIE D, KAPLAN J-C: Interaction between cytochrome b_5 and hemoglobin: Involvement of β66 (E10) and β95 (FG2) lysyl residues of hemoglobin. *Proc Natl Acad Sci USA* 77:1917, 1980.
29. JAFFÉ ER, NEUMANN G, ROTHBERG H, WILSON FT, WEBSTER RM, WOLFF JA: Hereditary methemoglobinemia with and without mental retardation: A study of three families. *Am J Med* 41:42, 1966.
30. COHEN RJ, SACHS JR, WICKER DJ, CONRAD ME: Methemoglobinemia provoked by malarial chemoprophylaxis in Vietnam. *N Engl J Med* 279:1127, 1968.
31. HORNE MK, WATERMAN MR, SIMON LM, GARRIOTT JC, FOERSTER EH: Methemoglobinemia from sniffing butyl nitrite. *Ann Intern Med* 91:417, 1979.
32. DALY JS, HULTQUIST DE, RUCKNAGEL DL: Phenazopyridine induced methaemoglobinaemia associated with decreased activity of erythrocyte cytochrome b_5 reductase. *J Med Genet* 20:307, 1983.
33. ROSS JD: Deficient activity of DPNH-dependent methemoglobin diaphorase in cord blood erythrocytes. *Blood* 21:51, 1963.
34. KANAZAWA Y, HATTORI M, KOSAKA K, NAKAO K: The relationship of NADH-dependent diaphorase activity and methemoglobin reduction in human erythrocytes. *Clin Chim Acta* 19:524, 1968.
35. WINTERBOURN CC: Free-radical production and oxidative reactions of hemoglobin. *Environ Health Perspect* 64:321, 1985.
36. WITTENBERG JB, WITTENBERG BA, PEISACH J, BLUMBERG WE: On the state of the iron and the nature of the ligand in oxyhemoglobin. *Proc Natl Acad Sci USA* 67:1846, 1970.
37. MANSOURI A, WINTERHALTER KH: Nonequivalence of chains in haemoglobin oxidation. *Biochemistry* 12:4946, 1973.
38. TOMODA A, YONEYAMA Y, TSUJI A: Changes in intermediate haemoglobins during autoxidation of haemoglobin. *Biochem J* 195:485, 1981.
39. BROOKS J: The oxidation of haemoglobin to methaemoglobin by oxygen. II. The relation between the rate of oxidation and the partial pressure of oxygen. *Proc R Soc London (B)* 118:560, 1935.
40. TOMODA A, YONEYAMA Y: Analysis of intermediate hemoglobins in solutions of hemoglobin partially oxidized with ferricyanide. *Biochim Biophys Acta* 581:128, 1979.
41. WINTERBOURN CC, CARRELL RC: Oxidation of human haemoglobin by copper. *Biochem J* 165:141, 1977.
42. MOHLER DN, MAJERUS PW, MINNICH V, HESS CE, GARRICK MD: Glutathi-

one synthetase deficiency as a cause of hereditary hemolytic disease. *N Engl J Med* 283:1253, 1970.

43. VESTLING CS: The reduction of methemoglobin by ascorbic acid. *J Biol Chem* 143:439, 1942.

44. TOMODA A, TSUJI A, MATSUKAWA S, TAKESHITA M, YONEYAMA Y: Mechanism of methemoglobin reduction by ascorbic acid under anaerobic conditions. *J Biol Chem* 253:7420, 1978.

45. SASS MD, CARUSO CJ, FARHANGI M: TPNH-methemoglobin reductase deficiency: A new red-cell enzyme defect. *J Lab Clin Med* 70:760, 1967.

46. KIESE M: Die Reduktion des Hämiglobins. *Biochem Z* 316:264, 1944.

47. WARBURG O, KUBOWITZ F, CHRISTIAN W: Über die katalytische Wirkung von Methylenblau in lebenden Zellen. *Biochem Z* 227:245, 1930.

48. YUBISUI T, MATSUKI T, TAKESHITA M, YONEYAMA Y: Characterization of the purified NADPH-flavin reductase of human erythrocytes. *J Biochem (Tokyo)* 85:719, 1979.

49. YUBISUI T, TAKESHITA M, YONEYAMA Y: Reduction of methemoglobin through flavin at the physiological concentration by NADPH-flavin reductase of human erythrocytes. *J Biochem (Tokyo)* 87:1715, 1980.

50. TOMODA A, YUBISUI T, TSUJI A, YONEYAMA Y: Changes in intermediate haemoglobins during methaemoglobin reduction by NADPH-flavin reductase. *Biochem J* 179:227, 1979.

51. SCOTT EM, McGRAW JC: Purification and properties of diphosphopyridine nucleotide diaphorase of human erythrocytes. *J Biol Chem* 237:249, 1962.

52. SCOTT EM, DUNCAN IW, EKSTRAND V: The reduced pyridine nucleotide dehydrogenases of human erythrocytes. *J Biol Chem* 240:481, 1965.

53. HEGESH E, AVRON M: The enzymatic reduction of ferrihemoglobin. II. Purification of a ferrihemoglobin reductase from human erythrocytes. *Biochim Biophys Acta* 146:397, 1967.

54. NIETHAMMER D, HUENNEKENS FM: Electrophoretic separation and characterization of the multiple forms of methemoglobin reductase. *Arch Biochem Biophys* 146:564, 1971.

55. SUGITA Y, NOMURA S, YONEYAMA Y: Purification of reduced pyridine nucleotide dehydrogenase from human erythrocytes and methemoglobin reduction by the enzyme. *J Biol Chem* 246:6072, 1971.

56. PASSON PG, HULTQUIST DE: Soluble cytochrome b₅ reductase from human erythrocytes. *Biochim Biophys Acta* 275:62, 1972.

57. KUMA F, INOMATA H: Studies on methemoglobin reductase. II. The purification and molecular properties of reduced nicotinamide adenine dinucleotide-dependent methemoglobin reductase. *J Biol Chem* 247:556, 1972.

58. YUBISUI T, TAKESHITA M: Characterization of the purified NADH-cytochrome b₅ reductase of human erythrocytes as a FAD-containing enzyme. *J Biol Chem* 255:2454, 1980.

59. HEGESH E, AVRON M: The enzymatic reduction of ferrihemoglobin. I. The reduction of ferrihemoglobin in red blood cells and hemolysates. *Biochim Biophys Acta* 146:91, 1967.

60. REISS A, SCHWARTZ JS, PATEL S: Mechanism of the enzyme-dependent reduction of methemoglobin in the presence of NADH and ferrocyanide. *Blood* 50 suppl 1:84, 1977.

61. TAKETA F, CHEN JY: Activation of the NADH-methemoglobin reductase reaction by inositol hexaphosphate. *Biochem Biophys Res Commun* 75:389, 1977.

62. YUBISUI T, MIYATA T, IWANAGA S, TAMURA M, TAKESHITA M: Complete amino acid sequence of NADH-cytochrome b₅ reductase purified from human erythrocytes. *J Biochem (Tokyo)* 99:407, 1986.

63. TAKESHITA M, TAMURA M, KUGI M, YONEYAMA Y: Exponential decay of cytochrome b₅ and cytochrome b₅ reductase during senescence of erythrocytes: Relation to the increased methemoglobin content. *J Biochem (Tokyo)* 93:931, 1983.

64. YUBISUI T, TAMURA M, TAKESHITA M: Studies on NADH-cytochrome b₅ reductase activities in hemolysates of human and rabbit red cells by isoelectric focusing. *Biochem Biophys Res Commun* 102:860, 1981.

65. ZAMUDIO I, CANESSA M: Nicotinamide-adenine dinucleotide dehydrogenase activity of human erythrocyte membranes. *Biochim Biophys Acta* 120:165, 1966.

66. WANG C-S, ALAUPOVIC P: Isolation and parital characterization of human erythrocyte membrane NADH: (acceptor) oxidoreductase. *J Supramol Str* 9:1, 1978.

67. GOTO-TAMURA R, TAKESUE Y, TAKESUE S: Immunological similarity between NADH-cytochrome b₅ reductase of erythrocytes and liver microsomes. *Biochim Biophys Acta* 423:293, 1976.

68. CHOURY D, LEROUX A, KAPLAN J-C: Membrane-bound cytochrome b₅ reductase (methemoglobin reductase) in human erythrocytes. Study in normal and methemoglobinemic subjects. *J Clin Invest* 67:149:1981.

69. KITAJIMA S, YASUKOCHI Y, MINAKAMI S: Purification and properties of human erythrocyte membrane NADH-cytochrome b₅ reductase. *Arch Biochem Biophys* 210:330, 1981.

70. CHOURY D, REGHIS A, PICHARD A-L, KAPLAN J-C: Endogenous proteolysis

of membrane-bound red cell cytochrome b₅ reductase in adults and newborns: Its possible relevance to the generation of the soluble "methemoglobin reductase." *Blood* 61:894, 1983.

71. HULTQUIST DE, REED DW, PASSON PG: Isolation, characterization, and enzymatic reduction of cytochrome B (556) from human erythrocytes. *Fed Proc* 28:862, 1969.

72. PASSON PG, HULTQUIST DE: Participation of erythrocyte cytochrome b₅ in methemoglobin reduction and evidence for the occurrence of erythrocyte P-420. *Fed Proc* 29:732, 1970.

73. PASSON PG, REED DW, HULTQUIST DE: Soluble cytochrome b₅ from human erythrocytes. *Biochim Biophys Acta* 275:51, 1972.

74. HULTQUIST DE, DEAN RT, DOUBLAS RH: Homogeneous cytochrome b₅ from human erythrocytes. *Biochem Biophys Res Commun* 60:28, 1974.

75. CAPALNA S: The erythrocyte cytochrome b₅. *Physiologie* 14:85, 1977.

76. DOUGLAS RH, HULTQUIST DE: Evidence that two forms of bovine erythrocyte cytochrome b₅ are identical to segments of microsomal cytochrome b₅. *Proc Natl Acad Sci USA* 75:3118, 1978.

77. SLAUGHTER SR, HULTQUIST DE: Membrane-bound redox proteins of the murine Friend virus-induced erythroleukemia cell. *J Cell Biol* 83:231, 1979.

78. HULTQUIST DE, REED DW, PASSON PG, ANDREWS WE: Purification and properties of S-protein (hemoprotein 559) from human erythrocytes. *Biochim Biophys Acta* 229:33, 1971.

79. ABE K, SUGITA Y: Properties of cytochrome b₅ and methemoglobin reduction in human erythrocytes. *Eur J Biochem* 101:423, 1979.

80. ABE K, KIMURA S, KIZAWA R, ANAN FK, SUGITA Y: Amino acid sequences of cytochrome b₅ from human, porcine, and bovine erythrocytes and comparison with liver microsomal cytochrome b₅. *J Biochem (Tokyo)* 97:1659, 1985.

81. SLAUGHTER SR, WILLIAMS CH, HULTQUIST DE: Demonstration that bovine erythrocyte cytochrome b₅ is the hydrophilic segment of liver microsomal cytochrome b₅. *Biochim Biophys Acta* 705:228, 1982.

82. SCHAFER DA, HULTQUIST DE: Purification and structural studies of rabbit erythrocyte cytochrome b₅. *Biochem Biophys Res Commun* 115:807, 1983.

83. IMOTO M: The purification and primary structure of human erythrocyte cytochrome b₅. *Juzen Igakkai Zasshi* 86:256, 1977.

84. HULTQUIST DE, SLAUGHTER SR, DOUGLAS RH, SANNES LJ, SAHAGIAN GG: Erythrocyte cytochrome b₅: Structure, role in methemoglobin reduction, and solubilization from endoplasmic reticulum. *Prog Clin Biol Res* 21:199, 1978.

85. TAKESHITA M, YUBISUI T, TANISHIMA K, YONEYAMA Y: A simple enzymatic microdetermination of cytochrome b₅ in erythrocytes. *Anal Biochem* 107:305, 1980.

86. KAFTORY A, HEGESH E: Improved determination of cytochrome b₅ in human erythrocytes. *Clin Chem* 30:1344, 1984.

87. OZOLS J, STRITTMATTER P: Correction of the amino acid sequence of calf liver microsomal cytochrome b₅. *J Biol Chem* 244:6617, 1969.

88. LEROUX A, KAPLAN J-C: Presence of red cell type NADH-methemoglobin reductase (NADH-diaphorase) in human nonerythroid cells. *Biochem Biophys Res Commun* 49:945, 1972.

89. KUMA F, PROUGH RA, MASTERS BSS: Studies on methemoglobin reductase. Immunochemical similarity of soluble methemoglobin reductase and cytochrome b₅ of human erythrocytes with NADH-cytochrome b₅ reductase and cytochrome b₅ of rat liver microsomes. *Arch Biochem Biophys* 172:600, 1976.

90. LEROUX A, JUNIEN C, KAPLAN J-C, BAMBERGER J: Generalised deficiency of cytochrome b₅ reductase in congenital methaemoglobinemia with mental retardation. *Nature* 258:619, 1975.

91. HULTQUIST DE, SANNES LJ, SCHAFER DA: The NADH/NADPH-methemoglobin reduction system of erythrocytes. *Prog Clin Biol Res* 55:291, 1981.

92. HULTQUIST DE, PETERS CL, SCHAFER DA: Proteolytic generation of erythrocyte cytochrome b₅ and cytochrome b₅ reductase from endoplasmic reticulum (ER). *Proc XIth Intl Cong Biochem* 490, 1979.

93. YUBISUI T, NAITOH Y, ZENNO S, TAMURA M, TAKESHITA M, SAKAKI Y: Molecular cloning of cDNAs of human liver and placenta NADH-cytochrome b₅ reductase. *Proc Natl Acad Sci USA* 84:3609, 1987.

94. HULTQUIST DE, DOUGLAS RH, DEAN RT: The methemoglobin reduction system of erythrocytes. *Prog Clin Biol Res* 1:297, 1975.

95. SCHAFER DA, HULTQUIST DE: Isolation of an acid protease from rabbit reticulocytes and evidence for its role in processing redox proteins during erythroid maturation. *Biochem Biophys Res Commun* 100:1555, 1981.

96. SCHAFER DA, HULTQUIST DE: Isolation and characterization of cathepsin D from reticulocyte membranes. *Prog Clin Biol Res* 165:549, 1984.

97. RAW I, DiFINI F: The possible role of ATP-dependent proteolysis on the solubilization of methemoglobin reductase during reticulocyte maturation. *Biochim Biophys Res Commun* 116:357, 1983.

98. CHOURY D, WAJCMAN H, BOISSEL JP, KAPLAN J-C: Evidence for endoge-

nous proteolytic solubilization of human red-cell membrane NADH-cytochrome b$_5$ reductase. *FEBS Lett* 126:172, 1981.

99. PETRAGNANI N, NOGUEIRA OC, RAW I: Methaemoglobin reduction through cytochrome b$_5$. *Nature* 184:1651, 1959.

100. SANNES LJ, HULTQUIST DE: Effects of hemolysate concentration, ionic strength and cytochrome b$_5$ concentration on the rate of methemoglobin reduction in hemolysates of human erythrocytes. *Biochem Biophys Acta* 544:547, 1978.

101. TOMODA A, YUBISUI T, TSUJI A, YONEYAMA Y: Kinetic studies of methemoglobin reduction by human red cell NADH cytochrome b$_5$ reductase. *J Biol Chem* 254:3119, 1979.

102. KUMA F: Properties of methemoglobin reductase and kinetic study of methemoglobin reduction. *J Biol Chem* 256:5518, 1981.

103. JUCKETT DA, HULTQUIST DE: Magnetic circular dichroism studies of hemoglobin. The reduction of ferrihemoglobin by ferrocytochrome b$_5$ and characterization of the high-spin hydroxy species of mixed-valence hemoglobin. *Biophys Chem* 19:321, 1984.

104. HULTQUIST DE, SANNES LJ, JUCKETT DA: Catalysis of methemoglobin reduction, in DeLuca M, Lardy H, Cross RL (eds): *Current Topics in Cellular Regulation.* New York, Academic, 1984, vol 24, p 287.

105. LOSTANLEN D, GACON G, KAPLAN J-C: Direct enzyme titration curve of NADH:cytochrome b$_5$ reductase by combined isoelectric focusing/electrophoresis. *Eur J Biochem* 112:179, 1980.

106. STRITTMATTER P: NADH-cytochrome b$_5$ reductase, in Slater EC (ed): *Flavins and Flavoproteins.* New York, Elsevier, 1966, p 325.

107. DAILEY HA, STRITTMATTER P: Modification and identification of cytochrome b$_5$ carboxyl groups involved in protein-protein interaction with cytochrome b$_5$ reductase. *J Biol Chem* 254:5388, 1979.

108. RIGHETTI PG, GACON G, GIANAZZA E, LOSTANLEN D, KAPLAN J-C: Titration curves of interacting cytochrome b$_5$ and hemoglobin by isoelectric focusing-electrophoresis. *Biochem Biophys Res Commun* 85:1575, 1978.

109. MAUK MR, MAUK AG: Interaction between cytochrome b$_5$ and human methemoglobin. *Biochemistry* 21:4730, 1982.

110. MAUK MR, REID LS, MAUK AG: Conversion of oxyhaemoglobin into methaemoglobin by ferricytochrome b$_5$. *Biochem J* 221:297, 1984.

111. POULOS TL, MAUK AG: Models for the complexes formed between cytochrome b$_5$ and the subunits of methemoglobin. *J Biol Chem* 258:7369, 1983.

112. FINCH CA: Methemoglobinemia and sulfhemoglobinemia. *N Engl J Med* 239:470, 1948.

113. JAFFÉ ER: Enzymopenic hereditary methemoglobinemia: A clinical/biochemical classification. *Blood Cells* 12:81, 1986.

114. WORSTER-DROUGHT C, WHITE JC, SARGENT F: Familial idiopathic methemoglobinaemia associated with mental deficiency and neurological abnormalities. *Br Med J* 2:114, 1953.

115. KAPLAN JC, LEROUX A, BEAUVAIS P: Formes cliniques et biologiques du déficit en cytochrome b$_5$ réductase. *CR Seances Soc Biol* 173:368, 1979.

116. KAPLAN JC, LEROUX A, BAKOURI S, GRANGAUD JP, BENABADJI M: La lésion enzymatique dans la méthémoglobinémie congénitale récessive avec encéphalopathie. *Nouv Rev Fr Hematol* 14:755, 1974.

117. HIRONO H: Lipids of myelin, white matter and gray matter in a case of generalized deficiency of cytochrome b$_5$ reductase in congenital methemoglobinemia with mental retardation. *Lipids* 15:272, 1980.

118. HIRONO H: Lipids of liver, kidney, spleen and muscle in a case of generalized deficiency of cytochrome b$_5$ reductase in congenital methemoglobinemia with mental retardation. *Lipids* 19:60, 1984.

119. JUNIEN C, LEROUX A, LOSTANLEN D, REGHIS A, BOUE J, NICOLAS H, BOUE A, KAPLAN JC: Prenatal diagnosis of congenital enzymopenic methaemoglobinaemia with mental retardation due to generalized cytochrome b$_5$ reductase deficiency: First report of two cases. *Prenat Diagn* 1:17, 1981.

120. ARNOLD H, BÖTCHER HW, HUFNAGEL D, LÖHR GW: Hereditary methemoglobinemia due to methemoglobin reductase deficiency in erythrocytes and leukocytes without neurological symptoms. *Abstracts, XVII Congress of the International Society of Hematology,* Paris, 1978, p 752.

121. TANISHIMA K, TANIMOTO K, TOMODA A, MAWATARI K, MATSUKAWA S, YONEYAMA Y, OHKUWA H, TAKAZAKURA E: Hereditary methemoglobinemia due to cytochrome b$_5$ reductase deficiency in blood cells without associated neurologic and mental disorders. *Blood* 66:1288, 1985.

122. FISHER RA, POVEY S, BORROW M, SOLOMON E, BOYD Y, CARRITT B: Assignment of the DIA/1 locus to chromosome 22. *Ann Hum Genet* 41:151, 1977.

123. JUNIEN C, VIBERT M, WEIL D, VAN-CONG N, KAPLAN J-C: Assignment of NADH-cytochrome b$_5$ reductase (DIA$_1$ locus) to human chromosome 22. *Hum Genet* 42:233, 1978.

124. KAPLAN J-C, BEUTLER E: Electrophoresis of red cell NADH- and NADPH-diaphorases in human subjects and patients with congenital methemoglobinemia. *Biochem Biophys Res Commun* 29:605, 1967.

125. HOPKINSON DA, CORNEY G, COOK PJL, ROBSON EB, HARRIS H: Genetically determined electrophoretic variants of human red cell NADH diaphorase. *Ann Hum Genet* 34:1, 1970.

126. JAFFÉ ER: Methemoglobinemia in the differential diagnosis of cyanosis. *Hosp Pract* 20:92, 1985.

127. SCHWARTZ JM, PARESS PS, ROSS JM, DIPILLO F, RIZEK R: Unstable variant of NADH methemoglobin reductase in Puerto Ricans with hereditary methemoglobinemia. *J Clin Invest* 51:1594, 1972.

128. FEIG SA, NATHAN DG, GERALD PS, ZARKOWSKI HS: Congenital methemoglobinemia: The result of age-dependent decay of methemoglobin reductase. *Blood* 39:407, 1972.

129. BEUTLER E: Selectivity of proteases as a basis for tissue distribution of enzymes in hereditary deficiencies. *Proc Natl Acad Sci USA* 80:3767, 1983.

130. SHARP CW, STILLMAN RC: Blush not with nitrites. *Ann Intern Med* 92:700, 1980 (editorial).

131. HEGESH E, CALMANOVICI N, AVRON M: New method for determining ferrihemoglobin reductase (NADH-methemoglobin reductase) in erythrocytes. *J Lab Clin Med* 72:339, 1968.

132. BOARD PG: NADH-ferricyanide reductase, a convenient approach to the evaluation of NADH-methaemoglobin reductase in human erythrocytes. *Clin Chim Acta* 109:233, 1981.

133. KAPLAN J-C, NICOLAS AM, HANZLICKOVA-LEROUX A, BEUTLER E: A simple spot screening test for fast detection of red cell NADH-diaphorase deficiency. *Blood* 36:330, 1970.

134. KAPLAN JC, CHIROUZE M: Therapy of recessive congenital methaemoglobinaemia by oral riboflavine. *Lancet* 2:1043, 1978.

CHAPTER 93

THE HEMOGLOBINOPATHIES

D. J. WEATHERALL
J. B. CLEGG
D. R. HIGGS
W. G. WOOD

1. The inherited disorders of hemoglobin fall into three overlapping groups: structural variants; thalassemias, all characterized by a reduced rate of synthesis of one or more of the globin chains of hemoglobin; and conditions in which fetal hemoglobin synthesis persists beyond the neonatal period, known collectively as hereditary persistence of fetal hemoglobin. Taken together, they are the most common single gene disorders in the world population. Because they coexist at a high frequency in many populations and individuals may inherit more than one type, they are responsible for an extremely complex series of clinical phenotypes.

2. The molecular pathology of these disorders has been elucidated in many cases, and a start has been made in relating primary molecular defects to associated clinical phenotypes. The development of rapid methods for studying the globin genes has also made it possible to analyze their population genetics and the mechanisms that underlie their high gene frequencies.

3. Because the carrier states for most of the important hemoglobin disorders are easily identifiable, they are amenable to population control by prenatal diagnosis. There is no definitive treatment, and management is symptomatic.

The inherited disorders of hemoglobin are the most common single gene conditions in humans. Recently the World Health Organization has suggested that, at a conservative estimate, about 5 percent of the world's population are carriers for different inherited disorders of hemoglobin and that about 300,000 severely affected homozygotes or compound heterozygotes are born each year.[1] In the developing countries, in which there is still a very high mortality from infection and malnutrition in the first year of life, many of these conditions go unrecognized. However, as economic conditions improve and infant death rates fall, they pose an increasingly heavy burden on health services.

As the result of mass migrations of populations from high prevalence areas, the hemoglobin disorders are being seen with increasing frequency in parts of the world in which they have not been recognized previously. Because some of them, particularly sickle cell anemia and the more severe forms of thalassemia, can produce life-threatening medical emergencies or chronic ill health, it is important for clinicians in all countries of the world to have a working knowledge of their clinical features, genetic transmission, management, and, in particular, prevention. The other reason the hemoglobin disorders are of particular current interest is that they were the first diseases to be analyzed by the methods of recombinant DNA technology. More is known about their molecular pathology than about any other genetic disease, and it is likely that their study has already given us a relatively complete picture of the repertoire of mutations that underlie single gene disorders.

In this chapter we review the main clinical, genetic, and population aspects of these conditions. It is not possible to provide an all-encompassing picture of the enormous amount of work that has been carried out in this field. Those who wish to study this subject in greater depth are referred to two extensive monographs on the subject.[2,3]

HISTORICAL BACKGROUND

The fascinating story of the evolution and development of the human hemoglobin field has been the subject of several reviews and monographs that contain extensive bibliographies.[3–6]

In trying to understand why the human hemoglobin field has paved the way for the application of molecular biology to the study of human disease, it is helpful to trace three historical threads that finally came together in the 1950s. The first is the story of the discovery of hemoglobin and the elucidation of its structure and function. The second encompasses the early description of sickle cell anemia, the realization that it is an inherited disease, and the characterization of its molecular pathology. And, finally, there is the even more complex saga of the gradual amalgamation of observations from many parts of the world that led to the notion that the thalassemias are also genetic disorders of hemoglobin with many features in common with the structural hemoglobin variants. The final chapter of this biologic detective story is not yet complete. However, given all this diverse information and the new tools of molecular and cell biology, it has been possible in less than 10 years to describe so much of the molecular pathology of hemoglobin that, at the time of writing, it is likely that we already have a very good idea about the repertoire of the molecular defects that underlie single gene disorders.

Following the studies of William Harvey on the circulation of the blood, two English workers, Robert Boyle and the Oxford eccentric Richard Lower, established that the function of the pulmonary circulation is to aerate venous blood. The mechanism of the binding of oxygen to blood was a subject of intense interest during the second half of the nineteenth century, and in 1862 Hoppe-Seyler first used the term *hemoglobin* to describe the oxygen-carrying pigment. The structure of heme was worked out by Kuster in 1912, but it was not until the mid-1950s, following pioneering work on protein structure by Sanger, that Ingram, Rhinesmith, Schroeder, Pauling, and others established that hemoglobin is a tetramer composed of two pairs of unlike peptide chains, α and β. Using the newly developed techniques of amino acid sequence analysis the primary structures of these chains were rapidly determined. At the same time Perutz and his colleagues, after years of painstaking work, were gradually arriving at a solution for the three-dimensional structure of hemoglobin by x-ray analysis. Thus by the early 1960s a start could be made in relating the structure of hemoglobin to its functional properties, as elegantly described by Bohr and Krogh in Denmark; Barcroft, Haldane, Hill, and Roughton in England; and Henderson in the United States.

This new knowledge, together with the discovery of the abnormal hemoglobins, led to rapid progress toward an understanding of the genetic control of human hemoglobin. But part of the work that laid the basis for this remarkably productive period of hemoglobin research had started half a century before with the discovery of sickle cell anemia.

The first description of sickle cell anemia appeared in 1910 in Herrick's classic paper.[7] The genetic basis of this disease was established by workers in the United States, particularly Neel, and in Africa, notably by the Lambotte-Legrands and Beet. The discovery that sickle cell anemia results from a structural change in hemoglobin, following the famous conversation between Castle and Pauling in 1945, was announced by Pauling and his colleagues in 1949,[8] and the amino acid substitution in Hb S was determined by Ingram in 1956.[9] Once it was realized that there are two globin chains, α and β, and that the amino acid substitution in sickle hemoglobin is in the β chain, the one gene/one enzyme (or peptide chain) concept, which had been proposed earlier by Beadle and Tatum from their work on *Neurospora*, was confirmed for higher organisms. More hemoglobin variants were soon discovered by electrophoresis, and, by studying families in which genes for both α- and β-globin variants segregated, the independent genetic control of the α and β chains was established. The different chains of fetal and the adult minor hemoglobin, A_2, were characterized, and by careful analysis of families with different genetic variants, and appropriate linkage studies, a reasonable working model of the order of the α-like and β-like globin genes on their respective chromosomes was obtained.

The third thread in the story starts in 1927 with the first description of thalassemia by Cooley and Lee.[10] Although the carrier state for this condition was probably identified at about the same time in Italy,[6] it was more than a quarter of a century before the genetic transmission of thalassemia was fully appreciated. During this period reports of the disease appeared from all over the world, and as soon as hemoglobin analysis became part of the armamentarium of clinicians during the 1950s it was soon realized that thalassemia is not only one of the most common genetic diseases but also extremely heterogeneous. Studies of the hemoglobin patterns of patients with different types of thalassemia and structural hemoglobin variants carried out in the late 1950s led to the suggestion by Ingram and Stretton[11] that there might be two main types, α and β thalassemia. The development of a method for studying hemoglobin synthesis in the test tube[12,13] led to the experimental validation of this hypothesis and to the further analysis of thalassemia, so that by the early 1970s it was known that there are many different forms, and it was also possible to make a guess at their underlying defects.

Thus by the mid-1970s a great deal was known about the genetic control of human hemoglobin, the structural variants, and the biosynthetic defects and remarkable heterogeneity of the thalassemias. The field was ready for the techniques of recombinant DNA. Over the last 10 years these methods have been used successfully to determine the molecular pathology of the globin disorders, so paving the way toward an understanding of the molecular basis for many single gene disorders.

THE STRUCTURE, GENETIC CONTROL, AND SYNTHESIS OF HEMOGLOBIN

Structure

All normal hemoglobins (Hb) have a tetrameric structure consisting of two pairs of unlike peptide chains (Fig. 93-1). In normal adults the major component, constituting about 97 percent of the total, is Hb A ($\alpha_2\beta_2$) with the remainder being Hb A_2 ($\alpha_2\delta_2$). The main hemoglobin in fetal life is Hb F ($\alpha_2\gamma_2$) (although traces of it (≈ 0.5 percent) are found in adults), and this is preceded in the embryo by Hb Gower 1 ($\zeta_2\epsilon_2$), Hb Gower 2 ($\alpha_2\epsilon_2$), and Hb Portland ($\zeta_2\gamma_2$). There are also various minor components that are the result of postsynthetic modifications that take place in vivo. The most common of these are Hb A_{Ic}, formed by reaction of glucose with hemoglobin, and Hb F_I, an acetylated form of fetal hemoglobin. The amino acid sequences of all the normal globins are known, and they are clearly related to each other, retaining many key features in common. Broadly speaking, they can be regarded as α-like (ζ and α, each of 141 amino acids) and β-like (ϵ, γ, δ, and β, 146 amino acids), and it appears that they arose from a single ancestral globin by successive duplications and divergence of the duplicated genes (see below, "The Hemoglobin Genes").

The three-dimensional structure of human hemoglobin has been determined by Perutz and colleagues to a resolution better than 2.7 Å by x-ray crystallography.[14,15] It consists of an ellipsoid approximately $64 \times 55 \times 50$ Å in which the subunits are oriented in a unit with a twofold symmetry axis running down a central water-filled cavity. Seventy-five percent of the native hemoglobin molecule is in the form of an α helix. Where the α-helix is interrupted (for example, by a proline residue) the polypeptide chains can turn corners, thus enabling them to fold and take up the compact shape seen in the tetrameric molecule. Within the tetramer individual polypeptide chains have only a limited contact with each other, and there is relatively little interaction between them compared with the forces that maintain their individual secondary and tertiary structures. The individual subunit chains of Hb have similar three-dimensional structures, with analogous helical segments. Eight helical regions (A to H) are present in the β chain and seven in α, which lacks a region corresponding to the β-chain D helix. Amino acids can thus be identified with specific helical positions.

The interiors of the subunits are made up almost entirely of nonpolar (hydrophobic) residues, which contact neighboring residues by low energy, short range (van der Waal's) forces. All the side chains that are ionizable under normal physiological conditions are on the surface of the subunits, as are most of the polar (hydrophilic) side groups. The exterior surface of hemoglobin is thus covered with polar groups that generally interact with water rather than other hydrophilic groups.

Oxygen Binding

Binding of oxygen to hemoglobin is mediated by the prosthetic group, heme, a ferroporphyrin molecule in which the iron atom is located at the center of the porphyrin ring (Fig. 93-2). The heme is situated within clefts in the globin subunits that are lined with nonpolar residues and lies between two histidines, one of which (the "proximal" histidine) is bonded directly to the heme iron atom through the nitrogen atom of

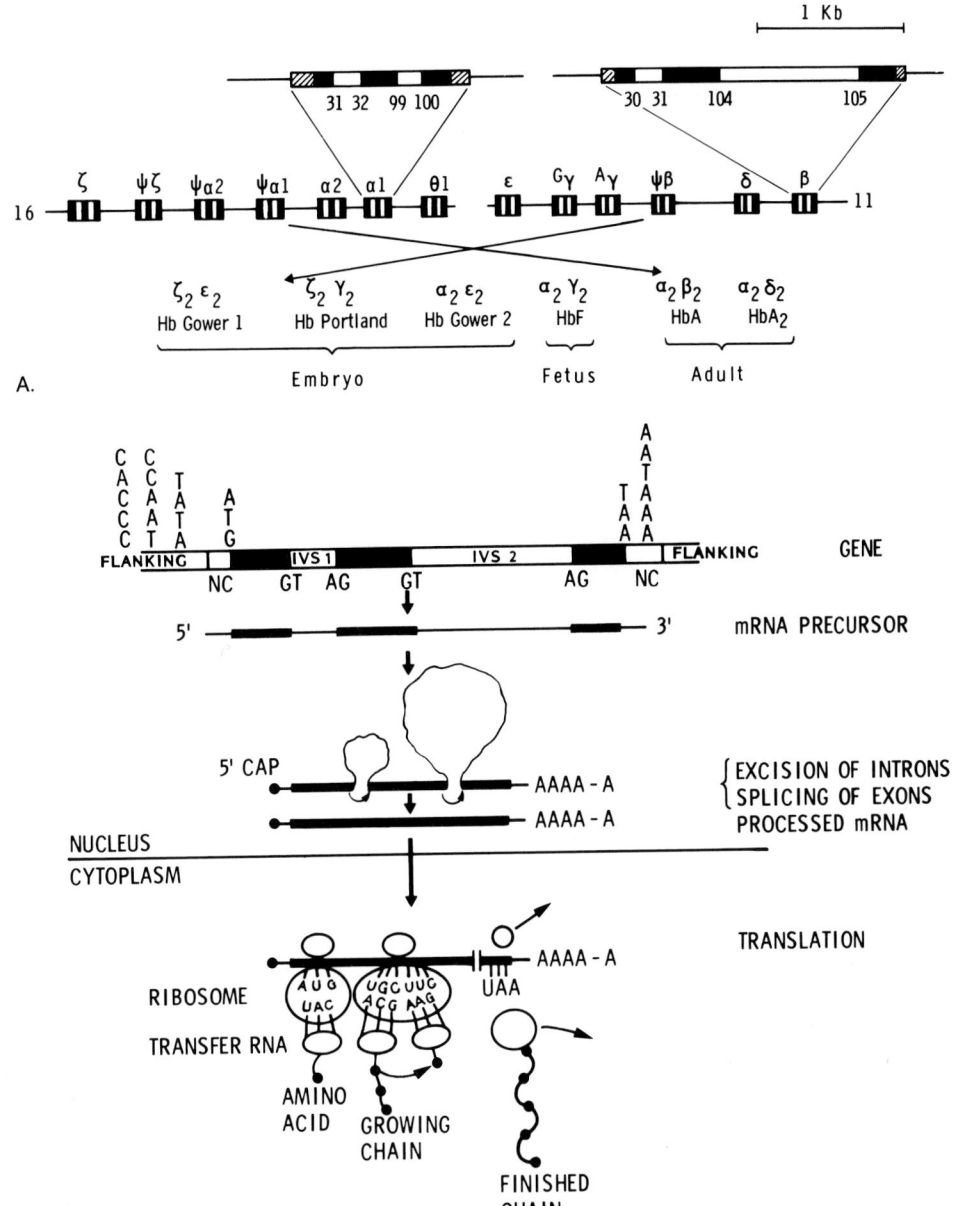

Fig. 93-1 The genetic control of human hemoglobin. *A.* The human hemoglobins and globin gene clusters. *B.* The mechanism of globin synthesis. The exons are shown in dark shading and the introns (IVS 1 and IVS 2) unshaded. The positions of the 5′ regulatory boxes and the 5′ and 3′ noncoding (NC) regions are also shown.

its imidazole group, while the other "distal" histidine lies opposite the oxygen binding site, but is not directly attached to the heme (Fig. 93-2). The orientation of the heme within the pocket allows its nonpolar vinyl groups to be buried within the hydrophobic interior while the polar proprionic acid groups reside on the hydrophilic surface of the globin subunit. A large number of interatomic contacts (<4 Å) between the heme and side chains of amino acid residues of the E and F helices stabilize this structure.

The residues that surround the heme group are invariant throughout the animal kingdom, suggesting a highly conservative structure that is essential if it is to function normally as an oxygen carrier. Indeed, hemoglobin variants with mutations in the heme pocket often show profound alterations in their stability or oxygen-binding properties.

There is a marked difference in the three-dimensional structures of the oxy and deoxy forms of hemoglobin, implying that the subunit chains change their relative orientation with re-

spect to each other during oxygenation and vice versa. In the tetramer each α chain is in contact with the two β chains; the two contacts can thus be defined as $\alpha_1\beta_1$ and $\alpha_1\beta_2$, and the twofold symmetry generates the structurally identical $\alpha_2\beta_1$ and $\alpha_2\beta_2$ contacts (Fig. 93-3). Most of the movement during oxygenation-deoxygenation takes place at the $\alpha_1\beta_2$ ($\alpha_2\beta_1$) interfaces, while the $\alpha_1\beta_1$ ($\alpha_2\beta_2$) interfaces remain relatively immobile, in keeping with the much greater number of contacts (40) at the latter interface compared with the 17 at the weaker $\alpha_1\beta_2$ interface.[16]

Good contacts between subunits can be made only when key regions of the two $\alpha\beta$ dimers are in the same relative orientation, thus favoring the formation of two specific quaternary states, oxy or "relaxed" (R) and deoxy or "tense" (T), without any stable intermediates.[17,18] Owing to the movement that occurs at the $\alpha_1\beta_2$ interface, the nature and number of contacts change during oxygenation-deoxygenation. In the deoxy state there are about 40 contacts (which include 19 hydrogen

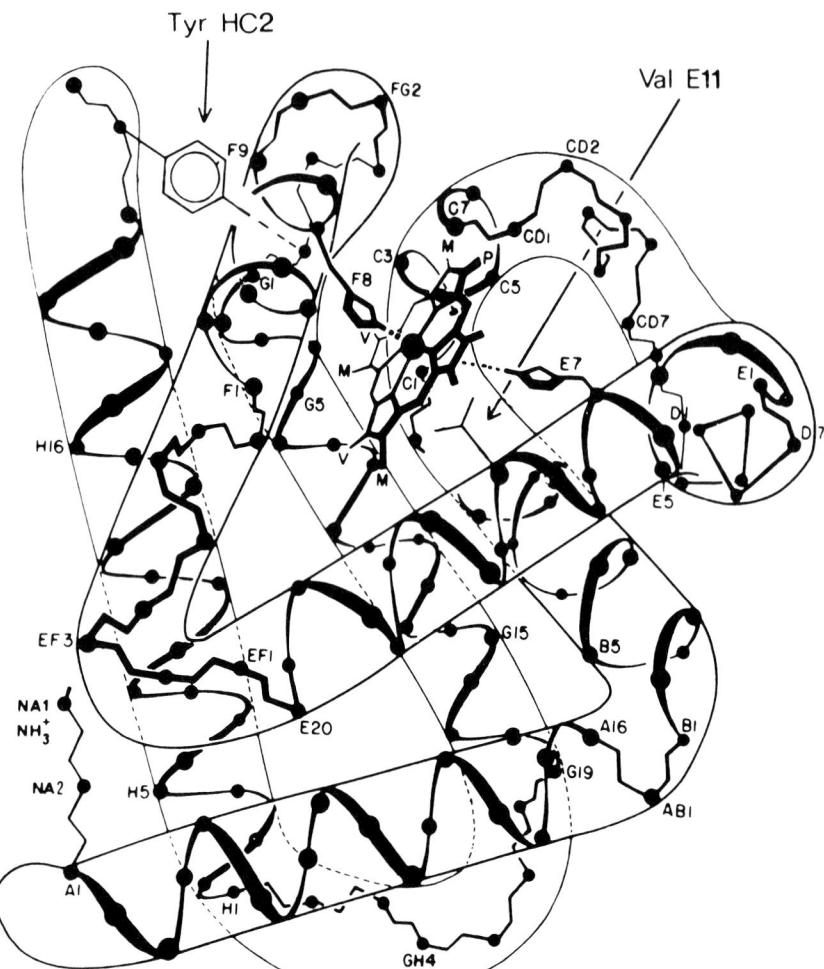

Tyr HC2

Val E11

Fig. 93-2 The α-globin subunit showing the structure and relationships of the heme pocket.

bonds), and this drops by almost a half (to 22 and 12, respectively) in the oxy state. Not surprisingly, the $\alpha_1\beta_2$ contact, like the heme pocket, is a highly conserved structure, which has been retained unchanged through long periods of evolutionary time. Mutations involving residues in this contact can have drastic functional consequences.

Deoxyhemoglobin has a more stable quaternary structure than oxyhemoglobin because of the increased number of contacts at the $\alpha_1\beta_2$ interface, and because there are additional inter- and intrasubunit salt linkages that are absent or much weaker in oxyhemoglobin. Thus the carboxyl group of the C-terminal arginine of one α chain interacts with the ϵ-amino group of a lysine residue at position 132 (H10) in the other α-chain, and the guanidine group of this same C-terminal arginine interacts with the carboxyl group of the aspartic acid residue at position 131 (H9) of the other α chain. There is also a chloride ion-mediated link between the C-terminal guanidine group and the opposite α chain's α-NH$_2$ group. None of these α-α salt linkages can be formed in oxyhemoglobin because of steric hindrance effects.[18] In a similar manner the β-chain C-terminal histidines are involved in two interactions: through the imidazole group with the aspartate residue at position 94 (FG1) of the same β chain, and through the carboxyl group with the ϵ-NH$_2$ group of lysine α40 (C5) forming a salt bridge that spans the $\alpha_1\beta_2$ interface. In oxyhemoglobin these residues are displaced too far for these interactions to occur, and no salt bridges are formed.

Physiological measurements indicate that there is a free energy change of 10 to 12 cal/mol of tetramer upon the transition of oxy to deoxy states, a figure in accordance with the energy estimated to reside in the salt bridges of 1 to 2 cal per bond. The salt bridges thus represent a considerable reservoir of stored energy, maintaining the deoxyhemoglobin molecule in a high-energy, or tense (T), state.

Structure-Function Relationships

The role of hemoglobin as oxygen carrier depends on its ability to absorb and release oxygen in response to the relatively small changes in partial pressures encountered under physiological conditions. The function of oxygen bound versus partial pressure is sigmoid, a property that depends crucially on a heterotetrameric structure [it does not occur in monomeric myoglobin or in the homotetrameric hemoglobins H(β_4) and Barts (γ_4)] and that is achieved by cooperative interactions between the heme groups as the oxygenation at one enhances the subsequent O$_2$ binding at others. Hemoglobin thus behaves as an allosteric molecule. In addition, O$_2$ binding is influenced by the interaction of small molecules such as 2,3-diphosphoglycerate (2,3-DPG) and is sensitive to changes in pH, a phenomenon known as the Bohr effect.

Heme-Heme Interaction. The heme-heme interaction that promotes the cooperative binding of oxygen is dependent on small rearrangements that occur when oxygen is taken up. During oxygenation the β-chain hemes move apart by about 7 Å in a process that is dependent on interactions between the

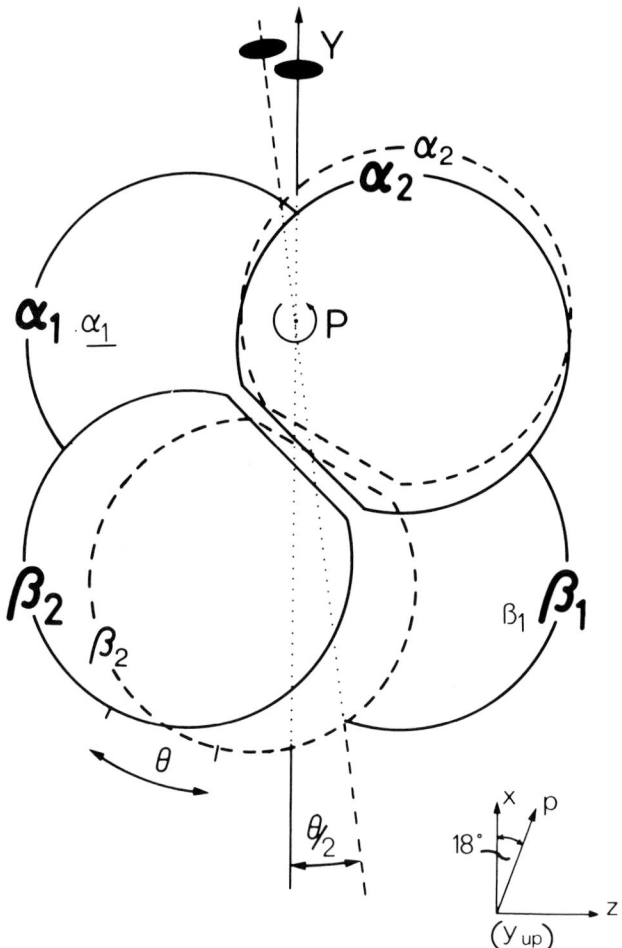

Fig. 93-3 Schematic diagram of quaternary structure of hemoglobin and the relative changes in orientation of the subunits during oxygenation. Bold: deoxy; light: oxy. (*From Haemoglobin and Myoglobin by G. Fermi and M.F. Perutz, Oxford University Press. Used by permission.*)

α and β subunits. It is likely that the $\alpha_1\beta_2$ contact is particularly important in these cooperative interactions. The three-dimensional structure indicates that α_1 and β_2 (or α_2 and β_1) subunits can have much more direct interaction than can α_1 and β_1 (or α_2 and β_2). Furthermore, oxygenation of the β_2 subunit causes it to rotate much more with respect to α_1 than does oxygenation of the β_1 subunit. And, as we have seen earlier, the overall structure of the $\alpha_1\beta_2$ contact has remained invariant throughout mammalian evolution. Most Hb variants with abnormalities in heme-heme interactions have mutations in or close to the $\alpha_1\beta_2$ interface.

The molecular origin for the conformational changes that take place in the subunits during oxygenation lies in the heme molecule. When there is no O_2 molecule bound, the atomic diameter of the iron atom is too great to allow it to sit flush in the plane of the porphyrin ring and it is thus displaced 0.6 Å toward the proximal histidine residue. When the heme iron binds oxygen, the resulting changes in the distribution of electrons orbiting the iron atom nucleus lead to an effective reduction in its atomic diameter and it can move into the plane of the porphyrin ring. This movement results in a tilt of the heme in its pocket, and this is amplified as a change in the tertiary structure of the subunit which ultimately pushes the penultimate tyrosine from between the F and H helices, resulting in rupture of the C-terminal salt bridges. The transition of the quaternary structure from the deoxy (T) to oxy

(R) conformation occurs abruptly as the salt bridges successively break apart, and constraints on the $\alpha_1\beta_2$ interface are relaxed. Since the α-subunit hemes are relatively more accessible to oxygen, they are probably oxygenated first. The shift from T to R structure then opens up the clefts of the unliganded β-chain hemes, greatly increasing their affinity for oxygen.

Modification of Oxygen Binding Properties by 2,3-DPG. Some organic phosphates increase the stability of deoxyhemoglobin. In human erythrocytes the major effector of this type is 2,3-diphosphoglycerate (2,3-DPG).[19,20] This binds specifically to the β chains of hemoglobin in the T state through electrostatic bonds between the 2,3-DPG phosphate groups and the N-terminal amino and imidazole groups of the β2 and β143 histidine residues and the ε-amino group of β82 lysine.[21] When the structure changes from the T to the R state the bound 2,3-DPG molecules are released because the β-chain H helices are now too close and the N-terminal amino groups too far apart for the 2,3-DPG to bind. Thus 2,3-DPG and oxygen binding are mutually exclusive, and the overall effect is that 2,3-DPG reduces the oxygen affinity of hemoglobin by stabilizing the deoxy (T) form. The cellular concentration of 2,3-DPG thus has an important influence on oxygen affinity. Differences in oxygen affinity between fetal and adult red cells are largely due to the fact that 2,3-DPG has only a weak affinity for deoxyhemoglobin F.[22,23]

The Bohr Effect. The binding of oxygen to hemoglobin is sensitive to changes in pH, a phenomenon that has physiological importance through its effects on the transport of CO_2 in the blood. Carbon dioxide released on respiration is too insoluble to be transported in any quantity in the blood except as bicarbonate ion, produced by reaction with water.

$$CO_2 + H_2O \rightarrow HCO_3^- + H^+$$

The released protons can combine with hemoglobin, forcing the reaction toward bicarbonate formation. Protons stabilize the deoxy state of the hemoglobin molecule, thus favoring oxygen release in the tissues. On oxygen binding (in the lungs) the converse occurs. Protons are released, driving the bicarbonate/CO_2 reaction toward CO_2 formation and thus release from the blood. The Bohr effect therefore mediates a reciprocal CO_2/O_2 exchange.[24,25]

Hemoglobin is also responsible for the direct transport of about 10 percent of respired CO_2 through the formation of a carbamate linkage with the N-terminal amino groups. Since CO_2 binds more readily to the deoxy form, this again facilitates the removal of CO_2 from the circulation.

The Hemoglobin Genes

Organization and Chromosomal Location. Six different types of globin chain (α, β, γ, δ, ε, ζ) are found in normal human hemoglobins at different stages of development, thus requiring as a minimum six different structural genes. Genetic analysis of families in which abnormal Hb variants were segregating established that the α- and β-globin genes were on separate chromosomes, and that it was likely that the fetal and adult non-α genes were present in a single cluster. The relationships between the amino acid sequences of the ζ and α chains, and ε, γ, δ, and β chains suggested that they had arisen by successive duplications and divergences of ancestral genes.

The localization of these groups of genes to specific chromosomes was achieved by the use of hybrid rodent/human somatic cell lines containing one or a few human chromosomes. The α-gene cluster was found on chromosome 16 and the β-like genes on chromosome 11[26–28] (Fig. 93-1). These assignments have been refined by *in situ* hybridization studies and by gene mapping of cell lines containing different translocations and deletions. Such analyses place the β-like cluster distal to band p14 on the short arm of chromosome 11,[29–33] and the α-like cluster in band 16p13.1.[34,35]

Restriction enzyme mapping of genomic DNA coupled with fine structure mapping of cloned DNA from the globin gene complexes on chromosomes 11 and 16 has enabled a very detailed picture to be built up of the precise chromosomal organization of the two complexes. The conclusions that had been reached by conventional genetic and structural analyses of hemoglobin variants have been vindicated by the molecular analyses and in addition the loci for the embryonic ζ and ε genes have been found to be linked to the clusters containing the adult genes (Fig. 93-1).[36–38]

Unexpectedly, other genes or genelike structures, unsuspected prior to these molecular analyses and with considerable structural homology to the "real" genes, have been identified within the clusters, one (ψβ[39,40]) between the ^Aγ and δ genes and no fewer than four (ψζ,[41] ψα1,[38] ψα2,[42] and θ1[43]) in the α cluster (Fig. 93-1). These (nonfunctional) genes are designated pseudogenes and are thought to be relics of past evolutionary changes within the globin gene clusters.

Evolution. By comparing the nucleotide sequences of the genes and using estimates of the average rates of nucleotide substitution derived from species comparisons, it is possible to establish an evolutionary history for the human globin genes. Various estimates put the time of α- and β-gene divergence from a single ancestral gene at approximately 450 million years (my) ago, during early vertebrate evolution.[44] In birds and mammals the α- and β-gene clusters subsequently became established on different chromosomes. The ζ-α gene split (400 my) was probably the most ancient of the subsequent duplications[44] followed by β/γ at 200 my, and γ/ε at 100 my.[45] The δ/β divergence appears at 40 my, although this is probably the time of a gene conversion following on from a much more ancient event.[46] Duplication of the α genes, like the ζ-α split, appears to have been a relatively early event, while the γ duplication is more recent, with the subsequent near-identity of the two α genes and two γ genes being maintained by rounds of gene conversion. From this history it can be inferred that developmental patterns of hemoglobin synthesis have changed considerably during evolution, presumably a reflection in part of the changing physiological and environmental circumstances that hemoglobin has had to respond to.

It can be seen from Fig. 93-1 that the globin genes are arranged in the order in which they are expressed and are all in the same transcriptional orientation. The significance of this, which is a feature of many (but not all, chicken and goat are exceptions) animal species, in terms of the developmental changes in gene expression that take place during development is at present unclear.

Individual Variation of Globin Gene Structure. The effort involved in producing very fine structure (down to the nucleotide level) maps of the globin gene clusters has been consid-

erable. Consequently, most of the sequence information available has come from intensive analyses of just one or two chromosomes, and it gives little indication of the variation that might be found if large numbers of individuals are studied. The initial indications that sequence variations might be relatively common came from the work of Jeffreys[47] who found two *Hind*III polymorphisms in the γ genes of a number of individuals and estimated that perhaps 1 percent of nucleotide sites might be polymorphic. Subsequent studies have shown many such polymorphisms spread throughout the globin gene clusters. Some of these are common and present in all racial groups, while others may have a much more restricted distribution.

Of particular interest and importance is the fact that in general the polymorphisms do not normally occur in association with each other in a random fashion, rather they are present in linked groups called *haplotypes*[48,49] (Fig. 93-4). Within any given population there are usually a small number of haplotypes that are common and a larger number of rarer haplotypes, only some of which are clearly related to the more common types, for example by a difference at a single site. The frequency and types of haplotype present in various populations can provide some interesting insights into racial affinities and evolution.[49,50] At a more practical level, the fact that haplotypes exist at all implies that within the region defined by the restriction enzyme cleavage sites constituting the haplotype, there has been little if any recombination between chromosomes (since, if there had been, the nonrandom association between polymorphic sites would have been destroyed). The knowledge that these chromosome arrangements are relatively stable has thus enabled the polymorphisms constituting the various haplotypes to be used in linkage analysis of hereditary disorders affecting globin genes. For example, establishing the particular haplotype carrying a β-thalassemia defect enables the affected chromosome to be followed within a pedigree, and it can also be used for prenatal diagnostic purposes by analysis of DNA from fetuses at risk.[51,52]

Although the features of the α- and β-like clusters noted in Fig. 93-1 are the norm, many examples are now known of individuals with various rearrangements within the clusters, most of which have little or no phenotypic effects of clinical significance. Most often seen are the variations in copy number of those genes that are usually duplicated (or have an associated, nearly identical, pseudogene such as ζ). Thus many individuals with triplicated ζ,[53] γ,[54] and α[55] genes have been documented and even quadruplicate α and γ arrangements are known. Likewise, there are numerous examples of single ζ-[53] (i.e., lacking ψζ), α-,[56,57] and γ-[58] gene chromosomes that have probably arisen through unequal crossing-over events. While most of these rearrangements are found at very low frequency in most populations, the single α-gene chromosomes are extremely common in many tropical countries because they appear to be at a selective advantage in malarial environments[59,60] (see below).

Rare cases of homogenization of the ^Gγ or ^Aγ genes, to form ^Gγ-^Gγ or ^Aγ-^Aγ arrangements,[61] are also known, possibly the result of localized gene conversion events.

Structural Features of Globin Genes. Since 1977 it has been apparent that the coding regions of most mammalian genes, and globin genes are no exception, are interrupted by stretches of noncoding DNA, usually referred to as *intervening sequence*, or *intron DNA*. All globin genes possess two introns in identical positions relative to the coding sequence but of variable

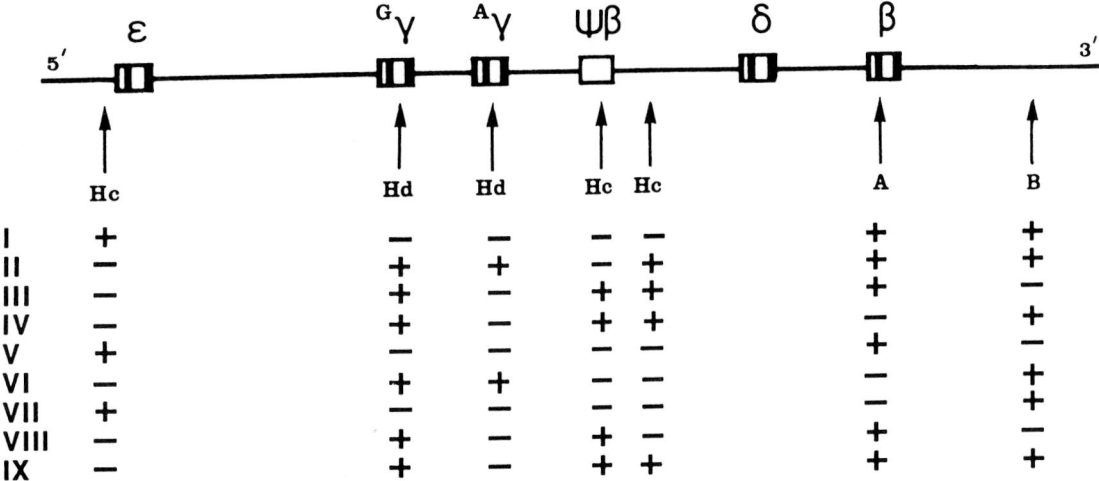

	ε		$^G\gamma$	$^A\gamma$	ψβ		δ	β	
	Hc		Hd	Hd	Hc	Hc		A	B
I	+		−	−	−	−		+	+
II	−		+	+	−	+		+	+
III	−		+	−	+	+		+	−
IV	−		+	−	+	+		−	+
V	+		−	−	−	−		+	−
VI	−		+	+	−	−		−	+
VII	+		−	−	−	−		+	+
VIII	−		+	−	+	−		+	−
IX	−		+	−	+	+		+	+

Fig. 93-4 Polymorphic restriction sites in the human β-globin complex and nine of the common haplotypes derived from them.

length, the shortest being the first intron (IVS1) of the α genes at 117 bp and the largest of 1264 bp in IVS1 of the ζ gene. The fact that introns are found in identical positions in all globin genes suggests that they were in place before the expansion of the globin gene repertoire from an ancestral gene took place. Molecular sequence analysis of the β-like genes reveals little or no homology among the larger IVS2 introns, except in the case of the duplicated $^G\gamma$ and $^A\gamma$ genes, and variable homology among the smaller IVS1 introns. Within the α-like genes, the duplicated α_1 and α_2 genes show considerable homology between IVS1 and IVS2 of those genes but very little with the linked upstream ζ gene or the ψζ gene.

Comparisons of the sequences of introns from many different genes reveal only a few common features, most notably in the sequences immediately adjacent to and around the coding sequences they interrupt[62] and a sequence 20 to 40 bases from the 3′ end involved in the formation of the branched splicing intermediate. Intron sequences are removed from (spliced out of) the initial precursor mRNA transcript in order to form the final mature mRNA product and the necessary signals for correct splicing reside at the 5′ (consensus sequence ^C_AAG ↓ GU^A_GAGU) and 3′ (consensus $^{(U)}_{(C)}$X$^{(C)}_U$AG ↓ G) ends of the introns.[63] The importance of these sequences is illustrated by the fact that mutations within them can interfere with, or even abolish, correct splicing, leading to abnormal processing of globin mRNA precursors, the molecular basis of a number of the thalassemias (see below).

The regions flanking the coding sequences of globin genes contain a number of sequence motifs that are necessary for correct expression[64] (Fig. 93-1B). The first of these is the *ATA* box, which serves to accurately locate the site of transcription initiation at the *cap* site, usually about 30 bases downstream, and which also appears to influence the level of transcription,[45] since natural mutations within the ATA region can reduce transcription quite markedly. Seventy or eighty base pairs upstream is a second conserved sequence, the *CCAAT* box. (In δ the sequence is CCAAC, and the γ genes have a duplicated structure.) In model systems, mutations introduced into CCAAT sequences also lead to reductions in the level of transcription.[45,65] Further 5′, approximately 80 to 100 bp from the cap site, is a GC-rich region with general structure GGGG^T_CG or C^A_GCCCC, which can be inverted and/or duplicated. These sequences resemble those required for optimal transcription of the SV40 early region, and mutations with this region in β-globin genes adversely affect expression.[66,67]

Other nonglobin mammalian genes contain similar conserved sequences upstream of the mRNA cap sites, each of which has been shown to be necessary for normal gene expression, presumably because they provide binding sites or regulatory signals for RNA polymerase II. In vitro experiments involving modification or deletion of the sequences confirm this, and natural mutations within them may result in decreased expression of the associated gene (see below).

Globin Gene Expression. The mechanism of protein synthesis in eukaryotes has been elucidated in considerable detail (for reviews see Refs. 68 to 74). In this section, only those aspects of globin gene expression that are particularly relevant to the molecular basis of the hemoglobinopathies are considered.[64]

Transcription of the globin genes initiates at the cap site, which is ≈50 bp upstream of the AUG initiation codon and which becomes the 5′ end of the mature mRNA after processing. Although mature mRNA terminates 10 to 20 bp downstream of the AATAAA polyadenylation signal, there is evidence from in vitro studies that the initial transcript may run well beyond this site and that the specific cleavage distal to the polyadenylation signal takes place subsequently. Supporting this is evidence from a case of β thalassemia with a mutation in the AATAAA sequence,[75] in which elongated β-gene transcripts were observed in RNA isolated from erythroid cells of the affected individual and in vitro experiments on a similar case of α thalassemia.[76]

The large initial precursor mRNA transcript is rapidly processed after synthesis. The first events—capping the 5′ end and polyadenylation of the 3′ end—probably serve to stabilize the transcript and prevent attack by exonucleases. Capping involves a GTP-mediated modification of the 5′ residue, usually an A, to form a 5′ppp5′ linkage, while polyadenylation, as the term implies, results in the addition of a long string of A residues (>50) to the 3′ end of the transcript formed by cleavage of the initial precursor 10 to 20 bp downstream of the AATAAA signal.

Subsequent to these steps the intervening sequences are removed from the pre-mRNA in a two-stage process. In the first, pre-mRNA is cut at the 5′ splice site to generate two intermediates—a linear first exon and a branched lariat-type molecule containing the intron and second exon. In the second step, the 3′ splice site is cleaved, the lariat intron released, and the two exons joined.[63] Introns may be removed in a sequential manner until the mature mRNA is produced. This is then transported from the nucleus into the cytoplasm where ribosomal translation of mRNA into globin can take place.

The details of the translation phase of protein synthesis are well known and have been extensively reviewed.[68–74] The synthesis of globin closely follows the pattern of other eukaryotic proteins; indeed, many aspects of the general mechanism were elucidated with cell-free systems synthesizing rabbit globins.

Regulation of Globin Gene Expression. Little is known of the mechanisms responsible for achieving the tissue-specific expression of the globin genes. Since globin genes have the same structure in all cells and are capable of being expressed in any cell, while globin synthesis is confined to erythroid cells, mechanisms must exist to achieve this specificity and to ensure that globin genes are expressed at the correct phase of erythroid cell development. While the precise mechanism remains to be elucidated, some important features that differentiate expressed from nonexpressed genes have been discovered.

METHYLATION. The methylation state of a gene has an important influence on its ability to be expressed, and as a general but not exclusive rule actively transcribed genes are almost always hypomethylated and vice versa.[77,78] Methylation mostly occurs at the C residue of CG dinucleotide sequences; nearly three quarters of all human CG sequences are, in fact, methylated.

In human and other animal tissues, globin genes are found to be extensively methylated in nonerythroid tissues and to be relatively undermethylated when they are being expressed.[64] For example, in the 5' flanking region of the human γ genes, CG sites within the CCAAT-ATA region are hypomethylated in fetal liver erythroid cells but become methylated in adult bone marrow, where HbF expression is effectively turned off. In vitro experiments also indicate that methylation of γ genes in the 5' flanking region can effectively prevent their expression in tissue culture cells. While hypomethylation of 5' flanking DNA appears to be a necessary prerequisite for normal globin gene expression, it appears not to be the primary signal for expression, since situations are known where globin genes are hypomethylated but not expressed. Methylation state is thus more of a permissive control on gene expression than a positive expression signal.

CHROMATIN. Genes in mammalian cells are present not as simple strands of DNA, but complexed with histones and other proteins in chromatin. One of the consequences of this packaging of DNA is that the transcriptional activity of the genome can be quite limited, such that in erythroid cells for example, only a few percent of the total DNA sequences capable of being expressed are active, among them the globin genes. Some of this selectivity is achieved by gross alterations in chromatin structure which can be revealed experimentally by an increased sensitivity to digestion by nucleases such as DNAse I.[79] DNAse I sensitivity as applied to globin gene expression has been most extensively studied in the nucleated erythroid cells of chickens[80–82] in which a number of different DNAse I sensitivity states have been defined: (1) there is an increased sensitivity affecting a considerable region of DNA surrounding the active gene which appears to signify that a specific region is capable of being expressed; (2) a more specific region of markedly higher sensitivity correlates with active transcription; and (3) DNAse I hypersensitive sites are usually found in the 5' flanking sequences of actively transcribed genes. Increased sensitivity to DNAse I appears to be related to the binding of a group of nonhistone proteins, high

mobility group (HMG) 14 and 17, to the active gene.[79] HMG proteins are present in all cell types and do not act in a gene-specific manner. The different levels of DNAse I sensitivity correlate well with the developmental stages of globin gene expression, in which embryonic chick erythroid cells that are relatively insensitive to DNAse I and are not synthesizing hemoglobin show an increased sensitivity around the globin genes after the start of hemoglobin synthesis.

Experiments on normal human erythroid cells, and on erythroleukemic cells such as K562 and MEL, which have abnormal patterns of globin synthesis, support the general conclusions that DNAse I sensitivity is associated with globin gene expression.[83–85] Thus activity of globin genes is associated with a change in chromatin configuration which appears to precede gene expression rather than initiate it. This clearly parallels the situation with methylation in which the changes that take place occur in response to other influences, rather than themselves being the initiators of expression.

INFLUENCE OF TRANS-ACTING FACTORS. Most of the genetic defects that impair globin synthesis are cis-acting; that is, a mutation on one chromosome does not appear to affect the activity of genes on the homologous chromosome. However, protein/DNA interactions are required for gene expression, and while it is clear that many of the characteristic changes in chromatin structure that accompany gene expression are nonspecific (for example, the binding of the HMG 14 and 17 proteins), it seems likely that some specific factors must be required to achieve tissue-specific expression—restriction of globin gene expression to erythroid cells, the differential expression of fetal γ and adult β genes, and so on. A number of independent observations point to the existence of soluble factors that may be responsible for the activation-inactivation of globin genes:

1. Studies of a small number of families with certain types of heterocellular hereditary persistence of fetal hemoglobin indicate that the genetic determinant is *unlinked* to the γ-β gene cluster (and is probably on a separate chromosome).[86]
2. Gene transfer experiments using K562, HEL, or MEL cells have shown that genes that are inactive in the abnormal cell lines can be expressed when transferred to "normal" hosts. Thus, inactive K562 β genes are expressed normally in a heterologous system,[87–89] and normal β genes fail to express when introduced into K562 cells,[88] suggesting that the cells lack an activating factor (or contain a β-gene suppressor).

Experiments using hybrid mouse erythroleukemia (MEL) cells containing human chromosome 16 from K562 cells in contrast express human α, but not the embryonic ζ which is normally actively synthesized in K562.[90,91] Since MEL cells are of adult origin, these results suggest that they contain a factor(s) that represses embryonic gene expression or, alternatively, that factors are present in embryonic cells that promote ζ-gene expression (in K562) and these are missing in the adult-derived MEL cells.

Developmental Changes in Hemoglobin Synthesis. The pattern of Hb synthesis changes during development. In the very early embryo Hb synthesis is restricted to the yolk sac and the production of Hb Gower 1 ($\zeta_2\epsilon_2$), Hb Gower 2 ($\alpha_2\epsilon_2$), and Hb Portland ($\zeta_2\gamma_2$). Subsequently, at about 8 weeks of gestation, the fetal liver takes over, synthesizing predominantly Hb F ($\alpha_2\gamma_2$) and a small amount (<10 percent) of Hb A. Between about 18 weeks and birth, liver is progressively replaced by bone marrow as the major site of red cell production, and this is accompanied in the later stages of gestation with a reciprocal switch in production of Hb F and Hb A, which continues until the end of the first year when Hb F production has dropped to less than 2 percent (Fig. 93-5).

The mechanism by which fetal erythroid cells switch from the production of Hb F to Hb A remains elusive and has been (and still is) the subject of a considerable research effort, not only for its own intrinsic interest but also because of the important therapeutic implications that would arise from the ability to manipulate the switching process.

In humans the switch from Hb F to Hb A production seems to be closely related to the gestational age of the fetus and largely independent of environmental factors. Experiments in sheep (which provide a good model system with close developmental parallels to humans) have shown that while various treatments, such as fetal hypophysectomy in the lamb, may alter the *rate* at which the developmental changes occur, they do not affect the *time* of switching.[92]

Similarly, transplantation experiments involving introducing fetal (liver) cells into lethally irradiated adult animals shows that the pattern of hemoglobin synthesis in the treated adults is that expected of a fetus of the same age as the donor cells, with switching to the production of adult hemoglobin only at the appropriate time.[93] The reverse experiments, of transplanting adult cells in a fetus in utero, showed continued production of adult Hb in the fetal environment, until the appropriate time for switching when the fetus began producing its own adult Hb.[94]

All these observations thus provide evidence of preprogrammed globin gene expression that is not appreciably affected by environmental changes. These general conclusions provide no insight into the mechanism(s) that bring about these changes, and one of the intriguing questions concerns the cell populations involved in the switching transition. Does the same cell type switch over from Hb F to Hb A production, or is a cell line that predominantly synthesizes Hb F progressively replaced by one that produces Hb A? During the switching period virtually all red cells contain both Hb A and Hb F but in quite variable amounts. This is consistent with these cells being derived from a single stem cell pool, rather than two separate pools, one producing Hb F cells and the other Hb A cells. On the other hand tissue culture studies of hemoglobin synthesis in erythroid colonies derived from newborn infant's blood suggests that two different colony populations are present, one unique to cord blood in which the proportion of fetal γ-globin chain was inversely related to that of β globin and a second population of cells where there was no relationship between the proportions of γ and β chains synthesized, analogous to adult colonies.[95] These findings do not, of course necessarily point to distinct populations of stem cells. Differences in maturation or differentiation of cells from a single unique pool could equally be responsible.

Regulation of Hemoglobin Synthesis. While the overall processes of gene expression, transcription, and translation are reasonably well understood, there is still a dearth of information on how these processes are actually regulated: What governs the amounts of globin mRNA and globin protein produced? The cytoplasmic phase of protein synthesis appears to exert only a minimal influence on the final tally of globin synthesized, which is determined to a large extent by the amount of mRNA delivered to the cytoplasm and its life span there. While the bulk of the regulation appears to occur within the nucleus, by determining the overall output of the α- and β-gene complexes, the actual mechanisms involved remain obscure.

It is clear that at the cytoplasmic level, chain initiation is the rate limiting step in globin synthesis. β-Globin mRNA initiates synthesis more effectively than α by a factor of about 1.5, and this is compensated for by a higher level of α mRNA in red cell precursors. The net effect is that the numbers of α and β chains synthesized are roughly equal; there is, in fact, a slight excess of α globin, which is removed proteolytically.

The differential regulation of globin synthesis is achieved against a background of predetermined cytoplasmic mRNA levels, but how α and β mRNA outputs from two different and unlinked chromosomal complexes are controlled is unknown. Some general feedback mechanisms must exist. For example, normal red cells accumulate about 30 pg of hemoglobin at a concentration of about 33 g/liter. In conditions that

Fig. 93-5 Globin synthesis at various stages of embryonic and fetal development.

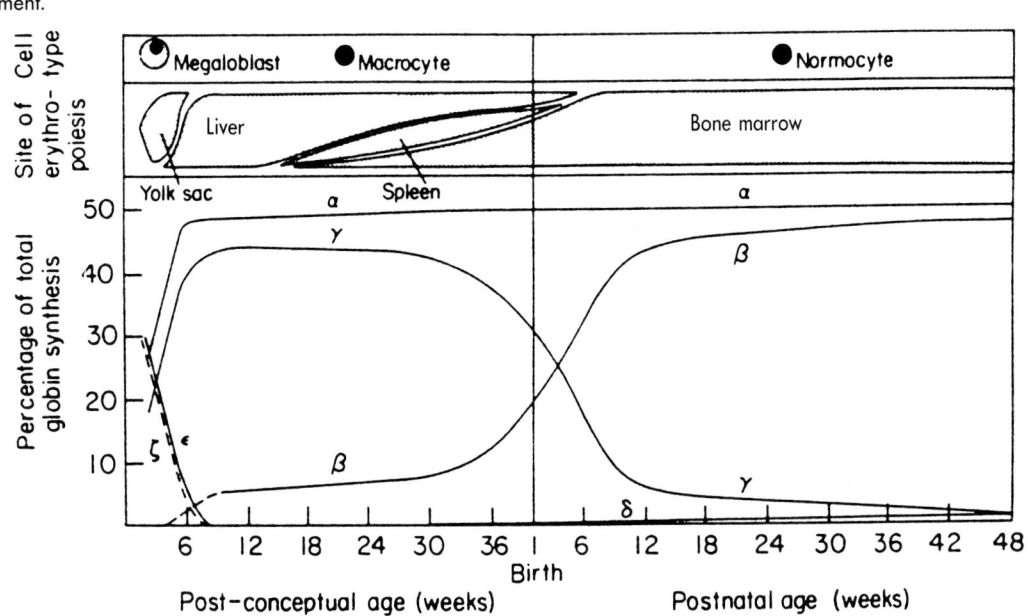

result in impaired globin synthesis such as thalassemia, the small cells that result have less hemoglobin than normal, but its final concentration is close to normal levels. And in both α and β thalassemia loss of activity of a gene is not usually accompanied by a proportionate decrease in globin synthesis,[2] indicating that the remaining normal genes compensate for the lost output, to some extent.[96]

For effective hemoglobin synthesis, the production of heme and globin have to be coordinated. The biosynthesis of heme takes place partly in the mitochondrion, partly in the cytoplasm through a series of coordinated enzyme reactions starting with the condensation of glycine and succinyl-CoA. The level of heme in red cell precursors has an important effect on the efficiency of protein synthesis, since in conditions of heme deficiency a specific initiation fraction IEF-2b is inactivated through binding to phosphorylated IEF-2, itself produced as a direct result of heme deficiency. Conditions in which heme synthesis is impaired, such as iron deficiency or lead poisoning, therefore have a direct inhibitory effect on globin synthesis.

CLASSIFICATION OF HEMOGLOBIN DISORDERS

The main groups of hemoglobin disorders are summarized in Table 93-1. They are divided into those in which there is a structural change in a globin chain and those in which there is a reduced rate of production of one or more of the globin chains, the thalassemias. In addition, there is a group of conditions that are characterized by a defect in the normal switching of fetal to adult hemoglobin production, known collectively as *hereditary persistence of fetal hemoglobin*. Although the latter are of no clinical significance, they are useful models for studying the regulation of gene switching during development.

Although offering a useful conceptual framework on which to describe the hemoglobin disorders this classification is not entirely satisfactory. In particular, there is an overlap between the structural hemoglobin variants and the thalassemias; some abnormal hemoglobins are produced at a reduced rate and are associated with the clinical phenotype of thalassemia.

Table 93-1 Genetic Disorders of Hemoglobin

Structural hemoglobin variants
  α Chain
  β Chain
  γ Chain
  δ Chain
  Fusion chains
    δβ
    βδ
    γβ
Thalassemias
  α Thalassemia
  β Thalassemia
  δβ Thalassemia
  γδβ Thalassemia
  γ Thalassemia
  δ Thalassemia
Hereditary persistence of fetal hemoglobin
  Deletion
  Nondeletion
    Linked to β-globin gene cluster
    Unlinked to β-globin gene cluster

It should be remembered that in many populations there is a high incidence of structural hemoglobin variants *and* different forms of thalassemia. It is not uncommon, therefore, for an individual to have inherited more than one genetic determinant for a hemoglobin variant and/or different forms of thalassemia. In some countries these interactions produce a bewildering collection of genetic disorders of hemoglobin production with widely varying clinical phenotypes; in Thailand, for example, over 60 different combinations have been observed.[2]

THE STRUCTURAL HEMOGLOBIN VARIANTS

Extensive population studies using hemoglobin electrophoresis and analyses of the hemoglobin of patients with specific hematologic conditions have led to the discovery of over 400 structural hemoglobin variants. In this section only those abnormal hemoglobins that are associated with clinical disorders are described in detail. Complete lists of the human hemoglobin variants together with their structural alterations and functional properties are listed in a recent monograph.[3]

Nomenclature

When the first hemoglobin variants were described after the discovery of sickle cell hemoglobin in 1949,[8] they were designated by letters of the alphabet. By the late 1950s all the letters of the alphabet had been used, and it became customary to name a new hemoglobin by its place of origin. As pointed out by Bunn and Forget[3] there is no consistent usage. Names range from the exotic (Hb Aida), through the chauvinistic (Hb Brigham) or parochial (Hb Riverdale-Bronx) to the patriotic (Hb Abraham Lincoln); they could also have added the poetic (Hb Constant Spring).

Although for many years there have been no formal recommendations for nomenclature of the abnormal hemoglobins, certain conventions are observed in the hemoglobin literature. Heterozygotes for hemoglobin variants are usually described as having the trait, e.g., sickle cell trait, Hb C trait. Homozygotes are described as having the disease, e.g., sickle cell disease, Hb C disease, Hb D disease. In fact, with the exception of the three β-globin variants that occur in polymorphic frequencies in many populations, Hb S, Hb C, and Hb E, the homozygous states for other β-chain variants are extremely rare and have usually been encountered in consanguineous marriages.[3] Individuals who inherit a different β-globin chain variant from each parent, that is, compound heterozygotes, are described as having SC, SD, or SE disease, and so on. Similarly, a person who has inherited a β-globin chain variant such as Hb S from one parent and a β-thalassemia gene from the other is said to have Hb S β thalassemia. The homozygous state for α-chain variants is also extremely uncommon, and because there are two α-globin genes per haploid genome, such individuals also have hemoglobin A.

There are a number of γ- and δ-chain variants that result from single amino acid substitutions.[3] Abnormal fetal hemoglobins that contain γ-chain variants are usually described after their place of origin, Hb F_{Malta} and Hb F_{Poole}, for example. The first structural δ-chain variant was called Hb A_2' or Hb B_2. Subsequently they were named after their place of discovery, Hb $A_{2Canada}$ for example.

Since α chains are shared by Hb F, Hb A, and Hb A_2, it follows that heterozygotes for α-chain variants will have both normal Hb F, Hb A, and Hb A_2 and variant forms composed of abnormal α chains combined with normal γ, β, and δ chains, respectively. These abnormal fetal and adult hemoglobins are usually named after the α-chain variant. For example, individuals heterozygous for the α variant Hb G$_{Philadelphia}$ have an abnormal fetal hemoglobin variant, Hb GF ($\alpha_2^G\gamma_2$), and an abnormal Hb A_2 called Hb G_2 ($\alpha_2^G\delta_2$).

The situation becomes even more complex when an individual is heterozygous for both an α-chain variant and a β-chain variant. Random association of subunits produces four main hemoglobin species. For instance, an individual who has inherited an α-globin variant designated X and a β-chain variant Y would have the following hemoglobins: $\alpha_2^A\beta_2^A$, $\alpha_2^X\beta_2^A$, $\alpha_2^A\beta_2^Y$, and $\alpha_2^X\beta_2^Y$. If the β-chain variant were Hb S and the α-chain variant Hb G, these hemoglobins would become A, G, S, and SG. Of course things are even more complicated because such individuals also have an abnormal form of Hb A_2 and an abnormal fetal hemoglobin due to the association of abnormal α chains with δ and γ chains. Thus in adult life they would have six hemoglobins and during the switch from fetal to adult hemoglobin would have eight.

Molecular Pathology

The majority of the 400 or more human hemoglobin variants that have been isolated to date result from single amino acid substitutions in one of the globin chains. In addition, there are a few variants with either elongated or shortened globin chains or chains that are fusion products, part β and part δ or part β and part γ.

Single-Base Substitutions. The single amino acid replacements that are found in the structural hemoglobin variants nearly all result from a single base substitution in the corresponding triplet codon of the particular globin gene. A few variants have amino acid replacements at two different sites on the same subunit. Three of them involve the Hb S substitution. It is believed that they arose either by a new mutation on the β^S gene or by crossing-over between the β^S gene and a β gene containing another structural variant.[3]

A total of 2583 single base substitutions are possible for the 140 residues of the α chain and the 146 residues of the β chain.[3] Of these, 1690 would result in an amino acid replacement but only one-third of these would cause a change in charge allowing the identification of the variant by electrophoresis. Remarkably, about 45 percent of these charged variants have already been discovered. The relatively few known hemoglobin variants with neutral mutations have been discovered because the amino acid substitution has altered the stability of the hemoglobin molecule and hence caused a hemolytic anemia.

Elongated Globin Chain Variants. Ten different elongated globin chain variants have been discovered (Table 93-2). They are caused by either single base substitutions in a chain termination codon, frameshift mutations, or mutations that cause failure of cleavage of the initiator methionine residue.

The chain termination mutants are all α-chain variants in which there is a single base substitution in the chain termination codon UAA[97] (Fig. 93-6). Thus, instead of coding for "termination," an amino acid is inserted into the growing peptide chain. Messenger RNA that is not normally translated is

Table 93-2 Hemoglobin Variants with Elongated or Shortened Subunits[3,97–101]

Elongated globin chains	
Chain termination mutations	Hbs Constant Spring, Icaria, Koya Dora
Frameshift mutations	Hbs Wayne, Saverne, Tak, Cranston
Reduplication	Hb Grady
Persistent *N*-terminal Met	Hbs Marseille, S. Florida, Long Island
Shortened globin chains	
Deletions	Hbs Leiden, Lyon, Freiburg, Gunn Hill, McKees Rocks, and others

then read through until another in-phase chain termination codon is reached. The result is an elongated α chain. For example, Hb Constant Spring has an α chain with 31 additional amino acid residues at its C-terminal end. The residue at position 142, next to what is normally the C-terminal arginine residue, is glutamine. This is because of a single base change in the chain termination codon UAA to CAA; the latter codes for glutamine. In fact there is a family of α-chain termination variants, all of which differ at position 142 but have identical residues in their elongated portions (Fig. 93-6). These variants all reflect different base substitutions in the chain termination codon. Because Hb Constant Spring and its related family of elongated α chain variants are all associated with the clinical phenotype of α thalassemia,[97] they will be considered further in a later section.

Several elongated hemoglobin variants have been found that appear to result from frameshift mutations. Hb Wayne is an α-chain variant that has five additional amino acid residues at its C-terminal end.[98] This results from the loss of a single base at codons 138 or 139 that throws the reading frame out of phase and hence generates a completely new sequence. Since the α-chain termination codon is also out of phase, translation continues until a new in-phase termination codon is reached. The elongated β-globin chain variant Hb Tak also appears to have arisen by a frameshift mutation involving the duplication of two bases, CA at positions 146/147 or AC at position 147.[99] Another elongated β-chain variant, Hb Cranston, has also arisen from a frameshift mutation.[100]

Hemoglobin Grady has an α chain which is normal in every way except for the insertion of nine bases that result in repetition of the Glu-Phe-Thr sequence at positions 116 to 118.[101] Several mechanisms have been suggested for its generation, including unequal crossing over between allelic α-chain genes or, as seems more likely, the production of a break in a DNA strand, mispairing at an adjacent short repeated dinucleotide sequence, and filling in and repair with the insertion of the additional bases, in this case the in-phase codons for Glu-Phe-Thr.

Several hemoglobin variants with elongated amino terminal ends have been found; in each case there is an additional methionine residue. For example, Hb Long Island[102] has two amino acid substitutions in the β chain; an extension of the amino terminus by a methionine residue and a histidine-to-proline change at the normal second position. Hemoglobin Marseille[103] has the same structure, while Hb South Florida[104] has an extra N-terminal methionine, and the normal N-terminal valine is replaced by methionine. Methionine is the first residue to be incorporated during translation of globin chains and many other peptide chains. During translation of the nascent peptide chain the amino-terminal methionine is normally cleaved leaving, in the case of the β-globin chain, valine as the

(a)

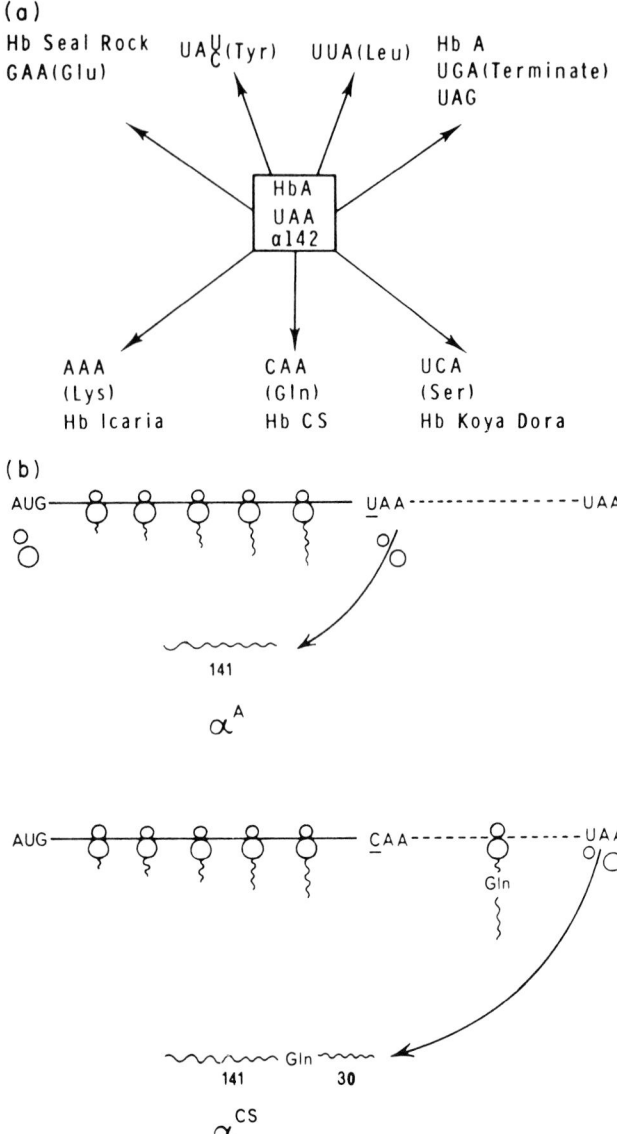

(b)

Fig. 93-6 The α-chain termination mutants. A. The various replacements in the α-chain termination codon which give rise to the family of termination mutants. B. Schematic representation of the synthesis of the elongated α chain of Hb Constant Spring (α^{CS}). *(From Weatherall and Clegg.[2] Used by permission.)*

amino-terminal residue. It has been suggested that the amino acid substitutions in these variants somehow inhibit the activity of a peptidase that normally cleaves the amino terminal methionine.[102] Thus they are all single amino-acid replacements; the additional N-terminal methionine reflects post-translational modification.

None of these elongated globin-chain variants, with the exception of the α-chain termination mutants, is associated with any major hematologic abnormalities.

Shortened Globin Chains.[3] Several hemoglobin variants with shortened globin chains have been described (Table 93-2). In each case one or more adjacent amino acids are missing from the abnormal chains, and the remainder of the chain is completely normal. These variants probably involve deletion of one or more intact codons; if an entire codon is lost, the reading frame will remain in phase and the remainder of the amino acid sequence will not differ from normal. In some cases, Hb Gun Hill,[105] for example, the deletion results in molecular in-

stability and the clinical picture of an unstable hemoglobin disorder (see below, "The Unstable Hemoglobin Disorders"). It is interesting to note that the sequence of globin mRNA in the regions where these deletions have occurred always shows a reiterated nucleotide sequence from two to eight bases in length. These deletion mutants may have arisen by chromosomal mispairing and nonhomologous crossing-over in these regions.

One hemoglobin variant with a shortened β chain, Hb McKees Rocks, may have arisen from a nonsense mutation, that is, a single base change that results in a chain termination codon within the coding region of the β-globin gene.[106] Although, as we see later, this is the cause of several forms of β thalassemia, in the case of this variant the premature termination codon is at position 145, thus producing a viable globin chain lacking its two C-terminal residues, tyrosine and histidine.

Fusion Hemoglobins. There are several hemoglobin variants that contain fused or hybrid globin chains. The first of these to be discovered, Hb Lepore, contains normal α chains and non-α chains that consist of the first 50 to 80 amino acid residues of the δ chains and the last 60 to 90 residues of the normal C-terminal amino acid sequence of the β chains.[107] Thus the Hb Lepore non-α chain is a δβ fusion chain. Three different varieties of Hb Lepore have been described in which the transition from δ to β sequences occurs at different points.[107–109] Hemoglobin Kenya is analogous except that the abnormal hybrid chain contains γ and β sequences, that is, it is a γβ fusion chain.[110]

The fusion chains have probably arisen by nonhomologous crossing-over, for instance, between part of the δ locus on one chromosome and part of the β locus on the complementary chromosome (Fig. 93-7). This event results from misalignment of chromosome pairing during meiosis so that a δ-chain gene pairs with a β-chain gene instead of its homologous partner. As shown in Fig. 93-7 such a mechanism should give rise to two abnormal chromosomes; the first, the Lepore chromosome, will have no normal δ or β loci but simply a δβ fusion gene. On the opposite of the homologous pairs of chromosomes there should be an anti-Lepore (βδ) fusion gene together with normal δ and β loci. Similarly, in the case of Hb Kenya there should be an anti-Kenya chromosome with intact ^{A}γ, δ, and β loci. A variety of anti-Lepore-like hemoglobins have been discovered, including hemoglobins Miyada, P-Congo, Lincoln Park, and P-Nilotic.[111–114]

Another variant with fusion chains, Hb Parchman, is more complex in that the non-α chain has a δ sequence at the N- *and* C-terminal ends and a β sequence in the middle. It seems likely that this arose by a double crossover event.[115]

The Lepore variants result in the clinical phenotype of β or δβ thalassemia and hence will be considered further in a later section. The anti-Lepore variants and Hb Kenya are not associated with any significant hematologic changes.[2]

Structural Hemoglobin Variants of Clinical Importance

The structural hemoglobin variants that cause clinical disorders are summarized in Table 93-3. The three that reach polymorphic frequencies, and hence cause a major public health problem, are Hb S, Hb C, and Hb E. The other clinically important variants are much less common. They fall into two major groups. First there are those that alter the oxygen

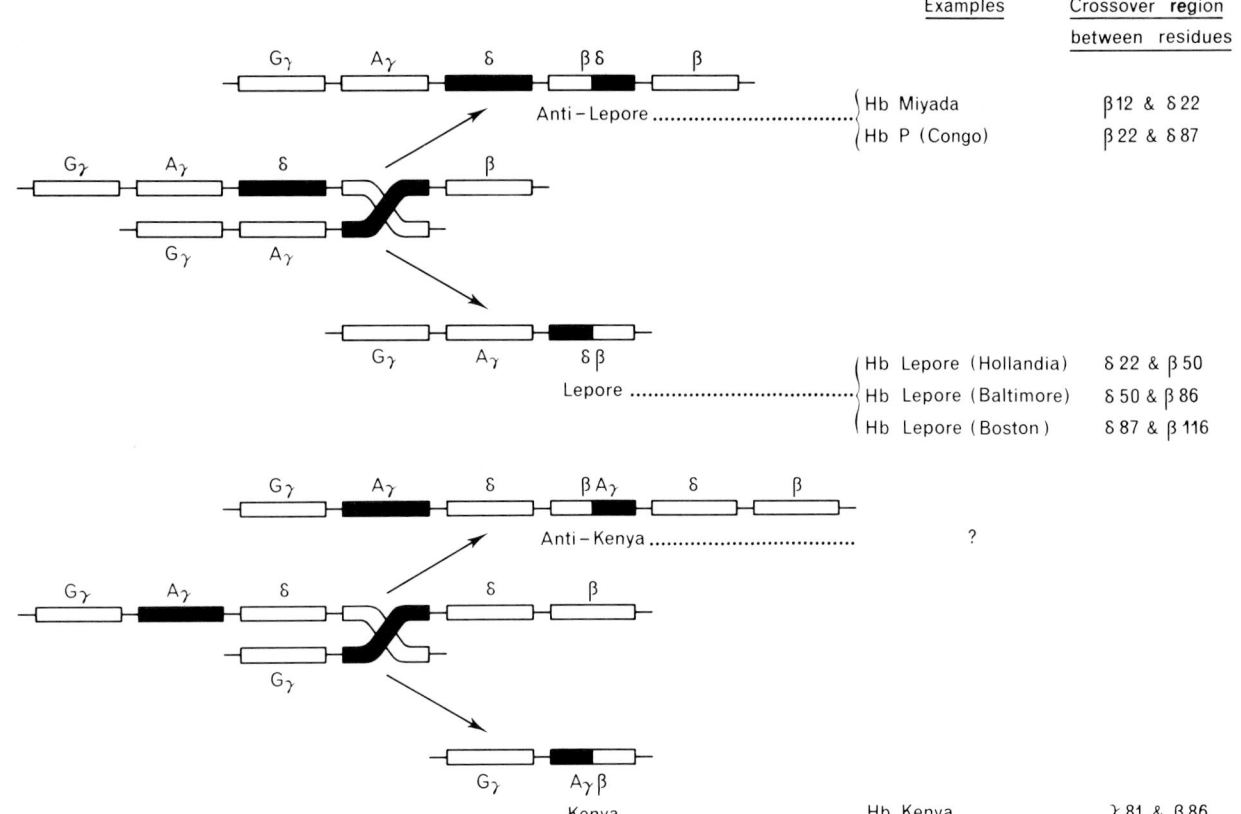

	Examples	Crossover region between residues
Anti-Lepore	Hb Miyada	β12 & δ22
	Hb P (Congo)	β22 & δ87
Lepore	Hb Lepore (Hollandia)	δ22 & β50
	Hb Lepore (Baltimore)	δ50 & β86
	Hb Lepore (Boston)	δ87 & β116
Anti-Kenya		?
Kenya	Hb Kenya	γ81 & β86

Fig. 93-7 The generation of Hb Lepore and Hb Kenya. *(From Weatherall and Clegg.[2] Used by permission.)*

carrying properties of hemoglobin and result either in hereditary polycythemia or methemoglobinemia. The second group comprises unstable variants that produce a hemolytic anemia of varying severity. Finally, there are several hemoglobin variants that are ineffectively synthesized and that are therefore associated with the clinical phenotype of α or β thalassemia.

The Sickling Disorders

Hemoglobin S was the first hemoglobin variant to be discovered[8] and the first to have its amino acid substitution determined.[9] Sickle cell anemia is the cause of considerable mortality and morbidity in Africa and in every population where there has been migration of individuals of African descent, in parts of the Mediterranean region, and in the Middle East and Indian subcontinent. However, despite the fact that the molecular lesion has been known for nearly 30 years, many questions remain about its pathophysiology, clinical heterogeneity, prognosis, and, above all, its clinical management.

Classification (Table 93-4). The sickling disorders include the heterozygous state [sickle cell trait (AS)], the homozygous condition [sickle cell disease (SS)], and the compound heterozygous states for the sickle cell gene in association with other β-globin chain variants such as Hbs C and D (SC and SD disease) or β thalassemia (Hb S β thalassemia). The sickle cell gene also occurs in association with α-chain variants and different forms of α thalassemia.

Molecular Pathology. Hemoglobin S differs from hemoglobin A by the substitution of valine for glutamic acid at position 6 of the β-globin chain.[9] This reflects an A→T substitution in the triplet codon for the sixth residue of the β-globin chain. In concentrated hemoglobin solutions that are partially or fully deoxygenated this amino acid substitution leads to polymerization and the formation of intracellular fibers that cause the sickle cell deformity. The latter results in reduced deformability of the red cell and hence in its defective passage through the microcirculation. This is the basis for the vasoocclusive manifestations of sickle cell disease. In addition, these structural changes of the red cell lead to a shortened survival and a chronic hemolytic anemia.

Despite an enormous amount of work over the last half-century the final story of how sickle cells actually sickle remains to be told. Early workers in the field observed that sickling is associated with the formation of liquid crystals or tactoids.[116] Electron micrographs of sickled erythrocytes show long, thin bundles of Hb S fibers that tend to run parallel to

Table 93-3 Spectrum of Clinical Disorders Due to Structural Hemoglobin Variants

Hemolytic anemia
  Sickling disorders
  Hb C
  Unstable variants
Abnormal oxygen transport
  High affinity variants
  Low affinity variants
Thalassemia phenotypes
  Ineffectively synthesized variants
    Hb E
    Hb Knossos
  Chain termination variants
  Fusion variants
  Highly unstable variants
    Hb Indianapolis

Table 93-4 The Common Sickling Disorders

Disorder	Genotype	Hemoglobins
Homozygous for Hb S		
Sickle cell disease	$\alpha\alpha/\alpha\alpha\ \beta^S\beta^S$	S, F, A_2
With α thalassemia	$-\alpha/-\alpha\ \beta^S\beta^S$	S, F, $A_2\uparrow$
	$-\alpha/\alpha\alpha\ \beta^S\beta^S$	S, F, A_2
Heterozygous for Hb S		
Sickle cell trait	$\alpha\alpha/\alpha\alpha\ \beta^A\beta^S$	A, S, A_2
With α thalassemia	$-\alpha/-\alpha\ \beta^A\beta^S$	A, $S\downarrow$, A_2
	$-\alpha/\alpha\alpha\ \beta^A\beta^S$	A, S, $A_2\uparrow$
With β thalassemia*	$\alpha\alpha/\alpha\alpha\ \beta^0\beta^S$	S, F, $A_2\uparrow$
	$\alpha\alpha/\alpha\alpha\ \beta^+\beta^S$	S, A, F, $A_2\uparrow$
With β-chain variants	$\alpha\alpha/\alpha\alpha\ \beta^S\beta^C$	S, C, A_2
	$\alpha\alpha/\alpha\alpha\ \beta^S\beta^D$	S, D, A_2
	$\alpha\alpha/\alpha\alpha\ \beta^S\beta^O_{Arab}$	S, O_{Arab}, A_2
	Many others	
With α-chain variants	$\alpha^G\alpha/\alpha\alpha\ \beta^A\beta^S$	A, S, G, A_2, G_2, SG
	Several other interactions	
With HPFH†	$\alpha\alpha/\alpha\alpha\ \beta^S -$	S, F, A_2

*β^0 and β^+ indicate β thalassemia with complete and partial deficiency of β-chains-gene.
†Represents a chromosome with a deleted β-chain gene.

the long axis of the cell and which are probably responsible for its abnormal morphology[117,118] (Fig. 93-8). The precise ultrastructure of these fibers has been the subject of considerable controversy. A number of different models have been proposed in which 6, 8, or, more recently, 14 strands are twisted in a helical configuration to form hollow fibers with an external diameter of 170 to 220 Å.[119,120] The stabilization of these structures is dependent on interactions between individual globin chains. The precise localization of the contact points and the identification of the amino acid residues involved has been derived from a variety of techniques, particularly x-ray diffraction studies. One model based on x-ray data identifies β6 Val, β73 Asp, β121 Glu, and α23 Glu as being among a number of residues that are probably important in generating intermolecular contacts[121]; many others may be implicated.[3]

POLYMER FORMATION. The way in which Hb S polymerizes to form a large molecular weight gel that is in equilibrium with monomeric hemoglobin solution is not fully understood. Monomers are stable in solution at a particular concentration of Hb S, pH, ionic strength, and temperature. However, small alterations in any of these variables lead to a rapid change to the gel form of Hb S. It is probably this sol-to-gel transition that leads to the viscosity changes, abnormalities of cell morphology, and sludging in the microcirculation and organ infarction, which are the hallmarks of the sickling disorders.

The sol-to-gel transformations have been studied using many different techniques including light scattering and turbidometry,[122,123] sedimentation,[124] birefringence optics,[125] calorimetry,[126] and nuclear magnetic resonance.[127] Although no unifying model has arisen from these studies, several important factors emerge. There appear to be two distinct steps in the transition. The first is a lag phase that corresponds to the construction of a polymer of a critical size. Once this has occurred, the reaction proceeds more rapidly and results in the formation of a high molecular weight polymer with closely aligned fibers. The delay time varies as the 30th power of the hemoglobin concentration; it has been calculated that, by decreasing the intracellular hemoglobin concentration from 35 to 34 g/dl, the delay phase is doubled. The sol-to-gel transformation is also extremely sensitive to changes in temperature and pH.

The kinetics of gel formation by Hb S in red cells is probably similar to that in solution. The delay time has important pathophysiological consequences. Oxygenation and deoxygenation of red cells in the circulation take approximately the same time as the sol-to-gel transformation of Hb S in solution.[128] This means that in the pulmonary circulation, at a high oxygen tension, Hb S gels melt in less than half a second. They will remain more or less in this state in the arterial circulation, but in the microcirculation, where oxygen saturation rapidly declines, there will be a concomitant reduction in hemoglobin solubility. The red cell spends approximately 1 s in the capillary circulation; if the delay time is less than this, cells will sickle and occlude the microcirculation. On the other hand, if the delay time is prolonged, sickling should not occur in the capillaries, and hence the microcirculation will remain patent. In other words, if the transit time is shorter than the delay time, occlusion will not occur. The type of environment that red cells may encounter in the renal medulla or spleen, where there may be a low pH, high hemoglobin concentration, and high ionic strength, all of which shorten the delay time, will favor sickling.

INTERACTIONS BETWEEN SICKLE AND OTHER HEMOGLOBINS. If known proportions of solutions of purified Hb S and other hemoglobins are mixed under appropriate conditions and are then completely deoxygenated, the degree of interaction of a particular hemoglobin in the sickling process can be assessed by determining the minimum concentration of the final mixture in grams per deciliter at which gelling occurs (MGC).[129] Hence a low MGC indicates an increased tendency to sickle, a high MGC vice versa. For example, mixtures of Hb S and Hb C have a higher MGC than solutions of Hb S alone, indicating that the substitution of the basic lysine does not cause sickling as efficiently as a hydrophobic valine. Hemoglobins D and O_{Arab} involve substitutions in the β121 region, an area that x-ray data suggest is an important contact region. Gelation studies show that these variants interact with sickle cell hemoglobin and support sickling as efficiently as Hb S. On the other hand experiments of this type show that Hbs A and F have an inhibitory effect on sickling. It is interesting to note that x-ray studies that have analyzed contacts between double strands have provided information that is in very good agreement with the location of mutations that affect gelation. The extensive data that have been generated on the various contact points and intermolecular interactions that may be important in the genesis of sickling are all consistent with a 14-strand structure of the sickle cell fiber.[3,128,130]

CELLULAR HETEROGENEITY. Films prepared from well-oxygenated blood samples from patients with sickle cell anemia show a number of sickled forms. Such irreversibly sickled cells (ISCs) are derived from a relatively young erythrocyte population with a low content of Hb F.[131] They are thought to be the end result of cycles of sickling and unsickling.[132] The ISC is a particularly rigid cell that is partly responsible for the abnormal viscosity of oxygenated whole blood of patients with sickle cell anemia. Their decreased deformability is related directly to the degree of cellular dehydration.

The formation of the ISC is thought to occur in several stages. Cycles of sickling cause damage to the red cell membrane that becomes abnormally permeable to cations, resulting in a low K^+, high Na^+, high Ca^{2+} concentration. In an effort to restore cation homeostasis ATP-dependent pumps are activated with a consequent decrease in intracellular ATP. At this

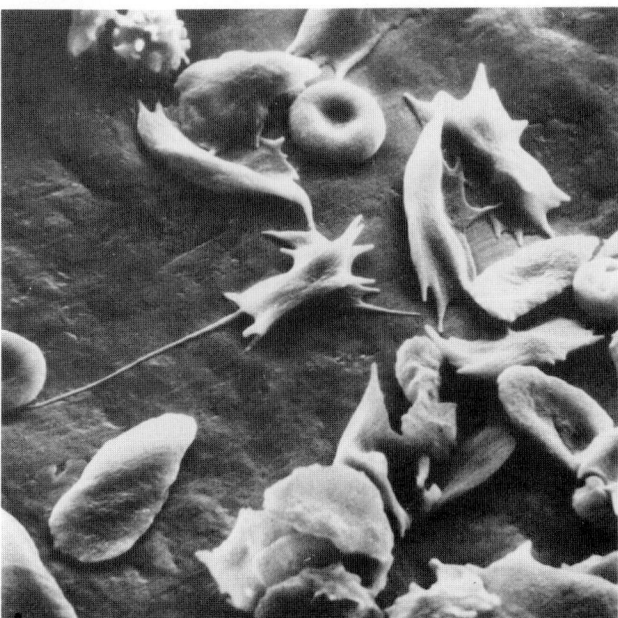

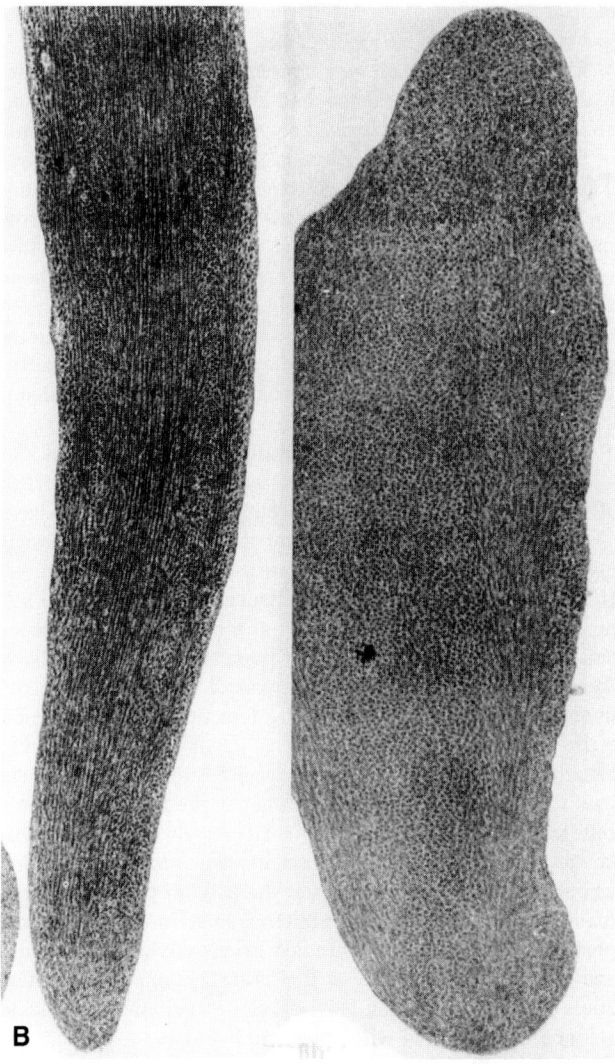

Fig. 93-8 Sickle cells. A. Scanning electron-microscopic appearances showing deoxygenated sickle cells with bizarre shapes and long filaments, short spicules, and chiseled surfaces. B. Electron microscopy (×17,655). The cells are shown in longitudinal section on the *left* and in cross section on the *right*. The figures are of deoxygenated irreversibly sickled cells (ICS). In contrast to a more random pattern of filaments in deoxygenated non-ISC there is a distinctive regularity of filament arrangements. *(From Bertles and Dobler.[131] Used by permission.)*

stage the erythrocyte is calcium-loaded and ATP-depleted and hence may undergo the "Gardos effect," i.e., gross dehydration with loss of potassium and water.[130] It is believed that this dehydrated cell, with a very high MCHC, has a decreased delay time and hence tends to remain in the sickled configuration. It seems likely that the low level of Hb F in these cells is a major factor in their termination in the irreversibly sickled state.

RHEOLOGY.[133] The transition from the sol to gel state is accompanied by a marked increase in viscosity. Hemoglobin, whether in free solution or in red cells, is a non-Newtonian fluid. This means that its viscosity is critically dependent on sheer rate. Above minimum gelling concentration of deoxy Hb S the viscosity increases dramatically; the rheological properties of the gel are probably the most immediate cause of the vasoocclusive manifestations of the sickling disorders.

OXYGEN AFFINITY. Although Hb S in dilute solution has a normal oxygen dissociation curve, blood from patients with sickle cell anemia shows a decreased oxygen affinity.[3] There are probably several factors responsible for the shift in the oxygen dissociation curve. Though individuals with sickle cell anemia have higher levels of red cell 2,3-DPG, the major cause is intracellular polymerization of Hb S.

Pathophysiology. The sickling disorders are all characterized by two major pathologic processes, anemia and vasoocclusion.

ANEMIA. The anemia of sickle cell disease has an extremely complex pathophysiology. It seems likely that physical trapping of sickled erythrocytes in the microcirculation due to their decreased deformability plays a major role in shortening the red cell survival. It turns out that, even when fully oxy-

genated, sickle cells exhibit decreased deformability. Both static and dynamic deformability of oxygenated sickle cells decrease with increasing dehydration.[134,135] Since polymerization of HbS is highly dependent on hemoglobin concentration, dehydrated sickled red cells show the most marked changes during partial deoxygenation. The decreased deformability is thought to cause trapping of rigid cells in small vessels.

There are other mechanisms that may be of importance in causing premature red cell destruction. Sickle cells have a tendency to adhere to vascular endothelial cells.[136] Furthermore, in vitro studies have shown that these cells are recognized more actively by monocytes and macrophages, suggesting that one component of the anemia of the sickling disorders is accelerated erythrophagocytosis.[137] Although the mechanism is not known, it has been suggested that it reflects the appearance of charged phospholipid, phosphatidyl serine in the outer monolayer of the membranes together with excessive binding of anti-α galactosyl IgG to the membrane.[138] It is also possible that autooxidation plays a role. Sickle cell membranes have increased amounts of membrane-associated hemichrome that is known to have the property of targeting autooxidative damage to membrane components. Excessive amounts of the by-products of lipid peroxidation and the modification of membrane constituents by potential cross-linking agents such as malonyldialdehyde have also been demonstrated.[139] These oxidative mechanisms may render sickle cells open to immunologic attack; there is an antibody in normal serums that opsonizes malonyldialdehyde-modified red cells.[140]

We have already seen how irreversibly sickled cells are dehydrated, have a high calcium and low potassium content, and are extremely rigid. It seems likely, therefore, that the anemia of the sickling disorders reflects a shortened red cell survival consequent upon decreased deformability, adherence to endothelial cells, erythrophagocytosis, autooxidation, and gross membrane abnormalities. Finally, it has been observed that there may be a suboptimal proliferative response by the bone marrow in this condition, probably because of the low oxygen affinity of Hb S in red cells.[141] Thus part of the anemia of patients with sickle-cell anemia may be a physiological adaptation to the altered oxygen carrying properties of their blood.

VASOOCCLUSION. The vasoocclusive manifestations of the sickling disorders result from the altered rheological properties of red cells containing a high concentration of Hb S. We have already considered the delay factor in the sickling phenomenon and its relevance to flow kinetics in the microcirculation. It seems quite likely that the tendency for sickle cells to adhere to vascular endothelium may also be involved in vasoocclusion. The normally deforming population of sickle cells is the most adherent, and there is evidence that plasma constituents play a critical role in their interaction with endothelial cells.[142] Adherent cells may retard the flow of other sickle cells, thereby increasing the time available for sickling as cells pass through hypoxic tissues. Ultimately the mass of adherent cells and sickle cells free within small vessels may lead to microvascular occlusion and subsequent tissue infarction. To this complicated picture we must add the flow properties and regulation of the diameter of the microcirculation itself. This important topic has not been studied extensively, although such evidence as there is suggests that there are important differences in microcirculation flow kinetics in patients with sickle cell anemia compared with normal individuals.[3]

The Sickle Cell Trait. The life expectancy of individuals with the sickle cell trait is probably the same as normal persons.[3,143] Although a number of clinical abnormalities have been reported in individuals with the trait, most of them are anecdotal and the association may be coincidental. It seems likely that such persons are at risk for splenic infarction when flying at high altitudes under conditions of inadequate cabin pressurization. Except in very unusual circumstances, this problem should not be encountered in commercial aircraft. There is no justification for denial of employment or life insurance to individuals with the sickle cell trait who fly in normally pressurized aircraft.

There is some evidence that otherwise unexplained hematuria may be associated with the sickle cell trait, as may the ability to concentrate urine. Other associations, based on less firm data, include a slightly increased risk of pulmonary embolism, renal papillary necrosis, and avascular necrosis of bone. There have been a few reports of infarctive episodes following the application of a limb tourniquet for orthopedic procedures or following a poorly administered anesthetic.

Sickle Cell Anemia. Sickle cell anemia is characterized by a lifelong hemolytic anemia, the occurence of acute exacerbations called *crises*, and a variety of complications resulting from an increased propensity to infection and the deleterious effects of repeated vasoocclusive episodes. Despite so much knowledge about the molecular pathology of the condition, the

reason the course of the illness is so variable, even within individual sibships let alone between different racial groups, is poorly understood. In this section we describe the typical features of sickle cell anemia and then attempt to define what is known about the factors that modify the clinical phenotype.

CLINICAL AND HEMATOLOGIC FEATURES AND COURSE OF THE ILLNESS.[3,144] Sickle cell anemia usually presents during the first or second year of life, although in milder cases later presentation is common and some patients may be ascertained only as adults during family studies or by chance. The usual presenting features are failure to thrive, repeated infections in infancy, attacks of painful dactylitis (the hand-foot syndrome; see below) or pallor. At this stage the infant looks pale, there may be slight icterus, and the spleen is usually palpable. By this time the typical hematologic findings of sickle cell anemia are established. The hemoglobin value varies between 7 and 11 g/dl, although higher levels are encountered with unusually mild forms of the illness. There are typical features of hemolysis with a raised reticulocyte count in the 10 to 20 percent range, marked variation in the depth of staining of the red cells, and some sickled erythrocytes on the blood film. The serum bilirubin level is slightly elevated, and the urinary urobilinogen level is increased.

The subsequent course is variable. Overall, patients with this disorder show early retardation of growth; weight is affected more than height. Although the mean height is generally reduced in childhood, data from studies in older children and adolescents are less clear. Usually by the age of 20 the height curves in males approach those of control groups and in females may actually exceed those of normal individuals.[144] Although there has been much controversy, it appears that patients with sickle cell disease have an abnormal body habitus characterized by long limbs and hence a decrease in the upper/lower segment ratio. Other features of abnormal anthropometry include narrow pectoral and pelvic girdles, increased anteroposterior chest diameters, a reduced arm circumference, and thinner skin folds. The onset of puberty is usually delayed.

The only other consistent finding in this condition is splenomegaly. This is usually present in infancy and early childhood; in a large Jamaican study 77 percent of patients had palpable spleens by the age of 24 months.[144] The organ gradually becomes impalpable in the majority of patients during later childhood; persistent splenomegaly occurs in patients with high levels of Hb F and in those who are homozygous for α^+ thalassemia (see below). The gradual splenic fibrosis and atrophy reflect repeated infarction of the organ. These changes in spleen size are mirrored by the presence of pitted red cells that result from reduced splenic function[145]; the pitted red cell count in sickle cell anemia correlates with other assessments of splenic function such as the clearance of heat-damaged autologous red cells and the uptake of labeled sulfacolloid.[146] Apart from the changes in developmental pattern and splenomegaly, there are no other characteristic physical signs.

Because of the right-shifted oxygen dissociation curve, patients with sickle cell anemia tend to compensate well for their anemia, and exercise tolerance is good. The main clinical problems that are encountered early in life are crises (see next section) and an increased propensity to infection.

It is clear that children with this condition have an increased susceptibility to infection although many of the published studies lack adequate controls. There is no doubt, however, that they have an increased incidence of infections due to

Streptococcus pneumoniae, Salmonella, Escherichia coli, and *Hemophilus influenzae.*[144] The Salmonella infections may be gastrointestinal, but osteomyelitis is also common and probably results from infection of infarcted bone. The pattern of other infections is also variable, but pneumococcal pneumonia and septicemia are particulary important; overwhelming septicemia and shock is a common pattern of death, particularly during infancy and childhood.

Undoubtedly a major cause for this proneness to infection is impaired splenic function together with generalized reticuloendothelial blockade; the pattern of infection in childhood is very similar to that of children who have had their spleens removed for other causes. The precise mechanism whereby splenic hypofunction increases susceptibility to infection is not clear; both antibody production and antigen processing may be involved. There may be other factors involved in children with sickle cell anemia, including defective neutrophil function and abnormalities of the alternate pathway of complement activation although such changes are only found in a small proportion of patients.[144] Infection is a major cause of death at all ages, an observation that suggests that hyposplenism is not the only factor involved in increased susceptibility.

CRISES. Acute exacerbations of the illness in patients with sickle cell anemia are called *crises.* They can take many clinical forms. Although the subdivision of crises into specific entities is useful for descriptive purposes, it should be emphasized that in many sickling crises a number of different pathophysiological mechanisms seem to be involved.

The *painful crisis*[144] is the most common and important manifestation of sickle cell anemia. These episodes are characterized by the rapid onset of pain in the limbs, back, abdomen, or chest. The mechanism is still unknown. There is good epidemiologic evidence that cold may be a factor, and in some cases there may be an underlying infection. But in many instances no precipitating factor can be found. There are no consistent changes in blood platelets or coagulation factors. It is clear, however, that these are vasoocclusive episodes; bone marrow biopsy over regions of bone pain invariably shows infarcted marrow. On theoretical grounds a vasoocclusive episode of this type could be caused either by enhancement of intravascular sickling or an alteration in the flow kinetics in the microcirculation. Other factors that may be involved include acidosis, hypoxia, and dehydration, all of which are known to potentiate intracellular polymerization.

The clinical course of the painful crisis is characteristic. The pain follows no particular pattern and tends to be severe for two or three days, after which it settles spontaneously. It is quite common to see a mild pyrexia in the second or third day of a crisis even in patients in whom an extensive search has not demonstrated any source of infection. This is presumably due to bone infarction. In an uncomplicated painful crisis the hematologic findings remain unchanged.

One particularly important form of painful crisis, which occurs early in infancy, is the so-called hand-foot syndrome. This is a dactylitis characterized by the sudden onset of painful swelling of the dorsum of the hands and feet. Two factors are probably responsible for this unusual distribution at a young age.[144] First, the bones are growing rapidly and may have a limited blood supply. Second, the occlusion of vessels by sickled cells may not be easily compensated by a coaxial blood supply to the bone. Autopsy studies have shown complete necrosis of the marrow and the inner third of the cortex, lesions similar to those that can be produced in experimental

animals by interruption of both the metaphyseal and nutrient artery supplies to long bones. In later life almost any bone can be involved in a painful crisis, and local swelling of the bone, that presumably reflects a periosteal reaction over an infarct, is commonly observed. Although painful crises always settle, repeated vasoocclusive episodes may lead to destruction of bone and soft tissue.

While painful crises are usually self-limiting, and therefore are not life-threatening, there are other forms of acute exacerbation of the clinical course of sickle cell anemia that are more serious and, together with infection, are the most common causes of death. There are a variety of *sequestration crises.* The most common type involves the spleen in the first 2 years of life.[144,147] The clinical picture is characterized by a rapid enlargement of the spleen that becomes engorged with sickled erythrocytes. This may progress to a stage at which a large proportion of the circulating blood volume is entrapped in the spleen leading to profound anemia and death. These episodes may occur more than once, particularly in children with persistent splenomegaly. A similar type of sequestration may occur in the liver in later life; the organ rapidly enlarges, while at the same time there is a dramatic fall in the hematocrit.

Another important type of sequestration crisis is called the *chest syndrome.*[148] This is being recognized increasingly as a cause of morbidity and mortality in patients of all ages. It is characterized by pleuritic pain, fever, cough, and increasing dyspnea. Initially there may be no radiologic findings, but as the condition develops pulmonary infiltrates appear and may progress to an almost complete "white-out" of the lung fields. Blood-gas analysis shows increasing hypoxemia. It is often very difficult to distinguish between an acute chest syndrome and a chest infection, and it is possible that infection may precipitate the syndrome in some cases. A previous history of an upper respiratory infection, infected sputum, a marked leukocytosis on presentation, and lower lobe disease is more in keeping with a pneumonia,[130] but these features are by no means always present and the distinction may be extremely difficult. Recent studies in the United Kingdom suggest that a falling hematocrit and/or platelet count, and rapidly deteriorating pO_2 values are useful indicators of an impending chest syndrome.[148]

Attacks of acute abdominal pain resembling a "surgical abdomen" occur frequently in patients with sickle cell anemia and constitute an *abdominal crisis.*[144] The pain is usually widespread and may be associated with tenderness without guarding, distension, and reduction or absence of bowel sounds. These features may be difficult to distinguish from peritonitis, although in the abdominal crisis rebound tenderness is absent and the patient's general condition is usually not so poor as in those with peritonitis. It is very important that this syndrome is recognized if unnecessary surgical exploration is to be avoided.

Another important cause of death in patients with sickle cell anemia of all ages is the *aplastic crisis.* Recent studies have implicated a human parvoviruslike agent as the most common cause of this condition.[149] Infection with this agent in normal people causes transient erythroid hypoplasia and a slight drop in the hemoglobin level. In patients with sickle cell anemia, who have a very short red cell survival, temporary marrow aplasia may lead to profound anemia. This is characterized by a very sudden drop in the hematocrit and the disappearance of reticulocytes from the peripheral blood. The bone marrow shows a marked reduction or absence of erythroid precursors. Recovery occurs in a few days and is heralded by a rising reticulocyte count. Aplastic crises occur in epidemics and often involve more than one family member. This reflects the periodic epidemicity of parvovirus infections in the general population.

Other crises have been defined as separate entities. The *neurologic crisis* is a vasoocclusive episode involving the central nervous system which may present in a variety of ways including the sudden onset of hemiplegia, fits, or other manifestations of focal neurologic damage.[144,150] The term *hemolytic crisis* is often used to describe an acute exacerbation of the hemolytic component of sickle cell anemia. In patients with intercurrent infection or painful crises the reticulocyte count may rise, but it is doubtful if the hemolytic crisis is a separate entity. *Priapism* occurs acutely and results from occlusion of the outflow vessels from the corpora cavernosa by sickled cells. This distressing complication may last for several days and may lead to permanent deformity of the penis.

CHRONIC ORGAN DAMAGE. Repeated vasoocclusive episodes may lead to chronic organ damage resulting from repeated infarction with subsequent healing and fibrosis.

Renal involvement occurs in virtually every patient with sickle cell anemia.[144] In early life there is impairment of renal function that is correctable by blood transfusion. In later life this defect is irreversible. It probably results from derangement of the normal countercurrent distribution in the medullary circulation; blood flow to the glomeruli is maintained, whereas flow to the vasa recta in the medulla is reduced. Injection of kidneys at autopsy has demonstrated decreased filling of these vessels, with dilated capillaries and extravasation of contrast media from ruptured vessels. In addition there may be a mild form of distal tubular acidosis. Otherwise unexplained hematuria is common and probably results from lesions of the papillae. It is now realized that chronic progressive renal failure is a common form of death in adults with the sickling disorders.[144]

In early life the concentrating defect of the kidney may be reflected in thirst and polyuria, and it is thought that nocturnal enuresis is common. In addition there have been a number of reports of a true nephrotic syndrome, although more recent analyses have cast doubt on the true association between the sickling disorders and nephrosis. So far, reports of the response of patients with sickle cell disease and chronic renal failure to renal transplantation are limited, although in small series the 1-year graft survival rate did not differ from that of the general population.[151]

Many other organs may be involved in the chronic damage resulting from vascular blockage.[144] Permanent penile deformity has already been mentioned. *Avascular necrosis* of the femoral or humoral heads occurs (Fig. 93-9) although it is not clear whether this is as common in sickle cell disease as in Hb SC disease (see below). Involvement of the mandible, skull, ribs and sternum, and vertebral bodies may all give rise to deformity or chronic bone tenderness. Chronic *leg ulceration* is also very common. The lesions occur just above the medial malleoli; presumably this reflects the precarious vascularization of the skin of this region. *Proliferative retinopathy* also occurs in sickle cell anemia, although it is more common in hemoglobin SC disease; it is described in a later section. The *central nervous system* may be involved in a variety of chronic complications. Stroke is the most important; two-thirds of strokes occur in children, and in many cases there is a second or third episode.[150] Although there may be a remarkable degree of restoration of neurologic function, many children are

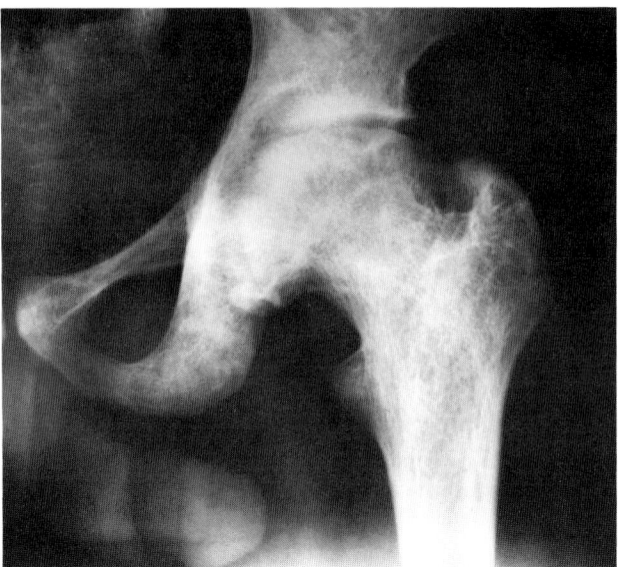

Fig. 93-9 Aseptic necrosis of the head of the left humerus in a patient with Hb SC disease. (*From Weatherall and Clegg.[2] Used by permission.*)

left with permanent defects in cognitive, sensory, and motor function. *Hepatic* involvement occurs in a variety of forms. There is invariably iron loading of the Kupffer cells and hepatocytes, and true macronodular cirrhosis has been observed, although the frequency of this condition seems to vary; for example, it is very rare in Jamaica. *Cholelithiasis* is very common, with all the associated complications. *Chronic pulmonary involvement* with progressive obliteration of the pulmonary vascular bed and associated pulmonary hypertension and right ventricular hypertrophy seems to be very uncommon, although this topic requires further study. Similarly, the *heart* seems to escape infarction. There is nearly always some degree of cardiac enlargement and a variety of flow murmurs have been described together with all the other manifestations of a hyperdynamic circulation. It is surprising that, although the myocardium extracts more oxygen than any other tissue, vasoocclusive episodes involving the myocardium do not seem to occur and coronary occlusion is not a recognized complication. This probably reflects the rapidity of blood flow in the myocardium, especially in a hyperdynamic heart. The question of whether there is a specific sickle *myocardiopathy* remains open, although autopsy series have revealed only minor histologic changes in cardiac muscle.[144]

OTHER COMPLICATIONS. There is much literature on the effects of sickle cell anemia on *pregnancy*. The most recent series estimate a very low maternal mortality, although it should be noted that most of these studies have been carried out in developed Western societies.[144] Such data as are available from Nigeria indicate that there is still a high maternal mortality.[152] Fetal wastage from abortion, stillbirth, and neonatal death is increased in all populations.[144] The anemia is exacerbated, and there appears to be an increased incidence of crises during pregnancy; the acute chest syndrome is particularly important. The association of preeclamptic toxemia remains controversial.

Because of the rapid marrow turnover, *folate deficiency* may occur, particularly in pregnancy, although this seems to be uncommon in patients maintained on adequate diets. Plasma zinc levels are significantly lower than in normal controls.[153] There is controversy about the clinical significance of zinc deficiency, which has been associated with a variety of complications including growth retardation and hypogonadism; these observations require confirmation on larger studies. Although *Plasmodium falciparum* malaria may be less severe in sickle cell heterozygotes, there is no doubt that it is a major cause of morbidity and mortality in homozygotes living in endemic areas. Audiometry has revealed *sensorineural hearing loss* in about 12 percent of patients with sickle cell anemia.[144] However this is usually subclinical; rarely, sudden deafness may occur during a painful crisis.

FACTORS THAT INFLUENCE PROGNOSIS. Surprisingly little is known about the natural history of sickle cell anemia except for the pioneering studies of Serjeant and his colleagues in Jamaica. Until recently it appeared that in both the United States and Jamaica there was a 10 percent mortality in the first few years of life. The most important causes of death were infection and splenic sequestration, with a number of sudden, unexpected deaths of uncertain etiology. With the advent of cord blood screening in the United States, it appears that this early mortality peak may be diminishing.[154] Recent studies from Jamaica indicate a 10-year survival of 84 percent, with the suggestion of a second peak in the mortality curve in the 20- to 24-year age group; data about longevity are extremely sparse.[144] Similarly, little is known about the prognosis for the disease in rural Africa, although such data as are available suggest that few patients survive to adult life. As mentioned earlier, infection remains the most common cause of death at all ages but, at least in Jamaica, progressive renal failure is being seen with increasing frequency in older age groups.[144]

Unfortunately, knowledge about the factors that modify the course of sickle cell anemia is extremely scanty. In certain populations such as those of eastern Saudi Arabia and Orissa, India, there is a particularly mild form of the disease.[155,156] This is characterized by fewer crises, higher hemoglobin levels, lower reticulocyte counts, persistence of splenomegaly into adult life, and a lower mortality. In both these populations the majority of patients have unusually high levels of fetal hemoglobin in the 15 to 25 percent range. There is no doubt that this must be a major protective factor; many studies have confirmed that high levels of fetal hemoglobin protect against sickling.[144,157] In some families it is possible to observe the segregation of a specific genetic determinant for persistent fetal hemoglobin production, that is, one or other form of hereditary persistence of fetal hemoglobin (see later section). But in Saudi Arabia and India such determinants have not been defined, although there is recent evidence that one factor that is responsible for elevating the fetal hemoglobin may segregate within the β-globin gene cluster.[158] It seems likely that the regulation of Hb F production in adults is under the control of more than one gene, however.

Another factor that clearly modifies the course of sickle cell anemia is the coinheritance of α thalassemia.[159] About 2 percent of American black and Jamaican populations are homozygous for the deletion form of α⁺ thalassemia. Comparison of such individuals, who also have sickle cell anemia, with those who have sickle cell anemia without α thalassemia shows that the α-thalassemic group has higher hemoglobin levels, typical thalassemic red cell indices, a greater likelihood of splenomegaly after childhood, and, possibly, fewer episodes of the acute chest syndrome and chronic leg ulceration. They also have lower levels of Hb F. In vitro studies show that the deformability of sickle cells is enhanced if α thalassemia is also present, providing a cellular basis for these observations.[160]

Evidence about the effect on survival of the coinheritance of α thalassemia remains conflicting.

But if high levels of Hb F and α thalassemia are excluded, the clinical picture of sickle cell anemia still remains remarkably heterogeneous and the factors that are involved in modifying the course are not understood. As we see later, a second mutation in the β-globin gene might account for some of this heterogeneity, but undoubtedly other factors remain to be identified.

THE HEMOGLOBIN CONSTITUTION. In the sickle cell trait there is usually about 30 percent Hb S with a normal Hb A$_2$ level (Fig. 93-10). The relative amount of Hb S varies. The main factor that seems to be responsible is the number of active α-globin genes. Individuals with the sickle cell trait who are also heterozygous for α⁰ thalassemia, or heterozygous or homozygous for α⁺ thalassemia have lower levels of Hb S. Those with triplicated α-globin genes have higher levels.[161]

In sickle cell anemia the hemoglobin consists mainly of Hb S with a normal Hb A$_2$ level and a variable amount of Hb F ranging from 1 or 2 percent up to 30 percent. Hemoglobin S can be distinguished from other variants with a similar electrophoretic migration on standard electrophoresis at alkaline pH by its different properties on agar gel electrophoresis (Fig. 93-11). However, the presence of Hb S should always be confirmed by carrying out a test for sickling.

Other Sickling Disorders. The sickle cell gene has been found in association with many structural hemoglobin variants.[3,144] However, only a minority of these conditions are common enough to warrant separate description. Recently a new sickling syndrome has been described that is symptomatic in the heterozygous state and that results from the coinheritance of a second mutation in a β-globin gene containing the sickle cell mutation.

Fig. 93-10 Hemoglobin electrophoresis (starch gel; protein stain, pH 8.6). The following are shown from left to right: 1 = sickle cell trait; 2 = normal; 3 = sickle cell anemia; 4 = normal. (*From Weatherall and Clegg.[2] Used by permission.*)

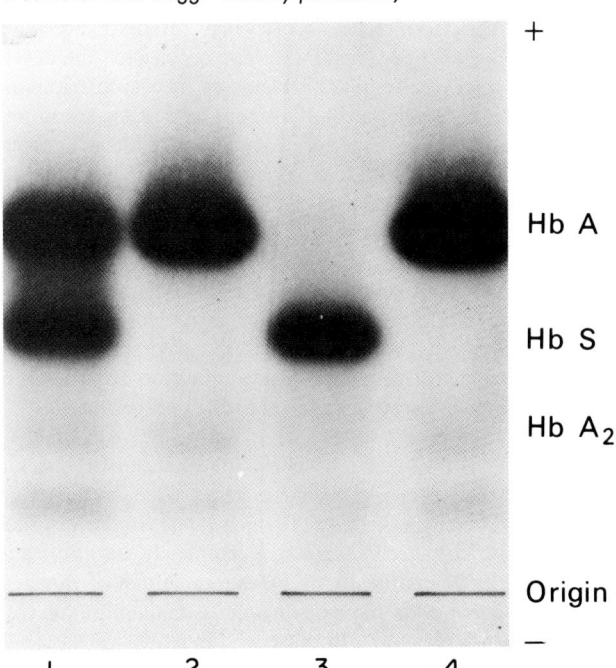

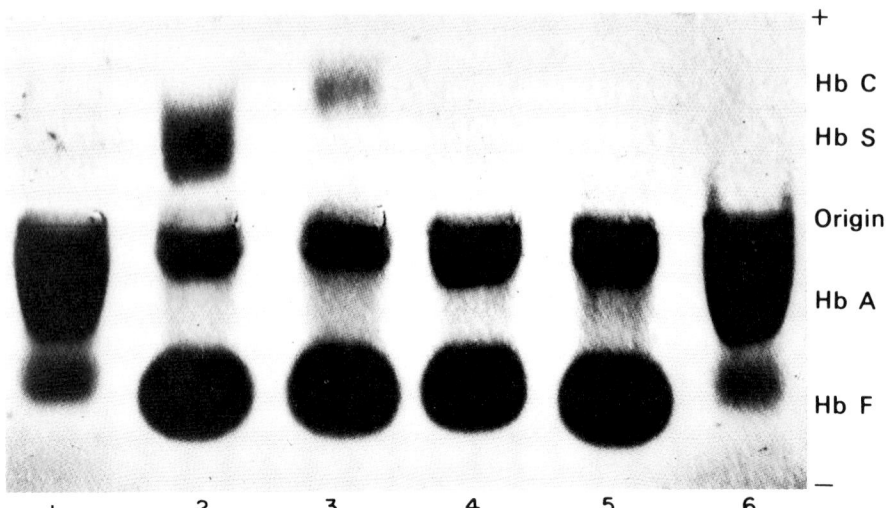

+

Hb C

Hb S

Origin

Hb A

Hb F

−

Fig. 93-11 Hemoglobin electrophoresis (agar gel, pH 6.0). The following are shown from left to right: 1 = normal; 2 = sickle cell trait in newborn period; 3 = Hb C trait in newborn period; 4 and 5 = normal newborns; 6 = normal adult. *(From Weatherall and Clegg.[2] Used by permission.)*

HEMOGLOBIN SC DISEASE. This condition[3,144] occurs in individuals of West African origin. It is a milder disorder than sickle cell anemia, although almost all the complications of the latter have been observed. Growth, development, and body habitus are normal, and the only abnormal physical sign is splenomegaly that occurs in about 65 percent of cases. The disease may not present until middle or even late in life with one of the complications. The blood picture shows a mild anemia with hemoglobin levels in the 11- to 13-g/dl range and a reticulocytosis of 3 to 5 percent. The peripheral blood film is particularly striking, showing sickled cells, many target cells, and cells that contain linear crystalline structures that tend to lie across their centers.

The main importance of Hb SC disease is that because it is mild it often goes unrecognized until a serious complication occurs. These include otherwise unexplained hematuria, aseptic necrosis of the femoral or humoral heads, and, particularly, ocular manifestations. All these changes reflect the abnormal rheology of red cells that contain both Hb S and Hb C; the pathophysiology of Hb C is considered in a later section.

The ocular complications are particularly important and are characterized by what is termed a *proliferative sickle retinopathy (PSR)*.[144] The latter seems to develop through successive stages starting with peripheral arteriolar occlusions, the development of arteriolar-venular anastomoses, neovascularization, and, finally, the development of vitreous hemorrhages and retinal detachment. In a large series studied in Jamaica[162] about one-third of patients with hemoglobin SC disease have PSR at varying stages of development, and this complication seems to be more prevalent in those with higher steady-state hematocrits.

The other serious complication of Hb SC disease is the development of widespread pulmonary vasoocclusion with the rapid onset of a typical chest syndrome as described in the section on sickle cell anemia. This complication occurs particularly commonly during pregnancy or the puerperium.

SICKLE CELL β THALASSEMIA.[3] The coinheritance of the sickle cell and β-thalassemia genes generates a wide spectrum of clinical disorders, the severity of which range from a disorder identical with sickle cell anemia to a completely asymptomatic condition that is identified only by chance. Much of this heterogeneity depends on the type of β-thalassemia mutation (see "β Thalassemia," below). In those who inherit β⁰ thalassemia the clinical disorder is very similar to sickle cell anemia. In

those who have a mild β⁺ thalassemia mutation there may be as much as 30 percent hemoglobin A in the red cells, and the clinical picture is no more severe than sickle cell or β-thalassemia trait.

OTHER COMPOUND HETEROZYGOUS DISORDERS.[13,144] *Hemoglobin S/D_{Los Angeles}* is a relatively severe disorder that resembles sickle cell anemia; this reflects the enhanced copolymerization of Hb D_{Los Angeles} with Hb S due to the β121 substitution at an important contact point in the sickle cell fiber. *Hemoglobin S/O_{Arab}* is also a severe disorder that is very similar to sickle cell anemia. The various combinations of *Hb S with hereditary persistence of fetal hemoglobin* are all extremely mild. There are numerous other examples of the interaction of α- or β-globin chain variants with Hb S. In most cases they result in an asymptomatic disorder identical with the sickle cell trait. The effects of α-thalassemia on the course of sickle cell anemia were considered in an earlier section.

SICKLE CELL DISEASE IN HETEROZYGOTES; HB S_{ANTILLES}. Recently a "new" sickling hemoglobin has been found with two substitutions in the β-globin chain, 6 Glu→Val and 23 Val→Ile.[163] This variant has the same electrophoretic mobility as Hb S, and the erythrocytes of heterozygotes tend to sickle at partial pressures of oxygen similar to those that induce sickling in Hb SC disease. Heterozygotes have a mild hemolytic anemia, splenomegaly, and, in some cases, painful crises. Thus the condition resembles Hb SC disease. Nuclear magnetic spin resonance studies suggest that the β23 substitution causes slight structural perturbations throughout the β subunit.

The discovery of this mutation is of particular interest because it raises the possibility that some of the reported heterogeneity of the sickle cell trait and sickle cell anemia might result from substitutions of this type that do not alter the charge of sickle hemoglobin and hence that cannot be identified on routine electrophoresis.

Other Common Hemoglobin Variants

The only other hemoglobin variants that are encountered commonly are Hb C, Hb D, and Hb E.

Hemoglobin C. This was the second variant to be identified electrophoretically. It results from the substitution of lysine for glutamic acid at position 6 in the β chain.[164] It is restricted in its distribution to areas of West Africa and countries in which there has been movement of populations from this region. The gene frequency in American blacks, for example, ranges from 0.01 to 0.02.

A number of observations suggest that Hb C is less soluble than Hb A, and hence it tends to crystallize within red cells.[165] This is probably due to intermolecular interactions arising from the β6 substitution. It is interesting that crystal formation is favored by the oxyhemoglobin configuration and the crystals tend to melt when red cells undergo deoxygenation in the capillaries.[166] The red cells of Hb C homozygotes contain less water than normal and have an enhanced rate of potassium efflux. It has been suggested that these changes result from the direct interaction of the positively charged Hb C with negatively charged proteins on the cytoplasmic surface of the red cell membrane.[167] Because of the resulting increased MCHC and the tendency to crystal formation, red cells containing Hb C are less deformable than normal. It seems likely that this is the major mechanism whereby their survival is shortened in the circulation. They also have decreased oxygen affinity.

Hemoglobin C heterozygotes have no hematologic changes except for an increased number of target cells on a stained blood film. The homozygous state for Hb C is characterized by a mild hemolytic anemia with splenomegaly. The blood film shows nearly 100 percent target cells, and there is a slightly elevated reticulocyte count. The peripheral blood film also shows a number of intracellular crystals.

The important interactions of Hb C are with Hb S (see previous section) and with β thalassemia. The compound heterozygous state with β⁰ thalassemia produces a clinical picture very similar to homozygous Hb C disease.

Hemoglobin D. Hemoglobin D is the term used to describe a number of hemoglobin variants that have an identical rate of migration with Hb S on electrophoresis at an alkaline pH. The only common abnormal hemoglobin with these properties is Hb D$_{Los Angeles}$ (D$_{Punjab}$). This variant occurs frequently in the Punjab region, and a number of homozygotes have been reported.[168] Their hemoglobin pattern shows almost all Hb D with normal levels of Hb A$_2$ and normal or only slightly elevated levels of Hb F. They have a normal or only slightly reduced hemoglobin level, and their red cells are normal except for increased numbers of target forms.

Hemoglobin E. This is probably the most common hemoglobin variant in the world population. It results from the substitution of glutamic acid by lysine at position 26 in the β chain.[169] It occurs mainly in a region stretching east from Bangladesh through Burma and reaches its highest frequency in eastern Thailand and Laos. It occurs in parts of China, and its distribution extends south into the Indonesian islands. Gene frequencies in these populations are considered in a later section.

The pathophysiology of Hb E is still not fully understood. There seems little doubt that it is synthesized inefficiently compared with Hb A and hence is associated with the clinical phenotype of a mild form of β thalassemia.[170] One reason for this is that the base substitution that is responsible for Hb E may also activate a cryptic splice site within exon 1 leading to abnormal splicing of β-globin mRNA.[171] But there is also evidence for decreased stability of β^E mRNA and of Hb E itself.[170] Presumably all these mechanisms are involved in set-

ting the final level of Hb E, although their relative importance remains to be clarified.

The heterozygous state for Hb E is associated with no clinical disability and with normal hemoglobin levels, although the red cells are slightly microcytic and hypochromic. There is usually about 30 to 35 percent Hb E. Similarly, Hb E homozygotes are asymptomatic and are only slightly anemic although they have red cell indices that are very similar to those of heterozygous β-thalassemia patients.

The importance of Hb E lies in the different phenotypes that result from its interaction with β thalassemia.[172] Compound heterozygotes for Hb E and β thalassemia have a variable clinical picture ranging from a condition indistinguishable from homozygous β thalassemia to a mild form of β thalassemia intermedia (see "Thalassemia," below). The hemoglobin pattern varies; in Hb E β⁰ thalassemia compound heterozygotes there is usually about 50 to 70 percent Hb F, the remainder being Hb E. Compound heterozygotes for Hb E and β⁺ thalassemia tend to have a milder disorder and produce variable amounts of Hb A. The reason for the severity of these interactions is not absolutely clear but probably reflects gross chain imbalance together with the abnormal properties of Hb E.[173]

In Southeast Asia there is a family of disorders due to the coinheritance of Hb E with different forms of α thalassemia. Heterozygotes for Hb E who inherit either α⁺ or α⁰ thalassemia have unusually low levels of Hb E.[172] The heterozygous state for Hb E in association with the genotype that produces Hb H disease (see "α Thalassemia," below) is responsible for a well-defined clinical syndrome characterized by moderate anemia, splenomegaly, and a hemoglobin pattern consisting of Hb A, Hb E, and Hb Bart's. The reason such patients produce Hb Bart's and not Hb H is not clear, although one factor may be the increased affinity of α chains for normal β chains as compared with β^E chains and the inability of the latter to form stable tetramers. Another complex group of anemias results from the various interactions of α thalassemia with the homozygous state for Hb E.[2,172]

The Unstable Hemoglobin Disorders

Over 90 different unstable hemoglobins have been reported.[3] However the term *unstable hemoglobin disorder* is usually reserved for the clinical phenotype associated with variants, the instability of which is sufficient to cause clinically recognizable hemolysis. The clinical picture associated with such abnormal hemoglobins is also called *congenital Heinz body hemolytic anemia* (CHBA).

Molecular Basis of Hemoglobin Instability.[3,174–176] There are five different classes of mutations that can result in instability of the hemoglobin molecule (Fig. 93-12). The first comprises amino acid substitutions in the vicinity of the heme pocket. The binding of heme to globin involves specific interactions with particular nonpolar amino acid residues in the CD, E, F, and FG regions of the globin subunits. Most of these residues are invariant, and hence it is not surprising that their substitution leads to a decrease in the stability of the binding of heme to globin; some examples are summarized in Fig. 93-12. At least three of these variants have amino acid substitutions at the proximal (heme-linked) histidine; two others have substitutions at the distal histidine. Some abnormal hemoglobins of this type are particularly susceptible to drug-induced pre-

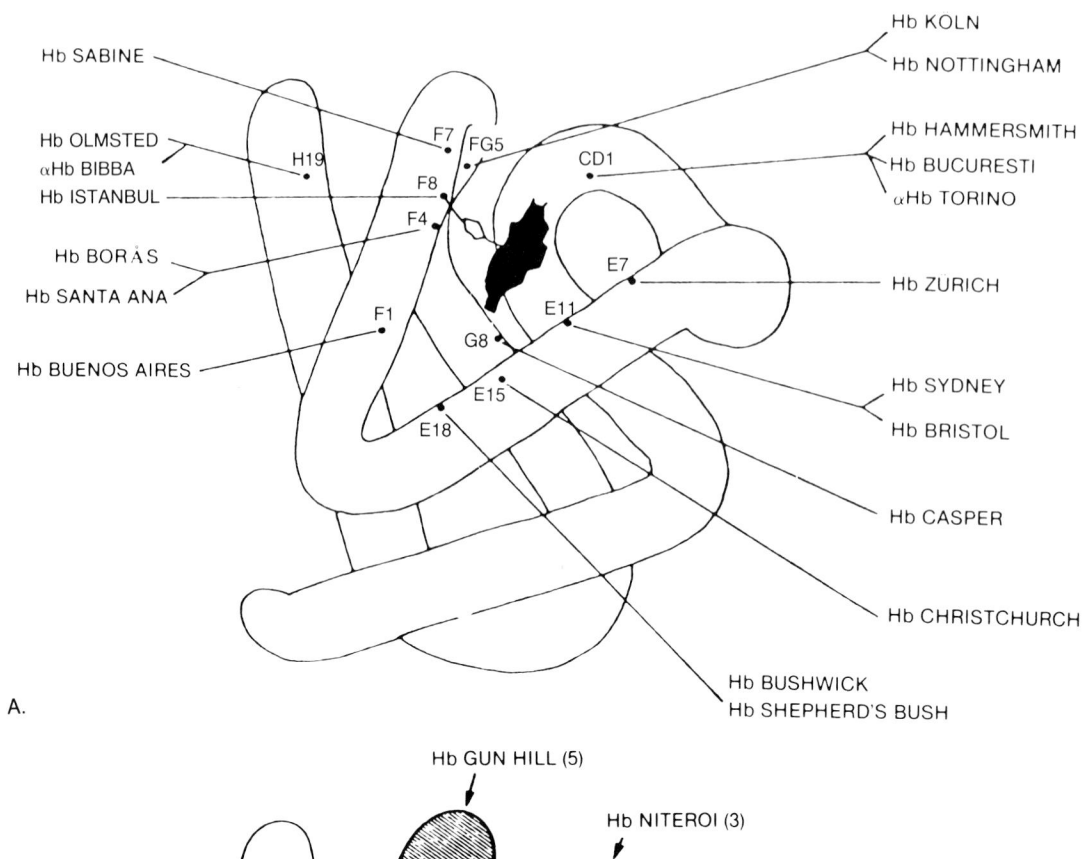

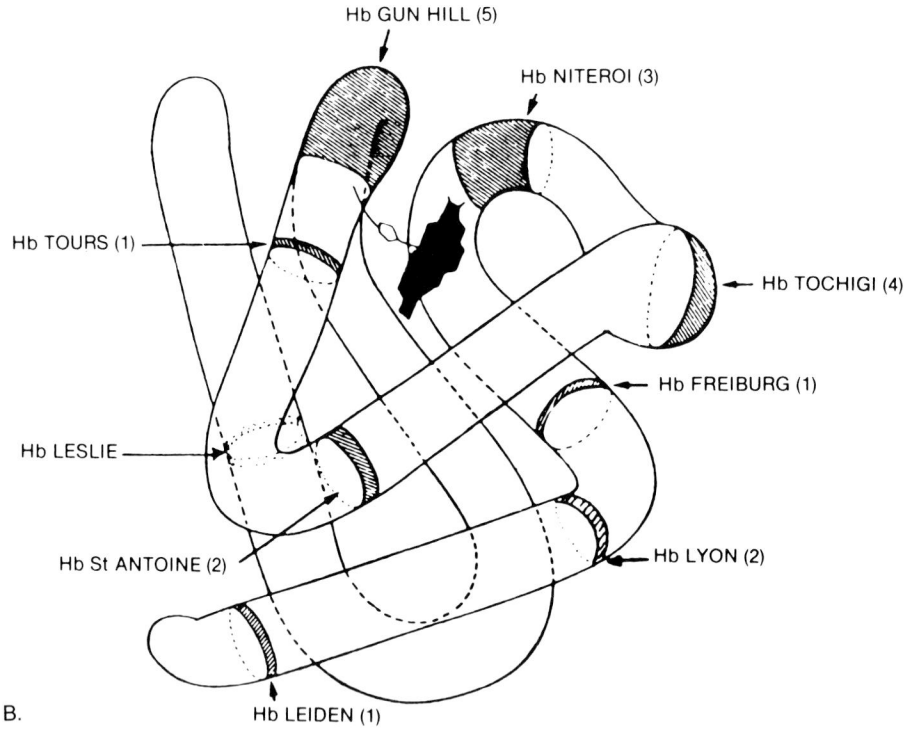

Fig. 93-12   The unstable hemoglobin variants. A. Three-dimensional representation of the β chain showing sites of amino acid substitutions at the heme pocket. B. Three-dimensional representation of the β chain showing sites of amino acid deletions that cause unstable hemoglobins. *(From Milner and Wrightstone.*[176] *Used by permission.)*

cipitation and hemolysis. Hemoglobin Zurich, for example, has a substitution that leaves the heme pocket wide open, thus allowing drugs like sulfonamides ready access to the heme iron.

A second group of unstable variants result from amino acid substitutions that disrupt the secondary structure of the globin chains. About 75 percent of globin is in the form of an α helix in which proline cannot participate except as part of one of the initial three residues. Eleven unstable hemoglobin variants have been described that result from the substitution of pro-

line for leucine, five that are caused by an alanine-to-proline change and three in which proline is substituted by histidine. Another group of variants that cause disruption of the normal configuration of the hemoglobin molecule involves internal substitutions that interfere with its stabilization by hydrophobic interactions. Some of these variants result in alterations in tertiary structure and hence allow access of water to the hydrophobic interior of globin subunits.

Finally, there are two groups of unstable hemoglobins that result from gross structural abnormalities of the globin subunits. At least 11 variants have been found that contain deletions ranging from one to five residues, many of which involve regions at or near interhelical corners. A few unstable variants have elongated globin chains. For example, Hb Cranston and Hb Saverne are associated with a mild hemolysis that is probably due to the hydrophobic segments attached to the C-terminal ends of their β-globin chains.

The Mechanism of Hemoglobin Denaturation.[174–176] The major result of these substitutions is the precipitation of hemoglobin with the formation of a rigid Heinz body. The latter causes retardation of the passage of red cells through the microcirculation and hence leads to their premature destruction.

Although the precise details of the mechanisms of hemoglobin precipitation in these disorders are unknown, a general pattern has emerged. Hemoglobin can autooxidize into methemoglobin with the dissociation of superoxide anion. The latter, and its reduction product, hydrogen peroxide, are able to generate more methemoglobin. The unstable hemoglobins show a more rapid rate of autooxidation than normal hemoglobin. Furthermore, methemoglobin can be converted into hemichrome in which globin undergoes sufficient internal distortion to allow direct bonding of an amino acid side chain to the distal aspect of the heme iron. Initially this process is reversible, but ultimately irreversible hemichrome formation occurs, and this is followed by precipitation of hemoglobin with the production of a Heinz body. In addition, some unstable variants interact with glutathione to form mixed disulfides. Furthermore, as mentioned above, the formation of methemoglobin favors the dissociation of heme from globin.

A scheme for the denaturation of unstable hemoglobin with the production of Heinz bodies is shown in Fig. 93-13.

Mechanism of Hemolysis.[177–180] Red cells that contain Heinz bodies have decreased pliability and hence negotiate the microcirculation with difficulty. These cells are trapped during their transit between the cords and sinuses of the spleen. In this way a Heinz body may be "pulled out" of the cell during its passage through the spleen, after which the remainder of the cell reseals. This process causes membrane damage that also may be mediated by the adherence of Heinz bodies to the inner surface of the red cell membrane. The red cells of patients with unstable hemoglobin disorders show an increased rate of potassium leak and, in some cases, reduced levels of ATP. Furthermore, because unstable hemoglobins may favor release of reactive oxidants such as hydrogen peroxide, superoxide, and free hydroxyl radical, these toxic side products may also damage the red cell membrane by causing lipid peroxidation and cross-linking of membrane proteins.

Clinical and Hematologic Findings. Patients with CHBA have a varying degree of hemolysis that is inherited as autosomal dominant. In several cases no affected relatives have been found, and the hemoglobin variants are thought to be the result of new mutations.[179]

The clinical course is characterized by anemia and splenomegaly, and the intermittent passage of dark urine. The last is not due to hemoglobinuria but to pigmenturia; the pigments have not been identified with certainty but may be related to dipyrrolmethanes of the mesobilifuscin group. Hematologic studies show the features of a hemolytic anemia with a raised reticulocyte count and variation in the shape and size of the

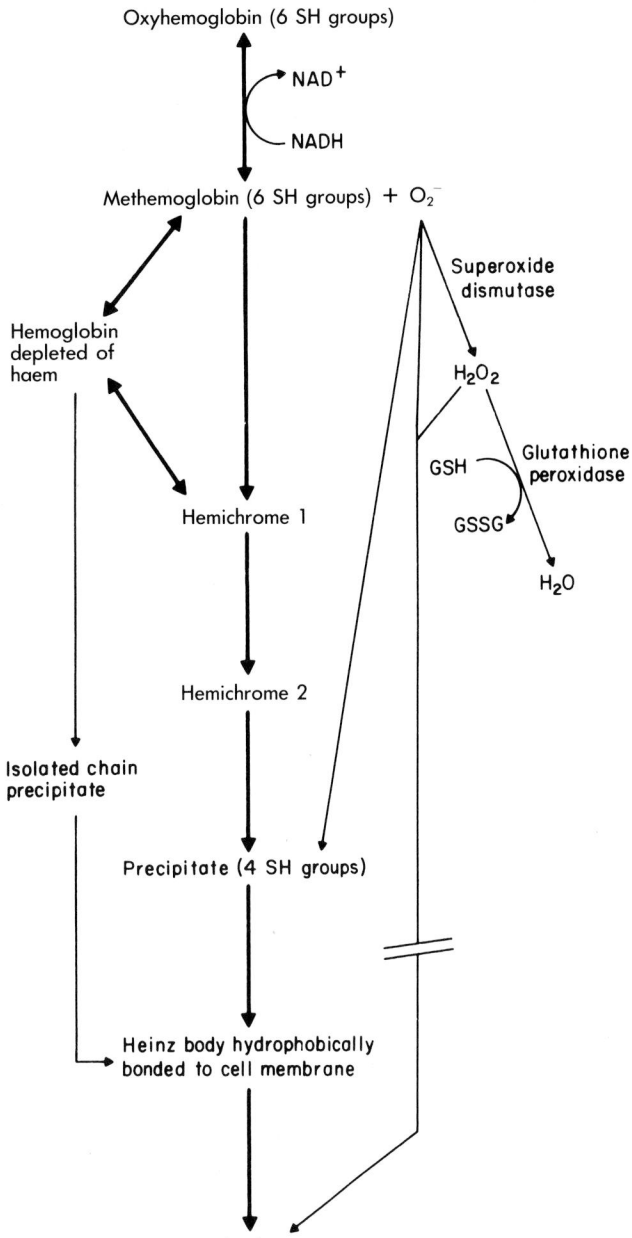

Fig. 93-13 Schematic representation of the mechanism of hemoglobin precipitation in the unstable hemoglobin disorders. *(From Weatherall and Clegg.[2] Used by permission.)*

red cells. In patients with an intact spleen this may be all that is found. However, after splenectomy many of the red cells contain Heinz bodies.

The hemoglobin variants that are associated with this condition often have neutral mutations; i.e., they cannot be identified by electrophoresis. However, if dilute hemoglobin solutions are incubated in a neutral phosphate buffer at 50° for 1 to 2 h, unstable variants precipitate. A similar effect can be induced by incubation of hemolysates in 17% isopropanol at 37°. Hemoglobin electrophoresis may show no abnormality, but sometimes after the red cell lysate has been stored for a few days a variety of bands appear, some of which are heme-depleted and therefore are only seen with a protein stain. The hemoglobin A_2 level may be slightly increased in patients with unstable β-chain variants. The position of the oxygen dissociation curve varies; both high and low affinity unstable hemoglobins have been reported.

Course and Prognosis. The majority of patients with CHBA have a mild anemia and are not incapacitated. Because some of these variants are precipitated by oxidant drugs, exacerbations may occur after drug therapy or with intercurrent illnesses, particularly infection. Rarely, there may be progressive splenomegaly with hypersplenism. Sustained thrombocytosis has been observed after splenectomy.

Hemoglobin Variants with Abnormal Oxygen Binding

Several clinical syndromes result from abnormalities of oxygen binding by abnormal hemoglobins. Both low and high oxygen affinity variants have been encountered. About a third of the unstable variants described in the previous section have increased oxygen affinity, but in these disorders the clinical manifestations are due to accelerated red cell destruction; the hemoglobin level may be modified by the oxygen affinity of the particular variant. There are, however, over 40 abnormal hemoglobins in which increased oxygen affinity occurs without instability. These variants are sometimes associated with the clinical syndrome of genetic polycythemia. On the other hand, variants characterized by a low oxygen affinity may result in a dominantly inherited form of cyanosis.

High Oxygen Affinity Variants and Hereditary Polycythemia.[3,181-183] As mentioned earlier, hemoglobin exists in equilibrium between two quaternary conformations, R and T. When it is fully deoxygenated, it assumes the T, or tense, state in which it has a low affinity for oxygen and a relatively high affinity for allosteric molecules such as Bohr protons and 2,3-DPG. On the other hand, oxyhemoglobin exists in the R or relaxed state in which it has a high affinity for oxygen and a low affinity for allosteric effectors. The transition between these two conformations requires cooperativity between the subunits that is the molecular basis for heme-heme interaction. Most of the high affinity variants result from mutations that cause amino acid substitutions that affect the equilibrium between the R and T states. Many of them are found at the $\alpha_1\beta_2$ interface, the C-terminal end of the β chain, and the 2,3-DPG binding sites (Table 93-5).

The clinical findings vary in patients with high oxygen affinity hemoglobin variants. There is usually an erythrocytosis with an elevated hemoglobin level but no changes in the white cell or platelet counts and no splenomegaly, features that distinguish these conditions from polycythemia vera, a myeloproliferative disorder involving hemopoietic stem cells. The whole blood oxygen dissociation curve is shifted to the left with a reduced p50; many of the high affinity hemoglobins also show a decreased alkaline Bohr effect. In some cases there is reduced interaction with 2,3-DPG. The other physiological properties of these variants have been the subject of a number of extensive reviews.[182,183]

The majority of patients with high oxygen affinity variants are asymptomatic and are ascertained only because they are found to have a modest erythrocytosis on routine hematologic examination. The diagnosis is made by ruling out other causes of polycythemia and by demonstrating a decreased p50 associated with a hemoglobin variant. It is important to remember that there are other causes of a left shifted oxygen dissociation curve, methemoglobin or carboxyhemoglobin, for example, that must be excluded by spectroscopic analysis.

Low Oxygen Affinity Variants. There are far fewer hemoglobin variants with low oxygen affinities (Table 93-5). As mentioned earlier, some unstable variants fall into this group, and some of the M hemoglobins also have decreased oxygen affinity.

The best studied low oxygen variant is Hb Kansas.[184] Carriers have normal hemoglobin levels but are cyanosed from birth. The condition is associated with a reduced oxygen saturation of the arterial blood despite a Pa_{O_2} of 100 mmHg. When these individuals breathe 100 percent oxygen, the oxygen saturation increases by about 30 percent, suggesting that there is a marked decrease in whole blood oxygen affinity. Hemoglobin Kansas has a threonine substitution for asparagine at position 102 in the β chain. It is interesting that this residue is at the $\alpha1\beta2$ interface, similar to some of the high affinity variants described earlier. The low affinity of Hb Kansas seems to be due in part to a relatively unstable R structure, although the precise mechanism is not understood. The clinical picture associated with two other low affinity variants, hemoglobins Beth Israel and St. Mande, is similar.

Congenital Cyanosis due to Hemoglobin Variants. Congenital methemoglobinemia may result from either an inherited structural hemoglobin variant or from a defect in one of the enzyme systems involved in maintaining a normal level of reduced hemoglobin in the red cells; the latter group of conditions is considered in Chap. 92.

The five structural hemoglobin variants that are associated with methemoglobinemia are all designated *Hb M*; they are further defined by their place of discovery, i.e., Hb M_{Boston}, Hb $M_{Hyde Park}$, and so on. Their structure-function relationships have been the subject of several detailed reviews.[3,184a] As mentioned earlier in this chapter, the iron atom of heme is normally linked to the imidazole group of the proximal histidine residue of the α and β chains. There is another histidine residue on the opposite side, near the sixth coordination position of the heme iron; this, the so-called distal histidine residue, is the normal binding site for oxygen. The imidazole group of the distal histidine does not form a bond with heme iron except, as mentioned earlier, in the pathologic conditions in which hemichrome is formed.

Four of the five M hemoglobins result from the substitution of a tyrosine for either the proximal or distal histidine residues in either the α or β chains. It is likely that the phenolic group of the abnormal tyrosine residue forms a covalent link with the heme iron, thus stabilizing the iron atom in the oxidized

Table 93-5 Hemoglobin Variants with Altered Oxygen Affinity

High oxygen affinity variants	
Mutations at $\alpha_1\beta_2$ contacts	
Hb Chesapeake	α92 Arg → Leu
Hb J-Cape Town	α92 Arg → Gln
Hb Tarrant	α126 Asp → Asn
Hb Legnano	α141 Arg → Leu
Mutations at 2,3-DPG binding sites	
Hb Rahere	β86 Lys → Thr
Hb Helsinki	β82 Lys → Met
Hb Providence	β82 Lys → Asn
Heme binding site	
Hb Heathrow	β103 Phe → Leu
Low oxygen affinity variants	
Mutations at $\alpha_1\beta_2$ contact	
Hb Kansas	β102 Asn → Thr
Hb Beth Israel	β102 Asn → Ser
Mutations at 2,3-DPG binding site	
Hb Raleigh	β1 Val → Acet.Ala

NOTE: A complete list with references is given in Ref. 3.

(Fe^{3+}) configuration. The first three hemoglobin Ms to be discovered were Hb M$_{Boston}$ (α58 His→Tyr), Hb M$_{Saskatoon}$ (β63 His→Tyr), and Hb M$_{Milwaukee-1}$ (β67 Val→Glu). Another variant, Hb M$_{Iwate}$ (α87 His→Tyr), was discovered later in Japan, although it subsequently turned up in other populations. A fifth variant, Hb M$_{Hyde\ Park}$ (β92 His→Tyr) was first encountered in the United Kingdom. Recently a fetal hemoglobin variant associated with methemoglobinemia, Hb FM$_{Osaka}$ (γ63 His→Tyr) has been found in a Japanese infant.

X-ray crystallographic studies have confirmed that these amino acid substitutions stabilize the heme group of the mutant hemoglobins in the oxidized forms. Once in this form the abnormal subunit is resitant to reduction by both enzymes and reducing agents.

Individuals who are heterozygous for the M hemoglobins are cyanosed from early in life but are otherwise asymptomatic. The condition can often be distinguished from congenital methemoglobinemia due to an enzyme defect by the family history; the pattern of inheritance of Hb M is typically dominant. Furthermore, if the cyanosis is present from birth, it is usually due to an α-chain Hb M hemoglobin variant; alternatively if cyanosis appears only during the first few months of life, the disorder is likely to be due to a β-chain variant. It is interesting that conjunctival cyanosis is present in children with methemoglobinemia but not in those in whom the cyanosis is due to defective oxygenation of the blood; the conjunctival sac provides such close apposition of the red cells to air that it acts as a "second lung"; even in cases of severe cyanotic heart disease or pulmonary disease conjunctival cyanosis is usually absent.

The diagnosis of methemoglobinemia is made by demonstrating increased amounts of methemoglobin in the red cells. The M hemoglobins give a characteristic spectral abnormality provided the hemoglobin is completely oxidized to the Fe^{3+} state with ferricyanide. They are not demonstrable by hemoglobin electrophoresis under routine conditions, although some of them separate on agar gel at pH 7.1. They can be demonstrated more effectively if the red cell lysate is first oxidized with ferricyanide.

No treatment is required for congenital methemoglobinemia due to an M hemoglobin. Affected individuals tolerate major surgery without difficulty; the main task for the clinician is to arrive at an accurate diagnosis and to provide adequate reassurance.

THALASSEMIA

The thalassemias are the most common single gene disorders in the world population. They have been the subject of several monographs[2,6,185] and reviews.[186–188] In this section, after defining and classifying these conditions, we describe their pathophysiology as a group; since they are very heterogeneous they share much in common with respect to the mechanisms of disordered erythropoiesis and red cell destruction. We then describe the molecular pathology and clinical and hematologic features of each of the main varieties.

Definition and Classification

The thalassemias are a heterogeneous group of inherited disorders of hemoglobin synthesis, all characterized by the absence or reduced output of one or more of the globin chains of hemoglobin. This leads to imbalanced globin chain synthesis that is the hallmark of all the thalassemia syndromes.[3]

The main types of thalassemia are summarized in Table 93-6. The most common and clinically most important forms are α, β, and $\delta\beta$ thalassemia. Each of these can be classified into disorders in which no chains are produced from the affected chromosomes, α^0, β^0, and $(\delta\beta)^0$ thalassemia, and those in which some chains are synthesized, but at a reduced rate, α^+, β^+, and $(\delta\beta)^+$ thalassemia. The related condition, hereditary persistence of fetal hemoglobin, can be regarded as a particularly mild form of β or $\delta\beta$ thalassemia in which defective β-chain production is fully compensated by persistent γ-chain synthesis beyond the neonatal period.

In many populations the thalassemias coexist with a variety of different structural hemoglobin variants. Thus it is quite common to inherit both types of condition. Furthermore, it is equally common for individuals to receive genes for more than one type of thalassemia. These complex interactions give rise to an extremely diverse series of clinical disorders that, taken together, constitute the thalassemia syndromes.[3]

Pathophysiology

One of the most remarkable aspects of the thalassemia field is how it has been possible to relate the diverse clinical manifestations, that may affect almost any organ system, to primary molecular defects in the α- or β-globin genes. In fact it is possible to trace almost all the pathophysiological features of these conditions back to a primary imbalance of globin chain synthesis (Fig 93-14). It is this phenomenon that makes the thalassemias fundamentally different from all the other genetic and acquired disorders of hemoglobin production and, to a large extent, explains their extreme severity in the homozygous or compound heterozygous states.

Imbalanced Globin Chain Synthesis. Measurements of in vitro globin chain synthesis in the peripheral blood or bone marrows of patients with different types of thalassemia,[12,173] together with genetic studies that enable the action of the thalassemia genes to be examined in patients who have also

Table 93-6 The Thalassemias and Related Disorders

α Thalassemia
α^0
α^+ Deletion, nondeletion
With α-chain Hb variants
With β-chain Hb variants
With β thalassemia
β Thalassemia
β^0
β^+
With β-chain Hb variants
With α-chain Hb variants
With α thalassemia
$\delta\beta$ Thalassemia
$(\delta\beta)^0$ Thalassemia
$(^A\gamma\delta\beta)^0$ Thalassemia
$(\epsilon\gamma\delta\beta)^0$ Thalassemia
δ Thalassemia
γ Thalassemia
Hereditary persistence of fetal hemoglobin
Deletion
$(\delta\beta)^0$ HPFH
Nondeletion
Linked to β-globin gene cluster
Unlinked to β-globin gene cluster

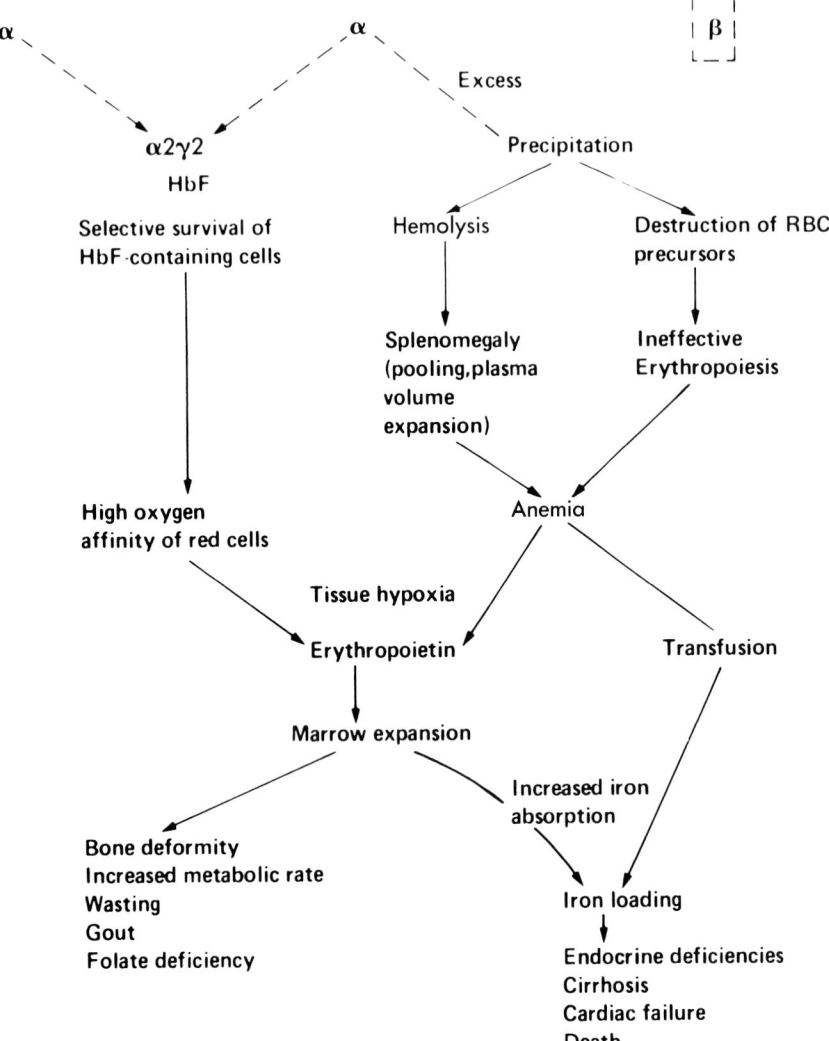

Fig. 93-14 The pathophysiology of β thalassemia.

inherited α- or β-globin structural variants, provide a clear picture of the action of the thalassemia determinants.[3,11] In homozygous β thalassemia β-globin synthesis may be either absent or markedly reduced. This results in the production of an excess of α-globin chains. Unpaired α-globin chains are incapable of forming a viable hemoglobin tetramer and hence precipitate in red cell precursors.[189-191] The resulting inclusion bodies can be demonstrated by both light and electron microscopy (Fig. 93-15). In the bone marrow, precipitation can be seen in the earliest hemoglobinized precursors and right through the erythroid maturation pathway.[192] These large inclusions are responsible for the intramedullary destruction of red cell precursors and hence the ineffective erythropoiesis that characterizes all the β thalassemias. It has been calculated that a large proportion of the developing erythroblasts are destroyed within the bone marrow in severe cases.[193] Such red cells as are released are prematurely destroyed by mechanisms that are considered below.

β-Thalassemia heterozygotes also have imbalanced globin chain synthesis, but in this case the magnitude of the excess of α chains is much less and presumably can be dealt with successfully by the proteolytic enzymes of the red cell precursors.[194] Notwithstanding, there is a mild degree of ineffective erythropoiesis.

From these considerations it is clear that the anemia of β thalassemia has three major components. First and most important, there is ineffective erythropoiesis with intramedullary

destruction of a variable proportion of the developing red cell precursors. Second, there is a hemolytic component due to destruction of mature red cells containing α-chain inclusions. Finally, because of the overall reduction in hemoglobin synthesis, the red cells are hypochromic and microcytic.

Because the primary defect in β thalassemia is in β-chain production, the synthesis of hemoglobins F and A_2 should be unaffected. Fetal hemoglobin production in utero is normal, and it is only when the neonatal switch from γ- to β-chain production occurs that the clinical manifestations of thalassemia first appear. However, fetal hemoglobin synthesis persists beyond the neonatal period in nearly all forms of β thalassemia; we return to the reasons for this in a later section. In β-thalassemia heterozygotes there is an elevated level of Hb A_2. This appears to reflect both a relative decrease in Hb A due to defective β-chain synthesis but also an absolute increase in the output of δ chains both cis and trans to the mutant β-globin gene.[3] The question of Hb A_2 production in homozygous β thalassemia is extremely complex and is discussed in a later section.

The consequences of excess non-α chain production in the α thalassemias are quite different. α Chains are shared by both fetal and adult hemoglobin, and therefore defective α-chain production is manifest in both fetal and adult life. In the fetus a reduced output of α chains leads to excess γ-chain production; similarly, in the adult excess β chains are produced. Excess γ chains combine to form γ_4 homotetramers or Hb

Bart's[195]; excess β chains form β₄ homotetramers or Hb H.[196] It is this ability of γ and β chains to form homotetramers that is the basis of the fundamental difference in the pathophysiology of α and β thalassemia. Because γ_4 and β_4 tetramers are soluble, they do not precipitate to any significant degree in the bone marrow, and therefore the α thalassemias are not characterized by a severe degree of ineffective erythropoiesis. However, β_4 tetramers precipitate as red cells age, with the formation of inclusion bodies. Thus the anemia of the more severe forms of α thalassemia in the adult is due mainly to a shortened red cell survival consequent on their damage in the microvasculature of the spleen due to the presence of the inclusions. In addition, because of the defect in hemoglobin synthesis the cells are hypochromic and microcytic. Hemoglobin Bart's is more stable than Hb H and does not appear to form inclusions.

But there is another factor that exacerbates the tissue hypoxia of the anemia of the α thalassemias. Both Hb Bart's and Hb H show no heme-heme interaction and have almost hyperbolic oxygen dissociation curves with very high oxygen affinities. Thus they are not able to give up oxygen at physiological tissue tensions and are, in effect, useless as oxygen carriers.[3]

It follows, therefore, that infants with high levels of Hb Bart's have severe intrauterine hypoxia. This is a major component of the clinical picture of homozygous α^0 thalassemia, which results in the stillbirth of hydropic infants late in pregnancy or at term. Severe intrauterine oxygen deprivation is reflected by the grossly hydropic state of the infant, presumably due to an increase in capillary permeability consequent on hypoxia, and severe erythroblastosis. Deficient fetal oxygenation is probably responsible for the enormously hypertrophied placentas that occur with the severe forms of intrauterine α thalassemia.[197]

Persistent Fetal Hemoglobin Production and Cellular Heterogeneity.
One of the earliest observations on the hemoglobin patterns of children with severe thalassemia was that there

Fig. 93-15 Inclusion bodies in the red cell precursors in homozygous β thalassemia. Electron microscopy, ×6,570. *From Weatherall and Clegg.[2] Used by permission; original preparations supplied by Dr. A. Polliack.)*

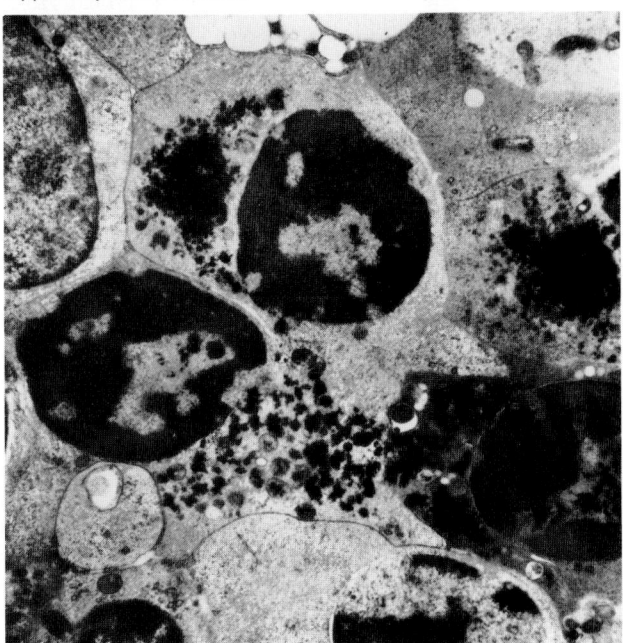

is a variable amount of Hb F production that persists into childhood and later.[3] Indeed, in the β^0 thalassemias, except for small amounts of Hb A_2, Hb F is the only hemoglobin produced. Examination of the peripheral blood using staining methods that are specific for Hb F show that it is heterogeneously distributed among the red cells. Persistent Hb F production is not a feature of the more severe forms of α thalassemia, although in some cases persistent γ-chain synthesis is reflected by the presence of Hb Bart's after the first 6 months of life.

There are still many unanswered questions about the mechanisms of persistent γ-chain synthesis in the thalassemias. Normal adults have small quantities of Hb F that is heterogeneously distributed among the red cells; cells with demonstrable Hb F are called *F cells*. It is clear that one important mechanism for persistent Hb F production in β thalassemia is cell selection.[3,198,199] As already mentioned, the major cause of ineffective erythropoiesis and shortened red cell survival in β thalassemia is the deleterious effects of excess α chains on erythroid maturation and survival of red cells in the blood. It follows, therefore, that any red cell precursors that produce significant numbers of γ chains will be at an advantage in an environment in which there are excess α chains; the latter will combine with γ chains to produce Hb F, and therefore the magnitude of α-chain precipitation will be less. Differential centrifugation experiments[199] and in vivo labeling studies[198] have shown that populations of red cells with relatively large amounts of Hb F are more efficiently produced and survive longer in the peripheral blood than those with low levels or no Hb F. The peripheral blood of homozygous β-thalassemia patients shows remarkable cellular heterogeneity with respect to red cell survival times; there are populations of cells that contain predominantly Hb A that are very rapidly destroyed in the spleen and elsewhere, cells with a much longer survival that contain relatively more Hb F, and populations of intermediate age and hemoglobin constitution.[3,186]

Whether cell selection of this type is the only mechanism for persistent γ-chain production in β thalassemia is not clear. It is possible that there may be an absolute increase in Hb F production; this is certainly so in some milder forms of homozygous β thalassemia, but in these cases there may be other genetic factors that are responsible for the relatively high level of γ-chain synthesis (see later section).

Since there is a reciprocal relation between γ- and δ-chain synthesis, it follows that the red cells of β-thalassemia homozygotes that contain large amounts of Hb F have relatively low levels of Hb A_2.[3,199] Thus the measured percent Hb A_2 in these individuals is the average of a very heterogeneous cell population. This probably accounts for the extreme variability in the levels of Hb A_2 reported in patients with this disorder.

A further consequence of the persistence of Hb F in β thalassemia is that the red cells have a high oxygen affinity. Thalassemic red cells adapt poorly to anemia, as reflected by inappropriately low levels of 2,3-DPG and a high oxygen affinity.[3]

Consequences of Compensatory Mechanisms for the Anemia of Thalassemia.
The profound anemia of homozygous β thalassemia combined with the high oxygen affinity of such blood as is produced combines to produce severe tissue hypoxia. Because of the properties of Hb Bart's and Hb H, a similar defect in tissue oxygenation occurs in the more severe

forms of α thalassemia. The major response is erythropoietin production and expansion of the dyserythropoietic bone marrow. This in turn leads to deformities of the skull and face, and porosity of the long bones.[2] In extreme cases extramedullary hemopoietic tumors may develop. Apart from the production of severe skeletal deformities, bone marrow expansion may cause pathologic fractures, sinus disease, and chronic middle ear infection.

Another effect of the enormous expansion of the marrow mass in severe thalassemia is to divert calories required for normal development to the ineffective red cell precursor population. Thus severely affected thalassemia patients show poor development and wasting. The massive turnover of erythroid precursors may result in secondary hyperuricemia and gout, and severe folate deficiency.

The effects of gross intrauterine hypoxia in homozygous α⁰ thalassemia have already been described. In the symptomatic forms of α thalassemia such as Hb H disease, which are compatible with survival into adult life, bone changes and other consequences of erythroid expansion are seen, although to a much lesser degree than in β thalassemia.

Splenomegaly; Dilutional Anemia. The constant bombardment of the spleen with abnormal red cells gives rise to the phenomenon of *work hypertrophy*. Progressive splenomegaly occurs in both α and β thalassemia and may exacerbate the anemia.[3,185] Large spleens act as a sump for red cells and may sequestrate a considerable proportion of the peripheral red cell mass. Furthermore, splenomegaly may also cause plasma volume expansion, a complication that may be exacerbated by massive expansion of the erythroid bone marrow. The combination of pooling of the red cells in the spleen together with plasma volume expansion may cause worsening of the anemia in both α and β thalassemia. The same process may occur in an enlarged liver, particularly after splenectomy.

Abnormal Iron Metabolism. In β-thalassemia homozygotes who are anemic there is an increase in intestinal iron absorption that is related to the degree of expansion of the red cell precursor population; iron absorption is decreased by blood transfusion.[185] Increased absorption causes a steady accumulation of iron, first in the Kupffer cells of the liver and in the reticuloendothelial (RE) cells of the spleen but later in the parenchymal cells of the liver (Fig. 93-16). Most homozygous β-thalassemia patients require regular blood transfusion, and thus transfusional siderosis adds to the iron accumulation. As well as the liver, iron accumulates in the endocrine glands, particularly the parathyroids and adrenals, pancreas, skin, and most importantly, in the myocardium. The latter leads to death, either by involving the conducting tissues or by causing intractable cardiac failure. Other consequences of iron loading include diabetes, hyperparathyroidism, and hypogonadism, mainly due to end-organ failure.[200-202]

Disordered iron metabolism is less common in the adult forms of α thalassemia. The reason is not clear, but the milder degree of anemia, less marked erythroid expansion of the marrow, and the fact that Hb H may not bind to haptoglobin and may be excreted in the urine all play a part.

There appears to be an increased susceptibility to bacterial infection in all forms of severe thalassemia.[3,185,203] The reason is not known. It has been suggested that the relatively high serum iron levels may favor bacterial growth. Another possible mechanism is blockage of the RE system due to the increased

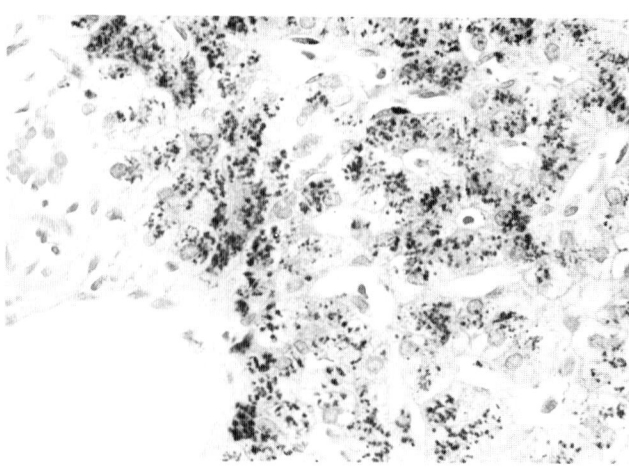

Fig. 93-16 Iron loading of the liver in β thalassemia intermedia. ×306, iron stain.

rate of destruction of red cells. No consistent defects in white cell or immune function have been demonstrated, but it remains to be shown unequivocally that high serum iron levels are an important factor.

Disordered Red Cell Metabolism. As we have seen, the presence of α- or β-chain inclusions in the red cells of thalassemia patients is explanation enough for their shortened survival. However, many abnormalities of red cell metabolism that might also play a role have been demonstrated.[3,185,204] These include oxidant damage to the membrane as a consequence of lipid peroxidation resulting from generation of superoxide and the formation of hemichrome by the precipitated globin chains. The significance of hemichromes was discussed in the section that deals with the unstable hemoglobin disorders. These abnormalities may be enhanced by vitamin E deficiency and excess iron in the red cells. Damage to the red cell membrane is reflected by a variety of abnormalities of permeability including an increase in the rate of potassium loss from the cells of both homozygotes and heterozygotes for β thalassemia and of individuals with the more severe forms of α thalassemia. Centrifugation experiments show that these changes are more severe in the fast-turning-over, low Hb F/high Hb A population of red cells of β-thalassemia patients.[204]

Clinical Heterogeneity. The pathophysiological mechanisms outlined in the previous sections provide a basis for the remarkable clinical diversity of the thalassemia syndromes. It is clear that all the clinical manifestations of β thalassemia can be related to excess α-chain production. It follows that any mechanism that tends to reduce the excess of α chains in β thalassemia should modify the clinical course of the disease. A number of elegant experiments of nature have shown that this is the case. For example, β-thalassemia homozygotes who inherit one or more α-thalassemia genes tend to run a much milder course than those with β thalassemia alone.[205-207] Similarly, the coinheritance of one or more genetic determinants that favor persistent γ-chain synthesis after the neonatal period ameliorates the condition. In other words if α thalassemia is coinherited, the magnitude of excess α chains is less; if there is a higher than usual output of γ chains, some of the excess α chains combine with γ chains to produce Hb F. In either case the overall excess of α chains is less, and therefore the degree of ineffective erythropoiesis and hemolysis is reduced. These clinical observations have provided strong support for the various pathophysiological concepts outlined in the previous sections.

It is clear that if patients with β thalassemia are adequately transfused, most of the consequences of excess α-chain production can be overcome. The drive to erythroid expansion is diminished, and hence the skeletal and growth abnormalities do not develop. Iron absorption from the gastrointestinal tract is reduced, and because endogenous red cell production is turned off, hepatosplenomegaly does not occur. Thus adequately transfused thalassemic children grow and develop normally, although if iron is not removed by chelation therapy, they succumb to the effects of iron loading of the tissues in the second or third decade.

α Thalassemia

Classification. Until the late 1970s the various determinants of α thalassemia could be defined only in terms of their effect on the phenotype (MCV, MCH, α/β-globin chain synthesis ratio) and the way in which they interact to produce the carrier states for α thalassemia (α thalassemia minor), Hb H disease, or the Hb Bart's hydrops fetalis syndrome (Table 93-7).[2] More recently, many of the underlying molecular defects have been identified, and therefore it is possible to establish a more comprehensive system for classifying the mutant alleles.

α Thalassemias in which no normal α globin is produced from the α-gene complex are called α^0 thalassemia, and those in which the output is reduced are referred to as α^+ thalassemias. This brings the classification of the α thalassemias in line with that for the β thalassemias. The α^0 and α^+ thalassemias can be further subdivided, according to the precise nature of the underlying molecular defect, into deletion and nondeletion types.

The α-globin haplotype may be written αα, representing the α_2 and α_1 genes, respectively. Therefore, a normal individual has the genotype αα/αα. A deletion involving one $(-\alpha)$ or both $(--)$ α genes may be further classified on the basis of its size, written as a superscript; thus $-\alpha^{3.7}$ indicates a deletion of 3.7-kb DNA including one α gene. Where the size of a deletion has not yet been established, a superscript describing the geographical or individual origin of the deletion is used; thus $--^{MED}$ describes a deletion of both α genes first

identified in individuals of Mediterranean origin. In those thalassemic haplotypes where both genes are intact, the nomenclature $\alpha\alpha^T$ is given, but when the precise molecular defect is known, as in Hb Constant Spring,[97] for example, $\alpha\alpha^T$ can be replaced by the more informative $\alpha^{CS}\alpha$.

This system provides an accurate shorthand way of describing various interactions. For example, the genotype $--^{SEA}/\alpha^{CS}\alpha$ denotes an interaction of the Hb Constant Spring mutation with the common Southeast Asian α^0 defect. The relationship of these genotypes to the commonly observed phenotypes of α thalassemia are outlined in Table 93.7 and discussed in detail in a later section.

Molecular Pathology.

α^+ THALASSEMIA DUE TO DELETIONS. The most common molecular defects underlying α thalassemia $(-\alpha^{3.7}$ and $-\alpha^{4.2})$ involve the deletion of one or other of the duplicated α-globin genes (Fig. 93-17). One or both of these determinants occur in all populations in which thalassemia is common.

The mechanism by which the α^+ thalassemia deletions occur has now been established, and it is clearly related to the underlying molecular structure of the α-globin complex.[38,211] Each α gene is located within a region of homology approximately 4 kb long, interrupted by two small nonhomologous regions (Fig. 93-18). It is thought that the homologous regions result from an ancient duplication event. Subsequently, during evolution, these homologous segments were subdivided, presumably by insertions and deletions, to give three homologous subsegments referred to as X, Y, and Z (Fig. 93-18). The duplicated Z boxes are 3.7 kb apart, and the X boxes are 4.2 kb apart. Misalignment and reciprocal crossover between these segments at meiosis can given rise to chromosomes with either single $(-\alpha)^{211}$ or triplicated $(\alpha\alpha\alpha)^{55,212-214}$ α-globin genes (Fig. 93-19). Such an occurrence between homologous Z boxes deletes 3.7 kb of DNA (referred to as a rightward deletion, $-\alpha^{3.7}$), whereas a similar crossover between the two X blocks deletes 4.2 kb of DNA (referred to as a leftward deletion, $-\alpha^{4.2}$). The corresponding triplicated α-gene arrangements are referred to as $\alpha\alpha\alpha^{anti\,3.7}$ and $\alpha\alpha\alpha^{anti\,4.2}$. Further examples of chromosomes with four α genes $(\alpha\alpha\alpha\alpha^{anti\,3.7}$ and $\alpha\alpha\alpha\alpha^{anti\,4.2})$ presumably result from similar crossovers involving the $\alpha\alpha\alpha^{anti\,3.7}$ and $\alpha\alpha\alpha^{anti\,4.2}$ chromosomes, respectively.[215]

Table 93-7 Clinical Phenotypes and Genotypes of α Thalassemia

Phenotype	Equivalent number of functional α genes	Level of† Hb Bart's at birth, %	% Hb H (inclusions)	MCV‡ (fl)	MCH‡ (pg)	α/β-globin chain synthesis ratio	Interacting¶ haplotypes	Most frequently encountered genotypes
Normal	4	0§	0 (none)	85–100	~28	~1.0	α/α	αα/αα
α Thalassemia* minor (mild)	3	0–2	0 (rare)	75–85	~24	~0.8	α^+/α	$-\alpha/\alpha\alpha$
α Thalassemia* minor (severe)	2	2–8	0 (occasional)	65–75	~20	~0.6	α^0/α or α^+/α^+	$--/\alpha\alpha$ $\alpha\alpha^T/\alpha\alpha$ $-\alpha/-\alpha$
Hb H disease	1	10–40	2–40 (many)	55–65	~20	~0.3	α^0/α^+ or α^+/α^+	$--/\alpha-$ $--/\alpha\alpha^T$ $\alpha\alpha^T/\alpha\alpha^T$
Hb Bart's hydrops fetalis	0	~80	Present (present)	110–120	Reduced	0.0	α^0/α^0	$--/--$ $--/\alpha\alpha^T$

*The mild and severe forms of α-thalassemia trait are often referred to as α-thalassemia-2 and α-thalassemia-1, respectively.
†Hb Bart's gradually disappears from peripheral blood in the 3 to 6 months following birth.
‡These values vary considerably depending on the age of the patient,[208] and the figures given are a guide to the indices seen in adults.[209]
§Very small amounts of Hb Bart's have been detected in normal infants at birth.[210]
¶α Refers to a normal haplotype, α^+ to α^+ thalassemia, and α^0 to α^0 thalassemia.

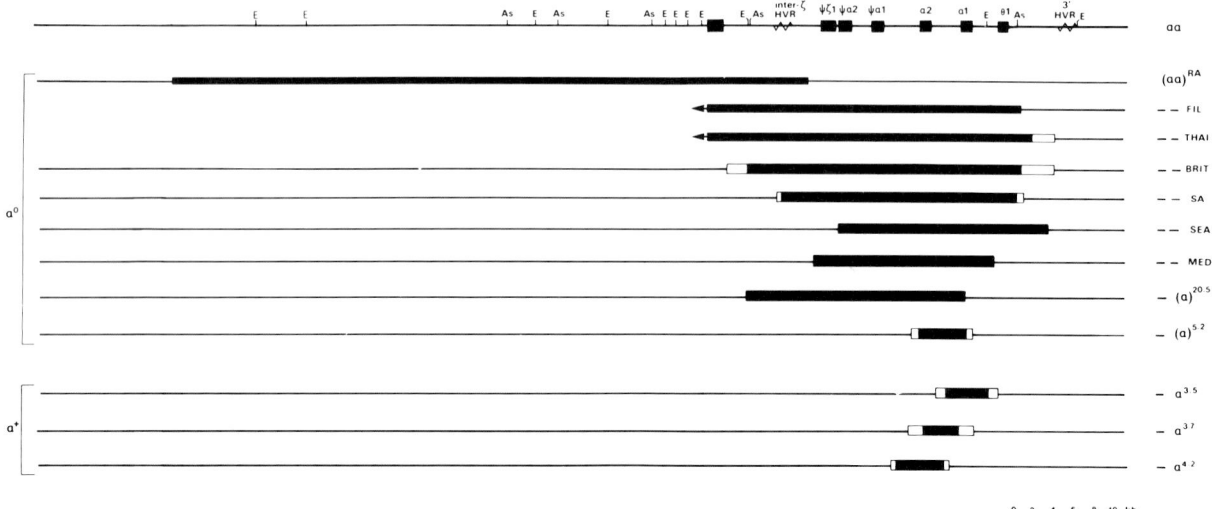

Fig. 93-17 Map of the human α-globin gene locus (*above*) with a summary of currently described deletions (*below*). The positions of restriction enzymes (A, *Asp* 718, and E, *Eco* RI) are shown on the map. Solid blocks represent genes and pseudogenes; zigzag lines denote hypervariable regions of DNA. The deletions are represented by black bars and when the precise break points are not known (e.g., − −BRIT) the regions of uncertainty are denoted by white bars. The first nine deletions affect both α genes (α° thalassemia) and the last three affect one of the duplicated α genes (α+ thalassemia).

Crossovers between single −α and duplicated αα chromosomes have also been described.[216] Indeed, several independent lines of evidence suggest that this type of homologous genetic recombination occurs relatively frequently in globin[217,218] and other[219,220] loci. At present it is not known whether such rearrangements take place between misaligned chromosomes or between chromatids during meiosis.

The mechanism by which the recently described −α3.5 deletion,[221] identified in an Asian Indian patient, has arisen is not yet clear. It will be interesting to determine the sequence of this break point to see if it involves a homologous (as in the −α3.7 and −α4.2) or illegitimate recombination event.

From the geographic distribution and relative frequencies of these −α chromosomes it appears that rearrangements involving the Z box are more frequent than those involving the X or Y regions. Recently it has been possible to subdivide the common Z box rearrangements into three types (−α3.7I, −α3.7II, −α3.7III) depending on exactly where the crossover has taken place with respect to three restriction enzyme sites that differ between the α2 and α1 Z boxes (see Fig. 93-18).[217] In general

Fig. 93-18 Fine structure around the duplicated α-globin genes (*above*) and a summary of deletions involving one of the pairs of α genes (*below*). The pseudo-α gene (ψα1) and duplicated α genes (α2 and α1) are shown. Black boxes indicate exons and the white boxes show the size and positions of introns. Below the two X, Y, and Z boxes are shown, marking the positions and extent of the duplication that gave rise to the two α genes. Above, the relative levels of expression of the α2 and α1 genes are shown. The deletions that involve one or other of the α genes are shown below. Black bars indicate the extent of the deletions and white bars the regions of uncertainty for the break points.

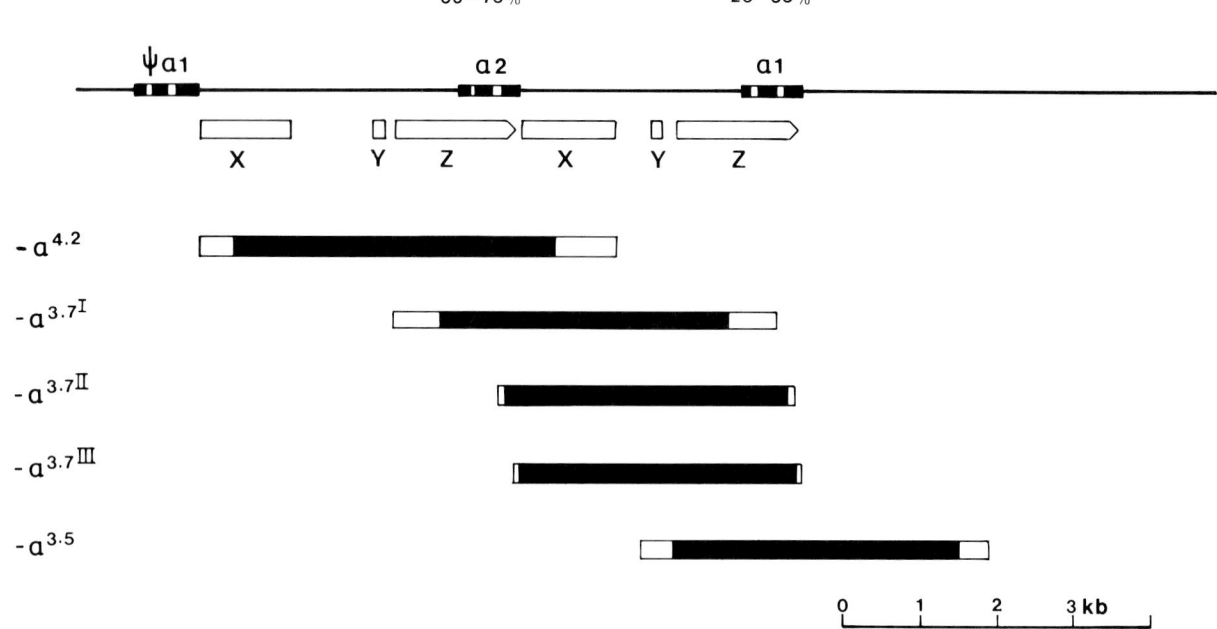

(A)

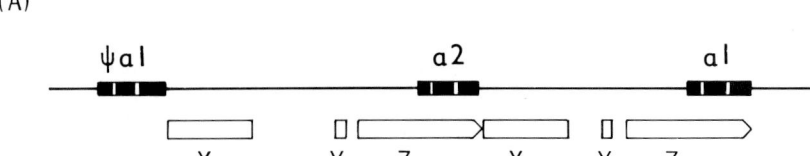

(B) RIGHTWARD CROSSOVER

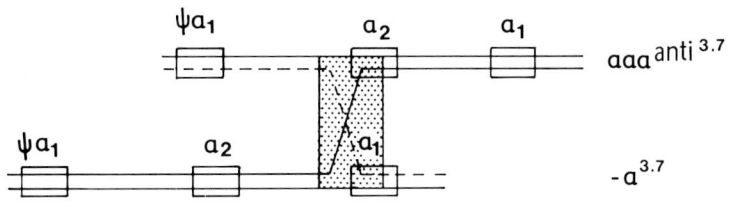

(C) LEFTWARD CROSSOVER

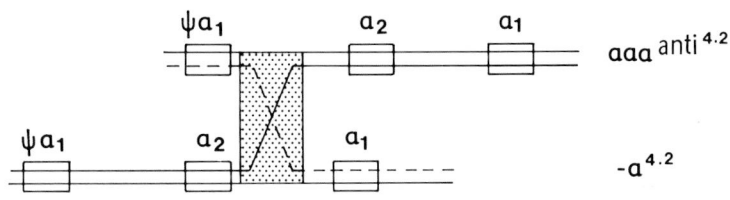

Fig. 93-19 The mechanism of unequal crossover that gives rise to the $-\alpha^{3.7}$ and $-\alpha^{4.2}$ deletions. A. The fine structural detail of the duplicated α-globin gene is shown as in the previous figure. B. The rightward crossover occurs when genetic exchange takes place between the misaligned homologous Z boxes giving rise to chromosomes with either one ($-\alpha^{3.7}$) or three $\alpha\alpha\alpha^{anti\ 3.7}$) α-globin genes. C. The leftward crossover occurs when genetic exchange takes place between the misaligned homologous X boxes giving rise to chromosomes with either one ($-\alpha^{4.2}$) or three ($\alpha\alpha\alpha^{anti\ 4.2}$) α-globin genes.

it appears that the frequency of each of these subtypes ($\alpha^{3.7I}$, $-\alpha^{3.7II}$, $-\alpha^{3.7III}$, and $-\alpha^{4.2}$; Y box crossovers have not been identified) is simply related to the length of homology within each subsegment. It remains to be seen whether more complex physical constraints also play a role in determining the relative frequency of recombination in this region.

The level of expression of the remaining α gene from these chromosomes ($-\alpha$) can be assessed by the effect of the deletions on phenotype (see Table 93-7) and more directly by measuring the production of α-specific mRNA from such chromosomes. The level of expression of the α_2 gene is two to three times greater than that of the α_1 gene, and this appears to be controlled at the level of transcription.[222-225] All five deletions ($-\alpha^{3.7I}$, $-\alpha^{3.7II}$, $-\alpha^{3.7III}$, $-\alpha^{4.2}$, $-\alpha^{3.5}$) reduce α-chain production from the affected chromosome. The similar phenotypes of homozygotes for the $-\alpha^{4.2}$ determinant, in which both α_2 genes are removed, and $-\alpha^{3.7III}$ homozygotes, in which effectively the α_1 genes are deleted, suggests that removal of the α_2 gene results in a partial, compensatory increase in the expression of the remaining α_1 gene on the -$\alpha^{4.2}$ chromosome[226]; increased expression of the α_1 gene has been clearly demonstrated at the level of mRNA.[96] Thus like other deletions of the α- and β-globin clusters, these deletions appear to exert an effect on the expression of nearby genes. At present there are insufficient phenotypic data to compare the relative levels of expression of the other $-\alpha$ chromosomes.

α^0 THALASSEMIA DUE TO DELETIONS. To date, 11 deletions have been described that involve both α genes and thereby abolish α-chain production from the affected chromosome (Fig. 93-17). In general, they are large deletions (5.2 to 62 kb) and, unlike in the $-\alpha^{3.7}$ and $-\alpha^{4.2}$ defects, there seem to be several mechanisms by which they can arise.

Recently, some of these deletions have been analyzed in detail to see if any underlying mechanism could be estab-lished.[227] Several features have emerged; first there appears to be a clustering of break points. Several of the 3' break points fall within a 6- to 8-kb region at the 3' end of the α-globin complex, suggesting that this may represent a break-point cluster region similar to those observed in the chromosomal translocations associated with certain malignant diseases.[228,229]

In a subset of the deletions ($- -^{MED}$, $- -^{SEA}$, $- -^{20.5}$, $- -^{SA}$, $- -^{BRIT}$), the 5' break points also appear to cluster. This gives rise to a situation in which the 5' break points are located approximately the same distance apart and in the same order along the chromosome as their respective 3' break points. These findings are consistent with similar observations on a group of deletions in the β-globin cluster.[230] In both cases it has been proposed that such staggered deletions may result from illegitimate recombination events deleting an integral number of chromatin loops as they pass through their nuclear attachment points during replication.[230]

One of these deletions ($- -^{MED}$) also involves a more complex rearrangement that introduces a new piece of DNA bridging the two break points in the α cluster (Fig. 93-17). This new DNA originates upstream from the α cluster and appears to have been replicated into the junction in a manner that suggests that the upstream segment of DNA also lies at the base of a replication loop. This region probably lies close to the bases of the proposed replication loops involved in the group of clustered deletions described above.

Sequence analysis has shown that members of the dispersed family of *Alu* repeats[231] are frequently found at or near the break points of these deletions. In one case ($\alpha\alpha^{RA}$) the deletion resulted from simple homologous recombination between two *Alu* repeats that are normally 62 kb apart. It will be interesting to see if *Alu* family repeats are frequently found in similar recombination events elsewhere in the genome. These repeats may simply provide partially homologous sequences that promote DNA strand exchanges during replication, or possibly a subset of *Alu* sequences may be more actively involved in the process, particularly if they function as origins of replication.[231]

In contrast to the $-\alpha^{3.7}$ and $-\alpha^{4.2}$ defects, this set of deletions is of limited geographical distribution,[232] and each one probably represents a single example of an uncommon type of genetic mishap. Nevertheless, this type of molecular defect probably underlies many common genetic disorders.

Since both α genes are involved in this group of deletions, α-globin synthesis is clearly abolished by these mutants. The similarity of these deletions to deletions of the β cluster that give rise to hereditary persistence of fetal hemoglobin (HPFH), $\delta\beta$ thalassemia, and $\gamma\delta\beta$ thalassemia raises the question of how they affect the expression of neighboring genes. The $\alpha\alpha^{RA}$ 62-kb deletion, identified in a British individual, appears to be similar to the cases of $\gamma\delta\beta$ thalassemia; a large deletion upstream of the α genes appears to inactivate these genes although there is as yet no definite proof that the DNA sequence of these α genes is entirely normal. The other large deletions (e.g., $--^{MED}$ and $--^{SEA}$), that can be compared with the HPFH deletions of the β cluster, are not associated with any major change in ζ-globin expression in the heterozygous state ($--^{SEA}/\alpha\alpha$). However it has been shown using a sensitive radioimmunoassay that there is a very small increase in ζ-globin expression in such individuals.[233,234] In homozygotes for these mutants ($--^{SEA}/--^{SEA}$ and $--^{MED}/--^{MED}$) large amounts (≈ 20 to 30 percent) of Hb Portland ($\zeta_2\gamma_2$) are produced. However, it seems more likely that this results from intensive cell selection rather than specific enhancement of ζ-globin expression. Hence the change in pattern of gene expression in these deletions should not be compared with the more dramatic changes in γ expression associated with HPFH. Perhaps it is more relevant to ask why the expression of the embryonic genes, ζ and ϵ, is not much changed by these deletions of the α- and β-globin cluster, whereas γ-gene expression is markedly altered.

α^+ THALASSEMIA DUE TO NONDELETION DEFECTS. The nondeletion α thalassemias are classified in this way because analysis of DNA from patients with these disorders reveals no gross abnormality by Southern blotting. In fact, in most cases they result from single or oligonucleotide mutations at regions of the α-gene sequence that are critical for normal expression. Similar mutations in the β-globin gene are much more common and are discussed in detail in a later section.

Since expression of the α_2 gene is two to three times greater than that of the α_1 gene[222-225] it is not surprising that most of the nondeletion mutants affect predominantly the expression of the α_2 gene. Clearly such mutations have greater effect on phenotype and presumably a greater selective advantage. Unlike the deletion of the α_2 gene in the $-\alpha^{4.2}$ defect, which results in a compensatory increase in the expression of the remaining α_1 gene, there appears to be no increase in expression of the α_1 gene when the α_2 gene is inactivated by a point mutation. Therefore the nondeletion α thalassemias have a greater effect on phenotype than the $-\alpha$ mutants.

The molecular lesions that underlie nondeletion forms of α thalassemia are relatively uncommon when compared with the $-\alpha^{3.7}$ and $-\alpha^{4.2}$ mutants; furthermore the geographic distribution of each mutant is quite limited (Table 93-8). As for the β-thalassemia mutants, they may be classified according to the level of gene expression that they affect (Table 93-8). Two nondeletion mutants that affect processing of the primary mRNA transcript have been identified. The first consists of a pentanucleotide deletion, including the 5' splice site of IVS I of the α_2-globin gene ($\alpha^{Hph}\alpha$). This deletion involves the invariant GT donor splicing sequence ($GGTGAGGCT \rightarrow GGCT$) thus abolishing the normal removal of IVS I during processing.[235,236] The second mutant in this group, $\alpha\alpha^{T\ SAUDI}$, involves the poly (A) addition signal (AATAAA-AATAAG) and down-regulates the α_2 gene by interfering with 3' end processing[75,237] and possibly with termination of transcription.[238] At present it is not clear whether a failure to correctly terminate transcription of the α_2 gene also down-regulates the linked α_1 gene.[237] Whatever the mechanism, it appears that both α_2 and α_1 genes are affected by this mutation.[236]

Mutations in a second group exert their effect by interfering with the translation of mature mRNA. In one case ($\alpha^{Nco}\alpha$) the initiation codon is completely inactivated by a T→C transi-

Table 93-8 Nondeletion Mutants That Cause α Thalassemia

	Affected gene	Affected sequence	Nomenclature	Geographic distribution
RNA processing	α_2	IVS I donor site	$\alpha^{Hph}\alpha$	Mediterranean
	α_2*	Poly (A) addition	$\alpha\alpha^{T\ Saudi}$	Mediterranean, Middle East
RNA translation	α_2	Initiator codon	$\alpha^{Nco}\alpha$	Mediterranean
	$-\alpha^{3.7II}$	Initiator codon	$-\alpha^{3.7T}$	North African, Mediterranean
	α_2	In-phase terminator	$\alpha^{MS}\alpha$	Black
	α_2	Terminator codon	$\alpha^{CS}\alpha$	Southeast Asia
	α_2	Terminator codon	$\alpha^{ic}\alpha$	Mediterranean
	α_2	Terminator codon	$\alpha^{KD}\alpha$	India
	α_2	Terminator codon	$\alpha^{SR}\alpha$	Black
Posttranslational instability	α_2	Exon III (125)	$\alpha^{QS}\alpha$	Southeast Asia
	$(\alpha_1$ or $\alpha_2)$	Exon III (109)	Suan Dok	Southeast Asia
	$(\alpha_1$ or $\alpha_2)$	Exon III (110)	Petah Tikvah	Middle East
	$-\alpha$	Exon I	Evanston	Black
Uncharacterized	?	Unknown	$\alpha\alpha^T$	Several populations
	?	Unknown	$\alpha\alpha^T$	Greek†
	$-\alpha$	Unknown	$-\alpha^T$	Black
	?	Unknown	$\alpha\alpha^{Karditsa}$	Greek†

*This mutation has been found in both α_2 like genes on an $\alpha\alpha\alpha^{anti\ 3.7}$ chromosome from a Saudi Arabian individual.[237]

†Its interaction with α^0 thalassemia to produce the Hb Bart's hydrops fetalis syndrome suggests that both α-globin genes are affected.

tion (CCA*T*GG→CCA*C*GG),[239] and in another the efficiency of initiation is reduced by a dinucleotide deletion in the consensus sequence around the start signal (CCCACC*ATG*→CCC*C*ATG).[240] Four mutations that affect termination of translation and give rise to elongated α-globin chains have been identified (Hb Constant Spring $\alpha^{CS}\alpha$, Hb Icaria $\alpha^{Ic}\alpha$, Hb Koya Dora $\alpha^{KD}\alpha$, and Hb Seal Rock $\alpha^{SR}\alpha$). Each specifically changes the termination codon (TAA).[97] Another mutation, identified in a black patient from Mississippi $(\alpha^{MS}\alpha)$,[241] causes premature termination of translation by changing codon 116 in exon III to an in-phase terminator (GAG→UAG).

A group of four structural mutations that cause α thalassemia give rise to highly unstable α-globin chains; these are Hb Quong Sze $(\alpha^{QS}\alpha)$,[242] Hb Suan Dok $(\alpha\alpha^{SD})$,[243] Hb Petah Tikvah $(\alpha\alpha^{PT})$,[244] and Hb Evanston.[245]

Many nondeletion α-thalassemia mutations remain to be characterized.[246–249] Of particular interest are those that are associated with the Hb Bart's hydrops fetalis syndrome where the nondeletion chromosome presumably has a substantially reduced α-chain production.[246,248,249] Perhaps these will turn out to be similar to the Saudi Arabian type of defect in which both α_2 and α_1 genes appear to be down-regulated, or possibly they represent yet more severe defects.

Interactions of α Thalassemia Haplotypes. At the present time more than 30 α haplotypes have been described, and thus there are potentially more than 465 interactions. Phenotypically, these result in one of four broad categories: a normal phenotype; α thalassemia minor, in which there are mild hematologic changes but no major clinical abnormalities; Hb H disease; and the Hb Bart's hydrops fetalis syndrome. These clinical syndromes and the broad classes of interactions that underlie them are summarized in Table 93-7 and are reviewed in detail in the following sections.

NORMAL PHENOTYPE. Although the majority of normal individuals have four α-globin genes (αα/αα), about 2 percent in most populations have five α genes (ααα/αα). Furthermore, in populations where α thalassemia is common, the genotype −α/ααα also occurs.[161] It has been shown that the additional α gene in the ααα haplotype produces a slight excess of α_2 mRNA,[223] although this is not always reflected in the α/β-globin chain synthesis ratio[55] or at the phenotypic level; individuals with these interactions are often indistinguishable from normal individuals.[55] Rare individuals with αααα/αα or αααα/ααα may produce excess α globin, but again their phenotype is essentially normal.[215]

It should also be noted that within normal individuals there is a considerable amount of variation in the sequence and structure of the α-globin complex with no apparent effect on the expression of the α-globin genes.[49]

α THALASSEMIA MINOR. This most frequently results from the interaction of a normal haplotype (αα) with one of the α^+ or α^0 thalassemia determinants (e.g., $-\alpha^{3.7}/\alpha\alpha$, $-\alpha^{4.2}/\alpha\alpha$, or $\alpha\alpha^T/\alpha\alpha$). In populations where α thalassemia is common, two α^+ thalassemias can also interact to produce α thalassemia minor, $-\alpha^{3.7}/-\alpha^{3.7}$. Since each α thalassemia determinant may be associated with a different degree of suppression of α-globin chain synthesis, these interactions produce a spectrum of disorders spanning a clinical and hematologic picture of a normal phenotype to Hb H disease (see Table 93-7). The variation of severity of the α^+ and α^0 mutations is demonstrated

by the degree of anemia, MCV, MCH, α/β-globin chain synthesis ratio, and level of Hb Bart's at birth when different determinants interact with each other or a normal chromosome (Fig. 93-20).

In general, chromosomes with a single α gene (−α) produce the mildest phenotype, with the $-\alpha^{4.2}$ producing a greater reduction in α-globin chain synthesis than $-\alpha^{3.7}$.[226] Nondeletion mutants $(\alpha\alpha^T)$ that affect the predominant α2 gene (see Table 93-8) cause a more pronounced reduction in α-chain synthesis, and deletion mutants involving both α genes (e.g., $--^{MED}$ and $--^{SEA}$) lead to the most severe phenotype. As shown in Fig. 93-20, it is not possible to predict accurately the genotype from any given phenotype and in some cases, −α/αα, for example, it may be impossible to diagnose a carrier of α thalassemia using any of the conventional phenotypic criteria. Therefore, to perform accurate genetic counseling in families with α thalassemia, genotype determination is essential.

HOMOZYGOTES FOR Hb CONSTANT SPRING. The chain termination mutant Hb Constant Spring causes a severe reduction in α_2-globin expression from the affected chromosome. Sufficient homozygotes $(\alpha^{CS}\alpha/\alpha^{CS}\alpha)$ have been described to establish that the phenotype is more severe than α thalassemia minor but not as severe as most cases of Hb H disease.[250] The subjects are anemic with thalassemic red cell changes and a reticulocytosis. Basophilic stippling of the red cells is often prominent. They have mild jaundice and a variable degree of hepatosplenomegaly and are therefore quite unlike patients with α thalassemia minor. Patients homozygous for the chain termination mutant Koya Dora $(\alpha^{KD}\alpha/\alpha^{KD}\alpha)$ have been described, but their phenotype was not given.[251]

The only other homozygotes for mutations affecting the predominant α2 gene are a single Sardinian patient with a very mild form of Hb H disease $(\alpha^{Nco}\alpha/\alpha^{Nco}\alpha)$[239] and Saudi Arabian patients with typical Hb H disease $(\alpha\alpha^{T\,SAUDI}/\alpha\alpha^{T\,SAUDI})$.[75,237] Comparing the phenotype of homozygotes for Hb CS $(\alpha^{CS}\alpha/\alpha^{CS}\alpha)$ with the Sardinian patients $(\alpha^{Nco}\alpha/\alpha^{Nco}\alpha)$, it appears that these interactions may lie on either side of a critical level of α-chain synthesis below which the syndrome of Hb H disease occurs.

Hb H DISEASE. Hb H disease most frequently results from the interaction of α^+ and α^0 thalassemia, and therefore it is predominantly found in Southeast Asia (commonly $--^{SEA}/-\alpha^{3.7}$) and the Mediterranean basin (commonly $--^{MED}/-\alpha^{3.7}$) where both α^+ and α^0 thalassemia are common. Hb H disease may also result from the interaction of nondeletion mutations affecting the predominant α2 globin gene $(\alpha^{Nco}\alpha/\alpha^{Nco}\alpha$, $\alpha\alpha^{T\,SAUDI}/\alpha\alpha^{T\,SAUDI}$, and $\alpha\alpha\alpha^{T\,SAUDI}/\alpha\alpha^{T\,SAUDI})$. In Algeria, homozygotes for the $-\alpha^{3.7II\,T}$ defect $(-\alpha^{3.7II\,T}/-\alpha^{3.7II\,T})$ (see Table 93-7) have typical Hb H disease.[238]

The genetic basis for Hb H disease is diverse, and as more molecular defects are characterized, the underlying interactions will become even more complex. It is not yet clear to what extent this molecular diversity is reflected in the variable clinical and hematologic features of Hb H disease. The clinical picture of hemoglobin H disease is usually thalassemia intermedia, although there is considerable variation in the severity of this condition. The predominant features are a hypochromic, microcytic anemia, with jaundice and hepatosplenomegaly. Since the main mechanism of the anemia is hemolysis rather than dyserythropoiesis, only one-third of patients have clinical evidence of an expanded erythron. The most common

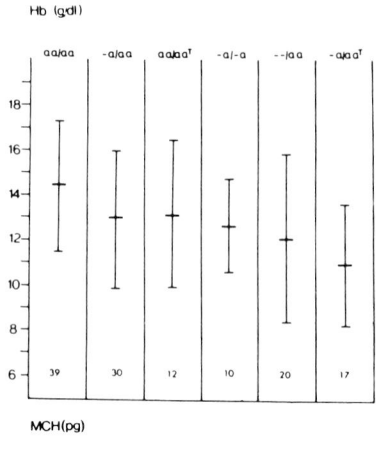

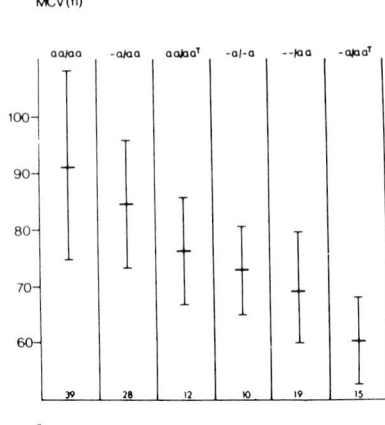

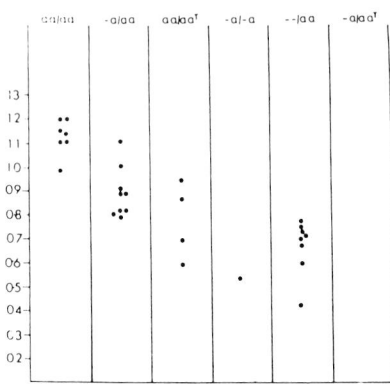

Fig. 93-20 Hematologic parameters (Hb, MCV, MCH) in patients with a variety of α-thalassemia interactions that give rise to α-thalassemia trait. The figures at the bottom of each column indicate the number of individuals studied. The results given are the mean ± 2 SD. α/β-Globin chain synthesis ratios in such patients are shown in the *bottom right-hand panel*, where each dot represents a single result.

complication is the development of severe splenomegaly with hypersplenism. Others include infection, leg ulcers, gallstones and folic acid deficiency.

The hematologic features of Hb H disease are also quite variable. Hemoglobin levels ranging from 2.6 to 12.4 g/dl have been recorded, in association with reticulocytosis and typical thalassemic changes of the red cell indices. The hemoglobin consists of Hb A with a variable amount of Hb H and sometimes Hb Bart's. The proportion of Hb H varies from 2 to 40 percent. When peripheral blood is incubated with redox dyes, this is reflected in the number of cells that contain typical Hb H inclusions (Fig. 93-21A).

As yet there have been no systematic attempts to correlate the genotype with the phenotype of Hb H disease. However, in general it appears that, as expected, patients with a non-deletion defect (affecting the predominant α_2 gene) interacting with an α^0- thalassemia determinant $(--/\alpha\alpha^T)$ have higher levels of Hb H (β_4), a greater degree of anemia and, anecdotally, a more severe clinical course than patients with the $--/-\alpha$ genotype. At the extreme of this spectrum, three patients have been described in whom severe Hb H disease was associated with hydrops fetalis.[246,248,249]

In Thailand, where there is an abundance of well-documented cases of Hb H disease, it is known that despite the relatively homogenous nature of the molecular basis $(--^{SEA}/-\alpha^{3.7}$ in 80 percent),[252] the clinical course is quite variable. This suggests that other genetic and environmental factors play an important role in the clinical and hematologic variation seen in this syndrome.

THE HEMOGLOBIN BART'S HYDROPS FETALIS SYNDROME. Nearly all cases of this syndrome are due to the interaction of two α^0 thalassemia determinants. As with Hb H disease, this condition is almost exclusively seen in patients of Southeast Asian

(commonly $--^{SEA}/--^{SEA}$) or Mediterranean (commonly $--^{MED}/--^{MED}$) origin. Infants with this syndrome either die in utero (30 to 40 weeks gestation) or soon after birth (Fig. 93-21). Recently, however, two infants with this syndrome were delivered at 28 and 32 weeks, transfused, and intensively nursed such that they have survived to 17 months and 14 months, respectively.[253,254]

Usually, the clinical picture is a pale edematous infant with signs of cardiac failure and prolonged intrauterine hypoxia (Fig. 93-21B). Hepatosplenomegaly is always present, and there are often other congenital abnormalities. The hemoglobin levels range from 3 to 10 g/dl, and the blood film is characterized by anisopoikilocytosis with large hypochromic macrocytes; many nucleated cells are present in the peripheral blood. The hemoglobin consists of ≈80 percent Hb Bart's, the remainder being hemoglobins H and Portland. Of these hemoglobins, only Hb Portland is efficient in the transport of oxygen, hence the severe degree of fetal hypoxia. There is a high incidence of maternal complications, including toxemia and postpartum hemorrhage.

Although the Hb Bart's hydrops syndrome is usually associated with a complete absence of α-globin chain synthesis, there have been a few recent reports of hydrops fetalis, in three Greek[246,249,255] and one Southeast Asian infant,[248] with very low levels of α-chain synthesis. Gene mapping shows that they result from the interaction of common α^0 determinants with nondeletion mutations $(\alpha\alpha^T)$, although the latter have not been characterized. The Greek mutation has been called $\alpha\alpha^T$ Karditsa[249,255] (Table 93-8). It is possible that the nondeletion mutations in these cases are like the $\alpha\alpha^{T\,SAUDI}$ defect in that the output of the two α genes is less than expected for the α_1 gene alone. Thus α-chain production falls below 12 percent of normal.

A recent survey of Chinese infants has shown that some hy-

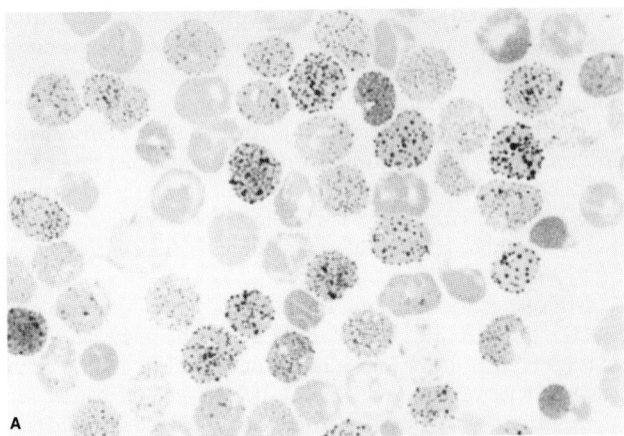

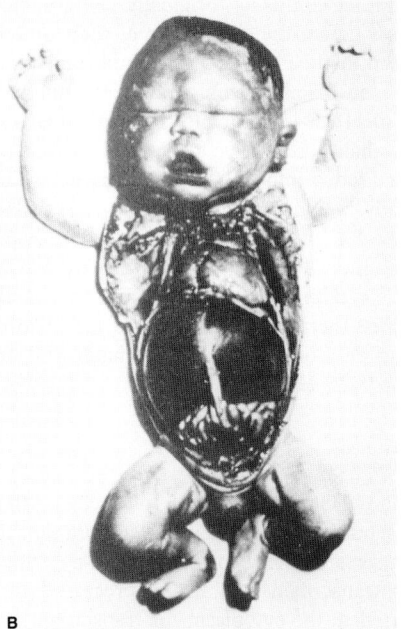

Fig. 93-21 Clinical manifestations of α thalassemia. A. A blood smear of a patient with Hb H disease. The cells were supravitally stained with brilliant cresyl blue to demonstrate Hb H inclusions. B. An infant with the hemoglobin Bart's hydrops fetalis syndrome.

dropic babies have a nondeletion mutation in which there is no α-chain production, thus identifying an entirely new type of αα^T disorder.[256] Finally, a stillborn hydropic infant of Iraqi-Kurdish origin has been reported, and in this case the infant had thalassemic red cell changes but only 40 percent Hb Bart's.[257] It is possible that this child was hydropic for other reasons.

Acquired Lesions of the α-Globin Genes.

α THALASSEMIA ASSOCIATED WITH MYELOPROLIFERATIVE DISORDERS. Most cases of Hb H disease result from inheritance of the α-thalassemia determinants described in the previous sections. However, several individuals have now been described in whom Hb H disease appears to be an acquired disorder associated with the development of a myeloproliferative syndrome[258]; previous hematologic assessments in these patients were entirely normal. This particular form of α thalassemia seems to be much more frequent in males than females. The structure of the α-globin complex appears to be normal, but there is a severe reduction in α-specific mRNA and α-globin chain synthesis. The molecular basis for this syndrome thus appears to involve an acquired defect in transcription of the α genes,[258] although the precise mechanism and its relationship to the hematologic malignancy is not yet known.

α THALASSEMIA ASSOCIATED WITH MENTAL RETARDATION. A second unusual type of α thalassemia is associated with mental retardation.[259] The pattern of inheritance of Hb H disease in these children is unusual in that neither parent is a carrier for a severe α-thalassemia determinant. However, family studies show that in each case at least one chromosome 16 has been affected by a *de novo* mutation causing α thalassemia. This new mutation is concurrently associated with mental retardation (IQ range <50 to 76) and a variety of other developmental abnormalities including microcephaly, hypogonadism, hypotonia, telocanthus, and mild skeletal changes.

In two cases there has been a *de novo* deletion involving the entire α complex and extending for at least 27 kb. In the remaining cases there is no detectable rearrangement around the α complex, and the nature of the molecular defect is not clear. Cytogenetic analysis has not revealed any gross abnormality of chromosome 16 in any of these cases.

It seems possible that this condition falls into the class of

contiguous gene syndromes (exemplified by retinoblastoma/mental retardation, Wilms tumor/aniridia/mental retardation, DiGiorge syndrome, Prader-Willi syndrome, and Beckwith-Wiedemann syndrome.[260]) By analogy, in the cases where the α genes are deleted it is possible that a variable number of other critical neighboring genes are also removed, giving rise to the associated developmental abnormalities. In those cases where the α gene complex appears to be intact, expression of genes may be affected by deletions of the neighboring genes that do not extend into the α complex.

Other well-documented large deletions of the α and β complexes apparently affect only globin gene expression. By comparison, we might expect the deletions involved in this syndrome to affect several other genes and therefore to extend a considerable distance (possibly hundreds of kilobases) on either side of the α-globin complex.

The β and δβ Thalassemias and Hereditary Persistence of Fetal Hemoglobin

The β and δβ thalassemias show considerable heterogeneity, not only in clinical severity but also in the phenotypic characteristics revealed by hematologic measurements and hemoglobin analysis. When the underlying defect is studied at the DNA level, it is clear that the phenotypic diversity hides even further molecular heterogeneity. The equally diverse group of conditions called, collectively, *hereditary persistence of fetal hemoglobin,* can be regarded as very mild β or δβ thalassemias in which defective β-chain production is compensated for by γ-chain production.

Classification. There are two approaches to subdividing this group of disorders. For clinical purposes they can be described as thalassemia major (transfusion-dependent), intermedia (of intermediate severity), and minor (asymptomatic). At the biosynthetic level they are categorized by the affected globin chains and whether there is a partial or complete defect in globin-chain production (see Table 93-6).

The β thalassemias are subdivided into β^0 and β$^+$, representing disorders with complete or partial defects in β-chain production. The nomenclature of the δβ thalassemias and

HPFH conditions is rather confusing, originally being named for their clinical effects before the similarities of their underlying defects were identified. The δβ thalassemias and most HPFH disorders have no δ- or β-chain production but have relatively high levels of Hb F in adult life. Homozygotes and heterozygotes for δβ thalassemia have thalassemic stigmata. The condition can be divided into (δβ)⁰ thalassemia, in which the Hb F contains both $^G\gamma$ and $^A\gamma$ chains, and $(^A\gamma\delta\beta)^0$ thalassemia, in which only $^G\gamma$ chains are produced. The (δβ)⁰ HPFH conditions are clinically asymptomatic, but are associated with higher levels of Hb F containing $^G\gamma$ and $^A\gamma$ chains. HPFH variants in which there is β-chain synthesis in cis produce Hb F containing only one of the two γ chains and are referred to as $^G\gamma\beta^+$ or $^A\gamma\beta^+$ HPFH.

Molecular Pathology.

β THALASSEMIA. The deficiency or absence of β chains that characterizes β thalassemia could potentially arise from defects affecting any of the stages in the complex process by which the β-globin gene is transcribed into RNA, processed into mRNA, and transported to the cytoplasm for translation into polypeptide chains. The molecular basis has been determined in more than 40 different β-thalassemia alleles, largely by cloning the abnormal gene and then comparing its sequence with that of the normal β^A gene. The identification of new defects has been greatly facilitated by the observation that within any population, each mutation is in strong linkage disequilibrium with specific restriction fragment length polymorphism (RFLP) haplotypes.[67] The defects characterized to date are listed in Table 93-9, grouped according to the mechanism by which they inactivate β-gene expression.

GENE DELETIONS. Four different deletions affecting only the β-globin gene have been described. Of these, only the 619-bp deletion at the 3' end of the β gene is common, and even that is restricted to the Sind populations of India and Pakistan, where it accounts for ≈30 percent of the β-thalassemia alleles.[261]

The other three deletions are all rare and all result in the phenotype of unusually high Hb A₂ β thalassemia.[262–264] In each of these cases (and only in these three cases), the 5' end of the β gene is missing while the δ gene remains intact. It is not clear whether the increased δ-chain production results from increased δ-gene transcription and, if so, whether it is only the gene in cis that is unusually active, as might occur as a direct effect of a conformational change induced by the deletion, or from both genes, possibly as a result of reduced competition for transcriptional factors.

MUTATIONS AFFECTING THE RATE OF TRANSCRIPTION. A number of β^+-thalassemia genes have a single base substitution in two regions immediately in front of the cap site close to or within the CCAAT and ATA boxes that are known to be important in transcriptional efficiency. These mutant genes show decreased β mRNA production in transient expression systems ranging from 10 to 25 percent of the output from a normal gene, confirming that these substitutions are responsible for the thalassemic nature of these genes.[265] In general, the level of expression in vitro correlates well with the clinical severity of the condition, where this is known. The A → G substitution at position −29 is responsible for the common mild β^+ form of thalassemia found in individuals of African origin.[266]

SPLICE SITE MUTATIONS. The boundaries of exons and introns are marked by almost invariant dinucleotides, GT at the donor (5') site and AG at the acceptor (3') site (see earlier section). Base substitutions that affect either of those sites totally abolish normal splicing and result in β⁰ thalassemia. Transcription of these genes appears to be normal, but abnormal processing products accumulate at low levels both in erythroid cells in vivo and in in vitro expression systems, as a result of splicing to cryptic splice sites in the surrounding exon or intron.[3]

SPLICE SITE CONSENSUS SEQUENCE MUTATIONS. Although only the GT dinucleotide is invariant at the donor splice site, there is conservation of the surrounding nucleotides, and a consensus sequence of these regions can be derived (see earlier section). Mutations within this sequence can reduce the efficiency of splicing to varying degrees, with alternative splicing occurring at the surrounding cryptic splice sites.[3] Mutations of the G at position 5 of IVS1 to C or T result in moderately severe β^+ thalassemia,[267] whereas the substitution of C for T at position 6 leads to the very mild β^+ thalassemia (Portuguese type) that is fairly common in the Mediterranean.[207,268]

MUTATIONS IN CRYPTIC SITES IN EXONS. One of the cryptic splice sites used for alternative splicing in mutations affecting the IVS1 donor site covers codons 24 to 27 of exon 1 (Fig. 93-22). This site contains a GT dinucleotide and substitutions surrounding this dinucleotide that alter the cryptic site so that it more closely resembles the consensus donor splice site result in some use of this site even though the normal splice site is intact.[269] Mutation of codon 24 from GGT to GGA does not alter the amino acid (glycine), but because some splicing occurs at this site instead of the exon-intron boundary, it results in a moderately severe β^+-thalassemia phenotype.[270]

Mutations of codons 26 (GAG → AAG) and 27 (GCC → TCC) result in both reduced production of β mRNA[171,271] and an amino acid substitution when the mRNA which is spliced normally is translated into protein. The abnormal hemoglobins produced are Hbs E and Knossos. It may be the mild thalassemic nature of the β^E allele that is responsible for its high prevalence in Southeast Asia, rather than an altered property resulting from the amino acid change.

MUTATIONS AT CRYPTIC SITES IN INTRONS. Cryptic splice sites within introns can also undergo mutations that cause them to be used even though the normal site remains intact. The first β-thalassemia mutation characterized was of this type, a base substitution at position 110 in IVS1.[272,273] This region contains a sequence similar to a 3' acceptor splice site but lacks the invariant AG dinucleotide. Mutation of the G at 110 to an A supplies the dinucleotide, and ≈90 percent of the RNA transcripts splice at this site and only ≈10 percent splice at the normal site, resulting in a phenotype of severe β^+ thalassemia. The result of the abnormal splicing is a nonfunctional mRNA molecule containing an extra 19 nucleotides from IVS1 that can be detected in low amounts in reticulocyte or marrow RNA. This lesion is the most common β^+-thalassemia mutation among Mediterraneans.[67]

Other mutations in cryptic splice sites in introns act in a similar way, although several of them appear to result in a β⁰ rather than a β^+-thalassemia phenotype.[3]

POLYADENYLATION SIGNAL MUTATION. The sequence AAUAAA in the 3' untranslated region of β mRNA is the signal for cleavage and polyadenylation of the β-gene tran-

Table 93-9 The Molecular Basis of the β Thalassemias

Type of mutation	Phenotype	Population	Direct detection	Haplotype*
Deletion				
1 619 bp	β⁰	Indian	Southern blot	
2 1.35 kb	High HbA₂ β⁰	Black	Southern blot	
3 ~10 kb	High HbA₂ β⁰	Dutch	Southern blot	
4 4.237 kb	High HbA₂ β⁰	Czech	Southern blot	
Transcriptional mutants				
5 −88 C→T	β⁺	Black, Indian		0 − − − + + + − + − + − + −
6 −87 C→G	β⁺	Mediterranean	AvrII	− + − + − + −
7 −31 A→G	β⁺	Japanese		
8 −29 A→G	β⁺⁺	Black, Chinese		0 + − + + + +
9 −28 A→C	β⁺	Kurdish		0 + + − + − +
10 −28 A→G	β⁺	Chinese		
Processing mutants				
Splice junction				
11 IVS1 5′ GT→AT	β⁰	Mediterranean		+ − − − − + −
12 IVS1 5′ GT→TT	β⁰	Indian		− + − + + + +
13 IVS2 5′ GT→AT	β⁰	Mediterranean, Black	Hpa I	{ − + − + + + − { + − − − − + −
14 IVS2 3′ AG→CG	β⁰	Black		
15 IVS2 3′ AG→GG	β⁰	Black	Alu I	0 − − − + − +
16 IVS2 3′ −17bp	β⁰	Kuwaiti	Fnu 4H, Mst II	− + − + + + +
17 IVS 3′ −25bp	β⁰	Indian	Fnu 4H, Mst II	− + − + + + +
Consensus sequence				
18 IVS1 position 5 G→C	β⁺	Indian, Chinese		{ 0 − − − − + + { + − − − − − +
19 IVS1 position 5 G→T	β⁺	Greek, N. European		+ − + − − + −
20 IVS1 position 5 G→A	β⁺	Greek, Algerian	EcoRV	
21 IVS1 position 6 T→C	β⁺⁺	Mediterranean	SfaN1	− + + − − − +
Cryptic splice sites in exons				
22 codon 24 T→A	β⁺	Black		0 + − − + + +
23 codon 26 G→A	β⁺⁺ βᴱ	S.E. Asian	Hb E, Mnl I	{ − + − + + + − { − + − + + − + { + − − − + + −
24 codon 27 G→T	β⁺, β^Knossos	Mediterranean	Hb Knossos	+ − − − − +
Cryptic splice sites in introns				
25 IVS1 position 110 G→A	β⁺	Mediterranean		{ + − − − − + + { − + + − + + + { − + − + + + +
26 IVS1 position 116 T→G	β⁰	Mediterranean	Mae I	+ − − − − + +
27 IVS2 position 654 C→T	β⁰	Chinese		+ − − − − + +
28 IVS2 position 705 T→G	β⁰	Mediterranean		
29 IVS2 position 745 C→G	β⁺	Mediterranean	Rsa I	+ − − − − − +
Polyadenylation signal				
30 AATAAA → AACAAA	β⁺	Black		0 − − − − + +
Nonsense mutants				
31 codon 15 C→A	β⁰	Indian		+ − − − − + +
32 codon 17 A→T	β⁰	Chinese	Mae I	
33 codon 37 G→A	β⁰	Arab	Ava II	
34 codon 39 C→T	β⁰	Mediterranean	Mae I	{ + − − − − + + { − + + − + + + { + − − − − − + { − + − + + + +
35 codon 121 G→T	β⁰	Polish	EcoRI	+ − − − − − +
Frameshift mutants				
36 codon 6 −1	β⁰	Mediterranean	Mst II	{ + − − − − + + { + − − − − + − { − + − + + + +
37 codon 8 −2	β⁰	Turkish		− + − + + + +
38 codon 8/9 +1	β⁰	Indian, Iranian		+ − − − − + +
39 codon 16 −1	β⁰	Indian		+ − − − − + +
40 codon 41/42 −4	β⁰	Indian, S.E. Asian		{ − + − + + + { + − − − − + −
41 codon 44 −1	β⁰	Kurdish		
42 codon 73/72 +1	β⁰	Chinese		+ − − − − − +

SOURCE: References 2, 3, 187, 188, and 269.
*Haplotypes as described in Fig. 93-4.

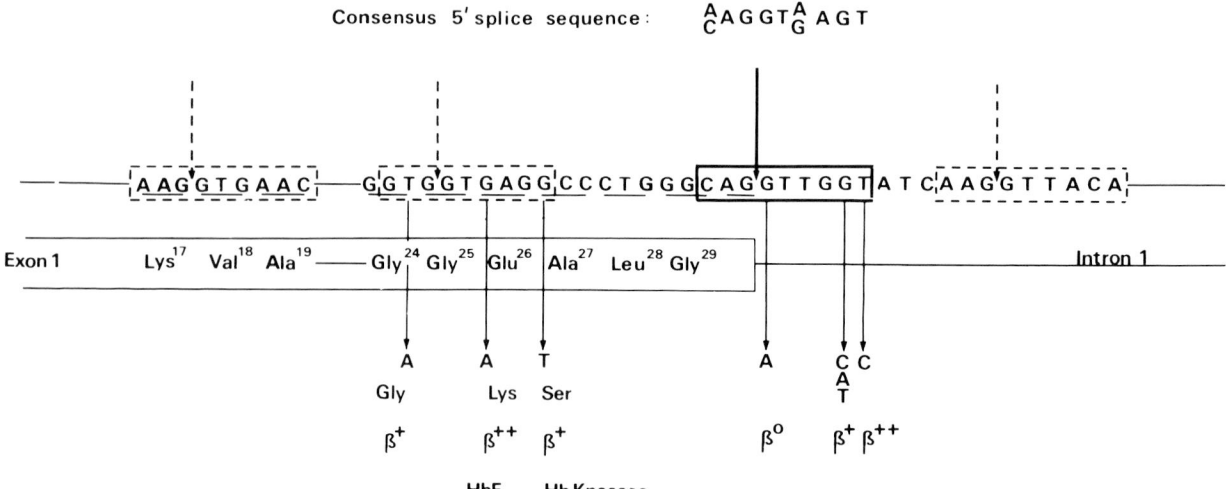

Fig. 93-22 Normal and abnormal splicing at the boundary of exon 1 and intron 1 of the β-globin gene. Solid box and arrow: normal splice site showing consensus sequence and site of cleavage. Dashed boxes and arrows: alternative splice sites used in various β-thalassaemia lesions.

script. A T → C substitution in the DNA leads to only one-tenth of the normal amount of β-globin mRNA and hence β$^+$ thalassemia.[76] A small amount of an extended β mRNA molecule is found in reticulocytes, presumably polyadenylated at a downstream site and probably unstable.

MUTATIONS TO TERMINATION CODONS. Base substitutions that change an amino acid codon to a chain termination codon prevent translation of the mRNA and result in β^0 thalassemia. Several mutations of this type have been described, the codon 17 mutation[274] being common in Southeast Asia and the codon 39 mutation[275] occurring at a high frequency in the Mediterranean. The low levels of nuclear and cytoplasmic RNA found in cells with these mutations have yet to be explained.[276,277]

FRAME-SHIFT MUTATIONS. The insertion or deletion of one or a few nucleotides in the coding region of the β-globin gene disrupts the normal reading frame and results, on translation of the mRNA, in the addition of anomalous amino acids until a termination codon is reached in the new reading frame. The abnormal mRNA is found only in very low levels in erythroid cells. This type of mutation leads to β^0 thalassemia, and one, the deletion of four nucleotides in codons 41 and 42, is common in Southeast Asia.

DELETIONS CAUSING δβ THALASSEMIA OR HPFH. The majority of the $(δβ)^0$ and $(^Aγδβ)^0$ thalassemias, as well as different forms of $(δβ)^0$ HPFH (including Hb Kenya) are the result of deletions affecting various parts of the β-globin locus. These disorders have attracted considerable interest, since an understanding of how the deletions result in the γ genes remaining active in adult life may provide valuable insight into the normal developmental regulation of the globin genes. Over 20 deletions have now been characterized, and in many cases the break points have been cloned and sequenced. These are summarized in Fig. 93-23. The mechanisms by which they arose are largely unknown. While Hb Lepore, Hb Kenya, and the γ thalassemias occur as a result of misaligned crossovers between homologous genes, the remaining deletions all involve some type of illegitimate recombination, with little or no sequence homology at the break points.

The $(δβ)^0$-thalassemia deletions remove or inactivate only the δ and β genes. They are relatively small and are contained within the β-gene cluster. One exception however is the Spanish type[278] that extends much further on the 3' side, beyond the 3' end of $(δβ)^0$ HPFH lesions. Phenotypically they are all similar, except that Hb Lepore is associated with a minimal increase in Hb F production.

The $(^Aγδβ)^0$ thalassemias extend into or beyond the $^Aγ$ gene on the 5' side as well as removing the δ and β genes. On the 3' side, most of them terminate within 20 kb of the β gene, but again there is one exception, the Chinese type, that extends much further. The Indian form is not a simple linear deletion but a complex rearrangement with two deletions, one affecting the $^Aγ$ gene and the other the δ and β genes; the intervening region remains but is inverted.[279,280] Again, the phenotypic results of these very different deletions are quite similar. The overall level of Hb F production is similar to that in the $(δβ)^0$ thalassemias, but in this case only the $^Gγ$ gene is active, not both.

The two African forms of $(δβ)^0$ HPFH are both due to extensive deletions, of similar length (>70 kb) but with staggered ends, differing phenotypically only in the proportions of $^Gγ$ and $^Aγ$ chains produced.[281] The third type (Indian) is somewhat smaller and, although producing a similar amount of Hb F in heterozygotes, has a more severe phenotype than the other two when coinherited with β thalassemia.[282]

The $(εγδβ)^0$ thalassemias differ from the previous ones in that the deletions begin a long way upstream of the β complex (>55 kb 5' to ε) and terminate within the cluster. In the two cases (Dutch and English) that spare the β-globin gene, no β-chain production occurs, even though the gene is expressed in heterologous systems.[283–285]

DELETION-PHENOTYPE ANALYSIS. Analysis of the size and position of these deletions does not provide any simple explanation for the persistent γ-chain synthesis in adult life that characterizes these disorders, nor does it explain the differences in phenotype of affected heterozygotes. However, several points can be made.

1. Deletions starting 5' to the complex apparently inactivate the β-like genes that remain. This could be due to the negative influence in erythroid cells of the sequence newly apposed to the surviving genes or to the removal of a sequence necessary to activate the whole of the β-globin domain.

2. Deletions starting within the complex and extending 3' to it appear to leave the surviving γ genes active in adult life when they would normally be repressed. While this could be the result of the newly apposed 3′ sequences, the number of different deletions of this type make it difficult to imagine that each one has a similar effect. Furthermore, two of the deletions [Hb Kenya and India ($^A\gamma\delta\beta$)^0 thalassemia] leave the 3′ end of the β gene and beyond intact.

3. Comparison of (δβ)^0 thalassemia and (δβ)^0 HPFH does not identify any single region between the $^A\gamma$ and δ genes that remains intact in the one but is lost in the other, precluding any simple explanation for the difference in γ-gene output between these two conditions. ($^A\gamma\delta\beta$)^0 thalassemia appears to act more like (δβ)^0 HPFH in terms of output per gene. Furthermore, the internal deletion that results in one form of normal Hb A$_2$ β thalassemia removes much of the area in which a putative switching sequence might reside, yet causes little or no increase in Hb F in heterozygotes.[286]

Overall, therefore, analysis of the deletions has yet to explain their phenotypic consequences. The pattern of the 5′ and 3′ deletions suggests some form of polarity within the globin gene complex, and hypotheses involving fetal and adult gene domains,[287] which require intact start and stop sites, may still be tenable. However, it is equally possible that there is more than one mechanism by which deletions within the complex affect the expression of the surviving genes. In fact, one important lesson that can be learned from these conditions is that, within this cluster, the genes are not regulated solely by the sequences immediately surrounding them but are subject to control acting over a considerable distance.

NONDELETION HPFH. Analysis of the nondeletion forms of HPFH by cloning and sequencing of the overexpressed gene has revealed, in each case, a single base substitution in the region immediately upstream from the transcription start site (Table 93-10).[288–292] The clustering of these substitutions and the lack of similar changes in normal γ genes suggest that they are responsible for the persistent Hb F production. This position is strengthened by the finding that when these promotor regions are mutated, the amount of transcription in transfected erythroid cells relative to the normal promoter is increased. It seems likely that these alterations affect the binding of a trans-acting protein involved in the normal developmental repression of γ-gene expression, either by decreasing the affinity for an inhibitory factor normally present in adult life or increasing the affinity for a factor promoting gene expression. The decrease in β-chain production that accompanies the persistent γ-chain synthesis has yet to be explained, but the fact that it is only the β gene in cis that is affected precludes any simple explanation involving competition for trans-acting factors.

As discussed in a later section, it is becoming clear that nondeletion HPFH is very heterogeneous. In some cases the genetic determinant is unlinked to the β-globin gene cluster. The molecular basis for many of these conditions remains to be determined.

Clinical and Hematologic Characteristics of the β Thalassemias.[2,185]

β THALASSEMIA MAJOR. This condition may result from the homozygous state for a β-thalassemia mutation or, more commonly, from the compound heterozygous state for two different β thalassemias.

At birth, when Hb F production is still high, β-thalassemia homozygotes are asymptomatic, but as Hb F production declines, affected infants present with severe anemia, usually during the first 1 to 2 years of life. Left untreated, they are incapable of maintaining a hemoglobin level above 5 g/dl and

Fig. 93-23 Deletions affecting the β-globin gene cluster, arranged according to their phenotypic effects. (Note the discontinuities at the 5′ and 3′ ends and the change of scale at the 3′ end.)

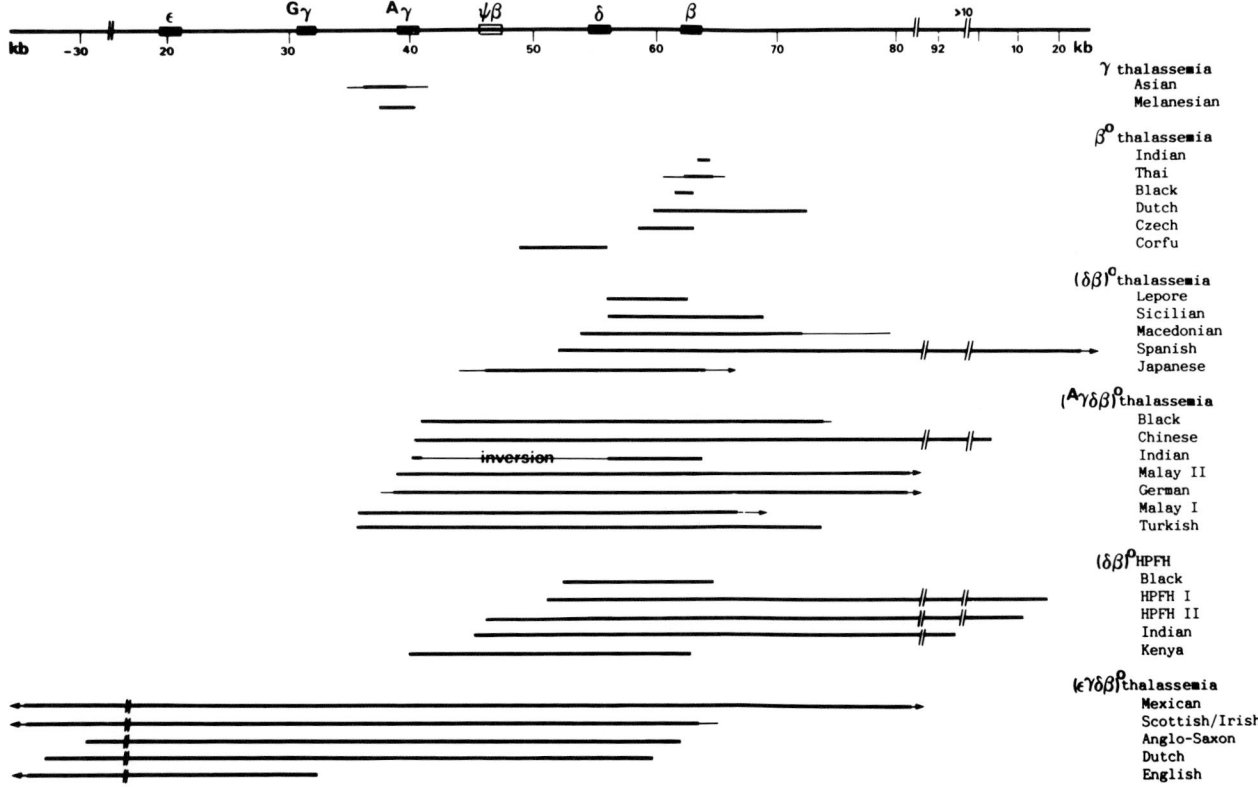

Table 93-10 Upstream Mutations Associated with the γ Genes in Nondeletion HPFH

Gene	Position*	Base substitution	% Hb F in heterozygote	Origin
$^G\gamma$	−175	T→C	~20	Black
$^G\gamma$	−202	G→C	14–20	Black
$^A\gamma$	−117	G→A	10–20	Greek
$^A\gamma$	−196	C→T	10–20	Italian, Chinese
$^A\gamma$	−198	T→C	3–10	British

*Position relative to transcription start site.
NOTE: References given in text.

show marked growth retardation. The skin shows pallor and icterus, often accompanied by brown pigmentation. Expansion of the bone marrow in response to anemia leads to characteristic skeletal changes including the development of "thalassemic" facies due to frontal bossing of the skull and protrusion of the jaws and cheekbones. On radiography, the skull has a "hair-on-end" appearance, while the long bones show considerable thinning and trabeculation and are prone to repeated fractures. The magnitude of the increase in erythropoiesis (estimated to be as much as 20- to 30-fold) may result in extramedullary masses, arising usually from the sternum and ribs. Progressive hepatosplenomegaly is a constant finding, often leading to secondary dilutional anemia, leukopenia, and thrombocytopenia. Gallstones and leg ulcers are common. Intercurrent infections are a frequent complication and in inadequately transfused patients are a major cause of morbidity and mortality.

With frequent transfusions to maintain a hemoglobin level above 11 g/dl, growth and development are relatively normal until early puberty. Splenectomy is often necessary during this period to reduce the transfusion requirements but is associated with an increased incidence of septicemia. By the age of 10 to 11 years, treated patients begin to show signs of progressive hepatic, cardiac, and endocrine disturbances associated with a reduced or absent pubertal growth spurt and failure of sexual maturation. These changes are due largely to accumulation of iron from transfusion and its deposition in the tissues. Unless iron overload is controlled by chelation therapy, it results in death in the second or third decade, usually from cardiac failure.

The peripheral blood shows grossly abnormal red cell morphology (Fig. 93-24). There are marked anisocytosis and poikilocytosis, target cells, and red cell fragments, all associated with extreme hypochromia. Nucleated red cells are usually present in the blood and often contain inclusion bodies, particularly after splenectomy. White cell and platelet counts are usually normal or elevated, unless there is hypersplenism.

The bone marrow shows intense erythroid hyperplasia (M : E ratio ≈ 0.1) with a shift to the less mature basophilic forms. Hypochromia is evident, and inclusion bodies of precipitated α chains can be demonstrated in many of the normoblasts.[190–192] Nuclear and cytoplasmic abnormalities, typical of ineffective erythropoiesis, and increased phagocytic activity are also prominent. This pattern of highly expanded but ineffective erythropoiesis has been confirmed by ferrokinetic and erythrokinetic studies.[193] Those cells that do survive to enter the circulation show a markedly reduced red cell life span of 7 to 22 days.

Hemoglobin analysis in untransfused patients usually shows a high proportion of Hb F. In those patients with no β-chain production there is a corresponding lack of Hb A, and except for a small proportion of Hb A_2 (1 to 3 percent) the remainder is Hb F. In those with reduced β-chain output, a variable amount of Hb A is present, but this rarely exceeds 30 percent. After transfusion, endogenous erythropoiesis is suppressed and analysis of hemoglobin composition, even immediately prior to transfusion, is unreliable as an indicator of the type of β thalassemia.

More detailed clinical descriptions of severe β thalassemia can be found in two monographs.[2,185]

THALASSEMIA INTERMEDIA. Thalassemia intermedia is an ill-defined clinical term used to describe patients with anemia and splenomegaly but without the full spectrum of clinical severity found in thalassemia major.[2,185] Although far less common than thalassemia major, the condition encompasses a much broader clinical spectrum so that it is sometimes further divided into mild or severe thalassemia intermedia. The criteria on which the diagnosis is made are that patients do not present until later in life relative to those with thalassemia major and that they are capable of maintaining a hemoglobin level above 6 g/dl without transfusion.

At the severe end of the spectrum, patients present between the ages of 2 and 6 years, and although they are capable of surviving with a hemoglobin level of 5 to 7 g/dl, it is clear that they will not develop normally and will show many of the skeletal and facial changes seen in untreated thalassemia major. Thus they are treated with transfusion, but their blood requirement is not as great as in those with thalassemia major. In general, they are prone to the same complications though they may occur later in life.

At the other end of the spectrum, patients may not become symptomatic until they reach adult life and may remain transfusion-free, with hemoglobin levels of 8 to 10 g/dl except at times of infection. There is usually some degree of hepatosplenomegaly, and the development of hypersplenism may render patients transfusion-dependent; this may be reversed by splenectomy. Sexual development may be normal, and several successful pregnancies have been reported, although the anemia is exacerbated in the later stages.

Even those who have few transfusions tend to accumulate iron with age, presumably as a result of increased absorption

Fig. 93-24 Blood film in homozygous β thalassemia. (Geimsa stain, × 492). *(From Weatherall and Clegg.[2] Used by permission.)*

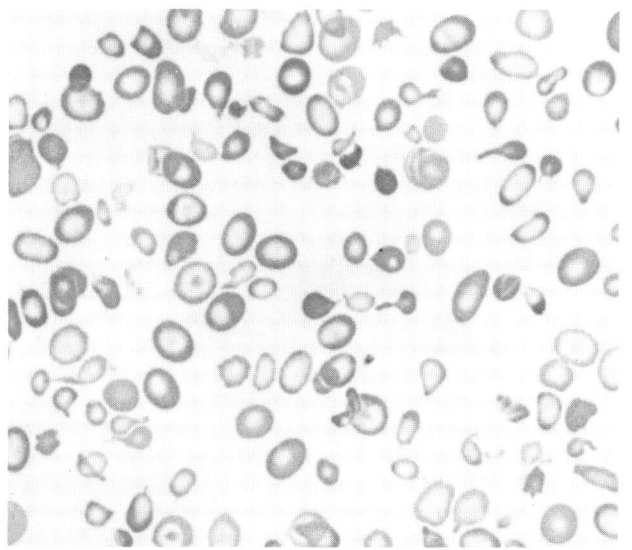

Table 93-11 Causes of β Thalassemia Intermedia

Mild β chain deficit
  Homozygous β^{++} thalassemia*
  Compound heterozygous β^+/β^{++} thalassemia
  Homozygous normal Hb A_2 β thalassemia type I
  Compound heterozygous β^+ or β^0/normal Hb A_2 β thalassemia
    type 1
  Severe heterozygous β thalassemia
Interacting α thalassemia
  Homozygous β^+/β^+ thalassemia with $\alpha\alpha/-\alpha$
  Homozygous β^0/β^0 thalassemia with $-\alpha/-\alpha$
  Compound heterozygous β^0/β^+ thalassemia with $-\alpha/-\alpha$
  Hb E/β^0 thalassemia with $-\alpha/-\alpha$
Increased Hb F production
  Homozygous $(\delta\beta)^0$ thalassemia
  Homozygous $(^A\gamma\delta\beta)^0$ thalassemia
  Compound heterozygous β^+ or $\beta^0/(\delta\beta)^0$ thalassemia
  Homozygous β^0/β^0 thalassemia with $-+-++$ haplotype (see text)
  Homozygous β^+ or β^0 thalassemia with high Hb F determinant
    (allelic or nonallelic)
  Homozygous Hb Lepore, Hb Lepore/$(\delta\beta)^0$ thalassemia, and Hb
    Lepore/β^0 thalassemia

*β^{++} Thalassemia indicates a particular mild defect in β chain synthesis.

in response to the chronic anemia. Thus, evidence of iron overload may develop in the third and fourth decades, with diabetes mellitus and impairment of other endocrine functions. The chronic hemolysis and ineffective erythropoiesis lead to a high incidence of gallstones. Presumably because of marrow expansion, some patients develop bone and joint disease later in life.

The hematologic picture of thalassemia intermedia, except for the severity of the anemia, is similar to that for thalassemia major. The hemoglobin composition is extremely variable. Rare cases are homozygous for β^0 thalassemia and hence have only Hb F and Hb A_2, while in others the level of Hb F may be as low as 5 to 10 percent. This variability reflects the wide genetic heterogeneity that can produce this clinical picture; this is summarized in Table 93.11.

The main causes of a mild phenotype in β-thalassemia homozygotes are "mild" β-thalassemia mutations and the coinheritance of α thalassemia or various genetic determinants that increase Hb F production (Table 93-11). The latter interactions are described in a later section. However there are many cases in which the mild course remains unexplained.

HETEROZYGOUS β THALASSEMIA. The heterozygous state for β thalassemia is asymptomatic and, despite the genetic heterogeneity, remarkably uniform hematologically. The diagnosis is usually straightforward, and is based on a low MCV and MCH together with an increased proportion of Hb A_2. This is an important consideration for genetic counseling and prenatal diagnosis. The hematologic findings are listed in Table 93-12. The peripheral blood film shows hypochromia and microcytosis with some aniso- and poikilocytosis and basophilic stippling. Red cell survival is almost normal.

Hemoglobin analysis shows a raised level of Hb A_2, to 3.5 to 6.5 percent (mean $\approx$ 5%), that is found only in this condition and occurs in nearly all cases. It may be accompanied by a slight increase (1 to 3 percent) in Hb F in about half of the cases. Although there is globin chain imbalance with an α-chain excess of about twofold, there is little evidence of ineffective erythropoiesis or of free α chains remaining in the red cell. It appears that the proteolytic mechanisms within the red cell have the capacity to deal with this degree of chain imbalance.

SUBTYPES OF β THALASSEMIA. The phenotypes of the various forms of β thalassemia that are detectable by hemoglobin analysis are listed in Table 93-12. Numerically, the β^0 and β^+ forms are by far the most important; the other types shown in Table 93-12, although widespread, do not usually account for more than 10 percent of the β-thalassemia alleles within a population.

β^0 Thalassemia genes are found in all affected populations although they are rare in those of African origin. In the homozygous state they are detected by the lack of Hb A in untransfused patients, whose hemoglobin pattern comprises Hb F plus 1 to 3 percent Hb A_2. The β^0 gene can also be distinguished in compound heterozygotes with a β-chain variant such as Hb S. In populations with both β^0 and β^+ alleles, distinction between β^0/β^+ compound heterozygotes and β^+/β^+ homozygotes is not usually possible because of the considerable overlap in the amount of Hb A produced in the two conditions. Heterozygotes for β^0 thalassemia cannot be distinguished from individuals heterozygous for the common β^+ forms of thalassemia.

There are numerous β^+-thalassemia alleles with variable levels of residual β-chain production, and several may be relatively common within the same population. By and large the extent of the β-chain deficit determines the clinical severity, but homozygosity or double heterozygosity for most of the common alleles causes thalassemia major. The extent of the deficiency in β-chain production dictated by specific β^+-thalassemia alleles can be determined only by the amount of Hb A in compound heterozygotes with β-chain structural variants.

Table 93-12 Phenotypic Characteristics of the β Thalassemias

		Heterozygotes			Homozygotes		
Condition	MCH, pg	% Hb A_2	% Hb F	% Hb A	% Hb F	Clinical status	
β^0 Thalassemia	21 ± 2	3.8–6.5	<4	0	~98	Major	
β^+ Thalassemia	22 ± 2	3.8–6.5	<4	5–50	50–90	Major	
β^{++} Thalassemia	24 ± 2	3.8–6.5	<2	50–90	10–50	Intermedia	
High Hb A_2 β thalassemia	21 ± 2	6.0–10.0	3–10	0	~98	Intermedia	
Normal Hb A_2 β thalassemia I	27 ± 2	2.3–3.4	<2	75–90	5–25	Intermedia	
Normal Hb A_2 β thalassemia II	23 ± 2	2.8–3.5	<2	—			
Severe heterozygous β thalassemia	21 ± 2	3.5–5.3	1–12	—			

SOURCE: Ref. 2.

Since many alleles have not been observed in such an association and the molecular defect has not been established in many of those that have, the correlation between the molecular lesion and the extent of β-chain deficit remains to be established in most cases.

In some cases the deficit in β-chain production is so mild that a separate category of β[++] *thalassemia* may be warranted. Homozygotes may not come to clinical attention, and compound heterozygotes with β[0] or the more severe β[+] alleles may be thalassemia intermedias. These mild alleles have been observed in West Africa[293] and also appear throughout the Mediterranean.[268,207]

NORMAL Hb A₂ β THALASSEMIA. Family studies of β-thalassemia patients occasionally reveal a parent without the raised Hb A₂ level characteristic of most heterozygotes. Two forms of this condition have been described,[294] type 1 in which the red cell indices are almost normal but in which deficient β-chain production is observed when the globin synthesis ratio is measured and type 2 in which only the Hb A₂ level differs from the normal heterozygous β-thalassemia picture.

The type 1 form, also known as *silent β thalassemia*,[295] appears to be another mild β-thalassemia allele although there is probably heterogeneity within this phenotype. Some, but not all, cases have been shown to be associated with an abnormal β-chain variant, Hb Knossos (β27 Ala→Ser), which is silent on standard hemoglobin electrophoresis but detectable by isoelectric focusing.[296,297] The β Knossos chain is produced in reduced amounts, hence the mild thalassemia phenotype which interacts with typical β-thalassemia alleles to produce the clinical picture of thalassemia intermedia.

There is also heterogeneity within type 2 normal Hb A₂ β thalassemia, and several different defects have been observed. Many cases are likely to be due to the coinheritance of a defective δ gene (δ thalassemia) which may occur either cis or trans to the β thalassemia gene, which itself may be of the β[0] or β[+] type. Gene mapping is usually normal,[298] but in a few isolated cases deletions within the β-globin gene complex have been detected. Deletion of the complete complex results in this phenotype,[299,300] as do deletions that remove the ε and [G]γ or ε [G]γ[A]γ and δ genes but spare the β gene.[283,285,301] These conditions, known as γδβ thalassemia, may result in an unusually severe hemolytic anemia at birth which disappears within the first few months.[302] One other deletion results in normal Hb A₂ β thalassemia type 2. It removes only part of the δ gene and ≈7 kb upstream.[286] In all these deletion cases, the surviving β gene is apparently not expressed even though it retains that capability in exogeneous systems.

UNUSUALLY HIGH Hb A₂ β THALASSEMIA. Several β thalassemias have been described in which the proportion of Hb A₂ in heterozygotes is unusually high, >7 percent. This phenotype appears to identify certain specific β[0]-thalassemia defects in which there is a deletion involving at least the 5′ end of the β gene but sparing the δ gene (see above).

SEVERE HETEROZYGOUS β THALASSEMIA. Several families have been described in which the inheritance of a mild thalassemia intermedia phenotype follows a dominant pattern. In some cases in which the defect has been identified it has been due to the inheritance of a β-chain structural variant which is highly unstable (e.g., Hb Indianapolis).[303] The more severe phenotype of these conditions may well be the result of the cells' capacity for destroying excess or abnormal chains being overcome by the combination of the unstable β-chain and the concomitant α-chain excess.

The coinheritance of the ααα gene arrangement with heterozygous β thalassemia may also produce this pattern of inheritance.

The δβ Thalassemias (Table 93-13).

HB LEPORE. The structures and molecular mechanisms underlying the Lepore hemoglobins were described in an earlier section.

Homozygotes for Hb Lepore produce only Hb Lepore (15 to 20 percent) and Hb F. Clinically their course is either thalassemia major or thalassemia intermedia; the basis for this variable phenotype is not well understood.[304] Although cases have been described from many racial groups, it appears to be relatively common only in the Campania region of Italy.[305]

(δβ)[0] THALASSEMIAS. (δβ)[0] Thalassemias are widely distributed but are relatively rare, reaching a significant proportion of the β thalassemias only in the Mediterranean They are characterized in the homozygous state by a clinical picture of thalassemia intermedia, while hemoglobin analysis shows 100 percent Hb F containing a mixture of both [G]γ and [A]γ chains. Hematologic changes are less marked than in β-thalassemia homozygotes.

Heterozygotes are distinguished from β-thalassemia heterozygotes by normal levels of Hb A₂, together with an increased Hb F level of 5 to 20 percent. The Hb F is heterogeneously distributed, with only a proportion of cells positive after acid elution. The red cell indices of heterozygotes are reduced but not as severely as in β-thalassemia heterozygotes.[306]

In general the clinical and hematologic findings appear to be very similar in all these disorders, regardless of their underlying defects, although too few cases have been studied in which the underlying lesion is known to be sure that there are no phenotypic differences.

Table 93-13 Characteristics of the Deletion Forms of δβ Thalassemia and HPFH

	Heterozygotes			Homozygotes		
Condition	MCH, pg	% Hb F	% [G]γ	% Hb F	% [G]γ	Clinical status
Hb Lepore	22 ± 2	1–3	20–45	70–90	48–62	Intermedia/major
(δβ)[0] Thalassemia	23 ± 2	5–18	25–56	100	47–64	Intermedia
([A]γδβ)[0] Thalassemia	24 ± 2	9–18	96–100	100	100	Intermedia
(δβ)[0] HPFH	27 ± 3	17–35	25–75	100	52–65*	Normal
Hb Kenya	26 ± 3	4–9	100	—	—	

*African type I 51 ± 4%, type II 32 ± 5%; Indian type 69 ± 4%
SOURCE: Ref. 2.

($^A\gamma\delta\beta$)^0 THALASSEMIA. These are also rare but widespread disorders. Clinically and hematologically they are very similar to the ($\delta\beta$)^0 thalassemias, with a similar amount and distribution of Hb F. They can be distinguished only by analysis of the γ-chain composition of the Hb F, which in the ($^A\gamma\delta\beta$)^0 thalassemias consists only of $^G\gamma$ chains. Again, there are few if any phenotypic differences between the various types which have been distinguished by the size and position of the underlying gene deletions.[307]

Hereditary Persistence of Fetal Hemoglobin (HPFH) (Table 93-13).

HPFH is the term used to describe any genetically determined increase in Hb F in adult life, a nomenclature that was introduced before the nature of these varied disorders was understood. We can now distinguish three major types of lesion that come under this definition: (1) deletions similar to those observed in ($\delta\beta$)^0 and ($^A\gamma\delta\beta$)^0 thalassemia removing the δ and β genes and differing only in that the resulting level of Hb F is sufficient to make the condition asymptomatic; (2) nondeletion disorders in which fairly high levels of Hb F in heterozygotes (5 to 15 percent) are associated with continued, but reduced, β-chain output from the same chromosome; (3) a group of conditions, probably heterogeneous, in which much lower levels of Hb F (2 to 5 percent) are found in otherwise normal families. There is evidence that in some of these cases the genetic determinant may not be linked to the β-globin gene cluster.

($\delta\beta$)^0 HPFH. This condition is usually found in individuals of African origin, although cases have been described from India and Southeast Asia. Homozygotes have 100 percent Hb F containing a mixture of both $^G\gamma$ and $^A\gamma$ chains, but are clinically asymptomatic. Their red cells are microcytic and hypochromic, and globin chain imbalance can be demonstrated ($\alpha/\gamma \approx$ 2.0), but they maintain Hb levels above 15 g/dl, compensating for the increased oxygen affinity associated with having only Hb F. Heterozygotes have normal hematology and 20 to 35 percent Hb F which has a pancellular but uneven distribution. Three different deletions of the globin gene complex have been found in Africans, affecting the phenotype only in the proportion of $^G\gamma$ chains (30 or 70 percent). A fourth similar deletion underlies the Indian form, giving $\approx$50 percent $^G\gamma$. While the phenotype of the Indian heterozygotes is similar to that of their African counterparts, the two conditions produce different effects on interaction with β thalassemia. The African compound heterozygotes are similar to β-thalassemia heterozygotes, while Indians with this combination have thalassemia intermedia, similar to that seen in a ($\delta\beta$)^0/β^0 thalassemia combination. This underlines the overlap in the clinical and hematologic effects of ($\delta\beta$)^0 thalassemia and ($\delta\beta$)^0 HPFH.

HB KENYA. Misaligned crossing-over between the $^A\gamma$ and β genes results in a fusion $^A\gamma\beta$ gene which produces the non-α chain of Hb Kenya.[110] This condition has not been observed in the homozygous state, but heterozygotes and compound heterozygotes with Hb S have been found in East Africa.

In the few families studied, the level of Hb Kenya in heterozygotes appears to fall into two groups, constituting 7 to 12 and 20 to 23 percent of the total[308-310]; it is not clear whether this reflects further genetic heterogeneity. This condition is also accompanied by persistent Hb F, with levels of 5 to 10 percent containing only $^G\gamma$ chains. Red cell morphology is normal, and globin synthesis is balanced.

NONDELETION TYPES OF HPFH. Compound heterozygotes for HPFH and β-chain variants do not usually produce any Hb A, but a few cases have been found in which this is not the case. Family studies have made it clear that these genetic defects are tightly linked to the β-globin locus and that there is β-chain production from the chromosome responsible for the increased γ-chain output. Several types have been described (Table 93-6), and unlike the forms of HPFH discussed above, none is associated with any deletion. Sequencing of the overproduced γ gene has demonstrated various single base substitutions within the promoter region in each of these types.

Compound heterozygotes for $^G\gamma\beta^+$ HPFH[311-313] and Hb S or Hb C produce 45 percent of the abnormal hemoglobin, 30 percent Hb A and 20 percent Hb F containing only $^G\gamma$ chains. Similar Hb F levels are seen in simple heterozygotes. Globin synthesis is balanced, and so the combined output of $^G\gamma$ and β^A chains from the affected chromosome is equal to the normal β-chain output. This rare condition has been found only in those of African origin and is not associated with hematologic abnormalities or clinical symptoms. Two different molecular defects have been described (see previous section).

The most common of the nondeletion types of HPFH, $^A\gamma\beta^+$ HPFH,[314-316] is found in Greeks, where it is still rare. Heterozygotes are hematologically normal but have 10 to 20 percent Hb F, almost all of the $^A\gamma$ type. Compound heterozygotes with β thalassemia have a hematologic phenotype slightly more severe than β-thalassemia trait (with high Hb F levels), and the presence of Hb A in compound heterozygotes with β^0 thalassemia demonstrates that the β gene cis to the HPFH defect is active.

Conditions with a similar phenotype have also been described in a Southern Italian[289] and a Chinese family,[317] but in those two cases a different promotor mutation underlies the defect.

A fourth similar molecular defect[292] producing $^A\gamma\beta^+$ HPFH was found in a single British family.[318] This family, in which heterozygotes have 3.5 to 10 percent Hb F, consisting mostly of $^A\gamma$ chains, contains the only known homozygotes for nondeletion HPFH. They are all hematologically normal, have balanced globin chain synthesis, and were characterized on hemoglobin analysis by low normal levels of Hb A$_2$ and Hb F levels of $\approx$20 percent. The offspring of one of these homozygotes, obligate heterozygotes, had normal levels of Hb F and normal $^G\gamma/^A\gamma$ ratios at birth, suggesting that the γ genes function normally during fetal life.[319] After birth however, they show a markedly delayed decline in Hb F levels accompanied by a rapid decline in $^G\gamma$ chain production.

HPFH WITH LOW LEVELS OF Hb F. The majority of normal adults have less than 1 percent Hb F. However, it has been recognized for many years that slightly elevated levels of Hb F (1 to 3 percent) can be traced through families and hence have a genetic component.[320] Later studies have confirmed this,[321] although neither the pattern of inheritance nor the amount of genetic heterogeneity which might underlie the condition has been elucidated. The importance of this (or these) condition(s) is that their coinheritance with the more severe forms of β thalassemia can lead to a considerable amelioration of the clinical severity through the increased ability to produce Hb F.[322,323]

It is clear from family studies of some cases of β thalassemia or Hb S with unusually high F levels that the high F level is genetically determined and that the determinant is not linked to the β-globin locus.[86,324] Other families, however, have been reported in which the high Hb F determinant does appear to be linked to the cluster. In most of these cases, only the nuclear family has been studied, and the small numbers of individuals give limited opportunities for assortment. Given the possibility of genetic heterogeneity of this condition, combining results from several families for genetic analysis may be misleading, and it is not clear to what degree ascertainment bias may have contributed to the published reports.

One further difficulty in genetic studies of such families is whether the determinant shows complete penetrance. In the largest family of this type studied to date,[324] there appeared to be clearcut examples of impenetrance, and this may well be why the genetics of this disorder have not been clarified in Mendelian terms, even within single families. This may be related to the observation that the high Hb F determinant may be expressed to a much greater degree under conditions of erythroid stress. Thus families in which β-thalassemia heterozygotes coinherit a high Hb F determinant and produce ≈5 percent Hb F may contain β-thalassemia homozygotes whose level of Hb F production (10 to 12 g/dl) is sufficient to produce a very mild or asymptomatic condition.

HAPLOTYPE-ASSOCIATED INCREASED Hb F DETERMINANTS. In addition to the mild β-thalassemia homozygotes described above, in whom the ability to produce increased Hb F can be traced in heterozygous relatives, there are other β-thalassemia homozygotes with a mild clinical course due to high levels of Hb F in whom family studies show no increased levels of Hb F.[325,326] Many of these cases share a common RFLP haplotype in the region 5′ to the β gene encompassing the ε, $^G\gamma^A\gamma$, and $\psi\beta$ genes, − + − + + (Fig. 93-4). Homozygotes for β^0 thalassemia who are homozygous for this haplotype tend to have thalassemia intermedia rather than the expected thalassemia major, while in β^+-thalassemia homozygotes it appears that if one of the chromosomes carries this haplotype the patient is likely to have a milder disease. Therefore the inheritance of this haplotype apparently confers the ability to increase Hb F production, but only under conditions of erythroid stress.

The − + − + + haplotype is also associated with higher Hb F production in patients with sickle cell disease[327,328] and is very similar to the + + − + + haplotype associated with very high Hb F production (≈20 percent) in sickle cell patients from Saudi Arabia and India.[329,330] In these cases too, there is no evidence of increased Hb F values in AS relatives. Both of these haplotypes, but none of the common haplotypes, contain an *Xmn* I restriction site 5′ to the $^G\gamma$ gene at position − 158.[331] It is not clear whether this *Xmn* I polymorphism is a further marker within the haplotype linked to the high Hb F determinant or whether the − 158 substitution might itself be the determinant since it is within the region where the substitutions responsible for the nondeletion HPFH conditions occur (see above).

The Interaction of β Thalassemia with α-Gene Mutations. The geographic distribution of α and β thalassemias is largely coincident, and relatively high frequencies of both occur in many populations. At least among Mediterraneans, the clinical and hematologic consequences of their coinheritance have been established, and the findings are likely to be applicable to other groups.

HOMOZYGOUS β THALASSEMIA AND α THALASSEMIA. In early studies it was established that β-thalassemia homozygotes who also inherited an α-thalassemia allele sometimes ran a milder

clinical course.[205] Since much of the pathology of β thalassemia is due to the pool of excess α chains, this observation can be readily explained, since the effect of α thalassemia is to reduce α-chain synthesis and hence the degree of excess chains. However, until gene mapping allowed the ready detection of α thalassemia, it was not clear to what extent α thalassemia played a part in producing the milder forms of the disease.

Two large series have now established that α thalassemia is an important factor in reducing the severity of homozygous β thalassemia to a clinical picture of thalassemia intermedia. In Cyprus, where the common lesion is a severe β^+ form of thalassemia (IVS1 110), 14 out of 27 cases of β-thalassemia intermedia had some form of deletion α thalassemia [α − /αα (9); α − /α − (1); αα/ − − (2); and α − / − − (2)] while only 4 of 30 thalassemia major cases had an α-thalassemia gene (all α − / αα). Furthermore, in four of five intermedia cases with a normal α genotype studied, one parent showed evidence of a nondeletion form of α thalassemia on the basis of globin chain synthesis studies. Clearly, the presence of one or more α-thalassemia genes can significantly modify the severity of the disease.[332]

In Sardinia, where the major β-thalassemia determinant is a β^0 type (codon 39 nonsense mutation), many of those with a single α-gene deletion (α − /αα) remained transfusion-dependent, but there was a significantly higher incidence of α − /αα and particularly α − /α − cases among β-thalassemia homozygotes than in the general population.[333] Presumably, in the face of the more severe deficit in β-chain production in Sardinia, the effect of one α gene deleted is not sufficient to reduce the chain imbalance enough to prevent transfusion dependence, while in the Cypriot β^+ cases it does.

HETEROZYGOUS β THALASSEMIA AND α THALASSEMIA. Studies of β-thalassemia heterozygotes who also have α thalassemia (as determined by gene mapping) show reduced amount of chain imbalance and less hematologic abnormalities.[334,335] Hemoglobin levels, MCV, and MCH all increase across the series αα/ αα, α − /αα, and α − α − but decrease again in those with α − / − − (Table 93-14). These results point to a potential problem in screening for β thalassemia on electronic counters by the reduced MCV, since in β-thalassemia heterozygotes with an α − /α − genotype, there is considerable overlap with normal values. However, screening by Hb A_2 levels should not be affected since the levels remain raised in all these groups. We return to this question later when considering population screening.

HOMOZYGOUS β THALASSEMIA AND ααα. Given the frequency of the ααα genotype in many populations, it will undoubtedly occur in β-thalassemia homozygotes, and individuals with this interaction and the picture of thalassemia major have been reported. Unexpectedly, four homozygotes with this genotype have been described with the milder pattern of thalassemia intermedia. It is probable that in at least some of these cases, there are nondeletion α-thalassemia mutations affecting genes within the triplicated α-gene arrangement.[336]

HETEROZYGOUS β THALASSEMIA AND ααα. The clinical and hematologic picture of double heterozygotes for β thalassemia and the triplicated α-gene arrangement (Table 93-14) may be indistinguishable from simple heterozygotes for β thalassemia in some cases,[336] while others present with thalassemia intermedia.[337–339] The reason for this difference remains unex-

Table 93-14 Hematologic Findings in Heterozygous β Thalassemia with Normal or Abnormal α-Gene Rearrangements

Condition	n	Hb, g/dl	MCV, fl	MCH, pg	Hb A$_2$, %	Hb F, %	α/β ratio
αα/αα	53	12.5 ± 1.2	65 ± 4	21 ± 1	4.9 ± 0.7	1.3 ± 1.1	2.2 ± 0.3
αα/−α	36	13.0 ± 1.4	67 ± 4	22 ± 1	5.2 ± 0.7	1.2 ± 0.3	1.4 ± 0.1
−α/−α	11	13.9 ± 1.1	77 ± 3	25 ± 1	5.1 ± 0.6	1.1 ± 0.7	0.8 ± 0.1
−α/−−	6	11.8 ± 0.8	55 ± 3	18 ± 1	4.6 ± 0.2	—	0.5 ± 0.1
αα/ααα*	7	11.7 ± 1.9	65 ± 5	21 ± 2	5.0 ± 0.9	2.3 ± 1.5	2.1 ± 0.4
	11	9.1 ± 0.9	70 ± 8	21 ± 2	4.9 ± 0.6	4.3 ± 2.1	2.9 ± 0.6
ααα/ααα	3	9.3 ± 0.9	65 ± 3	21 ± 1	4.6 ± 0.3	6.8 ± 2.9	4.0 ± 0.4

*Seven cases presenting with phenotype of thalassemia trait, 11 presenting as thalassemia intermedia.

plained; it does not seem to be due to the nature of the β-thalassemia allele, and in several of the asymptomatic patients all three α genes on the triple α chromosome appeared to be active. Both phenotypes may coexist within the same family.[340]

β-Thalassemia heterozygotes who are homozygous for the ααα arrangement present with thalassemia intermedia.[341,342]

The Interaction of β Thalassemia with Structural Variants. The association of β thalassemia with Hb S, Hb C, and Hb E was described in an earlier section.

Although β thalassemia has been reported in association with several other hemoglobin variants, few result in any clinical disability. Hb D/β thalassemia is not uncommon in parts of India but, apart from a mild anemia which may be exacerbated in pregnancy, is largely asymptomatic.

Hb O Arab/β^0 thalassemia causes a moderately severe disorder with a hemoglobin level of 6 to 8 g/dl and splenomegaly. Several cases with this combination have been reported from Bulgaria. It is not clear why this interaction is so severe, but homozygotes for Hb O Arab are also anemic.

WORLD DISTRIBUTION AND POPULATION GENETICS

Although our knowledge of the prevalence and distribution of the hemoglobin disorders is still scanty, enough information has been obtained to suggest that they are the most common single gene disorders. Very conservative data compiled by the World Health Organization indicate that about 5 percent of the world population are carriers for important hemoglobin disorders.[1] Since these data were compiled before anything was known about the distribution of α thalassemia, as assessed by more recently developed gene mapping techniques, it is clear that these figures represent a considerable underestimate of the total problem.

The Structural Hemoglobin Variants

The only structural hemoglobin variants to reach polymorphic frequencies are Hb S, Hb C, and Hb E. The sickle-cell gene is most concentrated in West Africa although its distribution spreads across central Africa, and it is found at lower frequencies in some non-African Mediterranean populations.[3,144] It also occurs patchily throughout the Middle East and central India, but, apart from some Indian populations in north Malaya, it has not been observed in Southeast Asia. Hemoglobin

C is restricted to parts of West Africa,[3] while Hb E is distributed in a region stretching from the eastern parts of India through Burma to Southeast Asia where it reaches its highest frequency in parts of Thailand, Laos, and Cambodia. Hemoglobin E is found sporadically in parts of southern China, and it extends in a line stretching south through Thailand and down the Malay peninsula and into some of the island populations of Indonesia.[3]

The approximate gene frequencies for the structural hemoglobin variants, where known, have been catalogued by several workers.[3,343] In parts of west central Africa, Nigeria, Ghana, Gabon, and Zaire for example, the gene frequency for Hb S can exceed 0.15; in other words heterozygotes constitute over 25 percent of the newborn population. Similar frequencies are found in parts of eastern Saudi Arabia, and the condition is almost as common in parts of central India. Hemoglobin C is found exclusively in African populations and reaches its highest frequency in Ghana and Upper Volta with gene frequencies approaching 0.15. The gene frequency for Hb E in Thailand and Burma is 0.05 to 0.10, although higher values have been recorded in parts of eastern Thailand near the Vietnamese border, the so-called Hb E triangle. At a minimum estimate there are about 30 million heterozygotes for Hb E and about 1 million homozygotes in Southeast Asia. For more extensive population data, broken down into different racial groups, readers are referred to the catalog of Livingstone.[343]

These remarkably high gene frequencies pose two important questions. How did these variants become distributed among the high incidence populations, and what are the factors that have maintained these polymorphisms?

Population Distribution. Before it was possible to analyze human DNA directly, a great deal was written about the distribution of the sickle cell gene and other hemoglobin variants under the assumption that population movements could be derived from the distribution of genetic markers of this type. It was believed, reasonably, that the distribution of the β^S gene in the New World is based entirely on emigration from West Africa during the transportation of slaves. But it was also thought that the high prevalence of the sickle cell gene in Saudi Arabia and India may have reflected migrations out of East Africa; the transport of slaves from East Africa to the Persian Gulf flourished from 200 to 1500 A.D.

More recently, however, it has been possible to analyze the origins of the sickle cell gene and other structural hemoglobin variants by examining the pattern of restriction fragment length polymorphisms (RFLPs) in and around the β-globin gene carrying the sickle mutation. The first study of this type employed a single polymorphism identified by the enzyme

Hpa I.[344] Nearly all Caucasians and about 97 percent of individuals of African origin with a normal hemoglobin phenotype have a 7.6-kb or, less commonly, a 7.0-kb *Hpa* I fragment that encompasses the entire β-globin gene. Only 3 percent have a 13-kb fragment. In contrast, among American blacks who have Hb S, nearly 70 percent have the 13-kb fragment. Similarly, blacks with Hb C nearly all have the 13-kb fragment. How can this type of linkage disequilibrium be explained? It seems likely that the β[S] and β[C] mutations both arose on a β gene carrying the 13-kb mutation, which may have occurred in a relatively small geographic area corresponding to what is now called Upper Volta and Ghana. Presumably because the β[S] and β[C] genes offered protection against malaria (see below), their frequency increased and the linked 13-kb mutation "hitchhiked" along with them. On the other hand, the prevalence of the ancestral 13-kb β[A] gene remained low because it lacked a selective advantage. The β[S]/13-kb fragment association has also been found in North Africans and Sicilians although not in individuals from East Africa, Saudi Arabia or India. These observations suggested an independent origin of the sickle cell gene in West and East Africa.[344]

More recently extensive RFLP analyses using a variety of single point polymorphisms in the β-globin gene cluster have been carried out in many populations in an attempt to obtain further information about the origins of both the sickle cell and Hb E mutations.[345–347] The particular arrangement of RFLPs is referred to as the *β-globin gene haplotype*. Studies in both Jamaica and West Africa indicate that the β[S] mutation can be found in association with a wide variety of haplotypes. At first sight these results suggest that the mutation may have had multiple origins. However, these data must be interpreted with caution because it is possible that a number of gene con-

version events could have given rise to at least some of the variability in β[S]/haplotype associations. However, the occurrence of a common haplotype associated with a β[S] gene in parts of eastern Saudi Arabia and Orissa in central India, and the finding of completely different haplotypes in some African populations, make it more likely that the β[S] mutation had at least two origins, one in east Africa and the other in the Middle East or India[329] (Fig. 93-25).

Similar haplotype data suggests that the β[E] mutation may have occured on more than one occasion.[348] The same reservations apply as in the case of Hb S; gene conversion events might also account for these different haplotypes.

Maintenance of the Polymorphism for Structural Hemoglobin Variants. In 1949 J. B. S. Haldane suggested that individuals with red cell disorders such as thalassemia might be protected against malaria.[349] Early epidemiologic studies in Africa suggested that Hb S heterozygotes are protected against *P. falciparum* malaria.[350] Recent work in Nigeria confirms these studies.[351] For example, the prevalence of the sickle cell trait in Nigerian newborns was 24 percent compared with 29 percent over the age of 5 years. Above this age no differences were noted. These data suggest that the Hb S trait confers a relative fitness of about 0.20 compared with normal individuals in the same population. This figure gives a calculated gene frequency of about 0.15, a value very close to that observed in Nigeria. Furthermore, it can be calculated that it would take about 50 generations (representing 1000 years) to reach the present equilibrium, assuming that the homozygous condition is 100 percent lethal.

These recent studies in Nigeria have been supported by analysis of the frequency of malarial parasites on peripheral

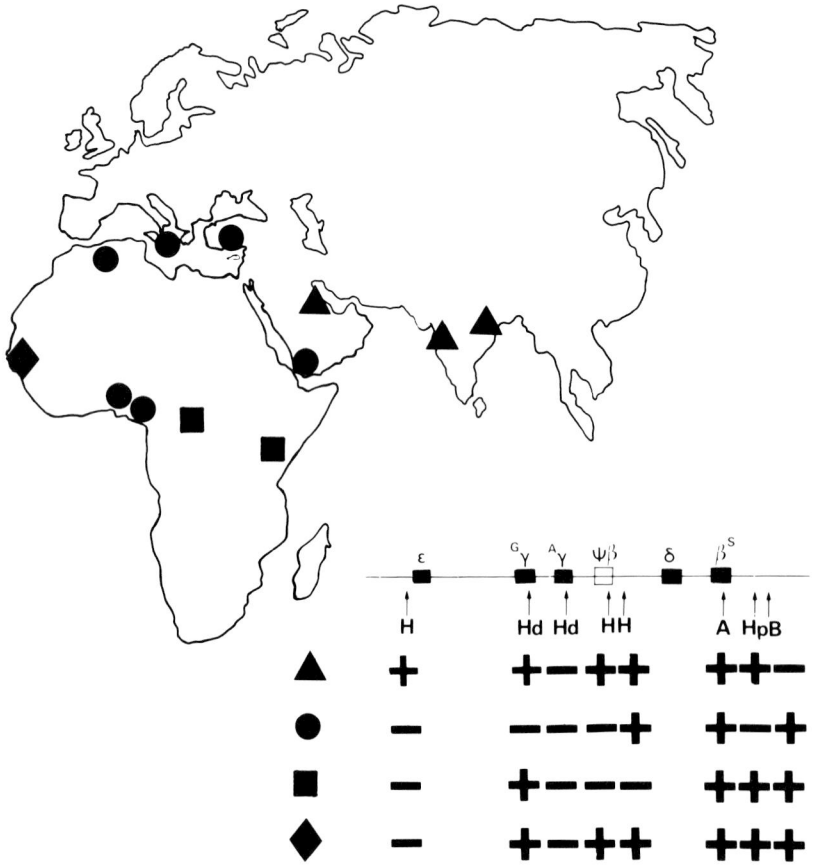

Fig. 93-25 β-Globin gene haplotypes in individuals with sickle cell gene from different populations. *(From Kulozik et al.[329] Used by permission.)*

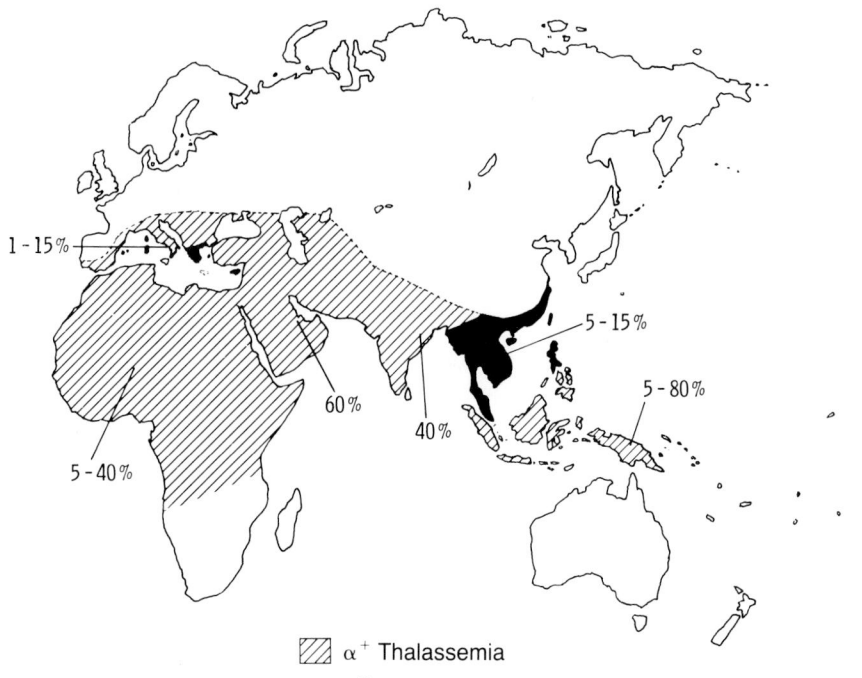

Fig. 93-26 The world distribution of α thalassemia.

◰ α⁺ Thalassemia

◼ α⁰ Thalassemia

blood smears of Hb S heterozygotes of different ages. The relative numbers of parasites were reduced in carriers aged 30–60 weeks, but not in older children.

If relative protection against *P. falciparum* malaria is the major mechanism for maintaining the Hb S polymorphism, how is this effect mediated? This problem has been approached by studying the rates of sickling of parasitized and nonparasitized cells under reduced oxygen tension and by examining the patterns of invasion and growth of parasites in red cells containing Hb S using in vitro culture systems. At least three possible protective mechanisms have been demonstrated. First, it has been found that under low oxygen tensions AS cells containing *P. falciparum* sickle more readily than nonparasitized cells. It has been suggested, therefore, that in vivo sickling may provide a mechanism for the rapid clearance of parasitized cells and their subsequent destruction in the RE system. It would follow that the parasite could not complete its life cycle.[352] In vitro culture studies have shown that, under ambient oxygen tensions, parasites invade and grow in sickle cells at the same rate as in normal cells.[353,354] However, under reduced oxygen conditions both invasion and growth are inhibited. It has been suggested that this effect may be mediated by the relatively low levels of potassium in AS cells that have undergone sickling.[355]

It is possible that several mechanisms are involved; the major reason the entrapment of sickle cells has been favored is the observation that individuals who are homozygous for the sickle cell gene undergo severe malarial infection, an observation that would be hard to explain if parasites could not survive adequately in cells containing a large concentration of Hb S. On the other hand, even a mild malaria infection might have catastrophic consequences for a child with sickle cell anemia.

In vitro studies of invasion and growth of *P. falciparum* in the cells of Hb E heterozygotes or homozygotes have not provided a clear answer as to why Hb E might be protective against malaria. However, since the Hb E mutation produces a thalassemic phenotype, we shall return to this problem in a later section.

The Thalassemias

The world distribution of the α and β thalassemias is summarized in Figs. 93-26 and 93-27; a more detailed breakdown of published data for the gene frequencies of different forms of thalassemia will be found in several monographs.[2,3,343]

True gene frequency data for β thalassemia are available only for a small number of populations. It is clear that, with a few exceptions such as Liberia, the condition occurs at only a low frequency throughout tropical Africa although higher frequencies have been observed in North Africa. The disease is common throughout the Mediterranean region, parts of the Middle East, and India and Burma, although accurate gene frequency data are sparse. It is also common throughout Southeast Asia in a line starting in southern China, stretching through Thailand, Cambodia, and Laos, and down the Malay peninsula into some of the island populations. It is distributed sporadically in Melanesia.

The world distribution of the α thalassemias is summarized in Fig. 93-26. The α⁺ thalassemias are extremely common in parts of Africa, the Mediterranean region, the Middle East, and throughout Southeast Asia and the Pacific island populations. Indeed, α⁺ thalassemia appears to be reaching fixation in some regions, notably the coastal regions of Papua New Guinea. On the other hand, α⁰ thalassemia is restricted to the Mediterranean island populations and to Southeast Asia where it occurs frequently in China, Thailand, Laos, and the Malay peninsula; it is not found in the Pacific island populations. Since α⁰ thalassemia is necessary for the Hb Bart's hydrops fetalis and Hb H disease phenotypes, it follows that these conditions are restricted to the Mediterranean region and Southeast Asia.

Population Distribution. As was the case for the sickle cell gene, before the advent of DNA technology and the realization of the remarkable heterogeneity of β thalassemia much was written about the movement of populations based on the distribution of the β-thalassemia mutations. However, more

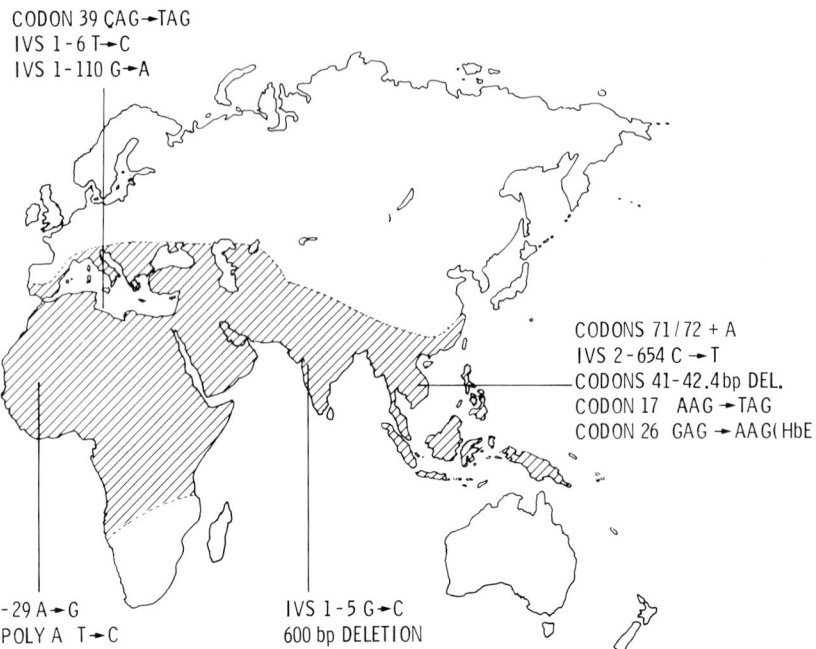

CODON 39 CAG→TAG
IVS 1-6 T→C
IVS 1-110 G→A

CODONS 71/72 + A
IVS 2-654 C → T
CODONS 41-42. 4bp DEL.
CODON 17 AAG→TAG
CODON 26 GAG → AAG(HbE)

-29 A→G
POLY A T→C

IVS 1-5 G→C
600 bp DELETION

Fig. 93-27 The world distribution of β thalassemia.

recent work, in which the precise molecular lesions have been defined and β-globin gene RFLP haplotypes determined, has provided a much clearer picture about the population distribution of the β thalassemias.[48,356,357]

It is now apparent that in each of the high frequency areas there are a few common mutations together with varying numbers of rare ones (Fig. 93-27). Furthermore, in each of these regions the pattern of mutations is different. And even where the same mutation occurs in different populations, it is usually found together with a different β-globin gene RFLP haplotype. Thus, although much of this work is at a very preliminary stage, it seems very likely that the β-thalassemia mutations have arisen independently in different populations and then achieved their high frequency by selection. Although there may have been some movement of the β-thalassemia genes between populations by drift and so on, there is little doubt that independent mutation and selection provide the overall basis for the world distribution of β thalassemia.

Recent molecular studies of the α thalassemias lead to similar conclusions.[60,232,247] The deletions that cause α⁰ thalassemia in the Mediterranean and Southeast Asia are different.[358] Furthermore, detailed analysis of the RFLP haplotypes in the α-globin gene cluster, together with studies of the crossover events that produce the α⁺ thalassemias, have shown that the common form of α⁺ thalassemia due to a 3.7-kb deletion (type I), has occured on many different occasions in different populations. α⁺ Thalassemia type III is, on the other hand, confined to parts of Melanesia. Haplotype analysis suggests that the α⁺ thalassemias arose *de novo* in Melanesia and reached their high frequencies by selection[60]; haplotypes of the α⁺ thalassemias in Southeast Asia are completely different. These studies suggest that, even allowing for a certain amount of drift and founder effect, the different types of α⁺ thalassemia have arisen independently in different populations.

Maintenance of the Thalassemia Polymorphism. Haldane's suggestion that thalassemia has been maintained at a high frequency by the protection of heterozygotes against *P. falciparum* malaria was an extremely attractive hypothesis, but it has been very difficult to provide the experimental data with which to validate it.

Studies in Sardinia, which showed that β thalassemia is less common in the mountainous regions where malarial transmission is relatively low, suggested that β thalassemia might have reached its high frequency because of protection against malarial infection.[359] For many years these data remained the only convincing evidence for the protective effect of thalassemia against malaria. However, recent studies utilizing malaria endemicity data and globin gene mapping have shown a very clear altitude-related effect on the frequency of α thalassemia in Papua New Guinea.[60] Furthermore, a sharp decline in the frequency of α thalassemia has been found in a region stretching north from Papua New Guinea, through the island populations of Melanesia to New Caledonia. A similar gradient in the distribution of malaria has been demonstrated from parasite and spleen rate data collected in this region over many years. This relationship might, of course, have resulted from gene drift and founder effect in these island populations. In other words, a population with a high frequency of α thalassemia might have moved through the islands from the north and the gene frequency been diluted during the migration southward. This explanation is unlikely, however, because there is a random pattern of the distribution of other DNA polymorphisms throughout these island populations.[60] Thus the frequency of α⁺ thalassemia, but not other DNA polymorphisms, shows an altitude- and latitude-dependent correlation with malarial endemicity throughout Melanesia. This is probably the best evidence to date that protection against *P. falciparum* is the major factor responsible for the high frequencies of the α thalassemias in many parts of the world.

The remarkable diversity of the different thalassemia mutations and their widespread distribution, taken together with population data that indicate that heterozygotes are protected against *P. falciparum* malaria, suggest that there may be properties common to the cells of carriers for different forms of thalassemia that in some way make them less attractive to the malarial parasite. However, there are no convincing experimental data to point to how such protection might be mediated. It has been found that cells containing relatively large amounts of Hb F tend to show a reduced rate of parasite growth[360] and it has been found that the rate of decline of Hb F is retarded in β-thalassemia heterozygotes. However the cells of both α- and β-thalassemia heterozygotes are invaded at the same rate as normal cells by parasites in in vitro culture systems, and the patterns of parasite growth and development are also the same as in normal cells in these systems. In vitro studies have shown that the red cell membrane in heterozygous thalassemia is particularly susceptible to damage by oxidation and that infection with the malarial parasite may produce sufficient oxidative stress to alter intracellular metabolism in a manner that might lead to the premature death of the parasite.[361] However, these experiments were carried out under very unphysiological conditions, and their in vivo relevance is uncertain.

Very recently it has been found that there is a strong correlation between the degree of parasite invasion and the deformability of erythrocytes. If this is confirmed, it would provide a unifying mechanism whereby the cells of heterozygotes for all types of thalassemia, because of their relative lack of deformability, might be less susceptible to invasion by malarial parasites.[362]

DIAGNOSIS, PREVENTION, AND TREATMENT

The practical aspects of the diagnosis, prevention, and management of the hemoglobinopathies are the subject of a number of monographs and reviews[2,3,185,363] and will only be outlined here.

Diagnosis

The diagnosis of a hemoglobin disorder involves the characterization of the homozygous or compound heterozygous state for a structural hemoglobin variant or one or other form of thalassemia in a patient with an appropriate clinical picture, or the identification of a heterozygote as part of a family study or population screening program. In the routine clinical laboratory a few relatively simple investigations will lead to a diagnosis in the majority of cases. These include the preparation of a well-stained blood film, analysis of the hemoglobin level and hematocrit together with a determination of the red cell indices with an electronic cell counter, hemoglobin electrophoresis, estimation of the Hb F level by alkali denaturation, and a quantitative assessment of the Hb A_2 level. To this may be added a heat stability or isopropanol test for unstable hemoglobin. Figure 93-28 shows a flow chart of the order in which these investigations should be carried out to obtain maximum information. In addition it may be necessary to carry out confirmatory investigations for the sickling disorders such as the metabisulfite or solubility tests and, in cases of suspected high or low affinity hemoglobin variants, to determine the p50.

This simple battery of investigations will allow the identification of the important sickling disorders, hemoglobins C and E, the high oxygen affinity variants, and the unstable hemoglobins. For unequivocal structural identification it is necessary to "fingerprint" and determine the amino acid substitution, but this is rarely required in clinical practice.

The diagnosis of the common sickling disorders is usually straightforward. In sickle cell anemia the Hb A_2 level is normal, and both parents show the sickle cell trait. The other common sickling disorders, such as SC, SD, and S/O$_{Arab}$ diseases, can be identified provisionally by agar gel electrophoresis or isoelectric focusing. Sickle cell β^0 thalassemia is diagnosed by finding the β thalassemia trait in one parent and a raised Hb A_2. It is important to carry out family studies when a raised Hb A_2 is found in an individual who is apparently homozygous for the sickle cell gene because the coexistence of α thalassemia and homozygous Hb S can also produce a raised Hb A_2 level; in this case both parents have the sickle cell trait and hematologic evidence of coexistent α thalassemia.

It is usually easy to diagnose the homozygous or compound

Fig. 93-28 A flowchart showing the approach to the laboratory diagnosis of the hemoglobin disorders. *(From Weatherall and Clegg.[2] Used by permission.)*

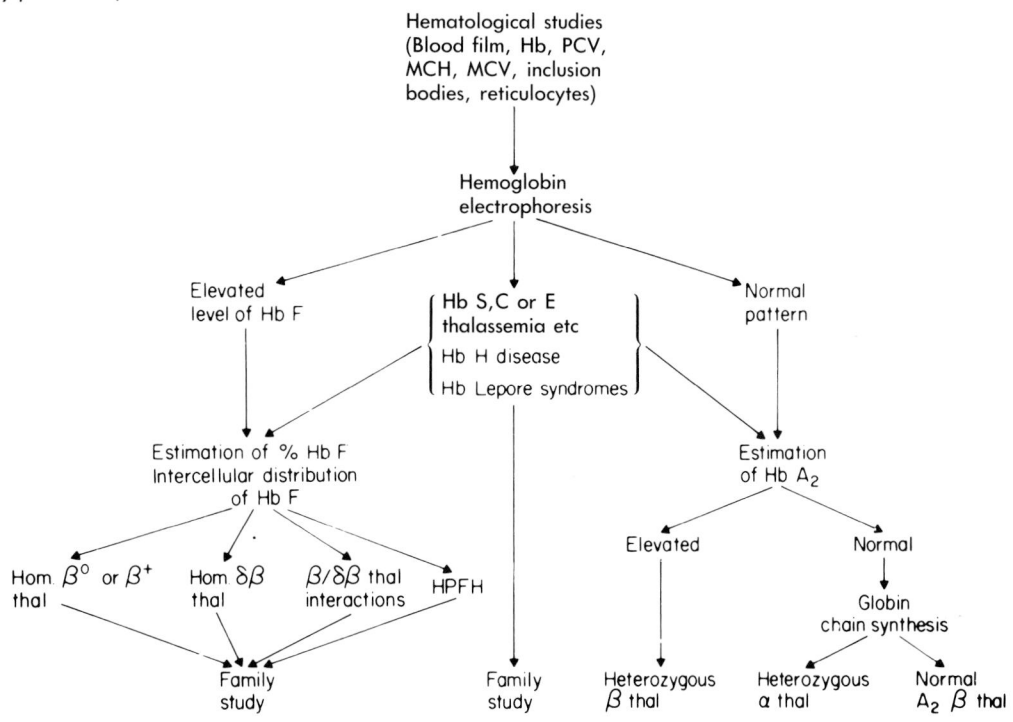

heterozygous states for the important forms of β and δβ thalassemia by measuring Hb F levels and carrying out a family study. The hemoglobin pattern of heterozygotes for these conditions is quite characteristic; β-thalassemia heterozygotes have typical thalassemic indices and a raised Hb A_2, while δβ-thalassemia heterozygotes have a normal Hb A_2 but Hb F levels in the 5 to 15 percent range. In homozygous β-thalassemia patients who have been transfused before referral, it may be necessary to repeat the investigations after an interval or to carry out globin chain synthesis studies on the marrow or blood.

The diagnosis of the Hb Bart's hydrops syndrome and Hb H disease usually presents no difficulties. It should be remembered that the level of Hb H varies considerably in Hb H disease, and, because Hb H is unstable, it is necessary to examine fresh red cell lysates. It is also important to carry out hemoglobin electrophoresis on concentrated red cell lysates so as not to miss the form of Hb H disease associated with Hb Constant Spring or one of the other α-chain termination mutants.

The diagnosis of the α thalassemia carrier states is more difficult. Heterozygous $α^0$ thalassemia is characterized by typical thalassemic red cell indices with a normal Hb A_2; a small proportion of the cells usually contain Hb H bodies. Heterozygous $α^+$ thalassemia is extremely difficult to identify as the red cell indices may be normal. The heterozygous state for $α^0$ thalassemia and the homozygous state for $α^+$ thalassemia produce identical red cell changes, and the two conditions can be distinguished only in an individual patient by a family study or, better, by α-gene mapping.

Screening. Screening for the hemoglobin variants and thalassemias is required for the prenatal identification of the carrier states for important disorders such as Hb S, β thalassemia, and $α^0$ thalassemia. It may also be required for identification of the sickling disorders or thalassemias in newborn infants or as part of a population screening program.

Screening for the sickle cell trait in adults can be carried out by hemoglobin electrophoresis or one of the solubility tests for Hb S. Screening for thalassemia is best done by determining the red cell indices and, if they suggest thalassemia, by carrying out a serum iron estimation to exclude iron deficiency. Once thalassemia is suspected, a Hb A_2 estimation should be done. In most cases this will serve to distinguish β-thalassemia trait from $α^0$-thalassemia trait. In populations in which β thalassemia with a normal Hb A_2 level is common, it is necessary to carry out globin chain synthesis or gene mapping analysis to distinguish this condition from heterozygous $α^0$ thalassemia. There is one pitfall that may be encountered in populations in which α and β thalassemia are common. Individuals who are heterozygous for both α and β thalassemia may have relatively normal red cell indices. Thus in these populations it is wise to use a Hb A_2 estimation as the initial screening procedure because such doubly affected heterozygotes have an elevated Hb A_2.[364] Typical red cell indices for the different heterozygous forms of thalassemia are summarized in Table 93-14.

Neonatal screening for the sickle cell gene is best carried out using agar gel electrophoresis. Screening for α thalassemia can be carried out by estimating Hb Bart's levels on cord blood, although this will miss a number of cases of heterozygous $α^+$ thalassemia. The diagnosis of β thalassemia can be made at birth but only by globin chain synthesis; where het-

erozygous or homozygous β thalassemia is suspected, it is better to delay hemoglobin analysis until after the first 6 months of life, at which time the typical changes are usually well established.

Prevention

Programs for the prevention of the common hemoglobinopathies can be carried out either by population screening of high school students or young adults, followed by marital advice, or by screening pregnant women and, in cases in which their husbands are also carriers, offering prenatal diagnosis followed, where appropriate, by termination of pregnancy. In the few studies that have been adequately documented, the former approach has both succeeded,[365] and not succeeded,[365a] and currently prenatal diagnosis is the most widely used approach to the prevention of the common hemoglobin disorders.

Prenatal diagnosis can be carried out either in the second trimester of pregnancy by fetal blood sampling or examination of the DNA of amniotic fluid cells, or by chorion villus sampling and DNA analysis in the first trimester.[366–369] Fetal blood sampling followed by globin chain synthesis analysis has been applied widely for the prenatal diagnosis of the hemoglobin disorders.[366] The method is extremely effective for the recognition of the sickling disorders and β thalassemias. It carries a 1 to 2 percent fetal loss rate, and there is about a 1 percent error rate. It has been used widely throughout the Mediterranean region, the Middle East, and in Britain and North America, and data are available on over 4000 cases.[366,367] The application of this method has reduced the incidence of homozygous β thalassemia very considerably in a number of Mediterranean populations.

More recently fetal DNA analysis following chorion villus sampling has been developed and is now being used widely for the prenatal diagnosis of all the important hemoglobin disorders.[368–370] It is currently estimated that the fetal loss following this procedure is in the region of 1 to 2 percent. So far there are no good follow-up data on infants who have been born following this procedure, and therefore its safety is still *sub judice*. It is possible to obtain 20 to 100 μg of fetal DNA from chorion villus material and, if the procedure is carried out correctly, it is usually uncontaminated by maternal cells. There is a variety of diagnostic approaches available for identifying the common hemoglobin disorders by DNA analysis. In some cases, sickle cell anemia, the deletion forms of α thalassemia, and some forms of β thalassemia, for example, the diagnosis can be made directly by Southern blotting. This is because the underlying mutations alter restriction enzyme sites or result in deletions or major gene rearrangements, all of which can be identified directly. If this is not possible, prenatal diagnosis can often be achieved by RFLP linkage analysis. This entails carrying out a family study to attempt to track the parental chromosomes that carry the particular mutations with an RFLP. Extensive studies in Europe have shown that this approach is feasible in about 80 percent of families of Mediterranean background;[368] a typical example is shown in Fig. 93-29. The success rate is higher if an RFLP can be found that is in strong linkage disequilibrium with a common β-thalassemia mutation.[371] Finally, if the precise mutation is known, it is possible to construct an oligonucleotide probe for its direct detection in fetal DNA.

To develop a comprehensive prenatal diagnosis for β

Direct Analysis : Bgl II   Indian   β⁰-thalassemia

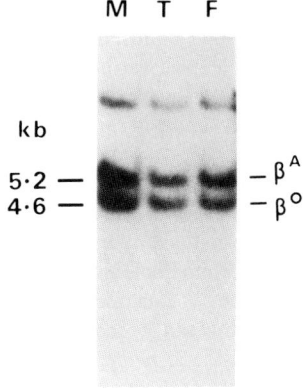

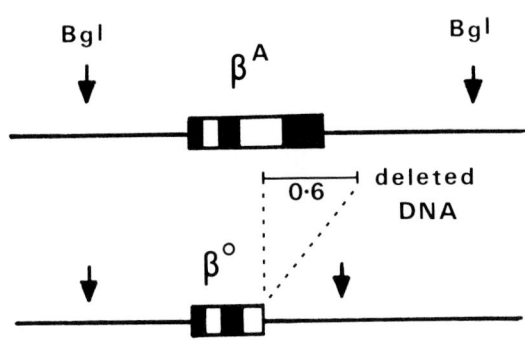

β⁰-thalassemia

Fig. 93-29 The prenatal diagnosis of β thalassemia. The panel on the right shows the ≈600-base deletion of the β-globin gene and the Bgl II sites. On the left is shown a Southern blot of a prenatal diagnosis: M = mother; F = father; T = trophoblast DNA obtained by chorion villus sampling. The normal β gene (β^A) generates a 5.2-kb Bgl II fragment; the β-thalassemia gene (β^T) generates a 4.6-Kb Bgl II fragment. The fetus was a heterozygote and the pregnancy was not terminated. (*Figure prepared by Dr. John Old.*)

thalassemia[364] the first step is to determine the common mutations in the population. When this has been done, a large proportion of cases can be identified with oligonucleotide probes or, if particular forms of thalassemia exist that can be identified with restriction enzymes, directly by Southern blotting. For cases in which the mutation is not known, RFLP linkage analysis can be carried out. Where DNA analysis is not possible, it will be necessary to have the backup of fetal blood sampling. Several large series of first trimester prenatal diagnosis have now been published and it is quite clear that the approach is feasible.[368,370] Potential difficulties include plasmid contamination, crossovers, and nonpaternity. In these early studies the error rate is about the same as that for fetal blood sampling followed by globin chain synthesis.

Treatment

There is no definitive treatment for any of the important hemoglobin disorders, but there has been considerable improvement in their symptomatic management.[2,185]

The Sickling Disorders.[144] Individuals with the sickle cell trait require no treatment beyond simple genetic counseling and the avoidance of conditions of extreme oxygen deprivation or dehydration.

Because so many of the serious complications occur in the first 2 years of life, the diagnosis of sickle cell anemia should be made as early as possible. Once established, the parents should be counseled about the dangers of infection during the early years of life. Although there are only limited data, there is a good case for the use of prophylactic penicillin in infants and young children.[144] The use of polyvalent pneumococcal vaccines is still under evaluation. The parents and family physician should be advised to seek hospital advice at the onset of any unusual symptoms. Mothers can be counseled about

splenic sequestration and taught to assess spleen size. No other treatment is required for sickle cell anemia in the steady state; folic acid supplements are often given but are probably unnecessary if the infant is receiving a good diet.

The management of sickle cell crises usually requires hospital admission and an extremely competent level of clinical care. The painful crisis is managed by bed rest, hydration, and adequate analgesia. Although it may be possible to manage mild painful crisis with first line analgesics such as paracetamol, more powerful agents are often required, at least for a few days; although there is a risk of addiction, patients cannot be left in excruciating pain. A source of infection should be sought and the hematocrit and reticulocyte count monitored twice daily. There is no indication for blood transfusion unless the hematocrit is falling. Splenic or hepatic sequestration crises should be managed by prompt transfusion; if the spleen remains large, there is a good case for splenectomy to prevent second episodes. Lung crisis should be managed by treatment of any associated infection, adequate oxygenation, and hydration, and, if the patient is deteriorating despite these measures, exchange transfusion. Neurologic crises should be treated by hypertransfusion or, if the initial hematocrit is relatively high, by exchange transfusion. The management of priapism is difficult. If treated conservatively, the condition usually fails to resolve and there may be permanent penile deformity. It has been suggested recently that the best approach is to use adequate hydration and analgesia for 24 h followed by an exchange transfusion or hypertransfusion for a further 24 h. If the condition does not resolve after these measures, a cavernosal-spongiosal shunt should be carried out.[144]

Hemoglobin SC disease should be managed in the same way as sickle cell anemia. There is increasing evidence that the retinal complications of this disorder may progress to blindness, and therefore all patients with this condition, and probably sickle cell anemia as well, should have regular ophthalmologic surveillance and laser therapy when indicated.

The management of pregnancy in sickle cell anemia is still controversial. Although hypertransfusion regimes have been advocated in the United Kingdom, there is no evidence that they are effective. Probably the best compromise is to follow the patient very carefully and transfuse only if there are recurrent crises or a fall in the hematocrit during late pregnancy.

The recent observation that aplastic crises in sickle cell anemia result from parvovirus infections has important implications. This condition should be suspected in any patient with sickle cell anemia with a falling hematocrit, particularly if the reticulocyte count is also reduced. It requires very careful hospital observation and early transfusion. The possibility of developing a vaccine may make it possible to prevent this life-threatening complication.

There is an enormous literature on potential antisickling agents.[3] Currently none of them has been found to be useful in clinical practice.

Unstable Hemoglobin Variants. The majority of patients require no treatment. If there is severe hemolysis with a large spleen, splenectomy may be helpful. There are, however, insufficient data to fully evaluate the likely benefit.

Thalassemia. No treatment is required for α- or β-thalassemia heterozygotes, although they should be followed carefully during pregnancy because they may become anemic during the second and third trimesters. They should receive appropriate genetic counseling.

The clinical management of homozygous β thalassemia is unsatisfactory. It has been the subject of an enormous amount of work,[3,185] and only a few principles can be outlined here. When the condition is suspected in early infancy, patients should be observed carefully to make sure that they are going to fall into the transfusion-dependent category. This usually becomes obvious by the end of the first year; the infant fails to thrive, feeding is difficult, and the hemoglobin level falls below 6 to 7 g/dl. It is important not to transfuse before this stage because a child with thalassemia intermedia may be wrongly categorized. Transfusion-dependent homozygous β-thalassemia patients require regular blood, chelating agents, and in some cases splenectomy.

Transfusion-dependent thalassemic children grow and develop best if their hemoglobin levels are maintained as close to normal as possible. This entails regular transfusions to maintain hemoglobin values between 10 and 14 g/dl. They should receive washed or frozen red cells uncontaminated by white cells and plasma proteins. There are a number of excellent accounts of the transfusion procedures to be followed.[185,372]

Where possible a program of chelation with desferrioxamine should be instituted. The precise age when this can be started varies, but it should not be delayed much after the second year. The ideal route is subcutaneously into the abdominal wall using an overnight infusion with a clockwork or electric pump.[373,374] The dose of desferrioxamine varies according to age, and in any case it should be monitored by regular measurement of urinary iron excretion. The best response to desferrioxamine is obtained in ascorbate-replete patients, although high doses of ascorbate should be avoided. Because of the rare ocular complications of desferrioxamine therapy, children treated in this way should have regular ophthalmologic surveillance. Where it is not possible to use subcutaneous desferrioxamine, bolus injections can be given, although they are much less effective. There is increasing evidence that children

maintained on an adequate transfusion regime and subcutaneous desferrioxamine will grow and develop normally and that secondary sexual development at puberty may be normal.[185] So far there are insufficient long-term follow up data to be absolutely sure about the prognosis for these patients. There is some evidence that children who are already grossly iron-loaded, even if they have cardiac involvement, may be rescued at least temporarily by the use of large doses of desferrioxamine given intravenously in an attempt to remove large amounts of iron.[375]

Hypersplenism is unusual in children who have been adequately transfused. However, in those who have not been so fortunate, or in non-transfusion-dependent patients with β thalassemia intermedia, hypersplenism is common and the spleen should be removed.[185] The operation should be avoided in the first few years of life and in any case should be followed up by the use of prophylactic penicillin for an indefinite period. Splenectomy is also indicated occasionally in patients with Hb H disease, although it should be done only if there is severe hypersplenism. There are several reports of migrating thrombophlebitis and more severe thromboembolic disease in splenectomized patients with Hb H disease[3]; the reason this occurs with this condition and not in β-thalassemia patients is not clear.

Good general pediatric care is essential for thalassemic children. If they are inadequately transfused, they are prone to infection and to a variety of skeletal complications due to expansion of the bone marrow. They should receive regular examination of their throats and ears. Where iron loading leads to delayed puberty, they should have a hormone profile carried out and, if indicated, careful replacement therapy instituted. Unfortunately this is not always successful because sexual underdevelopment is often due to target-organ unresponsiveness due to iron deposition.

Recently there has been considerable interest in bone marrow transplantation for homozygous β thalassemia.[376] The place of this form of treatment is still uncertain, and because of the high risk of graft-versus-host disease it probably has a limited role, particularly for children who can be adequately transfused and chelated.

In the future it is hoped that direct gene therapy or manipulation of hemoglobin F switching may be more definitive approaches to the management of sickle cell anemia and β thalassemia. A number of attempts have been made to raise Hb F levels in patients with these conditions.[377-381] Methods studied include the use of demethylating agents such as 5-azacytidine or cytotoxic agents like hydroxyurea. So far success has been limited, and the toxicity of these agents renders them unsatisfactory for long-term use.

REFERENCES

1. WHO WORKING GROUP: Hereditary anaemias: Genetic basis, clinical features, diagnosis and treatment. *Bull WHO* 60:643, 1982.
2. WEATHERALL DJ, CLEGG JB: *The Thalassaemia Syndromes*, 3d ed. Oxford, Blackwell, 1981.
3. BUNN HF, FORGET BG: *Hemoglobin: Molecular, Genetic and Clinical Aspects*. Philadelphia, Saunders, 1986.
4. CONLEY CL: Sickle-cell anemia—The first molecular disease, in Wintrobe MM (ed): *Blood, Pure and Eloquent*. New York, McGraw-Hill, 1980, p 319.
5. WEATHERALL DJ: Toward an understanding of the molecular biology of some common inherited anemias: The story of thalassemia, in Wintrobe MM (ed): *Blood, Pure and Eloquent*. New York, McGraw-Hill, 1980, p 373.

6. BANNERMAN RM: *Thalassemia. A Survey of Some Aspects.* New York, Grune & Stratton, 1961.

7. HERRICK JB: Peculiar elongated and sickle-shaped red blood corpuscles in a case of severe anemia. *Arch Intern Med* 6:517, 1910.

8. PAULING L, ITANO HA, SINGER SJ, WELLS IG: Sickle-cell anemia, a molecular disease. *Science* 110:543, 1949.

9. INGRAM VM: Specific chemical difference between the globins of normal human and sickle-cell anaemia haemoglobin. *Nature* 178:792, 1956.

10. COOLEY TB, LEE P: A series of cases of splenomegaly in children with anemia and peculiar bone changes. *Trans Am Pediatr Soc* 37:29, 1925.

11. INGRAM VM, STRETTEN AOW: Genetic basis of the thalassaemia diseases. *Nature* 184:1903, 1959.

12. WEATHERALL DJ, CLEGG JB, NAUGHTON MA: Globin synthesis in thalassemia: An *in vitro* study. *Nature* 208:1061, 1966.

13. CLEGG JB, NAUGHTON MA, WEATHERALL DJ: Abnormal human haemoglobins. Separation and characterisation of the α and β chains by chromatography, and the determination of two new variants Hb Chesapeake and Hb J (Bangkok). *J Mol Biol* 19:91, 1966.

14. FERMI G, PERUTZ MF, SHAANAN B, FOURME B: The crystal structure of human deoxyhemoglobin at 1.7 Å resolution. *J Mol Biol* 175:159, 1984.

15. BALDWIN JM: The structure of human carbonmonoxyhaemoglobin at 2.7 Å resolution. *J Mol Biol* 136:103, 1980.

16. PERUTZ MF: Stereochemistry of cooperative effects in haemoglobin. *Nature* 228:726, 1970.

17. PERUTZ MF: Stereochemical mechanism of oxygen transport by haemoglobin. *Proc R Soc Lond B* 208:135, 1980.

18. BALDWIN J: Structure and cooperativity of haemoglobin. *Trends Biol Sci* 5:224, 1980.

19. CHANUTIN A, CURNISH RR: Effect of organic and inorganic phosphates on the oxygen equilibrium of human erythrocytes. *Arch Biochem Biophys* 121:96, 1967.

20. BENESCH R, BENESCH RE: The effect of organic phosphates from the human erythrocyte on the allosteric properties of hemoglobin. *Biochem Biophys Res Comm* 26:162, 1967.

21. ARNONE A: X-ray diffraction study of binding of 2,3 diphosphoglycerate to human deoxyhaemoglobin. *Nature* 237:146, 1972.

22. BAUER C, LUDWIG I, LUDWIG M: Different effects of 2,3 diphosphoglycerate and adenosine triphosphate on the oxygen affinity of adult and foetal human haemoglobin. *Life* 7:1339, 1968.

23. TYMUA I, SHIMIZU K: Different response to organic phosphates of human fetal and adult hemoglobins. *Arch Biochem Biophys* 129:404, 1969.

24. PERUTZ MF: The Bohr effect and combination with organic phosphates. *Nature* 228:734, 1970.

25. PERUTZ MF: Stereochemistry of cooperative effects in haemoglobin. *Nature* 228:726, 1970.

26. DEISSEROTH A, VELES R, NIENHUIS AW: Hemoglobin synthesis in somatic cell hybrids. Independent segregation of the human alpha- and beta-globin genes. *Science* 191:1262, 1976.

27. DEISSEROTH A, NIENHUIS A, TURNER P, VELEZ R, ANDERSON WF, RUDDLE F, LAWRENCE J, CREAGAN R, KUCHERLAPATI R: Localization of the human α-globin structural gene to chromosome 16 in somatic cell hybrids by molecular hybridization assay. *Cell* 12:205, 1977.

28. DEISSEROTH A, NIENHUIS A, LAWRENCE J, GILES R, TURNER P, RUDDLE FH: Chromosomal localization of human β globin gene on human chromosome 11 in somatic cell hybrids. *Proc Natl Acad Sci USA* 75:1456, 1978.

29. GUSELLA JF, VARSANYI-BREINER A, KAO FT, JONES C, PUCK TT, KEYS C, ORKIN S, HOUSMAN D: Precise localization of human β-globin gene complex on chromosome 11. *Proc Natl Acad Sci USA* 76:5239, 1979.

30. JEFFREYS AJ, CRAIG IW, FRANCKE U: Localisation of the $^Gγ^Aγδ$ and β globin genes on the short arm of chromosome 11. *Nature* 281:606, 1979.

31. LEBO RV, CARRANO AV, BURKHARDT-SCHULTZ K, DOZY AM, YU L-C, KAN YW: Assignment of human β-, γ- and ζ-globin genes to the short arm of chromosome 11 by chromosome sorting and DNA restriction analysis. *Proc Natl Acad Sci USA* 76:5804, 1979.

32. SANDERS-HAIGH L, ANDERSON WF, FRANCKE U: The β-globin gene is on the short arm of human chromosome 11. *Nature* 283:683, 1980.

33. SCOTT AF, PHILLIPS JA, MIGEON BR: DNA endonuclease analysis for localisation of human β- and δ-globin genes on chromosome 11. *Proc Natl Acad Sci USA* 76:4563, 1979.

34. KOEFFLER HP, SPARKES RS, STANG H, MOHANDAS T: Regional assignment of genes for human α globin and phosphoglycolate phosphatase to the short arm of chromosome 16. *Proc Natl Acad Sci USA* 78:7015, 1981.

35. NICHOLLS RD, JONASSON JA, MCGEE JOD, PATIL S, IONASESCU VV, WEATHERALL DJ, HIGGS DR: High resolution mapping of the human α-globin locus. *J Med Genet* 24:39, 1987.

36. LAWN RM, FRITSCH EF, PARKER RC, BLAKE G, MANIATIS T: The isolation and characterization of linked γ and β-globin genes from a cloned library of human DNA. *Cell* 15:1157, 1978.

37. FRITSCH EF, LAWN RM, MANIATIS T: Molecular cloning and characterization of the human β-like globin gene cluster. *Cell* 19:959, 1980.

38. LAUER J, SHEN C-KJ, MANIATIS T: The chromosomal arrangement of human α-like globin genes: Sequence homology and α-globin gene deletions. *Cell* 20:119, 1980.

39. JAGADEESWARAN P, PAN J, FORGET BG, WEISSMAN SM: Sequences of human repetitive DNA, non-α-globin genes, and major histocompatibility locus genes. II. Sequences of non-α-globin genes in man. *Cold Spring Harbor Symp Quant Biol* 47:1081, 1983.

40. CHANG L-YE, SLIGHTOM JL: Isolation and nucleotide sequence analysis of β-type globin pseudogene from human, gorilla and chimpanzee. *J Mol Biol* 180:767, 1984.

41. PROUDFOOT NJ, GILL A, MANIATIS T: The structure of the human zeta-globin gene and a closely linked, nearly identical pseudogene. *Cell* 31:553, 1982.

42. HARDISON RC, SAWADA I, CHENG J-F, SHEN C-KJ, SCHMID CW: A previously undetected pseudogene in the human alpha globin gene cluster. *Nucleic Acids Res* 14:1903, 1986.

43. MARKS J, SHAW J-P, SHEN C-KJ: Sequence organization and genomic complexity of primate θ globin gene, a novel α-globin-like gene. *Nature* 321:785, 1986.

44. GOODMAN M, KOOP BF, CZELUSNIAK J, WEISS ML: The η-globin gene. Its long evolutionary history in the β-globin gene family of mammals. *J Mol Biol* 180:804, 1984.

45. EFSTRATIADIS A, POSAKONY JW, MANIATIS T, LAWN RM, O'CONNELL C, SPRITZ RA, DeRIEL JK, FORGET BG, WEISSMAN SM, SLIGHTOM JL, BLECHL AE, SMITHIES O, BARALLE FE, SHOULDERS CC, PROUDFOOT NJ: The structure and evolution of the human β-globin gene family. *Cell* 21:653, 1980.

46. HARDISON RL, MARGOT JB: Rabbit-globin pseudogene Ψβ2 is a hybrid of δ- and β-globin gene sequences. *Mol Biol Evol* 1:302, 1984.

47. JEFFREYS AJ: DNA sequence variants in the $^Gγ$-, $^Aγ$-, δ- and β-globin genes of man. *Cell* 18:1, 1979.

48. ANTONARAKIS SE, BOEHM CD, GIARDINA PJV, KAZAZIAN HH: Non random association of polymorphic restriction sites in the β-globin gene complex. *Proc Natl Acad Sci USA* 70:137, 1982.

49. HIGGS DR, WAINSCOAT JS, FLINT J, HILL AVS, THEIN SL, NICHOLLS RD, TEAL H, AYYUB H, PETO TEA, JARMAN A, CLEGG JB, WEATHERALL DJ: Analysis of the human α globin gene cluster reveals a highly informative genetic locus. *Proc Natl Acad Sci USA* 83:5165, 1985.

50. WAINSCOAT JS, HILL AVS, BOYCE A, FLINT J, HERNANDEZ M, THEIN SL, LYNCH JR, FALUSI Y, WEATHERALL DJ, CLEGG JB: Evolutionary relationships of human populations from an analysis of nuclear DNA polymorphisms. *Nature* 319:491, 1986.

51. BOEHM CD, ANTONARAKIS SE, PHILLIPS JA, STETTEN G, KAZAZIAN HH: Prenatal diagnosis using DNA polymorphisms. *N Engl J Med* 308:1054, 1983.

52. OLD JM, WAINSCOAT JS: A new DNA polymorphism in the β-globin gene cluster can be used for antenatal diagnosis of β thalassaemia. *Br J Haematol* 53:336, 1983.

53. WINICHAGOON P, HIGGS DR, GOODBOURN SEY, CLEGG JB, WEATHERALL DJ: Multiple arrangement of the human embryonic zeta globin genes. *Nucleic Acids Res* 10:5853, 1982.

54. TRENT RJ, BOWDEN DK, OLD JM, WAINSCOAT JS, CLEGG JB, WEATHERALL DJ: A novel rearrangement of the human α-like globin gene cluster. *Nucleic Acids Res* 9:6723, 1981.

55. HIGGS DR, OLD JM, PRESSLEY L, CLEGG JB, WEATHERALL DJ: A novel α-globin gene arrangement in man. *Nature* 284:632, 1980.

56. HIGGS DR, OLD JM, CLEGG JB, PRESSLEY L, HUNT DM, WEATHERALL DJ, SERJEANT GR: Negro α-thalassaemia is caused by deletion of a single α-globin gene. *Lancet* ii:272, 1979.

57. DOZY AM, KAN YW, EMBURY SH, MENTZER WC, WANG WC, LUBIN B, DAVIS JR, KOENIG HM: α-globin gene organisation in blacks precludes the severe form of α-thalassaemia. *Nature* 280:605, 1979.

58. SUKUMARAN PK, NAKATSUJI T, GARDINER MB, REESE AL, GILMAN JG, HUISMAN THJ: Gamma thalassaemia resulting from the deletion of a γ-globin gene. *Nucleic Acids Res* 11:4635, 1983.

59. HILL AVS: The population genetics of α thalassemia and the malaria hypothesis, in Watson JD (ed): *Symposium on Quantitative Biology.* Cold Spring Harbor, 1986, p 99.

60. FLINT J, HILL AVS, BOWDEN DK, OPPENHEIMER SJ, SILL PR, SERJEANTSON SW, BANA-KOIRI J, BHATIA K, ALPERS MP, BOYCE AJ, WEATHERALL DJ, CLEGG JB: High frequencies of α thalassaemia are the result of natural selection by malaria. *Nature* 321:744, 1986.

61. POWERS PA, ALTAY C, HUISMAN THJ, SMITHIES O: Two novel arrangements of the human fetal globin genes: Gγ-Gγ and Aγ-Aγ. *Nucleic Acids Res* 12:7023, 1984.

62. MOUNT SM: A catalogue of splice junction sequences. *Nucleic Acids Res* 10:10, 1982.

63. GREEN MR: Pre-mRNA splicing. *Annu Rev Genet* 20:671, 1986.

64. COLLINS FS, WEISSMAN SM: The molecular genetics of human hemoglobin, in Cohn WE, Moldave K: *Progress in Nucleic Acids Research and Molecular Biology*. New York, Academic, 1984, p 315.

65. GROSVELD GC, DE BOER E, SHEWMAKER CK, FLAVELL RA: DNA sequences necessary for transcription of the rabbit β-globin gene *in vitro*. *Nature* 295:120, 1982.

66. ORKIN SH, ANTONARAKIS SE, KAZAZIAN HH: Base substitution at Position-88 in a β-thalassemic globin gene: Further evidence for the role of the distal promoter element ACACCC. *J Biol Chem* 259:8679, 1984.

67. ORKIN SH, KAZAZIAN HH, ANTONARAKIS SE, GOFF SC, BOEHM CD, SEXTON JP, WABER PG, GIARDINA PJV: Linkage of β-thalassaemia mutations and β-globin gene polymorphisms with DNA polymorphisms in human β globin gene cluster. *Nature* 296:627, 1982.

68. LEWIN B: *Genes*. New York, Wiley, 1983.

69. ALBERTS B, BRAY D, LEWIS J, RAFF M, ROBERTS R, WATSON JD: *Molecular Biology of the Cell*. New York, Garland, 1983.

70. MAITRA V, STRINGER EA, CHAUDHORI A: Initiation factors in protein synthesis. *Annu Rev Genet* 51:869, 1982.

71. MILLER DM, WEISSBACH H: Factors involved in the transfer of aminoacyl-tRNA to the ribosome, in Weissbach H, Pestka S: *Molecular Mechanisms of Protein Biosynthesis*. New York, Academic, 1977, pp 323–373.

72. BROT N: Translocation, in Weissbach H, Pestka S: *Molecular Mechanisms of Protein Biosynthesis*. New York, Academic, 1977, pp. 375–411.

73. HARRIS RJ, PESTKA S: Peptide bond formation, in Weissbach H, Pestka S: *Molecular Mechanisms of Protein Biosynthesis*. New York, Academic, 1977, pp 413–442.

74. CASKEY CT: Peptide chain termination, in Weissbach H, Pestka S: *Molecular Mechanisms of Protein Biosynthesis*. New York, Academic, 1977, pp 443–465.

75. ORKIN SH, CHENG T-C, ANTONARAKIS SE, KAZAZIAN HH: Thalassaemia due to a mutation in the cleavage-polyadenylation signal of the human β-globin gene. *EMBO J* 4:453, 1985.

76. HIGGS DR, GOODBOURN SEY, LAMB J, CLEGG JB, WEATHERALL DJ, PROUDFOOT NJ: α-thalassaemia caused by a polyadenylation signal mutation. *Nature* 306:398, 1983.

77. SHEN CK: DNA methylation and developmental regulation of eukaryotic globin gene transcription, in Razin A, Cedar H, Riggs A (eds): *DNA Methylation*. New York, Springer-Verlag, 1984.

78. BUSSLINGER M, HURST J, FLAVELL RA: DNA methylation and the regulation of globin gene expression. *Cell* 34:197, 1983.

79. WEISBROD S: Active chromatin. *Nature* 197:289, 1982.

80. STALDER J, GROUDINE M, DODGSON JB, ENGLE JD, WEINTRAUB H: Hb switching in chickens. *Cell* 19:973, 1980.

81. STALDER J, LARSEN A, ENGEL JD, DOLAN M, GROUDINE M, WEINTRAUB H: Tissue-specific DNA cleavages in the globin chromatin domain introduced by DNAase 1. *Cell* 20:451, 1980.

82. ELGIN SCR: DNAase I-hypersensitive sites of chromatin. *Cell* 27:413, 1981.

83. LACHMAN HM, MEARS JG: DNase I hypersensitivity in the γ globin gene locus of K562 cells. *Nucleic Acids Res* 11:6065, 1983.

84. GROUDINE M, KOHWI-SHIGEMATSU T, GELINAS R, STAMATOYANNOPOULOS G, PAPAYANNOPOULOU T: Human fetal to adult hemoglobin switching: Changes in chromatin structure of the β-globin gene locus. *Proc Natl Acad Sci USA* 80:7551, 1983.

85. TUAN D, LONDON IM: Mapping of DNase I-hypersensitive sites in the upstream DNA of human embryonic ε-globin gene in K562 leukemia cells. *Proc Natl Acad Sci USA* 81:2718, 1984.

86. GIANNI AM, BREGNI M, CAPPELLINI MD, FIORELLI G, TARAMELLI R, GIGLIONI B, COMI P, OTTOLENGHI S: A gene controlling fetal hemoglobin expression in adults is not linked to the non-α globin cluster. *EMBO J* 2:921, 1983.

87. FORDIS CM, ANAGNOU NP, DEAN A, NIENHUIS AW, SCHECHTER AM: A β-globin gene, inactive in the K562 leukemic cell, functions normally in a heterologous expression system. *Proc Natl Acad Sci USA* 81:4485, 1984.

88. DONOVAN-PELUSO M, YOUNG K, DOBKIN C, BANK A: Erythroleukemia (K562) cells contain a functional β globin gene. *Mol Cell Biol* 4:2553, 1984.

89. PAPAYANNOPOULOU T, LINDSLEY D, KURACHI S, LEWISON K, HEMENWAY T, MELIS M, ANAGNOU NP, NAJELD V: Adult and fetal human globin genes are expressed following chromosomal transfer into MEL cells. *Proc Natl Acad Sci USA* 82:780, 1985.

90. ANAGNOU NP, YUAN TY, LIM E, HELDER J, WIEDER S, GLAISTER D, MARKS B, WANG A, COLBERT D, DEISSEROTH A: Regulatory factors specific for adult and embryonic globin genes may govern their expression in erythroleukemia cells. *Blood* 65:705, 1985.

91. ZEITLIN HC, WEATHERALL DJ: Selective expression within the human α globin gene complex following chromosome-dependent transfer into diploid mouse erythroleukaemia cells. *Mol Biol Med* 1:489, 1983.

92. WOOD WG, PEARCE K, CLEGG JB, WEATHERALL DJ, ROBINSON JS, THORBURN GD, DAWES G: The switch from fetal to adult haemoglobin synthesis in normal and hypophysectomised sheep. *Nature* 264:799, 1976.

93. WOOD WG, BUNCH C, KELLY SJ, GUNN Y, BRECKON G: Control of hemoglobin switching by a developmental clock? *Nature* 313:320, 1985.

94. ZANJANI ED, LIM G, MCGLAVE PB, CLAPP JF, MANN LI, NORWOOD TH, STAMATOYANNOPOULOS G: Adult haemopoietic cells transplanted to sheep fetuses continue to produce adult globins. *Nature* 295:244, 1982.

95. WEINBERG RS, GOLDBERG JD, SCHOFIELD JM, LENES AL, STYCZYNSKI R, ALTER BP: Switch from fetal to adult hemoglobin is associated with a change in progenitor cell population. *J Clin Invest* 71:785, 1983.

96. LIEBHABER SA, CASH FE, MAIN DM: Compensatory increase in α1-globin gene expression in individuals heterozygous for the α-thalassemia-2 deletion. *J Clin Invest* 76:1957, 1985.

97. WEATHERALL DJ, CLEGG JB: The α-chain termination mutants and their relationship to the α-thalassaemias. *Philos Trans R Soc Lond Ser B* 271:411, 1975.

98. SEID-AKHAVEN M, WINTER WP, ABRAMSON RK, RUCKNAGEL DL: Hemoglobin Wayne: A frameshift mutation detected in human hemoglobin alpha chains. *Proc Natl Acad Sci USA* 73:882, 1976.

99. LEHMANN H, CASEY R, LANG A, STATHOPOULOU R, IMAI K, TUCHINDA S, VINAI P, FLATZ G: Haemoglobin Tak: A β-chain elongation. *Br J Haematol* 31:119, 1975.

100. BUNN HF, SCHMIDT GJ, HANEY DN, DLUHY RG: Hemoglobin Cranston, an unstable variant having an elongated β chain due to nonhomologous crossover between two normal β chain genes. *Proc Natl Acad Sci USA* 72:3609, 1975.

101. HUISMAN THJ, WILSON JB, GRAVELY M, HUBBARD M: Hemoglobin Grady: The first example of a variant with elongated chains due to an insertion of residues. *Proc Natl Acad Sci USA* 71:3270, 1974.

102. PRCHAL JT, CASHMAN DP, KAN YW: Hemoglobin Long Island is caused by a single mutation (adenine to cytosine) resulting in a failure to cleave amino-terminal methionine. *Proc Natl Acad Sci USA* 83:24, 1986.

103. BLOUQUIT Y, LENA-RUSSO D, DELANOE J, AROUS N, BARDAKJIAN J, LANCOMBE C, ORSINI A, ROSA J, GALACTEROS F: Hb Marseille ($\alpha_2\beta_2$ 1(A1) NH→Met, 2(A2) His→3(A3) Pro: First variant having a N-terminal elongated β chain. *Blood* 64:55, 1984.

104. BROISSEL J-P, KASPER T, SHAH SC, MALONE JI, BUNN HF: NH$_2$-terminal processing of protein: Hb South Florida. *Proc Natl Acad Sci USA* 82:8448, 1985.

105. RIEDER RF, BRADLEY TB: Hemoglobin Gun Hill: An unstable protein associated with chronic hemolysis. *Blood* 32:355, 1968.

106. WINSLOW RM, SWENBERG ML, GROSS E, CHERVENICK P, BUCHMAN RR, ANDERSON WF: Hemoglobin McKees Rocks ($\alpha_2\beta_2^{145Tyr-Term}$), a human "nonsense" mutation leading to a shortened β-chain. *Am J Hum Genet* 27:95, 1975.

107. BAGLIONI C: The fusion of two peptide chains in hemoglobin Lepore and its interpretation as a genetic deletion. *Proc Natl Acad Sci USA* 48:1880, 1962.

108. BARNABAS J, MULLER CJ: Haemoglobin Lepore Hollandia. *Nature* 194:931, 1962.

109. OSTERTAG W, SMITH EW: Hb Lepore Baltimore, a third type of a δβ crossover (δ^{50}, β^{86}). *Eur J Biochem* 10:371, 1969.

110. HUISMAN THJ, WRIGHTSTONE RN, WILSON JB, SCHROEDER WA, KENDALL AG: Hemoglobin Kenya, the product of a fusion of γ and β polypeptide chains. *Arch Biochem Biophys* 153:850, 1972.

111. OHTA Y, YAMAOKA K, SUMIDA I, FUJITA S, FUJIMURA T, HANADA M, YANASE T: Two structural and synthetical variants, Hb Miyada and homozygous δ-thalassaemia, discovered in Japan. *XIII Int Cong Haematol*. Munich, JF Lehmanns Verlag, 1970, 233.

112. LEHMANN H, CHARLESWORTH D: Observations on hemoglobin P (Congo type). *Biochem J* 119:43, 1970.

113. HONIG GR, MASON RG, TREMAINE LM, VIDA LN: Unbalanced globin chain synthesis by Hb Lincoln park (anti-Lepore) reticulocytes. *Am J Hematol* 5:335, 1978.

114. BADR FM, LORKIN PA, LEHMANN H: Haemoglobin P-Nilotic: Containing β-δ chain. *Nature* 242:107, 1973.

115. ADAMS JG III, MORRISON WT, STEINBERG MH: Double crossover within a single human gene. *Science* 218:291, 1982.

116. HARRIS JW: Studies on the destruction of red blood cells. VII. Molecular orientation in sickle cell hemoglobin solutions. *Proc Soc Exp Biol Med* 75:197, 1950.

117. EDELSTEIN SJ, TELFORD JN, CREPEAU RH: Structure of fibers of sickle cell hemoglobin. *Proc Natl Acad Sci USA* 70:1104, 1973.

118. FINCH JT, PERUTZ MF, BERTLES JF, DOBLER J: Structure of sickled eryth-

rocytes and of sickle-cell hemoglobin fibers. *Proc Natl Acad Sci USA* 70:718, 1973.

119. GARRELL RL, CREPEAU RH, EDELSTEIN SJ: Cross-sectional views of hemoglobin S fibers by electron microscopy and computer modeling. *Proc Natl Acad Sci USA* 76:1140, 1979.

120. DYKES G, CREPEAU R, EDELSTEIN SJ: Three-dimensional reconstruction of the fibres of sickle cell haemoglobin. *Nature* 272:506, 1978.

121. WISHNER BC, HANSON JC, RINGLE WM, LOVE WE: Crystal structure of sickle cell deoxyhemoglobin, in Hercules JI, Cottam GL, Waterman MR, Schechter AN (eds): *Aspects of Sickle Cell Disease. Proc Symp Mol Cell.* US Dept HEW Publ No (NIH) 76-10017, Bethesda, p 1, 1976.

122. WILSON WW, LUZZANA MR, PENNISTON JT, JOHNSON CS: Pregelation aggregation of sickle cell hemoglobin. *Proc Natl Acad Sci USA* 71:1260, 1974.

123. MORRAT K, GIBSON QH: The rates of polymerization and depolymerization of sickle cell hemoglobin. *Biochem Biophys Res Comm* 61:237, 1974.

124. WILLIAMS RC: Concerted formation of the gel of hemoglobin S. *Proc Natl Acad Sci USA* 70:1506, 1973.

125. HOFRICHTER J, ROSS PD, EATON WA: Supersaturation in sickle cell hemoglobin solution. *Proc Natl Acad Sci USA* 73:3035, 1976.

126. ROSS PD, HOFRICHTER J, EATON WA: Calorimetric and optical characterization of sickle cell haemoglobin gelation. *J Mol Biol* 96:239, 1975.

127. ZIPP A, JAMES TL, KUNTZ ID, SHOHET SB: Water proton magnetic resonance studies of normal and sickle erythrocytes. Temperature and volume dependence. *Biochim Biophys Acta* 428:291, 1976.

128. EATON WA, HOFRICHTER J, ROSS PD: Delay time in gelation: A possible determinant of clinical severity in sickle cell disease. *Blood* 47:621, 1976.

129. SINGER K, SINGER L: Studies on abnormal hemoglobins. VIII. The gelling phenomenon of sickle cell hemoglobin: Its biologic and diagnostic significance. *Blood* 8:1008, 1953.

130. PLATT O, NATHAN DG: Sickle cell disease, in Nathan DG, Oski FA (eds): *Hematology of Infancy and Childhood*, 2d ed. Saunders, Philadelphia, 1981, p 687.

131. BERTLES JF, DOBLER J: Reversible and irreversible sickling; a distinction by electron microscopy. *Blood* 33:884, 1969.

132. MESSNER MJ, HAHN JA, BRADLEY TB: The kinetics of sickling and unsickling of red cells under physiologic conditions: Rheologic and ultrastructural correlations. Hercules JI, Cottam GL, Waterman MR, Schechter AN (eds): *Aspects of Sickle Cell Disease. Proc Symp Mol Cell.* US Dept HEW Publ No (NIH) 76-10017, Bethesda, 1976, p 225.

133. WALLACH DFH: *The Function of Red Blood Cells: Erythrocyte Pathobiology.* New York, AR Liss, 1981.

134. EVANS E, MOHANDAS N, LEUNG A: Static and dynamic rigidities of normal and sickle erythrocytes: Major influence of cell hemoglobin concentration. *J Clin Invest* 73:116, 1984.

135. KAUL DK, FABRY ME, WINDISCH P, BAEZ S, NAGEL RL: Erythrocytes in sickle cell anemia are heterogeneous in their rheological and hemodynamic characteristics. *J Clin Invest* 72:22, 1983.

136. HEBBEL RP, SCHWARTZ RS, MOHANDAS N: The adhesive sickle erythrocyte: Cause and consequence of abnormal interactions with endothelium, monocytes/macrophages and model membranes. *Clin Haemat* 14:141, 1985.

137. HEBBEL RP, MILLER WJ: Phagocytosis of sickle erythrocytes: Immunologic and oxidative determinants of hemolytic anemia. *Blood* 64:733, 1984.

138. GALILI U, CLARK MR, SHOHET SB: Excessive binding of natural anti-alpha galactosyl immunoglobulin G to sickle erythrocytes may contribute to extravascular cell destruction. *J Clin Invest* 77:27, 1986.

139. HEBBEL RP: Auto-oxidation and a membrane-associated "Fenton Reagent": A possible explanation for development of membrane lesions in sickle erythrocytes. *Clin Haemat* 14:129, 1985.

140. KAY MMB, GOODMAN SR, SORENSEN K, WHITFIELD CF, WONG P, ZAKI L, RUDLOFF V: Senescent cell antigen is immunologically related to band 3. *Proc Natl Acad Sci USA* 80:1631, 1983.

141. SHERWOOD JB, GOLDWASSER E, CHILCOTE E, CARMICHAEL LD, NAGEL RL: Sickle cell anemia patients have low erythropoietin levels for their degree of anemia. *Blood* 67:46, 1986.

142. MOHANDAS N, EVANS E: Sickle cell adherence to vascular endothelium: Morphologic correlates and the requirement for divalent cations and collagen binding plasma proteins. *J Clin Invest* 76:1605, 1985.

143. HELLER P, BEST WR, NELSON RB, BECKTEL J: Clinical implications of sickle cell trait and glucose-6-phosphate dehydrogenase deficiency in hospitalized black male patients. *N Engl J Med* 300:1001, 1979.

144. SERJEANT GR: *Sickle Cell Disease.* Oxford, Oxford University Press, 1985.

145. ROGERS DW, SERJEANT BE, SERJEANT GR: Early rise in "pitted" red cell count as a guide to susceptibility to infection in childhood sickle cell anaemia. *Arch Dis Child* 57:338, 1982.

146. ZAGO MA, BOTTURA C: Splenic function in sickle-cell diseases. *Clin Sci* 65:297, 1983.

147. ROGERS DW, CLARKE JM, CUPIDORE L, RAMLAL AM, SPARKE BR, SERJEANT GR: Early deaths in Jamaican children with sickle cell disease. *Br Med J* i:1515, 1978.

148. DAVIES SC, LUCE PG, WIN AA, RIORDAN JF, BROZOVIC M: Acute chest syndrome in sickle-cell disease. *Lancet* i:36, 1984.

149. PATTISON JR, JONES SE, HODGSON J, DAVIS LR, WHITE JM, STROUD CE, MURTAZA L: Parvovirus infections and hypoplastic crises in sickle-cell anaemia. *Lancet* i:664, 1981.

150. POWARS D, WILSON B, IMBUS C, PEGELOW C, ALLEN J: The natural history of stroke in sickle cell disease. *Am J Med* 65:461, 1978.

151. CHATTERJEE SN: National study on natural history of renal allografts in sickle cell disease or trait. *Nephron* 25:199, 1980.

152. HENDRICKSE JP DEV, HARRISON KA, WATSON-WILLIAMS EJ, LUZZATTO L, AJABOR LN: Pregnancy in homozygous sickle-cell anaemia. *J Obstet Gynaecol Br Commonw* 79:396, 1972.

153. NIELL HB, LEACH BE, KRAUS AP: Zinc metabolism in sickle cell anemia. *JAMA* 242:2686, 1979.

154. ROWLEY PT, HUNTZINGER DJ: Newborn sickle cell screening. Benefits and burdens realized. *Am J Dis Child* 137:341, 1983.

155. PERRINE RP, BROWN MJ, CLEGG JB, WEATHERALL DJ, MAY A: Benign sickle-cell anaemia. *Lancet* ii:1163, 1972.

156. KAR BC, SATAPATHY RK, KULOZIK AE, KULOZIK M, SIRR S, SERJEANT BE, SERJEANT GR: Sickle cell disease in Orissa State, India. *Lancet* ii:1198, 1986.

157. SERJEANT GR: Fetal haemoglobin in homozygous sickle cell disease. *Clin Haemat* 4:109, 1975.

158. WAINSCOAT JS, THEIN SL, HIGGS DR, BELL JI, WEATHERALL DJ, AL-AWAMY B, SERJEANT GR: A genetic marker for elevated levels of haemoglobin F in homozygous sickle cell disease. *Br J Haemat* 60:261, 1985.

159. HIGGS DR, ALDRIDGE BE, LAMB J, CLEGG JB, WEATHERALL DJ, HAYES RJ, GRANDISON Y, LOWRIE Y, MASON KP, SERJEANT BE, SERJEANT GR: The interaction of alpha-thalassemia and homozygous sickle-cell disease. *N Engl J Med* 306:1441, 1982.

160. NOGUCHI CT, DOVER GJ, RODGERS GP, SERJEANT GR, ANTONARAKIS SE, ANAGNOU NP, HIGGS DR, WEATHERALL DJ, SCHECHTER AN: α thalassemia changes erythrocyte heterogeneity in sickle cell disease. *J Clin Invest* 75:1632, 1985.

161. HIGGS DR, CLEGG JB, WEATHERALL DJ, SERJEANT BE, SERJEANT GR: Interaction of the ααα globin gene haplotype and sickle haemoglobin. *Br J Haemat* 58:671, 1984.

162. CONDON PI, GRAY R, SERJEANT GR: Ocular findings in children with sickle cell haemoglobin C disease in Jamaica. *Br J Ophthal* 58:644, 1974.

163. MONPLAISIR N, MERAULT G, POYART C, RHODE M-D, CRAESCU C, VIDAUD M, GALACTEROS F, BLOUQUIT Y, ROSA J: Hemoglobin S Antilles: A variant with lower solubility than hemoglobin S and producing sickle cell disease in heterozygotes. *Proc Natl Acad Sci USA* 83:9363, 1986.

164. ITANO HA, NEEL JV: A new inherited abnormality of human hemoglobin. *Proc Natl Acad Sci USA* 36:613, 1950.

165. DIGGS LW, KRAUS AO, MORRISON DB, RUDNICKI RPT: Intra-erythrocyte crystals in a white patient with hemoglobin C in the absence of other types of hemoglobin. *Blood* 9:1172, 1954.

166. HIRSCH RE, RAVENTOS-SUAREZ C, OLSON JA, NAGEL RL: Ligand state of intraerythrocyte circulating Hb C crystals in homozygote CC patients. *Blood* 66:775, 1985.

167. REISS G, RANNEY HM, SHAKLAI N: The association of hemoglobin C with red cell ghosts. *J Clin Invest* 70:946, 1982.

168. VELLA F, LEHMANN H: Haemoglobin D Punjab (D Los Angeles). *J Med Genet* 11:341, 1974.

169. HUNT JA, INGRAM VM: Abnormal human haemoglobins. VI. The chemical difference between haemoglobins A and E. *Biochim Biophys Acta* 49:520, 1961.

170. TRAEGER J, WOOD WG, CLEGG JB, WEATHERALL DJ, WASI P: Defective synthesis of HbE is due to reduced levels of β^E mRNA. *Nature* 288:497, 1980.

171. ORKIN SH, KAZAZIAN HH, ANTONARAKIS SE, OSTRER H, GOFF SC, SEXTON JP: Abnormal RNA processing due to the exon mutation of β^E-globin gene. *Nature* 300:768, 1982.

172. WASI P, NA-NAKORN S, POOTRAKUL S, SOOKANEK M, DISTHASONGCHAN P, PORNPATKUL M, PANICH V: Alpha- and beta-thalassemia in Thailand. *Ann NY Acad Sci* 165:60, 1969.

173. WEATHERALL DJ, CLEGG JB, NA-NAKORN S, WASI P: The pattern of disordered haemoglobin synthesis in homozygous and heterozygous β-thalassemia. *Br J Haemat* 16:251, 1969.

174. WINTERBOURN CC, CARRELL RW: Studies of hemoglobin denaturation and Heinz body formation in the unstable hemoglobins. *J Clin Invest* 54:678, 1974.

175. RACHMILEWITZ EA: Denaturation of the normal and abnormal hemoglobin molecule. *Semin Hemat* 11:441, 1974.

176. MILNER PF, WRIGHTSTONE RN: The unstable hemoglobins: A review, in Wallach DFH (ed): *The Function of Red Blood Cells: Erythrocyte Pathobiology.* New York, AR Liss, 1981, p 197.

177. RIFKIND RA: Heinz body anemia: An ultrastructural study. II Red cell sequestration and destruction. *Blood* 26:433, 1965.

178. JANDL JH, SIMMONS RL, CASTLE WB: Red cell filtration and the pathogenesis of certain hemolytic anemias. *Blood* 18:133, 1961.

179. MILLER DR, WEED RI, STAMATOYANNOPOULOS G, YOSHIDA A: Hemoglobin Koln disease occurring as a fresh mutation: Erythrocyte metabolism and survival. *Blood* 38:715, 1971.

180. FLYNN TP, ALLEN DW, JOHNSON GJ, WHITE JC: Oxidant damage of the lipids and proteins of the erythrocyte membranes in unstable hemoglobin disease. Evidence for the role of lipid peroxidation. *J Clin Invest* 71:1215, 1983.

181. CHARACHE S, WEATHERALL DJ, CLEGG JB: Polycythemia associated with a hemoglobinopathy. *J Clin Invest* 45:813, 1966.

182. CHARACHE S: Haemoglobins with altered oxygen affinity. *Clin Haemat* 3:357, 1974.

183. ADAMSON JW: Familial polycythemia. *Semin Hemat* 12:383, 1975.

184. BONAVENTURA J, RIGGS A: Hemoglobin Kansas, a human hemoglobin with a neutral amino acid substitution and an abnormal oxygen equilibrium. *J Biol Chem* 243:980, 1968.

184a. NAGEL RL, BOOKCHIN RM: Human hemoglobin mutants with abnormal oxygen binding. *Semin Hematol* 11:385, 1974.

185. MODELL CB, BERDOUKAS VA: *The Clinical Approach to Thalassemia.* New York, Grune & Stratton, 1983.

186. NATHAN DG, GUNN RB: Thalassemia: The consequences of unbalanced hemoglobin synthesis. *Am J Med* 41:815, 1966.

187. WEATHERALL DJ, WAINSCOAT JS: The molecular pathology of thalassaemia, in Hoffbrand AV (ed): *Recent Advances in Haematology*, 4th ed. Edinburgh, Churchill Livingstone, 1985, p 63.

188. NIENHUIS AW, ANAGNOU NP, LEY TJ: Advances in thalassaemia research. *Blood* 63:738, 1984.

189. BARGELLESI A, PONTREMOLI S, MENINI C, CONCONI F: Excess of alpha globin synthesis in homozygous beta-thalassemia and its removal from the red blood cell cytoplasm. *Eur J Biochem* 3:354, 1968.

190. FESSAS P: Inclusions of hemoglobin in erythroblasts and erythrocytes of thalassemia. *Blood* 21:21, 1963.

191. WICKRAMASINGHE SN, HUGHES M: Some features of bone marrow macrophages in patients with homozygous β-thalassaemia. *Br J Haemat* 38:23, 1978.

192. YATAGANAS X, FESSAS P: The pattern of hemoglobin precipitation in thalassemia and its significance. *Ann NY Acad Sci* 165:270, 1969.

193. FINCH CA, DEUBELBEISS K, COOK JD, ESCHBACH JW, HARKER LA, FUNK DD, MARSAGLIA G, HILLMAN RS, SLICHTER S, ADAMSON JW, GANZONI A, GIBLETT ER: Ferrokinetics in man. *Medicine (Baltimore)* 49:17, 1970.

194. CHALEVELAKIS G, CLEGG JB, WEATHERALL DJ: Imbalanced globin chain synthesis in heterozygous β-thalassemic bone marrow. *Proc Natl Acad Sci USA* 72:3853, 1975.

195. AGER JAM, LEHMANN H: Observations on some "fast" haemoglobins: K,J,N, and "Bart's." *Br Med J* i:929, 1958.

196. RIGAS DA, KOHLER RD, OSGOOD EE: New hemoglobin possessing a higher electrophoretic mobility than normal adult hemoglobin. *Science* 121:372, 1955.

197. WASI P, NA-NAKORN S, POOTRAKUL S: The α-thalassaemias. *Clin Haemat* 3:383, 1974.

198. GABUZDA TG, NATHAN DG, GARDNER FH: The turnover of hemoglobins A, F and A₂ in the peripheral blood of three patients with thalassemia. *J Clin Invest* 42:1678, 1963.

199. LOUKOPOULOS D, FESSAS P: The distribution of hemoglobin types in thalassemic erythrocytes. *J Clin Invest* 44:231, 1965.

200. COSTIN G, KOGUT MD, HYMAN CB, OREGA JA: Endocrine abnormalities in thalassemia major. *Am J Dis Child* 133:497, 1979.

201. CANALE VC, STEINHERZ P, NEW M, ERLANDSON M: Endocrine function in thalassemia major. *Ann NY Acad Sci* 232:333, 1974.

202. LASSMAN MN, O'BRIEN RT, PEARSON HA, WISE JK, DONANEDIAN RK, FELIG P, GENEL M: Endocrine evaluation in thalassemia major. *Ann NY Acad Sci* 232:226, 1974.

203. SMITH CH, ERLANDSON ME, STERN G, HILGARTNER MW: Postsplenectomy infection in Cooley's anemia. *Ann NY Acad Sci* 119:748, 1964.

204. NATHAN DG, STOSSEL TB, GUNN RB, ZARKOWSKY HS, LAFORET MT: Influence of hemoglobin precipitation on erythrocyte metabolism in alpha and beta thalassemia. *J Clin Invest* 48:33, 1969.

205. KAN YW, NATHAN DG: Mild thalassemia: The result of interactions of alpha and beta thalassemia genes. *J Clin Invest* 49:635, 1970.

206. WEATHERALL DJ, PRESSLEY L, WOOD WG, HIGGS DR, CLEGG JB: The molecular basis for mild forms of homozygous β thalassaemia. *Lancet* i:527, 1981.

207. WAINSCOAT JS, OLD JM, WEATHERALL DJ, ORKIN SH: The molecular basis for the clinical diversity of β thalassaemia in Cypriots. *Lancet* i:1235, 1983.

208. MAUDE GH, HIGGS DR, BECKFORD M, GRANDISON Y, MASON K, TAYLOR B, SERJEANT BE, SERJEANT GR: Alpha thalassemia and the hematology of normal Jamaican children. *Clin Lab Haemat* 7:289, 1985.

209. PORNPATKUL M, WASI P, NA-NAKORN S: Hematologic parameters in obligatory alpha-thalassemia traits. *J Med Assoc Thailand* 52:801, 1969.

210. WEATHERALL DJ, CLEGG JB, BOON WH: The haemoglobin constitution of infants with the haemoglobin Bart's hydrops foetalis syndrome. *Br J Haemat* 18:357, 1970.

211. EMBURY SH, MILLER JA, DOZY AM, KAN YW, CHAN V, TODD D: Two different molecular organizations account for the single α-globin gene of the α-thalassemia-2 genotype. *J Clin Invest* 66:1319, 1980.

212. GOOSSENS M, DOZY AM, EMBURY SH, ZACHARIADES Z, HADJIMINAS MG, STAMATOYANNOPOULOS G, KAN YW: Triplicated α-globin loci in humans. *Proc Natl Acad Sci USA* 77:518, 1980.

213. TRENT RJ, HIGGS DR, CLEGG JB, WEATHERALL DJ: A new triplicated α-globin gene arrangement in man. *Br J Haemat* 49:149, 1981.

214. LIE-INJO LE, HERRERA AR, KAN YW: Two types of triplicated α globin loci in humans. *Nucleic Acids Res* 9:3707, 1981.

215. GU YC, LANDMAN H, HUISMAN THJ: Two different quadruplicated α globin gene arrangements. *Br J Haemat* 66:245, 1987.

216. RAMSAY M, JENKINS T: The αααanti−3.7 globin haplotype with an additional Bgl III site mutation (αααanti−3.7 Bgl II(−)). *Hemoglobin* 9:385, 1985.

217. HIGGS DR, HILL AVS, BOWDEN DK, WEATHERALL DJ, CLEGG JB: Independent recombination events between duplicated human α globin genes: Implications for their concerted evolution. *Nucleic Acids Res* 12:6965, 1984.

218. POWERS PA, SMITHIES O: Short gene conversions in the human fetal globin gene region: A by-product of chromosome pairing during meiosis? *Genetics* 112:343, 1986.

219. NATHANS J, PIANTANIDA TP, EDDY RL, SHOWS TB, HOGNESS DS: Molecular genetics of inherited variation in human color vision. *Science* 232:203, 1986.

220. TAUB RA, HOLLIS GF, HIETER PA, KORSMEYER S, WALDMANN TA, LEDER P: Variable amplification of immunoglobulin κ light-chain genes in human populations. *Nature* 304:172, 1983.

221. KULOZIK A, KAR BC, SERJEANT BE, SERJEANT GR, WEATHERALL DJ: Alpha thalassemia in India: Its interaction with sickle cell disease. *Blood* 71:467, 1988.

222. ORKIN SH, GOFF SC: The duplicated human α-globin genes: Their relative expression as measured by RNA analysis. *Cell* 24:345, 1981.

223. LIEBHABER SA, KAN YW: Differentiation of the mRNA transcripts originating from the α1- and α2-globin loci in normals and α-thalassemics. *J Clin Invest* 68:439, 1981.

224. SHAKIN SH, LIEBHABER SA: Translational profiles of alpha 1-, alpha 2-, and beta-globin messenger ribonucleic acids in human reticulocytes. *J Clin Invest* 78:1125, 1986.

225. LIEBHABER SA, CASH FE, BALLAS SK: Human α-globin gene expression. The dominant role of the α2-locus in mRNA and protein synthesis. *J Biol Chem* 261:15327, 1986.

226. BOWDEN DK, HILL AVS, HIGGS DR, OPPENHEIMER SJ, WEATHERALL DJ, CLEGG JB: Different hematologic phenotypes are associated with leftward (-α4.2) and rightward (-α3.7) α+-thalassemia deletions. *J Clin Invest* 79:39, 1987.

227. NICHOLLS RD, FISCHEL-GHODSIAN N, HIGGS DR: Recombination at the human α-globin gene cluster: Sequence features and topological constraints. *Cell* 49:369, 1987.

228. TSUJIMOTO Y, COSSMAN J, JAFFE E, CROCE CM: Involvement of the Bcl-2 gene in human follicular lymphomas. *Science* 228:1440, 1985.

229. PICCOLI SP, CAIMI PG, COLE MD: A conserved sequence at c-myc oncogene chromosomal translocation breakpoints in plasmacytomas. *Nature* 310:327, 1984.

230. VANIN EF, HENTHORN PS, KIOUSSIS D, GROSVELD F, SMITHIES O: Unexpected relationships between four large deletions in the human β-globin gene cluster. *Cell* 35:701, 1983.

231. JELINEK WR, SCHMID CW: Repetitive sequences in eukaryotic DNA and their expression. *Annu Rev Biochem* 51:813, 1982.

232. HIGGS DR, WEATHERALL DJ: Alpha Thalassemia, in Piomelli S, Yachnin S (eds): *Current Topics in Hematology*, 4th ed. New York, AR Liss, 1983, p 37.

233. CHUNG S-W, WONG SC, CLARKE BJ, PATTERSON M, WALKER WHC, CHUI

DHK: Human embryonic ζ-globin chains in adult patients with α-thalassemias. *Proc Natl Acad Sci USA* 81:6188, 1984.

234. CHUI DHK, WONG SC, CHUNG S-W, PATTERSON M, BHARGAVA S, POON M-C: Embryonic ζ-globin chains in adults: A marker for α-thalassemia-1 haplotype due to a >17.5 kb deletion. *N Engl J Med* 31:76, 1986.

235. ORKIN SH, GOFF SC, HECTMAN RL: Mutation in an intervening sequence splice junction in man. *Proc Natl Acad Sci USA* 78:5041, 1981.

236. FELBER BK, ORKIN SH, HAMER DH: Abnormal RNA splicing causes one form of α thalassemia. *Cell* 29:895, 1982.

237. THEIN SL, WALLACE RB, PRESSLEY L, CLEGG JB, WEATHERALL DJ, HIGGS DR: Phenotypic expression of the polyadenylation site mutation in the α-globin gene cluster. *Blood* 71:313, 1988.

238. WHITELAW E, PROUDFOOT N. α-thalassemia caused by a poly(A) site mutation reveals that transcriptional termination is linked to 3′ end processing in the human α2 globin gene. *EMBO J* 5:2915, 1986.

239. PIRASTU M, SAGLIO G, CHANG JC, CAO A, KAN YW: Initiation codon mutation as a cause of α thalassemia. *J Biol Chem* 259:12315, 1984.

240. MORLE F, LOPEZ B, HENNI T, GODET J: α-thalassaemia associated with the deletion of two nucleotides at position −2 and −3 preceding the AUG codon. *EMBO J* 4:1245, 1985.

241. LEIBHABER SA, COLEMAN MB, ADAMS JG III, CASH FE, STEINBERG MH: Non-deletion α-thalassemia in a Black kindred resulting from a nonsense mutation (α2 116GAG-UAG). *Blood* 68:75, 1986.

242. LIEBHABER SA, KAN YW: α-thalassemia caused by an unstable α-globin mutant. *J Clin Invest* 71:461, 1983.

243. SANGUANSERMSRI T, MATRAGOON S, CHANGLOAH L, FLATZ G: Hemoglobin Suan-Dok (α2^{109(G16)LEU-ARG}β2): An unstable variant associated with α thalassemia. *Hemoglobin* 3:161, 1979.

244. HONIG GR, SHAMSUDDIN M, ZAIZOV R, STEINHERZ M, SOLAR I, KIRSCHMAN C: Hemoglobin Petah Tikva (α110 Ala →Asp): A new unstable variant with α-thalassemia-like expression. *Blood* 57:705, 1981.

245. HONIG GR, SHAMSUDDIN M, VIDA LN, MOMPOINT M, VALCOURT E, BOWIE LJ, JONES EC, POWERS PA, SPRITZ RA, GUIS M, EMBURY SH, CONBOY J, KAN YW, MENTZER WC, WEIL SC, HIRATA RK, WALOCH J, O'RIORDAN JF, GOLDSTICK TK: Hemoglobin Evanston (α14 Trp→Arg): An unstable α-chain variant expressed as α-thalassemia. *J Clin Invest* 73:1740, 1984.

246. LOUKOPOULOS D: Personal communication.

247. HILL AVS: *The Distribution and Molecular Basis of Thalassemia in Oceania.* PhD Thesis, Oxford University, 1986.

248. CHAN V, CHAN TK, LIANG ST, GHOSH A, YAN YW, TODD D: Hydrops fetalis due to an unusual form of Hb H disease. *Blood* 66:224, 1985.

249. TRENT RJ, WILKINSON T, YAKAS J, CARTER J, LAMMI A, KRONENBERG H: Molecular defects in 2 examples of severe Hb H disease. *Scand J Haemat* 36:272, 1986.

250. LIE-INJO LE, GANESAN J, CLEGG JB, WEATHERALL DJ: Homozygous state for Hb Constant Spring (slow-moving Hb X components). *Blood* 43:251, 1974.

251. DE JONG WW, KHAN PM, BERNINI LF: Hemoglobin Koya Dora: High frequency of a chain termination mutant. *Am J Hum Genet* 27:81, 1975.

252. WINICHAGOON P, HIGGS DR, GOODBOURN SEY, CLEGG JB, WEATHERALL DJ, WASI P: The molecular basis of α thalassaemia in Thailand. *EMBO J* 3:1813, 1984.

253. BEAUDRY MA, FERGUSON DJ, PEARSE K, YANOFSKY RA, RUBIN EM, KAN YW: Survival of a hydropic infant with homozygous α-thalassemia-1. *J Pediatr* 108:713, 1986.

254. BIANCHI DW, BEYER EC, STARK AR, SAFFAN D, SACHS BP, WOLFE L: Normal long-term survival with α-thalassemia. *J Pediatr* 108:716, 1986.

255. SHARMA RS, YU V, WALTERS WAW: Haemoglobin Bart's hydrops fetalis syndrome in an infant of Greek origin and prenatal diagnosis of alpha-thalassemia. *Med J Aust* 2:433, 1979.

256. TODD D: Personal communication.

257. HALBRECHT I, SHABITA F: An unusual case of hemoglobin Bart's hydrops fetalis. *Acta Genet Med Gemellol (Roma)* 24:97, 1975.

258. HIGGS DR, WOOD WG, BARTON C, WEATHERALL DJ: Clinical features and molecular analysis of acquired Hb H disease. *Am J Med* 75:181, 1983.

259. WEATHERALL DJ, HIGGS DR, BUNCH C, OLD JM, HUNT DM, PRESSLEY L, CLEGG JB, BETHLENFALVAY NC, SJOLIN S, KOLER RD, MAGENIS E, FRANCIS JL, BEBBINGTON D: Hemoglobin H disease and mental retardation. A new syndrome or a remarkable coincidence? *N Engl J Med* 305:607, 1981.

260. SCHMICKEL RD: Contiguous gene syndromes: A component of recognizable syndromes. *J Pediatr* 109:231, 1986.

261. THEIN SL, OLD JM, WAINSCOAT JS, WEATHERALL DJ: Population and genetic studies suggest a single origin for the Indian deletion β⁰ thalassemia. *Brit J Haemat* 57:271, 1984.

262. GILMAN JG, HUISMAN THJ, ABELS J: Dutch β⁰-thalassaemia: A 10 kilobase DNA deletion associated with significant γ-chain production. *Br J Haemat* 56:339, 1984.

263. PADANILAM BJ, FELICE AE, HUISMAN THJ: Partial deletion of the 5′ β globin gene region causes β⁰ thalassemia in members of an American black family. *Blood* 64:941, 1984.

264. POPOVICH BW, ROSENBLATT DS, KENDALL AG, NISHIOKA Y: Molecular characterization of an atypical β-thalassemia caused by a large deletion in the 5′ β-globin gene region. *Am J Hum Genet* 39:797, 1986.

265. ORKIN SH, SEXTON JP, CHENG TC, GOFF SC, GIARDINA PJV, LEE JI, KAZAZIAN HH: ATA box transcription mutation in β-thalassemia. *Nucleic Acids Res* 11:4727. 1983.

266. ANTONARAKIS SE, ORKIN SH, CHENG T-C, SCOTT AF, SEXTON JB, TRUSKO S, CHARACHE S, KAZAZIAN HH: β-thalassemia in American blacks: Novel mutations in the TATA box and IVS-2 acceptor splice site. *Proc Natl Acad Sci USA* 81:1154, 1984.

267. KAZAZIAN HH, ORKIN SH, ANTONARAKIS SE, SEXTON JP, BOEHM CD, GOFF SC, WABER PG: Molecular characterization of seven β-thalassemia mutations in Asian Indians. *EMBO J* 3:593, 1984.

268. TAMAGNINI GP, LOPES MC, CASTANHEIRA ME, WAINSCOAT JS, WOOD WG: β⁺ thalassaemia—Portuguese type: Clinical, haematological and molecular studies of a newly defined form of β thalassaemia. *Br J Haemat* 54:189, 1983.

269. ORKIN SK, KAZAZIAN HH: The mutation and polymorphism of the human β-globin gene and its surrounding DNA. *Annu Rev Genet* 18:131, 1984.

270. GOLDSMITH ME, HUMPHRIES RK, LEY T, CLINE A, KANTOR JA, NIENHUIS AW: "Silent" nucleotide substitution in β⁺ thalassemia globin gene activates splice site in coding sequence RNA. *Proc Natl Acad Sci USA* 80:2318, 1983.

271. ORKIN SH, ANTONARAKIS SE, LOUKOPOULOS D: Abnormal processing of β Knossos RNA. *Blood* 64:311, 1984.

272. SPRITZ RA, JAGADEESWARAN P, CHOUDARY PV, BIRO PA, ELDER JT, DE RIEL JK, MANLEY JL, GEFTER ML, FORGET BG, WEISSMAN SM: Base substitution in an intervening sequence of a β⁺ thalassemic human globin gene. *Proc Natl Acad Sci USA* 78:2455, 1981.

273. BUSSLINGER M, MOSCHONAS N, FLAVELL RA: β⁺ thalassemia: Aberrant splicing results from a single point mutation in an intron. *Cell* 27:289, 1981.

274. CHANG JC, KAN YW: β-thalassemia: A nonsense mutation in man. *Proc Natl Acad Sci USA* 76:2886, 1979.

275. TRECARTIN RF, LIEBHABER SA, CHANG JC, LEE KY, KAN YW, FURBETTA M, ANGIUS A, CAO A: β thalassemia in Sardinia is caused by a nonsense mutation. *J Clin Invest* 68:1012, 1981.

276. TAKESHITA K, FORGET BG, SCARPA A, BENZ EJ: Intranuclear defect in β globin mRNA accumulation to a premature termination codon. *Blood* 64:13, 1984.

277. HUMPHRIES RK, LEY TJ, ANAGNOU NP, BAUR AW, NIENHUIS AW: β⁰-39-thalassemia gene: A premature termination codon causes β mRNA deficiency without changing cytoplasmic β mRNA stability. *Blood* 64:23, 1984.

278. OTTOLENGHI S, GIGLIONI B, TARAMELLI R, COMI P, MAZZA U, SAGLIO G, CAMASCHELLA C, IZZO P, CAO A, GALANELLO R, GIMFERRER E, BAIGET M, GIANNI AM: Molecular comparison of δβ-thalassemia and hereditary persistence of fetal hemoglobin DNAs: Evidence of a regulatory area. *Proc Natl Acad Sci USA* 79:2347, 1982.

279. JONES RW, OLD JM, TRENT RJ, CLEGG JB, WEATHERALL DJ: Major rearrangement in the human β-globin gene cluster. *Nature* 291:39, 1981.

280. JENNINGS MW, JONES RW, WOOD WG, WEATHERALL DJ: Analysis of an inversion within the human beta globin gene cluster. *Nucleic Acids Res* 13:2897, 1985.

281. KUTLAR A, GARDINER MB, HEADLEE MG, REESE AL, CLEEK MP, NAGLE S, SUKUMARAN PK, HUISMAN THJ: Heterogeneity in the molecular basis of three types of hereditary persistence of fetal hemoglobin and the relative synthesis of the ^Gγ and ^Aγ types of γ chain. *Biochem Genet* 22:21, 1984.

282. WAINSCOAT JS, OLD JM, WOOD WG, TRENT RJ, WEATHERALL DJ: Characterization of an Indian (δβ)⁰ thalassaemia. *Br J Haemat* 58:353, 1984.

283. VAN DER PLOEG LHT, KONINGS A, OORT M, ROOS D, BERNINI L, FLAVELL RA: γ-β-thalassaemia studies showing that deletion of the γ- and δ-genes influences β-globin gene expression in man. *Nature* 283:637, 1980.

284. TARAMELLI R, KIOUSSIS D, VANIN E, BARTRAM K, GROFFEN J, HURST J, GROSVELD FG: γδβ-thalassaemia 1 and 2 are the result of a 100 kbp deletion in the human β-globin cluster. *Nucleic Acids Res* 14:7017, 1986.

285. CURTIN P, PIRASTU M, KAN YW, GOBERT-JONES JA, STEPHENS AD, LEHMANN H: A distant gene deletion affects β-globin gene function in an atypical γδβ-thalassemia. *J Clin Invest* 76:1554, 1985.

286. WAINSCOAT JS, THEIN SL, WOOD WG, WEATHERALL DJ, TZOTOS S, KAN-

AVAKIS E, METAXATOU-MAVROMATI A, KATTAMIS C: A novel deletion in the β globin gene complex. *Ann NY Acad Sci* 445:20, 1985.

287. BERNARDS R, FLAVELL RA: Physical mapping of the globin gene deletion in hereditary persistence of foetal hemoglobin (HPFH). *Nucleic Acids Res* 8:1521, 1980.

288. COLLINS FS, STOECKERT CJ, SERJEANT GR, FORGET BG, WEISSMAN SM: $^G\gamma\beta^+$ hereditary persistence of fetal hemoglobin: Cosmid cloning and identification of a specific mutation 5' to the $^G\gamma$ gene. *Proc Natl Acad Sci USA* 81:4894, 1984.

289. GIGLIONI B, CASINI C, MANTOVANI R, MERLI S, COMI P, OTTOLENGHI S, SAGLIO G, CAMASCHELLA C, MAZZA U: A molecular study of a family with Greek hereditary persistence of fetal hemoglobin and β-thalassemia. *EMBO J* 3:2641, 1984.

290. COLLINS FS, METHERALL JE, YAMAKAWA M, PAN J, WEISSMAN SM, FORGET BG: A point mutation in the $^A\gamma$-globin gene promoter in Greek hereditary persistence of fetal hemoglobin. *Nature* 313:325, 1985.

291. GELINAS R, ENDLICH B, PFEIFFER C, YAGI M, STAMATOYANNOPOULOS G: G to A substitution in the distal CCAAT box of the $^A\gamma$-globin gene in Greek hereditary persistence of fetal haemoglobin. *Nature* 313:323, 1985.

292. TATE VE, WOOD WG, WEATHERALL DJ: The British form of hereditary persistence of fetal hemoglobin results from a single base mutation adjacent to an S1 hypersensitive site 5' to the $^A\gamma$ globin gene. *Blood* 68:1389, 1986.

293. WILLCOX MC, WEATHERALL DJ, CLEGG JB: Homozygous β thalassaemia in Liberia. *J Med Genet* 12:165, 1975.

294. KATTAMIS C, METAXATOU-MAVROMATI A, WOOD WG, NASH JR, WEATHERALL DJ: The heterogeneity of normal Hb A_2-β thalassaemia in Greece. *Br J Haemat* 42:109, 1979.

295. SCHWARTZ E: The silent carrier of beta thalassemia. *N Engl J Med* 281:1327, 1969.

296. AROUS N, GALACTEROS F, FESSAS P, LOUKOPOULOS D, BLOUQUIT Y, KOMIS G, SELLAYE M, BOUSSIOU M, ROSA J: Structural study of hemoglobin Knossos, β27 (B9) Ala-Ser. A new abnormal hemoglobin present as a silent β-thalassaemia. *FEBS Lett* 147:247, 1982.

297. FESSAS P, LOUKOPOULOS D, LOUTRADI-ANAGNOSTOU A, KOMES G: "Silent" β thalassaemia caused by a "silent" β chain mutant: The pathogenesis of a syndrome of thalassaemia intermedia. *Br J Haemat* 51:577, 1982.

298. KANAVAKIS E, METAXATOU-MAVROMATI A, KATTAMIS C, AKSOY M, WEATHERALL DJ, WOOD WG: Globin gene mapping in normal HbA_2 types of β thalassaemia. *Br J Haemat* 51:59, 1982.

299. FEARON EF, KAZAZIAN HH, WABER PG, LEE JI, ANTONARAKIS E, ORKIN SH, VANIN EF, HENTHORN PA, GROSVELD FG, SCOTT F, BUCHANAN GR: The entire β-globin gene cluster is deleted in a form of γδβ-thalassaemia. *Blood* 61:1269, 1983.

300. PIRASTU M, KAN YW, LIN CC, BAINE R, HOLBROOK CT: Hemolytic disease of the newborn caused by a new deletion of the entire β-globin cluster. *J Clin Invest* 72:602, 1983.

301. ORKIN SH, GOFF SC, NATHAN DG: Heterogeneity of DNA deletion in γδβ-thalassaemia. *J Clin Invest* 67:878, 1981.

302. KAN YW, FORGET BG, NATHAN DG: Gamma-beta thalassemia: A cause of hemolytic disease of the newborn. *N Engl J Med* 286:129, 1972.

303. ADAMS JG, BOXER LA, BAEHNER RL, FORGET BG, TSISTRAKIS GA, STEINBERG MA: Hemoglobin Indianapolis (β112 (G14) arginine): An unstable β chain variant producing the phenotype of severe β thalassemia. *J Clin Invest* 69:931, 1979.

304. EFREMOV GD: Hemoglobins Lepore and anti-Lepore. *Hemoglobin* 2:197, 1978.

305. QUATTRIN N, VENTRUTO V: Hemoglobin Lepore: Its significance for thalassemia and clinical manifestations. *Ann NY Acad Sci* 232:65, 1974.

306. WOOD WG, CLEGG JB, WEATHERALL DJ: Hereditary persistence of fetal haemoglobin (HPFH) and δβ-thalassaemia. *Br J Haemat* 43:509, 1979.

307. TRENT RJ, JONES RW, CLEGG JB, WEATHERALL DJ, DAVIDSON R, WOOD WG: $(^A\gamma\delta\beta)^0$ thalassaemia: Similarity of phenotype in four different molecular defects, including one newly described. *Br J Haemat* 57:279, 1984.

308. KENDALL AG, OJWANG PJ, SCHROEDER WA, HUISMAN THJ: Hemoglobin Kenya, the product of a γ-β fusion gene: Studies of the family. *Am J Hum Genet* 25:548, 1973.

309. SMITH DH, CLEGG JB, WEATHERALL DJ, GILLES HM: Hereditary persistence of foetal haemoglobin associated with a γβ fusion variant, Haemoglobin Kenya. *Nature* 246:184, 1973.

310. NUTE PE, WOOD WG, STAMATOYANNOPOULOS G, OLWENY C, FIALKOW PJ: The Kenya form of hereditary persistence of fetal haemoglobin; structural studies and evidence for homogeneous distribution of haemoglobin F using fluorescent anti-haemoglobin F antibodies. *Br J Haemat* 32:55, 1976.

311. HUISMAN THJ, MILLER A, SCHROEDER WA: A $^G\gamma$ type of the hereditary persistence of fetal hemoglobin with β chain production in cis. *Am J Hum Genet* 27:765, 1975.

312. FRIEDMAN S, SCHWARTZ E: Hereditary persistence of foetal haemoglobin with β-chain synthesis in cis position $(^G\gamma\text{-}\beta^+\text{-HPFH})$ in a negro family. *Nature* 259:138, 1976.

313. HIGGS DR, CLEGG JB, WOOD WG, WEATHERALL DJ: $^G\gamma\beta^+$ type of hereditary persistence of fetal haemoglobin in association with HbC. *J Med Genet* 16:288, 1979.

314. FESSAS P, STAMATOYANNOPOULOS G: Hereditary persistence of fetal hemoglobin in Greece. A study and a comparison. *Blood* 24:223, 1964.

315. SOFRONIADOU K, WOOD WG, NUTE PE, STAMATOYANNOPOULOS G: Globin chain synthesis in Greek type $(^A\gamma)$ of hereditary persistence of fetal haemoglobin. *Br J Haemat* 29:137, 1975.

316. CLEGG JB, METAXATOU-MAVROMATI A, KATTAMIS C, SOFRONIADOU K, WOOD WG, WEATHERALL DJ: Occurrence of $^G\gamma$ Hb F in Greek HPFH: Analysis of heterozygotes and compound heterozygotes with β thalassaemia. *Br J Haemat* 43:521, 1979.

317. FARQUHAR M, GELINAS R, TATSIS B, MURRAY J, YAGI M, MUELLER R, STAMATOYANNOPOULOS G: Restriction endonuclease mapping of γ-δ-β globin region in $^G\gamma(\beta)^+$ HPFH and a Chinese $^A\gamma$ HPFH variant. *Am J Hum Genet* 35:611, 1983.

318. WEATHERALL DJ, CARTNER R, CLEGG JB, WOOD WG, MACRAE I, MACKENZIE A: A form of hereditary persistence of fetal haemoglobin characterised by uneven cellular distribution of haemoglobin F and the production of haemoglobins A and A_2 in homozygotes. *Br J Haemat* 29:205, 1975.

319. WOOD WG, MACRAE IA, DARBRE PD, CLEGG JB, WEATHERALL DJ: The British type of non-deletion HPFH: Characterisation of developmental changes *in vivo* and erythroid growth *in vitro*. *Br J Haemat* 50:401, 1982.

320. MARTI HR: Normale und abnormale menschliche Haemoglobine. Berlin, Springer-Verlag, 1963.

321. ZAGO MA, WOOD WG, CLEGG JB, WEATHERALL DJ, O'SULLIVAN M, GUNSON HH: Genetic control of F-cells in human adults. *Blood* 53:977, 1979.

322. WOOD WG, WEATHERALL DJ, CLEGG JB: Interaction of heterocellular hereditary persistence of foetal haemoglobin with β thalassaemia and sickle cell anaemia. *Nature* 264:247, 1976.

323. CAPPELLINI MD, FIORELLI G, BERNINI LF: Interaction between homozygous β^0 thalassaemia and the Swiss type of hereditary persistence of fetal haemoglobin. *Br J Haemat* 48:561, 1981.

324. JEFFREYS AJ, WILSON V, THEIN SL, WEATHERALL DJ, PONDER BAJ: DNA "fingerprints" and segregation analysis of multiple markers in human pedigrees. *Am J Hum Genet* 39:11, 1986.

325. LABIE D, DUNDA-BELKHODJA O, ROUABHI F, PAGNIER J, RAGUSA A, NAGEL RL: The -158 site 5' to the $^G\gamma$ gene and $^G\gamma$ expression. *Blood* 66:1463, 1985.

326. THEIN SL, WAINSCOAT JS, SAMPIETRO M, OLD JM, CAPPELLINI D, FIORELLI G, MODELL B, WEATHERALL DJ: Association of thalassaemia intermedia with a beta-globin gene haplotype. *Br J Haemat* 65:367, 1987.

327. GILMAN JG, HUISMAN THJ: Two independent genetic factors in the β-globin gene cluster are associated with high $^G\gamma$-levels in the Hb F of SS patients. *Blood* 64:452, 1984.

328. NAGEL RL, FABRY ME, PAGNIER J, ZOHOUN I, WAJCMAN H, BAUDIN V, LABIE D: Hematologically and genetically distinct forms of sickle cell anemia in Africa. *N Engl J Med* 312:880, 1985.

329. KULOZIK AE, WAINSCOAT JS, SERJEANT GR, KAR BC, AL-AWAMY B, ESSAN GJF, FALUSI AG, HAQUE SK, HILALI AM, KARE S, RANASINGHE WAEP, WEATHERALL DJ: Geographical survey of β^S-globin gene haplotypes: Evidence for an independent Asian origin of the sickle-cell mutation. *Am J Hum Genet* 39:239, 1986.

330. KULOZIK AE, KAR BC, SATAPATHY RK, SERJEANT BE, SERJEANT GR, WEATHERALL DJ: Fetal hemoglobin levels and β^S globin haplotypes in an Indian population with sickle cell disease. *Blood* 69:1742, 1981.

331. GILMAN JG, HUISMAN THJ: DNA sequence variation associated with elevated fetal $^G\gamma$ globin production. *Blood* 66:783, 1985.

332. WAINSCOAT JS, KANAVAKIS E, WOOD WG, LETSKY EA, HUEHNS ER, MARSH GW, HIGGS DR, CLEGG JB, WEATHERALL DJ: Thalassaemia intermedia in Cyprus—The interaction of α- and β-thalassaemia. *Br J Haemat* 53:411, 1983.

333. WAINSCOAT JS, BELL JI, OLD JM, WEATHERALL DJ, FURBETTA M, GALANELLO R, CAO A: Globin gene mapping studies in Sardinian patients homozygous for β^0 thalassaemia. *Mol Biol Med* 1:1, 1983.

334. KANAVAKIS E, WAINSCOAT JS, WOOD WG, WEATHERALL DJ, CAO A, FURBETA M, GALANELLO R, GEORGIOU D, SOPHOCLEOUS T: The interaction of α thalassaemia with heterozygous β thalassaemia. *Br J Haemat* 52:465, 1982.

335. ROSATELLI C, FALCHI AM, SCALAS MT, TUVERI T, FURBETTA M, CAO A: Hematological phenotype of double heterozygous state for alpha and beta thalassemia. *Hemoglobin* 8:25, 1984.

336. KANAVAKIS E, METAXATOU-MAVROMATI A, KATTAMIS C, WAINSCOAT JS,

WOOD WG: The triplicated α gene locus and β thalassaemia. *Br J Haemat* 54:201, 1983.

337. SAMPIETRO M, CAZZOLA M, CAPPELLINI MD, FIORELLI G: The triplicated alpha-gene locus and heterozygous beta thalassemia: A case of thalassaemia intermedia. *Br J Haemat* 55:709, 1983.

338. KULOZIK AE, THEIN SL, WAINSCOAT JS, GALE R, KAY L, WOOD JK, WEATHERALL DJ, HUEHNS ER: Thalassaemia intermedia: Interaction of the triple α-globin gene arrangement and heterozygous β-thalassaemia. *Br J Haemot* 66:109, 1987.

339. CAMASCHELLA C, BERTERO MT, SERRA A, DALL'ACQUA M, GASPARINI P, TRENTO M, VETTOSE L, PERONA G, SAGLIO G, MAZZA U: A benign form of thalassemia intermedia may be determined by the interaction of triplicated α locus and heterozygous β thalassemia. *Br J Haemat* 66:103, 1987.

340. ACUTO S, BUTTICE G, SAITTA B, PIRRONE AM, GAMBINO R, COSTA C, GIAMBINA A, LO GIOCO P, DI MARZO R, MAGGIO A: αααα$^{anti\ 4.2}$ haplotype and heterozygous β^0 thalassemia in a Sicilian family. *Hum Genet* 70:31, 1985.

341. GALANELLO R, RUGGERI R, PAGLIETTI E, ADDIS M, MELIS A, CAO A: A family with segregating triplicated alpha globin loci and beta thalassemia. *Blood* 62:1035, 1983.

342. THEIN SL, AL-HAKIN I, HOFFBRAND AV: Thalassaemia intermedia—A new molecular basis. *Br J Haemat* 56:333, 1984.

343. LIVINGSTONE FB: *Frequencies of Hemoglobin Variants.* New York, Oxford University Press, 1985.

344. KAN YW, DOZY AM: Evolution of the hemoglobin S and C genes in world populations. *Science* 209:388, 1980.

345. MEARS JG, LACHMAN HM: Sickle gene: Its origin and diffusion from West Africa. *J Clin Invest* 68:606, 1981.

346. ANTONARAKIS SE, BOEHM CD, SERJEANT GR, THEISEN CE, DOVER GJ, KAZAZIAN HH: Origin of the β^S-globin gene in blacks; The contribution of recurrent mutation or gene conversion or both. *Proc Natl Acad Sci USA* 81:853, 1984.

347. WAINSCOAT JS, BELL JI, THEIN SL, HIGGS DR, SERJEANT GR, PETO TEA, WEATHERALL DJ: Multiple origins of the sickle mutation: Evidence from β^S globin gene cluster polymorphisms. *Mol Biol Med* 1:191, 1983.

348. KAZAZIAN HH, WABER PG, BOEHM CD, LEE JI, ANTONARAKIS SE, FAIRBANK VF: Hemoglobin E in Europeans—Further evidence for multiple origins of the beta-E-globin gene. *Am J Hum Genet* 36:212, 1984.

349. HALDANE JBS: The rate of mutation of human genes. *Proc VIII Int Cong Genet Hered, suppl.* 35, 1949.

350. ALLISON AC: Protection afforded by sickle cell trait against subtertian malarial infection. *Br Med J* i:290, 1954.

351. FLEMING AF, STOREY J, MOLINEAUX L, IROKO EA, ATTAI EDE: Abnormal haemoglobins in the Sudan savanna of Nigeria. I. Prevalence of haemoglobins and relationships between sickle cell trait, malaria and survival. *Ann Trop Med Parasitol* 73:161, 1979.

352. LUZZATTO L, NWACHUKU ES, REDDY S: Increased sickling of parasitized erythrocytes is mechanism of resistance against malaria in the sickle trait. *Lancet* i:319, 1970.

353. FRIEDMAN MJ: Erythrocytic mechanism of sickle cell resistance to malaria. *Proc Natl Acad Sci USA* 75:1994, 1978.

354. PASVOL G, WEATHERALL DJ: A mechanism for the protective effect of haemoglobin S against *P falciparum* malaria. *Nature* 274:701, 1978.

355. FRIEDMAN MJ, ROTH EF, NAGEL RL, TRAGER W: Plasmodium falciparum: Physiological interactions with the human sickle cell. *Exp Parasitol* 47:73, 1979.

356. ORKIN SH, ANTONARAKIS SE, KAZAZIAN HH: Polymorphism and molecular pathology of the human β-globin gene. *Prog Hematol* 13:49, 1983.

357. ORKIN SH, KAZAZIAN HH: The mutation and polymorphism of the human β-globin gene and its surrounding DNA. *Annu Rev Genet* 18:131, 1984.

358. PRESSLEY L, HIGGS DR, CLEGG JB, WEATHERALL DJ: Gene deletions in a α thalassaemia prove that the 5' ζ locus is functional. *Proc Natl Acad Sci USA* 77:3586, 1980.

359. SINISCALCO M, BERNINI L, FILIPPI G, LATTE B, KHAN M, PIOMELLI S, RATTAZZI M: Population genetics of haemoglobin variants, thalassemia and glucose-6-phosphate dehydrogenase deficiency, with particular reference to malaria hypothesis. *Bull WHO* 34:379, 1966.

360. PASVOL G, WEATHERALL DJ, WILSON RJM: Effects of foetal haemoglobin on susceptibility of red cells to *plasmodium falciparum. Nature* 270:171, 1977.

361. FRIEDMAN MJ, TRAEGER W: The biochemistry of resistance to malaria. *Sci Am* 244:154, 1981.

362. PASVOL G, CHASIS JA, MOHANDAS N, ANSTEE DJ, TANNER MJA, MAWBY WJ, MERRY AH: Monoclonal antibodies and Fab fragments to the external portion of glycophorin may inhibit the invasion of red cells by *Plasmodium falciparum* by decreasing membrane deformability. Submitted for publication.

363. WEATHERALL DJ (ed): *Methods in Hematology, The Thalassemias.* Edinburgh, Churchill Livingstone, 1983.

364. WEATHERALL DJ: Prenatal diagnosis of inherited blood diseases. *Clin Haemat* 14:747, 1985.

365. SCRIVER CR, BARDANIS M, CARTIER L, CLOW CL, LANCASTER GA, OSTROWSKY JT: β Thalassemia disease prevention: Genetic medicine applied. *Am J Hum Genet* 36:1024, 1984.

365a. STAMATOYANNOPOULOS G: Problems of screening and counselling in the hemoglobinopathies. *Proc IV Int Conf Birth Defects,* Vienna, 1973, p 268.

366. ALTER BP: Advances in the prenatal diagnosis of hematologic diseases. *Blood* 64:329, 1984.

367. ALTER BP: Antenatal diagnosis of thalassemia: A review. *Ann NY Acad Sci* 445:393, 1985.

368. OLD JM, FITCHES A, HEATH C, THEIN SL, WEATHERALL DJ, WARREN R, MCKENZIE C, RODECK CH, MODELL B, PETROU M, WARD RHT: First trimester fetal diagnosis for haemoglobinopathies: Report on 200 cases. *Lancet* ii:763, 1986.

369. OLD JM, WARD RHT, PETROU M, KARAGOZLU F, MODELL B, WEATHERALL DJ: First trimester diagnosis for haemoglobinopathies: A report of 3 cases. *Lancet* ii:1413, 1982.

370. GOOSSENS M, DUMEZ Y, KAPLAN L, LUPKER M, CHABRET C, HENRION R, ROSA J: Prenatal diagnosis of sickle-cell anemia in the first trimester of pregnancy. *N Engl J Med* 309:831, 1983.

371. WAINSCOAT JS, OLD JM, THEIN SL, WEATHERALL DJ: A new DNA polymorphism for prenatal diagnosis of β-thalassaemia in Mediterranean populations. *Lancet* ii:1299, 1985.

372. PROPPER RD: Transfusion management of thalassemia, in Weatherall DJ (ed): *Methods in Hematology, The Thalassemias.* Edinburgh, Churchill Livingstone, 1983, p 145.

373. PROPPER RD, COOPER B, RUFO RR, NIENHUIS AW, ANDERSON WF, BUNN HF, ROSENTHAL A, NATHAN DG: Continuous subcutaneous administration of desferoxamine in patients with iron overload. *N Engl J Med* 297:418, 1977.

374. PIPPARD MJ, CALLENDER ST, LETSKY EA, WEATHERALL DJ: Prevention of iron loading in transfusion-dependent thalassaemia. *Lancet* i:1178, 1978.

375. WOLFE L, OLIVIERA N, SALLAN D, COLAN S, ROSE V, PROPPER R, FREEDMAN MH, NATHAN DG: Prevention of cardiac disease by subcutaneous desferoxamine in patients with thalassemia major. *N Engl J Med* 311:600, 1985.

376. THOMAS ED, BUCKNER CD, SANDERS JE, PAPAYANNOPOULOU T, BORGNAPIGNATTI C, DESTEFANO P, SULLIVAN KM, CLIFT RA, STORB R: Marrow transplantation for thalassaemia. *Lancet* ii:227, 1982.

377. LEY TJ, DESIMONE J, ANAGNOU NP, KELLER GH, HUMPHRIES RK, TURNER PH, YOUNG NS, HELLER P, NIENHUIS AW: 5-Azacytidine selectively increases gamma-globin synthesis in a patient with beta-plus thalassemia. *N Engl J Med* 307:1469, 1982.

378. LEY TJ, DESIMONE J, NOGUCHI CT, TURNER PR, SCHECHTER AN, HELLER P, NIENHUIS AW: 5-Azacytidine increases γ-globin synthesis and reduces the proportion of dense cells in patients with sickle cell anemia. *Blood* 62:370, 1983.

379. CHARACHE S, DOVER GJ, SMITH KD, TALBOT CC: Treatment of sickle cell anemia with 5-azacytidine results in increased fetal hemoglobin production and is associated with non-random hypomethylation of DNA around the γ-δ-β globin gene complex. *Proc Natl Acad Sci USA* 80:4842, 1983.

380. PLATT OS, ORKIN SH, DOVER G, BEARDSLEY GP, MILLER B, NATHAN DG: Hydroxyurea enhances fetal hemoglobin production in sickle cell anemia. *J Clin Invest* 74:652, 1984.

381. VEITH R, GALANELLO R, PAPAYANNOPOULOU T, STAMATOYANNOPOULOS G: Stimulation of F-cell production in patients with sickle-cell anemia treated with cytarabine or hydroxyurea. *N Engl J Med* 313:1571, 1985.

CHAPTER 94

PYRUVATE KINASE AND OTHER ENZYME DEFICIENCY DISORDERS OF THE ERYTHROCYTE

WILLIAM N. VALENTINE
KOUICHI R. TANAKA
DONALD E. PAGLIA

1. *Pyruvate kinase (PK) deficiency hemolytic anemia is the first-described, best-studied, and clearly most common of the hemolytic anemias associated with an enzymopathy of the Embden-Meyerhof pathway. The disorder occurs worldwide and is characterized clinically by lifelong hemolytic anemia of variable, but often moderately severe degree. Splenectomy usually results in some improvement in severely affected patients but does not provide a clinical cure. Metabolically, the main abnormalities in the deficient red cells are decreased ATP and increased 2,3-DPG concentrations in comparison to normal erythrocytes of the same age. Diagnosis depends upon the results of assays of red cell PK.*

2. *PK deficiency is inherited as an autosomal recessive disorder. Heterozygotes most often demonstrate about half-normal red cell PK activity on assay but are clinically and hematologically normal. In the absence of consanguinity, the clinically affected patients are usually compound heterozygotes for two defective mutant genes. On a molecular basis, there is strong evidence that most, if not all, mutations involve the structural gene coding for L-type PK. Enormous polymorphism for the PK gene exists. Characterization of the abnormal products of the mutant genes is increasing our understanding of the relationship of the defective enzyme and clinical findings.*

3. *Severe deficiencies of hexokinase, glucosephosphate isomerase, phosphofructokinase (PFK), aldolase, triosephosphate isomerase (TPI), phosphoglycerate kinase (PGK), 2,3-diphosphoglyceromutase and phosphatase, and lactate dehydrogenase (LDH) have also been identified. All are recessively transmitted except that of phosphoglycerate kinase, which is X-linked. LDH deficiency is not associated with hemolysis, but in one form there is myopathy. Deficiencies of 2,3-DPG mutase and 2,3-DPG phosphatase are associated with mild erythrocytosis secondary to near absence of 2,3-DPG. Hemolysis is not present. The mutase and phosphatase activities reside on a single protein.*

4. *In human beings PFK is a tetrameric protein with three basic subunits which are under separate genetic control: types M, muscle; L, liver; P or F, platelet or fibroblast. Normal red cell PFK possesses five isozymes reflecting combinations of M and L subunits. The first-described deficient subjects exhibited severe myopathy, compensated hemolysis, diminished levels of 2,3-DPG, and severe deficiency in subunit M. Several other phenotypes are now recognized, including hemolytic anemia*

without overt myopathy, and these phenotypes reflect different genetic lesions and hence different subunit composition and stability of red cell and muscle PFK.

5. *TPI deficiency, when severe, is a multisystem disorder characterized by hemolytic anemia, devastating neurologic deficits, and usually death in childhood, sometimes associated with cardiac dysfunction. All body tissues investigated are deficient in TPI. PGK deficiency in hemizygous males most frequently is accompanied by hemolytic anemia and a variety of neurologic and behavioral abnormalities. However, the phenotypic picture is variable. Heterozygous females may exhibit hemolytic anemia alone. The latter is variable depending on random X-inactivation. Aldolase deficiency is very rare, but is associated with hemolytic anemia and possibly other manifestations in some subjects.*

6. *Enzyme deficiencies involving the pentose phosphate shunt and associated glutathione metabolism are documented. Severe deficiency of 6-phosphogluconate dehydrogenase appears unassociated with clinical manifestations. Partial deficiency of glutathione peroxidase has been reported in association with hemolytic syndromes, but requires additional evaluation since half-normal activity is observed in entirely healthy subjects in certain ethnic groups. Most reported instances of glutathione reductase deficiency have proved to be secondary to inadequate flavin cofactor. A single kindred with documented apoenzyme deficiency lacked clinical manifestations other than an episode of hemolysis associated with fava bean ingestion in one affected member.*

7. *A kindred with near absence of red cell gluthathione secondary to deficiency of γ-glutamylcysteine synthetase had two members with hemolytic anemia and spinocerebellar degeneration. Deficiency of the second enzyme of glutathione synthesis, glutathione synthetase, presents as two phenotypes. The first exhibits hemolytic anemia alone; the second, presumably due to a generalized deficiency of the enzyme, is characterized by variable hemolysis, metabolic acidosis, variable neurologic manifestations, and the excretion of large amounts of pyroglutamate in urine.*

8. *Disturbances in erythrocyte nucleotide metabolism that are clearly associated with shortened red cell life span and hemolytic anemia of variable severity include (1) overproduction of biochemically normal adenosine deaminase and (2) severe de-*

Nonstandard abbreviations used in this chapter are: 2,3-DPG = 2,3-diphosphoglycerate; F-6-P = fructose-6-phosphate; F-1,6-P$_2$ = fructose-1,6-diphosphate; G-6-P = glucose-6-phosphate; G-6-PD = glucose-6-phosphate dehydrogenase; GPI = glucosephosphate isomerase; GSH = reduced glutathione; GSSG = oxidized glutathione; LDH = lactate dehydrogenase; PEP = phosphoenolpyruvate: PFK = phosphofructokinase; PGK = phosphoglycerate kinase; PK = pyruvate kinase; PP-ribose-P = 5-phosphoribosyl-1-pyrophosphate; and TPI = triosephosphate isomerase.

ficiency of pyrimidine nucleotidase. Overproduction of adenosine deaminase is a dominantly inherited disorder characterized by decreases in total erythrocyte adenine nucleotides (less than half-normal values), elevations in pyrimidine nucleotidase activity (three- to fourfold), and approximately a hundredfold elevations in adenosine deaminase activity. Severe deficiency of pyrimidine nucleotidase is inherited as an autosomal recessive disorder or is acquired secondary to lead toxicity. It is characterized by ineffective clearance of RNA degradation products from maturing reticulocytes with consequent accumulation of diverse pyrimidine conjugates and ribonucleotides, prominent basophilic stippling, twofold increased concentrations of erythrocyte glutathione, and intermediate (25 percent) reductions in ribosephosphate pyrophosphokinase activity.

9. *Adenylate kinase deficiency, previously thought to induce hemolytic anemia, may not do so without certain coexistent abnormalities, since a severe deficiency state (< 0.1 percent of normal mean) has been observed with no adverse hematologic effects.*

10. *The pathogenesis of hemolysis in enzymopathies of the pentose phosphate shunt is associated with increased susceptibility of hemoglobin to oxidant damage, denatured hemoglobin in the form of Heinz bodies, reduced glutathione stability, and damage to the plasma membrane of the red cell. There is no consensus as to the primary pathogenic event in enzymopathies of anaerobic glycolysis. We favor metabolic depletion secondary to block of glycolysis as a result of a wide variety of structural gene mutations and gene products as the dominant factor in pathogenesis. Secondary, but important, phenomena would then be accumulation of glycolytic intermediates, diminished ATP, translocation of Ca^{2+}, loss of membrane deformability, shape alterations and loss of membrane by budding, and increased susceptibility to phagocytosis by macrophages.*

11. *The pathogenesis of hemolysis in pyrimidine nucleotidase deficiency is speculative, but the accumulated pyrimidine ribonucleotides may interfere with normal glycolysis by virtue of their demonstrated ability to bind to sites on crucial enzymes where adenosine phosphates are preferred and far more efficient. The hemolytic syndrome, associated with great increases in the activity of red cell adenosine deaminase and greatly diminished ATP, presumably results from removal of an important substrate, adenosine, from a salvage pathway for renewal of the adenine nucleotide pool of the red cell. ATP depletion results.*

12. *Erythrocyte enzymopathies may also have hematologic expression other than hemolysis, may have no obvious deleterious consequences, or may be associated with clinical disorders affecting other than hematopoietic tissue.*

The nonnucleated human erythrocyte beyond the reticulocyte stage lacks organelles, lacks the capacity to synthesize proteins or lipids, and possesses only ineffectual vestiges of the enzymatic machinery essential for oxidative phosphorylation. It is unable to synthesize ATP *de novo* from small molecules or to salvage hypoxanthine, inosine, or IMP to replenish losses from the adenine nucleotide pool. Ninety-five percent of its protein is hemoglobin, devoted exclusively to the transport of oxygen and carbon dioxide, a role requiring neither expenditure nor gain of energy. Its energy requirements are met by generation of ATP via glycolysis, the catabolism of 1 mol glucose to 2 mol lactate in the simplest situation, requiring expenditure of 2 mol ATP and generation of 4. This theoretical net gain of two ATP for each cycle of anaerobic glycolysis is modified by the Rapoport-Luebering shunt.[1] About the middle of the anaerobic glycolytic pathway, triose may bypass the ATP-generating step mediated by phosphoglyceratekinase and be mutated to 2,3-diphosphoglycerate (2,3-DPG). The latter has

regulatory effects on the oxygen dissociation curve of hemoglobin,[2] and may constitute up to 50 percent or more of red cell organic phosphate. It is returned to the mainstream of glycolysis by 2,3-DPG phosphatase, an activity residing in the same protein as the mutase responsible for 2,3-DPG formation.[3,4] Depending on variations in the proportion of glucose traversing the shunt, the net gain in ATP varies from 1 to 2 mol per mole of glucose glycolysed. Figure 94-1 depicts certain important metabolic pathways available to the human erythrocyte.

The red cell also possesses an aerobic glycolytic pathway, the pentose phosphate shunt.[5] This includes the two dehydrogenases converting hexose to pentose and the enzymatic capacity to synthesize, oxidize, and reduce glutathione. For the shunt to function, the pyridine cofactor NADP must be cycled, being reduced at each dehydrogenase step and reoxidized at the step catalyzed by glutathione reductase. Pentose generated aerobically reenters the glycolytic mainstream via the action of transketolase and transaldolase. The proportion of glucose metabolized via the shunt varies widely with environmental oxidative stress and is dependent upon the rate at which reduced glutathione (GSH) is oxidized.

The pyridine cofactor of anaerobic glycolysis is nicotinamide dinucleotide (NAD), and this is reduced midway in glycolysis and reoxidized at the terminal lactate dehydrogenase step. NADH is a necessary cofactor for enzymatic reduction of cytochrome B_5, which in turn nonenzymatically reduces the nonfunctional methemoglobin continuously being formed in small amounts in the red cell.[6]

Despite being metabolically underprivileged, the normal red cell circulates about 120 days before senescence results in its ultimate demise. Far from being an inert bag of hemoglobin, it also possesses the machinery to rid itself of unwanted pyrimidine nucleotides, to salvage adenosine for its adenine nucleotide pool, to pump cations against electrochemical gradients, and to carry out other functions essential to the maintenance of its structure and shape. Given its limited metabolic options, it is not surprising that inborn or acquired molecular lesions should result in greatly shortened life span and overt hemolytic anemia. With some such lesions, hemolysis is but one component of multisystem disease.[7]

The definition of hemolytic syndromes secondary to red cell enzymopathies had roots in studies culminating in the recognition of glucose-6-phosphate dehydrogenase (G-6-PD) deficiency[8] as well as in the investigations, initiated by Dacie and his colleagues[9,10] and extended by others,[11-13] of certain hereditary anemias termed *nonspherocytic* to distinguish them from the better-defined disorder of hereditary spherocytosis. The first enzyme deficiency of anaerobic glycolysis incriminated in the pathogenesis of hereditary hemolytic anemia was pyruvate kinase (PK).[14,15] Since then, deficiencies of other glycolytic enzymes; of enzymes of the pentose phosphate shunt and closely related glutathione metabolism; and of enzymes of nucleotide metabolism have emerged as causes of hemolytic anemia (see reviews since 1976).[16-25]

PYRUVATE KINASE DEFICIENCY

Clinical Aspects

Prevalence. Pyruvate kinase (PK) deficiency is clearly the most common glycolytic enzyme defect associated with

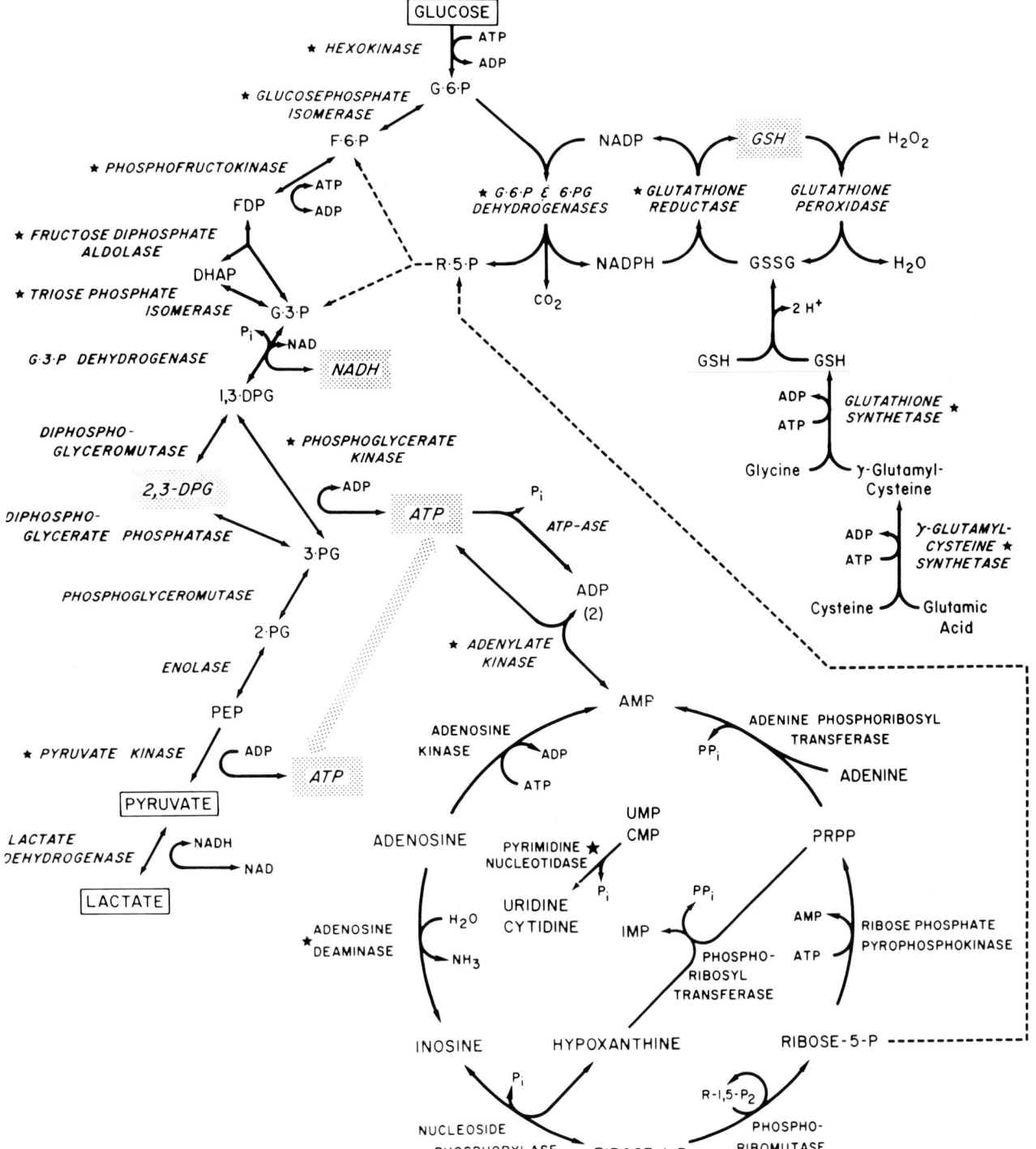

Fig. 94-1 Pathways of energy metabolism in human erythrocytes. Glucose-6-phosphate (G-6-P) may be degraded anaerobically to 2 mol lactate via the Embden-Meyerhof pathway on the left, or oxidatively via the dehydrogenases of the pentose phosphate pathway. Ribose-5-phosphate (R-5-P) can reenter anaerobic glycolysis as fructose-6-phosphate (F-6-P) and glyceraldehyde-3-phosphate (G-3-P) after conversion by enzymes of the terminal pentose phosphate pathway and is also a product of adenosine or inosine degradation. 2,3-Diphosphoglycerate (2,3-DPG) may be generated instead of ATP by diversion of triose through the Rapoport-Luebering shunt. Glutathione may be directly synthesized from constituent amino acids, and its cycling from oxidized (GSSG) to reduced form (GSH) is dependent upon reduced pyridine cofactor (NADPH) generation. Stars indicate those enzymes found defective in association with hereditary hemolytic anemia.

chronic hemolytic anemia and accounts for more than 80 percent of the cases involving the Embden-Meyerhof pathway.[16,22,24,26–30] Well over 300 patients with hemolytic anemia due to PK deficiency have been reported[17,24,30–32] since its initial description in 1961.[14,15] PK deficiency and G-6-PD deficiency (class I type) are about equally common and together constitute most of the cases of chronic hemolytic anemia due

to erythrocyte enzymopathies. Other inborn errors of the Embden-Meyerhof pathway as well as those involving glutathione and pyrimidine metabolism, which have been noted subsequently and are discussed later in this chapter, are comparatively uncommon or rare.

Patients with this disorder have been found primarily in the United States, Western Europe, and Japan but also in Canada,

Australia, New Zealand, Hong Kong, Spain, and Venezuela.[30,33] The disease is most common in people of Northern European ancestry but has also been reported from countries in the Mediterranean area such as Italy and Syria.[30] PK deficiency has also been noted in an Arabic woman,[34] a Senegalese,[31] Filipinos, Mexicans, American blacks, and in patients with part American Indian ancestry.[26,30,35] Distribution appears to be worldwide, but its prevalence in many parts of the world is still unknown. An especially high prevalence of this disorder has been identified in the Mifflin County (Pennsylvania) Amish deme.[36] Both sexes are affected equally.[15,26]

Clinical Features. Patients with PK deficiency hemolytic anemia have no distinguishing or pathognomonic clinical features. They have the usual hallmarks of chronic hemolytic processes, such as variable degrees of jaundice, slight to moderate splenomegaly, and an increased incidence of gallstones. The spectrum of clinical disease varies considerably, ranging from severe neonatal anemia requiring exchange or multiple transfusions to sustain life to a fully compensated hemolytic process in apparently healthy adults.[22,24,26,30,37] On the whole, PK deficiency is a more severe disease than hereditary spherocytosis.[38]

In most cases, anemia or jaundice or both are noted in infancy or early childhood, but some patients apparently escape detection until adulthood, even to age 72.[39] Typically, the early onset form of the disease is severe or moderate in nature, requiring many transfusions or often culminating in splenectomy during the first years of life. Thereafter, most of these patients maintain, usually without transfusions, a stable but moderately low hemoglobin level which they tolerate rather well, perhaps due to the right shift in the oxygen dissociation curve as a result of the characteristic elevation of red cell 2,3-DPG levels.[40-42] Patients having a later onset of symptoms generally have a milder form of the disease. They are often asymptomatic and may be diagnosed during investigations of an intercurrent acute illness[24,30] or during pregnancy.[34]

General development is usually normal, but growth retardation and frontal bossing have been observed in some of the severely affected children.[26,30] Kernicterus,[36] chronic leg ulcers,[43,46] acute pancreatitis secondary to biliary tract disease,[47] development of iron overload,[43,48-50] splenic abscess,[51] spinal cord compression by extramedullary hematopoietic tissue,[52] and migratory phlebitis with arterial thrombosis[53] are rare complications.

The chronic hemolytic process may be exacerbated by various acute illnesses, particularly viral infections and pregnancy.[30,54] Women with PK deficiency have tolerated pregnancy rather well, although blood transfusions were required in almost all of these patients who otherwise had not previously been transfused or who rarely needed transfusions.[26,30,50,55] Aplastic crises may result from infections with parvovirus-like virus.[56] Impairment of pentose phosphate shunt activity may decrease the ability of the erythrocyte to handle oxidant stress and may explain the acute exacerbations of hemolytic anemia observed in patients with PK deficiency.[57]

Most patients survive to adulthood, but a particularly severe form found in the Amish kindreds is often fatal in early childhood unless splenectomy is performed.[58] Only individuals homozygous or compound heterozygous for the red cell PK defect manifest clinical disease,[24,30,59] except in rare instances,[60] although certain erythrocyte biochemical abnormalities may be demonstrable in heterozygotes.[26]

Hematologic Findings. Red cell morphologic abnormalities are not a prominent feature of PK deficiency anemia. The erythrocytes are normochromic with only an occasional spiculated or irregularly contracted cell, except in some infants or young children with severe anemia. Slight to marked macrocytosis is related to the degree of reticulocytosis and not due to folic acid or vitamin B_{12} deficiency.[26,30] Certain features such as Pappenheimer bodies, siderocytes, Howell-Jolly bodies, and target cells may appear following splenectomy but are not specific for this disorder. The presence of many crenated red cells of unusual form (shrunken echinocytes) on a postsplenectomy blood smear is suggestive of PK deficiency.[61] The levels of hemoglobin and packed red cell volumes vary widely among patients but generally fall in the range of 6 to 12 g/dl and 0.17 to 0.37 liter/liter, respectively.[26,30] The frequent paradoxical rise in the percentage of circulating reticulocytes after splenectomy is characteristic but not pathognomonic of PK deficiency; very high values (40 to 70 percent range) are observed only after splenectomy.[26,29,55,61-63] The white blood count and platelet count are normal or slightly increased.

As expected, the serum indirect bilirubin level is elevated, serum haptoglobin may be decreased, and fecal urobilinogen excretion is increased.[26,30] The osmotic fragility of fresh red cells is usually normal, but the incubated osmotic fragility test may show varying degrees of abnormality.[30]

The Coombs' test and acid serum (Ham's) test results are negative. Donath-Landsteiner antibody and cold agglutinins are also absent. Hemoglobin is of the normal adult type (AA); fetal hemoglobin and hemoglobin A_2 are within normal limits. Incubated Heinz body formation is increased.[57]

Other Laboratory Findings. PK deficiency is not associated with specific organ dysfunction other than hemolytic anemia with its manifestations and complications. In particular, liver function test results are normal (except for the bilirubinemia already mentioned), even though the liver L-type PK has been shown to exhibit some of the molecular anomalies characterizing the deficient red cell PK variant.[17] Bone changes consistent with a hyperplastic marrow as seen in other chronic hemolytic anemias may be demonstrated roentgenologically in some of the severe cases.[30,64]

Erythrokinetics. Ferrokinetic studies utilizing ^{59}Fe demonstrate a short plasma clearance time and usually rapid maximal appearance of radioiron in circulating erythrocytes.[26] ^{59}Fe organ scans indicate that the spleen and liver are major sites of destruction of the newly formed PK-deficient red cells.[65]

Red cell life span as determined with the ^{51}Cr procedure for erythrocyte labeling is moderately to severely shortened in most instances. Biphasic ^{51}Cr survival curves obtained in some studies suggest that two populations of cells are present, one doomed to almost immediate destruction and the other with a more favorable outlook for survival.[30,66,67]

Although the ^{51}Cr data in regard to splenic sequestration are conflicting, PK-deficient poorly deformable reticulocytes may be selectively sequestered in the spleen, where they undergo irreversible damage and ultimately premature destruction.[68] Splenectomy permits longer survival of newly formed cells; thus, the reticulocyte count usually rises after removal of the spleen in this disorder.

Pathology. The bone marrow, as expected, reveals normoblastic hyperplasia. Chromosome aberrations have been observed in bone marrow cells but not in cultured lymphocytes.[69] There are no specific histologic findings in the spleen by light microscopy; reticuloendothelial hyperplasia, variable degrees of congestion, deposits of hemosiderin, erythrophagocytosis, and foci of extramedullary hematopoiesis have been noted.[26] The frequent presence of reticulocytes in the sinuses and their phagocytosis by cordal macrophages as demonstrated by electron microscopy are characteristic of PK deficiency.[66,70,71] Histologic examination of the liver is usually normal; rarely, iron overload has been noted.[30,48–50] As in any chronic hemolytic disease, cholelithiasis is common and may occur at an early age. To date, there is a paucity of autopsy information.[26,36,50]

Diagnosis

The diagnosis of PK deficiency hemolytic disease depends on the specific demonstration of quantitatively reduced activity or qualitative abnormalities of the erythrocyte enzyme. This is readily achieved by spectrophotometric assay of a hemolysate prepared from red cells carefully freed of white cells.[72,73] Contaminating leukocytes may obscure correct results, since the white cell/red cell PK activity is about 300:1 on a per cell basis, and leukocytes are not affected in PK deficiency.[15] The assay procedure uses phosphoenolpyruvate (PEP) as substrate for PK, crystalline lactate dehydrogenase, and NADH. The product is quantitated in terms of the linked reaction by which pyruvate formed is transformed to lactate with the conversion of NADH to NAD.

The quantitative procedure has proved a fairly reliable index for separating homozygous, heterozygous, and normal subjects.[26] More sophisticated examination of the enzyme at low concentrations of PEP with and without the allosteric effector fructose-1,6-diphosphate (F-1,6-P_2) may be necessary whenever a variant form of PK is suspected. Recommended methods for the characterization of PK variants have been published.[74] Two screening methods[75,76] have been described but have not been used extensively.

Most PK-deficient patients have about 5 to 25 percent of the normal (mean) red cell enzyme level, and heterozygotes have about half of the normal activity. Although assayed activity varies considerably within the homozygous and heterozygous ranges, the values usually do not overlap. Family studies may be helpful in difficult cases. The possibility of a kinetically aberrant mutant PK should be considered whenever clinically affected patients have PK values in the heterozygous, normal, or even increased activity range.[30] The poor correlation between PK activity and clinical severity and the fact that some asymptomatic heterozygotes have PK values within the homozygous range indicate that the assay, although useful, does not provide a precise quantitative measure of the metabolic derangement in the intact cell.

Red cell PK activity is elevated in reticulocytes. Thus, hemolytic anemias other than PK deficiency or conditions characterized by young red cell populations have slight to marked increases of PK activity. Acquired PK deficiency is discussed later.

The autohemolysis test demonstrates that erythrocytes of many patients with PK deficiency have increased hemolysis after 48 h of sterile incubation, which is not corrected by glucose (type II), as originally defined by Selwyn and Dacie.[10] However, the autohemolysis pattern is variable,[26] and the test is no longer useful in the diagnosis of this disorder.

Genetics

Erythrocyte PK deficiency is transmitted as an autosomal recessive trait.[14,15,22,26] With rare exceptions, only homozygous or compound heterozygous subjects develop clinically overt hemolytic disease. Since parents are usually not consanguineous, most patients with PK deficiency are compound heterozygotes for two PK variants rather than being homozygous for a single mutant gene. There is now ample evidence that PK deficiency is a heterogenous disorder, even more so than G-6-PD deficiency. This is to be expected because there is no evidence of heterozygote advantage in PK deficiency, and two genes for PK which are likely to be different in the absence of consanguinity are expressed in each red cell precursor.[22]

The increased incidence of consanguinity in PK deficiency[22,36,45] has permitted study of true homozygotes for the characterization of PK variants.[63,77] A recent report indicates that all cases of PK deficiency in the Amish arose from a common ancestral pair.[77]

Heterozygotes most commonly demonstrate about half the normal PK activity on assay and are not anemic. Their erythrocytes contain a mixture of normal (wild) PK isozyme and defective isozyme. The rare instance of a dominant transmission of the hemolytic symptom has been reported.[78]

To date no linkage of PK deficiency with serum or blood group antigens has been observed.[26] Geographic distribution of the mutant gene is worldwide; however, patients to date have been recognized most often among peoples of Northern European descent. The prevalence of heterozygosity for PK deficiency has been noted to be 1.2 percent in Boston,[79] 1.4 percent in Los Angeles,[26] 1.4 percent in Germany,[80] 0.24 percent in Spain,[81] 1.38 percent in Japan,[82] and 2.2 percent in China.[83]

The yeast PK gene has been sequenced and contains no introns,[84] but the chicken PK gene is interrupted by at least 10 introns.[85] The structural gene for PK of human white blood cells has been assigned to chromosome 15q22-qter.[86] The chromosomal location of the red cell PK gene remains to be defined. Preliminary examination of the organization of the PK gene in both normal DNA and DNA derived from leukocytes of several PK-deficient patients using rat L-type PK cDNA as a probe revealed no deletions or rearrangements.[23]

An animal model for PK deficiency exists in basenji dogs, in which this disorder is common.[87] PK deficiency also occurs in beagles.[88]

Biochemistry and Metabolism

Normal and Mutant Pyruvate Kinase. Pyruvate kinase (ATP:pyruvate 2-0-phosphotransferase, EC 2.7.1.40) is one of the rate-limiting key enzymes of the glycolytic pathway.[89] PK catalyzes the conversion of phosphoenolpyruvate to pyruvate with regeneration of ATP (Fig. 94-1). Pyruvate kinase is an ancient protein that has been found to have an overall structure that is similar in bacteria, fungi, and animals—a tetramer composed of identical 50- to 60-kDa subunits.[90] Initial observations that hereditary deficiency of pyruvate kinase was restricted to erythrocytes suggested that this enzyme might exist in more than one molecular form. In mammals, four isozymes of PK have been recognized, which are named types L, R, M_1, and M_2.[91–93] These forms all consist of four identical subunits of about 60 kDa, but differ in enzymatic properties.[94] All are allosterically regulated except for the M_1 type.

Expression of PK isozymes in mammals is regulated developmentally and is tissue-specific in adults.[94] The M_2 type is the only form detected in early fetal tissues[92]; transition occurs from the fetal to adult type in the late fetal to early postnatal period. In adult human tissues, the L type is the major isozyme in liver, the M_1 type is the main form in muscle, the R type is detected only in red cells, and leukocytes and platelets contain M_2-type PK.

A relationship between L and R was suggested in 1968 when Bigley and Koler[95] found that there was decreased PK activity in the erythrocytes and liver of a patient with hereditary hemolytic anemia. In 1973, Imamura et al.[96] noted qualitative abnormalities of erythrocyte PK and liver L-PK in two patients with PK Tokyo. Impairment of liver function has not been demonstrated, probably because the nucleated liver parenchymal cells are capable of continuing the synthesis of enzyme molecules. These initial reports of defective L-type PK in the liver of PK deficiency patients have been confirmed.[60,93,97,98] Investigations on the L-R subunit relationship were developed by Nakashima[99] and extended by Kahn's group,[100,101] who reported that proteolytic processing of a precursor subunit might be involved. More recently, however, they have demonstrated that the difference in L- and R-type isozymes is reflected in tissue-specific mRNAs.[102] On the other hand, on the basis of a patient with a red cell PK mutant with normal L-type PK in the liver, Etiemble and colleagues[103] have suggested that the mechanism that governs liver PK expression may be due to a modification of gene arrangement rather than to differences in RNA processing.

The L type is very similar but not identical to the R type in amino acid composition, peptide fingerprint patterns, and immunologic properties.[91,101,104] An important difference between these two enzymes is that the L-type enzyme is under hormonal and dietary control, whereas the erythrocyte enzyme is not.[91,105] The complete amino acid sequence of a rat L-type isozyme of PK deduced from the cDNA sequence has been reported recently.[106] A close relationship also exists between the M_1 and M_2 types.[104,107–111] Recent evidence suggests that M_1 and M_2 isozymes are produced from the same gene,[108,110] probably by alternative RNA splicing.[111]

Human red cell PK has been purified 40,000 times and shown to be antigenically identical to liver L-type enzyme.[112] Electrophoretically, erythrocytes show two interconvertible bands, designated R_1 and R_2, with different migration from L-type PK.[96,99] PK-R_1 predominates in young red cells, but the major form of erythrocyte enzyme is PK-R_2.[17,99,113] The predominance of R_2 in mature red cells favorably influences the molecular behavior and improves the regulatory properties of the PK enzyme.[101,114] For instance, R_1 is less stable and has a lower affinity for PEP than R_2. In the reticulocytes of hereditary deficiency of PK activity, the mutated R_1 form is predominant and may contribute to the marked sensitivity to hemolysis of the PK-deficient reticulocyte.[65] During erythroid maturation there is a progressive change from the predominant M_2 type PK in proerythroblasts to R type PK in basophilic or polychromatophilic erythroblasts.[115] Cases of PK deficiency with M_2-type and other "immature" bands in their mature red cells have been observed.[93,96,116–119] A similar persistence of M_2-type PK occurs in the PK-deficient basenji dog.[120]

Extensive studies of the kinetics of erythrocyte PK have been performed. The activity of erythrocyte PK is regulated by allosteric effectors, such as fructose-1,6-diphosphate and ATP.[121,122] The data for PK[121–124] are consistent in general with the two-state (R⇌T) conformational model for allosteric enzymes of Monod, Wyman, and Changeux,[125] but this model does not explain adequately the properties of some variants.[35,126] In vitro studies of activation and inhibition of human erythrocyte PK suggest that the in vivo regulation of the enzyme is likely to be complex and will depend on the cellular environment. The regulatory role in vivo of phosphorylation-dephosphorylation of PK still remains to be delineated[127–129]; decreased phosphorylation of variant erythrocyte PK possibly secondary to increased 2,3-DPG has been reported.[130]

Historically, PK deficiency was first detected by marked decrements in measurable in vitro activity even though a wide range of clinical severity was recognized.[14,15] It soon became evident that the severity of hemolysis did not always correlate with residual PK activity as assayed conventionally.[22,26,30] These observations are now explained in large part by the realization that phenotypically normal heterozygotes harbor many different mutant genes which code for mutant PK enzyme proteins differing in catalytic capacity, thermostability, kinetics, electrophoretic mobility, pH optima, and behavior toward allosteric modifiers and nucleotide cofactors, as well as in other ways.[26,30–32,35,43,63,93,116,117,119,124,126,131–142] Recently the complete amino acid sequence of human L-type pyruvate kinase, the isozyme associated with hemolytic anemia in humans, has been determined.[142a] L-type PK cDNA contains 1629 base pairs encoding 543 amino acids, 68 base pairs of 5'-noncoding sequence, and 734 base pairs of 3'-noncoding sequence. Rat L-type PK was 86.9 percent similar at the nucleotide sequence level and 92.4 percent at the amino acid sequence level. While amino acid sequencing data are still lacking for mutant human erythrocyte PK, it appears that in most instances a structural gene mutation is involved. Thus, in the absence of consanguinity, most patients are genetic compounds with two different mutant structural genes, and hence their erythrocytes contain two separate mutant proteins within each cell. Therefore, the enzyme in each cell may represent an assortment of tetramers containing different kinds of subunits; there is some recent evidence for this possibility in human erythrocyte PK variants.[143]

In addition to the problem of dealing with two mutant proteins mentioned above, most variants were identified initially by using crude hemolysates, a variety of techniques, and inadequate parameters. Thus, interpretation of data is difficult.[16,22,30] Recommended methods for the characterization of PK variants have now been developed by the International Committee for Standardization in Haematology.[74] By utilization of these methods, seven true homozygotes from consanguineous marriages were characterized in Japan and designated PK Tokyo, PK Nagasaki, PK Sapporo, PK Maebashi, PK Itabashi, PK Fukushima, and PK Aizu.[63] In these variants, low substrate (PEP) affinity and thermal instability appeared to play major roles in causing defective enzyme function resulting in chronic hemolysis, while product inhibition of PK by ATP often had an additional role. Other examples of homozygosity for the mutant gene, such as PK Wouw[144] and PK Fukien,[140] are rare. In addition, the expression of a single mutant PK isozyme can occur, despite inheritance of two separate abnormal genes, when the catalytic activity of one of the two gene products is absent or negligible,[136] as in PK Greenville.[35]

From our laboratories 12 presumed genetic compounds[119] and an additional 13 from Japan[32] have been characterized using the International Committee recommended methods. These reports, as well as others utilizing partially purified enzymes,[17,31,35,117,136,139,142] indicate that there is a definite relationship between properties of the defective PK enzymes and the severity of hemolysis. The most important characteristics of mutant PK enzymes involved in clinical expression of red cell PK deficiency appear to be very low residual activity, decreased affinity for PEP, thermal instability, increased inhibition by ATP, and decreased activation by F-1,6-P_2. However, decreased enzyme protein,[126] impaired kinetics affecting the ADP-combining site,[137] and increased affinity for PEP[124] have also been reported. These factors modulating the PK enzyme are schematically summarized in Fig. 94-2.

Red Cell Metabolism in Pyruvate Kinase Deficiency. The specific deficiency of red cell PK occurs near the final step of glycolysis (Fig. 94-1). All other reactions of the Embden-Meyerhof pathway, as well as a number of nonglycolytic reactions, are normally active. In fact, as expected in erythrocyte populations of young mean cell age, the activities of other age-related enzymatic activities are increased.

Pyruvate kinase deficiency results in impaired glycolysis and diminished capacity to generate ATP and to cycle NAD. Red cell ATP is usually low in PK deficiency, but patients with very high reticulocyte counts often have normal or even elevated ATP levels.[26,30,55,62] The latter finding is explained by the observation that PK-deficient reticulocytes depend almost entirely on mitochondrial oxidative phosphorylation rather than on glycolysis to maintain ATP levels.[62] The reliance of such cells on oxidative phosphorylation is supported further by the increased oxygen consumption of PK-deficient reticulocytes compared with normal reticulocytes.[65] Upon loss of oxidative phosphorylation during maturation, the subsequent obligatory dependence on glycolytic ATP synthesis dooms the PK-deficient erythrocytes. Less severely affected red cells are able to survive maturation long enough to demonstrate their impaired glycolytic energy production. As a consequence, ATP levels in mild cases may be anomalously lower than in severe cases.[62]

If oxidative phosphorylation in PK-deficient reticulocytes is inhibited in vitro or possibly compromised in the splenic environment, ATP levels decline rapidly, producing alterations in the red cell membrane which result in marked loss of potassium and water. The result is a shrunken, spiculated, viscous cell whose rheologic properties would favor its sequestration by the reticuloendothelial system.[65]

Glycolytic intermediates proximal to the PK enzyme defect are usually increased substantially, whereas pyruvate and lactate levels are generally normal or occasionally decreased.[26,30] The hallmark of PK deficiency is the markedly elevated concentration of 2,3-DPG, which may reach two or three times the normal range. The content of NAD and NADH is reduced to approximately half of normal, impairing the rate of the glyceraldehyde-3-dehydrogenase reaction in vivo.[145,146] This decrease in total NAD is due in part to impaired NAD synthesis in PK-deficient erythrocytes secondary to decreased ATP formation as a result of the PK deficiency.[147] The concentration of total adenine nucleotides (AMP, ADP, and ATP) is also decreased.[145] 5-Phosphoribosyl-1-pyrophosphate (PP-ribose-P) is an intermediate in the synthesis of adenine nucleotides and NAD. The enzyme responsible for its synthesis, PP-ribose-P synthetase, may be less active in vivo in PK-deficient red cells due to decreased ATP and increased 2,3-DPG concentrations.[148] Impaired PP-ribose-P formation has recently been observed in intact PK-deficient red cells.[149]

Glucose utilization is defective in PK deficiency in spite of the increased percentage of reticulocytes with their extremely high capacity for glucose comsumption.[15,26,62] Pyruvate kinase is normally operating far below saturation with respect to phosphoenolpyruvate. PK-deficient cells reach much higher and even saturating levels of PEP in order to utilize a larger proportion of their enzyme. Complex regulatory mechanisms control glycolysis in the PK-deficient and normal red cell in vivo.[150]

Recent studies suggest that increased concentrations of 2,3-DPG in PK-deficient red cells are sufficiently high to suppress stimulated pentose phosphate shunt activity.[57] Incubated Heinz body formation is increased[57] and the ascorbate cyanide test is positive,[57,151] but the content of reduced glutathione is normal.[15,26] This suppression may be an additional factor contributing to hemolytic anemia of PK deficiency, particularly during periods of infection or metabolic stress.

Although the PK heterozygote has a normal hemogram, some metabolic impairment of the red cells may result from the partial reduction in PK activity. ATP content may be low or unstable on incubation.[26] Occasionally, the content of 2,3-DPG may be slightly increased or the level of PEP may be elevated.[152] Red cell life span is usually normal, but may be

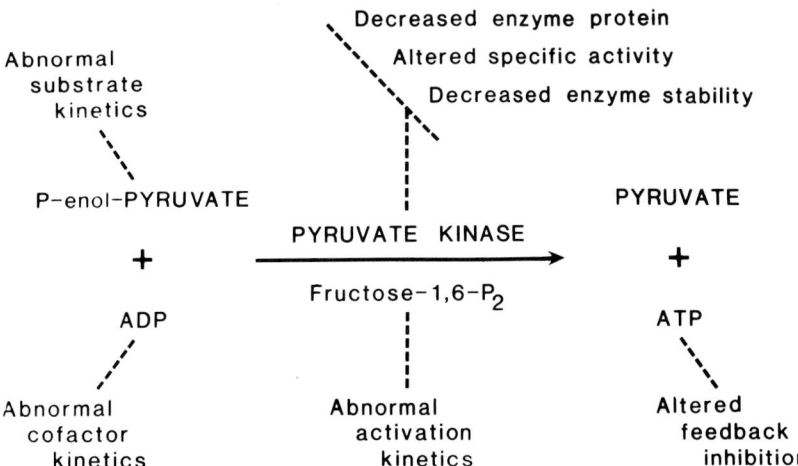

Fig. 94-2 The pyruvate kinase reaction. Broken lines indicate alterations of reaction components observed in association with various mutant isozymes.

minimally decreased in heterozygotes.[26] Rare instances of mild chronic hemolytic anemia in presumed heterozygotes have been reported.[40,60]

Treatment

There is no specific therapy. The usual hematopoietic agents as well as steroids are ineffective.[26,153] Supportive treatment consists primarily of red cell transfusions as deemed necessary. Beyond the early childhood period, most PK patients maintain a tolerable hemoglobin level without transfusions except during exacerbations, for example, following parvovirus infection or during pregnancy.[24]

Splenectomy is not curative but is frequently of distinct value, especially in infants and young children with severe disease. The hemoglobin concentration often increases 1 to 3 g/dl, reducing or, at times, eliminating transfusion requirements. Following splenectomy, growth and development in severely affected children may be accelerated.[26,153] Splenectomy may be lifesaving in the severely affected Amish patients.[58] On the other hand, anemia in mild cases may be unchanged by the procedure.

In contrast to splenectomy in hereditary spherocytosis, hemolysis clearly persists, and aplastic or hemolytic crises may still occur.[26,56] Erythrocyte survival and sequestration studies utilizing ^{51}Cr-labeled cells are not generally useful in selecting patients for surgery.

Experimental approaches with agents which either modify enzyme activity or circumvent the metabolic aberrations induced by the defective enzyme have been attempted. The administration of AMP, magnesium, riboflavin, methylene blue and ascorbic acid, oral mannose, galactose, and fructose, and the infusion of adenine, inosine, and guanosine, mostly in single cases, have produced no convincing clinical improvement and should be considered experimental.[30]

Hereditary Pyruvate Kinase Deficiency in Combination with Other Disorders

Partial deficiency of PK has been observed in combination with β-thalassemia,[154] hereditary spherocytosis,[155] and hereditary elliptocytosis.[156] A woman who was heterozygous for both G-6-PD and PK deficiency demonstrated mild reticulocytosis and a shortened survival of ^{51}Cr-labeled red cells.[157] Coexistence of α-thalassemia (silent carrier state) and a variant, PK Fukien, has been described in a boy of Chinese ancestry.[140]

There is some,[155,157] but as yet insufficient, evidence to implicate interaction between PK deficiency and other disorders of the red cell. In a case of Gaucher disease, however, cerebroside storage was probably enhanced by the hemolysis due to homozygous PK deficiency.[158] An accelerated level of hemolysis was observed when an acute Coombs-positive hemolytic anemia developed during the course of infectious mononucleosis in a patient with PK deficiency anemia.[159]

Acquired Pyruvate Kinase Deficiency

Acquired PK is much more prevalent than hereditary deficiency, but its clinical significance is still unclear. Reduced PK and pyrimidine-5'-nucleotidase activities are the most frequent findings among multiple enzymatic aberrations of the erythrocyte described in a variety of hematologic malignan-

cies.[22,30,160–163] PK deficiency has been noted particularly in acute myeloblastic leukemia and refractory sideroblastic anemia. Decreased activity of PK is also common following chemotherapy,[164,165] but occurs occasionally prior to treatment of cancer.[164] In most instances of acquired deficiency, PK values are only slightly to moderately reduced, but on occasion may be markedly decreased. Accumulation of glycolytic intermediates prior to the PK step may occur but probably does not result in shortened red cell survival.[166]

The mechanism of acquired enzyme defects is still unclear, but four hypotheses have been proposed: partial reversion to a fetal form of erythropoiesis, disturbance in gene expression, somatic mutations, and postsynthetic modifications of the enzyme. Arguments exist in favor of each of these hypothetical mechanisms.[30,162]

Differentiation between acquired and hereditary PK deficiency (usually the heterozygous state) is occasionally difficult; family studies or follow-up may be necessary.

Pyruvate Kinase and High ATP Syndrome

The association of PK hyperactivity (two- to fourfold increase), high ATP (about twice normal), and low 2,3-DPG content in the red cells has been reported in several families.[167–170] In some affected individuals, erythrocytosis developed secondary to a left shift in the oxygen dissociation curve as a result of the low 2,3-DPG content. The mode of inheritance is autosomal dominant. The high PK activity may be based either on the presence of the M_2-type PK in addition to the L-type in the erythrocytes,[168,169] or alternatively, on a shift in the R⇌T equilibrium to the R form (resulting in increased affinity for PEP) together with increased enzyme synthesis or decreased degradation.[170]

OTHER ERYTHROENZYMOPATHIES OF ANAEROBIC GLYCOLYSIS

Hexokinase

Hexokinase, a monomer of 100 kDa, like phosphofructokinase and pyruvate kinase catalyzes an essentially irreversible rate-limiting and regulatory step in glycolysis to produce glucose-6-phosphate (G-6-P).

$$\text{Glucose} + \text{ATP} \xrightarrow{\text{hexokinase}} \text{G-6-P} + \text{ADP}$$

In red cell populations of normal mean cell age, it has the lowest catalytic activity of any glycolytic enzyme.[171–175] However, it also exhibits the sharpest curve of activity decay with age. The curve is biphasic, with as much as an eight- to tenfold loss of activity in the short period that the reticulocyte matures.[174] This is unassociated with loss of a particulate fraction, since essentially all red cell hexokinase appears to be cytosolic. Hexokinase exists as four isozymes, with the red cell possessing chiefly type I, whose structural gene resides on chromosome 10.[176] Hexokinase I has three major forms, designated Ia, Ib, and Ic. Hexokinase Ib predominates in the young red cell.

While erythrocyte hexokinase deficiency occasionally is one of a constellation of abnormalities associated with multiple malformations (as in Fanconi pancytopenia),[177] in some 14 patients it has been identified as a single, usually recessively transmitted enzymopathy causing lifelong hemolytic anemia. In the first reported case,[171] glucose and fructose were converted to lactate at rates well below those expected for reticulocyte-rich blood. Splenectomy appears to result in partial benefit when transfusion requirements exist, though vigorous hemolysis persists after the procedure.[178] The concentration of 2,3-DPG, which is formed after the deficient glycolytic step, is usually subnormal. Despite the rarity of severe deficiency, genetic polymorphism is the rule[171,178–187] and is manifest by differing kinetics for glucose and Mg^{2+}–ATP^{4-}, differing electrophoretic patterns, and variable thermostability.

Hexokinase is inhibited by its product, G-6-P, by glucose-1,6-diphosphate, and by 2,3-DPG, and is stimulated by inorganic phosphorus (P_i). Abnormalities of regulation by inhibitors and of insensitivity to P_i have also been documented.[181,188] In severely deficient subjects, hexokinase may assay in the normal or modestly subnormal range, but far below the activity expected in reticulocyte-rich red cell populations. On the hexokinase scale of aging, reticulocytes in such deficient patients are already senescent and lack the metabolic machinery necessary for normal survival. While transmission of severe deficiency with overt hemolysis has usually been clearly recessive, in two cases there has been evidence of dominant inheritance of the hemolytic syndrome.[179,180]

Glucosephosphate Isomerase

Of glycolytic enzymopathies associated with hemolytic syndromes, glucosephosphate isomerase (GPI) deficiency is second only to that of PK[189] and has been identified in more than 40 subjects with hemolysis.[190–220] The enzyme is a dimer of 134 kDa[221] and is encoded by a gene on chromosome 19.[222] Tissue-specific isozymes are not believed to exist, and hence in severely deficient subjects not only the red cells but leukocytes, plasma, platelets, muscle, liver,[221,223] and presumably other tissues possess decreased GPI activity. Despite this, multisystem disease is exceedingly rare, perhaps reflecting the fact that nearly all documented mutant variant GPIs have been manifested chiefly by thermoinstability. As discussed for other enzymes, instability of an activity in the red cell, devoid of any mechanism for renewal by ongoing protein synthesis, has uncompensated consequences at least partially avoidable in nucleated tissues. Rare, stable mutant enzymes have been identified in association with hemolytic syndromes,[220] as has combined GPI and G-6-PD deficiency.[198,199] Clinical manifestations vary from mild to severe. When the latter are present, splenectomy results in partial benefit despite continuing hemolysis. Anemia may improve, transfusion requirements abate, and in rare instances, the procedure may be lifesaving.

While enzymopathies of erythrocytes may require exchange transfusion for hyperbilirubinemia at times in the neonate, they have rarely been implicated etiologically in hydrops fetalis or newborn death. In 260 cases,[191] only four such immediate neonatal deaths could be documented, one of which was attributed to severe GPI deficiency. However, more recently, five of six pregnancies in a consanguineous family from Southern India are reported to have resulted either in stillbirth or early neonatal death, one with hydrops.[193] In this family, there was no evidence of ABO incompatibility, thalassemia, or other evident causative pathophysiology. The sixth child subsequently was delivered early, noted to have hydrops fetalis, and successfully salvaged by immediate exchange transfusion. Un-

til splenectomy at age 3 brought substantial clinical improvement and subsidence of transfusion requirements, the clinical course was stormy. Red cell enzyme studies indicate homozygosity for an extremely thermolabile GPI variant (GPI Tadikonda).[193] Rarely, therefore, GPI deficiency is implicated as causing hydrops fetalis. Antenatal diagnosis is possible as early as the second trimester of pregnancy based on characterization of GPI from cultured amniotic fluid cells.[192]

GPI variants have been extensively polymorphic in terms of electrophoretic mobility, catalytic activity, thermostability, and other parameters.[190–220] At times, red cell G-6-P concentration is demonstrably increased. Evolution of $^{14}CO_2$ from glucose labeled at C2 depends on recycling of pentose through the pentose phosphate shunt following its conversion to fructose-6-phosphate (F-6-P) by transketolase and transaldolase. This requires traversing the GPI step to form G-6-P before reentering the shunt. In severe GPI deficiency, this recycling capacity may be as low as 0.2 to 10 percent of normal.[189,190]

Phosphofructokinase Deficiency

Phosphofructokinase (PFK) catalyzes the essentially irreversible phosphorlyation:

$$F\text{-}6\text{-}P + ATP \xrightarrow{\text{PFK}} F\text{-}1,6\text{-}P_2 + ADP$$

It is a key rate-limiting step in glycolysis and highly regulated by complex interactions with ATP, 2,3-DPG, and other metabolites.[224–232] Its product, $F\text{-}1,6\text{-}P_2$, is an essential allosteric activator of pyruvate kinase, the catalyst of a more distal, regulatory reaction.

PFK exists as tetrameric isozymes derived from three different subunits (types M, muscle; L, liver; P or F, platelet or fibroblast).[226–230] The subunits are encoded on chromosome 1 cen $\rightarrow$ q32 for M, chromosome 21q 22.3 for L, and chromosome 10 for P or F.[233–236] Muscle (M_4) and liver and fat (L_4) PFK are homotetramers. Leukocyte PFK is largely type L, while that of platelets is a hybrid of P and L. The red cell enzyme is expressed as five isozymes, M_4, M_3L, M_2L_2, ML_3, and L_4, the subunits M and L normally being generated in approximately equal amounts.

Severe PFK deficiency as originally described by Tarui et al.[237,238] and Layzer et al.[239] and sometimes known as Tarui disease classically presents with prominent myopathy and compensated hemolytic anemia. The former is manifested by variable muscle weakness and pain, exercise intolerance, and sometimes myoglobinuria and rhabdomyolysis. The hemolytic syndrome is clearly demonstrable, but asymptomatic. The myopathy varies markedly in severity, probably due to heterogeneous molecular lesions and degree of sedentary lifestyle. Early appearance of gout is common. However, other clinical phenotypes are well recognized.[240–248] In some, hemolysis without myopathy has been unequivocally documented.[240–243] In others, reductions in red cell PFK comparable in degree to those observed in classical Tarui disease have been unaccompanied by either hemolysis or myopathy. Rare reports of severe and progressive myopathy require additional data before PFK deficiency alone is incriminated as causative. A fatal infantile form of myopathy associated with less than 2 percent of normal mean PFK activity but normal amounts of immunologic cross-reacting activity has been reported.[248] Late onset myopathic manifestations also occur,[249] though it is not clear that subclinical or unrecognized muscle dysfunction, perhaps exacerbated by aging muscles with impaired perfusion, may not have been present lifelong.

Careful evaluation in the laboratory has gone far to clarify the variation in clinical phenotypes.[242,250–252] Biopsies show increased muscle glycogen, and the disorder has been alternatively designated as *glycogenosis type VII* (see Chap. 12).[253] The ischemic exercise tolerance test evokes little or no increase in venous pyruvate or lactate. The predisposition for gout appears secondary to excessive degradation of purines in exercising PFK-deficient muscles. Ammonia, inosine, and hypoxanthine are increased abnormally in venous blood after forearm exercise.[254] Muscle biopsies classically reveal virtually absent PFK activity while that of the red cell is about one-half normal.[237–239,250] Symptomatic subjects possess only the L isozyme in their red cells, as expected for homozygous deficiency of M subunits.[251,252] However, in one subject with late onset myopathy, the red cells contained a small but detectable complement of M PFK.[249] In entirely asymptomatic subjects with comparably low erythrocyte PFK, the latter can be associated with heterozygosity for either M or L subunit deficiency, and hence have available some M subunits in both muscle and red cells.[251] The absence of hemolysis in these circumstances despite assayable PFK activity of around 50 percent implies that M and L subunits in the erythrocyte have differing regulatory capabilities, and that the former are essential in maintaining an adequate flow of glycolytic intermediates when assayable PFK is half-normal.[251] Hemolysis without myopathy[251] may be related to a molecular lesion characterized by expression of a catalytically active but unstable mutant enzyme in some genetic variants. Ongoing subunit synthesis, possible in muscle but denied to the anucleate erythrocyte, could maintain a reduced but present cohort of functioning PFK in muscle alone. Clinical manifestations limited to myopathy and hemolysis are compatible with known tissue isozymic patterns and the special dependence of erythrocytes and exercising muscle on anaerobic glycolysis. The former, devoid of organelles, can maintain ATP to support viability solely through the glycolytic pathway; the latter, possessing only M_4 PFK, depends on an adequate anaerobic glycolytic flux during ischemia of severe exertion. The hemoglobin levels in Tarui disease, despite reticulocytosis and impaired red cell survival, are usually normal or possibly slightly increased.[251] Molecular lesions, such as hexokinase and PFK deficiency, proximal to the formation of 2,3-DPG result in diminished levels of 2,3-DPG.[255] This, in turn, unfavorably shifts the hemoglobin-oxygen dissociation curve, diminishes oxygen delivery to tissues, and stimulates erythropoietin production, thus favoring expansion of the erythron.

More than 20 unrelated kindreds with PFK deficiency are documented. An animal analogue, English springer spaniel dogs, manifests chronic hemolysis, alkalemia-induced hemolytic crises, and only mild myopathy in conjunction with autosomal recessively inherited severe PFK deficiency.[256,257] There is proven striking structural homology between human and rabbit muscle PFKs.[257]

Aldolase

Aldolase (Ald) catalyzes the interconversion of $F-1,6-P_2$ and the trioses dihydroxyacetone phosphate and glyceraldehyde-3-phosphate. A severe deficiency associated with hemolysis and a galaxy of malformations related possibly causatively, but possibly fortuitously, to deficient Ald, has been docu-

mented.[258] Two patients in a second kindred exhibited hemolysis alone, and Ald had an increased $K_{0.5s}$ (F-1,6,-P_2) and was thermolabile.[259] A cDNA for aldolase A was cloned using RNA isolated from a lymphoblastoid cell line from one of these patients. Nucleotide sequence analysis revealed a single amino acid substitution of $Asp_{128}\rightarrow Gly$ caused by a G to A alteration in the sense strand of the mutant sequence.[259a] Aldolase is a tetramer of 158 kDa, and three tissue isozymes (A, B, and C) are recognized.[260]

Triosephosphate Isomerase Deficiency

Triosephosphate isomerase (TPI), a dimer with two identical subunits containing 248 amino acids and with a calculated subunit mass of 26,750 Da,[261] catalyzes the reversible isomerization of dihydroxyacetone phosphate and glyceraldehyde-3-phosphate. It has the highest catalytic efficiency of any enzyme of human glycolysis and requires no cofactors or metal ions; prokaryotic and eukaryotic TPI have a highly selective homology.

Severe, autosomal recessive deficiency in human beings is characterized by multisystem disease,[262–264] including moderately severe, nonspherocytic hemolytic anemia, devastating neurologic dysfunction appearing first at about 6 months to 7 years of age, a propensity for sudden cardiac death, presumably due to arrhythmia,[265,266] and clinically increased susceptibility to infection.[263] The hemolytic anemia is exacerbated by myelosuppressive events, and improvement after splenectomy has not been documented. The clinical impression of predisposition to infection has not been associated with a detectable abnormality in any granulocyte function test.[262,267]

The severe, progressive neurologic dysfunction, unrelated to kernicterus or anoxemia secondary to anemia, includes diffuse weakness, hypotonia, absent limb reflexes, unintelligible speech, and eventually fixed deformities of hands and legs.[262,265,268,269] A recent thorough neurologic evaluation of two sibs with severe TPI deficiency also reviewed the available literature.[269] Intellect is preserved, sensory impairment is absent, and cerebrospinal fluid has been normal when studied, as have been computed tomographic brain scans and electroencephalogram in two patients.[269] Lower motor neuron involvement documented by electromyogram is an integral part of the disorder, while pyramidal tract signs, tremor, dystonia, and dyskinesia point to involvement of brainstem and basal ganglia in addition to the spinal cord. The cerebral cortex appears spared.

TPI deficiency appears to involve all the tissues of the body,[263,264] and activity is greatly reduced in skin fibroblasts, plasma, spinal fluid, skeletal muscle, and blood cells. The dihydroxyacetone phosphate concentration in the red cell is increased some twenty- to fortyfold.[270] TPI is encoded by a single locus on chromosome 12.[271,272] A multiplicity of electrophoretic forms are due to posttranslational deamination of the parent molecule at asparagines 15 and 71.[273]

Null alleles (with 50 percent TPI activity and 50 percent of the usual immunologic cross-reacting material) have been the most prevalent abnormality detected in surveys.[274,275] However, red cells of severely deficient subjects characteristically possess 5 to 20 percent of normal TPI activity, and homozygosity for truly null alleles is unknown, probably due to lethality in utero.[276] There is clear evidence of heterogeneity among deficient patients.[276,277] However, a single amino acid substitution, Glu-104→Asp-104, was present in a TPI allele from two unrelated patients with severe TPI deficiency and resulted in a thermolabile enzyme.[278] Each DNA-associated sequence exhibited a GC to CG transversion in the codon for amino acid 104. The importance of Glu-104 to TPI structure and function is suggested by its conservation in TPI of all species thus far characterized.[278] The syndrome of severe TPI deficiency in human beings has been documented in about 25 patients.[262,265-269,279-282] Recently, seven new homozygous cases were documented by investigators in France.[282] In one case, parents were first cousins.

Phosphoglyceratekinase

Phosphoglyceratekinase (PGK), a monomer of 45,000 Da,[283] was first demonstrated to be deficient in a woman with hemolytic anemia as her sole manifestation.[284] Nearly simultaneously, PGK deficiency was documented in association with more severe hemolysis, neurologic manifestations, and sometimes early deaths in male members of a large Chinese kindred, with mild hemolytic anemia in the mother and grandmother of the proband.[285,286] The clinical features strongly suggested an X-linked structural gene.[286] This was subsequently confirmed, and the PGK locus assigned to the long arm of X.[287-289] PGK catalyzes the reversible interconversion of 3-phosphoglycerate and 1,3-diphosphoglycerate and generates 2 mol ATP from each mole of glucose metabolized.

$$\text{1,3-diphosphoglycerate} + \text{ADP} \overset{\text{PGK}}{\rightleftharpoons} \text{3-phosphoglycerate} + \text{ATP}$$

In the Chinese kindred described initially, all afflicted male members had chronic hemolytic anemia subject to crises with enhanced reticulocytosis, sometimes hemoglobinuria, the appearance of spherocytes on stained blood films, and the necessity for transfusion.[285,286,290] Neurologic manifestations were varied, but included behavioral abnormalities, emotional lability, impaired speech, variable mental retardation, seizures, extrapyramidal tract disease, and even hemiplegia and deep coma during neurologic crises accompanying exacerbation of hemolysis. Recovery in some instances was remarkably rapid. Affected females, possessing a mosaic of PGK-deficient and normal cells, have exhibited moderate to no hemolysis and are essentially asymptomatic. However, PGK deficiency is clinically, biochemically, and genetically polymorphic.[285-287,290-304]

About half of the 12 reported variants with reduced activity[283] have been associated with neurologic and mental aberrations varying from minimal to severe. However, one variant, PGK München, with 21 percent of normal red cell activity had neither hemolysis nor neurologic abnormalities.[294] The enzyme activity was considerably higher than the 5 percent normal activity found in the initial Chinese kindred, and was unaccompanied by kinetic abnormalities or by the abnormal pattern of metabolic intermediates seen in the hemolytic syndrome. Two other patients have had myopathic symptoms with rhabdomyolysis without demonstrable hemolysis.[296,297] In one variant in a male,[296] there was severe PGK deficiency in muscle, leukocytes, platelets, and red cells, but the most severe kinetic abnormality involved a sixteenfold increase in K_m for ATP in the backward reaction and a threefold increase in that for ADP in the forward reaction. It should be noted that restoration of glycogen stores after muscle exertion via gluconeogenesis requires the backward PGK reaction, whereas the

latter serves no obvious beneficial function in the red cell. In a second variant in a male,[297] PGK activity in muscle was 5 percent of the normal mean, but 17.5 percent in erythrocytes. Again, activity was reduced, but not to the same point as in some other patients with hemolysis.

In males with hemolysis in the first kindred studied, PGK activity was very low in red cells, was less than 5 percent of normal in platelets and lymphocytes, and was 0.1 to 5 percent of normal in brain, skeletal muscle, liver, and cardiac muscle obtained at autopsy in one subject.[290,305] In three affected males,[290] ATP levels were low (one-half normal), while 2,3-DPG was increased almost twofold. Obligate female heterozygotes had normal to modestly reduced PGK activity and modest increases in 2,3-DPG (120 to 150 percent of normal). In the autopsied patient, specific PGK activity in a variety of PGK-deficient tissues was 1 to 4 percent of normal, indicating that in this particular kindred a variant protein of low activity was produced. Studies on the purified variant enzyme demonstrated an abnormal tendency to form aggregates, increased heat sensitivity, and altered nucleotide substrate specificity.[291] In contrast to normal PGK, GTP and ITP were more active phosphoryl group donors than was ATP. A major fraction ($\geq$ 95 percent) of the mutant enzyme could not be purified by the same procedures effective with normal PGK. A minor fraction behaved similarly to the normal enzyme. Although there was no clinical bleeding disorder in this kindred, male propositi had very low PGK activity in platelets, whereas hexokinase and pyruvate kinase activities were increased 40 to 60 percent and three- to fivefold, respectively.[290] One interpretation suggests that diminished platelet survival, though compensated, was reflected by increased activity of age-dependent enzymes.

Normal PGK has been completely sequenced,[306-308] as have four other variants. In PGK II, a normal activity but electrophoretic variant in South Pacific populations, asparagine has been substituted for threonine at position 352 (now 351).[309] In PGK Uppsala,[310] characterized by hemolysis and mild mental aberrations, proline has replaced arginine at position 205. In PGK München, asparagine has displaced aspartate at position 267.[311] PGK Tokyo[312] is associated with hemolysis, neurologic defects, 5 to 10 percent normal activity in cultured lymphoblastoid cells, abnormal thermostability and kinetics, and diminished specific activity. Valine has been substituted for methionine at position 265. Although the original sequence of normal PGK postulated 417 amino acids, later indications substantiate only 416.[307]

2,3-Diphosphoglycerate Mutase (Bisphosphoglycerate Mutase, E.C.2.7.5.4.) and Phosphatase

The conversion of 1,3-DPG to 2,3-DPG is catalyzed by 2,3-DPG mutase. 2,3-DPG phosphatase returns 2,3-DPG to the mainstream of glycolysis as 3-phosphoglycerate, bypassing the ATP-generating step mediated by phosphoglycerate kinase. The two activities constitute the Rapoport-Leubering shunt[1] which is not directly related to energy production. Autosomal recessive, severe deficiency of 2,3-DPG mutase was manifested in a proband by nearly undetectable levels of red blood cell 2,3-DPG. Deficiency of both 2,3-DPG mutase and 2,3-DPG phosphatase confirmed that both enzymatic activities of the shunt reside in the same protein.[3,4] Lack of 2,3-DPG resulted in increased oxygen affinity for hemoglobin, diminished delivery of oxygen to tissues at any given partial pressure,[2] and a compensatory modest increase in the circulating red cell mass, but there was no hemolysis, and clinical manifestations were absent. Both parents had partial deficiencies of 2,3-DPG mutase and 2,3-DPG phosphatase. Although 2,3-DPG mutase deficiency has been inferred in certain patients with hemolysis,[313] puzzling features and the indirect nature of evidence in some cases have demanded reservations. The kindred described above,[3] however, appears to document unequivocally the biochemical and hematologic characteristics of severe, nearly complete 2,3-DPG mutase and 2,3-DPG phosphatase deficiency, and hemolysis is notably absent.

The original published sequence of human erythrocyte 2,3-DPG mutase[314] has recently been extensively revised and confirmed by the determination of the amino acid composition of the encoded protein (258 amino acid residues and molecular weight 29,840).[315,316] The nucleotide sequence data were identical in five different cDNA clones. The enzyme also expresses a third activity, identical with, but quantitatively much less than that of, human red cell monophosphoglyceromutase (E.C. 2.7.5.3.). The latter requires catalytic traces of 2,3-DPG, apparently present in sufficient residual amounts in the erythrocytes of the kindred discribed above. 2,3-DPG mutase and monophosphoglyceromutase are structurally very similar and clearly have diverged relatively recently from a common mutase precursor.[317]

Lactate Dehydrogenase (LDH)

A severe deficiency of LDH due to genetic abnormality of the H subunit has been well-documented in a Japanese kindred.[318,319] While pyruvate and lactate formed within the erythrocyte are diffusible, and hence can be disposed of elsewhere, it might have been surmised that LDH deficiency would impair NADH oxidation and produce significant derangement in NAD/NADH ratios. While the latter were not entirely normal, sufficiently rapid cycling of NAD/NADH to maintain glycolysis occurred (probably by way of a multiplicity of reactions), and overt hemolysis was absent. More recently, myopathy without hemolysis and associated with a complete lack of subunit M in muscle, plasma, red cells, and leukocytes has been documented in four members of a Japanese family.[320]

ENZYMOPATHIES INVOLVING THE PENTOSE PHOSPHATE SHUNT AND RELATED GLUTATHIONE METABOLISM

6-Phosphogluconate Dehydrogenase and 6-Phosphogluconolactonase

Severe deficiency of 6-phosphogluconate dehydrogenase, the second dehydrogenase of the pentose phosphate shunt, while well-documented,[321–323] has never been incriminated in the pathogenesis of a hemolytic syndrome. In fact, subjects with <5 percent of normal activity in red cells have been found in population surveys,[321] but were entirely asymptomatic. The actual product of the G-6-PD reaction is 6-phosphogluconolactone, an unstable intermediate hydrolyzed rapidly to 6-phosphogluconate. While often neglected because the nonenzy-

matic hydrolysis is rapid, nonetheless, red cell 6-phosphogluconate dehydrogenase catalyzes the formation of 6-phosphogluconate some two and one-half to five times faster than nonenzymatic hydrolysis when NADPH is being rapidly reduced and reformed.[324] Recently, partial deficiency of 6-phosphogluconate dehydrogenase coexisting with G-6-PD deficiency was found associated with hemolysis, whereas the G-6-PD variant itself was not.[325] The question is whether the synergism of the two enzymopathies was or was not responsible for hemolytic anemia in the proband.

Glutathione Peroxidase

The enzymatic conversion of harmful peroxides to water and alcohols is catalyzed by the selenoenzyme glutathione peroxidase.[326–329] Glutathione (GSH) is simultaneously oxidized. While partial deficiency of glutathione peroxidase has been documented in conjunction with otherwise unexplained hemolytic syndromes,[330–336] the latter could represent fortuitous association with a not uncommon variant in a healthy population. Approximately half-normal glutathione peroxidase activity has been demonstrated in the red cells of large numbers of persons of Jewish and Mediterranean origin.[337] In untraveled residents of certain areas of New Zealand, where soil is uniquely selenium-poor, a linear relationship with enzyme activity has been reported for erythrocyte concentrations of Se less than about 0.14 μg/ml packed cells.[338,339] There was no documentation of coexistent hemolysis. The role of deficient glutathione peroxidase activity in the pathogenesis of a hemolytic syndrome in human beings remains unsettled.[337]

Glutathione Reductase

A wide diversity of syndromes including neurologic disorders, hemolytic anemias, and panmyelopathies have been reported in association with diminished glutathione (GSSG) reductase activity in red cells.[340–346] Beutler's observations that many subjects with such disorders suffered from inadequate synthesis of the cofactor flavin adenine dinucleotide (FAD) secondary to nutritional riboflavin deficiency or to its defective metabolism did much to resolve this paradox.[347–350] GSSG reductase deficiency, except when extremely severe, is not associated with hemolysis.[18,343] Since nutritional and metabolic aberrations accompany many illnesses, it is not surprising that diminished GSSG reductase activity is more common in hospitalized patients than in the general population.[346] A common cause of enzyme deficiency in malignancy is the inclusion of 1,3-bis(2-chloroethyl)-1-nitrosourea (BCNU) in the therapeutic regimen.[351] This agent produces severe, generalized, and specific reduction in GSSG reductase activity[351,352] within minutes after injection. Inhibition is dependent upon the enzyme being reduced by its cofactor, NADPH. However, virtually complete absence of apoenzyme activity has been firmly documented in three sibs, and partial deficiency was found in their obligate heterozygous parents.[353] This was uncorrected by FAD, was concomitantly present in leukocytes, and was associated with unstable GSH on incubating red cells with acetylphenylhydrazine. One sib had a hemolytic crisis after ingesting fava beans, two had cataracts possibly related to the deficiency, but otherwise the homozygous deficiency lacked clinical counterparts. GSSG reductase is encoded by a single gene on the short arm of chromosome 8. It is now clear that its deficiency may be accounted for by nutritionally or metabolically induced deficiency of FAD, by irreversible inhibition by BCNU employed chemotherapeutically, or by genetic alterations of the apoenzyme.

Enzyme Deficiencies of Glutathione Synthesis: γ-Glutamylcysteine Synthetase and Glutathione Synthetase

The tripeptide GSH is synthesized in two ATP-dependent steps catalyzed respectively by γ-glutamylcysteine and glutathione synthetase:[354,355]

$$\text{L-glutamate} + \text{L-cysteine} + \text{ATP} \xrightarrow{\text{γ-glutamylcysteine synthetase}}$$
$$\text{L-γ-glutamylcysteine} + \text{ADP} + \text{P}_i \quad (1)$$

$$\text{L-γ-glutamylcysteine} + \text{glycine} + \text{ATP} \xrightarrow{\text{glutathione synthetase}}$$
$$\text{GSH} + \text{ADP} + \text{P}_i \quad (2)$$

The end product, GSH, is present in red cells at the high concentration of 2 mM and plays an important role in protecting the cell from oxidative damage. GSH and its oxidized form, GSSG, are essential for function of the pentose phosphate shunt. In addition to participation in the enzymatic destruction of peroxides, GSH serves to preserve the functional —SH groups of proteins in their reduced state and forms conjugates with a variety of xenobiotics through the mediation of an abundant red cell enzyme, glutathione S-transferase.[356]

Severe glutathione synthetase deficiency is manifested as two phenotypes,[357] one consisting of hemolytic anemia alone[358–362] and one as multisystem disease with metabolic acidosis, massive 5-oxoprolinuria, and often neurologic dysfunction accompanying a hemolytic syndrome (see Chap. 31). Hemolytic anemia alone or in concert with multisystem disease is exacerbated by agents causing hemolysis in subjects with G-6-PD deficiency, and the Heinz body test is strongly positive. The erythrocytes have been reported to be extremely sensitive to damage by chromate, precluding the use of ^{51}Cr labeling as conventionally performed.[358] When multisystem disease is absent, tissues other than the red cell are presumed to have sufficient residual glutathione synthetase activity to support normal function.

The first patient with generalized glutathione synthetase deficiency was mentally retarded with severe organic brain disease, progressive neurologic deterioration, and death at age 28.[363] At autopsy there was selective atrophy of the granular cell layer of the cerebellum, and focal lesions in the frontoparietal cortex, visual cortex, and thalamus.[364] Generalized enzyme deficiency has been reported in additional patients,[366–372] many, but not all, exhibiting central nervous system involvement. It is difficult to ascertain whether neurologic dysfunction results from the enzyme deficiency or is secondary to severe metabolic acidosis and the concomitant 5-oxoprolinemia and 5-oxoprolinuria. GSH normally controls its own synthesis[357] by inhibiting formation of its precursor, γ-glutamylcysteine. In its absence, unimpeded synthesis of the latter results. In many tissues, a six-enzyme-catalyzed series of reactions, the γ-glutamyl cycle, controls GSH metabolism.[357,373,374] The large overproduction of γ-glutamylcysteine

results, in turn, in accumulation of 5-oxoproline, a metabolite in the cycle. When this exceeds the capacity of 5-oxoprolinase to convert it to glutamate, severe metabolic acidosis is the result. A metabolite derived from a GSH precursor no longer subject to feedback inhibition by GSH itself is thus incriminated in the most serious clinical manifestations of the syndrome. In generalized deficiency, severe lack of enzyme activity is demonstrated in placenta and cultured skin fibroblasts as well as red cells.[365] The heterogeneity of glutathione synthetase deficiency may be related to varying effects of unstable mutant enzymes in different tissues, but possibly also to differing tissue distribution of proteases.[375] In all phenotypes of glutathione synthetase deficiency, obligate heterozygotes have about half-normal enzyme activity, are asymptomatic, and have normal tissue concentrations of GSH. The treatment of the generalized disease is essentially ongoing control of the metabolic acidosis by administration of bicarbonate, which might, if instituted sufficiently early, modify central nervous system dysfunction. Glutathione synthetase deficiency, when severe, is accompanied by glutathione-S-transferase deficiency as well.[356] The latter is not genetically determined but secondary to increased susceptibility to denaturation when GSH is nearly absent.

Similarly severe, near-total lack of GSH results from the rarer, also autosomal recessive deficiency of γ-glutamylcysteine synthetase, in which there is inability to form the dipeptide of glutamate and cysteine. The initial probands, brother and sister, were diagnosed in adulthood, had moderate hemolytic anemia, red cell GSH only 2 to 3 percent of normal, and progressive spinocerebellar ataxia.[376,377] GSH concentration in muscle and leukocytes was 25 and 50 percent of normal, respectively, but there was no overt myopathy or granulocyte dysfunction. The brother, age 37, had ataxia, weakness, impaired vibratory and position sensation, absent lower extremity deep tendon reflexes, dysmetria, dysdiadochokinesia, and, later, irregular staccato speech. The spinocerebellar dysfunction was limited to the two family members with γ-glutamylcysteine synthetase deficiency, implying strongly a causative relationship, though the mechanism remains undefined.[378]

Syndromes with Increased Erythrocyte Glutathione (GSH)

The author's laboratory has studied members of a kindred with lifelong hemolytic anemia in which the only abnormality detected thus far is increased red cell GSH from 3 to 6 SD above the normal mean.[379,380] Both the male proband, his half sister, and the son of the latter have clear evidence of ongoing hemolysis. The proband and his half sister have different fathers. The mode of transmission appears to be autosomal dominant, though X-linkage is not unequivocally excluded by available data. Red cell GSH was normally stable and was authentic as evidenced by specific enzyme assay utilizing GSH-dependent glyoxalase I. The two dehydrogenases of the oxidative pentose phosphate shunt, GSH peroxidase and GSSG reductase, pyrimidine 5'-nucleotidase, and a number of nonglycolytic enzyme activities exhibited no abnormalities. No abnormalities of transport of oxidized glutathione were demonstrable in the red cell. There was no evidence of dyserythropoiesis. Increased red cell GSH is normally observed in cord blood, is not infrequent in a variety of dyserythropoietic syndromes, and is an epiphenomenon in severe pyrimidine-5'-nucleotidase deficiency and in the erythrocytes of the Lesch-Nyhan syndrome.[380,381]

DISTURBANCES IN ENZYMES OF NUCLEOTIDE METABOLISM

The metabolic reactions outlined in Fig. 94-1 are delicately balanced to provide optimal concentrations of reducing compounds and high-energy phosphates. Because many crucial cell functions depend specifically upon ATP, perturbations in its generation via glycolysis or its maintenance via salvage pathways often have deleterious effects on erythrocyte function and longevity. Within the adenine nucleotide pool, AMP is in particular jeopardy. AMP deamination, either before or after dephosphorylation, yields inosine monophosphate or diffusible inosine, and mechanisms do not exist in mature erythrocytes to retrieve the purine moiety from these compounds. This may have special importance in older erythrocytes in which salvage mechanisms likely assume relatively greater metabolic roles as glycolytic capacity diminishes with cell age.

Disorders of nucleotide metabolism in erythrocytes include both deficient and hyperactive enzymes.[382] Many of these conditions (for example, severe deficiencies of adenosine deaminase, nucleoside phosphorylase, adenine and hypoxanthine-guanine phosphoribosyl transferases, and hyperactive ribosephosphate pyrophosphokinase) have no discernible detrimental effects on erythrocytes. A few cases of ribosephosphate pyrophosphokinase and hypoxanthine-guanine phosphoribosyl transferase deficiencies have been associated with megaloblastic changes, but these may have been due to relative folate deficiency rather than to the enzymopathies per se. Megaloblastic features have also been described in cases with severe deficiencies of orotate phosphoribosyl transferase and orotidine 5'-decarboxylase in hereditary orotic aciduria, perhaps reflecting broader disturbances in purine and pyrimidine biosynthesis.

Three principal disorders of nucleotide metabolism have been reported in association with shortened erythrocyte life span and hemolytic anemia of varying severity: hereditary hyperactivity of adenosine deaminase, hereditary deficiency of adenylate kinase, and severe hereditary or acquired deficiencies of pyrimidine nucleotidase.

Hemolytic anemia secondary to hyperactive adenosine deaminase (adenosine aminohydrolase, E.C.3.5.4.4) has been identified in three unrelated kindreds in the United States, Japan, and France.[383–387] Affected individuals may be asymptomatic with well-compensated chronic hemolysis, but they can be identified by moderate reticulocytosis, decrements in erythrocyte ATP to less than one-half expected concentrations, three- to fourfold increases in pyrimidine nucleotidase activity, and markedly hyperactive (increased on the order of a hundredfold) adenosine deaminase. The cause and/or effects of elevated pyrimidine nucleotidase activities associated with this disorder remain an enigma. There is no evidence that this nucleotidase is capable of dephosphorylating AMP to cause the observed reductions in ATP.

The adenosine deaminase molecule itself is normal by all conventional biochemical criteria, including electrophoretic migration, kinetics for various substrates and inhibitors, heat stability, specific activity, pH optimum, immunologic reactivity, amino acid composition, and peptide patterns. The basic abnormality appears to result from overproduction of structurally normal enzyme protein due to abnormal translational control.[388]

The defect is transmitted as a genetic dominant and appears to be confined to erythroid elements, since granulocytes, lymphocytes, and cultured skin fibroblasts from affected individuals exhibit normal activities. If increased activity were due to altered molecular structure, as in the case of hyperactive ribosephosphate pyrophosphokinase, then specific activity would be increased and other tissues with the same isozyme would be expected to share the anomaly. In adenosine deaminase deficiency associated with immune incompetence, all tissues exhibit decreased activities. This is consistent with evidence that tissue-specific isozymes of adenosine deaminase share a common protein,[389,390] the production of which is governed by a single genetic locus on chromosome 20.[391] The structure and sequence of this gene have been determined (see Chap. 40).[392]

Reductions in the adenine nucleotide pool of affected erythrocytes are thought to result from perturbation of the normal delicate balance between adenosine deaminase and adenosine kinase activities. These two enzymes compete for micromolar amounts of substrate available in the plasma. Under certain conditions, adenosine may be preferentially converted to inosine because adenosine deaminase is normally much more active than the kinase[393,394] and is also in close physical association with the membrane components responsible for facilitated transport of adenosine.[395] At very low adenosine concentrations, however, phosphorylation may predominate, because the kinase has a twentyfold lower Michaelis constant than the deaminase.[394]

In the affected cells, adenosine deaminase activity is increased almost two orders of magnitude, perhaps even more in subpopulations. This might effectively divert adenosine away from the kinase-mediated pathway, depriving the cells of an effective means to compensate for random nucleotide losses, and low concentrations of adenine nucleotides would result. Parenthetically, the converse situation exists in some cases of immunodeficiency disease in which severe impairment of adenosine deaminase activity is associated with markedly increased concentrations of cellular adenine deoxynucleotides.[396–400] The absence of deaminase activity apparently allows an inordinate amount of adenosine or deoxyadenosine to be phosphorylated to AMP or dAMP, and the cell's nucleotide pool is consequently expanded. The biochemical abnormalities in these two distinct genetic anomalies strongly suggest that the availability of adenosine, and a balanced competition for it between adenosine kinase and deaminase, are necessary for normal maintenance of the adenine nucleotide pool in mature erythrocytes.

An equally rare disorder, hereditary deficiency of adenylate kinase (myokinase) (ATP:AMP phosphotransferase, E.C.2.7.4.3.), has been detected in four kindreds, but a causal relation between the deficiency and premature hemolysis remains uncertain. Adenylate kinase activities 10 percent or less of normal mean value were observed in an Israeli Arab[401,402] and a French family,[403] and 44 percent of the normal mean value in a Japanese child[404] with moderate to severe hemolytic anemia. In one case, anemia was associated with partial G-6-PD deficiency and in another with psychomotor retardation. Parents in each kindred possessed the common adenylate kinase-1 electrophoretic phenotype. Family studies suggested an autosomal recessive (or dominant with variable penetrance) transmission. Nonanemic heterozygotes were identifiable by enzyme activities approximately one-half the normal mean value.

Studies of a fourth kindred with this disorder, a black American family,[405] cast serious doubt that severe adenylate kinase deficiency alone is capable of inducing shortened erythrocyte survival. Of two children with virtually undetectable adenylate kinase activities, only one had hemolytic anemia, whereas the other was hematologically normal. Erythrocyte concentrations of all adenine nucleotides were only slightly decreased, if at all. The possibility of compound defects was again raised by the presence of slightly decreased pyruvate kinase activities and increased 2,3-diphosphoglycerate concentrations, but these changes were of comparable degrees in erythrocytes from both children.

AMP, generated from adenine by adenine phosphoribosyl transferase or from adenosine by adenosine kinase (Fig. 94-1), cannot be incorporated effectively into ADP and ATP without some minimal amount of kinase activity. Data from this family indicate that less than 0.1 percent of normal activity may be sufficient to maintain normal ATP/ADP concentrations in circulating erythrocytes, despite irreversible losses of the adenine moiety by deamination mediated by adenosine deaminase or adenylate deaminase. Since severe deficiency of adenine phosphoribosyl transferase is also not associated with premature hemolysis (see Chap. 39),[406] this salvage pathway appears less important for maintenance of the ATP/ADP pool than that mediated by adenosine kinase.

The most common enzyme defect within the category of nucleotide anomalies in red cells is that of pyrimidine nucleotidase deficiency.[407] Nucleotidases (5'-ribonucleotide phosphohydrolases, E.C.3.1.3.5.) are widely distributed throughout nature as a heterogeneous group of isozymes, all of which react with both purine and pyrimidine substrates with variable effectiveness. Catalytic capability of erythrocyte nucleotidase, however, is largely restricted to pyrimidine substrates,[408] an almost mandatory adaptation in erythrocytes, since a nucleotidase also capable of dephosphorylating AMP would impose a constant drain on the adenine nucleotide pool. Recently, a second normal isozyme of erythrocyte nucleotidase has been identified, a deoxynucleotidase that acts principally on both purine and pyrimidine deoxyribomononucleotides.[409]

Severe hereditary deficiency states of pyrimidine nucleotidase have been identified in a relatively large number of individuals with wide geographic distribution.[407] Those of peri-Mediterranean, Jewish, or African ancestry may be particularly susceptible. The genetic defect is transmitted as an autosomal recessive trait. Heterozygotes exhibit intermediate decrements in nucleotidase activity but are otherwise hematologically and biochemically normal.

Pyrimidine nucleotidase probably functions only during reticulocyte maturation, serving to dephosphorylate the pyrimidine products of RNA degradation without jeopardizing the purine components.[410] Severe nucleotidase deficiency, therefore, may result in accumulation of pyrimidines which cannot diffuse from the cells as long as they remain phosphorylated. Impaired degradation of RNA results in aggregates of intact or partially degraded ribosomal nucleoprotein. This provides the most distinctive hematologic finding in this disease: pronounced basophilic stippling on the Wright's stained peripheral smears (Fig. 94-3).

The diagnosis of pyrimidine nucleotidase deficiency is established by demonstration of significantly decreased enzyme activities, generally to about 5 percent of the level observed in comparably young normal cell populations, and/or the identification of an array of intracellular pyrimidine compounds, none of which is normally detectable in erythrocytes. These include conjugates, such as CDP-choline, CDP-ethanolamine, and UDP-glucose, as well as mono-, di-, and triphosphates. Chromatographic techniques are required to identify specific pyrimidines, but shifts in the ultraviolet absorption spectrum of cell extracts can readily detect their presence.[407,410] In subjects with severe hereditary or acquired nucleotidase deficiency, the presence of significant intracellular concentrations of pyrimidine compounds produces spectra with maximal absorption in the region of 265 to 270 nm rather than the usual 257 nm characteristic of adenine compounds. Since the accumulated nucleotides often consist of as much as 80 percent pyrimidine compounds, the adenine nucleotide pool is actually

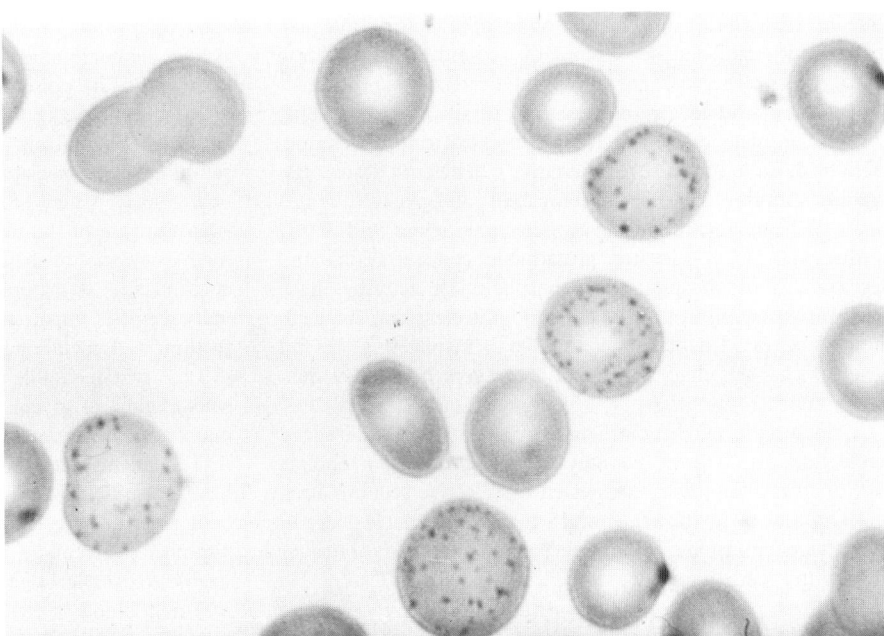

Fig. 94-3 Basophilic stippling in peripheral erythrocytes from a patient with severe hereditary deficiency of pyrimidine nucleotidase (Wright's stain).

diminished on an absolute scale, and this may be at least partially responsible for premature hemolysis.

Two epiphenomena have been consistently observed in this disorder: erythrocyte glutathione concentrations are frequently twice normal, and ribosephosphate pyrophosphokinase activities are usually reduced to about one-fourth normal. The etiology of these changes and their pathophysiological significance, if any, remain speculative. Evidence has been presented that pyrimidine nucleotides interfere with the membrane transport system that normally removes oxidized glutathione from the cell.[411] Pyrimidine compounds do not appear to alter the enzymes of glutathione biosynthesis or redox cycling.[412]

At least six different procedures for partial purification of erythrocyte nucleotidases have been applied in attempts to characterize normal and mutant isozymes of erythrocyte nucleotidases. Studies of cases of pyrimidine nucleotidase deficiency have allowed detection and assessment of the biochemical characteristics of residual deoxyribonucleotidase,[409,413-416] but deficiency states for this normal isozyme have not yet been observed. As with other erythrocyte enzymes, the methods of purification and assay strongly influence measurements of maximal activities, kinetic constants, and other biochemical properties, making accurate comparisons untenable.

Pyrimidine nucleotidase and deoxyribonucleotidase may be complementary systems that serve physiologically to clear the cytosol of RNA and DNA degradation products during maturation of erythroid elements by conversion of nucleotide monophosphates to diffusible nucleosides. This implies that erythroid precursors may not lose nuclear material entirely by pitting, but require a deoxynucleotidase system to catabolize residual nucleotides derived from karyolysis or mitochondrial degradation.[409,414,416]

Deficiencies of pyrimidine nucleotidase may also occur on an acquired basis secondary to lead toxicity. The remarkable sensitivity of this enzyme to inactivation by lead and certain other heavy metals[408] and the common feature of basophilic stippling led to elucidation of its role in the pathogenesis of lead-induced hemolytic anemia. Concentrations of lead that totally obliterate pyrimidine nucleotidase activity have minimal effects on most glycolytic and many other erythrocyte enzymes, although they may adversely affect heme biosynthesis. Humans exposed to chronic low-level overburden of industrial lead insufficient to cause anemia or basophilic stippling may still exhibit significant depressions of pyrimidine nucleotidase activity with otherwise normal glycolytic enzyme profiles.[417] When blood lead levels approach 200 μg/dl of packed cells, pyrimidine nucleotidase activity is depressed to levels comparable to those found in severe hereditary deficiency states. Basophilic stippling then becomes apparent, and pyrimidine nucleotides begin to accumulate to detectable levels within the erythrocytes.[418-420] Elevated glutathione concentrations and decreased ribosephosphate pyrophosphokinase activities have also been observed in isolated cases, so it is clear that the lead-induced acquired deficiency is capable of manifesting the full array of changes characteristic of the severe hereditary deficiency state.

A single case of chronic hemolytic anemia with deranged nucleotide metabolism, possibly involving defective choline phosphotransferase, was manifested by selective accumulation of CDP-choline in the range of 15 to 25 times normal erythrocyte concentrations.[421] No other abnormal nucleotides or metabolites were detected.

The three principal conditions reviewed here, hyperactivity of adenosine deaminase and deficiencies of adenylate kinase

and of pyrimidine nucleotidase, have all been reported to occur in association with hemolytic anemias of variable severities. The first two are very rare, and it now seems doubtful that pure adenylate kinase deficiency alone can induce premature hemolysis. The anemia of hyperactive adenosine deaminase may be subclinical or totally compensated. Life-threatening anemia has been observed in some cases of adenylate kinase deficiency, but these may have been complicated by other compound defects, since at least one case of severe deficiency has shown no hematologic effects. Pyrimidine nucleotidase deficiency is one of the more common erythroenzymopathies and is associated with hemolytic anemia of intermediate severity, infrequently necessitating transfusions. Acquired deficiencies of pyrimidine nucleotidase activity induced by lead overburden, if sufficiently severe, almost completely recapitulate the syndrome associated with severe hereditary deficiency states. Splenectomy in these disorders has not been consistently effective but may be useful in selected cases with heavy transfusion dependence. Therapy has been largely restricted to supportive measures.

Studies of cellular perturbations resulting from these defects have provided a broader understanding of normal erythrocyte metabolism, as well as the pathophysiology of underlying hemolytic mechanisms.

MECHANISMS OF HEMOLYSIS

In erythroenzymopathies associated with grossly inadequate function of the pentose-phosphate shunt, there is general agreement that impaired defense from harmful oxidants, oxidant denaturation of hemoglobin, and Heinz body formation are primary in the pathogenesis of hemolysis. The prototype enzymopathy is that associated with G-6-PD deficiency, but severe deficiencies of either of the enzymes of glutathione synthesis or very severe impairment of glutathione reductase activity may be associated with hemolytic episodes when oxidant medications or fava beans are ingested. The course of events appears to be denaturation of hemoglobin with Heinz body formation, membrane damage, and red cell damage when the red cells are pitted by the spleen. Most commonly the damaged cells undergo intravascular destruction with hemoglobinemia, hemoglobinuria, and/or hemosiderinuria, and usually such events are episodic and precipitated by harmful oxidants or infection. In the most severe forms of G-6-PD deficiency, continuous hemolysis with ongoing nonspherocytic anemia resembling that associated with erythroenzymopathies of anaerobic glycolysis may be present.

In the case of the hemolytic syndromes associated with defective enzymes of the Embden-Meyerhof pathway, there is no consensus as to pathogenesis.[422-423] In our opinion, the primary event is impaired energy metabolism and metabolic depletion.[422] A metabolic block at any step in anaerobic glycolysis has two inevitable consequences. If sufficiently severe, the smooth flow of glycolytic intermediates is interrupted and is manifested in terms of less than expected glycolytic rates and ATP concentrations and (except for deficient activity due to hexokinase deficiency) more subtly by accumulation of metabolic intermediates proximal to the molecular lesion. Indeed, diminished glycolytic rates and ATP are commonly demonstrable, particularly when appropriate comparison to reticulocyte-rich blood is made. The severity of depletion may be partially masked for several reasons: (1) The plentiful reticulocytes possess aerobic energy–generating machinery soon to be lost together with intracellular organelles; (2) the population assayed, by definition, still retains sufficient compensating capacities to survive; and (3) premature metabolic depletion does not preclude red cell survival for a limited time. However, if related to the pathogenesis of a significant hemolytic syndrome, premature metabolic depletion must intervene a priori long before it does in the normal erythrocyte. Observed poor correlation between enzyme activities as assayed in vitro and the clinical severity of the hemolytic syndrome has often been invoked as an unexplained discrepancy. However, with better realization of the enormous polymorphism of the mutant gene products associated with hemolysis, such discrepancies have been greatly clarified and narrowed. The variant enzymes differ in terms of catalytic activity, kinetics with substrate and cofactors, reaction with regulatory metabolites, thermostability, and other properties. These are often not resolved by assays with unphysiological concentrations of substrate and cofactors. When sufficient investigations are performed, the vast majority of the anaerobic glycolytic erythroenzymopathies are associated with grossly impaired enzyme function under conditions existing in the body. This does not deny, however, that unexplained and troublesome exceptions do exist and await elucidation or alternative explanation.

Invoking metabolic depletion as a primary event in no way denies the pathogenetic impact of secondary phenomena: diminished ATP/ADP ratios, altered cation fluxes, translocation of Ca^{2+} and its consequences, loss of membrane plasticity, budding and loss of plasma membrane constituents without initial loss of hemoglobin, disk-echinocyte-spherocyte transformation, and increased susceptibility to phagocytosis by the macrophage. Nor is a contributory role for deleterious effects secondary to altered patterns of metabolic intermediates in special cases ruled out. For example, diminished function of the pentose phosphate shunt and hence potentially diminished defense against oxidant damage has been demonstrated in pyruvate kinase deficiency.[57] However, despite the multiplicity of molecular lesions now identified with hemolytic syndromes due to mutant enzymes of anaerobic glycolysis, the latter are associated with strikingly similar clinical and hematologic manifestations despite widely disparate patterns of intermediates. In severe hexokinase deficiency there are no proximal intermediates to be invoked, though some distal abnormalities such as diminished 2,3-DPG can be noted. A lack of consensus, however, demands that future investigations define more precisely those issues that are now subject to divergent views.

The pathogenesis of the nonspherocytic hemolytic anemia secondary to severe pyrimidine-5′-nucleotidase deficiency remains unclear. The accumulated pyrimidine nucleotides have been shown to impair function of the pentose phosphate shunt. However, they also compete, largely to an unknown degree, with preferred adenine nucleotide cofactors in a number of important enzyme reactions. They represent a unique situation in which a host of unknown in vivo effects are possible and regarding which essentially no data are available.

The hemolytic syndrome associated with large excesses of adenosine deaminase activity and low red cell ATP appears to have a logical explanation. Adenosine is depleted by excessive deamination, and insufficient adenosine is available for the salvage pathway to replenish normal losses from the adenine nucleotide pool of mature red cells. Deaminated plasma adenosine is no longer available for phosphorylative reactions converting it to AMP.

Certain reported studies from the authors' laboratories were supported by National Institutes of Health Research Grants HLB 12944 and AM 14898.

REFERENCES

1. RAPOPORT S, LUEBERING J: The formation of 2,3-diphosphoglycerate in rabbit erythrocytes: The existence of a diphosphoglycerate mutase. *J Biol Chem* 183:507, 1950.

2. BENESCH R, BENESCH RE: Intracellular organic phosphate as regulators of oxygen release by haemoglobin. *Nature* 221:618, 1969.

3. ROSA R, PREHU M-O, BEUZARD Y, ROSA J: The first case of a complete deficiency of diphosphoglycerate mutase in human erythrocytes. *J Clin Invest* 62:907, 1978.

4. ROSA R, GAILLARDON J, ROSA J: Diphosphoglycerate mutase and 2,3-diphosphoglycerate phosphatase activities of red cells: Comparative electrophoretic study. *Biochem Biophys Res Commun* 51:536, 1973.

5. BEUTLER E: Glucose-6-phosphate dehydrogenase activity, in Stanbury JB, Wyngaarden JB, Fredrickson DS, Goldstein JL, Brown MS (eds): *The Metabolic Basis of Inherited Disease*, 5th ed. New York, McGraw-Hill, 1982.

6. HULTQUIST DC, PASSON PG: Catalysis of methaemoglobin reduction by erythrocyte cytochrome b_5 and cytochrome b_5 reductase. *Nature* 229:252, 1971.

7. VALENTINE WN, PAGLIA DE: Erythrocyte enzymopathies, hemolytic anemia, and multisystem disease. *Blood* 64:583, 1984.

8. CARSON PE, FLANAGAN CL, ICKES CE, ALVING AS: Enzymatic deficiency in primaquine-sensitive erythrocytes. *Science* 124:484, 1956.

9. DACIE JV, MOLLISON PL, RICHARDSON N, SELWYN JG, SHAPIRO L: Atypical congenital haemolytic anaemia. *Q J Med* 22:79, 1953.

10. SELWYN JG, DACIE JV: Autohemolysis and other changes resulting from the incubation in vitro of red cells from patients with congenital hemolytic anemia. *Blood* 9:414, 1954.

11. DE GRUCHY GC, CRAWFORD H, MORTON D: Atypical (nonspherocytic) congenital haemolytic anaemia. *Proc VII Congr Int Soc Hematol, Rome, II Pensiero Scientifico*, 1958, vol 2, pt 1, p 425.

12. DE GRUCHY GC, SANTAMARIA JN, PARSONS IC, CRAWFORD H: Nonspherocytic congenital hemolytic anemia. *Blood* 16:1371, 1960.

13. ROBINSON MA, LODER PB, DE GRUCHY GC: Red-cell metabolism in nonspherocytic congenital haemolytic anaemia. *Br J Haematol* 7:327, 1961.

14. VALENTINE WN, TANAKA KR, MIWA S: A specific erythrocyte glycolytic enzyme defect (pyruvate kinase) in three subjects with congenital nonspherocytic hemolytic anemia. *Trans Assoc Am Physicians* 74:100, 1961.

15. TANAKA KR, VALENTINE WN, MIWA S: Pyruvate kinase (PK) deficiency hereditary nonspherocytic hemolytic anemia. *Blood* 19:267, 1962.

16. PIOMELLI S, CORASH L: Hereditary hemolytic anemia due to enzyme defects in glycolysis. *Adv Hum Genet* 6:165, 1976.

17. KAHN A, KAPLAN J-C, DREYFUS J-C: Advances in hereditary red cell enzyme anomalies. *Hum Genet* 50:1, 1979.

18. BEUTLER E: Red cell enzyme defects as nondiseases and as diseases. *Blood* 54:1, 1979.

19. VALENTINE WN: The Stratton lecture: Hemolytic anemia and inborn errors of metabolism. *Blood* 54:549, 1979.

20. MIWA S: Significance of the determination of red cell enzyme activities. *Am J Hematol* 6:163, 1979.

21. VALENTINE WN, PAGLIA DE: Genetic defects of the human red cell and hemolytic anemia, in Atkinson DE, Fox CF (eds): *Modulation of Protein Function*. New York, Academic, 1979, p 423.

22. BEUTLER E: Hemolytic anemia in disorders of red cell metabolism, in Wintrobe MM (ed): *Topics in Hematology*. New York, Plenum, 1978.

23. MIWA S, FUJII H: Molecular aspects of erythroenzymopathies associated with hereditary hemolytic anemia. *Am J Hematol* 19:293, 1985.

24. VALENTINE WN, TANAKA KR, PAGLIA DE: Hemolytic anemias and erythrocyte enzymopathies. *Ann Intern Med* 103, 249, 1985.

25. DACIE J: *The Haemolytic Anaemias. The Hereditary Haemolytic Anaemias*, 3d ed. New York, Churchill Livingston, 1985, vol 1, pp 282–363, 419–429.

26. TANAKA KR, PAGLIA DE: Pyruvate kinase deficiency. *Semin Hematol* 8:367, 1971.

27. SULLIVAN DW, GLADER BE: Erythrocyte enzyme disorders in children. *Pediatr Clin North Am* 27:449, 1980.

28. MIWA S: Hereditary disorders of red cell enzymes in the Embden-Meyerhof pathway. *Am J Hematol* 14:381, 1983.

29. MENTZER WC JR: Pyruvate kinase deficiency and disorders of glycolysis, in Nathan DG, Oski FA (eds): *Hematology of Infancy and Childhood*. Philadelphia, Saunders, 1981, p 566.

30. VALENTINE WN, TANAKA KR, PAGLIA DE: Pyruvate kinase and other enzyme deficiency disorders of the erythrocyte, in Stanbury JB, Wyngaarden JB, Fredrickson DS, Goldstein JL, Brown MS (eds): *The Metabolic Basis of Inherited Disease,* 5th ed. New York, McGraw-Hill, 1983, p 1606.

31. MARIE J, ZANELLA A, VIVES-CORRONS JL, NAJMAN A, KAHN A: Significance of the electrophoretic modifications of defective pyruvate kinase variants. Study of six new observations. *Clin Chim Acta* 93:61, 1979.

32. ISHIDA Y, MIWA S, FUJII H, FUJINAMI N, TAKEGAWA S, YAMATO K: Thirteen cases of pyruvate kinase deficiency found in Japan. *Am J Hematol* 10:239, 1981.

33. VIVES-CORRONS JL, PUJADES MA, AGUILAR JL, FELIU E, JOU JM: Anemia hemolitica por deficit hereditario de piruvatokinasa eritrocitaria. Estudio clinico-familiar y biologico de diez casos. *Sangre (Barc)* 25:51, 1980.

34. LEVINSKI U, FAJNHOLC N, DJALDETTI M, DE VRIES A: Hemolytic anemia in pregnancy associated with erythrocyte pyruvate kinase deficiency. *Clin Sci* 11:43, 1974.

35. PAGLIA DE, VALENTINE WN, HOLBROOK CT, BROCKWAY R: Pyruvate kinase isozyme (PK-Greenville) with defective allosteric activation by fructose-1-6-diphosphate: The role of F-1,6-P$_2$ modulation in normal erythrocyte metabolism. *Blood* 62:972, 1983.

36. BOWMAN HS, MCKUSICK VA, DRONAMRAJU KR: Pyruvate kinase deficient hemolytic anemia in an Amish isolate. *Am J Hum Genet* 17:1, 1965.

37. KAHN A, MARIE J, VIVES-CORRONS JL, MAIGRET P, NAJMAN A: Search for a relationship between molecular anomalies of the mutant erythrocyte pyruvate kinase variants and their pathological expression. *Hum Genet* 57:172, 1981.

38. DACIE JV: Recent advances in knowledge of the hereditary haemolytic anaemias. *Schweiz Med Wochenschr* 98:1624, 1968.

39. SCHROTER W, TILLMANN W: Membrane-localized pyruvate kinase of red blood cells in hemolytic anemia associated with pyruvate kinase deficiency. *Klin Wochenschr* 53:1101, 1975.

40. VAN EYS J, GARMS P: Pyruvate kinase deficiency hemolytic anemia: A model for correlation of clinical syndrome and biochemical anomalies. *Adv Pediatr* 18:203, 1971.

41. DELIVORIA-PAPADOPOULOS M, OSKI FA, GOTTLIEB AJ: Oxygen-hemoglobin dissociation curves: Effect of inherited enzyme defects of the red cell. *Science* 165:601, 1969.

42. OSKI FA, MARSHALL BE, COHEN PJ, SUGERMAN HJ, MILLER LD: Exercise with anemia. The role of the left-shifted or right-shifted oxygen-hemoglobin equilibrium curve. *Ann Intern Med* 74:44, 1971.

43. VIVES-CORRONS JL, MARIE J, PUJADES MA, KAHN A: Hereditary erythrocyte pyruvate-kinase (PK) deficiency and chronic hemolytic anemia: Clinical, genetic and molecular studies in six new Spanish patients. *Hum Genet* 53:401, 1980.

44. TANAKA KR, VALENTINE WN, SCHNEIDER AS: Pyruvate kinase deficiency in hereditary nonspherocytic hemolytic anemia: An inborn error of metabolism, in *Proc IX Congr Eur Soc Haemat.* Basel, Karger, 1963, p 739.

45. MULLER-SOYANO A, DE ROURA ET, DUKE PR, DE ACQUATELLA GC, ARENDS T, GUINTO E, BEUTLER E: Pyruvate kinase deficiency and leg ulcers. *Blood.* 47:807, 1976.

46. CURIEL CARIAS D, VELASQUEZ GA, PAPA R, SOMOZA DE MARTINEZ R, LINARES F, SMITH P, RIOS DE VIELMA H, De ACQUATELLA G: Hemolytic anemia and leg ulcers due to pyruvate kinase deficiency. Report of the second Venezuelan family. *Sangre (Barc)* 22:64, 1977.

47. MAHOUR GH, LYNN HB, HILL RW: Acute pancreatitis with biliary disease in erythrocyte pyruvate-kinase deficiency. *Clin Pediatr (Phila)* 8:608, 1969.

48. SALEM HH, VAN DER WEYDEN MB, FIRKIN BJ: Iron overload in congenital erythrocyte pyruvate kinase deficiency. *Med J Aust* 1:531, 1980.

49. ROWBOTHAM B, ROESER HP: Iron overload associated with congenital pyruvate kinase deficiency and high dose ascorbic acid ingestion. *Aust NZ J Med* 14:667, 1984.

50. TANAKA KR: Unpublished data.

51. LINOS DA, NAGORNEY DM, MCILRATH DC: Splenic abscess—The importance of early diagnosis. *Mayo Clin Proc* 58:261, 1983.

52. RUTGERS MJ, VAN DER LUGT PJ, VAN TURNHOUT JM: Spinal cord compression by extramedullary hemopoietic tissue in pyruvate-kinase-deficiency-caused hemolytic anemia. *Neurology* 29:510, 1979.

53. BERTRAND P, FEREMANS WW, BARROY JP, DEREUME JP, GOLDSTEIN M: Vascular complications in a case of hemolytic anemia due to pyruvate kinase deficiency. *Acta Chir Belg* 82:533, 1982.

54. AMANKWAH KS, DICK BW, DODGE S: Hemolytic anemia and pyruvate kinase deficiency in pregnancy. *Obstet Gynecol* 55:42S, 1980.

55. TANAKA KR, VALENTINE WN: Pyruvate kinase deficiency, in Beutler E (ed): *Hereditary Disorders of Erythrocyte Metabolism.* New York, Grune & Stratton, 1968, p 229.

56. DUNCAN JR, POTTER CG, CAPPELLINI MD, KURTZ JB, ANDERSON MJ,

57. TOMODA A, LACHANT NA, NOBLE NA, TANAKA KR: Inhibition of the pentose phosphate shunt by 2,3-diphosphoglycerate in erythrocyte pyruvate kinase deficiency. *Br J Haematol* 54:475, 1983.

58. BOWMAN HS, PROCOPIO F: Hereditary non-spherocytic hemolytic anemia of the pyruvate-kinase deficient type. *Ann Intern Med* 58:567, 1963.

59. PAGLIA DE, VALENTINE WN, RUCKNAGEL DL: Defective erythrocyte pyruvate kinase with impaired kinetics and reduced optimal activity. *Br J Haematol* 22:651, 1972.

60. KAHN A, MARIE J, GALAND C, BOIVIN P: Chronic haemolytic anaemia in two patients heterozygous for erythrocyte pyruvate kinase deficiency. Electrofocusing and immunological studies of erythrocyte and liver pyruvate kinase. *Scand J Haematol* 16:250, 1976.

61. LEBLOND PF, LYONNAIS J, DELAGE JM: Erythrocyte populations in pyruvate kinase deficiency anaemia following splenectomy I. Cell morphology. *Br J Haematol* 39:55, 1978.

62. KEITT AS: Pyruvate kinase deficiency and related disorders of red cell glycolysis. *Am J Med* 41:762, 1966.

63. MIWA S, FUJII H, TAKEGAWA S, NAKATSUJI T, YAMATO K, ISHIDA Y, NINOMIYA N: Seven pyruvate kinase variants characterized by the ICSH recommended methods. *Br J Haematol* 45:575, 1980.

64. BECKER MH, GENIESER NB, PIOMELLI S, DOVE D, MENDOZA RD: Roentgenographic manifestations of pyruvate kinase deficiency hemolytic anemia. *Am J Roentgenol Radium Ther Nucl Med* 113:491, 1971.

65. MENTZER WC JR, BAEHNER RL, SCHMIDT-SCHONBEIN H, ROBINSON SH, NATHAN DG: Selective reticulocyte destruction in erythrocyte pyruvate kinase deficiency. *J Clin Invest* 50:688, 1971.

66. BOWMAN HS, OSKI FA: Laboratory studies of erythrocytic pyruvate kinase deficiency. *Am J Clin Pathol* 70:259, 1978.

67. WAZEWSKA-CZYZEWSKA M, GUMINSKA M: Congenital non-spherocytic haemolytic anaemia variants with primary and secondary pyruvate kinase deficiency I. Erythrokinetic patterns. *Br J Haematol* 41:115, 1979.

68. LEBLOND PF, LYONNAIS J, DELAGE J-M: Erythrocyte populations in pyruvate kinase deficiency anaemia following splenectomy II. Cell deformability. *Br J Haematol* 39:63, 1978.

69. MIWA S: Hereditary hemolytic anemia due to erythrocyte enzyme deficiency. *Acta Haematol (Japan)* 36:573, 1973.

70. MATSUMOTO N, ISHIHARA T, NAKASHIMA K, MIWA S, UCHINO F, KONDO M: Sequestration and destruction of reticulocytes in the spleen in pyruvate kinase deficiency hereditary nonspherocytic hemolytic anemia. *Acta Haematol (Japan)* 35:525, 1972.

71. MATSUMOTO N, ISHIHARA T, MIWA S, UCHINO F: The mechanism of mitochondrial extrusion from reticulocytes in the spleen from patients with erythrocyte pyruvate kinase (PK) deficiency. *Acta Haematol (Japan)* 37:25, 1974.

72. TANAKA KR: Pyruvate kinase, in Yunis JJ (ed): *Biochemical Methods in Red Cell Genetics,* New York, Academic, 1969, p 167.

73. BEUTLER E: *Red Cell Metabolism. A Manual of Biochemical Methods,* 3d ed. Orlando, Grune & Stratton, 1984.

74. MIWA S, BOIVIN P, BLUME KG, ARNOLD H, BLACK JA, KAHN A, STAAL GEJ, NAKASHIMA K, TANAKA KR, PAGLIA DE, VALENTINE WN, YOSHIDA A, BEUTLER E: Recommended methods for the characterization of red cell pyruvate kinase variants. International Committee for Standardization in Haematology. *Br J Haematol* 43:275, 1979.

75. BRUNETTI P, NENCI G: A screening method for the detection of erythrocyte pyruvate kinase deficiency. *Enzymol Biol Clin* 4:51, 1964.

76. BEUTLER E: A series of new screening procedures for pyruvate kinase deficiency and glutathione reductase deficiency. *Blood* 28:553, 1966.

77. MUIR WA, BEUTLER E, WASSON C: Erythrocyte pyruvate kinase deficiency in the Ohio Amish: Origin and characterization of the mutant enzyme. *Am J Hum Genet* 36:634, 1984.

78. ETIEMBLE J, PICAT C, DHERMY D, BUC HA, MORIN M, BOIVIN P: Erythrocytic pyruvate kinase deficiency and hemolytic anemia inherited as a dominant trait. *Am J Hematol* 17:251, 1984.

79. VALAES T, NECHELES TF, RAI U, TSOCHANTZIS-YIANNOPOULOS K: The role of hemolysis and red-cell enzyme defects in neonatal jaundice, in Stern L, Friis-Hansen B, Kildeberg P (eds): *Intensive Care in the Newborn.* New York, Masson, 1976, p 157.

80. BLUME KG, LOHR GW, PRAETSCH O, RUDIGER HW: Beitrag zur populationsgenetik der pyruvatkinase menschlicher erythrocyten. *Humangenetik* 6:261, 1968.

81. GARCIA SC, MORAGON AC, LOPEZ-FERNANDEZ ME: Frequency of glutathione reductase, pyruvate kinase and glucose-6-phosphate dehydrogenase deficiency in a Spanish population. *Hum Hered* 29:310, 1979.

82. SATOH C, NEEL JV, YAMASHITA A, GORIKI K, FUJITA M, HAMILTON HB: The frequency among Japanese of heterozygotes for deficiency variants of 11 enzymes. *Am J Hum Genet* 35:656, 1983.

83. WU Z-L, YU W-D, CHEN S-C: Frequency of erythrocyte pyruvate kinase deficiency in Chinese infants. *Am J Hematol* 20:139, 1985.

84. BURKE RL, TEKAMP-OLSON P, NAJARIAN R: The isolation, characterization, and sequence of the pyruvate kinase gene of Saccharomyces cerevisiae. *J Biol Chem* 258:2193, 1983.

85. LONBERG N, GILBERT W: Intron/exon structure of the chicken pyruvate kinase gene. *Cell* 40:81, 1985.

86. CHERN CJ, KENNETT R, ENGEL E, MELLMAN WJ, CROCE CM: Assignment of the structural genes for the α subunit of hexosaminidase A, mannose-phosphate isomerase, and pyruvate kinase to the region q22-qter of human chromosome 15. *Somatic Cell Genet* 3:553, 1977.

87. SEARCY GP, MILLER DR, TASKER JB: Congenital hemolytic anemia in the Basenji dog due to erythrocytic pyruvate kinase deficiency. *Can J Comp Med* 35:67, 1971.

88. PRASSE KW, CROUSER D, BEUTLER E, WALKER M, SCHALL WD: Pyruvate kinase deficiency anemia with terminal myelofibrosis and osteosclerosis in a Beagle. *J Am Vet Med Assoc* 166:1170, 1975.

89. RAKSHIT MM, BASU AK: Activity of erythrocytic pyruvate kinase (PK) in leukaemia. *Bull Calcutta Sch Trop Med* 21:24, 1973.

90. KAYNE FJ: Pyruvate kinase, in Boyer PD (ed): *The Enzymes*, 3d ed. New York, Academic, 1974, p 353, vol 8.

91. TANAKA T, HARANO Y, SUE F, MORIMURA H: Crystallization, characterization and metabolic regulation of two types of pyruvate kinase isolated from rat tissues. *J Biochem* 62:71, 1967.

92. IMAMURA K, TANAKA T: Multimolecular forms of pyruvate kinase from rat and other mammalian tissues. *J Biochem* 71:1043, 1972.

93. NAKASHIMA K, MIWA S, ODA S, TANAKA T, IMAMURA K, NISHINA T: Electrophoretic and kinetic studies of mutant erythrocyte pyruvate kinases. *Blood* 43:537, 1974.

94. IMAMURA K, TANAKA T: Pyruvate kinase isozymes from rat, in Colowick SP, Kaplan NO (eds): *Methods in Enzymology*. vol 90, Wood WA (ed): *Carbohydrate Metabolism*, Part E, New York, Academic, 1982, p 150.

95. BIGLEY RH, KOLER RD: Liver pyruvate kinase (PK) isozymes in a PK-deficient patient. *Ann Hum Genet* 31:383, 1968.

96. IMAMURA K, TANAKA T, NISHINA T, NAKASHIMA K, MIWA S: Studies on pyruvate kinase (PK) deficiency. II. Electrophoretic, kinetic, and immunological studies on pyruvate kinase of erythrocytes and other tissues. *J Biochem* 74:1165, 1973.

97. NAKASHIMA K, MIWA S, FUJII H, SHINOHARA K, YAMAUCHI K, TSUJI Y, YANAI M: Characterization of pyruvate kinase from the liver of a patient with aberrant erythrocyte pyruvate kinase, PK Nagasaki. *J Lab Clin Med* 90:1012, 1977.

98. STAAL GEJ, RIJKSEN G, VLUG AMC, VROMEN-VAN DEN BOS B, AKKERMAN JWN, GORTER G, DIERICK J, PETERMANS M: Extreme deficiency of L-type pyruvate kinase with moderate clinical expression. *Clin Chim Acta* 118:241, 1982.

99. NAKASHIMA K: Further evidence of molecular alteration and aberration of erythrocyte pyruvate kinase. *Clin Chim Acta* 55:245, 1974.

100. MARIE J, GARREAU H, KAHN A: Evidence for a postsynthetic proteolytic transformation of human erythrocyte pyruvate kinase into L-type enzyme. *FEBS Lett* 78:91, 1977.

101. KAHN A, MARIE J, GARREAU H, SPRENGERS ED: The genetic system of the L-type pyruvate kinase forms in man. Subunit structure, interrelation and kinetic characteristics of the pyruvate kinase enzymes from erythrocytes and liver. *Biochim Biophys Acta* 523:59, 1978.

102. MARIE J, SIMON M-P, DREYFUS J-C, KAHN A: One gene, but two messenger RNAs encode liver L and red cell L' pyruvate kinase subunits. *Nature* 292:70, 1981.

103. ETIEMBLE J, PICAT C, BOIVIN P: A red cell pyruvate kinase mutant with normal L-type PK in the liver. *Hum Genet* 61:256, 1982.

104. SAHEKI S, SAHEKI K, TANAKA T: Peptide structures of pyruvate kinase isozymes. I. Comparison of the four pyruvate kinase isozymes of the rat. *Biochim Biophys Acta* 704:484, 1982.

105. NOGUCHI T, INOUE H, CHEN H-L, MATSUBARA K, TANAKA T: Molecular cloning of DNA complementary to rat L-type pyruvate kinase mRNA. *J Biol Chem* 258:15220, 1983.

106. INOUE H, NOGUCHI T, TANAKA T: Complete amino acid sequence of rat L-type pyruvate kinase deduced from the cDNA sequence. *Eur J Biochem* 154:465, 1986.

107. IMAMURA K, TANIUCHI K, TANAKA T: Multimolecular forms of pyruvate kinase. II. Purification of M_2-type pyruvate kinase from Yoshida ascites hepatoma 130 cells and comparative studies on the enzymological and immunological properties of the three types of pyruvate kinases, L, M_1, and M_2. *J Biochem* 72:1001, 1972.

108. PETERS J, NASH HR, EICHER EM, BULFIELD G: Polymorphism of kidney pyruvate kinase in the mouse is determined by a gene, Pk-3, on chromosome 9. *Biochem Genet* 19:757, 1981.

109. NOGUCHI T, TANAKA T: The M_1 and M_2 subunits of rat pyruvate kinase are encoded by different messenger RNAs. *J Biol Chem* 257:1110, 1982.

110. HANCE AJ, LEE J, FEITELSON M: The M_1 and M_2 isozymes of pyruvate kinase are the products of the same gene. *Biochem Biophys Res Commun* 106:492, 1982.

111. NOGUCHI T, INOUE H, TANAKA T: The M_1 and M_2-type isozymes of rat pyruvate kinase are produced from the same gene by alternative RNA splicing. *J Biol Chem* 261:13807, 1986.

112. MARIE J, KAHN A, BOIVIN P: Human erythrocyte pyruvate kinase. Total purification and evidence for its antigenic identity with L-type enzyme. *Biochim Biophys Acta* 481:96, 1977.

113. ODA S, ODA E, TANAKA KR: Relationship of density distribution and pyruvate kinase electrophoretic pattern of erythrocytes in sickle cell diseases and other disorders. *Acta Haematol* 60:201, 1978.

114. SPRENGERS ED, STAAL GEJ: Functional changes associated with the sequential transformation of L'_4 into L_4 pyruvate kinase. *Biochim Biophys Acta* 570:259, 1979.

115. TAKEGAWA S, FUJII H, MIWA S: Change of pyruvate kinase isozymes from M_2-to-L-type during development of the red cell. *Br J Haematol* 54:467, 1983.

116. MIWA S, NAKASHIMA K, ARIYOSHI K, SHINOHARA K, ODA E, TANAKA T: Four new pyruvate kinase (PK) variants and a classical PK deficiency. *Br J Haematol* 29:157, 1975.

117. BLACK JA, RITTENBERG MB, BIGLEY RH, KOLER RD: Hemolytic anemia due to pyruvate kinase deficiency: Characterization of the enzymatic activity from eight patients. *Am J Hum Genet* 31:300, 1979.

118. KAHN A, DREYFUS JC: Molecular basis of the hereditary defects of enzyme activity, in Schewe T, Rapoport S (eds): *Molecular Diseases*. New York, Pergamon, 1979, vol 56, p 1.

119. SHINOHARA K, TANAKA KR: Pyruvate kinase deficiency hemolytic anemia: Enzymatic characterization studies in twelve patients. *Hemoglobin* 4:611, 1980.

120. BLACK JA, RITTENBERG MB, STANDERFER RJ, PETERSON JS: Hereditary persistence of fetal erythrocyte pyruvate kinase in the basenji dog, in *The Red Cell*. New York, AR Liss, 1978, p 275.

121. STAAL GEJ, KOSTER JF, KAMP H, VAN MILLIGEN-BOERSMA L, VEEGER C: Human erythrocyte pyruvate kinase. Its purification and some properties. *Biochim Biophys Acta* 227:86, 1971.

122. BLACK JA, HENDERSON MH: Activation and inhibition of human erythrocyte pyruvate kinase by organic phosphates, amino acids, dipeptides and anions. *Biochim Biophys Acta* 284:115, 1972.

123. STAAL GEJ, CEERDINK RP, VLUG AMC, HAMELINK ML: Defective erythrocyte pyruvate kinase. *Clin Chim Acta* 68:11, 1976.

124. ELDER GE, LAPPIN TRJ, LAWSON BE, BRIDGES JM: Three pyruvate kinase variants with increased affinity for PEP. *Br J Haematol* 47:371, 1981.

125. MONOD J, WYMAN J, CHANGEUX JP: On the nature of allosteric transitions: A plausible model. *J Mol Biol* 12:88, 1965.

126. MARIE J, VIVES-CORRONS JL, KAHN A: Hereditary erythrocyte pyruvate kinase deficiency: Molecular and functional studies of four mutant PK variants detected in Spain. *Clin Chim Acta* 81:153, 1977.

127. FUJII S, NAKASHIMA K, KANEKO T: Regulation of erythrocyte pyruvate kinase by cyclic AMP-dependent protein kinase and 2,3-diphosphoglycerate. *Biomed Res* 1:230, 1980.

128. FUJII S, NAKASHIMA K, KANEKO T: Evidence of in vivo phosphorylation of erythrocyte and liver pyruvate kinases. *Biomed Res* 2:316, 1981.

129. NAKASHIMA K, FUJII S, KAKU K, KANEKO T: Calcium-calmodulin dependent phosphorylation of erythrocyte pyruvate kinase. *Biochem Biophys Res Commun* 104:285, 1982.

130. FUJII S, NAKASHIMA K, YANAGIHARA T, SHINOHARA K, KANEKO T: Cyclic AMP-dependent phosphorylation of erythrocyte variant pyruvate kinase. *Biochem Med* 31:47, 1984.

131. PAGLIA DE, VALENTINE WN, BAUGHAN MA, MILLER DR, REED CF, MCINTYRE OR: An inherited molecular lesion of erythrocyte pyruvate kinase. Identification of a kinetically aberrant isozyme associated with premature hemolysis. *J Clin Invest* 47:1929, 1968.

132. PAGLIA DE, KONRAD PN, WOLFF JA, VALENTINE WN: Biphasic reaction kinetics in an anomalous isozyme of erythrocyte pyruvate kinase. *Clin Chim Acta* 73:395, 1976.

133. SHINOHARA K, MIWA S, NAKASHIMA K, ODA E, KAGEOKA T, TSUJINO G: A new pyruvate kinase variant (PK Osaka) demonstrated by partial purification and condensation. *Am J Hum Genet* 28:474, 1976.

134. KAHN A, MARIE J, GALAND C, BOIVIN P: Molecular mechanism of erythrocyte pyruvate kinase deficiency. *Humangenetik* 29:271, 1975.

135. PAGLIA DE, VALENTINE WN, WILLIAMS KO, KONRAD PN: An isozyme of erythrocyte pyruvate kinase (PK-Los Angeles) with impaired kinetics corrected by fructose-1, 6-diphosphate. *Am J Clin Pathol* 68:229, 1977.

136. ZANELLA A, REBULLA P, IZZO C, ZANUSO F, SIRCHIA G: Concomitance of

an active and an inactive mutant of red cell pyruvate kinase (PK). *Scand J Haematol* 22:145, 1979.

137. PAGLIA DE, VALENTINE WN: Molecular lesion affecting the ADP-combining site in a mutant isozyme of erythrocyte pyruvate kinase. *Proc Natl Acad Sci* USA 78:5175, 1981.

138. DENTE L, D'URSO M, DiMAIO S, BRANCACCIO V, LUZZATTO L: Pyruvate kinase deficiency: Characterization of two new genetic variants. *Clin Chim Acta* 126:143, 1982.

139. PAGLIA DE, KEITT AS, VALENTINE WN, GORDON S: Biochemical characterization of three mutant isozymes of erythrocyte pyruvate kinase: PK-"Gainesville," PK-"San Juan," and PK-"Cape Canaveral." *Am J Hematol* 14:335, 1983.

140. BEUTLER E AND FORMAN L: Coexistence of α-thalassemia and a new pyruvate kinase variant: PK Fukien. *Acta Haematol* 69:3, 1983.

141. SCHROTER W, LAKOMEK M, SCHARNETZKY M, TILLMANN W, WINKLER H: Pyruvate kinase "Gottingen": Congenital hemolytic anemia, evidence of heterozygosity, and lack of enzyme cooperativity. *Hum Genet* 60:381, 1982.

142. LAKOMEK M, WINKLER H, SCHARNETZKY M, TILLMANN W, LAIER G, MARTI HR, SCHROTER W: Erythrocyte pyruvate kinase deficiency: Characterization of a new variant (PK "Aarau"). *Blut* 48:123, 1984.

142a. TANI K, FUJII H, NAGATA S, MIWA S: Human liver type pyruvate kinase: Complete amino acid sequence and the expression in mammalian cells. *Proc Natl Acad Sci* USA 85:1792, 1988.

143. VALENTINE WN, HERRING WB, PAGLIA DE, STEUTERMAN MC, BROCKWAY RA, NAKATANI M: Pyruvate kinase Greensboro. A four-generation study of a high $K_{0.5s}$ (phosphoenolpyruvate) variant. *Blood* (in press).

144. SPRENGERS ED, BEEMER FA, STAAL GEJ: A new pyruvate kinase variant: PK-Wouw. *J Mol Med* 3:271, 1978.

145. GRIMES AJ, MEISLER A, DACIE JV: Hereditary non-spherocytic haemolytic anaemia. A study of red-cell carbohydrate metabolism in twelve cases of pyruvate-kinase deficiency. *Br J Haematol* 10:403, 1964.

146. LODER PB, DE GRUCHY GC: Red cell enzymes and co-enzymes in non-spherocytic congenital haemolytic anaemias. *Br J Haematol* 11:21, 1965.

147. ZEREZ CR, TANAKA KR: Impaired nicotinamide adenine dinucleotide synthesis in pyruvate kinase-deficient human erythrocytes: A mechanism for decreased total NAD content and a possible secondary cause of hemolysis. *Blood* 69:999, 1987.

148. ZEREZ CR, LACHANT NA, TANAKA KR: Decrease in subunit aggregation of phosphoribosylpyrophosphate synthetase: A mechanism for decreased nucleotide concentrations in pyruvate kinase-deficient human erythrocytes. *Blood* 68:1024, 1986.

149. ZEREZ CR, WONG MD, TANAKA KR: Impaired phosphoribosylpyrophosphate (PRPP) formation in intact pyruvate kinase deficient RBC: A mechanism for decreased nucleotide content and hemolysis. *Blood* 68:59a, 1986.

150. ROSE IA, WARMS JVB: Control of glycolysis in the human red blood cell. *J Biol Chem* 241:4848, 1966.

151. FAIRBANKS VF, FERNANDEZ MN: The identification of metabolic errors associated with hemolytic anemia. *JAMA* 208:316, 1969.

152. MIWA S, NISHINA T: Studies on pyruvate kinase (PK) deficiency I. Clinical, hematological and erythrocyte enzyme studies. *Acta Haematol (Japan)* 37:1, 1974.

153. TANAKA KR: Hemolytic anemia due to abnormalities of enzymes of anaerobic glycolysis and nucleotide metabolism, in Brain MC and Carbone PP (eds): *Current Therapy in Hematology-Oncology*. Philadelphia, Decker, 1985, p 24.

154. BAUGHAN MA, PAGLIA DE, SCHNEIDER AS, VALENTINE WN: An unusual hematological syndrome with pyruvate-kinase deficiency and thalassemia minor in the kindreds. *Acta Haematol* 39:345, 1968.

155. BROOK J, TANAKA KR: Combination of pyruvate kinase (PK) deficiency and hereditary spherocytosis (HS). *Clin Res* 18:176, 1970.

156. NEUMANN VE, SCHWARZMEIER J, HONETZ H: Hereditare elliptozytose und pyruvatkinasemangel der erythrozyten. *Wien Klin Wochenschr* 84:712, 1972.

157. OSKI FA, NATHAN DG, SIDEL VW, DIAMOND LK: Extreme hemolysis and red-cell distortion in erythrocyte pyruvate kinase deficiency I. Morphology, erythrokinetics, and family enzyme studies. *N Engl J Med* 270:1023, 1964.

158. EULDERINK F, CLETON FJ: Gaucher's disease with severe renal involvement combined with pyruvate-kinase deficiency. *Pathol Eur* 5:409, 1970.

159. DHARMKRONG-AT A, BLOOM GE: Acquired hemolytic anemia associated with infectious mononucleosis in a patient with congenital pyruvate kinase deficiency. *Clin Pediatr* 12:119, 1973.

160. VIVES-CORRONS JL, PUJADES MA, SIERRA J, RIBERA JM: Characteristics of red cell pyruvate kinase (PK) and pyrimidine 5'-nucleotidase (P5N) abnormalities in acute leukaemia and chronic lymphoid diseases with leukaemic expression. *Br J Haematol* 63:173, 1987.

161. LINTULA R: Red cell enzymes in myelodysplastic syndromes: A review. *Scand J Haematol* 36:56, 1986.

162. KAHN A: Abnormalities of erythrocyte enzymes in dyserythropoiesis and malignancies. *Clin Haematol* 10:123, 1981.

163. LIEBERMAN JE, GORDON-SMITH EC: Red cell pyrimidine 5'-nucleotidase and glutathione in myeloproliferative and lymphoproliferative disorders. *Br J Haematol* 44:425, 1980.

164. RENOUX M, BERNARD JF, TORRES M, SCHLEGEL N, AMAR M, LOPEZ M, BOIVIN P: Erythrocyte abnormalities induced by chemotherapy and radiotherapy: Induction of preleukaemic states? *Scand J Haematol* 21:323, 1978.

165. ETIEMBLE J, BERNARD JF, PICAT CH, BELPOMME D, BOIVIN P: Red blood cell enzyme abnormalities in patients treated with chemotherapy. *Br J Haematol* 42:391, 1979.

166. ABE S: Secondary red cell pyruvate kinase deficiency. I. Study of 30 subjects of malignant hematological disorders. *Acta Haematol (Japan)* 39:247, 1976.

167. ZURCHER C, LOOS JA, PRINS HK: Hereditary high ATP content of human erythrocytes. *Folia Haematol (Leipz)* 83:366, 1965.

168. MAX-AUDIT I, ROSA R, MARIE J: Pyruvate kinase hyperactivity genetically determined: Metabolic consequences and molecular characterization. *Blood* 56:902, 1980.

169. ROSA R, MAX-AUDIT I, IZRAEL V, BEUZARD Y, THILLET J, ROSA J: Hereditary pyruvate kinase abnormalities associated with erythrocytes. *Am J Hematol* 10:47, 1981.

170. STAAL GEJ, JANSEN G, ROOS D: Pyruvate kinase and the "high ATP syndrome." *J Clin Invest* 74:231, 1984.

171. VALENTINE WN, OSKI FA, PAGLIA DE, BAUGHAN MA, SCHNEIDER AS, NAIMAN JL: Hereditary hemolytic anemia with hexokinase deficiency. Role of hexokinase in erythrocyte aging. *N Engl J Med* 276:1, 1967.

172. BROK F, RAMOT B, ZWANG E, DANON D: Enzyme activities in human red blood cells of different age groups. *Isr J Med Sci* 2:291, 1966.

173. ROGERS PA, FISHER RA, HARRIS H: An examination of the age-related patterns of decay of the hexokinases of human red cells. *Clin Chim Acta* 65:291, 1975.

174. JANSEN G, KUENDERMAN L, RIJKSEN G, CATS BP, STAAL GEJ: Characteristics of hexokinase, pyruvate kinase, and glucose-6-phosphate dehydrogenase during adult and neonatal reticulocyte maturation. *Am J Hematol* 20:203, 1985.

175. VALENTINE WN, OSKI FA, PAGLIA DE, BAUGHAN MA, SCHNEIDER AS, NAIMAN JL: Erythrocyte hexokinase and hereditary hemolytic anemia, in Beutler E (ed): *Hereditary Disorders of Erythrocyte Metabolism*. New York, Grune & Stratton, 1968, p 288.

176. MAGNANI M, DALLAPICCOLA B: Regional mapping of the locus for hexokinase-1 (HK1). *Hum Genet* 62:181, 1982.

177. LOHR GW, WALLER HD, ANSCHUTZ F, KNOOP A: Biochemische Defekte in den Blutzellen bei familiarer Panmyelopathie (Typ Fanconi). *Humangenetik* 1:383, 1965.

178. PAGLIA DE, SHENDE A, LANZKOWSKY P, VALENTINE WN: Hexokinase "New Hyde Park": A low activity erythrocyte isozyme in a Chinese kindred. *Am J Hematol* 10:107, 1981.

179. NEWMAN P, MUIR A, PARKER AC: Non-spherocytic haemolytic anaemia in mother and son associated with hexokinase deficiency. *Br J Haematol* 46:537, 1980.

180. SIIMES MA, RAHIALA E-L, LEISTI J: Hexokinase deficiency in erythrocytes: A new variant in 5 members of a Finnish family. *Scand J Haematol* 22:214, 1979.

181. RIJKSEN G, STAAL GEJ: Human erythrocyte hexokinase deficiency. Characterization of a mutant enzyme with abnormal regulatory properties. *J Clin Invest* 62:294, 1978.

182. KEITT AS: Hemolytic anemia with impaired hexokinase activity. *J Clin Invest* 48:1997, 1969.

183. NECHELES TF, RAI US, CAMERON D: Congenital nonspherocytic hemolytic anemia associated with an unusual erythrocyte hexokinase abnormality. *J Lab Clin Med* 76:593, 1970.

184. MOSER K, CIRESA M, SCHWARZMEIER J: Hexokinasemangel bei hamolytischer anamie. *Med Welt* 46:1977, 1970.

185. GILSANZ F, MEYER E, PAGLIA DE, VALENTINE WN: Congenital hemolytic anemia due to hexokinase deficiency. *Am J Dis Child* 132:637, 1978.

186. BOARD PG, TRUEWORTHY R, SMITH JE, MOORE K: Congenital nonspherocytic hemolytic anemia with an unstable hexokinase variant. *Blood* 51:111, 1978.

187. BEUTLER E, DYMENT PG, MATSUMOTO F: Hereditary nonspherocytic hemolytic anemia and hexokinase deficiency. *Blood* 51:935, 1978.

188. RIJKSEN G, STAAL GEJ: Regulation of human erythrocyte hexokinase. The influence of glycolytic intermediates and inorganic phosphate. *Biochim Biophys Acta* 485:75, 1977.

189. PAGLIA DE, VALENTINE WN: Hereditary glucosephosphate isomerase deficiency. A review. *Am J Clin Pathol* 62:740, 1974.

190. BAUGHAN MA, VALENTINE WN, PAGLIA DE, WAYS PO, SIMON ER, DEMARSH QB: Hereditary hemolytic anemia associated with glucosephosphate isomerase (GPI) deficiency—A new enzyme defect of human erythrocytes. *Blood* 32:236, 1968.

191. MATHAY KK, MENTZER WC: Erythrocyte enzymopathies in the newborn. *Clin Haematol* 10:31, 1981.

192. WHITELAW AGL, ROGERS PA, HOPKINSON DA, GORDON H, EMERSON PM, DARLEY JH, REID C, CRAWFORD M d'A: Congenital haemolytic anaemia resulting from glucose phosphate isomerase deficiency: Genetics, clinical picture and pre-natal diagnosis. *J Med Genet* 16:189, 1979.

193. RAVINDRANATH Y, PAGLIA DE, WARRIER I, VALENTINE WN, NAKATANI M, BROCKWAY RA: Defective glucosephosphate isomerase as a cause of hydrops fetalis. *N Engl J Med* 316:258, 1987.

194. PAGLIA DE, HOLLAND P, BAUGHAN MA, VALENTINE WN: Occurrence of defective hexosephosphate isomerization in human erythrocytes and leukocytes. *N Engl J Med* 280:66, 1969.

195. CARTER P, TEMKINE H, GRISCELLI C: Étude biochimique d'une anemie hemolytique avec deficit familial en phosphohexosisomerase. *Enzymol Biol Clin* 10:439, 1969.

196. ARNOLD H, BLUME KG, BUSCH D, LENKEIT U, LOHR GW, LUBS E: Klinische und biochemische untersuchungen zur glucosephosphatisomerase normaler menschlicher erythrocyten und bei glucosephosphatisomerasemangel. *Klin Wochenschr* 48:1299, 1970.

197. TARIVERDIAN G, ARNOLD H, BLUME KG, LENKEIT U, LOHR GW: Zur formalgenetik der phosphoglucoseisomerase (EC 5.3.1.9). Untersuchung einer sippe mit PGI-defizienz. *Humangenetik* 10:218, 1970.

198. SCHROTER W, BRITTINGER G, ZIMMERSCHMITT E, KONIG E: A new haemolytic syndrome with glucosephosphate isomerase (GPI) and glucose-6-phosphate dehydrogenase (G6PD) deficiency of the erythrocytes. Biochemical studies. *Eur J Clin Invest* 1:145, 1970.

199. SCHROTER W, BRITTINGER G, ZIMMERSCHMITT E, KONIG E, SCHRADER D: Combined glucosephosphate isomerase and glucose-6-phosphate dehydrogenase deficiency of the erythrocytes: A new haemolytic syndrome. *Br J Haematol* 20:249, 1971.

200. OSKI F, FULLER E: Glucose-phosphate isomerase (GPI) deficiency associated with abnormal osmotic fragility and spherocytes. *Clin Res* 19:427, 1971.

201. BLUME KG, HRYNIUK W, POWARS D, TRINIDAD F, WEST C, BEUTLER E: Characterization of two new variants of glucose-phosphate-isomerase deficiency with hereditary nonspherocytic hemolytic anemia. *J Lab Clin Med* 79:942, 1972.

202. ARNOLD H, ENGELHARDT R, LOHR GW, JACOBI H, LIEBOLD I: Glucosephosphateisomerase Typ Recklinghausen: eine neue defektvariante mit hamolytischer anamie. *Klin Wochenschr* 51:1198, 1973.

203. LOHR GW, ARNOLD H, BLUME KG, ENGELHARDT R, BEUTLER E: Hereditary deficiency of glucosephosphate isomerase as a cause of nonspherocytic hemolytic anemia. *Blut* 26:393, 1973.

204. MIWA S, NAKASHIMA K, ODA S, MATSUMOTO N, OGAWA H, KOBAYASHI R, KOTANI M, HARATA A, ONAYA T, YAMADA T: Glucosephosphate isomerase (GPI) deficiency hereditary nonspherocytic hemolytic anemia. Report of the second case found in Japan. *Acta Haematol (Japan)* 36:70, 1973.

205. NAKASHIMA K, MIWA S, ODA S, ODA E, MATSUMOTO N, FUKUMOTO Y, YAMADA T: Electrophoretic and kinetic studies of glucose-phosphate isomerase (GPI) in two different Japanese families with GPI deficiency. *Am J Hum Genet* 25:294, 1973.

206. ARNOLD H, BLUME KG, ENGELHARDT R, LOHR GW: Glucosephosphate isomerase deficiency: Evidence for in vivo instability of an enzyme variant with hemolysis. *Blood* 41:691, 1973.

207. ARNOLD H, BLUME KG, LOHR GW, SCHROTER W, KOCH HH, WONNEBERGER B: Glucose phosphate isomerase deficiency with congenital nonspherocytic hemolytic anemia: A new variant type (type Nordhorn). II. Purification and biochemical properties of the defective enzyme. *Pediatr Res* 8:26, 1974.

208. SCHROTER W, KOCH HH, WONNEBERGER B, KALINOWSKY W, ARNOLD H, BLUME KG, HUTHER W: Glucose phosphate isomerase deficiency with congenital nonspherocytic hemolytic anemia: A new variant (type Nordhorn): I. Clinical and genetic studies. *Pediatr Res* 8:18, 1974.

209. CHILCOTE RR, BAEHNER RL: Red cell (RBC) glucose phosphate isomerase deficiency (GPI): Clinical and laboratory evidence of increased blood viscosity. *Pediatr Res* 8:398, 1974.

210. HUTTON JJ, CHILCOTE RR: Glucose phosphate isomerase deficiency with hereditary nonspherocytic hemolytic anemia. *J Pediatr* 85:494, 1974.

211. PAGLIA DE, PAREDES R, VALENTINE WN, DORANTES S, KONRAD PN: Unique phenotypic expression of glucosephosphate isomerase deficiency. *Am J Hum Genet* 27:62, 1975.

212. ARNOLD H, DODINVAL-VERSIE J, LAMBOTTE C, LOHR GW, VAN DER HOFSTADT J: Glucosephosphate isomerase deficiency type Liege: A new variant with congenital nonspherocytic hemolytic anemia. *Blut* 35:187, 1977.

213. KAHN A, BUC HA, GIROT R, COTTREAU D, GRISCELLI C: Molecular and functional anomalies in two new mutant glucose-phosphate-isomerase variants with enzyme deficiency and chronic hemolysis. *Hum Genet* 40:293, 1978.

214. SCHROTER W, TILLMAN W: Congenital nonspherocytic hemolytic anemia associated with glucose-phosphate isomerase deficiency: Variant Paderborn. *Klin Wochenschr* 55:393, 1977.

215. van BIERVLIET JP, van MILLIGEN-BOERSMA L, STAAL GEJ: A new variant of glucosephosphate isomerase deficiency: GPI Utrecht. *Clin Chim Acta* 65:157, 1975.

216. van BIERVLIET JP, VLUG A, BARTSTRA H, ROTTEVEEL JJ, DE VAAN GAM, STAAL GEJ: A new variant of glucosephosphate isomerase deficiency. *Hum Genet* 30:35, 1975.

217. KAHN A, VIVES-CORRONS JL, BERTRAND O, COTTREAU D, MARIE J, BOIVIN P: Glucosephosphate isomerase deficiency due to a new variant (GPI Barcelona) and to a silent gene: Biochemical, immunological, and genetic studies. *Clin Chim Acta* 66:145, 1976.

218. STAAL GEJ, AKKERMAN JWN, EGGERMONT E, van BIERVLIET JP: A new variant of glucosephosphate isomerase: G.P.I.-Kortrijk. *Clin Chim Acta* 78:121, 1977.

219. GALAND C, TORRES M, BOIVIN P, BOURGEAUD JP: A new variant of glucosephosphate isomerase deficiency with mild haemolytic anaemia (GPI-Mytho). *Scand J Haematol* 20:77, 1978.

220. ZANELLA A, IZZO C, REBULLA P, PERRONI L, MARIANI M, CANESTRI G, SANSONE G, SIRCHIA G: The first stable variant of erythrocyte glucosephosphate isomerase associated with severe hemolytic anemia. *Am J Hematol* 9:1, 1980.

221. CARTER ND, YOSHIDA A: Purification and characterization of human phosphoglucose isomerase. *Biochim Biophys Acta* 181:12, 1969.

222. MCKUSICK VA: The anatomy of the human genome. *Am J Med* 69:267, 1980.

223. PAYNE DM, PORTER DW, GRACY RW: Evidence against the occurrence of tissue-specific variants and isoenzymes of phosphoglucose isomerase. *Arch Biochem Biophys* 151:122, 1972.

224. LAYZER RB, ROWLAND LP, BANK WJ: Physical and kinetic properties of human phosphofructokinase from skeletal muscle and erythrocytes. *J Biol Chem* 244:3823, 1969.

225. STAAL GEJ, KOSTER JF, BANZIGER CJM, VAN MILLIGEN-BOERSMA L: Human erythrocyte phosphofructokinase: Its purification and some properties. *Biochim Biophys Acta* 276:113, 1972.

226. COTTREAU D, LEVIN MJ, KAHN A: Purification and partial characterization of different forms of phosphofructokinase in man. *Biochim Biophys Acta* 568:183, 1979.

227. KAHN A, MEIENHOFER M-C, COTTREAU D, LAGRANGE J-L, DREYFUS J-C: Phosphofructokinase (PFK) isozymes in man. 1. Studies of adult human tissues. *Hum Genet* 48:93, 1979.

228. MEIENHOFER M-C, LAGRANGE J-L, COTTREAU D, LENOIR G, DREYFUS J-C, KAHN A: Phosphofructokinase in human blood cells. *Blood* 54:389, 1979.

229. VORA S, SEAMAN C, DURHAM S, PIOMELLI S: Isozymes of human phosphofructokinase: Identification and subunit structural characterization of a new system. *Proc Natl Acad Sci USA* 77:62, 1980.

230. KAHN A, COTTREAU D, MEIENHOFER M-C: Purification of F₄ phosphofructokinase from human platelets and comparison with the other phosphofructokinase forms. *Biochim Biophys Acta* 611:114, 1980.

231. VORA S: Isozymes of phosphofructokinase, in Rattazzi MC, Scandalios JG, Whitt GS (eds): *Isozymes. Current Topics in Biological and Medical Research.* New York, AR Liss, 1982, vol 6, p 119.

232. TSAI MY, GONZALEZ F, KEMP RG: Physiological significance of phosphofructokinase isozymes, in Markert CL (ed): *Isozymes. II. Physiological Function.* New York, Academic, 1975, p 819.

233. VORA S, DURHAM S, DE MARTINVILLE B, GEORGE DL, FRANCKE U: Assignment of the human gene for muscle-type phosphofructokinase (PFKM) to chromosome 1 (region cen → q32) using somatic cell hybrids and monoclonal anti-M antibody. *Somatic Cell Genet* 8:95, 1982.

234. VORA S, FRANCKE U: Assignment of the human gene for liver-type 6-phosphofructokinase isozyme (PFKL) to chromosome 21 by using somatic cell hybrids and monoclonal anti-L antibody. *Proc Natl Acad Sci USA* 78:3738, 1981.

235. VORA S, MIRANDA A, HERNANDEZ E, FRANCKE U: Regional assignment of the human gene for platelet-type phosphofructokinase (PFKP) to chromosome 10p: Novel use of poly-specific rodent antisera to localize human enzyme genes. *Hum Genet* 63:374, 1983.

236. VAN KEUREN M, DRABKIN H, HART I, HARKER D, PATTERSON D, VORA S: Regional assignment of human liver-type-6-phosphofructokinase to chromosome 21q 22.3 by using somatic cell hybrids and a monoclonal anti-L antibody. *Hum Genet* 74:34, 1986.

237. TARUI S, OKUNO G, IKURA Y, TANAKA T, SUDA M, NISHIKAWA M: Phosphofructokinase deficiency in skeletal muscle: A new type of glycogenosis. *Biochem Biophys Res Commun* 19:517, 1965.

238. TARUI S, KONO N, NASU T, NISHIKAWA M: Enzymatic basis for the coexistence of myopathy and hemolytic disease in inherited muscle phosphofructokinase deficiency. *Biochem Biophys Res Commun* 34:77, 1969.

239. LAYZER RB, ROWLAND LP, RANNEY HM: Muscle phosphofructokinase deficiency. *Arch Neurol* 17:512, 1967.

240. ETIEMBLE J, KAHN A, BOIVIN P, BERNARD JF, GOUDEMAND M: Hereditary hemolytic anemia with erythrocyte phosphofructokinase deficiency. Studies of some properties of erythrocyte and muscle enzyme. *Hum Genet* 31:83, 1976.

241. MIWA S, SATO T, MURAO H, KOZURU M, IBAYASHI H: A new type of phosphofructokinase deficiency hereditary nonspherocytic hemolytic anemia. *Acta Haematol (Japan)* 35:113, 1972.

242. ETIEMBLE J, PICAT C, SIMEON J, BLATRIX C, BOIVIN P: Inherited erythrocyte phosphofructokinase deficiency: Molecular mechanism. *Hum Genet* 55:383, 1980.

243. WATERBURY L, FRENKEL EP: Hereditary nonspherocytic hemolysis with erythrocyte phosphofructokinase deficiency. *Blood* 39:415, 1972.

244. SERRATRICE G, MONGES A, ROUX H: Forme myopathique due deficit en phosphofructokinase. *Rev Neurol* 120:271, 1969.

245. TOBIN WE, HUIJING F, PORRO RS, SALZMAN RT: Muscle phosphofructokinase deficiency. *Arch Neurol* 28:128, 1973.

246. BOULARD MR, MEIENHOFER MC, BOIS M, REVIRON M, NAJEAN Y: Red cell phosphofructokinase deficiency. *N Engl J Med* 291:978, 1974.

247. KAHN A, ETIEMBLE J, MEIENHOFER MC, BOIVIN P: Erythrocyte phosphofructokinase deficiency associated with an unstable variant of muscle phosphofructokinase. *Clin Chim Acta* 61:415, 1975.

248. SERVIDEI S, BONILLA E, DIEDRICH RG, DORNFIELD M, OATES JD, DAVIDSON M, VORA S, DiMAURO S: Fatal infantile form of muscle phosphofructokinase deficiency. *Neurology* 36:1465, 1986.

249. VORA S, DiMAURO S, SPEAR D, HARKER D, DANON MJ: Characterization of the enzymatic defect in late-onset muscle phosphofructokinase deficiency. New subtype of glycogen storage disease Type VII. *J Clin Invest* 80:1479, 1987.

250. LAYZER RB, RASMUSSEN J: The molecular basis of muscle phosphofructokinase deficiency. *Arch Neurol* 31:411, 1974.

251. VORA S, DAVIDSON M, SEAMAN C, MIRANDA AF, NOBLE NA, TANAKA KR, FRENKEL EP, DiMAURO S: Heterogeneity of the molecular lesions in inherited phosphofructokinase deficiency. *J Clin Invest* 72:1995, 1983.

252. VORA S, CORASH L, ENGEL WK, DURHAM S, SEAMAN C, PIOMELLI S: The molecular mechanism of the inherited phosphofructokinase deficiency associated with hemolysis and myopathy. *Blood* 55:629, 1980.

253. BROWN BI, BROWN DH: Glycogen-storage diseases: Types I, III, IV, V, VII and unclassified glycogenoses, in Dickens F, Randle PJ, Whelan WJ (eds): *Carbohydrate Metabolism and Its Disorders.* London, Academic, 1968, vol 2, p 123.

254. MINEO I, KONO N, SHIMIZU T, HARA N, YAMADA Y, SUMI S, NONAKA K, TARUI S: Excess purine degradation in exercising muscles of patients with glycogen storage disease Types V and VII. *J Clin Invest* 76:556, 1985.

255. TAURI S, KONO N, KUWAJIMA M, KITANI T: Hereditary and acquired abnormalities in erythrocyte phosphofructokinase activity: The close association with altered 2,3-diphosphoglycerate levels. *Hemoglobin* 4:581, 1980.

256. GIGER U, HARVEY JW, YAMAGUCHI RA, McNULTY PK, CHIAPELLA A, BEUTLER E: Inherited phosphofructokinase deficiency in dogs with hyperventilation-induced hemolysis: Increased *in vitro* and *in vivo* alkaline fragility of erythrocytes. *Blood* 65:345, 1985.

257. VORA S, GIGER V, TURCHEN S, HARVEY JW: Characterization of the enzymatic lesion in inherited phosphofructokinase deficiency in the dog: An animal analogue of human glycogen storage disease Type VII. *Proc Natl Acad Sci USA,* 82:8109, 1985.

258. BEUTLER E, SCOTT S, BISHOP A, MARGOLIS N, MATSUMOTO F, KUHL W: Red cell aldolase deficiency and hemolytic anemia: A new syndrome. *Trans Assoc Am Physicians* 86:154, 1973.

259. MIWA S, FUJII H, TANO K, TAKAHASHI K, TAKEGAWA S, FUJINAMI N, SAKURAI M, KUBO M, TANIMOTO Y, KATO T, MATSUMOTO N: Two cases of red cell aldolase deficiency associated with hereditary hemolytic anemia in a Japanese family. *Am J Hematol* 11:425, 1981.

259a. KISHI H, MUKAI T, HIRONO A, FUJII H, MIWA S, HORI K: Human aldolase A deficiency associated with hemolytic anemia: Thermolabile aldolase due to a single base mutation. *Proc Natl Acad Sci USA* 84:8623, 1987.

260. PENHOET E, RAJKUMAR T, RUTTER WJ: Multiple forms of fructose diphosphate aldolase in mammalian tissues. *Proc Natl Acad Sci USA* 56:1275, 1966.

261. LU HS, YUAN PM, GRACY RW: Primary structure of human triosephosphate isomerase. *J Biol Chem* 259:11958, 1984.

262. SCHNEIDER AS, VALENTINE WN, HATTORI M, HEINS HL JR: Hereditary hemolytic anemia with triosephosphate isomerase deficiency. *N Engl J Med* 272:229, 1965.

263. SCHNEIDER AS, VALENTINE WN, BAUGHAN MA, PAGLIA DE, SHORE NA, HEINS HL JR: Triosephosphate isomerase deficiency. A. A multi-system inherited enzyme disorder. Clinical and genetic aspects, in Beutler E (ed): *Hereditary Disorders of Erythrocyte Metabolism.* New York, Grune & Stratton, 1968, p 265.

264. VALENTINE WN, PAGLIA DE: Erythrocyte enzymopathies, hemolytic anemia, and multisystem disease: An annotated review. *Blood* 64:583, 1984.

265. VALENTINE WN, SCHNEIDER AS, BAUGHAN MA, PAGLIA DE, HEINS HL JR: Hereditary hemolytic anemia with triosephosphate isomerase deficiency. Studies in kindreds with coexistent sickle cell trait and erythrocyte glucose-6-phosphate dehydrogenase deficiency. *Am J Med* 41:27, 1966.

266. ANGELMAN H, BRAIN MC, MacIVER JE: A case of triosephosphate isomerase deficiency with sudden death, in *Abstr XIIIth Int Congr Hematol.* Munich, Germany, 1970, p 122.

267. VIVES-CORRONS J-L, RUBINSON-SKALA H, MATEO M, ESTELLA J, FELIU E, DREYFUS J-C: Triosephosphate isomerase deficiency with hemolytic anemia and severe neuromuscular disease: Familial and biochemical studies of a case found in Spain. *Hum Genet* 42:171, 1978.

268. HARRIS SR, PAGLIA DE, JAFFE ER, VALENTINE WN, KLEIN RL: Triosephosphate isomerase deficiency in an adult. *Clin Res* 18:529, 1970.

269. POLL-THE BT, AICARDI J, GIROT R, ROSA R: Neurological findings in triosephosphate isomerase deficiency. *Ann Neurol* 17:439, 1985.

270. SCHNEIDER AS, DUNN I, IBSEN KH, WEINSTEIN IM: Triosephosphate isomerase deficiency. B. Inherited triosephosphate isomerase deficiency. Erythrocyte carbohydrate metabolism and preliminary studies of the erythrocyte enzyme, in Beutler E (ed): *Hereditary Disorders of Erythrocyte Metabolism.* New York, Grune & Stratton, 1968, p 273.

271. JONGSMA APM, LOS WRT, HAGEMEIJER A: Evidence for synteny between the human loci for triosephosphate isomerase, lactate dehydrogenase-B and peptidase-B and the regional mapping of these loci on chromosome 12. *Cytogenet Cell Genet* 13:106, 1974.

272. JONGSMA APM, HAGAMEIJER J, MIERALHAN P: Regional mapping of TPI, LDH-B and PEP-B on chromosome 12 of man, in Second International Workshop on Human Gene Mapping, Rotterdam Conference, Basel, National Foundation, 1974, p 189.

273. YUAN PM, TALENT JM, GRACY RW: Molecular basis for the accumulation of acidic isozymes of triosephosphate isomerase in aging. *Mech Ageing Dev* 17:151, 1981.

274. NEEL JV, MOHRENWEISER HW, MEISLER MH: Rate of spontaneous mutation at human loci encoding protein structure. *Proc Natl Acad Sci USA* 77:6037, 1980.

275. GRACY RW: Glucosephosphate and triosephosphate isomerases: Significance of isozyme structural differences in evolution, physiology, and aging, in Rattazzi MC, Scandalios JG, Whitt GS (eds): *Isozymes. Current Topics in Biological and Medical Research.* New York, AR Liss, 1982, vol 6, p 183.

276. MAQUAT LE, CHILCOTE R, RYAN M: Human triosephosphate isomerase cDNA and protein structure. Studies of triosephosphate isomerase deficiency in man. *J Biol Chem* 260:3748, 1985.

277. KAPLAN JC, TEEPLE L, SHORE NA, BEUTLER E: Electrophoretic abnormality in triosephosphate isomerase deficiency. *Biochem Biophys Res Commun* 31:768, 1968.

278. DAAR IO, ARTYMIUK PJ, PHILLIPS DC, MAQUAT LE: Human triosephosphate isomerase deficiency: A single amino acid substitution results in a thermolabile enzyme. *Proc Natl Acad Sci USA* 83:7903, 1986.

279. EBER SW, DUNNWALD M, BELOHRADSKY BH, BIDLINGMAIER F, SCHIEVELBEIN H, WEINMANN HM, KRIETSCH WKG: Hereditary deficiency of triosephosphate isomerase in four unrelated families. *Eur J Clin Invest* 9:195, 1979.

280. SKALA H, DREYFUS J-C, VIVES-CORRONS JL, MATSUMOTO F, BEUTLER E: Triosphosphate isomerase deficiency. *Biochem Med* 18:226, 1977.

281. FREYCON F, LAURAS B, BOVIER-LAPIERRE F, DORCHE CL, GODDON R: Anemie hemolytique congenitale par deficit en triosephosphate isomerase. *Pediatrie* 30:55, 1975.

282. ROSA R, PREHU M-O, CALVIN MC, BADOVAL J, ALIX D, GIROD R: Hereditary triosephosphate isomerase deficiency: Seven new homozygous cases. *Hum Genet* 71:235, 1985.

283. VANDEBERG JL: The phosphoglycerate kinase isozyme system in mammals: Biochemical, genetic, developmental, and evolutionary aspects, in Rattazzi MC, Scandalios JG, Whitt GS (eds): *Isozymes. Current Topics in Biological and Medical Research.* New York, AR Liss, 1985, vol 12, p 133.

284. KRAUS AP, LANGSTON MF, LYNCH BL: Red cell phosphoglycerate kinase deficiency. A new cause of non-spherocytic hemolytic anemia. *Biochem Biophys Res Commun* 30:173, 1968.

285. VALENTINE WN, HSIEH H-S, PAGLIA DE, ANDERSON HM, BAUGHAN MA, JAFFE ER, GARSON OM: Hereditary hemolytic anemia: Association with phosphoglycerate kinase deficiency in erythrocytes and leukocytes. *Trans Assoc Am Physicians* 81:49, 1968.

286. VALENTINE WN, HSIEH H-S, PAGLIA DE, ANDERSON HM, BAUGHAN MA, JAFFE ER, GARSON OM: Hereditary hemolytic anemia associated with phosphoglycerate kinase deficiency in erythrocytes and leukocytes. A probable X-chromosome-linked syndrome. *N Engl J Med* 280:528, 1969.

287. CHEN S-H, MALCOLM LA, YOSHIDA A, GIBLETT ER: Phosphoglycerate kinase: An X-linked polymorphism in man. *Am J Hum Genet* 23:87, 1971.

288. MEERA KHAN P, WESTERVELD A, GRZESCHIK KH, DEYS BF, GARSON OM, SINISCALCO M: X-linkage of human phosphoglycerate kinase confirmed in man-mouse and man-Chinese hamster somatic cell hybrids. *Am J Hum Genet* 23:614, 1971.

289. DEYS BF, GRZESCHIK KH, GRZESCHIK A, JAFFE ER, SINISCALCO M: Human phosphoglycerate kinase and inactivation of the X chromosome. *Science* 175:1002, 1972.

290. SVIRKLYS LG: Phosphoglycerate kinase deficiency. Thesis for Degree of Doctor of Philosophy, School of Biochemistry, The University of New South Wales, Australia, 1984.

291. SVIRKLYS LG, LEE CS, O'SULLIVAN WJ: Phosphoglycerate kinase: Studies on normal and a mutant human enzyme. *J Inherited Metab Dis* 9:374, 1986.

292. MIWA S, NAKASHIMA K, ODA S, TAKAHASHI K, MOROOKA K, NAKASHIMA T: Evidence of the decreased muscle enzyme activity in erythrocyte phosphoglycerate kinase deficiency. *Acta Haematol (Japan)* 37:59, 1974.

293. STRAUSS RG, MCCARTHY DJ, MAUER AM: Neutrophil function in congenital phosphoglycerate kinase deficiency. *J Pediatr* 85:341, 1974.

294. KRIETSCH WKG, KRIETSCH H, KAISER W, DUNNWALD M, KUNTZ GWK, DUHM J, BUCHER T: Hereditary deficiency of phosphoglycerate kinase. A new variant in erythrocytes and leucocytes, not associated with haemolytic anaemia. *Eur J Clin Invest* 7:427, 1977.

295. KRIETSCH WKG, EBER SW, HAAS B, RUPPELT W, KUNTZ GWK: Characterization of a phosphoglycerate kinase deficiency variant not associated with hemolytic anemia. *Am J Hum Genet* 32:364, 1980.

296. ROSA R, GEORGE C, FARDEAU M, CALVIN M-C, RAPIN M, ROSA J: A new case of phosphoglycerate kinase deficiency: PGK Creteil associated with rhabdomyolysis and lacking hemolytic anemia. *Blood* 60:84, 1982.

297. DIMAURO S, DALAKAS M, MIRANDA AF: Phosphoglycerate kinase deficiency: Another cause of recurrent myoglobinuria. *Ann Neurol* 13:11, 1983.

298. MIWA S, NAKASHIMA K, ODA S, OGAWA H, NAGAFUJI H, ARIMA M, OKUNA T, NAKASHIMA T: Phosphoglycerate kinase (PGK) deficiency hereditary nonspherocytic hemolytic anemia: Report of a case found in Japanese family. *Acta Haematol (Japan)* 35:571, 1972.

299. ARESE P, BOSIA A, GALLO E, MAZZA U, PESCARMONA GP: Red cell glycolysis in a case of 3-phosphoglycerate kinase deficiency. *Eur J Clin Invest* 3:86, 1973.

300. KONRAD PN, MCCARTHY DJ, MAUER AM, VALENTINE WN, PAGLIA DE: Erythrocyte and leukocyte phosphoglycerate kinase deficiency with neurologic disease. *J Pediatr* 82:456, 1973.

301. CARTER P, HABIBI B, LEROUX JP, MARCHAD JC: Anemie hemolytique congenitale associee a un deficit en phosphoglycerate kinase dans les globules rouges, les polynucleaires, et les lymphocytes. *Nouv Rev Fr Hematol* 11:565, 1971.

302. BOIVIN P, HAKIM J, MANDEREAU J, GALAND G, DEGOS F, SCHAISON G: Deficit en 3-phosphoglycerate kinase erythrocytaire et leucocytaire. Étude des propriétés de l'enzyme, de la fonction phagocytaire des polynucleaires et revise de la litteratura. *Nouv Rev Fr Hematol* 14:495, 1974.

303. KAHN A, COTTREAU O, GALAND C, BOIVIN P: Human erythrocyte phosphoglycerate kinase deficiency. Presence in a deficient patient of a stable variant with lowered catalytic activity. *Clin Chim Acta* 69:21, 1976.

304. DODGSON SJ, LEE CS, HOLLAND RAB, O'SULLIVAN WJ, VOWELS MR: Erythrocyte phosphoglycerate kinase deficiency: Enzymatic and oxygen binding studies, *Aust NZ J Med* 10:614, 1980.

305. SVIRKLYS LG, O'SULLIVAN WJ: Tissue levels of glycolytic enzymes in phosphoglycerate kinase deficiency. *Clin Chim Acta* 108:309, 1980.

306. HUANG I-Y, WELCH CD, YOSHIDA A: Complete amino acid sequence of human phosphoglycerate kinase: Cyanogen bromide peptides and complete amino acid sequence. *J Biol Chem* 255:6412, 1980.

307. MICHELSON AM, MARKHAM AF, ORKIN SH: Isolation and DNA sequence of a full-length cDNA clone from human X chromosome-encoded phosphoglycerate kinase. *Proc Natl Acad Sci USA* 80:472, 1983.

308. HUANG I-Y, FUJII H, YOSHIDA A: Structure and function of normal and variant human phosphoglycerate kinase. *Hemoglobin* 4:601, 1980.

309. YOSHIDA A, WATANABE S: Human phosphoglycerate kinase. II. Structure of a variant enzyme. *J Biol Chem* 247:446, 1972.

310. FUJII H, YOSHIDA A: Molecular abnormality of phosphoglycerate kinase-Uppsala associated with chronic nonspherocytic hemolytic anemia. *Proc Natl Acad Sci USA* 77:5461, 1980.

311. FUJII H, KRIETSCH WKG, YOSHIDA A: A single amino acid substitution (Asp → Asn) in a phosphoglycerate kinase variant (PGK Munchen) associated with enzyme deficiency. *J Biol Chem* 255:6421, 1980.

312. FUJII H, CHEN S-H, AKATSUKA J, MIWA S, YOSHIDA A: Use of cultured lymphoblastoid cells for the study of abnormal enzymes. Molecular abnormality of a phosphoglycerate kinase variant associated with hemolytic anemia. *Proc Natl Acad Sci USA* 78:2587, 1981.

313. SCHROTER W: 2,3-diphosphoglyceratstoffwechsel und 2,3-diphosphoglyceratmutasemangel in erythrozyten. *Blut* 20:311, 1970.

314. HAGGERTY NW, DUNBAR B, FOTHERGILL LA: The complete amino acid sequence of human erythrocyte diphosphoglycerate mutase. *EMBO J* 2:1213, 1983.

315. JOULIN V, GAREL MC, PREHU MO, ROSA R, VALENTIN C, ROSA J, COHEN-SOLAL M: Cloning of the human 2,3-bisphosphoglycerate mutase cDNA and genomic arrangement. *Blood* (Suppl 1) 68:37a, 1986.

316. JOULIN V, PEDUZZI J, ROMEO P-H, ROSA R, VALENTIN C, DUBART A, LAPEYRE B, BLOUQUIT Y, GAREL M-C, GOOSSENS M, ROSA J, COHEN-SOLAL M: Molecular cloning and sequencing of the human erythrocyte 2,3-bisphosphoglycerate mutase cDNA: revised amino acid sequence. *EMBO J* 5:2275, 1986.

317. FOTHERGILL-GILMORE LA: The evolution of the glycolytic pathway. *Trends Biochem Sci* 11:47, 1986.

318. MIWA S, NISHINA T, KAKEHASHI Y, KITAMURA M, HIRATSUKA A, SHIZUME K: Studies on erythrocyte metabolism in a case with hereditary deficiency of H-subunit of lactate dehydrogenase. *Acta Haematol (Japan)* 34:228, 1971.

319. KITAMURA M, IIJIMA N, HASHIMOTO F, HIRATSUKA A: Hereditary deficiency of subunit H of lactate dehydrogenase. *Clin Chim Acta* 34:419, 1971.

320. KANNO T, SUDO K, TAKEUCHI I, KANDA S, HONDA N, NISHIMURA Y, OYAMA K: Hereditary deficiency of lactate dehydrogenase M-subunit. *Clin Chim Acta* 108:267, 1980.

321. PARR CW, FITCH LI: Inherited quantitative variations of human phosphogluconate dehydrogenase. *Ann Hum Genet* 30:339, 1967.

322. BREWER GJ, DERN RJ: A new inherited enzymatic deficiency of human erythrocytes: 6-phosphogluconate dehydrogenase deficiency. *Am J Hum Genet* 16:472, 1964.

323. DERN RJ, BREWER GJ, TASHIAN RE, SHOWS TB: Hereditary variation of erythrocytic 6-phosphogluconate dehydrogenase. *J Lab Clin Med* 67:255, 1966.

324. BEUTLER E, KUHL W: Limiting role of 6-phosphogluconolactonase in erythrocyte hexosemonophosphate pathway metabolism. *J Lab Clin Med* 106:573, 1985.

325. BEUTLER E, KUHL W, TERRI G: 6-phosphogluconolactonase deficiency, a hereditary erythrocyte enzyme deficiency: Possible interaction with glucose-6-phosphate dehydrogenase deficiency. *Proc Natl Acad Sci USA* 82:3876, 1985.

326. MILLS GC: The purification and properties of glutathione peroxidase of erythrocytes. *J Biol Chem* 234:502, 1959.

327. MILLS GC: Glutathione peroxidase and the destruction of hydrogen peroxide in animal tissues. *Arch Biochem Biophys* 86:1, 1960.

328. COHEN G, HOCHSTEIN P: Glutathione peroxidase: The primary agent for the elimination of hydrogen peroxide in erythrocytes. *Biochemistry* 2:1420, 1963.

329. PAGLIA DE, VALENTINE WN: Studies on the quantitative and qualitative characterization of erythrocyte glutathione peroxidase. *J Lab Clin Med* 70:158, 1967.

330. BOIVIN P, GALAND C, HAKIM J, ROGE J, GUEROULT N: Anémie hémolytique avec déficit en glutathion-peroxydase chez un adulte. *Enzymol Biol Clin* 10:68, 1969.

331. BOIVIN P, GALAND C, HAKIM J, BLERY M: Deficit en glutathionperoxydase erythrocytaire et anemie hemolytique medicamenteuse. *Presse Med* 78:171, 1970.

332. HOPKINS J, TUDHOPE GR: Glutathione peroxidase in human red cells in health and disease. *Br J Haematol* 25:563, 1973.

333. NECHELES TF, MALDONADO N, BARQUET-CHEDIAK A, ALLEN DM: Homozygous erythrocyte glutathione-peroxidase deficiency: Clinical and biochemical studies. *Blood* 33:164, 1969.

334. NECHELES TF, STEINBERG MH, CAMERON D: Erythrocyte glutathione-peroxidase deficiency. *Br J Haematol* 19:605, 1970.

335. STEINBERG M, BRAUER MJ, NECHELES TF: Acute hemolytic anemia associated with erythrocyte glutathione-peroxidase deficiency. *Arch Intern Med* 125:302, 1970.

336. STEINBERG M, NECHELES TF: Erythrocyte glutathione peroxidase deficiency. *Am J Med* 50:542, 1971.

337. BEUTLER E, MATSUMOTO F: Ethnic variation in red cell glutathione peroxidase activity. *Blood* 46:103, 1975.

338. REA HM, THOMSON CD, CAMPBELL DR, ROBINSON MF: Relation between erythrocyte selenium and glutathione peroxidase (E.C.1.11.1.9.) activities of New Zealand residents and visitors to New Zealand. *Br J Nutr* 42:201, 1979.

339. THOMSON CD, REA H, DOLSBURG VM, ROBINSON MF: Selenium concentrations and glutathione peroxidase activities in whole blood of New Zealand residents. *Br J Nutr* 37:457, 1977.

340. WALLER HD: Glutathione reductase deficiency, in Beutler E (ed): *Hereditary Disorders of Erythrocyte Metabolism*. New York, Grune & Stratton, 1968, p 185.

341. BLUME KG, GOTTWIK M, LOHR GW, RUDIGER HW: Familienuntersuchungen zum glutathionreduktase-mangel menschlicher erythrocyten. *Humangenetik* 6:163, 1968.

342. BEUTLER E: Drug-induced hemolytic anemia. *Pharmacol Rev* 21:73, 1969.

343. FRISCHER H, AHMAD T: Consequences of erythrocytic glutathione reductase deficiency. *J Lab Clin Med* 109:583, 1987.

344. FRISCHER H, BOWMAN JE, CARSON PE, RIECKMANN KH, WILLERSON D JR, COLWELL EJ: Erythrocytic glutathione reductase, glucose-6-phosphate dehydrogenase and 6-phosphogluconic dehydrogenase deficiencies in populations of the United States, South Vietnam, Iran and Ethiopia. *J Lab Clin Med* 81:603, 1973.

345. FRISCHER H, CARSON PE, BOWMAN JE, RIECKMANN KH: Visual test for erythrocytic glucose-6-phosphate dehydrogenase, 6-phosphogluconic dehydrogenase and glutathione reductase deficiencies. *J Lab Clin Med* 81:613, 1973.

346. FRISCHER H: Erythrocytic glutathione reductase deficiency in a hospital population in the United States. *Am J Hematol* 2:327, 1977.

347. BEUTLER E: Effect of flavin compounds on glutathione reductase activity: *in vivo* and *in vitro* studies. *J Clin Invest* 48:1957, 1969.

348. BEUTLER E: Glutathione reductase: Stimulation in normal subjects by riboflavin supplementation. *Science* 165:613, 1969.

349. BAMJI MS: Glutathione reductase activity in red blood cells and riboflavin nutritional status in humans. *Clin Chim Acta* 26:263, 1969.

350. BEUTLER E, SRIVASTAVA SK: Relationship between glutathione reductase activity and drug-induced haemolytic anaemia. *Nature* 226:759, 1970.

351. FRISCHER H, AHMAD T: Severe generalized glutathione reductase deficiency after antitumor chemotherapy with BCNU [1,3-bis(2-chloroethyl)-1-nitrosourea]. *J Lab Clin Med* 89:1080, 1977.

352. AHMAD T, FRISCHER H: Active site-specific inhibition by 1,3-bis(2-chlorethyl)-1-nitrosourea of two genetically homologous flavoenzymes: Glutathione reductase and lipoamide dehydrogenase. *J Lab Clin Med* 105:464, 1985.

353. LOOS H, ROOS D, WEENING R, HOUWERZIJL J: Familial deficiency of glutathione reductase in human blood cells. *Blood* 48:53, 1976.

354. MOOZ ED, MEISTER A: Tripeptide (glutathione) synthetase. Purification properties, and mechanism of action. *Biochemistry* 6:1722, 1967.

355. MAJERUS PW, BRAUNER MJ, SMITH MB, MINNICH V: Glutathione synthesis in human erythrocytes. II. Purification and properties of the enzymes of glutathione biosynthesis. *J Clin Invest* 50:1637, 1971.

356. BEUTLER E, GELBART T, PEGELOW C: Erythrocyte glutathione synthetase deficiency leads not only to glutathione but also to glutathione-S-transferase deficiency. *J Clin Invest* 77:38, 1986.

357. MEISTER A: 5-Oxoprolinuria (pyroglutamic aciduria) and other disorders of the γ-glutamyl cycle, in Stanbury JB, Wyngaarden JB, Fredrickson DS, Goldstein JL, Brown MS (eds): *The Metabolic Basis of Inherited Disease*, 5th ed. New York, McGraw-Hill, 1983, chap 17, p 348.

358. OORT M, LOOS JA, PRINS HK: Hereditary absence of reduced glutathione in the erythrocytes—A new clinical and biochemical entity? *Vox Sang* 6:370, 1961.

359. BOIVIN P, GALAND C, ANDRE R, DEBRAY J: Anémies hémolytiques congénitales avec déficit isolé en glutathion réduit par déficit en glutathion synthétase. *Nouv Rev Fr Hematol* 6:859, 1966.

360. PRINS HK, OORT M, LOOS JA, ZURCHER C, BECKERS T: Congenital nonspherocytic hemolytic anemia, associated with glutathione deficiency of the erythrocytes. Hematologic, biochemical and genetic studies. *Blood* 27:145, 1966.

361. MOHLER DN, MAJERUS PW, MINNICH V, HESS CE, GARRICK MD: Glutathione synthetase deficiency as a cause of hereditary hemolytic disease. *N Engl J Med* 283:1253, 1970.

362. BOIVIN P, GALAND C: La synthèse du glutathion au cours de l'anémie hémolytique congénitale avec déficit en glutathion reduit. Déficit congénital en glutathion-synthétase érythrocytaire? *Nouv Rev Fr Hematol* 5:707, 1965.

363. JELLUM E, KLUGE T, BORRESEN HC, STOKKE O, ELDJARN L: Pyroglutamic

aciduria—A new inborn error of metabolism. *Scand J Clin Lab Invest* 26:327, 1970.

364. SKULLERUD K, MARSTEIN S, SCHRADER H, BRUNDELET PJ, JELLUM E: The cerebral lesions in a patient with generalized glutathione deficiency and pyroglutamic aciduria (5-oxoprolinuria). *Acta Neuropathol (Berl)* 52:235, 1980.

365. WELLNER VP, SEKURA R, MEISTER A, LARSSON A: Glutathione synthetase deficiency, an inborn error of metabolism involving the γ-glutamyl cycle in patients with 5-oxoprolinuria (pyroglutamic aciduria). *Proc Natl Acad Sci USA* 71:2505, 1974.

366. BEUTLER E: Glutathione deficiency, pyroglutamic acidemia and amino acid transport. *N Engl J Med* 295:441, 1976.

367. SPIELBERG SP, GARRICK MD, CORASH LM, BUTLER JD, TIETZE F, ROGERS L, SCHULMAN JD: Biochemical heterogeneity in glutathione synthetase deficiency. *J Clin Invest* 61:1417, 1978.

368. ELDJARN L, JELLUM E, STOKKE O: Pyroglutamic aciduria: Studies on the enzymic block and on the metabolic origin of pyroglutamic acid. *Clin Chim Acta* 40:461, 1972.

369. LARSSON A, ZETTERSTROM R, HAGENFELDT L, ANDERSSON R, DREBORG S, HORNELL H: Pyroglutamic aciduria (5-oxoprolinuria), an inborn error in glutathione metabolism. *Pediatr Res* 8:852, 1974.

370. HAGENFELDT L, LARSSON A, ZETTERSTROM R: Pyroglutamic aciduria. Studies in an infant with chronic metabolic acidosis. *Acta Paediatr Scand* 63:1, 1974.

371. MARSTEIN S, JELLUM E, HALPERN B, ELDJARN L, PERRY TL: Biochemical studies of erythrocytes in a patient with pyroglutamic acidemia (5-oxoprolinemia). *N Engl J Med* 295:406, 1976.

372. LARSSON A, ZETTERSTROM R: Pyroglutamic aciduria (5-oxoprolinuria), an inborn error in glutathione metabolism. *Pediatr Res* 8:852, 1974.

373. ORLOWSKI M, MEISTER A: The γ-glutamyl cycle: A possible transport system for amino acids. *Proc Natl Acad Sci USA* 67:1248, 1970.

374. MEISTER A: Glutathione and the γ-glutamyl cycle, in Arias IM, Jacoby WB (eds): *Glutathione: Metabolism and Function*. New York, Raven, 1976, p 35.

375. BEUTLER E: Selectivity of proteases as a basis for tissue distribution of enzymes in hereditary deficiencies. *Proc Natl Acad Sci USA* 80:3767, 1983.

376. KONRAD PN, RICHARDS F, II, VALENTINE WN, PAGLIA DE: γ-glutamylcysteine synthetase deficiency. A cause of hereditary hemolytic anemia. *N Engl J Med* 286:557, 1972.

377. RICHARDS F, II, COOPER MR, PEARCE LA, COWAN RJ, SPURR CL: Familial spinocerebellar degeneration, hemolytic anemia, and glutathione deficiency. *Arch Intern Med* 134:534, 1974.

378. MEISTER A: Relation between ataxia and defects of the γ-glutamyl cycle. *Adv Neurol* 21:289, 1978.

379. VALENTINE WN, PAGLIA DE: Nonrecessively transmitted nonspherocytic hereditary haemolytic anaemia associated with increased red cell glutathione. *Br J Haematol* 42:231, 1979.

380. VALENTINE WN, PAGLIA DE: Syndromes with increased red cell glutathione (GSH). *Hemoglobin* 4:799, 1980.

381. KONRAD PN, VALENTINE WN, PAGLIA DE: Enzymatic activities and glutathione content of erythrocytes in the newborn: Comparison with red cells of older normal subjects and subjects with comparable reticulocytosis. *Acta Haematol* 48:192, 1972.

382. PAGLIA DE, VALENTINE WN: Haemolytic anemia associated with disorders of the purine and pyrimidine salvage pathways. *Clin Haematol* 10:81, 1981.

383. VALENTINE WN, PAGLIA DE, TARTAGLIA AP, GILSANZ F: Hereditary hemolytic anemia with increased red cell adenosine deaminase (45- to 70-fold) and decreased adenosine triphosphate. *Science* 195:783, 1977.

384. PAGLIA DE, VALENTINE WN, TARTAGLIA AP, GILSANZ F, SPARKES RS: Control of red blood cell adenine nucleotide metabolism. Studies of adenosine deaminase, in *The Red Cell*, New York, AR Liss, 1978, p 319.

385. MIWA S, FUJII H, MATSUMOTO N, NAKATSUJI T, ODA S, ASANO H, ASANO S, MIURA Y: A case of red-cell adenosine deaminase overproduction associated with hereditary hemolytic anemia found in Japan. *Am J Hematol* 5:107, 1978.

386. FUJII H, MIWA S, SUZUKI K: Purification and properties of adenosine deaminase in normal and hereditary hemolytic anemia with increased red cell activity. *Hemoglobin* 4:693, 1980.

387. PERIGNON JL, HAMET M, BUC HA, CARTIER P, DERYCKE M: Biochemical study of a case of hemolytic anemia with increased (85-fold) red cell adenosine deaminase. *Clin Chim Acta* 124:205, 1982.

388. CHOTTINER EG, CLOFT HJ, TARTAGLIA AP, MITCHELL BS: Elevated adenosine deaminase activity and hereditary hemolytic anemia. Evidence for abnormal translational control of protein synthesis. *J Clin Invest* 79:1001, 1987.

389. HIRSCHHORN R, LEVYTSKA V, POLLARA B, MEUWISSEN HJ: Evidence for control of several different tissue-specific isozymes of adenosine deaminase by a single genetic locus. *Nature* 246:200, 1973.

390. HIRSCHHORN R: Conversion of human erythrocyte-adenosine deaminase activity to different tissue-specific isozymes. Evidence for a common catalytic unit. *J Clin Invest* 55:661, 1975.

391. TISCHFIELD JA, CREAGAN RP, NICHOLS EA, RUDDLE FH: Assignment of a gene for adenosine deaminase to human chromosome 20. *Hum Hered* 24:1, 1974.

392. WIGINTON DA, KAPLAN DJ, STATES JC, AKESON AL, PERME CM, BILYK IJ, VAUGHN AJ, LATTIER DL, HUTTON JJ: Complete sequence and structure of the gene for human adenosine deaminase. *Biochemistry* 25:8234, 1986.

393. PARKS RE JR, BROWN PR: Incorporation of nucleosides into the nucleotide pools of human erythrocytes. Adenosine and its analogs. *Biochemistry* 12:3294, 1973.

394. PERRETT D, DEAN B: The function of adenosine deaminase in the human erythrocyte. *Biochem Biophys Res Commun* 77:374, 1977.

395. AGARWAL RP, PARKS RE JR: A possible association between the nucleoside transport system of human erythrocytes and adenosine deaminase. *Biochem Pharmacol* 24:547, 1975.

396. AGARWAL RP, CRABTREE GW, PARKS RE JR, NELSON JR, KEIGHTLEY R, PARKMAN R, ROSEN FS, STERN RS, POLMAR SH: Purine nucleoside metabolism in the erythrocytes of patients with adenosine deaminase deficiency and severe combined immunodeficiency. *J Clin Invest* 57:1025, 1976.

397. SCHMALSTIEG FC, GOLDMAN AS, MILLS GC, MONAHAN TM, NELSON JA, GOLDBLUM RM: Nucleotide metabolism in adenosine deaminase deficiency. *Pediatr Res* 10:393, 1976.

398. COHEN A, HIRSCHHORN R, HOROWITZ SD, RUBENSTEIN A, POLMAR SH, HONG R, MARTING DW JR: Deoxyadenosine triphosphate as a potentially toxic metabolite in adenosine deaminase deficiency. *Proc Natl Acad Sci USA* 75:472, 1978.

399. COLEMAN MS, DONOFRIO J, HUTTON JJ, HAHN L, DAOUD A, LAMPKIN B, DYMINSKI J: Identification and quantitation of adenine deoxynucleotides in erythrocytes of a patient with adenosine deaminase deficiency and severe combined immunodeficiency. *J Biol Chem* 253:1619, 1978.

400. NELSON JA, KUTTESCH JF, GOLDBLUM RN, GOLDMAN AS, SCHMALSTIEG FC: Analysis of adenosine and adenine nucleotides in severe combined immunodeficiency disease, in Baer HP, Drummond GI (eds): *Physiological and Regulatory Functions of Adenosine and Adenine Nucleotides*. New York, Raven, 1979, p 417.

401. SZEINBERG A, GAVENDO S, CAHANE D: Erythrocyte adenylate-kinase deficiency. *Lancet* 1:315, 1969.

402. SZEINBERG A, KAHANA D, GAVENDO S, ZAIDMAN J, BEN-EZZER J: Hereditary deficiency of adenylate kinase in red blood cells. *Acta Haematol* 42:111, 1969.

403. BOIVIN P, GALAND C, HAKIM J, SIMONY D, SELIGMAN M: Un nouvelle érythroenzymopathie. Anémie hémolytique congénitale non sphérocytaire et déficit héréditaire en adénylate-kinase érythrocytaire. *Presse Med* 79:215, 1971.

404. MIWA S, FUJII H, TANI K, TAKAHASHI K, TAKIZAWA T, IGARASHI T: Red cell adenylate kinase deficiency associated with hereditary nonspherocytic hemolytic anemia: Clinical and biochemical studies. *Am J Hematol* 14:325, 1983.

405. BEUTLER E, CARSON D, DANNAWI H, FORMAN L, KUHL W, WEST C, WESTWOOD B: Metabolic compensation for profound erythrocyte adenylate kinase deficiency. A hereditary defect without hemolytic anemia. *J Clin Invest* 72:648, 1983.

406. VAN ACKER KJ, SIMMONDS HA, POTTER C, CAMERON JS: Complete deficiency of adenine phosphoribosyltransferase. Report of a family. *N Engl J Med* 297:127, 1977.

407. PAGLIA DE, VALENTINE WN: Hereditary and acquired defects in the pyrimidine nucleotidase of human erythrocytes. *Curr Top Hematol* 3:75, 1980.

408. PAGLIA DE, VALENTINE WN: Characteristics of a pyrimidine-specific 5'-nucleotidase in human erythrocytes. *J Biol Chem* 250:7973, 1975.

409. PAGLIA DE, VALENTINE WN, BROCKWAY RA: Identification of thymidine nucleotidase and deoxyribonucleotidase activities among normal isozymes of 5'-nucleotidase in human erythrocytes. *Proc Natl Acad Sci USA* 81:588, 1984.

410. VALENTINE WN, FINK K, PAGLIA DE, HARRIS SR, ADAMS WS: Hereditary hemolytic anemia with human erythrocyte pyrimidine 5'-nucleotidase deficiency. *J Clin Invest* 54:866, 1974.

411. KONDO T, DALE GL, BEUTLER E: Glutathione transport by inside-out vesicles from human erythrocytes. *Proc Natl Acad Sci USA* 77:6359, 1980.

412. ZEREZ CR, LACHANT NA, TANAKA KR: Pyrimidine nucleotides do not affect the enzymes of glutathione biosynthesis. *Enzyme* 34:94, 1985.

413. SWALLOW DM, AZIZ I, HOPKINSON DA, MIWA S: Analysis of human erythrocyte 5'-nucleotidases in healthy individuals and a patient deficient in pyrimidine 5'-nucleotidase. *Ann Hum Genet* 47:19, 1983.

414. PAGLIA DE, VALENTINE WN, KEITT AS, BROCKWAY RA, NAKATANI M: Pyrimidine nucleotidase deficiency with active dephosphorylation of dTMP: Evidence for existence of thymidine nucleotidase in human erythrocytes. *Blood* 61:1147, 1983.

415. HIRONO A, FUJII H, NATORI H, KUROKAWA I, MIWA S: Chromatographic analysis of human erythrocyte 5'-nucleotidase from five patients with pyrimidine 5'-nucleotidase deficiency. *Br J Haematol* 65:35, 1987.

416. PAGLIA DE, VALENTINE WN, BROCKWAY RA, NAKATANI M: Substrate specificity and pH sensitivity of deoxyribonucleotidase and pyrimidine nucleotidase activities in human hemolysates. *Exp Hematol* 15:1041, 1987.

417. PAGLIA DE, VALENTINE WN, DAHLGREN JG: Effects of low-level lead exposure on pyrimidine 5'-nucleotidase and other erythrocyte enzymes. Possible role of pyrimidine 5'-nucleotidase in the pathogenesis of lead-induced anemia. *J Clin Invest* 56:1164, 1975.

418. VALENTINE WN, PAGLIA DE, FINK K, MADOKORO G: Lead poisoning. Association with hemolytic anemia, basophilic stippling, erythrocyte pyrimidine 5'-nucleotidase deficiency, and intraerythrocytic accumulation of pyrimidines. *J Clin Invest* 58:926, 1976.

419. PAGLIA DE, VALENTINE WN, FINK K: Lead poisoning. Further observations on erythrocyte pyrimidine-nucleotidase deficiency and intracellular accumulation of pyrimidine nucleotides. *J Clin Invest* 60:1362, 1977.

420. BUC HA, KAPLAN J-C: Red-cell pyrimidine 5'-nucleotidase and lead poisoning. *Clin Chim Acta* 87:49, 1978.

421. PAGLIA DE, VALENTINE WN, NAKATANI M, RAUTH BJ: Selective accumulation of cytosol CDP-choline as an isolated erythrocyte defect in chronic hemolysis. *Proc Natl Acad Sci USA* 80:3081, 1983.

422. VALENTINE WN, PAGLIA DE: The primary cause of hemolysis in enzymopathies of anaerobic glycolysis: A viewpoint. *Blood Cells* 6:819, 1980.

423. BEUTLER E: A commentary. *Blood Cells* 6:827, 1980.

CHAPTER 95

DISORDERS OF THE RED CELL MEMBRANE SKELETON: Hereditary Spherocytosis and Hereditary Elliptocytosis

SAMUEL E. LUX
PAMELA S. BECKER

1. The red blood cell membrane is composed of a bilayer of lipids and integral membrane proteins laminated to an underlying protein skeleton. The skeleton is a two-dimensional meshwork of spectrin tetramers and oligomers cross-linked by protein 4.1 and short actin filaments. It is joined to the membrane by interactions of spectrin with ankyrin and the integral membrane protein 3, and probably by interactions between protein 4.1 and glycophorin. The skeleton is a major determinant of membrane shape, strength, and flexibility and helps to control lipid organization and integral protein mobility and topography.

2. Hereditary spherocytosis (HS) is a congenital hemolytic anemia caused by an intrinsic red cell defect. The primary molecular lesion appears to reside in the membrane skeleton and somehow causes progressive loss of membrane surface area. The unifying feature of red cells from all or nearly all individuals with HS is spectrin deficiency. The progressive loss of membrane surface causes the HS red cell to become increasingly spheroidal, osmotically fragile, and rigid, and subjects it to detention in the splenic cords where the metabolically inhospitable environment and the high concentration of macrophages combine, in a still uncertain manner, to accentuate the basic membrane defect and enhance spheroidicity. This process is known as splenic conditioning. Conditioned red cells appear as microspherocytes in the peripheral circulation and are particularly susceptible to destruction in the spleen.

3. Patients with the common, autosomal dominant form of HS typically have mild to moderate anemia, modest splenomegaly, and intermittent mild jaundice. Individuals with compensated hemolysis and no anemia are common, and occasionally severe, transfusion-dependent anemia occurs. Other complications include neonatal jaundice, gallbladder disease, and intermittent aplastic crises. Although the common form of the disease is inherited as an autosomal dominant trait, in about 25 percent of families neither parent is discernibly abnormal. This apparently recessive form is more severe, on average, than dominant HS. Red cell conditioning and hemolysis abate following splenectomy, although the basic molecular defect persists.

4. Hereditary elliptocytosis (HE) is a heterogeneous group of congenital red cell disorders characterized by elliptically shaped cells and, in its more severe forms, by spherocytes, fragmented red cells, and other bizarre poikilocytes. Three distinct subtypes are discernible: common HE (HE_c), spherocytic HE (HE_s), and Melanesian (stomatocytic) HE. Common HE is further
divided into several different phenotypes: (1) Mild HE_c, the most common form, is a dominant condition with prominent elliptocytosis. Usually there is little or no hemolysis, but significant red cell destruction can occur in individuals who develop splenomegaly in response to exogenous stimuli. (2) Mild HE_c with poikilocytosis in infancy occurs primarily in black populations and is clinically similar to mild HE_c after the first year of life. Neonates with this disorder have moderate hemolytic anemia and marked red cell fragmentation which may be due to increased concentrations of unbound 2,3-diphosphoglycerate in fetal red cells. (3) Homozygous mild HE_c produces severe hemolysis. (4) Similar features are observed in hereditary pyropoikilocytosis (HPP), a rare recessive disorder manifested by severe hemolysis, marked poikilocytosis, and a characteristic sensitivity of the red cells to heat-induced fragmentation in vitro. Spherocytic HE (HE_s) clinically resembles HS, with moderate hemolytic anemia and both spherocytosis and elliptocytosis. Melanesian (stomatocytic) HE is a variant of HE observed in Indonesian and Melanesian peoples. It is characterized by a unique erythrocyte morphology, a rigid cell membrane, decreased expression of blood group antigens, resistance to malarial parasites, and little or no hemolysis. In the forms of HE associated with hemolysis, red cell destruction is mitigated by splenectomy.*

5. A number of defects in the membrane skeletal proteins have been identified in individuals with HE and HPP. Isolated skeletons retain the elliptocytic or poikilocytic shape of the original red cells. Some of the specific defects thus far identified include diminished spectrin-spectrin interactions, deficiency or dysfunction of protein 4.1, absence of normal protein 4.2, and glycophorin C deficiency. In many cases the specific structural defects of spectrin responsible for diminished self-association have been identified. These include truncated β chains and, especially, various types of aberrant α chains.

During its 4-month life span the average human red blood cell travels around the circulation 500,000 times, a distance of several hundred miles. To complete this journey, it must be durable enough to withstand strong circulatory shearing forces and flexible enough to negotiate repetitively the narrow portals connecting the splenic cords and sinuses. The flexibility and durability of the red cell are largely determined by the shape, strength, and pliancy of its membrane, and these properties,

---

Nonstandard abbreviations used in this chapter are: 2,3-DPG = 2,3-diphosphoglycerate; HE = hereditary elliptocytosis; HE_c = common hereditary elliptocytosis; HE_s = spherocytic hereditary elliptocytosis; HPP = hereditary pyropoikilocytosis; HS = hereditary spherocytosis; and SDS-PAGE = sodium dodecyl sulfate polyacrylamide gel electrophoresis.

in turn, are controlled by a submembranous meshwork of proteins termed the red cell membrane skeleton. All the major skeletal proteins have been purified, and many of their interconnections have been defined. Several defects in these proteins have been identified in hereditary disorders. This chapter focuses on the structure of the normal membrane skeleton and on two groups of disorders that are believed to be caused by genetic alterations of this structure: hereditary spherocytosis (HS) and hereditary elliptocytosis (HE).

Reviews are available covering various aspects of normal and abnormal red cell membrane structure[1-5a] and selected specific subjects including membrane lipids,[6] integral membrane proteins,[7-10] disorders of red cell permeability,[11] hereditary spherocytosis,[12] and hereditary elliptocytosis.[13] Damage to the red cell membrane also contributes to the pathophysiology of abetalipoproteinemia (Chap. 44B), lecithin-cholesterol acyltransferase deficiency (Chap. 46), Wilson disease (Chap. 54), the porphyrias (Chap. 52), the muscular dystrophies (Chap. 118), glucose-6-phosphate dehydrogenase deficiency (Chap. 91), and the hemoglobinopathies (Chap. 93).

STRUCTURE OF THE NORMAL RED CELL MEMBRANE SKELETON

General Aspects of Membrane Structure

The red cell membrane contains approximately equal parts of proteins and lipids (Table 95-1). Phospholipids (PL) and cholesterol (C) predominate and are present in nearly equal molar proportions (C/PL = 0.8). These and the other lipids are organized in an asymmetric planar bilayer. The glycolipids and most of the choline phospholipids (phosphatidylcholine and sphingomyelin) are located in the outer half of the bilayer, while phosphatidylinositols and the aminophospholipids (phosphatidylethanolamine and phosphatidylserine) are concentrated in the inner half[6,14,15,22,23] (Table 95-1). The 10 to

12 major membrane proteins are conventionally separated and classified by polyacrylamide gel electrophoresis in sodium dodecyl sulfate (SDS-PAGE) (Fig. 95-1) and fall into two general classes: integral and peripheral (Table 95-2).

Integral membrane proteins penetrate or traverse the lipid bilayer and interact with the hydrophobic lipid core.[29,30] They characteristically have hydrophobic surfaces exposed at such contact points and tend to aggregate or denature in aqueous solution. The red cell protein 3, which forms the anion exchange channel, and the sialic acid–bearing glycophorins are the major examples of this class (Table 95-2). These proteins have an external carbohydrate-bearing region, a membrane-spanning hydrophobic portion, and an internal, hydrophilic domain. It is likely that all integral proteins have similar amphipathic properties. Integral membrane proteins form the intramembranous particles seen on freeze-cleave electron microscopy of membranes. In the red cell the 8- to 10-nm intramembranous particles are randomly distributed and are believed to be protein 3 tetramers[31] or a complex of protein 3 tetramers and glycophorin molecules.[32,33]

Peripheral proteins are bound to the membrane via interactions with integral proteins or the polar portions of the lipid bilayer. In the red cell the major peripheral proteins are located on the cytoplasmic membrane surface and include enzymes such as glyceraldehyde-3-phosphate dehydrogenase (G3PD, protein 6) and the structural proteins of the membrane skeleton.

Components of the Membrane Skeleton

Operationally, the red cell membrane skeleton is the insoluble proteinaceous residue that remains after extraction of red cells[34] or their ghosts[35] with the nonionic detergent Triton X-100. It comprises 55 to 60 percent of the membrane protein mass and includes all the spectrin, actin, ankyrin, protein 4.1, and protein 4.9, and a portion of proteins 3, 4.2, and 7 (Fig. 95-1). Spectrin, actin, and proteins 4.1 and 4.9 form the core of the structure, since the skeleton retains its shape when

Table 95-1 Composition of Normal Human Erythrocyte Membranes (Ghosts)

Component	Wt, %	g/ghost, $\times 10^{13}$	Approximate number of molecules/ghost, $\times 10^6$	% in outer half of bilayer[a]	% in inner half of bilayer[a]
Proteins and glycoproteins	55	5.7[b]	5[c]		
Lipids					
Phospholipids[d]	28	3.0	250[e]		
Sphingomyelin	6.8	0.73	60	80	20
Phosphatidylcholine	7.0	0.75	63	75	25
Phosphatidylethanolamine	7.4	0.79	65	20	80
Phosphatidylserine	4.3	0.46	40	0	100
Phosphatidylinositols	1.0	0.10	8	0	100
Phosphatidylinositol	0.34	0.036	3		
Phosphatidylinositol-4-P	0.22	0.024	2		
Phosphatidylinositol-4,5-PP	0.39	0.042	3		
Phosphatidic acid	1.0	0.10	8	Unknown	Unknown
Other	0.6	0.06	6	Unknown	Unknown
Cholesterol[d]	13	1.3	195	~50	~50
Glycolipids[f]	3	0.3	10	100	100
Free fatty acids[g]	1	0.1	20	Unknown	Unknown
	100	10.4	480		

[a]Based on data in Refs. 14–16.
[b]An average of three reported values compiled in Ref. 17.
[c]Calculated from the data in Table 95-2.
[d]Based on compiled data in Ref. 18.
[e]Number of phospholipids per ghost based on an average molecular weight of 723 calculated from the average red cell phospholipid polar head group and fatty acid side chain composition (see Ref. 19).
[f]Based on data in Ref. 20.
[g]An average of two reported values compiled in Ref. 21.

Table 95-2 Major Erythrocyte Membrane Proteins

Protein band[a]	Approx. mol. wt.	Identification	Integral or peripheral	Approximate proportion, wt %[b]	Approximate copies/ghost[c]
1	240,000	Spectrin[d]	P	27	200,000[d]
2	220,000				
2.1	210,000				
2.2	195,000	Ankyrin[e]	P	6	100,000
2.3	175,000				
2.6	145,000				
—	103,000	Adducin	P	1	30,000
—	97,000				
3	100,000	Anion exchange protein	I	30	1,100,000
4.1	80,000/78,000[f]	Unnamed	P	5	200,000
4.2	72,000	Unnamed	P	5	250,000
4.9	48,000	Unnamed	P	0.5	30,000
5	43,000	Actin	P	5	400,000
6	35,000	Glyceraldehyde-3-phosphate dehydrogenase	P	5	500,000
7	29,000/27,000	Erythrocyte tropomyosin[g]	P	4	500,000
8	23,000	Unnamed	P	1–2	200,000
GPA	31,000	Glycophorin A	I	1.6	500,000[h]
GPB	~23,000[i]	Glycophorin B	I	0.3	100,000[h]
GPC	~28,000[i]	Glycophorin C	I	0.1	50,000[k]

[a]Numbering system of Fairbanks[19] and Steck[24] for proteins 1 to 8. GPA, GPB, and GPC refer to glycophorins A, B, and C, respectively.
[b]Proteins 1 to 8 estimated from Refs. 17 and 25 and unpublished studies of the author. Estimates of the glycophorins are from Refs. 26–28 and do not include the weight of the carbohydrate.
[c]Based on an estimate of 5.7×10^{-13} g protein per ghost (Ref. 17).
[d]Spectrin is a heterodimer of protein bands 1 and 2. These bands are also referred to as the α and β chains of spectrin, respectively. The number of copies per ghost shown refers to the $\alpha\beta$ dimer. The native spectrin species is the $\alpha_2\beta_2$ tetramer (100,000 copies/ghost).
[e]Protein 2.1 is intact ankyrin. Proteins 2.2, 2.3, and 2.6 are proteolytic degradation products or alternatively spliced forms of ankyrin that are present in the native erythrocyte.
[f]Protein 4.1 is present in two forms, 4.1a and 4.1b, which differ slightly in apparent molecular weight but are otherwise virtually identical in structure and function. It appears that 4.1b is the native species and 4.1a results from an unknown posttranslational modification.
[g]Only a portion of band 7 is erythrocyte tropomyosin (~130,000 copies/ghost). The protein contains two subunits: 29,000 and 27,000. The other band 7 proteins have a molecular weight of 27,000 daltons.
[h]Assumes 60% carbohydrate for all three glycophorins. This figure is accurately known only for glycophorin A (Refs. 26–28): hence, the number of glycophorin B molecules/ghost is only a rough estimate.
[i]Estimated from migration in SDS gels relative to glycophorin A and from Refs. 26–28.
[j]Determined from the sequence of GPC cDNA (Ref. 28a).
[k]Determined by binding of a GPC-specific monoclonal antibody (D. Anstee, personal communication).

other components are eluted with hypertonic KCl[34] but disintegrates if spectrin or actin are removed.[34] When the skeleton is isolated in relatively low concentrations of detergent, it contains some residual phospholipid, particularly sphingomyelin,[34,35] but this is not an integral part of the structure, since it is absent when higher concentrations of detergent are used.[34] The chromosomal locations of most of the membrane skeletal proteins are now known and are listed in Table 95-3.

Spectrin. Spectrin is the major skeleton protein and accounts for about 50 to 75 percent of the skeletal mass, depending on the method of preparation.[34,35] It contains two enormous polypeptide chains that are structurally similar but functionally distinct: α chain (protein 1; 240,000 daltons) and β chain (protein 2; 220,000 daltons).[36–38] These chains are aligned side by side in an antiparallel arrangement with respect to their amino- and carboxy-terminal ends.[39] Electron microscopy shows spectrin to be a slender, twisted wormlike molecule

Fig. 95-1 Schematic illustration of the SDS polyacrylamide gel electrophoresis patterns of the proteins of red cell membranes (M) and membrane skeletons (S) stained for proteins with Coomassie Blue (CB) and for sialoglycoproteins with periodic acid Schiff (PAS). The two gel systems in common use are shown: Fairbanks-Steck gels containing 5% acrylamide and Laemmli gels containing 11.5% acrylamide. GPA, GPB, and GPC refer to glycophorins A, B, and C, respectively. (GPA)₂ and (GPB)₂ are the dimers and GPA-GPB is the heterodimer of GPA and GPB.

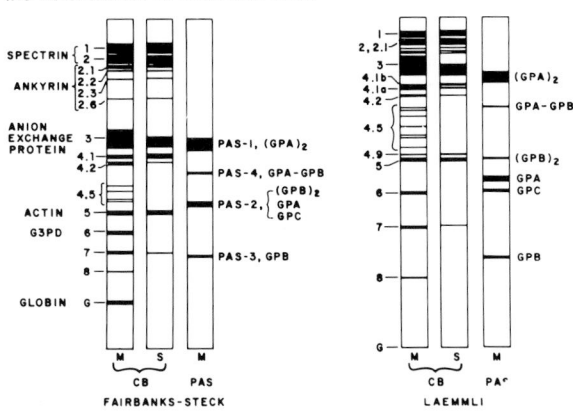

Table 95-3 Chromosomal Location of Human Erythrocyte Skeletal Protein Genes

Gene	Chromosome	Ref.
α-Spectrin	1q22-q25	65
Protein 4.1	1p36.2-p34	334
Glycophorin C	2q14-q21	335
Glycophorin A	4q28-q31	336
Glycophorin B	4q28-q31	336
β-Actin	7pter-q22	333
Ankyrin	8p11-p21	336a
β-Spectrin	14	66
Protein 3	17	337

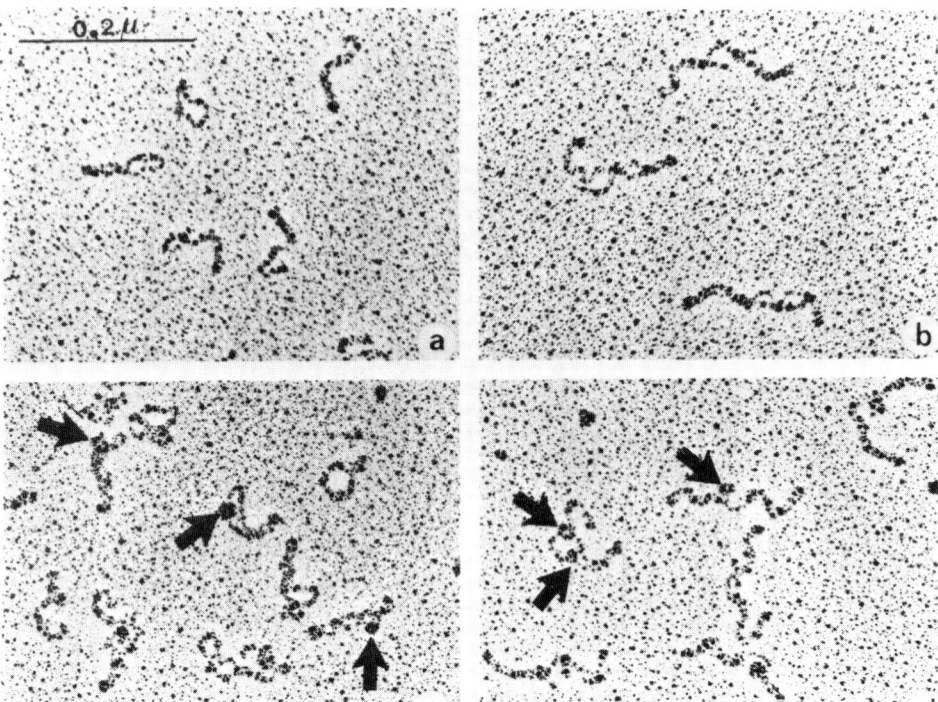

Fig. 95-2 Electron micrographs of rotary-shadowed specimens of red cell membrane skeletal proteins: (A) spectrin dimers; (B) spectrin tetramers; (C) spectrin dimers with bound ankyrin (arrows); (D) spectrin tetramers with bound ankyrin (arrows). (By permission of D. Branton, Cell, 24: 24, 1981.)

(Fig. 95-2) that extends to a total length of about 100 nm.[40,41] The protein is highly flexible[40-44] and assumes a variety of conformations, an unusual property that may be critical for normal membrane pliancy.

The initial model of spectrin structure based on biophysical studies suggested the presence of rigid globular regions containing ionic side chains and α-helical structure joined by hy-drophobic, flexible sections of polypeptide chain.[45] Chemical data disclosed a linear arrangement of proteolytically resistant domains joined by protease-sensitive regions[39,46] (Fig. 95-3). There are nine such domains, five on the α chain, designated α-I through α-V, and four on the β chain, β-I through B-IV.[46,47] As will be shown, many of the molecular defects in HE have been identified as abnormalities in spectrin domain

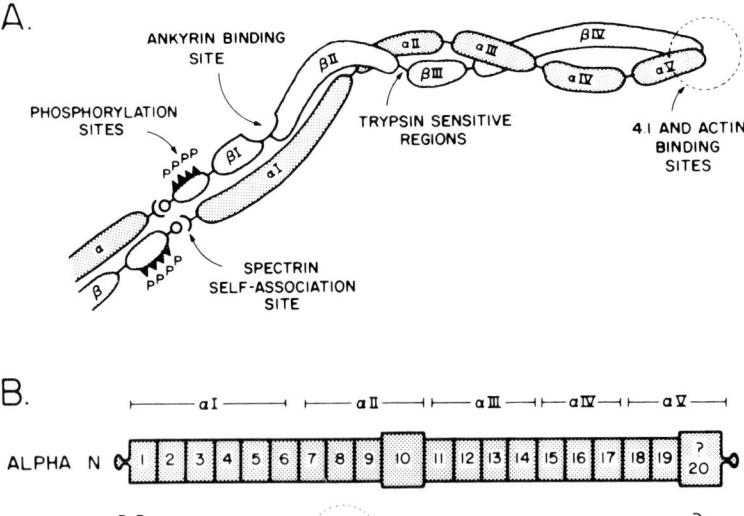

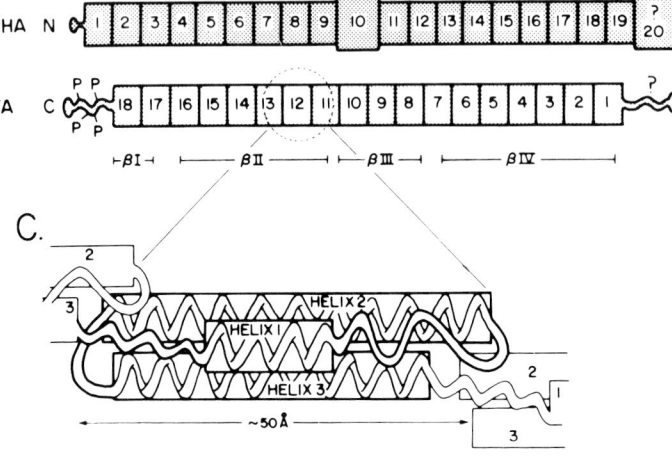

Fig. 95-3 Model of spectrin structure. A. Domain structure. The α and β chains of spectrin form a series of domains connected by trypsin-sensitive regions. The domains are numbered from the proximal ("head") end of the molecule, the end which contains the spectrin self-association site. The amino-terminal α-I domain contains one of these sites. It attaches to a complementary site in a small phosphorylated region at the carboxy-terminal end of the β chain. The ankyrin-binding site lies between the β-I and β-II domains. The binding sites for actin and protein 4.1 are near the distal ("tail") end of the molecule, but have not yet been assigned to specific domains. B. Subunit structure. Both spectrin chains are composed of a linked series of homologous 106-amino acid (12,000 dalton) subunits. The tenth and probably the twentieth subunits of the α chain differ from this pattern, as does the phosphorylated carboxy-terminus and, possibly, the amino-terminal end of the β chain. C. Subunit substructure. Although the amino acid sequences of the various subunits have diverged considerably during evolution, the length and overall structure of the subunits and the position of certain amino acid residues are highly conserved, for unknown reasons. Each subunit is believed to contain three helical regions linked by a short nonhelical sequence. The repeat distance is approximately 5 nm. The subunits are probably staggered, leading to supercoiling of the molecule and the twisted appearance observed in electron micrographs.

maps after proteolytic digestion. The protein sequencing of much of the spectrin molecule demonstrates repeating subunit structure, and the current model consists of 38 homologous segments of 106 amino acids, each a triple helix with nonhelical connecting chains[38] (Fig. 95-3).

Spectrin has the capability to associate to tetramers and higher oligomers.[48–50] This is accomplished by binding in a head-to-head configuration[41,49,50] (Fig. 95-2). Both tetramers and oligomers are believed to exist on the intact membrane,[49,50] but tetramers predominate,[50] probably because the association constant for formation of tetramers is substantially higher than for the larger species.[50a] At low ionic strength and physiological temperature (37°C), spectrin dissociates into dimers,[50,51] while physiological ionic strength and lower temperatures (25°C) favor the tetramer and oligomer species. At 4°C the equilibrium is kinetically frozen because of its high activation energy.[48] It is possible to extract spectrin from the membrane at such temperatures and examine its association state directly. Spectrin also binds to other proteins, including anykrin, protein 4.1, and actin (to be discussed).

Spectrin is synthesized very early in erythroid development. It is plentiful in pronormoblasts[52] and is detectable in undifferentiated erythroleukemia cells[53] and possibly in mature committed erythroid stem cells (CFU-E).[54] It is ubiquitous in both vertebrate[55] and invertebrate[56–58] red cells. Even in the most primitive organisms, regions of the molecule are immunochemically (and hence structurally) similar to the human protein.[56–58] This evolutionary conservation suggests that some spectrin function is critical for the survival of the erythrocyte. Moreover, a structural and functional analogue of spectrin, fodrin, has been identified in many other cell types,[59–64] and its role in those cells is now being elucidated.

The α-spectrin gene is located on chromosome 1 in the q22-q25 segment,[65] near the Duffy blood group. β-Spectrin is located somewhere on chromosome 14.[66] In chickens and mice, α-spectrin is synthesized in threefold excess relative to β-spectrin,[67,68] and is degraded by a different, slower pathway.[69] The limited synthesis and more rapid degradation of β-spectrin (at least in chickens) suggests that its association with the membrane is the rate-limiting step in spectrin assembly.[69,70]

Actin. Red cell actin is very similar to other actins, both structurally[71] and functionally.[71–74] It is the β type,[25] a subtype that is also found in a variety of other nonmuscle cells.[75] Unlike the actin in other cells, red cell actin appears to be organized as short, double-helical F-actin filaments ("protofilaments") about 12 to 16 monomers long.[76,77] It appears that these short filaments are stabilized by their interactions with spectrin and protein 4.1 (see below), although the existence of a capping protein or proteins has not been excluded. In fact, there is also evidence that the spectrin-actin-4.1 complex may cap the slow-growing ("pointed") end of actin filaments in the membrane,[78] although this is controversial.[79]

There is also evidence that the state of actin polymerization is functionally important to the red cell, since compounds that inhibit actin polymerization increase membrane flexibility, while compounds that promote its polymerization rigidify the membrane.[80] Spectrin dimers bind to the side of actin filaments at a site near the tail end of the spectrin molecule[81,82] (Fig. 95-4). It appears that both the α and β chains contribute to this interaction.[83] Spectrin tetramers are therefore bivalent and can cross-link actin filaments; however binding is weak ($K_d \sim 10^{-3} M$) and ineffectual in the absence of protein 4.1.[81,83–85]

Protein 4.1. This globular protein (78 to 80 kDa, a 5.7-nm sphere)[86] is a core skeletal component and is necessary for normal skeletal stability.[68,76–79] It binds tightly ($K_d \sim 10^{-7} M$) to spectrin at the tail end of the molecule, very near the actin-binding site[82,86] (Fig. 95-4) probably on the β chain[86a,86b] and greatly amplifies the otherwise weak spectrin-actin interaction.[81,83–85] In a discontinous SDS-PAGE system,[87] protein 4.1 appears as a doublet, designated 4.1a and 4.1b. Both proteins copurify, and both are phosphorylated and sequence-related.[88,89] Component 4.1b is more prominent in younger erythrocytes.[90,90a] The molecule is polarized, with an acidic end and a basic end.[89] A central 10-kDa fragment appears to contain the region responsible for spectrin-actin binding.[91] Protein 4.1 appears to bind spectrin in one-to-one stoichiometry and, with actin, results in a ternary complex with an association constant of $10^{12} M^{-2}$.[85]

Protein 4.1 also binds to one or more transmembrane proteins. It has been shown to associate with the cytoplasmic portions of both glycophorins A[92] and C.[93,94] The interaction with glycophorin A is regulated by polyphosphoinositides[95] and has received more attention, but the available evidence suggests that binding to glycophorin C may predominate in vivo.[96] The protein may also interact with protein 3[97] and with phosphatidylserine.[98] Thus, protein 4.1 may serve to attach the skeleton, through spectrin, to the lipid bilayer.

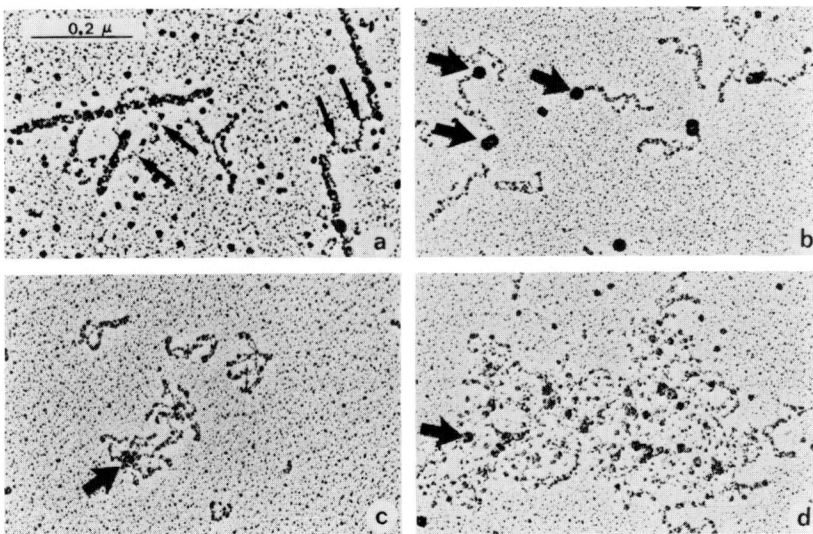

Fig. 95-4 Electron micrographs of rotary-shadowed specimens of red cell membrane skeletal proteins: (A) spectrin tetramers bound to actin filaments in the presence of protein 4.1; (B) ferritin-labeled protein 4.1 (arrows) bound to spectrin tetramers; (C) complexes of spectrin dimer, actin, and protein 4.1 formed at molar ratios close to those found in the normal red cell (arrow indicates putative actin protofilament); (D) complexes formed as in (C) except that spectrin tetramer was used instead of dimer, leading to the formation of an extended network (arrow indicates putative actin protofilament). (*By permission of D. Branton, Cell 24:24, 1981.*)

Actin-Associated Proteins: Protein 4.9, Adducin, and Tropomyosin.

PROTEIN 4.9- This 48,000-dalton protein is a core skeletal component along with spectrin, actin, and protein 4.1.[34] The protein must also attach to a lipid or integral membrane protein, since it remains associated with the membrane when the other skeletal proteins are extracted; however, this site has not been identified. The native protein is a trimer and is phosphorylated by a cAMP-dependent kinase and protein kinase C.[99–101] Nothing is known about the function of the protein in vivo. In vitro it binds to actin and bundles actin filaments into cables.[102] This action is abolished by phosphorylation at the cAMP-dependent site.[103]

ADDUCIN. This protein is a heterodimer containing α (103,000-dalton) and β (97,000-dalton) subunits.[104] There are 30,000 copies per cell or one per actin protofilament. The protein binds to actin and, like protein 4.1, increases the binding of spectrin to actin.[105] However, unlike protein 4.1, adducin does not interact directly with spectrin in the absence of actin.

The adducin-spectrin-actin complex fosters binding of a second spectrin, a reaction that is blocked by calmodulin.[105] The protein is phosphorylated by protein kinase C, but the function of this phosphorylation is unknown.[99–101]

TROPOMYOSIN. Erythrocyte tropomyosin is a heterodimer of 27,000- and 29,000-dalton subunits which run on SDS-PAGE in the region of band 7.[106] The red cell analogue is similar to other nonmuscle tropomyosins by many criteria.[106] There is one copy for each 6 to 8 actin monomers, which is just enough to cover all of the red cell actin protofilaments. The length of tropomyosin and the length of the protofilaments also correspond. This suggests a model in which each protofilament bears two tropomyosins, one in each of the two filament grooves.

Ankyrin (Protein Bands 2.1, 2.2, 2.3, and 2.6).

Ankyrin is a large, pyramid-shaped (8.3×10 nm) protein[86] that serves as the high affinity ($K_d \sim 10^{-7} M$) binding site for the attachment of spectrin to the inner membrane surface.[107–110] Ankyrin binds to spectrin at a site 20 nm from the end of the molecule involved in dimer-tetramer interactions[86] (Fig. 95-2). Proteolytic fragments of spectrin and ankyrin containing the respective binding sites have been isolated and partially characterized.[47,110,111] Judging from its relative abundance (Table 95-2), each spectrin tetramer probably binds on average only one ankyrin molecule, even though two binding sites are available. There is evidence that ankyrin binds about 10 times more avidly to spectrin tetramer ($10^{-7} M$) than to spectrin dimer ($10^{-6} M$),[112,113] which is surprising considering the distance of the ankyrin binding and spectrin self-association sites from each other (Fig. 95-3). Ankyrin, in turn, is bound with high affinity to the cytoplasmic portion of protein 3, the true anchor for the membrane skeleton.[114–116] The ankyrin molecule contains two separate binding domains that can be separated by gentle proteolysis. The spectrin-binding site is contained in a 72,000-dalton fragment.[114,117–119] Phosphorylation of this fragment abolishes the preferential interaction of ankyrin with spectrin tetramer.[120] A complementary 90,000-dalton fragment binds to the cytoplasmic domain of protein 3.[118,119] Ankyrin also contains binding sites for protein 4.2[121] and one or more

covalently bound fatty acids.[122] Neither of these sites has been localized to a specific domain. Preliminary studies of a patient whose red cells lack 4.2 (to be discussed) suggest this protein may modulate ankyrin–protein 3 interactions.[123] The function of the fatty acid is unknown.

Ankyrin is very sensitive to proteolysis and is easily pared from its native 210,000-dalton size to a number of lower molecular weight species (protein bands 2.2, 2.3, and 2.6).[124,125] Similar forms are present in all normal red cells, but it is not known whether these are proteolytic products of normal ankyrin or whether some are alternatively spliced proteins or even separate gene products. Protein 2.2 binds to more high affinity protein 3 sites than whole ankyrin and has a threefold higher affinity for spectrin.[126] This suggests that the 20-kDa fragment that is missing from protein 2.2 is a negative regulator of ankyrin function.

Anion Exchange Protein (Protein 3).

Protein 3, the major red cell membrane protein ($\sim 1 \times 10^6$ copies per cell), is a 100,000-dalton transmembrane glycoprotein that probably exists in the membrane as a noncovalently linked tetramer.[31,116,126a] Six to seven percent of the population is heterozygous for a slightly larger, but apparently functionally normal, variant.[127] The protein is divided into two structurally and functionally unique domains.[128–130] The carboxy-terminal end (52,000 daltons) forms the physiologically important anion exchange channel that enables the red cell to exchange Cl^- for HCO_3^- and transport CO_2 from the tissues to the lung. This part of the protein is mostly composed of transmembrane helices. These presumably cluster together to form the transport channel(s); however, their exact arrangement and mechanism of action are unknown. A single carbohydrate side chain attached at the outer membrane surface binds concanavalin A[131] and bears the I,i blood group antigens.[132] The glycosylation is heterogeneous, which accounts for the diffuse electrophoretic mobility of the protein on SDS gels.[133,134]

The 43,000-dalton cytoplasmic (amino-terminal) domain contains the binding sites for a large number of red cell proteins including: hemoglobin;[135] protein 4.1;[97] protein 4.2;[121] ankyrin;[114–116] and the glycolytic enzymes glyceraldehyde-3-phosphate dehydrogenase,[136,137] phosphofructokinase,[138,139] phosphoglycerate kinase,[140] and aldolase.[138,141] Hemoglobin and the glycolytic enzymes bind to a very acidic segment located at the extreme amino terminus.[135] The binding sites for ankyrin and proteins 4.1 and 4.2 are not well-localized but are more distal. Usually one ankyrin molecule binds avidly ($K_d \sim 10^{-8} M$) to each protein 3 tetramer.[116] With this stoichiometry, approximately 30 to 40 percent of the protein 3 molecules will be bound to ankyrin and the membrane skeleton. So far no differences have been detected in the protein 3 molecules that are bound and those that are not.[114–116] There is relatively little information about what proportion of protein 3 interacts with the other proteins noted above or what purpose these binding reactions serve. There is some evidence that the kinetics of the various glycolytic enzymes are altered by binding,[137,141,142] but it is not clear that this is a physiologically significant phenomenon.

As noted earlier, protein 3 may also interact with glycophorin A, the other major integral membrane protein.[32,33] If so, the interaction is weak, since glycophorin and protein 3 are not associated when they are extracted (and diluted) in nonionic detergents.

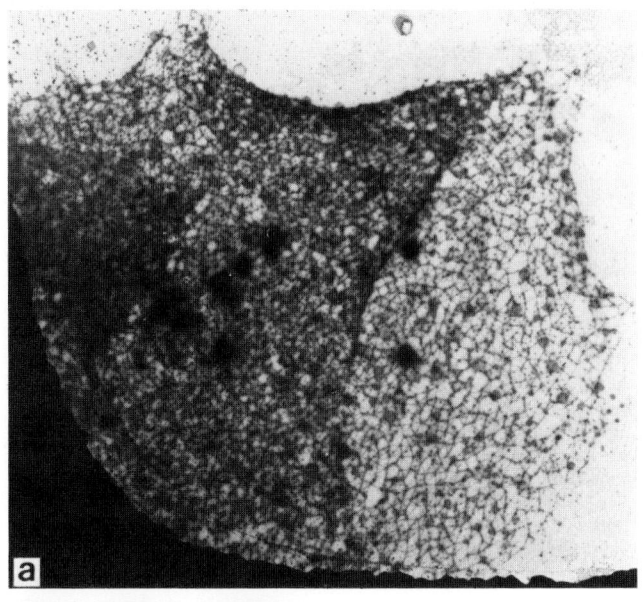

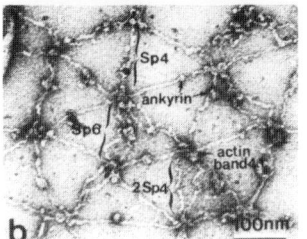

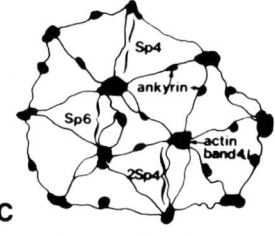

Fig. 95-5 Electron microscopy of negatively stained erythrocyte membrane skeletons. A, Low power view of spread skeleton. B, High power view, illustrated schematically in C, showing a hexagonal lattice of junctional complexes, presumably composed of F-actin protofilaments and protein 4.1 molecules cross-linked by spectrin tetramers (Sp4), three-armed spectrin hexamers (Sp6), and double spectrin filaments (2Sp4). Globular structures of ankyrin or ankyrin-containing complexes are attached to the spectrin molecules at the ankyrin-binding site. (From Liu, Derick, and Palek.[146] Used by permission of the Journal of Cell Biology.)

Organization of the Membrane Skeleton

Early electron micrographs of the membrane skeleton showed an anastomosing network of twisted, relatively unordered microfilaments.[143,144] Because of the poor resolution, it was difficult to define the specific components. More recent studies with high resolution negative-staining electron microscopy[77,145,146] enable visualization of junctional complexes of F-actin cross-linked by spectrin molecules (Fig. 95-5). Most frequently, spectrin tetramers and three-legged hexamers join the F-actin junctional complexes.[146] Ankyrin-containing globular complexes are also noted. These attach to spectrin about 80 nm from its distal end or 20 nm from the site of self-association.[146] The average thickness of the skeletal protein layer has been estimated to be 3 to 6 nm from x-ray diffraction data[148] and 7 to 10 nm from electron micrographs.[144,148] These dimensions suggest the skeleton is only one or two molecules thick on average, which means it must cover about 25 to 35 percent of the inner membrane surface area.

Models of spectrin and the membrane skeleton based on some of the available evidence are shown in Figs. 95-3 and 95-6. Spectrin dimer is depicted as a twisted, flexible polymer of protein bands 1 and 2, joined head to head to form tetramers and higher order oligomers. An 80,000-dalton domain at the amino-terminal end of the spectrin α chain contains one of the two interacting sites;[47] location of the complementary site lies near the phosphorylated region at the carboxy-terminal end of the β subunit,[149] since truncated β chains lacking this region are defective in self-association.[150,151] Spectrin molecules are linked into a two-dimensional network by interactions with a complex of actin protofilaments, protein 4.1, protein 4.9, adducin, and tropomyosin.[81–86,102–106] These associations occur at the tail ends of the bifunctional spectrin tetramer. The predicted complexes are morphologically similar to isolated spectrin-actin-4.1 complexes (Fig. 95-3) and to structures observed *in situ* in normal ghosts (Fig. 95-5). They appear to serve as a molecular junction or branch point in skeletal construction.

Individual spectrin tetramers and oligomers are attached to the overlying lipid bilayer through high affinity interactions with ankyrin and protein 3.[107–120] Current evidence suggests that protein 3 is a tetramer in the membrane[31,116,126] and that this tetramer probably binds only one molecule of ankyrin.[116] If so, about 40 percent of the protein 3 molecules are involved in anchoring the membrane skeleton. The ankyrin-binding site on spectrin is located 20 nm from the end of the molecule that participates in dimer-dimer binding.[47,86] Although the spectrin tetramer contains two such sites, on average only one

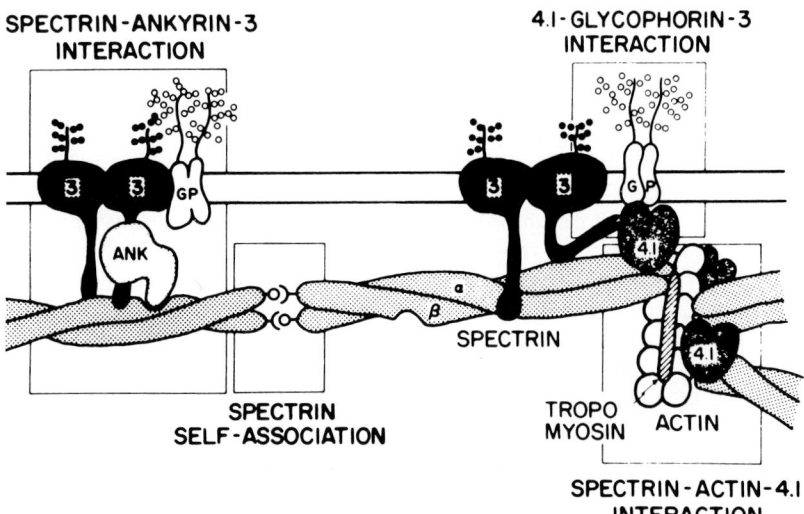

Fig. 95-6 Model (not to scale) of red cell membrane organization. Ank = ankyrin; GP = glycophorin A and/or C.

site per tetramer can be filled. Interactions between protein 4.1 and either glycophorin A, glycophorin C, or protein 3[92-97] provide secondary sites of attachment. Recent observations suggest that most spectrin molecules probably fold up to about one-third their length and do not extensively overlap or intertwine.[77,145,146]

Modulation of Membrane Skeletal Structure

Polyanions. Physiological concentrations of organic polyanions such as 2,3-diphosphoglycerate (2,3-DPG) and adenosine triphosphate (ATP) weaken and dissociate the membrane skeleton[152,153] and increase the lateral mobility of protein 3 in ghosts.[154] At the molecular level these compounds dramatically inhibit spectrin-actin interactions, even in the presence of protein 4.1.[155] Whether these or other polyanions (e.g., polyphosphorylated phosphoinositides) are "physiological" mediators in vivo is unknown, although recent studies suggest that even supraphysiological concentrations of 2,3-DPG have little or no effect on *intact* erythrocytes.[155a]

Phosphorylation. Almost all of the membrane skeletal proteins are phosphorylated by one or more protein kinases. These include cAMP-independent kinases (spectrin, protein 3);[156,157] cAMP-dependent kinases (ankyrin, proteins 4.1 and 4.9);[158-160] tyrosine kinase (protein 3);[99-101] and protein kinase C (proteins 4.1 and 4.9).[99-101] Recent studies have shown that ankyrin phosphorylation abolishes the preference of ankyrin for spectrin tetramer.[120] Phosphorylation of protein 4.1 also diminishes its binding to spectrin[162] and phosphorylation of the distal tyrosine at the amino terminus of protein 3 blocks the binding of glycolytic enzymes[162a] and, presumably, hemoglobin. In contrast, despite extensive study,[149,163,164] no functional effect of spectrin phosphorylation has yet been identified.

Calmodulin. Recent evidence indicates that calmodulin binds to the spectrin β chain in a Ca^{2+}-dependent manner and inhibits the protein 4.1–stimulated binding of spectrin to actin.[164a] However, the affinity of spectrin for calmodulin is not great, and it is unclear whether this effect occurs at the concentrations of calmodulin that exist in erythrocytes.

Functions of the Membrane Skeleton

Membrane Flexibility and Durability. Biochemical analyses of the red cell membrane suggest that its structural properties are determined almost entirely by the membrane skeleton. The best evidence for this hypothesis comes from studies of four mouse mutants with very severe, inherited hemolytic anemias.[68,165,166] The red cells of these mice are spherocytic and fragile and spontaneously vesiculate in the circulation (Fig. 95-7). All the mutants lack spectrin, and the degree of spectrin deficiency correlates with the apparent clinical severity.[166] Red cells from the more deficient mutants lack elasticity, show marked plastic deformation (see following section), and mechanically resemble lipid bilayers. Reconstitution of mutant ghosts with normal spectrin restores membrane stability.[167]

Numerous other observations attest to the structural importance of the skeleton. In intact red cells, denaturation of spectrin by exposure to heat[168-170] or low pH[169,171,172] destabilizes and rigidifies the membrane and promotes membrane fragmentation and spherocytosis. In isolated membranes, vesicu-

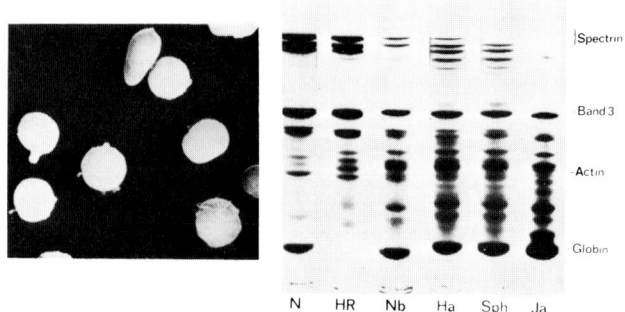

Fig. 95-7 Spectrin-deficient mouse mutants. *(Left)* Scanning electron micrograph of red cell from a mouse with the *sph/sph* mutation. Note the intense spherocytosis and membrane budding. Often budding is even more intense, with long strands of linked vesicles dangling from the surface. *(Right)* SDS gels of red cell membranes from normal (N) and high reticulocyte control (HR) mice, and from mice with the "normoblastosis," *nb/nb* (Nb); "hemolytic anemia," *sph^ha/sph^ha* (Ha); "spherocytosis," *sph/sph* (Sph); and "jaundiced," *ja/ja* (Ja) mutations. *(From Lux.[166] Used by permission of Seminars in Hematology.)*

lation occurs when spectrin is extracted at low ionic strength[173] or even when spectrin-actin bonds are weakened by 2,3-DPG.[152] Similarly, isolated skeletons become mechanically fragile when spectrin tetramers are converted to dimers by in vitro manipulations of temperature and ionic strength.[174] In contrast, cross-linking of membrane skeletal proteins by a variety of mechanisms increases membrane rigidity.[175-178]

Red Cell Shape. In general, isolated membrane skeletons retain the shape of the ghosts from which they are derived.[179,180] This and other observations[181,182] confirm the role of the skeleton in maintaining cell shape. Biomechanical analyses and modeling studies[183] suggest that a membrane formed by a phospholipid bilayer bonded to a membrane skeletal network will assume a biconcave shape spontaneously to minimize mechanical strain. Normally the red cell rapidly regains this shape if it is temporarily deformed, but if the distortion is maintained for some time, the cell will remain misshapen. This phenomenon, known as *plastic deformation*, is probably due to realignment of dynamic skeletal interactions in response to the stress of distortion.[184,185] Diminished skeletal interactions would presumably accelerate this process and foster poikilocytosis. More severe skeletal weakness would permit membrane budding and fragmentation and, in the most extreme cases, lead to the spherical shape characteristic of isolated phospholipid vesicles and spectrin-deficient mouse red cells.[166]

Integral Protein Distribution and Mobility. Perturbations that cause spectrin molecules to precipitate or aggregate on the inner membrane surfaces immobilize integral proteins in clusters directly over the spectrin aggregates.[186-189] Conversely, congenital absence of spectrin in mice, partial displacement of spectrin from the membrane by a proteolytic fragment of ankyrin, or weakening of spectrin-actin interactions with 2,3-DPG enhances the lateral diffusion of integral proteins in the bilayer plane.[154,190,191] These experiments clearly show that the membrane skeleton normally restricts the mobility of some integral membrane proteins. The mechanism of this restriction is uncertain. Presumably it is at least partially due to the association between protein 3 and the spectrin-ankyrin complex, but because only 30 to 40 percent of the protein 3 molecules participate in this interaction,[116] other constituents are probably also involved. Perhaps the cytoplasmic domains of many integral proteins are simply trapped in the skeletal meshwork. Alternatively, poorly described interactions between the skeleton and membrane lipids or between the skeleton and other integral proteins such as the glycophorins may be important.

There is some evidence that the distribution of integral membrane proteins influences the interaction of red cells with other cells they encounter in the circulation. The only well-studied example is the abnormal adherence of sickle cells and cultured human umbilical vein endothelial cells.[192–194] This appears to be related to surface charge topography, since it is normalized by desialylation, and since negative charges on the sickle-cell surface (presumably sialic acids on glycophorin molecules) are abnormally clustered.[192] Sialic acids are also clustered on thalassemic red cells,[195] but the interaction of these cells with endothelial cells has not been tested. It is not known whether the charge clustering in either type of cell is exacerbated by recently identified defects in the membrane skeleton,[196–198] although this is a reasonable possibility.

Membrane Endocytosis and Fusion. In addition to its probable importance in cell-cell interactions, skeletal control of integral protein topography appears to help regulate membrane endocytosis and fusion. Studies have shown that endocytic vacuoles in red cells and ghosts are spectrin-depleted and arise from spectrin-free areas of the membrane, produced by rearrangement of the membrane skeleton.[199,200] Pretreatment of ghosts with alkaline phosphatase blocks endocytosis and spectrin rearrangement, suggesting that phosphorylation of some membrane component is required.[199] The identity of this component has not been established.

It appears that a similar process occurs during membrane fusion. Early in the fusion process, integral membrane proteins cluster to produce areas of protein-free lipid bilayer.[201,202] Apparently fusion results when such bare areas contact each other, if the lipids are in a proper configuration.[202] It is known that spectrin is involved in this process.[167,203–206] Antispectrin antibodies inhibit the fusion of red cell membranes induced by Sendai virus,[204] and crude spectrin extracts prevent Ca^{2+}-induced fusion of phosphatidylserine vesicles.[205] In addition spectrin-deficient mouse red cells readily fuse with one another in the absence of any inducing agent,[167] a defect that is corrected by reconstituting the cells with normal mouse spectrin.[167] Thus, by immobilizing integral proteins in a diffuse distribution, the membrane skeleton protects the red cell from fusing with the many other cells it encounters in the circulation.

Membrane Lipid Asymmetry. In model systems, spectrin and protein 4.1 interact with negatively charged phospholipids, such as phosphatidylserine.[206–210] It is likely that similar inter-

actions occur in the red cell membrane, but this is difficult to prove. About 30 to 50 percent of inner membrane phosphatidylserine and phosphatidylethanolamine becomes accessible at the outer membrane surface when intact red cells are oxidized with agents that selectively cross-link spectrin.[211–215] Such studies are limited by the inability to be certain that only spectrin is damaged by oxidation. However, phospholipid asymmetry is also lost in red cells that are congenitally deficient in spectrin[216] or protein 4.1[210b] and in sickle cells[217] in which damage to both of these proteins occurs.[196–198] These observations suggest that one or more components of the skeleton normally help to stabilize the asymmetric distribution of phospholipids.

HEREDITARY SPHEROCYTOSIS

Hereditary spherocytosis (HS), or congenital hemolytic jaundice, is an important, dominantly inherited hemolytic anemia in which an incompletely characterized defect of the membrane skeleton leads to spheroidal, osmotically fragile, spectrin-deficient cells that are selectively trapped in the spleen and that survive almost normally after splenectomy.

History

Hereditary spherocytosis was first described more than 100 years ago by the Belgian physicians Vanlair and Masius.[218] They portrayed a young woman who developed recurrent abdominal pain over her enlarged spleen associated with prostration, vomiting, jaundice, anemia, aphonia, and marked muscular weakness. At the time of this attack (presumably a hemolytic crisis), the authors noted that the majority of the red cells were spherical and much smaller than normal (4-μm diameter!). They termed these cells *microcytes* and named the disease *microcythemia*. The unstained cells were illustrated in a beautiful lithograph drawn and tinted by Vanlair (Fig. 95-8). The drawing clearly shows spherocytosis [although the relatively large number of elliptocytes (19 percent of the evaluable cells) raises the question whether the true diagnosis may not have been spherocytic elliptocytosis]. Later, when the patient had improved, her red cells were somewhat larger, but still abnormal, and her spleen remained enlarged.

Vanlair and Masius thought the microcytes were senile normal cells ("globules atrophiques") and that the spleen assisted in their aging. They argued that when red cells are sequestered in the pulp of the spleen, they are removed from the active circulation, lose volume, and become dense, spherical, and microcytic. They believed an enlarged spleen produces

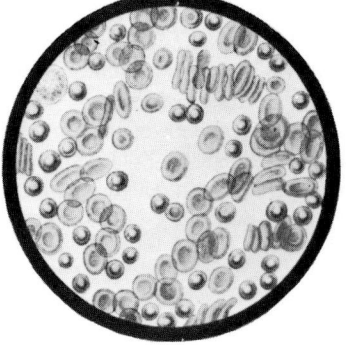
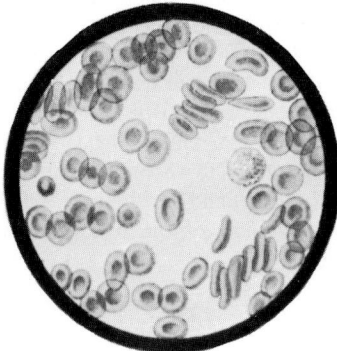

Fig. 95-8 Lithograph of normal red cells *(right)* and cells from a patient *(left)* with "microcythemia" described by Vanlair and Masius in 1871.[218]

even more of such cells than a normal spleen and that the liver completes the work of the spleen by destroying the microcytes it receives via the splenic vein. They suggested that the large number of microcytes in their patient was due in part to splenomegaly and in part to atrophy of the liver. Finally, they noted that the patient's older sister had suffered from an identical illness and had died during an apparent crisis. The mother was also subject to jaundice.

This remarkable paper must rank among the most prescient in hematology. Not only did the authors describe the first example of hereditary hemolytic anemia well before the microscope was in general use in the analysis of blood diseases, but their deductions concerning the pathophysiology, particularly the role of the spleen, predated Ham and Castle's concept of erythrostasis[219] by more than two-thirds of a century! Their analysis is placed in better perspective when one realizes that 40 to 65 years later HS was ascribed to causes as diverse as hereditary syphilis[220] and splenic hemolysins.[221]

Unfortunately, Vanlair and Masius's report and subsequent descriptions of HS by Wilson and Stanley in the 1890s[222,223] went largely unnoticed. The latter authors clearly recognized the hereditary nature of the disease and were the first to describe the pathology of the spleen, which, at autopsy, was grossly firm and dark and microscopically engorged with red cells. A report by Minkowski in 1900[224] received wide attention, and many additional papers soon appeared,[225,226] including Chauffard's historic definition of osmotic fragility[227] and reticulocytosis[228] as hallmarks of the disease.

At about the same time, Widal[229,230] differentiated an acquired form of "congenital hemolytic jaundice" (now recognizable as Coombs' test–positive immunohemolytic anemia). Because Hayem had previously reported similar cases,[231] the acquired form of the disease soon became the Hayem-Widal type, while the congenital form was given the Minkowski-Chauffard eponym.

The use of splenectomy was soon advocated, and in 1911 Micheli[232] removed the spleen from a patient with acquired hemolytic jaundice. The fortunately brilliant result, combined with the subsequent success of splenectomy in the congenital disease,[233,234] soon led to widespread acceptance of the procedure. Actually, the first successful splenectomy for HS was unintentionally performed by Spencer Wells in England in 1887 (3 years before Wilson's description of the disease in that country!).[235] Operating on a jaundiced woman for a supposed uterine fibroid, he instead encountered and removed an enormous spleen. The patient recovered and the jaundice disappeared. Forty years later Dawson restudied the woman and her son and found the characteristic osmotic fragility.[235]

Thus, by the time of Tileston's[236] and Gänsslen's[237] reviews in 1922, almost all the major clinical features of HS were documented, the spleen was thought to be involved in the hemolysis, and splenectomy was known to be curative. Nevertheless, with the exception of Vanlair and Masius's farsighted (and still unrecognized) premonitions, nothing substantive was known about the basic mechanism of the disorder or its pathogenesis. These aspects of the disease will be discussed in the sections that follow. Readers interested in more details of the history of HS should consult the superb chapters by Dacie, Wintrobe, and Crosby in *Blood, Pure and Eloquent*, a delightful account of the history of hematology, edited by Wintrobe.[238]

Prevalence and Genetics

HS is the most common hemolytic anemia in people of Northern European extraction. In this population the prevalence is roughly 1 in 5000,[239] and there is evidence, based on data obtained with sensitive osmotic fragility methods, that very mild forms of the disease may be four or five times more common.[240] The disease occurs, but is less frequent, in other races and ethnic groups. Recent studies indicate that there are at least two hereditary forms of HS. Approximately 75 percent of families show the classic autosomal dominant pattern.[239,241] No definite homozygotes for this form of HS have ever been identified, which suggests that homozygosity for the typical dominant disease may be incompatible with life. A family reported by Race[241] supports this supposition. He described a mating between first cousins in which both parents and three children were affected, one child was normal, and two miscarriages had occurred. A French family with 13 successive affected children[242] is sometimes said to be an example of homozygosity, but the mother was normal and the father was not clinically worse than his offspring (as his productivity attests). Three groups have reported complementary data on chromosomal translocations or deletions that localize at least one form of dominant HS to the short arm of chromosome 8 (8p11.1).[243–245] Extensive linkage studies in 42 families (Table 95-4) have failed to identify other loci responsible for the dominant form of the disease.[245a,245b]

Some of the remaining 25 percent of families are probably examples of an autosomal recessive form of the disease.[246–248] Others may be examples of dominant HS with reduced penetrance or may be new mutations. It will not be possible to definitively distinguish between these alternatives until specific molecular or genetic markers are identified that can detect heterozygotes.

Etiology

Cross-transfusion experiments clearly show that hereditary spherocytes are intrinsically defective.[249–251] Despite decades of intensive research, the precise molecular defect or defects are still uncertain in most patients. Many abnormalities have been identified in HS red cells, but the majority are believed to be secondary and do not represent primary hereditary defects. These include metabolic derangements, alterations in cation transport, abnormal membrane protein phosphorylation, and altered membrane lipid composition. The identified defects are listed in Table 95-5 and are discussed in the previous edition.[252] We will focus on defects of the membrane skeletal proteins, since these are probably responsible for the disease.

Loss of Membrane Surface. The membrane lesion is expressed as a loss of surface area, but whether this is due to an actual physical loss (i.e., fragmentation) or to contraction of the membrane surface is not completely clear. Most of the evidence favors fragmentation. Careful biomechanical measurements show that the force required to fragment HS membranes is diminished and proportional to the density of spectrin on the membrane.[270,271] Membrane elasticity and bending stiffness are also reduced and proportional to spectrin density.[272,273] In addition, HS red cells lose membrane much more

Table 95-4 Linkage Data for 42 Families with Dominant HS

Chromosome	Locus	Name	Linkage	Comment
1p36	PGD	6-Phosphogluconate dehydrogenase	No	Close to protein 4.1
1p34-p36	RH	Rhesus blood group	No	Close to protein 4.1
1p22	PGM1	Phosphoglucomutase-1	No	
1q12-q21	FY	Duffy blood group	No	Close to α-spectrin
2p	JK	Kidd blood group	No	
2p25	ACP1	Acid phosphatase-1	No	
2p12	KM	κ light chain	No	
4q28-q31	MNS	MNS blood group	No	Glycophorins A and B
4q11-q13	HP	Haptoglobin	No	
4q12	GC	Group-specific component	No	
6	P	P blood group	No	
6p21	HLA	HLA tissue type	No	
6p21	GLO1	Glyoxalase I	No	
7	DIA2	Diaphorase-2	No	
9q34	ABO	ABO blood group	No	
9q34	AK1	Adenylate kinase-1	No	
13q14	ESD	Esterase D	No	
14q32	PI	α_1-Antitrypsin	No	? Close to β-spectrin
14p32	GM	IgG heavy chain	*	? Close to β-spectrin
16	GPT1	Glutamate pyruvate transaminase	No	
16p13	PGP	Phosphoglycolate phosphatase	No	
19p13	C3	C3 complement	No	
19p13	LU	Luthern blood group	No	
20q13	ADA	Adenosine deaminase	No	

*Kimberling et al.[338] found linkage between GM and HS at a recombination fraction of 0.22 by assuming that HS was homogeneous and combining observations on 70 patients in 11 informative families. No linkage with the neighboring PI locus was found. However, subsequently de Jongh et al.[339] found no linkage between GM (or PI) and HS in a larger study of 250 HS patients in 19 families.
SOURCE: Kimberling et al.[338] and de Jongh et al.[339]

readily than normal when metabolically deprived.[274–277] This has not been shown to occur in metabolically maintained spherocytes, but the surface loss probably occurs slowly under these conditions (~1 to 2 percent per day), and none of the reported studies has been conducted for long periods of time. The phospholipid and cholesterol contents of isolated spherocytes are decreased by 15 to 20 percent, consistent with the loss of surface area.[274,279–281] Presumably integral membrane proteins are also lost, but no quantitative measurements have been made. Since budding red cells are only rarely observed in HS blood smears, membrane loss either occurs fairly rapidly (i.e., in seconds to minutes) or occurs in bywaters of the circulation such as the reticuloendothelial system.

The major evidence that surface loss involves more than simple fragmentation is that the surface deficit exceeds the measured lipid loss. After splenectomy, HS red cells are deficient in lipid compared with splenectomized controls, but their lipid content is similar to that of normal cells from unsplenectomized individuals, despite the fact that they are more spherical and more osmotically fragile.[279] The explanation of this discrepancy is unknown. It is possible that red cell lipids are more tightly packed in hereditary spherocytes or that the surface is contracted in some other way, but it is not easy to understand how this could occur. Alternatively, integral proteins may be disproportionately lost during fragmentation, or HS red cells may undergo internal as well as external fragmentation. The latter process would decrease surface area without causing a measurable loss of membrane lipid. Thin-section electron micrographs do not show cytoplasmic vesicles in hereditary spherocytes,[278] but a careful search has not been reported.

Mouse Mutants with Hereditary Spherocytic Anemia. The structural instability of HS membranes suggests a defect in the membrane skeleton. As noted earlier (see "Functions of the Membrane Skeleton"), this structure is the major determinant of membrane strength and durability and is defective in certain mutants of the common house mouse, *Mus musculus*.

Five types of murine hereditary hemolytic anemia have been identified. These anemias resemble human hereditary spherocytosis and may share similar genetic defects. They are designated *ja/ja* (jaundice), *sph/sph* (spherocytosis), *sph*[ha]/*sph*[ha] (hemolytic anemia), *sph*[2BC]/*sph*[2BC] (anemia), and *nb/nb* (normoblastosis).[321] The nomenclature indicates that anemia is observed only in the homozygous state and that the five mutants represent three loci: *ja*, *sph*, and *nb*. The mutants *sph*, *sph*[ha], and *sph*[2BC] represent different alleles at the sph locus. All of the mutants have severe hemolysis, with reticulocyte counts approaching 100 percent, along with marked spherocytosis, jaundice, bilirubin gallstones, and massive hepatosplenomegaly. The defects are autosomal recessive, and the homozygotes have drastically impaired viability. There is a similar but much milder condition in the deer mouse, *Peromyscus maniculatus*, designated *sp/sp*.[322]

Studies of these mouse mutants have revealed various membrane skeletal abnormalities. As noted earlier, all of the mutants are spectrin-deficient (Fig. 95-7), and the degree of deficiency correlates with clinical severity. The *ja/ja* mutant has no detectable spectrin. The *sph/sph* variants lack spectrin α chains but have small amounts of β-spectrin; *nb/nb* mutants have 50 to 70 percent of the normal quantity of spectrin.[166] Bone marrow transplantation transfers the mutations, confirming their erythroid origin.[321]

Table 95-5 Reported Abnormalities of Hereditary Spherocytes

Findings	References
Cellular properties	
Stomatocytic to spherocytic shape	253
Decreased deformability and filterability	253–257
Hemoglobin	
Increased MCHC (mean corpuscular hemoglobin concentration)	258
Metabolism	
Increased ATP turnover[a]	259–261
Increased glycolysis[b]	259, 260
Decreased 2,3-DPG[c]	264, 265
Decreased intracellular pH	266, 267
Membrane (general)	
Wrinkled and pitted membrane surface	268, 269
Decreased tension required for membrane fragmentation	270
Decreased membrane elasticity and bending stiffness	271–273
Increased membrane loss during ATP depletion	274–277
Diminished endocytosis	278
Lipids	
Decreased phospholipids and cholesterol per cell[d]	279–281
Decreased long-chain fatty acids in some phospholipids[d]	282, 282a
Increased lipid viscosity[e]	284, 285
Loss of phospholipid asymmetry[f]	216
Cations and transport	
Increased Na$^+$ permeability	259, 287, 288
Increased Ca^{2+} content[g]	289
Decreased Ca^{2+} efflux[g]	291
Decreased Ca^{2+}-ATPase[g]	292, 293
Decreased phosphoenolpyruvate transport	309
Phosphorylation	
Abnormal membrane protein phosphorylation[h]	294–299
Decreased phosphorylation-induced gelation of skeletal protein fragments	320
Proteins	
Increased membrane skeletal dissociation[i]	304
Increased membrane-bound hemoglobin and catalase	305
Decreased cation-induced aggregation of solubilized proteins	306–308
Decreased spectrin	246–248
Decreased spectrin and ankyrin[j]	310
Decreased binding of protein 4.1 to HS spectrin[j]	311–313
Absence of protein 4.2[j,k]	123, 314
Inextractable spectrin[i]	315–317
Enolase deficiency[j]	319

[a]Not confirmed by other investigators.[262]
[b]Not confirmed by other investigators.[263]
[c]Not confirmed by other investigators.[261]
[d]Not confirmed by other investigators.[283]
[e]Not confirmed by other investigators.[286]
[f]Only in patients with severe spectrin deficiency.
[g]Not confirmed by other investigators.[290]
[h]It should be noted that the various investigators referenced have reported an extraordinary range of different phosphorylation defects. Other investigators have found no phosphorylation defects in most HS red cells.[300–303]
[i]But more recent studies have shown that this effect is dependent on preparation of the skeletons with aged Triton X-100.
[j]Defect observed only in a subset of HS kindreds.
[k]This disease is discussed in the section on spherocytic elliptocytosis.

Recent studies of spectrin synthesis[323,324] in these mice suggest that *ja* mutants lack the ability to synthesize β chains, and the various *sph* mutants have defects in α-spectrin synthesis and/or stability. The *sph* mutation and the mouse α-spectrin gene have both been mapped to chromosome 1,[324] which is consistent with this conclusion. The *nb* mutants have normal spectrin synthesis.[323,324] It appears they lack spectrin because their ankyrin is very unstable.[325,326] The *nb* defect is localized on mouse chromosome 8, near the glutathione reductase gene.[326]

Recessively Inherited Spherocytosis in Humans. This disorder was originally described in siblings whose parents were fourth cousins.[246] The clinical condition was characterized by life-threatening anemia, frequent jaundice, and massive splenomegaly. Unlike typical dominant HS, hemolysis improved but was not eliminated by splenectomy. The red cells were microcytic with some acanthocytes and bizarre forms in addition to spherocytes. As compared to protein 3, the red cell membranes had only 40 to 50 percent of the normal amount of spectrin by SDS-PAGE and only 26 to 29 percent by radioimmunoassay.[246] The spectrin functioned normally in its ability to self-associate and bind to inside-out vesicles. This severe form of recessive HS is fortunately quite rare; however, less severe variants are common and may affect up to 25 percent of all HS patients.[247]

The mechanism of spectrin deficiency in these patients is unknown. The most straightforward explanations are reduced spectrin synthesis, synthesis of an unstable spectrin, or impaired binding of spectrin to the membrane. As noted earlier, in chickens,[67] mice,[68] and probably humans,[327] α-spectrin synthesis exceeds β- by a factor of 2 to 3. Thus heterozygotes for defects in α-spectrin synthesis would still make enough normal α-spectrin to pair with all or nearly all the β chains produced, so spectrin deficiency would only be evident in the homozygous state. This is exactly what is observed in patients with recessive HS.[246,247] In addition, recent investigations show the disease is genetically linked to polymorphisms in α-spectrin.[328]

Autosomal Dominant HS. It is now clear that *erythrocyte membranes from almost all HS patients are spectrin-deficient, including both the dominant and recessive forms of the disease, and that the degree of spectrin deficiency correlates closely with the severity of the disease and with the degree of spherocytosis, as measured by the median osmotic fragility of the red cells.*[247,248] Moreover, the degree of spectrin deficiency predicts the patient's status after splenectomy, as judged by reticulocyte count, haptoglobin level, and hematocrit[247] (Fig. 95-9). In general the dominant forms of HS are milder than the recessive variant(s), although significant overlap is observed.[247] The effect of spectrin deficiency on the hemolytic anemia may be partly explained by the finding that the membrane elastic shear modulus and bending stiffness are directly proportional to the surface density of spectrin.[273] These mechanical membrane properties may relate to the ability of the spectrin-deficient HS red cells to withstand circulatory stresses.

Expanding on the reasoning in the previous section, spectrin deficiency in dominant HS might be due to diminished synthesis (or instability) of the relatively scarce spectrin β chains or to a lack of ankyrin molecules, which bind the β chains. Either of these defects should limit the formation of stable, membrane associated heterodimers and be expressed as a dominant trait. In theory protein 3 might also be a culprit, since ankyrin and spectrin do not bind to the membrane until protein 3 is expressed,[332] and there is good evidence that only a fraction of the protein 3 molecules are available to bind ankyrin.[116] As described in the following sections, probable examples of primary spectrin and ankyrin defects have recently been described. However, these mutations have only been identified in a small fraction of patients with dominant HS. In the great majority of patients no cause for spectrin deficiency has yet been identified.

SPECTRIN-PROTEIN 4.1 INTERACTIONS. A subset of families with autosomal dominant HS have spectrin that is defective in its capacity to bind protein 4.1 (Fig. 95-10). This defect has been observed by two groups in a total of four kindreds.[311-313,329] The other binding functions of spectrin, such as ankyrin binding and self-association, are preserved.[311-313] Heterozygous individuals have two types of spectrin. The abnormal fraction, approximately 40 percent, lacks the ability to bind protein 4.1 and therefore attaches only weakly to actin.[312,313] Enzymatic digestions with trypsin[311] or chymotrypsin[313] reveal defects toward the tail of the spectrin β chain, near the site where protein 4.1 binds.[82,86-86b] The mutant spectrin is unstable and susceptible to thiol oxidation.[313] This oxidation causes or exacerbates the defect in binding to protein 4.1, since chemical reduction almost completely restores normal binding activity.[313] Interestingly, very mild oxidation of *normal* spectrin[330] or storage of normal cells under aerobic conditions in the blood bank[331] produces similar defects in spectrin-4.1 interactions.

Patients with the spectrin-4.1 binding defect are also spectrin-deficient, with spectrin content being only 80 percent of normal.[313] Presumably the defective spectrin detaches from the membrane more easily than normal and falls prey to proteases that specifically degrade unbound spectrin chains.[69] Loss of the abnormal spectrin explains why the ratio of normal to abnormal spectrin is 60:40 instead of the expected 50:50.

The fraction of patients with the spectrin-4.1 defect is unknown since no surveys have been done. A crude estimate would be approximately 10 percent. Clinically, these patients have typical dominant HS with symptoms proportional to the degree of spectrin deficiency. In one family, acanthocytes (5 to 15 percent) were present on the peripheral smear in addition to spherocytes,[312] but it is not clear whether this is characteristic of the spectrin-4.1 binding defect.

DEFICIENCY OF SPECTRIN AND ANKYRIN. Recently Coetzer and her colleagues[310] have described two patients with a new, apparently dominantly inherited, disease characterized by transfusion-dependent hemolytic anemia, marked spherocytosis, bizarre poikilocytosis, and only a partial response to splenectomy. Red cell membranes are deficient in both spectrin *and ankyrin* (about 50 to 60 percent of normal levels). The disease appears to be due to an inability to adequately synthesize ankyrin,[327] rather than to synthesis of an unstable or defective molecule or to a defect in the ankyrin-binding capacity of protein 3.[310] Very recently Costa and his colleagues have shown

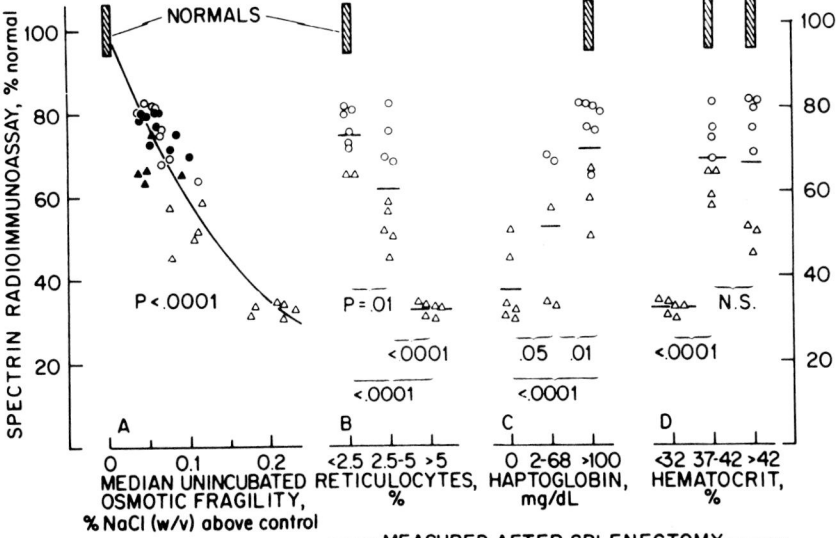

Fig. 95-9 Correlation of red cell spectrin content with osmotic fragility and measures of hemolysis after splenectomy. The hatched rectangles indicate the normal range for each index. Patients with nondominant (i.e., probably recessive) form of HS are indicated by triangles, those with the dominant form by circles, and those who have previously undergone splenectomy by open circles or triangles. (From Agre, Asimos, Casello, and McMillan.[247] Used by permission of the New England Journal of Medicine.)

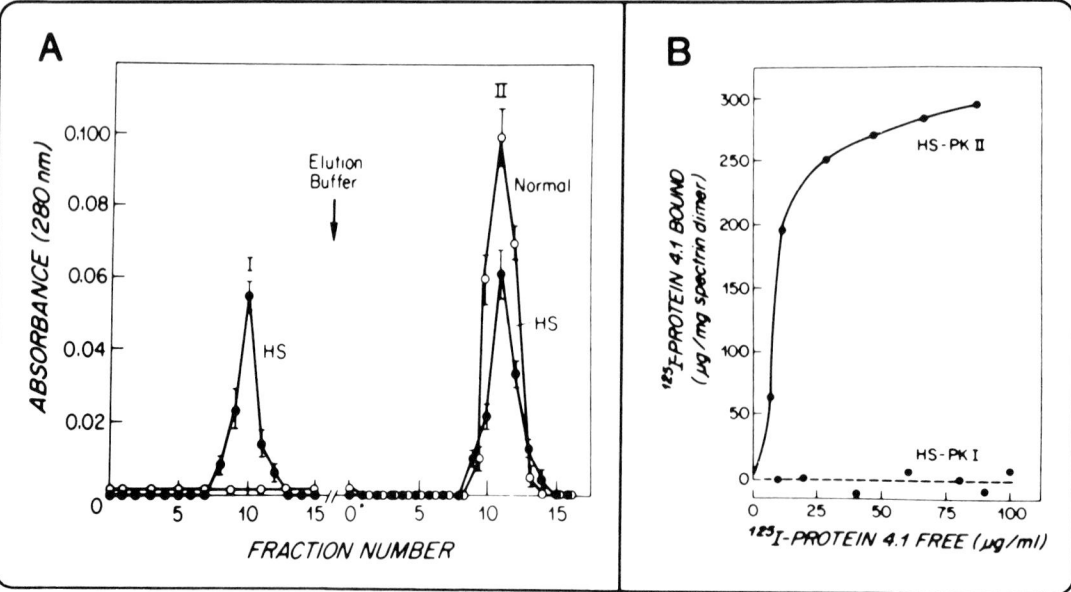

Fig. 95-10 Purification of mutant HS spectrin that is defective in binding to protein 4.1. *A.* Separation of HS spectrin dimers into normal and defective subpopulations by affinity chromatography on a column of immobilized normal 4.1. Note that all normal spectrin was retained but that 40 percent of the HS spectrin failed to bind and emerged in the void volume (peak I). Chromatography was then switched (arrow) to conditions that released all the normal spectrin and the remaining HS spectrin (peak II). *B.* Binding of HS peak I and peak II spectrins to normal ^{125}I-protein 4.1. Note that the peak I spectrin lacked all binding activity, while the peak II spectrin bound 4.1 normally. (*From Palek and Lux.*[562] *Used by permission of Seminars in Hematology.*)

that HS is genetically linked to the ankyrin gene in a large family with only 15 percent spectrin deficiency and clinically typical dominant HS.[336b] Further studies will be needed to define the ankyrin defect in this family and determine how frequently such defects are responsible for HS.

SPHEROCYTOSIS AND MENTAL RETARDATION. Four patients in three families have been identified with moderate to severe splenectomy-responsive anemia, spherocytosis, dysmorphic features, psychomotor retardation, and heterozygous deletion of a portion of the short arm of chromosome 8 (8p11.1-p21.1).[245,327a,327b] A similar hematological picture has been observed in two other families with balanced translocations involving the same region of chromosome 8.[243,244] This locus (SPH1) lies close to glutathione reductase in a position analogous to the *nb* locus on mouse chromosome 8.[326] We have recently found that the ankyrin gene is located at this position on chromosome 8 (Table 95-3).[336a] Two unrelated patients with the chromosome 8 deletion were studied. Both had only half the normal number of ankyrin genes by quantitative Southern blotting, and red cells from the one patient tested were very ankyrin-deficient (about 60 percent of normal).[336a]

INEXTRACTABLE SPECTRIN. A decreased ability to extract spectrin from the membranes of patients with dominant HS has been observed in a small number of Australian HS patients.[315–317] Inexplicably, the extracted spectrin also resisted reassociation with spectrin-depleted membranes.[316,317] The molecular investigations needed to explain these curious and apparently contradictory findings have not yet been done.

ENOLASE DEFICIENCY. A preliminary report of HS combined with partial enolase deficiency (~50 percent) in four generations of a Caucasian family has recently appeared.[319] The authors note that the spherocytic red cells resist lysis in the acidified glycerol lysis test (a characteristic of typical HS) and suggest this indicates that enolase-deficient HS is unique.

However, in a previously reported family with enolase deficiency (6 percent of normal) no hemolysis or spherocytosis was evident except during a hemolytic crisis.[318]

Pathophysiology

The major problems of the hereditary spherocyte are the rheological consequences of its decreased surface/volume ratio. The red cell membrane is very flexible, but it can expand its surface area only about 3 percent before rupturing.[340] Consequently, as the red cell becomes more and more spherical, it becomes less and less deformable, an impairment that Jandl has likened to "an obese man attempting to bend at the waist."[254] In the case of HS red cells this poor deformability is a hindrance only in the spleen, since hereditary spherocytes survive well after splenectomy.[341,342]

The Spleen. In the spleen most of the arterial blood empties directly into the cords: a narrow, honeycombed maze of passages formed by reticular cells and by phagocytes.[269,343,344] Histologically this is an "open" circulation, but apparently most of the blood that enters the cords travels in fairly direct (i.e., functionally "closed") pathways.[344,345] If flow through these passages is impeded, red cells are diverted deeper into the labyrinthine portions of the cords where blood flow is slow, and the cells may be detained for minutes to hours. To exit and return to the venous circulation, red cells must squeeze between the endothelial cells that form the walls of the venous sinusoids. Even when maximally distended, these narrow, elliptical fenestrations are much smaller than red cells (Fig. 95-11),[300] which must undergo considerable contortion during their passage.[343,344,346]

It is clear that spherocytic red cells are considerably hindered at this point in the circulation. Isolated hereditary spherocytes are poorly deformable and pass 3- to 5-μm filters with difficulty,[254,257,347] sometimes bursting in the process.[257]

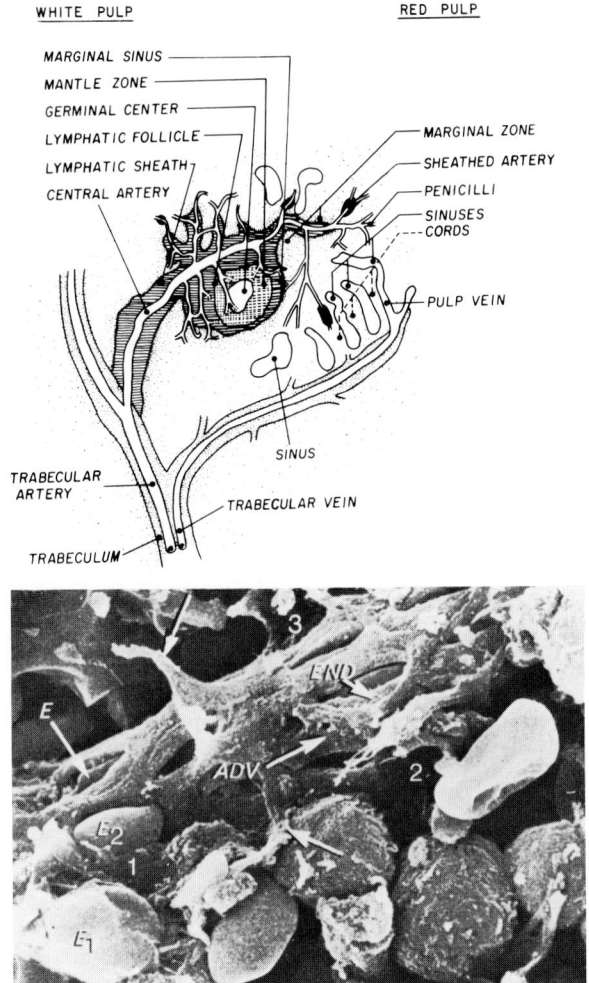

Fig. 95-11 *(Top)* Schematic illustration of the anatomy of the spleen. Note that blood entering the splenic cords must pass through the walls of the splenic sinuses to reenter the venous circulation. *(Bottom)* Scanning electron micrograph of a splenic sinus wall viewed from a splenic cord. A portion of the overlying cordal structure has been removed. The narrow transmural slits between the endothelial (END) and adventitial (ADV) cells of the sinus wall are easily seen. It is likely that these cells are normally apposed and that the slits are "potential" structures rather than fixed pores.[269] They are evident here because of a drying artifact. Note that the adjacent erythrocytes (E_1 and E_2) are considerably larger than these slits and must be flexible to pass through them into the splenic sinus. *(From Lux and Glader.[373] Used by permission of W. B. Saunders Co.)*

HS red cells are trapped in the cords during in vitro perfusion through spleens removed from patients with idiopathic thrombocytopenic purpura,[348] and ^{51}Cr-labeled spherocytes are selectively sequestered in the spleen in vivo.[349–354] As a consequence, HS spleens characteristically show massively congested cords and relatively empty venous sinuses on light microscopy,[269,355–357] and electron micrographs show relatively few spherocytes traversing the sinus wall,[269,357–359] in contrast to normal spleens, where such cells are easily found.[344]

It is also clear that spherocytes are damaged by their detention in the cords. In unsplenectomized HS patients, two populations of spherocytes are detectable—a minor population of hyperchromic "microspherocytes" that form the "tail" of very fragile cells on unincubated osmotic fragility tests and a major population of cells that may be only slightly more spheroidal than normal. Although it was known as early as 1913 that red cells obtained from the splenic vein were more osmotically

fragile than those in the peripheral circulation,[360] the significance of this observation was not fully appreciated until the classic studies of Emerson[249] and Young[348] and their colleagues, published in the early 1950s. These investigators clearly showed that osmotically fragile microspherocytes are concentrated in and apparently emanate from the splenic pulp. After splenectomy the tail of hyperfragile cells is no longer evident, although the major population of moderately fragile spherocytes persists.[249,348,355] These and other data led to the conclusion that the spleen detains and conditions circulating HS red cells in a way that increases their spheroidicity and hastens their demise.[249,348] The kinetics of this process were beautifully illustrated in vivo by Griggs and his coworkers,[353] who showed that a cohort of ^{59}Fe-labeled HS red cells gradually shifted from the major, less fragile, population to the minor, more fragile, population during their circulation in vivo. Although most conditioned HS red cells are probably recaptured and destroyed in the spleen, the damage incurred is sufficient to permit their recognition and destruction in extrasplenic sites since conditioned spherocytes isolated from the spleen at the time of splenectomy and reinfused postoperatively are rapidly destroyed.[353,365]

The mechanism of splenic conditioning is less clear. It is difficult to obtain precise information about the cordal environment, but the data that exist suggest the climate is inhospitable. Arteries supplying the white pulp skim off plasma and dramatically increase congestion in the cords where the crowded red cells must compete with metabolically voracious phagocytes for limited supplies of glucose.[362] Even if glucose were available, it is questionable whether the HS red cell could use it effectively. Because of the stagnant circulation, lactic acid accumulates[347] and the extracellular pH falls, probably to between 6.5 and 7.0.[249,347,363] Intracellular pH must also decline, inhibiting hexokinase[364] and phosphofructokinase,[365] the rate-limiting enzymes of glycolysis, and retarding glucose utilization. Under these conditions stores of 2,3-DPG will be metabolized to provide energy for the cell. The loss of this polyvalent anion, combined with the decreased anionic charge on hemoglobin that occurs in an acid environment, is compensated by the entry of monovalent chloride ions.[366] The resulting increase in osmolarity causes water to enter the HS red cell and must worsen its already compromising spheroidicity. Thus, the spherocyte, detained in the splenic cords because of its surface deficiency, is severely stressed by erythrostasis in a metabolically threatening environment. Whether this is sufficient to cause its demise is a matter of continuing debate.

Erythrostasis. As Ham and Castle[219] and Dacie[367] first recognized, the HS red cell is particularly vulnerable to erythrostasis. When incubated in the absence of glucose, their physiological substrate, all red cells undergo a series of changes that culminate in autohemolysis. As shown in Fig. 95-12, these changes are accelerated in hereditary spherocytes. HS red cells are initially jeopardized by an increase in the permeability of their membranes to sodium.[259,287] This is normally balanced by increased ATP-dependent sodium pumping and increased glycolysis,[259] a response that is impaired in erythrostasis where substrate is limited. Consequently spherocytes exhaust serum glucose and become ATP-depleted more rapidly than normal (Fig. 95-12, *panel A*). As ATP levels fall, cation pumps fail and the cells gain sodium and water and swell (Fig. 95-12, *panel B*). Later, when ATP reaches very low levels, intracellular calcium also rises owing to failure of the calcium

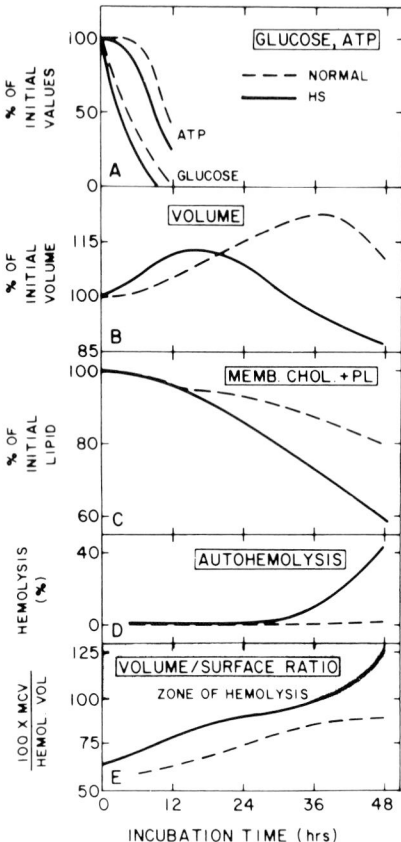

ERYTHROSTASIS OF
NORMAL AND HS RBC's

Fig. 95-12 The effects of erythrostasis on normal (– – –) and HS (—) red cells incubated at 37°C in their own serum at hematocrit values of 25 to 45 percent. Because HS red cells are more permeable to sodium than normal, they require excess ATP for sodium transport and exhaust available serum glucose and red cell ATP more rapidly than normal (panel A). This leads to cell swelling, which is followed by cell shrinkage due to calcium accumulation and potassium loss (Gardos phenomenon) (panel B). The relatively more rapid loss of membrane fragments (panel C) gradually increases the volume/surface ratio (panel E) until the critical hemolytic volume is reached (volume/surface ratio = 100) and autohemolysis ensues (panel D). (From Lux and Glader.[373] Used by permission of W. B. Saunders Co.)

pump. This leads to a selective efflux of red cell potassium, the so-called Gardos phenomenon.[368,369] The molecular mechanism of this permeability change is not well-understood, but its consequences are well-defined: as intracellular potassium declines, water exits in response to the change in osmolarity and cells shrink (Fig. 95-12, panel B). The sodium gain is accelerated in HS red cells but is insufficient by itself to induce hemolysis in vitro since cation-mediated cell swelling peaks as 12 to 16 h (Fig. 95-12, panel B), long before autohemolysis occurs (Fig. 95-12, panel D). HS red cells are doubly jeopardized. As noted earlier, they are inherently unstable and fragment excessively during metabolic depletion.[274–277] Membrane lipids are lost at more than twice the normal rate (Fig. 95-12, panel C).[276] It is not known whether a proportional loss of integral membrane proteins occurs, although this seems likely. At first this surface loss is balanced by cell dehydration (as shown by stabilization of the calculated volume/surface ratio between 20 and 30 h in Fig. 95-12, panel E), but eventually membrane loss predominates, the cells exceed their

critical hemolytic volume (volume/surface ratio >100), and autohemolysis ensues (Fig. 95-12, panel E).

Dynamics of Splenic Trapping. One of the major unanswered issues about the pathophysiology of HS is whether the events that lead to conditioning and destruction of HS red cells in the spleen are the same as those that lead to increased spheroidicity and autohemolysis during erythrostasis in vitro. In the past many investigators have assumed this was the case, and argument focused on the relative importance of membrane leakiness[259,370] versus membrane fragility[274,275,277,371,372] in the spherocytes' demise. Estimates of the dynamics of splenic blood flow in HS[373] and measurements of the metabolic status of HS red cells trapped in the splenic cords raise questions about this assumption.

In the first place it appears that most HS red cells are not detained in the splenic cords long enough for damage to occur by simple erythrostasis. The normal adult spleen has a red cell volume of about 30 to 40 ml[373] and normally receives about 3 percent of the resting cardiac output.[374,375] As noted earlier, most of this blood probably travels through relatively direct channels in the red pulp and is diverted into the more stagnant portions of the cords only if flow through this pathway is impeded. One can calculate (see Table 16-7 of Ref. 373) that the average normal red cell, traveling the direct pathway, will spend only 30 to 40 s in the splenic cords, a time that corresponds closely to measured transit times in isolated perfused canine spleens.[362]

The average spleen of an adult patient with HS contains a much larger red cell volume (~450 to 500 ml) but also receives a larger share of the cardiac output (~8 to 10 percent).[374] Mixing experiments with labeled HS red cells indicate that 90 to 99 percent of this blood is shunted rapidly through the spleen, presumably via the direct cordal pathways, and only 1 to 10 percent[350–352,376] is detained in the congested cords. Even so, the calculated residence time of the average HS red cell in the splenic cords is only 10 to 100 min[373]—far too short a time for any significant metabolic depletion to occur at the rates shown in Fig. 95-12. One could argue that a completely stagnant cordal subpopulation exists that is not detected in such mixing experiments, but if such a compartment were large enough to account for the turnover of HS red cells (4 to 8 percent per day) by simple erythrostasis (i.e., over the 36- to 48-h period required for autohemolysis) it would have to occupy 30 to 80 percent of the splenic red cell volume.[373] There is no evidence for such a large static compartment.

Thus, if HS red cells are conditioned by metabolic deprivation, the damage must occur repetitively. This is conceivable, since under conditions where the average red cell spends 1 h in the splenic cords, a small fraction of the cells will be trapped for a considerably longer time and may become significantly ATP-depleted. It is often assumed that if such cells escape the spleen, they will return to the cords within minutes, but their actual recirculation time may be much longer. When splenic cordal flow is low (1 percent of splenic blood flow) and cordal residence time is greatest (~100 min), one can calculate that the average red cell will not reenter the stagnant part of the cordal circulation for nearly 400 min.[373] Judged from in vitro studies,[377] this should be more than enough time to rejuvenate even moderately ATP-depleted cells. However, some consequences of ATP depletion (e.g., potassium and lipid loss) are not reversible. These changes would promote longer detention and more rapid recapture and could eventually lead to irreversible splenic sequestration and hemolysis.

This scenario is supported by direct analysis of splenic red cells. As shown in Table 95-6, HS red cells obtained from the splenic pulp immediately after splenectomy and containing approximately 90 percent conditioned cells are moderately cation-depleted and show changes in ADP and 2,3-DPG concentrations consistent with metabolism in an acidic environment, but their ATP levels are normal.[378] Others have reported similar findings.[351,352] Thus, if splenic conditioning is caused by metabolic depletion, it must occur by an intermittent process which allows most of the cells to recover and maintain normal or near-normal concentrations of ATP.

The data in Table 95-6 may also be taken to indicate that splenic conditioning is not caused by ATP depletion. The effects of other aspects of the splenic environment on hereditary spherocytes have not been carefully investigated. It is possible, for example, that potassium loss and membrane instability are aggravated by the low pH of the splenic cords and lead to the changes depicted in the table. Alternatively, membrane damage by macrophages may contribute to the cation and surface loss of hereditary spherocytes. The latter possibility is supported by the careful, but frequently ignored, observations of Coleman and Finch.[379] These investigators found that large doses of cortisone (400 mg/day) markedly ameliorated HS in nonsplenectomized patients. The effects were similar to those produced by splenectomy. Hemoglobin production, reticulocytosis, and fecal urobilinogen declined; red cell life span doubled, and hyperspheroidal, conditioned red cells disappeared from the circulation. It is well known that similar doses of corticosteroids inhibit splenic processing and destruction of IgG- or C3b-coated red cells in patients with immunohemolytic anemias, probably by suppressing macrophage-induced red cell sphering and phagocytosis.[380,381] Early light-microscopic studies showed little evidence for splenic erythrophagocytosis in HS,[355,356] but electron microscopy indicates that this is common, particularly in the splenic cords.[357,358] In addition, phagocytes expressed from the cords of HS patients contain bits of ghostlike membrane debris,[382] presumably resulting from membrane fragmentation. These observations suggest that macrophage processing may be a critical factor in splenic conditioning. It should be noted that no direct evidence for this speculation is presently available, and other explanations for the improvement induced by corticosteroids, such as changes in splenic size or alterations in the membrane properties of hereditary spherocytes, cannot be excluded.

In summary, it is clear that HS red cells are selectively detained by the spleen and this custody is detrimental, leading to a loss of membrane surface that fosters further splenic trapping and eventual destruction (Fig. 95-13). Indeed, recent

Table 95-6 Comparison of Splenic Cordal and Circulating Red Cells in Hereditary Spherocytosis

	Peripheral RBCs, 30% conditioned*	Splenic cordal RBCs, 90% conditioned*
Na$^+$, meq/liter RBC	10 ± 2	17 ± 3
K$^+$, meq/liter RBC	78 ± 7	58 ± 12
Na$^+$ + K$^+$, meq/liter RBC	89 ± 9	75 ± 13
ATP, mmol/liter RBC	1.48 ± 0.16	1.46 ± 0.18
ADP, mmol/liter RBC	0.40 ± 0.08	0.85 ± 0.14
2,3-DPG, mmol/liter RBC	4.72 ± 0.35	3.02 ± 0.57
ATP turnover, relative specific activity	$102 \pm 9\%$	$93 \pm 7\%$

*As measured by osmotic fragility tests.
SOURCE: Data from Mayman and Zipursky.[378]

studies show that the mean splenic transit time correlates inversely ($r = -0.96$) with red cell survival in HS.[382a] It appears likely that splenic trapping is initially promoted by membrane skeletal instability, but the details of how the molecular defect leads to splenic entrapment have yet to be defined. The mechanisms of splenic conditioning and red cell destruction are also uncertain. Kinetic considerations make it unlikely that red cells are continuously trapped within the cords for the long periods required to induce passive sphering and autohemolysis by metabolic depletion. Repetitious metabolic damage remains a possibility. A special susceptibility of the HS red cell to the acidic environment of the spleen and active intervention of macrophages in the processing of erythrostatically damaged spherocytes must also be considered, but direct evidence for these two hypotheses remains to be established.

Clinical Features

The characteristic clinical features of HS are pallor, jaundice, and splenomegaly. The disease typically presents in infancy or childhood, but may present at any age.[386a] As noted earlier, in most patients the degree of hemolysis, anemia, and spherocytosis; the need for transfusions (or no need); and the response to splenectomy closely parallel the degree of spectrin deficiency.[247]

Neonatal HS. HS frequently presents as jaundice in the first few days of life.[383–386] The combination of hemolysis and the reduced capacity of the neonatal liver to conjugate bilirubin can cause serum concentrations of unconjugated bilirubin to rise rapidly, and because kernicterus is a risk,[385] exchange transfusions are sometimes necessary. Mild anemia is common

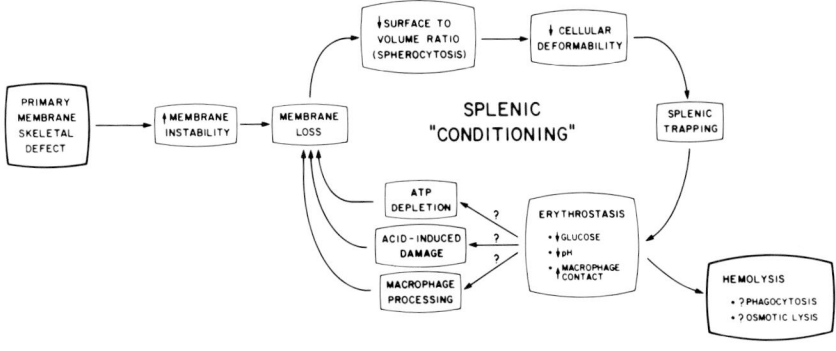

Fig. 95-13 Pathophysiology of the splenic conditioning and destruction of red cells observed in hereditary spherocytosis. (*From Lux and Glader.*[373] *Used by permission of W. B. Saunders Co.*)

at this time, but severe anemia is rare. There is no evidence that patients with HS who are symptomatic as neonates have a more severe form of the disease. Indeed most become asymptomatic within the first few weeks of life. However, some infants become progressively more anemic during the first few months of life and require transfusion. In our experience this usually occurs because the marrow response to anemia is more sluggish than normal. Fortunately, the problem is transient, except in rare patients with severe subtypes of HS, and usually remits after one or two transfusions. Subsequently the course of the disease depends on the equilibrium established between the rates of red cell production and destruction.

Mild HS. In a surprisingly large number of patients ($\sim$20 to 30 percent), red cell production and destruction are balanced, and no anemia is present.[258,387] These individuals are said to have "compensated" hemolysis. They are often asymptomatic, and in some cases diagnosis may be difficult since hemolysis, spherocytosis, and splenomegaly are usually mild. Hemolysis may become severe with illnesses that cause the spleen to enlarge, such as infectious mononucleosis.[388] Hemolysis is also exacerbated by pregnancy[389] and by intensive physical effort, to the point where it may impair athletic performance in endurance sports, even in patients with mild disease.[390] Many of these patients are diagnosed during family studies or are discovered as adults when splenomegaly or gallstones are noticed or transient episodes of jaundice appear. Although mild HS is usually familial, it also develops sporadically in families with more severely affected members.[258] Presumably this is due to the inheritance of modifying genes, such as those affecting splenic function.

One of the interesting mysteries about HS is why patients with "compensated" hemolysis continue to have erythroid hyperproduction when their hemoglobin levels are normal. The phenomenon is difficult to reconcile with the generally accepted theory that erythropoiesis is controlled by tissue hypoxia. One possible factor is the low concentration of 2,3-DPG in hereditary spherocytes[264,265] prior to splenectomy. Low red cell 2,3-DPG would increase oxygen affinity and promote erythropoiesis, but this effect is apparently balanced by other factors since the P_{50} (oxygen tension of the blood at which 50 percent of oxygen is released from red cells) of HS blood is normal.[265]

Typical HS. The majority of HS patients ($\sim$60 to 75 percent) have incompletely compensated hemolysis and mild to moderate anemia. Intermittent subtle jaundice is common, particularly in children, and is sometimes associated with mild viral infections, presumably due to reticuloendothelial stimulation and an increase in hemolysis. The spleen is palpable in about 50 percent of these patients during infancy and in 75 to 95 percent during late childhood and adult life.[258,391,392] Splenomegaly is usually modest, but it may be massive.[235,236,393,394] There is no published evidence that the size of the spleen correlates with the severity of HS, although such a correlation probably exists, considering the pathophysiology of the disease (Fig. 95-13).

Severe HS. A small proportion of HS patients ($\sim$5 to 10 percent) have severe and sometimes transfusion-dependent anemia. These individuals may present diagnostic difficulties if transfusions are begun before HS is diagnosed, since the abnormal cells may be destroyed so rapidly in the most severe cases that, except for a few spherocytic reticulocytes, only transfused cells are available for testing.[373] In addition to the risks of recurrent transfusions, these patients often suffer from aplastic crises (to be discussed) and may develop growth retardation,[393,394] delayed sexual maturation,[393] and frontal bossing or other changes in the facial bones similar to those observed in thalassemia.[393]

Laboratory Features

The major laboratory findings are those common to all hemolytic processes: hyperplasia of erythroid percursors in the bone marrow, an increased concentration of reticulocytes, a slight to moderate rise in unconjugated (indirect) bilirubin in the plasma, and an elevated fecal excretion of urobilinogens.[258,392,395] Plasma hemoglobin is normal,[396] and haptoglobin is only variably reduced,[397] because most of the hemoglobin that is released from destroyed hereditary spherocytes is catabolized to bilirubin at the site of destruction (so-called extravascular hemolysis).

Red Cell Morphology and Indexes. Spherocytosis is the hallmark of HS and, with reticulocytosis, is the most reliable finding. In 20 to 25 percent of patients, the typical hyperchromic, conditioned microspherocytes are relatively sparse.[258,392] Peripheral blood smears from these patients may sometimes mistakenly be considered normal, even by relatively experienced observers.[258] Interestingly, although hereditary spherocytes, and particularly the conditioned cells, appear spheroidal in conventional dried smears, most are actually thickened discocytes or spherostomatocytes when examined by scanning electron microscopy.[253] The various types of HS have different morphologic patterns on blood smears, as shown in Fig. 95-14. Patients with classic autosomal dominant HS and most patients with recessive HS have only spherocytes and microspherocytes. Patients with more severe spectrin deficiency have proportionally more misshapen spherocytes, spiculated red cells, and bizarre poikilocytes. In the most severe cases, these may dominate the blood smear[246,310] (Fig. 95-14D). Spiculated red cells (acanthocytes) may also be observed in the protein 4.1–binding defect of spectrin (Fig. 95-14C). Oblong spherocytes combined with elliptocytes suggest a variant of hereditary elliptocytosis (HE), spherocytic HE. Because the morphologic defect is acquired gradually in the circulation, HS erythroblasts are morphologically and rheologically normal,[255] and circulating reticulocytes are only slightly spheroidal.[398]

The mean corpuscular hemoglobin concentration (MCHC) of HS red cells is increased owing to mild cellular dehydration and exceeds the upper limit of normal (36 percent) in about half of the patients.[258] Red cell sodium concentrations are normal or slightly elevated, but cell potassium and water are low,[371,378,399] particularly in cells removed from the splenic pulp.[378] The mean corpuscular hemoglobin (MCH) and mean corpuscular volume (MCV) fall within the normal range,[258] but because young red cells normally have a high cell volume, the MCV in HS is actually relatively low.

Fragility and Autohemolysis Tests. The osmotic fragility test, particularly its incubated variant, is the most sensitive test generally available for the diagnosis of HS. The unincubated osmotic fragility test provides interesting information on the proportion of conditioned cells in the circulation,[249,348,355]

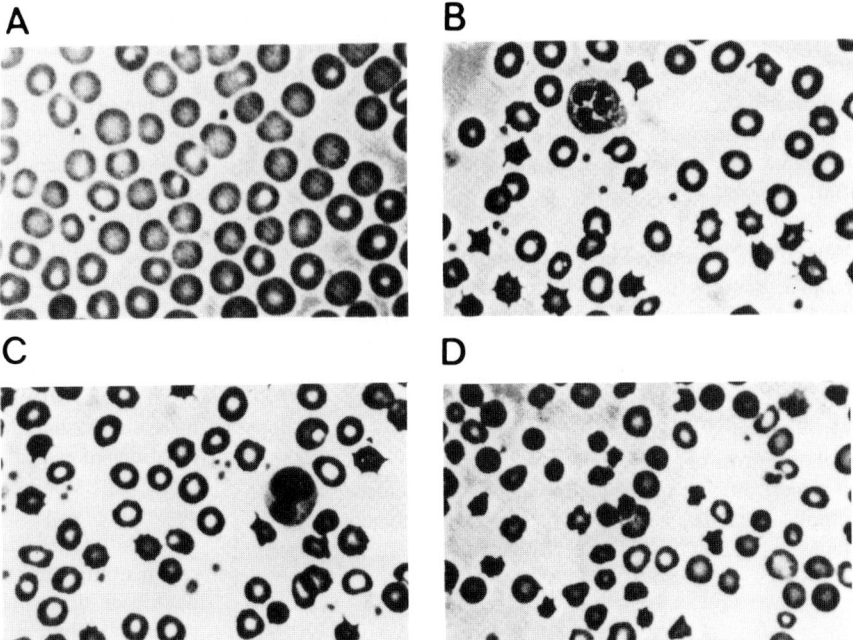

Fig. 95-14 Peripheral blood smears of patients with hereditary spherocytosis. A. Typical autosomal dominant HS: spherocytes and cells of normal appearance. B and C. Autosomal dominant HS with protein 4.1–binding defect of spectrin: acanthocytes, spherocytes, and normal appearing cells. D. Autosomal recessive HS with severe spectrin deficiency: microspherocytes, spherocytes, acanthocytes, poikilocytes, and schistocytes. (From Becker and Lux.[12] Used by permission of Clinical Haematology.)

information that is lost in the incubated osmotic fragility test. The test is performed by suspending the cells in aqueous solutions containing various concentrations of sodium chloride.[249] Since there is almost no exchange of cations during the short duration of the test, osmotic equilibrium is achieved almost entirely by the rapid movement of water across the membrane. In hypotonic solutions, red cells swell until they become spheres and then burst. Cells with a decreased surface/volume ratio, such as hereditary spherocytes, can tolerate less swelling than normal and are termed *osmotically fragile*. From 20 to 25 percent of HS patients have a normal or near-normal unincubated osmotic fragility test prior to splenectomy—particularly the mildly affected patients who are most difficult to diagnose.[391,400] The incubated osmotic fragility test, in contrast, is more often positive,[400] since hereditary spherocytes become metabolically depleted and lose membrane surface more rapidly than normal cells during the period of preincubation (24 h at 37°C) (Fig. 95-12), which accentuates their spheroidicity and enhances the sensitivity of the test. Occasional patients with normal incubated osmotic fragility tests have been reported,[401,402] and it seems likely that such patients are even more common than these rare reports suggest, since the osmotic fragility test detects a secondary property of HS red cells (their loss of membrane surface) rather than the primary molecular defect.

The autohemolysis test was first described by Ham and Castle[219] and was carefully standardized by Dacie[367] and Young[391,403] and their coworkers. The principle of the test is illustrated in Fig. 95-12. Autohemolysis of HS red cells, incubated in their own plasma in the absence of added glucose, is increased at 48 h. In most HS patients, much less autohemolysis is observed if supplemental glucose is added.[371,391,403,404] This is not true in patients with large numbers of conditioned spherocytes,[405] an exception that can lead to considerable diagnostic confusion, since autohemolysis that is unresponsive in glucose is a common feature of a number of hemolytic anemias.[403,404] In general the test is quite sensitive and is occasionally useful in confirming the diagnosis of HS (e.g., in mild, sporadic cases); however, we do not use it routinely. Other tests for HS are available including the mechanical fragility test,[249,391] the rate of hemolysis in acidified

glycerol,[402,406,407] and the ouabain osmotic fragility test.[408] The former test lacks specificity and has no proven diagnostic benefit, but the latter two procedures appear to be somewhat more sensitive than the standard OF and autohemolysis tests[402,408] (but see Ref. 408a for a contradictory view concerning the acidified glycerol lysis test) and may prove diagnostically useful if further studies confirm this increased sensitivity.

Complications

Crises. Patients with HS, like patients with other hemolytic processes, are subject to various "crises." Mild hemolytic crises are probably most frequent,[258] although this is controversial.[409] They usually occur with common viral syndromes and are characterized by a mild, transient increase in jaundice, splenomegaly, anemia, and reticulocytosis. Severe hemolytic crises are rare but have been reported.[393,410]

Aplastic crises, on the other hand, are less frequent but are often more serious, since severe anemia and even death[235,393] can result. They are mostly[411] caused by infection with the human parvovirus B19[412–416] and typically present with fever, vomiting, abdominal pain, arthralgias, headache, pallor, and symptoms of anemia.[409,412,414–417] A maculopapular rash[416] or even an illness resembling Henoch-Schönlein purpura[411] may also be seen. Sometimes multiple family members or even whole communities are affected simultaneously.[415,418] During the aplastic phase, the hematocrit level and reticulocyte count fall, marrow erythroblasts disappear, and unused iron accumulates in the serum.[409] Mild granulocytopenia and thrombocytopenia are common but are not invariably present. Since production of new HS red cells is halted, the cells that remain age, and microspherocytosis and osmotic fragility increase.[404,419] The bilirubin level declines owing to a decrease in the number of abnormal red cells that have to be destroyed. Since the usual aplastic crisis lasts 10 to 14 days[409] (about half the life span of HS red cells), the hemoglobin concentration typically falls to about half its usual value before recovery ensues. It is not uncommon for this severe stress to be the first sign of HS in previously well-compensated patients.[414] The return of marrow function is heralded by a fall in serum iron concentration, a rise in granulocytes and platelets to normal levels, and reticulocytosis.[409]

Megaloblastic crises result when the dietary intake of folic acid is insufficient for the increased needs of the erythroid HS bone marrow. They are usually observed during pregnancy[420,421] when the need for folic acid is particularly high.

Gallbladder Disease. The most common complication of HS from its first reports[222,223] to the present day has been gallbladder disease. Pigment gallstones have been detected in patients as young as 3 years old[419] but are most prevalent in adolescents and adults.[422] The available data indicate that 55 to 85 percent of untreated HS patients will eventually acquire stones[391,422,423] and that roughly half of these individuals will have symptoms of cholecystitis or, less commonly, biliary obstruction.[235,410,423] However, much more accurate data on the incidence of these complications are needed in patients with bilirubinate gallstones to accurately assess the risk/benefit ratio of splenectomy in HS.

Other Complications. Rare patients with HS develop gout,[236,424] indolent leg ulcers,[425] or a chronic erythematous dermatitis on the legs.[426] Occasionally patients also develop extramedullary masses of hematopoietic tissue, particularly alongside the posterior thoracic or lumbar spine.[235,424,427] These gradually enlarge with time and may be mistaken for neoplasms.[424] Interestingly, Schaeffer and his colleagues have suggested that untreated HS may predispose patients to a true neoplasm—multiple myeloma.[428] Four patients with HS and myeloma have been reported.[428-430] None was splenectomized, two had gallbladder disease, and one had silicosis. They argue that the association may be due to chronic reticuloendothelial stimulation since splenic clearance of abnormal red cells induces proliferation of lymphocytes and plasma cells as well as macrophages.[431] HS patients have a mild, polyclonal hypergammaglobulinemia,[428,432] and there is evidence favoring the association of myeloma and chronic gallbladder disease.[428,433] Untreated HS may also exacerbate hemochromatosis in patients who are heterozygous for the hereditary disease,[434-437] and several of the reported patients subsequently died of liver failure or hepatoma.[427,438,439]

Diagnostic Problems

In general, HS is easily diagnosed and differentiated from other causes of spherocytosis, but there are several situations in which diagnosis can be difficult. In the neonatal period it may be hard to differentiate HS from ABO incompatibility since microspherocytosis is prominent in both and the Coombs' test is frequently negative in ABO disease.[440] Fortunately, in most affected infants with ABO incompatibility, anti-A (or -B) antibodies can be eluted from the red cells, and free anti-A (or -B) IgG antibodies can be detected in the infant's serum. Occasionally older patients with immunohemolytic anemias and spherocytosis also have so few antibody molecules attached to their red cells that the Coombs' test is negative, and differentiation of the disease from HS is possible only with the use of radioactive antiglobulin reagents.[441]

Diagnostic difficulties also arise in patients who present during an aplastic crisis. Early in the crisis the acute nature of the symptoms may suggest an acquired process, and the absence of reticulocytes may divert the physician from a diagnosis of hemolytic anemia. Later, as marrow function returns, the physician may be misled by the fact that the emerging young HS red cells are initially less spherocytic and osmotically fragile than usual[398] and acquire their typical microspherocytic form only with age and reticuloendothelial conditioning. HS may also be camouflaged by association with disorders that increase the surface/volume ratio of the red cells, such as iron deficiency[442] or obstructive jaundice.[279] Iron deficiency corrects the abnormal shape and fragility of hereditary spherocytes but does not improve their life span,[442] whereas obstructive jaundice improves both shape and survival.[279]

The rare patients with "atypical" HS may also cause diagnostic confusion. Most such patients actually represent combinations of typical HS and diseases affecting other organ systems,[443,444] Coombs-negative immunohemolytic anemias (see above), or very severe HS in which large numbers of very defective spherocytes remain in the circulation owing to saturation of the reticuloendothelial system.[445,446] A few families have been described with unusual forms of hereditary spherocytic hemolytic anemias that resemble HS in some respects but not in others. For example, Boivin and his colleagues have reported a family with a dominantly inherited hemolytic anemia characterized by spherocytosis, decreased spectrin phosphorylation, and failure to improve following splenectomy.[263] And Zail and his coworkers have described a family with a dominantly inherited disorder characterized by spherocytosis and mild compensated hemolysis in which fresh red cells had a normal or decreased osmotic fragility and ^{51}Cr-labeled red cells lacked the characteristic pattern of splenic sequestration that is typical of HS.[447] The relationship of these patients to each other and to typical HS is unclear.

Splenectomy

It is one of the rare absolutes in medicine that patients with true, uncomplicated HS always respond dramatically to splenectomy. The degree of response correlates closely with the degree of spectrin deficiency,[247] and is incomplete in the most severe patients. The major issues today are which patients should be splenectomized and how they should be treated postoperatively. The most devastating complication of splenectomy is postsplenectomy sepsis. The data in the literature indicate that overwhelming sepsis occurs in 3.5 percent of patients with HS and that 60 percent of these patients die.[448,449] However, the studies are seriously flawed,[450,451] and the true incidence of fulminant sepsis is undoubtedly much less. The only adequate epidemiologic study suggests an incidence of 0.2 cases per 100 person-years for adults, and this rate can presumably be further reduced by use of pneumococcal[452] and perhaps other bacterial vaccines. These topics are beyond the scope of the present chapter but are covered in detail in recent hematology textbooks (e.g., see Ref. 451).

Following splenectomy, spherocytosis persists, but conditioned microspherocytes disappear, and changes typical of the postsplenectomy state, including Howell-Jolly bodies, target cells, acanthocytes, and siderocytes, appear in the peripheral smear.[355,405] Reticulocyte counts fall to normal or near-normal levels, although red cell life span, if carefully measured, remains slightly shortened (96 ± 13 days).[341] In all cases anemia and jaundice remit and do not recur except in the rare case of regrowth of a missed accessory spleen. This is the only proven cause of postsplenectomy failure in HS and is sometimes overlooked, since it may not become evident for years[453] or even decades.[454]

HEREDITARY ELLIPTOCYTOSIS

Hereditary elliptocytosis (HE) is a relatively common, clinically and genetically heterogeneous disorder characterized by the presence of a large number of elliptically shaped red cells in the peripheral blood. These cells are sometimes called *ovalocytes*, but elliptocytes and elliptocytosis are the more accurate designations as the cells are elliptical rather than egg-shaped. In the more severe forms of the disease, spherocytes or bizarre poikilocytes are also present, and sometimes these shapes predominate. Hereditary pyropoikilocytosis (HPP) is an example of the latter situation. Although HPP was previously considered to be a separate entity, emerging biochemical and genetic information clearly indicates it is related to HE, at least in some families, and the two disorders will be considered together here.

History

According to Lambrecht,[455] elliptocytosis was first observed by Goltz in Konigsburg, Germany, in 1860, but no written report of this observation is known. The disease was first reported in 1904 by Dresbach, a physiologist at Ohio State University, in one of his histology students during a laboratory exercise in which the students were examining their own blood.[456] His brief report elicited some controversy as the student died soon thereafter, leading the prominent American physician Austin Flint to suggest that he had actually had incipient pernicious anemia.[457] Dresbach replied that the student died of acute rheumatic carditis and took his slides to Germany where famous pathologists such as Ewing, Ehrlich, and Arneth supported his view that the red cell disorder was primary.[458] This was substantiated during the next two decades by the reports of Bishop,[459] Sydenstricker,[460] and Huck and Bigelow.[461] Hunter's demonstration of elliptocytosis in three generations of one family firmly established the hereditary nature of the disease.[462,463]

In the 1930s and early 1940s, there was considerable debate about whether HE was a disease or simply a morphologic curiosity. This is surprising in retrospect, since a number of individuals with hemolytic HE were described during this interval,[455,464–468] and some authors had clearly differentiated hemolytic and nonhemolytic forms.[455,464,465] In fact as early as 1928 van den Bergh even reported that anemia and jaundice cleared following splenectomy in one patient.[467] Early on, some confusion also existed in differentiating HE from sickle-cell anemia[469,470] and "hypochromic elliptocytosis" (probably thalassemia)[471] and later in differentiating hemolytic HE from hereditary spherocytosis.[472] These reports illustrate a point that will be emphasized later—namely, that HE, particularly its hemolytic variants, can sometimes be morphologically deceptive.

For the reader interested in the historical and clinical features of the disease, the reports of Wyandt and her coworkers,[472] Wolman and Ozge,[473] Dacie,[474] Josephs and Avery,[475] Weiss,[476] and Cutting and his coworkers[477] are particularly recommended.

Prevalence and Genetics

HE is clearly heterogeneous from a clinical, genetic, and biochemical point of view. This was not appreciated by early investigators, and recent workers have not classified subtypes of the disease in a consistent way. In most papers all patients with HE are simply lumped together. Accordingly it is difficult to relate much of the available information to the different clinical forms of the disease.

The prevalence of all forms of HE in the United States is about 250 to 500 per million.[472,478] Elliptocytic red cells have been observed in all racial and ethnic groups, but the distribution of some of the clinical phenotypes is clearly restricted. With the exception of HPP the disease is inherited as an autosomal dominant trait with complete penetrance. No instance of a spontaneous mutation has been recorded in the past 50 years.

Genetic studies show that one of the elliptocytosis genes (El_1) is closely linked to the Rh locus on the short arm of chromosome 1 (1p36-p34).[480–483] This is the location of the protein 4.1 gene.[334] Another gene (El_2) is located on the long arm of chromosome 1, near the Duffy blood group locus (1q24),[484] in the region where the spectrin α-chain gene is located (1q22-q25).[485]

Clinical Syndromes

Most of the reported cases of HE can be classified into one of three categories: common HE (HE_c), spherocytic HE (HE_s), and Melanesian or stomatocytic HE (Table 95-7). These categories can be further subdivided on the basis of clinical severity and other characteristic features (Table 95-7). It must be emphasized that these appellations denote clinical phenotypes and not specific molecular or genetic etiologies. Several defects in the membrane proteins of hereditary elliptocytosis have recently been identified and the various types of HE can also be classified based on these defects.

Mild HE (HE_c). This is the most prevalent form of HE. It can be divided into several subtypes.

SILENT CARRIER STATE. This condition has recently been identified by analyzing asymptomatic members of kindreds with HE or hereditary pyropoikilocytosis (HPP). The affected persons have normal red cell shape and no evidence of hemolysis, but careful measurements show a subtle defect in their membrane skeletons, with decreased red cell thermal stability, decreased mechanical stability of isolated skeletons, abnormal tryptic peptide maps of spectrin, and various combinations of these defects.[13,486,507,532,562] (These tests will be discussed in more detail in a later section). Typically at least one of the parents of patients with HPP is a silent carrier.

MILD HE_c. As implied by the name, this form of the disease is mild.[472,487–491] Typically it is dominantly inherited and patients have no anemia or splenomegaly (Table 95-7). Some-

Table 95-7 Clinical Phenotypes of Hereditary Elliptocytosis

Phenotype	Hemolysis	Anemia	Splenomegaly	Blood smear
Common HE (HE$_c$)				
One abnormal gene				
Silent carrier	None	None	None	Normal
Mild HE$_c$	Mild or none	None	None	Prominent elliptocytes, rod forms
HE$_c$ with chronic hemolysis	Mild-moderate	Mild-moderate	Variable	Elliptocytes, rod forms, variable poikilocytes and fragments
HE$_c$ with infantile poikilocytosis	Moderate	Mild-moderate	Variable	Budding, fragments, bizarre poikilocytes
HE$_c$ with dyserythropoiesis	Mild-moderate	Moderate	Usual	Rounded elliptocytes
Two abnormal genes				
Homozygous mild HE$_c$	Severe	Moderate-severe	Usual	Elliptocytes, budding red cells, fragments, spherocytes, bizarre poikilocytes
Hereditary pyropoikilocytosis	Moderate-severe	Moderate-severe	Usual	Budding fragments, spherocytes, bizarre poikilocytes, $\pm$ elliptocytes
Spherocytic HE (HE$_s$)				
One abnormal gene				
HE$_s$ with chronic hemolysis	Mild-moderate	Mild	Usual	Rounded elliptocytes, spherocytes, variable morphology within kindred
Melanesian (stomatocytic) HE (HE$_m$)				
One abnormal gene	None	None	None	Rounded elliptocytes, some with transverse bars (stomatocytic elliptocytes) or knizocytic, elliptocytic macrocytes

times red cell survival is normal,[488,563] but more often there is very mild, compensated hemolysis with a slight reticulocytosis and a decreased haptoglobin level.[472,490,491] In these patients, HE is little more than a morphologic curiosity. The peripheral blood smear shows prominent elliptocytosis with little red cell budding or fragmentation and spherocytosis. Elliptocytes almost always exceed 30 percent of the red cells and sometimes approach 100 percent (Fig. 95-15).[472,487,490] Very elongated elliptocytes (rod forms) are common (>10 percent). In contrast, normal individuals have less than 15 percent elliptocytes and less than 5 percent rod-shaped cells.[472,487,490] Somewhat higher proportions are seen in patients with anemia, particularly megaloblastic and hypochromic-microcytic anemias, but even in these individuals, elliptocytes and rod forms do not exceed 35 percent and 15 percent, respectively.[487] Hence the morphologic diagnosis of mild HE is rarely difficult. This may not be true in the neonatal period. Some investigators have noted that elliptocytes are infrequent in the cord blood of infants with mild HE and become more prominent with time.[463,472,564] For example, Wyandt and coworkers detected only 11 percent elliptocytes at birth in one infant, whereas by 4 months of age 80 percent of the cells were elliptical.[472] These observations, although few, suggest that the disease may be expressed differently in fetal red cells, a point that will be discussed in more detail in the following section. Early workers used a complex system for quantitating ellipticity,[565] but the method is time-consuming and has not proved more useful in diagnosing HE than simple subjective estimation.[487] In addition it is not prognostically useful, since there is no correlation between the proportion of elliptocytes or their ellipticity and the severity of the disease.

Phenotypically identical mild HE$_c$ is caused by more than one molecular lesion, since in some families mild HE$_c$ is linked to the Rh gene, and in other families it is not.[482,566] The best example of the Rh-linked disease is the large Dutch-American family first described by Hunter[462,463] and van den Bergh[567] and their associates and more recently restudied by Geerdink et al.[490,566] Moreover, multiple protein defects have been associated with the mild phenotype, including those involving α-spectrin, β-spectrin, and protein 4.1 (see Table 95-8). These specific defects will be discussed in detail in a later section.

HE$_c$ WITH ACUTE OR CHRONIC HEMOLYSIS. In many large kindreds with typical compensated mild HE, a minority (5 to 20 percent) of the patients have more severe hemolysis and anemia.[491,492] The etiology of this variation is not always clear. In some instances it is a transient acquired state due to hyperplasia of the spleen in response to a variety of stimuli (e.g., cirrhosis,[568] infectious mononucleosis,[491,493] bacterial infections,[491] or malaria[569,570]). For unknown reasons pregnancy may also transiently aggravate the disease[491] as may transplant rejection[13] and cobalamin (vitamin B$_{12}$) deficiency.

In other apparently sporadic cases *chronic* hemolysis exists in the absence of any detectable disease process. It is generally assumed that the latter individuals have inherited one or more modifier genes that aggravate the basic membrane defect or improve the performance of the spleen, but this hypothesis remains to be proved. If true, such genes must be relatively common to explain how a mother with compensated mild HE bore two children with the uncompensated disease from unrelated fathers.[571]

Except for signs of increased hemolysis and anemia, patients with uncompensated mild HE are similar to their less severely affected relatives. Splenomegaly and morphologic evidence of red cell destruction (e.g., fragmentation and poikilocytosis) are somewhat more prevalent in this group but are not reliable differentiating features. It appears that most of these patients

Osmotic fragility	Genetics	Other	Selected references
N	One parent a silent HE carrier or has HE$_c$ with $\alpha^{I/74}$	——	13, 486, 507
N or ↓	All races, one parent with mild HE$_c$	Significant hemolysis with diseases producing splenomegaly.	472, 487–493, 527
N or ↓	Sporadic in families with mild HE$_c$	Responds well to splenectomy.	465, 490–492, 494
N	Especially in blacks, one parent with mild HE$_c$	Neonatal jaundice; ↑ thermal sensitivity of red cells. Disease converts to mild HE$_c$ during first year of life.	153, 475, 495–497
N	Sporadic in some Italian families with mild HE$_c$	Gradual onset of erythroid dysplasia and ineffective erythropoiesis; incomplete response to splenectomy.	498
↑ ↑	Both parents with mild HE$_c$	Low MCV due to fragmentation; responds well to splenectomy.	472, 492, 499–504
↑ ↑	Autosomal recessive; usually both parents asymptomatic, sometimes one with mild HE$_c$	Low MCV due to fragmentation; ↑ ↑ thermal sensitivity of red cells; responds well to splenectomy.	486, 497, 505–511
↑	One parent with HE$_s$; especially Northern Europeans	↑ Glucose-responsive autohemolysis; responds well to splenectomy.	123, 464, 476, 477, 479, 513
N	One parent with HE$_m$; especially Melanesians and Malaysians	↓ Expression of blood groups; rigid red cells; protection against some forms of malaria.	514–526

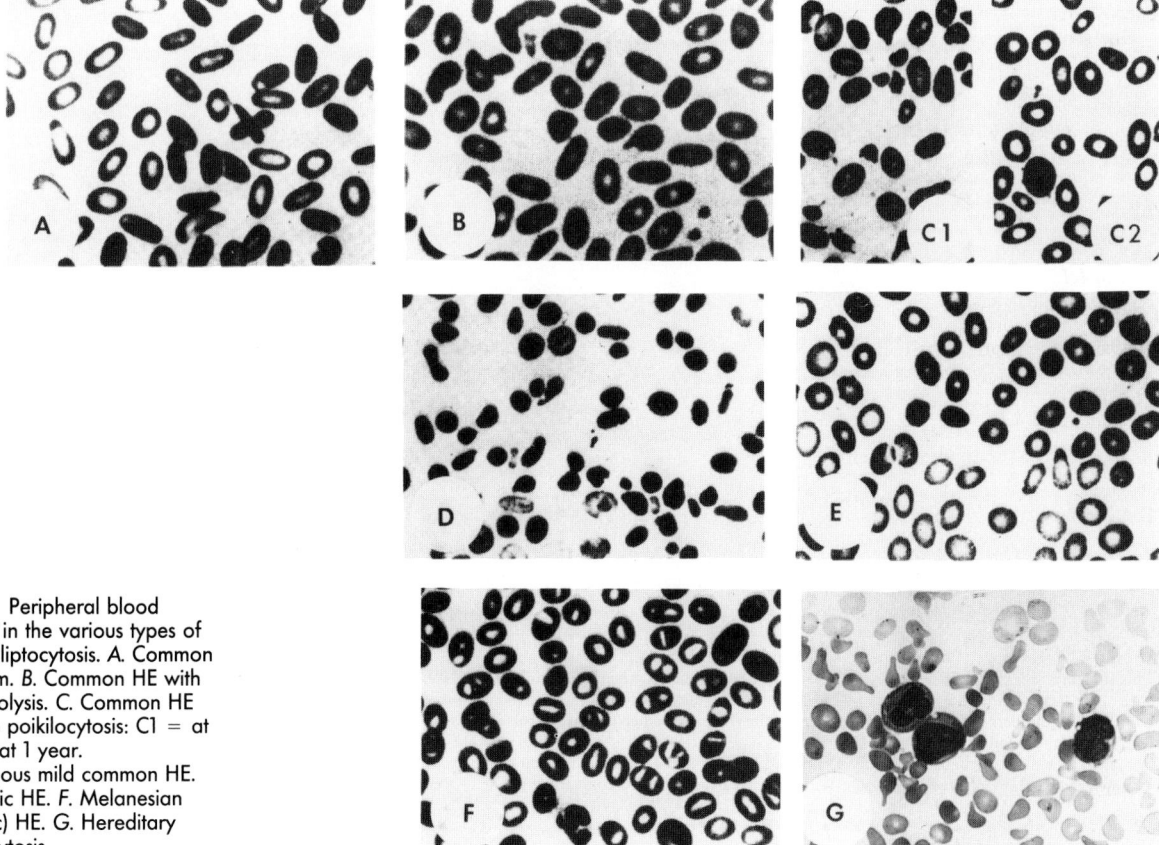

Fig. 95-15. Peripheral blood morphology in the various types of hereditary elliptocytosis. *A.* Common HE, mild form. *B.* Common HE with chronic hemolysis. *C.* Common HE with infantile poikilocytosis: C1 = at birth, C2 = at 1 year. *D.* Homozygous mild common HE. *E.* Spherocytic HE. *F.* Melanesian (stomatocytic) HE. *G.* Hereditary pyropoikilocytosis.

Table 95-8 Hereditary Defects of Membrane Skeletal Proteins

Defects	Estimated prevalence	Clinical expression	Mechanical stability of ghosts and skeletons[a]	Thermal stability of red cells[b]
Spectrin				
Primary spectrin deficiency				
Dominant type				
One gene abnormal	Common?	HS: mild-moderate	↓ in proportion to spectrin deficiency	Normal
Recessive type				
One gene abnormal	Very common?	Silent carrier	?	Normal
Two genes abnormal	Moderately common	HS: moderate-severe	↓ in proportion to spectrin deficiency	Normal
Self-association—α chain $\alpha^{I/78}$, $\alpha^{I/74}$, $\alpha^{I/65}$ (or $\alpha^{I/68}$), $\alpha^{I/46}$ (or $\alpha^{I/50a}$), $\alpha^{I/50b}$, $\alpha^{I/42-43}$, α^{234}				
One gene abnormal	Common	Silent carrier	Normal or slightly ↓	± Slightly ↓
		Mild HE_c	↓	Slightly ↓ to ↓↓
		HE_c with infant poikilocytosis	↓↓	↓↓
Two genes abnormal[e]	Rare	Homozygous HE or HPP	↓↓	↓↓
Self-association—β chain				
One gene abnormal	Rare	HE_c ± chronic hemolysis	↓	?
Spectrin-ankyrin				
One gene abnormal	?	Silent carrier state	?	Normal
Spectrin-4.1				
One gene abnormal	Uncommon	HS: mild-moderate	↓	?
Ankyrin				
Ankyrin deficiency				
One gene abnormal	?	HS: moderate-severe	?	?
Protein 4.1				
Primary 4.1 deficiency				
One gene abnormal	Common	Mild HE_c, ?HE_s	↓	Normal
Two genes abnormal	Rare	Homozygous HE	↓↓	Normal
Dysfunctional 4.1	Rare?	HE_c with chronic hemolysis	?	Normal
High molecular wt. 4.1	Rare	Mild HE_c	?	?

[a]Measured by resistance of membranes[561] or membrane skeletons[13] to fluid shear stress.
[b]This indicates the ability of red cells to withstand budding and fragmentation on heating. Normal red cells disintegrate at 49°C after short periods of heating (10–15 min). ↓ indicates a thermal stability of 47 to 48°C; ↓↓ indicates 45 to 46°C.
[c]Expressed as the percentage of spectrin dimers in the dimer-tetramer pool. Controls have 8 ± 3% spectrin dimer.
[d]OF = Osmotic fragility.
[e]In many cases the patients are probably compound heterozygotes for two different α-spectrin defects (homozygous HE) or for a defect in α-spectrin and a second, unknown defect (HPP). In addition some HPP patients have no detectable defect in the α-spectrin inherited from either parent.

Percentage of spectrin dimer in 0°C extracts[c]	Other characteristics	Method(s) of detection	Selected references
2–14% (i.e., normal)	↑ OF[d], spherocytosis; decreased spectrin/RBC (60 to 85% of normal).	(1) SDS gel electrophoresis or (2) Radioimmunoassay of spectrin/RBC	246–248
2–14%?	Normal shape; ?normal spectrin/cell.		
2–14%	↑ ↑ OF, marked spherocytosis; decreased spectrin/RBC (30 to 75% of normal).		
15–40%	Normal shape; observed with $\alpha^{I/74}$ and $\alpha^{I/46}$.	(1) Nondenaturing gel electrophoresis of 0°C spectrin extracts and/or (2) Limited tryptic digestion of spectrin, then domain mapping ± immunoblotting with antispectrin α^I antibody	13, 486, 503, 507–512, 527, 543
15–40%	Elliptocytosis; observed with $\alpha^{I/78}$, $\alpha^{I/74}$, $\alpha^{I/65}$, $\alpha^{I/46}$, and α^{234}.		
15–40%	Poikilocytosis (infant) → elliptocytosis (older child, adult); $\alpha^{I/74}$ and α^{234}.		
50–80%	Marked poikilocytosis; observed with $\alpha^{I/74}$, $\alpha^{I/65}$, and possibly $\alpha^{I/42-43}$, ↑ ↑ OF; decreased spectrin/RBC (~70% of normal).		
~50%	Deletion of 6-kDa phosphorylated region at C-terminal of spectrin β chain. Elliptocytosis with mild poikilocytosis.	(1) SDS gel electrophoresis and (2) Spectrin phosphorylation and (3) Nondenaturing gel electrophoresis of 0°C spectrin extracts	150, 151, 544
?	So far only patient described also has defect in spectrin self-association. Both defects together produce HE[c] with chronic hemolysis.	(1) Spectrin binding to inside-out membrane vesicles and/or (2) Spectrin binding to ankyrin	545
2–14%	↑ OF, spherocytosis; some patients with mild acanthocytosis; decreased spectrin/RBC (80% of normal).	(1) Spectrin binding to F-actin ± 4.1 and/or (2) Spectrin binding to 4.1	311–313
2–14%	↑ ↑ OF, spherocytosis and dense, irregular poikilocytes. Spectrin and ankyrin each ~50% of normal: Decreased ankyrin synthesis. Normal ankyrin peptide maps.	(1) SDS gel electrophoresis or (2) Radioimmunoassay or immunoblots of ankyrin	310, 327
2–14%	Normal or ? ↑ OF; elliptocytosis.	(1) SDS gel electrophoresis and (2) Immunoblots with anti-4.1	504, 546–550
?	↑ ↑ OF; marked poikilocytosis; associated deficiency of glycophorin C and/or protein 4.9 in some patients.		
2–14%	Patients' 4.1 with decreased ability to promote spectrin-actin interaction; some smaller 4.1 species—? due to proteolysis.	(1) and (2) as immediately above, + (3) Binding of 4.1 to spectrin or spectrin + actin	551
?	Half of 4.1 is abnormally large species (95 kDa) due to insertion in portion of protein responsible for spectrin-actin binding. ?Spectrin-actin binding abnormal.	(1) Immunoblots with anti-4.1 or (2) Northern blots with 4.1 cDNA	552, 553

Continued.

Table 95-8 Hereditary Defects of Membrane Skeletal Proteins—Continued

Defects	Estimated prevalence	Clinical expression	Mechanical stability of ghosts and skeletons[a]	Thermal stability of red cells[b]
Protein 4.2 Primary 4.2 deficiency ? Two genes abnormal	Rare?	HE$_s$: mild-moderate	?	?
Glycophorin C Primary glycophorin C deficiency	Rare	Mild HE$_c$, ?HE$_s$	?	?
Protein 3 Ankyrin-3	Rare	Atypical "HE" with marked poikilocytosis	?	Normal
Dysfunctional protein 3	Rare	Acanthocytosis (20–25%); no anemia	?	?

respond well to splenectomy, although extensive data are not available.[494,541,572]

MILD HE WITH POIKILOCYTOSIS IN INFANCY. Infants with this form of "mild" HE often begin life with moderately severe hemolytic anemia characterized by marked red cell budding, fragmentation, and poikilocytosis (Table 95-7) (Fig. 95-15) and neonatal jaundice.[153,475,495,496,573] In most cases sufficient elliptocytes are present to suggest the diagnosis, but sometimes this is not so, and the disorder may be mistaken for infantile pyknocytosis, hereditary pyropoikilocytosis, or a microangiopathic or oxidant-induced hemolytic anemia.[495,496] The correct diagnosis is easily made if the parents' smears are examined, since one will have mild HE$_c$. With time, fragmentation and hemolysis decline, and the clinical picture of mild HE$_c$ emerges. This transition requires from 4 months to 2 years. The change in morphology often occurs somewhat faster than the decline in hemolysis.[573] Subsequently the disease is clinically indistinguishable from typical mild HE$_c$. The unusual neonatal course and the fact that most of the patients are black strongly suggest that this is a unique clinical entity. The prevalence is unknown, but in our experience[453] this is the most common form of HE in black families and is not rare (approximately 30 percent of the kindreds with HE$_c$ seen at Children's Hospital Medical Center, Boston, in the past 5 years). The disorder is not restricted to blacks. We have observed it in one Puerto Rican family, and a possible example in an Italian kindred is recorded.[575]

The fragmenting neonatal red cells are very sensitive to heat, like hereditary pyropoikilocytes (see below), but red cells differ from pyropoikilocytes in that this sensitivity lessens as the patients mature.[573] The dense poikilocytic red cells are rich in hemoglobin F,[574] which suggests that the change in the course of the disease is due to the conversion from fetal to adult erythropoiesis. If so, interactions between the genetically defective protein and other skeletal proteins must differ in fetal and adult red cells. Mentzer has made the interesting suggestion that 2,3-DPG is the critical agent.[153] Free 2,3-DPG is elevated in fetal red cells since it is not bound by hemoglobin F. The free anion is known to weaken spectrin-actin

bonds[154,155] and to increase the fragility of isolated ghosts at *physiological* concentrations;[153] though it is controversial whether it does so at physiological concentrations in *intact* red cells.[155a] If so, this would certainly aggravate the underlying defect in spectrin self-association (to be discussed below). However, presumably the effect would have to be limited to certain specific molecular defects to explain why all infants with HE do not show poikilocytosis and hemolysis in infancy.

MILD HE WITH DYSERYTHROPOIESIS. In a small number of families with otherwise typical mild HE$_c$, the sporadic occurrence of hemolysis and anemia is at least partially due to the development of dysplastic and ineffective erythropoiesis. All the reported patients[498] and from Central and Southern Italy, have somewhat less elongated red cells than is typical for mild HE$_c$, and show the characteristic findings of ineffective erythropoiesis (high bilirubin, serum iron, and plasma iron turnover; relatively low reticulocyte count; and low incorporation of iron into circulating erythroid cells).[498] Their bone marrows are hyperplastic, with excessive intermediate erythroblasts, and have some dysplastic features including asynchrony of nuclear-cytoplasmic maturation, binuclearity, and small numbers of ringed sideroblasts. Anemia and presumably erythroid dysplasia usually commence during adolescence or early adult life and advance gradually over a number of years. Because dysplasia persists after splenectomy, response to the operation is incomplete. The available data suggest that dysplasia and elliptocytosis cosegregate, since no individuals with dysplasia have been observed who did not also carry the elliptocytosis gene. If so, these families must represent a unique subtype of mild HE. However, the numbers are small, and it is not clear that the nonelliptocytic members of the reported kindreds have been thoroughly examined.[498]

HOMOZYGOUS MILD HE. A few patients with apparently homozygous mild HE have been reported.[472,492,499–504] Most have had a very severe or even fatal[501] transfusion-dependent hemolytic anemia (hemoglobin = 2 to 5 g/dl) with marked fragmentation, poikilocytosis, spherocytosis, and elliptocytosis

Percentage of spectrin dimer in 0°C extracts[c]	Other characteristics	Method(s) of detection	Selected references
?	Primarily Japanese? ↑ OF, spherocytes, rounded elliptocytes; small amount large (74-kDa) protein 4.2. Normal 4.2-binding sites. Decreased binding of ankyrin to protein 3; mild decrease in protein 3.	(1) SDS gel electrophoresis _or_ (2) Immunoblots with anti-4.2	123, 554
2–14%	Leach phenotype of Gerbich-negative blood group; ↑ OF; mild decrease in protein 4.1; inheritance uncertain.	(1) SDS gel electrophoresis (Laemmli method) with PAS stain	555–558
?	Defective ankyrin-3 interaction, possibly due to altered arrangement of protein 3 on the membrane. Only observed in association with defect in spectrin self-association.	(1) Binding of ankyrin to ankyrin-depleted inside-out vesicles	560
?	Protein 3 larger (97–99 kDa) than normal (95 kDa) on SDS gels; ↑ anion transport; ↑ ankyrin binding (~50%) but apparently normal ankyrin content.	(1) SDS gel electrophoresis (Laemmli)	559

(Table 95-7, Fig. 95-15), but in a few patients hemolysis was less rampant (hemoglobin = 7 to 11 g/dl).[472,492,576] It appears these differences reflect differences in the severity of the many α-spectrin mutations that produce mild HE$_c$ (Table 95-8). Clinically, the disease is very similar to hereditary pyropoikilocytosis (to be described). All treated patients have responded dramatically to splenectomy.

HEREDITARY PYROPOIKILOCYTOSIS (HPP). This interesting, rare, apparently recessive disease presents in infancy or early childhood as a severe hemolytic anemia (Table 95-7) characterized by extreme poikilocytosis with budding red cells, fragments, spherocytes, elliptocytes, triangulocytes, and other bizarre-shaped cells[497,505–507] (Fig. 95-15). The morphology is similar to that observed in homozygous mild HE$_c$ and mild HE$_c$ with poikilocytosis in infancy. Most but not all of the cases have occurred in blacks. Complications of severe anemia including growth retardation,[505] frontal bossing,[505] and early gallbladder disease[505] are reported. Osmotic fragility tests are very abnormal, particularly after incubation,[497,505,506] and autohemolysis is greatly elevated.[497,505,506] The mean corpuscular volume (MCV) is very low (25 to 55 μm³) because of the large number of fragmented red cells.[505,506]

Another characteristic feature of these cells is their remarkable thermal sensitivity. Hereditary pyropoikilocytes fragment at 45 to 46°C (normal = 49°C) after short periods of heating (10 to 15 min).[497] With prolonged heating (>6 h) they fragment even at body temperatures.[497] Following splenectomy, hemolysis is greatly lessened but not eliminated.[497,505] Typically the hemoglobin after splenectomy is 7.5 to 10 g/dl with 3 to 7 percent reticulocytes.[13]

Although HPP is often considered as a separate disease, there is reasonably convincing evidence that it is related to HE. First, as noted above, the HPP is clinically and morphologically similar to the more severe forms of hemolytic elliptocytosis and shares the characteristic of red cell heat sensitivity observed in infants with mild HE$_c$ and poikilocytosis. In addition, in approximately 30 percent of cases one of the parents or siblings has typical mild HE$_c$.[13,497,506,562] In some of these kindreds, an apparently identical functional defect in spectrin (see the following section) is observed in sibs with phenotypically different diseases (i.e., HPP and mild HE$_c$). In other families, all the first-degree relatives are phenotypically normal. These finding suggest that HPP is genetically heterogeneous. At present the best hypothesis is that the HPP phenotype can be produced by homozygosity for an HPP gene, homozygosity for certain elliptocytosis genes,[576] or double heterozygosity (heterozygosity at two loci) for HPP and HE.

Spherocytic HE (HE$_s$). This form of HE is a phenotypic hybrid of mild HE and hereditary spherocytosis. It has been reported in white families of European descent and possibly in Japanese families. It is not linked to the Rh gene, and appears to be a unique subtype (Table 95-7).[123,464,476,477,512,513] Its prevalence is unknown, but, judging from the number of published reports and our own experience, it probably doesn't account for more than about 10 to 20 percent of all HE cases in these populations. Unlike mild HE$_c$, almost all the affected patients have some hemolysis. This is usually mild to moderate and is often incompletely compensated. The elliptocytes are less prominent and less elongated than in mild HE$_c$, and some spherocytes, microspherocytes, and microelliptocytes are usually present (Fig. 95-15). _Red cell morphology varies greatly, even within the same family._ Some family members may have relatively prominent spherocytes and as few as 15 to 25 percent elliptocytes, while in others elliptocytes predominate and spherocytes are rare.[464,477] This may cause diagnostic confusion initially, particularly if the propositus has few elliptocytes. Family studies will almost always reveal some members with obvious elliptocytosis.

As in HS, the red cells in spherocytic HE are osmotically fragile, particularly after incubation.[476,477,513] Increased autohemolysis that responds to glucose is also characteristic, as is excessive mechanical fragility.[476,477,512,577] Gallbladder disease is common,[477,513] and aplastic crises are a risk. The splenic pathology also mimics HS.[578,579] Splenic sequestration is evident,[477] red cells are conditioned during splenic passage,[512] and hemolysis abates following splenectomy.[123,474,476,477,512,513,578]

Melanesian (Stomatocytic) HE. This fascinating condition, also known as hereditary ovalocytosis or Melanesian ovalocytosis, is still incompletely defined. So far it has been reported only in the aboriginal populations of Melanesia and Indonesia[514,516–518,520,521] and in one Filipino family.[515] The gene is very common in Melanesia, particularly in lowland tribes where malaria is endemic.[518–520,522] In these tribes 5 to 25 percent of the natives are affected. In vivo there is evidence that Melanesian HE provides some protection against malaria, particularly *Plasmodium vivax* and probably *Plasmodium falciparum*, but protection is incomplete.[518–520,522] In vitro, Melanesian elliptocytes are very resistant to invasion by all forms of malaria,[520,523,524] apparently because the membrane is much more rigid than normal.[525,526] Other membrane characteristics reflect this property. For example, the cells are usually heat-resistant. They easily withstand heating to 49°C, at which temperature normal red cells disintegrate, and do not undergo endocytosis in response to drugs that produce dramatic endocytosis in normal cells, and they strongly resist crenation,[523,524] even after several days storage in plasma or buffered salt solutions. This property, combined with the distinctive red cell morphology (see below), provides a simple means of diagnosing the disease.

The molecular explanation of these remarkable membrane characteristics is a mystery. The membrane protein composition and lipid bilayer fluidity are normal,[523–526] and specific membrane protein interactions are just beginning to be examined. Genetic studies initially suggested autosomal recessive inheritance,[517] but recent work points to an autosomal dominant pattern.[518,520–522]

The morphology is unique and is characterized by elliptical stomatocytes and roundish elliptocytes traversed by one or two transverse bars (elliptical knizocytes) (Fig. 95-15).[514–516,517,520] Hemolysis is apparently mild or absent,[514–516,520] although extensive hematologic data have not been published. In one well-studied patient, red cell Na$^+$ and K$^+$ permeability was increased, glucose consumption was elevated to compensate for increased cation pumping, autohemolysis was increased, and the cells were osmotically resistant.[517] Curiously, many blood group antigens are poorly expressed on the surface of these cells;[517] conceivably this may occur because the rigid membrane skeleton inhibits their clustering and impedes agglutination. Whatever the explanation, it may prove to be an important property, because specific blood group antigens are required for the attachment and invasion of red cells by malarial parasites.[580–582]

Etiology

In all HE patients studied so far, isolated ghosts and membrane skeletons retain the elliptocytic or poikilocytic shape of the parent red cells[180] (Fig. 95-16). The membrane skeletons isolated from individuals with HE are unstable when exposed

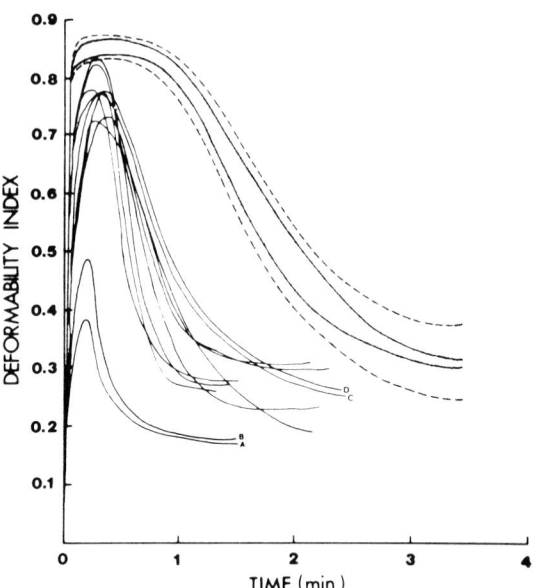

Fig. 95-17 Increased mechanical fragility of red cell membranes from patients with various elliptocytic disorders. Isolated membranes are resealed and subjected to a constant, high shear stress in a laser diffraction viscometer (ektacytometer). The deformability signal (deformability index) that the instrument provides progressively declines as the deformable cells are sheared into more spheroidal, less deformable fragments. The fragmentation rate for normal cells is shown by the shaded area within the dashed lines. The two curves in this area are from patients with elliptocytosis (60 percent) secondary to myelofibrosis. The curves with intermediate increases in fragmentation are from patients with the typical mild form of common HE due to defects in spectrin self-association (unlabeled curves) or to partial deficiency of protein 4.1 (*C,D*). Two patients with homozygous HE due to absence of protein 4.1 (*A,B*) show the greatest membrane fragility. Patients with hereditary pyropoikilocytosis have very similar curves. (*From Mohandas et al.*[561] *Used by permission of Blood.*)

to mechanical shaking[531] or shear stress[561] (Fig. 95-17). These findings suggest that the molecular defects lie in the skeletal proteins.

Several abnormalities in membrane skeletal protein content and function have already been defined.

Thermal Sensitivity of Spectrin. It has been known for more than a century that red cells heated to temperatures approaching 50°C for short periods of time become unstable and fragment spontaneously.[580a] Recent work shows that this phenomenon is due to denaturation of spectrin. Normal spectrin denatures at 49°C (10-min exposure),[180,529] and normal red cells fragment at the same temperature.[180] As noted earlier, all patients with HPP and some patients with other forms of HE have thermally sensitive red cells. Hereditary pyropoikilocytes and red cells from infants with mild HE$_c$ and poikilocytosis fragment after 10 min at 44 to 46°C.[497,573] Red cells from some but not all patients with mild HE$_c$ fragment at 47 to 48°C.[180] As expected, purified spectrin from these red cells is also heat-sensitive.[180,529] The thermal instability of HE red cells and spectrin is either present or absent in all the affected patients in a kindred.[180,497] This increased thermal sensitivity was the first clue that spectrin was abnormal in many patients with HE$_c$ and HPP.

Abnormal Spectrin Oligomerization. Thirty percent of patients with HE$_c$ (sometimes designated HE-I) and all patients thus far tested with HPP have a defect in their ability to associate the dimer form to tetramers and higher order oligo-

Fig. 95-16 The morphology of HE red cells (*left*), ghosts (*center*), and membrane skeletons (*right*). Essentially all the elliptocytic ghosts form elliptocytic membrane skeletons. (*From Tomaselli, John, and Lux.*[180] *Used by permission of the Proceedings of the National Academy of Science of the United States of America.*)

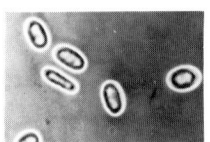 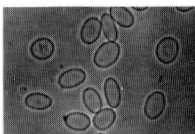 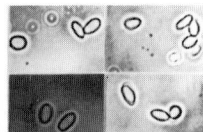

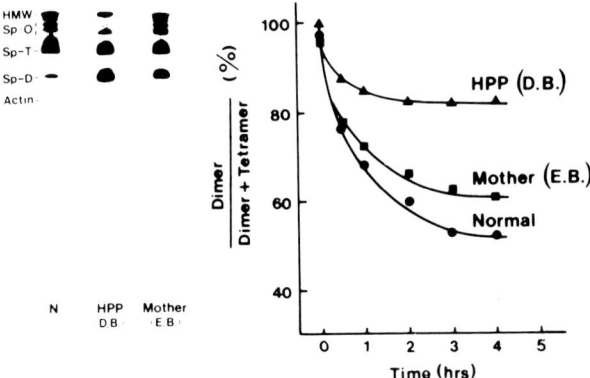

Fig. 95-18 Abnormality in spectrin dimer-tetramer equilibrium in hereditary pyropoikilocytosis. *(Left)* Nondenaturing polyacrylamide gel electrophoresis of spectrin extracts from normal, HPP, and HPP carrier red cell membranes. The positions of high molecular weight spectrin complexes (complex), spectrin tetramers (Sp-T), and spectrin dimers (Sp-D) are indicated. Note the increased proportion of spectrin dimer in the HPP patient (38 percent) and his asymptomatic mother (20 percent) (HPP carrier) compared with normal (5 percent). *(Right)* Kinetics of dimer to tetramer conversion at 30°C of normal, HPP, and HPP carrier spectrin. *(From Liu, Palek, Prochal, and Castelberry.[509] Used by permission of the Journal of Clinical Investigation.)*

mers (Fig. 95-18).[13] Abnormally high proportions of spectrin dimer are present in 0°C spectrin extracts.[509,510,532,538] At 0°C the equilibrium between spectrin dimer and tetramer is immobile,[48] and the proportion of each spectrin species reflects its relative proportion on the membrane.[50] As described previously, the head end of the spectrin dimer, consisting of the amino terminus of the α chain and the carboxy terminus of the β chain, is the functional site for spectrin self-association.[47] In the kindreds with HE_c and HPP possessing a defect in spectrin self-association, abnormalities of α- and β-chain structure have been identified.

Only one β-spectrin abnormality has been found, namely, a truncated chain of molecular weight 214,000 lacking the carboxy-terminal phosphorylation sites[149] (Fig. 95-19). Functionally, this deletion results in diminished spectrin self-association. Low temperature spectrin extracts contain increased spectrin dimer (~50 percent of the dimer-tetramer pool) and

Fig. 95-19 Densitometric tracings of SDS polyacrylamide gels of spectrin from a patient with HE due to deletion of the carboxy-terminal end of the spectrin β chain. A. Normal spectrin extract. B. Patient's spectrin extract. C and D. Patient's purified spectrin tetramer and dimer, respectively. Note the presence of an abnormally small (214-kDa) β component in all of the patient's spectrin preparations, but especially in the spectrin dimer fraction in panel D. This suggests that the mutant spectrin cannot participate to a normal extent in spectrin dimer self-association. *(From Palek.[13] Used by permission of Clinical Haematology.)*

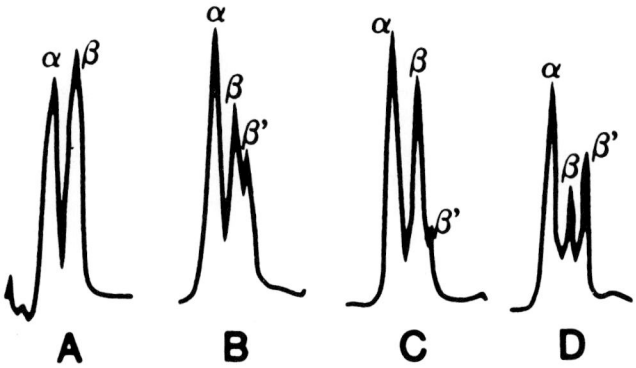

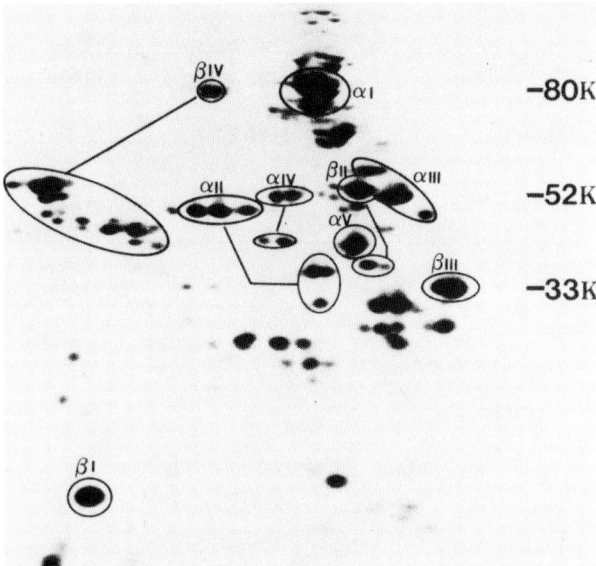

Fig. 95-20 Tryptic domains of spectrin separated by two-dimensional isoelectric focusing, pH 7.2 to 4.5 *(left to right)*, followed by SDS gel electrophoresis *(top to bottom)*. The major α- and β-chain domains are labeled. In some cases subdomains derived from further tryptic cleavage of a parent domain are also shown. *(From Marchesi et al.[538] Used by permission of Blood.)*

nearly all of the deleted β²¹⁴-spectrin is found in the dimer fraction (Fig. 95-19)[150,151,544] indicating that β²¹⁴ is responsible for the functional defect. Three such cases have been described in unrelated patients with hereditary elliptocytosis.[150,151,544] Clinically, these patients have mild to moderate hemolysis with prominent elliptocytosis and some fragmented red cells. Osmotic fragility is normal. Thermal stability is unusual; the red cells become echinocytic at 47°C (normal = 49°C) but do not fragment.[105]

The story of the α-spectrin defects is more complicated, with seven distinct types of α-chain variants described so far, at least six involving the amino-terminal α-I 80-kDa domain. These six were initially identified by two-dimensional spectrin polypeptide ("domain") maps. An example of a normal map is shown in Fig. 95-20. All six are characterized by a decrease or absence of the normal α-I 80-kDa domain and appearance of smaller proteolytic fragments, including: (1) a new 78-kDa peptide (α^{I/78} defect),[527] (2) a new 74-kDa peptide (α^{I/74} defect),[486,532–534,543] (3) a new 65-kDa (or 68-kDa) peptide (α^{I/65} or α^{I/68} defect),[503,536,539,543] (4) two new 46- and 17-kDa (or 50- and 21-kDa) peptides (α^{I/46} or α^{I/50a} defect),[532,535,538,543] (5) another 50-kDa peptide with a more basic isoelectric point (α^{I/50b}),[583] and (6) a defect with two new peptides (α^{I/42-43} defect).[540]

A major advance has recently been made in the specific identification of the mutations responsible for hereditary elliptocytosis, in that the amino acid sequence abnormalities have been elucidated in three of the α-chain variants. The α-I domain has been entirely sequenced,[584] and thus the variant amino acid sequences could be compared to the known normal sequence. The α^{I/50a} variant contains proline instead of the normal leucine at residue 254. The α^{I/50b} variant contains a proline instead of a glutamine at residue 465, and the α^{I/65} variant contains an extra leucine inserted after residue 150 (Fig. 95-21).[583] Presumably these mutations are responsible for the abnormal spectrin structure and function, and ultimately for the elliptocytic shape and membrane properties of HE red cells. The primary molecular defects in the α^{I/78}, α^{I/74},

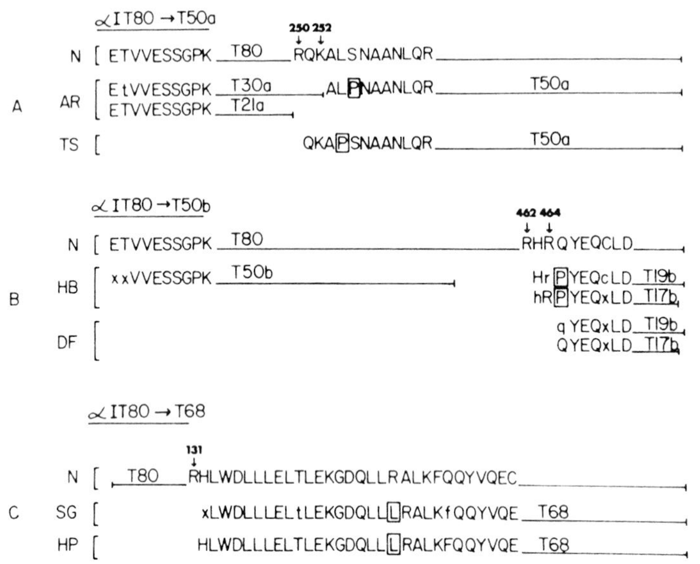

Fig. 95-21 Partial amino acid sequence of α-I domain peptides from HE spectrins that exhibit a defect in self-association. *A.* Partial sequences of the 50-kDa (T50a), 30-kDa (T30a), and 21-kDa (T21a) tryptic peptides derived from the α-I domain of patients with $\alpha^{I/50a}$ spectrin (also called $\alpha^{I/46}$). *B.* Partial sequence of 50-kDa, 19-kDa, and 17-kDa tryptic peptides of $\alpha^{I/50b}$ spectrin. *C.* Partial sequence of the 68-kDa tryptic peptide of $\alpha^{I/68}$ spectrin (also called $\alpha^{I/65}$). Arrows and numbers mark cleavage sites at lysine (K) or arginine (R) residues. Unidentified residues are represented as x and tentatively identified residues are given in lowercase letters. See Fig. 1-5 in Chap. 1 for single letter amino acid code. (*From Marchesi et al.*[583] Used by permission of the Journal of Clinical Investigation.)

and $\alpha^{I/42-43}$ mutations have not yet been defined. All six defects produce a similar functional phenotype: diminished spectrin self-association, decreased thermal stability,[497,573] and diminished resistance to isolated membranes or membrane skeletons to shear stress.[13,561]

The seventh abnormality is a short α-spectrin chain (234-kDa, α^{234} defect).[541,542] Although spectrin containing this mutant chain also fails to properly self-associate, studies so far surprisingly suggest the primary defect may lie at the opposite end of the molecule, in the α-IV domain.[541] Another curious feature of this disease is that the amount of the α^{234} chain varies widely: from 10 to 45 percent of the spectrin in different individuals. The proportion is constant in each patient and correlates directly with disease severity and membrane fragility.[541] No explanation of this remarkable variation is currently available.

Several clinical syndromes are associated with these α-chain defects (Table 95-8). In general, patients bearing only a single abnormal allele are either silent carriers or have mild HE$_c$ or HE$_c$ with infantile poikilocytosis.[13,486,503,507,511,527,528,532–539,541,543] The factors responsible for the differences in clinical expression are not understood; however, preliminary studies of compound heterozygotes suggest that different mutations are expressed differently.[576] Specifically the $\alpha^{I/74}$ defect produces severe disease with a greater proportion of spectrin dimers. In the homozygous state, hemolysis is life-threatening. In contrast, homozygous $\alpha^{I/65}$ spectrin is associated with only mild hemolysis and a lesser defect in spectrin self-association.[576] The $\alpha^{I/46}$ mutation appears to be of intermediate severity. In the limited surveys made so far these three mutations are more common than $\alpha^{I/78}$, $\alpha^{I/50b}$, or $\alpha^{I/42-43}$. Most of the defects have been observed in black families, but so far only the $\alpha^{I/74}$ alleles have been observed in patients with HE$_c$ and infantile poikilocytosis.[13,541] Patients with HPP have had either the $\alpha^{I/74}$ or $\alpha^{I/46}$ defects.[13,510,511] The clinical syndrome associated with $\alpha^{I/42-43}$ is somewhat unique.[540] Red cell morphology is very bizarre, and resembles HPP, but hemolysis is very mild like mild HE$_c$. Thermal sensitivity and spectrin self-association also mimic HE, but the red cells are spectrin-deficient, like HPP.[540]

Patients with HPP either carry two abnormal α-I genes or are double heterozygotes for one of the α-I defects and another unknown defect that augments its expression.[13,510,511] This is reflected in greater membrane instability to shear stress and

thermal challenge and a greater proportion of spectrin dimers in 0°C extracts (Table 95-8). In addition, the HPP patients with the mysterious "silent" defect, and perhaps all HPP patients, are also spectrin deficient (~30 percent).[512] This has led Palek to suggest that the silent defect is actually a regulatory mutation affecting α-spectrin synthesis,[13] similar or identical to the postulated defect in the recessive form of HS (Table 95-8). Decreased synthesis of normal α-spectrin would increase the proportion of the mutant α chain, augmenting the functional defect. The combination of decreased α-spectrin synthesis and the known thermal instability of the mutant α-I spectrins[529] could account for the deficit in membrane spectrin. This interesting hypothesis should be testable using recently isolated α-spectrin cDNA probes.[65]

Defective Binding of Spectrin to Ankyrin. This defect has been reported in only one family.[545] The *abnormal spectrin* binds poorly (70 to 80 percent of normal) to inside-out membranes and to the 72-kDa fragment of ankyrin that contains the spectrin-binding site. In the heterozygous state this mild defect is clinically silent, but when combined with a defect in spectrin self-association, the spectrin-ankyrin binding defect is greatly augmented (30 percent of normal) and a severe HPP-like syndrome results.[545,585] This is consistent with the observation that spectrin tetramers bind ankyrin better than do spectrin dimers.[117]

Protein 4.1 Deficiency. In several kindreds with HE, protein 4.1 was found to be either partially or fully deficient[504,546–550,586,587] (Fig. 95-22). This variant appears to be more common in patients of French and North African descent.[504,546,547] Protein 4.1 is decreased about 50 percent in heterozygotes and is absent in homozygotes. Clinically the heterozygotes have a mild form of HE with little or no hemolysis. At present it is not clear whether they have mild HE$_c$ or a variant of spherocytic HE, since there is disagreement as to whether osmotic fragility tests are or are not positive. In any case the degree of spherocytosis and hemolysis is clearly less than what is typically reported for spherocytic HE.[123,464,476,477,513] In contrast, homozygotes have a severe transfusion-dependent hemolytic anemia with marked osmotic fragility, normal thermal stability, bizarre red cell morphology, and a very good response to splenectomy.[504] The homozygous 4.1-deficient membranes are very fragile, but stability can be restored by reconstitution

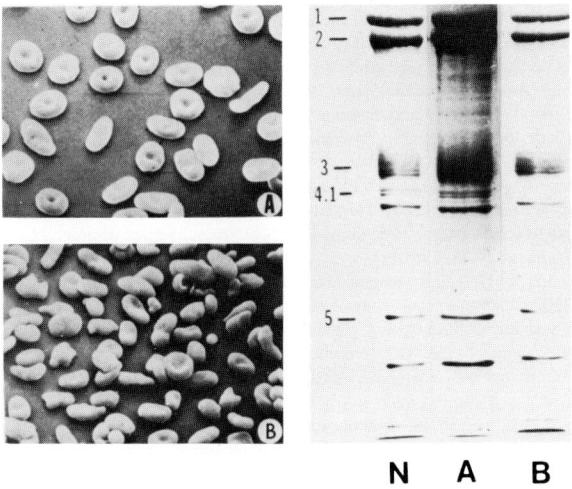

Fig. 95-22 *Deficiency of protein 4.1 in spherocytic HE. (Right)* SDS polyacrylamide gels (Laemmli system, see Fig. 95-1) of red cell membranes from a normal individual (N), a heterozygous parent with 50 percent of the normal amount of protein 4.1 (A), and a homozygous-deficient daughter (B). Note that both components of protein 4.1 (4.1a and 4.1b) are decreased (relative to protein 3) in the parent and missing in the daughter and that other proteins are present in normal concentrations. *(Left)* Scanning electron micrographs of red cells from the parent (A) and daughter (B). Note that the homozygous-deficient daughter shows marked fragmentation, spherocytosis, elliptocytosis, and bizarre poikilocytosis, while the heterozygous-deficient parent displays only modest elliptocytosis and slightly spheroidal discocytes. *(From Tchernia, Mohandas, and Shohet.*[504] *Used by permission of the Journal of Clinical Investigation.)*

with purified protein 4.1.[548] Molecular genetic studies suggest that the disease is caused by a mutation on chromosome 1 that produces a DNA rearrangement upstream from the initiation codon of protein 4.1 and results in an aberrantly spliced mRNA.[550]

In addition to deficiency in protein 4.1, some of these patients are also missing (partially) other proteins, such as protein 4.9[504] or glycophorin C.[549,587] The deficiency in glycophorin C lends support to the theory that protein 4.1 interacts with this glycoprotein.[557]

Structural and Functional Defects of Protein 4.1. Three structural defects of protein 4.1 have been described. One occurred in two generations of a French family with mild HE_c and moderate chronic hemolysis.[551] The disorder is characterized by prominent elliptocytosis with relatively dense and undeformable cells. Osmotic and thermal stability and spectrin self-association are normal. SDS gels show a 50 percent decrease in protein 4.1 and two faint new bands just below protein 4.2, that are immunologically related to 4.1.[551] Functionally, the patient's 4.1 bound to a crude mixture of normal spectrin and actin only 40 percent as well as normal. The most straightforward interpretation is that the affected members are heterozygous for a mutant protein 4.1 that is unstable and lacks the ability to promote normal spectrin-actin interactions; however, more detailed studies are needed to confirm this hypothesis.

The second defect has been identified in a single kindred with mild HE_c. The patients are heterozygous for a large variant of protein 4.1 (95 kDa) that comigrates with protein 3 and is detected with immunoblots.[552,553] The primary defect is an insertion of 34 amino acids at the border of the region of 4.1 where spectrin and actin interact (Ref. 552; S. Marchesi,

personal communication). Fortunately the insertion does not markedly alter spectrin-actin binding, which probably accounts for its relatively mild clinical phenotype.

The third variant is a shortened protein 4.1 that migrates as a doublet with apparent molecular weights of 73 and 74 kDa.[588] Remarkably, heterozygosity for the abnormal species does not produce any clinical defect.

Deficiency of Glycophorin C. Deficiency of this minor sialoglycoprotein occurs in homozygous protein 4.1 deficiency, as described above, and in patients with the rare Leach phenotype of Gerbich-negative (Ge−) red cells. The Gerbich antigen system is carried on glycophorin C. Patients with the Leach subtype of Ge− lack all three components of the glycophorin C complex: β, $β_1$, and γ.[556,558] These patients, but not other patients with Ge− red cells (who lack the antigen but *not* glycophorin C), have mild elliptocytosis[556,558] with *increased osmotic fragility* (i.e., HE_s). Their red cells contain near-normal levels of protein 4.1, but it extracts more easily than normal, indicating a weakened interaction with the membrane.[93] This and other information, discussed earlier, strongly suggests glycophorin C is an important binding site for protein 4.1 in normal red cells. In contrast to glycophorin C deficiency, patients lacking glycophorin A, glycophorin B, or both are entirely asymptomatic and have normal red cell morphology.

Deficiency of Protein 4.2. Several *Japanese* patients have been described with an apparently *recessive* disease characterized by moderately severe, splenectomy-responsive hemolytic anemia and complete or nearly complete absence of protein 4.2.[123,268,590] Although HS was diagnosed, the published red cell morphology is most compatible with spherocytic elliptocytosis (HE_s),[123,268] with numerous rounded elliptocytes.[123] In the best-studied patient, red cells contain traces of an abnormally large protein 4.2, suggesting that an unstable molecule is produced.[123]

Interestingly, protein 4.2 is reportedly also diminished or absent in some Japanese patients during episodes of biliary obstruction but returns to normal levels when the obstruction is relieved.[591] The explanation of this curious finding and its relationship to the hemolysis observed in patients with congenital 4.2 deficiency is unknown.

Defects in Protein 3. As noted earlier, 6 to 7 percent of the population is heterozygous for a slightly large, but functionally normal variant that produces no apparent disease.[127] In contrast, a recently described variant of similar size (98 kDa) is associated with acanthocytosis (without hemolysis), enhanced anion transport, and decreased ankyrin binding.[559] The difference is probably due to the fact that the extra peptide material appears to be inserted in the cytoplasmic domain in the first variant[127] and in the first part of the transmembrane domain in the second.[559]

Two other relatively poorly characterized protein 3 variants are reported: another slightly large, poorly phosphorylated mutant in a patient with HS;[592] and a complex membrane alteration including decreased protein 4.1 (70 percent of normal) and an apparently small protein 3 in a patient with a severe congenital poikilocytic hemolytic anemia whose parents are related.[593]

Other Considerations. As the previous sections illustrate, HE and HPP are very heterogeneous disorders associated with a large number of molecular defects. In some kindreds, the actual amino acid sequence abnormalities have been identified. However, despite our knowledge of the defective structure and function of the specific membrane proteins, we still do not understand how those abnormalities lead to an elliptical shape.

Any explanation of the various forms of HE must consider the fact that nucleated elliptocytic precursors are round, and elongate or fragment only gradually as they circulate. This process resembles the gradual development of spherocytosis in hereditary spherocytes[255,398] and aging normal cells, and is consistent with the concept that the change in shape is secondary to the intrinsic structural instability of the skeleton. According to this hypothesis, mild membrane skeletal defects lead to elliptocytosis by increasing membrane plasticity (i.e., plastic deformation). As noted earlier, normal red cells rapidly regain their shape if they are transiently deformed, but they remain misshapen if the distortion is maintained for long periods of time (minutes to hours).[184,185] Presumably, dynamic skeletal interactions realign in response to stress. In a cell with weakened skeletal interactions, like the hereditary elliptocyte, this process would be accelerated. In vivo, red cells are deformed into a stable elliptical or torpedo shape in very small capillaries and are sometimes detained for short periods of time. It is easy to imagine how this distortion, repeated thousands of times per day, could cause red cells to gradually elongate and assume their characteristic shape in typical mild HE$_c$. Whether this is, in fact, the pathophysiological mechanism remains to be proved.

Red cells with more severe skeletal defects would also tend to elongate, but if skeletal instability were sufficiently compromised, they would be unable to withstand the shear stresses experienced in the normal circulation, and fragmentation or combinations of fragmentation and shape change induced by plastic deformation (i.e., bizarre-shaped poikilocytes) would predominate. This process would explain the nearly identical morphology observed in homozygous HE and hereditary pyropoikilocytosis, and in neonates with mild HE$_c$ and poikilocytosis.

In spite of the uncertainties about the molecular mechanisms involved in the different subtypes of HE, the available information suggests that red cell death in the various hemolytic forms follows a similar pathway. In all cases hemolysis is markedly ameliorated by splenectomy, and where examined, splenic pathology shows cordal congestion essentially identical to that observed in HS.[494,578,579,594] As in HS, the specific pathophysiological mechanism(s) responsible for splenic sequestration and red cell destruction remain to be defined.

REFERENCES

1. BENNETT V: The membrane skeleton of human erythrocytes and its implications for more complex cells. *Annu Rev Biochem* 54:273, 1985.
2. COHEN CM: The molecular organization of the red cell membrane skeleton. *Semin Hematol* 20:141, 1983.
3. MARCHESI VT: Structure and function of the erythrocyte membrane skeleton. *Prog Clin Biol Res* 159:1, 1984.
4. MOHANDAS N, CHASIS JA, SHOHET SB: The influence of the membrane skeleton on red cell deformability, membrane material properties, and shape. *Semin Hematol* 20:225, 1983.
5. GOODMAN SR, SHIFFER K: The spectrin membrane skeleton of normal and abnormal human erythrocytes: A review. *Am J Physiol* 244:C121, 1983.
6. SCHWARTZ RS, CHIU DT, LUBIN B: Plasma membrane phospholipid organization in human erythrocytes. *Curr Top Hematol* 5:63, 1985.
7. ANSTEE DJ, TANNER MJ: Structure and function of the red cell membrane sialoglycoproteins. *Br J Haematol* 64:211, 1986.
8. JENNINGS ML: Kinetics and mechanism of anion transport in red blood cells. *Annu Rev Physiol* 47:519, 1985.
9. JAY D, CANTLEY L: Structural aspects of the red cell anion exchange protein. *Annu Rev Biochem* 55:38, 1986.
10. LOW PS: Structure and function of the cytoplasmic domain of band 3: Center of erythrocyte membrane-peripheral protein interactions. *Biochim Biophys Acta* 864:145, 1986.
11. LANDE WM, MENTZER WC: Haemolytic anaemia associated with increased cation permeability. *Clin Haematol* 14:89, 1985.
12. BECKER PS, LUX SE: Hereditary spherocytosis and related disorders. *Clin Haematol* 14:15, 1985.
13. PALEK J: Hereditary elliptocytosis and related disorders. *Clin Haematol* 14:45, 1985.
14. VERKLEIJ AJ, ZWAAL RFA, ROELOFSEN B, CONFURIUS P, KASTELIJN D, VAN DEENAN LLM: The asymmetric distribution of phospholipids in the human red cell membrane. A combined study using phospholipase and freeze-etch electron microscopy. *Biochim Biophys Acta* 323:178, 1973.
15. LOW MG, FINEAN JB: Modification of erythrocyte membranes by a purified phosphatidylinositol-specific phospholipase C (Staphylococcus aureus). *Biochem J* 162:235, 1972.
16. BLAIR L, BITTMAN R: Cholesterol distribution between the two halves of the lipid bilayer of human erythrocyte ghost membranes. *J Biol Chem* 253:8366, 1978.
17. FAIRBANKS G, STECK TL, WALLACH DFH: Electrophoretic analysis of the major polypeptides of the human erythrocyte membrane. *Biochemistry* 10:2606, 1971.
18. FERREL JE JR, HUESTIS WH: Phosphoinositide metabolism and the morphology of human erythrocytes. *J Cell Biol* 98:1992, 1984.
19. VAN DEENAN LLM, DEGIER J: Lipids of the red blood cell membrane, in Surgenor DM (ed): *The Red Blood Cell*. New York, Academic, 1974, p 48.
20. SWEELEY CC, DAWSON G: Lipids of the erythrocyte, in Jamieson GA, Greenwalt TJ (eds): *Red Cell Membrane Structure and Function*. Philadelphia, Lippincott, 1969, p 172.
21. COOPER RA: Lipids of human red cell membranes: Normal composition and variability in disease. *Semin Hematol* 7:269, 1970.
22. ROTHMAN JE, LENARD J: Membrane asymmetry. *Science* 195:743, 1977.
23. BERGELSON LD, BARSUKOV LI: Topological asymmetry of phospholipids in membranes. *Science* 197:224, 1977.
24. STECK TL: The organization of proteins in the human red cell membrane. *J Cell Biol* 62:1, 1974.
25. PINDER JC, GRATZER WB: Structural and dynamic states of actin in the erythrocyte. *J Cell Biol* 96:768, 1983.
26. ANSTEE DJ: The blood group MNSs-active sialoglycoproteins. *Semin Hematol* 15:13, 1981.
27. FURTHMAYR H: Structural comparison of glycophorins and immunochemical analysis of genetic variants. *Nature* 271:519, 1978.
28. FURTHMAYR H: Glycophorins A, B, and C: A family of sialoglycoproteins. Isolation and preliminary characterization of trypsin derived peptides, in Lux SE, Marchesi VT, Fox CF (eds): *Normal and Abnormal Red Cell Membranes*. New York, AR Liss, 1979, p 195.
28a. COLIN Y, RAHUEL C, LONDON J, ROMEO P-H, d'AURIOL L, GALBIBERT F, CARTON J-P: Isolation of cDNA clones and complete amino acid sequence of human erythrocyte glycophorin C. *J Biol Chem* 261:229, 1986.
29. BERCOVICH T, GITLER C: 5-[^{125}I]iodonaphthyl azide, a reagent to determine the penetration of proteins into the lipid bilayer of biological membranes. *Biochemistry* 17:1484, 1978.
30. KAHANE I, GITLER C: Red cell membrane glycophorin labelling from within the lipid bilayer. *Science* 201:351, 1978.
31. WEINSTEIN RS, KHODADAD JK, STECK TL: The band 3 protein intramembrane particle of the human red blood cell, in Lassen UV, Ussing HH, Wieth JO (eds): *Membrane Transport in Erythrocytes*. Copenhagen, Munksgaard, 1980, p 35.
32. GAHMBERG CG, TAUREN G, VIRTANEN I, WARTIOVAARA J: Distribution of glycophorin on the surface of human erythrocyte membranes and its association with intramembrane particles: An immunochemical and freeze fracture study of normal and En(a−) erythrocytes, in Lux SE, Marchesi VT, Fox CF (eds): *Normal and Abnormal Red Cell Membranes*. New York, AR Liss, 1979, p 59.
33. NIGG EA, BRON C, GIRARDET M, CHERRY RJ: Band 3-glycophorin A association in erythrocyte membranes demonstrated by combining protein diffusion measurements with antibody-induced cross-linking. *Biochemistry* 19:1887, 1980.
34. SHEETZ MP: Integral membrane protein interaction with Triton cytoskeletons of erythrocytes. *Biochim Biophys Acta* 557:122, 1979.
35. YU J, FISCHMAN DA, STECK TL: Selective solubilization of proteins and phospholipids of red blood cell membranes by nonionic detergents. *J Supramol Struct* 1:233, 1973.

36. DUNN MJ, KEMP RB, MADDY AH: The similarity of the two high-molecular weight polypeptides of erythrocyte spectrin. *Biochem J* 173:197, 1978.

37. ANDERSON JM: Structural studies on human spectrin. Comparison of subunits and fragmentation of native spectrin. *J Biol Chem* 254:939, 1979.

38. SPEICHER DW, MARCHESI VT: Erythrocyte spectrin is comprised of many homologous triple helical segments. *Nature* 311:177, 1984.

39. SPEICHER DW, MORROW JS, KNOWLES WJ, MARCHESI VT: A structural model of human erythrocyte spectrin: Alignment of chemical and functional domains. *J Biol Chem* 257:9093, 1982.

40. ELGSAETER A: Human spectrin. I. A classical light scattering study. *Biochim Biophys Acta* 536:235, 1978.

41. SHOTTON DM, BURKE BE, BRANTON D: The molecular structure of human erythrocyte spectrin. Biophysical and electron microscopic studies. *J Mol Biol* 131:303, 1979.

42. BOE A, ELGSAETER A, OFTEDAL G, STRAND KA: Human spectrin. III. A study based on dynamic and static light scattering. *Acta Chem Scand* A33:245, 1979.

43. STOKKE BT, ELGSAETER A: Human spectrin VI. A viscometric study. *Biochim Biophys Acta* 640:640, 1981.

44. DUNBAR JC, RALSTON GB: Hydrodynamic characterization of the heterodimer of spectrin. *Biochim Biophys Acta* 667:177, 1981.

45. CALVERT R, UNGEWICKELL E, GRATZER W: A conformational study of human spectrin. *Eur J Biochem* 107:363, 1980.

46. SPEICHER DW, MORROW JS, KNOWLES WJ, MARCHESI VT: Identification of proteolytically resistant domains of human erythrocyte spectrin. *Proc Natl Acad Sci USA* 77:5673, 1980.

47. MORROW JS, SPEICHER DW, KNOWLES WJ, HSU CJ, MARCHESI VT: Identification of functional domains of human erythrocyte spectrin. *Proc Natl Acad Sci USA* 77:6592, 1980.

48. UNGEWICKELL E, GRATZER W: Self-association of human spectrin. A thermodynamic and kinetic study. *Eur J Biochem* 88:379, 1978.

49. MORROW JS, MARCHESI VT: Self-assembly of spectrin oligomers in vitro: A basis for a dynamic cytoskeleton. *J Cell Biol* 88:463, 1981.

50. LIU SC, WINDISCH P, KIM S, PALEK J: Oligomeric states of spectrin in normal erythrocyte membranes. Biochemical and electron microscopic studies. *Cell* 37:587, 1984.

50a. SHAHBAKHTI F, GRATZER WB: Analysis of the self-association of human red cell spectrin. *Biochemistry* 25:5969, 1986.

51. RALSTON G, DUNBAR J, WHITE M: The temperature-dependent dissociation of spectrin. *Biochim Biophys Acta* 491:345, 1977.

52. GEIDUSCHEK JB, SINGER SJ: Molecular changes in the membranes of mouse erythroid cells accompanying differentiation. *Cell* 16:149, 1979.

53. EISEN H, BACH R, EMERY R: Induction of spectrin in erythroleukemic cells transformed by Friend virus. *Proc Natl Acad Sci USA* 74:3898, 1977.

54. HASTHORPE S: Quantification of spectrin-containing erythroid precursor cells in normal and perturbed erythropoiesis. *Exp Hematol* 8:1001, 1980.

55. TILLACK TW, MARCHESI SL, MARCHESI VT, STEERS E JR: A comparative study of spectrin: A protein isolated from red blood cell membranes. *Biochim Biophys Acta* 200:125, 1970.

56. PINDER JC, PHETHEAN J, GRATZER WB: Spectrin in primitive erythrocytes. *FEBS Lett* 97:278, 1978.

57. DUBREUIL R, BYERS TJ, BRANTON D, GOLDSTEIN CS, KIEHART DP: Drosophila spectrin. I. Characterization of the purified protein. *J Cell Biol* 105:2095, 1987.

58. BYERS TJ, DUBREUIL R, BRANTON D, KIEHART DP, GOLDSTEIN LS: Drosophila spectrin. II. Conserved features of the alpha subunit are revealed by analysis of cDNA clones and fusion proteins. *J Cell Biol* 105:2103, 1987.

59. GOODMAN SR, ZAGON IS, KULIKOWSKI RR: Identification of a spectrin-like protein in nonerythroid cells. *Proc Natl Acad Sci USA* 78:7570, 1981.

60. BURRIDGE K, KELLEY J, MANGEOT P: Nonerythrocyte spectrins: Actin-membrane attachment proteins occurring in many cell types. *J Cell Biol* 95:478, 1982.

61. RAPASKY EA, GRANGER BL, LAZARIDES E: Widespread occurrence of avian spectrin in nonerythroid cells. *Cell* 29:821, 1982.

62. NELSON WJ, LAZARIDES E: Expression of the β subunit of spectrin in nonerythroid cells. *Proc Natl Acad Sci USA* 80:363, 1983.

63. BENNETT V, DAVIS J, FOWLER WE: Brain spectrin, a membrane-associated protein related in structure and function to erythrocyte spectrin. *Nature* 299:126, 1982.

64. GLENNEY JR, GLENNEY P: Fodrin is the general spectrin-like protein found in most cells whereas spectrin and the TW protein have a restricted distribution. *Cell* 34:503, 1983.

65. HUEBNER K, PALUMBO AP, ISOBE M, KOZAK CA, MONACO S, ROVERA G, CROCE CM, CURTIS PJ: The α-spectrin gene is on chromosome 1 in mouse and man. *Proc Natl Acad Sci USA* 82:3790, 1985.

66. PRCHAL JT, MORLEY BJ, YOON S-H, COETZER TL, PALEK J, CONBOY JG,

KAN YW: Isolation and characterization of cDNA clones for human erythrocyte β-spectrin. *Proc Natl Acad Sci USA* 84:7468, 1987.

67. MOON RT, LAZARIDES E: β-Spectrin limits α-spectrin assembly on membranes following synthesis in a chicken erythroid cell lysate. *Nature* 305:62, 1983.

68. BODINE DM, BIRKENMEIER CS, BARKER JE: Spectrin deficient inherited hemolytic anemias in the mouse: Characterization by spectrin synthesis and mRNA activity in reticulocytes. *Cell* 37:721, 1984.

69. WOODS CM, LAZARIDES E: Degradation of unassembled α- and β-spectrin by distinct intracellular pathways: Regulation of spectrin topogenesis by β-spectrin degradation. *Cell* 40:959, 1985.

70. MOOD RT, LAZARIDES E: Biogenesis of the avian erythroid membrane skeleton: Receptor-mediated assembly and stabilization of ankyrin (globin) and spectrin. *J Cell Biol* 98:1899, 1984.

71. PUSZKIN S, PUSZKIN E, MAIMON J, ROUAULT C, SCHOOK W, ORES C, KOCHWA S, ROSENFIELD R: Alpha-actinin and tropomyosin interaction with a hybrid complex of erythrocyte actin and muscle myosin. *J Biol Chem* 252:5529, 1977.

72. TILNEY LG, DETMERS P: Actin in erythrocyte ghosts in its association with spectrin: Evidence for a nonfilamentous form of these two molecules in situ. *J Cell Biol* 66:508, 1975.

73. SHEETZ MP, PAINTER RG, SINGER SJ: Relationships of the spectrin complex of human erythrocyte membranes to the actomyosins of muscle cells. *Biochemistry* 15:4486, 1976.

74. OHNISHI T: Isolation and characterization of an actin-like protein from membranes of human red cells. *Br J Haematol* 35:453, 1977.

75. SHETEVLINE P: *Mechanisms of Cell Motility. Molecular Aspects of Contractility.* New York, Academic, 1983, p 36.

76. BRENNER SL, KORN ED: Spectrin/actin complex isolated from sheep erythrocytes accelerates actin polymerization by simple nucleation. Evidence for oligomeric actin in the erythrocyte cytoskeleton. *J Biol Chem* 255:1670, 1980.

77. BYERS T, BRANTON D: Visualization of the protein associations in the erythrocyte membrane skeleton. *Proc Natl Acad Sci USA* 82:6153, 1985.

78. PINDER JC, WEEDS AG, GRATZER WB: Study of actin filament ends in the human red cell membrane. *J Mol Biol* 191:461, 1986.

79. TSUKITA S, TSUKITA S, ISHIKAWA H: Bidirectional polymerization of G-actin on the human erythrocyte membrane. *J Cell Biol* 98:1102, 1984.

80. NAKASHIMA K, BEUTLER E: Comparison of structure and function of human erythrocyte and human muscle actin. *Proc Natl Acad Sci USA* 76:935, 1979.

81. UNGEWICKELL E, BENNETT PM, CALVERT R, OHANIAN V, GRATZER WB: In vitro formation of a complex between cytoskeletal proteins of the human erythrocyte. *Nature* 280:811, 1979.

82. COHEN CM, TYLER JM, BRANTON D: Spectrin-actin associations studied by electron microscopy of shadowed preparations. *Cell* 21:875, 1980.

83. COHEN CM, LANGLEY RC JR: Functional characterization of human erythrocyte spectrin alpha and beta chains: Association with actin and erythrocyte protein 4.1. *Biochemistry* 23:4488, 1984.

84. COHEN CM, FOLEY SF: The role of band 4.1 in the association of actin with erythrocyte membranes. *Biochim Biophys Acta* 688:691, 1982.

85. OHANIAN V, WOLFE LC, JOHN KM, PINDER JC, LUX SE, GRATZER WB: Analysis of the ternary interaction of the red cell membrane skeletal proteins spectrin, actin and protein 4.1. *Biochemistry* 23:4416, 1984.

86. TYLER JM, REINHARDT BN, BRANTON D: Associations of erythrocyte membrane proteins. Binding of purified bands 2.1 and 4.1 to spectrin. *J Biol Chem* 255:7034, 1980.

86a. BECKER PS, LUX SE: Protein 4.1 binding peptides of human spectrin identified by use of radiolabel-transfer cross-linker. *J Cell Biol* 99:113a, 1984.

86b. COLEMAN TR, HARRIS AS, MISCHE SM, MOOSEKER MS, MORROW JS: Beta spectrin bestows protein 4.1 sensitivity on spectrin-actin interactions. *J Cell Biol* 104:519, 1987.

87. LAEMMLI UK: Cleavage of structural proteins during the assembly of the head of bacteriophage T4. *Nature* 227:680, 1970.

88. GOODMAN SR, YU J, WHITFIELD CF, CULP EN, POSNAK EJ: Erythrocyte membrane skeletal protein bands 4.1 a and b are sequence related phosphoproteins. *J Biol Chem* 257:4564, 1982.

89. LETO TL, MARCHESI VT: A structural model of human erythrocyte protein 4.1. *J Biol Chem* 259:4603, 1984.

90. SAUBERMAN N, FORTIER NL, FAIRBANKS G, O'CONNOR RJ, SNYDER LM: Red cell membranes in hemolytic disease. Studies on variables affecting electrophoretic analysis. *Biochim Biophys Acta* 556:292, 1979.

90a. MUELLER TJ, JACKSON CW, DOCKLER ME, MORRISON M: Membrane skeletal alterations during in vivo mouse red cell aging. Increase in the band 4.1a:4.1b ratio. *J Clin Invest* 79:492, 1987.

91. CORREAS I, LETO TL, SPEICHER DW, MARCHESI VT: Identification of the functional site of erythrocyte protein 4.1 involved in spectrin-actin associations. *J Biol Chem* 261:3310, 1986.

92. ANDERSON RA, LOVRIEN RE: Glycophorin is linked to band 4.1 protein in the human erythrocyte membrane skeleton. *Nature* 307:655, 1984.

93. MUELLER TJ: The red cell skeletal protein 4.1 binds to PAS 2 in the membrane. *J Cell Biochem [Suppl]* 9B:17, 1985.

94. MUELLER T: A band 4.1 glycoconnectin (PAS 2) complex mediates the association of the red cell membrane skeleton with the bilayer domain. *Fed Proc* 43:1849, 1984.

95. ANDERSON RA, MARCHESI VT: Regulation of the association of membrane skeletal protein 4.1 with glycophorin by polyphosphoinositide. *Nature* 318:295, 1985.

96. WHITFIELD CF, CULP EN, GOODMAN SR: Transfer of label from protein 4.1-crosslinker complex to 4.1 membrane binding sites. *J Cell Biol* 103:542a, 1986.

97. PASTERNACK GR, ANDERSON RA, LETO TL, MARCHESI VT: Interactions between protein 4.1 and band 3. An alternative binding site for an element of the membrane skeleton. *J Biol Chem* 260:3676, 1985.

98. SATO SB, OHNISHI S: Interaction of a peripheral protein of the erythrocyte membrane, band 4.1, with phosphatidylserine-containing liposomes and erythrocyte inside-out vesicles. *Eur J Biochem* 130:19, 1983.

99. HORNE WC, LETO TL, MARCHESI VT: Differential phosphorylation of multiple sites in protein 4.1 and protein 4.9 by phorbol ester-activated and cyclic AMP-dependent protein kinases. *J Biol Chem* 260:9073, 1985.

100. PALFREY HC, WASEEM A: Protein kinase C in the human erythrocyte. Translocation to the plasma membrane and phosphorylation of bands 4.1 and 4.9 and other membrane proteins. *J Biol Chem* 260:16021, 1985.

101. FAQUIN WC, CHAHWALA SB, CANTLEY LC, BRANTON D: Protein kinase C of human erythrocytes phosphorylates bands 4.1 and 4.9. *Biochim Biophys Acta* 887:142, 1986.

102. SIEGEL DL, BRANTON D: Partial purification and characterization of an actin-binding protein, band 4.9, from human erythrocytes. *J Cell Biol* 100:775, 1985.

103. HUSAIN A, BRANTON D: Phosphorylation regulates actin-bundling activity of erythrocyte protein 4.9. *J Cell Biol* 105:39a, 1987.

104. GARDNER K, BENNETT V: Protein kinase C phosphorylates a recently identified membrane skeleton-associated calmodulin-binding protein in human erythrocytes. *J Biol Chem* 260:1339, 1986.

105. GARDNER K, BENNETT V: Modulation of spectrin-actin assembly by erythrocyte adducin. *Nature* 328:359, 1987.

106. FOWLER VM, BENNETT V: Tropomyosin: A new component of the erythrocyte membrane skeleton, in Kruckeberg WC, Eaton JW (eds): *Erythrocyte Membrane 3: Recent Clinical and Experimental Advances*. New York, AR Liss, 1984, p 57.

107. BENNETT V, STENBUCK PJ: Identification and partial purification of ankyrin, the high affinity membrane attachment site for human erythrocyte spectrin. *J Biol Chem* 254:2533, 1979.

108. LUNA EJ, KIDD GH, BRANTON D: Identification by peptide analysis of the spectrin-binding protein in human erythrocytes. *J Biol Chem* 254:2526, 1979.

109. YU J, GOODMAN S: Syndeins: The spectrin-binding protein(s) of the human erythrocyte membrane. *Proc Natl Acad Sci USA* 76:2340, 1979.

110. BENNETT V, STENBUCK PJ: Human erythrocyte ankyrin. Purification and properties. *J Biol Chem* 255:2540, 1980.

111. BENNETT V: Purification of an active proteolytic fragment of the membrane attachment site for human erythrocyte spectrin. *J Biol Chem* 253:2292, 1978.

112. WEAVER DC, MARCHESI VT: The structural basis of ankyrin function. I. Identification of two structural domains. *J Biol Chem* 259:6165, 1984.

113. WEAVER DC, PASTERNACK GR, MARCHESI VT: The structural basis of ankyrin function. II. Identification of two functional domains. *J Biol Chem* 259:6170, 1984.

114. BENNETT V, STENBUCK, PJ: The membrane attachment protein for spectrin is associated with band 3 in human erythrocyte membranes. *Nature* 280:468, 1979.

115. BENNETT V, STENBUCK PJ: Association between ankyrin and the cytoplasmic domain of band 3 isolated from the human erythrocyte membrane. *J Biol Chem* 255:6424, 1980.

116. HARGREAVES WR, GIEDD KN, VERKLEIJ A, BRANTON D: Reassociation of ankyrin with band 3 in erythrocyte membranes and in lipid vesicles. *J Biol Chem* 255:11965, 1980.

117. WEAVER DC, PASTERNACK GR, MARCHESI VT: The structural basis of ankyrin function. II. Identification of two functional domains. *J Biol Chem* 259:6170, 1984.

118. WEAVER DC, MARCHESI VT: The structural basis of ankyrin function. I. Identification of two structural domains. *J Biol Chem* 259:6165, 1984.

119. WALLIN R, CULP EN, COLEMAN DB, GOODMAN SR: A structural model of human erythrocyte band 2.1: Alignment of chemical and functional domains. *Proc Natl Acad Sci USA* 81:4095, 1984.

120. LU PW, SOONG C-J, TAO M: Phosphorylation of ankyrin decreases its affinity for spectrin tetramer. *J Biol Chem* 260:14958, 1985.

121. COHEN CM, FOLEY SF: Phorbol ester-and Ca^{2+}-dependent phosphorylation of human red cell membrane skeletal proteins. *J Biol Chem* 261:7701, 1986.

122. STAUFENBIEL M, LAZARIDES E: Ankyrin is fatty acid acylated in erythrocyte. *Proc Natl Acad Sci USA* 83:318, 1986.

123. RYBICKI AC, HEATH R, WOLF JL, LUBIN B, SCHWARTZ RS: Deficiency of protein 4.2 in erythrocytes from a patient with a Coombs negative hemolytic anemia. Evidence for a role of protein 4.2 in stabilizing ankyrin on the membrane. *J Clin Invest* 81:893, 1988.

124. SIEGEL DL, GOODMAN SR, BRANTON D: The effect of endogenous proteases on the spectrin binding proteins of human erythrocytes. *Biochim Biophys Acta* 598:517, 1980.

125. LUNA EJ, KIDD GH, BRANTON D: Identification of peptide analysis of the spectrin binding protein in human erythrocytes. *J Biol Chem* 254:2526, 1979.

126. HALL TC, BENNETT V: Erythrocyte ankyrin is functionally modulated by proteolytic cleavage of small regulatory domains. *Fed Proc* 46:2197, 1987.

126a. NIGG EA, CHERRY RJ: Anchorage of a band 3 population at the erythrocyte cytoplasmic membrane surface: Protein rotational diffusion measurements. *Proc Natl Acad Sci USA* 77:4702, 1980.

127. MUELLER TJ, MORRISON M: Detection of a variant of protein 3, the major transmembrane protein of the human erythrocyte. *J Biol Chem* 252:6573, 1977.

128. STECK TL, RAMOS B, STRAPAZON E: Proteolytic dissection of band 3, the predominant transmembrane polypeptide of human erythrocyte membrane. *Biochemistry* 15:1154, 1976.

129. DRICKAMER LK: Fragmentation of the band 3 polypeptide from human erythrocyte membranes. *J Biol Chem* 252:6909, 1977.

130. KOPITO RR, LODISH HF: Primary structure and transmembrane orientation of the murine anion exchange protein. *Nature* 316:234, 1985.

131. WEST CM, MCMAHON D, MOLDAY RS: Identification of glycoproteins, using lectins as probes, in plasma membranes from Dictyostelium discoideum and human erythrocytes. *J Biol Chem* 253:1716, 1978.

132. CHILDS RA, FEIZI T, FUKUDA M, HAKAMORI S: Blood group I activity associated with band 3, the major intrinsic membrane protein of human erythrocytes. *Biochem J* 173:333, 1978.

133. YU J, STECK TL: Isolation and characterization of band 3, the predominant polypeptide of the human erythrocyte membrane. *J Biol Chem* 250:9170, 1975.

134. MUELLER TJ, LI Y-T, MORRISON M: Effect of endo-beta-galactosidase on intact human erythrocytes. *J Biol Chem* 254:8103, 1979.

135. WALDER JA, CHATTERJEE R, STECK TL, LOW PS, MUSSO GF, KAISER ET, ROGERS PH, ARNONE A: The interaction of hemoglobin with the cytoplasmic domain of band 3 of the human erythrocyte membrane. *J Biol Chem* 259:10238, 1984.

136. KLIMAN HJ, STECK TL: Association of glyceraldehyde-3-phosphate dehydrogenase with the human red cell membrane. A kinetic analysis. *J Biol Chem* 255:6314, 1980.

137. TSAI I-H, MURTHY SNP, STECK TL: Effect of red cell membrane binding on the catalytic activity of glyceraldehyde-3-phosphate dehydrogenase with the human red cell membrane. *J Biol Chem* 259:1438, 1982.

138. JENKINS JD, MADDEN DP, STECK TL: Association of phosphofructokinase and aldolase with the membrane of the intact erythrocyte. *J Biol Chem* 259:9374, 1984.

139. HIGASHI T, RICHARDS CS, UYEDA K: The interaction of phosphofructokinase with erythrocyte membranes. *J Biol Chem* 254:9542, 1979.

140. DE BK, KIRTLEY ME: Interaction of phosphoglycerate kinase with human erythrocyte membranes. *J Biol Chem* 252:6715, 1977.

141. STRAPAZON E, STECK TL: Interaction of the aldolase and the membrane of human erythrocytes. *Biochemistry* 16:2966, 1977.

142. KARADSHEH NS, UYEDA K: Changes in the allosteric properties of phosphofructokinase bound to erythrocyte membranes. *J Biol Chem* 252:7418, 1977.

143. HAINFELD JF, STECK TL: The submembrane reticulum of the human erythrocyte: A scanning electron microscope study. *J Supramol Struct* 6:301, 1977.

144. TSUKITA S, TSUKITA S, ISHIKAWA H: Cytoskeletal network underlying the human erythrocyte membrane. Thin-section electron microscopy. *J Cell Biol* 85:567, 1980.

145. SHEN BW, JOSEPHS R, STECK TL: Ultrastructure of the intact skeleton of the human erythrocyte membrane. *J Cell Biol* 102:997, 1986.

146. LIU S-C, DERICK LH, PALEK J: Visualization of the hexagonal lattice in the erythrocyte membrane skeleton. *J Cell Biol* 104:527, 1987.

147. PAPE EH, KLOTT K, KREUTZ W: The determination of the electron density profile of the human erythrocyte ghost membrane by small-angle X-ray diffraction. *Biophys J* 19:141, 1977.

148. MCCAUGHAN L, KRIMM S: X-ray and neutron scattering density profiles of the intact human red blood cell membrane. *Science* 207:1481, 1980.

149. HARRIS HW JR, LUX SE: Structural characterization of the phosphorylation sites of human erythrocyte spectrin. *J Biol Chem* 255:11512, 1980.

150. DHERMY D, LECOMTE MC, GARBARZ M, BOURNIER O, GALAND C, GAUTERS H, FEO C, ALLOISIO N, DELAUNAY J, BOIVIN P: Spectrin beta-chain variant associated with hereditary elliptocytosis. *J Clin Invest* 70:707, 1982.

151. OHANIAN V, EVANS JP, GRATZER WB: A case of elliptocytosis associated with a truncated spectrin chain. *Br J Haematol* 61:31, 1985.

152. SHEETZ MP, CASALY J: 2,3-Diphosphoglycerate and ATP dissociate erythrocyte membrane skeletons. *J Biol Chem* 255:9955, 1980.

153. MENTZER WC JR, IAROCCI TA, MOHANDAS N, LANE PA, SMITH B, LAZERSON J, HAYES T: Modulation of erythrocyte membrane mechanical stability by 2,3-diphosphoglycerate in the neonatal poikilocytosis/elliptocytosis syndrome. *J Clin Invest* 79:943, 1987.

154. SCHINDLER M, KOPPEL D, SHEETZ MP: Modulation of membrane protein lateral mobility by polyphosphates and polyamines. *Proc Natl Acad Sci USA* 77:1457, 1980.

155. WOLFE LC, LUX SE, OHANIAN V: Spectrin-actin binding in vitro; effect of protein 4.1 and polyphosphates. *J Supramol Struct Cell Biochem* [*suppl*]5:123, 1981.

155a. WAUGH RE: Effects of 2,3-diphosphoglycerate on the mechanical properties of erythrocyte membrane. *Blood* 68:231, 1986.

156. AVRUCH J, FAIRBANKS G: Phosphorylation of endogenous substrates by erythrocyte membrane protein kinases. I. A monovalent cation-stimulated reaction. *Biochemistry* 13:5507, 1974.

157. PLUT DA, HOSEY MM, TAO M: Evidence for the participation of cytosolic protein kinases in membrane phosphorylation in intact erythrocytes. *Eur J Biochem* 82:333, 1978.

158. FAIRBANKS G, AVRUCH J: Phosphorylation of endogenous substrates by erythrocyte protein kinases. II. Cyclic adenosine monophosphate-stimulated reactions. *Biochemistry* 13:5514, 1974.

159. THOMAS EL, KING LE JR, MORRISON M: The uptake of cyclic AMP by human erythrocytes and its effect on membrane phosphorylation. *Arch Biochem Biophys* 196:459, 1979.

160. TAO M, CONWAY R, CHETA S: Purification and characterization of a membrane-bound protein kinase from human erythrocytes. *J Biol Chem* 255:2563, 1980.

161. DEKOWSKI SA, RYBICKI A, DRICKAMER K: A tyrosine kinase associated with the red cell membrane phosphorylates band 3. *J Biol Chem* 258:2750, 1983.

162. EDER PS, SOONG CJ, TAO M: Phosphorylation reduces the affinity of protein 4.1 for spectrin. *Biochemistry* 25:1764, 1986.

162a. LOW PS, ALLEN DP, ZIONCHECK TF, CHARI P, WILLARDSON BM, GEAHLEN RL, HAMSON ML: Tyrosine phosphorylation of band 3 inhibits peripheral protein binding. *J Biol Chem* 262:4592, 1987.

163. HARRIS HW JR, LEVIN N, LUX SE: Comparison of the phosphorylation of human erythrocyte spectrin in the intact red cell and in various cell-free systems. *J Biol Chem* 255:11521, 1980.

164. ANDERSON JM, TYLER JM: State of spectrin phosphorylation does not affect erythrocyte shape or spectrin binding to erythrocyte membranes. *J Biol Chem* 255:1259, 1980.

164a. ANDERSON JP, MORROW JS: The interaction of calmodulin with erythrocyte spectrin. Inhibition of protein 4.1-stimulated actin binding. *J Biol Chem* 262:6365, 1987.

165. GREENQUIST AC, SHOHET SB, BERNSTEIN SE: Marked reduction of spectrin in hereditary spherocytosis in the common house mouse. *Blood* 51:1149, 1978.

166. LUX SE: Spectrin-actin membrane skeleton of normal and abnormal red blood cells. *Semin Hematol* 16:21, 1979.

167. SHOHET SB: Reconstruction of spectrin-deficient spherocytic mouse erythrocyte membranes. *J Clin Invest* 64:483, 1979.

168. MOHANDAS N, GREENQUIST AC, SHOHET SB: Effects of heat and metabolic depletion on erythrocyte deformability, spectrin extractability, and phosphorylation, in Brewer GJ (ed): *The Red Cell*. New York, AR Liss, 1978, p 435.

169. LUX SE, JOHN KM, UKENA TE: Diminished spectrin extraction from ATP-depleted human erythrocytes. Evidence relating spectrin to changes in erythrocyte shape and deformability. *J Clin Invest* 61:815, 1978.

170. DEELEY JDT, CRUM LA, COAKLEY WT: The influence of temperature and incubation time on deformability of human erythrocytes. *Biochim Biophys Acta* 556:90, 1979.

171. SMITH BD, LaCELLE PL: Parallel decrease of erythrocyte membrane deformability and spectrin solubility at low pH. *Blood* 53:15, 1979.

172. CRANDALL ED, CRITZ AM, OSHER AS, KELJO DJ, FORSTER RE: Influence of pH on elastic deformability of the human erythrocyte membrane. *Am J Physiol* 235:C269, 1978.

173. MARCHESI VT, STEERS E JR: Selective solubilization of a protein component of the red cell membrane. *Science* 159:203, 1968.

174. LIU SC, PALEK J: Spectrin tetramer-dimer equilibrium and the stability of erythrocyte membrane skeletons. *Nature* 285, 1980.

175. NAKASHIMA K, BEUTLER E: Effect of antispectrin antibody and ATP on deformability of resealed erythrocyte membranes. *Proc Natl Acad Sci USA* 75:3823, 1978.

176. FISCHER TM, HAEST CWM, STOHR M, KAMP D, DEUTICKE B: Selective alteration of erythrocyte deformability by SH-reagents. Evidence for an involvement of spectrin in membrane shear elasticity. *Biochim Biophys Acta* 510:270, 1978.

177. HAEST CWM, FISCHER TM, PLASA G, DEUTICKE B: Stabilization of erythrocyte shape by a chemical increase in membrane shear stiffness. *Blood Cells* 6:539, 1980.

178. JOHNSON GJ, ALLEN DW, FLYNN TP, FINKEL B, WHITE JG: Decreased survival in vivo of diamide-incubated dog erythrocytes. A model of oxidant-induced hemolysis. *J Clin Invest* 66:955, 1980.

179. LUX SE, JOHN KM, KARNOVSKY MJ: Irreversible deformation of the spectrin-actin lattice in irreversibly sickled cells. *J Clin Invest* 58:955, 1976.

180. TOMASELLI MB, JOHN KM, LUX SE: Elliptical erythrocyte membrane skeletons and heat-sensitive spectrin in hereditary elliptocytosis. *Proc Natl Acad Sci USA* 78:1911, 1981.

181. SHEETZ MP, SINGER SJ: On the mechanism of ATP-induced shape changes in human erythrocyte membranes. I. The role of the spectrin complex. *J Cell Biol* 73:638, 1977.

182. JOHNSON RM, TAYLOR G, MEYER DB: Shape and volume changes in erythrocyte ghosts and spectrin-actin networks. *J Cell Biol* 86:371, 1980.

183. ELGSAETER A, STOKKE BT, MIKKELSEN A, BRANTON D: The molecular basis of erythrocyte shape. *Science* 234:1217, 1986.

184. HOCHMUTH RM, EVANS EA, COLVARD DF: Viscosity of human red cell membranes in plastic flow. *Microvasc Res* 11:155, 1976.

185. CHIEN S, SUNG K-LP, SKALAK R, USAMI S, TOZEREN A: Theoretical and experimental studies on viscoelastic properties of erythrocyte membranes. *Biophys J* 24:463, 1978.

186. NICOLSON GL, PAINTER RG: Anionic sites of human erythrocyte membranes. II. Anti-spectrin-induced transmembrane aggregation of the binding sites for positively charged colloidal particles. *J Cell Biol* 59:395, 1973.

187. ELGSAETER A, BRANTON D: Intramembrane particle aggregation in erythrocyte ghosts. I. The effects of protein removal. *J Cell Biol* 63:1018, 1974.

188. ELGSAETER A, SHOTTON DM, BRANTON D: Intramembrane particle aggregation in erythrocyte ghosts. II. The influence of spectrin aggregation. *Biochim Biophys Acta* 426:101, 1976.

189. SHOTTON D, THOMPSON K, WOFSY L, BRANTON D: Appearance and distribution of surface proteins of the human erythrocyte membrane. An electron microscope and immunochemical labeling study. *J Cell Biol* 76:512, 1978.

190. FOWLER V, BENNETT V: Association of spectrin with its membrane attachment site restricts lateral mobility of human erythrocyte integral membrane proteins. *J Supramol Struct* 8:215, 1978.

191. SHEETZ MP, SCHINDLER M, KOPPEL DE: Lateral mobility of integral membrane proteins is increased in spherocytic erythrocytes. *Nature* 285:510, 1980.

192. HEBBEL RP, YAMADA O, MOLDOW CF, JACOB HS, WHITE JG, EATON JW: Abnormal adherence of sickle erythrocytes to cultured vascular endothelium. Possible mechanism for microvascular occlusion in sickle cell disease. *J Clin Invest* 65:154, 1980.

193. HEBBEL RP, BOOGAERTS MA, EATON JW, STEINBERG MH: Erythrocyte adherence to endothelium in sickle-cell anemia. A possible determinant of disease severity. *N Engl J Med* 302:992, 1980.

194. MOHANDAS N, EVANS E: Adherence of sickle erythrocytes to vascular endothelial cells: Requirement for both cell membrane changes and plasma factors. *Blood* 64:282, 1984.

195. KAHANE I, POLLIACK A, RACHMILEWITZ EA, SKUTELSKY E: Distribution of sialic acids on the red blood cell membrane in beta thalassaemia. *Nature* 271:674, 1978.

196. PLATT OS, FALCONE JF, LUX SE: Molecular defect in the sickle erythrocyte membrane skeleton: Abnormal spectrin binding to sickle inside-out vesicles. *J Clin Invest* 75:266, 1985.

197. SCHWARTZ RS, RYBICKI AC, HEATH RH, LUBIN BH: Protein 4.1 in sickle erythrocytes. Evidence for oxidative damage. *J Biol Chem* 262:15666, 1987.

198. SHINAR E, SHALEV O, RACHMILEWITZ EA: Erythrocyte membrane skeleton abnormalities in severe beta-thalassemia. *Blood* 70:158, 1987.

199. HARDY B, BENSCH KG, SCHRIER SL: Spectrin rearrangement early in erythrocyte ghost endocytosis. *J Cell Biol* 82:654, 1979.

200. TOKUYASU KT, SCHEKMAN R, SINGER SJ: Domains of receptor mobility and endocytosis in the membranes of neonatal human erythrocytes and reticulocytes are deficient in spectrin. *J Cell Biol* 80:481, 1979.

201. ZAKAI N, KULKA RG, LOYTER A: Fusion of human erythrocyte ghosts by the combined action of calcium and phosphate ions. *Nature* 263:696, 1976.

202. CULLIS PR, HOPE MJ: Effects of fusogenic agents on membrane structure of erythrocyte ghosts and the mechanism of membrane fusion. *Nature* 271:672, 1978.

203. SEKIGUCHI K, ASANO A: Participation of spectrin in Sendai virus-induced fusion of human erythrocyte ghosts. *Proc Natl Acad Sci USA* 75:1740, 1978.

204. LALAZAR A, LOYTER A: Involvement of spectrin in membrane fusion: Induction of fusion in human erythrocyte ghosts by proteolytic enzymes and its inhibition by antispectrin antibody. *Proc Natl Acad Sci USA* 76:318, 1979.

205. PORTIS A, NEWTON C, PANGBORN W, PAPAHADJOPOULOS D: Studies on the mechanism of membrane fusion: Evidence for an intermembrane Ca^{2+}-phospholipid complex, synergism with Mg^{2+}, and inhibition by spectrin. *Biochemistry* 18:780, 1979.

206. MOMBERS C, VERKLEIG AJ, DE GIER J, VAN DEENAN LLM: The interaction of spectrin-actin and synthetic phospholipids. II. The interaction with phosphatidyl serine. *Biochim Biophys Acta* 551:279, 1979.

207. MOMBERS C, DE GIER J, DEMEL RA, VAN DEENAN LLM: Spectrin-phospholipid interaction. A monolayer study. *Biochim Biophys Acta* 603:52, 1980.

208. BONNET D, BEGARD E: Interaction of anilinonaphthyl labelled spectrin with fatty acids and phospholipids: A fluorescence study. *Biochem Biophys Res Commun* 120:344, 1984.

209. TYLER JM, HARGREAVES WR, BRANTON D: Purification of two spectrin-binding proteins: Biochemical and electron microscopical evidence for site specific reassociation between spectrin bands 2.1 and 4.1. *Proc Natl Acad Sci USA* 76:5192, 1979.

210. SATO SB, OHNISHI S: Interaction of a peripheral protein of the erythrocyte membrane, band 4.1, with phosphatidylserine-containing liposomes and erythrocyte inside-out vesicles. *Eur J Biochem* 130:19, 1983.

210a. COHEN AM, LIU S-C, DERICK LJ, PALEK J: Ultrastructural studies of the interaction of spectrin with phosphatidylserine liposomes. *Blood* 68:920, 1986.

210b. RYBICKI AC, HEATH R, LUBIN B, SCHWARTZ RS: Human erythrocyte protein 4.1 is a phosphatidylserine binding protein. *J Clin Invest* 81:255, 1988.

211. HAEST CWM, PLASA G, KAMP D, DEUTICKE B: Spectrin as a stabilizer of the phospholipid asymmetry in the human erythrocyte membrane. *Biochim Biophys Acta* 509:21, 1978.

212. FRANCK PFH, ROELOFSEN B, OP DEN KAMP JA: Complete exchange of phosphatidylcholine from intact erythrocytes after protein crosslinking. *Biochim Biophys Acta* 687:105, 1982.

213. DEUTICKE B, POSER B, LUTKEMEIER P, HAEST CW: Formation of aqueous pores in the human erythrocyte membrane after oxidative cross-linking of spectrin by diamide. *Biochim Biophys Acta* 731:196, 1983.

214. BERGMANN WL, DRESSLER V, HAEST CW, DEUTICKE B: Crosslinking of SH groups in the membrane enhances transbilayer orientation of phospholipids. Evidence for a limited access of phospholipids to the reorientation sites. *Biochim Biophys Acta* 796:390, 1984.

215. DRESSLER V, HAEST CWM, PLASA G, DEUTICKE B, ERUSALIMSKY JD: Stabilizing factors of phospholipid asymmetry in the erythrocyte membrane. *Biochim Biophys Acta* 775:189, 1984.

216. LUBIN B, CHIU D, et al: Abnormalities in membrane phospholipid organization in spectrin deficient human red cells. *Blood [suppl]* 62:34a, 1983.

217. LUBIN B, CHIN D, SCHWARTZ RS, COOPER B, JOHN K, WOLFE L, LUX SE: Abnormal membrane phospholipid organization in spectrin deficient human red cells. *Blood [suppl]* 62:34a, 1983.

218. VANLAIR CF, MASIUS JB: De la microcythemie. *Bull R Acad Med Belg* 5:515, 1871.

219. HAM TH, CASTLE WB: Studies on destruction of red blood cells. *Proc Am Phil Soc* 82:411, 1940.

220. CHAUFFARD A: Pathogenie de l'ictere hemolytique congenitale. *Ann Med* 1:3, 1914.

221. DAMESHEK W, SCHWARTZ SO: Hemolysins as the cause of clinical and experimental hemolytic anemias. With particular reference to the nature of spherocytosis and increased fragility. *Am J Med Sci* 196:769, 1938.

222. WILSON C: Some cases showing hereditary enlargement of the spleen. *Trans Clin Soc Lond* 23:162, 1890.

223. WILSON C, STANLEY D: A sequel to some cases showing hereditary enlargement of the spleen. *Trans Clin Soc Lond* 26:163, 1893.

224. MINKOWSKI O: Ueber eine hereditare, unter dem Bilde eines chronischen Ikterus mit Urobilinurie, Splenomegalie und Nierensiderosis verlaufende Affection. *Verh Dtsch Kongr Inn Med* 18:316, 1900.

225. BARLOW T, SHAW HB: Inheritance of recurrent attacks of jaundice and of abdominal crises with hepatosplenomegaly. *Trans Clin Soc Lond* 35:155, 1902.

226. GILBERT A, CASTAIGNE J, LEREBOULLET P: De l'ictere familial. Contribution a l'etude de la diathese biliaire. *Bull Mem Soc Med Hop Paris* 17:948, 1900.

227. CHAUFFARD MA: Pathogene de l'ictere congenital de l'adulte. *Semin Med (Paris)* 27:25, 1907.

228. CHAUFFARD MA: Les icteres hemolytique. *Semin Med* 28:49, 1908.

229. WIDAL F, ABRAMI P, BRULE M: Differenciation de plusieurs types d'icteres hemolytiques par le procede des hematies deplasmatisees. *Presse Med* 15:641, 1907.

230. WIDAL F, ABRAMI P, BRULE M: Les icterus d'origine hemolytique. *Arch Mal Coeur* 1:193, 1908.

231. HAYEM G: Sur une variete particuliere d'ictere chronique. Ictere infectieux chronique splenomegalique. *Presse Med* 6:121, 1898.

232. MICHELI F: Unmittelbare Effecte der Splenektomie bei einem Fall von erworbenem hamolytischen Splenomegalischen Ikterus Typus Hayem-Widal (Splenohamolytischer Ikterus). *Wien Klin Wochenschr* 24:1269, 1911.

233. WYNTER WE: Case of acholuric jaundice after splenectomy. *Proc R Soc Med (Clin Sec)* 6:80, 1912.

234. GIFFIN HZ: Haemolytic jaundice: A review of 17 cases. *Surg Gynecol Obstet* 25:152, 1917.

235. DAWSON OF PENN: The Hume Lectures on haemolytic icterus. *Br Med J* 1:921, 1931.

236. TILESTON W: Hemolytic jaundice. *Medicine.* 1:355, 1922.

237. GANSSLEN M: Uber hamolytischen Ikterus. *Dtsch Arch Klin Med* 140:210, 1922.

238. WINTROBE MM: *Blood, Pure and Eloquent.* New York, McGraw-Hill, 1980.

239. MORTON NE, MacKINNEY AA, KOSOWER N, SCHILLING RF, GRAY MP: Genetics of spherocytosis. *Am J Hum Genet* 14:170, 1962.

240. GODOL HC, HEIST H: High prevalence of increased osmotic fragility of red blood cells among Norwegian donors. *Scand J Haematol* 27:30, 1981.

241. RACE RR: On the inheritance and linkage relations of acholuric jaundice. *Ann Eugen* 11:365, 1942.

242. BERNARD J, BOIRON M, ESTAGER J: Une grand famille hemolytique. Treize cas de maladie de Minkowski-Chauffard observes dans la meme fratne. *Semin Hop* 28:3741, 1952.

243. KIMBERLING WJ, TAYLOR PA, CHAPMAN RG, LUBS HA: Linkage and gene localization of hereditary spherocytosis (HS). *Blood* 52:859, 1978.

244. BASS EB, SMITH SW, STEVENSON RE, ROSSE WF: Further evidence for location of the spherocytosis gene on chromosome 8. *Ann Intern Med* 99:192, 1983.

245. CHILCOTE RR, LeBEAU MM, DAMPLER C, PERGAMENT E, VERLINSKY Y, MOHANDAS N, FRISCHER H, ROWLEY JD: Association of red cell spherocytosis with deletion of the short arm of chromosome 8. *Blood* 69:156, 1987.

246. AGRE P, ORRINGER EP, BENNETT V: Deficient red-cell spectrin in severe, recessively inherited spherocytosis. *N Engl J Med* 306:1155, 1982.

247. AGRE P, ASIMOS A, CASELLA JF, MCMILLAN D: Inheritance pattern and clinical response to splenectomy as a reflection of erythrocyte spectrin deficiency in hereditary spherocytosis. *N Engl J Med* 315:1579, 1986.

248. AGRE P, CASELLA JF, ZINKHAM WH, MCMILLAN C, BENNETT V: Partial deficiency of erythrocyte spectrin in hereditary spherocytosis. *Nature* 314:380, 1985.

249. EMERSON CP JR, SHEN SC, et al: Studies on the destruction of red blood cells. IX. Quantitative methods for determining the osmotic and mechanical fragility of red cells in the peripheral blood and splenic pulp; the mechanism of increased hemolysis in hereditary spherocytosis (congenital hemolytic jaundice) as related to the function of the spleen. *Arch Intern Med* 97:1, 1956.

250. DACIE JV, MOLLISON PL: Survival of normal erythrocytes after transfusion to patients with familial haemolytic anaemia (acholuric jaundice). *Lancet* 1:550, 1943.

251. WILEY JS: Red cell survival in hereditary spherocytosis. *J Clin Invest* 49:555, 1970.

252. LUX SE: Disorders of the red cell membrane skeleton: Hereditary spherocytosis and hereditary elliptocytosis, in Stanbury JB, Wyngaarden JB, Fredrickson DS, Goldstein JL, Brown MS (eds): *The Metabolic Basis of Inherited Disease,* 5th ed. New York, McGraw-Hill, 1983.

253. LEBLOND PF, DE BOISFLEURY A, BESSIS M: La forme des érythrocytes dans la sphérocytose héréditaire. Étude au microscope à balayage. Relation avec leur déformabilité. *Nouv Rev Fr Hematol* 13:873, 1973.

254. JANDL JH, SIMMONS RL, CASTLE WB: Red cell filtration and the pathogenesis of certain hemolytic anemias. *Blood* 18:133, 1961.

255. LEBLOND PF, LaCELLE PL, WEED RI: Rheologie des érythroblastes et des érythrocytes dans la sphérocytose congénitale. *Nouv Rev Fr Hematol* 11:537, 1971.

256. LaCELLE PL: Pathologic erythrocytes in the capillary microcirculation. *Blood Cells* 1:269, 1975.

257. JOHNSSON R, VUOPIO P: Studies on red cell flexibility in spherocytosis using a polycarbonate membrane filtration method. *Acta Haematol* 60:329, 1978.

258. MacKINNEY AA JR, MORTON NE, KOSOWER NS, SCHILLING RF: Ascertaining genetic carriers of hereditary spherocytosis by statistical analysis of multiple laboratory tests. *J Clin Invest* 41:554, 1962.

259. JACOB HS, JANDL JH: Cell membrane permeability in the pathogenesis of hereditary spherocytosis (HS). *J Clin Invest* 43:1704, 1964.

260. MOHLER DN: Adenosine triphosphate metabolism in hereditary spherocytosis. *J Clin Invest* 44:1417, 1965.

261. LODER PB, BABARCZY G, DE GRUCHY GC: Red cell metabolism in hereditary spherocytosis. *Br J Haematol* 13:95, 1967.

262. REED CF, YOUNG LE: Erythrocyte energy metabolism in hereditary spherocytosis. *J Clin Invest* 46:1196, 1967.

263. DUNN I, IBSEN KH, COLE EL, SCHNEIDER AS, WEINSTEIN IM: Erythrocyte carbohydrate metabolism in hereditary spherocytosis. *J Clin Invest* 42:1535, 1963.

264. PALEK J, MIRČEVOVÁ L, BRABEC V: 2,3-Diphosphoglycerate metabolism in hereditary spherocytosis. *Br J Haematol* 17:59, 1969.

265. FERNANDEZ LA, ERSLEV AJ: Oxygen affinity and compensated hemolysis in hereditary spherocytosis. *J Lab Clin Med* 80:780, 1972.

266. BROMBERG PA, THEODORE J, ROBIN ED, JENSEN WN: Human erythrocyte pH with special reference to intracellular acidosis in hereditary spherocytosis. *J Clin Invest* 41:1349, 1962.

267. KAGIMOTO T, HAYASHI F, YAMASAKI M, MORINO Y, AKASAKA K, KISHIMOTO S: Phosphorus-31-NMR study on nucleotides and intracellular pH of hereditary spherocytes. *Experientia* 34:1092, 1978.

268. NOZAWA Y, NOGUCHI T, IIDA H, FUKUSHIMA T, SEKIYA T, ITO Y: Erythrocyte membranes of hereditary spherocytosis: Alteration in surface ultrastructure and membrane proteins, as inferred by scanning electron microscopy and SDS-disc gel electrophoresis. *Clin Chim Acta* 55:81, 1974.

269. BARNHART MT, LUSHER JM: The human spleen as revealed by scanning electron microscopy. *Am J Hematol* 1:243, 1976.

270. WAUGH RE, LaCELLE PL: Abnormalities in the membrane material properties of hereditary spherocytes. *J Biomech Eng* 102:240, 1980.

271. WAUGH RE: Effects of abnormal cytoskeletal structure on erythrocyte membrane mechanical properties. *Cell Motility* 3:609, 1983.

272. WAUGH RE: Effects of inherited membrane abnormalities on the viscoelastic properties of erythrocyte membranes. *Biophys J* 51:363, 1987.

273. WAUGH RE, AGRE P: Reductions of erythrocyte membrane viscoelastic coefficients reflect spectrin deficiencies in hereditary spherocytosis. *J Clin Invest* 81:133, 1988.

274. REED CF, SWISHER SN: Erythrocyte lipid loss in hereditary spheroccytosis. *J Clin Invest* 45:777, 1966.

275. WEED RI, BOWDLER AJ: Metabolic dependence of the critical hemolytic volume of human erythrocytes: Relationship to osmotic fragility and autohemolysis in hereditary spherocytosis and normal red cells. *J Clin Invest* 45:1137, 1966.

276. COOPER RA, JANDL JH: The selective and conjoint loss of red cell lipids. *J Clin Invest* 48:906, 1969.

277. SNYDER LM, LUTZ HU, SAUBERMAN N, JACOBS J, FORTIER NL: Fragmentation and myelin formation in hereditary xerocytosis and other hemolytic anemias. *Blood* 52:750, 1978.

278. SCHRIER SL, BEN-BASSAT I, BENSCH K, SEEGER M, JUNGA I: Erythrocyte membrane vacuole formation in hereditary spherocytosis. *Br J Haematol* 26:59, 1974.

279. COOPER RA, JANDL JH: The role of membrane lipids in the survival of red cells in hereditary spherocytosis. *J Clin Invest* 48:736, 1969.

280. LANGLEY GR, FELDERHOF CH: Atypical autohemolysis in hereditary spherocytosis as a reflection of two cell populations: Relationship of cell lipids to conditioning by the spleen. *Blood* 32:569, 1968.

281. JOHNSSON R: Red cell membrane proteins and lipids in spherocytosis. *Scand J Haematol* 20:341, 1978.

282. LUTZ HU, LIU S, PALEK J: Release of spectrin-free vesicles from human erythrocytes during ATP depletion. *J Cell Biol* 73:548, 1977.

282a. KUIPER PJC, LIVNE A: Differences in fatty acid composition between normal erythrocytes and hereditary spherocytosis affected cells. *Biochim Biophys Acta* 260:755, 1972.

283. ZAIL SS, PICKERING A: Fatty acid composition of erythrocytes in hereditary spherocytosis. *Br J Haematol* 42:399, 1979.

284. ALONI B, SHINITZKY M, MOSES S, LIVNE A: Elevated microviscosity in membranes of erythrocytes affected by hereditary spherocytosis. *Br J Haematol* 31:117, 1975.

285. JANSSON S-E, JOHNSSON R, GRIPENBERG J, VUOPIO P: The fluidity gradient in erythrocyte membranes in hereditary spherocytosis: A spin label study. *Br J Haematol* 46:73, 1980.

286. COOPER RA, SAWYER WH, LESLIE MH, HILL JS, GILL FM, WILEY JS: Normal fluidity of red cell membranes in hereditary spherocytosis. *Br J Haematol* 46:299, 1980.

287. BERTLES JE: Sodium transport across the surface membrane of red blood cells in hereditary spherocytosis. *J Clin Invest* 36:816, 1957.

288. ZIPURSKY A, ISRAELS LG: Significance of erythrocyte sodium flux in the pathophysiology and genetic expression of hereditary spherocytosis. *Pediatr Res* 5:614, 1971.

289. FEIG SA, BASSILAN S: Increased erythrocyte Ca^{2+} content in hereditary spherocytosis. *Pediatr Res* 9:928, 1975.

290. ZAIL SS, VAN DEN HOEK AK: Studies on calcium transport and calcium-dependent adenosine triphosphatase activity of erythrocyte membranes in hereditary spherocytosis. *Br J Haematol* 34:605, 1976.

291. JOHNSSON R, SANTAHOLMA S, SARIS NE: Calcium transport and adenosine triphosphatase activities of erythrocyte membranes in congenital spherocytosis. *Scand J Clin Lab Invest* 38:121, 1978.

292. FEIG SA, GUIDOTTI G: Relative deficiency of Ca^{2+}-dependent adenosine triphosphatase activity of red cell membranes in hereditary spherocytosis. *Biochem Biophys Res Commun* 58:487, 1974.

293. KIRKPATRICK FH, WOODS GM, LaCELLE PL: Absence of one component of spectrin adenosine triphosphate in hereditary spherocytosis. *Blood* 46:945, 1975.

294. BOIVIN P, DELAUNAY J, GALAND C: Altered erythrocyte membrane protein phosphorylation in an unusual case of hereditary spherocytosis. *Scand J Haematol* 23:251, 1979.

295. GREENQUIST AC, SHOHET SB: Phosphorylation in erythrocyte membranes from abnormally shaped cells. *Blood* 48:877, 1976.

296. BEUTLER E, GUINTO E, JOHNSON C: Human red cell protein kinase in normal subjects and patients with hereditary spherocytosis, sickle cell disease, and autoimmune hemolytic anemia. *Blood* 48:887, 1976.

297. MATSUMOTO N, YAWATA Y, JACOB HS: Association of decreased membrane protein phosphorylation with red blood cell spherocytosis. *Blood* 49:233, 1977.

298. YAWATA Y, KORESAWA S, MIYASHIMA K: Membrane protein phosphorylation and protein kinases in normal and hereditary spherocytosis red cells. *Hemoglobin* 4:717, 1980.

299. NAKAO M, FUJII Y, HARA Y, NOMURA T, NAKAO T, KANATSU Y: Membrane protein phosphorylation of intact normal and hereditary spherocytic human erythrocytes. *J Biochem* 88:327, 1980.

300. BOIVIN P, DELAUNAY J: Altered erythrocyte membrane protein phosphorylation in an unusual case of hereditary spherocytosis. *Scand J Haematol* 23:251, 1979.

301. ZAIL SS, VAN DEN HOEK AK: Studies of protein kinase activity and the binding of adenosine 3'5'-monophosphate by membranes of hereditary spherocytosis erythrocytes. *Biochem Biophys Res Commun* 66:1078, 1975.

302. BOIVIN P, GALAND G: Erythrocyte membrane phosphorylation in hereditary spherocytosis. *Biomedicine* 27:34, 1977.

303. WOLFE LC, LUX SE: Membrane protein phosphorylation of intact normal and hereditary spherocytic erythrocytes. *J Biol Chem* 253:3336, 1978.

304. WOLFE LC, LUX SE: Diminished stability of red cell membrane skeletons in hereditary spherocytosis. *Blood (suppl)* 52:106, 1978.

305. ALLEN DW, CADMAN S, McCANN SR, FINKEL B: Increased membrane binding of erythrocyte catalase in hereditary spherocytosis and in metabolically stressed normal cells. *Blood* 49:113, 1977.

306. JACOB HS, RUBY A, OVERLAND ES, MAZIA D: Abnormal membrane protein of red blood cells in hereditary spherocytosis. *J Clin Invest* 50:1800, 1971.

307. JACOB HS: The abnormal red cell membrane in hereditary spherocytosis: Evidence for the causal role of mutant microfilaments. *Br J Haematol* 23:35, 1972.

308. ENGLEHARDT R: Impaired reassemblance of red blood cell membrane components in hereditary spherocytosis, in Bolis L, Hoffman JF, Leaf A (eds): *Membranes and Disease.* New York, Raven, 1976, p 75.

309. IDEGUCHI H, HAMASAKI N, IKEHARA Y: Abnormal phosphoenolpyruvate transport in erythrocytes of hereditary spherocytosis. *Blood* 58:426, 1981.

310. COETZER TL, LAWLER J, LIU S-C, PRCHAL J, GUALTIERI RJ, BRAIN MC, DACIE JV, PALEK J: Partial ankyrin and spectrin deficiency in severe, atypical hereditary spherocytosis. *N Engl J Med* 318:230, 1988.

311. GOODMAN SR, SHIFFER KA, CASORIA LA, EYSTER ME: Identification of the molecular defect in the erythrocyte membrane skeleton of some kindreds with hereditary spherocytosis. *Blood* 60:772, 1982.

312. WOLFE LC, JOHN KM, FALCONE JC, BYRNE AM, LUX SE: A genetic defect in the binding of protein 4.1 to spectrin in a kindred with hereditary spherocytosis. *N Engl J Med* 307:1367, 1982.

313. BECKER PS, MORROW JS, LUX SE: Abnormal oxidant sensitivity and beta-chain structure of spectrin in hereditary spherocytosis associated with defective spectrin-protein 4.1 binding. *J Clin Invest* 80:557, 1987.

314. IANAKA T: Abnormality in a specific protein of the erythrocyte membrane in hereditary spherocytosis. *Biochem Biophys Res Commun* 57:1038, 1974.

315. SHEEHY R, RALSTON GB: Abnormal binding of spectrin to the membrane of erythrocytes in some cases of hereditary spherocytosis. *Blut* 36:145, 1978.

316. HILL JS, SAWYER WH, HOWLETT GJ, WILEY JS: Hereditary spherocytosis of man: Altered binding of cytoskeletal components to the erythrocyte membrane. *Biochem J* 201:259, 1981.

317. SAWYER WH, HILL JS, HOWLETT GH, WILEY JS: Hereditary spherocytosis of man: Detective cytoskeletal interactions in the erythrocyte membrane. *Biochem J* 211:349, 1983.

318. STEFANINI M: Chronic hemolytic anemia associated with erythrocyte enolase deficiency exacerbated by ingestion of nitrofurantoin. *Am J Clin Pathol* 58:408, 1972.

319. LACHANT NA, JENNINGS MA, TANAKA KR: Partial erythrocyte enolase deficiency: A hereditary disorder with variable clinical expression. *Blood* [suppl]:55a, 1986.

320. PINDER JC, PHERMY D, BAINES AJ, LUX SE, GRATZER WB: A phenomenological difference between membrane skeletal protein complexes isolated from normal and hereditary spherocytosis erythrocytes. *Br J Haematol* 55:455, 1983.

321. BERNSTEIN SE: Inherited hemolytic disease in mice: A review and update. *Lab Anim Sci* 30:197, 1980.

322. ANDERSON R, HUESTIS RR, MOTULSKY AG: Hereditary spherocytosis in the deer mouse. Its similarity to the human disease. *Blood* 15:491, 1960.

323. BODINE DM, BIRKENMEIER CS, BARKER JE: Spectrin-deficient inherited hemolytic anemias in the mouse: Characterization by spectrin synthesis and mRNA activity in reticulocytes. *Cell* 37:721, 1984.

324. BARKER JE, BODINE DM, et al: Synthesis of spectrin and its assembly into the red cell membrane cytoskeleton of normal and mutant mice. *J Cell Biochem* [suppl] 9B:3, 1985.

325. FALCONE JC, LUX SE: Unpublished observations.

326. WHITE R, BARKER J: Normoblastosis, a mutant mouse with severe hemolytic anemia. *Blood* [suppl] 70:57a, 1987.

327. HANSPAL M, PRCHAL JT, HANSPAL J, PALEK J: Synthesis and assembly of spectrin and ankyrin in atypical hereditary spherocytosis (HS) associated with spectrin and ankyrin deficiency. *Blood* [suppl] 70:53a, 1987.

327a. KITANTANI M, CHIYO H, OZAKI M, SHIKE S, MIWA S: Localization of the spherocytosis gene to chromosome segment 8p11.22→8p21.1. *Hum Genet* 78:94, 1988.

327b. MARCHESI S, MCINTOSH S, COLLINS F, FRANCKE U: Unpublished observations

328. WINKLEMAN JC, MARCHESI SL, WATKINS P, LINNENBACK AJ, AGRE P, FORGET BG: Recessive hereditary spherocytosis is associated with an abnormal α spectrin subunit. *Clin Res* 34:474a, 1987.

329. WOLFE LC, LUX SE: Unpublished observations.

330. BECKER PS, COHEN CM, LUX SE: The effect of mild diamide oxidation on the structure and function of human erythrocyte spectrin. *J Biol Chem* 261:4620, 1986.

331. WOLFE LC, BYRNE AM, LUX SE: Molecular defect in the membrane skeleton of blood bank-stored red cells. Abnormal spectrin-protein 4.1-actin complex formation. *J Clin Invest* 78:1681, 1986.

332. WOODS CM, BOYER B, VOGT PK, LAZARIDES E: Control of erythroid differentiation: Asynchronous expression of the anion transporter and the peripheral components of the membrane skeleton in AEV and S13-transformed cells. *J Cell Biol* 103:1789, 1986.

333. MCKUSICK VA: *The Human Gene Map* (April 15, 1987). Available from Victor A McKusick, The Johns Hopkins Hospital, Baltimore MD 21205.

334. CONBOY J, KAN YW, SHOHET SB, MOHANDES N: Molecular cloning of protein 4.1, a major structural element of the human erythrocyte membrane skeleton. *Proc Natl Acad Sci USA* 83:9512, 1986.

335. MATTEI MG, COLIN Y, LE VAN KIM C, MATTEI JF, CARTRON JP: Localization of the gene for human erythrocyte glycophorin C to chromosome 2, q14-q21. *Hum Genet* 74:420, 1986.

336. CARTRON JP: Personal communication.

336a. LUX S, JOHN K, SHALER O, FORGET B, CHILCOTE R, MARCHESI S, MCINTOSH S, HARRIS P, WATKINS P, BENNETT V: Red cell ankyrin is located on chromosome 8 and is deleted or defective in some patients with hereditary spherocytosis. *Blood* [Suppl], 72:46a, 1988.

336b. COSTA F, LUX S, AGRE P, WATKINS P, JOHN K, FORGET BG: Dominant hereditary spherocytosis is linked to the gene for the erythrocyte membrane protein ankyrin. *Blood* [Suppl], 72:38a, 1988.

337. LUX SE, HARRIS P, KOPITO R, LODISH HF: Unpublished observation.

338. KIMBERLING WJ, TAYLOR RA, CHAPMAN RG, LUBS HA: Linkage and gene localization of hereditary spherocytosis. *Blood* 52:859, 1978.

339. DE JONGH BM, BLACKLOCK HA, REEKERS P, VOLKERS WS, MEERA KHAN P, BERNINI LF, NIJENHUIS LE, VAN LOGHEM E, SCHREUDER GMT, ROOD JJ: Absence of close linkage between *Hereditary Spherocytosis* (*SPH*) and 24 genetic marker systems including *HLA* and *GM*. *Ann Hum Genet* 47:55, 1983.

340. EVANS EA, WAUGH R, MELNIK C: Elastic area compressibility modulus of red cell membranes. *Biophys J* 16:585, 1976.

341. CHAPMAN RG: Red cell life span after splenectomy in hereditary spherocytosis. *J Clin Invest* 47:2263, 1968.

342. BAIRD R, MCPHERSON AS, RICHMOND J: Red blood cell survival after splenectomy in congenital spherocytosis. *Lancet* 1:1060, 1971.

343. CHEN L-T, WEISS L: Electron microscopy of red pulp of human spleen. *Am J Anat* 134:425, 1972.

344. WEISS L: A scanning electron microscopic study of the spleen. *Blood* 43:665, 1974.

345. KNISELY MH: Spleen studies. I. Microscopic observations of the circulating system of living unstimulated mammalian spleen. *Anat Rec* 65:23, 1936.

346. CHEN L-T, WEISS L: The role of the sinus wall in the passage of erythrocytes through the spleen. *Blood* 41:529, 1973.

347. MURPHY JR: The influence of pH and temperature on some physical properties of normal erythrocytes and erythrocytes from patients with hereditary spherocytosis. *J Lab Clin Med* 69:758, 1967.

348. YOUNG LE, PLATZER RF, ERVIN DM, IZZO MJ: Hereditary spherocytosis. II. Observations on the role of the spleen. *Blood* 6:1099, 1951.

349. JANDL JH, GREENBERG MS, YONEMOTO R, CASTLE WB: Clinical determination of the sites of red cell sequestration in hemolytic anemias. *J Clin Invest* 35:842, 1956.

350. HARRIS IM, MCALISTER J, PRANKERD TAJ: Splenomegaly and the circulating red cell. *Br J Haematol* 4:97, 1958.

351. MOTULSKY AG, CASSERD F, GIBLETT ER, BROUN GO JR, FINCH CA: Anemia and the spleen. *N Engl J Med* 259:1164, 1212, 1958.

352. PRANKERD TAJ: Studies on the pathogenesis of haemolysis in hereditary spherocytosis. *Q J Med* 24:199, 1960.

353. GRIGGS RC, WEISMAN R JR, HARRIS JW: Alterations in osmotic and mechanical fragility related to in vivo erythrocyte aging and splenic sequestration in hereditary spherocytosis. *J Clin Invest* 39:89, 1960.

354. PRANKARD TAJ: The spleen and anaemia. *Br Med J* 2:517, 1963.

355. DACIE JV: Familial haemolytic anaemia (acholuric jaundice), with particular reference to changes in fragility produced by splenectomy. *Q J Med* 12:101, 1943.

356. WILAND OK, SMITH EB: The morphology of the spleen in congenital hemolytic anemia (hereditary spherocytosis). *Am J Clin Pathol* 26:619, 1956.

357. MOLNAR Z, RAPPAPORT H: Fine structure of the red pulp of the spleen in hereditary spherocytosis. *Blood* 39:81, 1972.

358. MATSUMOTO N, ISHIHARA T, SHIBATA M, UCHINO F, NAKASHIMA K, MIWA S: Electron microscopic studies of the spleen and liver in hereditary spherocytosis. *Acta Pathol Jpn* 23:507, 1973.

359. FUJITA T, KASHIMURA M, ADACH K: Scanning electron microscopy (SEM) studies of the spleen—normal and pathological. *Scanning Electron Microsc* 1:435, 1982.

360. BANTI G: Splenomegalie hemolytique et hemopoietique: Le role de la rate dans l'hemolyse. *Semin Med* 33:313, 1913.

361. MacPHERSON AIS, RICHMOND J, DONALDSON GWK, MUIR AR: The role of the spleen in congenital spherocytosis. *Am J Med* 50:35, 1971.

362. JANDL JH, ASTER RH: Increased splenic pooling and the pathogenesis of hypersplenism. *Am J Med Sci* 253:383, 1967.

363. LACELLE PL: pH in the mouse spleen and its effect on erythrocyte flow properties. *Blood* 44:910, 1974.

364. RAKITZIS ET, MILLS GC: Relation of red cell hexokinase activity to extracellular pH. *Biochim Biophys Acta* 192:157, 1969.

365. MINAKAMI S, YOSHIKAWA H: Studies on erythrocyte glycolysis. III. The effects of active cation transport, pH and inorganic phosphate concentration on erythrocyte glycolysis. *J Biochem (Tokyo)* 59:145, 1966.

366. PARKER JC: Ouabain-insensitive effects of metabolism on ion and water content in red blood cells. *Am J Physiol* 221:338, 1971.

367. DACIE JV: Observations on autohemolysis in familial acholuric jaundice. *J Pathol Bacteriol* 52:331, 1941.

368. GARDOS G: The role of calcium in the potassium permeability of human erythrocytes. *Acta Physiol Acad Sci Hung* 15:121, 1959.

369. SACHS JR, KNAUF PA, DUNHAM PB: Transport through red cell membranes, in Surgenor D, Mac N (ed): *The Red Blood Cell*, 2d ed. New York, Academic, 1975, vol 2, p 613.

370. JANDL JH: Hereditary spherocytosis, in Beutler E (ed): *Hereditary Disorders of Erythrocyte Metabolism*. New York, Grune & Stratton, 1968, p 209.

371. SELWYN JG, DACIE JV: Autohemolysis and other changes resulting from the incubation in vitro of red cells from patients with congenital hemolytic anemia. *Blood* 9:414, 1954.

372. LANGLEY GR, AXELL M: Changes in erythrocyte membranes and autohaemolysis during in vitro incubation. *Br J Haematol* 14:593, 1968.

373. LUX SE, GLADER BE: Disorders of the red cell membrane, in Nathan DG,

Oski FA (eds): *Hematology of Infancy and Childhood*, 2d ed. Philadelphia, Saunders, 1981, p 456.

374. BLENDIS LM, BANKS DC, RAMBOER C, WILLIAMS R: Spleen blood flow and splanchic haemodynamics in blood dyscrasia and other splenomegalies. *Clin Sci* 38:73, 1970.

375. HUCHZERMEYER H, SCHMITZ-FEUERHAKE T, RABLIN T: Determination of splenic blood flow by inhalation of radioactive rare gases. *Eur J Clin Invest* 7:345, 1977.

376. TOGHILL PJ: Red cell pooling in enlarged spleens. *Br J Haematol* 10:347, 1964.

377. PALEK J, LIU PA, LIU SC: Polymerization of red cell membrane protein contributes to spheroechinocyte shape irreversibility. *Nature* 274:505, 1978.

378. MAYMAN D, ZIPURSKY A: Hereditary spherocytosis: The metabolism of erythrocytes in the peripheral blood and in the splenic pulp. *Br J Haematol* 27:201, 1974.

379. COLEMAN DH, FINCH CA: Effect of adrenal steroids in hereditary spherocytic anemia. *J Lab Clin Med* 47:602, 1956.

380. ATKINSON JP, SCHREIBER AS, FRANK MM: Effects of corticosteroids and splenectomy on the immune clearance and destruction of erythrocytes. *J Clin Invest* 52:1509, 1973.

381. SCHREIBER AD, PARSONS J, MCDERMOTT P, COOPER RA: Effect of corticosteroids on the human monocyte IgG and complement receptors. *J Clin Invest* 56:1189, 1975.

382. BOWMAN HS, OSKI FA: Splenic macrophage interaction with red cells in pyruvate kinase deficiency and hereditary spherocytosis. *Vox Sang* 19:168, 1970.

382a. FERRANT A, LENERS N, MICHAUX JL, VERWILGHEN RL, SOKAL G: The spleen and haemolysis: Evaluation of the intrasplenic transit time. *Br J Haematol* 65:331, 1987.

383. TRUCCO JI, BROWN AK: Neonatal manifestations of hereditary spherocytosis. *Am J Dis Child* 113:263, 1967.

384. STAMEY CC, DIAMOND LK: Congenital hemolytic anemia in the newborn. *Am J Dis Child* 94:616, 1957.

385. BURMAN D: Congenital spherocytosis in infancy. *Arch Dis Child* 33:335, 1958.

386. ERLANDSON ME, HILGARTNER M: Hemolytic disease in the neonatal period and early infancy. *J Pediatr* 54:566, 1959.

386a. MANDELBAUM H: Congenital hemolytic jaundice: Report of a case on congenital hemolytic jaundice. Initial hemolytic crisis occurring at the age of 75: Splenectomy followed by recovery. *Ann Intern Med* 13:872, 1939.

387. ZANELLA A, MILANI S, FAGNANI G, MARIANI M, SIRCHIA G: Diagnostic value of the glycerol lysis test. *J Lab Clin Med* 102:743, 1983.

388. GELBACH SH, COOPER BA: Haemolytic anaemia in infectious mononucleosis due to inapparent congenital spherocytosis. *Scand J Haematol* 7:141, 1970.

389. HO-YEN DO: Hereditary spherocytosis presenting in pregnancy. *Acta Haematol (Basel)* 72:29, 1984.

390. GODAL HC, REFSUM HE: Haemolysis in athletes due to hereditary spherocytosis. *Scand J Haematol* 22:83, 1954.

391. YOUNG LE, IZZO MJ, PLATZER RF: Hereditary spherocytosis. I. Clinical, hematologic and genetic features in 28 cases, with particular reference to the osmotic and mechanical fragility of incubated erythrocytes. *Blood* 6:1073, 1951.

392. KRUEGER HC, BURGERT EO: Hereditary spherocytosis in 100 children. *Mayo Clin Proc* 41:821, 1966.

393. DEBRE R, LAMY M, SEE G, SCHRAMECK G: Congenital and familial hemolytic disease in children. *Am J Dis Child* 56:1189, 1938.

394. DIAMOND LK: Indications for splenectomy in childhood. Results in fifty-two operated cases. *Am J Surg* 39:400, 1938.

395. WATSON CJ: Studies of urobilinogen. III. The per diem excretion of urobilinogen in the common forms of jaundice and disease of the liver. *Arch Intern Med* 59:206, 1937.

396. SEARS DA, ANDERSON RP, FOY AL, WILLIAMS HL, CROSBY WH: Urinary iron excretion and renal metabolism of hemoglobin in hemolytic disease. *Blood* 28:708, 1966.

397. MULLER-EBERHARD U, JAVID J, LIEM HH, HANSTEIN A, HANNA M: Plasma concentrations of hemopexin, haptoglobin and heme in patients with various hemolytic diseases. *Blood* 32:811, 1968.

398. PAOLINO W: Variations of the mean diameter in the ripening of the erythrocyte. *Acta Med Scand* 136:141, 1949.

399. MAIZELS M: The anion and cation content of normal and anaemic bloods. *Biochem J* 30:821, 1936.

400. YOUNG LE: Observations on inheritance and heterogeneity of chronic spherocytosis. *Trans Assoc Am Physicians* 68:141, 1955.

401. JACOB HS: Hereditary spherocytosis: A disease of the red cell membrane. *Semin Hematol* 2:139, 1965.

402. ZANELLA A, IZZO C, REBULLA P, ZANUSO F, PERRONI L, SIRCHIA G: Acidified glycerol lysis test: A screening test for spherocytosis. *Br J Haematol* 45:481, 1980.

403. YOUNG LE, IZZO MJ, ALTMAN KI, SWISHER SN: Studies on spontaneous in vitro autohemolysis in hemolytic disorders. *Blood* 11:977, 1956.

404. DACIE JV: *The Hemolytic Anaemias, Congenital and Acquired. Part I. The Congenital Anaemias*, 2d ed. London, J & A Churchill, 1960, p 82.

405. LANGLEY GR, FELDERHOF CH: Atypical autohemolysis in hereditary spherocytosis as a reflection of two cell populations: Relationship of cell lipids to conditioning by the spleen. *Blood* 32:569, 1968.

406. GOTTFRIED EL, ROBERTSON NA: Glycerol lysis time of incubated erythrocytes in the diagnosis of hereditary spherocytosis. *J Lab Clin Med* 84:746, 1974.

407. GOTTFRIED EL: Acidified glycerol lysis test. *Br J Haematol* 47:323, 1981.

408. JOHNSSON R, SALMINEN S: Effect of ouabain on osmotic resistance and monovalent cation transport of red cells in hereditary spherocytosis. *Scand J Haematol* 29:323, 1980.

408a. RUTHERFORD CJ, POSTLEWAIGHT BF, HALLOWES M: An evaluation of the acidified glycerol lysis test. *Br J Haematol* 63:119, 1986.

409. OWREN PA: Congenital hemolytic jaundice. The pathogenesis of the hemolytic crisis. *Blood* 3:231, 1948.

410. BARKER K, MARTIN FRR: Splenectomy in congenital microspherocytosis. *Br J Surg* 56:561, 1969.

411. LEFRERE JJ, COUROUCE AM, BERTRAND Y, SOULIER JP: Infections a parvovirus B19. *Rev Fr Transfus Immunohematol* 29:149, 1986.

412. SERJEANT GR, TOPLEY JM, MASON K, SERJEANT BE, PATTISON JR, JONES SE, MOHAMED R: Outbreak of aplastic crises in sickle cell anaemia associated with parvovirus-like agent. *Lancet* 2:595, 1981.

413. SUMMERS J, JONES SE, ANDERSON MJ: Characterization of the genome of the agent of erythrocyte aplasia permits its classification as a human parvovirus. *J Gen Virol* 64:2527, 1983.

414. LEFRERE JJ, COUROUCE MA, GIROT R, BERTRAND Y, SOULIER JP: Six cases of hereditary spherocytosis revealed by human parvovirus infection. *Br J Haematol* 62:653, 1986.

415. SAARINEN UM, CHORBA TL, TATTERSALL P, YOUNG NS, ANDERSON LJ, PALMER E, COCELA PF: Human parvovirus B19-induced epidemic acute red cell aplasia in patients with hereditary hemolytic anemia. *Blood* 67:1411, 1986.

416. NUNOVE T, KOIKE T, KOIKE R, SANODA M, TSUKODA T, MORTIMER PP, COHEN BJ: Infection with human parvovirus infection. *Br J Haematol* 62:653, 1986.

417. CONKLIN GT, GEORGE JN, SEARS DA: Transient erythroid aplasia in hemolytic anemia: A review of the literature with two case reports. *Tex Rep Biol Med* 32:391, 1974.

418. ROBINS MM: Familial crisis in hereditary spherocytosis: Report of six affected siblings. *Clin Pediatr* 4:210, 1965.

419. GAIRDNER D: The association of gallstones with acholuric jaundice in children. *Arch Dis Child* 14:109, 1939.

420. DELAMORE IW, RICHMOND J, DAVIES SH: Megaloblastic anaemia in congenital spherocytosis. *Br Med J* 1:543, 1961.

421. KOHLER HG, MEYNELL MJ, COOKE WT: Spherocytic anaemia, complicated by megaloblastic anaemia of pregnancy. *Br Med J* 1:779, 1960.

422. BATES GC, BROWN CH: Incidence of gallbladder disease in chronic hemolytic anemia (spherocytosis). *Gastroenterology* 21:104, 1952.

423. LAWRIE GM, HAM JM: The surgical treatment of hereditary spherocytosis. *Surg Gynecol Obstet* 139:208, 1974.

424. HANFORD RB, SCHNEIDER GF, MacCARTHY JD: Massive thoracic extramedullary hemopoieses. *N Engl J Med* 263:120, 1960.

425. TAYLOR ES: Chronic ulcer of the leg associated with congenital jaundice. *JAMA* 112:1574, 1939.

426. BEINHAUER LG, GRUHN JG: Dermatologic aspects of congenital spherocytic anemia. *Arch Dermatol* 75:642, 1957.

427. BARRY M, SCHEUER PJ, SHERLOCK S, ROSS CF, WILLIAMS R: Hereditary spherocytosis with secondary haemochromatosis. *Lancet* 2:481, 1968.

428. SCHAFER AI, MILLER JB, LESTER EP, BOWERS TK, JACOB HS: Monoclonal gammopathy in hereditary spherocytosis: A possible pathogenic relation. *Ann Intern Med* 88:45, 1978.

429. LEMPERT KD: Gammopathy and spherocytosis. *Ann Intern Med* 89:145, 1978.

430. FUKATA S, TAMAI H, NOGAI K, MATSUBAYASHI S, NAGATO H, TASHIRO T, YASUDA M, KUMAGAI LF: A patient with hereditary spherocytosis and silicosis who developed an IgA (lambda) monoclonal gammopathy. *Jpn J Med* 26:81, 1987.

431. JANDL JH, FILES NM, BARNETT SB, MacDONALD RA: Proliferative response of the spleen and liver to hemolysis. *J Exp Med* 122:299, 1965.

432. SCHILLING RF: Hereditary spherocytosis; a study of splenectomized persons. *Semin Hematol* 13:169, 1976.

433. ISOBE T, OSSERMAN EF: Pathologic conditions associated with plasma cell dyscrasias: A study of 806 cases. *Ann NY Acad Sci* 190:507, 1071.

434. BLACKLOCK H, MERKIN M: Serum ferritin in patients with hereditary spherocytosis. *Br J Haematol* 49:117, 1981.

435. EDWARDS CQ, SKOLNICK MH, DADONE MM, KUSHNER JP: Iron overload in hereditary spherocytosis: Association with HLA-linked hemachromatosis. *Am J Hematol* 13:101, 1982.

436. FARGION S, CAPPELLINI MD, PIPERNO A, PANAJOTOPOULOUS N, RONCHI G, FIORELLI G: Association of hereditary spherocytosis and idiopathic hemochromatosis. A synergistic effect in determining iron overload. *Am J Clin Pathol* 86:645, 1986.

437. MOHLER DN, WHEBY MS: Hemochromatosis heterozygotes may have significant iron overload when they also have hereditary spherocytosis. *Am J Med Sci* 292:320, 1986.

438. LAWRENCE RD: Haemochromatosis in three families and in a woman. *Lancet* 1:736, 1949.

439. WILSON JD, SCOTT PJ, NORTH JDK: Hemochromatosis in association with hereditary spherocytosis. *Arch Intern Med* 120:701, 1967.

440. ZIPURSKY A: Isoimmune hemolytic diseases, in Nathan DG, Oski FA (eds): *Hematology of Infancy and Childhood*, 3d ed. Philadelphia, Saunders, 1987, p 44.

441. GILLILAND BC, BAXTER E, EVANS RS: Red cell antibodies in acquired hemolytic anemia with negative antiglobulin serum tests. *N Engl J Med* 285:252, 1971.

442. CROSBY WH, CONRAD ME: Hereditary spherocytosis: Observations on hemolytic mechanisms and iron metabolism. *Blood* 15:662, 1960.

443. MCCANN SR, JACOB HS: Spinal cord disease in hereditary spherocytosis: Report of two cases with a hypothesized common mechanism for neurologic and red cell abnormalities. *Blood* 48:259, 1976.

444. ZETTERSTROM R, STRINDBERG B: Sporadic congenital spherocytosis associated with congenital hypoplastic thrombocytopenia and malformations. *Acta Paediatr* 47:14, 1958.

445. WILEY JS, FIRKIN BG: An unusual variant of hereditary spherocytosis. *Am J Med* 48:63, 1970.

446. GARWICZ S: Atypical spherocytosis, a disease of spleen as well as of red blood cells. *Lancet* 1:956, 1975.

447. ZAIL SS, KRAWITZ P, VILJOEN E, METZ J: Atypical hereditary spherocytosis: Biochemical studies and sites of erythrocyte destruction. *Br J Haematol* 13:323, 1967.

448. SINGER DB: Postsplenectomy sepsis, in Rosenberg HS, Bolande RP (eds): *Perspectives in Pediatric Pathology*. Chicago, Yearbook Medical Publishers, 1973, vol 1, p 285.

449. KRIVIT W: Overwhelming post-splenectomy infection. *Am J Hematol* 2:193, 1977.

450. SCHWARTZ PE, STERIOFF S, MUCHA P, MELTON LJ, OFFORD KP: Postsplenectomy sepsis and mortality in adults. *JAMA* 248:2279, 1982.

451. LUX SE: Disorders of the red cell membrane, in Nathan DG, Oski FA (eds): *Hematology of Infancy and Childhood*, 3d ed. Philadelphia, Saunders, 1987, p 443.

452. SCHWARTZ JS: Pneumococcal vaccine: Clinical efficacy and effectiveness. *Ann Intern Med* 96:208, 1982.

453. MacKENZIE FAF, ELLIOT DH, EASTCOTT HHG, HUGHES-JONES NC, BARKHAN P, MOLLISON PL: Relapse in hereditary spherocytosis with proven splenunculus. *Lancet* 1:1102, 1962.

454. BART JB, APPEL MF: Recurrent hemolytic anemia secondary to accessory spleens. *South Med J* 71:608, 1978.

455. LAMBRECHT K: Die Elliptocytose (Ovalocytose) und ihre klinische Bedeutung. *Ergeb Inn Med Kinderheilkd* 55:295, 1938.

456. DRESBACH M: Elliptical human red corpuscles. *Science* 19:469, 1904.

457. FLINT A: Elliptical human erythrocytes. *Science* 19:796, 1904.

458. DRESBACH M: Elliptical human erythrocytes. *Science* 21:473, 1905.

459. BISHOP FW: Elliptical human erythrocytes. *Arch Intern Med* 14:388, 1914.

460. SYDENSTRICKER VP: Elliptic human erythrocytes. *JAMA* 81:113, 1923.

461. HUCK JG, BIGELOW RM: Poikilocytes in otherwise normal blood (elliptical human erythrocytes). *Bull Johns Hopkins Hosp* 34:390, 1923.

462. HUNTER WC, ADAMS RB: Hematologic study of three generations of a white family showing elliptical erythrocytes. *Ann Intern Med* 2:1162, 1929.

463. HUNTER WC: Further study of a white family showing elliptical erythrocytes. *Ann Intern Med* 6:775, 1932.

464. GIFFIN HZ, WATKINS CH: Ovalocytosis with features of hemolytic icterus. *Trans Assoc Am Physicians* 54:355, 1939.

465. PENFOLD J, LIPSCOMB JM: Elliptocytosis in man, associated with hereditary haemorrhagic telangiectasis. *Q J Med* 12:157, 1943.

466. GRZEGORZEWSKI H: Ueber familiares Vorkommennis elliptische Erythrozyten beim Menschen. *Folia Haematol* 50:260, 1933.

467. VAN DEN BERGH AAH: Elliptische rote Blutkorperchen. *Dtsch Med Wochenschr* 54:1244, 1928.

468. MASON VR: Ovalocytosis (elliptical human erythrocytes), in Downey H (ed): *Handbook of Hematology*. New York, Paul B Hoeber, 1938, vol III, p 2351.

469. LAWRENCE JS: Elliptical and sickle-shaped erythrocytes in the circulating blood of white persons. *J Clin Invest* 5:31, 1927.

470. POLLOCK LH, DAMESHEK W: Elongation of red blood cells in a Jewish family. *Am J Med Sci* 188:822, 1934.

471. INTROZZI P: Anaemia ipocromica splenomegalica emolitica con ovalocitosi (ellipticitosi), poichilocitosi ed aumento della resistenza osmotica der globuli rossi, splenectomia. *Haematologica* 16:525, 1935.

472. WYANDT H, BANCROFT PM, WINSHIP TO: Elliptic erythrocytes in man. *Arch Intern Med* 68:1043, 1941.

473. WOLMAN IJ, OZGE A: Studies on elliptocytosis. I. Hereditary elliptocytosis in the pediatric age period: A review of recent literature. *Am J Med Sci* 234:702, 1957.

474. DACIE JV: *The Hemolytic Anaemias, Congenital and Acquired, Part I. The Congenital Anaemias*, 2d ed. London, J & A Churchill, 1960, p 151.

475. JOSEPHS HW, AVERY ME: Hereditary elliptocytosis associated with increased hemolysis. *Pediatrics* 16:741, 1955.

476. WEISS HJ: Hereditary elliptocytosis with hemolytic anemia. *Am J Med* 35:455, 1963.

477. CUTTING HO, MCHUGH, CONRAD FG, MARLOW AA: Autosomal dominant hemolytic anemia characterized by ovalocytosis. A family study of seven involved members. *Am J Med* 39:21, 1965.

478. MCCARTY SH: Elliptical red blood cells in man. A report of eleven cases. *J Lab Clin Med* 19:612, 1934.

479. DAVIDSON RJL, STRAUSS WT: Hereditary elliptocytic anaemia. *J Clin Pathol* 14:615, 1961.

480. GOODALL HB, HENDRY DWW, LAWLER SD, STEPHEN SA: Data on linkage in man: Elliptocytosis and blood groups. II. Family 3. *Ann Eugen* 17:272, 1953.

481. MORTON NE: The detection and estimation of linkage between the genes for elliptocytosis and the Rh blood type. *Am J Hum Genet* 8:80, 1956.

482. BANNERMAN RM, RENWICK JH: The hereditary elliptocytoses: Clinical and linkage data. *Ann Hum Genet* 26:23, 1962.

483. COOK PJL, NOODES JE, NEWTON MS, DE MEY R: On the orientation of the Rh El, linkage group. *Ann Hum Genet* 41:157, 1977.

484. KEATS BJB: Another elliptocytosis locus on chromosome 1? *Hum Genet* 50:227, 1979.

485. HUEBNER K, PALUMBO AP, ISOBE M, KOZAK CA, MONACO S, ROVERA G, CROCE CM, CURTIS PJ: The alpha-spectrin gene is on chromosome 1 in mouse and man. *Proc Natl Acad Sci USA* 82:3790, 1985.

486. LAWLER J, LIU SC, PALEK J, PRCHAL J: Molecular defect of spectrin in hereditary pyropoikilocytosis: Alterations in the trypsin-resistant domain involved in spectrin self-association. *J Clin Invest* 70:1019, 1982.

487. FLORMAN AL, WINTROBE MM: Human elliptical red corpuscles. *Bull Johns Hopkins Hosp* 63:209, 1938.

488. MOTULSKY AG, SINGER K, CROSBY WH, SMITH V: The life span of the elliptocyte. Hereditary elliptocytosis and its relationship to other familial hemolytic diseases. *Blood* 9:57, 1954.

489. GARRDO-LACCA G, MERINO C, LUNA G: Hereditary elliptocytosis in a Peruvian family. *N Engl J Med* 256:311, 1957.

490. GEERDINK RA, HELLEMAN PW, VERLOOP MC: Hereditary elliptocytosis and hyperhaemolysis. A comparative study of 6 families with 145 patients. *Acta Med Scand* 179:715, 1966.

491. JENSSON O, JONASSON TH, OLAFSSON O: Hereditary elliptocytosis in Iceland. *Br J Haematol* 13:844, 1967.

492. GRECH JL, CACHIA EA, CALLEJA F, PULLICINO F: Hereditary elliptocytosis in two Maltese families. *J Clin Pathol* 14:365, 1961.

493. MCCURDY PR: Clinical, genetic and physiological studies in hereditary elliptocytosis. In *Proceedings of the IX Congress International Society of Hematology*. Mexico City, Universidad Nacional Autonoma de Mexico, vol 1, 1964, p 155.

494. BLACKBURN EK, JORDAN A, LYTLE WJ, SWAN HT, TUDHOPE GR: Hereditary elliptocytic haemolytic anaemia. *J Clin Pathol* 11:316, 1958.

495. AUSTIN RF, DESFORGES JF: Hereditary elliptocytosis: An unusual presentation of hemolysis in the new born associated with transient morphologic abnormalities. *Pediatrics* 44:196, 1969.

496. CARPENTIERI U, GUSTAVSON LP, HAGGARD ME: Pyknocytosis in a neonate: An unusual presentation of hereditary elliptocytosis. *Clin Pediatr* 16c:76, 1977.

497. ZARKOWSKY HS, MOHANDAS N, SPEAKER CB, SHOHET SB: A congenital haemolytic anaemia with thermal sensitivity of the erythrocyte membrane. *Br J Haematol* 29:537, 1975.

498. TORLONTANO G, FIORITONI G, SALVATI AM: Hereditary haemolytic ovalocytosis with defective erythropoiesis. *Br J Haematol* 43:435, 1979.

499. LIPTON EL: Elliptocytosis with hemolytic anemia; the effects of splenectomy. *Pediatrics* 15:67, 1955.

500. PRIOR DS, PITNEY WR: Hereditary elliptocytosis: A report of two families from New Guinea. *Br J Haematol* 13:126, 1967.

501. NIELSEN JA, STRUNK KW: Homozygous hereditary elliptocytosis as a cause of haemolytic anaemia in infancy. *Scand J Haematol* 5:486, 1968.

502. EVANS JPM, BAINES AJ, HANN IM, AL-HAKIM I, KNOWLES SM: Defective spectrin dimer-dimer association in a family with transfusion dependent homozygous hereditary elliptocytosis. *Br J Haematol* 54:163, 1983.

503. GARBARZ M, LeCOMTE MC, DHERMY D, FEO C, CHAVETOCHE I, GAUTERO H, BOURNIER O, PICAT C, GOEPP A, BOIVIN P: Double inheritance of an alpha I/65 spectrin variant in a child with homozygous elliptocytosis. *Blood* 67:1661, 1986.

504. TCHERNIA G, MOHANDAS N, SHOHET SB: Deficiency of cytoskeletal membrane protein band 4.1 in homozygous hereditary elliptocytosis: Implications for erythrocyte membrane stability. *J Clin Invest* 68:454, 1981.

505. WILEY JS, GILL FM: Red cell calcium leak in congenital hemolytic anemia with extreme microcytosis. *Blood* 47:197, 1976.

506. DACIE JV, MOLLISON PL, RICHARDSON N, SELWYN JG, SHAPIRO L: Atypical congenital haemolytic anaemia. *Q J Med* 22:79, 1953.

507. MENTZER WC, TURETSKY T, MOHANDAS N, SCHRIER S, WU CS: Identification of the hereditary pyropoikilocytosis carrier state. *Blood* 63:1439, 1984.

508. PALEK J, LIU SC, LIU PY, PRCHAL J, CASTLEBERRY RP: Altered assembly of spectrin in red cell membranes in hereditary pyropoikilocytosis. *Blood* 57:130, 1981.

509. LIU SC, PALEK J, PRCHAL J, CASTLEBERRY RP: Altered spectrin dimer-dimer association and instability of erythrocyte membrane skeletons in hereditary pyropoikilocytosis. *J Clin Invest* 68:597, 1981.

510. KNOWLES WJ, MORROW JS, SPEICHER DW, ZARKOWSKY AS, MOHANDAS N, MENTZER WC, SHOHET SB, MARCHESI VT: Molecular and functional changes in spectrin from patients with hereditary pyropoikilocytosis. *J Clin Invest* 71:1867, 1983.

511. LAWLER J, PALEK J, LIU SC, PRCHAL J, BUTLER E: Molecular heterogeneity of a hereditary pyropoikilocytosis: Identification of a second variant of the spectrin α-subunit. *Blood* 62:1182, 1983.

512. COETZER TL, PALEK J: Partial spectrin deficiency in hereditary pyropoikilocytosis. *Blood* 67:919, 1986.

513. GREENBERG LH, TANAKA KR: Hereditary elliptocytosis with hemolytic anemia—A family study of five affected members. *Calif Med* 110:389, 1969.

514. AMATO D, BOOTH PB: Hereditary ovalocytosis in Melanesians. *Papua New Guinea Med J* 20:26, 1977.

515. HONIG GR, LACSON PS: A new familial disorder with abnormal erythrocyte morphology and increased permeability of the erythrocytes to sodium and potassium. *Pediatr Res* 5:159, 1971.

516. HARRISON KL, COLLINS KA, McKENNA HW: Hereditary elliptical stomatocytosis; a case report. *Pathology* 8:307, 1976.

517. BOOTH PB, SERJEANTSON S, WOODFIELD DG, AMATO D: Selective depression of blood group antigens associated with hereditary ovalocytosis among Melanesians. *Vox Sang* 32:99, 1977.

518. BAER A, LIE-INJO LE, WELCH QB, LEWIS AN: Genetic factors and malaria in the Temuan. *Am J Hum Genet* 28:179, 1976.

519. SERJEANTSON S, BRYSON K, AMATO D, BABONA D: Malaria and hereditary ovalocytosis. *Hum Genet* 37:161, 1977.

520. CATTANI JA: The ovalocytosis polymorphism and malaria resistance in Papua New Guinea: An epidemiological study. Ph.D. Dissertation. Univeristy of California, Berkeley, 1984, p 1.

521. FIX AG, BAER AS, LIE-INJO LE: The mode of inheritance of ovalocytosis/elliptocytosis in Malaysian Orang Asli families. *Hum Genet* 61:250, 1982.

522. CASTELINO D, SAUL A, MYLER P, KIDSON C, THOMAS H, COOKE R: Ovalocytosis in Papua New Guinea—dominantly inherited resistance to malaria. *Southeast Asian J Trop Med Public Health* 12:549, 1981.

523. KIDSON C, LAMONT G, SAUL A, NURSE G: Ovalocytic erythrocytes from Melanesians are resistant to invasion by malaria parasites in culture. *Proc Natl Acad Sci USA* 78:5829, 1981.

524. HADLEY T, SAUL A, LAMONT G, HUDSON DE, MILLER LH, KIDSON C: Resistance of Melanesian elliptocytes (ovalocytes) to invasion by Plasmodium knowlesi and Plasmodium falciparum malaria parasites in vitro. *J Clin Invest* 71:780, 1983.

525. MOHANDAS N, LIE-INJO LE, FRIEDMAN M, MAK JW: Rigid membranes of Malayan ovalocytes: A likely genetic barrier against malaria. *Blood* 63:1385, 1984.

526. SAUL A, LAMONT G, SAWYER WH, KIDSON C: Decreased membrane deformability in Melanesian ovalocytes from Papua New Guinea. *J Cell Biol* 98:1348, 1984.

527. MORLE L, ALLOISIO N, DUCLUZEAU MT, POTHIER B, BLIBECH R, KASTALLY R, DELAUNAY J: Spectrin Tunis (α$^{1/78}$): a new αI variant that causes asymptomatic hereditary elliptocytosis in the heterozygous state. *Blood* 71:508, 1988.

528. EVANS JPM, BAINES AJ, HANN IM, AL-HAKIM I, KNOWLES SM, HOFFBRAND AV: Defective spectrin dimer-dimer association in a family with transfusion dependent homozygous hereditary elliptocytosis. *Br J Haematol* 54:163, 1983.

529. CHANG K, WILLIAMSON JR, ET AL: Effect of heat on the circular dichroism of spectrin in hereditary pyropoikilocytosis. *J Clin Invest* 64:326, 1979.

530. COETZER T, ZAIL S: Spectrin tetramer-dimer equilibrium in hereditary elliptocytosis. *Blood* 59:900, 1982.

531. LIU SC, PALEK J, PRCHAL J: Defective spectrin dimer-dimer association in hereditary elliptocytosis. *Proc Natl Acad Sci USA* 79:2072, 1982.

532. LAWLER J, LIU SC, PALEK J, PRCHAL J: Molecular defect of spectrin in a subgroup of patients with hereditary elliptocytosis: Alteration in the α subunit involved in spectrin self association. *J Clin Invest* 73:1688, 1984.

533. LeCOMTE MC, DHERMY D, GARBARZ M, GAUTERO H, BOURNIER O, GALAND C, BOIVIN P: Hereditary elliptocytosis with spectrin molecular defect in a white patient. *Acta Haematol (Basel)* 71:235, 1984.

534. DHERMY D, LeCOMTE MC, GARBARZ M, FEO C, GAUTER H, BOURNIER O, GALAND C, HERRERA A, GRETILLAT F, BOIVIN P: Molecular defect of spectrin in the family of a child with congenital hemolytic poikilocytic anemia. *Pediatr Res* 18:1005, 1984.

535. LeCOMTE MC, DHERMY D, GANBARZ M, FEO C, GANTERO H, BOURNIER O, PICAT C, CHAREROCHE I, ESTER A, GALARD C: Pathologic and non-pathologic variants of the spectrin molecule in two black families with hereditary elliptocytosis. *Hum Genet* 71:351, 1985.

536. LeCOMTE MC, DHERMY D, SOLIS A, ESTER A, FEO C, GAUTERS H, BOURNIER O, BOIVIN P: A new abnormal variant of spectrin in black patients with hereditary elliptocytosis. *Blood* 65:1208, 1985.

537. LAWLER J, COETZER TL, PALEK J, JACOB HS, LUBAN N: Sp α I/65: a new variant of the α subunit of spectrin in hereditary elliptocytosis. *Blood* 66:706, 1985.

538. MARCHESI SL, KNOWLES WT, MORROW JS, BOLOGNA M, MARCHESI VT: Abnormal spectrin in hereditary elliptocytosis. *Blood* 67:141, 1986.

539. ALLOISIO N, GUETORNI D, MERLE L, POTHIER B, DUCHIZEAU MT, SOUN A, COLONNA P, CLERC M, PHILIPPE N, DELAUNAY J: Sp α I/65 hereditary elliptocytosis in North Africa. *Am J Hematol* 23:113, 1986.

540. LAMBERT S, ZAIL S: A new variant of the α subunit of spectrin in hereditary elliptocytosis. *Blood* 69:473, 1987.

541. LANE PA, SHEW RL, IAROCCI TA, MOHANDAS N, HAYS T, MENTZER WC: Unique α-spectrin mutant in a kindred with common hereditary elliptocytosis. *J Clin Invest* 79:989, 1987.

542. DHERMY D, LeCOMTE MC, GORBARZ M, FEO C, GOLAND C, BOURNIER O, GANTERO H, BOIVIN P: A new kindred of hereditary elliptocytosis (HE) with a shortened spectrin alpha chain. *Blood [suppl]* 70:52a, 1987.

543. DHERMY D, GARBARZ M, LeCOMTE MC, FEO C, BOURNIER D, CHAREROCHE I, GAUTERS H, GALAND C, BOIVIN P: Hereditary elliptocytosis: Clinical, morphological, and biochemical studies of 38 cases. *Nouv Rev Fr Hematol* 28:129, 1986.

544. EBER SW, MORRIS SA, SCHROTER W, GRATZER WB: Interactions of spectrin in hereditary elliptocytes containing truncated spectrin beta-chains. *J Clin Invest* 81:523, 1988.

545. ZAIL SS, COETZER TL: Defective binding of spectrin to ankyrin in a kindred with recessively inherited hereditary elliptocytosis. *J Clin Invest* 74:753, 1984.

546. ALLOISIO N, MARK L, DORLEAI E, GENTILHOMME O, BACHIER D, GUETARNI D, COLENNA P, BOST M, ZOUAOUI Z, RODA L: The heterozygous form of 4.1(−) hereditary elliptocytosis [the 4.1(−) trait]. *Blood* 65:46, 1985.

547. ALLOISIO N, DORLEAC E, GIROT R, DELAUNAY J: Analysis of the red cell membrane in a family with hereditary elliptocytosis—total or partial of protein 4.1. *Hum Genet* 59:68, 1981.

548. TALAKUWAN Y, TCHERNIA G, ROSSI M, BENABADJI M, MOHANDAS N: Restoration of normal membrane stability to unstable protein 4.1-deficient erythrocyte membranes by incorporation of purified protein 4.1. *J Clin Invest* 78:80, 1986.

549. ALLOISIO N, MERLE L, BACHIR D, GUETARNI D, COLONNA P, DELAUNAY J: Red cell membrane sialoglycoprotein beta in homozygous and heterozygous 4.1(−) hereditary elliptocytosis. *Biochim Biophys Acta* 816:57, 1985.

550. CONBOY J, MOHANDAS N, TCHERNIA G, KAN YW: Molecular basis of hereditary spherocytosis due to protein 4.1 deficiency. *N Engl J Med* 315:680, 1986.

551. GARBARZ M, DHERMY D, LeCOMTE MC, FEO C, CHAVEROCHE I, GALAND C, BOURNIER O, BERTRAND O, BOIVIN P: A variant of erythrocyte membrane skeletal protein band 4.1 associated with hereditary elliptocytosis. *Blood* 64:1006, 1984.

552. LETSINGER JT, AGRE P, MARCHESI SL: High molecular weight protein 4.1 in the cytoskeletons of hereditary elliptocytes. *Blood [suppl]* 68:38a, 1986.

553. CONBOY J, KAN YW, AGRE P, MOHANDAS N: Molecular characterization of hereditary elliptocytosis due to an elongated protein 4.1. *Blood [suppl]* 68:34a, 1986.

554. RYBICKI AC, HEATH R, WOLF JR, LUBIN B, SCHWARTZ RS: Protein 4.2 stabilizes ankyrin in human erythrocyte membranes. *Blood [suppl]* 70:42a, 1987.

555. ANSTEE DJ, PARSONS SF, RIDGWELL K, RIDGWELL K, TANNER MJ, MERRY AH, THOMSON EE, JUDSON PA, JOHNSON P, BATES S, FRASER ID: Two individuals with elliptocytic red cells apparently lack three major sialoglycoproteins. *Biochem J* 218:615, 1984.

556. ANSTEE DJ, RIDGWELL K, TANNER MJ, DANIELS GL, PARSONS SF: Individuals lacking the Gerbich blood-group antigen have alterations in the human erythrocyte membrane sialoglycoproteins β and γ. *Biochem J* 221:97, 1984.

557. MUELLER T, MANSON M: Glycoconnectin (PAS2), a membrane attachment site for the human erythrocyte cytoskeleton, in Kruckeberg W, Eaton J, Greuner G (eds): *Erythrocyte Membranes 2: Recent Clinical and Experimental Advances.* New York, AR Liss, p 95.

558. DAHR W, MOULDS J, BAUMEISTER G, MOULDS M, KIEDROWSKI S: Altered membrane sialoglycoproteins in human erythrocytes lacking the Gerbich blood group antigen. *Biol Chem Hoppe Seyler* 366:201, 1985.

559. KAY MMB, GIELJAN JC, BOSMAN GM, LAWRENCE C: Functional topography of band 3: Specific structural alteration linked to functional alterations in human erythrocytes. *Proc Natl Acad Sci USA* 85:492, 1988.

560. AGRE P, ORRINGER EP, CHUI DHK, BENNETT V: A molecular defect in the families with hemolytic poikilocytic anemia. Reduction of high affinity membrane binding sites for ankyrin. *J Clin Invest* 68:1566.

561. MOHANDAS N, CLARK MR, HEALTH BP, ROSSI M, WOLFE LC, LUX SE, SHOHET SB: A technique to detect reduced mechanical stability of red cell membranes: Relevance to elliptocytic disorders. *Blood* 59:768, 1982.

562. PALEK J, LUX SE: Red cell membrane skeletal defects in hereditary and acquired hemolytic anemias. *Semin Hematol* 20:189, 1983.

563. TRINICK RH: Elliptocytosis. *Lancet* 1:963, 1948.

564. HELZ MK, MENTEN ML: Elliptocytosis, a report of two cases. *J Lab Clin Med* 29:185, 1944.

565. GUNTHER H: Die Klinische Bedeutung der Ellipsenformen der Erythrozyten. *Dtsch Arch Klin Med* 162:215, 1928.

566. GEERDINK RA, NIJENHUIS LE, HUIZINGA J: Hereditary elliptocytosis: Linkage data in man. *Ann Hum Genet* 30:363, 1967.

567. VAN DEN BERGH AAH, REHORST K: A propos des hematies elliptiques (ovalocytose). *Rev Belg Sci Med* 3:683, 1931.

568. OZER L, MILLS GC: Eliptocytosis with haemolytic anaemia. *Br J Haematol* 10:468, 1964.

569. NKRUMAH FK: Hereditary elliptocytosis associated with severe haemolytic anaemia and malaria. *Afr J Med Sci* 3:131, 1972.

570. KRUATRACHUO M, ASAWAPOKEE N: Hereditary elliptocytosis and Plasmodium falciparum malaria. *Ann Trop Med Parasitol* 66:161, 1972.

571. PEARSON HA: The genetic basis of hereditary elliptocytosis with hemolysis. *Blood* 32:972, 1968.

572. BAKER SJ, JACOB E, RAJAN KT, GAULT EW: Hereditary haemolytic anaemia associated with elliptocytosis: A study of three families. *Br J Haematol* 7:210, 1961.

573. ZARKOWSKY HS: Heat-induced erythrocyte fragmentation in neonatal elliptocytosis. *Br J Haematol* 41:515, 1979.

574. LUX SE, JOHN KM: Unpublished observations.

575. SCHOLNIK AP, VAN TILBURG CP, HOFFMAN GC: Hereditary elliptocytosis. *Cleve Clin Q* 41:23, 1974.

575a. HONIG GR, LACSON PS, MAURER HS: A new familial disorder with abnormal erythrocyte morphology and increased permeability of the erythrocytes to sodium and potassium. *Pediatr Res* 5:159, 1971.

576. PALEK J, COETZER T, LAHAV M, JAROLIM P, LAWLER J, WANG W, PRCHAL JT: Clinical and biochemical expression of homozygotes and double heterozygotes for α spectrin mutants that involve the spectrin heterodimer self-association site. *Blood [suppl]* 70:55a, 1987.

577. DE GRUCHY GC, LODER PB, HENNESSY IV: Haemolysis and glycolytic metabolism in hereditary elliptocytosis. *Br J Haematol* 8:168, 1962.

578. WILSON HE, LONG MJ: Hereditary ovalocytosis (elliptocytosis) with hypersplenism. *Arch Intern Med* 95:438, 1955.

579. MATSUMOTO N, ISHIHARA T, TAKAHASHI M, UCHINO F, ONO J, MIWA S, KIYOMITSU Y: Fine structure of the spleen in hereditary elliptocytosis. *Acta Pathol Jpn* 26:533, 1976.

580. MILLER LH, MASON SJ, DVORAK JA, MCGINNISS MLT, ROTHMAN IK: Erythrocyte receptors for (Plasmodium knowlesi) malaria: Duffy blood group determinants. *Science* 189:561, 1975.

580a. SCHULTZE M: Ein heizbarer objectisch und seine verwendung bei untersuchungen des blutes. *Arch Mikrok Anat* 1:1, 1865.

581. PERKINS M: Inhibitory effects of erythrocyte membrane proteins on the in vitro invasion of the human malarial parasite (Plasmodium falciparum) into its host cell. *J Cell Biol* 90:563, 1981.

582. HERMENTIN P, ENDERS B: Erythrocyte invasion by malaria (Plasmodium falciparum) merozoites: Recent advantages in the evaluation of receptor sites. *Behring Inst Mitt* 1984, p 121.

583. MARCHESI SL, LETSINGER JT, SPEICHER DW, MARCHESI VT, AGRE P, HYUN B, GULATI G: Mutant forms of spectrin α-subunits in hereditary elliptocytosis. *J Clin Invest* 80:191, 1987.

584. SPEICHER DW, DAVIS G, MARCHESI VT: Structure of human erythrocyte spectrin. II. The sequence of the α-I domain. *J Biol Chem* 258:14938, 1983.

585. GOMPERTS ED, CAYANNIS F, METZ J, ZAIL SS: A red cell membrane protein abnormality in hereditary elliptocytosis. *Br J Haematol* 25:415, 1973.

586. FEO CJ, FISCHER S, PIAU JP: Premiere observation de l'absence d'une proteine de la membrane erythrocytaire (band 4.1) dans un cas d'anemie elliptocytaire familiale. *Nouv Rev Fr Hematol* 22:315, 1981.

587. MUELLER TJ, WILLIAM J, WANG W, MORRISON M: Cytoskeletal alterations in hereditary elliptocytosis. *Blood* 58:47a, 1981.

588. MORLE L, GARBARZ M, ALLOISIO N, GIROT R, CHAVEROCHE I, BOIVIN P, DELAUNAY J: The characterization of protein 4.1 Presles, a shortened variant of red cell membrane protein 4.1. *Blood* 65:1151, 1985.

589. ANSTEE D: Personal communication.

590. HAYASHI S, KOOMOTO R, YANO A, ISHIGAMI S, TSUJINO G, SAEKI S, TANAKA T: Abnormality in a specific protein of the erythrocyte membrane in hereditary spherocytosis. *Biochem Biophys Res Commun* 57:1038, 1974.

591. IIDA H, HASEGAWA I, NOZAWA Y: Biochemical studies on abnormal membranes. Protein abnormality of erythrocyte membrane in biliary obstruction. *Biochem Biophys Acta* 443:394, 1976.

592. IMAMURA T, MATSUO T, YANASE T, KAGIYAMA S: Hereditary spherocytosis associated with a variant of band 3 protein in the erythrocyte membrane. *Jpn J Med* 23:216, 1984.

593. MORLE L, POTHIER B, ALLOISIO N, DUCLUZEAU MT, MARQUES S, OLIM G, MARTINS E, SILVA J, FEO C, GARBARZ M, CHAVEROCHE I, ET AL: Red cell membrane alteration involving protein 4.1 and protein 3 in a case of recessively inherited anemia. *Eur J Haematol* 38:447, 1987.

594. SCHNEIDMAN D, KIESSLING P, ONSTAD J, WOLF P: Red pulp of the spleen in hereditary elliptocytosis. *Virchows Arch (A)* 372:337, 1977.

α_1-ANTITRYPSIN DEFICIENCY

DIANE WILSON COX

1. *Alpha₁-antitrypsin (α1AT), a glycoprotein of molecular weight 52kDa, is a major plasma protease inhibitor. The major physiological substrate is elastase, particularly in the lower respiratory tract.*

2. *The locus (PI locus) for α1AT is on chromosome 14 at 14q32.1, close to the locus for the protease inhibitor α₁-antichymotrypsin. The gene is 10.2 kb long and contains four introns. α1AT produced in macrophages has a longer RNA transcript, beginning in exons 5' to the first exon for hepatocyte α1AT.*

3. *α1AT shows considerable genetic variability, having more than 60 genetic variants (PI types), the majority of which are associated with quantitatively and qualitatively normal α1AT. Further variation can be revealed at the DNA level, where a number of restriction enzymes reveal polymorphisms.*

4. *The PI★Z allele is the most common deficiency variant. PI ZZ homozygotes have 15 to 20 percent of the normal plasma concentration of α1AT, with a corresponding reduction in concentration in bronchoalveolar lavage fluid. The deficiency is due to lack of secretion of Z α1AT from the hepatocyte, where inclusions are formed in the rough endoplasmic reticulum. The lack of secretion is probably a result of increased aggregation. There are several rare deficiency types, including those which show lack of secretion and those which have no product (null).*

5. *A deficiency of α1AT results in a protease/protease inhibitor imbalance in the lung, allowing destruction of the alveolar walls. The resultant obstructive lung disease is the most prevalent clinical manifestation of α1AT deficiency. Basal lung regions are most severely affected. In nonsmokers, onset of dyspnea occurs at a mean age of 45 to 50 years, and in smokers at about 35 years of age. Smokers show a considerably increased rate of lung destruction and have a poorer survival rate than nonsmokers with the deficiency. Smoking enhances oxidation and inactivation of α1AT in the lung.*

6. *Symptoms of liver abnormalities in infancy are expressed in about 17 percent of all individuals with α1AT deficiency. Only a few percent of all patients with the deficiency have a poor prognosis following early liver symptoms. Other familial factors may influence the prognosis.*

7. *α1AT may be involved in the immune system, and a deficiency may contribute to diseases with an autoimmune component.*

8. *Prenatal diagnosis can be carried out using either synthetic oligonucleotide probes or restriction fragment length polymorphisms.*

9. *Replacement therapy with α1AT and the use of other protease inhibitors are under investigation as possible ways to prevent the chronic destruction of the lung. Antioxidants could potentially delay lung destruction. Lung and liver transplants offer potential therapy for end-stage destruction of these organs.*

α_1-Antitrypsin (α1AT) has a central role as a protease inhibitor in controlling tissue degradation and has led us to a better understanding of the pathogenesis of pulmonary emphysema. The role of α1AT in disease began with the astute observation of an abnormal protein pattern on electrophoresis.

α1AT, was isolated by Schultz et al.[1] as α₁-3,5-glycoprotein.

They later suggested the name α_1-*antitrypsin*,[2] as most of the serum trypsin inhibitory activity was associated with the α_1-globulin fraction and particularly with the protein they had isolated. A discussion of the early studies can be found in previous reviews.[3,4]

α1AT, as a major protease inhibitor in human plasma, can complex with a broad spectrum of proteases including elastase, trypsin, chymotrypsin, thrombin, and bacterial proteases. The most important inhibitor action is that against leukocyte elastase, a protease which degrades elastin of the alveolar walls as well as other structural proteins of a variety of tissues.

α1AT became of clinical interest when C. B. Laurell in Malmo, Sweden, in an examination of protein electrophoretic patterns on agarose gel, noted that a number of patients were lacking an α_1-globulin band. The samples in question had been sent from a pulmonary hospital, and the possibility of sample degradation was soon eliminated (Laurell, personal communication). The α1AT component deficiency was found to occur in a number of patients with early onset emphysema[5] and was associated with a low serum trypsin inhibitory capacity.[6] A study of this deficiency became the subject of a thesis by S. Eriksson,[7] and laid the foundation for much of our basic knowledge of the clinical effects of this deficiency. The codominant nature of the trait was expressed as a partial deficiency of serum trypsin inhibitory activity in heterozygotes and a marked deficiency in homozygotes. Confirmation of these studies was made in many parts of the world, and the picture emerged of progressive obstructive pulmonary disease, with preferential destruction in the bases of the lungs, in both males and females, beginning in the second and third decades, and particularly in smokers.

At about the same time, Fagerhol and Braend[8] were examining electrophoretic variation in the prealbumin (Pr) region, using starch gel electrophoresis. They suspected that the Pr bands might be α1AT, and this was soon shown.[9] A symbol Pi (now PI) for protease inhibitor was chosen as the name for the polymorphism α1AT, in consultation with Dr. Schultz, since it was already recognized that α1AT was an effective inhibitor for other proteases in addition to trypsin.[10] The first normal variant, PI X, was easily recognized as a doublet in agarose gel electrophoresis.[11] However, the extensive polymorphism of α1AT was recognized through the use of an unusual combination of buffers and high quality hydrolized potato starch, a system developed by Fagerhol.[12] The starch gel system was not easily reproduced because of the need for high quality starch and of the requirement for the addition of immunologic methods for the reliable detection of the deficiency variants. The system has now generally been replaced by high resolution isoelectric focusing in acrylamide gels.

Another observation of major importance came in 1969 when Sharp and coworkers noted that α1AT deficiency was associated with liver disease in children.[13] We now know that the liver disease is not usually as devastating as first suspected.

The association between α1AT deficiency and obstructive lung disease has led to extensive studies of the mechanisms of protease tissue destruction and the important role of a balance between proteases and their inhibitors. Studies of α1AT have also examined the role of protease inhibitors in immune mechanisms, nondisjunction, and recombination. The extensive genetic variation has led to population and evolution studies.

The deficiency state is unusual in that it results from abnormal plasma protein secretion from the hepatocyte, and the study of the basic defect enhances our understanding of glycoprotein secretion mechanisms. Studies at the molecular level provide possibilities for examining recombination events within and around a cluster of genes forming a protease inhibitor complex.

In the two decades or so since the original exciting observations of the clinical effects of α1AT deficiency, extensive biochemical, clinical, population, and molecular studies have been carried out. For some of the other plasma protease inhibitors, such as α_2-macroglobulin and α_1-antichymotrypsin, a deficiency state has not yet been discovered. However, in future years, they too may prove to be as complex and interesting.

STRUCTURE OF α_1-ANTITRYPSIN

Protein Structure

α1AT is a glycoprotein consisting of a single polypeptide chain of 394 residues and a carbohydrate content of 12 percent, resulting in a molecular mass of 52 kDa. Methods for purification and details of characterization of the protein have been reviewed.[10,14,15] The small size of the protein allows diffusion through interstitial body fluids and into tissues such as the lung. The high negative charge of α1AT in plasma (isoelectric point of 4.4 to 4.7[16,17]) may be important in preventing the loss of this small protein across the negatively charged glomerular membrane.[18] A somewhat larger molecule, including a 24-residue hydrophobic signal peptide, is produced within the liver, and in vitro.[19,20] Sequencing of cDNA has confirmed the presence of the signal peptide, with an N-terminal methionine.[21-23]

α1AT, while not crystallizable in its active form, does crystallize after proteolytic cleavage at its reactive site.[24] Analysis of the crystal structure indicates that the single polypeptide chain is organized into well defined secondary structural elements: three β sheets and eight α helixes. The first 150 residues preferentially form the α helixes. α1AT contains one cysteine residue, as indicated both by protein and DNA analysis. No disulfide bridge is present in the protein, although the thiol group can form a disulfide bond with other proteins. Linkage with the thiol group of immunoglobulin κ light chain is the basis for a method for purification[25] and can also produce artifacts on isoelectric focusing, which disappear when α1AT is reduced. About 1 percent of plasma α1AT is linked by disulfide bridging to the IgA heavy chain.[26]

Microheterogeneity

A characteristic microheterogeneity of α1AT is observed in acid starch gel electrophoresis,[9,27] in agarose electrophoresis in acid buffers,[28] and in polyacrylamide isoelectric focusing (PIEF), as generally noted for glycoproteins when near their isoelectric point. Eight bands were originally noted, numbered from 1 (anodal) to 8 (cathodal); bands 4 and 6 contain 40 and 35 percent, respectively, of the total α1AT,[9] and their isoelectric points are 4.52 and 4.59.[17] Much of the heterogeneity is due to differences in the type of carbohydrate side chain.[29] The number and type of carbohydrate side chains has been controversial. The current evidence indicates three carbohydrate side chains per molecule, attached at asparagine residues 46, 83, and 247.[30] The carbohydrate chains may be biantennary or triantennary, terminating in two or three N-acetylneuraminic acid residues.[31,32] The biantennary carbohydrate chains bind to concanavalin A with a higher affinity than do the triantennary chains.[33,34] The electrophoretic mobility of α1AT is sequentially shifted cathodally by incubation with neuraminidase as N-acetyl-neuraminic acid residues are removed. Isoelectric focusing after total desialylation results in one major fraction and two minor ones, one anodal, which may represent a deamidation product, and one cathodal, representing the asialo form of bands 7 and 8.[17] Conflicting results reported for earlier studies[10] appear to be due to the difficulty of completely removing neuraminic acid residues from the protein. The two minor cathodal components (M7 and M8) have been shown to have the same carbohydrate structure as the major bands (4 and 6), but the first five amino acids (Glu-Asp-Pro-Glu-Gly) have been removed, apparently by posttranslational cleavage.[34] The carbohydrate side chains found in each α1AT component separated by PIEF are shown in Fig. 96-1. Alterations in the usual pattern of microheterogeneity are observed in newborns and upon estrogen administration, with an increase in bands 6 and 8 relative to bands 4 and 7 (see Ref. 10). During inflammation or with high levels of estrogen, 80 percent of the increase in concentration of plasma α1AT occurs in bands 2 and 4.[29] This can be explained by the replacement of biantennary by triantennary oligosaccharides.[29,32,34]

Fig. 96-1 Distribution of biantennary and triantennary oligosaccharide chains responsible for the microheterogeneity of α1AT. Attachments for the oligosaccharide chains are at the Asn positions 46, 83, and 246. M7 and M8 lack the first five N-terminal amino acids. The isoelectric points for each fraction are indicated. (Modified from Jeppsson, Lilja, and Johansson.[34] Used by permission of J. Chromotography.)

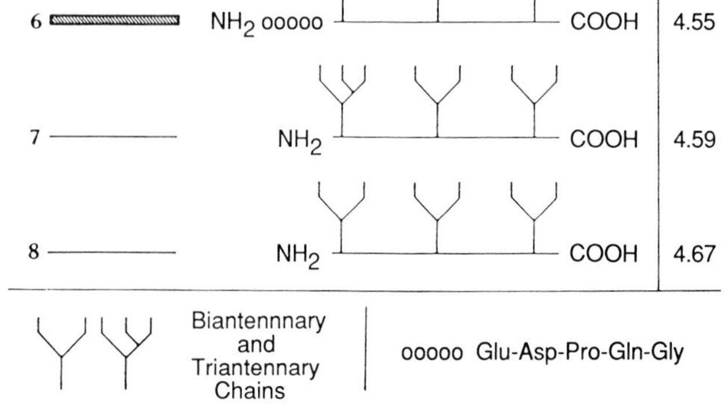

Table 96-1 Reactive Centers of Selected Protease Inhibitors

Inhibitor	Substrate	Reactive center*					
		P_1	$P_{1'}$	$P_{2'}$	$P_{3'}$	$P_{4'}$	$P_{5'}$
Human α1AT	Elastase	Met	Ser	Ile	Pro	Pro	Glu
Human α₁-antichymotrypsin	Chymotrypsin	Leu	Ser	Ala	Leu	Val	Glu
Mouse α1AT	Elastase	Tyr	Ser	Met	Pro	Pro	Ile
Mouse α₁-antichymotrypsin†	Trypsin	Lys	Ala	Ile	Leu	Pro	Ala
Human α-antithrombin III	Thrombin	Arg	Ser	Leu	Asn	Pro	Asn

*From Ref. 41.
†Also called *contrapsin*.

Reactive Site

Protease inhibition by α1AT occurs by formation of a tightly bound 1:1 complex between α1AT and the target protease, which can be one of a number of serine proteases, but is mainly elastase. Specificity is determined by crucial amino acids in the reactive site of α1AT. The methionine residue, at position 358,[22,35] close to the C terminus of the molecule, is important for functional activity.[36] The intact inhibitor has a strand containing the methionine residue which appears to be exposed on the surface of the molecule in a loop formation, as proposed for the general mechanism for protease inhibitors.[37] This loop fits precisely the conformation of the reactive site of the target protease. Proteolytic cleavage at the reactive site causes release of the strand and its subsequent incorporation into a β sheet.[24] As predicted by this model, proteolytic cleavage increases the stability of α1AT.[38] The exposed position of the reactive site allows ready access for oxidation.[38] According to this model, methionine, when oxidized to methionine sulfoxide, can no longer physically complex with elastase, and α1AT becomes inactive.[38] There is a 1000-fold decrease in the association constant for oxidized as compared with native α1AT.[39] The oxidization of methionine may be advantageous in some situations, for example, by allowing local tissue breakdown in areas of inflammation, by release of oxygen radicals from leukocytes.[40]

The reactive sites of several of the serine protease inhibitors are similar to each other, and also to those of low molecular weight plant protease inhibitors. Some of these reactive sites are shown in Table 96-1. Substrate specificity is determined by the composition of the reactive site. The specificity for methionine at amino acid 358 has been proven in a naturally occurring mutant of α1AT, PI Pittsburgh, in which arginine is substituted for methionine at the active site.[42] This mutant loses its capacity to inhibit porcine pancreatic elastase, and is a highly effective inhibitor of thrombin.

Gene Structure

The gene coding for the liver form of α1AT is 10.2 kb in length, including a 1434-bp coding region.[22] The gene contains four introns; exon 1, the 5′ portion of exon 2, and the 3′ portion of exon 5 are noncoding regions[22] (Fig. 96-2). The first intron, 5.3 kb in length, contains a 143-amino acid open reading frame, an Alu family sequence, and a pseudo-transcription initiation region. The open reading frame does not appear to be an actual protein coding region.

The region beginning 721 kb 5′ to the transcription start site is necessary for efficient expression of the α1AT gene and for its cell-specific expression.[43] In leukocytes and in lung, an initiation site 5′ to the hepatocyte initiation site is used, and a longer RNA transcript is produced.[44] This alternative form of α1AT, expressed in macrophages and monocytes, has separate promoter and transcription initiation sites, and includes three additional exons 5′ to exon 1 of the hepatocyte form.[45] The second of these three additional macrophage exons is optionally transcribed in macrophage α1AT, resulting in two forms of macrophage mRNA.[45]

Homologous Proteins

DNA and protein sequencing studies have indicated homologies, not only between some of the protease inhibitors but also between inhibitors and other plasma proteins, as well as with chicken ovalbumin.[46] An unexpectedly high degree of homology has been observed between human thryoxin binding globulin on the X chromosome and human α₁-antichymotrypsin nucleotide sequences, when compared with α1AT (58 and 53 percent, respectively).[47] For amino acids there is 42 percent homology between sequences for human α₁-antichymotrypsin and α1AT[41], 28 percent between antithrombin III and α1AT,[48] and 27 percent between Cl inhibitor and α1AT.[49] A similar degree of homology is observed in amino acid sequences between portions of chick ovalbumin and α1AT[46,50]; the position and number of introns are very different, probably indicating a relatively ancient divergence from a common ancestral gene several hundred million years ago.[50]

Localization of the Structural Gene

The gene encoding α1AT was localized to chromosome 14 by linkage studies with Gm, the system of inherited markers of the gamma immunoglobulins,[51] by analysis of protein production by somatic cell hybrids[52,53] and by DNA analysis of somatic cell hybrids.[54] The PI locus was regionally localized to 14q24.1 → q32.1 in a family with a paracentric inversion,[55] more specifically to q31-q32 by *in situ* hybridization,[56,57] and to band 14q32.1 by DNA analysis of translocated chromosomes.[58] A region homologous to α1AT was also localized to

Fig. 96-2 α1AT gene and flanking regions. Coding regions are solid, introns open, untranslated dotted rectangles. Cross-hatched regions are exons of macrophage DNA. Asterisk indicates sites of polymorphisms for the following restriction enzymes (those in square bracket at the right indicate polymorphisms in the 3′ homologous region): A = *Ava* II; Ma = *Mae* III; T = *Taq* I; RI = *Eco* RI; Ss = *Sst* site; S and Z circled = sites of mutations in PIS and PIZ, respectively. Genomic probes, 4.6 and 6.5 kb, are indicated.

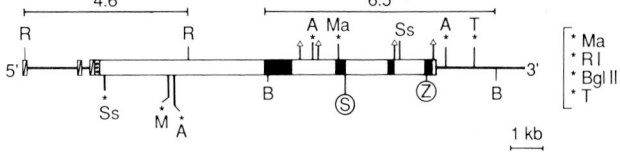

chromosome 14[54] and has been shown to lie 8.2 kb 3' of the α1AT gene.[44,59] It is not known if this homologous region is a functional gene.

Another partially homologous plasma protease inhibitor, α₁-antichymotrypsin, has been shown to lie within the same chromosomal region,[57] as further indicated by pulsed field electrophoresis results.[60]

PHYSIOLOGY OF α₁-ANTITRYPSIN

Function of α₁-Antitrypsin

α1AT inhibits a broad spectrum of serine proteases. Because of its efficiency of inhibition, broad substrate specificity, and ready access to tissue, α1AT plays an important role in defending tissue from proteolysis. As the name implies, α1AT inhibits pancreatic trypsin.[61] Because it is far more effective in inhibiting other serine proteases,[39] the name α₁-proteinase inhibitor has been proposed.[62] The original nomenclature has been retained here because of its extensive previous use, particularly in the clinical literature.

α1AT inhibits most serine proteases tested to date, including pancreatic and neutrophil elastase, neutrophil cathepsin G, pancreatic trypsin and chymotrypsin, collagenase from skin and from synovia, acrosin, kallikrein, urokinase, and renin (see Refs. 10 and 39). Proteases within the clotting and fibrinolytic systems which are inhibited include plasmin and thrombin, factor XI, and Hageman factor cofactor.[10] Some of these inhibitory activities may reflect only in vitro phenomena with no physiological importance because of the presence of other, more potent inhibitors for each specific protease.

α1AT complex formation results in inactivation of the protease and proteolytic cleavage of the inhibitor. The rate of inactivation of α1AT with specific proteases varies considerably but is greatest with neutrophil elastase, for which the association constant is $6.5 \times 10^7 \text{ M}^{-1} \cdot \text{s}^{-1}$, more than 10^6 times higher than that with thrombin.[39] Evidence for the important role of α1AT as a neutrophil elastase inhibitor, reviewed previously,[63] is provided by a large number of studies showing the effectiveness of human neutrophil elastase at inducing emphysema in experimental animals. Study of these animal models has demonstrated that the destruction of elastin fibers is of primary importance for producing the type of lung disease typical of emphysema.[63] α1AT provides approximately 90 percent of the antielastase activity in plasma. The other plasma inhibitor of elastase, α₂-macroglobulin, is largely inaccessible to the lower respiratory tract because of its high molecular mass (725 kDa); the small amounts of α₂-macroglobulin in the lower respiratory tract[64] may be produced locally by lung fibroblasts[65] or by macrophages.

Although a number of proteases in the clotting cascade are inhibited by α1AT, these reactions do not appear to be of prime physiological significance, probably because of the presence of other more effective inhibitors. Individuals with α1AT deficiency have not been reported to have abnormalities in coagulation or fibrinolysis. However, the change of only one amino acid at the active center (in PI Pittsburgh) converts α1AT into a potent inhibitor of thrombin and factor XI, producing a severe bleeding disorder during acute phase response.[66]

The possible function of trypsin inhibitors as potential antibacterial agents has been noted.[67] Since α1AT increases dur-

ing the acute phase response, trypsin inhibitors may play some role in resistance to infection.[67,68] The early discovery of the weak but definite antiproteolytic action by antibiotics such as penicillin[68] is currently being exploited in a different group of antibiotics to offer potential therapy for patients with α1AT deficiency (see further discussion under "Therapy").

Function in the Immune Response

Proteases have been shown, in a number of studies, to affect the immune response (reviewed in Ref. 10). Trypsin and chymotrypsin have been shown to act as mitogens on B lymphocytes. Trypsin or neutrophil elastase and cathepsin G can substitute for helper T cells in B-cell mitogen assays. Mouse thymocytes are triggered to synthesize DNA by neutrophils or macrophages, or substances released from them. Direct links with α1AT have been noted, although conflicting results have been reported, perhaps due to inadequate separation of cell types or to contaminants in purified α1AT.[69] Human lymphocytes have α1AT bound to their plasma membrane after concanavalin A-induced blastogenic transformation.[70] Enhanced lymphocyte responsiveness to phytohemagglutinin has been observed in α1AT-deficient individuals, which decreases with the addition of highly purified α1AT.[71] These studies have shown that α1AT has a direct affect on adherent cells but not on proliferating T cells. α1AT inhibition of the phytohemagglutinin adherent cell response may be due to inhibition of an elastaselike enzyme on the surface of macrophages.[69] In addition to mitogenic activity, proteases also cleave IgG, liberating the Fc fragment which can augment lymphocyte response.[71]

α1AT has been reported to inhibit antibody-dependent cell-mediated cytotoxicity, T-cell-mediated cytotoxicity, and natural killer activity. The hypothesis has been presented that a deficiency of α1AT leads to increased T-helper activity and to B-cell activation, producing the exaggerated cell-mediated immunity, and marked acceleration of delayed hypersensitivity responses, which have been demonstrated in vivo.[69] There is still much to be clarified regarding the mechanism and extent of involvement of α1AT in immune regulation.

Synthesis

Most α1AT is synthesized in the parenchymal cells of the liver, and studies supporting this have been reviewed.[10] Direct evidence is provided by the observed change of the genetic type of α1AT to that of the donor after liver transplantation.[72–74] Cultured human fetal liver cells synthesize and secrete α1AT; the secretion of α1AT is suppressed by increasing concentrations of α1AT in the medium, suggesting a feedback control mechanism.[75]

The production of α1AT by monocytes[76] and alveolar macrophages[77] may be important in regulation of local tissue injury. Transcription and translation of the α1AT gene, followed by posttranslational processing, and secretion of α1AT in a functionally active form has been demonstrated in human peripheral blood monocytes and bronchoalveolar and macrophages from breast milk; there is no production by B or T lymphocytes.[78] Although the amount of α1AT produced is very small, macrophage production could be important in the defense system of the lung.

Analysis of tissue RNA indicates, in addition to the predominant production of α1AT in liver, low levels of production in kidney, lung, and intestine.[44] The low level of mRNA production in kidney and intestine also occurs when human α1AT is introduced into transgenic mice.[44,79] The function and importance of α1AT in kidney and intestine are yet to be discovered.

The turnover of the normal type of α1AT in plasma has been estimated at 6.7 days.[80] Removal of 20 and 100 percent of the sialiac acid residues reduced the half-life to 4.0 and 0.8 days, respectively.[81]

Plasma Concentration

The average plasma concentration of α1AT in healthy individuals (PI type MM) has been estimated to be 1.3 mg/ml.[17] However, concentration varies according to PI type.

The concentration of α1AT in plasma can be measured either by functional assays or by immunochemical methods. Functional assays which evaluate inhibition of trypsin or elastase can utilize protein substrates[82,83] or synthetic substrates such as alpha-N-benzoyl-DL-arginine-p-nitroanilide (BAPNA) for trypsin[84] and N-tert-butoxycarbonyl-L-alanine-p-nitrophenyl-ester (NBA)[85] or N-succinyl-L-alanyl-L-alanyl-L-alalyl-L-alanine-p-nitroanilide (SLAPN)[86] for elastase. Appropriate immunologic methods include radial immunodiffusion,[87] electroimmunoassay,[88] or automated nephelometric methods. The immunologic methods frequently vary considerably between laboratories because of differences in commercial standards supplied. For this reason, many laboratories express normal values as percent of a normal pool of a large number of normal healthy individuals not pregnant or on medication, which can be assigned the value of 1.3 mg/ml.[17] Correlation between these methods is generally high,[83,89] but the functional assays include a component due to α₂-macroglobulin activity. Details of methodology and references have been published.[90]

As an acute phase protein, α1AT can show a fourfold increase in plasma concentration during infection. A marked increase in concentration occurs in a wide range of inflammatory conditions—in response to typhoid vaccine injection, in cancer, in liver disease (reviewed in Ref. 10). More modest increases of concentration are induced by estrogen during pregnancy or when administered as therapy.[91]

In addition to the deficiency variants, low levels of α1AT occur secondary to the respiratory distress syndrome in newborns,[92] to severe protein losing conditions,[7] to terminal liver failure,[93] and during the course of cystic fibrosis.[93]

GENETIC VARIATION

Protein (PI) Variants

α1AT shows a considerable amount of genetic variability. *PI*M*, which can be further classified into subtypes, is the most common allele in all populations described to date. The *PI*S* allele reaches polymorphic frequencies in many populations, as does the *PI*Z* allele, which produces a deficiency of α1AT.

In addition to common variants of α1AT, a large number of rare variants of α1AT have been identified. The inheritance is described as codominant, as both of two different variants can be observed in the heterozygote by various electrophoretic techniques. The PI (protease inhibitor) variants, initially identified primarily by the method of acid starch gel electropho-

resis developed by Fagerhol, were named in order of their relative mobility in the acid starch gel system: F (fast), M (medium), S (slow), and Z (the most cathodal).[12] Additional variants were given alphabetic designations according to their mobility in starch. In 1974, isoelectric focusing in polyacrylamide was used for resolution of PI variants.[16,94,95] Nomenclature guidelines were established, with the relative position by PIEF as the criterion for designation of subsequent variants.[96] Place names were used to designate the more rare alleles, using the birthplace of the oldest tested individual in the pedigree. These designations have been abbreviated by using the first three letters of the place name. According to the nomenclature guidelines,[96] with subsequent modification according to general guidelines for human gene nomenclature,[97] alleles at the PI locus are designated *PI*M*, *PI*S*, etc. Phenotypes are designated as PI MZ, PI M (or MM if confirmed in family studies). Genotype is indicated as *PI*M/PI*Z*, etc. Alleles which produce no detectable α1AT in serum, originally designated as *PI*null*, were originally represented in genotypes by a dash:—, PI M—, etc. According to the general nomenclature guidelines, the null alleles are designated *PI*QO*. This can be followed by a place name as for the other variants.

The earlier methods for identification of PI variants, including starch gel electrophoresis, isoelectric focusing, and agarose electrophoresis, have been reviewed.[10] PIEF offers increased resolution of the variants, better reproducibility, and the possibility of typing many (up to 50) samples on a single gel. A suitable method for PI typing by PIEF has been described,[98] and many modifications have been developed. Very narrow range ampholytes improved the resolving power of PIEF[99] and are now available commercially, as stock or in commercially prepared gels. The resolving power of PIEF has also been improved by the use of separators.[100–102] These methods resolved a further M subtype, M4, and other variants. As the limits of this approach were reached, immobilized pH gradients were applied to PI typing[103,104] and various modifications have been described.[105,106] The use of ultrathin PIEF gels and a narrow pH gradient, e.g., 4.2 to 4.9, appears to produce resolution similar to that of immobilized gradients.[107]

Typical results using PIEF and narrow-range ampholytes for the most clinically important PI variants are shown in Fig. 96-3A. The improved resolution which can be obtained with immobilized pH gradients and the additional, probably rare, M subtypes which can be differentiated are shown in Fig. 96-3B. The diagram in Fig. 96-4 indicates the relative position by PIEF of a number of the earliest described variants, summarized by the PI Nomenclature Committee.[96] These should serve as guidelines for those wishing to identify unusual variants. A complete list, with references, of those variants reported up to 1981 has been published.[10,108] Approximately 65 variants have been compared in our laboratory using immobilized gradient gels (Cox and Clark, unpublished data).

Most of the PI variants are associated with normal concentrations of α1AT. The exceptions are PI I, associated on average with 68 percent of the normal concentration of α1AT,[109] PI S at 60 percent of normal,[27] and PI P at 30 percent of normal.[110] (A number of variants with a mobility relatively close to P have a normal concentration of α1AT.) The types considered to be associated with a deficiency all have less than 20 percent of the normal concentration of α1AT, and are discussed subsequently. The normal ranges for PI types commonly found in the population are as follows, expressed as percent of a normal plasma pool ± 1 standard deviation[111] (similar to previous values)[27]: M, 100 ± 23.5; MZ, 64 ±

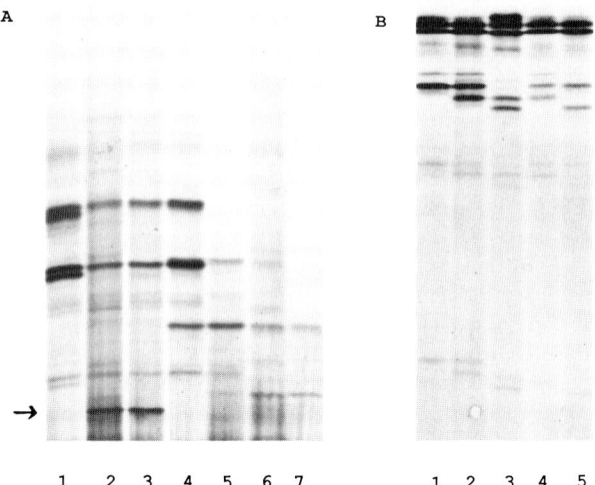

Fig. 96-3 Selected PI variants observed in human sera using isoelectric focusing, polyacrylamide gel. Anode is at the top. A. Routine PIEF, as described[98,108] but using Pharmalyte pH 4.5 to 5.5. Lane 1 = M1M2; 2 = M1Z; 3 = M1; 4 = M1S; 5 = SZ; 6 = ZZ with pronounced anodal components similar to position of S; 7 = ZZ. Dots indicate major Z bands. Lanes 2 and 3 have a cathodal component (arrow) occasionally found in patients with liver disease. B. Increased separation of PI M variants by hybrid PIEF, and an ultranarrow immobilized pH gradient, 4.5 to 4.75. Lane 1 = M1; 2 = M1M3; 3 = M2M3; 4 = M1M4; 5 = M1M2. (*Photographs courtesy of S. Weidinger and H. Cleve.[104] Used by permission of Pergamon Press.*)

15.2; MS, 86 ± 20.5. Most of the quantitative variation is accounted for by PI type.[112]

Not all variation observed electrophoretically is due to genetic differences. The cysteine in α1AT appears to be able to react with a variety of other plasma components to produce artifacts, which usually disappear by reduction of plasma samples prior to PIEF.[98] Anodal variants are observed in patients with liver disease and can be mistaken for the F or E variants. A variant cathodal to Z has been described in a child with cytomegalovirus and fatty liver[113] and is also noted in other patients, predominantly those with liver disease (Fig. 96-3A). Sometimes the additional bands which appear to be α1AT are due to other proteins and are not observed when immunofixation is used. Repeat testing of patients frequently indicates the transitory nature of these unusual patterns. Family studies

are a prerequisite to show that variants are truly genetic. All electrophoretic variants tested to date have normal functional capacity.[114] No nonfunctional variants have been observed. Two thermally unstable M-like variants have been reported.[115,116]

Amino Acid Sequence of PI Variants

The amino acid sequence has been determined for a number of types of α1AT, either by amino acid or DNA sequence analysis. The mutations identified are listed in Table 96-2, and their position in the molecule is shown in Fig. 96-5. An alanine-valine substitution at amino acid position 213, noted in amino acid sequencing studies,[35] was further identified by DNA studies of both Z and M1.[117] The alanine substitution is found in about 34 percent of *PI*M1* alleles[117,118] and differentiates two subtypes of M1: M1(Ala213) and M1(Val213). The *PI*Z* allele has the Ala213 substitution; however, PI types M2, M3, and S all have valine at position 213.[117,118] The Z and S variant sites have been confirmed by both amino acid[119–121] and DNA sequencing[22,11]; P,[122] Pittsburgh,[42] Xchr (XChristchurch),[123] and X (J.-O. Jeppsson, personal communication), by amino acid sequencing only. Sequencing of the two X variants demonstrates that variants with similar electrophoretic properties do not necessarily have identical mutations. Amino acid sequencing of M3[124] indicated a mutation compatible with a reported variant DNA sequence.[125]

Population Studies

Distribution of the PI alleles has now been determined for many populations. In all populations, *PI*M* is the most common allele. The earliest population studies were carried out by starch gel electrophoresis, and have been summarized.[3,126] These studies showed a low frequency of variants in Finns, Lapps, and Asians, and a high frequency of *PI*S* in Spain and Portugal. Since crossed immunoelectrophoresis was not used in the early studies, the *PI*Z* allele frequency could have been underestimated.

In later studies, PI typing was carried out by acid starch gel electrophoresis with crossed immunoelectrophoresis, or by PIEF. A number of the population studies, up to 1985, have been summarized.[10,67,127]

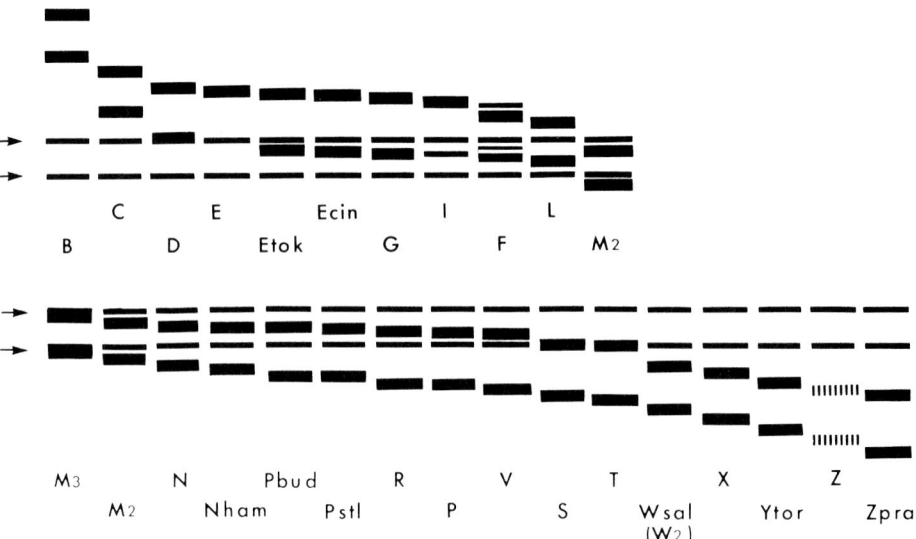

Fig. 96-4 Diagram of selected anodal (*top arrow*) and cathodal (*bottom row*) PI variants, by isoelectric focusing in acrylamide. Arrows in corresponding bands indicate position of two major bands of M1. Anode at top. (*Modified from Fagerhol and Cox[10] and Cox et al.[96] Used by permission of Plenum Press.*)

Table 96-2 Sequenced α₁-Antitrypsin Variants

PI type	Amino acid number	Normal amino acid	DNA codon	Mutant amino acid*	DNA codon†
Z	342	Glutamic acid	G̲AG	Lysine	A̲AG
Z, some M1	213	Valine	G̲TG	Alanine	G̲CG
S	264	Glutamic acid	GA̲A	Valine	GT̲A
M3	376	Glutamic acid	GA̲A	Asparagine	GA̲C
P	256	Asparagine	GA̲T	Valine	(G̲TT)
X	204	Glutamic acid	G̲AG	Lysine	(A̲AG)
Xchr	363	Glutamic acid	G̲AG	Lysine	(A̲AG)
Pittsburg	358	Methionine	A̲TG	Arginine	(A̲GG)

*References in text.

†Codons in parentheses are predicted as most likely from amino acid sequence.

Data from selected recent population studies, including PI M subtype frequencies, are presented in Table 96-3. These represent only a few of the populations studied to illustrate the major population differences. The frequency of *PI*M1* is the highest in all populations studied, with *M2* the next most frequent, and *M3* relatively uncommon. The additional subtype allele, *PI*M4*, has been described in several populations, at a frequency of 0.002 to 0.050.[100,101,129] In many studies, no differentiation was made between PI types M3 and M4. The *PI*S* allele is rare or absent in black and oriental populations, highest in Spain and Portugal, next most frequent in France, and low generally in other parts of Europe. The frequency of *PI*Z* (discussed subsequently) is highest in Scandinavian countries and is absent from oriental and black populations, except in those populations known to have admixture, as in the United States. There are two unusual exceptions for distribution of the *PI*Z* allele. The black Somalians have been reported to have a relatively high frequency of the *PI*Z* allele.[135] However, the apparent PI ZZ types could have been produced by sample degradation and were not confirmed by family studies (G. Massi, personal communication, 1987). Some babies could have had European admixture, explaining the PI MZ results. A coastal group of New Zealand Maoris were reported to have a high frequency of the *Z* allele[136] which could have been introduced by English seamen in the mid-eighteenth century.

DNA Polymorphisms

In addition to the extensive variation found in the protein by electrophoretic methods, further variation is found in the DNA sequence, as recognized by restriction enzymes, producing restriction fragment length polymorphisms (RFLPs). DNA variation was found to be rare when first examined using a cDNA probe: only two rare DNA polymorphisms were found, including one with *Taq* I.[137] Using cloned genomic sequences as probes, numerous DNA polymorphisms have been found with a variety of restriction enzymes. Several genomic sequences have been obtained[22,43,44]; those used as probes in our laboratory (provided by Dr. S. L. C. Woo) are shown in Fig. 96-2. The probe designated 4.6 includes the first exon, and the probed designated 6.5 includes the coding region and some of the 3′ flanking region.[138,139] Both were cloned from a phage clone α-AT 35.[50] Three polymorphisms have been described with probe 4.6, using the restriction enzymes *Sst* I, *Msp* I, and *Ava* II.[139] The allele frequencies are shown in Table 96-4, and the extent of variability is expressed by the polymorphism information content, or PIC.[140] These polymorphisms are all within the first intron of the α1AT gene, as shown in Fig. 96-5, and in spite of their close proximity, do not show strong linkage disequilibrium, suggesting that this may be a region of increased recombination.[139,141]

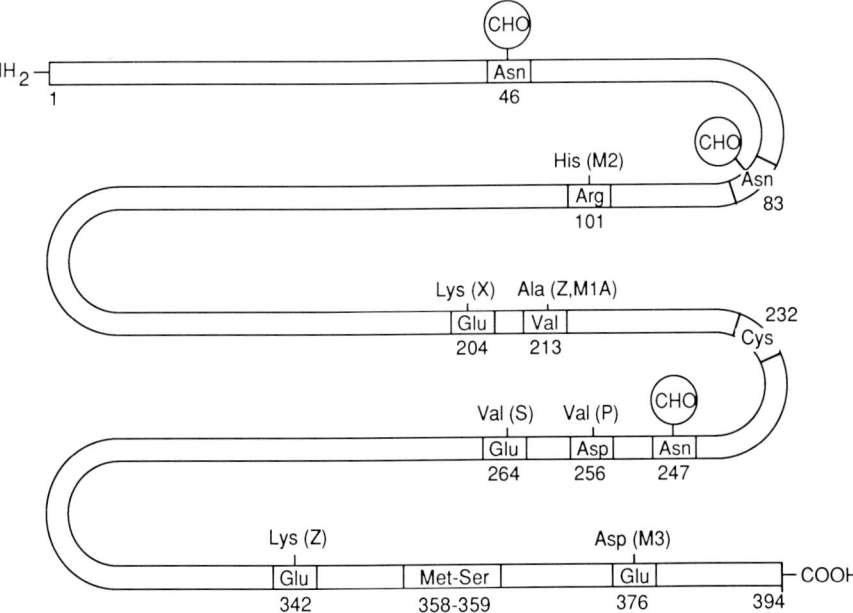

Fig. 96-5 Schematic diagram of important sites in the α1AT molecule. Positions of three oligosaccharide chains are indicated (CHO). The amino acid substitutions for sequenced PI variants (in parentheses) are shown (see also Table 96-2). Residues 358–359 are key positions in the reactive site. (*Courtesy of J.-O. Jeppsson.*)

Table 96-3 Allele Frequencies in Selected Populations

Population origin	No. tested	PI alleles M1	M2	M3	S	Z	Other	Ref.
Denmark	909	0.728	0.136	0.082	0.022	0.023	0.009	128
Netherlands	357	0.679	0.147	0.129*	0.029	0.013	0.003	129
Portugal	900	0.510	0.260	0.053	0.150	0.009	0.018	130
U.S. (white)	904	0.724	0.137	0.095	0.023	0.014	0.007	131
U.S. (black)	549	0.982	—	—	0.015	0.004	—	132
China†	1010	0.709	0.209	0.070	—	—	0.012	133
Japan	746	0.786	0.153	0.062	—	—	—	134

*Frequency of PI*M3 plus PI*M4.
†Mean of five Chinese populations.

Polymorphisms are detected with probe 6.5 using the restriction enzymes *Ava* II, *Mae* III, *BstE* II, *Taq* I, and *Eco* RI. *Ava* II detects polymorphisms both in the α1AT gene and the homologous sequence and was the first enzyme shown to produce a unique DNA haplotype for PI ZZ individuals.[139,141] Polymorphic fragments produced by Ava II (Fig. 96-6A) include one within the α1AT gene (bands 2/3), one which probably lies 3′ to the α1AT gene (bands 5/7), and one apparently within the downstream α1AT-like region (bands 1/4). The specific *Ava* II DNA haplotype for Z was found in association with all 52 PI*Z alleles for which the DNA haplotype was determined.[142]

When amino acid 213 is alanine, as found in Z and a portion of M1 α1AT, a restriction site for *BstE* II[117] and *Mae* III[118,141] is not present as it is in those PI types with valine at amino acid 213. When *Mae* III is used to detect this difference, a polymorphism outside the gene, presumably in the 3′ homologous region, is detected in addition to the polymorphism in the α1AT gene (Fig. 96-6B). The unique *Mae* III polymorphism has been found in association with all 31 PI*Z alleles tested.[142] As for *Mae* III, a restriction site for *BstE* II is lost adjacent to amino acid 213 in Z and in some M1 sequences,[117] but the difference in length would not be detectable using *BstE* II only. The polymorphism can be recognized using a double digest such as *BstE* II and *Bgl* II.[143] *Bgl* II recognizes a polymorphism outside the α1AT gene, apparently in the α1-AT-like region,[144] producing a unique haplotype associated with PI*Z.[143]

A *Taq* polymorphism in the flanking region immediately 3′ to the α1AT gene has been detected both by genomic probes[139,145] and by a cDNA probe.[137] An *Eco* RI polymorphism has been detected in the α1AT-like sequence.[146]

Most of the polymorphisms detected with probe 6.5 do not lie within the α1AT gene, as determined by examination of the known sequence but instead lie in the downstream homologous sequence. cDNA probe might detect these polymorphisms in the homologous sequence, but they may have been missed previously because the fragments appear much less intense on autoradiograms than those within the α1AT gene.

There is extensive linkage disequilibrium throughout the α1AT gene[141] so that the use of some of these polymorphisms will not provide additional genetic variation. With probe 6.5, the most useful combination is any enzyme providing a polymorphism within the α1AT gene (e.g., *Ava* II, *Mae* III, or *BstE* II) in combination with a restriction enzyme detecting polymorphism in the downstream region which does not show complete equilibrium,[141] such as *Taq* I or *Bgl* II.

The study of DNA polymorphisms shows a number of interesting features in the α1AT region. A study of the DNA haplotypes associated with the PI*Z allele indicates a single origin for all PI*Z alleles.[139] A specific DNA haplotype has been found associated with 53 PI*Z alleles, with two differing at either the 5′ or 3′ marker positions, irrespective of ethnic group within Northern Europe, and independent of the presence or type of clinical disease.[139,142] There appears to have been an early division between M1 subtypes, and the M1A (M1A1a213) subtype which has preceded the Z allele has the same amino acid at 213[117,141] as found in the baboon.[48] M1 (Val213) appears to have evolved into other PI subtypes such as M2, M3, and S.[141] A study of linkage disequilibrium be-

Table 96-4 Allele Frequencies for DNA Polymorphisms

Probe	Restriction enzyme	Alleles, kb	Allele frequency* +	−	0	No. of haplotypes	PIC†
4.6	Sst I	1.8, 1.9	0.69	0.31	—	2	0.33
	Msp I	0.95, 0.98	0.47	0.53	—	2	0.38
	Ava II	0.9, 1.1	0.65	0.35	—	2	0.35
6.5	Mae III	2.3, 2.5	0.71	0.29			
	Mae III (3′)	0.5, 0.7	0.65	0.35	—	4	0.33
	Ava II (5/7)	0.48, 0.68	0.22	0.78	—	4	0.44
	Ava II (1/4)(3′)	0.72, 2.7	0.29	0.71	—		
	Taq I	1.4, 2.0	0.97	0.03	—	4	0.58
	Taq I (3′)	4.8, 6.7, 0	0.53	0.26	0.21		
	Eco RI (3′)	5.7, 8.6	0.23	0.77	—	2	0.29

*+ = Presence of restriction site; − = absence of site; 0 = no fragment.
†Polymorphism information content.[140]
NOTE: Data for 4.6 probe from Refs. 139 and 141; data for 6.5 probe from Ref. 141 except Eco RI from Ref. 146.

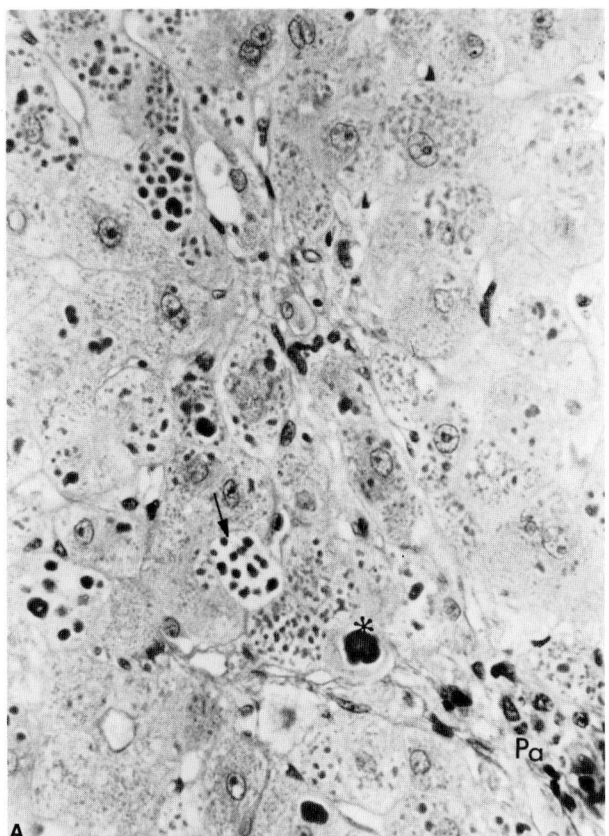

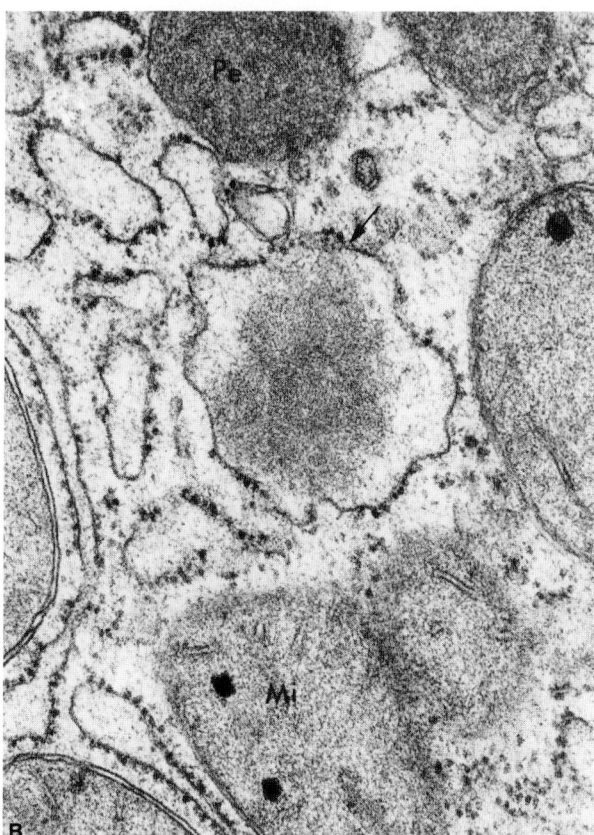

Fig. 96-6 A. Appearance of hepatic inclusions with PAS-D stain. Arrow indicates multiple small inclusions of α1AT; asterisk indicates large inclusion. Fibrosis is noted in the portal area (Pa). (PAS-D; x800). B. Hepatic inclusion as seen with electron microscope (EM). . Arrow indicates inclusion formed from dilation of rough endoplasmic reticulum, with numerous ribosomes visible on the outer membrane. Mi = mitochondria; Pe = peroxysome. x70,000. *(Photographs courtesy of E. Cutz. Used by permission of Masson Publishing.)*

tween each of the polymorphisms indicates a possible region of increased recombination in intron I, extensive linkage disequilibrium throughout the coding region of α1AT, occasional rare recombination events just 3' to the α1AT gene, and another area of occasional recombination within or near the 3' flanking of the region related sequence.[141]

α₁-ANTITRYPSIN DEFICIENCY

A modest reduction in the plasma concentration of α1AT is associated with the rare alleles I and P, and the common allele S. There is no firm evidence that any of these alleles are associated with disease. Even in association with the *PI*Z* allele, the risk for disease does not appear to be appreciable and will be presented in discussions of associated diseases. In this section we consider those alleles that produce a marked deficiency of α1AT.

Deficiency Due to PI*Z Allele

The most common of the deficiency alleles is *PI*Z*, and the majority of individuals with α1AT deficiency will be of PI type ZZ. As noted from population studies of PI variants, the *PI*Z* allele appears to be restricted to white, and occurs in blacks and orientals apparently only in populations with white admixture. The estimated frequency of the *PI*Z* allele in

North American white populations is 0.0122, corresponding to a frequency of PI ZZ homozygotes of 1 in 6,700.[147,148] The frequency of *PI*Z* is higher in Scandinavia: 0.018, as calculated from 200,000 Swedish newborns in a screening program.[149]

Plasma Concentration of α1AT

The plasma concentration of α1AT associated with PI type ZZ is usually in the range of 12 to 18 percent of normal. In one series of 105 PI ZZ individuals, the mean ± 1 standard deviation plasma α1AT concentration was 18 ± 5 percent of normal,[147] with a range of 9 to 27 percent in another series.[3] The plasma concentration of α1AT in 75 PI ZZ children was similar (17 ± 3 percent)[148]; however, for children or infants with liver disease, the concentrations of α1AT are frequently higher and can rise to 40 percent of normal.[150]

Diagnosis

α1AT deficiency should be considered in the differential diagnosis for patients with emphysema, jaundice in infancy, liver disease in childhood, and liver disease in adults.

An approximate concentration of α1AT can be estimated by serum protein electrophoresis. In most cases, the α₁-globulin peak on cellulose acetate electrophoresis will be absent or markedly reduced. We have occasionally observed an α₁ component in plasma of children of PI type ZZ. The use of computer printouts of these scans is unreliable, as the position of the baseline sometimes causes a normal concentration to be read when a visual examination of the scan clearly indicates a deficiency. In many laboratories, electrophoresis in agarose[151] has replaced cellulose acetate electrophoresis, with visual evaluation or densiometric scanning of the protein peaks. This method can be regarded only as a screening technique. In those clinical conditions with a relatively high probability of α1AT deficiency, a more specific measure of α1AT should be carried out. Immunologic assays (radial immunodiffusion, electroimmunoassay, or nephelometry) are most specific. Functional assays include a fraction of inhibitory capacity due to other inhibitors such as α_2-macroglobulin, which can prevent diagnosis of the deficiency.

In order to confirm the diagnosis of α1AT deficiency, PI typing must be carried out. The plasma concentration below which PI typing is carried out must be high enough to avoid missing affected individuals. Since patients with inflammation or liver disease, particularly in children, may have a concentration of α1AT up to about 40 percent of normal, PI typing for plasma with less than 40 percent of the normal mean concentration should detect all individuals of PI type ZZ.

Liver Inclusions

Normal α1AT is secreted rapidly from the liver. Z-type α1AT is retained in hepatocytes where it forms characteristic intracytoplasmic inclusions, providing another sign of α1AT deficiency.[72] Features of the inclusions have been described in detail[152] and are shown in Fig. 96-6. The hepatocyte inclusions can be identified by several histochemical stains. By routine hematoxylin-eosin, the inclusions appear as round to oval, slightly eosinophilic hyalinlike globules, localized predominantly in periportal hepatocytes. With PAS stain following diastase treatment (PAS-D), the α1AT inclusions are easily visualized as brilliant pink globules of various sizes. Large inclusions can be up to 15 μm in diameter. In infants with α1AT deficiency, the inclusions may be fine and granular. Large inclusions stain brick red with Masson trichrome stain and dark purple with phosphotungstic acid-hematoxylin (PTAH) stain.

The content of these inclusions was demonstrated to be α1AT by immunohistochemical methods, using specific antiserums against human α1AT.[72,153] The direct immunofluorescence method, with fluorescein- or peroxidase-labeled α1AT antibody, is used preferably on frozen sections, but formalin fixed tissue even after paraffin embedding can also be used.[154] Immunologic identification of α1AT is useful for confirming the presence of α1AT, particularly where other liver inclusions are present.

By electron microscopy, the hepatic inclusions appear as moderately electron dense membrane-bound masses. The storage of α1AT occurs within the membranes of the endoplasmic reticulum (ER), particularly in rough ER.[152,153]

There is considerable variability in the extent of inclusion formation. In general, the number and size of liver inclusions increases with age.[152] The presence of these inclusions indicates only the presence of at least one *PI*Z* allele. In individuals heterozygous for α1AT deficiency, PI MZ, who have liver disease, numerous and large inclusions may be observed. It is not possible to differentiate heterozygotes from homozygous deficient individuals by an examination of liver inclusions.

The occurrence of this type of liver inclusion is almost al-

ways due to the presence of a deficiency allele for α1AT. Rare deficiency alleles, with a defect in synthesis similar to that of Z, produce typical α1AT inclusions.[155] In some cases in which typical inclusions have been found in individuals said to be of normal PI type M or variant PI type S, other non-Z deficiency variants have not been excluded.[156–158] In occasional patients with alcoholic liver disease, small scattered PAS-D globules have been observed, with no electron microscopy confirmation of α1AT retention.[155] Deposits of lipofusion can produce PAS-D material, distinctly different from α1AT inclusions.[155] Rarely, patients with severe systemic diseases have typical PAS-D-positive globules positive for α1AT by immunofluorescence in periportal areas, present apparently because the rate of α1AT synthesis exceeds the capacity of the processing enzymes involved in secretion.[159,160]

The Basic Defect

Three of the deficiency variants, Z, Mmalton, and Mduarte, show an accumulation of α1AT in liver inclusions, although most studies of the basic defect contributing to the deficiency have been carried out with Z α1AT. The decreased plasma levels are not associated with an increased catabolic rate for Z or Mmalton.[81] The rates of synthesis of M and Z α1AT are identical in in vitro systems,[161,162] suggesting a defect in secretion, consistent with accumulation of liver inclusions.

The protein within the liver inclusions has been shown to have an abnormal carbohydrate composition, lacking terminal N-acetyl-neuraminic acid, and having a mannose-rich core, typical of incompletely processed glycoproteins.[163–166] Incomplete processing appears to be secondary to the basic defect, since reduced secretion in comparison with M α1AT also occurs when Z mRNA is injected into Xenopus oocytes.[167,168] Amino acid analysis indicates that the signal sequences in M and Z proteins are identical[19,169]; therefore an abnormal signal is unlikely to be the cause of the secretion defect.

The liver inclusions do not readily dissociate,[164,165] but when solubilized, Z α1AT binds elastase and is functionally active as an inhibitor.[166] Z protein has a strong tendency to aggregate, even in plasma, and aggregation is particularly pronounced in the presence of pH and salt concentrations typical of the hepatic intracellular fluid.[170] This tendency to aggregate is also observed with Mmalton α1AT.[170] Studies of production of M and Z α1AT in oocytes indicate that the secretion defect is observed for the nonglycosylated α1AT.[167] The reason for such aggregation or insolubility may be explained by an examination of the three-dimensional structure of α1AT. In the Z protein, lysine at position 342 replaces glutamic acid in normal M α1AT.[119,120] The three-dimensional structure obtained by x-ray crystallography indicates that this amino acid residue is involved in a salt bridge important for stabilization of the molecule and occurs at a sharp bend in the major β sheet.[24] Disruption of the salt bridge could decrease the rate of folding.[24] However, when amino acid 290, glutamic acid, the other component of the 290–342 salt bridge, was altered to lysine by site-directed mutagenesis, secretion of the α1AT was normal after injection of mRNA into oocytes.[171] This result suggests that alteration at the critical bend by lysine may be more important than the salt bridge for normal folding. Apparently, the α1AT produced immediately forms aggregates of increasing size in the liver, eventually producing large inclusions. Accumulation of Z α1AT appears to proceed slowly and continuously. Stimulation of lysosomal enzymes by nonse-

Table 96-5 Rare Deficiency Alleles of α_1-Antitrypsin

Allele	Position by IEF	Plasma concentration, % of normal	Inclusions in liver	Disease of Lung	Disease of Liver	Defect	References
Mduarte	= M3	6	+	+	–	?	173
Mmalton	< M2	12	+	+/–	+/–	Aggregates	170, 174
Mheerlen	< M3	2	–	+	–	aa369: pro → leu	175, 176
Zaugsburg	< Z	<10	?	+	–	?	177
M-like	= M	4	?	+	–	?	178
Unusual	< Z*	2	?	+	–	?	179
Mprocida	< M3†	4	?	+	?	aa41: leu → pro	180

*Tested by starch and agarose electrophoresis, not IEF.
†Tested in our laboratory; provided by R. G. Crystal.

creted α1AT may help to remove the abnormal Z protein.[172] Feedback inhibition may also occur, as indicated by the inhibition of synthesis in vitro by α1AT secreted in medium.[74]

Rare Deficiency Alleles

Several deficiency alleles have been reported, in which the amount of α1AT produced is similar to that of the *PI*Z* allele, or somewhat less, generally in the range of bout 2 to 15 percent of normal. These variants are summarized in Table 96-5.

Mmalton α1AT can be distinguished easily from Z α1AT by its different mobility both by agarose electrophoresis and isoelectric focusing in acrylamide.[147,174] The mean concentration of plasma α1AT in Mmalton homozygotes is similar to that in PI ZZ homozygotes (Table 96-5). Homozygotes would be predicted to have the same risk for obstructive lung disease as PI ZZ individuals, a hypothesis supported by the few cases reported. PI MmaltonZ heterozygotes developed obstructive airways disease similar to PI ZZ individuals, dependent on smoking history.[181,182] Heterozygotes with a partial deficiency, i.e., PI MMmalton, appeared similar to PI MZ heterozygotes in that some of the smokers showed impairment in some tests of lung function.[181]

Too few Mmalton homozytoes have been reported to assess the risk for liver disease. However, one adult patient has been reported with liver disease.[183] A study of the liver in a heterozygote, PI MMmalton, has shown PAS-positive inclusions identical with those found in association with PI Z.[155] The amino acid substitution in PI Mmalton has not yet been identified, but the protein has been shown to have a high tendency to aggregate.[170]

*PI*Mduarte*, producing about 6 percent of the normal α1AT concentration, was first reported in a 48-year-old woman with severe bullous emphysema.[173] PI Mduarte migrates in acid starch gel and agarose similarly to PI M,[173] and the isoelectric point is similar to that of M3, as determined by isoelectric focusing.[147] PAS-D globules were present in the liver,[173] indicating that this deficient variant also has, like Z and Mmalton, a defect in secretion from the liver.

Both *PI*Mmalton* and *PI*Mduarte* are relatively rare alleles, about 1/100th and 1/200th the frequency of the *PI*Z* allele, respectively (Table 96-6). Their presence must be considerd when no Z α1AT can be observed in plasma from a patient with apparent α1AT deficiency. Furthermore, these PI types will produce α1AT inclusions in the liver, particularly in heterozygotes, in the presence of an apparently normal M phenotype. When isoelectric focusing is used, the Mmalton α1AT can be identified even in the presence of a normal M allele. Mduarte can be detected in a heterozygote with an S or Z allele, but depending on the degree of resolution with PIEF, may not be detectable in the presence of a normal M allele. Family studies should help to confirm the presence of these rare deficiency alles. Unless their presence has been definitely excluded, the association of PAS-D-positive globules in hepatocytes cannot be associated with certainty with a PI Z-bearing phenotype.

Other rare deficiency variants have been observed. A German patient has been reported with heterozygosity for PI M and for a rare deficiency allele, *PI*Zaugsburg*, which has a position in isoelectric focusing more basic than that of PI Z.[177] Homozygosity for a variant reported in a 35-year-old Dutch smoker with obstructive lung disease and about 2 percent of the normal plasma concentration of α1AT has been called PI Mheerlen.[175] Although we have found the protein position by PIEF similar to Mduarte (unpublished), they are unlikely to be the same as Mduarte is associated with PAS-D hepatic inclusions and Mheerlen is not.[175] An M-like phenotype was described in a 38-year-old woman with chronic obstructive lung disease and an α1AT concentration of about 4 percent of normal.[178] This variant could have been identical with Mmalton or Mduarte; however, direct comparisons were not made. Homozygosity for a deficiency allele in a 15-year-old child from a consanguineous mating was associated with a plasma α1AT concentration of about 2 percent of normal. The mobility on agarose appeared to be slower than that of Z in both starch and agarose,[179] suggesting a variant similar to Zaugsburg.

The Null Alleles

The deficiency alleles Z, Mmalton, and Mduarte all apparently lead to a plasma deficiency because of lack of secretion of an

Table 96-6 Frequency of Deficiency Alleles in 112 Patients with α_1-Antitrypsin Deficiency

Allele	Frequency*
Z	1.22×10^{-2}
Mmalton	1.69×10^{-4}
Mduarte	0.56×10^{-4}
Null	1.69×10^{-4}

*From Ref. 147.

abnormal protein from the liver. In contrast, the null alleles probably produce no α1AT, or less than 1 percent of the normal amount of plasma α1AT. According to current nomenclature for the description of polymorphisms, these alleles should be designated as PI*QO and homozygotes designated as PI QOQO. While the PI*Z allele has been reported only in white populations, the null alleles, as expected, are widespread. We have previously estimated the frequency of the null "allele" to be 1.7×10^{-4},[147] about 1/100th the frequency of the PI*Z allele in a North American white population. Based on data from newborn screening, the frequency of the PI null allele(s) has been estimated at 1.34×10^{-4}.[149] The PI QOQO homozygote and other rare deficiency data published or known to us are listed in Table 96-7. Many PI MQO heterozygotes have been described.

Clinical information on all reported null homozygotes has been summarized,[191] although sometimes inadequately described, in published reports. Liver pathology has been examined in only one null homozygote, a Portugese girl, who had no liver inclusions.[184] She was found to have 1/200th the normal amount of plasma α1AT of normal type M mobility, which was named Mrouen, or QOrouen.[185] Obstructive airways disease occurs as early as the second or third decade, even in nonsmokers. Data indicate that null homozygotes have more severe obstructive airways disease than individuals of PI type ZZ, whose low concentrations of α1AT apparently provide some protection to lung tissue.[191] These individuals may particularly benefit from new methods of therapy under development. The presence of even trace amounts of α1AT in null homozygotes may help prevent the formation of α1AT antibodies during long-term therapy with injection of α1AT.

There appear to be a variety of null mutants, each with the final result of interference with the production of α1AT. The molecular defect has been reported in three of the null homozygotes (Table 96-7) and is different for each. The use of DNA haplotypes, as described for studies of normal alleles of α1AT, can be useful in delineating different null alleles. We have examined the DNA haplotype for six null alleles to date and have found each to have a different haplotype, probably reflecting different mutations.[192] This approach is useful for an initial identification of mutant alleles. Further study of the molecular defects in such mutants will indicate what type of defects interfere with production of α1AT.

Selective Mechanisms for Deficiency Alleles

Since the combined frequency of PI*QO alleles is about 1.7×10^{-4}, then the frequency of each allele should be considerably less. If selective advantage has allowed the frequency of the PI*Z allele to increase, then it is interesting that the frequency of other deficient alleles has not similarly increased. Possible explanations are that the PI*Z allele has some unique selective advantage in comparison with other deficiency alleles, that other deficiency alleles have arisen much more recently than PI*Z, or that chance factors have been responsible for the increase in PI*Z.

The analysis of DNA haplotypes has indicated a single origin for the PI*Z allele with a subsequent spread of the mutation through northern white populations.[139] Increased fertility of heterozygotes has been discussed as one possible mechanism for increasing the PI*Z allele frequency.[10] Preferential survival of heterozygotes is another possible selection pressure, and preferential survival from tuberculosis has been suggested.[193] This is entirely speculative at present, although data suggesting the frequency of MZ individuals is increased among older blood donors, who were adults prior to tuberculosis therapy, is of interest.[194]

Previously suggested preferential transmission of the Z allele from MZ heterozygotes, a means of increasing the PI*Z (or S) frequency, has not been supported for the Z[195,196] or S[197] alleles.

OBSTRUCTIVE LUNG DISEASE

Clinical Features

Chronic obstructive pulmonary disease (COPD), specifically emphysema, is the most prevalent clinical disorder associated with α1AT deficiency and was noted in the first patients described.[5] In a larger group of 33 patients reported by Eriksson in 1965,[7] the first symptoms of pulmonary disease were reported to occur below 40 years of age in 60 percent and below 50 years of age in 90 percent. The association of α1AT deficiency was confirmed in many subsequent studies. The early studies, suggesting a high proportion of emphysema in patients with α1AT deficiency, were biased by the ascertainment

Table 96-7 Clinical Features of Homozygotes and Basic Defect for Null Alleles (PI*QO) and Other Rare Deficiency Alleles of α₁-Antitrypsin

Allele	Ethnic origin	Sex	Disease of Lung	Disease of Liver	Mutation	Reference
Mrouen	Portuguese	F	−	−	?	184, 185
QOboston	American, white	M	+	−	?	186
QOhongkong	Oriental (sibs)	F, F	+	−	aa 317, 318: leu-ser → leu-arg CTCTCC → CTCC	187, 188
QObellingham	American, white	M	+	−	aa 217: lys → stop AAG → TAG	189
QOgranitefalls	American	M	+	−	aa 160, 161: tyr-val → stop TACGTG → TAGTG	190
QOmattawa	French, Greek (sibs)	F, F, F	+	−	?	191
QOoslo	Norwegian	M	+	−	?	Fagerhol*

*Unpublished, personal communication.

of patients through their illness. It is now appreciated that α1AT deficient patients who avoid smoking have a much delayed onset of clinical symptoms and may have an almost normal life span.

Surveys from several countries of groups of patients with COPD are in agreement with the initial report[5] that only 1 or 2 percent of all patients have α1AT deficiency[198] (earlier studies reviewed in Refs. 67 and 199). The frequency may be considerably higher: 18 percent of patients with emphysema in one study, when the referral pattern favors young and more severely affected patients.[111] The male/female ratio is at least 2:1,[198,200] which may be related to smoking exposure.

Emphysema associated with α1AT deficiency typically involves more basilar portions than apical portions of the lungs. Although the majority of patients present with emphysema, some present with symptoms of bronchial asthma or chronic bronchitis.[198,200] Thoracic x-rays show a symmetric decrease in peripheral vasculature most prominent in the lower lungs, but only in those patients with well established emphysema and not in asymptomatic individuals.[201] Radioisotope ventilation and perfusion scans are usually abnormal[198] and may show slight abnormalities in asymptomatic patients.[201] Changes in lung mechanics are similar to those found in other patients with emphysema, with reduction in lung volumes and expiratory flow rates. The decreased expiratory flow rate can be attributed to loss of elastic recoil. The most sensitive parameters for detecting abnormalities in asymptomatic α1AT-deficient patients have been reported to be closing volume, nitrogen washout volume, and lung mechanics, as well established for other types of emphysema.

Clinical features of pulmonary disease have been discussed extensively in the preceding edition of this text.[63]

Age of Onset and Course of Obstructive Lung Disease

The onset and severity of disease symptoms show considerable variability. Reports of emphysema in children with α1AT deficiency are extremely rare and may be due to the coexistence of other genetic abnormalities.[202] Nonsmokers may have normal lung function tests at least to 30 years of age.[191] In patients ascertained through an affected relative, females tend to show less rapid deterioration of lung function with age[200] and better survival.[203]

Smoking has a major effect on both the age of onset of pulmonary symptoms and on the course of pulmonary deterioration. In a review of patients from the literature (30 nonsmokers and 84 smokers), the mean age of onset of dyspnea was 35 years in smokers and 44 years in nonsmokers.[198] A study of 33 patients with emphysema and α1AT deficiency in New Zealand indicated a mean age for onset of dyspnea of 32 years in smokers and 51 years in nonsmokers.[204] Onset of dyspnea appears to be rare before 40 years of age in nonsmokers.[203] Lung function deteriorates continuously with time as the alveolar walls are destroyed. The rate of deterioration of lung function, as measured by decline in FEV₁ (volume of air expired during the first second of forced vital capacity) showed a marked difference between six α1AT deficient smokers (316 ± 80 ml/year) versus seven nonsmokers (80 + 38 ml/year).[203] The rate of decline of FEV₁ for PI ZZ subjects (17 percent smokers) with clinically significant pulmonary disease as reflected by an initial FEV₁ of 30 to 60 percent of predicted, was 111 ± 102 ml.[205] The subjects were tested in several U.S. cities. A comparable decline in nonsmoking controls is 36 ml/year.[206] Effects of smoking should be particularly detrimental in α1AT deficiency as in normal individuals when begun during adolescence, as attainment of maximal lung function is prevented.[207]

True survival figures for patients with α1AT deficiency are not known, as it is certain that many PI ZZ individuals are never identified. Survival to the sixth and seventh decade is possible. The most extensive survival data have been obtained from Sweden and are summarized in Fig. 96-7. Mortality figures in this study differ markedly for smokers and nonsmokers. About 98 percent of nonsmoking females and 65 percent of nonsmoking males are alive at age 55, whereas only 30 percent and 18 percent of females and males, respectively, who smoke are alive at the same age.[203]

The Role of Proteases in Lung Destruction

The alveolar destruction characteristic of emphysema is now generally considered to be due to an imbalance between proteolytic enzymes, particularly elastase, and their inhibitors. Support for this concept is derived from several types of studies. Experimental studies in animals demonstrated that porcine pancreatic elastase[208] and human neutrophil elastase[209,210] produce experimental emphysema in animals. Further evidence has come from the studies of patients with α1AT deficiency. α1AT, because of its small molecular size, enters lung tissue and has been recovered in bronchoalveolar lavage fluid. A plasma deficiency of α1AT is also reflected as a deficiency of α1AT in the lung.[211] The absence of adequate inhibitor allows continued destruction of lung tissue. Direct evidence for the complexing of α1AT with elastase in the lung has been provided by the finding of elastase-α1AT complexes in bronchoalveolar lavage fluid of normal smokers and nonsmokers, accounting for less than 1 percent of the total α1AT in the fluid.[212]

The role of α1AT as the major inhibitor of elastase at the epithelial lining has been demonstrated in a homozygous null individual, in whom the antineutrophil elastase capacity of lavage fluid was less than 15 percent of normal.[213] Other poten-

Fig. 96-7 Cumulative probability of survival to specified ages for normal males, normal females, PI ZZ smokers, PI ZZ nonsmokers as indicated in upper right. (*Based on data published by Larsson.*[203])

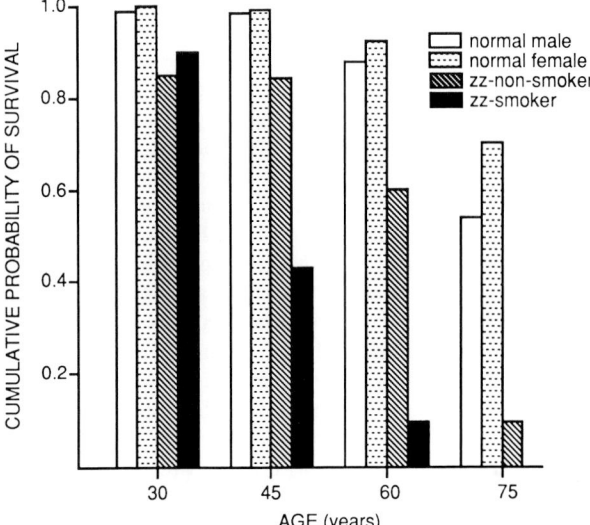

tial elastase inhibitors in lung tissue, such as a low molecular weight protease inhibitor[214–216] or locally produced α_2-macroglobulin,[65] apparently make a minor contribution.

Numerous other studies supporting the protease inhibitor imbalance hypothesis[217] and expanding upon the role of neutrophils[218] have been reviewed.

Mechanisms of Enhancement of Lung Destruction by Smoking

Mechanisms of lung destruction in normal smokers would be expected to have an even more detrimental effect in those with α1AT deficiency. One of the important mechanisms for the increased destruction of lung tissue in smokers appears to be oxidation, since oxidation of methionine residues interferes dramatically with complex formation of α1AT with elastase. Since the gas phase of tobacco smoke is rich in oxidizing agents, a direct effect of smoke on α1AT could be anticipated. In vitro, both a crude tar fraction of cigarette smoke and aqueous extracts of freshly generated cigarette smoke significantly inactivate α1AT (reviewed in Ref. 217).

In vivo studies assessing effects expressed in serum of smokers have produced conflicting results. Although some studies have shown a decrease of elastase inhibitor activity in serum from smokers compared with nonsmokers,[86,219] other studies have not shown a difference,[220] even when carried out with careful control of sample timing in relation to smoking.[221] In view of the generous supply of antioxidants in plasma, a measurable effect on α1AT in plasma would seem unlikely. A reduction of elastase inhibitor activity in lavage fluid of smokers has been reported. In a study of acute effects of smoking, there appeared to be no increase in elastaselike enzyme activity in smokers, but an increase in immunologic elastase levels indicated possible release of neutrophil elastase in the bronchioalveolar lavage fluid.[222] Slight inactivation of α1AT was noted in lavage fluid immediately after smoking.[223] α1AT with oxidized methionine and reduced inhibitory activity has been recovered from lungs of smokers.[224]

In addition to oxidation, smoking can act upon neutrophils, present in increased numbers in smokers. Triggered neutrophils release oxidants which in a local area can allow proteolytic cleavage of α1AT by elastase.[225] Smoking causes release of elastase from neutrophils. Neutrophils are also a source of myeloperoxidase, which inactivates α1AT.[226,227] This can also help account for the increased amount of proteolytically cleaved α1AT in smokers.[228] Smoking causes impaired adherence of alveolar macrophages and promotes increased synthesis and secretion of elastase from macrophages from nonsmokers (reviewed in Refs. 70 and 218). Smoking acts directly upon elastin by impairing its cross-linking.[229]

Evidence of increased breakdown of alveolar elastin in smokers can be detected directly by an increase in the amount of elastin-derived peptides in the plasma of smokers[230] and in patients with α1AT deficiency.[231]

Other Factors Influencing the Extent of Lung Destruction

Genetic Factors. No large studies of clinical variation in α1AT deficiency have been reported within sibships. A number of population studies have indicated that respiratory symptoms show familial aggregation (reviewed in Ref. 232) and genetic factors no doubt influence disease severity in

α1AT deficiency. In a study of 256 monozygotic and 158 dizygotic adult twins, a large proportion of measured variability in pulmonary function tests was accounted for by genetic influences.[232] A number of metabolic parameters may have a hereditary component and could alter susceptibility to lung destruction. These include number of neutrophils, extent of elastase released from neutrophils, or differences in elastase quality or quantity within neutrophils. Detrimental effects could be produced by an increased production of myeloperoxidase to cause local inactivation of α1AT, low levels of catalase which blocks H_2O_2 production by myeloperoxidase, low concentrations of antioxidants, or characteristics of lung tissue which result in susceptibility to degradation. There has been little investigation to date of most of these factors.

Neutrophil Protease Content. Neutrophil proteases, particularly elastase, cause lung degradation when inadequately inhibited. Any increase in the neutrophil content of such proteases might be expected to increase the rate of lung degradation. A number of studies have been carried out to compare neutrophil proteases in COPD, and in individuals of PI type MZ and ZZ, all with appropriate controls (reviewed in Ref. 10).

In summary, no pronounced differences in neutrophil elastase concentration were found between individuals with normal lung function and those with COPD. However, the mean values were somewhat increased in patients with COPD and may indicate that occasional individuals have exceptionally high concentrations of neutrophil elastase. For PI MZ and Z individuals, there was no significant difference between those with COPD and those with normal lung function.

Antioxidant Status. Oxidation appears to play an important role in proteolytic degradation of the lung. The obvious corollary is that antioxidants should play an important role in limiting this destruction. The damaging effects of both chemical oxidants, such as those from cigarette smoke, and those produced by neutrophils should be modified by antioxidants present in lung tissue. Normal plasma and tissue components which may contribute to antioxidant activity include ascorbate, ceruloplasmin, transferrin, vitamin E, reduced glutathione through the activity of glutathione peroxidase, NADPH reductase, methionine sulfoxide reductase, and superoxide dismutase.[233] The total antioxidant activity of plasma is somewhat reduced in smokers in comparison with nonsmokers,[234,235] and there is a suggestion that those with a family history of lung disease also have reduced plasma antioxidants.[234] In vitro studies of the antioxidants ascorbate, cysteine, and dapsone demonstrate that all these can protect α1AT loss of inhibitory activity due to activated neutrophils.[236] However they are not able to activate α1AT once inactivation has occurred. The protective effects of these antioxidants are proposed to be related to their ability to scavenge superoxide and oxidants generated by the neutrophils. In this study, it was pointed out that the concentrations of these agents having such a protective effect are attainable in vivo. Vitamin E is particularly important as a tissue antioxidant, believed to act predominantly on cell membranes. Animal experiments have demonstrated that vitamin E can neutralize free radicals and decrease lung susceptibility to oxidant injury (reviewed in Ref. 237). Serum levels of vitamin E and the oxidative metabolite vitamin E quinone are similar in young asymptomatic smokers and nonsmokers; however smokers show a marked decrease in vitamin E and vitamin E quinone in bronchoalveolar lavage fluid when compared with non-smokers, possibly owing to increased oxidative metabolism of vitamin E in smokers.[237] The difference was only partly corrected by vitamin E supplementation. Vitamin E was shown to have a protective role for the lung in experiments demonstrating that the killing of normal rat lung parenchymal cells by smoke or alveolar macrophages was inversely related to the vitamin E content of the parenchymal cells.[237] This study suggests that vitamin E is an important antioxidant in the lower respiratory tract and its role in therapy should be seriously considered.

Risk for Lung Disease in Heterozygotes

The extent of the risk for PI MZ heterozygotes to develop COPD has been controversial. Assessment of risk for these individuals is important since they constitute 2 to 5 percent of most populations. Surveys of patients with COPD have generally shown an increased frequency of individuals of PI type MZ in comparison with those of PI type M, although the difference between the two populations has varied from slight to considerable (reviewed in Ref. 111). In these studies, usually no separation has been made of smokers from nonsmokers. In studies of PI MZ subjects and appropriate PI MM controls, not ascertained through disease, a small decrease in lung function in nonsmokers and a larger decrease in smokers was noted for parameters reflecting loss of elastic recoil.[238] Differences were not found to be significant in a multicenter study of 143 PI MZ subjects.[239] Both studies have included adults of varying ages, and corrections have been made for age. In a study of 39 Swedish PI MZ heterozygotes ascertained from the general population, no significant differences were noted between PI MZ and M nonsmokers.[240] In contrast, PI MZ smokers showed a significant loss of elastic recoil, large residual volumes, and increased closing capacity, and most reported mild dyspnea on exertion. Six years later, 32 PI MZ heterozygotes and their controls were retested, and the PI MZ smokers but not nonsmokers showed a significantly increased mean annual reduction in FEV$_1$ (75 and 40 ml/year respectively).[241] No increased prevalence of clinical obstructive lung disease was noted in this study, although there have been numerous isolated reports in the literature of severely affected individuals of PI type MZ. The conclusion from these studies appears to be that PI MZ nonsmokers have little if any increased risk for COPD. PI MZ smokers have an increased rate of loss of lung elasticity but usually do not develop sufficient impairment to be recognized as clinical disease. There may be certain families in which other genetic predisposing factors coexist with α1AT heterozygosity to produce clinical disease.

An increased frequency of MZ or MS heterozygotes has been reported in association with asthma (reviewed in Ref. 10). Deficiency types of α1AT may lead to more severe lung damage for asthmatics.[10]

Individuals of PI type SZ should be more at risk than individuals of PI type MZ for developing a protease/protease inhibitor imbalance in the lungs. The risk for them to develop COPD must not be high, as surveys of patients with COPD have revealed few if any individuals of PI type SZ. Studies of small numbers of asymptomatic adults of PI type SZ and isolated reports of affected individuals suggest that smokers particularly may have a tendency to impaired lung function.[242]

Although the *PI*F* allele is not associated with a decrease

of α1AT concentration, there is a suggestion that PI FM heterozygotes may be more susceptible to pulmonary function impairment, particularly when exposed to industrial pollutants.[243,244] α1AT of the F type appears to have an increased tendency to oxidation, as reflected by its altered electrophoretic pattern after aging,[108] and this increased tendency to oxidation may make PI FM individuals susceptible to lung destruction in a polluted environment.

LIVER DISEASE

Childhood Onset

An association of α1AT deficiency and liver disease in children was first reported by Sharp and colleagues.[13] When originally reported, the prognosis for liver disease with α1AT deficiency was believed to be poor since all of the patients identified had cirrhosis. Later studies have shown the prognosis to be more favorable.

Liver abnormalities occur in only a portion of infants of PI type ZZ. The only prospective study carried out to date is a screening of 200,000 Swedish newborns, from which follow-up was carried out on 120 children of PI type ZZ (and two of PI type Z−).[245] Approximately 18 percent of PI Z children developed clinically recognizable liver abnormalities: 7.3 percent had prolonged obstructive jaundice with marked evidence of liver disease, 4.1 percent had prolonged jaundice with mild liver disease, and 6.4 percent had other abnormalities suggestive of liver disease such as hepatomegaly, splenomegaly, unexplained failure to thrive, or stated history of prolonged jaundice without medical documentation.[245]

The most common sign of liver abnormality associated with α1AT deficiency is the "neonatal hepatitis syndrome," characterized by conjugated hyperbilirubinemia and raised serum aminotransferases, frequently with hepatosplenomegaly. Varying degrees of failure to thrive have been noted. The serum bilirubin concentration can be very high, rising to 12 to 17 mg percent (normal less than 1).[245,246] Signs of cholestasis generally appear between 4 days and 2 months of age and can persist for a few weeks up to 8 months.[150,246] Cholestasis in α1AT deficiency may be severe enough to cause acholic stools, as in extrahepatic biliary atresia. α1AT deficiency should always be considered in a child with prolonged jaundice (conjugated hyperbilirubinemia) of unexplained origin, and PI typing should be an early diagnostic procedure. From 14 to 29 percent of infants with neonatal hepatitis have been found to have α1AT deficiency, PI type ZZ.[150,246] While presentation as neonatal hepatitis is the most common, hepatomegaly without jaundice in infancy or childhood has been noted as the presenting symptom. In one series of 18 children of PI type ZZ, 14 (78.6 percent) presented with the neonatal hepatitis syndrome, 3 (16.7 percent) with hepatomegaly, and 1 with hematemesis.[247]

The pathologic features of α1AT deficiency associated with liver disease in children have been reviewed.[150] The typical PAS-D positive inclusions, described previously, are observed in children with liver disease. They may be difficult to identify in percutaneous liver biopsy specimens from infants. Liver biopsies from young, asymptomatic children usually show only very small inclusions by PAS-D stain but more extensive deposition by immunofluorescence. The amount and size of liver inclusions shows no clear correlation with severity of liver disease. Livers of older PI Z patients, particularly those in whom cirrhosis develops, contain larger amounts of α1AT, and inclusions usually occupy 50 to 80 percent of the parenchyma. Regenerative nodules may contain focal depositions of α1AT while others may show no depositions.

In those children presenting with neonatal hepatitis, the constant histopathologic features include intrahepatic cholestasis, varying degrees of hepatocellular injury, and moderate fibrosis with inflammatory cells in portal areas. Giant cell transformation is common. Initial liver biopsy occasionally shows marked ductular proliferation with bile plugging suggestive of biliary atresia, in the presence of a normal extrahepatic biliary tree,[150] or with patent narrowed extrahepatic bile ducts.[247] Some infants have a significant decrease in the number of interlobular bile ducts. In infants who develop later cirrhosis, liver biopsies show moderate to heavy periportal inflammatory cell infiltrate and hepatocyte swelling with patchy necrosis but no evidence of cholestasis. In infants whose liver disease apparently resolves, the main abnormality observed on later biopsy was mild to moderate portal fibrosis with a few inflammatory cells; none of these children showed hepatocellular necrosis, cholestasis, or bile ductular changes.[150]

Once the diagnosis of α1AT deficiency has been established, liver biopsy is usually unnecessary. Biopsy has been reported to be useful in establishing a long-term prognosis, since portal fibrosis and ductular proliferation appear less frequently in patients with a favorable course of the disease. However, even patients with these liver abnormalities can have a favorable outcome.[248] Surgery has been reported to not affect the course of the disease adversely although no supporting data were given.[249] The prognosis for infants who undergo laparotomy has not been carefully examined. Earlier onset and longer persistence of jaundice appear to occur in children who progress to an unfavorable outcome,[247] although this has not been observed in all studies.[150] The level of liver enzymes such as serum alanine aminotransferase and serum glutamyl transpeptidase can be very high in PI ZZ infants,[245,246] and the degree of elevation does not appear to be correlated with prognosis. However, persistent elevation of liver enzymes at greater than three times the normal upper limit tends to be associated with a poor prognosis.[245,247,248,250] From birth through 8 years of age, many children who appear to be clinically well still have an elevation of liver-derived serum enzymes. The serum concentration of alanine aminotransferase in 4-year-olds from the Swedish study is shown in Fig. 96-8. An elevation of enzymes of up to two or three times normal does not appear to be associated with a poor prognosis.[250] Measurement of urinary bile acids has been suggested to be useful for evaluating liver status in affected children.[251] Total bile acids remained consistently high in children whose early liver abnormalities progressed to cirrhosis.

Contrary to the initial indications of a poor prognosis in children with α1AT deficiency and early liver symptoms, it now appears that at least two-thirds of children show recovery from their liver damage.[150] In a retrospective study from England, 20 of 82 children (24.4 percent) developed cirrhosis, 19 had a persistently raised level of liver enzymes associated with clinical normality, and 23 had no evidence of liver disease.[252] At The Hospital for Sick Children, Toronto, we have estimated that, at most, 37 percent of a series of PI ZZ children with liver abnormalities in the early months of life have developed chronic severe liver disease, a figure which may be biased

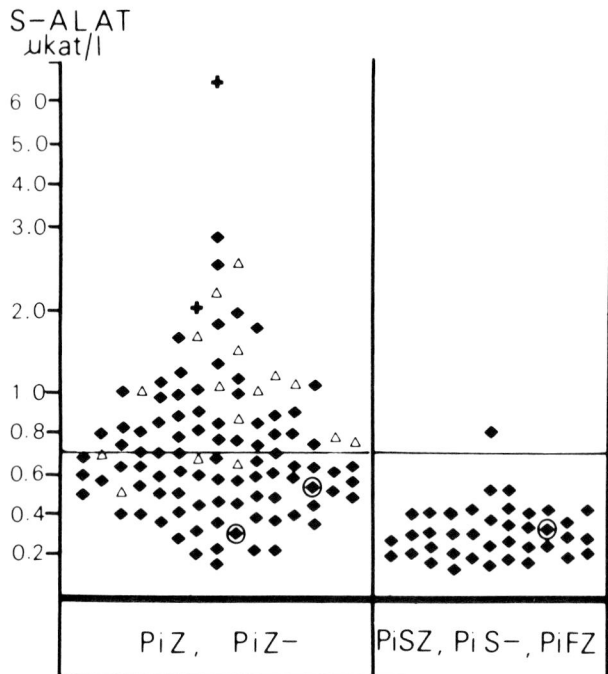

Fig. 96-8   Level of serum alanine aminotransferase (S-ALAT) of children with α1AT deficiency at follow-up at 4 years of age. Upper normal limit is 0.7 μkat/liter. PI types of children are indicated. + = children with liver cirrhosis; Δ = children with clinical symptoms of liver disease in the neonatal period; ▲ = children with no clinical signs of neonatal liver disease; ○ = children with null allele (PI Z−, S−). *(From Sveger and Thelin.[250] Used by permission of Acta Paediatrica Scandinavica.)*

upward because of ascertainment of more severely affected children early in the study.[150,253] At follow-up, at 8 years of age, of 122 PI Z (included 2 PI Z−) α1AT-deficient children identified from the Swedish screening program, 2 of 14 children with prolonged obstructive jaundice had died of liver cirrhosis. An additional PI ZZ child with clinical symptoms of neonatal liver disease without jaundice died of aplastic anemia at 4 years of age, with incipient liver cirrhosis at autopsy. Serum glutamic-oxaloacetic transaminase (SGOT) was elevated in 40 percent of the clinically healthy PI ZZ children. Liver cirrhosis with early death therefore occurred in only 3 of 122 PI ZZ children (2.4 percent), or in 13.6 percent of those PI Z children with clinical evidence of liver abnormalities in infancy.[254]

Factors predisposing to the development of progressive disease in the one-third of children who develop neonatal hepatitis have not been identified. Several studies have indicated that clinical and biochemical signs of cholestasis in PI ZZ infants occurred more frequently in males,[245,254] suggesting hormonal effects. A poorer prognosis for males has been suggested,[245,254] but it is not consistent in all series.[150,249,252] Hepatitis B virus infection, a suggested triggering factor for liver disease in PI ZZ infants,[255] has not been noted in other studies.[150,245,246]

The risk for progression of the liver disease has been reported to be reduced in infants who are breast-fed during the first month of life compared with those who are bottle-fed.[256] Excluding small for gestational age infants, 1 of 12 breast-fed infants and 8 of 20 bottle-fed infants developed severe liver disease. In the prospective Swedish study in which PI ZZ infants were identified through screening, 8 of 71 infants (11.3

percent) breast-fed for more than 1 month and 12 of 47 infants (25.5 percent) breast-fed for less than 1 month developed clinical signs of liver disease, and liver function tests were less abnormal than for the bottle-fed infants.[257] These differences were statistically significant. The two children who died of cirrhosis were both breast-fed for more than 1 month (T. Sveger, personal communication). A rationale for the effectiveness of breast-feeding has been proposed by which protease inhibitors in human milk help limit protease uptake and subsequent transport to the liver via the portal circulation.[258] Breast-feeding does not offer absolute protection against the development of severe liver disease but may decrease the likelihood of showing initial signs of liver abnormality and lead to a better prognosis. Further data are required to resolve this issue.

Some speculation might be made regarding factors which lead to progression of disease. Intracellular accumulation of α1AT has been shown to increase lysosomal enzyme activity,[172] which could contribute to liver damage. The presence of stored α1AT has not been established as the cause of fibrosis or cirrhosis. However, prior to cirrhosis, cell necrosis has been observed only in periportal hepatocytes with dilated endoplastic reticulum storing α1AT.[259] An autoimmune type of cellular damage could also be considered, with abnormal α1AT in hepatic inclusions stimulating an immune response. As hepatocytes containing α1AT are destroyed, the α1AT may be released and recognized as a foreign antigen. The α1AT in inclusions has some unique antigenic sites in comparison with normal M α1AT, since monoclonal antibody specific for Z α1AT has been produced.[260] Glomerular lesions found in patients with α1AT deficiency and cirrhosis is suggestive of an autoimmune response.[261] Children with impaired biliary secretion may develop deficiencies of fat-soluble vitamins. A deficiency of vitamin E in the liver could lead to excessively high oxidant levels, promoting membrane damage of haptocytes. Vitamin E therapy has been shown to improve liver function in a small number of children with cholestasis.[262] These speculations suggest further avenues for research and for potential therapy.

Unidentified genetic factors may be important in determining the prognosis in children with liver abnormalities in infancy. Sibship data from our hospital and from other series reporting a number of sibs of probands with liver disease have been reviewed.[263] In these studies, 32 families have been reported in which one or more sibs have been born in a family with a PI ZZ sib with liver abnormalities. In 15 families in which a PI ZZ sib has been born after a proband with resolved or no liver disease, 13 percent of subsequent sibs have developed liver disease. In 17 families in which the PI ZZ proband has developed severe liver disease, 40 percent of subsequent PI ZZ sibs have developed severe liver disease. The rate of recurrence for development of severe liver disease in a subsequent sib varies considerably between studies, with the highest risk, at 67 percent, reported from Great Britain.[252] The risk for a subsequent child to develop severe liver disease after a proband with resolved or no liver disease may not differ significantly from that of the general population, estimated to be about 2 percent.[254] In view of the great variability between studies, further follow-up studies with larger numbers are needed, and present risk estimates must be considered as approximate. There may be a tendency for sibs to follow the same clinical disease course, but normal healthy children with no liver involvement can be born subsequent to PI ZZ children developing severe liver disease.

Therapy

In some children with cirrhosis and recurrent gastrointestinal bleeding, portacaval shunt was thought to have been effective in slowing progression of the liver disease, with survival for 9 to 18 years following surgery.[248,264] It is difficult to know if the course of the disease would have differed without surgical intervention, since progression of disease often continues for years. The proposed benefit of this procedure is that absorbed intestinal proteases may be diverted from the liver to the systemic circulation, sparing the liver from further injury.[264] For seriously ill patients, the shunt procedure has been rapidly fatal.[265]

Since the cause of progressive liver disease in some PI ZZ children is unknown, there is no rationale for replacement therapy with α1AT. If the protease load from the intestine is crucial in the early weeks of life, then this is the period in which replacement therapy might be considered. The effects of such therapy would be extremely difficult to monitor, since the majority of children recover spontaneously from their liver abnormalities.

The end-stage treatment for liver disease is liver transplantation, which, if successful, provides a cure because the α1AT produced is that of the donor.[73]

Adult Onset

Cirrhosis and fibrosis of the liver were noted in Swedish adults with α1AT deficiency.[266] In a series of 246 Swedish PI Z patients ascertained through hospital admissions, 12 percent were found to have liver cirrhosis.[203] Of the PI ZZ individuals over 50 years of age, 19 percent had cirrhosis, apparently without a history of neonatal hepatitis. In a series of 115 adults with α1AT deficiency, 3.5 percent had biopsy or autopsy-proven cirrhosis and another had definite biochemical evidence of liver disease, providing a total figure of 5.2 percent affected with liver disease.[267] When these patients were classified by sex and age, the risks for development of liver disease for males and females, respectively, were as follows: age 20 to 40 years, 1.9 and 2.2 percent; age 41 to 50 years, 6.2 and 3.2 percent; age 51 to 60 years, 15.4 and 0 percent. These numbers should be considered as approximate because of the small numbers in each class; no corresponding figures for the normal population are available. However, they indicate an appreciable risk for the development of cirrhosis, particularly in males over 50 years of age. In an epidemiologic study based on autopsy cases of α1AT deficiency in a Swedish city, a strong relation was found between α1AT deficiency and cirrhosis, and also with primary liver cancer. These associations were statistically significant only for male patients.[268] The liver disease in adults appears to show rapid progression, and in most patients death has occurred within 2 years of the diagnosis of cirrhosis.[267,269] Perhaps the cirrhosis is advanced before diagnosis, with symptoms of cirrhosis having been masked by the presence of fatigue and dyspnea from pulmonary disease. Alcohol consumption does not appear to have been an important factor in the production of liver disease. In view of the appreciable risk for development of liver disease, particularly in males, avoidance of significant amounts of alcohol and environmental toxins would be prudent.

Primary Liver Carcinoma

Some patients with α1AT deficiency develop hepatocellular carcinoma (hepatoma), with or without cirrhosis, although the risk appears to be relatively small. High frequencies in some groups of patients may be due to bias of ascertainment. In an assessment of hepatic tissue from 14 adults of PI type Z, some of whom were also included in a later report,[270] cirrhosis of the liver was found in 5, fibrosis in 3, and 3 of the 8 had hepatoma.[266] α-Fetoprotein, usually elevated in hepatoma, is infrequently elevated in PI ZZ or MZ patients with hepatoma.[266,270]

Of 246 PI Z patients over 20 years of age admitted to Swedish hospitals, hepatoma was present in 3 percent,[203] possibly an underestimate, as 46 percent of the patients were under 50 years of age. A significant increase in primary liver cancer in males only with α1AT deficiency has been observed in Sweden in comparison with population controls.[268] Among a series of 140 adult Canadian patients of PI type Z,[267] two had hepatoma, one had cirrhosis without lung disease, one had lung disease without evidence of liver disease. Another patient with emphysema and no evidence of cirrhosis has also been reported to have hepatoma.[271] These data suggest that primary liver carcinoma apparently can occur in α1AT-deficient individuals without preexisting cirrhosis and may be due to the accumulation of α1AT in the liver.

In studies in which PI typing of patients with hepatoma has been carried out, homozygotes have not been found,[271,272] consistent with the rarity of α1AT deficiency in the population and the associated small risk for developing hepatoma. α1AT deficiency (homozygous or heterozygous) was not found in a series of 58 black South Africans with hepatoma,[273,274] not unexpected in view of the absence of *PI*Z in black populations. Studies of pathologic tissues have yielded conflicting and unreliable results. Of 56 Danish patients with hepatoma, 23 percent were found to have PAS-D-positive globules, taken to be indicative of the presence of Z-type α1AT, in the homozygous or heterozygous state.[275] Livers of 2 of 42 patients in England with hepatoma had PAS-D-positive granules, not more than expected in the normal population.[276] These studies are difficult to interpret since PI MZ individuals do not always show PAS granules in the liver, and tumor tissues can show PAS-D granules where no such granules are present in the nontumor tissue.[277] In general, the reports suggest an increased frequency of hepatocellular carcinoma, or hepatoma, associated with α1AT deficiency.

Risk for Heterozygotes

PI Type SZ Heterozygotes. A number of isolated cases of liver disease occurring in individuals of PI type SZ have been reported and have led to the conclusion by some that these individuals are at increased risk for liver disease.[278] The reports of isolated cases in both adults and children can be explained by chance, since about 1 in 700 to 1500 of the general population is of PI type SZ. The strongest evidence for lack of risk for childhood disease comes from the Swedish screening study, which has shown a modest elevation of liver enzymes in a portion of children of PI type SZ during the early months of life but with no clinical abnormalities or elevation

of liver enzymes by 8 years of age.[254] Screening of 857 Swedish adults with liver disease revealed seven of PI type SZ where one was expected, suggesting a possible increased risk for PI SZ adults.[270] Smaller studies have not confirmed this association.

PI Type MZ Heterozygotes. An increased risk for PI MZ individuals to develop cirrhosis has been suggested by isolated reports. However, since 2 to 4 percent of white populations are of PI type MZ, chance associations with liver disease would not be unexpected. In such surveys, appropriate PI typing must be carried out, as it is not possible to determine the phenotype based on PAS-D-positive inclusions in the liver. Individuals of both PI types MZ and ZZ can have inclusions. Furthermore, the presence of an anodal electrophoretic band migrating close to a major band of Z α1AT can cause such patients to be misdiagnosed as being of PI type MZ (Fig. 96-3A).

In a study in France of 159 adults with liver cirrhosis, 132 of which had chronic alcoholism, a small and nonsignificant increase in the number of PI MZ individuals in both alcoholic and nonalcoholic groups was found.[279] Of 857 Swedish patients with liver disease, 7.6 percent rather than the expected 4.8 percent were identified using a monoclonal antibody for detecting PI Z and were confirmed as of PI type MZ.[270] This difference, similar to those in previous studies, was significant with the larger patient number. In a study of English patients with various types of liver disease, a significant increase in PI MZ individuals was found only in patients with cirrhosis.[280] Among this group with cirrhosis, PI type MZ was found in 21 percent of all patients with HBsAg*-negative chronic active hepatitis and 21 percent of patients with cryptogenic cirrhosis. Conflicting data have been reported from England[156]; however, the latter study may not have identified those PI MZ individuals with normal plasma levels of α1AT. No other study has confirmed this high risk. If the risk is associated with a low concentration of α1AT, it is surprising that an even greater increase in frequency of PI SZ individuals has not been apparent in the various studies which have found an increased frequency of PI type MZ.

In summary, the risk for individuals heterozygous for α1AT deficiency does not appear to be appreciable. The possible but inconsistent association with HBsAg-negative chronic active hepatitis, which requires confirmation, suggests that environmental agents can trigger chronic active hepatitis in susceptible individuals.

OTHER DISEASE ASSOCIATIONS

Disorders with an Immune Component

The experimental evidence for involvement of α1AT in the immune response has been outlined. Clinical reports further support this involvement.

Kidney Disease. Membranoproliferative glomerulonephritis (MPGN) has occasionally been reported in patients with α1AT. Multiple immune complex disorders have been reported in two adults with α1AT deficiency, obstructive lung disease, progressive glomerulonephritis, and, in addition, mild

---

*HBsAG = hepatitis B antigen.

liver disease and necrotizing angiitis,[281] or cutaneous vasculitis and colitis.[282] MPGN has been identified in eight PI ZZ children who have also had liver disease.[261,283,284] Low levels of compliment C3 were reported in two of these patients and circulating immune complex in the one patient tested.[284] Deposits of α1AT were detected along the glomerular basement membrane, using immunofluorescent techniques, in autopsy specimens in two patients[150,283] but not in the one biopsy specimen examined.[284] Deposits of immunoglobulins IgG, M, and A, and C3, frequently found in cases of MPGN, were also identified.[150,283] One hypothesis is that abnormal α1AT from liver inclusions participates in the formation of an immune complex. All the children in whom MPGN was identified had severe liver disease, suggesting that the kidney abnormality was a consequence of the liver disease. However, in a study of 246 Swedish PI Z patients, 37 (15 percent) showed signs of glomerular renal damage, indicated by constant or recurrent proteinuria or hematuria.[203] Three patients (1 percent) developed advanced renal failure. Since these patients were all ascertained through hospitalization, the probability for PI Z patients to develop severe renal disease appears to be low, although its association with liver disease in this condition may be relatively high. α1AT deficiency is not a common cause of MPGN. Among 53 patients with idiopathic MPGN, none were homozygous or heterozygous for PI Z.[284]

Rheumatoid Arthritis. An increased frequency of the heterozygous deficiency PI types MZ and SZ was reported in adults with rheumatoid arthritis.[285] Subsequent studies have been carried out in different populations with conflicting results. This disagreement could be due to geographic difference, but more likely to differences in patient selection. In a U.S. study, no increase in Z heterozygosity was found among patients mostly off medication and therefore probably not severely affected.[286] No increase in Z heterozygotes was found in patients, not selected for disease severity, in Sweden[287] or Switzerland.[288] However, in another Swedish study, in whom all 200 patients had erosive rheumatoid arthritis, an increase in Z heterozygotes was found.[289] A significant increase in PI MZ patients has been shown in three British studies[290–292] and in Australia.[69] The report of an increase in PI type MS[69] must be interpreted with caution because of marked differences in population frequencies for the *PI*S* allele. These data seem to be compatible with our conclusion that an increased frequency of Z heterozygosity occurs particularly in individuals with seropositive erosive arthritis.[293] In the Swedish study of 246 hospitalized PI Z patients, 4.4 percent had rheumatoid arthritis and another 3 percent had a history of considerable joint pain with no confirmed diagnosis.[203] We have concluded that tissue destruction occurs more readily in the PI Z heterozygote because of inadequate α1AT present in the joint fluid to prevent leukocyte elastase, cathepsin G, and collagenase from attacking the structural proteins of joint cartilage.[293]

A numeric but nonsignificant increase in Z heterozygotes was found in children with juvenile rheumatoid arthritis,[293] and a study of more severely affected British children showed a significantly increased frequency of PI type MZ.[294] Juvenile arthritis consists of a number of different subgroups, and perhaps some but not all of these subgroups show increased susceptibilty.

Other Immune Disorders. Anterior uveitis, an immunologically mediated inflammatory eye disease, has been reported to be associated with an increased frequency of Z heterozygotes,[295,296] with an increase also in PI type MS in the latter study. The association was not confirmed in a study of 57 white American patients.[297] These discrepancies may be due to the type of patients selected. In posterior uveitis, 2 of 16 patients were of PI type MZ,[296] and further studies of these types of patients are required. Studies of PI MZ frequency in psoriasis have been contradictory.[298,299] Isolated cases of PI Z individuals with persistent cutaneous vasculitis,[300] panarteritis in association with emphysema and glomerular nephritis,[281] Hashimoto's thyroiditis,[301] and severe combined immunodeficiency[302] have been reported. Among five patients with panniculitis (Weber Christian Disease), two severely affected had α1AT deficiency.[303] Two of three sibs of PI type ZZ were reported to have panniculitis.[304] In one PI Z patient, panniculitis was found to be due to histoplasmosis,[305] and it would be of interest to know if this might have been a precipitating factor in the other affected individuals. A slight but nonstatistically significant increase of PI MZ from 3 to 7 percent was observed in systemic lupus erythematosia.[69] SLE occurred in 2 of 246 adult Swedish patients.[203]

The above associations all suggest that individuals with reduced levels of α1AT may show some hyperactivity of the immune system, leading to an increased risk for certain disorders with an autoimmune component. This increased susceptibility may be further enhanced by a decreased ability to control local inflammation. Further aspects of associations with immune disorders have been reviewed.[69]

Other Associations

Idiopathic Hemachromotosis. The isolated reports in PI MZ heterozygotes and in homozygotes[306,307] may be due to chance association, or hemachrometosis could promote cirrhosis when coexisting with α1AT deficiency. The PI Z gene, as detected by a monoclonal antibody, has not been found in either the heterozygous or homozygous state in 27 male patients with idiopathic hemachromotosis, all from the same region of Sweden.[308]

Chromosome Anomalies. An increased frequency of chromosome aberrations was reported with PI types other than M, but not with Z heterozygosity.[309] An increase of Z heterozygotes was found among parents of 21 probands with X-chromosome mosaicism.[310] The overall frequency of Z heterozygosity among patients with Down syndrome appears to be similar to that of the normal population (reviewed in Ref. 10). Proteolytic enzymes are involved in fertilization in cell division and could potentially be disturbed in the presence of inadequate protease inhibition.[309] Perhaps the same mechanisms are involved in the suggested slight increase in twinning associated with MZ[311] and MS[312] heterozygotes.

A variety of single case reports involving other disorders have been reviewed.[67]

PRENATAL DIAGNOSIS

Prenatal diagnosis can be carried out by PI typing of fetal blood obtained at fetoscopy. Because of the relatively high risk to the fetus, DNA analysis is preferable. The source of fetal DNA can be amniocytes or chorion villi.

Reliable PI typing is a crucial first step in prenatal diagnosis to determine that both parents have the Z allele and that there is no rare deficiency or null allele present in either parent.

Fetal Blood Analysis

Prenatal diagnsois of α1AT deficiency was first carried out on fetal blood samples obtained at fetoscopy.[313,314] Fetal blood was obtained as a mixture with amniotic fluid following puncture of a placental vessel, or pure fetal blood was obtained by cannulation of a fetal vessel. A fetal loss of 5 percent has been reported using this procedure.[315] Prenatal diagnosis was carried out in England by fetal sampling in 25 pregnancies at 17 to 20 weeks gestation.[316] Test results were confirmed postnatally, but two pregnancies ended in spontaneous abortion at 20 to 22 weeks and one was delivered prematurely at 31 weeks gestation. Probably the death of two (16 percent) of these fetuses was associated with the procedure. The possible high risk of pregnancy loss and the late stage for testing are undesirable features of this approach.

Recombinant DNA Methods

Prenatal diagnosis using DNA markers offers the advantages of a lower risk of fetal loss and testing at an earlier stage of pregnancy, particularly when chorion villus biopsy samples are used. There are two approaches to diagnosis of α1AT deficiency, and both can be applied equally well on cultured amniocytes or uncultured chorion villus. These two approaches involve the use of either synthetic oligonucleotide probes or genomic probes for the identification of genetic polymorphisms.

Synthetic Oligonucleotide Probes. Appropriate probes recognize a single base pair mutation and therefore can be used in any disorder for which the mutant site has been identified. Specific oligonucleotide probes have been prepared around the Z mutant site in amino acid 342 for normal M and deficiency Z DNA sequences.[138] These probes have been used for prenatal diagnosis.[317] Specific restriction enzymes are used to cut the DNA into fragments, which are separated by gel electrophoresis, hybridized with appropriate "oligo" probes, followed by gel washing alternately under high and low stringency conditions. Precise control of stringency, by temperature and salt concentration, is required to optimize conditions so that only the sequence specific to the given probe (normal or mutant) will hybridize. A 15- to 18-mg biopsy sample of chorion villus will yield about 15 μg of DNA. In some laboratories, a minimum of 10 to 15 μg of DNA is required for the procedure, particularly when probe hybridization is carried out directly in the gel. In a study of 16 prenatal diagnoses in which synthetic and genomic probes were compared, the oligonucleotide method required three times the quantity of fetal DNA.[318]

Improvement in technology is allowing less DNA, about 3 μg, to be adequate. Methods for gene amplification which allow the use of nanogram amounts of DNA have recently been developed,[319] providing the possibility of smaller chorion villus samples or the use of uncultured amniocytes. This method requires that the presence of a Z allele is definitely established in both parents, as the probes will not recognize the rare deficiency mutations.

Restriction Site Polymorphisms. Genomic probes from the α1AT gene can be used to identify polymorphic restriction fragments which predict the PI type of the fetus. In the typical type of prenatal diagnosis using restriction fragment length polymorphisms, the particular DNA fragments segregating with the disease gene vary in each family and must be established by testing parents and sibs of the at-risk fetus. Recombination between the marker and the gene can occur when the marker is outside the disease gene but usually does not occur within a gene of average size. Genomic probes used for diagnosis of α1AT deficiency lie within the gene and detect polymorphisms both of α1AT and the α1AT-homologous region. α1AT deficiency is unusual, to date, in that the DNA haplotype associated with the PI*Z allele has been found to be specific and unique. Studies of parents and sibs are theoretically unnecessary, although in practice they are advisable because of the possibility of rare exceptions. Polymorphisms in the α1AT region have been discussed. Each restriction digest requires about 3 μg of DNA; therefore, small amounts of DNA from fetal samples are adequate. Using genomic probes only, culture of chorion villus is not required, and is undesirable, to avoid possible maternal contamination. Two different restriction enzyme digests are advisable for verification of results.

The most useful probe for prenatal diagnosis is genomic probe 6.5 (Fig. 96-2). The restriction enzymes which have been found to be particularly useful for prenatal diagnosis are Ava II, Mae III, and a combination of BstE II and Bgl II. Ava II was the first enzyme to be applied in prenatal diagnosis.[263,318,320] The Ava II polymorphism can be used for analysis using cultured amniocytes but is less satisfactory for chorion villus DNA. An additonal Ava II site is cleaved in chorion villus DNA, presumably as a consequence of a difference in methylation, resulting in an altered pattern.[263] Resolution of the fragments must be extremely good to avoid a misdiagnosis, and, because of the intensity of the additional fragment, a weak band 4 may be not visible. Therefore, for chorion villus, additional restriction enzymes should be used. This approach has been used successfully for 16 pregnancies, for which cultured amniotic cells (11 pregnancies), or cultured chorion villus (5 pregnancies)[318] were used. The 16 fetal tissues were tested both by oligonucleotide probes and by restriction fragment analysis.

The restriction enzyme Mae III also produces a unique haplotype for PI*Z. As noted previously, Z and a portion of M1 alleles lack a site for the restriction enzyme Mae III, which is present in association with other PI variants.[118,139] This enzyme has been used in prenatal diagnosis,[118] and, in those pregnancies where one or both parents have the Mae III site in their α1AT gene, a result for the fetal DNA can be obtained quickly because of the intensity of the major α1AT fragments.

A third enzyme system producing a unique haplotype is a combined digest with BstE II and Bgl II, which has also been useful in prenatal diagnosis.[141]

The Taq I and Eco RI polymorphisms produce a high degree of heterozygosity and can be used as confirmatory enzymes if desired. However, the enzymes described which produce unique haplotypes are most useful.

If previous PI typing in the family has indicated the presence of a rare deficiency allele or a PI null allele, the DNA polymorphisms can still be used for prenatal diagnosis in a more conventional way, by following segregation of markers in the family.

POPULATION SCREENING

The screening of 200,000 Swedish infants has demonstrated that newborn screening is feasible.[149,245] In this study, a disk was punched from a dried blood sample on filter paper and eluted for semiquantitative assay of both α1AT and of transferrin, as internal standard, by electroimmunoassay. Infants with less than 40 percent of normal α1AT had a blood sample drawn for PI typing. The majority of the infants ascertained in this way were found to be of PI type ZZ; 28 percent of those PI typed were of PI type SZ. Although electroimmunoassay was used in this population screening, automated nephelometry could be used for the quantitation of α1AT and transferrin. The screening program could be conveniently carried out on the same dried blood spots used for the Guthrie test for newborns for phenylketonuria. PI typing can be carried out on the dried blood samples by using silver stain following PIEF.[321]

At present, the main value of a population screening program would be to counsel the parents to encourage their affected children to avoid smoking later in life. Further, the message of avoidance of smoking must be reinforced directly with the children as they reach teen years. Even with such reinforcement, we do not know if young adults who are then healthy will avoid smoking. Because of the known increased risk of respiratory disease in children of cigarette smokers, parents of children with α1AT deficiency should be advised not to smoke. At 4-year follow-up of the Swedish children screened for α1AT deficiency, 26 percent of parents had stopped smoking specifically because of their child's deficiency. However 44 percent of mothers and 33 percent of fathers continued smoking.[250] The data are very clear, as discussed, in indicating that if smoking is avoided, the onset of obstructive pulmonary disease will be considerably delayed.

An extensive follow-up of psychological consequences of the Swedish screening program has been undertaken.[322] In this study, 78 percent of the mothers and 58 percent of the fathers reported having immediately negative emotional reactions to the news of their infants' α1AT deficiency, and a majority initially conceived α1AT deficiency as an imminent and serious threat to their child's health.[323] These negative feelings were still found to be present in 58 percent of mothers and 44 percent of fathers when interviewed 5 to 7 years after the initial identification of α1AT deficiency.[324] If population screening is undertaken in newborns, parents should be informed that the testing is to be undertaken and should be informed of the presence of the deficiency in their infant by an individual knowledgeable about the condition. Repeated long-term follow-up beyond the first year of life may be unnecessary for those children who show no signs of liver disturbance. Some provision must be made for later reinforcement of the need for avoidance of smoking, which may be difficult in families with a high degree of mobility.

While screening during the newborn period, in combination with other neonatal screening, is probably most efficient, the avoidance of smoking later in life may be more effectively accomplished by a screening program later in childhood.

The Swedish study has provided valuable information on the risk for development of liver disease and on the course and prognosis for affected children. However, at the present time, no treatment is available for those children who develop early liver abnormalities followed by progressive liver disease. The encouragement of breast-feeding may be beneficial, although further data will be required to determine if this does truly influence the prognosis. Replacement therapy may become available in future for affected children.

THERAPY

Therapy for Lung Destruction

Preventative Therapy. The most effective therapy for the lung destruction of α1AT deficiency is prevention, predominantly through avoidance of smoking. In those individuals who begin to show relatively early signs of lung destruction, the rate of destruction may be slowed by the restoration of the protease-inhibitor balance in the lung through administration of suitable protease inhibitors.

In the earliest studies of α1AT deficiency, subjects were ascertained mainly through pulmonary clinics, leading to the impression that most individuals with the deficiency would eventually develop emphysema. However, the outlook for those with α1AT deficiency now appears to be more positive. In order to prevent lung destruction, the most important message for patients with the deficiency is to avoid exposure to smoke at all ages.

In view of the previously discussed mechanisms for lung damage to be potentiated through oxidation, consideration should be given to maintaining maximal antioxidant activity in lung tissue. The vitamin E status may be important in determining individual susceptibility to lung destruction. Administration of vitamin E in doses which adequately cover the daily requirements may help to protect lung tissue.

Danazol Therapy. The rationale behind consideration of danazol therapy was that the plasma concentration of α1AT could be increased by inducing increased production of α1AT in the liver, therefore increasing the plasma concentration. At one time, this was proposed as potential therapy for the deficiency.[63] Danazol is an isoxazole derivative of the synthetic steroid 17-ethinyl testosterone, which lacks major androgenic properties and has been used successfully in the treatment of a deficiency of the serine protease inhibitor C1 esterase in hereditary angioedema.[325] Of 43 patients with α1AT deficiency treated with danazol for 1 month, approximately 50 percent, mainly males, responded with an increased serum concentration of α1AT. The mean peak response was 44 mg/dl, or about 19 percent of normal.[326] A response of this magnitude is below the concentration found in SZ individuals, about 35 percent of normal, which may be sufficient to protect against lung destruction. However, after a 1-month trial of danazol, a number of adverse side effects were noted, including an increase in liver transaminases in 19 percent of patients.[326] Since increased production of PI Z α1AT leads to an increased accumulation of aggregated α1AT in the liver, and if this abnormal storage is responsible for the liver disease, danazol therapy might potentiate liver damage. Other similar agents intended to increase the plasma α1AT concentration, such as tamoxifen,[327] could present a similar risk. Since these individuals already have an increased risk for the development of liver disease, this type of therapy seems inappropriate.[328]

Replacement of α₁-Antitrypsin. Administration of α1AT to increase the plasma concentration to that found in PI SZ heterozygotes or preferably PI MZ heterozygotes (35 to 60 percent of normal) should delay the rate of lung deterioration or, if administered early, should prevent it. Because the lung destruction is a chronic lifetime process, constant maintenance of an increased blood level of α1AT would be required. The half-life of plasma α1AT is 6.7 days.[80] Therefore successful therapy requires continuous infusion at frequent time intervals to maintain an adequate protective blood concentration of α1AT. Because of the variation between individuals in rate of lung decline, a properly controlled clinical study, with monitoring of decline in lung function or mortality rate, would be exceedingly difficult and costly. To demonstrate a 40 percent decrease in the decline of FEV_1 would require 500 patients and controls studied for a 3-year period.[329] Therefore, proof of efficacy of therapeutic products has been considered to be established if the product raises α1AT plasma concentration to levels found in patients of PI type MZ and if active α1AT is found in lung wash fluids of treated patients.[330] Preliminary studies in PI Z individuals with emphysema showed that crude concentrate from human plasma infused once weekly established a normal elastase-antielastase balance within the lower respiratory tract.[331] A therapeutic trial, for PI Z patients, in which 60 mg of active α1AT was infused weekly, has been reported for 5 patients for 1 month and 18 patients for 6 months.[332] Serum α1AT levels were maintained above a threshold level of 40 percent of normal, and antielastase levels in lung lavage fluids were increased from 0.46 ± 0.16 to 1.89 ± 0.17 μM (26 percent of normal) at minimum. The threshold protective lavage fluid concentration of α1AT, estimated to be 1.3 μM, was surpassed 83 percent of the time. Since this type of therapy should not cause an increased storage of α1AT in the liver, no increased risk to the liver would be predicted, although long-term studies have not been carried out. A disadvantage is the requirement for weekly injections of large amounts of α1AT. Possibly, in the nonsmoker, sufficient protection can be achieved through the use of α1AT infusions only during periods of respiratory infection. This therapy has been used over a short time period in a null homozygote[213]; potential antibody formation in patients who completely lack α1AT must be monitored carefully for long-term therapy.

Replacement with Synthetic α1AT. Because of the requirements for large amounts of α1AT and the potential risk of infection in using human blood products, large scale synthesis of human α1AT through recombinant DNA methodology is potentially useful.

Normal human α1AT has been produced at high levels in *Escherichia coli*.[21,333,334] and in yeast.[23] In both hosts, the α1AT was found to be functionally active as an elastase inhibitor, with comparable activity of neutrophil elastase inhibition in the presence of α1AT-deficient plasma.[335] A modified α1AT resistant to oxidative inactivation has been produced by site-directed mutagenesis, substituting valine for methionine at amino acid 385.[23,333,336] The valine form produced in yeast has been shown to have as effective inhibition against neutrophil and pancreatic elastase as the normal methionine form, but it does not inhibit cathepsin G, pancreatic trypsin, plasmin, factor Xa, or thrombin.[337] The valine form is also effective at inhibiting proteolysis of glomerular basement membrane by neutrophils.[336] This form shows effective resistance to oxida-

tion by a variety of oxidants including *N*-chlorosuccinimide, myeloperoxidase, activated neutrophils, and smoke, although sufficiently long exposure to these agents brings about some inactivation.[338] Since some oxidation occurs with the valine mutant, other methionine residues in the protein may also be oxidized.[339]

The α1AT produced in yeast and *E. coli* completely lacks carbohydrate side chains. While functional characteristics of the synthetic α1AT are normal, heat stability is decreased, indicating that the carbohydrate side chains are important for normal stability.[332] Lack of side chains presents a major problem for the use of these synthetic forms, as their half-life is extremely short. The valine and methionine mutants in yeast have a half-life of 8.5 h in the rabbit, in comparison with the normal human α1AT of 2.2 days.[337] An advantage of the use of the valine form is that, because of its resistance to oxidation, lower doses may be required. However, frequent administration of the synthetic α1AT would still be necessary and the potential for antibody formation in null homozygotes would remain.

Other Therapeutic Approaches. Low molecular weight inhibitors offer potential for therapy. They usually disappear rapidly from the circulation, but direct therapy to the lungs by aerosol administration may be possible. A number of chloromethyl ketone peptides[339] and peptide aldehydes are potent elastase-specific inhibitors. The latter are resistant to oxidation[340] and in animal studies are effective in preventing or decreasing lung destruction resulting from instilled or injected elastase.[340–342] If nontoxic, such inhibitors may show promise for therapy.[343] Other potentially useful agents are cephalosporin antibiotics, which can be modified to become potent elastase inhibitors.[344]

As is the case for liver disease, organ transplantation offers the only treatment for end-stage tissue destruction. Recent advances in this area indicate that such treatment may become more feasible in future. Double lung transplant is required, since hyperinflatability of an affected lung would preclude use of a single transplant. Advances in this area are proceeding rapidly. At the time of writing, more than 100 heart-lung transplants have been performed worldwide, and 1-year survival appears to be about 50 percent.[345] Obliterative broncheolitis may present a problem in long-term, i.e., greater than 1-year, survivors.[346] Double lung transplants have been carried out recently in Toronto, Canada, and two of the three recipients have α1AT deficiency (J. Cooper, personal communication). Potential problems for such patients are inadequate defense from leukocyte elastase produced during infection and the possibility of toxic effects on the kidney in individuals who may already be predisposed to renal damage. The feasibility of lung transplantation for patients with α1AT deficiency therefore awaits further experience and follow-up studies. The approaches of preventative therapy with protease inhibitors, with antioxidants, and lung transplantation when disease is advanced offer future hope for affected individuals.

This chapter is dedicated to the late Andrew Sass-Kortsak, M.D., F.R.C.P. (C), my teacher, mentor, and friend, who was responsible for initiation of studies of α1AT and provided continuous support.

I acknowledge with thanks Dr. Jan-Olaf Jeppsson, Dr. Thomas Sveger, Dr. Eve Roberts, Dr. Henry Levison, and Dr. Gail Fraizer for review and helpful comments; Gail Billingsley for assistance in manuscript preparation, Mary Grace Brubacher for preparing some of the figures, and Sharon Kerbel for typing the manuscript.

REFERENCES

1. SCHULTZE HE, GOLLNER I, HEIDE K, SCHONENBERGER M, SCHWICK G: Zur Kenntnis der alpha globuline des menschlichen normalserums. *Z Naturforsch* 10:463, 1955.

2. SCHULTZE HE, HEIDE K, HAUPT H: α_1-Antitrypsin aus humanserum. *Klin Wochenschr* 40:427, 1962.

3. FAGERHOL MK, LAURELL C-B: The Pi system—Inherited variants of serum α-antitrypsin, in Steinberg A, Bearn A (eds): *Progress in Medical Genetics.* New York, Grune & Stratton, 1970, vol VII, p 96.

4. KUEPPERS F: Inherited differences in alpha$_1$-antitrypsin, in L'enfant C (ed): *Lung Biology in Health and Disease* New York, Marcel Dekker, 1978, vol 13, p 23.

5. LAURELL C-B, ERIKSSON S: The electrophoretic α_1-globulin pattern of serum in α_1-antitrypsin deficiency. *Scand J Clin Lab Invest* 15:132, 1963.

6. ERIKSSON S: Pulmonary emphysema and alpha$_1$-antitrypsin deficiency. *Acta Med Scand* 175:197, 1964.

7. ERIKSSON S: Studies in α_1-antitrypsin deficiency. *Acta Med Scand* 177 suppl 432:5, 1965.

8. FAGERHOL MK, BRAEND M: Serum prealbumin: Polymorphism in man. *Science* 149:986, 1965.

9. FAGERHOL MK, LAURELL C-B: The polymorphism of "prealbumins" and α_1-antitrypsin in human sera. *Clin Chim Acta* 16:199, 1967.

10. FAGERHOL MK, COX DW: The Pi polymorphism: Genetic, biochemical and clinical aspects of human α_1-antitrypsin, in Harris H, Hirschhorn K (eds): *Advances in Human Genetics.* New York, London, Plenum, 1981, vol 11, p 1.

11. AXELSON U, LAURELL C-B: Hereditary variants of serum α_1-antitrypsin. *Am J Hum Genet* 17:466, 1965.

12. FAGERHOL MK: Serum Pi types in Norwegians. *Acta Pathol Microbiol Scand* 70:421, 1967.

13. SHARP HL, BRIDGES RA, KRIVIT W: Cirrhosis associated with alpha-1-antritrypsin deficiency: A previously unrecognized inherited disorder. *J Lab Clin Med* 73:934, 1969.

14. LAURELL C-B, JEPPSSON J-O, 1975. Protease inhibitors in plasma, in Putnam F (ed): *The Plasma Proteins* New York, Academic, 1975, vol I, p 229.

15. TRAVIS J, SALVESEN GS: Human plasma proteinase inhibitors. *Annu Rev Biochem* 52:655, 1983.

16. ALLEN RC, HARLEY RA, TALAMO RC: A new method for determination of alpha$_1$-antitrypsin phenotypes using isoelectric focusing on polyacrylamide gel slabs. *Am J Clin Pathol* 62:732, 1974.

17. JEPPSSON J-O, LAURELL C-B, FAGERHOL MK: Properties of isolated α_1-antitrypsin of Pi types M, S and Z. *Eur J Biochem* 83:143, 1978.

18. CARRELL RW, OWEN MC: α_1-Antitrypsin.: Structure, variation and disease. *Essays Med Biochem* 4:83, 1978.

19. VERBANAC KM, HEATH EC: Biosynthesis, processing, and secretion of M and Z variant human α_1-antitrypsin. *J Biol Chem* 261:9979, 1986.

20. CARLSON J, STENFO J: The biosynthesis of rat α_1-antitrypsin. *J Biol Chem* 257:12987, 1982.

21. BOLLEN A, HERZOG A, CRAVADOR A, HERION P, CHUCHANA P, VANDER STRATEN A, LORIAU R, JACOBS P, VAN ELSEN A: Cloning and expression in Escherichia coli of full-length complementary DNA coding for human α_1-antitrypsin. *DNA* 2:255, 1983.

22. LONG GI, CHANDRA T, WOO SLC, DAVIE EW, KURACHI K: Complete sequence of the cDNA for human α_1-antitrypsin and the gene for the S variant. *Biochemistry* 23:4828, 1984.

23. ROSENBERG S, BARR, PJ, NAJARIAN RC, HALLEWELL RA: Synthesis in yeast of a functional oxidation-resistant mutant of human α_1-antitrypsin. *Nature* 312:77, 1984.

24. LOEBERMANN H, TOKUOKA R, DEISENHOFER J, HUBER R: Human alph$_1$-proteinase inhibitor. Crystal structure analysis of two crystal modifications, molecular model and preliminary analysis of the implications for function. *J Mol Biol* 177:531, 1984.

25. LAURELL C-B, PIERCE J, PERSSON U, THULIN E: Purification of α_1-antitrypsin from plasma through thiol-disulfide interchange. *Eur J Biochem* 57:107, 1975.

26. LAUREL C-B, THULIN E: Complexes in human plasma between α_1-antitrypsin and IgA, and α_1-antitrypsin and fibrinogen. *Scand J Immunol* 4:7, 1975.

27. FAGERHOL MK: Quantitative studies on the inherited variants of serum α_1-antitrypsin. *Scand J Clin Lab Infest* 23:97, 1969.

28. LAURELL C-B, PERSSON U: Analysis of plasma α_1-antitrypsin variants and their microheterogeneity. *Biochim Biophys Acta* 310:500, 1972.

29. VAUGHAN L, LORIER MA, CARRELL RW: α_1-Antitrypsin microheterogeneity isolation and physiological significance of isoforms. *Biochim Biophys Acta* 701:339, 1982.

30. CARRELL RW, JEPPSSON J-O, VAUGHAN SO, BRENNAN SO, OWEN MC, BOSWELL DR: Human α_1-antitrypsin: Carbohydrate attachment and sequence homology. *FEBS Lett* 135:301, 1981.

31. CHAN SK, REES DC, LI S-C, LI Y-T: Linear structure of oligosaccharide chains in α_1-protease inhibitor isolated from human plasma. *J Biol Chem* 251:471, 1976.

32. MEGA T, LUJAN E, YOSHIDA A: Studes on the oligosaccharide chains of human α_1-protease inhibitor. *J Biol Chem* 255:4053, 1980.

33. BAYARD B, KERCKAERT J-P, LAINE A, HAYEM A: Uniformity of glycans within molecular variants of α_1-protease inhibitor with distinct affinity for conconavalin-A. *J Biochem* 124:371, 1982.

34. JEPPSSON J-O, LILJA H, JOHANSSON M: Isolation and characterization of two minor fractions of α_1-antitrypsin by high-performance liquid chromatographic chromatofocusing. *J Chromatogr* 327:173, 1985.

35. CARRELL RW, JEPPSSON J-O, LAURELL C-B, BRENNAN SO, OWEN MC, VAUGHAN L, BOSWELL DR: Structure and variation of human α1-antitrypsin. *Nature* 298:329, 1982.

36. JOHNSON D, TRAVIS J: Structural evidence for methionine at the reactive site of human α-1-proteinase inhibitor. *J Biol Chem* 253:7142, 1978.

37. LASKOWSKI M Jr, KATO I: Protein inhibitors of proteinases. *Annu Rev Biochem* 49:593, 1980.

38. JOHNSON D, TRAVIS J: The oxidative inactivation of human α-1-proteinase inhibitor. *J Biol Chem* 254:4022, 1979.

39. BEATTY K, BIETH J, TRAVIS J: Kinetics of association of serine proteinases with native and oxidized α-1-proteinase inhibitor and α-1-antichymotrypsin. *J Biol Chem* 255:3931, 1980.

40. CARRELL RW, OWEN MC: Plakalbumin, α_1-antitrypsin, antithrombin and the mechanism of inflammatory thrombosis. *Nature* 317:730, 1985.

41. HILL RE, SHAW PH, BOYD PA, BAUMANN H, HASTIE ND: Plasma protease inhibitors in mouse and man: Divergence within the reactive centre regions. *Nature* 311:175, 1984.

42. OWEN MC, BRENNAN SO, LEWIS JH, CARREL RW: Mutation of antitrypsin to antithrombin: α_1 antitrypsin-Pittsburgh (358 Met → Arg), a fatal bleeding disorder. *N Engl J Med* 309:694, 1983.

43. CILIBERTO G, DENTE L, CORTESE R: Cell-specific expression of a transfected human α_1-antitrypsin gene. *Cell* 4:531, 1985.

44. KELSEY GD, POVEY S, BYGRAVE AE, LOVELL-BADGE RH: Species-and-tissue-specific expression of human α_1-antitrypsin in transgenic mice. *Genes Dev* 1:161, 1987.

45. PERLINO E, CORTESE R, CILIBERTO G: The human α_1-antitrypsin gene is transcribed from two different promoters in macrophages and hepatocytes. *EMBO J* 6:2767, 1987.

46. HUNT LT, DAYHOFF MO: A surprising new protein superfamily containing ovalbumin, anti-thrombin-III, and alpha$_1$-proteinase inhibitor. *Biochem Biophys Res Commun* 95:864, 1980.

47. FLINK IL, BAILEY TJ, GUSTAFSON TA, MARKHAM BE, MORKIN E: Complete amino acid sequence of human thyroxine-binding globulin deduced from cloned DNA: Close homology to the serine antiproteases. *Proc Natl Acad Sci USA* 83:7708, 1986.

48. KURACHI K, CHANDRA T, FRIEZNER DEGEN SJ, WHITE TT, MARCHIORO TL, WOO SLC, DAVIE EW: Cloning and sequence of cDNA coding for α_1-antitrypsin. *Proc Natl Acad Sci USA* 78:6826, 1981.

49. TOSI M, DUPONCHEL C, BOURGAREL P, COLOMB M, MEO T: Molecular cloning of human C1 inhibitor: Sequence homologies with α_1-antitrypsin and other members of the serpins super family. *Gene* 42:265, 1986.

50. LEICHT M, LONG GL, CHANDRA T, KURACHI K, KIDD VJ, MACE M JR, DAVIE EW, WOO SLC: Sequence homology and structural comparison between the chromosomal human α_1-antitrypsin and chicken ovalbumin genes. *Nature* 297:655, 1982.

51. GEDDE-DAHL T, FAHERHOL MK, COOK PJL, NOADES J: Autosomal linkage between the Gm and Pi loci in man. *Ann Hum Genet* 35:393, 1972.

52. DARLINGTON GJ, ASTRIN KH, MUIRHEAD SP, DESNICK RJ, SMITH M: Assignment of the human alpha-1-antitrypsin gene to chromosome 14 by somatic cell hybrid analysis. *Proc Natl Acad Sci USA* 79:870, 1982.

53. PEARSON SJ, TETRI P, GEORGE DL, FRANCKE U: Activation of human alpha$_1$-antitrypsin gene in rat hepatoma x human fetal liver cell hybrids depends on the presence of human chromosome 14. *Somatic Cell Genet* 5:567, 1983.

54. LAI EC, KAO F-T, LAW ML, WOO SLC: Assignment of the α_1-antitrypsin

gene and a sequence-related gene to human chromosome 14 by molecular hybridization. *Am J Hum Genet* 35:385, 1983.

55. COX DW, MARKOVIC VD, TESHIMA IE: Genes for immunoglobulin heavy chains and for alpha-1-antitrypsin are localized to specific regions of chromosome 14q. *Nature* 297:428, 1982.

56. SCHROEDER WT, MILLER MF, WOO SLC, SAUNDERS GF: Chromosomal localization of the human α_1-antitrypsin gene (PI) to 14q31-32. *Am J Hum Genet* 37:868, 1985.

57. RABIN M, WATSON M, KIDD V, WOO SLC, BREG RW, RUDDLE FH: Regional location of α_1-antichymotrypsin and α_1-antitrypsin genes on human chromosome 14. *Somatic Cell Mol Genet* 12:209, 1986.

58. PURRELLO M, ALHADEFF B, WHITTINGTON E, BUCKTON KE, DANIEL A, ARNAUD P, ROCCHI M, ARCHIDIACOMO N, FILIPPI G, SINISCALCO M: Comparison of cytologic and genetic distances between long arm subtelomeric markers of human autosome 14 suggests uneven distribution of crossing-over. *Cytogenet Cell Genet* 44:32, 1987.

59. HOFKER MH, NELEN M, KLASEN EC, FRANTS RR, NUKIWA T, CRYSTAL RC: A highly polymorphic alpha-1-antitrypsin-like gene maps within 8 kb 3' of the normal gene. *Hum Gene Mapping* 9, Paris, 1987.

60. WALTER MA, COX DW: A restrictive map generated by pulsed field gel electrophrosis of the human protease inhibitor cluster on human chromosome 14. *Hum Gene Mapping* 9, Paris, 1987.

61. SCHWICK HG, HEIMBURGER N, HAPT H: Antiproteasen des Humanserums. *Z Gesamte Inn Med* 21:193, 1966.

62. PANNELL RD, JOHNSON D, TRAVIS J: Isolation and properties of human plasma α_1-proteinase inhibitor. *Biochemistry* 13:5439, 1974.

63. GADEK JE, CRYSTAL RG: α_1-antitrypsin deficiency, in Stanbury JB, Wyngaarden JB, Fredrickson DS, Goldstein JL, Brown MS (eds): *Metabolic Basis of Inherited Disease*, 5th ed. New York, McGraw-Hill, 1983, p 1450.

64. GADEK JE, ZIMMERMAN RL, FELLS GA, CRYSTAL RG: Antielastases of the human alveolar structures: Assessment of the protease-antiprotease theory of emphysema. *J Clin Invest* 68:889, 1981.

65. BRISSENDEN JE, COX DW: α_2-Macroglobulin production by cultured human fibroblasts. *Somatic Cell Genet* 8:289, 1982.

66. SCOTT CF, CARRELL RW, GLASER CB, KUEPPERS F, LEWIS JH, COLMAN RW: Alpha-1-antitrypsin-Pittsburgh. A potent inhibitor of human plasma factor XIa, Kallikrein and factor XII. *J Clin Invest* 77:631, 1986.

67. LIEBERMAN J: Alpha$_1$-antitrypsin deficiency and related disorders. *Princ Pract Med Genet* 2:911, 1983.

68. MIRSKY IA, FOLEY G: Antibiotic actions of trypsin inhibitors. *Proc Soc Exp Biol Med* 59:34, 1945.

69. BREIT SN, WAKEFIELD D, ROBINSON JP, LUCKHURST E, CLARK P, PENNY R: The role of alpha$_1$-antitrypsin deficiency in the pathogenesis of immune disorders. *Clin Immun Immunopathol* 35:363, 1985.

70. LIPSKY JJ, BERNINGER RW, HYMAN LR, TALAMO RC: Presence of alpha-1-antitrypsin on mitogen stimulated human lymphocytes. *J Immunol* 122:24, 1979.

71. FOLDS JD, PRINCE II, SPITZNAGEL JK: Limited cleavage of human immunoglobulins by elastase of human neutrophil polymorphonuclear granulocytes. Possible modulator of immune complex disease. *Lab Invest* 39:313, 1978.

72. SHARP HL: Alpha$_1$-antitrypsin deficiency. *Hosp Pract* 5:83, 1971.

73. HOOD JM, KOEP LJ, PETERS RL, SCHROTER GPJ, WEIL R, REDEKER AG, STARZI TE: Liver transplantation for advanced liver disease with alpha-1-antitrypsin deficiency. *N Engl J Med* 302:272, 1980.

74. ALPER CA, RAUM D, AWDEH ZL, PETERSEN BH, TAYLOR PD, STARZL TE: Studies of hepatic synthesis in vivo of plasma proteins, including orosomucoid, transferrin, alpha-1-antitrypsin, C8, and factor B. *Clin Immunol Immunopathol* 16:84, 1980.

75. ERIKSSON S, ALM R, ASTEDT B: Organ cultures of human fetal hepatocytes in the study of extra- and intracellular α_1-antitrypsin. *Biochim Biophys Acta* 542:496, 1978.

76. ISAACSON P, JONES DB, MILLWORD-SADLER GH, JUDD MA, PAYNE S: Alpha-1-antitrypsin in human macrophages. *Lancet* 2:964, 1979.

77. COHEN AB: Interrelationships between the human alveolar macrophage and alpha-1-antitrypsin. *J Clin Invest* 52:2793, 1973.

78. PERLMUTTER DH, COLE FS, KILBRIDGE P, ROSSING TH, COLTEN HR: Expression of the alpha$_1$-proteinase inhibitor gene in human monocytes and macrophages. *Proc Natl Acad Sci USA* 82:795, 1985.

79. SIFERS RN, CARLSON JA, CLIFT SM, DEMAYO FJ, BULLOCK DW, WOO SLC: Tissue specific expression of the human alpha-1-antitrypsin gene in transgenic mice. *Nucleic Acids Res* 15:1459, 1987.

80. LAURELL C-B, NOSSLIN B, JEPPSSON J-O: Catabolic rate of α_1-antitrypsin of Pi type M and Z in man. *Clin Sci Mol Med* 52:457, 1977.

81. JEPPSSON J-O, LAURELL CB, NOSSLIN B, COX DW: Catabolic rate of α_1-antitrypsin of Pi types S and Mmalton and of asialylated M protein in man. *Clin Sci Mol Med* 55:103, 1978.

82. SENIOR RM, HEUBNER PF, PIERCE JA: Serum elastase inhibition capacity

as measure of serum α_1-antitrypsin concentrations, in Mittman C (ed): *Pulmonary Emphysema and Proteolysis*. New York, Academic, 1972, p 179.

83. BILLINGSLEY GD, COX DW: Functional assay of α_1-antitrypsin in obstructive lung disease. *Am Rev Respir Dis* 121:161, 1980.

84. ERLANGER BF, KOKOWSKY N, COHEN W: The preparation and properties of two new chromogenic substrates of trypsin. *Arch Biochem* 95:271, 1961.

85. VISSER L, BLOUT E: The use of *p*-nitrophenyl N-*tert*-butyloxycarbonyl-L-alaninate as substrate for elastase. *Biochim Biophys Acta* 268:257, 1972.

86. BEATTY K, ROBERTIE P, SENIOR RM, TRAVIS J: Determination of oxidized alpha-1-proteinase inhibitor in serum. *J Lab Clin Med* 100:186, 1982.

87. MANCINI G, CARBONARA AO, HEREMANS JE: Immunochemical quantitation of antigens by single radial immunodiffusion. *Immunochemistry* 2:235, 1965.

88. LAURELL C-B: Quantitative estimation of proteins by electrophoresis in agarose gel containing antibodies. *Anal Biochem* 15:45, 1966.

89. TALAMO RC, LANGLEY CE, HYSLOP NE JR: A comparison of functional and immunological measurements of serum α_1-antitrypsin, in Mittman C (ed): *Pulmonary Emphysema and Proteolysis*. New York, Academic, 1972, p 167.

90. TALAMO RC, BRUCE RM, LANGLEY CE, BERNINGER RW, PIERCE JA, BRYANT LJ, DUNCAN DB: *Alpha$_1$-antitrypsin Laboratory Manual* U.S. Department of Health, Education and Welfare, Publ No (NIH) 78, 1978.

91. LAURELL C-B, KULLANDER S, THORELL J: Effect of administration of a combined estrogen-progestin contraceptive on the level of individual plasma proteins. *Scan J Clin Lab Invest* 21:337, 1968.

92. EVANS HE, LEVI M, MANDL I: Serum enzyme inhibitor concentrations in the respiratory distress syndrome. *Am Rev Respir Dis* 101:359, 1970.

93. TALAMO RC: Basic and clinical aspects of the α_1-antitrypsin. *Pediatrics* 56:91, 1975.

94. ARNAUD P, CHAPUIS-CELLIER C, CREYSSEL R: Polymorphisme de l'alpha-1-antitrypsin plasmatique (système Pi). Mise en évidence par électrofocalisation sur gel de polyacrylamide. *C R Soc Biol Paris* 168:58, 1974.

95. LEBAS J, HAYEM A, MARTIN JP: Étude des variants génétiques de l'alpha-1-antitrypsin en immunofocalisation bidimensionelle. *C R Acad Sci Paris* 258:2359, 1974.

96. COX DW, JOHNSON AM, FAGERHOL MK: Report of nomenclature meeting for α_1-antitrypsin. INSERM. Rouen/Bois-Guillaume-1978. *Hum Genet* 53:429, 1980.

97. SHOWS TB, ALPER CA, BOOTSMA D, DORI M: et al: International system for human gene nomenclature. *Cytogenet Cell Genet* 25:96, 1979.

98. JEPPSSON J-O, FRANZEN B: Typing of genetic variants of α_1-antitrypsin by electrofocusing. *Clin Chem* 28:219, 1982.

99. CHARLIONET R, MARTIN J-P, SESBOUE R, MADEC PJ, LEFEBVRE F: Synthesis of highly diversified carrier ampholytes. Evaluation of the resolving power of isoelectric focusing in the Pi system (alpha-1-antitrypsin genetic polymorphism). *J Chromatogr* 176:89, 1979.

100. FRANTS RR, NOORDHOEK GT, ERIKSSON AW: Separator isoelectric focusing for identification of α-1-antitrypsin (PiM) subtype. *Scand J Clin Invest* 38:457, 1978.

101. CONSTANS J, VIAU M, GOUAILLARD C: An additional Pi$_M$ subtype. *Hum Genet* 55:119, 1980.

102. KLASEN EC, RIGUTTI A: Isoelectric focusing of α_1-antitrypsin (PI) using restricted pH-range carrier ampholytes in combination with a highly cross-linked gel and a separator. *Electrophoresis* 3:168, 1982.

103. GORG A, POSTEL W, WESER J, WEIDINGER S, PATUTSCHNICK W, CLEVE H: Isoelectric focusing in immobolized pH gradients for the determination of the genetic Pi (α_1-antitrypsin) variants. *Electrophoresis* 4:153, 1983.

104. WEIDINGER S, CLEVE H: High resolution of alpha-1-antitrypsin PI M subtypes by isoelectric focusing with a modified immobilized pH gradient. *Electrophoresis* 5:223, 1984.

105. PASCALI VL, CONTE G: Improved classification of alpha-1-antitrypsin in immobilized pH gradients containing sucrose. *Electrophoresis* 6:402, 1985.

106. WEIDINGER S, CLEVE H: Hybrid isoelectric focusing for classification of α-1-antitrypsin variants. *Protein Biol Fluids* 34:863, 1986.

107. BUDOWLE B, MURCH RS: A high resolution, rapid procedure for alpha 1-antitrypsin phenotyping. *Electrophoresis* 6:523, 1985.

108. COX DW: New variants of α_1-antitrypsin: Comparison of PI typing techniques. *Am J Hum Genet* 33:354, 1981.

109. ARNAUD P, CHAPUIS CELLIER C, VITTOZ P, FUDENBERG H: Genetic polymorphism of serum alpha-1-protease inhibitor (alpha-1-antitrypsin): Pi I, a deficient allele of the Pi system. *J Lab Clin Med* 92:177, 1978.

110. FAGERHOL MK, HAUGE HE: The PI phenotype MP. Discovery of a ninth allele belonging to the system of inherited variants of serum α_1-antitrypsin. *Vox Sang* 15:396, 1968.

111. COX DW, HOEPPNER VH, LEVISON H: Protease inhibitors in patients with chronic obstructive pulmonary disease: The alpha$_1$-antitrypsin heterozygote controversy. *Am Rev Respir Dis* 113:601, 1976.

112. MARTIN NG, CLARK P, OFULUE AF, EAVES LJ, COREY LA, NANCE WE: Does the PI polymorphism alone control alpha-1-antitrypsin expression? *Am J Hum Genet* 40:267, 1987.

113. HUG G, CHUCK G, BOWLES B: Alpha$_1$-antitrypsin phenotype: Transient cathodal shift in serum of infant girl with urinary cytomegalovirus and fatty liver. *Pediatr Res* 16:192, 1982.

114. BILLINGSLEY GD, COX DW: Functional assessment of genetic variants of α_1-antitrypsin. *Hum Genet* 61:118, 1982.

115. LIE-INJO LE: α_1-antitrypsin with unusual behavior. *Clin Chim Acta* 72:83, 1976.

116. TAYLOR JC, COLIN M, INAMIZU T, MITTMAN C: Familial temperature sensitive alpha 1 protease inhibitor (M1Anaheim). *Clin Chim Acta* 104:301, 1980.

117. NUKIWA T, BRANTLY M, OGUSHI F, FELLS G, SATOH K, STIER L, COURTNEY M, CRYSTAL RG: Characterization of the M1(ala^{213}) type of α1-antitrypsin, a newly recognized, common "normal" α1-antitrypsin haplotype. *Biochemistry* 26:5259, 1987.

118. COX DW, BILLINGSLEY GD: Restriction enzyme *Mae*III for prenatal diagnosis of alpha$_1$-antitrypsin deficiency. *Lancet* ii:741, 1986.

119. JEPPSSON J-O: Amino acid substitution Gly-Lys in α_1-antitrypsin Pi Z. *FEBS Lett* 65:195, 1976.

120. YOSHIDA L, LIEBERMAN J, GAIDULIS L, EWING C: Molecular abnormality of human α_1-antitrypsin variant (PiZ) associated with plasma activity deficiency. *Proc Natl Acad Sci USA* 73:1324, 1976.

121. OWEN MC, CARRELL RW, BRENNAN SO: The abnormality of the S variant of human α_1-antitrypsin. *Biochim Biophys Acta* 453:257, 1976.

122. WEIDINGER S, JEPPSSON J-O: Genetic study of the deficient alpha-1-antitrypsin variant PI P. *Proc Int Congr Hum Genet Berlin* 1986:435.

123. BRENNAN SO, CARRELL RW: α_1-Antitrypsin Christchurch, 363 Glu $\rightarrow$ Lys: mutation at the P'5 position does not affect inhibitory activity. *Biochim Biophys Acta* 873:13, 1986.

124. JEPPSSON J-O: Presented at α_1-Antitrypsin: Molecules and Medicine. Cambridge, England, Sept 9, 1985.

125. ROGERS J, KALSHEKER N, WALLIS S, SPEER A, COUTELLE CH, WOODS D, HUMPHRIES SE: The isolation of a clone for human α_1-antitrypsin and the detection of α_1-antitrypsin in mRNA from liver and leukocytes. *Biochem Biophys Res Commun* 116:375, 1983.

126. KELLERMANN G, WALTER H: Investigations on the population genetics of the α_1-antitrypsin polymorphism. *Humangenetik* 10:145, 1970.

127. KAMBOH MI: Biochemical and genetic aspects of human serum α_1-proteinase inhibitor protein. *Dis Markers* 3:135, 1985.

128. THYMANN M: Distribution of alpha-1-antitrypsin (Pi) phenotypes in Denmark determined by separator isoelectric focusing in agarose gel. *Hum Hered* 36:19, 1986.

129. KLASEN ED, BOS A, SIMMELINK HD: Pi (α_1-antitrypsin) subtypes: Frequency of PI*M4 in several populations. *Hum Genet* 62:139, 1982.

130. SANTOS ROSA MA, ROBALO CORDEIRO AJA: Alpha-1-proteinase inhibitor phenotypes in Portuguese population. *Eur J Respir Dis* 69(suppl 146):167, 1986.

131. DYKES DD, MILLER SA, POLESKY HF: Distribution of α_1-antitrypsin variants in a US white population. *Hum Hered* 34:308, 1984.

132. EVANS HE, BOGNACKI NS, PERROTT LM, GLASS L: Prevalence of alpha^1-antitrypsin Pi types among newborn infants of different ethnic backgrounds. *J Pediatr* 90:621, 1977.

133. YING Q-L, ZHANG M-L, LIANG C-C, CHEN L-C, CHEN L-F, HUANG Y-W, WANG R-X, ZHANG N-J, LI H-J, LIU S-S, GAO EX: Alpha-1-antitrypsin types in five Chinese national minorities. *Hum Genet* 71:225, 1985.

134. OHTANI H, SAITO M: Alpha-1-antitrypsin: Frequencies of PiM subtypes and serum concentration in the Japanese population. *Hum Hered* 35:62, 1985.

135. MASSI G, VECCHIO FM: Alpha-1-antitrypsin phenotypes in a group of newborn infants in Somalia. *Hum Gen* 38:265, 1977.

136. JANUS EE, SHEAT JM, CARRELL RW: Alpha-1-antitrypsin variants in New Zealand. *NZ Med J* 82:289, 1975.

137. MATTESON KJ, OSTRER H, CHAKRAVARTI A, BUETOW KH, O'BRIEN WE, BEAUDET AL, PHILLIPS JA: A study of restriction fragment length polymorphisms at the human alpha-1-antitrypsin locus. *Hum Genet* 69:263, 1985.

138. KIDD VJ, WALLACE RB, ITAKURA K, WOO SLC: α_1-antitrypsin deficiency detection by direct analysis of the mutation in the gene. *Nature* 304:230, 1983.

139. COX DW, WOO SLC, MANSFIELD T: DNA restriction fragments associated with alpha$_1$-antitrypsin indicate a single origin for deficiency allele PIZ. *Nature* 316:79, 1985.

140. BOTSTEIN D, WHITE RL, SKOLNICK M, DAVIS RW: Construction of a genetic linkage map in man using restriction fragment length polymorphisms. *Am J Hum Genet* 32:314, 1980.

141. COX DW, BILLINGSLEY GD, MANSFIELD T: DNA restriction site polymorphisms associated with the alpha$_1$-antitrypsin gene. *Am J Hum Genet* 41:891, 1987.

142. COX DW: DNA polymorphisms associated with α_1-antitrypsin and their clinical applications, in Mittman C, Taylor C (eds): *Pulmonary Emphysema and Proteolysis.* New York, Academic, 1987, vol. II.

143. COX DW, COULSEN SE, BILLINGSLEY GD: Unique DNA polymorphisms associated with α_1-antitrypsin Z deficiency allele: Application to prenatal diagnosis, in Peters H (ed): *Protides of the Biological Fluids.* 35:123, 1987.

144. COX DW, COULSON SE: BglII polymorphism for the α_1-antitrypsin-related gene on chromosome 14. *Nucleic Acids Res* 15:4701, 1987.

145. HODGSON I, KALSHEKER N: DNA polymorphisms of the human α_1 antitrypsin gene in normal subjects and in patients with pulmonary emphysema. *J Med Genet* 24:47, 1987.

146. HODGSON I, KALSHEKER N: RFLP for a gene-related sequence of alpha 1-antitrypsin (AAT). *Nucleic Acids Res* 14:6779, 1986.

147. COX DW, BILLINGSLEY GD, SMYTH S: Rare types of α1-antitrypsin associated with deficiency, in Allen RC, Arnaud P (eds): *Electrophoresis, Proc Third Int Conf Electrophoresis.* New York, de Gruyter, 1981, p 505.

148. SVEGER T: Plasma protease inhibitors in α_1-antitrypsin-deficient children. *Pediatr Res* 19:834, 1985.

149. LAURELL C-B, SVEGER T: Mass screening of newborn Swedish infants for α_1-antitrypsin deficiency. *Am J Hum Genet* 27:213, 1975.

150. MOROZ SP, CUTZ E, COX DW, SASS-KORTSAK A: Liver disease associated with alpha$_1$-antitrypsin deficiency in childhood. *J Pediatr* 88:19, 1976.

151. JOHANSSON BG: Agarose gel electrophoresis. *Scand J Clin Lab Invest* 29(suppl):124:7, 1972.

152. CUTZ E, COX DW: α_1-antitrypsin deficiency: The spectrum of pathology and pathophysiology, in Rosenberg HS, Bolande RP (eds): *Perspectives in Pediatric Pathology.* New York, Masson, 1979, p 1.

153. FELDMANN G, MARTIN J-P, SESBOUE P, ROPARTZ C, PERELMAN R, NATHANSON M, SERINGE P, BENHAMOU J-P: Hepatocyte ultrastructure changes in α_1-antitrypsin deficiency. *Gastroenterology* 67:1214, 1974.

154. HUANG S-N, MINASSIAN H, MORE JD: Application of immunofluorescent staining on paraffin sections improved by trypsin digestion. *Lab Invest* 35:383, 1976.

155. ROBERTS EA, COX DW, MEDLINE A, WANLESS IR: Occurrence of alpha-1-antitrypsin deficiency in 155 patients with alcoholic liver disease. *Am J Clin Pathol* 82:424, 1984.

156. FISHER RL, TAYLOR L, SHERLOCK S: α-1-antitrypsin deficiency in liver disease: The extent of the problem. *Gastroenterology* 71:646, 1976.

157. KELLY JK, TAYLOR TV, MILFORD-WARD A: Alpha-1-antitrypsin PiS phenotype and liver cell inclusion bodies in alcoholic hepatitis. *J Clin Pathol* 32:706, 1979.

158. PARIENTE E-A, DEGOTT C, MARTIN J-P, FELDMAN G, POTET F, BENHAMOU J-P: Hepatocytic PAS-positive diastase-resistant inclusions in the absence of alpha-1-antitrypsin deficiency—High prevalence in alcoholic cirrhosis. *Am J Clin Pathol* 76:299, 1981.

159. CARLSON J, ERIKSSON S, HAGERSTRAND I: Intra- and extracellular alpha$_1$-antitrypsin in liver disease with special reference to Pi phenotype. *J Clin Pathol* 34:1020, 1981.

160. BRADFIELD JWB, BLENKINSOPP WK: Alpha-1-antitrypsin globules in the liver and PiM phenotype. *J Clin Pathol* 30:464, 1977.

161. ERRINGTON DM, BATHURST IC, JANUS ED, CARELL RW: In vitro synthesis of M and Z forms of human α_1-antitrypsin. *FEBS Lett* 148:83, 1982.

162. BATHURST IC, STENFLO J, ERRINGTON DM, CARRELL RW: Translation and processing of normal (PiMM) and abnormal (PiZZ) human α_1-antitrypsin. *FEBS Lett* 153:270, 1983.

163. JEPPSSON J-O, LARSSON C, ERIKSSON S: Characterization of α_1-antitrypsin in the inclusion bodies from the liver in α_1-antitrypsin deficiency. *N Engl J Med* 293:576, 1975.

164. ERIKSSON S, LARSSON C: Purification and partial characterization of PAS-positive inclusion bodies from the liver in alpha$_1$-antitrypsin deficiency. *N Engl J Med* 292:176, 1975.

165. HERCZ A, KATONA E, CUTZ E, WILSON JR, BARTON M: α_1-antitrypsin: The presence of excess mannose in the Z variant isolated from liver. *Science* 201:1229, 1978.

166. BATHURST IC, TRAVIS J, GEORGE PM, CARRELL RW: Structural and functional characterization of the abnormal Z α_1-antitrypsin isolated from human liver. *FEBS Lett* 177:179, 1984.

167. FOREMAN RC, JUDAH JD, COLMAN A: Xenopus oocytes can synthesize but do not secrete the Z variant of human α_1-antitrypsin. *FEBS Lett* 168:84, 1984.

168. ERRINGTON DM, BATHURST IC, CARRELL RW: Human α_1-antitrypsin expression in Xenopus oocytes: Secretion of the normal (PiM) and abnormal (PiZ) forms. *Eur J Biochem* 153:361, 1985.

169. JEPPSSON J-O, ERIKSSON S: The N-terminal amino acid sequence from α_1-antitrypsin isolated from liver inclusion bodies. *Biochim Biophys Acta* 831:30, 1985.

170. COX DW, BILLINGSLEY GD, CALLAHAN JW: Aggregation of plasma Z type α_1-antitrypsin suggests basic defect for the deficiency. *FEBS Lett* 205:255, 1986.

171. FOREMAN RC: Disruption of the Lys 290-Glu 342 salt bridge in human alpha-1-antitrypsin does not prevent its synthesis and secretion. *FEBS Lett* 216:79, 1987.

172. BATHURST IC, ERRINGTON DM, FOREMAN RC, JUDAH JD, CARRELL RW: Human Z α_1-antitrypsin accumulates intracellularly and stimulates lysosomal activity when synthesized in the Xenopus oocyte. *FEBS Lett* 183:304, 1985.

173. LIEBERMAN J, GAIDULIS L, KLOTZ SD: A new deficient variant of α_1-antitrypsin (MDuarte). Inability to detect the heterozygous state by antitrypsin phenotyping. *Am Rev Respir Dis* 113:31, 1976.

174. COX DW: A new deficiency allele of alpha-1-antitrypsin: Pi Mmalton, in Peters H (ed): *Protides of the Biological Fluids.* Oxford, Pergamon Press, 1976, vol 23, p 375.

175. KRAMPS JA, BROUWERS JW, MAESEN F, DIJKMAN JH: Pi^{Mheerlen}, a Pi^M allele reulting in very low α_1-antitrypsin serum levels. *Hum Genet* 59:104, 1981.

176. HOFKER MH, NUKIWA T, VAN PAASSEN HMB, NELEN M, FRANTS RR, KRAMPS JA, KLASEN EC, CRYSTAL RG: A pro → leu substitution in codon 369 in the α_1-antitrypsin deficiency variant PI Mheerlen. *Am J Hum Genet* in press, 1987.

177. WEIDINGER S, JAHN W, CUJNIK F, SCHWARZFISCHER F: Alpha-1-antitrypsin: Evidence for a fifth PI M subtype and a new deficiency allele *PI*Z Augsburg*. *Hum Genet* 71:27, 1985.

178. KUEPPERS F, UTZ G, SIMON B: Alpha$_1$-antitrypsin deficiency with M-like phenotype. *J Med Genet* 14:183, 1977.

179. LANGLEY CE, BERNINGER RW, WOLFSON SL, TALAMO RC: An unusual type of α_1-antitrypsin deficiency in a child. *Johns Hopkins Med J* 144:161, 1979.

180. TAKAHASHI H, NUKIWA K, SATOH K, OGUSHI F, BRANTLEY M, FELLS G, STIER L, COURTNEY M, CRYSTAL RG: Characterization of the gene and protein of the α1-antitrypsin "deficiency" allele Mprocida. *J Biol Chem* in press, 1988.

181. SPROULE BJ, COX DW, HSU K, SALKIE ML, HERBERT FA: Pulmonary function associated with the Mmalton deficient variant of alpha$_1$-antitrypsin. *Am Rev Respir Dis* 127:237, 1983.

182. ALLEN MB, WARD AM, PERKS WH: Alpha$_1$ antitrypsin deficiency due to M^{Malton}Z phenotype: case report and family study. *Thorax* 41:568, 1986.

183. REID CL, WIENER GJ, COX DW, RICHTER JE, GEISINGER KR: Diffuse hepatocellular dysplasia and carcinoma associated with the Mmalton variant of alpha$_1$-antitrypsin. *Gastroenterology* 93:181, 1987.

184. FELDMANN G, MARTIN J-P, SESBOUE R, ROPARTZ C, PERELMAN R, NATHANSON M, SERINGE P, BENHAMOU J-P: The ultrastructure of hepatocytes in alpha-1-antitrypsin deficiency with the genotype PI--. *Gut* 135:796, 1975.

185. MARTIN J-P, SESBOUE R, CHARLIONET R, ROPARTZ C: Does alpha$_1$-antitrypsin PI null phenotype exist? *Humangenetik* 30:121, 1975.

186. TALAMO RC, LANGLEY CE, REED CE, MAKINO S: α_1-Antitrypsin deficiency: A variant with no detectable α_1-antitrypsin. *Science* 181:70, 1973.

187. MUENSCH H, GAIDULIS L, KUEPPERS F, SO SY, ESCANO G, KIDD VJ, WOO SLC: Complete absence of serum alpha-1-antitrypsin in conjunction with an apparently normal gene structure. *Am J Hum Genet* 38:898, 1986.

188. HARDICK C, SIFERS R, CARLSON J, KIDD V, WOO SLC: A null allele of the human alpha-1-antitrypsin gene is caused by a frame-shift mutation. *Am J Hum Genet* 39 suppl Philadelphia, 1986.

189. SATOH K, NUKIWA T, BRANTLY M, GARVER RI JR, HOFKER M, COURTNEY M, CRYSTAL RG: Emphysema associated with complete absence of α_1-antitrypsin in serum and the homozygous inheritance of a stop codon in an α_1-antitrypsin coding exon. *Am J Hum Genet* 42:77, 1988.

190. NUKIWA T, TAKAHASHI H, BRANTLY M, COURTNEY M, CRYSTAL RG: α_1-Antitrypsin null$_{Granite Falls}$, a non-expressing α_1-antitrypsin gene associated with a frameshift to stop mutation in a coding exon. *J Biol Chem* 262:11999, 1987.

191. COX DW, LEVISON H: Emphysema of early onset associated with a complete deficiency of alpha$_1$-antitrypsin (null homozygotes). *Am Rev Respir Dis* 137:371, 1988.

192. FRAIZER GC, COULSON SE, COX DW: Molecular analysis of rare deficiency (PI) alleles of alpha$_1$-antitrypsin. *Am J Hum Genet* 40 suppl:A214, 1987.

193. CARRELL RW: α_1-Antitrypsin, emphysema and smoking. *N Z Med J* 97:327, 1984.

194. PIERCE JA, ERADIO B, DEW TA: Antitrypsin phenotypes in St Louis. *JAMA* 238:609, 1975.

195. COX DW: Transmission of Z allele from MZ heterozygotes for α_1-antitrypsin deficiency. *Am J Hum Genet* 32:455, 1980.

196. MITTMAN C, MADISON R: Additional supporting data (letter). *Am J Hum Genet* 32:458, 1980.

197. SUAREZ B, PIERCE JA, RESTA R, HARLAN F, REICH T: Alpha-1-antitrypsin allele Pi^S fails to show segregation distortion. *Hum Hered* 32:246, 1982.

198. KUEPPERS F, BLACK LF: α_1-antitrypsin and its deficiency. *Am Rev Respir Dis* 110:176, 1974.

199. MORSE JO: Alpha$_1$-antitrypsin deficiency. *N Engl J Med* 299:1045, 1978.

200. TOBIN MJ, COOK PJL, HUTCHINSON DCS: Alpha$_1$-antitrypsin deficiency: The clinical and physiological features of pulmonary emphysema in subjects homozygous for Pi Type Z. *Br J Dis Chest* 77:14, 1983.

201. LIEBERMAN J, WINTER B, SASTRE A: Alpha$_1$-antitrypsin pi-types in 965 COPD patients. *Chest* 89:370, 1986.

202. COX DW, TALAMO RC: Genetic aspects of pediatric lung disease. *Pediatr Clin North Am* 26:467, 1979.

203. LARSSON C: Natural history and life expectancy in severe alpha$_1$-antitrypsin deficiency, PiZ. *Acta Med Scand* 204:345, 1978.

204. JANUS ED, PHILLIPS NT, CARRELL RW: Smoking, lung function, and α_1-antitrypsin deficiency. *Lancet* i:152, 1985.

205. BUIST AS, BURROWS B, ERIKSSON S, MITTMAN C, WU M: The natural history of air-flow obstruction in PiZ emphysema. *Am Rev Respir Dis* 127 suppl:43, 1983.

206. FLETCHER CM, PETO R, TINKER C, SPEIZER FE: *The Natural History of Chronic Bronchitis and Emphysema.* Oxford, Oxford University Press, 1976.

207. TAGER IB, MUNOZ A, ROSNER B, WEISS ST, CAREY V, SPEIZER FE: Effect of cigarette smoking on the pulmonary function of children and adolescents. *Am Rev Respir Dis* 131:752, 1985.

208. KAPLAN PD, KUHN CC, PIERCE JA: The induction of emphysema with elastase. I. The evolution of the lesion and the influence of serum. *J Lab Clin Med* 82:349, 1973.

209. JANOFF A, SLOAN B, WEINBAUM G, DAMIANO V, SANDHAUS RA, ELIAS J, KIMBEL P: Experimental emphysema induced with purified human neutrophil elastase: Tissue localization of the instilled protease. *Am Rev Respir Dis* 115:461, 1977.

210. SENIOR RM, TEGNER H, KUHN C, OHLSSON K, STARCHER BC, PIERCE JA: The induction of pulmonary emphysema with leukocyte elastase. *Am Rev Respir Dis* 116:469, 1977.

211. GADEK JE, HUNNINGHAKE GW, FELLS GA, ZIMMERMAN RL, KEOGH BA, CRYSTAL RG: Evaluation of the protease-antiprotease theory of human destructive lung disease. *Bull Eur Physiopathol Respir* 16:27, 1980.

212. JOCHUM M, PELLETIER A, BOUDIER C, PAULI G, BIETH JG: The concentration of leukocyte elastase-α1-proteinase inhibitor complex in bronchoalveolar lavage fluids from healthy human subjects. *Am Rev Respir Dis* 132:913, 1985.

213. WEWERS MD, CASOLARO MA, CRYSTAL RG: Comparison of alpha-1-antitrypsin levels and antineutrophil elastase capacity of blood and lung in a patient with the alpha-1-antitrypsin phenotype null-null before and during alpha-1-antitrypsin augmentation therapy. *Am Rev Respir Dis* 135:539, 1987.

214. OHLSSON K. Interactions between granulocyte proteases and protease inhibitors in the lung. *Bull Eur Physiopathol Respir* 16 suppl:209, 1980.

215. GAUTHIER F, FRYSMARK U, OHLSSON K, BIETH JG: Kinetics of the inhibition of leukocyte elastase by the bronchial inhibitor. *Biochem Biophys Acta* 700:178, 1982.

216. STOCKLEY RA, MORRISON HM, SMITH S, TETLEY T: Low molecular mass bronchial proteinase inhibitor and α1-proteinase inhibitor in sputum and bronchoalveolar lavage. *Hoppe-Seyler's Z Physiol Chem* 365:587, 1984.

217. JANOFF A: Elastases and emphysema. Current assessment of the protease-antiprotease hypothesis. *Am Rev Respir Dis* 132:417, 1985.

218. COHEN AB, ROSSI M: Neutrophils in normal lungs. *Am Rev Respir Dis* 127:S3, 1983.

219. JANOFF A, CARP H, LEE DK, DREW RT: Cigarette smoke inhalation decreases α_1-antitrypsin activity in rat lung. *Science* 206:1313, 1979.

220. STONE PJ, CALORE JD, MCGOWAN SE, BERNARDO J, SNIDER GL, FRANZBLAU C: Functional α_1-protease inhibitor in the lower respiratory tract of cigarette smokers is not decreased. *Science* 221:1187, 1983.

221. COX DW, BILLINGSLEY GD: Oxidation of plasma alpha$_1$-antitrypsin in smokers and nonsmokers and by an oxidizing agent. *Am Rev Respir Dis* 130:594, 1984.

222. FERA T, ABBOUD RT, RICHTER A, JOHAL SS: Acute effect of smoking on elastaselike esterase activity and immunologic neutrophil elastase levels in bronchoalveolar lavage fluid. *Am Res Respir Dis* 133:568, 1986.

223. ABBOUD RT, FERA T, RICHTER A, TABONA MZ, JOHAL SS: Acute effect of smoking on the functional activity of alpha$_1$-protease inhibitor in bronchoalveolar lavage fluid. *Am Res Respir Dis* 131:79, 1985.

224. CARP H, MILLER F, HOIDAL JR, JANOFF A: Potential mechanism of emphysema: α_1-proteinase inhibitor recovered from lungs of cigarette smok-

ers contains oxidized methionine and has decreased elastase inhibitory capacity. *Proc Natl Acad Sci USA* 79:2041, 1982.

225. OSSANNA PJ, TEST ST, MATHESON NR, REGIANI S, WEISS SJ: Oxidative regulation of neutrophil elastase-alpha-1-proteinase inhibitor interactions. *J Clin Invest* 77:1939, 1986.

226. MATHESON NR, WONG PS, TRAVIS J: Enzymatic inactivation of human alpha-1-proteinase inhibitor by neutrophil myeloperoxidase. *Biochem Biophys Res Commun* 88:402, 1979.

227. CLARK RA, STONE PJ, HAG AE, CALORE JD, FRANZBLAU C: Myeloperoxidase-catalyzed inactivation of α₁-protease inhibitor by human neutrophils. *J Biol Chem* 256:3348, 1981.

228. STOCKLEY RA, AFFORD SC: Qualitative studies of lung lavage α₁-proteinase inhibitor. *Hoppe-Seyler's Z Physiol Chem* 365:503, 1984.

229. LAURENT P, JANOFF A, KAGAN HM: Cigarette smoke blocks cross-linking of elastin *in vitro*. *Am Rev Respir Dis* 127:189, 1983.

230. KUCICH U, CHRISTNER P, LIFFMANN M, FEIN A, GOLDBERG A, KIMBEL P, WEINBAUM G, ROSENBLOOM J: Immunologic measurement of elastin-derived peptides in human serum. *Am Rev Respir Dis* 127:S28, 1983.

231. WEITZ JI, LANDMAN SL, CROWLEY KA, BIRKEN S, MORGAN FJ: Development of an assay for in vivo human neutrophil elastase activity. Increased elastase activity in patients with α₁-proteinase inhibitor deficiency. *J Clin Invest* 78:155, 1986.

232. REDLINE S, TISHLER PV, LEWITTER FI, TAGER IB, MUNOZ A, SPEIZER FE: Assessment of genetic and nongenetic influences on pulmonary function. A twin study. *Am Rev Respir Dis* 135:217, 1987.

233. TRAVIS J: Oxidants and antioxidants in the lung. Editorial. *Am Rev Respir Dis* 127, suppl:773, 1983.

234. TAYLOR JC, MADISON R, KOSINSKA D: Is antioxidant deficiency related to chronic obstructive pulmonary disease? *Am Rev Respir Dis* 134:285, 1986.

235. GALDSTON M, FELDMAN JG, LEVYTSKA V, MAGNUSSON B: Antioxidant activity of serum ceruloplasmin and transferrin available iron-binding capacity in smokers and nonsmokers. *Am Rev Respir Dis* 135:783, 1987.

236. THERON A, ANDERSON R: Investigation of the protective effects of the antioxidants ascorbate, cysteine, and dapsone on the phagocyte-mediated oxidative inactivation of human alpha-1-protease inhibitor in vitro. *Am Rev Respir Dis* 132:1049, 1985.

237. PACHT ER, KASEKI H, MOHAMMED JR, CORNWELL DG, DAVIS WB: Deficiency of vitamin E in the alveolar fluid of cigarette smokers. Influence on alveolar macrophage cytotoxicity. *J Clin Invest* 77:789, 1986.

238. COOPER DM, HOEPPNER VH, COX DW, ZAMEL N, BRYAN AC, LEVISON H: Lung function in alpha₁-antitrypsin heterozygotes (Pi type MZ). *Am Rev Respir Dis* 110:708, 1974.

239. BRUCE RM, COHEN BH, DIAMOND EL, FALLAT RJ, KNUDSON RJ, LEBOWITZ MD, MITTMAN C, PATTERSON CD, TOCKMAN MS: Collaborative study to assess risk of lung disease in Pi MZ phenotype subjects. *Am Rev Respir Dis* 130:386, 1984.

240. LARSSON C, ERIKSSON S, DIRKSEN H: Smoking and intermediate alpha₁-antitrypsin deficiency and lung function in middle-aged men. *Br Med J* 2:922, 1977.

241. ERIKSSON S, LINDELL SE, WIBERG R: Effects of smoking and intermediate α₁-antitrypsin deficiency (Pi MZ) on lung function. *Eur J Respir Dis* 67:279, 1985.

242. LARSSON C, DIRKSEN H, SUNSTRÖM G, ERIKSSON S: Lung function studies in asymptomatic individuals with moderately (PiSZ) and severely (PiZ) reduced levels of α₁-antitrypsin. *Scand J Respir Dis* 57:267, 1976.

243. BECKMAN G, BECKMAN L, MICHAELSSON O, RUDOLPHI N, STJERNBERG N, WIMAN L-G: Alpha-1-antitrypsin types and chronic obstructive lung disease in an industrial community in Northern Sweden. *Hum Hered* 30:299, 1980.

244. BECKMAN G, STJERNBERG NL, EKLUND A: Is the Pi^F allele of α₁-antitrypsin associated with pulmonary disease? *Clin Genet* 25:491, 1984.

245. SVEGER T: Liver disease in alpha₁-antitrypsin deficiency detected by screening of 200,000 infants. *N Engl J Med* 294:1316, 1976.

246. COTTRALL K, COOK PJL, MOWAT AP: Neonatal hepatitis syndrome and alpha-1-antitrypsin deficiency: An epidemiological study in south-east England. *Postgrad Med J* 50:376, 1974.

247. ODIEVRE M, MARTIN JP, HADCHOUEL M, ALAGILLE D: Alpha₁-antitrypsin deficiency and liver disease in children: Phenotypes, manifestations, and prognosis. *Pediatrics* 57:226, 1976.

248. NEBBIA G, HADCHOUEL M, ODIEVRE M, ALAGILLE D: Early assessment of evolution of liver disease associated with α₁-antitrypsin deficiency in childhood. *J Pediatr* 102:661, 1983.

249. ALAGILLE D: α-1-Antitrypsin deficiency. *Hepatology* 4(suppl):11, 1984.

250. SVEGER T, THELIN T: Four-year-old children with alpha₁-antitrypsin deficiency: Clinical follow-up and parental attitudes towards neonatal screening. *Acta Pediatr Scand* 70:171, 1981.

251. KARLAGANIS G, NEMETH A, HAMMARSKJOLD B, STRANDVIK B, SJOVALL J: Urinary excretion of bile alcohols in normal children and patients with α₁-antitrypsin deficiency during development of liver disease. *Eur J Clin Invest* 12:399, 1982.

252. PSACHAROPOULOS HT, MOWAT AP, COOK PJL, CARLILLE PA, PORTMANN B, RODECK CH: Outcome of liver disease associated wtih alpha₁-antitrypsin deficiency (PiZ). *Arch Dis Child* 58:882, 1983.

253. COX DW: α₁-antitrypsin deficiency, in Fisher MM, Roy CC (eds): *Pediatric Liver Disease: Hepatology Research and Clinical Issues*. New York, Plenum, 1983, vol 5, pp 271–282.

254. SVEGER T: Prospective study of children with α₁-antitrypsin deficiency; Eight-year-old follow-up. *J Pediatr* 104:91, 1984.

255. PORTER CA, MOWAT AP, COOK PJL, HAYNES DWG, SHILKIN KB, WILLIAMS R: α₁-antitrypsin deficiency and neonatal hepatitis. *Br Med J* 3:435, 1972.

256. UDALL JN, DIXON M, NEWMAN AP, WRIGHT JA: Liver disease in alpha₁-antitrypsin deficiency: A retrospective analysis of the influence of early breast- vs bottle-feeding. *JAMA* 253:2679, 1985.

257. SVEGER T: Breast-feeding, α₁-antitrypsin deficiency, and liver disease? *JAMA* (Letter) 254:3036, 1985.

258. UDALL JN, BLOCH KJ, WALKER WA: Transport of proteases across neonatal intestine and development of liver disease in infants with α₁-antitrypsin deficiency. *Lancet* I:1441, 1982.

259. HULTCRANTZ R, MENGARELLI S: Ultrastructure liver pathology in patients with minimal liver disease and alpha₁-antitrypsin deficiency: A comparison between heterozygous and homozygous patients. *Hepatology* 4:937, 1984.

260. WALLMARK A, ALM R, ERIKSSON S: Monoclonal antibody specific for the mutant PiZ α₁-antitrypsin and its application in an ELISA procedure for identification of PiZ gene carriers. *Proc Natl Acad Sci USA* 81:5690, 1984.

261. MOROZ SP, CUTZ E, BALFE JW, SASS-KORTSAK A: Membranoproliferative glomerulonephritis in childhood cirrhosis associated with alpha₁-antitrypsin deficiency. *Pediatrics* 57:232, 1976.

262. SOKOL RJ, HEUBI JE, MCGRAW C, BALISTRERI WF: Correction of vitamin E deficiency in children with chronic cholestasis. II. Effect on gastrointestinal and hepatic function. *Hepatology* 6:1263, 1986.

263. COX DW, MANSFIELD T: Prenatal diagnosis of alpha₁-antitrypsin deficiency and estimates of fetal risk for disease. *J Med Genet* 24:52, 1987.

264. STARZL TE, PORTER KA, FRANCAVILLA A, IWATSUKI S: Reversal of hepatic alpha-1-antitrypsin deposition after portacaval shunt. *Lancet* 2:424, 1983.

265. KAPLAN MM, KUSHNER DC: Case Record 24-1980. *N Engl J Med* 302:1405, 1980.

266. BERG NO, ERIKSSON S: Liver disease in adults with alpha₁-antitrypsin deficiency. *N Engl J Med* 287:1264, 1972.

267. COX DW, SMYTH S: Risk for liver disease in adults with α₁-antitrypsin deficiency. *Am J Med* 74:221, 1983.

268. ERIKSSON S, CARLSON J, VELEZ R: Risk of cirrhosis and primary liver cancer in alpha₁-antitrypsin deficiency. *N Engl J Med* 314:736, 1986.

269. ERIKSSON S, HAGERSTRAND I: Cirrhosis and malignant hepatoma in α₁-antitrypsin deficiency. *Acta Med Scand* 195:451, 1974.

270. CARLSON J, ERIKSSON S: Chronic "cryptogenic" liver disease in malignant hepatoma in intermediate alpha₁-antitrypsin deficiency identified by a PI Z-specific monoclonal antibody. *Scand J Gastroenterol* 20:835, 1985.

271. SCHLEISSNER IA, COHEN AH: Alpha-1-antitrypsin deficiency and hepatic carcinoma. *Am Rev Respir Dis* 111:863, 1975.

272. GOVINDARAJAN S, ASHCAVAI M, PETERS RL: α-1-antitrypsin phenotypes in hepatocellular carcinoma. *Hepatology* 1:628, 1981.

273. THEODOROPOULOS A, FERTAKIS A, ARCHIMANDRITIS A, KAPORDELIS C, ANGELOPOULOS B: Alpha-1-antitrypsin phenotypes in cirrhosis and hepatoma. *Acta Hepato-Gastroenterol* 23:114, 1976.

274. CLERC M, LE BRAS M, LOUBIERE R, HOUVET D: Cancer primitif du foie: Incidence de déficit en alpha-1-antitrypsin. *Nouv Presse Med* 6:3061, 1977.

275. REINTOFT I, HAGERSTRAND IE: Does the Z gene variant of alpha-1-antitrypsin predispose to hepatic carcinoma? *Hum Pathol* 10:419, 1979.

276. KELLY JK, DAVIES JS, JONES AW: Alpha-1-antitrypsin deficiency and hepatocellular carcinoma. *J Clin Pathol* 32:373, 1979.

277. PALMER PE, UCCI AA, WOLFE HJ: Expression of protein markers in malignant hepatoma. Evidence for genetic and epigenetic mechanisms. *Cancer* 45:1424, 1980.

278. NUKIWA T, BRANTLY M, GARVER R, PAUL L, COURTNEY M, LECOCQ J-P, CRYSTAL RG: Evaluation of "at risk" alpha-1-antitrypsin genotype SZ with synthetic oligonucleotide gene probes. *J Clin Invest* 77:528, 1986.

279. MORIN T, FELDMANN G, MARTIN J-P, RUEFF B, BENHAMOU J-P, ROPARTZ C: Heterozygous alpha₁-antitrypsin deficiency and cirrhosis in adults, a fortuitous association. *Lancet* 1:250, 1975.

280. HODGES JR, MILLWARD-SADLER GH, BARBATIS C, WRIGHT R: Heterozygous MZ alpha₁-antitrypsin deficiency in adults with chronic active hepatitis and cryptogenic cirrhosis. *N Engl J Med* 304:557, 1981.

281. MILLER F, KUSCHNER M: Alpha₁-antitrypsin deficiency, emphysema, necrotizing angiitis and glomerulonephritis. *Am J Med* 46:615, 1969.

282. LEWIS M, KALLENBACH J, ZALTZMAN M, LEVY H, LURIE D, BAYNES R, KING P, MEYERS A: Severe deficiency of alpha₁-antitrypsin associated with cutaneous vasculitis, rapidly progressive glomerulonephritis, and colitis. *Am J Med* 79:489, 1985.

283. MILFORD WARD A, PICKERING JD, SHORTLAND JR: The renal manifestations of Pi Z, in Martin J-P (ed): *L'Alpha-1-antitrypsine et le Système Pi.* Paris, INSERM, 1975, p 131.

284. STRIFE CF, HUG G, CHUCK G, MCADAMS AJ, DAVIS CA, KLINE JJ: Membrano-proliferative glomerulonephritis and α₁-antitrypsin deficiency in children. *Pediatrics* 71:88, 1983.

285. COX DW, HUBER O: Rheumatoid arthritis and alpha-1-antitrypsin. *Lancet* 1:1216, 1976.

286. COLLINS RL, TURNER RA, JOHNSON AM: Obstructive pulmonary disease in rheumatoid arthritis. *Arthritis Rheum* 19:623, 1976.

287. SJOBLOM KG, WOLLHEIM FA: Alpha-1-antitrypsin phenotypes and rheumatic diseases. *Lancet* 2:41, 1977.

288. BRACKERTZ D, KUEPPERS F: Alpha-1-antitrypsin phenotypes in rheumatoid arthritis. *Lancet* 2:934, 1977.

289. BECKMAN G, BECKMAN L, BJELLE A, RANTAPÄÄ DAHLQVIST S: Alpha-1-antitrypsin types and rheumatoid arthritis. *Clin Genet* 25:496, 1984.

290. GEDDES DM, WEBLEY M, BREWERTON DA, TURTON DW, TURNER-WARWICK M, MURPHY AH, MILFORD WARD A: α₁-antitrypsin phenotypes in fibrosing alveolitis and rheumatoid arthritis. *Lancet* 2:1049, 1977.

291. BUISSERET PD, PEMBREY ME, LESSOF MH: α₁-antitrypsin phenotypes in rheumatoid arthritis and ankylosing spondylitis. *Lancet* 2:1358, 1977.

292. ARNAUD P, GALBRAITH RM, FAULK WP, BLACK C: Pi phenotypes of alpha₁-antitrypsin in southern England: Identification of M subtypes and implications for genetic studies. *Clin Genet* 15:406, 1979.

293. COX DW, HUBER O: Association of severe rheumatoid arthritis with heterozygosity for α₁-antitrypsin deficiency. *Clin Genet* 17:153, 1980.

294. ARNAUD P, GALBRAITH R, FAULK WP, ANSELL BM: Increased frequency of the MZ phenotype of alpha-1-protease inhibitor in juvenile chronic polyarthritis. *J Clin Invest* 60:1442, 1977.

295. BREWERTON DA, WEBLEY M, MURPHY AH, MILFORD WARD AM: The α₁-antitrypsin phenotype MZ in acute anterior uveitis. *Lancet* 1:1103, 1978.

296. WAKEFIELD D, BREIT SN, CLARK P, PENNY R: Immunogenetic factors in inflammatory eye disease. Influence of HLA-B27 and alpha₁-antitrypsin phenotypes on disease expression. *Arthritis Rheum* 25:1431, 1982.

297. BROWN WT, MAMELOK AE, BEARN AG: Anterior uveitis and alpha-1-antitrypsin. *Lancet* 2:646, 1979.

298. BECKMAN G, BECKMAN L, LIDEN S: Association between psoriasis and the α₁-antitrypsin deficiency gene Z. *Acta Dermatovener* 60:163, 1980.

299. LIPKIN G, GALDSTON M, KUEPPERS F: Alpha₁-antitrypsin deficiency genes: Contributory defect in a subset of psoriatics? *J Am Acad Dermatol* 11:615, 1984.

300. BRANDRUP F, OSTERGAARD PA: α₁-antitrypsin deficiency associated with persistent cutaneous vasculitis. *Arch Dermatol* 114:921, 1978.

301. NICHOLLS MG, JANUS ED: Hashimoto's thyroiditis and homozygous alpha₁-antitrypsin deficiency. *Aust NZ J Med* 3:516, 1973.

302. GELFAND EW, COX DW, LIN MT, DOSCH H-M: Severe combined immunodeficiency disease in a patient with α₁-antitrypsin deficiency. *Lancet* 2:202, 1979.

303. RUBINSTEIN HM, JAFFER AM, KUDRNA JC, LERTRATANAKUL Y, CHANDRASEKHAR AJ, SLATER D, SCHMID FR: Alpha₁-antitrypsin deficiency with severe panniculitis. *Ann Intern Med* 86:742, 1977.

304. BREIT SN, CLARK P, ROBINSON JP, LUCKHURST E, DAWKINS RL, PENNY R: Familial occurrence of α₁-antitrypsin deficiency and Weber-Christian disease. *Arch Dermatol* 119:198, 1983.

305. POTTAGE JC JR, TRENHOLME GM, ARONSON IK, HARRIS AA: Panniculitis associated with histoplasmosis and alpha₁-antitrypsin deficiency. *Am J Med* 75:150, 1983.

306. ANAND S, SCHADE R, BENDETTI C, KELLEY R, RABIN BS, KRAUSE J, STARZL TE, IWATSUKI S, VAN THIEL DH: Idiopathic hemochromatosis and α₁-antitrypsin deficiency: Coexistence in a family with progressive liver disease in the proband. *Hepatology* 3:714, 1983.

307. ERIKSSON S, LINDMARK B: A Swedish family with alpha₁-antitrypsin deficiency, hemochromatosis, haemoglobinopathy D and early death in liver cirrhosis. *J Hepatol* 2:65, 1986.

308. ERIKSSON S, LINDMARK B, OLSSON S: Lack of association between hemochromatosis and α-antitrypsin deficiency. *Acta Med Scand* 219:291, 1986.

309. AARSKOG D, FAGERHOL MK: Protease inhibitor (Pi) phenotypes in chromosome aberrations. *J Med Genet* 7:367, 1970.

310. KUEPPERS F, O'BRIEN P, PASSARGE E, RUDIGER HW: Alpha₁-antitrypsin phenotypes in sex chromosome mosaicism. *J Med Genet* 12:263, 1975.

311. LIEBERMAN J, BORHANI NO, FEINLEIB M: α₁-antitrypsin deficiency in twins and parents-of-twins. *Clin Gen* 15:29, 1979.

312. CLARK P, MARTIN NG: An excess of the Piˢ allele in dizygotic twins and their mothers. *Hum Genet* 61:171, 1982.

313. JEPPSSON J-O, FRANZEN B, SVEGER T, CORDESIUS E, STROMBERG P, GUSTABII B: Prenatal exclusion of alpha₁-antitrypsin deficiency in a high-risk fetus. *N Engl J Med* 300:1441, 1979.

314. JEPPSSON J-O, CORDESIUS E, GUSTAVII B, LOFBERG L, FRANZEN B, STROMBERG P, SVEGER T: Prenatal diagnosis of alpha-1-antitrypsin deficiency by analysis of fetal blood obtained at fetoscopy. *Pediatr Res* 15:254, 1981.

315. ALTER BP: Advances in the prenatal diagnosis of hematologic diseases. *Blood* 64:329, 1984.

316. CORNEY G, WHITEHOUSE DB, HOPKINSON DA: Prenatal diagnosis of alpha-1-antitrypsin deficiency by fetal blood sampling. *Prenat Diag* 7:101, 1987.

317. KIDD VJ, GOLBUS MS, WALLACE RB, ITAKURA K, WOO SLC: Prenatal diagnosis of alpha₁-antitrypsin deficiency by direct analysis of the mutation site in the gene. *N Engl J Med* 310:639, 1984.

318. HEJTMANCIK JF, SIFERS RN, WARD PA, HARRIS S, MANSFIELD T, COX DW: Prenatal diagnosis of alpha₁-antitrypsin deficiency using restriction fragment linked polymorphism analysis and comparison with oligonucleotide synthetic probe analysis. *Lancet* ii:767, 1986.

319. SAIKI RK, BUGAWAN TL, HORN GT, MULLIS KB, ERLICH HA: Analysis of enzymatically amplified β-globin and HLA-DQα DNA with allele-specific oligonucleotide probes. *Nature* 324:163, 1986.

320. COX DW, MANSFIELD T: Prenatal diagnosis for alpha₁-antitrypsin deficiency. *Lancet* i:230, 1985.

321. JEPPSSON JO, SVEGER T: Typing of genetic variants of α₁-antitrypsin from dried blood. *Scand J Clin Lab Invest* 44:413, 1984.

322. MCNEIL TF, THELIN T, ASPERGREN-JANSSON E, SVEGER T, HARTY B: Psychological factors in cost-benefit analysis of somatic prevention. A study of the psychological effects of neonatal screening for α₁-antitrypsin deficiency. *Acta Paediatr Scand* 74:427, 1985.

323. THELIN T, MCNEIL TF, ASPERGREN-JANSSON E, SVEGER T: Psychological consequences of neonatal screening for α₁-antitrypsin deficiency. Parental reactions to the first news of their infants' deficiency. *Acta Paediatr Scand* 74:787, 1985.

324. THELIN T, MCNEIL TF, ASPERGREN-JANSSON E, SVEGER T: Identifying children at high somatic risk: Parents' long-term emotional adjustment to their children's alpha₁-antitrypsin deficiency. *Acta Psychiatr Scand* 72:323, 1985.

325. GELFAND JA, SHERINS RJ, ALLING DW, FRANK MM: Treatment of heriditary angioedema with danazol: Reversal of clinical and biochemical abnormalities. *N Engl J Med* 295:1444, 1976.

326. WEWERS MD, GADEK JE, KEOGH BA, FELLS GA, CRYSTAL RG: Evaluation of danazol therapy for patients with PiZZ alpha-1-antitrypsin deficiency. *Am Rev Respir Dis* 134:476, 1986.

327. WEWERS MD, BRANTLY ML, CASOLARO MA, CRYSTAL RG: Evaluation of tamoxifen as a therapy to augment alpha-1-antitrypsin concentrations in Z homozygous alpha-1-antitrypsin-deficient subjects. *Am Rev Respir Dis* 135:401, 1987.

328. Editorial. *Lancet* ii:812, 1985.

329. BURROWS B: A clinical trial of efficacy of antiproteolytic therapy: Can it be done? *Am Rev Respir Dis* 127:S42, 1983.

330. COHEN AB: The clinical usefulness of different forms of alpha-1-protease inhibitor. *Am Rev Respir Dis* 133:349, 1986.

331. GADEK JE, KLEIN HG, HOLLAND PV, CRYSTAL RG: Replacement therapy of alpha-1-antitrypsin deficiency: Reversal of protease-antiprotease imbalance within the alveolar structures of PiZ subjects. *J Clin Invest* 68:1158, 1981.

332. WEWERS MD, CASOLARO MA, SELLERS SE, SWAYZE SC, MCPHAUL KM, WITTES JT, CRYSTAL RG: Replacement therapy for alpha₁-antitrypsin deficiency associated with emphysema. *N Engl J Med* 316:1055, 1987.

333. COURTNEY M, JALLAT S, TESSIER L-H, BENAVENTE A, CRYSTAL RG, LECOCQ J-P: Synthesis in E. Coli of α₁-antitrypsin variants of therapeutic potential for emphysema and thrombosis. *Nature* 313:149, 1985.

334. COURTNEY M, BUCHWALDER A, TESSIER L-H, JAYE M, BENAVENTE A, BALLAND A, KOHLI V, LATHE R, TOLSTOSHEV P, LECOCQ J-P: High-level production of biologically active human α₁-antitrypsin in Escherichia coli. *Proc Natl Acad Sci USA* 81:669, 1984.

335. STRAUS SD, FELLS GA, WEWERS MD, COURTNEY M, TESSIER L-H, TOLSTOSHEV P, LECOCQ J-P, CRYSTAL RG: Evaluation of recombinant DNA-directed E. coli produced α₁-antitrypsin as an anti-neutrophil elastase for potential use as replacement therapy of α₁-antitrypsin deficiency. Biochem Biophys Res Commun 130:1177, 1985.

336. GEORGE PM, VISSERS MCM, TRAVIS J, WINTERBOURN CC, CARRELL RW: A genetically engineered mutant of α₁-antitrypsin protects connective tissue from neutrophil damage and may be useful in lung disease. *Lancet* 2:1426, 1984.

337. TRAVIS J, OWEN MC, GEORGE P, CARREL RW, ROSENBERG S, HALLEWELL RA, BARR PJ: Isolation and properties of recombinant DNA produced var-

iants of human alpha₁-proteinase inhibitor. *J Biol Chem* 260:4384, 1985.

338. JANOFF A, GEORGE-NASCIMENTO C, ROSENBERG S: A genetically engineered, mutant human alpha₁-proteinase inhibitor is more resistant than the normal inhibitor to oxidative inactivation by chemicals, enzymes, cells, and cigarette smoke. *Am Rev Respir Dis* 133:353, 1986.

339. POWERS JC, GUPTON BF, HARLEY AD, NISHINO N, WHITLEY RJ: Specificity of porcine pancreatic elastase, human leukocytes elastase and cathepsin-G. Inhibition with chloromethyl ketone peptides. *Biochim Biophys Acta* 485:156, 1977.

340. ROBERTS NA, SURGENOR AE: Comparison of peptide aldehydes with α₁-antitrypsin as elastase inhibitors for use in emphysema. *Biochem Biophys Res Commun* 139:896, 1986.

341. JANOFF A, DEARING R: Prevention of elastase-induced experimental emphysema by oral administration of synthetic elastase inhibitor. *Am Rev Respir Dis* 121:1025, 1980.

342. KLEINERMAN J, RANGA V, RYNBRANDT D, IP MPC, SORENSEN J, POWERS JC: The effect of the specific elastase inhibitor alanyl alanyl prolyl alanine chloromethylketone, on elastase-induced emphysema. *Am Rev Respir Dis* 121:381, 1980.

343. POWERS JC: Synthetic elastase inhibitors: Prospects for use in the treatment of emphysema. *Am Rev Respir Dis* 127:S54, 1983.

344. DOHERTY JB, ASHE BM, ARGENBRIGHT LW, BARKER PL, BONNEY RJ, CHANDLER GO, DAHLGREN ME, DORN CP JR, FINKE PE, FIRESTONE RA, FLETCHER D, HAGMANN WK, MUMFORD R, O'GRADY L, MAYCOCK AL, PISANO JM, SHAH SK, THOMPSON KR, ZIMMERMAN M: Cephalosporin antibiotics can be modified to inhibit human leukocyte elastase. *Nature* 322:192, 1986.

345. GRIFFITH BP, HARDESTY RL, TRENTO A, PARADIS IL, DUQUESNOY RJ, ZEEVI A, DAUBER JH, DUMMER JS, THOMPSON ME, GRYZAN S, BAHNSON HT: Heart-lung transplantation: Lessons learned and future hopes. *Ann Thorac Surg* 43:6, 1987.

346. BURKE CM, THEODORE J, BALDWIN JC, TAZELAAR HD, MORRIS AJ, MCGREGOR C, SHUMWAY NE, ROBIN ED, JAMIESON S: Twenty-eight cases of human heart-lung transplantation. *Lancet* i:517, 1986.

347. PATTERSON GA, COOPER JD, DARK JH, JONES MT, AND THE TORONTO LUNG TRANSPLANT GROUP: Experimental and clinical double lung transplantation. *J Thorac Cardiovasc Surg* 95:70, 1988.

CHAPTER 97

AMYLOIDOSIS

MERRILL D. BENSON
MARGARET R. WALLACE

1. Hereditary amyloidosis is characterized by the extracellular accumulation of protein fibrils having β-pleated sheet structure. Actually there are a number of forms of amyloidosis, each characterized by the protein which is the basic subunit of the amyloid fibril. In hereditary systemic amyloidosis the most frequent subunit protein is plasma prealbumin (transthyretin). In immunoglobulin (primary) amyloidosis the subunit protein is the variable portion of the immunoglobulin light chain or a portion thereof. In reactive (secondary) amyloidosis the subunit protein is a degradation product, amyloid A (AA), of a serum acute phase protein called serum amyloid A (SAA). All forms of amyloidosis cause illness and death by physical encroachment on normal organ structures. In the autosomal dominant hereditary amyloidoses, these deposits usually occur in peripheral nerves and cause polyneuropathy. In addition, varying degrees of infiltration in vital organs such as heart, kidney, and bowel result in varied syndromes which usually lead to death.

2. Hereditary amyloidosis is a late onset disease with clinical symptoms beginning in most kindreds within the third to seventh decades of life. The clinical disease usually progresses over 5 to 15 years and ends with death from cardiac failure, renal failure, or malnutrition. Gene carriers in some kindreds with late onset disease, however, have lived past age 90. Gene prevalence is not known, since there are a number of mutations, and many of the kindreds have been characterized only recently. In the United States, the prevalence of variant prealbumin genes is certainly greater than 1 in 1,000,000 and maybe as much as 1 in 100,000.

3. The primary defect in autosomal dominant prealbumin amyloidosis results from one of a number of mutations in the gene for prealbumin, which is a single copy sequence on chromosome 18. To date, seven single amino acid substitutions in the prealbumin molecule have been shown to be associated with hereditary amyloidosis. Six of these have been proven to be due to single nucleotide changes in the gene.

4. Direct DNA tests have been developed for five of the variant genes for prealbumin. These tests involve using either cDNA or genomic probes in Southern blot analysis and are based upon unique recognition sites for restriction endonucleases. In addition, there are a number of reported kindreds with hereditary amyloidosis in which the deposits have been shown to contain prealbumin, but a presumed mutation has not yet been identified. At the present time the DNA tests that have been established for certain prealbumin variants are being used for genetic counseling.

5. Prenatal diagnosis has been developed for at least one type of prealbumin amyloidosis, using specific oligonucleotide hybridization techniques.

6. Other forms of autosomal dominant amyloidosis that are defined by their subunit protein include: (1) hereditary cerebral amyloidosis with hemorrhage (γ trace protein or cystatin C), (2) Alzheimer disease (amyloid beta protein or A4 protein), (3) Iowa FAP III (apolipoprotein A-I), (4) medullary carcinoma of the thyroid (procalcitonin).

The amyloidoses are deposition diseases in which homogeneous subunit protein molecules aggregate into an ordered structure to make fibrils measuring 75 to 100 Å in cross section and having indeterminate length.[1] These fibrils accumulate in extracellular spaces to form deposits which, because of the ordered structure, have the crystalline property of birefringence and have selective affinities for certain histochemical dyes such as Congo red.

There are several types of amyloidosis defined by the basic protein constituent of the fibrils. Some of these disorders are systemic while the amyloid deposition is restricted in others to particular organ systems. Although each type of amyloidosis is a separate disease with its own etiology and pathogenic mechanisms, all share the physicochemical properties of the amyloid fibril and cause illness in the same way. As the extracellular deposits enlarge, they displace normal tissue structures, causing disruption of cell function and ultimately cell death. The signs and symptoms of the disease depend on the strategic location and size of the fibril deposits, but the basic mechanisms and end result of their presence is the same in all types of amyloidosis. Despite this final common pathway, the etiology, pathogenesis, prognosis, and therapeutic intervention for the different forms of amyloidosis must be considered separately. To set the stage for such discussion and prepare us for handling the rapidly accumulating data in this area, it is important to have some historical perspective.

HISTORY

Although amyloidosis has undoubtedly occurred for centuries, it was not until the mid-1800s that attention was brought to the condition. Rokitansky[2] in 1842 wrote about the "lardaceous liver" found at autopsy in patients with chronic diseases, and Virchow (1854) subsequently showed that these tissues gave a unique color reaction with iodine and sulfuric acid.[3,4] Virchow coined the term *amyloid*, which means starch-like, because of this reaction which led him to believe that amyloid represented deposits of carbohydrates. However, in 1859, Friedreich and Kekule reported evidence that the amyloid deposits were composed mainly of protein.[5] Over the next

---

Nonstandard abbreviations used in this chapter are: AA = amyloid A; AH = amyloidosis of hereditary type; AL = amyloidosis with light chain immunoglobulin deposition; FAP = familial amyloid polyneuropathy; FMF = familial Mediterranean fever; RBP = retinol binding protein; SAA = serum amyloid A; TTR = transthyretin.

100 years, amyloidosis associated with chronic diseases was studied histologically and epidemiologically.[6] It became obvious that some patients with amyloidosis had no predisposing illness and that amyloidosis was occasionally seen in familial patterns. Eventually the term *primary* was applied to the sporadic form of amyloidosis and *secondary* to amyloidosis that developed in individuals with chronic inflammatory diseases such as tuberculosis, osteomyelitis, and rheumatoid arthritis. Hereditary amyloidosis was not really described as such until Andrade (1952) published his finding of amyloidosis in families with polyneuropathy in northern Portugal.[7] Reviews of the literature show that, as early as the 1920s, familial occurrence of amyloidotic polyneuropathy had been described, but these cases were classified as *primary*.[8,9]

Characterization of amyloid remained relatively static until 1959 when Cohen and Calkins[10] and Spiro[11] showed by electron microscopy that amyloid deposits contained nonbranching fibrils with diameters of 75 to 100 Å and indeterminate length. Chemical characterization of this fibril material was hindered by its resistance to solubilization in practically all solvents. However, in 1971 using strong chaotropic agents, Glenner et al.[12] were able to solubilize amyloid fibrils from the tissues of patients with primary amyloidosis and isolate the major subunit proteins. Amino acid sequencing revealed that these subunits were homologous to the variable segment of immunoglobulin light chains.[12] This breakthrough in amyloid research at the chemical level was quickly followed by the demonstration that amyloid fibrils from patients with secondary amyloidosis were composed of a previously undescribed protein which was subsequently named amyloid A protein (AA).[13-15] Further studies showed that AA was derived from an acute phase serum amyloid A (SAA) protein synthesized in the liver.[16-22] In 1978, Costa et al. found that amyloid material from patients with hereditary amyloidosis was composed of a subunit protein which reacted with antiserum to plasma prealbumin.[23] The presence of prealbumin in hereditary amyloid deposits was confirmed at the structural level by 1981,[24] and since then several variants of this plasma protein have been found to be associated with hereditary amyloidosis.[25-30] This brings us to the present time where we can discuss amyloidosis at the physicochemical level and consider hypotheses on the etiology and pathogenic mechanisms of the various types.

PHYSICAL PROPERTIES OF AMYLOID FIBRILS

By light microscopy of hematoxylin and eosin stained preparations, amyloid deposits of all kinds are amorphous and eosinophilic (Fig. 97-1). The deposits are extracellular and often give the appearance of crowding the cells aside. This phenomenon is best appreciated in peripheral nerves where the typical nerve bundles and Schwann cell nuclei traverse around large accumulations of amyloid (Fig. 97-2). In other tissues, amyloid may accumulate along margins of cells. This is seen in the liver where columns of amyloid separate the hepatic cords and in the heart where cross-sectional preparations show rings of amyloid around the myocardial fibers. In some tissues, large collections of amyloid may be completely void of cellular elements.

While amyloid deposits of all kinds are eosinophilic, they also show unique staining properties which are useful in diagnosis. In the past, methylviolet and crystalviolet, which give

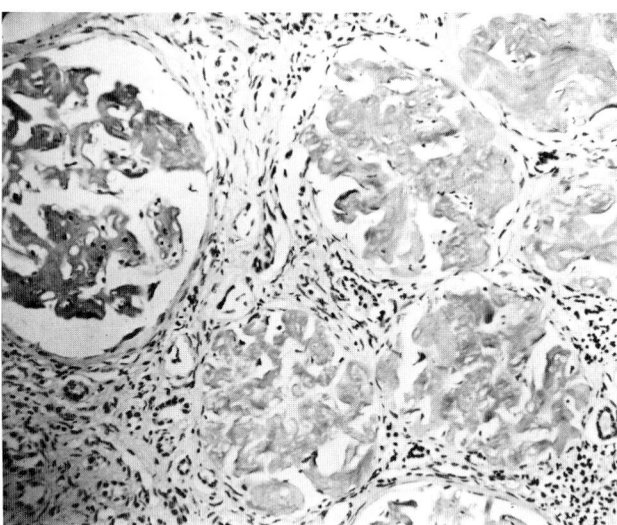

Fig. 97-1 Amyloid deposits obliterating renal glomeruli in a patient with hereditary amyloidosis. Hematoxylin and eosin stain.

metachromatic reactions with amyloid, were used to stain amyloid deposits. Now Congo red has become the standard for identification of amyloid on histologic sections[31] (Fig. 97-3). In tissue sections stained with alkaline Congo red, amyloid deposits take up the dye and give a characteristic green color when viewed in the polarizing microscope. This specific marker for amyloid is due to the birefringent nature of the amyloid fibrils and to their ability to bind Congo red. Collagen is also birefringent in histologic sections, but collagen does not bind Congo red, and, therefore, the green birefrigence is not seen. The fluorescent bioflavin dyes have also been used to localize amyloid but have not been universally accepted.

At the level of electron microscopy amyloid deposits contain characteristic fibrillar structures which are often in linear array, but lack of ordered structure is the rule (Fig. 97-4). Deep invaginations of the fibrils into the cytoplasmic membranes of reticuloendothelial cells are frequently seen and have been postulated as the sites of amyloid formation, but controversy persists on where actual fibril formation occurs. When amyloid fibrils are physically extracted from tissue deposits, nega-

Fig. 97-2 Amyloid deposits within peripheral nerve displacing nerve fibers and supporting cells. Congo red counterstained with hematoxylin.

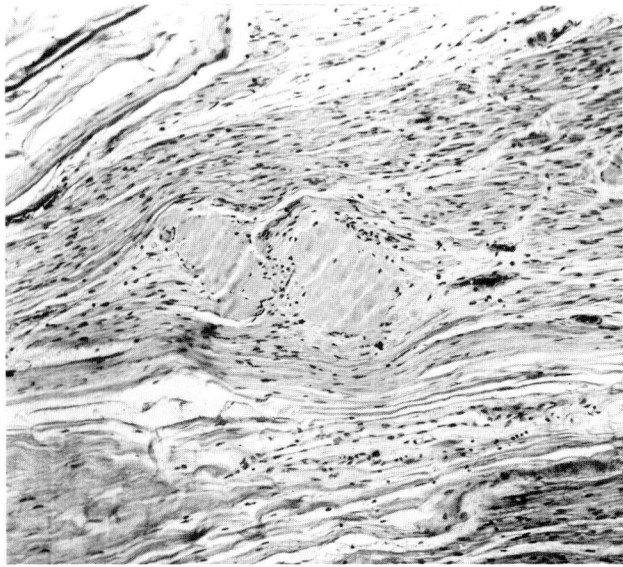

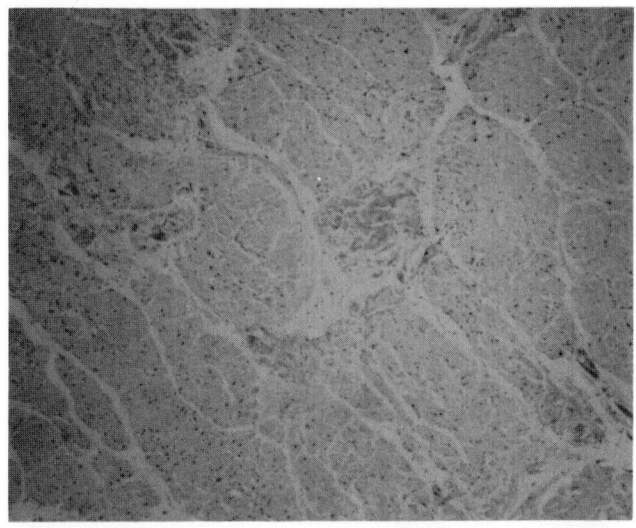

A.

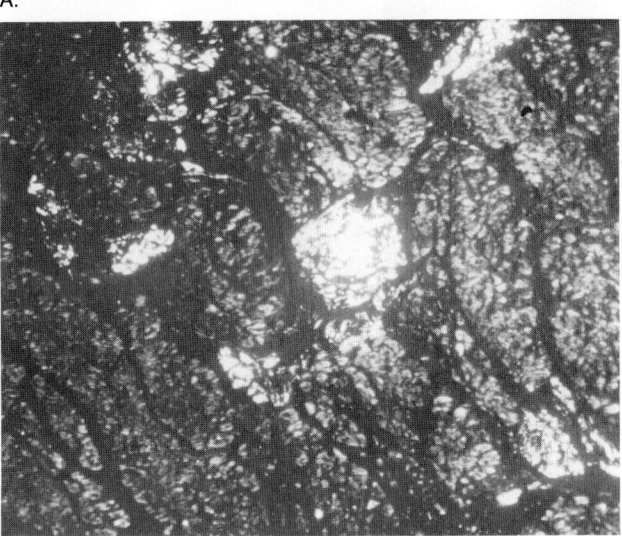

B.

Fig. 97-3 Amyloid deposits within myocardium stained with Congo red. *Panel A* is a light microscopic view, while *panel B* is the same section viewed through crossed polars. Congo red-stained amyloid deposits show green birefringence. Ring structures caused by amyloid deposits around myocardial fiber bundles also become apparent in the polarizing microscope. Congo red counterstained with hematoxylin.

tively stained with uranyl acetate or phosphotungstic acid, and studied by high resolution electron microscopy, the non-branching fibrils appear to consist of two to several parallel subunit filaments.[32] Helical twisting of these subunits, which measure about 25 to 35 Å in width, may give a beaded appearance to the fibrils. While a fair degree of structural diversity is seen from one fibril preparation to another, no ultrastructural features which distinguish immunoglobulin, AA, or prealbumin amyloid fibrils have been reported.

The substructure of amyloid fibrils has been studied by x-ray diffraction.[33,34] While amyloid fibrils basically have a crystalline structure which gives them their birefringence, it has not been possible to solubilize and recrystallize amyloid fibrils to study crystal lattice by x-ray diffraction. Chemical studies suggest that other substances (e.g., proteoglycans) may be involved in fibril formation, and, therefore, fibrils are a mixture of substances other than just the basic protein subunit. X-ray powder patterns, however, are consistent with β structure,

and this has been the basis for developing the antiparallel β pleated sheet model of amyloid fibrils (Fig. 97-5). This is supported by x-ray crystallographic data on two of the amyloid fibril subunit proteins, immunoglobulin light chain and prealbumin. Immunoglobulin light chain domains have extensive antiparallel β configuration.[35] Similarly, the prealbumin monomer is composed of extensive β structure with eight polypeptide segments running in an antiparallel fashion in two planes.[36] Tertiary structure of AA protein in reactive amyloidosis is not as well understood, and structural models suggest that alpha helices may be involved in intrinsic fibril formation.

OVERALL CLASSIFICATION OF THE AMYLOIDOSES

Although the term *amyloid* turned out to be a misnomer, we have all become accustomed to using the term amyloidosis to denote the syndromes characterized by the deposition of the β pleated sheet fibrils. There have been some attempts to change the designation of these diseases to the β *fibrilloses* since the β pleated sheet fibril appears to be the most unifying feature of all the diseases we call *amyloidosis*.[1] Even this has a shortcoming, since fibril formation may not always be necessary to give pathology. For instance, we now recognize a condition called *immunoglobulin light chain deposition disease*, a B-lymphocyte dyscrasia in which monoclonal light chain proteins (usually κ) accumulate in organs such as kidney and result in death but evidently do not have the capability of forming fibrils.[37,38] This condition would appear to be very closely related to immunoglobulin amyloidosis, since there have now been reports of patients who had immunoglobulin light chain deposition disease in whom postmortem examinations showed actual amyloid fibril deposits in organs other than the kidney.[39,40] Thus, we think it is best to retain the term *amyloidosis* and direct our attention to constructing a modern day classification of the amyloidoses based on the chemical composition of the amyloid deposits. Such a classification will have to be modified for clinical usage, since patterns of organ involvement will continue to be important. For instance, systemic amyloidosis versus localized amyloidosis has far reaching significance in treatment and prognosis. Therefore, it is best to classify the systemic amyloidoses separately from the localized forms and then use subclassifications based on chemical compositions.

Historically, for the want of a better method, the amyloidoses were classified according to the clinical features of each syndrome. Primary amyloidosis was used to designate those syndromes in which there was no obvious predisposing disease. Secondary amyloidosis referred to those cases in which there was a predisposing chronic inflammatory disease. Heredofamilial or hereditary amyloidosis was used whenever there was a definite familial pattern. A few confusing terms were used, and these need to be mentioned because they, of course, persist in the old literature. First, patients with amyloidosis associated with multiple myeloma were frequently said to have amyloidosis "secondary" to multiple myeloma. The use of the term *secondary* in this context is unfortunate since chemical analysis now shows that myeloma associated amyloidosis is chemically the same as primary amyloidosis. These two groups should be and are presently classified as *immunoglobulin amyloidosis*. Further confusion has been caused by the use of the term *primary* in some of the reports of hereditary amyloidosis.

At the present time, the best classification of the amyloi-

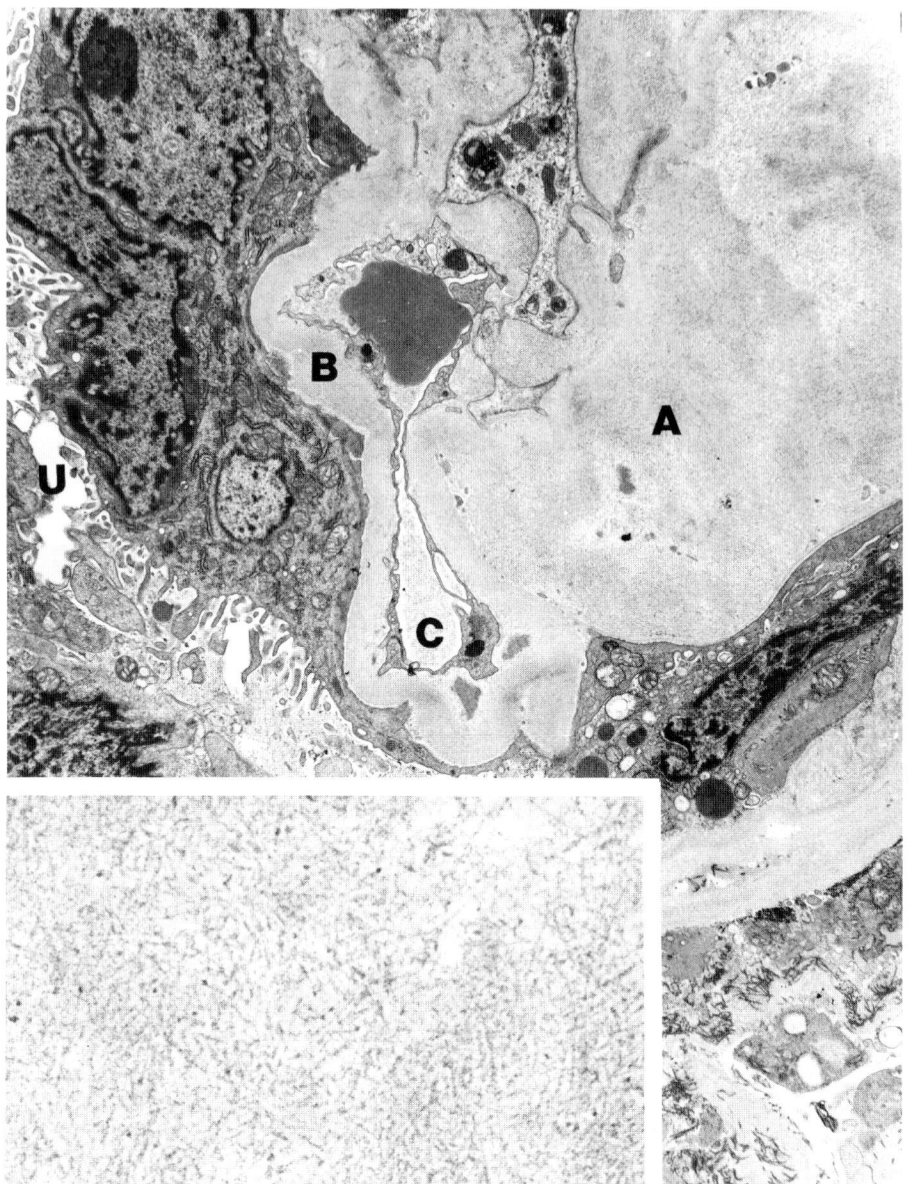

Fig. 97-4 Electron micrograph of a renal biopsy. Amyloid deposits are present throughout the basement membrane and in adjacent structures. *Inset* is higher power micrograph showing the fibrillar structures that are characteristic of all types of amyloid deposits. A = amyloid; B = basement membrane; C = capillary loop; U = urinary space.

doses is based upon the chemical composition of the amyloid fibrils. This is of particular value in the systemic amyloidoses where we recognize three distinct entities and know the chemical basis for each. A word of caution, however, since there may be other forms of systemic amyloidosis, particularly in the hereditary group, for which we may find as yet undescribed amyloid subunits. In the localized forms of amyloidosis, few subunit proteins have been characterized biochemically, so it remains necessary to classify them by a combination of factors including organ system involvement and chemical composition, where known. It is important to realize that some hereditary amyloidoses are systemic and others are localized. In the systemic group are the autosomal dominant forms which usually show peripheral neuropathy and in which many variant forms of prealbumin have been described.[41] In addition, there is the systemic amyloidosis associated with familial Mediterranean fever in which the pattern of inheritance is autosomal recessive.[42] Hereditary amyloid syndromes with localized deposits include medullary carcinoma of the thyroid,[43,44] familial cutaneous amyloidosis,[45,46] and those forms of Alzheimer disease in which there is a familial pattern.[47] Localized forms of amyloidosis without

an apparent hereditary pattern include amyloid in the islets of Langerhans in diabetes mellitus, amyloid of the larynx and upper respiratory tract, the sporadic occurrence of amyloid tumors in the genitourinary tract, some cutaneous amyloidoses, and nonfamilial cerebral amyloid angiopathy and most Alzheimer disease.

THE SYSTEMIC AMYLOIDOSES

There are three major types of systemic amyloidosis that have been recognized in humans: (1) immunoglobulin (primary), (2) reactive (secondary), and (3) hereditary (Table 97-1). A fourth type which thus far has been described only in patients on chronic hemodialysis has deposits containing β_2-microglobulin.[48,49] This type, in which deposition seems restricted to bones and joints, has not yet been accepted as a systemic disease. In this chapter we are principally interested in the hereditary forms of amyloidosis, but it is important to have an understanding of the other types of human systemic amyloidosis for two reasons. First, at the clinical level, the three types of

A.

B.

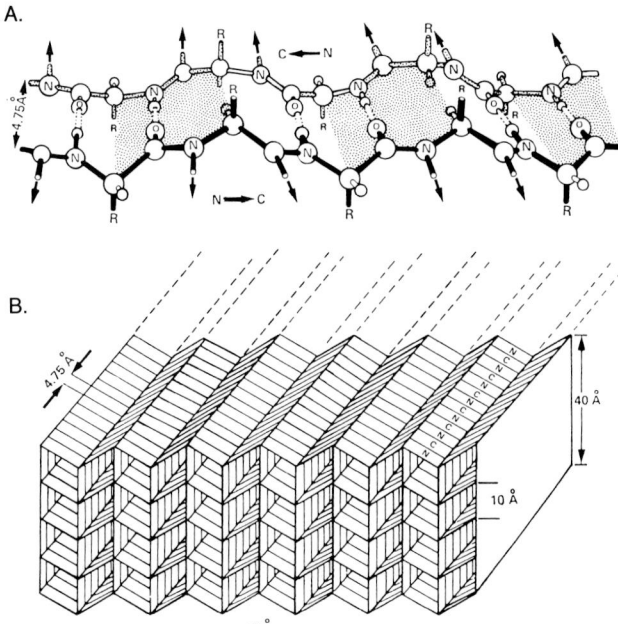

Fig. 97-5 Proposed model of antiparallel β structure. A. The polypeptide chain is depicted running left to right as indicated from amino terminus to carboxyl terminus. The peptide then folds back on itself with the second strand held by hydrogen bonding with an interchain distance of approximately 4.75 Å. B. The proposed structure of amyloid fibril is shown with basic dimensions of 40 X 40 Å with indefinite length. Two or more of these fibrils probably associate by twisting along the long axis to form the amyloid fibril. (Modified from G. H. Sack et al.[156] Used by permission.)

systemic amyloidosis may be very similar. They all may affect the same organ systems to varying degrees. One form of amyloidosis may be easily mistaken for another, especially in situations where a family history is not available or informative, or when chronic inflammatory disease which may predispose to reactive amyloidosis is not readily apparent. Second, it has become increasingly evident that there is a genetic basis to both the immunoglobulin and the reactive types of amyloidosis. The monoclonal immunoglobulin light chains, which are the subunit proteins of immunoglobulin amyloidosis, are the products of intricate gene rearrangement mechanisms in β-lymphocyte clones. Limited structural studies of amyloid light chain proteins suggest that only certain structures are amyloidogenic (having the capability of forming amyloid fibrils). Whatever pathogenic mechanisms are involved in immunoglobulin amyloid formation, DNA rearrangements are an integral part of the process. In reactive amyloidosis, the precursor protein SAA is synthesized by the liver. There are multiple genes coding for this protein and, again, while structural data are limited, they suggest that only certain forms of SAA are processed to make amyloid fibrils. While no inheritance pattern of reactive amyloidosis has been shown other

than in familial Mediterranean fever and Muckle-Wells syndrome, the fact that only certain SAA gene products are associated with amyloid fibrils suggest that there is a genetic basis for reactive amyloidosis as well. Therefore, we review the clinical, pathogenic, and biochemical aspects of the two classic forms of systemic amyloidosis before we turn our attention to the hereditary amyloidoses.

Immunoglobulin-Type Amyloidosis

Immunoglobulin amyloidosis includes all cases in which the basic building block of the amyloid fibril is immunoglobulin light chain protein. This type is referred to as *AL amyloidosis* for amyloidosis light chain. This group of disorders includes not only primary amyloidosis but also amyloidosis associated with multiple myeloma and other plasma cell dyscrasias such as Waldenström macroglobulinemia and the heavy chain diseases. The unifying factor in these amyloidoses is the overproduction of monoclonal immunoglobulin protein, with the light chain protein of the clonal product becoming the subunit of the amyloid fibril.

Incidence. Immunoglobulin amyloidosis is the most common form of systemic amyloidosis. There are no good prevalence data, but in a large medical center there should be several patients with this disease each year.[50] Unfortunately, a fair percentage of patients with immunoglobulin amyloidosis die without the benefit of a correct diagnosis. Even with correct diagnosis, the lack of a proven form of therapy often leads to failure on the part of the primary physician to refer the patient to a specialty center where that person would be entered into the published statistics. The predilection of immunoglobulin amyloidosis to affect the heart and cause heart failure or fatal arrhythmia probably adds to the number of undiagnosed cases.

Clinical Presentation. It is frequently noted that immunoglobulin amyloidosis affects the mesenchymal derived organs such as heart, skeletal muscle, and nerve. These structures are involved much more frequently than in reactive (secondary) amyloidosis. Still, the most common presentation for immunoglobulin amyloidosis is renal involvement with nephrotic syndrome.[51] Some patients may present with hepatomegaly, and there are a small number of patients who present with clotting factor X deficiency which may be related to amyloid infiltration of the spleen.[52] Immunoglobulin amyloidosis has become recognized increasingly in patients with cardiomyopathy and also in patients with life-threatening ventricular arrhythmias. Bowel involvement with chronic diarrhea and weight loss is common, and autonomic nervous system involvement with orthostatic hypotension and sexual impotence is also frequent. Vascular involvement in the skin may give

Table 97-1 Systemic Amyloidoses

Type	Previous name	Subunit protein	Distinguishing feature
Immunoglobulin (AL)	Primary Myeloma-associated	Ig light chains Kappa Lambda	Monoclonal immunoglobulin
Reactive (AA)	Secondary	Amyloid A	Inflammatory disease
Hereditary (AH)	Familial Heredofamilial FAP	Prealbumin	Autosomal dominant

purpura. A smaller number of patients will have carpal tunnel syndrome, and some will have generalized neuropathy due to amyloid infiltration of nerves.[53] These latter cases may be confused with the hereditary syndromes.

Laboratory Findings. Laboratory tests will reflect which organ systems are infiltrated by amyloid. Electrocardiograms often show decreased voltage and evidence of anteroseptal myocardial infarction. Numerous studies have shown that no such infarction exists in these patients and that the septal Q waves and voltage abnormalities are most likely due to amyloid deposits in the muscle. Echocardiography may show thickened ventricular walls and poor contractility. Valve thickening is much less common in this type of amyloidosis than in the hereditary syndromes. Renal amyloid usually causes proteinuria in the nephrotic range; in later stages there is increasing azotemia. Heart failure and orthostatic hypotension can frequently give prerenal azotemia. Protein electrophoresis and immunoelectrophoresis of serum and urine will detect monoclonal immunoglobulin components in approximately 80 percent of patients with immunoglobulin amyloidosis. The bone marrow frequently has increased numbers of plasma cells which, in classic primary amyloidosis, lack malignant features but often have increased cytoplasm which probably indicates active immunoglobulin synthesis. The percentage of plasma cells in the bone marrow is frequently in the 3 to 5 percent range but may be 20 percent or more. In patients with overt myeloma, the plasma cells will have malignant features and may constitute 50 percent or more of the bone marrow population. Quantitation of Bence-Jones protein in serum or urine is not always useful in distinguishing multiple myeloma from primary amyloidosis, but it is often used as one of the parameters to diagnose multiple myeloma. If multiple myeloma does exist, lytic lesions in the skull or the spine may be seen on x-ray. The clinician needs to be wary, however, since amyloid deposits in such structures as the femoral head may occasionally completely replace the bone and be misinterpreted as evidence of myeloma.

Clinical Course and Prognosis. Immunoglobulin amyloidosis is a variable disease, with prognosis depending on which organ system is involved. The best statistics show that the median survival of patients with primary amyloidosis is 12 to 14 months.[50] Survival ranges from less than 4 months for patients with serum creatinines greater than 4 mg/dl or with congestive heart failure to several years for patients who present with only neuropathy or carpal tunnel syndrome. Of the three types of systemic amyloidosis, the immunoglobulin type has the worst prognosis. The prognosis is especially grim for patients with multiple myeloma and amyloidosis, and many die within 6 months of diagnosis.

Pathogenesis. Since all immunoglobulin-type amyloid deposits are composed of monoclonal immunoglobulin light chain proteins, we know that a basic factor in the pathogenesis of this disease is the overproduction of immunoglobulin light chains by a particular B-lymphocyte clone. The factors responsible for the initiation of this process are unknown. In multiple myeloma it may be due to the malignant nature of the cell, but in most cases of classic primary amyloidosis, it would appear that normal metabolic processes are altered so that light chains are either overproduced or cannot be degraded completely. Clinical studies have suggested that certain immunoglobulin light chains are more amyloidogenic than

others. For instance, more λ light chain proteins are associated with amyloid than κ proteins.[1] Since the ratio of κ to λ in the immune system is 2:1, this suggests that λ light chains are more amyloidogenic. This result may be partly due to the fact that free Bence-Jones proteins in plasma usually exist as dimers, and λ light chains have a higher association constant than κ light chains. Much less is known about why certain monoclonal light chains deposit in any particular organ. Vascular organs such as kidney, liver, spleen, and heart are very prone to amyloid deposition, but bowel and nerve are also commonly involved. The light chain protein is usually processed when incorporated into fibrils so that most amyloid subunit proteins include the entire variable segment of the light chain plus approximately the first tryptic peptide of the constant region. Since both the variable segment and the constant segment have extensive β structure, they evidently are easily incorporated into the β pleated sheet of the amyloid fibril.[35] Practically no data are available on whether the light chains are cleaved prior to incorporation into the fibril or whether incorporation occurs and then the bulk of the constant region is clipped off during the aggregation process. Occasionally amyloid fibrils are found in which the entire light chain is incorporated into the fibril. Thus far, no fragments of heavy chain proteins have been found in amyloid fibrils, and there is no evidence to suggest that *polyclonal* light chains are incorporated into the fibrils. Fibril synthesis, therefore, appears to be a very selective process.

Treatment. The most frequent treatment for immunoglobulin amyloidosis is chemotherapy with alkylating agents such as melphalan coupled with prednisone.[54] This has been standard therapy for multiple myeloma for many years and in selected cases appears to be effective in immunoglobulin amyloidosis. Patients with Waldenström macroglobulinemia and amyloidosis are often treated with chlorambucil. In recent years, colchicine has been added to this regimen or used alone, because it has been shown that it is effective in preventing amyloid fibril formation in the murine model of amyloidosis. It should be noted that in the murine model the amyloid is of the reactive (AA) type, and these data have been extrapolated to the other forms of systemic amyloidosis. The efficacy of colchicine has not been documented.[55-57]

Numerous supportive measures have been shown to prolong the survival of patients with immunoglobulin amyloidosis. Potent diuretics can alleviate the nephrotic syndrome and congestive heart failure, and antiarrhythmia medications may prevent fatal arrhythmias. These often increase the problems of restrictive cardiomyopathy, however. Renal failure can be treated with dialysis, and some patients have received renal transplants. These transplanted organs usually develop amyloidosis if the patient lives long enough, but in selected cases prolongation of survival is definitely noted. Bleeding diathesis from factor X deficiency has been corrected by splenectomy in a few patients.[58]

Reactive Amyloidosis

Reactive (secondary) amyloidosis is usually found in individuals with chronic inflammatory disease. Many diseases will predispose to reactive amyloidosis, but the most frequent include inflammatory arthritis such as rheumatoid or psoriatic, granulomatous bowel disease, tuberculosis, leprosy, osteomyelitis, and suppurative infections, as may be seen in patients with quadraplegia or paraplegia. Reactive amyloidosis has also been reported in patients with cystic fibrosis, systemic lupus erythematosus, and bronchiectasis. In recent years there has been an increasing number of reports of reactive amyloidosis in intravenous drug users, presumably associated with chronic skin and other organ infection. Occasionally, reactive amyloidosis will be seen in a patient with no predisposing disease. Reactive amyloidosis occurs in a familial pattern in patients with familial Mediterranean fever. This association will be discussed in the section on hereditary amyloidosis. The acronym classification for reactive amyloidosis is AA, which stands for amyloid A to reflect the subunit protein of the fibrils.

Incidence. Recent studies suggest that the incidence of reactive amyloidosis is decreasing. In the early part of this century, amyloidosis was common in patients with suppurative tuberculous lesions such as empyema. A lower incidence is noted in chronic cavitary disease, and now that tuberculosis is usually treated satisfactorily, it is quite uncommon to see a patient with amyloidosis associated with tuberculosis. The incidence in patients with rheumatoid arthritis has been reported to be high in the past, but the figures probably reflect selection bias. Most clinicians would agree that amyloidosis is seen in less than 5 percent of patients with inflammatory arthritis such as rheumatoid arthritis. The relatively high incidence in patients with quadriplegia or paraplegia persists despite the use of antibiotics. In certain equatorial parts of the world, leprosy is frequently associated with reactive amyloidosis.

Clinical Presentation. Reactive amyloid deposits usually involve the kidney, liver, and spleen early in the course of the disease. Many patients present with the nephrotic syndrome, and this may persist for months or years before azotemia occurs. By the time of death, major liver and spleen involvement is common. The gastrointestinal tract is commonly involved, but motility is less affected than in the immunoglobulin and hereditary amyloidoses. However, gastrointestinal bleeding, which may be life-threatening, is quite frequent, and often no definite site of bleeding can be found on clinical evaluation. Cardiac and skeletal muscle are much less commonly involved, and neuropathy has not been reported. Length of survival with reactive amyloidosis depends on how early in the course the diagnosis is made. Renal disease usually progresses slowly, and a patient may be nephrotic for 3 to 5 years before becoming significantly azotemic. Hemodialysis or peritoneal dialysis may prolong life. Amyloid infiltration in blood vessel walls, however, causes increased risk of hemorrhage, and involvement of other organs such as the liver eventually leads to death.

Pathogenesis. The precursor protein of reactive amyloid fibrils is serum amyloid A, which is synthesized mainly in the liver.[16,22,59] There is some evidence that other tissues produce SAA, but hepatic synthesis far outweighs any other origin. SAA is both an acute phase reactant and an apolipoprotein.[60,61] The kinetics of hepatic SAA production are very simiiar to those for C-reactive protein, another acute phase reactant.[20,21] Numerous studies suggest that both of these proteins are synthesized under the direction of an inducer produced by macrophages. This inducer is probably interleukin 1, which stimulates hepatocytes either alone or in concert with other factors to produce SAA through induction of transcription of SAA genes.[62,63] In the human, there are at least two SAA

genes with multiple alleles located on the short arm of chromosome 11.[64] In the mouse there are three SAA genes, and these are localized to chromosome 7.[65–67] Only two forms of SAA proteins have been identified in the mouse even though all three mRNA species are present.[68,69] In the mouse, only one of the SAA species is found in amyloid fibrils.[70] In humans it is not yet clear whether certain forms of SAA are amyloidogenic while others are not. Human SAA has 104 amino acid residues in a single polypeptide chain.[64,71,72] In amyloidosis the SAA is usually processed by cleavage between residues 76 and 77, and the amino-terminal 76 residues are incorporated into amyloid fibrils. There have been some data to suggest that patients who develop reactive amyloidosis have a defect in normal degradation of SAA proteins.[73] Reactive amyloidosis has been the most thoroughly studied type because there are several animal models of this disease which lend themselves nicely to laboratory investigation (see "Animal Models of Amyloidosis" below).

Treatment. There is no specific treatment for reactive amyloidosis. Chronic colchicine administration has been shown to prevent the occurrence of reactive amyloidosis in patients with familial Mediterranean fever, but no such finding has been reported for sporadic reactive amyloidosis.[74] Chemotherapy would seem not to be indicated since, in some animal models, cytotoxic drugs may accelerate the formation of amyloid deposits. Supportive measures are often very effective and can add significant time to survival. These include not only renal dialysis but also the judicious use of diuretics, antibiotics, and measures to treat the primary inflammatory disease.

Animal Models of Amyloidosis

Systemic amyloidosis occurs in many animals species, most often as a sporadic disease but occasionally with hereditary aspects. The amyloid fibrils from a number of species have been analyzed and shown to contain AA proteins and therefore reveal the reactive nature of the disease. AA proteins have been structurally characterized for the mouse, horse, cow, dog, cat, monkey, guinea pig, hamster, mink, and Pekin duck.[59,75–81] The duck is the only nonmammal so far in which AA of reactive amyloid has been characterized. In a certain strain of collie dog, amyloidosis is associated with hereditary cyclic neutropenia.[82] In Abysinnian cats, amyloidosis shows a hereditary pattern.[83] Some strains of mice have spontaneous amyloidosis which is not the AA type. SJL mice have old age onset amyloidosis in which the fibrils do not appear to contain AA protein.[84] The true subunit of these fibrils has not been characterized to date. In a strain of mice showing early senescense, amyloid deposits have been shown to be composed of apolipoprotein A-II.[85]

Reactive amyloidosis can be induced in most mammalian species. Kuczynski first demonstrated the production of amyloidosis in mice by the parenteral administration of sodium caseinate.[86,87] Subsequently, the murine model of induced systemic amyloidosis was used extensively as a model of the human disease. It has many features of the human disease with major deposition of fibrils in spleen, liver, and kidney. This form of amyloid can also be produced by administration of Freund's complete adjuvant and also by chronic administration of endotoxin. Studies using this model show that interleukin 1 is generated by macrophages[62,88] and that this induces the liver to synthesize SAA,[22] one form of which (SAA 2) is incorporated into amyloid fibrils.[70] There are recent DNA studies to show that some mouse species (e.g., SJL/J) lack the allele for the amyloidogenic isotype of SAA.[89] It is interesting that, of all the mammalian species studied thus far, the rat does not appear to synthesize SAA and has never been shown to develop reactive amyloidosis. The murine model of casein-induced amyloidosis has been used to show that high doses of colchicine will prevent amyloid fibril formation[56,57] and that discontinuation of casein administration will result in some resolution of the fibril deposits.[90]

Hereditary Amyloidosis

Of all the amyloidoses, the greatest progress in research over the past 10 years has been in the understanding of the hereditary forms. This progress is due to the combination of sophisticated protein chemistry coupled with the advent of molecular biology and an enhanced awareness of genetic diseases. While 10 years ago we did not know the composition of the amyloid deposits, we now know that a number of the autosomal dominant amyloidoses are associated with variants of the plasma protein prealbumin. We also know that prealbumin is not the only protein that is associated with autosomal dominant amyloidosis. The hereditary cerebral amyloidosis originally described in Iceland is associated with a variant of γ trace protein. In addition, there are a number of autosomal dominant amyloidoses in which the subunit protein of the deposits has not been characterized. Some of these may be prealbumin, but certainly some of them are not.

Classification. There are several ways to classify the hereditary amyloidoses. From the genetic viewpoint, there are autosomal dominant forms and also the autosomal recessive form associated with familial Mediterranean fever. Most of the autosomal dominant forms are systemic, but there are localized forms of hereditary amyloidosis such as those associated with medullary carcinoma of the thyroid and familial Alzheimer disease.[43,47] In the past, the hereditary amyloidoses were classified by clinical presentation and ethnic origin of the kindreds.[41] Clinically, most of the autosomal dominant forms present with peripheral neuropathy, and therefore the term *familial amyloidotic polyneuropathy (FAP)* was coined. Further subclassification was based on type of neuropathy. FAP I was assigned to the Portuguese, Japanese, and some Swedish families in which the first feature is lower extremity neuropathy; FAP II was assigned to the Indiana/Swiss family and the Maryland kindreds in which carpal tunnel syndrome is prominent. The Iowa kindred was called FAP III since marked nephrotic syndrome and an association with peptic ulcer disease seemed to set it apart from the Portuguese disease. The Finnish amyloidosis with prominent cranial neuropathy was called *FAP IV*. The term *FAP*, however, is now antiquated. While the clinical syndromes in general correspond to the genetic defect for these different kindreds, there is considerable overlap, and a more rigorous chemical classification of the hereditary amyloidoses is in order.

The Prealbumin Amyloidoses

The majority of the autosomal dominant amyloidoses characterized thus far are associated with variants of plasma prealbumin (transthyretin), and there is good evidence that more

prealbumin variants will be described in the future. To understand the pathogenesis of these forms of amyloidosis better, it is important to review the properties of prealbumin.

Prealbumin is a normal plasma protein. It was originally called *prealbumin* because it migrates ahead of albumin on standard protein electrophoresis. However, it shares no structural relationship to albumin. Various names for this protein have included thyroxine binding prealbumin,[91] plasma prealbumin,[92] and, more recently, transthyretin (TTR).[93] This last name was coined because of the transport properties of the protein, which binds both thyroxine and retinol binding protein (RBP). Indeed, the name *prealbumin* is somewhat misleading. For instance, studies in the mouse system have used the term *prealbumin* to apply to other serum proteins, mainly α_1-antitrypsin, rather than prealbumin (transthyretin), which actually migrates on electrophoresis within the plasma albumin range.[94] The term *transthyretin*, will most likely find increased usage in subsequent years. It should be noted, however, that any literature review will find many of the significant articles under the name *prealbumin*.

Plasma prealbumin is synthesized by the liver in a constitutive manner as a single polypeptide chain of 127 amino acid residues.[95] The primary structure has been known since 1974, and the secondary, tertiary, and quaternary structure has been defined by x-ray diffraction.[96] The entity circulating in plasma is a tetramer ($M_r = 55,000$) composed of four identical monomers[36] (Fig. 97-6). It would appear that two monomers

Fig. 97-6 Schematic drawing of prealbumin tetramer as viewed down the Z molecular axis. Thyroxine binds in the inner channel, and RBP attaches to the outside of the molecule. *(Modified from C. C. Blake et al.[36] Used by permission.)*

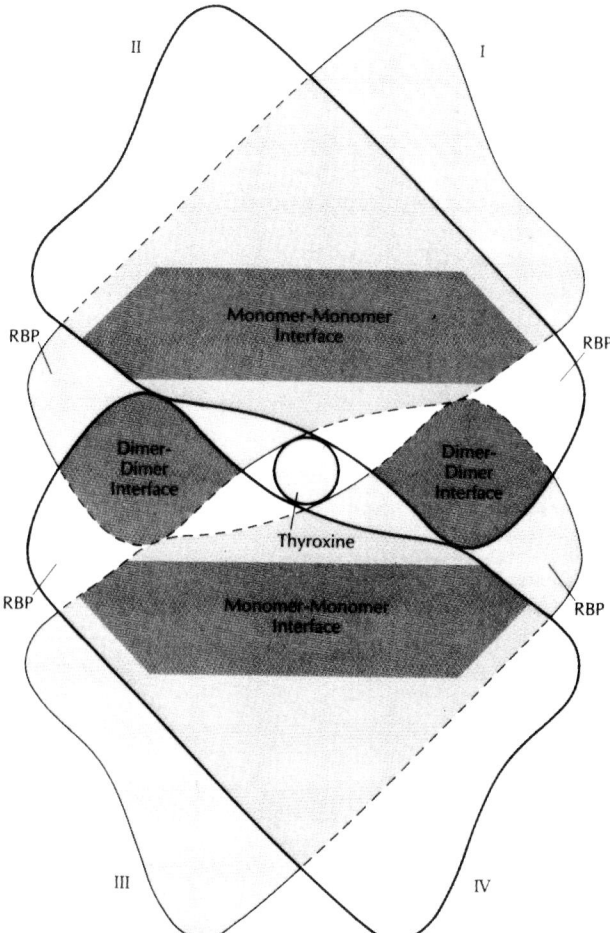

noncovalently combine to form a stable dimer, and then two dimers associate to form the tetramer with twofold symmetry. Down the center channel of the tetramer are two binding sites for thyroxine although binding studies suggest that these sites show negative cooperativity.[97] Prealbumin also binds retinol binding protein (RBP, $M_r = 21,000$), which is assumed to attach to the outside of the tetramer.[98] RBP must be saturated with retinol in order to bind to the carrier prealbumin molecule.

Prealbumin concentration in plasma ranges from 20 to 40 mg/dl in normal individuals and has been found to be significantly depressed in individuals with malnutrition. Prealbumin concentration also decreases at times of acute or chronic inflammation, and therefore prealbumin has been referred to as *a negative acute phase protein*. Prealbumin levels also are significantly depressed in many patients with the prealbumin amyloidoses, but the reason for this is unclear.[99–101] There is one gene for prealbumin, and this is located on human chromosome 18.[102] Almost all individuals with prealbumin amyloidosis have been found to be heterozygotes having one normal prealbumin allele and one variant prealbumin allele. Expression of the two alleles is probably equal, but most studies have shown slightly more of the normal gene product in the plasma than the variant.[103,104]

Prealbumin has extensive β structure with the monomers having eight β chains arranged in an antiparallel configuration in two planes[36] (Fig. 97-7). This configuration would appear to predispose toward amyloid fibril formation. Each of the amino acid substitutions that has been identified in variant prealbumins associated with hereditary amyloidosis can be hypothesized to alter the surface topography of the molecule. This alteration presumably would favor aggregation and fibril formation. Although no structural prealbumin variant has yet been identified which is not associated with amyloid formation, nonamyloid variants probably will be found.

The prealbumin cDNA sequence has been reported by a number of laboratories,[102,105,106] and the complete nucleotide sequence of the prealbumin gene in humans has been reported by two laboratories[107,108] (Fig. 97-8). The human gene has four exons (Fig. 97-9). The proximal upstream 5' region has sequences similar to those for binding of the glucocortocoid receptor.[109] However, in the mouse prealbumin gene, there appear to be additional regulatory sequences about 2 kb upstream from the coding regions.[94] Prealbumin mRNA has been identified in choroid plexus of rats[110–112] and humans,[113] so synthesis is not exclusively hepatic. The role of any extrahepatic prealbumin synthesis in the systemic manifestations of amyloidosis is unlikely, but occasional leptomeningeal involvement may be related to intracranial synthesis.

Autosomal Dominant Prealbumin-Associated Amyloidosis Syndromes

Clinical Features. Most of the autosomal dominant amyloidoses have peripheral neuropathy as a major clinical manifestation. Thus, these disorders have also been called *familial amyloidotic polyneuropathy*. In the past, clinical classification of the syndromes has been based on distinguishing between lower extremity neuropathy and upper extremity involvement as the presenting symptom.[41] This is less valid now, since the upper extremity neuropathy, which is really a compression neuropathy from the carpal tunnel syndrome, has been seen in several of the recently described kindreds, sometimes be-

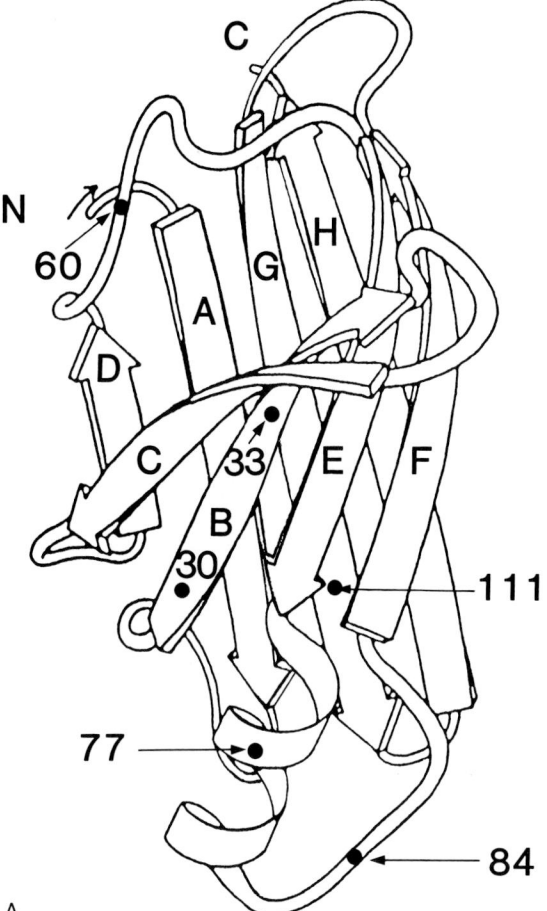

A.

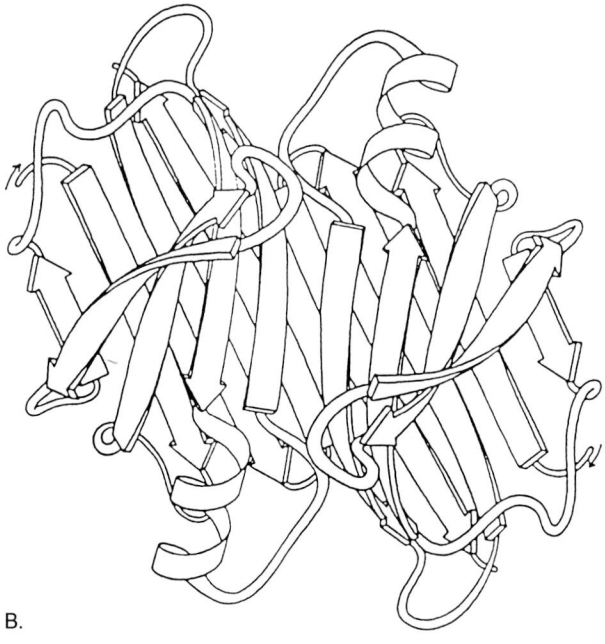

B.

Fig. 97-7 Subunit structure of prealbumin (transthyretin). *A.* Antiparallel β structure of prealbumin. Eight β strands are arranged in two parallel planes. Approximate locations of mutations associated with amyloidosis are indicated. *B.* Two prealbumin monomers associate to form a dimer. Two dimers then associate to give the tetramer depicted in Fig. 97-6. *(Modified from J.S. Richardson, Advances in Protein Chemistry 34:167, 1981. Used by permission.)*

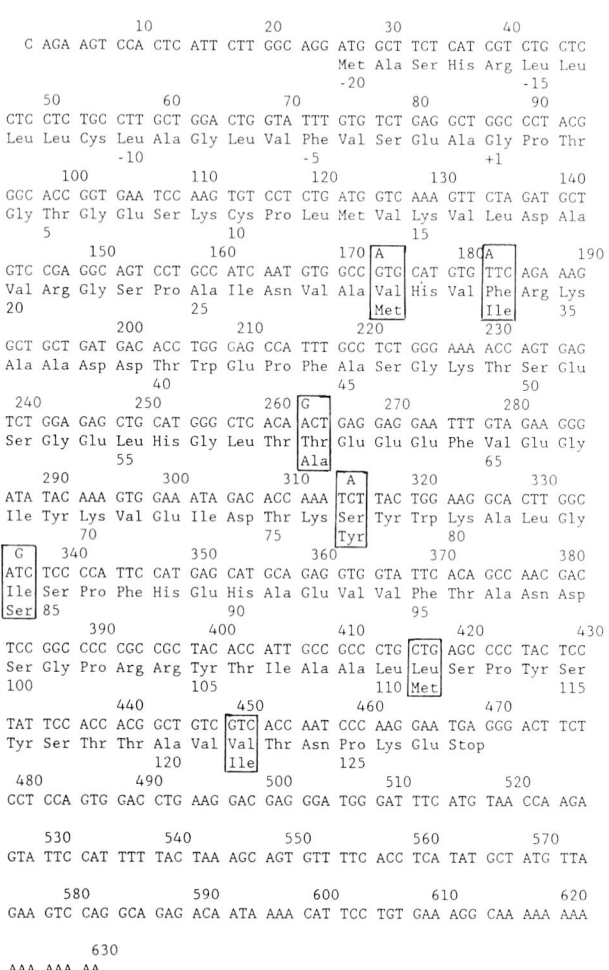

Fig. 97-8 Complete nucleotide sequence of prealbumin cDNA and protein amino acid sequence. Mutations associated with hereditary amyloidosis are indicated. The nucleotide substitution for Met 111 has not yet been proven.

ual impotence or gastrointestinal dysfunction. Sensory loss in the lower extremities follows a stocking distribution, and it has been noted that temperature and pain sensations are impaired earlier than proprioception. By the time sensory loss is noted at the level of the knees, the hands usually become involved by a sensory neuropathy with a glove distribution. Motor loss develops later and frequently gives footdrop, wrist-drop, and difficulty in hand function. Trophic ulcers on the lower extremities are common and were a common cause of infection and death before antibiotics came into use. Orthostatic hypotension is common and has profound significance in patients with cardiac amyloid. Gastrointestinal symptoms are due mainly to nerve dysfunction with patients frequently having constipation alternating with diarrhea. Delayed gastric emptying may lead to distension of the organ and poor appetite. Cachexia is a frequent feature and may be a significant factor in mortality.

Visual involvement has been known to occur in the Portuguese syndrome but is much more common in the Indiana/Swiss amyloidosis (FAP II). Amyloid within the vitreous humor of the eye often leads to loss of vision, but this can usually be corrected at least temporarily by surgical removal of the deposits (Fig. 97-12). The scalloped pupil deformity is another eye manifestation which has been described both in the Portuguese and in the Swedish varieties of FAP I. This is most likely due to involvement of ciliary nerves. Lattice corneal dystrophy, a third type of visual involvement, is seen in the Finnish syndrome (FAP IV), but vision is usually not affected until later in the disease. Autonomic neuropathy may cause urinary retention severe enough to require diversionary procedures to prevent renal damage. Hypohydrosis is also seen.

Other clinical manifestations of hereditary amyloidosis depend on which organ systems are involved. FAP I patients (Portuguese, Swedish, Japanese) may have renal amyloid with significant protein loss and subsequent renal insufficiency. In these patients, life may be prolonged by dialysis, but subsequent involvement of other organs is not prevented. The Indiana/Swiss kindred (FAP II) and the Appalachian kindred both have severe cardiac disease, and this is usually the cause of death. Cardiac conduction disturbances occur early and frequently require artificial pacing. The subsequent clinical picture is one of restrictive cardiomyopathy with low output heart failure. Heart failure and cardiomyopathy were prominent in the patients reported by Zalin et al. in England[114] and in the patients described by Frederiksen et al. in Denmark.[115]

Chemical Classification. A number of prealbumin (transthyretin) variants have been identified in the amyloid fibrils or plasma of patients with hereditary amyloidosis (Table 97-2). These findings have provided a biochemical basis for classify-

fore and sometimes after involvement of the lower extremities (Fig. 97-10).

The Portuguese neuropathy (FAP type I) shows the classic and most common features of hereditary amyloidosis (Fig. 97-11). The clinical disease usually starts in the third or fourth decade, although the onset of symptoms may be delayed until advanced age. The disease progresses over 10 to 20 years with peripheral sensorimotor neuropathy, autonomic neuropathy, and varying degrees of systemic organ involvement. The neuropathy starts in the lower extremities with parasthesias and often hypesthesia which can be debilitating. Autonomic neuropathy is an early feature, and patients may present with sex-

Fig. 97-9 Schematic drawing of human prealbumin gene showing four exons. Two mutations associated with amyloidosis have been identified in exon 2, three in exon 3, and two in exon 4. The

recognition sites for *Pvu* II are indicated (P) to show the DNA fragments generated in the test for the Ala 60 gene (see Fig. 97-16).

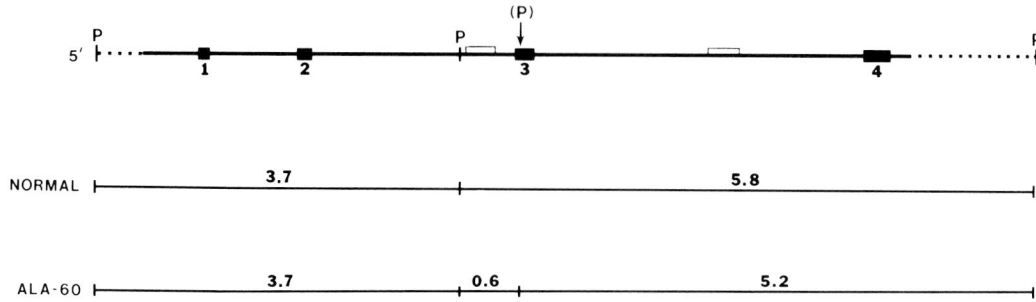

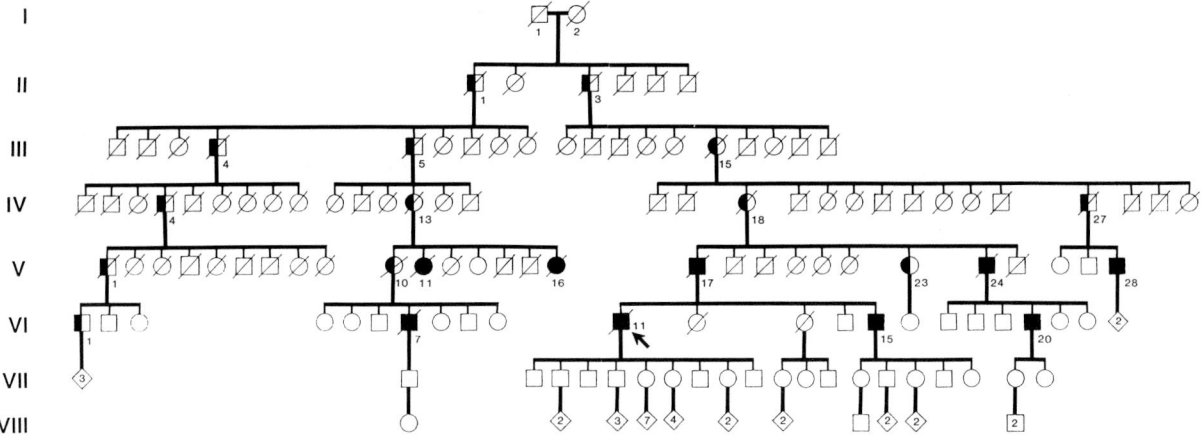

Fig. 97-10 Kindred with hereditary prealbumin amyloidosis associated with variant prealbumin showing the typical autosomal dominant pattern of inheritance. ■ = biopsy proven; ◩ = presumed affected; ◇ multiple sibs, sex unspecified.

ing the prealbumin amyloidoses and have shown that, while the old classification based on the clinical syndrome and ethnic origin was basically sound, there is a great degree of overlap among the syndromes. Identification of nonsymptomatic carriers of variant prealbumin genes in many of the kindreds has widened the recognized time span of clinical onset that is usually quoted for each syndrome. The following prealbumin variants have been identified in hereditary amyloidosis.

METHIONINE 30. The most common type of hereditary amyloidosis thus far reported is characterized by a substitution of methionine for valine at position 30 of the prealbumin molecule. This variant prealbumin has been found in many kindreds in Portugal and Japan, and also in American

Fig. 97-11 Pattern of sensory loss in familial amyloid polyneuropathy type I.

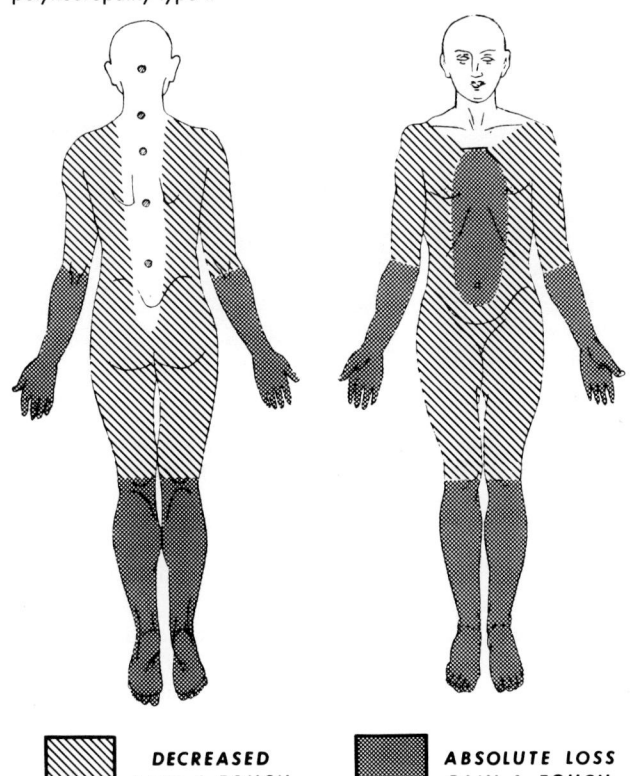

| DECREASED PAIN & TOUCH | | ABSOLUTE LOSS PAIN & TOUCH |

kindreds of Swedish and Greek origin.[25,104,106,116–119] The recent finding of high prevalence of the Met 30 gene in northern Sweden supports the Scandinavian origin of the Swedish/American trait.[120] Clinically, most of these kindreds have been classified as FAP I with neuropathy starting in the lower extremities. Varying degrees of renal and cardiac involvement have been reported, but autonomic and gastrointestinal symptoms are present in most patients. Vitreous deposits of amyloid have been reported, as has the scalloped pupil deformity.[7] In most families, clinical symptoms appear in the third or fourth decade with death by age 50. In the preantibiotic era, death was often from infected leg ulcers. More recently, renal failure and malnutrition due to bowel involvement have been frequent causes of death. Mental function is generally not affected, but amyloid may be present in the central nervous system and in the leptomeninges.[121] In some families the disease has a later onset with patients living into their 60s or 70s.[122,123]

ISOLEUCINE 33. This type of amyloidosis was originally called Jewish FAP. The study represents the smallest kindred that has been chemically characterized. One man who was born in Poland and immigrated to Israel subsequently developed neuropathy (beginning in the lower limbs), diarrhea, impotence, and vitreous deposits between age 25 and 30.[124] His father died from similar symptoms. Autopsy revealed amyloid in all major organs, particularly the thyroid, kidney, spleen, and nerves. Original studies of the amyloid isolated from thyroid showed that a significant proportion of the prealbumin molecules had been cleaved between amino acid positions 48 and 49. A substitution of glycine for threonine at position 49 was reported.[125,126] Subsequently, another group sequenced the amyloid subunit protein isolated from spleen of the same individual and found an isoleucine in place of phenylalanine at position 33.[127] To date no plasma prealbumin in this family has been studied. The controversy between glycine at 49 and isoleucine at 33 has not been completely resolved, but a recent report supports the isoleucine at 33 by restriction enzyme analysis of DNA.[128]

ALANINE 60. This type of amyloidosis (also called Appalachian type) was originally discovered in a large kindred from West Virginia in which the disease was traced to a couple having Irish, English, and German ancestry.[129,130] Recently, the alanine 60 prealbumin substitution was found in another U.S. amyloidosis family of Irish lineage, which supports a Gaelic origin for this mutation. Peripheral neuropathy is not a prominent feature of this syndrome. Some patients have carpal tunnel syndrome. Most have some degree of peripheral neuropa-

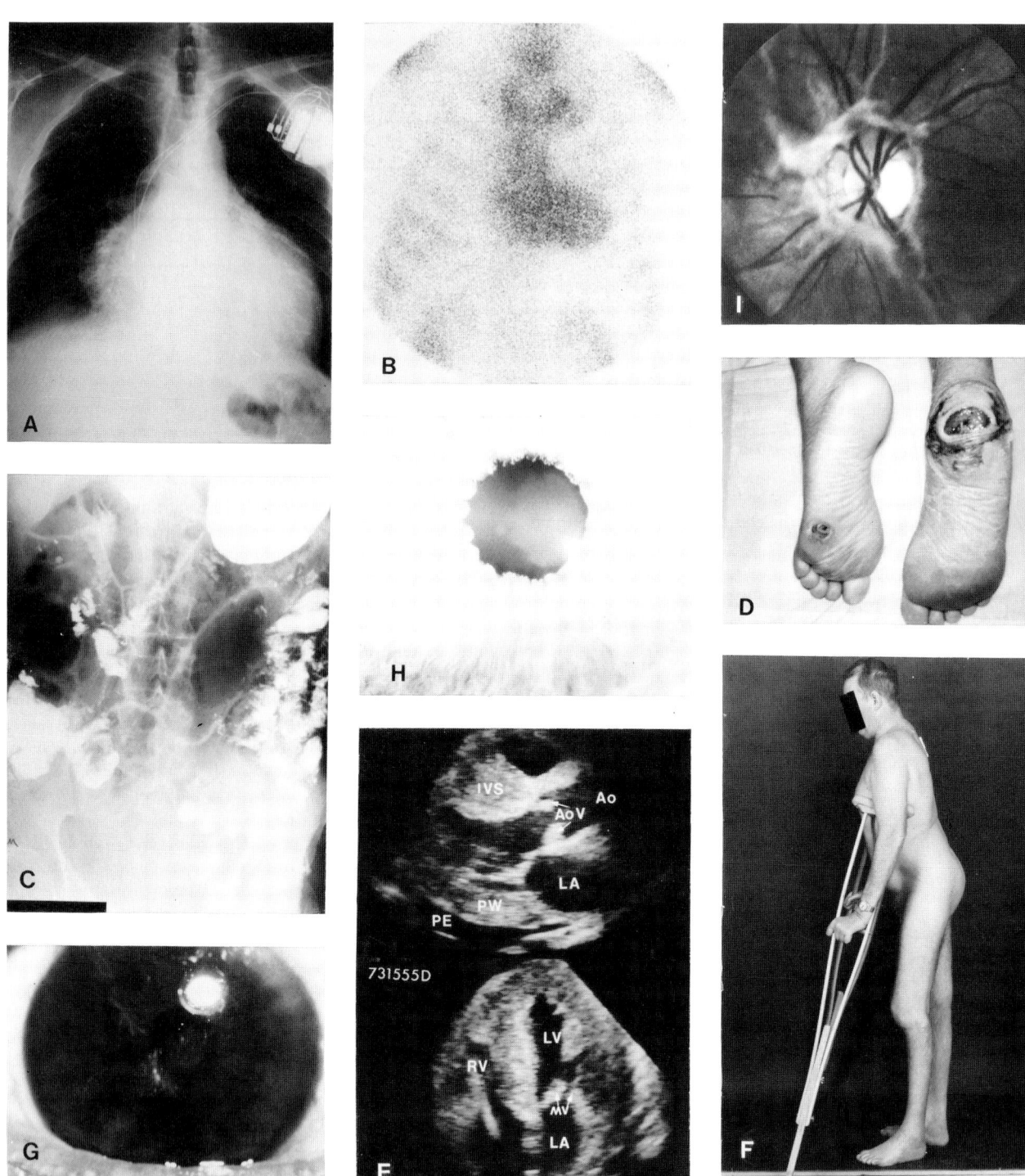

Fig. 97-12 Clinical features of the prealbumin amyloidoses. *A.* Cardiomegaly in Ser 84 amyloidosis. *B.* Technetium pyrophosphate uptake in cardiac amyloidosis. *C.* Gastric distension and dilated small bowel in Ala 60 amyloidosis. *D.* Neurogenic ulcer and calcaneal osteomyelitis in Met 30 amyloidosis. *E.* Two-dimensional echocardiography in Ser 84 amyloidosis showing thickening intraventricular septum (IVS), left ventricular wall (PW), aortic (AOV) and mitral valves (MV) plus dilated left atrium (LA). *F.* Typical neuropathy of Met 30 amyloidosis. This patient has neuropathic arthropathy (Charcot knee). *G.* Lattice corneal dystrophy of Finnish amyloidosis. *H.* Scalloped pupil in Met 30 amyloidosis. *I.* Vitreous deposits in Ser 84 amyloidosis.

thy in the lower extremities, but incapacitation is related more to bowel involvement and resultant malnutrition. Sexual impotence is common. These patients die of cardiomyopathy which usually starts after age 50 and may not begin until after age 60. The disease is progressive but may run a 10- to 20-year course. While most individuals have died in their 60s, some have been known to live past age 90. Postmortem examinations have shown amyloid in nerves, heart, and thyroid

(Fig. 97-13, Fig. 97-14). Significant amyloid in liver, kidney, and spleen has not been seen.

Of particular importance are the facts that cardiomyopathy may be expressed very late in life and that patients frequently suffer from misdiagnosis. At least one individual with this particular mutation has lived past age 90 without significant heart failure. Although these mildly affected individuals obviously have not had life shortened by this type of amyloidosis, some

Table 97-2 Prealbumin Amyloidoses

Amino acid substitution	Position	Clinical name	Clinical feature*	Geographic kindreds
Methionine	30	FAP I	LLN, Bowel, AN, Eye	Portugal/Japan/U.S./Sweden
Isoleucine	33	Jewish	LLN, Eye	Israel
Alanine	60	Appalachian	Heart, CTS, AN	U.S./West Virginia
Tyrosine	77	Il/German	Kidney, Bowel, LLN	U.S./Illinois
Serine	84	FAP II	Heart, CTS, Eye	U.S./Indiana
Methionine	111	Danish	Heart, no neuropathy	Denmark
Isoleucine	122	Senile Cardiac	Heart	U.S./Scand.

*Abbreviations are as follows: LLN = lower limb neuropathy; AN = autonomic neuropathy; and CTS = carpal tunnel syndrome.

of their children have developed the disease at a much earlier age. The original Appalachian kindred is very large and dispersed throughout the United States. The gene has also been detected in a large kindred in the Northeastern United States and in an Irish family that originally settled in the Chicago area.[131]

TYROSINE 77. Amyloidosis associated with the tyrosine 77 prealbumin variant has been described so far in only one family, from Illinois and of German extraction.[132] The clinical syndrome shows lower limb neuropathy and diarrhea starting about age 50. Historically, kidney failure has been the major cause of death. No postmortem tissues have been studied chemically, but biopsy material has shown amyloid deposits which stain selectively with antiprealbumin antiserum. Plasma prealbumin was isolated from one affected individual and was shown to contain a mixture of normal prealbumin and a variant with a tyrosine for serine substitution at position 77. DNA analysis from members of this kindred shows typical autosomal inheritance of the corresponding prealbumin mutation. Although cases of hereditary amyloidosis have been reported in Germany, no studies have yet connected these families with the Illinois/German kindred.

SERINE 84. This form of amyloidosis is commonly referred to as the *Indiana/Swiss type*. While originally reported by Falls et al. in 1954,[133] Rukavina's description of the kindred in 1956 caused his name to be used in identifying this type of heredi-

Fig. 97-13 Section of peripheral nerve stained with antiprealbumin by the avidin biotin peroxidase method. Amyloid deposits are found within the nerve structure, and the positive staining with antiprealbumin proves the diagnosis of hereditary amyloidosis. x100.

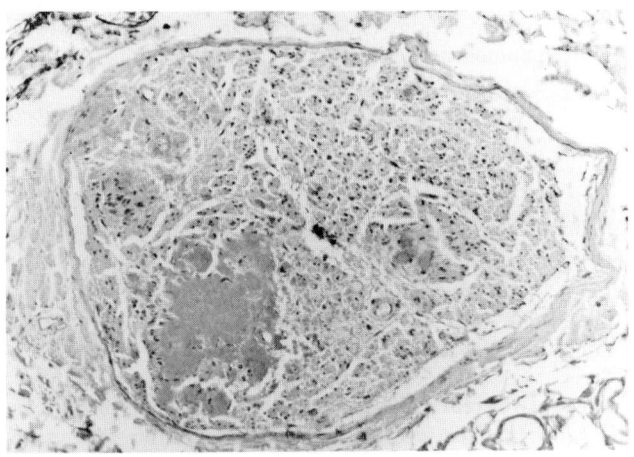

tary amyloidosis.[134] Unfortunately, it was originally called *primary* familial amyloidosis, and this has caused some confusion. In the past, the Indiana and Maryland kindreds were classified together as FAP II, since both have prominent carpal tunnel syndrome.[41] However, it now appears that the disease in the Maryland kindred has a different genetic basis. The Indiana/ Swiss syndrome is characterized by the early onset of carpal tunnel syndrome (a compression neuropathy) which may occur as early as the third decade of life. Infiltrative peripheral neuropathy tends to occur later in the course and can affect all four extremities. Another distinguishing feature is the presence in nearly all patients of vitreous deposits, which often lead to blindness.[133] Cardiomyopathy is the usual cause of death. Most patients die in their mid-50s or mid-60s, although at least one individual has reached age 80 with the help of a cardiac pacemaker. Sexual impotence is common in males, and bowel involvement with diarrhea and malabsorption is also common.

Gene carriers in this kindred, both affected and presymptomatic, have been shown to have significantly reduced plasma RBP concentrations.[135] This finding suggests that the area of the molecule around residue 84 may be involved in retinol binding. The depression in the serum RBP level is such that gene carriers can usually be identified by this measurement alone. Recent studies have shown 100 percent concordance between presence of the Ser 84 gene and the low RBP levels in this kindred.[136]

METHIONINE 111. In 1962, Frederiksen et al. described a kindred in Denmark with amyloid cardiomyopathy.[115] At that time no neuropathy was detected, and subsequent reexamination of this kindred showed no neuropathy. The clinical findings are those of restrictive cardiomyopathy. Pathologically, traces of amyloid can be found throughout the body, but the primary organ of involvement is the heart. Chemical analysis of postmortem tissues has shown that the amyloid contains prealbumin with a methionine-for-leucine substitution at position 111.[137–139] Similar symptomatology has been reported in a few families outside Denmark, but chemical confirmation of the methionine 111 is lacking. So far no DNA test has been devised for the variant prealbumin gene. This form of prealbumin amyloidosis could account for some of the apparently sporadic cases of senile cardiac amyloidosis, but this speculation has not been confirmed.

ISOLEUCINE 122. Amyloid cardiomyopathy in individuals with no family history of amyloidosis and little or no evidence of systemic disease has been called senile cardiac amyloidosis. This is a relatively rare condition and is often only appreciated

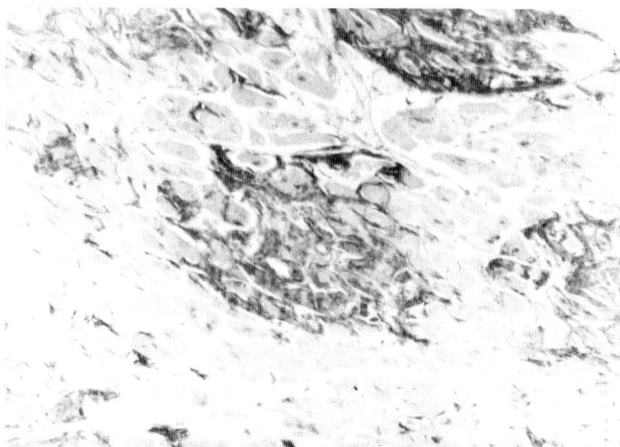

Fig. 97-14 Section of left ventricle stained immunohistochemically using antiprealbumin. Amyloid deposits displace myocardial fibrils and also form rings around the cardiac muscle bundles. x100.

postmortem. Most individuals having this disease die with restrictive cardiomyopathy, but some suffer fatal arrhythmias.[140–143] In 1980, Sletten et al. showed that amyloid isolated from a case of senile cardiac amyloidosis was homologous to prealbumin.[144] Recently, one such amyloid protein has been completely sequenced and found to be identical with prealbumin except for a valine-to-isoleucine change at position 122.[145] This finding suggests that at least some of the cases that have been classified as senile cardiac are hereditary and that the late onset of the disease has clouded the familial nature of the disease. While not reported yet, similar apparently sporadic cases of cardiac amyloidosis may be the alanine 60, serine 84 or methionine 111 types.

SENILE SYSTEMIC AMYLOIDOSIS. In addition to the characterized cases of senile cardiac amyloidosis, a number of postmortem studies have shown a high incidence of amyloid deposits in individuals dying after age 60. These deposits are often mainly in the heart, but varying degrees of systemic involvement have also been noted.

The term *senile systemic amyloidosis* has been used to classify these cases and also those previously labeled *senile cardiac*.[146] Immunohistochemical studies have shown that a number of these are prealbumin amyloid, but structure analysis has been reported for only the cardiac amyloids noted above.[147,148] Cornwell et al. noted that there may be multiple forms of cardiovascular amyloidosis with some not showing staining with antiprealbumin antiserums.[149]

Treatment of Prealbumin Amyloidosis. While there remains no specific treatment for autosomal dominant prealbumin amyloidosis, supportive measures can give significant prolongation of life. These include renal dialysis for patients who have severe nephropathy. The use of cardiac pacemakers has prolonged the life of many individuals in the Indiana/Swiss and also in the Appalachian and Swedish kindreds. Potent diuretics and drugs that give afterload reduction can significantly improve the quality of life of patients with restrictive cardiomyopathy. Bowel involvement can be devastating to some individuals, and the judicious use of antibiotics to reduce intestinal flora and agents such as metachlopramide to stimulate bowel motility have been helpful. Vitrectomy can restore vision to patients with eye involvement. Recently, plasmapheresis has been used experimentally, and anecdotal reports suggest some improvement in quality of life. Colchicine has

been used but may increase diarrhea and has not been shown to be effective in patients with the disease. Even so, the use of colchicine in presymptomatic carriers is often recommended with the idea that onset and progression of amyloid formation might be modulated early in the course of the disease. Preventive measures obviously will depend heavily on early detection of gene carriers by DNA analyses as discussed below.

Hereditary Amyloidosis Probably Associated with Prealbumin

Maryland Type. The Maryland type of autosomal dominant amyloidosis was classified as FAP II because of the clinical similarity to the Indiana/Swiss disease. There appears to be less cardiomyopathy and less vitreous involvement in the Maryland kindred, however. Mahloudji et al. traced the origin of this family to immigrants who came from Southern Germany in the 1740s.[150] Presently there are a large number of descendant families which have grown apart. Although many still live in Maryland and Eastern Pennsylvania, others now live in Florida, New England, and the Western United States. No definite genealogic association with European families of present time has been made. The disease shows prominent neuropathic symptoms. Carpal tunnel syndrome and severe and painful neuropathy are common. Onset of disease is frequently in the 40s, and patients may linger for many years with neuropathic symptoms.

Recent immunohistochemical studies have shown that the amyloid deposits contain prealbumin; however, no chemical analysis of the amyloid deposits has been reported. DNA analysis of two individuals in this kindred has been negative for the serine 84 prealbumin gene which shows that the two FAP II kindreds (Maryland and Indiana) are genetically different. Chemical classification of the Maryland-type amyloidosis awaits further study.

Finnish Type. In 1969, Meretoja described a familial amyloidosis with lattice corneal dystrophy, progressive cranial neuropathy, and skin changes with various internal symptoms.[151–153] The first manifestation of the disease is a dystrophic change of the cornea which is due to amyloid deposition. Over several decades, thickening of the skin on the forehead and back occurs, and patients may develop facial paralysis due to cranial neuropathies. Nephropathy due to renal amyloid may result in death. While the largest occurrence of this type of amyloidosis is in Finland, there have been reports of patients in the United States.[154–156] No chemical characterization of this type of amyloidosis has been reported; however, recent immunohistochemical studies have shown that the amyloid deposits do contain prealbumin.[157]

In addition to the immediately preceding well described kindreds, anecdotal reports of amyloid deposits staining with antiprealbumin have been published. Many such reports may relate to the known types of prealbumin amyloidosis but lack of data precludes any such analysis.

Hereditary Amyloidosis Not Associated with Prealbumin

Hereditary Cerebral Hemorrhage with Amyloid (Iceland). In 1972, Gudmundsson et al. described Icelandic families in which patients suffered premature strokes and intracranial bleeding, usually in the third or fourth decade of life.[158] The neurologic symptoms varied, depending on the location and the severity of hemorrhage. Some patients died abruptly, but others suffered numerous nonfatal cerebral accidents over several years before death. Postmortem examinations showed amyloid primarily restricted to cerebral blood vessels. Chemical analysis of this amyloid has shown a subunit which is a degradation product of γ trace protein (cystatin C).[159] The one reported amino acid sequence of the amyloid protein is lacking the first 10 residues of cystatin C, and, in addition, a glutamine was found at position 58 instead of the normal leucine.[160] The significance of this amino acid substitution in the etiology of the disease is not known at this time. Individuals affected with this disease show extremely low levels of γ trace protein in the cerebral spinal fluid, and this is a possible test for detection of carriers of the presumed gene.[161] While this type of amyloidosis may be considered a localized form, the extensive vascular involvement in the intracranial vessels justifies it being labeled systemic. Senile plaques containing amyloid of the type seen in Alzheimer disease are not a feature of the Icelandic amyloidosis. Since the original description of the syndrome in Iceland, several Dutch families have been found with a similar type of amyloidosis but without the low cerebrospinal fluid γ trace levels.[162,163] Recently chemical characterization of amyloid from one individual with the Dutch syndrome has shown that the vascular deposits contain the β protein of Alzheimer disease.[164]

Iowa Type. In 1969, Van Allen et al. described a kindred from Iowa of English, Irish, and Scottish descent with autosomal dominant amyloidosis.[165] Individuals in this kindred had prominent renal disease with nephrotic syndrome and/or renal insufficiency. Individuals in their 20s have been shown to be affected, but others have lived into their 70s. A striking incidence of peptic ulcers was seen in affected individuals. Lower limb neuropathy is characteristic of this syndrome. In the past this syndrome has been named *FAP III*, but a few reports have called it *FAP IV*.

Recent chemical studies on amyloid fibrils from an Iowa patient have found a degradation product of a variant form of apolipoprotein A-I.[166] No evidence for a prealbumin subunit was found. At present, it is not known whether the apolipoprotein A-I variant is definitely related to the expression of this disease, but the involvement of apolipoproteins in amyloid deposits is not without precedent. Reactive amyloidosis contains a degradation product of SAA, an apolipoprotein encoded on chromosome 11 as is apolipoprotein A-I. In addition, the senescent amyloid mouse model has been shown to have amyloid composed of apolipoprotein A-II.

Familial Mediterranean Fever. Familial Mediterranean fever (FMF) is the only syndrome in which systemic amyloidosis appears in a definite autosomal recessive pattern. Siegal first described FMF in 1945 and used the name *benign paroxysmal peritonitis*.[167] Other terms applied to this syndrome include *familial paroxysmal polyserositis* and *periodic fever*. Heller used the term *familial Mediterranean fever* and first noted the autosomal recessive inheritance.[168] A high percentage of patients with FMF develop systemic amyloidosis with prominent renal involvement.

FMF is seen most frequently in individuals of Mediterranean origin.[169,170] It is particularly prominent in Sephardic Jews and Armenians. The disease is characterized by periodic episodes of fever which may be accompanied by signs of per-

itonitis, synovitis, pleuritis, or an erythematous rash. These attacks may occur within the first decade of life and usually persist throughout life. The clinical manifestations have wide variability, however, and some patients have only mild abdominal discomfort during attacks. Large joint effusions can be seen, but these usually resolve without residual effects.[171] The etiology of these attacks is unknown, and biopsies of either peritoneum or pleura show nothing more than evidence of mild inflammation. The attacks are self-limiting and usually resolve after 2 or 3 days. Recently, low serum levels of C5a inhibitor in FMF patients have been reported, and this strongly suggests that complement activation is involved in pathogenesis of the syndrome.[172]

Genetic studies suggest that FMF is transmitted as a simple autosomal recessive trait. The FMF gene frequency in Sephardic Jews has been calculated as 0.22.[170,173] FMF-type illnesses have been described in other ethnic groups, however, and in some instances autosomal dominant inheritance with incomplete penetrance cannot be excluded. While systemic amyloidosis is common in patients with FMF, the relationship between the FMF and amyloidosis is not clear.[174] The development of amyloidosis does not correlate well with numbers or degrees of febrile attacks, and indeed some members of FMF kindreds have been described with amyloidosis but without the febrile attacks.[175] The incidence of amyloidosis in FMF patients of Armenian descent is lower than in Sephardic Jews, and this may indicate that FMF and amyloidosis are two separate traits which may be inherited with varying degrees of linkage.

The amyloidosis of FMF typically has a predilection for renal involvement with nephrotic syndrome followed by azotemia. Many patients die by their early 20s. Pathologically the renal disease shows glomerular deposits of amyloid. The spleen is commonly involved, and the thyroid may be heavily infiltrated. Vascular deposits throughout the body are common but rarely lead to organ dysfunction. Treatment with either chronic hemodialysis or peritoneal dialysis has yielded fair results, and kidney transplantation has been effective.[176] Over the past 10 years, it has been noted that treatment with colchicine has not only prevented the febrile attacks in most patients but has also been associated with a lack of progression of amyloidosis.[177] This has led to treatment of all FMF patients with colchicine. In studies by Zemer et al., only patients who did not maintain this therapeutic regimen have been noted to develop progressive renal disease.[178]

The amyloid fibrils of FMF contain protein AA, and on chemical grounds this amyloidosis is the reactive type.[13,16] Studies have shown that the serum SAA concentration increases during febrile attacks and returns to normal between attacks. Since SAA levels are elevated by the attacks of inflammation, it would appear that the amyloidosis of FMF is indeed a reactive type not only chemically but clinically, and that there are at least two determining factors acting in concert. Variables which may lead to the differences in expression of the amyloidosis include: (1) penetrance of the FMF genetic trait, (2) prevalence of an amyloidogenic SAA allele in the population at risk, and (3) environmental, dietary, and metabolic factors which may modulate the expression of the SAA genes or degradation of their protein products.

Muckle-Wells Syndrome. In 1962, Muckle and Wells described a syndrome characterized by nerve deafness, fever, urticaria, malaise, and "augey" bouts (attacks of urticaria or angioedemalike symptoms).[179] Nephrotic syndrome developed by middle age, and patients died of renal insufficiency. Post-mortem studies showed glomerular amyloidosis plus involvement of the adrenals and spleen. Families with similar syndromes have been described, including one of Norwegian descent.[180] While the original description supports autosomal dominant inheritance, this syndrome is similar to FMF because the amyloid has been shown to contain protein AA.[181] Clinically the two syndromes seem distinct, but since in some FMF families the disease appears to be autosomal dominant and in some Muckle-Wells families the pattern of inheritance is not clearly dominant, it may be that similar mechanisms are involved in expression of these two conditions. No reports on treatment of Muckle-Wells syndrome with colchicine have been noted to date, but such a therapeutic trial would certainly be indicated.

Miscellaneous Hereditary Amyloidosis Syndromes. In 1932, Ostertag described a familial syndrome of renal amyloidosis.[182] More recently Mornaghi et al. described a family of Irish-American origin with a similar clinical picture.[183] The main feature is renal involvement without neuropathy, with death resulting from renal insufficiency.[184] At postmortem the adrenals and spleen may be involved with amyloid as well as the kidneys. In one report immunohistochemical studies failed to show localization with antiprealbumin antiserum, which raises the possibility that this form of amyloidosis is associated with a different subunit protein.[183] In another family (Ohio kindred with oculoleptomeningeal amyloidosis), patients have CNS complications including dementia, seizures, strokes, abnormal gait, and vitreous deposits.[185] The Ohio family is of German origin, and postmortem examinations showed amyloid in the CNS, particularly in the leptomeninges and subarachnoid vessels. Traces of amyloid were found in peripheral nerves and skeletal muscles. The possible relationship to the Icelandic form of hereditary cerebral hemorrhage with amyloidosis has not been clarified.

Localized Hereditary Amyloidosis

Localized amyloidosis occurs in a number of syndromes. The first to be characterized chemically was the amyloid associated wtih medullary carcinoma of the thyroid. This carcinoma occurs in both sporadic and autosomal dominant patterns and is frequently associated with other endocrinopathies including pheochromocytomas.[186,187] This syndrome has been designated *multiple endocrine adenomatosis type II (MEA-II)*.[188] Chemically the amyloid is composed of peptides derived from precalcitonin and is limited to the thyroid or tumor metastases.[189,190]

Cutaneous amyloidosis has been reported in families and may be characterized as lichenoid changes of the skin.[191–194] This condition appeared to be autosomal dominant in a family reported by Rajagopalan and Tay,[195] but there have also been reports of X-linked disease.[196] Familial bullous cutaneous amyloid infiltration has also been reported.

Clinically perhaps the most important of the localized amyloidoses is associated with Alzheimer disease, a progressive dementia characterized by accumulations of amyloid substance in the brain.[47] Amyloid deposits (plaques) in cortical tissues are associated with neurofibrillary tangles and blood vessel deposits (congophilic angiopathy) which also stain histologically as amyloid. While only approximately 10 percent of Alzheimer cases are clearly inherited, this is a late onset disease and many familial cases may not be recognized.[197–199] The amyloid in

Alzheimer plaques and in congophilic angiopathy deposits contain a subunit protein (amyloid β protein, or A4 protein) of approximately 4000 molecular weight with a unique sequence.[200] The origin of this protein has not yet been determined, but most tissues contain homologous RNA and DNA sequences when analyzed with cDNA probes.[201,202] While in the past the cerebral amyloid deposits were thought to be the end result of some degenerative neuronal condition, recent characterization of the subunit protein suggests that perhaps amyloid formation is central to the pathogenesis of this disease. This is supported by localizations of both the amyloid β protein (A4) gene and the familial Alzheimer disease gene to chromosome 21. Interestingly, patients with trisomy 21 (Down syndrome) almost always develop Alzheimer disease by middle age as proven by postmortem examinations.

Other clinically recognized types of localized amyloidosis have been recognized by specific syndromes. Tumoral deposits of amyloid in the urinary tract are common. To date, chemical composition of these deposits has not been determined, but they are usually not associated with any systemic disease. Ureteral obstruction or hemorrhage from the bladder may lead to clinical recognition of these deposits.[203] Amyloid in the upper respiratory tract without systemic involvement has been frequently reported.[204] Again, chemical characterization of the amyloid substance has not been accomplished. Amyloid deposits in senile articular cartilage have been reported with or without association of calcium pyrophosphate deposition disease. It is possible that these deposits are related to the β_2-microglobulin articular amyloid that is seen in chronic dialysis patients, but no studies have been reported on this to date. None of these localized tumoral amyloidoses appear to be inherited.

DETECTION OF GENE CARRIERS IN HEREDITARY AMYLOIDOSIS

Identification of gene carriers prior to the development of clinical disease is important so that these individuals can plan for the future and benefit from any treatments that might be developed to prevent the disease. In particular, genetic counseling is of much greater value when coupled with means for detection of gene carriers. Significant progress has been made in preclinical diagnosis in the prealbumin amyloidoses.

Two methods for detection of gene carriers in the prealbumin amyloidoses have been developed. The first involves the isolation and characterization of the abnormal prealbumin protein. The other is a direct DNA analysis to detect abnormal prealbumin genes. Identification of variant prealbumin proteins involves purification and sequence analysis of prealbumin from relatively large quantities of plasma.[205] This is usually accomplished by detecting new peptides when prealbumin is digested with either trypsin, cyanogen bromide, or other means to split the prealbumin molecules, since the intact molecules of normal and variant prealbumin do not separate by standard methods. For the methionine 30 prealbumin, an efficient biochemical test using a small amount of plasma has been developed based on radioimmunoassay to recognize the aberrant peptide generated by cyanogen bromide cleavage at the methionine 30 residue.[206,207] Recently a method of separating several of the prealbumin variants by hybrid isoelectric focusing has also been described.[208] A serious drawback to these biochemical tests is the requirement for a rather large sample of blood, which makes prenatal diagnosis less feasible.

Direct DNA analysis promises greater utility and is applicable even prenatally using DNA from amniotic cells or chorionic villi. Thus far, DNA tests have been developed for five of the prealbumin variant genes associated with hereditary amyloidosis. These tests use the Southern blot analysis technique and are based on the loss or gain of specific restriction enzyme sites in the prealbumin gene due to the mutations. The patient's DNA is cut with one of these specific restriction enzymes, and the electrophoretically separated prealbumin gene sequences are examined by using a DNA probe (a radiolabeled piece of the prealbumin gene). DNA samples are usually obtained from peripheral leukocytes from a small blood sample but can also be obtained from cells of other tissues. The restriction enzyme used is specific for each prealbumin variant. The five known DNA tests are summarized in Table 97-3.

Sasaki et al.[209] developed the first DNA test for the methionine 30 gene. The protein substitution implied a single base change in the DNA coding for position 30. This change, G to A in the codon for residue 30, creates a recognition site for the restriction enzymes *Nsi*I and *Bal*I. Sasaki et al. and others have been able to show the presence of this extra site in the mutant prealbumin gene.[210–213] An example of this test, using *Nsi*I, is shown in Fig. 97-15. *Nsi*I digested DNA from a normal individual is in the middle lane. A prealbumin cDNA probe detects only two DNA fragments in normal DNA (6.7 and 3.2 kb). However, DNA samples from affected individuals (lanes 1 and 3) show two extra bands (5.1 and 1.6 kb) which result from cutting the 6.7-kb fragment in the mutant gene. Because these patients are heterozygous (as are most hereditary amyloidosis patients thus far identified), the normal DNA fragments are present as well. Thus, the enzymes *Nsi*I or *Bal*I, in combination with a prealbumin cDNA probe, can directly detect the methionine 30 gene.

The same type of test is used for the alanine 60 variant gene; however the enzyme *Pvu*II is required.[28] The DNA mutation is an A-to-G change in codon 60, which creates a *Pvu*II site. The prealbumin cDNA probe detects 5.8- and 3.7-kb *Pvu*II fragments in normal DNA. The extra *Pvu*II site in the alanine 60 gene reduces the 5.8-kb fragment to 5.2 kb, as seen in Fig. 97-16.

The tyrosine 77 variant gene has a C-to-A change in codon 77, creating an *Ssp*I site.[214] A genomic prealbumin probe rather than the cDNA is required to detect the variant gene due to limitations encountered when using a cDNA probe. The genomic probe described by Wallace et al. (1988) is an

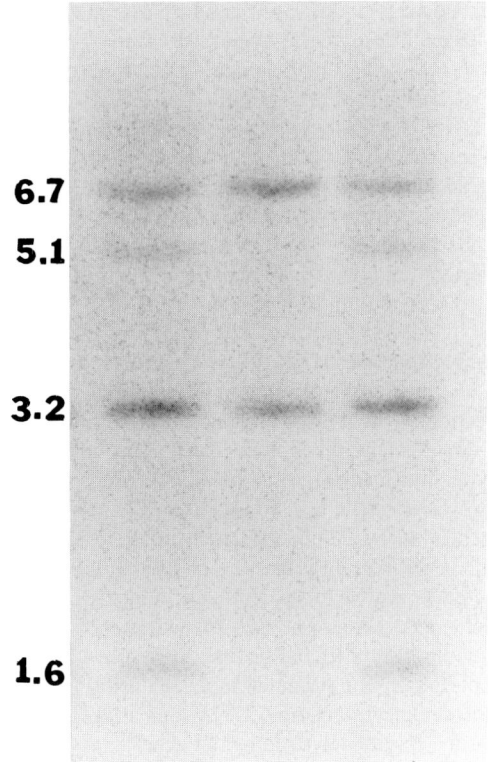

Fig. 97-15 Southern blot analysis for methionine 30 variant of prealbumin using *Nsi*I. The probe is the prealbumin cDNA which detects two fragments in normal DNA (6.7 and 3.2 kb in center lane). In affected individuals there are two extra bands (5.1 and 1.6 kb in outside lanes) which result from cutting the 6.7-kb fragment.

850-bp fragment from intron 2 of the prealbumin gene. It detects 1.4- and 0.6-kb fragments in normal DNA, with the 1.4-kb fragment being reduced to 1.1-kb in the tyrosine 77 gene. The tyrosine 77 carrier thus shows decreased intensity of the 1.4-kb band plus the variant 1.1-kb band.

For similar reasons, a genomic probe is required to detect the serine 84 prealbumin gene.[215] The enzyme used is *Alu*I, which cuts the mutant gene an additional time owing to a T-to-G mutation in codon 84. A genomic probe containing the

Fig. 97-16 Southern blot analysis of members of the kindred shown in Fig. 97-10. The propositus at the left and six of his relatives have an extra 5.2 kb band which is a result of the extra *Pvu*II site in the alanine 60 gene. The prealbumin cDNA is the probe.

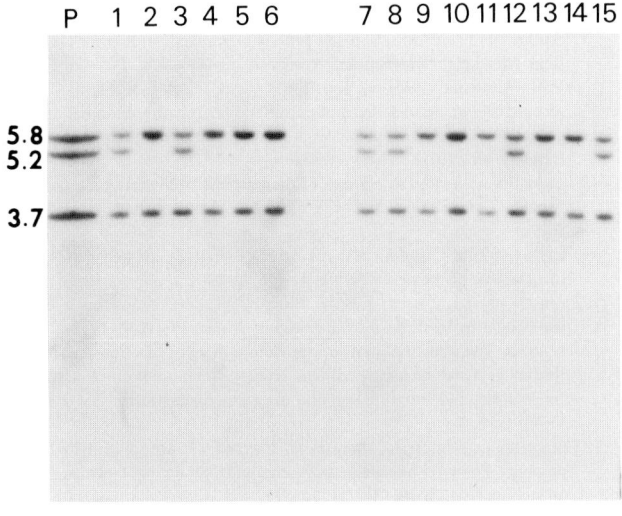

Table 97-3 Direct DNA Tests for Prealbumin Genetic Variants

Variant	Mutation	Restriction enzyme*	Probe
Methionine 30	G⟶A	*Nsi*I or *Bal*I	cDNA
Isoleucine 33	T⟶A	*Bcl*I	cDNA
Alanine 60	A⟶G	*Pvu*II	cDNA
Tyrosine 77	C⟶A	*Ssp*I	Genomic
Serine 84	T⟶G	*Alu*I	Genomic
Methionine 111	G⟶A†	*Dde*I†	?
Isoleucine 122	G⟶A	*Mae*III†	?

*All instances represent the gain of a restriction enzyme site except for isoleucine 122, and methionine 111, which would involve loss of an enzyme recognition site.
†Theoretical.

3' end of exon 3 detects an 880-bp fragment in normal DNA and detects both the 880- and a 790-bp fragment in carriers of the serine 84 gene. The 790-bp fragment arises from the additional *Alu*I cut in the 880-bp fragment.

Recently a DNA test has been described which can detect the mutation responsible for the phenylalanine-to-isoleucine substitution at position 33 of prealbumin in the Jewish type of amyloidosis. The restriction enzyme *Bcl*I in combination with the cDNA probe produces a new DNA pattern on Southern analysis in affected individuals, and therefore this test should be applicable to detection of carriers of this gene.[216]

These direct DNA tests for variant prealbumin genes are only the beginning of clinically useful tests that have resulted from research on hereditary amyloidosis. It is clear that a similar direct detection of the mutation using Southern blot analysis could be done for the methionine 111 variant associated with cardiomyopathy (Danish), since the Leu-to-Met change should destroy a *Dde*I site.

These molecular analyses, which can be used to identify carriers of mutant prealbumin genes, are of great value in the diagnosis of hereditary amyloidosis and have immediate application for genetic counseling. The next obvious step is to develop similiar methods for prenatal testing. Such a test has recently been reported for the serine 84 mutation using in vitro amplification of amniocyte genomic DNA and a labeled oligonucleotide probe specific for the amyloid gene.[217]

DNA tests, of course, can only identify individuals with the amyloid producing genes. While they may aid in diagnosis and subsequent treatment, they cannot change the course of the disease in affected individuals. Even more important at this time is to find means of modifying the disease process so that fibril synthesis is decreased or stopped. Possible answers may lie in developing methods to regulate expression of specific genes or to modify the biochemical fate of their protein products.

REFERENCES

1. GLENNER GG: Amyloid deposits and amyloidosis: The β-fibrilloses. *N Engl J Med* 302:1283, 1980.
2. ROKITANSKY KFV: *Handbuch der Pathologischen Anatomie.* Vienna, Braumueller and Seidel, 1842, vol 3.
3. VIRCHOW R: Zur Cellulose-Frage. *Virchows Arch (A)* 6:416, 1854.
4. VIRCHOW VR: Ueber einem Gehirn und Rueckenmark des Menschen aufgefundene Substanz mit der chemischen reaction der Cellulose. *Virchows Arch (A)* 6:135, 1854.
5. FRIEDREICH N, KEKULE A: Zur Amyloidfrage. *Virchows Arch (A)* 16:50, 1859.
6. COHEN AS: The constitution and genesis of amyloid, in Richter GW, Epstein MA (eds): *International Review of Experimental Pathology.* New York, Academic, 1965, vol 4, p 159.
7. ANDRADE C: A peculiar form of peripheral neuropathy. Familial atypical generalized amyloidosis with special involvement of the peripheral nerves. *Brain* 75:408, 1952.
8. DEBRUYN RS, STERN RO: A case of the progressive hypertrophic polyneuritis of Dejerine and Sottas with pathological examination. *Brain* 52:84, 1929.
9. DENAVASQUEZ S, TREBLE HA: A case of generalized amyloid disease with involvement of the nerves. *Brain* 61:116, 1938.
10. COHEN AS, CALKINS E: Electron microscopic observation on a fibrous component in amyloid of diverse origins. *Nature* 183:1202, 1959.
11. SPIRO D: The structural basis of proteinuria in man. Electron microscopic studies of renal biopsy specimens from patients with lipid nephrosis, amyloidosis, and subacute and chronic glomerulonephritis. *Am J Pathol* 35:47, 1959.
12. GLENNER GG, TERRY W, HARADA M, ISERSKY C, PAGE D: Amyloid fibril proteins: Proof of homology with immunoglobulin light chains by sequence analysis. *Science* 172:1150, 1971.
13. LEVIN M, FRANKLIN EC, FRANGIONE B, PRAS M: The amino acid sequence of a major nonimmunoglobulin component of some amyloid fibrils. *J Clin Invest* 51:2773, 1972.
14. HUSBY G, SLETTEN K, MICHAELSEN TE, NATVIG JB: Antigenic and chemical characterization of non-immunoglobulin amyloid proteins. *Scand J Immunol* 1:393, 1972.
15. SLETTEN K, HUSBY G: The complete amino acid sequence of non-immunoglobulin amyloid fibril protein AS in rheumatoid arthritis. *Eur J Biochem* 41:117, 1974.
16. LEVIN M, PRAS M, FRANKLIN EC: Immunologic studies of the major non-immunoglobulin protein of amyloid I. Identification and partial characterization of a related serum component. *J Exp Med* 138:373, 1973.
17. HUSBY G, NATVIG JB: A serum component related to immunoglobulin amyloid protein AS, a possible precursor of the fibrils. *J Clin Invest* 53:1054, 1974.
18. ROSENTHAL CJ, FRANKLIN EC: Variation with age and disease of an amyloid A protein-related serum component. *J Clin Invest* 55:746, 1975.
19. LINKE RP, SIPE JD, POLLOCK PS, IGNACZAK TF, GLENNER GG: Isolation of a low molecular weight serum component antigenically related to an amyloid fibril protein of unknown origin. *Proc Natl Acad Sci USA* 72:1473, 1975.
20. MCADAM KPWJ, SIPE JD: Murine model for human secondary amyloidosis: Genetic variability of the acute-phase serum protein SAA response to endotoxins and casein. *J Exp Med* 144:1121, 1976.
21. BENSON MD, SCHEINBERG MA, SHIRAHAMA T, CATHCART ES, SKINNER M: Kinetics of serum amyloid protein A in casein-induced murine amyloidosis. *J Clin Invest* 59:412, 1977.
22. BENSON MD, KLEINER E: Synthesis and secretion of serum amyloid protein A (SAA) by hepatocytes in mice treated with casein. *J Immunol* 124:495, 1980.
23. COSTA PP, FIGUERA AS, BRAVO FR: Amyloid fibril protein related to prealbumin in familial amyloidotic polyneuropathy. *Proc Natl Acad Sci USA* 75:4499, 1978.
24. BENSON MD: Partial amino acid sequence homology between an heredofamilial amyloid protein and human plasma prealbumin. *J Clin Invest* 67:1035, 1981.
25. DWULET FE, BENSON MD: Polymorphism of human plasma thyroxine binding prealbumin. *Biochem Biophys Res Commun* 114:657, 1983.
26. PRAS M, FRANKLIN EC, PRELLI F, FRANGIONE B: A variant of prealbumin from amyloid fibrils in familial polyneuropathy of Jewish origin. *J Exp Med* 154:989, 1981.
27. NAKASATO M, KANGAWA K, MINAMINOI N, TAWARA S, MATSUO H, ARAKI S: Revised analysis of amino acid replacement in a prealbumin variant (SKO-III) associated with familial amyloidotic polyneuropathy of Jewish origin. *Biochem Biophys Res Commun* 123:921, 1984.
28. WALLACE MR, DWULET FE, CONNEALLY PM, BENSON MD: Biochemical and molecular genetic characteristic of a new variant prealbumin associated with hereditary amyloidosis. *J Clin Invest* 78:6, 1986.
29. DWULET FE, BENSON MD: Characterization of prealbumin variant associated with familial amyloidotic polyneuropathy type II (Indiana/Swiss). *J Clin Invest* 78:880, 1986.
30. WALLACE MR, DWULET FE, WILLIAMS EC, CONNEALLY PM, BENSON MD: Identification of a new hereditary amyloid prealbumin variant, Tyr-77, associated wtih autosomal dominant amyloidosis. *J Clin Invest* 81:189, 1988.
31. PUCHTLER H, SWEAT F, LEVINE M: On the binding of Congo red by Amyloid. *J Histochem Cytochem* 10:355, 1962.
32. SHIRAHAMA T, COHEN AS: High resolution electron microscopic analysis of the amyloid fibril. *J Cell Biol* 33:679, 1967.
33. EANES ED, GLENNER GG: X-ray diffraction studies of amyloid filaments. *J Histochem Cytochem* 16:673, 1968.
34. BONAR L, COHEN AS, SKINNER MM: Characterization of the amyloid fibrils as a cross-B protein. *Proc Soc Exp Biol Med* 131:1373, 1969.
35. POLJAK RJ, ANZEL LM, EHCN BL, PHIZACKERLEY RP, SAUL F: The three-dimensional structure of the Fab' fragment of a human myeloma immunoglobulin at 2.0Å resolution. *Proc Natl Acad Sci USA* 71:3440, 1974.
36. BLAKE CCF, GEISOW MJ, OATLEY SJ: Structure of prealbumin: Secondary, tertiary and quaternary interactions determined by Fourier refinement at 1.8Å. *J Mol Biol* 121:339, 1978.
37. RANDALL RE, WILLIAMSON JR WC, MULLINAX F, TUNG MX, STILL WJS: Manifestations of light chain deposition. *Am J Med* 60:293, 1976.
38. PREUD'HOMME JL, MOREL-MAROGER L, BROVET JC, CERF M, MIGNON F, GUGLIELMI P, SELIGMANN M: Synthesis of abnormal immunoglobulin in lymphoplasmocytic disorders with visceral light chain deposition. *Am J Med* 69:703, 1980.
39. HOFMANN-GUILAINE C, NOCHY D, JACQUOT C, BARIETY J, CAMILLERI JP: Association light chain deposition disease (LCDD) and amyloidosis. *Pathol Res Pract* 180:214, 1985.

40. JACQUOT C, SAINT-ANDRE JP, TOUCHARD G, HOCHY D, DE LAMARTINIE CD, ORIOL R, DWULET P, BARIETY J: Association of systemic light-chain deposition disease and amyloidosis: A report of three patients with renal involvement. *Clin Nephrol* 24:93, 1985.

41. ANDRADE A, ARAKI S, BLOCK WD, COHEN AS, JACKSON CE, KUROIWA Y, MCKUSICK VA, NISSIM J, SOHAR E, VANALLEN MW: Hereditary amyloidosis. *Arthritis Rheum* 13:902, 1970.

42. HELLER H, SOHAR E, GAFNI J, HELLER J: Amyloidosis in familial Mediterranean fever. *Arch Intern Med* 107:539, 1961.

43. SCHIMKE RN, HARTMANN WH: Familial amyloid-producing medullary thyroid carcinoma and pheochromocytoma: Distinct genetic entity. *Ann Intern Med* 63:1027, 1965.

44. SIPPLE JH: The association of pheochromocytoma with carcinoma of the thyroid gland. *Am J Med* 31:163, 1961.

45. SAGHER F, SHANON J: Amyloid cutis: Familial occurrence in three generations. *Arch Dermatol* 87:171, 1963.

46. RAJACOPALAN K, TAY CH: Familial lichen amyloidosis: Report of 19 cases in 4 generations of a Chinese family in Malaysia. *Br J Dermatol* 87:123, 1972.

47. DAVIES P: The genetics of Alzheimer's disease: A review and a discussion of the implications. *Neurobiol Aging* 7:459, 1986.

48. BARDIN T, KUNTZ D, ZINGRAFF J, VOISIN M, ZELMAR A, LANSAMAN J: Synovial amyloidosis in patients undergoing long-term hemodialysis. *Arthritis Rheum* 28:1052, 1985.

49. GEJYO F, YAMADA T, ODANI S, NAKAGAWA Y, ARAKAWA M, KUNITOMO T, KATAOKA H, SUZUKI M, HIRASAWA Y, SHIRAHAMA T, COHEN AS, SCHMID K: A new form of amyloid protein associated with chronic hemodialysis was identified as B2-microglobulin. *Biochem Biophys Res Commun* 129:701, 1985.

50. KYLE RA, GREIPP PR: Amyloidosis (AL): Clinical and laboratory features in 229 cases. *Mayo Clin Proc* 58:665, 1983.

51. BRANDT KD, CATHCART ES, COHEN AS: A clinical analysis of the course and prognosis of 42 patients with amyloidosis. *Am J Med* 44:955, 1968.

52. GREIPP PR, KYLE RA, BOWIE WEJ: Factor-X deficiency in amyloidosis in a critical review. *Am J Hematol* 11:443, 1981.

53. BENSON MD, COHEN AS, BRANDT ES, CATHCART ES: Neuropathy, M-components and amyloid. *Lancet* 1:10, 1975.

54. KYLE RA, WAGONER RD, HOLLEY KE: Primary systemic amyloidosis: Resolution of the nephrotic syndrome with melphalan and prednisone. *Arch Intern Med* 142:1445, 1982.

55. BENSON MD: Treatment of AL amyloidosis with melphalan, prednisone and colchicine. *Arthritis Rheum* 29:683, 1986.

56. KEDAR (KEIZMAN) I, RAVID M, SOHAR E, GAFNI J: Colchicine inhibition of casein-induced amyloidosis in mice. *Isr J Med Sci* 10:787, 1974.

57. SHIRAHAMA T, COHEN AS: Blockage of amyloid induction by colchicine in an animal model. *J Exp Med* 140:1102, 1974.

58. GREIPP PR, KYLE RA, BOWIE EJW: Factor-X deficiency in primary amyloidosis: resolution after splenectomy. *N Engl J Med* 301:1050, 1979.

59. BENDITT EP, ERIKSEN N, HERMODSON MA, ERICSSON LH: The major proteins of human and monkey amyloid substance: Common properties including unusual N-terminal amino acid sequences. *FEBS* 19:169, 1971.

60. BENDITT EP, ERIKSEN N: Amyloid protein SAA is associated with high density lipoproteins from human serum. *Proc Natl Acad Sci USA* 74:4025, 1977.

61. BENDITT EP, ERIKSEN N, HANSON RH: Amyloid protein SAA is an apoprotein of mouse plasma high density lipoprotein. *Proc Natl Acad Sci USA* 76:4092, 1979.

62. SIPE JD, VOGEL SN, RYAN JL, MCADAMS KPWJ, ROSENSTREICH DL: Detection of a mediator derived from endotoxin-stimulated macrophages that induces the acute phase serum amyloid A response in Mice. *J Exp Med* 150:597, 1979.

63. MORROW JF, STEARMAN RS, PELTZMAN CG, POTTER DA: Induction of hepatic synthesis of serum amyloid A protein and actin. *Proc Natl Acad Sci USA* 78:4718, 1981.

64. KLUVE-BECKERMAN B, LONG GL, BENSON MD: DNA sequence evidence for polymorphic forms of human serum amyloid A (SAA). *Biochem Genet* 24:795, 1986.

65. TAYLOR BA, ROWE L: Genes for serum amyloid A proteins map to Chromosome 7 in the mouse. *Mol Gen Genet* 195:491, 1984.

66. YAMAMOTO K, MIGITA S: Complete primary structure of two major murine serum amyloids A proteins deduced from cDNA sequence. *Proc Natl Acad Sci USA* 82:2915, 1985.

67. LOWELL CA, POTTER DA, STEARMAN RS, MORROW JF: Structure of the murine serum amyloid A gene family. *J Biol Chem* 261:8442, 1986.

68. HOFFMAN JS, ERICSSON LH, ERIKSEN N, WALSH KA, BENDITT EP: Murine tissue amyloid protein AA NH2-terminal sequence identity with only one of two serum amyloid protein (ApoSAA) gene products. *J Exp Med* 159:641, 1984.

69. LOWELL CA, STEARMAN RS, MORROW JF: Transcriptional regulation of serum amyloid A gene expression. *J Biol Chem* 261:8453, 1986.

70. MEEK RL, HOFFMAN JS, BENDITT EP: Amyloidogenesis: One serum amyloid A isotype is selectively removed from the circulation. *J Exp Med* 163:499, 1986.

71. PARMALEE DC, TITANI K, ERICSSON LH, ERIKSEN N, BENDITT EP, WALSH KA: Amino acid sequence of amyloid related apoprotein (apoSAA) from human high-density lipoproteins. *Biochemistry* 21:3298, 1982.

72. SIPE JD, COLTEN HR, GOLDBERG D, EDGE MD, JACK BF, COHEN AS, WHITEHALL AS: Human serum amyloid A (SAA): Biosythesis and post-synthetic processing of pre SAA and structural variants defined by complementary DNA. *Biochemistry* 24:2931, 1985.

73. LAVIE G, ZUCKER-FRANKLIN D, FRANKLIN EC: Degradation of serum amyloid A protein by surface-associated enzymes of human blood monocytes. *J Exp Med* 148:1020, 1978.

74. ZEMER D, PRAS M, SOHAR E, MODAN M, CABILI S, GAFNI J: Colchicine in the prevention and treatment of the amyloidosis of familial Mediterranean fever. *N Engl J Med* 314:1001, 1986.

75. DWULET FE, BENSON MD: Primary structure of amyloid fibril protein AA in azocasein-induced amyloidosis of CBA/J mice. *J Lab Clin Med* 110:322, 1987.

76. WESTERMARK P, JOHNSON KH, WESTERMARK GT, SLETTEN K, HAYDEN DW: Bovine amyloid protein AA: Isolation and amino acid sequence analysis. *Comp Biochem Physiol* 85B:609, 1986.

77. BENSON MD, DWULET FE, DIBARTOLA SP: Identification and characterization of amyloid protein AA in spontaneous canine amyloidosis. *Lab Invest* 52:448, 1985.

78. DIBARTOLA SP, BENSON MD, DWULET FE, CORNACOFF JB: Isolation and characterization of amyloid protein AA in the Abyssinian cat. *Lab Invest* 52:485, 1985.

79. SKINNER M, CATHCART ES, COHEN AS, BENSON MD: Isolation and identification by sequence analysis of experimentally induced guinea pig amyloid fibrils. *J Exp Med* 140:871, 1974.

80. ANDERS RF, NORDSTOGA K, NATVIG JB, HUSBY G: Amyloid-related serum protein SAA in endotoxin-induced amyloidosis of the mink. *J Exp Med* 143:678, 1976.

81. GOREVIC PD, GREENWALD M, FRANGIONE B, PRAS M, FRANKLIN EC: The amino acid sequence of duck amyloid A (AA) protein. *J Immunol* 118:1113, 1977.

82. MACHADA EA, GREGORY RS, JONES JB, LANGE RD: The cyclic hematopoietic dog: A model for spontaneous secondary amyloidosis. *Am J Pathol* 92:23, 1978.

83. BOYCE JT, DIBARTOLA SP, CHEW DJ, GASPER PW: Familial renal amyloidosis in Abyssinian cats. *Vet Pathol* 21:33, 1984.

84. SCHEINBERG MA, CATHCART ES, EASTCOTT JW, SKINNER M, BENSON MD, SHIRAHAMA T, BENNETT M: The SJL/J mouse: A new model for spontaneous age-associated amyloidosis. Morphological and immunochemical aspects. *Lab Invest* 35:47, 1976.

85. HIGUCHI K, YONEZU T, KOGISHI K, MATSUMURA A, TAKASHITA S, KOHNO A, MATSUSHITA M, HOSOKAWA M, TAKEDA T: Purification and characterization of a senile amyloid-related antigenic substance (apoSASSAM) from mouse serum. *J Biol Chem* 261:12834, 1986.

86. KUCZYNSKI MH: Neue Beitraege zur Lehre vom Amyloid. *Klin Wochenschr* 2:727, 1923.

87. KUCZYNSKI MH: Weitere Beitraege zur Lehre vom Amyloid 3. Mitteilung, ueber die Rueckbildung des Amyloids. *Klin Wochenschr* 2:2193, 1923.

88. SIPE JD, MCADAMS KPWJ, UCHINO F: Biochemical evidence for the biphasic development of experimental amyloidosis. *Lab Invest* 38:110, 1978.

89. YAMAMOTO K, SHIROO M, MIGITA S: Diverse gene expression for isotypes of murine serum amyloid A protein during acute phase reaction. *Science* 232:227, 1986.

90. SHIRAHAMA T, COHEN AS: Redistribution of amyloid deposits. *Am J Pathol* 99:539, 1980.

91. BRANCH WT JR, ROBBINS J, EDELHOCK H: Thyroxine-binding prealbumin. *J Biol Chem* 246:6011, 1971.

92. ROBBINS J: Thyroxine-binding proteins. *Prog Clin Biol Res* 5:331, 1976.

93. NC-IUB and JCBN Newsletter, Nomenclature Committee of IUB. *J Biol Chem* 256:12, 1981.

94. COSTA RH, LAI E, DARNELL JE: Transcriptional control of the mouse prealbumin (Transthyretin) gene: Both promotor sequences and a distinct enhancer are cell specific. *Mol Cell Biol* 6:4697, 1986.

95. KANDA Y, GOODMAN DS, CANFIELD RE, MORGAN FJ: The amino acid sequence of human plasma prealbumin. *J Biol Chem* 249:6796, 1974.

96. BLAKE CCF, GEISOW MJ, SWAN IDA: Structure of human plasma prealbumin at 2.5 Å resolution. *J Mol Biol* 88:1, 1974.

97. OATLEY SJ, BLANEY JM, LANGRIDGE R, KOLLMAN PA: Molecular-mechan-

ical studies of hormone-protein interactions: The interaction of T4 and T3 with prealbumin. *Biopolymers* 23:2931, 1984.

98. GOODMAN DS: Retinol-binding protein, prealbumin and vitamin A transport. *Prog Clin Biol Res* 5:313, 1976.

99. BENSON MD, DWULET FE: Prealbumin and retinol binding protein serum concentrations in the Indiana type hereditary amyloidosis. *Arthritis Rheum* 26:1493, 1983.

100. SKINNER M, CONNORS LH, RUBINOW A, LIBBEY C, SIPE JD, COHEN AS: Lowered prealbumin levels in patients with familial amyloid polyneuropathy (FAP) and their non-affected but at risk relatives. *Am J Med Sci* 289:17, 1985.

101. WESTERMARK P, PITKANEN P, BENSON L, VAHLQUIST A, OLOFSSON BO, CORNWELL III GG: Serum prealbumin and retinol-binding protein in the prealbumin-related senile and familial forms of systemic amyloidosis. *Lab Invest* 52:314, 1985.

102. WALLACE MR, NAYLOR SL, KLUVE-BECKERMAN B, LONG GL, MCDONALD L, SHOWS TB, BENSON MD: Localization of the human prealbumin gene to chromosome 18. *Biochem Biophys Res Commun* 129:753, 1985.

103. BENSON MD, DWULET FE: Identification of carriers of a variant plasma prealbumin (transthyretin) associated with familial amyloidotic polyneuropathy type I. *J Clin Invest* 75:71, 1985.

104. DWULET FE, BENSON MD: Primary structure of an amyloid prealbumin and its plasma precursor in a heredofamilial polyneuropathy of Swedish origin. *Proc Natl Acad Sci USA* 81:694, 1984.

105. MITA S, MAEDA S, SHIMADA K, ARAKI S: Cloning and sequence analysis of cDNA for human prealbumin. *Biochem Biophys Res Commun* 124:558, 1984.

106. SASAKI H, SAKAKI Y, MATSUO H, GOTO I, KUROIWA Y, SAHASHI I, TAKAHASHI A, SHINODA T, ISOBE T, TAKAGI Y: Diagnosis of familial amyloidotic polyneuropathy by recombinant DNA techniques. *Biochem Biophys Res Commun* 125:636, 1984.

107. TSUZUKI T, MITA S, MAEDA S, ARAKI S, SHIMADA K: Structure of the human prealbumin gene. *J Biol Chem* 260:12224, 1985.

108. SASAKI H, YOSHIOKA N, TAKAGI Y, SAKAKI Y: Structure of the chromosomal gene for human serum prealbumin. *Gene* 37:191, 1985.

109. WAKASUGI S, MAEDA S, SHIMADA K: Structure and expression of the mouse prealbumin gene. *J Biochem* 100:49, 1986.

110. SOPRANO DR, HERBER J, SOPRANO KJ, SCHON EA, GOODMAN DS: Demonstration of transthyretin mRNA in the brain and other extrahepatic tissues in the rat. *J Biol Chem* 260:11793, 1985.

111. DICKSON PW, ALDRED AR, MARLEY PD, GUO-FEN T, HOWLETT GJ, SCHREIBER G: High prealbumin and transferrin mRNA levels in the choroid plexus of rat brain. *Biochem Biophys Res Commun* 127:890, 1985.

112. STAUDER AJ, DICKSON PW, ALDRED AR, SCHREIBER G, MENDELSOHN FAO, HUDSON P: Synthesis of transthyretin (prealbumin) mRNA in choroid plexus epithelial cells, localized by in situ hybridization in rat brain. *J Histochem Cytochem* 34:949, 1986.

113. DICKSON PW, SCHREIBER G: High levels of messenger RNA for transthyretin (prealbumin) in human choroid plexus. *Neurosci Lett* 66:311, 1986.

114. ZALIN A, DARBY A, VAUGHAN S, RAFTERY EB: Primary neuropathic amyloidosis in three brothers. *Br Med J* 1:65, 1974.

115. FREDERIKSEN T, GOTZSCHE H, HARBOE N, KIAER W, MELLEMGAARD K: Familial primary amyloidosis with severe amyloid heart disease. *Am J Med* 33:328, 1962.

116. SARAIVA MJM, BIRKEN S, COSTA PP, GOODMAN DS: Amyloid fibril protein in familial amyloidotic polyneuropathy, Portuguese type. *J Clin Invest* 74:104, 1984.

117. TAWARA S, NAKAZATO M, KANGAWA K, MATSUO H, ARAKI S: Identification of amyloid prealbumin variant in familial amyloidotic polyneuropathy (Japanese type). *Biochem Biophys Res Commun* 116:880, 1983.

118. SKINNER M, COHEN AS: The prealbumin nature of the amyloid protein in familial amyloid polyneuropathy (FAP)—Swedish variety. *Biochem Biophys Res Commun* 99:1326, 1981.

119. SARAIVA MJM, SHERMAN W, GOODMAN DS: Presence of a plasma transthyretin (prealbumin) variant in familial amyloidotic polyneuropathy in a kindred of Greek origin. *J Lab Clin Med* 108:17, 1986b.

120. HOLMGREN G, HOLMBERG E, LINDSTROM A, LINDSTROM E, NORDENSON I, SANDGREN O, STEEN L, SVENSSON B, LUNDGREN E, VON GABAIN A: Diagnosis of familial amyloidotic polyneuropathy in Sweden by RFLP analysis. *Clin Genet* 33:176, 1988.

121. BENSON MD, COHEN AS: Generalized amyloid in a family of Swedish origin. A study of 426 family members in 7 generations of a new kinship with neuropathy, nephropathy and central nervous system involvement. *Ann Intern Med* 86:419, 1977.

122. SARAIVA MJM, COSTA PP, GOODMAN DS: Genetic expression of a transthyretin mutation in typical and late-onset Portuguese families with familial amyloidotic polyneuropathy. *Neurology* 36:1413, 1986.

123. KINCAID JC, BENSON MD, DWULET FE, GREIPP PR, LAUTZENHEISER RL: A new family with hereditary amyloidosis. *Clin Res* 32:821A, 1984.

124. GAFNI J, FISCHEL B, REIF R, YARON M, PRAS M: Amyloidotic polyneuropathy in a Jewish family. Evidence for the genetic heterogeneity of the lower limb familial amyloidotic neuropathies. *Q J Med* 55:33, 1985.

125. PRAS M, FRANKLIN EC, PRELLI F, FRANGIONE B: A variant of prealbumin from amyloid fibrils in familial polyneuropathy of Jewish origin. *J Exp Med* 154:989, 1981.

126. PRAS M, PRELLI F, FRANKLIN EC, FRANGIONE B: Primary structure of an amyloid prealbumin variant in familial polyneuropathy of Jewish origin. *Proc Natl Acad Sci USA* 80:539, 1983.

127. NAKAZATO M, KANGAWA K, MINAMINO N, TAWARA S, MATSUO H, ARAKI S: Revised analysis of amino acid replacement in a prealbumin variant (SKO-III) associated with familial amyloidotic polyneuropathy of Jewish origin. *Biochem Biophys Res Commun* 123:921, 1984.

128. JACOBSON DR, SANTIAGO-SCHWARZ F, ROSENTHAL CJ, BUXBAUM J: Identification of new restriction fragment length polymorphisms associated with familial amyloidotic polyneuropathy. *Clin Res* 35:594A, 1987.

129. WALLACE MR, DWULET FE, CONNEALLY PM, BENSON MD: Biochemical and molecular genetic characterization of a new variant prealbumin associated wth hereditary amyloidosis. *J Clin Invest* 78:6, 1986.

130. BENSON MD, WALLACE MR, TEJADA E, BAUMANN H, PAGE B: Hereditary amyloidosis: Description of a new American kindred with late onset cardiomyopathy. *Arthritis Rheum* 30:195, 1987.

131. KOEPPEN AH, MITZEN EJ, HANS MB, PENG S, BAILEY RO: Familial amyloid polyneuropathy. *Muscle Nerve* 8:733, 1985.

132. WALLACE MR, DWULET FE, WILLIAMS EC, CONNEALLY PM, BENSON MD: Identification of a new hereditary amyloid prealbumin variant, Tyr-77, associated wtih autosomal dominant amyloidosis. *Am J Hum Genet* 39:A22, 1986.

133. FALLS HF, JACKSON JH, CAREY JG, RUKAVINA JG, BLOCK WD: Ocular manifestations of hereditary primary systemic amyloidosis. *Arch Opthalmol* 54:660, 1955.

134. RUKAVINA JG, BLOCK WD, JACKSON CE, FALLS HF, CAREY JH, CURTIS AC: Primary systemic amyloidosis: A review and an experimental, genetic, and clinical study of 29 cases with particular emphasis on the familial form. *Medicine (Baltimore)* 35:239, 1956.

135. BENSON MD, DWULET FE: Prealbumin and retinol binding protein serum concentrations in the Indiana type hereditary amyloidosis. *Arthritis Rheum* 26:1493, 1983.

136. DWULET FE, BENSON MD: Characterization of a transthyretin (prealbumin) variant associated wtih familial amyloidotic polyneuropathy type II (Indiana/Swiss). *J Clin Invest* 78:880, 1986.

137. NORDLE M, SLETTEN K, HUSBY G, RANLÖV PJ: A new prealbumin variant in familial amyloid cardiomyopathy of Danish origin. *Scand J Immunol* 27:119, 1988.

138. HUSBY G, RANLOV PJ, SLETTEN K, MARHAUG G: The amyloid in familial amyloid cardiomyopathy of Danish origin is related to prealbumin. *Clin Exp Immunol* 60:207, 1985.

139. HUSBY G, SLETTEN K: Chemical and clinical classification of amyloidosis 1985. *Scand J Immunol* 23:253, 1986.

140. BUERGER L, BRAUNSTEIN H: Senile cardiac amyloidosis. *Am J Med* 28:357, 1960.

141. POMERANCE A: The pathology of senile cardiac amyloidosis. *J Pathol Bacteriol* 91:357, 1966.

142. HODKINSON HM, POMERANCE A: The clinical significance of senile cardiac amyloidosis: A prospective clinico-pathological study. *Q J Med* 46:381, 1977.

143. WESTERMARK P, JOHANSSON B, NATVIG JB: Senile cardiac amyloidosis: Evidence of two different amyloid substances in the aging heart. *Scand J Immunol* 10:303, 1979.

144. SLETTEN K, WESTERMARK P, NATVIG JB: Senile cardiac amyloid is related to prealbumin. *Scand J Immunol* 12:503, 1980.

145. GOREVIC P: Personal communication.

146. PTIKANEN P, WESTERMARK P, CORNWELL GG: Senile systemic amyloidosis. *Am J Pathol* 117:391, 1984.

147. CORNWELL GG, WESTERMARK P, NATVIG JB, MURDOCH W: Senile cardiac amyloid: Evidence that fibrils contain a protein immunologically related to prealbumin. *Immunology* 44:447, 1981.

148. FELDING P, FEX G, WESTERMARK P, OLOFSSON O, PITKANEN P, BENSON L: Prealbumin in Swedish patients with senile systemic amyloidosis and familial amyloidotic polyneuropathy. *Scand J Immunol* 21:133, 1985.

149. CORNWELL GG, MURDOCH WL, KYLE RA, WESTERMARK P, PITKANEN P: Frequency and distribution of senile cardiovascular amyloid. *Am J Med* 75:618, 1983.

150. MAHLOUDJI M, TEASDALL RD, ADAMKIEWICZ JJ, HARTMANN WH, LAMBIRD PA, MCKUSICK VA: The genetic amyloidoses. With particular refer-

ence to hereditary neuropathic amyloidosis, type II (Indiana or Rukavina type). *Medicine (Baltimore)* 48:1, 1969.

151. MERETOJA J: Familial systemic paramyloidosis with lattice dystrophy of the cornea, progressive cranial neuropathy, skin changes and various internal symptoms. *Ann Clin Res* 1:314, 1969.

152. MERETOJA J: Genetic aspects of familial amyloidosis wtih corneal lattice dystrophy and cranial neuropathy. *Clin Genet* 4:173, 1973.

153. MERETOJA J, TEPPO L: Histopathological findings of familial amyloidosis with cranial neuropathy as principal manifestation. *Acta Pathol Microbiol Immunol Scand [A]* 79:432, 1971.

154. KLINTWORTH GK: Lattice corneal dystrophy. An inherited variety of amyloidosis restricted to the cornea. *Am J Pathol* 50:371, 1967.

155. DARRAS BT, ADELMAN LS, MORA JS, BODZINER RA, MUNSAT TL: Familial amyloidosis with cranial neuropathy and corneal lattice dystrophy. *Neurology* 36:432, 1986.

156. SACK GH, DUMARS KW, GUMMERSON KS, LAW A, MCKUSICK VA: Three forms of dominant amyloid neuropathy. *Johns Hopkins Med J* 149:239, 1981.

157. MAURY CPJ, TEPPO AM, KARINIEMI AL, KOEPPEN AH: Amyloid fibril protein in familial amyloidosis with cranial neuropathy and corneal lattice dystrophy (FAP type IV) is related to transthyretin. *Am J Clin Pathol* 89:359, 1988.

158. GUDMUNDSSON G, HALLGRIMSSON J, JONASSON TA, BJARNASON O: Hereditary cerebral hemorrhage with amyloidosis. *Brain* 95:387, 1972.

159. COHEN DH, FEINER H, JENSSON O, FRANGIONE B: Amyloid fibril in hereditary cerebral hemorrhage with amyloidosis (HCHWA) is related to gastroentero-pancreatic neuroendocrine protein, gamma trace. *J Exp Med* 158:623, 1983.

160. GHISO J, PONS-ESTEL B, FRANGIONE B: Hereditary cerebral amyloid angiopathy: The amyloid fibrils contain a protein which is a variant of cystatin C, an inhibitor of lysosomal cysteine proteases. *Biochem Biophys Res Commun* 136:548, 1986.

161. JENSSON O, GUDMUNDSSON G, ARNASON A, THORSTEINSSON L, BLONDAL H, GRUBB A, LOFBERG H, FRANGIONE B: Hereditary cystatin C (gamma trace) amyloid angiopathy of the central nervous system causing cerebral hemorrhage. *Acta Neurol Scand* 73:308, 1986.

162. JENSSON O, THORSTEINSSON L, BOTS GTAM, LUYENDIJK W, GUDMUNDSSON G, ARNASON A, LOFBERG H: Immunohistochemical comparison between the Dutch and the Icelandic form of hereditary central nervous system amyloid angiopathy. *Acta Neurol Scand* 73:312, 1986.

163. JENSSON O, LUYENDIJK W, PETURSDOTTIR I, ARNASON A, GUDMUNDSSON G, GRUBB A: Cystatin C values in the cerebrospinal fluid: Comparison between the Icelandic and the Dutch type of hereditary central nervous system amyloid angiopathy. *Acta Neurol Scand* 73:313, 1986.

164. VAN DUINEN SG, CASTANO EM, PRELLI F, BOTS GTAB, LUYENDIJK W, FRANGIONE B: Hereditary cerebral hemorrhage with amyloidosis in patients of Dutch origin is related to Alzheimer disease. *Proc Natl Acad Sci USA* 84:5991, 1987.

165. VAN ALLEN MW, FROHLICH JA, DAVIS JR: Inherited predisposition to generalized amyloidosis. *Neurology* 19:10, 1969.

166. NICHOLS WC, DWULET FE, BENSON MD: Apolipoprotein A1 in Iowa type hereditary amyloidosis (FAP type IV). *Clin Res* 35:595A, 1987.

167. SIEGAL S: Benign paroxysmal peritonitis. *Ann Intern Med* 23:1, 1945.

168. HELLER H, SOHAR E, SHERF L: Familial Mediterranean fever. *Arch Intern Med* 102:50, 1958.

169. SOHAR E, PRAS M, HELLER J, HELLER H: Genetics of familial Mediterranean fever (FMF). *Arch Intern Med* 107:529, 1961.

170. SOHAR E, GAFNI J, PRAS M, HELLER H: Familial Mediterranean fever. *Am J Med* 43:227, 1967.

171. HELLER H, GAFNI J, MICHAELI D, SHAHIN N, SOHAR E, ERLICH G, KARTEN I, SOKOLOFF L: The arthritis of familial Mediterranean fever (FMF). *Arthritis Rheum* 9:1, 1966.

172. MOTZNER Y, BRZOZINSKI A: C5a inhibitor deficiency in peritoneal fluids from patients with familial Mediterranean fever. *N Engl J Med* 311:287, 1984.

173. PRAS M, BRONSHPIGEL N, ZEMER D, GAFNI J: Variable incidence of amyloidosis in familial Mediterranean fever among different ethnic groups. *Johns Hopkins Med J* 150:22, 1982.

174. GAFNI J, RAVID M, SOHAR E: The role of amyloidosis in familial Mediterranean fever: A population study. *Isr J Med Sci* 4:995, 1968.

175. BLUM A, GAFNI J, SOHAR E, SHIBOLET S, HELLER H: Amyloidosis as the sole manifestation of familial Mediterranean fever (FMF). *Ann Intern Med* 57:795, 1962.

176. BENSON MD, SKINNER M, COHEN AS: Amyloid deposition in a renal transplant in familial Mediterranean fever. *Ann Intern Med* 87:31, 1977.

177. GOLDSTAIN RC, SCHWABE AD: Prophylactic colchicine therapy in familial Mediterranean fever: A controlled, double-blind study. *Ann Intern Med* 81:792, 1974.

178. ZEMER D, PRAS M, SOHAR E, MODAN M, CABILI S, GAFNI J: Colchicine in the prevention and treatment of the amyloidosis of familial Mediterranean fever. *N Engl J Med* 314:1001, 1986.

179. MUCKLE TJ, WELLS M: Urticaria, deafness and amyloidosis: A new heredofamilial syndrome. *Q J Med* 31:235, 1962.

180. BLACK JT: Amyloidosis, deafness, urticaria and limb pains: A hereditary syndrome. *Ann Intern Med* 70:989, 1969.

181. LINKE RP, HEILMAN KL, NATHRATH WBJ, EULITZ M: Identification of amyloid A protein in a sporadic Muckle-Wells syndrome. *Lab Invest* 48:698, 1983.

182. OSTERTAG B: Familiere Amyloid-Erkrankung. *Z Menschl Vererbungs Konstit Lehre* 30:105, 1950.

183. MORNAGHI R, RUBINSTEIN P, FRANKLIN EC: Familial renal amyloidosis. Case report and genetic studies. *AM J MED* 73:609, 1982.

184. WEISS SW, PAGE DL: Amyloid nephropathy of Ostertag with special reference to renal glomerular giant cells. *Am J Pathol* 72:447, 1973.

185. GOREN H, STEINBERG MC, FARBOODY GH: Familial oculoleptomeningeal amyloidosis. *Brain* 103:473, 1980.

186. SCHMIKE RN, HARTMANN WH: Familial amyloid-producing medullary thyroid carcinoma and pheochromocytoma. *Ann Intern Med* 63:1027, 1965.

187. SIPPLE JH: The association of pheochromocytoma with carcinoma of the thyroid gland. *Am J Med* 31:163, 1961.

188. KEISER HR, BEAVEN MA, DOPPMAN J, WELLS S, BUJA LM: Sipple's syndrome: Medullary thyroid carcinoma, pheochromocytoma, and parathyroid disease. *Ann Intern Med* 78:561, 1973.

189. TASHJIAN AH, WOLFE HJ, VOELKEL EF: Human calcitonin. Immunologic assay, cytologic localization and studies on medullary thyroid carcinoma. *Am J Med* 56:840, 1974.

190. SLETTEN K, WESTERMARK P, NATVIG JB: Characterization of amyloid fibril proteins from medullary carcinoma of the thyroid. *J Exp Med* 143:993, 1976.

191. ENG AM, COGAN L, GUNNAR RM, BLEKYS I: Familial generalized dyschromic amyloidosis cutis. *J Cutan Pathol* 3:102, 1976.

192. OZAKI M: Familial lichen amyloidosis. *Int J Dermatol* 23:190, 1984.

193. NEWTON JA, JAGJIVAN A, BHOGAL B, MCKEE PH, MCGIBBON DH: Familial primary cutaneous amyloidosis. *Br J Dermatol* 112:201, 1985.

194. DE PIETRO WP: Primary familial cutaneous amyloidosis. *Arch Dermatol* 117:639, 1981.

195. RAJAGOPALAN K, TAY CH: Familial lichen amyloidosis: Report of 19 cases in 4 generations of a Chinese family in Malaysia. *Br J Dermatol* 87:123, 1972.

196. PARTINGTON MW, MARRIOTT PJ, PRENTICE RSA, CAVAGLIA A, SIMPSON NE: Familial cutaneous amyloidosis with systemic manifestations in males. *Am J Med Genet* 10:65, 1981.

197. NEE LE, POLINSKY RJ, ELDRIDGE R, WEINGARTNER H, SMALLBERG S, EBERT M: A family with histologically confirmed Alzheimer's disease. *Arch Neurol* 40:203, 1983.

198. GOUDSMIT J, WHITE BJ, WEITKAMP LR, KEATS BJB, MORROW CH, GAJDUSEK DC: Familial Alzheimer's disease in two kindreds of the same geographic and ethnic origin. *J Neurol Sci* 49:79, 1981.

199. FELDMAN RG, CHANDLER KA, LEVY LL, GLASER GH: Familial Alzheimer's disease. *Neurology* 13:811, 1963.

200. GLENNER GG, WONG CD: Alzheimer's disease: Initial report of the purification and characterization of a novel cerebrovascular amyloid protein. *Biochem Biophys Res Commun* 120:885, 1984.

201. ST GEORGE-HYSLOP PH, TANZI RE, POLINSKY RJ, HAINES JL, NEE L, WATKINS PC, MYERS RH, FELDMAN RG, POLLEN D, DRACHMAN D, GROWDON J, BRUNI A, FONCIN JF, SALMON D, FROMMETT P, AMADUCCI L, SORBI S, PIACENTINI S, STEWART GD, HOBBS WJ, CONNEALLY PM, GUSELLA JF: The genetic defect causing familial Alzheimer's disease, maps on chromosome 21. *Science* 235:885, 1987.

202. TANZI RE, GUSELLA JF, WATKINS PC, BRUNS GAP, ST. GEORGE-HYSLOP P, VAN KEUREN ML, PATTERSON D, PAGAN S, KURNIT DM, NEVE RL: Amyloid beta protein gene: cDNA, mRNA distribution, and genetic linkage near the Alzheimer locus. *Science* 235:880, 1987.

203. FUJIHARA S, GLENNER GG: Primary localized amyloidosis of the genitourinary tract: Immunohistochemical study on eleven cases. *Lab Invest* 44:55, 1981.

204. THOMPSON PJ, CITRON KM: Amyloid and the lower respiratory tract. *Thorax* 38:84, 1983.

205. BENSON MD, DWULET FE: Identification of carriers of a variant plasma prealbumin (transthyretin) associated with familial amyloidotic polyneuropathy type I. *J Clin Invest* 75:71, 1985.

206. NAKAZATO M, KURIHARA T, MATSUKURA S, KANGAWA K, MATSUO H: Diagnostic radioimmunoassay for amyloidotic polyneuropathy before clinical onset. *J Clin Invest* 77:1699, 1986.

207. SARAIVA MJM, COSTA PP, GOODMAN DS: Biochemical marker in familial amyloidotic polyneuropathy, Portuguese type. *J Clin Invest* 76:2171, 1985.

208. ALTLAND K, BANZHOFF A: Separation by hybrid isoelectric focusing of normal human plasma transthyretin (prealbumin) and a variant with a methionine for valine substitution associated with familial amyloidotic polyneuropathy. *Electrophoresis* 7:529, 1986.

209. SASAKI H, SAKAKI Y, MATSUO H, GOTO I, KUROIWA Y, SAHASHI I, TAKAHASHI A, SHINODA T, ISOBE T, TAKAGI Y: Diagnosis of familial amyloidotic polyneuropathy by recombinant DNA techniques. *Biochem Biophys Res Commun* 125:636, 1984.

210. MITA S, MAEDA S, IDE M, TSUZUKI T, SHIMADA K, ARAKI S: Familial amyloidotic polyneuropathy diagnosed by cloned human prealbumin cDNA. *Neurology* 36:298, 1986.

211. SARAIVA MJM, COSTA PP, GOODMAN DS: Genetic expression of a transthyretin mutation in typical and late-onset Portuguese families with familial amyloidotic polyneuropathy. *Neurology* 36:1413, 1986.

212. IDE M, MITA S, IKEGAWA S, MAEDA S, SHIMADA K, ARAKI S: Identification of carriers of mutant prealbumin gene associated with familial amyloidotic polyneuropathy type I by Southern blot procedures: Study of six pedigrees in the Arao district of Japan. *Hum Genet* 73:281, 1986.

213. WALLACE MR, CONNEALLY PM, LONG GL, BENSON MD: Molecular detection of carriers of hereditary amyloidosis in a Swedish-American family. *Am J Med Genet* 25:335, 1986.

214. WALLACE MR, DWULET FE, WILLIAMS EC, CONNEALLY PM, BENSON MD: Identification of a new hereditary amyloidosis prealbumin variant, Tyr-77, and detection of the gene by DNA analysis. *J Clin Invest* 81:189, 1988.

215. WALLACE MR, CONNEALLY PM, BENSON MD: A DNA test for Indiana/Swiss hereditary amyloidosis (FAP II) *Am J Hum Genet* 43:182, 1988.

216. JACOBSON DR, SANTIAGO-SCHWARZ F, BUXBAUM J: Restriction fragment analysis confirms the position 33 mutation in transthyretin from an Israeli patient (SKO) with familial amyloidotic polyneuropathy. *Biochem Biophys Commun* 153:198, 1988.

217. NICHOLS WC, WALLACE MR, BENSON MD: Enzymatic amplification of prealbumin genomic sequences and potential use in diagnosis of hereditary amyloidosis. *Am J Hum Genet* 41:A230, 1987.

PART 15

MEMBRANE TRANSPORT SYSTEMS

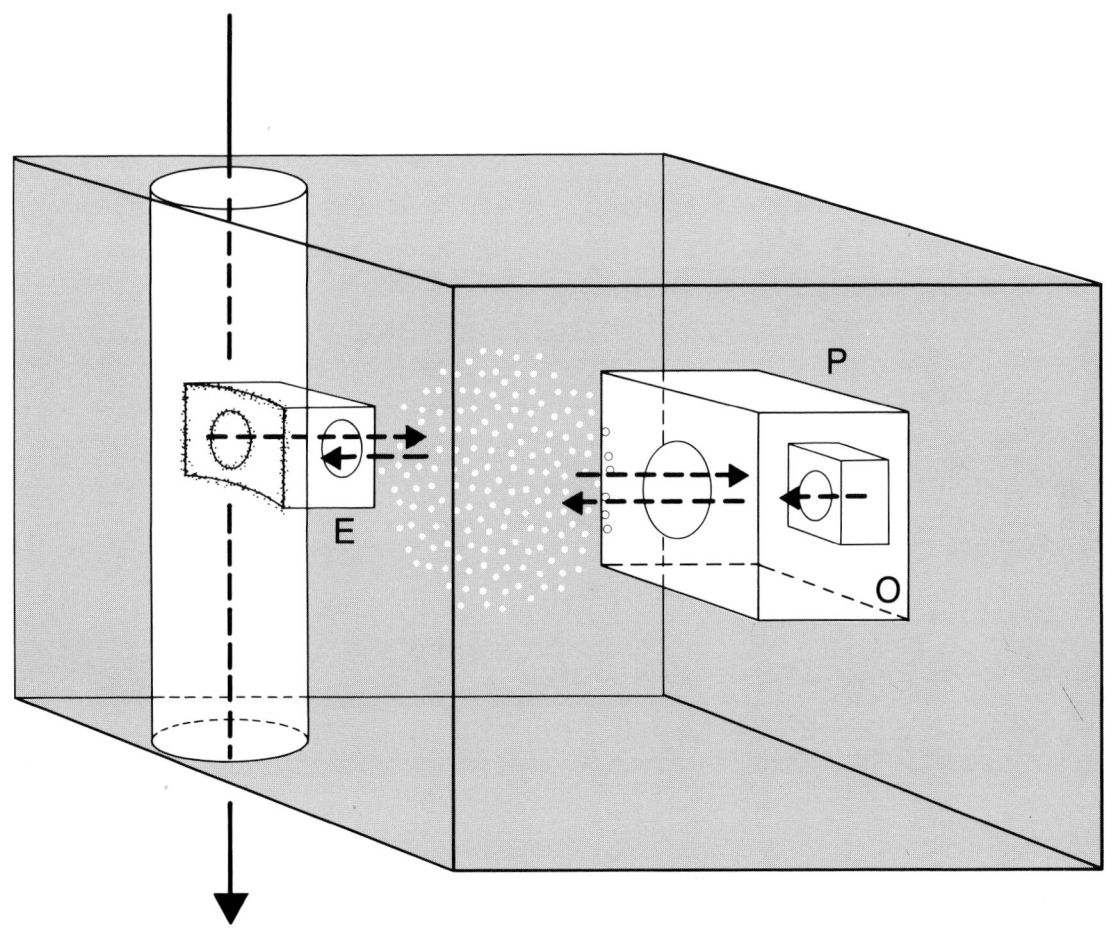

Membrane transport systems affect epithelial cells (E), parenchymal (P) cells, and organelles (O).

CHAPTER 98

CONGENITAL SELECTIVE Na$^+$, D-GLUCOSE COTRANSPORT DEFECTS LEADING TO RENAL GLYCOSURIA AND CONGENITAL SELECTIVE INTESTINAL MALABSORPTION OF GLUCOSE AND GALACTOSE

JEHAN-FRANÇOIS DESJEUX

1. The Na$^+$, D-glucose cotransport system is present in the luminal membrane of epithelial cells in the small intestine and the proximal tubule of the kidney. It is essential for the absorption from lumen to blood of glucose and galactose, but not fructose. Clinically, the congenital defect of the Na$^+$, D-glucose cotransport system(s) is expressed in two main entities: selective congenital glucose and galactose malabsorption by the small intestine and familial renal glycosuria.

2. Physiological studies and clinical observations strongly suggest that the Na$^+$, D-glucose transport system is heterogeneous. The main intestinal and renal transporters display different characteristics. A minimum of two mutations at the Na$^+$, D-glucose transport system loci are necessary to explain the clinical findings. The first, malabsorption, is characterized by severe impairment of hexose transport in the small intestine but only small deficit in the proximal tubule, and the second, glycosuria, affects reabsorption of glucose by the proximal tubule but does not involve any apparent intestinal defect.

3. Glucose and galactose malabsorption is a rare disease characterized by the neonatal onset of severe, watery, acidic diarrhea that quickly leads to remarkably severe dehydration. Related gastrointestinal symptoms are uncommon, but intermittent or constant glucosuria is a frequent finding. Intestinal malabsorption of glucose and galactose is easily identified by the hydrogen breath test. Dramatic improvement of the diarrhea with a glucose and galactose-free diet is typical of the disease. The diagnosis is established by direct determination of selective glucose and galactose intestinal malabsorption. Usually children and adults are able to live their lives once glucose and galactose are removed from the diet.

4. Renal glycosuria denotes the renal tubule abnormality displayed by individuals who excrete a variable amount of glucose in their urine with normal levels of blood glucose. Although more frequently encountered than glucose and galactose malabsorption, this condition is not common. It is a benign condition, usually without symptoms or physical consequences.

5. The intestinal defect displays only one phenotype, while renal glycosuria is a heterogeneous condition resulting from several mutations, as indicated by analysis of titration curves for glucose reabsorption. In type A, minimal renal glucose threshold and maximal tubular reabsorption are both reduced; in type B, the threshold is usually reduced, while maximal tubular reabsorption is normal with an increased splay; in type O, tubular reabsorption is virtually absent.

6. Comparison of the clinical consequences of defective glucose absorption in the proximal tubule and small intestine may provide insight into the specific roles of the kidney and intestinal tract.

D-Glucose is an important source of energy for most cells of the body, and enters them via the plasma membrane by an Na$^+$-independent transport system.

In the small intestine and proximal tubule of the kidney, D-glucose is absorbed by epithelial cells that both possess an Na$^+$, D-glucose cotransport system at luminal membrane level and an Na$^+$-independent transport system at the basolateral membrane level. This asymmetric distribution of the D-glucose transport system is essential for the vectorial transport of glucose from the lumen to the blood via the epithelial cells. The genetic functional defects of this cotransport system at luminal membrane level are expressed in two main clinical entities: selective congenital glucose and galactose malabsorption by the small intestine, and familial renal glycosuria. The first is characterized by severe impairment of hexose transport in the small intestine but only a small deficit in the proximal tubule; the second is a disorder affecting proximal tubular reabsorption of D-glucose but does not involve any corresponding intestinal defect.

At least two mutations at the chromosomal locus, or loci, for Na$^+$-dependent glucose transport are necessary to explain these clinical findings.

Until we know the molecular structure of the carrier(s), the nature of these mutations cannot be precisely identified. However, recent physiological studies indicate the presence of several Na$^+$, D-glucose transport systems in the small intestine and proximal tubule of the kidney, and the chemical structures of the D-glucose– and Na$^+$-binding sites in these organs are now under study.

The clinical consequences of the two mutations are very different. They are severe in the intestinal disease and benign in the kidney disorder. This difference is explained in part by the functional roles of the two organs.

GLUCOSE-GALACTOSE MALABSORPTION

Introduction and History

Glucose and galactose malabsorption (GGM) is a rare congenital disease resulting from a selective defect in the intestinal transport of glucose and galactose. It is characterized by the neonatal onset of severe, watery, acidic diarrhea. In the past, it usually resulted in death within the first weeks of life. Now that the disease has been identified, children recover if glucose and galactose are withdrawn from their diet. In 1962, it was simultaneously described in France as an "intolerance to actively transported sugars" by Laplane, Polonovski, et al.[1] and in Sweden by Lindquist and Meeuwisse as a "chronic diarrhea caused by monosaccharide malabsorption."[2] Twenty-five years later, approximately 40 cases have been reported in families of European, North American, and "Oriental-Iraqi Jewish" origin.[3–29]

Clinical Description

The clinical history of GGM was almost identical for all patients: Watery diarrhea is profuse, acidic, and contains sugar. In affected children given lactose, fecal sugar consists mainly of glucose and galactose, with only a small amount of lactose. For the equivalent amount of sugar given by mouth (2 g per kilogram of body weight), fecal excretion of galactose is much higher than that of glucose.[10] Incidentally, as the low stool pH results from the bacterial metabolism of the sugar in the colon, fecal acidity can be eliminated by antibiotics.[13]

Characteristically, diarrhea develops within 4 days of birth. Occasionally, it may be noticed later, within 2 weeks, or may be diagnosed in adults.[10,18,26]

Diarrhea quickly leads to remarkably severe dehydration. Thus, in a series of eight patients, weight losses of 17 to 24 percent were reported.[3] Metabolic acidosis and hyperosmolar dehydration gradually develop with serum protein concentrations of up to 7.6 g/dl and sodium concentrations of up to 173 meq/liter.

Related gastrointestinal signs and symptoms are uncommon. Abdominal distension and vomiting have been noticed. Anorexia is unusual. Apart from signs of severe dehydration, physical examination is normal.

Intermittent or permanent glycosuria after fasting or after a glucose load is a frequent finding. Thus, the combination of reducing sugars in water feces and of slight glycosuria despite low blood sugar levels is highly suggestive of GGM.[10] Three of the four patients in whom glycosuria was not present were from the same family.[21,29] Renal glycosuria has been studied by five authors,[4,8,11,25,28] but their results are contradictory. However, in general, the alterations they found in the renal glucose threshold and maximal glucose reabsorption were only moderate (Fig. 98-9).

Some of the laboratory tests carried out in order to exclude causes of diarrhea other than GGM have given conflicting results; thus, hypochromic anemia and moderate steatorrhea have been observed. Although normal values for xylose absorption are common in GGM, low or borderline values have sometimes been recorded. The histology of the biopsies taken after diarrhea had stopped was normal under light and electron microscopy. The fact that disaccharidase activities were found within the control range further indicates the integrity of the intestinal mucosa. During an episode of diarrhea, non-specific alterations in both histologic appearance and disaccharidase activity are sometimes observed.[3,9,10,13]

The abnormality of carbohydrate metabolism is confined to glucose transport in the small intestine and the proximal renal tubule. Glucose entry into the erythrocytes is normal,[31] and so is fasting blood glucose. Whereas galactose and glucose disappear from plasma at normal rates after intravenous infu-

sion,[4,11,14] oral sugar tolerance tests with glucose, galactose, and lactose yield flat blood glucose response curves. In contrast, blood glucose increases considerably after oral fructose loading. These results are the consequence of selective malabsorption of glucose and galactose. Although these tests are commonly performed, they are not very useful in identifying GGM for three reasons: (1) When glucose or galactose is given at the dose of 2 g per kilogram of body weight, watery diarrhea is usually produced, but this response is not specific to GGM and may aggravate the clinical status. (2) Approximately 25 percent of normal children have a flat blood glucose curve, and what is more, (3) in GGM, not all response curves are flat. The increase in blood glucose within 1 h may reach 1 mmol/liter. From the practical point of view, subjects undergoing oral sugar tests must be closely monitored for dehydration; stools must be collected, weighed, and immediately analyzed for pH, the presence of reducing sugars, and sugar identification.

Malabsorption of glucose and galactose is easily identified by the hydrogen breath test.[32] It is safe to perform the first test with a dose of 0.5 g glucose per kilogram of body weight. Usually, the breath hydrogen concentration exceeds 20 parts per million (ppm) within 3 h of glucose or galactose oral loading (Fig. 98-1).[3,33] However, after several days of glucose feeding, breath hydrogen production may decrease.[34]

The course of GGM under a glucose- and galactose-free diet is predictable. Very often, the diarrhea stops with intravenous feeding but resumes with standard oral feeding. An immediate improvement is seen as soon as children are put on a fructose-based milk formula free of glucose and galactose.

The diagnosis of GGM can be established later by direct determination of selective glucose and galactose intestinal malabsorption.

As affected children grow older and their diet becomes more diversified, the dietary restrictions are increasingly difficult to maintain, and both children and parents learn to "titrate" the symptoms according to carbohydrate tolerance. In older children and adults, tolerance of the offending carbohydrates im-

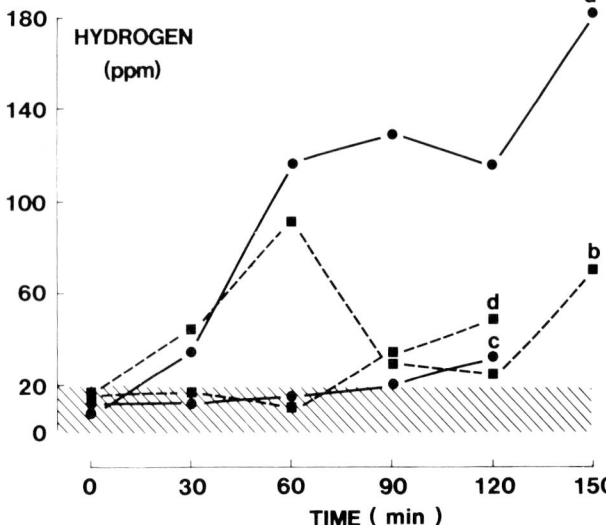

Fig. 98-1 Concentration of hydrogen expired after oral administration of glucose and galactose to two children with GGM. a = O.L., 2 g/kg glucose; b = O.L., 1 g/kg galactose; c = H.F., 0.5 g/kg glucose; d = H.F., 0.5 g/kg galactose. Shaded area shows control range. For greater clarity, the hydrogen expiration recorded after two challenges with 2 g/kg fructose has been omitted, but it never exceeded 20 ppm. (From Evans et al.[3])

proves,[3,10,17-19,35] although malabsorption of glucose and galactose in the small intestine remains unchanged. In most cases, growth and mental development have been normal when glucose and galactose were removed from the diet;[3] adults with GGM live relatively normal lives.[10,18,26]

Physiology of Glucose Absorption

In the first month of life, lactose constitutes the main source of carbohydrate. Full-term breast-fed children receive approximately 0.7 g/kg of lactose. This quantity increases rapidly and reaches 8.9 g/kg at the fifth day of life.[36]

After ingestion, lactose is hydrolyzed to free D-glucose and D-galactose by the lactase, a β-galactosidase on the luminal surface of the brush border membrane of enterocytes (see Chap. 120). The two monosaccharides, glucose and galactose, are then transported across the brush border membrane by a Na$^+$-monosaccharide transporter. The energy for this transport process is supplied by the Na$^+$ electrochemical gradient. Na$^+$ and the monosaccharide enter the brush border membrane by cotransport as follows: Na$^+$ enters the cell along its own electrochemical gradient, and the glucose accompanying it accumulates at the expense of the dissipation of the Na$^+$ gradient provided by the Na$^+$,K$^+$ATPase located at the basolateral membrane. The transport of glucose across the brush border membrane is therefore an example of secondary active transport. At the basolateral membrane, glucose and galactose are extruded into the blood by a facilitated diffusion system. Although this schematic view of glucose absorption from food is well-documented,[37-39] additional information is required to understand the symptoms associated with GGM. This information is essentially related to four factors:

(1) The glucose and galactose produced by lactose hydrolysis are absorbed mainly in the upper part of the small intestine, and the transport capacity for all monosaccharides declines from jejunum to ileum. In healthy breast-fed children, a portion of the carbohydrates they receive are metabolized in the colon, as indicated by increased hydrogen concentration in alveolar breath tests. In preterm and term infants, incomplete lactose absorption appears to be common and presumably is normal.[40] It constitutes neither a nutritional risk nor a cause of diarrhea, because inadequately absorbed carbohydrates are salvaged by colonic flora.[41,42]

(2) Lactose is not the sole source of carbohydrates in the first months of life. Sucrose, maltose, or maltodextrins may be present in infant formulas. The glucose thus arriving at the brush border membrane is transported by the Na$^+$-glucose cotransporter. The fructose is transported by another system, i.e., facilitated passive diffusion on a different carrier.[38,43] Most adult subjects absorb fructose incompletely if the fructose concentration is high.[44] Intestinal perfusion studies in adults whose absorption of disaccharides was compared to that of equivalent amounts of monosaccharide mixtures demonstrated that maltose and sucrose hydrolysis is fast. However, the rate of lactose hydrolysis in vivo is only about half that of sucrose. Hence, contrary to what is observed for sucrose and maltose, hydrolysis of lactose rather than glucose transport is the rate-limiting step for glucose assimilation.[45]

(3) There is a close relationship between intestinal absorption of glucose, Na$^+$, and water.[46] Between meals, water from digestive secretion enters the lumen of the small intestine and is reabsorbed passively following the active absorption of Na$^+$ by the epithelium covering the villi of the small intestine (Fig. 98-2). Consequently, little water is lost in the stools. After a meal, breast milk or formula, a large amount of water enters the intestinal lumen following the stimulation of digestive secretion. Glucose plays a key role in stimulating the reabsorption of Na$^+$, and therefore the reabsorption of water, by the epithelium covering the villi. Fructose, which is not cotransported with Na$^+$, does not stimulate water reabsorption. The widespread oral rehydration therapy that prevents or cures the dehydration caused by acute diarrhea is based on the relationship between glucose, Na, and water.[46,47] The hypernatremia frequently observed in the dehydration phase of GGM might indicate an upper limit for the glucose concentration in the oral rehydration solution used in treating acute diarrhea.[47]

(4) The Na$^+$-glucose cotransporter has been extensively studied in healthy animals, and is obviously also present in the jejunum of children. Everted sacs from 10-week-old human fetuses absorb glucose against a concentration gradient. By the age of 16 weeks, this absorption almost triples.[48] Using the transepithelial potential as an index of Na$^+$ absorption, Levin and Koldovsky demonstrated that glucose stimulates Na$^+$ absorption in the fetal jejunum as early as the fifteenth week of gestation.[49,50] In addition, the maximal absorption rates for glucose measured in vivo and normalized per centimeter of intestine were four to five times higher in adults than in infants.[51] This increased transport with age is due, at least in part, to the age-related increase in intestinal diameter and hence in surface area.[52]

The Na$^+$, D-glucose cotransporter can be studied in isolated jejunal epithelium of healthy children.[3,53,54] The use of isotopic D-glucose and Na$^+$ tracers makes it possible to determine

Fig. 98-2 Effect of sodium-solute-coupled transport on sodium and water reabsorption. Between meals (1), digestive secretions are balanced by intestinal sodium absorption. During meals (2), there is a sudden increase in the volume of fluid entering the intestinal lumen. Actively absorbed solutes, sugars, and amino acids present in the meal immediately increase sodium reabsorption by stimulating sodium-solute transport, thereby increasing water reabsorption. In glucose and galactose malabsorption (3), there is no increase in sodium reabsorption during meals. Therefore, water entering the intestine is poorly reabsorbed. (*From Desjeux et al.[46]*)

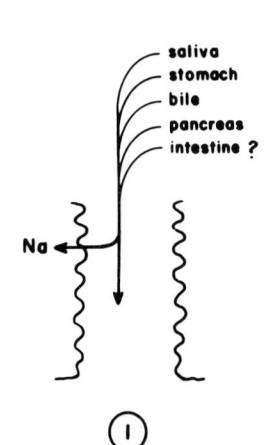

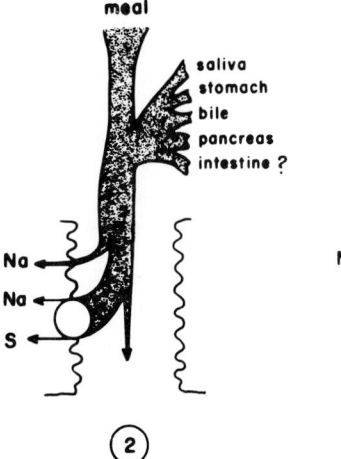

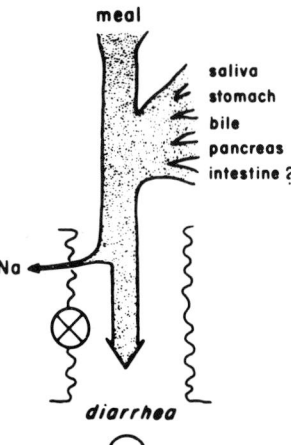

Table 98-1 Intracellular Substrate Concentration at Various Substrate Concentrations in the Medium in Jejunal Biopsies from Children

| | | C/M substrate | |
Substrate	Concentration, mM	Controls (n)	Patients (n)
Glucose (Glu)	10	3.84 ± 0.21 (34)	0.95 ± 0.12* (8)
Glu + phlor	10 + 0.5	2.99 ± 0.2 (7)	0.52 (1)
Galactose	10	1.54 ± 0.12 (6)	0.52 ± 0.11* (4)
Glucose	0.1	15.77 ± 1.55 (13)	2.98 ± 0.90* (4)
Galactose (Gala)	0.1	4.11 ± 0.33 (13)	ND
Gala + phlor	0.1 + 0.5	1.50 ± 0.70 (3)	ND
Xylose	10	1.10 ± 0.08 (13)	0.92 and 0.93
Alanine	0.8	13.33 ± 1.68 (4)	16.83 ± 3.54 (3)

*Significantly different from controls ($p < 0.001$).
NOTE: Results are expressed as intracellular over extracellular concentrations (C/M). n = Number of determinations; ND = not determined; phlor = phloridzin. The pieces of jejunum were placed in a beaker containing the oxygenated medium at 37°C, for 1 h. The C/M ratio is the result of steady state uptake from brush border and basolateral membranes. C/M > 1 represents uptake in excess of simple diffusion.
SOURCE: From Evans et al.[3]

simultaneously the intracellular concentration of D-glucose and Na^+ at the steady state. The method was originally described by Rosenberg et al. for amino acids.[55] Jejunal epithelial cells can accumulate 38 mM glucose in the intracellular water when the incubation medium contains 10 mM glucose (Table 98-1).[3,8,53,56] With 0.1 mM glucose in the medium, the cells can concentrate glucose sixteenfold. Their ability to concentrate galactose is four times less than their ability to concentrate glucose. In the meantime, the intracellular Na concentration is only one-third of the extracellular concentration (40 versus 140 mM). The electrochemical gradient for Na^+ is sufficient to explain the accumulation of glucose or galactose.[53] Ouabain, which inhibits the Na^+,K^+-ATPase, simultaneously reduces the Na^+ and glucose gradients, thus indicating that active glucose transport (against a concentration gradient) is Na^+-dependent (Fig. 98-3).

D-Glucose stimulates Na^+ absorption on the Na^+-glucose cotransporter. This is best studied by measuring the transepithelial potential difference (PD)[50] or the current produced by the active transport of Na^+, called *short-circuit current (Isc)*. The method shows that addition of glucose to the mucosal or luminal side of the tissue is followed by an immediate increase in PD and Isc.[53] Glucose does not stimulate Na^+ absorption by supplying the cell with more energy. Rather, this absorption is stimulated by the structure of D-glucose or its nonmetabolized analogue, 3-O-methylglucose, at the brush border membrane.[53] The importance of the structural role of glucose is further substantiated by the effect of phloridzin, a competitive inhibitor of glucose at the brush border membrane, which reduces glucose and galactose accumulation against a concentration gradient without altering the Na^+ gradient. Phloridzin decreases glucose entry at the luminal membrane, and the Isc stimulated by glucose declines.[57]

The relative permeability to glucose of the brush border membrane that contains the Na^+-glucose cotransporter and of

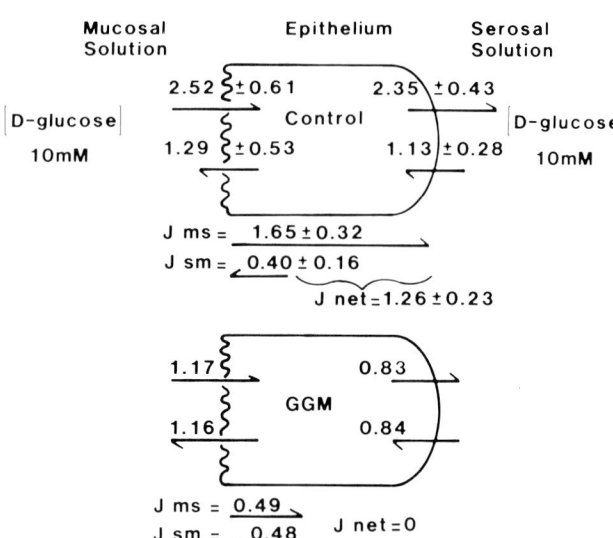

Fig. 98-3 Schematic representation of steady state unidirectional fluxes of D-glucose, calculated on the same piece of tissue according to Naftalin and Curran,[57] in control epithelium *(upper cell)* and epithelium from one patient with glucose and galactose malabsorption (GGM, *lower cell*). In the control epithelium (n = 6) the ratio of influx to efflux values calculated for the luminal membrane provides evidence for an energy-mediated event at the level of this membrane. In GGM (one patient), this ratio did not differ from unity, indicating a loss of the energy-mediated D-glucose transport. Consequently, D-glucose did not accumulate in the cell and the efflux at basolateral membrane level decreased; the influx did not alter, indicating that the apparent permeability of this membrane remained unchanged. *(Unpublished data.)*

the basolateral membrane that contains the facilitated diffusion system can be estimated by measuring the ratio of [³H]glucose entering the brush border membrane from the mucosal solution to the [¹⁴C]glucose entering the basolateral membrane from the blood side. When 10 mM glucose is present on both sides of the epithelium, the brush border membrane is twice as permeable as the basolateral membrane (Fig. 98-3).

These observations indicate the presence of an Na^+, D-glucose or D-galactose cotransporter at the brush border membrane level. Consequently, D-glucose can be absorbed from lumen to blood in the absence of a glucose concentration gradient across the epithelium.

The biochemistry of the Na^+-glucose cotransporter has been studied in small intestinal brush border membrane isolated from animal enterocytes.[60–63] Certain characteristics of the Na^+, D-glucose cotransporter are relevant to the understanding of the defect accounting for GGM and also, perhaps, for renal glycosuria:

(1) The Na^+, D-glucose transporter is a minor component of the brush border membrane (approximately 12 to 14 pmol per milligram of total protein).[64]

(2) Phosphatidylserine and cholesterol seem to be necessary for optimal transport of glucose.[65] If this is the case, the functional role of a protein inserted in a membrane may be dependent on the lipid composition of the membrane.

(3) In rabbit, a 72-kDa polypeptide constitutes all or part of the Na^+, D-glucose cotransporter across the intestinal brush border. As isolated by the use of monoclonal antibodies, this polypeptide is at least partly functional, since after isolation it still interacts with D-glucose and phloridzin. Peerce and Wright[62,63] suggest that the glucose- and phloridzin-binding site contains lysyl residues, while the Na-binding site contains

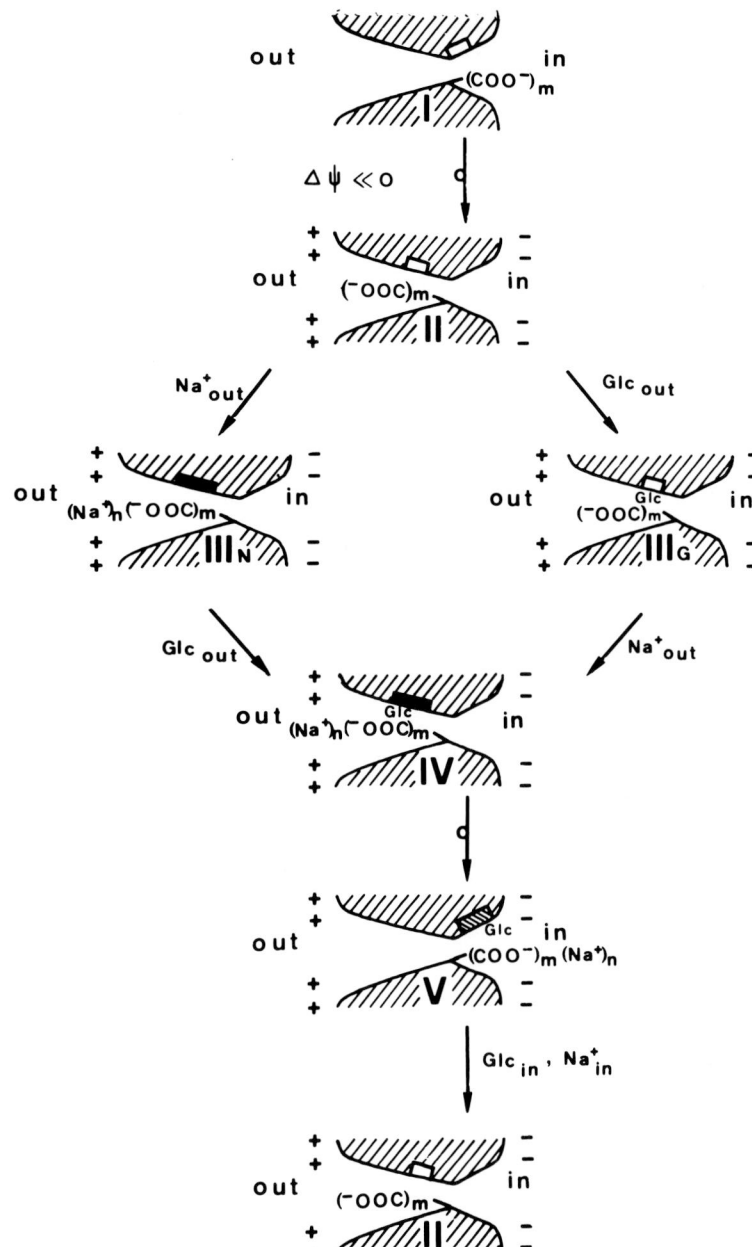

Fig. 98-4 A likely mode of functioning of the small intestinal Na⁺, D-glucose cotransporter: via an asymmetric gated channel or pore, responsive to Δψ. The D-glucose and phloridzin binding site is indicated by ▭, low affinity; ■, high affinity; ▨, indefinite affinity. For detailed discussion, see text. (*From Kessler and Semenza.*[59])

a tyrosyl residue. In addition, a specific cysteine group has been identified in the transporter.

(4) The Na⁺, D-glucose cotransporter penetrates into the brush border membrane asymmetrically in relation to the plane of the membrane, as shown in Fig. 98-4. It has the functional properties of a "gated channel or pore."[58] In particular, in the absence of an electrical potential across the membrane ($\Delta\psi = 0$) and at low substrate concentrations, all binding sites possess spontaneously directed inward orientation, i.e., toward the interior of the cell. Therefore, in form I of the transporter, Na⁺ and D-glucose inside the cell each has access to its respective binding site, and they trap the cotransporter as a slowly translocating or nontranslocating binary complex. In the presence of an electrical potential inside-negative ($\Delta\psi \ll 0$), the "gate" moves with the D-glucose–binding site toward the outside of the brush border or is made otherwise accessible from the outside in form II. When this happens, Na⁺ present outside can bind to the gate (III Na), which increases the affinity of the glucose-binding site. Alternatively, the glucose

may bind first to its outwardly exposed binding site (form II), leading to form III Glc. Neither form, III Na nor III Glc, of the cotransporter crosses the membrane fast.

The "fully occupied" form IV is generated from either form III Na or III Glc; its gate charge is neutralized by Na⁺, or may even be made positive if the gate carries a charge of -1 and can bind 2 Na⁺. This makes the gate snap back (form V) in the "spontaneous" inwardly directed position (as in form I), the more so as it is now positively charged. In form V, the binding sites and thus the substrates are exposed toward the inside, where the Na⁺ and sugar are released. Reappearance of the native charge in the gate makes it again respond to the electrical potential and snap toward the outside (form II).

Glucose transporters occur in various forms in the small intestine (Table 98-2). In 1962 Wilson[66] formulated the concept of a common, single transport mechanism for all actively transported sugars. Multiple transport systems were postulated as early as 1966,[67] and they are still under investigation. The fact that fasting, and the feeding of glucose, galactose, or

Table 98-2 Characteristics of Na^+, D-Glucose Transport in the Small Intestine of Various Animal Species

	I	II	References
K_m, mM			
Hamster	2.8	0.8	43
Rat	0.63	0.012	73
Rabbit	4.1	0.048	72
Rabbit	0.7–2	0.003–0.02	71
Cow	0.09–0.2	0.03	71
Guinea pig	24	0.5	75
Piglet	52	3.9	74
$\mathcal{J}_{max}$ glucose	I > II		
Hexose specificity	Common	Glc, Gala, 2-deoxyglucose	
Na^+/glucose	1:1–2:1	2:1–3:1	

NOTE: All experiments except those in hamster were performed on isolated brush border membrane under voltage-clamped, initial-rate zero-trans conditions (see Ref. 38). Only experiments with two transport systems are presented, i.e., with high K_m (I) and low K_m (II). Glc = glucose; Gala = galactose.

α-methylglucoside all have differential effects on the kinetics of absorption of these sugars in the rat jejunum is consistent with the concept that jejunal enterocytes possess multiple transport systems for actively transported sugars in vivo.[68,69]

The mutual inhibition of monosaccharides as well as the kinetics of the unidirectional monosaccharide influx across the luminal membrane of isolated and everted hamster small intestine were strongly suggestive of the presence of two carriers in the brush border membrane.[43,70] Carrier 1 would have a lower affinity for glucose and galactose and broad specificity, and would be common to glucose, galactose, 6-deoxyglucose, and 3-methylglucose. Carrier 2 would have a greater affinity for glucose and galactose and would mainly be specific for glucose and galactose. Both systems are Na^+-dependent. Two such carriers are present along the small intestine where the carrier 2/carrier 1 ratio is higher in the distal ileum than in the other sectors. At birth, carrier 1 is more abundant than carrier 2.

Recently, the kinetics of glucose transport were studied in vesicles of isolated brush border membrane. One group of investigators, who used voltage-clamped, initial-rate, zero-trans conditions, demonstrated the presence of a high affinity, minor saturable system and a low affinity, major saturable system in the rabbit, with a hundredfold difference between the K_m for glucose of the two systems.[71] Dorando and Crane[72] and Freeman and Quamme[73] reached the same conclusion by different methods. The results for two out of three bovine intestine preparations also suggested the existence of a major saturable system and a minor high affinity system.[71]

Two transport systems were identified by kinetic analysis in piglet intestine. In this preparation two piglets had been infected with transmissible gastroenteritis virus causing an acute diarrheal illness closely resembling human rotavirus enteritis. The pattern of glucose transport indicated a homogeneous population of low affinity carriers closely resembling those seen in control animals. Because previous studies strongly suggested that in acute transmissible gastroenteritis diarrhea the epithelium is composed of relatively undifferentiated crypt-type cells with loss of villus type cells, Keljo et al.[74] surmised that high affinity D-glucose carriers are lacking in normal epithelial crypt cells, and that they are incorporated into the brush border membranes of jejunal enterocytes as the cells differentiate in the course of their migration from crypt to villus.[74]

In guinea pig jejunum, two distinct D-glucose transport systems have been identified in the presence of Na^+ by Brot-Laroche et al.[75] (Fig. 98-5): One of them, which they called system I, is a low temperature–sensitive system, fully inhibited by D-glucose, D-galactose, and α-methylglucoside; it is the usual Na^+, D-glucose cotransport system, obligatorily dependent on Na^+ and insensitive to inhibition by cytochalasin B. System II is a high temperature–sensitive system, specific for D-glucose and D-galactose. Its cation specificity is unclear, but it appears to be sensitive to cytochalasin B inhibition. The heterogeneity of the glucose transport system was also suggested by Lindi et al.,[76] who studied the characteristics of glucose transport in four age groups of rats. They concluded that in very young animals the Na^+ chemical potential gradient seems to be responsible for D-glucose overshoot in brush border membrane vesicles. In young rats the Na^+ electrochemical potential is important, while in adult animals the electrical potential gradient represents the main driving force. In conclu-

Fig. 98-5 Na^+, D-glucose cotransport: effect of temperature. Vesicles were incubated for 2 s at either 25°C (●) or 35°C (■) in media containing one of the three following agents: (1) 10 mM HMBA buffer, pH 7.4, (2) 100 mM NaCl; (3) U-^{14}C-labeled D-glucose in a concentration range of 0.1 to 350 mM. All mediums contained sufficient sorbitol to keep the osmolarity constant. The data are illustrated as either (A) direct plots, v = f [S]; or (B) Eadie-Hofstee plots. Solid curves are the theoretical ones calculated by iteration. Straight dotted lines represent the breakdown of total uptake rates into their individual components. (From Brot-Laroche et al.[75])

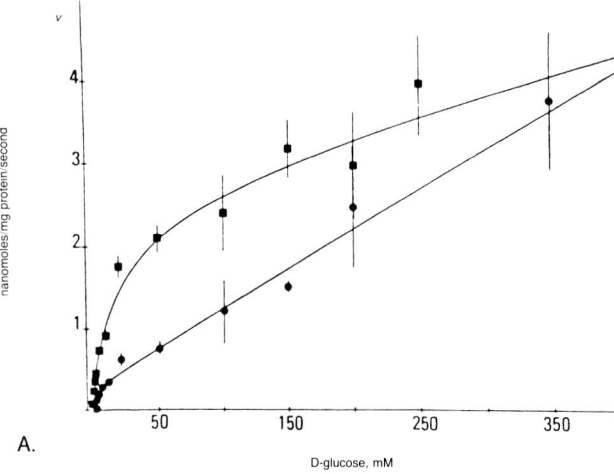

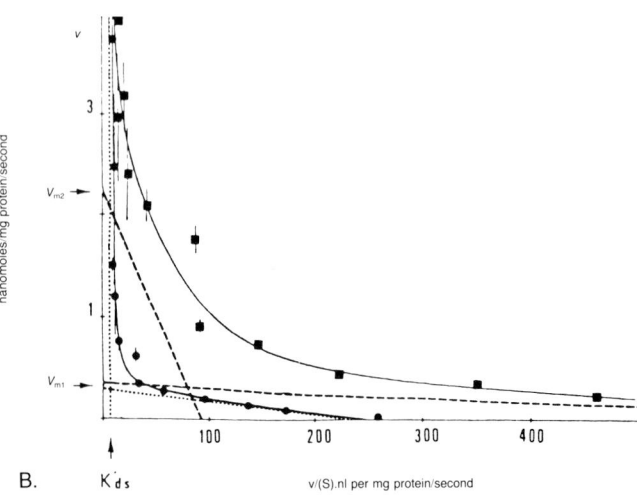

sion, several recent findings indicate the existence of many glucose transport systems. However, it is difficult to draw conclusions about the nature of this heterogeneity until we know more about the structure of the system and, in fact, other circumstantial evidence argues for a single major intestinal transporter.[37,38,59]

Pathophysiology

In GGM, the diarrhea is a consequence of the selective congenital defect in the absorption of these sugars from lumen to blood in the small intestine. This defect is situated at the brush border membrane, a conclusion essentially reached by means of in vivo intubation studies and investigation of in vitro transport in isolated pieces of jejunum. The main results of these experiments are discussed below.

The intubation studies were performed under various technical conditions. Initially, Meeuwisse et al.[10] compared the absorption of glucose and fructose after ingestion of a test meal containing the same concentrations of both sugars. Glucose was always absorbed more slowly than fructose. These authors also demonstrated that lactose, sucrose, and maltose were hydrolyzed in the patients tested. In the more recent experiments, the jejunum was perfused using either a double-lumen tube[18,22] or a four-lumen tube incorporating an occlusive balloon, in order to isolate effectively a 25-cm segment of bowel distal to the duodenojejunal junction.[26] This study was done in two adults and a 9-month-old child. The results were essentially the same, and may be summarized as follows:

Glucose and galactose were poorly absorbed. At low concentrations of 5.6 mM or less, a small amount of glucose was secreted in the lumen (Fig. 98-6). At high concentrations of up to 280 mM, glucose absorption was less than 10 percent of the control value. In one patient[26] the basal potential difference of the jejunal mucosa was normal, but did not respond to the addition of intraluminal glucose, a result that was in agreement with the absence of a functional Na+, D-glucose cotransporter. The jejunal mucosa secreted electrolytes and fluid, suggesting that under the prevailing experimental conditions, the combined glucose-sodium-water absorption process was defective.[26] Sucrose was hydrolyzed and fructose absorbed, suggesting that malabsorption of glucose and galactose is a selective defect.

The major characteristics of GGM is the lack of intracellular glucose or galactose accumulation against a concentration gradient (Table 98-1). This has been observed at a low glucose concentration (e.g., 0.1 mM) and at a high concentration (e.g., 10 mM). In principle, the disappearance of active glucose and galactose transport might be due either to a reduced driving force, i.e., a less steep Na+ electrochemical gradient, or to decreased permeability of the brush border membrane. However, there is no evidence for the first possibility, since when intracellular sodium was measured with isotopic tracers, it was found to be lower, and not higher, in patients with GGM than in controls, an observation that may in fact indicate a steeper Na+ electrochemical gradient.[3]

Furthermore, the transport of other solutes such as alanine or leucine via an Na+-solute cotransporter does not alter.[3,20,77] The autoradiographic studies of Stirling and Kinter et al.[13,78] clearly indicate a defect in glucose binding at the brush border membrane (Fig. 98-7). The diminished glucose influx across the luminal membrane and the selective absence of short-circuit current stimulation by glucose further substantiate this possibility. Taken together, these experimental findings indicate that the functional activity of the Na+, D-glucose cotransporter at the brush border membrane is either absent or reduced (Fig. 98-8). In addition, the participation of mutarotase in sugar transport was recently suggested, and the absence of this enzyme has been demonstrated in one case of glucose-galactose malabsorption.[79] However, fuller understanding of GGM requires additional information on the lipid composition of the membrane, and on the number, characteristics, and genetic control of its glucose transport system. In this connection, the cloning of epithelial cells of human origin that carry the Na+, D-glucose transport system is promising.[80-82] Recent data indicate the presence of such a system in a human intestinal epithelial cell live.[82a]

Fig. 98-6 Absorption of sugars from a 25-cm segment of jejunum in an adult with glucose and galactose malabsorption. Negative values represent secretion of glucose into the jejunum. Mean glucose absorption (± SE) for healthy controls is shown for comparison. (From Phillips and McGill.[26])

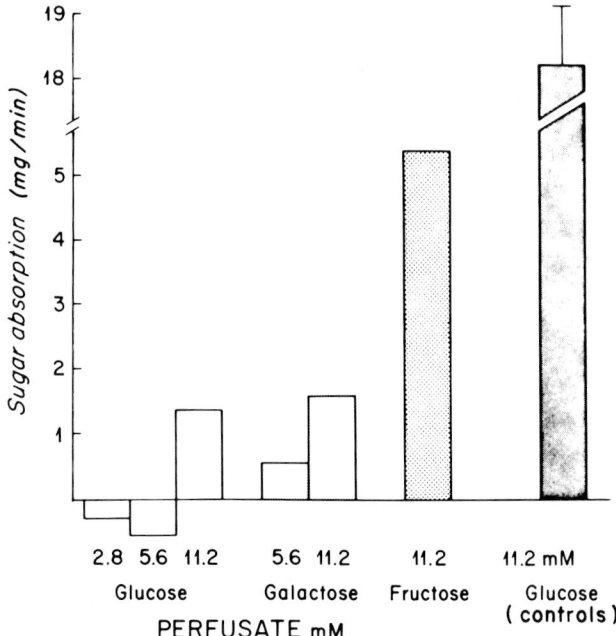

Fig. 98-7 Galactose-³H radioautographs of columnar epithelium from a patient at 3 years. Small pieces of tissue were incubated for 1, 5, and 30 min in medium containing 1 mM labeled galactose. Limited uphill accumulation of galactose inside absorptive cells had occurred by 30 min. ×1300. (From Stirling et al.[78])

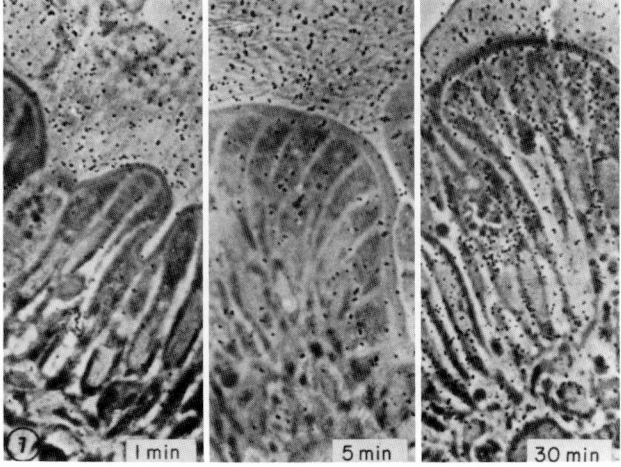

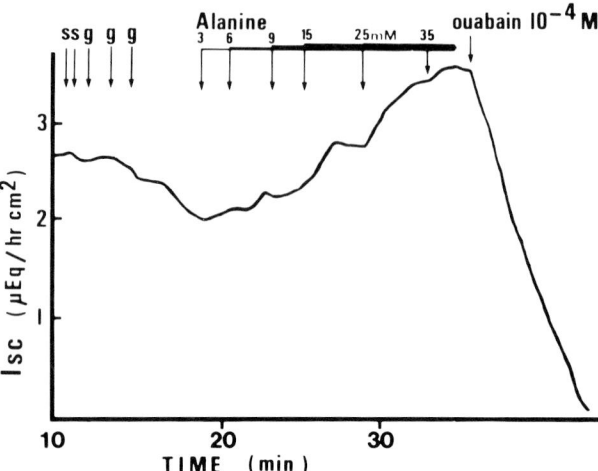

Fig. 98-8 Effects of sucrose (s), glucose (g), alanine, and ouabain on the short-circuit current (Isc), in a tissue sample from a patient with glucose and galactose malabsorption. Isc was recorded after successive addition to the incubation medium, on both sides of the tissue, of final concentrations of 13 mM sucrose, 33 mM glucose, 35 mM alanine, and 0.1 mM ouabain. *(From Evans et al.[3])*

Genetics

The children affected by GGM are of very diverse origin. Of the 39 cases reported 27 were girls.[3] The high consanguinity rate and the fact that no vertical transmission has been found argue in favor of an autosomal recessive mode of inheritance.[12] Although the proportion of siblings affected (6 of 16) may appear high, the true expression rate is masked by the small sample numbers, and the size of the family concerned cannot be used as an argument against this mode of inheritance. In addition, the high proportion of consanguineous mating implies that the mutant gene is very infrequent.[3]

Attempts to detect heterozygotes with reduced glucose intestinal absorption have been made in three familial studies. Meeuwisse and Dahlqvist[9] found reduced intestinal glucose accumulation in the father of one child, while the results were normal in the mother. Elsas et al.[8] demonstrated, in both parents of an affected child and also in a half-sister, that glucose accumulation dropped to a level intermediate between that of the controls and the proband. However, when we studied the father and mother of three children with GGM (one is reported in Ref. 3), they exhibited no clinical symptoms of the disease. Hydrogen breath tests after glucose and galactose were normal. With 50 g fructose we observed abdominal pain and diarrhea, as well as an increased hydrogen concentration; however, this response was probably physiological.[44] In one family, glucose accumulation in the intestine was normal. Further studies are required before we can draw firm conclusions on the mode of detection of heterozygotes.

Diagnosis

The primary diagnostic criterion is a history of watery diarrhea as soon as milk or sugar water is given. The diarrhea is watery, profuse, and acidic and contains reducing substances; it is frequently associated with mild glycosuria; it only improves if glucose and galactose are withdrawn from the diet, and will reappear within a few hours when ingestion of glucose

or galactose (usually in the form of lactose) is resumed. Substitution of sucrose for lactose may alleviate the condition.

The diagnosis of GGM is further substantiated by oral sugar loading tests, which we usually start at a dose of 0.5 g/kg glucose. Loading of glucose or galactose, but not of fructose, is followed by an increase in the output of stools containing the loaded sugar, an enhanced hydrogen concentration in alveolar breath air (more than 20 ppm in 3 h), little or no increase in blood sugar, and mild glycosuria (Fig. 98-1).

On clinical grounds alone, the following neonatal diseases may be difficult to differentiate from congenital glucose-galactose malabsorption: congenital lactose malabsorption, congenital sucrose-isomaltose malabsorption, familial chloride diarrhea, congenital sodium malabsorption, microvillus atrophy, and infectious diarrheas. Stool analysis for electrolytes and sugars and removal of glucose and galactose from the diet usually supply decisive information strongly suggestive that a child has GGM.

Acquired monosaccharide intolerance may occur after mucosal injury causing villus flattening or damage to the intestinal epithelium.[83,84] Disorders that often produce this lesion include infectious enteritis (rotavirus and giardiasis), gluten-sensitive enteropathy, radiation enteritis, drug-induced enteritis, and inflammatory bowel disease. However, this intolerance may also be of unknown origin.[85] Acquired monosaccharide intolerance differs from congenital GGM in that it is not usually present at birth, although its clinical presentation is essentially the same.[86]

Isolated fructose malabsorption has not often been described[87] and does not seem to occur at birth.

The decisive information for the diagnosis of GGM is obtained between the ages of 6 and 12 months, when the child displays no symptoms when on a glucose- and galactose-free diet. The glucose and galactose transport defect is best established in vitro by observing that the piece of jejunal biopsy does not accumulate glucose (and galactose) against a concentration gradient. It is also wise to check that alanine or leucine is actively transported[3] (Table 98-1). It should be noted that in acquired monosaccharide malabsorption with flat intestinal mucosa, the concentrative power of the remaining epithelium is still 30 percent that of the control intestine.[77,88] Alternatively, intestinal perfusion *in situ* has been used successfully to assess the diagnosis of GGM;[18,22,26] it is essential to use a well-defined methodology to obtain unequivocal results.[89–93]

Treatment

Treatment consists of immediate rehydration (oral rehydration solutions that contain glucose must be avoided) and feeding a glucose- and galactose-free diet. In the first 3 months of life, a commercial glucose- and galactose-free formula, such as Galactomine 19 from Nutricia, supplemented with iron and vitains, may be given. Alternatively, a special formula may be prepared containing calcium caseinate, 19 to 29 g/liter, fructose, 39 to 59 g/liter, and corn oil, 34 g/liter, to which electrolytes, vitamins, iron, and oligoelements should be added.[11]

After the age of 3 months, it is probably safe to add other foodstuffs either free of glucose and galactose (e.g., fish, meat, eggs, oil) or containing low quantities of these sugars (e.g., many vegetables and varieties of fruits and cheese). Honey, which children usually like, may also be given. Gradually the diet can be increasingly varied, and can include milk products and potatoes, bread, and other starch products, provided that there are no symptoms like abdominal cramps or diarrhea and that breath hydrogen production remains low.

RENAL GLYCOSURIA

Clinical Description

Renal glycosuria denotes the renal tubular abnormality displayed by individuals who excrete a variable amount of glucose in their urine with normal levels of blood glucose.[94] This chapter deals with the situation in which glucose excretion is the only apparent tubular defect. The following diagnostic criteria, proposed by Marble in 1947, are commonly accepted.[95]

1. Glycosuria is present without hyperglycemia. The amount of glucose excreted may vary from less than 10 g to more than 100 g/24 h; it remains essentially stable, except during prenancy, when it may increase.
2. The degree of glycosuria is largely independent of diet but may fluctuate according to the amount of carbohydrate ingested. In general, all specimens of urine examined, including those collected after an overnight fast, should contain sugar.
3. Levels of blood glucose are only slightly affected by dietary carbohydrates. The oral glucose tolerance curve is normal or slightly flat, and the levels of plasma insulin and free fatty acids are within control limits.[96] The percentage of glycosylated hemoglobin exhibits no increase.
4. The type of sugar excreted is glucose, identified by simple specific methods using glucose oxidase. Other sugars are not found (e.g., pentoses, fructose, galactose, lactose, sucrose, maltose, and heptulose).
5. Subjects with renal glycosuria are able to store and utilize carbohydrates normally.

When the above criteria are strictly applied, the condition is not common. For instance, only 94 cases have been observed among the 50,000 cases of melituria seen at the Joslin Clinic.[95] On the other hand, Lawrence proposed that renal glycosuria is proven wherever glycosuria occurs with a normal glucose tolerance test.[97] On the basis of this more liberal definition, he found that 65 percent of 800 selectees with glycosuria fell into this category. According to the same criteria, Lestradet et al.[96] who reported 103 cases in 24 years, found only 60 with glycosuria after an overnight fast. During that period, the latter authors observed 1700 children with insulin-dependent diabetes.

All the authors agree that renal glycosuria is a benign condition without symptoms or physical consequences, except in type 0 glycosuria, during pregnancy or starvation, when dehydration and ketosis may develop.[94] This rare, acute situation may lead to erroneous treatment of diabetic ketacidosis. Although renal glycosuria and insulin-dependent diabetes are two distinct entities, a combination of these two conditions has occasionally been reported.[94] In addition, immunologic abnormalities were found in a series of 11 patients.[98,99]

The age at which renal glycosuria is first recognized varies, depending on the frequency of urinary tests for reducing substances. The number of cases diagnosed seems to reach a peak at the age of military service, and in some countries at the age of the first vaccination; of the 103 cases in the French study referred to above,[96] 25 were detected before 6 years of age. Pregnancy and screening in the family of subjects with renal glycosuria occasioned the diagnosis of seven cases, whereas symptoms, including polyuria, excessive thirst, or abdominal pain, were the only reason for diagnosis in five cases.

Pathophysiology

In renal glycosuria, the presence of glucose in the urine results from a selective congenital defect in proximal tubule glucose reabsorption from the lumen into the blood. This definition is essentially based on four major clinical findings: (1) The metabolism of glucose, including its storage and utilization and insulin secretion, does not alter. (2) Glycosuria is present, but not hyperglycemia. (3) The only kidney function that alters is the increase in the urinary excretion of glucose, but there is no increase in the excretion of other solutes. The glomerular filtration, p-aminohippuric acid secretion, and phosphate and amino acid reabsorption are normal in patients with glycosuria.[100–102] (4) Renal glycosuria is usually not associated with anatomic abnormality, as assessed by routine histologic exploration including histochemistry and electron microscopy, thus indicating that the defect involved in renal glycosuria must be examined at the biochemical and biophysical levels. Taken together, these clinical observations strongly suggest that this defect is selectively expressed in the tubular glucose transport system.

At the same time, several observations relative to patients with renal glycosuria and kidney physiology suggest that the pathophysiology of renal glycosuria is more complex than the schematic view just presented. These observations concern three concepts.

The first is that the kidney is the only organ involved. This notion has been questioned, and a possible relationship with diabetes mellitus has been envisaged, because certain patients with an initial diagnosis of renal glycosuria were found to have hyperglycemia when retested after periods of 3 months to 13 years.[103] However, it is now clear that diabetes mellitus and renal glycosuria are two different conditions. Nevertheless, from the clinical point of view, it is important to check for the absence of transient or permanent hyperglycemia before the diagnosis of renal glycosuria is established. In addition to the fasting blood glucose concentration, it might be useful to measure the percentage of glycosylated hemoglobin and the increase in the plasma insulin concentration after glucose loading.

If renal glycosuria is indeed the genetic expression of a defect in the tubular glucose transport system, one would expect to observe symptoms in organs in which the same transport system exists, including first of all the small intestine. However, in renal glycosuria, glucose is well-absorbed in the small intestine, as assessed in vivo by oral glucose tolerance and in vitro by glucose accumulation against a concentration gradient in the intestinal epithelial cells.[9] This point will be further discussed blow.

The second is that structural integrity of the kidney may be in question.[101,104] However, the defects found are too small to explain a significant functional abnormality. Hence, it is prob-

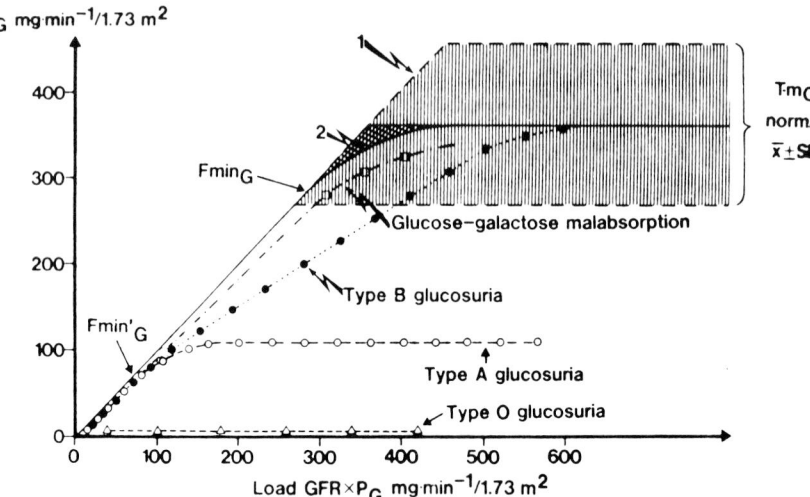

Fig. 98-9 Glucose titration curves showing renal tubular glucose reabsorption (T_G) as a function of filtered load (GFR x P_G). Schematic drawing of normal and pathologic states. 1 = theoretical curve; 2 = actual curve found in normal humans; F_{minG} = minimal renal glucose threshold in normal subjects; $\bar{F}_{min'G}$ = minimal renal glucose threshold in renal glycosuria. (From Oemar et al.[109])

ably safe to conclude that defective glucose transport in the proximal tubule is not related to anatomic abnormalities.

The third is that renal glycosuria might be due to an isolated selective defect in tubular glucose reabsorption. However, it is not clear whether this defect constitutes a single entity or is the result of several mutations. Reubi[105] and Bradley et al.[106] originally proposed that patients with renal glycosuria seemed to fall into two separate groups.

In this connection data were later obtained by the titration method of Smith[107] allowing a distinction to be made between the threshold glucose concentration (F_{minG}) and the maximum glucose transport rate (T_{mG}). The threshold concentration was defined as the plasma concentration at which glucose appears in the urine (i.e., for readily detectable concentrations far above normal trace values) and T_{mG}, as the plasma concentration required to saturate the reabsorptive capacity for glucose reabsorption.[108]

Analysis of titration curves for glucose reabsorption suggests that its values are heterogeneous in patients with renal glycosuria (Fig. 98-9). In type A, or classic, renal glycosuria[105] F_{minG} and T_{mG} are reduced, so that a significant amount of glucose spills over into the urine during fasting. In type B, F_{minG} is usually reduced while T_{mG} is normal but has an increased splay. Type A might well be a mutation reflecting a reduction in the capacity of the transport system. It is best explained by a diffuse defect involving all the nephrons. Type B might constitute a mutation reflected by a decrease in the affinity of the transport system. It might also be a consequence of functional or anatomic nephron heterogeneity.[56,94,108]

Recently, Oemar et al.[109] observed a new type of glycosuria that they called *type 0* in a 15-year-old boy who had complete absence of tubular glucose reabsorption. Of German origin, the parents, who were distant relatives, had a daily glycosuria of 1.1 g/1.73 m^2 for the father and 2.7 g/1.73 m^2 for the mother. Two of three siblings also had small loss of glucose. The proband's glycosuria was diagnosed when he was 11 years old and complained about persistent enuresis nocturna, polyuria, polydypsia, and episodes of polyphagia. He excreted daily 136 to 160 g/1.73 m^2 glucose accompanied by normal blood glucose levels between 75 and 105 mg/dl. The endogenous glucose clearance [112 to 160 ml/(min/1.73 m^2)] was nearly identical to inulin clearance [148 to 153 ml/(min·1.73 m^2)]. After intravenous glucose loading with a blood glucose concentration of 261 to 342 mg/dl, glucose clearance remained in the same range and tubular glucose reabsorption was virtually absent.

It should be stressed that titration curve analysis is not a simple method allowing constant clear discrimination between type A and type B glycosuria. For example, it is difficult to raise the blood glucose level without producing volume expansion, thus altering tubular sodium reabsorption and hormonal responses.[109] It is also difficult to obtain accurate values for F_{minG} by this method.[110] In conclusion, titration curve analysis underlines the diversity of the phenotypes, thus suggesting that no single defect characterizes all subjects with renal glycosuria.

Physiology of Renal Glucose Transport

Several features should be considered in connection with renal glycosuria:

(1) As glucose is completely filterable at the glomerulus, but is not normally detectable in voided urine, it must be reabsorbed from lumen to blood in the tubule.[108]

(2) Glucose reabsorption occurs through the epithelial cells of this tubule, and also crosses the epithelium by a paracellular route. Experimentally in the presence of phloridzin, an inhibitor of cellular absorption whose action mimics the inhibition occurring in renal glycosuria, glucose secretion may be demonstrated when the glucose concentration is lower in the tubular fluid than in the plasma.[111]

(3) The proximal tubule is the major site of glucose reabsorption. There is no evidence of glucose reabsorption in the loop of Henle or distal tubule. A small fraction of the filtered glucose may be reabsorbed in the collecting ducts. There are differences in glucose transport by the superficial and deep nephrons.[111,112]

(4) At the cellular level, D-glucose is reabsorbed from the urine in the proximal tubule via a sodium-coupled secondary active transport system located in the brush border membrane. As a result of this process, glucose is concentrated in the proximal tubule cells and subsequently passes down its concentration gradient into the blood via a facilitated transport system located in the antiluminal or plasma membrane. The driving force for D-glucose reabsorption is, thus, supplied by the electrochemical gradient for sodium across the brush border membrane. Phloridzin is a potent and highly specific inhibitor of the brush border membrane D-glucose transport system. The sodium electrochemical gradient is maintained by the activity of the Na$^+$,K$^+$-ATPase in the plasma membrane.

(5) Physiological studies strongly suggest that sodium-de-

Table 98-3 Characteristics of Na$^+$, D-Glucose Transport in the Proximal Tubule of Humans and Rabbits

	I *Early proximal* *(outer cortex, pars convoluta)*	*II* *Late proximal* *(outer medulla, pars recta)*
K_m glucose, mM	2.5–5.7	0.13–0.35
$\mathcal{J}_{max}$, nmol/(min·mg)	10	4
Hexose specificity	Glc $\gg$ Gala	Glc $=$ Gala
Na$^+$/glucose	1:1	2:1
Phloridzin inhibition	90%	60%

NOTE: Glc = glucose; Gala = galactose.
SOURCES: Barfuss and Schafer,[113] Turner and Silverman,[114] Turner and Moran.[115,116]

pendent D-glucose transport is heterogeneous along the proximal tubule. The transepithelial parameters of glucose transport were studied, using the isolated perfused tubule technique. Barfuss and Schafer[113] examined the properties of glucose transport in tubule segments thought to be representative of the three ultrastructurally defined cell types found in the proximal tubule. These are termed the S1, S2, and S3 cell types, which respectively predominate in the early proximal convoluted tubule (S1 segment), the early proximal straight tubule of the superficial nephrons (S2 segment), and the late proximal straight tubule (S3 segment). Active reabsorption of glucose was found to occur via a low affinity, high capacity system in S1 segments, a higher affinity, lower capacity system in S2 segments, and a still higher affinity and lower capacity system in S3 segments.

The heterogeneity of the sodium-dependent D-glucose system has been further examined by quantitative analysis of glucose transport kinetics in brush border membrane vesicles prepared from the whole cortex of human beings and dogs.[113] The curvilinear Eadie-Hofstee plots in both preparations cannot be accounted for by a single transporter obeying Michaelis-Menten kinetics. Turner and Moran[115] compared the glucose transport properties of proximal tubule brush border membrane vesicles prepared from two regions of rabbit kidney: the outer cortex, thought to contain S1 and some S2 cell types, and the outer medulla, thought to contain S3 cell types. In the outer cortical preparation, or the pars convoluta of the proximal tubule, the behavior of the sodium-dependent component of the D-glucose flux indicated the presence of a low affinity transport system with a K_m of 6 mM and a V_{max} of 10 nmol/min per milligram of mg protein, as measured at 17°C under zero-trans conditions (i.e., with initial intravesicular concentrations of sodium and glucose of zero). By contrast, in the outer medullary preparation, or pars recta of the proximal tubule, this flux component behaved like a high affinity system, as its K_m was 0.35 mM and its V_{max} 4 nmol/min per milligram of protein (Table 98-3).

The low affinity system was associated with a high affinity phloridzin-binding site. The sodium glucose stoichiometry for this system was 1:1. The high affinity phloridzin system was almost two orders of magnitude less sensitive to inhibition by phloridzin, and its sodium glucose stoichiometry was 2:1.

(6) Similarly, the uptake of D-galactose in vesicles from whole cortex seems to be mediated by a low affinity and a high affinity transport system.[117] More precisely, the D-galactose uptake from the pars recta was found to be mediated via a high affinity transport system ($K_m = 0.15 \pm 0.02$ mM) and was strictly Na$^+$-dependent. In the pars convoluta D-galactose uptake was mediated by a system that had a low affinity ($K_m = 15 \pm 2$ mM) and was Na$^+$-dependent.

(7) In the outer cortical preparation, the rate of uptake of D-glucose was much higher than that of D-galactose. D-Glucose and D-galactose were transported by a single Na$^+$-dependent transport by means of a high affinity system (K_ms for galactose and glucose: 0.15 ± 0.02 mM and 0.13 ± 0.02 mM, respectively).

Genetics

The preceding section appears to confirm the suggestion that no single defect characterizes all subjects with renal glycosuria. The conflicting data reported in the literature about the pattern of inheritance of renal glycosuria probably result from three factors.

First, in many of the reports describing families, information is incomplete or the techniques for detection are insensitive or inaccurate. Diagnostic criteria include the appearance of glucose in the urine during an otherwise normal glucose tolerance test, in the presence or absence of fasting glycosuria. The use of titration methods does not always allow clear separation of type A and type B glycosuria. Therefore, to better define the pattern of inheritance it seems appropriate to include the search for genetic markers in addition to the renal investigations.[118] Second, the genetic heterogeneity may be related to both the heterozygous and the homozygous state. Third, the genetic defect is not defined at the molecular level and may be heterogeneous involving, for instance, K_m, V_{max}, different locations on the tubule, activation of the transporter in the membrane, etc.

In 1927 Hjärne was able to obtain information about 141 out of 199 individuals belonging to generations with common ancestors in the eighteenth century.[119] He concluded that the defect was inherited as an autosomal dominant characteristic, in view of the following features: (1) Glycosuria occurred in both male and female members of the family. (2) When neither parent had glycosuria, none of the offspring had it either. (3) When either of the parents had glycosuria, some of the children generally had the defect. Similar conclusions regarding inheritance were reached in subsequent studies.[94]

More recently, De Marchi et al.[118] reported on five unrelated families affected by type A renal glycosuria. After careful examination of 25 patients and 40 healthy relatives (Fig. 98-10) these authors concluded that type A renal glycosuria was transmitted as an autosomal-dominant trait because in each family, the gene responsible for the tubular defect was segregated with the HLA complex. Two cases carried intra-HLA recombinant haplotypes, thus providing clues to the location of the abnormal gene on the sixth pair of chromosomes, i.e., closer to the HLA-A locus than to the HLA-B locus. Note that renal glycosuria was not associated with HLA-A, -B, or -C specific antigens.

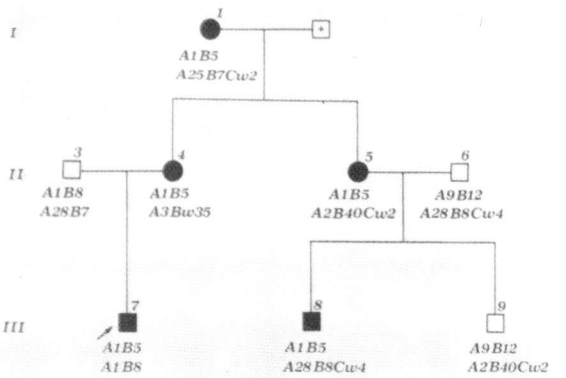

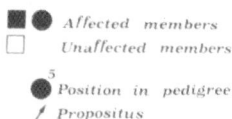

Fig. 98-10 Pedigree of "Mogl" family with HLA genotypes. All the affected members of the family carry the A1, B5 haplotype. *(From De Marchi et al.[118])*

The autosomal dominant mode of inheritance was queried by Elsas and Rosenberg,[120] who pointed out that the affected members of those pedigrees demonstrating a dominant pattern of inheritance might actually be heterozygotes and homozygotes for different mutations in the glucose transport process. They interpreted their own detailed study of two pedigrees as suggestive of autosomal recessive inheritance of renal glycosuria, with clinical disease resulting from a double dose of the mutant gene.

Relationship Between Renal Glycosuria and Glucose-Galactose Malabsorption?

On the basis of comparison of renal glycosuria and glucose-galactose malabsorption, Meeuwisse postulated in 1970[11] that two glucose transport systems are present in both the small intestine and proximal renal tubule; the same author also suggested that one of these systems with a similar affinity for galactose and glucose predominates in the intestine (he called it "the intestinal mechanism"), while the other, with little or no affinity for galactose, predominates in the kidney (this he called "the tubular mechanism"). According to Meeuwisse, the genetic defect in the intestine system causes GGM, while the defect in the tubular one causes renal glycosuria.

Based on the same comparison and with additional data, a similar but more precise suggestion was later made by Scriver et al.[30] about the heterogeneity of glucose carriers in the human kidney. The results of Turner and Moran[114–116] corroborate this hypothesis (Table 98-3).

Accordingly, at high concentrations, glucose is not absorbed in the intestine in GGM, on account of the absence of intestinal transport system. However, at low concentrations, glucose should be better absorbed if the tubular transport system is present. This was not found to be the case in perfusion studies.[26] However, the results of in vitro transport studies are consistent with this hypothesis, since when the glucose concentration in the incubation medium was low (0.1 mM) three of the four pieces of jejunum from GGM patients accumulated glucose against a concentration gradient (Table 98-1). Furthermore, addition of phloridzin to the incubation medium containing glucose reduced the intracellular glucose concentration gradient in GGM tissues to a lower level than in phloridzin-free medium. The presence of a minor glucose intestinal transport system was also suggested in a child referred to our department for failure to thrive, although he displayed no gastrointestinal symptoms and normal histology. Study of the child's jejunal mucosa showed a reduced glucose accumulation

(C/M = 6.9 at 0.1 mM glucose in the medium where C/M = intracellular over extracellular concentrations), but no decrease in galactose accumulation (C/M = 30.4 at 0.1 mM galactose in the medium).

Conversely a defect in the tubular transport system should be associated with renal glycosuria and the absence of digestive symptoms. This hypothesis is more difficult to test, as defects in a minor glucose transport system in the intestine are difficult to find and have, in fact, never been detected.[56] The presence in the kidney of a residual glucose transport system (i.e., the intestinal mechanism) must be postulated to explain why part of the glucose is reabsorbed in renal glycosuria. It is tempting to test the hypothesis of Meeuwisse and Scriver regarding the two transport systems in the light of the multiplicity of the glucose transport system recently found by physiologists in the brush border membrane of the kidney proximal tubule and small intestine.

At first sight, the characteristics of the glucose transport system found in the outer medulla (Tables 98-2 and 98-3) are also found in the high affinity glucose transport system in the intestine. They have in common the highest affinity and the lowest maximal transport rate; when tested, glucose and galactose may have the same affinity, and the flux ratio is 2 or 3 Na$^+$ to 1 glucose. However, as pointed out by Dorando and Crane,[72] the concordance of the data is not strict enough to establish that the two transport systems are identical. For example, in the kidney, the low affinity pathway for glucose has a high affinity for phloridzin, and the reverse is the case for the high affinity pathway.[114] Furthermore, 3-O-methylglucose is not a substrate for the low affinity pathway of the kidney.

To sum up, the studies of the two genetic diseases (GGM and renal glycosuria) and of glucose transport in the brush border membrane vesicles of the proximal tubule and small intestine both suggest the presence of a multiplicity of glucose transport systems. However, genetic studies suggest the existence of at least one transport system common to the intestine and kidney (the intestinal mechanism), while there is a marked difference in the kidney and intestinal systems described by physiologists. Therefore, it may be assumed that the kidney and intestinal carriers are not identical until it is shown that these differences are due to the use of different methods of measurement.[72]

Clinical Consequences

Comparison of the clinical consequences of defective glucose absorption in the proximal tubule and small intestine may provide insight into the specific roles of the kidney and intestinal tract. In renal glycosuria, tubular malabsorption of glucose does not cause severe polyuria or dehydration, but both these disorders are constant features in GGM. Moreover, to our knowledge, the consequences of defective tubular transport of glucose have not been specifically studied in renal glycosuria.

Nevertheless, the following sequence of events is conceivable in renal glycosuria: glucose is filtered together with water and electrolytes through the glomerular membrane. Then, in the proximal tubule, the decreased glucose reabsorption must be associated with diminished sodium and water reabsorption. The failure of this tubule to reabsorb 10 g or 55 mosmol of glucose might result in a 180-ml load in the distal tubule. In principle, water could be selectively reabsorbed in the distal tubule as a consequence of its increased hydraulic conductivity, which is regulated by the antidiuretic hormone vasopressin. However, in the absence of dehydration, there is no reason to suppose that vasopressin secretion is increased. Therefore, 10 g of glucose will be excreted together with an excess volume of urine of about 200 ml.

In the gastrointestinal tract, the situation is more complex, as shown by the following features.[39,121]

In GGM, glucose stimulates water and electrolyte secretion in the jejunum, as demonstrated by *in situ* perfusion.[22,26] The water secretion present in the absence of perfused sugar was stimulated by the presence of glucose, galactose, maltose, sucrose, and lactose, but not fructose.[26] Sodium, potassium, and chloride were always secreted together with water. However, the mechanism of this secretion is not clear, as the osmolarity of the solutions perfused was made isotonic with plasma (300 mosmol/kg). Water secretion during perfusion of solutions containing sucrose was also demonstrated by Launiala[122] in a case of sucrase-isomaltase deficiency during perfusion of solutions containing sucrose. It was identical to that observed in

Fig 98-11 Ileal input into the cecum and volume of stools. A wide range of ileal inputs was observed; diarrhea only appeared when the rate of ileal discharge exceeded the threshold of 6.3 ml/min. *(From Palma et al.[124])*

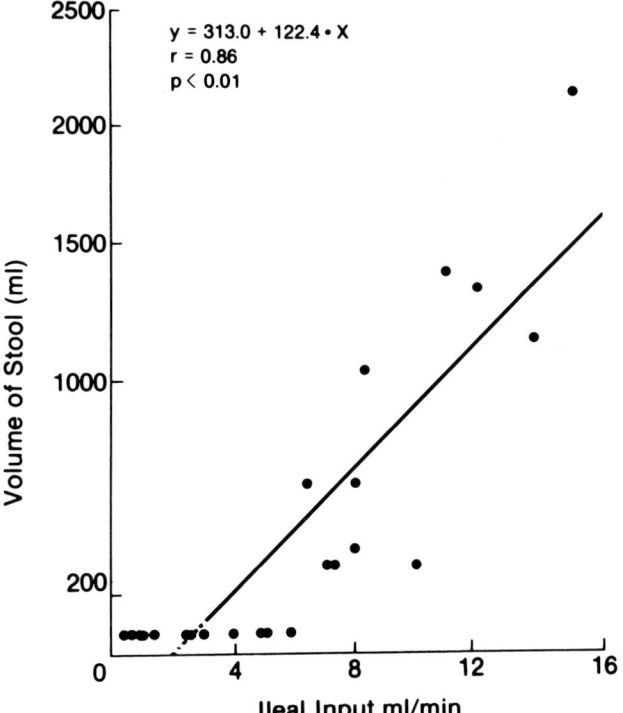

normal children during perfusion of mannitol, a poorly absorbed sugar. Thus, water and electrolyte secretion is related to the presence of unabsorbed sugar in the intestinal lumen.

Fluid secretion in the lumen of the small intestine is accompanied by a reduction in the transit time of the perfused solution, probably secondary to the increased flow rate in the segment under study.[122]

Unusually large amounts of water, electrolytes, and glucose enter the colon. In contrast to the distal tubule, the colon is known not to reabsorb water under active regulation of hydraulic conductivity (see Ref. 123). Consequently, the osmolality of fecal water is only slightly greater than that of plasma, and the colon must therefore adjust to acute loads of water and glucose by a mechanism other than hydraulic conductivity.

The role of the colon in handling water was recently examined in healthy adult volunteers by perfusing the stomach with an isotonic saline solution at an increasing rate.[124] The results indicate that diarrhea appeared when fluid entered the colon at a flow rate of 6.3 ml/min or more (Fig. 98-11). This threshold is about twice the colonic maximal absorption rate of 2.7 ml/min found in the same subjects. Therefore, under these experimental conditions, the colon is able to store about 1 liter of unabsorbed fluid before diarrhea starts.

The consequences of acute loading of glucose and other carbohydrates have been examined experimentally in animals and humans. Stool output was measured in healthy volunteers given an acute load of sugars poorly absorbed by the small intestine.[125] Diarrhea occurred when the load exceeded 120 to 220 mmol of mannitol, 73 to 146 mmol of lactulose, or 80 mmol of raffinose (Fig. 98-12). The significance of a colonic threshold for water and glucose loading is to be found in the three major activities of the colon: motility, absorption, and intraluminal bacterial metabolism. As we know very little about these activities in the human newborn, all we can do is to attempt to draw conclusions from studies performed at different ages. The magnitude and consequences of the osmotic load entering the adult colon in the form of glucose were examined by Bond and Levitt.[126] Carbohydrates may be broken into short-chain fatty acids by the bacteria that are active under anaerobic conditions of the colon lumen. The fatty acids not absorbed in their ionized form would then hold an equal number of milliequivalents of cation. Thus, failure to absorb only 10 g or 55 mosmol of glucose in the small bowel could result in a 220-mosmol load in the colon, which is the isotonic equivalent of about 650 ml of fecal water.

In fact, however, the short-chain fatty acids in the colon are absorbed and oxidized by the bacteria, and most of the remaining fecal glucose is converted into a larger molecular form with limited osmotic activity. Thus, the colonic flora benefits the host by reducing the osmotic load of unabsorbed carbohydrate and by salvaging of a large percentage of the calories of carbohydrate not absorbed in the small bowel.[126] When the colonic capacity to remove glucose is exceeded, it is the unabsorbed carbohydrate rather than the short-chain fatty acids that enhances the output of fecal water.[126]

This mechanism has been examined in transmissible gastroenteritis of 3-day-old and 3-week-old pigs. Infected animals did not absorb fluid and glucose in the small intestine. However, in contrast to the 3-day-old group, the large intestine of the 3-week-old infected pigs increased fluid absorption some six times over the control, and this compensatory response prevented diarrhea in these older animals.[127]

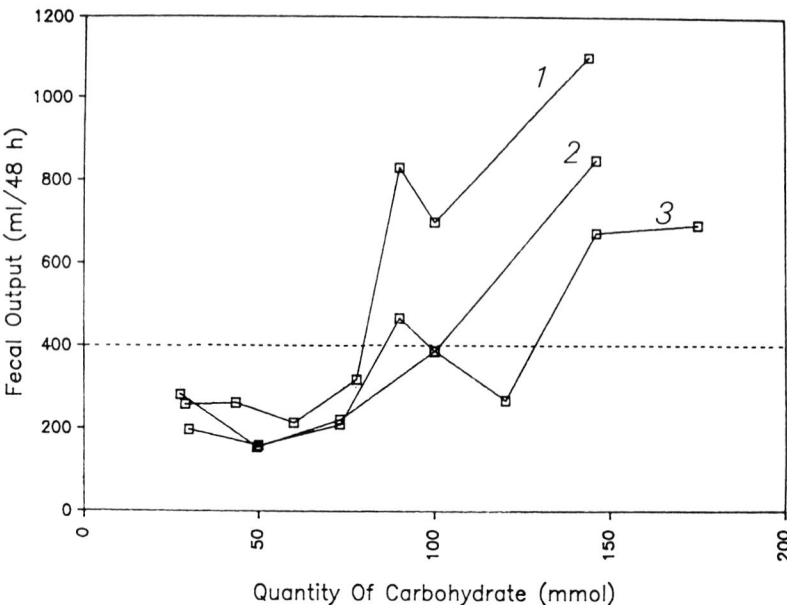

Fig. 98-12 Relationship between stool output and colonic carbohydrate load. 1 = raffinose, 2 = lactulose, 3 = mannitol. Points were obtained experimentally in one adult volunteer who could tolerate 80 to 100 mmol before fecal output of water exceeded 400 ml in 48 h or before test carbohydrate appeared in stools. (From Saunders and Wiggins.[125])

The adaptation of colonic flora to chronic glucose loading might also explain the ability to tolerate larger amounts of dietary glucose as patients with GGM grow older. This adaptation was examined in adults given a chronic load of lactulose, a nonabsorbable sugar.[128] After 8 days of a daily load of 20 g, fecal water and carbohydrate output declined, whereas galactosidase activity, free fatty acid production, and other bacterial colonic activities increased. Thus, chronic lactulose loading improved the efficiency of the carbohydrate digestion by flora. A similar adaptive mechanism was found in one patient with GGM who was given a moderate amount of glucose.[34]

In conclusion, comparison of the clinical consequences of defective glucose absorption in kidney or intestine stresses the importance of the colon in water economy. The control of the colonic threshold for water and glucose loading is the main compensatory mechanism that prevents diarrhea secondary to glucose malabsorption.

Recently, monoclonal antibodies were derived after immunization of mice either with highly purified renal brush border membranes or with apical membranes purified from LLC-PK_1, a cell line of pig renal proximal tubule origin. The chemical and functional properties of these antibodies indicate that the 75-kDa antigen recognized by these antibodies is a component of the renal Na^+-glucose cotransport system.[129]

In addition, the rabbit intestinal Na^+-glucose cotransporter was cloned and the cDNA sequenced.[130] These important discoveries should lead in the near future to the identification of the origin of the congenital defects in Na^+-glucose transport in children. However, the gene for the intestinal GGM transport system is on chromosome 22,[131] while a locus or chromosome 6 seems to encode the renal glycosuria phenotype.[118]

REFERENCES

1. LAPLANE R, POLONOVSKI C, ETIENNE M, DEBRAY P, LODS JC, PISSARO B: L'intolérance aux sucres à transfert intestinal actif. Ses rapports avec l'intolérance au lactose et le syndrome coeliaque. *Arch Fr Pediatr* 19:895, 1962.

2. LINDQUIST B, MEEUWISSE GW: Chronic diarrhoea caused by monosaccharide malabsorption. *Acta Paediatr* 51:674, 1962.

3. EVANS L, GRASSET E, HEYMAN M, DUMONTIER AM, BEAU JP, DESJEUX JF: Congenital selective malabsorption of glucose and galactose. *J Pediatr Gastroenterol Nutr* 4:878, 1985.

4. ABRAHAM JM, LEVIN B, OBERHOLZER VG, RUSSEL A: Glucose-galactose malabsorption. *Arch Dis Child* 42:592, 1967.

5. JEHAN P, JEZEQUEL C, COUTEL Y: Troubles du transfert actif du glucose. *Quest Med* 31:479, 1978.

6. GRASSET E, HEYMAN M, DUMONTIER AM, LESTRADET H, DESJEUX JF: Possible sodium and D-glucose cotransport in isolated jejunal epithelium of children. *Pediatr Res* 13:1240, 1979.

7. GERARD-BROCHOT E, BROCHOT JL, BOCQUET A, MENGET A, SCHIRRER J, RAFFI A: Malabsorption congénitale du glucose et du galactose. A propos d'un cas. *Med Hyg* 41:3897, 1983.

8. ELSAS LJ, HILLMAN RE, PATTERSON JH, ROSENBERG LE: Renal and intestinal hexose transport in familial glucose-galactose malabsorption. *J Clin Invest* 49:576, 1970.

9. MEEUWISSE GW, DAHLQVIST A: Glucose-galactose malabsorption. A study with biopsy of the small mucosa. *Acta Paediatr Scand* 57:273, 1968.

10. MEEUWISSE GW, MELIN K: Glucose-galactose malabsorption. A clinical study of 6 cases. *Acta Paediatr Scand Suppl* 188:3, 1969.

11. MEEUWISSE G: *Glucose-Galactose Malabsorption. An Inborn Error of Carrier-Mediated Transport.* University of Lund, Sweden, 1970, vol 7.

12. MELIN K, MEEUWISSE GW: Glucose-galactose malabsorption. A genetic study. *Acta Pediatr Scand Suppl* 188:19, 1969.

13. SCHNEIDER AJ, KINTER WB, STIRLING CE: Glucose-galactose malabsorption. Report of a case with autoradiographic studies of a mucosal biopsy. *N Engl J Med* 274:305, 1966.

14. PRUITT AW, ACHORD JL, FALES FW, PATTERSON JH: Glucose-galactose malabsorption complicated by monilial arthritis. *Pediatrics* 43:106, 1969.

15. KAIJSER K, OCKERMAN PA: Diagnostic problems in glucose-galactose malabsorption. *Acta Paediatr Scand* 59:214, 1970.

16. LINNEWEH F, SCHAUMLOFFEL E, BARTHELMAI W: Angeborene glucose-und galactose-malabsorption. *Klin Wochenschr* 43:405, 1965.

17. WIMBERLEY PD, HARRIES JT, BURGESS EA: Congenital glucose-galactose malabsorption. *Proc R Soc Med* 67:755, 1974.

18. HUGHES WS, SENIOR JR: The glucose-galactose malabsorption syndrome in a 23-year-old woman. *Gastroenterology* 68:142, 1975.

19. ANDERSON CM, KERRY KR, TOWNLEY RRW: An inborn defect of intestinal absorption of certain monosaccharides. *Arch Dis Child* 40:1, 1965.

20. EGGERMONT E, LOEB H: Glucose-galactose intolerance. *Lancet* 2:343, 1966.

21. DUBOIS R, LOEB H, EGGERMONT E, MAINGUET P: Étude clinique et biochimique d'un cas de malabsorption congénitale du glucose et du galactose. *Helv Paediatr Acta* 6:577, 1966.

22. FAIRCLOUGH PD, CLARK ML, DAWSON AM, SILK DBA, MILLA PJ, HARRIES JT: Absorption of glucose and maltose in congenital glucose-galactose malabsorption. *Pediatr Res* 12:1112, 1978.

23. DEPRETTERE AJR, VAN ACKER KJ, EGGERMONT E, CARCHOM H, EVENS M: Primary glucose-galactose malabsorption. *Acta Paediatr Belg* 33:121, 1980.

24. ESPOSITO G, FAELLI A, CAPRARO V: Sugar and electrolyte absorption in the rat intestine perfused "in vivo". *Pflugers Arch* 340:335, 1973.

25. LIU HY, ANDERSON GJ, TSAO MU, MOORE BF, GIDAY Z: Tm glucose in a case of congenital intestinal and renal malabsorption of monosaccharides. *Pediatr Res* 1:386, 1967.

26. PHILLIPS SF, MCGILL DB: Glucose-galactose malabsorption in an adult: Perfusion studies of sugar, electrolyte, and water transport. *Am J Dig Dis* 18:1017, 1973.

27. MARKS JF, NORTON JB, FORTRAN JS: Glucose-galactose malabsorption. *J Pediatr* 69:225, 1966.

28. BEAUVAIS P, VAUDOUR G, DESJEUX JF, LE BALLE JC, BIROT JY, BRISSAUD HE: La malabsorption congénitale du glucose-galactose. Un nouveau cas avec l'étude in vitro de l'absorption intestinale et étude du TmG. *Arch Fr Pediatr* 28:573, 1971.

29. LEBENTHAL E, GARTI R, MATHOTH Y, COHEN B, KATZENELSON D: Glucose-galactose malabsorption in an Oriental-Iraqi Jewish family. *J Pediatr* 78:844, 1971.

30. SCRIVER CR, CHESNEY RW, MCINNES RR: Genetic aspects of renal tubular transport: Diversity and topology of carriers. *Kidney Int* 9:149, 1976.

31. MEEUWISSE GW: Glucose-galactose malabsorption: A study on the transfer of glucose across the red cell membrane. *Scand J Clin Lab Invest* 25:145, 1970.

32. BOND JH, LEVITT MD: Investigation of small bowel transit time in man utilizing pulmonary hydrogen (H2) measurement. *J Lab Clin Med* 85:546, 1975.

33. DOUWES AC, VAN CAILLIE M, FERNANDES J, BIJLEVELD CMA, DESJEUX JF: Interval breath hydrogen test in glucose-galactose malabsorption. *Eur J Pediatr* 137:273, 1981.

34. SARLES J, COLLARD Y, ARNAUD-BATTANDIER F, BRESSON JL, SCHMITZ J, RICOUR C, REY J: Fermentation acide et production d'hydrogène par la flore colique dans un cas de malabsorption du glucose et du galactose. *Gastroenterol Clin Biol* 10:848, 1986.

35. ELSAS LJ, LAMBE DW: Familial glucose-galactose malabsorption: Remission of glucose intolerance. *J Pediatr* 83:226, 1973.

36. CASEY CE, NEIFERT MR, SEACAT JM, NEVILLE MC: Nutrient intake by breast-fed infants during the first five days after birth. *Am J Dis Child* 140:933, 1986.

37. KIMMICH GA: Intestinal absorption of sugar, in Johnson LR (ed): *Physiology of the Gastrointestinal Tract*. New York, Raven, 1981, p 1035.

38. HOPFER U: Membrane transport mechanisms for hexoses and amino acids in the small intestine, in Johnson LR (ed): *Physiology of the Gastrointestinal Tract*, 2d ed. New York, Raven, 1987, p 1499.

39. CASPARY WF: Diarrhoea associated with carbohydrate malabsorption. *Clin Gastroenterol* 15(3):631, 1986.

40. DOUWES AC, OOSTERKAMP RF, FERNANDES J, LOS T, JONGLOED A: Sugar malabsorption in healthy neonates estimated by breath hydrogen. *Arch Dis Child* 55:512, 1980.

41. MOBASSAIEH M, MONTGOMERY RK, BILLER JA, GRAND RJ: Development of carbohydrate absorption in the fetus and neonate. *Pediatrics* 75 (suppl):160, 1985.

42. LIFSCHITZ CH, O'BRIAN SMITH E, GARZA C: Delayed complete functional lactase sufficiency in breast-fed infants. *J Pediatr Gastroenterol Nutr* 2:478, 1983.

43. HONEGGER P, SEMENZA G: Multiplicity of carriers for free glucalogues in hamster small intestine. *Biochim Biophys Acta* 318:390, 1973.

44. RAVICH WJ, BAYLESS TM, THOMAS M: Fructose: Incomplete intestinal absorption in humans. *Gastroenterology* 84:26, 1983.

45. GRAY GM, SANTIAGO NA: Disaccharide absorption in normal and diseased human intestine. *Gastroenterology* 51:489, 1966.

46. DESJEUX JF, TANNENBAUM C, TAI YH, CURRAN PF: Effects of sugars and amino acids on sodium movement across small intestine. *Am J Dis Child* 131:331, 1977.

47. MAHALANABIS D, MERSON M: Development of an improved formulation of oral rehydration salts (ORS) with antidiarrhoeal and nutritional properties: A "super ORS," in Holmgren J, Lindberg A, Möllby R (eds): *Development of Vaccines and Drugs against Diarrhea*. 11th Nobel Conference, Stockholm, 1986, p 240.

48. JIROSOVA V, KOLDOVSKY O, HERINGOVA A, HOSKOVA J, JIRASEK J, UHER J: The development of the functions of the small intestine of human fetus. *Biol Neonate* 9:44, 1966.

49. LEVIN RJ, KOLDOVSKY O, HOSKOVA J, JIRSOVA V, UHER J: Electrical activity across human foetal small intestine associated with absorption processes. *Gut* 9:206, 1968.

50. KOLDOVSKY O, HERINGOVA A, JIRSOVA V, JIRASEK JE, UHER J: Transport of glucose against a concentration gradient in everted sacs of jejunum and ileum of human fetuses. *Gastroenterology* 48:185, 1965.

51. YOUNOSZAI MK: Jejunal absorption of hexose in infants and adults. *J Pediatr* 85:446, 1974.

52. KARASOV WH, DIAMOND JM: Adaptative regulation of sugar and amino acid transport by vertebrate intestine. *Am J Physiol* 245 (*Gastrointest Liver Physiol* 8):G443, 1983.

53. GRASSET E, HEYMAN M, DUMONTIER AM, LESTRADET H, DESJEUX JF: Possible sodium and D-glucose cotransport in isolated jejunal epithelium of children. *Pediatr Res* 13:1240, 1979.

54. HEYMAN M, DESJEUX JF, GRASSET E, DUMONTIER AM, LESTRADET H: Relationship between transport of D-xylose and other monosaccharides in jejunal mucosa of children. *Gastroenterology* 80:758, 1981.

55. ROSENBERG LE, BLAIR A, SEGAL S: Transport of amino acids by slices of rat-kidney cortex. *Biochim Biophys Acta* 54:479, 1961.

56. ELSAS LJ, ROSENBERG LE: Familial renal glycosuria: A genetic reappraisal of hexose transport by kidney and intestine. *J Clin Invest* 48:1845, 1969.

57. NAFTALIN R, CURRAN PF: Galactose transport in rabbit ileum. *J Membrane Biol* 16:257, 1974.

58. SEMENZA G, KESSLER M, HOSANG M, WEBER J, SCHMIDT U: Biochemistry of the Na$^+$, D-glucose cotransporter of the small-intestinal brush-border membrane. The state of the art in 1984. *Biochim Biophys Acta* 779:343, 1984.

59. KESSLER M, SEMENZA G: The small-intestinal Na$^+$, D-glucose cotransporter: An asymmetric gated channel (or pore) responsive to $\Delta\psi$. *J Membrane Biol* 76:27, 1983.

60. HOPFER U, NELSON K, PERROTTO J, ISSELBACHER K: Glucose transport in isolated brush border membrane from rat small intestine. *J Biol Chem* 248:25, 1973.

61. HOPFER U: Diabetes mellitus: Changes in the transport properties of isolated intestinal microvillous membranes. *Proc Natl Acad Sci USA* 6:2027, 1975.

62. PEERCE BE, WRIGHT EM: Conformational changes in the intestinal brush border sodium-glucose cotransporter labeled with fluorescein isothiocyanate. *Proc Natl Acad Sci USA* 81:2223, 1984.

63. PEERCE BE, WRIGHT EM: Sodium-induced conformational changes in the glucose transporter of intestinal brush borders. *J Biol Chem* 259:14105, 1984.

64. TOGGENBURGER G, KESSLER M, ROTHSTEIN A, SEMENZA G, TANNENBAUM C: Similarity in effects of Na$^+$ gradients and membrane potentials on D-glucose transport by, and phlorizin binding to, vesicles derived from brush borders of rabbit intestinal mucosal cells. *J Membrane Biol* 40:269, 1978.

65. DUCIS I, KOEPSELL H: Simple liposomal system to reconstitute and assay highly efficient Na$^+$/D-glucose cotransport from kidney brush-border membranes. *Biochim Biophys Acta* 730:119, 1983.

66. WILSON TH: *Intestinal Absorption*. Philadelphia, Saunders, 1962, p 91.

67. NEWEY H, SANFORD PA, SMYTH DH: The effect of uranyl nitrate on intestinal transfer of hexoses. *J Physiol* 186:493, 1966.

68. DEBNAM ES, LEVIN RJ: An experimental method of identifying and quantifying the active transfer electrogenic component from the diffusive component during sugar absorption measured in vivo. *J Physiol* 246:181, 1975.

69. DEBNAM ES, LEVIN RJ: Influence of specific dietary sugars on the jejunal mechanisms for glucose, galactose, and methylglucoside absorption: Evidence for multiple sugar carriers. *Gut* 17:92, 1976.

70. HONEGGER P, GERSHON E: Further evidence for the multiplicity of carriers for free glucalogues in hamster small intestine. *Biochim Biophys Acta* 352:127, 1974.

71. KAUNITZ JD, WRIGHT EM: Kinetics of sodium D-glucose cotransport in bovine intestinal brush border vesicles. *J Membrane Biol* 79:41, 1984.

72. DORANDO FC, CRANE RK: Studies of the kinetics of Na$^+$ gradient-coupled glucose transport as found in brush-border membrane vesicles from rabbit jejunum. *Biochim Biophys Acta* 772:273, 1984.

73. FREEMAN HJ, QUAMME GA: Age-related changes in sodium-dependent glucose transport in rat small intestine. *Am J Physiol* 251 (*Gastrointest Liver Physiol* 14):G208, 1986.

74. KELJO DJ, MACLEOD RJ, PERDUE MH, BUTLER DG, HAMILTON JR: Glucose transport in piglet jejunal brush border membranes: Insights from a disease model. *Am J Physiol* 249 (*Gastrointest Liver Physiol* 12):G751, 1985.

75. BROT-LAROCHE E, SERRANO MA, DELHOMME B, ALVARADO F: Temperature sensitivity and substrate specificity of two distinct Na$^+$-activated D-glucose transport systems in guinea pig jejunal brush border membrane vesicles. *J Biol Chem* 261:6168, 1986.

76. LINDI C, MARCIANI P, FAELLI A, ESPOSITO G: Intestinal sugar transport during ageing. *Biochim Biophys Acta* 816:411, 1985.

77. DESJEUX JF, SANDLER L, SASSIER P, LESTRADET H: Acquired and congenital disorders of intestinal transport of D-glucose in children. *Rev Eur Etud Clin Biol* 16:364, 1971.

78. STIRLING CE, SCHNEIDER AJ, WONG MD, KINTER WB: Quantitative radioautography of sugar transport in intestinal biopsies from normal humans and a patient with glucose-galactose malabsorption. *J Clin Invest* 51:438, 1972.

79. KESTON AS, MEEUWISSE G, FREDRIKSON B: Evidence for participation of mutarotase in sugar transport: Absence of the enzyme in a case of glucose-galactose malabsorption. *Biochem Biophys Res Commun* 108:1574, 1982.

80. MORAN A, TURNER RJ, HANDLER JS: Hexose regulation of sodium-hexose transport in LLC-PK₁ epithelia: The nature of the signal. *J Membrane Biol* 82:59, 1984.

81. MORAN A, TURNER RJ, HANDLER JS: Hexose regulation of sodium-luxose transport in LLC-PK₁ epithelia: The nature of the signal. *J Membrane Biol* 82:59, 1984.

82. WEISS ER, COOK JS: Separation of hexose-transporting from nontransporting LLC-PK₁ cells on density gradients. *Am J Physiol* 250 (*Cell Physiol* 19):C199, 1986.

82a. DESJEUX JF, NATH SK: Appearance of absorptive properties in a human epithelial cell live HRT-18. *J Physiol* (London) 396:22p, 1988.

83. BURKE V, ANDERSON CM: Sugar intolerance as a cause of protracted diarrhea following surgery of the gastrointestinal tract of neonates. *Aust Pediatr* 2:219, 1966.

84. LIFSHITZ F, COELLO-RAMIREZ P, GUTIERREZ-TOPETE G: Monosaccharide intolerance and hypoglycemia in infants with diarrhea. I. Clinical course of 23 infants. *J Pediatr* 77:595, 1970.

85. LIFSHITZ F, COELLO-RAMIREZ P, GUTIERREZ-TOPETE G: Monosaccharide intolerance and hypoglycemia in infants with diarrhea. II. Metabolic studies in 23 infants. *J Pediatr* 77:604, 1970.

86. NICHOLS BL: Pathogenesis of glucose malabsorption in acquired monosaccharide intolerance, in Lifshitz F (ed): *Carbohydrate Intolerance in Infancy*. New York, Basel, Marcel Dekker, 105, 1982.

87. BARNES G, MCKELLAR W, LAWRENCE S: Detection of fructose malabsorption by breath hydrogen test in a child with diarrhea. *J Pediatr* 103:575, 1983.

88. DESJEUX JF, SASSIER P, TICHET J, SARRUT S, LESTRADET H: Sugar absorption by flat jejunal mucosa. *Acta Paediatr Scand* 62:531, 1973.

89. MODIGLIANI R, BERNIER JJ: Absorption of glucose, sodium, and water by the human jejunum studied by intestinal perfusion with a proximal occluding balloon and at variable flow rates. *Gut* 12:184, 1971.

90. MODIGLIANI R, RAMBAUD JC, BERNIER JJ: The method of intraluminal perfusion of the human small intestine. I. Principle and technique. *Digestion* 9:176, 1973.

91. MODIGLIANI R, RAMBAUD JC, BERNIER JJ: The method of intraluminal perfusion of the human small intestine. II. Absorption studies in health. *Digestion* 9:264, 1973.

92. RAMBAUD JC, MODIGLIANI R, BERNIER JJ: The method of intraluminal perfusion of the human small intestine. III. Absorption studies in disease. *Digestion* 9:343, 1973.

93. REY F, DRILLET F, SCHMITZ J, REY J: Influence of flow rate on the kinetics of the intestinal absorption of glucose and lysine in children. *Gastroenterology* 66:79, 1974.

94. KRANE SM: Renal glycosuria, in Stanbury JB, Wyngaarden JB, Frederickson DS (eds): *The Metabolic Basis of Inherited Disease*, 4th ed. New York, McGraw-Hill, 1978.

95. MARBLE A: Non-diabetic melituria, in Joslin EP, Root HF, White P, Marble A (eds): *The Treatment of Diabetes Mellitus*. Philadelphia, Lea & Febiger, 1959.

96. LESTRADET H, LABRUNE B, DUVAL C, DESCHAMPS I: Le diabète rénal. A propos de 103 observations chez l'enfant. *Arch Fr Pediatr* 36:760, 1979.

97. LAWRENCE RD: Symptomless glycosurias: Differentiation by sugar tolerance tests. *Med Clin North Am* 31:289, 1947.

98. DE MARCHI S, CECCHIN E, BASILE A, PROTO G, DONADON W, SCHINELLA D, LENGO A, DE PAOLI P, JUS A, VILLALTA D, TESIO F, SANTINI G: Is renal glycosuria a benign condition? *Proc Eur Dial Transplant Assoc* 20:681, 1983.

99. DE PAOLI P, BATTISTIN S, JUS A, REITANO M, VILLALTA D, DE MARCHI S, CECCHIN E, BASILE A, SANTINI G: Immunological characterization of renal glycosuria patients. *Clin Exp Immunol* 56:289, 1984.

100. LEONARDI P, RUOL A, MUNARI R: Morphologic aspects of renal glycosuria. *Am J Med Sci* 239:721, 1960.

101. FREEMAN JA, ROBERTS KE: A fine structural study of renal glycosuria. *Exp Mol Pathol* 2:83, 1963.

102. MUDGE GH: Clinical patterns of tubular dysfunction. *Am J Med* 24:785, 1958.

103. ACKERMAN IP, FAJANS SS, CONN JW: The development of diabetes mellitus in patients with nondiabetic glycosuria. *Clin Res Proc* 6:251, 1958.

104. MONASTERIO G, OLIVER J, MUIESAN G, PARDELLI G, MARINOZZI V, MACDOWELL M: Renal diabetes as a congenital tubular dysplasia. *Am J Med* 37:44, 1964.

105. REUBI FC: Glucose titration in renal glycosuria, in *Ciba Foundation Symposium on the Kidney*. Boston, Little, Brown, 1954.

106. BRADLEY SE, BRADLEY GP, TYSON CJ, CURRY JJ, BLAKE WC: Renal function in renal diseases. *Am J Med* 9:766, 1950.

107. SMITH HW: *The Kidney: Structure and Function in Health and Disease*. New York, Oxford University Press, 1958.

108. MUDGE GH, BERNT WO, VALTIN H: Tubular transport of urea, glucose, phosphate, uric acid, sulfate, and thiosulfate, in Orloff J, Berliner RW (eds): *Renal Physiology, Handbook of Physiology*. Washington, DC, American Physiological Society, 1973.

109. OEMAR BS, BYRD DJ, BRODEHL J: Complete absence of tubular glucose reabsorption: A new type of renal glucosuria (type O). *Clin Nephrol* 27:156, 1987.

110. DARMAUN D, ROBERT JJ, CHEVROT M, DIETERLEN PH, REACH G, DESJEUX JF: Filtration glomérulaire et réabsorption tubulaire du glucose dans le diabète insulinodépendant de l'enfant. *Arch Fr Pediatr* 43:23, 1986.

111. LOESCHKE K, BAUMAN K, RENSCHLER H, ULLRICH KJ: Differenzierung zwischen aktiver und passiv komponente des D-glucosetransports a proximalen konvolut der ratteuniere. *Arch Ges Physiol* 305:118, 1969.

112. HOSHI T, KIKUTA Y: Effects of organic solute-sodium cotransport on the transmembrane potential resistance parameters of the proximal tubule of Triturus kidney, in Anagnostopoulos T (ed): *Electrophysiology of the Nephron*. Paris, INSERM, 1977, vol 67, p 135.

113. BARFUSS DW, SCHAFER JA: Differences in active and passive glucose transport along the proximal nephron. *Am J Physiol* 240 (*Renal Fluid Electrolyte Physiol* 9):F322, 1981.

114. TURNER RJ, SILVERMAN M: Sugar uptake into normal human renal brush border vesicles. *Proc Natl Acad Sci USA* 75:2825, 1977.

115. TURNER RJ, MORAN A: Heterogeneity of sodium-dependent D-glucose transport sites along the proximal tubule: Evidence from vesicle studies. *Am J Physiol* 242 (*Renal Fluid Electrolyte Physiol* 11):F406, 1982.

116. TURNER RJ, MORAN A: Further studies of proximal tubular brush border membrane D-glucose transport heterogeneity. *J Membrane Biol* 70:37, 1982.

117. ROIGAARD-PETERSEN H, JACOBSEN C, SHEIKH MI: Characteristics of D-galactose transport systems by luminal membrane vesicles from rabbit kidney. *Biochim Biophys Acta* 856:578, 1986.

118. DE MARCHI S, CECCHIN E, BASILE A, PROTO G, DONADON W, JENGO A, SCHINELLA D, JUS A, VILLALTA D, DE PAOLI P, SANTINI G, TESIO F: Close genetic linkage between HLA and renal glycosuria. *Am J Nephrol* 4:280, 1984.

119. HJÄRNE VA: Study of orthoglycaemic glycosuria with particular reference to its hereditability. *Acta Med Scand* 67:422, 1937.

120. ELSAS JJ, BUSSE D, ROSENBERG LE: Autosomal recessive inheritance of renal glycosuria. *Metabolism* 20:968, 1971.

121. GRAY GM: Intestinal disaccharidase deficiencies and glucose-galactose malabsorption, in Stanbury JB, Wyngaarden JB, Fredrickson DS (eds): *The Metabolic Basis of Inherited Disease*, 4th ed. New York, McGraw-Hill, 1978.

122. LAUNIALA K: The effect of unabsorbed sucrose and mannitol on the small intestinal flow rate and mean transit time. *Scand J Gastroenterol* 3:665, 1968.

123. BRIDGES RJ, RUMMEL W: Mechanistic basis of alterations in mucosal water and electrolyte transport. *Clin Gastroenterol* 15(3):491, 1986.

124. PALMA R, VIDON N, BERNIER JJ: Maximal capacity for fluid absorption in human bowel. *Dig Dis Sci* 26:929, 1981.

125. SAUNDERS DR, WIGGINS HS: Conservation of mannitol, lactulose and raffinose by the human colon. *Am J Physiol* 241 (*Gastrointest Liver Physiol* 4):G397, 1981.

126. BOND JH, LEVITT MD: Fate of soluble carbohydrate in the colon of rats and man. *J Clin Invest* 57:1158, 1976.

127. ARGENZIO RA, MOON HW, KEMENY LJ, WHIPP SC: Colonic compensation in transmissible gastroenteritis of swine. *Gastroenterology* 86:1501, 1984.

128. FLORENT C, FLOURIE B, LEBLOND A, RAUTUREAU M, BERNIER JJ, RAMBAUD JC: Influence of chronic lactulose ingestion on the colonic metabolism of lactulose in man (an in vivo study). *J Clin Invest* 75:608, 1985.

129. WU JSR, LEVER JE: Monoclonal antibodies that bind the renal Na⁺/glucose symport system. 1. Identification. *Biochemistry* 26:5783, 1987.

130. HEDIGER MA, COADY MJ, IKEDA TS, WRIGHT EM: Expression cloning and cDNA sequencing of the Na⁺/glucose co-transporter. *Nature* 330:379, 1987.

131. WRIGHT E: Personal communication.

CHAPTER 99

CYSTINURIA

STANTON SEGAL
SAMUEL O. THIER

1. Cystinuria is a disorder of amino acid transport affecting the epithelial cells of the renal tubule and the gastrointestinal tract. The defective transport of cystine, lysine, arginine, and ornithine is transmitted as an autosomal recessive trait. The heterozygous state may reflect true recessive or incompletely recessive inheritance. In the latter state the affected amino acids are excreted in urine in quantities greater than normal but less than in the homozygous state. By use of the intestinal transport system as a sensitive genetic marker, three types of cystinuric homozygotes can be defined, and the evidence is that these types result from allelic mutations.

2. The intestinal defect can be demonstrated in vivo by oral loading tests and by intestinal perfusion studies. Complementary data showing the defect have also been obtained by incubations in vitro measuring transport into mucosal biopsies. The dibasic amino acids can be absorbed by cystinuric subjects in a normal fashion as dipeptides.

3. The renal lesions for all four amino acids and the mixed disulfide of cysteine-homocysteine can be demonstrated by clearance studies. The clearance of cystine in both humans and dogs with cystinuria frequently exceeds the glomerular filtration rate. This suggests that secretion occurs. Studies in vitro of amino acid transport by renal cortical slices of affected kidneys demonstrate a defect for dibasic amino acids but not for cystine. There exist, in rat renal tubule fragments and isolated brush border membrane vesicles, multiple systems for cystine and lysine transport. Cystine and the dibasic amino acids appear to share the low K_m, high affinity system which is probably defective in the cystinuric kidney. Microperfusion of rat kidney tubules and studies of rat cortical transport in vivo indicate that there may be an interaction of cystine and dibasic amino acids at the luminal membrane of the renal tubule cells. Cysteine, the intracellular form of cystine, shares a cellular efflux system with dibasic amino acids. This interaction may play an important role in the regulation of cystine transport into renal cortical cells.

4. Cystinuria is expressed clinically as urinary tract calculus disease. Radiopaque cystine stones are formed, and hexagonal cystine crystals appear in the urine. Diagnosis may be pursued by testing urine with nitroprusside, high-voltage electrophoresis, or column amino acids analysis. Stones generally form at cystine excretion rates of greater than 300 mg cystine per gram of creatinine in acid urine. Cystinuric patients are susceptible to all complications of stone disease. Treatment is directed at reducing the concentration of cystine in urine by increasing urine volume, increasing cystine solubility by alkalinizing the urine, and reducing cystine excretion by use of D-penicillamine. D-Penicillamine, although extremely effective, is not without risk and should be reserved for patients who fail to respond to conservative therapy.

Other sulfhydryl-containing compounds such as mercaptopropionylglycine (MPG) and captopril have been shown to reduce cystine excretion and stone formation. MPG appears to be quite effective but has a significant frequency of side effects, particularly in patients who have had reactions to D-penicillamine. The place of captopril in the treatment of cystinuria has not been defined.

5. Models of human cystinuria have been described in animals. Studies of these models may help clarify the cellular defect in cystinuria and may provide a system for testing new drug therapy.

Cystinuria is an inheritable disorder of amino acid transport affecting the epithelial cells of the renal tubules and gastrointestinal tract. The disease is expressed clinically by the formation of calculi in the urinary tract, with the potential for obstruction, infections, and ultimately renal insufficiency. The disease is characterized primarily by the precipitation of cystine, the least soluble of the naturally occurring amino acids; lysine, arginine, ornithine and cysteine-homocysteine mixed disulfide are also present in excess in the urine. Since this aminoaciduria occurs with a normal or reduced filtered load of cystine and the dibasic amino acids, it was postulated earlier that cystinuria is a disorder of tubular transport in the kidney. The subsequent demonstration of comparably defective transport in the intestine established the present view of this disorder as an inherited defect in a specific transepithelial transport mechanism, which is expressed in two areas, the kidney and the intestine.

HISTORY

The historical development of a theory of the pathogenesis of cystinuria was anything but orderly. Although the data suggesting renal and intestinal lesions appeared in random order, it is easier to trace the history of the renal lesion before that of the intestinal defect.

In 1810 Wollaston analyzed two stones recovered from urinary bladders and discerned that they differed from all previously described calculi. Because of their bladder origin and supposed chemical nature, they were named cystic oxide stones.[1] In 1824 Stromeyer noted hexagonal platelike crystals in the urine of patients with cystinuria.[2] The finding of cystine crystals served for many years as the chief means of diagnosing the disease and remains helpful even today.

In 1833 Berzelius, recognizing that the compound was not an oxide, renamed the substance "cystine," perpetuating the fallacy that it originated in the bladder.[3] Although improved descriptions of the chemistry of cystine were developed over the next 70 years, it was not until 1902 that Friedman defined the chemical structure of cystine.[4] In his 1908 Croonian lec-

---

The nonstandard abbreviation used in this chapter is MPG = mercaptopropionylglycine.

tures, Garrod discussed cystinuria among the inborn errors of metabolism and postulated that a defect in the metabolism of cystine was responsible for the disorder.[5] During the next 40 years, in spite of the reports of increased lysine in the urine of cystinuric subjects, there was little advance in our understanding of the disease. The present concepts of cystinuria emerged after the advent of paper chromatography and development of polarographic and microbiologic assays. With these methods, Yeh et al. demonstrated in 1947 that lysinuria and argininuria also occur in cystinuria,[6] and Stein found that a large quantity of ornithine was also present.[7] Subsequently, Dent et al.[8] and Arrow and Westall[9] noted that plasma levels of cystine and of dibasic amino acids were normal or low. Dent and Rose observed that cystine and the dibasic amino acids had structural similarities, i.e., two amino groups separated by four to six chemical bonds. They postulated that there was a single renal transport mechanism shared by these amino acids and proposed that this mechanism was defective or absent in cystinuria[10] (Fig. 99-1). Although defective uptake of lysine and arginine has been demonstrable in tissue slices from cystinuric subjects, cystine uptake was unimpaired, and cystine did not appear to compete with the dibasic amino acids for transport.[11]

Recent studies with rat renal cortical tubule fragments[12] and isolated brush border membrane vesicles[13] indicate that there are two transport systems for cystine, one with a high affinity that is shared with dibasic amino acids, another with low affinity that is shared with dibasic amino acids, another with low affinity that is unshared. It appears that the latter system is the only one observable during in vitro studies with cortical slices and that the results of cystine uptake experiments with slices do not reveal an important aspect of the transport for this amino acid. The data with isolated brush border membranes[13] support the formulation of Dent and Rose and suggest that cystinuria may result from defective function of a common high affinity uptake system for cystine and dibasic amino acids. This explanation for the renal defect in cystinuria is complicated, however, by the occurrence of cystine clearances exceeding creatinine clearances in cystinuric patients. This indicates that cystine secretion may contribute to the aminoaciduria.[14-16]

The intestinal defect was not recognized as promptly. Von Udranszky and Baumann in 1889 observed that cadaverine and putrescine, decarboxylation products of lysine and arginine, were present in large amounts in urine of cystinuric subjects.[17] These findings were confirmed by Loewy and Neuberg.[18] Subsequently an increase of urinary cystine excretion was reported in cystinuria in response to protein feeding, but feeding of cystine itself was not observed to increase either serum or urine cystine.[19,20] After half a century these data were finally interpreted by Milne, who had already recognized the intestinal transport defect associated with the renal aminoaciduria in Hartnup disease.[21] Milne performed experiments which demonstrated reduced intestinal absorption of the dibasic amino acids in patients with cystinuria.[22,23] His findings

have been confirmed in vitro by studies of transport in jejunal biopsies.[24-26] The question of why malabsorption of an essential amino acid does not result in more serious problems of growth and development has been answered in part by the observation that oligopeptide absorption from the intestine may account for a significant proportion of amino acid absorption.[27,28] Lysine absorption from an oligopeptide may be normal in the same cystinuric subject who has poor absorption of free lysine.

CLINICAL ASPECTS

Although cystinuria is thought to be a rare disease because of the estimated prevalence of 1 per 100,000 in Sweden[29] and 1 per 20,000 in England[30,31]; there are populations where homozygous cystinuria is a frequently inherited disorder. The prevalence in Israeli Jews of Libyan origin has been estimated to be 1 in 2500.[32] Screening programs of newborn babies show the prevalence in England to be 1 in 2000[33]; in Australia, 1 in 4000[34]; and in the United States, 1 in 15,000.[35] According to Levy,[36] who summarized the results of newborn screening, the overall prevalence is 1 in 7000, which makes cystinuria one of the most common inherited disorders. The disease occurs equally in both sexes, but males are more severely affected and have a higher mortality rate. The greater severity of the disease in males may be related to urinary tract anatomy, with a greater likelihood of urethral obstruction in males. Although clinical expression of the disease may occur in the first year of life or as late as the ninth decade, the second and third decades appear to be the peak times for expression of cystinuria. Colic, the most common presentation, may be associated with obstruction of the urinary tract, subsequent infection, and eventual loss of function. Infection, hypertension, and renal failure may occur occasionally and cause the patient first to seek medical attention. The belief that cystinuric patients are shorter than the general population[37] has not been substantiated.[38]

Cystine Stones

Both cystine stones and uric acid stones form readily in acid urine, and the two are frequently confused. However, the cystine stone, with its yellow-brown color and maple sugar crystal surface, is much firmer than uric acid and is radiopaque.[39,40] The radiopacity of cystine is due to the density of the sulfur molecules. On roentgenograms cystine stones appear smooth and are less dense than calcium stones. Cystine calculi tend to occur as staghorn or multiple recurrent stones, frequently necessitating surgery (Fig. 99-2). Calcium and/or magnesium ammonium phosphate (struvite) stones may also be formed as a result of infection secondary to cystine calculi.

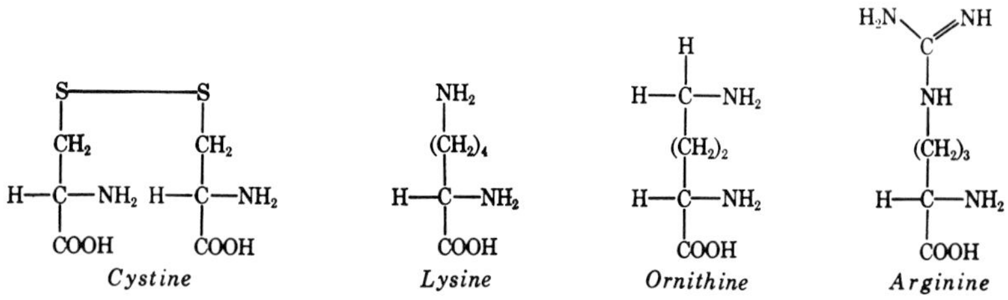

Fig. 99-1 Chemical structures of the amino acids excreted in excessive amounts in the urine in cystinuria.

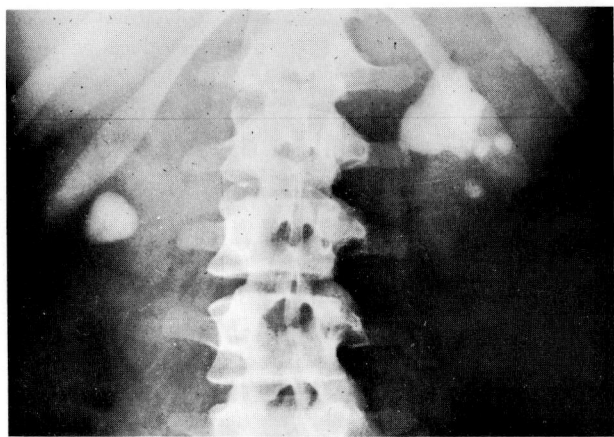

Fig. 99-2 Roentgenogram of the abdomen of a cystinuric patient showing bilateral radiopaque calculi.

DIAGNOSIS

The diagnosis of cystinuria should be entertained in every patient with urinary calculi or with urinary tract symptoms suggestive of calculi. The simplest diagnostic procedure is the microscopic examination of urinary sediment, preferably in the first voiding in the morning or other concentrated urine, for typical cystine crystals (Fig. 99-3). Acidification of a cooled concentrated urine specimen with acetic acid may precipitate cystine crystals that were not visible in a fresh urine specimen.

The cyanide-nitroprusside test has been widely applied as a chemical screening procedure.[41,42] It is important that the color obtained be compared with that of a specimen of normal urine to which cystine has been added. Since the lower limit of sensitivity of the reaction is about 75 to 125 mg/per gram of creatinine, the reaction permits easy detection of homozygous stone formers who usually excrete more than 250 mg/per gram of creatinine.[43,44] Some but not all of those heterozygotes with increased urinary cystine may also be detected by this procedure. A positive nitroprusside test may be seen in homocystinuria as well as in patients with acetonuria. Patients with crystalluria or a positive cyanide-nitroprusside test should be further studied for identification of urinary amino acids by such methods as thin-layer chromatography[45] or high-voltage electrophoresis.[46] Quantitation of cystine may be made easily following its electrolytic reduction to the thiol, which can be colorimetrically determined.[45] Quantitative ion-exchange chro-

Fig. 99-3 Cystine crystals as they appear in the urinary sediment in cystinuria.

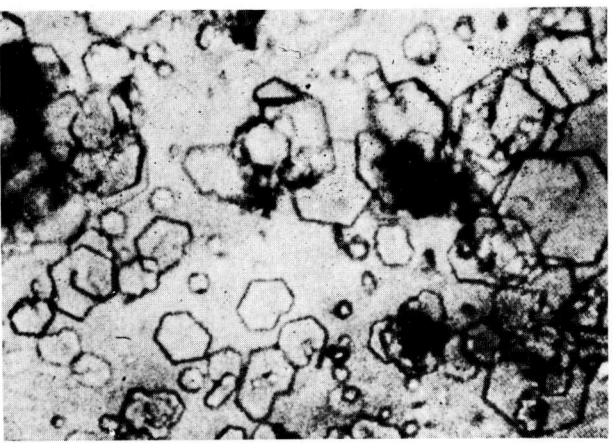

matography is the most sophisticated procedure and should be performed whenever possible.[47,48] By this method the upper limits of normal values for cystine, lysine, arginine, and ornithine in the adult are 18, 130, 16, and 22 mg per gram of creatinine, respectively.[31]

Cystinuria has been associated with hyperuricemia,[49] hemophilia,[50] retinitis pigmentosa,[51] muscular dystrophy,[52] muscular hypotonia,[53] mongolism,[54] and hereditary pancreatitis,[55] and it occurs as an isolated aminoaciduria with hypocalcemic tetany.[56] A urinary amino acid excretion pattern consistent with the cystinuric phenotype has been observed in infants with organic acidemias such as propionic,[57] methylmalonic,[58] and isovaleric acidemia.[59] In the latter instance the cystinuric pattern reverted to normal when the acute isovaleric acid toxicity state was successfully treated.

BIOCHEMISTRY OF CYSTINURIA

Consideration of cystinuria as an inborn error of metabolism by Garrod[5] was based on the assumption that an enzyme responsible for cystine catabolism was missing or defective. Although Garrod's concept of a missing enzyme in a metabolic pathway has been substantiated for the other diseases upon which his theory was based, this has not been done for cystinuria. Garrod was not truly incorrect about cystinuria, since the modern view that the disease is an inherited disorder of membrane transport supposes the genetic loss of a mechanism located in the membrane which is responsible for movement of extracellular cystine into the confines of the cell. The concept of a membrane transport mechanism involving an amino acid–binding site and genetic control is consistent with the function of a "carrier" protein. What Garrod did not anticipate was the membrane nature of the disorder and the primary involvement of the kidney and intestine.

Garrod's concept stimulated the elucidation of the transsulfuration metabolic pathway. The feeding experiments of Brand and his colleagues demonstrated that methionine[19] and proteins high in methionine[60] resulted in higher cystine excretion, since methionine is converted to cysteine and then to cystine. Feeding of cystine itself did not give rise to increased amounts of urinary cystine, but giving cysteine did.[20] This can now be interpreted on the basis of an intestinal defect in cystine absorption which does not involve cysteine (see below). The role of cystathionine as an intermediate was shown in du Vigneaud's laboratory when that compound gave rise to cystine.[61] Most recent observations have been concerned with the enzymes of the pathway in relation to homocystinuria[62] and cystathioninuria.[63] The observation that the body can convert methionine or homocystine to cystine by way of the transsulfuration pathway has relegated cystine to the position of a nonessential amino acid, but the demonstration that cystathionase is not active in fetal tissues implies that cystine may be an essential amino acid in fetal development.[64]

Relatively less seems to be known of the catabolism of cystine or cysteine to sulfate. Oxidation to cysteinesulfonate, taurine, cysteic acid, and sulfite appears to be involved (see Chap. 56).[65,66] Increased urinary sulfate excretion in cystinuric patients fed cystine may involve the oxidation of unabsorbed cystine in the gastrointestinal tract and subsequent absorption of the inorganic ion.[67]

These aspects of cystine catabolism may be more appropriately considered with regard to the human cystine storage disease, cystinosis,[68] which should not be confused with cystinuria. Although a generalized aminoaciduria is present with cystinosis, the large amounts of cystine and dibasic amino acids found with cystinuria are not found. Cystine storage disease is associated with deposition of cystine in various tissues; in cystinuria there is no tissue deposition, only urinary loss.

Of importance to a basic understanding of both human diseases involving cystine is the fact that the intracellular form of the amino acid is not the disulfide but the free thiol, cysteine.[69,70] When [^{35}S] cystine is incubated with kidney cortex slices or other tissues, the ^{35}S within the cell is mainly in cysteine or glutathione, little or none being maintained as cystine[70] (Table 99-1). Reduction of cystine to cysteine is believed to take place within the cell by a mechanism mediated by glutathione cysteine transhydrogenase[71] since cystine taken up by isolated renal brush border membrane vesicles is not reduced to the free thiol.[13]

RENAL TRANSPORT DEFECTS

Cystinuria is a classic example of a disorder of renal tubular function. In a discussion of aminoaciduria it should be kept clearly in mind that most aminoacidurias are not disorders of tubular function. Normally amino acids are filtered and are almost entirely reabsorbed in the proximal nephron. There is a maximal capacity to the reabsorptive mechanism which is exceeded in certain disorders. In most cases of aminoaciduria an extrarenal metabolic defect leads to the accumulation of an amino acid in the plasma, which is then filtered in amounts exceeding the normal capacity of the nephron for reabsorption. These are not disorders of tubular function. With normal or low plasma levels and diminished filtered loads of amino acid, if excessive loss still occurs in the urine, then the reabsorptive capacity of the tubule is said to be below normal and tubular dysfunction exists. The latter situation obtains in cystinuria. Excessive urinary losses of cystine and dibasic amino acids occur with normal or less than normal plasma levels of the affected amino acids.[8,9]

Of all amino acids studied, only cystine and the dibasic amino acids are involved in cystinuria. On the basis of this information Dent and Rose postulated a single transport mechanism shared by cystine and the dibasic amino acids which is defective in cystinuria.[10] Recent reports of clinical disorders in which cystine and dibasic aminoacidurias occur independently have complicated this interpretation and indicate that there may be separate systems for transport of cystine and lysine by the kidney tubule. Brodehl et al.[56] have found

isolated cystinuria without dibasic aminoaciduria, and Stephens and Perrett[72] reported a patient with cystine stones who had minimal dibasic aminoaciduria, a finding in many dogs with cystinuria and urolithiasis.[73] Conversely, dibasic aminoaciduria without cystinuria has been observed.[74,75] Lysinuric protein intolerance is characterized by lysinuria without cystinuria, and defective renal tubular reabsorption of lysine and competition among the dibasic amino acids have been demonstrated (see Chap. 100).[76]

Observations in Vivo

The increase in renal clearance of cystine and the dibasic amino acids reported first by Dent et al.[8] and then by Arrow and Westall[9] has also been found in more recent investigations.[77,78] Although in many patients the cystine clearance is equal to or somewhat less than the glomerular filtration rate, certain patients with cystinuria have a cystine clearance greater than glomerular filtration, with a $C_{cystine}/C_{inulin}$ ratio ranging between 1 and 2.[14–16] The clearance of lysine is usually about 50 to 70 percent of the glomerular filtration rate. Arginine and ornithine reabsorption is less defective than that of lysine.[78]

The postulate of Dent and Rose that there is a single shared transport mechanism for cystine and dibasic amino acids predicted that increasing the filtered load of one amino acid in the group should reduce the reabsorption of the others. Robson and Rose,[79] Lester and Cusworth,[77] and Kato[78] demonstrated that this was indeed true in normal humans. Similar data were derived in studies on normal dogs by Webber, Brown, and Pitts.[80] While Robson and Rose did not find that infusion of lysine increased cystine excretion by cystinuric subjects, both Lester and Cusworth[77] and Kato[78] observed such an effect on cystine, ornithine, and arginine excretion. Lester and Cusworth showed that lysine infusion caused the clearance of cystine to increase to a value greater than glomerular filtration, with a $C_{cystine}/C_{creatinine}$ ratio of 1.5 Kato[78] infused increasing amounts of arginine into three patients whose tubular reabsorption of cystine ranged from 10 to 50 percent (normal 99 percent). This reduced the cystine reabsorption to −25 percent.

A careful examination of the data of Webber, Brown, and Pitts[80] indicates that lysine infusion in a normal dog caused the cystine clearance to exceed the glomerular filtration rate. Segal and Bovee[81] have reported that infusion of lysine into cystinuric dogs can alter what appears to be a simple reabsorptive defect into cystine clearances greater than the glomerular filtration rate. The data are consistent with secretion of cystine under these conditions and raise the question of bidirectional cystine transport. The dibasic amino acid infusion data imply

Table 99-1 Intracellular Forms of ^{35}S after Incubation of Rat Kidney Cortex Slices with Labeled L-Cystine and L-Cysteine

Age of animal	Transported substrate	Concentration, mM	Intracellular form of ^{35}S as percent of intracellular ^{35}S			
			Cystine	Reduced glutathione	Cysteine	Other
5 days	Cystine	0.07	0	25	62	13
5 days	Cysteine	0.07	6	24	62	8
Adult	Cystine	0.07	0	12	68	20
Adult	Cysteine	0.07	14	20	64	8

SOURCE: From Segal and Smith.[69]

that these amino acids may not only compete with cystine for reabsorption but that by some enigmatic process they induce cystine secretion. The concept of amino acid secretion has been amply supported by experimental findings employing a variety of techniques.[82-84]

Additional studies in cystinuric patients have revealed a low renal threshold for lysine.[77] When homozygous subjects were infused with increasing amounts of lysine, they were unable to reabsorb the amino acid to any extent above the endogenous capacity until the filtered load was seven- to tenfold higher than the basal state. A further increase in the filtered load was associated with a tubular reabsorption in cystinuric patients that did not differ from the normal rate.[77] These findings are consistent with the function of dual systems for lysine transport, a low capacity system acting at low substrate concentrations which is defective in cystinurics, and a high capacity transport system predominating at high lysine levels which is unaffected. Such a dual transport system for lysine has been described in human renal cortical slices.[85] The occurrence of multiple systems for cystine and dibasic amino acids is also supported by Brodehl, who found that newborn human infants have diminished reabsorption of cystine and dibasic amino acids and that reabsorption capacity matured at different rates for each of the substrates.[86] Scriver et al.[87] have extended these observations on the urinary amino acid patterns of newborns. Of 340,000 newborns 730 had increased urinary cystine and dibasic amino acid excretion that persisted in 191. With further follow-up and matching of infants to their parental phenotypes (see "Genetics" below for explanation of types I, II, and III) it was noted that in heterozygotes but not homozygous infants, amino acid excretion fell with age to reach the level of their parental variants. With the exception of type I heterozygotes (who had clearly lower urinary amino acid levels) heterozygotes could not be differentiated from homozygotes during early infancy. These findings have important implications for genetic screening and counseling programs.

Examination of the extraction of cystine from blood flowing through the kidneys of cystinuric patients has revealed minimal arteriovenous differences[88,89] and no alteration from the normal. Assuming that total failure of tubular reabsorption of cystine accounts for cystinuria, a large arteriovenous difference for cystine should be discernible. The inability to demonstrate this has raised the possibility of cystine synthesis *de novo* or kidney protein catabolism to account for the presence of urinary cystine in the face of normal plasma extraction. Frimpter[90] has attempted to answer this by comparing the specific activity of plasma and urinary cystine after infusing [35S] cystine. The fact that these activities were the same argues against an endogenous kidney production of cystine, but it is possible that the long infusion period may have labeled the kidney pools of cystine so that the sought-for specific activity differences would not be detected.

The reduced form of cystine, cysteine, may play an important role in the underlying abnormality. Plasma cysteine in cystinuric patients is decreased proportionally more than cystine or the dibasic amino acids, but little cysteine appears in urine, and no increased conversion of cysteine to cystine has yet been demonstrated.[90,91] Frimpter,[88] having found an arteriovenous difference for cysteine but not for cystine across the kidney of a single patient, postulated that urinary cystine may be derived from plasma cysteine. Rosenberg et al.,[89] however, found no increase in cysteine extraction in two patients when compared with controls. An increase in cysteine clearance by

the kidney would seem an unlikely source of urinary cystine. The plasma level of cysteine is only about 25 percent of that of cystine, too low to explain the large amounts of urinary cystine on the basis of a total loss of filtered cysteine.

Results of microperfusion experiments with rat kidney tubules[92,93] show arginine inhibition of cystine and cysteine removal from the lumen of the tubule. Volkl and Silbernagl[94] in later microperfusion studies could not demonstrate saturability of cystine luminal uptake within the range of cystine solubility up to 0.4 mM. The fractional reabsorption rate of cystine was inhibited by a number of neutral amino acids, such as alanine, methionine, citrulline, α-aminoisobutyric acid, phenylalanine, and cycloleucine, but only methionine inhibited cysteine uptake.

Although these data suggest an interaction at the luminal membrane and the possibility of a shared transport system, it must be kept in mind that the cystine in the lumen is a resultant of fluxes and that the effect of arginine may not be a simple inhibition of uptake at the luminal membrane. Schafer and Watkins,[75] who examined unidirectional fluxes of [35S] cystine in isolated perfused segments of rabbit proximal straight tubule, found a saturable system of the lumen-to-bath flux with a K_m of 0.2 mM but a nonsaturable bath-to-lumen flux. Luminal lysine inhibited the absorptive cystine flux but did not affect bath-to-lumen flux, thus providing evidence for the absence of shared cystine-lysine transport system in the basolateral membrane.

A series of in vivo studies of lysine and cystine transport in rats attempted to demonstrate bidirectional transport by examining cellular accumulation after ureteral ligation and cessation of glomerular filtration.[96,97] The fact that cellular accumulation was maintained in the presence of ureteral ligation suggested that basolateral uptake had occurred, but this interpretation is open to question, since 1 to 2 h after ureteral obstruction in the rat the single nephron glomerular filtration rate is only slightly reduced.[99] The interaction of dibasic amino acids and cystine was also examined in the intact rat kidney.[96,97] The injection of a large amount of arginine increased the fractional excretion of lysine, while injection of a lysine load increased the excretion of cystine. An unexplained finding was that during the arginine-induced lysinuria, when less lysine would be thought to be entering the tubule cells from the lumen, the tubule cell content of radioactive lysine was greater than in cells of control rats. A similar type of result occurred during lysine-induced cystinuria, when an increase in tubule cell cysteine, the intracellular form of cystine, was noted. These increases varied with the depth of the cell from the kidney surface and were greatest in cells of the outer medulla. The significance of these observations is not clear, but they suggest a functional heterogeneity of kidney tubule cells with regard to cystine and dibasic amino acids. Schwartzman, Blair, and Segal[99] have reported that lysine inhibits cysteine efflux from renal tubule cells and have postulated an efflux system shared by lysine and cystine. An elevation of intracellular cysteine could result from an inhibition by lysine of the transfer of cysteine into the peritubular capillary at the basolateral aspect of the cell.

Observations in Vitro

Studies in vitro with slices of human renal cortex have demonstrated that the dibasic amino acids, lysine, arginine, and ornithine, share a common renal transport mechanism.[11] The ability of cortical slices from cystinuric persons to take up lysine and arginine is impaired[11] (Fig. 99-4). The cystinuric tissue has about 50 to 60 percent of the normal capacity to take up lysine. This corresponds to the reabsorptive defect observed during clearance experiments in vivo.[78] Evidence that the shared dibasic amino acid transport system is only partially defective is that the low uptake of lysine can be further suppressed by the addition of arginine. Rosenberg, Albrecht, and Segal[85] examined the concentration dependence of lysine uptake by normal and cystinuric renal cortex slices. Lineweaver-Burk plots were indicative of the presence of two distinct influx systems, one a high affinity, low capacity system and the other a low affinity, high capacity system. From the observed K_m and V_{max} parameters it appeared that the V_{max} of the high affinity, low K_m system was lower than normal. At a physiologic plasma lysine concentration of 0.1 mM the major lysine transport ability of normal renal tissue would result in the low K_m system, and that system appears to have a limited capacity in cystinuric kidney.

Neither the uptake of cystine[11] nor cysteine[100] is impaired in slices of renal cortex from cystinuric patients. Cystine and the dibasic amino acids did not appear to share a common transport system.[11] Although cysteine transport is effected by dual systems by human cortical slices,[100] only one system could be observed for cystine entry into human renal cells.[11] These unexpected findings stimulated an extensive investigation of the characteristics of cystine and dibasic amino acid transport by rat renal cortex slices, isolated tubule fragments, and brush border membrane vesicles.

Numerous experiments have been performed using kidney slice transport techniques. These clearly demonstrate that the transport systems for lysine and cystine in rat kidney cortex are not the same.[101–105] In addition to the lack of mutual inhibition between these two amino acids and their nonparticipation in heteroexchange diffusion, there are certain biochemical differences in their transport characteristics. Lysine transport is only partially dependent on the presence of sodium ion and aerobic conditions, and over a pH range of 6 to 8.5 there is little change of influx in rats.[103] Cystine transport, on the other hand, is completely dependent on sodium and oxygen and shows marked differences in influx with changes in pH, with an optimum of about pH 7.4.[104] While there is evidence for more than one lysine transport system in rat cor-

tical slices, only one system was evident for cystine, with a K_m of 0.8 mM. Kinetic studies in rat kidney cortex slices have furnished evidence, based on response to alteration of pH, temperature changes, oxygen lack, and sodium deprivation, that the kidney cystine and cysteine transport systems are different.[104] Confirmation of this supposition has come from ontogenetic studies which show a separate developmental time pattern for cystine and cysteine transport in rat kidney cortex.[70] An examination of the transport interaction of cysteine with dibasic amino acids in vitro showed no mutual inhibition of uptake.[99] Even so, incubation of cysteine with lysine causes an enhanced accumulation of the sulfur amino acid by kidney cortex.[99,102] Schwartzman, Blair, and Segal[99] have explained the lysine-enhanced accumulation of cystine by showing that the dibasic amino acids inhibit the efflux of intracellular cysteine into the incubation fluid. This interaction between the sulfur amino acids and the dibasic amino acids may have physiologic importance since the natural intracellular form is cysteine, even if cystine is the compound being transported.[69,70]

With the recent use of rat tubule fragments[12] and brush border membrane vesicles,[13,106] a more complete picture of cystine and dibasic amino acid transport in the proximal tubule has emerged. Cystine uptake by isolated cortical tubules occurred via two saturable transport systems with K_m values of 0.012 and 0.55 mM. Lysine inhibited cystine uptake via the low K_m system but appeared not to inhibit cystine uptake via the high K_m mechanism. Cystine inhibited the uptake of lysine by the tubules. Figure 99-5 shows the calculated percentages of cystine uptake mediated by the two systems present in tubule fragments at various cystine concentrations. At the concentration of about 0.05 mM present in plasma, about 50 percent would be handled by each system.[12]

With brush border membrane vesicles two comparable transport systems for cystine were demonstrated with dibasic amino acids inhibiting the low K_m high affinity system (Fig. 99-6).[13,106] Heteroexchange diffusion of lysine and cystine was demonstrated by the high affinity component.[106] In contrast to tubule fragments, where the cystine entering the cell was reduced to cysteine,[12] the intravesicular amino acid was cystine, indicating that the unreduced form was transported across the brush border membrane.[13,106] Also, unlike the findings in tubule cells where the intracellular cysteine is not bound to proteins, the intravesicular cystine became bound to the membrane. This emphasizes the importance of the intracellular

DISTRIBUTION RATIOS OF LYSINE AND ARGININE AFTER 30 MINUTES INCUBATION

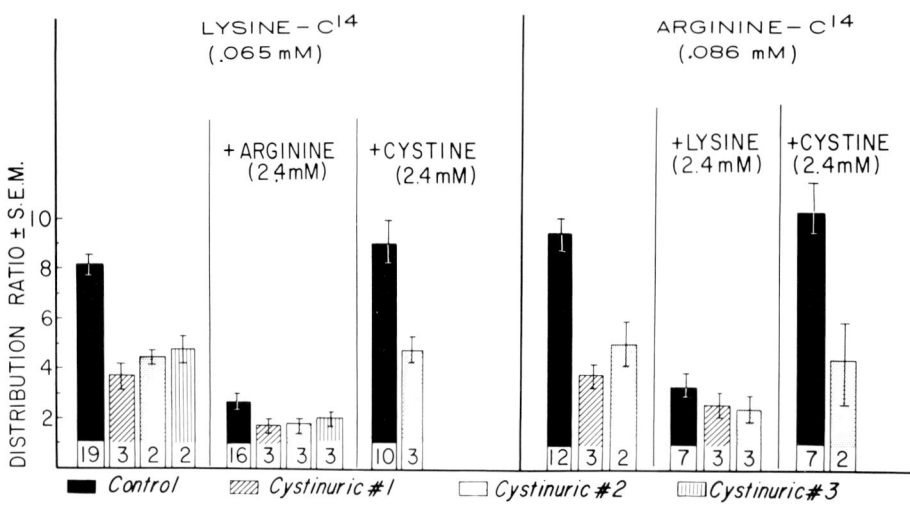

Fig. 99-4 Uptake of lysine and arginine by renal cortex slices from cystinuric and noncystinuric subjects. The distribution ratio is the ratio of radioactivity in counts per milliliter of intracellular fluid to counts per minute per milliliter of incubation media. (From data in Ref. 11)

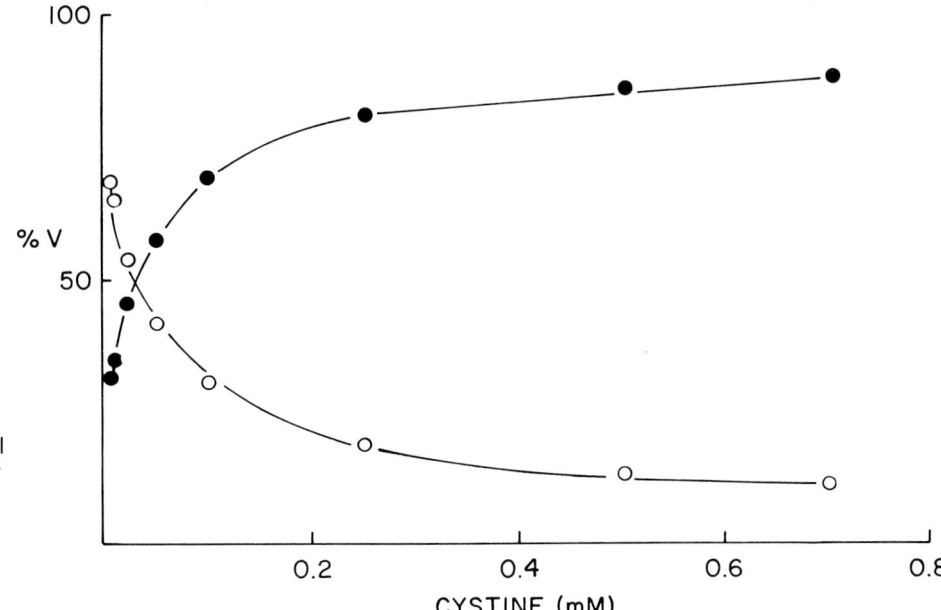

Fig. 99-5 The percentages of total velocity of cystine uptake by rat renal proximal tubules in vitro mediated by the high (closed circle) and low (open circle) K_m systems at various cystine concentrations. *(From Foreman, Hwang, and Segal.[12] Copyright 1980 by Grune & Stratton, Inc.)*

reducing process for maintaining free cysteine within the cell and this facilitates unhampered transcellular movement of the amino acid during the reabsorptive process. The renal brush border vesicle[110,111] system has been utilized to examine arginine[107–109] and lysine transport.[110,111] Rabbit vesicle lysine uptake on the basis of inhibition studies appeared to Mircheff et al.[110] to be mediated by two systems, one of which was shared with phenylalanine. On the basis of kinetic data with rat membranes McNamara et al.[112] concluded there is only one system for lysine uptake which is not dependent on sodium and shared with cystine.

The correlation of the dual cystine transport systems in tubule fragments and in brush border membrane vesicles indicates that transport across the luminal side of the proximal tubule cell can be observed when tubule fragments are studied. With renal cortical slices only one component of cystine transport is demonstrated and that corresponds to the high K_m system observed with both renal cortical tubules and brush border membrane vesicles. Since only the high K_m system is observed in slice experiments, an interaction between cystine and dibasic amino acids would not be expected; this interac-

Fig. 99-6 Concentration dependence of cystine on the initial rate of uptake by rat renal brush border membrane vesicles. Solid circles represent uptake of [14]L-cystine, and open circles show its uptake in the presence of 1 mmol/liter L-lysine. *(From Segal, McNamara, and Pepe.[13] Copyright 1977 by American Association for Advancement of Science.)*

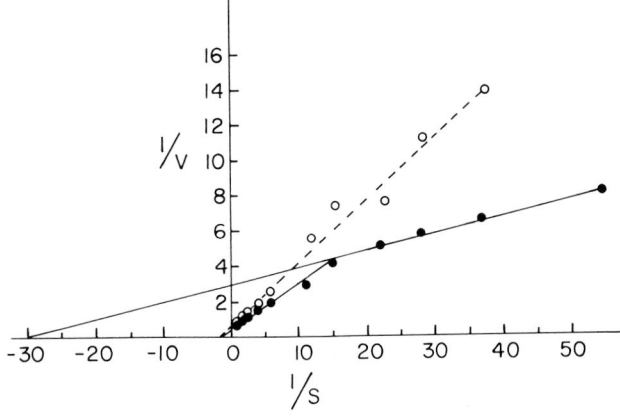

tion occurs on the low K_m shared system. Why the renal slice experiments give a broad picture of dibasic amino acid transport but only a truncated view of cystine transport is at present enigmatic. Equally enigmatic are the observations that in cultured human renal proximal tubule cells[113] and LLC-PK$_1$ cells derived from pig renal tubules[114] the cystine transport system is dissociated from that of the dibasic amino acids and becomes shared with glutamate transport. Such a cystine-glutamate exchange system has been observed in cultured human fibroblasts[115,116] and cultured rat hepatocytes.[117] An excellent review of cystine transport processes has been published by Bannai.[118]

The demonstration of a shared system for cystine and dibasic amino acids in the luminal membrane of the renal tubule cell substantiates the original hypothesis of Dent and Rose[10] that cystinuria results from defective reabsorption by a common transport process. The finding of another unshared system aids in interpreting some of the clinical observations. Figure 99-7 shows a possible model of the carrier systems in the brush border membrane for cystine and dibasic amino acids. A defective low K_m system would result in excessive amounts of cystine, lysine, arginine, and ornithine in urine, as in classic cystinuria. This is the system whose defective function has been observed in human cystinuric kidney slices when lysine was the transported substrate,[11] and which was inhibited by infusion of large amounts of lysine in humans and dogs.[77–81] Cystinuric patients, who do not have dibasic aminoaciduria, may have a defect in the high K_m unshared cystine system. Dibasic aminoaciduria without cystinuria[74,75] may be due to a defect in a dibasic transport system unshared with cystine. Remaining to be explained is the apparent secretion of cystine by some cystinuric patients[14–16] and dogs infused with lysine.[81]

URINARY EXCRETION OF OTHER AMINO ACIDS IN CYSTINURIA

Although hyperexcretion of lysine, arginine, ornithine, and cystine in the urine is the hallmark of cystinuria, other amino acids have been found in higher than normal amounts in the urine of some patients. These include glycine,[14] methionine,[119]

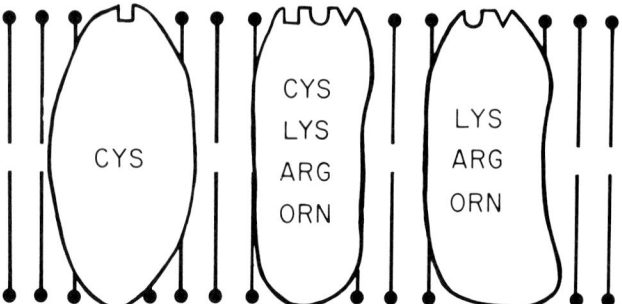

Fig. 99-7 Schematic diagram of a membrane from the renal proximal tubule cell showing the possible diversity of carrier proteins for cystine (cys), lysine (lys), arginine (arg), and ornithine (orn).

cystathionine,[120] and homocysteine-cysteine disulfide[121] (Fig. 99-8). The latter is most consistently present in variable amounts up to 224 mg/24 h,[88] the amount being related directly to the amount of cystine excreted.[122] This mixed disulfide has also been found in the urine of patients with Fanconi syndrome on the basis of Wilson disease, as well as in dogs with cystinuria.[88] Subsequently, the mixed disulfide was demonstrated in normal plasma and in increased amount in the plasma of a patient with homocystinuria.[123] Although it was thought at first to be uniquely associated with cystinuria, homocysteine-cysteine mixed dissulfide probably is a normal plasma constituent which is overexcreted because it participates in the renal tubular defect responsible for the loss of cystine.

INTESTINAL TRANSPORT DEFECTS

When an amino acid is fed, absorption occurs, and the unabsorbed amino acid will be used by the intestinal flora. The less an amino acid is absorbed, the lower the blood levels will be after feeding, and the greater will be the levels of bacterial breakdown products in the stool and perhaps also in plasma and urine. If bacterial flora are suppressed, the nonabsorbed amino acid should be demonstrable in the stool. Lysine, arginine, and ornithine are decarboxylated by bacteria in the intestine to the diamines cadaverine, agmatine, and putrescine. Piperidine is formed from lysine breakdown, and pyrrolidine from arginine and ornithine metabolism (Fig. 99-9). These heterocyclic amines are formed from the diamines. As mentioned earlier, the data suggesting an intestinal transport defect in cystinuric patients were available by the late nineteenth century, when diamines were detected in the urine of these patients.[17,18] It was only after Milne and coworkers demonstrated defective tryptophan absorption from the intestine of patients with the neutral aminoaciduria, Hartnup disease, in 1960, that the data on cystinuria were finally brought into focus.[21] Milne et al. observed increased putrescine and pyrrolidine in the urine after feeding arginine, and increased cadaverine, piperidine, and pyrrolidine after feeding lysine. Since the pyrrolidine could not have been derived from lysine, it was concluded that lysine was competitively inhibiting arginine transport in the intestine. The role of bacterial degradation in this process was proved in patients treated with oral neomycin; pyrrolidine and putrescine decreased in stool and urine, while lysine, arginine, and ornithine increased in the stool of patients so treated.[22,23] Evidence for a failure of cystine absorption was presented by Brand, Cahill, and Harris,[19] by

Dent et al.,[8] and more recently by London and Foley,[67] Rosenberg et al.,[89] and Silk et al.[124] using ion-exchange chromatography to measure plasma cystine concentration after oral loading. In all these studies cysteine absorption by cystinuria patients was not impaired.[124,125]

Double-lumen perfusion of the jejunum with low concentrations of lysine demonstrates defective dibasic amino acid transport in vivo, while in the same patient oral administration of a large dose results in a normal increase in the plasma concentration of lysine.[126] The response to a large oral dose of lysine suggests that diffusion or alternate transport routes may protect the cystinuric individuals from amino acid malnutrition. Perhaps a better explanation of why there is little evidence of dibasic amino acid malabsorption in cystinuria derives from recent studies indicating that oligopeptide transport is normal in these patients. In fact, in cystinuria administration of lysylglycine results in a greater increase in plasma lysine than equimolar feeding of free lysine plus glycine. Similarly, casein feeding produces a more rapid increase in plasma arginine and lysine than does a mixture of free amino acids derived from a casein hydrolysate.[127–131]

The concept of impaired intestinal amino acid transport derived from feeding experiments received direct confirmation by the demonstration in vitro of defective amino acid accumulation in specimens of jejunal mucosa obtained by peroral biopsy.[24–26] The results of further studies showed that there were some patients who had total impairment of cystine, lysine, and arginine accumulation, others who had small but detectable cystine transport but no dibasic amino acid transport, and still a third group who had normal or only slightly impaired cystine uptake and demonstrable but diminished lysine and arginine accumulation[132] (Fig. 99-10). Later experiments showed that intestinal mucosa from the different types of cystinuria had no impairment of cysteine accumulation in vitro.[133] This finding not only established the independence of the cystine and cysteine transport mechanism but with the results of studies of cystine uptake in vitro explained the many oral feeding experiments previously performed which showed a rise in plasma and urinary cystine after cysteine feeding but not after cystine feeding.[67,125]

Recent work suggests that in mucosal biopsy specimens from cystinuric patients there is diminished lysine permeability at the brush border membrane,[134] while in biopsied tissues of patients with lysinuric protein intolerance impaired flux of lysine exists at the basolateral membrane of the epithelial cells.[135] Measurement of cystine fluxes across intestinal biopsies suggests there is an increased efflux permeability at the luminal membrane to explain defective cystine uptake.[136]

Fig. 99-8 The structures of cystine and related compounds.

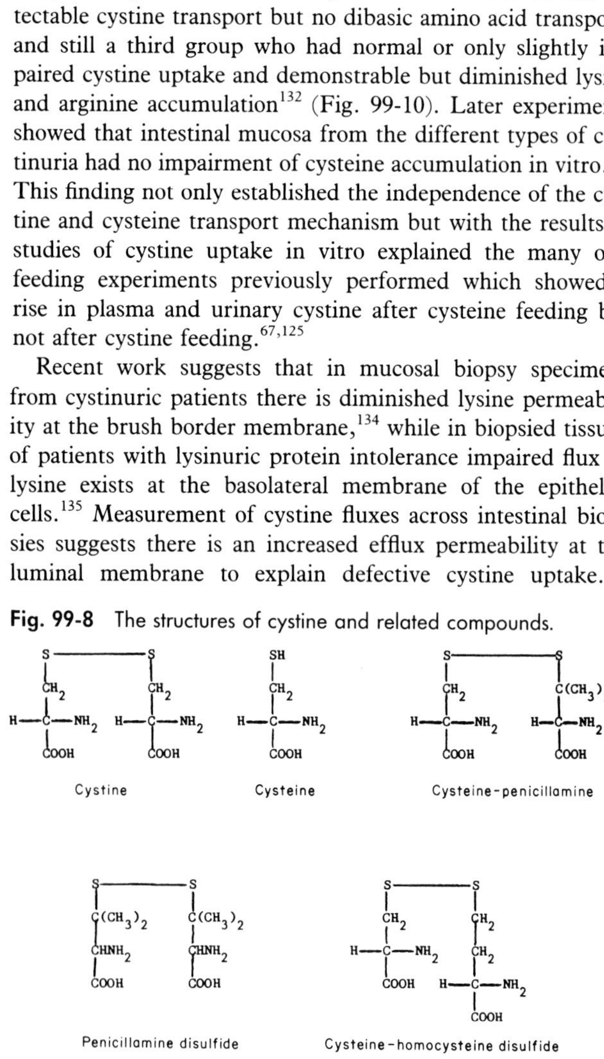

Cystine

Cysteine

Cysteine-penicillamine

Penicillamine disulfide

Cysteine-homocysteine disulfide

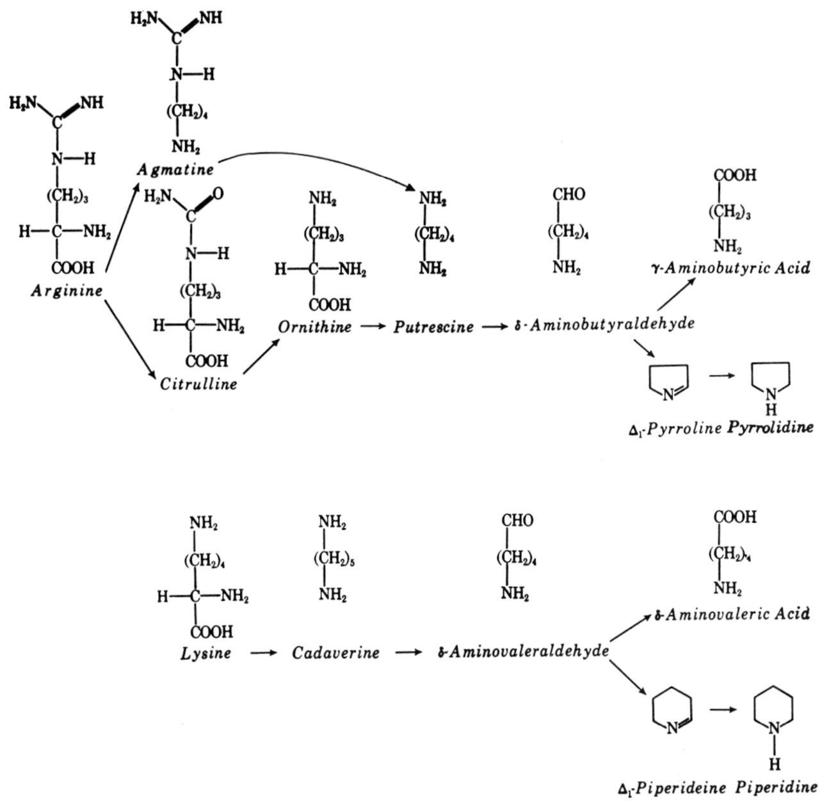

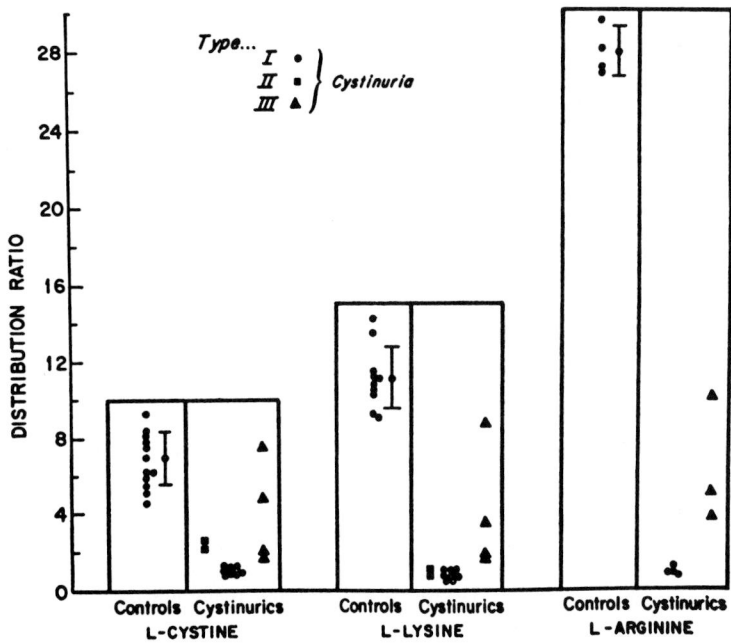

Fig. 99-9 Formation of putrescine and pyrrolidine from arginine and cadaverine and of piperidine from lysine. (After Crawhall and Watts.[30])

Since the intracellular form is cysteine and cysteine transport by biopsied mucosa is unimpaired,[133] the conclusions of Desjeux et al.[135,136] that efflux is increased await further evaluation.

Differences between the characteristics of intestinal and renal transport of lysine in vitro have been clearly demonstrated in the rat. Lysine uptake by intestinal mucosa is sodium- and oxygen-dependent and sensitive to pH changes; that by the kidney is only minimally affected by changes in sodium, oxygen, or pH.[137] Lysine[138] and cystine[139] uptake has been examined in rat intestinal brush border vesicles. A single system for cystine transport is present which is shared by lysine but other amino acids inhibit the system.[139]

Family studies of cystine excretion alone allowed differentiation of phenotypically identical cystinuric subjects into two genetically different groups.[43,140,141] Additional consideration of the intestinal mucosal transport patterns for the dibasic amino acids allows homozygous cystinuric subjects to be differentiated into three groups[132] (Table 99-2). In type I, which includes the majority of patients, there is no accumulation of either cystine or the dibasic amino acids against a gradient, and oral cystine loading fails to raise serum cystine levels (Fig. 99-11). In type II there is detectable active accumulation of cystine but no accumulation of dibasic amino acids; as in type I, oral loading fails to raise serum cystine levels. In type III accumulation of cystine and dibasic amino acids does occur

Fig. 99-10 Uptake of cystine, lysine, and arginine by jejunal mucosa from control and cystinuric subjects expressed as the distribution ratio, i.e., the ratio of radioactive amino acid inside the cell to that in the medium, after a 45-min incubation. (From Rosenberg, Downing, Durant, and Segal.[132])

Table 99-2 Classification of Cases of Cystinuria

Experimental observations	Type I	Type II	Type III
Intestine:			
In vitro transport	No transport of cystine, lysine, or arginine; normal cysteine transport	No transport of lysine; markedly reduced cystine transport	Transport of cystine reduced but may be normal; lysine variably reduced
Oral cystine administration	No plasma cystine elevation	No plasma cystine elevation	Slow increase in plasma cystine to normal elevation
Kidney:			
In vitro transport cortical slices	Reduced lysine transport		Reduced lysine transport
Urinary amino acid excretion	Increased cystine, lysine, arginine, ornithine excretion	Increased cystine, lysine, arginine, ornithine excretion	Increased cystine, lysine, arginine, ornithine excretion
Urinary amino acid excretion in heterozygotes	Normal	Cystine and lysine above normal	Cystine and lysine above normal

but not to the normal extent; oral cystine loading results in normal elevation of plasma cystine levels.

In an elegant study in which urinary excretion of amino acids, renal clearances, intestinal biopsies, and oral cystine loading were performed, Morin et al.[16] obtained data confirming the existence of types I and II cystinuria. They found no patients, however, with a condition corresponding to type III. Disorders suggestive of type III were found in persons produced by the mating of heterozygous carriers of type I and type II. The family studies based on this separation will be discussed under "Genetics."

The results of intestinal transport studies in vitro fit the postulate of Dent and Rose that cystine and dibasic amino acids share a common transport system. In the intestinal mucosa there is evidence of only a single shared system which in many patients is completely defective in its function.[26,132] That system corresponds to the low K_m high affinity shared component recently demonstrated in renal brush border membranes.[13,106] An important difference is that lysine transport by the cystinuric kidney is only partially impaired.[11] Although this intestinal defect may be of little clinical importance, it has served as an extremely sensitive genetic marker and has paved the way for a new genetic classification of cystinuria. The lack of amino acid transport defects in circulating leukocytes of cystinuric patients has precluded their usefulness for discerning genetic aspects of the disease.[142]

CYSTINURIA AND THE CENTRAL NERVOUS SYSTEM

There have been numerous reports of an association of cystinuria with central nervous system abnormalities. Scriver et al.[143] reported an increase in the prevalence of cystinuria in a group of mentally disturbed patients, and there have been reports of cystinuria patients with spastic paraplegia[144–146] Mental retardation has been described occasionally in homozygous patients,[147] but testing of a large group of homozygous cystinuric patients for mental deficiency did not reveal an increased prevalence.[148] Smith and Procopis[149] reported a 13 times higher incidence of heterozygous cystinuric subjects than would have been expected in a population of retarded persons in New South Wales, but no instances of homozygous cystinuria were detected. A pertinent question has been whether cystinuric patients are at a greater risk for cerebral dysfunction because there might be defective transport into the brain for an essential amino acid like lysine, or cystine in the neonatal

period,[64] as has been demonstrated in the intestine or kidney of affected subjects.

The relationship of cystine, cysteine, and lysine transport by isolated rat brain synaptosomes has been examined.[150–152] Dual systems for their uptake were described, but there was no inhibition of either mechanism of cystine entry by dibasic amino acids. Cysteine uptake was only slightly inhibited by lysine but was strongly affected by glycine. The low K_m lysine transport system was shared by other dibasic amino acids but not by cystine, as it is in the kidney or intestines. The uptake of cystine by isolated rat brain capillaries appeared to be independent of dibasic amino acid transport.[153] All the findings in vitro indicate that the systems for entry of these amino acids to brain differ from those of kidney and intestine and make it unlikely that cystinuric subjects are at risk because of transport abnormalities in the central nervous system.

GENETICS

An understanding of the genetics of cystinuria depends on a clear definition of the phenotypically homozygous state. This state is suggested by (1) the excretion of over 250 mg cystine per gram of creatinine, often with formation of urinary calculi, and (2) the presence of an intestinal absorptive defect for cystine and the dibasic amino acids. In the first large-scale genetic studies, Harris and coworkers divided cystinuria into two groups in which phenotypically homozygous subjects were in-

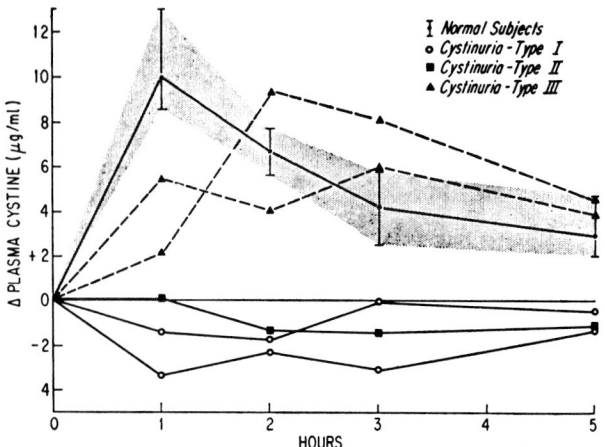

Fig. 99-11 The change of plasma cystine levels after oral cystine administration of 0.5 μmol/kg. (From Rosenberg, Downing, Durant, and Segal.[132])

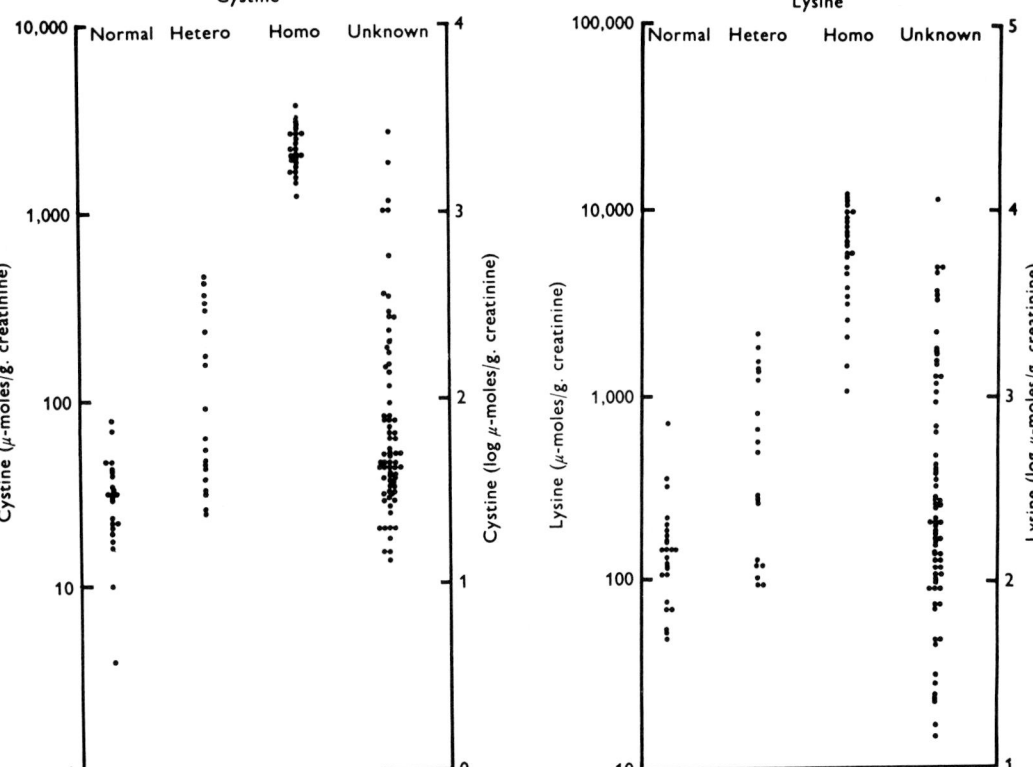

Fig. 99-12   The excretion of cystine and lysine by normal subjects, patients with cystinuria, heterozygotes for cystinuria, and relatives of cystinuric patients. *(From Crawhall, Purkiss, Watts, and Young.[31])*

distinguishable.[141] In one group the disease was transmitted as a true recessive trait; no family members other than the homozygous individual had aminoaciduria. The second group was designated as incompletely recessive; family members frequently excreted excessive amounts of cystine and lysine, although significantly less than homozygotes. The heterozygous incompletely recessive cystinuric subject did not form stones. On the basis of variable patterns of amino acid excretion in homozygous cystinuric patients Harris and Robson[154] postulated that this group might be under polygenic influences. The exhaustive analysis by Crawhall et al. of urinary cystine, lysine, and arginine excretions by cystine stone formers, their parents, other relatives, and normal persons seems to support this view.[31] After examination of many kindreds these workers emphasized the wide disparities among the amounts of individual amino acids excreted by different heterozygous and homozygous individuals (Figs. 99-12 and 99-13). Thus it appears that multiple genetic factors influence the quantities of the various amino acids excreted in the urine and the final phenotypic expression.

The availability of jejunal mucosa led to the recognition that more than one pattern of cystine and dibasic amino acid transport could be recognized in homozygotes, and that these patterns correlated with different modes of inheritance, as suggested by Harris. Homozygotes can now be differentiated without recourse to family studies. The pattern of jejunal mucosal transport discussed above under "Intestinal Transport Defects" is summarized in Table 99-2. Note that three classes of cystinuria may now be developed and that the last two were combined in the incompletely recessive group II of Harris.

With the ability to separate homozygous cystinuric subjects into distinct groups based on intestinal transport, Rosenberg restudied the families of these individuals and found distinc-

tive urinary amino acid patterns.[155] First-degree relatives of type I patients had no abnormal urinary amino acid excretion. Type II and type III heterozygous individuals excreted excessive amounts of cystine and the dibasic amino acids in their urine, and could be distinguished from each other. The quantities excreted were consistently higher in type II heterozygotes. Morin et al.,[16] on the other hand, in their study of the urinary amino acid excretion of cystinuric families, did not encounter more than two patterns in heterozygotes. The patterns of excretion that Rosenberg, Durant, and Albrecht[155] considered to indicate type III heterozygotes correspond to that of type I and type II compound heterozygotes (offspring of the mating of type I and type II carriers) found by Morin et al.[16]

The presence of at least three distinct genetic types raised the question of whether cystinuria represented a group of diseases with defects in separate steps of amino acid transport, or different defects in the same genetically controlled step; i.e., were the different types the result of nonallelic or allelic mutations? The results of matings between type I and type II or III heterozygous individuals could provide an answer. If the defects were allelic, a fully expressed homozygous state (a better term is "genetic compound") might appear in the offspring. If the defects were in separate genes, then only the expressed heterozygous state should appear in the offspring. The fact that "homozygous" children were found suggested that the defects were allelic.[156,157] Although studies in vitro of intestinal transport have defined what seem to be three phenotypes,[126] it should be pointed out that within the third type the cystine uptake by mucosal biopsies ranges from normal to an impairment almost as severe as in the first type (Fig. 99-10). The third type may be an expression of an even greater multiplicity of genetic factors involved in the intestinal transport phenotype.

Thus cystinuria is defined as a genetic disorder with a complex recessive mode of inheritance resulting from allelic mu-

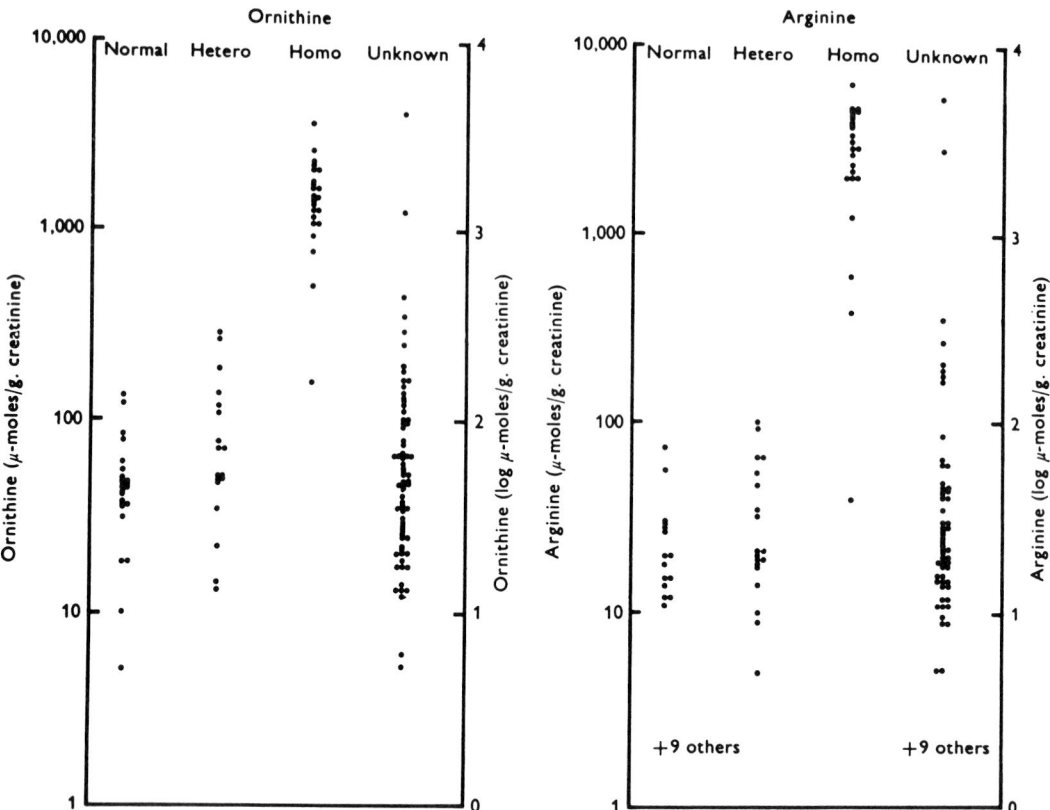

Fig. 99-13 The excretion of arginine and ornithine by normal subjects, cystinuric patients, heterozygotes for cystinuria, and relatives of cystinuric patients. *(From Crawhall, Purkiss, Watts, and Young.[31])*

tations. At least some of the mutations may be expressed in the heterozygous state, both as an aminoaciduria and in type II and III heterozygotes as an increased risk factor for stone formation.[158] The most sensitive means for differentiating the three types of homozygous cystinuric subjects is the study of the intestinal transport of cystine and the dibasic amino acids in vitro. Similar differentiation can be attempted from studies of urinary amino acid excretion in families of cystinuric subjects. This approach is neither as sensitive nor as direct as the study of transport in vitro.

ANIMAL MODELS OF CYSTINURIA

Several animal models have been suggested for the study of cystinuria. As a result of studies of amino acid excretion patterns of animals in the London Zoo, Harris thought that the blotched genet excreted large amounts of cystine.[159] The genet appeared to be unique in that "cystine" was excreted without the dibasic amino acids, and was excreted in concentrations far greater than would ordinarily remain in solution. Crawhall and Segal subsequently demonstrated that the genet excretes not cystine, but the far more soluble sulfur amino acid, S-sulfo-L-cysteine.[160] There is in fact no abnormality of cystine transport in the genet, and this apparent animal model must be discarded.

In 1956 a male mink with large numbers of apparently pure cystine stones was reported. This was a ranch mink on a higher than usual protein intake but otherwise unremarkable.[161] The presence of cystinuria in an animal group already carefully bred and therefore easily studied bears further inves-

tigation, but at present little further information is available.

Canine cystinuria represents potentially the most useful model for study. Although cystine stones in dogs were described as early as 1823, it was not until Brand and Cahill bred a group of Irish terriers with cystinuria that any systematic observations were made.[162–166] The expression of cystinuria corresponded to a sex-linked inheritance pattern. As in human beings, their animals responded with rises in cystine excretion after methionine feeding, and had no change after cystine feeding. Most, if not all, canine cystinuria has appeared in males. Though this may be due to the narrow urethra of male dogs, which brings stone production to clinical attention, amino acid chromatography has not revealed the disease in females to date.

The exact amino acid excretion pattern in canine cystinuria is not clear. Isolated cystinuria, cystinuria plus lysinuria, and the full pattern of cystine and all dibasic amino acids appearing in excess in the urine have been reported.[73,167,170] An intestinal defect in amino acid transport has been postulated.[171]

Recent application of transport techniques in vitro to both intestinal and kidney biopsies of cystine stone-forming dogs has disclosed a defect neither in cystine nor in lysine accumulation by either tissue.[73] The absence of a demonstrable lysine transport defect in these dog tissues is unlike the findings in human biopsies, while the absence of a cystine transport defect is consistent with findings in human beings. It would appear that canine cystinuria is a heterogeneous entity. The presence of large amounts of cystine in the urine of these dogs makes this strain an excellent model for evaluating the nature of hyperexcretion of cystine. Clearance studies have been performed on a group of cystinuric and control dogs.[81,172] What emerges is a striking cystinuria accompanied by variable degrees of dibasic aminoaciduria. The dibasic aminoaciduria does not correlate well with the degree of cystinuria. The extent of the cystinuria is variable and may reach clearances twice creatinine clearance, documenting the secretion of cystine. Infusion of lysine into cystinuric dogs may cause secretion of cystine.[81] Plasma concentrations of the cystine precursor methionine were elevated and correlated with plasma cystine levels and with fractional reabsorption of cystine. These observations suggest that canine cystinuria may be a metabolic disorder associated with cystine secretion. The cystinuric dog is also an excellent model for assessment of therapeutic approaches for decreasing the amounts of urinary cystine in human beings. To date, fluid intake, alkalinization, and D-penicillamine have all been observed to alter the clinical course favorably.[173]

Cystinuria has also been found in the maned wolf of Brazil.[174] Eighty percent of these wolves tested in zoos in the United States and abroad as well as animals whose urine was collected in the Brazilian jungle are affected. Several animals are known to have died in zoos because of cystine stones and urinary tract obstruction. Amino acid clearance studies in five affected wolves revealed variable cystine reabsorptive defects. In one animal there was evidence for secretion not only of cystine but of lysine, arginine, and ornithine as well.

One human experimental model has been described by Brown.[175] He produced increased urinary excretion of several amino acids (principally cystine, lysine, ornithine, and arginine) in amounts similar to homozygous cystinuria in patients fed the nonmetabolizable amino acid, cycloleucine. The rat also shows this response to cycloleucine administration.[176] Holtzapple et al.[177] have shown that cycloleucine is a competitive inhibitor of the transport of both neutral and dibasic amino acid by slices of human kidney cortex. Craan and Bergeron[93] have performed microperfusion experiments with rat renal tubules and have found that cycloleucine inhibits the reabsorption of both cystine and lysine.

Perhaps the most common animal model is the cystinuria that occurs in the neonatal rat[178] and dog[179] as well as in the human.[180] In vitro studies of cystine uptake by isolated dog renal tubules show diminished cellular influx of cystine.[179] The comparable experiments with rat tubules show no impairment of uptake[178] which may mean different mechanisms underlie the neonatal cystinuria.

TREATMENT

Were it not for the insolubility of cystine, cystinuria would be a metabolic oddity of no clinical significance except under conditions of critical limitation of protein intake. Therefore treatment is designed to reduce excretion and increase the solubility of cystine. Therapeutic approaches may be divided into three categories: (1) dietary restriction aimed at reducing cystine production and excretion, (2) attempts to increase cystine solubility, and (3) attempts to convert cystine to a more soluble compound. Surgical therapy can be divided into three categories: (1) attempts to dissolve cystine calculi by irrigation, (2) removal of cystine stones by lithotripsy or lithomony, and (3) renal transplantation to replace kidneys destroyed by cystinuria.

Dietary Therapy

Cystine production arises from the essential amino acid methionine. Numerous attempts have been made to design diets low in methionine, yet adequate for nutritional purposes. The results of use of such diets are extremely variable. Disappearance of cystinuria while the patient was on one of these diets has been reported by some investigators, whereas others have been unable to demonstrate any significant reduction in urinary cystine with careful methionine restriction.[181,182] The amount of sulfur amino acids in the diet of rats does not alter the transport of cystine by isolated membrane vesicles.[183] It is probably reasonable to avoid excessive methionine intake, but it is clear that discomforting diets are not indicated. High sodium intake will increase urinary amino acid excretion in patients with cystinuria. While it is not clear that severe sodium restriction is beneficial, it seems prudent to avoid sodium intakes of over 100 mg/day.[184]

Alteration of Cystine Solubility

At urinary pH values below 7.5 about 300 mg cystine per liter of urine will be in solution. Increasing urine volume provides a progressive reduction in urinary cystine concentration and reduces the likelihood of precipitation. Some reports of stone dissolution on high fluid intake programs have appeared.[185] Many cystinuric subjects excrete in the range of 1 g cystine per day and will require a fluid intake of 4 or more liters per day. Cystine solubility can also be enhanced by providing an alkaline pH, but the solubility does not increase significantly until the pH is above 7.5 (Fig. 99-14). Since the maximum urine pH which can be achieved is about 8, there is little leeway in the alkalinizing program. Administration of bicarbonate, citrate, and carbonic anhydrase inhibitors has been advocated for improving solubility, but while theoretically reasonable, it is not clear that much practical benefit occurs. Since varying physical factors, high fluid intake, and alkalinization are logical and simple, they should be included in the first therapeutic program in all cystinuric subjects. In considering high fluid intake therapy, Dent and Senior[186] pointed out the importance of preventing supersaturation of urine with cystine at night when urine flow is low. The intake of two glasses of water at bedtime repeated at 2 or 3 A.M. is recommended. Dent et al.[185] found hydration therapy to be successful in preventing stone formation in about two-thirds of patients who adhered to it, during a 10-year study. Their therapeutic hydration regimen is well outlined in their paper.

Fig. 99-14 The solubility of cystine in relation to urinary pH. (*From Dent and Senior.*[186])

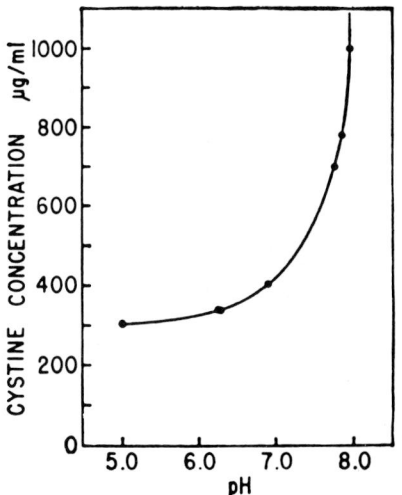

Conversion of Cystine to a More Soluble Compound

Penicillamine. In spite of the best and most controlled therapeutic efforts, some patients with cystinuria will repeatedly form and pass stones, and a significant number will require surgery for relief of urinary tract obstruction. For those who were apparently not helped by diet, fluid, and alkalinization, there was little to be done until Crawhall, Scowen, and Watts introduced the use of D-penicillamine (ββ-dimethylcysteine). Through a disulfide exchange reaction, this drug can produce the mixed disulfide of cysteine-penicillamine, which is significantly more soluble than cystine[187,188] (Fig. 99-8). On adequate penicillamine therapy, usually 1 to 2 g/24 h, cystine excretion may be kept below 200 mg/g creatinine, a level at which stone formation is minimal. The reduction of urinary cystine does not appear to be balanced by the amount of cysteine which is combined with penicillamine into the cysteine-penicillamine mixed disulfide. The total molar amount of half-cystine excreted on penicillamine therapy, i.e., the sum of cystine plus the cysteine moiety of the mixed disulfide, is much less than prior to drug treatment. This plus the reduction of plasma cystine levels by the drug suggests another biochemical effect of penicillamine besides disulfide exchange.[189-191] In contrast to the results on cystinuric subjects, the total molar amount of half-cystine in urine of normal individuals given penicillamine is greatly increased.[189] This finding has not been satisfactorily explained.

Although strikingly effective in preventing and dissolving cystine stones,[192,193] penicillamine has certain undesirable side effects. As many as 50 percent of patients receiving the drug will develop allergic reactions, usually fever and rash; rarely arthralgias appear.[189] More severe reactions include development of a nephrotic syndrome[194-196] and of pancytopenia.[197] Proteinuria of more than 500 mg/24 h occurs after several months of therapy in approximately one-third of patients treated with penicillamine. The proteinuria almost invariably clears when the drug is discontinued but usually recurs when the drug is started again.[198] Epidermolysis,[199-201] thrombocytosis,[202] and loss of taste (hypogeusia) have also been reported.[203] The hypogeusia may be reversed by copper.[204] The chelating property of penicillamine is responsible for increased copper and zinc excretion in the urine. It also has less significant effects on calcium, mercury, and iron excretion.[205-207] Part of the increase in copper excretion is independent of chelation[207] and is as yet unexplained. In addition, a possible problem resulting from inhibition of pyridoxine should be recognized and treated with supplemental pyridoxine phosphate. The possible reaction of penicillamine with pyridoxine to form a thiazolidine led to studies demonstrating a reduced pyridoxal effect in patients on penicillamine therapy (increased kynurenic acid excretion).[208] The hypogeusia may also be reversed by the administration of pyridoxine.[209,210] No interference with growth is seen in children, and pregnancies have been successfully completed in women receiving the drug.[193,211] Most recently the disturbing association of penicillamine therapy with a fatal Goodpasture-like syndrome has been reported.[212]

In view of the drawbacks of D-penicillamine therapy, its use should be restricted to patients in whom more conservative therapy has failed or who have lost one kidney from cystine stone disease. Therapy should be started in the hospital in order to monitor reactions of hypersensitivity. In those patients initially sensitive to the drug, adequate results have been obtained by readministering the medication in gradually increasing doses over a period of 1 to 2 months. A related compound, N-acetyl-D-penicillamine, has been developed which is effective in disulfide formation and thus in reducing cystine content; this compound appears to have fewer side effects, perhaps because of the unavailability of an amino group for chemical reaction.[31,213,215] Cross-sensitivity between penicillamine and penicillin has not been a problem.

Mercaptopropionylglycine. Another drug which may be of interest for therapy is mercaptopropionylglycine (MPG), which Timmerman et al.[216] suggested would be useful in dissolving renal calculi by renal pelvic perfusion. King first reported the use of MPG in cystinuria.[217] Subsequently a number of reports from Japan,[218-220] Germany,[231] and Greece[222] have suggested that oral MPG may substitute for penicillamine in the treatment of cystinuria. MPG has a higher oxidation-reduction potential than penicillamine and may be even more effective in a disulfide exchange reaction leading to the production of a mixed disulfide and cysteine. MPG has a mechanism of action similar to penicillamine and has been effective in cystinuria. Side effects have included skin rash, fever, nausea, and soft feces but not serious hematologic, hepatic, or renal toxicity. It is not known whether MPG will be tolerated by patients sensitive to penicillamine. Side effects have included skin rash, fever, proteinuria, nausea, and soft feces but not serious hematologic or hepatic toxicity. In controlled trials, MPG appears to be at least as effective as D-penicillamine. In a group of patients with a high incidence of untoward reactions to D-penicillamine approximately one-third will have serious reactions to MPG. The other two-thirds will be able to take MPG, though some will have tolerable side effects.[223] At present MPG is available on an experimental basis in the United States.

Captopril, a sulfhydryl compound, is an angiotensin-converting enzyme inhibitor that is effective as an antihypertensive agent. In two patients, captopril at a dose of 150 mg/day and 75 mg/day reduced cystine excretion by 70 and 93 percent. The fall in cystine excretion occurred over a period of several weeks and was greater than could be explained by the conversion of cystine to the far more soluble mixed disulfide of cysteine-captopril. (The mixed disulfide is approximately 200 times more soluble than cystine.) Questions remain about the predictability of the captopril effect, how well it can be sustained, and whether captopril will be tolerated by those with allergic reactions to D-penicillamine or MPG.[224]

Pharmacologic Reduction of Cystine Excretion

Glutamine administered orally or intravenously has been reported to reduce cystine excretion in cystinuria. The original report documented the effectiveness of glutamine in a single patient from Japan.[225] Subsequent studies from the United States failed to demonstrate reduced cystine excretion in patients receiving glutamine orally[226] or intravenously.[227]

Jaeger et al.[184] have clarified some of the confusion about glutamine. In patients with cystinuria enhanced by a high sodium intake, glutamine will lower cystine excretion to that seen on a low sodium intake. In patients on a low sodium intake, glutamine has no effect on cystine excretion. Thus, glutamine appears to have no therapeutic benefit beyond what can be achieved by avoiding a high sodium intake. The physiological significance of the glutamine-sodium-cystine interaction remains to be elucidated. Diazepoxide has been reported to reduce cystine-crystalluria.[228] Whether this drug directly alters cystine solubility is not known, but it bears further investigation.

Surgical Approaches

Catheter Irrigation. Reports of dissolution of cystine stones by irrigation of the urinary tract by ureteral catheters placed through supercutaneous nephrostomy have been encouraging.[229–231] Irrigation with alkaline solutions of N-acetylpenicillamine, D-penicillamine, and tromethamine has proved successful in dissolving cystine calculi in 1 week to several months. Although infection may be a complication, if this therapeutic approach is successful, surgery should be avoided.

Lithotripsy. The introduction of extracorporeal lithotripsy has not been of great benefit to patients with cystinuria. Cystine stones may be fractured for easier dissolution with alkalinizing solutions, but they are not as readily pulverized as other stones. Percutaneous lithotripsy is more effective, though cystine stones are still among those most resistant to disintegration. Nonetheless, the need for muscle-splitting lithotomy has been almost eliminated.[232,233]

Lithotomy. Surgical removal of obstructing stones or stones causing intractable pain remains a necessary form of treatment for the rare patient with cystinuria. Correct diagnosis, more effective medical treatment, and the judicious use of lithotripsy and/or irrigation should nearly eliminate the need for repeated lithotomies.

Transplantation. Occasionally cystinuria will cause sufficient renal injury to lead to chronic renal failure. In these rare circumstances renal transplantation may be effective. Since the defect in cystinuria resides in the transport epithelium of the genetically affected person, a kidney from a noncystinuric donor should remain disease-free. Normal amino acid excretion has been documented as long as 3½ years after transplantation for cystinuria.[234]

Supported by Grant AM 10894 from the National Institutes of Health.

REFERENCES

1. WOLLASTON WH: On cystic oxide: A new species of urinary calculus. *Trans R Soc London* 100:223, 1810.
2. NOEHDEN GH: Scientific notices—chemistry, cystic oxide—communicated in a letter from Dr. Noehden to Mr. Children. *Ann Philos* 7:146, 1824.
3. BERZELIUS JJ: Calculus urinaries. *Traite Chem* 7:424, 1833.
4. FRIEDMAN E: Der Kreislauf des Schwefels in der organischen Natur. *Ergebn Physiol* 1:15, 1902.
5. GARROD AE: Inborn errors of metabolism. *Lancet* 2, 1908. (Lecture I, p. 1; Lecture II, p 73; Lecture III, p 142; Lecture IV, p 214).
6. YEH HL, FRANKL W, DUNN MS, PARKER P, HUGHER B, GYORGY P: The urinary excretion of amino acids by a cystinuric subject. *Am J Med Sci* 214:507, 1947.
7. STEIN WH: Excretion of amino acids in cystinuria. *Proc Soc Exp Biol Med* 78:705, 1951.
8. DENT CE, SENIOR B, WALSHE JM: The pathogenesis of cystinuria. II. Polarographic studies of the metabolism of sulphur-containing aminoacids. *J Clin Invest* 33:1216, 1954.
9. ARROW VK, WESTALL RG: Amino acid clearances in cystinuria. *J Physiol* 142:141, 1958.
10. DENT CE, ROSE GA: Amino acid metabolism in cystinuria. *Q J Med* 20:205, 1951.
11. FOX M, THIER S, ROSENBERG LE, KISER W, SEGAL S: Evidence against a single renal transport defect in cystinuria. *N Engl J Med* 270:556, 1964.
12. FOREMAN JW, HWANG SM, SEGAL S: Transport interactions of cystine and dibasic amino acids in isolated rat renal tubules. *Metabolism* 29:53, 1980.
13. SEGAL S, MCNAMARA PD, PEPE LM: Transport interaction of cystine and dibasic amino acids in renal brush border vesicles. *Science* 197:169, 1977.
14. FRIMPTER GW, HORWITH M, FURTH E, FELLOWS RE, THOMPSON DD: Inulin and endogenous amino acid renal clearances in cystinuria: Evidence for tubular secretion. *J Clin Invest* 41:281, 1962.
15. CRAWHALL JC, SCOWEN EF, THOMPSON CJ, WATTS RWE: The renal clearance of amino acids in cystinuria. *J Clin Invest* 46:1162, 1967.
16. MORIN CL, THOMPSON MW, JACKSON SH, SASS-KORTSAK A: Biochemical and genetic studies in cystinuria: Observations on double heterozygotes of genotype I/II. *J Clin Invest* 50:1961, 1971.
17. von UDRANSZKY L, BAUMANN E: Ueber das Vorkommen von Diaminen, sogenannten Ptomainen, bei Cystinurie. *Z Physiol Chem* 13:562, 1889.
18. LOEWY A, NEUBERG C: Über Cystinurie. *Z Physiol Chem* 43:338, 1904.
19. BRAND E, CAHILL GF, HARRIS MM: Cystinuria. II. The metabolism of cysteine, methionine and glutathione. *J Biol Chem* 109:69, 1935.
20. BRAND E, CAHILL GF: Further studies on metabolism on sulfur compounds in cystinuria. *Proc Soc Exp Biol Med* 31:1247, 1934.
21. MILNE MD, CRAWFORD MA, GIRAO CB, LOUGHRIDGE LW: The metabolic disorder in Hartnup disease. *Q J Med* 29:407, 1960.
22. MILNE MD, ASATOOR AM, EDWARDS KDG, LOUGHRIDGE LW: The intestinal absorption defect in cystinuria. *Gut* 2:323, 1961.
23. ASATOOR AM, LACEY BW, LONDON DR, MILNE MD: Amino acid metabolism in cystinuria. *Clin Sci* 23:285, 1962.
24. THIER S, FOX M, SEGAL S, ROSENBERG LE: Cystinuria: In vitro demonstration of an intestinal transport defect. *Science* 143:482, 1964.
25. MCCARTHY CF, BORLAND JL, LYNCH HJ, OWEN EE, TYOR MPL: Defective uptake of basic amino acids and L-cystine by intestinal mucosa of patients with cystinuria. *J Clin Invest* 43:1518, 1964.
26. THIER S, SEGAL S, FOX M, BLAIR A, ROSENBERG LE: Cystinuria: Defective intestinal transport of dibasic amino acids and cystine. *J Clin Invest* 44:442, 1965.
27. HELLIER MD, PERRETT D, HOLDSWORTH CD: Dipeptide absorption in cystinuria. *Br Med J* 4:782, 1970.
28. SILK DBA: Progress report—peptide absorption in man. *Gut* 15:494, 1974.
29. BOSTROM H, HAMBRAEUS L: Cystinuria in Sweden. VII. Clinical histopathological and medico-social aspect of the disease. *Acta Med Scand* suppl 411, 1, 1964.
30. CRAWHALL JC, WATTS RWE: Cystinuria. *Am J Med* 45:736, 1968.
31. CRAWHALL JC, PURKISS P, WATTS RWE, YOUNG EP: The excretion of amino acids by cystinuric patients and their relatives. *Ann Hum Genet* 33:149, 1969.
32. WEINBERGER A, SPERLING O, RABINOVITZ M, BROSH S, ADAM A, De VRIES A: High frequency of cystinuria among Jews of Libyan origin. *Hum Hered* 24:568, 1974.
33. WOOLF LI: Large-scale screening for metabolic disease in the newborn in Great Britain, in Anderson JA, Swaiman KF (eds): *Phenylketonuria and Allied Metabolic Disorders.* U.S. Department of Health, Education and Welfare (Children's Bureau), Washington, 1967, pp 50–59.
34. TURNER B, BROWN DA: Amino acid excretion in infancy and early childhood: A survey of 200,000 infants. *Med J Aust* 1:62, 1972.
35. LEVY HL, SHIH VE, MADIGAN PM: Massachusetts metabolic disorders screening program. I. Technics and results of urine screening. *Pediatrics* 49:825, 1971.
36. LEVY HL: Genetic screening, in Harris H, Hirschhorn K (eds): *Advances in Human Genetics.* New York, Plenum, 1973, vol 4, p 1.
37. COLLIS JE, LEVI AJ, MILNE MD: Stature and nutrition in cystinuria and Hartnup disease. *Br Med J* 1:590, 1963.
38. SMITH A, YU JS, BROWN DA: Childhood cystinuria in New South Wales. *Arch Dis Child* 54:676, 1979.
39. RENANDER A: The roentgen density of the cystine calculus. *Acta Radiol* suppl 41, 1941.
40. HAMBRAEUS L, LAGERGREN C: Cystinuria in Sweden. VI, Biophysical and roentgenological studies of urinary calculi from cystinurics. *J Urol* 88:826, 1962.
41. BRAND E, HARRIS MM, BILOON S: Cystinuria: Excretion of a cystine complex which decomposes in the urine with the liberation of free cystine. *J Biol Chem* 86:315, 1930.
42. LEWIS HB: Cystinuria: A review of some recent investigations. *Yale J Biol Med* 4:437, 1932.
43. HARRIS H, MITTWOCH U, ROBSON EB, WARREN FL: Pattern of amino acid excretion in cystinuria. *Ann Hum Genet* 19:196, 1955.

44. HAMBRAEUS L: Comparative studies of the value of two cyanide-nitroprusside methods in the diagnosis of cystinuria. *Scand J Lab Clin Invest* 15:657, 1963.

45. CRAWHALL JC, SAUNDERS EP, THOMPSON CJ: Heterozygotes for cystinuria. *Ann Hum Genet* 29:257, 1966.

46. SACKETT DL: Adaptation of monodirectional high voltage electrophoresis on long papers to the rapid qualitative identification of urinary amino acids. *J Lab Clin Med* 63:306, 1964.

47. STEIN WH: A chromatographic investigation of the amino acid constituents of normal urine. *J Biol Chem* 201:45, 1953.

48. SOUPART P: Free amino acids of blood and urine in the human, in Holden JT (ed): *Amino Acid Pools.* Amsterdam, Elsevier, 1962, p 220.

49. MELONI CR, CANARY JJ: Cystinuria with hyperuricemia. *JAMA* 200:169, 1967.

50. DENT CE, HARRIS H: The genetics of cystinuria. *Ann Hum Genet* 16:60, 1951.

51. BROOKS WDW, HEASMAN MA, LOVELL RRH: Retinitis pigmentosa associated with cystinuria: 2 uncommon inherited conditions occurring in family. *Lancet* 1:1096, 1949.

52. HURWITZ LJ, CARSON NAJ, ALLEN IV, FANNIN TF, LYTTLE JA, NEILL DW: Clinical, biochemical and histopathological findings in a family with muscular dystrophy. *Brain* 90:799, 1967.

53. CLARA R, LOWENTHAL A: Familial and congenital lysine-cystinuria with benign myopathy and dwarfism. *J Neurol Sci* 3:434, 1966.

54. TANGUAY RB, GALINDO J: Cystinuria associated with mongolism and identification of an abnormal pyrrolidine compound in urine. *Am J Clin Pathol* 46:442, 1966.

55. GROSS JB, ULRICH JA, JONES JD: Urinary excretion of amino acids in a kindred with hereditary pancreatitis and aminoaciduria. *Gastroenterology* 47:41, 1964.

56. BRODEHL J, GALLISSEN K, KOWALEWSKI S: Isolated cystinuria (without lysine-ornithine-argininuria) in a family with hypocalcemic tetany. *Klin Wochenschr* 45:38, 1967.

57. PURKISS P, CHALMERS RA, BORUD O: Combined iminoglycinuria and cystine- and dibasic aminoaciduria in patients with propionic acidaemia and 3-methylcrotonylglycinuria. *J Inherited Metab Dis* 3:85, 1980.

58. DELVALLE JA, MERINERO B, GARCIA MJ, UGARTE M, GONZALEZ M, GRACIA R, PERALTA A: Biochemical findings in a patient with neonatal methylmalonic acidaemia. *J Inherited Metab Dis* 5:53, 1982.

59. SEGAL S: Unpublished.

60. BRAND E, BLOCK RJ, KASSELL B, CAHILL GF: Cystinuria. V. The metabolism of casein and lactalbumin. *J Biol Chem* 119:669, 1937.

61. RACHELE JR, REED LJ, KIDWAL AR, FERGER MF, DU VIGNEAUD V: Conversion of cystathionine labeled with S35 to cystine *in vivo*. *J Biol Chem* 185:817, 1950.

62. SCHIMKE RN, MCKUSICK VA, WEILBAECHER RG: Homocystinuria, in Nyhan WL (ed): *Amino Acid Metabolism and Genetic Variation.* New York, McGraw-Hill, 1967, pp 297-313.

63. FRIMPTER GW: Cystathionuria, in Nyhan WL (ed): *Amino Acid Metabolism and Genetic Variation.* New York, McGraw-Hill, 1967, pp 315-523.

64. STURMAN JA, GAULL G, RATHS NCR: Absence of cystathionase in human fetal liver: Is cystine essential? *Science* 169:74, 1970.

65. GAITONDE MK, GAULL G: A procedure for the quantitative analysis of the sulphur amino acids of rat tissues. *Biochem J* 102:959, 1967.

66. WHELDRAKE JF, PASTERNAK CA: The oxidation of cystine by mast-cell tumor P815, in culture. *Biochem J* 106:437, 1968.

67. LONDON DR, FOLEY TH: Cystine metabolism in cystinuria. *Clin Sci* 29:133, 1965.

68. CRAWHALL JC, LIETMAN PS, SCHNEIDER JA, SEEGMILLER JE: Cystinosis: Plasma cystine and cysteine concentration and effect of D-penicillamine and dietary treatment. *Am J Med* 44:330, 1968.

69. CRAWHALL JC, SEGAL S: The intracellular ratio of cysteine and cystine in various tissues. *Biochem J* 105:891, 1967.

70. SEGAL S, SMITH I: Delineation of cystine and cysteine transport systems in rat kidney cortex by development patterns. *Proc Natl Acad Sci USA* 63:926, 1969.

71. STATES B, SEGAL S: Distribution of glutathione-cystine transhydrogenase activity in subcellular fractions of rat intestinal mucosa. *Biochem J* 113:443, 1969.

72. STEPHENS AD, PERRETT D: Cystinuria: A new genetic variant. *Clin Sci Mol Med* 51:27, 1976.

73. HOLTZAPPLE PG, BOVEE K, REA CF, SEGAL S: Amino acid uptake by kidney and jejunal tissue from dogs with cystine stones. *Science* 166:1525, 1969.

74. WHELAN DT, SCRIVER CR: Hyperdibasic aminoaciduria: An inherited disorder of amino acid transport. *Pediatr Res* 2:525, 1968.

75. OYANGI K, MIURA R, YAMANOUGHI T: Congenital lysinuria: A new inherited transport disorder of dibasic amino acids. *J Pediatr* 77:259, 1970.

76. SIMELL O, PERHEENTUPA J: Renal handling of diamino acids in lysinuric protein intolerance. *J Clin Invest* 54:9, 1974.

77. LESTER FT, CUSWORTH DC: Lysine infusion in cystinuria: Theoretical renal thresholds for lysine. *Clin Sci* 44:99, 1973.

78. KATO T: Renal handling of dibasic amino acids and cystine in cystinuria. *Clin Sci Mol Med* 53:9, 1977.

79. ROBSON EB, ROSE GA: The effect of intravenous lysine on the renal clearances of cystine, arginine and ornithine in normal subjects, in patients with cystinuria and Fanconi syndrome and their relatives. *Clin Sci* 16:75, 1957.

80. WEBBER WA, BROWN JL, PITTS RF: Interactions of amino acids in renal tubular transport. *Am J Physiol* 200:380, 1961.

81. BOVEE KC, SEGAL S: Renal tubular reabsorption of amino acids after lysine loading of cystinuric dogs. *Metabolism* 33:602, 1984.

82. BERGERON M, VADEBONCOEUR M: Antiluminal transport of L-arginine and L-leucine following microinjections in peritubular capillaries of the rat. *Nephron* 8:355, 1971.

83. BERGERON M, VADEBONCOEUR M: Microinjections of L-leucine into tubules and peritubular capillaries of the rat. II. The maleic acid model. *Nephron* 8:367, 1971.

84. FOULKES EC: Effects of heavy metals on renal appartate transport and the nature of solute movement in kidney cortex slices. *Biochim Biophys Acta* 241:815, 1971.

85. ROSENBERG LE, ALBRECHT I, SEGAL S: Lysine transport in human kidney: Evidence for two systems. *Science* 155:1426, 1967.

86. BRODEHL J: Postnatal development of tubular amino acid reabsorption, in Silbernagel S, Lang F, Greger R (eds): *Amino Acid Transport and Uric Acid Transport.* Stuttgart, Georg Thieme Publishers, 1975, p 128.

87. SCRIVER C, GOODYER P, GIGUERE R: Ontogeny modifies manifestations of cystinuria genes: Implications for counseling. *J Pediatrics* 106:3, 1985.

88. FRIMPTER GW: Cystinuria: Metabolism of the disulfide of cysteine and homocysteine. *J Clin Invest* 42:1956, 1963.

89. ROSENBERG LE, DURANT JL, HOLLAND IM: Intestinal absorption and renal extraction of cystine and cysteine in cystinuria. *N Engl J Med* 273:1239, 1065.

90. FRIMPTER GW: Cystinuria: Intravenous administration of S35 cystine and S35 cysteine. *Clin Sci* 31:207, 1966.

91. STEIN WH, MOORE S: The free amino acids of human blood plasma. *J Biol Chem* 211:915, 1954.

92. SILBERNAGL S, DEETJEN P: The tubular reabsorption of L-cystine and L-cysteine: A common transport system with L-arginine or not? *Pfluegers Arch* 337:277, 1972.

93. CRAAN AG, BERGERON M: Experimental cystinuria: The cycloleucine model. I. Amino acid interactions in renal and intestinal epithelia. *Can J Physiol* 53:1027, 1975.

94. VOLKL H, SILBERNAGL S, ASCHER A: Mutual inhibition of L-cystine/L-cysteine and other neutral amino acids during tubular reabsorption. A microperfusion study in rat kidney. *Pflugers Arch* 395:190, 1982.

95. SCHAFER JA, WATKINS ML: Transport of L-cystine in isolated perfused proximal straight tubules. *Pflugers Arch* 401:143, 1984.

96. AUSIELLO DA, SEGAL S, THIER SO: Cellular accumulation of L-lysine in rat kidney cortex in vivo. *Am J Physiol* 222:1473, 1972.

97. GRETH WE, THIER SO, SEGAL S: Cellular accumulation of L-cystine in rat kidney cortex in vivo. *J Clin Invest* 52:454, 1973.

98. DAL CANTON A, STANZIALE R, CORRADI A, ANDREUCCI VE, MIGONE L: Effects of acute ureteral obstruction on glomerular hemodynamics in rat kidney. *Kidney Int* 12:403, 1977.

99. SCHWARTZMAN L, BLAIR A, SEGAL A: A common renal transport system for lysine, ornithine, arginine and cysteine. *Biochem Biophys Res Common* 23:220, 1966.

100. SEGAL S, CRAWHALL JC: Transport of cysteine by human kidney cortex. *Biochem Med* 1:141, 1967.

101. ROSENBERG IE, DOWNING SJ, SEGAL S: Competitive inhibition of dibasic amino acid transport in rat kidney. *J Biol Chem* 237:2265, 1962.

102. SCHWARTZMAN L, BLAIR A, SEGAL A: Exchange diffusion of dibasic amino acids in rat-kidney cortex slices. *Biochim Biophys Acta* 135:120, 1967.

103. SEGAL S, SCHWARTZMAN L, BLAIR A, BERTOLI D: Dibasic acid transport in rat kidney cortex slices. *Biochim Biophys Acta* 135:127, 1967.

104. SEGAL S, CRAWHALL JC: Characteristics of cystine and cysteine transport in rat kidney cortex slices. *Proc Natl Acad Sci USA* 59:231, 1968.

105. SEGAL S, SMITH I: Delineation of separate transport systems in rat-kidney cortex for L-lysine and L-cystine by developmental patterns. *Biochem Biophys Res Commun* 35:771, 1969.

106. MCNAMARA PD, PEPE LM, SEGAL S: Cystine uptake by renal brush border vesicles. *Biochem J* 194:443, 1981.

107. HAMMERMAN MR: Na+-independent L-arginine transport in rabbit renal brushborder membrane vesicles. *Biochim Biophys Acta* 685:17, 1982.

108. HILDEN SA, SACKTOR B: L-arginine uptake into renal brush border membrane vesicles. *Arch Biochem Biophys* 210:289, 1981.

109. JEAN T, RIPOCHE P, POUJEOL P: A sodium-independent mechanism for L-arginine uptake by rat renal brush border membrane vesicles. *Membr Biochem* 5:1, 1983.

110. MIRCHEFF AK, KIPPEN I, HIRAYAMA B, WRIGHT EM: Delineation of sodium-stimulated amino acid transport pathways in rabbit kidney brush border vesicles. *Membr Biol* 64:113, 1982.

111. STIEGER B, STANGE G, BIBER J, MURER H: Transport of L-lysine by rat renal brush border membrane vesicles. *Pflugers Arch* 397:106, 1983.

112. MCNAMARA PD, REA CT, SEGAL S: Lysine uptake by rat renal brush-border membrane vesicles. *Am J Physiol* 251:F734, 1986.

113. STATES B, FOREMAN JW, LEE J, HARRIS D, SEGAL S: Cystine and lysine transport in cultured human renal epithelial cells. *Metabolism* 36:356, 1987.

114. FOREMAN JW, LEE J, SEGAL S: Characteristics of cystine uptake by cultured LLC-PK$_1$ cells. *BBA* 968:323, 1988.

115. BANNAI S, KITAMURA E: Transport interaction of L-cystine and L-glutamate in human diploid fibroblasts in culture. *J Biol Chem* 255:2372, 1980.

116. BANNAI S: Exchange of cystine and glutamate across plasma membrane of human fibroblasts. *J Biol Chem* 261:2256, 1986.

117. TAKADA A, BANNAI S: Transport of cystine in isolated rat hepatocytes in primary culture. *J Biol Chem* 259:2441, 1984.

118. BANNAI S: Transport of cystine and cysteine in mammalian cells. *Biochim Biophys Acta* 779:289, 1984.

119. KING JS Jr, WAINER A: Cystinuria with hyperuricemia and methioninuria: Biochemical study of a case. *Am J Med* 43:125, 1967.

120. FRIMPTER GW: Cystathioninuria in a patient with cystinuria. *Am J Med* 46:832, 1969.

121. FRIMPTER GW: The disulfide of L-cysteine and L-homocysteine in urine of patients with cystinuria. *J Biol Chem* 236:651, 1961.

122. HAMBRAEUS L: Cystinuria in Sweden: Quantitative studies of urinary amino acid excretion in cystinurics. *Acta Soc Med Ups* 6:1, 1964.

123. SCHNEIDER JA, BRADLEY KH, SEEGMILLER JE: Identification and measurement of cysteine-homocysteine mixed disulfide in plasma. *J Lab Clin Med* 71:122, 1968.

124. SILK DB, PERRETT D, STEPHENS AD, CLARK ML, SCOWEN EF: Intestinal absorption of cystine and cysteine in normal human subjects and patients with cystinuria. *Clin Sci Mol Med* 47:393, 1974.

125. FOLEY TH, LONDON DR: Cysteine metabolism in cystinuria. *Clin Sci* 29:549, 1965.

126. HELLIER MD, HOLDSWORTH CD, PERRETT D: Dibasic amino acid absorption in man. *Gastroenterology* 65:613, 1973.

127. MAWER GE, NIXON E: The net absorption of amino acid constituents of a protein meal in normal and cystinuric subjects. *Clin Sci* 36:463, 1969.

128. MILNE MD: Amino acid metabolism in cystinuria. *Proc Biochem Soc* 122:9P, 1971.

129. ASATOOR AM, CROUCHMAN MR, HARRISON AR, LIGHT FW, LOUGHRIDGE LW, MILNE MD, RICHARDS AJ: Intestinal absorption of oligopeptides in cystinuria. *Clin Sci* 41:23, 1971.

130. HELLIER MD, PERRETT D, HOLDSWORTH CD, THIRUMALAI C: Absorption of dipeptides in normal and cystinuric subjects. *Gut* 12:496, 1971.

131. ASATOOR AM, HARRISON RDW, MILNE MD, PROSSER DI: Intestinal absorption of an arginine-containing peptide in cystinuria. *Gut* 13:95, 1972.

132. ROSENBERG LE, DOWNING S, DURANT JL, SEGAL S: Cystinuria: Biochemical evidence of three genetically distinct diseases. *J Clin Invest* 45:365, 1966.

133. ROSENBERG LE, CRAWHALL JC, SEGAL S: Intestinal transport of cystine and cysteine in man: Evidence for separate mechanisms. *J Clin Invest* 46:30, 1967.

134. COICADAN L, HEYMAN M, GRASSET E, DESJEUX JF: Cystinuria: Reduced lysine permeability at the brush border of intestinal membrane cells. *Pediatr Res* 14:109, 1980.

135. DESJEUX JF, SIMELL RJ, DUMONTIER AM, PERHEENTUPA J: Lysine fluxes across the jejunal epithelium in lysinuric protein intolerance. *J Clin Invest* 65:1382, 1980.

136. DESJEUX JF, VONLANTHEN M, DUMONTIER AM, SIMELL O, LEGRAIN M: Cystine fluxes across the isolated jejunal epithelium in cystinuria: Increased efflux permeability at the luminal membrane. *Pediatr Res* 21:477, 1987.

137. SEGAL S, LOWENSTEIN LM, WALLACE A: Comparison of the transport characteristics by rat intestine and kidney cortex. *Gastroenterology* 55:386, 1968.

138. CASSANO G, LESZCZYNSKA B, MURER H: Transport of L-lysine by rat intestinal brush border membrane vesicles. *Pflugers Arch* 397:114, 1983.

139. OZEGOVIC B, MCNAMARA PD, SEGAL S: Cystine uptake by rat jejunal brushborder membrane vesicles. *Biosci Rep* 2:913, 1982.

140. HARRIS H, WARREN FL: Quantitative studies on the urinary cystine in patients with cystine stone formation and their relatives. *Ann Eugen* 18:125, 1953.

141. HARRIS H, MITTWOCH U, ROBSON EB, WARREN FL: Phenotypes and genotypes in cystinuria. *Ann Hum Genet* 20:57, 1955.

142. ROSENBERG LE, DOWNING S: Transport of neutral and dibasic amino acids by human leucocytes: Absence of a defect in cystinuria. *J Clin Invest* 44:1382, 1965.

143. SCRIVER CR, WHELAN DT, CLOW CL, DALLAIRE L: Cystinuria: Increased prevalence in patients with mental disease. *N Engl J Med* 283:783, 1970.

144. BANERJI NK, MILLAR JHD: Paraplegia associated with cystinuria. *J Neurol Sci* 12:101, 1971.

145. DeMYER W, GEBHARD RL: Subacute combined degeneration of the spinal cord with cystinuria. *Neurology* 25:994, 1975.

146. BLACKBURN CR, MCLEOD JG: CNS lesions in cystinuria. *Arch Neurol* 32:638, 1977.

147. BERRY HK: Cystinuria in mentally retarded siblings with atypical osteogenesis imperfecta. *Am J Dis Child* 97:196, 1959.

148. GOLD RJM, DOBRINSKI MJ, GOLD DP: Cystinuria and mental deficiency. *Clin Gen* 12:329, 1977.

149. SMITH A, PROCOPIS PG: Cystinuria and its relationship to mental retardation. *Med J Aust* 2:932, 1975.

150. HWANG SM, SEGAL S: Developmental and other aspects of [^{35}S]cysteine transport by rat brain synaptosomes. *J Neurochem* 33:1303, 1979.

151. SEGAL S, HWANG SM: L-[^{35}S]cystine uptake by rat brain synaptosomes. *J Neurochem* 33:697, 1979.

152. HWANG SM, SEGAL S: Developmental and other characteristics of lysine uptake by rat brain synaptosomes. *Biochim Biophys Acta* 557:436, 1979.

153. HWANG SM, WEISS S, SEGAL S: Uptake of L-[^{35}S]cystine by isolated rat brain capillaries. *J Neurochem* 35:417, 1980.

154. HARRIS H, ROBSON EB: Variation in homozygous cystinuria. *Acta Genet (Basel)* 5:581, 1955.

155. ROSENBERG LE, DURANT JL, ALBRECHT I: Genetic heterogeneity in cystinuria: Evidence for allelism. *Trans Assoc Am Physicians* 79:284, 1966.

156. ROSENBERG LE: Genetic heterogeneity in cystinuria, in Nyhan WL (ed): *Amino Acid Metabolism and Genetic Variation.* McGraw-Hill, New York, 1967, p 341.

157. HERSHKO C, BEN-AMI E, PACIORKOVSKI J, LEVIN N: Alleomorphism in cystinuria. *Proc Tel-Hashomer Hosp* 4:21, 1965.

158. GIUGLIANI R, FERRARI I, GREENE LJ: Heterozygous cystinuria and urinary lithiasis. *Am J Med Genet* 22, 1986.

159. DATTA SP, HARRIS H: Urinary amino acid patterns of some mammals. *Ann Eugen* 18:107, 1953.

160. CRAWHALL JC, SEGAL S: Sulphocysteine in the urine of the blotched Kenya genet. *Nature* 208:1320, 1965.

161. OLDFIELD JE, ALLEN PH, ADAIR J: Identification of cystine calculi in mink. *Proc Soc Exp Biol Med* 91:560, 1956.

162. LASSAIGNE JL: Observation sur l'existence de l'oxide cystique dans un calcul vésical du chien, et essai analytique sur la composition élémentaire de cette substance particulière. *Ann Chim Phys* 2d ser, 23:328, 1823.

163. MORRIS ML, GREEN DF, DINKEL JH, BRAND E: Canine cystinuria. *North Am Vet* 16:16, 1935.

164. BRAND E, CAHILL GF: Canine cystinuria. III. *J Biol Chem* 114:XV, 1936.

165. BRAND E, CAHILL GF, KASSELL B: Canine cystinuria. V. Family history of two cystinuric Irish terriers and cystine determination in dog urine. *J Biol Chem* 133:431, 1940.

166. GREEN DG, MORRIS ML, CAHILL GF, BRAND E: Canine cystinuria. II. Analysis of cystine calculi and sulfur distribution in the urine. *J Biol Chem* 114:91, 1936.

167. CRANE CW, TURNER AW: Amino acid patterns of urine in blood plasma in a cystinuric Labrador dog. *Nature* 177:237, 1956.

168. TREACHER RJ: Amino acid excretion in canine cystine-stone disease. *Vet Rec* 74:503, 1962.

169. CORNELIUS CE, BISHOP JA, SCHAFFER MH: A quantitative study of amino aciduria in dachshunds with a history of cystine urolithiasis. *Cornell Vet* 177, April 1967.

170. GOULDEN BE, LEAVER JL: Low voltage paper electrophoresis as a screening test for the diagnosis of canine cystinuria. *Vet Rec* 80:244, 1967.

171. TREACHER RJ: Intestinal absorption of lysine in cystinuric dogs. *J Comp Pathol* 75:309, 1965.

172. BOVEE KC, THIER SO, REA C, SEGAL S: Renal clearance of amino acids in canine cystinuria. *Metabolism* 23:51, 1974.

173. FRIMPTER GW, THOUIN P, EWALDS BH: Penicillamine in canine cystinuria. *J Am Vet Med Assoc* 151:1084, 1967.

174. BOVEE KC, BUSH M, DIETZ J, JEZYK P, SEGAL S: Cystinuria in the maned wolf of South America. *Science* 212:919, 1981.

175. BROWN RR: Aminoaciduria resulting from cycloleucine administration in man. *Science* 157:432, 1967.

176. GOYER RA, REYNOLDS JO JR, ELSTON RC: Characteristics of the aminoaciduria resulting from cycloleucine administration in pair fed rats. *Proc Soc Exp Biol Med* 130:860, 1969.

177. HOLTZAPPLE P, REA C, GENEL M, SEGAL S: Cycloleucine inhibition of amino acid transport in human and rat kidney cortex. *J Lab Clin Med* 75:818, 1970.

178. HWANG SM, FOREMAN J, SEGAL S: Developmental pattern of cystine transport in isolated rat renal tubules. *Biochim Biophys Acta* 690:145, 1982.

179. MEDOW MS, FOREMAN JW, BOVEE KC, SEGAL S: Developmental changes of glycine transport in the dog. *Biochim Biophys Acta* 693:85, 1982.

180. BRODEHL J, GELISSEN K: Endogenous renal transport of free amino acids in infancy and childhood. *Pediatrics* 42:395, 1968.

181. KOLB FO, EARLL JM, HARRIS HA: Disappearance of cystinuria in a patient treated with prolonged low methionine diet. *Metabolism* 16:378, 1967.

182. ZINNEMAN HH, JONES JE: Dietary methionine and its influence on cystine excretion in cystinuric patients. *Metabolism* 15:915, 1966.

183. CHESNEY RW, GUSOWSKI N, PADILLA M, LIPPINCOTT S: Effect of amino acid intake on brush-border membrane uptake of sulfur amino acids. *Am J Physiol* F125, 1986.

184. JAEGER P, PORTMANN L, SAUNDERS A, ROSENBERG LE, THIER SO: Anticystinuric effects of glutamine and of dietary sodium restriction. *N Engl J Med* 315:1120, 1986.

185. DENT CE, FRIEDMANN M, GREEN H, WATSON LCA: Treatment of cystinuria. *Br Med J* 1:403, 1965.

186. DENT CE, SENIOR B: Studies on the treatment of cystinuria. *Br J Urol* 27:317, 1955.

187. CRAWHALL JC, SCOWEN EF, WATTS RWE: Effect of penicillamine on cystinuria. *Br Med J* 1:585, 1963.

188. CRAWHALL JC, SCOWEN EF, WATTS RWE: Further observations on use of D-penicillamine in cystinuria. *Br Med J* 1:1411, 1964.

189. BARTTER FC, LOTZ M, THIER S, ROSENBERG LE, POTTS JT: Cystinuria: Combined clinical staff conference at the National Institutes of Health. *Ann Intern Med* 62:796, 1965.

190. CRAWHALL JC, THOMPSON CJ: Cystinuria: Effect of D-penicillamine on plasma and urinary cystine concentrations. *Science* 147:1459, 1965.

191. LOTZ M, POTTS JT: Quantitation of the effects of pencillamine therapy in cystinuria. *J Clin Invest* 43:1293, 1964.

192. MCDONALD JE, HENNEMAN PH: Stone dissolution in vivo and control of cystinuria with D-penicillamine. *N Engl J Med* 273:578, 1965.

193. CRAWHALL JC, SCOWEN EF, THOMPSON CJ, WATTS RWE: Dissolution of cystine stones during D-penicillamine treatment of a pregnant patient with cystinuria. *Br Med J* 1:216, 1967.

194. FELLERS FX, SHAHIDI NT: The nephrotic syndrome induced by penicillamine therapy. *Am J Dis Child* 98:669, 1959.

195. ADAMS DA, GOLDMAN R, MAXWELL MH, LATTA H: Nephrotic syndrome associated with penicillamine therapy of Wilson's disease. *Am J Med* 36:330, 1964.

196. ROSENBERG LE, HAYSLETT JP: Nephrotoxic effects of penicillamine in cystinuria. *JAMA* 201:698, 1967.

197. CORCOS JM, SOLER-BECHERA J, MAYER K, FREYBERG RH, GOLDSTEIN R, JAFFÉ I: Neutrophilic agranulocytosis during administration of penicillamine. *JAMA* 189:265, 1964.

198. HALPERIN EC, THIER SO, ROSENBERG LE: The use of D-penicillamine in cystinuria: Efficacy and untoward reactions. *Yale J Biol Med* 54:439, 1981.

199. BEER WE, COOKE KB: Epidermolysis bullosa induced by penicillamine. *Br J Dermatol* 79:123, 1967.

200. KATZ R: Penicillamine-induced skin lesions, a possible example of human lathyrism. *Arch Dermatol Syphilol* 95:196, 1967.

201. HARRIS ED, SJOERDSMA A: Effect of penicillamine on human collagen and its possible application to treatment of scleroderma. *Lancet* 1:996, 1966.

202. FAWCETT NP, NYHAN WL, ANDERSON WW: Thrombocytosis during treatment of cystinuria with penicillamine. *J Pediatr* 69:976, 1966.

203. KEISER HR, HENKIN RI, BARTTER FC, SJOERDSMA A: Loss of taste during therapy with penicillamine. *JAMA* 203:381, 1968.

204. HENKIN RI, KEISER HR, JAFFE IA, STERNLIEB I, SCHEINBERG IH: Decreased taste sensitivity after D-penicillamine reversed by copper administration. *Lancet* 16:1268, 1967.

205. WALSH JM, PATSTON V: Effect of penicillamine on serum iron. *Arch Dis Child* 40:651, 1965.

206. BOSTROM H, WESTER PO: Excretion of trace elements in two penicillamine-treated cases of cystinuria. *Acta Med Scand* 181:475, 1967.

207. MCCALL JT, GOLDSTEIN NP, RANDALL RV, GROSS JB: Comparative metabolism of copper and zinc in patients with Wilson's disease (hepatolenticular degeneration). *Am J Med Sci* 254:35, 1967.

208. JAFFE IA, ALTMAN K, MERRYMAN P: The antipyridoxine effect of penicillamine in man. *J Clin Invest* 43:1969, 1964.

209. GIBBS K, WALSHE JM: Penicillamine and pyridoxine requirements in man. *Lancet* 175, January 1966.

210. HEDDLE JG, METTENY EW, BEATON GH: Penicillamine and vitamin B_6 interrelationships in the rat. *Can J Biochem Physiol* 42:1215, 1963.

211. PRUZANSKI W: Cystinuria and cystine urolithiasis in childhood. *Acta Paediatr Scand* 55:97, 1966.

212. STERNLIEB I, BENNETT B, SCHEINBERG IH: D-Penicillamine induced Goodpasture's syndrome in Wilson's disease. *Ann Intern Med* 82:673, 1975.

213. STOKES GS, POTTS JT, LOTZ M, BARTTER F: A new agent in the treatment of cystinuria: N-acetyl-D-penicillamine. *Br Med J* 1:284, 1968.

214. STEPHENS AD, WATTS RWE: The treatment of cystinuria with N-acetyl-D-penicillamine, a comparison with the results of D-penicillamine treatment. *QJ Med* 40:335, 1971.

215. MULVANEY WP, QUILTER T, MORTERA A: Experiences with acetylcysteine in cystinuric patients. *J Urol* 114:107, 1975.

216. TIMMERMAN A, KALLISTRATOS G, FENNER O, SOMMER E: A tentative map suggesting the possible role of urinary minerals for the formation of renal stones, in Hodgkinson A, Nordin BEC (eds): *Renal Stone Research Symposium* (Leeds, 1968). London, J & A Churchill, 1969.

217. KING JS: Treatment of cystinuria with α-mercaptopropionylglycine: A preliminary report. *Proc Soc Exp Biol Med* 129:927, 1968.

218. KINOSHITA K, YACHIKU S, KOTAKE T, TAKEUCHI M, SONODA T: Treatment of cystinuria with 2-mercaptopropionylglycine (MPG), *Proc 2nd Internat Sympos on Thiola*. Osaka, Santen Pharmaceutical Co, 1972, p 50.

219. SONODA T, KINOSHITA K, KOTAKE T, YACHIKU S, TAKEUCHI M: Effect of thiola on cystinuria, *Proc Int Symp Thiola*. Osaka, Santern Pharmaceutical Co, 1970, p 231.

220. NISHIMURA R, ISHIDO T, TAKAI S: Studies on cystinuria, *Proc 2nd Internat Sympos on Thiola*. Osaka, Santen Pharmaceutical Co, 1972, p 47.

221. HAUTMANN R, TERHORST B, STUHLSATZ HW, LUTZEYER W: Mercaptopropionylglycine: A progress in cystine stone therapy. *J Urol* 117:628, 1977.

222. KALLISTRATOS G, MITA I, VADALOYKA-KALFAKAKOU V: Management of cystinuric disorders with sulfhydryl drugs, in *The Management of Genetic Disorders*. New York, AR Liss, 1979, pp 255–263.

223. PAK YC, FULLER C, KHASHAYAR S, ZERWEKH JE, ADAMS BV, with investigators from collaborating units: Management of cystine nephrolithiasis with alpha-mercaptopropionylglycine. *J Urol* 136, 1986.

224. SLOAND JA, ISSO JL, Jr: Captopril reduces urinary cystine excretion in cystinuria. *Arch Intern Med* 147, 1987.

225. MIYAGI K, NAKADA S, OHSHIRO D: Effect of glutamine on cystine excretion in a patient with cystinuria. *N Engl J Med* 301:196, 1979.

226. SKOVBY F, ROSENBERG LE, THIER SO: No effect of L-glutamine on cystinuria. Letter to the editor. *N Engl J Med* 302:236, 1980.

227. VAN DEN BERG CJ, JONES JD, WILSON DM, SMITH LH: Glutamine therapy of cystinuria. *Invest Urol* 18:155, 1980.

228. FARISS BL, KOLB FO: Preliminary communications: Factors involved in crystal formation in cystinuria. *JAMA* 205:138, 1968.

229. SMITH AD, LANGE PH, MILLER RP, REINKE DB: Dissolution of cystine calculi by irrigation with acetylcysteine through percutaneous nephrostomy. *Urology* 13:422, 1979.

230. CRISSEY MM, GITTES RF: Dissolution of cystine ureteral calculus by irrigation with tromethamine. *J Urol* 121:811, 1979.

231. STARK H, SAVIR A: Dissolution of cystine calculi by pelviocaliceal irrigation with D-penicillamine. *J Urol* 124:895, 1980.

232. DRETLER S: Personal communication, December 1987.

233. LYTTON B: Personal communication, December 1987.

234. KELLY S, NOLAN DP: Letter to the editor, *JAMA* 243:1897, 1980.

CHAPTER 100

LYSINURIC PROTEIN INTOLERANCE AND OTHER CATIONIC AMINOACIDURIAS

OLLI SIMELL

1. *Membrane transport of cationic amino acids lysine, arginine, and ornithine is abnormal in four disease entities: classic cystinuria; lysinuric protein intolerance (hyperdibasic aminoaciduria type 2, or familial protein intolerance); hyperdibasic aminoaciduria type 1; and isolated lysinuria (lysine malabsorption syndrome). Cystinuria is the most common of these; it is dealt with in Chap. 99. About 80 patients with lysinuric protein intolerance (LPI) have been published or are known to me. Almost half of them are from Finland, where the prevalence of this autosomal recessive disease is 1 in 60,000. Autosomal dominant hyperdibasic aminoaciduria type 1 has been described in 13 of 33 members in a French Canadian pedigree and isolated lysinuria in one Japanese patient.*

Arginine and ornithine are intermediates in the urea cycle; lysine is an essential amino acid. In lysinuric protein intolerance, urinary excretion and clearance of all cationic amino acids, especially of lysine, are increased, and they are poorly absorbed from the intestine. Their plasma concentrations are low, and their body pools become depleted. The patients have periods of hyperammonemia caused by "functional" deficiency of ornithine, the backbone of the urea cycle. Consequently, nausea and vomiting occur, and aversion to protein-rich food develops. The patients fail to thrive, and symptoms of protein malnutrition are further aggravated by lysine deficiency.

2. *Patients with lysinuric protein intolerance are usually symptom-free when breast-fed, but have vomiting and diarrhea after weaning. Their appetite is poor, they fail to thrive, and if force-fed high protein milk or formulas, they may develop coma. After infancy, they reject high protein foods, grow poorly, and have enlarged liver and spleen, muscle hypotonia, and sparse hair. Osteoporosis is prominent. The mental prognosis varies from normal development to moderate retardation; most patients are normal. Four patients have had psychotic periods. The final height in treated patients has been slightly subnormal or low-normal. Pregnancies are risky: severe hemorrhage during labor and a toxemic crisis have occurred, but the children are normal if not damaged by delivery-related complications. Acute exacerbations of hyperammonemia have not been a frequent problem in treated patients but may have been the cause of the sudden death in one adult male after moderate alcohol ingestion. A severe complication of the disease is interstitial lung disease (undefined interstitial pneumonia). Patients present with fatigue, cough, dyspnea during exercise, fever, and, rarely, hemoptysis. Arterial PaO_2 is decreased, and interstitial changes are evident in the chest x-rays. Three patients have died of the condition, all of whom had "alveolar proteinosis" at autopsy. One symptomatic patient has been treated with prednisolone and is now in remission over 2 years after the occurrence of the symptoms.*

3. *The concentrations of the cationic amino acids in plasma are subnormal or low-normal, and the amounts of glutamine, al-anine, serine, proline, citrulline, and glycine are increased. Lysine is excreted in urine in massive excess and arginine and ornithine in moderate excess. Daily urine contains in the mean 4.13 (range 1.02 to 7.00) mmol lysine, 0.36 (0.08 to 0.69) mmol arginine, and 0.11 (0.09 to 0.13) mmol ornithine per 1.73 m^2 body surface area. The mean renal clearances are 25.7, 11.5, and 3.3 ml/min/1.73 m^2, respectively; occasional values suggest net tubular secretion of lysine. Cystine excretion may be slightly increased. Blood ammonia and urinary orotic acid excretion are normal during fasting but are increased after protein meals. Serum urea level is low to normal, and lactate dehydrogenase, ferritin, and thyroid-binding globulin are elevated.*

4. *The transport abnormality is expressed in the kidney tubules, intestine, cultured fibroblasts, and probably in the hepatocytes, but not in mature erythrocytes. In vivo and in vitro studies of the handling of cationic amino acids in the intestine and kidney strongly suggest that the transport defect is localized at the basolateral (antiluminal) membrane of the epithelial cells. In vivo, plasma concentrations increase poorly after oral loads of the cationic amino acids, but also if lysine is given as a lysine-containing dipeptide. Dipeptides and other oligopeptides utilize a different transport mechanism not shared with that of free amino acids. The dipeptide thus crosses the luminal membrane normally, and is hydrolyzed to free amino acids in the cytoplasm of the enterocyte. An efflux defect at the basolateral membrane explains why the dipeptide-derived lysine is unable to enter the plasma compartment in LPI. Direct measurements and calculations of unidirectional fluxes of lysine in intestinal biopsy specimens have confirmed that the defect indeed localizes at the basolateral cell surface. Similar cellular localization of the defect in the kidney tubules is suggested by infusions of citrulline, which not only cause citrullinuria, but also significant argininuria and ornithinuria. Because citrulline and the cationic amino acids do not share transport mechanisms in the tubules, part of citrulline is converted to arginine and further to ornithine in the tubular cells during reabsorption. A basolateral transport defect prohibits antiluminal efflux of arginine and ornithine, which accumulate and escape through the luminal membrane into the urine. The genetic mutations in LPI and possibly in all cationic aminoacidurias apparently lead to kinetic abnormalities in the transport protein(s) of the cationic amino acids. This is suggested by the fact that increases in the tubular load of a single cationic amino acid by intravenous infusion increases its tubular reabsorption, but reabsorption remains subnormal even at high loads. The other cationic amino acids are able to compete for the same transport site(s) also in LPI, but an increase in the load of one cationic amino acid frequently leads to net secretion of the others.*

The plasma membrane of cultured fibroblasts shows a defect in the trans-stimulated efflux of the cationic amino acids; i.e.,

---

Nonstandard abbreviations used in this chapter are: EEG = electroencephalogram; HDL = high density lipoprotein; HHH = hyperornithinemia-hyperammonemia-homocitrullinuria; LDL = low density lipoprotein; LPI = lysinuric protein intolerance; TBG = thyroxine-binding globulin.

their flux out of the cell is not stimulated by cationic amino acids present on the outside of the cell as efficiently as it is in the control fibroblasts. The percent of trans-stimulation of homoarginine efflux in the fibroblasts of the heterozygotes is halfway between that of the patients and controls.

5. *The exact cause of hyperammonemia in LPI remains unknown. The enzymes of the urea cycle have normal activities in the liver, and the brisk excretion of orotic acid during hyperammonemia supports the view that N-acetylglutamate and carbamyl phosphate are formed in sufficient quantities. Low plasma concentrations of arginine and ornithine suggest that the malfunction of the cycle is caused by deficiency of intramitochondrial ornithine. This hypothesis is supported by experiments in which hyperammonemia after protein or amino nitrogen loads is prevented by intravenous infusion of arginine or ornithine. Citrulline, a third urea cycle intermediate, abolishes hyperammonemia also if given orally, because as a neutral amino acid, it is well-absorbed from the intestine. The existence of ornithine deficiency has recently been questioned because cationic amino acids and their nonmetabolized analogues accumulate in higher than normal amounts in intestinal biopsy specimens and cultured fibroblasts of the patients in vitro and the concentrations of the cationic amino acids in liver biopsy samples are similar or higher in the patients when compared to these concentrations in the controls. If hyperammonemia is not due to simple deficiency of ornithine, it could be caused by inhibition of the urea cycle enzymes by the intracellularly accumulated lysine; by a coexisting defect in the mitochondrial ornithine transport necessary for the function of the urea cycle; or by actual deficiency of ornithine in the cytoplasm caused by abnormal pooling of the cationic amino acids into some cell organelle(s), most likely lysosomes. The latter two explanations imply that the transport defect is also expressed in the organelle(s).*

6. *Lysine is present in practically all proteins, including collagen. Lysine deficiency may cause many features of the disease which are not corrected by prevention of hyperammonemia, including enlargement of the liver and spleen, poor growth and delay in the bone age, and osteoporosis. Oral lysine supplement is poorly tolerated by the patients, because of its poor intestinal absorption. ε-N-Acetyl-L-lysine, but not homocitrulline, efficiently increases plasma concentration of lysine in the patients, but acetyllysine or other neutral lysine analogues have not been used for supplementation.*

7. *The treatment in lysinuric protein intolerance consists of protein restriction and oral citrulline supplementation, 3 to 8 g daily during meals. Patients are encouraged to increase modestly their protein intake during citrulline supplementation, but aversion to protein in most patients effectively inhibits them from accepting more than the minimal requirement. The treatment clearly improves the growth and well-being of the patients.*

8. *The clinical and biochemical findings in other cationic aminoacidurias differ slightly from those in protein intolerance. The symptoms of the index case with hyperdibasic aminoaciduria type 1 resemble those of LPI, but the other affected members of the pedigree are clinically healthy. The Japanese patient with isolated lysinuria has severe growth failure, seizures, and mental retardation. Her transport defect is apparently limited to lysine, and hyperammonemia is not a feature of the disease.*

Perheentupa and Visakorpi described the first three patients with *familial protein intolerance with deficient transport of basic amino acids* in 1965.[1] The disease is now called *lysinuric protein intolerance* (LPI) or *hyperdibasic aminoaciduria type 2.*[2–5] Over 80 patients with this autosomal recessive disease have been described or are known to me; 34 of them are Finns.[6–39] The incidence in Finland is 1 in 60,000 births, but varies considerably within the country.[2] Patients of black and white American, Japanese, Turkish, Moroccan, Italian, French, Dutch,

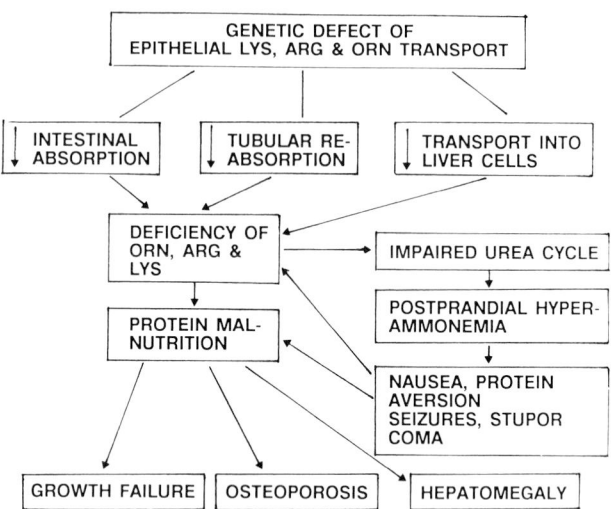

Fig. 100-1 The suggested pathogenesis of lysine, arginine, and ornithine deficiency, hyperammonemia, and aversion to protein in LPI.

Irish, Norwegian, Swedish, and Russian origin have also been described. The fascinating combination in the disease of a urea cycle failure, expressed as postprandial hyperammonemia, and a defect in the transport of the cationic amino acids lysine, arginine, and ornithine in the intestine and kidney tubules has led to extensive studies of the mechanisms that link these two phenomena. The mechanisms are still partly unresolved and the sequence of events leading to hyperammonemia is unclear. We can simplify our knowledge by saying that hyperammonemia is caused by "functional deficiency" of the urea cycle intermediates arginine and ornithine in the urea cycle[4,11,14,40] (Fig. 100-1). LPI has also been a productive model for studies of cellular transport: it is the first human disease in which the transport defect has been localized to the basolateral (antiluminal) membrane of the epithelial cells.[41–43] Further, in LPI the parenchymal cells show a defect in the trans-stimulated efflux of the cationic amino acids, suggesting that the basolateral membrane of the epithelial cells and the plasma membrane of the parenchymal cells have analogous functions.[44,45]

Recently, several patients with variant forms of cationic aminoaciduria have been described in which the protein tolerance often is better than in LPI, and the selectivity and severity of cationic aminoaciduria differs.[23,25,33,46,47] In the report by Whelan and Scriver[46] only the history of the index case suggested hyperammonemia, but other members of the pedigree have been symptom-free. The inheritance of this hyperdibasic aminoaciduria type 1 is autosomal dominant, implying that the patients are heterozygous for LPI or another type of hyperdibasic aminoaciduria.

CLINICAL ASPECTS

Lysinuric Protein Intolerance

Natural Course of the Disease. The pregnancies and deliveries have been uneventful.[4–6,9–11,35] Breast-fed infants usually thrive because of the low protein concentration in human milk, but symptoms of hyperammonemia may appear during the neonatal period and reflect exceptionally low protein tolerance or high protein content in the breast milk. Nausea, vomiting, and mild to severe diarrhea usually appear within 1 week of weaning or other increases in the protein content of the meals. Soy-based formulas are perhaps slightly better tolerated than cow's milk. The infants are poor feeders, they cease to thrive, and they have marked muscular hypotonia. The patients' liver and spleen are enlarged from the neonatal period onward. The association of episodes of vomiting with high protein feeds is not always apparent to the parents and may remain unnoticed even by trained physicians for years. Thus, the diagnosis frequently has been delayed until the preschool or school age.[35]

Around the age of 1 year most patients begin to reject cow's milk, meat, fish, and eggs. The diet then mainly contains cereals cooked in water, potatoes, rice and vegetables, fruits and juices, bread, butter, and candies. The frequency of vomiting and diarrhea decreases on this diet, but accidental increases in protein intake lead to dizziness, nausea, and vomiting. A few patients have lapsed into coma, to the point that the EEG became isoelectric when the children were force-fed protein-rich foods.[27,35] Hospitalizations and nasogastric feedings are a special danger for patients who have remained undiagnosed, because the protein concentration in enteral feedings is often high. Prolonged moderately increased intake of protein may lead to dizziness, psychotic periods, chronic abdominal pains, or suspicion of abdominal emergencies.

A few patients have had fractures of the long bones due to minimal trauma, and two patients have had compression fractures of the lumbar spine in early childhood.[14,35] The radiologic signs of osteoporosis are usually severe before puberty, but decrease with advancing age and during citrulline therapy (see "Therapy," below).[4,30,35,48]

Physical Findings. Muscular hypotonia and hypotrophy are usually noticeable from early infancy but are alleviated with advancing age.[35] Most patients are unable to perform long-lasting physical exercises, but acute performance is relatively good. The body proportions of patients after the first couple of years of life are characteristic; the extremities are thin, but the front view of the body is squarelike with abundant centripetal subcutaneous fat (Fig. 100-2). The hair is thin and sparse, the skin may be slightly hyperelastic, and the nails are normal. The liver is variably enlarged, and the spleen is often palpable and large in ultrasound.

Patients who have remained undiagnosed until the age of several years have had characteristics typical of protein-calorie malnutrition and frequently resemble patients with advanced celiac disease. The subcutaneous fat may be reduced and the skin "loose" and "too large for the body" (Fig. 100-1).

The skull and sella turcica have been normal in roentgenograms. The combined cortical thickness of the second left metacarpal has been below the normal median in all untreated patients and below the 10th percentile in 8 of 20 patients.[35] Osteoporosis has been the leading sign in one patient[30] and is a constant finding, especially in younger patients. Biopsies of the cortical bone from the iliac crests of two patients have shown extensive osteoporosis.[55] The relative volume of bone, the calcified bone volume, and the calcification rate were decreased in another patient in a bone biopsy performed after dual tetracycline labeling.[30] The ocular fundi have been normal by ophthalmoscopy.[35] Of 20 patients studied 14 had minute opacities in the anterior fetal Y suture of both lenses. In 10 patients the opacities were surrounded by minute satellites. The opacities were never large enough to cause visual impairment and have remained stable, in some patients now for over 20 years. The mechanism of the lens abnormalities is unknown.[49]

The dentition of the patients has been normal, and the patients do not appear to be especially prone to caries despite the high carbohydrate content of the diet.

Liver Pathology. In the youngest patients the histologic findings in liver biopsy specimens have been normal with only occasional fat droplets found in the hepatocytes.[8,35] In older patients delimited areas in periportal or central parts of the liver lobules contain hepatocytes with ample pale cytoplasm and small pyknotic nuclei. In these cells the glycogen content is decreased and glycogen appears in coarse particles. At the borders of the abnormal areas many nuclei are ghostlike with

Fig. 100-2 Two children with LPI. The pictures were taken at the time of diagnosis, A. at 12 years of age, B. at 6 years of age. Note the prominent abdomen, hypotrophic muscles, and "loose" skin. The thorax of the child in B. is deformed and her trunk shortened because of osteoporosis and pathologic fractures of the vertebrae.

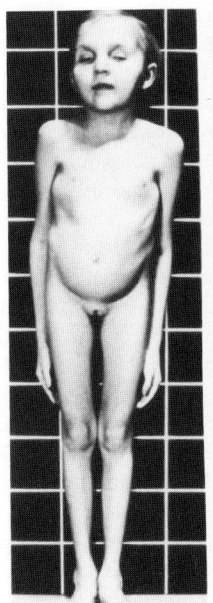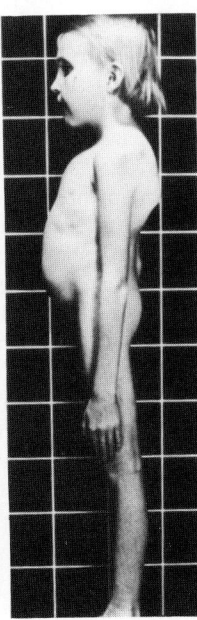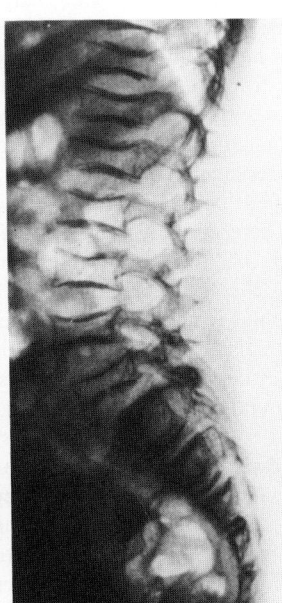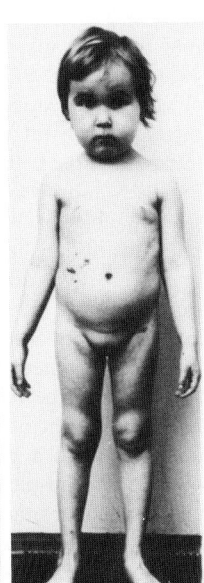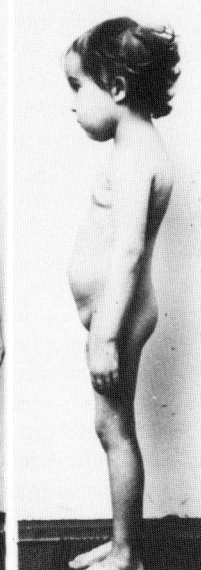

A.

B.

central inclusion bodies staining positively with periodic acid–Schiff. Cytoplasmic fat droplets occur especially in the periportal areas, and extensive fatty degeneration has been found in a few patients. Inflammatory cells have always been absent in the biopsy samples, but the periportal collagenous tissue may be increased.

Growth. Birth weights and lengths have been normal for gestational age, and postnatal growth is normal before weaning. The growth curves begin then to deviate progressively more from the normal mean, and at the time of diagnosis 16 of 20 Finnish patients were more than 2 SD below the mean height, 12 patients were more than 3 SD, 6 patients more than 4 SD, 2 patients more than 5 SD, and 1 patient 6 SD below the mean.[35] Skeletal maturation is considerably delayed. Thus, the growth continues longer than in healthy subjects, frequently until the age of 20 years. The final height of the patients has invariably been closer to the normal than the height measured during the time of diagnosis, because of therapy and the late cessation of growth. The head circumferences have been normal for age.

The body proportions are normal, but with advancing age moderate centripetal obesity, which is present from early childhood, becomes more obvious.

Performance in Adult Life. Mental development is normal in the majority of subjects. Performance is decreased particularly in patients with known histories of prolonged hyperammonemia. Altogether about 20 percent of patients with LPI reported in the literature or otherwise known to me are mentally retarded. Convulsions are uncommon, but periods of stupor have occasionally been misinterpreted as psychomotor seizures.[18] Four patients have had psychotic periods, which have clearly been precipitated by prolonged moderate hyperammonemia.[35]

Treatment with low protein diet and citrulline supplementation[11,14] (see "Therapy," below) has significantly improved the life quality of the patients. Episodes of vomiting and other signs of hyperammonemia have become a rare exception. The fitness of the patients is fair, and the only physical handicap seems to be diminished capacity for long-lasting heavy work: endurance is clearly limited. One patient, though, has worked for several years as a construction worker in a building company, but now finds the job too heavy; another one has been an active jogger for years and is capable of running 15 km without problems. The patients with prolonged periods of hyperammonemia in early infancy and childhood, who appeared severely retarded at the first presentation, have considerably and continuously improved their performance during therapy. All are now able to take care of the activities of daily life, and none is institutionalized. The most severely retarded patient, who had an IQ of 40 at the age of 12 years, lives in the custody of an elderly widow and is now at the age of 35 years capable of taking care of her daily activities; she also works in a protected environment outside home a few hours a day and helps routinely in the household. She is talkative, happy, and socially active. At the other end of the spectrum, one patient has graduated from a medical school and works successfully as an internist in a hospital, and several patients have graduated from high school or other schools and are permanently employed. The oldest known patient in Finland is now 45 years of age and retired because of back problems. He is mentally and physically active and takes care of the household duties of a small farmhouse. A Finnish-born

patient in Sweden is now 53 years old.[16,21,29] One male and five female patients are married.

Pregnancies of the Patients. Four of the five married females have had seven pregnancies. One of the mothers was treated during the pregnancy only with protein restriction; the others received citrulline supplementation during the pregnancies (8 to 14 pills of 0.414-g L-citrulline daily during meals). Anemia (hemoglobin < 85 g/liter) occurred in all, and platelet count decreased to less than 50×10^9/liter. A severe hemorrhage complicated both deliveries of one patient. Another patient had severe toxemia in her second pregnancy. The blood pressure increased to crisis values, she had prolonged convulsions and unconsciousness, but she recovered totally. In a third patient an ultrasound-guided amniotic fluid puncture led to a bleed and loss of the fetus at 35 gestational weeks. One patient has had two normal pregnancies and deliveries.

Of the six living children born to the patients, five are well at the ages of 4 to 9 years. One child, whose delivery was complicated by a severe hemorrhage of the mother, has hemiplegia and slightly delayed mental development, and another one was late in learning to speak but has later developed well.

The fertility of the male patients is unknown.

Complications. An unexpected and life-threatening complication in patients with LPI has been undefined interstitial pneumonia.[50,51] This disease is rare in healthy subjects, with lifetime incidences of about 5 per 100,000, but the disease is more common in many chronic diseases, including several liver and bowel diseases. Of the 34 Finnish patients, 3 have had interstitial pneumonia; 2 of them died. A Japanese patient has had a long-lasting, slowly progressive interstitial pneumonia,[36] and a Moroccan patient died with identical symptoms and autopsy findings (see below).[37] An American child with LPI presented with interstitial pneumonia at the age of 27 months.[38]

The symptoms of interstitial pneumonia in patients with LPI have started with progressive fatigue, cough, and mild to moderate fever, and one patient had blood in the sputum.[51] Dyspnea with marked air hunger during even minimal exercise has been a typical feature in all. Hemoglobin and platelet values fall, and arterial oxygen tension is decreased. The sedimentation rate is elevated, and the values of serum ferritin and lactate dehydrogenase, which are high also in normal circumstances, increase even further. In the two Finnish patients who died, the symptoms lasted from 2 to 4 weeks. The first patient died at the age of 10 years after 2 weeks of pulmonary symptoms. She was treated with a combination of antibiotics, and then with sulfamethoxazole-trimethoprim because of suspicion of *Pneumocystis carinii* infection; she showed no response to treatment. The other child was 14 years of age when she started coughing and had clear interstitial changes in chest x-rays. She was treated immediately with sulfamethoxazole-trimethoprim, but the symptoms progressed, and the child died 2 days after an open lung biopsy. No signs of *P. carinii* or other agents could be found in either patient in autopsy. The autopsy findings were otherwise those of alveolar proteinosis in which PAS-positive material fills the alveoli. The lung biopsy sample taken before death suggested interstitial pneumonia of undefined origin. The third patient was 23 years of age at the time when the symptoms appeared. He immediately had an open lung biopsy in which no pathogens were found, and the findings were typical for interstitial pneumonia. He was treated with high dose prednisolone. The symptoms and the radiologic changes in the lungs disappeared within a week. He has now had a small dose of prednisolone for over 2 years. He had a relapse when he started smoking 8 months after the initial bout of interstitial pneumonia; the symptoms and pulmonary changes again disappeared when he stopped smoking and the dose of prednisolone was temporarily increased.

It is likely that this complication is part of the symptomatology in patients with LPI. The pathophysiological mechanisms remain unknown, but the abnormal content of cationic amino acids in the bronchoalveolar lavage of the patients suggests that the transport of cationic amino acids may be abnormal also in the pulmonary alveolar epithelium.[52] How this transport defect affects gas exchange in the alveoli remains unknown. Because the complication appears to be treatable with prednisolone, and in severe cases possibly with bronchoalveolar lavage, all patients and their guardians should be warned of the symptoms.

One patient died while asleep at the age of 20 years after a few drinks in the evening. He may have died of an acute episode of hyperammonemia; the autopsy was noninformative.

Other Cationic Aminoacidurias

The propositus of Whelan and Scriver[46] has many clinical features of LPI, including recurrent vomiting during infancy, poor growth, and delayed bone age. The heights of the other members of the kindred with the dominantly inherited trait were also below the 3d percentile for normals, but they were otherwise healthy. The authors discuss the possibility that the trait was a heterozygous mainfestation of the LPI gene or some other recessive transport disorder. Interestingly, the obligate heterozygotes in the pedigree of Kihara et al.[33] had urinary excretion values similar to those of the subjects with the dominant trait described by Whelan and Scriver,[46] suggesting that the index case might be homozygous for hyperdibasic aminoaciduria type 1. Further pedigrees with the trait of hyperdibasic aminoaciduria type 1 are needed before firm conclusions of this relationship are possible.

So far, in my mind the patients described by Kihara et al.,[33] Oynagi et al.,[24,25] Brown et al.,[23] and others[13,18,20,22,28] have sufficiently clinical and biochemical features to be regarded as patients with LPI. The only significant clinical differences are the less marked protein intolerance,[25,28] less significant growth failure,[18,28] and some peculiar features (see below).[20,31–33] We now know that clinical protein tolerance may vary also in LPI, and that vomiting and aversion to high protein foods are not always prominent in confirmed patients. This variability may depend on the subject's capacity to handle waste nitrogen via other metabolic routes.[53–61]

Omura and coworkers[47] described a Japanese 21-month-old girl with severe mental retardation, convulsions, marked growth failure, and clear signs of malnutrition. She excreted excessive lysine in the urine, but arginine and ornithine excretions were at the upper limit of normal or only slightly increased, respectively. Her intestinal absorption of lysine was decreased, but arginine, ornithine, and cystine absorption did not differ from that of controls. Fasting blood ammonia and values after a load of cow's milk were normal. LPI cannot with certainty be excluded in this patient, but she likely represents another mutation affecting the transport of the cationic amino acids, and the disease should tentatively be regarded as an entity of its own, best called *isolated lysinuria*.

A few patients with biochemical LPI have had uncommon associated features, which may point to heterogeneity of the syndrome or may be random associations; because of the biochemical identity I have included these patients in the LPI group. A mentally retarded boy with biochemical features typical of LPI showed a peculiar response to phenothiazines which were prescribed to relieve his hyperactivity.[33] A Japanese 8-year-old girl had a prestage of systemic lupus erythematosus and showed multiple immunologic abnormalities, including impaired function of lymphocytes, presence of lupus erythematosus cells, antinuclear antibodies, and hypergammaglobulinemia.[31] Two Italian boys with LPI had striking joint hyperextensibility and prominent autophagy of erythroblasts by granulocytes and clusters of degenerated erythroblast nuclei in the bone marrow[20,32]; autophagy was found also in a patient of Turkish ancestry.[22] The findings in the bone marrow aspirates are interesting and may be a common phenomenon in the disease, but were not found in two Finnish patients.[35] The autophagocytosis might be linked with abnormalities in the peripheral red cells of the patients.[35,62] The mechanisms of the changes in blood cells should be further investigated.

BIOCHEMICAL INVESTIGATIONS

Plasma and Urine Amino Acids

Plasma and urinary amino acid concentrations and the renal clearances of plasma amino acids are given in Table 100-1. Plasma concentrations of lysine, arginine, and ornithine are one-third to one-half of the normal means, but occasionally may be well within the normal range.[8,14,19,25,33,35,63] The concentrations of serine, glycine, citrulline, proline, and, especially, alanine and glutamine are increased. The accumulation of amino nitrogen in these pools seems to be a regular feature of LPI. The increase in plasma citrulline is noteworthy.

Urinary excretion and renal clearance of lysine is massively increased, and that of arginine and ornithine is moderately increased. Because of the high plasma concentrations of serine, glycine, citrulline, proline, alanine, and glutamine, they are also found in excess in the urine, but their renal clearances are within the normal range.

In some patients, lysinuria and arginine-ornithinuria has been missed in thin-layer or paper chromatograms used for screening of inborn errors of metabolism. The reason for the low excretion in these patients has always been that the plasma concentration of the cationic amino acids has been exceptionally low. In such a situation the molar and relative excretion of the cationic amino acids can be minimal even though the clearances are high. I have seen this phenomenon a few times in older, undiagnosed patients who have spontaneously restricted their protein intake to the extreme, and who also have had clear signs of protein malnutrition. When protein intake has been increased, cationic aminoaciduria has become as prominent as in other patients.

The reabsorption defect in kidney tubules is most marked for lysine; arginine is less affected; and ornithine is absorbed best.[63] The measurements of tubular reabsorption of lysine have in some urine collections suggested net secretion. The reabsorption defect for arginine and ornithine and presumably for lysine remains significant also when plasma concentrations of these amino acids are increased, but at extremely high filtered loads, when plasma concentrations are at several milli-

Table 100-1 Plasma Concentration, Urinary Excretion, and Renal Clearance of Free Amino Acids in Patients with Lysinuric Protein Intolerance*

| | Plasma concentration, mM | | | Urinary excretion, mmol/(24 h·1.73 m²) | | Renal clearance, ml/(min·1.73 m²) | |
| | Range in normal children† | Patients with LPI | | | | | |
		Mean	Range	Mean	Range	Mean	Range
Alanine	0.173–0.305	0.772	0.417–1.017	1.068	0.465–1.586	0.953	0.698–1.324
α-amino-adipic acid	0.002	n.m.		0.609	0.405–0.821		
Arginine	0.023–0.086	0.027	0.012–0.058	0.356	0.076–0.687	11.508	3.175–22.300
Aspartic acid	0.004–0.023	n.m.		n.m.		n.m.	
Asparagine and glutamine	0.057–0.467	5.583	3.644–7.161	6.491	4.365–8.542	0.891	0.595–1.628
Citrulline	0.012–0.055‡	0.232	0.141–0.530	0.519	0.155–0.988	1.440	0.762–2.425
Cystine	0.048–0.140‡	0.080	0.057–0.105	0.120	0.059–0.209	0.175	0.050–0.324
Glutamic acid	0.023–0.250	0.049	0.021–0.081	0.047	0.040–0.051	0.853	0.427–0.839
Glycine	0.117–0.223	0.467	0.385–0.530	2.058	1.595–2.808	3.062	2.538–4.067
Histidine	0.024–0.085	0.110	0.084–0.139	0.637	0.155–1.232	4.374	1.184–10.221
Isoleucine	0.028–0.084	0.059	0.029–0.082	0.099	0.071–0.158	1.306	0.598–2.076
Leucine	0.056–0.178	0.090	0.050–0.126	0.101	0.067–0.142	0.830	0.596–1.184
Lysine	0.071–0.151	0.070	0.032–0.179	4.126	1.022–7.000	25.655	11.116–45.877
Methionine	0.011–0.016	0.032	0.021–0.048	0.050	0.038–0.063	1.356	0.976–2.044
Ornithine	0.027–0.086	0.021	0.002–0.083	0.106	0.091–0.134	3.268	2.709–5.357
Phenylalanine	0.026–0.061	0.049	0.033–0.084	0.078	0.056–0.094	1.268	0.574–1.966
Proline	0.068–0.148	0.189	0.158–0.268	n.m.		n.m.	
Serine	0.079–0.112	0.251	0.199–0.246	0.607	0.398–0.878	1.900	1.257–2.628
Threonine	0.042–0.095	0.113	0.030–0.172	0.277	0.111–0.554	1.825	1.235–2.578
Tyrosine	0.031–0.071	0.047	0.030–0.072	0.142	0.125–0.158	2.361	1.202–3.688
Valine	0.128–0.283	0.182	0.132–0.244	0.047	0.035–0.059	0.177	0.167–0.186

*The plasma concentrations were measured after an overnight fast, and the respective 24-h urines were collected when the patients were on a self-chosen hospital diet. The clearance values are calculated from the 24-h urinary excretion and from the fasting plasma concentration. Plasma lysine, arginine, and ornithine concentrations were measured on 33 occasions in the 20 patients; the other values are from four patients.
†From Dickenson et al.[198]
‡From Scriver & Davies.[199]
NOTE: n.m. = not measurable
SOURCE: From Simell, Perheentupa, Rapola, Visakorpi, and Eskelin.[35] Used by permission of *American Journal of Medicine*.

molar, the tubular reabsorption of arginine and ornithine reabsorption resembles normal. At these very high filtered loads, selective transport probably becomes unimportant and physical diffusion phenomena determine the rate of absorption. A significant increase in plasma concentration and, consequently, in the filtered load of one cationic amino acid leads easily to net tubular secretion of the other two cationic amino acids.

Blood Ammonium, Urinary Orotic Acid Excretion, and Serum Urea

Blood ammonium concentration is normal ($< 70 \mu M$) during fasting, but 100 to 560 μM after regular meals.[8,35] The extent of postprandial hyperammonemia depends on the protein content of the meal. The ammonium values usually return to the normal range 2 to 6 h later. Frequent ingestion of high protein foods, extensive fasting, acute infections, especially viral gastroenteritis, and severe physical or psychological stress increase blood ammonium in the patients and easily cause persisting hyperammonemia, which does not disappear during fasting.

Urinary orotic acid is increased more frequently than blood ammonium suggesting that orotic acid is a better indicator of urea cycle failure in these patients than hyperammonemia.[13,64–67] Urine samples collected during fasting frequently contain normal amounts of orotic acid [$< 0.03 \mu mol/(kg·h)$, or $< 11 \mu mol/mmol$ creatinine], but values are increased even during a self-chosen low protein diet [log mean, 0.52; range

0.05 to 3.77 $\mu mol/(kg·h)$ in 24-h urines] and increase massively if the protein intake is increased further.[64] Nitrogen loads given in the form of cow's milk protein (0.5 g/kg), ammonium lactate (2.5 mmol/kg), or intravenous alanine (6.6 mmol/kg during 90 min) can be given without clinical risk to the patients. In healthy subjects blood ammonium is stable after such loads, but blood ammonium and certainly urinary orotic acid excretion increase in the patients [log mean and range in the patients: 4.93; 1.61 to 11.19 μmol (kg·h) in 4- to 6-h urines; 0.61, 0.10 to 7.22 in 1.5-h urines; and 3.32, 0.30 to 11.73 in 6-h urines after the three loads, respectively]. Another advantage to orotic acid measurement is the stability of the compound: urine samples can be sent via post at room temperature for orotic acid measurement, but blood ammonium has to be measured immediately.

Serum urea concentration has been high-normal or even slightly elevated during the first few months of life, but later it has been constantly below the normal mean and often subnormal, the mean of 126 determinations in the patients being 3.7 μM (range 1.5 to 8.5 μM; normal 2 to 7 μM).[35] Serum urea increases slowly after nitrogen loads in the patients.[8,35]

Other Laboratory Tests

Slight normochromic or hypochromic anemia with anisocytosis and poikilocytosis is common.[8,35,62] Most patients have leukopenia, and the platelet count is decreased, in some young patients not uncommonly to less than 30,000/mm³. Reticulocyte count is often slightly elevated, the osmotic resistance of the erythrocytes, the red cell indexes, and serum iron level and iron-binding capacity are normal. In some patients autoerythrophagocytosis has been observed in the bone marrow,[20,22,32] and the number of megakaryocytes may be increased, but otherwise the marrows have been normal. Interestingly, the changes in the peripheral blood cells decrease in intensity during and after puberty and values in adults are usually within the range of healthy subjects.

The blood pH, serum concentrations of sodium, potassium, chloride, calcium, and phosphate are normal. Serum LDL and HDL cholesterol values are often high in older children and adults probably because the patients replace a large part of their protein calories by fat in the diet. In animals, high orotic acid concentrations influence lipoprotein metabolism,[68] but the possible link between orotic acidemia and hyperlipidemia in LPI is unclear. The triglycerides are usually slightly elevated in the patients.

No constant abnormal peaks have been found in analyses of organic acids in the urine.

Interestingly, several of the patients from different ethnic backgrounds and all the Finnish patients have constantly had significantly increased concentrations of lactate dehydrogenase (LDH) and ferritin in serum.[22,35,69] All LDH isoenzymes, but most significantly the liver isoenzyme, are affected; the values are usually two to five times higher than the upper limit of normal. The LDH and ferritin values increase further during complications of the disease, including undefined interstitial pneumonia (see "Complications," above). Thyroxine-binding globulin (TBG) is also elevated in the patients, and consequently, measurements of total T_4 give high values; free T_4 is normal, and the patients are clinically euthyroid.[34,35,70,71] Whether there is a general increase in hormone carrier proteins or only a specific increase in TBG is not known.

In two Japanese patients growth hormone responsiveness to glucagon-propranolol, arginine, and insulin was studied as a possible cause of the delayed growth and bone age of the patients.[34] The response to insulin was moderately decreased in the one patient studied before arginine supplementation was started, but all responses were normal when the patients had been on arginine supplementation for 8 months.

Kekomäki and coworkers[72] confirmed that the activities of the urea cycle enzymes in liver biopsy samples of the patients were normal. Glutaminase I activity, once suggested to be the basic defect in patients with LPI,[16,21,29] has later been proven to be normal both in leukocytes and liver.[73] Likewise, the activity of ornithine aminotransferase, the enzyme responsible for the main catabolic pathway of ornithine (see Chap. 19), has been normal or slightly elevated in the liver and cultural fibroblasts of the patients.[45,74,75] The concentration of *N*-acetylglutamine and the rate of its synthesis have not been measured in the patients, but the efficient production of orotic acid by the patients[13,22,64,76] strongly suggests that this cofactor and regulator of the carbamoyl-phosphate synthase activity[77] is available in sufficient quantities.

PATHOPHYSIOLOGY

Normal Cellular Transport of Cationic Amino Acids

In normal physiology, cationic and other amino acids reach the body only by passing through the intestinal wall in the process of absorption. They do this mainly as free amino ac-

ids, but partly also as dipeptides and other small peptides, which then are hydrolyzed to free amino acids at the luminal brush border and, predominantly, in the cytoplasm of the epithelial cells.[78-83] During absorption, the amino acids first cross the luminal membrane of the epithelial cell. A fraction of the amino acids is used in cellular metabolism in the cytoplasm ("metabolic runout"),[84,85] and the remainder must cross the basolateral (antiluminal) membrane of the cell to reach the body. In the cytoplasm, the amino acids may also enter the subcellular organelles (mitochondria, lysosomes, etc.) where some amino acids are metabolized. In adult intestine, only free amino acids, not peptides, are able to cross the whole cell in absorption.

Absorption of the cationic amino acids lysine, arginine, and ornithine has been extensively studied in the kidneys,[78,86-99] intestine,[100-102] and some parenchymal tissues[103-105] of animals and human beings. Most studies have included cyst(e)ine, because in cystinuria the transport of all four amino acids is affected.[90,100,106-121] In the kidney, reabsorption occurs along the full length of the nephron. The proximal segment of the tubule receives the highest load of filtered amino acids and, consequently, has to absorb a significant load quickly and efficiently, whereas further down in the tubules, a more selective reabsorption system would be more profitable. Such axial heterogeneity[85,122] in absorption has indeed been demonstrated for several amino acids, including the cationic amino acids. The net handling of the cationic amino acids in the kidney and their mutual interactions have been studied using amino acid loads after which the urinary excretion and renal clearances of the amino acids have been measured.[112,113,116,123-125] Microperfusion of animal nephrons[91,95,119,120] and flux measurements in segments of the nephrons or fragments of the tubules,[91,92,108,126] in renal cortical slices,[90,93,94,108] in cultured cells of the tubules,[127] and in isolated vesicles prepared from the brush border[88,97,114,118,128,129] or basolateral cell membrane[99] of the cells of the tubules have been performed. The transport of the cationic amino acids across the luminal membrane occurs via a shared, Na^+-dependent system. The system selective for the cationic amino acids in the proximal convoluted tubule has high capacity and low affinity,[92] whereas the system in the proximal straight segment has low capacity and high affinity and is shared with cystine.[91]

At the basolateral membrane in the kidney tubules, the transport of the cationic amino acids is not shared with cystine, and both high and low affinity systems are used. The transport from the cell to the pericellular space (efflux) occurs via Na^+-independent exchange diffusion that may be shared with cystine on the cytoplasmic surface.[85,99,108]

At the brush border of the intestinal epithelium the cationic amino acids are transported by a single Na^+-dependent system that has high affinity and is shared by all cationic amino acids and cystine.[130,131]

White and Christensen[104] and others[103,110,127,132] have carefully characterized transport of cationic amino acids in cultured or isolated cells using human fibroblasts,[103,110,133] permanent hepatoma cell lines, rat hepatocytes,[104] and other cells.[127,132] Transport of cationic amino acid into human fibroblasts occurs by a saturable mediation, which they designated system y^+, earlier called Ly^+. The system serves the flow of ω-guanidino amino acids and ω,α-diamino acids. The uptake of cationic substrates by system y^+ is Na^+-independent, pH-insensitive, stereoselective, and inhibitable by neutral amino acids in the presence of Na^+ ion. This system is not shared with cystine.[106,110] The uptake and efflux of the substrates are strongly stimulated by cationic amino acids inside and outside the cell, respectively. Arginine and homoarginine accumulate in human fibroblasts and can reach distribution ratios of more than 20 at physiological external amino acid concentrations.[103] The driving force appears to be the transmembrane voltage.

In hepatoma cell lines, the transport of cationic amino acids occurs by the saturable mediation of the system y^+.[104] The influx into hepatoma cells has all the characteristics seen also in the system y^+ of the fibroblasts, including strong stimulation by cationic amino acids inside the cell, i.e., trans-stimulation. In normal hepatocytes no significant trans-stimulation was observed, suggesting that the y^+ system is absent or altered in this cell. The rate at which arginine is transported at the hepatocyte plasma membrane suggests that transport is the rate-limiting step in hydrolysis of arginine by arginase.

Mutations in the Transport of Cationic Amino Acids

In a long series of studies Segal and coworkers,[118] States and coworkers,[127] and others[102,106,107,111–117,134] have analyzed the interactions of the cationic amino acids and cystine in transport mutations, especially in the cystinuric kidney (see Chap. 99). Recently, Scriver and coworkers have reviewed in detail current knowledge of the transport mutations in cystinuria and other cationic aminoacidurias.[85]

In classic cystinuria, reabsorption in the kidney tubules of cystine and the cationic amino acids is selectively impaired, occasionally to the extent that measurements show net tubular secretion of cystine or lysine[96,135] (see Chap. 99). In normal tubules, cystine, lysine, arginine, and ornithine mutually compete for transport. Intravenous loading studies in cystinuria suggest that the residual reclamation of cationic amino acids and cystine follows rules of competition similar to those in the normal tubules.[111,116] An absorption defect has also been found in the intestinal epithelium in vivo[117] and in biopsy samples of the jejunum.[100,102] Measurement of unidirectional and net fluxes of cationic amino acids in intestinal biopsy samples of patients with cystinuria clearly shows that the transport defect is localized at the luminal membrane of the epithelial cells.[130] Most likely, the efflux permeability of the luminal membrane is increased but the influx is normal.[131]

Is the transport defect in patients with LPI similar to that in cystinuria? In their first report on LPI, Perheentupa and Visakorpi[1] had access only to semiquantitative measurement of plasma and urinary amino acids, and they regarded the urinary amino acid excretion as identical to that in cystinuria. It soon became apparent that cystine was excreted in significantly smaller quantities than in cystinuria, and Kekomäki and coworkers[6,8] suggested that the mechanisms of the transport defects differ in the two diseases. Absorption of the cationic amino acids by the kidneys[10,15,25,63,98] and small intestine[9,23,24,33,41,136–138] in LPI has later been carefully characterized. In both organs, absorption of lysine, arginine, and ornithine is defective. The slight increase in renal cystine losses could be explained by the excessive tubular lysine load and normal competition for absorption in the kidney tubules. Oral loads with the dipeptide lysylglycine increased plasma glycine concentrations properly, but plasma lysine remained almost unchanged in the patients[41] (Fig. 100-3). This was in striking contrast to the controls in whom concentrations of both amino acids of the dipeptide increased in plasma. LPI was thus the first human disease in which a defect in peptide absorption was recognized. Because the transport of oligopep-

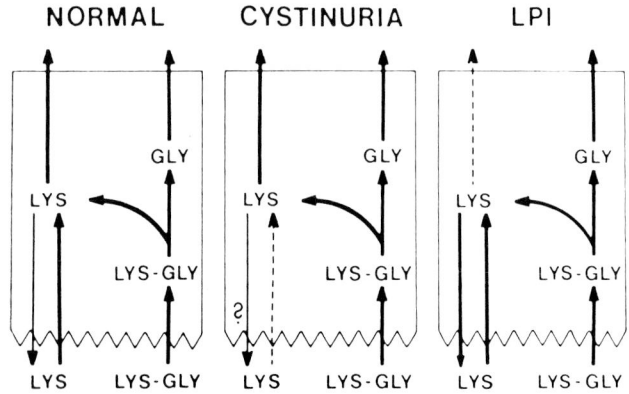

Fig. 100-3 Schematic representation of brush border cells of jejunal mucosa, showing absorption of diamino acids [here lysine (LYS) in free and dipeptide form] and suggested sites of defect in cystinuria and LPI. Defective fluxes are indicated by dashed arrows. (From Rajantie, Simell, and Perheentupa.[41] Used with permission of Lancet.)

tides is not shared with transport of free amino acids at the luminal membrane of the enterocyte, the lysine-containing dipeptide enters the cell normally in LPI. The absorbed peptides are hydrolyzed to free amino acids mainly in the cytoplasm of the enterocyte,[79,80,139] and they are able to cross the basolateral membrane only as free amino acids. The missing increase in plasma lysine after the lysylglycine load but normal increase in plasma glycine shows that the intracellularly released dipeptide-derived lysine is unable to cross the basolateral (antiluminal) membrane of the enterocyte and strongly suggests that the transport defect in LPI is localized at this membrane in the epithelial cells.

In vitro studies of unidirectional and net transport of cationic amino acids in jejunal biopsy samples of the patients soon proved even more directly that the transport defect situates at the basolateral (antiluminal) membrane of the epithelial cell.[43] These in vitro results differed clearly from identical experiments in cystinuria,[131] where the abnormality in lysine transport was located at the luminal membrane, and the defect in cystine absorption could perhaps best be explained by increased efflux permeability at the luminal membrane of the epithelium. Interestingly, in an earlier study of cationic amino acid accumulation in jejunal biopsy samples and uptake during intestinal perfusion in LPI no defects could be found.[136] This failure is understandable now when the defect in LPI has been localized at the antiluminal membrane and we know that the epithelial cells accumulate higher than normal concentrations of the cationic amino acids (see below).

Rajantie and coworkers[42] gave patients with LPI prolonged intravenous infusions of citrulline and measured plasma and urinary amino acids during the loads. Compared with controls, the plasma citrulline concentration of the patients increased normally but urinary citrulline excretion increased excessively. Rises in plasma arginine and ornithine during the load were subnormal, but massive argininuria and moderate ornithinuria appeared (Fig. 100-4). The excretion rates of lysine and other amino acids remained practically unaltered, thus excluding mutual competition as the cause for the increases. This finding is compatible with a transport defect at the basolateral membrane of the renal tubular cells and can be explained as follows: Citrulline as a neutral amino acid does not use the cationic amino acid transport system; citrulline is partly converted to arginine and further to ornithine in the tubular cell as an integral part of the reabsorption process; in

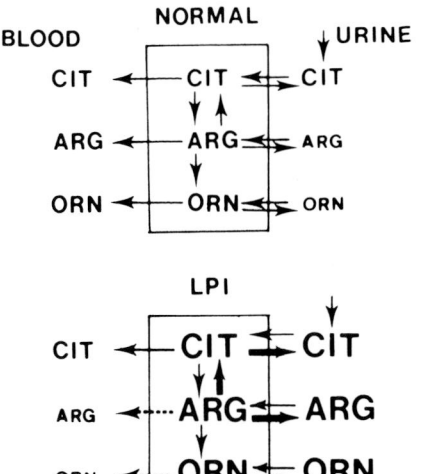

Fig. 100-4 Suggested mechanism of tubular reabsorption of citrulline in human beings and of pathophysiology of the massive argininuria and moderate citrullinuria and ornithinuria in LPI. Bold type and arrows indicate increased concentrations and fluxes; thin type and dotted arrows indicate decreased concentrations and impaired fluxes. (*From Rajantie, Simell, and Perheentupa.*[42] *Used with permission of Journal of Clinical Investigation.*)

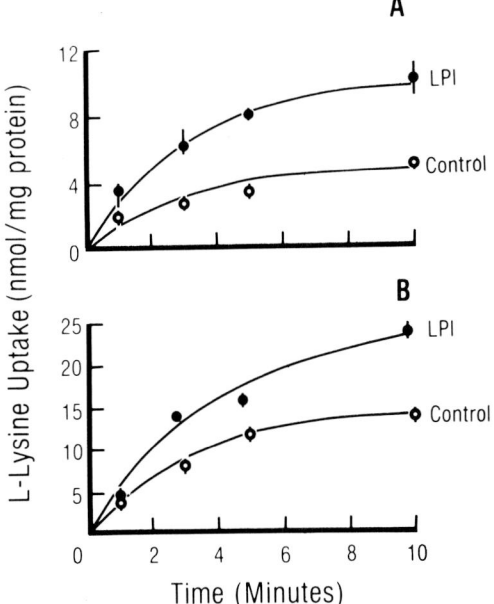

Fig. 100-5 L-Lysine uptake by cultured fibroblasts from a control subject (open circles) and a patient with LPI (solid circles). The cells were incubated for 90 min at 37°C in buffer without arginine (*A*) or in buffer containing 1 mM arginine (*B*), washed twice with PBS (37°C), then incubated for 1,3,5, or 10 min at 37°C in PBS containing 0.1 mM L-[³H] lysine. Data are means and ranges of two or three measurements. [*From Smith, Scriver, Tenenhouse, and Simell.*[44] *Used with permission of Proceedings of the National Academy of Sciences (U.S.A.).*]

LPI, formed arginine and ornithine are unable to exit at the antiluminal membrane, their intracellular concentrations increase, and backflux (argininuria and ornithinuria) into the lumen occurs; high intracellular arginine and ornithine concentrations inhibit citrulline metabolism in the tubular cell; intracellular citrulline concentration increases and leads to citrullinuria.

Reabsorption curves for arginine and ornithine have been produced in patients with LPI by stepwise increases in plasma concentrations of arginine or ornithine and simultaneous measurement of tubular filtration rate and plasma concentration and urinary excretion of the two amino acids.[63] The curves were clearly below those of healthy controls at all loads except at values close to the tubular reabsorption maxima of the controls, where the patients' curves approached those of the controls. It is possible that at such filtered loads (at plasma concentrations of several millimolar) active transport plays a minor part and physical factors regulate the amount of reabsorption. The extrarenal metabolic clearances of arginine and

Table 100-2 Steady State Amino Acid Concentrations in Intact Cultured Fibroblasts of a Control and a Patient with Lysinuric Protein Intolerance

	Concentration ratio	
Amino acid	*Control*	*LPI*
Lysine/alanine	0.23 ± 0.007	0.35 ± 0.014
Ornithine/alanine	0.11 ± 0.009	0.19 ± 0.008
Arginine/alanine	0.40 ± 0.024	0.54 ± 0.012
Leucine/alanine	0.30 ± 0.016	0.31 ± 0.015

NOTE: Human skin fibroblasts were maintained in culture medium 24 h prior to harvest with a rubber policeman. Cells were resuspended in 1 ml phosphate-buffered saline, sonicated, and deproteinized. The supernatants were assayed for amino acid content with a Durrum D-500 amino acid analyzer. Values are the mean ± SEM, *n* = 4. Amino acid values were normalized to fibroblast alanine concentrations which were 18 ± 1.3 and 17 ± 1.2 pmol/mg protein in control and LPI cells, respectively.

ornithine by tissues, calculated from the same infusion experiments, were significantly decreased in the patients.[140] This finding suggests that besides the defect in epithelial transport, transport in LPI is abnormal in other tissues as well.[132]

A direct proof of such an extraepithelial transport defect was obtained in studies of Smith and coworkers,[44] who investigated steady state amino acid concentrations in intact fibroblasts (Table 100-2) and influx (Figs. 100-5 and 100-6), efflux, and trans-stimulation of the transport of lysine and other cationic amino acids and their nonmetabolized analogues[141] in cultured fibroblasts of the patients (Fig. 100-7). In trans-stimulation experiments the amino acid in question, or another amino acid which uses the same transport system, is present on the other side of the membrane than the labeled amino studied. The influx at the plasma membrane was not different from controls in LPI; trans-stimulated efflux was. A defect in trans-stimulation was found also in fibroblasts of the heterozygotes with values about 50 percent of those in homozygotes, suggesting gene-dosage effect (Fig. 100-8). The results also imply that the basolateral membrane of epithelial cells and the plasma membrane of parenchymal cells are functionally analogous at least in transport of cationic amino acids, but it may well be that this analogy is a general physiological principle. Vesicles prepared from LPI fibroblast plasma membranes failed to show a transport defect for cationic amino acids.[142] This finding is possibly explained by the fact that the preparation of the vesicles favored equally formation of inside-out and right-side-out vesicles. If both forms are present in equal quantities and the defect is only expressed in efflux, the sum effect in the mixture of the vesicles will be the same as in controls.

Recently, Smith and others[143] measured transport of the cationic amino acids and their nonmetabolized analogues in isolated erythrocytes of the patients. The mutant erythrocytes

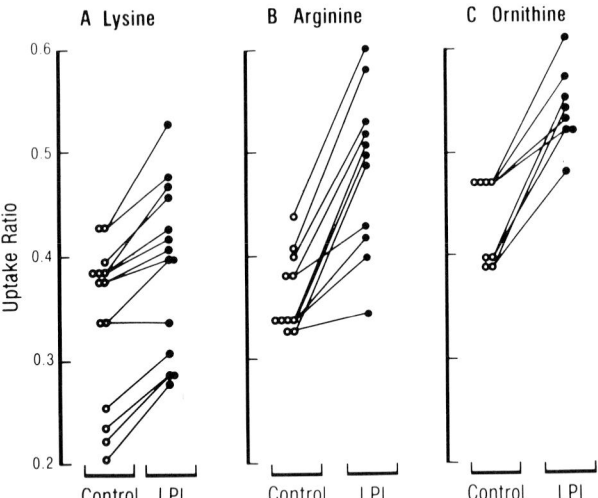

Fig. 100-6 Uptake ratios of the cationic amino acids vs. L-leucine at steady state in cultured fibroblasts of controls and patients with LPI. The cells were incubated for 10 min at 37°C in PBS containing 0.1 mM L-[³H] leucine and (A) 0.1 mM L-[¹⁴C] lysine, (B) L-[¹⁴C] arginine, or (C) L-[¹⁴C] ornithine. Each point represents a single measurement of the net isotopic molar uptake ratio (cationic amino acid/leucine) in paired control and LPI cell strains. The differences between control and LPI cells for uptake of L-lysine ($n = 13$, $P < 0.02$), L-arginine ($n = 16$, $p < 0.01$), and L-ornithine ($n = 8$, $p < 0.01$) are significant by the Wilcoxon signed rank test. [From Smith, Scriver, Tenenhouse, and Simell.[44] Used with permission of Proceedings of the National Academy of Sciences (U.S.A.).]

Fig. 100-7 Efflux of L-homoarginine from cultured skin fibroblasts of a control and LPI cell line. The cells were incubated for 40 min at 37°C in buffer containing (A) 0.1 mM L-[³H] homoarginine and (B) 0.1 mM L-[¹⁴C] leucine. The time course of efflux was measured into unlabeled incubation buffer (trans-zero condition, open circles) or into buffer containing 1 mM unlabeled amino acid (trans-stimulated condition, solid circles). Time course for efflux from the cellular pool is shown. Zero-time homoarginine content (100% value) was 2.8 ± 0.16 (control) and 2.9 ± 0.29 (LPI) nmol/mg protein; zero-time leucine content was 8.5 ± 0.37 (control) and 9.8 ± 0.59 (LPI) nmol/mg protein. The difference in the zero-time leucine content for LPI and control cells was not significant. Each point represents the mean and SEM of four determinations. [From Smith, Scriver, Tenenhouse, and Simell.[44] Used with permission of Proceedings of the National Academy of Sciences (U.S.A.).]

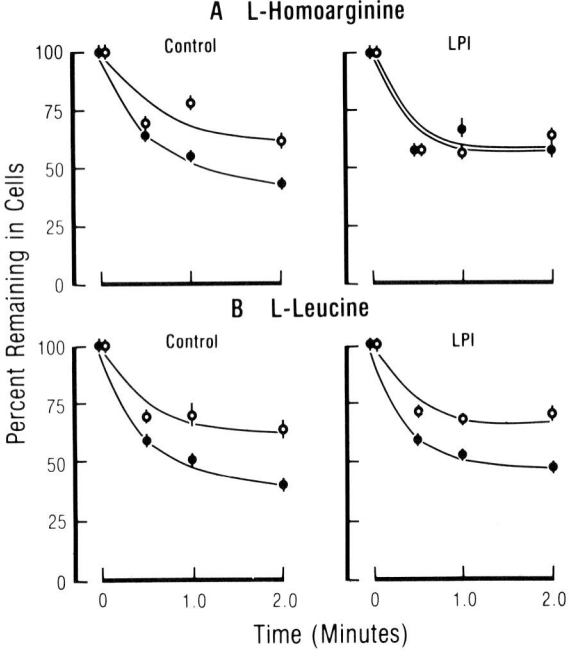

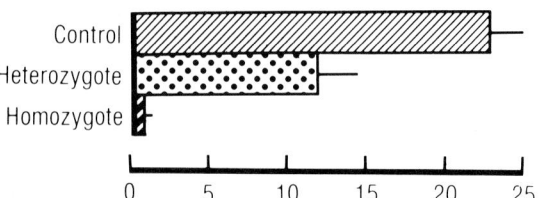

Fig. 100-8 Percent trans-stimulation of homoarginine efflux from cultured skin fibroblasts of control cells and cells from homozygotes and heterozygotes for LPI. The cells were preincubated for 40 min at 37°C in buffer containing 0.1 mM L-[³H] homoarginine and 0.1 mM L-[¹⁴C] leucine. The 1-min efflux of label was measured as described in Fig. 100-7. Trans-stimulation refers to the difference (increase) between trans-zero and trans-stimulated efflux, normalized to zero-time cellular isotope. Each value represents the mean of three or four determinations on one cell line; error bars indicate the range. [From Smith, Scriver, Tenenhouse, and Simell.[44] Used with permission of Proceedings of the National Academy of Sciences (U.S.A.).]

had transport characteristics identical to the controls, and the authors concluded that the mutant transporter is not expressed on the surface of mature human erythrocytes. The findings are in agreement with those of Gardner and Levy,[144] who noticed that the transport of dibasic amino acids in human erythrocytes is temperature-dependent, incapable of uphill transport, and not dependent on extracellular sodium or potassium concentrations or on energy derived from cellular metabolism. They further stated that lysine transport in human erythrocytes comprises two saturable, carrier-mediated processes operating in parallel: one is a high affinity, low capacity process that predominates at low lysine concentrations; the other is a low affinity, high capacity process that predominates at higher lysine concentrations. Further studies on cationic amino acid transport in rabbit reticulocytes[145] and human erythrocytes[146] have clarified details of the transport phenomena in these specialized cells.

Subcellular Transport of Cationic Amino Acids

In the urea cycle, the urea molecule is assembled on the ornithine backbone; cleavage of the urea from arginine regenerates free ornithine. During the cycle, ornithine has to gain access from the cytoplasm into the mitochondrial matrix to be carbamylated, and the formed citrulline has to be exported back to the cytoplasm to be further exposed by the enzyme argininosuccinic acid synthase. Whether or not mitochondrial transport processes are involved in the pathophysiology of LPI has remained an open question.[147] In rat liver mitochondria and in mitochondria of human cultured fibroblasts, ornithine and citrulline transport has been relatively well characterized. In the classic study of Gamble and Lehninger,[148] the entry of ornithine into the mitochondria of rat liver was mediated by a carrier that was respiratory-dependent and required permeant proton-yielding anions for function.

Ornithine fluxes in mitochondria have earlier been measured in the absence of active citrulline synthesis.[149–160] The study of Cohen and coworkers[155] avoided this pitfall: they analyzed the transport phenomena during the presence and absence of citrulline synthesis in respiring rat liver mitochondria. They were able to characterize both influx of ornithine and efflux of citrulline in the mitochondria. When respiring mitochondria were preloading with cold ornithine and then incubated in [³H]ornithine, the mitochondria produced citrulline of the same specific activity as that of external ornithine, but ornithine in mitochondrial matrix remained unlabeled. The concentration of ornithine in the matrix was also extremely low when the ornithine concentration in the incubation medium was less than 1 mM. Both findings imply that the ornithine molecule is not transported into the matrix randomly, but is channeled to the intramitochondrial enzymes for further processing to citrulline. The importance of ornithine catabolism by the matrix enzyme ornithine aminotransferase for the net movement of ornithine has remained open, but the activity in liver mitochondria is such that all ornithine not immediately used in the urea cycle is transaminated (see Chap. 19).

Studies of citrulline transport in rat liver mitochondria have suggested that the transport mechanisms do not depend on respiratory energy or the presence of permeant cations or anions.[148,154,155] Citrulline transport occurs in liver mitochondria, but not in mitochondria of the heart.[148] Some studies have also implied that an ornithine-citrulline antiporter exists in the mitochondrial membrane,[152] but this finding may have been an artifact caused by experimental circumstances in which citrulline was not formed.[153,155]

Recently, increasing evidence has accumulated suggesting that mitochondrial ornithine transport is genetically altered in another human urea cycle disease, the hyperornithinemia-hyperammonemia-homocitrullinuria (HHH) syndrome[53,157,158,160–168] (see Chap. 19). If the plasma membranes of cultured fibroblasts are made permeable to amino acids by digitonin, accumulation of labeled ornithine can be measured in the particulate fraction of the cells, which mainly contain mitochondria.[165,166] Such studies have suggested that ornithine accumulation in mitochondria is decreased in fibroblasts and liver of patients with the HHH syndrome.[162,163,165,166,169] If cultured HHH fibroblasts are incubated with labeled ornithine, a subnormal fraction of label is found in CO_2, implying that ornithine is unable to enter the mitochondria to be further metabolized.[157,158,160–163,167,169]

A mitochondrial transport defect also has been proposed to have a part in the pathophysiology of LPI.[147] This theory has been based on biochemical findings which speak against cytoplasmic ornithine deficiency in this disease. Firstly, biopsy samples from the intestinal epithelium accumulate higher than normal concentrations of the cationic amino acids in vitro.[43] Secondly, LPI fibroblasts also accumulate higher than normal concentrations of cationic amino acids.[44,45] Thirdly, direct measurements of concentrations of the cationic amino acids in liver biopsy samples of the patients contain normal or elevated concentrations of the cationic amino acids, even though their plasma concentrations are decreased.[24,147] Fourthly, there is evidence that citrulline formation is not impaired: plasma concentration of citrulline is constantly high normal or elevated in the patients[8,30,31,34,35]; citrulline concentration is high normal or increased in liver biopsy samples of the patients[24,147]; and the extrarenal metabolic clearance of citrulline and conversion of citrulline to arginine and ornithine are retarded[42,147] (Fig. 100-9).

These conflicting findings have been reconciled in a hypothesis which suggests that in LPI a defect in the efflux of the cationic amino acids exists at the plasma membrane of the liver cells or, if the cells retain polarity, at the basolateral membrane and that the transport defect is expressed also in the mitochondria.[147] Such a mitochondrial defect would further increase cytoplasmic concentrations of arginine and ornithine. Depletion of ornithine in the mitochondria would lead to accumulation of carbamyl phosphate and to hyperammo-

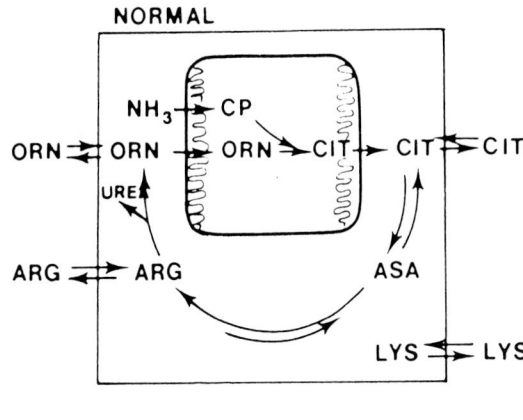

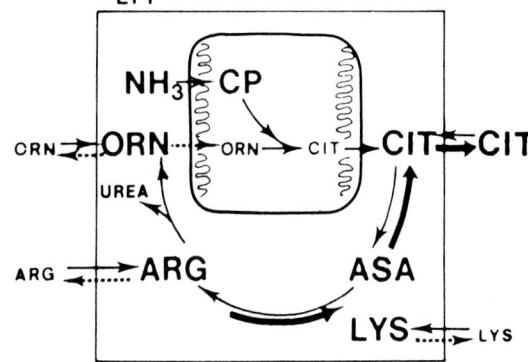

Fig. 100-9 Hypothetical mechanism of the elevated plasma citrulline concentration and the urea cycle failure in LPI. Bold type and arrows indicate supranormal concentrations and fluxes; thin type and dotted arrows, subnormal concentrations and impaired fluxes. For simplicity, only those fluxes are shown which are present at the "basolateral" and mitochondrial membranes of the liver cells. (*From Rajantie, Simell, and Perheentupa.*[147] *Used with permission of Acta Paediatrica Scandinavica.*)

nemia. This theory, though interesting, has recently been questioned because the oxidation of ornithine in cultured LPI fibroblasts proceeds normally.[45]

System y^+ for the cationic amino acids is expressed on the lysosomal membranes and used at least for influx of the cationic amino acids.[170] Normal lysosomes have active and selective efflux mechanisms for cystine, sialic acid, and probably other substances[171–176] (see Chap. 106). Efflux of other amino acids from the lysosomes is strictly limited, as is suggested by the disruption of rat liver lysosomes if they are filled by passive diffusion with amino acid methyl esters.[176] These esters are hydrolyzed by lysosomal enzymes, but the liberated amino acids cannot readily escape from the lysosomes, possibly because of their high polarity. They accumulate within the lysosomes, and may cause osmotic lysis of the organelles. In LPI the lysosomes might function as a metabolically excluded pool of lysine and other cationic amino acids so that the actual cytoplasmic lysine concentration would be relatively normal or even low. No direct proof of such a transport defect has been obtained, but the hypothesis is attractive.

Malfunction of the Urea Cycle

Patients with LPI have decreased nitrogen tolerance and develop hyperammonemia after ingestion of even moderate amounts of protein.[8,11,14,35,64] The urea cycle failure is clearly less severe than in the "first" enzyme defects of the cycle, i.e., in carbamyl-phosphate synthase, ornithine carbamoyltransferase, and N-acetylglutamate synthase deficiencies, or even argininosuccinate synthase or lyase deficiencies (see Chap. 20). The clinical impression is that the tendency to hyperammonemia in LPI closely resembles that seen in patients with the HHH syndrome.[53,161,163-165,168]

Already in the first description of the disease, Perheentupa and Visakorpi[1] noticed that intravenous infusion of ornithine during a load of protein or intravenous L-alanine prevented the hyperammonemia which otherwise followed the loads. An identical effect was later shown with arginine and citrulline when given intravenously.[8,11,14,35,64,137]

Oral supplementation with arginine and ornithine has been only minimally effective in the patients, because both amino acids are poorly absorbed from the intestine and easily produce diarrhea.[10,43,138,177] Obviously the absorption defect is not total because low protein diet and arginine or ornithine supplementation have improved growth and decreased hyperammonemia in patients with LPI.[6-8,13,17,28,32] A few variant patients tolerate arginine or ornithine supplementation well.[13,17,28,32] Awrich et al.[14] showed that the neutral amino acid citrulline, also an intermediate in the urea cycle, when taken as an oral supplement prevents hyperammonemia. It is well-tolerated by LPI patients,[11,30] and its effect in preventing hyperammonemia in LPI has now been well-documented.[64] As a neutral amino acid it passes the cell membranes normally in LPI and is rapidly converted in the body to arginine and then to ornithine.

Poor intestinal absorption, excessive loss in the urine, and low plasma concentration of the cationic amino acids arginine and ornithine strongly suggest that the malfunction of the urea cycle is caused by deficiency of these urea cycle intermediates (Fig. 100-1). The finding that hyperammonemia produced by amino nitrogen or protein loads could effectively be prevented by simultaneous intravenous infusion of arginine or ornithine led to the hypothesis that the malfunction of the cycle was caused by deficiency of ornithine in the liver cell.[1,4,178] Even now, when increasing evidence has accumulated supporting the view that intracellular concentration of the cationic amino acids is increased in the patients both in epithelial and in parenchymal cells,[24,147] the malfunction is best explained as a "functional deficiency" of the intermediates. In reality, it is possible that enzymes of the urea cycle are inhibited by increased intracellular concentration of lysine (see Chap. 19) or that a transport defect at the inner mitochondrial membrane prevents the entry of ornithine into the mitochondria, just as hypothesized in the HHH syndrome (see Chap. 19). Such a defect would decrease ornithine concentration in the mitochondrial matrix, decrease transcarbamylation, and slow down urea production. It is also possible that cytoplasmic concentrations of the cationic amino acids actually are diminished because of accumulation of these substances in an organelle, most likely the lysosome. In such a case, cytoplasmic ornithine concentration could be temporarily increased by supplementation of arginine or ornithine. We know that the lysosomal membrane exhibits specialized transport characteristics which can be modified by genetic mutations in human beings (see Chap. 106). The lysosomal transport mutations are all apparently defects in the efflux from the lysosomes; this is the case at least in cystinosis and the Salla disease. An efflux defect could theoretically explain pooling and cytoplasmic depletion of the cationic amino acids in LPI, but our knowledge of amino acid movements into and out of the lysosomes is too sparse, and no direct data to confirm the hypothesis of a lysosomal efflux defect exist.

Half of the urea nitrogen begins urea synthesis as free ammonium via carbamyl phosphate synthesis, but this nitrogen does not gain access to the liver cell as free ammonium.[179,180] Animal experiments have suggested that the amide nitrogen of glutamine is an important precursor of urea nitrogen; glutamine functions as a transport and storage form of ammonium ion to keep its tissue levels within tolerable ranges via the glutamine synthetase.[16] The ammonium for carbamyl phosphate synthesis is released from glutamine by intramitochondrial glutaminase, which was found to be defective in the leukocytes of one patient.[16,21] The suspected defect in glutaminase led to an interesting hypothesis of the mechanism of the transport disorder in LPI,[16] but later studies did not confirm the deficiency of glutaminase in leukocytes or liver biopsy samples of other patients.[73]

It is possible that during large nitrogen inflow, i.e., after protein meals, intrahepatic glutamine synthesis serves to trap free ammonium and amino groups from other amino acids. Plasma glutamine is constantly high in LPI, and its fluctuations seem to be related with the previous nitrogen load. Exact knowledge of the nitrogen flow in the liver during protein absorption is lacking, and the rate-limiting step in urea formation is not known. It may well be that the rate-limiting step varies and depends on several other factors, including the availability of the substrates.[148,150,155,156,159,181-183]

Patients with LPI efficiently produce orotic acid after nitrogen loads.[22,64] This cytoplasmic pathway could theoretically serve as a means to excrete excessive nitrogen from the body via carbamyl phosphate and aspartate, i.e., the same substrates as in the actual urea cycle.[184,185] The level of renal clearance and urinary excretion of orotic acid is very high, but the overall capacity of the pathway is limited, and only relatively small amounts of excess nitrogen can be excreted as orotate even during loading conditions.[76] Interestingly, uracil is also excreted in excess in LPI.[22]

Lysine Deficiency

Despite prevention of hyperammonemia by citrulline supplementation and low protein diet, several features of the disease have remained unaltered in treated patients. Growth has not totally normalized, bone age is delayed, liver and spleen are enlarged, and liver pathology is unchanged.[11,35] The hematologic abnormalities have also persisted during the therapy, and osteoporosis is practically unaltered. These are possibly signs caused by continuing deficiency of the essential amino acid lysine, the net bioavailability of which in the changeable body pool is significantly reduced by the poor intestinal absorption and heavy renal losses.[4,41,63,138] In addition to the transport defects in the epithelial cells, which lead to poor net reclamation of lysine in the body, the transport defect at the plasma membrane of the parenchymal cells and hypothetical transport defects in cell organelles may be important cofactors in the suspected lysine deficiency.[44,147]

Lysine is an integral part of practically all proteins and, relatively speaking, collagen is especially rich in lysine. The mechanisms of the often prominent osteoporosis in patients with LPI have remained open. It may well be that the osteoporosis is caused by lysine deficiency, which delays formation of the matrix of the bone and is an important factor for poor formation of other essential structural proteins and additional proteins.[186-190] Nothing is known of the acute or long-term effects of intravenous lysine infusions or oral supplementation of absorbable lysine derivatives in osteoporosis in LPI. Rajantie and coworkers found that ε-N-acetyllysine, but not homocitrulline, efficiently increases plasma lysine in patients with LPI.[191] Acetyllysine uses a transport system different from that of the cationic amino acids, making it suitable for oral use. Despite the apparently fast metabolism of acetyllysine to lysine in human beings, its suitability for lysine replacement may be limited. In mice fed on synthetic amino acid diets, substitution of L-lysine with ε-N-methyl-L-lysine, ε-N-dimethyl-L-lysine, and ε-N-trimethyl-L-lysine resulted in relative replacement values of about $\frac{1}{12}$, $\frac{1}{20}$, and $\frac{1}{25}$, respectively, of the value obtained with the standard lysine diet.[192] The α-N-acetyl-L-lysine was not utilized by mice and the replacement value of the ε-N-acetyllysine was about 3 percent that of lysine. Replacement of the charged ε-amino group in lysine with a sulfur-containing group led to weight reduction. N-Phosphorylated lysine has not been tested in this system.[193]

Arginine is an essential amino acid in inborn errors of the urea cycle and probably in growing children[55,56] and some animals, at least the cat.[194,195] However, arginine deficiency is unlikely to be a reason for the residual symptoms in LPI because ample amounts should be available during citrulline supplementation.[11,14,137]

Serum Ferritin, LDH, and TBG. Serum concentrations of ferritin, LDH, and TBG have constantly been elevated in the patients.[22,35] The cause of the high concentration of ferritin is its decreased catabolism in the liver,[62,69] but the reason for this is not known. High ferritin and LDH values have increased further during acute illnesses (see "Complications," above). The increase in TBG and the association increase in total T_4 has on some occasions led to suspicion of hyperthyroidism in these patients.

GENETICS

The inheritance of LPI follows a typical pattern for an autosomal recessive disease.[2] The incidence of the disease is 1 in 60,000 in Finland, but the birthplaces of the patients' grandparents are unevenly distributed in the country, with several clusters of families.[2,4,35] Most patients in other countries have been isolated cases[13–15,18,19,22,23,27,28,30,31,33] or children of one family.[17,20,25,26,32,34]

The hyperdibasic aminoaciduria type 1 described by Whelan and Scriver[46] showed autosomal dominant inheritance. Of the 33 subjects in the kindred, 13 had the trait. The suggestion that the affected members of the kindred are heterozygotes of an autosomal recessive disease seems likely, even though no confirmed homozygotes are known. The possibility exists that the patient of Kihara et al.[33] is a homozygote for the trait, as has been suggested by Scriver and Tenenhouse,[85] but this remains a hypothesis. The original proposal by the authors that the carriers of the trait could be heterozygous for LPI is at least equally attractive.

The expression of the mutant gene in heterozygotes for LPI has been poorly characterized. The constant finding of decreased epithelial transport of the cationic amino acids in homozygotes and, especially, the direct measurement of defective cationic amino acid transport in cultured fibroblasts of homozygotes and heterozygotes for LPI[44] strongly support the view that the mutation affects the transport protein at the basolateral cell membrane of the epithelial cells and at the plasma membrane of the parenchymal cells. Many LPI heterozygotes excrete slightly increased amounts of the cationic amino acids in the urine, but this has not been a constant finding.[2] More detailed studies of the characteristics of the heterozygotes are indeed needed.

There have been no attempts to characterize directly the protein(s) responsible for the transport of the cationic amino acids, nor to evaluate more closely the mutation(s) in DNA.

TREATMENT

Clinically the most severe symptom of the disease is hyperammonemia, which occurs after high protein meals, during prolonged fasting, or during severe infections. A diet in which the protein content has been moderately decreased—in children to 1.0 to 1.5 g/kg/day and in adults to 0.5 to 0.8 g/kg/day—forms the basis of successful treatment.[11,14,35] Acute symptoms disappear when the patients are on this diet, but in many infants, severe protein aversion leads to minimal energy intake as well, and even though nausea and vomiting can be avoided, pediatric patients usually eat very poorly during the first years of life. Supplementation with arginine or ornithine has been moderately helpful in some patients,[6–8,13,17,28,32] but the decreased intestinal absorption of cationic amino acids limits their usefulness, and supplementation often leads to osmotic diarrhea.[41,137,138] Citrulline is a neutral amino acid and utilizes another transport mechanism at the cell membrane. It is readily absorbed from the intestine and converted to arginine and further to ornithine in the body, especially in the liver. Citrulline supplementation guarantees that there are adequate numbers of urea cycle intermediates present at the site of urea synthesis, and, indeed, oral citrulline supplementation has clinically proved to prevent hyperammonemia as efficiently as intravenous arginine or ornithine.[11,14,64] The dose of citrulline supplementation has been 2.5 to 8.5 g (14 to 48 mmol) daily, divided into three to five doses and taken during the meals. The individual doses are first calculated according to the protein content of the meals, and then adjusted according to the clinical and biochemical responses of the patients. Most patients quickly learn to know how much citrulline they need for a specific portion of each high protein food. Citrulline can be given as powder dissolved in juice, or as pills (ours have 0.414-g L-citrulline) or capsules.

In acute hyperammonemic crisis in LPI, the best treatment has been total removal of protein and nitrogen from the nutrition. Intravenous glucose should be given to supply as much energy as possible. In hyperammonemia we have also infused ornithine, arginine, or citrulline intravenously, first a priming dose of 1 mmol/kg in 5 to 10 min, and then at a rate of about 0.5 to 1 mmol/kg/h until the symptoms have subsided. Sodium benzoate and sodium phenylacetate intravenously or orally[54,57,59,60] appear clinically effective in these episodes even though they do not correct alanine-induced hyperammonemia.[76]

Lysine has been given orally to the patients, but its intestinal absorption is poor and it causes diarrhea and abdominal pains in the patients.[11] A few patients have received lysine supplementation for longer periods of time, but the ability of lysine to correct signs of protein malnutrition has not been convincing. Interestingly, acute loads of ε-N-acetyllysine, a neutral analogue of lysine and a readily absorbed substance, increased plasma lysine concentrations in the patients as well as in the controls.[191] Homocitrulline had no effect on plasma lysine. Because of the limited availability and the high price of acetyllysine, it has not been used as long-term supplement in the patients.[197] Its usefulness as a replacement for lysine has recently been questioned.[192]

A potentially life-threatening complication in patients with LPI is acute interstitial pneumonia[50,51] (see "Complications," above). One patient has been treated efficiently with high dose prednisolone; the symptoms subsided rapidly after initiation of the therapy. The dose was soon tapered, but a 2.5-mg intermittent-day dose has been continued for over 2 years. The response to treatment is important, because three other patients with this complication died of insufficient gas exchange and oxygenation of the blood within a couple of weeks from the appearance of the symptoms.

This study was supported in part by grants from the Sigrid Juselius Foundation, the Finnish Academy, the Signe and Ane Gyllenberg Foundation, the Foundation for Pediatric Research, Finland, and the University Foundation, Turku, Finland. The skillful technical assistance of Ms. Marjatta Viikari in many of the original studies is acknowledged. I want to thank Ms. Anne Nurmi, Mrs. Marja Piippo, Mrs. Anneli Enlund, Mrs. Kaarina Renvall, and my wife, Tuula, for help in the processing of the manuscript.

REFERENCES

1. PERHEENTUPA J, VISAKORPI JK: Protein intolerance with deficient transport of basic amino acids. *Lancet* 2:813, 1965.
2. NORIO R, PERHEENTUPA J, KEKOMÄKI M, VISAKORPI JK: Lysinuric protein intolerance, an autosomal recessive disease. *Clin Genet* 2:214, 1971.
3. MCKUSICK VA: *Mendelian Inheritance in Man; Catalog of Autosomal Dominant, Autosomal Recessive and X-linked Phenotypes*, 6th ed. Baltimore, The Johns Hopkins University Press, 1983, pp 138, 682.
4. SIMELL O, RAJANTIE J, PERHEENTUPA J: Lysinuric protein intolerance, in Eriksson AW, Forsius H, Nevanlinna HR, Workman PL, Norio RK (eds): *Population Structure and Genetic Disorders*. London, Academic, 1980, p 633.
5. SIMELL O, SCRIVER CR: Hyperdibasic-aminoaciduria, in Bergsma D (ed): *Birth Defects Compendium*, 2d ed. New York, The National Foundation—March of Dimes, Inc, 1979, p 543.
6. KEKOMÄKI M: Familial protein intolerance. Studies on an inborn error of metabolism and related biochemical problems. Thesis, Helsinki, 1969.
7. KEKOMÄKI M, TOIVAKKA E, HÄKKINEN V, SALASPURO M: Familial protein intolerance with deficient transport of basic amino acids. Report on an adult patient with chronic hyperammonemia. *Acta Med Scand* 183:357, 1968.
8. KEKOMÄKI M, VISAKORPI JK, PERHEENTUPA J, SAXEN L: Familial protein intolerance with deficient transport of basic amino acids. An analysis of 10 patients. *Acta Paediatr Scand* 56:617, 1967.
9. RAJANTIE J: Lysinuric protein intolerance: Intestinal transport defect and treatment. Thesis, Helsinki, 1980.
10. SIMELL O: Lysinuric protein intolerance. Thesis, Helsinki, 1975.
11. RAJANTIE J, SIMELL O, RAPOLA J, PERHEENTUPA J: Lysinuric protein intolerance: A two-year trial of dietary supplementation therapy with citrulline and lysine. *J Pediatr* 97:927, 1980.
12. PERHEENTUPA J, SIMELL O: Lysinuric protein intolerance. *Birth Defects* 10(4):201, 1974.
13. RUSSELL A, SLATTER M, BEN-ZVI A: Ornithine administration as a therapeutic tool in dibasic aminoaciduric protein intolerance. *Hum Her* 27:206, 1977.
14. AWRICH AE, STACKHOUSE J, CANTRELL JE, PATTERSON JH, RUDMAN D: Hyperdibasicaminoaciduria, hyperammonemia, and growth retardation: Treatment with arginine, lysine, and citrulline. *J Pediatr* 87:731, 1975.
15. KATO T, TANAKA E, HORISAWA S: Hyperdibasicaminoaciduria and hyperammonemia in familial protein intolerance. *Am J Dis Child* 130:1340, 1976.
16. MALMQUIST J, JAGENBURG R, LINDSTEDT G: Familial protein intolerance: Possible nature of enzyme defect. *N Engl J Med* 284:997, 1971.
17. YOSHIMURA T, KATO M, GOTO I, KUROIWA Y: Lysinuric protein intoler-

ance—Two patients in a family with loss of consciousness and growth retardation. *Rinsho Shinkeigaku* 23:140, 1983.
18. KITAJIMA I, GOTO K, UMEHARA F, NAGAMATSU K, KANEHISA Y: A case of lysinuric protein intolerance with intermittent stupor looking like psychomotor seizure in adulthood. *Rinsho Shinkeigaku* 26:592, 1986.
19. CARSON NAJ, REDMOND OAB: Lysinuric protein intolerance. *Ann Clin Biochem* 14:135, 1977.
20. ANDRIA G, BATTAGLIA A, SEBASTIO G, STRISCIUGLIO P, AURICCHIO S: Lysinuric protein intolerance. *Rev Ital Pediatr* 2:386, 1977.
21. MALMQUIST J, HETTER B: Leucocyte glutaminase in familial protein intolerance. *Lancet* ii:129, 1970.
22. BEHBEHANI AW, GAHR M, SCHRÖTER W: Lysinuric protein intolerance. *Monatsschr Kinderheilkd* 131:784, 1983.
23. BROWN JH, FABRE LF JR, FARRELL GL, ADAMS ED: Hyperlysinuria with hyperammonemia. *Am J Dis Child* 124:127, 1972.
24. OYNAGI K, SOGAWA H, MINAWI R, NAKAO T, CHIBA T: The mechanism of hyperammonemia in congenital lysinuria. *J Pediatr* 94:255, 1979.
25. OYNAGI K, MIURA R, YAMANOUCHI T: Congenital lysinuria: A new inherited transport disorder of dibasic amino acids. *J Pediatr* 77:259, 1970.
26. KATO T, MIZUTANI N, BAN M: Hyperammonemia in lysinuric protein intolerance. *Pediatrics* 73:489, 1984.
27. CHAN H, BILLMEIER GJ JR, MOLINARY SV, TUCKER HN, SHIN B-C, SCHAFFER A, CAVALLO K: Prolonged coma and isoelectric electroencephalogram in a child with lysinuric protein intolerance. *J Pediatr* 91:79, 1977.
28. ENDRES W, ZOULEK G, SCHAUB J: Hyperdibasicaminoaciduria in a Turkish infant without evident protein intolerance. *Eur J Pediatr* 131:33, 1979.
29. JAGENBURG R, LINDSTEDT G, MALMQUIST J: Familjär (?) proteinintolerans med hyperammoniemi. *Läkartidningen* 67:5255, 1970.
30. CARPENTER TO, LEVY HL, HOLTROP ME, SHIH VE, ANAST CS: Lysinuric protein intolerance presenting as childhood osteoporosis. Clinical and skeletal response to citrulline therapy. *N Engl J Med* 312:290, 1985.
31. NAGATA M, SUZUKI M, KAWAMURA G, KONO S, KODA N, YAMAGUCHI S, AOKI K: Immunological abnormalities in a patient with lysinuric protein intolerance. *Eur J Pediatr* 146:427, 1987.
32. ANDRIA G, SEBASTIO G, STRISCIUGLIO P, DEL GIUDICE E: Lysinuric protein intolerance: Possible genetic heterogeneity? *J Inherited Metab Dis* 4:151, 1981.
33. KIHARA H, VALENTE M, PORTER MT, FLUHARTY AL: Hyperdibasicaminoaciduria in a mentally retarded homozygote with a peculiar response to phenothiazines. *Pediatrics* 51:223, 1973.
34. GOTO I, YOSHIMURA T, KUROIWA Y: Growth hormone studies in lysinuric protein intolerance. *Eur J Pediatr* 141:240, 1984.
35. SIMELL O, PERHEENTUPA J, RAPOLA J, VISAKORPI JK, ESKELIN L-E: Lysinuric protein intolerance. *Am J Med* 59:229, 1975.
36. YAMAGUCHI S: Personal communication, 1987.
37. SAUDUBRAY JM: Personal communication, 1987.
38. SPOCK A, COLEMAN R: Personal communication, 1988.
39. KRASNOPOLSKAIA KD, IAKOVENKO LP, MAZAEVA IV, LEBEDEV BV: Lysinuric protein intolerance, a hereditary defect of amino acid transport. *Pediatriia* 6:78, 1978.
40. SOGOWA H: Studies on the etiology of hyperammonemia associated with inborn errors of amino acid metabolism, part 2: Etiology of hyperammonemia associated with hyperdibasic aminoaciduria. *Sapporo Med J* 47:215, 1978.
41. RAJANTIE J, SIMELL O, PERHEENTUPA J: Basolateral-membrane transport defect for lysine in lysinuric protein intolerance. *Lancet* i:1219, 1980.
42. RAJANTIE J, SIMELL O, PERHEENTUPA J: Lysinuric protein intolerance. Basolateral transport defect in renal tubuli. *J Clin Invest* 67:1078, 1981.
43. DESJEUX J-F, RAJANTIE J, SIMELL O, DUMONTIER A-M, PERHEENTUPA J: Lysine fluxes across the jejunal epithelium in lysinuric protein intolerance. *J Clin Invest* 65:1382, 1980.
44. SMITH DW, SCRIVER CR, TENENHOUSE HS, SIMELL O: Lysinuric protein intolerance mutation is expressed in the plasma membrane of cultured skin fibroblasts. *Proc Natl Acad Sci USA* 84:7711, 1987.
45. BOTSCHNER J, SMITH DW, SIMELL O, SCRIVER CR: Comparison of ornithine metabolism in hyperornithinemia, hyperammonemia, and homocitrullinuria, lysinuric protein intolerance, and gyrate atrophy fibroblasts. *J Inherited Metab Dis*, in press, 1989.
46. WHELAN DT, SCRIVER CR: Hyperdibasicaminoaciduria: An inherited disorder of amino acid transport. *Pediatr Res* 2:525, 1968.
47. OMURA K, YAMANAKA N, HIGAMI S, MATSUOKA O, FUJIMOTO A, ISSIKI G, TADA K: Lysine malabsorption syndrome: A new type of transport defect. *Pediatrics* 57(1):102, 1976.
48. ANONYMOUS: Lysinuric protein intolerance: A rare cause of childhood osteoporosis. *Nutr Rev* 44:110, 1986.
49. MOSCHOS M, ANDREANOS D: Lysinuria and changes in the crystalline lens. *Bull Mem Soc Fr Ophthalmol* 96:322, 1985.
50. DALY WJ: Miscellaneous disease of the lung, in Stein JH, Cline MJ, Daly

WJ, Easton JD, Hutton JJ, Kohler PO, O'Rourke RA, Sande MA, Trier JS, Zvaifler NJ (eds): *Internal Medicine*. Boston, Little, Brown, 1983, p 397.

51. SIMELL OG, SIPILÄ I, PERHEENTUPA J, RAPOLA J: Lysinuric protein intolerance: Undefined interstitial pneumonia, a lethal or life-threatening complication. The Fourth International Congress of Inborn Errors of Metabolism. Sendai, Japan, 1987, p 38.

52. HALLMAN M, SIPILÄ I: Lysinuric protein intolerance (LPI): A possible defect in diamino acid transport in pulmonary alveolar epithelium. European Society for Pediatric Research, Annual Meeting, Oslo, Norway, June 26–29, 1988 (abstract).

53. SIMELL O, MacKENZIE S, CLOW CL, SCRIVER CR: Ornithine loading did not prevent induced hyperammonemia in a patient with HHH syndrome. *Pediatr Res* 19:1283, 1985.

54. COUDE FX, COUDE M, GRIMBER G, PELET A, CHARPENTIER C: Potentiation by piridoxilate of the synthesis of hippurate from benzoate in isolated rat hepatocytes. An approach to the determination of new pathways of nitrogen excretion in inborn errors of urea synthesis. *Clin Chim Acta* 136:211, 1984.

55. BRUSILOW SW: Arginine, an indispensable amino acid for patients with inborn errors of urea synthesis. *J Clin Invest* 74:2144, 1984.

56. VISEK WJ: Arginine needs, physiological state and usual diets. A reevaluation. *J Nutr* 116:36, 1986.

57. BRUSILOW SW, DANNEY M, WABER LJ, BATSHAW M, BURTON B, LEVITSKY L, ROTH K, MCKEETHREN C, WARD J: Treatment of episodic hyperammonemia in children with inborn errors of urea synthesis. *N Engl J Med* 310:1630, 1984.

58. BATSHAW ML, PAINTER MJ, SPROUL GT, SCHAFER IA, THOMAS GH, BRUSILOW S: Therapy of urea cycle enzymopathies: Three case studies. *Johns Hopkins Med J* 148:34, 1981.

59. BRUSILOW S, TINKER J, BATSHAW ML: Amino acid accumulation: A mechanism of nitrogen excretion in inborn errors of urea synthesis. *Science* 207:659, 1980.

60. SMITH I: The treatment of inborn errors of the urea cycle. *Nature* 291:378, 1981.

61. MCCORMICK K, VISCARDI RM, ROBINSON B, HEININGER J: Partial pyruvate decarboxylase deficiency with profound lactic acidosis and hyperammonemia: Responses to dichloroacetate and benzoate. *Am J Med Genet* 22:291, 1985.

62. RAJANTIE J, SIMELL O, PERHEENTUPA J, SIIMES M: Changes in peripheral blood cells and serum ferritin in lysinuric protein intolerance. *Acta Paediatr Scand* 69:741, 1980.

63. SIMELL O, PERHEENTUPA J: Renal handling of diamino acids in lysinuric protein intolerance. *J Clin Invest* 54:9, 1974.

64. RAJANTIE J: Orotic aciduria in lysinuric protein intolerance: Dependence on the urea cycle intermediates. *Pediatr Res* 15:115, 1981.

65. WENDLER PA, BLANDING JH, TREMBLAY GC: Interaction between the urea cycle and the orotate pathway: Studies with isolated hepatocytes. *Arch Biochem Biophys* 224:36, 1983.

66. MILNER JA, PRIOR RL, VISEK WJ: Arginine deficiency and orotic aciduria in mammals. *Proc Soc Exp Biol Med* 150:282, 1975.

67. MILNER JA, VISEK WJ: Urinary metabolites characteristic of urea-cycle amino acid deficiency. *Metabolism* 24:643, 1975.

68. KELLEY WN, GREENE ML, FOX IH, ROSENBLOOM FM, LEVY RI, SEEGMILLER JE: Effects of orotic acid on purine and lipoprotein metabolism in man. *Metabolism* 19:1025, 1970.

69. RAJANTIE J, RAPOLA J, SIIMES MA: Ferritinemia with subnormal iron stores in lysinuric protein intolerance. *Metabolism* 30:3, 1981.

70. LAMBERG B-A, SIMELL O, PERHEENTUPA J, SAARINEN P: Increase in TBG, T4, FT4 and T3 in the lysinuric protein intolerance. *Excerpta Med Int Cong Ser* 378:232, 1975.

71. LAMBERG BA, PERHEENTUPA J, RAJANTIE J, SIMELL O, SAARINEN P, EBELING P, WELIN M-G: Increase in thyroxine-binding globulin (TBG) in lysinuric protein intolerance. *Acta Endocrinol* 97:67, 1981.

72. KEKOMÄKI M, RÄIHÄ NCR, PERHEENTUPA J: Enzymes of urea synthesis in familial protein intolerance with deficient transport of basic amino acids. *Acta Paediatr Scand* 56:631, 1967.

73. SIMELL O, PERHEENTUPA J, VISAKORPI JK: Leukocyte and liver glutaminase in lysinuric protein intolerance. *Pediatr Res* 6:797, 1972.

74. KEKOMÄKI MP, RÄIHÄ NCR, BICKEL H: Ornithine-ketoacid aminotransferase in human liver with reference to patients with hyperornithinaemia and familial protein intolerance. *Clin Chim Acta* 23:203, 1969.

75. VALLE D: Personal communication, 1988.

76. SIMELL O, SIPILÄ I, RAJANTIE J, VALLE DL, BRUSILOW SW: Waste nitrogen excretion via amino acid acylation: Benzoate and phenylacetate in lysinuric protein intolerance. *Pediatr Res* 20:1117, 1986.

77. BACHMANN C, KRAHENBUHL S, COLOMBO JP, SCHUBIGER G, JAGGI KH, TONZ O: N-acetylglutamate synthetase deficiency: A disorder of ammonia detoxication. *N Engl J Med* 304:543, 1981.

78. HAMMERMAN MR: Na⁺-independent L-arginine transport in rabbit renal brush border membrane vesicles. *Biochim Biophys Acta* 685:71, 1982.

79. ADIBI SA: Intestinal transport of dipeptides in man: Relative importance of hydrolysis and intact absorption. *J Clin Invest* 50:2266, 1971.

80. MATTHEWS DM, ADIBI SA: Peptide absorption. *Gastroenterology* 71:151, 1976.

81. ASATOOR AM, GROUGHMAN MR, HARRISON AR, LIGHT FW, LOUGHRIDGE LW, MILNE MD, RICHARDS AJ: Intestinal absorption of oligopeptides in cystinuria. *Clin Sci* 41:23, 1971.

82. GANAPATHY V, MENDICINO JF, LEIBACH FH: Transport of glycyl-L-proline into intestinal and renal brush border vesicles from rabbit. *J Biol Chem* 256:118, 1981.

83. GANAPATHY V, MENDICINO J, PASHLEY DH, LEIBACH FH: Carrier-mediated transport of glycyl-L-proline in renal brush-border vesicles. *Biochem Biophys Res Commun* 97:1133, 1980.

84. SCRIVER CR, MCINNES RR, MOHYUDDIN F: Role of epithelial architecture and intracellular metabolism in proline uptake and transtubular reclamation in PRO/RR mouse kidney. *Proc Natl Acad Sci USA* 72:1431, 1975.

85. SCRIVER CR, TENENHOUSE HS: Mendelian phenotypes as "probes" of renal transport systems for amino acids and phosphate, in *Handbook of Renal Physiology*, in press, 1988.

86. WILSON OH, SCRIVER CR: Specificity of transport of neutral and basic amino acids in rat kidney. *Am J Physiol* 213:185, 1967.

87. WEBBER WA, BROWN JL, PITTS RF: Interactions of amino acids in renal tubular transport. *Am J Physiol* 200:380, 1961.

88. STEIGER B, STANGE G, BIBER J, MURER H: Transport of L-lysine by rat renal brush border membrane vesicles. *Pflugers Arch* 397:106, 1983.

89. SCRIVER CR, CLOW CL, READE TM, GOODYER P, AURAY-BLAIS C, GIGUERE R, LEMIEUX B: Ontogeny modifies manifestations of cystinuria genes. Implications for counseling. *J Pediatr* 106:411, 1985.

90. SCHWARTZMAN L, BLAIR A, SEGAL S: A common renal transport system for lysine, ornithine, arginine and cysteine. *Biochem Biophys Res Commun* 23:220, 1966.

91. SCHAFER JA, WATKINS ML: Transport of L-cystine in isolated perfused proximal straight tubules. *Pflugers Arch* 401:143, 1984.

92. SAMARZIJA I, FROMTER E: Electrophysiological analysis of rat renal sugar and amino acid transport IV. Basic amino acids. *Pflugers Arch* 393:199, 1982.

93. ROSENBERG LE, DOWNING SJ, SEGAL S: Competitive inhibition of dibasic amino acid transport in rat kidney. *J Biol Chem* 237:2265, 1962.

94. ROSENBERG LE, ALBRECHT I, SEGAL S: Lysine transport in human kidney: Evidence for two systems. *Science* 155:1426, 1967.

95. BERGERON M, MOREL F: Amino acid transport in rat renal tubules. *Am J Physiol* 216:1139, 1969.

96. CRAWHALL JC, SCOWEN EF, THOMPSON CJ, WATTS RWE: The renal clearance of amino acids in cystinuria. *J Clin Invest* 46:1162, 1967.

97. HILDEN SA, SACKTOR B: L-Arginine uptake into renal brush membrane vesicles. *Arch Biochem Biophys* 210:289, 1981.

98. KATO T, MIZUTANI N, BAN M: Renal transport of lysine and arginine in lysinuric protein intolerance. *Eur J Pediatr* 139:181, 1982.

99. LEOPOLDER A, BURCHHARDT G, MURER H: Transport of L-ornithine across isolated brush border membrane vesicles from proximal tubule. *Renal Physiol* 2:157, 1980.

100. MCCARTHY CF, BORLAND JL JR, LYNCH HJ JR, OWEN EE, TYOR MP: Defective uptake of basic amino acids and L-cystine by intestinal mucosa of patients with cystinuria. *J Clin Invest* 43:1518, 1964.

101. OZEGOVIC B, MCNAMARA D, SEGAL S: Cystine uptake by rat jejunal brush border membrane vesicles. *Biosci Rep* 2:913, 1982.

102. THIER SO, SEGAL S, FOX M, BLAIR A, ROSENBERG LE: Cystinuria: Defective intestinal transport of dibasic amino acids and cystine. *J Clin Invest* 44:442, 1965.

103. WHITE MF: The transport of cationic amino acids across the plasma membrane of mammalian cells. *Biochim Biophys Acta* 822:355, 1985.

104. WHITE MF, CHRISTENSEN HN: Cationic amino acid transport into cultured animal cells. II. Transport system barely perceptible in ordinary hepatocytes, but active in hepatoma cell lines. *J Biol Chem* 257:4450, 1982.

105. WHITE MF, GAZZOLA GC, CHRISTENSEN HN: Cationic amino acid transport into cultured animal cells. I. Influx into cultured human fibroblasts. *J Biol Chem* 257:4443, 1982.

106. BANNAI S: Transport of cystine and cysteine in mammalian cells. *Biochim Biophys Acta* 779:289, 1984.

107. DENT CE, ROSE GA: Aminoacid metabolism in cystinuria. *Q J Med* 79:205, 1951.

108. FOREMAN JW, HWANG S-M, SEGAL S: Transport interactions of cystine and dibasic amino acids in isolated rat renal tubules. *Metabolism* 29:53, 1980.

109. FOREMAN JW, MEDOW MS, BOVEE KC, SEGAL S: Developmental aspects of cystine transport in the dog. *Pediatr Res* 20:593, 1986.

110. GROTH U, ROSENBERG LE: Transport of dibasic amino acids, cystine, and

tryptophan by cultured human fibroblast: Absence of a defect in cystinuria and Harnup disease. *J Clin Invest* 51:2130, 1972.

111. KATO T: Renal handling of dibasic amino acids and cystine in cystinuria. *Clin Sci Mol Med* 53:9, 1977.

112. KATO T: Renal transport of lysine and arginine in cystinuria. *Tohoku J Exp Med* 139:9, 1983.

113. LESTER FT, CUSWORTH DC: Lysine infusion in cystinuria: theoretical renal thresholds for lysine. *Clin Sci* 44:99, 1973.

114. MCNAMARA D, PEPE M, SEGAL S: Cystine uptake by rat renal brush border vesicles. *Biochem J* 194:443, 1981.

115. MORIN CL, THOMPSON MW, JACKSON SH, SASS-KORTSAK A: Biochemical and genetic studies in cystinuria: Observations on double heterozygotes of genotype I/II. *J Clin Invest* 50:1961, 1971.

116. ROBSON EB, ROSE GA: The effect of intravenous lysine of the renal clearances of cystine, arginine and ornithine in normal subjects in patients with cystinuria and Fanconi syndrome and in their relatives. *Clin Sci* 16:75, 1957.

117. ROSENBERG LE: Cystinuria: Genetic heterogeneity and allelism. *Science* 154:1341, 1966.

118. SEGAL S, MCNAMARA PD, PEPE CM: Transport interaction of cystine and dibasic amino acids in renal brush border vesicles. *Science* 197:169, 1977.

119. VOLKL H, SILBERNAGL S: Mutual inhibition of L-cystine/cysteine and other neutral amino acids during tubular reabsorption. A microperfusion study in rat kidney. *Pflugers Arch* 395:190, 1982.

120. VOLKL H, SILBERNAGL S: Reexamination of the interplay between dibasic amino acids and L-cystine/L-cysteine during tubular reabsorption. *Pflugers Arch* 395:196, 1982.

121. THIER S, FOX M, SEGAL S: Cystinuria: In vitro demonstration of an intestinal transport defect. *Science* 143:482, 1964.

122. SCRIVER CR, CHESNEY RW, MCINNES RR: Genetic aspects of renal tubular transport. Diversity and topology of carriers. *Kidney Int* 9:149, 1976.

123. STRAUVEN T, MARDENS Y, CLARA R, TERHEGGEN H: Intravenous loading with arginine-hydrochloride and ornithine-aspartate in siblings of two families, presenting a familial neurological syndrome associated with cystinuria. *Biomedicine* 24:191, 1976.

124. FRIMPTER GW, HORWITH M, FURTH E, FELLOWS RE, THOMPSON DD: Inulin and endogenous amino acid renal clearances in cystinuria: Evidence for tubular secretion. *J Clin Invest* 41:281, 1962.

125. BOVEE KC, SEGAL S: Renal tubule reabsorption of amino acids after lysine loading of cystinuric dogs. *Metabolism* 33:602, 1984.

126. BOWRING MA, FOREMAN JW, LEE J, SEGAL S: Characteristics of lysine transport by isolated rat renal cortical tubule fragments. *Biochim Biophys Acta* 901:23, 1987.

127. STATES B, FOREMAN J, LEE J, HARRIS D, SEGAL S: Cystine and lysine transport in cultured human renal epithelial cells. *Metabolism* 36:356, 1987.

128. STEVENS BR, ROSS HJ, WRIGHT EM: Multiple transport pathways for neutral amino acids in rabbit jejunal brush border vesicles. *J Membr Biol* 66:213, 1982.

129. BUSSE D: Transport of L-Arginine in brush border vesicles derived from rabbit kidney cortex. *Arch Biochem Biophys* 191:551, 1978.

130. COICADAN L, HEYMAN M, GRASSET E, DESJEUX J-F: Cystinuria: Reduced lysine permeability at the brush border of intestinal membrane cells. *Pediatr Res* 14:109, 1980.

131. DESJEUX JF, VOLANTHEN M, DUMONTIER AM, SIMELL O, LEGRAIN M: Cystine fluxes across the isolated jejunal epithelium in cystinuria: Increased efflux permeability at the luminal membrane. *Pediatr Res* 21:477, 1987.

132. SIMELL O: Diamino acid transport into granulocytes and liver slices of patients with lysinuric protein intolerance. *Pediatr Res* 9:504, 1975.

133. METOKI K, HOMMES FA: The uptake of ornithine and lysine by isolated hepatocytes and fibroblasts. *Int J Biochem* 16:833, 1984.

134. SCRIVER CR: Cystinuria. *N Engl J Med* 315:1155, 1986.

135. FRIMPTER GW: Cystinuria: Metabolism of the disulfide of cysteine and homocysteine. *J Clin Invest* 42:1956, 1963.

136. KEKOMÄKI M: Intestinal absorption of l-arginine and l-lysine in familial protein intolerance. *Ann Paediatr Fenn* 14:18, 1968.

137. RAJANTIE J, SIMELL O, PERHEENTUPA J: Oral administration of urea cycle intermediates in lysinuric protein intolerance: Effect on plasma and urinary arginine and ornithine. *Metabolism* 32:49, 1983.

138. RAJANTIE J, SIMELL O, PERHEENTUPA J: Intestinal absorption in lysinuric protein intolerance: Impaired for diamino acids, normal for citrulline. *Gut* 21:519, 1980.

139. SILK DBA: Peptide absorption in man. *Gut* 15:494, 1974.

140. SIMELL O, PERHEENTUPA J: Defective metabolic clearance of plasma arginine and ornithine in lysinuric protein intolerance. *Metabolism* 23:691, 1974.

141. CHRISTENSEN HN, CULLEN AM: Synthesis of metabolism-resistant substrates for the transport system for cationic amino acids; their stimulation of the release of insulin and glucagon, and of the urinary loss of amino acids related to cystinuria. *Biochim Biophys Acta* 298:932, 1973.

142. BUCHANAN JA, ROSENBLATT DS, SCRIVER CR: Cultured human fibroblasts and plasma membrane vesicles to investigate transport function and the effects of genetic mutation. *Ann NY Acad Sci* 456:401, 1985.

143. SMITH DW, SCRIVER CR, SIMELL O: Lysinuric protein intolerance mutation is not expressed in the plasma membrane of erythrocytes. *Hum Genet*, in press.

144. GARDNER JD, LEVY AG: Transport of dibasic amino acids by human erythrocytes. *Metabolism* 21:413, 1972.

145. CHRISTENSEN HN, ANTONIOLI JA: Cationic amino acid transport in the rabbit reticulocyte. *J Biol Chem* 244:1497, 1969.

146. VADGAMA JV, CHRISTENSEN HN: Discrimination of Na^+-independent transport systems L, T, and ASC in erythrocytes. Na^+ independence of the latter a consequence of cell maturation? *J Biol Chem* 260:2912, 1985.

147. RAJANTIE J, SIMELL O, PERHEENTUPA J: "Basolateral" and mitochondrial membrane transport defect in the hepatocytes in lysinuric protein intolerance. *Acta Paediatr Scand* 72:65, 1983.

148. GAMBLE JG, LEHNINGER AL: Transport of ornithine and citrulline across the mitochondrial membrane. *J Biol Chem* 248:610, 1973.

149. ARONSON DL, DIWAN JJ: Uptake of ornithine by rat liver mitochondria. *Biochemistry* 20:7064, 1981.

150. METOKI K, HOMMES FA: A possible rate limiting factor in urea synthesis by isolated hepatocytes: The transport of ornithine into hepatocytes and mitochondria. *Int J Biochem* 16:1155, 1984.

151. HOMMES FA, KITCHINGS L, ELLER AG: The uptake of ornithine and lysine by rat liver mitochondria. *Biochem Med* 30:313, 1983.

152. BRADFORD NM, MCGIVAN JD: Evidence for the existence of an ornithine/citrulline antiporter in rat liver mitochondria. *FEBS Lett* 113:294, 1980.

153. RAIJMAN L: Citrulline synthesis in rat tissues and liver content of carbamoyl phosphate and ornithine. *Biochem J* 138:225, 1974.

154. BRYLA J, HARRIS EJ: Accumulation of ornithine and citrulline in rat liver mitochondria in relation to citrulline formation. *FEBS Lett* 72:331, 1976.

155. COHEN NS, CHEUNG C-W, RAIJMAN L: Channeling of extramitochondrial ornithine to matrix ornithine transcarbamylase. *J Biol Chem* 262:203, 1987.

156. COHEN NS, CHEUNG C-W, RAIJMAN L: The effects of ornithine on mitochondrial carbamyl phosphate synthesis. *J Biol Chem* 255:10248, 1980.

157. GRAY RGF, HILL SE, POLLITT RJ: Studies on the pathway from ornithine to proline in cultured skin fibroblasts with reference to the defect in hyperornithinaemia with hyperammonaemia and homocitrullinuria. *J Inherited Metab Dis* 6:143, 1983.

158. GRAY RGF, HILL SE, POLLITT RJ: Reduced ornithine catabolism in cultured fibroblasts and phytohaemagglutinin-stimulated lymphocytes from a patient with hyperornithinaemia, hyperammonaemia and homocitrullinuria. *Clin Chim Acta* 118:141, 1982.

159. SHIH VE: Regulation of ornithine metabolism. *Enzyme* 26:254, 1981.

160. SHIH VE, MANDELL R: Defective ornithine metabolism in the syndrome of hyperornithinaemia, hyperammonaemia and homocitrullinuria. *J Inherited Metab Dis* 4:95, 1981.

161. VICI CD, BACHMANN C, GAMBARARA M, COLOMBO JP, SABETTA G: Hyperornithinemia-hyperammonemia-homocitrullinuria syndrome: Low creatine excretion and effect of citrulline, arginine, or ornithine supplement. *Pediatr Res* 22:364, 1987.

162. INOUE I, SAHEKI T, KAYANUMA K, UONO M, NAKAJIMA M, TAKESHITA K, KOIKE R, YUASA T, MIYATAKE T, SAKODA K: Biochemical analysis of decreased ornithine transport activity in the liver mitochondria from patients with hyperornithinemia, hyperammonemia and homocitrullinuria. *Biochim Biophys Acta* 964:90, 1988.

163. INOUE I, KOURA M, SAHEKI T, KAYANUMA K, UONO M, NAKAJIMA M, TAKESHITA K, KOIKE R, YUASA T, MIYATAKE T, SAKODA K: Abnormality of citrulline synthesis in liver mitochondria from patients with hyperornithinaemia, hyperammonaemia and homocitrullinuria. *J Inherited Metab Dis* 10:277, 1987.

164. GATFIELD PD, TALLER E, WOLFE DM, HAUST DM: Hyperornithinemia, hyperammonemia, and homocitrullinuria associated with decreased carbamyl phosphate synthetase I activity. *Pediatr Res* 9:488, 1975.

165. HOMMES FA, ROESEL RA, METOKI K, HARTLAGE PL, DYKEN PR: Studies on a case of HHH-syndrome (hyperammonemia, hyperornithinemia, homocitrullinuria). *Neuropediatrics* 17:48, 1986.

166. HOMMES FA, HO CK, ROESEL RA, CORYELL ME: Decreased transport of ornithine across the inner mitochondrial membrane as a cause of hyperornithinaemia. *J Inherited Metab Dis* 5:41, 1982.

167. OYANAGI K, TSUCHIYAMA A, ITAKURA Y, SOGAWA H, WAGATSUMA K, NAKAO T: The mechanism of hyperammonaemia and hyperornithinaemia in the syndrome of hyperornithinaemia, hyperammonaemia with homocitrullinuria. *J Inherited Metab Dis* 6:133, 1983.

168. SHIH VE, EFRON ML, MOSER HW: Hyperornithinemia, hyperammonemia, and homocitrullinuria. A new disorder of amino acid metabolism associated with myoclonic seizures and mental retardation. *Am J Dis Child* 117:83, 1969.

169. KOIKE R, FUJIMORI K, YUASA T, MIYATAKE T, INOUE I, SAHEKI T: Hyperornithinemia, hyperammonemia, and homocitrullinuria: Case report and biochemical study. *Neurology* 37:1813, 1987.

170. PISONI RL, THOENE JG, CHRISTENSEN HN: Detection and characterization of carrier-mediated cationic amino acid transport in lysosomes of normal and cystinotic human fibroblasts. *J Biol Chem* 260:4791, 1985.

171. AULA P, AUTIO S, RAIVIO KO, RAPOLA J, THODEN C-J, KOSKELA S-L, YAMASHINA I: "Salla Disease." A new lysosomal storage disorder. *Arch Neurol* 36:88, 1979.

172. GAHL WA, BASHAN N, ITEZE F, BERNARDINI I, SCHULMAN JD: Cystine transport is defective in isolated leukocyte lysosomes from patients with cystinosis. *Science* 217:1263, 1982.

173. RENLUND M, AULA P, RAIVIO KO, AUTIO S, SAINIO K, RAPOLA J, KOSKELA S-L: Salla disease: A new lysosomal storage disorder with disturbed sialic acid metabolism. *Neurology* 33:57, 1983.

174. RENLUND M, KOVANEN PT, RAIVIO KO, AULA P, GAHMBERG CG, EHNHOLM C: Studies on the defect underlying the lysosomal storage of sialic acid in Salla disease. Lysosomal accumulation of sialic acid formed from N-acetyl-*mannosamine*? or derived from low density lipoprotein in cultured mutant fibroblasts. *J Clin Invest* 77:568, 1986.

175. RENLUND M, TIETZE F, GAHL WA: Defective sialic acid egress from isolated fibroblast lysosomes of patients with Salla disease. *Science* 232:759, 1986.

176. REEVES JP: Accumulation of amino acids by lysosomes incubated with amino acid methyl esters. *J Biol Chem* 254:8914, 1979.

177. DESJEUX JF, RAJANTIE J, SIMELL O, DUMONTIER AM, PERHEENTUPA J: Flux de lysine a travers l'epithelium du jejunum dans l'intolerance aux proteines avec lysinurie. *Gastroenterol Clin Biol* 4:31A, 1980.

178. PERHEENTUPA J, KEKOMÄKI M, VISAKORPI JK: Studies on aminonitrogen metabolism in familial protein intolerance. *Pediatr Res* 4:209, 1970.

179. RATNER S: Urea synthesis and metabolism of arginine and citrulline. *Adv Enzymol* 15:319, 1954.

180. MEISTER A: Metabolism of glutamine. *Physiol Rev* 36:103, 1956.

181. BACHMANN C, COLOMBO JP: Computer simulation of the urea cycle: Trials for an appropriate mode. *Enzyme* 26:259, 1981.

182. KREBS HA, HEMS R, LUND P, HALLIDAY D, READ WWC: Sources of ammonia for mammalian urea synthesis. *Biochem J* 176:733, 1978.

183. STUMPH DA, PARKS JK: Urea cycle regulation: I. Coupling of ornithine metabolism to mitochondrial oxidative phosphorylation. *Neurology* 30:178, 1980.

184. NATALE PJ, TREMBLAY GC: On the availability of intramitochondrial carbamylphosphate for the extramitochondrial biosynthesis of pyrimidines. *Biochem Biophys Res Commun* 37:512, 1969.

185. PAUSCH J, RASENACK J, HÄUSSINGER D, GEROK W: Hepatic carbamoyl phosphate in de novo pyrimidine synthesis. *Eur J Biochem* 150:189, 1985.

186. GRAHAM GG, MacLEAN WC JR, PLACKO RP: Plasma free amino acids of infants and children consuming wheat-based diets, with and without supplemental casein or lysine. *J Nutr* 111:1446, 1981.

187. CREE TC, SCHALCH DS: Protein utilization in growth: Effect of lysine deficiency on serum growth hormone, somatomedins, insulin, total thyroxine (T_4) and triiodothyronine, free T_4 index, and total corticosterone. *Endocrinology* 117:667, 1985.

188. BORUM PR, BROQUIST HP: Lysine deficiency and carnitine in male and female rats. *J Nutr* 107:1209, 1977.

189. JANSEN GR: Lysine in human nutrition. *J Nutr* 76:1, 1962.

190. HWANG S-M, SEGAL S: Developmental and other characteristics of lysine uptake by rat brain synaptosomes. *Biochim Biophys Acta* 557:436, 1979.

191. RAJANTIE J, SIMELL O, PERHEENTUPA J: Oral administration of ^{e}-N-acetyllysine and homocitrulline for lysinuric protein intolerance. *J Pediatr* 102:388, 1983.

192. FRIEDMAN M, GUMBMANN MR: Bioavailability of some lysine derivatives in mice. *J Nutr* 111:1362, 1981.

193. FUJITAKI JM, STEINER AW, NICHOLS SE, HELANDER ER, LIN YC, SMITH RA: A simple preparation of N-phosphorylated lysine and arginine. *Prep Biochem* 10(2):205, 1980.

194. MORRIS JG, ROGERS QR: Ammonia intoxication in the near-adult cat as a result of a dietary deficiency of arginine. *Science* 199:431, 1978.

195. MORRIS JG, ROGERS QR: Arginine: An essential amino acid for the cat. *J Nutr* 108:1944, 1978.

196. KACSER H, BURNS JA: The molecular basis of dominance. *Genetics* 97:639, 1981.

197. LI-CHAN E, NAKAI S: Covalent attachment of N^{e}-acetyl lysine, N^{e}-benzylidene lysine, and threonine to wheat gluten for nutritional improvement. *J Food Sci* 45(3):514, 1980.

198. DICKINSON JC, ROSENBLOM H, HAMILTON PB: Ion exchange chromatography of the free amino acids in the plasma of the newborn infant. *Pediatrics* 36:2, 1965.

199. SCRIVER CR, DAVIES E: Endogenous renal clearance rates of free amino acids in prepubertal children. *Pediatrics* 36:592, 1965.

CHAPTER 101

HARTNUP DISORDER

HARVEY L. LEVY

1. Hartnup disorder is an autosomal recessive impairment of neutral amino acid transport involving and limited to the kidneys and small intestine. It is believed to be due to a genetic defect of a specific system responsible for neutral amino acid transport across the brush border membrane of renal and intestinal epithelium. The diagnostic feature is a striking neutral hyperaminoaciduria. Most affected individuals also have increased excretion of indolic compounds, notably indican (indoxyl sulfate). These indoles originate in the gut from bacterial degradation of unabsorbed tryptophan. Reduced intestinal absorption of tryptophan and increased tryptophan loss in the urine lead to reduced availability of tryptophan for the synthesis of niacin.

2. Pellagra-like clinical features have been described in patients with the Hartnup disorder. These include a photosensitive skin rash, intermittent ataxia, and psychotic behavior. Some affected individuals have also been mentally retarded or mentally subnormal to a mild degree. Treatment with nicotinamide has often been associated with clearing of the rash and, on occasion, disappearance of the ataxia. This has led to the theory that the clinical abnormalities are due to niacin deficiency. Most subjects identified by routine newborn screening, however, as well as most affected sibs of probands have remained clinically normal. The most plausible explanation for the disparity in clinical expression is that while the disorder is monogenic, the "disease" is multifactorial and requires the presence of complicating environmental influences such as poor diet or diarrhea and perhaps also a polygenic influence such as tendency for low plasma amino acid values.

3. The renal and intestinal defects are not always expressed concordantly. Some individuals with the Hartnup hyperaminoaciduria do not have increased urinary excretion of indolic acids, suggesting that they have the renal defect without the intestinal defect. Conversely, a single individual with evidence of an intestinal neutral amino acid transport defect but without the Hartnup hyperaminoaciduria has been reported.

4. Maternal Hartnup disorder is probably benign to the fetus and to the pregnancy. At least 14 offspring from women with Hartnup disorder are known, and almost all have been normal. One man with Hartnup disorder has sired two normal children.

Hartnup disorder is a familial disorder of renal and intestinal amino acid transport. Its constant feature is a specific hyperaminoaciduria that is due to a diminished capacity for renal reabsorption of a group of monoaminomonocarboxylic ("neutral") acids which share a common, and in this case defective, transport system. In most affected individuals there is also reduced intestinal aborption of at least some of the neutral amino acids, notably tryptophan.

A decade ago when this chapter, written then by the late Dr. John Jepson, was last included in this book, Hartnup disorder was considered to be a rare and usually symptomatic "disease." Since then information derived from newborn urine screening has widened our view. We now know that Hartnup disorder is one of the most frequent of the hyperaminoacidurias and that most affected individuals remain asymptomatic,

as Mary Efron predicted over 20 years ago,[2] though symptoms can occur when complicating factors are present.[3]

Jepson accurately described the place that Hartnup disorder occupies in human biology when he stated, "The disorder has a physiologic interest out of all proportion to its rare clinical occurrence. . . . Its study has shed light on general problems of renal absorption, amino acid transport, protein digestion, nicotinamide metabolism, and intestinal bacterial reactions."[1]

This chapter will update that written by Jepson. Much of the original, which so clearly describes the history of this disorder and its biochemical phenotype, will remain largely unchanged.

THE HARTNUP FAMILY

In 1951, a boy, age 12, E. Hartnup, was admitted to the Middlesex Hospital, London, England, with mild cerebellar ataxia and a red, scaly rash on the exposed areas of his body. His mother avowed that he had pellagra, for her eldest daughter (P.H.), with identical symptoms, had been treated at the hospital in 1937 for that disease. Although the rash in E.H. was quite consistent with pellagra, other findings were not, and a diagnosis of pellagra as a dietary deficiency was untenable.

Apart from variable cerebellar signs and retarded mental development, the only abnormality detected at that time was in the urinary excretion of free amino acids. Paper chromatography of the urine disclosed an excretion pattern of amino acids quite unlike that seen in any other disease.

At the same time, P.H., then age 19, had a recurrence of ataxia (without a rash), similar to that which she had had in childhood when the pellagra-like rash was most severe. The excretion pattern of amino acids in her urine was identical to that of her brother, E.H.

It was then clear that these two sibs were affected by the same disease. An inherited condition seemed probable when it was learned that the parents were first cousins.

Neither parent and none of their other six children gave a clinical history to suggest that they were similarly affected, although one girl (M.H.) was mentally retarded. Two younger sibs, Jh. H. and H.H., also had gross aminoaciduria with the characteristic chromatographic pattern. No abnormality was detected in the urine of the other four sibs or in either parent. In the affected children, the amino acid excretion persisted unchanged in pattern and amount. The skin and neurologic disturbances gradually lessened in P.H. and E.H. but made a fleeting appearance in the younger boys.

The pedigree of the Hartnup family, with a diagrammatic representation of the amino acid chromatographic findings, is given in Fig. 101-1. No other relatives of the Hartnup parents showed the amino acid abnormality.

The publication which first fully reported this family and

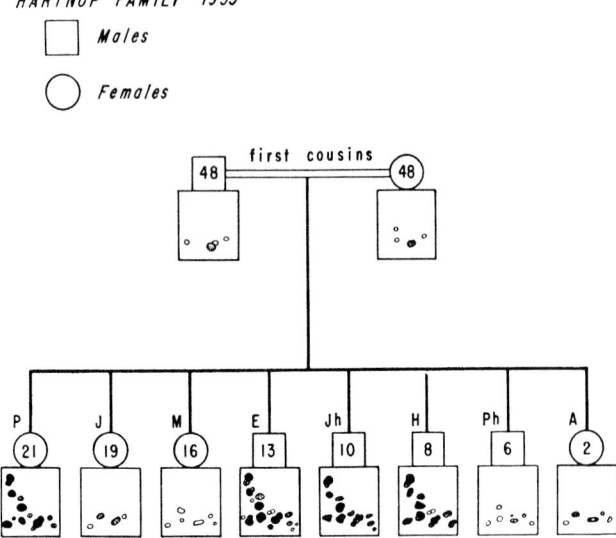

HARTNUP FAMILY - 1953

Fig. 101-1 The genealogy of Hartnup disorder as illustrated in the original Hartnup family. The parents were first cousins. The age of the subject in 1953 is indicated by the numbers; in the squares are the chromatography patterns of urine samples of two-dimensional chromatograms stained for amino acids.

the existence of this disorder was entitled "Hereditary Pellagra-like Skin Rash with Temporary Cerebellar Ataxia. Constant Renal Amino-Aciduria. And Other Bizarre Biochemical Features."[4] As a description of the fully expressed phenotype of the disorder this title cannot be bettered. The family in which the condition was first found consented to the use of their surname as an appropriate appellation.

BIOCHEMICAL PHENOTYPE

The diagnosis of Hartnup disorder is based on biochemical rather than clinical abnormalities. The characteristic pattern of neutral hyperaminoaciduria is the one constant feature and is considered the sine qua non for diagnosis. This is a consequence of the defect in renal amino acid transport. The feces contain increased free amino acids, a consequence of the defect in intestinal amino acid transport. The intestinal defect also accounts for the presence of indoles in the urine. Defective absorption of tryptophan allows bacterial enzymes to degrade tryptophan, releasing indole and related metabolites for absorption and further degradation within the body.

Amino Acids

Renal Defect. The pattern of hyperaminoaciduria in Hartnup disorder is distinctive and quite different from other forms of renal hyperaminoaciduria such as the generalized hyperaminoaciduria of the Fanconi syndrome, cystinuria, or iminoglycinuria. The neutral hyperaminoaciduria of Hartnup disorder consists of striking increases in the monoaminomonocarboxylic amino acids including alanine, serine, threonine, valine, leucine, isoleucine, phenylalanine, tyrosine, tryptophan, and histidine, as well as glutamine and asparagine, which are neutral monoaminodicarboxylic amides. These free amino acids are excreted in amounts 5 to 20 times normal (Fig. 101-2). Amino acids in the "acidic" (monoaminodicarboxylic) group, such as glutamic acid and aspartic acid, as well as those in the

"basic" (diaminomonocarboxylic) group, such as lysine and ornithine, are usually normal or present only in slightly increased amounts.[5] Methionine, a sulfur-containing neutral amino acid, is also usually normal, although it may be increased. Two affected sibs are known with markedly increased excretion of methionine in addition to the characteristic Hartnup hyperaminoaciduria. The β-amino acids, taurine and β-aminoisobutyric acid, are not detected in Hartnup urine. Notably, even the most sensitive methods fail to detect increased amounts of proline, hydroxyproline, or arginine. The absence of proline in particular distinguishes the Hartnup pattern from generalized hyperaminoaciduria.[6] The free amino acids are all of the L-configuration.[7]

The hyperaminoaciduria is of renal origin, not an "overflow" phenomenon. Plasma amino acid concentrations are not increased. The renal clearances of those amino acids that are excreted in excess are grossly elevated above normal, both in the fasting state[8] and following an oral load of casein,[9] while the clearances of the amino acids that are not excreted in excess are normal or only slightly elevated. Table 101-1 provides data on renal clearances from several studies.[9-12] Clearance of histidine has been reported as high as 140 ml/min,[13] approximating the glomerular filtration rate. One patient excreted 17 percent of an intravenous load of L-histidine unchanged within 4 h, while a control excreted only 0.3 percent.[11] For the other amino acids excreted in excess by Hartnup individuals, the tubular reabsorption of the filtered load at physiological concentrations is about 30 to 60 percent, compared to over 95 percent in normal subjects.

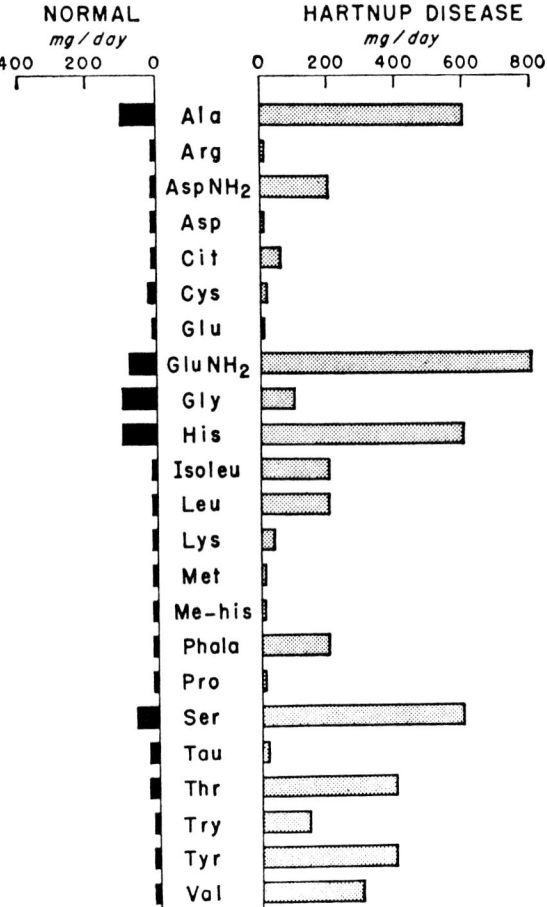

Fig. 101-2 The excretion of free amino acids in the urine of normal subjects and patients with the Hartnup disorder.

Table 101-1 Renal Clearance of Amino Acids in Hartnup Disorder

| Amino acid | Excretion in Hartnup disorder | Clearance ml/min* | |
		Hartnup	Normal
Total amino acid N			
Fasting	High	6–22	1.5
Maximum on oral protein load	Very high	25–50	3.0
Threonine	High	70	1.0
Tyrosine	High	66	1.5
Histidine	High	122	6.0
Taurine	Low	1.9	5.0
Proline	Low	0.3	0.1
Cystine	Low	0.4	0.5
Lysine	Low	3.0	0.4

*From Refs. 9–12.

These excretion studies indicate a disturbance in the renal tubular transport of a certain group of amino acids, viz., those of the neutral type, which share a common system for renal membrane transport.[14] The quartet of amino acids excreted in cystinuria (cystine, ornithine, lysine, and arginine; see Chap. 99) share another transport system, and this is obviously intact in Hartnup individuals, as is a third distinct transport system, for the glycine-imino acid group, the system which is defective in iminoglycinuria (see Chap. 102). This concept, that Hartnup disorder is one of a trio of genetic disorders each involving only one of the systems for amino acid transport, was first suggested by Milne et al.[15] and extended by them to apply to intestinal transport as well as of the renal tubule.

Despite the obvious defect, substantial renal tubular transport of the involved amino acids remains. As noted above, except for rare instances renal clearances do not approach the glomerular filtration rate. It is possible that the renal tubular defect is far from complete. A more likely explanation is that each amino acid is transported by more than one system.[16] One of these systems transports most of the neutral amino acids. This is most likely high capacity and is defective in Hartnup disorder. Specific low capacity systems may also exist for each amino acid, as is known to be the case for glycine (see "Iminoglycinuria," Chap. 102). Thus, in the Hartnup disorder renal tubular reabsorption of neutral amino acids may occur by a combination of specific amino acid transport, passive diffusion, and, perhaps, residual activity of the defective neutral amino acid transport system.

The amino acid excretion pattern is remarkably constant and is unchanged by nicotinamide or other vitamins, drugs, or antibiotics, despite isolated reports to the contrary.[17,18]

All other tests of renal tubular function and renal clearance have given normal results. One patient who came to autopsy had absence of the descending limb of the loop of Henle.[19] This child had unusual features that included fatty degeneration of the liver with liver failure and terminal myocardial involvement.[20] Microdissection of nephrons was not reported in a subsequent patient studied at autopsy.[21] The defect is certainly at a subcellular level, but in vitro studies of renal amino acid transport in Hartnup individuals have not yet been performed.

Intestinal Defect. More complicated than demonstrating the defect in renal transport is demonstrating that there is an analogous defect in intestinal absorption of free amino acids, but several studies have shown that: Hartnup patients excrete increased amounts of the affected amino acids in the feces; the

rise in plasma concentration of several of the involved amino acids following an oral load is abnormally low or delayed, although normal concentrations are found after intravenous administration; and bacterial degradation products from unabsorbed amino acids are found in excess in urine. This has been especially investigated for tryptophan.

The discovery that the defect in the Hartnup disorder affected intestinal transport of tryptophan[22] will be discussed below in the section on indolic compounds. Following this, Scriver and Shaw[23] and then Scriver[24] described a pattern of increased fecal amino acids that almost mirrored the typical Hartnup urinary pattern. Asatoor and coworkers[25] found that the feces of patients with Hartnup disorder contained greater quantities of tryptophan, phenylalanine, tyrosine, valine, and leucine/isoleucine than did the feces of normal individuals.

Other investigations, however, have not disclosed increased fecal amino acids in patients on regular diets.[26–28] This seemingly conflicting evidence stimulated investigation of transport with amino acid loads administered orally. In these studies intestinal transport of leucine, methionine, phenylalanine, and tyrosine was reduced in the Hartnup disorder,[26–31] whereas proline, glycine, and β-alanine, which have normal renal transport in the Hartnup disorder, had normal intestinal transport as well.[27–30] On the other hand, studies of intestinal transport of lysine and histidine have not produced consistent results, with evidence for reduced transport in the Hartnup disorder in some investigations[26,30] and normal transport in others.[11,26,28,32]

Impaired intestinal transport for several free amino acids has been demonstrated in vitro in the Hartnup disorder. Tarlow et al.[31,32] found that jejunal biopsy tissue in one patient showed very little accumulation of histidine when incubated with L-histidine. Shih and coworkers[28] studied the uptake of four amino acids by jejunal mucosa obtained through biopsy from two affected brothers. Tryptophan and methionine uptakes were markedly reduced, while lysine and glycine uptakes were slightly but significantly diminished. Jejunal mucosa has been histologically normal.[19,21,28,30]

The defective intestinal absorption of certain free neutral amino acids seems not to apply to their ketoacid analogues. Scriver[24] found that transport by the gut of indolepyruvic acid, the ketoacid of tryptophan (Fig. 101-3), was normal in the Hartnup disorder in contrast to the defective transport of tryptophan.

The defect also does not involve intestinal absorption of peptides. When histidine was given to a Hartnup subject in the form of oral carnosine (β-alanyl-L-histidine) rather than as free histidine, the plasma histidine response was normal.[29] This subject also absorbed phenylalanine and tryptophan better when they were in the dipeptide form than as the corresponding mixed free amino acids, while the reverse is true in normal individuals.[30] Analogous results were seen in another affected individual after oral administration of glycyl-tyrosine and free tyrosine.[32] When hydrolyzed casein was given to an individual with the Hartnup disorder, there was a rise in levels of plasma amino acids, but when a simulated mixture of amino acids was given, there was no comparable rise.[33] This suggests that amino acid nutrition in Hartnup disorder (and possibly in analogous situations) is maintained more by absorption of small peptides than by essential amino acids in free form.[34]

An intestinal defect in amino acid transport similar to that noted in the classic Harnup disorder defect can be present without the renal defect. Drummond et al.[35] reported intestinal malabsorption seemingly limited to tryptophan with nor-

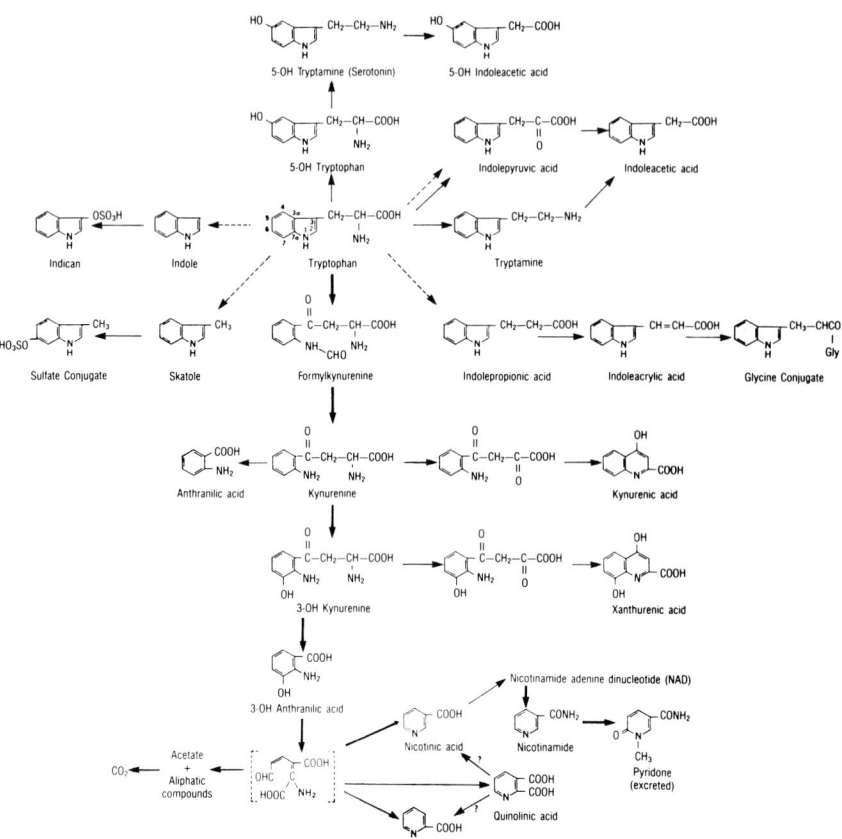

Fig. 101-3 Pathways of tryptophan catabolism. Broken arrows indicate intestinal catabolism by microorganisms.

mal urine amino acid excretion in one child and, most probably, also in a deceased sib (see below). Recently Hillman and coworkers[36] described an infant with markedly increased neutral amino acids in the stool and normal or near-normal urine amino acids. These cases, in combination with the diversity in intestinal amino acid transport suggested by the studies in those with the renal defect, indicate a substantial degree of heterogeneity in the linked renal and intestinal transport of neutral amino acids.

Blood Amino Acids. In all cases in which analysis of blood amino acids has been performed, the results have been either normal or low, as could be anticipated from the diminished absorption and increased excretion. When the quantities of the individual amino acids have been listed, the values have usually been within the normal range.[8,37,38] A recent study[3] disclosed slightly lower summed plasma values for the "Hartnup" amino acids in 21 Hartnup subjects as compared to 19 age-matched unaffected sibs (1552 ± 299 μmol/liter and 1657 ± 311 μmol/liter, respectively; $p = 0.16$ and 0.06 by Student's t-test and ANOVA, respectively). Summed plasma values for the "non-Hartnup" amino acids were also slightly lower in the Hartnup subjects.

Transport in Other Tissues. Sweat and saliva from Hartnup individuals have a normal amino acid composition.[4] Leukocytes[39] and cultured skin fibroblasts[40] from Hartnup patients transport tryptophan normally. These observations emphasize that many genetically independent transport mechanisms must exist in humans and that the Hartnup disorder affects only one of the different types and only in specific tissues.

Indole Compounds

Tryptophan Metabolism and Nicotinic Acid (Niacin). Among the clinical abnormalities recognized in the first individuals with the Hartnup disorder were psychosis, a photosensitive skin rash, and, occasionally, diarrhea.[4,41,42] Since these are features of pellagra, attention was early directed to the possible role of niacin deficiency in the disorder. However, these patients did not have a dietary history suggesting pellagra nor a deficiency of nicotinic acid derivatives in the urine. Additional tryptophan did not substantially increase the excretion of nicotinic acid derivatives, as would be expected in pellagra.[4] Furthermore, urine amino acids were normal in a patient with dietary-induced pellagra.[4] Nevertheless, there frequently seemed to be a clinical response to nicotinamide treatment.[4,41,42] Thus, a defect in the availability of niacin was suspected.

Nicotinic acid and nicotinamide can be synthesized from tryptophan. Hence, there is particular interest in the degradation of tryptophan in the Hartnup disorder. Figure 101-3 depicts the pathway for this synthesis, the major tryptophan catabolic pathway, as well as some of the many other pathways along which tryptophan catabolism can proceed. Tryptophan is first converted to formylkynurenine by the liver enzyme tryptophan pyrrolase; increased activity of this enzyme is readily brought about by tryptophan administration or by corticoids.[43,44] Formylkynurenine is hydrolyzed to kynurenine by the liver enzyme, kynurenine formylase. Kynurenine is hydroxylated to 3-hydroxykynurenine by the mitochondrial enzyme kynurenine-3-hydroxylase, which can be cleaved by the pyridoxal-requiring enzyme, kynureninase, to alanine and 3-hydroxyanthranilic acid. The latter product is oxidized to a labile ring-opened aldehyde intermediate. Ring closure and decarboxylation then occur simultaneously, with the formation of either nicotinic acid or picolinic acid, each by its specific enzyme. Nicotinic acid is further metabolized to nicotinamide adenine dinucleotide (NAD) and nicotinamide.

Little tryptophan appears to be converted to nicotinic acid under normal conditions. It is estimated that in the human 60 mg tryptophan is required to replace 1 mg dietary nicotinamide in the form of niacin.[45] Nevertheless, tryptophan may still be an important source of niacin, particularly in individuals with relatively poor protein diets.[46]

Several patients suspected of having a defect in tryptophan degradation have been reported. The most plausible are two sibs described by Snedden and coworkers[47] who had markedly increased plasma and urine tryptophan levels and reduced kynurenine.[47] A block in the conversion of tryptophan to kynurenine was postulated, but enzyme studies to confirm and locate the block were not performed. Tada and colleagues[48] and, later, Wong et al.[49] described children with growth and developmental delay, ataxia, and a photosensitive rash who had very mild increases in plasma tryptophan, accentuated by tryptophan loading. On the basis of reduced urinary kynurenine after tryptophan loading, they also postulated a block in the conversion of tryptophan to kynurenine, but, again, enzyme studies were not done. Komrower et al.[50] reported a child with borderline intelligence, short stature, and headaches who excreted large amounts of both kynurenine and 3-hydroxykynurenine. They suggested that she had a defect in kynureninase, which catalyzes the conversion of kynurenine to anthranilic acid as well as the degradation of 3-hydroxykynurenine. Other reports include a postulated defect in picolinate carboxylase,[51] a suggested partial defect in kynurenine-3-hydroxylase,[52] and the suggestion of an unspecified block proximal to 3-hydroxyanthranilic acid.[53] Common clinical features in several of these patients include photosensitive rash, ataxia, and mental subnormality.[48,49,51,53] Urinary excretion of N-methylnicotinamide was often reduced,[48,51,53] indicating that the block in tryptophan degradation limited nicotinic acid synthesis and that this limitation might have caused the clinical picture.

Other Tryptophan Derivatives. Serotonin (5-hydroxytryptamine), a monoamine neurotransmitter, is an important derivative of tryptophan, although little tryptophan is catabolized in this direction. Serotonin is usually estimated in urine or cerebrospinal fluid as its oxidation product, 5-hydroxyindoleacetic acid.

Another pathway of tryptophan metabolism is conversion to indolic acids. Normal urine contains a number of indolic acids, the major ones being indoleacetic acid, indolelactic acid, 5-hydroxyindoleacetic acid, and indoleacetylglutamine.[54] The indoleacetic acid is a product of metabolism by intestinal microorganisms and mammalian tissues.[55] This conversion occurs mainly by transamination of tryptophan to indolepyruvic acid, with subsequent decarboxylation to indoleacetic acid. Small amounts of tryptophan are also converted to indoleacetic acid by way of tryptamine. The normal tryptamine excretion by humans is very low but can be raised many-fold by the administration of monoamine oxidase inhibitors.[56]

If intestinal absorption of tryptophan is delayed, colonic bacteria can transform tryptophan into indolepropionic acid (Fig. 101-3). This is absorbed from the intestine and converted by tissues into indoleacrylic acid, which is excreted as the glycine conjugate.[57,58] Apparently mammalian tissue cannot produce either indolepropionic acid or indoleacrylic acid directly from tryptophan.

Other important products from the degradation of tryptophan by intestinal microorganisms are indole and skatole (3-methylindole).[59] These microorganisms contain tryptophanase, an enzyme which cleaves tryptophan to indole and pyruvic acid.[60] Indole is absorbed from the intestine, partly oxidized to oxindole and derivatives which are not detectable by standard tests for indoles,[61] and partly hydroxylated in the 3 position to form indoxyl and then its sulfate conjugate (indican). Skatole, the methylated derivative of indole, is converted to 6-hydroxyskatole and likewise conjugated with sulfate for excretion.[62]

Over the years many correlations have been sought between deranged tryptophan-indole metabolism and mental illness, particularly schizophrenia.[63] Unfortunately, nothing substantial has yet been established.

It is more certain that delayed tryptophan absorption can introduce abnormal urinary excretion of indoles that may mimic metabolic abnormalities.[64] Hartnup disorder is the most extreme of these situations, but many other examples can be found. Africans accustomed to consuming large quantities of matoke (cooked banana) excrete indolylacryloylglycine, presumably because enhanced intestinal motility speeds tryptophan down to colonic bacteria.[65] This effect is also obtained by administering tryptophan orally or per rectum, with a more rapid response by the latter route of administration[66]; sterilization of the gut eliminates this effect.[65,66] Indolylacryloylglycine has also been found in the urine of individuals with unusual intestinal flora.[67,68] Patients with blind-loop syndrome excrete vast amounts of indican.

A familial and specific intestinal malabsorption of tryptophan known as the "blue diaper syndrome" has been described by Drummond et al.[35] (see above). In this disorder intestinal bacteria convert much of the unabsorbed tryptophan to indican (hence the designation "blue diaper syndrome" from the indigotin—or indigo blue—the hydrolytic and oxidation product of indican identified in the urine). Other indolic acids are also excreted in abundance. Unlike Hartnup disorder, the defect affects only tryptophan and does not involve the renal tubule cells.

Indoles in Hartnup Disorder

Early in the investigations of the Hartnup family, a high but variable excretion of indoxylsulfate (indican) was apparent among affected members. This led to a survey that disclosed increased urinary excretion of other indole compounds as well.[4] Thus, increased excretion of indolic acids derived from tryptophan was revealed in the Hartnup disorder (Fig. 101-4).

Indican has been the most prominent of these urinary indoles; in some instances, Hartnup probands excreted almost 400 mg/day compared to approximately 100 mg/day by age-matched normal subjects.[69,70] As with normal individuals, urinary indican disappears when the gut is sterilized with antibiotic.[4,18,71–73] Antibiotics do not alter the urinary amino acid excretion, and the indoluria returns to its high level within a few days after cessation of treatment.

The indicanuria is raised dramatically by the oral administration of L-tryptophan, even in Hartnup patients showing a reasonably normal indican excretion in the basal state,[22] but

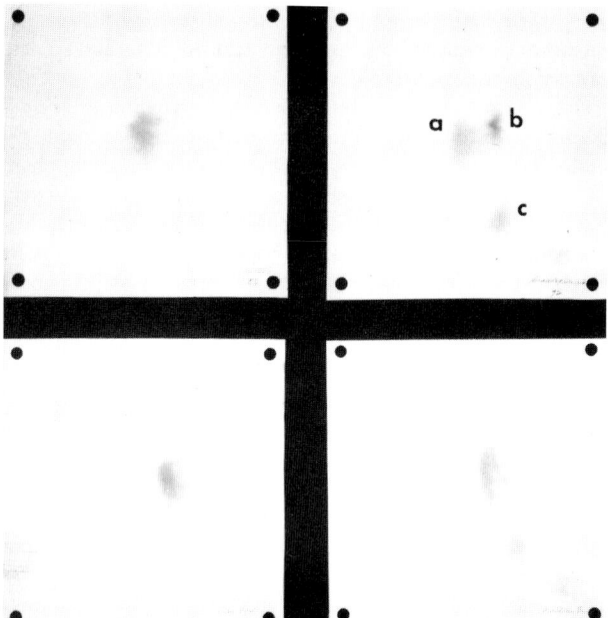

Fig. 101-4 Urine indole patterns (in standardized aliquots) in a normal control *(top left)*, his typical Hartnup sibling *(top right)*, a Hartnup proband with the variant allele *(bottom right)*, and her control sibling *(bottom left)*. The typical pattern shows an excess of indoxyl sulfate and tryptophan. The variant pattern shows an excess of tryptophan only. a = urea; b = indoxyl sulfate; c = tryptophan. *(From Scriver, Clow, and Levy, unpublished data.)*

not by intravenous L-tryptophan.[18,74] It was the demonstration of this response to oral tryptophan that led Milne and his group[22] to recognize that the transport defect in Hartnup disorder involves the intestine as well as the kidney. In normal subjects after administration of oral tryptophan there is a slight, variable rise in indican followed by a fall to normal within 12 h, representing a tryptophan-to-indican conversion of no more than 1.6 percent. By contrast, in Hartnup disorder there is a greatly increased indican excretion, which reaches a maximum after 12 h and persists for more than 24 h, with a conversion of 7 to 13 percent[22,74] (Fig. 101-5). A patient investigated by Srikantia et al.[75] is exceptional in showing a five-fold rise in urinary indican level within 1 h of an oral tryptophan load, which returned to normal within 3 h but peaked again 3 h later. This patient may have a variant of the intestinal defect in Hartnup disorder, although fecal amino acid values and in vitro studies of intestinal transport indicate considerable heterogeneity in the disorder (see "Intestinal Defect").

The urinary indoxyl derivatives are final excretion products, formed in the liver from indole absorbed from the colon. Here they must arise from the action of intestinal microorganisms on tryptophan not absorbed from the jejunum because of the transport defect. Studies of the indole-producing bacteria (*Escherichia coli*) from the feces of Hartnup patients[25] failed to show that chronic exposure to tryptophan alters the colonic flora in type or amount from that normally found. On the other hand, there is little or no excretion of 6-hydroxyskatole sulfate, the final product of intestinal skatole formation that may be seen in malabsorption syndromes.[64]

Other urinary indoles that are increased in Hartnup disorder include indoleacetic acid and its conjugate, indoleacetylglutamine.[70,76–78] Indolelactic acid and indoleacetylglucuronide, the other possible conjugate of indoleacetic acid, have also been reported, but only in moderate amounts.[78] The excretion

of these indolic acids, especially indoleacetic acid, has been particularly prominent during acute bouts of ataxia and rash in some patients.[4,73]

On the other hand, the urinary indolic acid pattern has been quite variable in Hartnup individuals and has often been normal under usual conditions as well as during acute clinical episodes.[22,29] Under the stimulus of an oral tryptophan load, however, indolic acid production becomes an obvious feature of Hartnup disorder. The oral administration of L-tryptophan to normal subjects in quantities of about 70 mg/kg body weight causes a sharp sixfold rise in free and conjugated urine indoleacetic acid.[22] The peak is reached at 2 h, and the excretion returns to its normal low level in 8 h. The total conversion of such a load to urinary indolic acids is about 0.2 percent. In Hartnup patients, the rise is several times larger, does not reach its peak until 8 or 10 h, and persists at a high level for at least 24 h (Fig. 101-5). The total conversion has been calculated at 1.3 to 1.7 percent in these patients.[22]

Hartnup patients on oral tryptophan loading also excrete large quantities of indolylacryloylglycine with the same 8-h lag period that applies to indoleacetic acid production[71,79]; they may even excrete small amounts of indolylacryloylglycine on a normal diet.[73] In contrast, normal individuals never produce indolylacryloylglycine even with a large oral load of tryptophan, provided that the usual intestinal transport mechanism are operative.

As with indoxyl derivatives, other indolic acids are derived from bacterial catabolism of tryptophan in the gut. This explanation is supported by two lines of evidence. First is the effect of intestinal antibiotics in Hartnup patients. Neomycin (with nystatin) not only lowers the excretion of all indolic acids to somewhat less than the usual level but virtually abol-

Fig. 101-5 Urinary excretion (mg/h) of tryptophan derivatives following oral L-tryptophan (about 70 mg/kg body weight) administered to normal subjects (N---) and to Hartnup patients (H---). These are idealized responses, averaged from the results of several investigators.

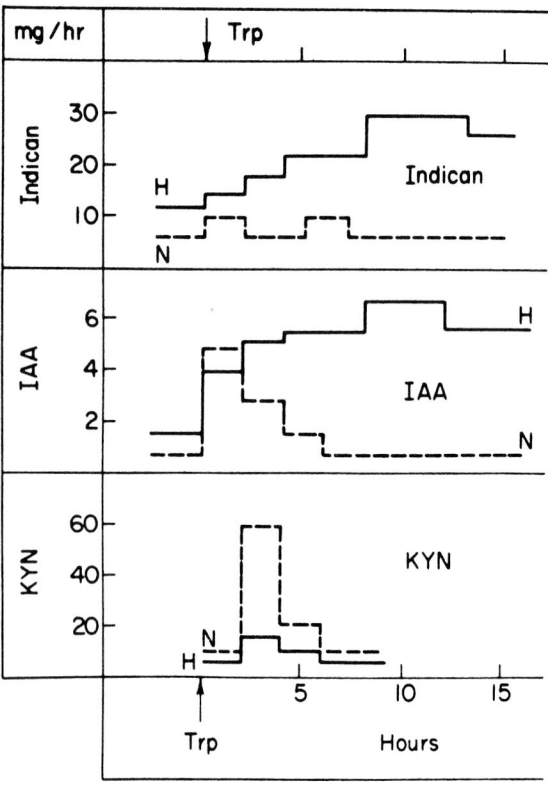

ishes any rise after oral tryptophan loading.[18,71,73] It is possible that neomycin slightly inhibits tryptophan or indoleacetic acid absorption from the intestine,[80] but this could not account for more than a small part of the dramatic effect. Second, intravenous tryptophan does not increase indolic acid excretion.[74]

Indolepyruvic acid and its decomposition products have not been detected in the urine of Hartnup patients.[81,82] The urinary excretion of tryptamine is within normal limits in these patients.[1] This may only be tryptamine produced in the kidney and might not reflect tryptamine formation in other tissues or in the intestine.[25] Tryptamine is catabolized to indoleacetic acid by way of the corresponding aldehyde. Experiments to see if the oxidation pathway could be diverted through a reductive pathway by the administration of ethanol[83] were unsuccessful; no urinary tryptophol or its conjugates were detectable in Hartnup or control subjects, before or after the consumption of large quantities of alcohol.[1]

Indoluria other than increased tryptophan may not be present in infants during the first 6 months of life.[84,85] This may reflect the more rapid transit of food through the gut during these early months with less time for bacteria to act upon the tryptophan. After age 6 months children originally identified by newborn urine amino acid screening have almost always had increased excretion of indolic compounds.[3,84]

Indolic Acids in the Blood. Whole blood indolic acids have been found normal.[70] The renal clearance values of indolic acids are normally very high.[86] The clearance of indolylacetylglutamine is at least 150 ml/min, and it may be synthesized, at least in part, from indoleacetic acid in the kidney.[1]

Serotonin Levels. Blood and urine levels for serotonin (5-hydroxytryptamine) have been within normal limits or on the low side of the normal range, in parallel with reduced urinary 5-hydroxyindoleacetic acid excretion.[1,70,72]

Jonas and Butler[87] recently reported substantially reduced concentrations of 5-hydroxyindoleacetic acid, the oxidation metabolite of serotonin, in the cerebrospinal fluid of a growth- and developmentally delayed child with the Hartnup disorder. Other neurotransmitter metabolite levels were normal. The tryptophan level in cerebrospinal fluid was also reduced, suggesting that this deficiency in the brain led to the reduced serotonin. In support of this suggestion was the response to intravenous tryptophan, which increased the level of 5-hydroxyindoleacetic acid in cerebrospinal fluid to a high normal value.

Nicotinic Acid Derivatives

The pellagra-like clinical features of some patients with the Hartnup disorder led to an early interest in the tryptophan-kynurenine-nicotinic acid pathway.[4] Surprisingly, the urinary excretion of nicotinic acid and derivatives such as nicotinamide and N-methylnicotinamide were within normal limits, albeit on the low side. Later reports supported these findings. Visakorpi et al.[20] found that niacin concentrations in blood and urine were normal and that derivatives of nicotinic acid such as the diphosphopyridine nucleotides (DPN and DPNH) also had normal concentrations in blood. Other studies, however, have found that Hartnup subjects may excrete less N-methylnicotinamide than normal individuals both in the basal state[37,39,72,88] and after an oral tryptophan load.[37,39,89]

These data might indicate that in Hartnup disorder nico-

tinic acid and its derivatives are not necessarily deficient, perhaps because ingested nicotinic acid is absorbed and metabolized normally,[88] but that lesser amounts are formed from ingested tryptophan. This is not due to a block in the major pathway of tryptophan catabolism through kynurenine (Fig. 101-3), as was once thought might be the case.[4] Tryptophan administered intravenously to Hartnup subjects produces normally enhanced excretion of kynurenine and N-methylnicotinamide.[18,74] Rather, it is due to less availability of ingested tryptophan, as evidenced by the formation of much less kynurenine[18,22,29,39,74] and xanthurenic acid[71] than in normal controls. Normal individuals converted 3 to 7 percent of oral L-tryptophan to urinary kynurenine, with a peak excretion rate of about 80 mg/h, while Hartnup patients converted only 0.5 to 1.5 percent to kynurenine, with a maximum excretion rate of 10 mg/h.[22] The reduced availability of ingested tryptophan is presumably a result of the defect in intestinal transport (see "Intestinal Defect").

CLINICAL PHENOTYPE

The clinical findings in at least two of the four affected children in the original Hartnup family were so much like those seen in pellagra that the investigators performed amino acid analyses on urine specimens from two other English children who had previously been reported as having pellagra.[41,42] In at least one of these children the diet was much better than that usually ingested by individuals with pellagra.[41] In both the amino acid pattern was like that seen in the affected members of the Hartnup family. Thus, it seemed that Hartnup disorder was closely linked to the clinical phenotype of pellagra.

Subsequent experience has not confirmed such a close association. In fact children with Hartnup disorder identified by routine newborn urine screening have almost always remained clinically normal.[3,84] This suggests that Hartnup disorder is usually benign. There is little doubt, however, that some individuals with the Hartnup biochemical phenotype develop clinical abnormalities. In addition, the unusual combination of a photosensitive rash and neuropsychiatric manifestations has been more often associated with the Hartnup pattern of neutral hyperaminoaciduria than would be expected by coincidence. The most likely explanation for the wide clinical spectrum, as proposed by Scriver et al.,[3] is that Hartnup disorder represents a monogenic transport defect with which polygenic and environmental factors interact. When these factors are aberrant, as occasionally they are, disease results. Thus the cause of Hartnup "disease" is multifactorial. Otherwise, the transport disorder is benign.

Skin Lesions

An unusual "pellagra-like" rash has been the most frequent clinical abnormality seen in Hartnup patients. The age of onset has varied from as early as 10 days[90] or 3 months[4,71,91,92] to as late as 13 years.[37] The photosensitive rash has appeared as "severe sunburn," and the patient becomes known as one who should avoid the sun. After unusual exposure to sunlight, blisters have formed much more readily than in normal individuals. The rash has been exclusively or predominantly on the exposed areas of the body, particularly the face, back of neck, back of hands and wrists, external surfaces of the arms and legs, anterior surfaces of the knees, and dorsal surfaces of the feet. In several individuals the rash has been pruritic[37,73,92] and, on occasion, has had the appearance of eczema.[4,20] In three patients the appearance of umbilicated bullae surrounded by erythematous halos suggested the diagnosis of hydroa vacciniforme.[21,93,94] Following the acute erythematous phase, the skin has frequently desquamated, exposing areas of depigmentation. Subsequently, the skin becomes dry and scaly with peripheral depigmentation. The rash has usually been bilateral. Minor skin manifestations were found at slightly higher frequency in Hartnup persons relative to their control sibs in a prospective study.[3]

Neurologic Manifestations

Ataxia. Intermittent ataxia has been the next most frequent abnormality reported among clinically affected patients and the most frequently noted neurologic aberration. The ataxia has usually appeared as unsteadiness while standing and as an unsteady, wide-based gait. In general, no unilaterality has been noted, although in two patients[4,77] the ataxia was more pronounced on the left side and in another patient[75] there was a tendency to fall to one side. The ataxia has usually begun later than the skin abnormalities, but in one case[13] it was the first clinical abnormality noted and in two other cases[75,77] it appeared at the same time as the rash. It has frequently been accompanied by other abnormalities such as nystagmus, diplopia, and tremors, suggesting a cerebellar origin. The most striking characteristic of the ataxia, however, has been its intermittency. In most instances it was present for only a few days or less at a time and then spontaneously disappeared. Precipitating factors in the ataxic episodes have usually not been identifiable, although *Shigella* dysentery seemed to cause an attack in one patient,[4] and exposure to sunlight was implicated in both the rash and ataxia in two other patients.[37]

Mental Development. Although the first two cases identified in the original Hartnup family were mentally retarded, the other two affected members were not retarded.[4] Most of the subsequently reported clinically affected Hartnup patients have not had frank intellectual retardation. School performance has been consistent with intelligence test scores and clinical estimates of intelligence[4,70,73,82] as have been the types of labor performed.[4,70,77] One of two symptomatic Hartnup patients in a prospective study[3] had delayed cognitive development relative to his non-Hartnup sibs.

Neurologic Signs. Other than the ataxia, there have been few specific neurologic findings. Increased muscle tone and increased deep-tendon reflexes have been reported, usually involving all extremities but, on occasion, only the lower extremities.[37,38,75] With the exception of a transient Babinski response in one patient,[21] the plantar reflex has been flexor. Pyramidal tract signs have only infrequently been present and when so, usually during ataxic episodes. One patient had decreased deep-tendon reflexes,[42] and another patient had decreased muscle tone.[95]

Electroencephalographic Findings. Electroencephalographic examinations have shown considerable, but variable, dysrhythmia which has defied interpretation. Interpretations have ranged from "electrical immaturity"[95] to "general cerebral dysrhythmia."[73] Increases in θ,[29,70] δ,[89] θ-δ,[37,73] and β[37] have been

mentioned. The abnormalities have usually been generalized, but specifically abnormal activities in the parietotemporal,[73] occipital,[89] and posterior temporal[29] areas have been noted. In one patient abnormal slow wave activity was recorded.[82]

All patients with abnormal electroencephalograms have had abnormal clinical findings referable to the central nervous system. In two patients these findings were as nonspecific as increased anxiety and irritability,[70] while in another case ataxia and mental retardation were present.[89] At least two patients with profound central nervous system disease had normal electroencephalograms.[27,82] Electroencephalographic findings have not been recorded in individuals with Hartnup disorder who were free of neurologic findings.

Other Neurologic Findings. One patient had choreiform movements when ataxia was pronounced.[4] Frequent headaches were noted in two patients.[4,73] A history of generalized seizures during early childhood was noted in a patient who also had deaf mutism and mental retardation.[27] One patient was prone to vasovagal attacks.[4]

Psychologic Changes

Most of the clinically affected Hartnup patients have had no psychiatric disturbances. Abnormalities of a psychiatric nature suggesting psychosis, however, were among the prominent findings in several of the early cases. The boy described by Hersov[41] was "irritable and morose." The first two members of the Hartnup family had marked emotional instability with depression and outbursts of temper accompanying ataxic episodes. Other patients have been "depressed and depersonalized" with suicidal tendencies,[70] severely anxious,[70] nervous and hallucinatory[37,73] continuously crying,[73,82] severely confused with hypomania, prone to meaningless utterances, and incontinent,[29] and markedly aggressive.[95] These disturbances have always been episodic and frequently were accompanied by ataxia.

General Somatic Abnormalities

Several different abnormalities of this nature have been described in patients with the Hartnup disorder. It is doubtful that most are related to the basic defect. Visakorpi et al.[20] described edema and hypoproteinemia with fatty degeneration of the liver and death from liver failure in a child whose affected sister had transient hypoproteinemia and urinary calculi but recovered. Edema and hypoproteinemia were also described in another child who was otherwise well.[96] The patient described by Daute et al.[21] had fever, diarrhea, anemia, and leukopenia and eventually died. Wong and Pillai[74] described recurrent vomiting in one patient. Oyanagi et al.[37] recorded fatty liver in one patient.

Two abnormalities may be related to the Hartnup disorder in some patients. The first of these is atrophic glossitis, present in at least six patients.[21,29,41,42,70,71] The second is small stature, noted in many of the reported cases. Although the general experience from prospective studies of cases identified by newborn screening[3,84] does not support the conclusion of Colliss et al.[97] that Hartnup subjects have a significant reduction in height, occasional children identified prospectively have had growth delay.[3] It is possible that either niacin deficiency or a general deficiency of amino acids[3] complicating certain cases of the Hartnup disorder could explain the glossitis and growth retardation.

Characteristics of Individuals Identified by Newborn Screening

Wilcken and her coworkers[84] studied 15 children with Hartnup disorder detected through routine newborn urine screening in New South Wales. Most did not receive nicotinamide treatment. Their intelligence and growth were considered normal and comparable to those of their unaffected sibs. None had abnormal neurologic findings, and only one had a photosensitive rash.

Scriver et al.[3] recently reported the study of 21 affected children who had come to attention through routine urine screening in Massachusetts and Quebec compared to 19 age-matched unaffected sib controls. None had received continual nicotinamide therapy. Two developed major clinical manifestations, considered to be due to factors acting in concert with the Hartnup defect (see "Is Hartnup Disorder a Disease?" below). Among the remaining 19 affected children, five developed skin lesions, three of which were eczematous and two psoriatic but none photosensitive; one unaffected sib had eczema ($p = 0.19$). One Hartnup subject had seizures and an abnormal electroencephalogram. The mean ± SD full-scale IQ scores for 12 Hartnup subjects and eight sib controls were 103 ± 10 and 108 ± 12, respectively. The difference was insignificant. School performances were similar for the two groups. Two Hartnup subjects had learning difficulties, one of whom was subsequently found to also have 47,XXX aneuploidy.[98] Somatic growth was normal in the affected children and comparable to their sib controls. Thus, it seems that most Hartnup subjects remain clinically normal.

DIAGNOSIS

The only constant feature of Hartnup disorder is the characteristic excretion of free amino acids, and it is upon this that the diagnosis must be based.[1,2] The *pattern* of urinary amino acids, rather than the total amino acid excretion, is the determining factor. Any of the simple two-dimensional paper or thin-layer chromatographic systems and location reagents for amino acids will serve.[99] Figure 101-2 indicates the urinary amino acids expected in excess in the Hartnup disorder.

Very little else even remotely resembles the Hartnup pattern. In generalized hyperaminoaciduria, with which the Hartnup pattern is most likely confused, proline is always a prominent amino acid and other amino acids such as cystine and the dibasic amino acids (lysine and ornithine) are excreted in excess. These compounds, particularly proline, are not increased in Hartnup disorder.[4] Fecal contamination of urine, which often produces factitious results in newborn screening,[100] causes an amino acid pattern much more like generalized hyperaminoaciduria than one resembling Hartnup disorder.[101]

The indolic excretion is not constant enough to be the basis of a diagnostic test. Even increased excretion of indolic acids after an oral tryptophan load might be misleading since an intestinal defect similar or identical to that in Hartnup disorder may be present without neutral hyperamioaciduria.[36] Conversely, Hartnup subjects may have only the renal defect.[3]

Thus, Hartnup disorder is not excluded by a normal indole excretion, but all patients with a high indican or other indolic acid excretion should be further examined for Hartnup disorder by urine amino acid analysis.

The only alternative diagnoses for the full clinical expression associated with Hartnup disorder would be pellagra or, possibly, a defect in the major pathway of tryptophan catabolism. In pellagra, amino acid excretion is low or normal.[4] Putative defects in tryptophan catabolism include familial disease with pellagra-like skin rash and ataxia, but renal and intestinal amino acid transport is normal.[48,49,51,53,102] Hartnup disorder should be suspected in patients with pellagra-like signs but without gross dietary deficiency; photosensitive rash, especially if accompanied by neurologic changes; intermittent ataxia, especially where sibs are similarly affected; or high excretion of indican or other indolic acids.

TREATMENT

The only rational treatment for this disorder is the administration of nicotinic acid, or better, nicotinamide to patients who have signs suggesting a deficiency of this vitamin. This has been used in amounts from 50 to 300 mg/day administered orally. In many instances the rash has cleared with this therapy.[73,103] Several investigators have also reported cessation of ataxia[37,41,77,89] and amelioration of psychotic-type behavior.[29,37,41,70,73,104] Despite reports to the contrary,[17,18] neither the hyperaminoaciduria nor the intestinal transport defect responds to this therapy.[26,88] In addition to nicotinamide a high protein diet or protein supplement might be beneficial in some instances,[1] particularly for patients with low plasma amino acid values[3] in whom symptomatic Hartnup episodes might be prevented. Intravenous nutrition has been beneficial in correcting an eczematoid rash and hypoproteinemic edema associated with low plasma amino acid levels in one patient.[3]

The efficacy of therapy is difficult to evaluate. Since the clinical abnormalities have generally been intermittent, their disappearance in most cases cannot clearly be designated as a therapeutic result. Furthermore, therapy with nicotinamide has not always achieved the desired result. In one patient the rash disappeared after treatment on one occasion but did not on another occasion.[4] However, it seems that patients with clinical abnormalities associated with Hartnup disorder should be given at least a trial of nicotinamide therapy.

GENETICS

Hartnup disorder has an autosomal recessive inheritance pattern; males and females are about equally represented, sibs are often affected,[1,3,4,84] and parents have normal urine amino acid profiles.[105] Consanguinity between parents has been reported in a number of families.[1,90,92]

There seems to be widespread distribution of Hartnup disorder with no ethnic predilection. Cases have been found wherever urine amino acid analysis has been conducted, including England, continental Europe, Canada, the United States, Australia, India, Japan, West Africa, and Israel.

Hartnup disorder is not associated with other genetic disorders. Jonxis[13] reported phenylketonuria and Hartnup disorder in one patient. Shih et al.[106] reported the coexistence of

Hartnup disorder and methylmalonic aciduria in two families. In one of these families the proband had both Hartnup disorder and methylmalonic aciduria but a sib had methylmalonic aciduria alone. The methylmalonic aciduria was B_{12}-unresponsive and considered to be a benign variant of methylmalonyl-CoA mutase deficiency.[107] In the second family an infant died with severe methylmalonic aciduria; his mother was subsequently found to have Hartnup disorder when she was evaluated for recurrent skin rashes. We are aware of 47,XXX aneuploidy in a girl with the Hartnup syndrome,[98] and Tarlow et al.[32] described the coexistence of celiac disease and Hartnup disorder in a boy. One girl identified in newborn screening by Wilcken developed juvenile diabetes mellitus.[107a] All of these combinations appear to be purely chance occurrences.

Heterozygotes for the Hartnup mutation, including parents and offspring of Hartnup subjects, have shown no evidence of the renal defect.[1,27,108] The mother of the original Hartnup children had a normal amino acid clearance, even in response to a casein load.[9] Tryptophan loading in heterozygotes, however, might elicit evidence of deficient intestinal transport. The parents of two Hartnup patients had a delayed peak for plasma tryptophan following an oral load.[74] Similarly challenged, all the children from two Hartnup patients excreted abnormally large amounts of indican, indoleacetic acid, indolylacryloylglycine, indoleacetylglutamine, and indoleacetamide.[27] There may also be a high incidence of photosensitivity among heterozygous individuals.[73,78]

The specific carrier responsible for neutral amino acid transport has not been identified. It is apparently located in the brush border membrane of cells expressing the Hartnup gene[29,30,33]; the gene is not expressed in parenchymal[40] and blood cells.[39] Similarly, the gene that encodes this protein has neither been mapped nor cloned. These discoveries may require an in vitro system in which the neutral amino acid transport mechanism can be isolated—perhaps cells cultured from kidney or intestine with the more specific transport mechanisms suppressed.

An animal model for Hartnup disorder has not yet been identified. Schiffer et al.[109] reported a monoaminomonocarboxylic hyperaminoaciduria in males of an inbred mouse strain, but the pattern differed somewhat from the Hartnup hyperaminoaciduria[110] and required testosterone for expression.

SCREENING AND INCIDENCE

Urine amino acid screening of individuals institutionalized for mental retardation has led to the identification of several Hartnup subjects. Among 729 such individuals screened in India, two Hartnup cases were found.[111] Two affected brothers were found among 2100 mentally defective persons screened in a Massachusetts institution.[28] A single case was discovered among an unspecified number of individuals screened in a New Hampshire institution for the mentally retarded.[27]

Finding only these few cases and the relatively small number of others identified as a result of amino acid screening for medical indications led to the belief that Hartnup disorder was very rare, and, therefore, the presence of clinical abnormalities in these individuals was highly significant. Routine newborn urine screening by paper or thin-layer chromatography, however, has demonstrated that the Hartnup finding is one of the

most frequent of the amino acid disorders.[99] The most recent newborn screening data include incidences of 1 in 42,000 among over 1 million screened infants in Quebec,[112] 1 in 18,000 among 750,000 screened in Massachusetts,[113] 1 in 33,000 among 300,000 screened in New South Wales, Australia,[84] and 1 in 25,000 among 127,000 screened in Manitoba.[114] Accordingly, the composite newborn screening experience is 82 affected infants identified among at least 2 million screened, an incidence of 1 in 24,000. Additional cases have been identified among sibs of these infants.[3,84,113] Thus, Hartnup disorder is quite comparable in frequency to cystinuria[112,113] and is not very much less frequent than phenylketonuria.[113]

IS HARTNUP DISORDER A DISEASE?

From prospective and retrospective studies of Hartnup subjects identified by routine newborn screening and followed for many years, most without therapy, it is clear that very few become symptomatic.[3,6,84] On this basis, Hartnup disorder could be considered benign. Furthermore, even the symptomatic few have not had the complete clinical phenotype that was once thought to be characteristic of the Hartnup disorder.[3] These observations together with the relatively high frequency of the Hartnup finding in the general population prompt the question of whether the symptoms described in patients with Hartnup disorder might be coincidental and not causally related to the genetic defect.

It is reasonable to propose that this is so. In addition to the preponderance of asymptomatic affected subjects identified by routine screening, the great majority of affected sibs identified by family screening of symptomatic probands have also been clinically normal.[6] Therapeutic correction of niacin deficiency, the factor that is believed to cause clinical abnormalities in the Hartnup disorder, does not always reverse the clinical findings and sometimes produces no benefit whatsoever.[1] Nevertheless, it is difficult to disregard the very striking and unusual pellagra-like phenotype observed in a number of affected individuals.

Attempts to reconcile these quite different observations in Hartnup subjects have produced several hypotheses. The first of these holds that symptomatic cases come from economically deprived families whose diets would be just adequate for normal individuals or are persons under the stress of temporary malnutrition.[5,115] Thus, dietary niacin deficiency compounds their inherent inability to form nicotinamide from its only precursor amino acid, tryptophan.[14] A second hypothesis is that at least the acute attacks of ataxia and, perhaps, psychosis are a result of toxicity to the central nervous system from indolic acids produced in large amounts in some patients by the bacterial degradation of unabsorbed tryptophan in the gut.[22] Supporting this is a report that the ingestion of indoleacetic acid or indolepropionic acid causes irritability and ataxia.[116] In another study, however, indoleacetic acid was given in huge quantities, apparently without ill effects.[117]

The most recent hypothesis is that of Scriver et al.,[3] which holds that liability to disease in the Hartnup disorder is determined by one or more polygenic factors, notably the plasma amino acid value. Accordingly, disease will not likely occur if the inherent aggregate value for plasma amino acids is normal but will occur, especially in response to environmental stress

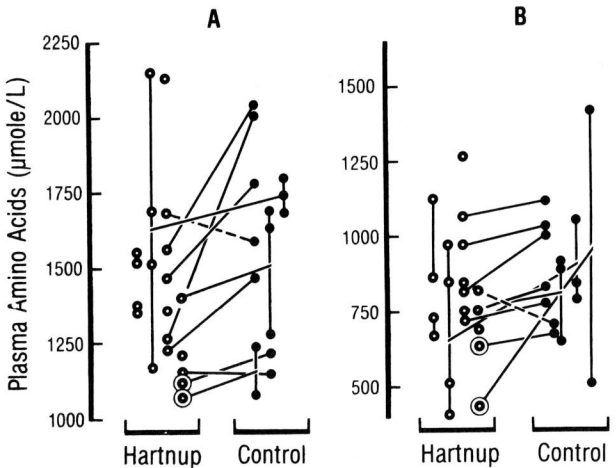

Fig. 101-6 Distributions of plasma amino acid values in Hartnup subjects (circles) and control sibs (black dots). Lines join the corresponding values for sibs (vertical lines, Hartnup vs. Hartnup and control vs. control; solid crossing lines, Hartnup value < control value; interrupted crossing line, Hartnup value > control value). *Panel A.* Aggregate values (μmol/liter) for 10 amino acids (excluding tryptophan) affected by Hartnup mutation. *Panel B.* Aggregate values for remaining amino acids. Two symptomatic probands are indicated by the bull's-eye symbol. *(From Scriver, Mahon, Levy, Clow, Reade, Kronick, Lemieux, and Laberge.[3] By permission of the American Journal of Human Genetics.)*

such as diarrhea, if the aggregate plasma amino acid value is low (Fig. 101-6). In this concept, the cause of disease in the Hartnup disorder is multifactorial.[3] It would seem that this theory is the most reasonable yet advanced to explain the clinical observations in Hartnup disorder.

MATERNAL HARTNUP DISORDER

Eleven offspring have been reported from four women with the Hartnup disorder.[27,106,108] In addition Seakins[5] mentions two offspring born to affected women who were described before their pregnancies,[29,77] and we know of a third offspring recently born to one of the women we reported.[108] Twelve of these 14 offspring were clinically normal, and none has had the Hartnup disorder. Of the two abnormal offspring, one had a severe neural tube defect characterized by meningomyelocele and hydrocephalus and died at age 3 months.[106] The other had methylmalonic acidemia with severe metabolic acidosis and died during early infancy.[106] Pregnancies have been normal in these women with the exception of one complicated by placenta previa.[108] It seems likely that the Hartnup disorder does not adversely affect pregnancy and is harmless to the fetus. The occurrences of methylmalonic acidemia in one offspring and neural tube defect in another were almost certainly coincidental.[106,108]

In one pregnancy the ratios between maternal and umbilical vein amino acids at delivery were normal, suggesting that the neutral amino acid transport defect is not expressed in the placenta when the mother has the Hartnup disorder.[108]

One man with Hartnup disorder has sired two normal non-Hartnup offspring.[27]

This chapter is a revision of the excellent one, entitled "Hartnup Disease," written by the late Dr. John B. Jepson for The Metabolic Basis of Inherited Disease, 4/e. Much of the text and several figures from that chapter have been retained.

REFERENCES

1. JEPSON JB; Hartnup disease, in Stanbury JB, Wyngaarden JB, Fredrickson DS (eds): *The Metabolic Basis of Inherited Disease*, 4th ed. New York, McGraw-Hill, 1978, p 1563.
2. EFRON M: Comments in Greer M: Hartnup's syndrome. *Trans Am Neurol Assoc* 90:53, 1965.
3. SCRIVER CR, MAHON B, LEVY HL, CLOW CL, READE TM, KRONICK J, LEMIEUX B, LABERGE C: The Hartnup phenotype: Mendelian transport disorder, multifactorial disease. *Am J Hum Genet* 40:401, 1987.
4. BARON DN, DENT CE, HARRIS H, HART EW, JEPSON JB: Hereditary pellagra-like skin rash with temporary cerebellar ataxia. Constant renal aminoaciduria. And other bizarre biochemical features. *Lancet* 2:421, 1956.
5. SEAKINS JWT: Hartnup disease, in Vinken PJ, Bruyn GW (eds): *Metabolic and Deficiency Diseases of the Nervous System*. Amsterdam, North-Holland, 1977, p 149.
6. LEVY HL: Hartnup disease, in Goldensohn ES, Appel SH (eds): *Scientific Approaches to Clinical Neurology*, Philadelphia, Lea & Febiger, 1977, p 75.
7. BONETTI E, DENT CE: The determination of optical configuration of naturally occurring amino acids using specific enzymes and paper chromatography. *Biochem J* 57:77, 1954.
8. CUSWORTH DC, DENT CE: Renal clearances of amino acids in normal adults and in patients with aminoaciduria. *Biochem J* 74:550, 1960.
9. DENT CE: The renal aminoacidurias. *Exp Med Surg* 12:229, 1954.
10. EVERED DF: The excretion of amino acids by the human: A quantitative study with ion-exchange chromatography. *Biochem J* 62:416, 1956.
11. HALVORSEN S, HYGSTEDT O, JAGENBURG R, SJAASTAD O: Cellular transport of L-histidine in Hartnup disease. *J Clin Invest* 48:1552, 1969.
12. TADA K, HIRONO H, ARAKAWA T: Endogenous renal clearance rates of free amino acids in prolinuric and Hartnup patients. *Tohoku J Exp Med* 93:57, 1967.
13. JONXIS JHP: Oligophrenia phenylpyruvica en de hartnupziekte. *Ned Tijdschr Geneeskd* 101:569, 1957.
14. SCRIVER CR, ROSENBERG LE: *Amino Acid Metabolism and Its Disorders*. Philadelphia, Saunders, 1973.
15. MILNE MD, ASATOOR A, LOUGHRIDGE L: Hartnup disease and cystinuria. *Lancet* 1:51, 1961.
16. SCRIVER CR, HECHTMAN P: Human genetics of membrane transport with emphasis on amino acids. *Adv Hum Genet* 1:211, 1970.
17. FOIS A, LECCHINI L: Acute cerebellar ataxia associated with some features of the Hartnup syndrome. *Helv Paediatr Acta* 19:42, 1964.
18. DE LAEY P, HOOFT C, TIMMERMANS J, SNOECK J: Biochemical aspects of Hartnup disease. *Ann Paediatr* 202:145, 321, 1964.
19. HJELT L, PAATELA M, VISAKORPI JK: Autopsy findings in Hartnup disease. *Proc 13th Northern Pediatr Cong*, Copenhagen, 1961.
20. VISAKORPI JK, HJELT L, LAHIKAINEN T, OHMAN S: Hartnup disease in two siblings: Clinical observations and biochemical studies. *Ann Paediatr Fenn* 10:42, 1964.
21. DAUTE K-H, DIETEL K, EBERT W: Das Hartnupsyndrom. Bericht über einen tödlichen Krankheitsverlauf. *Z Kinderheilkd* 95:103, 1966.
22. MILNE MD, CRAWFORD MA, GIRAO CB, LOUGHRIDGE LW. The metabolic disorder in Hartnup disease. *Q J Med* 29:407, 1960.
23. SCRIVER CR, SHAW KNF: Hartnup disease: An example of genetically determined defective cellular amino acid transport. *Can Med Assoc J* 86:232, 1962.
24. SCRIVER CR: Hartnup disease. A genetic modification of intestinal and renal transport of certain neutral alpha-amino acids. *N Engl J Med* 273:530, 1965.
25. ASATOOR AM, CRASKE J, LONDON DR, MILNE MD: Indole production in Hartnup disease. *Lancet* 1:126, 1963.
26. SEAKINS JWT, ERSSER RS: Effects of amino acid loads on a healthy infant with the biochemical features of Hartnup disease. *Arch Dis Child* 42:682, 1967.
27. POMEROY J, EFRON ML, DAYMAN J, HOEFNAGEL D: Hartnup disease in a New England family. *N Engl J Med* 278:1214, 1968.
28. SHIH VE, BIXBY EM, ALPERS DH, BARTSOCAS CS, THIER SO: Studies of intestinal transport defect in Hartnup disease. *Gastroenterology* 61:445, 1971.
29. NAVAB F, ASATOOR AM: Studies on intestinal absorption of amino acids and a dipeptide in a case of Hartnup disease. *Gut* 11:373, 1970.
30. ASATOOR AM, CHENG B, EDWARDS KDG, LANT AF, MATTHEWS DM, MILNE MD, NAVAB F, RICHARDS AJ: Intestinal absorption of two dipeptides in Hartnup disease. *Gut* 11:380, 1970.
31. TARLOW MJ, SEAKINS JWT, LLOYD JK, MATTHEWS DM, CHENG B, THOMAS AJ: Intestinal absorption and biopsy transport of peptides and amino acids in Hartnup disease. *Clin Sci* 39:18P, 1970.

32. TARLOW MJ, SEAKINS JWT, LLOYD JK, MATTHEWS DM, CHENG B, THOMAS AJ: Absorption of amino acids and peptides in a child with a variant of Hartnup disease and coexistent coeliac disease. *Arch Dis Child* 47:798, 1972.

33. LEONARD JV, MARRS TC, ADDISON JM, BURSTON D, CLEGG KM, LLOYD JK, MATTHEWS DM, SEAKINS JW: Intestinal absorption of amino acids and peptides in Hartnup disorder. *Pediatr Res* 10:246, 1976.

34. ASATOOR AM, CHENG B, EDWARDS KDG, LANT AF, MATTHEWS DM, MILNE MD, NAVAB F, RICHARDS AJ: Intestinal absorption of dipeptides and corresponding free amino acids in Hartnup disease. *Clin Sci* 39:1P, 1970.

35. DRUMMOND KN, MICHAEL AF, ULSTROM RA, GOOD RA: The blue diaper syndrome: Familial hypercalcemia with nephrocalcinosis and indicanuria. *Am J Med* 37:928, 1964.

36. HILLMAN RE, STEWART A, MILES JH: Aminoacid transport defect in intestine not affecting kidney. *Pediatr Res* 20:265A, 1986.

37. OYANAGI K, TAKAGI M, KITABATAKE M, NAKAO T: Hartnup disease. *Tohoku J Exp Med* 91:383, 1967.

38. NIELSEN EG, VEDSO S, ZIMMERMANN-NIELSEN C: Hartnup disease in three siblings. *Dan Med Bull* 13:155, 1966.

39. TADA K, MORIKAWA T, ARAKAWA T: Tryptophan load and uptake of tryptophan by leukocytes in Hartnup disease. *Tohoku J Exp Med* 90:337, 1966.

40. GROTH U, ROSENBERG LE: Transport of dibasic amino acids, cystine, and tryptophan by cultured human fibroblasts: Absence of a defect in cystinuria and Hartnup disease. *J Clin Invest* 51:2130, 1972.

41. HERSOV LA: A case of childhood pellagra with psychosis. *J Ment Sci* 101:878, 1955.

42. HICKISH GW: Pellagra in an English child. *Arch Dis Child* 30:195, 1955.

43. FEIGELSON P, FEIGELSON M, GREENGARD O: Comparison of the mechanisms of hormonal and substrate induction of rat liver tryptophan pyrrolase. *Recent Prog Horm Res* 18:491, 1962.

44. SCHIMKE RT, SWEENEY EW, BERLIN CM: The roles of synthesis and degradation in the control of rat liver tryptophan pyrrolase. *J Biol Chem* 240:322, 1965.

45. GOLDSMITH GA: Niacin-tryptophan relationships in man and niacin requirements. *Am J Clin Nutr* 6:479, 1958.

46. GOLDSMITH GA: The B vitamins: Thiamine, riboflavin, niacin, in Beaton GH, McHenry EW (eds): *Nutrition. A Comprehensive Treatise*. New York, Academic, 1964, vol 2, p 110.

47. SNEDDEN W, MELLOR CS, MARTIN JR: Familial hypertryptophanemia, tryptophanuria and indoleketonuria. *Clin Chim Acta* 131:247, 1983.

48. TADA K, ITO H, WADA Y, ARAKAWA T: Congenital tryptophanuria with dwarfism. *Tohoku J Exp Med* 80:118, 1963.

49. WONG PWK, FORMAN P, TABAHOFF B, JUSTICE P: A defect in tryptophan metabolism. *Pediatr Res* 10:725, 1976.

50. KOMROWER GM, WILSON V, CLAMP JR, WESTALL RG: Hydroxykynureninuria. A case of abnormal tryptophan metabolism probably due to a deficiency of kynureninase. *Arch Dis Child* 39:250, 1964.

51. SALIH MAM, BENDER DA, MCCREANOR GM: Lethal familial pellagra-like skin lesion associated with neurologic and developmental impairment and the development of cataracts. *Pediatrics* 76:787, 1985.

52. PRICE JM, YESS N, BROWN RR, JOHNSON SAM: Tryptophan metabolism. A hitherto unreported abnormality occurring in a family. *Arch Dermatol* 95:462, 1967.

53. FENTON DA, WILKINSON JD, TOSELAND PA: Family exhibiting cerebellar-like ataxia, photosensitivity and shortness of stature—A new inborn error of tryptophan metabolism. *J R Soc Med* 76:736, 1983.

54. ARMSTRONG MD, SHAW KNF, GORTATOWSKI MJ, SINGER H: The indole acids of human urine. *J Biol Chem* 232:17, 1958.

55. WEISSBACH H, KING W, SJOERDSMA A, UDENFRIEND S: Formation of indole-3-acetic acid and tryptamine in animals. *J Biol Chem* 234:81, 1959.

56. SJOERDSMA A, OATES JA, ZALTZMAN P, UDENFRIEND S: Identification and assay of urinary tryptamine. *J Pharmacol Exp Ther* 126:217, 1959.

57. SMITH HG, SMITH WRD, JEPSON JB: Interconversions of indolic acids by bacteria and rat tissue—Possible relevance to Hartnup disorder. *Clin Sci* 34:333, 1968.

58. SMITH HG, SMITH WRD, JEPSON JB, SORENSEN K: The metabolism and excretion of indolylacrylic acid in the rat., *Biochem Pharmacol* 19:1689, 1970.

59. FORDTRAN JS, SCROGGIE WB, POLTER DE: Colonic absorption of tryptophan metabolites in man. *J Lab Clin Med* 64:125, 1964.

60. HAPPOLD FC: Tryptophanase-tryptophan reaction. *Adv Enzymol* 10:51, 1950.

61. KING LJ, PARKE DV, WILLIAMS RT: Metabolism of indole-2-^{14}C. *Biochem J* 88:66P, 1963.

62. NAKAO A, BALL M: The appearance of a skatole derivative in the urine of schizophrenics. *J Nerv Ment Dis* 130:417, 1960.

63. SPRINCE H: Indole metabolism in mental illness. *Clin Chem* 7:203, 1961.

64. SCRIVER CR: Abnormalities of tryptophan metabolism in a patient with malabsorption syndrome. *J Lab Clin Med* 58:908, 1961.

65. CRAWFORD MA: Degradation of aminoacids in the large gut of East Africans and its possible significance. *East Afr Med J* 41:228, 1964.

66. CRAWFORD MA: Discussion of indole metabolism in Hartnup disease. *Adv Pharmacol* 6B:176, 1968.

67. MELLMAN WU, BARNESS LA, TEDESCO TA, BESSELMAN D: Indolylacryloyl-glycine excretion in a family with mental retardation. *Clin Chim Acta* 8:843, 1963.

68. SZEINBERG A, BAR-OR R, POLLACK S, COHEN BE, JEPSON JB: Observations on urinary excretion of indolylacryloyl-glycine. *Clin Chim Acta* 11:506, 1965.

69. RODNIGHT R, MCILWAIN H: Indicanuria and the psychosis of a pellagrin. *J Ment Sci* 101:884, 1955.

70. HERSOV LA, RODNIGHT R: Hartnup disease in psychiatric practice: Clinical and biochemical features of three cases. *J Neurol Neurosurg Psychiatry* 23:40, 1960.

71. SHAW KNF, REDLICH D, WRIGHT SW, JEPSON JB: Dependence of urinary indole excretion in Hartnup disease upon gut flora. *Fed Proc* 19:194, 1960.

72. HOOFT C, De LAEY P, TIMMERMANS J, SNOECK J: La maladie de Hartnup. *Acta Paediatr Belg* 16:281, 1962.

73. HALVORSEN K, HALVORSEN S: Hartnup disease. *Pediatrics* 31:29, 1963.

74. WONG PWK, PILLAI PM: Clinical and biochemical observations in two cases of Hartnup disease. *Arch Dis Child* 41:383, 1966.

75. SRIKANTIA SG, VENKATACHALAM PS, REDDY V: Clinical and biochemical features of a case of Hartnup disease. *Br Med J* 1:282, 1964.

76. JEPSON JB: Indolylacetyl-glutamine and other indole metabolites in Hartnup disease. *Biochem J* 64:14p, 1956.

77. HENDERSON W: A case of Hartnup disease. *Arch Dis Child* 33:114, 1958.

78. WEYERS H, BICKEL H: Photodermatose mit Aminoacidurie, Indolaceturie und cerebralen Manifestationen (Hartnup-Syndrom). *Klin Wochenschr* 36:893, 1958.

79. JEPSON JB: Indole metabolism in Hartnup disease. *Adv Pharmacol* 6B:171, 1968.

80. HVIDT S, KJELDSEN K: Malabsorption induced by small doses of neomycin sulfate. *Acta Med Scand* 173:699, 1963.

81. JEPSON JB: Indolylacetamide, a chromatographic artifact from the natural indoles indolylacetylglucosiduronic acid and indolylpyruvic acid. *Biochem J* 69:22P, 1958.

82. LOPEZ F, VELEZ H, TORO G: Hartnup disease in two Colombian siblings. *Neurology* 19:71, 1969.

83. DAVIS VE, BROWN H, HUFF JA, CASHAW JL: Alteration of serotonin metabolism to 5-hydroxytryptophol by ethanol ingestion in man. *J Lab Clin Med* 69:132, 1967.

84. WILCKEN B, YU JS, BROWN DA: Natural history of Hartnup disease. *Arch Dis Child* 52:38, 1977.

85. LEVY HL, SHIH VE, MACCREADY RA: Inborn errors of metabolism and transport. Prenatal and neonatal diagnosis. *Proc 13th Int Cong Pediatrics*. Vienna, 1971, vol 5, p 1.

86. DESPOPOULOS A, WEISSBACH H: Renal metabolism of 5-hydroxyindoleacetic acid. *Am J Physiol* 189:548, 1957.

87. JONAS AJ, BUTLER IJ: Neurotransmitter abnormalities in Hartnup disease. *Am J Hum Genet* 41:A8, 1987.

88. WONG PWK, LAMBERT AM, PILLAI PM, JONES PM: Observations on nicotinic acid therapy in Hartnup disease. *Arch Dis Child* 42:642, 1967.

89. ALBERS FH, WADMAN SK: Een patiënte met H-ziekte. *Maandschr Kindergeneeskd* 29:102, 1961.

90. SOMASUNDARAM O, PAPAKUMARI M: Hartnup disease. A report on two siblings. *Indian Pediatr* 10:455, 1973.

91. HAIM S, GILHAR A, COHEN A: Cutaneous manifestations associated with aminoaciduria. Report of two cases. *Dermatologica* 156:244, 1978.

92. STROBEL M, FALL M, KUAKUVI N, N'DIAYE B, SANOKHO A, MARCHAND J-P: Maladie de Hartnup. *Bull Soc Med Afr Noire Lgue Frse* 23:118, 1978.

93. ASHURST PJ: Hydroa vacciniforme occurring in association with Hartnup disease. *Br J Dermatol* 81:486, 1969.

94. KIMMIG J: Hartnup-syndrom. *Arch Klin Exp Dermatol* 219:753, 1964.

95. GUZZETTA F, MAZZAGLIA E: La malattia di Hartnup. *Minerva Pediatr* 22:480, 1970.

96. OZALP I, SAATCI U, HASSA R: A case of Hartnup disorder with hypoalbuminemia and edema. *Turk J Pediatr* 19:73, 1977.

97. COLLISS JE, LEVI AJ, MILNE MD: Stature and nutrition in cystinuria and Hartnup disease. *Br Med J* 1:590, 1963.

98. LEVY HL, KUPKE KG: Unpublished data.

99. LEVY HL: Genetic screening. *Adv Hum Genet* 4:1, 1973.

100. LEVY HL, COULOMBE JT, SHIH VE: Newborn urine screening, in Bickel H,

Guthrie R, Hammersen G (eds): *Neonatal Screening for Inborn Errors of Metabolism*. Heidelberg, Springer-Verlag, 1980, p 89.

101. LEVY HL, MADIGAN PM, LUM A: Fecal contamination in urine amino acid screening. Artifactual cause of hyperaminoaciduria. *Am J Clin Pathol* 51:765, 1969.

102. FREUNDLICH E, STATTER M, YATZIV S: Familial pellagra-like skin rash with neurologic manifestations. *Arch Dis Child* 56:146, 1981.

103. MILNE MD: Hartnup disease. *Biochem J* 111:3P, 1969.

104. BARTELHEIMER HK, GRÜTTNER R, SIMON HA: Das Hartnup-Syndrom. I. Diagnose, Therapie und klinischer Verlauf. *Monatsschr Kinderheilkd* 119:52, 1971.

105. LEVY HL: Unpublished data.

106. SHIH VE, COULOMBE JT, WADMAN SK, DURAN M, WAELKENS JJJ: Occurrences of methylmalonic aciduria and Hartnup disorder in the same family. *Clin Genet* 26:216, 1984.

107. LEDLEY FD, LEVY HL, SHIH VE, BENJAMIN R, MAHONEY MT: Benign methylmalonic aciduria. *N Engl J Med* 311:1015, 1984.

107a. WILCKEN B: Personal communication.

108. MAHON BE, LEVY HL: Maternal Hartnup disorder. *Am J Med Genet* 24:513, 1986.

109. SCHIFFER SP, JEZYK PF, PATTERSON DF, RODERICK TH: Characterization of aminoaciduria in P/J mice. *Lab Anim Sci* 36:586, 1986.

110. SCHIFFER SP: Personal communication.

111. RAO BS, NARAYANAN HS, REDDY GN: A clinical and biochemical survey of 729 cases of mental subnormality. *Br J Psychiatry* 118:505, 1971.

112. LEMIEUX B, AURAY-BLAIS C, GIGUÈRE R, SHAPCOTT D, SCRIVER CR: Newborn urine screening experience with over one million infants in the Quebec Network of Genetic Medicine. *J Inherited Metab Dis* 11:45, 1988.

113. LEVY HL, LAWLOR MG, SWENSON EF: Unpublished data.

114. FOX JG: Experience of the Manitoba Perinatal Screening Program, 1965–85. *Can Med Assoc J* 137:883, 1987.

115. JEPSON JB: Hartnup disease, in Benson PF (ed): *Cellular Organelles and Membranes in Mental Retardation*. Edinburgh, Churchill, Livingstone, 1971, p 55.

116. GREER M: Hartnup's syndrome. *Trans Am Neurol Assoc* 90:53, 1965.

117. MIRSKY JA: Insulinase, insulinase inhibitors and diabetes mellitus. *Recent Prog Horm Res* 13:429, 1957.

CHAPTER 102

FAMILIAL RENAL IMINOGLYCINURIA

CHARLES R. SCRIVER

1. Familial iminoglycinuria is a benign inborn error of membrane transport. It involves a membrane carrier in the renal tubule with preference for L-proline, hydroxy-L-proline, and glycine serving net reabsorption. The iminoglycinuria phenotype is autosomal recessive.

2. Homozygotes retain significant tubular reabsorption of the imino acids and glycine. The residual transport function is saturated at endogenous concentrations of substrate, and the normal competitive interactions between the imino acids and glycine during tubular reabsorption are not observed. These seemingly paradoxical observations can be explained if several carriers participate in the reabsorption of imino acids and glycine. Loss of a carrier shared by the imino acids and glycine and retention of other carriers with preferences for glycine and imino acids, but not both simultaneously, would account for the homozygous iminoglycinuric phenotype.

3. A variant phenotype in which imino acid reabsorption has a normal T_m value and the defect affects glycine reclamation more than proline indicates a K_m variant.

4. Impaired intestinal transport of L-proline has been demonstrated in some but not all homozygotes. A transport defect has not been demonstrated in the leukocytes or skin fibroblasts.

5. Obligate heterozygotes may be "hyperglycinuric" (incompletely recessive) or "silent" (completely recessive) for expression of the mutant allele. Phenotypic heterogeneity among probands and obligate heterozygotes indicates genetic heterogeneity.

6. The different mutations appear to be allelic. Probands inheriting two "silent" mutant alleles, or two "hyperglycinuric" alleles, or two different alleles have the same renal phenotype.

7. The differential diagnosis of familial iminoglycinuria includes: hyperprolinemia, in which iminoglycinuria occurs by a combined saturation-inhibition mechanism; the Fanconi syndrome, in which iminoglycinuria occurs as part of a generalized disturbance of transport; and the newborn, in whom hyperiminoglycinuria occurs in the first 6 months of life. Neonatal iminoglycinuria involves ontogeny of transport systems not controlled by the gene locus involved in hereditary iminoglycinuria.

8. Several different forms of renal hyperglycinuria are known, which must be distinguished from the hyperglycinuric phenotype of the "incompletely recessive" heterozygote with renal iminoglycinuria.

Familial renal iminoglycinuria is a Mendelian disorder expressed in homozygotes or genetic compounds as a selective hyperaminoaciduria. It is caused by several autosomal alleles, some of which are partially expressed in heterozygotes (incompletely recessive alleles). The disorder is not a disease, although ascertainment of the phenotype in probands with clinical signs suggested to early observers that it might be. Familial iminoglycinuria is significant because it provides evidence for a transport system selective for imino acids[*] and glycine in the renal tubule and intestine under the control of a single locus. In its medical context, the disorder enters into the differential diagnosis of several hyperaminoacidurias, and since the newborn infant has physiological iminoglycinuria, the ontogenetic and Mendelian phenotypes need to be discriminated from each other.

When Dent[4] applied chromatographic methods to the investigation of diseases, he fostered an exponential increase in the discovery of disorders of amino acid metabolism.[5] (Renal iminoglycinuria is one of those disorders.) Urine was a revealing mirror of metabolic disorders, and chromatography of urine amino acids evinced great interest.[6] It was soon recognized that urine of young infants normally contains a large quantity of the two imino acids, proline and hydroxyproline, and of the amino acid glycine.[7-10] It then became known that iminoaciduria disappeared as the infant reached about 3 months of age, and thereafter the urine normally did not contain detectable amounts of proline or hydroxyproline; the hyperglycinuria had disappeared by about 6 months. Impaired net tubular reabsorption explained neonatal iminoglycinuria (Fig. 102-1).

Persistence of iminoglycinuria beyond 6 months constitutes an abnormality. It occurs under three different circumstances:

1. As a "combined" aminoaciduria in the presence of hyperprolinemia or hyperhydroxyprolinemia (see Chap. 18).

2. As a component of a generalized disturbance of membrane transport, e.g., in the Fanconi syndrome (see Chap. 104).

3. As a specific inborn error of membrane transport of amino acids now usually known as familial (renal) iminoglycinuria (the subject of this chapter).

Most of the early reports of pathologic iminoglycinuria[12-34] testify that the condition was discovered during retrospective studies carried out for other purposes. The diversity of the clinical abnormalities in probands with familial iminoglycinuria suggests now that there is little or no direct relationship between the inherited disorder of membrane transport and the accompanying illness. It is appropriate to classify familial iminoglycinuria as a benign inborn error of membrane transport,[20-22] a conclusion borne out by the frequent occurrence of healthy iminoglycinuric sibs of probands and by the prospective discovery of probands, through newborn screening programs,[28,30] in whom follow-up observations have revealed no late-appearing illness.

---

[*]These compounds are also excreted in bound form as oligopeptides (see Chap. 18). Familial iminoglycinuria is a trait affecting only the free forms of proline, hydroxyproline, and glycine. "Imino acid" is a popular term used to distinguish the configuration of the secondary amino group (RC—NHCH—COOH) of the heterocyclic amino acids from the primary amino group (NH$_2$—CHR—COOH) of other amino acids. The term "imino acid" is freely used in standard texts on the biochemistry and metabolism of amino acids,[1,2] but reservations have been expressed about the accuracy of its use in this way.[3]

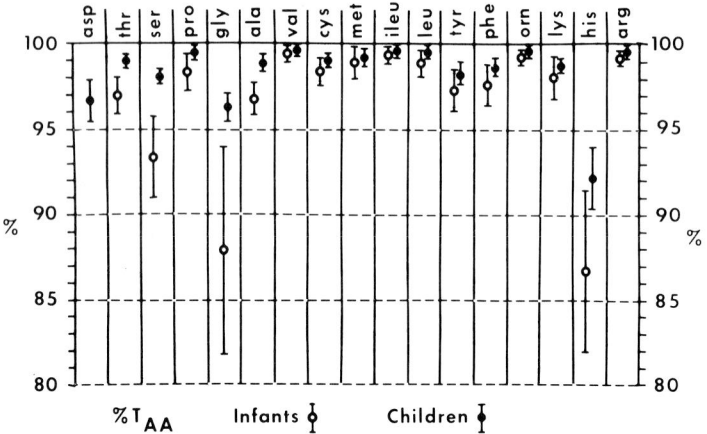

Fig. 102-1 Net tubular reabsorption of amino acids (expressed as percent of filtered load) is less efficient in the newborn human subject than in older subjects. Glycine reabsorption is particularly impaired, and the presence of imino acids in the urine of the neonate and young infant is noteworthy. *(Redrawn from Brodehl and Gellissen.*[10] *Reproduced from Pediatrics, with permission.)*

RENAL TRANSPORT OF IMINO ACIDS AND GLYCINE

Investigation into the cause of iminoglycinuria in another disorder, familial hyperprolinemia[35,36] (see Chap. 18), led to the concept that imino acids and glycine share a specific renal transport system which has preference for these three substrates.[11] Familial renal iminoglycinuria, the phenotype described here, corroborates this hypothesis. Many studies in humans and other mammals indicate that renal transport of amino acids is a complex process apparently involving several carriers presumably under the control of several genes. Carriers for the imino acids and glycine, of which there are also several, are among them.

Human Studies. There is a maximum rate for net tubular absorption of proline (T_m proline).[36] Hydroxy-L-proline reabsorption also exhibits a T_m value.[37] The capacity of the normal human renal tubule to transport proline and hydroxyproline is shown in Table 102-1. A T_m for glycine has not been demonstrated in human beings probably because there is extensive paracellular diffusion for glycine in the proximal tubule.[49] Infusion of one imino acid increases urinary excretion of the other and of glycine in humans;[36,37] this procedure has little or no influence on the excretion of other amino acids.

Patients with familial hyperprolinemia have hyperiminoglycinuria[35,36] directly proportional to the plasma concentration of proline when it exceeds 1 mM; this is the level at which proline saturates its own transport system and appears in the urine.[36] The data for imino acid and glycine transport by normal human subjects and by patients with disorders of imino acid catabolism are complementary. They indicate the presence of a renal transport process, selective in its preference for proline, hydroxyproline, and glycine, and finite in its capacity.

Reabsorption of substrate is initiated by events at the brush border membrane (see next section). Transport of imino acids and glycine has been measured in purified brush border membrane vesicles prepared from human renal cortex samples obtained at operation.[39] Two saturable uptake systems were identified: one has high affinity and is shared both by imino acids and by glycine; the other has low affinity, and it is not shared by glycine. The high affinity system can apparently accommodate most of the imino acid load at physiological concentrations in filtrate, and if it were placed distally in proximal nephron, for instance, in the straight segment, it would explain the absence of iminoaciduria in the mature subject (see "Nonhuman Studies" below).

Table 102-1 Renal Clearance, Net Tubular Absorption, and T_m of Amino Acids and Glycine in Familial Iminoglycinuria

	Proline			Hydroxyproline	
Phenotype	*Endog. clear., ml/(min·1.73 m²)*	*Reabsorbed, %*	*T_m, μmol/(min·1.73 m²)*	*Endog. clear., ml/(min·1.73 m²)*	*Reabsorbed, %*
Normal	0–0.03	>99.8	180–300	0	100
Homozygous mutant★ (classic type):					
Mean	6.7			13	
Range	0.5–19.6	77–99.5	10–18	1–33.6	65–99
Heterozygous† ("hyperglycinuric")	0	100	35–117	0	100
Heterozygous‡ ("silent")	0	100	?	0	100
Genetic compound (K_m variant)§	~0.3	>99	Normal with "splay"	2–4	<100

★Compiled from Goodman et al.,[18] Scriver,[17] Rosenberg et al.,[21] Hoefnagel and Pomeroy,[19] and Tada et al.[38] Includes genetic compound and homozygous probands.
†Compiled from Goodman et al.,[18] Scriver,[17] Rosenberg et al.,[21] and Hoefnagel and Pomeroy.[19]
‡Compiled from Scriver[17] and Hoefnagel and Pomeroy.[19]
§Compiled from Greene et al.[27]

Nonhuman Studies. Amino acid reabsorption in the mammalian nephron is accommodated by a mosaic of carriers in the brush border membrane with selective preferences for particular amino acids and groups of amino acids.[40,41] Moreover, there is a broad arrangement involving axial heterogeneity of carriers, those located in the more proximal segments of proximal nephron having higher capacity but broader specificity and lower affinity for substrate, those located more distally having lower capacity but higher affinity and, sometimes, narrower specificity.[42] Net reabsorption also involves mechanisms to prevent backflux whereby the effective concentration of substrate at the luminal pole of the cell is kept lower than the equilibrium concentration; the processes for this situation include intracellular metabolic runout and efflux of substrate at the basolateral pole of the cell by carriers with properties different from those of the carriers in the brush border membrane.[40–42] While the weight of evidence pertaining to reabsorption of imino acids and glycine is concordant with this general scheme, details have yet to be resolved, and it should be kept in mind that findings in the nonhuman nephron may not reflect the human case exactly. In fact, it is not possible from present evidence to develop an accurate taxonomy of the tubular transport systems for imino acids and glycine in human beings.

Selective interactions between imino acids and glycine occur in vivo during renal reabsorption in rat and dog.[43,44] Microperfusions *in vivo et situ* in the rat confirm this finding.[45–49] The reabsorption process is saturable, stereospecific (for L-proline), and Na^+-dependent. Electrophysiological studies[50] reveal two mechanisms for reabsorption of imino acids and glycine, both located at the renal brush border membrane of proximal convolutions: one with low affinity, presumably more proximal and apparently a general system shared by many neutral amino acids; the other with high affinity, apparently more specific for the triad of substrates and perhaps located more distally in proximal nephron. The latter study corroborates earlier findings obtained by the continuous microperfusion technique in rat[47,48] and with the brush border membrane vesicle preparation from human kidney.[39] The low capacity, high affinity system for proline is shared with glycine and hydroxyproline in human kidney.

Glycine transport was studied in great detail in the isolated perfused rabbit nephron segment.[51,52] Glycine is transported against a chemical gradient, from lumen to cell, by a saturable Na^+-dependent carrier. Two forms of glycine transport were identified; one in the proximal convoluted segments has high capacity and low affinity, the other in the proximal straight segment has low capacity and high affinity. A paracellular, diffusional bidirectional flux was also found. Glycine uptake from peritubular space to cell across the basolateral membrane is active and also Na^+-dependent. The inward-directed basolateral flux is greater in straight segments relative to convoluted segments. The lumen-to-peritubular transcellular flux exceeds the flux in the reverse direction at physiological concentrations of glycine. No observations were made, in this work, on interactions of imino acids with glycine during transport.

Studies with purified membrane vesicles segregate membrane events from the intracellular events which influence net reabsorption,[40,42] and they are valuable for this reason, provided one recognizes that vesicle and microperfusion experiments measure different quantities.[50] The vesicle studies[53–57] are both informative and confusing. Brush border and basolateral membranes have Na^+-dependent and Na^+-independent systems respectively for L-proline transport (Fig. 102-2). This indicates that brush border and basolateral membranes have carriers that are different in their function and therefore, presumably, in the genes that control them. Glycine transport by luminal membrane vesicles is Na^+-dependent[56] (Fig. 102-2); studies of glycine transport by basolateral membrane vesicles have not yet been reported. Imino acids interact with each other[54] but not with glycine[57] during uptake by rabbit renal brush border membrane vesicles; on the other hand, imino acids and glycine interact on a shared carrier in rat nephron vesicles.[56] It is unclear whether these functional differences reflect differences in species or in methodology, such as the nephron segment from which vesicles were isolated.

Renal transport of imino acids and glycine has been studied in rat cortex slices[58] and in rabbit isolated tubule fragments.[59,60] The slice preparation preferentially exposes the basolateral membrane,[61,62] while the tubule fragment preparation exposes both luminal and antiluminal membranes. There is heterogeneity of carriers for imino acids and glycine in the basolateral membrane with a high capacity, low affinity function shared by the three substrates and separate low capacity, high affinity functions for imino acids and glycine, respectively.

These descriptions are probably an oversimplification, particularly when one is trying to understand which carrier, in which membrane, of which nephron segment is affected by the human iminoglycinuria mutation. The apparent distribution of carriers for imino acids and glycine in proximal nephron is summarized in Table 102-2.

Intracellular Events Influencing Proline Reabsorption

A nonhuman mutation (PRO/Re in mouse) affecting renal proline oxidase activity[63] is informative about the overall mechanism for net reabsorption of L-proline. Mammalian renal cortex has a large capacity for proline oxidation.[58,64,65] This provides metabolic runout of proline[40] which, *in vivo et situ*, facilitates net reabsorption of the imino acid. Proline oxidation is blocked in the PRO/Re mouse (see Chap. 18), proline content of cortical cells is elevated, and net reabsorption is impaired because backflux from cell to lumen across the

(Continued)

Hydroxyproline	Glycine	
T_m, μmol/(min·1.73 m²)	Endog. clear., ml/(min·1.73 m²)	Reabsorbed, %
60–135	1.2–8.6	93–99
	27	
6	17.0–41.6	61–77
50	14.3	82–95
?	8.6–26.2	
	3.1–6.7	>93
	37–60	65

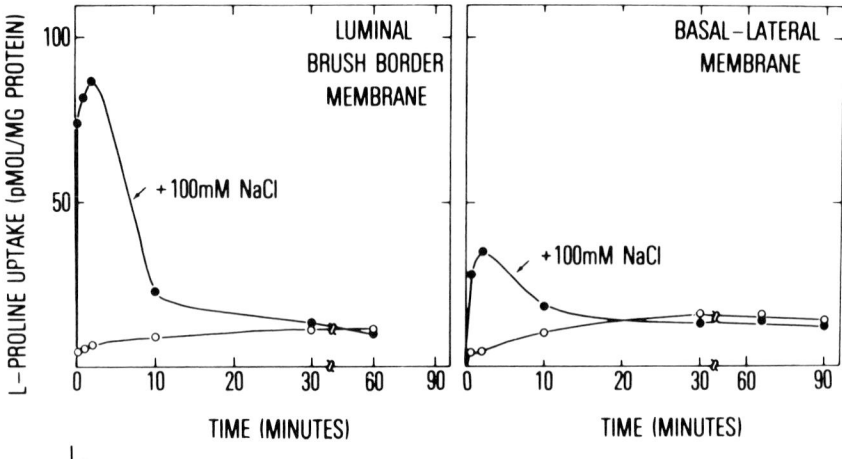

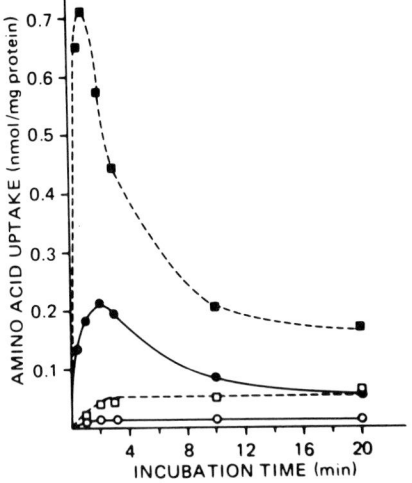

Fig. 102-2 *Upper panels:* Transport of L-proline (25 μM) by rabbit kidney brush border and basolateral membranes. ● = Na⁺ gradient. ○ = Na⁺-free medium. *(Taken from Barfuss and Schafer.[51]). Lower panel:* Transport of L-proline and glycine by rat renal brush border membranes. ■ □ = proline. ● ○ = glycine, both at 0.06 mM; closed symbols = Na⁺ gradient; open symbols = no Na⁺ gradient. *(Taken from Slack, Liang, and Sacktor, with permission[53]).* Graphs show sodium-dependent transport for proline and glycine transport at brush border membrane. Apparent Na⁺-dependence for a small component of proline transport in basolateral membranes reflects contamination of membrane fraction by brush borders during preparation.

brush border membrane is increased[63] (see Fig. 81-3 in the fifth edition of this book for further details).

Ontogeny of Renal Transport of Imino Acids and Glycine

Ontogeny affects renal transport of imino acids and glycine. When ontogeny is combined with Mendelian variation, the findings are revelatory. Hyperiminoglycinuria in the normal human newborn[6–10] reflects reduced net reabsorption of imino acids and glycine[10,66,67] (Fig. 102-1). The maturation of tubular transport functions observes independent schedules for proline and glycine,[66,67] suggesting that separate carriers are involved. This conclusion is given strong support by findings in probands homozygous for hereditary iminoglycinuria.[67]

Table 102-2 A Tentative Classification of Membrane Carriers by Segment, Side of Cell, and Preference for Imino Acids and Glycine in Mammalian Nephron

Segment	Brush border membrane	Basolateral membrane
PC	P + HP + (G?)	P + HP + G
	G alone?	p + hp + g
PS	p + hp + (g?)★	
	g	g

*System affected in familial renal iminoglycinuria (hypothesis only).
NOTE: Segment: PC = proximal convoluted; PS = proximal straight. Carrier kinetics: uppercase letters = high capacity, low affinity; lowercase letters = low capacity, high affinity. Substrates: G, g = glycine; HP, hp = hydroxyproline; P, p = proline.

Such individuals have near-total absence of tubular reabsorption for proline and glycine in the early postnatal period. As tubular function matures, reabsorptive activity for proline appears first, followed by the later appearance of a glycine reabsorptive activity (Fig. 102-3). The profile of maturing proline and glycine transport in the mutant homozygote indicates that there are independent carriers for proline and glycine not controlled by the gene locus affected by the mutation.

Transient postnatal iminoglycinuria is characteristic of mammals in general.[68] Postnatal maturation of membrane transport activities is believed to involve intensification of specific membrane functions,[69] for which an explanation may be improved efficiency in maintaining and coupling the inward-directed Na⁺ gradient, which is the driving force for uptake of amino acids at the brush border membrane.[70] Although there has been controversy about the process of ontogeny as it involves renal transport of proline and glycine,[71–74] several observations provide an overall insight. First, backflux of amino acids in the immature distal tubule is not a component of postnatal iminoglycinuria.[75] Second, diminished metabolic runout is not a significant cause of diminished net reabsorption.[71,75] Third, postnatal prolinuria in the rat is associated with low activity of the high affinity Na⁺-dependent proline transport system in nephron[75,76] in the brush border membrane.[76] Fourth, cortical tubule fragments[75] and slices[68,71,72] from newborn animals have impaired efflux of proline. Together, these findings suggest that ontogeny is associated with deficient activity of high affinity systems for imino acids and glycine that do not include the system controlled by the familial iminoglycinuria locus.

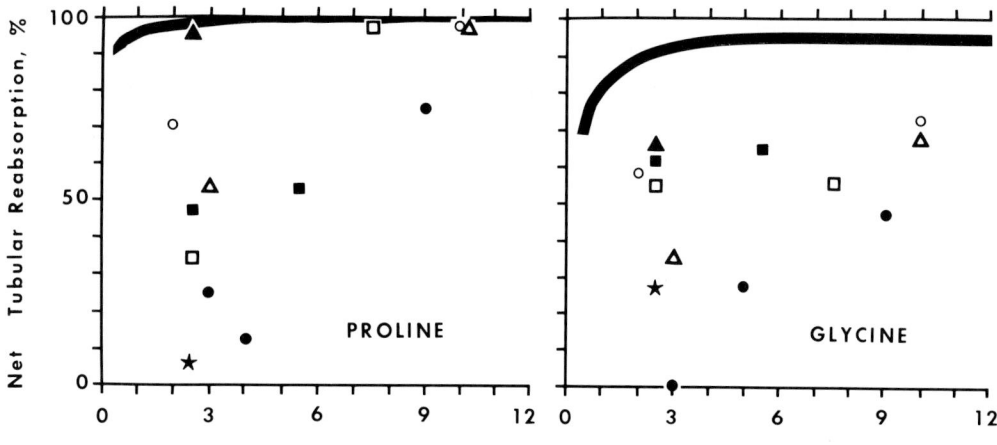

Age, months

Fig. 102-3 Tubular reabsorption data for proline and glycine in relation to age in seven probands (various symbols, from Ref. 67) with familial renal iminoglycinuria. Shaded region indicates reabsorption values in normal infants. *(From Brodehl.[66] Reproduced from Pediatric Research, with permission.)*

RENAL REABSORPTION OF IMINO ACIDS AND GLYCINE IN FAMILIAL IMINOGLYCINURIA

Endogenous renal clearance rates are elevated and net reabsorption is decreased in probands (Table 102-1). Two other observations are important: First, net tubular absorption of imino acids and glycine is not completely eliminated in homozygotes. Second, the abnormal prolinuria may disappear at low plasma proline concentrations in homozygotes (Fig. 102-4). The venous plasma "threshold" for prolinuria is very low in homozygotes (about 0.1 mM) compared with normal subjects (about 0.8 mM).

The ability of homozygotes with hereditary iminoglycinuria to retain a considerable fraction of their specific tubular ab-

Fig. 102-4 Endogenous renal clearance of L-proline related to its concentration in plasma in homozygotes with familial iminoglycinuria. The "venous plasma threshold concentration" at which prolinuria appears is about 0.1 mM; the normal value is about 0.8 mM.[36] Abnormal prolinuria disappears in mutant homozygotes at low plasma proline concentrations, indicating the existence of a small but efficient tubular capacity to transport proline. *(Redrawn from Scriver,[17] with permission of The Journal of Clinical Investigation, with data (symbol ○) added from Greene et al.[27] and other data (symbol ▲) added from Tada et al.[38])*

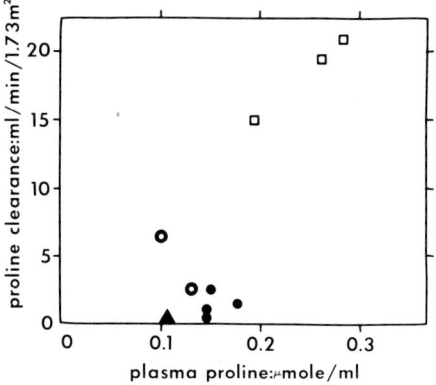

sorptive function is a feature shared by homozygotes with other inborn errors of membrane transport. For example, homozygotes with either classic cystinuria, isolated hypercystinuria, or Hartnup disorder usually retain some capacity to transport the relevant amino acids. A similar characteristic is also observed for hexose transport in glucose-galactose malabsorption in regard to renal tubular absorption of glucose.[40] One interpretation of this phenomenon in mutant phenotypes is that more than one type of transport system serves reabsorption of the specific substrate along the nephron, the different systems being controlled by different genes.

Transport at Saturation in the Mutant Iminoglycinuria Phenotype

T_m values were measured in mutant homozygotes and obligate heterozygotes infused with L-proline and hydroxy-L-proline.[16,17,21] Imino acid transport is present but saturated at normal plasma concentration of proline and hydroxyproline in the mutant homozygotes (Fig. 102-5). The heterozygote has a T_m value intermediate between normal and homozygous mutant values (Fig. 102-5); imino acid reabsorption is normal at concentrations below the T_m, suggesting that affinity of the available imino acid transport sites is normal in the heterozygote. Taken together, these findings indicate that the mutation causes deletion of a transport system which has a capacity well above the normal concentration of imino acids in filtrate. Another modality of uptake with a small but recognizable capacity and high affinity is retained.

Greene et al.[27] described a proband in whom the mutant allele did not delete the affected transport function but altered its affinity for substrate, so that glycine was very poorly reabsorbed and proline was less avidly transported by the mutant carrier (Fig. 102-5); a K_m variant was proposed.

Interactions Between Imino Acids and Glycine During Tubular Reabsorption in the Mutant Phenotype

Normal adult subjects infused with proline or hydroxyproline show brisk inhibition of glycine reabsorption; mutant homozygotes show no inhibition of the residual activity serving glycine reabsorption[17] (Fig. 102-6). The latter may represent transport of glycine on the high affinity system in proximal

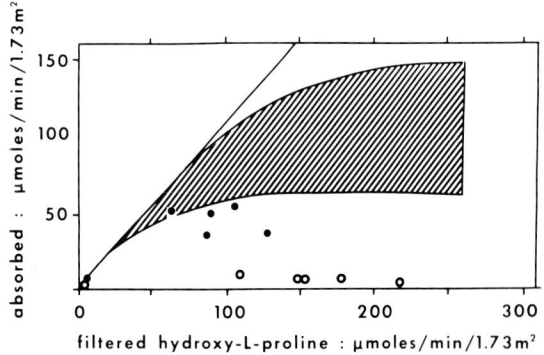

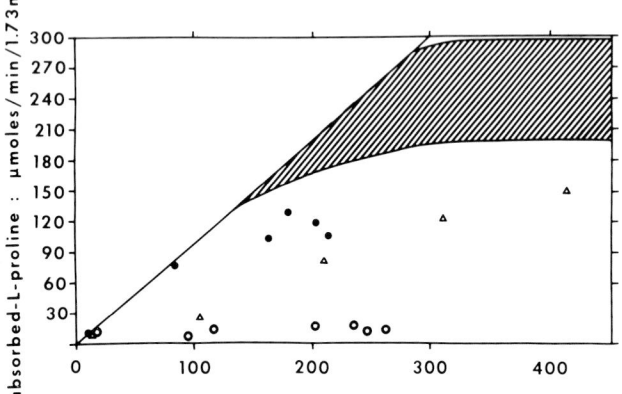

Fig. 102-5 Maximum rates of tubular reabsorption (T_m) of L-proline and hydroxy-L-proline in normal subjects (hatched), heterozygotes (solid circles), and mutant homozygotes (open circles) with classic iminoglycinuria. Data for patient with K_m variant of iminoglycinuria[27] are also shown ($\triangle$). (Redrawn from Scriver[17] and Greene et al.,[27] with permission.)

straight tubule or by the diffusional mode in proximal nephron.[51] Loss of a portion of the glycine transport activity in the mutant phenotype is somewhat discordant with an opinion[57] that imino acids and glycine do not share a transport system in the brush border membrane. The latter hypothesis implies that the iminoglycinuria mutation, which is at one locus, affects two transport systems; this could be explained if a polypeptide subunit were common to both carriers.

Infusion of one imino acid also impairs reabsorption of the other in normal subjects and in mutant homozygotes.[17] This finding in the mutant phenotype is compatible with inhibition of residual imino acid transport, on the broad-specificity, high capacity neutral amino acid system in proximal convolutions.[50]

Imino acids and glycine do share transport on a high capacity, low affinity system at the basolateral membrane.[58] However, some heterozygotes have hyperglycinuria at normal plasma glycine concentrations (Figs. 102-5 and 102-6). This finding is compatible with impaired transport activity at the brush border membrane and less so with impairment at the basolateral membrane (see Ref. 77 for explanation). Therefore, although we know that familial iminoglycinuria is a disorder involving a carrier selective for imino acids and glycine, it is still uncertain which carrier is affected.

Expression of Phenotype in Nonrenal Tissues

Intestine. Intestinal transport of L-proline has been examined in vivo[14,15,17,18,21] and in intestinal biopsy material.[21] Fecal excretion of amino acids has also been measured.[17,21] Two phenotypes have been identified. Some homozygotes have normal intestinal transport of L-proline and normal fecal excretion,[14,17,21] while others have impaired absorption and increased fecal excretion of proline.[15,18] The association of different intestinal phenotypes with a single renal phenotype suggests that more than one mutant allele is responsible for the iminoglycinuric trait.

The plasma response to glycine loading by mouth is normal in patients with and without demonstrable impairment of proline absorption.[15,18,21] This may indicate that transport by intestine is qualitatively different from that in kidney or that diffusional uptake of glycine, which would be unaffected by mutation, is significant in the intestine.

Leukocytes and Skin Fibroblasts. Net uptake of isotopically labeled proline at low extracellular concentrations (0.05 mM) by leukocytes and skin fibroblasts was apparently normal in the homozygote.[78] A negative finding has two interpretations: either the mutant system is not expressed in the plasma membrane of parenchymal cells; or the experiment did not test for uptake on the mutant system. The former explanation involves an understanding that plasma membranes of parenchymal cells share homologous transport functions with basolateral membranes of renal and intestinal epithelium but not necessarily with functions in the brush border membranes,[77,79] and renal iminoglycinuria appears to be a disorder of a brush border membrane carrier.

DIAGNOSIS

Criteria for Abnormal Iminoglycinuria

Any degree of iminoaciduria after 6 months of age may be considered abnormal. Hyperglycinuria may be recognized on

Fig. 102-6 Effect of L-proline and hydroxy-L-proline on net tubular reabsorption of glycine in normal subjects (hatched), heterozygotes (solid circles), and mutant homozygotes with classic iminoglycinuria. (Redrawn from Scriver[17] and Greene et al.,[27] with permission.)

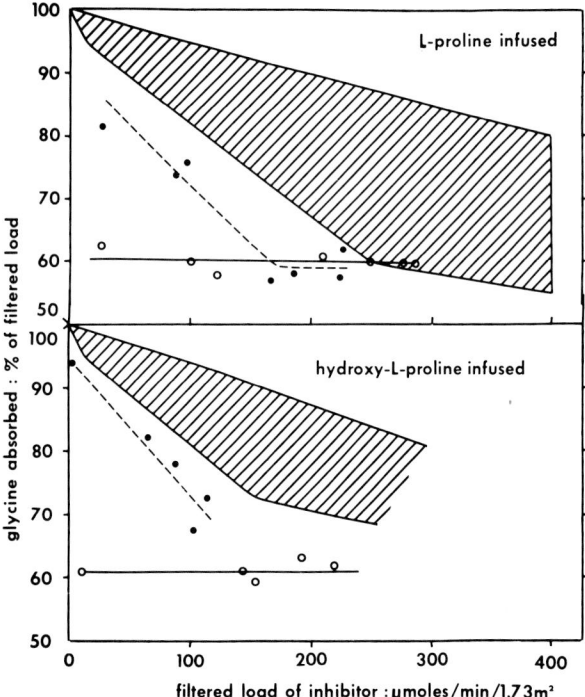

partition chromatograms when the glycine spot is disproportionately intense in comparison with other amino acids. The quantitative criteria for hyperglycinuria are urinary excretion exceeding 150 μmol per gram of total nitrogen,[20] or 150 mg/24 h,[80] or an endogenous clearance rate exceeding 8.6 ml/(min·1.73 m²).[81]

Differential Diagnosis

Hyperprolinemia and Hydroxyprolinemia. Iminoglycinuria occurs by a "combined" mechanism when there is hyperprolinemia in excess of about 0.8 mM.[36] Hyperprolinemia, type I or type II (see Chap. 18), is usually accompanied by iminoglycinuria. Patients with hydroxyprolinemia have not exhibited iminoglycinuria because the concentration of hydroxyproline in their plasma has not exceeded 0.4 mM; hydroxyproline must be present in plasma at this concentration at least to inhibit tubular absorption of proline and glycine competitively.[37] Hyperprolinemia and hydroxyprolinemia can be ruled out as a cause of iminoglycinuria if the concentration of both imino acids in plasma is normal in subjects with iminoglycinuria.

Fanconi Syndrome. Iminoglycinuria occurs in this syndrome as part of a generalized hyperaminoaciduria, in contrast to the selective hyperaminoaciduria in familial iminoglycinuria.

Neonatal Iminoglycinuria. The human infant normally has some degree of hyperiminoaciduria until about the third month of postnatal life; the hyperglycinuria subsides by the sixth month.

Renal Glycinuria. There have been numerous reports of hyperglycinuria without iminoaciduria. This phenotype may represent one form of the heterozygote with the iminoglycinuria mutation or the "K_m variant" form of renal iminoglycinuria.[27] Differential diagnosis includes:

1. Dominantly inherited renal hyperglycinuria and nephrolithiasis.[82,83]

2. Autosomal dominant glucoglycinuria.[84] Glucosuria occurs by the type B mechanism of Reubi, i.e., the renal threshold for glucosuria is low (79 mg/dl), but the T_{mG} is normal—386 mg/(min·173 m²). Of the 44 subjects examined,[84] 13 healthy relatives also had glucoglycinuria; no subjects with glucosuria or glycinuria alone were found.

3. X-linked hypophosphatemia with glucoglycinuria.[85,86] Glucosuria is Reubi type A (low T_m). A glycine carrier, shared with imino acids, is present, but it is operating inefficiently. The glucoglycinuria occurs through a mechanism different from that described in the autosomal dominant condition.[84]

These traits should all be distinguished from the "prerenal" form of hyperglycinuria found in hyperglycinemia.

GENETICS

Familial renal iminoglycinuria is the expressed phenotype of alleles at an autosomal locus which controls a membrane carrier shared by imino acids and glycine. Consanguinity in parents of iminoglycinuria probands has been reported[14,22] (Fig. 102-7).

In some pedigrees, obligate heterozygotes have hyperglycinuria (Fig. 102-7). This represents expression of an "incompletely recessive" allele, and the phenotype must be differentiated from other forms of dominantly inherited hyperglycinuria (see "Renal Glycinuria" above). Most heterozygotes for familial iminoglycinuria do not have hyperglycinuria; their

Fig. 102-7 Pedigrees of patients with familial iminoglycinuria. See Ref. 12 for pedigree A; Ref. 14, B,C; Ref. 15, D; Ref. 17, E; Ref. 18, F; Ref. 19, G; Ref. 17, H; Ref. 20, I; Ref. 21, J; Ref. 22, K; Ref. 23, L; Ref. 24, M; Ref. 25, N; Ref. 26, O; Ref. 27, P.

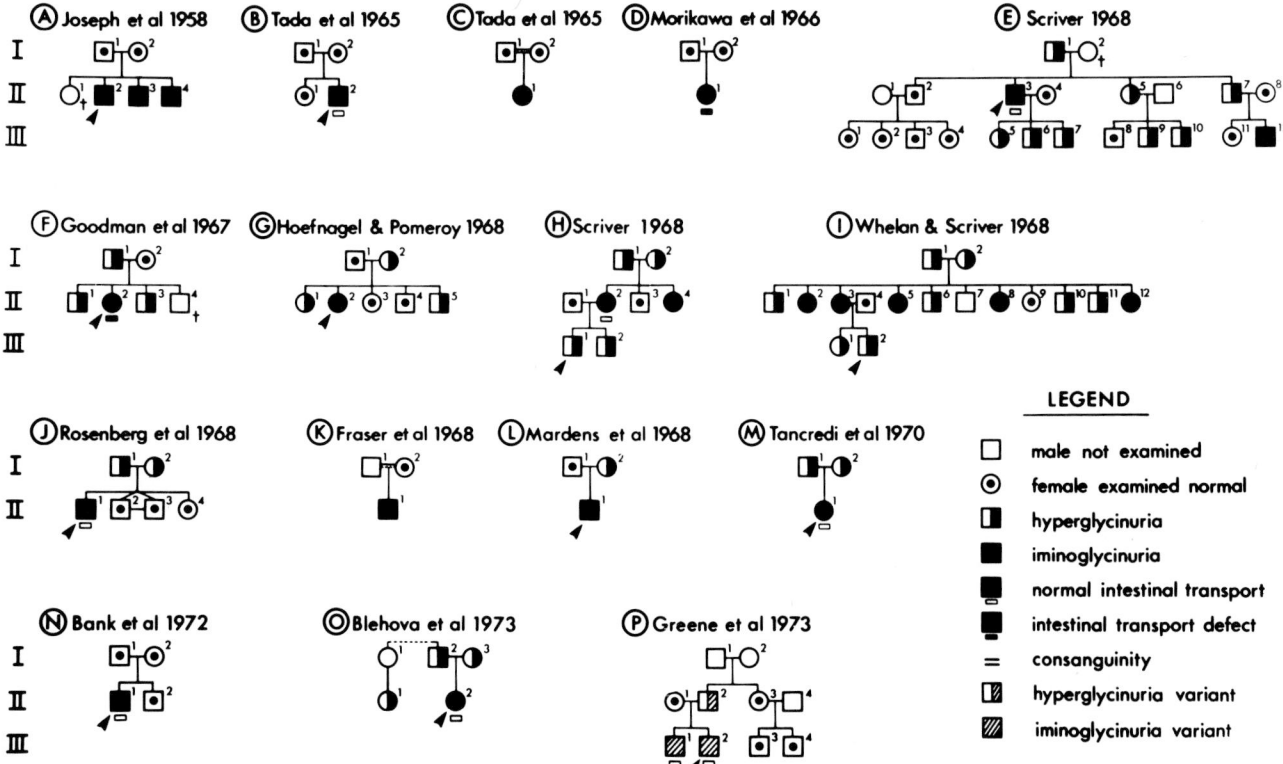

Table 102-3 Evidence for Allelic Mutations in Familial Renal Iminoglycinuria. Phenotype Heterogeneity among Homozygotes, "Genetic Compounds," and Obligate Heterozygotes

| Presumed allelic pair | Renal phenotype in | | Intestinal phenotype in homozygote (or compound) | Exemplary pedigrees in Fig. 102-7 |
	Homozygote or compound	Heterozygote		
I-I	IG	N	Present	D
II-II	IG	N	N	B, N
III-III	IG	G	N	E, H, J, M, O
I-III(or II)	IG	N or G	Present	F
	IG	N or G	Not tested	E, G, L
II-IV	iG(K_m)	N or G(K_m)	N	P

KEY: IG = iminoglycinuria (with loss of "high K_m" system); G = glycinuria alone; iG(K_m) = K_m variant involving "high K_m" system affecting glycine more than amino acids; N = normal; "Present" implies defective absorption of proline and/or glycine in test procedure.

mutant allele is "completely recessive." A third allele[27] is apparent in pedigree P (Fig. 102-7), in which a heterozygote and two affected offspring had hyperglycinuria associated with a mutant transport system expressing lowered affinity for glycine.

There are pedigrees (E, F, G, and L, Fig. 102-7) in which one parent is hyperglycinuric and the other is not; their offspring are indistinguishable from homozygotes with two hyperglycinuric parents or with two "silent" parents. When probands with the fully expressed phenotype have parents showing phenotypic heterogeneity (incomplete recessive × silent recessive) the probands are presumed to be genetic compounds for different alleles.

Some mutant homozygotes have impaired intestinal transport of proline (Fig. 102-7), whereas others do not. The intestinal phenotype is not consistently associated with any form of the heterozygous phenotypes. From the various combinations of phenotypes, including the K_m variant,[27] one can postulate four mutant alleles (Table 102-3). There has been no opportunity for analysis by molecular genetic methods to confirm this hypothesis.

Prevalence. Newborn screening data[27–29] indicate that the frequency of the presumed homozygote (or genetic compound) among Caucasians is about 1 in 15,000 live births. Accordingly, the frequency of heterozygotes in the population is about 2 percent, about half being incompletely recessive (hyperglycinuric phenotype). The corresponding frequencies of specific alleles (silent, incomplete, and K_m variant) are therefore lower than 1 percent. Since these alleles are presumably all neutral in terms of selection, their high frequency may reflect founder effect or high mutation rate at the locus.

TREATMENT

Familial iminoglycinuria is a benign condition involving nonessential amino acids, and no treatment is indicated. The considerable number of healthy subjects in whom iminoglycinuria was discovered quite incidentally (see Fig. 102-7, pedigree E, subjects II.3 and III.12; pedigree H, subjects II.2 and II.4; and all homozygous members of pedigree I) supports this interpretation. The various illnesses that have been associated with the iminoglycinuric trait apparently served only to bring the transport mutation to attention.

REFERENCES

1. GREENSTEIN JP, WINITZ M: *Chemistry of the Amino Acid.* New York, Wiley, 1961.
2. MEISTER A: *Biochemistry of the Amino Acid,* 2d ed. New York, Academic, 1965.
3. MCMILLAN DE: Letter to the editor. *N Engl J Med* 278:771, 1965.
4. DENT CE: Detection of amino acids in urine and other fluids. *Lancet* 2:637, 1946.
5. SCRIVER CR, ROSENBERG LE: *Amino Acid Metabolism and Its Disorders.* Philadelphia, Saunders, 1973.
6. SCRIVER CR: Hereditary aminoaciduria, in Bearn A, Steinberg AG (eds): *Progress in Medical Genetics.* New York, Grune & Stratton, 1962, vol 2, p 83.
7. SERENI F, MCNAMARA H, SHIBUYA M, KRETCHMER N, BARNETT HL: Concentration in plasma and rate of urinary excretion of amino acids in premature infants. *Pediatrics* 15:575, 1955.
8. WOOLF LI, NORMAN AP: The urinary excretion of amino acids and sugars in early infancy. *J Pediatr* 50:271, 1957.
9. O'BRIEN D, BUTTERFIELD LJ: Further studies on renal tubular conservation of free amino acids in early infancy. *Arch Dis Child* 38:437, 1963.
10. BRODEHL J, GELLISSEN K: Endogenous renal transport of free amino acids in infancy and childhood. *Pediatrics* 42:395, 1968.
11. SCRIVER CR, SCHAFER IA, EFRON ML: New renal tubular amino acid transport system and a new hereditary disorder of amino acid metabolism. *Nature* 192:672, 1961.
12. JOSEPH R, RIBIERRE M, JOB JC, GIRAULT M: Maladie familiale associante des convulsions a début très précoce, une hyperalbuminorachie et une hyperaminoacidurie. *Arch Fr Pediatr* 15:374, 1958.
13. MOZZICONACCI P, BOISSE J, LEMONNIER A, CHARPENTIER C: Les maladies métaboliques des acides amines avec arriération mentale (citation on p 249). Paris, L'Expansion Scientifique Francaise, 1968.
14. TADA K, MORIKAWA T, ANDO T, YOSHIDA T, MIRIGAWA A: Prolinuria: A new renal tubular defect in transport of proline and glycine. *Tohoku J Exp Med* 87:133, 1965.
15. MORIKAWA T, TADA K, ANDO T, YOSHIDA T, YOKOYAMA Y, ARAKAWA T: Prolinuria: Defect in intestinal absorption of imino acids and glycine. *Tohoku J Exp Med* 90:105, 1966.
16. SCRIVER CR, WILSON OH: Amino acid transport in human kidney: Evidence for genetic control of two types. *Science* 155:1428, 1967.
17. SCRIVER CR: Renal tubular transport of proline, hydroxyproline and glycine. III. Genetic basis for more than one mode of transport in human kidney. *J Clin Invest* 47:823, 1968.
18. GOODMAN SI, MCINTYRE CA, O'BRIEN D: Impaired intestinal transport of proline in a patient with familial iminoaciduria. *J Pediatr* 71:246, 1967.
19. HOEFNAGEL D, POMEROY J: Personal communication of unpublished data, 1968, 1969.
20. WHELAN DT, SCRIVER CR: Cystathioninuria and renal iminoglycinuria in a pedigree: A perspective on counseling. *N Engl J Med* 278:924, 1968.
21. ROSENBERG IE, DURANT JL, ELSAS LJ, II: Familial iminoglycinuria: An inborn error of renal tubular transport. *N Engl J Med* 278:1407, 1968.
22. FRASER GR, FRIEDMANN AI, PATTON VM, WADE DN, WOOLF LL: Iminoglycinuria—a "harmless" inborn error of metabolism? *Humangenetik* 6:362, 1968.
23. MARDENS Y, ANDRIAENSSENS K, Van SANDE M: Glycinurie et iminoaci-

durie rénales associés à une oligophrenie: Étude clinique et biochimique. *J Neurol Sci* 6:333, 1968.

24. TANCREDI F, GUAZZI G, AURICHIO S: Renal iminoglycinuria without intestinal malabsorption of glycine and imino acids. *J Pediatr* 7:386, 1970.

25. BANK H, CRISPIN M, EHRLICH D, SZEINBERG A: Iminoglycinuria: A defect of renal tubular transport. *Isr J Med Sci* 8:606, 1972.

26. BLEHOVÁ B, PAŽOUTOVÁ, HYÁNEK J, JIRÁSEK J: Iminoglycinuria in a child in Czechoslovakia. *Humangenetik* 19:207, 1973.

27. GREENE ML, LIETMAN PS, ROSENBERG LE, SEEGMILLER JE: Familial hyperglycinuria: New defect in renal tubular transport of glycine and imino acids. *Am J Med* 54:265, 1973.

28. LEVY HL: Genetic screening, in Harris H, Hirschhorn K (eds): *Advances in Human Genetics*. New York, Plenum, 1973, vol 4, p 1.

29. TURNER B, BROWN DA: Amino acid excretion in infancy and early childhood: A survey of 200,000 infants. *Med J Aust* 1:62, 1972.

30. PROCOPIS PG, TURNER B: Iminoaciduria: A benign renal tubular defect. *J Pediatr* 79:419, 1971.

31. PAINE RS: Evaluation of familial biochemically determined mental retardation in children, with special reference to aminoaciduria. *N Engl J Med* 262:658, 1966.

32. JONXIS JHP: Personal communications, 1962 (cited in Ref. 17), 1969.

33. MILLER M: Familial cirrhosis with hepatoma. *Am J Dig Dis* 12:633, 1967.

34. STATTER M, BEN-ZVI A, SHINA A, SCHEIN R, RUSSELL A: Familial iminoglycinuria with normal intestinal absorption of glycine and imino acids in association with profound mental retardation, a possible "cerebral phenotype." *Helv Paediatr Acta* 31:173, 1976.

35. SCHAFER IA, SCRIVER CR, EFRON ML: Familial hyperprolinema, cerebral dysfunction and renal anomalies occurring in a family with hereditary nephritis and deafness. *N Engl J Med* 267:51, 1962.

36. SCRIVER CR, EFRON ML, SCHAFER IA: Renal tubular transport of proline, hydroxyproline and glycine in health and in familial hyperprolinemia. *J Clin Invest* 43:374, 1964.

37. SCRIVER CR, GOLDMAN H: Renal tubular transport of proline, hydroxyproline and glycine. II. Hydroxy-L-proline as substrate and as inhibitor in-vivo. *J Clin Invest* 45:1357, 1966.

38. TADA K, HIRONO H, ARAKAWA T: Endogenous renal clearance rates of free amino acids in prolinuric and Hartnup patients. *Tokohu J Exp Med* 93:57, 1967.

39. FOREMAN JW, MCNAMARA PD, PEPE LM, GINKINGER K, SEGAL S: Uptake of proline by brushborder vesicles isolated from human kidney cortex. *Biochem Med* 34:304, 1985.

40. SCRIVER CR, CHESNEY RW, MCINNES RR: Genetic aspects of renal tubular transport: Diversity and topology of carriers. *Kidney Int* 9:149, 1976.

41. SCHAFER JA, BARFUSS DW: Membrane mechanisms for transepithelial amino acid absorption and secretion. *Am J Physiol* 238:F335, 1980.

42. SCRIVER CR, TENENHOUSE HS: Genetics and mammalian transport system. *Ann NY Acad Sci* 456:384, 1985.

43. WILSON OH, SCRIVER CR: Specificity of transport of neutral and basic amino acids in rat kidney. *Am J Physiol* 213:185, 1967.

44. WEBBER WA: Interactions of neutral and acidic amino acids in renal tubular transport. *Am Physiol* 202:577, 1962.

45. BERGERON M, MOREL F: Amino acid transport in rat renal tubules. *Am J Physiol* 216:1139, 1969.

46. DUBORD L, BERGERON M: Multiplicité des systèmes transporteurs à la membrane luminale du néphron chez le rat normal. *Rev Can Biol* 33:99, 1974.

47. VOLKL H, SILBERNAGL S, DEETJEN P: Kinetics of L-proline reabsorption in rat kidney studied by continuous microperfusion. *Pflugers Arch* 382:115, 1979.

48. VOLKL H, SILBERNAGL S: Molecular specificity of tubular reabsorption of L-proline. A microperfusion study in rat kidney. *Pflugers Arch* 387:253, 1980.

49. ULLRICH KJ, REIMRICH G, KLOSS S: Sodium dependence of the amino acid transport in the proximal convolution of the rat kidney. *Pflugers Arch* 351:49, 1974.

50. SAMARZIJA I, FROMTER E: Electrophysiological analysis of rat renal sugar and amino acid transport. III. Neutral amino acids. *Pflugers Arch* 393:199, 1982.

51. BARFUSS DW, SCHAFER JS: Active amino acid absorption by proximal convoluted and proximal straight tubules. *Am J Physiol* 236(2):F149, 1979.

52. BARFUSS DW, MAYS JM, SCHAFER JA: Peritubular uptake and transepithelial transport of glycine in isolated proximal tubules. *Am J Physiol* 238:F324, 1980.

53. SLACK EN, LIANG C-CT, SACKTOR B: Transport of L-proline and D-glucose in luminal (brush border) and contraluminal (basal-lateral) membrane vesicles from the renal cortex. *Biochem Biophys Res Commun* 77:891, 1977.

54. HAMMERMAN MR, SACKTOR B: Transport of amino acids in renal brush border membrane vesicles. Uptake of L-proline. *J Biol Chem* 252:591, 1977.

55. MCNAMARA PD, OZEGOVIC B, PEPE LM, SEGAL S: Proline and glycine uptake by renal brush border membrane vesicles. *Proc Natl Acad Sci USA* 73:4521, 1976.

56. MCNAMARA PD, PEPE LM, SEGAL S: Sodium gradient dependence of proline and glycine uptake in renal brush-border membrane vesicles. *Biochim Biophys Acta* 556:151, 1979.

57. HAMMERMAN MR, SACKTOR B: Na^+-dependent transport of glycine in renal brush border membrane vesicles. *Biochim Biophys Acta* 686:189, 1982.

58. MOHYUDDIN F, SCRIVER CR: Amino acid transport in mammalian kidney: Identification and analysis of multiple systems for iminoacids and glycine in rat kidney. *Am J Physiol* 219:1, 1970.

59. HILLMAN RE, ALBRECHT I, ROSENBERG LE: Identification and analysis of multiple glycine transport systems in isolated mammalian renal tubules. *J Biol Chem* 243:5566, 1968.

60. HILLMAN RE, ROSENBERG LE: Amino acid transport by isolated mammalian renal tubules. II. Transport systems for L-proline. *J Biol Chem* 244:4494, 1969.

61. WEDEEN RP, WEINER B: The distribution of p-aminohippuric acid in rat kidney slices. I. Tubular localization. *Kidney Int* 3:205, 1973.

62. ARTHUS MF, BERGERON M, SCRIVER CR: Topology of membrane exposure in the renal cortex slice. Studies of glutathione and maltose cleavage. *Biochim Biophys Acta* 692:371, 1982.

63. SCRIVER CR, MCINNES RR, MOHYUDDIN F: Role of epithelial architecture and intracellular metabolism in proline uptake and transtubular reclamation in PRO/Re mouse kidney. *Proc Natl Acad Sci USA* 72:1431, 1975.

64. HOLTZAPPLE P, GENEL M, REA C, SEGAL S: Metabolism and uptake of L-proline by human kidney cortex. *Pediatr Res* 7:818, 1973.

65. GRETH WE, THIER SO, SEGAL S: The transport and metabolism of L-proline-^{14}C in the rat and in vivo. *Metabolism* 27:975, 1978.

66. BRODEHL J: Postnatal development of tubular amino acid reabsorption in Silbernagl S, Lang F, Greger R (eds): *Amino Acid Transport and Uric Acid Transport*. Symposium Innsbruck, June 1975, Stuttgart, Thieme, 1976, p 128.

67. LASLEY L, SCRIVER CR: Ontogeny of amino acid reabsorption in human kidney. Evidence from the homozygous infant with familial renal iminoglycinuria for multiple proline and glycine systems. *Pediatr Res* 13:65, 1979.

68. BAERLOCHER K, SCRIVER CR, MOHYUDDIN F: Ontogeny of iminoglycine transport in mammalian kidney. *Proc Natl Acad Sci USA* 65:1009, 1970.

69. CHRISTENSEN HN: On the development of amino acid transport systems. *Fed Proc* 32:19, 1973.

70. MEDOW MS, ROTH KS, GOLDMANN DR, GINKINGER K, HSU BYL, SEGAL S: Developmental aspects of proline transport in rat renal brush border membranes. *Proc Natl Acad Sci USA* 83:7561, 1986.

71. BAERLOCHER KE, SCRIVER CR, MOHYUDDIN F: The ontogeny of amino acid transport in rat kidney. II. Kinetics of uptake and effect of anoxia. *Biochim Biophys Acta* 249:364, 1971.

72. BAERLOCHER KE, SCRIVER CR, MOHYUDDIN F: The ontogeny of amino acid transport in rat kidney. I. Effect on distribution ratios and intracellular metabolism of proline and glycine. *Biochim Biophys Acta* 249:353, 1971.

73. ROTH KS, HWANG S-M, LONDON JW, SEGAL S: Ontogeny of glycine transport in isolated rat renal tubules. *Am J Physiol* 233:F241, 1977.

74. REYNOLDS R, ROTH KS, HWANG SM, SEGAL S: On the development of glycine transport systems by rat renal cortex. *Biochim Biophys Acta* 511:274, 1979.

75. SCRIVER CR, ARTHUS MF, BERGERON M: Neonatal iminoglycinuria: Evidence that the prolinuria originates in selective deficiency of transport activity in proximal nephron. *Pediatr Res* 16:684, 1982.

76. GOLDMANN DR, ROTH KS, LANGFITT TW Jr, SEGAL S: L-proline transport by newborn rat kidney brush-border membrane vesicles. *Biochem J* 178:253, 1979.

77. SCRIVER CR, TENENHOUSE HS: Mendelian phenotypes as probes of renal transport system for amino acids and phosphate, in *Handbook on Renal Physiological*, 2d ed, Bethesda, American Physiological Society, in press, 1989.

78. TADA K, MORIKAWA T, ARAKAWA T: Prolinuria: Transport of proline by leukocytes. *Tokohu J Exp Med* 90:189, 1966.

79. SMITH DW, SCRIVER CR, TENENHOUSE HS, SIMELL D: The lysinuric protein intolerance mutation is expressed in plasma membrane of cultured skin fibroblasts. *Proc Natl Acad Sci (USA)* 84:7711, 1987.

80. CARVER MJ, PASKA R: Ion-exchange chromatography of urinary amino acids. I. Normal children. *Clin Chim Acta* 6:721, 1961.

81. SCRIVER CR, DAVIES E: Endogenous renal clearance rates of free amino acids in pre-pubertal children. *Pediatrics* 36:592, 1965.

82. DeVRIES A, KOCHWA S, LAZEBNIK J, FRANK M, DJALDETTI M: Glycinuria, a hereditary disorder associated with nephrolithiasis. *Am J Med* 23:408, 1957.

83. OBERITER V, PURETI CZ, FABE CI, C-SABADI V: Hyperglycinuria with nephrolithiasis. *Eur J Pediatr* 127:279, 1978.

84. KASER H, COTTIER P, ANTENER I: Glucoglycinuria, a new familial syndrome. *J Pediatr* 61:386, 1962.

85. SCRIVER CR, GOLDBLOOM RB, ROY CC: Hypophosphatemic rickets with renal hyperglycinuria, renal glucosuria and glycylprolinuria: A syndrome with evidence for renal tubular secretion of phosphorus. *Pediatrics* 34:357, 1964.

86. DENT CE, HARRIS H: Hereditary forms of rickets and osteomalacia. *J Bone Joint Surg* 38B:204, 1956.

CHAPTER 103

RENAL TUBULAR ACIDOSIS

THOMAS D. DuBOSE, Jr.
ROBERT J. ALPERN

1. *Renal tubular acidosis (RTA) is a clinical syndrome characterized by hyperchloremic metabolic acidosis secondary to an abnormality in renal acidification. The acidification defect may be manifest by an inappropriately high urine pH and bicarbonaturia, but is, by definition, always associated with reduced net acid excretion. Classic distal renal tubular acidosis and proximal renal tubular acidosis are frequently associated with hypokalemia. Distal renal tubular acidosis can also result from a generalized dysfunction of the distal nephron, in which case it is usually accompanied by hyperkalemia and may be associated with either hypoaldosteronism or aldosterone resistance.*

2. *Proximal renal tubular acidosis may result from an isolated defect of acidification in the proximal nephron. The isolated defect in acidification could be the result of selective dysfunction of the Na^+/H^+ antiporter, the proximal tubule H^+-ATPase, or the $Na^+(HCO_3^-)_3$ symporter.*

3. *More commonly, proximal renal tubular acidosis occurs as one manifestation of a generalized defect in proximal tubule function. Patients with this generalized abnormality, the Fanconi syndrome, usually have glycosuria, aminoaciduria, citraturia, and phosphaturia. The acidification defect associated with this generalized tubular dysfunction may be the result of: (1) impairment of Na^+,K^+-ATPase or (2) cellular phosphate depletion.*

4. *Vitamin D deficiency may be associated with the Fanconi lesion. The transport defect may be due to a combination of factors, including a reduction in 1,25-dihydroxyvitamin D_3 levels, elevated parathyroid hormone levels, hypocalcemia, and intracellular phosphate depletion.*

5. *The diagnosis of proximal renal tubular acidosis is based on the demonstration of a chronic hyperchloremic metabolic acidosis frequently associated with an acid urine pH. Correction of the metabolic acidosis with alkali raises the plasma bicarbonate level above the renal threshold and results in prominent bicarbonaturia and an alkaline urine pH. The fractional excretion of bicarbonate may exceed 15 percent of the filtered load in such conditions, and hypokalemia is common. Bone disease, which commonly accompanies this disorder, is expressed as rickets in children and as osteopenia in adults.*

6. *The goal of therapy in proximal renal tubular acidosis is to maintain a near normal serum bicarbonate concentration while avoiding potassium deficiency. Concomitant administration of thiazide diuretics to reduce intravascular volume and secondarily reduce the filtered load of bicarbonate is often beneficial.*

7. *The mechanisms underlying hypokalemic classic distal renal tubular acidosis are not fully understood. The hypokalemia suggests a lesion in the medullary collecting duct or a selective lesion in cortical collecting tubules. Possible mechanisms include: (1) an abnormal bicarbonate leak pathway or "gradient" lesion or (2) a "rate defect." An experimental model of a leak defect is induced by amphotericin B. The observed low urine-blood P_{CO_2} gradient in most patients with distal renal tubular acidosis argues against enhanced bicarbonate leak and suggests a rate defect as the underlying mechanism.*

8. *Classic hypokalemic distal renal tubular acidosis (type I RTA) is characterized clinically by an inability to acidify the urine appropriately during metabolic acidosis. Hypokalemia, hypercalciuria, and hypocitraturia frequently accompany this disorder, but proximal tubular reabsorptive function is preserved. Chronic metabolic acidosis results in calcium, magnesium, and phosphate wasting which in turn result in dissolution of bone. Nephrocalcinosis is common in this disorder. Most patients with classic hypokalemic distal renal tubular acidosis have the condition in association with a systemic illness.*

9. *Classic hypokalemic distal renal tubular acidosis also occurs as an isolated defect inherited as an autosomal dominant trait. Hypercalciuria and hypocitraturia may occur, in which case nephrocalcinosis usually develops.*

10. *Untreated classic distal renal tubular acidosis produces growth retardation, which is responsive to alkali therapy. Correction of the acidosis by alkali administration leads to correction of hypokalemia, sodium depletion, and hypercalciuria, and results in an increase in citrate excretion. Progression of nephrocalcinosis and nephrolithiasis are arrested. Restoration of normal growth and prevention of nephrocalcinosis are the major goals of therapy.*

11. *A generalized dysfunction of the distal nephron produces distal renal tubular acidosis with hyperkalemia. The acidification defect in this disorder may result from a "voltage" defect which limits the rate of proton secretion by the cortical collecting tubule at any given luminal pH. Such a transport defect is observed after amiloride administration and upon release of unilateral ureteral obstruction.*

12. *Aldosterone deficiency also results in hyperkalemia and metabolic acidosis by limiting proton secretion by the cortical collecting tubule. The hyperkalemia also has independent effects on net acid excretion by reducing renal ammoniagenesis. Mineralocorticoid resistance also causes hyperkalemic-hyperchloremic metabolic acidosis in children and adults.*

13. *Advanced renal insufficiency, especially due to diabetes and tubulointerstitial disease, produces a hyperkalemic distal renal tubular acidosis. The hyperkalemia is out of proportion to the reduction in glomerular filtration rate. Underlying this disorder is either mineralocorticoid deficiency or mineralocorticoid resistance. As in primary mineralocorticoid deficiency, metabolic acidosis is secondary, in part, to the hyperkalemia. Simply lowering blood potassium often results in improvement in the acidosis.*

14. *Patients with hyporeninemic hypoaldosteronism and chronic renal insufficiency may require cation exchange resins, alkali therapy, and a loop diuretic to enhance renal potassium excretion. Superphysiological doses of mineralocorticoids may be employed on occasion, but they usually must be adminstered in combination with a loop diuretic in order to avoid volume overexpansion and aggravation of hypertension.*

Renal tubular acidosis (RTA) is a clinical syndrome characterized by a hyperchloremic metabolic acidosis secondary to an abnormality in renal acidification. It can be demonstrated as either an inappropriately high urine pH, bicarbonaturia, or reduced net acid excretion (titratable acid and ammonium excretion). The clinical expression of the defect in acidification depends on the specific nephron segment in which the defect arises. The general types of RTA are summarized in Table 103-1. Renal tubular acidosis may occur clinically as a hyperchloremic metabolic acidosis with hypokalemia or hyperkalemia. Classic distal RTA (type I) and proximal RTA (type II) are frequently associated with hypokalemia. In contrast, a generalized dysfunction of the distal nephron, often associated with either hypoaldosteronism or aldosterone resistance, is usually seen in association with hyperkalemia. Since all varieties of RTA are associated with hyperchloremic metabolic acidosis when they are fully expressed, the differential diagnosis of hyperchloremia with metabolic acidosis and a normal anion gap is important.

HYPERCHLOREMIC METABOLIC ACIDOSIS

The diverse clinical disorders which may result in a hyperchloremic metabolic acidosis are outlined in Table 103-2. Since a reduced plasma HCO_3^- and elevated Cl^- concentration may also occur in chronic respiratory alkalosis, it is important to confirm acidosis by measuring arterial pH. In the absence of this information, a slightly elevated anion gap (12 to 16 meq/liter) and/or signs of pulmonary or hepatic disease suggest the presence of respiratory alkalosis. Hyperchloremic metabolic acidosis occurs most often as a result of loss of HCO_3^- from the gastrointestinal tract or as a result of a renal acidification defect. Hypokalemia may accompany both gastrointestinal loss of HCO_3^- and proximal and distal RTA.

Diarrhea results in the loss of large quantities of HCO_3^- and HCO_3^- decomposed by reaction with organic acids.[1] Since diarrheal stools contain a higher concentration of HCO_3^- and decomposed HCO_3^- than plasma, volume depletion and metabolic acidosis will develop. Hypokalemia exists because large quantities of K^+ are lost from stool and because volume depletion causes elaboration of renin and aldosterone, enhancing renal potassium secretion. Instead of an acid urine pH as anticipated with diarrhea, a pH of 6.0 or more is common.[2] This occurs because metabolic acidosis and hypokalemia increase renal ammonia synthesis and ammonium excretion, thus providing more urinary buffer, which increases urine pH. Metabolic acidosis due to gastrointestinal losses with a high urine pH can be differentiated from RTA, since urinary NH_4^+ excretion is typically low in RTA, while NH_4^+ excretion is high in patients with diarrhea.[3,4] Urinary NH_4^+ levels can be estimated, as suggested by Halperin and associates,[4,5] by calculating the negative urine anion gap (UAG):

$$UAG = [Na^+ + K^+]_u - [Cl]_u$$

When the urine chloride concentration exceeds the sum of the concentrations of Na^+ and K^+, the urine ammonium level is usually adequate, suggesting an extrarenal lesion. Conversely, if the sum of urine Na^+ and K^+ exceeds the Cl^- concentration, the urine NH_4^+ concentration would be predicted to be low, a condition compatible with RTA. Furthermore, the fractional excretion of sodium would be expected to be low

Table 103-1 Types of Renal Tubular Acidosis

Associated with hypokalemia
  Proximal RTA (type II)
  Distal RTA (type I)
Associated with hyperkalemia
  Aldosterone deficiency or resistance (type IV)
  Nonmineralocorticoid voltage defect (type IV)

(<1 to 2 percent) in patients with HCO_3^- loss from the gastrointestinal tract but usually exceeds 2 to 3 percent in RTA.[2]

In addition to gastrointestinal tract HCO_3^- loss, external loss of pancreatic and biliary secretions can also cause a hyperchloremic acidosis. Cholestyramine, calcium chloride, and magnesium sulfate ingestion can result in a hyperchloremic metabolic acidosis (Table 103-2), especially in patients with renal insufficiency, but the plasma potassium is typically normal, not depressed.[2,6]

Severe hyperchloremic metabolic acidosis with hypokalemia may occur on occasion in patients with ureteral diversion procedures. Since the ileum and colon are both endowed with Cl^-/HCO_3^- exchangers, when the Cl^- from the urine enters the gut, the HCO_3^- concentration increases as a result of the exchange process.[7] Moreover, K^+ secretion is stimulated which, together with HCO_3^- loss, can result in a hyperchloremic, hypokalemic metabolic acidosis. This defect is particularly common in patients with ureterosigmoidostomies and is more common with this type of diversion because of the prolonged transit time of urine due to stasis in the colonic segment.[8]

Loss of functioning renal parenchyma by progressive renal disease is known to be associated with metabolic acidosis. Typically, the acidosis is hyperchloremic when the glomerular infiltration rate (GFR) is between 20 and 50 ml/min but may convert to the typical acidosis of uremia with high anion gap with more advanced renal failure, i.e., when the GFR is < 15 ml/min.[2,9,10] It is generally assumed that such a progression is observed more commonly in patients with tubulointerstitial forms of renal disease, but hyperchloremic metabolic acidosis can occur with advanced glomerular disease.[11,12] The principal defect in acidification in advanced renal failure is that ammon-

Table 103-2 Differential Diagnosis of Hyperchloremic Metabolic Acidosis

Gastrointestinal bicarbonate loss
  Diarrhea
  External pancreatic or small bowel drainage
  Ureterosigmoidostomy, jejunal loop
  Drugs
    Calcium chloride
    Magnesium sulfate
    Cholestyramine
Renal acidosis
  Proximal RTA (type II)
  Distal (classic) RTA (type I)
  Generalized distal nephron dysfunction (type IV)
    Mineralocorticoid deficiency
    Mineralocorticoid resistance
    Nonmineralocorticoid voltage defects
  Renal insufficiency
Other
  Acid loads (ammonium chloride, arginine chloride, arginine hydrochloride, hyperalimentation, sulfur)
  Loss of potential bicarbonate—ketosis with ketone excretion
  Dilutional acidosis
  Posthypocapnic state

iagenesis is reduced in proportion to the loss of functional renal mass. In addition, medullary ammonia accumulation and trapping in the outer medullary collecting tubule may be impaired.[4] Because of adaptive increases in potassium secretion by the collecting duct[13] and colon,[14] the acidosis of chronic renal insufficiency is typically normokalemic.[12]

Dilutional acidosis, acidosis due to exogenous acid loads, and the posthypocapnic state can usually be excluded by history. When isotonic saline is infused rapidly, particularly in patients with temporary or permanent renal failure, the plasma bicarbonate will decline reciprocally in relation to chloride.[2] Addition of acid or acid equivalents (arginine HCl, lysine HCl, or NH$_4$Cl) to blood results in metabolic acidosis.[14a] A similar situation may arise from endogenous infusion of ketoacids during recovery from ketoacidosis when the sodium salts of ketones may be excreted by the kidneys and lost as potential bicarbonate.[2]

Hyperchloremic metabolic acidosis associated with hyperkalemia is almost always associated with a generalized dysfunction of the distal nephron. However, potassium-sparing diuretics, nonsteroidal anti-inflammatory drugs, angiotensin converting enzyme inhibitors and β blockers may mimic this disorder by causing hyperkalemia and a hyperchloremic acidosis. Such drugs should be discontinued before the diagnosis of a nonreversible, generalized defect of the distal nephron is considered.

The diverse clinical disorders associated with hyperchloremic metabolic acidosis should be considered and excluded before embarking upon an extensive evaluation of renal acidification and the diagnosis of RTA (Table 103-2).

PROXIMAL RENAL TUBULAR ACIDOSIS

Mechanism and Regulation of Proximal Acidification

The kidney filters approximately 4000 meq of HCO$_3^-$ per day. To maintain acid-base balance and to reabsorb the filtered load of HCO$_3^-$, the renal tubules must secrete 4000 meq of hydrogen ions. Although the kidney must secrete an additional 50 to 80 meq of hydrogen ions to titrate urinary buffers, the majority of hydrogen ion secretion is involved in the "reclamation" of filtered HCO$_3^-$. Approximately 80 to 90 percent of the HCO$_3^-$ is reabsorbed in the proximal tubule. Thus, while the distal nephron is responsible for the final acidification of the urine and the generation of large pH gradients, the proximal tubule represents a high capacity system and secretes the majority of hydrogen ions. Defects in proximal tubular reabsorption of HCO$_3^-$ are typically characterized by large amounts of bicarbonaturia.

Mechanism of H$^+$ Secretion/HCO$_3^-$ Absorption.

Reabsorption of HCO$_3^-$ in the proximal tubule depends on active secretion of hydrogen ions across the apical membrane.[15-17] This process is effected mostly by an apical membrane Na$^+$/H$^+$ antiporter, which results in hydrogen ion section into the lumen in exchange for sodium ions entering the cell.[18-24] The driving force for hydrogen ion secretion is provided by the low cell sodium concentration which is generated by the basolateral membrane Na$^+$/K$^+$-ATPase. Thus, ATP indirectly drives this active proton secretion. In parallel with the Na$^+$/H$^+$ antiporter is an H$^+$-ATPase which mediates a small frac-

tion of apical membrane H$^+$ secretion.[24-26] The base generated in the cell by these two transporters then exits the cell across the basolateral membrane via an electrogenic Na(HCO$_3$)$_3$ symporter which transports one sodium and three HCO$_3^-$ ions.[27-32] The driving force for this transporter is the negative cell potential.

Carbonic anhydrase is present in the cytoplasm and on both apical and basolateral membranes of the proximal tubule. The cytoplasmic form is very similar to the carbonic anhydrase II of red blood cells.[33,34] The membrane bound form is a different form which has been named *type IV*.[33,34] Carbonic anhydrase I, the most prevalent red blood cell carbonic anhydrase, is not present in the kidney.[35] The major function of carbonic anhydrase (CA) in the proximal tubule (and in the kidney in general) is to accelerate the reaction

$$H^+ + HCO_3^- \overset{CA}{\leftrightarrow} H_2CO_3 \leftrightarrow CO_2 + H_2O$$

Since in the lumen of the proximal tubule hydrogen ions are secreted into the HCO$_3^-$ containing filtrate, H$_2$CO$_3$ is formed. The H$_2$CO$_3$ is rapidly dehydrated by the luminal carbonic anhydrase to form CO$_2$ and H$_2$O. The CO$_2$ is freely diffusible and reabsorbed. This allows transmembrane pH gradients to be minimal, and facilitates further proton secretion and HCO$_3^-$ reabsorption.

In parallel with the active hydrogen ion secretory mechanisms is a leak through the paracellular pathway. Because luminal HCO$_3^-$ concentration is lower than that of blood, HCO$_3^-$ can back-diffuse into the lumen. While the proximal tubule is a leaky epithelium with relatively high paracellular permeabilities, the HCO$_3^-$ permeability is comparatively small.[36-40] Diffusion of hydrogen ions is even smaller in magnitude.[41] Thus, leak pathways tend to be unimportant under normal conditions.

Other Proximal Tubular Functions. Proximal renal tubular acidosis is usually associated with defects in other proximal tubular functions. The proximal tubule is the major site for reabsorption of glucose, amino acids, organic anions, and phosphate. All these solutes are reabsorbed across the apical membrane on transporters coupled to sodium transport. The low intracellular sodium concentration which is generated by the basolateral membrane Na$^+$/K$^+$-ATPase provides the driving force for these transporters to actively take up these solutes from the lumen. Most of these solutes are then either metabolized within the proximal tubular cell or passively exit across the basolateral membrane. These mechanisms lead to low concentrations of these solutes in the lumen, creating a driving force for back-diffusion of these solutes across the paracellular pathway. Once again, under normal conditions, these back-diffusing fluxes are present but small in magnitude.

Proximal absorption of Na$^+$ and Cl$^-$ is more complex. High rates of HCO$_3^-$ absorption, preferential to Cl$^-$, in the early proximal tubule lead to an increased concentration of Cl$^-$ in the late proximal tubule. This provides a chemical gradient for Cl$^-$ absorption which drives Cl$^-$ movement and causes a lumen-positive potential difference (P.D.) that secondarily drives Na$^+$ absorption. While 50 percent of proximal tubular NaCl absorption occurs by such a passive mechanism, there is an additional active transcellular component of NaCl absorption.[42-45] This, however, also appears to be related to acidification in that the apical membrane mechanism is Na^+/H^+ antiport and $Cl^-/base^-$ exchange in parallel.[46–49]

Thus, diseases which interfere with HCO_3^- absorption in any manner can interfere secondarily with passive Cl^- absorption by preventing the rise in luminal Cl^- concentration. In addition, any mechanism which interferes with the Na^+/K^+-ATPase or the Na^+/H^+ antiporter will also interfere with transcellular Cl^- absorption. In theory, if the inhibition of HCO_3^- and Cl^- absorption is in proportion to the plasma concentrations (corrected for differences in volume of distribution), the result will be a decrease in extracellular fluid volume with no change in the concentrations of HCO_3^- or Cl^-. In reality, the inhibition of HCO_3^- absorption in proximal renal tubular acidosis is proportionately greater than that of Cl^- absorption, resulting in a decrease in plasma HCO_3^- concentration and an increase in plasma Cl^- concentration.

Regulation of Proximal Tubular HCO_3^- Absorption. Pitts and Lotspeich[50] examined the effect of an HCO_3^- infusion on renal HCO_3^- absorption and excretion in normal dogs. The results are displayed in Fig. 103-1. As the plasma HCO_3^- concentration rises, renal HCO_3^- absorption also increases. At low plasma bicarbonate concentrations, nearly 100 percent of filtered HCO_3^- is absorbed. However, at higher plasma HCO_3^- concentrations, a threshold is reached where HCO_3^- first appears in the urine (the threshold for bicarbonaturia). As plasma HCO_3^- concentration increases further, HCO_3^- absorption continues to increase until a maximal level is reached, the so-called T_m for HCO_3^- absorption.

The initial interpretation of these studies was that HCO_3^- absorption was a saturable process such that at low filtered loads of HCO_3^- luminal transporters were able to reabsorb all the HCO_3^-, but as luminal HCO_3^- concentration increased, the transporters became saturated and fractional HCO_3^- absorption decreased. Recent microperfusion studies have demonstrated that this interpretation is only partly correct.[36,51] While proximal tubular HCO_3^- absorption does saturate as a function of luminal HCO_3^- concentration, a more important regulatory effect is that exerted by the peritubular HCO_3^- concentration. Increases in peritubular HCO_3^- concentration directly inhibit proximal tubular HCO_3^- absorption. Thus, when plasma HCO_3^- concentration is increased, both luminal and peritubular HCO_3^- concentration are increased. While the increase

in luminal HCO_3^- concentration leads toward saturation of the system, the increase in peritubular HCO_3^- concentration markedly inhibits proximal tubular HCO_3^- absorption. The net result produces the curve reported by Pitts and Lotspeich (Fig. 103-1).[50]

The studies of Pitts and Lotspeich form the basis for the most frequently used test to examine patients for proximal tubular acidification defects. These patients have apparently normal rates of renal HCO_3^- absorption at low plasma HCO_3^- concentrations. However, even at these low plasma HCO_3^- concentrations, proximal tubular HCO_3^- absorption is probably still subnormal; distal HCO_3^- delivery is low enough such that the distal nephron can reabsorb the excess HCO_3^-. Because the distal nephron acidification is not impaired, the urine can then be acidified appropriately. As plasma bicarbonate concentration increases, these patients are found to have a low threshold for bicarbonaturia, as shown in Fig. 103-2. At high plasma HCO_3^- concentrations, distal delivery of HCO_3^- exceeds the capacity of the distal nephron for HCO_3^- absorption, and there is significant bicarbonaturia. Patients with distal renal tubular acidification defects, on the other hand, may have small degrees of bicarbonaturia but never have large amounts of bicarbonaturia unless the patients are made frankly alkalotic. Figure 103-2 shows a typical HCO_3^- titration curve for a normal patient, a patient with proximal renal tubular acidosis and a patient with distal renal tubular acidosis.

Pathogenesis of Proximal Renal Tubular Acidosis

Possible Defects. Proximal renal tubular acidosis can be divided into two general categories, one in which acidification is the only defective function and one in which there is a more generalized proximal tubular dysfunction. A generalized proximal tubular defect could occur by one of two mechanisms. First, there could be an increase in the permeability of the paracellular pathway. This would lead to a backleak into the lumen of solutes for which the proximal tubule is the main site of reabsorption and whose concentration is thus low in the lumen. These solutes would include HCO_3^-, phosphate, glucose, amino acids, and organic anions. An alternative mechanism is a generalized disorder of cellular function which would inhibit absorption of all of these solutes. For example, any

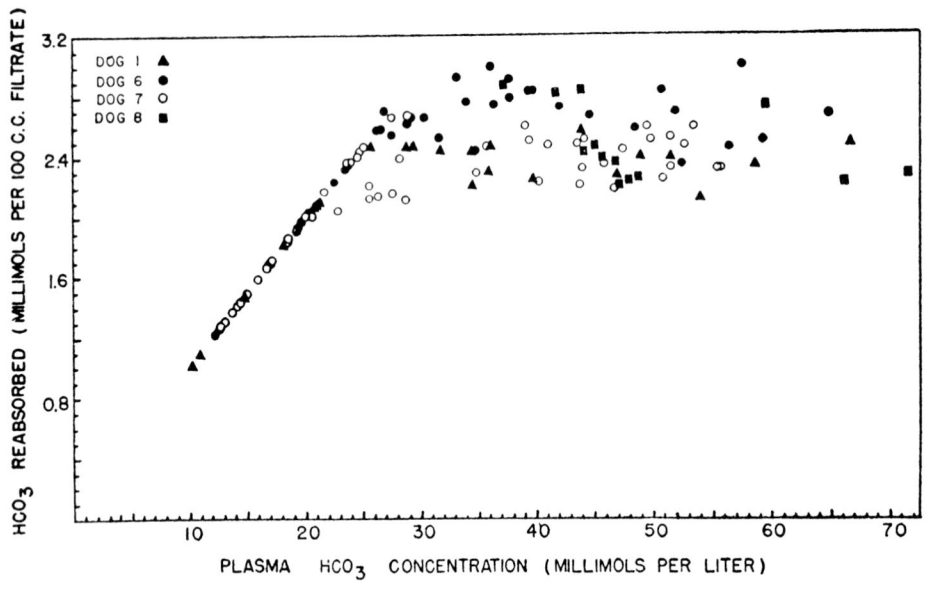

Fig. 103-1 Effect of varying plasma HCO_3^- concentration on renal bicarbonate absorption in normal dogs. (From R.F. Pitts and W.D. Lotspeich.[50] Used by permission.)

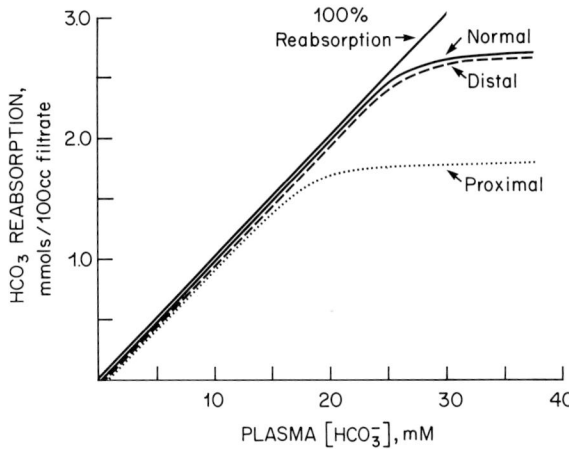

Fig. 103-2 Effect of plasma bicarbonate concentration on renal HCO_3^- absorption in normal patients (solid line), patients with hypokalemic distal renal tubular acidosis (broken line), and patients with proximal renal tubular acidosis (dotted line). Bold diagonal line represents 100 percent reabsorption of filtered bicarbonate. Note that in distal renal tubular acidosis, the threshold for bicarbonaturia (i.e., the plasma bicarbonate concentration at which renal bicarbonate absorption is not 100 percent of filtered load) is normal, while in patients with proximal renal tubular acidosis the threshold is decreased.

disorder which inhibits ATP production in the proximal tubule would lead to a generalized defect in reabsorption. Similarly, because reabsorption of these solutes as well as acidification are coupled to sodium transport, any disorder in which the Na^+/K^+-ATPase is abnormal would lead to a generalized defect in proximal tubular function.

A proximal tubular defect involving only acidification is rare. Such a disorder would have to involve a selective defect in the Na^+/H^+ antiporter, the H^+-ATPase, or the $Na^+/(HCO_3^-)_3$ symporter. Abnormalities of cell depolarization or abnormalities in carbonic anhydrase could also present in this manner.

Generalized Proximal Tubular Dysfunction. The majority of cases of proximal renal tubular acidosis fit into the category of generalized proximal tubular dysfunction with glycosuria, generalized aminoaciduria, hypercitraturia, and phosphaturia. The generalized failure of proximal tubular function is referred to as the *Fanconi syndrome*. As there is a separate chapter in this book dealing with this syndrome, we discuss the Fanconi syndrome only briefly as it relates to the mechanism of the acidification defect.

In 1950, Berliner et al.,[52] while examining the capacity of organic acids to serve as effective buffers for acidification, accidentally found that maleic acid infused intravenously into dogs caused a syndrome with proximal renal tubular acidosis and glycosuria. This condition, now referred to as *maleic acid nephropathy*, has been subsequently used to study the mechanism of the Fanconi syndrome. Al-Bander et al.,[53] using clearance techniques in dogs undergoing a free-water diuresis, found results suggesting that maleic acid inhibits proximal tubular solute and water absorption. While initial studies raised the possibility of abnormal proximal tubular leaks in the genesis of maleic acid nephropathy,[54] the techniques used were indirect and the conclusions have not been substantiated by more direct studies performed subsequently. One more recent study which found evidence for renal tubular leakage[55] exposed animals to maleic acid 20 h prior to studying renal function. In this study, tubules were leaky to lissamine green and

inulin, suggesting that nephrotoxicity had approached the level of acute tubular necrosis. Hoppe et al.[56] and Gougoux et al.[57] found that the effect of maleate on bicarbonaturia was additive to that of carbonic anhydrase inhibition, suggesting separate mechanisms. Gmaj et al.[58] found no effect of maleate on renal carbonic anhydrase activity.

In studies where the lumen of the proximal tubule was microperfused and rates of acidification measured, Bank et al.[59] found that previous maleic acid treatment inhibited the rates of HCO_3^- absorption and of sodium chloride absorption. These investigators found no inulin leak. In addition, in studies where tubules were perfused in the absence of HCO_3^- and the rate of HCO_3^- entrance was measured (a measure of paracellular HCO_3^- permeability), maleic acid had no effect. Thus, Bank et al. concluded that maleic acid acted by interfering with transcellular active HCO_3^- absorption rather than enhancing HCO_3^- backleak. Similar results were obtained by Reboucas et al.,[60] employing split droplet microperfusion. Rates of volume absorption were inhibited. In further studies with a pH electrode in the luminal fluid, these investigators measured the rates of luminal acidification and alkalinization. In tubules perfused with alkaline solutions, the rate of acidification was inhibited, a result consistent with either a transcellular defect or enhanced leak. However, in tubules perfused with very acid solutions, the rate of alkalization was also inhibited, a result consistent only with an inhibited transcellular flux and not consistent with enhanced leakiness. In addition, in these studies cell voltage was measured and found to be decreased consistent with inhibition of the Na^+/K^+-ATPase.[60] Günther et al.[61] examined the effect of maleic acid infusion on glycine absorption. Maleic acid infusion inhibited glycine absorption in the microperfused proximal tubule. However, when saturable transcellular glycine absorption was inhibited by excess phenylalanine in the lumen, maleic acid had no effect on glycine absorption.

These studies demonstrated that maleic acid nephropathy involves disruption of active transcellular absorption of HCO_3^-, amino acids, and other solutes. Such a defect could be due to a generalized disorder of apical membrane transporters, a disorder of the basolateral Na^+/K^+-ATPase, or a metabolic disorder which lowers intracellular ATP concentrations. Using the isolated brush border membrane technique, addition of maleic acid to vesicles did not affect the $Na^+/$glucose cotransporter.[62] In addition, the $Na^+/$glucose cotransporter isolated from either control animals or animals treated in vivo with maleic acid were similar in function. Addition of maleic acid to brush border membranes did not affect transport of α-methylglucoside, alanine, proline, or lysine.[63] Silverman and Huang[64] found that maleic acid addition to vesicles did not affect phlorizin binding to the $Na^+/$glucose cotransporter. Lastly, LeGrimellec et al.[65] found no effect of maleate on the fluidity of the lipids of brush border membranes. Thus, no abnormality of apical membrane transporters could be demonstrated.

Kramer and Gonick[66] found that maleic acid treatment of rats inhibited Na^+/K^+-ATPase activity in renal cortical homogenates prepared 1.0 h after treatment. There was no effect on Na^+/K^+-ATPase in medullary homogenates. Thus, inhibition of the Na^+/K^+-ATPase provides one mechanism by which all the transport defects in maleic acid nephropathy and in Fanconi syndrome could be produced.

In addition to the defect in Na^+/K^+-ATPase, Kramer and Gonick[66] found decreased ATP concentrations in renal cortical homogenates. One possible explanation for these decreased

ATP levels is inhibition of metabolism by maleic acid. Angielski and Rogulski[67] have found that maleic acid interferes with the Krebs cycle. While this effect occurs in many tissues, only kidney cells actively accumulated maleate. Another possible cause of decreased ATP levels is sequestration of intracellular phosphate. Al-Bander et al.[68] found that previous phosphate loading in dogs could markedly ameliorate the maleic acid-induced bicarbonaturia, natriuresis, and aminoaciduria. There was no effect of previous phosphate loading on the hypercitraturia. In subsequent studies, Al-Bander et al.[68a] found that prior phosphate loading attenuated the increased renal excretion of small molecular weight proteins and lysosomal enzymes seen in maleic acid treated kidneys.

Production of Fanconi syndrome by intracellular phosphate depletion has also been proposed in hereditary fructose intolerance where ingestion of fructose leads to accumulation of fructose-1-phosphate in the proximal tubule. Because these patients lack the enzyme fructose-1-phosphate aldolase, the fructose-1-phosphate cannot be further metabolized and intracellular phosphate is sequestered in this form. The renal lesion is confined to the proximal tubule because this is the only segment in the kidney that possesses the enzyme fructokinase.[69] Administration of large parenteral loads of fructose to rats leads to high intracellular concentrations of fructose-1-phosphate and low concentrations of ATP and GTP, as well as total adenine nucleotides.[69] Prior phosphate loading prevents the reductions in intracellular ATP, total adenine nucleotides, and phosphate.[70]

A clinical association which has occurred relatively frequently is that of vitamin D deficiency, resistance, or dependence, and generalized proximal tubular dysfunction. Numerous investigators have noted an association between vitamin D deficiency and a generalized Fanconi syndrome with proximal renal tubular acidosis, aminoaciduria, and hyperphosphaturia.[71–73] In these studies, correction of the vitamin D deficiency has caused correction of the proximal tubular dysfunction.[71,72] Similar results have been obtained in patients with vitamin D-dependent and vitamin D-resistant rickets treated with dihydrotachisterol.[74,75] While the existence of this association is undisputed, the mechanisms involved in the proximal tubular dysfunction are not yet clear.

Vitamin D deficiency states are associated with low levels of vitamin D, low levels of serum calcium, and high levels of parathormone (PTH). PTH has been demonstrated to be an important inhibitor of proximal tubular bicarbonate absorption.[76–79] This results from inhibition of active transcellular proton secretion rather than from an increase in bicarbonate backleak.[78,79] Although the mechanism of this inhibition is not yet settled, recent studies suggest a direct effect on the Na/H antiporter, mediated possibly by the cyclic AMP-dependent protein kinase.[80,81] While such an effect may explain proximal RTA, recent studies have suggested that chronic PTH administration does not lead to metabolic acidosis but rather to metabolic alkalosis.[82,83] This appears to be due to a stimulation of HCO_3^- absorption in more distal segments, either in the loop of Henle[84] or in the collecting tubule. Recent studies have suggested that increased distal phosphate delivery that is induced by PTH can stimulate distal nephron acidification.[85] Thus, in spite of the marked inhibitory effect of PTH on proximal tubular absorption of HCO_3^-, the effect on whole kidney HCO_3^- absorption appears to be small and, overall, there is a small stimulation of acidification.

Extracellular Ca^{2+} concentration is also a regulator of proximal tubular transport, although less potent than PTH. In the in vitro perfused proximal convoluted tubule, increases in extracellular Ca^{2+} concentration stimulate HCO_3^- absorption, and decreases in extracellular Ca^{2+} concentration inhibit HCO_3^- absorption.[86] However, in these studies large changes in Ca^{2+} concentrations produced only small effects on HCO_3^- absorption. Although the effects of vitamin D have not yet been studied in the perfused proximal tubule, clearance studies have found that administration of 25-hydroxyvitamin D stimulates renal absorption of Ca^{2+}, PO_4^{3-}, sodium, and HCO_3^-.[87,88] The exact nephron segment in which this effect occurs has not been established but is thought to be the proximal tubule.[89]

An additional pathophysiological mechanism for the proximal tubular defect in vitamin D deficiency could be intracellular phosphate depletion. Intracellular PO_4^{3-} depletion has been proposed as a cause of ATP depletion and the secondary Fanconi syndrome in maleic acid nephropathy and in hereditary fructose intolerance. High levels of PTH will inhibit proximal tubular PO_4^{3-} absorption. In addition, vitamin D may promote proximal tubular phosphate absorption, and its deficiency reduces PO_4^{3-} absorption, secondarily contributing to intracellular phosphate depletion. Grose and Scriver[90] created an experimental model of vitamin D deficiency in the rat and demonstrated hyperphosphaturia and aminoaciduria. These authors noted that aminoaciduria was not prominent until the animals had been on a vitamin D-deficient diet for 6 weeks. In addition, they noted that the aminoaciduria appeared 2 to 4 weeks after hyperphosphaturia, supporting a role for a more complex scheme than mere hormone presence or absence.

Further support for a role of the Ca^{2+}/PO_4^{3-}/PTH/vitamin D system in proximal RTA can be found from the results of Morris et al.[91] who found that hypoparathyroidism ameliorated the fructose-induced proximal tubular dysfunction in a patient with hereditary fructose intolerance. Administration of PTH to this hypoparathyroid patient enhanced the fructose-induced renal defect. As discussed above, intracellular PO_4^{3-} depletion has been proposed as the cause of Fanconi syndrome in hereditary fructose intolerance. Decreased levels of PTH could protect these patients by enhancing phosphate uptake by the proximal tubule. An alternative explanation is that the inhibition of PTH on acidification is additive to the effect of fructose-induced intracellular phosphate depletion.

The association between Fanconi syndrome and vitamin D disorders may be partially related to decreased 1α-hydroxylase activity in disorders of proximal tubule function. 1α-Hydroxylase, which is present in proximal tubular mitochondria, could be deficient in Fanconi syndrome. Brewer et al.[92] found that conversion of 25-hydroxy-D$_3$ to 1,25-dihydroxy-D$_3$ was impaired in maleic acid nephropathy. However, Chesney et al.[93] measured levels of vitamin D metabolites and found them to be normal in three patients with Fanconi syndrome. In summary, vitamin D deficiency is clearly associated with Fanconi syndrome. The defect is related to low levels of 1,25-dihydroxy-D$_3$, high levels of PTH, and low Ca^{2+}. These findings may be produced in part by intracellular phosphate depletion.

Isolated Proximal Tubular Acidosis. One model for selective inhibition of proximal tubular HCO_3^- absorption is that of lysine infusion. Walker et al.[94] reported that lysine caused marked bicarbonaturia in the dog. Chan and Kurtzman[95] examined the effect of microperfusing rat proximal tubules with lysine. Lysine was found to inhibit HCO_3^- absorption with no effect on volume absorption. This effect was seen only with L-lysine, not with D-lysine, and the dose response for this effect was similar to that of the concentration relationship for lysine absorption from the lumen. Although no specific mechanism for this effect was established, Frömter[96] and Hoshi et al.[97] have found that luminal lysine depolarizes the proximal tubular cell. Such an effect could inhibit HCO_3^- efflux across the basolateral membrane, secondarily alkalinizing the cell and inhibiting apical membrane proton secretion.

Another model for isolated proximal tubular acidosis is inherited carbonic anhydrase deficiency. Sly and associates[98,99] have reported an inherited syndrome with osteopetrosis, cerebral calcification, and renal tubular acidosis due to an inherited deficiency of carbonic anhydrase II. These patients may have a combined proximal and distal RTA but have no other evidence for proximal tubular dysfunction.[100,101] As discussed above, carbonic anhydrase II is present in the cytoplasm of renal cells, and thus an acidification defect occurring in association with its deficiency is not unexpected. This syndrome is discussed extensively in Chap. 117.

An association between renal tubular acidosis and an aberrant carbonic anhydrase I has also been reported.[102,103] These patients appear to have a combined proximal and distal renal tubular acidosis. While they had normal amounts of carbonic anhydrase I assayed antigenically, carbonic anhydrase I enzyme activity was decreased. Kondo et al.[102] proposed that this defect may be related to abnormal binding of zinc to carbonic anhydrase I. This association may have been a coincidence and not a causal one since biochemical studies have failed to demonstrate carbonic anhydrase I in the kidney.[35] In addition, in patients with a syndrome of inherited deficiency of carbonic anhydrase I, there is no disorder of renal function.[104]

Diagnosis of Proximal Renal Tubular Acidosis

The diagnosis of proximal renal tubular acidosis rests initially on the finding of a hyperchloremic metabolic acidosis. These patients will generally present with a chronic metabolic acidosis in the steady state with acid urine and a small amount of HCO_3^- excretion. Upon HCO_3^- infusion, as the plasma HCO_3^- rises above the threshold in these patients, bicarbonaturia ensues, and urine pH becomes alkaline. In its isolated form, this metabolic acidosis occurs alone or in association with mild hypokalemia. If for some reason bicarbonate intake has been large, the patients will have significant bicarbonaturia on presentation and hypokalemia may be marked.

The diagnosis thus rests on an appropriately acidified urine (pH < 5.5) in acidotic patients, and a high fractional excretion of HCO_3^- (>10 to 15 percent) in patients with a near-normal serum HCO_3^- concentration. An additional clue to the diagnosis is the difficulty with which plasma HCO_3^- concentration is corrected. In patients with proximal RTA, massive amounts of exogenous HCO_3^- are required.

In most patients, this acidification defect is part of a generalized proximal tubular dysfunction called *Fanconi syndrome*. These patients have hypophosphatemia, hyperphosphaturia, glycosuria, aminoaciduria, hypercitraturia, hypercalciuria, and proteinuria. In addition, this syndrome is frequently associated with bone disease which presents as rickets in children or osteopenia in adults.[105] The diagnostic approach to patients with RTA and the use of fractional excretion of HCO_3^- are discussed later in this chapter in the section on distal RTA.

Table 103-3 Disorders Associated with Proximal RTA

Isolated RTA
  Primary (sporadic or familial)
  Carbonic anhydrase
    Inhibition
      Acetazolamide
      Mafenide (sulfamylon)
    Deficiency
      Osteopetrosis with carbonic anhydrase II deficiency
Generalized
  Primary (sporadic or familial)
  Inborn error of metabolism
    Cystinosis
    Lowe syndrome
    Hereditary fructose intolerance
    Tyrosinemia
    Galactosemia
    Wilson's disease
    Pyruvate carboxylase deficiency
    Metachromatic leukodystrophy
    Glycogen storage disease
  Dysproteinemic states
    Multiple myeloma
    Light chain disease
    Monoclonal gammopathy
    Amyloidosis
  Vitamin D deficiency, dependence, or resistance
  Interstitial renal disease
    Sjögren syndrome
    Medullary cystic disease
    Renal transplantation rejection (early)
    Balkan nephropathy
    Chronic renal vein thrombosis
  Toxins
    Outdated tetracyclines
    Lead
    Mercury
    Gentamicin
    Cadmium
    Maleic acid
    Coumarin
    Streptozotocin
  Miscellaneous
    Nephrotic syndrome
    Paroxysmal nocturnal hemoglobinuria
    Malignancy
    Congenital heart disease

Clinical Spectrum

Table 103-3 lists the causes of proximal renal tubular acidosis. Isolated proximal renal tubular acidosis occurs either as an idiopathic or genetic condition, or is related to carbonic anhydrase insufficiency or inhibition. Syndromes of generalized proximal tubular dysfunction are discussed in depth in a subsequent chapter, but they generally fall into the categories of primary disease and those associated with inherited disorders of metabolism, dysproteinemic states, nephrotoxins, interstitial nephritis, and vitamin D deficiency states.

Associated Findings

Proximal renal tubular acidosis occurs in two forms: (1) as part of a broader syndrome of proximal tubular dysfunction, namely Fanconi syndrome, and (2) as an isolated defect. In Fanconi syndrome, because of the multiple tubular defects, the pathophysiological consequences are complex. In the pure form of proximal renal tubular acidosis, all the pathophysiological consequences can be explained by inhibition of proximal tubular HCO_3^- absorption.

Rodriguez-Soriano et al.[106] used clearance techniques to examine the distribution of NaCl and volume absorption in patients with proximal RTA. In these studies, the patients were found to have marked inhibition of proximal tubular NaCl and volume absorption with increased distal delivery. Distal NaCl absorption was normal. As discussed above, proximal tubular NaCl absorption is integrally related to proximal tubular acidification mechanisms. First, because proximal tubular bicarbonate absorption sets up the high luminal chloride concentrations which drive passive NaCl absorption, inhibition of acidification will lead to inhibition of passive NaCl absorption. Second, transcellular NaCl absorption is mediated by apical membrane Na^+/H^+ antiport, which may also be defective in proximal RTA.

In patients with proximal RTA who have a significant acidosis but are not excreting HCO_3^-, potassium handling is normal. Indeed, in two clinical studies of isolated proximal renal tubular acidosis, patients were found to have normal serum potassium, presumably because of a lack of significant bicarbonaturia in the steady state.[108,109] Patients with proximal RTA have renal potassium wasting only during bicarbonaturia. In fact, Sebastian et al.[107] found that the magnitude of potassium excretion correlated well with the magnitude of HCO_3^- excretion. The mechanism of the potassium wasting is related to increased distal delivery of sodium with a poorly reabsorbable anion (i.e., bicarbonate). In addition, inhibition of proximal tubular NaCl absorption leads to volume depletion, which leads to increased aldosterone levels and enhanced potassium secretion.

There is presently no evidence to suggest that proximal RTA causes hypercalciuria or hyperphosphaturia.[108,109] Phosphate wasting associated with proximal renal tubular acidosis appears to occur only in association with the Fanconi syndrome. The hypercalciuria frequently seen with chronic metabolic acidosis is not seen in this disorder, probably because increased distal HCO_3^- delivery enhances calcium absorption in the distal nephron.[110] In addition, hypercitraturia helps to prevent nephrocalcinosis and nephrolithiasis, which are not seen in proximal RTA. The rickets frequently seen in association with Fanconi syndrome is probably more related to phosphate wasting than to the proximal renal tubular acidosis.

Management and Prognosis

The goal of treatment in proximal renal tubular acidosis is to maintain a normal serum bicarbonate concentration and pH. This can be achieved only by the administration of large amounts of HCO_3^- or an equivalent organic anion such as citrate which consumes H^+ during metabolism in the liver. As described above, such treatment will be associated with massive bicarbonaturia which will be excreted in the form of $NaHCO_3$ and $KHCO_3$. Thus, the HCO_3^- or citrate administered should be administered as a mixture of the sodium and potassium salts depending on the moieties excreted (Polycitra or K-lyte) (Table 103-4). One approach to decreasing the magnitude of bicarbonate excretion is to administer thiazide diuretics,[111,112] a maneuver which lowers the filtered load of bicarbonate by decreasing GFR as a result of chronic extracellular fluid volume depletion. Although the prognosis varies according to the specific cause of the proximal tubular dysfunction, proximal renal tubular acidosis per se should

Table 103-4 Forms of Alkali Replacement

Shohl's solution	
Na citrate	1 meq/ml
Citric acid	1 meq/ml
$NaHCO_3$ tablets	3.9 meq/tablet (325 mg)
Baking soda	60 meq/teaspoon
K-Lyte	25 or 50 meq/tablet
Polycitra (K-Shohls)	
Na citrate	1 meq/ml
K citrate	1 meq/ml
Citric acid	1 meq/ml

cause no harm to the patient if the metabolic acidosis is corrected. While growth is stunted in children with isolated proximal RTA, this is corrected by correction of the acidosis. Some investigators have noted that the tubular defect improves over time in isolated proximal renal tubular acidosis presenting in childhood.[109]

DISTAL RENAL TUBULAR ACIDOSIS

Mechanism and Regulation of Distal Acidification

Most of the filtered HCO_3^- (90 percent) is reabsorbed in the proximal tubule. One of the functions of the distal nephron is to reabsorb the remainder of the filtered HCO_3^- (about 5 to 10 percent). In addition, the distal nephron must secrete a quantity of protons equal to that generated systemically by metabolism in order to maintain acid-base balance. While this quantity of protons, approximately 50 to 80 meq/day, is small, it must be secreted to prevent the cumulative development of chronic positive hydrogen ion balance and metabolic acidosis. It must also be buffered. Ten milliequivalents per liter of proton would be equivalent to a pH of 2.0 and would expose the urinary tract to extreme acidity if unbuffered. Moreover, to achieve a urine pH of this acidity, proton secretory mechanisms would be required to generate large gradients between blood and tubule fluid. To mitigate the development of limiting pH gradients and increase the rate of acid excretion, protons secreted in the collecting tubule are buffered by ammonia, phosphate, creatinine, and other miscellaneous buffers. Thus, the distal nephron reabsorbs a small fraction of filtered HCO_3^- and secretes 50 to 80 meq of acid per day in the form of NH_4^+ and titratable acid.

Anatomic and Physiological Components of the Distal Nephron. The mechanisms of acidification have been discussed extensively elsewhere[34] and are reviewed here as pertinent to the distal renal tubular acidosis. For the purpose of this discussion, the distal nephron can be considered to consist of two segments. The first is the cortical collecting tubule (CCT). This segment has three important characteristics. First, it is capable of HCO_3^- absorption and HCO_3^- secretion,[113,114] which are performed by separate cells in this segment.[115] Second, the relative numbers of these cells, and thus the relative magnitude of HCO_3^- absorption and secretion, can be modulated by the acid-base status of the animal.[115] Third, the CCT actively transports Na^+ and K^+ in addition to H^+/HCO_3^-. The CCT normally has a negative lumen voltage which is due to sodium transport and which can be modulated by variations in the rate of sodium transport.

It should be pointed out that a great deal of research on the mechanism of acidification has been conducted by micropuncture techniques in the superficial distal convoluted tubule of the rat. This segment of the nephron actually includes three distinct morphologic segments: the true distal convoluted tubule, the connecting tubule, and the initial cortical collecting tubule. When studied functionally with respect to acidification, however, this segment appears to have many characteristics which are similar to the cortical collecting tubule. For example, the superficial distal convoluted tubule actively absorbs sodium and secretes potassium, and is capable of absorption or secretion of HCO_3^-, depending on the acid-base status of the animal.[116–118] Thus, the superficial distal tubule and the cortical collecting tubule can be viewed as similar segments of the distal nephron.

The second major segment of the distal nephron which functions importantly in acidification is the outer medullary collecting tubule (OMCT). Lombard and colleagues[119] first demonstrated that the outer medullary collecting tubule (inner stripe) was capable of high rates of proton secretion. This segment absorbs HCO_3^- at rates exceeding that observed in the CCT. In addition, this segment does not actively transport sodium or potassium[120] and does not secrete HCO_3^- but only absorbs HCO_3^-.[119] Moreover, the rate of HCO_3^- absorption is unaffected by the chronic acid-base status of the animal.[119] Finally, as a result of these transport characteristics, specifically, active proton secretion, the luminal electrical potential difference is positive in this segment.[119] The importance of the inner medullary collecting tubule in acidification is controversial. While microcatheterization, micropuncture, and split-droplet microperfusion studies have all demonstrated that this segment is capable of acidificaiton of tubule fluid,[121–123] the exact mechanism involved and the relative magnitude of proton secretion is not yet fully appreciated.

Thus, acidification in the distal nephron can be viewed simplistically as occurring in two segments. The first segment, represented by the CCT, is a low capacity segment where acidification can be regulated by sodium transport-dependent changes in potential difference, as well as by chronic systemic acid-base balance. The second segment, represented by the outer medullary collecting tubule, has a higher capacity for proton secretion but is unaffected by chronic system acid-base changes and, because this segment does not transport sodium actively, should not be affected by sodium delivery.

H^+ Secretion/HCO_3^- Absorption. The mechanism of HCO_3^- absorption appears to be similar in all the segments of the distal nephron. Studies measuring disequilibrium pH have demonstrated that HCO_3^- absorption in the distal nephron is mediated by apical membrane secretion of hydrogen ions.[15–17] Because of the negative cell potential, secretion of hydrogen ions must be an active process which requires energy input. Numerous studies suggest that active proton secretion at the apical membrane is mediated by an ATP-dependent electrogenic proton pump. This conclusion is based on studies which have demonstrated electrogenicity and sodium-independence of HCO_3^- absorption.[124–126] Recently, a H^+-ATPase has been demonstrated in vesicles from renal medulla and has been purified.[127–130] This H^+-ATPase is similar to that found in endosomes, clathrin-coated vesicles, Golgi, and endoplasmic reticulum. In addition, antibodies directed against the purified H^+-ATPase stain the apical membrane of the hydrogen secreting cells in the CCT and OMCT.[131,132]

Active H^+ secretion by the apical membrane generates base

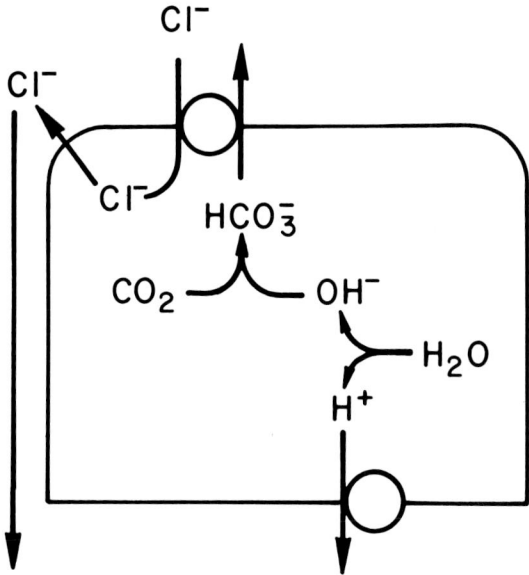

Fig. 103-3 Cell model for hydrogen ion secretion into the lumen of the collecting tubule (and bicarbonate absorption). *(From R.J. Alpern et al.[34] Used by permission.)*

in the cell which must exit the basolateral membrane. The mechanism of base exit appears to be Cl^-/HCO_3^- exchange. This conclusion is based on studies which have demonstrated that chloride is required for HCO_3^- absorption and proton secretion in the turtle urinary bladder and in the OMCT.[133,134] In addition, Cl^-/HCO_3^- exchange has been demonstrated directly on the basolateral membrane of proton secretory cells of the CCT by measuring cell pH.[115] Using antibodies against the red cell anion exchanger (Cl^-/HCO_3^-), an antigenically similar protein was detected in the basolateral membrane.[135] Chloride, which enters the cell in exchange for bicarbonate, exits the cell through a basolateral membrane chloride conductance.[136] Chloride then diffuses across the tight junction driven by the positive transepithelial voltage. The mechanism of bicarbonate absorption is summarized in Fig. 103-3.

Bicarbonate Secretion. When animals are pretreated with an alkaline diet, net bicarbonate secretion is observed in the CCT. A similar adaptation occurs in the turtle urinary bladder in which the mechanism of HCO_3^- secretion has been investigated extensively. Subsequent studies in the CCT have suggested that the turtle urinary bladder and the mammalian CCT share similar transport characteristics. As was true for HCO_3^- absorption, HCO_3^- secretion is dependent on the presence of chloride and independent of sodium.[137–139] Under control conditions, HCO_3^- secretion is electroneutral and active.[140] Based on these findings, it appears that HCO_3^- secretion is mediated by a basolateral membrane H^+-ATPase in series with an apical membrane Cl^--HCO_3^- exchanger (Fig. 103-4A and B). It is not clear whether the basolateral membrane H^+-ATPase in bicarbonate secreting cells is identical with the apical membrane H^+-ATPase in bicarbonate absorbing cells. However, antibodies raised against purified H^+-ATPase label the basolateral membranes of some CCT cells.[131] While apical membrane Cl^--HCO_3^- exchange has been demonstrated in HCO_3^- secreting cells by measuring cell pH, antibodies against the red cell Cl^--HCO_3^- exchanger do not stain the apical membrane in the CCT. The model which best explains the mechanism of electroneutral HCO_3^- secretion is shown in Fig. 103-4A.[20] Here, protons are actively secreted

(a) ELECTRONEUTRAL　　(b) ELECTROGENIC

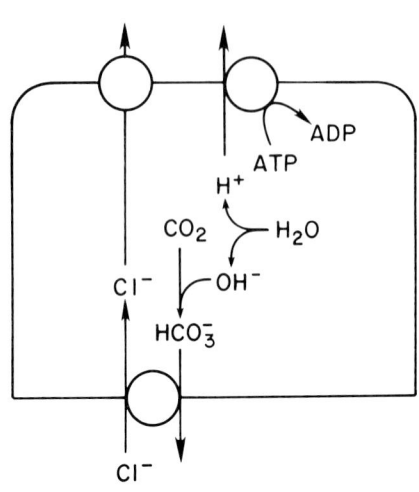 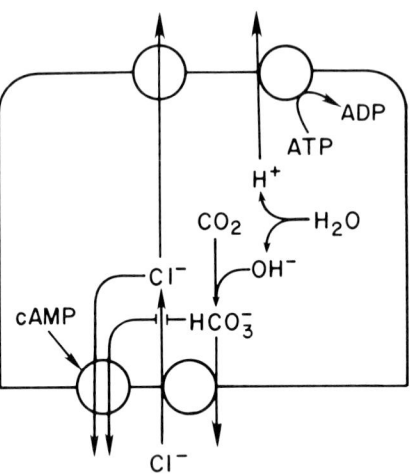

Fig. 103-4 Cell model for electroneutral (A) and electrogenic (B) bicarbonate secretion into the lumen of the cortical collecting tubule. Note that the H^+-ATPase is in the basolateral membrane in this model. (Used by permission from R.J. Alpern and F.C. Rector, Jr: Renal acidification: cellular mechanisms of tubular transport and regulation. In: Handbook of Physiology, edited by E.E. Windhager and G.H. Giebisch. Rockville Pike, Md.: American Physiological Society, in press.)

across the basolateral membrane, generating base within the cell. Base then exits across the apical membrane as HCO_3^- in exchange for chloride. The chloride exits across the basolateral membrane chloride conductance. This process is electroneutral since equal proton and chloride currents flow across the basolateral membrane.

It has been demonstrated clearly in the turtle urinary bladder that increases in intracellular cAMP levels stimulate HCO_3^- secretion and convert it from electroneutral to electrogenic.[141-143] These data are best explained by activation or appearance of an anion channel in the apical membrane which is conductive to chloride or HCO_3^-.[143] This has the effect of accelerating HCO_3^- secretion in several ways. First, an additional mechanism for apical membrane HCO_3^- exit has been added. Second, an additional mechanism for chloride efflux is added, which can then allow the Cl^--HCO_3^- exchanger to proceed at a faster rate. Last, addition of such a conductance pathway should depolarize the cell, allowing the H^+-ATPase to secrete at a faster rate. The mechanism of electrogenic HCO_3^- secretion is shown in Fig. 103-4B. Schuster recently demonstrated that cAMP increased HCO_3^- secretion in the CCT perfused in vitro.[144] However, electrogenicity was not demonstrated in these studies. It was shown that the hormone responsible for adenylate cyclase stimulation was β-catecholamine.

Buffers. As discussed above, secreted protons must be buffered to prevent extreme luminal acidity. These buffer systems are conveniently divided into two types: closed and open. A closed buffer system is one in which the concentration of total buffer is fixed. Addition of acid to the solution converts the basic form of the buffer to the acidic form. Such buffers are most efficient at the pK where 50 percent of total buffer is in the acid form and 50 percent is in the basic form. Because the total concentration of these buffers is fixed, we can calculate the contribution to renal acid secretion by titrating urine from the urinary pH back to blood pH (to simulate the pH of the fluid entering the renal tubules). As discussed above, this is referred to as *titratable acidity* and represents the contribution of titrated closed buffers to net acid excretion.

An open buffer system is one in which one of the moieties, the acid or base, can enter or leave the system. The concentration of the other component varies with pH. In biologic systems, the component which enters and leaves the system is lipid-soluble and capable of rapid transepithelial diffusion.

Such systems have greatest buffer capacity when the total buffer concentration is greatest. The contribution of these buffers to acidification is assessed by measuring the concentration of the impermeable form. One example of such a buffer system is $CO_2/H_2CO_3/HCO_3^-$. The concentration of carbonic acid is essentially fixed because of rapid dehydration to CO_2 which is highly permeable. Acid addition merely decreases the concentration of HCO_3^-.

Ammonia. Another important open buffer system is NH_3/NH_4^+. Since NH_3 permeability is high, proton secretion merely affects the concentration of NH_4^+. This process is referred to as *nonionic diffusion*. Addition of acid to the lumen causes NH_3 to be converted to NH_4^+, which lowers the concentration of NH_3 and causes NH_3 to diffuse (by nonionic transport) into the lumen. Recent studies have demonstrated that the tubular permeability to NH_3 is not as great as was previously thought so that, in some segments, transport of NH_4^+ can lead to gradients of NH_3 (ionic transport).

Ammonia is synthesized predominantly in the proximal tubule[145] and transported into the lumen of the proximal tubule by nonionic diffusion and direct transport of NH_4^+ on the Na^+/H^+ antiporter.[146-149] As tubule fluid leaves the proximal tubule and enters the loop of Henle, a number of processes lead to ammonia efflux and high medullary interstitial ammonia concentrations. First, luminal fluid is alkalinized in the thin descending limb due to water abstraction which concentrates bicarbonate.[150-152] Alkalinization creates a condition favorable for ammonia efflux by nonionic diffusion. In addition, direct NH_4^+ transport by the thick ascending limb has been demonstrated.[153] Ammonia is also capable of reentering the proximal straight tubule from the interstitium,[154] thus leading to countercurrent multiplication, where the "single effect" involves ammonia addition in the proximal tubule and active ammonia absorption in the thick ascending limb. The countercurrent system in the loop then multiplies the effect. The net result of this system is a medullary-to-cortical gradient for ammonia with medullary concentrations exceeding cortical concentrations manyfold. This allows most of the synthesized ammonia to be available for trapping in the collecting tubule and minimizes the amount of ammonia which can exit the kidney via the renal veins and be washed into the systemic circulation (where the liver is responsible for conversion of ammonia to glutamine and urea). The medullary interstitial ammonia then enters the lumen of the collecting tubule by nonionic diffusion where it is trapped as NH_4^+ in the lumen by acidification of tubule fluid.[155]

Regulation of Distal Acidification. As described above, distal acidification involves two processes: electrogenic bicarbonate absorption and bicarbonate secretion, which may be either electroneutral or electrogenic. These mechanisms are subjected to many forms of regulation which have been reviewed extensively elsewhere.[34] In this section, we discuss some of the aspects of regulation of bicarbonate absorption which are relevent to distal renal tubular acidosis.

The rate of proton secretion is very sensitive to luminal pH. This has been studied extensively in the turtle urinary bladder where the net proton secretory rate has been shown to be related linearly to luminal pH (Fig. 103-5).[156] Because leak pathways are extremely small in the distal nephron, this relationship is due to an effect of luminal pH on active transepithelial proton secretory rate.[156,157]

As discussed above, bicarbonate absorption or proton secretion is mediated by an electrogenic mechanism (proton-translocating ATPase). As such, it would be expected that the rate of this process would be affected by the transepithelial potential difference. This has been clearly demonstrated in the turtle urinary bladder where transepithelial voltage and transepithelial pH gradients (Fig. 103-5)[158] have been found to have similar effects on the rate of proton secretion. In the CCT, changes in transepithelial potential difference which occur secondary to changes in sodium transport affect the rate of proton secretion.[159] This provides a mechanism by which changes in sodium delivery and changes in the sodium avidity of the CCT, possibly related to mineralocorticoid levels, can affect acidification secondarily. Although the outer medullary collecting tubule also secretes protons by an electrogenic mechanism, this segment does not actively transport sodium, and thus transepithelial voltage would not be expected to be affected by sodium delivery. It is presently not established whether electrogenic HCO_3^- secretion occurs in the CCT. If this were the case, the HCO_3^- secretory rate could also be affected by sodium transport and secondary changes in transepithelial voltage. Lastly, it should be noted that anion gra-

Fig. 103-5 Effect of mucosal pH on rate of hydrogen ion secretion in the turtle urinary bladder. Note that hydrogen secretory rate is linearly related to mucosal pH rather than mucosal hydrogen ion concentration. (Adapted from Q. Al-Awqati: Am J Physiol 235:F77, 1978. Used by permission.)

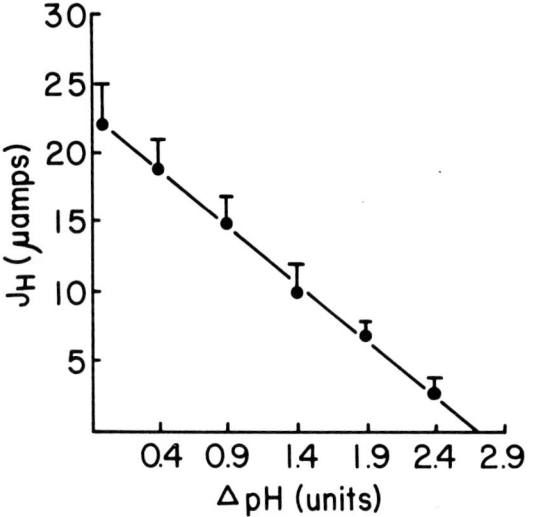

dients may affect the transepithelial potential difference in the CCT or OMCT and thus secondarily affect the rate of proton secretion.

Mineralocorticoid levels have also been demonstrated to be a potent determinant of the proton secretory rate. In the CCT, mineralocorticoids stimulate sodium absorption, which makes the transepithelial potential more negative and secondarily stimulates electrogenic proton secretion.[160,161] In addition, mineralocorticoids have been demonstrated to stimulate proton secretion directly in the turtle urinary bladder,[162,163] and cortical and outer medullary collecting tubule even in the absence of sodium.[124,126] When examined as a function of luminal pH, mineralocorticoids do not affect the limiting luminal pH gradient but rather affect the rate of H^+ secretion at high luminal pH.[162]

Finally, both hypokalemia and hyperkalemia should be regarded as important determinants of acidification. While clearance studies have suggested that potassium deficiency stimulates distal proton secretion, more direct studies in perfused segments have been conflicting.[164,165] Potassium status can affect distal nephron acidification by indirect mechanisms. First, the level of potassium is an important determinant of the aldosterone level which, as discussed above, is an important determinant of distal acidification. Even more important is the effect of potassium on ammonia synthesis in the proximal tubule.[166] Chronic potassium deficiency stimulates ammonia synthesis, while hyperkalemia suppresses ammonia synthesis. These changes in ammonia synthesis may also affect medullary interstitial ammonia concentration and buffer availability.

Pathogenesis of Distal RTA

Hypokalemic (Classic). The mechanisms involved in the pathogenesis of hypokalemic distal RTA are not yet resolved. Thus far, three lines of evidence have been used to address this question. First, the fact that these patients tend to be hypokalemic and are not hyperkalemic demonstrates that generalized CCT dysfunction or aldosterone deficiency is not causative. Some type of lesion in the medullary collecting duct, or a selective lesion of the CCT remain possibilities.

The second characteristic, often considered the cardinal feature of this entity, is an inability to maximally acidify the urine (to below pH 5.5). This characteristic has resulted in the designation of hypokalemic distal RTA as a *gradient lesion*, and has suggested to many the possibility of an abnormal leak pathway (see below).[167,168] Some investigators have also employed the response of urine pH to Na_2SO_4 infusion to classify the defect, arguing that an abnormal leak would result in an inability to maximally acidify the urine that would theoretically respond to Na_2SO_4.[169–171] However, as is discussed in detail below, a response to Na_2SO_4 infusion has many interpretations.

The last line of evidence which helps to elucidate the pathogenesis of the acidification defect in these patients is the response of the urine P_{CO_2} to HCO_3^- infusion. In patients given large infusions of sodium bicarbonate to produce a high HCO_3^- excretion rate, distal nephron hydrogen ion secretion will lead to the generation of a high CO_2 tension in the renal medulla and urine.[172] In fact, the magnitude of the urinary P_{CO_2} (often referred to as the urine-minus-blood P_{CO_2} or U-B P_{CO_2}) is quantitatively related to distal nephron hydrogen ion secretion in this setting.[121,173] Because of marked bicarbonaturia, this test offers an opportunity to examine distal nephron hydrogen ion secretion in the absence of blood-to-lumen HCO_3^- gradients.

However, it would be incorrect to assume that gradients for H^+ ions, H_2CO_3, and non-HCO_3^- buffers are absent in this setting. Because luminal carbonic anhydrase is not present in the collecting tubule, hydrogen ion secretion increases the concentration of these acid moieties in the lumen. Thus, while the luminal HCO_3^- concentrations may exceed that of the interstitium, gradients exists for backleak of H^+ ions, H_2CO_3, and acid non-HCO_3^- buffers out of the lumen. Backleak of any of these moieties or decreased rates of hydrogen ion secretion will lead to a low U-B P_{CO_2}. While this test has not been routinely performed in all patients with hypokalemic distal RTA, the U-B P_{CO_2} is generally subnormal except in amphotericin B-induced distal RTA.[172–174]

With this background, we now explore a number of possible mechanisms for defective distal tubular acidification. We orient this discussion along the lines of Fig. 103-6. In this figure, the line labeled *normal* represents the usual relationship between proton secretory rate and luminal pH in the collecting tubule, which is presumed to be similar to the relationship in the turtle bladder as displayed in Fig. 103-5. When luminal fluid is alkaline, proton secretion is rapid and leads to luminal acidification. The limiting luminal pH represents that pH at which net proton secretion ceases. In the collecting tubule, leak pathways are normally very small, so the limiting pH represents the pH at which active transepithelial proton secretion ceases.[158]

In Fig. 103-6 the line labeled *leak* represents an approximation of the expected relationship when an abnormal leak pathway is inserted into the collecting tubule. In the absence of a transepithelial pH gradient, the effect of such a leak would be minimal or absent. However, as luminal pH decreases, the leak would provide a pathway for base addition and acid efflux from the lumen which would markedly decrease net proton secretion. Thus, a leak would appear as a "gradient" defect, in which abnormal acidification would be most obvious when the filtered load of HCO_3^- is low and the need to excrete a highly acid urine is great.

The exact acid-base moiety which would leak is not known but could vary with the type of leak. Possibilities include H^+ or OH^- ions, H_2CO_3, HCO_3^-, or non-HCO_3^- buffers. Based on Fick's law of diffusion, the rate of diffusion is equal to the permeability times the concentration gradient. The HCO_3^- and non-HCO_3^- buffers, therefore, would be likely moieties to back-diffuse because of the large concentration gradients (millimolar range). Protons, because of high mobility in aqueous solutions, may leak back when the H^+ concentration is sufficiently high (i.e., low luminal pH). Carbonic acid would be unlikely to back-diffuse through an aqueous pore because of the low concentration in lumen and blood (micromolar). However, if the leak pathway were through lipids, possibly due to an alteration in membrane composition, H_2CO_3 diffusion could be important.

Two additional theoretical mechanisms exist by which a gradient distal renal tubular acidosis could occur. First, in the absence of an abnormal leak pathway, an inability to maximally acidify luminal fluid could represent an energetic problem such as an altered ATP or ADP ratio in the cell or an altered stoichiometry of a transporter (i.e., H^+-ATPase). Such defects would be expected to present as gradient lesions and could behave like an abnormal leak (Fig. 103-6) but have not yet been described. A second possible mechanism of a gra-

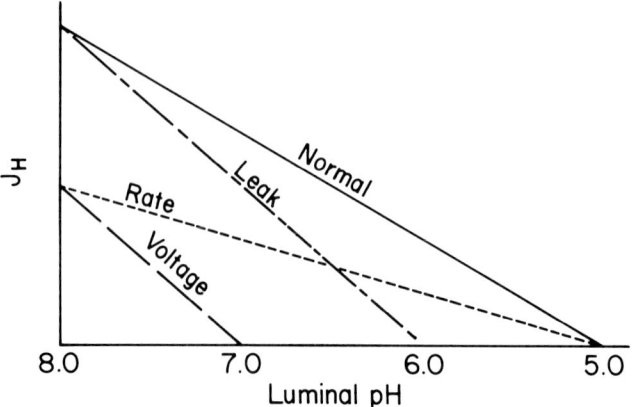

Fig. 103-6 Theoretical mechanisms for defect in hydrogen ion secretion. Rate of hydrogen ion secretion is expressed as a function of luminal pH. See text for explanation.

dient defect is an enhanced rate of active HCO_3^- secretion. This would lead to an inability to maximally acidify the urine along with lower rates of net hydrogen ion secretion. Such a lesion, however, has not yet been reported. An enhanced rate of HCO_3^- secretion would be associated with a normal U-B P_{CO_2}, which, when found, has always been associated with insertion of aqueous channels and increased HCO_3^- leak (see below). We therefore have not considered this possible mechanism in Fig. 103-6.

An alternative to a gradient lesion is denoted in Fig. 103-6 by the line labeled *rate*. In the absence of pH gradients, the rate of proton secretion is markedly depressed. However, the epithelium still retains the ability to achieve normal pH gradients and thus achieve maximal acidification. It is important to note that in the presence of a marked rate defect, achievement of maximal pH gradients may require an extremely long contact time, such that maximal acidification is never achieved. Based on the cell model for HCO_3^- absorption, a rate defect could involve an abnormality in the H^+-ATPase, the Cl^-/HCO_3^- exchanger, or the chloride conductance.

At present, the best experimental model representative of a "leak" defect is that induced by amphotericin B. Amphotericin B, when inserted into lipid membranes, forms an aqueous channel.[175,176] Animals treated with amphotericin B are unable to maximally acidify their urine under control conditions.[176–178] However, in response to Na_2SO_4 infusion, urinary pH is maximally acidified.[173,178] During HCO_3^- loading in amphotericin-treated rats, the U-B P_{CO_2} is normal.[173,177] In addition, DuBose and Caflisch[173] found a normal disequilibrium pH in the papillary collecting duct (also indicating a normal H^+ secretion rate) in association with a papillary P_{CO_2} elevated to levels similar to those achieved in control animals. These studies demonstrated that the hydrogen ion secretory rate is normal in this form of distal renal tubular acidosis and that the back-diffusing species is most likely HCO_3^-. As discussed above, back-diffusion of H^+ ions, H_2CO_3, or non-HCO_3^- buffers, would be expected to lower the U-B P_{CO_2}. Other toxins such as toluene have been suggested to produce a similar lesion, but this model has not been studied extensively.[179]

Unlike the situation with amphotericin, the pathophysiology of the acidification defect in classic hypokalemic distal RTA is unresolved. Under a number of different circumstances, including acute acid infusion, patients with classic hypokalemic distal renal tubular acidosis are unable to acidify their urine below pH 5.5.[2,3,12,167,168,170] In most of the reported studies, urine pH remains alkaline after Na_2SO_4 infusion.[180] In addition, patients with classic hypokalemic distal renal tubular acidosis can enhance net acid excretion in a normal manner in response to buffer infusion. Most of these findings are consistent with a gradient defect; however, patients with classic hypokalemic distal renal tubular acidosis have been found to have a low U-B P_{CO_2}.[3,172,180,181] This finding is not consistent with an enhanced HCO_3^- leak, as such a defect would not affect net proton secretion in the absence of a gradient (high tubular fluid HCO_3^- concentration). Rather, these data are consistent with a rate defect. The inability to acidify the urine below pH 5.5 could be due to the fact that rates of proton secretion are extremely limited in the most distal segments that can normally secrete protons against large gradients and establish a low urine pH. A normal response of net acid secretion to buffer infusion may be due to the fact that the diseased segments contribute little quantitatively to whole kidney hydrogen ion secretion in the absence of steep gradients.

An alternative explanation for the defect in classic hypokalemic distal renal tubular acidosis is an enhanced leakiness of the epithelium to H^+ ions, H_2CO_3, or non-HCO_3^- buffer. As discussed above, such a leak would explain the inability of these patients to create maximal pH gradients and acidify their urine below pH 5.5. In addition, this mechanism would explain the normal response in net acid excretion to a buffer infusion.[167] Lastly, as discussed above, such a leak would also explain the low U-B P_{CO_2}. Thus, the only difference between the amphotericin and classic lesion may be the moiety which leaks back across the tubule.

Patients with impaired collecting duct hydrogen ion secretion and classic distal RTA also have low excretory rates of ammonium when the degree of systemic acidosis is taken into account.[3–5] Low ammonium excretion in classic hypokalemic distal RTA could occur because of the failure to trap ammonia as ammonium in the medullary collecting duct as a result of a higher than normal tubular fluid pH in this segment.[150] In addition, since ammonium is normally trapped in the medulla by mechanisms involving the countercurrent system,[181] patients with classic distal RTA, who commonly have an associated urinary concentrating defect, may have normal rates of renal cortical ammoniagenesis but an inability to trap ammonium in the medullary countercurrent system.[3] This defect would reduce the normally favorable ammonia gradient from loop of Henle to medullary interstitium and secondarily medullary interstitium to outer medullary collecting duct.[181] Whether this type of defect contributes to the reduction in ammonium excretion in classic hypokalemic distal RTA requires further investigation. It seems reasonable, however, that an abnormality in medullary ammonium accumulation could occur in various forms of tubulointerstitial diseases involving the medulla.

In summary, hypokalemic distal RTA is characterized by an inability to acidify the urine below pH 5.5. In some patients, this is attributable to an enhanced backleak of HCO_3^- (amphotericin lesion). However, in most patients, the defect cannot be attributed to such a leak. In these patients a decreased rate of distal proton secretion or enhanced backleak of hydrogen ions, carbonic acid, or non-HCO_3^- buffer are the likely mechanisms. It should be emphasized that only a few reports exist where patients have been thoroughly evaluated with respect to minimal urine pH, response to Na_2SO_4, and response of urinary P_{CO_2} to HCO_3^- infusion. Delineation of the pathogenesis of classic hypokalemic distal RTA will require the examination of many more patients, the development of more precise and definitive clinical tests, and, most importantly, clinically relevant animal models.

Hyperkalemia in Association with an Acidification Defect: Generalized Distal Nephron Dysfunction. An additional mechanism by which the proton secretory rate can be affected is an altered transepithelial potential difference in the collecting tubule, which is also referred to as *short circuit* distal RTA.[182] The expected effect of such a defect on proton secretory rate is denoted by the line in Fig. 103-6 labeled *voltage*. As demonstrated in this figure, the effects of transepithelial potential difference and luminal pH are additive. Thus, an altered transepithelial potential will shift the line, thereby affecting both the limiting pH gradient and the rate of proton secretion at any given luminal pH. Any process inhibiting sodium transport in the cortical collecting tubule would be expected to cause such a defect. Moreover, in this setting, K^+ secretion in the CCT should also be decreased.

The best model of such a transport defect is that observed after amiloride administration. This agent inhibits sodium transport in the cortical collecting tubule and in the turtle urinary bladder, which decreases the negative transepithelial voltage in the lumen and secondarily inhibits proton secretion.[183] The ability to maximally acidify the urine is clearly impaired. Moreover, sodium sulfate infusion fails to restore the ability to lower urine pH during an acid challenge.[170,173,184] In addition, with buffer infusion to prevent pH gradients, H^+ secretory capacity remains low.[184] Recent micropuncture studies employing microelectrodes to measure disequilibrium pH as an index of proton secretion and P_{CO_2} in the papillary collecting duct in rats with the amiloride defect revealed that this lesion is associated with a reduction in proton secretion and, as anticipated, a reduction in P_{CO_2}.[173] Potassium secretion is also decreased secondarily to decreased voltage and may result in hyperkalemia.[173,185]

In contrast to the failure of the amiloride-induced acidification defect to respond to sodium sulfate infusion, the type of distal RTA produced by lithium administration is characterized by the development of a maximally acid urine pH during sodium sulfate infusion after an acid challenge.[170,173,186] The failure of urinary P_{CO_2} to increase above blood levels during HCO_3^- infusion in animals with lithium-induced distal RTA suggested that proton secretion was impaired.[187] Moreover, studies by Arruda et al. in the turtle urinary bladder under open-circuited conditions revealed that lithium impaired proton secretion by virtue of a detrimental effect on the electrical gradient favoring H^+ secretion.[188] As was noted with the amiloride defect, disequilibrium pH and papillary P_{CO_2} were reduced, indicating clearly impaired proton secretion in the lithium defect.[173]

It appears that the favorable response to sodium sulfate infusion in experimental animals with lithium-induced distal RTA can be explained by enhanced delivery of sodium and poorly reabsorbed anion to this segment, which thereby restores the lumen-negative potential difference.[171,180] Thus, the lithium defect is a "voltage-type" of gradient lesion which probably occurs in the cortical collecting tubule. Patients with this type of lesion have incomplete distal RTA, so metabolic acidosis is rarely seen.[189] Furthermore, hyperkalemia is not observed in patients undergoing lithium therapy or in lithium-induced complete distal RTA in the rat.[173] Although the explanation for this latter observation is not clear, there may be an effect of lithium on K^+ reabsorption in more proximal segments. Lithium therapy in humans, however, is associated with only a very mild distal acidification defect, as well as the more generally appreciated defect in urinary concentration.[189]

An excellent experimental model of voltage-mediated distal RTA associated with hyperkalemia is that induced by unilateral ureteral obstruction. Experimental findings in the postobstructed kidney are similar in all respects to amiloride.[171,173,180] Finally, pseudohypoaldosteronism (types I and II) may represent an additional clinical example of a voltage defect and is discussed below.

Since the cortical collecting tubule is responsible for sodium reabsorption by an aldosterone-dependent process, which enhances the lumen negative transepithelial potential difference and thereby favors the secretion of potassium and hydrogen, it is not surprising that aldosterone deficiency would cause hyperkalemia[190] and metabolic acidosis.[191] Moreover, aldosterone stimulates potassium secretion in the distal tubule and whole kidney, and hydrogen ion secretion in both the turtle urinary bladder[162] and medullary collecting tubule, independent of sodium transport.[126,134] Therefore, a decrease in the relative amount of aldosterone, or alternatively, a decrease in responsiveness of the collecting tubule to aldosterone, could result in a reduction in distal sodium reabsorption which would be expected to impair both potassium and hydrogen ion secretion.

Based on the direct and indirect (sodium transport-dependent voltage changes) effects, two mechanisms exist for defective collecting tubule proton secretion in aldosterone deficiency. When voltage changes are corrected for, low aldosterone levels cause a "rate" defect,[162] as displayed in Fig. 103-6. This would be associated with the ability to achieve a normal minimal urine pH, but low rates of proton secretion would be observed at higher luminal pH. As discussed above, a voltage-dependent lesion would be associated with an inability to achieve a normal minimal urine pH (Fig. 103-6). Such a defect is observed after administration of lithium or amiloride as well as after unilateral ureteral obstruction in the rat.[173,180] Whole kidney studies have revealed that during conditions associated with low buffer excretion (i.e., decreased ammonium excretion), a normal minimal urine pH can be achieved.[184] Such findings suggest that the rate defect is quantitatively more important than the "voltage" defect in hypoaldosteronism and implies that the direct effect of aldosterone on H^+ secretion is quantitatively more important than indirect effects mediated through voltage changes.

Additional evidence in this regard can be deduced from studies which have examined the effect of spironolactone on acidification. In the turtle urinary bladder, spironolactone blocks aldosterone-stimulated sodium absorption but serves as an agonist for the direct effect of mineralocorticoid on proton secretion.[192] The inability of spironolactone to cause a metabolic acidosis in the intact animal supports the relative unimportance of voltage-mediated changes in mineralocorticoid deficiency-induced distal RTA.[193]

In addition to impaired hydrogen and potassium secretion as a result of decreased activity of aldosterone, the development of hyperkalemia appears to have independent effects on net acid excretion.[194] Hyperkalemia per se inhibits renal ammoniagenesis and is associated with a decrease in excretion of ammonium which contributes to the development of metabolic acidosis.[190,195] The importance of hyperkalemia in the development of metabolic acidosis due to mineralocorticoid deficiency has been demonstrated further by correction of hyperkalemia with cation exchange resins. This correction was associated with a significant increase in net acid excretion (ammonium excretion).[194,198]

The integrity of urinary acidification capacity was investigated extensively in dogs with selective aldosterone deficiency.[191] In the absence of mineralocorticoid replacement, but in the presence of glucocorticoid replacement, net acid excretion falls, and a hyperkalemic hyperchloremic metabolic acidosis ensues.[191] The reduction in net acid excretion can be accounted for by reduction in urinary excretion of ammonium, which appears to be a direct result of a reduction in renal ammoniagenesis.[191] The hyperkalemia appears to be largely responsible for the reduction in ammonia production, since the ammonium excretion rate does not decrease if hyperkalemia is prevented during cessation of mineralocorticoid administration. Moreover, ammonium excretion varied inversely with plasma potassium. Such findings have been documented in mineralocorticoid-deficient animals and humans.[196-197] In adrenalectomized human subjects net acid excretion and plasma total CO_2 decreased when mineralocorticoid was selectively discontinued but increased when mineralocorticoid was reinitiated.[197] The change in plasma total CO_2 correlated directly with changes in net acid excretion, as expected, and inversely with corresponding changes in potassium balance.

Taken together these findings provide evidence that renal acidification is under the influence of mineralocorticoid, and that mineralocorticoid deficiency can cause acidosis and impairment of renal acidification even in the absence of renal disease or glucocorticoid deficiency. The potential for systemic metabolic acidosis in such a setting could be amplified greatly, however, in individuals with renal insufficiency and a decrease in functioning renal mass.

The role of aldosterone deficiency in the pathogenesis of metabolic acidosis in patients with renal insufficiency has been investigated further by the administration of fludrocortisone in the setting of hyperkalemia and hyporeninemic hypoaldosteronism.[197,198] With administration of fludrocortisone in physiological replacement amounts, net acid excretion increased and the hyperkalemia and systemic acidosis improved.[198] Initially, urine pH decreased as a result of mineralocorticoid-mediated enhanced hydrogen ion secretion, but as urinary NH_4^+ excretion increased over several days, urine pH increased as a result of the increase in urinary buffer. Thus, in patients with selective hypoaldosteronism and chronic renal insufficiency, mineralocorticoid administration enhances renal acid excretion directly by increasing renal hydrogen ion secretion, and indirectly by correcting hyperkalemia, which allows ammoniagenesis to increase.

Mineralocorticoid resistance also causes hyperkalemic-hyperchloremic metabolic acidosis in both children and adults. Pseudohypoaldosteronism is more common in children, and two types have been recognized. Classic pseudohypoaldosteronism of infancy (type I pseudohypoaldosteronism) may be familial and is characterized by renal salt wasting and a tendency toward hypotension.[199] Chronic hyperkalemia and metabolic acidosis may occur in the absence of diffuse renal parenchymal disease or a reduction in glomerular filtration rate.[200] Dehydration and hyponatremia due to renal salt wasting and hyperkalemia due to renal potassium retention are typically observed in association with distal renal tubular acidosis.[199,200] Plasma renin activity and plasma aldosterone concentrations are elevated, but deoxycorticosterone and corticosterone concentrations are within the normal range.[2,12,200] Supplemental salt administration can reverse the hyponatremia and hyperkalemia and allow improved growth.[200] After infancy the disorder typically abates permitting reduction or discontinuation of sodium chloride supplements. However, it may recur during periods of salt restriction. This disorder has been attributed to an abnormality in the aldosterone receptor in the cortical collecting tubule.[200] In one patient with pseudohypoaldosteronism I, binding of aldosterone was normal in mucosal cells obtained from the sigmoid colon.[201] In another patient with pseudohypoaldosteronism, however, mineralocorticoid stimulation of sodium and potassium transport was impaired in multiple target organs including salivary glands, sweat glands, the colon, and the kidney.[202] Such a defect could be explained by a deficiency of Na^+/K^+-ATPase. Renal Na^+/K^+-ATPase activity was undetectable in either the proximal or distal nephron segments in two studies.[203] This finding does not prove that a deficiency in renal Na^+/K^+-ATPase is the primary defect, since Na^+/K^+-ATPase activity can decrease under circumstances associated with a reduction in net renal sodium reabsorption.[204]

In summary, pseudohypoaldosteronism type I could be the result of a decrease in aldosterone receptor activity or occur as the result of a decrease in Na^+/K^+-ATPase activity. Additional possibilities include a decrease in apical membrane Na^+ transport or a generalized metabolic defect of the cortical collecting tubule. These latter defects would resemble the amiloride lesion.

Pseudohypoaldosteronism type II occurs in older children or adults and is most easily distinguished from type I pseudohypoaldosteronism by the presence of hypertension, volume expansion, and low to normal plasma aldosterone levels.[205–209] In contrast to patients with type I pseudohypoaldosteronism, patients with type II pseudohypoaldosteronism respond to diuretics and salt restriction.[206,210] Recent studies suggest that the disorder represents a unique abnormality in the distal nephron in which a marked avidity for sodium chloride results in volume overexpansion, suppressed renin activity, and reduced potassium secretion.[209] The primary defect appears to be an increase in the reabsorptive avidity for chloride relative to sodium in the distal nephron, which thereby reduces the sodium and mineralocorticoid-dependent voltage driving force for potassium and hydrogen secretion (less lumen negative).[209] This defect, which has been designated a *distal chloride shunt*, could occur as a result of an increase in the permeability of the distal nephron to chloride. During infusion of sodium bicarbonate or sodium sulfate, potassium secretion appears to respond to mineralocorticoid hormone by increasing into the normal range. The combination of shunting of the transepithelial potential difference and volume-mediated secondary hypoaldosteronism severely impairs distal potassium secretion, resulting in hyperkalemia. Hyperkalemia, in turn, is believed to decrease ammonia production and hydrogen ion secretion resulting in metabolic acidosis.[195] Such patients respond to either salt restriction, which reduces salt delivery to the distal tubule, or to thiazide diuretics, which reduce absorption in the distal tubule. Mineralocorticoid replacement is not required.[206,209,210] Such a series of events has been confirmed by Schambelan and associates.[209]

Hyporeninemic hypoaldosteronism has been recognized with increasing frequency in adults with chronic renal insufficiency as a cause of hyperkalemic, hyperchloremic metabolic acidosis. Patients with this disorder almost always exhibit mild to moderate renal insufficiency and acidosis in association with chronic hyperkalemia in the range of 5.5 to 6.5 meq/liter.[190,211,212] It is important to recognize that both the metabolic acidosis and the hyperkalemia are far out of proportion to the level of reduction in glomerular filtration rate. The most frequently associated renal diseases are diabetic nephropathy and tubulointerstitial disease.[212–214] For 80 to 85 percent of such patients there is a reduction in plasma renin activity that cannot be stimulated by the usual physiological maneuvers.[215] Aldosterone secretion, while low, can be increased by administration of angiotensin II or ACTH.[215] The degree of salt wasting associated with hyporeninemic hypoaldosteronism is generally not severe and is no worse than that seen in patients with chronic renal insufficiency at comparable levels of GFR.[216] Since approximately 30 percent of patients with hyporeninemic hypoaldosteronism are hypertensive,[12] the finding of a low plasma renin in such patients suggests a volume-dependent form of hypertension with physiological suppression of renin elaboration.[217] In general, patients with more advanced renal insufficiency as a result of glomerular disease rather than tubulointerstitial disease (e.g., diabetic nephropathy) are more commonly volume expanded.[12,217] Therefore, because either mild salt wasting or salt retention may occur in this disorder, the precise etiology of the decrease in plasma renin has not been established firmly. Primary destruction of cells of the juxtaglomerular (J-G) apparatus may be observed in diabetic nephropathy.[218,219] Deficient release of renin also occurs in diabetic autonomic insufficiency or in prostaglandin deficiency.[220,221] A defect in conversion of renin precursor to renin was suggested in some patients with diabetes as well.[222]

The pathogenesis of the metabolic acidosis in hyporeninemic hypoaldosteronism is complex. Proximal HCO_3^- reabsorption was shown to be mildly abnormal, and the fractional excretion of HCO_3^- ranges from 3 to 10 percent at a normal plasma HCO_3^- concentration.[190,223] Whether this degree of bicarbonate wasting is a result of a defect in proximal bicarbonate reabsorption is not established. The ability to acidify the urine during metabolic acidosis is intact, but there is typically a reduced rate of net acid excretion and ammonium excretion.[190] As mentioned above, impaired ammonium excretion is the combined result of impaired ammoniagenesis, a reduction in nephron mass, reduced proton secretion, and hyperkalemia.[212]

Based on the above discussion, acidification defects in the distal nephron can be grouped into three general categories: (1) an abnormal leak pathway resulting in back-diffusion of bicarbonate and hydrogen ion (e.g., amphotericin B defect), (2) a voltage-dependent defect associated with intact proton secretion but suppressed net acidification due to an abnormal transepithelial voltage (e.g., amiloride and pseudohypoaldosteronism type II), and (3) a rate or pump defect with decreased rates of transepithelial proton secretion (e.g., selective hypoaldosteronism). Classic hypokalemic distal RTA (excluding the amphotericin-induced gradient defect) appears to be a rate defect in transepithelial proton secretion based on the observed reduction in the U-B P_{CO_2} difference. The inability to acidify the urine maximally is most likely due to a severe rate defect in the terminal portion of the collecting duct, the only segment of the nephron shown to be capable of lowering urine pH below 5.5. However, as mentioned previously a leak of H^+, H_2CO_3, or non-HCO_3^- buffer cannot be excluded.

Diagnosis of Type of Defect: Provocative Tests of Urinary Acidification

Minimal Urine pH and Maximal Acid Excretion. Clinically, the measurement of urine pH is the initial step to assess the ability to acidify the urine. In the presence of systemic metabolic acidosis the urine pH should be below 5.5 and is often below 5.0.[3,12,170,180] A urine pH consistently above 5.5 in the presence of systemic metabolic acidosis suggests an acidification defect involving the more distal portions of the nephron. Several points regarding the urine pH must be stressed, however. A urine pH below 5.5 is also found in patients with proximal renal tubular acidosis when systemic acidosis is present and the filtered load of bicarbonate is low (i.e., below 15 meq/liter).[224] The explanation for this finding is that when the distal nephron is not impaired, reduced filtered loads of HCO_3^- can be reabsorbed in more distal segments so that HCO_3^- does not appear in the urine.[225] A urine pH below 5.5 is also characteristic of patients with selective aldosterone deficiency.[180] In this disorder low urinary buffer excretion allows the urine pH to reach a limiting pH gradient more rapidly. These findings emphasize that while urine pH is the most commonly used test of renal acidification, it does not measure total hydrogen ion excretion. Patients with chronic metabolic acidosis and normal renal function frequently have a higher urine pH as a result of the excretion of large quantities of ammonia.[3] A low urine pH, therefore, does not ensure that the proton secretory mechanism is either intact or appropriate for the level of acidosis, and a high urine pH does not prove an abnormality in acidification. The urine pH should be evaluated in conjunction with an estimate, or precise knowledge, of urine ammonium excretion.[3]

The urine pH should always be measured on freshly voided urine collected under mineral oil. In patients in which systemic acidosis is present, there is no need to perform an ammonium chloride loading test. If systemic acidosis is not present at the time of study, ammonium chloride can be given as a single dose orally (0.1 g/kg body weight) followed by hourly determinations of urine pH for 2 to 8 h.[226,227] Total CO_2 concentration in plasma should decrease by at least 3 to 5 meq/liter, and the urine pH should fall below 5.5. Many investigators prefer to administer ammonium chloride in the same dose daily over a 3- to 5-day period. In these studies, urine pH and urinary ammonium excretion are measured.[228] The latter value should be expected to increase three- to fivefold by the third day of ammonium chloride-induced metabolic acidosis. In patients with liver disease, an alternative acidifying agent is calcium chloride, which can be administered in a dose of 2 meq/kg body weight.[180,229] Arginine monohydrochloride has also been used as an acidifying agent in previous studies, but use of this agent is discouraged because proximal HCO_3^- wastage may be induced.[230]

Fractional Excretion of HCO_3^-. The fractional excretion of HCO_3^- during HCO_3^- loading, or at a time when the plasma HCO_3^- is normal, is a convenient means of distinguishing proximal renal tubular acidosis from other forms. In patients with distal RTA, HCO_3^- reabsorption, while incomplete at low plasma levels of HCO_3^-, increases with increasing plasma HCO_3^- concentrations. The fractional excretion of HCO_3^- $FE_{HCO_3^-}$%, calculated as the $(U/P_{[HCO_3^-]} \div U/P_{Cr} \times 100)$, is persistently elevated (> 10 to 15 percent) in patients with proximal RTA when plasma HCO_3^- is near the normal range

(>20 meq/liter).[12,225] Patients with hyperkalemic distal RTA may have an $FE_{HCO_3^-}$ between 5 and 10 percent. In contrast, in classic hypokalemic distal RTA, the fractional excretion of HCO_3^- is usually less than 5 percent except in children, where values may exceed 5 to 10 percent.[225,231]

HCO_3^- Administration and U-B P_{CO_2}. The increment in urinary P_{CO_2} during HCO_3^- infusion or oral HCO_3^- administration in amounts which result in excretion of a highly alkaline urine is a reliable and sensitive index of proton secretion by the terminal nephron.[121,172,173,232,233] After $NaHCO_3^-$ loading, the urine P_{CO_2} may reach a value at least 25 mmHg higher than systemic levels. The test is performed by infusing a solution containing 500 meq/liter $NaHCO_3$ at a rate of 3 ml/min into a peripheral vein.[228] Timed urine collections of approximately 15 to 30 min duration are obtained by having the patient void spontaneously while in the upright position. The test may be terminated after completion of at least three clearance periods when the urine pH is consistently 7.5 or greater. A steady state is usually achieved within 180 to 260 min after initiation of the bicarbonate infusion. Urine should always be collected under mineral oil for measurement of urine pH and P_{CO_2}. Patients with decreased rates of distal hydrogen secretion are expected to display subnormal values during HCO_3^- loading, since the U-B P_{CO_2} gradient will be lower than 10 to 15 mmHg.[172,234] In contrast, patients with a gradient or backleak defect of the type exemplified by the amphotericin B lesion are expected to retain the ability to generate high urinary CO_2 tensions during HCO_3^- loading.[173,177]

Urine Sodium Concentration. Since inadequate distal sodium delivery has been recognized as a feature of extracellular fluid volume depletion, such as that which can result from protracted diarrhea, and since Schwartz and associates[169] have suggested that the response to ammonium chloride loading is determined in part by sodium avidity and sodium delivery to the collecting tubule, the measurement of the urinary sodium concentration has been suggested to be a necessary part of the evaluation of urinary acidification in response to oral ammonium chloride. Battle and associates recently described a patient with a urinary pH persistently above 5.5 despite severe acidemia in whom distal sodium delivery, when enhanced by either furosemide or sodium sulfate, resulted in an appropriate decrease in urinary pH below 5.5.[235] The analysis of the laboratory findings in this patient with laxative abuse and chronic volume depletion stresses the importance of knowledge of distal nephron sodium delivery when evaluating urinary acidification, especially in patients in whom surreptitious laxative abuse is a possibility.

Sodium Sulfate Infusion. If normal subjects are reabsorbing sodium avidly, sodium sulfate administration will result in maximal acidification as assessed by a significant decrease in urine pH.[169] This evaluation requires that the patient be placed on a low salt diet to enhance distal sodium avidity. The delivery of sodium to the distal nephron is then promoted by administration of sodium accompanied by a poorly reabsorbable anion such as sulfate. This may be accomplished by infusion of 500 ml of 4% Na_2SO_4 over 1 h. One milligram of 9α-fludrocortisone administered orally 12 h preceding Na_2SO_4 infusion is usually required to ensure a sodium-avid state.[180] The typical response to sodium sulfate infusion in control subjects is a decrease in urine pH below 5.5 with or without systemic acidosis.[169,170] Urine collections should be continued for 2 to 3 h after discontinuing the sodium sulfate infusion because of a delayed response in some patients with distal RTA and in chronic renal insufficiency.[170,180] To assess the function of the collecting tubule, some investigators include assessment of distal potassium secretory capacity.[236] The failure to increase potassium excretion in response to sodium sulfate suggests the presence of decreased potassium secretory capacity in the cortical collecting tubule.[174] However, the mere presence of hyperkalemia in such patients suggests impaired K^+ secretory capacity, and it is not clear that the response to sodium sulfate provides additional useful information.

The acidification response to sodium sulfate infusion provides little help in elucidating the mechanisms involved in the acidification defect.[174] A stimulation of proton secretion in response to Na_2SO_4 would be expected in: (1) the gradient defect (e.g., amphotericin B lesion), (2) a sodium-responsive voltage lesion (e.g., lithium-induced RTA), or (3) a rate lesion with decreased pump activity in which the remaining activity is voltage-sensitive (e.g., hypoaldosteronism). In addition, if the defect does not involve the cortical collecting tubule at all (i.e., confined to deeper medullary structures), the normal transport mechanisms in the CCT could still respond to the associated increase in sodium delivery. The only conditions in which one would not anticipate a response to Na_2SO_4 are those in which either Na_2SO_4 cannot alter voltage (e.g., amiloride defect, medullary collecting duct lesion) or those in which acidification mechanisms in the CCT have been totally eliminated.

Furosemide Administration. Since administration of sodium sulfate is often cumbersome in the clinical setting, Batlle and associates have suggested that the response of urine pH and potassium excretion to a single oral dose of 80 mg of furosemide can be employed to characterize the defect in collecting tubule acidification in distal renal tubular acidosis.[174] In this test, furosemide is administered orally after completing baseline urine collections. Urine is then obtained at hourly intervals (or when convenient for the subject) and pH and potassium concentration are determined. In all instances in which furosemide has been studied concomitant with administration of sodium sulfate, the two tests have been shown to give the same result.[174] Batlle has reported that furosemide, when administered to normal subjects, stimulates voltage-dependent hydrogen and potassium secretion in the collecting tubule.[174] Based on such findings, he has suggested that furosemide can be used to disclose the segmental localization of the defect underlying distal RTA. Support for this hypothesis was obtained by observing that the fall in urine pH induced by furosemide was blocked by simultaneous administration of amiloride. In patients with classic hypokalemic distal renal tubular acidosis, furosemide did not produce a decrease in urine pH, but potassium excretion increased normally. In hyperkalemic distal renal tubular acidosis, furosemide failed to lower pH below 5.5 and was associated with a blunted increase in potassium excretion.[174] However, the same reservations regarding interpretation of such data as outlined for Na_2SO_4 infusion pertain to the furosemide effect on acidification.

Neutral Sodium Phosphate Infusion. Neutral sodium phosphate (0.6 mmol/kg of body weight diluted in 180 ml of normal saline) is infused at a rate of 1 ml/min for 3 h.[236] Under these conditions phosphate infusion usually results in a two-

to threefold increase in plasma phosphate concentration, and urinary phosphate concentration increases above 20 mM. When these conditions are satisfied, the U-B P_{CO_2} is measured and is consistently greater than 25 mmHg in both normal individuals and patients with renal insufficiency.[170,189,236] Sodium phosphate infusion could stimulate H^+ secretion by enhancing distal sodium delivery with nonreabsorbable anion or by providing more buffer. Kurtzman and Batlle found that the response to neutral phosphate infusion is identical to that obtained with sodium sulfate infusion.[180,236] However, the complexities in interpretation of the effects of nonreabsorbable anion infusion are complicated by additional possible mechanisms of action which limit the value of such tests clinically.

Urinary Anion Gap and Ammonium Excretion. Halperin and associates have recently proposed a means of estimating urinary ammonium excretion by consideration of the urinary anion gap.[3–5] This test relies on the assumption that a hyperchloremic metabolic acidosis due to extrarenal bicarbonate loss, such as with diarrhea, should be associated with high urinary ammonium concentrations, while a renal acidification defect is associated with a low urinary ammonium concentration.[5] Urinary ammonium levels can be estimated by calculating the negative urine anion gap (UAG): [UAG = (Na_u^+ + K_u^+) − Cl_u^+].[5] Therefore, when the urine chloride concentration is greater than the sum of sodium and potassium, the ammonium level is usually increased adequately, suggesting an extrarenal cause for the acidosis. Conversely, if the sum of urine Na + K exceeds the Cl concentration, the urine ammonium would be predicted to be low, a condition compatible with distal renal tubular acidosis.[5]

An Integrated Approach to the Diagnosis of RTA. Whether precise localization of the defect in distal renal tubule acidosis can be discerned by the application of such provocative tests of urinary acidification in any given patient with distal renal tubular acidosis has not yet been tested rigorously. Additional evaluation of these maneuvers in experimental models of distal renal tubular acidosis is necessary before wide application can be extended routinely to the clinical setting. As a result of the inherent limitations of these tests and the difficulties encountered when employing these maneuvers in the usual clinical setting, a number of investigators have suggested simplified approaches to the evaluation of patients with a suspected defect in acidification.[2,3,228,236] Such an approach is outlined in Table 103-5. Patients with a hyperchloremic metabolic acidosis which cannot be ascribed to bicarbonate loss from the gastrointestinal tract should be suspected of having a defect in urinary acidification. Patients with either classic distal renal tubular acidosis or proximal RTA usually have hypokalemia, while patients with generalized dysfunction of the distal nephron due to selective aldosterone deficiency or aldosterone resistance usually have hyperkalemia. Therefore, the serum potassium may provide a clue to the type of defect. If the urine pH with either spontaneous metabolic acidosis or after an ammonium chloride challenge is less than 5.0, the defect may either reside in the proximal tubule or may occur as a result of a generalized defect in distal nephron function with hyperkalemia associated with reduced ammoniagenesis. In proximal RTA the urine ammonium excretion will be high, and the urine anion gap will therefore be normal if the urine is acid.

Table 103-5 Diagnostic Studies in RTA

Finding	Type of RTA		
	Proximal (II)	Classic distal (I)	Generalized distal dysfunction (IV)
Plasma [K$^+$]	Low	Low	High
Urine pH with acidosis	<5.5	>5.5	<5.5
Urine anion gap	Normal	Low	Low
Fanconi lesion	Present	Absent	Absent
Fractional bicarbonate excretion	>10–15%	<5%	<5–10%
U-B P$_{CO_2}$	Normal	Low	Low
Response to therapy	Least readily	Readily	Less readily
Associated features	Fanconi syndrome	Nephrocalcinosis/ hyperglobuliemia	Renal insufficiency

A urine pH above 5.5 usually denotes a defect in distal nephron hydrogen ion secretion which can be confirmed by evaluating the U-B P$_{CO_2}$ following bicarbonate loading. The U-B P$_{CO_2}$ following bicarbonate loading is typically low in hypokalemic distal renal tubular acidosis of the secretory or rate type but not of the gradient type. Generalized distal nephron dysfunction is associated with a low U-B P$_{CO_2}$, while in proximal RTA the U-B P$_{CO_2}$ will be normal. Hyperkalemia in association with a low U-B P$_{CO_2}$ suggests simultaneous defects in hydrogen ion secretion and potassium secretion. This combination may be due to a failure to generate a normal transepithelial potential gradient in the collecting tubule due to a voltage defect, a defect in permeability to chloride, or low mineralocorticoid levels.

Observing the difficulty with which systemic metabolic acidosis is corrected may also provide more information about the diagnosis of the type of renal tubular acidosis. Proximal RTA is particularly difficult to correct because bicarbonate administration aggravates bicarbonate wasting and also increases urinary potassium excretion. Classic hypokalemic distal renal tubular acidosis typically responds readily to bicarbonate administration. Selective aldosterone deficiency generally responds more readily than proximal RTA but less readily than classic distal RTA. Finally, the accompanying features of the disorder will often allow the clinician to categorize the general type of lesion. For example, Fanconi syndrome is seen in association with proximal RTA; nephrocalcinosis and nephrolithiasis with hypokalemic distal RTA; and diabetic nephropathy, obstructive uropathy, or tubulointerstitial disease with a generalized dysfunction of the distal nephron associated with hyperkalemia.

Clinical Disorders of Impaired Net Acid Excretion with Hypokalemia: Classic Distal RTA

The hallmark of classic hypokalemic distal RTA is an inability to acidify the urine appropriately during spontaneous or chemically induced metabolic acidosis.[237] The reduction in distal acidification lowers ammonium and titratable acid excretion and results in positive acid balance, hyperchloremic metabolic acidosis, and volume depletion.[226,237] Hypokalemia and hypercalciuria[238] often accompany this disorder, but proximal tubule reabsorptive function is preserved as evidenced by the conspicuous absence of findings compatible with Fanconi syndrome.[12,239] The dissolution of bone, which may on occasion accompany distal RTA, appears to be the result of chronic positive acid balance which causes calcium, magnesium, and phosphate wasting.[2,12] Hypercalciuria is therefore typical of distal RTA. Since chronic metabolic acidosis also decreases renal excretion of citrate,[238,240] the resulting hypocitraturia in combination with hypercalciuria results in urinary stone formation and nephrocalcinosis.[238,241] Nephrocalcinosis appears to be a reliable marker of classic distal RTA since this disorder does not occur in proximal RTA or the generalized dysfunction of the nephron associated with hyperkalemia.[242] Pyelonephritis is one of the most common complications of distal renal

Table 103-6 Disorders Associated with 61 Classic Hypokalemic Distal RTA

Primary
 Familial
 Idiopathic
Acquired (secondary)
 Hyperglobulinemic states
  Hypergammaglobulinemia
  Hyperglobulinemic purpura
  Cryoglobulinemia
  Sjögren syndrome
  Thyroiditis
  Pulmonary fibrosis
  Chronic active hepatitis
  Primary biliary cirrhosis
  Systemic lupus erythematosus
 Hypercalciuria and nephrocalcinosis
  Primary hyperparathyroidism
  Vitamin D intoxication
  Hyperthyroidism
  Idiopathic hypercalciuria
  Medullary sponge kidney
 Drugs and toxins
  Amphotericin B
  Toluene
  Cyclamate
 Tubulointerstitial diseases
  Balkan nephropathy
  Chronic pyelonephritis
  Obstructive uropathy
  Renal transplantation
  Leprosy
  Jejunoileal bypass with hyperoxaluria
 Secondary to genetically transmitted diseases
  Ehler-Danlos syndrome
  Hereditary elliptocytosis
  Sickle-cell disease
  Medullary cystic disease
  Wilson's disease
  Fabry disease
  Hereditary hypercalciuria
 Miscellaneous
  Hepatic cirrhosis
  Osteopetrosis with carbonic anhydrase II deficiency

tubular acidosis, especially in the presence of nephrocalcinosis, and eradication of the causative organism may be difficult.[225]

The vast majority of patients with distal renal tubular acidosis have distal RTA in association with a systemic illness, which is referred to as *secondary* distal RTA. Conversely, distal renal tubular acidosis may occur as a part of an inherited defect in which there is no association with systemic disease. The clinical spectrum of classic distal renal tubular acidosis is outlined in Table 103-6.

Primary Distal RTA: Genetics. Classic distal renal tubular acidosis may occur in the absence of other diseases as an inherited defect (primary distal RTA). The majority of cases of isolated distal RTA occur sporadically, but approximately 30 families with classic hypokalemic distal renal tubular acidosis involving over 200 affected individuals have been reported.[225,239,241,243–252] Autosomal dominant and X-linked inheritance are reported, and the mode of inheritance is unclear in some families.[98,239,248,251–254] Among the genetic types of distal RTA, some are associated with hypercalciuria, nephrocalcinosis, and nephrolithiasis, while other forms are not associated with abnormalities in calcium transport.[238,239,242,251–253] The proposed sequence of events through which genetic defects are expressed is summarized in Fig. 103-7 for four reported kindred studies.[239,243,252,255]

Primary distal renal tubular acidosis occurs most often as an autosomal dominant trait characterized by chronic metabolic acidosis which may appear in the first few months of life.[239,243,246,249] The same genetic defect which apparently results in the acidification defect can give rise to nephrocalcinosis.[239,250] Patients with primary distal renal tubular acidosis and nephrocalcinosis most often have hypercalciuria and hypocitrituria.[243,244–246,250] In seven affected members of kindreds studied in San Francisco (Fig. 103-7), nephrocalcinosis was present radiographically as early as age 5, even in patients receiving alkali therapy.[243] However, in a later generation of patients in whom high dose alkali therapy had been initiated prior to 4 years of age, nephrocalcinosis or nephrolithiasis was not detectable for the period of follow-up which ranged from 10 to 20 years.[250] Moreover, the glomerular filtration rate remained normal during follow-up in these patients.[225] In these children and in other children treated similarly with autosomal dominant classic distal renal tubular acidosis, the hypercalciuria and hypocitraturia appear to be corrected by high dose alkali therapy.[225,250]

Wrong and Davies were the first to observe that patients with demonstrable acidification defects did not always display frank metabolic acidosis (incomplete distal RTA). Nephrocalcinosis was already present in some of these patients.[237] Buckalew et al. also observed that the genetically transmitted acidification defect of distal RTA can occur without frank acidosis in some affected members of certain large kindreds.[241] Thus, acidosis occurs in some patients with hereditary distal RTA but not in others. Buckalew and co-workers have reported a 64-member kindred comprising four generations in which hypercalciuria was the primary manifestation of the autosomal dominant defect (Atlanta kindred) (Fig. 103-7).[239] It was proposed by Buckalew et al. that the sequence of hypercalciuria, nephrocalcinosis, and renal damage was necessary for the development of the defect in renal acidification.[239] However, the existence of nephrocalcinosis in the complete absence of a demonstrable defect in renal acidification was not documented in other studies of families with an inability to acidify the urine after an acid challenge. In addition, in the patients in whom hypercalciuria was severe, aminoaciduria, lysozymuria, and other features were present, which suggested that the proximal tubule could also be involved. Therefore, the renal defect described in this kindred may be complex.

In a defect described by Norman and colleagues[255] in a

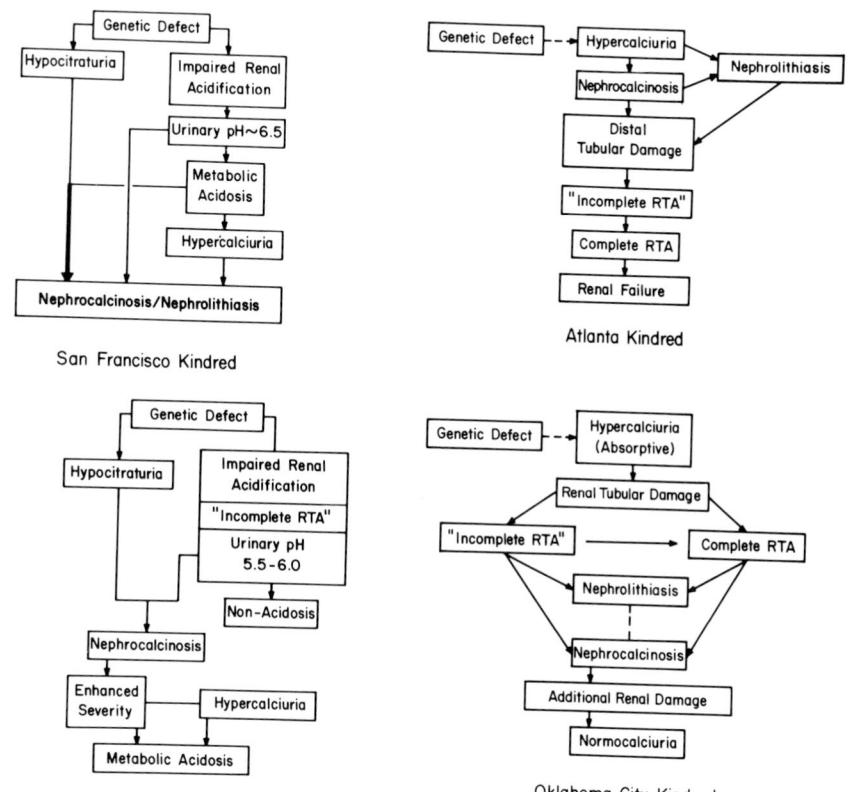

Fig. 103-7 Pathophysiology of development of distal RTA in four family groups designated by the city in which the investigation was conducted. Pathways depicted by dotted lines are assumed. The major differences in these disorders reflect the relationships between metabolic acidosis and hypercalciuria and the sequence in which full expression of the defect occurs. See text for explanation. (*Adapted from R.C. Morris and A. Sebastian.[225] Used by permission.*)

kindred from Philadelphia (Fig. 103-7), incomplete distal RTA was the defect expressed initially which apparently progressed to complete renal tubular acidosis only after the appearance of nephrocalcinosis. As occurs in other patients with hereditary distal RTA, severe hypocitraturia was observed in many affected individuals in the kindred. The hypocitraturia was successfully corrected with alkali therapy in high dose, but whether nephrocalcinosis could be prevented with early correction of hypocitraturia is not established. A similar sequence was reported by Coe and Parks, who found that alkali therapy in amounts adequate to elevate the plasma bicarbonate concentration to normal had little effect on the hypocitraturia but was associated with correction of hypercalciuria and reduction in the frequency of nephrolithiasis.[238] Thus, the observations of Norman, Coe, and Buckalew suggest that hypocitraturia and hypercalciuria may be primary metabolic manifestations of the disorder but that hypocitraturia in combination with hypercalciuria may be critical in the pathogenesis of nephrocalcinosis and nephrolithiasis with progression of incomplete distal RTA to complete distal RTA.

Finally, Hamed and associates have reported a large kindred from Oklahoma City in which hypercalciuria was the most frequent finding. The disorder was inherited as an autosomal dominant trait through four generations.[251] The hypercalciuria in this kindred was thought to be a result of augmented intestinal absorption, which appeared to precede both renal tubular acidosis and nephrocalcinosis. Thus, it was proposed that sustained hypercalciuria could damage the renal tubule and ultimately impair acidification, setting the stage for further damage and ultimately nephrocalcinosis.

Recently, Sly and associates have investigated 18 patients in 11 unrelated families with osteopetrosis, renal tubular acidosis, and cerebral calcification.[98,99] Carbonic anhydrase II has been shown to be virtually absent from red blood cells in all patients studied.[98] Moreover, reduced levels of carbonic anhydrase II were found in heterozygotes. These findings suggested that carbonic anhydrase II deficiency is the enzymatic basis for this autosomal recessive syndrome. The type of renal tubular acidosis present in this disorder has not been clearly delineated. While these patients generally exhibit frank bicarbonate wasting at normal plasma bicarbonate concentrations, suggesting a proximal defect, a number of patients have demonstrated an inability to acidify the urine during sustained systemic acidosis.[256] It is not clear if the bicarbonate wasting seen in such patients is a result of a distal defect alone, as is seen in prepubescent children with typical distal renal tubular acidosis, or if indeed a proximal defect is also present. A more detailed analysis of patients with this interesting syndrome can be found in Chap. 117.

Secondary Distal RTA. The disorders associated with acquired classic distal renal tubular acidosis are outlined in Table 103-7. The frequency with which hypokalemic distal RTA complicates the hyperglobulinemic states is especially striking. Failure to maximally acidify the urine can be demonstrated in up to 50 percent of patients with Sjögren syndrome and hyperglobulinemic purpura.[262-265] Round cell infiltration of the renal interstitium is frequently found in such disorders and, although yet unproven, the tubular dysfunction may have an immunologic basis. It is not known how hyperglobulinemia results in distal RTA, but it is clear that there is no correlation between the class or quantity of the circulating globulin and the renal defect.[262] The autoimmune and hyperglobulinemic states reported to be associated with distal RTA include hy-

perglobulinemic purpura,[263] cryoglobulinemia,[266] fibrosing alveolitis,[267] Sjögren syndrome,[268-270] thyroiditis,[271] primary biliary cirrhosis,[272] chronic active hepatitis,[273-277] and systemic lupus erythematous.[278-279]

The distal acidification defect that complicates the major disorders of calcium metabolism is usually, but not always, associated with nephrocalcinosis. Primary hyperparathyroidism, for example, appears to result in distal RTA only after the development of nephrocalcinosis.[280-282] Similarly, in the absence of nephrocalcinosis, distal RTA does not appear to be a characteristic complication of a number of other disorders, such as vitamin D intoxication,[282,283] hyperthyroidism,[284,285] idiopathic hypercalciuria,[286,287] medullary sponge kidney,[288,289] hereditary fructose intolerance,[290] Wilson disease, and Fabry disease.[291] The increased incidence of distal RTA with medullary sponge kidney suggests that cystic dilatation of collecting ducts may disrupt acid secretion.[292] Medullary sponge kidney is usually benign unless complicated by nephrocalcinosis, distal RTA, stones, or infection.[289]

Several drugs and toxins can result in a distal tubular acidification defect. These include amphotericin B,[293-295] toluene,[179] lithium carbonate,[189] cyclamate,[296] and analgesics.[297,298] Amphotericin B, as outlined in the section on pathophysiology, alters the permeability of the distal nephron allowing backleak of bicarbonate from blood to lumen and a reduction in net hydrogen secretion ("gradient defect").[173] A concentrating defect due to a direct antagonism by lithium of the effect of antidiuretic hormone on the collecting tubule is commonly observed.[180] Lithium also impairs distal acidification in therapeutic doses and may cause structural tubulointerstitial disease with chronic administration.[189] The renal tubular acidosis associated with renal transplantation may be of either the proximal or distal variety, but the distal variety is more common in association with chronic rejection.[299-301] Other associated tubulointerstitial diseases include leprosy,[302] hyperoxaluria,[303] obstructive uropathy,[304-306] and pyelonephritis secondary to urolithiasis.[307] Finally, distal renal tubular acidosis may occur in association with a variety of genetically transmitted disorders such as Ehler-Danlos syndrome,[257] hereditary elliptocytosis,[258] hereditary nerve deafness,[259] sickle-cell disease,[260] and medullary cystic disease.[261]

Bicarbonate Excretion in Adults and Children with Classic Distal RTA. In adults with classic hypokalemic distal RTA the fractional excretion of HCO_3^- is elevated at both normal and reduced plasma HCO_3^- concentrations but is usually less than 5 percent.[225] This contrasts with the typical finding in proximal RTA of frank HCO_3^- wasting at a normal plasma HCO_3^- concentration (fractional excretion of 10 to 15 percent)[308] (Table 103-5). The finding of a lower fractional excretion in adults with distal RTA implies that reabsorption of HCO_3^- in the proximal tubule is normal. Therefore, adult patients with distal RTA characteristically correct the metabolic acidosis if the amount of alkali needed to titrate the acid which enters the extracellular fluid from metabolism is replaced. This usually amounts to 1 to 1.5 meq/kg body weight per day and represents the average alkali replacement requirement in adults.[225] This explains the relative ease with which correction of the acidosis in distal RTA is achieved, in contrast to proximal RTA (Table 103-5).[1,2,3,12,225]

In children, however, renal HCO_3^- wasting accompanies the otherwise typical features of distal RTA. In infants with distal RTA, frank renal HCO_3^- wasting is present initially but may become apparent only after alkali therapy has been initiated.[243]

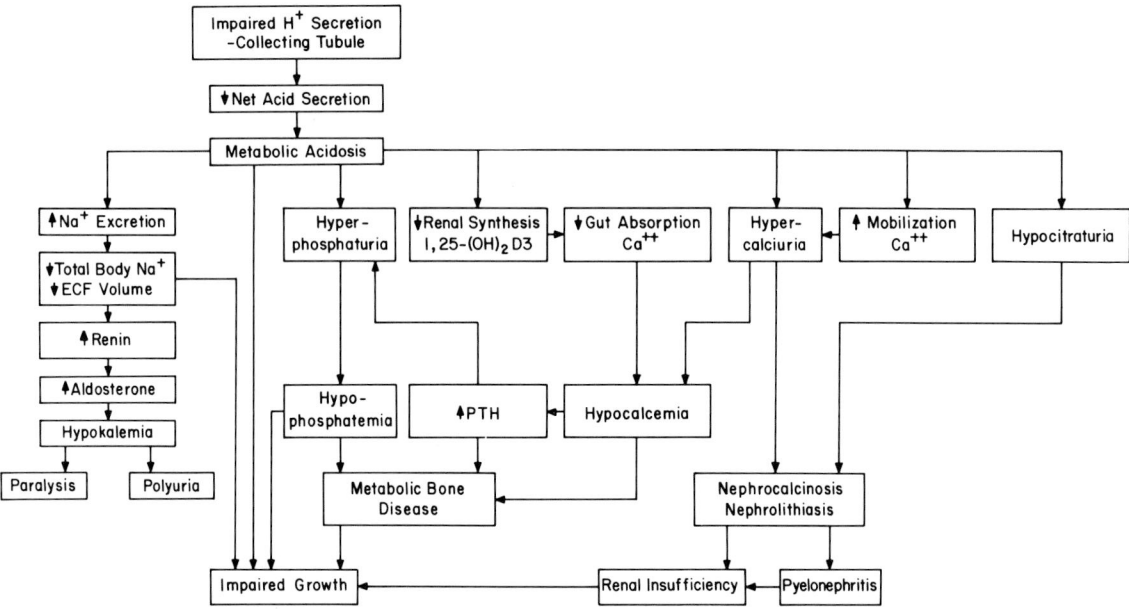

Fig. 103-8 Pathophysiological basis of the numerous clinical features which may accompany classical hypokalemic distal RTA. (*Modified and adapted from Morris and Sebastian.*[225] *Used by permission.*)

Endogenous acid production in prepubertal children can be as high as 3 meq/kg per day.[308,309] In older children, renal HCO_3^- wasting is often apparent during periods of accelerated growth.[309] McSherry and associates have shown that the fractional excretion of HCO_3^- in children with classic distal RTA may range as high as 6 to 14 percent.[243,308] Such findings led initially to the designation of this defect as type III RTA. It is now clear that children with hereditary distal RTA and bicarbonate wasting have affected parents who do not display renal HCO_3^- wasting. Since renal HCO_3^- wasting in these children usually subsides after puberty, the designation of type III RTA has been abandoned. Children with a distal acidification defect and renal HCO_3^- wasting are now thought to have classic distal RTA. The important practical point, however, is that renal HCO_3^- wasting should be anticipated in children with distal RTA and that adequate alkali replacement must be provided in order to assure normal growth and maturation.[243]

Associated Findings in Classic Distal RTA. The pathophysiological base of the associated clinical features of classic distal RTA are outlined schematically in Fig. 103-8. Abnormal calcium metabolism, as manifested by hypercalciuria, nephrocalcinosis, and nephrolithiasis, is a prominent feature in many patients with classic distal RTA. Low urinary citrate levels are presumed to be the result of chronic metabolic acidosis and probably facilitate development of nephrolithiasis.[310–311] Musculoskeletal complaints are frequent accompanying features of distal RTA, and hypocalcemic tetany may occur during alkali therapy.[312] Salt wasting also occurs in distal RTA and is seen more commonly in association with tubulointerstitial disease or advanced nephrocalcinosis.[313,314] Potassium wasting may be particularly severe during acidosis.[315]

Renal ammonium excretion may be normal in classic distal RTA when one allows for the prevailing urinary pH, but is clearly subnormal for the degree of acidosis and hypokalemia.[226,227] Aldosterone levels are often elevated because of volume contraction and are especially elevated considering the magnitude of hypokalemia.[225,315] In addition to hypercalciuria,

the increased renal clearance of phosphate occurs predictably during metabolic acidosis.[316] Calcium phosphate might be expected to be the major constituent of urinary stones in patients with classic distal RTA,[238] but calcium oxalate stones were reported with equal frequency in one study.[317] Hypocalcemia and hypophosphatemia, when occurring concomitantly, are usually related to the osteomalacia that may occur with chronic metabolic acidosis.[318,319] Chronic metabolic acidosis results in mobilization of skeletal calcium and inhibition of renal conversion of 25-hydroxyvitamin D_3 to 1,25-dihydroxyvitamin D_3.[320] In a recent series, radiologic evidence of bone disease was observed in only 1 of 44 patients with carefully documented classic distal RTA,[242] suggesting that overt bone disease, initially observed commonly in distal RTA, is now much less common in this disorder. It has also been emphasized that patients with distal RTA commonly have a urinary concentrating defect, perhaps as a result of tubulointerstitial disease. When a concentrating defect of a significant degree accompanies classic distal RTA, it appears to result from the underlying defect, such as tubulointerstitial disease or nephrocalcinosis.

In infants and young children with untreated distal RTA, abnormal growth is commonly observed.[243] The velocity of growth increases within several weeks after initiating alkali therapy. Within 3 to 6 months normal stature may be attained.[243] Older children may require several years to achieve normal height.[225,250] Renal HCO_3^- wasting tends to occur and increases in severity during periods of increased growth velocity.[243] As a result, in children with hypokalemic distal renal tubular acidosis, alkali therapy should be provided in an amount which allows sustained correction of the underlying metabolic acidosis. When initiated before the age of 3 years, it appears that alkali therapy sufficient to sustain correction of acidosis can prevent nephrocalcinosis.[243]

Treatment of Classic Hypokalemic Distal RTA. Correction of chronic metabolic acidosis can usually be achieved in patients with classic distal RTA by administration of alkali in the amount necessary to neutralize the production of metabolic acids derived from the diet. In adult patients with distal RTA this usually amounts to no more than 1 to 1.5 meq/kg per day.[12] In growing children endogenous acid production is usually greater, 2 to 3 meq/kg per day. However, renal HCO_3^- wasting in children may on occasion exceed 5 meq/kg per day. Therefore, larger amounts of bicarbonate must be administered to correct the acidosis and maintain normal growth.[243] Most children with distal RTA are able to take $NaHCO_3$ or HCO_3^- precursors in amounts necessary to sustain correction of acidosis.[243,250] The various forms of alkali replacement are outlined in Table 103-4. Most patients, especially children, tolerate Shohl's solution more readily than $NaHCO_3$. Compliance in adults is often limited by taste fatigue with Shohl's solution and by gastrointestinal discomfort with $NaHCO_3$ tablets. Alternating therapy among the numerous forms of alkali is often helpful. In patients with distal RTA, correction of acidosis with alkali therapy reduced urinary potassium excretion, and hypokalemia and sodium depletion may resolve with sustained correction of metabolic acidosis.[224,315,321] Therefore, in most patients with distal RTA potassium supplement is not necessary. Frank wasting of potassium may occur in a minority of patients in association with secondary hyperaldosteronism despite correction of the acidosis by the alkali therapy.[315] In some children, but not most adults, potassium supplement may be required even after the acidosis is corrected and may be given as potassium bicarbonate (K-Lyte or Polycitra).

On occasion, strikingly severe hypokalemia, metabolic acidosis, and hypocalcemia may require immediate therapy. This constellation of findings in an emergency setting has occurred with sufficient frequency to warrant the designation *crisis of distal RTA*. Since hypokalemia may be severe enough to result in paralysis and respiratory depression, immediate therapy with potassium replacement is necessary and should always be carried out prior to administering alkali.

Prognosis. The goal of therapy in distal RTA is to prevent the relentless progression of renal disease. The prognosis of well-managed patients appears to be excellent but is determined primarily by the severity of the underlying disease. The glomerular filtration rate should be expected to stabilize and remain constant during replacement with alkali therapy, even if initially reduced.[323]

Upon sustained correction of metabolic acidosis, hypercalciuria usually disappears, citrate excretion may increase, and intestinal reabsorption of calcium increases.[12,311,318,324,325] Moreover, the renal clearance of phosphate decreases, and the serum concentration of both phosphate and calcium may reach the normal level.[318] While nephrocalcinosis may persist, nephrolithiasis usually occurs much less frequently with adequate alkali therapy, and may correlate with a correction of citrate excretion.[238]

Disorders of Impaired Net Acid Excretion With Hyperkalemia: Generalized Distal Nephron Dysfunction

Although hyperchloremic metabolic acidosis and hyperkalemia occur with regularity in advanced renal insufficiency, patients selected because of severe hyperkalemia (>5.5 meq/liter) with diabetic nephropathy and tubulointerstial disease have hyperkalemia that is disproportionate to the reduction in glomerular filtration rate. In such patients a unique dysfunction of potassium and acid secretion by the collecting tubule coexists that can be attributed in most cases to selective hypoaldosteronism.[211,213] In patients presenting with this constellation of find-

Table 103-7 Disorders Associated with Aldosterone Deficiency or Resistance

Primary mineralcorticoid deficiency
  Combined gluco- and mineralcorticoid deficiency
    Addison disease
    Congenital adrenal enzyme defects
      21-Hydroxylase deficiency
      3-β-Hydroxydehydrogenase deficiency
      Desmolase deficiency
  Isolated mineralocorticoid deficiency
    Familial methyl oxidase deficiency
    Transient mineralocorticoid deficiency of infancy
    Chronic idiopathic hypoaldosteronism
Hyporeninemic hypoaldosteronism
  Diabetic nephropathy
  Tubulointerstitial disease
  Nonsteroidal anti-inflammatory drugs
Aldosterone resistance
  With salt wasting
    Pseudohypoaldosteronism I
    Adult form with renal insufficiency
    Tubulointerstitial disease
    Drugs
      Spironalactone
      Amiloride
      Triamterene
  Without salt wasting
    Sporadic
    Hereditary

ings, an evaluation of renin-aldosterone elaboration is indicated. A classification of the underlying disorders resulting in a generalized distal tubule dysfunction according to the production of and responsiveness to aldosterone are outlined in Table 103-7. Three general categories of lesions are noted: (1) a primary defect in the adrenal gland as a result of generalized dysfunction of the gland or abnormalities in mineralocorticoid synthesis; (2) defective stimulation of aldosterone elaboration because of suppressed or inadequate renin-angiotensin elaboration; and (3) resistance of the collecting tubule to mineralocorticoid action.

Primary Mineralocorticoid Deficiency. Destruction of the adrenal cortex by hemorrhage, infection, invasion by tumors, or autoimmune processes results in Addison disease. This causes combined glucocorticoid and mineralocorticoid deficiency and is recognized clinically by hypoglycemia, anorexia, weakness, and a failure to respond to stress. These defects can occur in association with renal salt wasting, hyperkalemia, and metabolic acidosis.[194,211-213] The most common congenital adrenal defect in steroid biosynthesis is 21-hydroxylase deficiency which is associated with salt wasting, hyperkalemia, and metabolic acidosis in a fraction of the patients.[326] Complete deficiency can be fatal unless diagnosed promptly, while less severe deficiency is compatible with survival without specific therapy. The adrenogenital syndrome occurs as a result of a shift of glucocorticoid precursors to androgen synthesis. 21-Hydroxylase deficiency accounts for 90 percent of all cases of adrenogenital syndrome. The defect may be isolated to the glucocorticoid pathway, sparing mineralocorticoid synthesis.[326] With the combined defect, mineralocorticoid deficiency typically results in salt wasting, hyperkalemia, and metabolic acidosis.[327,328]

Hyporeninemic Hypoaldosteronism. In contrast to patients with the primary adrenal disorder, patients in this group will exhibit low plasma renin activity. Hyperchloremic metabolic acidosis occurs in approximately 50 percent of patients with hyporeninemic hypoaldosteronism. This disorder has been recognized with increasing frequency in adults as a cause of hyperkalemic hyperchloremic metabolic acidosis and is most typically seen in older adults with diabetes mellitus or tubulointerstitial disease and renal insufficiency.[213,223] Patients will usually have mild to moderate renal insufficiency and acidosis with modest elevation in plasma potassium (5.5 to 6.0 meq/liter). Both the metabolic acidosis and the hyperkalemia are out of proportion to the degree of impairment in glomerular filtration rate.[211,213] Drugs may also cause a similar syndrome. The nonsteroidal anti-inflammatory drugs, in particular, have the ability to produce hyperkalemia with hyperchloremic metabolic acidosis in patients with renal insufficiency.[220,329,330] The principal defect in hyporeninemic hypoaldosteronism is a reduced level of plasma renin activity which appears to be unresponsive to the usual physiological stimuli.[211,215] Aldosterone secretion is low as a result, especially in view of the degree of hyperkalemia.[215] While reduction in plasma potassium by administration of cation exchange resins may reduce aldosterone levels, the beneficial effect of enhanced renal ammoniagenesis improves or corrects the metabolic acidosis and hyperkalemia.[194] The magnitude of salt wasting in hyporeninemic hypoaldosteronism is variable. While the capacity to conserve salt is diminished during salt restriction in patients with hyporeninemic hypoaldosteronism, the degree of salt wasting is no more severe than in patients with chronic renal insufficiency of a comparable magnitude without hyporeninemic hypoaldosteronism.[216,217] Hyponatremia does not usually occur in this setting. Mineralocorticoid replacement with 9α-fludrocortisone improves net acid excretion, put high doses (0.3 to 0.5 mg/day) may be required, particularly when some degree of renal tubular unresponsiveness is present, as is often the case.[198]

The means by which renin secretion is reduced have been discussed in the section on pathophysiology. The importance of volume expansion in this regard has not yet been established, but hypertensive patients with this disorder are often volume-overexpanded, suggesting physiological suppression of renin elaboration.[212] Orthostatic hypotension may accompany autonomic insufficiency in diabetic nephropathy and is not a reliable index of volume contraction. When volume overexpansion is present, diuresis would be expected to reverse the disorder.[217,331] Diuretics alone are frequently not sufficient to correct the abnormalities in acid-base and electrolyte balance.

Resistance to Mineralocorticoid. Mineralocorticoid resistance with hyperkalemia may occur with salt retention or with salt wasting. A number of patients have been reported with hyperkalemia, hyperchloremic metabolic acidosis, hypertension, undetectable plasma renin activity, and low aldosterone levels (pseudohypoaldosteronism type II).[205–210,332] These patients generally have not exhibited glomerular or tubulointerstitial disease. The acidosis in such patients is mild and can be accounted for by the magnitude of hyperkalemia. Furthermore, renal potassium secretion is resistant to mineralocorticoid administration. Renin and aldosterone levels both increase if volume expansion is corrected by diuretics or salt restriction.[206,209,310] The original patients were described by Paver and Pauline,[333] Arnold and Healy[205] and Gordon et al.[206] Schambelan has investigated this disorder in detail and has demonstrated that potassium excretion responds to sodium sulfate infusion but not sodium chloride infusion.[209] On the

basis of these findings it was suggested that a distal tubule "chloride shunt" which was reversed by administration of thiazide diuretics can explain this disorder. Presumably, if chloride shunting is responsible, a distal tubule diuretic such as a thiazide would serve to prevent distal tubule chloride reabsorption. A familial form of this disorder has also been described in children with short stature.[207]

Mineralocorticoid resistance with salt wasting also results in hyperkalemic-hyperchloremic acidosis because of a decrease in effectiveness of mineralocorticoid at the level of the cortical collecting tubule. Several distinct syndromes have been described and may be due to a primary genetic defect of the aldosterone receptor or a more generalized defect involving cortical collecting tubule function. Idiopathic pseudohypoaldosteronism type I occurs in young children, usually boys, without accompanying renal pathology.[199–202] While the defect improves as the child matures, high aldosterone levels are required to maintain acid and potassium balance. Patients with pseudohypoaldosteronism type I will require supplemental sodium chloride which can reverse the hyponatremia and hyperkalemia, improve the symptoms, and enhance growth.[212] After infancy the disorder typically abates sufficiently to permit reduction or discontinuation of sodium chloride supplements, but the findings can recur during periods of dietary salt restriction. Pseudohypoaldosteronism may be acquired in patients with systemic lupus erythematosus,[334] obstructive uropathy,[335] sickle-cell disease,[336] and drug induced interstitial hepatitis,[337] and in the postrenal transplant recipient.[338] Finally, Batlle and associates have emphasized that hyporeninemic hypoaldosteronism and classic distal renal tubule acidosis may coexist in patients with decreased responsiveness to mineralocorticoid.[170,174]

Drugs may also produce mineralocorticoid resistance and result in a clinical constellation which mimics the acidification defect seen in hyperkalemic distal RTA. These drugs and toxins are summarized in Table 103-8. The spironolactones act as competitive inhibitors of aldosterone, and they may cause hyperkalemia and metabolic acidosis when administered to patients with significant renal insufficiency.[193,339] Similarly, amiloride and triamterine may be associated with this disorder.[172,184] Finally, the inhibitors of cycloxygenase, the pivotal enzyme in the production of prostaglandins from arachidonic acid precursors, can produce hyperkalemia and metabolic acidosis.[329,330] Other drugs including converting enzyme inhibitors have been observed by the authors to be associated with this disorder. Drugs should be ruled out as a cause of hyperkalemia in metabolic acidosis in such patients.

Treatment (Table 103-9). In hyperkalemic, hyperchloremic, metabolic acidosis, documentation of the underlying disorder is necessary, particularly in adults with acquired disease.

Table 103-8 Drug-Induced Hyperchloremic Metabolic Acidosis

Hyperkalemia
 Potassium sparing diuretics (spironolactone, triamterene, amiloride)
 Potassium supplement (KCl, salt substitutes, dietary)
 Nonsteroidal anti-inflammatory drugs
 β Blockers
 Converting enzyme inhibitors
Hypokalemia
 Acetazolamide
 Amphotericin B
 Lithium carbonate

Table 103-9 Treatment of Generalized Dysfunction of the Nephron with Hyperkalemia

Alkali therapy
Loop diuretic (furosemide, bumetamide)
Sodium polysterene sulfonate (Kayexalate)
Fludrocortisone (0.1–0.3 mg/day)
  Avoid in hypertension, volume expansion, heart failure
  Combine with loop diuretic
Avoid drugs associated with hyperkalemia (Table 103-8)

Treatment of patients with hyperkalemia and metabolic acidosis with chronic renal insufficiency is not always necessary, and the decision to treat is often based on the severity of the hyperkalemia. Reduction in serum potassium often improves the metabolic acidosis. Patients with combined glucocorticoid and mineralocorticoid deficiency should receive both adrenal steroids in replacement dosages. Patients with hyporeninemic hypoaldosteronism may respond to cation exchange resins, alkali therapy, or treatment with a loop diuretic to induce renal potassium and salt excretion (Table 103-9). Volume depletion should be avoided unless the patient is volume-overexpanded or hypertensive. Superphysiological doses of mineralocorticoids may be necessary but should be administered in combination with a loop diuretic to avoid volume overexpansion and aggravation of hypertension.[331] Infants with pseudohypoaldosteronism type I should receive salt supplement in amounts sufficient to correct the syndrome and allow normal growth,[328] while patients with pseudohypoaldosteronism type II should receive thiazide diuretics and/or salt restriction.[209]

REFERENCES

1. TEREE TM, MIRABAL-FONT E, ORTIZ A, WALLACE WM: Stool losses and acidosis in diarrheal disease of infancy. *Pediatrics* 36:704, 1965.
2. EMMETT M, SELDIN DW: Clinical syndromes of metabolic acidosis and metabolic alkalosis, in Seldin DW, Giebisch G (eds): *The Kidney: Physiology and Pathophysiology.* New York, Raven, 1985, p 1567.
3. HALPERIN ML, GOLDSTEIN MB, RICHARDSON RMA, STINEBAUGH BJ: Distal renal tubular acidosis syndromes: A pathophysiogical approach. *Am J Nephrol* 5:1, 1985.
4. HALPERIN ML, GOLDSTEIN MB, JUNGAS RL, STEINBAUGH BJ: Biochemistry and physiology of ammonium excretion, in Seldin DW, Giebisch G (eds): *The Kidney: Physiology and Pathophysiology.* New York, Raven, 1985, p 1471.
5. GOLDSTEIN MB, BEAR R, RICHARDSON RMA, MARSDEN PA, HALPERIN ML: The urine anion gap: A clinically useful index of ammonium excretion. *Am J Med Sci* 292:198, 1986.
6. KLEINMAN PK: Cholestyramine and metabolic acidosis. *N Engl J Med* 290:861, 1974.
7. D'AGOSTINO A, LEADBETTER WF, SCHWARTZ WB: Alterations in the ionic composition of isotonic saline solution instilled into the colon. *J Clin Invest* 32:444, 1953.
8. STAMEY TA: The pathogenesis and implications of the electrolyte imbalance in ureterosigmoidostomy. *Surg Gynecol Obstet* 103:736, 1956.
9. DUBOSE TD JR: Acid-base balance, in Eknoyan G, Knochel JP (eds): *The Systemic Consequences of Renal Failure.* Orlando, Grune & Stratton, 1984, p 421.
10. WIDMER B, GERHARDT RE, HARRINGTON JT, COHEN JJ: The influence of graded degrees of chronic renal failure. *Arch Intern Med* 139:1099, 1979.
11. GONICK HC, KLEEMAN CR, RUBINI ME, MAXWELL MH: Functional impairment in chronic renal failure. *Nephron* 6:28, 1969.
12. COGAN MG, RECTOR FC JR: Acid-base disorders, in Brenner BM, Rector FC Jr (eds): *The Kidney,* 3d ed. Philadelphia, Saunders, 1986, p 457
13. FINE LG, YANAGAAWA N, SCHULTZ RG, BRICKER N: Functional profile of the isolated uremic nephron. Potassium adaptation in the rabbit cortical collecting tubule. *J Clin Invest* 64:1033, 1979.
14. VAN YPERSELE DE STRIHOU C: Potassium homeostasis in renal failure. *Kidney Int* 11:491, 1977.
14a. HEIRD WC, DELL RB, DRISCOLL JM, GREBIN B, WINTERS RW: Metabolic acidosis resulting from intravenous alimentation mixtures containing synthetic amino acids. *N Engl J Med* 287:943, 1972.
15. RECTOR RF JR, CARTER NW, SELDIN DW: The mechanism of bicarbonate reabsorption in the proximal and distal tubules of the kidney. *J Clin Invest* 44:278, 1968.
16. VIEIRA FL, MALNIC G: Hydrogen ion secretion by rat renal cortical tubules as studied by an antimony microelectrode. *Am J Physiol* 214:710, 1968.
17. DUBOSE TD JR, PUCACCO LR, CARTER NW: Determination of disequilibrium pH in the rat kidney in vivo: Evidence for hydrogen secretion. *Am J Physiol* 240:F138, 1981.
18. ALPERN RJ, CHAMBERS M: Cell pH in the rat proximal convoluted tubule. Regulation by luminal and peritubular pH and sodium concentration. *J Clin Invest* 78:502, 1986.
19. MURER H, HOPFER U, KINNE R: Sodium/proton antiport in brush-border membrane vesicles isolated from rat small intestine kidney. *Biochem J* 154:597, 1976.
20. WARNOCK DG, REENSTRA WW, YEE VJ: Na$^+$/H$^+$ antiporter of brush-border vesicles: Studies with acridine orange uptake. *Am J Physiol* 242:F733, 1982.
21. KINSELLA JL, ARONSON PS: Properties of the Na$^+$-H$^+$ exchanger in renal microvillus membrane vesicles. *Am J Physiol* 238:F461, 1980.
22. SCHWARTZ GJ: Na$^+$-dependent H$^+$ efflux from proximal tubule: Evidence for reversible Na$^+$-H$^+$ exchange. *Am J Physiol* 241:F380, 1981.
23. SASAKI S, SHIIGAI T, TAKEUCHI J: Intracellular pH in the isolated perfused rabbit proximal straight tubule. *Am J Physiol* 249:F417, 1985.
24. PREISIG PA, IVES HE, CRAGOE EJ JR, ALPERN RJ, RECTOR FC JR: The role of the Na$^+$/H$^+$ antiporter in rat proximal tubule bicarbonate absorption. *J Clin Invest* 80:970, 1987.
25. KINNE-SAFFRAN E, BEAUWENS R, KINNE R: An ATP-driven proton pump in brush-border membranes from rat renal cortex. *J Membrane Biol* 64:67, 1982.
26. CHAN YL, GIEBISCH G: Relationship between sodium and bicarbonate transport in the rat proximal convoluted tubule. *Am J Physiol* 240:F222, 1981.
27. ALPERN RJ: Mechanism of basolateral membrane H$^+$/OH$^-$/HCO$_3^-$ transport in the rat proximal convoluted tubule. A sodium-coupled electrogenic process. *J Gen Physiol* 86:613, 1985.
28. YOSHITOMI K, BURCKHARDT B-CH, FROMTER E: Rheogenic sodium-bicarbonate cotransport in the peritubular cell membrane of rat renal proximal tubule. *Pflügers Arch* 405:360, 1985.
29. BORON WF, BOULPAEP EL: Intracellular pH regulation in the renal proximal tubule of the salamander: Basolateral HCO$_3^-$ transport. *J Gen Physiol* 81:53, 1983.
30. AKIBA T, ALPERN RJ, EVELOFF J, CALAMINA J, WARNOCK DG: Electrogenic sodium/bicarbonate cotransport in rabbit renal cortical basolateral membrane vesicles. *J Clin Invest* 78:1472, 1986.
31. GRASSL SM, ARONSON PS: Na$^+$/HCO$_3^-$ co-transport in basolateral membrane vesicles isolated from rabbit renal cortex. *J Biol Chem* 19:8778, 1986.
32. SASAKI S, SHIIGAI T, YOSHIYAMA N, TAKEUCHI J: Mechanism of bicarbonate exit across basolateral membrane of rabbit proximal straight tubule. *Am J Physiol* 21:F11, 1987.
33. DOBYAN DC, BULGER RE: Renal carbonic anhydrase. *Am J Physiol* 243:F311, 1982.
34. ALPERN RJ, WARNOCK DG, RECTOR FC JR: Renal acidification mechanisms, in Brenner BM, Rector FC Jr (eds): *The Kidney,* 3d ed. Philadelphia, Saunders, 1986, p 206.
35. WAHLSTRAND T, WISTRAND PJ: Carbonic anhydrase C in the human renal medulla. *Ups J Med Sci* 85:7, 1980.
36. ALPERN RJ, COGAN MG, RECTOR FC JR: Effect of luminal bicarbonate concentration on proximal acidification in the rat. *Am J Physiol* 243:F53, 1982.
37. CHAN YL, MALNIC G, GIEBISCH G: Passive driving forces of proximal tubular fluid and bicarbonate transport: Gradient-dependence of H$^+$ secretion. *Am J Physiol* 245:F622, 1983.
38. HOLMBERG C, KOKKO JP, JACOBSON HR: Determination of chloride and bicarbonate permeabilities in proximal convoluted tubules. *Am J Physiol* 241:F386, 1981.
39. SASAKI S, BERRY CA, RECTOR FC JR: Effect of luminal and peritubular HCO$_3^-$ concentrations and PCO$_2$ on HCO$_3^-$ reabsorption in rabbit proximal convoluted tubules perfused in vitro. *J Clin Invest* 70:639, 1982.
40. WARNOCK DG, YEE VJ: Anion permeabilities of the isolated perfused rabbit proximal tubule. *Am J Physiol* 242:F395, 1982.
41. HAMM LL, PUCACCO LR, KOKKO JP JACOBSON HR: Hydrogen ion permeability of the rabbit proximal convoluted tubule. *Am J Physiol* 246:F3, 1984.
42. GREEN R, BISHOP JHV, GIEBISCH G: Ionic requirements of proximal tubular

sodium transport. III. Selective luminal anion substitution. *Am J Physiol* 236:F268, 1979.

43. JACOBSON HR: Characteristics of volume reabsorption in rabbit superficial and juxtamedullary proximal convoluted tubules. *J Clin Invest* 63:410, 1979.

44. BAUM M, BERRY CA: Evidence of neutral transcellular NaCl transport and neutral basolateral chloride exit in the rabbit proximal convoluted tubule. *J Clin Invest* 74:205, 1984.

45. ALPERN RJ, HOWLIN KJ, PREISIG PA: Active and passive components of chloride transport in the rat proximal convoluted tubule. *J Clin Invest* 76:1360, 1985.

46. LUCCI MS, WARNOCK DG: Effects of anion-transport inhibitors on NaCl reabsorption in the rat superficial proximal convoluted tubule. *J Clin Invest* 64:570, 1979.

47. BAUM M: Evidence that parallel Na^+-H^+ and Cl^--$HCO_3^-(OH^-)$ antiporters transport NaCl in the proximal tubule. *Am J Physiol* 252:F338, 1987.

48. KARNISKI LP, ARONSON PS: Chloride/formate exchange with formic acid recycling: A mechanism of active chloride transport across epithelial membranes. *Proc Natl Acad Sci USA* 82:6362, 1985.

49. ALPERN RJ: Apical membrane chloride/base exchange in the rat proximal convoluted tubule. *J Clin Invest* 79:1026, 1987.

50. PITTS RF, LOTSPEICH WD: Bicarbonate and the renal regulation of acid-base balance. *Am J Physiol* 147:138, 1946.

51. ALPERN RJ, COGAN MG, RECTOR FC JR: Effects of extracellular fluid volume and plasma bicarbonate concentration on proximal acidification in the rat. *J Clin Invest* 71:736, 1983.

52. BERLINER RW, KENNEDY TJ, HILTON JG: Effect of maleic acid on renal function. *Proc Soc Exp Biol Med* 75:791, 1951.

53. AL-BANDER HA, WEISS RA, HUMPHREYS MH, MORRIS RC JR: Dysfunction of the proximal tubule underlies maleic acid-induced type II renal tubular acidosis. *Am J Physiol* 243:F604, 1982.

54. BERGERON M, DUBORD L, HAUSSER C: Membrane permeability as a cause of transport defects in experimental Fanconi syndrome. A new hypothesis. *J Clin Invest* 57:1181, 1976.

55. MAISAKA JK, MCCAFFERY M: Evidence for renal tubular leakage in maleic acid-induced Fanconi syndrome. *Am J Physiol* 239:F507, 1980.

56. HOPPE A, GMAJ P, METLER M, ANGIELSKI S: Additive inhibition of renal bicarbonate reabsorption by maleate plus acetazolamide. *Am J Physiol* 231:1258, 1976.

57. GOUGOUX A, LEMIEUX G, LAVOIE N: Maleate-induced bicaronaturia in the dog: A carbonic anhydrase-independent effect. *Am J Physiol* 231:1010, 1976.

58. GMAJ P, HOPPE A, ANGIELSKI S, ROGULSKI J: Acid-base behavior of the kidney in maleate-treated rats. *Am J Physiol* 222:1182, 1972.

59. BANK N, AYNEDJIAN HS, MUTZ BF: Microperfusion study of proximal tubule bicarbonate transport in maleic acid-induced renal tubular acidosis. *Am J Physiol* 250:F476, 1986.

60. REBOUCAS NA, FERNANDES DT, ELIAS MM, DE MELLO-AIRES M, MALNIC G: Proximal tubular HCO_3^-, H^+ and fluid transport during maleate-induced acidification defect. *Pflugers Arch* 401:266, 1984.

61. GÜNTHER R, SILBERNAGL S, DEETJEN P: Maleic acid induced aminoaciduria, studied by free flow micropuncture and continuous microperfusion. *Pflugers Arch* 382:109, 1979.

62. SILVERMAN M: Mechanism of maleic acid nephropathy: Investigations using brush border membrane vesicles. *Memb Biochem* 4:63, 1981.

63. REYNOLDS R, MCNAMARA PD, SEGAL S: On the maleic acid induced Fanconi syndrome: Effects on transport by isolated rat kidney brushborder membrane vesicles. *Life Sci* 22:39, 1978.

64. SILVERMAN M, HUANG L: Mechanism of maleic acid-induced glucosuria in dog kidney. *Am J Physiol* 231:1024, 1976.

65. LE GRIMELLEC C, CARRIERE S, CARDINAL J, GIOCONDI MC: Effect of maleate on membrane physical state of brush border and basolateral membranes of the dog kidney. *Life Sci* 30:1107, 1982.

66. KRAMER HJ, GONICK HC: Experimental Fanconi syndrome. I. Effect of maleic acid on renal cortical Na-K-ATPase activity and ATP levels. *J Lab Clin Med* 76:799, 1970.

67. ANGIELSKI S, ROGULSKI J: Effect of maleic acid on the kidney. I. Oxidation of Krebs cycle intermediates by various tissues of maleate intoxicated rats. *Acta Biochim Polonica* 9:357, 1962.

68. AL-BANDER H, ETHEREDGE SB, PAUKERT T, HUMPHREYS MH, MORRIS RC JR: Phosphate loading attenuates renal tubular dysfunction induced by maleic acid in the dog. *Am J Physiol* 248:F513, 1985.

68a. AL-BANDER HA, MOCK DM, ETHEREDGE SB, PAUKERT TT, HUMPHREYS MH, MORRIS RC JR: Coordinately increased lysozymuria and lysosomal enzymuria induced by maleic acid. *Kidney Int* 30:804, 1987.

69. BURCH HB, CHOI S, DENCE CN, ALVEY TR, COLE BR, LOWRY OH: Metabolic effects of large fructose loads in different parts of the rat nephron. *J Biol Chem* 255:8239, 1980.

70. MORRIS RC JR, NIGON K, REED EB: Evidence that the severity of depletion of inorganic phosphate determines the severity of the disturbance of adenine nucleotide metabolism in the liver and renal cortex of the fructose-loaded rat. *J Clin Invest* 61:209, 1978.

71. FRASER D, KOOH SW, SCRIVER CR: Hyperparathyroidism as the cause of hyperaminoaciduria and phosphaturia in human vitamin D deficiency. *Pediatr Res* 1:425, 1967.

72. GUIGNARD JP, TORRADO A: Proximal renal tubular acidosis in vitamin D deficiency rickets. *Acta Paediatr Scand* 62:543, 1973.

73. VAINSEL M, MANDERLIER T, VIS HL: Proximal renal tubular acidosis in vitamin D deficiency rickets. *Biomedicine* 22:35, 1974.

74. READE TM, SCRIVER CR, GLORIEUX FH, NOGRADY B, DELVIN E, PIORIER R, HOLICK MF, DELUCA HF: Response to crystalline 1α-hydroxyvitamin D_3 in vitamin D dependency. *Pediatr Res* 9:593, 1975.

75. HUGUENIN M, SCHACHT R, DAVID R: Infantile rickets with severe proximal renal tubular acidosis, responsive to vitamin D. *Arch Dis Child* 49:955, 1974.

76. BANK N, AYNEDJIAN HS: A micropuncture study of the effect of parathyroid hormone on renal bicarbonate reabsorption. *J Clin Invest* 58:336, 1976.

77. IINO Y, BURG MB: Effect of parathyroid hormone on bicarbonate absorption by proximal tubules in vitro. *Am J Physiol* 236:F387, 1979.

78. MCKINNEY TD, MYERS P: PTH inhibition of bicarbonate transport by proximal convoluted tubules. *Am J Physiol* 239:F127, 1980.

79. MCKINNEY TD, MYERS P: Bicarbonate transport by proximal tubules: Effect of parathyroid hormone and dibutyryl cyclic AMP. *Am J Physiol* 238:F166, 1980.

80. POLLOCK AS, WARNOCK DG, STREWLER GJ: Parathyroid hormone inhibition of Na^+-H^+ antiporter activity in a cultured renal cell line. *Am J Physiol* 250:F217, 1986.

81. WEINMAN EJ, SHENOLIKAR S, KAHN AM: cAMP-associated inhibition of Na^+-H^+ exchanger in rabbit kidney brush-border membranes. *Am J Physiol* 252:F19, 1987.

82. HULTER HN, TOTO RD, ILNICKI LP, HALLORAN B, SEBASTIAN A: Metabolic alkalosis in models of primary and secondary hyperparathyroid states. *Am J Physiol* 245:F450, 1983.

83. MITNICK P, GREENBERG A, COFFMAN T, KELEPOURIS E, WOLF CJ, GOLDFARB S: Effects of two models of hypercalcemia on renal acid base metabolism. *Kidney Int* 21:613, 1982.

84. BICHARA M, MERCIER O, PAILLARD M, LEVIEL F: Effects of parathyroid hormone on urinary acidification. *Am J Physiol* 251:F444, 1986.

85. MERCIER O, BICHARA M, PAILLARD M, PRIGENT A: Effects of parathyroid hormone and urinary phosphate on collecting duct hydrogen secretion. *Am J Physiol* 251:F802, 1986.

86. MCKINNEY TD, MYERS P: Effect of calcium and phosphate on bicarbonate and fluid transport by proximal tubules in vitro. *Kidney Int* 21:433, 1982.

87. PERAINO RA, GHAFARY E, ROUSE D, STINEBAUGH BJ, SUKI WN: Effect of 25-hydroxycholecalciferol on renal handling of sodium, calcium, and phosphate during bicarbonate infusion. *Miner Electrolyte Metab* 1:321, 1978.

88. PUSCHETT JB, MORANZ J, KURNICK WS: Evidence for a direct action of cholecalciferol and 25-hydroxycholecalciferol on the renal transport of phosphate, sodium, and calcium. *J Clin Invest* 51:373, 1972.

89. GEKLE D, STRÖKER R, ROSTOCK D: The effect of vitamin D on renal inorganic phosphate reabsorption of normal rats, parathyroidectomized rats, and rats with rickets. *Pediastr Res* 5:40, 1971.

90. GROSE JH, SCRIVER CR: Parathyroid-dependent phosphaturia and aminoaciduria in the vitamin D-deficient rat. *Am J Physiol* 214:370, 1968.

91. MORRIS RC JR, MCSHERRY E, SEBASTIAN A: Modulation of experimental renal dysfunction of hereditary fructose intolerance by circulating parathyroid hormone. *Proc Natl Acad Sci USA* 68:132, 1971.

92. BREWER ED, TSAI HC, SZETO KS, MORRIS RC JR: Maleic acid-induced impaired conversion of $25(OH)D_3$ to $1,25(OH)_2D_3$: Implications for Fanconi's syndrome. *Kidney Int* 12:244, 1977.

93. CHESNEY RW, KAPLAN BS, PHELPS M, DELUCA HF: Renal tubular acidosis does not alter circulating values of calcitriol. *J Pediatr* 104:51, 1984.

94. WALKER WG, DICKERMAN H, JOST LJ: Mechanism of lysine-induced kaliuresis. *Am J Physiol* 206:409, 1964.

95. CHAN YL, KURTZMAN NA: Effects of lysine on bicarbonate and fluid absorption in the rat proximal tubule. *Am J Physiol* 242:F604, 1982.

96. FRÖMTER E: Solute transport across epithelia: What can we learn from micropuncture studies on kidney tubules? *J Physiol* 288:1, 1979.

97. HOSHI T, SUDO K, SUZUKI Y: Characteristics of changes in the intracellular potential associated with transport of neutral, dibasic and acidimic amino acids in Trituris proximal tubule. *Biochim Biophys Acta* 44:492, 1976.

98. SLY WS, WHYTE MP, SUNDARAM V, TASHIAN RE, HEWETT-EMMETT D, GUIBAUD P, VAINSEL M, BALUARTE HJ, GRUSKIN A, AL-MOSAWI M, SAKATI N, OHLSSON A: Carbonic anhydrase II deficiency in 12 families with the au-

tosomal recessive syndrome of osteopetrosis with renal tubular acidosis and cerebral calcification. *N Engl J Med* 313:139, 1985.

99. SLY WS, HEWETT-EMMETT D, WHYTE MP, YU YSL, TASHIAN RE: Carbonic anhydrase II deficiency identified as the primary defect in the autosomal recessive syndrome of osteopetrosis with renal tubular acidosis and cerebral calcification. *Proc Natl Acad Sci USA* 80:2752, 1983.

100. BREGMAN H, BROWN J, ROGERS A, BOURKE E: Osteopetrosis with combined proximal and distal renal tubular acidosis. *Am J Kidney Dis* 11:357, 1982.

101. BOURKE E, DELANEY VB, MOSAWI M, REAVEY P, WESTON M: Renal tubular acidosis and osteopetrosis in siblings. *Nephron* 28:268, 1981.

102. KONDO T, TANIGUCHI N, TANIGUCHI K, MATSUDA I, MURAO M: Inactive form of erythrocyte carbonic anhydrase B in patients with primary renal tubular acidosis. *J Clin Invest* 62:610, 1978.

103. SHAPIRA E, BEN-YOSEPH Y, EYAL FG, RUSSELL A: Enzymatically inactive red cell carbonic anhydrase B in a family with renal tubular acidosis. *J Clin Invest* 53:59, 1974.

104. KENDALL AG, TASHIAN RE: Erythrocyte carbonic anhydrase I: Inherited deficiency in humans. *Science* 197:471, 1977.

105. BRENNER RJ, SPRING DB, SEBASTIAN A, MCSHERRY EM, GENANT HK, PALUBINSKAS AJ, MORRIS RC JR: Incidence of radiographically evident bone disease, nephrocalcinosis, and nephrolithiasis in various types of renal tubular acidosis. *N Engl J Med* 307:217, 1982.

106. RODRIGUEZ-SORIANO J, VALLO A, CASTILLO G, OLIVEROS R: Renal handling of water and sodium in children with proximal and distal renal tubular acidosis. *Nephron* 25:193, 1980.

107. SEBASTIAN A, MCSHERRY E, MORRIS RC JR: On the mechanism of renal potassium wasting in renal tubular acidosis associated with the Fanconi syndrome (Type 2 RTA). *J Clin Invest* 50:231, 1971.

108. BRENES LG, BRENES JN, HERNANDEZ MM: Familial proximal renal tubular acidosis. A distinct clinical entity. *Am J Med* 63:244, 1977.

109. NASH MA, TORRADO AD, GREIFER I, SPITZER A, EDELMANN CM JR: Renal tubular acidosis in infants and children. *J Pediatr* 80:738, 1972.

110. PERAINO RA, SUKI WN: Urine HCO_3^- augments renal Ca^{2+} absorption independent of systemic acid-base changes. *Am J Physiol* 238:F394, 1980.

111. CALLIS L, CASTELLO F, FORTUNY G, VALLO A, BALLABRIGA A: Effect of hydrochlorothiazide on rickets and on renal tubular acidosis in two patients with cystinosis. *Helv Paediatr Acta* 6:602, 1970.

112. RAMPINI S, FANCONI A, ILLIG R, PRADER A: Effect of hydrochlorothiazide on proximal renal tubular acidosis in a patient with idiopathic "de Toni-Debre-Fanconi syndrome." *Helv Paediatr Acta* 1:13, 1968.

113. MCKINNEY TD, BURG MB: Bicarbonate transport by rabbit cortical collecting tubules; effect of acid and alkali loads in vivo on transport in vitro. *J Clin Invest* 60:766, 1977.

114. ATKINS JL, BURG MB: Bicarbonate transport by isolated perfused rat collecting ducts. *Am J Physiol* 249:F485, 1985.

115. SCHWARTZ GJ, BARASCH J, AL-AWQATI Q: Plasticity of functional epithelial polarity. *Nature* 318:368, 1985.

116. LUCCI MS, PUCACCO LR, CARTER NW, DUBOSE TD JR: Evaluation of bicarbonate transport in the rat distal tubule: Effects of acid-base status. *Am J Physiol* 243:F335, 1982.

117. LEVINE DZ: An in vivo microperfusion study of distal tubule bicarbonate reabsorption in normal and ammonium chloride rats. *J Clin Invest* 75:588, 1985.

118. IACOVITTI M, NASH L, PETERSON LN, ROCHON J, LEVINE DZ: Distal tubule bicarbonate accumulation in vivo. Effect of flow and transtubular bicarbonate gradients. *J Clin Invest* 78:1658, 1986.

119. LOMBARD WE, KOKKO JP, JACOBSON HR: Bicarbonate transport in cortical and outer medullary collecting tubules. *Am J Physiol* 244:F289, 1983.

120. STOKES JB: Na and K transport across the cortical and outer medullary collecting tubule of the rabbit: Evidence for diffusion across the outer medullary portion. *Am J Physiol* 242:F514, 1982.

121. DUBOSE TD JR: Hydrogen ion secretion by the collecting duct as a determinant of the urine to blood PCO_2 gradient in alakaline urine. *J Clin Invest* 69:145, 1982.

122. ULLRICH KJ, PAPAVASSILIOU F: Bicarbonate reabsorption in the papillary collecting duct of rats. *Pflugers Arch* 289:271, 1981.

123. GRABER ML, BENGELE HH, SCHWARTZ JH, ALEXANDER EA: pH and PCO_2 profiles of the rat inner medullary collecting duct. *Am J Physiol* 241:F659, 1981.

124. KOEPPEN BM, HELMAN SI: Acidification of luminal fluid by the rabbit cortical collecting tubule perfused in vitro. *Am J Physiol* 242:F521, 1982.

125. MCKINNEY TD, BURG MB: Bicarbonate absorption by rabbit cortical collecting tubules in vitro. *Am J Physiol* 234:F141, 1978.

126. STONE DS, SELDIN DW, KOKKO JP, JACOBSON HR: Mineralocorticoid modulation of rabbit medullary collecting duct acidification. A sodium-independent acidification. *J Clin Invest* 72:77, 1983.

127. GLUCK S, AL-AWQATI Q: An electrogenic proton-translocating adeno-

128. STONE DK, XIE XS, RACKER E: Comparison of the proton ATPase and chloride transporter from bovine clathrin-coated vesicles and renal medullary vesicles. *Kidney Int* 25:283, 1984.

129. DIAZ-DIAZ FD, LABELLE EF, EATON DC, DUBOSE TD JR: ATP-dependent proton transport in human renal medulla. *Am J Physiol* 20:F297, 1986.

130. KAUNITZ JD, GUNTHER RD, SACHS G: Characterization of an electrogenic ATP and chloride-dependent proton translocating pump from rat renal medulla. *J Biol Chem* 260:11567, 1985.

131. GLUCK S, HIRSCH S, BROWN D: Immunocytochemical localization of H^+-ATPASE in rat kidney. *Kidney Int* 31:167, 1987.

132. SILVA F, SCHULZ W, DAVIS L, XIE X-S, STONE DK: Immunocytochemical localization of the clathrin-coated vesicle proton pump (CCV-PP). *Kidney Int* 1:416, 1987.

133. FISHER JL, HUSTED RF, STEINMETZ PR: Chloride dependence of the HCO_3^- exit step in urinary acidification by the turtle bladder. *Am J Physiol* 245:F564, 1983.

134. STONE DK, SELDIN DW, KOKKO JP, JACOBSON HR: Anion dependence of rabbit medullary collecting duct acidification. *J Clin Invest* 71:1505, 1983.

135. SCHUSTER VL, BONSIB SM, JENNINGS ML: Two types of collecting duct mitochondria-rich (intercalated) cells: Lectin and band 3 cytochemistry. *Am J Physiol* 20:C347, 1986.

136. KOEPPEN BM: Conductive properties of the rabbit outer medullary collecting duct: Inner stripe. *Am J Physiol* 17:F500, 1985.

137. LESLIE BR, SCHWARTZ JH, STEINMETZ PR: Coupling between Cl^- absorption and HCO_3^- secretion in turtle urinary bladder. *Am J Physiol* 225:610, 1973.

138. HUSTED RF, EYMAN E: Chloride-bicarbonate exchange in the urinary bladder of the turtle: Independence from sodium ion. *Biochim Biophys Acta* 595:305, 1980.

139. STAR RA, BURG MB, KNEPPER MA: Bicarbonate secretion and chloride absorption by rabbit cortical collecting ducts: Role of chloride/bicarbonate exchange. *J Clin Invest* 76:1123, 1985.

140. OLIVER JA, HIMMELSTEIN AS, STEINMETZ PR: Energy dependence of urinary bicarbonate secretion in turtle bladder. *J Clin Invest* 55:1003, 1975.

141. SATAKE N, DURHAM JH, EHRENSPECK G, BRODSKY WA: Active electrogenic mechanisms for alkali and acid transport in turtle bladders. *Am J Physiol* 13:C259, 1983.

142. EHRENSPECK G: Effect of 3-isobutyl-1-methylxanthine on HCO_3^- transport in turtle bladder: Evidence of electrogenic HCO_3^- secretion. *Biochem Biophys Acta* 684:219, 1982.

143. STETSON DL, BEAUWENS R, PALMISANO J, MITCHELL PP, STEINMETZ PR: A double-membrane model for urinary bicarbonate secretion. *Am J Physiol* 18:F546, 1985.

144. SCHUSTER VL: Cyclic adenosine monophosphate-stimulated bicarbonate secretion in rabbit cortical collecting tubules. *J Clin Invest* 75:2056, 1985.

145. GOOD DW, BURG MB: Ammonia production by individual segments of the rat nephron. *J Clin Invest* 73:602, 1984.

146. KINSELLA JL, ARONSON PS: Interaction of NH_4^+ and Li^+ with the renal microvillus membrane Na^+-H^+ exchanger. *Am J Physiol* 241:C220, 1981.

147. NAGAMI GT, SONU CM, KUROKAWA K: Ammonia production by isolated mouse proximal tubule perfused in vitro. Effect of metabolic acidosis. *J Clin Invest* 78:124, 1986.

148. HAMM LL, TRIGG D, MARTIN D, GILLESPIE C, BUERKERT J: Transport of ammonia in the rabbit cortical collecting tubule. *J Clin Invest* 75:478, 1985.

149. GARVIN JL, BURG MB, KNEPPER MA: NH_3 and NH_4^+ transport by rabbit renal proximal straight tubules. *Am J Physiol* 21:F232, 1987.

150. DUBOSE TD JR, LUCCI MS, HOGG RJ, PUCACCO LR, KOKKO JP, CARTER NW: Comparison of acidification parameters in superficial and deep nephrons of the rat. *Am J Physiol* 13:F497, 1983.

151. BUERKERT J, MARTIN D, TRIGG G: Segmental analysis of the renal tubule in buffer production and net acid formation. *Am J Physiol* 244:F442, 1983.

152. GOTTSCHALK CW, LASSITER WE, MYLLE M: Localization of urine acidification in the mammalian kidney. *Am J Physiol* 198:581, 1960.

153. GOOD DW, KNEPPER MA, BURG MB: Ammonia and bicarbonate transport by thick ascending limb of rat kidney. *Am J Physiol* 247:F35, 1984.

154. KURTZ I, STAR R, BALABAN RS, GARVIN JL, KNEPPER MA: Spontaneous luminal disequilibrium pH in S_3 proximal tubules. Role in ammonia and bicarbonate transport. *J Clin Invest* 78:989, 1986.

155. KNEPPER MA, GOOD DW, BURG MB: Mechanism of ammonia secretion by cortical collecting ducts of rabbits. *Am J Physiol* 247:F729, 1984.

156. STEINMETZ PR, LAWSON LR: Effect of luminal pH on ion permeability and flows of Na^+ and H^+ in turtle bladder. *Am J Physiol* 220:1573, 1971.

sine triphosphatase from bovine kidney medulla. *J Clin Invest* 73:1704, 1984.

157. BEAUWENS R, AL-AWQATI Q: Active H$^+$ transport in the turtle urinary bladder: Coupling of transport of glucose oxidation. *J Gen Physiol* 68:421, 1976.

158. AL-AWQATI Q, MULLER A, STEINMETZ PR: Transport of H$^+$ against electrochemical gradients in turtle urinary bladder. *Am J Physiol* 233:F502, 1977.

159. LASKI ME, KURTZMAN NA: Characterization of acidification in the cortical and medullary collecting tubule of the rabbit. *J Clin Invest* 72:2050, 1983.

160. O'NEIL RG, HELMAN SI: Transport characteristics of renal collecting tubules: Influences of DOCA and diet. *Am J Physiol* 233:F544, 1977.

161. SCHWARTZ GJ, BURG MB: Mineralocorticoid effects on cation transport by cortical collecting tubule in vitro. *Am J Physiol* 235:F576, 1978.

162. AL-AWQATI Q, NORBY LH, MUELLER A, STEINMETZ PR: Characteristics of stimulation of H$^+$ transport by aldosterone in turtle urinary bladder. *J Clin Invest* 58:351, 1976.

163. AL-AWQATI A: Effect of aldosterone on the coupling between H$^+$ transport and glucose oxidation. *J Clin Invest* 60:1240, 1977.

164. MCKINNEY TD, DAVIDSON KK: Effect of potassium depletion and protein intake in vivo on renal tubular bicarbonate transport in vitro. *Am J Physiol* 21:F509, 1987.

165. HAYS SR, SELDIN DW, KOKKO JP, JACOBSON HR: Effect of K depletion on HCO$_3^-$ transport across rabbit collecting duct segments. *Kidney Int* 29:268A, 1986.

166. TANNEN RL, MCGILL J: Influences of potassium on renal ammonia production. *Am J Physiol* 231:1178, 1976.

167. SELDIN DW, WILSON JD: Renal tubular acidosis, in Stanbury JB, Wyngaarden JB, Fredrickson DS (eds): *The Metabolic Basis of Inherited Disease*, 3d ed. New York, McGraw-Hill, 1972, pp 1548–1566.

168. RECTOR FC JR: Acidification of the urine, in Orloff J, Berliner RW (eds): *Renal Physiology*. Baltimore, Williams and Wilkins, 1973, pp 431.

169. SCHWARTZ WB, JENSON RL, RELMAN AS: Acidification of the urine and increased ammonia excretion without change in acid-base equilibrium: Sodium reabsorption as a stimulus to the acidifying process. *J Clin Invest* 34:673, 1955.

170. BATLLE DC, SEHY JT, ROSEMAN MK, ARRUDA JAL, KURTZMAN NA: Clinical and pathophysiologic spectrum of acquired distal renal tubular acidosis. *Kidney Int* 20:389, 1981.

171. ARRUDA JAL, KURTZMAN NA: Mechanism and classification of deranged distal urinary acidification. *Am J Physiol* 8:F515, 1980.

172. HALPERIN ML, GOLDSTEIN MB, HAIG A, JOHNSON MD, STEINBAUGH BJ: Studies on the pathogenesis of type 1 (distal) renal tubular acidosis as revealed by the urinary PCO$_2$ tension. *J Clin Invest* 53:669, 1974.

173. DUBOSE TD JR, CAFLISCH CR: Validation of the difference in urine and blood CO$_2$ tension during bicarbonate loading as an index of distal nephron acidification in experimental models of distal renal tubular acidosis. *J Clin Invest* 75:1116, 1985.

174. BATLLE DC: Segmental characterization of defects in collecting tubule acidification. *Kidney Int* 30:546, 1986.

175. CAPASSO G, SCHULTZ H, VICKERMANN B, KINNE R: Amphotericin B and amphotericin B methylester: Effect on brush border membrane permeability. *Kidney Int* 30:311, 1986.

176. STEINMETZ PR, LAWSON LR: Defect in acidification induced in vitro by amphotericin B. *J Clin Invest* 49:596, 1970.

177. GARG LC: Lack of effect of amphotericin-B on urine-blood PCO$_2$ gradient in spite of urinary acidification defect. *Pfluegers Arch* 381:137, 1979.

178. JULKA N, ARRUDA JAL, KURTZMAN NA: The mechanism of amphotericin-induced distal acidification defect in rats. *Clin Sci* 56:555, 1979.

179. TAHER SM, ANDERSON RJ, McCARTNEY R, POPOVTZER MM, SCHRIER RW: Renal tubular acidosis associated with toluene "sniffing." *N Engl J Med* 290:765, 1974.

180. KURTZMAN NA: Acquired distal renal tubular acidosis. *Kidney Int* 24:807, 1983.

181. GOOD DW, CAFLISCH CR, DUBOSE TD JR: Transepithelial ammonia concentration gradients in inner medulla of the rat. *Am J Physiol* 252:F491, 1987.

182. KURTZMAN NA: "Short-circuit" renal tubular acidosis. *J Lab Clin Med* 95:633, 1980.

183. HUSTED RF, STEINMETZ PR: The effects of amiloride and ouabain on urinary acidification by turtle bladder. *J Pharmacol Exp Ther* 210:264, 1979.

184. ARRUDA JAL, SUBBARAYUDU K, DYTKO G, MOLA R, KURTZMAN NA: Voltage dependent distal acidification defect induced by amiloride. *J Lab Clin Med* 95:407, 1980.

185. HULTER HN, ILNICKI LP, LICHT JH, SEBASTIAN A: On the mechanism of diminished urinary carbon dioxide tension caused by amiloride. *Kidney Int* 21:8, 1982.

186. NASCIMENTO L, RADEMACKER D, HAMBURGER R, ARRUDA JAL, KURTZ-

MAN NA: On the mechanism of lithium-induced renal tubular acidosis. *J Lab Clin Med* 89:445, 1977.

187. ROSCOE M, GOLDSTEIN MB, HALPERIN MC, WILSON DR, STINEBAUGH BJ: Lithium-induced impairment of urine acidification. *Kidney Int* 9:344, 1976.

188. ARRUDA JAL, DYTKO G, MOLA R, KURTZMAN NA: On the mechanism of lithium-induced distal renal tubular acidosis: Studies in the turtle bladder. *Kidney Int* 17:196, 1980.

189. BATLLE DC, GAVIRIA M, GRUPP M, ARRUDA JAL, WYNN J, KURTZMAN NA: Distal nephron function in patients receiving chronic lithium therapy. *Kidney Int* 21:477, 1982.

190. SCHAMBELAN M, SEBASTIAN A, HULTER HN: Mineralocorticoid excess and deficiency syndromes, in Brenner BM, Stein JH (eds): *Contemporary Issues in Nephrology. Acid-Base and Potassium Homeostasis*. New York, Churchill Livingstone, 1978, vol 2, p 232.

191. HULTER HN, ILNICKI LP, HARBOTTLE JA, SEBASTIAN A: Impaired renal H$^+$ secretion and NH$_3$ production in mineralocorticoid-deficient glucocorticoid-replete dogs. *Am J Physiol* 326:F136, 1979.

192. STEINMETZ PR: Cellular mechanisms of urinary acidification. *Physiol Rev* 54:890, 1974.

193. HULTER HN, BONNER EL JR, GLYNN RD, SEBASTIAN A: Renal and systemic acid-base effects of chronic spironolactone administration. *Am J Physiol* 240:F381, 1981.

194. SZYLMAN P, BETTER OS, CHIAMOWITZ C, ROSLER A: Role of hyperkalemia in the metabolic acidosis of isolated hypoaldosteronism. *N Engl J Med* 294:361, 1975.

195. TANNEN RC: Relationship of renal ammonia production and potassium homeostasis. *Kidney Int* 11:453, 1977.

196. WILCOX CS, CEMERIKI DA, GIEBISCH G: Differential effects of acute mineralo- and glucocorticosteroid administration on renal acid elimination. *Kidney Int* 21:546, 1982.

197. SEBASTIAN A, SUTTON JM, HULTER HN, SCHAMBELAN M, POLAR SM: Effect of mineralocorticoid replacement therapy on renal acid-base homeostasis in adrenalectomized patients. *Kidney Int* 18:762, 1980.

198. SEBASTIAN A, SCHAMBELAN M, LINDENFELD S, MORRIS RC JR: Amelioration of metabolic acidosis with fluorocortisone therapy in hyperoreninemic hypoaldosteronism. *N Engl J Med* 297:576, 1977.

199. CHEEK DB, PERRY JW: A salt-wasting syndrome in infancy. *Arch Dis Child* 33:252, 1948.

200. DONNELL GN, LITMAN N, ROLDAN M: Pseudohypoadrenalocorticism; renal sodium loss; hyponatremia, and hyperkalemia due to renal tubular insensitivity to mineralocorticoids. *Am J Dis Child* 97:813, 1959.

201. POSTEL-VINAY MC, ALBERTI GM, RICOUR C, LIMAL JM, RAPPAPORT R, ROYER P: Pseudohypoaldosteronism: Persistence of hyperaldosteronism and evidence for renal tubular and intestinal responsiveness to endogenous aldosterone. *J Clin Endocrinol Metab* 39:1038, 1974.

202. OBERFIELD SE, LEVINE LS, CAREY RM, BEJAR R, NEW MI: Psuedohypoaldosteronism: Multiple target organ unresponsiveness to mineralocorticoid hormones. *J Clin Endocrinol Metab* 48:228, 1979.

203. BIERICH JR, SCHMIDT U: Tubular Na$^+$ K$^+$-ATPase deficiency the cause of congenital renal salt-losing syndrome. *Eur J Pediatr* 121:81, 1976.

204. WESTENFELDER C, AREVALO GJ, BARANOWSKI RL, KURTZMAN NA, KATZ AI: Relationship between mineralocorticoids and renal Na$^+$-K$^+$-ATPase: Sodium reabsorption. *Am J Physiol* 233:F593, 1977.

205. ARNOLD JE, HEALY JK: Hyperkalemia, hypertension and systemic acidosis without renal failure associated with a tubular defect in potassium excretion. *Am J Med* 47:461, 1969.

206. GORDON RD, GEDDES RA, PAWSEY CGK, O'HALLORAN NW: Hypertension and severe hyperkalemia associated with suppression of renin and aldosterone and completely reversed by dietary sodium restriction. *Aust Ann Med* 4:287, 1970.

207. SPITZER A, EDELMANN CM JR, GOLDBERG LD, HENNEMAN PH: Short stature hyperkalemia and acidosis: A defect in renal transport of potassium. *Kidney Int* 3:251, 1973.

208. WEINSTEIN SF, ALLAN DME, MENDOZA SA: Hyperkalemia, acidosis, and short stature associated with a defect in renal potassium excretion. *J Pediatr* 85:355, 1974.

209. SCHAMBELAN M, SEBASTIAN A, RECTOR FC JR: Mineralocorticoid-resistant renal hyperkalemia without salt wasting (type II pseudohypoaldosteronism): Role of increased renal chloride reabsorption. *Kidney Int* 19:716, 1981.

210. LEE MR, BALL SG, THOMAS TH, MORGAN DB: Hypertension and hyperkalemia responding to bendrofluazide. *Q J Med* 48:245, 1979.

211. SCHAMBELAN M, SEBASTIAN A, BIGLIERI EG: Prevalance, pathogenesis, and functional signficance of aldosterone deficiency in hyperkalemic patients with chronic renal insufficiency. *Kidney Int* 17:89, 1980.

212. SEBASTIAN A, SCHAMBELAN M, HULTER HN, MAHER T, KURTZ I, BIGLIERI EG, RECTOR FC JR, MORRIS RC JR: Hyperkalemic renal tubular acidosis, in

Gonick HC, Buckalew VM Jr (eds): *Renal Tubular Disorders. Pathophysiology, Diagnosis and Management.* New York, Marcel Dekker, 1985, p 307.

213. DEFRONZO RA: Hyperkalemia and hyporeninemic hypoaldosteronism. *Kidney Int* 17:118, 1980.

214. CARROL HJ, FARBER SJ: Hyperkalemia and hyperchloremic acidosis in chronic pyelonephritis. *Metabolism* 13:808, 1964.

215. SCHAMBELAN M, STOCKIGT JR, BIGLIERI M: Isolated hypoaldosteronism in adults. A renin-deficiency syndrome. *N Engl J Med* 287:573, 1972.

216. COLEMAN AJ, ARIAS M, CARTER NW, RECTOR FC JR, SELDIN DW: The mechanism of salt wastage in chronic renal disease. *J Clin Invest* 45:1116, 1966.

217. OH MS, CARROL HJ, CLEMMONS JE, VAGNUCCI AH, LEVISON SP, WHANG ESM: A mechanism for hyporeninemic hypoaldosteronism in chronic renal disease. *Metabolism* 23:1157, 1974.

218. SPARAGNA M: Hyporeninemic hypoaldosteronism associated with diabetic glomerulosclerosis. *J Steroid Biochem* 5:369, 1974.

219. SCHINDER AM, SOMMERS SC: Diabetic sclerosis of the renal juxtaglomerular apparatus. *Lab Invest* 15:877, 1966.

220. TAN SY, SHAPIRO R, FRANCO R, STOCKARD H, MULROW AJ: Indomethacin-induced prostaglandin inhibition with hyperkalemia. A reversible cause of hyporeninemic hypoaldosteronism. *Ann Intern Med* 90:783, 1979.

221. NORBY LH, RAMWELL P, WEIDIG J, SLOTKOFF L, FLAMENBAUM W: Possible role for impaired renal prostaglandin in production in pathogenesis of hyporeninemic hypoaldosteronism. *Lancet* 2:1118, 1978.

222. DELEIVA A, CHRISTLICH AR, MELBY JC, GRAHAM CA, DAY RP, LUETSCHER JA, ZAGER PG: Big renin and biosynthetic defect of aldosterone in diabetes mellitus. *N Engl J Med* 25:639, 1976.

223. PEREZ GO, OSTER JR, VAAMONDE CA: Renal acidosis and renal potassium handling in selective hypoaldosteronism. *Am J Med* 57:809, 1974.

224. MORRIS RC JR: Renal tubular acidosis. Mechanisms, classification and implications. *N Engl J Med* 281:1405, 1969.

225. MORRIS RC JR, SEBASTIAN A: Renal tubular acidosis and Fanconi syndrome, in Stanbury JB, Wyngaarden JB, Frederickson DS, Goldstein JL, Brown MS (eds): *The Metabolic Basis of Inherited Disease*, 5th ed. New York, McGraw-Hill, 1983, p 1808.

226. ELKINGTON JR, HUTH EJ, WEBSTER GD JR, McCANCE RA: The renal excretion of hydrogen ion in renal tubular acidosis. *Am J Med* 29:554, 1960.

227. WRONG O: Urinary hydrogen ion excretion. *J Clin Pathol* 18:520, 1965.

228. BATLLE DC, KURTZMAN NA: The defect in distal (type I) renal tubular acidosis, in Gonick HC, Buckalew VM Jr (eds): *Renal Tublar Disorders. Pathophysiology, Diagnosis and Management.* New York, Marcel Dekker, 1985, p 281.

229. OSTER JR, HOTCHKISS JL, CARBON M: A short duration renal acidification test using calcium chloride. *Nephron* 14:281, 1975.

230. LONEY LC, NORLING LL, ROBSON AM: The use of arginine hydrochloride infusion to assess urinary acidification. *J Pediatr* 100:95, 1982.

231. SEBASTIAN A, McSHERRY E MORRIS RC JR: Metabolic acidosis with special reference to renal acidosis, in Brenner BM, Rector FC Jr (eds): *The Kidney*, 2d ed. Philadelphia, Saunders, 1976, p 615.

232. ARRUDA JAL, NASCIMENTO L, MEHTA PK, RADEMACHER DR, SEHY JT, WESTENFELDER C, KURTZMAN NA: The critical importance of urinary concentration ability in the generation of urinary carbon dioxide tension. *J Clin Invest* 60:922, 1977.

233. KURTZMAN NA, ARRUDA JAL: Physiologic significance of urinary carbon dioxide tension. *Miner Electrolyte Metab* 1:241, 1978.

234. STINEBAUGH BJ, ESQUENAZI R, SCHLOEDER FX, SUKI WN, GOLDSTEIN MB, HALPERIN ML: Control of the urine-blood PCO_2 gradient in alkaline urine. *Kidney Int* 17:31, 1980.

235. BATLLE DC, RIOTTE A, SCHLUETER W: Urinary sodium in the evaluation of hyperchloremic metabolic acidosis. *N Engl J Med* 316:140, 1987.

236. BATLLE DC, KURTZMAN NA: Renal regulation of acid-base homeostasis; Integrated response, in Seldin DW, Giebisch G (eds): *The Kidney: Physiology and Pathophysiology.* New York, Raven, 1985, p 1539.

237. WRONG O, DAVIES HE: The excretion of acid in renal disease. *Q J Med* 28:259, 1959.

238. COE FL, PARKS JH: Stone disease in hereditary distal renal tubular acidosis. *Ann Intern Med* 93:60, 1980.

239. BUCKALEW VM JR, PURVIS ML, SHULMAN MG, HERNDON CN, RUDMAN D: Hereditary renal tubular acidosis. Report of a 64 member kindred with variable clinical expression including idiopathic hypercalcemia. *Medicine* 53:229, 1974.

240. SIMPSON DP: Influence of plasma bicarbonate concentration and pH on citrate excretion. *Am J Physiol* 206:875, 1964.

241. BUCKALEW VM JR, McCURDY DK, LUDWIG GD, CHAYKIN LB, ELKINTON JR: The syndrome of incomplete renal tubular acidosis. *Am J Med* 45:32, 1968.

242. BRENNER RJ, SPRING DB, SEBASTIAN A, MCSHERRY EM, GENANT HK, PALUBINSKAS AJ, MORRIS RC JR: Incidence of radiographically evident bone disease, nephrocalcinosis, and nephrolithiasis in various types of renal tubular acidosis. *N Engl J Med* 307:217, 1982.

243. MCSHERRY EM, MORRIS RC JR: Attainment and maintenance of normal stature with alkali therapy in infants and children with classic renal tubular acidosis. *J Clin Invest* 61:509, 1978.

244. PITTS HH, SCHULTE JW, SMITH DR: Nephrocalcinosis in a father and three children. *J Urol* 73:208, 1955.

245. RANDALL RE JR, TARGGART WH: Familial renal tubular acidosis. *Ann Intern Med* 54:1108, 1961.

246. RANDALL RE JR: Familial renal tubular acidosis revisited. *Ann Intern Med* 66:1024, 1967.

247. SEEDAT YK: Some observations of renal tubular acidosis: A family study. *S Afr Med J* 38:606, 1964.

248. GYORY AZ, EDWARDS KDG: Renal tubular acidosis: A family with an autosomal dominant genetic defect in renal hydrogen ion transport, with proximal tubular and collecting duct dysfunction and increased metabolism of citrate and ammonia. *Am J Med* 45:43, 1968.

249. RICHARDS P, WRONG OM: Dominant inheritance in a family with familial renal tubular acidosis. *Lancet* 2:998, 1978.

250. MCSHERRY EM, POKROY MV: The absence of nephrocalcinosis in children with type 1 RTA on high dose alkali therapy since infancy. *Clin Res* 26:470A, 1978.

251. HAMED IA, CZERWINSKI AW, COATS B, KAUFMAN C, ALTMILLER DH: Familial absorptive hypercalciuria and renal tubular acidosis. *Am J Med* 67:385, 1979.

252. BUCKALEW VM JR: Familial renal tubular acidosis. *Ann Intern Med* 69:1329, 1968.

253. DONCKERWOLCKE RA, VAN STEHELENBURG GJ, TIDDENS HA: A case of bicarbonate-losing renal tubular acidosis with defective carboanhydrase activity. *Arch Dis Child* 45:769, 1970.

254. SHAPIRA E, BEN-YOSEPH Y, EYAL FC, RUSSEL A: Enzymatically inactive red cell carbonic anhydrase B in a family with renal tubular acidosis. *J Clin Invest* 53:59, 1974.

255. NORMAN ME, COHN RM, McCURDY DK: Urinary citrate excretion in the diagnosis of distal renal tubular acidosis. *J Pediatr* 92:394, 1978.

256. BOURKE E, DELANEY VB, MOSAWI M, REAVY P, WESTON M: Renal tubular acidosis and osteopetrosis in siblings. *Nephron* 28:268, 1981.

257. LEVINE AS, MICHAEL AF JR: Ehler-Danlos syndrome with renal tubular acidosis and medullary sponge kidneys. *J Pediatr* 71:107, 1967.

258. BECHNER RL, GILCHRIST GS, ANDERSON EJ: Hereditary elliptocytosis and primary renal tubular acidosis in a single family. *Am J Dis Child* 115:414, 1968.

259. DUNGER DB, BRENTON DP, CAIN AR: Renal tubular acidosis and nerve deafness. *Arch Dis Child* 55:221, 1980.

260. OSTER JR, LESPIER LE, LEE SM, PELLEGRINI EL, VAAMONDE CA: Renal acidification in sickle-cell disease. *J Lab Clin Med* 88:389, 1976.

261. GISELSON N, HEINEGARD D, HOLMBERG CG, LINDBERG LG, LINDSTEDT G, SCHERSTEN B: Renal medullary cystic disease or familial juvenile nephronophthisis: A renal tubular disease. Biochemical findings in two siblings. *Am J Med* 48:174, 1970.

262. MORRIS RC JR, FUDENBERG HH: Impaired renal acidification in patients with hypergammaglobulinemia. *Medicine* 46:57, 1967.

263. COHEN A, WAY BJ: The association of renal tubular acidosis with hyperglobulinaemic purpura. *Australas Ann Med* 11:189, 1962.

264. MASON AMS, GOLDING PL: Hyperglobulinaemic renal tubular acidosis: A report of nine cases. *Br Med J* 3:143, 1970.

265. MARQUEZ-JULIO A, RAPOPORT A, WILANSKY DL, RABINOVICH S, CHAMBERLAIN D: Purpura associated with hypergammaglobulinemia, renal tubular acidosis and osteomalacia. *Can Med Assoc J* 116:53, 1977.

266. LOSPALLUTO J, DORWARD B, BILLER W, ZIFF M: Cryoglobulinemia based on interaction between a gamma macroglobulin and 7S gamma globulin. *Am J Med* 32:142, 1962.

267. MASON AMS, McILLMURRAY MB, GOLDING PL, HUGHES DTD: Fibrosing alveolitis associated with renal tubular acidosis. *Br Med J* 4:596, 1970.

268. TALAL N, ZISMAN E, SCHUR PH: Renal tubular acidosis, glomerulonephritis and immunologic factors in Sjogren's syndrome. *Arthritis Rheum* 2:774, 1968.

269. TALAL N: Sjogren's syndrome, lymphoproliferation, and renal tubular acidosis. *Ann Intern Med* 74:633, 1971.

270. SHIOJI R, FURUYAMA T, ONODERA S, SAITO H, ITO H, SASAKI Y: Sjogren's syndrome and renal tubular acidosis. *Am J Med* 48:456, 1970.

271. MASON AM, GOLDING PL: Renal tubular acidosis and autoimmune thyroid disease. *Lancet* 2:1104, 1970.

272. GOLDING PL: Renal tubular acidosis in chronic liver disease. *Postgrad Med J* 51:550, 1975.

273. BRIDI GS, FALCON PW, BRACKETT NC JR, STILL WJS, SPORN IN: Glomerulonephritis and renal tubular acidosis in a case of chronic active hepatitis with hyperimmunoglobulinemia. *Am J Med* 52:267, 1972.

274. READE AE, SHERLOCK S, HARRISON CV: Active "juvenile" cirrhosis considered as part of a systemic disease. *Gut* 4:378, 1963.

275. SEEDAT YK, RAINE ER: Active chronic hepatitis associated with renal tubular acidosis and successful pregnancy. *S Afr Med J* 39:595, 1965.

276. GOLDING PL, SMITH M, WILLIAMS R: Multisystem involvement in chronic liver disease. Studies on the incidence and pathogenesis. *Ann J Med* 55:772, 1973.

277. COCHRANE AM, TSANTOULOS DC, MOUSSOUROS A, MCFARLAND IG, EDDLESTON ALWF, WILLIAMS R: Lymphocyte cytotoxicity for kidney cells in renal tubular acidosis of autoimmune liver disease. *Br Med J* 2:276, 1976.

278. TU WH, SHEARN MA: Systemic lupus erythematosus and latent renal tubular dysfunction. *Ann Intern Med* 67:100, 1967.

279. JESSOP S, RABKIN R, MUMFORD G, EALES L: Renal tubular function in systemic lupus erythematosus. *S Afr Med J* 47:132, 1973.

280. REYNOLDS TB, BETHUNE JE: Renal tubular acidosis secondary to hyperparathyroidism. *Clin Res* 17:169, 1969.

281. COHEN SI, FITZGERALD MG, FOURMAN P, GRIFFITHS WJ, DEWARDENER HE: Polyuria in hyperparathyroidism. *Q J Med* 26:423, 1957.

282. FERRIS T, KASHGARIAN M, LEVITIN H, BRANDT I, EPSTEIN FH: Renal tubular acidosis and renal potassium wasting acquired as a result of hypercalcemic nephropathy. *N Engl J Med* 265:924, 1961.

283. ROCHMAN J, BETTER OS, WINAVER J, CHAIMOVITZ C, BARZILAI A, JACOBS R: Renal tubular acidosis due to the milk-allkali syndrome. *Isr J Med Sci* 13:609, 1977.

284. HUTH EJ, MAYOCK RL, KERR RM: Hyperthyroidism associated with renal tubular acidosis. *Am J Med* 26:818, 1959.

285. ZISMAN E, BUCCINO RA, GORDEN P, BARTTER FC: Hyperthyroidism and renal tubular acidosis. *Arch Intern Med* 121:118, 1968.

286. PARFITT AM, HIGGINS BA, NASSIM JR, COLLINS JA, HILB A: Metabolic studies in patients with hypercalciuria. *Clin Sci* 27:463, 1964.

287. DENT CE, HARPER CM, PARFIT AM: The effect of cellulose phosphate on calcium metabolism in patients with hypercalciuria. *Clin Sci* 27:417, 1964.

288. DECK MDF: Medullary sponge kidney with renal tubular acidosis: A report of 3 cases. *J Urol* 94:330, 1965.

289. MORRIS RC JR, YAMAUCHI H, PALUBINSKAS AJ, HOWENSTINE J: Medullary sponge kidney. *Am J Med* 38:883, 1965.

290. MASS RE, SMITH WR, WALSH JR: The association of hereditary fructose intolerance and renal tubular acidosis. *Am J Med Sci* 251:516, 1966.

291. YEOH SA: Fabry's disease with renal tubular acidosis. *Singapore Med J* 8:275, 1967.

292. HIGASHIRHARA E, NUTAHARA K, TAGO K, UENO A, NIIJIMA T: Medullary sponge kidney and renal acidification defect. *Kidney Int* 25:453, 1984.

293. PATTERSON RM, ACKERMAN GL: Renal tubular acidosis due to amphotericin B nephrotoxicity. *Arch Intern Med* 127:241, 1971.

294. DOUGLAS JB, HEALY JK: Nephrotoxic effects of amphotericin B, including renal tubular acidosis. *Am J Med* 46:154, 1969.

295. MCCURDY DK, FREDERIC M, ELKINTON JR: Renal tubular acidosis due to amphotericin B. *N Engl J Med* 278:124, 1968.

296. YONG JM, SANDERSON KV: Photosensitive dermatitis and renal tubular acidosis after ingestion of calcium cyclamate. *Lancet* 2:1273, 1969.

297. STEELE TW, GYORY AZ, EDWARDS KDG: Renal function in analgesic nephropathy. *Br Med J* 2:213, 1969.

298. STEELE TW, EDWARDS KDG: Analgesic nephropathy. *Med J Aust* 1:181, 1971.

299. GYORY AZ, STEWART JH, GEORGE CRP, TILLER DJ, EDWARDS KDG: Renal tubular acidosis, acidosis due to hyperkalemia, hypercalcaemia, disordered citrate metabolism and other tubular dysfunctions following human renal transplantation. *Q J Med* 38:231, 1969.

300. WILSON DR, SIDDIQUI AA: Renal tubular acidosis after kidney transplantation. *Ann Intern Med* 79:352, 1973.

301. BETTER OS, CHAIMOWITZ C, NAVEH Y, STEIN A, NAHIR AM, BARZILAI A, ERLIK D: Syndrome of incomplete renal tubular acidosis after cadaver kidney transplantation. *Ann Intern Med* 71:39, 1969.

302. DRUTZ DJ, GUTMAN RA: Renal tubular acidosis in leprosy. *Ann Intern Med* 75:475, 1971.

303. VAINDER M, KELLY J: Renal tubular dysfunction secondary to jejuno-ileal bypass. *JAMA* 235:1257, 1976.

304. BETTER OS, ARIEFF AI, MASSRY SG, KLEEMAN CR, MAXWELL MH: Studies on renal function after relief of complete unilateral ureteral obstruction of three months duration in man. *Am J Med* 54:234, 1973.

305. EARLEY LE: Extreme polyuria in obstructive uropathy. *N Engl J Med* 255:600, 1956.

306. BERLYNE GM: Distal tubular funcction in chronic hydronephrosis. *Q J Med* 30:339, 1961.

307. COCHRAN M, PEACOCK M, SMITH DA, NRODIN BEC: Renal tubular acidosis of pyelonephritis with renal stone disease. *Br Med J* 2:721, 1968.

308. MCSHERRY E, SEBASTIAN A, MORRIS RC JR: Renal tubular acidosis in infants: The several kinds, including bicarbonate wasting classic renal tubular acidosis. *J Clin Invest* 51:499, 1972.

309. RODRIQUEZ-SORIANO J, BOICHIS H, EDELMAN CM JR: Bicarbonate reabsorption and hydrogen ion excretion in children with renal tubular acidosis. *J Pediatr* 71:802, 1967.

310. DEDMON RE, WRONG O: The excretion of organic anion in renal tubular acidosis with particular reference to citrate. *Clin Sci* 22:19, 1962.

311. MORRISSEY JF, OCHOA M, LOTSPEICH WD, WATERHOUSE C: Citrate excretion in renal tubular acidosis. *Ann Intern Med* 58:159, 1963.

312. HARRINGTON TM, BUNCH TW, VAN DEN BERG C: Renal tubular acidosis. A new look at treatment of musculoskeletal and renal disease. *Mayo Clin Proc* 58:354, 1983.

313. SEBASTIAN A, MCSHERRY E, MORRIS RC JR: Impaired renal conservation of sodium and chloride during sustained correction of systemic acidosis in patients with Type I, classic renal tubular acidosis. *J Clin Invest* 58:454, 1976.

314. RODRIQUEZ-SORIANO J, VALLO A, CASTILLO G, OLIVEROS R: Renal handling of water and sodium in children with proximal and distal renal tubular acidosis. *Nephron* 25:193, 1980.

315. SEBASTIAN A, MCSHERRY E, MORRIS RC JR: Renal potassium wasting in renal tubular acidosis (RTA). Its occurrence in types 1 and 2 RTA despite sustained correction of systemic acidosis. *J Clin Invest* 50:667, 1971.

316. LEMANN J JR, LITZOW JR, LEMMON EJ: The effects of chronic acid loads in normal man: Further evidence for participation of bone mineral in the defense against chronic metabolic acidosis. *J Clin Invest* 45:1608, 1975.

317. BACKMAN U, DANIELSON BG, JOHANSSON G, LJUNGHALL S, WIKSTROM B: Incidence and clinical importance of renal tubular defects in recurrent stone formers. *Nephron* 25:96, 1980.

318. ALBRIGHT F, BURNETT CH, PARSON W, REIFENSTEIN ED JR, ROOS A: Osteomalacia and late rickets: The various etiologies met in the United States with emphasis on that resulting in a specific form of renal acidosis, the therapeutic indications for each etiological sub-group, and the relationship between osteomalacia and Milkman's syndrome. *Medicine* 25:399, 1946.

319. LIGHTWOOD R, PAYNE WW, BLACK JA: Infantile renal acidosis. *Pediatrics* 12:628, 1953.

320. LEE SW, RUSSEL JE, AVIOLI LV: 25-OHD$_3$ to 1,25-(OH)$_2$D$_3$ conversion impaired by systemic acidosis. *Science* 195:944, 1977.

321. SEBASTIAN A, MCSHERRY E, MORRIS RC JR: Impaired renal conservation of sodium and chloride during sustained correction of systemic acidosis in patients with type 1, classic renal tubular acidosis. *J Clin Invest* 58:454, 1976.

322. RODRIQUEZ-SORIANO JR, VALLO A, CASTILLO G, OLIVERAS R: Renal handling of water and sodium in children with proximal and distal renal tubular acidosis. *Nephron* 25:193, 1980.

323. MORRIS RC JR, SEBASTIAN A, MCSHERRY E: Therapeutic experience in patients with classic renal tubular acidosis. *Proc VII Intern Cong Nephrol.* Basel, Karger, 1978, p 345.

324. HARRINGTON TM, BUNCH TW, VAN DEN BERG C: Renal tubular acidosis. A new look at treatment of musculoskeletal and renal disease. *Mayo Clin Proc* 58:354, 1983.

325. HARRISON HE, CHISOLM JJ JR, HARRISON HC: Congenital renal tubular acidosis. *Am J Dis Child* 96:588, 1958.

326. OETLIKER OH, ZURBRUGG PRP: Renal tubular acidosis in salt-losing syndrome of congenital adrenal hyperplasia (CAH). *J Clin Endocrinol Metab* 31:447, 1970.

327. IVERSEN T: Congenital adrenocortical hyperplasia with disturbed electrolyte regulations: "dysadrenocorticism." *Pediatrics* 16:875, 1955.

328. NEW MI, DUPONT B, GRUMBACH K, LEVINE LS: Congenital adrenal hyperplasia and related conditions, in Wyngaarden JB, Fredrickson DS, Goldstein JL, Brown MS (eds): *Metabolic Basis of Inherited Disease.* New York, McGraw-Hill, 1983, p 973.

329. HENRICH WL: Nephrotoxicity of nonsteroidal anti-inflammatory agents. *Am J Kidney Dis* 2:478, 1983.

330. DUNN MJ: Nonsteroidal antiinflammatory drugs and renal function. *Annu Rev Med* 35:411, 1984.

331. SEBASTIAN A, SCHAMBELAN M, SUTTON JM: Amelioration of hyperchloremic acidosis with furosemide therapy in patients with chronic renal insufficiency and type 4 renal tubular acidosis. *Am J Nephrol* 4:287, 1984.

332. BRAUTBAR N, LEVI J, ROSLER A, LEITESDORF E, DJALDETI M, EPSTEIN M, KLEEMAN CR: Familial hyperkalemia, hypertension and hyporeninemia

with normal aldosterone levels. A tubular defect in potassium handling. *Arch Intern Med* 138:607, 1978.

333. PAVER WKA, PAULINE GJ: Hypertension and hyperpotassemia without renal disease in a young male. *Med J Aust* 2:305, 1964.

334. DEFRONZO RA, COOKE CR, GOLDBERG M, COW M, MYERS AR, AGUS ZS: Impaired renal tubular potassium secretion in systemic lupus erythematosus. *Ann Intern Med* 86:268, 1977.

335. BATLLE DC, ARRUDA JAL, KURTZMAN NA: Hyperkalemic distal renal tubular acidosis associated with obstructive uropathy. *N Engl J Med* 304:373, 1981.

336. BATLLE D, ITSARAYOUNGYVEN K, ARRUDA JAL, KURTZMAN NA: Hyper-

kalemic hyperchloremic metabolic acidosis in sickle cell hemoglobinopathies. *Am J Med* 72:188, 1982.

337. COGAN MG, ARIEFF AI: Sodium wasting, acidosis and hyperkalemia induced by methicillin interstitial nephritis. Evidence for selective distal tubular dysfunction. *Am J Med* 64:500, 1978.

338. DEFRONZO RA, GOLDBERG M, COOKE CR, BARKER C, GROSSMAN RA, AGUS ZS: Investigations into the mechanisms of hyperkalemia following renal transplantation. *Kidney Int* 11:357, 1977.

339. GABOW PA, MOORE S, SCHRIER RW: Spironalactone-induced hyperchloremic metabolic acidosis in cirrhosis. *Ann Intern Med* 90:338, 1979.

CHAPTER 104

THE RENAL FANCONI SYNDROME

MICHEL BERGERON
ANDRÉ GOUGOUX

1. The renal Fanconi syndrome consists of two components: (1) a generalized dysfunction of the proximal renal tubule leading to impaired proximal reabsorption of amino acids, glucose, phosphate, urate, and bicarbonate, and therefore increased urinary excretion of all these solutes and (2) a vitamin D–resistant metabolic bone disease, either rickets in growing children or osteomalacia in adults.

2. The renal Fanconi syndrome can be either associated with various inborn errors of metabolism or acquired from various etiologies. The inherited Fanconi syndrome may be idiopathic (in the absence of any metabolic disease) or observed with various primary Mendelian diseases. Cystinosis is the most common cause of the hereditary Fanconi syndrome in children. The degree of cystine accumulation determines three clinical forms of cystinosis: infantile, adolescent, and adult. The Fanconi syndrome disappears in patients with hereditary fructose intolerance, galactosemia, tyrosinemia, and Wilson disease when these disorders are treated by restriction of fructose, galactose, tyrosine, or copper, respectively. Expression of the Fanconi syndrome is linked to the abnormal gene product by way of reversible abnormality of renal metabolism. Other metabolic diseases can also be associated with the Fanconi syndrome: vitamin D dependency, glycogen storage disease, and oculocerebrorenal (Lowe) syndrome.

3. A wide variety of toxic and immunologic tubular injuries may produce the generalized renal dysfunction characteristic of the Fanconi syndrome. Heavy metals (cadmium, uranium, mercury, lead, and platinum), various drugs (especially antibiotics), the urinary excretion of abnormal proteins observed in dysproteinemias, and immunologic disorders are all known to induce a Fanconi syndrome. Maleate and cadmium can be used to produce experimental models in the animal. Finally, the Basenji dog can have a spontaneous Fanconi syndrome.

4. The renal Fanconi syndrome might theoretically result either from multiple transport dysfunctions restricted to the proximal tubule or from concomitant proximal and distal tubular dysfunctions. Some experimental data suggest that, in addition to the proximal disturbance, a distal nephron involvement may play a role in the final production of the aminoaciduria, glycosuria, and phosphaturia observed in the Fanconi syndrome. Alterations in membrane permeability can result in an increased influx of molecules into the cell or an increased efflux from the cell at its luminal pole. An impaired mitochondrial production of ATP and a reduced activity of the basolateral membrane Na^+, K^+-ATPase have also been suggested as pathogenetic mechanisms. However, further investigation with various experimental models is still needed to clarify: (1) the respective roles of proximal and distal tubule, (2) the contribution of a reduced influx and/or an accelerated efflux of molecules, and (3) the basic cellular defect(s) underlying the disturbed reabsorptive processes.

5. The clinical features of the renal Fanconi syndrome (mostly in affected children) are not specific and result from the renal losses of fluid and electrolytes and the characteristic vitamin D–resistant metabolic bone disease. The most frequent are polyuria, polydipsia, dehydration, hypokalemia, acidosis, impaired growth, and rickets.

In the absence of a specific treatment, the fluids and electrolytes lost have to be replaced, the metabolic bone disease resulting from Fanconi syndrome must be treated, and renal transplantation may be useful when children with nephropathic cystinosis become severely uremic.

DEFINITION

The renal Fanconi syndrome (Lignac-de Toni-Debré-Fanconi syndrome) is characterized by two components:

1. A generalized renal tubular dysfunction leading to impaired net proximal reabsorption of amino acids, glucose, phosphate, urate, and bicarbonate and therefore increased urinary excretion of all these solutes.

2. A vitamin D–resistant metabolic bone disease, either rickets in growing children or osteomalacia in adults. Water[1] and solutes, normally reabsorbed by the kidney, could also be lost in the urine: sodium, potassium, calcium, magnesium,[2-5] carnitine,[6] lysozyme,[7,8] and other low molecular weight proteins[9] such as peptide hormones, enzymes, and immunoglobulin light chains.

The clinical features are polyuria, dehydration, hypokalemia, acidosis, impaired growth, and rickets.

HISTORICAL SUMMARY

The disease was first recognized in 1903 by Abderhalden,[10] who found cystine crystals in the liver and spleen of a 21-month-old infant and called the disorder a "familial cystine diathesis," considered an inherited susceptibility conferring chemical individuality. In 1924, Lignac[11] described three similar cases in children with severe rickets, dwarfism, renal disease, and progressive wasting. In 1931, Fanconi described rickets and stunted growth in a child with glucosuria and albuminuria.[12] After de Toni in 1933[13] and Debré et al. in 1934[14] had reported similar cases, Fanconi in 1936 recognized the similarity between these few reported cases and suggested for this syndrome the name of "nephrotic-glycosuric dwarfism with hypophosphatemic rickets."[15] This name, which is sometimes referred to in the literature as the Lignac-de Toni-Debré-Fanconi syndrome, was reduced to *Fanconi syndrome* by McCune et al.[16] in 1943.

Table 104-1 Inherited Fanconi Syndrome

1. Idiopathic (22770, 22780)
2. Known primary Mendelian diseases in the Fanconi syndrome:
Cystinosis (21980, 21990, 22000)	Chap. 107
Hereditary fructose intolerance (22960)	Chap. 11
Galactosemia (23040)	Chap. 13
Hepatorenal tyrosinemia (tyrosinemia type I) (27670)	Chap. 16
Wilson disease (27790)	Chap. 54
Vitamin D–dependent rickets (26470)	Chap. 80
Glycogen storage disease type I (23220)	Chap. 12
Oculocerebrorenal (Lowe) syndrome (30900)	
3. The Fanconi syndrome in Basenji dogs

NOTE: Numbers in parentheses are from the McKusick catalogues. The inheritance of all these disorders is autosomal recessive except the Lowe syndrome, which is X-linked recessive. The chapter numbers indicate where these diseases are described in greater detail in this edition.

ETIOLOGIC CLASSIFICATION

The Fanconi syndrome can be associated either with various inborn errors of metabolism (Table 104-1) or acquired from a wide variety of experiences (Table 104-2).

Genetic Causes

Idiopathic. This condition occurs in the absence of any recognized inherited metabolic disease, and its diagnosis can be made only when all the possible acquired causes and various inborn errors of metabolism producing Fanconi syndrome can be excluded. Most cases are sporadic in occurrence, but some familial forms have also been described, most often transmitted in an autosomal dominant fashion.[17–19] Various abnormalities of carbohydrate metabolism have been described in some patients with idiopathic Fanconi syndrome.[20,21]

Known Primary Mendelian Diseases in the Fanconi Syndrome.

CYSTINOSIS. This autosomal recessive disorder associated with the intralysosomal accumulation of cystine in different tissues of the body is the inherited metabolic disease most commonly associated with Fanconi syndrome in children. According to the degree of cystine accumulation, three clinical forms of the disease have been recognized:

1. The infantile or nephropathic cystinosis, characterized by onset of signs and symptoms within the first year of life and progressive renal failure leading to terminal uremia toward the end of the first decade.[22,23]
2. The adolescent or intermediate cystinosis appearing during the second decade of life.[24]
3. The adult or benign form of cystinosis without Fanconi syndrome or impaired renal function.[25]

Only the infantile and adolescent forms are accompanied by Fanconi syndrome. Cystinosis is discussed further in Chap. 107.

HEREDITARY FRUCTOSE INTOLERANCE. In this autosomal recessive disorder associated with deficient activity of fructose-1-phosphate aldolase, the intravenous infusion of fructose rapidly induces an accumulation of fructose-1-phosphate, an intracellular depletion of inorganic phosphate, and a reversible

and complete Fanconi syndrome, with the markedly increased urinary excretion of the characteristic substances.[26,27] The renal toxicity is probably related to the accumulation of fructose-1-phosphate in the renal cortex. Because the infusion of fructose induces within minutes a reversible Fanconi syndrome, this is a very useful experimental model utilized to study the human Fanconi syndrome. Hereditary fructose intolerance is discussed in Chap. 11.

GALACTOSEMIA. The autosomal recessively inherited deficiency of galactose-1-phosphate uridyltransferase (catalyzing the transformation of galactose-1-phosphate into glucose-1-phosphate) leads to accumulation of galactose-1-phosphate. It is associated with an incomplete Fanconi syndrome that is reversible with the removal of lactose or galactose from the diet.[28] The toxic product is presumably the accumulated galactose-1-phosphate, which could also deplete the intracellular inorganic phosphate in a fashion similar to that observed in hereditary fructose intolerance. Galactosemia is discussed in Chap. 13.

HEPATORENAL TYROSINEMIA (TYROSINEMIA TYPE I). When the ingestion of tyrosine or phenylalanine is not restricted, the Fanconi syndrome is induced in patients with this autosomal recessive disease and will disappear with the dietary restriction of these two amino acids. However, this therapeutic maneuver does not prevent the progressive hepatic failure that is responsible for the death of these children within the first decade of life. The various disorders of tyrosine metabolism are discussed in Chap. 16.

WILSON DISEASE. This autosomal recessive disorder of copper metabolism, primarily affecting the liver and the brain (hepatolenticular degeneration), is also accompanied by copper accumulation in the renal cortex and the various tubular defects characteristic of Fanconi syndrome,[29] both of which can be reversed when copper is chelated by penicillamine.[30] The following clinical triad is characteristic of this disease: (1) hepatic

Table 104-2 Acquired Fanconi Syndrome

Heavy metals:
  Cadmium
  Uranium
  Mercury
  Lead
  Platinum
Drugs:
  Antibiotics: outdated tetracycline
            aminoglycosides: gentamicin and others
  Others: valproate
       6-mercaptopurine
       methyl-3-chromone
       Lysol
       paraquat
       toluene
Urinary excretion of abnormal proteins:
  Multiple myeloma
  Other dysproteinemias
Immunological disorders:
  Nephrotic syndrome
  Interstitial nephritis with anti-TBM antibodies
  Renal transplantation
  Malignancy
Experimental models:
  Maleate
  Cadmium
  Fructose (in hereditary fructose intolerance)

cirrhosis; (2) a wide variety of neurologic symptoms; and (3) the Kayser-Fleischer rings in the cornea. Wilson disease is discussed in Chap. 54.

VITAMIN D DEPENDENCY (TYPE I). In this autosomal recessive disorder, the 1α hydroxylation of 25-hydroxycholecalciferol in the kidney mitochondria is apparently defective, a phenomenon that induces decreased intestinal absorption of calcium, hypocalcemia, and parathyroid hormone (PTH) excess. This disease is discussed in Chap. 80.

GLYCOGEN STORAGE DISEASE (TYPE I). The type with autosomal recessive inheritance and galactose intolerance is associated with Fanconi syndrome.[31] Glycogen storage diseases are discussed in Chap. 12.

OCULOCEREBRORENAL (LOWE) SYNDROME. Originally described by Lowe and his coworkers in 1952[32] and characterized by a Fanconi syndrome, rickets (or osteomalacia in a few patients), growth retardation, bilateral congenital cataracts, glaucoma, generalized muscular hypotonia, hyporeflexia, and severe mental retardation, this syndrome often becomes apparent during the first year of life. In this familial disorder, probably transmitted as an X-linked recessive trait,[33] the great majority of the cases have been observed in males although a few have been reported in girls.[34] Cortical opacities can also be found in the lenses of heterozygotes,[35,36] suggesting the possibility of another mode of inheritance. There are three distinct phases in the natural history of this inborn error of metabolism: (1) during infancy, neurologic and ophthalmologic manifestations predominate, but the various tubular dysfunctions of the Fanconi syndrome may all appear within the first year of life; (2) during childhood, severe rickets, growth failure, and the Fanconi syndrome are obvious; (3) later, the patient dies from inanition, pneumonia, and chronic renal failure.

Although the specific defect responsible for Lowe syndrome remains unknown, the increased urinary excretion of mucopolysaccharides, chondroitin sulfate, and hydroxyproline[37,38] either suggests an abnormal metabolism in connective tissue or simply reflects the metabolic bone disease. Early in the course of the disease, renal dysfunction is tubular but is followed by a progressive reduction of glomerular filtration rate. The finding that the mitochondrial changes and the functional defects are both proximal suggests a relationship between anatomic and physiological abnormalities.[34] The tubular changes observed with renal biopsy are not specific[39] whereas variable pathologic changes have been described in the central nervous system, the eyes, the skeletal muscles, and other tissues. Since the possible biochemical abnormality underlying this disorder remains unknown, there is no specific diagnostic test and treatment. However, vitamin D therapy is useful to treat the metabolic bone disease, as is the case for the Fanconi syndrome associated with other inborn errors of metabolism.

Spontaneous Animal Model: The Basenji Dog. A spontaneous animal model resembling the human idiopathic Fanconi syndrome was recently found in basenji dogs.[40-42] They show clinical signs analogous to those found in humans: polydipsia, polyuria, dehydration, weight loss, and weakness; renal failure occurs after months or years. Plasma electrolytes in these dogs were normal with the exception of a moderate metabolic acidosis. Glucosuria, phosphaturia, and a generalized aminoaciduria along with elevated sodium, potassium, and urea excre-

tion were documented in all affected animals. Renal biopsies were normal, but when renal failure was present, various degrees of tubular and glomerular damage were found.

Acquired Causes

Table 104-2 lists a wide variety of toxic and immunologic renal tubular injuries that may produce the generalized impairment of net proximal tubular reabsorption characteristic of the Fanconi syndrome. In contrast to the Fanconi syndrome observed with various inherited metabolic diseases, these acquired Fanconi syndromes are seen primarily in adults, although some can occur at any age.

Heavy Metals. Among the heavy metals that can bind selectively to the proximal tubular cells and induce the reabsorptive dysfunctions characteristic of the Fanconi syndrome, lead was the most frequent cause but now cadmium is the agent most commonly responsible. These induced tubular dysfunctions are reversible when exposure to the toxic environment ceases.

CADMIUM. After a prolonged occupational or environmental exposure to cadmium, over many years, its excessive accumulation in the kidney is responsible for chronic nephrotoxicity.[43] The increased excretion of the low molecular weight β_2-microglobulin, an indicator of renal tubular damage, can allow the early detection of cadmium nephrotoxicity.[44]

Fanconi syndrome appears frequently among workers exposed to cadmium,[45] a finding which has stimulated many investigators to study the experimental cadmium-induced nephropathy in many animal models, including the rabbit[46,47] and the rat.[48-50] In Japan, exposure to soil contaminated with cadmium resulted in the severe osteomalacia characteristic of itai-itai disease.[50,51]

URANIUM. Exposure to gaseous uranium compounds has also been associated with Fanconi syndrome, uranium and cadmium being much more toxic metals than lead and mercury.[45]

MERCURY. The accumulation of mercury in the proximal tubular cells after exposure to inorganic mercury salts or organic mercury compounds (mercurial diuretics) can also produce a reversible Fanconi syndrome.[5]

LEAD. In lead poisoning, intranuclear inclusion bodies containing lead bound to a protein appear in proximal tubular cells,[52] and a reversible Fanconi syndrome has been observed, especially in acutely intoxicated children.[53]

PLATINUM. Cisplatin (cis-diaminedichloroplatinum II) is a new and potent chemotherapeutic agent used very effectively in the treatment of many carcinomas, particularly testicular and ovarian. Dose-dependent nephrotoxicity with reduced glomerular filtration rate results from the use of this drug.[54] Among the various tubular dysfunctions observed, the most important clinically is the severe urinary loss of magnesium, inducing severe magnesium depletion and hypomagnesemia.[55]

Drugs. The tubular dysfunctions characteristic of Fanconi syndrome have also been described with the utilization of several drugs and are reversible when the responsible agent is discontinued.

The ingestion of *outdated tetracycline* produces a reversible Fanconi syndrome.[56,57] Among the degradation products of tetracycline, outdated or stored in a moist warm environment, anhydro-4-*epi*-tetracycline has been shown to be the intoxicating substance responsible for the tubulopathy.[58] In the rat, this metabolite induces mitochondrial injury in proximal nephron and decreases oxidative enzymatic activity and energy production.[59] Most cases of Fanconi syndrome resulting from *aminoglycoside antibiotics* have been associated with the use of gentamicin. Renal magnesium and potassium wasting with severe hypomagnesemia and hypokalemia have also been observed with aminoglycoside antibiotics,[60,61] substances well known to accumulate selectively in proximal tubular cells.[62] A reversible Fanconi syndrome has been reported with the anticonvulsant *valproate*.[63] Some patients with nephrotic syndrome and receiving *6-mercaptopurine* have also developed Fanconi syndrome.[64] It is not easy in these patients to dissociate the respective contribution of the nephrotic syndrome and of the 6-mercaptopurine administration. The accidental ingestion of large amounts of *methyl-3-chromone*, a substance structurally related to tetracycline, has also been reported to induce a reversible Fanconi syndrome.[65] Finally, a Fanconi syndrome has been recognized following an extensive *Lysol* burn,[66] the ingestion of the herbicide *paraquat*,[67] and *toluene* inhalation.[68]

Urinary Excretion of Abnormal Proteins. *Multiple myeloma* and *other dysproteinemias* are a frequent cause of acquired Fanconi syndrome in adults,[69] which in some patients may even precede by many years the appearance of dysproteinemia.[70] Indeed, this diagnosis of dysproteinemia must be excluded in all adult patients with a Fanconi syndrome of obscure cause. Bence-Jones proteinuria is always present,[70] all patients having light chains of the κ variety except a few with λ light chains.[71] Crystalline inclusion bodies, probably representing light-chain accumulation, can be observed in the cytoplasm of proximal tubular cells.[69,70] These light chains might therefore be directly toxic to the proximal tubular cells or to a specific enzyme such as Na^+,K^+-ATPase.[72] Amyloidosis,[73,74] light-chain nephropathy,[75,76] and benign monoclonal gammopathy[77] are among the dysproteinemias other than multiple myeloma reported to induce Fanconi syndrome and urinary excretion of monoclonal light chains.

Immunologic Disorders. Fanconi syndrome has been reported in *nephrotic syndrome*,[78] most often with focal and segmental glomerular sclerosis,[79] but the pathogenesis remains uncertain. *Interstitial nephritis with antitubular basement membrane antibodies* (linear deposits along the basement membrane of the proximal tubules) may be accompanied by a Fanconi syndrome. A reversible Fanconi syndrome has also been observed in several patients following *renal transplantation*,[80–82] and the defects of proximal reabsorption, most probably resulting from immunologic tubular injury during acute rejection episodes, seem to disappear during the first year following transplantation. The immunosuppressive drug cyclosporine does not seem to be responsible for the various defects of proximal reabsorption.[83] Some tumors, such as nonossifying fibroma of bone, can also produce Fanconi syndrome, possibly through the release of a humoral factor.[84] Lymphoid *malignancies* with peritubular infiltrates have been associated with a Fanconi syndrome and could result either from immunologic tubular injury or from tubular destruction by tumor infiltration.[85] The simultaneous occurrence of a Fanconi syndrome

and other malignancies such as carcinoma of the lung,[86] liver,[87] pancreas,[88] and ovary[89] may be fortuitous.

Experimental Models. *Maleate*, first used by Berliner et al. in the dog,[90] was found by Harrison and Harrison[91] to induce a Fanconi syndrome in the rat. Maleate still remains a model widely used to study the mechanisms and pathogenesis of this complex renal tubular dysfunction. *Cadmium* has also been utilized.[47–50]

MECHANISMS AND PATHOGENESIS

General Characteristics

The pathogenetic mechanisms underlying the Fanconi syndrome remain to be elucidated. However, many conclusions can be drawn from study of the hereditary or the acquired diseases as well as of the experimental models.

1. The Fanconi syndrome clearly has *two components:* a multiple renal transport disorder and a metabolic bone disease, rickets in children or osteomalacia in adults. Since the bone disease is not always present, the primary disturbance in this syndrome could be thought to be renal. In fact, some of the etiologic agents might have direct effects on both bone and kidney, whereas others might have an effect only on kidney. The respective contributions of the proximal and distal nephron, the organelles involved, the membrane transport defects, or the possibly abnormal enzymatic activities remain to be elucidated.

2. Amino acids, glucose, phosphate, and other molecules are transported into the cells by multiple carriers; it is hard to visualize how point mutations could disturb so many of these. It is more likely that the various mutations associated with the Mendelian forms of the Fanconi syndrome affect components of the transport mechanism other than the carrier(s) per se.

3. In many pathologic cases, the Fanconi syndrome is expressed only when well-defined factors are present, such as the unrestricted intake of tyrosine and phenylalanine in tyrosinemia[92–94] or the ingestion of fructose in hereditary fructose intolerance.[26,27,95] Reciprocally, when galactose is removed in galactosemia,[28,96] fructose in hereditary fructose intolerance,[26,95] or tyrosine and phenylalanine in tyrosinemia,[97–100] the Fanconi syndrome is no longer expressed. These observations demonstrate the *reversibility* of the abnormality leading to the Fanconi syndrome. Furthermore, they suggest that the modified critical step has to be *global* enough to affect many transport functions. Such a step could be a disruption of the energy source, a generalized nonspecific membrane permeability defect, or a specific organelle pathology.

4. The *duration of exposure* to the specific agent also appears to be an important element but varies with the disease underlying the Fanconi syndrome. Within minutes of intravenous injection of small amounts of fructose to patients with hereditary fructose intolerance, the excretion of amino acids, phosphate, glucose, and other electrolytes will be increased in a dose-dependent fashion.[26,27] On the other hand, patients with galactosemia have to ingest galactose for days[28] before the renal dysfunction occurs, whereas, by contrast, hepatic dysfunction can be noted within minutes.[101] Renal tubular dysfunction caused by cadmium occurs after many years of occupational or environmental exposure.[43] Lead can induce a

Fanconi syndrome in acutely intoxicated children almost exclusively,[53,102] in experimental animals,[103] and, rarely, in chronic states.

5. *A specific biochemical sequence* of events can take place as illustrated in patients with hereditary fructose intolerance: following a fructose infusion, an accumulation of fructose-1-phosphate in proximal tubular cells is postulated to result from the deficiency of aldolase-B activity; a severe depletion of inorganic phosphate, ATP, and total adenine nucleotides ensues and might contribute to the multiple transport disorders of the Fanconi syndrome.[104] Any interruption of this sequence of events could prevent the pathologic manifestations. Since in normal humans, rats, and dogs the administration of large amounts of fructose does not induce a Fanconi syndrome, despite the hepatic and renal cortical accumulation of large amounts of fructose-1-phosphate,[105–107] Morris et al.[104] have suggested that the genetic defect is primary and that abnormalities other than the kinetic deficiency of the enzyme are finally involved.

Nephron Segment(s) Involved

In normal mammalian kidneys, the reabsorptive capacity of proximal tubular cells is immense for amino acids since most of the filtered load is reabsorbed within the first few millimeters of the proximal nephron;[108] in fact less than 2 percent of the filtered load of amino acids will appear in the urine with the exception of aspartic acid, glycine, and histidine, of which only 94 to 98 percent are reabsorbed.[109] In the Fanconi syndrome, the aminoaciduria is generalized, with the pattern of excretion appearing to be similar to the normal.[110] The absence of selective aminoaciduria does not point toward a specific lesion of a carrier or even to a specific segment.

Major morphologic lesions were not found in many reported cases of human Fanconi syndrome such as hereditary tyrosinemia,[94] galactosemia,[28] fructosemia,[104] heavy metal poisoning, and various other forms.[17,111] Renal biopsies from Basenji dogs having the Fanconi syndrome showed normal histology; various degrees of tubular and glomerular damage were found only when renal failure was present.[41,42] It should be pointed out, however, that the absence of morphologic lesions does not mean the absence of functional disturbance; for instance, histologic lesions are seldom observed in most specific transport defects such as hyperglycinuria, lysinuria, and hyperlysinuria.

A "swan-neck lesion," resulting from cell atrophy in the earliest portion of the proximal tubule, was found at the autopsy of a few patients with cystinosis and was thought for many years to be the cause of transport dysfunction.[112] This is not likely since micropuncture studies have demonstrated that the entire length and not only the early part of the proximal nephron has the capacity to reabsorb amino acids.[108] The popularitiy of this explanation can be attributed to the beauty of the image given as evidence rather than to a critical assessment of the data: this hypothesis should be forgotten. The cell atrophy observed is most probably secondary, since the emergence of the swan-neck lesion in cystinosis is progressive with age and not related to the transport dysfunction. Nonspecific tubular and glomerular lesions were also documented in renal biopsies of patients with Lowe syndrome.[33,113]

In the experimental models of Fanconi syndrome, ultrastructural modifications were always found in the proximal tubule[8,114–118] but varied from cell to cell: extensive cytoplasmic vacuolization, darkening or swelling of the mitochon-

drial matrix, enlargement of the lysosomes, disruption of cytoplasmic organization, distension of the granular endoplasmic reticulum, loss of basolateral membrane infoldings, and even cell necrosis. Maleate and heavy metals are readily filtered, and the early part of the proximal nephron is therefore first exposed to their deleterious effects; for instance, Gonick et al. showed that cadmium specifically accumulates in proximal tubular cells of the renal cortex.[50] Toxic compounds containing heavy metals also yielded similar lesions. All these ultrastructural changes are reversible within a few days after cessation of maleate or cadmium administration. Additional evidence of proximal nephron damage is also suggested by the significant impairment by maleate of the 1 hydroxylation of 25-OH-D$_3$ in the mitochondria of proximal cells.[119–121] Maleate also affects the γ-glutamyl transpeptidase, a membrane-bound enzyme of the proximal nephron.[122] Several investigators[114,117,118] have found maleate-induced morphologic injury restricted to proximal tubular cells, the distal tubule appearing normal. By contrast, the distal nephron was also found to be damaged when larger doses of maleate were given.[115,116]

The Fanconi syndrome might theoretically result either from multiple transport dysfunctions restricted to the proximal tubule or from concomitant proximal and distal tubular dysfunctions.[123] Therefore, based on morphologic alterations and on data obtained with micropuncture studies in rats[123] and dogs,[124] some investigators have suggested that maleate has additional sites of action located more distally than the proximal convoluted tubule, namely the thick ascending limb[125] or other parts of the distal nephron. Similarly, micropuncture and free water clearance studies have shown that maleate,[126,127] like acetazolamide,[128,129] has an effect on the thick ascending limb; while sodium chloride and sodium bicarbonate reabsorption were both inhibited in the proximal nephron, chloride but not bicarbonate was reabsorbed by the thick ascending limb. Bergeron et al.[123,130] suggested that maleate induces an accelerated cellular efflux of amino acids, glucose, and phosphate into the lumen of both proximal and distal nephron. However, in proximal tubular cells the membrane transport carriers still demonstrate the same structural requirements for their substrates, as observed in experimental animals[123,131,132] as well as in humans in whom a competitive inhibition between glycine and iminoacids has been reported.[133] Since they are still functioning, albeit at a reduced rate,[132] both the decreased cell entry and the increased efflux into the lumen can be partially or totally corrected downstream; such is not the case in the distal nephron where there is no reabsorption of amino acids[108] and little absorption of phosphate and glucose.[124] Molecules that exit at this distal site are irrevocably lost in the urine. Thus, in addition to the proximal disturbance, a distal nephron involvement may be a major determinant in the final production of the aminoaciduria, glycosuria, and phosphaturia seen in the Fanconi syndrome. This is further suggested by the increased urinary minus blood P$_{CO_2}$ gradient[134–137] and the increased kaliuresis in maleate-treated animals,[134] both of which could reflect an accelerated cellular exit of hydrogen and potassium ions into the lumen of the last segments of the nephron.

Membrane Permeability Alteration

It must be pointed out that increased urinary excretion of electrolytes and nonelectrolytes does not necessarily mean de-

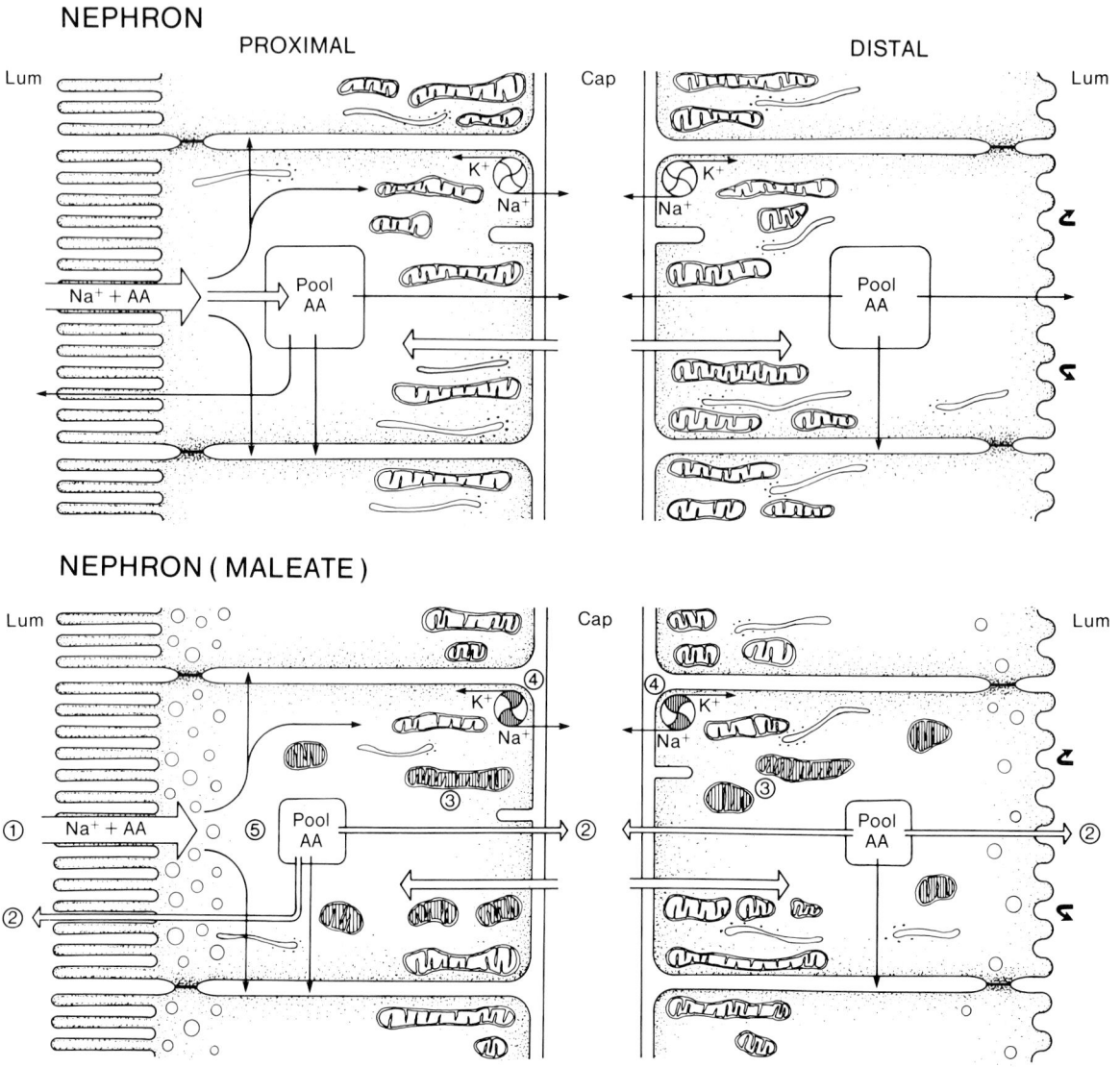

Fig. 104-1 Schematic representation of movements of amino acids in the normal nephron *(upper panel)*. At the proximal tubule, amino acids gain access to the cell through the apical microvilli or through the infoldings of the antiluminal membrane. The reabsorptive capacity of proximal cells, driven by the sodium gradient, is high for amino acids and monosaccharides. At the distal nephron sites, there is no absorption of amino acids and little, if any, of glucose and phosphate. Efflux (arrows) will take place at all membranes.

In the maleate model *(lower panel)*, morphologic modifications are dose-dependent and will vary from minor cytoplasmic vacuolization and mitochondrial swelling to cell disorganization and even necrosis; they are more extensive in proximal tubule cells. The intracellular pool of amino acids is decreased. Based on the maleate model, which has been extensively studied, the renal Fanconi syndrome could be explained by: (1) A *defective entry* of molecules at the proximal nephron. Most solutes lost in the urine are coupled to luminal reabsorption of sodium. (2) A *defective entry* in proximal cells coupled with an *increased backleak* of molecules from both proximal and distal cells. While backflux can be corrected downstream in the proximal tubule, molecules that exit at the distal nephron sites are irrevocably lost in the urine. This is why a distal nephron involvement, in addition to the defective entry at the proximal apical membrane, may be a major determinant. (3) *An impaired energy production.* Maleate, for example, decreases the mitochondrial oxidation of Krebs cycle intermediates (especially the CoA-dependent substrates). (4) A reduced Na^+, K^+-*ATPase activity* at the basolateral membranes which could affect the sodium gradient. (5) A derangement at *other possible cellular sites* such as the H^+-ATPase, the membrane carrier recycling mechanism, organellar organization (endoplasmic reticulum, mitochondrion, etc.).

creased proximal reabsorption. This final excretion could result at the tubular level either from defective entry into the cell or from an increased exit of molecules from the cell at its luminal pole. Both mechanisms appear to act in the maleate model.[123,124,130,132,138,139] The in vitro studies of Rosenberg and Segal,[138] later confirmed by in vivo studies of Bergeron et al.,[123,130] have clearly shown the preponderant role of cellular efflux as opposed to influx in explaining the low intracellular concentration of amino acids and sugars in maleate-treated kidneys.[140,141] These efflux data suggest a maleate-induced impairment of the barrier function of the membrane, as illustrated by the increased cellular exit of amino acids,[123,130,138]

sugars,[123,124,139] potassium,[134,142] and bicarbonate[126,134,137,143] (see Fig. 104-1).

Maleic anhydride was shown to react rapidly and specifically with the amino groups associated with the protein fraction of the red cell membrane: sodium and potassium permeability was increased while that of sulfate and chloride was reduced, suggesting a specific action of maleate on the membrane physicochemical properties.[144] In contrast, in the study of Le Grimellec et al.,[145] maleate did not alter the composition and the physical status of brush border and basolateral membranes obtained from dog kidney cortex; similarly, vesicles obtained from brush border membranes of rats[146] and dogs[147] were not influenceed by maleate, although this could be explained by the reversibility of the action of maleate.[110] Actually, maleate does not have to modify the physical chemistry of membranes to affect their permeability, since this could also be achieved by its chelating properties.[131,148] Maleate could chelate divalent cations (Mg^{2+} and Ca^{2+}) essential in the maintenance of membrane stability. Silverman and Huang[139] have shown that the cytoplasmic face of cell membranes appears to be modified by maleate: by using indicators to localize the interactions of various sugars at either the internal or external side of these membrane surfaces, they concluded that the glycosuria found in maleate-treated dogs could be related to the movement of cytoplasmic glucose back across the brush border into the urine or could be attributed to partial inhibition of glucose movement from the cytoplasm across the antiluminal membrane. Previous in vitro studies of Rosenberg and Segal[138] and in vivo studies of Bergeron et al.,[123] Wen,[124] Maesaka and McCaffery,[149] and Günther et al.[132] are all compatible with such a membrane effect of maleate at the cytoplasmic leaflet. Maleate could thus affect the membrane transfer of amino acids and other molecules at both proximal and distal nephron sites. Studies of the maleate-induced lysozymuria carried out by Christensen and Maunsbach[8] further illustrated the maleate-induced membrane derangement; they demonstrated that, in proximal cells, the transport of lysozyme from endocytic vacuoles to lysosomes was partially inhibited by maleate, leading to an accumulation of these vacuoles in the apical cytoplasm and a disappearance of apical tubules, and suggesting an altered recycling of membranes. The mere volume of these numerous vacuoles observed in all studies certainly contributes to organelle dysfunction; this distension factor has always been underestimated.

Maleate, cadmium, and tetracyclines all have specific, albeit reversible, effects not only on plasma membranes but also on organelles and their interrelationships.[50,116,117] Mitochondria seem to concentrate cadmium, mercury, and maleate.[48,50] The decreased activity of 25-OH-vitamin D_3-1-hydroxylase,[119] an enzyme localized in renal cortical mitochondria,[120] suggests that these chemicals can affect their membranes as well. A major modification between mitochondria and the network of perimitochondrial membranes was noted by Bergeron and Laporte[116] in the maleate model and by Gonick and Kramer[50] in the cadmium model.

The cadmium nephrotoxicity in humans occurs after many years of exposure to a polluted environment or to industrial cadmium (pigment, plastic, alloy, accumulator battery, nuclear and electronic industries).[43-46] A Fanconi syndrome can be detected, but an increased β_2-microglobulin urinary excretion is the early sign that may be useful as a screening test.[44] Many cases were described after World War II in Japan in middle-aged, postmenopausal, multiparous women, and their disease is known as the itai-itai, or "ouch-ouch," disease.[51,150,151] Intoxication came from soil and rice fields contaminated in the Jinzu River Basin.

An experimental model of the Fanconi syndrome has been produced in rats by repeated injections of cadmium chloride and was extensively studied by Gonick and collaborators.[50,152] The myriad of signs typical of Fanconi syndrome appeared abruptly after 3 weeks of injection and the total administration of about 2.25 mg cadmium. Mitochondrial enlargement and loss of basolateral membrane infoldings were the most conspicuous morphologic changes. ATP levels decreased by 38 percent and Na^+,K^+-ATPase activity by 60 percent. Kägi and Vallee[153] described the formation of a low molecular weight metalloprotein, methallothionein, which has a high sulfhydryl content (cysteine) and metal content (cadmium and zinc). The cadmium methallothionein is synthesized by the liver, filtered by the glomeruli, and reabsorbed proximally.[154] The proximal tubule appears to be more susceptible to the cadmium-methallothionein[155] or cadmium-cysteine[156] complexes than to the inorganic cadmium. The protein degradation in the kidney liberates the metal, which is then incorporated into nascent chains of thionein within the kidney. The delayed onset of renal tubular dysfunction seen in cadmium exposure is most likely related to its interaction with the thionein. Raghavan and Gonick[157] offered the hypothesis that the Fanconi syndrome resulted from a saturation of the cadmium-binding capacity of the renal cortical methallothionein; the excess cadmium was then free to "spill" over from the soluble cytoplasmic fraction to other subcellular fractions, in particular the microsomal and mitochondrial fractions containing cadmium-sensitive enzymes. As mentioned above, renal cortical ATP levels and Na^+,K^+-ATPase activities were reduced when the manifestations of the Fanconi syndrome were maximal in these animals (see Fig. 104-2).

The basenji dog model actually suggests a defect only at the

Fig. 104-2 Schematic summary of the possible sites of action of various agents producing the renal Fanconi syndrome at the proximal tubule cell. Most renal effects could be explained by a diminution in ATP synthesis or a reduction of the Na^+,K^+-ATPase activity, or both, through an accumulation or depletion of cofactors (see Ref. 50). The resultant decrease in the sodium gradient would affect luminal absorption of many substrates ultimately found in excess in the urine.

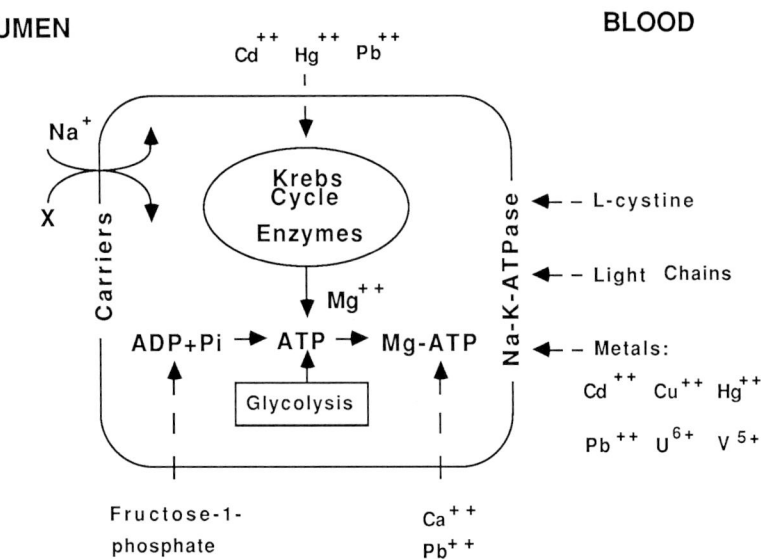

substrate entry step. As demonstrated by Bovee et al.,[41] glycine, lysine, and α-methyl-D-glucose uptake were all impaired in slices obtained from renal biopsies of affected dogs. The discrepancy between the maleate and the spontaneous animal model cannot be explained. One could ask which model is more related to the human genetic disease.

Basic Cellular Defect(s)

Maleate could directly inhibit the Na^+,K^+-ATPase activity at the basolateral membranes, a phenomenon which would affect secondarily the electrochemical sodium gradient across the luminal membrane; alternatively, maleate could interfere at some intracellular site (like the mitochondrion) and reduce the production of ATP required for active reabsorption. Either of these hypotheses could account for all the transport defects observed in the Fanconi syndrome. In this regard, it is of interest that the reabsorption of each solute lost in the urine is coupled to sodium reabsorption across the luminal membrane of proximal cells: Na^+-H^+ exchange (bicarbonate reabsorption), Na^+-glucose cotransport, Na^+–amino acid cotransport, and Na^+-phosphate cotransport. Therefore the following sequence of events might be postulated to account for the various tubular dysfunctions observed in the Fanconi syndrome: impaired mitochondrial metabolism $\longrightarrow$ decreased cytosolic ATP concentration $\longrightarrow$ reduced active sodium extrusion through basolateral membrane $\longrightarrow$ increased cytosolic sodium concentration $\longrightarrow$ decreased gradient-dependent luminal sodium entry $\longrightarrow$ decreased sodium-coupled transport processes through brush border membranes (H^+, glucose, amino acids, and phosphate) $\longrightarrow$ increased urinary excretion of bicarbonate, glucose, amino acids, and phosphate. As discussed above, a passive efflux of these substances into the lumen cannot be ruled out in the presence of an inhibited active influx.

Reductions in renal cortical ATP concentration[115,142,158] and renal cortical Na^+,K^+-ATPase activity[142] have been reported following maleate administration, but a causal relationship between the decreased ATP level and the inhibited tubular transport of various solutes has not been established unequivocally. Intestinal transport of glucose and amino acids was unaffected by maleate while sodium absorption and Na^+,K^+-ATPase activity were markedly impaired.[159] Maleate has been shown to decrease markedly the mitochondrial oxidation of Krebs cycle intermediates in the kidney,[160] especially the CoA-dependent substrates such as pyruvate and α-ketoglutarate.[158,161,162] Maleate has also been shown to impair significantly the 1 hydroxylation of 25-OH D_3 in the mitochondria of proximal tubular cells.[119–121]

The protective effect of acetoacetate on the maleate-induced bicarbonaturia and phosphaturia results from competition between acetoacetate (which is the physiological substrate for succinyl-CoA transferase) and maleate for the transfer of CoA.[163] Phosphate loading can also prevent the maleate-induced Fanconi syndrome and decrease the urinary excretion of bicarbonate, amino acids,[164] lysozyme, and lysosomal enzymes.[7] This protective effect of phosphate suggests that a phosphate-dependent metabolic abnormality in proximal tubular cells might play an important role in the pathogenesis of the maleate-induced Fanconi syndrome.

At the present time, when one considers the pathogenesis of Fanconi syndrome, an impaired energy production by the renal tubular cells cannot be dissociated from a defective transduction of this energy to the various membrane transport processes.

Because the pathophysiologic basis of the Fanconi syndrome remains uncertain, further investigation with various experimental models will be needed in order to clarify: (1) the respective role of the proximal and the distal nephron, (2) the contribution of a reduced influx and/or an accelerated efflux or backleak, and (3) the basic cellular defect(s) underlying the disturbed reabsorptive processes. In this respect the Basenji model may shed new light since the renal tubular defects are a likely consequence of a genetic factor.

CLINICAL SIGNS AND SYMPTOMS

The clinical manifestations of the Fanconi syndrome are not specific and result from the renal losses of fluid and electrolytes and the characteristic vitamin D–resistant metabolic bone disease. The renal loss of other substances such as glucose, amino acids, and uric acid will not induce any clinical signs or symptoms but may contribute in some patients to the diagnosis of Fanconi syndrome.

The age at which a child first becomes symptomatic can provide a clue for the specific inborn error of metabolism. For example, infants with galactosemia or hereditary fructose intolerance can present acute symptoms within the first few days of life if they ingest galactose or fructose, respectively. Children with nephropathic cystinosis present symptoms only after the age of 6 months. In Wilson disease, symptoms resulting from Fanconi syndrome will not appear before the end of the first decade of life. By contrast, it must be kept in mind that symptoms induced by acquired Fanconi syndrome may appear at any age.

Consequences of Renal Losses of Fluid and Electrolytes

The excessive urinary loss of water resulting from the renal concentration defect will produce polyuria, polydipsia, and, in infants and young children, dehydration, constipation, and unexplained recurrent fever. The chronic hyperchloremic metabolic acidosis resulting from the associated renal proximal tubular acidosis (renal tubular acidosis is discussed extensively in the previous chapter) can induce anorexia and episodic vomiting. Muscle weakness and even episodic paralysis can result from severe hypokalemia and potassium depletion.

Vitamin D–Resistant Metabolic Bone Disease

Hypophosphatemic rickets (in growing children) or osteomalacia (in adults) is produced at least in part by the exaggerated renal loss of phosphate and may dominate the clinical picture. An impaired renal tubular 1 hydroxylation of 25-OH D_3 into $1,25$-$(OH)_2D_3$ may also play a role in the pathogenesis of this metabolic bone disease; indeed this biologically active vitamin D metabolite was not found in the blood of five nonazotemic children with Fanconi syndrome.[119] The child with Fanconi syndrome will fail to grow and may present the characteristic clinical findings of rickets: frontal bossing, rachitic rosary, bowing deformities of the legs, metaphyseal widening at the wrists, knees, or ankles, and waddling gait. By contrast, patients with adult-onset Fanconi syndrome often complain of severe bone pain and spontaneous fractures.

THERAPY

Specific Treatment

Although the clinical management of Fanconi syndrome consists mostly of replacing the renal losses of substances not reabsorbed adequately by the kidney, one must always consider the possibility of a dramatic improvement when the responsible metabolite (in some inborn errors of metabolism) or the toxic agent (in acquired Fanconi syndrome) can be removed.

In the absence of a specific treatment (such as oral cysteamine therapy to reduce intracellular cystine levels in nephropathic cystinosis,[165]), fluids and electrolytes have to be replaced, the metabolic bone disease resulting from Fanconi syndrome must be treated, and renal transplantation may be useful when children with nephropathic cystinosis are severely uremic. By contrast, no therapy is required for the asymptomatic renal loss of other substances like glucose, amino acids, and uric acid.

Correction of Fluid and Electrolyte Disturbances

First, dehydration resulting from polyuria must be prevented by restoration of free water balance. Second, the correction of the hyperchloremic metabolic acidosis usually requires large amounts of alkali (more than 3 and up to 10 to 20 meq/(kg/day), a therapeutic maneuver that will aggravate the renal potassium wasting. Extracellular fluid volume contraction may also be induced by the restriction of sodium chloride and water[166] and the chronic administration of hydrochlorothiazide[167] in an attempt to reduce a very large alkali requirement to a level tolerable for the patient. Third, potassium supplements are always necessary in the presence of a severe hypokalemia or during the treatment of metabolic acidosis with alkali therapy. Potassium bicarbonate, citrate, or acetate will simultaneously improve the potassium depletion and the metabolic acidosis.

Treatment of Metabolic Bone Disease

Oral phosphate therapy to replace the renal phosphate loss helps to correct the rickets in children or osteomalacia in adults. Vitamin D therapy, in the form of its more biologically active metabolites, $1,25\text{-}(OH)_2D_3$ and $1\alpha\text{-}OHD_3$, is preferred because renal production of hormone could be impaired in patients with Fanconi syndrome.[119]

Renal Transplantation

Chronic dialysis and renal transplantation should be considered when patients with Fanconi syndrome become terminally uremic. Renal transplantation from either a cadaveric or a living related donor has been especially useful to treat young children with nephropathic cystinosis because the transplanted

kidney does not have the genetic defect and consequently there is no recurrence of renal cystinosis and Fanconi syndrome.[168,169] However, these transplanted cystinotic patients remain of short stature and often photophobic despite a successful renal transplantation. The severe mental retardation of patients like those with Lowe syndrome may prevent the utilization of chronic dialysis and/or renal transplantation in the treatment of their end-stage renal disease.

This investigation was supported by the Medical Research Council of Canada. We acknowledge the roles our colleagues Alfred Berteloot, Raynald Laprade, Jennifer McLeese, Stanton Segal, Georges Thiery, and Patrick Vinay have played in the development of the ideas expressed in this chapter; any errors are our sole responsibility, not theirs. The authors acknowledge the skillful assistance of Mrs. C. Laurier and Mssrs. J. Bernier, D. Cyr, and G. Filosi.

REFERENCES

1. RODRIGUEZ-SORIANO J, VALLO A, CASTILLO G, OLIVEROS R: Renal handling of water and sodium in children with proximal and distal renal tubular acidosis. *Nephron* 25:193, 1980.
2. HOUSTON IB, BOICHIS H, EDELMANN CM: Fanconi syndrome with renal sodium wasting and metabolic alkalosis. *Am J Med* 44:638, 1968.
3. SEBASTIAN A, McSHERRY E, MORRIS RC JR: On the mechanism of renal potassium wasting in renal tubular acidosis associated with the Fanconi syndrome (type 2 RTA). *J Clin Invest* 50:231, 1971.
4. RODRIGUEZ SORIANO J, HOUSTON IB, BOICHIS H, EDEMANN CM JR: Calcium and phosphorus metabolism in the Fanconi syndrome. *J Clin Endocrinol Metab* 28:1555, 1968.
5. LEE DBN, DRINKARD JP, ROSEN VJ, GONICK HC: The adult Fanconi syndrome: Observations on etiology, morphology, renal function and mineral metabolism in three patients. *Medicine* 51:107, 1972.
6. BERNARDINI I, RIZZO WB, DALAKAS M, BERNAR J, GAHL WA: Plasma and muscle free carnitine deficiency due to renal Fanconi syndrome. *J Clin Invest* 75:1124, 1985.
7. AL-BANDER HA, MOCK MD, ETHEREDGE SB, PAUKERT TT, HUMPHREYS MH, MORRIS RC JR: Coordinately increased lysozymuria and lysosomal enzymuria induced by maleic acid. *Kidney Int* 30:804, 1986.
8. CHRISTENSEN EI, MAUNSBACH AB: Proteinuria induced by sodium maleate in rats: Effects on ultrastructure and protein handling in renal proximal tubule. *Kidney Int* 17:771, 1980.
9. DILLARD MG, PESCE AF, POLLAK VE, BOREISHA I: Proteinuria and renal protein clearances in patients with renal tubular disorders. *J Lab Clin Med* 78:203, 1971.
10. ABDERHALDEN F: Familiare Cystindiathese. *Z Physiol Chem* 38:557, 1903.
11. LIGNAC GOE: Stooris der Cystine-stofwisseling byj Kinderen. *Ned Tijdschr Geneeskd* 68:2987, 1924.
12. FANCONI G: Die nicht diabetischen Glykosurien und Hyperglykamien des altern Kindes. *Jahrb Kinderheilk* 133:257, 1931.
13. DE TONI G: Remarks on the relations between renal rickets (renal dwarfism) and renal diabetes. *Acta Paediatr* 16:479, 1933.
14. DEBRE R, MARIE J, CLERET F, MESSIMY R: Rachitisme tardif coexistant avec une néphrite chronique et une glycosurie. *Arch Med Enf* 37:597, 1934.
15. FANCONI G: Der nephrotisch-glykosurische Zwergwuchs mit Hypophosphatámischer Rachitis. *Dtsch Med Wochenschr* 62:1169, 1936.
16. McCUNE DJ, MASON HH, CLARKE HT: Intractable hypophosphatemic rickets with renal glycosuria and acidosis (the Fanconi syndrome): Report of a case in which increased urinary organic acids were detected and identified, with a review of the literature. *Am J Dis Child* 65:81, 1943.
17. HUNT DD, STEARNS G, McKINLEY JB, FRONING E, HICKS P, BONFIGLIO M: Long-term study of family with Fanconi syndrome without cystinosis (DeToni-Debré-Fanconi syndrome). *Am J Med* 40:492, 1966.
18. FRIEDMAN AL, TRYGSTAD CW, CHESNEY RW: Autosomal dominant Fanconi syndrome with early renal failure. *Am J Med Genet* 2:225, 1978.
19. BRENTON DP, ISENBERG DA, CUSWORTH DC, GARROD P, KRYWAWYCH S, STAMP TCB: The adult presenting idiopathic Fanconi syndrome. *J Inherited Metab Dis* 4:211, 1981.

20. CHESNEY RW, KAPLAN BS, COLLE E, SCRIVER CR, MCINNES RR, DUPONT CH, DRUMMOND KN: Abnormalities of carbohydrate metabolism in idiopathic Fanconi syndrome. *Pediatr Res* 14:209, 1980.

21. CHESNEY RW, KAPLAN BS, TEITEL D, COLLE E, MCINNES RR, GOLDMAN H, SCRIVER CR: Metabolic abnormalities in the idiopathic Fanconi syndrome: Studies of carbohydrate metabolism in two patients. *Pediatrics* 67:113, 1981.

22. CRAWHALL JC, LIETMAN PS, SCHNEIDER JA, SEEGMILLER JE: Cystinosis: Plasma cystine and cysteine concentrations and the effect of D-penicillamine and dietary treatment. *Am J Med* 44:330, 1968.

23. SCHNEIDER JA, WONG V, SEEGMILLER JE: The early diagnosis of cystinosis. *J Pediatr* 74:114, 1969.

24. GOLDMAN H, SCRIVER CR, AARON K, DELVIN E, CANLAS Z: Adolescent cystinosis: Comparisons with infantile and adult forms. *Pediatrics* 47:979, 1971.

25. LIETMAN PS, FRAZIER PD, WONG VG, SHOTTON D, SEEGMILLER JE: Adult cystinosis: A benign disorder. *Am J Med* 40:511, 1966.

26. MORRIS RC JR: An experimental renal acidification defect in patients with hereditary fructose intolerance. I. Its resemblance to renal tubular acidosis. *J Clin Invest* 47:1389, 1968.

27. MORRIS RC JR: An experimental renal acidification defect in patients with hereditary fructose intolerance. II. Its distinction from classical renal tubular acidosis; its resemblance to the renal acidification defect associated with the Fanconi syndrome of children with cystinosis. *J Clin Invest* 47:1648, 1968.

28. HOLZEL A, KOMROWER GM, SCHWARZ V: Galactosemia. *Am J Med* 22:703, 1957.

29. MORGAN HG, STEWART WK, LOWE KG, STOWERS JM, JOHNSTONE JH: Wilson's disease and the Fanconi syndrome. *Q J Med* 31:361, 1962.

30. ELSAS LJ, HAYSLETT JP, SPARGO BH, DURANT JL, ROSENBERG LE: Wilson's disease with reversible renal tubular dysfunction: Correlation with proximal tubular ultrastructure. *Ann Intern Med* 75:427, 1971.

31. GARTY R, COOPER M, TABACHNIK E: The Fanconi syndrome associated with hepatic glycogenosis and abnormal metabolism of galactose. *J Pediatr* 85:821, 1974.

32. LOWE CU, TERREY M, MACLACHLAN EA: Organic-aciduria, decreased renal ammonia production, hydrophthalmos, and mental retardation: A clinical entity. *Am J Dis Child* 83:164, 1952.

33. ABBASSI V, LOWE CU, CALCAGNO PL: Oculo-cerebro-renal syndrome: A review. *Am J Dis Child* 115:145, 1968.

34. SAGEL I, ORES RO, YUCEOGLU AM: Renal function and morphology in a girl with oculocerebrorenal syndrome. *J Pediatr* 77:124, 1970.

35. GARDNER RJM, BROWN N: Lowe's syndrome: Identification of carriers by lens examination. *J Med Genet* 13:449, 1976.

36. HITTNER HM, CARROLL AJ, PRCHAL JT: Linkage studies in carriers of Lowe oculo-cerebro-renal syndrome. *Am J Hum Genet* 34:966, 1982.

37. AKASAKI M, FUKUI S, SAKANO T, TANAKA T, USUI T, YAMASHINA I: Urinary excretion of a large amount of bound sialic acid and of undersulfated chondroitin sulfate A by patients with the Lowe syndrome. *Clin Chim Acta* 89:119, 1978.

38. HAYASHI S, NAGATA T, KIMURA A, TSURUMI K: Urinary excretion of acid glycosaminoglycans and hydroxyproline in a patient with oculo-cerebro-renal syndrome. *Tohoku J Exp Med* 126:215, 1978.

39. HABIB R, BARGETON E, BRISSAUD HE, RAYNAUD J, LE BALL JC: Constatations anatomiques chez un enfant atteint d'un syndrome de Lowe. *Arch Fr Pediatr* 19:945, 1962.

40. EASLEY JR, BREITSCHWERDT EB: Glucosuria associated with renal tubular dysfunction in three Basenji dogs. *J Am Vet Med Assoc* 168:938, 1976.

41. BOVEE KC, JOYCE T, REYNOLDS R, SEGAL S: The Fanconi syndrome in Basenji dogs: A new model for renal transport defects. *Science* 201:1129, 1978.

42. BOVEE KC, JOYCE T, REYNOLDS R, SEGAL S: Spontaneous Fanconi syndrome in the dog. *Metabolism* 27:45, 1978.

43. ADAMS RG, HARRISON JF, SCOTT P: The development of cadmium-induced proteinuria, impaired renal function, and osteomalacia in alkaline battery workers. *Q J Med* 38:425, 1969.

44. BERNARD A, BUCHET JP, ROELS H, MASSON P, LAUWERYS R: Renal excretion of proteins and enzymes in workers exposed to cadmium. *Eur J Clin Invest* 9:11, 1979.

45. CLARKSON TW, KENCH JE: Urinary excretion of amino acids by men absorbing heavy metals. *Biochem J* 62:361, 1956.

46. AXELSSON B, DAHLGREN SE, PISCATOR M: Renal lesions in the rabbit after long-term exposure to cadmium. *Arch Environ Health* 17:24, 1968.

47. STOWE HD, WILSON M, GOYER RA: Clinical and morphologic effects of oral cadmium toxicity in rabbits. *Arch Pathol* 94:389, 1972.

48. NISHIZUMI M: Electron microscopic study of cadmium nephrotoxicity in the rat. *Arch Environ Health* 24:215, 1972.

49. RAGHAVAN SRV, GONICK HC: Experimental Fanconi syndrome. IV. Effect of repetitive injections of cadmium on tissue distribution and protein-binding of cadmium. *Miner Electrolyte Metab* 3:36, 1980.

50. GONICK HC, KRAMER HJ: Pathogenesis of the Fanconi syndrome, in Gonick HC, Buckalew VM Jr (eds): *Renal Tubular Disorders. Pathophysiology, Diagnosis and Management.* New York, Marcel Dekker, 1985, p 545.

51. NOMIYAMA K, SUGATA Y, MURATA I, NAKAGAWA S: Urinary low-molecular-weight proteins in itai-itai disease. *Environ Res* 6:373, 1973.

52. GOYER RA, MAY P, CATES MM, KRIGMAN MR: Lead and protein content of isolated intranuclear inclusion bodies from kidneys of lead-poisoned rats. *Lab Invest* 22:245, 1970.

53. CHISOLM JJ JR, HARRISON HC, EBERLEIN WR, HARRISON HE: Amino-aciduria, hypophosphatemia, and rickets in lead poisoning. *Am J Dis Child* 89:159, 1955.

54. BLACHLEY JD, HILL JB: Renal and electrolyte disturbances associated with cisplatin. *Ann Intern Med* 95:628, 1981.

55. SCHILSKY RL, ANDERSON T: Hypomagnesemia and renal magnesium wasting in patients receiving cisplatin. *Ann Intern Med* 90:929, 1979.

56. FRIMPTER GW, TIMPANELLI AE, EISENMENGER WJ, STEIN HS, EHRLICH LI: Reversible "Fanconi syndrome" caused by degraded tetracycline. *JAMA* 184:111, 1963.

57. GROSS JM: Fanconi syndrome (adult type) developing secondary to the ingestion of outdated tetracycline. *Ann Intern Med* 58:523, 1963.

58. BENITZ KF, DIERMEIER HF: Renal toxicity of tetracycline degradation products. *Proc Soc Exp Biol Med* 115:930, 1964.

59. LINDQUIST RR, FELLERS FX: Degraded tetracycline nephropathy: Functional, morphologic, and histochemical observations. *Lab Invest* 15:864, 1966.

60. BAR RS, WILSON HE, MAZZAFERRI EL: Hypomagnesemic hypocalcemia secondary to renal magnesium wasting: A possible consequence of high-dose gentamicin therapy. *Ann Intern Med* 82:646, 1975.

61. KELNAR CJH, TAOR WS, REYNOLDS DJ, SMITH DR, SLAVIN BM, BROOK CGD: Hypomagnesaemic hypocalcemia with hypokalaemia caused by treatment with high dose gentamicin. *Arch Dis Child* 53:817, 1978.

62. KUHAR MJ, MAK LL, LIETMAN PS: Autoradiographic localization of (^{3}H) gentamicin in the proximal renal tubules of mice. *Antimicrob Agents Chemother* 15:131, 1979.

63. LENOIR GR, PERIGNON JL, GUBLER MC, BROYER M: Valproic acid: A possible cause of proximal tubular renal syndrome. *J Pediatr* 98:503, 1981.

64. BUTLER HE JR, MORGAN JM, SMYTHE CM: Mercaptopurine and acquired tubular dysfunction in adult nephrosis. *Arch Intern Med* 116:853, 1965.

65. OTTEN J, VIS HL: Acute reversible renal tubular dysfunction following intoxication with methyl-3-chromone. *J Pediatr* 73:422, 1968.

66. SPENCER AG, FRANGLEN GT: Gross amino-aciduria following a Lysol burn. *Lancet* 1:190, 1952.

67. VAZIRI ND, NESS RL, FAIRSHTER RD, SMITH WR, ROSEN SM: Nephrotoxicity of paraquat in man. *Arch Intern Med* 139:172, 1979.

68. MOSS AH, GABOW PA, KAEHNY WD, GOODMAN SI, HAUT LL, HAUSSLER MR: Fanconi's syndrome and distal renal tubular acidosis after glue sniffing. *Ann Intern Med* 92:69, 1980.

69. COSTANZA DJ, SMOLLER M: Multiple myeloma with the Fanconi syndrome: Study of a case, with electron microscopy of the kidney. *Am J Med* 34:125, 1963.

70. MALDONADO JE, VELOSA JA, KYLE RA, WAGONER RD, HOLLEY KE, SALASSA RM: Fanconi syndrome in adults: A manifestation of a latent form of myeloma. *Am J Med* 58:354, 1975.

71. WALKER BR, ALEXANDER F, TANNENBAUM PJ: Fanconi syndrome with renal tubular acidosis and light chain proteinuria. *Nephron* 8:103, 1971.

72. MCGEOCH J, SMITH JF, LEDINGHAM J, ROSS B: Inhibition of active transport sodium-potassium-ATPase by myeloma protein. *Lancet* 2:17, 1978.

73. FINKEL PN, KRONENBERG K, PESCE AJ, POLLAK VE, PIRANI CL: Adult Fanconi syndrome, amyloidosis and marked x-light chain proteinuria. *Nephron* 10:1, 1973.

74. ROCHMAN J, LICHTIG C, OSTERWEILL D, TATARSKY I, EIDELMAN S: Adult Fanconi's syndrome with renal tubular acidosis in association with renal amyloidosis: Occurrence in a patient with chronic lymphocytic leukemia. *Arch Intern Med* 140:1361, 1980.

75. HARRISON JF, BLAINEY JD: Adult Fanconi syndrome with monoclonal abnormality of immunoglobulin light chain. *J Clin Pathol* 20:42, 1967.

76. SMITHLINE N, KASSIRER JP, COHEN JJ: Light-chain nephropathy: Renal tubular dysfunction associated with light-chain proteinuria. *N Engl J Med* 294:71, 1976.

77. DAHLSTROM U, MARFTENSSON J, LINDSTROM FD: Occurrence of adult Fanconi syndrome in benign monoclonal gammopathy. *Acta Med Scand* 208:425, 1980.

78. VAN HOOFT C, VERMASSEN A: DeToni-Debré-Fanconi syndrome in nephrotic children: A review. *Ann Pediatr* 194:193, 1960.

79. MCVICAR M, EXENI R, SUSIN M: Nephrotic syndrome and multiple tubular defects in children: An early sign of focal segmental glomerulosclerosis. *J Pediatr* 97:918, 1980.

80. FRIEDMAN A, CHESNEY R: Fanconi's syndrome in renal transplantation. *Am J Nephrol* 1:45, 1981.

81. VERTUNO LL, PREUSS HG, ARGY WP JR, SCHREINER GE: Fanconi syndrome following homotransplantation. *Arch Intern Med* 133:302, 1974.

82. VAZIRI ND, NELLANS RE, BRUEGGEMANN RM, BARTON CH, MARTIN DC: Renal tubular dysfunction in transplanted kidneys. *South Med J* 72:530, 1979.

83. PALESTINE AG, AUSTIN HA, NUSSENBLATT RB: Renal tubular function in cyclosporine-treated patients. *Am J Med* 81:419, 1986.

84. LEEHEY DJ, ING TS, DAUGIRDAS JT: Fanconi syndrome associated with a non-ossifying fibroma of bone. *Am J Med* 78:708, 1985.

85. GOLDSWEIG HG, BRISSON DE CHAMPLAIN ML, DAVIDMAN M: Proximal tubular dysfunction associated with Burkitt's lymphoma. *Cancer* 41:568, 1978.

86. WEINSTEIN B, IRREVERRE F, WATKIN DM: Lung carcinoma, hypouricemia and aminoaciduria. *Am J Med* 39:520, 1965.

87. STOWERS JM, DENT CE: Studies on the mechanism of the Fanconi syndrome. *Q J Med* 16:275, 1947.

88. MYERSON RM, PASTOR BH: The Fanconi syndrome and its clinical variants. *Am J Med Sci* 228:378, 1954.

89. CLAY RD, DARMADY EM, HAWKINS M: The nature of the renal lesion in the Fanconi syndrome. *J Pathol Bacteriol* 65:551, 1953.

90. BERLINER RW, KENNEDY TJ, HILTON JG: Effect of maleic acid on renal function. *Proc Soc Exp Biol Med* 75:791, 1950.

91. HARRISON HE, HARRISON HC: Experimental production of renal glycosuria, phosphaturia, and aminoaciduria by injection of maleic acid. *Science* 120:606, 1954.

92. FRITZELL S, JAGENBURG OR, SCHNURER LB: Familial cirrhosis of the liver, renal tubular defects with rickets and impaired tyrosine metabolism. *Acta Paediatr* 53:18, 1964.

93. HALVORSEN S, GJESSING LR: Studies on tyrosinosis: 1, Effect of low-tyrosine and low-phenylalanine diet. *Br Med J* 2:1171, 1964.

94. HARRIES JT, SEAKINS JWT, ERSSER RS, LLOYD JK: Recovery after dietary treatment of an infant with features of tyrosinosis. *Arch Dis Child* 44:258, 1969.

95. LEVIN B, SNODGRASS GJAI, OBERHOLZER VG, BURGESS EA, DOBBS RH: Fructosaemia: Observations on seven cases. *Am J Med* 45:826, 1968.

96. CUSWORTH DC, DENT CE, FLYNN FV: The amino-aciduria in galactosemia. *Arch Dis Child* 30:150, 1955.

97. JAGENBURG R, LINDBLAD B, DE MARE JM, RODJER S: Hereditary tyrosinemia: Metabolic studies in a patient with partial p-hydroxyphenylpyruvate hydroxylase activity. *J Pediatr* 80:994, 1972.

98. ARONSSON S, ENGLESON G, JAGENBURG R, PALMGREN B: Long-term dietary treatment of tyrosinosis. *J Pediatr* 72:620, 1968.

99. SCRIVER CR, SILVERBERG M, CLOW CL: Hereditary tyrosinemia and tyrosyluria: Clinical report of four patients. *Can Med Assoc J* 97:1047, 1967.

100. KANG ES, GERALD PS: Hereditary tyrosinemia and abnormal pyrrole metabolism. *J Pediatr* 77:397, 1970.

101. ISSELBACHER KJ: Galactosemia, in Stanbury JB, Wyngaarden JB, Fredrickson DS (eds): *The Metabolic Basis of Inherited Disease*, 2d ed. New York, McGraw-Hill, 1966, p 178.

102. CHISOLM JJ JR: Aminoaciduria as a manifestation of renal tubular injury in lead intoxication and a comparison with patterns of aminoaciduria seen in other diseases. *J Pediatr* 60:1, 1962.

103. GOYER RA: The renal tubule in lead poisoning. I. Mitochondrial swelling and aminoaciduria. *Lab Invest* 19:71, 1968.

104. MORRIS RC JR, MCINNES RR, EPSTEIN CJ, SEBASTIAN A, SCRIVER CR: Genetic and Metabolic Injury of the Kidney, in Brenner BM, Rector FC Jr (eds): *The Kidney*. Philadelphia, Saunders, 1976, p 1193.

105. BURCH HB, LOWRY OH, MEINHARDT L, MAX P JR, CHYU KJ: Effect of fructose, dihydroxyacetone, glycerol, and glucose on metabolites and related compounds in liver and kidney. *J Biol Chem* 245:2092, 1970.

106. WOODS HF, EGGLESTON LV, KREBS HA: The cause of hepatic accumulation of fructose-1-phosphate on fructose loading. *Biochem J* 119:501, 1970.

107. WOODS HF: Hepatic accumulation of metabolites after fructose loading. *Acta Med Scand Suppl* 542:87, 1972.

108. BERGERON M, MOREL F: Amino acid transport in rat renal tubules. *Am J Physiol* 216:1139, 1969.

109. BRODEHL J, BICKEL H: Aminoaciduria and hyperaminoaciduria in childhood. *Clin Nephrol* 1:149, 1973.

110. ROTH KS, FOREMAN JW, SEGAL S: The Fanconi syndrome and mechanisms of tubular transport dysfunction. *Kidney Int* 20:705, 1981.

111. SCHNEIDER JA, SEEGMILLER JE: Cystinosis and the Fanconi syndrome, in Stanbury JB, Wyngaarden JB, Fredrickson DS (eds): *The Metabolic Basis of Inherited Disease*, 3d ed. New York, McGraw-Hill, 1972.

112. DARMADY EM, STRANACK F: Microdissection of the nephron in disease. *Br Med Bull* 13:21, 1957.

113. WITZLEBEN CL, SCHOEN EJ, TU WH, MCDONALD LW: Progressive morphologic renal changes in the oculo-cerebro-renal syndrome of Lowe. *Am J Med* 44:319, 1968.

114. WORTHEN HG: Renal toxicity of maleic acid in the rat: Enzymatic and morphologic observations. *Lab Invest* 12:791, 1963.

115. SCHARER K, YOSHIDA T, VOYER L, BERLOW S, PIETRA G, METCOFF J: Impaired renal gluconeogenesis and energy metabolism in maleic acid–induced nephropathy in rats. *Res Exp Med* 157:136, 1972.

116. BERGERON M, LAPORTE P: Effet membranaire du maléate au niveau du néphron proximal et distal. *Rev Can Biol* 32:275, 1973.

117. ROSEN VJ, KRAMER HJ, GONICK HC: Experimental Fanconi syndrome. II. Effect of maleic acid on renal tubular ultrastructure. *Lab Invest* 28:446, 1973.

118. VERANI RR, BREWER ED, INCE A, GIBSON J, BULGER RE: Proximal tubular necrosis associated with maleic acid administration to the rat. *Lab Invest* 46:79, 1982.

119. BREWER ED, TSAI HC, SZETO KS, MORRIS RC JR: Maleic acid-induced impaired conversion of 25(OH)D$_3$ to 1,25(OH)$_2$D$_3$: Implications for Fanconi's syndrome. *Kidney Int* 12:244, 1977.

120. GRAY RW, OMDAHL JL, GHAZARIAN JG, DeLUCA HF: 25-hydroxycholecalciferol-1-hydroxylase: Subcellular location and properties. *J Biol Chem* 247:7528, 1972.

121. AKIBA T, ENDOU H, KOSEKI C, SAKAI F: Localization of 25-hydroxyvitamin D$_3$-1a-hydroxylase activity in the mammalian kidney. *Biochem Biophys Res Commun* 94:313, 1980.

122. TATE SS, MEISTER A: Stimulation of the hydrolytic activity and decrease of the transpeptidase activity of y-glutamyl transpeptidase by maleate; identify a rat kidney maleate-stimulated glutaminase and y-glutamyl transpeptidase. *Proc Natl Acad Sci USA* 71:3329, 1974.

123. BERGERON M, DUBORD L, HAUSSER C: Membrane permeability as a cause of transport defects in experimental Fanconi syndrome: A new hypothesis. *J Clin Invest* 57:1181, 1976.

124. WEN SF: Micropuncture studies of glucose transport in the dog: Mechanism of renal glycosuria. *Am J Physiol* 231:468, 1976.

125. BREWER ED, SENEKJIAN HO, INCE A, WEINMAN EJ: Maleic acid-induced reabsortive dysfunction in the proximal and distal nephron. *Am J Physiol* 245:F339, 1983.

126. BANK N, AYNEDJIAN HS, MUTZ BF: Microperfusion study of proximal tubule bicarbonate transport in maleic acid-induced renal tubular acidosis. *Am J Physiol* 250:F476, 1986.

127. AL-BANDER HA, WEISS RA, HUMPHREYS MH, MORRIS RC JR: Dysfunction of the proximal tubule underlies maleic acid-induced type II renal tubular acidosis. *Am J Physiol* 243:F604, 1982.

128. ROSIN JM, KATZ MA, RECTOR FC JR, SELDIN DW: Acetozolamide in studying sodium reabsorption in diluting segment. *Am J Physiol* 219:1731, 1970.

129. KUNAU RT JR: The influence of the carbonic anhydrase inhibitor, benzolamide (Cl-11,366), on the reabsorption of chloride, sodium, and bicarbonate in the proximal tubule of the rat. *J Clin Invest* 51:294, 1972.

130. BERGERON M, VADEBONCOEUR M: Microinjections of L-leucine into tubules and peritubular capillaries of the rat. II. The maleic acid model. *Nephron* 8:367, 1971.

131. BERGERON M, DUBORD L, LAPORTE P, HAUSSER C, ALLE-ANDO L: On the physiopathology of the Fanconi syndrome, in Silbernagl S, Lang F, Greger R (eds): *Amino Acid Transport and Uric Acid Transport*. Stuttgart, Georg Thieme, p 46.

132. GUNTHER R, SILBERNAGL S, DEETJEN P: Maleic acid induced aminoaciduria, studied by free flow miropuncture and continuous microperfusion. *Pflugers Arch* 382:109, 1979.

133. SCRIVER CR, CHESNEY RW, MCINNES RR: Genetic aspects of renal tubular transport: Diversity and topology of carriers. *Kidney Int* 9:149, 1976.

134. GOUGOUX A, LEMIEUX G, LAVOIE N: Maleate-induced bicarbonaturia in the dog: A carbonic anhydrase-independent effect. *Am J Physiol* 231:1010, 1976.

135. GMAJ P, HOPPE A, ANGIELSKI S, ROGULSKI J: Acid-base behavior of the kidney in maleate-treated rats. *Am J Physiol* 222:1182, 1972.

136. GMAJ P, HOPPE A, ANGIELSKI S, ROGULSKI J: Effects of maleate and arsenite on renal reabsorption of sodium and bicarbonate. *Am J Physiol* 225:90, 1973.

137. HOPPE A, GMAJ P, METLER M, ANGIELSKI S: Additive inhibition of renal bicarbonate reabsorption by maleate plus acetazolamide. *Am J Physiol* 231:1258, 1976.

138. ROSENBERG LE, SEGAL S: Maleic acid-induced inhibition of amino acid transport in rat kidney. *Biochem J* 92:345, 1964.

139. SILVERMAN M, HUANG L: Mechanism of maleic acid-induced glucosuria in dog kidney. *Am J Physiol* 231:1024, 1976.

140. BERGERON M: Renal amino acid accumulation in maleate treated rats. *Rev Can Biol* 30:267, 1971.

141. AUSIELLO DA, SEGAL S, THIER SO: Cellular accumulation of L-lysine in rat kidney cortex in vivo. *Am J Physiol* 222:1473, 1972.

142. KRAMER HJ, GONICK HC: Experimental Fanconi syndrome. I. Effect of maleic acid on renal cortical Na-K-ATPase acitivty and ATP levels. *J Lab Clin Med* 76:799, 1970.

143. REBOUCAS NA, FERNANDES DT, ELIAS MM, DE MELLO-AIRES M, MALNIC G: Proximal tubular HCO$_3^-$, H$^+$ and fluid transport during maleate-induced acidification defect. *Pflugers Arch* 401:266, 1984.

144. OBAID AL, REGA AF, GARRAHAN PJ: The effects of maleic anhydride on the ionic permeability of red cells. *J Membr Biol* 9:385, 1972.

145. LE GRIMELLEC C, CARRIERE S, CARDINAL J, GIOCONDI MC: Effect of maleate on membrane physical state of brush border and basolateral membranes of the dog kidney. *Life Sci* 30:1107, 1982.

146. REYNOLDS R, McNAMARA PD, SEGAL S: On the maleic acid induced Fanconi syndrome: Effects on transport by isolated rat kidney brushborder membrane vesicles. *Life Sci* 22:39, 1978.

147. SILVERMAN M: The mechanism of maleic acid nephropathy: Investigations using brush border membrane vesicles. *Membr Biochem* 4:63, 1981.

148. LAPRADE R, BEAUCHESNE G, BERGERON M: Effet membranaire du maléate: Étude à l'aide de membranes artificielles lipidiques. *Proc VIIth Intern Congr Nephrol* 1978, p M-6.

149. MAESAKA JK, McCAFFERY M: Evidence for renal tubular leakage in maleic acid-induced Fanconi syndrome. *Am J Physiol* 239:F507, 1980.

150. SAITO H, SHIOJI R, HURUKAWA Y, NAGAI K, ARIKAWA T, SAITO T, SASAKI Y, FURUYAMA T, YOSHINAGA K: Cadmium-induced proximal tubular dysfunction in a cadmium-polluted area. *Contrib Nephrol* 6:1, 1977.

151. BREWER ED: The Fanconi syndrome: Clinical disorders, in Gonick HC, Buckalew VM Jr (eds): *Renal Tubular Disorders. Pathophysiology, Diagnosis and Management.* New York, Marcel Dekker, 1985, p 475.

152. GONICK HC, INDRAPRASIT S, ROSEN VJ, NEUSTEIN H, VAN DE VELDE R, RAGHAVAN SRV: Experimental Fanconi Syndrome. III. Effect of cadmium on renal tubular function, the ATP-NA-K-ATPase transport system and renal tubular ultrastructure. *Miner Electrolyte Metab* 3:21, 1980.

153. KÄGI JHR, VALLEE BL: Metallothionein: A cadmium- and zinc-containing protein from equine renal cortex. *J Biol Chem* 235:3460, 1960.

154. FOULKES EC: Renal tubular transport of cadmium-metallothionein. *Toxicol Appl Pharmacol* 45:505, 1978.

155. NORDBERG GF, GOYER RA, NORDBERG M: Comparative toxicity of cadmium-metallothionein and cadmium chloride on mouse kidney. *Arch Pathol* 99:192, 1975.

156. GUNN SA, GOULD TC, ANDERSON WAD: Selectivity of organs response to cadmium injury and various protective measures. *J Pathol Bacteriol* 96:89, 1968.

157. RAGHAVAN SRV, GONICK HC: Experimental Fanconi Syndrome. IV. Effect of repetitive injections of cadmium on tissue distribution and protein-binding of cadmium. *Miner Electrolyte Metab* 3:36, 1980.

158. GOUGOUX A, VINAY P, DUPLAIN M: Maleate-induced stimulation of glutamine metabolism in the intact dog kidney. *Am J Physiol* 248:F585, 1985.

159. WAPNIR RA, EXENI RA, MCVICAR M, DE ROSAS FJ, LIFSHITZ F: Inhibition of sodium intestinal transport and mucosal (Na$^+$-K$^+$)-ATPase in experimental Fanconi syndrome. *Proc Soc Exptl Biol Med* 150:517, 1975.

160. ANGIELSKI S, ROGULSKI J: Effect of maleic acid on the kidney. I. Oxidation of Krebs cycle intermediates by various tissues of maleate intoxicated rats. *Acta Biochim Pol* 9:357, 1962.

161. ROGULSKI J, PACANIS A, ADAMOWICZ W, ANGIELSKI S: On the mechanism of maleate action on rat kidney mitochondria: Effect on oxidative metabolism. *Acta Biochim Pol* 21:403, 1974.

162. GOUGOUX A, VINAY P, DUPLAIN M: Maleate-induced stimulation of glutamine metabolism in dog renal cortical tubules. *Contrib Nephrol* 47:36, 1985.

163. SZCZEPANSKA M, ANGIELSKI S: Prevention of maleate-induced tubular dysfunction by acetoacetate. *Am J Physiol* 239:F50, 1980.

164. AL-BANDER H, ETHEREDGE SB, PAUKERT T, HUMPHREYS MH, MORRIS RC JR: Phosphate loading attenuates renal tubular dysfunction induced by maleic acid in the dog. *Am J Physiol* 248:F513, 1985.

165. GAHL WA, REED GF, THOENE JG, SCHULMAN JD, RIZZO WB, JONAS AJ, DENMAN DW, SCHLESSELMAN JJ, CORDEN BJ, SCHNEIDER JA: Cysteamine therapy for children with nephropathic cystinosis. *N Engl J Med* 316:971, 1987.

166. ARANT BS, GREIFER I, EDELMANN CM, SPITZER A: Effect of chronic salt and water loading on the tubular defects of a child with Fanconi syndrome (cystinosis). *Pediatrics* 58:370, 1976.

167. RAMPINI S, FANCONI A, ILLIG R, PRADER A: Effect of hydrochlorothiazide on proximal renal tubular acidosis in a patient with idiopathic "deToni-Debre-Fanconi syndrome." *Helv Paediatr Acta* 23:13, 1968.

168. MALEKZADEH MH, NEUSTEIN HB, SCHNEIDER JA, PENNISI AJ, ETTENGER RB, UITTENBOGAART CH, KOGUT MD, FINE RN: Cadaver renal transplantation in children with cystinosis. *Am J Med* 63:525, 1977.

169. WEST JC, GOODMAN SI, SCHROTER GP, BLOUSTEIN PA, HAMBIDGE KM, WELL R: Pediatric kidney transplantation for cystinosis. *J Pediatr Surg* 12:651, 1977.

CHAPTER 105

HYPOPHOSPHATEMIAS

HOWARD RASMUSSEN
HARRIET S. TENENHOUSE

1. There are two well characterized, inherited syndromes of hypophosphatemia. Each has a decrease in renal tubular phosphate reabsorption as a major underlying abnormality. Each is associated with rickets and osteomalacia and with specific changes in vitamin D metabolism.

2. The first disease is hereditary hypophosphatemic rickets with hypercalciuria (HHRH). The mode of inheritance is not yet clear but is consistent with an autosomal dominant trait with variable expressivity. It is characterized by hypophosphatemia, a reduced TmP/GFR, normocalcemia, hypercalciuria, a high plasma 1,25-dihydroxyvitamin D_3 concentration, a low parathyroid hormone concentration, and elevated plasma alkaline phosphatase activity. These defects are associated with growth retardation, bone pain, muscle weakness, femoral and tibial bowing, and radiologic and histomorphometric evidence of rickets and osteomalacia. A single defect in renal phosphate transport linked to a secondary stimulation of the renal 25-hydroxyvitamin D_3 1-α-hydroxylase appears to account for all the biochemical manifestations of the condition. Treatment with oral phosphate alone (2.0 to 3.0 g/day in divided doses) reduces bone pain, heals rickets, and stimulates skeletal growth. Family members with milder degrees of hypophosphatemia have been found to have hypercalciuria, elevated plasma 1,25-dihydroxyvitamin D_3, and nephrolithiasis without bone disease.

3. The predominant type of familial hypophosphatemic rickets (FHR) is inherited as an X-linked dominant trait. It is characterized by hypophosphatemia, normocalcemia, normal to low plasma 1,25-dihydroxyvitamin D_3 concentrations, normal parathyroid function, elevated plasma alkaline phosphatase activity, and a reduced TmP/GFR. Clinically, these changes are associated with growth retardation, femoral and tibial bowing, and radiologic and histomorphometric evidence of rickets and osteomalacia but no muscle weakness or tetany. This disease appears to result from a combined defect in renal tubular phosphate transport and abnormal regulation of renal 25-hydroxyvitamin D_3-1-α-hydroxylase. The most effective therapy is a combination of oral phosphate (1.0 to 2.0 g/day in four to five divided doses) and 1,25-dihydroxyvitamin D_3 or 1-α-hydroxyvitamin D_3 (1.0 to 3.0 μg/day).

4. Hypophosphatemic rickets in the mouse may be caused by mutation at one of two closely linked loci on the X chromosome. The more extensively studied Hyp mutation is a murine homologue of FHR and is associated with renal defects in brush border membrane Na^+-dependent phosphate transport and mitochondrial 25-hydroxyvitamin D_3 metabolism. The recently described Gy mutation is associated with extreme circulating behavior, deafness, and impaired renal brush border membrane Na^+-dependent phosphate transport. These mouse mutations provide useful animal models to examine the genetic and biochemical mechanisms for hypophosphatemic rickets and to assess treatment protocols.

Inorganic phosphate is an essential nutrient in terms of both cell function and skeletal mineralization. It is essential to the basic processes of glycolysis, gluconeogenesis, and ATP synthesis and turnover. It serves as the source of phosphate for such organic cell constituents as DNA, RNA, a variety of phosphorylated metabolic intermediates, and the phospholipid constituents of cellular membranes. In addition, phosphorylation of cellular proteins is a major mechanism by which cell function is controlled. The intracellular regulatory functions of phosphate involve such diverse effects as the control of aerobic metabolism, the control of the O_2 dissociation curve of hemoglobin in the intact red cell, and the regulation of cellular calcium metabolism.

Phosphate is sufficiently abundant in natural foods that dietary phosphate deficiency is unlikely to develop except under conditions of extreme starvation. Furthermore, the major portion of ingested phosphate (65 to 75 percent), either in the inorganic or organic form, is absorbed in the small intestine, and hormonal regulation of this process plays only a minor role in phosphate homeostasis. Absorbed phosphate is either eliminated by the kidney, incorporated into organic forms in proliferating cells, or deposited as a component of bone mineral (hydroxyapatite). Bone deposition accounts for a much larger percentage of retained phosphate during the growth period. However, even in the growing organism only a small percentage of the dietary phosphate is retained. Most of the absorbed phosphate is excreted in the urine. This means that phosphate homeostasis and plasma phosphate concentration depend primarily on the renal mechanisms which regulate tubular phosphate transport. In addition, during times of severe phosphate deprivation, particularly when caloric intake is adequate, the phosphate contained in bone mineral provides the only alternative source of phosphate for the needs of the organism. Hence, in severe phosphate deficiency, there is a net loss of phosphate from bone due to both inhibition of the mineralization process and stimulation of bone resorption.

In view of the central role of the kidney in phosphate homeostasis, it is not surprising that the tubular mechanisms which determine tubular phosphate reabsorption are complex and are regulated by a multiplicity of factors.[1-12] Nonetheless, two of these are of overriding importance to our present discussion: dietary phosphate intake and circulating parathyroid hormone. Conversely, the renal conversion of 25-hydroxyvitamin D_3 [25-$(OH)D_3$] to 1,25-dihydroxyvitamin D_3 [1,25-$(OH)_2D_3$], an active metabolite of vitamin D_3, is controlled by plasma phosphate concentration or some signal related to plasma phosphate concentrations.[13-15] These associations mean that diseases in which a renal tubule phosphate "leak" leads to a fall in plasma phosphate concentration are characterized by bone disease and disordered vitamin D metabolism. Three well-characterized conditions exemplify these states. Two, familial hypophosphatemic rickets (FHR) and hereditary hypophosphatemic rickets with hypercalciuria (HHRH), are inherited, and the third, oncogenic hypophosphatemic osteomalacia (OHO), is acquired. The latter is included in the present discussion because of its possible relevance to our understanding of the pathogenesis of FHR.

In spite of the fact that all three conditions are thought to have a primary renal phosphate leak [i.e., a reduced transfer maximum for phosphate per unit volume of glomerular filtrate (TmP/GFR) and hypophosphatemia], patients with the different diseases have different alterations in vitamin D metabolism. They also display different responses to alterations in dietary phosphate intake and parathyroid infusion, and they require different therapeutic measures. In the ensuing discussion, a consideration of phosphate homeostasis and the renal handling of phosphate is followed by a consideration of the pathogenic mechanisms involved in these three conditions. The clinical features of each syndrome and its treatment are presented. Emphasis is placed on more recent work, which has enhanced both our understanding of phosphate homeostasis and phosphate transport, and on the pathogenesis and treatment, particularly of FHR. A major factor that has contributed to this increased understanding is the study of an animal model of FHR, the *Hyp* mouse. The clinical and physiological manifestations of the altered metabolism of phosphate, vitamin D, and calcium in the *Hyp* mouse and in the human patient are so similar that a detailed comparison between the two states forms an important part of the ensuing discussion. For a discussion of earlier work relating to these conditions, the reader is referred to the discussion of FHR and the *Hyp* mouse which appeared in the previous edition of this work.[16]

One of the unexpected findings in both the FHR patient and the *Hyp* mouse is the disordered renal metabolism of 25-(OH)D$_3$, and the failure of hypophosphatemia to elicit an increase in 1,25-(OH)$_2$D$_3$ synthesis. The recent description of a new inherited disorder of renal phosphate reabsorption with hypophosphatemia and a marked increase in plasma 1,25-(OH)$_2$D$_3$ and hypercalciuria[17,18] provides a particularly important new element to considerations of the pathogenic mechanisms underlying the abnormal metabolism of 25-(OH)D$_3$ in FHR and the *Hyp* mouse.

PHOSPHATE HOMEOSTASIS

Under most ordinary circumstances, the major determinants of phosphate homeostasis are dietary phosphate intake, the absorption of phosphate from the intestine, and its reabsorption by the renal tubule. The cellular mechanisms underlying transport across the intestinal mucosal cell and the renal tubular cell are quite similar, but their hormonal and dietary controls are quite different.

Normal phosphate intake in adult humans is in the range of 800 to 1600 mg/day. This phosphate is in both the organic and the inorganic forms, but the organic forms, except for phytates, are degraded in the intestinal lumen to inorganic phosphates, and in this form absorbed. The absorptive rate for phosphate is highest in the jejunum and ileum with a lower rate in the duodenum. Essentially no absorption occurs in the colon.[19] This pattern contrasts with that of Ca^{2+} which is absorbed at highest rates in duodenum and ileum with lower rates in both jejunum and colon.

Although intestinal phosphate absorption is regulated by the vitamin D metabolites, 25-(OH)D$_3$ and 1,25-(OH)$_2$D$_3$,[20,21]

these normally play a relatively minor role. Between 65 and 75 percent of ingested phosphate is absorbed regardless of the dietary phosphate intake. In vitamin D deficiency, this percentage may fall to 50 to 60 percent, due largely to a failure to absorb Ca^{2+} and thereby reduce free phosphate concentration in the lumen, but also to a direct effect on the phosphate transport system in the mucosal cell.[22]

Over a large range of phosphate intake, plasma phosphate concentration remains normal while intestinal phosphate absorption increases proportionally to the phosphate content of the diet.[23–25] This means that the renal excretion of phosphate increases and decreases in direct relation to phosphate intake over a wide range of intake. The mechanism(s) underlying this important renal adaptation to phosphate intake is not completely understood.

Plasma inorganic phosphate concentration (measured as phosphorus) varies as a function of age in humans: in the range of 3.8 to 5.5 mg/dl in children and 3.0 to 4.5 mg/dl in adults [SI unit (mmol/liter) $\times$ 3.10 = mg/dl]. Of interest is the fact that a species difference in normal plasma phosphate values exists. This difference correlates with differences in basal metabolic rate. The higher this rate, the higher the plasma phosphate concentration.[26]

Although long-term changes in plasma phosphate concentration clearly depend on the balance between intestinal absorption and renal excretion, short-term changes in phosphate concentrations can occur as a consequence of the redistribution of phosphate between the extracellular fluid (ECF) and either bone or cell constituents. Since the ECF phosphate represents less than 1 percent of total body phosphate, either the mobilization of phosphate following tissue destruction or the mobilization of phosphate from bone mineral can lead to temporary increases in plasma phosphate concentration.

In measuring plasma phosphate concentration and relating this value to a clinical situation, it is necessary to bear in mind that there is a diurnal variation in plasma phosphate concentration with a nadir at 9:30 to 10:00 A.M. and a peak at 4 A.M.[27] The change in concentration from nadir to peak may be as much as 1 mg/dl, i.e., a 25 to 35 percent change in concentration. The factors determining this diurnal variation are not known but probably involve largely extrarenal mechanisms.

Phosphate Homeostasis in States of Altered Mineral Intake

In considering the mechanisms involved in the pathogenesis of the FHR, HHRH, and OHO, it is useful to discuss our present views of how the organism adapts to severe dietary restrictions of either phosphate or calcium.

Including a discussion of calcium homeostasis in a discussion of disorders of renal phosphate transport is necessary because of: (1) the intimate link between the transport of these ions across intestine and renal tubule; (2) their coexistence as components of bone mineral; (3) their interrelated effects on the regulation of vitamin D metabolism; and (4) the interrelated changes in their metabolism in response to parathyroid hormone (PTH), calcitonin (CT), and 1,25-(OH)$_2$D$_3$. (Refer to Chaps. 79 and 80 for more relevant discussion.)

The key tissues involved in Ca^{2+} and phosphate homeostasis are the gut, kidney, and bone; and the key hormonal regulators are PTH, CT, and 1,25-(OH)$_2$D$_3$.

Response to Severe Phosphate Deprivation. The changes in both phosphate and Ca^{2+} metabolism that occur as a consequence of severe dietary phosphate restriction are shown in Fig. 105-1.[1-5,13-15] The decrease in phosphate intake leads to a prompt fall in renal phosphate excretion due to a renal adaptive response so that within a few days renal phosphate excretion falls nearly to zero. During this transient period, plasma phosphate may fall only minimally, but with continued phosphate restriction plasma phosphate concentration falls and filtered load decreases. Either a change in the tubular phosphate transport or the change in plasma phosphate concentration leads to an increase in 25-$(OH)D_3$-1-α-hydroxylase (1-α-hydroxylase) activity in the proximal renal tubule. As a consequence, the plasma 1,25-$(OH)_2D_3$ rises. The fall in plasma phosphate leads to an inhibition of bone mineral deposition, and if bone resorption continues, there is a net shift of phosphate from skeleton to ECF. In fact, because the plasma 1,25-$(OH)_2D_3$ concentration increases, there is also an increase in rate of bone resorption,[28] which makes a further contribution to the net loss of phosphate from the skeleton. The increase in plasma 1,25-$(OH)_2D_3$ also stimulates intestinal phosphate transport both by a direct action on the mucosal phosphate transport system, and because 1,25-$(OH)_2D_3$ increases intestinal Ca^{2+} absorption.

As a consequence of the rise in plasma 1,25-$(OH)_2D_3$ concentration and the resultant increases in both intestinal Ca^{2+} absorption and bone resorption, the plasma Ca^{2+} concentration rises. This acts to inhibit PTH secretion. As a consequence, PTH concentration falls and the distal tubular reabsorption of Ca^{2+} is decreased: the increased influx of Ca^{2+} into the ECF from bone and gut is balanced by an increased renal loss. Theoretically, the decreased effect of PTH on tubular phosphate transport should also contribute to renal phosphate retention, but, in fact, the phosphate transport system in the tubules of the phosphate-deprived organism is insensitive to this action of PTH. Hence, even the infusion of PTH will not increase urinary phosphate excretion in the phosphate-deprived organism.

These homeostatic changes lead to a nearly complete renal conservation of phosphate coupled to the mobilization of phosphate from the skeleton to replace extrarenal loss (occur-

Fig. 105-1 A schematic representation of the changes in calcium *(left)* and phosphate *(right)* metabolism induced by severe dietary phosphate restriction. The triangle at the top of the figure represents the parathyroid gland, the solid block on the right hand side of each scheme represents bone mineral, and that on the left intestinal mineral. The figure in the center represents the plasma concentration of either calcium (Ca^{2+}) or phosphate (HPO_4^{2-}) ion. The arrow from the ion concentration to the bottom of the figure represents renal excretion of the particular ion, and the horizontal arrow at the bottom of each scheme the conversion of 25-hydroxyvitamin D_3 by the kidney. The arrows from bone and gut to plasma concentration represent net fluxes, and the broken arrows (---) the various control signals.

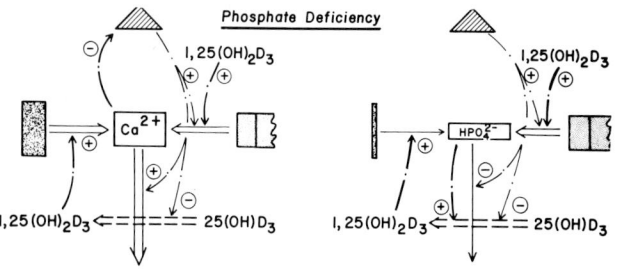

ring largely via the gastrointestinal tract). These changes in phosphate metabolism are associated with increased intestinal calcium absorption and hypercalciuria.

It might be predicted that a simple renal phosphate leak should lead to a similar sequence of events, and in particular, to increases in plasma 1,25-$(OH)_2D_3$ concentration and intestinal calcium absorption resulting in hypercalciuria. However, in the case of both FHR and OHO, the renal phosphate leak coexists with a disordered regulation of the 1-α-hydroxylase. On the other hand, in HHRH, the phosphate leak is associated with the triad of high plasma 1,25-$(OH)_2D_3$, increased calcium absorption, and hypercalciuria, the same triad as seen during dietary phosphate restriction.

Response to Calcium Deprivation. The changes in both Ca^{2+} and phosphate metabolism that occur in response to severe dietary calcium restriction are shown in Fig. 105-2. The decrease in calcium intake leads to a slight fall in plasma Ca^{2+} concentration, and a stimulation of PTH secretion. The resulting rise in plasma PTH concentration leads to: (1) an increase in bone resorption leading to a net loss of Ca^{2+} from bone; (2) an increase in the distal tubular reabsorption of Ca^{2+}; and (3) an increase in the rate of 1,25-$(OH)_2D_3$ synthesis by the proximal tubule. The resulting rise in plasma 1,25-$(OH)_2D_3$ leads to an increased efficiency of intestinal Ca^{2+} absorption, and acts synergistically with PTH to enhance resorption of bone.

As a result of the increases in plasma 1,25-$(OH)_2D_3$ concentration, intestinal phosphate absorption and the net removal of phosphate from bone increase. Bone phosphate removal is also increased by PTH. However, in spite of this increase in the net movement of phosphate into the ECF, the plasma phosphate concentration does not increase but rather falls slightly owing to the inhibitory action of PTH on renal tubular phosphate transport, and thus a decrease in TmP/GFR.

These homeostatic changes lead to a nearly complete renal conservation of calcium coupled with the mobilization of Ca^{2+} from the skeleton to replace extrarenal Ca^{2+} losses (gut and skin). These changes in Ca^{2+} metabolism are associated with increased movement of phosphate into the ECF, a fall in TmP/GFR, and hence a net loss of phosphate from the body.

Response to Phosphate Excess. Marked increases in dietary phosphate intake can occur without a marked change in plasma phosphate concentration because of the compensatory increase in renal phosphate clearance. However, with very high phosphate intakes, particularly if associated with a reduced calcium intake, plasma phosphate may rise sufficiently to reduce plasma ionized Ca^{2+}, leading to an increase in PTH secretion, a rise in plasma PTH, and a further reduction in

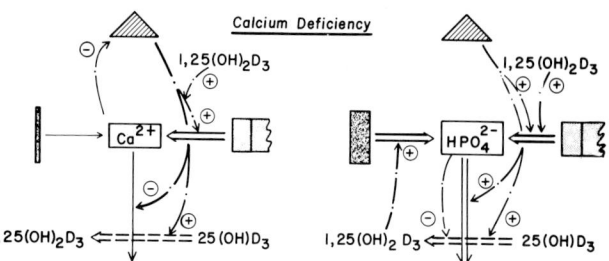

Fig. 105-2 A schematic representation of the changes in calcium *(left)* and phosphate *(right)* metabolism induced by severe dietary calcium restriction. Symbols as in Fig. 105-2.

renal tubular phosphate reabsorption. Under these circumstances, PTH causes less of an increase in 1,25-$(OH)_2D_3$ synthesis, but it does stimulate bone turnover. Whether or not this leads to a net removal of Ca^{2+} and phosphate from bone depends on the Ca^{2+} intake. The key point is that excessive phosphate intake can lead to a state of secondary hyperparathyroidism: a consideration in the therapeutic use of phosphate in humans.

RENAL PHOSPHATE TRANSPORT

The renal excretion of phosphate is determined by the balance between the rates of glomerular filtration and tubular reabsorption.[1-12] There is no convincing evidence for net tubular secretion of phosphate by the mammalian nephron. Not all the phosphate in plasma is ultrafilterable, so the phosphate concentration in the glomerular ultrafiltrate is approximately 90 percent of that in plasma.[29,30] This percentage decreases as the plasma Ca^{2+} concentration rises above 10.5 mg/dl. At a plasma Ca^{2+} concentration of 18 mg/dl, it is about 75 percent.[29]

As in the case of many transport processes, the transcellular transport of phosphate is a carrier-mediated, saturable process. Hence, we might anticipate that a transfer maximum, or Tm, for the renal reabsorption of this anion could be determined. However, because of the marked effect of phosphate intake on the renal handling of phosphate, the Tm varies considerably as dietary phosphate rises and falls. The best way to estimate the overall capacity of the renal phosphate transport system is to measure the Tm for phosphate per unit volume of glomerular filtrate (TmP/GFR) during acute phosphate infusions. In practice, an estimate of TmP/GFR can be made by measuring phosphate and creatinine excretions and plasma phosphate concentrations and using this information and the nomogram developed by Bijvoet[31] (showing the relationship between plasma phosphate concentration and the fractional excretion of phosphate) to derive this value. The use of this nomogram is limited to situations in which there are significant rates of urinary phosphate excretion.

Tubular Sites of Phosphate Reabsorption, PTH and CT Action, and 1,25-$(OH)_2D_3$ Synthesis

Considerable information from animal studies has accumulated in the past few years in terms of the tubular sites at which phosphate reabsorption occurs, at which PTH and CT act, and at which 1,25-$(OH)_2D_3$ synthesis occurs.[32-36,39,44,45] This information is summarized in Table 105-1.

The major site of phosphate reabsorption is in the proximal convoluted tubule. Reabsorption at this site normally accounts for approximately 60 percent of the filtered load. A second site accounting for another 15 to 20 percent is the proximal straight tubule. A small but variable reabsorption is also seen in the distal tubule. The importance of phosphate reabsorption at this latter site is difficult to define because of considerable heterogeneity between the ability of deep and superficial nephrons to conserve phosphate. Nonetheless, it does appear that small amounts of phosphate are reabsorbed distally, and these may be important in disorders involving defects in the mechanisms controlling phosphate reabsorption in the proximal nephron.

When the tubular locations of PTH-sensitive adenylate cyclase was defined, the enzyme was found at all three sites of phosphate transport: proximal convoluted tubule, proximal straight tubule, and distal tubule.[37-38] There is also clear evidence that PTH (or cAMP) will decrease phosphate reabsorption in both proximal convoluted tubule and proximal straight tubule, and probably in the distal tubule. From these observations, it has been concluded that PTH inhibits phosphate transport in each of these tubular segments via a cAMP-dependent process. Further, PTH stimulates 1-α-hydroxylase by a cAMP-dependent mechanism in the proximal convoluted tubule[39] and inhibits Na^+-H^+ exchange in this nephron segment[40,41] (but see "Short-Term Responses: PTH Action," below). Finally, PTH stimulates distal tubular Ca^{2+} reabsorption.[42,43]

In contrast to PTH, calcitonin-sensitive adenylate cyclase is localized in the medullary and cortical thick ascending limbs and in the distal tubule,[44] but the CT-sensitive 1-α-hydroxylase is localized in the proximal straight tubule.[44] CT acts in the proximal convoluted tubule and possibly proximal straight tubule to inhibit phosphate reabsorption. Given the fact that the effects of CT on both phosphate reabsorption and 1-α-hydroxylase activity occur at nephron sites which do not possess CT-sensitive adenylate cyclase,[45] it has been concluded that CT regulates these processes by a cAMP-independent mechanism. The nature of this mechanism remains to be defined. CT also acts on the medullary thick ascending limb to increase Ca^{2+} reabsorption presumably by a cAMP-dependent mechanism. The action of CT on the distal tubule remains undefined even though this is the segment with the most abundant CT-sensitive cyclase.

During dietary phosphate deprivation there is an increase in

Table 105-1 Renal Tubular Sites of Phosphate Transport, 1-α-Hydroxylase, and Hormone-Sensitive Adenylate Cyclase

	Phosphate transport	PTH-sensitive adenylate cyclase	PTH-sensitive 1-α-hydroxylase	CT-sensitive adenylate cyclase	CT-sensitive 1-α-hydroxylase	Phosphate sensitive 1-α-hydroxylase
PCT	+ + +	+ +	+ + + +	− −	− −	+ + +
PST	+ +	+	− −	− −	+ + +	?
MTAL	− −	− −	− −	+	− −	− −
CTAL	− −	+ + + +	− −	+ + +	− −	− −
DT	+	+ + +	− −	+ + + +	− −	− −
CT	− −	− −	− −	+ +	− −	− −

NOTE: PCT = proximal convoluted tubule; PST = proximal straight tubule; MTAL = medullary thick ascending limb; CTAL = cortical thick ascending limb; DT = distal tubule; CT = collecting tubule.

phosphate transport in all nephron segments,[46,47a] and probably an increase in 1-α-hydroxylase in the proximal convoluted tubule but not in the proximal straight tubule.

Cellular Mechanism of Phosphate Transport

The most detailed studies of the cellular mechanism for phosphate transport have been done in proximal tubules and cultured cells derived from them.[1,5,8–10,23,32,35,36,46–50] In these cells and tissues the process is essentially a unidirectional transport from luminal to basal cell surface. Based on present information, a model of phosphate transport can be constructed (Fig. 105-3) in which HPO_4^{2-} entry into the cell from the tubular fluid across the brush border membrane involves the secondary active transport of phosphate driven by the Na^+ gradient. The transport is via a Na^+-HPO_4^{2-} cotransport system in which $2Na^+$ enter with each phosphate. This means that when HPO_4^{2-} is the predominant species, the process is electroneutral but, when it is $H_2PO_4^-$, transport is electrogenic. The rate of phosphate transport is dependent on the magnitude of the Na^+ gradient maintained across the luminal membrane which, in turn, depends on the activity of the Na^+,K^+-ATPase or sodium pump on the basolateral membrane. Inhibition of this pump leads to an inhibition of phosphate transport. Further, the rate limiting step in transcellular transport is proably the Na^+-dependent entry of phosphate across the luminal membrane. This process has a low K_m for luminal phosphate (0.1 mM or less) so that it is possible for phosphate transport to be highly efficient.

An additional order of complexity has been introduced by the finding of multiple Na^+-dependent phosphate transport processes in the brush border membranes of proximal tubular cells from pig[51] and rat.[52] In the early proximal convoluted tubule, there appear to be two such systems: one of low affinity and high capacity, which appears to be responsible for the reabsorption of the bulk of the filtered load, and a high affinity, low capacity system, which is responsible for the remainder. In the proximal straight tubule, a single high affinity system is found. Studies with isolated proximal tubular segments derived from rabbit kidney also revealed two phosphate transport systems: a PTH-insensitive high capacity system in the proximal convoluted tubule and a PTH-sensitive low capacity system in the proximal straight tubule.[52a]

The phosphate which enters the cell is in rapid exchange with intracellular phosphate. There does not appear to be a separate transport pool. The efflux of phosphate out of the cell across the basolateral membrane appears to be a passive process driven by the electrical gradient existing across this membrane and occurring via an anion-exchange mechanism. In addition, there appears to be a small component of Na^+-linked secondary active influx of phosphate across the basolateral membrane which has a V_{max} only 10 percent of the luminal process.[53] This process can be distinguished from that in the brush border membrane because it has a lower K_m for phosphate (0.014 mM), is insensitive to pH, and is more electrogenic. However, this Na^+-dependent entry of phosphate across the basolateral membrane appears to be insufficient to maintain normal intracellular phosphate concentrations in the absence of luminal phosphate entry.

The difficulties in defining the transcellular transport process are: (1) an inability to measure the intracellular inorganic phosphate concentration accurately and (2) the inability to use tracer methods effectively to study the transcellular transport process because of the rapid mixing of the tracer with the metabolically active organic phosphate pools within the cell. Estimates of intracellular inorganic phosphate concentration range from 0.7 to 2.0 mM, with the former value obtained with the use of NMR spectroscopy.[54] A value between 0.6 and 1.0 mM is likely to be close to the true value.

Because intracellular phosphate is of key importance to cellular energy metabolism and its concentration is one factor determining the phosphate potential of the cell (ATP/ADP × P_i), we might anticipate that some type of functional coupling exists between the transport processes across the two cell surfaces so that large changes in free phosphate concentrations do not occur as a result of large changes in phosphate load.[46] However, the existence of such a homeostatic mechanism has not been clearly demonstrated. Under extreme nonphysiological circumstances removal of phosphate from tubular lumen in a perfused kidney leads to a fall in total cellular inorganic phosphate but a sustained near normal transcellular transport of Na^+ and an intracellular free phosphate concentration measured by ^{31}P NMR spectroscopy of 0.7 mM. In isolated perfused proximal tubules, removal of phosphate from the luminal but not the peritubular fluid leads to an inhibition of net fluid absorption, i.e., a decrease in transcellular Na^+ transport which can be reversed by removal of glucose from the medium; i.e., the phosphorylation of intracellular glucose and the resulting glycolytic intermediates along with a reduced luminal entry of phosphate lead to a sufficient fall in intracellular phosphate concentration to decrease the rate of ATP synthesis.[46]

Fig. 105-3 A model of the process of transcellular transport of inorganic phosphate (HPO_4^{2-}) in the cell of the proximal convoluted tubule of the mammalian kidney. The luminal or brush border membrane is depicted on the *left*, the basolateral plasma membrane on the *top*, *bottom*, and *right*, and the only intracellular organelle depicted is the mitochondrion. Both a Na^+-H^+ exchanger and a $2Na^+$-HPO_4^{2-} cotransporter operate in the luminal membrane. The HPO_4^{2-} which enters the cell across the luminal surface mixes with the metabolic pool of phosphate in the cell and is eventually transported out of the cell across the basolateral membrane via an anion (A^-) exchange mechanism. There is also a Na^+-HPO_4^{2-} cotransporter on the basolateral membrane and a Na^+,K^+-ATPase on this membrane. The activity of this ATPase transports the Na^+ (which enters the cell on its luminal side) out of the cell thereby maintaining the Na^+ gradient driving force for luminal phosphate entry.

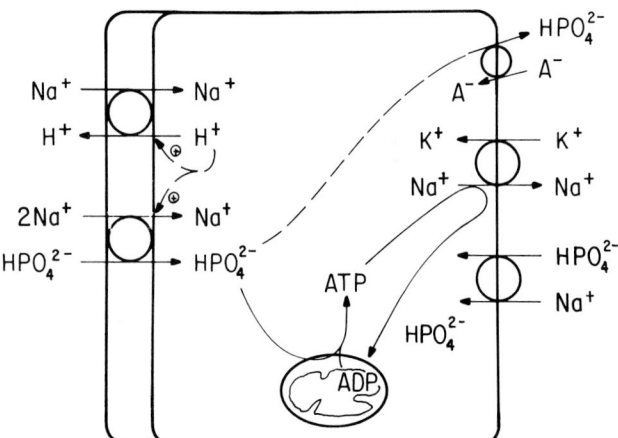

Regulation of Na$^+$-Phosphate Cotransport

If one assumes that the rate-limiting step in the transcellular transport of phosphate is its Na$^+$-dependent entry across the luminal membrane, then the major factors involved in regulating the overall process should act on this entry step. This prediction is borne out by the evidence from studies of dietary phosphate restriction, parathyroid hormone, thyroid hormone, glucocorticoid, and growth hormone actions. All influence the activity of the Na$^+$-phosphate cotransport system in the brush border membrane.[1-5,46,47,47a] These regulatory mechanisms consist of short-term effects which do not involve protein synthesis and longer-term changes which do. However, the two major factors particularly relevant to our discussion are dietary phosphate intake and parathyroid hormone.

Long-Term Responses. Dietary restriction of phosphate leads to a marked increase in proximal tubular phosphate transport and an increase in Na$^+$-phosphate cotransport in isolated brush border membrane vesicles from the kidneys of rats, mice, rabbits, humans, and pigs (Fig. 105-4). The effect is an increase in V_{max} without a change in K_m.[1-3,46,47a] This adaptive increase occurs rapidly within 2 to 4 h after dietary phosphate restriction at a time when plasma phosphate concentration has not changed significantly. The change is progressive and may lead to a three- to fivefold increase in V_{max}. The adaptive response is inhibited in animals treated with actinomycin D.

Fig. 105-4 The effect of dietary phosphate depletion on the initial velocity of Na$^+$-dependent phosphate entry into brush border membrane vesicles prepared from pig kidney. The initial velocity of phosphate transport into brush border membrane vesicles is plotted as a function of medium phosphate concentration with vesicles obtained from animals fed a high ($\bigcirc$, $\triangle$) or low phosphate ($\bullet$, $\blacktriangle$) diet. Vesicles are incubated in media containing no Na$^+$ ($\triangle$, $\blacktriangle$) or 100 mM Na$^+$ ($\bigcirc$, $\bullet$). Note the approximately threefold greater rate of Na$^+$-dependent phosphate transport in vesicles from the animals fed a low phosphate diet. (*From Barrett et al.[4] Used by permission.*)

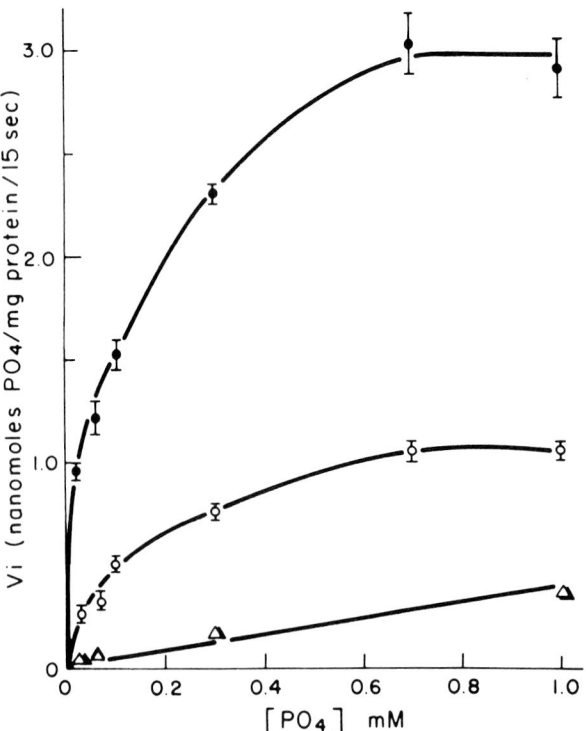

Studies in LLC-PK$_1$ cells (an epithelial line of cultured pig kidney cells) show that a reduction in the ambient phosphate concentration to 0.1 mM leads to an adaptive response which displays two components, an initial increase occurring within minutes and representing an approximately 30 percent increase in transport capacity which is independent of protein synthesis, and a longer-term increase taking hours, requiring protein synthesis, and leading eventually to a twofold increase in transport rate.[46] However, if such cells, exposed to low ambient phosphate, are replaced in normal phosphate media, the phosphate transport rate falls rapidly but can be rapidly increased, even in the presence of protein synthesis inhibitors, upon reincubation of the cells in a low phosphate environment.

These data from studies of cultured cells have been interpreted to mean that the adaptive response seen in vitro is due to a direct effect of phosphate depletion on renal tubular cells.[46] However, this seems an unlikely explanation because: (1) the plasma phosphate concentration barely changes early in the course of phosphate deprivation; (2) the adaptive responses seen in vivo are much greater than those seen in vitro; and (3) the in vitro responses are much more readily reversible than the in vivo ones. Based on these observations, it seems quite likely that some humoral messenger participates in this adaptive response.

The data from tubular and cellular studies have led to the proposal that the number of Na$^+$-phosphate cotransporter molecules in the brush border membrane is determined both by the distribution of transporters between the brush border membrane and an intracellular membrane vesicular pool[46] and by the rate of protein synthesis. Thus, during the first phase of the adaptive response, there is a shift of preformed transporters from the intracellular vesicular pool to the brush border membrane, and during the second phase there is the synthesis of new transporter-containing vesicles followed by their insertion into the brush border membrane.

Short-Term Responses: PTH Action. The original model of PTH action on proximal phosphate transport was one in which the interaction of PTH with its receptor on the basolateral membrane leads to the activation of adenylate cyclase resulting in an increase in cAMP, which diffuses across the cell and inhibits Na$^+$-phosphate cotransport by catalyzing the phosphorylation of one or more proteins in the brush border membrane.[1-3,46] However, there is no convincing evidence that such a mechanism actually operates. Further, larger changes in parathyroid hormone concentrations in vivo, which produce very marked changes in rates of phosphate excretion, bring about very small changes in the V_{max} of the Na$^+$-phosphate cotransporter in subsequently isolated brush border membrane vesicles. The largest changes in Na$^+$-phosphate cotransporter activity reported are in the range of 20 to 100 percent.[54a] These results are consistent with the notions that: (1) PTH may cause a small decrease in V_{max} of the transport process by causing a shift of Na$^+$-phosphate cotransporters from the brush border membrane to the intracellular vesicular pool and (2) PTH exerts another effect on transcellular transport, which does not persist in subsequently isolated brush border membrane vesicles and does not involve a change in the number of Na$^+$-phosphate cotransporters in the brush border membrane.

In order to consider what this second effect might be, it is necessary to summarize the known effects of PTH on proximal tubular function.[1-3,46,55,56] An increase in PTH leads to:

an increase in cAMP concentration; an increase in Ca^{2+} influx rate[57] and a transient increase in intracellular free Ca^{2+} concentration[58,59]; a Ca^{2+}- and cAMP-dependent activation of gluconeogenesis[60,61]; an inhibition of both phosphate and HCO_3^- reabsorption[62,63]; and an increase in the activity of 1-α-hydroxylase.[55] The unresolved issue is whether the effects on phosphate and HCO_3^- transport, gluconeogenesis and 1-α-hydroxylase, are separate effects of PTH or whether they are interrelated.[46,56] What is clear is that all four processes are sensitive to changes in cAMP, Ca^{2+}, and H^+ concentrations, but the cellular and molecular targets for the actions of these different messengers are not known.

A cultured cell line derived from the opossum kidney (OK cells) responds to PTH with an increase in cAMP and intracellular Ca^{2+} and an inhibition of Na^+-dependent phosphate uptake.[64–66] Also, when incubated in a medium without CO_2-HCO_3^- buffers and with a reduced Na^+ concentration, PTH induces a Na^+-dependent fall in intracellular pH, suggesting that PTH brings about an inhibition of luminal membrane Na^+-H^+ exchange.[66] These data argue that PTH through some combination of intracellular messengers, in particular Ca^{2+} and cAMP, brings about coordinate changes in the rate of Na^+-phosphate cotransport (an inhibition) and Na^+-H^+ exchange (an inhibition) at the luminal surface, and of 1-α-hydroxylase activity (an activation) and gluconeogenesis (an activation) at a mitochondrial locus. It seems likely that the changes in transport functions are a direct consequence of the changes in intracellular messenger activity and are not secondary to an increase in gluconeogenesis. However, it is possible that the PTH-induced increase in gluconeogenesis is a coordinate response to that of inhibition of Na^+-H^+ exchange, whereby the decrease in intracellular pH resulting from an inhibition of Na^+-H^+ exchange is minimized by an increase in gluconeogenic rate because gluconeogenesis is an H^+-consuming reaction sequence. On the other hand, key effects of PTH, mediated by intracellular messengers, on gluconeogenesis are exerted on steps in mitochondrial metabolism, as are the effects of PTH on 1-α-hydroxylase activity. Hence, a single mitochondrial effect could conceivably account for the changes in both mitochondrial functions.

It is also possible that a decrease in phosphate intake and an increase in PTH concentration act via some common intracellular messenger in regulating the 1-α-hydroxylase system, but the nature by which acute changes in 1-α-hydroxylase activity are brought about are not known. Nor it is known by what mechanisms long-term adaptations of 1-α-hydroxylase activity occur. During chronic phosphate depletion or during chronic exposure to PTH, the total 1-α-hydroxylase activity in the proximal nephron increases. The signals for this increase are not known. Hence, it is not clear whether there are two separate signals or a common one generated by these two separate metabolic changes.

The relevance of this discussion and this problem to the clinical situation is direct. Patients with HHRH have the expected increase in 1-α-hydroxylase activity in response to phosphate depletion. Patients with either FHR or OHO and the *Hyp* mouse do not display normal responses, in terms of changes in 1-α-hydroxylase activity, to either phosphate depletion or PTH treatment.

Effect of Ca^{2+} on Tubular Phosphate Transport.

There is a confusing literature on the effects of Ca^{2+} on phosphate transport. This has been reviewed by others.[1,3] The most important observation from a clinical point of view is that administration of Ca^{2+} or agents which raise plasma Ca^{2+} concentration [1,25-$(OH)_2D_3$ or PTH] lead to a reduction in TmP/GFR. The mechanism and tubular site(s) of this effect are not known.

CLINICAL DISORDERS OF PHOSPHATE TRANSPORT

The three clinical states to be discussed are HHRH, FHR, and OHO (Table 105-2). Even though the latter is an acquired disease, its discussion is warranted because of the similarity of its manifestations to those of FHR.

HEREDITARY HYPOPHOSPHATEMIC RICKETS WITH HYPERCALCIURIA

HHRH is a new entity which has recently been reported to occur in closely related members of a single Bedouin tribe in which intermarriage has been widely practiced for many generations.[17,18] The mode of inheritance is not yet clear. Either of two genetic mechanisms could account for the presently available data: (1) an autosomal recessive mechanism involving the additive effects of two genes each of which have two alternative alleles or (2) a mechanism involving one set of alleles with a dominant mode of inheritance and variable expressivity.

Clinical Features

Presumed Homozygotes. The major clinical features of the condition are bone pain, skeletal deformities, short stature, and muscle weakness with x-ray signs of rickets and osteomalacia. The biochemical findings include a reduced serum phosphate concentration, a reduced TmP/GFR, a normal serum Ca^{2+} concentration, low or low normal serum PTH and urinary cAMP concentrations, an elevated serum alkaline phosphatase, normal serum 25-$(OH)D_3$ and 24,25-$(OH)_2D_3$ concentrations, but an elevated serum 1,25-$(OH)_2D_3$ concentration associated with a marked increase in urinary calcium excretion.

The patient's response to either an oral calcium-loading or a phosphate-loading test show that there is hyperabsorption of both calcium and phosphate from the intestine. These changes are indicative of the fact that the intestinal mucosa in these patients is normally responsive to 1,25-$(OH)_2D_3$. The intravenous injection of parathyroid extract is found to reduce TmP/GFR even further and to increase urinary cAMP excretion.

Presumed Heterozygotes. In an extensive study of 59 closely related members of this tribe, nine individuals were identified with the characteristics just described. However, an additional 21 members were found to be clinically healthy but to display idiopathic hypercalciuria (IH) with slightly reduced serum phosphate concentrations, elevated serum 1,25-$(OH)_2D_3$ concentrations, and elevated urinary calcium excretion. The values seen in the patients with IH were intermediate between normal members of the same tribe and members with HHRH: urinary Ca^{2+} concentration 0.43 ± 0.14 mg/mg Cr for HHRH, 0.34 ± 0.07 for IH, and 0.14 ± 0.05 for normal

Table 105-2 Comparison of the Inherited Syndromes of Hypophosphatemic Rickets with Oncogenic Hypophosphatemic Osteomalacia

	FHR	HHRH	OHO
Inheritance	X-linked	AD (?)	— —
Age of onset	Early childhood	Early childhood	Any age
Clinical features			
Short stature	+ +	+ +	+ +
Bone pain	+ +	+ + +	+ + +
Femoral bowing	+ +	+ +	+ +
Muscle weakness	— —	+ +	+ +
Radiologic signs			
Rickets	+ +	+ +	+ +
Pseudofracture	+	+ +	+ +
Coarse trabeculi	+ +	+ +	+ +
Dental abnormalities	+ +	?	— —
Calcium metabolism			
Serum Ca^{2+}	N-LN	N-HN	N-LN
iPTH	N-HN	LN	H-HN
Ca_u	L	H	L
Ca absorption	L	H	L
Phosphate metabolism			
Serum phosphate	L	L	L
TmP/GFR	L	L	L
Alkaline phosphatase	H	H	H
Vitamin D metabolism			
25-$(OH)D_3$	N	N	N
1,25-$(OH)_2D_3$	N-LN	H	LN-L
25-$(OH)D_3$ 1-α-hydroxylase response to phosphate	Abnormal	Normal	Abnormal

NOTE: AD = autosomal dominant; iPTH = immunoreactive parathyroid hormone; N = normal; LN = low normal; H = high; HN = high normal; L = low.

individuals; serum 1,25-$(OH)_2D_3$, 303 pg/ml for HHRH, 145 pg/ml for IH, and 95 pg/ml for normal individuals; TmP/GFR was 3.05 SD units below the mean in HHRH and 1.15 below the mean in IH. Thus, the IH patients appear to have a milder metabolic defect characterized by elevated plasma 1,25-$(OH)_2D_3$ concentrations and hypercalciuria without evidence of bone disease or growth retardation.

Bone Morphology

Examination of undecalcified sections of bone from a single untreated patient with HHRH revealed wide osteoid seams, low osteoclastic activity, and a decrease in tetracycline labeling, findings consistent with a diagnosis of osteomalacia.

Pathogenesis

From the point of view of pathophysiology, these patients appear to have the biochemical and physiological responses appropriate to chronic phosphate deprivation, but they have high rates of urinary phosphate excretion and a low TmP/GFR. These latter two changes are not compatible with phosphate deprivation but indicate instead that the primary defect is the renal handling of phosphate leading to an appropriate increase in 1,25-$(OH)_2D_3$ synthesis, the hyperabsorption of both Ca^{2+} and phosphate from the gastrointestinal tract, a suppression of PTH secretion, but a persistent hypophosphatemia sufficient to lead to a reduction in the rate of bone mineralization and bone growth. The fact that these patients respond to oral phosphate therapy with an increase in iPTH, a fall in plasma 1,25-$(OH)_2D_3$ concentration, a fall in bone turn-

over, bone growth, and a healing of the rickets fits with this pathogenic mechanism. Unresolved is the location of the tubular segment which expresses the disorder in phosphate reabsorption.

Genetics

The genetic relationship in a single Bedouin tribe in which nine individuals have HHRH and 21 subjects have idiopathic hypercalciuria without clinical evidence of bone disease is shown in Fig. 105-5. The interrelationships emphasize the considerable intermarriage seen within the extended kindred. On the basis of this family tree, it is logical to assume that patients with HHRH and idiopathic hypercalciuria share a common inherited defect which leads to a milder degree of phosphate leak and attendant changes in vitamin D and calcium metabolism in patients with idiopathic hypercalciuria than in those with HHRH. The data are compatible with several modes of inheritance. An autosomal recessive mechanism involving the additive effects of two genes, each possessing two alleles (normal or deficient), could account for the findings. In this case, we might assume that most of the normal subjects are heterozygous for one of the two genes. Conversely, the data could be explained by a single gene and one variant allele exhibiting dominant inheritance with variable expressivity. The latter seems more likely.

It is not yet clear whether patients with idiopathic hypercalciuria and nephrolithiasis with a so-called phosphate leak who have been reported in this country and Europe[67–69] have the same disease as the subjects with idiopathic hypercalciuria seen in the HHRH kindred. There is a report of a single case of hypophosphatemic rickets with hypercalciuria from Ja-

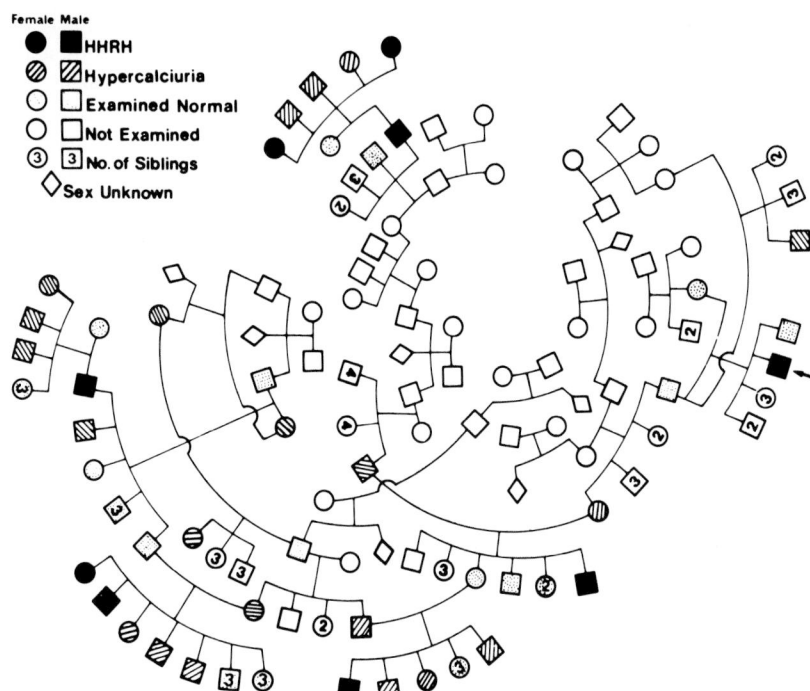

Fig. 105-5 Genetic relationship of nine patients with hereditary hypophosphatemic rickets and hypercalciuria and 21 subjects with "idiopathic" hypercalciuria alone. Arrow indicates index case. (Reprinted from Tieder et al.[18] Used by permission.)

pan.[70] This case did not respond to therapy with 1-α-hydroxy-vitamin D$_3$ but did respond to phosphate treatment. It seems quite likely that this patient has HHRH.

Treatment

Administration of 1–2.5 g of neutral phosphate daily, given in five divided doses leads to an increase in growth rate, disappearance of bone pain and muscle weakness, and disappearance of the radiologic signs of rickets. The serum phosphate concentration rises; the serum 1,25-(OH)$_2$D$_3$ concentration falls, as do the serum calcium and alkaline phosphatase concentrations. Likewise, urinary calcium excretion falls, the urinary cAMP rises, but TmP/GFR does not change. Bone biopsy of a treated subject reveals healing osteomalacia.

FAMILIAL HYPOPHOSPHATEMIC RICKETS

FHR is the most common inherited abnormality of renal tubular phosphate transport (Table 105-2). It is inherited as an X-linked dominant trait. It is also known as vitamin D–resistant rickets, X-linked hypophosphatemia, or hypophosphatemic vitamin D–resistant rickets.

Clinical Features

The most common features of FHR are short stature and femoral and/or tibial bowing presenting early in life (1 to 2 years) without muscle weakness, tetany, or convulsions.[16,71–75] The degree of growth retardation and of skeletal abnormalities is quite variable within a given kindred. Females often have less severe disease than do males. This difference has been ascribed to sex-dependent modulation of mutant gene expression and/or to the presence of normal active X chromosomes in the heterozygous female. The phenomenon of random X-chromosome inactivation may also contribute to the variable expression of the mutant phenotype in the female. In keeping with this concept, obligate heterozygous females without any evidence of bone disease have been described. However, even in affected males, there is a considerable variability in the severity of the bone disease and of the growth retardation.

Prenatal diagnosis is not yet possible. Nor is it easy to make the diagnosis in suspected cases during early infancy even in known kindreds. The plasma phosphate concentration may be normal at birth and remain so far 6 to 9 months. The most reliable early sign of the disease is an elevation of plasma alkaline phosphatase activity, which may occur as early as 4 to 6 months of age and is usually associated with early but definite radiologic signs of rickets. By 1 year of age, some retardation of growth usually occurs with established hypophosphatemia, elevated plasma alkaline phosphatase, and definite radiologic signs of rickets. Coarse trabeculation of bone consistent with osteomalacia is also seen. There may also be some retardation of bone age.

Other early manifestations of the disease are late dentition and recurrent dental abscesses. These may be associated with cranial synostosis. Fractures or pseudofractures in the growing child practically never occur even in untreated patients, but in such cases there is progressive femoral and/or tibial bowing usually resulting in genu valgum; however, in some cases genu varium is seen. Growth retardation and the radiologic signs are more apparent in the lower than upper extremity. These findings have led in part to the suggestion that growth failure is limited to the lower extremities. However, more recent analyses in which upper segment height was determined by subtracting sitting height from total length, have led to more reproducible measurement of upper and lower segment length.[76] The results from these measurements have shown that growth retardation involves both segments but is slightly greater in the lower than upper segment.

Once skeletal growth has ceased, the alkaline phosphatase falls into the normal range and progressive skeletal deformity usually does not occur. However, nearly all untreated adults have bone pain sufficient to restrict somewhat their physical activity. In spite of normal plasma alkaline phosphatase values, histomorphometric evaluation of undecalcified sections of transileal bone biopsies from such adults reveals significant osteomalacia, in both adult females and males[77] (unpublished). Even so, the majority of adults do not have progressive bone disease leading to severe osteomalacia and pseudofractures. However, bone abnormalities are common in all adults. In particular, bone overgrowth occurs at sites of major muscle attachments and around larger joints.[78] These changes may lead to joint pain and a restriction of motion of the elbow, shoulders, and/or hips. Occasionally this overgrowth occurs within the spinal canal, and is of sufficient extent to lead to cord compression requiring surgical intervention.[79,79a]

Spontaneous dental abscesses are common in both early and late childhood.[80] There is commonly a defect in dentine maturation with enlarged pulp chambers and, in many cases, a defect in enamel formation.[81,82] Under normal circumstances the dentin matrix calcifies by the formation of calcospheres containing calcium phosphate crystals. These coalesce to form a uniformly calcified dentin. In patients with FHR, the calcospheres fail to coalesce normally so that a distinct pattern of interglobular dentine forms and persists throughout life.

Laboratory Findings

The two most reliable markers for this disease are a reduced plasma phosphate concentration and a reduced TmP/GFR with otherwise normal renal tubular function. These are associated with a normal to slightly low plasma Ca^{2+} concentration, a normal to slightly high iPTH, an elevated serum alkaline phosphatase, a low or low normal plasma $1,25\text{-}(OH)_2D_3$ and normal $25(OH)D_3$ concentration, and a reduced urinary calcium excretion (unpublished observations). Upon administration of an oral calcium load, there is a very small increase in either plasma Ca^{2+} concentration or urinary Ca^{2+} excretion, implying a secondary defect in the absorption of calcium from the gastrointestinal tract. The serum $24,25\text{-}(OH)_2D_3$ content has been reported to be normal in children but low in untreated adults.

The severity of the bone disease does not correlate with the degree of hypophosphatemia or the TmP/GFR. Hence, hypophosphatemia is an important but not the sole determinant of bone disease.[75]

Radiologic Findings

Early in life, the predominant changes are the characteristic signs of rickets with fraying, widening, and cupping of the metaphyseal ends of the proximal and distal tibia, the distal femur, and the ulna and radius. As the child grows older, the changes at the wrist become minimal. Those at the knee become more pronounced and become associated with a widening of the metaphysis. During late childhood and adolescence the shafts of the long bones display thickened cortices and coarse, unusually dense trabecular bone. Bone mineral analysis usually reveals a normal value, which means that total bone (mineralized and unmineralized) is greater than normal, but there is a marked increase in incompletely mineralized bone. Parenthetically, successful treatment often leads to a remodeling of the skeleton and a decrease in cortical thickness and trabecular bone volume.

There is, with age, an increasing prevalence of calcification of tendon and ligament insertion and of joint capsules. These abnormalities are seen in 45 percent of patients under 20, in 78 percent of those between 20 and 40, and in nearly 100 percent of patients over 40 years of age. These deposits are found in the hand, sacroiliac joints, hips, and iliolumbar ligaments, and sites of tendon insertions on the lesser trochanter. When examined histologically, these calcifications are made up of intratendinous lamellar bone. The factors bringing about deposition of bone at these sites are not known.

Bone Morphology

In the few cases which it has been possible to study, the classic changes of rickets are found at the epiphyseal plate, an expanded proliferative zone with uncalcified or partially calcified cartilage and below this uncalcified or partially calcified primary bone.

Transileal biopsies have been performed in a number of patients.[83–85] These show evidence of osteomalacia in both the cortical and trabecular bone with an increase in osteoid volume, osteoid surface, and mean osteoid seam width. Using the technique of double tetracycline labeling, it has been possible to demonstrate a decrease in calcification rate, and a prolongation of mineralization lag time (the time between bone matrix deposition and its eventual calcification). It is also possible to estimate the occurrence rate of new remodeling units (BMU). This is markedly reduced. Hence, bone turnover is slow; there is a prolonged period of formation at a given remodeling site but a marked delay in mineralization at such a site and a decrease in resorption rate. These changes lead to an increase in total bone, with a normal or low normal amount of mineralized bone, but a significantly increased amount of unmineralized or partially mineralized osteoid. In association with these changes are a characteristic sign of this type of osteomalacia: areas of hypomineralization around osteocytes in the lamellar cortical bone.[86]

Given the finding of a nearly normal amount of mineralized bone as determined both by bone mineral analysis in vivo and in bone biopsy material in vitro, the question arises as to why bowing of the long bones, particularly the tibiae and femora, occurs. The answer appears to lie in the fact that areas of osteomalacia are not confined simply to bone surfaces but are distributed throughout the cortical bone so that the structural properties of the whole organ are adversely affected. The increase in total bone volume can be viewed as an effort to compensate for this lack of structural integrity at the organ level.

Genetics

A more complete discussion of the genetics of FHR is given in the previous edition of this text.[16] Only the salient features are summarized below.

When genetic evaluation was based simply on the appearance of bone disease, the mode of inheritance was not completely clear, but when Winters et al.[87] introduced hypophosphatemia as the criterion for the presence or absence of the trait, then a clear generation-to-generation transmission via an X-linked dominant trait was evident. Subsequent work has borne out this conclusion.[88,89] Critical to proper screening is the necessity of taking fasting blood samples in the early morning for the determination of the serum inorganic phosphate concentration. Equally important is the use of the normative data for the age-related normal serum phosphate concentrations developed by Greenberg et al.[90]

A summary of 143 subjects from several large kindreds showed that by definition all had hypophosphatemia, but only 97 (or 68 percent) had clinically evident bone disease. Further, in all instances each hypophosphatemic child had one hypophosphatemic parent, and the distribution of male and female offspring were nearly equal, but the number of affected females was half of the number of affected males. Furthermore, in the hypophosphatemic individuals without bone disease 47 were female and only 2 males.

These results support the notion of X-linked dominant inheritance, and further argue that affected males with the trait nearly always have clinically evident bone disease, but nearly 50 percent of females do not. At issue is the reason for this relative immunity of the affected female from severe skeletal disease. It is particularly important to note that the explanation does not lie in the degree of hypophosphatemia. Affected females have the same range of serum phosphate concentrations as males. It is not known whether the serum $1,25\text{-}(OH)_2D_3$ concentrations in males and females are similar, nor if there is a difference in $1,25\text{-}(OH)_2D_3$ values between affected females with and those without bone disease.

From a genetic perspective, three possible explanations have been offered to account for the relative immunity of the female from severe bone disease. First is the possibility that the presence of the normal allele on one X chromosome modifies the action of the abnormal gene so that the female escapes severe bone disease because of heterozygosity. Second is the possibility there is an X-linked factor independent of gene dose which confers a relative immunity to the effects of the abnormal gene. Third is the possibility that during the normal process of inactivation of one of the X chromosomes in the female mosaicism with respect to the presence or absence of the abnormal gene could lead to a reduction in the manifestations of the disease.[91]

The problem in deciding among these alternatives is a lack of a detailed study of phosphate and vitamin D metabolism in females with and without skeletal manifestations. It would be of particular interest to know whether these two groups display differences in TmP/GFR, serum $1,25\text{-}(OH)_2D_3$ concentrations, and whether their responses to phosphate restriction differ.

Although no genetic marker is available for prenatal diagnosis of FHR, recent progress has been made in determining the locus of the FHR gene (called HPDR I, McKusick no. 30780,[92] in which HPDR means *hypophosphatemic* vitamin D–resistant rickets). Read and coworkers[93] and Mächler et al.[94] have shown by linkage analysis that the gene is located on the distal short arm of the X chromosome close to the DXS41(99.6) and DXS43(D2) loci at XP22. To obtain a precise mapping of the disease locus in relation to these genetic loci, additional families were investigated using multilocus linkage analysis.[94a] In these studies, the hypophosphatemic rickets gene mapped distal to the DXS41(99.6) locus and proximal to the DXS43(D2) locus, thereby establishing two bridging genetic markers for the disease.[94a] The chromosomal location in humans is consistent with a scheme which relates the mouse and human X chromosome by two rearrangements.[95]

The *Hyp* Mouse

A major advance in the study of the underlying pathophysiology of FHR has taken place as a result of the discovery in 1976 of a mutation in the laboratory mouse which exhibits many of the phenotypic features of FHR.[96] The *Hyp* mouse is characterized by hypophosphatemia, decreased growth rate, rickets and osteomalacia, and reduced net tubular reabsorption of phosphate without hypocalcemia and secondary hyperparathyroidism. Moreover, the trait in the *Hyp* mouse is inherited as an X-linked dominant trait and has been mapped to the distal part of the X chromosome by linkage studies.

Because of the similar pattern of X-linked dominant inheritance and the similarity in phenotypic expression of the mutation in mice and humans, the *Hyp* mouse appears to be an appropriate model for the human disease, FHR. Hence, the ensuing discussion of pathophysiology considers data derived both from humans and mice. Before undertaking this discussion, a brief description of the mouse phenotype is given.

General Phenotype. Heterozygous *Hyp* females (*Hyp*/+) and hemizygous *Hyp* males (*Hyp*/Y) can be distinguished from their normal litter mates (+/+ and +/y) at 21 days of age by their shortened hind limbs and tail and reduced body weight. These features persist throughout life and become more obvious with age. Kyphosis of the thoracic vertebrae, rachitic rosary, and prominent bowing of the femur develop with age in mutant mice, and bone ash is significantly reduced.[96] The skeletal abnormalities are more uniformly severe in the hemizygous male compared to the heterozygous female[96,97] as in the case of the human disease, FHR.

The plasma concentration of inorganic phosphate is significantly reduced in both *Hyp* males and *Hyp* females when compared with that of normal litter mates.[96] These differences are apparent by 20 to 49 days of age and persist up to and beyond 400 days of age. In both genotypes, the plasma phosphate concentration is higher during rapid growth (20 to 49 days) than in mature adults (100 to 199 days). Whereas plasma phosphate continues to decline with age in normal mice (400 to 750 days), a comparable decrease is not apparent in the mutant strain.[96] Plasma calcium concentration is slightly but significantly reduced in *Hyp* males and *Hyp* females. Urinary phosphate excretion, in relation to plasma phosphate, is significantly elevated in *Hyp* mice. The phosphate excretion index is reduced in both genotypes by increasing the calcium/phosphate ratio in the diet (from 0.3 to 1.06), but the elevated urinary phosphate excretion index characteristic of the mutant strain persists under these conditions. The mutant mice appear to live a normal life span. *Hyp*/+ females are fertile and raise their young but not all *Hyp*/Y males can sire offspring.[96]

Renal Phenotype. PHOSPHATE TRANSPORT. As in human X-linked hypophosphatemia, *Hyp* mice exhibit an elevated excretion of phosphate in relation to plasma phosphate concentration.[96,98] Micropuncture studies have localized the phosphate transport defect to the proximal tubule of *Hyp* kidney.[99,100] The persistence of the phosphate leak after parathyroidectomy indicates that the tubular defect in phosphate transport is not dependent on PTH.[100,101] Recent studies have utilized cultured renal proximal tubular cells, derived from 30-day-old normal and *Hyp* mice, to establish the intrinsic nature of the mutant renal phenotype.[102] Using this culture system, the Na^+-dependent phosphate/Na^+-dependent α-methyl-Dglucoside transport ratio is found to be significantly decreased in confluent monolayers derived from *Hyp* mice when compared with those derived from normal mice.[103] These data demonstrate that the expression of the mutant renal phenotype is intrinsic to the kidney, and support the concept that the changes in renal function are not secondary to some humoral factor as is the case in OHO.

Phosphate uptake into renal cortex slices derived from *Hyp* mice is not impaired.[98] Because the basolateral surface of the renal epithelial cell is predominantly exposed in the renal slice preparation,[104] these results suggest that phosphate transport across the basolateral membrane is normal in *Hyp* mice. In contrast, Na^+-phosphate cotransport across the renal brush border membrane is 50 percent of normal in *Hyp* mice.[98,105]

The specificity of the renal brush border membrane phosphate transport defect in *Hyp* mice was established by the demonstration of normal Na^+-dependent glucose,[98,105] alanine,[106] and proline[107] uptake in vesicle preparations derived from mutant mouse kidney. The renal phosphate transport defect in *Hyp* mice is not secondary to alterations in brush border membrane sodium permeability.[107a] Kinetic analysis reveals that the renal brush border membrane phosphate transport defect is associated with a 50 percent decrease in the apparent V_{max} for phosphate transport.[108,109]

After 2 weeks on a very low phosphate diet (0.03% phosphate), a striking suppression in renal fractional excretion of phosphate is observed and a significant rise in Na^+-dependent phosphate transport in brush border membrane vesicles is seen in phosphate-deprived male and female mice bearing the X-linked *Hyp* mutation.[110,111] However, the genotypic difference in phosphate transport between normal and *Hyp* mice is still maintained under these conditions; i.e., Na^+-dependent phosphate uptake into brush border membrane vesicles is significantly lower in vesicles from phosphate-deprived *Hyp* mice as compared with that in phosphate-deprived normal litter mates (Fig. 105-6).[110,111]

VITAMIN D METABOLISM. The regulation of renal 25-$(OH)D_3$ metabolism is impaired in the X-linked *Hyp* mouse, as it is in the FHR human. The production of 1,25-$(OH)_2D_3$ in *Hyp* mice is markedly lower than that of normal mice with a comparable degree of hypophosphatemia, achieved by feeding the normal animals a low phosphate diet.[112,113] *Hyp* mice exhibit a significantly blunted renal 1-α-hydroxylase response to vitamin D^{114} or phosphate deficiency.[113,114a] The reduced synthesis of 1,25-$(OH)_2D_3$ in the mutant strain is independent of genotype differences in serum calcium[114] and parathyroid hormone levels[115] and is associated with a decrease in the apparent V_{max} for 1-α-hydroxylase with no change in apparent K_m.[115] *Hyp* mice also exhibit a significantly reduced renal 1-α-hydroxylase response to PTH infusion[116] and to calcium restriction.[116,117] Patients with FHR also show similar blunted 1-α-hydroxylase responses to both lowered plasma phosphate concentration[117a] and elevated PTH concentration.[117b] In contrast, the stimulation of renal 1,25-$(OH)_2D_3$ production in response to CT infusion is intact in the *Hyp* mouse.[118]

The finding of a difference between the effects of PTH[116] and CT[118] on 1-α-hydroxylase activity in *Hyp* mice provides genetic confirmation of the previously reported existence of two anatomically distinct, independently regulated renal 1-α-hydroxylase systems in mammalian kidney (Table 105-1), namely, a PTH-regulated system in the proximal convoluted tubule and a calcitonin-stimulated system in the proximal straight tubule.[39,44] These results support the notion that the

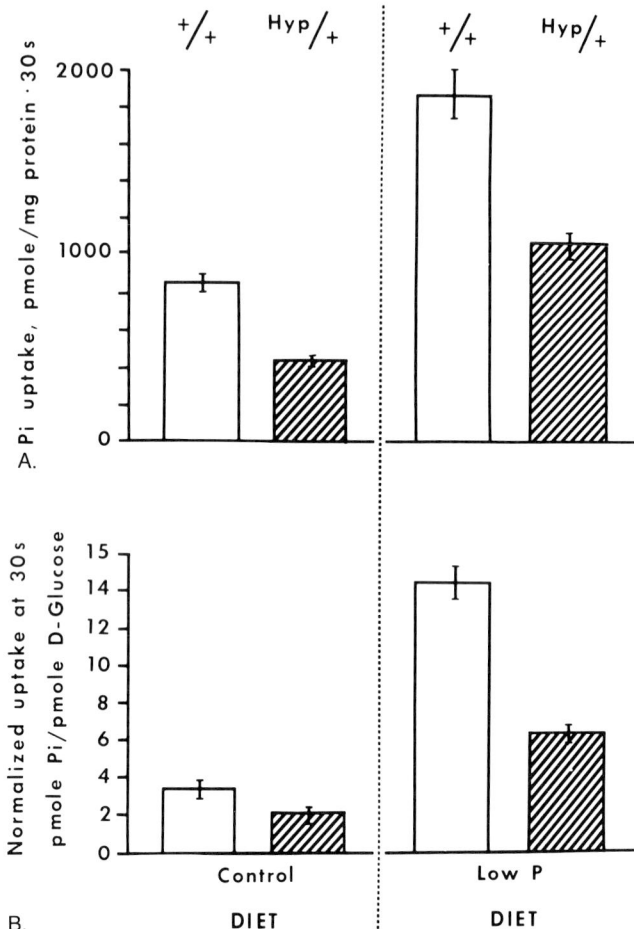

Fig. 105-6 Effect of the *Hyp* mutation on renal adaptation to phosphate deprivation. *A*. The Na^+-dependent cotransport of inorganic phosphate (100 μM) at 30 s, corrected for contribution of diffusional component, by renal brush border membrane vesicles prepared from normal female (+/+) (open bars) and heterozygous female (*Hyp*/+) (shaded bars) litter mates fed control (0.6% P) phosphorus and low phosphate (0.03%) diets for 2 weeks. Data show mean values ± SE of five determinations. *B*. data in *A* normalized to simultaneous uptake of D-glucose (20 μM) by Na^+-dependent cotransport. Values are mean ± SE. These data show that differences in transport between *Hyp* and normal animals and between low phosphate and control diet fed animals, as shown in *A*, are specific for phosphate. (*From Tenenhouse and Scriver.[110] Used by permission.*)

defective 1-α-hydroxylase of the *Hyp* mouse resides in the proximal convoluted tubule.

The renal mitochondrial production of 24,25-dihydroxyvitamin D_3 is significantly elevated in *Hyp* mice when compared with that of normal litter mates,[114,119,120] and this increase in renal 25-$(OH)D_3$-24-hydroxylase (24-hydroxylase) activity in *Hyp* mice is associated with an increase in apparent V_{max} with no change in affinity of the mutant enzyme for the 25-$(OH)D_3$ substrate.[121] Although isolated renal mitochondria from *Hyp* mice exhibit increased 24-hydroxylase activity, there is no evidence for elevated plasma levels of 24,25-$(OH)_2D_3$ in mutant mice.[122] The synthesis of 24,25-$(OH)_2D_3$ is significantly stimulated by 1,25-$(OH)_2D_3$ treatment in both normal and *Hyp* mice, and no differences in this 24-hydroxylase response is apparent.[121] However, after vitamin D and calcium deprivation, *Hyp* mice are more responsive to signals which induce 24-hydroxylase than are normal litter mates.[121]

The metabolism of 25-$(OH)D_3$ is also abnormal in cultured renal epithelial cells derived primarily from the proximal tubule of normal and *Hyp* mice. Cells from *Hyp* mice exhibit increased 24,25-$(OH)_2D_3$ production[103] and an abnormal regulation of 1,25-$(OH)_2D_3$ synthesis[123] when compared to cultured cells from normal mice. The demonstration of abnormal 25-$(OH)D_3$ metabolism in renal epithelial cells derived from *Hyp* mice after 8 days in culture provides further evidence in support of the concept that the expression of the mutant renal phenotype is independent of circulating factors and therefore intrinsic to the kidney.

Renal degradation of vitamin D_3 metabolites by the C-24 oxidation pathway is significantly increased in *Hyp* mice.[124,125] Figure 105-7 shows that the production of 1,24,25-trihydroxyvitamin D_3, 24-oxo-1,25-dihydroxyvitamin D_3, and 24-oxo-1,23,25-trihydroxyvitamin D_3 from 1,25-$(OH)_2D_3$ is twofold greater in renal mitochondria from *Hyp* mice than when compared with normal litter mates. These findings suggest that increased renal catabolism of the active vitamin D hormone, may indeed contribute to the clinical phenotype. The report of a modest increase in the plasma clearance of high doses of exogenous [^{3}H]1,25-$(OH)_2D_3$ in mutant *Hyp* mice[125a] is consistent with the in vitro findings.[124,125] Similarly, an increase in the 1,25-$(OH)_2D_3$ disappearance rate has been reported in patients with FHR.[126]

TISSUE PHOSPHATE. The precise relationship between the defect in brush border membrane phosphate transport and in mitochondrial 25-$(OH)D_3$ metabolism is poorly understood. One possibility is that the abnormalities in 24,25-$(OH)_2D_3$ and 1,25-$(OH)_2D_3$ synthesis are due to an altered renal cell phosphate concentration. Reduced renal cortical ribonucleoside triphosphate pools in *Hyp* mice have been reported,[126a] but both chemical and ^{31}P NMR methods have failed to demonstrate genotype differences in the intracellular concentration of inorganic phosphate[96,98,110,127] and phosphorylated compounds.[127]

PTH STATUS AND RESPONSE TO PTH. The persistence of the renal phosphate transport leak after parathyroidectomy of X-linked *Hyp* mice establishes that the brush border membrane phosphate transport defect is not secondary to hyperparathy-

roidism.[100–101] The PTH status of *Hyp* mice is, nevertheless, a controversial issue. Either normal or elevated levels of PTH by radioimmunoassay[96,115,128] or cytochemical bioassay[129] have been reported. The latter data are consistent with elevated urinary excretion of cAMP in *Hyp* mice[98,130] and the demonstration that parathyroidectomy elicits a greater fall in serum calcium concentration in *Hyp* mice than in normal litter mates.[101,131] Although the relative contribution of hyperparathyroidism to the mutant renal phenotype is difficult to ascertain, genotype differences in brush border membrane phosphate transport are equally apparent after comparable diet-induced hyperparathyroidism in both strains.[132] It is noteworthy that humans with FHR have high normal and, in some cases elevated, plasma PTH concentrations. The latter is particularly the case in infants between the ages of 6 months and 2 years (unpublished).

The effect of the *Hyp* mutation on the renal response to PTH has also been investigated. Subcutaneous injections of PTH elicits a dose-dependent increase in urine cAMP and in the fractional excretion index of phosphate in both normal and *Hyp* mice.[133] No evidence for hypersensitivity to PTH was documented, thereby ruling out one of the postulated mechanisms for this disorder.[133]

PROTEIN KINASES. Examination of renal cytosolic content of protein kinases and protein kinase inhibitor protein in normal and mutant mice[134] reveals that cAMP-dependent protein kinase and protein kinase inhibitor activity are not different in the two genotypes. Moreover, the pattern of cAMP-dependent brush border membrane protein phosphorylation is not different in both genotypes.[109,134a] Ca^{2+}-dependent, phospholipid-stimulated protein kinase activity (protein kinase C) is significantly elevated in renal cytosol of *Hyp* mice.[134] In contrast, an increase in protein kinase C is not apparent in supernatant fractions of heart, spleen, or liver prepared from *Hyp* mice.[134] These data suggest that the inappropriately high cytosolic protein kinase C activity is specific to *Hyp* kidney and may indeed be related to the defects in brush border membrane phosphate transport and/or mitochondrial vitamin D metabolism.

Intestinal Phenotype. Although early studies in everted gut sacs provided evidence for a defect in jejunal phosphate transport in the *Hyp* mouse,[135,136] these findings have not been confirmed in later studies.[137] Na^+-dependent phosphate and glucose transport in isolated jejunal brush border membrane vesicles and transmural transport of phosphate by everted gut sacs, prepared from duodenum to terminal ileum, are not different in normal mice and mutant litter mates.[137]

Examination of the effect of the *Hyp* mutation on the intestinal receptor for 1,25-$(OH)_2D_3$ has shown no significant difference in either K_D values (0.9 to 3.5 $\times$ 10^{-10} M) or receptor number in normal and *Hyp* mice.[138] Moreover, studies of renal and testicular 1,25-$(OH)_2D_3$ receptors failed to detect genotype differences.[138] These data, as well as the demonstration of similar amounts of 10K and 30K intestinal vitamin D–dependent calcium binding protein in normal and *Hyp* mice,[139] provide evidence against an intestinal resistance to 1,25-$(OH)_2D_3$ in the mutant strain. However, a different intestinal phenotype has recently been documented in the juvenile *Hyp* mouse. Evidence for malabsorption of calcium and phosphate in 5-week-old mutant mice is apparent by whole animal balance studies,[140] isolated duodenal segments,[141] or administration of oral isotopic calcium and phosphate.[142] In these animals lower levels of vitamin D–dependent calcium binding

Fig. 105-7 Effect of the *Hyp* mutation on C-24 oxidation of 1,25-$(OH)_2D_3$. Renal mitochondria from +/Y and Hyp/Y mice were incubated with 500 nM[^{3}H]1,25-$(OH)_2D_3$ for 15 min at 25°C. Each bar depicts mean ± SEM and is based on values derived from seven individual mice of each genotype. Genotype differences were significant for each product (p < 0.001) by Student's *t* test. (From Tenenhouse, Yip, and Jones.[125] Used by permission.)

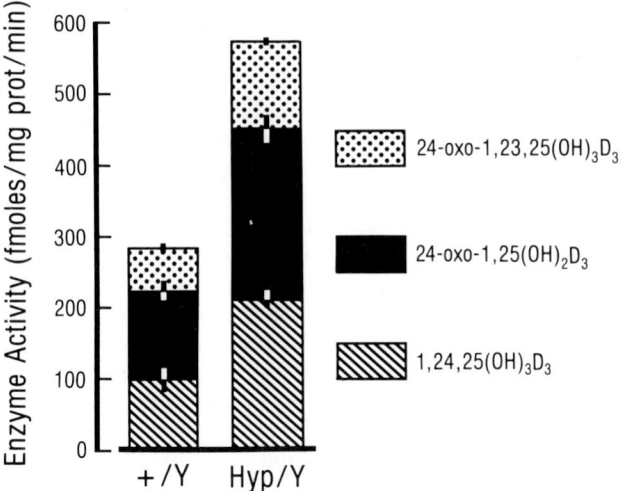

protein were detected in the duodenum of *Hyp* mice when compared with those of normal litter mates.[143] To identify the mechanism for this compromised intestinal function in juvenile *Hyp* mice, intestinal receptors for 1,25-(OH)$_2$D$_3$ and intestinal response to the vitamin D$_3$ hormone were examined. No evidence for intestinal resistance to 1,25-(OH)$_2$D$_3$ was apparent; 1,25-(OH)$_2$D$_3$ receptor number and binding affinity, and 1,25-(OH)$_2$D$_3$-stimulated calcium and phosphate transport and vitamin D–dependent calcium binding protein were normal in the juvenile *Hyp* mouse.[142] However, the plasma concentration of 1,25-(OH)$_2$D is lower than normal in 5-week-old mutants,[142] and young *Hyp* mice fail to exhibit an appropriate 1-hydroxylase response to dietary stress.[144] These results indicate that the intestinal phenotype of juvenile *Hyp* mice is most likely secondary to abnormal renal production of 1,25-(OH)$_2$D$_3$. The reduced Ca^{2+} absorption seen in young FHR patients probably has a similar basis.

Bone Phenotype. *Hyp* mice have shortened hind limbs and tail, reduced body size, kyphosis of the thoracic vertebrae, rachitic rosary, and prominent bowing of the femur.[96] Femur ash weight is less than half normal, yet, femur calcium/phosphate ratio is unaltered.[97] Histologically, the femur is characterized by wide osteoid borders and a wide epiphyseal plate. Reduced bone density and enlarged osteocyte lacunae are revealed by microradiography.[97] Abnormal skeletal development is apparent as early as 7 days after birth, and unexpected transitory metaphyseal radioopacity which peaks at 3 weeks occurs in the long bones.[145,146] Undecalcified bone sections reveal that an increased amount of trabecular bone in the metaphysis of *Hyp* mice accounts for this increased radioopacity. Craniosynostosis is present by 4 weeks of age and is apparently due to premature fusion of the coronal suture in *Hyp* mice.[147] Deficient linear growth of the nasal bone is considered the most important variable contributing to the overall difference in skull morphology between *Hyp* and normal mice.[148]

Analytical and histomorphometric methods reveal a shorter than normal vertebral length associated with a wider epiphyseal growth plate in *Hyp* mice. Moreover, impaired endosteal bone mineralization is present in the mutants as demonstrated by excessive osteoid surface and thickness, and decreased extent of the mineralization front.[149]

The temporal pattern of bone mineral accretion, estimated by measuring femoral ash weight and ash weight/femoral length ratio, is markedly different in males and females, independent of genotype. In females, femora continue to gain in mineral content with age, but in males there is no increase after 15 weeks of age.[150,151] These results demonstrate that, in young mice, genotype differences in mineral content are significant in both males and females, whereas by 52 weeks of age, only mutant males are different from normal; i.e., significant differences between normal females and heterozygous (*Hyp*/ +) or homozygous (*Hyp/Hyp*) mutant females are not apparent. Moreover, at all ages examined, bone parameters in *Hyp*/ + females and *Hyp/Hyp* females are not different.[150,151]

In view of comparable hypophosphatemia in all groups of *Hyp* mice (*Hyp*/ + , *Hyp/Hyp*, *Hyp*/Y), these data suggest that differences in expression of skeletal abnormalities between older *Hyp* males and *Hyp* females may be attributed to sexually determined factors rather than to lyonization. The failure to detect gene dosage may be attributed to the fact that some loci on the X chromosome can escape inactivation and that differential expression of active and inactive X-linked loci has been reported.[152] On the other hand, the failure to detect gene

dosage may be attributed to the secondary nature of the bone defect; i.e., abnormal mineralization of bone in *Hyp* mice may be the consequence of hypophosphatemia and inappropriate plasma 1,25-(OH)$_2$D$_3$ levels, both of which arise from a primary renal defect.

To examine the effect of the *Hyp* mutation on bone formation, the mineralization of subcutaneously implanted osteosarcoma-derived bone-inducing substance was investigated in normal and *Hyp* mice.[153] In both genotypes, cartilage formation was evident at 2 weeks after implantation, and, by 4 weeks, the cartilage was replaced by unmineralized bone matrix and hematopoietic bone marrow.[153] Osteoid tissue arising from the implantation of bone-inducing substance in the *Hyp* mouse showed no radiologic or histologic sign of calcification. In normal mice, however, calcification of implants was readily discernible. These results suggest that abnormal bone mineralization in *Hyp* mice is determined to a large extent by the hypophosphatemic environment and that the defect in bone formation may be secondary to the renal phosphate leak and/or the abnormality in renal vitamin D metabolism. On the other hand, studies by Glorieux and Ecarot-Charrier (personal communication) suggest that in addition to an effect of the environment on bone cell function, there is an intrinsic defect in bone cell function. This is demonstrable by differences in osteoid thickness of bone nodules induced by the injection of "osteoblasts" from mutant or normal mice into the gluteal muscle of normal mice. These investigators suggest that a defect in phosphate metabolism in osteoblasts may play a role in the pathogenesis of bone disease, and that this defect may act in concert with the extracellular ionic abnormal environment to determine the severity of the bone disease in a given patient.

Hyp mice exhibit dental abnormalities similar to those reported in patients with X-linked hypophosphatemia. The molars of *Hyp*/Y mice tend to have rather large pulp chambers and a wider predentine band that + /Y controls, with mutant dentine showing prominent interglobular areas of deficient mineralization.[154–156] In addition to these dental abnormalities, exposure of the dental pulp occurs frequently in *Hyp* mice, through developmental deficiency of the dentine.[156]

Other Phenotypic Characteristics. The phosphate content of milk was measured in lactating normal and *Hyp*/ + females 14 days after giving birth. No significant genotype differences are found in the concentration of inorganic and total phosphate[157] in the milk of lactating *Hyp*/ + and normal females. These data indicate that *Hyp*/ + females can accumulate a normal amount of phosphate in milk despite significant hypophosphatemia and provide evidence for the absence of a phosphate transport defect in mammary glands.[157]

Phosphate transport function of salivary glands derived from normal and *Hyp* mice was examined indirectly by determining the concentration of phosphate in saliva.[158] The inorganic and total phosphate concentrations are lower than normal in saliva from *Hyp* mice. However, in both genotypes, the phosphate content of saliva is decreased by feeding a low phosphate diet. Moreover, salivary phosphate of *Hyp* mice is similar to that of normal mice with comparable degrees of hypophosphatemia. These data indicate that the phosphate transport defect, which is expressed in the renal brush border membrane, is not expressed in the salivary gland.[158]

To explain the basis for greater food consumption in *Hyp* mice relative to that of normal litter mates, the metabolic rate was determined.[159] Oxygen consumption is elevated in *Hyp* mice, and this is accompanied by an increased percentage of cardiac output being delivered to organs of heat production (liver and skeletal muscle) and to skin. The T_4 levels are normal in *Hyp* mice and increased oxygen consumption is not affected by serum phosphate. The underlying mechanisms for the increased oxygen consumption in the mutant animals are not understood.

Hyp mice exhibit an abnormal hyperphosphatemic response to fasting.[160] Their inability to demonstrate a rise in serum phosphate following fasting has been attributed to their apparent failure to adapt to phosphate deprivation.[161] It has been proposed that the hyperphosphatemic response to fasting is related to the adaptive renal response, which prevents phosphate, mobilized from body stores during fasting, from being excreted in the urine. However, the demonstration of adaptation to phosphate deprivation at the renal brush border membrane of *Hyp* mice[110,111] casts doubt on the validity of this hypothesis.

Treatment. Phosphate supplementation of drinking water for 11 weeks postweaning leads to growth of hind limbs in *Hyp*/Y mice.[96] In addition, kyphosis of the thoracic spine does not develop. Examination of skeletal preparations reveals that long bones, tail bones, and skull bones of *Hyp* males are normal and that the rachitic changes are less pronounced following treatment with phosphate.[96]

The efficacy of phosphate supplementation was also assessed by histomorphometric analysis of bone.[149] Treatment of *Hyp* males with phosphate normalizes the endochondral calcification but does not correct the endosteal bone mineralization, as evidenced by a decreased mineralization front and increased mean osteoid seam thickness in treated *Hyp* males when compared with controls. Accordingly, as observed in the human disease, phosphate supplementation of *Hyp* mice can heal the epiphyseal but not the endosteal defect in bone mineralization. Moreover, secondary hyperparathyroidism arising from phosphate therapy appears to stimulate osteoblastic and osteoclastic recruitment and activity.[149]

Treatment of *Hyp* males with phosphate combined with either 25-$(OH)D_3$, 24,25-$(OH)_2D_3$ or 1,25-$(OH)_2D_3$ was also assessed by bone histomorphometry.[162] In this study the vitamin D_3 metabolites were administered for the last 3 weeks of a 20-week phosphate treatment protocol. Only 1,25-$(OH)_2D_3$ produced a dose-dependent rise in serum calcium and serum phosphate and greatly improved bone mineralization. The stimulation of bone turnover induced by phosphate supplementation alone was not apparent with the combined therapy. However, the persistence of osteomalacia despite the correction of serum mineral concentrations suggests that either there is a specific bone cell resistance to phosphate and 1,25-$(OH)_2D_3$ or 1,25-$(OH)_2D_3$ therapy was not initiated early enough.[162] When therapy with 1,25-$(OH)_2D_3$ alone was started in 21-day-old *Hyp* mice and continued for 4 weeks, epiphyseal, endosteal, and periosteal bone mineralization are improved in correlation with the dose of 1,25-$(OH)_2D_3$ and the rise in serum phosphate.[163] These data suggest that both rickets and osteomalacia can be healed by 1,25-$(OH)_2D_3$ in doses high enough to normalize serum mineral concentrations.

The improvement in phosphate homeostasis achieved by continuous subcutaneous administration of 1,25-$(OH)_2D_3$ to *Hyp* mice can be attributed to increased intestinal absorption of phosphate.[164] Everted gut sacs prepared from all segments of the small intestine of 1,25-$(OH)_2D_3$-treated *Hyp* mice exhibit significantly higher phosphate transport activity than sacs

from untreated mutants. In contrast, 1,25-$(OH)_2D_3$ treatment has no effect on renal brush border membrane phosphate transport and fails to correct the renal defect in phosphate reabsorption in *Hyp* mice.[164]

The efficiency of therapy with 1-α-hydroxyvitamin D_3 has also been assessed in *Hyp* mice.[165] This vitamin D_3 analogue significantly increases the intestinal transport of phosphate, elicits a dose-dependent rise in serum phosphate and serum calcium concentrations, and improves rachitic bone morphology.

In 1979, Meyer et al. reported that *Hyp* mice exhibit a slight elevation in serum magnesium and a lower than normal bone magnesium content.[97] The effect of magnesium supplementation was therefore assessed to establish whether reduced skeletal magnesium is involed in the pathogenesis of the bone disease in the mutant mice.[166] The results indicate that reduced bone magnesium appears to impair the skeletal responsiveness to PTH, since magnesium therapy restores osteoclastic bone resorption and improves bone mineralization. In the same study, lactose supplementation was found to partially inhibit bone resorption and improve renal phosphate conservation, probably through a calcium-induced suppression of PTH secretion. These studies suggest that secondary hyperparathyroidism contributes to the renal phosphate leak in *Hyp* mice as was suggested by other studies.[101,128,129,131]

Treatment of *Hyp* mice with thyroid hormones (T_3 or T_4) leads to a rise in serum phosphate, a decrease in urinary phosphate excretion, and a stimulation of renal brush border membrane Na^+-dependent phosphate transport.[107] The effect of thyroid hormone appears to be specific, since the transport of proline in the same brush border membrane preparation remains unchanged. Although the cellular mechanism for the effect of thyroid hormone on renal phosphate transport is not understood, the response appears to be independent of PTH and calcitonin. Because there is no evidence to suggest that *Hyp* mice are hypothyroid,[107,159] this treatment should be recognized as a pharmacologic maneuver and is not feasible in patients with the homologous disorder.

The *Gy* Mouse

Another X-linked mutation (gene symbol, *Gy*) in the mouse also perturbs phosphate homeostasis.[106] The *Gy* gene maps to an independent locus close to *Hyp* on the X chromosome. The *Gy* mutation confers a phenotype (designated *Gyro*) in males characterized by hypophosphatemia, dwarfism, rickets, extreme circling behavior, hyperactivity, abnormalities of the inner ear, and deafness.

Gy males exhibit an impairment in renal brush border membrane Na^+-dependent phosphate transport and, like *Hyp* males, have 50 percent of the activity of normal litter mates. The demonstration of normal Na^+-stimulated glucose and alanine transport in brush border membrane vesicles prepared from *Gy* males provides evidence for the specificity of the renal phosphate transport defect.

The *Gy* mutation reveals that there are two closely linked loci on the X chromosome, *Gy* and *Hyp*, that play a role in phosphate transport at the renal brush border membrane. Whether these gene loci code for gene products which operate at different steps of the phosphate transport process or represent separate components of a heteropolymeric phosphate transporter or function as putative controlling elements of the transport process remains to be elucidated.

It is of interest that perturbation of phosphate homeostasis itself is not the cause of the inner ear lesion in the *Gy* mouse. The nature of the *Gy* translation product that is common to the inner ear and renal brush border membrane is unknown.

Audiometric evaluation of 22 patients with FHR identified five individuals, including two mother-son pairs, with sensorial hearing deficits due to cochlear dysfunction, suggesting that FHR patients with the cochlear phenotype may be the human counterpart of the *Gy* phenotype in mouse.[106a]

Pathogenesis of FHR

The studies in the *Hyp* mouse complement and extend the data obtained from clinical studies in FHR patients. From these data, a clear idea of the pathogenesis of the various manifestations of the disease in FHR patients has emerged (Fig. 105-8). The renal phosphate leak, the secondary nature of the impaired absorption of Ca^{2+} and phosphate from the gut of both juvenile *Hyp* mice and young FHR patients, and the bone disease appear to be the same in the human and murine disorders. Likewise, renal adaptation to low phosphate is seen in both humans and mice in vivo, but at any level of plasma phosphate concentration the reabsorption of phosphate and the V_{max} for Na^+-phosphate cotransport in isolated brush border membrane vesicles are different between mutant and normal animals. Further, in both species an elevation of the plasma PTH concentration is not the major agent altering renal phosphate transport. Nonetheless, the kidney is respon-

sive to this hormone so that, in the absence of PTH, phosphate transport increases, but a clear difference between normal and mutant organisms persists. Additionally, the adaptive responses of the renal 1-α-hydroxylase systems in terms of either PTH infusion or phosphate deprivation are abnormal in both species. Neither an elevation of PTH nor a restriction of dietary phosphate leads to an appropriate increase in either renal 1-α-hydroxylase activity or in plasma 1,25-$(OH)_2D_3$ concentration. There is also evidence to suggest that in each species an increase in the metabolic clearance of 1,25-$(OH)_2D_3$ from the plasma is present. The importance of this change in clearance rate to the overall abnormality in vitamin D metabolism is not yet clear.

The close link between the abnormalities in phosphate transport and in the control of 1-α-hydroxylase activity, the demonstration that both defects persist in cultured cells derived from the proximal tubule, and the demonstration that CT elicits a normal stimulation of 1-α-hydroxylase in the kidney of the mutant mouse, all place the site of the primary renal lesion in the proximal convoluted tubule. The data argue that an intrinsic tubular defect exists. It apparently does not arise as a consequence of the generation of a humoral factor (see OHO discussion, below). The findings from the studies of the mineralization process in bone and bone cell explants from the *Hyp* mouse argue that both an intrinsic defect in the bone mineralization process and, in particular, an abnormal extracellular fluid environment are responsible for the mineralization defect.

The issues which remain to be clarified are: (1) the nature of the primary renal tubular defect; (2) the reason that in children with FHR there is a decrease in intestinal Ca^{2+} absorption in the face of a normal or low normal plasma 1,25-$(OH)_2D_3$ concentration; (3) the mechanisms by which the changes in the metabolism of phosphate and vitamin D lead to the skeletal changes; and (4) the reason that the female has a relative immunity to the development of severe bone disease.

The most important question in terms of pathogenesis is that of determining the difference in the nature of the primary defects which characterize FHR and HHRH. Why in HHRH is a renal phosphate leak associated with a normal adaptive response (increase) in 1-α-hydroxylase activity but in FHR with an abnormal adaptive response? At least two likely possibilities exist: either the phosphate transport defects in the two conditions exist at different sites within the nephron, or the defects exist in the same nephron segment but involve different sites within the cells of this segment.

If the defects in phosphate transport were at different tubular sites in the two conditions, then one could propose that the primary defect in FHR is in the proximal convoluted tubule and that in HHRH at some more distal site. In this view, in patients with HHRH, the hypophosphatemia resulting from the distal phosphate leak would act to stimulate the 1-α-hydroxylase activity in the proximal convoluted tubule. The difficulty with this hypothesis is that one would also expect an adaptive increase in phosphate transport in the proximal convoluted tubule as a consequence of phosphate depletion. This adaptation should be sufficient to bring about a nearly complete renal conservation of phosphate: an event which clearly does not occur.

The alternative possibility is that the primary defect in each of these two conditions is at the level of the proximal convoluted tubule, but the primary cellular site of the defect differs for the two conditions. To understand how differing primary

Fig. 105-8 The pathogenesis of FHR. A single proximal tubular defect leads to two important abnormalities: a decrease in *Tm* for phosphate and an altered regulation of 1,25-$(OH)_2D_3$ synthesis. The decrease in *Tm* leads to increased P_i excretion and a fall in serum phosphate concentration. This has two adverse effects on the skeleton: it decreases both the rate of growth and the rate of mineralization. Further, an intrinsic defect in phosphate transport in osteoblasts may contribute to the bone disease (not shown). Normally, the fall in serum phosphate concentration would act as a stimulus for the increased renal synthesis of 1,25-$(OH)_2D_3$, but in FHR this mechanism does not operate so that the serum 1,25-$(OH)_2D_3$ concentration is low or low normal. As a consequence, intestinal Ca^{2+} absorption is reduced, serum Ca^{2+} concentration falls to a low normal value, and urinary Ca^{2+} falls. The fall in serum Ca^{2+} concentration leads to a rise in serum PTH to a high normal value. This stimulus would normally act to increase 1,25-$(OH)_2D_3$ synthesis, but in the FHR patient this mechanism is impaired. Nonetheless, the rise in PTH acts to further enhance renal phosphate loss. This model provides the rationale for combined phosphate and 1,25-$(OH)_2D_3$ therapy in FHR.

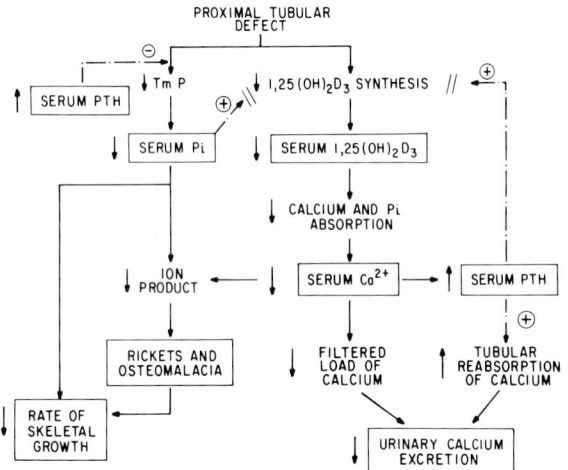

sites of cellular dysfunction might lead to the same decrease in Na^+-phosphate cotransport and hence to a fall in TmP/GFR, it is necessary to argue that during the transcellular transport of phosphate across the proximal tubular cell, there is a coupling of events at the two membrane sites, the brush border and the basolateral membranes, such that a decrease in phosphate efflux out of the cell across the basolateral membranes leads to a secondary decrease in phosphate entry across the luminal membrane and, conversely, that a primary decrease in phosphate entry leads to a secondary decrease in phosphate efflux. In this view, HHRH could develop from a primary defect in Na^+-phosphate entry across the luminal membrane resulting in a small fall in intracellular phosphate concentration and a consequent stimulation of 1-α-hydroxylase activity. Conversely, FHR could develop as a consequence of a primary defect in phosphate egress from the cell across the basolateral membrane, with a consequent slight rise in intracellular phosphate content leading to a partial inhibition of 1-α-hydroxylase activity as well as a secondary decrease in Na^+-phosphate entry across the luminal membrane leading to a reduction in TmP/GFR. Although in vitro studies in renal cortical slices suggested that efflux of phosphate across the basolateral membrane is not impaired in the *Hyp* mouse,[98] the ^{32}P-loaded cortical slice may not accurately reflect the efflux component of transcellular phosphate flux across the basolateral membrane in the intact proximal tubule in vivo.

Calcium Malabsorption. One of the enigmas in the young FHR patient is a reduced intestinal calcium absorption in the face of a low or low normal plasma 1,25-$(OH)_2$D concentration. A partial explanation for this dichotomy may be found in the results of recent studies in the juvenile *Hyp* mouse where a reduced level of calcium transport and vitamin D–dependent calcium binding protein (CaBP) were found in the intestinal mucosal cell.[142] These manifestations were secondary to a defect in 1,25-$(OH)_2D_3$ synthesis and not due to a defect in the responsiveness of the intestinal mucosal cell to actions of 1,25-$(OH)_2D_3$. A similar mechanism may be operative in the young FHR patient.

Bone Abnormalities and Skeletal Growth. It has been known for many years that young rats fed a severely restricted phosphate diet develop rickets and osteomalacia. Hence, in both FHR and HHRH the major pathogenic factor in the development of bone disease is hypophosphatemia. Rickets, a disorder of the epiphyseal growth plate, develops because the sequence of cartilage matrix formation → cartilage matrix mineralization → resorption of the mineralized cartilage matrix → deposition of primary bone matrix → mineralization of the bone matrix → resorption of the mineralized bone matrix, etc., is markedly retarded. This is the case largely because chondroclasts and osteoclasts selectively resorb mineralized matrix. Thus, an impairment of mineralization leads to a retardation of the overall remodeling sequence and eventually to a decrease in epiphyseal growth rate and a short stature. Theoretically, restoration of the plasma phosphate concentration to a normal value should lead to a complete restoration of the mineralization process and a reestablishment of a normal growth rate. In practice, this therapeutic objective is not often attainable. Administration of oral phosphate leads to a transient increase in plasma phosphate concentration lasting 2.5 to 3.0 h. Hence, what is usually achieved is a periodic increase in the phosphate level to normal values. Moreover, in patients with FHR, administration of phosphate alone invariably leads to secondary hyperparathyroidism because each time the plasma phosphate rises, bone and cartilage mineralization ensues and calcium as well as phosphate is deposited into the matrix. As a consequence, the plasma Ca^{2+} concentration falls and parathyroid hormone secretion is increased, but this does not cause the expected increase in 1,25-$(OH)_2D_3$ synthesis, and so Ca^{2+} absorption is not increased. This failure of an adaptive increase in intestinal Ca^{2+} absorption means that availability of Ca^{2+} restricts the mineralization of cartilage and bone in the patient treated with phosphate alone. Hence, the therapeutic objectives in patients with FHR are to increase the intestinal absorption of both Ca^{2+} and phosphate. This contrasts with the situation in HHRH, in which plasma 1,25-$(OH)_2D_3$ concentration and intestinal Ca^{2+} absorption are high.

It is not clear whether the low normal plasma 1,25-$(OH)_2D_3$ concentrations as well as the hypophosphatemia play a direct role in the abnormality in bone mineralization seen in patients with FHR, i.e., does 1,25-$(OH)_2D_3$ play a role in the regulation of the mineralization process. Considerable data exist to suggest that it does play such a role, but these data are outside the scope of the present discussion.

Treatment of FHR

Children. At present there is no completely satisfactory treatment for FHR.[16,72–75,83,84,167–171] Marked improvement in growth rate and the associated skeletal abnormalities can be achieved with oral phosphate combined with either vitamin D_3 or 1,25-$(OH)_2D_3$. However, even under optimal conditions, in the usual patient, subtle radiologic signs of the skeletal abnormalities are seen at the end of the long bones of the lower extremities and growth rates often remain subnormal when patients are treated in this way. Two persistent radiologic signs are common: a widening or flaring of the end of the bone (presumably due to the fact that a delay still exists in the rate of the remodeling process involved in reshaping the metaphyseal region as the bone grows in length) and a weblike abnormality of the medial segment of the growth plate particularly in the distal femoral epiphysis (unpublished). There are two major problems in achieving effective therapeutic results: the first, seen most often with vitamin D_3 therapy, is repeated episodes of vitamin D_3 intoxication; and the second is the matter of patient compliance. To be effective combined therapy must be started early in life and sustained at least through childhood, adolescence, and early adult life (see "Adults," below). This requires the administration of four to five daily doses of phosphate, an objective not easily attainable.

In employing the combined therapy, even with phosphate and 1,25-$(OH)_2D_3$, careful follow-up is required. The simplest method for instituting treatment is to administer oral neutral phosphate (neutraphos K) in divided doses (four to five per day) for a maximal daily dose of 1.25 to 1.5 g. The major difficulty in achieving this objective is the induction of diarrhea by the ingestion of oral phosphate. However, by introducing the phosphate in graded doses, a tolerance is usually built up so the objective can be attained. The administration of 1,25-$(OH)_2D_3$ in a dose of 0.5 to 0.75 μg/day is then begun and the dose increased gradually to attain a maximal suppression of parathyroid hormone secretion without inducing hypercalciuria or hypercalcemia. Even so, close monitoring of response is required because during the rapid healing phase the dose of 1,25-$(OH)_2D_3$ or 1-α-hydroxyvitamin D_3 needed to facilitate healing is greater than during the maintenance phase, particularly in younger children. If this therapy is instituted in the first to third year, there is considerable healing and a growth spurt is seen. Once the alkaline phosphatase is normal, then it is usually necessary to reduce the dose of 1,25-$(OH)_2D_3$, and this dose can then be maintained until the onset of puberty, at which time an increased need for 1,25-$(OH)_2D_3$ and phosphate develop and a readjustment of doses is required.

A major limitation of this treatment program is that of compliance. This more often involves a failure to ingest the required four to five daily doses of phosphate than a failure to ingest the 1,25-$(OH)_2D_3$. Since the two therapeutic modalities counterbalance each other's effects, such a failure of phosphate ingestion can lead to hypercalcemia and hypercalciuria. Thus, hypercalciuria can develop either because of an excessive dose of 1,25-$(OH)_2D_3$ in a patient with an adequate phosphate intake, in which case a reduction in 1,25-$(OH)_2D_3$ is indicated, or it can develop in a patient with an inadequate phosphate intake in which case an increase in phosphate intake is indicated. Measurement of the phosphate content in a random 24-h urine sample can help decide between these alternatives.

A different approach to therapy has been recommended, in which high doses (2 to 3 μg/day) of 1,25-$(OH)_2D_3$ are given along with phosphate (1 to 2 g) to initiate healing, and then once healing has occurred the doses of 1,25-$(OH)_2D_3$ are decreased when hypercalcemia and hypercalciuria develop.[172] However, in this study only one out of five patients was below the age of 13.5 years. Even so, this approach does not offer any advantage over the program outlined above and offers the major disadvantage of having most patients develop hypercalciuria and hypercalcemia, complications to be avoided (see "Complications of Therapy," below).

Another approach to adjuvant therapy has been recommended.[170,171] This is to treat patients with 1,25-$(OH)_2D_3$ and phosphate but add to this two additional medications, hydrochlorothiazide (25 to 75 mg/day) and amiloride (10 to 15 mg/day) to induce renal Ca^{2+} conservation and thereby improve bone healing and linear growth. The value of this long-term adjuvant therapy remains to be established.

Adults. Once the patient enters adulthood, the plasma alkaline phosphatase usually falls into the normal range even when the patient receives no specific therapy. This has usually been taken as an indication that the bone disease (osteomalacia) is no longer active. However, an examination of undecalcified sections of transileal bone biopsies from such patients show that nearly all have significant osteomalacia. The majority have a normal content of mineralized bone, and for this reason it has been recommended that these patients need no specific therapy throughout adult life. Nonetheless, careful questioning of such patients reveals that nearly all have bone pain (often not attributable to the joint problems), fatiguability, and an intolerance to long sustained exercise (unpublished). Treatment of these patients with 1,25-$(OH)_2D_3$ (or 1-α-hydroxyvitamin D_3) (1.0 to 2.0 μg/day), and oral phosphate (1 to 1.5 g/day) almost invariably leads to a significant mineralization of the osteoid tissue, symptomatic improvement with greater exercise tolerance, and less bone pain. Hence, it is our present policy to treat nearly all adults, except certain females with minimal disease during their growth period, with this combination therapy.

Complications of Therapy

The most serious complication of therapy is a reduction in renal function as a result of intoxication with vitamin D or its metabolites. Before the introduction of 1,25-$(OH)_2D_3$ as a therapeutic agent, the common treatment of FHR involved the combined administration of vitamin D and oral phosphate. The doses of vitamin D were quite large and led, in the majority of patients, to one or more episodes of vitamin D intoxication with hypercalciuria, hyperphosphatemia, and a marked reduction in renal function. A particularly striking feature of this renal failure with, for example, an 80 to 90 percent decrease in GFR, is that in most cases, at least during and following the first episode, it is nearly completely reversible. However, with the next and subsequent episodes, recovery is not complete and progressive renal failure can develop.

The introduction of 1,25-$(OH)_2D_3$ as a therapeutic agent has led to a marked reduction in this complication. Ideally, if one follows urinary calcium excretion, hypercalciurias will be observed before hypercalcemia or reduced renal function is found. Practically, this is not always the case, but even if hypercalcemia does occur, it can be rapidly reversed (within weeks) after cessation of 1,25-$(OH)_2D_3$ therapy. Experience with repeated hypercalcemic episodes due to 1,25-$(OH)_2D_3$ therapy is too limited to know whether repeated hypercalcemic episodes as a result of 1,25-$(OH)_2D_3$ excess can lead to sustained reductions in renal function.

Since 1,25-$(OH)_2D_3$ therapy has been employed for only 10 to 12 years, there still remain a significant number of patients who were treated in the past with vitamin D with (or without) phosphate, and who developed one or more episodes of vitamin D intoxication. These patients display unusual complications during subsequent treatment with 1,25-$(OH)_2D_3$ and phosphate. They develop tertiary hyperparathyroidism and a slowly progressive decrease in renal function[173,174] (unpublished).

Upon initiation of 1,25-$(OH)_2D_3$ therapy to a patient without a history of previous vitamin D intoxication, the plasma iPTH and nephrogenous cAMP (NcAMP) fall to normal values even if the patient has developed secondary hyperparathyroidism as a consequence of several months of phosphate therapy. In contrast, in a significant number of patients with a previous history of vitamin D intoxication, institution of combined treatment with phosphate and 1,25-$(OH)_2D_3$ leads initially to a healing of bone disease without a significant change in renal function, but as soon as the bone healing is well advanced, renal Ca^{2+} excretion increases and creatinine clearance falls. What is remarkable is that these events occur without a significant increase in plasma Ca^{2+} concentration or an abnormal increase in phosphate concentration (measured 1.5 h after ingestion of 250 mg phosphate). Even though plasma Ca^{2+} concentration is normal or high normal, plasma iPTH and NcAMP are elevated. Furthermore, cessation of phosphate therapy and administration of 1,25-$(OH)_2D_3$ alone, even for a period of several months, does not suppress PTH secretion, but, paradoxically, in some patients actually increases it. Even if the 1,25-$(OH)_2D_3$ dosage is decreased and combined therapy continued, there is usually a progressive decline in renal function. Cessation of all therapy leads to a stabilization or partial recovery of renal function.

In considering the pathogenesis of this state, the factor of overriding importance is a previous history of vitamin D intoxication (Fig. 105-9). This apparently has two consequences. The first is an altered sensitivity of the renal cell to Ca^{2+} (and

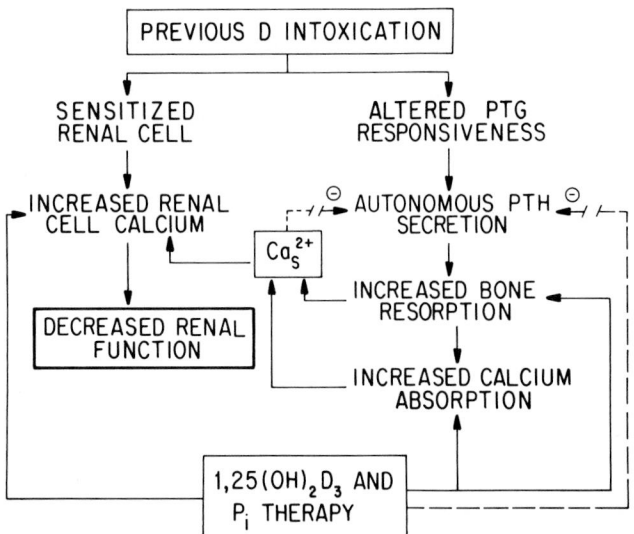

Fig. 105-9 The pathogenesis of decreased renal function in patients with FHR and a previous history of vitamin D intoxication. The previous episode of vitamin D intoxication alters both the responsiveness of the parathyroid gland to feedback inhibition of PTH secretion by either Ca^{2+} or $1,25-(OH)_2D_3$ and the sensitivity of renal cells poisoned by Ca^{2+}.

possibly phosphate) intoxication. Patients with primary hyperparathyroidism with comparable degrees of hypercalcemia, relatively autonomous PTH function, high plasma $1,25-(OH)_2D_3$, hypercalciuria, and hypophosphatemia can be treated with comparable doses of phosphate (as those given to FHR patients) without a significant reduction of renal function.

The second is an altered feedback control of PTH secretion as shown by the fact that elevation of neither Ca^{2+} nor $1,25-(OH)_2D_3$ leads to a suppression of PTH secretion.

If these abnormalities exist, the initiation of combined therapy with $1,25-(OH)_2D_3$ and phosphate leads to hypercalciuria, the uptake of Ca^{2+} and phosphate into the renal cell, and a decrease in renal function (Fig. 105-9). Given this situation, the physician has the choice of discontinuing all treatment, or of performing total parathyroidectomy with autotransplant. This operation is successful in reducing iPTH to low values, and allows one to safely reinstate combined $1,25-(OH)_2D_3$ and phosphate therapy for the bone disease. However, in the majority of patients treated in this way, the autotransplanted parathyroid tissue shows a considerable growth potential so that within 1 to 3 years postparathyroidectomy, tertiary hyperparathyroidism has recurred, and operative removal of the hyperplastic, autonomous functioning tissue from the graft site is required.

ONCOGENIC HYPOPHOSPHATEMIC OSTEOMALACIA

OHO is a rare, acquired form of hypophosphatemia which is of importance both because it may be confused with FHR and because the changes in proximal tubular function seen in FHR and OHO are so similar.[175-181]

Clinical Features

The disease is characterized by an insidious onset of fatiguability, bone pain, and skeletal deformities and, in children,

growth retardation. Proximal muscle weakness causing a waddling gait is also a prominent feature in contrast to the lack of this sign in FHR. Age of onset is usually in adult life but has been reported in patients ranging in age from 5 to 70 years.

The patients have the same key triad of abnormal laboratory findings as seen in FHR: a reduced TmP/GFR, hypophosphatemia, and a low plasma $1,25-(OH)_2D_3$. The reduction in serum phosphate and $1,25-(OH)_2D_3$ concentrations are usually more severe than those seen in the typical FHR patient. The presence of muscle weakness in OHO has been ascribed to the more profound hypophosphatemia. The serum Ca^{2+} and $25-(OH)D_3$ concentrations are normal or low normal with a normal or mildly elevated iPTH, but high iPTH with aminoaciduria and glycosuria have been reported. On bone biopsy, osteomalacia was present. Radiologic examination reveals decreased mineral density, occasional rib fractures or pseudofractures at other sites, and, in children, rickets.

The differential diagnosis between FHR and OHO is relatively easy when, as in most cases, OHO first appears later in life and leads to progressive disease. Usually the opposite is the case in FHR. It is rare for a patient with FHR who has minimal disease during childhood and adolescence to then display signs of severe disease in adult life. Even when OHO appears in children, its differentiation from sporadic FHR is usually possible based on: (1) FHR being considerably more likely than OHO; (2) a family history in FHR; (3) the signs of FHR appearing usually within the first 2 to 3 years of life; and (4) the plasma $1,25-(OH)_2D_3$ being higher in FHR than in OHO.

Pathogenesis

The most intriguing feature of OHO is its association with small mesenchymal tumors. These have been described as hemangiopericyloma, odontogenic tumor of the maxilla, fibroma, angiosarcoma, oat cell carcinoma, myoma, angiofibroma, sclerosing hemangiomas, ossifying mesenchymal tumor, or osteoblastoma. In spite of this variety of designations, the majority have been reported to have prominent vascularity and often osteoclast-like multinucleated giant cells. Additionally, patients with the linear sebaceous nevus syndrome have been found to have as a component of their disease a variant of this syndrome. The tumors have been found in the skin, subcutaneous tissue, nasopharynx, bone, paranasal sinuses, palm of the hand, and sole of the foot.

The tumor is usually small and may be extremely difficult to locate. Nevertheless, if found and successfully removed, the manifestations of the disease disappear completely. There is a restoration of normal renal function, the TmP/GFR becomes normal, plasma $1,25-(OH)_2D_3$ rises to supranormal values within a few days of the surgical removal of the tumor and then falls slowly to normal values, and with time the osteomalacia heals completely.

The working hypothesis is that the tumor produces a humoral factor(s) which acts specifically on the proximal renal tubule to bring about the same, or nearly the same, abnormalities in tubular phosphate transport and $1,25-(OH)_2D_3$ synthesis as seen in FHR. This fact raises the possibility that FHR is not a disease intrinsic to the kidney but represents a genetic defect which leads to the overproduction of the same humoral factor which is operative in OHO. Against this possibility are the findings that cultured renal cells from the *Hyp* mouse display defects in phosphate transport and vitamin D metabolism even when no longer exposed to their natural in vivo environment. On the other hand, a recent study of parabiotic animals in which a normal litter mate is linked to a *Hyp* mouse has led to the finding that the normal litter mate develops a renal phosphate leak. This result raises the possibility that a humoral factor may play a role in the pathogenesis of FHR.[182]

Treatment

The obvious therapy for patients with OHO is the surgical removal of the tumor which is the source of the presumed humoral factor. The difficulty is often that of finding the tumor. If no tumor can be found, then the alternative is treatment with combined phosphate and 1,25-(OH)$_2$D$_3$. These agents may ameliorate some of the signs and symptoms of the disease and may cause a partial healing of the osteomalacia, but they do not normally lead to a complete cure and often are quite ineffective.

HYPOPHOSPHATEMIC BONE DISEASE

Hypophosphatemic bone disease (HBD) is another hypophosphatemic phenotype with modest shortening of stature, bowing of lower limbs, and osteomalacic bone disease.[183] Several features distinguish this disorder from FHR: rickets is rarely present in patients with HBD; fractional tubular reabsorption of phosphate is normal at endogenous levels of filtered phosphate (a decrease in *TmP/GFR* is apparent only after infusion of patients with phosphate); the phosphaturic response to PTH is not blunted; the mode of inheritance does not appear to be X-linked; and patients with HBD respond to therapy with 1,25-(OH)$_2$D$_3$ alone.[184] The demonstration of normal plasma levels of 1,25-(OH)$_2$D[185] and normal urinary Ca^{2+} excretion (C. R. Scriver, personal communication) in patients with HBD suggests that this hypophosphatemic phenotype may also be distinct from HHRH.[17,18] However, the precise relationship between the mutant genes associated with HBD and HHRH will require further study.

REFERENCES

1. BONJOUR J-P, CAVERZASIO J: Phosphate transport in the kidney. *Rev Physiol Biochem Pharmacol* 100:162, 1984.
2. MURER H, BURCKHARDT G: Membrane transport of anions across epithelia of mammalian small intestine and kidney proximal tubule. *Rev Physiol Biochem Pharmacol* 96:1, 1983.
3. DENNIS VW, BRAZY PC: Divalent anion transport in isolated renal tubules. *Kidney Int* 22:498, 1982.
4. BARRETT PQ, GERTNER JM, RASMUSSEN H: Effect of dietary phosphate on transport properties of pig renal microvillus vesicles. *Am J Physiol* 239:F352, 1980.
5. BAUMANN K, DEROUFFIGNAC C, ROINEL N, RUMRICH G, ULLRICH KJ: Renal phosphate transport: Inhomogeneity of local proximal transport rates and sodium dependence. *Pflugers Arch* 356:287, 1975.
6. BERNDT TJ, KNOX FG: Proximal tubule site of inhibition of phosphate reabsorption by calcitonin. *Am J Physiol* 246:F927, 1984.
7. BERNDT TJ, KNOX FG: Nephron site of resistance to phosphaturic effect of PTH during respiratory alkalosis. *Am J Physiol* 249:F919, 1985.
8. BRAZY PC, MCKEOWN JW, HARRIS RH, DENNIS VW: Comparative effects of dietary phosphate, unilateral nephrectomy, and parathyroid hormone on phosphate transport by the rabbit proximal tubule. *Kidney Int* 17:788, 1980.
9. CHENG L, DERSCH C, KRAUS E, SPECTOR D, SACKTOR B: Renal adaptation

10. GULLANS SR, BRAZY PC, MANDEL LJ, DENNIS VW: Stimulation of phosphate transport in the proximal tubule by metabolic substrates. *Am J Physiol* 247:F582, 1984.
11. HAMM LL, KOKKO JP, JACOBSON HR: Effect of luminal pH and HCO$_3^-$ on phosphate reabsorption in the rabbit proximal convoluted tubule. *Am J Physiol* 247:F25, 1984.
12. HOPPE Z, METLER M, BERNDT TJ, KNOX G, ANGIELSKI S: Effect of respiratory alkalosis on renal phosphate excretion. *Am J Physiol* 243:F471, 1982.
13. HAUSSLER M, HUGHES M, BAYLINK D, LITTLEDIKE ET, CORK D, PITT M: Influence of phosphate depletion on the biosynthesis and circulating level of 1-alpha-25-dihydroxyvitamin D. *Adv Exp Med Biol* 31:233, 1977.
14. TANAKA Y, DELUCA HF: The control of 25-hydroxyvitamin D metabolism by inorganic phosphorus. *Arch Biochem Biophys* 154:566, 1973.
15. GRAY RW, NAPOLI JL: Dietary phosphate deprivation increases 1,25-dihydroxyvitamin D$_3$ synthesis in rat kidney *in vitro*. *J Biol Chem* 258:1152, 1983.
16. RASMUSSEN H, ANAST C: Familial hypophosphatemic rickets and vitamin D-dependent rickets, in Stanbury JB, Wyngaarden JB, Frederickson DS, Goldstein JL, Brown MS (eds): *The Metabolic Basis of Inherited Disease*, 5th ed. New York, McGraw-Hill, 1983, p 1743.
17. TIEDER M, MODAI D, SAMUEL R, ARIE R, HALABE A, BAB I, GABIZON D, LIBERMAN UA: Hereditary hypophosphatemic rickets with hypercalciuria. *N Engl J Med* 312:611, 1985.
18. TIEDER M, MODAI D, SHAKED U, SAMUEL R, ARIE R, HALABE A, MAOR J, WEISSGARTEN J, AVERBUKH Z, COHEN N, EDELSTEIN S, LIBERMAN UA: "Idiopathic" hypercalciuria and hereditary hypophosphatemic rickets. *N Engl J Med* 316:125, 1987.
19. WALLING MW: Intestinal Ca and phosphate transport: Differential responses to vitamin D$_3$ metabolites. *Am J Physiol* 233:E488, 1977.
20. LEE DBN, WALLING MW, BRAUTBAR N: Intestinal phosphate absorption: Influence of vitamin D and non-vitamin D factors. *Am J Physiol* 250:G369, 1986.
21. RIZZOLI R, FLEISCH H, BONJOUR J-P: Role of 1,25-dihydroxyvitamin D$_3$ on intestinal phosphate absorption in rats with a normal vitamin D supply. *J Clin Invest* 60:639, 1977.
22. MATSUMOTO T, FONTAINE O, RASMUSSEN H: Effects of 1,25-dihydroxyvitamin D$_3$ on phosphate uptake into chick intestinal brush border membrane vesicles. *J Biol Chem* 256:3354, 1981.
23. BRAZY P, MCKEOWN JW, HARRIS RH, DENNIS VW: Comparative effects of dietary phosphate, unilateral nephrectomy, and parathyroid hormone on phosphate transport by the rabbit proximal tubule. *Kidney Int* 17:788, 1980.
24. FRICK A: Reabsorption of inorganic phosphate in the rat kidney. I. Saturation of transport mechanism. II. Suppression of fractional phosphate reabsorption due to expansion of extracellular fluid volume. *Pflugers Arch* 304:351, 1968.
25. STEELE TH, DELUCA HF: Influence of dietary phosphorus on renal phosphate reabsorption in the parathyroidectomized rat. *J Clin Invest* 57:867, 1976.
26. SESTOFT L: Is the relationship between the plasma concentration of inorganic phosphate and the rate of oxygen consumption of significance in regulating energy metabolism in mammals? *Scand J Clin Invest* 39:191, 1979.
27. MARKOWITZ M, ROTKIN L, ROSEN JF: Circadian rhythms of blood minerals in humans. *Science* 213:672, 1981.
28. BAYLINK D, WERGEDAL J, STAEFFER M: Formation, mineralization and reabsorption of bone in hypophosphatemic rats. *J Clin Invest* 50:2519, 1971.
29. HARRIS CA, SUTTON RA, DIRKS JH: Effects of hypercalcemia and tubular calcium and phosphate ultrafilterability and tubular reabsorption in the rat. *Am J Physiol* 233:F201, 1977.
30. LEGRIMELLEC M: Micropuncture study along the proximal convoluted tubule. Electrolyte reabsorption in the first convolutions. *Pflugers Arch* 354:133, 1975.
31. BIJVOET O: The importance of the kidney in phosphate homeostasis, in Avioli L, Bordier P, Fleisch H, Massry S, Slatopolsky E (eds): *Phosphate Metabolism, Kidney and Bone*. Paris, Armour-Montagu, 1976, vol 19, p 421.
32. STRICKLER JC, THOMPSON DD, KLOSE RM, GIEBISCH G: Micropuncture study of inorganic phosphate excretion in the rat. *J Clin Invest* 43:1596, 1964.
33. KUNTZIGER H, AMIEL C, GAUDEBOUT C: Phosphate handling by the rat nephron during saline diuresis. *Kidney Int* 2:318, 1972.

34. LEGRIMELLEC C, ROINEL N, MOREL F: Simultaneous Mg, Ca, P, K Na and Cl analysis in rat tubular fluid. I. During perfusion of either inulin or ferrocyanide. *Pflugers Arch* 340:181, 1973.

35. WEN S-F: Micropuncture studies of phosphate transport in the proximal tubule of the dog. The relationship to sodium reabsorption. *J Clin Invest* 53:143, 1974.

36. GREGER R, LANG F, MARCHAND G, KNOX FG: Site of renal phosphate reabsorption: Micropuncture and microinfusion study. *Pflugers Arch* 369:111, 1977.

37. MOREL F: Sites of hormone action in the mammalian nephron. *Am J Physiol* 240:F159, 1981.

38. KNOX FG, HARAMATI A: Renal regulation of phosphate excretion, in Seldin DW, Giebisch G (eds): *The Kidney: Physiology and Pathophysiology.* New York, Raven Press, 1985, p 1381.

39. KAWASHIMA H, TORIKAI S, KUROKAWA K: Localization of 25-hydroxyvitamin D_3-1 alpha-hydroxylase and -24-hydroxylase in the rat nephron. *Proc Natl Acad Sci USA* 78:1199, 1981.

40. MCKINNEY TD, MYERS P: Bicarbonate transport by proximal tubules; effect of parathyroid hormone and dibutyryl cyclic AMP. *Am J Physiol* 238:F166, 1980.

41. HAMMERMAN MR, KLARH S, COHN DE: Renal failure, metabolic acidosis, and parathyroidectomy in the dog increase Na^+-H^+ exchange in isolated renal brush border membrane vesicles, in Forte J, Rector F (eds): *Hydrogen Ion Transport in Epithelia.* New York, Wiley, 1983, p 139.

42. SUKI WN: Calcium transport in the nephron. *Am J Physiol* 237:F1, 1979.

43. IMAI M: Effect of parathyroid hormone and N^6,O^2-dibutyryl cyclic AMP on Ca transport across the rabbit distal nephron segments perfused *in vitro. Pflugers Arch* 390:145, 1981.

44. KAWASHIMA H, TORIKAI S, KUROKAWA K: Calcitonin selectively stimulates 25-hydroxyvitamin D_3-1α-hydroxylase in the proximal straight tubule of rat kidney. *Nature* 291:327, 1981.

45. BERNDT TJ, KNOX FG: Proximal tubule site of inhibition of phosphate reabsorption by calcitonin. *Am J Physiol* 246:F927, 1984.

46. GMAJ P, MURER H: Cellular mechanisms of inorganic phosphate transport in kidney. *Physiol Rev* 66:36, 1986.

47. BERNER W, KINNE R, MURER H: Phosphate transport into brush-border membrane vesicles isolated from rat small intestine. *Biochem J* 160:467, 1976.

47a. MIZGALA CL, QUAMME GA: Renal handling of phosphate. *Physiol Rev* 65:431, 1985.

48. DENNIS VW, WOODHALL PB, ROBINSON RR: Characteristics of phosphate transport in isolated proximal tubule. *Am J Physiol* 231:979, 1976.

49. BRAZY PC, GULLANS SR, MANDEL LJ, DENNIS VW: Metabolic requirement for inorganic phosphate by the rabbit proximal tubule: Evidence for a Crabtree effect. *J Clin Invest* 70:53, 1982.

50. BURCKHARDT G, STERN H, MURER H: The influence of pH on phosphate transport into rat renal brush border membrane vesicles. *Pflugers Arch* 390:191, 1981.

51. WALKER JJ, YAN TS, QUAMME GA: Presence of multiple sodium-dependent phosphate transport processes in proximal brush border membranes. *Am J Physiol* 252:F226, 1987.

52. BINDELS RJM, van den BROEK LAM, van OS CH: Effect of pH on the kinetics of Na^+-dependent phosphate transport in rat renal brush border membranes. *Biochim Biophys Acta* 897:83, 1987.

52a. DENNIS VW, BELLO-REUSS E, ROBINSON RR: Response of phosphate transport to parathyroid hormone in segments of rabbit nephron. *Am J Physiol* 233:F29, 1977.

53. SCHWAB SJ, KLAHR S, HAMMERMAN MR: Na^+ gradient-dependent Pi uptake in basolateral membrane vesicles from dog kidney. *Am J Physiol* 246:F663, 1984.

54. FREEMAN D, BARTLETT S, RADDA G, ROSS B: Energetics of sodium transport in the kidney saturation transfer ^{31}P-NMR. *Biochim Biophys Acta* 762:325, 1983.

54a. HAMMERMAN MR, KARL IE, HRUSKA KA: Regulation of canine renal vesicle Pi transport by growth and parathyroid hormone. *Biochim Biophys Acta* 603:322, 1980.

55. KAWASHIMA H, KUROKAWA K: Metabolism and sites of action of vitamin D in the kidney. *Kidney Int* 29:98, 1986.

56. RASMUSSEN H, KOJIMA I, APFELDORF W, BARRETT P: Cellular calcium mechanism of hormone action in the kidney: Messenger function and cyclic AMP. *Kidney Int* 29:90, 1986.

57. BORLE AB, UCHIKAWA T: Effects of parathyroid hormone on the distribution and transport of calcium in cultured kidney cells. *Endocrinology* 101:1725, 1978.

58. HRUSKA KA, GOLIGORSKY M, SCOBLE J, TSUTSUMI M, WESTBROOK S, MOSKOWITZ D: Effects of parathyroid hormone on cytosolic calcium in renal proximal tubular primary cultures. *Am J Physiol* 251:F188, 198, 1986.

59. GOLIGORSKY MS, LOFTUS DJ, HRUSKA KA: Cytoplasmic calcium in individual proximal tubular cells in culture. *Am J Physiol* 251:F938, 1986.

60. KUROKAWA K, OHNO T, RASMUSSEN H: Ionic control of renal gluconeogenesis. II. The effects of Ca^{2+} and H^+ upon the response to parathyroid hormone and cyclic AMP. *Biochim Biophys Acta* 313:32, 1973.

61. KUROKAWA K: Mechanism of renal action of parathyroid hormone. *Adv Exp Med Biol* 81:291, 1977.

62. BANK K, AYNEDJIAN SH: A micropuncture study of the effect of parathyroid hormone on renal bicarbonate reabsorption. *J Clin Invest* 58:336, 1976.

63. MCKINNEY TD, MYERS P: Bicarbonate transport by proximal tubules: Effect of parathyroid hormone and dibutyryl cyclic AMP. *Am J Physiol* 238:F166, 1980.

64. TEITELBAUM AP, STREWLER GJ: Parathyroid hormone receptors coupled to cyclic adenosine monophosphate formation in an established renal cell line. *Endocrinology* 114:980, 1984.

65. KOYAMA H, GOODPASTURE C, MILLER MM, TEPLITZ RL, RIGGS D: Establishment and characterization of a cell line from the American Opossum (Didelphys Virginiana). *In Vitro* 14:239, 1978.

65a. MALMSTROM K, MURER H: Parathyroid hormone inhibits phosphate transport OK cells but not in LLC-PK_1 and JTC-12·P3 cells. *Am J Physiol* 251:C23, 1986.

65b. CAVERZASIO J, RIZZOLI R, BONJOUR J-P: Sodium-dependent phosphate transport inhibited by parathyroid hormone and cyclic AMP stimulation in an opossum kidney cell line. *J Biol Chem* 261:3233, 1986.

66. POLLOCK AS, WARNOCK GS, STREWLER GJ: Parathyroid hormone inhibition of $-Na^+$-H^+-antiporter activity in a cultured renal cell line. *Am J Physiol* 250:F217, 1986.

67. BROADUS AE, INSOGNA KL, LANG R, ELLISON AF, DREYER BE: Evidence for disordered control of 1,25-dihydroxyvitamin D production in absorptive hypercalciuria. *N Engl J Med* 311:73, 1984.

68. TIEDER M, STARK H, SHAINKIN-KASTENBAUM R: Pathophysiologic studies in idiopathic hypercalciuria presenting in childhood. *Int J Pediatr Nephrol* 4:197, 1983.

69. BROADUS AE, INSOGNA KL, LANG R, et al: A consideration of the hormonal basis and phosphate leak hypothesis of absorptive hypercalciuria. *J Clin Endocrinol Metab* 58:161, 1984.

70. NISHIYAMA S, INOUE F, MAKUDA I: A single case of hypophosphatemic rickets with hypercalciuria. *J Pediatr Gastroenterol Nutr* 5:826, 1986.

71. LAPATSANES PD, SBYRAKIS S, MEGRELI CHR, EDELSTEIN S: The management of siblings with familial hypophosphatemic rickets. *Helv Paediatr Acta* 38:373, 1983.

72. CHAN JC, ALON U, HIRSHMAN GM: Renal hypophosphatemic rickets. *J Pediatr* 106:533, 1985.

73. SCHIMERT G, FANCONI A: Early history of familial hypophosphatemic vitamin D-resistant rickets. *Helv Paediatr Acta* 38:383, 1983.

74. HERWEIJER TJ, STEENDIJK R: The relation between attained adult height and the metaphyseal lesions in hypophosphatemic vitamin D-resistant rickets. *Acta Paediatr Scand* 74:196, 1985.

75. HARRISON HE: Primary hypophosphatemic rickets and growth retardation. *Growth* 2:1, 1986.

76. STEENDIJK R, HERWEIJER TJ: Height, sitting height and leg length in patients with hypophosphatemic rickets. *Acta Paediatr Scand* 73:181, 1984.

77. MARIE PJ, GLORIEUX FH: Bone histomorphometry in asymptomatic adults with hereditary hypophosphatemic vitamin D-resistant osteomalacia. *Metab Bone Dis Rel Res* 4:429, 1982.

78. POLISSON PP, MARTINEZ S, KHOURY M: Calcification of entheses associated with X-linked hypophosphatemic osteomalacia. *N Engl J Med* 313:1, 1985.

79. CARTWRIGHT DW, MASEL JP, LATHAM SC: The lumbar spine canal in hypophosphatemic vitamin D-resistant rickets. *Aust NZ J Med* 11:154, 1981.

79a. MASEL JP, CARTWRIGHT DW, LATHAM SC: Hypophosphatemic vitamin D-resistant rickets—A cause of spinal stenosis in adults. *Aust J Radiol* 25:264, 1981.

80. TULLOCH EN, ANDREWS FFH: The association of dental abscesses with vitamin D-resistant rickets. *Br Dent J* 154:136, 1983.

81. RAKOCZ M, KEATING J III, JOHNSON R: Management of the primary dentition in vitamin D-resistant rickets. *Oral Surg* 54:166, 1982.

82. HERBERT FL: Hereditary hypophosphatemic rickets: An important awareness for dentists. *ASCS J Dent Child* 53:223, 1986.

83. DREZNER MK, LYLES KW, HAUSSLER MR, HARRELSON JM: Evaluation of a role for 1,25-dihydroxyvitamin D_3 in the pathogenesis and treatment of X-linked hypophosphatemic rickets and osteomalacia. *J Clin Invest* 66:1020, 1980.

84. RASMUSSEN H, PECHET M, ANAST C, MAZUR H, GERTNER J, BROADUS AE:

Long term treatment of familial hypophosphatemic rickets with oral phosphate and 1α-hydroxyvitamin D₃. *J Pediatr* 99:16, 1981.

85. MARIE PJ, GLORIEUX FH: Histomorphometric study of bone remodeling in hypophosphatemic vitamin D-resistant rickets. *Metab Bone Dis Rel Res* 3:31, 1981.

86. CHOUFOER JH, STINDJIK R: Distribution of the perilacuna hypomineralized areas in cortical bone of patients with familial hypophosphatemic (vitamin D-resistant) rickets. *Calcif Tissue Int* 27:101, 1979.

87. WINTERS RW, GRAHAM JB, WILLIAMS TF, MCFALK VW, BURNETT CH: A genetic study of familial hypophosphatemia and vitamin D-resistant rickets with a review of the literature. *Medicine (Baltimore)* 37:97, 1958.

88. GRAHAM JB, MCFALLS VW, WINTERS RW: Familial hypophosphatemia with vitamin D-resistant rickets. II. Three additional kindred of sex-linked dominant type with a genetic analysis of four such families. *Am J Hum Genet* 11:311, 1959.

89. BURNETT CH, DENT CE, HARPER C, WARLAND BJ: Vitamin D-resistant rickets: Analysis of 24 pedigrees with hereditary and sporadic cases. *Am J Med* 36:222, 1964.

90. GREENBERG BG, WINTERS RW, GRAHAM JB: The normal range of serum inorganic phosphorus and its utility as a discriminant in the diagnosis of congenital hypophosphatemia. *J Clin Endocrinol* 20:364, 1960.

91. LYON MF: Sex chromatin and gene action in the mammalian x-chromosome. *Am J Hum Genet* 14:135, 1962.

92. MCKUSICK VA: *Mendelian Inheritance in Man,* 7th ed. Baltimore, Johns Hopkins University Press, 1986, p 1394.

93. READ AP, THAKKER RV, DAVIES KE, MOUNTFORD RC, BRENTON DP, DAVIES M, GLORIEUX F, HARRIS R, HENDY GN, KING A, MCGLADE S, PEACOCK CJ, SMITH R, O'RIORDAN JLH: Mapping of human X-linked hypophosphatemic rickets by multilocus linkage analysis. *Hum Genet* 73:267, 1986.

94. MÄCHLER M, FREY D, GAL A, ORTH U, WIENKER TF, FANCONI A, SCHMID W: X-linked dominant hypophosphatemia is closely linked to DNA markers DXS41 and DCS43 at Xp22. *Hum Genet* 73:271, 1986.

94a. THAKKER RV, READ AP, DAVIES KE, WHYTE M, WEKSBERG R, GLORIEUX F, DAVIES M, MOUNTFORD RC, HARRIS R, KING A, KIM GS, FRASER D, KOOH SW, O'RIORDAN JLH: Bridging markers defining the map position of X-linked hypophosphatemic rickets. *J Med Genet* 24:756, 1987.

95. BUCKLE VJ, EDWARDS JF, EVANS EP, JONASSON JA, LYON MF, PETERS J, SEARLE AG: Comparative maps of human and mouse x-chromosomes. *Cytogenet Cell Genet* 40:594, 1985.

96. EICHER EM, SOUTHARD JL, SCRIVER CR, GLORIEUX FH: Hypophosphatemia: Mouse model for human familial hypophosphatemic (vitamin D-resistant) rickets. *Proc Natl Acad Sci USA* 73:4667, 1976.

97. MEYER JR, JOWSEY J, MEYER MH: Osteomalacia and altered magnesium metabolism in the X-linked hypophosphatemic mouse. *Calcif Tissue Int* 27:19, 1979.

98. TENENHOUSE HS, SCRIVER CR, MCINNES RR, GLORIEUX FH: Renal handling of phosphate *in vivo* and *in vitro* by the X-linked hypophosphatemic male mouse: Evidence for a defect in the brush border membrane. *Kidney Int* 14:236, 1978.

99. GIASSON SD, BRUNETTE MG, DANAN G, VIGNEAULT N, CARRIERE S: Micropuncture study of renal phosphorus transport in hypophosphatemic vitamin D resistant mice. *Pflugers Arch* 371:33, 1977.

100. COWGILL LD, GOLDFARB S, LAU K, SLATOPOLSKY E, AGUS ZS: Evidence for an intrinsic renal tubular defect in mice with genetic hypophosphatemic rickets. *J Clin Invest* 63:1203, 1979.

101. KIEBZAK GM, MEYER RA, MISH PM: X-linked hypophosphatemic mice respond to thyroparathyroidectomy. *Miner Electrolyte Metab* 6:153, 1981.

102. BELL CL, TENENHOUSE HS, SCRIVER CR: Isolation and culture of murine proximal tubule cells: A system to study solute transport in mutants. *Ann NY Acad Sci* 456:398, 1985.

103. BELL CL, TENENHOUSE HS, SCRIVER CR: Primary cultures of renal epithelial cells from X-linked hypophosphatemic (Hyp) mice express defects in phosphate transport and vitamin D metabolism. *Am J Hum Genet* 43:1988 (in press).

104. ARTHUS MF, BERGERON M, SCRIVER CR: Topology of membrane exposure in the renal cortex. Studies of glutathione and maltose cleavage. *Biochem Biophys Acta* 692:371, 1982.

105. TENENHOUSE HS, SCRIVER CR: The defect in transcellular transport of phosphate in the nephron is located in brush-border membranes in X-linked hypophosphatemia (Hyp mouse model). *Can J Biochem* 56:640, 1978.

106. LYON MF, SCRIVER CR, BAKER LRI, TENENHOUSE HS, KRONICK J, MANDLA S: The Gy mutation: Another cause of X-linked hypophosphatemia in mouse. *Proc Natl Acad Sci USA* 83:4899, 1986.

106a. BONEH A, READE TM, SCRIVER CR, RISHIKOF E: Audiometric evidence for two forms of X-linked hypophosphatemia in humans, apparent counterparts of Hyp and Gy mutations in mouse. *Am J Hum Genet* 27:997, 1987.

107. KIEBZAK GM, DOUSA TP: Thyroid hormones increase renal brush border membrane transport of phosphate in X-linked hypophosphatemic (Hyp) mice. *Endocrinology* 117:613, 1985.

107a. BRUNETTE MG, MERNISSI GE, DOUCET A: Renal sodium transport in vitamin D resistant hypophosphatemic rickets. *Can J Physiol Pharmacol* 63:1339, 1985.

108. TENENHOUSE HS, COLE DEC, SCRIVER CR: Mendelian hypophosphatemias as probes of phosphate and sulphate transport by mammalian kidney, in Belton NR, Toothill C (eds): *Transport and Inherited Disease.* New York, MTP Press, 1981, p 231.

109. HAMMERMAN MR, CHASE LR: Pᵢ transport, phosphorylation, and dephosphorylation in renal membranes from Hyp/Y mice. *Am J Physiol* 245:F701, 1983.

110. TENENHOUSE HS, SCRIVER CR: Renal adaptation to phosphate deprivation in the Hyp mouse with X-linked hypophosphatemia. *Can J Biochem* 57:938, 1979.

111. TENENHOUSE HS, SCRIVER CR: Renal brush border membrane adaptation to phosphorus deprivation in the Hyp/Y mouse. *Nature* 281:225, 1979.

112. LOBAUGH B, DREZNER MK: Abnormal regulation of renal 25-hydroxyvitamin D-1α-hydroxylase activity in the X-linked hypophosphatemic mouse. *J Clin Invest* 71:400, 1983.

113. YAMAOKA K, SEINO Y, SATOMURA K, TANAKA Y, YABUUCHI H, HAUSSLER MR: Abnormal relationship between serum phosphate concentration and renal 25-hydroxycholecalciferol-1-alpha-hydroxylase activity in X-linked hypophosphatemic mice. *Miner Electrolyte Metab* 12:194, 1986.

114. TENENHOUSE HS: Abnormal renal mitochondrial 25-hydroxyvitamin D₃-1-hydroxylase activity in the vitamin D and calcium deficient X-linked Hyp mouse. *Endocrinology* 113:816, 1983.

114a. MEYER RA, GRAY RW, MEYER MH: Abnormal vitamin D metabolism in the X-linked hypophosphatemic mouse. *Endocrinology* 107:1577, 1980.

115. TENENHOUSE HS: Investigation of the mechanism for abnormal renal 25-hydroxyvitamin D₃-1-hydroxylase activity in the X-linked Hyp mouse. *Endocrinology* 115:634, 1984.

116. NESBITT T, DREZNER MK, LOBAUGH B: Abnormal parathyroid hormone stimulation of 25-hydroxyvitamin D-1α-hydroxylase activity in the hypophosphatemic mouse. *J Clin Invest* 77:181, 1986.

117. TENENHOUSE H: Metabolism of 25-hydroxyvitamin D₃ in renal slices from the X-linked hypophosphatemic (Hyp) mouse: Abnormal response to fall in serum calcium. *Cell Calcium* 5:43, 1984.

117a. INSOGNA KL, BROADUS AE, GERTNER JM: Impaired phosphorus conservation and 1,25-dihydroxyvitamin D generation during phosphorus deprivation in familial hypophosphatemic rickets. *J Clin Invest* 71:1562, 1983.

117b. LYLES KW, DREZNER MK: Parathyroid hormone effects on serum 1,25-dihydroxyvitamin D levels in patients with X-linked hypophosphatemic rickets: Evidence for abnormal 25-hydroxyvitamin D-1-hydroxylase. *J Clin Endocrinol Metab* 54:638, 1982.

118. NESBITT T, LOBAUGH B, DREZNER MK: Calcitonin stimulation of renal 25-hydroxyvitamin D-1α-hydroxylase activity in hypophosphatemic mice. Evidence that the regulation of calcitriol production is not universally abnormal in X-linked hypophosphatemia. *J Clin Invest* 79:15, 1987.

119. TENENHOUSE HS: Metabolism of 25-[26,27-³H]-hydroxyvitamin D₃ [25(OH)-D₃] by renal mitochondria of normal and hypophosphatemic (Hyp) mice, in Norman AW, Schaefer K, Herrath DV, Grigoleit HG (eds): *Vitamin D. Chemical, Biochemical and Clinical Endocrinology of Calcium Metabolism.* Berlin, New York, Walter de Gruyter, 1982, p 471.

120. CUNNINGHAM J, GOMES H, SEINO Y, CHASE LR: Abnormal 24-hydroxylation of 25-hydroxyvitamin D in the X-linked hypophosphatemic mouse. *Endocrinology* 112:633, 1983.

121. TENENHOUSE HS, JONES G: Effect of the X-linked Hyp mutation and vitamin D status on induction of renal 25-hydroxyvitamin D₃-24-hydroxylase. *Endocrinology* 120:609, 1987.

122. MEYER RA Jr, MEYER MH, GRAY RW: Metabolites of vitamin D in normal and X-linked hypophosphatemic mice. *Calcif Tissue Int* 36:662, 1984.

123. FUKASE M, AVIOLI LV, BIRGE SJ, CHASE LR: Abnormal regulation of 25-hydroxyvitamin D₃-1α-hydroxylase activity by calcium and calcitonin in renal cortex from hypophosphatemic (Hyp) mice. *Endocrinology* 114:1203, 1984.

124. JONES G, YIP A, TENENHOUSE HS: Side chain oxidation of vitamin D₃ in mouse kidney mitochondria: Effect of the Hyp mutation and 1,25-dihydroxyvitamin D₃ treatment. *Biochem Cell Biol* 65:853, 1987.

125. TENENHOUSE HS, YIP A, JONES G: Increased renal catabolism of 1,25-dihydroxyvitamin D₃ in murine X-linked hypophosphatemic rickets. *J Clin Invest* 81:461, 1988.

125a. SEINO Y, YAMAOKA K, ISHIDA M, TANAKA Y, KUROSE H, YABUUCHI H, TOHIRA Y, FUKUSHIMA M, NISHII Y: Plasma clearance for high doses of exogenous 1,25-dihydroxy [23,24(n)-³H] cholecalciferol in X-linked hypophosphatemic mice. *Biomed Res* 3:683, 1982.

126. SEINO Y, SATOMURA K, YAMAOKA K, TANAKA Y, TANAKA H, YAMAMOTO T, ISHIDA M, YABUCICHI H: Activity of renal 25-hydroxyvitamin D₃-1α-

hydroxylase in a case of X-linked hypophosphatemic rickets. *Eur J Pediatr* 142:219, 1984.

126a. SABINA RL, DREZNER MK, HOLMES EW: Reduced renal cortical ribonucleoside triphosphate pools in three different hypophosphatemic animal models. *Biochem Biophys Res Commun* 109:649, 1982.

127. BROWN CE, WILKIE CA, MEYER MH, MEYER RA Jr: Response of tissue phosphate content to acute dietary phosphate deprivation in the X-linked hypophosphatemic mouse. *Calcif Tissue Int* 37:423, 1985.

128. KIEBZAK GM, ROOS BA, MEYER RA Jr: Secondary hyperparathyroidism in X-linked hypophosphatemic mice. *Endocrinology* 111:650, 1982.

129. POSILLICO TJ, LOBAUGH B, MUHLBAIER LH, DREZNER MK: Abnormal parathyroid function in the X-linked hypophosphatemic mouse. *Calcif Tissue Int* 37:418, 1985.

130. KIEBZAK GM, MEYER RA, MISH PM: Increased urinary excretion of cyclic nucleotides in X-linked hypophosphatemic (*Hyp*) mice. *Experientia* 37:978, 1981.

131. MUHLBAUER RC, BONJOUR J-P, FLEISCH H: Decrease in the tubular reabsorption of calcium with evidence for compensatory hyperparathyroidism in X-linked hypophosphataemia in mice. *Clin Sci* 62:503, 1982.

132. TENENHOUSE HS, VEKSLER A: Effect of the *Hyp* mutation and diet-induced hyperparathyroidism on renal parathyroid hormone- and forskolin-stimulated adenosine 3',5'–monophosphate production and brush border membrane phosphate transport. *Endocrinology* 118:1047, 1986.

133. KIEBZAK GM, MEYER RA Jr: X-linked hypophosphatemic mice are not hypersensitive to parathyroid hormone. *Endocrinology* 110:1030, 1982.

134. TENENHOUSE HS, HENRY HL: Protein kinase activity and protein kinase inhibitor in mouse kidney: Effect of the X-linked *Hyp* mutation and vitamin D status. *Endocrinology* 117:1719, 1985.

134a. BRUNETTE MG, ALLARD S, BELIVEAU R: Renal brush border membranes from mice with X-linked hypophosphatemia: Protein composition, phosphate binding capacity, and protein kinase activity. *Can J Physiol Pharmacol* 62:1394, 1984.

135. O'DOHERTY PJA, DELUCA HF: Intestinal calcium and phosphate transport in genetic hypophosphatemic mice. *Biochem Biophys Res Commun* 71:617, 1976.

136. O'DOHERTY PJA, DELUCA HF, EICHER EM: Lack of effect of vitamin D and its metabolites on intestinal phosphate transport in familial hypophosphatemia of mice. *Endocrinology* 101:1325, 1977.

137. TENENHOUSE HS, FAST DK, SCRIVER CR, KOLTAY M: Intestinal transport of phosphate anion is not impaired in the *Hyp* (hypophosphatemic) mouse. *Biochem Biophys Res Commun* 100:537, 1981.

138. SEINO Y, SIERRA RI, ICHIKAWA M, AVIOLI LV: 1,25-Dihydroxyvitamin D₃ receptor in the X-linked hypophosphatemic mouse. *Endocrinology* 111:329, 1982.

139. BAKER LRI, CLARK ML, FAIRCLOUGH PD, GOBLE H: Identification of two intestinal vitamin D-dependent calcium-binding proteins in the X-linked hypophosphatemic mouse. *Biochem Biophys Res Commun* 119:850, 1984.

140. MEYER MH, MEYER RA Jr, IORIO RJ: A role for the intestine in the bone disease of juvenile X-linked hypophosphatemic mice: Malabsorption of calcium and reduced skeletal mineralization. *Endocrinology* 115:1464, 1984.

141. MEYER RA Jr, MEYER MH, ERICKSON PR, KORKOR AB: Reduced absorption of ⁴⁵Calcium from isolated duodenal segments "*in vivo*" in juvenile but not adult X-linked hypophosphatemic mice. *Calcif Tissue Int* 38:95, 1986.

142. MEYER RA, MEYER M, GRAY RW, BRUNS ME: Evidence that low plasma 1,25-dihydroxyvitamin D causes intestinal malabsorption of calcium and phosphate in juvenile X-linked hypophosphatemic mice. *J Bone Miner Res* 2:67, 1987.

143. BRUNS ME, MEYER RA Jr, MEYER MH: Low levels of intestinal vitamin D-dependent calcium binding protein in juvenile X-linked hypophosphatemic mice. *Endocrinology* 115:1459, 1984.

144. TENENHOUSE HS: Effect of age and the X-linked *Hyp* mutation on renal adaptation to vitamin D and calcium deficiency. *Comp Biochem Physiol* 81A:367, 1985.

145. IORIO RJ, MURRAY G, MEYER RA: Craniometric measurements of craniofacial malformations in mice with X-linked, dominant hypophosphatemia (Vitamin D-resistant rickets). *Teratology* 22:291, 1980.

146. MOSTAFA YA, MEYER RA Jr: Increased metaphyseal bone mass in the young X-linked hypophosphatemic (*Hyp*) mouse. *Clin Orthop* 161:326, 1981.

147. ROY WA, IORIO RJ, MEYER GA: Craniosynostosis in vitamin D-resistant rickets. *J Neurosurg* 55:265, 1981.

148. MOSTAFA YA, EL-MANGOURY NH, MEYER RA Jr, IORIO RJ: Deficient nasal bone growth in the X-linked hypophosphatemic (*Hyp*) mouse and its implication in craniofacial growth. *Arch Oral Biol* 27:311, 1982.

149. MARIE PJ, TRAVERS R, GLORIEUX FH: Healing of rickets with phosphate supplementation in the hypophosphatemic male mouse. *J Clin Invest* 67:911, 1981.

150. KAY MA, MEYER MH, DELZER PR, MEYER RA Jr: Changing patterns of femoral and skeletal mineralization during growth in juvenile X-linked hypophosphatemic mice. *Miner Electrolyte Metab* 11:374, 1985.

151. BRAULT BA, MEYER MH, MEYER RA, IORIO RJ: Mineral uptake by the femora of older female *Hyp* mice but not older male *Hyp* mice. *Clin Orthop* 222:289, 1987.

152. MIGEON BR, SHAPIRO LJ, NORUM RA, MOHANDAS T, AXELMAN J, DABORA RL: Differential expression of steroid sulphatase locus on active and inactive human X chromosome. *Nature* 299:838, 1982.

153. YOSHIKAWA H, MASUHARA K, TAKAOKA K, ONO K, TANAKA H, SEINO Y: Abnormal bone formation induced by implantation of osteosarcoma-derived bone-inducing substance in the X-linked hypophosphatemic mouse. *Bone* 6:235, 1985.

154. IORIO RJ, BELL WA, MEYER MH, MEYER RA: Radiographic evidence of craniofacial and dental abnormalities in the X-linked hypophosphatemic mouse. *Ann Dent* 38:31, 1979.

155. IORIO RJ, BELL WA, MEYER MH, MEYER RA: Histologic evidence of calcification abnormalities in teeth and alveolar bone of mice with X-linked dominant hypophosphatemia (VDRR). *Ann Dent* 38:38, 1979.

156. SOFAER JA, SOUTHAM JC: Naturally-occurring exposure of the dental-pulp in mice with inherited hypophosphatemia. *Arch Oral Biol* 27:701, 1982.

157. DELZER PR, MEYER RA Jr: Normal milk composition in lactating X-linked hypophosphatemic mice despite continued hypophosphatemia. *Calcif Tissue Int* 35:750, 1983.

158. DELZER PR, MEYER RA Jr: Normal handling of phosphate in the salivary glands of X-linked hypophosphatemic mice. *Arch Oral Biol* 29:1009, 1984.

159. VAUGHN LK, MEYER RA Jr, MEYER MH: Increased metabolic rate in X-linked hypophosphatemic mice. *Endocrinology* 118:441, 1986.

160. MUHLBAUER RC, BONJOUR J-P, FLEISCH H: Abnormal hyperphosphatemic response to fasting in X-linked hypophosphatemic mouse. *Miner Electrolyte Metab* 10:362, 1984.

161. MUHLBAUER RC, BONJOUR J-P, FLEISCH H: Abnormal tubular adaptation to dietary P₁ restriction in X-linked hypophosphatemic mice. *Am J Physiol* 242:F353, 1982.

162. MARIE PJ, TRAVERS R, GLORIEUX FH: Bone response to phosphate and vitamin D metabolites in the hypophosphatemic male mouse. *Calcif Tissue Int* 34:158, 1982.

163. MARIE PJ, TRAVERS R, GLORIEUX FH: Healing of bone lesions with 1,25-dihydroxyvitamin D₃ in the young X-linked hypophosphatemic male mouse. *Endocrinology* 111:904, 1982.

164. TENENHOUSE HS, SCRIVER CR: Effect of 1,25-dihydroxyvitamin D₃ on phosphate homeostasis in the X-linked hypophosphatemic (*Hyp*) mouse. *Endocrinology* 109:658, 1981.

165. BEAMER WG, WILSON MC, DELUCA HF: Successful treatment of genetically hypophosphatemic mice by 1α-hydroxyvitamin D₃ but not 1,25-dihydroxyvitamin D₃. *Endocrinology* 106:1949, 1980.

166. MARIE PJ, TRAVERS R: Effects of magnesium and lactose supplementation on bone metabolism in the X-linked hypophosphatemic mouse. *Metabol Clin Exp* 32:165, 1983.

167. ALON V, CHAN JCM: Effects of parathyroid hormone and 1,25-dihydroxyvitamin D₃ on tubular handling of phosphate in hypophosphatemic rickets. *J Clin Endocrinol Metab* 58:671, 1984.

167a. GLORIEUX FH, SCRIVER CR, READE TM, GOLDMAN H, ROSEBOROUGH A: Use of phosphate and vitamin D to prevent dwarfism and rickets in X-linked hypophosphatemia. *N Engl J Med* 287:481, 1972.

168. LOEFFLER RD, SHERMAN FC: The effect of treatment on growth and deformity in hypophosphatemic vitamin D-resistant rickets. *Clin Orthop* 162:4, 1982.

169. CHESNEY RW, MAZESS RB, ROSE P, HAMSTRA AJ, DELUCA HF, BREED AL: Long-term influence of calcitriol (1,25-dihydroxyvitamin D) and supplemental phosphate in X-linked hypophosphatemic rickets. *Pediatrics* 71:559, 1983.

170. ALON U, CHAN JCM: Effect of hydrochlorothiazide and amiloride in renal hypophosphatemic rickets. *Pediatrics* 75:754, 1985.

171. ALON U, COSTANZO L, CHAN JCM: Additive hypocalciuric effects of amiloride and hydrochlorothiazide in patients treated with calcitriol. *Miner Electrolyte Metab* 10:379, 1984.

172. HARRELL RM, LYLES KW, HARRELSON JM, FRIEDMAN NE, DREZNER MK: Healing of bone disease in X-linked hypophosphatemic rickets/osteomalacia. *J Clin Invest* 75:1858, 1985.

173. KINDER B, RASMUSSEN H: New applications of total parathyroidectomy and autotransplant: Use in proximal renal tubular dysfunction. *World J Surg* 9:156, 1985.

174. ALON U, NEWSOME H Jr, CHAN JC: Hyperparathyroidism in patients with X-linked dominant hypophosphatemic rickets. *Int J Pediatr Nephrol* 5:39, 1984.

175. EVANS DJ, AZZOPARDI JG: Distinctive tumours of bone and soft tissue causing acquired vitamin D-resistant osteomalacia. *Lancet* i:353, 1972.

176. SIVELL RA, MALES JL, HAMSTRA AJ, DELUCA HF: Vitamin D metabolite levels in oncogenic osteomalacia. *Am Int Med* 93:279, 1980.

177. ASNES RS, BERDON WE, BASSETT A: Hypophosphatemic rickets in an adolescent cured by excision of a monossifying fibroma. *Clin Pediatr* 20:646, 1981.

178. AGUS ZS: Oncogenic hypophosphatemic osteomalacia. *Kidney Int* 24;113, 1983.

179. WEISS D, BAR RS, WEIDNER N, WENER M, LEE F: Oncogenic osteomalacia: Strange tumours in strange places. *Postgrad Med J* 61:349, 1985.

180. GITELIS S, RYAN WG, ROSENBERG AG, TEMPLETON AC: Adult-onset hypophosphatemic osteomalacia secondary to neoplasm. *J Bone Joint Surg* 68A:134, 1986.

180a. CAREY DE, DREZNER MK, HARNDAN JA, MANGE M, AHARAD MS, MUBARAK S, NYHAN WL: Hypophosphatemic rickets/osteomalacia in linear sebaceous nevus syndrome: A variant of tumor-induced osteomalacia. *J Pediatr* 109:994, 1986.

181. RYAN WG, GITELIS S, CHARTERS JR: Studies in a patient with tumor-induced hypophosphatemic osteomalacia. *Calcif Tissue Int* 38:358, 1986.

182. MEYER RA, MEYER MH, GRAY RW: Humoral origin of X-linked hypophosphatemia in mice suggested by parabiosis. *Fed Proc* 46:1393, 1987.

183. SCRIVER CR, MacDONALD W, READE T, GLORIEUX FH, NOGRADY B: Hypophosphatemic nonrachitic bone disease: An entity distinct from X-linked hypophosphatemia in the renal defect, bone involvement and inheritance. *Am J Med Gen* 1:101, 1977.

184. SCRIVER CR, READE T, HALAL F, COSTA T, COLE DEC: Autosomal hypophosphatemic bone disease responds to 1,25-(OH)$_2$D$_3$. *Arch Dis Child* 56:203, 1981.

185. SCRIVER CR, READE TM, DELUCA HF, HAMSTRA AJ: Serum 1,25-dihydroxyvitamin D levels in normal subjects and in patients with hereditary rickets or bone disease. *N Engl J Med* 299:976, 1978.

CHAPTER 106

HEREDITARY RENAL HYPOURICEMIA

ODED SPERLING

1. Hereditary renal hypouricemia is an inborn error of membrane transport, presumably in urate reabsorption in the proximal tubule. It is inherited in an autosomal recessive mode. In homozygotes, it is manifest as hypouricemia and increased renal urate clearance. Heterozygosity may be detected by moderately decreased serum urate levels and moderately, but significantly, increased renal urate clearance.

2. The homozygosity is associated with moderate or excessive uricosuria, reflecting the diversion of intestinal urate elimination to urinary urate excretion consequent to the hypouricemia. There is no evidence for purine overproduction. Hypercalciuria, probably of the hyperabsorptive type, is associated with renal hypouricemia in about 30 percent of the propositi. The mechanism for this abnormality is not yet clarified. The hyperuricosuria and/or hypercalciuria are etiologic factors in uric acid or calcium oxalate urolithiasis, occurring in about 25 percent of the propositi.

3. Transport of urate through the intestinal wall and thorough the erythrocyte membrane appears to be normal.

4. The differential diagnosis of hereditary renal hypouricemia includes familial conditions in which the defective renal urate transport is one component in a generalized transport abnormality, such as Hartnup syndrome or the group of diseases with the Fanconi renal tubulopathy (Wilson disease, cystinosis, galactosemia, and hereditary fructose intolerance).

5. The model of the renal handling of urate in the human includes four components: free glomerular filtration, net early proximal tubular reabsorption (segment S_1), net tubular secretion (segment S_2), and net postsecretory tubular reabsorption (segment S_3). It is assumed that reabsorption and secretion of urate in the proximal tubule occur simultaneously and that the manifestation of net reabsorption or secretion at the various segments reflects different intensities of the two processes. The residual urinary urate in the S_1 region derives originally from filtration, whereas that in the S_3 segment arises from secretion in the S_2 segment.

6. Several types of renal hypouricemia may be distinguished according to the nature and site of the transport defect, as reflected in the fractional clearance of urate and the effects on this parameter of pyrazinamide (inhibiting urate secretion) and probenecid (inhibiting urate reabsorption). The most common type of hereditary renal hypouricemia appears to be a presecretory reabsorption defect. Some of the cases may have a total transport defect (no reabsorption, no secretion) or a total reabsorption defect. A postsecretory reabsorption defect has not been documented in hereditary renal hypouricemia but was found to characterize acquired renal hypouricemia and familial conditions in which renal hypouricemia is a part of a generalized tubular reabsorption defect (Fanconi syndrome). A hypersecretion defect was suggested in three cases of isolated renal hypouricemia without evidence for familiality.

INTRODUCTION

It is common knowledge that a certain proportion of the inborn errors of metabolism in humans represent extremely rare and benign diseases. Yet the discovery and study of such defects are often of utmost importance in that the work contributes to our understanding of the metabolic pathways or processes that occur in the normal human cell or organ. In humans, the renal handling of urate, the final waste product of purine metabolism, is complex; its exact nature has not been conclusively clarified. Hereditary renal hypouricemia is a rare, almost harmless (except for urolithiasis in some of the patients), inborn error in membrane urate transport in the kidney. It represents an "experiment of nature" in human renal handling of urate, furnishing valuable information on urate handling in the normal kidney. Indeed, the first case of this syndrome, reported in 1950, although it lacked conclusive evidence for familiality,[1] furnished the first indication of renal tubular secretion of urate in human beings. The study of the 21 cases with true hereditary renal hypouricemia, first documented in 1972, provided data supporting the presently accepted four-component model of the renal handling of urate in human beings. Furthermore, the results of these studies suggested that the two reabsorption components in the model, namely the presecretory and the postsecretory, are controlled by different genes.

DEFINITION AND DIFFERENTIAL DIAGNOSIS

Hereditary renal hypouricemia refers to the hereditary condition of increased renal urate clearance (see Table 106-2 for normal values) caused by a specific (isolated) inborn error of membrane transport for urate in the renal proximal tubule. This condition is manifested by hypouricemia as defined by a serum urate less than 2.5 mg/dl for adult males and less than 2.1 mg/dl for adult women using a colorimetric determination.[2-5] Hereditary renal hypouricemia should be differentiated from other hereditary conditions of renal hypouricemia, in which the urate transport defect is only one component in a generalized disturbance of membrane transport, e.g., Fanconi (see Chap. 104)[6-8] and Hartnup (see Chap. 101)[9] syndromes. It should also be distinguished from genetically determined metabolic hypouricemia, such as in xanthinuria (see Chap. 42)[10,11] and in purine nucleoside phosphorylase deficiency (see Chap. 40).[12] In the latter conditions, decreased production of uric

---

Nonstandard abbreviations used in this chapter are: FC_{ur} = fractional urate clearance; PAH = para-aminohippuric acid; SITS = 4-acetamido-4′-isothiocyanostilbene-2,2′-disulfonic acid; T_m = maximal rate for net tubular absorption.

acid due to specific enzyme abnormalities is manifested by very low uric acid levels in both serum and urine.

According to the above definition, subjects with persistent hypouricemia with normal or somewhat excessive (see below) urinary excretion of uric acid, i.e., increased renal urate clearance, should be investigated for hereditary renal hypouricemia. In all reported cases, the classification of hereditary, isolated renal hypouricemia was established by demonstration of familiality and by refuting the presence of other renal tubular reabsorption defects. In order to establish the familiality of the defect, sibs and other family members should be screened for hypouricemia (see "Genetics" below). Finding an additional affected hypouricemic (homozygous) sib is proof of familiality. Finding parents or offspring with intermediate blood levels of uric acid (2.5 to 3.5 mg/dl) associated with significantly increased renal urate clearance may be taken to indicate heterozygosity. When familial renal hypouricemia is established, the isolated type can be verified by ruling out the presence of other tubular abnormalities. The presence of the following hereditary diseases should be excluded: Wilson disease,[13-16] cystinosis,[17] galactosemia,[18] and hereditary fructose intolerance[19] (see Chaps. 54, 107, 13, and 11 respectively). All these diseases are associated with the Fanconi syndrome, in which uric acid reabsorption in the proximal tubule is decreased, along with that of other crystalloid solutes. Renal hypouricemia is also part of the Hartnup syndrome, which should also be excluded (see Chap. 101).[9]

Subjects with persistent renal hypouricemia who have no sibs or other relatives may be classified as having suspected hereditary renal hypouricemia if proven to have the isolated defect in uric acid transport and when the presence of acquired renal hypouricemia is excluded beyond doubt. Acquired renal hypouricemia may accompany conditions of extracellular fluid volume expansion, such as inappropriate antidiuretic hormone secretion,[20-22] and various malignancies, such as multiple myeloma,[23] lymphomas,[24] and pulmonary neoplasms.[25-28] In some of the neoplasms the renal hypouricemia is part of a broader, Fanconi-like tubulopathy, whereas in others, like Hodgkin's disease, it appears as an isolated defect. In the latter disease, the degree of renal urate clearance was found to correlate with the activity of the neoplastic process.[24] Renal hypouricemia may also occur in heavy metal intoxication[29,30] and following use of outdated tetracyclines.[31] In both conditions, the renal hypouricemia is part of a general tubulopathy of the type of the Fanconi syndrome. It can also occur in liver disease, such as jaundice,[32] in which the degree of renal urate clearance has been shown to improve (decrease) with recovery, and cirrhosis,[33] in which an inverse correlation was found between serum bilirubin and urate.

Further support for (but by no means proof of) the presence of hereditary renal hypouricemia in subjects with persistent renal hypouricemia who show no evidence of acquired conditions but who lack conclusive evidence of familiality may be obtained by demonstration of the presecretory reabsorption type of defect in renal urate handling. This is because of the apparently characteristic presence of this type of defect in subjects with hereditary renal hypouricemia (see below).

HISTORY

True hereditary renal hypouricemia—due to an isolated tubular defect for urate transport—was described in human

beings first by Greene et al. in 1972.[34] This condition was described by Praetorius and Kirk[1] in 1950, but in their patient there was no evidence of genetic transmission. The second true case of hereditary renal hypouricemia was documented in 1973 by Khachadurian et al.[35] In 1974, Sperling et al. reported a new hereditary syndrome that included hypouricemia, hypercalciuria, and decreased bone density.[36] Since then, another 18 families have been documented[34-49] with true hereditary renal hypouricemia. An additional 12 patients were reported[1,38,50-56] who could fit into this category but in whom the genetic transmission was not established.

RENAL HANDLING OF URATE IN NORMAL HUMANS

Since hereditary renal hypouricemia is believed to be caused by a primary defect in the renal handling of urate, our present knowledge of the normal handling of urate in the human kidney will first be reviewed. The exact nature of the renal handling of urate in human beings has not been clarified conclusively. This is due in part to the lack of an identical animal model. Experiments in humans were limited to the study of the effects of urate loading[57,58] and of various drugs[58-61] on uric acid excretion. In addition, important information was furnished by "experiments of nature," i.e., inborn defects in renal urate reabsorption, the subject of this chapter. In constructing a plausible model for the renal handling of urate in the human being, information from animals was selected according to its compatibility with the information obtained for humans. Data were obtained from a wide range of laboratory animals, such as reptiles, rats, dogs, Cebus monkeys, and chimpanzees. In these animals, stop-flow, micropuncture, and microperfusion experiments in vivo, as well as vesicle studies in vitro, furnished the basic information on the renal handling of urate and the mechanism of renal urate transport. The species which were found to resemble ours most closely were the chimpanzee and Cebus monkey.[62]

The Components of Renal Handling of Urate

Glomerular Filtration of Uric Acid. Urate is probably bound to plasma proteins, the amount of binding being approximately 5 to 10 percent;[63,64] however, the data regarding binding are conflicting. Practically, urate is freely filtered at the glomerulus, since the binding of urate to plasma proteins is offset by the plasma negative Gibbs-Donnan potential generated across the glomerular membrane.[65] Indeed, determinations of the concentrations of urate in glomerular ultrafiltrate and plasma water indicate that they are almost equal.[66-68]

Reabsorption of Uric Acid. In a number of species, the fraction of filtered urate excreted in the urine is less than 100 percent, indicating net reabsorption. This is true for cat, some monkeys, rat, mongrel dog, Cebus monkey, chimpanzee, and human beings.[62] In humans, the fractional clearance of urate in relation to that of inulin or creatinine is about 7 to 10 percent, indicating very efficient reabsorption. In all animals in which urate reabsorption has been localized, including the Cebus monkey,[69] it was found to occur largely in the proximal tubules, although it is possible that some degree of urate reabsorption occurs in some animals in more distal segments. Urate reabsorption may proceed by two mechanisms, a saturable, mediated pathway through the cell and a nonsaturable, noninhibitable pathway across the tight junction.[70] That urate reabsorption is an active transport process is evident from several findings. In free-flow, micropuncture studies, the ratio between urate concentration in the proximal tubule fluid to that in plasma was shown to be less than 1.[71] Similar results were obtained in microperfusion studies.[72] In addition, in nonhuman primates and in humans, diuresis and inhibition of urate secretion by pyrazinoate caused the concentration of urate in urine to approach 10 percent of the plasma concentration.[73] In the chimpanzee and Cebus monkey, urate concentration in the tubular fluid was found to be from 20 to 60 percent of plasma urate concentration.[74] The relationship between the active absorption of urate and the intraluminal concentration of urate was found to follow first-order kinetics.[70] The urate reabsorption process was found to be affected by alterations in the reabsorption of sodium,[75] but could be dissociated from that of the sodium by pharmacologic agents[76,77] and by expansion of the extracellular fluid volume.[78] That urate and sodium reabsorption are not linked intimately was also confirmed in vesicle studies.[79,80] Studies in the rat in vivo and in vesicles in vitro demonstrated that urate reabsorption is inhibited by a number of substances, such as probenecid, furosemide, para-aminohippuric acid (PAH), and the anion exchange inhibitors 4-acetamido-4'-isothiocyanostilbene-2,2'-disulfonic acid (SITS) and 4,4'-diisothiocyanostilbene-2,2'-disulfonic acid, and thus that urate reabsorption is mediated by an anion-exchange mechanism.

Secretion of Uric Acid. The first evidence for tubular urate secretion in human beings was found in 1950[1] in the first subject with renal hypouricemia, in whom the fractional urate clearance (FC_{ur}, urate/inulin clearance ratio) was 1.46. This early evidence for the bidirectional tubular transport of urate was subsequently augmented by studies in human beings, in which the FC_{ur} was increased artificially to as high as 1.23 by use of urate loading, mannitol diuresis, and probenecid.[58] In humans, the exact localization of urate secretion has not been conclusively established. In one study,[81] the proximal nephron was found to transport urate to the tubular fluid, whereas the distal nephron was unable to do so. Net secretion of urate occurs in many species, such as birds, reptiles, guinea pigs, Dalmatian coach dogs, some individual rabbits, and certain species of monkeys. In virtually all of these animals, there is evidence for bidirectional urate transport. In the rat, urate secretion occurs by both saturable transcellular and nonsaturable paracellular pathways.[82] The relationship between the mediated secretory flux of urate and the urate concentration in the peritubular capillaries demonstrates first-order kinetics.[82] In vivo microperfusion and microinjection studies indicated that, similar to the reabsorption of urate, the secretory process is a result of an anion exchange mechanism. The secretory flux of urate was inhibited by probenecid, p-chloromercuribenzoate, SITS, PAH, and pyrazinoate.[82-84] Accordingly it was concluded that the secretory urate exchanger has affinity for PAH and pyrazinoate. Several experiments indicated the presence of an uphill transport step for urate in the rat proximal tubule, probably at the basolateral membrane. When rat kidney slices were incubated in a medium containing urate, the slice-to-medium urate ratio was 0.71.[85] Intravenous loading of rats with urate accompanied by administration of the uricase inhibitor oxonate resulted in a mean fractional delivery of urate to the early proximal tubule of 130 percent.[71] Also in the

rabbit, an uphill transport site for urate secretion was firmly implicated in the proximal tubule[86,87] at the basolateral membrane.[85,88] An interesting finding in the rabbit is that urate secretion is modulated by a serum protein that affects the basolateral transporter by allosteric modification.[87] This finding may be taken to suggest that abnormalities in renal urate handling may also reflect primary defects in such modulators of secretion or reabsorption (see below). In the rabbit, urate secretion was demonstrated to increase markedly with plasma urate concentration.[89,90]

A Model for Urate Transport. The studies with renal brush border and basolateral membrane vesicles from the rat and brush border vesicles from the dog[90-97] led Kahn and Weinman to the construction of a model for the bidirectional transport of urate in the proximal tubule of the rat.[65] According to this model (Fig. 106-1), urate reabsorption from the lumen to the cell is mediated by the brush border anion exchanger, exchanging urate for intracellular anions. Anions such as hydroxyl or bicarbonate are above electrochemical equilibrium within the cell, and thus their exchange with urate allows uphill reabsorption of urate. Other anions, such as lactate, pyruvate, and succinate, may also exchange with urate. These anions may either be produced in the cell or transported from the lumen via a sodium cotransport system. The transport of urate from the cell into the interstitium could occur by simple diffusion or through an anion exchange mechanism, e.g., for chloride. According to this model of urate reabsorption, compounds such as probenecid, PAH, or furosemide inhibit urate reabsorption from the lumen to the proximal tubule cell by blocking the brush border anion exchanger. In the secretion process, urate transport from plasma to cell through the basolateral membrane is mediated via anion exchange with cellular chloride or other anions not yet identified. These cellular anions should be above electrochemical equilibrium with respect to the interstitium to allow uphill urate secretion. Another transport mechanism that could mediate uphill urate transport from interstitium to the cell is a sodium-urate trans-

Fig. 106-1 Proposed scheme for urate reabsorption (A) and secretion (B) in the proximal tubule of the rat. The luminal surface is to the right. (From Kahn and Weinman.[65] Used by permission.)

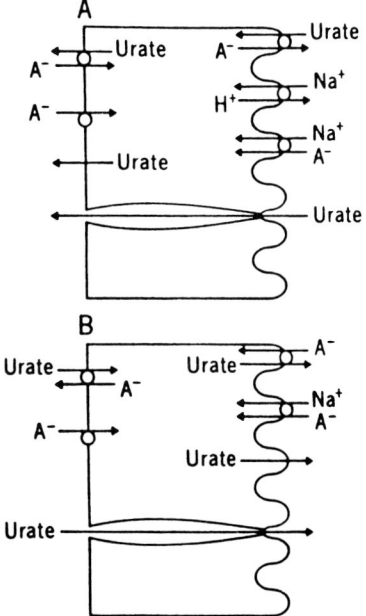

port system. However, this system has not as yet been demonstrated. The flux of urate from the tubule cell to the lumen could occur by simple diffusion or could be mediated by an anion exchanger, most likely in exchange for chloride.

Models for Urate Handling in Human Beings

Studies on renal handling of urate in human beings generated models of a two-, a three-, and finally a four-component system. The first model, suggested in 1950 by Berliner et al.,[57] included glomerular filtration followed by extensive, though incomplete, tubular reabsorption. Three years later, following the demonstration of uric acid secretion in humans, this third component was added by Gutman and Yu.[98] More recently, a fourth component, postsecretory reabsorption, was added in order to explain the effects of pyrazinamide in some patients or conditions which otherwise, according to the three-component model, could only be interpreted as enhanced tubular secretion of urate. These effects of pyrazinamide included the suppression of the increased uric acid clearance in patients with Wilson disease[16] and Hodgkin's disease[24] and the suppression in normal subjects, by pretreatment with pyrazinamide, of probenecid-induced uricosuria, the uricosuric response to intravenous chlorothiazide,[98] and the increased urate clearance of volume expansion associated with hypertonic sodium chloride administration.[99] The four-component model (Fig. 106-2) was suggested in 1973 by Steele and Boner,[100] by Steele,[101] by Diamond and Paolino,[102] and in 1974 by Rieselbach and Steele.[103] It includes glomerular filtration, early proximal reabsorption, later proximal secretion, and extensive postsecretory reabsorption, which could occur at the same location as the secretion, separate and distal to it, or both. Evidence for the existence of the postsecretory reabsorption site with a different mechanism than that of the presecretory reabsorption site was obtained in several patients with renal hy-

Fig. 106-2 Model for the renal handling of urate in humans. The size and direction of arrows indicate intensity and direction of urate transport. The stippled arrow represents filtered urate; the solid arrow, urate reabsorption; and the open arrow, urate secretion or urate remaining in tubular fluid after reabsorption. Numerical values indicate hypothetical orders of magnitude of the transport processes. (From Rieselbach and Steele.[103] Used by permission.)

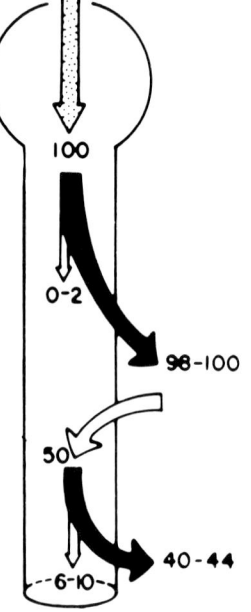

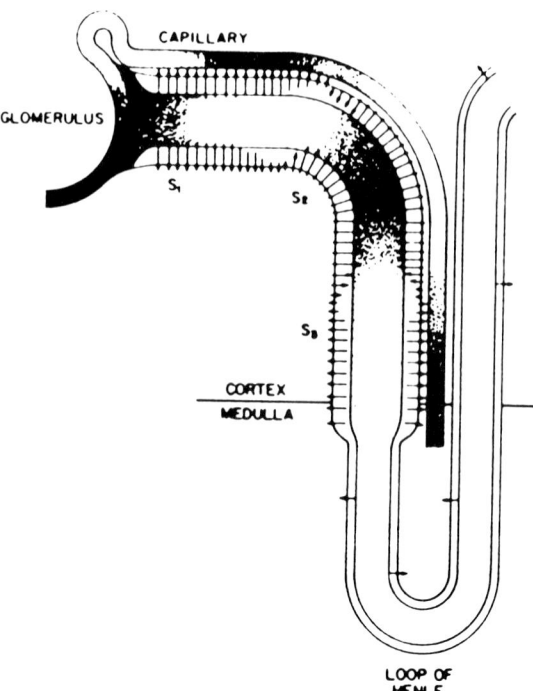

Fig. 106-3 Mode of renal handling of urate in humans. The size and direction of arrows indicate intensity and direction of urate transport. The density of shading in the tubule and the capillary indicates the relative amounts of urate (not concentration) in the lumina. (From Grantham and Chonko.[107] Used by permission.)

pouricemia (see below), in whom the increased urate clearance was attributed to a defect in postsecretory reabsorption.[8,16,24,104–106]

Recently another model has been proposed (Fig. 106-3).[107] It includes the same four components as the former model, but reabsorption and secretion of urate occur simultaneously along all the proximal tubule, each at different intensities at the different segments of the tubule. The model suggests a higher density of reabsorption transporters at the S_1 segment compared with S_2 and S_3, and a higher intensity of secretion at the S_2 region of the tubule. These differences in the intensities of reabsorption and secretion along the tubule result in initial net reabsorption of urate in the S_1 segment followed by net secretion in the S_2 segment and net reabsorption in the S_3 segment. According to both models the residual urinary urate in the S_1 region is derived originally from filtration whereas that in the S_3 segment arises from secretion in the S_2 segment.

Factors That Affect Renal Handling of Urate in Humans

Age and Sex. Urate excretion becomes less efficient with age.[108–110] Accordingly, plasma urate levels increase with age. This change with maturation has been attributed to increased urate reabsorption rather than a decrease in urate secretion.[110] The mean clearance of urate is 1.2 to 2.3 ml/min higher in females than males.[111,112] Exogenous estrogen was found to produce a significant increase in urate clearance in transsexual males.[113]

Extracellular Fluid Volume and Urine Flow Rate. The extracellular fluid volume or, more precisely, the volume of the effective arterial circulation is one of the most dominant factors in renal urate handling.[75,114–118] Volume expansion, like that associated with administration of isotonic or hypertonic saline, increases urate clearance, whereas volume contraction, like that associated with restricted sodium chloride intake, decreases urate clearance. Presumably, these effects of changes in extracellular volume are mediated through alterations in urate reabsorption in the proximal tubule.[75,117,118] The rate of urinary flow affects urinary urate concentration and therefore may affect the back-diffusion of urate in the relatively impermeable terminal renal tubules.[119,120] Nevertheless, these effects are probably minor in relation to those of the extracellular fluid volume, as can be judged from the values of renal urate clearance in patients with inappropriate secretion of antidiuretic hormone and in patients with nephrogenic diabetes insipidus. In the former patients with expanded extracellular fluid volume, renal urate clearance is high despite slow urinary flow rate.[20,21,121] In the latter patients with contracted extracellular fluid volume, urinary urate clearance is decreased despite rapid urinary flow rate.[122]

Drugs. Many drugs affect renal urate excretion.[107,123] A biphasic effect (different effect at low and high concentration of the drug) was documented for some of the drugs and suggested for all others.[123] Pyrazinamide, probenecid, phenylbutazone, and salicylate inhibit urate secretion at low doses, but inhibit urate reabsorption at high doses.[67,98,124,125] Diuretic drugs are initially uricosuric by direct inhibition of urate reabsorption, but their chronic administration is associated with contraction of the extracellular fluid volume resulting in antiuricosuria.[98,126–130] An additional property of some of the diuretic drugs is their tendency to compete with tubular urate secretion, decreasing further urate excretion.[128]

RENAL HANDLING OF URATE IN HEREDITARY RENAL HYPOURICEMIA

Renal Clearance of Urate

The data on the renal handling of urate in the propositi of the 21 families documented to have true hereditary renal hypouricemia are summarized in Table 106-1. As can be seen from the table, all the propositi have significantly decreased plasma urate levels, ranging from 0.2 to 1.5 mg/dl. Indeed, these markedly low serum urate values were unexpected in almost all cases, being found during investigation for unrelated medical problems (to exclude urolithiasis, see below). Urinary urate excretion in the propositi is normal or excessive, and renal urate clearance is markedly elevated, ranging from 39.5 to 144 ml/min, the fractional clearance of urate (FC_{ur}) ranging from 36 to 169 percent. However, the FC_{ur} was found to exceed 100 percent in only four out of the 21 propositi. Seventeen of the propositi were males, and four were females; their age at diagnosis ranged from 3 to 74 years.

The group of 12 subjects with renal hypouricemia in whom no conclusive evidence for familiality could be obtained[1,38,50–56] had levels of uric acid in serum and urine similar to those of the propositi with the familial disorder.

Two normouricemic subjects were reported[52,61] with a renal defect for uric acid handling, which was manifested as increased renal urate clearance only under conditions of purine load. The familiality of this type of defect in the renal handling of urate is not clarified.

Nature of the Renal Transport Defect

Increased renal urate clearance could be caused by defective reabsorption or by increased secretion. Based on the models of urate transport in the proximal tubule (Fig. 106-1) and of renal handling of urate in human beings (Figs. 106-2 and 106-3), as presented above, five main possibilities of specific abnormalities in the active urate transport processes that may cause renal hypouricemia should be considered:

A. Total transport defect (no reabsorption and no secretion)

B. Total reabsorption defect

C. Presecretory reabsorption defect

D. Postsecretory reabsorption defect

E. Increased secretion

Renal hypouricemia being an inborn error, this classification depends, of course, on the genetic control of each of the active transport processes. Accordingly, possibility A is based on the assumption of a common genetic control for all transport processes (implying that reabsorption and secretion of urate in the renal proximal tubules reflect only inverse positioning of the same mechanism), possibility B, on the assumption of a common genetic control for all reabsorption processes, and possibilities C and D, on the assumption of separate genetic control for the two reabsorption processes.

Effects of Pyrazinamide and Probenecid on FC_{ur}. According to the simple model of the renal handling of urate in human beings, as depicted in Fig. 106-2, one may distinguish between the above types of transport defects by use of drugs inhibiting urate reabsorption or secretion. In the localization of the tubular defect in renal hypouricemia, two drugs, probenecid and pyrazinamide, are employed. Probenecid [p-(di-n-propylsulfamyl)-benzoic acid] has a dual action on urinary urate excretion. When administered by the oral or intravenous route at the usual "high" doses, it increases renal urate clearance markedly (Table 106-2). On the other hand, at low doses, the drug causes a so-called paradoxical urate retention.[131] While the increase of renal urate clearance at the high probenecid dose appears to be due solely to inhibition of tubular reabsorption, the paradoxical urate retention at low doses has been explained by inhibition of tubular secretion. In any event, the net effect of a high probenecid dose (2 to 3 g orally) is a substantial rise in urate excretion. There are several reasons for the assumption that probenecid inhibits tubular urate reabsorption chiefly at the postsecretory site. Firstly, in the plasma, probenecid is largely bound to albumin,[132] and thus the amount filtered is relatively small. Secondly, probenecid appears in the urine chiefly by tubular secretion, possibly by the same mechanism as uric acid.[133] The tubular secretion of probenecid would explain both its paradoxical urate-retaining action (at low doses) by competition with urate at the secretory site, and its reabsorption due to inhibitory action (at high doses) at a postsecretory tubular site.

Whether and to what extent probenecid also inhibits presecretory tubular reabsorption is still an open question. Evidently, the many-fold increase of urate clearance in response to probenecid in normal subjects is compatible with the dominance of postsecretory absorption in the normal regulation of renal urate excretion. On the other hand, in subjects with renal hypouricemia, the probenecid response should be attenuated, its magnitude depending on the tubular site of the de-

Table 106-1 Data on Renal Handling of Urate in Hereditary Renal Hypouricemia

First author (Ref.)	Year	Propositus Age at diagnosis	Propositus Sex	Plasma urate, mg/dl	Urinary urate, mg/24 h	C_{ur}, ml/min	FC_{ur} (C_{ur}/GFR), %
1. Greene (34)	1972	23	M	0.9	640	46	38
2. Khachadurian (35)	1973	57	M	0.2	797	173	148
3. Sperling (36)	1974	53	M	0.6	691	55	70.6
4. Akaoka (37)	1975	28	M	0.4	690	88.5	107.3
5. Akaoka (38)	1977	40	M	0.54	596	99	75
6. Akaoka (38)	1977	41	M	0.48	627	114	95
7. Benjamin (39)	1977	37	F	1.1	662	39.5	37.6
8. Benjamin (40)	1978	48	M	1.2	750	50.9	38.5
9. Frank (41)	1979	39	M	1.0	>1000	80	47.9
10. Frank (41)	1979	37	M	1.0	>1000	60	45
11. Weitz (42)	1980	8	M	0.7	355	35.2	43.7
12. Hedley (43)	1980	63	M	<1.3	1042	–	169
13. Fujiwara (44)	1980	24	M	0.9	961	74.1	56.8
14. Delevelle (45)	1980	74	M	0.43	526	85	80
15. Garty (46)	1981	10	M	1.5	286	45.8	36
16. Matsuda (47)	1982	43	F	0.5	667	83	91.7
17. Vinay (48)	1983	43	F	0.3	1040	144	77
18. Takeda (49)	1985	3	F	0.8	662	75	90
19. Takeda (49)	1985	10	M	1.0	1310	117	88
20. Takeda (49)	1985	12	F	0.7	1530	93	102
21. Takeda (49)	1985	4	M	0.8	1142	102	146

NOTE: Values given for serum urate are the lowest or average values reported for each subject. Values given for urinary urate excretion, for C_{ur}, and for FC_{ur} are the highest or average values reported for each subject.

fect, whether postsecretory, presecretory, or both. In the case where the defect is exclusively postsecretory and complete (type D), probenecid will have no effect on urinary urate excretion. However, where the defect is presecretory (type C), the probenecid response will be maintained but may be of lesser magnitude than normal. Where the defect in tubular urate reabsorption is combined presecretory and postsecretory (type B), the probenecid response will be nil.

The separation between the reabsorption sites, as well as the very existence of the postsecretory site, was postulated according to data obtained by the use of pyrazinamide, although the exact effect of this drug on renal urate handling is still under dispute. Following administration of pyrazinamide, urinary uric acid is transiently reduced to very low levels, without change of glomerular filtration rate (Table 106-2).[134,135] This

effect may be attributed to inhibition of urate secretion, a property demonstrated for this drug in the dog[136] and rat.[137] Indeed, this property has been extensively used as a pharmacologic aid in quantitating urate reabsorption and secretion. The pyrazinamide suppression test in humans[101] is based on the assumption that pyrazinamide blocks completely and specifically only urate secretion. It is performed by determining uric acid excretion before and immediately after administration of pyrazinamide in a dose sufficient to give maximal suppression of uric acid excretion (usually 3 g, administered orally). The difference between the amount of urate filtered and that excreted under maximal effect of the drug is taken to represent urate reabsorption, which was found to be 98 to 99 percent complete in normal humans. On the other hand, the decrement in uric acid excretion observed under maximal ef-

Table 106-2 The Effects of Pyrazinamide and Probenecid on FC_{ur} in Control Subjects and Differentiation by These Effects Between the Various Types of Renal Hypouricemia*

No. of control subjects	FC_{ur}, %	Effect on FC_{ur}, % Pyrazinamide	Effect on FC_{ur}, % Probenecid
10[a]	9.8 ± 3.4	Decrease to 2.15 ± 1.7	
14[b]	10.3 ± 4	Decrease to 1.2 ± 1.1	
10[c]	8.2 ± 0.6	Decrease to 1.8	Increase to 40.4 ± 8
10[d]	9.3 ± 2.6	Decrease to 1.13 ± 0.35	
5[e]	8.4 ± 2.7		Increase to 46.7 ± 8.3

Type of renal hypouricemia			
A. Total transport defect (reabsorption and secretion)	100	No effect	No effect
B. Total reabsorption defect	>100	Attenuated effect decreasing FC_{ur} to 1	No effect
C. Presecretory reabsorption defect	?	Attenuated effect	Attenuated effect
D. Postsecretory reabsorption defect	<100	Normal effect	No effect
E. Increased secretion	<100	Normal effect	Normal effect

*Values represent mean ± SD. SOURCES: a = Steele and Rieselbach;[134] b = Tofuku et al;[53] c = Meisel and Diamond,[8] values represent C_{ur} in ml/min instead of FC_{ur}, 1 g probenecid administered IV; d = Akaoka et al;[38] Kawabe et al;[51] Fujiwara et al;[44] and Shichiri et al;[54] e = Fujiwara et al.[44] and Shichiri et al.[54]

fect of pyrazinamide is taken to represent tubular urate secretion. The latter was found to account for 80 to 85 percent of excreted urate in normal subjects.[134,138] In recent years, data obtained in vivo and in vitro indicate, however, that explaining the suppression of uric acid excretion by pyrazinamide as a specific effect of blocked tubular urate secretion is an oversimplification. Evidence was first obtained that the effect of pyrazinamide depends on its concentration and that at high concentrations it also inhibits urate reabsorption, increasing urate excretion.[139] Support for the dual effect of the drug was indicated by the findings that pyrazinamide inhibited the precession of [^{14}C]urate relative to [^{3}H]inulin into the urine when the compounds were simultaneously injected into a peritubular capillary[83] and that pyrazinoate inhibited the reabsorption of [^{14}C]urate injected into the rat proximal tubule.[140] In addition to its inhibitory effect on urate reabsorption and secretion, pyrazinamide was also found to enhance urate reabsorption.[141] Thus, the suppression effect of pyrazinamide on urate excretion may reflect both inhibition of urate secretion and enhancement of urate reabsorption. Recently, studies in isolated membranes have indicated that pyrazinoate has affinity for the urate anion exchanger in the brush border membrane.[80,95,142] Accordingly, when in the lumen, this drug will inhibit urate reabsorption, but when in the cell, it will enhance urate reabsorption. These effects were recently demonstrated in studies with dog brush border vesicles.[65] Although in view of the foregoing data the interpretation of the pyrazinamide effect in normal subjects, as well as in subjects with increased renal urate clearance, should be made with reservation and regarded as tentative, the pyrazinamide response may be still interpreted as mainly reflecting the inhibitory effect of the drug on tubular urate secretion, even though the magnitude of the response need not be an exact measure of it. In normal subjects in whom tubular secretion is the main source of urinary urate, pyrazinamide response is expected to be of great magnitude (Table 106-2). On the other hand, in subjects with increased urate clearance due to a defect in tubular urate reabsorption, the pyrazinamide response could vary according to the site of the defect, whether presecretory or postsecretory. In case of a postsecretory defect in urate reabsorption (type D), pyrazinamide will markedly reduce urinary urate excretion, bringing it to a level similar to that reached in pyrazinamide-treated normal subjects. In the case of a presecretory defect (type C), however, the pyrazinamide response will be attenuated. In the case of combined presecretory and postsecretory defective tubular urate reabsorption (type B), in which the clearance of urate exceeds the glomerular filtration rate (GFR), pyrazinamide will reduce the elevated urate clearance to a value close or equal to GFR. In patients with a total transport defect (type A), pyrazinamide will have no effect, but in case of increased secretion (type E), the effect of the drug will be normal.

According to the above considerations on the renal urate handling and the action of pyrazinamide and probenecid, the five types of renal hypouricemia would be expected to conform to the following responses (Table 106-2). In a total transport defect (type A), FC$_{ur}$ should be about 1, and this value should not be altered by administration of pyrazinamide or probenecid. In a total reabsorption defect (type B), i.e., absence of reabsorption at both the presecretory and postsecretory sites but presence of normal secretion, FC$_{ur}$ should be greater than 1. In such a defect, blocking secretion by pyrazinamide will result in an attenuated decrease in FC$_{ur}$ which should approach the value of 1. Administration of probenecid will not alter FC$_{ur}$. In a presecretory reabsorption defect (type C), FC$_{ur}$

cannot be estimated, since the maximal rate for net tubular absorption (T_m) for urate at the postsecretory site is unknown. If, indeed, the excreted urate represents the amount of secreted urate escaping reabsorption at the postsecretory reabsorption site, one can expect a substantial proportion, probably the majority of the filtered load (not reabsorbed at the presecretory site), to escape the postsecretory reabsorption, too. If this is the case, then FC$_{ur}$ in a presecretory reabsorption defect will be greater than 1. In a presecretory reabsorption defect, administration of pyrazinamide will decrease FC$_{ur}$ and administration of probenecid will increase this parameter, but both effects will be attenuated. In defective reabsorption at the postsecretory site (type D), FC$_{ur}$ will be smaller than 1 if the amount secreted is smaller than that filtered. In the presence of such a defect, administration of pyrazinamide will decrease FC$_{ur}$ to normal level, but administration of probenecid will have no effect. In case of a defect manifested in increased secretion (type E), FC$_{ur}$ will probably be smaller than 1 (unless the secretion is increased to such a level that its fraction escaping reabsorption will exceed the amounts of filtered urate). In such a defect, the administration of pyrazinamide and of probenecid will result in normal response.

Type of Defect in Hereditary Renal Hypouricemia

The greatest proportion of the propositi (12 subjects) had FC$_{ur}$ values between 36 to 85 percent and exhibited attenuated responses to the administration of pyrazinamide and probenecid. These propositi,[34,36,38–42,44,45,47] may be classified as type C, affected with presecretory reabsorption defect. In some of these subjects,[40–42] the effect of pyrazinamide was somewhat greater than in the others, but the lowest FC$_{ur}$ values, obtained under the maximal effect of the drug, did not reach the normal level.

Two cases studied by Akaoka,[37,38] one studied by Matsuda,[47] and three of the propositi studied by Takeda[49] had FC$_{ur}$ values close to 1 which were not affected significantly by administration of pyrazinamide and probenecid. These six cases may fit with either type C or type A. In only three of the propositi were FC$_{ur}$ values clearly greater than 1. In two of them, the pyrazinamide and probenecid tests were not done. In the third case, a 4-year-old Japanese boy,[49] the tests were done, but under different conditions than those adopted by all other investigators. In this boy, pyrazinamide had almost no effect, whereas benzbromarone (employed instead of probenecid) had an inverse effect, decreasing FC$_{ur}$. This case could fit with total reabsorption defect (type B). None of the propositi could be conclusively classified with type D or E. Thus, of the 19 propositi studied for the effects of the drugs, 12 could definitely be classified as type C (presecretory reabsorption defect), 6 as type C or A (total transport defect), and 1 as type B (total reabsorption defect). None of the propositi could be classified as type D (postsecretory reabsorption defect) or E (increased secretion).

Nature of the Defect in Other Conditions of Renal Hypouricemia

The pyrazinamide and probenecid tests were done in patients with the Fanconi syndrome,[8,105] Wilson disease,[16] Hodgkin's disease,[24] and hyperparathyroidism.[106] In some of these patients the renal hypouricemia was part of a generalized tubular reabsorption defect, such as in the Fanconi syndrome, whereas in the others it represented an isolated defect. Interestingly, most, if not all, of these subjects could be classified as type D (postsecretory reabsorption defect), which was not found in the subjects with hereditary isolated renal hypouricemia. Two subjects with Hodgkin's disease who exhibited normal response to pyrazinamide were classified as having increased secretion.[24] Nevertheless, the probenecid effect was not studied in these patients, and therefore the normal pyrazinamide effect could also be interpreted to reflect a postsecretory reabsorption defect. The subjects reported with isolated renal hypouricemia but without proof for familiality represent a heterogeneous group. One of these subjects[53] could be classified as type D. Three subjects[54,55] could be classified as type E. They had moderately increased FC_{ur} values, which were normally affected by both pyrazinamide and probenecid or sulfinpyrazone.[55] This type was not found among the patients with hereditary renal hypouricemia. Only three of the subjects[53,56] could be classified as type C, the most common type in the group with hereditary renal hypouricemia. In the rest of the subjects of this group, the results of the pyrazinamide and probenecid tests did not allow classification.

In the two normouricemic subjects, in whom increased FC_{ur} was found only following purine load,[52,61] the effect of pyrazinamide was normal. In one of these subjects,[52] the defect was suggested to be at the postsecretory reabsorption site, in view of an attenuated response of FC_{ur} to administration of benzbromarone (given instead of probenecid). In the other subject,[61] a high rate of secretion was demonstrated following RNA administration, but the probenecid test was not performed.

The above data may be taken to suggest that type C is the most common (if not the only type) among the subjects with hereditary (isolated) renal hypouricemia, whereas type D is the most common in patients with the acquired renal hypouricemia and in patients with hereditary renal hypouricemia associated with a generalized renal tubular reabsorption defect. According to the foregoing discussion, demonstration of a presecretory reabsorption defect may be taken to support the classification of true hereditary renal hypouricemia, whereas demonstration of the postsecretory reabsorption defect may be taken to refute this classification.

Urate Transport in Nonrenal Tissues

Assuming that deletion of a specific carrier is the primary abnormality leading to the defective reabsorption of urate in the renal tubules of subjects with hereditary renal hypouricemia, the tissue specificity of this defect was investigated.[48,143]

Erythrocytes. Uric acid transport into normal human erythrocytes has been shown to be partially inhibited by hypoxanthine,[144] and this is presumed to represent active uric acid transport mediated by an enzymatic system. This active system was suggested to be lacking in the Dalmatian coach hound[145] but later was found to be normal in these dogs.[48] Uric acid transport into erythrocytes was studied in five hypouricemic subjects.[48,143] In all these subjects, urate uptake by the erythrocytes, both total uptake as well as that inhibited by hypoxanthine, was normal (Figs. 106-4 and 106-5). The lack of expression of the transport defect in the erythrocytes is not surprising, since to our knowledge none of the known renal tubular transport disorders could be demonstrated in erythrocytes.

Intestine. Active urate transport through the normal intestinal wall has not been demonstrated.[146,147] Nevertheless, the intestinal uptake of urate was studied in one hypouricemic subject[143] because genetically determined renal transport defects may also be expressed in the intestinal mucosa, as in cystinuria,[148] iminoglycinuria,[149] and the Hartnup syndrome.[150] The intestinal absorption of uric acid was gauged by the 7-day cumulative urinary excretion of [^{14}C], following oral administration of [^{14}C]urate in presence of bacteriostasis. The value in the hypouricemic subject was similar to that obtained in two control subjects (Fig. 106-6). The apparently accelerated urinary excretion of labeled uric acid in the patient may be taken to reflect his increased uric acid clearance.

Presence of an Endogenous Uricosuric Agent

In all the above considerations, the existence of an inborn primary renal tubular urate transport defect was presumed. However, in making this assumption and the interpretations as to the location of the tubular defect given above, caution should be exercised in view of the possibility that the renal tubular abnormalities may be secondary to an abnormal metabolite produced elsewhere in the body or to qualitative or quantitative alterations in modulators affecting urate transport processes. The presence of a humoral uricosuric factor may be possible in some conditions with acquired renal hypouricemia in which the transitory nature of the defect was demonstrated.

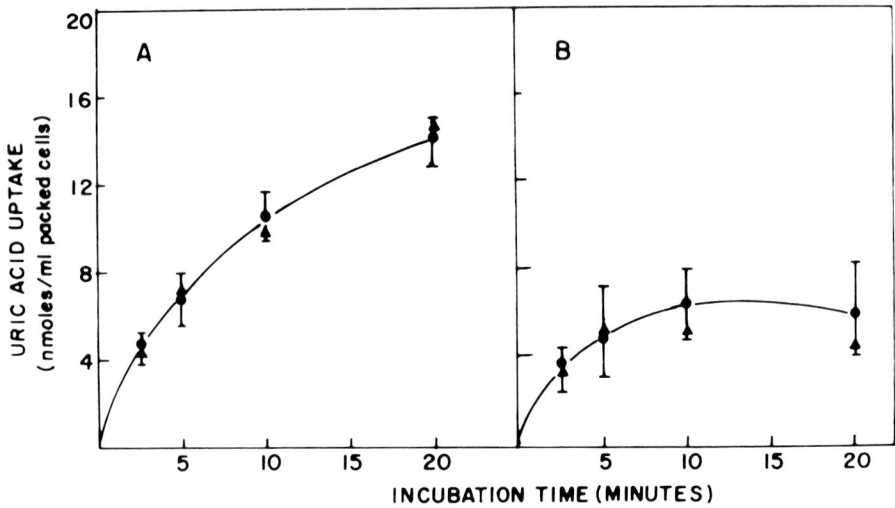

Fig. 106-4 Uptake of uric acid by erythrocytes. The range and mean of five normal subjects (●) and the mean of two experiments for a patient with renal hypouricenia (▲) are presented. A total uptake; B hypoxanthine-inhibited uptake. (*From Sperling et al.[143] Used by permission.*)

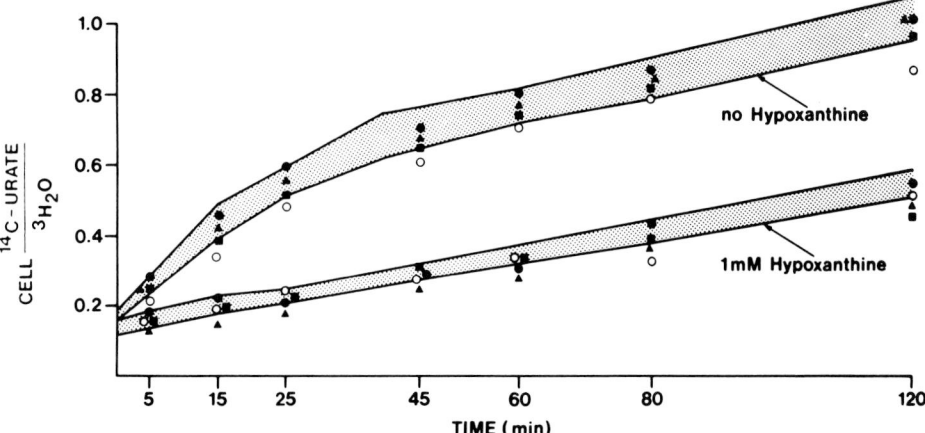

Fig. 106-5 Transport of urate into erythrocytes. The transport is expressed as the ratio of [^{14}C]labeled urate space to tritiated water space, with and without hypoxanthine in the buffer. Hatched areas represent range for normal controls; symbols represent values for four hypouricemic patients. (*From Vinay et al.[48] Used by permission.*)

In Hodgkin's disease, serum uric acid and renal uric acid clearance became normal following chemotherapy, but the hypouricemia and increased renal clearance of urate reappeared with recrudescence of disease.[24] Similarly, with severe burns the increased renal urate clearance was found to decrease to normal with recovery.[151] Nevertheless, until today, no experimental evidence could be obtained for the presence of a uricosuric agent in the plasma of patients with acquired or hereditary renal hypouricemia. Infusing the plasma of a hypouricemic patient with Hodgkin's disease into a *Cebus albifrons* monkey did not affect urate clearance.[152] Furthermore, studies in rabbit kidney slices failed to detect any abnormal uricosuric agent in the plasma of several renal hypouricemic subjects.[153]

The Dalmatian Coach Hound. This breed of dogs is of interest in this connection. It differs from other dogs in that it is relatively hyperuricemic and hyperuricosuric and exhibits increased renal urate clearance.[154–161] The relative hyperuricemia and hyperuricosuria in this breed of dogs was demonstrated to reflect a defective uric acid transport into hepatocytes, the uricase-containing tissue.[162] On the other hand, the reason for the increased renal urate clearance has not been clarified. It could

reflect a urate transport defect in the kidney or in all tissues.[164] Moreover, data are available which suggest that the increased renal urate clearance in this dog reflects the presence of a uricosuric substance produced in the Dalmatian liver. The results of the liver transplantation experiments performed by Kuster et al.[163,164] support this hypothesis. These investigators found that when non-Dalmatian dogs received Dalmatian livers, the renal clearance and excretion of uric acid increased to values typical of Dalmatians and that when Dalmatians received non-Dalmatian livers, the parameters diminished to those typical for non-Dalmatians. These results were taken to indicate that the Dalmatian liver is responsible for both the increased amount of excreted urate and the increased renal urate clearance. According to the results of this study, the increased renal urate clearance in the Dalmatian is caused by an abnormal metabolite produced in the liver.

An additional support for the possibility that a humoral substance may affect renal urate transport and therefore that abnormality in such a substance may be the primary defect in hereditary renal hypouricemia may be drawn from the finding that in the rabbit a serum protein was found to modulate, by allosteric modification, the basolateral transporter associated with urate secretion (see above).[87]

Fig. 106-6 Urine excretion of orally administered [^{14}C]labeled uric acid. (●) indicates patient with hereditary renal hypouricemia; (○) and (△) are normal subjects. (*From Sperling et al.[143] Used by permission.*)

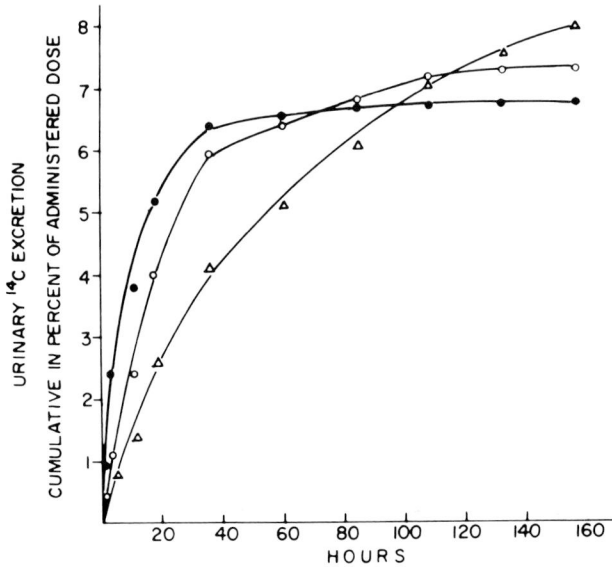

CLINICAL SIGNIFICANCE

The hypouricemia in the syndrome is generally discovered during screening procedures mainly for various diseases such as osteoporosis, familial hypercholesterolemia, urolithiasis, polyarthralgia, stomatitis, neurologic disorders, glomerulonephritis, idiopathic edema, noncongenital colloid goiter, etc. All these diseases, except for urolithiasis, are unrelated to the renal hypouricemia.

Hypouricemia. The hypouricemia as such has, as far as is known, no clinical significance. Indeed, speculatively, the hypouricemia might be advantageous in avoiding the risks associated with hyperuricemia, mainly the various clinical manifestations of urate crystal deposition disease.

Hyperuricosuria. In three patients with hereditary renal hypouricemia, the hypouricemia was associated with a marked hyperuricosuria, the urinary uric acid excretion exceeding 1000 mg/day. Furthermore, hyperuricosuria, although moderate, was present in many of the other hypouricemic propositi. Thus, hyperuricosuria appears to be a constant feature of isolated renal hypouricemia. Principally, the hyperuricosuria might reflect purine overproduction or diversion of intestinal urate elimination to urinary urate excretion consequent to the hypouricemia. There is no evidence in the hypouricemic-hyperuricosuric subjects for purine overproduction. Incorporation of [^{12}N]glycine into urinary uric acid was measured in one such patient and was found to be moderately excessive,[38] probably reflecting the decreased intestinal urate disposal. Normal [^{15}N]glycine incorporation was found in another hypouricemic uric acid stone–forming patient as well as in two hypouricemic patients in whom familiality was not proven.[51]

Hypercalciuria. Hypercalciuria was found to accompany the renal hypouricemia in six of the propositi.[34,36,41,42,46] It may be classified as "idiopathic hypercalciuria" in all of these subjects, as there was no detectable etiology. In three,[34,41] the hypercalciuria was proven to be of the hyperabsorptive type, e.g., secondary to increased intestinal calcium absorption. Thus far, evidence has not been obtained for a primary abnormality in renal calcium handling in any of these hypouricemic–idiopathic hypercalciuric patients. Thus, at this stage of knowledge, the renal tubular defect leading to hypouricemia may be considered as isolated tubular abnormality in these subjects until proven otherwise. The apparently frequent association between the renal defect for urate handling and intestinal calcium hyperabsorption is as yet unexplained.

Urolithiasis. Five out of the 21 propositi with inborn isolated renal hypouricemia[34,39,41,43] had urinary calculi. Three uric acid stones, one calcium oxalate stone, and one stone of unidentified composition were identified. In four other propositi,[49] urolithiasis was present in other family members. The

high incidence of urolithiasis among the subjects with hereditary renal hypouricemia may be explained by the occurrence of hyperuricosuria and of hypercalciuria among these subjects. Indeed, the patients who had uric acid stones had the most significant hyperuricosuria (more than 1000 mg/day). It is not surprising that not all the hypouricemic patients had evidence of urolithiasis since hyperuricosuria or hypercalciuria are important, but not the only determinants in the causation of stone formation.

Decreased Bone Density. Decreased bone density was found to be associated with the hypercalciuria in two renal hypouricemic sibs,[36] and osteoporosis was found in a 4-year-old boy with hereditary renal hypouricemia.[49] Similar abnormalities have not been observed in the other reported hypouricemic families. The association between renal hypouricemia and decreased bone density remains therefore unexplained.

Genetics

Hereditary renal hypouricemia occurs when two mutant autosomal alleles occur at the locus which controls the urate transport site. Known consanguinity in parents of hypouricemic children in 5 out of the 21 families,[35–38,42] demonstrates the recessive mode of inheritance of the trait (Fig. 106-7). In one family,[43] a dominant mode was suggested in view of the finding that the propositus had three hypouricemic daughters, without consanguinity. Nevertheless, the serum uric acid levels reported for these daughters (2.0, 2.2, and 2.4 mg/dl) could very well represent heterozygosity rather than homozygosity. There is no evidence for X-linkage in the reported pedigrees. In at least five of the pedigrees,[35–37,40,41] both sexes were affected.

It is of interest that in addition to exhibiting the same mode of inheritance, the vast majority of patients with hereditary renal hypouricemia (12 to 18 out of the 19 propositi in whom the pyrazinamide and probenecid tests were performed) were

Fig. 106-7 Pedigrees of consanguineous families with hereditary renal hypouricemia. (A from Akaoka et al.;[37] B from Akaoka et al.;[38] C from Weitz and Sperling;[42] D from Sperling et al.;[36] all used by permission.)

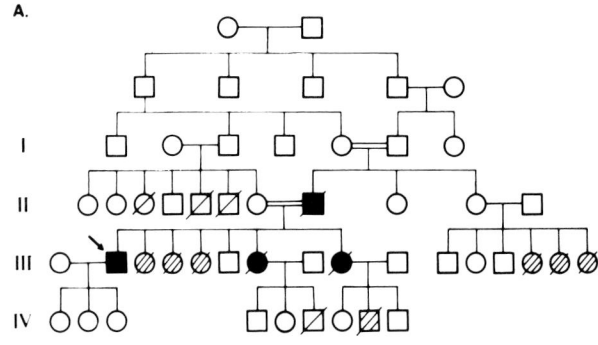

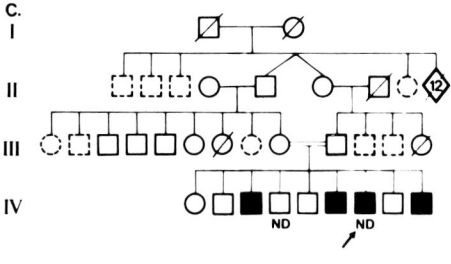

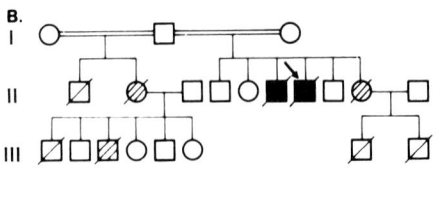

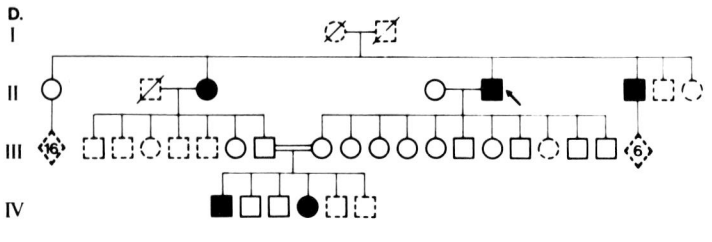

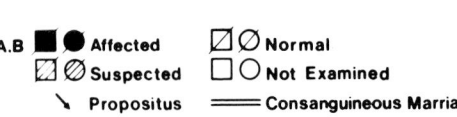

A,B ■● Affected   ▨⊘ Normal
    ▨⊘ Suspected □○ Not Examined
    ＼ Propositus ══ Consanguineous Marriage

C,D ■● Affected   ▨⊘ Deceased
    □○ Normal   ＼ Propositus
    ⸨⸩○ Not Examined   ND= Neurological Disorder

classified as affected with the same type of reabsorption defect—at the presecretory site. Moreover, in none of the families with hereditary renal hypouricemia could an isolated defect for the postsecretory reabsorption site be demonstrated, although such a defect was suggested in other conditions of renal hypouricemia (see above). These findings may be taken to suggest that the presecretory and postsecretory reabsorption sites for urate in the proximal tubule are controlled by different genes.

Another point of interest is that all cases of hereditary renal hypouricemia reported from Israel[36,39–42,46] were Jews of non-Ashkenazic (i.e., Sephardic) origin: five were Iraqi, one was Libyan, and one was Turkish. It appears likely, therefore, that hereditary renal hypouricemia is relatively common among non-Ashkenazic Jews.

Treatment

As indicated above, urolithiasis is the only clinical manifestation which may be associated with hereditary renal hypouricemia. The urolithiasis is probably the result of the hyperuricosuria and the hypercalciuria found to be common in these patients. Thus, it is advisable to study the affected subjects carefully for these parameters and to treat them accordingly. High fluid intake and control of urinary pH may suffice to prevent uric acid stones.[165] In some cases, in which uric acid excretion is markedly excessive, allopurinol may be needed to reduce uric acid excretion. For prevention of calcium stones, patients exhibiting marked hypercalciuria should be treated by conventional means.

REFERENCES

1. PRAETORIUS E, KIRK JE: Hypouricemia with evidence for tubular elimination of uric acid. *J Lab Clin Med* 35:856, 1950.
2. MIKKELSEN WM, DODGE HJ, VALKENBURG H: The distribution of serum uric acid values in a population unselected as to gout or hypouricemia. *Am J Med* 39:242, 1965.
3. RAMSDELL CM, KELLEY WN: The clinical significance of hypouricemia. *Ann Intern Med* 78:239, 1973.
4. DWOSH IL, RONCARI DAK, MARLISS E, FOX IH: Hypouricemia in disease: A study of different mechanisms. *J Lab Clin Med* 90:153, 1977.
5. WYNGAARDEN JB, KELLEY WN: Miscellaneous forms of hypouricemia, in *Gout and Hyperuricemia*. New York, Grune & Stratton, 1976, p 411.
6. WALLIS IA, EAGLE RI: The adult Fanconi syndrome. II. Review of eighteen cases. *Am J Med* 22:13, 1957.
7. LEE DBN, DRINKARD JP, ROSEN VJ, GNICK HC: The adult Fanconi syndrome: Observation on etiology, morphology, renal functions and mineral metabolism in three patients. *Medicine* 51:107, 1972.
8. MEISEL AD, DIAMOND HS: Hyperuricosuria in the Fanconi syndrome. *Am J Med Sci* 274:109, 1977.
9. BARON DN, DENT CE, HARRIS H, HARD EW, JEBSON JB: Hereditary pellagra-like skin rash with temporary cerebellar ataxia, constant renal aminoaciduria and other bizarre biochemical features. *Lancet* 2:421, 1956.
10. DENT CE, PHILPOT GR: Xanthinuria, an inborn error (or deviation) of metabolism. *Lancet* 1:182, 1954.
11. HOLMES EW, WYNGAARDEN JB: Hereditary xanthinuria, in Stanbury JB, Wyngaarden JB, Fredrickson DS, Goldstein JL, Brown MS (eds): *The Metabolic Basis of Inherited Disease*, 5th ed. New York, McGraw-Hill, 1983, p 1192.
12. GIBLETT ER, AMMAN AJ, SANDMAN R, WARA DW, DIAMOND LK: Nucleoside phosphorylase deficiency in a child with severely defective T-cell immunity and normal B-cell immunity. *Lancet* 1:1010, 1975.
13. MORGAN HG, STEEWART WK, LOWE KG, STOWERS JM, JOHNSTONE JH: Wilson's disease and the Fanconi syndrome. *Q J Med* 31:361, 1962.
14. LEU ML, STRICKLAND GT, GUTMAN RA: Renal function in Wilson's disease: Response to penicillamine therapy. *Am J Med Sci* 250:381, 1970.
15. ELSAS LJ, HAYSLETT JP, SPARGO BH, DURANT JL, ROSENBERG LE: Wilson's disease with reversible renal tubular dysfunction. *Ann Intern Med* 75:127, 1971.
16. WILSON DB, GOLDSTEIN NP: Renal urate excretion in patients with Wilson's disease. *Kidney Int* 4:331, 1973.
17. SCHNEIDER JA, SCHULMAN JD, SEEGMILLER JE: Cystinosis and the Fanconi syndrome, in Stanbury JB, Wyngaarden JB, Fredrickson DS (eds): *The Metabolic Basis of Inherited Disease*, 4th ed. New York, McGraw-Hill, 1978, p 1660.
18. CUSWORTH DC, DENT CE, FLYNN FV: The amino-aciduria in galactosaemia. *Arch Dis Child* 30:150, 1955.
19. LAMIERE N, MUSSCHE M, BACLE G, KINT J, RINGOIR S: Hereditary fructose intolerance: A difficult diagnosis in the adult. *Am J Med* 65:416, 1978.
20. BECK IH: Hypouricemia in the syndrome of inappropriate secretion of antidiuretic hormone. *N Engl J Med* 301:528, 1979.
21. OSTERLIND K, HANSEN M, DOMBERNOWSKY P: Hypouricemia and inappropriate secretion of antidiuretic hormone in small cell bronchogenic carcinoma. *Acta Med Scand* 209:289, 1981.
22. WEINBERGER A, SANTO M, SOLOMON F, SHALIT M, PINKHAS J, SPERLING O: Abnormality in renal urate handling in the syndrome of inappropriate secretion of antidiuretic hormone. *Isr J Med Sci* 18:711, 1982.
23. SMITHLINE N, KASSIRER JP, COHEN JJ: Light-chain nephropathy. *N Engl J Med* 294:71, 1976.
24. BENNETT JS, BOND J, SINGER I, GOTTLIEB AJ: Hypouricemia in Hodgkin's disease. *Ann Intern Med* 76:751, 1972.
25. WEINSTEIN B, IRREVERRE F, WATKIN DM: Lung carcinoma, hypouricemia and aminoaciduria. *Am J Med* 39:520, 1965.
26. COOPER DS: Oat-cell carcinoma and severe hypouricemia. *N Engl J Med* 288:321, 1973.
27. GORSHEIN D, ASBELL S: Ectopic production of hormones in tumors. *JAMA* 235:2716, 1976.
28. WEINBERGER A, PINKHAS J, SPERLING O, DE VRIES A: Frequency and causes of hypouricemia in hospital patients. *Isr J Med Sci* 13:529, 1977.
29. CHISHOLM JJ JR, HARRISON HC, EVERLEIN WR, HARRISON HE: Amino-aciduria, hypophosphatemia and rickets in lead poisoning, *Am J Dis Child* 89:159, 1955.
30. CLARKSON TW, KENCH JE: Urinary excretion of amino acids by men absorbing heavy metals. *Biochem J* 62:361, 1965.
31. GROSS JM: Fanconi syndrome (adult type) developing secondary to the ingestion of outdated tetracycline. *Ann Intern Med* 48:523, 1963.
32. SCHLOSSTEIN L, KIPPEN I, BLUESTONE R, WHITEHOUSE MW, KLINENBERG JR: Association between hypouricemia and jaundice. *Ann Rheum Dis* 33:308, 1974.
33. MICHELIS MF, WARMS PC, FUSCO RD, DAVIS BB: Hypouricemia and hyperuricosuria in Laennec cirrhosis. *Arch Intern Med* 134:681, 1974.
34. GREENE ML, MARCUS R, AURBACH GD, KAZAM ES, SEEGMILLER JH: Hypouricemia due to isolated renal tubular defect. *Am J Med* 53:361, 1972.
35. KHACHADURIAN AK, ARSLANIAN MJ: Hypouricemia due to renal uricosuria. *Ann Intern Med* 78:547, 1972.
36. SPERLING O, WEINBERGER A, OLIVER I, LIBERMAN UA, DE VRIES A: Hypouricemia, hypercalciuria and decreased bone density: A hereditary syndrome. *Ann Intern Med* 80:482, 1974.
37. AKAOKA I, NISHIZAWA T, YANO E, TAKEUCHI A, NISHIDA Y, YOSHIMURA T, HORIUCHI Y: Familial hypouricemia due to renal tubular defect of urate transport. *Ann Clin Res* 7:316, 1975.
38. AKAOKA I, NISHIZAWA T, YANO E, KAMATANI N, NISHIDA T, SASAKI S: Renal urate excretion in five cases of hypouricemia with an isolated renal defect of urate transport. *J Rheumatol* 4:1, 1977.
39. BENJAMIN D, SPERLING O, WEINBERGER A, PINKHAS J, DE VRIES A: Familial hypouricemia due to isolated renal tubular defect. *Nephron* 18:220, 1977.
40. BENJAMIN D, SPERLING O, WEINBERGER A, PINKHAS J: Familial hypouricemia due to isolated renal tubular defect. *Biomedicine* 29:54, 1978.
41. FRANK M, MANY M, SPERLING O: Familial renal hypouricemia: Two additional cases with uric acid lithiasis. *Br J Urol* 51:88, 1979.
42. WEITZ R, SPERLING O: Hereditary renal hypouricemia: Isolated tubular defect of urate reabsorption. *J Pediatr* 96:850, 1980.
43. HEDLEY JM, PHILLIPS PJ: Familial hypouricemia and uric acid calculi: Case report. *J Clin Pathol* 33:971, 1980.
44. FUJIWARA J, TAKAMITSUE J, UEDA N, ORITA Y, ABE H: Hypouricemia due to an isolated defect in renal tubular urate reabsorption. *Clin Nephrol* 13:44, 1980.
45. DELEVELLE F, TROMBERT JC, BOUVIER MF, CANARELLI G: Hypouricemie renale idiopathique: L'observation. *Nouv Presse Med* 35:2578, 1980.
46. GARTY BZ, NITZAN M, SPERLING O: Inborn hypouricemia due to isolated defect in renal tubular uric acid transport. *Isr J Med Sci* 17:295, 1981.
47. MATSUDA O, SHIIGAI T, ITO Y, AONUMA K, TAKEUCHI J: A case of familial renal hypouricemia associated with increased secretion of PAH and idiopathic edema. *Nephron* 30:178, 1982.

48. VINAY P, GATTEREAN A, MOULIN B, GOUGOUX A, LEMIEUX G: Normal urate transport into erythrocytes in familial renal hypouricemia and in Dalmatian dog. *Can Med Assoc J* 128:545, 1983.

49. TAKEDA E, KURODA T, ITO M, TOSHIMA K, WATANABE T, ITO M, NAIKO E, YOKOTA I, HUWANG TJ, MIYAO M: Hereditary renal hypouricemia in children. *J Pediatr* 107:71, 1985.

50. SIMKIN PA, SKEITH DA, HEALY LA: Suppression of uric acid secretion in a patient with renal hypouricemia. *Adv Exp Med Biol* 41B:723, 1974.

51. KAWABE K, MURAYAMA T, AKAOKA I: A case of uric acid renal stone with hypouricemia caused by tubular reabsorption defect of uric acid. *J Urol* 116:690, 1976.

52. SORENSEN LB, LEVINSON DJ: Isolated defect in postsecretory reabsorption of uric acid. *Ann Rheum Dis* 39:180, 1980.

53. TOFUKU Y, KURODA M, TEKADA R: Hypouricemia due to renal urate wasting. *Nephron* 30:39, 1982.

54. SHICHIRI M, MATSUDA O, SHIIGAI T, TAKEUCHI J, KANAYAMA M: Hypouricemia due to an increment in renal tubular urate secretion. *Arch Intern Med* 142:1855, 1982.

55. DUMONT I, DECAUX G: Hypouricemia related to a hypersecretional tubulopathy. *Nephron* 34:256, 1983.

56. SMETANA SS, BAR-KHAYIM J: Hypouricemia due to renal tubular defect: A study with the probenecid-pyrazinamide test. *Arch Intern Med* 145:1200, 1985.

57. BERLINER RW, HILTON JG, YU TF, KENNEDY TJ JR: The renal mechanism for urate excretion in man. *J Clin Invest* 29:396, 1950.

58. GUTMAN AB, YU TF, BERGER L: Tubular secretion of urate in man. *J Clin Invest* 38:1778, 1959.

59. YU TF, BERGER L, STONE DJ, WOLF J, GUTMAN AB: Effect of pyrazinamide and pyrazinoic acid on urate clearance and other discrete renal functions. *Proc Soc Exp Biol (NY)* 96:264, 1957.

60. YU TF, BERGER L, GUTMAN AB: Suppression of tubular secretion of urate by pyrazinamide in the dog. *Proc Soc Exp Biol (NY)* 107:905, 1961.

61. STEELE TH, RIESELBACH RE: The renal mechanism for urate homeostasis in normal man. *Am J Med* 43:868, 1967.

62. WEINER IM: Urate transport in the nephron. *Am J Physiol* 237:F85, 1979.

63. ABRAMSON RG, LEVITT MF: Micropuncture study of uric acid in rat kidney. *Am J Physiol* 228:1597, 1975.

64. WYNGAARDEN JB, KELLEY WN: Gout, in Stanbury JB, Wyngaarden JB, Fredrickson DS, Goldstein JL, Brown MS (eds): *The Metabolic Basis of Inherited Disease*, 5th ed. New York, McGraw-Hill, 1983, p 1043.

65. KAHN AM, WEINMAN EJ: Urate transport in the proximal tubule: In vivo and vesicle studies. *Am J Physiol* 249:F789, 1985.

66. ROCH-RAMEL F, DIEZI-CHOMETY F, DE ROUGEMONT D, TELLIER M, WIDMER J, PETERS G: Renal excretion of uric acid in the rat: A micropuncture and microperfusion study. *Am J Physiol* 230:768, 1976.

67. ROCH-RAMEL F, DIEZI-CHOMETY F, ROTH L, WEINER IM: A micropuncture study of urate excretion by Cebus monkeys employing high performance liquid chromatography with amperometric detection of urate. *Pflugers Arch* 383:203, 1980.

68. WEINMAN EJ, STEPLOCK D, SANSOM SC, KNIGHT TF, SENEKJIAN HO: Use of high-performance liquid chromatography for determination of urate concentrations in nanoliter quantities of fluid. *Kidney Int* 19:83, 1981.

69. ROCH-RAMEL F, WEINER IM: Excretion of urate by the kidney of Cebus monkeys: A micropuncture study. *Am J Physiol* 224:1369, 1973.

70. SANSOM SC, SENEKJIAN HO, KNIGHT TF, BABINO H, STEPLOCK D, WEINMAN EJ: Determination of the apparent transport constants for urate absorption in the rat proximal tubule. *Am J Physiol* 240:F406, 1981.

71. DE ROUGEMONT D, HENCHOZ M, ROCH-RAMEL F: Renal urate excretion at various plasma concentrations in the rat: A free-flow micropuncture study. *Am J Physiol* 231:387, 1976.

72. WEINMAN EJ, SENEKJIAN HO, SANSOM SC, STEPLOCK D, SHETH A, KNIGHT TF: Evidence for active and passive urate transport in the rat proximal tubule. *Am J Physiol* 240:F90, 1981.

73. FANELLI GM JR, WEINER IM: Pyrazinoate excretion in the chimpanzee: Relation to urate disposition and the actions of uricosuric drugs. *J Clin Invest* 52:1946, 1973.

74. WEINER IM, FANELLI GM JR: Renal urate excretion in animal models. *Nephron* 14:33, 1975.

75. WEINMAN EJ, EKNOYAN G, SUKI WN: The influence of the extracellular fluid volume on the tubular reabsorption of uric acid. *J Clin Invest* 55:283, 1975.

76. WEINMAN EJ, KNIGHT TF, MCKENZIE R, EKNOYAN G: Dissociation of urate from sodium transport in the rat proximal tubule. *Kidney Int* 10:295, 1976.

77. WEINMAN EJ, STEPLOCK D, SUKI WN, EKNOYAN G: Urate reabsorption in proximal convoluted tubule of the rat kidney. *Am J Physiol* 231:509, 1976.

78. SENEKJIAN HO, KNIGHT TF, SANSOM SC, WEINMAN EJ: Effect of flow rate and the extracellular fluid volume on proximal urate and water absorption. *Kidney Int* 17:155, 1980.

79. KAHN AM, ARONSON PS: Urate transport via anion exchange in dog renal microvillus membrane vesicles. *Am J Physiol* 244:F56, 1983.

80. KAHN AM, BRANHAM S, WEINMAN EJ: Mechanism of urate and p-aminohippurate transport in rat renal microvillus membrane vesicles. *Am J Physiol* 245:F151, 1983.

81. PODEVIN R, ARDAILLOU R, PAILLARD F, FONTANELLE J, RICHET G: Étude chez l'homme de la cinetique d'apparition dans purine de l'acide urique 2 ^{14}C. *Nephron* 5:134, 1968.

82. WEINMAN EJ, SANSOM SC, STEPLOCK DA, SHETH AU, KNIGHT TF, SENEKJIAN HO: Secretion of urate in the proximal convoluted tubule of the rat. *Am J Physiol* 239:F383, 1980.

83. KRAMP RA, LENOIR RH: Characteristics of urate influx in the rat nephron. *Am J Physiol* 229:1654, 1975.

84. WEINMAN EJ, SANSOM SC, BENNETT S, KAHN AM: Effect of anion exchange inhibitors and para-aminohippurate on the transport of urate in the rat proximal tubule. *Kidney Int* 23:832, 1983.

85. PLATTS MM, MUDGE GH: Accumulation of uric acid by slices of kidney cortex. *Am J Physiol* 200:387, 1961.

86. SENEKJIAN HO, KNIGHT TF, WEINMAN EJ: Urate transport by the isolated perfused S$_2$ segment of the rabbit. *Am J Physiol* 240:F530, 1981.

87. SHIMOMURA A, CHONKO A, TANNER RM, EDWARDS R, GRANTHAM JJ: Nature of urate transport in isolated rabbit proximal tubules. *Am J Physiol* 241:F565, 1981.

88. TANNER EJ, CHONKO AM, EDWARDS RM, GRANTHAM JJ: Evidence for an inhibitor of renal urate and PAH secretion in rabbit blood. *Am J Physiol* 244:F590, 1983.

89. MOLER JV: The relation between secretion of urate and p-aminohippurate in the rabbit kidney. *J Physiol (Lond)* 192:505, 1967.

90. POULSEN H, PRAETORIUS E: Tubular excretion of uric acid in rabbits. *Acta Pharmacol Toxicol* 10:371, 1954.

91. ABRAMSON RG, KING VF, REIF MC, LEAL-PINTO E, BARUCH SB: Urate uptake in membrane vesicles of rat renal cortex: Effect of copper. *Am J Physiol* 242:F158, 1982.

92. ABRAMSON RG, LIPKOWITZ MS: Carrier-mediated concentrative urate transport in rat renal membrane vesicles. *Am J Physiol* 248:F574, 1985.

93. BLOMSTEDT JW, ARONSON PS: pH Gradient-stimulated transport of urate and p-aminohippurate in dog renal microvillus membrane vesicles. *J Clin Invest* 65:931, 1980.

94. BOUMENDIL-PODEVIN EF, PODEVIN RA, PRIOL C: Uric acid transport in brush border membrane vesicles isolated from rabbit kidney. *Am J Physiol* 236:F519, 1979.

95. GUGGINO SE, ARONSON PS: Paradoxical effects of pyrazinoate (PZA) on urate transport in dog renal brush border membrane vesicles (BBMV). *Kidney Int* 23:256, 1983.

96. KIPPEN I, HIRAYAMA B, KLINENBERG JR, WRIGHT EM: Transport of p-aminohippuric acid and glucose in highly purified rabbit renal brush border membranes. *Biochim Biophys Acta* 556:161, 1979.

97. NORD E, WRIGHT SH, KIPPEN IM, WRIGHT EM: Pathways for carboxylic acid transport by rabbit renal brush border membrane vesicles. *Am J Physiol* 243:F456, 1982.

98. GUTMAN AB, YU TF: A three-component system for regulation of renal excretion of uric acid in man. *Trans Assoc Am Physicians* 74:353, 1961.

99. MANUEL MA, STEELE TH: Pyrazinamide suppression of the uricosuric response to sodium chloride infusion. *J Lab Clin Med* 83:417, 1974.

100. STEELE TH, BONER G: Origins of the uricosuric response. *J Clin Invest* 52:1368, 1973.

101. STEELE TH: Urate secretion in man: The pyrazinamide suppression test. *Ann Intern Med* 79:734, 1973.

102. DIAMOND HS, PAOLINO JS: Evidence for a post-secretory reabsorptive site for uric acid in man. *J Clin Invest* 52:1491, 1973.

103. RIESELBACH RE, STEELE TH: Influence of the kidney upon urate homeostasis in health and disease. *Am J Med* 56:665, 1974.

104. SORENSEN LB, LEVINSON DJ: Isolated defect in postsecretory reabsorption of uric acid. *Ann Rheum Dis* 39:180, 1980.

105. ARIE R, SPERLING O: In preparation.

106. GIBSON T, SIMS HP, JIMENEZ SA: Hypouricemia and increased renal urate clearance associated with hyperparathyroidism. *Ann Rheum Dis* 35:372, 1976.

107. GRANTHAM JJ, CHONKO AM: Renal handling of organic anions and cations; metabolism and excretion of uric acid, in Brenner BM (ed): *The Kidney*, 3d ed. Philadelphia, Saunders, 1986, p 663.

108. HARKNESS RA, NICOL AD: Plasma uric acid levels in children. *Arch Dis Child* 44:773, 1969.

109. STAPELTON FB, LINSHAWM MA, HASSANCIN K, GRUSKIN AB: Uric acid excretion in normal children. *J Pediatr* 92:911, 1978.

110. STAPELTON FB: Renal uric acid clearance in human neonates. *J Pediatr* 103:290, 1983.

111. WOLFSON WO, HUNT HJ, LEVINE E, GUTTERMAN HS, COHN C, ROSENBERG EF, HUDDLESTUN B, KADOTA IC: The transport and excretion of uric acid in man V. A sex differential in urate metabolism; with a note on clinical and laboratory findings in gouty women. *J Clin Exp* 9:749, 1949.

112. SCOTT JT, POLLARD AC: Uric acid excretion in relatives of patients with gout. *Ann Rheum Dis* 29:397, 1970.

113. NICHOLLS A, SNAITH MZ, SCOTT JT: Effect of estrogen therapy on plasma and urinary levels of uric acid. *Br Med J* 1:449, 1973.

114. STEELE TH: Evidence for altered renal urate reabsorption during changes in volume of the extracellular fluid. *J Lab Clin Med* 74:288, 1969.

115. CANNON PJ, SVAHN DS, DEMARTINI FF: The influence of hypertonic saline infusions upon the fractional reabsorption of urate and other ions in normal and hypertensive man. *Circulation* 41:97, 1970.

116. DIAMOND H, MEISEL A: Influence of volume expansion, serum sodium and fractional excretion of sodium on urate excretion. *Pflugers Arch* 356:47, 1975.

117. STEELE TH, OPPENHEIMER S: Factors affecting urate excretion following diuretic administration in man. *Am J Med* 47:564, 1969.

118. STEELE TH, MANUEL MA, BONER G: Diuretics, urate excretion and sodium reabsorption: A test of acetazolamide and urinary alkalinization. *Nephron* 11:48, 1975.

119. ENGLE JE, STEELE TH: Variation of urate excretion with urine flow in normal man. *Nephron* 16:50, 1976.

120. MEISEL A, DIAMOND H: Effect of vasopressin on uric acid excretion: Evidence for distal nephron reabsorption of urate in man. *Clin Sci Mol Med* 51:33, 1976.

121. MEES EJD, BLOM VAN ASSENDELFT P, NIEUVEENHUIS MG: Elevation of uric acid clearance caused by inappropriate antidiuretic hormone secretion. *Acta Med Scand* 189:69, 1971.

122. GORDON P, ROBERTSON GL, SEEGMILLER JE: Hyperuricemia, a concomitant congenital vasopressin-resistant diabetes insipidus in the adult. *N Engl J Med* 284:1057, 1971.

123. EMMERSON BT: Abnormal urate excretion associated with renal and systemic disorders, drugs and toxins, in Kelley WN, Weiner IM (eds): *Handbook of Experimental Pharmacology, Uric Acid*. Berlin, Springer-Verlag, 1978, vol 51, p 287.

124. YU TF, GUTMAN AB: Paradoxical retention of uric acid by uricosuric drugs in low dosage. *Proc Soc Exp Biol Med* 90:542, 1955.

125. YU TF, GUTMAN AB: Study of the paradoxical effects of salicylate in low, intermediate and high dosage on the renal mechanisms for excretion of urate in man. *J Clin Invest* 38:1298, 1959.

126. MANUEL MA, STEELE TH: Changes in renal urate handling after prolonged thiazide treatment. *Am J Med* 57:741, 1974.

127. DEMARTINI FE: Hypouricemia induced by drugs. *Arthritis Rheum* 8:823, 1965.

128. STEWART RJ, CHONKO AM: Pharmacologic inhibition of urate transport across perfused and non-perfused rabbit proximal straight tubules. *Kidney Int* 19:258, 1981.

129. REESE OG JR, STEELE TH: Renal transport of urate during diuretic-induced hypouricemia. *Am J Med* 60:973, 1978.

130. NEMATI M, KYLE MC, FREIS ED: Clinical study of ticrynafen. *JAMA* 237:652, 1977.

131. GROBNER TO, ZOLLNER N: Uricosuria, in Gicht, *Handbuch der Inn Med*, 5th ed, vol 7, *Stoff wechsel krankheiten*, part 3. Berlin, Heidelberg, New York, Springer, 1976, p 491.

132. DAYTON PG, YU TF, CHEN W, BERGER L, WESTM LA, GUTMAN AB: The physiological disposition of probenecid, including renal clearance in man, studied by an improved method for its estimation in biological material. *J Pharmacol Exp Ther* 140:278, 1963.

133. DE VRIES A, SPERLING O: Implications of disorders of purine metabolism for the kidney and the urinary tract, in *Purine and Pyrimidine Metabolism, Ciba Foundation Symp 48 (New Series)*. Amsterdam, Elsevier, 1977, p 179.

134. STEELE TH, RIESELBACH RE: The renal mechanism for urate homeostasis in normal man. *Am J Med* 43:868, 1967.

135. YU TF, BERGER L, STONE DJ, WOLF J, GUTMAN AB: Effects of pyrazinamide and pyrazinoic acid on urate clearance and other discrete renal functions. *Proc Soc Exp Biol Med* 96:264, 1957.

136. YU TF, BERGER L, GUTMAN AB: Suppression of the tubular secretion of urate by pyrazinamide in the dog. *Proc Soc Exp Biol Med* 107:905, 1961.

137. DAVIS BB, FIELD JB, RODNAN GP, KEDES LH: Localization and pyrazinamide inhibition of distal transtubular movement of uric acid-2-^{14}C with a modified stop-flow technique. *J Clin Invest* 44:716, 1965.

138. GUTMAN A, YU TF, BERGER L: Renal function in gout. III. Estimation of tubular secretion and reabsorption of uric acid by use of pyrazinamide (pyrazinoic acid). *Am J Med* 47:575, 1969.

139. WEINER IM, TINKER JP: Pharmacology of pyrazinamide: Metabolic and renal function studies related to the mechanism of drug-induced urate retention. *J Pharmacol Exp Ther* 180:411, 1972.

140. KRAMP RA, LASSITER WE, GOTTSCHALK CW: Urate-2-^{14}C transport in the rat nephron. *J Clin Invest* 50:35, 1971.

141. FRANKFURT SJ, WEINMAN EJ: Pyrazinoic acid and urate transport in the rat. *Proc Soc Exp Biol Med* 159:16, 1978.

142. GUGGINO SE, ARONSON PS: Paradoxical effects of pyrazinoate and nicotinate on urate transport in dog renal microvillus membranes. *J Clin Invest* 76:543, 1985.

143. SPERLING O, BOER P, WEINBERGER A, DE VRIES A: Transport into erythrocytes and intestinal absorption of uric acid in hereditary renal hypouricemia. *Biomedicine* 23:157, 1975.

144. HANSEN KO, LASSEN UV: Active transport of uric acid through the human erythrocyte membrane. *Nature* 4685:553, 1959.

145. HARVEY AM, CHRISTENSEN HN: Uric acid transport system. Apparent absence in erythrocytes of Dalmatian coach hounds. *Science* 145:826, 1964.

146. OH JH, DOSSETOR JB, BECK IT: Kinetics of uric acid transport and its production in rat small intestine. *Can J Physiol Pharmacol* 45:121, 1967.

147. WILSON DW, WILSON HC: Studies "in vitro" of the digestion and absorption of purine ribonucleotides by the intestine. *J Biol Chem* 237:1643, 1962.

148. THIER SO, SEGAL S: Cystinuria, in Stanbury JB, Wyngaarden JB, Fredrickson DS (eds): *The Metabolic Basis of Inherited Disease*, 3d ed. New York, McGraw-Hill, 1972, p 1504.

149. SCRIVER CR: Familial iminoglycinuria, in Stanbury JB, Wyngaarden JB, Fredrickson DS (eds): *The Metabolic Basis of Inherited Disease*, 3d ed. New York, McGraw-Hill, 1972, p 1520.

150. JEPSON JB: Hartnup disease, in Stanbury JB, Wyngaarden JB, Fredrickson DS (eds): *The Metabolic Basis of Inherited Disease*, 3d ed. New York, McGraw-Hill, 1972, p 1486.

151. WEINBERGER A, WEINBERGER A, SPERLING O, BEN-BASSAT M, KAPLAN I, PINKHAS J: Increased uric acid clearance in patients with burns. *Biomed Express* 27:277, 1977.

152. KAY NE, GOTLIEB AJ: Hypouricemia in Hodgkin's disease: Report of an additional case. *Cancer* 32:1508, 1973.

153. GARTI M, SPERLING O: Unpublished observations.

154. BRIGGS OM, SPERLING O: Uric acid metabolism in the Dalmatian coach hound. *J S Afr Vet Assoc* 53:201, 1982.

155. FRIEDMAN M, BYERS SD: Observations concerning the causes of the excess excretion of uric acid in the Dalmatian dog. *J Biol Chem* 175:727, 1948.

156. KESSLER RH, HIERHOLZER K, GURD RS: Localization of urate transport in the nephron of mongrel and Dalmatian dog kidney. *Am J Physiol Ther* 197:601, 1959.

157. MUDGE GH, GUCCHI J, PLATTS M, O'CONNELL JMB, BERNDT WO: Renal excretion of uric acid in the dog. *Am J Physiol* 215:404, 1968.

158. MUDGE GH, BERNDT WO, VALTIN H: Tubular transport of urea, glucose, phosphate, uric acid, sulphate and thiosulphate, in Orloff J, Berliner BW (eds): *Handbook of Physiology: Renal Physiology*. Washington, DC, American Physiological Society 1973, vol 19, p 587.

159. MYERS VC, HANZAL RF: The metabolism of methylxanthines and their related methyluric acids. *J Biol Chem* 162:309, 1946.

160. YOUNG EG, CONWAY CF, CRANDALL WA: On the purine metabolism of the Dalmatian coach hound. *Biochem J* 32:1138, 1938.

161. ZINS GR, WEINER IM: Bidirectional urate transport limited to the proximal tubule in dogs. *Am J Physiol* 215:411, 1968.

162. KLEMPERER FW, TRIMBLE HC, HASTINGS AB: The uricase of dogs, including the Dalmatian. *J Biol Chem* 125:445, 1938.

163. KUSTER G, SHORTER RG, DAWSON B, HALLENBECK GA: Effect of allogenic hepatic transplantation between Dalmatian and mongrel dogs on urinary excretion of uric acid. *Surg Forum* 18:360, 1967.

164. KUSTER G, SHORTER RG, DAWSON B, HALLENBECK GA: Uric acid metabolism in Dalmatian and other dogs. *Arch Intern Med* 129:492, 1972.

165. SPERLING O: Uric acid nephrolithiasis, in Wickham JEA, Buck AC (eds): *Renal Tract Stone, Metabolic Basis and Clinical Practice*. London, Churchill Livingstone, in press.

CHAPTER 107

LYSOSOMAL TRANSPORT DISORDERS:
Cystinosis and Sialic Acid Storage Disorders

WILLIAM A. GAHL
MARTIN RENLUND
JESS G. THOENE

1. *Cystinosis and Salla disease are rare lysosomal disorders due to defective carrier-mediated transport of the amino acid cystine and the charged monosaccharide sialic acid, respectively, across the lysosomal membrane. The major clinical manifestation of cystinosis is renal failure at approximately 10 years of age. Salla disease is characterized by various degrees of psychomotor retardation. Both are autosomal recessively inherited disorders.*

2. *In cystinosis, free, nonprotein cystine accumulates to 10 to 1000 times normal levels and forms crystals within the lysosomes of most tissues, which are damaged at different rates. Cystinosis can be diagnosed by the elevated cystine content of leukocytes or cultured fibroblasts or by slit-lamp examination showing corneal crystals in patients over 1 year of age.*

3. *Children with cystinosis are normal at birth but develop signs of the renal tubular Fanconi syndrome, generally between 6 and 12 months of age. These include dehydration, acidosis, vomiting, electrolyte imbalances, hypophosphatemic rickets, and failure to grow. Weight is proportional to height. Head circumference and intelligence are spared. Other manifestations of cystinosis include photophobia, hypothyroidism, and decreased ability to sweat. Renal glomerular damage progresses inexorably, requiring dialysis or transplantation at 6 to 12 years of age. Cystine storage does not occur in the donor kidney, but continued accumulation in the host tissue results in blindness, corneal erosions, diabetes mellitus, and neurologic deterioration in a significant number of postrenal transplant patients 13 to 30 years old.*

4. *Therapy for cystinosis includes replacement of renal losses due to the Fanconi syndrome, provision of thyroxine and insulin for deficient patients, and symptomatic care of ophthalmic complaints. In young patients, chronic cystine-depleting therapy with the free thiol cysteamine improves growth and preserves renal function. Cysteamine eye drops can dissolve corneal crystals in young children.*

5. *The clinical course and severity of cystine accumulation in cystinosis varies in different kindreds, from benign cystinosis in adults with corneal crystals but no renal disease to intermediate cystinosis in adolescents with late-onset renal deterioration, and finally to classic nephropathic cystinosis in infants. Heterozygotes for all types of cystinosis are entirely normal clinically. Cystinosis can be diagnosed in utero by cystine measurements in amniocytes or chorionic villi.*

6. *The free sialic acid storage disorders include Salla disease and the more severe infantile free sialic acid storage disease (ISSD). Patients with these two diseases store, respectively, approximately 10- and 100-fold normal amounts of unbound N-acetylneuraminic acid in their tissues, and excrete 10 and 100 times normal amounts in the urine. Cellular lysomes are engorged by the storage material, which accumulates due to impaired free sialic acid transport across the lysosomal membrane.*

7. *Patients with Salla disease, a disorder largely of the Finnish population, are normal at birth, but develop psychomotor delay and ataxia between 3 and 12 months of age. Intelligence is moderately to severely impaired, but life span is only slightly reduced. In contrast, patients with ISSD can present at birth and succumb in the first few years of life. They generally have hepatosplenomegaly, dysostosis multiplex, coarse facial features, and severe mental and motor retardation. There are fewer than 100 Salla disease patients known and fewer than 10 ISSD cases reported.*

8. *Both sialic acid storage disorders can be diagnosed based on the presence of sialuria and histologic evidence of lysosomal storage. Prenatal diagnosis is available. Only symptomatic therapy can be offered for patients with these diseases.*

Cystinosis and Salla disease are specific lysosomal storage disorders resulting from defective transport of cystine and sialic acid (Fig. 107-1), respectively, across the lysosomal membrane. The term *cystinosis* can refer to one of several variants of the disease but, unless specified, here denotes nephropathic cystinosis, which results in renal failure at approximately 10 years of age. Salla disease, a disorder most prevalent in Finland, represents the most common inborn error associated with lysosomal storage of free sialic acid; patients with more extensive clinical and biochemical involvement are considered to have infantile free sialic acid storage disease (ISSD). All patients with sialic acid storage disorders suffer some degree of psychomotor retardation. Cystine and sialic acid serve as prototypes for amino acids and monosaccharides having carriers within the lysosomal membrane, and cystinosis and free sialic acid storage diseases represent examples of an emerging group of metabolic disorders due to defective integral lysosomal membrane proteins.

CYSTINOSIS

Historical Aspects

The current understanding of cystinosis as an inherited, multisystemic disease resulting from failure of lysosomal cystine transport follows from more than eight decades of both clinical and laboratory research. A number of basic issues required

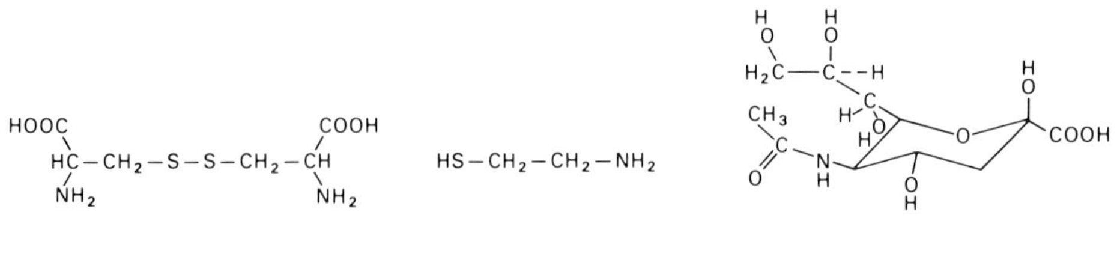

Fig. 107-1 Structures of the disulfide amino acid cystine, which is stored in cystinosis; the aminothiol cysteamine, which depletes cells of cystine; and the charged sugar N-acetylneuraminic acid, which is stored in free sialic acid storage disorders.

investigation: (1) What is the clinical phenotype of the disease? (2) Is cystinosis different from renal Fanconi syndrome and cystinuria? (3) Where is the cystine stored? (4) Do the crystals form *in situ* or are they phagocytosed from preformed crystals in the extracellular fluid? (5) What is the source of the stored cystine? (6) Why does the cystine accumulate? (7) What causes the renal failure in cystinosis? (8) How can the disease be treated? The answers to these questions are now known, but with various degrees of certitude.

The first known description of cystinosis appeared in 1903 in a publication in the *Zeitschrift f. Physiologie Chemie* by Emil Abderhalden in which a family from Basel was described.[1] The propositus was a 21½-month-old boy who died of inanition and whose organs had a grossly white appearance with punctate lesions throughout. Classic chemical analysis demonstrated an identity between the stored material and the amino acid cystine. Two sibs had died of inanition similar to the index case. Two other children and a grandfather were reported to excrete excessive amounts of cystine in the urine. If correct, this could be explained by the possibility that the genes for both cystinosis and cystinuria were present in this family.

Subsequent work appearing in the 1930s identified cystinosis as one cause of nondiabetic glycosuria and noted the association of renal rickets and primary growth failure[2] in the disorder which at that time was termed *De Toni-Fabre'-Fanconi* syndrome. In 1937, cystine crystals in the glomeruli were described in a condition called *Cystinkrankheit*.[3] Aminoaciduria in cystinosis, first described in 1936 by Fanconi, was extensively studied by Dent who, in 1947, also quantified the extent of polyuria, glucosuria, phosphaturia, and proteinuria.[4] Dent also noted that the generalized aminoaciduria in cystinosis was not due to "overflow" of plasma amino acids and that no obvious error of sulfur amino acid metabolism was present in these patients. Further details on the early investigations of this disorder are available elsewhere.[5–7]

The clear distinction between cystinosis and cystinuria was first provided in 1949,[8] when the familial nature of both diseases was recognized and the rarity of cystine stones in patients with cystinosis was appreciated.

In 1952, Bickel and colleagues proposed the name *Lignac-Fanconi disease* for the condition known as *cystinosis* and described it as cystine storage disease with aminoaciduria.[9] They emphasized the pathognomonic finding of cystine crystals in the cornea and bone marrow. The generalized aminoaciduria present in cystinosis was distinguished from the specific aminoaciduria found in cystinuria, phenylketonuria, and other inborn errors known at that time. It was incorrectly concluded that cystinosis and renal tubular Fanconi syndrome of childhood were one and the same disease but correctly surmised that the cystine storage and aminoaciduria were not the result of a primary kidney dysfunction, but rather of a generalized disturbance of amino acid metabolism. A review of the occur-

rence of de Toni-Fanconi syndrome and cystinosis was provided by Worthen and Good in 1958.[10]

In 1962, electron microscopy of renal biopsy specimens demonstrated hexagonal crystals between tubules in the kidney, and the pathognomonic "swan neck" deformity of the proximal tubule was confirmed on light microscopy.[11] Vacuolation and swelling of the endoplasmic reticulum were noted, and cytoplasmic bodies were found in the apical and central portions of the cell, frequently with coarse granules in the proximal convoluted tubule. It was concluded that crystallization of cystine between cells, secondary to some unknown primary metabolic or enzymatic defect, led to the renal pathology.

In 1925, the nephrotoxic effects of both oral and intravenous cystine were investigated. Feeding cystine to rabbits produced albuminuria and azotemia, without cystinuria.[12] The intravenous injection of gram quantities of cystine into dogs produced glomerular necrosis and calcium deposition.[13] Other amino acids similarly administered did not cause renal injury. In these studies, it was apparent that increased extracellular cystine damaged renal cells. In cystinosis, crystallizing levels of intracellular cystine, i.e., lysosomal cystine, also produce renal damage, perhaps by breaking open the lysosomes and releasing their toxic contents.

The modern era of clinical investigation into cystinosis began in 1967 when the intracellular nature of the cystine storage was defined. These studies not only identified the lysosome as a focal point for future research, they also established the feasibility of using cultured fibroblasts for such pursuits. They led to an exposition of the mechanism of cystine storage in cystinosis, a demonstration of cystine depletion and clinical benefit attributable to treatment with the free thiol cysteamine, and the discovery of a new class of inborn errors of metabolism due to defective transport of small molecules across the lysosomal membrane. In this process, cystinosis proved a paradigm for the interaction of clinical and basic research, and it continues to serve in that capacity.

The Basic Defect

Cystine. Cystine, the disulfide of the amino acid cysteine, has a molecular weight of 240.3. Cystine and cysteine participate in a reversible oxidation-reduction reaction whose redox potential is -0.22 eV[14] or even more negative.[15] In the presence of oxygen, cysteine is rapidly oxidized to cystine. Cystine's two carboxyl groups and two amine residues have pK_a's of <1, 1.7, 7.48, and 9.02, respectively[16]; its net charge at physiological pH is zero, and its pI is 4.60.[16] The disulfide's solubility in water at 25°C approximates only 0.5 mM at pH 7.0,[12] but heating or the use of small volumes of dilute (0.01 N) acid or alkali facilitates crystal dissolution. Human plasma at 37°C and pH 7.3 can dissolve approximately 1.67 mM cystine.[5] Cystine's insolubility in alcohol provides the basis for proper preservation of cystine crystals in tissue specimens, i.e., alcohol fixation.

CYSTINE METABOLISM. Cysteine results from protein hydrolysis and from *de novo* synthesis, its sulfur atom derived from the essential amino acid, methionine. In the metabolism of methionine, the transsulfuration pathway yields homocysteine, which combines with serine to form cystathionine, the proximate precursor of cysteine through the enzymatic activity of cystathionase (see Chap. 23). In conditions in which cystathionine β-synthase or cystathionase is deficient,[17] e.g., in homocystinuria or cystathioninuria, or in normal human fetuses and neonates,[18] cysteine becomes an essential amino acid. Cysteine or cystine is also required for the growth of normal human fibroblasts[19] but not normal human lymphoid cells[20] in culture. In vivo, cysteine is oxidized to inorganic sulfate for excretion in the urine, or is reutilized for protein synthesis and the formation of free thiols such as glutathione (GSH, γ-glutamylcysteinylglycine).

Most cellular cyst(e)ine exists as the free thiol, cysteine, because of an abundance of GSH and the enzymatic reducing systems for disulfides present within the cytosol. These consist of two types, nucleotide-dependent reductases and GSH-disulfide transhydrogenases.[21] The latter system appears more important, since the reduced glutathione concentration of cells approaches 10 mM, at least in liver.[22] Cystine and free thiols such as GSH participate in a disulfide interchange reaction[23] to form cysteine and cysteine-GSH mixed disulfide; a second reaction between reduced GSH and the mixed disulfide produces cysteine and oxidized glutathione. The same type of reaction provides the basis for the reduction of cystine by cysteamine (see "Mechanism of Cystine Depletion," below). These disulfide interchange reactions and their products occur within the cytosol, and isolated reports of lysosomal cystine-reducing systems[24] have not been supported in subsequent investigations.[25] Cystine-reducing systems have been extensively discussed elsewhere.[7,21]

METHODS OF ASSAY. Cystine can be reduced to cysteine and measured qualitatively by the cyanide-nitroprusside reaction.[26] This procedure is not particularly useful in cystinosis diagnosis or research. Routine, subnanomolar quantitation of cystine by amino acid analysis involves separation from other amino acids by ion-exchange chromatography and identification by ninhydrin staining.[27] The procedure measures total cystine plus cysteine; it cannot differentiate the two. This explains the conventional use of "half-cystine" to express amounts of the disulfide. Picomole quantities of free cystine can be measured in protein-free extracts of physiological fluids and tissues using an *Escherichia coli* cystine-binding protein.[28] The assay involves competition by unknown quantities of nonradioactive cystine for [^{14}C]cystine bound to the protein, with trapping of protein-bound radioactivity on nitrocellulose filters. The less radioactivity trapped, the greater the competing nonradioactive cystine. This sensitive and specific assay played a crucial role in determining the basic defect in cystinosis. Other cystine assays employ ion-exchange, paper,[29] or thin-layer chromatography.[30] In all experimental systems where both cysteine and cystine are present, care must be taken to prevent the spontaneous oxidation of cysteine to cystine, which would spuriously raise measured cystine levels. This can be accomplished using iodoacetate, iodoacetamide, or *N*-ethylmaleim-

ide, which forms an essentially irreversible adduct with free thiols such as cysteine.

Lysosomal Storage in Cystinosis. Plasma cystine concentrations are normal in cystinosis.[5] Intestinal absorption of cystine is normal, and urinary cystine levels are no more elevated than those of other amino acids. Thus, the accumulation of cystine in cystinosis is an intracellular phenomenon. Cystine crystals have been identified in many tissues (Fig. 107-2), including kidney,[31] liver,[32] lung, pancreas,[33] intestine,[34,35] appendix,[36] spleen,[37] conjunctiva and cornea,[38] lymph node,[39] polymorphonuclear leukocyte and monocyte,[40] bone marrow,[41] thyroid,[42] thymus,[43] and choroid plexus.[44,45] Crystals have even been found in the Kupffer cells of a 22-week fetus with cystinosis.[46] The crystals can be rectangular, in which case they are birefringent, or hexagonal, in which case they are not.[5] Recently, cystine crystals were photographed in the retina of an older, postrenal transplant cystinosis patient.[47] Many cystinotic cell types, including muscle, brain, various peripheral leukocyte populations,[48] and all cells in culture, remain devoid of crystals but accumulate 5 to 500 times normal amounts of cystine (Table 107-1). Tissues which contain crystals, e.g., kidney, conjunctiva, and liver, have 100 times the cystine concentrations of those without crystals, e.g., brain, with a great deal of variation among samples obtained from different individuals. Brain white matter and gray matter in a young cystinosis patient have appeared entirely spared of cystine accumulation[49] but have shown several-fold increased cystine levels when measured in a 25-year-old woman with cystinosis.[50]

Circulating leukocytes and cultured cells from cystinotic individuals are more uniform in their cystine content than crystal-laden tissues (Table 107-1) and exhibit normal morphology and growth. Cysteine concentrations are normal in cystinotic leukocytes.[61] Cystinotic fibroblasts contain 50 to 100 times normal amounts of cystine. Cultured lymphoblasts store only fivefold normal amounts of cystine, or one-tenth the concentration of other cell types. Cystinotic corneal cells in culture accumulate cystine to subcrystalline levels (Table 107-1) even though corneas in vivo are packed with crystals. If we estimate that tissues are 10% protein, the peripheral leukocyte and fibroblast levels of cystine are one or two orders of magnitude less than in crystal-containing tissues. This may be related to more rapid cell division by the leukocytes and cultured cells. It may also take a considerable amount of time for tissue crystals to form. We measured hepatic cystine levels in a 22-week fetus with cystinosis and in boys 6 and 12 years old with cystinosis. The values were 8, 92, and 528 nmol half-cystine per milligram protein, respectively, suggesting that cystine may accumulate gradually in this tissue. Muscle cystine levels also exhibited a pattern of increasing values with age.[56] In addition, leukocyte cystine values may be slightly greater in older than in younger cystinotics, since 10 patients under 3 years of age averaged 6.1 ± 2.4 nmol half-cystine per milligram protein compared with 10.4 ± 4.1 nmol half-cystine per milligram protein for 15 patients 13 to 28 years old.[58]

The lysosomal localization of stored cystine was determined by several different methods. Subcellular fractionation of cystinotic leukocytes[61] and fibroblasts[59] by differential centrifugation demonstrated that the bulk of stored cystine co-sedimented in granular fractions with the lysosomal enzyme acid phosphatase. Similar findings were obtained using cells from individuals heterozygous for cystinosis.[69] Electron microscopy

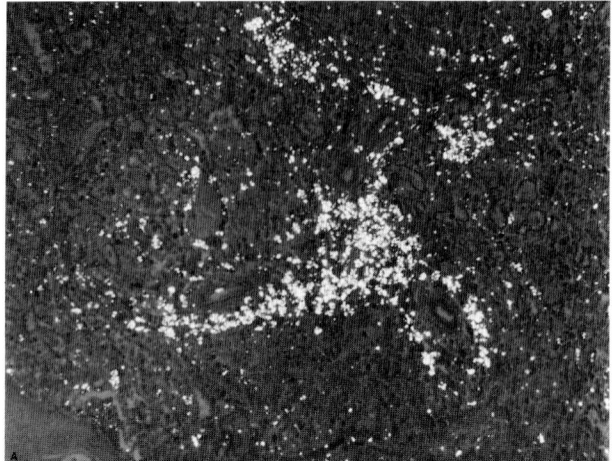

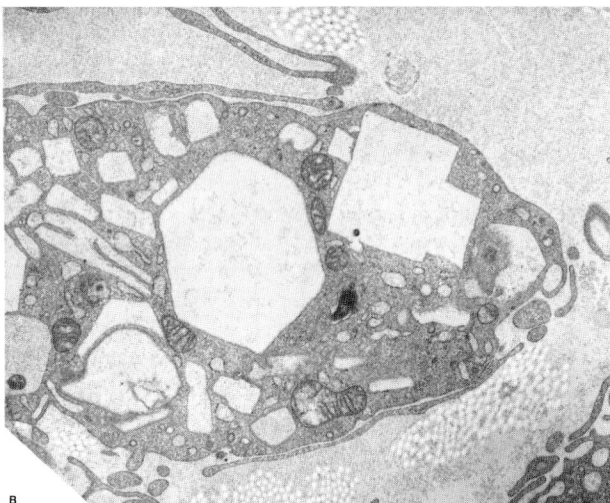

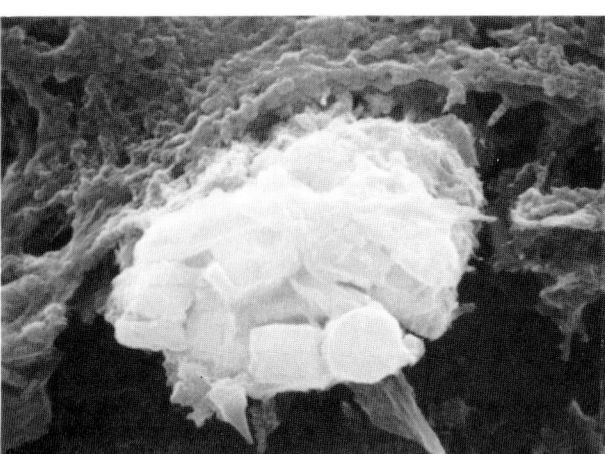

Fig. 107-2 Cystine crystals in cystinotic tissue. A. Light microscopy of spleen tissue showing cystine crystals under cross-polarizing light. × 44. B. Cystine crystals within lysosomes of a histiocyte in conjunctival stroma. Electron micrograph × 9250. (*Courtesy of T. Kuwabara, M.D., National Eye Institute, Bethesda, Maryland.*) C. Three-dimensional appearance of cystine crystals in a Kupffer cell. Scanning electron micrograph × 1800. (*Courtesy of K. G. Ishak, M.D., Ph.D., Armed Forces Institute of Pathology, Washington, D.C.*)

of cystinotic lymph node cells revealed a crystal surrounded by acid phosphatase-staining material, all within an intact limiting membrane.[39] This finding was confirmed by similar electron-microscopic findings in cystinotic histiocytes[70] and rectal mucosal cells.[71] Additional work using ferritin to label lyso-

somes also demonstrated the lysosomal location of the cystine storage.[72] Other studies employed sucrose density gradients to demonstrate compartmentalization of cystine within leukocyte lysosomes,[73] and exposure to L-cysteine-D-penicillamine disulfide to selectively induce vacuolation in cystinotic fibroblasts.[74] This crucial body of work accurately defined the lysosome as the proper target of future investigations into the primary defect in cystinosis.

Early Investigations. Based upon the possibility that cystine was stored within lysosomes secondary to a nonlysosomal abnormality, several studies investigated cyst(e)ine metabolism and plasma membrane transport in normal and cystinotic cells. Cystine uptake by cystinotic fibroblasts was reported as normal in one study[75] but increased in another report, with slower than normal efflux as well.[76] Others found [^{35}S]cysteine uptake and oxidation to [^{35}S]cystine greater in cystinotic compared with normal leukocytes,[29] and cystinotic fibroblasts were found to be less susceptible to cysteine toxicity than normal cells.[77] ^{35}S incorporation into glutathione appeared normal in these studies but was reduced in cystinotic fibroblasts exposed to [^{35}S]cystine.[78] The ratio of reduced to oxidized glutathione was reported as increased approximately twofold in cystinotic fibroblasts,[79] although glutathione and cysteine concentrations were normal in such cells.[80]

Several enzymatic activities have been investigated. Pantetheinase was found normal in cystinotic fibroblasts and leukocytes.[81] Cystinotic γ-glutamyltranspeptidase activity has been reported normal[82] or, with enormous variability among cell strains, moderately increased,[83] and γ-glutamyltranspeptidase inhibitors decreased the cystine content of cystinotic fibroblasts.[84] Cysteinyl tRNA synthetase, as well as tRNA$_{cys}$, are normal in cystinotic fibroblasts.[85] Arylsulfatase B[86] and β-galactosidase[87] were reported reduced in cystinotic fibroblasts, and β-alanine has been found increased in cystinotic lymphocytes and platelets[88]; none of these findings has been pursued by more than one laboratory. Several thiol-dependent enzyme activities were shown to be slightly diminished in postmortem cystinotic livers, but this was considered a result rather than a cause of the cystine accumulation in cystinosis.[52]

A central issue in cystinosis research was whether cystine reducing systems were defective in this disease. Some investigators examined whole blood[89] or erythrocyte hemolysate[90] levels of NADH-dependent cystine reductase and cysteine-glutathione transhydrogenase,[91] i.e., cysteine-glutathione thioltransferase. Others pursued cellular systems. In cystinotic liver specimens obtained at autopsy, both cystine reductase and cysteine glutathione thioltransferase were shown to be normal, and several cysteine oxidizing systems were also intact in the patients' livers.[92] Data from cystinotic fibroblasts later confirmed normal amounts of cystine reductase, glutathione reductase, and cysteine glutathione thioltransferase,[93] although one report of an inexplicable increase in cystine-reducing activity appeared.[94] Despite some evidence for cystine reduction in rat liver lysosomes,[95] extensive studies in human leukocytes demonstrated that virtually all glutathione-cysteine thioltransferase activity occurred in the cytoplasm rather than in lysosome-rich granular fractions and that this activity was normal in cystinotic cells.[25] Thus, rather exhaustive studies by several investigators failed to reveal a defect in cystine reduction or cysteine metabolism in cystinosis.

Lysosomal Transport Studies. An alternative hypothesis to explain cystine storage in cystinosis was that a transport mech-

Table 107-1 Cystine Content of Cystinotic Tissue and Cells

		Cystinotic			Normal		
	N	x̄ ± SD	Range	N	x̄ ± SD	Range	Reference
Tissues		*nmol half-cystine/mg wet weight*			*nmol half-cystine/mg wet weight*		
Kidney	4	94.8 ± 79.7	24.6–29.5	1	0.25	—	49
	5	51.4 ± 32.6	16.7–101.7	?	—	<0.29	51
	3	64.7 ± 22.2	39.2–80.0	—			52
	1	—	19.8, 21.0	—			53
Conjunctiva	7	117.9 ± 115.3	5.2–314.0	13	—	<0.38	54, 55
Muscle	10	0.77 ± 0.53	0.05–1.94	10	0.023 ± 0.003	—	56
	3	0.31 ± 0.23	0.06–0.95	1	0.003	—	57
Brain	2	—	0.02–0.08	1	0.17	—	49
	1	—	0.05–0.20	—			53
Lung	1	44.5		—			58
Pancreas	1	35.8		—			58
Liver	3	73.0 ± 35.0	45.8 ± 112.5	2	—	0.58, 0.92	52
	1	69.1		—			58
	1	—	34.5, 42.4	—			53
Cells		*nmol half-cystine/mg protein*			*nmol half-cystine/mg protein*		
Polymorphonuclear leukocytes	9	6.4 ± 2.8	4.0–13.2	9	0.08 ± 0.06	<0.2	59–61
	3	—	6.9–10.0	2	—	<0.1	62
	29	8.9 ± 4.7	2.6–23.1	29	0.14 ± 0.06	0.04–0.28	58, 63
Cultured fibroblasts	6	8.4 ± 1.3	6.6–10.6	9	0.07 ± 0.05	<0.2	59, 60
	6	—	6.7–14.3	3	—	<0.1	62
Cultured leukocytes	3	—	0.31–3.10	3	—	<0.03	64
Epstein-Barr virus–transformed lymphoblasts	3	0.46 ± 0.10	—	3	0.10 ± 0.02	—	65
Cultured myoblasts/myotubes	1*	29.8 ± 10.8	16.7–41.2	1	0.31	—	57
Cultured cornea	1	23.2 ± 14.1	11.0–38.7	1	0.27†	—	66
Cultured renal cells	1	8.0 ± 0.6	—	1‡	0.06 ± 0.02	—	68

*When a single individual's cells were studied, the mean ± SD for at least three separate cultures is given.
†Another reported normal value is ≤0.40.[67]
‡Madin-Darby canine kidney epithelial cells; human renal cells in culture were not available.

anism in the lysosomal membrane was defective in the mutant cells. The possibility that the movement of small molecules across the lysosomal membrane was carrier-mediated, and even energy requiring, was mentioned in a 1969 article.[96] The concept gained credibility through vacuolation studies showing that mouse macrophages took up nonhydrolyzable peptides by pinocytosis. If the peptide were of molecular weight over 220 to 230, cellular lysosomes became vacuolated, presumably because the peptide could not freely traverse the lysosomal membrane but, instead, accumulated.[97] This permeability characteristic of the lysosomal membrane was exploited in experiments showing that cystinotic but not normal fibroblasts formed vacuoles on exposure to high concentrations of L-cysteine-D-penicillamine disulfide.[98] It followed that some product of the disulfide, e.g., cystine, might be blocked in its egress from cystinotic lysosomes.

It was difficult to compare rates of cystine movement out of a highly loaded compartment, the cystinotic lysosome, with rates out of a virtually empty compartment, the normal lysosome. A means for loading normal lysosomes to cystinotic levels of cystine was needed. This was achieved by the use of cystine dimethylester. It had been shown that some amino acid methylesters permeate the membranes of rat liver lysosomes because of their lysosomotropic properties and were specifically broken down within lysosomes by acid hydrolases, yielding methanol and the corresponding free amino acids.[99,100] The amino acids, having acquired a charge by virtue of the lysosome's acidity, accumulated to levels high enough to specifically swell lysosomes and even burst them by osmotic lysis.[101] Any such high level of amino acid loading required a rate of methylester hydrolysis much greater than the rate of

egress of the resultant amino acid and depended on the fact that the methylester was an appropriate substrate for some lysosomal hydrolase.

Cystine dimethylester proved a suitable substrate. This compound was shown to load isolated lysosomes from human leukocytes with cystine in vitro.[102] These experiments were performed on isolated lysosome-rich granular fractions and employed 2.5 mM [35S]cystine dimethylester for loading and glass filters for trapping and washing the lysosomes. They revealed slow rates of cystine loss from both normal and cystinotic granular fractions, with no difference between the two.[103] In retrospect, this appeared due to enormous nonspecific binding of 35S to normal and cystinotic particles, obscuring recognition of the loss of 35S-cystine from the normal granules.

This type of interference was not encountered in whole cell experiments in which leukocytes were exposed to 0.25 mM cystine dimethylester.[103] In these studies, the leukocyte lysosomes were specifically loaded, as predicted from earlier studies with other amino acid methylesters.[99,100] This was evident from the finding of abnormally distended myeloperoxidase-positive granules in loaded leukocytes (much more frequently in cystinotic leukocytes than in normal cells similarly treated). In experiments employing [35S]cystine dimethylester for loading and high voltage electrophoresis for [35S]cystine determinations, [35S]cystine was cleared much more slowly from the cystinotic cells ($t_{1/2}$ 80 to over 500 min) than from normal cells (mean $t_{1/2}$ = 42.7 ± 3.1 min). A factor confounding interpretation of these differences was the possibility of dilution of the specific radioactivity of [35S]cystine by the large endogenous cystine pool of the cystinotic, but not the normal cells. If this had occurred, then the slow clearance of [35S]cystine radioactivity from the cystinotic cells might actually represent an enormous loss of total (radioactive and nonradioactive) cystine, meaning that the cystinotic did not really have a slower rate of cystine loss compared with normal. The problem was obviated by the use of nonradioactive cystine dimethylester for loading, with subsequent measurement of nonradioactive cystine by the cystine binding protein method.[28] Under these conditions, leukocytes from two normal individuals lost half their total cystine in 27 and 67 min, respectively, compared with 366 min and infinity for leukocytes from two cystinotic patients.[103] The initial cystine loading in the normal leukocytes, 11.2 and 38.4 nmol half-cystine per milligram protein, approximated that in the cystinotic cells, 9.6 and 34.5 nmol half-cystine per milligram protein, making comparisons of half-times legitimate reflections of differences in rate. The finding of impaired cystine clearance in cystinosis was supported by radioactive experiments in fibroblasts, although the issue of dilution of specific radioactivity was not addressed.[103] Other experiments in fibroblasts used cysteamine-depleted cystinotic cells and normal cells, both exposed to 30 mM cysteine-glutathione mixed disulfide as a source of cystine. Starting with 0.5 to 0.8 nmol cystine per milligram protein, the normal cells lost half their cystine in 20 min, while the cystinotic fibroblasts lost virtually none in 90 min.[104] Clearly, the whole cell experiments pointed to an impairment of lysosomal cystine clearance in cystinosis.

LYSOSOMAL CYSTINE EGRESS STUDIES. Cystine egress was studied by loading leukocyte granular fractions with cystine and measuring the amount remaining after different times of incubation at 37°C.[105] In radioactive experiments, [^{35}S]cystine was lost from 13 normal granular fractions with a mean $t_{1/2}$ of 26.1 ± 1.4 SEM min and from 12 cystinotic granular fractions with a mean $t_{1/2}$ of 80.8 ± 10.7 min. In nonradioactive experiments, the $t_{1/2}$ for normal cystine egress ranged from 34 to 60 min, regardless of the initial level of cystine loading (7.6 to 52.2 nmol half-cystine per milligram protein); the $t_{1/2}$ for cystinotic granular fractions was 142 min to infinity, whether the initial loading was 2.9 or 86.8 nmol half-cystine per milligram protein. In contrast to cystine, methionine and tryptophan were removed from cystinotic granular fractions with normal half-times, i.e., approximately 17 and 27 minutes, respectively. This suggested that cystinosis did not represent a generalized defect in lysosomal amino acid clearance. Indeed, other amino acids do not accumulate in cystinotic lysosomes.[106]

Measurements of velocities of cystine egress out of normal and cystinotic lysosomes, rather than half-times, were made possible by several methodological innovations. First, cystine lost from loaded granular fractions was shown to be recovered, as cystine, outside the lysosomes, even in the presence of the thiol-trapping agent, N-ethylmaleimide.[107] This eliminated the possibility that cystine was first reduced to cysteine and then reoxidized to cystine during transport through the lysosomal membrane. Second, cystine appearance outside lysosomes was linear with time through at least 80 min, meaning that an initial velocity of egress could be calculated after a 40-min incubation.[107] Third, N-ethylmaleimide had no effect on rates of cystine loss from lysosomes.[107] This meant that extralysosomal cystine measurements would reflect only the cystine that was outside the lysosome due to egress from inside the lysosome. There would be no spurious contributions from oxidation of contaminating cysteine, which would be trapped by the N-ethylmaleimide. Fourth, rates of cystine exodus from lyso-

somes were normalized to amounts of a uniquely lysosomal enzyme, β-hexosaminidase, so that results of experiments using granular fractions of variable purity could be compared. With this background (Fig. 107-3), using normal leukocyte granular fractions, the initial velocity of cystine appearance outside lysosomes increased with loading and then leveled off, indicating saturation kinetics (Fig. 107-3). The V_{max} was approximately 23 pmol half-cystine per unit of hexosaminidase per minute. Cystinotic granular fractions displayed negligible velocity of cystine egress, regardless of the level of cystine loading. Heterozygotes for cystinosis exhibited a V_{max} half that of normal individuals.[107]

An impaired egress of cystine from other types of cystinotic cells was also demonstrated. Using Epstein-Barr virus (EBV)–transformed lymphoblasts loaded by exposure to cystine dimethylester, the velocity of cystine egress from normal granular fractions was two to three times that for cystinotic granular fractions.[65] Impaired clearance of cystine from cystinotic fibroblast granular fractions was conclusively demonstrated, using both radioactive[108,109] and nonradioactive cystine,[109] bringing to three the number of cell types and the number of different laboratories revealing the defect in cystinosis.

COUNTERTRANSPORT STUDIES. A classic means of verifying carrier-mediated as opposed to diffusional transport is the demonstration of countertransport, or transstimulation. If transstimulation exists in a system, tracer amounts of a radiolabeled substance will cross a membrane at an increased rate if there is a substantial concentration of the nonradioactive substance on the opposite side of the membrane.[110] Thus, if nonradioactive cystine-loaded lysosomes take up [^{3}H]cystine (present in tracer concentrations) more rapidly than lysosomes not loaded with cystine, then a carrier for cystine must be present in the lysosomal membrane. Not only was this phe-

Fig. 107-3 Initial velocity of cystine transport as a function of lysosomal cystine loading using human leukocytes. Normal egress velocity increased with loading and then plateaued, indicating saturation kinetics. Heterozygotes for cystinosis followed a similar pattern but reached only half the normal maximal velocity. Cystinotic patients displayed negligible egress velocity regardless of the level of loading. Values were normalized to the activity of hexosaminidase, a lysosomal enzyme. *(From Gahl et al.: "Cystine Transport Is Defective in Isolated Leukocyte Lysosomes from Patient with Cystinosis," Science, Sept. 24, 1982, vol. 217, pp. 1263–1265. Copyright 1982 by the American Association for the Advancement of Science.)*

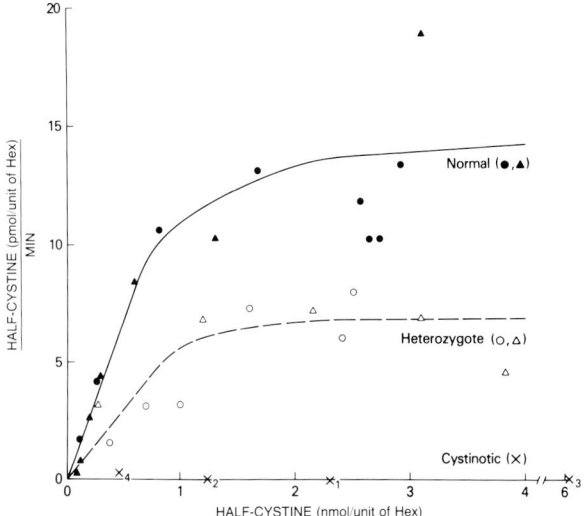

nomenon demonstrated for normal leukocyte granular fractions, but the [³H]cystine uptake was proportional to the level of nonradioactive cystine loading up to 3 nmol half-cystine per unit of hexosaminidase, above which uptake plateaued (Fig. 107-4).[111] Cystinotic granular fractions took up virtually no [³H]cystine, regardless of the level of loading. Obligate heterozygotes for cystinosis exhibited half the normal [³H]cystine countertransport.[63] Normal, cystine-loaded granular fractions did not countertransport other amino acids except, to a certain extent, cystathionine. Normal cystine countertransport was relatively independent of extralysosomal sodium or potassium ion concentration, but was temperature-dependent, with a Q_{10} of approximately 2.0 and an energy of activation of 11.4 kcal/mol. Extralysosomal nonradioactive L-cystine, but not D-cystine, competed with [³H]cystine for uptake into cystine-loaded normal granular fractions,[111] establishing the stereospecificity of the carrier for the L isomer. Certain sulfur compounds resembling cystine, such as cystathionine and cysteamine, were presumably also recognized by the carrier since they competed for countertransport. Since the dibasic amino acid, arginine, did not compete with cystine, the carrier was presumed to be different from the plasma membrane carrier for dibasic amino acids in renal tubular and intestinal epithelial cells (see Chap. 100). Several other amino acids, i.e., methionine, alanine, tryptophan, tyrosine, glutamate, and homocystine, as well as β-carboxyethyl-L-thiocysteine and other cystine analogues, did not compete.[111] The cystine carrier appeared specific for compounds of chain length 6 (not 8) sulfur or methylene units having an amine (but not necessarily a carboxyl) group at each end. The structural specificity and stereospecificity, along with the temperature dependence, countertransport, and saturation kinetics, confirmed that cystine transport across the lysosomal membrane was carrier-mediated. The virtual absence of such transport in cystinotic cells, as well as the gene-dosage effect demonstrable in velocity[107] and countertransport[63] measurements in heterozygotes, verified that impaired lysosomal cystine transport was the genetic defect in nephropathic cystinosis.

OTHER CHARACTERISTICS. The lysosomal cystine carrier did not appear to operate through γ-glutamyltranspeptidase activity, since a patient deficient in this enzyme exhibited normal

Fig. 107-4 Cystine countertransport as a function of cystine loading in leukocyte lysosomes. The ordinate represents [³H]cystine uptake into nonradioactive cystine-loaded lysosomes, minus uptake into lysosomes not loaded with cystine. The hourly rate of this uptake (representing an initial velocity) increased linearly with initial cystine loading in normal lysosomes but was negligible for cystinotic lysosomes at every level of loading. (*Reprinted by permission from Biochemical Journal, 216:393, 1983, copyright 1983 by The Biochemical Society, London*).

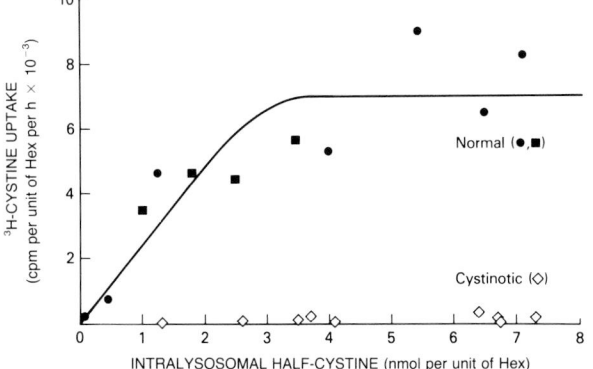

lysosomal cystine transport in his leukocytes.[112] The lysosomal carrier was also considered genetically distinct from the plasma membrane cystine carrier in fibroblasts, which transports both cystine and glutamate.[113] The plasma membrane carrier exhibited an identical pH dependence of cystine uptake by normal and cystinotic fibroblasts.[114] Moreover, at physiological pH (≈7.4), cystine exists as a mixture of tetrapolar neutral and tripolar acidic forms. The latter are structurally similar to glutamate. At lysosomal pH (≈5.0), cystine exists exclusively as the tetrapolar neutral form and does not resemble glutamate. Therefore, the finding that glutamate does not compete with cystine for lysosomal transport[111] supports the conclusion that the lysosomal transport system for cystine is genetically distinct from the plasma membrane system. Similar results have been found for lysosomal membrane transport systems involving other amino acids.[115]

Normal lysosomal cystine transport was further characterized by examining its energy or ATP requirements. Results of these investigations were difficult to interpret because ATP not only provides energy but also effects lysosomal acidification through a divalent cation–dependent proton pump,[116] and this process itself might influence transport.

ATP did stimulate normal transport twofold in polymorphonuclear leukocytes,[107] but the effect required the presence of both 90 mM potassium chloride and 2 mM magnesium chloride.[117] Later, even greater stimulation of cystine efflux was demonstrated when lysosomal membranes were made permeable to potassium ions either by an ionophore such as valinomycin or by the presence of a permeant anion.[118] The potassium-valinomycin effects were present in cystinotic lysosomes as well, suggesting that they were not mediated through the carrier system deficient in cystinosis. The ability of magnesium chloride to stimulate lysosomal cystine transport was concentration-dependent up to 5 mM and, at least at pH 5.5, could be divorced from the effects of ATP.[117] The possibility that ATP's stimulation of cystine egress was due to lysosomal acidification was examined by measuring cystine transport in the presence of the protonophore, CCCP (carbonyl cyanide m-chlorophenylhydrazone), the alkalinizing agents ammonium chloride and methylamine, the anion transport inhibitor DIDS (4,4'-diisothiocyanostilbene-2,2'-disulfonate), and an inhibitor of ATP-dependent acidification, DCCD (NN'-dicyclohexylcarbodiimide), all of which diminish the proton gradient across the lysosomal membrane.[119–121] None of these reagents decreased cystine transport either in the absence or in the presence of Mg-ATP.[117]

Different results were reported for EBV-transformed human lymphoblasts. In this system, 2 mM Mg-ATP stimulated the loss of cystine from normal granular fractions, but the stimulation was inhibited by CCCP and the nonhydrolyzable ATP analogue 5-adenylylimidophosphate.[65] This study showed that nucleotides such as ITP, GTP, and UTP, which acidified lysosomes by at least 0.2 pH units, stimulated cystine efflux to exactly the same extent as ATP; ADP and AMP, which did not acidify lysosomes, did not stimulate cystine egress.[122] Inhibition of acidification by reagents such as N-ethylmaleimide also correlated with inhibition of cystine efflux. At the same time, ATP-dependent acidification and ATPase activity of lymphoblast lysosomes[122] and the intralysosomal pH of fibroblast lysosomes[123] were demonstrated to be normal in cystinotic cells.

In rat liver lysosomes purified 89-fold, Mg-ATP stimulated lysosomal acidification and, in separate preparations, stimulated the efflux of cystine, but not leucine, methionine, or tyrosine.[124] Divalent cations also stimulated cystine efflux, and the calcium ionophore A23187, which altered the lysosomal membrane potential, inhibited the cation-stimulated cystine efflux. Ionophores which reduced the proton gradient across the lysosomal membrane also decreased cystine efflux rates. These results, as well as more recent studies using normal fibroblast lysosomes, have led to the conclusion that both decreased membrane potentials and increased pH gradients stimulate lysosomal cystine transport.[125] Cystine loading itself may affect the membrane potential, and it would be informative to measure the extent to which the membrane potential is altered by ionophores using cystine-loaded lysosomes.

The differences between the findings in human leukocytes and lymphoblasts may be related to technical aspects of the studies or to properties intrinsic to the two cell types. Recent evidence indicates that ATP may stimulate cystine exodus from leukocyte granular fractions only at low levels of cystine loading and in the absence of N-ethylmaleimide.[126] Standard leukocyte experiments were performed at high levels of cystine loading in the presence of N-ethylmaleimide but not magnesium chloride, and the appearance of cystine outside highly loaded lysosomes was measured. Lymphoblast experiments were done at low levels of cystine loading in the absence of N-ethylmaleimide but with magnesium chloride present, and the disappearance of cystine from less well loaded lysosomes was measured. Both employed crude granular fractions, but experiments on purified rat liver lysosomes supported the lymphoblast results. The leukocyte and lymphoblast may also differ in lysosomal pH or level of endogenous ATP retained after preparation of the granular fraction. No pH or ATP measurements were made in the leukocyte experiments. The issue of whether cystine transport requires lysosomal acidification may be resolved when the cystine carrier is isolated, incorporated into liposomes, and studied under defined conditions. At present, there is no evidence for a direct energy requirement for lysosomal cystine transport, and all systems tested exhibit some lysosomal cystine transport in the absence of *added* Mg-ATP. Since any cystine that leaves the lysosome is rapidly reduced to cysteine in the cytoplasm, cystine would be expected to always move down its concentration gradient, and energy might not be required for this process.

Mechanism of Cystine Depletion. The most studied cystine-depleting agent to date is cysteamine, an aminothiol demonstrated in 1976 to rapidly and extensively lower the cystine content of cystinotic fibroblasts.[127] It was suggested that cysteamine reacted with cystine to form cysteine and cysteine-cysteamine mixed disulfide; the cysteine would leave cystinotic lysosomes freely,[105] and the mixed disulfide would also "diffuse out" of the lysosome because its molecular weight was less than 220 daltons, the accepted upper limit for free movement of amino acids and di- and tripeptides across the lysosomal membrane.[97] Subsequent work demonstrated that because cysteine-cysteamine mixed disulfide resembles lysine structurally and because cystinotic fibroblasts have an intact lysosomal transport system for lysine, the mixed disulfide was transported across cystinotic lysosomal membranes in a carrier-mediated fashion, by the intact lysine porter.[108] In fact, experiments in leukocytes demonstrated that cysteine-cysteamine mixed disulfide was cleared at a significant rate from cystinotic granular fractions, in contrast to cystine, which remained trapped inside the lysosomes.[128] These two studies essentially verified the hypothesis put forth 9 years earlier concerning the mechanism of cystine depletion by cysteamine.[127]

Several other reagents were also investigated for their cystine-depleting ability. Many were even enclosed in liposomes for presentation to cells.[129] Dithiothreitol lowered the cystine content of intact cystinotic fibroblasts[130] and, later, of leukocyte granular fractions,[128] presumably by penetrating the lysosome and reducing cystine to cysteine. Ascorbic acid caused a 50 percent decrease in the cystine content of cultured fibroblasts, perhaps by its effects on properties of the lysosomal membrane.[131] Pantethine, which depleted intact cystinotic fibroblasts[132] but not leukocyte granular fractions of cystine,[128] was reported to function by being degraded to cysteamine by pantetheinase,[133] an enzyme present in human fibroblasts.[81] The aminothiol WR 1065, or N-(2'-mercaptoethyl)-1,3-propanediamine, and WR 638, or phosphocysteamine, were also proposed to produce cysteamine as the active cystine-depleting agent.[134,135]

Source of Lysosomal Cystine. The hypothesis that phagocytosis of preformed crystals accounted for intralysosomal cystine accumulation in cystinosis was rejected based on previous histologic studies in 1951,[136] on the absence of cystine crystals in urine and extracellular fluid, and on the solubility of cystine in plasma.[5] Rather, crystals were considered to form from a saturated cystine solution within lysosomes.[72] In cultured cells, the source of this cystine was proposed to be cystine itself in the presence of exogenous cystine and to be protein catabolism in the absence of exogenous cystine.[137] In cystinotic fibroblasts depleted by cysteamine and grown in the absence of cystine, lysosomal cystine was derived from the degradation of cystine-containing proteins, both intracellular and extracellular.[138,139] In fact, the lysosomal cystine content varied directly with the concentration in the medium of the cystine-rich protein, bovine serum albumin.[140] Other cystine-rich proteins, but not cysteine-rich proteins, also gave rise to lysosomal cystine storage.[138] The process involved consists of pinocytosis of proteins followed by proteolysis, the rate of which is normal in cystinotic fibroblasts.[140,141] Glutathione has also been mentioned as a source of cystine because inhibitors of γ-glutamyltranspeptidase prevented cystine from accumulating from glutathione-cysteine mixed disulfide.[142] But the high concentrations of inhibitor employed and the fact that glutathione-cysteine undergoes disulfide interchange reactions to form cystine made these experiments difficult to interpret. Other studies using [^{35}S]cystine demonstrated cystine accumulation only when the protein pool was labeled and not when the glutathione pool alone was labeled.[139] *De novo* cysteine synthesis through the cystathionine β-synthase pathway was shown not to be the source of stored cystine in cystinosis.[139,143]

In cystinotic fibroblasts depleted by cysteamine but grown in cystine-containing medium, cystine accumulation varies linearly with its extracellular concentration.[138,144] Cystine acquired in this fashion could enter the lysosome by pinocytosis, without traversing the reducing environment of the cytosol, but experiments demonstrated that fluid-phase pinocytosis in cystinotic fibroblasts accounted for only 1 to 2 percent of observed cystine accumulation.[138] Alternatively, cystine might bind nonspecifically to the plasma membrane and enter the cell by adsorptive pinocytosis, but this is unlikely to be a high flux process, since the uptake of another amino acid, D-alanine, was no greater than the basal pinocytosis rate.[145] Evidence has recently been presented that exogenous cystine enters lysosomes by two routes.[146] One is rapid, low-capacity, chloroquine-inhibitable, and involves movement through the plasma membrane, cytosol, and lysosomal membrane. The other is slow, high capacity, stimulated by chloroquine and low medium pH, and might involve pinocytosis, with fusion of pinosomes and lysosomes.

We currently do not know why cystine is lost from cystinotic fibroblasts when they are placed at acid pH,[147] in chloroquine-containing medium,[148] at an elevated temperature,[149] or when they are labeled with [35S]cystine and placed in cystine-free medium. This latter occurrence may be due to exocytosis, since the kinetics of [35S]cystine egress resemble those of tritiated sucrose and tritiated mannitol, fluid-phase markers of endocytosis and exocytosis.[150]

Genetics

The inheritance of cystinosis follows an autosomal recessive pattern in all pedigrees of all variants studied. The frequency of consanguinity is increased among cystinotic families. The incidence of nephropathic cystinosis has been estimated at about 1 in 100,000 to 1 in 200,000 live births. This approximates the incidence of other rare inborn errors of metabolism and corresponds to a carrier frequency of roughly 1 in 200 in the general population. Although cystinosis has been described in most major ethnic groups,[151,152] it occurs rarely among most populations except for an isolate in the province of Brittany, France, where the frequency has been estimated at 1 in 26,000.[153] Ascertainment of patients with cystinosis is suspected to be grossly incomplete, with many undiagnosed infants dying of dehydration. In a survey study of affected patients in Germany,[154] the ratio of males to females was 58:43. In a European collaborative study,[155] it was 115:90. Of 58 cystinosis patients examined at the NICHD, 31 were males. This slight preponderance of affecting living males remains unexplained.

As expected for an autosomal recessive condition, individuals heterozygous for the cystinosis gene are entirely asymptomatic. Detection is based on finding an intermediate level of cystine in circulating leukocytes or in cultured fibroblasts.[60] Peripheral leukocytes of obligate heterozygotes for cystinosis have exhibited approximately half-normal rates of lysosomal cystine egress[107] and countertransport.[63]

In view of the phenotypic heterogeneity of cystinosis and the presumably complex pathway for targeting and processing of lysosomal carriers, it seems likely that several different mutations could result in lysosomal cystine storage. Some patients may be compound heterozygotes for allelic mutations; others may be homozygotes for a mutation at a locus different from the classically mutated locus. No chromosomal location for a cystinosis gene has been identified.

No linkage between cystinosis and HLA loci has been found.[156] Cystinosis and Fabry disease have been reported in the same family[157]; cystinosis and cystic fibrosis have been diagnosed in the same individual, a boy who died at 6 years of age.[158]

Clinical Features and Pathology

Presentation and General Course (Fig. 107-5). As for most lysosomal storage disorders, patients with nephropathic cystinosis are entirely normal at birth, except perhaps for lighter skin and hair pigmentation than their sibs. Development proceeds normally until the second half of the first year of life, when an affected baby may fail to grow and gain weight, eat poorly, appear fussy, urinate and drink excessively, or suffer isolated or recurrent episodes of acidosis, dehydration, and, consequently, fever. These findings all result from renal tubular Fanconi syndrome; glucosuria may also eventually lead to a diagnosis of cystinosis. In the early 1970s, the mean age of diagnosis, determined for patients living in 1985, was approximately 28 months,[159] but this has probably decreased with improved ascertainment.

The natural history of cystinosis after infancy dictates that an affected child will manifest normal intelligence but continue to grow poorly, develop photophobia, and gradually lose

Fig. 107-5 Patients with nephropathic cystinosis. *(Courtesy of National Institutes of Health Clinical Center.) A. A 21-month-old boy with light hair and complexion. B. A 4 9/12-year-old boy with protruberant abdomen and short stature. C. A 20-year-old man with renal transplant at age 13. Note short stature.*

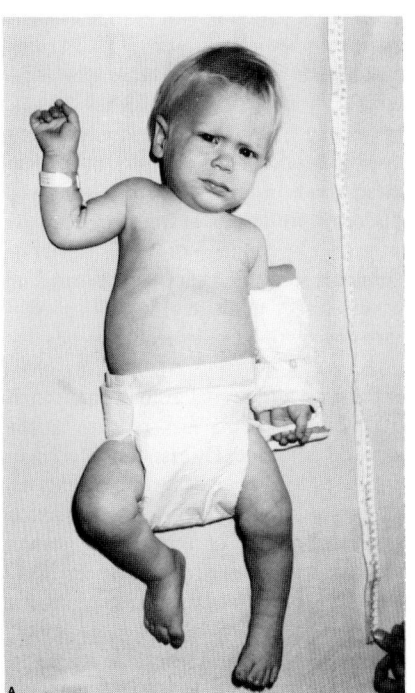
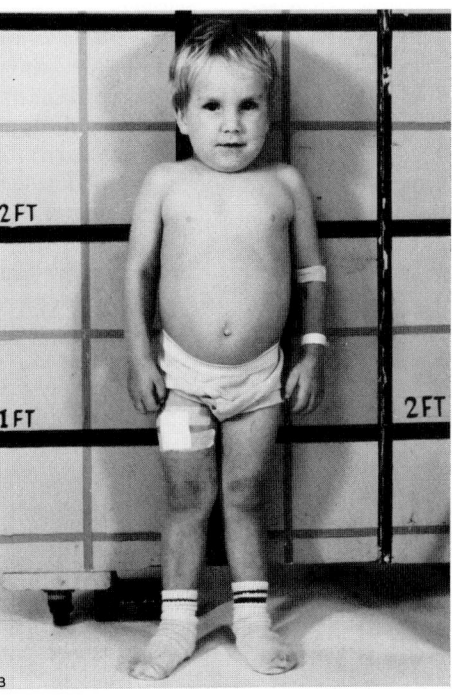
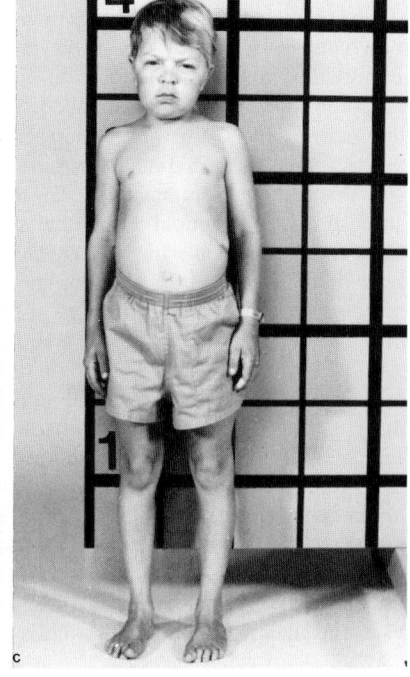

renal glomerular function, requiring renal transplantation after a decade of life. The child will not have a predisposition to infections, although certain abnormalities in phagocytic cells have been reported in cystinotic children.[160] After kidney transplantation, renal function is normalized, but the inexorable accumulation of cystine in other organs creates newly recognized threats to their proper functioning. A composite history for a typical cystinotic child has been published.[161]

Renal Tubular Involvement. Initially, the renal abnormality in cystinosis consists of the Fanconi syndrome, or failure of the tubules to properly reabsorb small molecules. The pathologic correlates of the Fanconi syndrome appear to be the "swan neck" deformity of the proximal convoluted tubule[162] and the disorganized and poorly developed tubules, seen in a cystinotic patient's kidney even prior to the onset of frank Fanconi syndrome.[163] Cystinosis represents the most common identifiable cause of renal tubular Fanconi syndrome in children.

The Fanconi syndrome results in excessive urinary losses of glucose, amino acids, phosphate, calcium, magnesium, sodium, potassium, bicarbonate, carnitine, water, and, undoubtedly, other small molecules yet to be identified. Children with cystinosis may initially receive a diagnosis of Bartter syndrome, nephrogenic diabetes insipidus, or pseudohypoaldosteronism.[164-166] A "tubular" proteinuria, in which proteins of molecular weight 10 to 50,000 are excreted in fiftyfold normal amounts, can also develop.[167] Microscopic hematuria is occasionally present. Renal calculi of urate and calcium oxalate have been reported in cystinosis.[168] Although blood glucose levels are normal, glucosuria and polyuria can lead to the mistaken diagnosis of juvenile onset diabetes mellitus. The polyuria consists of 2 to 6 liters of dilute urine (less than 300 mosmol/liter) excreted daily, may contribute to persistent enuresis in some children, and represents a particular threat to the well-being of an infant suffering acute gastroenteritis. Dehydration in such a patient is rapid and can be associated with a mild chronic fever. Acidosis can be profound due to renal losses of bicarbonate. Hyponatremia and hypokalemia with its risk of arrhythmias also occur. Hypocalcemia, and occasionally hypomagnesemia, result in tetany, especially when acidosis is acutely reversed by alkali therapy. Phosphaturia leads to hypophosphatemic rickets with typical metaphyseal widening, rachitic rosary, frontal bossing, genu valgum, and often failure to walk. Elevated serum alkaline phosphatase levels reflect active rickets. Vitamin D metabolites are normal in cystinosis.[169] A generalized aminoaciduria results in excretion of an average of over 1 mmol/kg/per day of 21 measurable amino acids; this is over tenfold the normal amino acid excretion.[170] Carnitine, a small molecule required for transport of free fatty acids into mitochondria for subsequent energy production, represents the latest nutrient found to be abnormally excreted in Fanconi syndrome patients. Normally 97 percent reabsorbed, carnitine is only 70 percent reabsorbed in cystinotic patients, resulting in plasma and muscle deficiency.[170] The muscle deficit causes lipid droplet accumulation on oil-red-O staining, and may be related to the poor muscle development of cystinotic children. The full ramifications of Fanconi syndrome in cystinosis have not yet been determined, but they include the failure to thrive characteristic of the disorder.

Glomerular Damage. The glomerular deterioration that provides the clinical hallmark of cystinosis proceeds inexorably in untreated patients. Pathologically, the cystinotic kidney manifests different stages of destruction[171] with giant cell transformation of the glomerular epithelium,[172] hyperplasia and hypertrophy of the juxtaglomerular apparatus,[7,56] and occasional "dark" cells and cytoplasmic inclusions.[31] But the ultimate result remains a classic end-stage kidney with scarring and fibrosis, chronic interstitial nephritis, and tubular degeneration.[44,173] Crystals, identified as L-cystine,[174] are abundant, but renal stones do not form, as in cystinuria. Clinically, most patients have proteinuria and many have granular casts and microscopic hematuria. Although creatinine clearance may fall within the first 2 years of life, a rise in serum creatinine generally does not appear until approximately 5 years of age. Once this occurs, the reciprocal of serum creatinine decreases linearly with age, as for other renal diseases.[175] Apparent improvement in the Fanconi syndrome, i.e., lessening of renal losses, may actually reflect reduced filtration; neither the tubular nor the glomerular damage in cystinosis is reversible. Some patients have unexplained plateaus in their renal function lasting months to years; others suffer a rapid deterioration of renal function with the onset of an acute infection or, in infants, with hypoperfusion secondary to dehydration. Cystinosis patients with uremia can die in congestive heart failure. The average age at renal death in cystinosis is 9.2 years.[155]

Growth. Growth retardation represents a significant part of the clinical picture of nephropathic cystinosis, yet it does not commence *in utero*. Length and weight are normal at birth. During the first year of life, linear growth begins to decrease. Height falls to the third percentile by one year of age. In untreated patients, this continuing growth impairment results in substantial dwarfing by the end of the second year of life (Fig. 107-6).[7,176] Bone age follows height age, which soon lags years behind chronological age.[161,177,178] Since height and weight are equally delayed, the children appear proportional except for a relative macrocephaly caused by sparing of head circumference.

The pathogenesis of the growth impairment in cystinosis has been the object of some study. Children with renal failure due to other causes generally do not show the profound impairment of growth exhibited by patients with cystinosis, who by age 8 have an average size of a normal 4 year old. Certainly renal failure, chronic acidosis, and renal rickets result in growth impairment, but the cystine storage in other organs, including growth plates in long bones and developing myofibrils, may exert a noxious influence on the ability of cells to replicate. This hypothesis finds support in the improved growth observed in children chronically cystine-depleted by oral cysteamine treatment.[176] Single growth hormone measurements[179] and somatomedin-C levels[177] are normal in patients with cystinosis; the direct pathogenesis linking lysosomal cystine storage with growth impairment has not yet been determined.

Growth of cystinosis patients after renal transplantation is extremely variable.[56] Of 15 such patients seen recently at the National Institute of Child Health and Human Development (NICHD), the tallest was 162 cm at age 17 years and the shortest 113 cm at 14 years of age.[178] Children transplanted before adolescence have some chance of realizing a growth spurt and achieving near-normal height. This prospect is remote for patients grafted after 16 years of age, despite a bone age several years delayed.[178] Daily steroids and other immunosuppressive agents may impair growth in these patients.

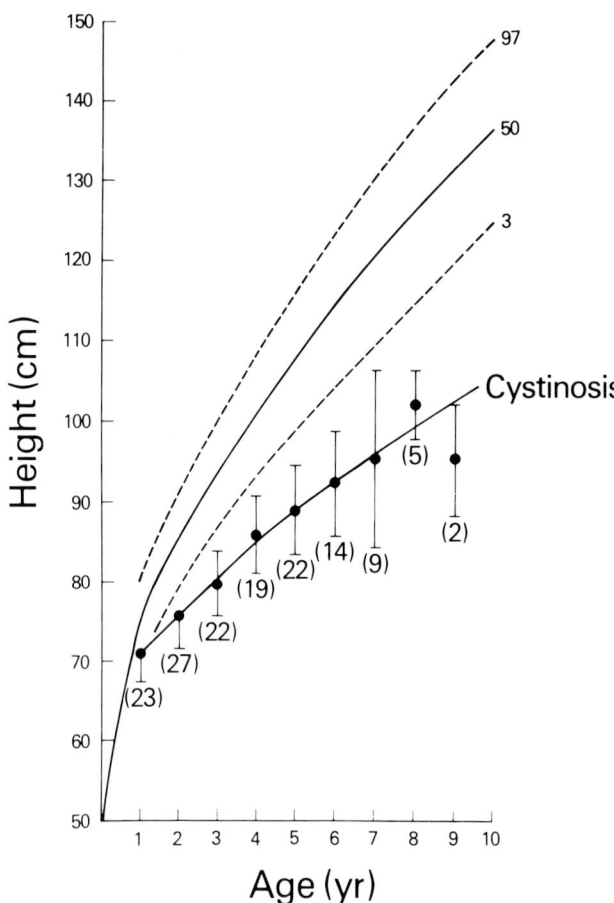

Fig. 107-6 Height of 143 cystinotic children prior to cystine-depleting therapy. The natural history of this disease reflects a growth velocity 50 to 60 percent of normal after the first year of life. (*From Gahl et al: New England Journal of Medicine, vol. 316, pp. 971–977, 1987. Reprinted with permission.*)

Ocular Damage. Cystinosis eventually affects most of the structures[180] and many of the functions of the eye, but with variable rates of progression. Several reviews have detailed the early[181,182] and late[47,56,178] ocular findings in cystinosis.

RETINA. A characteristic peripheral retinopathy, consisting of a patchy depigmentation of the retina with pigment clumps of various sizes, typifies nephropathic cystinosis.[183] This finding is not present at birth, although vacuolization of retinal pigment epithelial cells has been reported in a 21-week cystinotic fetus.[184] A pigment retinopathy has been reported in a 5-week-old girl subsequently diagnosed as having cystinosis.[41] Despite the "blond fundus" resulting from degeneration of the retinal pigment epithelium, visual acuity, visual fields, night vision, and electroretinography have been normal in young children with cystinosis.[182] But posttransplant patients, whose retinas have accumulated cystine for one to three decades, exhibit a disconcerting frequency of visual impairment. Although visual acuity was subjectively normal in a series of 10 patients age 11 to 19, electroretinography was abnormal in one individual.[185] Of 16 patients in a French study, three exhibited marked visual impairment and eight had abnormal electroretinography.[56] In a survey of 80 patients over the age of 10 in North America, one-third had decreased visual acuity[134] and 5 of 15 patients examined at the National Eye Institute had objective evidence of seriously impaired vision, with color vision and dark adaptation deficits as well.[178] Electroretinography con-

firmed the clinical findings in affected patients,[47,178] and the presence of retinal crystals was documented by photography in one individual.[47] Color vision deficits appear to precede problems with acuity.

CORNEA. Corneal crystals, first described in cystinosis in 1941,[186] are pathognomonic of the disorder when seen on slit-lamp examination by a trained ophthalmologist (Fig. 107-7). Descriptions of the pathology of cystinotic corneal tissue are numerous.[181,182,187–189] Fusiform crystals involve the anterior portion of the central cornea but occupy the full thickness of the peripheral cornea.[38,182] They are absent at birth and at 3 months of age[38] but are generally present by 1 year of age.[182] A patchy pattern is occasionally observed between 1 and 2 years, and the presence of crystals not apparent on slit-lamp examination in a moving infant can occasionally be documented by photography. By 3 or 4 years, cystinotic corneas are packed with crystals, and by 10 to 20 years of age, corneas often develop a characteristic haziness.[47] At this time, exquisitely painful corneal erosions, documented by fluorescein testing, can recur several times a month and seriously interfere with normal activities.[47,178,190] In one patient whose cornea was examined immunohistologically, an inflammatory component appeared to be involved.[191] In rabbits fed L-cystine, a keratopathy has been described.[192]

CONJUNCTIVA. The conjunctiva and uvea contain birefringent hexagonal and rectangular crystals[38] shown by x-ray diffraction studies to be made of L-cystine.[189] These can produce a ground-glass appearance on slit-lamp examination, but do not cause inflammation.[182] Electron microscopy of conjunctival tissue has been used to demonstrate the lysosomal location of the crystals.[193] Cystine measurements in conjunctival biopsies have been suggested for the early diagnosis of cystinosis,[54] but leukocyte assays are less invasive.

Photophobia of variable onset produces various degrees of discomfort in children with cystinosis, who often avoid sun-

Fig. 107-7 Slit-lamp demonstration of cystine crystals packing the cornea of a 5 7/12-year-old girl. (*Courtesy of Dr. M. I. Kaiser-Kupfer, National Eye Institute, National Institutes of Health, Bethesda, Maryland.*)

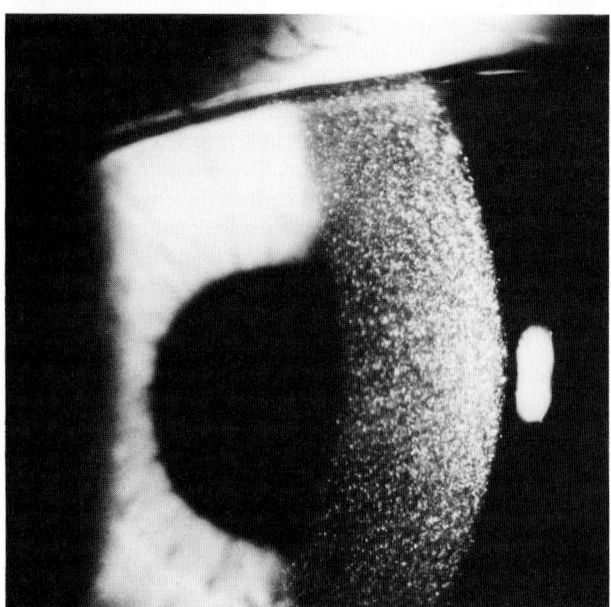

light. The photophobia, which may result from retinal depigmentation or from reflections of light off corneal and conjunctival crystals, appears progressive in its severity.[47]

OTHER OCULAR TISSUES. Cystine crystals are present in the uvea and sclera of cystinotic patients.[182] The irides also contain crystals, especially in older individuals,[47] and crystals have been documented overlying the lenses of posttransplant patients.[47,190] The presence of crystals in these locations may give rise to tissue reactions which result in posterior synechiae, observed in five posttransplant cystinotics 13 to 27 years old.[47,178] This complication may in turn lead to glaucoma, which has been observed in two patients 19 and 27 years old.[47,178,193] Refractory blepharospasm, apparently a result of constant guarding against painful photophobia, has been found in a few older individuals.[47,178] In an occasional young patient in whom Schirmer testing was possible, tear production was diminished.[194]

Endocrine Involvement. Children with cystinosis frequently develop hypothyroidism, with atrophy and crystal formation in follicular cells.[42] This apparently reduces the thyroid's functional reserve and causes compensated hypothyroidism, i.e., an increase in thyrotropin (TSH) prior to the onset of frank hypothyroidism.[179,195] In particular, the α subunit of TSH is often elevated.[196] Hypothyroidism clearly represents an age-related phenomenon. In one study, 3 of 15 patients examined before age 13 years were clinically hypothyroid.[42] Fifteen of twenty-seven French children of all ages with cystinosis were hypothyroid.[56] And more than 70 percent of 80 North American patients over 10 years of age required thyroid replacement, with an average age of 10 years at the initiation of therapy.[157] Hypothyroidism in cystinosis may be associated with pituitary resistance to thyroid hormone.[197]

The pancreas may also be affected by long-standing cystine accumulation. Although nonsuppressible insulinlike activity is normal in young children with cystinosis,[179] several patients have developed insulin-dependent diabetes mellitus after the age of 10.[33,56,198] In some, the diabetes appeared steroid-induced and transient, but in others it persisted even when prednisone was reduced to a low, every-other-day dosage. Insulin levels in affected individuals point to poor insulin production rather than peripheral resistance to insulin.[33] Recently, a 13-month-old infant was reported with cystinosis and diabetes mellitus,[199] and β-cell hyperplasia has been found in cystinotic pancreases examined postmortem.[200]

Histologic study of pituitary glands revealed occasional hyperplasia of thyrotrophs and refractile crystals.[42] Growth hormone,[179] somatomedin-C,[177] and cortisol response to ACTH[179] have been reported normal in children with cystinosis. Studies of gonadotropin levels in cystinosis are limited.[179] In general, patients eventually experience puberty, but it is delayed to approximately 16 to 17 years of age, with a normal sequence of events.[178] One 20-year-old woman with cystinosis and a renal transplant gave birth to a normal boy in late 1986.[200a] Older male patients can experience erections but produce a very low volume ejaculate or none at all.[200b] Some male patients in their twenties have primary hypogonadism.[200b]

Central Nervous System Involvement. The central nervous system had been considered clinically spared in cystinosis, consistent with the apparent lack of cystine storage there (Table 107-1).[49] This is true only for younger children. In one 25-year-old woman with nephropathic cystinosis, postmortem ex-

amination showed cystine storage in all portions of the central nervous system, including cystine levels one to three orders of magnitude elevated in all parenchymal nervous tissues tested.[50] These biochemical findings are consistent with increasingly widespread neurologic involvement in posttransplant patients. Cerebral atrophy on CT scan has been reported in three cystinotic patients in chronic renal failure,[201] in seven of nine posttransplant patients,[202] in a group of 10 cystinosis patients with neurologic symptoms such as seizures, tremor, mental retardation, or pyramidal syndrome,[203] and in 11 of 13 unselected cystinotic patients age 13 to 25.[178] Cerebral cortical atrophy can result from slow virus infections in immunosuppressed patients and can be seen in pediatric patients with end-stage renal disease,[204] but the frequency in cystinosis seems excessive, and one study controlled for this.[203] Other cerebral involvement has been reported in cystinosis, including nonabsorptive hydrocephalus,[205] demyelination of the internal capsule and brachium pontis,[45] and calcification of the internal capsule or basal ganglia and paraventricular areas.[206] The patient with the latter problem, a 25-year-old man with a renal transplant for 14 years, had difficulty swallowing, slow speech, loss of recent memory, extremity weakness, and a gait disturbance confining him to a wheelchair. Another 21-year-old man with a renal transplant also had difficulty swallowing, as well as generalized weakness of all extremities.[206] Most recently, deficits of short-term visual memory, not based upon ophthalmologic abnormalities, have been reported in cystinosis.[207] All these clinical findings may very well be unrelated to the cerebral atrophy seen on CT scan, since nearly all cystinotic patients with atrophy have entirely normal neurologic examinations.[206]

The older patients become, the more likely some cerebral involvement appears. Four of seven cystinotic individuals in their third decade of life examined at the NICHD appeared prematurely aged, with jowled facies (Fig. 107-5c) and slow, raspy, and repetitive speech.[58] More and more these and other late central nervous system abnormalities appear to result from the disease cystinosis and not chronic renal failure, kidney transplantation, or its attendant immunosuppression.

Young patients with cystinosis have average intelligence and school performance.[208] Psychosocial problems occur because of their chronic illness, and adjusting to a life of short stature often proves difficult.[161] Some children avoid school and others fail to extricate themselves from dependence on their parents.

Hepatic and Gastrointestinal Complications. Hepatomegaly has been reported in 7 of 16 dialysis and transplant patients[56] and in 42 percent of 80 patients with cystinosis over the age of 10.[157] Many children under age 5 also have hepatomegaly, whose etiology is unknown. In general, it is not associated with elevated serum liver enzymes or clinical abnormalities. Esophageal varices in two patients[56] and bleeding gastric varices in another[209] did result from portal hypertension. Hypersplenism syndrome has been seen in occasional patients[56,178] and the incidence of splenomegaly among patients over 10 is 27 percent.[157] Liver pathology has demonstrated crystals[32] and hepatic venoocclusive disease[209] but not cirrhosis.[56]

Cystine crystals occur in the appendix,[36] rectal mucosa,[34] and intestinal mucosa.[35] Their presence may contribute to the morning nausea and vomiting observed among some children with cystinosis, many of whom are also poor eaters with penchants for hot, spicy foods.[161] One 7-year-old boy with severe cystinosis has been diagnosed with ulcerative colitis,[58] and an

18-year-old woman has objective evidence of pancreatic exocrine insufficiency.[210]

Other Clinical and Laboratory Abnormalities. Caucasian (not Hispanic or black) patients with cystinosis have skin and hair pigmentation noticeably lighter than their unaffected sibs. This may be related to an impairment of pigment formation by the melanosomes, which are the melanocyte counterparts of lysosomes. This hypothesis is entirely speculative.

Most children with nephropathic cystinosis also display an inability to produce a normal volume of sweat, although sweat electrolyte concentrations are normal.[211] This deficiency results in heat intolerance and avoidance, flushing, hyperthermia, and vomiting in small children. The cause is unknown. Stimulated salivary flow rates were also decreased below the normal range in 10 of 18 cystinotic patients.[212]

In several patients undergoing open muscle biopsy, resorbable sutures failed to dissolve, leaving larger than normal surgical scars.[58] This finding invites speculation regarding cystine's effect on the lysosome's hydrolytic functions.

For reasons that remain mysterious, several laboratory values are chronically elevated in cystinosis, including the sedimentation rate, total serum cholesterol, and platelet count.[161,178] The platelet count normalizes after renal transplant.[178] A mild anemia becomes severe with the onset of uremia, with a hematocrit of 15 to 20 percent accompanying a serum creatinine of 3 to 8 mg/dl. The anemia, not due to iron deficiency, probably results largely from decreased erythropoietin production by a damaged kidney and, later, from uremia, since posttransplant patients have normal hematocrits.[178] The renal Fanconi syndrome causes many laboratory abnormalities in cystinosis, such as increased electrolyte excretion and an elevated heat-labile serum alkaline phosphatase in active rickets.

In view of the increasing number of older cystinosis patients alive by virtue of their renal allografts[56,157] we can expect that the clinical and laboratory ramifications of long-standing cystine storage in nonrenal organs will continue to define themselves. The oldest patient with nephropathic cystinosis of whom we are aware is 30 years old.

Diagnosis

Postnatal. Testing for cystinosis often depends upon an index of suspicion on the part of the attending physician, whether aroused by a child's clinical course or by a history of an affected sib. Physician awareness is apparently increasing, since the age at which children are diagnosed has been gradually decreasing.[157] The most direct method of diagnosis is measurement of leukocyte cystine content.[61] Leukocytes are prepared from whole blood by acid citrate-dextran sedimentation, followed by hypotonic lysis of erythrocytes. The leukocyte pellet is suspended in a buffer containing N-ethylmaleimide to prevent oxidation of any free cysteine to cystine. Cystine is then measured either by an automated amino acid analyzer using column chromatography or by a cystine-binding protein assay.[28] Leukocytes of patients homozygous for cystinosis have approximately 8 nmol half-cystine per milligram protein, or 50 to 100 times the normal value (Table 107-1).[59-63]

Cultured skin fibroblasts also store cystine, to levels between 6 and 14 nmol half-cystine per milligram protein (Table 107-1).[59,60,62] Cells heterozygous for nephropathic cystinosis contain approximately 0.4 nmol half-cystine per milligram

protein.[59] The fibroblast cystine content of cystinotics varies somewhat with cell preparation and storage,[213] cell passage number and confluency,[143] and the cystine and protein content of the culture medium.[138,140]

Cystinosis can also be diagnosed immediately by ophthalmologic examination, revealing the typical crystalline keratopathy in children over 1 year of age[182] and/or a salt and pepper retinopathy in infants even younger.[41] Abnormal eye findings have also been identified in an abortus affected with cystinosis.[184] Detection of the typical retinopathy requires use of an indirect ophthalmoscope and generally is successfully accomplished in the newborn only by an ophthalmologist using either local or general anesthesia.

Other ways to diagnose cystinosis include measurement of hair cystine by infrared spectroscopy[214] and demonstration of characteristic birefringent crystals in either a conjunctival biopsy,[38] rectal mucosal biopsy,[34] or bone marrow aspirate, where the hexagonal and monoclinic cystine crystals are obvious under crossed polarizing prisms.[41] Currently, direct measurement of leukocyte cystine provides the least traumatic, most rapid, and, therefore, the preferred method of diagnosing cystinosis.

There is no newborn screening program for cystinosis because of the labor-intensive nature of current diagnostic tests.

Prenatal. Parenchymal tissue and amniocytes from cystinotic fetuses store 20 to 100 times normal amounts of cystine.[184,215,216] Prenatal diagnosis of cystinosis has been accomplished by using [^{35}S]cystine (1 mCi/ml) pulse labeling[29,217] of cultured amniocytes obtained at 14 to 18 weeks gestation.[184,215,216] After 18 h of incubation to label the lysosomal cystine pool, the cells are lysed in buffer containing N-ethylmaleimide and the labeled metabolites separated by column chromatography or high voltage electrophoresis on paper.[217] Normal fibroblasts show negligible radioactivity in cystine and virtually all the radioactivity is found in glutathione and reduced cysteine-N-ethylmaleimide. Cystinotic fibroblasts contain about 30 percent of radioactivity as the disulfide cystine and about 60 percent as glutathione and the free thiol cysteine. A few percent are found at the origin as taurine. The amniotic fluid cystine level was normal in an affected pregnancy.[184]

Recently, diagnosis has also been accomplished by chorionic villus sampling at 9 weeks of gestation, with direct measurement of the cystine content (34.7 nmol half-cystine per milligram protein) by the cystine binding protein assay.[218] Normal cystine levels using chorionic villi of wet weight at least 5 mg are 0.102 ± 0.011 (SEM) nmol half-cystine per milligram protein.[219]

Heterozygotes. Diagnosis of heterozygotes in the past has rested upon finding a leukocyte (or fibroblast) cystine concentration intermediate between homozygotes (6 to 9 nmol half-cystine per milligram protein, Table 107-1) and normal individuals (less than 0.2 nmol half-cystine per milligram protein). Heterozygotes store less than 1.0.[59-63] In one report, a majority of obligate heterozygotes displayed normal leukocyte cystine values,[63] but the method of preparation may have favored nonpolymorphonuclear leukocytes which accumulate very little cystine in homozygotes and heterozygotes. When polymorphonuclear leukocytes were prepared using a discontinuous gradient of Ficoll-Hypaque, there was no overlap between values for 29 obligate heterozygotes and 18 normal controls.[220] Other methods based on retention[221] or countertransport[63] of [^{35}S]cystine by leukocyte lysosomes can distinguish heterozygotes from homozygotes and normal individuals but are technically very difficult to perform.

Therapy

Symptomatic. Patients with cystinosis develop the renal Fanconi syndrome early in life with attendant renal tubular wastage of glucose, water, sodium, potassium, bicarbonate, phosphorus, and carnitine. Hypoglycemia is not a recognized problem in the usual clinical management of nephropathic cystinosis, but severe electrolyte imbalances due to renal losses of water and electrolytes can cause fatal dehydration, particularly during summer months and during episodes of gastroenteritis. Acute, life-threatening imbalances must be promptly treated with enormous intravenous replacement of fluids and electrolytes. Daily losses during periods of health are managed by oral replacement therapy. Estimates of appropriate amounts of intravenous and oral supplements are discussed elsewhere.[161] Electrolyte supplementation is usually accomplished by some combination of sodium and potassium along with bicarbonate. Polycitra provides 1 meq of sodium and 1 meq of potassium, along with 2 meq of bicarbonate anion (as citrate) in each milliliter.[222] The drug is produced as an intensely orange-flavored syrup which conveniently masks the taste of cysteamine (*vide infra*). In patients with normal potassium, sodium citrate alone (Bicitra) may be substituted. Some patients, in whom bicarbonate wastage is less severe than other electrolyte losses, may require only sodium or potassium chloride. Some children also require oral calcium or magnesium replacement to prevent tetany. Progressive urinary losses of phosphate can be replaced using sodium phosphate (Nutraphos®), which contains 765 mg of phosphate in 2.5 oz. If gastrointestinal disturbances do not interfere with the administration of the phosphate preparation, any existing rickets should be cured within 2 to 3 months. Of utmost importance is ad libitum access to salt and water at all times. All children with nephropathic cystinosis have profound salt and water craving and will regulate themselves very well if not denied access to fluids and salty foods. Particularly enjoyed and often craved by these patients are pickles, pretzels, pizza, salted chips and soft drinks. Indomethacin has been successfully employed to reduce polyuria and polydipsia in cystinotic children,[223,224] but this treatment can also cause a reversible reduction in glomerular filtration rate.[225]

Carnitine deficiency due to Fanconi syndrome[170] can be treated with oral L-carnitine replacement. Plasma carnitine levels return promptly to normal, but because of enormous ongoing urinary losses, the muscle compartment will take years to replete, at least at 100 mg/kg per day of L-carnitine given in divided doses each 6 h.[226]

Although children with cystinosis have generalized and profound aminoaciduria, nitrogen wastage has not been documented.[227]

As renal failure supervenes, the functioning renal mass diminishes and supplementation with pharmacologic doses of vitamin D is required, e.g., 0.25 µg 1,25-dihydroxycholecalciferol every other day or daily, depending on the response of plasma calcium and phosphorus. The need for other supplementation simultaneously decreases, and plasma electrolytes and other chemistries must be followed to avoid hyperkalemia and hyperphosphatemia. Patients also often develop hypothyroidism by the end of the first decade of life[157,179] and respond

well to standard doses of L-thyroxine.[228] Similarly, insulin-deficient patients are benefited by insulin therapy.[33] Older patients with recurrent corneal erosions are sometimes afforded relief by the use of hourly over-the-counter eyedrops or bandage contact lenses. One 12-year-old boy with incapacitating corneal erosions underwent a penetrating keratoplasty in his most affected eye, with gratifying results. The cornea was clear 14 months after the procedure.[190]

Renal Allografts. Once uremia ensues in cystinosis, dialysis or renal transplantation becomes essential. Hemodialysis of a cystinotic boy was reported in 1966[229] and rapidly became part of the standard of care for uremic patients. It has recently been supplanted in some areas by peritoneal dialysis, which can be continuous or intermittent, inpatient or ambulatory. Dialysis represents a temporizing measure for patients awaiting renal transplant.

To our knowledge, the first such allograft in a cystinosis patient took place in 1968. Many more transplants were performed as it became apparent that cystinotic children were appropriate candidates for the procedure.[56,157,178,198,228,230–232] With prednisone, azathioprine, and, occasionally, cyclosporine as immunosuppressive agents, transplanted kidneys are expected to function for at least 15 to 20 years, i.e., the natural life span of a grafted kidney. Several cystinotic patients have undergone multiple renal transplants.[157] The procedure cures the renal disease in cystinosis, and the Fanconi syndrome does not recur[51,231]; supplementation for renal losses becomes unnecessary after transplantation.[51] The histology of donor kidneys examined after transplantation has been described as relatively normal.[51]

As for transplanted cornea,[190] donor kidneys do not store cystine.[51] This follows from the nature of the metabolic defect in cystinosis which is intrinsic to each cell. The increased cystine content occasionally observed in a grafted kidney results from interstitial infiltration of host mononuclear cells.[51,228,231] Parents or sibs heterozygous for cystinosis serve as very suitable donors, and the best immunologic match should always be sought. In one sampling of 14 posttransplant patients with cystinosis, kidneys from living related donors performed better and longer than cadaveric kidneys.[178] Neither dialysis nor transplantation would be expected to reduce cystine levels in nonrenal tissues.

Specific Treatment to Reduce Cystine Storage. Dietary restriction of methionine and cystine to reduce cystine storage has proven of no benefit in cystinosis.[5,227,233] In retrospect, this seems logical since intracellular protein serves as an abundant source of cystine in cystinotic fibroblasts.[139]

Specific drug therapy has been directed toward the reduction of cystine to cysteine. In 1961, penicillamine was proposed to serve this function,[234] but subsequent clinical trials demonstrated a conclusive lack of efficacy.[233,235] It was later apparent that penicillamine did not efficiently deplete either cystinotic fibroblasts[127] or leukocyte granular fractions[128] of cystine, probably because its size or configuration prevented entry into lysosomes.

Dithiothreitol was the first thiol-reducing agent to prove to be an effective cystine-depleting agent in cultured fibroblasts[130]; cystine could be mobilized by either dithiothreitol disulfide or free thiol.[236] Although oral dithiothreitol therapy produced moderate reductions in leukocyte cystine content in two children treated for 8 months at a time,[53] longer-term stabilization of renal function has not been demonstrated, and dithiothreitol has not been widely used during the past 10 years.

Ascorbic acid reduced the cystine content of cultured cystinotic fibroblasts by 50 percent[131] but did not benefit renal function in 32 cystinotic children treated for 28 months in a placebo-controlled clinical trial.[237]

The largest and best experience with cystine-depleting drugs in cystinosis involves cysteamine* (β-mercaptoethylamine), whose mechanism of action has already been described (see "Mechanism of Cystine Depletion," above). In 1976, in vitro experiments demonstrating cystine-depleting efficacy in cystinotic fibroblasts provided the basis for in vivo administration of the drug.[127] A cystinotic patient with end-stage renal disease tolerated up to 90 mg/kg per day of cysteamine hydrochloride with marked cystine depletion in circulating leukocytes, but suffered a seizure, presumably due to her advanced renal failure.[127] That trial was discontinued, but other workers studying the effect of relatively short-term cysteamine therapy in a small number of patients with advanced renal failure noted no significant improvement.[238] Anecdotal reports of short-term cysteamine use are referred to in a previous edition of this chapter.[7]

In 1978, a multicenter collaborative trial was begun at the University of Michigan and concurrently at the NICHD and the University of California, San Diego. Patients were treated with a mean dose of 51.3 mg/kg per day of cysteamine free base for up to 73 months. The drug was given every 6 h because of its short duration of cystine-depleting action.[127] The mean leukocyte depletion of the 93 children treated with cysteamine was 82 percent. When the patients were studied at age 6, 17 of 27 children treated with cysteamine for at least a year had a serum creatinine of less than 1.0 mg/dl, compared with only 2 of 17 in an historical control group not treated with cysteamine ($p = 0.002$). When the study was terminated, the mean creatinine clearance was 38.5 ± 2.5 ml/min per 1.73 m^2 for cysteamine-treated patients and 29.7 ± 2.0 for patients not receiving cysteamine ($p = 0.015$). In addition, significant improvement of growth was noted during the first year on cysteamine and every year thereafter. Between 2 and 3 years of age, patients treated with cysteamine had 93.1 percent of the normal growth velocity, whereas in untreated children growth was only 53.5 percent of normal. Although the renal tubular dysfunction did not improve and the crystalline keratopathy did not resolve, some children at least temporarily avoided otherwise inevitable renal failure at age 10 years.[176]

Cysteamine has served as a duodenal ulcerogen in rats,[239] and it depletes somatostatin[240] and pituitary prolactin[241] in rats given doses much larger than those used in humans. Blood levels of cysteamine in treated cystinotic children reach only 54 μM 1 h after a dose.[242] Standard treatment of patients with cysteamine has revealed inhibition of glycine turnover,[243] blunting of a prolactin response to thyrotropin-releasing hormone,[244] and conversion of apolipoprotein E$_3$ to an apolipoprotein E$_4$ phenotype on isoelectric focusing,[245] but no clinical ramifications have accompanied these laboratory findings. Three patients whose cysteamine dose was abruptly started at up to 70 mg/kg per day experienced a Stevens-Johnson-like rash, central nervous system disorientation and lethargy, or

neutropenia, all of which resolved on discontinuing of the drug.[246] With the gradual incremental dosing over 6 to 8 weeks used in the long-term study, the only significant side effect was nausea and vomiting observed in approximately 14 percent of patients.[176] Cysteamine, a free thiol, has the odor and taste of rotten eggs. The hepatic venoocclusive disease reportedly due to cysteamine therapy[209] appears more likely a complication of cystinosis itself.[247] Hepatomegaly is no more frequent among patients treated with cysteamine than among those who never received cysteamine.[159]

Cysteamine has recently been shown to prevent the development of renal Fanconi syndrome in a patient treated from 5 weeks of age[248] but not in one treated from 9 weeks.[249] The renal damage in cystinosis, whether tubular or glomerular, appears irreversible. In contrast, corneal crystal formation may be reversible, as two patients under the age of 2 years exhibited a clearing of corneal crystals after 5 months of therapy using 10 mM cysteamine eye drops.[66] No toxicity was observed in this double-masked, placebo-controlled study.

In utero therapy with cysteamine might seem reasonable because cystine accumulation begins early in fetal life, but the risks of teratogenic effects of the free thiol appear prohibitive at this time. Animal studies may alter this conclusion. The use of cysteamine is now being considered to prevent the late nonrenal complications of cystinosis. Perhaps the best gauge of the efficacy of cysteamine in this population will be provided by a comparison of the frequency of nonrenal involvement among current patients age 10 to 30 and future patients the same age who will have been treated for 10 to 15 years with cysteamine.

Because of cysteamine hydrochloride's foul taste and odor, other means of delivering the free thiol have been pursued. Cysteamine in gelatin capsules using 0.2% silicic acid as a dessicant has been recommended.[250] Pantetheine, when degraded by pantetheinase,[81] produces cysteamine, but pantetheine's cystine-depleting efficacy appears inferior to that of cysteamine.[251] Phosphocysteamine (WR-638, the phosphothioester of cysteamine developed by Walter Reed Army Hospital as a radioprotective agent) lacks the odor and smell of cysteamine. In tissue culture experiments and in limited clinical trials, phosphocysteamine had the same cystine-depleting properties on a molar basis as cysteamine itself,[135] to which it is converted in vivo.[252] Phosphocysteamine will be the next subject of collaborative clinical studies in the United States designed to investigate the efficacy of cystine-depleting agents in preserving renal function in cystinosis.

Support Group. The Cystinosis Foundation,[253] established in 1983, provides a forum for the interaction of families and physicians concerned with cystinosis.

Cystinosis Variants

The preceding discussion has been related to the infantile nephropathic type of cystinosis. However, some patients are more mildly affected than the classic cases. This was first appreciated with the description in 1957 of an individual with adult or benign cystinosis.[254] Since then, at least eight patients age 23 to 53 years from six different sibships have been identified by the presence of corneal cystine crystals,[60,254–258] usually noted incidentally on ophthalmologic examination. A previous edition of this chapter gives further references to

---

*This drug had not been approved by the Food and Drug Administration at the time of writing.

cystinosis variants.[7] In general, benign cystinosis patients do not suffer renal disease of any kind, grow normally, and manifest normal skin and retinal pigmentation. They require no therapy and their lives are entirely normal in length and quality except, perhaps, for photophobia.[60,256,258] Cystine crystals have been found in the cornea, conjunctiva, bone marrow, and even in peripheral leukocytes, but not in the kidney.[254,256,258] Biochemical measurement of kidney cystine was performed in only one case of adult cystinosis, in which the extremely low patient value, compared with controls, rendered the data unhelpful.[258] Conjunctival cystine levels in benign cystinosis resemble those in nephropathic cystinosis.[54]

An intermediate variety of cystinosis, first described in 1971, has been called adolescent, juvenile, or late-onset. The hallmark of this variant is renal disease appearing between 18 months and 17 years of age.[259–265] Intermediate cystinosis can involve tubular dysfunction; the first patient described had polyuria in infancy.[62] Glomerular deterioration always occurs but proceeds much more slowly than in classic infantile cystinosis. At least seven patients with intermediate cystinosis have had significant renal damage (creatinine clearance 40 to 50 ml/min per 1.73 m^2, serum creatinine 1.5 to 2.2 mg/dl) at age 13 to 17 years.[259,261,264,265] Photophobia, impairment of growth, and decreased skin and retinal pigmentation are variably present in intermediate cystinosis. Cystine crystals are found in the cornea, conjunctiva, bone marrow, and, when specifically sought after, in the kidney.[264] Some young patients considered on clinical grounds to have benign cystinosis may later develop renal disease and require reclassification as intermediate variants. This sequence of events has been documented for two sibs who became uremic at ages 14 and 15.[265] The same outcome may be possible for two youths 11 and 16 years old[266] and for a boy 13 years old recently described as having benign cystinosis.[267] Consideration should be given to offering cysteamine therapy to any young patient with cystine storage, even in the absence of renal tubular or glomerular damage.

As for infantile nephropathic cystinosis, both the benign and intermediate variants of cystinosis "breed true," i.e., have similar clinical manifestations within sibships. Inheritance follows an autosomal recessive pattern, supported by the finding of consanguinity[256] and multiple affected sibs within some families.[256,259,263] The incidence of benign cystinosis is most likely much greater than the number of reported cases would indicate, since the method of diagnosis, i.e., the recognition of crystals on a slit-lamp examination performed for unrelated reasons, makes ascertainment very poor.

The clinical severity of cystinosis, perhaps best gauged by effects on renal function, correlates well with the amount of cystine stored within leukocytes in each of the variant types of the disease. In the benign type, leukocyte cystine levels vary between 1 and 3.6 nmol half-cystine per milligram protein,[62] and these individuals suffer no renal disease. Intermediate cystinosis patients have levels of 2.5 to 5.0 nmol half-cystine per milligram protein in their leukocytes[62,261,264,265] and become uremic in their second or third decade of life. Heterozygotes for intermediate[62] and benign cystinosis[266] have cystine levels similar to heterozygotes for nephropathic cystinosis. Infantile nephropathic cystinosis patients, with leukocyte cystine levels usually over 4 nmol half-cystine per milligram protein (Table 107-1), suffer terminal renal failure by age 10. In untreated cystinosis patients, leukocyte cystine levels may correlate with kidney cystine levels, which may be directly related to renal damage.

Leukocyte cystine levels also appear inversely related to the amount of residual cystine-carrying capacity within the lysosomal membrane. Figure 107-8 illustrates the concept that a continuum of cystine-carrying capacities (from 0 to 100 percent of normal) and leukocyte cystine levels (from 0.04 to 23.1 nmol half-cystine per milligram protein) are likely to exist in a population. Specific clinical manifestations appear as levels of stored cystine exceed discrete thresholds. The scheme suggests that there exist a large number of different types of cystinosis, with clinical expression of the disease determined by the amount of residual cystine-carrying capacity. Only three variants have been formally delineated because our current ability to differentiate among phenotypes depends on relatively gross clinical parameters. But, in the future, biochemical and molecular genetic techniques will permit discrimination among an enormous number of cystinosis variants.

Somatic cell fusion has demonstrated that benign and nephropathic cystinosis cells do not complement each other,[268] suggesting that their mutations are at the same locus. This may not be true for all combinations of fused cystinotic variants. Fused hybrids of normal and nephropathic cystinotic fibroblasts do not store cystine[269]; apparently the provision of lysosomal cystine carrier genes by the normal cells is sufficient to prevent the expression of a heterozygous phenotype with respect to cystine storage.

Future Research in Cystinosis

As occurs so frequently a genetic disorder, in this case cystinosis, has revealed a metabolic function, i.e., lysosomal membrane transport, previously unrecognized because it was op-

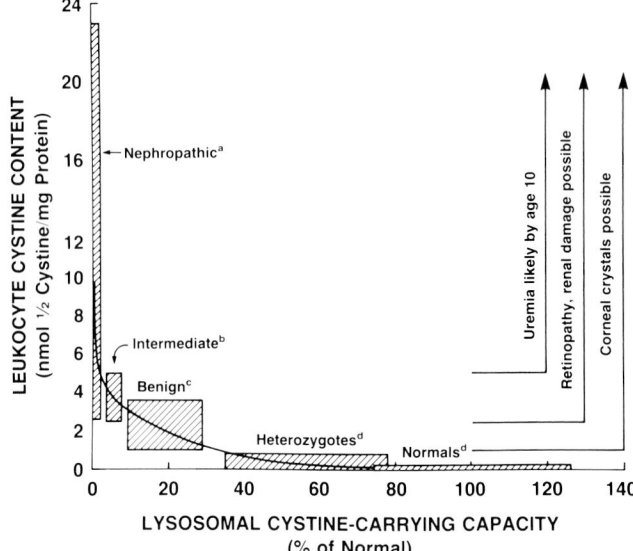

Fig. 107-8 Relationship between lysosomal cystine-carrying activity, leukocyte cystine content, and clinical manifestations for various cystinosis genotypes and phenotypes. Vertical dimension of each box gives a range; horizontal dimension gives 1 SD for normals and heterozygotes, and an *estimate* for cystinosis variants. Line passes through the means for each group. a = from Table 107-1, Ref. 111; b = Refs. 62, 260, 262, 265, 266; no data are available on cystine-carrying capacity in this variant; c = Refs. 255–259; cystine-carrying capacity based on one patient, Ref. 268; d = Ref. 63.

erating normally. The precedent set by the elucidation of the defect in cystinosis has prompted a search for other inborn errors caused by lysosomal transport defects and deeper investigations into the structure and function of the lysosomal membrane's cystine porter.

Isolating the lysosomal cystine carrier will prove exceedingly difficult; no transport protein has yet been purified from any subcellular organelle. Strategies may include the application of innovative protein separative techniques to lysosomal membranes to isolate the carrier protein or the use of transfection procedures which "cure" cystinotic fibroblasts of their cystinosis; subsequent recovery of the transfecting DNA might yield the "curing" gene. This genetic approach must involve steps which select for cured cells, and can take advantage of the immortality offered by SV40-transformed cystinotic fibroblasts.[270] A clear goal of this type of research will be to determine the nucleotide sequence of the gene defective in cystinosis. This would allow characterization of all the mutations which result in cystinosis, and should prompt accurate prenatal diagnosis by restriction fragment length polymorphism analysis in informative families. At this writing, these feats remain in the indefinite future.

The cystine carrier represents a functional integral lysosomal membrane protein. Therefore, once a probe such as a specific antibody is found, the intracellular movement and processing of the carrier can be followed. Cells from cystinosis patients will provide appropriate negative controls. Cells from patients with mucolipidosis II- or I-cell disease, who lack the enzyme responsible for placing the recognition marker, mannose-6-phosphate, on lysosomal enzymes (see Chap. 62) also have a cystine transport defect. I-cell fibroblasts store cystine (but not other amino acids)[271] and display impaired egress of cystine out of their lysosomes.[109,272] This may occur because the lysosomal cystine carrier is not properly processed in the absence of a full contingent of hydrolytic enzymes within the I-cell lysosomes. Once the cystine carrier is isolated, this hypothesis can be tested.

Cystinotic fibroblasts can also be used to study the relative rates of lysosomal and cytoplasmic proteolysis. Since cystinotic lysosomes accumulate cystine from the degradation of disulfide proteins, the rate of lysosomal cystine accumulation provides a measure of lysosomal proteolysis.[138–140,273] Other protease systems, one of which requires ATP and ubiquitin, have now been demonstrated to be cytosolic systems. Under conditions of nutritional deprivation, cells switch from cytosolic to lysosomal proteolysis. The advantage and mechanism of this switch is unknown. If cystinotic fibroblasts are exposed to proteins labeled with [^{35}S]cystine, then the amount of lysosomal ^{35}S-cystine accumulation will provide an assay by which to follow the switch to lysosomal proteolysis and the mechanisms which control it.

Clinically, many issues require pursuit. For example, what are the full nutritional ramifications of the renal Fanconi syndrome in children with cystinosis? Can oral carnitine therapy ever replete cystinotic muscle? What are the pathophysiological bases for kidney damage, growth impairment, cerebral calcifications and atrophy, and hypopigmentation in cystinosis? Why do patients with the adult variant of cystinosis escape kidney disease? Will any organ be spared eventual damage in cystinosis? Will cysteamine therapy benefit nonrenal organs to the same extent as the kidneys? The answers to these and many other questions await further clinical investigation.

SIALIC ACID STORAGE DISORDERS

Salla disease and infantile free sialic acid storage disease are two lysosomal storage disorders which share qualitative biochemical and histologic features but which differ in the severity of their clinical manifestations. Both disorders are characterized by severe psychomotor retardation, with Salla disease patients less affected than ISSD patients. Intermediate forms may exist. The major biochemical feature of these disorders is intralysosomal accumulation of free sialic acid or N-acetylneuraminic acid (Fig. 107-1).

Historical Aspects

The first description of sialic acid storage disease appeared in 1979 when four patients with severe psychomotor retardation and lysosomal storage were reported.[274] The eponym *Salla disease* was adopted because most of the affected patients originated from an area in northern Finland with that name. A tenfold increase in urinary excretion of free sialic acid was found in the original patients and in nine similar individuals subsequently described.[275] No other abnormalities were detected in the urine. Since 1979, over 70 patients with Salla disease have been identified by screening mentally retarded individuals in Finland for sialuria. Approximately half of the patients were from northern Finland; a few patients of non-Finnish descent have been described.[276–278]

Recently, the clinical features of six children[279] and 34 older individuals[280] with Salla disease were described. All had ataxia in infancy as well as early-onset psychomotor retardation of a moderate to severe degree. Life expectancy was nearly normal. The spectrum of sialic acid storage disorders was widened in 1982 by reports of severely impaired infants with clinical and histologic evidence of lysosomal storage and vastly increased tissue and urine levels of free sialic acid.[281,282] Even more severely affected newborns have been reported,[283] and intermediate forms of free sialic acid storage disease have been described.[284]

The Basic Defect

Sialic Acid Metabolism. The sialic acids are a family of over 30 compounds derived from neuraminic acid, with many biologic roles.[285,286] In humans, the predominant sialic acid is N-acetylneuraminic acid, a negatively charged compound of molecular weight 309 and pK 2.6, which we refer to as sialic acid. While a small portion of total sialic acid is free in tissues and body fluids, most is bound by an α-glycosidic linkage to glycoconjugates. Sialic acid provides these macromolecules with a negatively charged terminal sugar that serves many functions,[287] but no direct biologic role has been attributed to unbound sialic acid.

The synthesis of sialic acid begins with glucose, which undergoes several modifications to become activated UDP-N-acetyl-D-glucosamine. This central metabolite is converted to N-acetylmannosamine (ManNAc) in a reaction that is subject to feedback inhibition by cytidine monophosphate (CMP)-sialic acid[288,289] (Fig. 107-9). ManNAc is modified in stepwise fashion to produce N-acetylmannosamine-6-phosphate, N-acetylneuraminic acid-9-phosphate, and N-acetylneuraminic acid

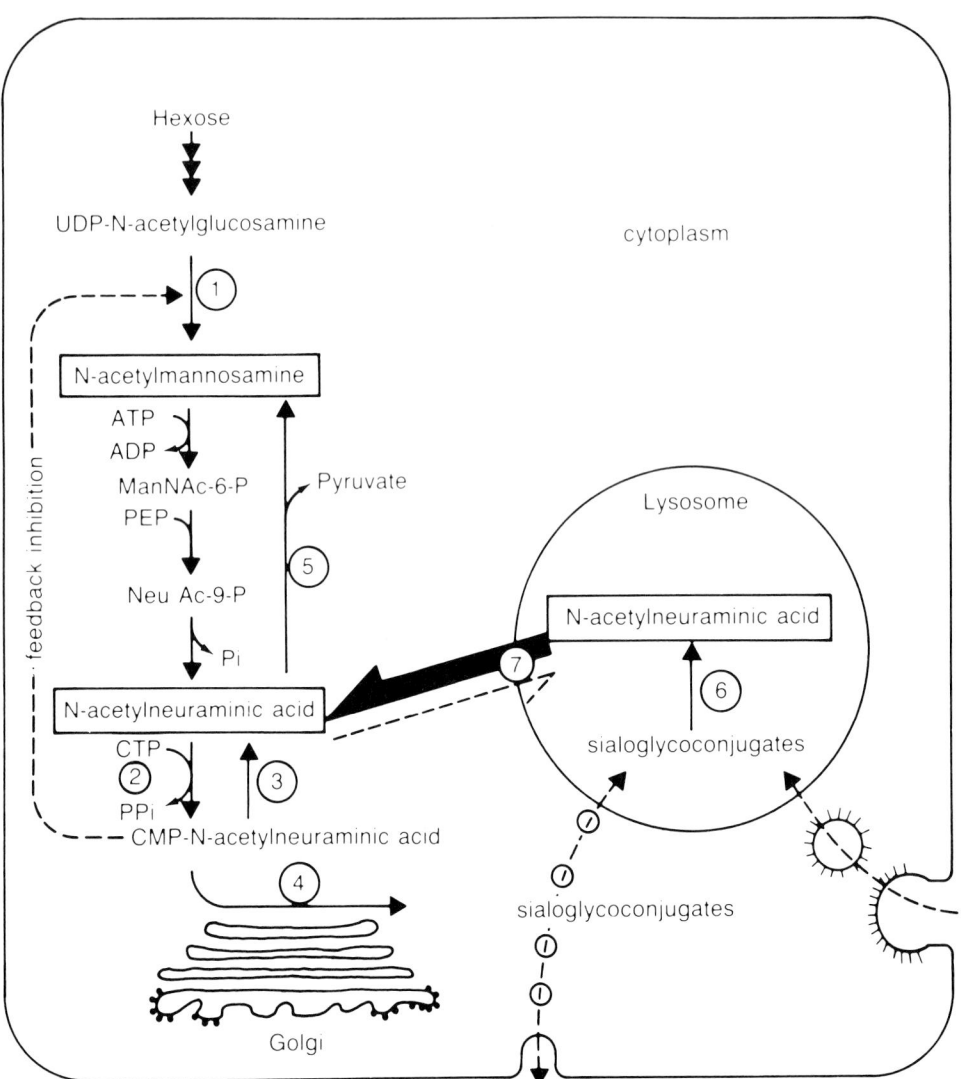

Fig. 107-9 *Main steps in mammalian sialic acid metabolism. Enzymes and reactions indicated in the pathway are: (1) UDP-N-acetylglucosamine-2-epimerase (EC 5.1.3.14); (2) acylneuraminate cytidylyltransferase (EC 2.7.7.43); (3) CMP-N-acylneuraminate phosphodiesterase (EC 3.1.4.40); (4) sialyltransferases (EC 2.4.99.1-9); (5) N-acetylneuraminate lyase (EC 4.1.3.3); (6) sialidase (EC 3.2.1.18); (7) putative lysosomal membrane free sialic acid carrier, defective in the sialic acid storage disease. ManNAc-6-P = N-acetylmannosamine-6-phosphate; NeuAC-9-P = N-acetylneuraminic acid-9-phosphate.*

(sialic acid) in reactions apparently not subject to feedback inhibition.[288,290] Sialic acid is then incorporated into glycoconjugates by a cytoplasmic process utilizing CMP as a carrier.

The degradation of sialoglycoconjugates occurs within lysosomes by sequential hydrolysis of terminal glycosidic linkages, usually initiated by the removal of one or more sialic acid residues by an acid sialidase. The free sialic acid produced can be reutilized or degraded by N-acetylneuraminate lyase,[291] a cytoplasmic enzyme apparently not present within lysosomes.[292,293] This suggests that sialic acid must be removed from the lysosomes for further metabolism. Prior to the discovery of free sialic acid storage disorders the requirement for such a transport process was unrecognized.

Sialic Acid Storage and Localization. All patients with Salla disease or ISSD excrete increased amounts of free sialic acid in their urine (Table 107-2). Compared with age-matched controls, this increase is five- to tenfold in Salla disease and 20- to 200-fold in ISSD. An increase of urinary 2-deoxy-2,3-dehydro-N-acetylneuraminic acid has also been reported in one patient with ISSD.[282] The increased urinary excretion of free

sialic acid may result from an increased serum level, variously reported in ISSD.[284,297,298] The elevated serum level probably results from intracellular accumulation of free sialic acid, which has been identified in all tissues studied from patients with sialic acid storage disease (Table 107-2). These include liver, kidney, brain, leukocytes, and cultured fibroblasts. In Salla disease the amount of free sialic acid in tissues is increased approximately 10- to 30-fold, while in ISSD it is increased up to 200-fold. Gas-liquid chromatography/mass spectrometry and [13]C- or H-nuclear magnetic resonance spectroscopy have verified that the sialic acid excreted in the urine and stored within tissues is authentic N-acetylneuraminic acid.[275,281,284,292,295,296]

Experiments using radiolabeled sialic acid precursors, e.g., ManNAc or glucosamine, demonstrated that ISSD fibroblasts accumulated sialic acid in free form and that excretion of free sialic acid into the culture medium was negligible.[281,301] Other investigators found seven times the normal amount of labeled free sialic acid in cultured ISSD fibroblasts after incubation with ^{3}H-ManNAc for 72 h.[296] Similar results were obtained for Salla disease fibroblasts.[302] A prolonged retention of la-

Table 107-2 Free and Total Sialic Acid of Tissues, Cells, and Urine from Patients with Salla Disease or ISSD

	Mutants			Controls			
	N	Free	Total	N	Free	Total	Reference
Liver, μmol/g wet weight							
Salla	2	0.9–1.1	1.9–2.4	3	0.03–0.09	0.8–1.3	292
ISSD	1	18	21	—	—	—	281
Cultured fibroblasts, nmol/mg protein							
Salla	11	6–33	16–39	9	0.4–1.6	10–21	292, 294
	1	20	22	7	6.6	7	277
ISSD	1	(3, 5)★	(4, 7)★	NA†	(0.2)★	(0.9)★	295
	2	35, 52	56, 61	20	0–3.9	6–14	282
	1	40	65	NA	1.2–2.1	20	296
	1	63	90	3	0	11–12	297
	1	88	102	14	3.1	24	297
	1	33	41	5	0–2.6	8–18	298
Cultured amniocytes, nmol/mg protein							
Salla	1	3	19	14	0.5	19	294
ISSD	1	25	38	5	0.4	15	299
Urine, nmol/mg creatinine							
Salla	1	700	1050–1250	NA	90	345	276
	1	1370	1680	4	126	280	277
	1	2460	—	NA	430	—	278
Adults	13	160–450	360–1000	24	7–28	84–250	275
Children	6	640–2100	—	74	100–650	—	280
ISSD	1	2240	3530	5	18–50	290–540	298
	1	5230	5450	6	34–617	140–1350	297
	1	12330	12650	8	215	480	297

★ μmol/g wet weight.
†NA = not available.

beled ManNAc-derived free sialic acid was also observed by investigators studying both Salla disease[302] and ISSD fibroblasts.[281,296,301]

Bound sialic acid has appeared normal in most individuals with sialic acid storage[281,292,295] but was reported up to sixfold increased in one Salla disease[277] and one ISSD patient.[284] In studies of liver, brain, and cultured fibroblasts in Salla disease and ISSD, gangliosides, neutral glycolipids, and membrane-bound sialoglycoconjugates were normal.[292,295,300] In ISSD, slight biochemical abnormalities consistent with neurodegeneration have been reported, i.e., moderately increased levels of simple gangliosides and low levels of brain galactosylceramide and sulfogalactosylceramide.[281] The incorporation of labeled ManNAc-derived sialic acid into sialoglycoconjugates has been reported as normal[296] or slightly elevated in ISSD fibroblasts.[295]

The intralysosomal localization of sialic acid was first indicated in Salla disease by histochemical methods using the sialic acid–specific lectin Limulus polyphemus agglutinin.[303] Studies employing ISSD fibroblasts and differential centrifugation demonstrated the accumulation of free sialic acid in a lysosome-rich subcellular fraction.[295] Salla disease fibroblast studies using low density lipoprotein labeled with tritium in the sialic acid moiety gave similar results.[302] The binding, internalization, lysosomal degradation, and exit of products of lipoprotein catabolism were normal, but the accumulation of labeled sialic acid liberated within the mutant cells was two- to threefold increased compared with controls. Chase studies showed that the labeled free sialic acid decreased by 70 to 80 percent within 24 h in normal cells, but by only 10 to 30 percent in mutant cells. Retained free sialic acid was localized mainly in the lysosomal compartment, as indicated by Percoll gradient fractionation of postnuclear preparations of the fibro-

blasts.[302] ³H-sialic acid labeled fetuin was also used to demonstrate accumulation of labeled free sialic acid in ISSD fibroblasts,[304] and differential latency studies using digitonin supported these results.[301]

Direct evidence of intralysosomal localization has recently been provided by Percoll gradient fractionation of ISSD[305,306] and Salla disease[305] fibroblasts. In these cells, free sialic acid fractionated with the lysosomal enzyme hexosaminidase. It has also been reported that ISSD lysosomes are more buoyant than normal lysosomes.[306] The concentration of endogenous free sialic acid in ISSD lysosomes has been estimated to be 40 mM.[284]

These biochemical findings supported previous histologic evidence for lysosomal accumulation in the free sialic acid storage disorders (Fig. 107-10). On electron microscopy, the appearance of enlarged lysosomes was similar in Salla disease and ISSD, but more striking in the latter. Single membrane-bound vacuoles containing fibrillogranular material and occasional dark staining globules were readily apparent. Multilinear arrays or lamellar stacks were reported in one patient with Salla disease[277] and several ISSD patients.[282,297,298] Enlarged lysosomes were prominent in both Salla disease and ISSD in fibrocytes, Schwann cells, Kupffer cells, perilobular hepatocytes, epithelial cells, sweat gland cells, and endothelial cells of the blood and lymphatic capillaries. They were also occasionally seen in various other cell types. In ISSD, bone marrow mononuclear cells were shown by some investigators to contain enlarged lysosomes[282,284] and by others to be spared.[297] Vacuolation has been demonstrated in ISSD central nervous system neurons and glomerular epithelial cells,[283] and in renal tubular, cardiac muscle, alveolar, spleen, and glial cells.[297] Peripheral lymphocytes are commonly vacuolated in ISSD patients but not in all patients with Salla dis-

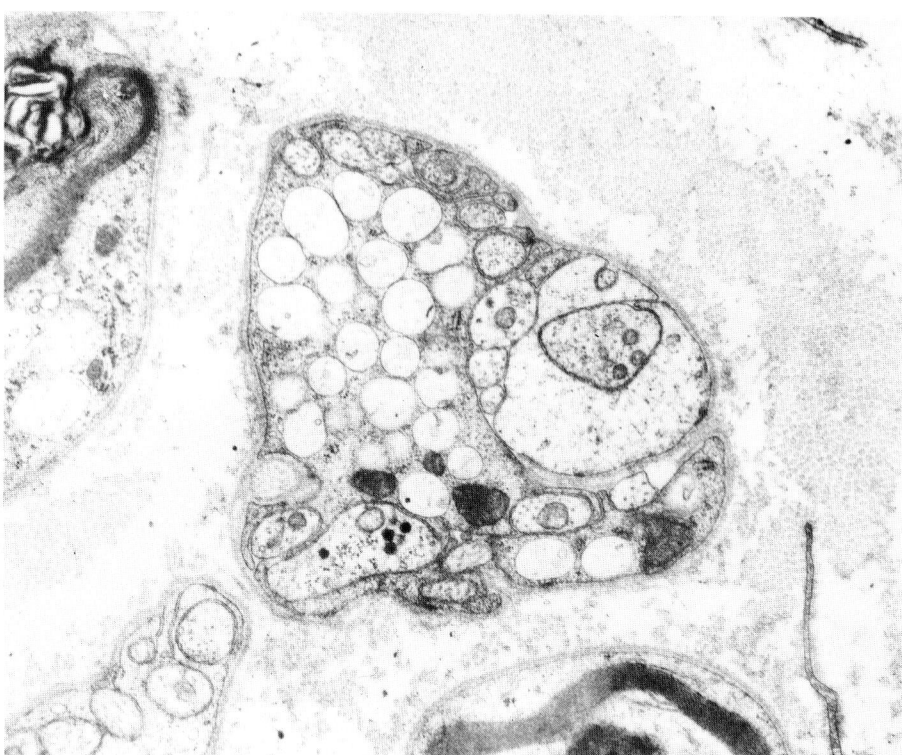

Fig. 107-10 Electron photomicrograph of unmyelinated dermal nerve Schwann cell from a skin biopsy of a patient with Salla disease. Enlarged single membrane-bound vesicles are filled with amorphous fibrillo-granular material. ×11,220. *(From Archives of Neurology, 1979, vol. 36, pp. 88–94, copyright 1979, American Medical Association.)*

ease.[278,279,307] Cultured fibroblasts can exhibit vacuolation on phase contrast and electron microscopy both in ISSD[281,297,298] and, to a lesser extent, in Salla disease.[274] Epidermal cells did not appear vacuolated in either Salla disease[274] or ISSD.[282]

Sialic Acid Metabolism in the Storage Disorders. Recognition of free sialic acid as the storage compound prompted metabolic studies of the turnover of this molecule. Using cultured fibroblasts and liver from normal and affected individuals, it was shown that the major enzymes involved in the metabolism of sialic acid (Fig. 107-9) were normal. These studies included assays of N-acetylneuraminate lyase, sialidase, CMP-N-acylneuraminate phosphodiesterase, and acylneuraminate cytidylyltransferase.[292,295] In fibroblasts the activity of sialidase was reported to be normal by most investigators, although two authors reported three- to fivefold increases.[296,297] Sialidase was also reported increased in the lymphocytes of one patient with Salla disease.[276] All other lysosomal enzymes studied have been normal in ISSD and Salla disease.

Lysosomal Transport Studies. The existence of a cytoplasmic but not a lysosomal enzyme for the catabolism of free sialic acid suggested that impaired transport across the lysosomal membrane might be the cause of sialic acid storage in Salla disease and ISSD. As for cystinosis, a means of loading normal lysosomes to mutant levels of the stored compound was required in order to compare rates of egress. Such loading was approached by exposure of normal fibroblasts to 30 to 100 mM ManNAc, a precursor of sialic acid (Fig. 107-9), for 3 to 10 days; this procedure was previously shown to introduce large amounts of sialic acid into intact fibroblasts.[290] Absolute amounts of free sialic acid were measured by high-performance liquid chromatography.[308] The loading procedure achieved free sialic levels in normal lysosome-rich granular fractions equivalent to endogenous free sialic acid concentrations in Salla disease granular fractions.[309] In addition, Percoll density gradients of normal granular fractions indicated that a portion of the ManNAc-derived free sialic acid fractionated with lysosomal marker enzymes,[305] and egress experiments verified that ManNAc-derived and endogenous sialic acid were handled by mutant granular fractions in an identical fashion.[309] Using ManNAc-loaded fibroblasts, it was first shown that free sialic acid lost from inside normal lysosome-rich granular fractions was recovered outside, that the velocity of this reaction was linear with time through 15 min, and that Salla disease granular fractions did not exhibit a similar loss of sialic acid over the same period of time. Subsequent determinations of initial rate demonstrated that the velocity of normal sialic acid egress increased linearly with loading up to 90 pmol per unit of hexosaminidase (Fig. 107-11); four different Salla disease fibroblast strains displayed a negligible egress velocity regardless of the initial sialic acid loading. The velocity of cystine egress was normal in Salla disease lysosomes, indicating some specificity for the putative lysosomal sialic acid carrier. Egress of sialic acid from normal lysosome-rich granular fractions was temperature-dependent, with a Q_{10} of 2.3,[305] suggesting a carrier-mediated transport process. In addition, the existence of an inherited defect in sialic acid transport provided strong evidence that the movement of sialic acid across the lysosomal membrane was carrier-mediated. The failure to demonstrate saturation kinetics was probably due to an inability to load normal lysosomes sufficiently.

Loading and velocity experiments performed on ISSD fibroblasts yielded results resembling those for Salla disease. Although ISSD loading, with or without ManNAc exposure, was several times that of ManNAc-loaded normal granular fractions, these mutant granules lost virtually no free sialic acid during a 30-min egress period.[305]

Similar results were found when purified normal lysosomes were loaded by direct exposure to 200 mM sialic acid[310] and compared with lysosomes from ISSD fibroblasts (identified as Salla disease cells). In 3 min, normal lysosomes lost 60 percent of their sialic acid, while ISSD lysosomes lost only 10 percent,

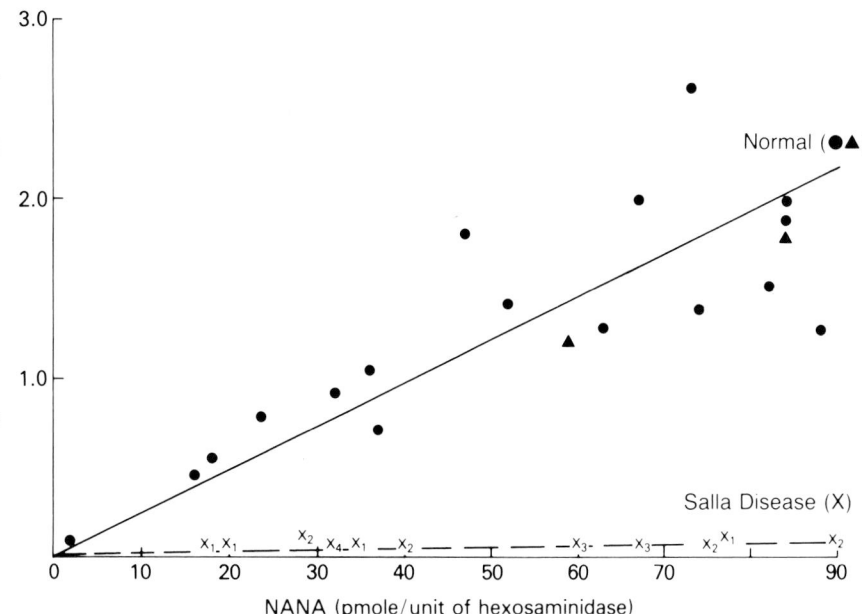

Fig. 107-11 Initial velocity of sialic acid (NANA) transport out of lysosomes plotted against lysosomal sialic acid loading in normal and Salla disease fibroblasts. Normal egress velocity increased with loading. Salla disease granular fractions exhibited negligible egress regardless of loading. Values were corrected for lysosomal rupture as judged by the release of the lysosomal enzyme hexosaminidase. *(From Renlund et al.: "Defective Sialic Acid Egress from Isolated Fibroblast Lysosomes of Patients with Salla Disease," Science, May 9, 1986, vol. 232, pp. 759-762. Copyright 1986 by the American Association for the Advancement of Science.)*

but the initial loading of the mutant lysosomes was 229 nmol per unit of hexosaminidase compared with only 5 nmol per unit of hexosaminidase for the normal individuals. In other experiments, Salla disease, ISSD, and normal control fibroblasts were exposed to [³H]sialic acid methyl ester, and a portion of the radioactivity appeared in lysosomes as authentic free sialic acid.[311] This radioactivity was followed to demonstrate a prolonged $t_{1/2}$ of sialic acid egress from the mutant lysosomes compared with normal, although the specific radioactivity was almost certainly diluted by the high endogenous sialic acid content of Salla disease and ISSD lysosomes. In cases of grossly unequal loading, velocity measurements based on the detection of absolute amounts of free sialic acid are crucial in comparing normal and mutant transport.

Genetics and Epidemiology

Genealogic studies of Salla disease families suggest an autosomal recessive mode of inheritance; consanguinity was demonstrated in several families. Males and females are equally affected, and the corrected proportion of affected sibs was 0.24 in 23 families studied.[280] The carrier frequency has been estimated at 1:40 in northern Finland, with further clustering in subpopulations.[312] The majority of the Salla disease patients have been reported from Finland, but recently occasional patients have been detected in Sweden,[276] Germany,[277] and France.[278] Fewer than 10 patients with ISSD have been described. The presence of patients of both sexes suggests that it is an autosomal disorder.

Obligate heterozygotes for both Salla disease and ISSD are entirely unaffected, and detection of carriers is not currently possible. The urinary excretion of free sialic acid[276,294,297] and the free sialic acid content of cultured fibroblasts of Salla disease and ISSD heterozygotes[294,297,299] have been within the normal range.

Clinical and Pathologic Features

Salla Disease (Fig. 107-12). Intrauterine growth, pregnancy, delivery, and the neonatal period have been normal in all cases

of Salla disease. A few infants have appeared jittery shortly after birth.[276] All patients have delayed motor development of variable severity, first observed between 3 and 12 months of age. Most infants are hypotonic, but many older patients have increased muscular tone in the lower extremities. Mild to se-

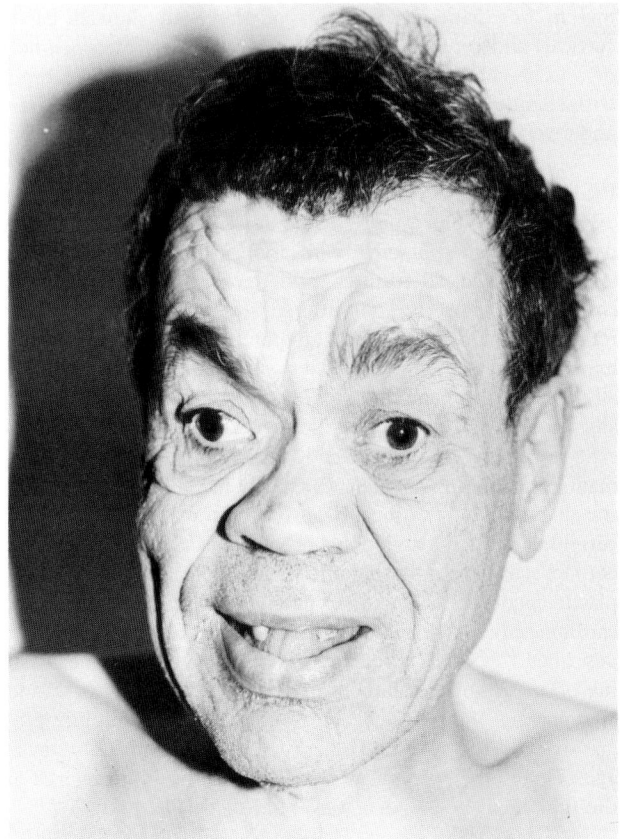

Fig. 107-12 Salla disease patient, 63 years of age. Note slightly coarse features and external strabismus. [*From P. Aula, S. Autio, K.O. Raivio, J. Rapola, M. Renlund: Salla disease in Genetic Errors of Glycoprotein Metabolism. P. Durand and J. S. O'Brien, (eds): New York, Springer-Verlag, 1982. Copyright Edi. Ermes. Used by permission.*]

vere limb and truncal ataxia is present in all affected infants during the first year of life, and approximately half of the patients followed have had nystagmus presenting in the first months of life and disappearing by 5 years of age. Psychomotor development progresses slowly during the first two decades.[279,280] A third of the patients never learn to walk and have progressive spasticity of the lower extremities; a few had spastic tetraparesis, and most had brisk deep tendon reflexes and extensor plantar responses.[274,276,278] Others learned to walk between 1.5 and 12 years of age. Most patients speak single words or short sentences, but the speech is dysarthric and dyspraxic. Understanding appears superior to expressive language. After 10 to 30 years of age, a slow deterioration begins, with more pronounced spasticity and athetosis and slow deterioration of gait, speech, and mental functions. Intelligence quotas decrease with age, so that adults have IQs below 50, in most cases below 20. A small proportion of patients have had generalized or myoclonic convulsions beginning in childhood, while several adults had absence episodes, sometimes leading to prolonged hemiparesis and postical confusion.

The disease affects life span only moderately; the oldest patient is 70 years of age. The adult patient is severely retarded with gait ataxia and has a friendly disposition. He has short stature and mildly coarse facial features but no evidence of organomegaly. The only skeletal abnormalities encountered have been gradual thickening of the calvarium and a thoracic bone deformation.[277] A mild ocular hypertelorism may occur. No corneal nor fundal changes have been detected, but half of the patients are myopic and about half have divergent strabismus, starting during the first and second decades of life. On electroencephalography, brain-wave amplitude decreased gradually with increasing age. In the few patients studied, nerve conduction velocities, electroretinograms, and electromyograms were normal. Visual evoked potentials were occasionally extinguished; auditory evoked potentials were abnormal in one patient. CT scans of the head showed basal, cortical, and cerebellar atrophy in a few cases. Neuropathologic examinations of two adult patients showed a firm brain with slightly enlarged ventricles, striking loss of white matter, and a very thin corpus callosum.[300]

ISSD. The clinical features of ISSD resemble those of Salla disease but are much more severe. Two of the seven reported patients presented at birth with ascites, hepatosplenomegaly, mildly coarse facial features, and developmental delay. The children grew poorly and suffered severe mental and motor retardation, with marked axial hypotonia and lower extremity hypertonia. Deep tendon reflexes were brisk in most, but not all,[298] cases. All patients had hepatosplenomegaly and unusually fair skin and hair. The children had a mild anemia, recurrent respiratory infections, and, occasionally, skeletal abnormalities including punctate calcifications, mild expansion of the diaphyses of the long bones, elongation of the posterior vertebral pedicles, and dolichocephaly. Mild hypertelorism, equinovarus deformity, inguinal and umbilical hernias, hyperplastic epiglottic folds and laryngomalacia, recurrent diarrhea, cardiomegaly, seizures, and divergent strabismus have been described.[282,297,298] Two patients had vascular changes consisting of aneurysmal dilatation of conjunctival capillaries[282] and angiomata of the pinnae.[297] For four patients, the rapidly progressive course led to death between 28 days and 3.3 years of age. Three other patients were alive but severely impaired at the time their case reports were published.

Diagnosis

Postnatal. The diagnosis of sialic acid storage disorders depends on the demonstration of elevated urinary excretion of free sialic acid, histologic evidence of lysosomal storage, demonstration of intracellular free sialic acid, and the clinical findings of neurologic and physical impairment. The differentiation between Salla disease and ISSD can be made on clinical grounds since only patients with the latter disease have visceral and skeletal involvement. It can also be made on biochemical grounds, since the amount of free sialic acid excreted in the urine and accumulated in tissues also reflects the severity of the disease; ISSD patients are much more severely affected than Salla disease patients. It may sometimes be difficult to assign a patient to either disorder, since intermediate variants have been described.[284]

Prenatal. Prenatal diagnosis has been accomplished in both Salla disease and ISSD.[294,299] Free sialic acid is greatly elevated in cultured amniocytes and amniotic fluid of ISSD but only moderately increased in Salla disease amniocytes. The free sialic acid level of the amniotic fluid in Salla disease did not distinguish an affected pregnancy from controls. Phase microscopic study of ISSD amniocytes revealed vacuolation, allowing an identification of the affected pregnancy. No vacuolation was observed in the amniocytes from a pregnancy affected with Salla disease. In ISSD amniocytes, labeling with [³H]sialic acid fetuin resulted in a much higher accumulation of radiolabeled free sialic acid, and a reduced rate of disappearance upon chase, compared with normal control cells.

Chorionic villi of two ISSD pregnancies showed lysosomal storage on electron microscopy.[283,299] The diagnosis was verified by the finding of greatly elevated amounts of sialic acid in the liver, brain, kidney, and cultured fibroblasts of the affected fetus.

Differential Diagnosis. Newborns with ISSD and those with infantile forms of sialidosis, G_{M1} gangliosidosis, Wolman disease, Gaucher disease, and some of the mucopolysaccharidoses, share several clinical features, including ascites and visceral and skeletal involvement.[283,313,314] The disorders can be readily distinguished by examination of urinary metabolites, by intracellular free sialic acid measurements, or by determination of activities of the lysosomal enzymes deficient in these disorders.

In Salla disease, the slow progression of the symptoms can mimic cerebral palsy of the ataxic type, or aspartylglucosaminuria, another lysosomal storage disease. A demonstration of increased urinary sialic acid enables proper diagnosis.

Increased urinary excretion of free sialic acid has been observed in several patients without concomitant lysosomal storage. In a unique French patient with mental retardation, seizures, and mildly dysmorphic features,[315–317] the sialic acid excretion was 10,000-fold increased compared with controls. This patient also had increased levels of free sialic acid in tissues but no lysosomal storage. The metabolic defect in this disease appears to be defective feedback inhibition of the enzyme UDP-N-acetylglucosamine-2-epimerase (Fig. 107-9), leading to a massive overproduction of free sialic acid.[318] Other cases with sialuria without lysosomal involvement have been described.[319–321] In these patients, no increase of free sialic acid could be detected in cultured fibroblasts,[321] and the metabolic defect remains unknown. Three Australian patients with sialuria and elevated sialic acid in their fibroblasts have been described[322]; the basic defect in these cases has also not been determined.

Therapy

Only supportive and not directed therapy exists for the sialic acid storage diseases. A few patients with Salla disease who have severe spasticity of the lower extremities have benefited from surgical release of Achilles tendons and hip adductors, but this has offered only temporary relief. No attempts have been made to specifically deplete lysosomes of the accumulated free sialic acid. For some families with an affected child, prenatal diagnosis may permit assurance of an unaffected sib.

POTENTIAL LYSOSOMAL TRANSPORT DEFECTS

Inborn errors of lysosomal membrane transport can be recognized if there exists a carrier for a given compound and if impairment of that carrier is not universally lethal. Lysosomal transport systems have already been identified for a variety of small molecules besides cystine and sialic acid.

In human fibroblast lysosomes, transport systems for cationic amino acids[108] and small neutral amino acids such as alanine, serine, and threonine[115] have been described. There also exists a carrier for tyrosine and other neutral amino acids in cultured rat thyroid cells[323]; this system recognizes the iodotyrosines and iodothyronines.[58] A defect in any of these carriers might lead to lysosomal storage, although it may not be clinically apparent or significant.

Sialic acid probably represents only one of several monosaccharides transported by lysosomal membrane carriers. Studies using both osmotic lysis, which gives a measure of lysosomal membrane permeability, and radiolabeled sugar uptake have demonstrated that glucose and other sugars cross the membranes of rat liver lysosomes in a facilitated fashion.[324,325] The evidence included the findings of specificity, inhibition, and competition and a Q_{10} of 2.8. In addition, it is speculated that the uronic acids glucoronate and iduronate may require a carrier for transport across the lysosomal membrane.[326]

A disorder of lysosomal storage of vitamin B_{12} has been described as resulting from impaired transport of cobalamin across the lysosomal membrane.[327] The single affected patient had only developmental delay and mild methylmalonic aciduria. Her fibroblasts produced free cobalamin from a transcobalamin II–vitamin B_{12} complex within lysosomes but did not release cobalamin into the cytoplasm. The defect has been termed the *cobalamin F mutation*[328] (see Chap. 82).

Other small molecules produced by lysosomal hydrolysis may also require carriers to leave lysosomes, and other inborn errors may result from defects in these transport systems. The diverse clinical presentations of cystinosis and Salla disease warn us that future transport defects need not have stereotypic features. The cobalamin F mutation, if it proves due to impaired free cobalamin transport, demonstrates that some mutations of lysosomal transport may present with signs of product deficiency rather than lysosomal storage. In the future, this complex, growing area of investigation will benefit from the astute eye and the focused mind of metabolism-oriented clinicians and researchers alike.

REFERENCES

1. ABDERHALDEN E: Familiare cystindiathese. *Z Physiol Chem* 38:557, 1903.
2. FANCONI G: Der fruhinfantile nephrotisch-glycosurische Zwergwuchs mit hypophosphatamischer Rachitis. *Jahrb Kinderheilk* 147:299, 1936.
3. BEUMER H, WEPLER W: Über die cystinkrankheit der ersten Lebenzeit. *Klin Wochenschr* 16:8, 1937.
4. DENT CE: The amino-aciduria in Fanconi syndrome. A study making extensive use of techniques based on paper partition chromatography. *Biochem J* 41:240, 1947.
5. SEEGMILLLER JE, FRIEDMANN T, HARRISON HE, WONG V, SCHNEIDER JA: Cystinosis. *Ann Intern Med* 68:883, 1968.
6. SCHULMAN JD: Historical perspective, in Schulman JD (ed): *Cystinosis.* Washington, DC, DHEW Publication no (NIH) 72-249, Government Printing Office, 1973, p 1.
7. SCHNEIDER JA, SEEGMILLER JE: Cystinosis, in Stanbury JB, Wyngaarden JB, Fredrickson DS, Goldstein JL, Brown MS (eds): *The Metabolic Basis of Inherited Disease*, 5th ed. New York, McGraw-Hill, 1983, pp 1844–1866.
8. FREUDENBERG E: Cystinosis: Cystine disease (Lignac's disease) in children. *Adv Pediatr* 4:265, 1949.
9. BICKEL H, SMALLWOOD WC, SMELLIE JM, BAAR HS, HICKMANS EM: Cystine storage disease with aminoaciduria and dwarfism (Lignac-Fanconi disease). *Acta Paediatr* 42 (suppl 90):1, 1952.
10. WORTHEN HG, GOOD RA: The de Toni-Fanconi syndrome with cystinosis. *Am J Dis Child* 95:653, 1958.
11. JACKSON JD, SMITH FG, LITMAN NN, YUILE CL, LATTA H: The Fanconi syndrome with cystinosis. Electron microscopy of renal biopsy specimens from five patients. *Am J Med* 33:893, 1962.
12. LEWIS H: The metabolism of sulfur IX. The effect of repeated administration of small amounts of cystine. *J Biol Chem* 65:187, 1925.
13. NEWBURGH LH, MARSH PL: Renal injuries by aminoacids. *Arch Intern Med* 36:682, 1925.
14. JOCELYN PC: The standard redox potential of cysteine-cystine from the thiol-disulphide exchange reaction with glutathione and lipoic acid. *Eur J Biochem* 2:327, 1967.
15. GORIN G, DOUGHTY G: Equilibrium constants for the reaction of glutathione with cystine and their relative oxidation-reduction potentials. *Arch Biochem Biophys* 126:547, 1968.
16. MEISTER A: *Biochemistry of the Amino Acids.* New York, Academic, 1965, vol I, p 28.
17. BRENTON DP, CUSWORTH DC, DENT DE, JONES EE: Homocystinuria. Clinical and dietary studies. *Q J Med* 35:325, 1966.
18. STURMAN JA, GAULL G, RAIHA NCR: Absence of cystathionase in human fetal liver: Is cystine essential? *Science* 169:74, 1970.
19. EAGLE H, PIEZ KA, OYAMA VI: The biosynthesis of cystine in human cell cultures. *J Biol Chem* 236:1425, 1961.
20. IGLEHART JD, YORK RM, MODEST AP, LAZARUS H, LIVINGSTON DM: Cystine requirement of continuous human lymphoid cell lines of normal and leukemic origin. *J Biol Chem* 252:7184, 1977.
21. TIETZE F: Enzymic reduction of cystine and other disulfides, in Schulman JD (ed): *Cystinosis.* Washington, DC, DHEW Publication no (NIH) 72-249, Government Printing Office, 1973, p 147.
22. JOCELYN PC: Glutathione metabolism in animals, in Crook EM (ed): *Glutathione.* Cambridge, England, Cambridge University Press, 1959, Biochemical Society Symposium No 17, p 43.
23. ELDJARN L, PIHL A: Equilibrium constants and oxidation-reduction potentials of some thiol-disulfide systems. *J Am Chem Soc* 79:4589, 1957.
24. STATES B, SEGAL S: Distribution of glutathione-cystine transhydrogenase activity in subcellular fractions of rat intestinal mucosa. *Biochem J* 113:443, 1969.
25. TIETZE F, BRADLEY KH, SCHULMAN JD: Enzymatic reduction of cystine by subcellular fractions of cultured and peripheral leukocytes from normal and cystinotic individuals. *Pediatr Res* 6:649, 1972.
26. BRAND E, HARRIS MM, BILOON S: Cystinuria. The excretion of a cystine complex which decomposes in the urine with the liberation of free cystine. *J Biol Chem* 86:315, 1930.
27. LEE PLY: Single-column systems for accelerated amino acid analysis of physiological fluids using five lithium buffers. *Biochem Med* 10:107, 1974.
28. OSHIMA RG, WILLIS RC, FURLONG CE, SCHNEIDER JA: Binding assays for amino acids: The utilization of a cystine binding protein from *Escherichia coli* for the determination of acid-soluble cystine in small physiological samples. *J Biol Chem* 249:6033, 1974.
29. SCHNEIDER JA, BRADLEY KH, SEEGMILLER JE: Transport and intracellular fate of cysteine-^{35}S in leukocytes from normal subjects and patients with cystinosis. *Pediatr Res* 2:441, 1968.

30. STATES B, SEGAL S: Thin-layer chromatographic separation of cystine and the N-ethylmaleimide adducts of cysteine and glutathione. *Anal Biochem* 27:323, 1969.

31. SPEARS GS, SLUSSER RJ, TOUSIMIS AJ, TAYLOR CG, SCHULMAN JD: Cystinosis: An ultrastructural and electron-probe study of the kidney with unusual findings. *Arch Pathol* 9:206, 1971.

32. SCOTTO JM, STRALIN HG: Ultrastructure of the liver in a case of childhood cystinosis. *Virchows Arch (A)* 377:43, 1977.

33. FIVUSH B, GREEN OC, PORTER CC, BALFE JW, O'REGAN S, GAHL WA: Pancreatic endocrine insufficiency in post-transplant cystinosis. *Am J Dis Child* 141:1087, 1987.

34. HOLTZAPPLE PG, GENEL M, YAKOVAC WC, HUMMELER K, SEGAL S: Diagnosis of cystinosis by rectal biopsy. *N Engl J Med* 281:143, 1969.

35. MORECKI R, PAUNIER L, HAMILTON JR: Intestinal mucosa in cystinosis. A fine structure study. *Arch Pathol* 86:297, 1968.

36. SCHNEIDER JA, NOLAN SP, SEEGMILLER JE: Appendicitis in a child with cystinosis. *Arch Surg* 97:565, 1968.

37. GROSS U, MASSHOFF W, KORZ R: Die milz in allgemein pathologischer sicht. *Internist (Berlin)* 9:1, 1968.

38. COGAN DG, KUWABARA T: Ocular pathology of cystinosis. *Arch Ophthalmol* 63:51, 1960.

39. PATRICK AD, LAKE BD: Cystinosis: Electron microscopic evidence of lysosomal storage of cystine in lymph node. *J Clin Pathol* 21:571, 1968.

40. KORN D: Demonstration of cystine crystals in peripheral white blood cells in a patient with cystinosis. *N Engl J Med* 262:545, 1960.

41. SCHNEIDER JA, WONG V, SEEGMILLER JE: The early diagnosis of cystinosis. *J Pediatr* 74:114, 1969.

42. CHAN AM, LYNCH MJG, BAILEY JD, EZRIN C, FRASER D: Hypothyroidism in cystinosis. *Am J Med* 48:678, 1970.

43. CASEY TP: Cystine storage disease. A case report with a note on the extraction of cystine from formalin-fixed tissues. *Aust Ann Med* 15:61, 1966.

44. BAAR HS, BICKEL H: Morbid anatomy, histology, and pathogenesis of Lignac-Fanconi disease. *Acta Paediatr (suppl 90)* 42:171, 1952.

45. LEVINE S, PAPARO G: Brain lesions in a case of cystinosis. *Acta Neuropathol (Berlin)* 57:217, 1982.

46. HAYNES MD, CARTER RF, POLLARD AC, CAREY WF: Light and electron microscopy of infantile and foetal tissues in cystinosis. *Micron* 11:443, 1980.

47. KAISER-KUPFER MI, CARUSO RC, MINKLER DS, GAHL WA: Long-term ocular manifestations in nephropathic cystinosis. *Arch Ophthalmol* 104:706, 1986.

48. SCHULMAN JD, WONG VG, KUWABARA T, BRADLEY KH, SEEGMILLER JE: Intracellular cystine content of leukocyte populations in cystinosis. *Arch Intern Med* 125:660, 1970.

49. SCHULMAN JD: Cystine storage disease: Investigations at the cellular and subcellular levels, in Carson NAJ, Raine DN (eds): *Inherited Disorders of Sulphur Metabolism.* Edinburgh and London, Churchill Livingstone, 1971, p 123.

50. JONAS AJ, CONLEY SB, MARSHALL R, JOHNSON RA, MARKS M, ROSENBERG H: Nephropathic cystinosis with central nervous system involvement. *Am J Med* 83:966, 1987.

51. GOODMAN SI, HAMBIDGE KM, MAHONEY CP, STRIKER GE: Renal homotransplantation in the treatment of cystinosis, in Schulman JD (ed): *Cystinosis.* Washington, DC, HEW Publication no (NIH) 72-249, Government Printing Office, 1973, p 227.

52. PATRICK AD: Deficiencies of SH-dependent enzymes in cystinosis. *Clin Sci* 28:427, 1965.

53. DEPAPE-BRIGGER D, GOLDMAN H, SCRIVER CR, DELVIN E, MAMER O: The in vivo use of dithiothreitol in cystinosis. *Pediatr Res* 11:124, 1977.

54. SCHULMAN JD, WONG VG, BRADLEY KH, SEEGMILLER JE: A simple technique for the biochemical diagnosis of cystinosis. *J Pediatr* 76:289, 1970.

55. WONG VG, SCHULMAN JD, SEEGMILLER JE: Conjunctival biopsy for the biochemical diagnosis of cystinosis. *Am J Ophthalmol* 70:278, 1970.

56. BROYER M, GUILLOT M, GUBLER M-C, HABIB R: Infantile cystinosis: A reappraisal of early and late symptoms, in Hamburger J, Crosnier J, Grünfeld J-P, Maxwell MH (eds): *Advances in Nephrology.* Chicago, Year Book, 1981, p 137.

57. HARPER GS, BERNARDINI I, HURKO O, ZUURVELD J, GAHL WA: Cystine storage in cystinotic myotubes. *Biochem J* 243:841, 1987.

58. GAHL WA: Unpublished data.

59. SCHNEIDER JA, ROSENBLOOM FM, BRADLEY KH, SEEGMILLER JE: Increased free-cystine content of fibroblasts cultured from patients with cystinosis. *Biochem Biophys Res Commun* 29:527, 1967.

60. SCHNEIDER JA, WONG V, BRADLEY KH, SEEGMILLER JE: Biochemical comparisons of the adult and childhood forms of cystinosis. *N Engl J Med* 279:1253, 1968.

61. SCHNEIDER JA, BRADLEY K, SEEGMILLER JE: Increased cystine in leukocytes from individuals homozygous and heterozygous for cystinosis. *Science* 157:1321, 1967.

62. GOLDMAN H, SCRIVER CR, AARON K, DELVIN E, CANLOS Z: Adolescent cystinosis: Comparisons with infantile and adult forms. *Pediatrics* 47:979, 1971.

63. GAHL WA, BASHAN N, TIETZE F, SCHULMAN JD: Lysosomal cystine countertransport in heterozygotes for cystinosis. *Am J Hum Genet* 36:277, 1984.

64. SCHULMAN JD, BRADLEY KH, BEREZESKY IK, GRIMLEY PM, DODSON WE, AL-AISH MS: Biochemical, morphologic and cytogenetic studies of leukocytes growing in continuous culture from normal individuals and from patients with cystinosis. *Pediatr Res* 5:501, 1971.

65. JONAS AJ, SMITH ML, SCHNEIDER JA: ATP-dependent lysosomal cystine efflux is defective in cystinosis. *J Biol Chem* 257:13185, 1982.

66. KAISER-KUPFER MI, FUJIKAWA L, KUWABARA T, JAIN S, GAHL WA: Removal of corneal crystals by topical cysteamine in nephropathic cystinosis. *N Engl J Med* 316:775, 1987.

67. HARMS E, KRAUSS-MACKIW E, LUTZ P: Cystine concentration of cultivated cells from skin and cornea. *Metab Pediatr Ophthalmol* 3:157, 1979.

68. PELLET OL, SMITH ML, THOENE JG, SCHNEIDER JA, JONAS AJ: Renal cell culture using autopsy material from children with cystinosis. *In Vitro* 20:53, 1984.

69. SCHULMAN JD, SCHNEIDER JA, BRADLEY KH, SEEGMILLER JE: Heterozygote studies in cystinosis. *Clin Chim Acta* 29:73, 1970.

70. WONG VG, KUWABARA T, BRUBAKER R, OLSON W, SCHULMAN J, SEEGMILLER JE: Intralysosomal cystine crystals in cystinosis. *Invest Ophthalmol* 9:83, 1970.

71. HUMMELER K, ZAJAC BA, GENEL M, HOLTZAPPLE PG, SEGAL S: Human cystinosis: Intracellular deposition of cystine. *Science* 168:859, 1970.

72. SCHULMAN JD, WONG V, OLSON WH, SEEGMILLER JE: Lysosomal site of crystalline deposits of cystinosis as shown by ferritin uptake. *Arch Pathol* 90:259, 1970.

73. SCHULMAN JD, BRADLEY KH, SEEGMILLER JE: Cystine: Compartmentalization within lysosomes in cystinotic leukocytes. *Science* 166:1152, 1969.

74. SCHULMAN JD, BRADLEY KH: Cystinosis: Selective induction of vacuolation in fibroblasts by L-cysteine-D-penicillamine disulfide. *Science* 169:595, 1970.

75. KAYE CI, NADLER HL: Transport of L-cystine by cultivated skin fibroblasts of normal subjects and patients with cystinosis. *Pediatr Res* 10:637, 1976.

76. STATES B, HARRIS D, SEGAL S: Uptake and utilization of exogenous cystine by cystinotic and normal fibroblasts. *J Clin Invest* 53:1003, 1974.

77. ORLOFF S, MUKHERJEE AB, BUTLER JD, FOLEY B, SCHULMAN JD: Cystinotic and normal fibroblasts: Differential susceptibility of cysteine toxicity in vitro. *In Vitro* 16:655, 1980.

78. OSHIMA RG, RHEAD WJ, THOENE JG, SCHNEIDER JA: Cystine metabolism in human fibroblasts. Comparison of normal, cystinotic and gamma-glutamylcysteine synthetase-deficient cells. *J Biol Chem* 251:4287, 1976.

79. STATES B, SCARDIGLI K, SEGAL S: Glutathione in fibroblasts from normal and cystinotic children. *Life Sci* 22:31, 1977.

80. SCHULMAN JD, SCHNEIDER JA, BRADLEY KH, SEEGMILLER JE: Cystine, cysteine, and glutathione metabolism in normal and cystinotic fibroblasts in vitro and in cultured amniotic fluid cells. *Clin Chim Acta* 35:383, 1971.

81. ORLOFF S, BUTLER J, TOWNE D, MUKHERJEE AB, SCHULMAN JD: Pantetheinase activity and cysteamine content in cystinotic and normal fibroblasts and leukocytes. *Pediatr Res* 15:1063, 1981.

82. PATRICK AD, BERLIN RD, SCHULMAN JD: Gamma-glutamyl transferase: Studies of normal and cystinotic human leukocytes, rabbit neutrophiles, and rat liver. *Pediatr Res* 13:1058, 1979.

83. STATES B, SEGAL S: Levels of gamma-glutamyltranspeptidase in cultured skin fibroblasts from cystinotics and normals. *Life Sci* 27:1985, 1980.

84. BUTLER JD, SPEILBERG S: Depletion of cystine accumulation in cystinotic cells by inhibitors of gamma-glutamyl transpeptidase. *J Biol Chem* 256:4160, 1981.

85. WATERSON JR, WINTER WP, SCHMICKEL RD: Cysteine activation in cultured cystinotic cells. The specific activity of cysteinyl-tRNA synthetase and tRNA$_{Cys}$ and the determination of the Michaelis-Menten constants for cysteinyl-tRNA synthetase. *J Clin Invest* 54:182, 1974.

86. FURUSHO K, VETRELLA M, LATTA E: Abnormal arysulphatase activities of fibroblasts cultured from patients with mucopolysaccharidosis and cystinosis. *Z Kinderheilkd* 110:324, 1971.

87. SCARDIGLI K, KOLDOVSKY O, PALMIERI M, SEGAL S, STATES B: Activities of acid hydrolases in fibroblasts from normal and cystinotic children. *Clin Chim Acta* 75:12, 1977.

88. WENSKE G, LINNEWEH F: Beta-Alanin-Vermehrung in Lympho- und Thrombocyten zur biochemischen Diagnose der Cystinose. *Klin Wochenschr* 50:1082, 1972.

89. WORTHEN HG, GOOD RA: The pathogenesis of cystinosis. *Am J Dis Child* 102:494, 1961.

90. MAHONEY CP, TRUMP BF: Studies in cystinosis. *Am J Dis Child* 104:563, 1962.

91. SEEGMILLER JE, HOWELL RR: Cystine metabolism in deToni-Fanconi syndrome with cystinosis. *Clin Res* 9:189, 1961.

92. PATRICK AD: The degradative metabolism of L-cysteine and L-cystine *in vitro* by liver in cystinosis. *Biochem J* 83:248, 1962.

93. KAYE CI, NADLER HL: Enzymic reduction of cystine and glutathione in cultivated human fibroblasts from normal subjects and patients with cystinosis. *J Lab Clin Med* 86:422, 1975.

94. STATES B, HARRIS D, SEGAL S: Patterns of cystine reduction by fibroblasts from normal and cystinotic children. *Pediatr Res* 11:685, 1977.

95. GRIFFITHS PA, LLOYD JB: Evidence of lysosomal reduction of cystine residues. *Biochem Biophys Res Commun* 89:428, 1979.

96. LUCY JA: Lysosomal membranes, in Dingle JT, Fell HB (eds): *Lysosomes in Biology and Pathology*. New York, American Elsevier, 1969, vol 2, p 313.

97. EHRENREICH BA, COHN ZA: The fate of peptides pinocytosed by macrophages *in vitro*. *J Exp Med* 129:227, 1969.

98. SCHULMAN JD, BRADLEY KH: Metabolism of amino acids, peptides and disulfides in the lysosomes of fibroblasts cultured from normal individuals and those with cystinosis. *J Exp Med* 132:1090, 1970.

99. GOLDMAN R, KAPLAN A: Rupture of rat liver lysosomes mediated by L-amino acid esters. *Biochim Biophys Acta* 318:205, 1973.

100. REEVES JP: Accumulation of amino acids by lysosomes incubated with amino acid methyl esters. *J Biol Chem* 254:8914, 1979.

101. REEVES JP, DECKER RS, CRIE JS, WILDENTHAL K: Intracellular disruption of rat heart lysosomes by leucine methylester: Effects on protein degradation. *Proc Natl Acad Sci USA* 78:4426, 1981.

102. STEINHERZ R, TIETZE F, RAIFORD D, GAHL WA, SCHULMAN JD: Patterns of amino acid efflux from isolated normal and cystinotic human leucocyte lysosomes. *J Biol Chem* 257:6041, 1982.

103. STEINHERZ R, TIETZE F, GAHL WA, TRICHE TJ, CHIANG H, MODESTI A, SCHULMAN JD: Cystine accumulation and clearance by normal and cystinotic leukocytes exposed to cystine dimethyl ester. *Proc Natl Acad Sci USA* 79:4446, 1982.

104. JONAS AJ, GREENE AA, SMITH ML, SCHNEIDER JA: Cystine accumulation and loss in normal, heterozygous, and cystinotic fibroblasts. *Proc Natl Acad Sci USA* 79:4442, 1982.

105. GAHL WA, TIETZE F, BASHAN N, STEINHERZ R, SCHULMAN JD: Defective cystine exodus from isolated lysosome-rich fractions of cystinotic leucocytes. *J Biol Chem* 257:9570, 1982.

106. HARMS E, SCHNEIDER JA: The lysosomal localization of free-cystine in normal and cystinotic cells. *Clin Res* 27:457A, 1979.

107. GAHL WA, BASHAN N, TIETZE F, BERNARDINI I, SCHULMAN JD: Cystine transport is defective in isolated leukocyte lysosomes from patients with cystinosis. *Science* 217:1263, 1982.

108. PISONI RL, THOENE JG, CHRISTENSEN HN: Detection and characterization of carrier-mediated cationic amino acid transport in lysosomes of normal and cystinotic human fibroblasts. Role in therapeutic cystine removal. *J Biol Chem* 260:4791, 1985.

109. TIETZE F, ROME LH, BUTLER JDEB, HARPER GS, GAHL WA: Impaired clearance of free cystine from lysosome-enriched granular fractions of I-cell-disease fibroblasts. *Biochem J* 237:9, 1986.

110. CHRISTENSEN HN: *Biological Transport*, 2d ed. London, WA Benjamin, 1975.

111. GAHL WA, TIETZE F, BASHAN N, BERNARDINI I, RAIFORD D, SCHULMAN JD: Characteristics of cystine counter-transport in normal and cystinotic lysosome-rich leucocyte granular fractions. *Biochem J* 216:393, 1983.

112. SCHULMAN JD, GAHL WA, TIETZE F, BASHAN N, STEINHERZ R, RIZZO WB, BUTLER J: Gamma-glutamyl transpeptidase deficiency and cystinosis, in Larsson A (ed): *Functions of Glutathione: Biochemical, Physiological, Toxicological, and Clinical Aspects*. New York, Raven, 1983, p 355.

113. BANNAI S, KITAMURA E: Transport interaction of L-cystine and L-glutamate in human diploid fibroblasts in culture. *J Biol Chem* 255:2372, 1980.

114. FORSTER S, LLOYD JB: pH profile of cystine and glutamate transport in normal and cystinotic human fibroblasts. *Biochim Biophys Acta* 814:398, 1985.

115. PISONI R, FLICKINGER K, THOENE J, CHRISTENSEN H: Characterization of carrier-mediated transport systems for small neutral aminoacids in human fibroblast lysosomes. *J Biol Chem* 262:6010, 1987.

116. OKHUMA S, MORIYAMA Y, TAKANO T: Identification and characterization of a proton pump on lysosomes by fluorescein isothyocyanate-dextran fluorescence. *Proc Natl Acad Sci USA* 79:2758, 1982.

117. GAHL WA, TIETZE F: pH effects on cystine transport in lysosome-rich leucocyte granular fractions. *Biochem J* 228:263, 1985.

118. BASHAN N, GAHL WA, TIETZE F, BERNARDINI I, SCHULMAN JD: The effect of ions and ionophores on cystine egress from human leucocyte lysosome-rich granular fraction. *Biochim Biophys Acta* 777:267, 1984.

119. SCHNEIDER DL: ATP-dependent acidification of intact and disrupted lysosomes. Evidence for an ATP-driven proton pump. *J Biol Chem* 256:3858, 1981.

120. STONE DK, XIE X, RACKER E: An ATP-driven proton pump in clathrin-coated vesicles. *J Biol Chem* 258:4059, 1983.

121. XIE X, STONE DK, RACKER E: Determinants of clathrin-coated vesicle acidification. *J Biol Chem* 258:14834, 1983.

122. JONAS AJ, SMITH ML, ALLISON WS, LAIKIND PK, GREENE AA, SCHNEIDER JA: Proton-translocating ATPase and lysosomal cystine transport. *J Biol Chem* 258:11727, 1983.

123. OUDE ELFERINK RPJ, HARMS E, STRIJLAND A, TAGER JM: The intralysosomal pH in cultured human skin fibroblasts in relation to cystine accumulation in patients with cystinosis. *Biochem Biophys Res Commun* 116:154, 1983.

124. JONAS AJ: Cystine transport in purified rat liver lysosomes. *Biochem J* 236:671, 1986.

125. SMITH ML, GREENE AA, POTASHNIK R, MENDOZA SA, SCHNEIDER JA: Lysosomal cystine transport. Effect of intralysosomal pH and membrane potential. *J Biol Chem* 262:1253, 1987.

126. GREENE AA, CLARK KF, SMITH ML, SCHNEIDER JA: Cystine exodus from leukocyte granular fractions is stimulated by ATP at sub-saturating cystine levels. *Pediatr Res* 21:290A, 1987.

127. THOENE JG, OSHIMA RG, CRAWHALL J, OLSON D, SCHNEIDER JA: Cystinosis: Intracellular cystine depletion by aminothiols in vitro and in vivo. *J Clin Invest* 58:180, 1976.

128. GAHL WA, TIETZE F, BUTLER JDEB, SCHULMAN JD: Cysteamine depletes cystinotic leucocyte granular fractions of cystine by the mechanism of disulfide interchange. *Biochem J* 228:545, 1985.

129. BUTLER JDEB, TIETZE F, PELLEFIGUE F, SPIELBERG SP, SCHULMAN JD: Depletion of cystine in cystinotic fibroblasts by drugs enclosed in liposomes. *Pediatr Res* 12:46, 1978.

130. GOLDMAN H, SCRIVER CR, AARON K, PINSKY L: Use of dithiothreitol to correct cystine storage in cultured cystinotic fibroblasts. *Lancet* I:811, 1970.

131. KROLL WA, SCHNEIDER JA: Decrease in free cystine content of cultured cystinotic fibroblasts by ascorbic acid. *Science* 186:1040, 1974.

132. BUTLER JDEB, ZATZ M: Pantethine depletes cystinotic fibroblasts of cystine. *J Pediatr* 102:796, 1983.

133. BUTLER JDEB, ZATZ M: Pantethine and cystamine deplete cystine from cystinotic fibroblasts via efflux of cysteamine-cysteine mixed disulfide. *J Clin Invest* 74:411, 1984.

134. BUTLER JDEB, GAHL WA, TIETZE F: Cystine depletion by WR-1065 in cystinotic cells. Mechanism of action. *Biochem Pharmacol* 34:2179, 1985.

135. THOENE J, LEMONS R: Cystine depletion of cystinotic tissues by phosphocysteamine (WR 638). *J Pediatr* 96:1043, 1980.

136. BAAR HS: Pathologie des aminosauren-diabetes. *Monatschr Kinderheilk* 99:35, 1951.

137. DANPURE CJ: The effect of chloroquine on the metabolism of [^{35}S]cystine in normal and cystinotic human fibroblasts. *Biochem J* 200:555, 1981.

138. THOENE J, LEMONS R: Cystine accumulation in cystinotic fibroblasts from free and protein-linked cystine but not cysteine. *Biochem J* 208:823, 1982.

139. THOENE J, OSHIMA R, RITCHIE D, SCHNEIDER J: Cystinotic fibroblasts accumulate cystine from intracellular protein degradation. *Proc Natl Acad Sci USA* 74:4505, 1977.

140. THOENE J, LEMONS R: Modulation of the intracellular cystine content of cystinotic fibroblasts by extracellular albumin. *Pediatr Res* 14:785, 1980.

141. KOOISTRA T, LLOYD JB: Pinocytosis and degradation of exogenous proteins by cystinotic fibroblasts. *Biochim Biophys Acta* 887:182, 1986.

142. BUTLER J, SPIELBERG S: Accumulation of cystine from glutathione-cysteine mixed disulfide in cystinotic fibroblasts. Blockade by an inhibitor of gamma-glutamyl transpeptidase. *Life Sci* 31:2563, 1982.

143. CRAWHALL J, OSHIMA R, SCHNEIDER J: Factors controlling the non-protein cystine content of cystinotic fibroblasts. *Pediatr Res* 11:41, 1977.

144. SCHULMAN JD, BRADLEY KH: Cystinosis: Therapeutic implications of in vitro studies of cultured fibroblasts. *J Pediatr* 78:833, 1971.

145. THOENE J, FORSTER S, LLOYD J: The role of pinocytosis in the cellular uptake of an aminoacid. *Biochem Biophys Res Commun* 127:733, 1985.

146. DANPURE CJ, JENNINGS PR, FYFE DA: Further studies on the effect of chloroquine on the uptake, metabolism and intracellular translocation of [^{35}S]cystine in cystinotic fibroblasts. *Biochim Biophys Acta* 885:256, 1986.

147. RITCHIE DG, JONAS AJ, OSHIMA RG, NEAL P, SCHNEIDER JA: Cystinotic fibroblasts are depleted of free-cystine by acid pH medium. *Pediatr Res* 15:1492, 1981.

148. STATES B, LEE J, SEGAL S: Effect of chloroquine on handling of cystine by cystinotic fibroblasts. *Metabolism* 32:272, 1983.

149. LEMONS RM, PISONI RL, CHRISTENSEN HN, THOENE JG: Elevated temperature produces cystine depletion in cystinotic fibroblasts. *Biochim Biophys Acta* 884:429, 1986.

150. THOENE J: Unpublished data.

151. JONAS A, SCHULMAN J, MATALON R, VELAZQUEZ A, BREWER E, CHEN H, BOYER M, BRANDWEIN E, ARBUS G, MORRIS C, SCHNEIDER J: Cystinosis in non Caucasian children. *Johns Hopkins Med J* 151:117, 1982.

152. SOCHETT E, PETTIFOR JM, MILNER L, THOMSON PD, BERKOWITZ F: Nephropathic cystinosis in black children. *S Afr Med J* 65:397, 1984.

153. BOIS E, FEINGOLD J, FRENAY P, BRIARD ML: Infantile cystinosis in France—Genetics, incidence, geographic distribution. *J Med Genet* 13:434, 1976.

154. MANZ F, GRETZ N: Cystinosis in the Federal Republic of Germany: Coordination and analysis of data. *J Inherited Metab Dis* 8:2, 1985.

155. GRETZ N, MANZ F, AUGUSTIN R: Survival time in cystinosis. A collaborative study. *Proc Eur Dial Transplant Assoc* 19:582, 1982.

156. STEINHERZ R, RAIFORD D, MITTAL KK, SCHULMAN JD: Association of certain human leukocyte antigens with nephropathic cystinosis in the absence of linkage between these loci. *Am J Hum Genet* 33:227, 1981.

157. GAHL WA, ADAMSON M, KAISER-KUPFER MI, LUDWIG IH, O'CONNELL HJ, COHEN W, BARRANGER J: Biochemical phenotyping of a single sibship with both cystinosis and Fabry disease. *J Inherited Metab Dis* 8:127, 1985.

158. KASKEL R: Unpublished information.

159. GAHL WA, SCHNEIDER JA, THOENE JG, CHESNEY R: Course of nephropathic cystinosis after age 10 years. *J Pediatr* 109:605, 1986.

160. MORELL GP, NIAUDET P, JEAN G, DESCAMPS-LATSCHA B: Altered oxidative metabolism, motility, and adherence in phagocytic cells from cystinotic children. *Pediatr Res* 19:1318, 1985.

161. GAHL WA: Cystinosis coming of age. *Adv Pediatr* 33:95, 1986.

162. CLAY RD, DARMADY EM, HAWKINS M: The nature of the renal lesion in Fanconi syndrome. *J Pathol Bacteriol* 65:511, 1953.

163. TEREE TM, FRIEDMAN AB, KEST LM, FETTERMAN GH: Cystinosis and proximal tubular nephropathy in siblings. Progressive development of the physiological and anatomical lesion. *Am J Dis Child* 119:481, 1970.

164. LEMIRE J, KAPLAN BS, SCRIVER CR: Presentation of cystinosis as Bartter's syndrome and conversion to Fanconi Syndrome on indomethacin treatment. *Pediatr Res* 12:544, 1978.

165. O'REGAN S, MONGEAU J-G, ROBITAILLE P: A patient with cystinosis presenting with the features of Bartter syndrome. *Acta Paediatr Belg* 33:51, 1980.

166. LEMIRE J, KAPLAN BS: The various renal manifestations of the nephropathic form of cystinosis. *Am J Nephrol* 4:81, 1984.

167. BÜRKI VE: Ueber die Cystinkrankheit im Klienkindesalter unter besonderer Berücksichtigung des Augenbefundes. *Ophthalmologica* 101:257, 1941.

168. BLACK J, STAPLETON B, ROY S III, WARD J, NOE HN: Varied types of urinary calculi in a patient with cystinosis without renal tubular acidosis. *Pediatr* 78:295, 1986.

169. STEINHERZ R, CHESNEY RW, SCHULMAN JD, DELUCA HF, PHELPS M: Circulating vitamin D metabolites in nephropathic cystinosis. *J Pediatr* 102:592, 1983.

170. BERNARDINI I, RIZZO WB, DALAKAS M, BERNAR J, GAHL WA: Plasma and muscle free carnitine deficiency due to renal Fanconi syndrome. *J Clin Invest* 75:1124, 1985.

171. SPEAR GS: The pathology of the kidney, in Schulman JD (ed): *Cystinosis.* Washington, DC, DHEW Publication no (NIH) 72-249, Government Printing Office, 1973, p 37.

172. SPEAR GS, SLUSSER RJ, SCHULMAN JD, ALEXANDER F: Polykaryocytosis in the visceral glomerular epithelium in cystinosis with description of an unusual clinical variant. *Johns Hopkins Med J* 129:83, 1971.

173. SPEAR GS: Pathology of the kidney in cystinosis, in Sommers SC (ed): *Pathology Annual.* New York, Appleton-Century-Crofts, 1974, p 81.

174. JACKSON JD, SMITH FG, LITMAN NN, YUILE CL, LATTA H: The Fanconi syndrome with cystinosis. Electron microscopy of renal biopsy specimens from five patients. *Am J Med* 33:893, 1962.

175. LEUMANN EP: Progression of renal insufficiency in pediatric patients: Estimation from serum creatinine. *Helv Paediatr Acta* 33:25, 1978.

176. GAHL WA, REED GF, THOENE JF, SCHULMAN JD, RIZZO WB, JONAS AJ, DENMAN DW, SCHLESSELMAN JJ, CORDEN BJ, SCHNEIDER JA: Cysteamine therapy for children with nephropathic cystinosis. *N Engl J Med* 316:971, 1987.

177. BERCU BB, RIZZO WB, CORDEN BJ, REED GF, SCHULMAN JD: Circulating somatomedin-C levels in nephropathic cystinosis. *Isr J Med Sci* 20:236, 1984.

178. GAHL WA, KAISER-KUPFER MI: Complications of nephropathic cystinosis after renal failure. *Pediatr Nephrol* 1:260, 1987.

179. LUCKY AW, HOWLEY PM, MEGYLESI K, SPIELBERG SP, SCHULMAN JD: Endocrine studies in cystinosis: Compensated primary hypothyroidism. *J Pediatr* 91:204, 1977.

180. SANDERSON PO, KUWABARA T, STARKER J, WONG VG, COLLINS EM: Cystinosis: A clinical, histopathologic and ultrastructure study. *Arch Ophthalmol* 91:270, 1974.

181. FRANCOIS J, HANSSENS M, COPPIETERS R, EVENS L: Cystinosis. A clinical and histopathologic study. *Am J Ophthalmol* 73:643, 1972.

182. WONG VG: The eye and cystinosis, in Schulman JD (ed): *Cystinosis.* Washington, DC, DHEW Publication no (NIH) 72-249, Government Printing Office, 1973, p 23.

183. WONG VG, LIETMAN PS, SEEGMILLER JE: Alterations of pigment epithelium in cystinosis. *Arch Ophthalmol* 77:361, 1967.

184. SCHNEIDER JA, VERROUST FM, KROLL WA, GARVIN AJ, HORGER EO III, WONG VG, SPEAR GS, JACOBSON C, PELLETT OL, BECKER FLA: Prenatal diagnosis of cystinosis. *N Engl J Med* 290:878, 1974.

185. YAMAMOTO GK, SCHULMAN JD, SCHNEIDER JA, WONG VG: Long-term ocular changes in cystinosis: Observations in renal transplant recipients. *J Pediatr Ophthalmol Strabismus* 16:21, 1979.

186. WALDMAN TA, MOGIELNICKI RP, STROBER W: The proteinuria of cystinosis: Its pattern and pathogenesis, in Schulman JD (ed): *Cystinosis.* Washington, DC, DHEW Publication no (NIH) 72-249, Government Printing Office, 1973, p 55.

187. COGAN DG, KUWABARA T, KINOSHITA J, SUDARSKY D, RING H: Ocular manifestations of systemic cystinosis. *Arch Ophthalmol* 55:36, 1956.

188. KENYON ER, SENSENBRENNER JA: Electron microscopy of cornea and conjunctiva in childhood cystinosis. *Am J Ophthalmol* 78:68, 1974.

189. FRAZIER PD, WONG VG: Cystinosis: Histologic and crystallographic examination of crystal in eye tissues. *Arch Ophthalmol* 80:87, 1968.

190. KAISER-KUPFER MI, DATILES MB, GAHL WA: Corneal transplant in a twelve-year-old boy with nephropathic cystinosis. *Lancet* I:331, 1987.

191. KAISER-KUPFER MI, CHAN C-C, RODRIGUES M, DATILES MB, GAHL WA: Nephropathic cystinosis: Immunohistochemical and histopathologic studies of cornea, conjunctiva and iris. *Curr Eye Res* 6:617, 1987.

192. WEBER U, SONS HU, BERNSMEIER H, LENZ W: Experimentally induced cystine keratopathy in rabbits. *Graefes Arch Clin Exp Ophthalmol* 224:443, 1986.

193. WAN WL, MINCKLER DS, RAO NA: Pupillary-block glaucoma associated with childhood cystinosis. *Am J Ophthalmol* 101:700, 1986.

194. KAISER-KUPFER MI, GAHL WA: Unpublished information.

195. BURKE JR, EL-BISHTI MM, MAISEY MN, CHANTLER C: Hypothyroidism in children with cystinosis. *Arch Dis Child* 53:947, 1978.

196. BERCU BB, SCHULMAN JD: Pituitary secretion of α and β subunits of thyroid-stimulating hormone in nephropathic cystinosis. *Isr J Med Sci* 20:179, 1984.

197. BERCU BB, ORLOFF S, SCHULMAN JD: Pituitary resistance to thyroid hormone in cystinosis. *J Clin Endocrinol Metab* 51:1262, 1980.

198. CHANTLER C, CARTER JE, BEWICK M, COUNAHAN R, CAMERON JS, OGG CS, WILLIAMS DG, WINDER E: 10 year's experience with regular haemodialysis and renal transplantation. *Arch Dis Child* 55:435, 1980.

199. AMMENTI A, GROSSI A, BERNASCONTI S: Infantile cystinosis and insulin-dependent diabetes mellitus. *Eur J Pediatr* 145:548, 1986.

200. MILNER RDG, WIRDNAM PK: The pancreatic β-cell fraction in children with errors of amino acid metabolism. *Pediatr Res* 16:213, 1982.

200a. REISS RE, KUNABARA T, SMITH ML, GAHL WA: Successful pregnancy despite placental cystine crystals in a woman with nephropathic cystinosis. *N Engl J Med* 319:223, 1988.

200b. CHIK CL, GAHL WA, MERRIAM GR: Unpublished data.

201. EHRICH JHH, STOEPPLER L, OFFNER G, BRODEHL J: Evidence for cerebral involvement in nephropathic cystinosis. *Neuropädiatrie* 10:128, 1979.

202. BRODEHL J, EHRICH JHH, KROHN JP, OFFNER G, BYRD D: Kidney transplantation in nephropathic cystinosis, in Brodehl J, Ehrich JHH (eds): *Pediatric Nephrology.* Berlin, Springer-Verlag, 1984, p 172.

203. COCHAT P, DRACHMAN R, GAGNADOUX M-F, PARIENTE D, BROYER M: Cerebral atrophy and nephropathic cystinosis. *Arch Dis Child* 61:401, 1986.

204. SCHNAPER HW, COLE BR, HODGES FJ, ROBSON AM: Cerebral cortical atrophy in pediatric patients with end-stage renal disease. *Am J Kidney Dis* 2:645, 1983.

205. ROSS DL, STRIFE CF, TOWBIN R, BOVE KE: Nonabsorptive hydrocephalus associated with nephropathic cystinosis. *Neurology* 32:1330, 1982.

206. FINK JK, BROUWERS P, BARTON N, MALEK M, SATO S, COHEN W, FIVUSH B, HILL S, GAHL WA: Neurologic complications of longstanding nephropathic cystinosis. Submitted, 1988.

207. TRAUNER DA, CHASE CH, SCHELLER JM, FONTANESI J, KATZ B, SCHNEIDER JA: Neurologic and cognitive deficits in cystinosis. *Pediatr Res* 21:498A, 1987.

208. WOLF G, EHRICH JHH, OFFNER G, BRODEHL J: Psychosocial and intellectual development in 12 patients with infantile nephropathic cystinosis. *Acta Paediatr Scand* 71:1007, 1982.

209. AVNER ED, ELLIS D, JAFFE R: Veno-occlusive disease of the liver associated with cysteamine treatment of nephropathic cystinosis. *J Pediatr* 102:793, 1983.

210. FIVUSH B, FLICK JA, GAHL WA: Pancreatic exocrine insufficiency in a patient with nephropathic cystinosis. *J Pediatr* 112:49, 1988.

211. GAHL WA, HUBBARD VS, ORLOFF S: Decreased sweat production in cystinosis. *J Pediatr* 104:904, 1984.

212. FOX PC, BAUM BJ, GAHL WA: Unpublished information.

213. KROLL WA, BECKER FLA, SCHNEIDER JA: Measurement of intracellular amino acids in cultured skin fibroblasts. *Biochem Med* 10:368, 1974.

214. LUBEC G, NAUER G, POLLACK A: Non-invasive diagnosis of cystinosis by infra-red spectroscopy of hair. *Lancet* II:623, 1983.

215. STATES B, BLAZER B, HARRIS D, SEGAL S: Prenatal diagnosis of cystinosis. *J Pediatr* 87:558, 1975.

216. BOMAN H, SCHNEIDER JA: Prenatal diagnosis of nephropathic cystinosis. *Acta Paediatr Scand* 70:389, 1981.

217. SCHULMAN JD, FUJIMOTO WY, BRADLEY DH, SEEGMILLER JE: Identification of heterozygous genotype for cystinosis in utero by a new pulse-labeling technique: Preliminary report. *J Pediatr* 77:468, 1970.

218. SMITH ML, PELLET OL, CASS MMJ, KENNAWAY NG, BUIST NRM, BUCKMASTER J, GOLBUS M, SPEAR GS, SCHNEIDER JA: Prenatal diagnosis of cystinosis utilizing chorionic villus sampling. *Prenat Diagn* 6:195, 1986.

219. GAHL WA, DORFMANN A, EVANS MI, KARSON EM, LANDSBERGER FJ, FABRO SE, SCHULMAN JD: Chorionic biopsy in the prenatal diagnosis of nephropathic cystinosis, in Fraccaro M, Simmoni G, Brambti B (eds): *First Trimester Fetal Diagnosis*. Berlin, Springer-Verlag, 1985, p 260.

220. SMOLIN LA, CLARK KF, SCHNEIDER JA: An improved method for heterozygote detection in cystinosis using polymorphonuclear leukocytes. *Am J Hum Genet* 41:266, 1987.

221. STEINHERZ R, TIETZE F, TRICHE T, MODESTI A, GAHL WA, SCHULMAN JD: Heterozygote detection in cystinosis, using leukocytes exposed to cystine dimethyl ester. *N Engl J Med* 306:1468, 1982.

222. SCHNEIDER JA: Clinical aspects of cystinosis, in Schulman JD (ed): *Cystinosis*. Washington, DC, DHEW Publication No (NIH) 72-249, 1973, p 11.

223. HAYCOCK GB, AL-DAHHAN J, MAK RHK, CHANTLER C: Effect of indomethacin on clinical progress and renal function in cystinosis. *Arch Dis Child* 57:934, 1982.

224. BETEND B, DAVID L, VINCENT M, HERMIER M, FRANCOIS R: Successful indomethacin treatment of two pediatric patients with severe tubulopathies. A boy with an unusual hypercalciuria and a girl with cystinosis. *Helv Paediatr Acta* 34:339, 1979.

225. LEMIRE J, KAPLAN BS: Prolonged use of indomethacin in cystinosis. *Pediatr Res* 15:696, 1981.

226. GAHL WA, BERNAR J, BERNARDINI I, DALAKAS M, RIZZO WB, HARPER GS, HOEG JM, HURKO O: Oral carnitine replacement in children with cystinosis and renal Fanconi syndrome. *J Clin Invest* 81:549, 1988.

227. BICKEL H, LUTZ P, SCHMIDT H: The treatment of cystinosis with diet or drugs, in Schulman JD (ed): *Cystinosis*. Washington, DC, DHEW Publication no (NIH) 72-249, 1973, p 199.

228. MALEKZADEH MH, NEUSTEIN HB, SCHNEIDER JA, PENNISI AJ, ETTENGER RB, UITTENBOGAART CH, KOGUT MD, FINE RN: Cadaver renal transplantation in children with cystinosis. *Am J Med* 63:525, 1977.

229. MAHONEY CP, MANNING GB, HICKMAN RO: Hemodialysis in a patient with cystinosis. *Am J Dis Child* 112:65, 1966.

230. LANGLOIS RP, O'REGAN S, PELLETIER M, ROBITAILLE P: Kidney transplantation in uremic children with cystinosis. *Nephron* 28:273, 1981.

231. MAHONEY CP, STRIKER GE, HICKMAN RO, MANNING GB, MARCHIORO TL: Renal transplantation for childhood cystinosis. *N Engl J Med* 283:397, 1970.

232. WEST JC, GOODMAN SI, SCHROTER GP, BLOUSTEIN PA, HAMBIDGE KM, WEIL R: Pediatric kidney transplantation for cystinosis. *J Pediatr Surg* 12:651, 1977.

233. CRAWHALL JC, LIETMANN PS, SCHNEIDER JA, SEEGMILLER JE: Cystinosis: Plasma cystine and cysteine concentrations and the effect of D-penicillamine and dietary treatment. *Am J Med* 44:330, 1968.

234. CLAYTON BE, PATRICK AD: Use of dimercaprol or penicillamine in the treatment of cystinosis. *Lancet* 2:909, 1961.

235. HAMBREAUS L, BROBERGER O: Penicillamine treatment of cystinosis. *Acta Paediatr Scand* 56:243, 1967.

236. LANCASTER GA, SCRIVER CR: Cystinotic and normal fibroblasts: Differential protection by cystine-free medium by dithiothreitol. *Pediatr Res* 15:86, 1981.

237. SCHNEIDER JA, SCHLESSELMAN JJ, MENDOZA SA, ORLOFF S, THOENE JG, KROLL WA, GODFREY AD, SCHULMAN JD: Ineffectiveness of ascorbic acid therapy in nephropathic cystinosis. *N Engl J Med* 300:756, 1979.

238. YUDKOFF M, FOREMAN JW, SEGAL S: Effects of cysteamine therapy in nephropathic cystinosis. *N Engl J Med* 304:141, 1981.

239. SELYE H, SZABO S: Experimental model for production of perforating duodenal ulcers by cysteamine in the rat. *Nature* 244:458, 1973.

240. SZABO S, REICHLIN S: Somatostatin in rat tissues is depleted by cysteamine administration. *Endocrinology* 109:2255, 1981.

241. SCAMMELL JG, DANNES PS: Depletion of pituitary prolactin by cysteamine is due to loss of immunologic activity. *Endocrinology* 114:712, 1984.

242. JONAS AJ, SCHNEIDER JA: Plasma cysteamine concentrations in children treated for cystinosis. *J Pediatr* 100:321, 1982.

243. YUDKOFF M, NISSIM I, SCHNEIDER A, SEGAL S: Cysteamine inhibition of ^{15}N-glycine turnover in cystinosis and of the glycine cleavage system *in vitro*. *Metabolism* 30:1096, 1981.

244. GAHL WA, BERCU BB: Blunted prolactin response to thyrotropin-releasing hormone stimulation in cystinotic children receiving cysteamine. *J Clin Endocrinol Metab* 60:793, 1985.

245. GAHL WA, GREGG RE, HOEG JM, FISHER E: *In vivo* alteration of a mutant human protein using the free thiol cysteamine. *Am J Med Genet* 20:409, 1985.

246. CORDEN BJ, SCHULMAN JD, SCHNEIDER JA, THOENE JG: Adverse reactions to oral cysteamine use in nephropathic cystinosis. *Dev Pharmacol Ther* 3:25, 1981.

247. GAHL WA, SCHULMAN JD, THOENE JG: Hepatotoxicity of cysteamine. *J Pediatr* 103:1008, 1983.

248. DA SILVA VA, ZURBRUGG RP, LAVANCHY P, BLUMBERG A, SUTER H, WYSS SR, LUTHY CM, OETLIKER OH: Long-term treatment of infantile mephropathic cystinosis with cysteamine. *N Engl J Med* 313:1460, 1985.

249. GRADUS DB, CARMI R, POTASHNIK R, MOSES S, BASHAN N: Treatment of infantile nephropathic cystinosis with cysteamine. *N Engl J Med* 314:1319, 1986.

250. BERGON ZI E, HERREN A, LAVANCHY P, BUHLMAN C, WYSS SR, LUTHY C, OETLIKER O: Treatment of cystinosis with cysteamine. A pilot study determining dose and form of application. *Helv Paediatr Acta* 36:437, 1981.

251. WITTWER CT, GAHL WA, BUTLER JDEB, ZATZ M, THOENE JG: Metabolism of pantethine in cystinosis. *J Clin Invest* 76:1665, 1985.

252. SMOLIN L, SCHNEIDER JA: Personal communication.

253. 477 15th St, Suite 200, Oakland, CA 94612.

254. COGAN DG, KUWABARA T, KINOSHITA J, SHEEHAN L, MEROLA L: Cystinosis in an adult. *JAMA* 164:394, 1957.

255. COGAN DG, KUWABARA T, HURLBUT CS, MCMURRAY V: Further observations on cystinosis in the adult. *JAMA* 166:1725, 1958.

256. LIETMAN PS, FRAZIER PD, WONG VG, SHOTTON D, SEEGMILLER JE: Adult cystinosis—A benign disorder. *Am J Med* 40:511, 1966.

257. KRAUS E, LUTZ P: Ocular cystine deposits in an adult. *Arch Ophthalmol* 85:690, 1971.

258. DODD MG, PUSIN SM, GREEN WR: Adult cystinosis: A case report. *Arch Ophthalmol* 96:1054, 1978.

259. AARON K, GOLDMAN H, SCRIVER CR: Cystinosis: New observations: 1. Adolescent (type III) form. 2. Correction of phenotypes in vitro with dithiothreitol, in Carson NAJ, Raine DN (eds): *Inherited Disorders of Sulphur Metabolism*. Edinburgh, Churchill Livingstone, 1971, p 150.

260. HOOFT C, CARTON D, DE SCHRIJVER F, DELBEKE MJ, SAMJIN W, KINT J: Juvenile cystinosis in two siblings, in Carson NAJ, Raine DN (eds): *Inherited Disorders of Sulphur Metabolism*, Edinburgh, Churchill Livingstone, 1971, p 141.

261. HAUGLUSTAINE D, CORBEEL L, VAN DAMME B, SERRUS M, MICHIELSEN P: Glomerulonephritis in late-onset cystinosis. Report of two cases and review of the literature. *Clin Nephrol* 6:529, 1976.

262. PABICO RC, PANNER BJ, MCKENNA BA, BRYSON MF: Glomerular lesions in patients with late-onset cystinosis with massive proteinuria. *Renal Physiol* 3:347, 1980.

263. DALE RT, RAO GN, AQUAVELLA JV, METZ HS: Adolescent cystinosis: A clinical and specular microscopic study of an unusual sibship. *Br J Ophthalmol* 65:828, 1981.

264. MANZ F, HARMS E, LUTZ P, WALDHERR R, SCHARER K: Adolescent cystinosis: Renal function and morphology. *Eur J Pediatr* 138:354, 1982.

265. LANGMAN CB, MOORE ES, THOENE JG, SCHNEIDER JA: Renal failure in a sibship with late-onset cystinosis. *J Pediatr* 107:755, 1985.

266. BRUBAKER RF, WONG VG, SCHULMAN JD, SEEGMILLER JE, KUWABARA T: Benign cystinosis: The clinical, biochemical and morphologic findings in a family with two affected siblings. *Am J Med* 49:546, 1970.

267. GAHL WA, TIETZE F: Lysosomal cystine transport in cystinosis variants and their parents. *Pediatr Res* 21:193, 1987.

268. PELLET OL, SMITH ML, GREENE AA, SCHNEIDER JA: Lack of complementation in somatic cell hybrids between fibroblasts from patients with different forms of cystinosis. *Proc Natl Acad Sci USA* 85:3531, 1988.

269. SCHNEIDER JA, FRANCKE U, HAMMOND DS, PELLETT OL, BECKER FLA: Properties of cystinotic fibroblast-D98 cell hybrids studied by somatic cell hybridization. *Nature* 244:289, 1973.

270. OSHIMA RG, PELLETT OL, ROBB JA, SCHNEIDER JA: Transformation of hu-

man cystinotic fibroblasts by SV40: Characteristics of transformed cells with limited and unlimited growth potential. *J Cell Physiol* 93:129, 1977.

271. TIETZE F, BUTLER JDeB: Elevated cystine levels in cultured skin fibroblasts from patients with I-cell disease. *Pediatr Res* 13:1350, 1979.

272. GREENE AA, JONAS AJ, HARMS E, SMITH ML, PELLETT OL, BUMP EA, MILLER AL, SCHNEIDER JA: Lysosomal cystine storage in cystinosis and mucolipidosis II. *Pediatr Res* 19:1170, 1985.

273. THOENE JG, LEMONS R, BOSKOVICH S, BORYSKO K: Inhibitors of protein synthesis also inhibit lysosomal proteolysis. *J Clin Invest* 75:370, 1985.

274. AULA P, AUTIO S, RAIVIO KO, RAPOLA J, THODEN CJ, KOSKELA SL, YAMASHINA I: Salla disease, a new lysosomal storage disorder. *Arch Neurol* 36:88, 1979.

275. RENLUND M, CHESTER AM, LUNDBLAD A, AULA P, RAIVIO KO, KOSKELA SL: Increased urinary excretion of free N-acetylneuraminic acid in thirteen patients with Salla disease. *Eur J Biochem* 101:245, 1979.

276. YLITALO V, HAGBERG B, RAPOLA J, MÅNSSON JE, SVENNERHOLM L, SANNER G, TONNBY B: Salla disease variants. Sialoylaciduric encephalopathy with increased sialidase activity in two non-Finnish children. *Neuropediatrics* 17:44, 1986.

277. WOLBURG-BUCHHOLZ K, SCHOLTE W, BAUMKÖTTER J, CANTZ M, HOLDER H, HARZER K: Familial lysosomal storage disease with generalized vacuolization and sialic aciduria. Sporadic Salla disease. *Neuropediatrics* 16:67, 1985.

278. ECHENNE B, VIDAL M, MAIRE I, MICHALSKI JC, BALDET P, ASTRUC J: Salla disease in one non-Finnish patient. *Eur J Pediatr* 145:320, 1986.

279. RENLUND M: Clinical and laboratory diagnosis of Salla disease in infancy and childhood. *J Pediatr* 104:232, 1984.

280. RENLUND M, AULA P, RAIVIO KO, AUTIO S, SAINIO K, RAPOLA J, KOSKELA SL: Salla disease: A new lysosomal storage disorder with disturbed sialic acid metabolism. *Neurology* 33:57, 1983.

281. HANCOCK LW, THALER MM, HORWITZ AL, DAWSON G: Generalized N-acetylneuraminic acid storage disease: Quantitation and identification of the monosaccharide accumulating in brain and other tissues. *J Neurochem* 38:803, 1982.

282. TONDEUR M, LIBERT J, VAMOS E, VAN HOOF F, THOMAS GH, STRECKER G: Infantile form of sialic acid storage disorder: Clinical, ultrastructural, and biochemical studies in two siblings. *Eur J Pediatr* 139:142, 1982.

283. GILLAN JE, PATH MRC, LOWDEN JA, GASKIN K, CUTZ E: Congenital ascites as a presenting sign of lysosomal storage disease. *J Pediatr* 104:225, 1984.

284. BAUMKOTTER J, CANTZ M, MENDLA K, BAUMANN W, FRIEBOLIN H, GEHLER J, SPRANGER J: N-acetylneuraminic acid storage disease. *Hum Genet* 71:155, 1985.

285. SCHAUER R: *Sialic Acids: Chemistry, Metabolism and Function.* New York, Springer-Verlag, 1982.

286. SCHAUER R: Sialic acids: Chemistry, metabolism and functions of sialic acids. *Adv Carbohydr Chem Biochem* 40:131, 1982.

287. SCHAUER R: Sialic acids and their role as biological masks. *Trends Biochem Sci* 10:357, 1985.

288. KORNFELD S, KORNFELD R, NEUFELD EF, O'BRIEN PJ: The feedback control of sugar nucleotide biosynthesis in liver. *Proc Natl Acad Sci USA* 52:371, 1964.

289. SOMMAR KM, ELLIS DB: Uridine diphosphate N-acetyl-D-glucosamine 2-epimerase from rat liver. Catalytic and regulatory properties. *Biochim Biophys Acta* 268:581, 1972.

290. THOMAS GH, SCOCCA J, MILLER CS, REYNOLDS LW: Accumulation of N-acetylneuraminic acid (sialic acid) in human fibroblasts cultured in the presence of N-acetylmannosamine. *Biochim Biophys Acta* 846:37, 1985.

291. KOLISIS FN, HERVAGAULT JF: Theoretical and experimental studies on the competition of NAN-aldolase and cytidine-5'-monophosphate synthetase for their common substrate N-acetylneuraminic acid. *Biochem Int* 13:493, 1986.

292. RENLUND M, CHESTER AM, LUNDBLAD A, PARKKINEN J, KRUSIUS T: Free N-acetylneuraminic acid in tissues in Salla disease and the enzymes involved in its metabolism. *Eur J Biochem* 130:39, 1983.

293. BRUNETTI P, JOURDIAN GW, ROSEMAN S: The sialic acids. III. Distribution and properties of animal N-acetylneuraminic acid aldolase. *J Biol Chem* 237:2447, 1962.

294. RENLUND M, AULA P: Prenatal detection of Salla disease based upon increased free sialic acid in amniocytes. *Am J Med Genet* 28:377, 1987.

295. HANCOCK LW, HORWITZ AL, DAWSON G: N-acetylneuraminic acid sialoglycoconjugate metabolism in fibroblasts from a patient with generalized N-acetylneuraminic acid storage disease. *Biochim Biophys Acta* 760:42, 1983.

296. THOMAS GH, SCOCCA J, LIBERT J, VAMOS E, MILLER CS, REYNOLDS LW: Alterations in cultured fibroblasts of sibs with an infantile form of a free (unbound) sialic acid storage disease. *Pediatr Res* 17:307, 1983.

297. STEVENSON RE, LUBINSKY M, TAYLOR HA, WENGER DA, SCHROER RJ, OLM-

298. STEAD PM: Sialic acid storage disease with sialuria: Clinical and biochemical features in the severe infantile type. *Pediatrics* 72:441, 1983.

298. PASCHKE E, TRINKL G, ERWA W, PAVELKA M, MUTZ I, ROSCHER A: Infantile type of sialic acid storage disease with sialuria. *Clin Genet* 29:417, 1986.

299. VAMOS E, LIBERT J, ELKHAZEN N, JAUNIAUX E, HUSTIN J, WILKIN P, BAUMKÖTTER J, MENDLA K, CANTZ M, STRECKER G: Prenatal diagnosis and confirmation of infantile sialic acid storage disease. *Prenat Diagn* 6:437, 1986.

300. AUTO-HARMAINEN H, OLDFORS A, RENLUND M, DAMMERT K, RAUVALA H, SIMILÄ S, SOURANDER P: Neuropathology of Salla disease. A morphologic study of two patients. Submitted for publication, 1988.

301. PASCHKE E, HÖFLER G, ROSCHER A: Infantile sialic acid storage disease: The fate of biosynthetically labeled N-acetyl-[3H]-neuraminic acid in cultured human fibroblasts. *Pediatr Res* 20:773, 1986.

302. RENLUND M, KOVANEN P, RAIVIO KO, AULA P, GAHMBERG CG, EHNHOLM C: Studies on the defect underlying the lysosomal storage of sialic acid in Salla disease. Lysosomal accumulation of sialic acid formed from N-acetylmannosamine or derived from low density lipoprotein in cultured mutant fibroblasts. *J Clin Invest* 77:568, 1986.

303. VIRTANEN I, EKBLOM P, LAURILA P, NORDLING S, RAIVIO KO, AULA P: Characterization of storage material in cultured fibroblasts by specific lectin binding in lysosomal storage diseases. *Pediatr Res* 14:1199, 1980.

304. BAUMKÖTTER J, MENDLA K, ROSENAU C, GEHLER J, SPRANGER J, CANTZ M: Neuraminic acid storage disease. Studies in cultured fibroblasts. *Abstr. Third International Symposium on Inborn Errors of Metabolism in Humans.* Munich, March 7–9, 1984. Basel, Karger, 1984, p 89.

305. TIETZE F, RENLUND M, THOMAS GH, HARPER GS, GAHL WA: Unpublished observations.

306. HILDRETH IV J, SACKS L, HANCOCK L: N-acetylneuraminic acid accumulation in a buoyant lysosomal fraction of cultured fibroblasts from patients with infantile generalized N-acetylneuraminic acid storage disease. *Biochem Biophys Res Commun* 139:838, 1986.

307. SIMILÄ S, LINNA SL, VÄYRYNEN M, AUTIO-HARMAINEN H, VON WENDT L, RUOKONEN A: Finnish type of sialic acid storage disease with sialuria (Salla disease): The occurrence and diagnostic significance of cytoplasmic vacuoles in blood lymphocytes. *J Ment Defic Res* 29:179, 1985.

308. SILVER HKG, KARIM KA, GREY MA, SALINA FA: High performance liquid chromatography quantitation of N-acetylneuraminic acid in malignant melanoma and breast carcinoma. *J Chromatogr* 224:381, 1981.

309. RENLUND M, TIETZE F, GAHL WA: Defective sialic acid egress from isolated fibroblast lysosomes of patients with Salla disease. *Science* 232:759, 1986.

310. JONAS AJ: Studies of lysosomal sialic acid metabolism: Retention of sialic acid by Salla disease lysosomes. *Biochem Biophys Res Commun* 137:175, 1986.

311. MANCINI GMS, VERHEIJEN FW, GALJAARD H: Free N-acetylneuraminic acid (NANA) storage disorders: Evidence for defective NANA transport across the lysosomal membrane. *Hum Genet* 73:214, 1986.

312. AULA P, RENLUND M, RAIVIO KO, KOSKELA SL: Screening of inherited oligosacchariduriass among mentally retarded patients in northern Finland. *J Ment Defic Res* 30:365, 1986.

313. NELSON A, PETERSON L, FRAMPTON B, SLY WS: Mucopolysaccharidosis VII (β-glucuronidase deficiency) presenting as nonimmune hydrops fetalis. *J Pediatr* 101:574, 1982.

314. ABU-DALU KI, TAMARY H, LIVNI N, RIVKIND AI, YATZIV S: GM1-gangliosidosis presenting as neonatal ascites. *J Pediatr* 100:940, 1982.

315. DUPONT A, FARRIAUX JP, BISERTE G, MONTREUIL J, FONTAINE G: Particularite de l'ultrastructure hepatique chez un enfant presentant une sialurie. *Lille Med* 12:654, 1967.

316. FONTAINE G, BISERTE G, MONTREUIL J, DUPONT A, FERRIAUX JP, STRECKER G, SPIK G, PUVION E, PUVION-DUTILLEUL F, SEZILLE G, PIQUE MT: La sialurie: Un trouble metabolique original. *Helv Paediat Acta 23* (suppl XVII):3, 1968.

317. MONTREUIL J, BISERTE G, STRECKER G, SPIK G, FONTAINE G, FARRIAUX JP: Description d'un nouveau type de melituries: La sialurie. *Clin Chim Acta* 21:61, 1968.

318. THOMAS GH, REYNOLDS LW, MILLER CS: Overproduction of N-acetylneuraminic acid (sialic acid) by sialuria fibroblasts. *Pediatr Res* 19:451, 1985.

319. PALO J, RAUVALA H, FINNE J, HALTIA M, PALMGREN K: Hyperexcretion of free N-actylneuraminic acid—A novel type of sialuria. *Clin Chim Acta* 145:237, 1986.

320. ROESEL RA, BYRNE KM, HOMMES F, TREFZ J, KELLOES C, NELSON AM, CARROL JE: Infantile type of sialuria without lysosomal storage. *Pediatr Neurol*, in press, 1988.

321. WILCKEN B, DON N, GREENAWAY R, HAMMOND J, SOSULA L: Sialuria: A second case. *J Inherited Metab Dis* 10:97, 1987.

322. CLEMENTS PR, TAYLOR JA, HOPWOOD JJ: Biochemical characterization of

patients and prenatal diagnosis of sialic acid storage disease for three families. *J Inherited Metab Dis* 11:30, 1988.

323. BERNAR J, TIETZE F, KOHN LD, BERNARDINI I, HARPER GS, GROLLMAN EF, GAHL WA: Characteristics of a lysosomal membrane transport system for tyrosine and other neutral amino acids in rat thyroid cells. *J Biol Chem* 261:17107, 1986.

324. DOCHERTY K, BRENCHLEY GV, HALES CN: The permeability of rat liver lysosomes to sugars. Evidence for carrier-mediated facilitated diffusion. *Biochem J* 178:361, 1979.

325. MAGUIRE GA, DOCHERTY K, HALES CN: Sugar transport in rat liver lysosomes. Direct demonstration by using labelled sugars. *Biochem J* 212:211, 1983.

326. WILLIAMS JC: Personal communication, 1986.

327. ROSENBLATT DS, HOSACK A, MATIASZUK NV, COOPER BA, LAFRAMOBOISE R: Defect in vitamin B_{12} metabolism. *Science* 228:1319, 1985.

328. WATKINS D, ROSENBLATT DS: Failure of lysosomal release of vitamin B_{12}: A new complementation group causing methylmalonic aciduria (Cb1F). *Am J Hum Genet* 39:404, 1986

CHAPTER 108

CYSTIC FIBROSIS

THOMAS F. BOAT
MICHAEL J. WELSH
ARTHUR L. BEAUDET

1. Cystic fibrosis (CF) is the most common fatal autosomal recessive disease affecting Caucasian populations, with an incidence of 1 in 2000 to 3000 births in various groups. The CF locus is mapped to chromosome 7q31 within a region of approximately 600 kb, but the gene is not cloned, and its product is not yet known.

2. Pulmonary obstruction and infection are the most life-threatening clinical manifestations of CF. Thick mucous secretions are associated initially with chronic obstructive lung diease, predominantly involving the small airways. Recurrent and persistent infections, especially with Pseudomonas and Staphylococcus, lead to bronchiectasis and respiratory failure, often accompanied by cor pulmonale and death. In the majority of cases, exocrine pancreatic dysfunction begins in utero and causes postnatal steatorrhea and failure to thrive. Neonatal meconium ileus occurs in 5 to 10 percent and is virtually diagnostic. Other manifestations include cirrhosis of the liver; infertility, especially in males; and abnormally high levels of sweat sodium and chloride.

3. The diagnosis is suggested by the clinical features of chronic obstructive lung disease, persistent pulmonary infection, particularly with mucoid strains of Pseudomonas, meconium ileus, pancreatic insufficiency with failure to thrive, or a positive family history. In the presence of such features, the diagnosis is confirmed by a sweat chloride concentration greater than 60 meq/liter. Newborn screening is possible using dried blood specimens for quantitation of immunoreactive trypsin. Newborn screening is not routine, but utilization may increase if early medical intervention is proven to be of value.

4. Treatment involves a comprehensive approach to provide postural drainage with chest percussion, inpatient and outpatient antibiotics, pancreatic enzyme replacement, proper nutrition, and psychosocial support. The prognosis has improved greatly, with 75 percent survival to late teens, 50 percent survival to the mid-20s, and about 40 percent survival to the fourth decade.

5. The basic biochemical defect in CF is unknown. Mucous secretions in CF are abnormal. Electrolyte transport, particularly chloride (Cl⁻) transport, is abnormal in the apical membrane of several epithelia in CF. Abnormalities of Cl⁻ transport are reflected in vivo in the sweat electrolyte abnormality and by an increased transepithelial voltage in CF airways. Abnormalities of Cl⁻ channel function can also be demonstrated in vitro using patch-clamp techniques to study primary cultured cells from sweat glands and from tracheal epithelium. There is evidence that the relevant Cl⁻ channel is present, but its function or regulation is impaired, and the basic defect in CF may involve the regulation of electrolyte transport. These studies indicate that the CF gene product is expressed in primary cultured cells, and they provide a potential functional assay for the gene product.

6. The CF locus has been mapped to chromosome 7q31 using DNA polymorphisms. Very tightly linked markers are available, allowing prenatal diagnosis and heterozygote detection within CF families. Analysis of microvillar intestinal enzymes in amniotic fluid can also be used for prenatal diagnosis. There is strong linkage disequilibrium between some DNA markers and the CF locus, which suggests that a large fraction of mutant genes in the population are descended from a single mutational event, but there is also some evidence for allelic heterogeneity. There are extensive efforts to clone the CF gene using a reverse genetic approach. A CF antigen, which is elevated in the plasma of heterozygotes and homozygotes, has homologies suggesting a calcium-binding function and has been cloned and mapped to chromosome 1.

INTRODUCTION AND HISTORICAL PERSPECTIVES

Cystic fibrosis (CF) is a complex, inherited disorder affecting children, many of whom now live into adulthood. It is characterized chiefly by chronic obstruction and infection of the respiratory tract, exocrine pancreatic insufficiency and its nutritional consequences, and elevated levels of sweat electrolytes. This condition represents the most common life-threatening recessive genetic trait in the Caucasian population. Dysfunction of exocrine glands appears to be the predominant pathogenetic mechanism and is responsible for a broad and variable array of presenting manifestations and subsequent complications.

CF is an important medical problem. It is the predominant etiology of severe chronic lung disease in children and has become an important cause of lung-related morbidity and mortality in young adults. CF is responsible for most of the exocrine pancreatic insufficiency of childhood and early adulthood and for much of the nasal polyposis, pansinusitis, rectal prolapse, nonketotic insulin-dependent hyperglycemia, and biliary cirrhosis seen at these ages. Therefore, CF enters into the differential diagnosis of many pediatric and young adult patients. Finally, investigators and clinicians have been intrigued by the elusive basic defect in CF and encouraged by recent opportunities to detect the CF gene, to approach gene isolation, and to identify its aberrant product. This chapter will review rapid advances toward these goals and toward the understanding of related epithelial cell pathophysiology.

CF was first described as a distinct clinical entity in the late 1930s. However, numerous references to infants and children with meconium ileus and typical pancreatic and lung disease are sprinkled throughout the literature from as early as 1650. Of interest are references in European folklore to the association of salty skin and early demise.[1] In 1936, Fanconi reported a child with the clinical features of CF, but failed to recognize the scope or importance of this syndrome.[2] Anderson is usually credited with the first comprehensive description of CF in

1938.[3] She coined the term "cystic fibrosis of the pancreas." In 1945, Farber suggested that CF is a disease of exocrine glands, characterized largely by failure to clear their mucous secretory product.[4] He introduced the term *mucoviscidosis*, which was popular in the medical literature for a number of years. Chronic infection of the lungs was recognized early as a major contributing factor, and antibiotics were first used for the treatment of CF in the 1940s. At that time, an autosomal recessive inheritance pattern for CF was suggested by Anderson and Hodges.[5] In 1953, di Sant'Agnese and colleagues investigated salt depletion in children with CF during a summertime heat wave and concluded that excessive loss of salt occurred via the sweat.[6] They subsequently documented that sodium and chloride levels in sweat are elevated in virtually all individuals with CF. This observation led to a description by Gibson and Cooke of the pilocarpine iontophoresis method for sweat testing,[7] a method which remains the diagnostic standard to this day. By the late 1950s, CF was reported occasionally in older children and young adults. Soon therefater, comprehensive and aggressive approaches to the care of patients were instituted in many treatment centers, and have been credited with a steadily increasing survival to adulthood of CF patients. In the past 30 years, a progressively more refined description of the CF syndrome and its complications has emerged.

Two recent sets of observations appear to be particularly important. In the early 1980s, Knowles, Boucher, and coworkers described altered electrical properties of CF respiratory epithelium associated with abnormalities of both sodium and chloride transport.[8] Soon thereafter, Quinton and coworkers[9] documented chloride impermeability of CF sweat gland ducts. These observations have focused attention on a pathogenetic role for electrolyte and water movement across CF epithelia and have provided for the first time a basis for understanding both sweat gland and lung dysfunction in this disease. Recent observations of isolated membrane patches from cultured respiratory epithelial cells have strongly suggested that the fundamental problem occurs at the level of cellular regulation of transport or secretory processes.[10] In 1985–86, several laboratories, using restriction fragment length polymorphism (RFLP) analysis, mapped the CF gene to a small segment of the long arm of chromosome 7.[11–13] These observations have laid the groundwork for rapid advances in the integration of genetic and pathophysiological information relevant to the abnormal gene product.

PATHOLOGIC AND CLINICAL FEATURES

CF presents in many different ways and mimics a number of other clinical entities. Usual presentations include persistent cough and recurrent or refractory lung infiltrates. Usual presentations also reflect gastrointestinal disturbance and include meconium ileus in approximately 10 percent of patients, as well as failure to thrive with steatorrhea. A number of individuals with a family history of CF are detected before the onset of symptoms. A surprising number of individuals escape detection in the first decade or two of life, often because symptoms are unusual, subtle, or even absent. A list of unusual presentations is compiled in Table 108-1. Recognition of the protean manifestations of CF and a high index of suspicion are required to detect all cases, either in childhood or later in life.

Table 108-1 Unusual Presentations of Cystic Fibrosis

Respiratory

Bronchiolitis/asthma
Pseudomonas aeruginosa
  colonization of the respiratory tract
Staphylococcal pneumonia
Nasal polyposis

Gastrointestinal

Meconium plug syndrome
Rectal prolapse
Recurrent abdominal pain and/or right lower quadrant
  mass
Hypoproteinemic edema
Prolonged neonatal jaundice
Biliary cirrhosis with portal hypertension
Pseudotumor cerebri
Vitamin deficiency states (A, D, E, K)
Acrodermatitis enteropathica–like eruption with fatty acid
  and zinc deficiency
Recurrent pancreatitis
Volvulus in fetal life

Genitourinary

Male infertility
Female infertility

Other

Hypochloremic, hyponatremic alkalosis
Mother of a child with cystic fibrosis

Respiratory Tract

Pathology. Mucous obstruction and infection, the major pathologic events in the lung, are confined, at least initially, to the conducting airways. In fact, the earliest consistent pathologic lesion is said to be mucous obstruction of bronchioles with accompanying bronchiolar wall inflammation.[14] It is clear that conducting airways disease is acquired postnatally. The airways of children with CF who have died within the first days of life display no obvious abnormalities.[15] For example, numbers and distribution of mucous-producing goblet cells and the numbers and size of submucosal glands appear to be within normal range at birth. A careful morphometric analysis of CF airways early in life has demonstrated dilated acinar and duct lumens in submucosal glands before reaction to chronic infection would be expected.[16] This finding suggests either hypersecretion or accumulation of secretions with abnormal properties at an early age and provides strong evidence that the primary pathogenetic event is accumulation of secretions rather than infection.

With progression of lung disease, evidence for bronchiolitis and bronchitis becomes more prominent, the submucosal glands hypertrophy, and goblet cells not only increase in number but extend distally into the bronchioles. Focal areas of squamous metaplasia develop and may impair clearance of mucus. Some small airways are obstructed completely by secretions (Fig. 108-1). Bronchiolectasis and then bronchiectasis are consequences of repetitive cycles of obstruction and infection. Extensive bronchiectasis is a usual finding by the second decade of life, but often is noted much earlier. Pneumonia, when present, generally is distributed in a peribronchial pattern.[17]

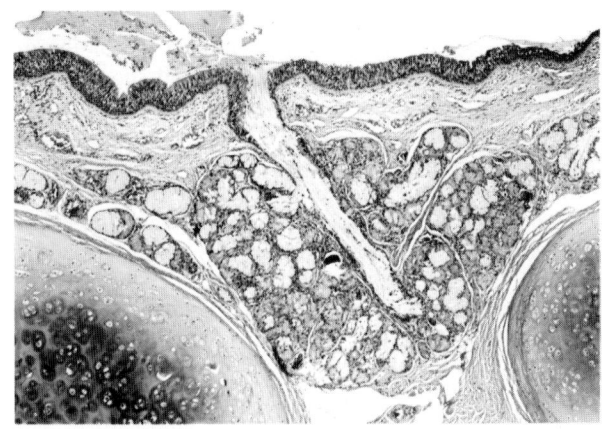

A.

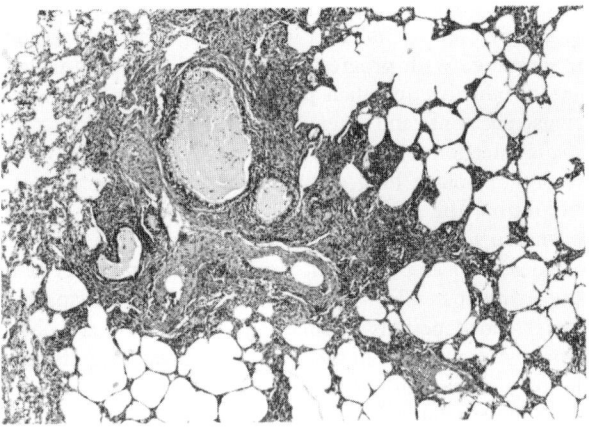

B.

Fig. 108-1 Tracheobronchial pathology in CF. A. Hypertrophied submucosal gland in the trachea of an 18-year-old woman with CF. Mucus-containing acini are distended. The duct lumen is distended with secretions which contain inflammatory and/or epithelial cells. H & E, × 42 (original magnification). B. Large and small bronchioles in the lungs of a 21-year-old male with CF. These airways are completely obstructed with secretions and display chronic inflammation of the walls and surrounding tissues. Peribronchiolar fibrosis also can be demonstrated with appropriate stains. Air space enlargement is prominent *(right)*, but more normal appearing peripheral lung is present *(left)*. H & E, × 42.

Detailed pathologic descriptions of lung disease are based on examination of lungs at autopsy and reflect advanced lung disease. Bronchiectatic cysts, initially most prominent in the upper lobes, occupy as much as 50 percent of the cross-sectional area of the lung.[18] In addition to dilatation, bronchioles undergo stenosis or even obliteration.[19] At autopsy, the lungs also show extensive overinflation of air spaces. Scattered areas of destructive emphysema (Fig. 108-1) are seen in patients who have lived for two or three decades.[20] Absence of more extensive alveolar wall destruction can be explained by effective confinement of chronic infection to conducting airways. Several patterns of interstitial pneumonia also have been described.[21] Peribronchiolar and peribronchial fibrosis accelerates with time and contributes to the restrictive lung function pattern which is superimposed on obstruction in advanced lung disease. Subpleural cysts eventually occur on the mediastinal surfaces of the upper lobes and seem to be related to the occurrence of pneumothorax in patients with advanced lung disease.[22] Bronchial arteries become large and tortuous,[23] contributing to a propensity for hemoptysis in ectatic airways.

Pulmonary arteries display varying degrees of change reflecting secondary pulmonary hypertension.[24]

Hypertrophy and hyperplasia of secretory elements, mucus accumulation, and chronic inflammatory changes also are characteristic of paranasal sinuses and the nasal passages. A common feature of nasal pathology is inflammatory edema of the mucosa with subsequent pedunculation and formation of polyps.[25]

Pathogenesis of Lung Infection. While mucous obstruction is likely to be the primary pathophysiological event, chronic infection in the respiratory tract appears to be the more destructive process. The chronic airways infection of CF may be unique, particularly with respect to its confinement to the endobronchial space and the organisms involved, primarily *Staphylococcus aureus* and *Pseudomonas aeruginosa*. Once established, infection of the lungs is nearly impossible to eradicate. Bacterial infection extending beyond the lungs is distinctly uncommon. Therefore, local rather than general host defense mechanisms must be compromised.

A potential reason for failure of lung defense and bacterial colonization of airways is defective mucociliary clearance. However, mucus transport velocity in the central airways is not consistently or profoundly diminished.[26] Clearance from the more peripheral airways, where mucus first accumulates, has not been assessed directly. Studies to date suggest that cilia morphology and beat frequency are normal.[27,28] Therefore, most investigators assume that abnormal physical properties or excessive volumes of secretions are responsible for retention of mucus. No matter what the basis, failure to clear secretions is likely to provide an environment which is conducive to the establishment of chronic endobronchial infection.

The role played by *Pseudomonas aeruginosa* and *Staphylococcus aureus* in endobronchial infection has prompted suggestions that surface properties of CF airways are altered in a fashion that promotes adherence of these organisms. *P. aeruginosa* adheres more avidly to buccal epithelial cells of patients with CF than to cells from age-matched control patients.[29] Furthermore, *P. aeruginosa* binds to cell surface carbohydrates of upper and lower airway epithelial cells,[30] but comparisons of CF and control respiratory cell interactions with *P. aeruginosa* or other organisms have not been reported. Another observation suggests that interactions of bacteria with epithelial cells may be important for CF lung disease; mucoid strains of *P. aeruginosa* seen frequently in CF lungs have enhanced adherence properties.[31]

Pulmonary immunology has also been investigated extensively in an effort to identify host defense abnormalities. There is little reason to believe that a primary deficiency state exists. Although CF subjects tend to have low levels of serum IgG in the first decade of life, these levels increase dramatically as chronic infection is established.[32] Secretory antibody levels appear to be normal or enhanced.[33] IgG harvested from the serum of patients with CF lacks a full complement of sugars on the termini of oligosaccharide chains. However, this alteration may reflect enhanced deglycosylation rather than a biosynthetic abnormality.[34] Antibody responses specific for infecting organisms in the respiratory tract are brisk.[35] Numbers of B lymphocytes and B cells that differentiate into immunoglobulin-secreting cells are not depressed.[36] T-lymphocyte numbers are adequate, and these lymphocytes proliferate in response to nonspecific mitogens.[37] With advancing severity of pulmonary disease, lymphocytes of CF patients proliferate less briskly when challenged with *P. aeruginosa* and other gram-negative organisms.[38] Blood lymphocytes of CF patients who are experiencing exacerbation of lung infection also display depressed production of interleukin 2.[39] These acquired dysfunctions can be reversed in some patients by intensive antibiotic treatment of *P. aeruginosa*, but may contribute to antimicrobial therapy failures associated with end-stage lung disease.

Polymorphonuclear leukocytes (neutrophils) and alveolar macrophages are plentiful in CF airways. Bacterial endotoxins or immune complexes in CF sputum appear to prime neutrophils for enhanced oxidative function following activation.[40] However, several investigators have examined the possibility that phagocytic cells are not fully functional in the CF respiratory tract. This notion gained credence from observations that CF serum inhibits the phagocytosis of *P. aeruginosa* organisms (but not several other bacteria) by rabbit and human alveolar macrophages.[41] On the other hand, CF pulmonary alveolar macrophages function normally when removed from their usual environment.[42] The putative phagocytic defect in cystic fibrosis appears to be related to deficient opsonic activity, is seen only in patients who have established *P. aeruginosa* infection, and may be caused by proteolytic fragmentation of IgG.[43] In addition, recent work suggests that the major subclass of IgG in serum and lungs and attached to lung organisms of CF subjects is IgG₂. Because alveolar macrophages have receptors largely for other subclasses of IgG, a preponderance of IgG₂ would be expected to interfere with opsonin-mediated phagocytic clearance.[44] In all phagocytic studies, abnormalities appear to be secondary to chronic lung infection rather than a primary contributor.

Whole complement activity is normal in CF. Decreased activity of the alternate complement pathway has been documented, and circulating immune complexes are present, largely in patients with severe lung disease.[45] The roles of complement abnormalities and immune complexes in the pathogenesis of lung disease are uncertain. Neither is likely to be primary. A number of investigators have attempted to relate *S. aureus* infection of CF lungs to fatty acid, particularly linoleic acid, deficiency.[46] Fatty acid deficiency is most likely secondary to the fat maldigestion of exocrine pancreatic insufficiency. Although CF patients who maintain exocrine pancreatic function experience less rapid progression of lung disease,[47] there is no evidence that this subpopulation avoids *S. aureus* colonization and infection of the airways. Other factors which may favor staphylococcal colonization are as yet unrecognized.

The mechanisms by which chronic infection produces airways obstruction and destruction of airways walls have received little attention. Recently, the role of proteinases has been considered. Both leukocyte and bacterial elastases are known to generate C5a nonimmunologically in CF secretions.[48] High levels of this chemotactic factor may be responsible for the brisk polymorphonuclear leukocyte response characteristic of infected CF airways. Elastases and other proteases are potent stimulators of goblet-cell secretion.[49] Furthermore, proteolytic enzymes introduced into the airways of animals produce marked hyperplasia of mucus-secreting cells in the surface epithelium.[50] Airways secretions of CF patients with chronic lung disease contain large amounts of uninhibited proteolytic enzyme activity.[51] Therefore, it is likely that these enzymes play a role in the development and perpetuation of the striking hypersecretion of mucus in CF. Proteinases also are capable of interfering with ciliary function[52] and enhance bacterial adherence to epithelial cells.[53] Furthermore, proteolytic injury to airway walls may be a factor contributing to structural damage and the development of widespread bronchiolectasis and bronchiectasis. The fact that destructive emphysema is not a prominent feature of cystic fibrosis lungs, especially early in the course of lung disease, may be attributed to confinement of infection to endobronchial spaces in mild to moderate lung disease. Detrimental chronic inflammatory reactions in conducting airways also may be fueled by immunologic responses to microbial residents.[54] Other mechanisms of conducting airways tissue injury undoubtedly exist but have not been described in detail.

Clinical Manifestations. The earliest manifestation of CF lung disease is generally cough. At first it is intermittent, coinciding with episodes of acute respiratory tract infection but persisting longer than expected. With time, the cough becomes a daily event. It is often worse at night and on arising in the morning. With progression of lung disease, the cough becomes productive and then paroxysmal. Sputum is usually tenacious, purulent, and often green, the latter reflecting *P. aeruginosa* infection. Hyperinflation of the lungs is noted early in the progression of lung disease. Wheezing may occur, especially during the first 2 years of life, due to inflammation and edema in small airways. Wheezing also may be associated with evidence for atopy, which, according to some observers, is more frequent in CF.[55] Lung sounds are often unremarkable for extended periods of time, sometimes for years. Not infrequently, diminution in the intensity of breath sounds may be the only abnormality noted, usually correlating with the extent of hyperinflation. Coarse crackles frequently are heard first over the right upper lobe but eventually achieve general distribution.

CF patients may have only bronchitic symptoms for long periods of time, in some cases for a decade or two, but eventually periods of relative stability are punctuated with exacerbations of symptoms including increased intensity of cough, tachypnea, shortness of breath, decreased activity and appetite, and weight loss. These exacerbations may be triggered by acute respiratory infections, perhaps of viral or mycoplasmal origin, although studies differ concerning evidence for these infections during early stages of increasing lung symptoms.[56,57] Intensive antibiotic therapy and assistance with clearance of mucus are usually required to control exacerbations of lung symptoms and to improve lung function. Exacerbations characteristically occur with increasing frequency. However, frank limitation of activity is associated only with end-stage lung disease, and heralds a sequence of terminal events including substantial hypoxemia, pulmonary hypertension, cor pulmonale, and death.

Most patients with cystic fibrosis have chronic rhinitis with increased volumes of upper airways secretions and moderate airflow obstruction. Nasal polyps occur in 15 to 20 percent of patients and are most common toward the end of the first decade and during the second decade of life.[58] Manifestations include severe or complete obstruction of airflow, profuse rhinorrhea, and, occasionally, widening of the bridge of the nose. Even though all sinuses usually display roentgenographic opacification, symptoms of acute or chronic sinusitis are infrequent. Cultures of the maxillary antra in 20 patients were remarkable for the presence of *P. aeruginosa* in 13 and the lack of recovery of *S. aureus*.[59] Mucocele of the paranasal sinuses is an infrequent finding and can be complicated by infection.[60] Middle ear disease is surprisingly uncommon.[61]

MICROBIOLOGY. The airways of individuals with CF are colonized early with bacteria, and once established, infection is rarely if ever eradicated. *S. aureus* and *Hemophilus influenza* are often the first organisms detected.[62] *P. aeruginosa* characteristically is cultured from respiratory secretions months to years later, although this organism is present at diagnosis with increasing frequency. With progression of lung disease, *P. aeruginosa* is often the only organism recovered from sputum, and may be present in several colonial forms, all with different antibiotic sensitivity patterns. Typically, one of these types is mucoid, due to elaboration of large amounts of alginate, a polyuronic acid. Mucoid properties were first thought to be associated with more rapid progression of lung disease, but they seem to have little effect on antibiotic susceptibility[63] or clearance from guinea pig lungs.[64] The recovery of *P. aeruginosa*, particularly the mucoid form, from the lower respiratory tract of a child or young adult with chronic lung symptoms is virtually diagnostic of CF. Recently, other species of *Pseudomonas* have been recovered from CF lungs with increasing frequency, particularly *P. cepacia* and *P. maltophilia*. The former is now recovered from a substantial number of patients followed by an increasing number of CF care centers, and is particularly difficult to control because of its resistance to most antimicrobial agents.[65] *P. cepacia* colonization has been linked to the rapid demise of a number of patients.[66] Occasionally other gram-negative rods are present in sputum including a mucoid *Escherichia coli*, *Klebsiella*, and *Proteus*. Anaerobes or microaerophilic organisms have been recovered from CF lung tissue, may be undetected pathogens, and on rare occasions are found in large abscess cavities.[67] Sputum bacteriology correlates reasonably well with specimens obtained directly from the lower respiratory tract. Quantitative bacteriology may be particularly useful for determining the relative contributions of the multiple organisms isolated.[68] A large number of sputum specimens contain yeast and *Aspergillus fumigatus*. Neither organism is often a serious pathogen, although the latter occasionally causes the symptoms of allergic aspergillosis. Infection of lungs with rapidly growing mycobacteria[69] or *Mycobacterium tuberculosis*[70] is unusual.

RADIOLOGY. The earliest radiographic change is usually hyperinflation of the lungs.[62] As bronchitis progresses, peribronchial cuffing becomes increasingly prominent, creating linear densities in the lung fields (Fig. 108-2). Impaction of mucus in airways may be seen as branching, fingerlike shadows. Evidence for bronchiectasis such as enlarged ring shadows and cysts is common by 5 to 10 years of age. Frequently, peripheral rounded densities are noted during acute exacerbations and may clear with treatment, leaving residual cysts. For reasons which remain unexplained, the right upper lobe usually displays the earliest and most severe changes. With advancing disease, the pulmonary artery segments are increasingly prominent. A relatively small and vertical cardiac shadow enlarges appreciably with evidence for systemic venous congestion. Hilar adenopathy is rarely prominent radiographically. Lobar or segmental atelectasis is uncommon.

Roentgenographic improvement with intensive treatment is not readily appreciated because of the fixed nature of changes in the airways. The most striking evidence for improvement often is diminished inflation of the lungs, which tends to make the fixed markings more prominent.

Bronchograms are not indicated unless lobectomy is a strong consideration. Computed tomography of the chest may be useful for definition of unusual lesions, but is not used routinely. There is little experience with magnetic resonance imaging of the chest in CF. Preliminary reports suggest that this imaging modality provides better definition of bronchiectasis, mucoid impaction, and inflammatory cuffing of the bronchi, and may be useful for distinguishing nodes from large pulmonary vessels at the hilum.[71]

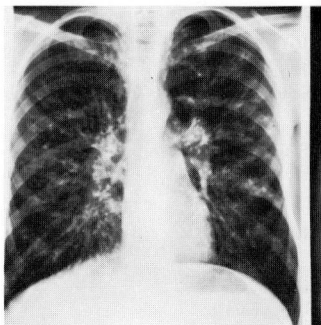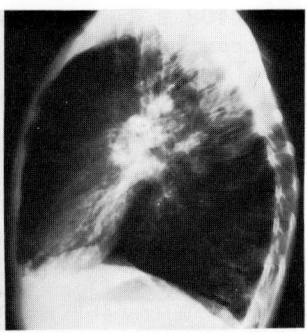

Fig. 108-2 Advanced changes of CF seen on this chest radiograph include: hyperinflation, bronchial wall thickening due to bronchiectasis, mucus plugs, and enlarged hila probably due to large pulmonary arteries.

LUNG FUNCTION. Newborns are thought to have normal lung function. However, within weeks to months, many infants with CF show evidence for increased airways resistance, gas trapping, and diminished flow rates.[62] When children reach an age ensuring cooperation, more complete testing first demonstrates obstruction of small airways as evidenced by reduced maximum midexpiratory flow rates, reduced flows at low lung volumes, and elevation of the ratio of residual volume to total lung capacity (RV/TLC).[72] Another sensitive indicator of lung pathology is an increased alveolar-arterial oxygen gradient, reflecting ventilation-perfusion inequalities.[62] Tests which are used most often to follow the course of pulmonary function include spirometry, lung volume measurements, and measures of oxygenation. In general, patients progress from initial reductions in maximum midexpiratory flow rates to reductions in FEV_1/FVC and then to diminished vital capacity and total lung volumes. This progression from peripheral airways obstruction to more generalized obstruction to acquisition of a restrictive component is illustrated in Table 108-2.

By the time a diagnosis is made, many children with CF display mild decrements of Pa_{O_2}. Oxygenation declines slowly throughout life. As a rule, patients who maintain satisfactory oxygenation continue to do well clinically, independent of the extent of the obstructive lesion. When Pa_{O_2} values dip below 55 mmHg on a sustained basis, symptomatic pulmonary hypertension should be expected.[73] Nocturnal and postural desaturation experienced by CF individuals may be a contributing factor.[74,75] Hypoxemia generally is not accompanied by polycythemia, at least in part due to an expanded plasma volume[76] and in some individuals also to suppressed erythropoiesis secondary to chronic infection. Tissue oxygenation appears to be further compromised by failure of CF erythrocytes to adequately increase their 2,3-diphosphoglycerate levels as pulmonary involvement progresses.[77] Elevation of Pa_{CO_2} generally occurs with FEV_1 values less than 30 percent predicted; thereafter, survival averages 29 months.[78]

Airway reactivity is a common feature of CF lung disease. Up to 68 percent of the CF population demonstrates decreased flows after histamine, and flows improve in as many as 40 percent of patients with aerosolized bronchodilators.[79,80] In con-

Table 108-2 Representative Pulmonary Function Test Results From Three Young Adult Males with Mild (A), Moderate (B) and Severe (C) Lung Disease*

	Patients		
	A	B	C
FVC	98	72	48
FEV$_1$	92	46	34
FEV$_1$/FVC	(.81)	(.70)	(.64)
MMEF	83	15	6
V_{max}, 50%	91	19	11
V_{max}, 25%	52	10	5
FRC	162	112	75
RV	189	200	120
TLC	131	105	62
RV/TLC	(.29)	(.45)	(.50)
Pa$_{O_2}$ (room air)	[87]	[74]	[48]

NOTE: Values are % predicted, except those in parenthesis, which are simple ratios, and those in brackets, which are torr. Patient A coughs several times a day, occasionally produces sputum, and shows no restriction of activity. Patient B coughs frequently, expectorates moderately large amounts of mucus, but is able to jog 3 miles daily and is a full-time student in a professional school. Patient C has chronic right heart failure, but is able to work daily as a hair stylist.

trast to cross-sectional studies, repeated tests every 1 to 3 months for a year have demonstrated bronchodilator responsiveness at least once in 95 percent of subjects.[81] Responsiveness seems to be more prevalent during winter months and diminishes with exacerbations of lung disease. The pathogenesis of bronchial reactivity in CF is unclear.

COMPLICATIONS OF RESPIRATORY TRACT DISEASE. Lobar and segmental *atelectasis* occurs in approximately 5 percent of patients.[82] This complication is most common in the first 5 years of life. Many episodes occur in conjunction with an exacerbation of clinical symptoms, but silent atelectasis has been noted. Occasionally volume loss is associated with allergic aspergillosis and endobronchial mucus plugging of other etiologies. However, in most instances, a discrete mucus plug is not evident on bronchoscopy.

Pneumothorax is a more frequent complication and, in contrast to atelectasis, has an increasing incidence with age.[83] In the 1960s, pneumothorax occurred in approximately 5 percent of all patients. There are now strong indications that this problem occurs more frequently, probably related to the prolonged course of chronic lung disease. Pneumothorax occurs equally often in both sexes and is more frequent in the right chest. Not uncommonly, a small asymptomatic pneumothorax may be discovered at the time of routine chest roentgenographic examination. More commonly, patients present with acute onset of shortness of breath, chest pain, and hemoptysis. The incidence of tension is probably higher in CF than in patients with less severe or no lung disease, and under these circumstances, the accumulation of pleural air may become a life-threatening event. Simultaneous bilateral pneumothoraces have been described and constitute a crisis. Once an initial pneumothorax has been recognized, the rate of recurrence is high.[84]

Hemoptysis is a common event in older CF patients and correlates with clinical and radiologic evidence for bronchiectasis. In most cases, hemoptysis is not associated with vigorous ac-

tivity, trauma to the chest, or other suspected contributory factors. Most frequently, only blood streaking of the mucus occurs. A few patients will occasionally cough up a mouthful of blood. Massive hemoptysis occurs in approximately 5 percent of individuals.[85] There is a strong correlation between the occurrence of both small and large volume hemoptysis and exacerbation of lung infection. Patients with relatively large volume hemoptysis may be able to localize the site of bleeding by describing a bubbling or gurgling sensation in one area of the chest. However, localization usually is difficult. Even immediate bronchoscopy seldom identifies the source of blood loss. Patients who experience massive hemoptysis originally were considered to have a poor prognosis.[86] The immediate mortality may be as high as 10 percent, but a more recent analysis suggests that massive hemoptysis usually is not a harbinger of terminal events.[85]

In one study, more than 50 percent of patients with CF had precipitating antibodies to *A. fumigatus* in their serum, and this organism can be recovered from the sputum with a similar frequency.[87] A small number of patients develop the syndrome of allergic aspergillosis, including new lung infiltrates, increased cough, respiratory distress, and often wheezing. The expectoration of rusty brown plugs of sputum suggests this diagnosis. Occasionally plugging of bronchi with hyphae-laden mucus causes lobar or segmental atelectasis.

Digital *clubbing* occurs in virtually all patients with cystic fibrosis and is usually present early in the course of symptomatic lung disease. The etiology is unknown, but the extent of clubbing seems to correlate with the severity of lung disease.[88] *Hypertrophic pulmonary osteoarthropathy* occurs in as many as 15 percent of older adolescents and adults.[89] If roentgenographic evidence for periostitis is used as the definition, the incidence is 8 percent. The most common sites are the distal aspects of the tibia, fibula, radius, and ulna. Signs and symptoms include pain, bone tenderness, swelling, and warmth over the involved areas. Effusions in nearby joints may occur. Often there is discomfort with ambulation. Symptoms of hypertrophic pulmonary osteoarthropathy frequently intensify with pulmonary exacerbations and tend to subside when control of pulmonary disease is achieved.

Pleural disease is uncommon in cystic fibrosis. Occasionally pleuritic symptoms and signs may accompany exacerbations of lung infection. Sympathetic effusions are distinctly uncommon, even during episodes of frank pneumonia. Staphylococcal empyema has been described in a rare patient,[90] but by and large, respiratory tract infections spare the pleural space.

Respiratory failure and *cor pulmonale* are late events. While progressive hypoxemia is characteristic of this disease, hypercapnea usually occurs only weeks to months before death. Similarly, liver congestion and peripheral edema associated with pulmonary hypertension appear on average 8 months prior to death,[91] although occasional patients may live with systemic venous congestion for 5 or more years. Unless associated with a reversible event such as influenza virus infection, hypercapnea and cor pulmonale generally persist once they have been detected.

Gastrointestinal Tract

Symptoms related to the gastrointestinal tract may predominate, although they are rarely life-threatening if properly treated.

Intestinal Tract.

PATHOLOGY. Changes in the intestinal tract itself are not prominent.[92] Brunner's glands of the duodenum are hypertrophied, with dilated ducts and acinar lumens filled with mucus. There is little if any primary change of the small intestinal tract mucosa. The appendix frequently displays goblet-cell hyperplasia of the epithelium and accumulation of secretions within crypts and in the lumen, changes which may be diagnostic of CF. In the past, a number of investigators have claimed the ability to diagnose CF by rectal biopsy, based on goblet-cell hyperplasia and accumulation of mucus in the crypts. However, subsequent studies have demonstrated that these findings are not consistent in CF rectal mucosa.[93]

CLINICAL MANIFESTATIONS. Meconium ileus occurs in 5 to 10 percent of newborns with CF and is virtually diagnostic.[92] Its pathogenesis is generally ascribed to failure of pancreatic enzyme secretion and digestion of intraluminal contents in utero. However, dehydration of intestinal contents due to epithelial transport dysfunction also has been suggested. These infants fail to pass meconium in the first day or two of life, develop abdominal distension, and proceed to bilious emesis. Occasionally, perforation occurs and peritonitis accompanied by shock intervenes. Flat and upright abdominal films reveal multiple dilated loops of intestine with fluid levels (Fig. 108-3). The lower abdomen often takes on a granular appearance, representing accumulated meconium containing small air bubbles. Barium enema demonstrates a small, unexpanded colon, and if contrast material can be refluxed into the ileum, the point of ileal obstruction is identified. Occasionally in utero perforation results in peritoneal and scrotal calcifications. In other newborns, obstruction may occur in the large intestine and only delay passage of meconium. This condition is termed the *meconium plug syndrome* and is less specific for CF.[94]

Beyond the newborn period, small bowel obstruction may occur for a variety of reasons. Perhaps the most common (occurring in 20 percent of patients) has been called *meconium ileus equivalent* or the *distal intestinal obstruction syndrome*.[92,95] As with meconium ileus of the newborn, obstruction occurs in the terminal ileum and is usually associated with voluminous, sticky, incompletely digested intestinal contents. Complete obstruction is associated with failure to pass stools, abdominal distension, and vomiting. In some instances, a partial obstruction occurs, accompanied only by intermittent abdominal pain. A mobile right lower quadrant mass may be palpable.

Fig. 108-3 Newborn with intestinal obstruction. Abdomen film *(left)* shows distended bowel loops with "bubbly" pattern of inspissated meconium in terminal ileum *(arrow)*. Barium enema *(right)* shows a microcolon from disuse secondary to intrauterine obstruction.

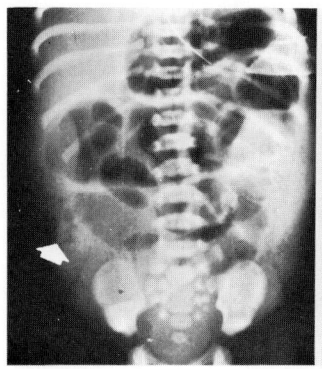
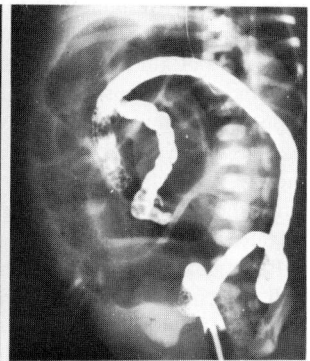

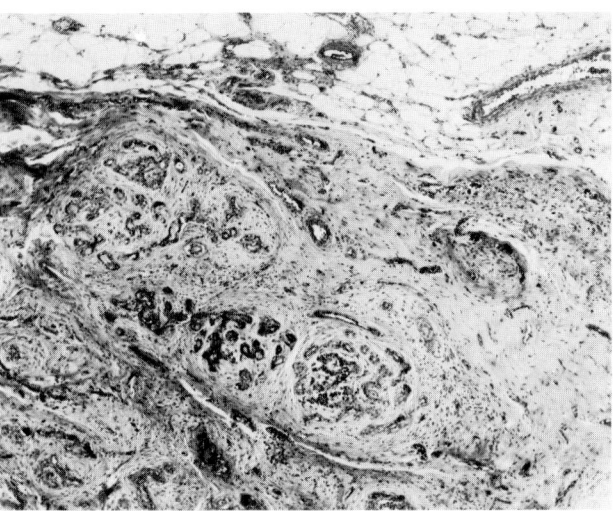

Fig. 108-4 Histologic section of pancreas from 12-year-old girl which shows changes typical of CF, including: extensive fibrosis of acini, dilatation of ductules, plugs within acini, and focal acinar calcifications. H & E, × 310.

These episodes of obstruction often follow ingestion of large, fatty meals, or are a consequence of noncompliance with pancreatic enzyme replacement therapy. Other causes of abdominal pain associated with obstruction include intussusception and intestinal adhesions from previous abdominal surgery, which seem to be a particular problem for individuals with CF. Lower abdominal pain also may attend low grade appendicitis (partially suppressed by antibiotic therapy) and periappendiceal abscess.[96] Nonfilling of the appendix on contrast enema is frequent in CF, even in the absence of appendicitis[97] and is due to accumulation of secretions.[98] Diverticulosis of the appendix has been reported in 14 percent of autopsy and surgical cases, a much greater incidence than is found in control populations.[99] Duodenal irritation, caused by failure to buffer gastric acid, may be responsible for recurrent epigastric pain and radiographic changes such as thickened, redundant mucosal folds in this area.[100]

Rectal prolapse occurs in nearly 20 percent of children, but is an infrequent event for adults with cystic fibrosis.[101] In fact, CF is one of the most common causes of rectal prolapse in the United States. Factors contributing to rectal prolapse include the presence of bulky, sticky stools which adhere to rectal mucosa, loss of perirectal fat which normally supports the rectum, and increased frequency of high intraabdominal pressure due to paroxysmal coughing. Pneumatosis coli has been reported in association with rectal prolapse in an 18-year-old with CF.[102]

Pancreatic Disease. Exocrine pancreatic insufficiency is present in the large majority of patients with CF from birth.[103]

PATHOLOGY (Fig. 108-4). The pancreas is abnormal in almost all cases and is virtually destroyed in most cases at autopsy.[103] Obstruction of ducts by inspissated secretions is an early feature, followed by dilatation of secretory ducts and acini and flattening of the epithelium. Loss of acinar cells is widespread, and areas of destruction are replaced by fibrous tissue and fat. Intraluminal calcifications may occur and be noted roentgenographically. Small cysts are common and generally represent dilated ducts. Inflammatory changes are not prominent. The islets of Langerhans are relatively spared, at least for extended periods of time. Late changes of the islets include distortion by fibrous tissue which may provide a barrier between hormone secreting cells and the vascular spaces[104] or disrupt blood flow. Changes in the distribution of islet cell types also have been noted.[105] Pathologic changes in the pancreas are used occasionally to make a postmortem diagnosis in atypical or missed cases of CF.

CLINICAL MANIFESTATIONS. Pancreatic enzyme deficiency causes fat and protein maldigestion, producing a distended abdomen and frequent, bulky, greasy, foul-smelling stools. Uncorrected maldigestion results in failure to gain weight, and, ultimately, a failure of linear growth. However, poor growth also may be associated with increased expenditure of energy to accomplish the work of breathing, a point that is often overlooked in the assessment of patients who are short or excessively thin. Fat loss in stools may be small or as high as 50 to 70 percent of total intake. Residual lipolytic activity has been ascribed to lingual lipase.[106] This lipase has a low pH optimum (5.4) for activity and can act in the stomach as well as the duodenum. In fact, its activity in the CF duodenum may be enhanced because of diminished bicarbonate secretion from the pancreas. Nitrogen malabsorption is roughly comparable or perhaps somewhat less severe. In general, carbohydrates are adequately absorbed in CF.[107] Deficient absorption of fat-soluble vitamins occasionally produces symptoms. Vitamin A deficiency, initially a prominent part of the CF syndrome, is now rare, occurring only in patients who do not take supplementary vitamins or pancreatic enzymes. Increased intracranial pressure, xerophthalmia, and night blindness may result. Vitamin D–deficiency rickets is rarely seen, but serum levels of 25-hydroxyvitamin D may be reduced. Bone demineralization is present in up to 40 percent of all patients, and is most prevalent in older females.[108] Diminished bone density seems to occur largely after the first decade of life. Calcitriol levels in serum of older CF patients are seasonal and appear to be correlated with extent of sun exposure.[109] Osteomalacia has been reported in an adult with CF and biliary cirrhosis.[110] Vitamin E deficiency is common in unsupplemented patients, but only rarely causes detectable abnormalities such as decreased red blood cell survival due to low grade hemolysis[111] and neuroaxonal dystrophy.[112] Additional evidence for vitamin E deficiency seen at autopsy includes focal necrosis of striated muscle and ceroid pigment deposition in intestinal smooth muscle.[113] Vitamin K–dependent coagulation factors may also be deficient, occasionally resulting in a severe hemorrhagic diathesis.[114] More commonly, vitamin K deficiency results in depression of factor II (prothrombin) coagulant activity without changes of antigen level or of the prothrombin time.[115] In addition to fat malabsorption, frequent use of antimicrobials and hepatic dysfunction may be contributing factors. While severe hemorrhagic problems have occurred in young children, bleeding problems associated with vitamin K deficiency, such as hemoptysis, are occasionally seen in older patients. Vitamin B_{12} deficiency occurs infrequently and can be corrected by administration of pancreatic enzymes.[116] More often, serum vitamin B_{12} levels are high, probably related to hepatic dysfunction.[117] Pyridoxal-5′-phosphate levels also may be low in plasma of CF patients, correlating inversely with liver function test values,[118] but there are no currently recognized adverse consequences. An acrodermatitis-type rash has been reported in an infant with Zn^{2+} deficiency. Both the deficiency state and the skin problem cleared with introduction of pancreatic enzyme therapy.[119]

Increased fecal losses of bile acids also appear to contribute to fat maldigestion. CF patients with steatorrhea have up to a sevenfold increase in bile acid excretion,[120] probably due to interference with bile acid absorption in the ileum. Interruption of the enterohepatic circulation can be explained largely by binding of bile acids to undigested intestinal contents, including proteins as well as lipids.[121] Kinetic studies show that bile acid synthesis is accelerated, that the bile acid pool is contracted, and that the bile acid pool increases with pancreatic enzyme therapy.[121] However, pancreatic enzymes do not normalize bile acid excretion,[121] an expected finding because exogenous enzyme therapy rarely eliminates steatorrhea. Ileal reabsorption and hepatic secretion of conjugated bile acids in response to cholecystokinin and secretin seem to be intact.[122,123] The functional consequence is that intraluminal solubilization of lipid may be deficient and contribute to the fat malabsorption characteristic of CF. For reasons that are not clear, fecal loss of bile acids diminishes with age.[123]

Severe maldigestion and malnutrition during the first 6 months of life may induce hypoproteinemia and anasarca.[124] This syndrome, accompanied in some cases by hemolytic anemia and hepatic steatosis,[125] may be the presenting manifestation in up to 8 percent of patients with CF. In many instances, the introduction of a soy protein–based formula has preceded development of profound hypoproteinemia,[125] suggesting that these formulas are a suboptimal source of protein for CF infants.

It is now recognized that symptoms of pancreatitis are encountered in less than 1 percent of adolescent or adult CF patients, especially those who have retained some exocrine pancreatic function.[126] The genesis of this problem is probably ongoing ductal obstruction and extravasation of secreted enzymes, causing pancreatic cell damage and secondary inflammation. Pancreatic calcifications are occasionally seen roentgenographically, but do not seem to correlate with symptomatic pancreatitis.

DIABETES. Endocrine pancreatic dysfunction has a predilection for older CF patients, although it has presented in the first year of life. This complication was noted in the first comprehensive description of CF in 1938.[3] A study of patients 12 years of age and older demonstrated a 57 percent incidence of abnormal glucose tolerance.[127] Other studies using different populations and criteria for impaired tolerance have identified this abnormality in 27 and 42 percent of study patients.[104,128] Surveys of two populations including 536 patients older than 11 years of age have found an 8 percent incidence of fasting hyperglycemia, glycosuria, and a requirement for insulin therapy.[95,127]

Insulin responses to an oral glucose load are delayed in nearly all subjects with CF. Individuals with glucose intolerance have a response which is even more delayed and variably subnormal.[104] Responses to tolbutamide, glucagon, and intravenous arginine are more prompt, but clearly meager.[104,129] Responses of glucagon to arginine may be variable,[130] but frequently are diminished.[129] Glucose administration does not suppress plasma glucagon levels. Insulin and glucagon responses of CF subjects with fasting hyperglycemia differ from those of patients with genetic diabetes mellitus, who demonstrate more profound insulinopenia and an increased response of glucagon to arginine stimulation.[127]

Functional assessments of pancreatic islets in CF correlate well with morphometric analyses of cell types in islets of CF patients at autopsy.[105] β cells occupy 28 percent of the islet surface area, compared with less than 10 percent in diabetes mellitus and greater than 50 percent in controls. Surface area occupied by glucagon-producing cells is normal, not increased as in people with type I diabetes. Somatostatin-producing cells are increased in all CF subjects, with and without hyperglycemia. These figures must be interpreted in the light of other observations that numbers of islets are diminished in most CF pancreases, so that the total number of β cells, as an example, may be profoundly diminished.

Insulin receptors on circulating monocytes are increased in number but have impaired affinity.[131] This does not seem to be true for CF red cells.[127] One study suggests that peripheral tissue sensitivity to insulin of CF subjects without diabetes is increased and may compensate for impaired insulin secretion.[132] However, another study has demonstrated decreased peripheral response to insulin by CF subjects with fasting hyperglycemia.[127]

The presentation of symptomatic hyperglycemia is the same for subjects with CF and genetic diabetes mellitus, namely, abrupt onset of thirst, polyuria, and weight loss. The hyperglycemia of CF does induce microvascular changes in the retina and the kidney if the course of the metabolic disorder is sufficiently long.[133,134] A striking feature of CF-associated endocrine pancreatic insufficiency is the virtual absence of ketoacidosis.[127] The reason for this difference from type I diabetes mellitus is unknown, but may be related to the relatively better preservation of insulin secretion as well as a less brisk glucagon response.

Considerable discussion has surrounded the question of the effects of fasting hyperglycemia and glycosuria on progression of CF-related organ dysfunction. While appearance of a diabetes-like state complicates therapy and may be psychologically devastating, recent evidence suggests that CF-associated diabetes does not influence the rate of deterioration of pulmonary function[135] and, therefore, presumably, longevity. However, diabetes may have a more profound influence on well-being of individuals with CF if survival is extended substantially.

Hepatobiliary Disease. Liver changes are variable. In 25 percent or more of all autopsies, islands of relatively normal lobules are surrounded by fibrotic bands, creating a distinctive multilobular appearance.[136] Microscopically (Fig. 108-5), this focal biliary cirrhosis is characterized by inspissation of secretions within the bile ductules, biliary duct proliferation, periportal inflammatory reaction and fibrosis, and a paucity of evidence for bile stasis.[137] Antemortem focal biliary cirrhosis may be identifiable only by elevation of hepatic alkaline phosphatase levels in serum.[138,139] Occasionally, prolonged neonatal jaundice with cirrhosis is encountered.[140] Thereafter, symptomatic biliary cirrhosis occurs in 2 to 5 percent of patients and presents with hyperbilirubinemia, ascites and peripheral edema, or massive hematemesis due to esophageal varices.[127,141] Evidence for hypersplenism is frequent in these cases. The presence of hepatosplenomegaly is virtually diagnostic for cirrhosis with portal hypertension. Bleeding from esophageal varices is the most feared complication of CF-related hepatobiliary disease, and may even be the presenting manifestation of CF.[142] At times, lobulation of the liver characteristic of the multilobular biliary cirrhosis can be appreciated by palpation. Especially early in life, a large liver may be due to massive fatty infiltration.[143] Infiltration by fat often is a response to inadequate nutrition and can be detected as increased radiolucency of the liver.[144] Unlike focal biliary cirrhosis, this condition responds favorably to dietary treatment.

Cholelithiasis, sometimes with biliary colic, is diagnosed before death in up to 12 percent of older patients[145] and has been detected as early as at 3 years of age.[146] Cholesterol stones are found in both extrahepatic and intrahepatic sites.[147] At autopsy, the gallbladder is abnormal in many more cases.[148] Alterations include hypoplasia (microgallbladder), a content of thick, colorless mucus (white bile), and calculi. In one study, calculi, nonvisualization, or structural abnormalities were noted in 45 percent of cholecystograms.[149] Bile in patients with CF who are not receiving pancreatic enzyme supplements is lithogenic because of a high content of cholesterol.[150] Enzyme treatment reduces cholesterol levels to a normal range.

Genitourinary Tract

More than 95 percent of male patients with cystic fibrosis have altered Wolffian duct structures.[151–154] The vas deferens, tail and body of the epididymis, and seminal vesicles are atrophic, fibrotic, or completely absent. The pathogenesis of these structural changes probably relates to early, often intrauterine, obstruction of the genital tract with inspissated secretions.[152] Developmental failure cannot be excluded at this time. A relatively high incidence of inguinal hernia, hydrocele, and undescended testis has also been noted.[155] Failure of reproductive function does not become an issue until well into the second decade of life. Because 2 to 3 percent of males with cystic fibrosis are fertile, a semen analysis should be performed on all males at an appropriate time after puberty. The volume of ejaculate is usually one-third to one-half of normal. There is complete absence of spermatazoa and a number of chemical abnormalities of semen including increased acidity, decreased fructose concentration, and increased levels of citric acid and acid phosphatase. These chemical changes reflect absence of secretions from the seminal vesicles.[153] A testicular biopsy will demonstrate spermatogenesis,[156] indicating that the functional CF genitourinary abnormality should be termed *azoospermia*. However, it is not necessary to perform a biopsy unless a diagnosis of cystic fibrosis is in question after the usual diagnostic criteria are examined.[157] Sexual function is usually normal and only limited by physical stamina and psychological factors.[158]

Fig. 108-5 Histologic section of liver from 12-year-old girl with CF which shows focal biliary cirrhosis. The periportal area shows fibrosis, chronic inflammation, and bile duct proliferation with intracanalicular bile plugs. H & E, ×620.

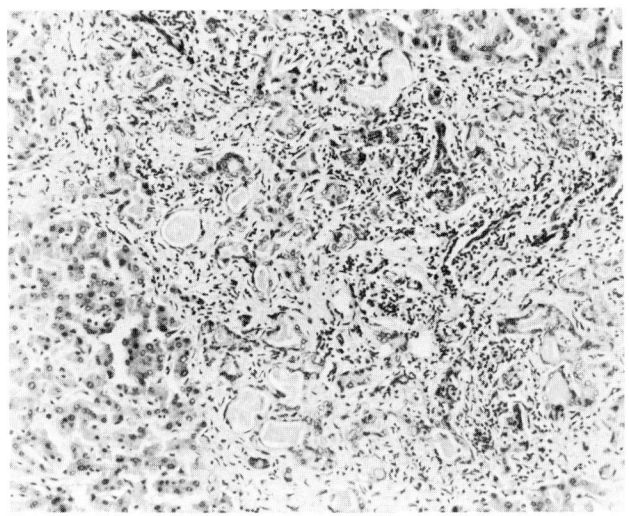

Fertility in women with CF is most likely greater than 10 percent,[159] but reliable figures are not available. Menstrual irregularity and oligomenorrhea are common.[160] Many women with CF are anovulatory because of poor nutrition and chronic lung infection. Another major obstacle to conception may be the presence of a thick, tenacious mucus plug which is very difficult to dislodge from the cervical os. Cystic fibrosis cervical mucus is dehydrated and has abnormal electrolyte concentrations, preventing the usual ferning at midcycle and perhaps impeding normal sperm migration.[161] Endocervicitis and polyp formation are also commonly noted.

A survey of cystic fibrosis centers in 1980 documented 129 pregnancies in 100 patients.[162] Seventy-five percent of the pregnancies were completed, and 89 percent of completed pregnancies produced a viable infant. Five percent of pregnancies resulted in spontaneous abortion, and one maternal death occurred during pregnancy. Therapeutic abortion was carried out in approximately 20 percent. Women with CF can breast-feed successfully. Analysis of CF breast milk has demonstrated essentially normal protein and electrolyte composition,[163] and minor variations in phospholipid composition, similar to those found in blood.[164]

Delayed onset of puberty is common in both males and females with CF. Reproductive endocrine function is intact, and delays in age-related increments of FSH (follicle-stimulating hormone) and LH (luteinizing hormone) secretion are thought to be consequences of chronic lung disease and inadequate nutrition. Most patients with cystic fibrosis do complete sexual maturation, sometimes at an appropriate age but frequently with a 2- to 4-year delay.[160,165] Height is in the normal range for greater than 90 percent of adults, although mean height is somewhat below that of the normal population.[127]

Sweat Glands

The most consistent functional alteration in CF has been elevated concentrations of chloride, sodium, and potassium in eccrine sweat. The number of sweat glands is normal.[166] Sweat rates are stimulated as in normal subjects by cholinomimetic drugs, but the usual response to β-adrenergic agonists is missing.[167] However, the pathophysiology of the sweat electrolyte disturbance relates primarily to a failure to reabsorb chloride along the sweat gland duct and is discussed in detail below. There is no structural abnormality of eccrine sweat glands.[168] In contrast, apocrine sweat glands of children with CF are more dilated and filled with retained secretions than glands of control subjects.[169]

Children with CF may "taste salty" or display salt crystals on their skin following profuse sweating. Excessive loss of salt in the sweat provokes both the release of aldosterone and attempts at salt retention by the kidneys.[170] The CF sweat gland is relatively refractory to mineralocorticoids.[171] Young children are predisposed to salt depletion episodes, especially at times when there is extra salt loss due to vomiting or diarrhea. These children develop profound hypochloremia, less impressive hyponatremia, and alkalosis.[172] They present with lethargy, anorexia, and hypochloremic alkalosis, an occurrence that is more common in warm, arid zones.[173] Hypochloremic alkalosis is rarely seen in older children and adults. Hypokalemia is not commonly recognized even though increased amounts of potassium are also present in sweat. Young adults with CF have on average lower systolic and diastolic blood pressures than age- and sex-matched controls, perhaps attributable to chronic, low-grade salt depletion.[174]

Other Manifestations

A number of other minor or infrequent pathologic and clinical manifestations of CF include enlarged submandibular, sublingual, and submucosal salivary glands with scattered histologic evidence for diluted ducts, inspissated secretions, and eventual atrophy of acini.[146] The parotid glands, which are not mucus-secreting, show no morphologic change. Other reported findings include seronegative, nondisabling arthritis,[175] painful subcutaneous nodules,[176] palpable purpura,[177] brain abscess,[178] and inappropriate ADH (antidiuretic hormone) secretion.[179] Several neoplasms have been reported,[180,181] but it is not possible to say whether individuals with CF are at increased risk. Amyloidosis, a recognized complication of chronic infection, has now been reported in a number of older individuals with CF.[182]

DIAGNOSIS AND COURSE OF DISEASE

A diagnosis of CF is based on carefully defined clinical criteria and analysis of sweat chloride levels. Accepted diagnostic criteria are listed in Table 108-3. Any one of these clinical features if accompanied by a sweat chloride level >60 meq/liter is sufficient to make the diagnosis. A number of individuals with sweat chloride values persistently in the diagnostic range but without clinical features of CF or a family history have been identified. As long as they remain symptom-free, a diagnosis of CF cannot be made. Other clinical entities may be accompanied by elevated sweat chloride concentrations. These are listed in Table 108-4. None of these disorders is easily confused with CF. It is now recognized that a very small percentage of individuals with CF have sweat chloride values in an intermediate (40 to 60 meq/liter) or even in a frankly normal range.[183]

For the 1 to 2 percent of patients with compatible clinical features but normal sweat chloride levels, several approaches to the diagnosis have been proposed. Documentation of azoospermia in sexually mature males may be of considerable value.[157] Attempts to document pancreatic insufficiency by collection of duodenal fluid following stimulation with secretin and pancreozymin are also informative but have fallen into disfavor because of the extraordinary time and technical expertise required, and the discomfort to individuals tested. Other tests of pancreatic function are more easily performed but less direct and specific. For example, serum trypsinogin levels may be abnormal in 80 to 85 percent of individuals with CF, and these values only correlate with pancreatic function after 7 years of age.[184] The discovery that bioelectrical potential differences across respiratory epithelia are elevated in individuals with CF at all ages[185] offers a second diagnostic test

Table 108-3 Criteria for Diagnosis of Cystic Fibrosis

1. Typical pulmonary manifestations, and/or
2. Typical gastrointestinal manifestations, and/or
3. A history of cystic fibrosis in the immediate family, plus
4. Sweat chloride concentration >60 meq/liter

Table 108-4 Conditions Other than Cystic Fibrosis Associated with Elevated Sweat Chloride Levels

1. Adrenal insufficiency
2. Pseudohypoaldosteronism
3. Hypothyroidism
4. Hypoparathyroidism
5. Nephrogenic diabetes insipidus
6. Ectodermal dysplasia
7. Glycogen storage disease (type I)
8. Mucopolysaccharidoses
9. Fucosidosis
10. Malnutrition
11. Mauriac syndrome
12. Familial cholestasis syndrome
13. Pancreatitis
14. Prostaglandin E_1 administration

that may be useful in the evaluation of atypical patients.[186] Most importantly, DNA analysis techniques are now available for detection of the CF gene, but this approach currently is useful only in situations in which individuals can be studied along with other family members including an individual affected with CF. The availability of a DNA probe which directly detects the CF gene may be close at hand and will have distinct advantages over current diagnostic approaches.

Until better alternatives are available, the sweat test remains the diagnostic standard. A single methodology is recognized as adequate for the definitive diagnosis of CF. This test involves collection of sweat by pilocarpine iontophoresis coupled with chemical determination of the chloride concentration.[187] Simultaneous analysis of sodium levels does not provide further information. The procedure must be carried out in a meticulous fashion in order to avoid errors which frequently contribute to misleading values. As many as 40 percent of patients referred to CF centers are inaccurately diagnosed because of false positive or false negative sweat test results.[188] In addition to frequent laboratory errors, faulty values can be obtained if the sweat rate is not sufficiently high. At least 50 mg of sweat must be collected in a 45-min period. Potential pitfalls in interpretation include the presence of hypoproteinemic edema, failure to consider age-related effects, and concurrent administration of corticosteroids. Though 60 meq/liter of chloride in sweat appears to discriminate nearly all adults with cystic fibrosis from those with other lung conditions,[189] normal values of sweat chloride do increase with age, and some insist on documentation of sweat chloride levels in excess of 80 meq/liter for the diagnosis of CF in adults.

Sweat electrolyte levels are elevated even in the first days of life. However, collection of sufficient amounts of sweat in newborns is frequently a problem. In addition, sweat electrolyte levels may be elevated for normal infants on the first day or two of life.[190] Therefore, testing is usually delayed for several weeks, unless diagnostic information is urgently needed.

Newborn screening for CF can be carried out using dried blood specimens for analysis of immunoreactive trypsin.[191] Although most newborns with CF are identified with this test,[192] routine screening has not been recommended up to the present.[193] Newborn screening is discussed further under "Genetics," below.

In the past, several approaches to antenatal diagnosis based on chemical assays of amniotic fluid have been proposed, but none has gained widespread acceptance. Recent identification of DNA probes linked to the CF gene has allowed accurate antenatal diagnosis for families who have had a previous child with CF and for whom specimens from the affected child and parents can be analyzed in parallel with amnionic fluid specimens (see "Genetics," below). Using the several probes available, more than 95 percent of families are informative. DNA analysis can also be used to identify carriers of the CF gene within the same family constellation. More specific gene probes hopefully will provide very accurate antenatal diagnosis and opportunities to screen extensively for the carrier state. Achievement of this goal should permit more accurate and timely genetic counseling.

CF runs a highly variable course, ranging from death due to complications of meconium ileus in the first days of life or death from severe respiratory tract problems within the first months of life to essentially asymptomatic existence for 10 to 20 years[142] and protracted survival. Individuals with CF do live into the fifth and sixth decades of life.[194] Nearly 3300 patients, or more than 20 percent of the individuals in the 1986 United States CF patient registry, are 18 years of age or older.

At most care centers, patients with CF are monitored by general clinical assessment which often involves the use of a scoring system,[195-197] periodic monitoring of respiratory tract pathogens, periodic chest x-rays, serial pulmonary function testing, and ongoing nutritional assessment. Initial intensive treatment is often followed by improvement of chest roentgenograms and pulmonary function as well as substantial improvement of weight-to-height ratios and accelerated linear growth. Following initial improvement and/or stabilization, there is often an extended period of stable lung function which may last 5, 10, or 15 years. However, longitudinal patterns of pulmonary function in older individuals with CF, while highly variable,[198,199] usually show slow deterioration.

Statistics from the U.S. Cystic Fibrosis Foundation indicate that 50 percent of patients can be expected to survive to 26 years of age. These data were generated on all patients under care in cystic fibrosis–sponsored centers in 1986 (Fig. 108-6). Analyses of survival curves over the years have suggested that survival has increased steadily to the present time. Some of the improvement in survival may have resulted from the diagnosis of milder forms of the disease. However, improved

Fig. 108-6 Survival curve for CF patients followed in all U.S. centers, 1986 data. These curves demonstrate the median survival age, or age to which 50 percent of the population may be expected to survive, using data from the year 1986 (*upper curve*) or cumulative data representing the 10-year span from 1977 through 1986. It is apparent from these curves that prognosis has improved during the 10-year period. (*Data from the Patient Registry, Cystic Fibrosis Foundation, Bethesda, Maryland.*)

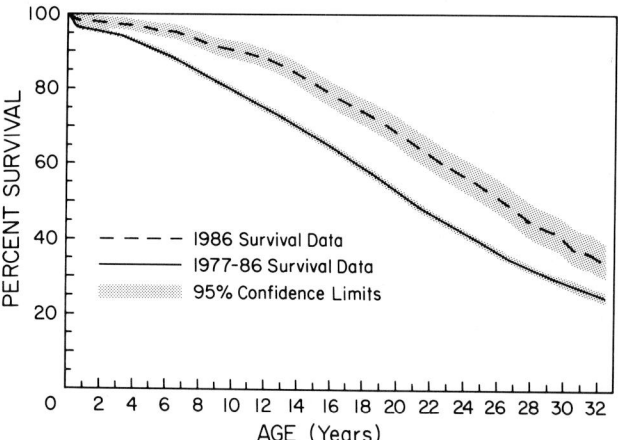

symptomatic therapy undoubtedly also has contributed to better survival.

Multiple factors determine the prognosis for individuals with CF.[200] Data from all U.S. cystic fibrosis centers suggest that survival is better for patients living in northern climates as compared with those in the South. On average, males live 3 years longer than females. Blacks who survive the first several years of life may have a better prognosis than whites. Age at diagnosis has not emerged as a clear determinant of survival. However, a study of sibling pairs suggests that a younger sibling who is diagnosed before 1 year of age, prior to the onset of symptoms, usually has better pulmonary function at 7 years of age than does the older sibling diagnosed because of symptoms.[201] Outcome analyses of patients who have been identified at birth by screening procedures and those who have been diagnosed after onset of symptoms should provide more definitive evidence for the efficacy of early diagnosis and treatment. Several studies suggest that clinical features at presentation do make a difference. Patients who present only with steatorrhea and failure to thrive generally improve remarkably after institution of therapy and do well for extended periods of time. On the other hand, patients who present with respiratory tract symptoms usually continue to have respiratory tract manifestations and have a less favorable prognosis.[202] When the entire CF population is considered, those patients who retain pancreatic function display a slower progression of pulmonary disease.[47] Meconium ileus does not influence longevity if the patient survives the first months of life.[203] Claims that CF patients with allergic manifestations have improved survival cannot be substantiated.[204] There are numerous indicators of poor prognosis once lung disease has been established, including colonization of the respiratory tract with *P. aeruginosa* or *P. cepacia* and the occurrence of pulmonary complications such as pneumothorax and massive hemoptysis.[205]

Little is known about the influence of medical care on longevity. Individuals followed at establshed care centers appear to have a greater median survival than those who receive care in nonspecialized settings.[206] In addition, recent evidence suggests that center-to-center variation in survival of patients is directly related to the intensity of care rendered in each center, including frequency of monitoring, use of antibiotics, and hospitalization for treatment of pulmonary exacerbations.[207]

Finally, psychosocial factors undoubtedly play a prominent role in outcome, although this is difficult to document. The role of a supportive family is crucial. Suicide is uncommon. However, it is widely recognized that a substantial number of adolescent and adult patients do not comply fully with therapy regimens because of denial, unresolved dependence-independence issues, and depression. Clearly, attitude and the ability to cope with a fatal illness during maturation and early adulthood do influence quality of life and survival.[208]

Even though faced with a life-threatening illness and burdened with staggering demands on time, energy, and financial resources to comply with therapy, many adolescents and young adults are coping admirably and are able to achieve a satisfactory quality of life. Meaningful relationships, an advanced education, and full occupation are frequently achieved, indicating that independent lifestyles and substantial participation in life events are attainable goals for many.[209]

TREATMENT

The primary objectives of CF treatment are to control infection, promote mucus clearance, and improve nutrition. In addition, experience has repeatedly demonstrated that attention to preventive aspects of lung care and psychosocial factors is important. The efficacy of a number of therapeutic approaches has become the focus of several collaborative studies.

Ambulatory Care

At diagnosis, most patients are introduced to a care program including postural drainage with chest percussion, administration of antimicrobials as indicated, and a nutritional regimen including pancreatic enzymes and fat-soluble vitamins. Other therapeutic modalities are prescribed on an individualized basis.

Postural Drainage with Chest Percussion. This approach to clearance of mucus is based on the idea that cough clears mucus from large airways but vibrations are necessary to remove secretions from the small airways, where expiratory flow rates are low. Pulmonary function evaluations before and after this procedure in some cases have and in other cases have not shown improvements in airflow.[210,211] Postural drainage alone may be helpful.[212] The most compelling argument for the use of this therapeutic modality comes from a study of older children with mild to moderate airflow limitation.[213] When patients were receiving chest physical therapy on a regular basis, little effect of a single therapy session could be documented. However, after 3 weeks without chest physical therapy, when both forced vital capacity and flow rates were significantly reduced, lung function could be improved with reinstitution of therapy. Most care centers prescribe this therapy one to four times a day, depending on severity of illness. A question has been raised about the advisability of chest physical therapy for patients who have minimal cough and no apparent sputum production. Experimental results are not available to answer this question. Several studies in the literature suggest that voluntary coughing,[214] positive expiratory pressure[215] or repeated forced expiratory maneuvers, and vigorous exercise[216] may substitute for chest physical therapy. In the absence of definitive supporting data, others have suggested that these should be considered adjunct therapies.

Antimicrobials. Lung infection is the major source of morbidity and mortality in CF. Therefore, antibiotic therapy is the mainstay of therapy designed to control progression of disease. In general, antibiotic therapy should be predicated on the presence of symptoms and guided by the identification of organisms from the lower respiratory tract. There is evidence that early and vigorous use of antibiotics produces better results than administration of antibiotics after symptoms are well-developed or advanced.[217] Some have advocated the early use of continuous antibiotic therapy.[218] Data justifying this approach are lacking. Another principle of antimicrobial therapy in cystic fibrosis is that dosages need to be higher than for non-CF-related chest infections. Both total-body clearance and volume of distribution are considerably greater for CF than for other patients.[219] In addition, large doses are needed to achieve therapeutic levels in infected and mucus- or pus-filled endobronchial spaces. Sputum levels achieved are highly variable, ranging from less than 10 percent to nearly 50 percent of levels measured in serum.[220] Experience has also led many caretakers of CF patients to use longer-than-usual courses of antibiotics, e.g., courses of at least 2 weeks or, not infrequently, 3 or 4 weeks. Continuous coverage is dictated by repeated, prompt increase in lung symptoms after antibiotic therapy is discontinued.

The choice of antibiotics optimally should be based on the results of sputum culture and appropriate sensitivity testing. If *S. aureus* is present or expected, the choice may include a semisynthetic penicillin, a combination of ampicillin and clavulanic acid, a cephalosporin, clindamycin, or chloramphenicol. Drugs and dosages are listed in Table 108-5. *Hemophilus* infections are best treated with ampicillin, trimethoprim-sulfamethoxazole, or chloramphenicol. In the majority of cases, these antibiotics will temporarily eradicate *S. aureus* and *H. influenzae* from the airways. In older children and adults, tetracyclines may provide useful empirical therapy. Efficacious oral anti-*Pseudomonas* preparations have not been available. However, ciprofloxacin, a new oral antimicrobial, appears to control symptoms and reduces numbers of *Pseudomonas* organisms in CF airways. Its usefulness may be limited by rapid emergence of resistant organisms and potential side effects in growing children.[221]

Because the treatment of *Pseudomonas* with oral antibiotics is frequently ineffective, intravenous preparations of aminoglycosides or other antibiotics have been delivered to the lower respiratory tract by aerosol. Several studies now suggest that symptoms can be controlled better and numbers of hospitalizations can be reduced with this approach.[222-224] Surprisingly, emergence of resistant organisms has not been a great problem with aerosolized antibiotic therapy.

Aerosol Therapy. Other solutions given by aerosol have the objective of providing water to hydrate inspissated mucous secretions. One frequently used solution contains 0.45% saline, another, 0.125% phenylephrine and 10% USP propylene glycol. The efficacy of this approach has not been substantiated. In the past, patients were encouraged to sleep in mist tents. This therapy has been largely abandoned due to lack of evidence for benefit and the aggravation for patients and families. New approaches to the hydration of airway secretions, e.g., inhibition of sodium and water reabsorption by respiratory epithelium, are in the experimental stage.[225]

Bronchodilators. As detailed above in "Clinical Manifestations," many patients demonstrate bronchial lability, prompting frequent use of bronchodilators, particularly β-adrenergic agonists.[226] While immediate effectiveness can be documented in the pulmonary function laboratory, overall improvement or long-term benefit has not been established. Indications for the use of bronchodilators include troublesome wheezing or a doc-

Table 108-5 Antimicrobial Agents Used to Treat CF Lung Infection

Organism	Agent	Dose		Doses/day
		Pediatric, mg/(kg·day)	Adult, g/day	
Oral route				
S. aureus	Cloxacillin	50–100	2–4	3–4
	Cefaclor	40–60	3–4	3
	Clindamycin	20	0.6–1.2	3–4
	Erythromycin	50–100	2	3–4
	Amoxicillin/clavulanate	40	2	3
H. influenza	Amoxicillin	50–100	2	3
	Trimethoprim-sulfamethoxazole (trimethoprim)	20	0.32–0.64	2–4
	Chloramphenicol	50–100	2	3–4
P. aeruginosa	Ciprofloxacin	—	1.5	3
Empirical	Tetracycline	50–100	2	3–4
Intravenous route				
S. aureus	Oxacillin	150–200	★	4
P. aeruginosa	Gentamicin or tobramycin	8–20	★	3
	Amikacin	15–30	★	2–3
	Netilmicin	6–12	★	2–3
	Carbenicillin or ticarcillin	250–500	★	4–6
	Piperacillin, mezlocillin, or azlocillin	250–450	★	4–6
	Ticarcillin/clavulanate	250–450	★	4–6
	Imipenim/cilastatin	45–90	4	3–4
P. aeruginosa and *cepacia*	Ceftazidime	150	4–6	3
Aerosol route		*mg/dose*	*mg/dose*	
P. aeruginosa	Gentamicin	40–80	80–160	2–4
	Tobramycin	40–80	80–160	2–4
	Carbenicillin	—	2000–4000	2–4

★Usually dosed by mg/(kg·day), as with children.

umented improvement in pulmonary function, e.g., at least a 15 percent improvement of FEV_1. β agonists can be nebulized, administered from meter-dosed inhalers, or given orally. There are no data suggesting that one route or one preparation is clearly superior. Caution should be introduced concerning long-term therapy with these agents, because animal studies show that administration of large amounts of β-adrenergic agonists causes submucosal gland hypertrophy and presumably a hypersecretory state.[227] Theophylline preparations also may be effective in selected cases. However, CF patients seem to be less tolerant of theophylline, because of frequent gastrointestinal irritation.[228] Inhaled atropine improves airflow in CF patients,[229] but systemic side effects prohibit clinical use. Newer, poorly absorbed, inhaled anticholinergics, such as ipratropium bromide, may provide effective therapy without adverse consequences. Cromolyn sodium has also been used, but claims of efficacy are only anecdotal. This preparation has the advantage of avoiding the rather substantial adverse effects of other bronchodilators.

Corticosteroids. A double-blind controlled study of alternate-day corticosteroid administration has demonstrated better maintenance of pulmonary function and fewer exacerbations of lung disease requiring hospitalization over a 4-year period in the treatment group.[230] A large multicenter study of corticosteroids administered in this fashion currently is being conducted. Widespread use of corticosteroids cannot be advocated at this time. It should be noted that in the initial study, subjects were children, up to 12 years of age, who had relatively good lung function. The effect on subjects with more advanced lung disease has not been studied systematically. In addition, corticosteroids may promote the emergence of hyperglycemia and glycosuria in CF patients. Nonsteroidal, anti-inflammatory agents have been proposed as an alternative for the control of airways inflammation and its adverse consequences, but data are not available to document either efficacy or toxicity.

Other Respiratory Therapies. Mucolytics, expectorants, and cough suppressants have been used for relief of chest symptoms. In general, cough is an important mechanism for clearance of mucus in patients with CF and should not be suppressed. Currently formulated expectorants, which by definition should increase the amount of water in secretions, probably do not achieve that objective. Rather than being helpful, long-term administration of iodides to patients with CF has been associated with a high incidence of goiter and hypothyroidism.[231] Mucolytics such as N-acetylcysteine are injurious to respiratory epithelium and when used regularly promote bronchitis. Therefore, this substance should be aerosolized selectively and only for short periods.

Exercise is generally considered to be beneficial for patients with CF and should be encouraged for all but those with the most severe lung disease. In one study, 12 of 29 patients with an FEV_1 <50 percent of FVC dropped their Sa_{O_2} below 90 percent with peak exercise, compared with no drop in patients with less obstruction.[232] A 12-week exercise program consisting of three 1-h sessions a week during which jogging produced a heart rate averaging 70 to 85 percent of peak heart rate has been shown to increase exercise tolerance and cardiorespiratory fitness, probably by increasing respiratory muscle endurance.[233] However, this program did not improve pulmonary function. Weight training appears to be safe, and may promote weight gain as well as strength.[234] Most caretakers of

patients with CF feel that regular, vigorous exercise promotes a positive self-concept and increases the perception of wellness. Although CF patients have normal thermoregulatory responses to exercise, they do lose more salt through the skin, and with exercise plus heat stress their serum sodium and chloride concentrations drop.[235]

Nutrition. Approximately 90 percent of patients with cystic fibrosis require pancreatic enzyme supplementation. This is accomplished by mealtime administration of enzyme extract, usually administered as encapsulated microspheres coated with acid-resistant material to promote delivery to the small intestine. Enzyme replacement diminishes but does not normalize the amount of fat and nitrogen excreted in stools.[236] One to four capsules per meal or snack generally is adequate. Numbers of capsules taken should be adjusted, based on weight gain or loss, presence or absence of abdominal cramping, and the character of stools. Because postprandial pH is low in the CF duodenum, the encapsulated spheres may not dissolve optimally in the proximal small intestine.[237] Complications of pancreatic enzyme replacement therapy include oral and perianal ulcerations and hyperuricosuria[238] when large amounts of pancreatic extract are given. Vitamins A and D are generally supplied by a daily multiple-vitamin preparation. Vitamin E, 100 to 200 units daily, also is recommended because serum levels are generally low in unsupplemented patients. Vitamin K usually is given sporadically to treat bleeding complications or correct prolonged prothrombin times. Other vitamins and trace minerals may be deficient and require supplementation on a selective basis.

Many individuals with CF have a higher than normal caloric need because of the increased work of breathing. In general, patients should be encouraged to eat a balanced diet including at least a moderate amount of fat. When the anorexia of chronic infection supervenes, failure to gain weight or weight loss occurs. Further encouragement to eat high calorie foods may be helpful. Supplementation with elemental dietary preparations by mouth is unlikely to be sustained over an extended period of time. Some CF care centers have begun to administer supplementary elemental feedings nocturnally by nasogastric tube or by percutaneous duodenostomy.[239] While short-term benefits such as increased weight gain can be achieved, long-term benefits including effects on pulmonary function and psychological consequences have not been established.

Patients with CF who retain exocrine pancreatic function and maintain good nutrition experience a slower rate of decline of pulmonary function than those with no demonstrable pancreatic function.[47] This observation has been used as a rationale for emphasizing nutritional interventions. However, it may be more efficacious to maintain good nutrition by preventing progression of lung disease than to maintain good lung function by emphasizing nutritional therapy. A combination of these approaches is probably optimal. The more favorable pulmonary function in patients who retain pancreatic function could reflect the presence of an allele causing a milder phenotype (see "Linkage Disequilibrium," below).

Psychosocial Factors. As with any chronic disease, compliance with therapy and ability to function fully are highly dependent on patient attitude. Therefore, approaches which promote a positive self-concept, foster the ability of individuals to take control of their medical management, and allow them to participate fully in life events are likely to promote well-being and perhaps longevity. However, caretakers of patients with

CF must recognize that these individuals may participate in harmful behaviors, such as substance abuse,[240] just like their healthy peers. Medical care which provides continuity and fosters trust may pay large dividends. Personnel who specifically provide psychosocial support are important contributors to CF care teams.

Prevention of Lung Disease. Rubeola, pertussis, and influenza infections are particularly injurious to CF lungs and may trigger a downward spiral of lung function. Adequate immunization early in life for pertussis and measles is mandatory. In addition, patients of all ages should be adequately immunized for influenza virus infection on a yearly basis. The early use of amantidine for acute respiratory illnesses during epidemics of influenza A infections may further prevent adverse consequences of this infection. There is no evidence that administration of the pneumococcal vaccine is useful. Cigarette smoke and other air pollutants are likely to have adverse effects, but their role in the decline of lung function is undetermined.

Hospital Therapy

Indications for hospitalization and intensive pulmonary therapy include increased cough or wheezing, respiratory distress with decreased activity tolerance, weight loss, sustained downward trend in pulmonary function, increasing hypoxemia, or one of the pulmonary complications of CF. Although all the modalities of therapy can be intensified in the hospital, the major advantage of hospitalization has been the ability to administer intravenous antimicrobial agents which control *Pseudomonas* infection.

Antibiotics for intravenous administration should be selected on the basis of respiratory tract cultures and susceptibility studies. Two-drug treatment of *Pseudomonas* infection is the rule. A third antibiotic may be added as necessary for control of *S. aureus* or other organisms. Drugs and dosages currently used for intravenous therapy are listed in Table 108-5. A response often is not seen for 4 to 7 days after initiation of therapy. In general, a 2-week course provides good improvement in pulmonary function[241] and more sustained benefit. With refractory infection, treatment for 3 or more weeks is not unusual. Some advocate intensive therapy until pulmonary function has returned to a previous baseline or until improvement has reached a plateau. Prolonged courses of antibiotic therapy should include weekly monitoring of respiratory tract organisms and their sensitivities, as shifts in either are not uncommon. In general, determination of minimum inhibitory concentrations provides more useful information about susceptibility of *Pseudomonas* organisms than do disk methods of sensitivity testing.

Aminoglycosides have been the mainstay of anti-*Pseudomonas* therapy for more than 15 years. A major advantage is the ability to monitor and adjust blood levels. For gentamicin or tobramycin, dosage three times a day and achievement of peaks in the range of 10 μg/ml and troughs <2 μg/ml seems to be optimal. The same daily dose of aminoglycosides can be given once or twice daily, and the high peak levels achieved under these conditions are well-tolerated.[242] Patients should be monitored during aminoglycoside therapy for nephrotoxicity and ototoxicity. An aminoglycoside is usually paired with one of the penicillin derivatives or with ceftazadime.

Individuals with cystic fibrosis, particularly those who are

in school or holding full-time jobs, may opt to administer intravenous antibiotics for all or a portion of the treatment course at home. Properly administered intravenous therapy at home appears to be nearly as efficacious as in-hospital treatment.[243] For patients requiring long-term home antibiotic therapy, central intravenous catheters have been surgically placed and used for prolonged periods.

Interest in bronchial lavage as a therapeutic modality has been tempered by the realization that long-term benefits are unlikely to accrue from this approach and that acute deterioration of lung function is a possible outcome.[244] In fact, there is no evidence that bronchoscopy and lavage, whether it be whole-lung, lobar, or segmental, is superior to intensive antibiotic therapy and chest percussion.

Treatment of Complications. The most feared complications of CF lung disease are pulmonary hypertension with right heart failure and respiratory failure. Low-flow oxygen is effective in alleviating nocturnal hypoxemia and does not cause clinically important hypercapnea.[245] However, there is no evidence that this approach is effective in preventing pulmonary hypertension or postponing the onset of symptomatic right heart failure, as may be the case with older patients who have chronic bronchitis. If systemic venous congestion is present, furosemide, 1 mg/kg, administered intravenously usually results in brisk diuresis and reduces fluid retention.[246] If needed, long-term diuretic therapy with spironolactone prevents potassium depletion and seems to be helpful. Digitalis is not effective in the face of pure right-sided failure, but it may be useful when there is associated left-sided dysfunction.[247] Pharmacologic relief of high pulmonary artery pressures has been achieved acutely with tolazoline[248] but not with other pulmonary vasodilators.[249] Evidence for sustained improvement with drug therapy has not been forthcoming. The most effective approach to relief of right heart failure is improvement of oxygenation through intensive pulmonary therapy. A moderate limitation of salt intake, i.e., 2 g sodium per day, may be helpful. Carbenicillin and related drugs may promote fluid retention because of their relatively high sodium content.

Respiratory failure is best managed with vigorous medical therapy of lung disease. All evidence to date suggests that respiratory insufficiency in a patient who has experienced slow deterioration in lung function over months to years will not be reversed by assisted ventilation. In fact, the usual outcome of intubation and ventilatory assistance is prolonged ventilator dependence.[250] For this reason, assisted ventilation is recommended only for patients who have had at least moderately good lung function and who have experienced rapid deterioration because of a reversible insult to the lungs, such as influenza virus infection.

Atelectasis is best treated with vigorous antibiotic therapy and frequent chest percussion and drainage. Corticosteroids may be helpful in the face of reactive airways disease or evidence for allergic aspergillosis. There is no evidence that bronchoscopy and lavage hasten the expansion of collapsed segments or lobes.[82] However, fiberoptic bronchoscopy and the sampling of secretions from an atelectatic area of the lung for cytologic and microbiologic assessment may be helpful.

Pneumothorax can be watched if it is small (<10 percent of the hemithorax cross-sectional area) and is asymptomatic. Because of a tendency toward persistent air leak and a high recurrence rate, many advocate instillation of a sclerosing agent such as atabrine or limited thoracotomy with both oversewing of obvious areas of leakage and pleural abrasion or stripping.[84]

In general, these interventions are well-tolerated by patients and shorten rather than lengthen hospitalization for pneumothorax.

Small volume hemoptysis requires no specific therapy other than aggressive treatment of lung infection and vitamin K supplements if indicated. Large volume hemoptysis usually subsides spontaneously,[85] but if persistent, has been treated successfully by bronchial artery embolization.[251] Allergic aspergillosis usually responds to systemic corticosteroid therapy and is self-limiting.[252] For refractory cases, aerosolized amphotericin B may be helpful. There is no specific therapy for hypertrophic osteoarthropathy. Symptoms usually wane as control of lung infection is achieved. Gastroesophageal reflux has been documented in about 20 percent of infants and children with cystic fibrosis,[253,254] probably due to increased intraabdominal pressure secondary to obstructive lung disease and frequent coughing. It may contribute to airways obstruction and lung infiltrates by reflex mechanisms or aspiration. Medical therapy for reflux reduces symptoms in most of these patients but several have required fundoplication.[253] Use of bethanecol to treat reflux has resulted in marked deterioration of lung function[255] presumably secondary to enhanced bronchospasm and secretion of mucus.

Treatment of Gastrointestinal Complications. Meconium ileus can often be relieved with enemas using Gastrografin or other contrast materials which are refluxed into the terminal ileum under fluoroscopy.[92] If this fails, or if there is evidence of perforation, surgical intervention is required. Distal intestinal obstruction syndrome also can be relieved with contrast enemas which reach the terminal ileum.[256] Some success is also claimed for oral administration of N-acetylcysteine[257] and peroral lavage with large volumes of physiological fluids containing polyethylene glycol.[258] Occasionally surgical intervention is necessary. Rectal prolapse usually can be reduced voluntarily by older patients, using abdominal, perineal, and gluteal muscles, but in small children it must be reduced manually by continuous gentle pressure with the patient in the knee-chest position.[101] Sedation may be helpful. Adequate pancreatic enzyme therapy, decreased fat in the diet, and control of pulmonary infection usually eliminate recurrences. An infrequent patient may require surgical stabilization of the rectum. Cirrhosis is generally focal and usually does not require specific therapy. Bleeding varices usually can be managed with sclerotherapy. In the past, significant bleeding has been treated successfully with portal-systemic shunting.[141] Splenorenal anastomoses have been most effective, and hepatic encephalopathy has not been a problem. Occasionally, pronounced hypersplenism may require splenectomy. Liver failure and ascites are treated as in other patients. Similarly, pancreatitis, when it occurs in adolescents or young adults with CF, is treated with standard regimens.

Hyperglycemia attending cystic fibrosis can occur at any age, but is generally a problem of the second and third decades of life. Ketoacidosis is rarely encountered. When blood glucose levels are only intermittently elevated and glycosuria does not intervene, no treatment is necessary. With the advent of sustained glycosuria, insulin treatment should be instituted. Oral hypoglycemic agents usually are not effective. Vascular disease affecting the retina and the kidneys has been documented in CF patients with prolonged hyperglycemia. Therefore, consistent control of blood sugar levels is desirable, although caution must be exercised with insulin therapy in that CF subjects frequently become hypoglycemic.[127]

Many of the complications of CF are iatrogenic. A number of therapy-related medical problems are listed in Table 108-6.

Surgical Therapy. The most common reason for surgery in cystic fibrosis is nasal polypectomy. This may be required when the nasal passages are completely obstructed, when rhinorrhea is particularly bothersome, or if the polyps cause internal pressure and widen the bridge of the nose. Elective surgery should be avoided during exacerbations of lung disease. Intensive pulmonary therapy for several days before surgery may be useful, and careful monitoring postoperatively is essential for preventing postanesthetic problems.[25] Polyps do tend to recur after surgical removal, but the incidence of polyposis wanes after the second decade of life. Removal of lung segments or lobes because of chronic atelectasis or severe focal lung disease is attempted infrequently. In carefully selected patients this approach may provide additional years with fewer symptoms. However, lobectomy should be undertaken with the knowledge that postoperative complications are not uncommon and removal of any functioning lung tissue may be detrimental for patients who have a progressive, generalized pulmonary disease. Abdominal surgery for intestinal obstruction, appendicitis, or cholelithiasis is occasionally indicated and usually is well-tolerated if attention is paid to care of the lungs.

Heart-lung transplantation had been attempted in more than 40 individuals with CF by July 1988. Initial results have been encouraging, with more than half of recipients surviving the immediate postoperative period and at least one surviving for more than 2 years. The epithelium of transplanted lungs retains the electrochemical properties of normal tissue,[259] and infection typical of CF is reportedly not a problem in transplanted lungs. Lung function of survivors has approached normal.

BIOLOGY OF THE BASIC DEFECT

The biochemical lesion responsible for cystic fibrosis has eluded detection for more than four decades. Numerous theories of pathogenesis have been proposed, but until recently, no single theory has adequately explained the major physiological abnormalities, namely, abnormal electrolyte content of exocrine sections and failure to clear mucous secretions.

Table 108-6 Complications of Therapy for CF

Complication	Agent
1. Renal dysfunction	
a. Tubular	Aminoglycosides
b. Interstitial nephritis	Semisynthetic penicillins
2. Hearing loss	Aminoglycosides
3. Peripheral neuropathy and/or optic atrophy	Chloramphenicol (prolonged course)
4. Hypomagnesemia	Aminoglycosides
5. Hyperuricemia, hyperuricosuria	Pancreatic extracts (very large doses)
6. Goiter	Iodine-containing expectorants
7. Gynecomastia	Spironolactone
8. Enamel hypoplasia/staining	Tetracyclines (used in first 8 years of life)

NOTE: Common hypersensitivity reactions to drugs are not included.

Macromolecule Secretion

Following Farber's report of mucous obstruction in many exocrine glands, a search was initiated for abnormal macromolecules or abnormal quantities of macromolecules which might change the physical properties of CF exocrine secretions. Particular emphasis has been placed on analysis of mucous glycoproteins (mucins), the high molecular weight glycoconjugates that are putative determinants of the viscoelastic properties of mucus.[260] Isolation and characterization of CF mucous glycoproteins from respiratory, gastrointestinal, and genitourinary sources has now been achieved in several laboratories. One of the difficulties in comparing these substances from CF and control subjects is that they are susceptible to proteolytic and perhaps other degradative enzymes to which they are exposed in vivo and so may not be recovered from patients in their native form.[261] In addition, these glycoproteins display extensive microheterogeneity of carbohydrate constituents and therefore are difficult to compare from subject to subject or even from patient group to control group.

Overall, mucins from CF patients and control subjects show considerable similarity. In addition, attempts to document rheologic differences between CF patients' respiratory tract secretions and controls' secretions have met with little success. However, this may reflect difficulty in obtaining unaltered secretions and in developing sensitive methods for analysis of the physical properties of mucus.

Suggestions that the fucose content of CF mucins is elevated and the sialic acid content is decreased seem to be true for gastrointestinal mucins[262] but not for those of respiratory tract origin.[263] Perhaps more importantly, there is evidence that CF mucous glycoproteins are excessively glycosylated. Mucins isolated from the tracheobronchial secretions of individuals with CF have oligosaccharide chains which on average are longer by several sugar residues than mucins from control subjects.[264] Similarly, mucins extracted from CF small intestinal epithelium appear to possess longer than normal oligosaccharide chains.[262] The biosynthetic basis for this observation is not readily apparent. Attempts to determine glycosyltransferase activities, which are key to oligosaccharide chain assembly, have not provided helpful data,[260] in large part because enzyme specificities have not been carefully documented and because most studies have been carried out using body fluids, tissues, or cells other than epithelial cells, which are the major target of the CF gene. If, indeed, CF epithelial cells elaborate mucins with longer or more complex side chains, altered viscosity or elasticity could result. Studies of submandibular mucins suggest that carbohydrate-to-carbohydrate interactions are a major determinant of the physical properties of mucin solutions or gels.[265] Thus, increased glycosylation could relate to retention of mucous secretions in CF.

Recent reports also suggest that more fatty acids are covalently linked to CF than to control gastric mucins.[266] In addition, CF patients' rectal mucosa contains more glycoprotein fatty acyltransferase than that of control subjects.[267] Mucins containing covalently linked fatty acids may be resistant to proteolysis[268] and may form more viscous fluids.[269] However, other investigators have either been unable to confirm these findings[270] or have found that lipid associated with CF respiratory mucins is dependent on the extent of lung infection.[271,272] The role of covalently and noncovalently bound lipid in CF mucous secretions needs to be clarified further.

In addition, several investigators have reported that cystic fibrosis glycoconjugates from both respiratory and gastrointes-

tinal sources stain more intensely for sulfate groups[273] and contain increased numbers of sulfated sugars.[274,275] Goblet cells within the bronchial epithelium of patients with cystic fibrosis have an elevated sulfur content.[276] If sulfur is present as sulfate, this observation could reflect either increased levels of free sulfate or greater amounts of sulfated intracellular glycoconjugates. Studies of CF nasal epithelial cells in primary culture substantiate increased glycoconjugate sulfation.[277] The reason for this enhanced sulfation is unclear. Although serum sulfate levels are normal in patients with CF,[278] studies of CF fibroblasts do suggest an increased influx of this anion.[279] Comparable studies of sulfate transport by CF epithelial cells have not been reported.

It is also apparent that increased amounts of mucin are secreted by CF epithelia *in situ*. What is not clear is whether the quantitative differences in CF are related to a primary cell dysfunction or whether they are secondary to the effect of chronic infection on the cells. For example, studies of the rate of radiolabeled glycoprotein secretion by explants obtained from CF tracheas at autopsy do not demonstrate increased rates of secretion beyond what can be accounted for by goblet-cell hyperplasia and gland hypertrophy.[280,281] For this reason, studies of macromolecule secretion by CF airway cells, dissociated by proteases and grown to confluence on collagen matrices, are particularly valuable.

Increased lengths and degree of sulfation of mucin oligosaccharide chains may be related, since sulfate in respiratory tract mucins resides predominantly on long oligosaccharide chains.[282,283] These observations may have further relevance in that increased sulfation may be linked to the viscoelastic or gelation properties of mucins by increasing ionic interactions or by contributing to an extended conformation of the mucin peptide.[259]

Another intriguing observation is that CF mucins interact more avidly with influenza virus than do comparable mucins from control subjects.[284] Virus binds to sialic acid sites on mucins, but this interaction is also enhanced by the presence of sulfated sugars.[263] The mechanisms by which sulfated sugars influence virus binding are unidentified. However, depending on the protective role that mucins play and whether glycoconjugates on the surface of CF respiratory epithelial cells reflect the altered virus-binding properties of mucins, CF subjects may have a greater susceptibility to attachment and epithelial-cell infection by this virus.

Abnormalities of membrane glycoproteins from CF cells of various types have been described. These reports, which have been reviewed previously,[259] show no consistent trends. However, it is likely that the biosynthetic mechanism for elaboration of secreted and membrane glycoconjugates are similar and that a CF-related abnormality would be expressed in both pathways. It is intriguing to speculate that the adherence of bacteria such as *P. aeruginosa* to respiratory epithelial cells is enhanced in CF because of differences in the abundance of binding sites which reside in cell surface glycoconjugates.[285]

It has been difficult to discern how altered macromolecules relate to the observed electrolyte transport abnormalities of CF epithelial cells. However, recent evidence (see "Epithelial Transport Abnormalities," below) strongly suggests that chloride and perhaps sodium transport abnormalities are the products of altered intracellular regulatory processes. If so, it is conceivable that cellular control of processes such as sulfate uptake, glycosylation and sulfation of macromolecules, or acylation of mucins is also perturbed in CF epithelia. Further studies of cultured epithelial cells are required to investigate these possibilities. It appears that initial suggestions of alterations in mucus permeability in CF[286] have not been confirmed by more rigorous assessments.[287]

Claims for alterations of other types of glycoproteins in CF have been made but do not fit clearly into a pathophysiological scheme. IgG purified from CF serum is underglycosylated, missing primarily the peripheral sugars, sialic acid and galactose, on their N-linked oligosaccharide chains.[34] The best explanation for this observation seems to be that these sugars are removed from IgG in the circulation, perhaps by glycosidases released from leukocytes or bacteria in the lung. A biosynthetic abnormality cannot be excluded at this time. Similarly, altered glycosylation of fibroblast membrane glycoproteins has been described, the most striking deviation being increased fucose content.[288] However, there is no evidence that fibroblast function is affected by this putative difference. Studies of glycopeptides released from CF lymphocytes demonstrate no alteration of carbohydrate composition.[289] In addition, potential mechanisms such as altered levels of fucosyltransferase or α-L-fucosidase activity[259] are not apparent in CF tissues or cells. Other studies of fibroblasts have demonstrated both normal metabolic labeling of cell surface glycoproteins[259] and ability to completely synthesize viral glycoproteins in infected cells.[290]

A number of investigators also have attempted to relate phase changes of CF secretions to interactions of mucins with other constituents in mucous secretions. For example, albumin and intestinal mucins interact to enhance the viscosity of fluids in which they reside.[291] This finding may have special relevance to meconium ileus in that the CF intestine early in life contains elevated levels of albumin in addition to mucins. As another example, calcium interactions with mucins have been postulated to decrease the solubility of secretory macromolecules and to contribute to phase changes in secretions.[292] These hypotheses derive from several sets of observations which could be related. The calcium content of CF epithelial and other cells is elevated.[293,294] Although calcium transport via ATPase-dependent mechanisms is probably intact[295] and calmodulin levels are normal,[296] excess amounts of calcium are secreted into several body fluids, including submaxillary saliva, nasal secretions, and perhaps tracheobronchial secretions.[259] However, evidence to the contrary also is reported for

tracheobronchial fluids.[259] Interactions between calcium and a low molecular weight phosphoprotein result in precipitation of the protein and turbidity of CF submandibular saliva. This interaction can be explained entirely by the high calcium levels of CF saliva and the fact that the solubility product for calcium and the phosphoprotein is exceeded.[297] Turbidity of CF submandibular saliva appears to have little pathophysiological consequence. While calcium in large amounts decreases the solubility of rat intestinal mucin,[291] there is no direct evidence that inspissation of CF mucous secretions is the result of calcium-mucin interactions.

Analyses of other macromolecular secretory products from patients with CF have failed to uncover substantial differences.[259] These macromolecules have included α-amylase, ribonuclease, and lysozyme from salivary secretions and pancreatic enzymes including chymotrypsin, trypsin, carboxypeptidase, amylase, and lipase.

Epithelial Transport Abnormalities

Since the previous edition of this chapter, it has become clear that electrolyte transport, particularly chloride (Cl⁻) transport, is abnormal in several CF epithelia. The work that led to this conclusion was prompted by two clinical aspects of the disease. First, the three organs classically involved by CF—sweat glands, airways, and pancreas—are each composed of epithelia, as are several other affected organs including salivary glands, epididymis, and intestine. Second, secretions from several organs are abnormally thick and dehydrated; consequently they produce obstruction of gland ducts. These observations led to basic studies of electrolyte transport by CF epithelia. The resultant finding of abnormal electrolyte transport provides a unifying hypothesis about the defect in epithelia and relates the research observations to the pathophysiology. The following discussion considers abnormalities of electrolyte transport in each organ system.

Sweat Gland Duct. The sweat gland is composed of two different regions, the secretory coil and the reabsorptive duct; Fig. 108-7 shows a schematic representation. The secretory coil produces nearly isotonic sweat. Then, as the sweat passes up through the water-impermeable duct, NaCl is absorbed, and a hypotonic fluid emerges at the surface of the skin. In the coil, active Cl⁻ transport drives fluid secretion; in the duct, active Na⁺ transport drives electrolyte absorption. In each case, the counterion appears to follow passively.

The clinical observation that Cl⁻ and Na⁺ concentrations are increased in CF sweat led Quinton and colleagues to examine the ion transport properties of the sweat duct.[9,299,300] They found both in vivo and in vitro that CF ducts had a higher transepithelial voltage than normal ducts. Normal isolated, perfused ducts generated a voltage of about −7 mV; CF ducts had a voltage of −76 mV (lumen voltage with respect to bath). When luminal Cl⁻ (or NaCl) concentration was reduced in normal ducts, luminal voltage became more negative; this finding indicates that Cl⁻ transport is electrically conductive. In contrast, when luminal Cl⁻ was decreased in CF ducts, transepithelial voltage became more positive. These results indicate that the CF sweat duct is Cl⁻-impermeable and suggest that the increased transepithelial voltage results from a normal Na⁺-absorptive mechanism in the presence of Cl⁻ impermeability.

Studies of transepithelial electrical conductance support and

Fig. 108-7 Schematic representation of electrolyte transport by the sweat gland. ACh = acetylcholine; Iso = isoproterenol. *(From Welsh and Fick[298] with permission of the Journal of Clinical Investigation.)*

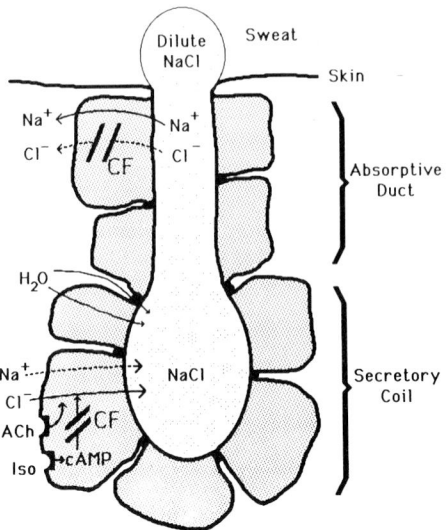

extend the conclusion that the sweat duct is Cl^--impermeable.[301,302] Normal sweat ducts have a transepithelial conductance of approximately 100 to 125 mS/cm^2, 90 percent of which results from the Cl^- conductance. Although the conclusion is not yet certain, the data suggest that the conductive Cl^- flow is predominantly through the cells (transcellular) rather than between the cells through the tight junctions (paracellular). In contrast to normal ducts, CF ducts have a conductance of 10 to 20 mS/cm^2 because Cl^- conductance is low or absent. It is unclear how normal sweat ducts transport ions or regulate their transport, so it is impossible to define the specific abnormality in CF. However, the decreased Cl^- conductance explains the pathophysiology; Cl^- cannot follow active Na^+ absorption; hence, NaCl absorption is prevented and the NaCl concentration in the sweat increases.

Sweat Gland Secretory Coil. The secretory coil of the CF sweat gland also transports ions abnormally.[167] Either cholinergic (muscarinic) or β-adrenergic agonists can stimulate sweat production. Methacholine stimulates secretion to the same extent in normal and CF secretory coils; however, the β-adrenergic agonist isoproterenol fails to stimulate secretion by CF secretory coils. The abnormality does not result from a defective interaction between hormone and receptor since isoproterenol-induced cAMP accumulation is normal in CF glands. These results suggest a defect in the cAMP-mediated regulation of Cl^- secretion. At present it is not clear whether isoproterenol and methacholine stimulate different cells in the gland, different secretory mechanisms in the same cell, or the same secretory mechanism via different intracellular regulatory mechanisms.

Airway Epithelia. Figure 108-8 schematically represents the airway epithelium. Transepithelial electrolyte transport controls the quantity and composition of the respiratory tract fluid; thus, it is important in effecting normal mucociliary clearance. The epithelium can actively transport Cl^- from the submucosal to the mucosal surface, thereby driving fluid secretion, or it can actively absorb Na^+, driving fluid in the opposite direction.[303] In both cases, the counterion is thought to move passively through the paracellular pathway. The relative magnitude of the two active transport processes is determined by the airway region and the neurohumoral environ-

ment, with chloride secretion being acutely stimulated by agents such as β-adrenergic agonists and prostaglandins.

The clinical observation that CF airway secretions are thick and dehydrated led to studies of electrolyte transport by CF respiratory epithelium. Knowles et al.[8] found that in vivo the voltage across upper (nasal) and lower (tracheal and bronchial) airway epithelia was higher in CF patients (-50 mV, lumen with respect to submucosa) than in normal subjects or disease controls (-20 to -25 mV). This finding suggested some defect in electrolyte transport. An abnormal response to Cl^- substitution studies in vivo and decreased Cl^- fluxes in vitro indicated a decreased epithelial Cl^- permeability in CF.[304,305]

Subsequent studies of primary cultures of airway epithelial cells showed abnormalities similar to those observed in native tissue. CF epithelia were Cl^--impermeable and failed to secrete Cl^- when stimulated with isoproterenol.[306–308] These results indicated that the Cl^- impermeability was a property of the epithelial cells themselves and that a circulating "factor" was not the cause of the ion transport defect. Intracellular microelectrode and ion substitution studies have localized the Cl^- impermeability to the cellular pathway and specifically to the apical membrane.[306,309]

Using the single-channel patch-clamp technique,[310] researchers have asked why the apical membrane is impermeable to Cl^- in CF patients. In normal cells, they found Cl^- channels with properties that suggest they produce the apical membrane Cl^- conductance,[311,312] and in cell-attached patches of membrane, isoproterenol opened Cl^- channels. Importantly, isoproterenol did not open Cl^- channels in CF cells.[10,312] The failure of channels to open appropriately did not result from the absence of Cl^- channels because CF cells contained Cl^- channels with conductive properties identical to those of normal cells. Cl^- channels from both normal and CF cells opened when patches of membrane were excised from the cell and when cell Ca^{2+} was increased by addition of the calcium ionophore A-23187,[10,312,313] even though cytosolic Ca^{2+} does not appear to be the primary regulator of the Cl^- channel via a ligand-type interaction. There does not appear to be a defective interaction between hormone and receptor, since the secretagogue isoproterenol increased cellular levels of cAMP appropriately in CF cells and addition of secretagogue opened a Ca^{2+}-activated K^+ channel in CF cells.[10,313] Moreover bypassing the receptor by addition of 8-bromo-cAMP or forskolin failed to open CF Cl^- channels. Because many of the physiological effects of cAMP result from activation of cAMP-dependent protein kinase, investigators asked whether the kinase controls the apical membrane Cl^- channel. To determine if cAMP-dependent protein kinase regulates the channel, they used excised, cell-free patches of membrane and examined the effect of adding ATP and the catalytic subunit of cAMP-dependent protein kinase. The purified catalytic subunit activated Cl^- channels from normal cells but failed to activate Cl^- channels from CF cells.[313a,313b] Those results indicate that in normal cells, the cAMP-dependent protein kinase phosphorylates the Cl^- channel or an associated regulatory protein, causing the channel to open. The failure of CF Cl^- channels to open suggests a defect either in the channel or in such an associated regulatory protein. It is also possible that some other pathway which also regulates the Cl^- channel is defective accounting for the abnormal response.

The increased transepithelial voltage in CF airway epithelia and the dehydrated airway secretions also suggest that Na^+ absorption may be abnormal in CF. In excised, short-circuited CF nasal epithelium, the rate of active Na^+ absorption aver-

Fig. 108-8 Schematic representation of electrolyte transport by airway epithelium. *(From Welsh and Fick[298] with permission of the Journal of Clinical Investigation.)*

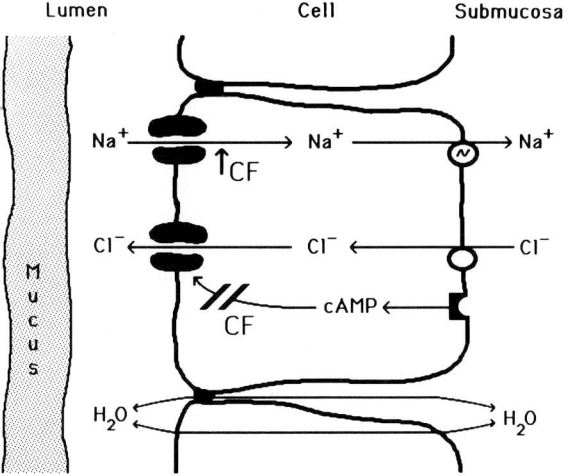

aged twice the rate in non-CF epithelium.[314] More significantly, in CF epithelia, β-adrenergic agonists and forskolin, both of which increase cellular concentrations of cAMP, paradoxically stimulated Na^+ absorption. The explanation for the abnormal regulation of Na^+ absorption is uncertain; it may be a direct result of the genetic abnormality, or it may be secondary to the Cl^- impermeability.[315]

Pancreas. Because CF patients develop pancreatic failure, electrolyte transport has also been investigated in this organ. However, because the pancreatic architecture is complex and because viable CF pancreas is difficult to obtain for in vitro studies, investigators have studied pancreatic function in vivo. Kopelman and colleagues[316] studied pancreatic secretions from CF subjects before total organ failure developed and from control subjects with similar levels of pancreatic acinar function. In CF secretions, they found higher concentrations of protein than in controls, primarily because CF pancreas secreted less fluid at all levels of pancreatic function. Because anion secretion appears to be important for production of pancreatic fluid, the results suggest that anion secretion is abnormally decreased in CF pancreas. This is an attractive hypothesis because it is consistent with observations in airway and sweat gland epithelium. Moreover, defective anion secretion might explain the pathology of pancreatic disease, if dehydrated secretions block the ducts and eventually destroy the gland.

GENETICS

Although alternative hypotheses have been put forward over the years, cystic fibrosis is well established as an autosomal recessive disorder with an unusually high incidence. Considerable recent information is available including the identification of closely linked DNA markers, the mapping of the CF locus to chromosome 7, and the discovery of DNA polymorphisms in strong linkage disequilibrium with the CF locus. More detailed discussions of the genetics of CF prior to the identification of linkage are available elsewhere.[317–319]

Incidence

CF is the most common autosomal recessive fatal disorder in Caucasians, with an incidence of 1 in 1700 to 1 in 6500 reported in various larger populations (Table 108-7). Most older studies represent epidemiologic surveys; data based on newborn screening have been available only within the last few years. Epidemiologic data and newborn screening data from Australia have yielded similar incidences (approximately 1 in 2500).[320,321,343] A moderately wide range of incidence has been reported in the United States, and newborn screening data indicate a slightly lower incidence compared to epidemiologic studies (Table 108-7). Examples of higher incidence presumably due to random genetic drift and founder effect have been reported from smaller populations with incidences of 1 in 377 in parts of Brittany,[324] 1 in 640 to 1 in 1200 in an American Amish poplation,[346] and 1 in 1192 in Southwest Africa.[329] The disease is rare in Finland.[347] The disease has been reported but is definitely much less frequent in American Indians, Africans, and Asians (see Refs. 318 and 319 for further references). Reliable incidence figures are not available for non-Caucasians

Table 108-7 The Incidence of Cystic Fibrosis in Various Populations

Country	Incidence	References
Epidemologic studies		
Australia	1 in 2450; 1 in 2550	320, 321
Czechoslovakia	1 in 2600; 1 in 3300	322, 323
Brittany, France	1 in 1800	324
Germany	1 in 3300	325
Israel	1 in 5000	326
Italy	1 in 2000	327,* 328
South Africa	1 in 6500	329
Sweden	1 in 7700	330
England: Caucasian	1 in 2400 to 1 in 3000	331–333
England: Asian	1 in 10,000	334
Northern Ireland	1 in 1700; 1 in 1900	335, 336
United States: Caucasian	1 in 1900 to 1 in 3700	337–340
United States: black	1 in 17,000	341
Hawaii: Caucasian	1 in 3800	342
Hawaii: Oriental	1 in 90,000	342
Newborn screening		
Australia: New South Wales	1 in 2564	343
United States: Colorado	1 in 5227	192
United States: Wisconsin	1 in 4200	344
Italy: Veneto	1 in 3944	192, 345
England: Peterboro	1 in 2669	192
Total newborn	1 in 3190	192

*This earlier report of a frequency of 1 in 15,000 is inconsistent with subsequent studies of the same population (personal communication, G. Romeo).

with the exception of Hawaiian Orientals in whom Wright and Morton[342] estimated a frequency of 1 in 90,000.

Newborn Screening

Early attempts at newborn screening for CF involved assessment of the albumin content of meconium. In 1979 it was found that newborns with CF had elevated immunoreactive trypsin in the blood and that dried blood samples already being collected for newborn screening could be tested using a radioimmunoassay to quantitate trypsin.[191,348] Subsequently, enzyme immunoassays using monoclonal antibodies have been developed and adapted for high volume screening.[349] Extensive experience in New South Wales, Australia; Colorado, United States; New Zealand; and Veneto, Italy indicate that at least 95 percent of CF patients can be detected by this strategy.[192,350–352] Approximately 1 in 200 screenees require repeat sampling. One program in Wisconsin is screening one-half of the population by random selection in order to evaluate the potential benefits of newborn screening.[344,352]

The potential benefits and risks of newborn screening for CF have been reviewed.[192,193,353,354] The characteristics of the test, the usefulness in making reproductive decisions, and the effectiveness of presymptomatic treatment are all issues which require further study. A position paper from an ad hoc task force of the United States Cystic Fibrosis Foundation[193] subsequently endorsed by the American Academy of Pediatrics[353] said in 1983 that "until sufficient information related to these and other issues can be obtained, the task force strongly recommends that no mass population screening for cystic fibrosis be implemented, even if a valid and reliable test is available." A statement in 1986 by some directors of major screening programs[192] concluded as follows: "All in all we feel that the case for screening is now strong." This conclusion was based in part on evidence of short-term benefits such as reduced hospitalization costs in the first year of life and on the presumption that early diagnosis will lead to improved reproductive counseling, particularly since reliable prenatal diagnosis is available. There is also evidence of correctable nutritional deficits prior to 2 months of age in some infants.[355] Newborn screening could become a major evaluation tool if population-based heterozygote screening programs are implemented in the future. Eventually, newborn screening could become unnecessary if all cases of CF were anticipated by population-based heterozygote detection. In the short term, greater utilization of newborn screening for CF may occur.

Classic Genetics

The high incidence of CF in Caucasian populations and the low incidence in other races has raised many questions regarding the number of loci causing the CF phenotype, the number of alleles causing the phenotype, and the possibility of some form of selective advantage. Even before linkage data were available, the prevailing view expressed in numerous reports[318–320,339,356] was that CF represented an autosomal recessive disorder at a single locus with a high probability that a single mutant allele accounted for the majority of abnormal genes in the population. This view has largely been substantiated by linkage studies.

Arguments for and against the possibility of multiple loci (i.e., nonallelic heterogeneity) are chronicled elsewhere.[317,318] Population studies comparing the incidence of CF in cousins of affected individuals to the normal population and comparing the frequency of consanguineous matings among CF families and normal families can be used to assess the presence of nonallelic heterogeneity. These studies largely argued against the possibility of multiple loci,[320,328,339,356] but some data were interpreted as indicative of multiple loci.[357] One study was erroneously interpreted as evidence for multiple loci[321] but was later reinterpreted as favoring a single locus.[358] The power of these approaches is extremely limited in comparison to linkage analysis.[359,360] Linkage studies eliminate the possibility of significant nonallelic heterogeneity.[360,361]

The possibility of allelic heterogeneity has long been suggested by the extensive phenotypic variation in CF.[362] The tendency for meconium ileus to recur in the same family[363] can be interpreted as evidence favoring allelic heterogeneity. Phenotypic heterogeneity can be explained to some extent by stochastic factors, environmental factors, and genetic effects of modifier loci. Linkage disequilibrium data to be discussed in greater detail below suggest that a single allele may account for a large fraction of the mutant genes in the population.[364]

There has been a long-standing debate as to whether some form of genetic advantage is associated with the CF mutation or whether the high frequency can be explained by chance factors such as genetic drift and founder effect. Increased fertility or higher reproductive capacity has been suggested as a possible mechanism for increased frequency.[320,357,365] Any hypothesis to explain the high incidence of CF must take into account the dramatic differences in racial distribution. A disproportionately high mutation rate is not a consideration given recent linkage disequilibrium data. Although increased resistance to tuberculosis in CF heterozygotes has been suggested as a possible mechanism,[366,367] there are no data to support

this hypothesis. Some form of meiotic drive leading to preferential transmission of the mutant allele is a theoretical possibility. The magnitude of any heterozygote advantage, differential fitness, or meiotic drive need only be very small and should not be detectable given the samples available. It has been estimated that a sample of approximately 26,000 offspring of carriers would be required to detect at the 5 percent level a differential fitness or meiotic drive accounting for an equilibrium frequency of 1 in 40 for the CF gene.[360] A recent suggestion of unusual segregation of the CF allele to males is likely to be attributable to a small sample size, and the relevance, if confirmed, of a distortion in the sex ratio of homozygous normal sibs of CF patients is unclear.[368]

A selective advantage for the CF gene in Caucasian populations is not proven. Rao and Morton[369] pointed out that large deviations in the incidence of genetic diseases are not improbable and could occur due to chance alone. Presumably founder effect and inbreeding can account for the very high incidence in some small populations as in Brittany,[324] Southwest Africa,[329] and American Amish populations.[346] Although the DNA sequence of mutant CF alleles might be known soon, there is no assurance that these data will clarify whether the high incidence of CF is attributable to some genetic advantage or to chance.

Genetic Linkage and Reverse Genetics

With the concept of an RFLP map for the human genome,[370,371] the possibility of obtaining DNA markers linked to the CF locus became a major focus in many research laboratories. At the time of the Human Gene Mapping Workshop in Helsinki in summer of 1985, negative linkage data for CF were available for many parts of the human genome.[360,372–374] At that time, Eiberg and colleagues presented evidence for linkage between CF and paraoxonase (PON).[375] This provided reassurance that CF represented a single locus, but PON was not mapped to a particular human chromosome. Very shortly thereafter, Tsui, Buchwald, and colleagues, using an anonymous, unmapped DNA probe from Donis-Keller and colleagues, also found linkage to CF.[11] Unlike PON, this DNA probe (DOCRI-917) could be rapidly assigned to a human chromosome, and the CF locus was thus mapped to chromosome 7q.[376] Promptly, White et al. reported very tight linkage between CF and the *met* oncogene locus,[12] while Wainwright et al.[13] reported very tight linkage to another anonymous DNA probe, J3.11 (D7S8). A collaborative study using these probes in over 200 families with CF indicated a recombination fraction of approximately 0.01 between CF and MET and between CF and D7S8 and the data favored the order of centromere/MET/CF/D7S8/telomere.[361] Other DNA probes linked to CF were identified including 7c22(D7S16),[377] B79a (D7S13),[378] genomic fragments of the MET locus,[379] and anonymous probes.[380]

It was extremely fortuitous that the *met* oncogene mapped very close to the CF locus. This oncogene had been isolated by DNA-mediated gene transfer from a mutagenized tumor cell cell line into 3T3 mouse cells. The transforming ability of the altered *met* oncogene facilitated the use of chromosome-mediated gene transfer to isolate small chromosomal segments near the CF locus in a rodent cell line. Scambler et al. used this approach to transfer a number of tightly linked DNA markers into rodent cells.[381] These transfers were used to isolate a series of cosmid clones from the CF region.[382] The Williamson laboratory proceeded to identify a candidate gene locus for CF, taking advantage of the presence of methylation-free islands to locate a functional gene.[364] Using DNA probes from the vicinity of this candidate gene, this group identified RFLPs which demonstrated strong linkage disequilibrium with the CF mutation. The linkage disequilibrium provided confirmatory evidence that these DNA segments were extremely close to the CF locus. The linkage disequilibrium data from European and North American populations are remarkably similar (Table 108-8), with 85 percent of CF chromosomes found with a single haplotype while that haplotype is found with only 15 percent of normal chromosomes. The linkage disequilibrium data suggest that a large fraction of the CF genes in the population originate from one or a few mutational events. Subsequent sequence analysis of the first candidate gene revealed homology with the oncogene *int*-1.[383] Analysis of crossovers has indicated that this candidate gene, designated IRP, for *int*-related protein, is not the CF gene.[384]

Other strategies directed at cloning the CF gene have included chromosome jumping, long-range restriction mapping using pulsed-field gel electrophoresis, and analysis of biologic candidate genes. Chromosome jumping has been used to proceed in a telomeric direction from the *met* oncogene.[385] A detailed genetic and physical map of the region surrounding the CF locus is now available through the work of a number of laboratories (Figs. 108-9 and 108-10).[364,386,387] The probes KM-19, XV-2c, and CS.7 reveal the greatest linkage disequilibrium with the CF locus.[364,388,389] Crossovers involving these tightly linked loci suggest that the CF locus is located telomeric to this cluster and to the gene for IRP.[384,390] As of mid-1988, the gene for CF appears to be localized between the IRP locus and the anonymous probe D7S8, and it is widely expected that the gene should be cloned in the foreseeable future.

Although numerous biologic candidate genes have been suggested, perhaps the most interesting possibility would involve the cloning of chloride channel proteins. The band 3 protein mediates reversible exchange of chloride and bicarbonate anions across the plasma membrane of erythrocytes. The murine gene for band 3 has been cloned and characterized.[391] The human band 3 gene is not the CF gene. Although related gene sequences that might represent other chloride channels have been identified, no sequence that maps to the CF region has been identified.[392] A variety of other candidate genes involved in cyclic AMP and calcium metabolism have been studied, but no candidate clone that is linked to the CF locus has been identified.

Prenatal Diagnosis and Heterozygote Detection

Biochemical Methods. Prenatal diagnosis for cystic fibrosis remained an elusive goal through the early 1980s. A variety of strategies proved unreliable, including metachromasia in fibroblasts, analysis of mucociliary inhibitors, response to Tamm-Horsfall glycoprotein, enhanced resistance against dexamethasone, leakage of lysosomal enzymes and alkaline phosphatase, α-mannosidase activity, and inhibition of oxygen consumption, as reviewed elsewhere.[318] Quantitation of proteases that hydrolyzed methylumbelliferylguanidinobenzoate in amniotic fluid suggested generally lower values in affected pregnancies,[393,394] but ultimately this approach proved unreliable.[318]

In 1983, it was reported that measurement of various microvillar intestinal enzymes in amniotic fluid provided a more reliable approach to prenatal diagnosis of CF.[395-397] Levels of intestinal alkaline phosphatase, γ-glutamyltranspeptidase, leucine aminopeptidase, trehalase, and intestinal disaccharidases are reduced in the amniotic fluid of affected pregnancies. The cumulative experience of various laboratories[398-400] suggests a false positive rate of 2 to 5 percent and a false negative rate of 2 to 10 percent. Intestinal enzyme analysis is generally not useful if the prior risk of CF for the fetus is low, since an abnormal result will more likely represent a false positive than an affected fetus. Intestinal enzyme analysis has largely been replaced by DNA analysis for fetuses at 1 in 4 risk where DNA is available from the index case, although it is still useful when DNA from the index case is not available.

There is evidence that echogenic densities may be detected in the abdomen of fetuses affected by CF,[401] but this is not a reliable method for prenatal diagnosis of CF. Detection of ultrasound abnormalities in a pregnancy in which there is no family history of CF is rarely explained by the presence of CF in the fetus.[402-404] Ultrasonographic abnormalities and decreased levels of microvillar intestinal enzymes are found with numerous other pathologic conditions, including intestinal obstruction and chromosomal abnormality.[405] Some infants are normal at birth despite ultrasound and intestinal enzyme abnormalities in utero.[403,404]

Biochemical, histologic, and histochemical criteria have been described for the diagnosis of CF in fetal specimens taken after termination of pregnancy.[406,407] However, these methods are probably not reliable enough to justify their use to validate or disprove diagnoses made on the basis of fully informative linkage analysis.

Molecular Prenatal Diagnosis. With the availability of tightly linked DNA markers, numerous groups have demonstrated the reliability of prenatal diagnosis by linkage analysis.[404,408-412]

Table 108-8 Linkage Disequilibrium and Cystic Fibrosis

Haplotype*		CF alleles			Normal alleles		
XV-2c	KM-19	Number	%E†	%NA†	Number	%E†	%NA†
−	−	26	5.1	6.7	120	28.9	29.6
−	+	367	84.7	86.5	61	16.4	14.0
+	−	19	6.8	2.8	180	44.0	44.0
+	+	16	3.4	4.0	48	10.7	12.4

*Minus (−) indicates the absence of a polymorphic restriction enzyme site and plus (+) indicates the presence of the site.
†E indicates European data (176 CF chromosomes and 159 normal chromosomes),[388] and NA indicates North American data (252 CF chromosomes and 250 normal chromosomes).[389,417]

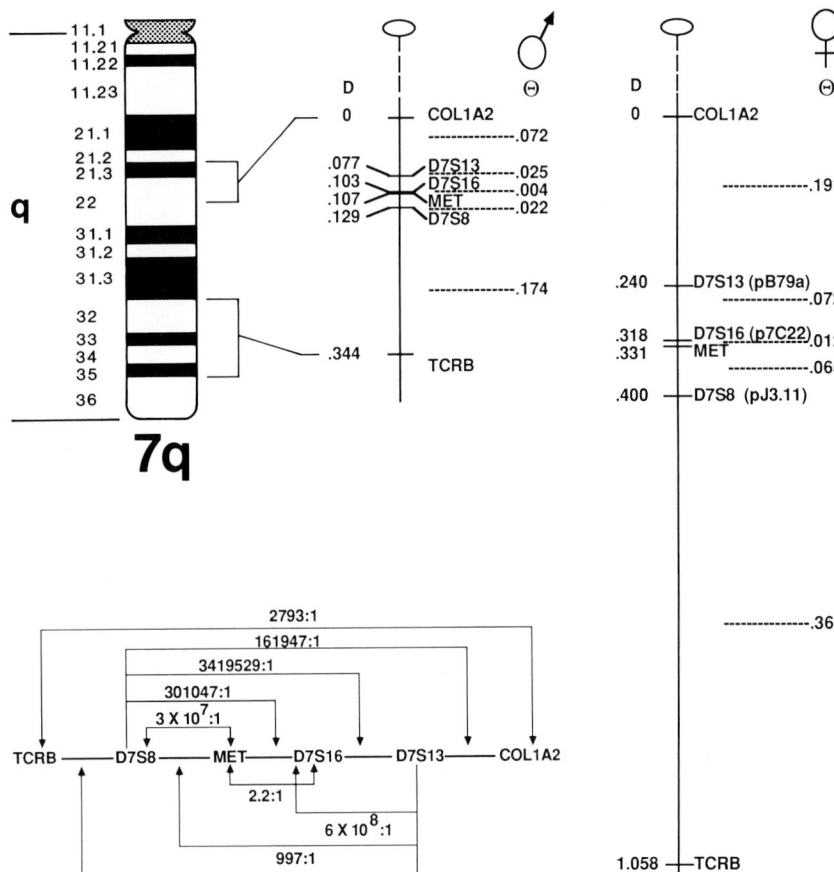

Fig. 108-9 Map of chromosome 7q, showing genetic locations of six marker loci and the CF gene under the best-supported gene order, as well as the odds against certain alternative orders. Physical locations are also shown for the α2 chain of type I collagen (COL1A2) and the β subunit of the T-cell receptor (TCRB). θ = recombination fraction; D = genetic distance in Morgans. *(From Lathrop et al.*[386] *with permission of the American Journal of Human Genetics.)*

DNA analysis is fully informative in virtually all families,[408–413] particularly when the more recently available probes are utilized.[388,389] The accuracy of molecular prenatal diagnosis can be determined from linkage studies in CF families. Although the linkage map in the region of the CF gene has been refined, indicating some greater distances than were determined ear-

lier,[386] the probability of diagnostic accuracy is extremely high if the most tightly linked probes are informative or if flanking markers are informative. Presumably the accuracy of molecular prenatal diagnosis will continue to increase until such time as direct detection of the mutation or the gene product becomes a reality. The KM-19 and CS.7 polymorphisms have been analyzed using the polymerase chain reaction for rapid diagnosis.[414,415] Cells from buccal mucosa can be used for analysis with the polymerase chain reaction, and this sampling method could facilitate population-based screening programs.[416]

Linkage Disequilibrium. The strong linkage disequilibrium detected with the DNA probes CS.7, XV-2c, and KM-19 not only indicates that these RFLPs are near the CF gene but also makes these probes particularly useful for genetic counseling. Assuming a gene frequency of 1 in 50 (equivalent to a carrier frequency of approximately 1 in 25), the probability that a chromosome of a given RFLP haplotype carries a CF mutation can be calculated to be as high as 1 in 9 or as low as 1 in 770. An individual homozygous for the highest risk haplotypes has a probability of 1 in 5 for carrier status while an individual homozygous for the lowest risk haplotypes has a 1 in 380 carrier risk.[388,389,417] The linkage disequilibrium data can be used in conjunction with microvillar intestinal enzyme analysis and linkage analysis in families to provide genetic counseling and prenatal diagnosis for couples with a close relative affected with CF. Use of extended haplotypes probably can further increase the predictive power of the linkage disequilibrium data.

There is a suggestion of a difference in linkage disequilib-

Fig. 108-10 Physical map of the region surrounding the CF locus. The direction of transcription is indicated for the MET and IRP loci. The locations for other DNA markers are indicated below the lines. The upper section is a map based on pulsed-field gel electrophoresis with letters indicating restriction enzyme sites as follows: A = *Nae*I, B = *Bss*HII, C = *Sac*II, M = *Mlu*I, R = *Nru*I, N = *Not*I, and F = *Sfi*I. Asterisk indicates a polymorphic *Not*I site. *(Upper section modified from Drumm et al.*[387] *and lower section modified from Estivill et al.,*[388] *both with permission of Genomics.)*

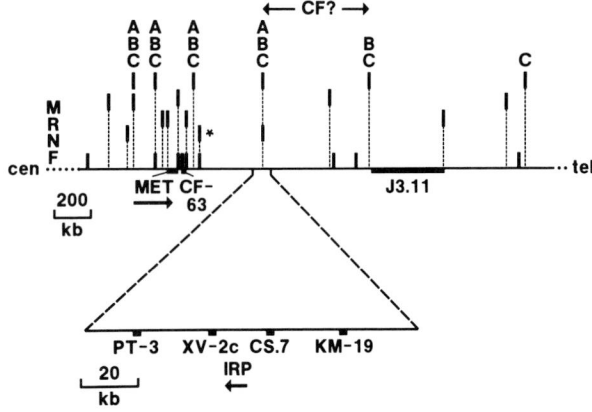

rium findings in individuals affected with meconium ileus.[418] Although the linkage disequilibrium data suggest that a single mutation might account for the majority of mutant CF genes in the population, there may be mutant alleles specifically associated with meconium ileus. There is also a suggestion of different haplotype frequencies in American blacks,[419] which might be consistent with the occurrence of different mutations in that population. It has also been suggested on the basis of linkage disequilibrium data that CF patients without pancreatic insufficiency may show an increased frequency of RFLP haplotypes which are not usually associated with CF.[420,421] This may prove to be the strongest evidence to date for allelic heterogeneity.

Heterozygote Detection and Genetic Counseling. Heterozygote detection can be provided with great accuracy for close relatives of CF patients using linkage analysis. Prenatal diagnosis can be provided for fetuses at 1 in 4 risk and for fetuses at less than 1 in 4 risk using the approaches described above. There is evidence that couples who have given birth to a child with CF choose to undergo sterilization with a greater frequency and at a younger age than comparable controls.[422] A large educational effort will be required if population-based heterozygote detection programs are offered to various populations. The effect of such programs on the incidence of CF is likely to vary widely in relationship to cultural background, educational status, socioeconomic status, and availability of health care services. Selective reproduction, artificial insemination by noncarrier donors, and prenatal diagnosis with selective abortion could lead to a marked reduction in the incidence of CF, but the utilization of such approaches is difficult to predict given the CF phenotype and its variations. There is evidence of limited knowledge of CF in various populations, even in families with affected children.[423]

Other Biochemical Genetic Observations

Innumerable biochemical genetic findings have been reported in CF as reviewed partially in the previous edition of this book. Data regarding the CF antigen are of particular note. The identification of this protein began with the detection of elevated levels of the protein using isoelectric focusing of serum samples.[424] Ultimately, monoclonal antibodies to this protein were obtained, the gene was mapped to chromosome 1, and a cDNA clone was obtained.[425,426] The cDNA sequence indicated homology with various calcium-binding proteins.[427] At this time, it appears that the CF antigen may be identical to the macrophage protein MRP-8, also known as the light chain of leukocyte L-1 protein.[428,429] Although levels of the CF antigen are elevated in the serum of heterozygotes, overlap with the normal range precludes its use as a reliable heterozygote detection method. Elevated levels in heterozygotes might indicate some functional proximity to the basic defect in CF, but the mapping of this antigen to chromosome 1 excludes it as the direct product of the CF gene. The relationship of the CF antigen to the basic defect is unclear at present.

It has been suggested that the basic defect in CF might involve regulation of arachidonic acid release[430] or might involve a magainin.[431] Magainins are a class of recently discovered antimicrobial peptides.

REFERENCES

1. TAUSSIG LM: Cystic fibrosis: An overview, in Taussig LM (ed): *Cystic Fibrosis*. New York, Thieme-Stratton, 1984, pp 1–9.
2. FANCONI G, UEHLLINGER E, KNAUER C: Das coeliakiesyndrom be: Angeborener zysticher pankreas fibromatose und bronkiektasien. *Wien Med Wochenschr* 86:753, 1936.
3. ANDERSON DH: Cystic fibrosis of the pancreas and its relation to celiac disease: A clinical and pathological study. *Am J Dis Child* 56:344, 1938.
4. FARBER S: Some organic digestive disturbances in early life. *J Michigan Med Soc* 44:587, 1945.
5. ANDERSON DH, HODGES RG: Celiac syndrome. V. Genetics of cystic fibrosis of the pancreas with a consideration of etiology. *Am J Dis Child* 72:62, 1946.
6. DI SANT'AGNESE PA, DARLING RC, PERERA GA, SHEA E: Abnormal electrolytic composition of sweat in cystic fibrosis of the pancreas. Clinical significance and relationship of the disease. *Pediatrics* 12:549, 1953.
7. GIBSON LE, COOKE RE: A test for concentration of electrolytes in sweat in cystic fibrosis of the pancreas utilizing pilocarpine by iontophoresis. *Pediatrics* 23:545, 1959.
8. KNOWLES M, GATZY J, BOUCHER R: Increased bioelectric potential difference across respiratory epithelia in cystic fibrosis. *N Engl J Med* 305:1489, 1981.
9. QUINTON PM, BIJMAN J: Higher bioelectric potentials due to decreased chloride absorption in the sweat glands of patients with cystic fibrosis. *N Engl J Med* 308:1185, 1983.
10. WELSH MJ, LIEDTKE CM: Chloride and potassium channels in cystic fibrosis airways epithelia. *Nature* 322:467, 1986.
11. TSUI LC, BUCHWALD M, BARKER D, BRAMAN JC, KNOWLTON R, SCHRUMM JW, EIBERG H, MOHR J, KENNEDY D, PLAVIC N: Cystic fibrosis locus defined by a genetically linked polymorphic DNA marker. *Science* 230:1054, 1985.
12. WHITE R, WOODWARD W, LEPPERT M, O'CONNELL PO, HOFF M, HERBST F, LALOUEL FM, DEAN M, VANDE WONDE G: A closely linked genetic marker for cystic fibrosis. *Nature* 318:382, 1985.
13. WAINWRIGHT BJ, SCAMBLER PJ, SCHMIDTKE J, WATSON EA, LAW H-Y, FARRELL M, COOKE HJ, EIBERG H, WILLIAMSON R: Localization of cystic fibrosis locus to human chromosome 7 cen-q22. *Nature* 318:384, 1985.
14. ZUELZER WW, NEWTON WA JR: The pathogenesis of fibrocystic disease of the pancreas. A study of 36 cases with special reference to the pulmonary lesions. *Pediatrics* 4:53, 1949.
15. STURGESS J, IMRIE J: Quantitative evaluations of the development of tracheal submucosal glands in infants with cystic fibrosis and control infants. *Am J Pathol* 106:303, 1982.
16. STURGESS J: Morphologic characteristics of the bronchial mucosa in cystic fibrosis, in Quinton P, Martinez R, Hopfer U (eds): *Fluid and Electrolyte Abnormalities in Exocrine Glands in Cystic Fibrosis*. San Francisco, San Francisco Press, 1982, p 254.
17. BEDROSSIAN CWM, GREENBERG SD, SINGER DB, HANSEN JJ, ROSENBERG HS: The lung in cystic fibrosis. *Hum Pathol* 7:195, 1976.
18. TOMASHEFSKI JF JR, BRUCE M, GOLDBERG HI, DEARBORN DG: Regional distribution of macroscopic lung disease in cystic fibrosis. *Am Rev Respir Dis* 133:535, 1986.
19. SOBONYA RE, TAUSSIG LM: Quantitative aspects of lung pathology in cystic fibrosis. *Am Rev Respir Dis* 134:290, 1986.
20. TOMASHEFSKI JF JR, BRUCE M, STERN RC, DEARBORN DG, DAHMS B: The pathology of pulmonary air cysts in cystic fibrosis, relation to radiologic findings and history of pneumothorax. *Hum Pathol* 16:253, 1985.
21. TOMASHEFSKI JF JR, KONSTAN MW, BRUCE M: The pathology of interstitial pneumonia in cystic fibrosis. *Am Rev Respir Dis* 133:A365, 1986.
22. BOAT TF, DI SANT'AGNESE PA, WARWICK W, HANDWERGER S: Pneumothorax in cystic fibrosis. *JAMA* 209:1498, 1969.
23. MACK JF, MOSS AF, HARPER WW, O'LOUGHLIN BJ: The bronchial arteries in cystic fibrosis. *Br J Radiol* 38:422, 1965.
24. RYLAND D, REID L: The pulmonary circulation in cystic fibrosis. *Thorax* 30:285, 1975.
25. STERN RC, BOAT TF, WOOD RE, MATTHEWS LW, DOERSHUK CF: Treatment and prognosis of nasal polyps in cystic fibrosis. *Am J Dis Child* 136:1067, 1982.
26. WOOD RE, WANNER A, HIRSCH J, FARRELL PM: Tracheal mucociliary transport in patients with cystic fibrosis and its stimulation by terbutaline. *Am Rev Respir Dis* 111:733, 1975.
27. KATZ SM, HOLSCLAW DS: Ultrastructural features of respiratory cilia in cystic fibrosis. *Am J Clin Pathol* 73:682, 1980.
28. RUTLAND J, COLE PJ: Nasal mucociliary clearance and ciliary beat fre-

quency in cystic fibrosis compared with sinusitis and bronchiectasis. *Thorax* 36:654, 1981.

29. WOODS DE, BASS JA, JOHANSON WG, STRAUS DC: Role of adherence in the pathogenesis of *Pseudomonas aeruginosa* lung infection in cystic fibrosis patients. *Infect Immun* 30:694, 1980.

30. NIEDERMAN MS, RAFFERTY TD, SASAKI CT, MERRILL WW, MATTHAY RA, REYNOLDS HY: Comparison of bacterial adherence to ciliated and squamous epithelial cells obtained from the respiratory tract. *Am Rev Respir Dis* 127:85, 1983.

31. RAMPHAL R, PIER GB: Role of *Pseudomonas aeruginosa* mucoid exopolysaccharide in adherence to tracheal cells. *Infect Immun* 47:1, 1985.

32. MATTHEWS WJ, WILLIAMS M, OLIPHINT B, GEHA R, COLTEN RH: Hypogammaglobulinemia in patients with cystic fibrosis. *N Engl J Med* 302:245, 1980.

33. GUGLER E, PALLAVICINI JD, SWERDLOW TL: Immunological studies of submaxillary saliva from patients with cystic fibrosis and normal children. *J Pediatr* 73:548, 1968.

34. MARGOLIES R, GRAY B, BOAT TG: Identification of a major heparin-precipitable protein in human serum and its relationship to cystic fibrosis. *Pediatr Res* 16:181, 1982.

35. BALTIMORE RS, FICK RB, FINO L: Antibody to multiple mucoid strains of *Pseudomonas aeruginosa* in patients with cystic fibrosis, measured by an enzyme-linked immunosorbent assay. *Pediatr Res* 20:1085, 1986.

36. SORENSEN RU, RUUSKANEN O, MILLER K, STERN RC: B-lymphocyte function in cystic fibrosis. *Eur J Respir Dis* 64:524, 1983.

37. SORENSEN RU, STERN RC, POLMAR SH: Cellular immunity to bacteria: Impairment of in vitro lymphocyte response to *Pseudomonas aeruginosa* in cystic fibrosis patients. *Infect Immun* 18:735, 1977.

38. SORENSEN RU, STERN RC, CHASE P, POLMAR SH: Defective cellular immunity to gram-negative bacteria in cystic fibrosis patients. *Infect Immun* 23:398, 1979.

39. MILLER TJ, OLDS LC: Interleukin-2 production by lymphocytes from blood of children with arthritis is less suppressed than in systemic lupus or cystic fibrosis. *J Rheumatol* 14:736, 1987.

40. KHARAZMI A, RECHNITZER C, SCHIETZ PO, JENSEN R, BAEK L, HOIBY N: Priming of neutrophils for enhanced oxidative burst by sputum from cystic fibrosis patients with *Pseudomonas aeruginosa* infection. *Eur J Clin Invest* 17:256, 1987.

41. THOMASSEN MJ, BOXERBAUM B, DEMKO CA, KUCHENBROD PJ, DEARBORN DG, WOOD RE: Inhibitory effect of cystic fibrosis serum on pseudomonas phagocytosis by rabbit and human alveolar macrophages. *Pediatr Res* 13:1085, 1979.

42. THOMASSEN MJ, DEMKO CA, WOOD RE, TANDLER B, DEARBORN DG, BOXERBAUM B, KUCHENBROD PJ: Ultrastructure and function of alveolar macrophages from cystic fibrosis patients. *Pediatr Res* 14:715, 1980.

43. FICK RB, NAEGEL GP, SQUIER SU, WOOD RE, GEE BL, REYNOLDS HY: Proteins of the cystic fibrosis respiratory tract: Fragmented immunoglobulin G opsonic antibody causing defective opsonophagocytosis. *J Clin Invest* 74:236, 1984.

44. FICK RB, OLCHOWSKI J, SQUIER SU, MERRILL WW, REYNOLDS HY: Immunoglobulin-G subclasses in cystic fibrosis: IgG$_2$ response to *Pseudomonas aeruginosa* lipopolysaccharide. *Am Rev Respir Dis* 133:418, 1986.

45. WISNIESKI JJ, TODD EW, FULLER RK, JONES PK, DEARBORN DG, BOAT TF, NAFF GB: Immune complexes and complement abnormalities in patients with cystic fibrosis. *Am Rev Respir Dis* 132:770, 1986.

46. CAMPBELL IM, CROZIER DN, SILVER J, BUIVIDS IA: The effect of fatty acids on *Staphylococcus aureus* in vitro, in Sturgess JM (ed): *Perspectives in Cystic Fibrosis.* Mississauga, Ontario, Canada, Imperial Press, 1980, p 359.

47. GASKIN K, GURWITZ D, COREY M, LEVISON H, FORSTNER G: Improved pulmonary function in cystic fibrosis patients without pancreatic insufficiency, in Sturgess JM (ed): *Perspectives in Cystic Fibrosis.* Mississauga, Ontario, Canada, Imperial Press, 1980, p 226.

48. FICK RB Jr, ROBBINS RV, SQUIER SU, ROBBINS RA, SQUIER SU, SCHODERBEK WE, RUSS WO: Complement activation in cystic fibrosis respiratory fluids: *in vivo* and *in vitro* generation of C5a and chemotactic activity. *Pediatr Res* 20:1258, 1986.

49. KLINGER JD, TANDLER B, LIEDTKE CM, BOAT TF: Proteinases of *Pseudomonas aeruginosa* evoke mucin release by tracheal epithelium. *J Clin Invest* 74:1669, 1984.

50. CHRISTENSEN TG, KORTHY AL, SNIDER GL, HAYES JA: Irreversible bronchial goblet cell metaplasia in hamsters with elastase induced panacinar emphysema. *J Clin Invest* 59:397, 1977.

51. GOLDSTEIN W, DORING G: Lysosomal enzymes with polymorphonuclear leukocytes and proteinase inhibitors in patients with cystic fibrosis. *Am Rev Respir Dis* 134:49, 1986.

52. HINGLEY ST, HASTIE AT, KUEPPERS F, HIGGINS ML: Disruption of respiratory cilia by proteases including those of *Pseudomonas aeruginosa. Infect Immun* 54:379, 1986.

53. NIEDERMAN MS, MERRILL WW, POLOMSKI LM, REYNOLDS HY, GEE BL: Influence of sputum IgA and elastase on tracheal cell bacterial adherence. *Am Rev Respir Dis* 133:255, 1986.

54. SCHIOTZ PO, NIELSEN H, HOIBY N, GLIKMANN G, SVEHAG SE: Immune complexes in the sputum of patients with cystic fibrosis suffering from chronic *Pseudomonas aeruginosa* lung infection. *Acta Pathol Microbiol Scand* 86:37, 1978.

55. TALAMO RC, SCHWARTZ RH: Immunologic and allergic manifestations, in Taussig LM (ed): *Cystic Fibrosis,* New York, Thieme-Stratton, 1984, p 175.

56. WANG EEL, PROBER CG, MANSON B, COREY M, LEVISON H: Association of respiratory viral infections with pulmonary deterioration of patients with cystic fibrosis. *N Engl J Med* 311:1653, 1984.

57. PETERSON NT, HOIBY N, MORDHORST CH, LIND K, FLENSBORO EW, BRUNN B: Respiratory infections in cystic fibrosis patients caused by virus, chlamydia, and mycoplasma: Possible synergism with *Pseudomonas aeruginosa. Acta Pediatr Scand* 70:623, 1981.

58. STERN RC, BOAT TF, WOOD RE, MATTHEWS LW, DOERSHUK CF: Treatment and prognosis of nasal polyps in cystic fibrosis. *Am J Dis Child* 136:1067, 1982.

59. SHAPIRO ED, MILMOE GJ, WALD ER, RODMAN JB, BOWEN A: Bacteriology of the maxillary sinuses in patients with cystic fibrosis. *J Infect Dis* 146:589, 1982.

60. STRAUSS RG, WEST PJ, SILVERMAN FN: Unilateral proptosis in cystic fibrosis. *Pediatrics* 43:297, 1969.

61. FORMAN-FRANCO B, ABRAMSON AL, GARVOY JD, STEIN T: Cystic fibrosis and hearing loss. *Arch Otolaryngol* 105:338, 1979.

62. TAUSSIG LM, LANDAU LI, MARKS MI: Respiratory system, in Taussig LM (ed): *Cystic Fibrosis.* New York, Thieme-Stratton, 1984, p 115.

63. DEMKO CA, THOMASEN MJ: Effect of mucoid property on antibiotic susceptibility of *Pseudomonas aeruginosa. Curr Microbiol* 4:69, 1980.

64. BLACKWOOD L, PENNINGTON JE: Influence of mucoid coating on clearance of *Pseudomonas aeruginosa* from lungs. *Infect Immun* 32:443, 1981.

65. ISLES A, MACLUSKY I, COREY M, GOLD R, PROBER C, FLEMING P, LEVISON H: *Pseudomonas cepacia* infection in cystic fibrosis: An emerging problem. *J Pediatr* 104:206, 1984.

66. THOMASSEN MJ, DEMKO AC, KLINGER JD, STERN RC: *Pseudomonas cepacia* colonization among patients with cystic fibrosis. *Am Rev Respir Dis* 131:791, 1985.

67. LESTER LA, EGGE A, HUBBARD VS, DI SANT'AGNESE PA: Aspiration and lung abscess in cystic fibrosis. *Am Rev Respir Dis* 127:786, 1983.

68. KILBOURN JP, CAMPBELL RA, GRACH JL: Quantitative bacteriology of sputum. *Am Rev Respir Dis* 98:810, 1968.

69. BOXERBAUM B: Isolation of rapidly growing mycobacteria in patients with cystic fibrosis. *J Pediatr* 96:689, 1980.

70. WOOD RE, BOAT TF, DOERSHUK CF: State of the art: Cystic fibrosis. *Am Rev Respir Dis* 113:833, 1976.

71. GOODING CA, LALLEMAND DP, BRASCH RC, WESLEY GE, DAVIS B: Magnetic resonance imaging in cystic fibrosis. *J Pediatr* 105:384, 1984.

72. LEVISON H, GODFREY S: Pulmonary aspects of cystic fibrosis, in Mangos JA, Talamo RE (eds): *Cystic Fibrosis: Projections into the Future,* New York, Stratten Intercontinental Medical Book, 1976, p 3.

73. SIASSI B, MOSS AJ, DOOLEY RR: Clinical recognition of cor pulmonale in cystic fibrosis. *J Pediatr* 78:794, 1971.

74. FRANCIS PWJ, MULLER NL, GURWITZ D, MILLIGAN DWA, LEVISON H, BRYAN AC: Hemoglobin desaturation. Its occurrence during sleep in patients with cystic fibrosis. *Am J Dis Child* 134:734, 1980.

75. STOKES DC, WOHL ME, KHAW KT, STRIEDER DJ: Postural hypoxemia in cystic fibrosis. *Chest* 87:785, 1985.

76. WAGENER JS, McNEIL GC, TAUSSIG LM, CORRIGAN JJ, LEMEN R: Ferrokenetic and hematologic studies in cystic fibrosis patients. *Am J Pediatr Hematol Oncol* 5:153, 1983.

77. ROSENTHAL A, KHAW KT, SHWACHMAN H: Hemoglobin-oxygen equilibrium in cystic fibrosis. *Pediatrics* 59:919, 1977.

78. WAGENER JS, TAUSSIG LM, BURROWS B, HERNRIED L, BOAT T: Comparison of lung infection and survival patterns between cystic fibrosis and emphysema or chronic bronchitis patients, in Sturgess JM (ed): *Perspectives in Cystic Fibrosis.* Mississauga, Ontario, Imperial Press, 1980, p 236.

79. HALUSZKA J, SCISLICKI A: Bronchial lability in children suffering from some diseases of the bronchi. *Respiration* 32:217, 1975.

80. LARSEN GL, BARRON RJ, COTTEN EK, BROOKS JG: A comparative study of

inhaled atropine sulfate and isoproterenol hydrochloride in cystic fibrosis. *Am Rev Respir Dis* 119:399, 1979.

81. HORDVIK NL, KONIG P, MORRIS D, KREUTZ C, BARBERO GF: A longitudinal study of bronchodilator responsiveness in cystic fibrosis. *Am Rev Respir Dis* 131:889, 1985.

82. STERN RC, BOAT TF, ORENSTEIN DM, WOOD RE, MATTHEWS LW, DOERSHUK CF: Treatment and prognosis of lobar and segmental atelectasis in cystic fibrosis. *Am Rev Respir Dis* 118:821, 1978.

83. BOAT TF, DI SANT'AGNESE PA, WARWICK W, HANDWERGER S: Pneumothorax in cystic fibrosis. *JAMA* 209:1948, 1969.

84. STOWE SM, BOAT TF, MENDELSOHN H, STERN RC, TUCKER AS, DOERSHUK CF, MATTHEWS LW: Open thoracotomy for pneumothorax in cystic fibrosis. *Am Rev Respir Dis* 111:611, 1975.

85. STERN RC, WOOD RE, BOAT TF, MATTHEWS LW, TUCKER AS, DOERSHUK CF: Treatment and prognosis of massive hemoptysis in cystic fibrosis. *Am Rev Respir Dis* 117:825, 1978.

86. HOLSCLAW DS, GRAND RJ, SCHWACHMAN H: Massive hemoptysis in cystic fibrosis. *J Pediatr* 76:829, 1970.

87. SCHONHEYDER H, JENSEN T, HOIBY N, ANDERSEN P, KOCH C: Frequency of *Aspergillus fumagatus* isolates and antibodies to aspergillus antigens in cystic fibrosis. *Acta Pathol Microbiol Immunol Scand* 93:105, 1985.

88. LEMEN RJ, GATES AJ, MATHE AA, WARING WW, HYMAN AL, KADOWITZ PD: Relationships among digital clubbing, disease severity, and serum prostaglandins F_2 OC and E concentrations in cystic fibrosis patients. *Am Rev Respir Dis* 117:639, 1978.

89. COHEN AM, YULISH BS, WASSER KB, VIGNOS PJ, JONES PK, SORIN SB: Evaluation of pulmonary hypertrophic osteoarthropathy in cystic fibrosis. *Am J Dis Child* 140:74, 1986.

90. TAUSSIG LM, BELMONTE M, BEAUDRY PH: *Staphylococcus aureus* empyema in cystic fibrosis. *J Pediatr* 84:724, 1974.

91. STERN RC, BORKAT G, HIRSCHFIELD SS, BOAT TF, MATTHEWS LW, LIEBMAN G, DOERSHUK CF: Heart failure in cystic fibrosis. *Am J Dis Child* 134:267, 1980.

92. DI SANT'AGNESE PA, HUBBARD VS: The gastrointestinal tract, in Taussig LM (ed): *Cystic Fibrosis.* New York, Thieme-Stratton, 1984, p 212.

93. NEUTRA MR, TRIER JS: The rectal mucosa in cystic fibrosis: Morphologic features before and after short term organ culture. *Gastroenterology* 75:701, 1978.

94. ROSENSTEIN BJ, LANGBAUM TS: Incidence of meconium abnormalities in newborn infants with cystic fibrosis. *Am J Dis Child* 134:72, 1980.

95. DI SANT'AGNESE PA, DAVIS PB: Cystic fibrosis in adults: 75 cases and a review of 232 cases in the literature. *Am J Med* 66:121, 1979.

96. MCCARTHY VP, MISCHLER EJ, HUBBARD VS, CHERNICK MS, DI SANT'AGNESE PA: Appendiceal abscess in cystic fibrosis: A diagnostic challenge. *Gastroenterology* 86:564, 1984.

97. FLETCHER BD, ABRAMOWSKY CR: Contrast enemas in cystic fibrosis: Implications of appendiceal nonfilling. *AJR* 137:323, 1981.

98. DOLAN TF, MEYERS A: Mild cystic fibrosis presenting as an asymptomatic distended appendiceal mass: A case report. *Clin Pediatr* 14:862, 1975.

99. GEORGE DH: Diverticulosis of the vermiform appendix in patients with cystic fibrosis. *Hum Pathol* 18:75, 1987.

100. TAUSSIG LM, SALDINE RM, DI SANT'AGNESE PA: Radiographic abnormalities of the duodenum and small bowel in cystic fibrosis of the pancreas. *Radiology* 106:369, 1973.

101. STERN RC, IZANT RJ, BOAT TF, WOOD RE, MATTHEWS LW, DOERSHUK CF: Treatment and prognosis of rectal prolapse in cystic fibrosis. *Gastroenterology* 82:707, 1982.

102. WOOD RE, HERMAN CJ, JOHNSON KW, DI SANT'AGNESE PA: Pneumatosis coli in cystic fibrosis. Clinical, radiologic and pathologic features. *Am J Dis Child* 129:246, 1975.

103. DI SANT'AGNESE PA, HUBBARD VS: The pancreas, in Taussig LM (ed): *Cystic Fibrosis.* New York, Thieme-Stratton, 1984, p 230.

104. HANDWERGER S, ROTH J, GORDEN P, DI SANT'AGNESE PA, CARPENTER DF, PETER G: Glucose intolerance in cystic fibrosis. *N Engl J Med* 281:451, 1969.

105. ABDUL-KARIM FW, DAHMS BB, VELASCO ME, RODMAN HM: Islets of Langerhans in adolescents and adults with cystic fibrosis. *Arch Pathol Lab Med* 110:602, 1986.

106. ABRAMS CK, HAMOSH M, HUBBARD VS, DATTA SK, HAMESH P: Lingual lipase in cystic fibrosis. *J Clin Invest* 73:374, 1984.

107. HOFFMAN RD, ISENBERG JN, POWELL GK: Carbohydrate malabsorption is minimal in school-age cystic fibrosis children. *Dig Dis Sci* 32:1071, 1987.

108. MISCHLER EH, CHESNEY PJ, CHESNEY RW, MAZESS RB: Demineralization in cystic fibrosis. *Am J Dis Child* 133:632, 1979.

109. REITER EO, BRUGMAN SM, PIKE JW, PITT M, DOKOH S, HAUSSLER MR, GERSTLE RS, TAUSSIG LM: Vitamin D metabolites in adolescents and young adults with cystic fibrosis. *J Pediatr* 106:21, 1985.

110. FRIEDMAN HZ, LANGMAN CB, FAVUS MJ: Vitamin D metabolism and osteomalacia in cystic fibrosis. *Gastroenterology* 88:803, 1985.

111. FARRELL PM, BIERI JG, FRATANTONI JF, WOOD RE, DI SANT'AGNESE PA: The occurrence and effects of human vitamin E deficiency: A study in patients with cystic fibrosis. *J Clin Invest* 60:233, 1977.

112. ELIAS E, MULLER DPR, SCOTT J: Association of spinocerebellar disorders with cystic fibrosis or chronic childhood cholestasis and very low serum vitamin E. *Lancet* 2:1319, 1981.

113. BLANC WA, REID JD, ANDERSON DH: Avitaminosis E in cystic fibrosis of the pancreas. *Pediatrics* 22:494, 1958.

114. TORSTENSON OL, HUMPHREY GB, EDSON JR: Cystic fibrosis presenting with severe hemorrhage due to vitamin K malabsorption: A report of three cases. *Pediatrics* 45:857, 1970.

115. CORRIGAN JJ, TAUSSIG LM, BECKERMAN R, WAGENER JS: Factor II (prothrombin) coagulant activity and immunoreactive protein: Detection of vitamin K deficiency and liver disease in patients with cystic fibrosis. *J Pediatr* 99:254, 1981.

116. DEREN JJ, ARORA B, TOSKES PP, HANSELL J, SIBINGA MD: Malabsorption of crystalline vitamin B_{12} in cystic fibrosis. *N Engl J Med* 288:949, 1973.

117. LINDEMANS J, ABELS J, NEIJENS HJ, KERREBIJN KF: Elevated serum vitamin B_{12} in cystic fibrosis. *Acta Paediatr Scand* 73:768, 1984.

118. FARAJ BA, CAPLAN DB, CAMP VM, PILZER E, KUTNER M: Low levels of pyridoxal 5'-phosphate in patients with cystic fibrosis. *Pediatrics* 78:278, 1986.

119. HANSEN RC, LEMEN R, REVSIN B: Cystic fibrosis manifesting with acrodermatitis enteropathica-like eruption. *Arch Dermatol* 119:51, 1983.

120. WEBER A, ROY CC, MORIN CL, LaSALLE R: Malabsorption of bile acids in children with cystic fibrosis. *N Engl J Med* 289:1001, 1973.

121. WATKINS JB, TERCYAK AM, SZCZEPANIK P, KLEIN PD: Bile salt kinetics in cystic fibrosis: Influence of pancreatic enzyme replacement. *Gastroenterology* 73:1023, 1977.

122. ROBB TA, DAVIDSON GP, KIRUBAKARON C: Conjugated bile acids in serum and secretions in response to cholecystokinin/secretin stimulation in children with cystic fibrosis. *Gut* 26:1246, 1985.

123. DI SANT'AGNESE PA, HUBBARD VS: The hepatobiliary system, in Taussig LM (ed): *Cystic Fibrosis.* New York, Thieme-Stratton, 1984, p 296.

124. FLEISCHER DA, DiGEORGE AM, BARNESS LA, CORNFIELD D: Hypoproteinemia and edema in infants with cystic fibrosis of the pancreas. *J Pediatr* 64:341, 1964.

125. LEE PA, ROLOFF DW, HOWATT WF: Hypoproteinemia and anemia in infants with cystic fibrosis. *JAMA* 228:585, 1974.

126. SHWACHMAN H, LEBENTHAL E, KHAW KT: Recurrent acute pancreatitis in patients with cystic fibrosis with normal pancreatic enzymes. *Pediatrics* 55:86, 1975.

127. RODMAN HM, MATTHEWS LW: Hyperglycemia in cystic fibrosis: A review of the literature and our own patient experience, in Warwick WJ (ed): *1000 Years of Cystic Fibrosis.* Minneapolis, MN, University of Minnesota Press, 1981, p 67.

128. MILNER AD: Blood glucose and serum insulin levels in children with cystic fibrosis. *Arch Dis Child* 44:351, 1969.

129. LIPPE B, SPERLING MA, DOOLEY RR: Pancreatic alpha and beta cell functions in cystic fibrosis. *J Pediatr* 90:751, 1977.

130. REDMOND AO, BUCHMAN KD, TRIMBLE ER: Insulin and glucagon response to arginine infusion in cystic fibrosis. *Acta Pediatr Scand* 66:199, 1977.

131. LIPPE BM, KAPLAN SA, NEUFELD ND, SMITH A, SCOTT M: Insulin receptors in cystic fibrosis: Increased receptor number and altered affinity. *Pediatrics* 65:1018, 1980.

132. WILMSHURST EG, SOELDNER JS, HOLSCLAW DS, KAUFMAN RL, SCHWACHMAN H, ASKI TT, GLEASON RE: Endogenous and exogenous insulin responses in patients with cystic fibrosis. *Pediatrics* 55:75, 1975.

133. RODMAN HM, WALTMAN SR, KRUPIN T, LEE AT, FRANK KE, MATTHEWS LW: Quantitative vitreous fluorophotometry in insulin-treated cystic fibrosis patients. *Diabetes* 32:505, 1983.

134. ALLEN JL: Progressive nephropathy in a patient with cystic fibrosis and diabetes. *N Engl J Med* 315:764, 1986.

135. RODMAN HM, DOERSHUK CF, ROLAND JM: The interactions of two diseases: Diabetes mellitus and cystic fibrosis. *Medicine* 65:389, 1986.

136. DI SANT'AGNESE PA, BLANC WA: A distinctive type of biliary cirrhosis of the liver associated with cystic fibrosis of the pancreas. *Pediatrics* 18:387, 1956.

137. CRAIG JM, HADDAD H, SHWACHMAN H: The pathological changes in the liver in cystic fibrosis of the pancreas. *Am J Dis Child* 93:357, 1957.

138. KATTWINKEL J, TAUSSIG LM, STATLAND BE, VERTER JI: The effects of age on alkaline phosphatase and other serologic liver function tests in normal subjects and patients with cystic fibrosis. *J Pediatr* 82:234, 1973.

139. BOAT TF, DOERSHUK CF, STERN RC, MATTHEWS LW: Serum alkaline phosphatase in cystic fibrosis. *Clin Pediatr* 13:505, 1974.

140. VALMAN HB, FRANCE NE, WALLIS PG: Prolonged neonatal jaundice in cystic fibrosis. *Arch Dis Child* 46:805, 1971.

141. STERN RC, STEVENS DP, BOAT TF, DOERSHUK CF, IZANT RF, MATTHEWS LW: Symptomatic hepatic disease in cystic fibrosis: Incidence, course, and outcome of portal systemic shunting. *Gastroenterology* 70:645, 1976.

142. STERN RC, BOAT TF, DOERSHUK CF, TUCKER AS, MILLER RB, MATTHEWS LW: Cystic fibrosis diagnosed after age 13. *Ann Intern Med* 87:188, 1977.

143. SCHWARTZ HP, KRAEMER R, THURNHEER U, ROSSI E: Liver involvement in cystic fibrosis: A report of 9 cases. *Helv Paediatr Acta* 33:351, 1978.

144. GRISCOM NT, CAPITANIO MA, WAGONER ML, CULHAM G, MORRIS L: The visibly fatty liver. *Radiology* 117:385, 1975.

145. L'HEUREUX PR, ISENBERG JN, SHARP HL, WARWICK WJ: Gallbladder disease in cystic fibrosis. *Am J Roentgenol* 128:953, 1977.

146. OPPENHEIMER EH, ESTERLY JR: Pathology of cystic fibrosis: Review of the literature and comparison with 146 autopsied cases, in Rosenberg HS, Bolande RP (eds): *Perspectives in Pediatric Pathology.* New York, Yearbook Medical Publishers, 1975, vol 2, p 241.

147. ESTERLY JR, OPPENHEIMER EH: Observation in cystic fibrosis. 1. The gallbladder. *Bull Johns Hopkins Hosp* 110:247, 1962.

148. BASS S, CONNON JJ, HO CS: Biliary tree in cystic fibrosis. *Gastroenterology* 84:1592, 1985.

149. ISENBERG JN, L'HEUREUX PR, WARWICK WJ, SHARP HL: Clinical observations on the biliary system in cystic fibrosis. *Am J Gastroenterol* 65:134, 1976.

150. ROY CC, WEBER AM, MORIN CL, COMBES JC, NUSSLE D, MEGEVAND A, LASALLE R: Abnormal biliary lipid composition in cystic fibrosis: Effect of pancreatic enzymes. *N Engl J Med* 297:1301, 1977.

151. LANDING BH, WELLS TR, WANG CI: Abnormality of the epididymis and vas deferens in cystic fibrosis. *Arch Pathol* 88:570, 1969.

152. TAUSSIG LM, LOBECK CC, DI SANT'AGNESE PA, ACKERMAN DR, KATTWINKEL J: Fertility in males with cystic fibrosis. *N Engl J Med* 287:586, 1972.

153. KAPLAN E, SHWACHMAN H, PERLMUTTER AD, RULE A, KHAW KT, HOLSCLAW DS: Reproductive failure in males with cystic fibrosis. *N Engl J Med* 279:65, 1968.

154. VALMAN HB, FRANCE NE: The vas deferens in cystic fibrosis. *Lancet* 2:566, 1969.

155. HOLSCLAW DS, SHWACHMAN H: Increased incidence of inguinal hernia hydrocele, and undescended testicle in males with cystic fibrosis. *Pediatrics* 48:442, 1971.

156. DENNING CR, SOMMERS SC, QUIGLEY HJ JR: Infertility in male patients with cystic fibrosis. *Pediatrics* 41:7, 1968.

157. STERN RC, BOAT TF, DOERSHUK CF: Obstructive azoospermia as a diagnostic criterion for the cystic fibrosis syndrome. *Lancet* 1:1401, 1982.

158. LEVINE SB, STERN RC: Sexual function in cystic fibrosis. *Chest* 81:422, 1982.

159. SHWACHMAN H, KOWALSKI M, KHAW KT: Cystic fibrosis: A new outlook. *Medicine (Baltimore)* 56:129, 1977.

160. NEINSTEIN LS, STEWART D, WANG CI, JOHNSON I: Menstrual dysfunction in cystic fibrosis. *J Adolesc Health Care* 4:153, 1983.

161. KAPITO LE, KOSASKY HJ, SHWACHMAN H: Water and electrolytes in cervical mucus from patients with CF. *Fertil Steril* 24:512, 1973.

162. COHEN LF, DI SANT'AGNESE PA, FRIEDLANDER J: Cystic fibrosis and pregnancy: A national survey. *Lancet* 2:842, 1980.

163. ALPERT SE, CORMIER AD: Normal electrolyte and protein content in milk from mothers with cystic fibrosis. *J Pediatr* 102:77, 1983.

164. BITMAN J, HAMOSH M, WOOD DL, FREED LM, HAMOSH P: Lipid composition of milk from mothers with cystic fibrosis. *Pediatrics* 80:927, 1987.

165. MITCHELL-HEGGS P, MEARNS M, BATTEN JC: Cystic fibrosis in adolescents and adults. *Q J Med* 179:479, 1976.

166. GIBSON LE, DI SANT'AGNESE PA: Studies of salt excretion in sweat. *J Pediatr* 62:855, 1963.

167. SATO K, SATO F: Defective beta-adrenergic response of cystic fibrosis sweat glands *in vivo* and *in vitro. J Clin Invest* 73:1763, 1984.

168. MUNGER B, BRUSILOW S, COOKE R: An electron microscopic study of eccrine sweat glands in patients with cystic fibrosis of the pancreas. *J Pediatr* 59:497, 1961.

169. ESTERLY NB, OPPENHEIMER EH, ESTERLY JR: Observations on cystic fibrosis of the pancreas: The apocrine sweat gland. *Am J Dis Child* 123:200, 1972.

170. SIMOPOULOUS AP, LAPEY A, BOAT TF, DI SANT'AGNESE PA, BARTTER FC: The renin-angiotensin-aldosterone system in patients with cystic fibrosis of the pancreas. *Pediatr Res* 5:626, 1971.

171. GRAND RJ, DI SANT'AGNESE PA, TALAMO RC, PALLAVICINNI JC: The effects of exogenous aldosterone on sweat electrolytes. II. Patients with cystic fibrosis of the pancreas. *J Pediatr* 70:357, 1967.

172. NUSSBAUM E, BOAT TF, WOOD RE, DOERSHUK CF: Cystic fibrosis with acute hypoelectrolytemia and metabolic acidosis in infancy. *Am J Dis Child* 133:965, 1979.

173. BECKERMAN RC, TAUSSIG LM: Hyperelectrolytemia. *Pediatrics* 63:580, 1979.

174. LIEBERMAN J, RODBARD S: Low blood pressure in young adults with cystic fibrosis. *Ann Intern Med* 82:806, 1975.

175. NEWMAN AJ, ANSELL BM: Episodic arthritis in children with cystic fibrosis. *J Pediatr* 94:594, 1979.

176. SCHIDLOW DV, GOLDSMITH DP, PALMER J, HUANG NN: Arthritis in cystic fibrosis. *Arch Dis Child* 59:377, 1984.

177. SOTER NA, MIHM MC, COLTEN HR: Cutaneous necrotizing venulitis in patients with cystic fibrosis. *J Pediatr* 95:197, 1979.

178. FISCHER EG, SHWACHMAN H, WEPSIE JG: Brain abscess and cystic fibrosis. *J Pediatr* 95:385, 1979.

179. COHEN LF, DI SANT'AGNESE PA, TAYLOR A, GILL JR: The syndrome of inappropriate antidiuretic hormone secretion as a cause of hyponatremia in cystic fibrosis. *J Pediatr* 90:574, 1977.

180. MILLER RW: Childhood cancer and congenital defects: A study of U.S. death certificates during the period 1960–1966. *Pediatr Res* 3:389, 1969.

181. ABDUL-KARIM FW, KING TA, DAHMS BB, GAUDERER MW, BOAT TF: Carcinoma of extrahepatic biliary system in an adult with cystic fibrosis. *Gastroenterology* 82:758, 1982.

182. CASTILE R, SHWACHMAN H, TRAVIS W, HADLEY CA, WARWICK W, MISSMAHL HP: Amyloidosis as a complication of cystic fibrosis. *Am J Dis Child* 139:728, 1985.

183. STERN RC, BOAT TF, ABRAMOWSKY CR, MATTHEWS LW, WOOD RE, DOERSHUK CR: Intermediate-range sweat chloride concentration and pseudomonas bronchitis. A cystic fibrosis variant with preservation of exocrine pancreatic function. *JAMA* 239:2676, 1978.

184. DURIE PR, FORSTNER GG, GASKIN KJ, MOORE DJ, CLEGHORN GD, WONG SS, COREY ML: Age-related alterations of immunoreactive pancreatic cationic trypsinogen in sera from cystic fibrosis patients with and without pancreatic insufficiency. *Pediatr Res* 20:209, 1986.

185. GOWEN CW, LAWSON EE, GINGRAS-LEATHERMAN J, GATZY JT, BOUCHER RC, KNOWLES MR: Increased nasal potential difference and amiloride sensitivity in neonates with cystic fibrosis. *J Pediatr* 108:517, 1986.

186. SAUDER RA, CHESROWN SE, LOUGHLIN GM: Clinical application of transepithelial potential difference measurements in cystic fibrosis. *J Pediatr* 111:353, 1987.

187. DENNING CR, HUANG NN, CUASAY LR, SHWACHMAN H, TOCCI P, WARWICK WJ, GIBSON LE: Cooperative study comparing three methods of performing sweat tests to diagnose cystic fibrosis. *Pediatrics* 66:752, 1980.

188. ROSENSTEIN BJ, LANGBAUM TS: Diagnosis, in Taussig LM (ed): *Cystic Fibrosis.* New York, Thieme-Stratton, 1984, p 85.

189. DAVIS PB, DEL RIO S, MUNTZ JA, DIECKMAN L: Sweat chloride concentration in adults with pulmonary disease. *Am Rev Respir Dis* 138:34, 1983.

190. HARDY JD, DAVISON SHH, HIGGINS MU, POLYCARPOU PN: Sweat tests in the newborn period. *Arch Dis Child* 48:316, 1973.

191. CROSSLEY JR, ELLIOTT RB, SMITH PA: Dried-blood spot screening for cystic fibrosis in the newborn. *Lancet* 1:472, 1979.

192. HAMMOND K, NAYLOR E, WILCKEN B: in Therrell BL (ed): *Advances in Neonatal Screening.* New York, Excerpta Medica, 1987, p 377.

193. AD HOC TASK FORCE ON NEONATAL SCREENING, CYSTIC FIBROSIS FOUNDATION: Neonatal screening for cystic fibrosis: Position paper. *Pediatrics* 72:741, 1983.

194. SANDERS JS, PROYER TD, WEDEL MK: Prolonged survival in an adult with cystic fibrosis. *Chest* 77:226, 1980.

195. SHWACHMAN H, KULCZYCK LL: Long-term study of 105 patients with cystic fibrosis. Studies made over a 5 to 14 year period. *Am J Dis Child* 96:6, 1958.

196. TAUSSIG LM, KATTWINKEL J, FRIEDERWALD WT, DI SANT'AGNESE PA: A new prognostic score and clinical evaluation system for cystic fibrosis. *J Pediatr* 82:380, 1973.

197. BRASFIELD D, HICKS G, SOONG S-J: The chest roentgenogram in cystic fibrosis. A new scoring system. *Pediatrics* 63:24, 1979.

198. FINK RJ, DOERSHUK CF, TUCKER AS, STERN RC, BOAT TF, MATTHEWS LW: Pulmonary function and morbidity in 40 adult patients with cystic fibrosis. *Chest* 74:643, 1978.

199. COREY M, LEVISON H, CROZIER D: Five-to-seven year course of pulmonary function in cystic fibrosis. *Am Rev Respir Dis* 114:1085, 1976.

200. WOOD RE: Prognosis, in Taussig LM (ed): *Cystic Fibrosis.* New York, Thieme-Stratton, 1984, p 434.

201. ORENSTEIN DM, BOAT TF, STERN RC, TUCKER AS, CHARNOCK EL, MATTHEWS LW, DOERSHUK CF: The effect of early diagnosis and treatment on progression of the pulmonary disease in cystic fibrosis. *Am J Dis Child* 131:973, 1977.

202. KATZ JN, HOROWITZ RI, DOLAN TF, SHAPIRO ED: Clinical features as pre-

dictors of functional status in children with cystic fibrosis. *J Pediatr* 108:352, 1986.

203. GASKIN K, GURWITZ D, COREY M, LEVISON H, FORSTNER G: Improved pulmonary function in cystic fibrosis patients without pancreatic insufficiency, in Sturgess JM (ed): *Perspectives in Cystic Fibrosis*. Mississauga, Ontario, Canada, Imperial Press, 1980, p 226.

204. WILMOTT WR, TYSON SL, MATTHEW DJ: Cystic fibrosis survival rates: The influences of allergy and *Pseudomonas aeruginosa*. *Am J Dis Child* 139:669, 1985.

205. KNOKE JD, STERN RC, DOERSHUK CF, BOAT TF, MATTHEWS LW: Cystic fibrosis: The prognosis for five-year survival. *Pediatr Res* 12:676, 1978.

206. HILL DJS, MARTIN AJ, DAVISON GP, SMITH GS: Survival of cystic fibrosis patients in South Australia. *Med J Aust* 143:230, 1985.

207. WOOD RE: Determinants of survival in cystic fibrosis. *CF Club Abstracts* 26:69, 1985.

208. DENNING CR, GLUCKSON MM: Psychosocial aspects of cystic fibrosis, in Taussig LM (ed): *Cystic Fibrosis*. New York, Thieme-Stratton, 1984, p 461.

209. LEWISTON NJ: Psychosocial impact of cystic fibrosis. *Semin Respir Med* 6:321, 1985.

210. ZINMAN R: Cough versus chest physiotherapy: A comparison of the acute effects on pulmonary function in patients with cystic fibrosis. *Am Rev Respir Dis* 129:182, 1984.

211. ZAPLETAL A, STEFANOVA J, HORAK J, VAVROVA V, SAMANEK M: Chest physiotherapy and airway obstruction in patients with cystic fibrosis—A negative report. *Eur J Respir Dis* 64:426, 1983.

212. WONG JW, KEENS TG, WANNAMAKER EM, CROZIER DN, LEVISON H, ASPIN J: Effects of gravity on tracheal mucus transport rates in normal subjects and in patients with cystic fibrosis. *Pediatrics* 60:146, 1977.

213. DESMOND KJ, SCHWENK F, THOMAS E, BEAUDRY PH, COATS AL: Immediate and long-term effects of chest physiotherapy in patients with cystic fibrosis. *J Pediatr* 103:538, 1983.

214. DE BOECK C, ZINMAN R: Cough versus chest physiotherapy: A comparison of the acute effects on pulmonary function in patients with cystic fibrosis. *Am Rev Respir Dis* 129:182, 1984.

215. FALK M, KELSTRUP M, ANDERSON JB, KINOSHITA T, FALK P, STOVRING S, GOTHGEN I: Improving the ketchup bottle method with positive expiratory pressure, PEP, in cystic fibrosis. *Eur J Respir Dis* 65:423, 1984.

216. BLEMQUIST M, FREYSCHUSS U, WIMAN L-G, STRANDVIK B: Physical activity and self-treatment in cystic fibrosis. *Arch Dis Child* 61:362, 1986.

217. SZAFF M, HOIBY N, FLENSBERG EW: Frequent antibiotic therapy improves survival of cystic fibrosis patients with chronic *Pseudomonas aeruginosa* therapy. *Acta Paediatr Scand* 72:651, 1983.

218. LAWSON D, PORTER J: Serum precipitins against respiratory tract pathogens in 522 "normal" children and 48 cases of cystic fibrosis treated with cloxacillin. *Arch Dis Child* 51:890, 1976.

219. BOSSO JA, TOWNSEND PL, HERBST JJ, MATSEN JM: Pharmacokinetics and dosage requirements of netilmicin in cystic fibrosis. *Antimicrob Agents Chemother* 28:829, 1985.

220. MENDELMAN PM, SMITH AL, LEVY J, WEBER A, RAMSEY B, DAVIS R: Aminoglycoside penetration, inactivation, and efficacy in cystic fibrosis sputum. *Am Rev Respir Dis* 132:761, 1985.

221. LEBEL M, BERGERON MG, VALLEE F, FISET C, CHASSE G, BIGONESSE P, RIVARD G: Pharmacokinetics and pharmacodynamics of ciprofloxacin in cystic fibrosis patients. *Antimicrob Agents Chemother* 30:260, 1986.

222. HUDSON ME, PENKETH ARL, BATTEN JC: Aerosol carbenicillin and gentamicin treatment of *Pseudomonas aeruginosa* infection in patients with cystic fibrosis. *Lancet* 2:1137, 1981.

223. WALL MA, TERRY AB, EISENBERG J, MCNAMARA M: Inhaled antibiotics in cystic fibrosis. *Lancet* 1:1325, 1983.

224. KUN P, LANDAU LI, PHELAN PD: Nebulized gentamicin in children and adolescents with cystic fibrosis. *Aust Pediatr* 20:43, 1984.

225. WALTNER WE, CHURCH NL, GATZY JT, BOUCHER RC, KNOWLES MR: Toxicity and pharmacokinetics of acute amiloride aerosol in normal and cystic fibrosis subjects. *CF Club Abstracts* 27:121, 1986.

226. HORDVIK NL, KONIG P, MORRIS D, KREUTZ C, BARBERO GJ: A longitudinal study of bronchodilator responsiveness in cystic fibrosis. *Am Rev Respir Dis* 131:889, 1985.

227. STURGESS J, REID L: The effect of isoprenaline and pilocarpine on a) bronchial mucus-secreting tissue and b) pancreas, salivary glands, heart, thymus, liver, and spleen. *Br J Exp Pathol* 54:388, 1973.

228. SHAPIRO GG, BAMMAN J, KANAREK P, BIERMAN CW: The paradoxical effect of adrenergic and methylxanthine drugs in cystic fibrosis. *Pediatrics* 58:740, 1976.

229. LARSEN GL, BARRON RJ, COTTON EK, BROOKS JG: A comparative study of inhaled atropine sulfate and isoproterenol hydrochloride in cystic fibrosis. *Am Rev Respir Dis* 119:399, 1979.

230. AUERBACH HS, WILLIAMS M, KIRKPATRICK JA, COLTEN HR: Alternate-day prednisone reduces morbidity and improves pulmonary function in cystic fibrosis. *Lancet* 2:686, 1985.

231. DONLAN TF, GIBSON LE: Complications of iodide therapy in patients with cystic fibrosis. *J Pediatr* 79:684, 1971.

232. HENKE KG, ORENSTEIN DM: Oxygen saturation during exercise in cystic fibrosis. *Am Rev Respir Dis* 129:708, 1984.

233. ORENSTEIN DM, FRANKLIN BA, DOERSHUK CF, HELLERSTEIN HK, GERMANN KZ, HOROWITZ ZG, STERN RC: Exercise conditioning and cardiopulmonary fitness in cystic fibrosis. *Chest* 80:392, 1981.

234. STRAUSS GD, OSHER A, WANG C-I, GOODRICH E, GOLD F, COLMAN W, STABILE M, DOBRENCHUK A, KEENS TG: Variable weight training in cystic fibrosis. *Chest* 92:273, 1987.

235. ORENSTEIN DM, HENKE KG, COSTILL DL, DOERSHUK CF, LEMON PJ, STERN RD: Exercise and heat stress in cystic fibrosis patients. *Pediatr Res* 17:267, 1983.

236. LAPEY A, KATTWINKEL J, DI SANT'AGNESE PA, LASTER L: Steatorrhea and azotorrhea and their relation to growth and nutrition in adolescents and young adults with cystic fibrosis. *J Pediatr* 84:328, 1974.

237. YOUNGBERG CA, BERARDI RR, HOWATT WF, HYNECK ML, AMIDON GL, MEYER JH, DRESSMAN JB: The comparison of gastrointestinal pH in cystic fibrosis and healthy subjects. *Dig Dis Sci* 32:472, 1987.

238. STAPLETON FB, KENNEDY J, NOUSIA-ARVANITAKIS S, LINSHAW MA: Hyperuricosuria due to high-dose pancreatic extract therapy in cystic fibrosis. *N Engl J Med* 295:246, 1976.

239. BERTRAND JM, MORIN CL, LASALLE R, PATRICK R, COATES AL: Short-term clinical, nutritional, and functional effects of continuous elemental enteral alimentation in children with cystic fibrosis. *J Pediatr* 104:41, 1984.

240. STERN RC, BYARD PJ, TOMASHEFSKI JF, DOERSHUK CF: Recreational use of psychoactive drugs by patients with cystic fibrosis. *J Pediatr* 111:293, 1987.

241. REDDING GJ, RESTUCCIA R, COTTON EK, BROOKS JG: Serial changes in pulmonary functions in children hospitalized with cystic fibrosis. *Am Rev Respir Dis* 126:31, 1982.

242. POWELL SH, THOMPSON WL, LUTHE MA, STERN RC, GROSSNIKLAUS DA, BLOXHAM DD, GRODEN DL, GACOLOS MR, DISCENNA AO, CASH HA, KLINGER JD: Once daily vs. continuous aminoglycoside dosing: Efficacy and toxicity in animal and clinical studies of gentamicin, netilmicin, and tobramycin. *J Infect Dis* 147:918, 1983.

243. DONATI MA, GUENETTE G, AUERBACH H: Prospective controlled study of home and hospital therapy of cystic fibrosis pulmonary disease. *J Pediatr* 111:28, 1987.

244. BRAUNSTEIN MS, FLEEGLER B: Failure of bronchopulmonary lavage in cystic fibrosis. *Chest* 66:96, 1974.

245. SPIER S, RIVLIN J, HUGHES D, LEVISON H: The effect of oxygen on sleep, blood gases and ventilation in cystic fibrosis. *Am Rev Respir Dis* 129:712, 1984.

246. WHITMAN V, STERN RC, BELLET P, DOERSHUK CF, LIEBMAN Z, BOAT TF, BORKAT G, MATTHEWS LW: Studies on cor pulmonale in cystic fibrosis: 1. Effects of diuresis. *Pediatrics* 55:83, 1975.

247. BENSON LN, NEWTH CJL, DESOUZA M, LOBRAICO R, KARTODIHARDJO W, CONKEY C, GILDAY D, OLLEY PM: Radionuclide assessment of right and left ventricular function during bicycle exercise in young patients with cystic fibrosis. *Am Rev Respir Dis* 130:987, 1984.

248. LIEBMAN J, LUCAS RV, MOSS A, ROSENTHAL A: Cor pulmonale and related cardiovascular effects of cystic fibrosis, in Mangos JA, Talamo RC (eds): *Cystic Fibrosis: Projections into the Future*. New York, Stratton Intercontinental Medical Book, 1976, p 41.

249. GEGGEL RL, DOZOR AJ, FYLER DC, REID LM: Effect of vasodilators at rest and during exercise in young adults with cystic fibrosis and chronic cor pulmonale. *Am Rev Respir Dis* 131:531, 1985.

250. DAVIS PB, DI SANT'AGNESE PA: Assisted ventilation for patients with cystic fibrosis. *JAMA* 239:1851, 1978.

251. FELLOWS KE, KHAW K-T, SCHUSTER S, SHWACHMAN H: Bronchial artery embolization in cystic fibrosis. Technique and long-term results. *J Pediatr* 95:959, 1979.

252. VOSS MJ, BUSH RK, MISCHLER EH, PETERS ME: Association of allergic bronchopulmonary aspergillosis and cystic fibrosis. *J Allergy Clin Immunol* 69:539, 1982.

253. VINCOUR CD, MARMON L, SCHIDLOW DV, WEINTRAUB WH: Gastroesophageal reflux in the infant with cystic fibrosis. *Am J Surg* 149:182, 1985.

254. SCOTT RB, O'LOUGHLIN EV, GALL DG: Gastroesophageal reflux in patients with cystic fibrosis. *J Pediatr* 106:223, 1985.

255. DOLLY T, ROTHBERG RM, LESTER LA: Cystic fibrosis and gastroesophageal reflux in infancy. *Am J Dis Child* 139:66, 1985.

256. O'HALLORAN SM, GILBERT J, MCKENDRICK OM, CARTY HML, HEAF DP: Gastrografin in acute meconium ileus equivalent. *Arch Dis Child* 61:1128, 1986.

257. LILLIBRIDGE CB, DOCTER JM, EIDELMAN S: Oral administration of n-ace-

tyl cysteine in the prophylaxis of meconium ileus equivalent. *J Pediatr* 71:887, 1967.

258. CLEGHORN GJ, FORSTNER GG, STRINGER DA, DURIE PR: Treatment of distal intestinal obstruction syndrome in cystic fibrosis with a balanced intestinal lavage solution. *Lancet* 1:8, 1986.

259. ALTON EWFW, BATTEN J, HODSON M, WALLWORK J, HIGGINBOTTOM T, GEDDES DM: Measurement of lower airways' potential difference in CF following heart-lung transplantation. *Pediatr Pulmonol* S1:111, 1987.

260. BOAT TF, DEARBORN DG: Etiology and pathogenesis, in Taussig LM (ed): *Cystic Fibrosis.* New York, Thieme-Stratton, 1984, p 25.

261. ROSE MC, BROWN CF, JACOBY JZ, LYNN WS, KAUFMAN B: Biochemical properties of tracheobronchial mucins from cystic fibrosis and non-cystic fibrosis individuals. *Pediatr Res* 22:545, 1987.

262. WESLEY A, FORSTNER J, QURESHI R, MANTLE M, FORSTNER G: Human intestinal mucin in cystic fibrosis. *Pediatr Res* 17:65, 1983.

263. BOAT TF, CHENG PW, IYER R, CARLSON DM, POLONY I: Human respiratory tract secretions: Mucous glycoproteins of nonpurulent tracheobronchial secretions and sputum of patients with bronchitis and cystic fibrosis. *Arch Biochem Biophys* 177:95, 1976.

264. LAMBLIN G, LAFITTE JJ, LHERMITTE M, DEGAND P, ROUSSEL P: Mucins from cystic fibrosis sputum. *Mod Probl Paediatr* 19:153, 1977.

265. HILL HD, REYNOLDS JA, HILL RL: Purification, composition, molecular weight, and subunit structure of ovine submaxillary mucin. *J Biol Chem* 252:3791, 1977.

266. SLOMIANY A, WITAS H, AONA M, SLOMIANY BL: Covalently linked fatty acids in gastric mucus glycoprotein of cystic fibrosis patients. *J Biol Chem* 258:8535, 1983.

267. SLOMIANY A, LIAU YH, CARTER SR, NEWMAN LJ, SLOMIANY BL: Mucus glycoprotein fatty acyltransferase in patients with cystic fibrosis: Effect on the glycoprotein viscosity. *Biochem Biophys Res Commun* 132:199, 1985.

268. SLOMIANY A, JOSWIAK Z, TAKAGI A, SLOMIANY BL: The role of covalently bound fatty acids in the degradation of human gastric mucus glycoprotein. *Arch Biochem Biophys* 229:560, 1984.

269. SLOMIANY BL, MURTY VLN, CARTER SR, SLOMIANY A: Effect of covalently bound fatty acids and associated lipids on the viscosity of gastric mucus glycoprotein in cystic fibrosis. *Digestion* 34:275, 1986.

270. MANTLE M, FORSTNER JF: The effects of delipidation on the major antigenic determinant of purified human intestinal mucin. *Biochem Cell Biol* 64:223, 1986.

271. HOUDRET N, PERINI J-M, GALABERT C, SCHARFMAN A, HUMBERT P, LAMBLIN G, ROUSSEL P: The high lipid content of respiratory mucins in cystic fibrosis is related to infection. *Biochim Biophys Acta* 880:54, 1986.

272. GALABERT C, JACQUOT J, ZAHM JM, PUCHELLE E: Relationships between the lipid content and the rheological properties of airway secretions in cystic fibrosis. *Clin Chim Acta* 164:139, 1987.

273. LEV R, SPICER SS: Histochemical comparison of human epithelial mucins in normal and in hypersecretory states including pancreatic cystic fibrosis. *Am J Pathol* 46:23, 1965.

274. BOAT TF, KLEINERMAN JI, CARLSON DM, MALONEY WH, MATTHEWS LW: Mucous glycoproteins secreted by cultured nasal polyp epithelium from subjects with allergic rhinitis and with cystic fibrosis. *Am Rev Respir Dis* 110:428, 1974.

275. FRATES RC, KAIZU T, LAST JA: Mucus glycoproteins secreted by respiratory epithelial tissue from cystic fibrosis patients. *Pediatr Res* 17:30, 1983.

276. ROOMAN GM, VON EULER AM, MULLER RM, GILLJAM H: X-ray microanalysis of goblet cells in brochial epithelium of patients with cystic fibrosis. *J Submicrosc Cytol* 18:613, 1986.

277. CHENG PW, BOUCHER RC, YANKASKAS JM, BOAT TF: Glycoconjugates secreted by cultured human nasal epithelial cells, in Quinton P, Mastella G (eds): *Cellular and Molecular Basis of Cystic Fibrosis.* San Francisco, San Francisco Press, 1988, p 233.

278. PILLION DJ, NEUMEIER TT, MEEZAN E: Serum sulfate levels in patients with cystic fibrosis. *Clin Chim Acta* 142:241, 1984.

279. MEEZAN E, ELGAVISH A: Sulfate incorporation into a cell-associated macromolecular fraction in human lung fibroblasts (IMR-90). *Pediatr Pulmonol* S1:115, 1987.

280. NEUTRA MR, GRAND RJ, TRIER JS: Glycoprotein synthesis, transport, and secretion by epithelial cells of human rectal mucosa: Normal and cystic fibrosis. *Lab Invest* 36:535, 1977.

281. BOAT TF, CHENG PW: Mucous glycoproteins, in Mangos JA, Talamo RC (eds): *Cystic Fibrosis: Projection into the Future.* Miami, Symposia Specialists, 1976, p 165.

282. ROUSSEL P, LAMBLIN G, DEGAND P, WALKER-NASIR E, JEANLOZ RW: Heterogeneity of the carbohydrate chains of sulfated bronchial glycoproteins isolated from a patient suffering from cystic fibrosis. *J Biol Chem* 250:2114, 1975.

283. MAWHINNEY TP, ADELSTEIN E, MORRIS D, MAWHINNEY AM, BARBERO G: Structure determination of five sulfated oligosaccharides derived from tracheobronchial mucus glycoproteins. *J Biol Chem* 262:2994, 1987.

284. BOAT TF, DAVIS J, STERN RD, CHENG PW: Effect of blood group determinants on binding of human salivary mucous glycoproteins to influenza virus, in Gregory JD, Jeanloz RW (eds): *Glycoconjugate Research.* New York, Academic, 1979, vol 1, p 503.

285. VISHWANATH S, RAMPHAL R: Tracheobronchial mucin receptor for *Pseudomonas aeruginosa:* Predominance of amino sugars in binding sites. *Infect Immun* 48:331, 1985.

286. GIBSON LE, MATTHEWS WJ JR, MINIHAN PT: Relating mucus, calcium, and sweat in a new concept of cystic fibrosis. *Pediatrics* 48:695, 1971.

287. LUKIE BE: Entry of (^{3}H) water and (1,2-^{14}C) polyethylene glycol 4000 into normal and cystic fibrosis salivary mucus. *J Lab Clin Med* 101:426, 1983.

288. SCANLIN TF, WANG YM, GLICK MC: Altered fucosylation of membrane glycoproteins from cystic fibrosis fibroblasts. *Pediatr Res* 19:368, 1985.

289. MALER T, RIORDAN JR: Altered fucose handling by cystic fibrosis lymphoblasts, in Sturgess JM (ed): *Perspectives in Cystic Fibrosis.* Mississauga, Ontario, Canada, Imperial Press, 1980, p 58.

290. HUNT LA, SUMMERS DF: Glycosylation of VSV glycoprotein is similar in cystic fibrosis, heterozygote carrier, and normal human fibroblasts. *J Supramol Struct* 7:213, 1977.

291. LIST SJ, FINDLAY BP, FORSTNER GG, FORSTNER JF: Enhancement of the viscosity of mucin by serum albumin. *Biochem J* 175:565, 1978.

292. FORSTNER JF, FORSTNER GG: Calcium binding to intestinal goblet cell mucin. *Biochim Biophys Acta* 386:283, 1975.

293. ROOMANS GM: Calcium and cystic fibrosis. *Scanning Electron Microscopy* 1:165, 1986.

294. SCHONI MH, SCHONI-AFFOLTER F, JEFFERY D, KATZ S: Intracellular free calcium levels in mononuclear cells of patients with cystic fibrosis and normal controls. *Cell Calcium* 8:53, 1987.

295. DEARBORN DG, WITYK RJ, JOHNSON LR, PONCZ L, STERN RC: Calcium-ATPase activity in cystic fibrosis enthrocyte membranes: Decreased activity in patients with pancreatic insufficiency. *Pediatr Res* 18:890, 1984.

296. TALLANT EA, WALLACE RW: Altered binding of ^{125}I-labeled calmodulin to a 46/5-kilodalton protein in skin fibroblasts cultured from patients with cystic fibrosis. *J Clin Invest* 79:643, 1987.

297. BOAT TJ, WIESMAN UN, PALLAVICINI JC: Purification and properties of the calcium precipitable protein in submaxillary saliva of normal and cystic fibrosis subjects. *Pediatr Res* 8:531, 1974.

298. WELSH MJ, FICK RB: Perspective: Cystic fibrosis. *J Clin Invest* 80:1523, 1987.

299. QUINTON PM: Chloride impermeability in cystic fibrosis. *Nature* 301:421, 1983.

300. BIJMAN J, QUINTON P: Permeability properties of cell membranes and tight junctions of normal and cystic fibrosis sweat ducts. *Pflugers Arch* 408:505, 1987.

301. QUINTON PM: Missing Cl conductance in cystic fibrosis. *Am J Physiol* 251:C649, 1986.

302. BIJMAN J, FROMTER E: Direct demonstration of high transepithelial chloride-conductance in normal human sweat duct which is absent in cystic fibrosis. *Pflugers Arch* 407:S123, 1987.

303. WELSH MJ: Electrolyte transport by airway epithelia. *Phys Rev* 67:1143, 1987.

304. KNOWLES M, GATZY J, BOUCHER R: Relative ion permeability of normal and cystic fibrosis nasal epithelium. *J Clin Invest* 71:1410, 1983.

305. KNOWLES MR, STUTTS MJ, SPOCK A, FISCHER NL, GATZY JT, BOUCHER RC: Abnormal ion permeation through cystic fibrosis respiratory epithelium. *Science* 221:1067, 1983.

306. WIDDICOMBE JH, WELSCH MJ, FINKBEINER WE: Cystic fibrosis decreases the apical membrane chloride permeability of monolayers cultured from cells of tracheal epithelium. *Proc Natl Acad Sci USA* 82:6167, 1985.

307. YANKASKAS JR, COTTON CU, KNOWLES MR, GATZY JT, BOUCHER RC: Culture of human nasal epithelial cells on collagen matrix supports: A comparison of bioelectric properties of normal and cystic fibrosis epithelia. *Am Rev Respir Dis* 132:1281, 1985.

308. YANKASKAS JR, GATZY JT, KNOWLES MR, BOUCHER RC: Persistence of abnormal chloride ion permeability in cystic fibrosis nasal epithelial cells in heterologous culture. *Lancet* 1:8435:954, 1985.

309. COTTON CU, STUTTS MJ, KNOWLES MR, GATZY JT, BOUCHER RC: Abnormal apical cell membrane in cystic fibrosis respiratory epithelium: An in vitro electrophysiologic analysis. *J Clin Invest* 79:30, 1987.

310. HAMILL OP, MARTY A, NEHER E, SAKMANN B, SIGWORTH FJ: Improved patch-clamp techniques for high-resolution current recording from cells and cell-free membrane patches. *Pflugers Arch* 391:85, 1981.

311. WELSH MJ: An apical membrane chloride channel in human tracheal epithelium. *Science* 232:1648, 1986.

312. FRIZZELL RA, RECHKEMMER G, SHOEMAKER RL: Altered regulation of air-

way epithelial cell chloride channels in cystic fibrosis. *Science* 233:558, 1986.

313. WIDDICOMBE JH: Cystic fibrosis and β-adrenergic response of airway epithelial cell cultures. *Am J Physiol* 251:R818, 1986.

313a. LI M, MCCANN JD, LIEDTKE CM, NAIRN AC, GREENGARD P, WELSH MJ: Cyclic AMP-dependent protein kinase opens chloride channels in normal but not cystic fibrosis airway epithelium. *Nature* 331:358, 1988.

313b. SCHOUMACHER RA, SHOEMAKER RL, HALM DR, TALLANT EA, WALLACE RW, FRIZZELL RA: Phosphorylation fails to activate chloride channels from cystic fibrosis airway cells. *Nature* 330:752, 1987.

314. BOUCHER RC, STUTTS MJ, KNOWLES MR, CANTLEY L, GATZY JT: Na⁺ transport in cystic fibrosis respiratory epithelia: Abnormal basal rate and response to adenylate cyclase activation. *J Clin Invest* 78:1245, 1986.

315. CULLEN JJ, WELSH MJ: Regulation of sodium absorption by canine tracheal epithelium. *J Clin Invest* 79:1, 1987.

316. KOPELMAN H, DURIE P, GASKIN K, WEIZMAN Z, FORSTNER G: Pancreatic fluid secretion and protein hyperconcentration in cystic fibrosis. *N Engl J Med* 312:329, 1985.

317. NADLER HL, GIRIMAJI JS, RAO JS, TAUSSIG LM: Cystic fibrosis, in Stanbury JB, Wyngaarden JB, Fredrickson DS (eds): *The Metabolic Basis of Inherited Disease*, 4th ed. New York, McGraw-Hill, 1978, p 1683.

318. NADLER HL, BEN-YOSEPH Y: Genetics, in Taussig LM (ed): *Cystic Fibrosis*. New York, Thieme-Stratton, 1984, p 10.

319. THOMPSON MW: Genetics of cystic fibrosis, in Sturgess JM (ed): *Perspectives in Cystic Fibrosis*. Mississauga, Ontario, Canada, Imperial Press, 1980, p 281.

320. DANKS DM, ALLAN J, ANDERSON CM: A genetic study of fibrocystic disease of the pancreas. *Ann Hum Genet* 28:323, 1965.

321. DANKS DM, ALLAN J, PHELAN PD, CHAPMAN C: Mutations at more than one locus may be involved in cystic fibrosis—Evidence based on first-cousin data and direct counting of cases. *Am J Hum Genet* 35:838, 1983.

322. HOUSTEK J, VÁVROVÁ V: Notre expérience à propos de la mucoviscidose. *Rev Méd Liège* 22:421, 1967.

323. BRUNECKÝ Z: The incidence and genetics of cystic fibrosis. *J Med Genet* 9:33, 1972.

324. BOIS E, FEINGOLD J, DEMENAIS F, RUNAVOT Y, JEHANNE M, TOUDIC L: Cluster of cystic fibrosis cases in a limited area of Brittany (France). *Clin Genet* 14:73, 1978.

325. VIVELL VO, JACOBI H, MÜNCHBACH K: Zur Mucoviscidosis im Kindesalter. *Monatsschr Kinderheilkd* 111:62, 1963.

326. LEVIN S: Fibrocystic disease of the pancreas, in Goldschmidt E (ed): *Genetics of Migrant and Isolate Populations*. Baltimore, Williams and Wilkins, 1963, p 294.

327. ANTONELLI M, DONFRANCESCO A: Indagine clinico-statistica sulla epidemiologia della fibrosi cistica (F.C.) in Italia nel quadriennio. *Fracastoro* 63:207, 1970.

328. ROMEO G, BIANCO M, DEVOTO M, MENOZZI P, MASTELLA G, GIUNTA AM, MICALIZZI C, ANTONELLI M, BATTISTINI A, SANTAMARIA F, CASTELLO D, MARIANELLI A, MARCHI AG, MANCA A, MIANO A: Incidence in Italy, genetic heterogeneity, and segregation analysis of cystic fibrosis. *Am J Hum Genet* 37:338, 1985.

329. SUPER M: Factors influencing the frequency of cystic fibrosis in South West Africa. *Monogr Paediatr* 10:106, 1979.

330. SELANDER P: The frequency of cystic fibrosis of the pancreas in Sweden. *Acta Paediatr* 51:65, 1962.

331. CARTER CO: Genetic aspects of cystic fibrosis of the pancreas. *Mod Probl Pediatr* 10:372, 1967.

332. PUGH RJ, PICKUP JD: Cystic fibrosis in Leeds region: Incidence and life expectancy. *Arch Dis Child* 42:544, 1967.

333. HALL BD, SIMPKISS MJ: Inheritance of fibrocystic disease in Wessex. *J Med Genet* 5:262, 1968.

334. GOODCHILD MC, INSLEY J, RUSHTON DI, GAZE H: Cystic fibrosis in 3 Pakistani children. *Arch Dis Child* 49:739, 1974.

335. STEVENSON AC: The load of hereditary defects in human populations. *Radiat Res Suppl* 1:306, 1959.

336. NEVIN GB, NEVIN NC, REDMOND AD: Cystic fibrosis in Northern Ireland. *J Med Genet* 16:122, 1979.

337. STEINBERG AG, BROWN DC: On the incidence of cystic fibrosis of the pancreas. *Am J Hum Genet* 12:416, 1960.

338. KRAMM ER, CRANE MM, SIRKIN MG, BROWN ML: A cystic fibrosis pilot survey in three New England states. *Am J Public Health* 52:2041, 1962.

339. MERRITT AD, HANNA BL, TODD CW, MYERS TL: Incidence and mode of inheritance of cystic fibrosis. *J Lab Clin Med* 60:998, 1962.

340. SULTZ HA, SCHLESINGER ER, MOSHE WE: The Erie County survey of long term childhood illness. *Am J Public Health* 56:1461, 1966.

341. KULCZYCKI IL, SCHAUF V: Cystic fibrosis in Blacks in Washington, D.C. *Am J Dis Child* 127:64, 1974.

342. WRIGHT SE, MORTON NE: Genetic studies on cystic fibrosis in Hawaii. *Am J Hum Genet* 20:157, 1968.

343. WILCKEN B, BROWN ARD: Screening for cystic fibrosis in New South Wales, Australia: Evaluation of the results of screening 400,000 babies, in Therrell BL (ed): *Advances in Neonatal Screening*. New York, Excerpta Medica, 1987, p 385.

344. FARRELL P, ROCK M, MISCHLER E, BRUNS WT, PALTA M, LAESSIG R, HASSEMER D: Infant screening test for cystic fibrosis (CF). *Pediatr Res* 23:563A, 1988.

345. PEDERZINI F, ARMANI P, BARBATO A, BORGO G: Newborn screening for cystic fibrosis. Two methods compared on 229,626 newborns tested in 8 years in the Veneto region. *Ital J Pediatr* 9:445, 1983.

346. KLINGER KW: Cystic fibrosis in the Ohio Amish: Gene frequency and founder effect. *Hum Genet* 65:94, 1983.

347. NORIO R, NEVALINNA HR, PERHEENTUPA J: Herditary diseases in Finland: Rare flora in rare soil. *Ann Clin Res* 5:109, 1973.

348. KING DN, HEELEY AF, WALSH MP, KUZEMKO JA: Sensitive trypsin assay for dried blood specimens as a screening procedure for early detection of cystic fibrosis. *Lancet* 2:1217, 1979.

349. BOWLING FG, RYLATT DB, BUNCH RJ, WATSON ARA, ELLIOTT JE, BUNDESEN PG: Monoclonal antibody-based enzyme immunoassay for trypsinogen in neonatal screening for cystic fibrosis. *Lancet* 1:826, 1987.

350. WILCKEN B, BROWN ARD, URWIN R, BROWN DA: Cystic fibrosis screening by dried blood-spot trypsin assay: results in 75,000 newborn infants. *J Pediatr* 102:383, 1983.

351. HAMMOND KB, REARDON MC, ACCURSO FJ, ABMAN SH, COTTON EK, PINNEY M, FISHER C, SOKOL RJ, ASK CG, WATTS DC, BONNER A-M: Early detection and follow-up of cystic fibrosis in newborns: The Colorado experience, in Carter TP, Willey AM (eds): *Genetic Disease Screening and Management*. New York, Alan R. Liss, Inc., 1986.

352. HASSEMER DJ: Neonatal screening for cystic fibrosis in Wisconsin, in Therrell BL (ed): *Advances in Neonatal Screening*. New York, Excerpta Medica, 1987, p 393.

353. HOLTZMAN NA: Routine screening of newborns for cystic fibrosis: Not yet. *Pediatrics* 73:98, 1984.

354. FARRELL PM: Early diagnosis of cystic fibrosis: To screen or not to screen—An important question. *Pediatrics* 73:115, 1984.

355. REARDON MC, HAMMOND KB, ACCURSO FJ, FISHER CD, MCCABE ERB, COTTON EK, BOWMAN CM: Nutritional deficits exist before 2 months of age in some infants with cystic fibrosis identified by screening test. *J Pediatr* 105:271, 1984.

356. CROW JF: Problems of ascertainment in the analysis of family data, in Neel JV, Shaw MW, Schull WJ (eds): *Genetics and Epidemiology of Chronic Diseases*. U.S. Public Health Service Publication 1163, 1965, p 23.

357. CONNEALLY PM, MERRITT AD, YU P: Cystic fibrosis: Population genetics. *Tex Rep Biol Med* 31:639, 1973.

358. DANKS DM, PHELAN PD, CHAPMAN C: Retraction: No evidence for more than one locus in cystic fibrosis. *Am J Hum Genet* 36:1401, 1984.

359. GEDSCHOLD J, KROPF S, SZIBOR R, BERGER M: Cystic fibrosis—A single locus disease? Results of a population genetics study. *Hum Genet* 75:277, 1987.

360. BOWCOCK AM, CRANDALL J, DANESHVAR L, LEE GM, YOUNG B, ZUNZUNEGUI V, CRAIK C, CAVALLI-SFORZA LL, KING M-C: Genetic analysis of cystic fibrosis: linkage of DNA and classical markers in multiplex families. *Am J Hum Genet* 39:699, 1986.

361. BEAUDET A, BOWCOCK A, BUCHWALD M, CAVALLI-SFORZA L, FARRALL M, KING M-C, KLINGER K, LALOUEL J-M, LATHROP G, NAYLOR S, OTT J, TSUI L-C, WAINWRIGHT B, WATKINS P, WHITE R, WILLIAMSON R: Linkage of cystic fibrosis to two tightly linked DNA markers: Joint report from a collaborative study. *Am J Hum Genet* 39:681, 1986.

362. SING CF, RISSER DR, HOWATT WF, ERICKSON RP: Phenotypic heterogeneity in cystic fibrosis. *Am J Med Genet* 13:179, 1982.

363. ALLAN JL, ROBBIE M, PHELAN PD, DANKS DM: Familial occurrence of meconium ileus. *Eur J Pediatr* 135:291, 1981.

364. ESTIVILL X, FARRALL M, SCAMBLER PJ, BELL GM, HAWLEY KMF, LENCH NJ, BATES GP, KRUYER HC, FREDERICK PA, STANIER P, WATSON EK, WILLIAMSON R, WAINWRIGHT J: A candidate for the cystic fibrosis locus isolated by selection for methylation-free islands. *Nature* 326:840, 1987.

365. KNUDSEN AG JR, WAYNE L, HALLETT WY: On selective advantage of cystic fibrosis heterozygotes. *Am J Hum Genet* 19:388, 1967.

366. CRAWFORD MD: A genetic study including evidence for heterosis in cystic fibrosis of the pancreas. *Heredity* 29:126, 1972.

367. MEINDL RS: Hypothesis: A selective advantage for cystic fibrosis heterozygotes. *Am J Phys Anthropol* 74:39, 1987.

368. KITZIS A, CHOMEL JC, KAPLAN JC, GIRAUD G, LABBE A, DASTUGUE B, DUMUR V, FARRIAUX JP, ROUSSEL P, WILLIAMSON R, FEINGOLD J: Unusual segregation of cystic fibrosis allele to males. *Nature* 333:215, 1988.

369. RAO DC, MORTON NE: Large deviations in the distribution of rare genes. *Am J Hum Genet* 25:594, 1973.

370. SOLOMON E, BODMER WF: Evolution of sickle variant gene. *Lancet* 1:923, 1979.

371. BOTSTEIN D, WHITE RL, SKOLNICK M, DAVIS RW: Construction of a genetic linkage map in man using restriction fragment length polymorphisms. *Am J Hum Genet* 32:314, 1980.

372. TSUI L-C, COX DW, MCALPINE PJ, BUCHWALD M: Cystic fibrosis: Analysis of linkage of the disease locus to red cell and plasma protein markers. *Cytogenet Cell Genet* 39:238, 1985.

373. TSUI L-C, ZSIGA M, KENNEDY D, PLAVSIC N, MARKIEWICZ D, BUCHWALD M: Cystic fibrosis: Progress in mapping the disease locus using polymorphic DNA markers. I. *Cytogenet Cell Genet* 39:299, 1985.

374. SCAMBLER PJ, BELL G, WATSON E, FARRALL M, BATES G, DAVIES K, LENCH N, ASHWORTH A, WILLIAMSON R, TIPPET P, WAINWRIGHT B: Cystic fibrosis linkage exclusion data. *Cytogenet Cell Genet* 41:62, 1986.

375. SCHMIEGELOW K, EIBERG H, TSUI L-C, BUCHWALD M, PHELAN PD, WILLIAMSON R, WARWICK W, NIEBUHR E, MOHR J, SCHWARTZ M, KOCH C: Linkage between the loci for cystic fibrosis and paraoxonase. *Clin Genet* 29:374, 1986.

376. KNOWLTON RG, COHEN-HAGUENAUER O, CONG NV, FRÉZAL J, BROWN VA, BARKER D, BRAMAN JC, SCHUMM JW, TSUI L-C, BUCHWALD M, DONIS-KELLER H: A polymorphic DNA marker linked to cystic fibrosis is located on chromosome 7. *Nature* 318:380, 1985.

377. SCAMBLER PJ, WAINWRIGHT BJ, WATSON E, BATES G, BELL G, WILLIAMSON R, FARRALL M: Isolation of a further anonymous informative DNA sequence from chromosome seven closely linked to cystic fibrosis. *Nucleic Acids Res* 14:1951, 1986.

378. ESTIVILL X, SCHMIDTKE J, WILLIAMSON R, WAINWRIGHT B: Chromosome assignment and restriction fragment length polymorphism analysis of the anonymous DNA probe B79a at 7q22 (HMG8 assignment D7S13). *Hum Genet* 74:320, 1986.

379. DEAN M, O'CONNELL P, LEPPERT M, PARK M, AMOS JA, PHILLIPS DG, WHITE R, VANDE WOUDE GF: Three additional DNA polymorphisms in the *met* gene and D7S8 locus: Use in prenatal diagnosis of cystic fibrosis. *J Pediatr* 111:490, 1987.

380. BARKER D, GREEN P, KNOWLTON R, SCHUMM J, LANDER E, OLIPHANT A, WILLARD H, AKOTS G, BROWN V, GRAVIUS T, HELMS C, NELSON C, PARKER C, REDIKER K, RISING M, WATT D, WEIFFENBACH B, DONIS-KELLER H: Genetic linkage map of human chromosome 7 with 63 DNA markers. *Proc Natl Acad Sci USA* 84:8006, 1987.

381. SCAMBLER PJ, LAW H-Y, WILLIAMSON R, COOPER CS: Chromosome mediated gene transfer of six DNA markers linked to the cystic fibrosis locus on human chromosome seven. *Nucleic Acids Res* 14:7159, 1986.

382. SCAMBLER PJ, ESTIVILL X, BELL G, FARRALL M, MCLEAN C, NEWMAN R, LITTLE PFR, FREDERICK P, HAWLEY K, WAINWRIGHT BJ, WILLIAMSON R, LENCH NJ: Physical and genetic analysis of cosmids from the vicinity of the cystic fibrosis locus. *Nucleic Acids Res* 15:3639, 1987.

383. WAINWRIGHT BJ, SCAMBLER PJ, STANIER P, WATSON EK, BELL G, WICKING C, ESTIVILL X, COURTNEY M, BOVE A, PEDERSEN PS, WILLIAMSON R, FARRALL M: Isolation of a human gene with protein sequence similarity to human and murine int-1 and the *Drosophila* segment polarity mutant *wingless*. *EMBO J* 7:1743, 1988.

384. FARRALL MP, STANIER G, FELDMAN G, BEAUDET AL, HALLBY D, SIMON M, DICKERMAN L, ROMEO G, KAPLAN J-C, KITZIS A, WILLIAMSON R: Recombinations between IRP and cystic fibrosis. *Am J Hum Genet,* 43:471, 1988.

385. COLLINS FS, DRUMM JL, COLE JL, LOCKWOOD WK, VANDE WOUDE GF, IANNUZZI MC: Construction of a general human chromosome jumping library, with application to cystic fibrosis. *Science* 235:1046, 1987.

386. LATHROP GM, FARRALL M, O'CONNELL P, WAINWRIGHT B, LEPPERT M, NAKAMURA Y, LENCH N, KRUYER H, DEAN M, PARK M, VANDE WOUDE G, LALOUEL J-M, WILLIAMSON R, WHITE R: Refined linkage map of chromosome 7 in the region of the cystic fibrosis gene. *Am J Hum Genet* 42:38, 1988.

387. DRUMM ML, SMITH CL, DEAN M, COLE JL, IANNUZZI MC, COLLINS FS: Physical mapping of the cystic fibrosis region by pulsed-field gel electrophoresis. *Genomics* 2:346, 1988.

388. ESTIVILL X, SCAMBLER PJ, WAINWRIGHT JB, HAWLEY K, FREDERICK P, SCHWARTZ M, BAIGET M, KERE J, WILLIAMSON R, FARRALL M: Patterns of polymorphism and linkage disequilibrium for cystic fibrosis. *Genomics* 1:257, 1987.

389. BEAUDET AL, SPENCE JE, MONTES M, O'BRIEN WE, ESTIVILL X, FARRALL M, WILLIAMSON R: Experience with new DNA markers for the diagnosis of cystic fibrosis. *N Engl J Med* 318:50, 1988.

390. BERGER W, HEIN J, GEDSCHOLD J, BAUER I, SPEER A, FARRALL M, WILLIAMSON R, COUTELLE C: Crossovers in two German cystic fibrosis families determine probe order for MET, 7C22 and XV-2c/CS.7. *Hum Genet* 77:197, 1987.

391. KOPITO RR, LODISH HF: Primary structure and transmembrane orientation of the murine anion exchange protein. *Nature* 316:234, 1985.

392. PALUMBO AP, ISOBE M, HUEBNER K, SHANE S, ROVERA G, DEMUTH D, CURTIS PJ, BALLANTINE M, CROCE CM, SHOWE LC: Chromosomal localization of a human band 3-like gene to region 7q35→7q36. *Am J Hum Genet* 39:307, 1986.

393. BROCK DJH, HAYWARD C: Methylumbelliferylguanidinobenzoate reactive proteases and prenatal diagnosis of cystic fibrosis. *Lancet* 1:1244, 1979.

394. WALSH MMJ, NADLER HL: Methylumbelliferylguanidinobenzoate-reactive proteases in human amniotic fluid: Promising marker for the intrauterine detection of cystic fibrosis. *Am J Obstet Gynecol* 137:978, 1980.

395. CARBARNS NJB, GOSDEN C, BROCK DJH: Microvillar peptidase activity in amniotic fluid: Possible use in the prenatal diagnosis of cystic fibrosis. *Lancet* 1:329, 1983.

396. BROCK DJH: Amniotic fluid alkaline phosphatase isoenzymes in early prenatal diagnosis of cystic fibrosis. *Lancet* 2:941, 1983.

397. VAN DIGGELEN OP, JANSE HC, KLEIJER WJ: Disaccharidases in amniotic fluid as possible prenatal marker for cystic fibrosis. *Lancet* 1:817, 1983.

398. MULIVOR RA, COOK D, MULLER F, BOUÉ A, GILBERT F, MENNUTI M, PERGAMENT E, POTIER M, NADLER H, PUNNETT H, HARRIS H: Analysis of fetal intestinal enzymes in amniotic fluid for the prenatal diagnosis of cystic fibrosis. *Am J Hum Genet* 40:131, 1987.

399. BOUÉ A, MULLER F, NEZELOF C, OURY JF, DUCHATEL F, DUMEZ Y, AUBRY MC, BOUÉ J: Prenatal diagnosis in 200 pregnancies with a 1-in-4 risk of cystic fibrosis. *Hum Genet* 74:288, 1986.

400. BROCK DJH, CLARKE HAK, BARRON L: Prenatal diagnosis of cystic fibrosis by microvillar enzyme assay on a sequence of 258 pregnancies. *Hum Genet* 78:271, 1988.

401. MULLER F, AUBRY MC, GASSER B, DUCHATEL F, BOUÉ J, BOUÉ A: Prenatal diagnosis of cystic fibrosis. II. Meconium ileus in affected fetuses. *Prenat Diagn* 5:109, 1985.

402. FOSTER MA, NYBERG DA, MAHONY BS, MACK LA, MARKS WM, RAABE RD: Meconium peritonitis: Prenatal sonographic findings and their clinical significance. *Radiology* 165:661, 1987.

403. SHARPLES PM, HOPE PL, WILKINSON AR: False positive in prenatal diagnosis of cystic fibrosis. *Lancet* 1:595, 1988.

404. GILBERT F, TSAO K-L, MENDOZA A, MULIVOR R, GLUCKSON MM, DENNING CR: Prenatal diagnostic options in cystic fibrosis. *Am J Obstet Gynecol* 158:947, 1988.

405. MORIN PR, MELANÇON SB, DALLAIRE L, POTIER M: Prenatal detection of intestinal obstructions, aneuploidy syndromes, and cystic fibrosis by microvillar enzyme assays (disaccharidases, alkaline phosphatase, and glutamyltransferase) in amniotic fluid. *Am J Med Genet* 26:405, 1987.

406. BROCK DJH, BARRON L: Biochemical analysis of meconium in fetuses presumed to have cystic fibrosis. *Prenat Diagn* 6:291, 1986.

407. ORNOY A, ARNON J, KATZNELSON D, GRANAT M, CASPI B, CHEMKE J: Pathological confirmation of cystic fibrosis in the fetus following prenatal diagnosis. *Am J Med Genet* 28:935, 1987.

408. FARRALL M, LAW H-Y, RODECK CH, WARREN R, STANIER P, SUPER M, LISSENS W, SCAMBLER P, WATSON E, WAINWRIGHT B, WILLIAMSON R: First-trimester prenatal diagnosis of cystic fibrosis with linked DNA probes. *Lancet* 1:1402, 1986.

409. SPENCE JE, BUFFONE GJ, ROSENBLOOM CL, FERNBACH SD, CURRY MR, CARPENTER RJ, LEDBETTER DH, O'BRIEN WE, BEAUDET AL: Prenatal diagnosis of cystic fibrosis using linked DNA markers and microvillar intestinal enzyme analysis. *Hum Genet* 76:5, 1987.

410. FELDMAN GL, LEWISTON N, FERNBACH SD, O'BRIEN WE, BEAUDET AL: Prenatal diagnosis of cystic fibrosis using linked DNA markers in 119 pregnancies at 1 in 4 risk. (submitted)

411. NUGENT CE, GRAVIUS T, GREEN P, LARSEN JW, MacMILLIN MD, DONIS-KELLER H: Prenatal diagnosis of cystic fibrosis by chorionic villus sampling using 12 polymorphic deoxyribonucleic acid markers. *Obstet Gynecol* 71:213, 1988.

412. SUPER M, SCHWARZ M, ELLES RG, IVINSON A, GILES L, READ AP, HARRIS R: Clinic experience of prenatal diagnosis of cystic fibrosis by use of linked DNA probes. *Lancet* 2:782, 1987.

413. MATHY L, KAMPMANN W, HIGUCHI M, SCHWARTENBECK G, BARTHOLOMÉ K, DRIESEL AJ, GRZESCHIK K-H, OLEK K: Cystic fibrosis: Typing 48 German families with linked DNA probes. *Hum Genet* 75:359, 1987.

414. WILLIAMS C, WILLIAMSON R, COUTELLE C, LOEFFLER F, SMITH J, IVINSON A: Same day first trimester antenatal diagnosis for cystic fibrosis using gene amplification. *Lancet* 2:102, 1988.

415. FELDMAN GL, WILLIAMSON R, BEAUDET AL, O'BRIEN WE: Prenatal diagnosis of cystic fibrosis using DNA amplification for detection of the KM-19 polymorphism. *Lancet* 2:102, 1988.

416. LENCH N, STANIER P, WILLIAMSON R: Simple non-invasive method to obtain DNA for gene analysis. *Lancet* 1:1356, 1988.

417. BEAUDET AL, FELDMAN GL, FERNBACH SD, BUFFONE GG, O'BRIEN WE:

Linkage disequilibrium, cystic fibrosis and genetic counseling. *Am J Hum Genet*, in press.

418. MORNET E, SERRE JL, FARRAL M, BOUÉ J, SIMON-BOUY B, ESTIVILL X, WILLIAMSON R, BOUÉ A: Genetic differences between cystic fibrosis with and without meconium ileus. *Lancet* 1:376, 1988.

419. CUTTING GR, ANTONARAKIS SE, KASCH LM, ROSENSTEIN BJ, KAZAZIAN HH: KM19/XV2C haplotype analysis suggests that several mutations of the cystic fibrosis gene may exist. *Pediatr Res* 23:328A, 1988.

420. DEVOTO M, ANTONELLI M, BELLINI F, BORGO G, CASTIGLIONE O, CURCIO L, DALLAPICCOLA B, FERRARI M, GASPARINI P, GIUNTA A, MARIANELLI L, MASTELLA G, NOVELLI G, PIGNATTI PF, ROMANO L, ROMEO G, SEIA M: Rarer alleles of DNA RFLP's closely linked to the CF gene are significantly more frequent in Italian CF patients without pancreatic insufficiency. *Am J Hum Genet* 43:A82, 1988.

421. BUCHANAN JA, KAREM B, COREY ML, BUCHWALD M, TSUI L-C: Marker haplotype association with pancreatic sufficiency in cystic fibrosis. *Am J Hum Genet* 43:A79, 1988.

422. KABACK M, ZIPPIN D, BOYD P, CANTOR R: Attitudes toward prenatal diagnosis of cystic fibrosis among parents of affected children, in Lawson D (ed): *Cystic Fibrosis: Horizons*. New York, Wiley, 1984, p 15.

423. PASSARGE E, ECKERLAND B, STEPHAN U: Genetic counselling in cystic fibrosis: Results of a survey of 572 families. *Eur J Pediatr* 143:54, 1984.

424. WILSON GB, FUDENBERG HH, JAHN TL: Studies on cystic fibrosis using isoelectric focusing. I. An assay for detection of cystic fibrosis homozygotes and heterozygote carriers from serum. *Pediatr Res* 9:635, 1975.

425. VAN HEYNINGEN V, HAYWARD C, FLETCHER J, MCAULEY: Tissue localization and chromosomal assignment of a serum protein that tracks the cystic fibrosis gene. *Nature* 315:513, 1985.

426. DORIN JR, NOVAK M, HILL RE, BROCK DJH, SECHER DS, VAN HEYNINGEN V: A clue to the basic defect in cystic fibrosis from cloning the CF antigen gene. *Nature* 326:614, 1987.

427. VAN HEYNINGEN V, BROCK DJH, DORIN JR, HAYWARD C, NOVAK M, WILKINSON M: Calcium binding protein homology of cystic fibrosis associated serum protein: a clue to the basic defect, in Mastella G, Quinton PM (eds): *Cellular and Molecular Basis of Cystic Fibrosis*. San Francisco, San Francisco Press, 1988, p 90.

428. ODINK K, CERLETTI N, BRÜGGEN J, CLERC RG, TARCSAY L, ZWADLO G, GERHARDS G, SCHLEGEL R, SORG C: Two calcium-binding proteins in infiltrate macrophages of rheumatoid arthritis. *Nature* 330:80, 1987.

429. ANDERSSON KB, SLETTEN K, BERNTZEN HB, FAGERHOL MK, DALE I, BRANDTZAEG P, JELLUM E: Leukocyte L1 protein and the cystic fibrosis antigen. *Nature* 332:688, 1988.

430. CARLSTEDT-DUKE J, BRÖNNEGÅRD M, STRANDVIK B: Pathological regulation of arachidonic acid release in cystic fibrosis: The putative basic defect. *Proc Natl Acad Sci USA* 83:9202, 1986.

431. ZASLOFF M: Magainins, a class of antimicrobial peptides from Xenopus skin: Isolation, characterization of two active forms, and partial cDNA sequence of a precursor. *Proc Natl Acad Sci USA* 84:5449, 1987.

PART 16

DEFENSE AND IMMUNE MECHANISMS

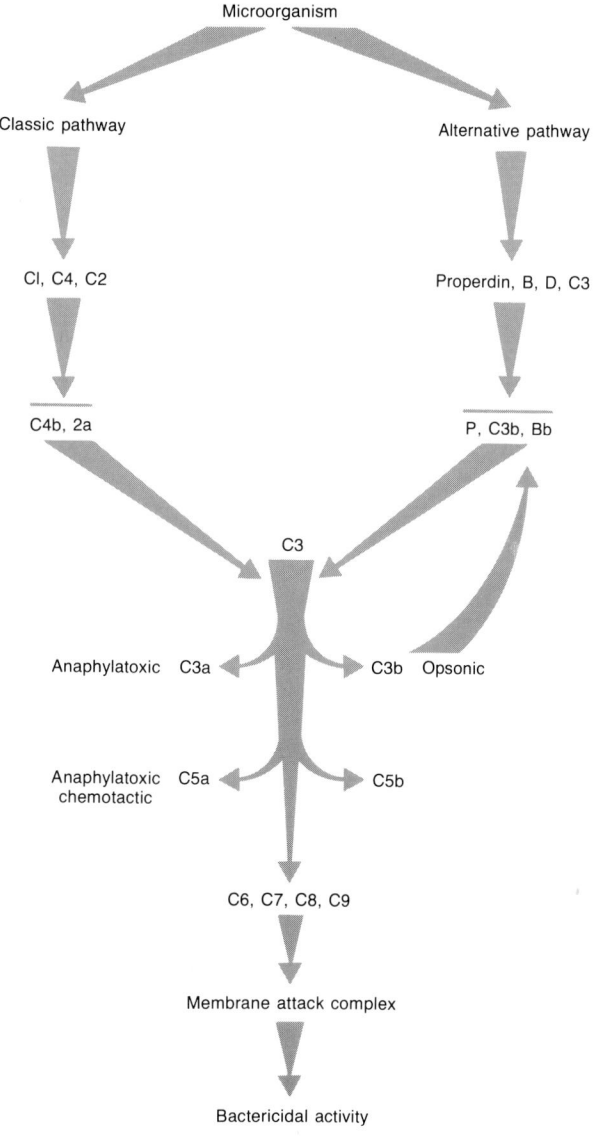

Microorganism

Classic pathway

Alternative pathway

Cl, C4, C2

Properdin, B, D, C3

C4b, 2a

P, C3b, Bb

C3

Anaphylatoxic C3a

C3b Opsonic

Anaphylatoxic
chemotactic C5a

C5b

C6, C7, C8, C9

Membrane attack complex

Bactericidal activity

Complement activation

CHAPTER 109

ANTIBODY DEFICIENCY DISEASES

JOSEPH L BUTLER
MAX D. COOPER

1. Antibodies are protein molecules that specifically recognize and bind to antigens. They are produced by B cells in response to antigen and serve to protect the host from microbial infection. Antibodies can be divided into five immunoglobulin (Ig) classes based on their physiochemical or serologic properties: IgG, IgM, IgA, IgD, and IgE. There are four subclasses of IgG that are numbered according to their relative abundance in the circulation: IgG1>IgG2>IgG3>IgG4. There are two subclasses of IgA, i.e., IgA1 and IgA2. Thus, there are nine different isotypes of antibodies, each of which has special biologic advantages.

2. B cells are produced in the bone marrow where stem-cell progeny undergo an orderly developmental sequence to become pre-B cells, then mature B cells. Newly formed B cells are seeded to the spleen and other peripheral lymphoid tissues, where they may respond to antigen stimulation and T-cell help to become mature antibody-secreting plasma cells. Aberrations in normal B-cell development and differentiation lead to diseases characterized by antibody deficiency. The level of the B-cell differentiation arrest influences the clinical and laboratory characteristics of the immunodeficiency disease.

3. Primary antibody deficiency diseases may be inherited in X-linked recessive or autosomal recessive transmission patterns. In some cases, a mode of inheritance is not apparent. The hallmark of these diseases is recurrent infections. Treatment by antibody replacement reduces the number and severity of infections in many of these immunodeficient patients. When abortive T-cell development accompanies the B-cell deficiency, bone marrow transplantation may result in normal immunologic function.

The immune system consists of four major components which productively interact to protect the individual against microbes and other agents capable of producing disease. These components consist of the antibody, or humoral, immune system, the cellular immune system, the complement system, and the phagocytic system. Abnormalities in the development or function of any one of these components may lead to altered immune responsiveness manifested by immunodeficiency or autoimmunity.

In this chapter, we discuss deficiencies of antibody-mediated immunity. First, the structure and function of the immunoglobulin classes are considered. Next, we review the generation of B cells from stem-cell precursors and the steps involved in their terminal differentiation into antibody-secreting plasma cells. Particular attention is given to the molecular mechanisms of immunoglobulin gene rearrangement and isotype switching and to the events involved in B-cell activation. This information is incorporated into a model of the normal development and differentiation of B cells.

Using this developmental model, we review the antibody deficiency diseases. The inherited and acquired defects in B cell development which produce these diseases are discussed. The clinical and laboratory features of each disease are considered, and useful diagnostic tests outlined. Finally, we provide an overview of treatment options, with particular emphasis on antibody replacement.

IMMUNOGLOBULIN STRUCTURE AND FUNCTION

Immunoglobulin (Ig) molecules are glycoproteins composed of 80 to 95 percent polypeptide and 5 to 18 percent carbohydrate. The biologic properties of the molecules are determined primarily by their polypeptide moieties, but the function of the carbohydrate components is poorly understood. In their monomeric form, immunoglobulin molecules are composed of two identical heavy chains and two identical light chains as shown in Fig. 109-1.[1] Antigenic differences in the heavy chains can be used to separate immunoglobulins into the five major isotypes: G, M, A, D, and E. Similarly, light chains

Fig. 109-1 A simplified schematic model for an IgG human antibody molecule. Heavy double lines symbolize inter- and intra-chain disulfide bonds; V_L and V_H indicate the variable region of light and heavy chains, respectively. C denotes the constant region. Only one of the two antigen-binding sites is indicated.

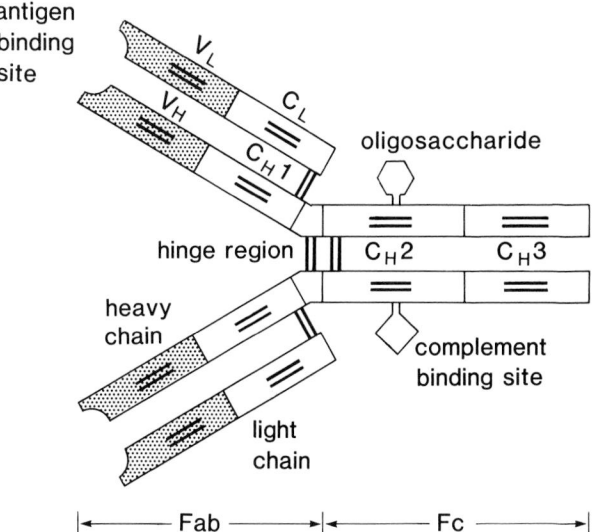

antigen binding site

Nonstandard abbreviations used in this chapter are: C1 = the first component of complement; C3 = the third component of complement; Fab = the antibody-binding or amino-terminal fragment of papain-cleaved immunoglobulin; Fc = the crystallizable or carboxy-terminal fragment of papain-cleaved immunoglobulin; Ig = immunoglobulin; and SCID = severe combined immunodeficiency.

can be divided into κ and λ types. An individual antibody molecule has either κ or λ chains but not both, and the usual κ/λ percentage ratio of Ig molecules is 65 : 35 in human beings. This ratio may vary for different antibodies, suggesting that changes in the κ and λ constituents may be important in recognition of certain antigens. Both types of light chains consist of a single 23,000-Da polypeptide structure. Interchain disulfide bonds formed between cysteine residues are essential to the development of a stable three-dimensional structure. Intrachain bonds separate the chains into domains of relatively constant size, each containing approximately 100 amino acid residues. Greater variability in the amino acid sequence occurs in the N-terminal portion of each chain. These domains, termed the *variable regions* of heavy and light chains, contribute to the antigenic specificity of the immunoglobulin molecule. The C-terminal domains are designated as *constant regions* and are responsible for secondary biologic properties such as transmembrane transport, histamine release from mast cells, and complement fixation.[2]

Studies elucidating immunoglobulin structure were facilitated by the discovery that enzymes could be used to cleave the molecule at specific sites. Treatment with papain cleaves the molecule on the N-terminal side of the disulfide bonds connecting the heavy chains.[3] Three fragments of similar size are produced: one crystallizable fragment (Fc) consisting of the C-terminal ends of the heavy chains and two antibody-binding fragments (Fab) made up of the N-terminal portions of the heavy and light chains. The two Fab fragments from an antibody molecule are identical, and their variable regions make them uniquely suited to recognize and bind the antigenic determinant. The Fc fragment contains binding sites for components of the classic complement system and for surface receptors (Fc receptor) on neutrophils, macrophages, and monocytes. If IgG is digested with pepsin, the molecule is cleaved on the C-terminal side of the interchain disulfide bonds, producing a large F(ab)′2 fragment.[4] The Fc fragment is sensitive to pepsin degradation and is extensively digested.

The immunoglobulins represent a wide variety of proteins that share structural similarities but exhibit diverse antigenic specificity and biologic functions. Differences in the sequence of amino acids produce structural changes in the molecule which, in turn, dictate the biologic properties. The characteristic properties of each immunoglobulin isotype are summarized in Table 109-1.

Immunoglobulin G

IgG is the most plentiful and widely distributed immunoglobulin, accounting for 70 to 80 percent of the total serum immunoglobulins. Four IgG subclasses have been identified and are designated IgG1 to IgG4 on the basis of their relative concentrations in the serum:[5,6] IgG1, 60 to 70 percent; IgG2, 15 to 20 percent; IgG3, 5 to 8 percent; and IgG4, 1 to 5 percent of the total IgG (Table 109-2). The constant region of each IgG subclass is encoded by a separate gene, yet they share greater than 95 percent homology in amino acid sequence.[7] Sequence differences are found primarily in the hinge region of the molecule. The hinge of IgG3 is expanded to more than 100 amino acid residues, accounting for the higher molecular weight of IgG3 compared to other subclasses.[8] Unlike other isotypes, all of the IgG subclasses are passively transferred across the placenta. The half-life of IgG is inversely related to the pool size but normally is 3 to 4 weeks. Maternally derived IgG thus constitutes the majority of the newborn's serum immunoglobulins until endogenous IgG production becomes prevalent at 4 to 6 months of age. Physiological hypogammaglobulinemia occurs during this transitional period but is rarely of clinical significance.

On initial antigen exposure, production of IgG antibodies follows IgM antibody production. Subsequent exposure to antigen induces a rapid and prolonged IgG response, with greater than 90 percent of the antibodies produced in the secondary response being IgG. This anamnestic response and the long half-life of IgG make it well-suited for prolonged immunity. All four subclasses participate in this antibody response but with some selectivity. The IgG1 and IgG3 subclasses contain most of the antibodies to protein antigens. If the antigen is a carbohydrate, IgG2 is the predominate antibody produced.[9] IgG1, IgG2, and IgG3 can fix the classic complement components via their interaction with a specific complement-binding region located in C_H2 domain. IgG4 lacks this ability but may be able to activate the alternate complement pathway. In addition to complement-mediated killing, IgG antibodies promoted microbial opsonization, as macrophages and neutrophils bear receptors for the Fc portion of the IgG complexes. The IgG1 and IgG3 antibody-antigen complexes bind to these cells with greater affinity than do IgG2 and IgG4 complexes. The binding site on the IgG molecule resides in the C_H3 domain, and its interaction with the target cell may result in upregulation of chemotaxis, phagocytosis, mediator release,

Table 109-1 Properties of the Human Immunoglobulin Classes

Property	IgG	IgM	IgA	IgD	IgE
Chains:					
Heavy	γ	μ	α	δ	ε
Light	κ,λ	κ,λ	κ,λ	κ,λ	κ,λ
Number of subclasses	4	2	2	0	0
Molecular weight	150,000	900,000	160–500,000	180,000	200,000
Sedimentation coefficient (S)	6–7	19	7	7–8	8
Percent carbohydrate	4	15	10	18	18
Serum concentration, approximate, in mg/dl	658–1522	54–238	52–364	1–3	0.01–0.05
Serum half-life, days	23	5	6	2–8	1–5
Placental transfer	+	0	0	0	0
Complement fixation (classic pathway)	+	+ + + +	0	0	0
Opsonization	+	+ +	0	0	0
Agglutination	+	+ +	0	0	0
Reaginic activity	0	0	0	0	+ + +

Table 109-2 Properties of the Human IgG Subclasses

Property	IgG1	IgG2	IgG3	IgG4
Molecular weight	146,000	146,000	165,000	146,000
Percent of total IgG	60–70	15–20	5–8	1–5
Serum half-life, days	23–25	23	9–11	21–25
Placental transfer	+	+	+	+
Complement fixation (classic pathway)	+ + + +	+ +	+ + + +	0
Reactivity with staphylococcal protein A	+	+	0	+
Lymphocyte receptors	+	+	+	+
Monocyte receptors	+	0	+	0
Neutrophil receptors	+	+	+	+

and cytotoxicity. All IgG1, IgG2, and IgG4 antibodies bind to protein A present in the cell walls of staphylococci, but the biologic significance of this phenomenon is unknown.

Immunoglobulin M

IgM is the largest of the polymeric immunoglobulins. It normally exists in a 900,000-Da pentameric form in the serum, but is expressed as a monomer on the surface of most B cells and in the serum in various hypergammaglobulinemic conditions. The five structural monomers in pentameric IgM antibodies are arranged in a radial distribution, connected by interchain disulfide bonds and a joining (J) chain. The J chain is a 15,000-Da polypeptide associated with all polymeric immunoglobulin molecules.[10] IgM constitutes 8 to 10 percent of total immunoglobulin and is the first antibody produced during fetal life. The first antibody to be produced after antigen exposure, IgM provides the initial line of humoral defense against infections. Passive transfer of IgM to the fetus does not occur, and consequently elevated levels of IgM in the newborn have been used as an indicator of congenital infection.[11] Its short half-life precludes its ability to provide sustained immunity in the absence of chronic antigen exposure. Stimulation with polysaccharide antigens induces high levels of serum IgM, as exemplified by the antibody response to erythrocyte ABO antigens and endotoxins of gram-negative bacteria.

Each pentameric IgM molecule has 10 antigen combining sites that make it extremely effective in the opsonization and agglutination of bacteria. These properties lead to increased clearance of antigens by the reticuloendothelial system. IgM is also the most efficient complement-fixing antibody. Through its interaction with the first component of complement (C1), one molecule of IgM can activate the classic complement pathway. This property provides an important biologic advantage in the eradication of bacterial infection, but it may also be detrimental as in the case of complement-mediated autoimmune hemolytic anemias. Pentameric IgM is more efficient than the monomeric form in antigen agglutination and complement fixation. Approximately 80 percent of the total IgM is localized to the intravascular space, but exocrine secretions also contain IgM. Secretory levels are particularly high in selective IgA-deficient individuals. Such a compensatory increase in IgM may explain why some individuals with total absence of secretory IgA are asymptomatic.

Immunoglobulin A

IgA antibodies are an important component of the mucosal immune system, being the major immunoglobulin isotype in body secretions. IgA1 exists as a monomer of 160,000 Da and predominates in the circulation, while polymeric IgA2 is slightly more prevalent in secretions.[12,13] Dimeric IgA is by far the most common polymer in exocrine secretions. Secretory IgA is composed of two immunoglobulin molecules connected by a J chain and a secretory component. The secretory component binds specifically to dimeric IgA1 and IgA2 molecules.[14] This 60,000-Da polypeptide recognizes IgA2, binds to it, and facilitates transport of the IgA dimers through epithelial cells to the mucous membrane surface. IgA-producing plasma cells are abundant in the lamina propriae of the intestinal and respiratory tracts, and most of the IgA found in secretions is synthesized locally by these cells.

The role of IgA in the immune response is not precisely understood. It is rarely produced in the fetus in the absence of a congenital infection, and it is the last immunoglobulin to reach adult levels (by the age of 12 to 14 years). IgA antibodies do not activate complement through the classic pathway but may have antibacterial activity in body secretions through their interaction with alternate pathway components. IgA is important in the immune response to orally or nasally administered vaccines such as polio and may be similarly crucial to naturally encountered infectious agents. The primary functions of IgA antibodies may be to prevent the entry of antigen via the mucosal surfaces and to remove antigens from the circulation. The latter function is achieved via the selective transport of IgA-antigen complexes into the biliary collecting systems. Its inability to initiate inflammation by complement activation also makes IgA ideal for removing antigens that have leaked into the circulation from the gut or respiratory tract. Otherwise, a different class of antibody could bind to the antigen and induce a harmful inflammatory reaction though the formation of immune complexes and the activation of complement. The high incidence of autoantibody production and autoimmune diseases in IgA-deficient individuals supports this view.

Immunoglobulin D

This immunoglobulin is coexpressed with IgM on the surface of most B cells but is present in very low concentrations in human serum. The mature B cell represents the first stage of differentiation where IgD expression occurs.[15] Expression ceases following B-cell activation and progression toward terminal plasma-cell differentiation. The specific function of IgD is unknown. Surface IgD can serve as a functional antigen receptor through its ability to bind antigen.[16,17] Stimulation of B cells with anti-IgD antibodies produces increased intracellular concentrations of free calcium and inositol phospholipids, both of which are indicative of early cell activation.[18,19] Thus, IgD may function on the B-cell surface as an important component of the clonal activation mechanism. The small amount of IgD present in the serum makes the investigation of its role as a circulatory antibody difficult, but it is possible that secreted IgD molecules could serve an immunoregulatory role.

Immunoglobulin E

IgE constitutes only a small fraction of the total serum immunoglobulins (0.05 mg/ml); the majority is bound to basophils and mast cells and exists as a 190,000-Da monomer. The fetus does not receive maternal IgE but is capable of limited endogenous synthesis. The low levels of IgE in the newborn gradually increase to adult values before 10 years of age. IgE has the shortest serum half-life of any immunoglobulin class (approximately 2.5 days) and the lowest rate of synthesis (4 to 5 μg per kilogram of body weight per day). The wide distribution of IgE-producing plasma cells in the lymphoid tissue of the gut and respiratory tract suggests that IgE may function in local mucosal immunity. Unlike other species, IgE responses in human beings are long-lived.

IgE antibodies are increased in individuals with allergic diseases and play an important role in hypersensitivity through their characteristic property of high-affinity binding to the Fc receptors on basophils and mast cells.[20] Cross-linkage of this surface-bound IgE by antigens such as ragweed or insect venom induces the release of pharmacologic mediators capable of producing wheal-and-flare skin reactions, bronchospasm, and, in rare cases, fatal anaphylaxis.[21] In addition to its activity in immediate hypersensitivity diseases, IgE is produced in response to parasitic diseases, particularly helminthic infestations. The role that it plays in the immune response to parasites is unclear, but its serum concentration is significantly increased in areas of the world where parasitic diseases are endemic and varies proportionally to the level of parasitic infestation. IgE is similarly increased in selective IgA deficiency and in immunodeficiency diseases characterized by defective

T-cell function (DiGeorge, Wiskott-Aldrich, and hyper-IgE syndromes), suggesting that normal suppressor T cells are involved in the regulation of IgE synthesis.[22-24]

GENERATION OF B CELLS

The development of B lineage cells can be divided into two distinct phases: an antigen-independent pre-B-cell phase and an antigen-dependent B-cell phase (Fig. 109-2). Abortive B-cell development may result from inherited or acquired defects at specific points along this differentiation continuum, as shown in Fig. 109-3. Therefore, the analysis of antibody deficiency diseases is dependent on an understanding of the normal development and differentiation of B lineage cells.

Pluripotential stem cells of mesenchymal origin initially give rise to erythroid and myeloid cells in blood islands of the yolk sac. At approximately 8 weeks of gestation, these cells migrate to the fetal liver, where differentiation along B lineage begins.[25,26] The bone marrow is also populated by stem cells and becomes the primary site of B-cell hemopoiesis later in fetal development and throughout life. Development of B cells begins at the pre-B-cell phase when stem cells give rise to large, immature pre-B cells which do not express immunoglobulin

Fig. 109-2 The development of B lineage cells showing the early antigen-independent and the later antigen-dependent phases. μ indicates μ heavy chain in the cytoplasm of a pre-B cell. Uppercase letters denote immunoglobulin isotypes, and subclasses are indicated by numbers. Secreted immunoglobulin is symbolized by curved arrows. *(Adapted by permission of M.D. Cooper, New England Journal of Medicine; in press.)*

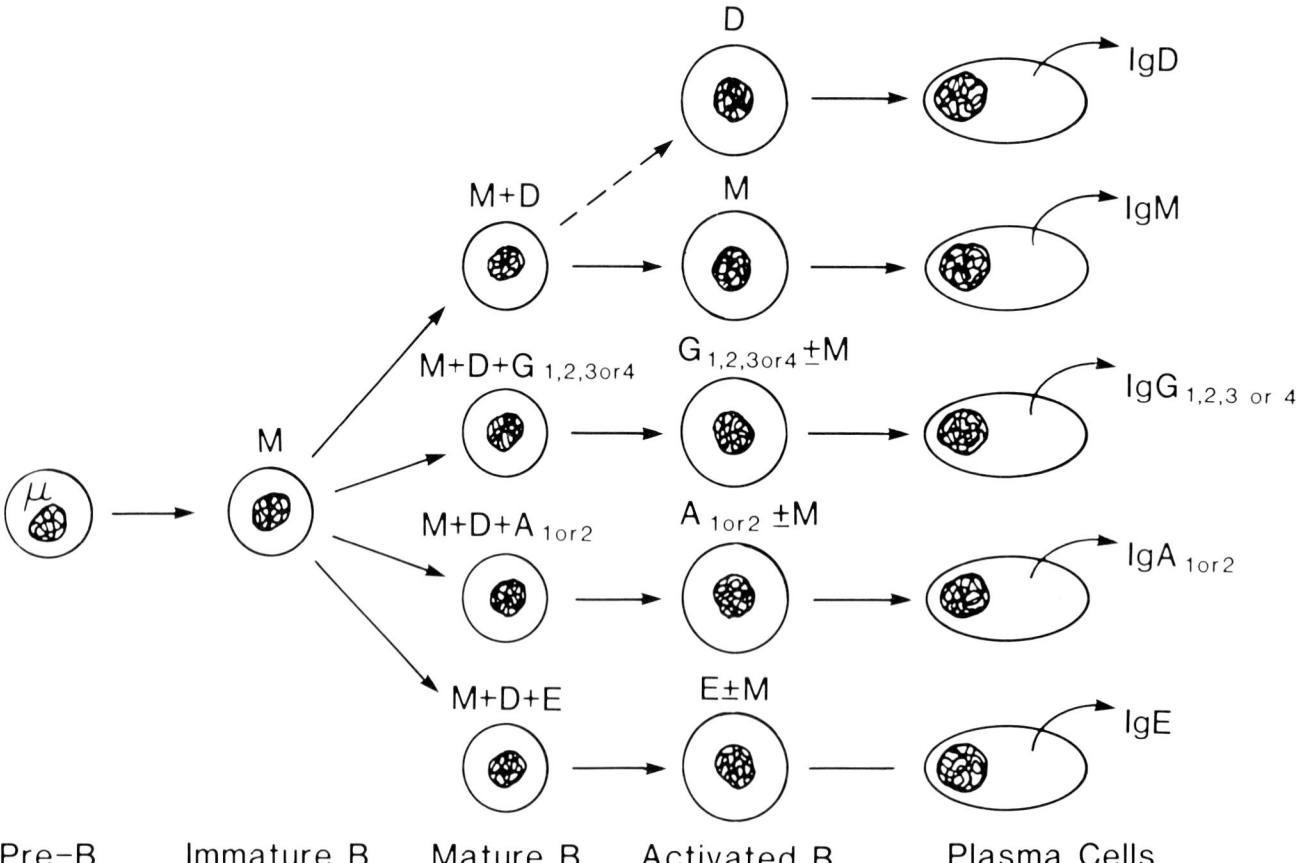

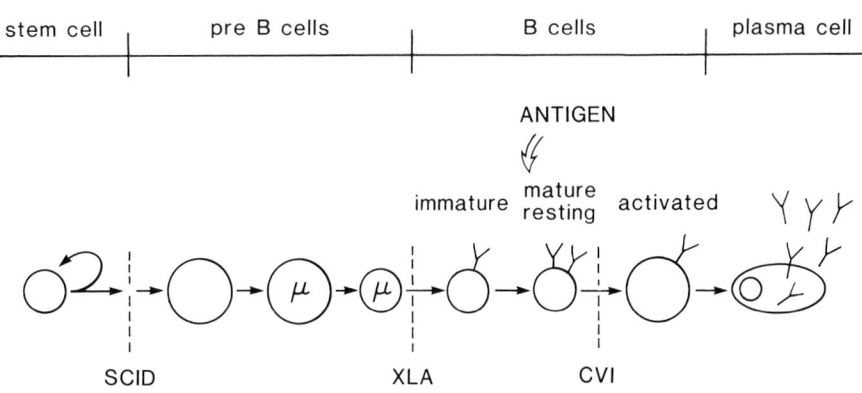

Fig. 109-3 A model of B cell differentiation. μ indicates cytoplasmic μ heavy chain in pre-B cells; Y denotes immunoglobulin molecules. Dashed lines symbolize points along the differentiation pathway where defects may occur in severe combined immunodeficiency (SCID), X-linked agammaglobulinemia (XLA), and common variable immunodeficiency (CVI). (*Adapted by permission of M.D. Cooper, New England Journal of Medicine, in press.*)

heavy or light chains.[27] The subsequent differentiation of large numbers of clonally diverse B cells is dependent on two processes that take place during the antigen-independent phase. The first is an organized sequence of DNA rearrangements and expression of the variable region genes. The second is polyclonal cell proliferation.

IMMUNOGLOBULIN GENE REARRANGEMENTS

Humans produce well over a million antibodies, each with a different antigenic specificity. If each antibody molecule were coded for by a separate gene, the entire human genome would quickly be exceeded. This apparent paradox is answered through an understanding of the pattern of arrangement of genetic information in higher organisms. The nucleic acid message for antibody structure is arranged into patches of DNA coding sequences separated by noncoding intervening segments. These split genes, both DNA coding and noncoding sequences, are first transcribed into RNA. The intervening segments are removed by splicing, and the pertinent coding sequences are joined to form messenger RNA from which the antibody molecule is synthesized. This recombination of gene pieces allows remarkable diversity in the antibody repertoire within the constraints of the genetic information available.

Immunoglobulin heavy and light chains are encoded by genes located on different chromosomes. The heavy-chain genes are present on chromosome 14, κ genes on chromosome 2, and λ genes on chromosome 22. As shown in Fig. 109-4, heavy-chain variable region genes on chromosome 14 are selected for the first DNA rearrangements by translocation of one of the 20 or more diversity (D) genes in juxtaposition with one of six joining (J_H) genes and deletion of the interposed DNA.[28–31] Next, the complete variable region of the heavy chains is encoded by translocating a variable region (V_H) gene on one chromosome to the downstream DJ_H segment to form a VDJ complex. Such an arrangement allows transcriptional enhancer sequences located within the intervening sequence between the J_H and Vμ genes to influence the promoter DNA sequence located 5′ to the transposed V_H leader sequence.[32,33] The constant region (Cu) gene complex is then transcribed and the transcript processed into μ chain mRNA. A "nonproductive" VDJ_H rearrangement occurs when a defective V_H gene is transposed or V-DJ splicing is defective. To prevent an individual B cell from making two heavy chains with different antibody specificities, V_H rearrangement occurs on only one chromosome when a nonproductive VDJ_H rearrangement occurs on the other. The successful completion of heavy-chain

gene rearrangements is demonstrated by the expression of μ heavy chains in the cytoplasm of large pre-B cells.[34–36]

When the VDJ_H rearrangement is productive, a signal is given to begin rearrangement of light-chain variable region genes. The light-chain gene rearrangements occur primarily in small, postmitotic pre-B cells and are usually initiated in the κ gene loci on chromosome 2.[37] The pattern of VJ_L rearrangement and expression is comparable to that described for the VDJ_H gene complex. Transcription begins when a productive VJ_L rearrangement occurs in one light-chain gene locus. When light chain mRNA is formed from the transcript, further VJ_L rearrangements on other chromosomes stop. If a productive VJ_K rearrangement fails on the other chromosome 2, the rearrangement mechanism proceeds to the λ family on chromosome 22.

When the V_L gene is transposed, transcriptional enhancers located between the J_L and C_L genes influence the V_L promoter sequence to make it receptive to binding by regulatory nuclear proteins. Ultimately, transcription of the light-chain gene complex is initiated. When this process is successful, light chains are assembled, and the pre-B cell is converted to an immature B cell expressing IgM molecules on its surface.[36] The expression of surface immunoglobulin molecules is a unique feature of B cells and is necessary for their activation and clonal selection by antigen. Thus, light-chain synthesis heralds the antigen-dependent B-cell phase.

Normal individuals generate millions (approximately 10^9) of B cells in the bone marrow each day. Each clone differs in its immunoglobulin heavy- and light-chain genes and in the antigenic specificity that these genes determine. Newly formed B cells leave the bone marrow microenvironment and migrate to the spleen and then to lymph nodes and other lymphoid tissues.

ISOTYPE SWITCHING

Isotype switching describes the phenomenon by which members of each B-cell clone undergo a change in the heavy chain class of their antibodies from IgM to the production of a different isotype (Fig. 109-2). Switching does not result in a loss or change in antigenic specificity and involves two types of molecular pathways. The first is used by all mature B cells to express IgD on their surface and requires the production of a long VDJ-Cμ-Cδ transcript.[38–40] The transcript is differentially spliced into VDJ-Cμ and VDJ-Cδ messenger RNAs which are used to produce intact μ and δ heavy chains. Mature B cells use this mechanism to express surface IgM and IgD molecules with identical antigenic specificity. The second

A. Human heavy chain genes

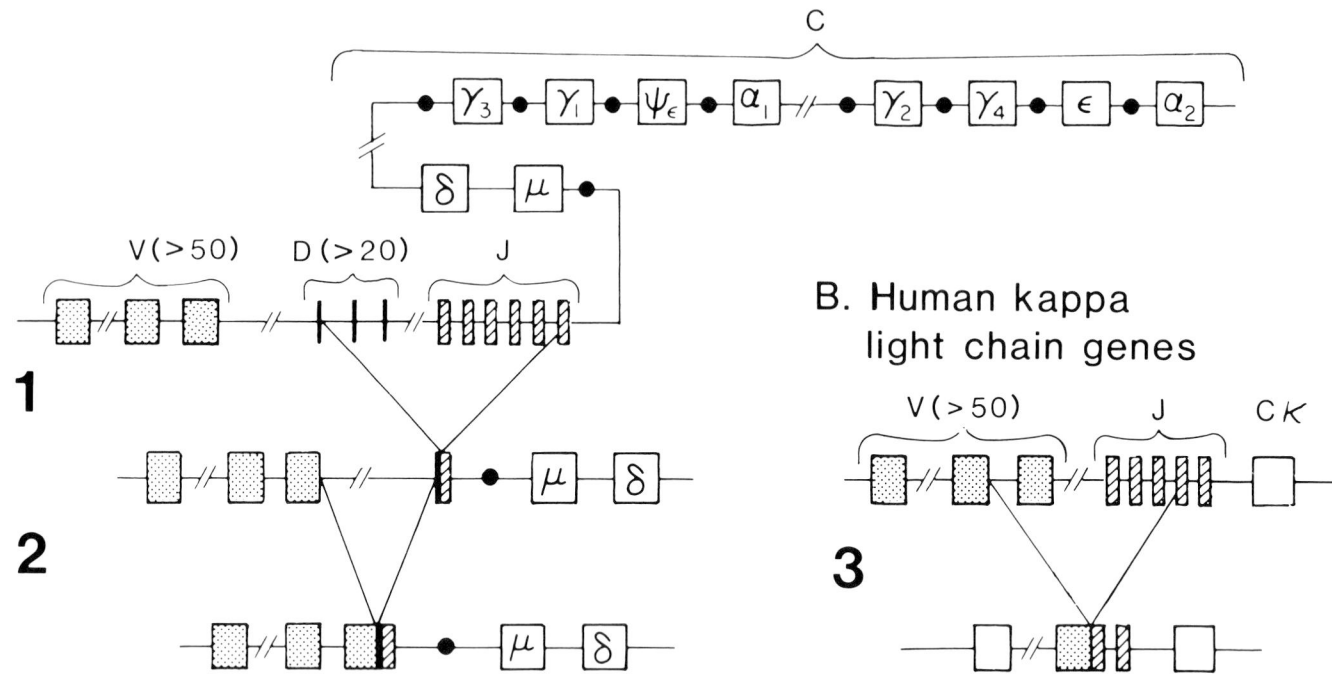

Fig. 109-4 Schematic representation of rearrangement of the human (A) heavy- and (B) light (κ)-chain genes. Open squares indicate the constant (C) region exons; stippled squares symbolize the variable (V) regions; hatched squares and heavy lines denote the joining (J) and diversity (D) segments, respectively. Heavy-chain isotype switch sequences are indicated by solid circles. In Step **1,**

one of the D genes is translocated in proximity to a J gene with deletion of the intervening DNA. Step **2** is completed when a V-region gene combines with the DJH segment to form a VDJ_H complex. Step **3** shows a productive VJ_L rearrangement in one κ light-chain locus. (*Adapted by permission of M.D. Cooper, New England Journal of Medicine, in press.*)

isotype switch mechanism is used by some members of each B-cell clone in the last step in the sequence of immunoglobulin gene rearrangements. Repetitive DNA sequences in a switch (S) region 5' of the Cμ gene are recombined with an S region 5' of a downstream C_H gene to be expressed.[41,42] This recombination event results in the transient coexpression of surface IgM and non-IgM isotypes in B cells undergoing an isotype switch. Relatively few B cells successfully complete the switch from IgM to IgD by deletion of the Cμ gene because there is no well-formed switch sequence between the Cμ and Cδ genes.

B-CELL ACTIVATION AND DIFFERENTIATION

The end product of the humoral immune response is the generation of specific antibody molecules by antigen-stimulated B cells. However, only a small number of the 10^9 cells produced daily participate in this response. The majority die within a few days after migrating to the peripheral lymphoid tissues.[43] B-cell clones which encounter antigens or nonspecific mitogens are selected for survival on the basis of their antibody specificity. Surface immunoglobulin molecules provide the recognition link between the B cell and its specific antigen.[44] Antigen bound to surface antibody molecules is internalized, partially degraded, and reexpressed on the cell surface in association with class II molecules of the major histocompatibil-

ity complex (MHC). Helper T cells recognize the antigen–MHC class II aggregate with their antigen receptor and thus are stimulated to produce B-cell growth and differentiation factors.[45–47] If the antigen is multivalent, antigen-antibody binding results in cross-linkage of surface immunoglobulin molecules and acts as a stimulus to drive the small, resting B cell into the cell cycle.

One of the first steps in the cell activation process is the induction of a membrane phospholipase.[48,49] This enzyme catalyzes the metabolism of membrane inositol phospholipids to inositol triphosphate and diacylglycerol. These metabolites trigger the mobilization of calcium from intracellular stores, resulting in a rapid increase in intracellular free calcium.[50] This may amplify the activity of protein kinase C or modulate the hydrolysis of phosphatidylinositol, leading to increased production of diacylglycerol and secondary activation of protein kinase C. B-cell mitogens such as lipopolysaccharide and phorbol esters may bypass the activation pathway used by ligands which cross-link surface immunoglobulin.[51,52] They interact with the B cell to activate protein kinase C without affecting phospholipid metabolism and intracellular calcium concentrations. Regardless of the activation pathway used, the resultant phosphorylation of intracellular proteins leads to the transmission of external signals to the nuclear genome.

A variety of B surface receptors other than immunoglobulin are expressed during cell activation and differentiation. These molecules serve as communication links between the B cell and other immunocompetent cells to facilitate antibody production. B cells express receptors for B cell stimulatory factor

1 (BSF-1) and interleukin 2, soluble factors produced by activated T helper cells.[53-56] These lymphokines enhance B-cell proliferation and induce the expression of receptors for additional growth and differentiation factors such as transferrin and γ-interferon. Other surface molecules serve as receptors for the C3b and C3d fragments of the third complement component (C3). The C3d receptor also binds the Epstein-Barr virus,[57] indicating that some of these surface molecules have binding sites for multiple ligands.

As differentiation proceeds toward the mature plasma-cell stage, surface immunoglobulin, HLA-DR molecule, and complement receptor expression decline as high rate synthesis and secretion of immunoglobulin molecules ($>10^3$/s) begin. Plasma cells rarely divide and have life spans of only a few days, so their B-cell precursors must be continuously replaced by hemopoiesis in the bone marrow.

A subpopulation of activated B-cell clones do not complete terminal plasma-cell differentiation. These cells, termed *memory B cells,* are characterized by their long life span and heightened antibody responses on secondary exposure to antigen.[58,59]

The age of the individual and the pattern of exposure to environmental antigens influence changes in the B-cell population. This is best illustrated in the ability to generate antibodies to polysaccharide antigens. The capacity to synthesize IgG2, the predominant antibody produced to these antigens, is acquired relatively late in infancy.[60] Immunization with carbohydrate antigens before the age of 2 years produces an IgM antibody response which does not result in durable immunity. Immune responses requiring IgA antibodies are the last to mature. This developmental pattern is reflected in the sequential attainment of adult levels of serum immunoglobulins; IgM at 1 year; IgG at 5 to 6 years; and IgA at 10 to 14 years.

IMMUNOGLOBULIN DEFICIENCY SYNDROMES

Antibody deficiency diseases range from asymptomatic selective deficiency of a single immunoglobulin class to panhypogammaglobulinemia associated with severe, recurrent infections (Table 109-3). This broad spectrum of clinical expression results from variability in the nature and extent of the defect in B-cell development and function. In general, individuals with lower levels of serum immunoglobulins have increased risk of recurrent infections with bacterial, viral, and protozoan pathogens. Unless a defect in T-cell function accompanies hypogammaglobulinemia, fungal infections are rarely a significant problem. Quantitation of serum immunoglobulins permits a rapid diagnosis of antibody deficiency, and when coupled with enumeration of lymphocytes via their differentiation antigens, the stage of the B-cell developmental defect can be determined. Antibody replacement provides effective therapy for many of these diseases.

Congenital X-Linked Agammaglobulinemia

In 1952, Bruton described a young boy with profound hypogammaglobulinemia and recurrent bacterial infections.[61] His report provided the first clinical description of an immunode-

Table 109-3 Antibody Deficiency Diseases

Nomenclature	Presumed pathogenic defect	Serum immunoglobulin levels	B cell number	Inheritance*
X-linked agammaglobulinemia	Block in differentiation from pre-B to B cell	Decrease in all isotypes	Reduced to absent	XL
X-linked agammaglobulinemia with growth hormone deficiency	Unknown	Decrease in all isotypes	Reduced to absent	XL
Common variable immunodeficiency	Low B cell numbers; B-cell maturation arrest; defective T cell help; autoantibodies to B and T cells	Decrease in multiple isotypes	Normal, increased, or decreased	AR, autosomal dominant, or unknown
Selective IgA deficiency	Failure of IgA-B cells to undergo terminal differentiation	Decrease in IgA1 and/or IgA2 +/− IgG subclass deficiency	Normal but with immature phenotype	Unknown
IgG subclass deficiency	Defect in Ig heavy-chain genes or in isotype switching	Variable decreases in IgG1, IgG2, IgG3, and IgG4	Normal	Unknown
Immunodeficiency with elevated IgM	Defective isotype switching	Elevated IgM and IgD; low IgG and IgA	Reduced IgG- and IgA-bearing cells	XL,AR
Severe combined immunodeficiency†	Defective stem-cell differentiation	Decrease in all isotypes	Decreased	XL,AR
Light-chain deficiencies	Intrinsic B-cell defect	Decreased Ig (κ or λ); IgA deficiency in some cases	Normal or decreased	Unknown
Immunodeficiency with thymoma	Intrinsic B-cell defect in some; lack of T-cell help in others	Decrease in all isotypes	Decreased	Unknown

*XL = X-linked; AR = autosomal recessive.
†Severe combined immunodeficiency is classified as a combined immunodeficiency but is included as an important cause of panhypogammaglobulinemia.
Transient hypogammaglobulinemia of infancy has been excluded from this list.

ficiency disease which was long thought to be the result of a developmental defect affecting all B lineage cells. Improved understanding of B cell ontogeny has clarified the pathogenesis of this and other antibody deficiency diseases. Affected males synthesize small amounts of immunoglobulins, making agammaglobulinemia a misnomer. They have normal numbers of bone marrow pre-B cells and a paucity of B cells in the circulation and peripheral lymphoid tissues.[62–64] In contrast, a few patients with X-linked agammaglobulinemia have had normal numbers of B cells, suggesting that there may be two distinct forms of this disease. Heterozygous mothers have normal antibody levels because all of their B cells utilize the normal X chromosome. This evidence suggests that the developmental arrest in X-linked agammaglobulinemia is an intrinsic defect of B lineage cells that prevents the differentiation of pre-B to B cells[65,66] (Fig. 109-3). Epstein-Barr virus infection of bone marrow cells from affected individuals results in transformation of cells at each stage of B-cell development, with the greatest frequency represented by pre-B cells.[67–69] Both pre-B and B-cell lines established in this manner exhibit normal immunoglobulin gene rearrangements and gene product expression. Although the specific defect in X-linked agammaglobulinemia is unknown, it may represent an X-chromosomal defect that inhibits B-cell maturation or a rate-limiting abnormality in VJ_L gene rearrangement.

Patients with X-linked agammaglobulinemia usually remain asymptomatic during the first 6 months of life. At that time passively transferred maternal IgG reaches its nadir, and recurrent infections, particularly otitis media, begin. Subsequently, sinopulmonary infections with *Streptococcus pneumoniae* and *Hemophilus influenzae* assume increasing importance. Repeated infections result in chronic pulmonary disease manifested by abnormal pulmonary function tests and radiographic evidence of bronchiectasis. In unusual cases, pneumonia caused by *Pneumocystis carinii* may be the presenting complaint.[70] Patients usually have intact cellular immunity and respond normally to infections with viruses such as varicella and rubeola.[71,72] Defective production of protective antibodies does not confer long-lasting immunity to viral infections, and patients may develop multiple episodes of chickenpox and measles. Certain viruses pose particular hazards to the agammaglobulinemic patient. Echoviruses and adenoviruses may cause an encephalitis whose course varies from chronic to rapidly progressive and fatal.[73] This central nervous system infection is sometimes associated with a dermatomyositis-like illness.[74] Poliomyelitis has occurred following live-virus vaccination in some patients.[75] Consequently, only killed vaccines should be used in immunodeficient patients. Agammaglobulinemic patients fail to clear hepatitis B virus from their circulation and have a progressive, often fatal, course.[76] Other clinical manifestations of severe antibody deficiency include chronic diarrhea and malabsorption associated with *Giardia lamblia* infestation[77] or rotavirus infection.[78] Children with agammaglobulinemia may develop arthritis indistinguishable from juvenile chronic arthritis,[79,80] and mycoplasma arthritis has been reported.[81] Physical findings include evidence of chronic pyogenic infections, dermatitis, and absent tonsils and peripheral lymph nodes.

The laboratory abnormalities are characterized by extremely low levels of serum immunoglobulins. IgG is usually less than 200 mg/dl, and IgM, IgA, IgD, and IgE are low to undetectable. The presence of maternal IgG in the serum may delay the diagnosis of agammaglobulinemia in infants less than 6 months of age, making IgM and IgA measurements especially useful for early diagnosis. Failure to produce specific antibody following immunization is also helpful to establishing the diagnosis. Pre-B cells are present in normal numbers in the bone marrow of affected individuals, but circulating B cells are rare. T cells are present in normal to increased numbers, and cellular immunity is intact as shown by normal responses to T-cell mitogens and positive delayed hypersensitivity skin tests. Lymph node biopsies, though rarely necessary for diagnostic purposes, demonstrate a lack of primary and secondary follicles.

Antibody replacement with commercial γ-globulin products is the treatment of choice to prevent recurrent bacterial infections. Maintenance of serum IgG levels between 150 and 300 mg/dl is sufficient to prevent most life-threatening infections, but may be inadequate to eradicate chronic sinopulmonary infections and prevent secondary bronchiectasis. These serum levels can usually be achieved by intramuscular injection of 100 mg/kg of IgG at monthly intervals, preceded by a loading dose of 200 mg/kg. Such large doses of γ-globulin make intramuscular replacement uncomfortable for some adult patients. The widespread availability of intravenous IgG preparations provide a needed alternative mode of antibody replacement therapy.[82–85] These preparations provide antibodies of good stability with intact structural and biologic properties. Intravenous γ-globulin in doses of 100 to 400 mg/kg offers the major advantage of delivering increased amounts of antibodies with less discomfort. Intravenous replacement is usually once monthly due to the 28 day half-life of IgG and, in contrast to the intramuscular route, results in significant elevation of serum IgG levels.[86,87] After several weeks of administration, a steady state level is achieved which may be within the normal range for serum IgG until the next infusion is given. Recent evidence suggests that high-dose intravenous γ-globulin replacement is superior to intramuscular therapy in preventing chronic sinopulmonary complications of hypogammaglobulinemia.[88]

Adverse reactions to γ-globulin administration include a symptom complex of diaphoresis, musculoskeletal pain, tachycardia, and hypotension immediately following intramuscular injections or during intravenous infusion.[82,89] These reactions are thought to be mediated by aggregates of IgG in the γ-globulin preparations and can often be avoided by changing to another commercial source. It should be emphasized that commercial γ-globulin is not capable of transmitting virus, particularly the human immunodeficiency virus.

Infusion of fresh plasma, 10 to 20 ml/kg at intervals of 3 to 4 weeks, may be necessary in agammaglobulinemic patients who fail to respond to maximum doses of γ-globulin. This therapy has the advantage of replacing IgM and IgA as well as IgG, although both IgM and IgA have half-lives of only a few days. Plasma therapy has the major disadvantage of potentially transmitting a virus which can produce a devastating infection in the immunodeficient patient. This risk can be reduced by the careful screening of selected donors, usually family members, for the absence of viral infections such as hepatitis B or HIV viruses.

Prophylactic antibiotics may be necessary in some patients with chronic sinopulmonary disease and bronchiectasis. Provision of good pulmonary toilet with regular postural drainage is an important part of the management of these individuals.

X-Linked Agammaglobulinemia with Growth Hormone Deficiency

The association of retarded physical growth and antibody deficiency has been described.[90] In this report, two brothers and their maternal uncles were variably affected with recurrent infections secondary to hypogammaglobulinemia. Marked reduction of all immunoglobulin isotypes was present in three individuals, while the fourth had normal serum levels of IgM and IgA. No circulating B cells were detected in the panhypogammaglobulinemic individuals, and the B-cell number was reduced in the fourth. Immunization failed to induce antibody responses in all. All tests of cellular immunity were normal, suggesting that the immunodeficiency was the result of an isolated B-cell defect. Growth hormone levels were reduced in response to insulin-arginine stimulation, and the reduction was manifested clinically by short stature, delayed puberty, and retarded bone age. A common developmental or biochemical defect explaining the coexistence of antibody and growth hormone deficiency has not been elucidated.

Common Variable Immunodeficiency

This group of immunodeficiency diseases which may be congenital or acquired affects males and females of all ages. Antibody deficiency usually involves all isotypes but can be limited to IgG and IgA, or rarely to selective IgG deficiency. An autosomal recessive mode of inheritance has been demonstrated in certain families,[91] but no definite pattern of genetic transmission can be demonstrated in the majority of cases.

Common variable immunodeficiency can result from many causes.[92] Many cases are due to arrested B-cell maturation (Fig. 109-3). Normal to increased numbers of clonally diverse B cells are produced, but the cells are phenotypically immature and may not be activated by cross-linkage of surface immunoglobulin (Fig. 109-3). Subsequent differentiation to antibody-producing plasma cells does not occur. That the B cells can be activated by phorbol esters, calcium ionophores, and Epstein-Barr virus suggests that an abnormality in signal transduction via surface immunoglobulin could account for the defective plasma-cell differentiation at least in some individuals with this disease.[93] Autoantibodies to B or T cells have been implicated in the pathogenesis of the immunodeficiency in other patients. Abnormalities of cellular immunity, manifested by alterations in T-cell subpopulations, absent delayed hypersensitivity skin test responses, and reduced T-cell proliferation to mitogens, can be demonstrated in a significant number of patients.[94-96] In other common variable immunodeficiency syndromes, deficient lymphokine production or responsiveness has been described.[97-99]

Patients with the acquired form of common variable immunodeficiency can present at any age, although clinical disease is most common during the second through the fourth decades. The pattern of recurrent infections is similar to that seen in X-linked agammaglobulinemia. Respiratory infections predominate and often produce bronchiectasis if inadequately treated. Recurrent or chronic infection with *Giardia* produces diarrhea and malabsorption severe enough to impair adequate nutrition in some patients. Due to the block in B-cell differentiation, large numbers of B cells may accumulate in antigen-stimulated lymphoid tissues to give rise to marked peripheral lymphadenopathy and splenomegaly suggestive of malignancy. Some patients develop intestinal lymphoid hyperplasia and malignancies. Still others manifest findings of autoimmunity, which may include pernicious anemia, hemolytic anemia, idiopathic thrombocytopenic purpura, endocrinopathies, rheumatoid arthritis, systemic lupus erythematosus, and dermatomyositis. Similar autoimmune disorders occur with high frequency in first-degree relatives.

Immunoglobulin levels are usually slightly higher than in X-linked agammaglobulinemia, with IgG values usually less than 250 mg/dl. Specific antibody responses are markedly reduced or absent. A small subpopulation of patients have reduced numbers of circulating B cells, while the remainder have normal or increased numbers of phenotypically immature cells.[100,101] The same treatment principles outlined for X-linked agammaglobulinemia apply to this disease.

Selective IgA Deficiency

This is the most common immunodeficiency, occurring with a frequency of approximately 1 in 600 persons of European ancestry.[102-104] Its occurrence is usually sporadic, but several instances of familial IgA deficiency have been reported. The mode of genetic transmission in these cases has not been determined. IgA deficiency may also result from environmental factors including administration of drugs such as phenytoin[105,106] or as a consequence of congenital intrauterine infection with rubella, toxoplasmosis, or cytomegalovirus.[107] IgA deficiency has been reported in association with abnormalities of chromosome 18,[108] but the vast majority of individuals with the antibody deficiency have no evidence of chromosomal aberrations.[109]

The pathogenesis of IgA deficiency is poorly understood. Almost all affected individuals have IgA-bearing B cells, demonstrating the presence and expression of the $C\alpha_1$ and $C\alpha_2$ genes.[110] Thus, the disorder appears to be a consequence of reduced synthesis and secretion of IgA antibodies.

Most affected individuals are asymptomatic in spite of their inability to make either IgA1 or IgA2 antibodies, but some have an increased number of respiratory gastrointestinal infections as would be anticipated from IgA's role in mucosal immunity. Respiratory tract infections include otitis media, sinusitis, bronchitis, and pneumonia. The infections tend to be less severe than in the panhypogammaglobulinemic patient. In particular, chronic pulmonary disease with secondary bronchiectasis is unusual. Gastrointestinal disease can range from occasional diarrhea to a syndrome of malabsorption and weight loss resulting from gluten-sensitive enteropathy.[111] The pathologic association of IgA deficiency with this enteropathy is unclear, and the gastrointestinal symptoms may resolve when gluten is eliminated from the diet. Infections may increase in frequency and severity as a consequence of reduced antibody response to polysaccharide antigens when IgG2 and IgG4 subclass deficiencies occur in association with IgA deficiency.[112-115] IgA-deficient patients have a high incidence of IgE-mediated asthma and other allergic diseases. Autoimmune diseases such as systemic lupus erythematosus, rheumatoid arthritis, thyroiditis, and dermatomyositis occur with increased frequency in IgA-deficient individuals. These diseases may be mediated by autoantibodies which occur to human immunoglobulins, thyroid antigens, basement membrane antigens, and collagen.[102]

Serum and secretory forms of IgA are markedly reduced or absent, and levels of IgM and IgG are normal. B-cell numbers in the circulation are normal, but IgA-bearing cells appear immature; most of these coexpress IgM.[105] IgG2 and IgG4 subclasses may be diminished, and their decrease is not reflected by the total IgG serum level since they contribute only a small percentage to the total IgG. IgE levels are usually normal but may vary widely from increased amounts in IgA deficiency with atopy to reduced levels in nonatopic patients.[116]

There is no definitive treatment for IgA deficiency. Symptomatic use of antibiotics is the mainstay of therapy. IgA replacement is impractical due to its short half-life. γ-Globulin may be useful in the patient deficient in IgA-IgG who fails to respond to appropriate antibiotic therapy.[117] Administration of any IgA-containing blood products must be performed with extreme caution, however, due to the risk of fatal anaphylaxis mediated by anti-IgA antibodies.[118–121]

IgG Subclass Deficiency

Antibody deficiency resulting from reduced levels of one or more IgG subclasses is being increasingly recognized as a cause of recurrent infections.[112,115] Serum IgG subclass abnormalities may occur in monoclonal gammopathies[122] and in other primary immunodeficiency diseases, notably IgA deficiency,[112] common variable hypogammaglobulinemia,[123] Wiskott-Aldrich syndrome,[124] and ataxia-telangiectasia.[125] The specific defect that causes IgG subclass deficiency is unknown, but there is evidence to suggest a defect in the heavy-chain genes or in the regulation of the isotype switch.[126] Antibodies to protein antigens are primarily IgG1 and IgG3, while the IgG2 subclass constitutes the major source of antibodies to the carbohydrate antigens.[9,127]

Recurrent infections often occur in IgG2-deficient individuals and are manifested by sinopulmonary infections with the encapsulated bacteria *Pneumococcus* and *Hemophilus*. These children also exhibit impaired antibody responses to immunization with the capsular polysaccharide of *Hemophilus influenzae* type B.[128] Progressive impairment in pulmonary function tests has been documented in patients with IgA and IgG2 and/or IgG3 subclass deficiencies.[117] Nonatopic children with chronic lower respiratory symptoms have been shown to have reduced levels of IgG1, IgG2, and IgG4.[129]

Although the diagnosis may be suspected in individuals with recurrent pyogenic infections and low IgG and/or IgA levels, quantitation of the IgG subclasses should be performed. Treatment of the symptomatic individual requires appropriate antibiotics and in severe cases, γ-globulin replacement may be beneficial.

Transient Hypogammaglobulinemia of Infancy

Transient hypogammaglobulinemia results from delayed B-cell development in which normal physiological hypogammaglobulinemia is exaggerated. The actual number of well-documented cases is small, although the incidence has been reported to be from 0.001 to 18 percent of patients investigated for immunodeficiency diseases.[130,131] This apparent discrepancy may be explained by differences in the age-related normal IgG values used for diagnosis. A small group of affected

individuals have immunodeficient family members,[132,133] but the significance of this association has not been determined.

Serum IgG levels fall to 300 to 400 mg/dL between 3 and 6 months of postnatal life as passively transferred maternal IgG is catabolized. Since most transplacental IgG transfer occurs in the last trimester of gestation, premature infants have lower serum IgG levels than full-term newborns and more depressed nadirs. As antigenic stimulation increases, the infant responds by progressive production of antibodies. Normal levels of IgM are attained first, followed by IgG and IgA.

In transient hypogammaglobulinemia, IgG levels remain low for variable periods of time, but all infants recover during the first 2 years of life. There is often no deficiency of IgM and IgA, and the number of circulating B cells is normal. Abnormalities in cellular immunity may contribute to the hypogammaglobulinemia in some cases.[134] Immunization usually induces good antibody responses in these infants. Careful immunologic assessment and periodic reevaluation are essential to differentiate this disorder from other forms of antibody deficiency.

Treatment includes appropriate antibiotics for infections. γ-Globulin replacement may be necessary in rare cases of severe or recurrent infections.

Immunodeficiency with Elevated IgM

The hyperimmunoglobulinemia M syndrome (elevated IgM and IgD and low IgG and IgA levels) can be inherited in both X-linked and autosomal recessive patterns.[135] In other cases this pattern of immunodeficiency follows congenital rubella infections or may be acquired later in life. Defective mechanisms regulating the isotype switch are presumed to be responsible for the defect as there are no detectable abnormalities in the heavy-chain genes or in their switch regions.[136] B cells are essentially normal in number except for an absence of IgG- and IgA-bearing B-cell subpopularions. Chronic antigenic stimulation may underlie the excessive IgM production as a result of the lack of negative feedback control normally provided by IgG antibodies.[137] The pattern of recurrent pyogenic infections is similar to that seen in other antibody deficiency diseases. Specific IgM antibodies may be made following immunization, and antibodies to naturally occurring carbohydrate blood group antigens may be elevated. Neutropenia may accompany the hypogammaglobulinemia and increase the risk of severe infections. Hemolytic anemia, aplastic anemia, and lymphoid malignancy have been associated with this immunodeficiency. Treatment of recurrent infections is similar to that of X-linked agammaglobulinemia. Intravenous γ-globulin replacement may correct the neutropenia.

Severe Combined Immunodeficiency

This profound developmental defect affects both B and T lineage cells and is characterized by impairment of humoral and cell-mediated immunity.[135,138–140] The disease occurs sporadically or can be inherited in either an X-linked[141] or autosomal recessive pattern.[142] It is associated with a variety of biochemical and developmental defects affecting immunocompetent cells. Survival beyond 1 year of age is unusual without treatment.

The Swiss type of severe combined immunodeficiency

(SCID), transmitted in an autosomal recessive manner, is characterized by significant reduction in B- and T-cell numbers. The defect seems to result from faulty differentiation of a common stem-cell precursor (Fig. 109-3). Deficiency of either adenosine deaminase[143] or purine nucleoside phosphoorylase[144] is another cause of SCID. These enzymes are necessary for the normal catabolism of purines, and defects in their production are inherited in an autosomal recessive pattern. Affected individuals accumulate metabolic products toxic for lymphoid cells (see Chap. 40 for a detailed account of these enzyme deficiencies). DNA synthesis is impaired, and variable degrees of immunodeficiency result. An X-linked form of SCID is associated with a marked reduction in circulating T cells and variable numbers of B cells.

Patients with SCID usually die early in life from overwhelming infections with bacteria, fungi, viruses, or protozoa. They are particularly susceptible to infections with *Pneumocystis carinii, Candida albicans,* and cytomegalovirus. During the early months of life, bacterial infections are prevented to some extent by the presence of maternal IgG antibodies. Subsequently, profound panhypogammaglobulinemia becomes evident, and specific antibodies are not made following exposure to antigen. The thymus is small and composed almost entirely of epithelial and stromal elements, and all tests of cellular immunity are abnormal.

The disease can be successfully treated with transplantation of histocompatible bone marrow, usually obtained from a sib.[145–148] Reconstitution of cellular immunity occurs 3 to 6 months after transplantation, while normal antibody production may be delayed by 1 to 3 years.[149] γ-Globulin replacement provides protection from recurrent pyogenic infections until normal humoral immunity is established. Graft-versus-host disease may develop following bone marrow transplantation or after blood transfusion in the untreated patient. Due to the varied nature of infections in these infants, aggressive measures should be used to establish a diagnosis to ensure that appropriate treatment is given. All patients should receive antibiotic prophylaxis for *Pneumocystis* as long as cellular immunity is impaired.

Light-Chain Deficiencies

Variable abnormalities of light-chain synthesis have been reported.[150–152] Primary light-chain deficiency was described in three patients with κ-chain deficiency and one patient with λ-chain deficiency, all of whom had significant distortion in κ/λ chain ratios. Their clinical presentations were varied and included recurrent respiratory infections, diarrhea, achlorhydria, and megaloblastic anemia. One patient with κ-chain deficiency and selective IgA deficiency also had cystic fibrosis and malabsorption. In this case, the immunoglobulins in serum and lymphocytes were completely devoid of κ chains, and when the lymphocytes were stimulated with pokeweed mitogen, the antibodies produced contained only λ chains. In other patients with selective IgA deficiency and/or hypogammaglobulinemia, less severe light-chain abnormalities have been demonstrated. Patients with light-chain deficiency had normal tests of cellular immunity. Antibody responses were diminished in some patients, and in others the number of antibody-producing cells in the bone marrow and gastrointestinal tract was decreased. These findings suggest that a regulatory defect in B lineage cells may account for the disease.

Immunodeficiency with Thymoma

The association of hypogammaglobulinemia with thymoma has been recognized for many years,[153] but the pathogenic link between the two is unknown. In contrast to most patients with common variable immunodeficiency, patients with thymoma and immunodeficiency have reduced numbers of circulating B cells. They also have a significant deficiency of pre-B cells in their bone marrow,[65,154] a feature distinctive from X-linked agammaglobulinemia. These observations suggest that the immunodeficiency results from defective stem-cell differentiation into B lineage cells. Most affected individuals have reduced levels of all classes of immunoglobulins and exhibit impaired responsiveness to antigenic stimulation. The number of circulating T cells is usually normal, but functional tests of cell-mediated immunity such as skin graft rejection and positive delayed hypersensitivity skin tests are often abnormal.

Recurrent sinopulmonary infections are the most common consequence of the hypogammaglobulinemia. Chronic diarrhea, urinary tract infection, dermatitis, stomatitis, and arthritis may also occur. Hematologic abnormalities are common and include thrombocytopenia, anemia (aplastic, hemolytic, or pernicious), leukopenia, and the characteristic feature of profound eosinopenia. Myasthenia gravis has also been associated with thymoma.

Removal of the thymoma often results in improvement in the associated red cell aplasia or myasthenia gravis, but not in the immunodeficiency. Treatment with γ-globulin replacement may be of benefit in preventing recurrent pyogenic infections.

Supported by grants CA 13148, CA 16673, and AM 03555 awarded by the National Institutes of Health; and grant 1-608 from the March of Dimes Birth Defects Foundation.

REFERENCES

1. WASSERMAN RL, CAPRA JD: Immunoglobulins, in Horowitz MI, Pigman W (eds): *The Glycoproteins.* New York, Academic, 1977, p 323.
2. HILSCHMANN N, CRAIG LC: Amino acid sequence studies with Bence Jones proteins. *Proc Natl Acad Sci USA* 53:1403, 1965.
3. PORTER RR: The hydrolysis of rabbit γ-globulin and antibodies with crystalline papain. *Biochem J* 73:119, 1959.
4. EISEN HN: *Immunology,* 2d ed. Hagerstown, Harper & Row, 1980.
5. GREY HM, KUNKEL HG: H chain subgroups of myeloma proteins and normal 7S gamma-globulin. *J Exp Med* 120:253, 1964.
6. TERRY WD, FAHEY JL: Subclasses of human gamma 2-globulin based on differences in the heavy polypeptide chains. *Science* 146:400, 1964.
7. ELLISON J, HOOD L: Linkage and sequence homology of two immunoglobulin heavy chain constant region genes. *Proc Natl Acad Sci USA* 79:1984, 1982.
8. MICHAELSON TE, FRANGIONE B, FRANKLIN EC: Primary structure of the "hinge" region of human IgG3. *J Biol Chem* 252:83, 1977.
9. SIBER GR, SCHUR PH, AISENBURG AC, WEITZMAN SA, SCHIFFMAN G: Correlation between serum IgG-2 concentrations and the antibody response to bacterial polysaccharide antigens. *N Engl J Med* 303:178, 1980.
10. WILDE CE, KOSHLAND ME: Molecular size and shape of the J chain for polymeric immunoglobulin. *Biochemistry* 12:3218, 1973.
11. ALFORD CA JR, WU LYF, BLANCO A: Developmental humoral immunity and congenital infections in man, in Neter J, Milgram F (eds): *The Immune System and Infectious Diseases.* Basel, Karger, 1974, p 42.
12. KUNKEL HG, PRENDERGAST RA: Subgroups of A immune globulins. *Proc Soc Exp Biol Med* 122:910, 1966.
13. KUNKEL HG, SMITH WK, JOSLIN FG, NATVIG JB, LITWIN SD: Genetic marker of the gamma-A2 subgroup of gamma-A immunoglobulins. *Nature* 223:1247, 1969.
14. TOMASI TB JR: Secretory immunoglobulins. *N Engl J Med* 287:500, 1972.

15. VITETTA ES, UHR JW: Cell surface Ig. XV. The presence of IgM and IgD-like receptors on murine B cells. *J Exp Med* 144:852, 1976.

16. SIEKMANN DG, SCHER I, ASOFSKY R, MOSIER DE, PAUL WE: Activation of mouse lymphocytes by anti-immunoglobulin. II. A thymus-independent response by a mature subset of B lymphocytes. *J Exp Med* 148:1628, 1978.

17. SCOTT DW, LAYTON JE, NOSSAL GJV: Role of IgD in the immune response and tolerance. I. Anti-δ pretreatment facilitates tolerance induction in adult B cells in vitro. *J Exp Med* 146:1473, 1977.

18. POZZAN T, ARSLAN P, TSIEN RY, RINK JJ: Anti-immunoglobulin, cytoplasmic free calcium, and capping in B lymphocytes. *J Cell Biol* 94:335, 1982.

19. COGGESHALL KM, CAMBIER J: B cell activation. VIII. Membrane immunoglobulins transduce signals via activation of phosphatidylinositol hydrolysis. *J Immunol* 133:3382, 1984.

20. ISHIZAKA K, ISHIZAKA T, LEE EH: Biologic function of Fc fragments of E myeloma proteins. *Immunochemistry* 7:687, 1970.

21. ISHIZAKA K, ISHIZAKA T: Immune mechanisms of reversed type reaginic hypersensitivity. *J Immunol* 103:588, 1969.

22. POLMAR SH, WALDMANN TA, BALESTRA ST, JOST MC, TERRY WE: Immunoglobulin E in immunologic deficiency diseases. *J Clin Invest* 51:326, 1972.

23. WALDMANN TA, POLMAR SH, BALESTRA ST, JOST MC, BRUCE RM, TERRY WD: Immunoglobulin E in immunologic deficiency diseases. II. Serum IgE concentration of patients with acquired hypogammaglobulinemia, myotonic dystrophy, intestinal lymphangiectasia, and Wiskott-Aldrich syndrome. *J Immunol* 109:304, 1972.

24. BUCKLEY RH, FISCUS SA: Serum IgD and IgE concentrations in immunodeficiency diseases. *J Clin Invest* 55:157, 1975.

25. GATHINGS WE, LAWTON AR, COOPER MD: Immunofluorescent studies of the development of pre-B cells, B lymphocytes and immunoglobulin isotype diversity in humans. *Eur J Immunol* 7:804, 1977.

26. KAMPS WA, COOPER MD: Microenvironmental studies of pre-B and B cell development in human and mouse fetuses. *J Immunol* 129:526, 1982.

27. LANDRETH KS, ROSSE C, CLAGETT J: Myelogenous production and maturation of B lymphocytes in the mouse. *J Immunol* 127:2027, 1981.

28. TONEGAWA S: Somatic generation of antibody diversity. *Nature* 302:575, 1983.

29. ALT FW, YANCOPOULOS GD, BLACKWELL TK, WOOD C, THOMAS E, BOSS M, COFFMAN, R, ROSENBERG N, TONEGAWA S, BALTIMORE D: Ordered rearrangement of immunoglobulin heavy chain variable region segments. *EMBO J* 3:1209, 1984.

30. MAKI R, KEARNEY J, PAIGE C, TONEGAWA S: Immunoglobulin gene rearrangement in immature cells. *Science* 209:1366, 1980.

31. PERRY RP, KELLEY DE, COLECLOUGH C, KEARNEY JF: Organization and expression of immunoglobulin genes in fetal liver hybridomas. *Proc Natl Acad Sci USA* 78:247, 1981.

32. GILLIES DS, MORRISON KSL, OI VT, TONEGAWA S: A tissue-specific transcription enhancer element is located in the major intron of a rearranged immunoglobulin heavy chain gene. *Cell* 33:717, 1983.

33. WABL M, BURROWS PD: Expression of immunoglobulin heavy chain at a high level in the absence of a proposed immunoglobulin enhancer element in cis. *Proc Natl Acad Sci USA* 81:2452, 1984.

34. RAFF MC, MEGSON M, OWEN JJT, COOPER MD: Early production of intracellular IgM by B-lymphocyte precursors in mouse. *Nature* 259:224, 1976.

35. BURROWS PD, LEJEUNE M, KEARNEY JF: Evidence that murine pre-B cells synthesize μ heavy chains but not light chains. *Nature* 280:838, 1979.

36. LEVITT D, COOPER MD: Mouse pre-B cells synthesize and secrete μ heavy chains but not light chains. *Cell* 19:617, 1980.

37. HIETER PA, KORSEMEYER SJ, WALDMANN TA, LEDER P: Human immunoglobulin light-chain genes are deleted or rearranged in λ-producing B cells. *Nature* 290:368, 1981.

38. BLATTNER FR, TUCKER PW: The molecular biology of immunoglobulin D. *Nature* 307:417, 1984.

39. MOORE KW, ROGERS J, HUNKAPILLER T, EARLY P, NOTTENBURG C, WEISSMAN I, BAZIN H, WALL R, HOOK LE: Expression of IgD may use both DNA rearrangement and RNA splicing mechanisms. *Proc Natl Acad Sci USA* 78:1800, 1981.

40. MAKI R, ROEDER W, TRAUNECKER A, SIDMAN C, WABL M, RASCHKE W, TONEGAWA S: The role of DNA rearrangement and alternative RNA processing in the expression of immunoglobulin delta genes. *Cell* 24:353, 1981.

41. DAVIS MM, KIM SK, HOOD LE: DNA sequence mediating class switching in α immunoglobulins. *Science* 209:1360, 1980.

42. HONJO T: Immunoglobulin genes. *Annu Rev Immunol* 1:499, 1983.

43. DEFREITAS AA, COUTINHO A: Very rapid decay of mature B lymphocytes in the spleen. *J Exp Med* 154:994, 1981.

44. RAFF MC, OWEN JJT, COOPER MD, LAWTON AR III, MEGSON M, GATHINGS WE: Differences in susceptibility of mature and immature mouse B lymphocytes to anti-immunoglobulin-induced immunoglobulin suppression *in vitro*: Possible implications for B cell tolerance to self. *J Exp Med* 142:1052, 1975.

45. RIENHERTZ EL, SCHLOSSMAN SF: The differentiation and function of human T lymphocytes. *Cell* 19:821, 1980.

46. REINHERTZ EL, MEUER SC, SCHLOSSMAN SF: The human T cell receptor: Analysis with cytotoxic T cell clones. *Immunol Rev* 74:83, 1983.

47. ACUTO O, FABBI M, BENSUSSON A, MILANESE C, CAMPEN TJ, ROYER HD, REINHERZ EL: The human T-cell receptor. *J Clin Immunol* 5:141, 1985.

48. MICHELL RH: Inositol phospholipids and cell surface receptor function. *Biochim Biophys Acta* 415:81, 1975.

49. HIRATA F, TOYOSHIMA S, AXELROD J, WAXDAL MJ: Phospholipid methylation: A biochemical signal modulating lymphocyte mitogenesis. *Proc Natl Acad Sci USA* 77:862, 1980.

50. FREEDMAN MH: Early biochemical events in lymphocyte activation. I. Investigations on the nature and significance of early calcium fluxes observed in mitogen-induced T and B lymphocytes. *Cell Immunol* 44:290, 1979.

51. SUZUKI T, BUTLER JL, COOPER MD: Human B cell responsiveness to B cell growth factor following activation by phorbol ester and monoclonal anti-μ antibody. *J Immunol* 134:2470, 1985.

52. MONROE JG, NIEDEL JE, CAMBIER JC: B cell activation. IV. Induction of cell membrane depolarization and hyper-I-A expression by phorbol diesters suggests a role for protein kinase C in murine B lymphocyte activation. *J Immunol* 132:1472, 1984.

53. RABIN EM, OHARA J, PAUL WE: B cell stimulatory factor (BSF)-1 activates resting B cells. *Proc Natl Acad Sci USA* 82:2935, 1985.

54. VITETTA ES, OHARA J, MYERS C, LAYTON J, KRAMMER PH, PAUL W: Serological, biochemical and functional identity of B cell stimulatory factor-1 and B cell differentiation factor for IgG1. *J Exp Med* 162:1726, 1985.

55. MURAGUCHI A, KEHRL JH, LONGO DL, VOLKMAN DL, SMITH KA, FAUCI AS: Interleukin 2 receptors on human B cells. Implications for the role of interleukin 2 in human B cell function. *J Exp Med* 161:181, 1985.

56. MIYAWAKI T, SUZUKI T, BUTLER JL, COOPER MD: Interleukin 2 effects on human B cells activated in vivo. *J Clin Immunol* 7:277, 1987.

57. FINGEROTH JD, WEISS JJ, TEDDER TF, STROMINGER JL, BIRO PA, FEARON DT: The Epstein-Barr virus receptor of human B lymphocytes is the C3d receptor (CR2). *Proc Natl Acad Sci USA* 81:4510, 1984.

58. ASKONAS BA, WILLIAMSON AR: Factors affecting the propagation of a B cell clone forming antibody to the 2,4 dinitrophenyl group. *Eur J Immunol* 2:487, 1972.

59. BLACK SJ, TOKUHISA T, HERZENBERG LA, HERZENBERG LA: Memory B cells at successive stages of differentiation: Expression of surface IgD and capacity for self renewal. *Eur J Immunol* 10:846, 1980.

60. ANDERSSON U, BIRD G, BRITTON S: Humoral and cellular immunity in humans studied at the cell level from birth to two years of age. *Immunol Rev* 57:5, 1981.

61. BRUTON OC: Agammaglobulinemia. *Pediatrics* 9:722, 1952.

62. COOPER MD, LAWTON AR: Circulating B-cells in patients with immunodeficiency. *Am J Pathol* 69:513, 1972.

63. PREUD'HOMME JL, SELIGMANN M: Primary immunodeficiency with increased numbers of circulating B lymphocytes contrasting with hypogammaglobulinemia. *Lancet* 1:442, 1972.

64. LUCKASEN JR, SABAD A, GAJL-PECZALSKA KJ, KENSEY JH: Lymphocytes bearing complement receptors, surface immunoglobulins and sheep erythrocyte receptors in primary immunodeficiency diseases. *Clin Exp Immunol* 16:535, 1974.

65. PEARL ER, VOGLER LB, OKOS AJ, CRIST WM, LAWTON AR, COOPER MD: B lymphocyte precursors in human bone marrow: An analysis of normal individuals and patients with antibody-deficiency status. *J Immunol* 120:1169, 1978.

66. TEDDER TF, CRAIN MJ, KUBAGAWA H, CLEMENT LT, COOPER MD: Evaluation of lymphocyte differentiation in primary and secondary immunodeficiency diseases. *J Immunol* 135:1786, 1985.

67. SCWABER J, LAZARUS H, ROSEN FS: Bone marrow-derived lymphoid cell lines from patients with agammaglobulinemia. *J Clin Invest* 62:302, 1978.

68. FU SM, HURLEY JN, MCCUNE JM, KUNKEL HG, GOOD RA: Pre-B cells and other possible precursor lymphoid cell lines derived from patients with X-linked agammaglobulinemia. *J Exp Med* 152:1519, 1980.

69. LEVITT D, OCHS H, WEDGEWOOD RJ: Epstein-Barr virus-induced lymphoblastoid cell lines derived from the peripheral blood of patients with X-linked agammaglobulinemia can secrete IgM. *J Clin Immunol* 4:143, 1984.

70. SAULSBURY FT, BERNSTEIN MT, WINKELSTEIN JA: Pneumocystis carinii pneumonia as the presenting infection in congenital hypogammaglobulinemia. *J Pediatr* 95:559, 1979.

71. JANEWAY CA, APT L, GITLIN D: "Agammaglobulinemia." *Trans Assoc Am Physicians* 66:200, 1953.

72. GOOD RA, ZAK SJ: Disturbances in gamma globulin synthesis as "experiments of nature." *Pediatrics* 18:109, 1956.

73. WILFERT CM, BUCKLEY RH, MOHANAKUMAR T, GRIFFITH JF, KATZ SL, WHISNANT JK, EGGLESTON PA, MOORE M, TREADWELL E, OXMAN MN, ROSEN FS: Persistent and fatal central-nervous system ECHO virus infection in patients with agammaglobulinemia. *N Engl J Med* 296:1485, 1977.

74. MEASE PJ, OCHS HD, WEDGWOOD RJ: Successful treatment of echovirus meningoencephalitis and myositis-fascitis with intravenous immune globulin therapy in a patient with X-linked agammaglobulinemia. *N Engl J Med* 304:1278, 1981.

75. WRIGHT PF, HATCH MH, KASSELBERG AG, LOWRY SP, WADLINGTON WB, KARZON DT: Vaccine-associated poliomyelitis in a child with sex-linked agammaglobulinemia. *J Pediatr* 91:408, 1977.

76. GOOD RA, PAGE AR: Fatal complications of virus hepatitis in two patients with agammaglobulinemia. *Am J Med* 29:804, 1960.

77. OCHS HD, AMENT ME, DAVIS SD: Giardiasis with malabsorption in X-linked agammaglobulinemia. *N Engl J Med* 287:341, 1972.

78. SAULSBURY FT, WINKLESTEIN JA, YOLKEN RH: Chronic rotavirus infection in immunodeficiency. *J Pediatr* 97:71, 1980.

79. JANEWAY CA, GITLIN D, CRAIG JM, GRICE DS: Collagen disease in patients with congenital agammaglobulinemia. *Trans Assoc Am Physicians* 69:93, 1956.

80. GOOD RA, ROTSTEIN J: Rheumatoid arthritis and agammaglobulinemia. *Bull Rheum Dis* 10:203, 1960.

81. STUCKEY M, QUINN PA, GELFAND EW: Identification of ureaplasma urealyticum (T-strain mycoplasma) in patient with polyarthritis. *Lancet* 2:917, 1978.

82. BARANDUN S, KISTLER P, JEUNET F, ISLIKER H: Intravenous administration of human gamma globulin. *Vox Sang* 7:157, 1962.

83. AMMANN AJ, ASHMAN RF, BUCKLEY RH, et al: Use of intravenous γ-globulin in antibody immunodeficiency: Results of a multicenter controlled trial. *Clin Immunol Immunopathol* 22:60, 1982.

84. ROMER J, MORGENTHALER J-J, SCHERZ R, SKVARIL F: Characterization of various immunoglobulin preparations for intravenous application. I. Protein composition and antibody content. *Vox Sang* 42:62, 1982.

85. BUCKLEY RH: Gamma globulin replacement. *Clin Immunol Allergy* 5:141, 1985.

86. MORELL A, SCHNOZ M, BARANDUN S: Build-up and maintenance of IgG serum concentrations with intravenous gammaglobulin in patients with primary humoral immunodeficiency. *Vox Sang* 43:212, 1982.

87. OCHS HD, FISHER SH, WEDGWOOD RJ, WARA DW, COWAN MJ, AMMANN AJ, SAXON A, BUDINGER MD, ALLRED RU, ROUSELL RH: Comparison of high-dose and low-dose intravenous immunoglobulin therapy in patients with primary immunodeficiency diseases, in *Proceedings of Symposium on Intravenous Immune Globulin and the Compromised Host. Am J Med* 76(3A):78, 1984.

88. ROIFMAN CM, LEVISON H, GELFAND EW: High-dose versus low-dose intravenous immunoglobulin in hypogammaglobulinemia and chronic lung disease. *Lancet* 1(8541):1075, 1987.

89. ALVING BM, TANKENSLEY DL, MASON BL, ROSSI F, ARONSON DL, FINLAYSON JS: Contact activated factors: Contaminants of immunoglobulin preparations with coagulant and vasoactive properties. *J Lab Clin Med* 96:334, 1980.

90. FLEISHER TA, WHITE RM, BRODER S, NISSLEY SP, BLAESE RM, MULVIHILL JJ, OLIVE G, WALDMANN TA: X-linked hypogammaglobulinemia and isolated growth hormone deficiency. *N Engl J Med* 302:1429, 1980.

91. WOLLHEIM FA, BELFRAGE S, COSTER C, LINDHOLM H: Primary "acquired" hypogammaglobulinemia, clinical and genetic aspects of nine cases. *Acta Med Scand* 176:1, 1964.

92. ROSEN FS, WEDGWOOD RJ, EIBL M, AIUTI F, COOPER MD, GOOD RA, GRISCELLI C, HANSON LA, HITZIG WH, MATSUMOTO S, SELIGMANN M, SOOTHILL JF, WALDMANN TA: Primary immunodeficiency diseases. *Clin Immunol Immunopathol* 40:166, 1986.

93. CHIEN M, YOKOYAMA W, ASHMAN R: Abnormal membrane depolarization response to anti-μ plus B cell growth factor (BCGF) in B cells from patients with common variable hypogammaglobulinemia. *Fed Proc* 45:982, 1986.

94. WALDMANN TA, BRODER S, BLAESE RM, DURM M, BLACKMAN M, STROBER W: Role of suppressor cells in the pathogenesis of common variable hypogammaglobulinemia. *Lancet* 2:609, 1974.

95. MORITO T, BANKHURST AD, WILLIAMS RC JR: Studies of T- and B-cell interactions in adult patients with combined immunodeficiency. *J Clin Invest* 65:422, 1980.

96. REINHERZ EL, COOPER MD, SCHLOSSMAN SF, ROSEN FS: Abnormalities of T cell maturation and regulation in human beings with immunodeficiency disorders. *J Clin Invest* 68:699, 1981.

97. SAIKI O, SHIMIZU M, SAEK Y, KISHIMOTO S, KISHIMOTO T: Dissociation in the production of B cell stimulating factors (BCGF and BCDF) and interleukin 2 by T cells from a common variable immunodeficient patient. *J Immunol* 133:1920, 1984.

98. PERRI RT, WEISDORF DJ: Impaired responsiveness to B cell growth factor in a patient with common variable hypogammaglobulinemia. *Blood* 66:345, 1985.

99. MATHESON DS, GREEN BJ: Defect in production of B cell differentiation factor-like activity by mononuclear cells from a boy with hypogammaglobulinemia. *J Immunol* 138:2469, 1987.

100. COOPER MD, LAWTON AR, BACKMAN DE: Agammaglobulinemia with B lymphocytes: specific defect of plasma-cell differentiation. *Lancet* 2:791, 1971.

101. PREUD'HOMME JL, GRISCELLI C, SELIGMANN M: Immunoglobulins on the surface of lymphocytes in fifty patients with primary immunodeficiency diseases. *Clin Immunol Immunopathol* 1:241, 1973.

102. AMMANN AJ, HONG R: Selective IgA deficiency: Presentation of 30 cases and a review of the literature. *Medicine* 50:223, 1971.

103. BUCKLEY RH: Clinical and immunologic features of selective IgA deficiency, in Bergsma D, Good RA, Finstad J, Paul NW (eds): *Immunodeficiency in Man and Animals*. Sunderland, MA: Sinauer, 1975, p 134.

104. ROPARS C, MULLER A, PAINT N, BEIG D, AVENARD G: Large scale detection of IgA deficient blood donors. *J Immunol Methods* 54:183, 1982.

105. SEAGER J, JAMISON DL, WILSON J, HAYWARD AR, SOOTHILL JF: IgA deficiency, epilepsy, and phenytoin treatment. *Lancet* 2:632, 1975.

106. DOSCH H-M, JASON J, GELFAND EW: Transient antibody deficiency and abnormal T suppressor cells induced by phenytoin. *N Engl J Med* 306:406, 1982.

107. ROSEN FS: Immune deficiencies: An overview, in Gelfand EW, Dosch H-M (eds): *Biological Basis of Immunodeficiency*. New York, Raven, 1980, p 1.

108. FEINGOLD M, SCHWARTZ RS, ATKINS L, ANDERSON L, BARTSUCAS CS, PAGE DL, LITTLEFIELD JW: IgA deficiency associated with partial deletion of chromosome 18. *Am J Dis Child* 117:129, 1969.

109. HERRMANN RP, CHIPPER L, BELL S: Chromosomal studies in health blood donors with IgA deficiency. *Clin Genet* 22:231, 1982.

110. CONLEY ME, COOPER MD: Immature IgA B cells in IgA-deficient patients. *N Engl J Med* 305:495, 1981.

111. MANN JG, BROWN WR, KERN F: The subtle and variable clinical expressions of gluten-induced enteropathy (adult celiac disease, non-topical spue). An analysis of twenty-one consecutive cases. *Am J Med* 48:357, 1970.

112. OXELIUS V-A, LAURELL A-B, LINDQUIST B, GOLEBIOWSKA H, AXELSSON U, BJÖRKANDER J, HANSON LÅ: IgG subclasses in selective IgA deficiency: importance of IgG2-IgA deficiency. *N Engl J Med* 304:1476, 1981.

113. LUZI G, KUBAGAWA H, CRAIN MJ, COOPER MD: Analysis of IgG subclass production in cell cultures from IgA deficient patients and in normal controls as a function of age. *Clin Exp Immunol* 65:434, 1986.

114. CUNNINGHAM-RUNDLES C, OXELIUS V-A, GOOD RA: IgG2 and IgG3 subclass deficiencies in selective IgA deficiency in the United States. *Birth Defects* 19:173, 1983.

115. UGAZIO AG, OUT TA, PLEBANI A, DUSE M, MONAFO V, NESPOLI L, BURGIO GR: Recurrent infections in children with "selective" IgA deficiency: Association with IgG2 and IgG4 deficiency. *Birth Defects* 19(x):169, 1983.

116. ZEISS CR: Immunologic aspects of immediate hypersensitivity, in Patterson R (ed): *Allergic Diseases*. Philadelphia, Lippincott, 1985, p 52.

117. BJÖRKANDER J, BJÖRN B, OXELIUS V-A, HANSON LÅ: Impaired lung function in patients with IgA deficiency and low levels of IgG2 or IgG3. *N Engl J Med* 313:720, 1985.

118. VYAS GN, PERKINS HA, FUDENBERG HH: Anaphylactoid transfusion reactions associated with anti-IgA. *Lancet* 2:312, 1968.

119. RIVAT L, RIVAT C, DAVEAU M, ROPARTZ C: Comparative frequencies of anti-IgA antibodies among patients with anaphylactic transfusion reactions and among normal blood donors. *Clin Immunol Immunopathol* 7:340, 1977.

120. KOISTINEN J, HEIKKILÄ M, LEIKOLA J: Gammaglobulin treatment and anti-IgA antibodies in IgA-deficient patients. *Br Med J* 2:923, 1978.

121. BURKS AW, SAMPSON HA, BUCKLEY RH: Anaphylactic reactions after gamma globulin administration in patients with hypogammaglobulinemia. *N Engl J Med* 314:560, 1986.

122. SCHUR PH, KYLE RA, BLOCH KJ, HAMMACK WJ, RIVERS SL, SARGENT A, RITCHIE RF, MCINTYRE OR, MOLONEY WC, WOLFSON L: IgG subclasses: Relationship to clinical aspects of multiple myeloma and frequency distribution among M-components. *Scand J Haematol* 12:60, 1974.

123. YOUNT WJ, HONG R, SELIGMANN M, GOOD R, KUNKEL HG: Imbalances of gamma globulin subgroups and gene defects in patients with primary hypogammaglobulinemia. *J Clin Invest* 49:1957, 1970.

124. OXELIUS V-A: Quantitative and qualitative investigations of serum IgG subclasses in immunodeficiency diseases. *Clin Exp Immunol* 36:112, 1979.

125. OXELIUS V-A, BERKEL AI, HANSON LÀ: IgG2 deficiency in ataxia-telangiectasia. *N Engl J Med* 306:515, 1982.

126. HAMMARSTROM L, GRAMSTROM M, OXELIUS V, PERSSON MAA, SMITH CIE: IgG subclass distribution of antibodies against *S. aureus* teichoic acid and α-toxin in normal and immunodeficient donors. *Clin Exp Immunol* 55:593, 1984.

127. STEVENS R, DICHEK D, KELD B, HEINER D: IgG1 is the predominant subclass of in vivo- and in vitro-produced anti-tetanus toxoid antibodies and also serves as the membrane IgG molecule for delivering inhibitory signals to anti-tetanus toxoid antibody-producing B cells. *J Clin Immunol* 3:65, 1983.

128. UMETSU DT, AMBROSINO DM, QUINTI I, SIBER GR, GEHA RS: Recurrent sinopulmonary infection and impaired antibody response to bacterial capsular polysaccharide antigen in children with selective IgG-subclass deficiency. *N Engl J Med* 313:1247, 1985.

129. SMITH TF, MORRIS EC, BAIN RP: IgG subclasses in nonallergic children with chronic chest symptoms. *Pediatrics* 105:896, 1984.

130. HAYAKAWA H, IWATA T, YATA J, KOBAYASHI N: Primary immunodeficiency syndrome in Japan. I. Overview of a nationwide survey on primary immunodeficiency syndromes. *J Clin Immunol* 1:31, 1981.

131. TILLER TL JR, BUCKLEY RH: Transient hypogammaglobulinemia of infancy: Review of the literature, clinical and immunologic features of 11 new cases, and long-term follow-up. *J Pediatr* 92:347, 1978.

132. SOOTHILL JF: Immunoglobulins in first-degree relatives of patients with hypogammaglobulinemia: Transient hypogammaglobulinemia: A possible manifestation of heterozygocity. *Lancet* 1:1001, 1968.

133. RIEGER CHI, NELSON LA, PERI BA, LUSTIG JV, NEWCOMB RW: Transient hypogammaglobulinemia of infancy. *J Pediatr* 91:601, 1977.

134. SIEGEL RL, ISSEKUTZ T, SCHWABER J, ROSEN FS, GEHA RS: Deficiency of T helper cells in transient hypogammaglobulinemia of infancy. *N Engl J Med* 305:1307, 1981.

135. ROSEN FS, COOPER MD, WEDGWOOD RJP: The primary immunodeficiencies. *N Engl J Med* 311:235, 1984.

136. BURROWS PD, KUBAGAWA H, BORZILLO GV, COOPER MD: Immunoglobulin isotype switching in humans, in Singhal SK, Delovitch TL (eds): *Mediators of Immune Regulation and Immunotherapy*. New York, Elsevier, 1986, p 158.

137. GOLDMAN AS, RITZMANN SE, HOUSTON EW, SIDWELL S, BRATCHER R, LEVIN WC: Dysgammaglobulinemic antibody deficiency syndrome: Increased M-globulins and decreased G- and A-globulins. *J Pediatr* 70:16, 1967.

138. GLANZMANN E, RINIKER P: Essentielle lymphocytophthise. Ein neues Krankheitsbild aus der Sauglings-pathologie. *Ann Paediatr (Basel)* 175:1, 1950.

139. COTTIER H: Zur Histopathologie des Antikorpermangel-syndroms. *Trans 6th Congr Eur Soc Haematol, Copenhagen, 1957*. Basel, Karger, 1958.

140. HITZIG WH, BIRO Z, BOSCH H, HUSER HJ: Agammaglobulinamie und Alymphozytose mit Schwund des lymphatischen Gewebest. *Helv Paediatr Acta* 13:551, 1958.

141. GITLIN D, CRAIG JM: The thymus and other lymphoid tissues in congenital agammaglobulinemia. I. Thymic alymphoplasia and lymphocytic hypoplasia and their relation to infection. *Pediatrics* 32:417, 1963.

142. TOBLER R, COTTIER H: Familiare lymphopenie mit Agammaglobulinamie und schwere Moniliasis: Die "essentielle Lymphocytophthise" als besondere Form der fruhkindlichen Agammaglobulinamie. *Helv Paediatr Acta* 13:313, 1958.

143. GIBLETT ER, ANDERSON JE, COHEN F, POLLARA B, MEUWISSEN JH: Adenosinedeaminase deficiency in two patients with severely impaired cellular immunity. *Lancet* 2:1067, 1972.

144. GIBLETT ER, AMMANN AJ, WARA DW, SANDMAN R, DIAMOND LK: Nucleoside-phosphorylase deficiency in a child with severely defective T-cell immunity and normal B-cell immunity. *Lancet* 1:1010, 1975.

145. GATTI RA, MEUWISSEN HJ, ALLEN HD, HONG R, GOOD RA: Immunological reconstitution of sex-linked lymphopenic immunological deficiency. *Lancet* 2:1366, 1968.

146. LEVEY RH, KLEMPERER MR, GELFAND WE, SANDERSON AR, BATCHELOR RJ, BERKEL AI, ROSEN FS: Bone-marrow transplantation in severe combined immunodeficiency syndrome. *Lancet* 2:571, 1971.

147. RADL J, DOOREN LJ, EJSVOOGEL VP, VAN WENT JJ, HIJMANS W: An immunological study during post-transplantation follow-up of a case of severe combined immunodeficiency. *Clin Exp Immunol* 10:367, 1972.

148. O'REILLY RJ, DUPONT B, PAHWA S, GRIMES E, SMITHWICK EM, PAHWA R, SCHWARTZ S, HANSEN JA, SIEGAL FP, SORRELL M, SVEJGAARD A, JERSILD C, THOMSEN M, PLATZ P, L'ESPERANCE P, GOOD RA: Reconstitution in severe combined immunodeficiency by transplantation of marrow from an unrelated donor. *N Engl J Med* 297:1311, 1971.

149. BUCKLEY RH, SCHIFF SE, SAMPSON HA, SCHIFF RI, MARKERT JML, KNUTSEN AP, HERSHFIELD MS, HUANG AT, MICKEY GH, WARD FE: Development of immunity in human severe primary T cell deficiency following haplo-identical bone marrow stem cell transplantation. *J Immunol* 136:2398, 1986.

150. BERNIER GM, GUNDERMAN JR, RUYMANN FB: Kappa-chain deficiency. *Blood* 40:795, 1972.

151. BARANDUN S, MORRELL A, SKVARIL F, OBERDORFER A: Deficiency of κ- or λ-type immunoglobulins. *Blood* 47:79, 1976.

152. ZEGERS BJM, MAETZDORF WJ, VAN LOGHEM E, MUL NAJ, STOOP JW, VAN DER LAAG J, VOSSEN JJ, BALLIEUX RE: Kappa-chain deficiency. An immunoglobulin disorder. *N Engl J Med* 294:1026, 1976.

153. JEUNET FS, GOOD RA: Thymoma, immunologic deficiencies and hematologic abnormalities, in Bergsma D, Good RA (eds): *Immunologic Deficiency Diseases in Man*. National Foundation: *Birth Defects* vol 4, no 1. Baltimore, Williams & Wilkins, 1968, p 192.

154. LITWIN SD: Immunodeficiency with thymoma: Failure to induce Ig production in immunodeficiency lymphocytes cocultured with normal T cells. *J Immunol* 122:728, 1979.

CHAPTER 110

GENETIC IMMUNODEFICIENCY SYNDROMES WITH DEFECTS IN BOTH T- AND B-LYMPHOCYTE FUNCTIONS

R. MICHAEL BLAESE

1. *During the development of mature T- and B-lymphocyte populations, similar molecular mechanisms are involved in the assembly of receptors from discontinuous genetic elements coding for variable and constant regions of these receptor molecules. When T cells or B cells fail to function appropriately, distinct clinical disorders occur which are characterized by increased infections with different classes of microorganisms.*

2. *Severe combined immunodeficiency (SCID) is a heterogeneous group of disorders characterized by profound functional deficiency in both cellular (T-cell) and humoral (B-cell) immunity. SCID may be inherited as an autosomal recessive or X-linked trait. About 30 percent of SCID is associated with deficiency of the purine catabolic enzyme adenosine deaminase (ADA). SCID may occur along with agranulocytosis (reticular dysgenesis), an absence of cell surface major histocompatibility antigens (bare lymphocyte syndrome), absence of all lymphocytes (Swiss type), and with preserved B-cell numbers (SCID with B cells). The biochemical defect leading to the dual system immunodeficiency in SCID is not known except in the case of ADA deficiency. Carrier heterozygotes with ADA deficiency can be identified because they express only half-normal ADA levels. Carriers of X-linked SCID can also be detected, because these females demonstrate unbalanced X-chromosome inactivation in their peripheral T cells.*

3. *Ataxia telangiectasia (AT) is an autosomal recessive multisystem disorder consisting of profound neurologic disability, oculocutaneous telangiectasia, and variable immunologic deficiency. The patients develop disabling cerebellar ataxia and chorioathetosis early in life with recurrent infections appearing somewhat later and correlating with the degree of immunodeficiency. Both humoral and cellular immune responses may be defective, and the patients have a high incidence of neoplasia. The thymus is embryonic in appearance, and patients have persistent production of α-fetoprotein. Fibroblasts from AT patients have a markedly reduced colony-forming ability in vitro following x irradiation and are presumed to have a defect in DNA repair. There is a very high incidence of chromosomal translocations and breaks in T-cell leukemias and lymphoblastoid cell lines from AT patients, centered in areas of the T-cell receptor genes and the immunoglobulin genes, genetic segments known to undergo breaks, rearrangements, deletions, and repair of DNA.*

4. *The Wiskott-Aldrich syndrome is an X-linked disease defined by the triad of recurrent infections with all classes of microorganisms, hemorrhage secondary to thrombocytopenia with microplatelets, and eczema. These patients have a unique dual system immunodeficiency with selective defects in both the T- and B-cell systems as well as selective functional defects in monocytes, granulocytes, and platelets. Their selective inability to produce antibodies to polysaccharide antigens is an immunologic defect unique to this disease. Autoimmune disease is a major complicating factor, and malignancy also occurs in high frequency. Splenectomy corrects the thrombocytopenia and results in conversion of the platelets from small to normal size, indicating that this part of the "classic" triad is a secondary phenomenon. The primary defect is unknown, but defects in the cell membrane glycoprotein sialophorin have been demonstrated. Carriers can be detected because they demonstrate a nonrandom pattern of X-chromosome inactivation in their T cells, B cells, and granulocytes.*

Until the 1960s, immunodeficiency was a vaguely defined concept developed in response to patients who were experiencing an increased susceptibility to infections. Confusion existed because classes of infectious agents that seemed to dominate the clinical picture in one patient appeared to cause no difficulty at all for another patient. Understanding of the immunodeficiency diseases was greatly enhanced when the two-component makeup of the immune system was delineated. Studies in mice and chickens established the presence of two distinct and complementary systems, the T-cell, or cellular immune, system, and the B-cell, or humoral immune, system.[1]

The T-cell population consists of lymphocytes that arise from precursor cells migrating to the thymus, an epithelial structure embryonically derived from the third and fourth pharyngeal pouches. T cells mature into subsets that perform an array of different functions ranging from the killing by cytotoxic cells of virus-infected host tissues or foreign tissue grafts, to the synthesis and secretion of biologically active mediator molecules (the lymphokines), to important immunoregulatory functions such as helper and suppressor activities.

B cells arise in the bursa of Fabricius in birds and in the fetal liver and bone marrow in mammals and mature to cells specialized for antibody secretion. The T-cell system and the B-cell system interact in an exquisitely complex dance involving positive and negative regulatory effects resulting in the final expression of immunity. Because of the complexity of the interactions involved, there are many potential sites where defects can occur leading to altered immune function.

Study of patients with severe T-cell defects revealed an increased incidence of serious infections with agents such as *Monilia*, *Pneumocystis carinii*, herpes zoster, cytomegalovirus,

---

Nonstandard abbreviations used in this chapter are: ADA = adenosine deaminase; AT = ataxia telangiectasia; GVHD = graft-versus-host disease; MHC = major histocompatibility; PEG = polyethylene glycol; SCID = severe combined immunodeficiency; WAS = Wiskott-Aldrich syndrome.

and other "opportunistic organisms." These patients experience chronic thrush, interstitial pneumonitis, and intractable diarrhea. They frequently develop generalized vaccinia following smallpox vaccination and generalized BCGosis if immunized with viable Bacille Calmette-Guérin. By contrast, patients with defective antibody production experience recurrent infections with high grade encapsulated organisms such as pneumococci and *Hemophilus influenzae*. These patients present with recurrent otitis media, sinusitis, bronchitis, and pneumonia. Fulminant bacterial sepsis and meningitis are commonly seen whereas significant infection with herpesviruses such as varicella-zoster or cytomegalovirus are not.

DIFFERENTIATION OF B AND T CELLS AND THEIR ANTIGEN RECEPTORS

Antibody-producing cells develop through a series of differentiation stages that mirror the molecular events leading to the expression of immunoglobulin molecules.[2] In the first recognizable stage along the B-cell pathway, hematopoietic precursors differentiate to become cells containing μ immunoglobulin heavy-chain molecules in their cytoplasm.[3] This is termed the *pre-B cell stage*, and since pre-B cells lack surface expressed immunoglobulin molecules, they are not directly stimulated by antigens in their environment.

Pre-B cells divide and then begin to synthesize immunoglobulin light-chain molecules. These combine with the μ heavy chains to form complete IgM molecules which then become expressed on the cell surface. These immature B cells (or Bμ cells) differentiate further to express both IgM and IgD on their surfaces (B$\mu\delta$). These cells may then undergo class switch to form B cells expressing other membrane-bound immunoglobulin isotypes and ultimately mature to become plasma cells. At this stage there is conversion from the synthesis of membrane to secretory type immunoglobulin and an increase in the production rate of the secretory immunoglobulin molecules (IgM, IgG, IgA, and IgE).

The genes that specify the structure of each antibody (or T-cell receptor) are not present as such in the germline. They are found as discontinuous DNA segments in the nonlymphoid cells of the body.[4–8] During differentiation of precursor stem cells to antibody-producing cells, a series of rearrangements of the immunoglobulin genes occurs that both activates these genes and serves to amplify the diversity of the resulting gene products. Individual mutations also increase the diversity of B-cell products such that millions of different distinct immunoglobulin molecules can be generated by the B-cell system. In T cells, genes encoding the antigen receptor are also shuffled as precursor cells develop into mature T lymphocytes resulting in diversity of these immune receptors in a similar fashion.

The detailed account of immunoglobulin gene rearrangement and activation has been presented in Chap. 109. The immunoglobulin chain genes are located at band q32 of chromosome 14, the κ light-chain genes at band p11 of chromosome 2, and the λ light-chain genes at band q11 on chromosome 22.[9–12] As the precursor stem cells differentiate to pre-B cells, DNA rearrangement occurs, bringing the separate gene segments found in the germline into continuity. The heavy-chain gene family contains several hundred variable (V_H) re-

gion genes that encode the first 95 amino acids of the variable portion of the heavy chain, more than 20 diversity (D) region genes that encode the next few amino acids, six joining (J_H) region genes that encode the final 13 amino acids of the variable region, and then a series of nine functional constant (C_H) region genes.[13] As the initial event, a single D_H segment is combined with a single J_H through a process of DNA rearrangement. Following DJ_H joining, a single V_H element is combined with this DJ segment. As a consequence of this VDJ_H joining, a promotor sequence present 5' to the V_H segment is brought close to a tissue-specific enhancer sequence located 3' to the J region, between the J and C genes.[14,15] This then activates the gene complex, increasing transcription of mRNA for the heavy-chain gene utilizing the first of the C_H gene segments, that for μ. This results in production of cytoplasmic μ chain and thus the appearance of the pre-B cell.

Following an effective heavy-chain gene rearrangement, the light-chain genes rearrange beginning with the κ locus. If the κ genes fail to achieve an effective rearrangement, activation of the λ genes occurs.[16,17] With the generation of an effective light-chain gene, mRNA is translated into intact light chains, and this is followed by the assembly of complete IgM molecules and their expression on the cell surface, marking the B-cell stage of differentiation. B cells and their progeny produce only one of the two possible light-chain types. However, B cells can produce both IgM and IgD simultaneously and are capable of switching subsequently to produce other immunoglobulin isotypes. The simultaneous production of IgM and IgD as well as the transition from membrane-bound Ig to the production of the secreted form involves alternative mRNA splicing.[18,19] The conversion of a B cell expressing IgM and IgD to a B cell expressing another isotype involves a process known as *heavy-chain class switch*. The heavy-chain constant region genes are found on chromosome 14 in the order 5'-Cμ-Cδ-Cγ_3-Cγ_1-C(pseudo)ϵ-Cα_1-C(pseudo)γ-Cγ_2-Cγ_4-Cϵ-Cα_2-3'.[20] In class switch, an area known as the *switch region* located 5' to each C_H gene is spliced to the switch region of the downstream heavy-chain C region to be expressed.[21–24] During such recombination, deletion of the DNA between the two switch regions occurs allowing a new constant region to be transcribed with the preexisting VDJ_H recombined variable region gene.

T cells are also derived from pleuripotent stem cells which mature and differentiate under the influence of the microenvironment of the thymus. During maturation, T cells express a variety of cell membrane glycoproteins which correlate with the functional properties of the differentiated cells.[25,26] The most primitive cells in the thymus express CD7 (3A1, leu9) and the receptor for sheep red cells, CD2 (T_{11}). Subsequently, thymocytes coexpress CD4 (leu3, T4) and CD8 (leu2, T8) and finally express CD3 (leu4, T3) as well as the T-cell receptor for antigen. Mature T cells leaving the thymus express CD4 or CD8, but not both, and these cell populations represent distinct functional classes of cells. While the immoglobulin receptors on B cells can recognize free antigen, T lymphocytes recognize only antigens that have been "processed" or degraded and are presented on the surface of macrophages and other cells in conjunction with membrane molecules of the major histocompatibility locus (MHC). Helper T cells corecognize antigen in association with MHC class II (HLA-DR,-DS,-DQ) molecules, with the T-cell CD4 molecules involved in this class II restricted recognition process. Thus,

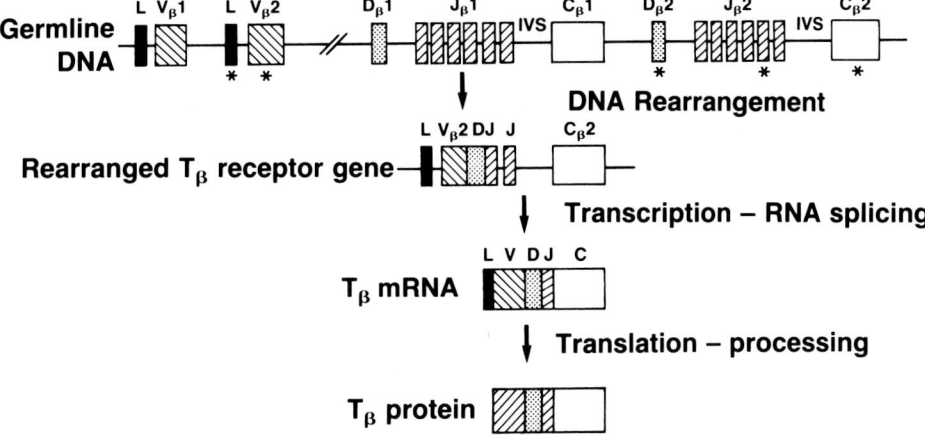

Fig. 110-1 The arrangement of the human T-cell receptor β-chain gene locus. Multiple variable (Vβ) regions exist, each with an associated leader (L) sequence. There are two alternative diversity (Dβ) segments and two sets of six alternative joining (Jβ) segments encoding the remainder of the variable region. There are also two alternative constant (Cβ) region elements per allele. DNA rearrangements lead to the juncture of a single V with a single D and a single J element. When the gene is activated, RNA is transcribed and the intervening sequences (IVS) are removed by RNA splicing. The leader sequence is removed after translation and the processed protein is inserted into the T-cell surface membrane in association with the T-cell receptor α-chain protein and the molecules of the T3 complex. In this example, the germline elements marked (*) have rearranged to form the active gene.

most helper T cells are included in the CD4 T-cell subpopulation.[27,28] Cytotoxic T cells also recognize foreign antigens associated with MHC. In those cases in which the cytotoxic T cell responds to antigens in association with class I MHC molecules (HLA-ABC), the CD8 T-cell subpopulation is involved.[28] When the cytotoxic T cell recognizes antigens in association with class II MHC molecules, the T cells are in the CD4 subset.

The T-cell receptor for antigen is a disulfide-linked heterodimer consisting of a 45- to 50-kDa α subunit and a 40- to 45-kDa β subunit.[29-31] Both α and β chains consist of constant and variable domains, and these two chains are part of a macromolecular complex including several nonpolymorphic polypeptides recognized by anti-CD3 monoclonal antibodies. The α and β chains appear to recognize antigen, while the CD3 complex appears to transduce the signal to the nucleus, initiating cellular activation.

The α and β genes of the T-cell receptor have variable (V), joining (J), and constant (C) regions similar to those of the immunoglobulin genes, and diversity (D) region elements have been identified for at least the β chain (Fig. 110-1). The Tα genes are located at q11 of chromosome 14. The Tβ genes are at q32 on chromosome 7. In addition to the α- and β-chain genes, other rearranging genetic elements have been found in some T cells. These elements code for the γ and δ chains, which appear to mark a T-cell subpopulation bearing a different type of antigen receptor. The Tγ genes are found at p15 on chromosome 7.[32-42]

Although the details of T-cell receptor molecular genetics are less well understood than those of the B-cell immunoglobulins, the recombinatorial processes for the generation of the T-cell antigen receptor are roughly similar to those used by the B-cell immunoglobulin genes. In fact, a common recombinase performs all of the many variable region gene assembly events of both B and T cells. When unjoined Dβ and Jβ T-cell receptor gene segments were introduced into B-cell precursor lines that carry out immunoglobulin gene rearrangements, the T-cell segments rearranged as efficiently as did the immunoglobulin D_H and J_H gene segments.[43]

SEVERE COMBINED IMMUNODEFICIENCY

Severe combined immunodeficiency (SCID) is the most extreme form of the inherited primary immunodeficiency diseases. It is characterized by profound defects in both the humoral and cell-mediated immune systems. A positive family history is obtained in about 50 percent of cases with SCID. Within this disease classification are several distinct disorders that have different modes of inheritance and different patterns of cellular deficiency. Both autosomal recessive and X-linked modes of inheritance have been demonstrated in SCID.[44,45] Other forms of SCID are characterized by an absence of all lymphocytes, or by an absence of T cells with preservation of B-cell numbers. By definition SCID is a disorder of infancy, since the immune deficit is so profound that children usually die of infection in the first weeks or months of life.

Clinical Features

Infants with SCID present with infections within the first weeks of life. Recurrent pneumonia, failure to thrive, chronic diarrhea, and persistent *Candida* infection of the mouth, esophagus, and skin of the face and diaper area are common. These children are susceptible to infections with all types of microorganisms, but infections with opportunistic pathogens tend to dominate the clinical picture. Death has resulted from generalized chickenpox, measles with Hecht pneumonia and cytomegalovirus and adenovirus infection. In addition to infections, many children with SCID have developed graft-versus-host disease (GVHD) following transfusions of whole blood containing immunocompetent T lymphocytes from adult donors. Maternal lymphocytes entering the fetal circulation during labor and delivery or during gestation have also caused GVHD in infants with SCID.[46] When smallpox vaccination was routinely employed, inoculated SCID infants regularly developed generalized vaccinia. Paralytic poliomyelitis has also occurred following administration of live attenuated polio vaccine to infants with SCID.

The physical examination of infants with SCID shows evidence of acute and chronic infection and failure to thrive. Lymph nodes are not palpable, and the tonsils and adenoids are absent. Chest x-ray may show evidence of infection but will also reveal the absence of a thymic shadow.

Immunologic Defects

SCID is a dual system immune deficiency disease with profound functional defects in both the T and B immune systems. Careful laboratory evaluation may disclose considerable heterogeneity with certain portions of the immune system preserved essentially intact in some patients. The levels of serum IgM, IgA, and IgG are usually extremely low, but a few patients have been found with normal amounts of one or more of the immunoglobulin isotypes.[47] Antibody responses, however, have been almost universally absent. B lymphocytes may be absent in some SCID patients, while others may have almost normal numbers of B cells. In these patients B cells may account for all the circulating lymphocytes, since T-cell deficiency is the norm for their disease.

All tests of cell-mediated immunity are abnormal in SCID. Numbers of peripheral blood T cells are depressed to less than 10 percent of normal in 90 percent of SCID patients.[48] All patients are anergic to recall skin test antigens and cannot be sensitized to new antigens. They are even unresponsive to intradermal administration of phytohemagglutinin and have a profound defect in skin allograft rejection.[49] In vitro T-cell function tests are markedly impaired with defective proliferative responses to mitogens, lack of cytotoxic T-cell activity, and absent T-cell immunoregulatory activity.

Genetics and Pathogenesis

SCID is a diagnostic category containing a heterogeneous group of disorders with the presence of dual system immunodeficiency as the common feature, and therefore no single pathogenic mechanism is operative in all cases. There are autosomal recessive as well as X-linked forms of SCID. Many of the immundeficiency diseases of human beings appear to represent disorders of lymphocyte differentiation, and several of the various forms of SCID also fit this pattern.

SCID with Generalized Hematopoietic Hypoplasia (Reticular Dysgenesis)

Reticular dysgenesis is the most severe form of SCID, since it is characterized by agranulocytosis as well as profound dual system immunodeficiency. These patients die of overwhelming infection within hours or days of birth because of the lack of both specific immunity and a critical nonspecific defense agent, the polymorphonuclear leukocyte. It has been proposed that this disorder represents a defect in differentiation of the primitive hematopoietic stem-cell precursor of all leukocytes, resulting in the failure of development of both myeloid and lymphoid lineages.[50-53]

SCID with Failure of Lymphoid Stem-Cell Development (Swiss Type)

"Swiss-type" agammaglobulemia is a form of SCID thought to result from defective lymphoid stem-cell development, since these infants lack both T and B lymphocytes.[54] This very rare disorder is inherited as an autosomal recessive trait, and these infants usually die during the first months of life. The status of the recombinase enzyme involved in rearrangement of the genes for the T-cell antigen receptor and the immunoglobulin molecules has not been reported in any human disease. However, the lack of both T and B cells in Swiss type makes deficiency of this enzyme one attractive candidate for the genetic defect underlying this disorder.

SCID with Normal B Cells

Some patients with SCID have normal or even increased numbers of B lymphocytes despite profound T-cell deficiency. They may produce small amounts of IgM but fail to produce specific antibody after antigenic challenge. In these cases the primary defect is a failure of T-cell development, with the lack of B-lymphocyte maturation occurring as a secondary event. Defects at the level of the prethymic T-lymphocyte precursor, the intrathymic T lymphocyte, and the post-thymic T-cell precursor have all been demonstrated.[55,56] B cells from some of these patients have been shown to produce IgG and IgA as well as IgM in response to stimulation with pokeweed mitogen in vitro when cocultured with T cells from a normal individual. In this case, the normal T cells provided appropriate helper-T-cell activity which permitted the patient's B cells to function normally.[57,58]

SCID with MHC Class I and/or Class II Deficiency ("Bare Lymphocyte Syndrome")

A unique form of SCID has been found in several kindreds of North African descent in which lymphocytes do not express membrane MHC class I[59,60] and/or class II[61,62] cell surface antigens (Fig. 110-2). This disorder is transmitted as an autosomal recessive trait, but inheritance is not linked to genes on chromosome 6, the chromosomal location of the MHC genes. Therefore, the defect is postulated to involve a transacting regulatory gene controlling MHC antigen expression on the cell surface.[59-61] Since T cells "see" antigen after it is processed and then presented in association with MHC antigens, the lack of MHC expression cripples the T-cell recognition process. Both initial antigen presentation (class II MHC) and later T-cell functions (CD8 cells interact with class I molecules, CD4 cells interact with class II molecules) are disrupted by abnormal MHC gene product expression.

X-Linked SCID

Male infants with X-linked SCID are profoundly deficient in both T cells and B cells, but the nature of the genetic defect on the X chromosome causing this deficiency is unknown. Interestingly, female carriers of this mutant gene are immunologically normal. Normal function in the carriers would be expected if all their T cells were derived from precursors whose

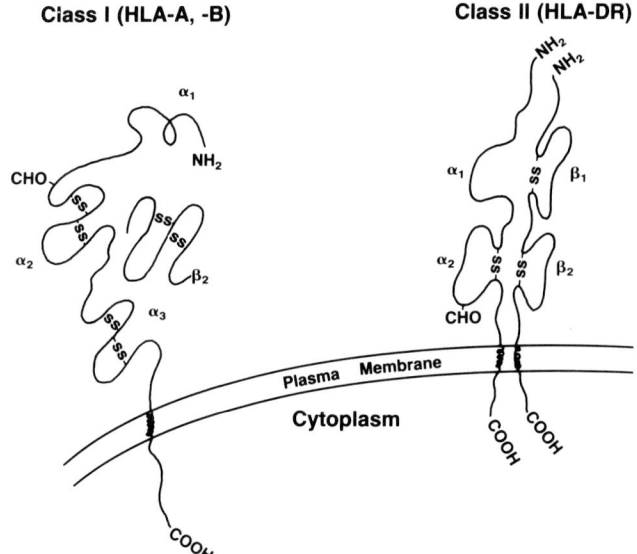

Fig. 110-2 Schematic representation of the class I and class II HLA antigen molecules. The class 1 MHC encoded chain has three domains termed α_1, α_2, and α_3. The α_3 domain is closely associated with a non-MHC-encoded chain, β_2-microglobulin. The alloantigenic sites which carry the determinants specific for each unique HLA type are found on domains α_1 and α_2. The HLA class II antigens consist of two nonidentical, noncovalently bound chains (α and β) which also have globular domains. This domain structure is similar to the structure found in immunoglobulin molecules and constitutes one of the common features of this supergene family.

X chromosomes bearing the defective X-SCID gene were inactivated. With a normal pattern of X inactivation (lyonization), approximately 50 percent of a female's cells utilize the maternally derived X chromosome, and in the other half the paternally derived X chromosome is active. As predicted, the peripheral T cells of carriers of X-SCID demonstrate an unbalanced pattern of X-chromosome inactivation with the same X chromosome inactive in all circulating cells. This has been demonstrated by using the restriction fragment length polymorphism (RFLP) pattern to distinguish the maternally from the paternally derived X.[63] In this technique, somatic cell hybrids are produced by fusion of T cells from the potential car-

rier with hypoxanthine-phosphoribosyl transferase (HPRT)–deficient hamster cell line. Successful hybrids carrying an active human X chromosome (the site of the human HPRT gene) are selected by growth in culture conditions requiring reconstituted HPRT activity for hybrid survival. Multiple individual hybrid clones are then examined for the RFLP pattern of the human X chromosome contained in the hybrid. In normal noncarrier females, roughly equal proportions of the clones contain either the paternally derived X chromosome or the maternally derived X. By contrast, hybrid clones established from obligate carriers of X-SCID *all* had an identical pattern with the same X chromosome active in each. Although this method is capable of identifying carrier females, it is tedious and expensive to perform and therefore is not likely to be adopted outside a research setting.

SCID with Adenosine Deaminase Deficiency, ADA(−) SCID

ADA(−) SCID was the first of the primary immunodeficiency diseases in which the specific enzyme defect was identified.[64] The disorder (discussed in detail in Chap. 40) is inherited as an autosomal recessive trait and is indistinguishable clinically from cases of SCID with normal ADA.[65,66] The diagnosis is usually made by measurement of the ADA concentration in red blood cells. ADA activity is present in fetal cells so that prenatal diagnosis of ADA deficiency is possible.[67–69]

ADA is a 38-kDa enzyme coded for by a gene on chromosome 20.[70,71] The enzyme catalyzes the conversion of adenosine and deoxyadenosine to inosine and deoxyinosine, respectively. The mechanism by which ADA deficiency results in immune deficiency is not completely understood, but it is probably related to the accumulation of ADA substrates rather than from a deficiency of a product of ADA enzyme action (Fig. 110-3). The ADA substrates adenosine and 2′-deoxyadenosine accumulate in high concentration, and both compounds are toxic to lymphocytes, particularly T cells.[72] Many mechanisms have been proposed, but none alone adequately explains all the findings in this disorder. ADA deficiency can result in elevated levels of cyclic AMP, pyrimidine starvation, diminished cellular phosphoribosyl pyrophosphate, inhibition

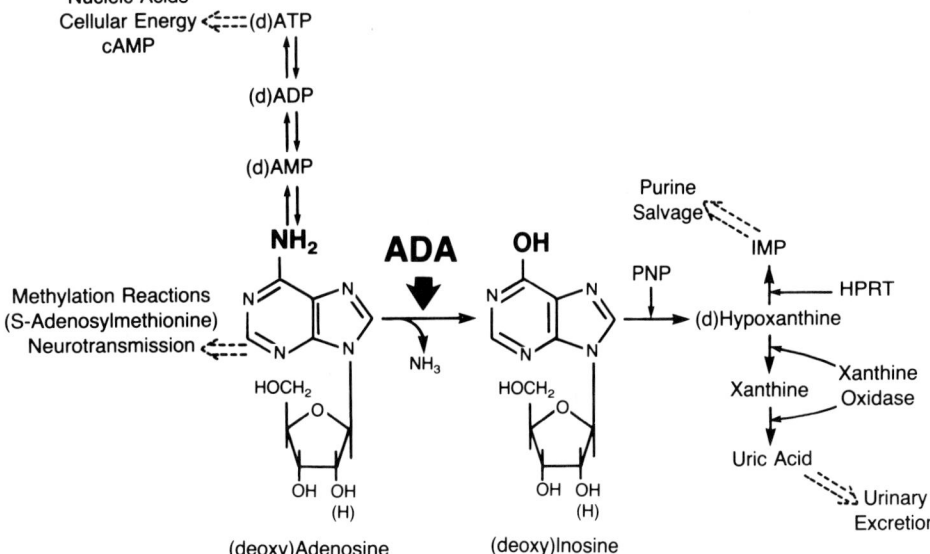

Fig. 110-3 The pathway of purine metabolism illustrating the site of action of adenosine deaminase (ADA). The accumulation of deoxyadenosine and dATP as a consequence of the ADA deficiency leads to lymphocytotoxicity and subsequent combined T-cell and B-cell immunodeficiency.

of ribonucleotide reductase and *S*-adenosylhomocystine hydrolase, and accelerated poly(ADP)ribose synthesis with NAD and ATP depletion. Other effects are also likely, and probably several mechanisms cooperate in the pathophysiology of this disease.[73–86]

Treatment of SCID

The need to develop effective treatment for these desperately ill children has been one of the greatest challenges for clinical immunology. In 1968, bone marrow transplantation was introduced to clinical medicine when an infant with SCID was given bone marrow from a histocompatible sibling.[87] The transplanted marrow affected total immunologic reconstitution in this infant and opened a new era in therapy for this and many other immunologic and hematologic disorders. In the two decades since its introduction, bone marrow transplantation has been performed in several hundred infants with SCID. When the donor is a genotypically identical HLA-matched sibling and the infant is transplanted when free of serious infection, over 80 percent of SCID recipients have had long-lasting immunologic reconstitution.

Since only a minority of patients have had an HLA-matched sibling donor available, many alternative transplantation strategies have been tried. Transplantation with whole bone marrow from HLA-incompatible donors has been almost universally unsuccessful because of the development of fatal GVHD. To avoid this, transplants with embryonic lymphoid tissues such as the fetal thymus and fetal liver have been attempted. Initially the rate of immunologic reconstitution in SCID recipients of fetal tissue was less than 20 percent and was frequently limited to partial T-cell recovery without any B-cell reconstitution. More recently it has been found that children maintained in a germ-free environment for several months after fetal liver transplantation have an enhanced rate of immune reconstitution, perhaps because of the slow pace of repopulation of the lymphoid population when fetal grafts are used.

More recently, reconstitution using HLA-nonidentical bone marrow treated to remove mature T lymphocytes has shown very promising results.[88] In this approach, parents are used as marrow donors so that at least 50 percent identity is maintained between the donor and recipient to enhance MHC-dependent interactions between the donor immune cells and the host tissues. T cells in the donor marrow are eliminated by treatment with lectins, monoclonal antibodies and complement, or immunotoxins to remove the cells capable of causing graft-versus-host disease.[89,90] The success rate with this technique in infants with SCID is now approaching that of transplants using HLA-identical siblings as the marrow donors, offering potential cure to almost every infant with this disease.

Bone marrow transplantation has been successful in the treatment of both ADA(+) and ADA(−) SCID.[91] Enzyme replacement has also been attempted in the treatment of ADA(−) SCID. Initially, exchange transfusions with irradiated whole blood were used since erythrocytes are a rich source of ADA.[92] In practice, erythrocyte transfusions have not been effective in correcting the immunodeficiency in ADA(−) SCID patients. They have, however, resulted in transient improvement in lymphocyte function in vitro and correction of the levels of deoxyadenosine in the blood and deoxy ATP in the lymphoid cells of these patients. Recently, Herschfield and colleagues have administered large amounts of bovine ADA conjugated to polyethylene glycol (PEG-ADA) to

ADA(−) SCID patients.[93] The PEG conjugation renders the bovine enzyme nonimmunogenic and increases its serum half-life from just minutes to several hours. Weekly intramuscular injections of PEG-ADA to two patients have resulted in a striking improvement in the biochemical and immunologic defects seen in these patients. Although it is too early to determine whether PEG-ADA therapy will result in total reconstruction of immune function in these children and if the effects will be long-lasting, these initial results are very promising. In the future, ADA(−) SCID may well be one of the earliest diseases treated with gene therapy.[94] It has been shown that the biochemical abnormalities in ADA(−) T cells can be corrected in vitro by treatment with a recombinant murine retrovirus carrying the human gene for ADA.[95]

ATAXIA TELANGIECTASIA

Ataxia telangiectasia (AT) is an autosomal recessive disorder characterized by variable immunodeficiency, oculocutaneous telangiectasia, and cerebellar ataxia. Onset of the neurologic deficit typically occurs in early childhood and dominates the clinical picture throughout.[96–98]

Clinical Features

Neurologic symptoms are the usual presenting problem in these patients, with difficulty in learning to walk commonplace. The early manifestation of cerebellar dysfunction as ataxia is followed somewhat later by chorioathetosis, myoclonic jerking, and oculomotor abnormalities. The telangiectasia characteristic of this disease usually appear by 2 to 7 years of age. They initially appear on the bulbar conjunctiva (Fig. 110-4) and develop later on the skin in exposed areas and areas of trauma such as the nasal bridge, the ears, and flexor folds on the neck and extremities. Other cutaneous manifestations include vitiligo, café au lait spots, an early loss of subcutaneous fat, and premature graying of the hair. Endocrine abnormalities are also very common and may involve multiple organs. More than 50 percent of patients display glucose intolerance.[99] Delayed or absent development of secondary sexual characteristics in females is associated with absent or hypoplastic ovaries. Hypogonadism is a less consistent finding in males. Half the patients have mild elevations in liver enzymes, which is usually associated with fatty infiltration and round-cell accumulation in the portal areas.

An increased incidence of cancer is a feature of several of the primary immunodeficiency diseases and is prominent in AT with up to 15 percent of the patients ultimately dying of malignancy.[100,101] Non-Hodgkin's lymphomas predominate in childhood AT patients as they do in other primary immunodeficiency diseases. Adult male patients have an estimated seventyfold increased incidence of carcinoma of the stomach compared to the general population. Interestingly, these cases of carcinoma all have occurred in AT patients lacking serum IgA, although IgA deficiency is seen in only 70 percent of ataxia telangiectasia patients overall.[102] Rare forms of lymphoid leukemia have been observed including subacute T-cell lymphocytic leukemia and T-cell chronic lymphocytic leukemia. In these T-cell malignancies, chromosomal translocations have been defined for several patients with a high incidence of breakpoints clustered on chromosomes 14q11, 7p13-15, and

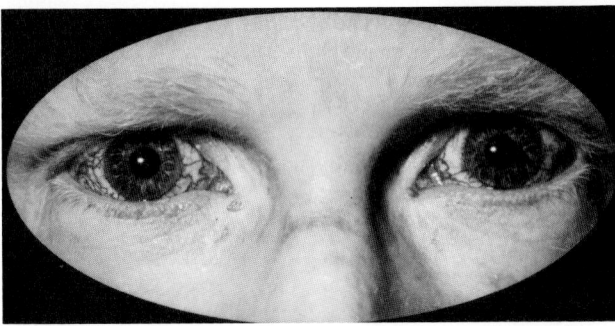

Fig. 110-4 Telangiectatic blood vessels on the bulbar conjunctiva and nasal bridge of a 22-year-old patient with ataxia telangiectasia. The recognition of these vascular abnormalities is frequently the initial clue leading to the correct diagnosis in a child being evaluated for cerebellar ataxia.

7q32-35.[103–106] These are the chromosomal regions that undergo rearrangement to generate active T-cell receptor genes.[38] In addition, breaks and translocations involving chromosome 14q32, the site of the immunoglobulin heavy-chain genes, are frequent in AT.

Recurrent infections are a major feature in some patients, while others seem to have little problem with infection. In general there is a good correlation between the severity of infectious illnesses and the immunologic status of the patient.[96] Sinopulmonary infections are the most common problem. Chronic pulmonary disease contributed to by both the im-

Fig. 110-5 The levels of α-fetoprotein in the serum of patients with ataxia telangiectasia (AT), their normal sibs and parents, and a group of normal donors. Elevated α-fetoprotein is one of the most consistent findings in this disorder and may be useful in early diagnosis of affected patients. (*Courtesy of Dr. Thomas A. Waldmann.*)

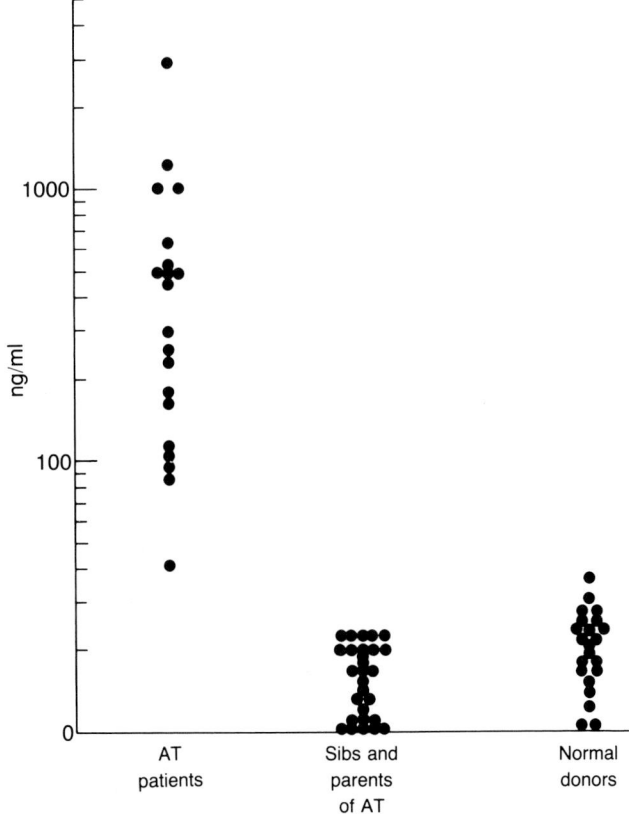

mune deficiency and recurrent aspiration of oral secretions secondary to the neurologic deficit results in pulmonary failure as a common terminal event.

Immunologic Defects

AT has a variable pattern of immunodeficiency with considerable differences from patient to patient even within the same family. Defects in both humoral and cellular immunity have been described, but few of the abnormalities occur in all or even the majority of patients.[96,107] The most consistent B-lymphocyte defects are an absence of serum IgA in about 75 percent and of serum IgE in about 85 percent of patients. The IgA and IgE deficiencies may occur independently of one another, and siblings within a family may have different patterns of immunoglobulin deficiency. IgG2 and IgG4 may also be deficient in this disorder.[108] In addition, 80 percent of patients have serum IgM in a monomeric 7S form rather than as the pentameric 19S molecule usually found in serum. Total B-lymphocyte numbers are normal, as are IgA-bearing B cells. Antibody responses to a variety of specific antigens have been variable, with no consistent pattern of deficiency present. Autoantibodies to self antigens are common in AT. Included are antibodies to mitochondria, basement membranes, muscle, thyroid, and even immunoglobulins.[109]

The cellular immune system also shows variable degrees of impairment. Many patients are anergic to delayed hypersensitivity skin testing, and a few have had delayed skin allograft rejection. Half of the patients have depressed lymphocyte proliferative responses to mitogens and even more have defective proliferative and cytotoxic T-cell responses to viral pathogens.[110] Immunoregulatory T-cell function has also been variable with defects in helper-T-cell function and in vitro immunoglobulin production observed in more than half the patients studied.[111]

Pathogenesis

The fundamental biochemical defect underlying AT is unknown. However, the constellation of findings in the patients has led to the development of two major hypotheses. One of the most striking and consistent pathologic features of this disease is that the thymus is small or absent, lacks Hassall corpuscles, and is embryonic in appearance.[112] This observation led to the proposal that the disorder is a consequence of a defect in tissue differentiation.[113] Auerbach[114] first showed that thymic development is dependent on the interaction of ectodermal and mesodermal elements. The postulated defect in AT involved a failure in the development and maturation of tissues that require an essential interaction between primitive mesoderm and ectoderm. Supporting this hypothesis was the observation that AT patients have high circulating concentrations of oncofetal antigens, which are ordinarily found only with immaturity. α-Fetoprotein, a protein produced normally by the fetal liver, was shown to be elevated in 59 of 60 AT patients but not in their parents or in patients with other immunodeficiency diseases (Fig. 110-5).[115] AT patients have also been reported to have elevated levels of carcinoembryonic antigen as well.[116] As an additional correlative observation, ovarian agenesis is frequently seen in these patients.

Another hypothesis advanced to explain some of the manifestations of this disease was developed after the observation that patients with AT have an increased sensitivity to ionizing radiation and radiomimetic drugs.[117,118] Furthermore, cultured fibroblasts from AT patients have a markedly reduced colony-forming ability following x-irradiation, but are not unusually sensitive to ultraviolet irradiation as are the cells from patients with xeroderma pigmentosum. There is presumably a defect in DNA repair in these cells following x-irradiation, but convincing evidence for a specific biochemical defect has not been presented.[119–121] Fibroblasts from different patients have been fused and found to cross-correct the defect in x-ray sensitivity. At least five complementation groups have been defined by this technique.[122,123] The AT cells examined failed to pause sufficiently after x-ray for DNA repair to be completed. Rather, they launch directly into DNA replication.

As mentioned earlier, there is a high incidence of chromosomal translocations in the leukemic cells of these patients as well as in vitro lymphocyte lines established from AT patients. These translocations usually involve chromosomes 7 and 14, the sites of the T-cell receptor genes and the immunoglobulin heavy-chain genes. These are chromosomal regions that undergo DNA rearrangements, deletions, and repair to generate active receptor genes. Further, site-specific DNA breaks and subsequent repair are involved in immunoglobulin heavy-chain class switch. If such breaks are not normally repaired in AT patients, they could contribute to the immune deficiency as well as the neoplasia observed. For example, AT patients frequently have reduced or absent IgA, IgG2, IgG4, and IgE, the immunoglobulins encoded by the genes at the 3' end of the heavy-chain gene cluster.[108,124] These are Ig classes that are dependent on additional steps of site-specific DNA breaking and rejoining to generate an active gene and could be expected to be more severely affected by an abnormality in this cellular mechanism.

Treatment

There is no form of therapy that has proved to be effective in either preventing the progression of the neurologic disability or in reconstituting the immune system defects in this disease. Immunoglobulin replacement therapy and blood transfusions have been associated with severe and even fatal episodes of anaphylaxis in IgA-deficient AT patients. The mechanism of this anaphylaxis is the spontaneous production of anti-IgA antibodies in these patients which then react with IgA in the infused blood products resulting in the systemic allergic response.

THE WISKOTT-ALDRICH SYNDROME

The Wiskott-Aldrich syndrome (WAS) is an X-linked condition characterized by the clinical triad of recurrent infections with all types of microorganisms, hemorrhages secondary to thrombocytopenia, and eczema of the skin.[125,126] The onset of symptoms typically occurs during the first 6 months of life with the recognition of the presence of petechia and the development of infections such as otitis media.[127]

Clinical Features

Boys affected with WAS have a great variety of clinical problems. The severity of their immune deficiency is second only to SCID, leading to infections with high grade encapsulated organisms such as *Hemophilus influenzae* and pneumococci as well as with opportunistic pathogens such as *Pneumocystis carinii*, cytomegalovirus, and *Candida albicans*. WAS patients have died with disseminated herpes simplex infections, and varicella has also been fatal, particularly in patients treated with corticosteroids.

The thrombocytopenia is often profound with platelet counts averaging in the 15,000 to 30,000 range. Bleeding accounts for about 30 percent of the mortality in this disease, with intracranial hemorrhage the greatest threat. The thrombocytopenia is unique because WAS is the only disease regularly associated with small-sized platelets.[128] The mean platelet volume in idiopathic thrombocytopenic purpura by contrast is increased.

In addition to eczema, the third component of the classic clinical triad, these patients have a high incidence of severe autoimmune disease. This autoimmunity may take the form of Coombs' positive hemolytic anemia, a juvenile rheumatoid arthritis–like syndrome with hectic fever and joint involvement, a leukocytoclastic vasculitis primarily involving the legs, and large vessel vasculitis affecting the coronary or cerebral arteries. An autoimmune thrombocytopenia with high levels of platelet-associated IgG may be superimposed on the preexisting low platelet count or may be the cause of the reappearance of thrombocytopenia following splenectomy. High levels of circulating immune complexes may be found intermittently. The development of this aggressive autoimmune disorder may be an ominous sign of clinical deterioration.

Another striking feature of this disease is a high incidence of malignancy. In some series over 20 percent of the patients develop cancer, usually a form of non-Hodgkin's lymphoma. Almost 50 percent of these have lymphoma involving the brain, sometimes as the primary site. It appears that the incidence of lymphoma has lessened since the introduction of splenectomy and routine autobiotic prophylaxis. A confusing clinical issue is the frequent development of marked peripheral lymphadenopathy in these boys. These isolated nodes almost never contain lymphoma unless widely disseminated cancer is present.[102,129,130]

Immunologic Defects

WAS has selective defects involving parts of each of the major host defense systems in contrast to SCID where more global defects are found.[131,132] The patients may have normal immunoglobulin levels, but the most common pattern is normal IgG, high levels of IgA and IgE, and IgM levels about half-normal. Antibody responses to many antigens are normal, while responses to others are completely absent. WAS is the only described disorder in which patients fail to produce antibodies to an entire class of antigens, the polysaccharides. Therefore, these patients have low or absent isohemagglutinins. They produce antibodies to tetanus toxoid, a protein antigen, but not to the capsular polysaccharides of *H. influenzae* or the pneumococcus.[133] This unique defect explains their susceptibility to infection with these encapsulated organisms despite normal or elevated total immunoglubulin levels in the serum.

Another unique abnormality in WAS is the observation that these patients hypercatabolize their serum immunoglobulins and albumin. The serum half-life of IgG, IgM, IgA, and albumin is shortened to one-third to one-half of normal. Therefore, to maintain normal serum levels, WAS patients actually synthesize immunoglobulin and albumin at far greater than normal rates.[134]

The cellular immune system also demonstrates selective defects. The boys are generally anergic when tested for cutaneous delayed hypersensitivity, and even have prolonged survival of skin allografts.[133] However, they have nearly normal absolute T-lymphocyte numbers and a normal ratio of CD4 and CD8 cells. In vitro their lymphocytes can proliferate well when stimulated with mitogens such as phytohemagglutinin[135] and produce substantial amounts of the lymphokines, IL-1 and IL-2. Nevertheless, their T cells proliferate very poorly to antigens or allogeneic cells, and they do not develop self-restricted virus-specific cytotoxic T cells even though they may produce antibody to the same virus.

The lymphocytes from WAS patients have been reported to have a characteristic appearance by scanning electron microscopy which may be useful as a diagnostic test for this disease.[136] Carefully performed size analysis of the platelets in these patients has shown a mean platelet volume of more than 3 SD below the mean normal volume in 17 of 18 of our patients. This is probably the most reliable single test to confirm the diagnosis of WAS.[128]

The polymorphonuclear leukocytes from WAS patients have been reported to have a defect in chemotactic responsiveness, as do the monocytes from these patients.[137,138] Their monocytes also have a defect in killer activity in antibody dependent cellular cytotoxicity (ADCC) and in cytotoxicity mediated via the mannosyl-fucosyl membrane receptor.[139,140]

Pathogenesis and Genetics

The fundamental defect responsible for the diverse manifestations of WAS is unknown. There are at least seven distinct immunodeficiency diseases inherited as X-linked traits, and each of those studied by linkage analysis has mapped to a different region of the X chromosome. WAS is most tightly linked to markers that map near the centromere on the short arm of X.[141]

The selective defects in cellular function involving T cells, B cells, granulocytes, platelets, and the mononuclear phagocytes demonstrate that this disorder is not the result of a defect in differentiation of just a single immune cellular element as is the case in a disorder like X-linked agammaglobulinemia. Parkman and colleagues have described a deficiency of a cell membrane glycoprotein, GP115, on lymphocytes from WAS patients as well as from another immunodeficient subject.[142–146] The glycosylation of this molecule, recently named sialophorin,[146] appears to be abnormal in that some sialic acid residues are more labile than normal and are lost from the surface of WAS cells more rapidly than from normal cells. There may be a more generalized defect in cell membrane glycoproteins since platelets, which normally lack sialophorin, also have been reported to have an abnormal pattern of surface glycoprotein in WAS patients. Further, the sialophorin gene does not seem to map to the X chromosome. Perhaps an X-linked *trans*-acting factor involved in membrane structure or stability is defective in this disease.

As with most X-linked immunodeficiency diseases, the carriers of the WAS are immunologically and hematologically normal, demonstrating none of the defects found in the affected males. Carrier identification therefore has not been possible except for a few situations in large families where linkage

analysis using RFLP markers has been successful.[141] Since females are functional mosaics for genes encoded on the X chromosome, it would be expected that some defect in immune or platelet function should be detected in the carrier females. This would be true unless all their peripheral cells were derived from precursors whose X chromosomes bearing the defective WAS genes were inactivated. Because random X inactivation (lyonization) occurs in the very early embryo, essentially all cell lineages in the female body have the same ratio of cells in which each of the parental X chromosomes is active. Under average conditions, approximately 50 percent of a female's cells use the maternally derived X chromosome and the remaining half use the paternally derived X. Using RFLPs for the genes phosphoglycerol kinase and hypoxanthine-phosphoribosyl transferase to distinguish the maternally and paternally derived X chromosomes and methylation-sensitive restriction endonucleases to distinguish the active from inactive chromosomes, it has been possible to evaluate the pattern of X inactivation in the peripheral blood cells of WAS carriers. Skin biopsies from the carriers showed a normal random pattern of X inactivation. However, all T cells, B cells, and granulocytes in each of the carriers had a nonrandom pattern of X inactivation such that one homologue was used preferentially as the active X (Fig. 110-6). This strikingly unbalanced pattern was seen in each of the 14 informative carriers studied and was not observed in any of over 80 normal female controls. In the one family studied where linkage phase could be determined, the X bearing the normal allele at the WAS locus was utilized as the active X. Gealy and colleagues[148] have shown that a similar unbalanced X-chromosome utilization occurs in carrier platelets by evaluating isozymes of glucose-6-phosphate dehydrogenase in rare double heterozygotes for

Fig. 110-6 Unbalanced X-chromosome inactivation in a carrier of the Wiskott-Aldrich syndrome (WAS). A probe for the X-linked gene phosphoglycerate kinase (PGK) was hybridized to DNA extracted from various cell populations from normal females and carriers of the disease. B indicates DNA samples digested with the restriction endonuclease BglI, which is used to identify females who are heterozygous for an RFLP at this locus (1.7-kb and 1.3-kb alleles). In heterozygous females, another aliquot of DNA was further digested with HpaII (B + H). Methylated PGK gene segments are resistant to digestion by HpaII, and therefore the extent of digestion of the two alleles by HpaII indicates the relative proportion of methylated (i.e., inactive) to unmethylated (i.e., active) DNA. In the T cells and granulocytes (PMNs) of normal females, HpaII digestion, as expected, affects both alleles with a reduction in the intensity of both the 1.7- and 1.3-kb bands and generation of fragments of smaller size. Similarly, the skin sample from the WAS carrier also shows a balanced pattern of X inactivation. By contrast, the DNA from the T cells and PMNs from the WAS carrier show a striking unbalanced pattern of X inactivation with the 1.3-kb allele totally digested (i.e., active) and the 1.7-kb allele unchanged (i.e., inactive). This pattern indicates that all of the peripheral blood T cells and granulocytes from this carrier have the same X chromosome active rather than the mixed usage seen with her skin cells or in the T cells and granulocytes of the normal female.

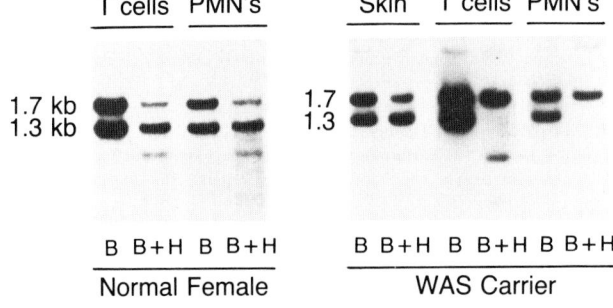

T cells	PMN's		Skin	T cells	PMN's

1.7 kb
1.3 kb

1.7
1.3

B B+H B B+H   B B+H B B+H B B+H

Normal Female   WAS Carrier

both glucose-6-phosphate dehydrogenase deficiency and WAS. These results provide the basis for carrier identification and also give unique insights into the extent of the cell lineages affected by the WAS genetic defect.

Treatment

There are several potential forms of therapy for the WAS. HLA-matched bone marrow transplantation has a higher rate of success in this disease than in any other condition.[149,150] In over 30 patients treated, the level of cure exceeds 90 percent. Interestingly, following successful transplantation all of the immune and hematologic abnormalities are corrected, as is the eczema.

The choice of treatment for patients lacking an HLA-matched sibling donor is more complex. T cell–depleted haploidentical bone marrow transplantation has been successful in only about 50 percent of the cases, with failure of engraftment a fatal complication in several. Splenectomy cures the thrombocytopenia in over 90 percent of cases and has had a major impact on the patient's quality of life and medical management of this disease.[151] Interestingly, the platelet size also normalizes following splenectomy.[128] Early experience with splenectomy was very poor, because many of the patients experienced overwhelming infections.[152] The use of routine prophylactic antibiotics and/or intravenous γ-globulin to prevent infections with high grade pathogens has been essential to the successful use of splenectomy and seems to result in an overall lessened problem with infection as well.

The autoaggressive syndrome[153] which frequently complicates WAS may be very difficult to treat. Bone marrow transplantation has been used in this setting and has been successful. The thrombocytopenia which occasionally appears after splenectomy most commonly resolves without specific treatment. Corticosteroids, high dose intravenous γ-globulin, and vinblastine have all been used with success in treating more prolonged episodes of this thrombocytopenia. The juvenile rheumatoid arthritis–like syndrome frequently responds to nonsteroidal anti-inflammatory treatment, but occasionally high dose steroid therapy may be needed to control severe vasculitis. As with all cases of severe T-cell deficiency, all blood and platelets for transfusion should be irradiated to prevent the possibility of GVHD.

REFERENCES

1. COOPER MD, PETERSON RDA, SOUTH MA, GOOD RA: The functions of the thymus system and the bursa system in chickens. *J Exp Med* 123:75, 1966.
2. COOPER MD: Pre B cells: Normal and abnormal development. *J Clin Immunol* 1:81, 1981.
3. COOPER MD, KEARNEY J, SCHER I: B lymphocytes, in Paul WE (ed): *Fundamental Immunology*. New York, Raven, 1984, p 43.
4. LEDER P: The genetics of antibody diversity. *Sci Am* 246:102, 1982.
5. HONJO T: Immunoglobulin genes. *Annu Rev Immunol* 1:499, 1983.
6. TONEGAWA S: Somatic generation of antibody diversity. *Nature* 302:575, 1983.
7. HOOD LE, WEISSMAN IL, WOOD WB, WILSON JH: *Immunology*, 2d ed. Menlo Park, CA, The Benjamin/Cummings Publishing Co, 1984, p 81.
8. WALDMANN TA: The arrangement of immunoglobulin and T cell receptor genes in human lymphoproliferative disorders. *Adv Immunol* 40:247, 1987.
9. CROCE CM, SHANDER M, MARTINIS J, CICUREL L, D'ANCONA GG, DOLBY TW, KOPROWSKI H: Chromosomal locations of the human genes for immunoglobulin heavy chains. *Proc Natl Acad Sci USA* 76:3416, 1979.
10. ERIKSON J, MARTINIS J, CROCE CM: Assignment of the genes for human γ immunoglobulin chains to chromosome 22. *Nature* 295:173, 1981.
11. MALCOLM S, BARTON P, MURPHY C, FERGUSON-SMITH MA, BENTLEY DL, RABBITTS TH: Localization of human immunoglobulin κ light chain variable region genes to the short arm of chromosome 2 by in situ hybridization. *Proc Natl Acad Sci USA* 79:4957, 1982.
12. MCBRIDE OW, HIETER PA, HOLLIS GF, SWAN D, OTEY MC, LEDER P: Chromosomal location of human kappa and lambda immunoglobulin light chain constant region genes. *J Exp Med* 155:1480, 1982.
13. EARLY P, HUANG H, DAVIS M, CALAME K, HOOD L: An immunoglobulin heavy chain variable region gene is generated from three segments of DNA: V$_H$, D and J$_H$. *Cell* 19:981, 1980.
14. GILLIS SD, MORRISON SL, OI VT, TONEGAWA S: A tissue-specific transcription enhancer element is located in the major intron of a rearranged immunoglobulin heavy chain gene. *Cell* 33:717, 1983.
15. QUEEN C, BALTIMORE D: Immunoglobulin gene transcription is activated by downstream sequence elements. *Cell* 33:741, 1983.
16. KORSMEYER SJ, HIETER RA, RAVETCH JV, POPLACK DG, WALDMANN TA, LEDER P: Developmental hierarchy of immunoglobulin gene rearrangements in human leukemia pre-B cells. *Proc Natl Acad Sci USA* 78:7096, 1981.
17. KORSMEYER SJ, WALDMANN TA: Immunoglobulin genes: Rearrangement and translocation in human lymphoid malignancy. *J Clin Immunol* 4:1, 1984.
18. EARLY P, ROGERS J, DAVIS M, CALAME K, BOND M, WALL R, HOOD L: Two mRNAs can be produced from a single immunoglobulin μ gene by alternative RNA processing pathways. *Cell* 20:313, 1980.
19. MOORE KW, ROGERS J, HUNKAPILLER T, EARLY P, NOTTENBURG C, WEISSMAN I, BAZIN H, WALL R, HOOD LE: Expression of IgD may use both DNA rearrangement and RNA splicing mechanisms. *Proc Natl Acad Sci USA* 78:1800, 1981.
20. FLANAGAN JG, RABBITTS TH: Arrangement of human immunoglobulin heavy chain constant region genes implies evolutionary duplication of a segment containing γ, ε, and α genes. *Nature* 300:709, 1982.
21. CORY S, JACKSON J, ADAMS JM: Deletions in the constant region locus can account for switches in immunoglobulin heavy chain expression. *Nature* 285:450, 1980.
22. DAVIS MM, KIM SK, HOOD LE: DNA sequences mediating class switching in α-immunoglobulins. *Science* 209:1360, 1980.
23. KATAOKA T, MIYATA T, HONJO T: Repetitive sequences in class-switch recombination regions of immunoglobulin heavy chain genes. *Cell* 23:357, 1981.
24. MARCU KB, COOPER MD: New views of the immunoglobulin heavy-chain switch. *Nature* 298:327, 1982.
25. REINHERZ EL, SCHLOSSMAN SF: The differentiation and function of human T lymphocytes. *Cell* 19:821, 1980.
26. REINHERZ EL, SCHLOSSMAN SF: The characterization and function of human immunoregulatory T lymphocyte subsets. *Immunol Today* 2:69, 1981.
27. MORETTA L, MINGARI MC, SEKALY PR, MORETTA A, CHAPUIS B, CEROTTINI C: Surface markers of cloned human T cells with various cytolytic activities. *J Exp Med* 154:569, 1981.
28. ENGLEMAN EG, BENIKE CJ, GRUMET FC, EVANS RL: Activation of human T-lymphocyte subsets: Helper and suppressor/cytotoxic T cells recognize and respond to distinct histocompatibility antigens. *J Immunol* 127:2124, 1981.
29. ALLISON JP, MCINTYRE BW, BLOCH D: Tumor-specific antigen of murine T lymphoma defined with monoclonal antibody. *J Immunol* 129:2293, 1982.
30. MEUER SC, FITZGERALD KA, HUSSEY RE, HODGDON JC, SCHLOSSMAN SF, REINHERZ EL: Clonotypic structures involved in antigen-specific human T-cell function. *J Exp Med* 157:705, 1983.
31. HASKINS K, KUBO R, WHITE J, PIGEON M, KAPPLER J, MARRACK P: The major histocompatibility complex-restricted antigen receptor on T cells. Isolations with a monoclonal antibody. *J Exp Med* 157:1149, 1983.
32. CHIEN YH, BECKER DM, LINDSTEN T, OKAMURAS M, COHEN DI, DAVIS MM: A third type of murine T-cell receptor gene. *Nature* 312:31, 1984.
33. HEDRICK SM, NIELSEN EA, KAVALER J, COHEN DI, DAVID MM: Sequence relationships between putative T-cell receptor polypeptides and immunoglobulins. *Nature* 308:153, 1984.
34. SAITO H, KRANZ DM, TAKAGAKI Y, HAYDAY AC, EISEN HN, TONEGAWA S: A third rearranged and expressed gene in a clone of cytotoxic T lymphocytes. *Nature* 312:36, 1984.
35. SIM GK, YAGUE J, NELSON J, MARRACK P, PALMER E, AUGUSTIN A, KAPPLER J: Primary structure of human T-cell receptor α-chain. *Nature* 312:771, 1984.
36. YANAGI Y, YOSHIKAI Y, LEGGETT K, CLARK SP, ALEKSANDER I, MAK TW:

A human T cell–specific cDNA clone encodes a protein having extensive homology to immunoglobulin chains. *Nature* 308:145, 1984.

37. HAYDAY AC, SAITO H, GILLIES SD, KRANZ DM, TANIGAWA G, EISEN HN, TONEGAWA S: Structure, organization and somatic rearrangement of T-cell gamma genes. *Cell* 40:259, 1985.

38. MURRE C, WALDMANN RA, MORTON CC, WALDMANN TA, BONGIOVANNI KF, SHOUS TB, EDDY RL, SEIDMAN JG: Another gene that rearranges in human T cells maps to the short arm of chromosome 7. *Nature* 316:549, 1985.

39. CACCIA N, BRUNS GAP, KIRSCH IR, HOLLIS GH, BERTNESS V, MAK TW: T-cell receptor α chain genes are located on chromosome 14 at 14q11 in humans. *J Exp Med* 161:1255, 1985.

40. RABBITTS TH, LEFRANC MP, STINSON MA, SIMS JE, SCHROEDER J, STEIN-METZ M, SPURR NL, SOLOMON E, GOODFELLOW PW: The chromosomal localization of a T-cell receptor gene and a T-cell rearranging gene: Possible correlation with specific translocation in human T-cell leukemia. *EMBO J* 4:1461, 1985.

41. ISOBE M, ERIKSON J, EMANUEL BS, NOWEL PC, CROCHE CM: Localization of gene for β subunit of human T-cell receptor at band 7q35, a region prone to rearrangements in T cells. *Science* 228:580, 1985.

42. MORTON CC, DUBY AD, EDDY RL, SHOUS TB, SEIDMAN JG: Genes for β gene of human T-cell antigen receptor map to regions of chromosomal rearrangement in T cells. *Science* 228:582, 1985.

43. YANCOPOULOS GD, BLACKWELL TK, SUH H, HOOD L, ALT FW: Introduced T cell receptor variable region gene segments recombine in pre-B cells; Evidence that B and T cells use a common recombinase. *Cell* 44:251, 1986.

44. HITZIG WH: Congenital thymic and lymphocytic deficiency disorders, in Stiehm ER, Fulginiti V (eds): *Immunologic Disorders in Infants and Children.* Philadelphia, WB Saunders, 1973.

45. HOYER JR, COOPER MD, GABRIELSON AE, GOOD RA: Lymphopenic forms of congenital immunologic deficiency diseases. *Medicine* 47:201, 1968.

46. POLLACK MS, KIRKPATRICK D, KAPOOR N, DUPONT B, O'REILLY R: Identification by HLA typing of intrauterine derived maternal T cells in four patients with severe combined immunodeficiency. *N Engl J Med* 307:662, 1982.

47. PAHWA SG, PAHWA RN, GOOD RA: Heterogeneity of B lymphocyte differentiation in severe combined immunodeficiency disease. *J Clin Invest* 66:543, 1980.

48. HITZIG WH: Protean appearances of immunodeficiencies: Syndromes and inborn errors involving other systems which express associated primary immunodeficiency, in Wedgwood R, Rosen FS, Paul NW (eds): *Primary Immunodeficiency Diseases.* New York, AR Liss, 1983, p 307.

49. BLAESE RM, WEIDEN PL, OPPENHEIM JJ, WALDMANN TA: Phytohemagglutinin as a skin test for the evaluation of cellular immune competence in man. *J Lab Clin Med* 81:538, 1973.

50. DEVAAL OM, SEYNHAEVE V: Reticular dysgenesia. *Lancet* 2:1123, 1959.

51. HAAS RJ, NIETHAMMER D, GOLDMAN SF, HEIT W, BIENZLE U, KLEIHAUER E: Congenital immunodeficiency and agammaglobulinemia (reticular dysgenesis). *Acta Paediatr Scand* 66:279, 1977.

52. LEVINSKY RJ, TIEDEMAN K: Successful bone-marrow transplantation for reticular dysgenesis. *Lancet* 1:671, 1983.

53. OWNBY DR, PIZZO S, BLACKMON L, GALL SA, BUCKLEY RH: Severe combined immunodeficiency with leukopenia (reticular dysgenesis) in siblings: Immunologic and histopathologic findings. *J Pediatr* 89:382, 1976.

54. HITZIG WH, LANDOLT R, MILLER G, BODMER P: Heterogeneity of phenotypic expression in a family with Swiss-type agammaglobulinemia: Observations on the acquisition of agammaglobulinemia. *J Pediatr* 78:968, 1971.

55. PYKE KW, DOSCH HM, IPP MM, GELFAND EW: Demonstration of an intrathymic defect in a case of severe combined immunodeficiency disease. *N Engl J Med* 193:424, 1975.

56. INCEFY GS, O'REILLY RJ, KAPOOR N, IWATA T, GOOD RA: In vitro differentiation of human marrow T cell precursors by thymic factors in severe combined immunodeficiency. *Transplantation* 32:299, 1981.

57. SEEGER RC, ROBINS RA, STEVENS RH, KLEIN RB, WALDMANN DJ, ZELTZER PM, KESSLER SW: Severe combined immunodeficiency with B lymphocytes: In vitro correlation of defective immunoglobulin production by addition of normal T lymphocytes. *Clin Exp Immunol* 26:1, 1976.

58. BUCKLEY RH, GILBERTSEN RB, SCHIFF RI, FERREIRA E, SANAL SO, WALDMANN TA: Heterogeneity of lymphocyte subpopulations in severe combined immunodeficiency: Evidence against a stem cell defect. *J Clin Invest* 58:130, 1976.

59. TOURAINE J-L, BETUEL H, SOUILLET G, JEUNE M: Combined immunodeficiency disease associated with absence of cell-surface HLA-A and -B antigens. *J Pediatr* 93:47, 1978.

60. SCHUURMAN RKB, VAN ROOD JJ, VOSSEN JM, SCHELLEKENS PTA, FELT-

KAMP-VROOM TM, DOYER E, GMELIG-MEYLING F, VISSER HKA: Failure of lymphocyte-membrane HLA A and B expression in two siblings with combined immunodeficiency. *Clin Immunol Immunopathol* 14:418, 1979.

61. DePREVAL C, LISOWSKA-GROSPIERRE B, LOCHE M, GRISCELLI C, MACH B: A *trans*-acting class II regulatory gene unlinked to the MHC control expression of HLA class II genes. *Nature* 318:291, 1985.

62. GRISCELLI C, FISCHER A, DURANDY A, LISOWSKA-GROSPIERRE B, BREMARD C, CERF-BENSUSSAN N, LE DEIST F, MARCADET A, DE PREVAL C: Defective synthesis of HLA class I and II molecules associated with combined immunodeficiency, in Eibl MM, Rosen FS (eds): *Primary Immunodeficiency Diseases.* Amsterdam, Elsevier, 1986.

63. PUCH JM, NUSSBAUM RL, CONLEY ME: Carrier detection in X-linked severe combined immunodeficiency based on patterns of X chromosome inactivation. *J Clin Invest* 79:1395, 1987.

64. GIBLETT ER, ANDERSON JE, COHEN F, POLLARA B, MEUWISSEN HJ: Adenosine-deaminase deficiency in two patients with severely impaired cellular immunity. *Lancet* 2:1067, 1972.

65. MEUWISSEN HJ, POLLARA B, PICKERING RJ: Combined immunodeficiency disease associated with adenosine deficiency. *J Pediatr* 86:169, 1975.

66. WARA DW, AMMANN AJ: Laboratory data, in Meuwissen HJ, Pickering RJ, Pollara B, Porter IH (eds): *Combined Immunodeficiency Disease and Adenosine Deaminase Deficiency, a Molecular Defect.* New York, Academic, 1975.

67. CHEN S-H, SCOTT CR, SWEDBERG KR: Heterogeneity for adenosine deaminase deficiency: Expression of the enzyme in cultured skin fibroblasts and amniotic fluid cells. *Am J Hum Genet* 27:46, 1975.

68. HIRSCHHORN R, BERATIS N, ROSEN FS: Characterization of residual enzyme activity in fibroblasts from patients with adenosine deaminase deficiency and combined immunodeficiency: Evidence for a mutant enzyme. *Proc Natl Acad Sci USA* 73:213, 1976.

69. CARSON DA, GOLDBLUM R, SEEGMILLER JE: Quantitative immunoassay for adenosine deaminase in combined immunodeficiency disease. *J Immunol* 118:270, 1977.

70. DADDONA PE, KELLEY WN: Human adenosine deaminase: Purification and subunit structure. *J Biol Chem* 252:110, 1977.

71. TISCHFIELD JA, CREAGAN RP, NICHOLS EA, RUDDLE FH: Assignment of a gene for adenosine deaminase to human chromosome 20. *Hum Hered* 24:1, 1974.

72. COHEN A, HIRSCHHORN R, HOROWITZ SD, RUBENSTEIN A, POLMAR SH, HONG R, MARTIN DW: Deoxyadenosine triphosphate as a potentially toxic metabolite in adenosine deaminase deficiency. *Proc Natl Acad Sci USA* 75:472, 1978.

73. GELFAND EW, COHEN A: Disorders of purine metabolism and immunodeficiency, in Gallin JI, Fauci AS (eds): *Advances in Host Defense Mechanisms.* New York, Raven, 1983, vol 2.

74. KREDICK NM: The methylation hypothesis of adenosine toxicity, in *Ciba Found Symp Ser 68.* Amsterdam, Elsevier, 1979.

75. CARSON DA, KAYE J, SEEGMILLER JE: Lymphospecific toxicity in adenosine deaminase deficiency and purine nucleoside phosphorylase deficiency: Possible role of nucleoside kinase(s). *Proc Natl Acad Sci USA* 24:5677, 1977.

76. CARSON DA, KAYE J, SEEGMILLER JE: Differential sensitivity of human leukemic T cell lines and B cell lines to growth inhibition by deoxyadenosine. *J Immunol* 121:1726, 1978.

77. MITCHELL BS, MEJIAS E, DADDONA PE, KELLEY WN: Purinogenic immunodeficiency diseases: Selective toxicity of deoxyribonucleosides for T cells. *Proc Natl Acad Sci USA* 75:5011, 1978.

78. WILSON JM, MITCHELL BS, DADDONA PE, KELLEY WN: Purinogenic immunodeficiency diseases: Differential effects of deoxyadenosine and deoxyguanosine on DNA synthesis in human T-lymphoblasts. *J Clin Invest* 64:1475, 1979.

79. MEJIAS E, MITCHELL B, CASSIDY J, KELLEY WN: Deoxyribonucleotide pools in immunodeficiency states. III. International Symposium on Purine Metabolism in Man. *Clin Res* 27:331A, 1979.

80. HERSHFIELD MS, KREDICH NM, OWNBY DR, OWNBY H, BUCKLEY R: In vivo inactivation of erythrocyte S-adenosylhomocysteine hydrolase by 2'-deoxyadenosine in adenosine deaminase-deficient patients. *J Clin Invest* 63:807, 1979.

81. CARSON DA, SETO S, WASSON DB: Lymphocyte dysfunction after DNA damage by toxic oxygen species: A model of immunodeficiency. *J Exp Med* 163:746, 1986.

82. MARKERT ML, HERSHFIELD MS, WIGINTON DA, STATES JC, WARD FE, BIGNER SH, BUCKLEY RH, KAUFMAN RE, HUTTON JJ: Identification of a deletion in the adenosine deaminase gene in a child with severe combined immunodeficiency. *J Immunol* 138:3203, 1987.

83. HIRSCHHORN R, ELLENBOGEN A: Genetic heterogeneity in adenosine deaminase (ADA) deficiency: Five different mutations in five new patients with partial ADA deficiency. *Am J Hum Genet* 38:13, 1986.

84. AKESON AL, WIGINTON DA, STATES JC, PERME CM, DUSING CM, HUTTON JJ: Mutations in the human adenosine deaminase gene that affect protein structure and RNA splicing. *Proc Natl Acad Sci USA* 84:5947, 1987.

85. CARSON DA, WASSON DB, LAKOW E, KAMATANI N: Possible metabolic basis for the different immunodeficient states associated with genetic deficiencies of adenosine deaminase and purine nucleoside phosphorylase. *Proc Natl Acad Sci USA* 79:3848, 1982.

86. HIRSCHHORN R: Inherited enzyme deficiencies and immunodeficiency: Adenosine deaminase (ADA) and purine nucleoside phosphorylase (PNP) deficiencies. *Clin Immunol Immunopathol* 40:157, 1986.

87. GATTI RA, ALLEN HD, MEUWISSEN HJ, HONG R, GOOD RA: Immunological reconstitution of sex-linked lymphopenic immunological deficiency. *Lancet* 2:1366, 1968.

88. REISNER Y, KAPOOR N, KIRKPATRICK D, POLLACK MS, DUPONT B, ROOD RA, O'REILLY RJ: Transplantation of acute leukemia with HLA-A and B identical parental marrow cells fractionated with soybean agglutinin and sheep red blood cells. *Lancet* 2:327, 1981.

89. O'REILLY RJ, KAPOOR N, KIRKPATRICK D, FLOMENBERG N, POLLACK MS, DUPONT B, GOOD RA, REISNER Y: Transplantation of hematopoietic cells for lethal congenital immunodeficiencies, in Wedgwood R, Rosen FS, Paul NW (eds): *Primary Immunodeficiency Diseases.* New York, AR Liss, 1983, p 307.

90. FISCHER A, GRISCHELLI C, BLANCHE S, LeDEIST F, VEBER F, LOPEZ M, DELAAGE M, OLIVE D, MAWAS C, JANOSSY G: Prevention of graft failure by an anti-HLFA-1 monoclonal antibody in HLA-mismatched bone marrow transplantation. *Lancet* 2:1058, 1986.

91. MARKERT ML, HERSHFIELD MS, SCHIFF RI, BUCKLEY RH: Adenosine deaminase and purine nucleoside phosphorylase deficiencies: Evaluation of therapeutic interventions in eight patients. *J Clin Immunol* 7:389, 1987.

92. POLMAR SH, STERN RC, SCHWARTZ AL, WETZLER EM, CHASE PA, HIRSCHHORN R: Enzyme replacement therapy for adenosine deaminase deficiency and severe combined immunodeficiency. *N Engl J Med* 295:1337, 1976.

93. HERSHFIELD MS, BUCKLEY RH, GREENBERG ML, MELTON AL, SCHIFF R, HATEM C, KURTZBERG J, MARKERT ML, KOBAYASHI RH, KOBAYASHI AL, ET AL: Treatment of adenosine deaminase deficiency with polyethylene glycol-modified adenosine deaminase. *N Engl J Med* 136:589, 1987.

94. ANDERSON WF: Prospects for human gene therapy. *Science* 226:401, 1984.

95. KANTOFF PW, KOHN DB, MITSUYA H, ARMENTANO D, SIEBERG M, ZWIEBEL JA, EGLITIS MA, MCLACHLIN JR, WIGINTON DA, HUTTON JJ, HOROWITZZ SD, GILBOA E, BLAESE RM, ANDERSON WF: Correction of adenosine deaminase deficiency in cultured human T and B cells by retrovirus-mediated gene transfer. *Proc Natl Acad Sci USA* 83:6563, 1986.

96. MCFARLIN DE, STROBER W, WALDMANN TA: Ataxia-telangiectasia. *Medicine* 51:281, 1972.

97. BODER E: Ataxia-telangiectasia: Some historic, clinical and pathologic observations, in Bergsma D, Good RA, Finstad J, Paul NW (eds): *Immunodeficiency in Man and Animals.* Sunderland, MA, Sinauer Press, 1975, p 255.

98. GATTI RA, SWIFT M (eds): *Ataxia Telangiectasia: Genetics, Neuropathology and Immunology of a Degenerative Disease of Childhood.* KROC Foundation Series, 1985, vol 19.

99. BAR RS, LEVIS MR, RECHLER MM, HARRISON LC, SIEBERT C, PODSKALNY J, ROTH J, MUGGEO M: Extreme insulin resistance in ataxia telangiectasia: Defect in affinity of insulin receptors. *N Engl J Med* 298:1164, 1978.

100. WALDMANN TA, STROBER W, BLAESE RM: Immunodeficiency disease and malignancy. *Ann Intern Med* 77:605, 1972.

101. SPECTOR BD, PERRY GS, KERSEY JH: Genetically determined immunodeficiency diseases (GDID) and malignancy: Report from the Immunodeficiency-Cancer Registry. *Clin Immunol Immunopathol* 11:12, 1978.

102. FILIPOVICH AH, ZERBE D, SPECTOR BD, KERSEY J: Lymphomas in persons with naturally occurring immune deficiency disorders, in MaGroth IT, O'Connor GT, Ramot B (eds): *Pathogenesis of Leukemias and Lymphomas: Environmental Influences.* New York, Raven, 1984, p 225.

103. COHEN MM, SHAHAM M, DAGAN J, SHMUELI E, KOHN G: Cytogenetic investigations in families with ataxia-telangiectasia. *Cytogenet Cell Genet* 15:338, 1975.

104. MCCAW BK, HECHT F, HARNDEN DG, TEPLITZ KL: Somatic rearrangement of chromosome 14 in human lymphocytes. *Proc Natl Acad Sci USA* 72:2071, 1975.

105. OXFORD JM, HARNDEN DG, PARRINGTON JM, DELHANTY JDA: Specific chromosome aberrations in ataxia-telangiectasia. *J Med Genet* 12:251, 1975.

106. HECHT F, HECHT BK: Chromosome changes connect immunodeficiency and cancer in ataxia-telangiectasia. *Am J Pediatr Hematol Oncol* 9:185, 1987.

107. MCFARLIN DE, OPPENHEIM JJ: Impaired lymphocyte transformation in ataxia-telangiectasia in part due to a plasma inhibitory factor. *J Immunol* 103:1212, 1969.

108. OXELIUS VA, BERKEL AI, HANSEN LA: IgG2 deficiency in ataxia-telangiectasia. *N Engl J Med* 306:515, 1982.

109. AMMANN AJ, HONG R: Autoimmune phenomena in ataxia telangiectasia. *J Pediatr* 78:821, 1971.

110. WALDMANN TA, MISITI J, NELSON D, KRAEMER KH: Ataxia telangiectasia: A multi-system hereditary disease with immunodeficiency, impaired organ maturation, X-ray hypersensitivity, and a high incidence of neoplasia. A combined staff conference of the NIH. *Ann Intern Med* 99:367, 1983.

111. WALDMANN TA, BRODER S, GOLDMAN CK, FROST K, KORSMEYER SJ, MEDICI MA: Disorders of B cells and helper T cells in the pathogenesis of the immunoglobulin deficiency of patients with ataxia-telangiectasia. *J Clin Invest* 71:282, 1983.

112. PETERSON RDA, KELLY WD, GOOD RA: Ataxia-telangiectasia: Its association with a defective thymus, immunological-deficiency disease and malignancy. *Lancet* 1:1189, 1964.

113. PETERSON RDA, COOPER MD, GOOD RA: Lymphoid tissue abnormalities associated with ataxia-telangiectasia. *Am J Med* 41:342, 1966.

114. AUERBACH R: Morphogenetic interactions in the development of the mouse thymus gland. *Dev Biol* 2:271, 1960.

115. WALDMAN TA, MCINTIRE KR: Serum-alpha-fetoprotein levels in patients with ataxia-telangiectasia. *Lancet* 2:1112, 1972.

116. SUGIMOTO T, SAWADA T, TOZAWA M, KIDOWAKI T, KUSUNOKI T, YAMAGUCHI N: Plasma levels of carcinoembryonic antigen in patients with ataxia-telangiectasia. *J Pediatr* 92:436, 1978.

117. GOTOFF SP, AMIRMOKRI E, LIEBNER EJ: Ataxia telangiectasia: Neoplasia, untoward response to X-irradiation and tuberous sclerosis. *Am J Dis Child* 114:617, 1967.

118. CUNLIFFE PN, MANN JR, CAMERON AH, ROBERTS KD, WARD HWC: Radiosensitivity in ataxia telangiectasia. *Br J Radiol* 48:374, 1975.

119. TAYLOR AMR, HARNDEN DG, ARLETT CF, HARCOURT SA, LEHMANN AR, STEVENS S, BRIDGES BA: Ataxia telangiectasia: A human mutation with abnormal radiation sensitivity. *Nature* 258:427, 1975.

120. BRIDGES BA: Some DNA repair-deficient human syndromes and their implications for human health. *Proc R Soc Lond [Biol]* 212:263, 1981.

121. TAYLOR AMR, METCALFE JA, OXFORD JM, HARNDEN DG: Is chromatid-type damage in ataxia telangiectasia after irradiation at G_0 a consequence of defective repair? *Nature* 260:441, 1976.

122. JASPERS NGJ, BOOTSMA D: Genetic heterogeneity in ataxia-telangiectasia studied by cell fusion. *Proc Natl Acad Sci USA* 79:2641, 1982.

123. MURNANE JP, PAINTER RB: Complementation of the defects in DNA synthesis in irradiated and unirradiated ataxia-telangiectasia cells. *Proc Natl Acad Sci USA* 79:1960, 1982.

124. PYUN KH, OCHS HD, XANG X, WEDGWOOD RJ: Antibody deficiency in ataxia-telangiectasia, a defect in heavy chain constant gene rearrangement. *Clin Res* 35:218A, 1987.

125. ALDRICH RA, STEINBERG AG, CAMPBELL DC: Pedigree demonstrating a sex-linked recessive condition characterized by draining ears, czematoid dermatitis and bloody diarrhea. *Pediatrics* 13:133, 1954.

126. KRIVIT W, GOOD RA: Aldrich's syndrome (thrombocytopenia, eczema and infection) in infants. *Am J Dis Child* 97:137, 1959.

127. PERRY GS III, SPECTOR BD, SCHUMAN LM, MANDEL JS, ANDERSON E, MCHUGH RB, HANSON MR, FAHLSTORM SM, KRIVIT W, KERSEY JH: The Wiskott-Aldrich syndrome in the United States and Canada (1892–1979). *J Pediatr* 97:72, 1980.

128. CORASH L, SHAFER B, BLAESE RM: Platelet-associated immunoglobulin, platelet size, and the effect of splenectomy in the Wiskott-Aldrich syndrome. *Blood* 65:1439, 1985.

129. BLAESE RM: Defects in the afferent limb of the immune system, in Waldmann TA (moderator), Immunodeficiency disease and malignancy. *Ann Intern Med* 77:605, 1972.

130. COTELINGHAM JD, WITEBSKY FG, HSU SM, BLAESE RM, JAFFE ES: Malignant lymphoma in patients with the Wiskott-Aldrich syndrome. *Cancer Invest* 3:515, 1985.

131. BLAESE RM, STROBER W, WALDMANN TA: Immunodeficiency in the Wiskott-Aldrich syndrome, in Bergsma D (ed): *Immunodeficiency in Man and Animals. Birth Defects.* Sunderland, MA, Sinauer Associates, 1975, p 250.

132. COOPER MD, CHASE HP, LOWMAN JT, KRIVIT W, GOOD RA: Wiskott-Aldrich syndrome: An immunologic deficiency disease involving the afferent limb of immunity. *Am J Med* 44:499, 1968.

133. BLAESE RM, STROBER W, BROWN RS, WALDMANN TA: The Wiskott-Aldrich syndrome. A disorder with a possible defect in antigen processing or recognition. *Lancet* 1:1056, 1968.

134. BLAESE RM, STROBER W, LEVY AL, WALDMANN TA: Hypercatabolism of IgG, IgA, IgM and albumin in the Wiskott-Aldrich syndrome. *J Clin Invest* 50:2331, 1971.

135. OPPENHEIM JJ, BLAESE RM, WALDMANN TA: Defective lymphocyte transformation and delayed hypersensitivity in Wiskott-Aldrich syndrome. *J Immunol* 104:835, 1970.

136. KENNEY D, CAIRNS L, REMOLD-O'DONNELL E, PETERSON J, ROSEN FS, PARKMAN R: Morphological abnormalities in the lymphocytes of patients with the Wiskott-Aldrich syndrome. *Blood* 68:1329, 1986.

137. OCHS HD, SLICHTER SJ, HARKER LA, VON BEHRENS WE, CLARK RA, WEDGWOOD RJ: The Wiskott-Aldrich syndrome: Studies of lymphocytes, granulocytes, and platelets. *Blood* 55:243, 1980.

138. ALTMAN LC, SNYDERMAN R, BLAESE RM: Abnormalities of chemotactic lymphokine synthesis and mononuclear leukocyte chemotaxis in Wiskott-Aldrich syndrome. *J Clin Invest* 54:486, 1974.

139. POPLACK DG, BONNARD GD, HOLIMAN BJ, BLAESE RM: Monocyte-mediated antibody-dependent cellular cytotoxicity: A clinical test of monocyte function. *Blood* 48:809, 1976.

140. BLAESE RM, MUCHMORE AV, LAWRENCE EC, POPLACK DG: The cytolytic effector function of monocytes in immunodeficiency disease, in Seligmann M, Hitzig W (eds): *Proceedings of the 3rd International Symposium on Primary Immunodeficiency Diseases of Man.* Amsterdam, Elsevier/North Holland, 1980, p 391.

141. PEACOCKE M, SIMINOVITCH KA: Linkage of the Wiskott-Aldrich syndrome with polymorphic DNA sequences from the human X chromosome. *Proc Natl Acad Sci USA* 84:3430, 1987.

142. PARKMAN R, KENNEY DM, REMOLD-O'DONNELL PS, ROSEN FS: Surface protein abnormalities in lymphocytes and platelets from patients with Wiskott-Aldrich syndrome. *Lancet* 2:1387, 1982.

143. REISINGER D, PARKMAN R: Molecular heterogeneity of a lymphocyte glycoprotein in immunodeficient patients. *J Clin Invest* 79:595, 1987.

144. REMOLD-O'DONNEL E, KENNEY DM, PARKMAN R, CAIRNS L, SAVAGE B, ROSEN FS: Characterization of a human lymphocyte surface sialoglycoprotein that is defective in Wiskott-Aldrich syndrome. *J Exp Med* 159:1705, 1984.

145. REMOLD-O'DONNELL E, ZIMMERMAN C, KENNEY D, ROSEN FS: Expression on blood cells of sialophorin, the surface glycoprotein that is defective in Wiskott-Aldrich syndrome. *Blood* 70:104, 1987.

146. MENTZER SJ, REMOLD-O'DONNELL E, CRIMMINS MAV, BIERER BE, ROSEN FS, BURAKOFF SJ: Sialophorin, a surface sialoglycoprotein defective in the Wiskott-Aldrich Syndrome, is involved in human T lymphocyte proliferation. *J Exp Med* 165:1383, 1987.

147. KOH DB, FEARON ER, WINKELSTEIN JA, VOGELSTEIN B, BLAESE RM: Wiskott-Aldrich carrier detection by X-chromosome inactivation analysis. *Pediatr Res* 21:838, 1987.

148. GEALY WJ, DWYER JM, HARLEY JB: Allelic exclusion of glucose-6-dehydrogenase in platelets and T lymphocytes from a Wiskott-Aldrich syndrome carrier. *Lancet* 1:63, 1980.

149. PARKMAN R, RAPPEPORT J, GEHA R, BELLI J, CASSIDY R, LEVEY R, NATHAN DG, ROSEN FS: Complete correction of the Wiskott-Aldrich syndrome by allogeneic bone marrow transplantation. *N Engl J Med* 298:921, 1978.

150. KAPOOR N, KIRKPATRICK D, BLAESE RM, OLESKE J, HILGARTNER MH, CHAGANTI RSK, GOOD RA, O'REILLY RJ: Reconstitution of normal megakaryocytopoiesis and immunologic functions in Wiskott-Aldrich syndrome by marrow transplantation following myeloablation and immunosuppression with busulfan and cyclophosphamide. *Blood* 57:692, 1981.

151. LUM LG, TUBERGEN DG, CORASH L, BLAESE RM: Splenectomy in the management of the thrombocytopenia of the Wiskott-Aldrich syndrome. *N Engl J Med* 302:892, 1980.

152. WEIDEN PL, BLAESE RM: Hereditary thrombocytopenia: Relation to the Wiskott-Aldrich syndrome with special reference to splenectomy. *J Pediatr* 80:226, 1972.

153. FILIPOVICH AH, KRIVIT W, KERSEY JH, BURKE BA: Fatal arteries as a complication of Wiskott-Aldrich syndrome. *J Pediatr* 95:742, 1979.

CHAPTER 111

GENETICALLY DETERMINED DISORDERS OF THE COMPLEMENT SYSTEM

JERRY A. WINKELSTEIN
HARVEY R. COLTEN

1. The complement system is composed of a series of plasma proteins and membrane receptors which, when functioning in an ordered and integrated fashion, serve as important mediators of host defense and inflammation. In order for the individual components of complement to subserve their biologic functions, they must first be activated. Activation of the complement system can occur via either the classical activating pathway of the alternative activating pathway. Once activated, individual components act as opsonins, possess chemotactic activity, are potent anaphylatoxins, and can assemble into the membrane attack complex and generate cytolytic activity. In addition, the complement system is important in the processing of immune complexes and the generation of a normal antibody response.

2. Some of the complement genes have been grouped into supergene families based on similarities in their structure, function, and chromosomal location. For example, the genes encoding C2, factor B, and C4 constitute the class III genes of the major histocompatibility complex on chromosome 6; the products of these genes are constituents of the enzymes that activate C3 and C5. The genes for C4-binding protein, factor H, decay-accelerating factor, and two of the receptors for C3 cleavage products make up another family of complement genes located on the long arm of chromosome 1; the products of these genes share their ability to interact with the activation products of C4 and C3. The synthesis of a number of components of complement is regulated by cytokines such as interleukin 1 (IL-1) and γ-interferon and by endotoxic lipopolysaccharide.

3. Genetically determined deficiencies have been described for most of the individual components of complement. The usual mode of inheritance of disorders is autosomal recessive with only two exceptions: C1 inhibitor deficiency is inherited in an autosomal dominant fashion, and properdin deficiency appears to be an X-linked recessive disorder. The clinical manifestations of individuals with complement deficiencies have varied. Most individuals have had either an increased susceptibility to infection, a variety of rheumatic disorders, or angioedema. Patients with a deficiency of C3 or with a deficiency of a component in either of the two pathways necessary for the activation of C3

have an increased susceptibility to encapsulated bacteria for which C3b-dependent opsonization is an important host defense. Patients with deficiencies of terminal components, C5 through C9, are markedly susceptible to systemic neisserial infections, since serum bactericidal activity is an important host defense against these organisms. The prevalence of rheumatic disorders is highest in patients deficient in components of the classical activating pathway (C1, C4, and C2) and of C3. They include a lupuslike syndrome, vasculitis, membranoproliferative glomerulonephritis, and dermatomyositis. The pathophysiological basis for the occurrence of these disorders in complement-deficient patients is unknown.

The complement system was first described around the turn of the century as a cytolytic mechanism responsible for lysing bacteria or erythrocytes sensitized with antibody.[1] The term *complement* was used since the cytolytic principle *complemented* the action of antibody. Nearly 100 years later, it is now appreciated that the complement system is composed of a series of proteins which, when functioning in an ordered and integrated fashion, serve as important mediators of host defense and inflammation.[2] In addition to its cytolytic function, the complement system subserves a variety of other biologically significant functions. Individual components of the complement system act as opsonins, possess chemotactic activity, or are potent anaphylatoxins. In addition, the complement system has been implicated in the processing of immune complexes and the generation of a normal antibody response. When its activation is controlled and directed against invading microorganisms, the complement system is an important mechanism of defense and is beneficial to the host. However, when its activation proceeds in an uncontrolled manner or is directed against the host, the complement system is an important mediator of immunopathologic damage and is detrimental to the host.

The first description of an individual with a genetically de-

---

Nonstandard abbreviations used in this chapter are: Ba = the smaller cleavage product of factor B; Bb = the larger cleavage product of factor B; CH_{50} = total serum hemolytic complement; C1-INH = C1 esterase inhibitor; C1q, C1r, C1s = the subcomponents of C1; C1r̄ = activated C1r; C1s̄ = activated C1s; C1–C9 = the first through ninth components of complement; C2a = the smaller cleavage product of C2; C2b = the larger cleavage product of C2; C3a = the smaller cleavage fragment of C3; C3b = the larger cleavage fragment of C3; C3,Bb = the priming C3 convertase; C3b,Bb = the amplification C3 convertase; C3a-desArg = the molecule produced by removal of the C-terminal Arg from C3a; (C3b)$_2$,Bb = the alternative pathway C5 convertase; C4a = the smaller cleavage product of C4; C4b = the larger cleavage product of C4; C4b,2a = the C3 convertase produced by the classical pathway; C4b,2a,3b = the C5 convertase produced by the classical pathway; C4-bp = C4-binding protein; C4c = the large cleavage product of C4b; C4d = the small cleavage product of C4b which remains bound to the cell surface; C5a = the smaller cleavage fragment of C5; C5a-desArg = the molecule produced by removal of the C-terminal Arg from C5a; DAF = decay-accelerating factor; HAE = hereditary angioedema; iC3b = inactive C3b; I1-1 = interleukin 1; IFN-γ = γ-interferon; LFA-1 = lymphocyte function–associated antigens; LPS = endotoxic lipopdysaccharide; MHC = major histocompatibility complex; 21-OH = steroid 21-hydroxylase; P = properdin; *QO = a null allele at a complement component locus; SERPIN = serine proteinase inhibitor; TNF = tumor necrosis factor/cachectin.

termined deficiency of one of the components of complement was in 1960.[3] Since then, genetically determined deficiencies of nearly all of the components of the complement system have been described in human beings.[4,5] The discovery of individuals with genetically determined abnormalities of the complement system has not only identified a new group of patients with inborn errors of metabolism but, through the elucidation of pathophysiology in these patients, has also led to a better understanding of the physiological role of complement in normal individuals.

The following chapter will review the biochemistry, biology, and molecular genetics of the normal complement system and relate these to the genetically determined disorders of the complement system in human beings.

BIOCHEMISTRY AND BIOLOGY OF THE COMPLEMENT SYSTEM

The complement system is composed of a series of individual proteins (Table 111-1). The majority of the biologically significant effects of the complement system are mediated by C3 and the terminal components, C5, C6, C7, C8, and C9. In order to subserve their biologic functions, however, C3–C9 must first be activated. Activation of C3–C9 may occur through at least two mechanisms, the classical pathway and the alternative pathway (Fig. 111-1).

The Classical Pathway

Activation of the classical pathway is usually initiated by antigen-antibody complexes (Fig. 111-2). Antibodies of the appropriate class or subclass (IgG1, IgG2, IgG3, and IgM) combine

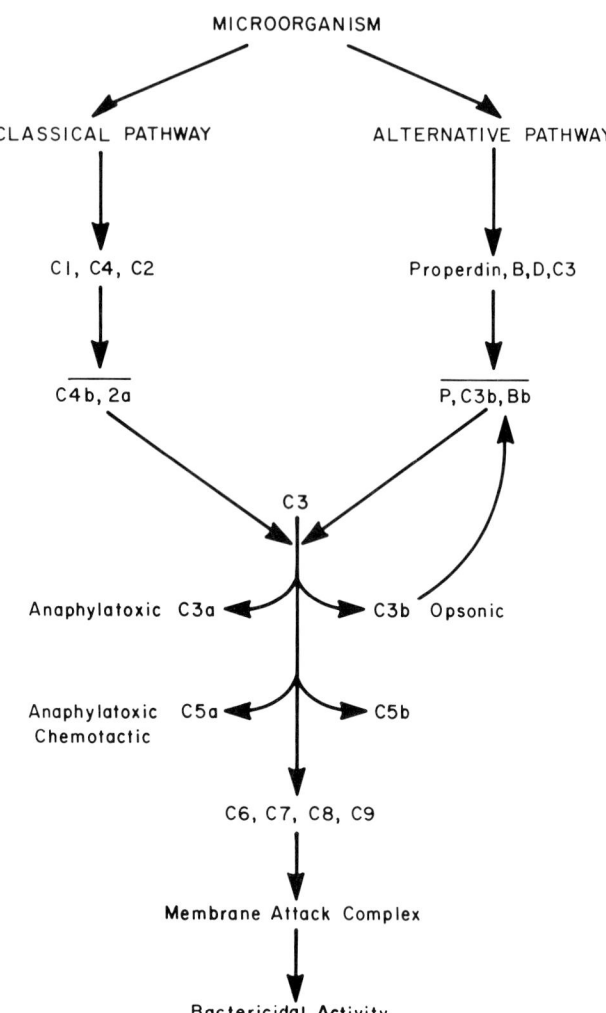

Fig. 111-1 The activation of C3 and the terminal components (C5–C9) of complement by microorganisms. Should the microorganism combine with antibody to form an immune complex, then activation of the classical pathway occurs. Cell wall polysaccharides of many microorganisms can also activate the alternative pathway directly and in the absence of antibody.

with an antigen to form an immune complex, which is then capable of binding and activating the first component of complement (C1) (reviewed in Ref. 6). In its native state, a single molecule of C1 is a macromolecular, Ca^{2+}-dependent complex composed of three biochemically distinct subcomponents, designated C1q, C1r, and C1s,[7] which are present in molar ratios of 1:2:2.[8] It is the C1q that binds to the immunoglobulin molecules in the immune complex.[9] Each C1q is composed of 18 chains arranged in a series of triple helices to give six subunits,[6] with each subunit resembling a tulip on the end of a stalk.[10] Each of the six stalks contains collagenlike amino acid sequences, and they are closely associated to form a common stem. The six globular regions radiate out from the common stem, permitting them to interact with the immunoglobulin molecules in an immune complex.[11] When the antigen is bound to a cell surface or an integral membrane constituent, the C1q binds to the heavy chains of two adjacent IgG molecules or to two heavy chains of a single, pentameric IgM molecule.

Binding of C1q to the immune complex results in the activation of C1r. Presumably a conformational change in C1r exposes a proteolytic site which initiates the autocatalytic cleavage of C1r and thereby converts the single chain zymogen form (C1r) to the disulfide-linked heterodimer that is the ac-

Table 111-1 Components of Human Complement

Component	Approximate molecular weight, kDa	Peptide chains
Classical pathway:		
C1q	460	6A, 6B, 6C
C1r	83	Single
C1s	83	Single
C4	200	1 α, 1 β, 1 γ
C2	102	Single
Alternative pathway:		
Factor D	25	Single
Factor B	93	Single
C3 and terminal components:		
C3	185	1 α, 1 β
C5	190	1 α, 1 β
C6	128	Single
C7	120	Single
C8	163	1 α, 1 β, 1 γ
C9	79	Single
Control proteins:		
C1 inhibitor	105	Single
C4-binding protein	550	7–8 identical
Factor H	150	Single
Factor I	100	1 α, 1 β
Properdin	223	4 identical
Membrane-receptor proteins:		
Decay-accelerating factor	70	Single
CR1	250	Single
CR2	145	Single
CR3	250	1 α, 1 β

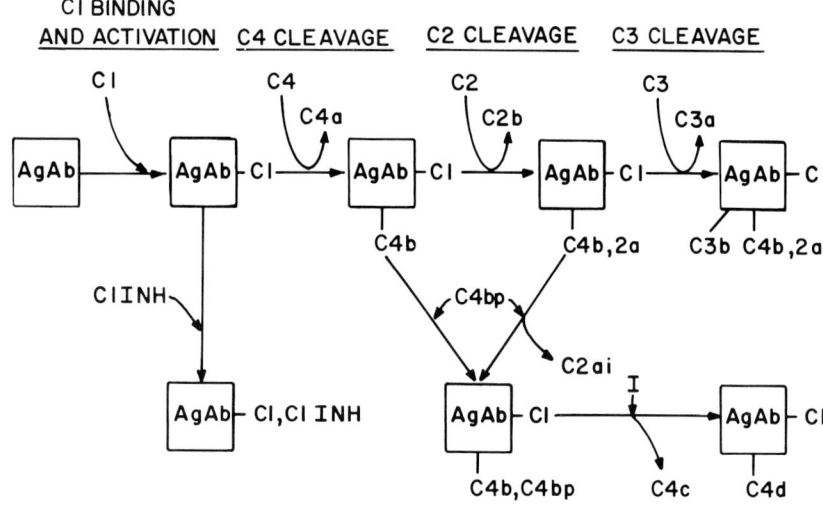

Fig. 111-2 The classical pathway of C3 activation. Activation of the pathway is initiated by immune complexes (AgAb) which activate C1. Activated C1 then cleaves C4 and C2, generating cleavage products that form a bimolecular complex, C4b,2a, which is the classical pathway C3 convertase. The generation and expression of the C3 convertase is regulated by the control proteins, C1 inhibitor (C1-INH), C4-binding protein (C4-bp), and factor I (I). (*Modified from Stanbury et al., The Metabolic Basis of Inherited Disease, 5th edition. New York: McGraw-Hill. Used with permission.*)

tive enzyme (C$\overline{1r}$).[12,13] A serine esterase, C$\overline{1r}$, then converts C1s to its active form, C$\overline{1s}$. Native C1s is present in serum as a single polypeptide chain and is similar in molecular mass and amino acid sequence to C1r. Upon activation by C$\overline{1r}$, C1s is cleaved into two disulfide-linked chains, and its serine esterase activity is expressed.[14,15]

Activated C$\overline{1s}$ then activates its natural substrate, the fourth component of complement (C4), by cleavage. Native C4 is composed of three disulfide-linked chains (α, β, γ).[16] Activation of C4 is accomplished by cleaving a peptide (C4a) of 6 kDa from the N-terminal portion of the largest of the three chains, the α chain.[16] This exposes an intrachain reactive thiolester bond in the remaining portion of the α chain of the larger cleavage product (C4b). The nascent C4b is then able to bind covalently to cell surfaces or to immunoglobulins through either esterification of hydroxyl groups on polysaccharides or amidation of amino groups on proteins by the acyl group of the reactive thiolester.[17,18] The internal thiolester bond of the C4b is highly labile, however, and if transesterification or amidation does not occur quickly, the C4b is inactivated by hydrolysis in the fluid phase and unable to bind to the cell surface or immunoglobulin. It is the lability of the reactive thiolester that limits the binding of the nascent C4b to the immediate vicinity of the immune complex and thereby helps to restrict the activation of the complete cascade to the area in which it was initiated. The reaction continues with the cleavage of the second component (C2) by the C$\overline{1s}$.[19] In order for most efficient activation of native C2 to occur, however, the C2 must first complex, through Mg^{2+}-dependent binding, with C4b molecules that are in close proximity to the C$\overline{1s}$. Cleavage of the C2 results in the liberation of a small peptide (C2b) and the formation of a new bimolecular enzyme C$\overline{4b,2a}$, which is responsible for activating C3[20] and initiating the assembly of the terminal components (C5–C9) into the membrane attack complex.

If the activation of the classical pathway were to proceed in an uncontrolled fashion, the generation of the C$\overline{4b,2a}$ enzyme would lead to the continuous activation of C3, C5, and the other terminal components. This, in turn, could result in the generation of excessive amounts of the phlogistic fragments of complement, which could cause widespread immunopathologic damage to the host. Fortunately, a number of mecha-

nisms act to control the assembly and expression of the classical pathway C3 convertase, C$\overline{4b,2a}$. First, the enzymatic actions of C$\overline{1r}$ and C$\overline{1s}$ can be inhibited by a control protein, C1 esterase inhibitor (C1-INH).[21] The C1-INH is a naturally occurring glycoprotein that binds covalently to C1r and C1s, leading to dissociation of the C1 macromolecular complex.[22] A second inhibitor, C4-binding protein (C4-bp), inhibits the C$\overline{4b,2a}$ enzyme by limiting the uptake of C2 by the C4b, by accelerating the decay-dissociation of the C2a once it has complexed with the C4b, and by enhancing the ability of yet another inhibitor, factor I (C3b/C4b inactivator), to cleave and inactivate C4b.[23,24] Factor I is a serine protease that inhibits the activity of the C4b of the classical pathway C3-cleaving enzyme but also inhibits the C3b of the alternative pathway C3-cleaving enzyme (see below). In the case of C4b, factor I cleaves the α chain so as to release a large cleavage product (C4c) of the C4b into the fluid phase, leaving a smaller fragment of the α chain (C4d) still covalently attached to the cell surface but no longer able to bind native C2.[24] Finally, a fourth inhibitor, decay-accelerating factor (DAF), an integral membrane protein found in erythrocytes and a variety of other cells, also accelerates the release of C2a from the C$\overline{4b,2a}$ enzyme.[25] Thus, in the usual situation, the assembly and expression of the C$\overline{4b,C2a}$ enzyme, and the activation of C3, proceeds in a controlled fashion and is limited to the immediate vicinity of the initiating substance (e.g., a microbial surface or an immune complex).

Activation of the classical pathway is usually initiated by antigen-antibody complexes and therefore is considered to be especially important in acquired immunity. However, some enveloped RNA viruses,[26] some mycoplasma species,[27] and certain strains and species of both gram-negative[28] and gram-positive bacteria[29] can bind C1q directly and activate the classical pathway. Thus, under some circumstances, the classical pathway may be activated in an antibody-independent fashion and function in "natural" immunity (reviewed in Ref. 30).

The Alternative Pathway

Activation of the alternative pathway begins with the C3 molecule (reviewed in Ref. 31) (Fig. 111-3). Like C4 (see above),

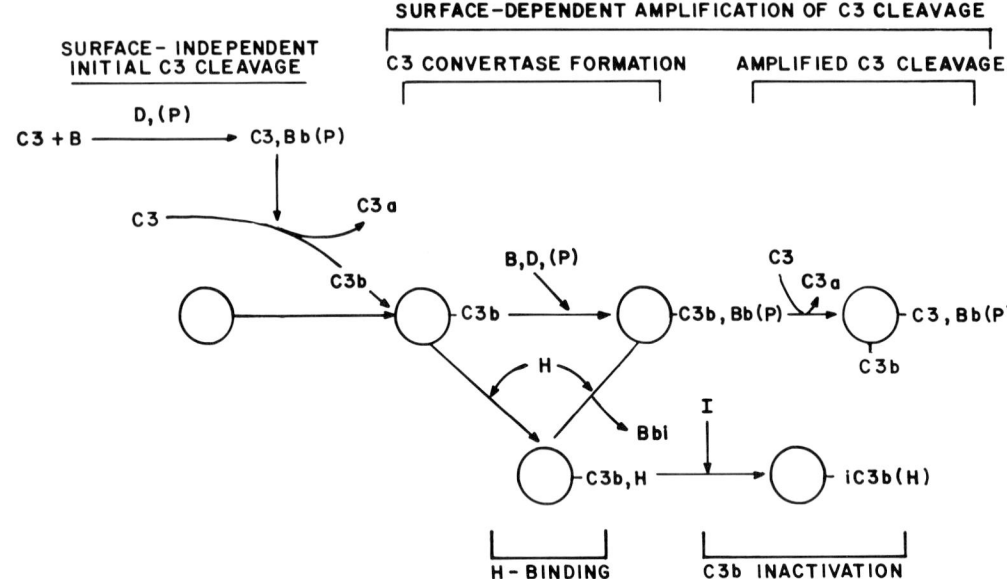

Fig. 111-3 The alternative pathway of C3 activation. There is a continuous, low-grade generation of C3b by a "priming" C3 convertase (C3,Bb,P) in the fluid phase. If the nascent C3b attaches to a cell surface which is an "activator" of the alternative pathway, then the amplification C3 convertase (C3b,Bb,P) is formed, additional C3 is cleaved, and more C3b is deposited on the surface. However, if the nascent C3b attaches to a "nonactivating" surface, then the control proteins, factors H and I, act to prevent the generation and expression of the amplification C3 convertase. The circle represents a cell. (*Modified from Stanbury et al., The Metabolic Basis of Inherited Disease, 5th edition. New York: McGraw-Hill, 1983. Used with permission.*)

native C3 contains an internal thiolester in its α chain.[32] It has been suggested that under normal conditions there is the slow and continuous low grade hydrolysis of this internal thiolester to create a C3b-like molecule.[33] The "C3b-like" C3 then can bind native factor B and allow its cleavage by a serine protease, factor D.[34] Two cleavage products of factor B are generated, a larger carboxy-terminal product, Bb, and a smaller, amino-terminal product, Ba. The association of the hydrolyzed C3 with Bb then creates a C3-cleaving enzyme, C3,Bb, (termed the "priming" C3 convertase),[31] which is responsible for a continuous, low grade cleavage of C3 and hence, the generation of nascent C3b. As with the activation of C4, the cleavage of native C3 exposes the reactive thiolester, allowing transesterification with, or amidation of, suitable acceptor sites on the cell surface. Should a suitable surface not be available, then hydrolysis of the thiolester results in an inactive C3b molecule. On the other hand, if the nascent C3b binds to a suitable surface, it forms a Mg^{2+}-dependent, reversible complex with native factor B, which is then cleaved by factor D to create a highly efficient C3-cleaving enzyme, C3b,Bb, termed the "amplification" C3 convertase.[31]

A number of opposing factors influence the activity of the alternative pathway C3 convertase.[31] The enzyme is relatively labile, and under physiological conditions rapidly undergoes intrinsic decay through dissociation of Bb. One of the proteins of the alternative pathway, properdin (P), stabilizes the binding of Bb to C3b and thereby retards its intrinsic decay.[35] Two other control proteins, factor H and factor I, act to inhibit the generation and/or expression of the C3b,Bb enzyme. Factor H not only competes with B for binding to C3b in the assembly of the alternative pathway C3 convertase,[36] but also can displace Bb from the C3b,Bb complex once the C3 convertase has formed.[37] Factor I inhibits the alternative pathway C3 convertase by inactivating cell-bound C3b through proteolytic cleavage, creating iC3b; its rate of inactivation of C3b is markedly accelerated by factor H.[38]

Certain particles, such as yeast cells,[39] rabbit erythrocytes,[40] and some bacteria,[30,41] are potent activators of the alternative pathway. They do so, in part, by virtue of their ability to bind nascent C3b and to protect the C3b,Bb enzyme from the inhibitory actions of factors H and I.[42] At least one molecular mechanism by which a particle protects the alternative pathway C3 convertase from these two control proteins has been elucidated. The binding of factor H to a particle, and thus its inhibitory effects on the alternative pathway C3-cleaving enzyme, is favored by the presence of sialic acid residues on the particle.[36,43]

Antibody is not required for the activation of the alternative pathway, and thus, the alternative pathway is generally viewed as an important mechanism of natural immunity (reviewed in Ref. 30). However, antibody can participate functionally in the activation of the alternative pathway by a variety of particles, including bacteria[44,45] and virus-infected cells.[46] The mechanism by which antibody enhances activation of the alternative pathway probably differs depending on the nature of the initiating particle and class of antibody involved.[45,47,48]

Two final points regarding the relationship of the classical and alternative pathways to the activation of C3 and C5–C9 deserve emphasis. First, since C3b is both the product of the alternative pathway C3 convertase and also forms part of the alternative pathway C3 convertase, the activation of C3 via the alternative pathway creates a positive feedback amplification loop (Fig. 111-1). Second, activation of the classical pathway, by creating nascent C3b, can lead to activation of the alternative pathway. Thus, the alternative pathway can act to amplify the action of the classical pathway.

Activation of C3 and the Terminal Components

Whether C3 is activated via the classical or alternative pathways, the α chain of the C3 is cleaved, generating two fragments of unequal size, C3a and C3b (Fig. 111-4). In the classical pathway C3 convertase, the C2a carries the active site.[20]

In the alternative pathway C3 convertase, the Bb carries the active site.[49] The activation of C3 by either of the two C3 convertases represents an amplification step, since hundreds of C3 molecules can be cleaved by one C3 convertase. Cleavage of native C3 by either convertase releases a small peptide (C3a) from the α chain into the fluid phase, where it acts as an anaphylatoxin (see below). Most of the nascent C3b is also released into the fluid phase, where it rapidly is inactivated through hydrolysis. Other molecules of C3b, however, bind covalently to the cell surface or immunoglobulins through transesterification with hydroxyl groups of polysaccharides or amidation of amino groups on proteins (reviewed in Ref. 50). The cell-bound C3b may then be degraded by factor I and other proteases, yielding a variety of cleavage products (Fig. 111-4). If the cell-bound C3 is not degraded, it is then able to act as an opsonin (see below) or combine with either of the C3 convertases to create two new enzymes, the alternative and classical pathway C5 convertases. The classical pathway C5-cleaving enzyme is composed of $\overline{C4b,2a,3b}$.[51] In this complex the C3b acts to bind the native C5 while the C2a carries the active enzymatic site. In the alternative pathway, the C5-cleaving enzyme is composed of $(C3b)_2,Bb$.[52] Apparently, in this enzymatic complex more than one C3b is needed to bind native C5 in a suitable position for cleavage by Bb.

Activation of C5 by either the alternative or classical pathway C5 convertases results in cleavage of the α chain of the native molecule to create a small molecular weight product,

Fig. 111-4 The proteolytic cleavage of C3. Step 1 involves the cleavage of the α chain by either the alternative pathway or classical pathway C3 convertases. Step 2 results from the action of factor I, with factor H or the CR1 (C3b) receptor serving as cofactors. Step 3 is also mediated by factor I and CR1. Step 4 involves cleavage by plasmin, trypsin, leukocyte elastase, and cathepsin G. (Modified from *Fearon and Wong.*[60])

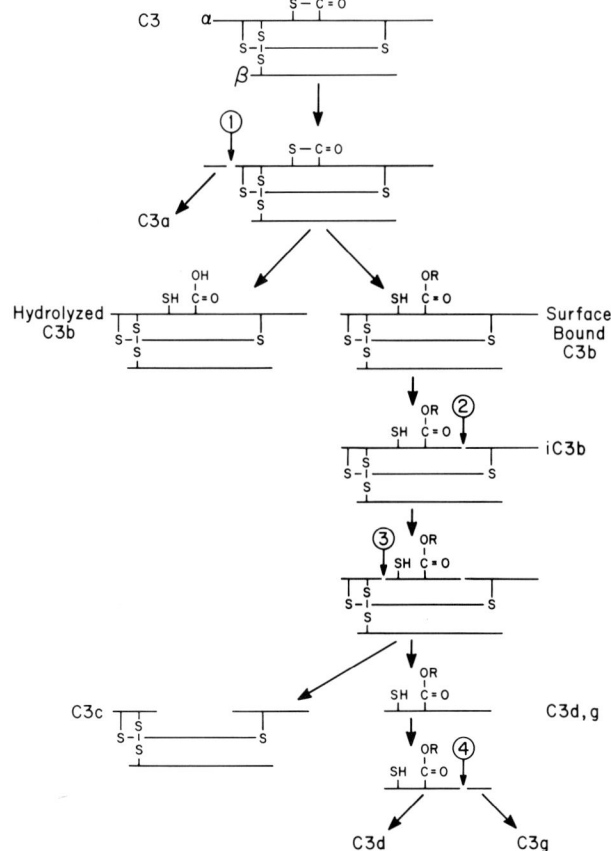

C5a, and a larger molecular weight product, C5b. The smaller cleavage product, C5a, is released into the fluid phase where it, like C3a, can act as an anaphylatoxin (see below). In addition, C5a possesses potent chemotactic activity (see below). If the C5b combines with native C6 while it is still attached to the C5 convertase, it is stabilized and can initiate formation of the membrane attack complex, a multimolecular assembly of C5b, C6, C7, C8, and C9 which is capable of cytolytic activity.[1,53] The initial event is stabilization of the nascent C5b by C6.[54] Addition of C7 to form the C5b,6,7 complex leads to insertion of hydrophobic domains of this trimolecular complex into the cell membrane and results in stable binding to the cell membrane.[55-57] The addition of C8 leads to further insertion of the complex and the generation of small and unstable pores in the membrane through which small molecules can pass.[53,58] On reaction of C5b-8 with C9, and polymerization of C9, a large and stable transmembrane channel is formed, leading to accelerated lysis of the target cell.[59]

BIOLOGIC CONSEQUENCES OF COMPLEMENT ACTIVATION

Complement Receptors

Receptors for many of the cleavage products of individual components of complement exist on a variety of cells (reviewed in Ref. 60). In general, two types of cleavage products are generated as the result of complement activation: small molecular weight, diffusible fragments, such as C4a, C3a, and C5a, and large molecular weight fragments, primarily C3b and its degradation products, which fix to the activating material.

Receptors for C3a, C4a, and C5a are present on mast cells, and receptors for C5a are also found on neutrophils, monocytes, and macrophages.[61] Presumably, the interactions of C3a, C4a, and C5a with these receptors are responsible for initiating the anaphylatoxic and chemotactic responses of these cells.

There are three distinct receptors for C3b and its cleavage products. The CR1 receptor (C3b-C4b receptor) is found on polymorphonuclear leukocytes, eosinophils, monocytes, macrophages, mast cells, glomerular podocytes, B lymphocytes, and some T lymphocytes (reviewed in Ref. 60). In addition, it is found on the erythrocytes of primates, including human beings.[62] Although C3b is the primary ligand for the CR1 receptor, it is also capable of binding C4b. One of the more important functions of the CR1 receptor is to enhance the phagocytosis of particles opsonized with C3b.[63] In addition, its presence on erythrocytes may allow them to bind circulating immune complexes bearing C3b and to transport the immune complexes to cells of the reticuloendothelial system.[64] Finally, CR1 can act to dissociate Bb from the C3b,Bb enzyme and act as a cofactor in the factor I–mediated cleavage of C3b to iC3b,[65] functions it holds in common with factor H. In an analogous fashion, it can dissociate C2a from the $\overline{C4b,2a}$ enzyme and act as cofactor in the cleavage of C4b to iC4b by factor I.[66]

The CR2 receptor is found on B lymphocytes and binds C3d,g and C3d as well as iC3b. The functional significance of CR2 on B lymphocytes is unclear but may relate in some way to the role of C3 in humoral immunity. The CR3 receptor is found on the same cells as the CR1 receptor and its primary ligand appears to be iC3b.

Anaphylatoxic Activity

The smaller cleavage products of both C3 and C5 (C3a and C5a) possess anaphylatoxic activity.[67] Each of these small molecular polypeptides (9000 and 11,000 Da, respectively) is cleaved from the N-terminal portion of the α chain of their respective parent molecules. When compared on a molar basis, C5a is a more potent anaphylatoxin than C3a.[68] Both of these anaphylatoxins are subject to attack by a serum carboxypeptidase. This enzyme rapidly cleaves the C-terminal arginine that is common to both these molecules and in each case creates a new molecule (C3a-desArg and C5a-desArg, respectively) that is a significantly less potent anaphylatoxin than the parent molecule. It should also be noted that C4a also possesses some anaphylatoxic activity but much less so than either C3a or C5a[69]; its biologic significance is unclear.

Complement-derived anaphylatoxins possess a variety of activities of biologic significance. They were originally identified through their abilities to cause histamine release from basophils and certain tissue mast cells, to promote smooth-muscle contraction, and to increase vascular permeability (reviewed in Ref. 61). More recently, additional functions of these peptides have been identified (reviewed in Ref. 68). Anaphylatoxins can promote the aggregation of platelets and the subsequent release of arachidonic acid metabolites from them. In addition, they can cause leukocytes to aggregate, to generate arachidonic acid metabolites, to produce toxic oxygen radicals, and to discharge their granular enzymes.

Chemotactic Activity

The smaller cleavage product of C5, C5a, is also a potent chemotactic factor causing the directed movement of polymorphonuclear leukocytes and monocytes as well as eosinophils and basophils (reviewed in Ref. 70). When the terminal arginine is removed by the action of carboxypeptidase B, producing C5a-desArg, the molecule loses approximately 90 percent of its activity.[71] Interestingly, C5a-desArg has a lower affinity than native C5a for the C5a receptor, which corresponds to its lower biologic potential for chemotactic activity. In addition to its role in cell movement, C5a also promotes adherence of phagocytic cells to vascular endothelium,[72] a necessary prerequisite to their exit from the intravascular compartment. A variety of in vivo studies have demonstrated that C5a plays an important role in attracting phagocytic cells to local sites of microbial invasion.[73,74]

Opsonic Activity

The larger cleavage product of C3, C3b, acts as a potent opsonin when fixed to the surface of a microorganism.[75] It appears that C3b subserves different opsonic functions depending on the nature of the phagocytic cell and its state of activation. In the case of neutrophils and nonactivated macrophages, C3b promotes attachment of the particle, whereas immunoglobulin G acts to favor ingestion.[76] In the case of activated macrophages, C3b serves to aid in both attachment and ingestion.[77]

There is a great deal of data suggesting that C3-dependent opsonic activity is one of the more important activities of the complement system. Studies in experimental animals have shown that C3 is an important opsonin in both the nonim-

mune host,[78] as well as in hosts who have high levels of antibody.[79]

Bactericidal Activity

The generation of complement-mediated serum bactericidal activity requires the participation of the entire terminal complement sequence (reviewed in Ref. 80). Although bactericidal activity can occur in the absence of C9, killing proceeds at a very much slower rate.[81] Only gram-negative bacteria can be killed by complement. Although protoplasts of gram-positive organisms are susceptible to lysis by complement,[82] intact gram-positive organisms are not, suggesting that their thick cell wall somehow interferes with the bactericidal action of C5–C9. The site of action of C5–C9 appears to be the outer lipid membrane of gram-negative organisms,[83] but the exact mechanism by which killing occurs is unclear.[84]

Processing of Immune Complexes

The complement system also appears to play an important role in the processing of immune complexes (reviewed in Ref. 85). There are a number of mechanisms by which the complement system could modify the structure and/or influence the biologic activities of immune complexes. First, the activation of C3 via the classical pathway can retard the formation of large complexes and prevent, to some degree, their precipitation from serum.[86] Second, once complexes are formed, they can be solubilized by the complement system.[87] Apparently, it is much easier to prevent immune precipitation than it is to solubilize the complexes once they have formed. The mechanisms by which complement modifies the structure of immune complexes are incompletely understood. Clearly, the covalent binding of C3b to the immune complex is important in both the prevention of precipitation and the solubilization of preformed complexes. The biologic significance of the role of C3 in the inhibition and/or solubilization of immune complexes in

Fig. 111-5 *Upper panel:* Chromosomal localization of the human complement genes. The order and orientation of complement genes on chromosome 1 is not known. *Lower panel:* organization of the human major histocompatibility complex on chromosome 6p. Class I, II, and III genes are shown.

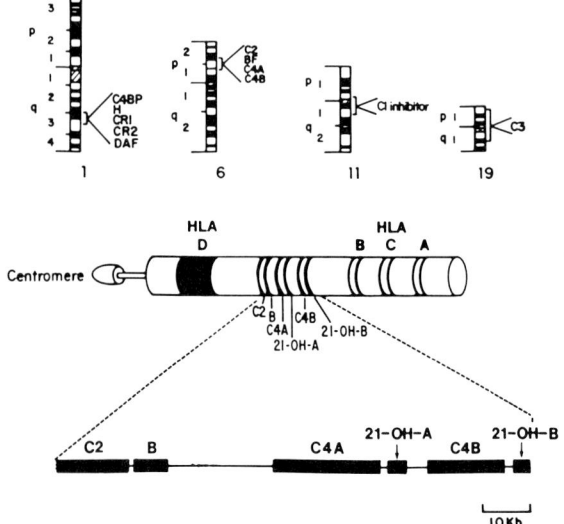

vivo is not fully understood. However, in an experimental model of serum sickness, C3 was shown to be necessary for the efficient removal of immune complexes in the kidney, suggesting that C3 may play an important role in solubilization of immune complexes in vivo.[88]

Opsonically active C3b can also enhance the uptake of immune complexes by macrophages in vivo,[89] suggesting that phagocytic cells of the reticuloendothelial system can clear circulating immune complexes in vivo. Primates may have an additional complement-mediated mechanism available for handling immune complexes. Primates possess receptors for C3b on their erythrocytes,[62] and circulating immune complexes bearing C3b will fix to erythrocytes through these receptors. The erythrocyte-bound complexes are then transported to the liver, where they are stripped from the erythrocytes and cleared from the circulation.[64] In this manner, erythrocytes may serve as a buffer for the disposal of circulating immune complexes in human beings.

Role of Complement in Antibody Formation

Interest in the role of complement in antibody formation has been stimulated by a number of independent but related observations. Monocytes, macrophages, B lymphocytes, and a subset of T lymphocytes all have receptors for C3 and/or C5 cleavage products,[60] and it is therefore possible that their participation in the generation of a normal antibody response could be influenced by the complement system. In fact, a variety of in vitro studies have shown that cleavage products of both C3 and C5 can either enhance or inhibit a number of cellular functions important in the generation of a normal antibody response.[90] The in vivo significance of these in vitro studies has been difficult to predict since the inhibitory or enhancing effects of these different C3 and C5 cleavage products operate at different steps in a complex series of cell-to-cell interactions.

In vivo studies, however, using experimental animals pharmacologically depleted of C3[91] or using animals with genetically determined deficiencies of C4[92] or C3,[93] have clearly shown the complement system to be important in the generation of a normal antibody response. The antibody response to T-dependent antigens is relatively more dependent on an intact complement system than is the response to T-independent antigens. In addition, an intact complement system is needed for the isotype switch from IgM to IgG in the normal immune response. The mechanisms by which the complement system participates in antibody formation are unknown.

MOLECULAR GENETICS OF COMPLEMENT: GENERAL CONSIDERATIONS

Gene Families

The complement genes have been grouped into supergene families on the basis of similarities in structure, function, and chromosomal localization. For instance, the genes encoding C2, factor B, and C4 constitute the class III genes of the major histocompatibility complex (MHC) on human chromosome 6 (Fig. 111-5). The 3' terminus of the C2 gene is upstream of,

and close to, the 5' terminus of the factor B gene (<500 base pairs).[94] The two C4 genes (C4A and C4B) lie approximately 30 kb downstream from the C2 and factor B genes. The C4 loci are separated by 10 kb, and each has a cytochrome P_{450} steroid 21-hydroxylase (21-OH) gene within 1.5 kb of the 3' terminus.[95–97] The order of the genes in the direction of transcription is C2-BF-C4A-210HA-C4B-210HB, and they have been mapped within a 0.7-cM region between HLA-B and HLA-DR.[98,99] Factor B and C2 are similar in structural and functional features, suggesting that the genes were derived from a common ancestral gene.[100] The topology of the MHC class III genes is highly conserved in evolution, as shown in several studies of the corresponding region in mice.[101,102]

The genes encoding complement receptors CR1 and CR2, C4-binding protein, factor H, and decay-accelerating factor (DAF) may be considered members of another supergene family because they are closely clustered on the long arm of chromosome 1[103–106] and their products share several structural and functional characteristics. Direct sequence analyses of genes within this family have recently demonstrated repeating homology units of approximately 60 residues which are also seen in the sequence of C2,[100] factor B,[107,108] and C1r.[109] One property common to all the proteins that have these highly conserved repeating homology units is their capacity to bind fragments of C3 and C4. Therefore, the complement regulatory genes on chromosome 1 and the genes encoded in the class III region of the MHC on chromosome 6 may be considered parts of a larger supergene family related because of their capacity to interact with the activation fragments of C3 and C4 (reviewed in Ref. 109). These repeating homology units are also found in noncomplement proteins such as the IL-2 receptor, β_2-glycoprotein 1, the haptoglobin α chain, and the herpes simplex virus glycoprotein C, all proteins that have not been shown to interact with C3 or C4. The presence of these repetitive homologous sequences in herpes simplex virus glycoprotein C may reflect fortuitous or directed insertion of the viral genome at one or several of the loci of this gene family during evolution; i.e., homologies based not on divergence from an ancestral gene but on encounter with infectious agents.

The genes for complement proteins C3, C4, and C5 have been described as a family that shares similar gene structure and primary protein structural and functional properties with α_2-macroglobulin and the pregnancy zone protein. These genes all encode multichain disulfide-linked molecules. Except for C5, a thiolester reactive site is a distinct characteristic of this family. These genes do not appear to be clustered in a specific chromosomal region, however.

Based on primary sequence homologies, several of the proteins of the membrane attack complex also appear to be members of a single gene family.[110–112] That is, the C8 α chain, the C8 β chain (encoded by separate messenger RNAs), C9, and the cytolytic protein derived from natural killer cells, perforin, share sequence and domain homologies.

C1 inhibitor shares structural and functional characteristics with several serine proteinase inhibitors, so that it is often included in the "SERPIN" (serine proteinase inhibitor) supergene family (see below). The chromosomal localization of several SERPIN genes has been determined. C1 inhibitor maps to human chromosome 11,[113] whereas another member of this family, α_1-proteinase inhibitor, is localized on chromosome 14.

Protein Polymorphism

Approximately two decades ago genetically determined electrophoretic variants of the C3 protein were observed (reviewed in Ref. 114). The relatively high concentrations of C3 in serum permits direct visualization of C3 variants in prolonged agarose gel electrophoresis. The common C3 variants are found in all major racial groups, and about 20 rare variants have been detected in one or several populations. Other methods have been used to detect genetic variants, at the protein level, of the other polymorphic complement proteins such as factor B, C2, C4, C6, C7, C8, and factor D.[114] In some instances the structural basis for this genetic variation has been determined by extensive sequence analysis of cDNA clones.[115] A number of studies have reported associations between polymorphic forms of individual components of complement and certain diseases (reviewed in Refs. 114, 116, 117), but the bases for the associations are not known.

Considerable attention has been given to an analysis of the complement proteins encoded by genes within the MHC. Studies of protein polymorphisms of the C2, factor B, C4A, and C4B loci, together with typing of the class I and class II genes, have generated the concept of "extended" haplotypes.[118] This concept derives from data in haplotypes showing a decreased frequency of recombinant events extending over a 7 to 14 megabase region of chromosome 6. Taken together, the extended halotypes account for nearly 30 percent of haplotypes in normal Caucasian populations studied thus far. These observations have relevance for the well-recognized association of a number of diseases with the extended haplotypes and the remarkable finding that mixed lymphocyte cultures from unrelated individuals sharing the same two extended haplotypes exhibit low or absent reactivity.[119] The latter has considerable implications for transplantation biology.[120,121]

MOLECULAR GENETICS OF COMPLEMENT: SPECIFIC COMPONENTS

C1

As noted earlier, C1 is a macromolecule consisting of three noncovalently bound subcomponents: C1q, C1r, and C1s. Biosynthesis of the C1 macromolecular complex has been demonstrated in primary and long-term epithelial cell cultures, in mononuclear phagocytes, and in fibroblasts.[122] In addition, hepatoma-derived cell lines[123] synthesize the subcomponents C1r and C1s. These studies and others[124] indicate that the regulation of C1q synthesis is independent of the control of C1r and C1s synthesis.

The C1q B chain gene is 2.6 kb long and has a single 1.1-kb intron in its coding region.[125] This intron is located in the middle of a region coding for the collagenlike moiety of the molecule, interrupting the collagen sequence exactly at the site at which the triple helix of C1q bends when viewed in the electron microscope. This is one of several features that distinguishes C1q from the human collagen proteins.[126] Complementary DNA sequences for the A and C chain of C1q have not been reported. Further information about the structure of C1q may allow the elucidation of the molecular mechanisms for several variants that have been described: a form of C1q deficiency characterized by a C1q molecule with apparent molecular mass of 155 kDa (normal is 460 kDa)[127]; fibroblast C1q with an apparent molecular mass of 800 kDa[128]; colostral C1q with an unusually large apparent molecular mass[129]; and a form of C1q which apparently functions as an immunoglobulin (Fc) receptor on the surface of guinea pig peritoneal macrophages.[130]

Isolation of cDNA clones for the C1 subcomponents C1r and C1s has been reported in a preliminary communication.[131] These two subcomponents are similar in enzymatic activity and subunit structure, but differ in other characteristics and appear to be under distinct regulatory controls.[132]

C4

The fourth component of complement is a three-chain disulfide-linked glycoprotein (≈ 200 kDa). Hepatic synthesis of the 185-kDa single-chain precursor of C4, pro-C4,[133,134] is directed by a polyadenylated mRNA of approximately 5 kb.[135,136] Posttranslational modification involves proteolytic excision of two intersubunit-linking peptides,[137,138] sulfation,[139] modification of residues generating the thiolester reactive site,[140] and glycosylation of the α and β subunits.[141,142] There is also a specific proteolytic cleavage of a carboxy-terminal fragment of the C4 α chain which is mediated by a metalloenzyme.[143,144]

The complete nucleotide sequences of the two human C4 genes, C4A and C4B, have been determined.[145,146] The C4A gene is 22 kb in size. A variation in size of the C4B gene (16 kb in some individuals and 22 kb in other individuals) is a result of the absence or presence of a 6.8 kb intron toward the 5′ terminus of the C4B gene.[95,147] There are only four amino acid differences between the two genes.[115] This variation in sequence is located around the active site, the thiolester region of the C4 α chain, and is thought to explain the differences in functional activity of the C4A and C4B gene products. C4B reacts more effectively with hydroxyl groups and is two- to fourfold more effective in complement activation, while C4A reacts more readily with amino groups, such as those displayed by immune aggregates.[148,149] The variation in sequence between C4A and C4B does not explain the apparent 2-kDa difference in α-chain size between the two isotypes.[150]

A relatively high frequency of duplications, deletions, and rearrangements leads to polymorphic variation in the human C4 genes. Many of the variants and null alleles ascribed to these genes are based on electrophoretic mobility of the C4 protein. By direct analysis of gene structure several additional polymorphic variations have been defined, and estimates of the frequency of homoduplications and deletions have been revised.[115,151,152]

Synthesis of human C4 is regulated by immune interferon (IFN-γ), but the effects of this mediator differ for C4A and C4B.[153] That is, interferon induces a fivefold increase in steady state levels of C4A mRNA and in the rate of C4A synthesis, but only a 1.5- to 2.0-fold increase in C4B expression. Since C4 is not responsive to IL-1 or tumor necrosis factor (TNF) cachectin, it is likely that its acute response is predominantly mediated by interferon.

Factor B and C2

Human factor B is encoded at a single genetic locus.[94,154] The human factor B gene is approximately 6 kb long and is divided into 18 exons.[94] Three exons coding for regions within the Ba fragment show significant sequence homology with each other, i.e., they may be products of tandem duplication. These exons encode repeating homology units of 60 amino acids that are also found in C2, C1r, C4-bp, CR1, factor H, IL-2 receptor, β_2-glycoprotein 1, and clotting factor XIII.[109] The organization of the factor B gene in the region encoding the carboxy terminus of the Bb fragment is similar, with the exception of a single exon, to that observed in chymotrypsin, elastase, kallikrein, and trypsin. The amino terminus of the Bb fragment is encoded by five exons that do not bear any homology with other serine proteases. This is consistent with the observation that both factor B and C2 are unique among the serine proteases; i.e., the catalytic chains are approximately twice the size of other serine proteases.[94]

A high degree of structural conservation of factor B has been noted in a comparison of mice and humans,[155] with 83 percent of the residues in mice identical with the corresponding regions of the human protein in the coding region. In addition, the 3' untranslated region displays 59 percent sequence identity between the two species. The functional significance of homology in noncoding sequences in the 3'-flanking region is unknown, but conservation of structure in this region may be of functional importance in expression of the factor B protein.

The fine details of C2 genomic structure have not been published, but preliminary data suggest many similarities between the C2 and factor B genes even though there is only approximately 35 percent homology in the derived amino acid sequences.[94,100,154] There is a significantly lower frequency of polymorphic variation in C2 and factor B than in C4 or the class I and class II MHC gene products. Nevertheless, several allelic forms of these two proteins have been defined by electrophoretic techniques[114,120] and by restriction endonuclease digestion.[156-158]

C2 mRNA programs the translation of three distinct polypeptides.[159] The three forms of C2 are probably derived from differential transcription or posttranscriptional processing. Translation of the most abundant C2 mRNA ($\approx$2.8 kb) generates a product that is secreted within 1 to 2 h. Two forms of C2 of lower molecular mass remain cell-associated. These multiple forms of C2 have also been detected in murine L cells transfected with a genomic fragment bearing the human C2 and factor B genes,[102] but the significance of the multiplicity is not yet appreciated.

In extrahepatic mononuclear phagocytes, the proportion of C2-producing cells and the rates of synthesis per cell vary as a function of cellular maturation and tissue origin.[160] For example, the proportion of C2-producing cells increases from 0 detected in bone marrow mononuclear cells and 10 percent in blood monocytes to 45 percent in spleen and peritoneal cavity. Only 2.5 percent of lung (bronchoalveolar lavage) macrophages produce C2, but the higher rate of synthesis of C2 per bronchoalveolar cell compensates for the lower proportion of C2-producing cells.[161] Local C2 synthesis is affected during an inflammatory response, at least in part, by a pretranslational regulatory mechanism. That is, the net tissue concentration of C2 is augmented not only by an increase in cell number but also by increases in C2 mRNA and rate of synthesis of C2 per cell.[162,163] γ-Interferon (IFN-γ) is one of the mediators of this change in C2 expression.

Synthesis of the factor B primary translation product is directed by a 2.6-kb polyadenylated mRNA.[164] The synthesis and secretion of factor B is similar to that described for C2, but important differences, including the response to cytokines that regulate factor B and C2 gene expression, have been ob-

served. Control of factor B synthesis is rather complex and almost certainly is exerted at multiple levels. Recent data demonstrate a genetically determined independent regulation of factor B and C2 in murine hepatocytes and macrophages. Peritoneal macrophages elicited with starch or thioglycollate synthesize factor B at about the same rate as resident cells, but specific signals (e.g., LPS, IFN-γ) can also trigger rather significant changes in expression of the factor B gene.

In human mononuclear phagocytes, a small but significant increase in C2 and factor B mRNA is induced by the lipid A component of endotoxin (LPS).[165] A corresponding increase in factor B protein synthesis (two- to threefold) is noted, but net C2 protein synthesis is not affected by lipopolysaccharide. These findings suggest that an increase in C2 translation rate requires a second signal, or that there is increased catabolism of C2 protein in the presence of LPS. Endotoxin injection elicits a dose-dependent increase in factor B gene expression in liver and in extrahepatic tissues (e.g., lung, kidney, intestine, spleen, heart, and peritoneal macrophages).[166]

IL-1 regulates factor B expression in murine hepatocytes and in human hepatoma cell lines[167,168] and in extrahepatic sites. Whether extrahepatic factor B gene expression (especially in peritoneal macrophages) is regulated directly by IL-1 (autocrine or paracrine regulation) or via another cytokine (e.g., IFN-γ) is uncertain.

In primary hepatocyte cultures, IL-1 induces a dose- and time-dependent, reversible increase in expression of the factor B gene and a decrease in albumin gene expression.[168] This regulation is pretranslational, since the kinetics and direction of change in specific mRNA for factor B and albumin correspond to the change in synthesis of the respective proteins. The small size of the factor B 5'-flanking region (limited by the 3' terminus of the IL-1–unresponsive C2 gene) provides a well-defined region to probe the structural basis for the differential effect of IL-1 on factor B and the closely related gene for C2. Murine fibroblasts transfected with human DNA bearing the C2 and Bf genes synthesize and secrete C2 and factor B proteins.[167] In the transfectant, human factor B gene expression, but not C2 gene expression, is increased when the cells are incubated with IL-1.

IFN-γ regulates expression of both the C2 and factor B genes in primary cell culture and in the MHC class III transfectants.[169] IFN-γ induces a dose-dependent increase in synthesis of C2 and factor B protein. Regulation is pretranslational, but the kinetics and magnitude of the response to IFN-γ for the two proteins is different. In both primary cultures of human monocytes and in the class III transfectants, the IFN-γ–induced increase in factor B always precedes and exceeds the increase in C2 gene expression.

C3

The human C3 gene has been mapped to chromosome 19.[170] The human and murine C3 genes show considerable similarities in size ($\approx$24 kb) and, to the extent known, in organization. Pro C3 is a 185-kDa two-chain disulfide-linked glycoprotein, which is synthesized as a single chain precursor, pre-pro-C3. The synthesis of pre-pro-C3 is programmed by a $\approx$5-kb mRNA. Postsynthetic cleavage by signal peptidase and a plasminlike enzyme generates native C3.[171-174] As in the case for the precursors of C4 (pro-C4) and C5 (pro-C5), the β chain is the amino-terminal segment in pro-C3. The complete nucleotide sequences of human and murine C3 cDNA clones have been reported.[175,176] The human C3 precursor contains a signal peptide of 22 amino acids, a region of 645 residues corresponding to the β chain and a 992-amino acid α chain. A region of four basic amino acids separating the β and α chain is the intersubunit peptide cleaved during processing to the mature two-chain molecule.

Expression of the C3 gene is regulated by several mediators. Bacterial LPS increases net C3 protein synthesis five- to thirtyfold in adult human mononuclear phagocytes,[165] by a pretranslational mechanism; i.e., the concentration of C3-specific mRNA is increased at least fivefold. C3 gene expression in hepatocytes is regulated by IL-1 and by TNF[167,169,177] and in extrahepatic sites by IL-1 and IFN-γ. Hence, well-defined mediators of hepatocyte and macrophage function affect expression of this key component of the complement cascade.

C5

C5 is synthesized in hepatocytes and macrophages as a single chain precursor, pro-C5.[178,179] Pro-C5 undergoes posttranslational processing to generate a two-chain disulfide-linked molecule with β-α–chain orientation.[180] Most of the coding sequences of human and murine C5 have been determined[180,181] and are homologous from positions 372 to 812. The sequences include an open reading frame of 4920 base pairs specifying 1640-amino acid residues. Comparison of the derived murine C5 sequence with previously determined sequences for murine C3 and C4 reveals a high degree of primary structural homology, but in C5 there is substitution of serine for cysteine and alanine for the proximal glutamine which gives rise to the intramolecular thiolester bond in C3 and C4.

Components of the Membrane Attack Complex: C6 to C9

Relatively little information about the structural and functional properties of C6 and C7 is available. C8 consists of three chains, two of which (α and γ) are disulfide-linked. Each C8 polypeptide is synthesized in the liver. The cDNAs for α and β subunits of human C8 have been cloned.[110,111] The translated portion of the α subunit is 1659 bases long with a leader sequence of 30 amino acids and a region of 10 amino acids followed by an arginine-rich tetrapeptide typical for propeptides. A 2.5-kb mRNA in human hepatoma cells hybridizes with this cDNA probe. The β subunit cDNA has an open reading frame of 1608 base pairs. Features of these cDNA clones and the message sizes suggest that separate mRNAs code for the α and γ subunits making it likely that three distinct messenger RNA species encode the C8 protein.[110] There is considerable homology between the α and β subunits, C9, and the LDL receptor. Allelic variants of the C8 α-γ subunit have been identified by isoelectric focusing.[182–184] Family studies of one of these variants has suggested linkage with markers known to be localized to chromosome 1.[184]

The primary amino acid sequence of C9 consists of 573 residues as deduced from cDNA sequencing.[185–187] The amino-terminal portion is hydrophilic, and the carboxy terminus is hydrophobic in nature. This structure is consistent with previous studies, suggesting that the carboxy terminus of C9 is inserted into phospholipid membranes during the formation of complement-mediated membrane lesions. In the amino-terminal portion of the molecule there is a region with multiple cysteine residues which is highly homologous to a cysteine-rich domain in the LDL receptor. As indicated previously, there is also structural homology between C9 and perforin, a product of cytolytic lymphocytes.[188]

Factor D

Factor D is a 25-kDa single chain glycoprotein. It is synthesized by monocytes and macrophages.[189,190] The mechanism of activation of factor D and regulation of its synthesis have not been studied. These studies should prove to be especially interesting since factor D is apparently synthesized as an active enzyme, i.e., it is not produced in zymogen form.

C1 Inhibitor

C1 inhibitor is a glycoprotein with an estimated molecular mass of 105 kDa and total carbohydrate content of 33 percent.[191] Liver is the major source of plasma C1 inhibitor,[123,192–194] but mononuclear phagocytes from extrahepatic sites also synthesize the inhibitor protein as well as the enzymes C1s and C1r.[132,195] Synthesis of C1s and C1 inhibitor in these cells is controlled independently by a product or products of activated lymphocytes.[132]

The primary sequence of the C1 inhibitor has been determined.[113,196] It has approximately 20 percent homology with serine protease inhibitors α₁-proteinase inhibitor, α₁-antichymotrypsin, antithrombin III, and angiotensinogen. The intron-exon structure of C1 inhibitor is also similar to that of antithrombin III, α₁-proteinase inhibitor, and rat angiotensinogen. There is, however, an amino-terminal domain of C1 inhibitor that shares no homology with the other serine proteinase inhibitors.

C4-Binding Protein

C4-binding protein (C4-bp) is a 550-kDa polypeptide that is composed of seven to eight identical 70-kDa disulfide-linked chains. It is synthesized in human liver.[197] Complementary DNA clones for human C4-bp have allowed determination of the complete nucleotide sequence of the C4-bp mRNA.[197] Human C4-bp contains 549 amino acids with the 491 amino-terminal amino acids divided into eight 60-amino acid homologous repeating units with a characteristic framework of highly conserved residues. C4-bp appears in the electron microscope as a spiderlike structure with "tentacles" connected at one end to a central "core," making it likely that the repeating units are arranged with the nonhomologous carboxy-terminal residues constituting the core.[109,198]

Several polymorphic variants of C4-bp have been demonstrated by isoelectric focusing.[199] Comparison of the derived amino acid sequence of human C4-bp and amino acid sequence determined for the protein purified from pooled human plasma suggest that there are at least two regions in which variability is likely to occur.[200]

Decay-Accelerating Factor

Decay-accelerating factor (DAF) has an apparent molecular mass of 75 to 80 kDa. It is heavily glycosylated, especially with serine- and threonine-linked carbohydrate.[201] There appear to be both plasma membrane and secreted forms of the molecule,[201,202] generated by alternative posttranscriptional splicing pathways that lead to distinct mRNAs encoding the membrane and secreted forms of DAF.[203] DAF is expressed in many cell types, including erythrocytes, granulocytes, monocytes, and endothelial cells.[204] The complete nucleotide sequence of human DAF cDNA has been determined.[205] This cDNA sequence codes for 347 amino acids beginning at the amino terminus with four contiguous 61 amino acids consensus repeats similar to those described above. There is a serine- and threonine-rich sequence similar to that of the LDL receptor. The carboxy-terminal segment consists of a hydrophobic sequence similar to that of most integral membrane proteins.

Factor H

Factor H (H) is a 150-kDa single chain glycoprotein that regulates the activity of C3b. Factor H is synthesized in liver and macrophages. It is composed of 20 homologous repeating units starting from the amino terminus of the processed protein and similar to those of C4-bp and the other structurally related proteins mentioned above.[108] There is relatively little information about the regulation of H or the other complement regulatory proteins available.

Factor I

Factor I is a heterodimer composed of disulfide-linked 50-kDa and 38-kDa subunits; 11 to 20 percent of its weight constitutes asparagine-linked carbohydrate. The light chain bears homology with the classic serine proteinases, especially the plasminogen activators. It is synthesized in human hepatoma cells as a single chain precursor, pro-I, and undergoes posttranslational proteolysis to generate the mature protein.[206] It is also synthesized in human mononuclear phagocytes.[190] cDNA clones for factor I have been isolated and the gene localized to chromosome 4.[207]

Complement C3 Receptors: CR1, CR2, and CR3

A partial cDNA sequence for the human C3b-C4b receptor (CR1) has been published[208] from which an estimated 78 percent of the coding sequence has now been determined. Three long homologous repeats, each of 450 amino acids, are present in the extracellular domain. Within each long homologous repeat are seven consensus repeats of 60 to 70 amino acids each. Invariant residues in these consensus repeats include four half-cystines, a tryptophan, and a glycine similar to those in factor H, C4-bp, CR2, Ba, C2b, IL-2 receptor, β₂-glycoprotein 1, C1r, factor XIIIb subunit, and haptoglobin α chain. Limited sequence analysis of CR1 genomic clones suggests that each repeat is encoded by a distinct exon, as is the case for the Ba fragment of factor B. A nonrepetitive sequence has been identified in the carboxy-terminal portion of CR1. A hydrophobic segment of 25 amino acids followed by four positively charged amino acids is probably the membrane spanning segment, and 43 amino acids at the carboxy terminus probably represent the cytoplasmic tail. There is a six-residue sequence in the cytoplasmic tail that has 65 percent homology with the protein kinase C phosphorylation site in the epidermal growth factor receptor and the erb B oncogene.

Several structural polymorphisms of CR1 have been identified. Three allotype variants, S, F, and F′, are associated with proteins of different apparent molecular mass.[209–211] Another variant resulting in a lower number of CR1 molecules per cell but without a change in structure[212] has recently been associated with a specific restriction fragment length polymorphism.[213]

CR2 is the C3d–Epstein-Barr virus receptor of B lymphocytes and follicular dendritic cells of the spleen. It is a 145-kDa glycoprotein composed of a single polypeptide and 8 to 11 asparagine-linked oligosaccharides.[214] It has been partially characterized by molecular cloning.[215] CR2 is highly homologous to CR1, having repeating units of 60 amino acids with conserved residues at 10 to 14 positions. Both genes have been localized to band q3.2 of human chromosome 1.

CR3 (also known as MO1) is the receptor that recognizes bound iC3b. It is composed of two subunits, a 155-kDa α chain and a 94-kDa β chain. The β subunit is shared by two other membrane proteins, LFA-1 (lymphocyte function–associated antigen) and p150,94.[216] Partial sequence analysis of cDNA clones for the common β subunit and p150,95 α subunit is now available.[217] The β subunit is 760 amino acids long, including a 22-amino acid signal sequence, a cystine-rich external domain with three to four tandem duplications, a single hydrophobic membrane-spanning region, and a 46-amino acid cytoplasmic tail. The β subunit also bears homology with the chicken fibronectin and the laminin receptor. The p150,95 α subunit is homologous with the human vitronectin receptor and platelet IIbIIa.

COMPLEMENT DEFICIENCIES: GENERAL CONSIDERATIONS

Genetically determined deficiencies have been described for nearly all of the individual components of the complement system[4,5,218] (Table 111-2). The usual mode of inheritance of the clinical phenotype is as an autosomal recessive trait. However, codominant expression of the defect is usually apparent at the protein level. There are two disorders which are not inherited as autosomal recessive traits. Deficiency of C1 esterase inhibitor has an autosomal dominant mode of inheritance, while properdin deficiency appears to be inherited as an X-linked recessive disorder.

Diagnosis

Most of the genetically determined deficiencies of the classical activating pathway (C1, C4, and C2), of C3, and of the terminal components (C5, C6, C7, C8, and C9) can be detected using antibody-sensitized sheep erythrocytes in a total serum hemolytic complement (CH₅₀) assay. Since this assay depends on the functional integrity of C1 through C9, severe deficiencies of any of these components lead to a marked reduction or absence of total hemolytic complement activity. There is one exception, however. The lysis of sensitized erythrocytes can occur in the absence of C9,[58] although at a much slower rate and to a lesser extent than in the presence of C9. Therefore, patients with C9 deficiency do have some serum hemolytic complement activity, but it is reduced to between one-third and one-half of the lower limit of normal.[219]

Table 111-2 Complement Deficiencies in Humans

Deficiency	Inheritance	Approximate number patients/kindreds	Major clinical manifestations
C1q	Autosomal recessive	17/10	Rheumatic disorders and pyogenic infections
C1r/s	Autosomal recessive	9/5	Rheumatic disorders
C4	Autosomal recessive	16/11	Rheumatic disorders and pyogenic infections
C2	Autosomal recessive	77/56	Rheumatic disorders and pyogenic infections
C3	Autosomal recessive	14/9	Pyogenic infections
C5	Autosomal recessive	17/11	Meningococcal sepsis and meningitis
C6	Autosomal recessive	33/24	Meningococcal sepsis and meningitis
C7	Autosomal recessive	22/16	Meningococcal sepsis and meningitis
C8	Autosomal recessive	33/22	Meningococcal sepsis and meningitis
C9	Autosomal recessive	5/5	Asymptomatic
Factor H	Autosomal recessive	2/1	Hemolytic uremic syndrome
Factor I	Autosomal recessive	6/5	Pyogenic infections
Properdin	X-linked recessive	6/2	Meningococcal sepsis and meningitis
C1 inhibitor	Autosomal dominant	100s/100s	Angioedema

SOURCE: Adapted from Ross and Densen[4] and Rother and Rother.[5]

Deficiencies of factor H, factor I, and properdin of the alternative activating pathway can be detected by a hemolytic assay that assesses lysis of rabbit erythrocytes mediated by the alternative pathway.[220] Rabbit erythrocytes are potent activators of the alternative pathway,[40] due in part to the fact that they have very low levels of surface sialic acid.[31,221] Obviously the serum of patients with deficiencies of C3 or C5–C9 will also be abnormal when tested in the rabbit erythrocyte assay (as well as in the CH_{50} assay), since the lysis of rabbit erythrocytes depends on these components as well as components of the alternative activating pathway.

The identification of the specific component that is deficient usually rests on both functional and immunochemical tests. Highly specific functional assays have been developed for each of the individual components.[222] They usually depend on reagents that lack the specific component in question but possess the other components of the hemolytic pathway in excess. Monospecific antibodies are also available for each of the individual components, allowing for their detection by immunochemical techniques. In most cases both functional and immunochemical assessment of the specific component will show the deficiency. There are some exceptions, however. For example, one form of C1 inhibitor deficiency[223] and one form of C1q deficiency[224] are characterized by dysfunctional proteins that can be detected by using immunochemical assays but are markedly reduced in functional activity. In addition, most forms of C8 deficiency are the result of deficiencies of only one portion of the complete three-chain molecule.[225] This, too, may lead to the detection of C8 antigen in the serum of such patients while their C8 function is markedly reduced.

Individuals who are heterozygous for a single component deficiency usually have normal total serum hemolytic complement (CH_{50}) levels, since this assay is not sensitive enough to reliably detect mild to moderate reductions in a single component. As a group, individuals who are heterozygous deficient usually have levels of the specific component that are approximately one-third to one-half the average level of normal. However, assignment of a given individual as a hetero-

zygote may be difficult since the range of values for normals may be quite wide and the levels in some heterozygotes may overlap the lower limit of normal. In some instances, such as in C2 deficiency[226] and C4 deficiency,[227] the gene for the deficiency is closely linked to the major histocompatibility complex, thus allowing family members of deficient individuals to be assigned as heterozygotes based on HLA typing. Similarly, it is possible to identify heterozygotes for C2 deficiency in populations[228] based on the fact that the gene for this deficiency is in linkage disequilibrium with specific HLA haplotypes.[229]

Clinical Presentation

The clinical presentation of individuals with genetically determined deficiencies of complement components has varied. While some individuals are asymptomatic, most have presented with either an increased susceptibility to infection, a variety of rheumatic diseases, or angioedema.[4,5,218] For each specific deficiency the fraction of individuals who are symptomatic is not known and probably varies depending on the individual component and the significance of its role in homeostasis.

An increased susceptibility to infection has been a prominent clinical finding in patients with complement deficiencies.[4,5,218] The kinds of infections that occur in patients with deficiencies of individual components relate to the biologic functions of those components. The third component of complement is an important opsonic ligand in both the nonimmune and the immune host.[78,79] Therefore, patients with a deficiency of C3, or with a deficiency of a component in either of the two pathways necessary for the activation of C3, have an increased susceptibility to encapsulated bacteria for which opsonization is the primary host defense (e.g., the pneumococcus, streptococci, and *Hemophilus influenzae*). Similarly, C5 through C9 form the membrane attack complex and are therefore responsible for the bactericidal-bacteriolytic functions of complement. Thus, patients with deficiencies of C5–C9 can opsonize bacteria normally and are not unduly susceptible to infection by bacteria for which opsonization is the primary host defense. These patients are, however, markedly susceptible to gram-negative bacteria, most notably neisserial species, since serum bactericidal activity is an important host defense against these organisms.

Although there may be some selection bias favoring the ascertainment of complement deficiencies in patients with an increased susceptibility to infection, there nevertheless appears to be a significant association between the two. For example, the prevalence of genetically determined complement deficiencies in unselected patients with systemic meningococcal disease is between 10 and 20 percent.[230,231] In addition, an analysis of all the reported individuals with complement deficiencies has shown that nonproband homozygous deficient individuals, ascertained as the result of family studies, also have a significantly higher number of serious bacterial infections (pneumonia, bacteremia, and meningitis) than does the general population.[4]

Patients with complement deficiencies also have a variety of clinical conditions that can best be characterized as rheumatic disorders.[4,5,218] These include disorders resembling discoid lupus or systemic lupus erythematosis (SLE) as well as glomerulonephritis, dermatomyositis, anaphylactoid purpura, and vasculitis. Although the prevalence of these inflammatory disorders is highest in those patients with deficiencies of the classical activating pathway (C1, C4, and C2) and of C3, they are nevertheless occasionally seen in patients with deficiencies of one of the terminal components as well.[4,5]

The pathophysiological basis for the association between these rheumatic disorders and complement deficiencies is unclear, but a number of possibilities exist. First, several studies have shown that components of the complement system can neutralize and/or lyse certain viruses in vitro,[232] while other studies in experimental animals have shown that C3 and C5 are important mechanisms of antiviral host defense in vivo.[233,234] Thus in some instances the rheumatic disorders seen in complement-deficient patients might be the consequence of an altered host response to recurrent or chronic viral infections. Second, the genes for three of the individual components of complement (C4, C2, and factor B) are located within the major histocompatibility complex and are in linkage disequilibrium with specific HLA haplotyes.[114,116,118,120,121] It is possible, therefore, that in other instances, the rheumatic disorders seen in complement-deficient patients are due in part to other genes within the major histocompatibility complex which in some manner influence immune function rather than to the deficiency in complement itself. Third, as mentioned above, C1, C4, C2, and C3 play an important role in the processing of immune complexes.[85] In fact, serums from patients deficient in these early components of the classical pathway do not inhibit the precipitation of immune complexes as well as normal serum.[85] Thus, the rheumatic diseases seen in these patients may reflect their inability to handle immune complexes normally. Finally, since the complement system appears to play some role in the generation of a normal antibody response,[90] the rheumatic diseases seen in complement-deficient patients could result from disordered humoral immunity.

There are some interesting and important differences between the rheumatic diseases seen in complement-deficient patients and their counterparts in "normal" non-complement-deficient individuals. For example, the SLE-like illness seen in complement-deficient individuals is usually characterized by an early onset (often in childhood), prominent annular photosensitive skin lesions resembling discoid lupus (Fig. 111-6), relatively limited renal and pleuropericardial involvement, and a relatively infrequent occurrence of immunoglobulin and C3 in the skin.[4,5,218] In addition, complement-deficient individuals with the lupuslike syndrome usually have absent or relatively low titers of both antinuclear antibodies and antinative DNA antibodies, and their lupus preparations are often negative.[218,228,235,236] In contrast, the incidence of anti-Ro (SSA) antibodies is significantly higher in complement-deficient patients with the lupuslike illness than it is in non-complement-deficient patients with lupus.[235,236] Thus, both with respect to some of their clinical manifestations and with respect to their serologic findings, complement-deficient patients with lupuslike syndromes bear a striking resemblance to a subgroup of lupus patients who are "ANA-negative."[237,238]

As with the relationship between complement deficiencies and infection, although there may be some selection bias favoring the ascertainment of complement deficiencies in patients with rheumatic disorders such as lupus or glomerulonephritis, there nevertheless appears to be a significant association between the two.[4] Individuals who are homozygous deficient for C1, C4, C2, or C3 but have been ascertained as a result of family studies also have a relatively high prevalence of SLE, discoid lupus, and/or glomerulonephritis. Additional evidence that there is a causal relationship between complement deficiencies and renal disease is provided by dogs with an inherited deficiency of C3 who have a very high incidence of membranoproliferative glomerulonephritis.[239]

COMPLEMENT DEFICIENCIES: SPECIFIC DISORDERS

C1q Deficiency

Only a limited number of individuals with C1q deficiency have been described.[4,240] In those instances in which a genetic basis has been determined, the deficiency appears to be inherited as an autosomal recessive trait.

Individuals with C1q deficiency generally have markedly reduced levels of both total hemolytic complement (CH$_{50}$) and C1 functional activity in their serums. Their levels of the other components of complement, including C1r and C1s, are generally normal. There appear to be at least two distinct forms of C1q deficiency.[240] In one form, no C1q can be detected by either functional or immunochemical analysis. In the other form, immunochemical C1q is present, but it lacks functional activity (dysfunctional C1q). Studies of the dysfunctional C1q in two different families have shown that it is antigenically deficient when compared to normal C1q.[224,241] In the one family in which it has been studied, heterozygotes have both normal C1q and the antigenically deficient molecule in their serum.[224] The dysfunctional C1q does not bind to immunoglobulin[127,241] nor does it interact with C1r and C1s.[127] The dysfunctional C1q found in one family is not the same as in another since the two abnormal molecules differ in molecular mass from each other as well as from normal C1q[127,241]; i.e., the deficiency is genetically heterogeneous.

The predominant clinical presentation associated with either form of C1q deficiency has been a lupuslike syndrome.[4,240] Although the disease has varied from patient to patient, both between and within families, skin lesions, fevers, arthralgias, and nephritis have been relatively common. As with other genetically determined complement deficiencies in which a lupuslike illness develops, ANA and anti-DNA antibodies are absent or present in low titers and LE preparations may be negative. Some patients with C1q deficiency also have an increased susceptibility to infection. In fact, three C1q-deficient patients have died of sepsis and/or meningitis.

C1r-C1s Deficiency

An inherited deficiency of C1r has been described in which C1r is markedly reduced (<1 percent of normal) and C1s is moderately reduced (between 20 and 50 percent of normal).[4,240] The disorder is inherited in an autosomal recessive fashion.

Patients with C1r-C1s deficiency have markedly reduced CH_{50} activity and C1 functional activity in their serums. Their C1q levels are normal. The basis for the association of the moderately reduced levels of C1s with the absence of C1r in these patients is unknown, but is quite interesting in view of the structural and functional similarities between C1r and C1s.

The clinical features of C1r-C1s deficiency are similar to those found in the other deficiencies of the classical activating pathway. Rheumatic disorders resembling lupus and glomerulonephritis have each been seen. In addition, some patients ascertained through family studies have been clinically well.

C4 Deficiency

Only a few patients with a genetically determined total C4 deficiency have been identified.[4,242] There are two loci within the major histocompatibility complex for C4, C4A and C4B.[243] Although the products of the two loci share functional, structural, and antigenic characteristics that identify them as C4, they differ with respect to electrophoretic mobility,[244] molecular weight of the α chain,[245] and functional hemolytic activity.[244] In addition, their antigenic display is in part different, since the product of the C4A locus is responsible for the serum- and red cell–associated Rogers blood group antigen and the product of the C4B locus is responsible for the Chido serum and red cell–associated blood group antigens.[246] Since there are two loci controlling the synthesis of C4, patients with

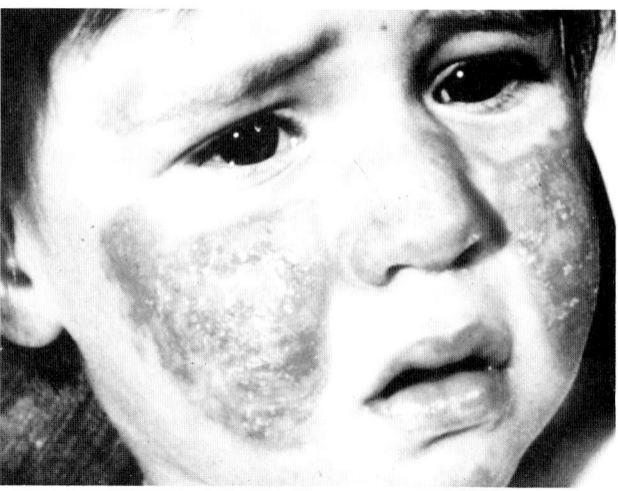

Fig. 111-6 Photosensitive skin lesions on the face of a child with C4 deficiency. *(Courtesy of Dr. Georges Hauptmann.)*

total C4 deficiency are homozygous for a double null C4 haplotype, C4A*QO, C4B*QO.[244] As expected, the deficiency is closely linked to other genes of the major histocompatibility complex (MHC).[227]

Patients with C4 deficiency usually have severely depressed serum levels of both antigenic and functional C4 (<1 percent). Individuals who are heterozygous for C4 deficiency, at either or both of the C4 loci, as a group will have serum C4 levels that generally reflect the number of active genes.[247,248] However, assignment of a given individual as heterozygous for the deficiency is complicated by the fact that the range of C4 levels in normals is quite wide and a deficiency of C4 at one or the other locus is relatively common in normals.[244] Accordingly, assignment of an individual as heterozygous for the deficiency is usually based on kindred analysis using HLA linkage,[227] DNA blot analysis,[151] or electrophoretic analysis of C4 allotypes in serum.[249]

Patients with C4 deficiency have a markedly decreased ability to activate C3 via the classical pathway, and thus their total serum hemolytic complement activity, as assessed by antibody-sensitized erythrocytes, is virtually absent. In contrast, those serum activities which can be mediated via the alternative pathway, such as opsonic, chemotactic, and bactericidal activities, are present although usually reduced because of a lack of an intact classical pathway.[250,251]

The predominant clinical manifestation of C4 deficiency has been an SLE-like illness[4,218,242] (Fig. 111-6). Although most of the patients have had many of the clinical features of SLE, such as photosensitive skin rashes, renal disease, and occasionally arthritis, they have rarely had antinuclear antibodies in their serum, and, if present, these have been of relatively low titer. Biopsies of the affected skin have shown histologic features characteristic of lupus.[252] Although some of the patients have demonstrated an increased susceptibility to infection, these have been patients in whom the SLE-like illness has also been present.[251,252] As with many of the other complement deficiency diseases, there have been a few asymptomatic C4-deficient patients ascertained as the result of family studies.

A second form of C4 deficiency has been described in which the deficiency is incomplete (serum levels 2 to 5 percent of normal).[253] This variant of C4 deficiency appears to be inherited as an autosomal dominant trait and is not linked to genes of the major histocompatability complex. Like patients with the common form of C4 deficiency, the patient had lupus.

There is a relatively high frequency of null alleles at either the C4A or C4B locus among both blacks[254] and whites.[244] For example, the frequency of C4A*QO among Caucasians has been estimated as between 13 and 14 percent and that of C4B*QO as between 15 and 16 percent. The corresponding frequencies of homozygous null individuals at each locus would be just over 1 percent for C4A and just under 3 percent for C4B. These are clearly minimal estimates as revealed by direct studies of the C4A and C4B genes by Southern blotting.[151] A number of studies have shown a statistically significant association of C4A*QO with SLE[255–257] and of both C4A*QO and C4B*QO with insulin-dependent diabetes mellitus[258,259] and IgA nephropathy or anaphylactoid purpura.[260] It is difficult to assign a direct relationship between C4 null genes and these diseases since the C4 null genes may be in linkage disequilibrium with other genes of the major histocompatibility complex, which in turn may be responsible for the association. However, in at least one study, the risk of SLE associated with the C4A null gene was independent of other loci within the MHC.[257] Moreover, the striking difference in C4A and C4B functional activity and response of the corresponding genes to IFN-γ (see above) supports a direct effect of the gene product on the propensity for immune complex diseases.

C2 Deficiency

Genetically determined C2 deficiency is the most common of the inherited complement deficiencies.[4,218,261] The frequency of the gene for C2 deficiency has been estimated at between 1 and 1.5 percent in the normal population[228,262] with homozygous deficients as common as 1 in 10,000.[261] Analyses of affected kindreds using polymorphisms of the protein have shown that the deficiency is the consequence of so-called "null" or silent alleles of the structural gene for C2.[263] Studies using cDNA probes for C2 have shown that the gene for C2 is present and has not undergone a major deletion or rearrangement.[264] Apparently, a pretranslational defect in C2 gene expression leads to a lack of C2 mRNA and a lack of synthesis and secretion of C2 protein.[264,265]

A number of studies have shown that the gene for C2 deficiency (C2★QO) is closely linked to genes of the MHC and that it is in linkage disequilibrium with a number of the products of the MHC.[226,229,262,266–269] Thus, the C2QO allele is often part of an extended haplotype consisting of HLA-A25, B18, C2QO, BfS, C4A4, C4B2, and D/DR2.[261,269,270]

Individuals homozygous for C2 deficiency generally have less than 1 percent of the normal amount of C2 functional activity and undetectable C2 by immunochemical analysis.[271] Heterozygotes for C2 deficiency generally have C2 levels between 30 and 70 percent of the average values for normal individuals.[271] The wide range of C2 levels in both normal individuals and individuals who are heterozygous for C2 deficiency, combined with the fact that there is some overlap between the two groups, may, on some occasions, make assignment of heterozygous status based on C2 levels alone difficult. Family studies and/or analysis of MHC haplotypes with which C2 deficiency is in linkage disequilibrium may be necessary for assignment of a given individual as a heterozygote for C2 deficiency.[228]

Complement-mediated serum activities, such as opsonization and chemotaxis, are present in patients with C2 deficiency, presumably because their alternative pathway is intact.[272–274] However, when assessed carefully and compared to those in normals with an intact classical pathway, these activities are not generated as quickly or to the same degree.[75,274,275,276]

The clinical manifestations of C2 deficiency vary and have included individuals who are asymptomatic and individuals who are clinically affected with an increased susceptibility to infection and/or rheumatic diseases.[4,218,261] A number of C2-deficient patients have had an increased susceptibility to bacterial infections. For the most part, the infections have been blood-borne and systemic (e.g., sepsis, meningitis, arthritis, and osteomyelitis) and caused by encapsulated organisms (e.g., pneumococcus, *H. influenzae*, and meningococcus).[4,218,261,273,277,278]

A variety of rheumatic diseases have been seen in association with C2 deficiency.[4,218,261] The most common of these have been disorders that resemble systemic lupus erythematosis and discoid lupus. Although these patients possess many of the characteristic clinical features of SLE, there are some distinctions. In general, although fulminant glomerulonephri-

tis can occur,[279] progressive nephritis and renal failure are uncommon.[218,261] Similarly, although there are reports of central nervous system involvement, it is relatively uncommon. Arthralgias may be present, but frank arthritis is rare. Cutaneous lesions are seen relatively often among C2-deficient patients with "lupuslike" illnesses, and many patients have characteristic annular photosensitive lesions.[280] In addition, unlike the situation in typical SLE, biopsies of uninvolved skin do not show deposits of C3 or immunoglobulin at the dermal-epidermal junction.[261,280] The incidence of anti-DNA and antinuclear antigen antibodies is relatively low in C2-deficient patients with the "lupuslike" illness[218,228,235]; however, they do have a relatively high prevalence of anti-Ro(SSA) antibody (75 percent).[235] Thus, based on both clinical and serologic criteria, C2-deficient patients with the "lupuslike" illness resemble non-complement-deficient patients with "ANA-negative" lupus[237] and/or subacute, cutaneous lupus erythematosis.[238] A number of other "rheumatic diseases" have been described in patients with C2 deficiency.[4,218,261] Chief among these have been glomerulonephritis,[281] dermatomyositis,[282] anaphylactoid purpura,[283] and vasculitis.[274]

Certain rheumatic diseases have also been seen with increased frequency in individuals who are heterozygous for C2 deficiency. In one prospective study involving large numbers of patients with SLE, juvenile rheumatoid arthritis (JRA), and rheumatoid arthritis, 5.9 percent of the SLE patients and 3.7 percent of the JRA patients were heterozygotes for C2 deficiency as compared to 1.2 percent of normal controls.[228] As with homozygous C2-deficient patients, ANA titers were significantly lower than in lupus patients who did not have C2 deficiency. In contrast, in a study of familial lupus, only one of eight kindreds had members who were heterozygous for C2 deficiency; each of these had either clinical lupus or serologic abnormalities.[284] In the same kindred, however, there were other family members who did not carry the C2★QO gene but had lupus and/or serologic abnormalities.

C3 Deficiency

Genetically determined C3 deficiency is inherited as an autosomal recessive trait.[4,218] Genetic studies using allotypic analysis have shown that the gene for C3 deficiency is a so-called "null" or silent allele of the structural gene for C3.[285–287] Although these patients have severely depressed levels of C3 in their serum (<1 percent of normal), some C3 antigen and function can be detected using highly sensitive techniques.[288] In addition, when monocytes from C3-deficient individuals are cultured in vitro, they produce approximately 25 percent of the normal amount of C3.[173] Thus, it is likely that C3 deficiency is due to a biosynthetic regulatory defect rather than a structural gene defect.

As mentioned above, C3-deficient patients have less than 1 percent of the normal amount of C3 in their serum, whether the level of C3 is assessed based on its antigenic activity or its functional activity. Heterozygotes have approximately 50 percent of the normal amount of C3 in their serum. Those serum functions either directly dependent on C3, or indirectly dependent on C3 because of its role in the activation of C5–C9, are also markedly reduced. Thus, serum opsonic, chemotactic, and bactericidal activities are either absent or markedly diminished in patients with C3 deficiency.[288–293]

The clinical manifestations of C3 deficiency in human beings have included both an increased susceptibility to infection and rheumatic disorders. Patients with C3 deficiency have had a variety of infections, including pneumonia, bacteremia, meningitis, and osteomyelitis, caused by encapsulated pyogenic bacteria, such as the pneumococcus, meningococcus, *Klebsiella pneumonia*, and *Escherichia coli*.[4,288,289,291–295] To this date, no patient with C3 deficiency has had an unusually severe or recurrent viral or fungal infection. A variety of rheumatic diseases have been seen in C3 deficiency patients. A number of patients have presented with arthralgias and vasculitic skin rashes.[290,291] In two of these patients (sisters), a clinical picture consistent with systemic lupus erythematosus was present with arthritis, alopecia, malar rash, and photosensitivity.[291] Interestingly, although certain clinical features of lupus or a "lupuslike" illness are present in some patients with C3 deficiency, as with other complement-deficient patients, they do not have serologic evidence of lupus. Renal disease has also been seen in C3-deficient patients.[287,296,297] Histologically, the lesions most closely resemble membranoproliferative glomerulonephritis and are often characterized by mesangial cell proliferation, an increased mesangial matrix, and electron-dense deposits in both the mesangium and the subendothelium of capillary loops.[296,297] Immunofluorescent studies have revealed all major immunoglobulin classes to be present, but no C3. In one of the cases of renal disease, as well as in some of the cases of vasculitis or the lupuslike syndrome in which there was no apparent renal disease, circulating immune complexes were found in the serum.[291,293,296]

C3 is highly polymorphic with at least 20 identified allelic variants.[114] The two most common alleles, C3 Fast (CS*F) and C3 Slow (C3*S), can be distinguished by their electrophoretic mobility and are found in over 98 percent of the population. Two particularly rare variants have been described that are indistinguishable from C3 Slow and C3 Fast by electrophoretic mobility but are associated with decreased staining after electrophoresis and reduced levels of serum C3. Termed *hypomorphic C3 slow* (C3*s) and *hypomorphic C3 fast* (C3*f), these variants have been identified in patients with a variety of rheumatic disorders. Hypomorphic C3 fast has been described in a patient with glomerulonephritis and arthritis,[298] cutaneous vasculitis,[299] and recurrent hemolytic-uremic syndrome[300] as well as in normal individuals.[301] Hypomorphic C3 slow has been described in a patient with nephritis and in his asymptomatic family members.[302]

C5 Deficiency

Genetically determined C5 deficiency has been identified in a number of different families.[4,218,303] The deficiency appears to be inherited as an autosomal recessive trait.

Homozygous deficient individuals usually have markedly reduced levels of C5 functional activity (<1 percent), and no C5 antigen is detectable in their serum. In one instance, however, the patient had as much as 1 to 2 percent of the normal amount of C5 functional activity although her homozygous deficient sister had less than 0.1 percent.[304] Heterozygotes usually have between one-third and one-half of the average amount of C5 in their serum. The serums of patients with C5 deficiency are unable to generate normal amounts of chemotactic or bactericidal activity.[305–308] As expected, serum opsonic activity is intact, since the activation of C3 can proceed without the participation of C5.[305,307]

Although the initial patient identified as C5-deficient had SLE and membranoproliferative glomerulonephritis,[304] subsequent patients have been identified because of either meningococcal meningitis or disseminated gonococcal infections.[305–308] A few C5-deficient patients have been asymptomatic, having been ascertained through family studies.

C6 Deficiency

Deficiency of C6 is inherited in an autosomal recessive fashion.[4,218,309] Studies on a number of families, using analyses of C6 protein polymorphism, have shown that the gene for C6 deficiency is a "null" or silent allele of the structural gene for C6.[310]

Individuals who are homozygous deficient generally have less than 1 percent of the normal amount of C6 in their serum, whether it is assessed immunochemically or functionally.[310] The only abnormality relating to their serum complement system is a marked deficiency of serum bactericidal activity.[311–314] The rest of their complement-mediated serum activities which depend only on the activation of C3 and C5, such as opsonic activity and chemotactic activity, are normal.[311–314]

The major clinical manifestation of C6 deficiency has been disseminated neisserial infections.[4,218] While most patients have had meningococcal sepsis and meningitis, others have had disseminated gonococcal infections. One patient with C6 deficiency presented with a lupuslike syndrome.[315]

A patient with a genetically determined combined deficiency of both C6 and C7 has been described.[316] The patient had extremely low levels of both C6 (1 to 5 percent of normal) and C7 (3 to 9 percent of normal). When concentrated from the patient's serum, the C6 was found to be smaller in size (110 kDa) than normal C6 (140 kDa) and antigenically deficient, while the C7 appeared normal. The nature of this patient's unique genetic defect has not been elucidated but may relate to the fact that C6 and C7 share some structural and functional characteristics.[317]

C7 Deficiency

Only a few patients with C7 deficiency have been identified.[4,218,318] The defect appears to be inherited as an autosomal recessive trait.

For the most part, homozygous deficient individuals have severely reduced (<1 percent) levels of C7 in their serum. In one case, however, the patient's serum level of functionally active C7 varied over time, reaching levels as high as 3.5 percent of normal.[319] At the time when the level of C7 function was at its highest, C7 antigen also appeared in the serum. As expected, C7-deficient patients have little if any total hemolytic complement activity in their serum. Similarly, serum bactericidal activity is also markedly reduced in those patients in whom it has been tested.[320–322]

A number of clinical presentations have been associated with C7 deficiency.[4,218,318] As with the other deficiencies of terminal components, systemic meningococcal infections and/or disseminated gonococcal infections have predominated. Individual patients have also presented with a lupuslike syndrome,[323] rheumatoid arthritis,[324] and scleroderma.[319] Finally, there have been a few patients with C7 deficiency who have been clinically well.

C8 Deficiency

Genetically determined C8 deficiency is inherited in an autosomal recessive fashion[4,218,325] and is the result of a "null" or silent gene.[326]

Normal C8 is composed of three chains (α, β, and γ).[327] The α and γ chains are covalently joined to form one subunit (C8 α-γ), which is joined to the other subunit, composed of the β chain (C8 β), by noncovalent bonds.[328] In one form of C8 deficiency patients lack the C8 α-γ subunit, while in the other form the C8 β subunit is deficient.[325,329] In each case, C8 functional activity is markedly reduced (<1 percent of normal).

In the case of C8 β-subunit deficiency, C8 antigen can be detected in the serum of affected individuals using standard immunodiffusion techniques, but it lacks antigenic determinants present in the intact C8 molecule.[330] Isolation of the C8 antigen from the serum of patients with C8 β-subunit deficiency has shown it to be identical to the normal C8 α-γ subunit.[331,332] Addition of C8 β subunit, purified from normal C8, to the serum from patients with C8 β-subunit deficiency restores C8 functional activity, offering additional evidence that the C8 α-γ subunit in these patients' serums is normal.[331,332]

In the case of C8 α-γ subunit deficiency, initial analysis of serum from these patients using standard immunodiffusion techniques failed to detect any C8 antigen.[333,334] However, when serums from these patients is immunoprecipitated with antiserum to C8 and the precipitates examined using SDS-page analysis, the C8 β subunit can be detected.[329] Addition of purified C8 α-γ from normal serum restores C8 functional hemolytic activity to C8 α-γ-subunit-deficient serums.[329] As expected, when C8 α-γ subunit-deficient serums are mixed with C8 β-deficient serums, hemolytic activity is also restored.[329]

The only functional defect in C8-deficient serums is a marked reduction in bacteriolytic activity.[333,335] Other complement-mediated serum activities, such as opsonization, are intact.

The clinical presentation of C8 deficiency has been similar to the other deficiencies in terminal complement components.[4,218,325] Meningococcemia, meningococcal meningitis, and disseminated gonococcal infections have predominated, but SLE has also rarely been seen.

C9 Deficiency

Only a few patients with C9 deficiency have been identified in the West,[4,218,336] but it appears to be the most common complement deficiency in Japan.[337] In those patients whose family members have been available for testing, the disease appears to be inherited as an autosomal recessive trait.

Most affected individuals have markedly reduced levels of C9, whether tested immunochemically or by functional analysis. In one case, however, a patient had trace amounts of C9 antigen detectable in her serum and between 10 and 15 percent of the normal amount of C9 functional hemolytic activity.[338] The hemolysis of sensitized erythrocytes can be mediated by a membrane attack complex composed of C5b-8 and is not therefore strictly dependent on C9.[58] Therefore, patients with C9 deficiency have some total hemolytic complement activity, although it is usually between one-third and one-half of

the lower limit of normal.[339,340] Similarly, their serums possess some bactericidal activity, although the rate of killing is significantly reduced.[338]

Only one patient with C9 deficiency has had clinical problems that might relate to her complement deficiency.[341] She had meningococcal sepsis and meningitis. It is difficult, however, to be sure that the systemic meningococcal infection was causally related to her C9 deficiency, since there may have been ascertainment bias because of the known association of meningococcal infections with deficiencies of the other terminal components.

Factor I Deficiency

Genetically determined factor I deficiency has been described in only a few families.[4,218] It is inherited as an autosomal recessive trait. The concentrations of factor I in the serums of heterozygous deficient individuals are approximately one-half the average level in normals.

Patients with factor I deficiency have an uncontrolled activation of C3 via the alternative pathway.[342–345] As mentioned earlier, there is the continuous low grade generation of an alternative pathway C3 convertase, C3b,Bb, which is inhibited by factors H and I. In the absence of factor I there is no control imposed on the formation and expression of the alternative pathway C3 convertase, and as a result, there is the continued activation and cleavage of C3.[346] Patients with factor I deficiency, therefore, have a secondary consumption of native C3 with markedly reduced levels of antigenic C3 in their serum, most of which is not in the form of native C3 but rather of the cleavage product, C3b.[342] Serum levels of other components of the alternative pathway, factors B, factor H, and properdin, are also reduced, reflecting continuing activation of the alternative pathway.[345]

As expected, those serum activities that depend on C3 either directly or indirectly, such as bactericidal activity, opsonic activity, and chemotactic activity, are reduced in patients with factor I deficiency.[342]

In at least one instance, purified factor I has been infused into a patient with factor I deficiency.[345] Levels of factor B and properdin rose within 24 h of the infusion. The level of the C3 cleavage product, C3b, fell and was followed by a rise in the level of native C3. Apparently, the replacement of factor I corrected the metabolic defect by reestablishing control of the alternative pathway and stopping the activation and consumption of native C3. As a result, the patients' serum hemolytic and opsonic activities also became normal.

The most common clinical expression of factor I deficiency is an increased susceptibility to infection.[342,344,347–350] As with primary C3 deficiency, infections have included both localized infections on mucosal surfaces and systemic infections. The organisms most commonly responsible for these infections have been encapsulated, pyogenic bacteria such as the streptococcus, the pneumococcus, the meningococcus, and *H. influenzae*, organisms for which C3 is an important opsonic ligand. In addition to problems with infection, some patients have had elevated levels of circulating immune complexes.[348,349] There have as yet been no reports of patients with factor I deficiency developing chronic renal disease as has been the case with C3 deficiency. However, there has been one report of a transient illness resembling serum sickness and characterized by fever, rash, arthralgia, hematuria, and protein-uria.[348]

Factor H Deficiency

Genetically determined factor H deficiency has been described in only one family.[351] The deficiency appears to be inherited as an autosomal recessive trait. The parents were first cousins and had approximately one-half the normal level of factor H, as did some of the other family members.

Factor H levels in the serum of the two affected brothers were detectable but reduced to less than 10 percent of normal. In addition, the levels of alternative pathway factor B and of properdin were reduced, but not to the same degree as factor H. Similarly, the serum levels of C3 were reduced and the majority of the C3 that was present was in the form of an activation-cleavage product (C3d). Presumably, the markedly reduced level of factor H leads to continuous activation of the alternative pathway and the resultant depletion of C3 and other proteins of the alternative pathway.

One of the brothers had the hemolytic uremic syndrome with anemia, elevated fibrin split products, and nephritis. In addition, he had a positive Coombs test for C3d on his red cells. His brother, who also had factor H deficiency, was clinically well and had no previous illnesses.

Properdin Deficiency

Only two families with genetically determined properdin deficiency have been identified to this date.[352,353] The deficiency appears to be inherited as an X-linked recessive disorder.

Properdin is undetectable (less than 2 percent of normal) in the serums of affected males using immunochemical assays. The ability of their serums to support the activation of C3, or the lysis of rabbit erythrocytes, via the alternative pathway is also reduced. Finally, the opsonization of endotoxin particles via the alternative pathway is reduced. Each of the functional abnormalities of the alternative pathway can be corrected by the addition of purified properdin. The only clinical manifestation of properdin deficiency in either family has been fulminant meningococcemia and meningococcal meningitis.

C1 Inhibitor Deficiency

A genetically determined deficiency of C1 esterase inhibitor (C1-INH) is responsible for the clinical disorder termed *hereditary angioedema* (HAE).[354] Although isolated cases of angioedema were described as early as the mid-nineteenth century, the first complete clinical description and discussion of the familial nature of the disorder was published in 1988 by Sir William Osler.[355] Since that time a number of reports have summarized the clinical manifestations as well as confirmed the hereditary nature of the disorder.[356–359]

HAE is inherited in an autosomal dominant fashion. There are at least two forms of C1-INH deficiency.[223,360] In the commonest form (type I), accounting for approximately 85 percent of the patients, the serum of affected individuals is deficient in both C1-INH protein (5 to 30 percent of normal) and C1-INH activity.[354,358–360] In the other, less common form (type II), a dysfunctional protein is present in normal or elevated concentrations, but the functional activity of C1-INH is mark-

edly reduced.[223,358–360] In patients with type I HAE, the diagnosis can be established easily by demonstrating a decrease in serum C1-INH protein when assessed by immunochemical techniques. However, in patients with type II HAE the diagnosis must rest on demonstrating a decrease in C1-INH functional activity. In either case, C4 levels and C2 levels are usually reduced below the lower limit of normal during attacks,[358,361,362] presumably due to their uncontrolled cleavage by $C\overline{1}s$. The level of C4 in serum is also commonly reduced between attacks, making it a useful diagnostic clue.[358,362]

A number of studies have examined the dysfunctional C1-INH molecules from different families and found that they not only differ from normal C1-INH but from each other. Although they appear to be immunochemically identical to normal C1-INH,[223,360,363,364] some, but not all, have a different electrophoretic mobility than normal.[360] In addition, they differ from normal C1-INH, and from each other, with respect to their ability to bind to C1s and their ability to inhibit the cleavage of a synthetic substrate, N-acetyl-tyrosine-ethyl-ester, by $C\overline{1}s$.[360] Normal C1-INH also inhibits plasma kallikrein, activated Hageman factor, and plasmin. In one study comparing the dysfunctional C1-INH molecules from eight different kindreds, each dysfunctional C1-INH was unique with respect to its spectrum of inhibitory activities against these enzymes,[364] although none of the dysfunctional proteins inhibited plasmin.

The levels of normal C1-INH in patients with either type of HAE are lower than one might expect in a heterozygote: 5 to 30 percent of normal in type I C1-INH deficiency and little or none in type II C1-INH deficiency. In addition, the levels of the dysfunctional protein in the type II disorder are usually equivalent to normal or higher than normal, rather than the expected 50 percent of normal. In an attempt to explain this apparent discrepancy, metabolic studies using both normal and dysfunctional proteins have been performed in normal and deficient subjects.[365] As expected, the synthesis of the normal C1-INH in the type I disorder was reduced, findings consistent with earlier studies showing reduced content of the normal protein in the livers of patients with C1-INH deficiency.[194] The fractional catabolic rate of normal C1-INH in both types of patients with HAE was significantly elevated. Finally, the fractional catabolic rates of two different dysfunctional C1-INH proteins were different from each other and from normal; in one the fractional catabolic rate was near normal, and in the other it was strikingly reduced.

These studies have been used to create a model to explain the low levels of C1-INH found in the type I disorder and the elevated levels of dysfunctional protein found in the type II disorder.[366] The model proposes that there are two catabolic routes for normal C1-INH, one in which the inhibitor complexes with the enzymes with which it reacts in vivo, and another independent of inhibitor-enzyme complexes and representing the normal catabolism of any serum protein. Thus, it has been suggested that in the type I disorder the markedly lowered levels of C1-INH are the result of both decreased synthesis and increased catabolism consequent to the complexing of the normal C1-INH with the activated enzymes which it normally inhibits. Similarly, it has been suggested that the low levels of normal C1-INH and elevated levels of dysfunctional C1-INH in the type II disorder are the result of decreased synthesis and increased catabolism of the normal C1-INH and, at least in some cases, decreased catabolism of the dysfunctional C1-INH consequent to its inability to complex with C1 and other enzymes.

The pathophysiological mechanism(s) by which the absence of C1-INH activity leads to the angioedema characteristic of the disorder are still incompletely understood. Neither the mediators responsible for producing the edema nor the mechanisms initiating their production have been clearly identified. There is a great deal of evidence implicating complement in the pathogenesis of the edema. Clearly, $\overline{C1s}$ activity is present in the serum of patients during an attack.[367] Furthermore, when purified $\overline{C1s}$ is injected into either normal or HAE patients' skin, angioedema is produced.[368] The intradermal response to $\overline{C1s}$ in C2-deficient individuals is markedly diminished, while it is preserved in C3-deficient individuals, suggesting the direct involvement of C2 in the production of the angioedema.[368] Other evidence suggests that the plasma kallikrein system may also be involved in the generation of the edema. C1-INH is capable of inhibiting the ability of activated Hageman factor to initiate kinin generation, fibrinolysis, and coagulation.[369] It also inhibits kallikrein of the kinin system, plasma thromboplastin antecedent (factor XIa) of the clotting system, and plasmin of the fibrinolytic system (reviewed in Ref. 358). It is possible, therefore, that products of the kinin system could be involved in the edema formation. In fact, blister fluids from HAE patients contain active plasma kallikrein,[370] and their serum has decreased amounts of prekallikrein and kininogen,[371] suggesting activation of the kinin system during attacks of edema.

The clinical symptoms of HAE are the result of submucosal or subcutaneous edema. The lesions are characterized by noninflammatory edema associated with capillary and venule dilation.[372] The postcapillary venule also demonstrates gaps between the endothelial cells.[372] The three most prominent areas of involvement are the skin, respiratory tract, and gastrointes-

Fig. 111-7 A patient with C1 inhibitor deficiency during an attack of angioedema. (Courtesy of Dr. Fred S. Rosen. From Nathan DC & Oski FA (eds.): Hematology of Infancy and Childhood. Philadelphia, Saunders, 1987. With permission.)

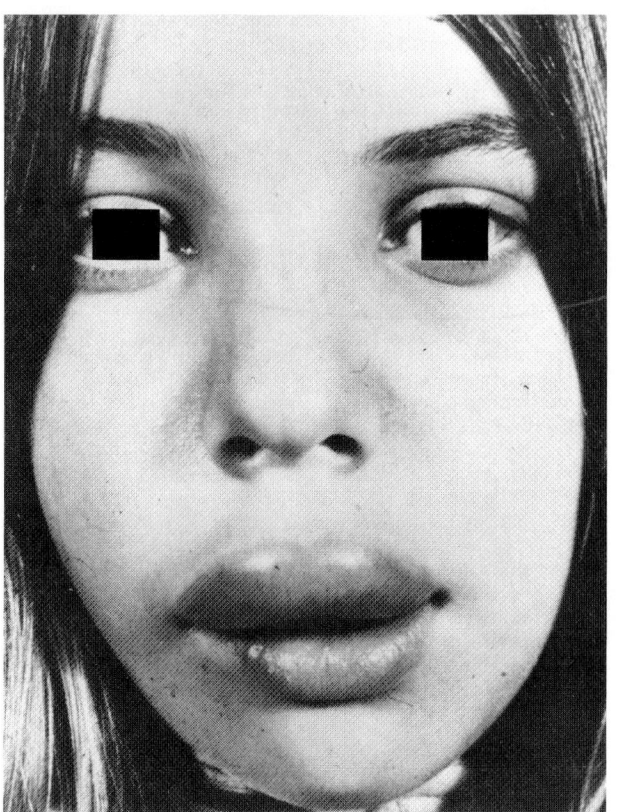

tinal tract.[357–359] Although symptoms during attacks may relate to only one of these areas, they are not mutually exclusive and may be seen in combination.

Attacks involving the skin may occur on an extremity, the face, or the genitalia (Fig. 111-7). In some instances, there may be changes just preceding the edema such as mottling, a transient serpiginous erythema, or frank erythema marginatum. The edema usually expands centripetally from a single site and may vary in size from a few centimeters to involvement of a whole extremity. The lesions are pale rather than red, are usually not warm, and characteristically are nonpruritic. There may be, however, a feeling of tightness in the skin due to the accumulation of subcutaneous fluid. Attacks usually progress for 1 to 2 days and resolve over an additional 2 to 3 days.

Attacks involving the upper respiratory tract represent a serious threat to the patient with HAE. In one series, pharyngeal edema had occurred at least once in nearly two-thirds of the patients.[358] The patient may initially experience a "tightness" in the throat, and swelling of the tongue, buccal mucosa, and oropharynx follows. In some instances laryngeal edema, accompanied by hoarseness and stridor, occurs, progresses to respiratory obstruction, and represents a life-threatening emergency. In fact, in one series, tracheostomies had been performed in one out of every six patients with HAE.[358]

The gastrointestinal tract can also be affected by HAE. Symptoms are probably related to edema of the bowel wall, and may include anorexia, dull aching of the abdomen, vomiting, and in some cases crampy abdominal pain. Abdominal symptoms can occur in the absence of concurrent cutaneous or pharyngeal involvement. In some instances, abdominal symptoms may be the only symptoms the patient has ever had, leading to difficulty in diagnosis.

The onset of symptoms referable to HAE occurs in over half the patients before adolescence,[358,359] but in some patients, their first symptoms do not occur until they are well into adult life. Although in just over half of the patients no specific events can be clearly identified as initiating attacks, trauma and anxiety and/or stress are frequently cited.[357–359] Dental extractions and tonsillectomy can initiate edema of the upper airway, and cutaneous edema may follow trauma to an extremity. Some patients report attacks following the use of tight-fitting clothing or shoes, while others have related cold exposure to the onset of symptoms.

The therapy of HAE can be conveniently considered to fall into three categories: (1) the long-term prophylaxis of attacks, (2) the short-term prophylaxis of attacks, and (3) the treatment of acute attacks.[358] In those patients who have had laryngeal obstruction or have suffered frequent and debilitating attacks that have interfered with work or other responsibilities, the long-term prevention of attacks may be indicated. Antifibrinolytic agents, such as ϵ-aminocaproic acid or its cyclic analogue, tranexamic acid, have been used with some success in the long-term prevention of attacks.[373,374] Improvement consisted of a decreased frequency of attacks in most patients and a decrease in severity in the others. The mechanisms by which these agents exert their protective effect is unclear.

More recently, "impeded" androgens, such as danazol and stanozolol, which have attenuated androgenic potential have been found to be useful in the long-term prophylaxis of HAE.[375] The basis for their use lies in an earlier observation that methyltestosterone therapy was effective in HAE.[376] During a double-blind controlled study of danazol, only 1 of 46 courses of danazol therapy was accompanied by attacks of angioedema while 44 of 47 courses of placebo therapy were interrupted by an attack.[375] Danazol therapy appears to be effective for extended periods of time, but because of dose-related adverse reactions (e.g., weight gain, abnormal liver function tests, microscopic hematuria, and altered libido), therapy needs to be closely monitored.[377] Danazol may act by stimulating the synthesis of functionally intact C1-INH by the normal gene in these patients, whether they have the form of the disease characterized by low levels of C1-INH (type I) or the form characterized by a dysfunctional protein (type II).[375,378]

In some instances, patients may need short-term prophylactic therapy, such as before oral surgery.[379] In these circumstances danazol therapy may be initiated 1 week before surgery or ϵ-aminocaproic acid the day before surgery. There is some controversy concerning the use of fresh frozen plasma during an acute attack, since the plasma not only supplies the missing C1-INH but also C1 enzyme and substrates such as C4 and C2. Nevertheless, the use of plasma transfusions 12 h before elective surgery may prevent morbidity from the procedure.[380]

A number of drugs have been used in an attempt to interrupt an attack of HAE once it has begun. Epinephrine, antihistamines, and corticosteroids are of no proven benefit. Recent trials with partially purified C1-INH have been encouraging. Infusion of C1-INH has been accompanied by resolution of edema and symptoms within a few hours.[380,381]

REFERENCES

1. MAYER MM: Complement: Historical perspectives and current issues. *Complement* 1:2, 1984.
2. FRANK MM: The complement system in host defense and inflammation. *Rev Infect Dis* 1:483, 1979.
3. SILVERSTEIN AM: Essential hypocomplementemia: Report of a case. *Blood* 16:1338, 1960.
4. ROSS SC, DENSEN P: Complement deficiency states and infection: Epidemiology, pathogenesis and consequences of neisserial and other infections in an immune deficiency. *Medicine* 63:243, 1984.
5. ROTHER K, ROTHER V: Hereditary and acquired complement deficiencies in animals and man. *Prog Allergy* 39:1986.
6. PORTER RR, REID KBM: The biochemistry of complement. *Nature* 275:699, 1978.
7. LEPOW IH, NAFF GB, TODD EW, PENSKY J, HINZ CF: Chromatographic resolution of the first component of complement into three activities. *J Exp Med* 117:983, 1963.
8. GIGLI I, PORTER RR, SIM RB: The unactivated form of the first component of human complement, C1. *Biochem J* 157:541, 1976.
9. MULLER-EBERHARD HJ, KUNKEL H: Isolation of a thermolabile serum protein which precipitates gammaglobulin aggregates and participates in immune hemolysis. *Proc Soc Exp Biol Med* 106:291, 1961.
10. SHELTON E, YONEMASU K, STROUD RM: Ultrastructure of human complement component, C1. *Proc Natl Acad Sci USA* 69:65, 1972.
11. KNOBEL HR, HEUSSER C, RODRICH ML, ISLIKER H: Enzymatic digestion of the first component of human complement. *J Immunol* 112:2094, 1974.
12. LIN TY, FLETCHER DS: Activation of human complement C1 by the third subcomponent C1q. *J Biol Chem* 255:7756, 1980.
13. ZICCARDI RJ, COOPER NR: Activation of C1r by proteolytic cleavage. *J Immunol* 116:504, 1976.
14. VALET G, COOPER NR: Isolation of the proenzyme forms of C1r and C1s from human serum. *J Immunol* 111:292, 1973.
15. SAKAI K, STROUD RM: Purification, molecular properties and activation of C1 proesterase, C1. *J Immunol* 110:1010, 1973.
16. SCHREIBER RD, MULLER-EBERHARD HJ: Fourth component of human complement: Description of a three polypeptide chain structure. *J Exp Med* 140:1324, 1974.
17. LAW SK, LICHTENBERG NA, HOLCOMBE FH, LEVINE RP: Interaction between the labile binding sites of the fourth and fifth components of complement and erythrocyte cell membranes. *J Immunol* 125:634, 1980.
18. TACK BF: The beta-cys-gamma-glu thiolester bond in C4, C3, and alpha$_2$-macroglobulin. *Spring Semin Immunopathol* 6:259, 1983.
19. NAGASAWA S, STROUD RM: Cleavage of C2 by C1s into antigenically distinct fragments, C2a and C2b: Demonstration of binding of C2a to C4b. *Proc Natl Acad Sci USA* 74:2998, 1977.
20. SHIN HS, MAYER MM: The third component of the guinea pig complement system. II. Kinetic study of the reaction of EAC 4,2a with guinea pig C3. *Biochemistry* 7:2997, 1968.
21. PENSKY J, LEVY LR, LEPOW IH: Partial purification of a serum inhibitor of C'1-esterase. *J Biol Chem* 236:1674, 1961.
22. HARPEL PC, COOPER NR: Studies on human plasma C1 inactivator-enzyme interactions. I. Mechanisms of interactions with C1s, plasmin, and trypsin. *J Clin Invest* 55:593, 1975.
23. GIGLI I, FUJITA T, NUSSENZWEIG V: Modulation of the classical pathway C3 convertase by the plasma proteins, C4-binding protein and C3b inactivator. *Proc Natl Acad Sci USA* 76:6596, 1979.
24. NAGASAWA S, ICHIBARA C, STROUD RM: Cleavage of C4b by C3b inactivator: Production of a nicked form of C4b, C4b', as an intermediate cleavage product of C4b by C3b inactivator. *J Immunol* 125:578, 1980.
25. NICHOLSON-WELLER A, BURGE J, FEARON DT, WELLER PF, AUSTEN KF: Isolation of a human erythrocytes membrane glycoprotein with decay-accelerating activity for C3 convertases of the complement system. *J Immunol* 129:184, 1982.
26. HIRSCH RL, WINKELSTEIN JA, GRIFFIN DE: The role of complement in viral infections. III. Activation of the classical and alternative pathways by sindbis virus. *J Immunol* 124:2507, 1980.
27. BREDT W, WELLEK B, BRUNNER H, LOOS M: Interactions between *Mycoplasma pneumoniae* and the first component of complement. *Infect Immun* 15:7, 1977.
28. LOOS M, WELLEK B, THESEN R, OPFERKUCH W: Antibody-independent interaction of the first component of complement with gram-negative bacteria. *Infect Immunol* 22:5, 1978.
29. EADS ME, LEVY NJ, KASPER DL, BAKER CJ, NICHOLSON-WELLER A: Antibody-independent activation of C1 by type 1a group B streptococci. *J Infect Dis* 146:665, 1982.
30. WINKELSTEIN JA: Complement and natural immunity. *Clin Immunol Allergy* 3:421, 1983.
31. FEARON DT: Activation of the alternative complement pathway. *CRC Crit Rev Immunol* 1:1, 1979.
32. TACK BF, HARRISON RA, JANOTOVA J, THOMAS ML, PRAHL JW: Evidence for presence of an internal thiolester bond in third component of human complement. *Proc Natl Acad Sci USA* 77:5764, 1980.
33. PANGBURN MK, MULLER-EBERHARD HJ: Relation of a putative thioester bond in C3 to activation of the alternative pathway and the binding of C3b to biological targets of complement. *J Exp Med* 152:1102, 1980.
34. FEARON DT, AUSTEN KF: Initiation of C3 cleavage in the alternative complement pathway. *J Immunol* 115:1357, 1975.
35. FEARON DT, AUSTEN KF: Properdin: Binding to C3b and stabilization of the C3b-dependent C3 convertase. *J Exp Med* 142:856, 1975.
36. KAZATCHKINE MD, FEARON DT, AUSTEN KF: Human alternative complement pathway: Membrane-associated sialic acid regulates the competition between B and β1H for cell-bound C3b. *J Immunol* 122:75, 1979.
37. WEILER JM, DAHA MR, AUSTEN KF, FEARON DT: Control of the amplification convertase of complement by the plasma protein, β1H. *Proc Natl Acad Sci USA* 73:3268, 1976.
38. WHALEY K, RUDDY S: Modulation of the alternative complement pathway by β1H globulin. *J Exp Med* 144:1147, 1976.
39. PILLEMER L, BLUM L, LEPOW IH, ROSS OA, TODD EW, WARDLAW AC: The properdin system and immunity. I. Demonstration and isolation of a new serum protein, properdin, and its role in immune phenomena. *Science* 120:279, 1954.
40. PLATTS-MILLS TAE, ISHIZAKAH K: Activation of the alternate pathway of human complement by rabbit cells. *J Immunol* 113:348, 1974.
41. WINKELSTEIN JA, SHIN HS, WOOD WB JR: Heat labile opsonins to pneumococcus. III. Participation of immunoglobulin and of the alternative pathway of C3 activation. *J Immunol* 108:1681, 1972.
42. FEARON DT, AUSTEN KF: Activation of the alternative complement pathway due to resistance of zymosan-bound amplification convertase to endogenous regulatory mechanisms. *Proc Natl Acad Sci USA* 74:1683, 1977.
43. FEARON DT: Regulation by membrane sialic acid of β1H-dependent decay/dissociation of amplification C3 convertase of the alternative pathway. *Proc Natl Acad Sci USA* 75:1971, 1978.
44. WINKELSTEIN JA, SHIN HS: The role of immunoglobulin in the interaction of pneumococci and the properdin pathway: Evidence for its specificity and lack of requirement for the Fc portion of the molecule. *J Immunol* 112:1635, 1974.
45. EDWARDS MS, NICHOLSON-WELLER A, BAKER CJ, KASPER DL: The role of specific antibody in alternative complement pathway mediated opsonophagocytosis of type III, group B streptococcus. *J Exp Med* 151:1275, 1980.

46. PERRIN LH, JOSEPH BS, COOPER NR, OLDSTONE MBA: Mechanism of injury of virus-infected cells by antiviral antibody and complement: Participation of IgG, F(ab')₂ and the alternative pathway. *J Exp Med* 143:1027, 1976.

47. MOORE FD JR, FEARON DT, AUSTEN KF: IgG on mouse erythrocytes augments activation of the human alternative complement pathway by enhancing deposition of C3b. *J Immunol* 126:1805, 1981.

48. NICHOLSON-WELLER A, DAHA MR, AUSTEN KF: Different functions for specific guinea pig IgG1 and IgG2 in the lysis of sheep erythrocytes by C4-deficient guinea pig serum. *J Immunol* 126:1800, 1981.

49. FEARON DT, AUSTEN KF, RUDDY S: Formation of a hemolytically active cellular intermediate by the interaction between properdin factors B and D and the activated third component of complement. *J Exp Med* 138:1305, 1973.

50. HOSTETTER MK, GORDON DL: Biochemistry of C3 and related thiolester proteins in infection and inflammation. *Rev Infect Dis* 9:97, 1987.

51. SHIN HS, PICKERING RJ, MAYER MM: The fifth component of the guinea pig complement system. II. Mechanisms of SAC1,4,2,3,5b formation and C5 consumption by EAC1,4,2,3. *J Immunol* 106:473, 1971.

52. DAHA MR, FEARON DT, AUSTEN KF: C3 requirements for formation of alternative pathway C3 convertase. *J Immunol* 117:630, 1976.

53. MAYER MM, MICHAELS DW, RAMM LE, SHIN ML, WHITLOW MB, WILLOUGHBY JB: Membrane damage by complement. *CRC Crit Rev Immunol* 2:133, 1981.

54. THOMPSON RA, LACHMAN PJ: Reactive lysis: The complement mediated lysis of unsensitized cells. II. The characterization of activated reactor as C5b and the participation of C8 and C9. *J Exp Med* 131:643, 1970.

55. SHIN ML, PAZNEKAS WA, ABROMOVITZ AS, MAYER MM: On the mechanism of membrane damage by complement: Exposure of hydrophobic sites on activated complement proteins. *J Immunol* 119:1358, 1977.

56. HAMMER CH, NICHOLSON A, MAYER MM: On the mechanism of cytotysis by complement: Evidence on insertion of C5b and C7 subunits of the C5b,6,7 complex into phospholipid bilayers of erythrocyte membranes. *Proc Natl Acad Sci USA* 72:5076, 1975.

57. HU VW, ESSER SF, PODACK ER, WISNIESHIS BJ: The membrane attack mechanism of complement: Photolabelling reveals insertion of terminal proteins into target membranes. *J Immunol* 27:380, 1981.

58. STOLFI RL: Immune lytic transformation. A state of irreversible damage generated as a result of the reaction of the eighth component in the guinea pig complement system. *J Immunol* 100:46, 1968.

59. TSCHOPP J, PODACK ER, MULLER-EBERHARD HJ: The membrane attack complex of complement; C5b-8 complex as accelerator of C9 polymerization. *J Immunol* 134:495, 1985.

60. FEARON DT, WONG WW: Complement ligand-receptor interactions that mediate biological responses. *Annu Rev Immunol* 1:243, 1983.

61. HUGLI TE: The structural basis for anaphylatoxin and chemotactic functions of C3a, C4a and C5a. *CRC Crit Rev Immunol* 2:321, 1981.

62. FEARON DT: Identification of the membrane glycoprotein that is the C3b receptor of the human erythrocyte, polymorphonuclear leukocyte, B lymphocyte and monocyte. *J Exp Med* 152:20, 1980.

63. EHLENBERGER AG, NUSSENZWEIG V: The role of membrane receptors for C3b and C3d in phagocytosis. *J Exp Med* 145:357, 1977.

64. CORNACOFF JB, HEBERT LA, SMEAD WL, VAN AMAN ME, BIRMINGHAM DJ, WAXMAN FJ: Primate erythrocyte-immune complex-clearing mechanism. *J Clin Invest* 71:236, 1983.

65. FEARON DT: Regulation of the amplification C3 convertase of human complement by an inhibitory protein isolated from human erythrocyte membranes. *Proc Natl Acad Sci USA* 76:5867, 1979.

66. IIDA K, NUSSENZWEIG V: Complement receptor is an inhibitor of the complement cascade. *J Exp Med* 153:1138, 1981.

67. COCHRANE CG, MULLER-EBERHARD HJ: The derivation of two distinct anaphylatoxins from the third and fifth components of human complement. *J Exp Med* 127:371, 1968.

68. VOGT W: Anaphylatoxins: Possible roles in diseases. *Complement* 3:177, 1986.

69. GORSKI J, HUGLI TE, MULLER-EBERHARD JH: C4a: The third anaphylatoxin of the human complement system. *Proc Natl Acad Sci USA* 76:5299, 1979.

70. SYNDERMAN R, GOETZL EJ: Molecular and cellular mechanisms of leukocyte chemotaxins. *Science* 213:830, 1981.

71. PEREZ HD, GOLDSTEIN IM, CHERNOFF D, WEBSTER RO, HENSON PM: Chemotactic activity of C5a des arg: Evidence of a requirement for an anionic peptide "helper factor" and inhibition by a cationic protein in serum from patients with systemic lupus erythematosis. *Mol Immunol* 17:163, 1980.

72. HOOVER RL, BRIGGS RT, KARNOVSKY MJ: The adhesive interaction between polymorphonuclear leukocytes and endothelial cells in vitro. *Cell* 14:423, 1978.

73. SNYDERMAN R, PHILLIPS JK, MERGENHAGEN SE: Biological activity of complement *in vivo*: Role of C5 in the accumulation of polymorphonuclear leukocytes in inflammatory exudates. *J Exp Med* 134:1131, 1971.

74. LARSEN GL, MITCHELL BC, HENSON PM: The pulmonary response of C5 sufficient and deficient mice to immune complexes. *Am Rev Respir Dis* 123:434, 1981.

75. JOHNSTON RB JR, KLEMPERER MR, ALPER CA, ROSEN FS: The enhancement of bacterial phagocytosis by serum. The role of complement components and two co-factors. *J Exp Med* 129:1275, 1969.

76. MANTOVANI B, RABINOVITCH M, NUSSENZWEIG V: Phagocytosis of immune complexes by macrophages. Different roles of the macrophage receptor sites for complement (C3) and for immunoglobulin (IgG). *J Exp Med* 135:780, 1972.

77. BIANCO C, GRIFFIN FM JR, SILVERSTEIN SC: Studies on the macrophage complement receptor: Alteration of receptor function upon macrophage activation. *J Exp Med* 141:1278, 1975.

78. WINKELSTEIN JA, SMITH MR, SHIN HS: The role of C3 as an opsonin in the early stages of infection. *Proc Soc Exp Biol Med* 149:397, 1975.

79. HOSEA SW, BROWN EJ, FRANK MM: The critical role of complement in experimental pneumococcal sepsis. *J Infect Dis* 142:903, 1980.

80. MUSCHEL LH, FONG JSC: Serum bactericidal activity and complement, in NK Day, RA Good (eds): *Comprehensive Immunology*, New York, Plenum, 1977, p 137.

81. HARRIMAN GR, ESSER AF, PODACK ER, WUNDERLICH AC, BRAUDE AI, LINT TF, CURD JG: The role of C9 in complement-mediated killing of Neisseria. *J Immunol* 127:2386, 1981.

82. SAULSBURY FT, WINKELSTEIN JA: Activation of the alternative complement pathway by L-phase variants of gram-positive bacteria. *Infect Immun* 23:711, 1979.

83. WRIGHT SD, LEVINE RP: How complement kills E. coli. I. Location of the lethal lesion. *J Immunol* 127:1146, 1981.

84. TAYLOR PW, KROLL HP: Effect of lethal doses of complement on the functional integrity of target enterobacteria. *Curr Top Microbiol Immunol* 121:135, 1985.

85. SCHIFFERLI JA, NG YC, PETERS DK: The role of complement and its receptor in the elimination of immune complexes. *N Engl J Med* 315:488, 1986.

86. SCHIFFERLI JA, BARTOLOTTI SR, PETERS DK: Inhibition of immune precipitation by complement. *Clin Exp Immunol* 42:387, 1980.

87. MILLER GW, NUSSENZWEIG V: A new complement function: solubilization of antigen-antibody aggregates. *Proc Natl Acad Sci USA* 72:418, 1975.

88. BARTOLOTTI SR, PETERS DK: Delayed removal of renal-bound antigen in decomplemented rabbits with acute serum sickness. *Clin Exp Immunol* 32:199, 1978.

89. van SNICK JL, MASSON PL: The effect of complement on the ingestion of soluble antigen-antibody complexes and IgM aggregates by mouse peritoneal macrophages. *J Exp Med* 148:903, 1978.

90. WEILER JM, BALLAS ZK, NEEDLEMAN BW, HOBBS MV, FELDBUSH TL: Complement fragments suppress lymphocyte immune responses. *Immunol Today* 3:238, 1982.

91. PEPYS MB: The role of complement in induction of antibody production in vivo. *J Exp Med* 140:126, 1974.

92. OCHS HD, WEDGEWOOD RJ, FRANK MM, HELLER SR, HOSEA: The role of complement in the induction of antibody responses. *Clin Exp Immunol* 53:208, 1983.

93. O'NEIL KM, OCHS HD, HELLER SR, CORK LC, WINKELSTEIN JA: Deficient humoral immunity in C3-deficient dogs. *J Immunol* 140:1939, 1988.

94. CAMPBELL RD, BENTLEY DR, MORLEY BJ: The factor B and C2 genes. *Philos Trans R Soc Lond B* 306:367, 1984.

95. CARROLL MC, PALSDOTTIR A, BELT KT, PORTER RR: Deletion of complement C4 and steroid 21-hydroxylase genes in the HLA class III region. *EMBO J* 4:2547, 1985.

96. CARROLL MC, CAMBELL RD, PORTER RR: Mapping of steroid 21-hydroxylase genes adjacent to complement component C4 genes in HLA, the major histocompatibility complex in man. *Proc Natl Acad Sci USA* 82:521, 1985.

97. WHITE PC, GROSSBERGER D, ONUFER BJ, CHAPLIN DD, NEW MI, DUPONT B, STROMINGER JL: Two genes encoding 21-hydroxylase are located near the genes encoding the fourth component of complement in man. *Proc Natl Acad Sci USA* 82:5111, 1985.

98. OLAISEN B, TEISBERG R, JONASSEN R, THORSBY E, GEDDE-DAHL T: Gene order and gene distance in the HLA regions studied by the haplotype method. *Am Hum Genet* 47:285, 1983.

99. WHITEHEAD AS, COLTEN HR, CHANG CC, DEMARS R: Localization of MHC-linked complement genes between HLA-B and HLA-DR by using HLA mutant cell lines. *J Immunol* 134:641, 1985.

100. BENTLEY DR: Primary structure of human complement component C2. Homology to two unrelated protein families. *Biochem J* 239:339, 1986.

101. CHAPLIN DD, WOODS DE, WHITEHEAD AS, GOLDBERGER G, COLTEN HR, SEIDMAN JG: Molecular map of the murine S region. *Proc Natl Acad Sci USA* 80:6947, 1985.

102. PERLMUTTER DH, COLTEN HR, GROSSBERGER D, STROMINGER J, SEIDMAN JD, CHAPLIN DD: Expression of complement proteins C2 and factor B in transfected L cells. *J Clin Invest* 76:1449, 1985.

103. KLICKSTEIN LB, WONG WW, SMITH JA, MORTON C, FEARON DT, WEIS JH: Identification of long homologous repeats in human Crl. *Complement* 2:44, 1985.

104. LUBLIN DM, LEMONS RS, LEBEAU MM, HOLERS VM, TYKOCINSKI ML, MEDOF ME, ATKINSON JP: The gene encoding decay-accelerating factor is located in the complement regulator locus on the long arm of chromosome 1. *Clin Res* 35:460A, 1987.

105. RODRIQUEZ de CORDOBA S, LUBLIN DM, RUBINSTEIN P, ATKINSON JP: Human genes for 3 complement compontents that regulate the activation of C3 are tightly linked. *J Exp Med* 161:1189, 1985.

106. WEIS JH, MORTON CC, BRUNS GAP, WEIS JJ, KLICKSTEIN LB, WONG WW, FEARON DT: A complement receptor locus: Genes encoding C3b/C4b receptor and C3d/Epstein-Barr virus receptor map to 1q32. *J Immunol* 138:312, 1987.

107. MORLEY BJ, CAMPBELL RD: Internal homologies of the Ba fragment from human complement component factor B, a class III MHC antigen. *EMBO J* 3:153, 1984.

108. KRISTENSEN T, WETSEL RA, TACK BF: Structural analysis of human complement protein H: Homology with C4b binding protein, beta-2-glycoprotein 1 and Ba fragment of B. *J Immunol* 136:3407, 1986.

109. REID KBM, BENTLEY DR, CAMPBELL RD, CHUNG LP, SIM RB, KRISTENSEN T, TACK BF: Complement system proteins which interact with C3B or C4B. A super family of structurally related proteins. *Immunol Today* 7:230, 1986.

110. RAO AG, HOWARD OMZ, NG S, WHITEHEAD AS, COLTEN HR, SODETZ JM: cDNA and derived amino acid sequence of the alpha subunit of human complement protein C8: Evidence for the existence of separate alpha subunit mRNA. *Biochemistry* 26:3556, 1987.

111. HOWARD OMZ, RAO AG, SODETZ JM: cDNA and derived amino acid sequence of the beta subunit of human complement protein C8: Identification of a close structural and ancestral relationship to the alpha subunit and C9. *Biochemistry* 26:3565, 1987.

112. STANLEY KK, KOCHER HP, LUZIO JP, JACKSON P, TSCHOPP J: The sequence and topology of human complement component C9. *EMBO J* 4:375, 1985.

113. DAVIS AE, WHITEHEAD AS, HARRISON RA, DAUPHINAIS A, BRUNS GAP, CICARDI M, ROSEN FS: Human inhibitor of the first component of complement, C1: Characterization of cDNA clones and localization of the gene to chromosome 11. *Proc Natl Acad Sci USA* 83:3161, 1986.

114. RAUM D, DONALDSON VH, ROSEN FS, ALPER CA: Genetics of complement. *Curr Top Hematol* 3:111, 1980.

115. YU CY, BELT KT, GILES CM, CAMPBELL RD, PORTER RR: Structural basis of the polymorphism of human complement components C4A and C4B: Gene size, reactivity and antigenicity. *EMBO J* 5:2873, 1986.

116. SCHUR PH: Inherited complement component abnormalities. *Annu Rev Med* 37:333, 1986.

117. MCLEAN RH, WINKELSTEIN JA: Genetically determined variation in the complement system: Relationship to disease. *J Pediatr* 105:179, 1984.

118. AWDEH ZL, RAUM D, YUNIS EJ, ALPER CA: Extended HLA/complement allele haplotypes: Evidence for T/t-like complex in man. *Proc Natl Acad Sci USA* 80:259, 1983.

119. AWDEH ZL, ALPER CA, EYNON E, ALOSCO SM, STEIN R, AND YUNIS EJ: Unrelated individuals matched for MHC extended haplotypes and HLA-identical siblings show comparable responses in mixed lymphocyte culture. *Lancet* II:853, 1985.

120. ALPER CA: Complement and the MHC, in Dorf ME (ed): *The Role of the Major Histocompatibility Complex in Immunology.* New York, Garland Press, 1981, p 173.

121. COLTEN HR: Genetics and synthesis of components of the complement system, in Ross GD (ed): *Immunobiology of the Complement System.* New York, Academic, 1986, p 163.

122. MORRIS KM, COLTEN HR, BING DH: The first component of complement: A quantitative comparison of its biosynthesis in culture by human epithelial and mesenchymal cells. *J Exp Med* 148:1007, 1978.

123. MORRIS KM, ADEN DP, KNOWLES BB, COLTEN HR: Complement biosynthesis by the human hepatoma-derived cell line. HepG2. *J Clin Invest* 70:906, 1982.

124. MULLER W, HANAUSKE-ABEL H, LOOS M: Biosynthesis of the first component of complement by human and guinea pig peritoneal macrophages: Evidence for independent production of the C1 subunits. *J Immunol* 121:1578, 1978.

125. REID KBM, BENTLEY DR, WOOD KJ: Cloning and characterization of the complementary DNA for the B chain of normal human serum C1q. *Philos Trans R Soc Lond B* 306:345, 1984.

126. CHU ML, DEWET W, BERNARD M, DING JF, MOSABITO LM, MAYERS J, WILLIAMS C, RAMIREZ F: Human pro alpha 1 (1) collagen gene structure reveals evolutionary conservation of a pattern of introns and exons. *Nature* 310:337, 1984.

127. REID KBM, THOMPSON RA: Characterization of a non functional form of C1q found in patients with a genetically linked deficiency of C1q activity. *Mol Immunol* 20:117, 1983.

128. REID KBM, SOLOMAN E: Biosynthesis of the first component of complement by human fibroblasts. *Biochem J* 167:647, 1977.

129. YONEMASU K, KITAJUMA H, TANABE S, OCHI T, SHINKAI H: Effect of age on C1q and C3 levels in human serum and their presence in colostrum. *Immunology* 35:523, 1979.

130. LOOS M: Biosynthesis of the collagen-like C1q molecule and its receptor functions for Fc and polyanionic molecules on macrophages. *Curr Top Microbiol Immunol* 102:1, 1983.

131. TOSI M, JOURNET A, COLOMB M, MEO T: Construction, isolation and characterization of cDNA clones encoding human C1r and C1s. *Complement* 2:79, 1985.

132. BENSA JC, REBOUL A, COLOMB MG: Biosynthesis in vitro of complement subcomponents C1q, C1s and C1 inhibitor by resting and stimulated human monocytes. *Biochem J* 216:385, 1983.

133. HALL RE, COLTEN HR: Cell-free synthesis of the fourth component of guinea pig complement (C4): Identification of a precursor of serum C4 (pro-C4). *Proc Natl Acad Sci USA* 74:1707, 1977.

134. ROOS MH, ATKINSON JP, SHREFFLER DC: Molecular characterization of SS and S1p (C4) proteins of the mouse H-2 complex: Subunit composition, chain size, polymorphism and an intracellular (pro-Ss) precursor. *J Immunol* 121:1106, 1978.

135. OGATA R, SHREFFLER D, SEPICH D, LILLY S: cDNA clone spanning the alpha-gamma subunit junction in the precursor of the murine fourth complement component. *Proc Natl Acad Sci USA* 80:5061, 1983.

136. WHITEHEAD AS, WOODS DE, FLEISHNICK E, CHIN JE, KATZ AJ, GERALD PS, ALPER CA, COLTEN HR: DNA polymorphism of the C4 gene: A new marker for analysis of the major histocompatibility complex. *N Engl J Med* 310:88, 1984.

137. GOLDBERGER G, COLTEN HR: Precursor complement protein (pro-C4) is converted in vitro by plasmin. *Nature* 286:514, 1980.

138. GOLDBERGER G, ABRAHAM GN, WILLIAMS J, COLTEN HR: Amino terminal sequence analysis of pro-C4, the precursor of the fourth component of guinea pig complement. *J Biol Chem* 250:7071, 1980.

139. KARP DR: Post-translational modification of the fourth component of complement. Sulfation of the alpha chain. *J Biol Chem* 258:12745, 1983.

140. KARP DR: Post-translational modification of the fourth component of complement. Effect of the tunicamycin and amino acid analogs on the formation of the internal thiolester and disulfide bonds. *J Biol Chem* 258:14490, 1983.

141. MATTHEWS WJ, GOLDBERGER G, MARINO JT, EINSTEIN LP, GASH DJ, COLTEN HR: Complement proteins C2, C4 and factor B: Effect of glycosylation on their secretion and catabolism. *Biochem J* 204:839, 1982.

142. ROOS MH, KORNFELD S, SHREFFLER DC: Characterization of the oligosaccharide units of the fourth component of complement (Ss protein) synthesized by murine hepatocytes. *J Immunol* 124:2860, 1980.

143. CHAN AC, MITCHELL KR, MUNNS TW, KARP DR, ATKINSON JP: Identification and partial characterization of the secreted form of the fourth component of human complement: Evidence that it is different from the major plasma form. *Proc Natl Acad Sci USA* 80:268, 1983.

144. HORTIN G, CHANGE AS, FOK KF, STRAUSS AW, ATKINSON JP: Sequence analysis of the COOH terminus of the alpha chain of the fourth complement of human complement: Identification of the site of its extracellular cleavage. *J Biol Chem* 261:9065, 1986.

145. BELT KT, CARROLL MC, PORTER RR: The structural basis of the multiple forms of human complement component C4. *Cell* 36:907, 1984.

146. BELT KT, YU CY, CARROLL MC, PORTER RR: Polymorphism of the human complement component C4. *Immunogenetics* 21:173, 1985.

147. PRENTICE HL, SCHNEIDER PM, STROMINGER JL: C4B gene polymorphism detected in human cosmid clone. *Immunogenetics* 23:274, 1986.

148. ISENMAN DE, YOUNG JR: The molecular basis for the difference in immune hemolysis activity of the Chido and Rodgers isotypes of human complement component C4. *J Immunol* 132:3019, 1984.

149. LAW SKA, DODDS AW, PORTER RR: A comparison of the properties of the two classes, C4A and C4B, of the human complement component C4. *EMBO J* 3:1819, 1984.

150. ROOS MH, MOLLENHAUER E, DEMANT P, RITTNER C: A molecular basis for the two locus model of human complement component C4. *Nature* 298:854, 1982.

151. SCHNEIDER PM, CARROLL MC, ALPER CA, RITTNER C, WHITEHEAD AS, YU-

NIS EJ, COLTEN HR: Polymorphism of the human complement C4 and steroid 21-hydroxylase gene. Restriction fragment length polymorphisms revealing structural deletions, homoduplications and size variants. *J Clin Invest* 78:650, 1986.

152. WHITEHEAD AS, WOODS DE, FLEISHNICK E, CHIN JE, KATZ AJ, GERALD PS, ALPER CA, COLTEN HR: DNA polymorphism of the C4 gene: A new marker for analysis of the major histocompatibility complex. *N Engl J Med* 310:88, 1984.

153. MIURA N, PRENTICE H, SCHNEIDER PM, PERLMUTTER DH: Synthesis and regulation of the two human complement C4 genes in stable transfected mouse fibroblasts. *J Biol Chem* 262:7298, 1987.

154. CARROLL MC, CAMPBELL RD, BENTLEY DR, PORTER RR: A molecular map of the human major histocompatibility complex class III region linking complement genes C4, C2 and factor B. *Nature* 307:237, 1984.

155. SACKSTEIN R, COLTEN HR, WOODS DE: Phylogenetic conservation of class III major histocompatibility complex antigen, factor B: Isolation and nucleotide sequence of mouse factor B cDNA clones. *J Biol Chem* 258:14693, 1983.

156. CROSS SJ, EDWARDS JM, BENTLEY DR, CAMBELL RD: DNA polymorphism of the C2 and factor B genes. Detection of a restriction fragment length polymorphism which subdivides haplotypes carrying the C2C and factor B F alleles. *Immunogenetics* 21:39, 1985.

157. FALUS A, WAKELAND EK, McCONNELL TJ, GITLIN J, WHITEHEAD AS, COLTEN HR: DNA polymorphism of MHC class III genes in inbred and wild mouse strains. *Immunogenetics* 25:290, 1987.

158. WOODS DE, EDGE MD, COLTEN HR: Isolation of a cDNA clone for the human complement protein C2 and its use in identification of a restriction fragment length polymorphism. *J Clin Invest* 74:634, 1984.

159. PERLMUTTER DH, COLE FS, GOLDBERGER G, COLTEN HR: Distinct primary translation products from human liver mRNA give rise to secreted and cell-associated forms of complement C2. *J Biol Chem* 259:10380, 1984.

160. ALPERT SE, AUERBACH HS, COLE FS, COLTEN HR: Macrophage maturation: Differences in complement secretion by marrow, monocyte, and tissue macrophages detected with an improved hemolytic plaque assay. *J Immunol* 130:102, 1983.

161. COLE FS, MATTHEWS WJ, MARINO JT, GASH DJ, COLTEN HR: Control of complement synthesis and secretion in bronchoalveolar and peritoneal macrophages. *J Immunol* 125:1120, 1980.

162. COLE FS, AUERBACH HS, GOLDBERGER G, COLTEN HR: Mechanisms regulating complement production during monocyte-macrophage maturation. *Immunobiology* 164:224, 1983.

163. COLE FS, AUERBACH HS, GOLDBERGER G, COLTEN HR: Tissue-specific pretranslational regulation of complement production in human mononuclear phagocytes. *J Immunol* 134:2610, 1985.

164. WOODS DE, MARKHAM A, RICKER A, GOLDBERGER G, COLTEN HR: Isolation of cDNA clones for the human complement protein factor B, a class III major histocompatibility complex gene product. *Proc Natl Acad Sci USA* 79:5661, 1982.

165. STRUNK RC, WHITEHEAD AS, COLE FS: Pretranslational regulation of the synthesis of the third component of complement in human mononuclear phagocytes by the lipid A portion of lipopolysaccharide. *J Clin Invest* 76:985, 1985.

166. RAMADORI G, SIPE J, COLTEN HR: Expression and regulation of the murine serum amyloid A (SAA) gene in extrahepatic sites. *J Immunol* 135:3645, 1985.

167. PERLMUTTER DH, GOLDBERGER G, DINARELLO CA, MIZEL SB, COLTEN HR: Regulation of class III major histocompatibility complex gene products by interleukin-1. *Science* 232:850, 1986.

168. RAMADORI G, SIPE JD, DINARELLO CA, MIZEL SB, COLTEN HR: Pretranslational modulation of acute phase hepatic protein synthesis by murine recombinant interleukin (IL-1) and purified human IL-1. *J Exp Med* 162:930, 1985.

169. STRUNK RC, COLE FS, PERLMUTTER DH, COLTEN HR: Gamma interferon increases expression of class III complement genes C2 and factor B in human monocytes and in murine fibroblasts transfected with human C2 and factor B genes. *J Biol Chem* 260:15280, 1985.

170. WHITEHEAD AS, SOLOMON E, CHAMBERS S, BODMER WF, POVEY S, FEY G: Assignment of the structural gene for the third component of human complement to chromosome 19. *Proc Natl Acad Sci USA* 79:5021, 1982.

171. BRADE V, HALL RW, COLTEN HR: Biosynthesis of pro-C3, a precursor of the third component of complement. *J Exp Med* 146:759, 1977.

172. DOMDEY M, WIEBAUER K, KAZMAIR M, MULLER V, ODINK K, FEY G: Characterization of the mRNA and cloned cDNA specifying the third component of mouse complement. *Proc Natl Acad Sci USA* 79:7619, 1982.

173. EINSTEIN LP, HANSEN PJ, BALLOW M, DAVIS AE, DAVIS JS, ALPER CA, ROSEN FS, COLTEN HR: Biosynthesis of the third component of complement (C3) in vitro by monocytes from both normal and homozygous C3-deficient humans. *J Clin Invest* 60:963, 1977.

174. MORRIS KM, GOLDBERGER G, COLTEN HR, ADEN DP, KNOWLES BB: Biosynthesis and processing of a human precursor complement protein, pro-C3, in a hepatoma-derived cell line. *Science* 215:399, 1982.

175. de BRUIJN MHL, FEY G: Human complement component C3: cDNA coding sequence and derived primary structure. *Proc Natl Acad Sci USA* 82:708, 1985.

176. FEY GH, LUNDWALL A, WETSEL RA, TACK BF, de BRUIJN MHL, DOMDEY H: Nucleotide sequence of complementary DNA and derived amino acid sequence of murine complement component C3. *Philos Trans R Soc Lond B* 306:333, 1984.

177. PERLMUTTER DH, COLTEN HR: Molecular immunobiology of complement biosynthesis: A model of single cell control of effector-inhibitor balance. *Annu Rev Immunol* 4:231, 1986.

178. OOI YM, COLTEN HR: Biosynthesis and post-synthetic modification of a precursor (Pro-C5) of the fifth component of mouse complement (C5). *J Immunol* 123:2494, 1979.

179. PATEL F, MINTA JO: Biosynthesis of a single chain pro-C5 by normal mouse liver mRNA: Analysis of the molecular basis of C5 deficiency in AKR/J mice. *J Immunol* 123:2408, 1979.

180. LUNDWALL AB, WETSEL RA, KRISTENSEN T, WHITEHEAD AS, WOODS DE, OGDEN RL, COLTEN HR, TACK BF: Isolation of a cDNA clone encoding the fifth component of human complement. *J Biol Chem* 260:2108, 1985.

181. WETSEL RA, OGATA RT, TACK BF: Primary structure of the fifth component of murine complement. *Biochemistry* 26:737, 1987.

182. PETERSEN BH, GRAHAM JA, BROOKS GF: Human deficiency of the eighth component of complement. The requirement of C8 for serum *Neisseria gonorrhoeae* bactericidal activity. *J Clin Invest* 57:283, 1976.

183. RAUM D, SPENCER MA, BALAVITCH D, TIDOMAN S, MERRITT AD, TAGGART RT, PETERSEN BH, DAY NR, ALPER CA: Genetic control of the eighth component of complement. *J Clin Invest* 64:648, 1979.

184. RITTNER C, SCHNEIDER PM: Genetics and polymorphism of the complement components, in Rother K, Till GO (ed): *The Complement System.* Heidelberg, Springer-Verlag, 1988.

185. DISCIPIO RG, GEHRING MR, PODACK ER, KAN CC, HUGLI TE, FEY GH: Nucleotide sequence of human complement component C9. *Proc Natl Acad Sci USA* 81:7298, 1984.

186. STANLEY KK, LUZIO JP: Construction of a new family of high efficiency bacterial expression vectors: Identification of cDNA clones for human liver proteins. *EMBO J* 3:11429, 1984.

187. STANLEY KK, KOCHER HP, LUZIO JP, JACKSON P, TSCHOPP J: The sequence and topology of human complement component C9. *EMBO J* 4:375, 1985.

188. YOUNG JDE, CHON ZA, PODACK ER: The ninth component of complement and the pore-forming protein (perforin 1) from cytotoxic T cells: Structural, immunological and functional similarities. *Science* 233:184, 1986.

189. BARNUM SR, VOLANAKIS JE: In vitro biosynthesis of complement protein D by U937 cells. *J Immunol* 143:1799, 1985.

190. WHALEY K: Biosynthesis of complement components and the regulatory proteins of the alternative complement pathway by human peripheral blood monocytes. *J Exp Med* 151:501, 1980.

191. HARRISON RA: Human C1 inhibitor: Improved isolation and preliminary structural characterization. *Biochemistry* 22:5001, 1983.

192. COLTEN HR: Ontogeny of the human complement system: in vitro biosynthesis of individual complement components by fetal tissues. *J Clin Invest* 51:725, 1972.

193. GITLIN D, BIASUCCI A: Development of gamma G, gamma A, gamma M, beta-1-C/beta-1-A, C1 esterase inhibitor, ceruloplasmin, transferrin, hemopexin, haptoglobin, fibrinogen, plasminogen, alpha₁ antitrypsin, orosomucoid, beta-lipoprotein, alpha₂ macroglobulin and prealbumin in the human conceptus. *J Clin Invest* 48:1433, 1969.

194. JOHNSON AM, ALPER CA, ROSEN FS, CRAIG FM: C1 inhibitor: Evidence for decreased hepatic synthesis in hereditary angioneurotic edema. *Science* 173:553, 1971.

195. YEUNG-LAIWAH AC, JONES L, HAMILTON AD, WHALEY K: Complement subcomponent-C1 inhibitor synthesis by human monocytes. *Biochem J* 226:199, 1985.

196. BOCK SC, SKRIVER K, NEILSON E, THOGERSEN HC, WIMAN B, DONALDSON VH, EDDY RL, MUARINAN J, RODZIEJEWSKA E, HUBER R, SHOWS TB, MAGNUSSON S: Human C1 inhibitor: Primary structure, cDNA cloning and chromosomal localization. *Biochemistry* 25:4294, 1986.

197. CHUNG LP, BENTLEY DR, REID KBM: Molecular cloning and characterization of the cDNA coding for C4b-binding protein a regulatory protein of the classical pathway of the human complement system. *Biochem J* 230:133, 1985.

198. DAHLBACK B, SMITH CA, MULLER-EBERHARD HJ: Visualization of human

C4b-binding protein and its complexes with vitamin K-dependent protein S and complement protein C4B. *Proc Natl Acad Sci USA* 80:3461, 1983.

199. RODRIQUEZ de CORDOBA S, FERREIRA A, NUSSENZWEIG V, RUBINSTEIN P: Genetic polymorphism of human C4 binding protein. *J Immunol* 131:1565, 1983.

200. REID KBM: Application of molecular cloning to studies on the complement system. *Immunology* 55:185, 1985.

201. LUBLIN DM, DRSEK-STAPLES J, PANGBURM MK, ATKINSON JP: Biosynthesis and glycosylation of the human complement regulatory protein decay-accelerating factor. *J Immunol* 137:1629, 1986.

202. MEDOF ME, HAAS R, WALKER EI, ROSENBERRY TL: Decay-accelerating factor (DAF) is anchored to membranes by a C-terminal glycolipid. *Biochemistry* 25:6740, 1986.

203. CARAS IW, DAVITZ MA, RHEE L, WEDDELL G, MARTIN DW, NUSSENZWEIG V: Cloning of decay-accelerating factor suggests novel use of splicing to generate two proteins. *Nature* 325:545, 1987.

204. ASCH AS, KINOSHITA T, JAFFE EA, NUSSENZWEIG V: Decay-accelerating factor is present on cultured human umbilical vein endothelial cells. *J Exp Med* 163:221, 1986.

205. MEDOF ME, LUBLIN DM, HOLERS VM, AYERS DJ, GETTY RR, LEYKAM JF, ATKINSON JP, TYKOCINSKI ML: Cloning and characterization of cDNAs encoding the complete sequence of decay-accelerating factor of human complement. *Proc Natl Acad Sci USA* 84:2007, 1987.

206. GOLDBERGER G, ARNAOUT MA, ADEN D, KAY R, RITS M, COLTEN HR: Biosynthesis and postsynthetic processing of human C3b/C4b inactivator (factor I) in the three hepatoma cell lines. *J Biol Chem* 259:6492, 1984.

207. GOLDBERGER G, BRUNS GAP, RITS M, EDGE MD, KWIATKOWSKI DJ: Human complement factor I. Analysis of cDNA-derived primary structure and assignment of its gene to chromosome 4. *J Biol Chem* 262:10065, 1987.

208. WONG WW, KLICKSTEIN LB, SMITH JA, WEIS JH, FEARON DT: Identification of a partial cDNA clone for the human receptor for complement fragments C3b/C4b. *Proc Natl Acad Sci USA* 82:7711, 1985.

209. DYCKMAN TR, COLE JL, IIDA K, ATKINSON JP: Polymorphism of the human erythrocyte C3b/C4b receptor. *Proc Natl Acad Sci USA* 80:1698, 1983.

210. DYCKMAN TR, HATCH J, ATKINSON JP: Polymorphism of the human C3b/C4b receptor: Identification of a third allele and analysis of receptor phenotypes in families and patients with systemic lupus erythematosus. *J Exp Med* 159:691, 1984.

211. WONG WW, WILSON JG, FEARON DT: Genetic regulation of a structural polymorphism of human C3b receptor. *J Clin Invest* 72:685, 1983.

212. WILSON JG, WONG WW, SCHUR PH, FEARON DT: Mode of inheritance of decreased C3b receptors on erythrocytes of patients with systemic lupus erythematosus. *N Engl J Med* 307:981, 1982.

213. WILSON JG, MURPHY EF, WONG WW, KLICKSTEIN LB, WEIS JH, FEARON DT: Identification of a restriction fragment length polymorphism by a CR1 cDNA that correlated with the number of CR1 on erythrocytes. *J Exp Med* 164:50, 1986.

214. WEIS JJ, FEARON DT: The identification of N-linked oligosaccharides on the human CR2/Epstein-Barr virus receptor and their function in receptor metabolism, plasma membrane expression, and ligand binding. *J Biol Chem* 260:13824, 1985.

215. WEIS JJ, FEARON DT, KLICKSTEIN LB, WONG WW, RICHARDS SA, DEBRUYN KOPS A, SMITH JA, WEIS JH: Identification of a partial cDNA clone for the C3d/Epstein-Barr virus receptor of human B lymphocytes: Homology with the receptor for fragments C3b and C4b of the third and fourth components of complement. *Proc Natl Acad Sci USA* 83:5639, 1986.

216. SANCHEZ-MADRID F, NAGY JA, ROBBINS E, SIMON P, SPRINGER TA: Characterization of human leukocyte differentiation antigen family with distinct alpha subunits and a common beta subunit: The lymphocyte function associated antigen (LFA-1), the C3bi complement receptor (OKM1/Mac-1) and the p150,94 molecule. *J Exp Med* 158:1785, 1983.

217. SASTRE L, ROMAN JM, TEPLOW DB, DREYER WJ, GEE CE, LARSON RS, ROBERTS TM, SPRINGER TA: A partial genomic DNA clone for the alpha subunit of the mouse complement receptor type 3 and cellular adhesion molecule Mac-1. *Proc Natl Acad Sci USA* 83:5644, 1986.

218. AGNELLO V: Complement deficiency states. *Medicine* 57:1, 1978.

219. LINT TF, ZEITZ HJ, GEWURZ H: Inherited deficiency of the ninth component of complement in man. *J Immunol* 125:2252, 1980.

220. POLHILL RB JR, PRUITT KM, JOHNSTON RB JR: Kinetic assessment of alternative pathway activity in a hemolytic system. I. Experimental and kinetic analysis. *J Immunol* 121:363, 1978.

221. AMINOFF D, BELL WC, FULTON I, INGEBRIGTSEN N: Effect of sialidase on the viability of erythrocytes in circulation. *Am J Hematol* 1:419, 1976.

222. NELSON RA JR, JENSEN J, GIGLI I, TAMURA N: Methods for the separation, purification and measurement of the nine components of the hemolytic complement in guinea pig serum. *Immunochemistry* 3:111, 1966.

223. ROSEN FS, CHARACHE P, PENSKY J, DONALDSON V: Hereditary angioneurotic edema: Two genetic variants. *Science* 148:957, 1965.

224. THOMPSON RA, HAENEY R, REID KBM, DAVIES JG, WHITE RHR, CAMERON AH: A genetic defect of the C1q subcomponent of complement associated with childhood (immune complex) nephritis. *N Engl J Med* 303:22, 1980.

225. TEDESCO F, DENSEN P, VILLA MA, PETERSEN BH, SIRCHIA G: Two types of dysfunctional eighth component of complement (C8) molecules in C8 deficiency in man: Reconstitution of normal C8 from the mixture of two abnormal C8 molecules. *J Clin Invest* 71:183, 1983.

226. FU SM, KUNKEL HG, BRUSMAN HP, ALLEN FH JR, FOTINO M: Evidence for linkage between HL-A histocompatibility genes and those involved in the synthesis of the second component of complement. *J Exp Med* 140:1108, 1975.

227. OCHS HD, ROSENFELD SI, THOMAS ED, GIBLETT ER, ALPER CA, DUPONT B, SCHALLER JG, GILLILAND BC, HANSEN JA, WEDGEWOOD RJ: Linkage between the gene (or genes) controlling synthesis of the fourth component of complement and the major histocompatibility complex. *N Engl J Med* 296:470, 1977.

228. GLASS D, RAUM D, GIBSON D, STILLMAN JS, SCHUR P: Inherited deficiency of the second component of complement: Rheumatic disease associations. *J Clin Invest* 58:853, 1976.

229. GIBSON DJ, GLASS D, CARPENTER CB, SCHUR PH: Hereditary C2 deficiency: Diagnosis and HLA gene complex associations: *J Immunol* 116:1065, 1976.

230. ELLISON RT, KOHLER PH, CURD JG, JUDSON FN, RELLER LB: Prevalence of congenital or acquired complement deficiency in patients with sporadic meningococcal disease. *N Engl J Med* 308:913, 1983.

231. LEGGIARDRO RJ, WINKELSTEIN JA: Prevalence of complement deficiencies in children with systemic meningococcal infections. *Pediatr Inf Dis* 6:75, 1987.

232. HIRSCH RL: The complement system: Its importance in the host response to viral infection. *Microbiol Rev* 46:71, 1982.

233. HIRSCH RL, GRIFFIN DE, WINKELSTEIN JA: The effect of complement depletion on the course of sindbis virus infection in mice. *J Immunol* 121:1276, 1978.

234. HICKS JT, ENNIS FA, KIM E, VERBONITZ M: The importance of an intact complement pathway in recovery from a primary viral infection. Influenza in decomplemented and in C5-deficient mice. *J Immunol* 121:1437, 1978.

235. PROVOST TT, ARNETT FC, REICHLIN M: Homozygous C2 deficiency, lupus erythematosis, and anti-Ro (SSA) antibodies. *Arthritis Rheum* 26:1279, 1983.

236. MEYER O, HAUPTMANN G, TAPPEINER G, OCHS HD, MASCART-LEMONE F: Genetic deficiency of C4, C2 or C1q and lupus syndromes. Association with anti-Ro (SS-A) antibodies. *Clin Exp Immunol* 62:678, 1985.

237. MADDISON PJ, PROVOST TT, REICHLIN M: Serologic findings in patients with "ANA-negative" SLE. *Medicine* 60:87, 1981.

238. SONTHEIMER RD, STASTNY P, MADDISON P, REICHLIN M, GILLIAM JN: Serologic and HLA associations in subacute cutaneous lupus erythematosis (SCLE): A clinical subset of lupus erythematosis. *Ann Intern Med* 97:664, 1982.

239. BLUM JR, CORK LC, MORRIS JM, OLSEN JL, WINKELSTEIN JA: The clinical manifestations of a genetically determined deficiency of the third component of complement in the dog. *Clin Immunol Immunopathol* 34:304, 1985.

240. LOOS M, HEINZ HP: Component deficiencies: The first component: C1q, C1r, C1s. *Prog Allergy* 39:212, 1986.

241. CHAPUIS RM, HAUPTMANN G, GROSSHANS E, ISLIKER H: Structural and functional studies in C1q deficiency. *J Immunol* 129:1509, 1982.

242. HAUPTMANN G, GOETZ J, URING-LAMBERT B, GROSSHANS E: Component deficiencies: The fourth component. *Prog Allergy* 39:232, 1986.

243. O'NEILL GJ, YANG SY, DUPONT B: Two HLA-linked loci controlling the fourth component of human complement. *Proc Natl Acad Sci USA* 75:5165, 1978.

244. AWDEH ZL, ALPER CA: Inherited structural polymorphism of the fourth component of human complement. *Proc Natl Acad Sci USA* 77:3576, 1978.

245. ROOS MH, MOLLENHAUER E, DEMANT P, RITTNER CH: A molecular basis for the two model of human complement component C4. *Nature* 298:854, 1982.

246. O'NEILL GJ, YANG SY, TEGOLI J, BERGER R, DUPONT B: Chido and Rogers blood groups are distinct antigenic components of human complement C4. *Nature* 273:668, 1978.

247. AWDEH ZL, OCHS HD, ALPER CA: Genetic analysis of C4 deficiency. *J Clin Invest* 67:260, 1981.

248. WELCH TR, BEISCHEL L, BERRY A, FORRISTAL J, WEST CD: The effect of null C4 alleles on complement function. *Clin Immunol Immunopathol* 34:316, 1985.

249. AWDEH ZL, RAUM D, ALPER CA: Genetic polymorphism of human complement C4 and detection of heterozygotes. *Nature* 282:205, 1979.

250. CLARK RA, KLEBANOFF SJ: Role of the classical and alternative complement pathways in chemotaxis and opsonization: Studies of human serum deficient in C4. *J Immunol* 120:1102, 1978.

251. MASCART-LEMONE F, HAUPTMANN G, GOETZ J, DUCHATEAU J, DELESPESSE G, VRAY B, DAB I: Genetic deficiency of C4 presenting with recurrent infections and a SLE-like disease. *Am J Med* 75:295, 1983.

252. TAPPEINER G, HINTNER H, SCHOLZ S, ALBERT E, LINERT J, WOLFF K: Systemic lupus erythematosis in hereditary deficiency of the fourth component of complement. *J Am Acad Dermatol* 7:66, 1982.

253. MUIR WA, HEDRICH S, ALPER CA, RATNOFF OD, SCHACTER B, WISNIESKI JJ: Inherited incomplete deficiency of the fourth component of complement (C4) determined by a gene not linked to human histocompatibility leukocyte antigens. *J Clin Invest* 74:1509, 1984.

254. BUDOWLE B, ROSEMAN JM, GO RCP, LOUV W, BARGER BO, ACTON RT: Phenotypes of the fourth component (C4) in black americans from the southeastern United States. *J Immunogenet* 10:199, 1983.

255. CHRISTIANSEN FT, DAWKINS RL, UKO G, MCCLUSKY J, KAY PH, ZILKO PJ: Complement allotyping in SLE: Association with C4A null. *Aust NZ J Med* 13:483, 1983.

256. FIEDLER AHL, WALPORT MJ, BATCHELOR JR, RYNES RI, BLACK CM, DODI IA, HUGHES GRV: Family study of the major histocompatibility complex in patients with sytemic lupus erythematosis: Importance of null alleles of C4A and C4B in determining disease susceptibility. *Br Med J* 286:425, 1983.

257. HOWARD PF, HOCHBERG MC, BIAS WB, ARNETT FC, MCLEAN RH: Relationship between C4 null genes, HLA-D region antigens, and genetic susceptibility to systemic lupus erythematosis in caucasian and black americans. *Am J Med* 81:187, 1986.

258. MIJOVIC C, FLETCHER J, BRADWELL AR, HARVEY T, BARNETT AH: Relation of gene expression (allotypes) of the fourth component of complement to insulin dependent diabetes and its microangiopathic complications. *Br Med J* 291:9, 1985.

259. PARTANEN J, KOSKIMIES S, ILONEN J, KNIP M: MLA antigens and complotypes in insulin-dependent diabetes mellitus. *Tissue Antigens* 27:291, 1986.

260. MCLEAN RH, WYATT RJ, JULIAN BA: Complement phenotypes in glomerulonephritis: Increased frequency of homozygous null C4 phenotypes in IgA nephropathy and Henoch-Schonlein purpura. *Kidney Int* 26:855, 1984.

261. RUDDY S: Component Deficiencies: The second component. *Prog Allergy* 39:250, 1986.

262. RHYNES RI, BRITTEN AF, PICHERING RJ: Deficiency of the second component of complement association with the HLA haplotype A10, B18 in a normal population. *Ann Rheum Dis* 41:93, 1982.

263. PARISER KM, RAUM D, BERKMAN EM, ALPER CA, AGNELLO V: Evidence for a silent or null gene in hereditary C2 deficiency. *J Immunol* 121:2580, 1978.

264. COLE FS, WHITEHEAD AS, AUERBACH HS, LINT TL, ZEITZ HJ, KILBRIDGE P, COLTEN HR: The molecular basis for genetic deficiency of the second component of human complement. *N Engl J Med* 313:11, 1985.

265. EINSTEIN LP, ALPER CA, BLOCK KJ, HERRIN JT, ROSEN FS, DAVID JR, COLTEN HR: Biosynthetic defect in monocytes from human beings with genetic deficiency of the second component of complement. *N Engl J Med* 292:1169, 1975.

266. FU SM, STERN R, KUNKEL HG, DUPONT B, HANSEN JA, DAY NK, GOOD RA, JERSILD C, FOTINO M: Mixed lymphocyte culture determinants and C2 deficiency. LD-7a associated with C2 deficiency in four families. *J Exp Med* 142:495, 1975.

267. DAY NK, L'ESPERANCE P, GOOD RA, MICHAEL AF, HANSEN JA, DUPONT B, JERSILD C: Hereditary C2 deficiency. Genetic studies and association with the HL-A system. *J Exp Med* 141:1464, 1975.

268. WOLSKI KP, SCHMID FR, MITTAL K: Genetic linkage between the HL-A system and a deficient of the second component (C2) of complement. *Science* 188:1020, 1975.

269. AWDEH ZL, RAUM DD, GLASS D, AGNELLO V, SCHUR PH, JOHNSTON RB JR, GELFAND EW, BALLOW M, YUNIS E, ALPER CA: Complement-human histocompatibility antigen haplotypes in C2 deficiency. *J Clin Invest* 67:581, 1981.

270. HAUPTMANN G, TONGIO MM, GOETZ J, MAYER S, FAUCHET R, SOBEL A, GRISCEL C, BERTHOUX F, RIVAT C, ROTHER U: Association of the C2-deficiency gene (C2*Q0) with the C4A*4, C4B*2 genes. *J Immunogenet* 9:127, 1982.

271. RUDDY S, KLEMPERER MR, ROSEN FS, AUSTEN KF, KUMATE J: Hereditary deficiency of the second component of complement in man: Correlation of C2 hemolytic activity with immunochemical measurements of C2 protein. *Immunology* 18:943, 1970.

272. JOHNSON FR, AGNELLO V, WILLIAMS RC JR: Opsonic activity in human serum deficient in C2. *J Immunol* 109:141, 1971.

273. SAMPSON HA, WALCHNER AM, BAKER PJ: Recurrent pyogenic infections in individuals with absence of the second component of complement. *J Clin Immunol* 2:39, 1982.

274. FRIEND P, RAPINE J, KIM Y, CLAWSON CC, MICHAEL AF: Deficiency of the second component of complement (C2) with chronic vasculitis. *Ann Intern Med* 83:813, 1975.

275. REPINE JE, CLAWSON CC, FRIEND PS: Influence of a deficiency of the second component of complement on the bactericidal activity of neutrophils in vitro. *J Clin Invest* 59:802, 1977.

276. GEIBINK GS, VERHOEFF J, PETERSON PK, QUIE PG: Opsonic requirements for phagocytosis of streptococcus pneumoniae types VI, XVIII, XXIII and XXV. *Infect Immunol* 18:291, 1977.

277. NEWMAN SL, VOGLER LB, FIEGEN RD, JOHNSTON RB JR: Recurrent septicemia associated with congenital deficiency of C2 and partial deficiency of factor B of the alternative pathway. *N Engl J Med* 299:290, 1978.

278. HYATT AC, ALTENBURGER KM, JOHNSTON RB, WINKELSTEIN JA: Increased susceptibility to severe pyogenic infections in patients with an inherited deficiency of the second component of complement. *J Pediatr* 98:417, 1981.

279. GEWURZ A, LINT TF, ROBERTS JL, ZEITZ H, GEWURZ H: Homozygous C2 deficiency with fulminant lupus erythematosus. Severe nephritis via the alternative complement pathway. *Arthritis Rheum* 21:28, 1978.

280. LEVY SB, PINNELL SR, MEADOWS L, SNYDERMAN R, WARD FE: Hereditary C2 deficiency associated with cutaneous lupus erythematosus. *Arch Dermatol* 115:57, 1979.

281. KIM Y, FRIEND PS, DRESNER IG, YUNIS EJ, MICHAEL AF: Inherited deficiency of the second component of complement (C2) with membranoproliferative glomerulonephritis. *Am J Med* 62:765, 1977.

282. LEDDY JP, GRIGGS RC, KLEMPERER MR, FRANK MM: Hereditary complement (C2) deficiency with dermatomyositis. *Am J Med* 58:83, 1975.

283. GELFAND EW, CLARKSON JO, MINTA JO: Selective deficiency of the second component of complement in a patient with anaphylactoid purpura. *Clin Immunol Immunopathol* 4:269, 1975.

284. REVIELLE JD, BIAS WB, WINKELSTEIN JA, PROVOST TT, DORSCH CA, ARNETT FC: Familial systemic lupus erythematosis: Immunogenetic studies in eight families. *Medicine* 62:21, 1983.

285. ALPER CA, PROPP RP, KLEMPERER MR, ROSEN FS: Inherited deficiency of the third component of complement (C3). *J Clin Invest* 48:553, 1969.

286. ALPER CA, COLTEN HR, GEAR JSS, ROBSON AR, ROSEN FS: Homozygous human C3 deficiency: The role of C3 in antibody production, C1s-induced vasopermiability, and cobra venom-induced passive hemolysis. *J Clin Invest* 57:222, 1976.

287. PUSSELL BA, BOURKE E, NAYEF M, MORRIS S, PETERS DK: Complement deficiency and nephritis: A report of a family. *Lancet* i:675, 1980.

288. DAVIS AE III, DAVIS JS IV, ROBSON AR, OSOFSKY SG, COLTEN HR, ROSEN FS, ALPER CA: Homozygous C3 deficiency: Detection of C3 by radioimmunoassay. *Clin Immun Immunopathol* 8:543, 1977.

289. BALLOW M, SHIRA JE, HARDEN L, YANG SY, DAY NK: Complete absence of the third component of complement in man. *J Clin Invest* 56:703, 1975.

290. OSOFSKY SG, THOMPSON BH, LINT TF, GEWURZ H: Hereditary deficiency of the third component of complement in a child with fever, skin rash, and arthralgias: Response to transfusion of whole blood. *J Pediatr* 90:180, 1977.

291. ROORD JJ, DAHA M, KUIS W, VERBRUGH HA, VERHOEF J, ZEGERS BJM, STOOP JW: Inherited deficiency of the third component of complement associated with recurrent pyogenic infections, circulating immune complexes, and vasculitis in a dutch family. *Pediatrics* 71:81, 1983.

292. HSIEH K-H, LIN C-Y, LEE T-C: Complete absence of the third component of complement in a patient with repeated infections. *Clin Immunol Immunopathol* 20:305, 1981.

293. SANO Y, NISHINUKAI H, KITAMURA H, NAGAKI K, INAI S, HAMASAKI Y, MARUYAMA I, IGATA A: Hereditary deficiency of the third component of complement in two sisters with systemic lupus erythematosis-like symptoms. *Arthritis Rheum* 24:1255, 1981.

294. ALPER CA, COLTEN HR, ROSEN FS, ROBSON AR, MacNAB GM, GEAR JSS: Homozygous deficiency of C3 in a patient with repeated infections. *Lancet* ii:1179, 1972.

295. GRACE HJ, BRERETON-STILES GG, VOS GH, SCHONLAND M: A family with partial and total deficiency of complement C3. *S Afr Med J* 50:139, 1976.

296. BERGER M, BALOW JE, WILSON CB, FRANK MM: Circulating immune complexes and glomerulonephritis in a patient with congenital absence of the third component of complement. *N Engl J Med* 308:1009, 1983.

297. BORZY MS, HOUGHTON D: Mixed-pattern immune deposit glomerulonephritis in a child with inherited deficiency of the third component of complement. *Am J Kidney Dis* 5:54, 1985.

298. MCLEAN RH, WEINSTEIN A, DAMJANOV I, ROTHFIELD N: Hypomorphic variant of C3, arthritis, and chronic glomerulonephritis. *J Pediatr* 93:937, 1978.

299. MCLEAN RH, WEINSTEIN A, CHAPITIS J, LOWENSTEIN M, ROTHFIELD N: Familial partial deficiency of the third component of complement (C3) and the hypocomplementemic cutaneous vasculitis syndrome. *Am J Med* 68:549, 1980.

300. WYATT RJ, JONES D, STAPLETON FB, ROY S, ODOM TW, MCLEAN RH: Recurrent hemolytic-uremic syndrome with the hypomorphic fast allele of the third component of complement. *J Pediatr* 107:564, 1985.

301. ALPER CA, ROSEN FS: Studies of a hypomorphic variant of human C3. *J Clin Invest* 50:324, 1971.

302. MCLEAN RH, BRYAN RK, WINKELSTEIN JA: Hypomorphic variant of the slow allele of C3 associated with hypocomplementemia and hematuria. *Am J Med* 78:865, 1985.

303. MCCARTY GA, SNYDERMAN R: Component deficiencies. The fifth component. *Prog Allergy* 39:271, 1986.

304. ROSENFELD SI, KELLY ME, LEDDY JP: Hereditary deficiency of the fifth component of complement in man. I. Clinical, immunochemical, and family studies. *J Clin Invest* 57:1626, 1976.

305. ROSENFELD SI, BAUM J, STEIGBIGEL RT, LEDDY JP: Hereditary deficiency of the fifth component of complement in man. II. Biological properties of C5-deficient human serum. *J Clin Invest* 57:1635, 1976.

306. SNYDERMAN R, DURACK DT, MCCARTY GA, WARD FE, MEADOWS L: Deficiency of the fifth component of complement in human subjects. Clinical genetic and immunologic studies in a large kindred. *Am J Med* 67:638, 1979.

307. MCLEAN R, PETER G, GOLD R, GUERRA L, YUNIS EJ, KRUETZER DL: Familial deficiency of C5 in humans: Intact but deficient alternative complement pathway activity. *Clin Immunol Immunopathol* 21:62, 1981.

308. PETER G, WEIGERT MB, BISSEL AR, GOLD R, KRUETZER D, MCLEAN RH: Meningococcal meningitis in familial deficiency of the fifth component of complement. *Pediatrics* 67:882, 1981.

309. ROTHER U: Component deficiencies. The sixth component. *Prog Allergy* 39:283, 1986.

310. GLASS D, RAUM D, BALAVITCH D, KAGAN E, ROBSON A, SCHUR PH, ALPER CA: Inherited deficiency of the sixth component of complement: A silent or null gene. *J Immunol* 120:538, 1978.

311. LEDDY JP, FRANK MM, GAITHER T, BAUM J, KLEMPERER MR: Hereditary deficiency of the sixth component of complement in man. I. Immunochemical, biologic, and family studies. *J Clin Invest* 53:544, 1974.

312. LIM D, GEWURZ Z, LINT TF, GHAZE M, SEPHARI B, GEWURZ H: Absence of the sixth component of complement in a patient with repeated episodes of meningococcal meningitis. *J Pediatr* 89:42, 1976.

313. VOGLER LB, NEWMAN SL, STROUD RM, JOHNSTON RB JR: Recurrent meningococcal meningitis with absence of the sixth component of complement: An evaluation of underlying immunologic mechanisms. *Pediatrics* 64:465, 1979.

314. LEE TJ, SNYDERMAN R, PATTERSON J, RAUCHBACH AS, FOLDS JD, YOUNT WJ: Neisseria meningitidis bacteremia in association with deficiency of the sixth component of complement. *Infect Immun* 24:656, 1979.

315. TEDESCO F, SILVANI CM, AGELLI M, GIOVANETTI AM, BOMBARDIERI S: A lupus-like syndrome in a patient with deficiency of the sixth component of complement. *Arthritis Rheum* 24:1438, 1981.

316. LACHMAN PJ, HOBART MJ, WOO P: Combined genetic deficiency of C6 and C7 in man. *Clin Exp Immunol* 33:193, 1978.

317. PODACK ER, KOLB WP, MULLER-EBERHARD HJ: Purification of the sixth and seventh components of human complement. *J Immunol* 116:263, 1978.

318. ZEITZ HJ, LINT TF, GEWURZ A, GEWURZ H: Component deficiencies. The seventh component. *Prog Allergy* 39:289, 1986.

319. BOYER JT, GALL EP, NORMAN ME, NILSSON UR, ZIMMERMAN TS: Hereditary deficiency of the seventh component of complement. *J Clin Invest* 56:905, 1975.

320. WELLEK B, OPFERKUCH W: A case of deficiency of the seventh component of complement in man: Biological properties of a C7-deficient serum and description of a C7-inactivating principle. *Clin Exp Immunol* 19:223, 1975.

321. LEE TJ, UTSINGER PD, SNYDERMAN R, YOUNT WJ, SPARLING PF: Familial deficiency of the seventh component of complement associated with recurrent bacteremic infections due to Neisseria. *J Infect Dis* 138:359, 1978.

322. LOIRAT C, BURIOT D, PELTIER AP, BERCHE P, AUJARD Y, GRISCELLI C, MATHIEU H: Fulminant meningococcemia in a child with hereditary deficiency of the seventh component of complement and proteinuria. *Acta Paediatr Scand* 69:553, 1980.

323. ZEITZ HJ, MILLER GW, LINT TF, ALI MA, GEWURZ H: Deficiency of C7

324. ALCALAY M, BONTOUX D, PELTIER A: C7 deficiency, abnormal platelet aggregation and rheumatoid arthritis. *Arthritis Rheum* 24:102, 1981.

325. TEDESCO F: Component deficiencies. The eighth component. *Prog Allergy* 39:295, 1986.

326. RAUM D, SPENCE MA, BALAVITCH D, TIDEMAN S, MERRITT AD, TAGGART RT, PETERSEN BH, DAY NK, ALPER CA: Genetic control of the eighth component of complement. *J Clin Invest* 64:858, 1979.

327. KOLB WP, MULLER-EBERHARD HJ: The membrane attack mechanism of complement. The three polypeptide chain structure of the eighth coment (C8). *J Exp Med* 143:1131, 1976.

328. STECKEL EW, YORK RG, MONAHAN JB, SODETY JM: The eighth component of human complement. Purification and physicochemical characterization of its unusual subunit structure. *J Biol Chem* 255:11997, 1980.

329. TEDESCO F, DENSEN P, VILLA MA, PETERSEN BH, SIRCHIA G: Two types of dysfunctional eighth component of complement (C8) molecules in C8 deficiency in man: Reconstitution of normal C8 from the mixture of the two abnormal C8 molecules. *J Clin Invest* 71:183, 1983.

330. TEDESCO F, BARDARE M, GIOVANETTI AM, SIRCHIA G: A familial dysfunction of the eighth component of complement (C8). *Clin Immunol Immunopathol* 16:180, 1980.

331. TSCHOPP J, ESSER AF, SPIRA TJ, MULLER-EBERHARD HJ: Occurrence of an incomplete molecule in homozygous C8 deficiency in man. *J Exp Med* 154:1599, 1981.

332. TEDESCO F, VILLA MA, DENSEN P, SIRCHIA G: Beta chain deficiency in three patients with dysfunctional C8 molecules. *Mol Immunol* 20:47, 1983.

333. PETERSEN BH, GRAHAM JA, BROOKS GF: Human deficiency of the eighth component of complement. The requirement of C8 for serum Neisseria gonorrhoeae bactericidal activity. *J Clin Invest* 57:283, 1976.

334. JASIN HE: Absence of the eighth component of complement in association with system lupus erythematosis-like disease. *J Clin Invest* 60:709, 1977.

335. NICHOLSON A, LEPOW I: Host defense against Neisseria meningitidis requires a complement-dependent bactericidal activity. *Science* 205:298, 1979.

336. LINT TF, GEWURZ H: Component deficiencies. The ninth component. *Prog Allergy* 39:307, 1986.

337. YOSHIMURA K, FUKUMORI Y, OHNOKI S, O KUBO Y, YAMAGUCHI H, TANAKA M, AKAGARI Y, INAI S: Studies on complement deficiencies in blood donors in Osaka area of Japan. *Jpn J Hum Genet* 28:120, 1983.

338. HARRIMAN GR, ESSER AF, PODACK ER, WUNDERLICH AC, BRAUDE AI, LINT TF, CURD JG: The role of C9 in complement-mediated killing of Neisseria. *J Immunol* 127:2386, 1981.

339. INAI S, HITAMURA H, HIRAMATSU S, NAGAKI K: Deficiency of the ninth component of complement in man. *J Clin Lab Immunol* 2:85, 1979.

340. LINT TF, ZEITZ HJ, GEWURZ H: Inherited deficiency of the ninth component of complement in man. *J Immunol* 125:2252, 1980.

341. FINE DP, GEWURZ H, GRIFFIS M, LINT TF: Meningococcal meningitis in a woman with inherited deficiency of the ninth component of complement. *Clin Immunol Immunopathol* 28:413, 1983.

342. ALPER CA, ABRAMSON N, JOHNSTON RB JR, JANDL JH, ROSEN FS: Increased susceptibility to infection associated with abnormalities of complement-mediated functions and of the third component of complement (C3). *N Engl J Med* 282:349, 1970.

343. ALPER CA, ABRAMSON N, JOHNSTON RB, JANDL JH, ROSEN FS: Studies in vivo and in vitro on an abnormality in the metabolism of C3 in a patient with increased susceptibility to infection. *J Clin Invest* 49:1975, 1970.

344. ABRAMSON N, ALPER CA, LACHMANN PJ, ROSEN FS, JANDL JH: Deficiency of C3 inactivator in man. *J Immunol* 107:19, 1971.

345. ZEIGLER JB, ALPER CA, ROSEN FS, LACHMANN PJ, SHERINGTON L: Restoration by purified C3b inactivator of complement-mediated function in vivo in a patient with C3b inactivator deficiency. *J Clin Invest* 55:668, 1975.

346. NICOL PAE, LACHMANN PJ: The alternative pathway of complement activation. The role of C3 and its inactivator (KAF). *Immunology* 24:259, 1973.

347. WAHN V, ROTHER V, RAUTERBERG EW, DAY NK, LAURELL AB: C3b inactivator deficiency: Association with an alpha-migrating factor H. *J Clin Immunol* 1:228, 1981.

348. SOLAL-CELIGNY P, LAVIOLETTE M, HEBERT J, ATKINS PC, SIROIS M, BRUN G, LEHNER-NETSCH G, DELAGE JM: C3b inactivator deficiency with immune complex manifestations. *Clin Exp Immunol* 47:197, 1982.

349. TEISNER B, BRANDSLUND I, FOLKERSON J, RASMUSSEN JM, PAULSEN LO, SVEHOG SE: Factor I deficiency and C3 nephritic factor: Immunochemical findings and association with Neisseria meningitidis infection in two patients. *Scand J Immunol* 20:291, 1984.

350. THOMPSON RA, LACHMANN PJ: A second case of human C3b inhibitor (KAF) deficiency. *Clin Exp Immunol* 27:23, 1977.

351. THOMPSON RA, WINTERBORN MH: Hypocomplementaemia due to a genetic deficiency of beta-1H globulin. *Clin Exp Immunol* 46:110, 1981.

352. SJOHOLM AG, BRACONIER JH, SODERSTROM C: Properdin deficiency in a family with fulminant meningococcal infections. *Clin Exp Immunol* 50:291, 1982.

353. DENSEN P, WEILER JM, GRIFFISS JM, HOFFMANN LG: Familial properdin deficiency and fatal meningococcemia: Correction of the bactericidal defect by vaccination. *N Engl J Med* 316:922, 1987.

354. DONALDSON VH, EVANS RR: A biochemical abnormality in hereditary angioneurotic edema. Absence of serum inhibitor of C1-esterase. *Am J Med* 35:37, 1963.

355. OSLER W: Hereditary angio-neurotic aedema. *Am J Med Sci* 95:362, 1888.

356. LANDERMAN NS: Hereditary angioneurotic edema. I. Case reports and review of the literature. *J Allergy* 33:316, 1962.

357. DONALDSON VH, ROSEN FS: Hereditary angioneurotic edema: A clinical survey. *Pediatrics* 37:1017, 1966.

358. FRANK MM, GELFAND JA, ATKINSON JP: Hereditary angioedema: The clinical syndrome and its management. *Ann Intern Med* 84:580, 1976.

359. CICARDI M, BERGAMASCHINI L, MARASINI B, BOCCASSINI G, TUCCI A, AGOSTINI A: Hereditary angioedema: An appraisal of 104 cases. *Am J Med Sci* 284:2, 1982.

360. ROSEN FS, ALPER CA, PENSKY J, KLEMPERER MR, DONALDSON VH: Genetically determined heterogeneity of the C1 esterase inhibitor in patients with hereditary angioneurotic edema. *J Clin Invest* 50:2143, 1971.

361. AUSTEN KF, SHEFFER AL: Detection of hereditary angioneurotic edema by demonstration of a reduction in the second component of human complement. *N Engl J Med* 272:649, 1965.

362. PICKERING RJ, GEWURZ H, KELLY JR, GOOD RA: The complement system in hereditary angioneurotic oedema—A new perspective. *Clin Exp Immunol* 3:423, 1968.

363. HARPEL PC, HUGLI TE, COOPER NR: Studies on human plasma C1 inactivator-enzyme interactions: II Structural features of an abnormal C1 inactivator from a kindred with hereditary angioneurotic edema. *J Clin Invest* 55:605, 1975.

364. DONALDSON VH, HARRISON RA, ROSEN FS, BEING DH, KINDNESS G, CANAR J, WAGNER CJ, AWAD S: Variability in purified dysfunctional C1-inhibitor proteins from patients with hereditary angioneurotic edema. Functional and analytical gel studies. *J Clin Invest* 75:124, 1985.

365. QUASTEL M, HARRISON R, CICARDI M, ALPER CA, ROSEN FS: Behavior in vivo of normal and dysfunctional C1 inhibitor in normal subjects and patients with hereditary angioneurotic edema. *J Clin Invest* 83:1041, 1983.

366. LACHMAN PJ, ROSEN FS: The catabolism of C1-inhibitor and the pathogenesis of hereditary angio-edema. *Acta Pathol Microbiol Immunol Scand* 92:35, 1984.

367. DONALDSON VH, ROSEN FS: Action of complement in hereditary angioneurotic edema: Role of C1-esterase. *J Clin Invest* 43:2204, 1964.

368. KLEMPERER MR, DONALDSON VH, ROSEN FS: Effect of C1 esterase on vascular permiability in man: Studies in normal and complement-deficient individuals and in patients with hereditary angioneurotic edema. *J Clin Invest* 47:604, 1968.

369. SCHREIBER AP, KAPLAN AP, AUSTEN KF: Inhibition by C1INH of Hageman factor fragment activation of coagulation, fibrinolysis, and kinin generation. *J Clin Invest* 52:1402, 1973.

370. CURD JG, PROGAIS LJ JR, COCHRANE CG: Detection of active kallikrein in induced blister fluids of hereditary angioedema patients. *J Exp Med* 152:742, 1980.

371. SCHAPIRA M, SILVER LD, SCOTT CF, SCHMAIER AH, PROGRAIS LJ, CURD JG, COLMAN RW: Prekallikrein activation and high-molecular-weight kininogen consumption in hereditary angioedema. *N Engl J Med* 308:1050, 1983.

372. SHEFFER AL, CRAIG JM, WILLMS-KRETSCHMER K, AUSTEN KF, ROSEN FS: Histopathological and ultrastructural observations on tissues from patients with hereditary angioneurotic edema. *J Allergy* 47:292, 1971.

373. SHEFFER AL, AUSTEN KF, ROSEN FS: Tranexamic acid therapy in hereditary angioneurotic edema. *N Engl J Med* 287:452, 1972.

374. FRANK MM, SERGENT JS, KANE MA, ALLING DW: Epsilon aminocaproic acid therapy of hereditary and angioneurotic edema: A double blind study. *N Engl J Med* 286:808, 1972.

375. GELFAND JA, SHERINS RJ, ALLING DW, FRANK MM: Treatment of hereditary angioedema with danazol: Reversal of clinical and biochemical abnormalities. *N Engl J Med* 295:1444, 1976.

376. SPAULDING WB: Methyltestosterone therapy for hereditary episodic edema (hereditary angioneurotic edema). *Ann Intern Med* 53:739, 1960.

377. HOSEA SW, SANTAELLA ML, BROWN EJ, BERGER M, KATUSHA K, FRANK MM: Long-term therapy of hereditary angioedema with danazol. *Ann Intern Med* 93:809, 1980.

378. GADEK JE, HOSEA SW, GELFAND JA, FRANK MM: Response of variant hereditary angioedema phenotypes to danazol therapy. *J Clin Invest* 64:280, 1979.

379. JAFFE CJ, ATKINSON JP, GELFAND JA, FRANK MM: Hereditary angioedema: The use of fresh frozen plasma for prophylaxis in patients undergoing oral surgery. *J Allergy Clin Immunol* 55:386, 1975.

380. GADEK JE, HOSEA SW, GELFAND JA, SANTAELLA M, WICKERHAUSER M, TRIANTAPHYLLOPOULOS DC, FRANK MM: Replacement therapy in hereditary angioedema: Successful treatment of acute episodes of angioedema with partly purified C1 inhibitor. *N Engl J Med* 304:542, 1980.

381. BERGAMASCHINI L, CICARDI M, TUCCI A, GARDINELI M, FRANGI D, VALLE C, AGOSTONI A: C1-IHN concentrate in the therapy of hereditary angioedema. *Allergy* 38:81, 1983.

CHAPTER 112

IMMOTILE-CILIA SYNDROME (Primary Ciliary Dyskinesia), INCLUDING KARTAGENER SYNDROME

BJÖRN A. AFZELIUS
BJÖRN MOSSBERG

1. *The immotile-cilia syndrome is a genetically determined disorder characterized by dysmotility or even complete immotility of the cilia in the airways and elsewhere. Spermatozoa also are either immotile or poorly motile.*

2. *Kartagener syndrome is a subgroup of the immotile-cilia syndrome and is further characterized by situs inversus viscerum. Situs inversus, bronchiectasis, and chronic sinusitis form the classic Kartagener triad.*

3. *The reason for the ciliary immotility or dysmotility can usually be seen with an electron-microscopic investigation of a ciliated mucosal biopsy or of the spermatozoa of an ejaculate. Certain specific defects in the ciliary axoneme that may be found are pathognomonic of the syndrome. These defects include a lack or deficiency of dynein arms, abnormally short dynein arms, short spokes and no central sheath, and missing central microtubules with displacement of one of the nine peripheral microtubular doublets. Cilia and sperm tails normally exhibit the same defects in the same patient. Motility can be evaluated by light-microscopic examination of living cilia or spermatozoa, and the functional capacity of cilia by measurement of mucociliary transport.*

4. *The clinical consequences of the immotile-cilia syndrome include chronic cough and expectoration, bronchiectasis, chronic rhinitis and nasal polyposis, chronic or recurrent sinusitis, and often an agenesis of the frontal sinuses. Otosalpingitis and otitis are common. Obstructive lung disease may develop and is expressed as chronic airflow limitation. Most clinical manifestations date from early childhood. Neonatal asphyxia often occurs.*

5. *Males are usually sterile. Females may be fertile or infertile.*

6. *Treatment is symptomatic and directed against complications in the upper and lower respiratory tract. Physiotherapy with postural drainage should probably be started early in life. With modern care and abstinence from smoking the prognosis in the immotile-cilia syndrome is good.*

7. *The immotile-cilia syndrome clearly is a genetically heterogeneous disease, although its clinical profile is fairly uniform. Many genes participate in the construction of a cilium, and an error in anyone of them will prevent the cilia from working properly. The inheritance in most cases is autosomal recessive. In families in which the immotile-cilia syndrome occurs, half the affected sibs have situs inversus. Presumably chance alone decides between situs inversus and situs solitus in homozygotes of the syndrome.*

In a paper in 1933 Manes Kartagener published the case histories of four persons who all had situs inversus totalis, bronchiectasis, and chronic sinusitis.[1] This combination of symptoms has later come to be known as *Kartagener syndrome* or *Kartagener triad*. In the Soviet Union it is sometimes called *Siewert* or *Zivert syndrome*. Siewert wrote a description of a person with situs inversus combined with bronchiectasis, initially (1902) in Russian and somewhat later in German.[2]

Kartagener's paper, entitled "Zur Pathogenese der Bronchiektasien," is an attempt to explain the pathogenesis of bronchiectasis. Kartagener wrote, "In transposition of the viscera there is often a weakness of the bronchi, possibly due to a deficiency of elastic tissue, which renders those with it liable to develop bronchiectasis."

The frequent association between bronchiectasis and situs inversus has been confirmed by numerous investigators, but the explanation given by Kartagener has been superseded by another theory of pathogenesis: Kartagener syndrome is caused by a structural and generalized abnormality of cilia. Because of this abnormality the cilia are immotile, feebly motile, or dysmotile,[3,4] and, hence, they are nonfunctional. Ciliary dysmotility is associated with situs inversus in only about half the cases; thus there are about as many cases with bronchiectasis and chronic sinusitis due to ciliary defects but without situs inversus as there are cases with Kartagener syndrome.

For this reason, and because situs inversus per se usually has no serious implications, this chapter will treat the immotile-cilia syndrome in its entirety and will include Kartagener syndrome as a subgroup of the immotile-cilia syndrome.

PREVALENCE

Most authors estimate the prevalence of Kartagener syndrome at 1 in 30,000 to 1 in 60,000.[5,6] Different values will be obtained depending on how strictly the investigator adheres to the original definition. For example, a generalized bronchitis rather than demonstrated bronchiectasis may be regarded as part of Kartagener syndrome, since bronchiectasis is not congenital but develops during life.

The prevalence of the immotile-cilia syndrome can be estimated from the following data. Situs inversus has been estimated to have a prevalence in Europe and the United States of 1 in 8000 to 1 in 11,000.[5,7] By analyzing cohorts of newborns and men liable for military service in Sweden, Svartengren et al. recently found an incidence of situs inversus of 1 in 25,000, i.e., a somewhat lower figure than previously estimated.[8] Roughly one-fourth to one-fifth of all persons with situs inversus also have bronchiectasis and chronic sinusitus.[7] A somewhat higher fraction has generalized bronchitis but not (yet) bronchiectasis. This gives a figure of the prevalence of Kartagener syndrome on the order of 1 in 40,000 to 1 in

120,000. If it is true, as assumed,[3] that 50 percent of patients with the immotile-cilia syndrome have situs inversus, then the prevalence of this syndrome will be twice that of Kartagener syndrome, or about 1 in 20,000 to 1 in 60,000.

A somewhat higher value for the prevalence may be found among newborns, if infants with Kartagener syndrome have an increased mortality.

Geographic and Racial Distribution

Kartagener syndrome has been described in all major races and from most countries with medical journals. Detailed pedigrees have been published from Austria,[9] Canada,[10] France,[11] Germany,[12-14] Great Britain,[15] Israel,[16] Japan,[17] Sweden,[18] the United States,[19-21] and other countries. In all these publications it was remarked that one or several sibs of the propositus had the same bronchial and sinusoidal symptoms as the propositus but had no situs inversus. Sometimes these sibs have been claimed to have an "incomplete Kartagener syndrome." The seemingly equal number of affected sibs with and without situs inversus supports the idea that the immotile-cilia syndrome is inherited as a recessive disorder and that chance alone determines whether the viscera take up the normal or the reversed position during embryogenesis.[3]

The Polynesian population of New Zealand may be a special case. According to Wakefield and Waite[22] 12 Polynesians were diagnosed as having nonfunctioning cilia although none of them had situs inversus. Bronchiectasis is relatively common among the Polynesians in New Zealand, Samoa, and elsewhere, and they may have a particular disease where ciliary defects develop during childhood and therefore do not involve a risk of situs inversus.[22]

Reports from Nonhuman Species

Some investigators have reported cases of Kartagener syndrome or of the immotile-cilia syndrome in the dog.[23-27] The symptoms are the same as in humans: chronic rhinitis and bronchopneumonia and poorly developed nasal turbinals, and, in about one-half of the cases, situs inversus. In one case the autopsy showed the brain ventricles to have approximately twice the normal size, thus approaching hydrocephalus.[26]

Ciliary disorders of genetic origin are also known from the mouse, mainly the male-sterile mutant called hpy/hpy.[28] In this mouse strain the cilia are defective because of a lack of dynein arms (see below), and the animals are prone to develop hydrocephalus and polydactyly.

The model organism for ciliary (or flagellar) mutants is the unicellular alga *Chlamydomonas*, in which a great variety of mutants have been isolated. Biochemical and genetical studies of this organism have shown that ciliary (or, more properly, flagellar) immotility is a heterogeneous condition; anyone of a great number of different genes may be involved.[29-31] Ciliary mutants have also been described from other organisms, as reviewed by Afzelius.[32]

CILIA IN THE HUMAN BODY

The symptoms of the immotile-cilia syndrome and of its subgroup, Kartagener syndrome, cannot be understood with-

out a knowledge of the distribution in the body of cilia and of the normal ciliary anatomy.

Cilia and sperm tails are outgrowths from centrioles (basal bodies) with an architecture as shown in Figs. 112-1 to 112-3. The central axis is called the *axoneme* and consists of nine microtubular doublets in a ring around two single microtubules. These 11 units are joined by three types of bonds:

1. Two rows of arms along each doublet. The outer arms have a complex structure while the inner arms are somewhat shorter and simpler. The arms contain the major ATPases that are responsible for the ciliary work; they are proteins called *dynein*. The dynein arms make temporary bonds that are formed and broken several times during each ciliary beat.

2. Nexin links, which also connect the doublets and which are presumed to act like resistant elastic bonds that keep the axoneme together.

3. Spokes which extend from the outer doublets to a central sheath that surrounds the two central microtubules.

The two main protein components of the cilium are the tubulins and the dyneins, which make up the microtubules and the dynein arms, respectively. There is a functional analogy between the tubulin-dynein system in cilia and the actin-myosin system in muscles. Thus, the dynein arms are structures which are instrumental in the sliding of microtubules during ciliary work, as are myosin bridges during muscle contraction. Like myosin, the dynein molecules have a high molecular weight and are ATPases. The dynein arms can thus be considered to provide the motor force for beating of cilia. Cilia with no outer dynein arms are capable of slow beatings whereas the inner dynein arms seem to be indispensible for ciliary movements.[31,33]

The nexin links presumably are responsible for the maintenance of axoneme structure during sliding. They seem to limit the sliding by being stretchable only to a certain degree. It has also been suggested that the nexin links pull the doublets to-

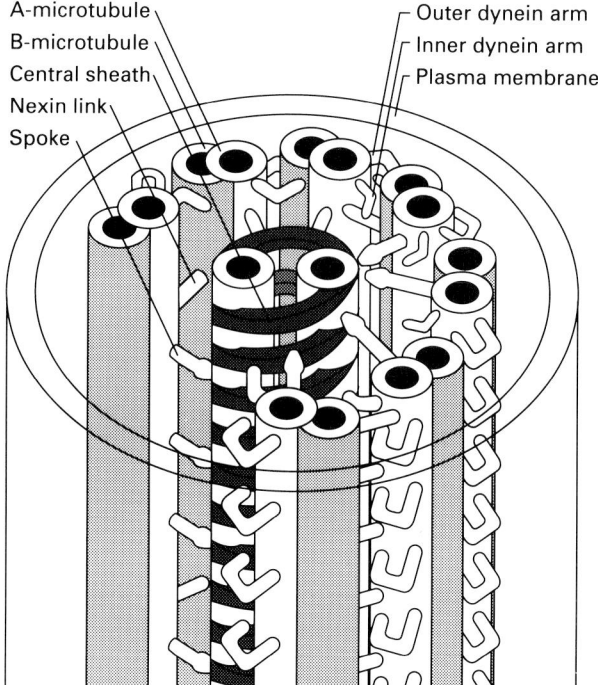

Fig. 112-1 Three-dimensional reconstruction of the cilium. (*From Klaus Hausmann. Reproduced by permission of* Biologie in unserer Zeit.)

A-microtubule
B-microtubule
Central sheath
Nexin link
Spoke

Outer dynein arm
Inner dynein arm
Plasma membrane

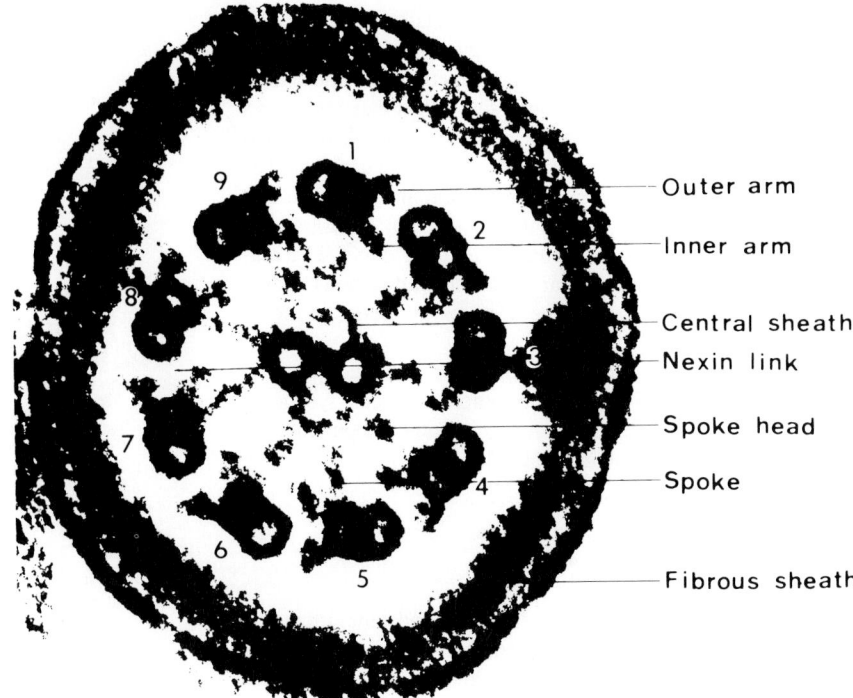

Fig. 112-2 Electron micrograph of a transversely sectioned human sperm tail from a healthy man. The central part of the sperm tail has the same structure as that of a cilium. There are nine outer microtubular doublets in a ring around two central microtubules. The terms used for some of the components are given. (*From Afzelius.[45] Reproduced by permission of Journal of Ultrastructure Research.*)

Fig. 112-3 Cilia from the bronchial mucosa of a person who has normal cilia. Note that the cilia have a fairly ordered orientation best seen in the two central microtubules.

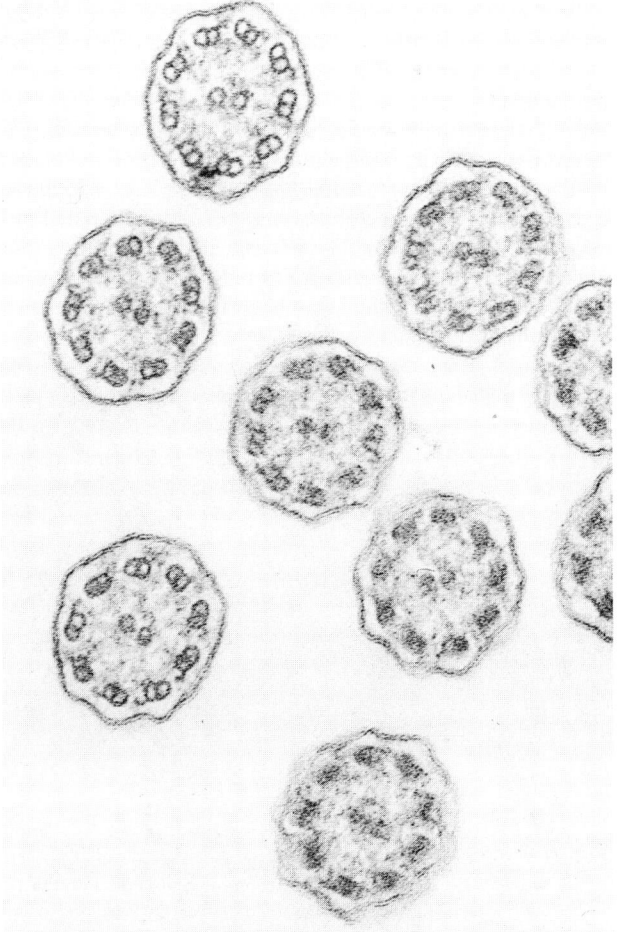

gether in the initial phase of bend induction, allowing the dynein arms to interact with adjacent doublets.

The spokes may interact with the central sheath at the start of bending as a part of the mechanism for converting sliding into bending. It also appears probable that the spokes give the cilium a certain rigidity, preventing it from making sharp nicks, while allowing it to bend. Further details of the ciliary machinery and its mode of action can be found in Refs. 5 and 34 to 39.

Ciliated epithelia are found in the following places in the human body: the upper airways (i.e., the nasal passages, the paranasal sinuses, the eustachian tubes, the middle ear mucosa, and the nasopharynx); the trachea and bronchi down to the respiratory bronchioles; the lacrimal sac; the ependymal lining of the brain and central canal of the spinal cord; the endometrial lining of the deeper parts of the cervix; the fallopian tubes; and the ductuli efferentes on the border between the testis and epididymis.

Some epithelia have a single cilium per cell, sometimes called a primary cilium, a solitary cilium, or a monocilium. This is true for the thyroid gland,[40] the inner corneal endothelium, the trabecular meshwork, and the choroid of the eye[41] as well as of several of the embryonic epithelia.[5] Primary cilia have been found to beat, but whether their beatings can perform work is unknown.[42]

Certain sensory cells carry a sensory hair that is a modified cilium. The tail of the human spermatozoon has an axoneme, with the typical structure of a cilium, although it is much longer and has a flagellar beat. Cilia are about 6 μm long, sperm tails about 40 μm.

Our knowledge about the normal functions of the cilia is incomplete. The epithelium of the upper and lower airways and of the middle ear is a mixture of ciliated and nonciliated cells. The epithelium secretes a serous fluid which forms a 5-μm-thick layer (the sol layer) in which the cilia beat. The goblet cells and the mucous glands secrete a mucous layer (the gel layer) which forms a blanket overlying the ciliary tips that also is about 5 μm wide and that is either patchy or continuous.[34]

Although a very accurate alignment of mucus-propelling cilia may be unnecessary, most cilia are aligned in a way such that their effective stroke is in the same direction and the ciliary beatings form a metachronal wave. The ciliary beating moves the mucous blanket toward the esophagus, and the mucus is swallowed. The speed of movement of the mucus blanket is on the order of 2 mm/min in the intrapulmonary bronchi and increases to about 10 mm/min in the trachea; its volume is about 0.5 ml per kilogram of body weight per day.[36] The mucous blanket traps inhaled particles and endogenous debris which are then eliminated by the mucociliary clearance mechanism.

The role of cilia in the fallopian tubes, the ductuli efferentes, and the ependyma of the central nervous system is largely speculative. Similarly, nothing is known about the role of single cilia on monociliated epithelia.

Ultrastructure of Cilia and Sperm Tails in the Immotile-Cilia Syndrome

The essential feature of the immotile-cilia syndrome, including Kartagener syndrome, is the abnormal structure and function of cilia. Usually an immotility or a dysmotility can be detected by light microscopical videorecording, and an abnormal ciliary ultrastructure can be seen by electron microscopy. Most—possibly all—clinical data of this syndrome can be explained by the ciliary work being defective.

Cilia and sperm tails from hundreds of persons have been examined as to their motility or immotility and ultrastructure and the data from different laboratories are in essential agreement. It is evident that the immotile-cilia syndrome is a heterogeneous disease and that several subgroups can be found. The following subgroups can be defined:

1. Dynein arms are practically absent in both rows[3,5,43–52] (Figs. 112-4 and 112-5).
2. Both outer and inner dynein arms are reduced in number, often to about half the normal one.[18,52–54]
3. The outer dynein arms are short, and the inner dynein arms may be missing.[44,48,55–57]
4. Only outer dynein arms are missing[44,45,51,52,58] (Fig. 112-6).
5. Only inner dynein arms are missing.[52,55,56,60]
6. The entire spokes or the spoke heads as well as the central sheath are missing; the two inner microtubules often are off-center: "the spoke defect"[5,45,46,50,61] (Fig. 112-7).

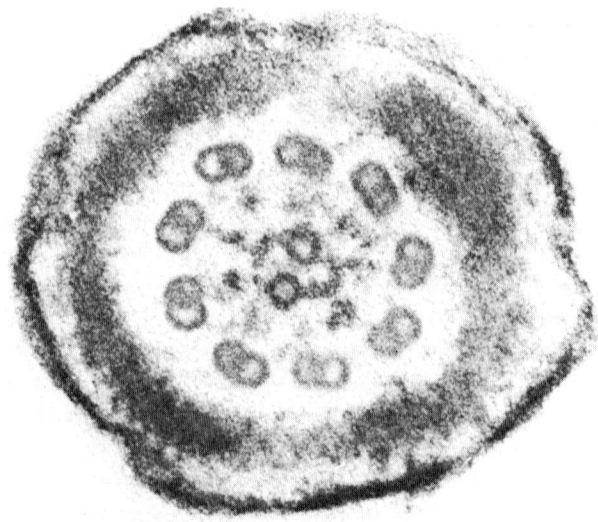

Fig. 112-4 The sperm tail of a man with the immotile-cilia syndrome. In this man the sperm tails and the cilia are characterized by a total or nearly total lack of both the outer and inner dynein arms.

7. The central microtubules are short or absent, and microtubular doublet no. 1 is transposed to a central position; the inner dynein arms may be absent: "microtubular transposition defect."[47,50,62]
8. Nexin links, spokes, and the inner dynein arms are missing, and the circle of microtubular doublets is disrupted: "disorganized" axoneme.[45,48,59]
9. The two central microtubules and the inner dynein arms are missing.[63]
10. Cilia have a normal ultrastructure as seen in sections but are immotile[64,65] or "hypermotile" although nonfunctional.[66] In some cases the cilia have approximately twice the normal length.[67]
11. Cilia and basal bodies may be completely lacking. Ciliated cells in the nasal epithelium only[68] or in the nasal epithelium and tracheobronchial tree may be replaced by cells that have long microvilli; these cells may be undifferentiated mucous cells or brush cells.[44,69–72] It should be noted here that viral or bacterial infections tend to reduce the number of ciliated cells, and that it thus may be difficult to distinguish between inherited and acquired diseases.[73]

Other subgroups may well exist. In many of the patients in subgroups 1 to 7 the cilia are further characterized by the

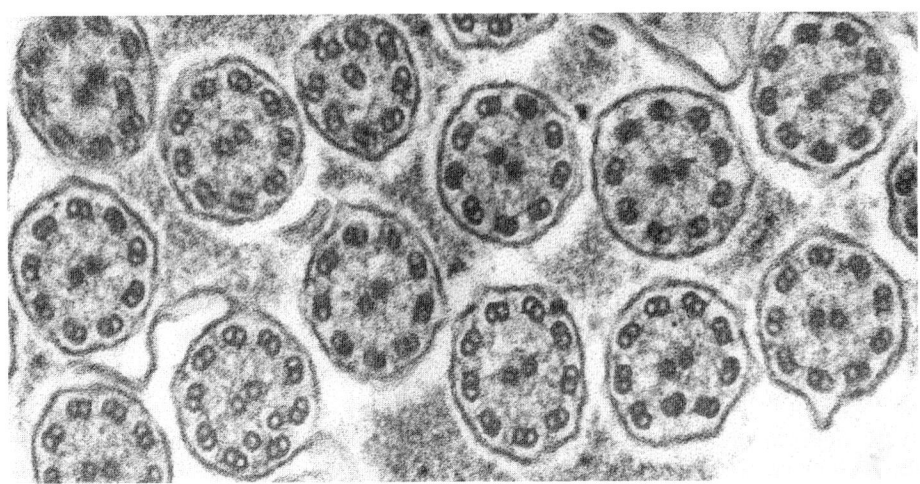

Fig. 112-5 Cilia from the nasal epithelium of a woman with the immotile-cilia syndrome. The dynein arms are missing.

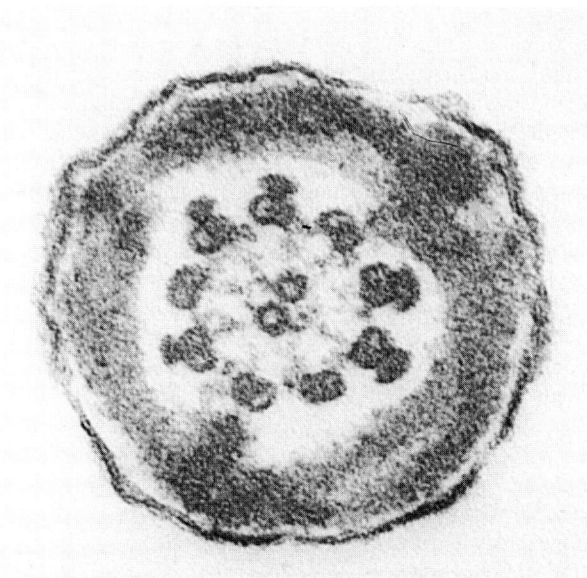

Fig. 112-6 The sperm tail of a man with the immotile-cilia syndrome and characterized by the presence of inner dynein arms but no, or very few, outer dynein arms. The spermatozoa had some degree of motility.

presence of supernumerary or missing microtubules in the axoneme. Cilia also tend to be rather poorly aligned; the range of orientation of the basal feet or of the two central microtubules thus is wider than in controls.[74] Although it seems that a very accurate alignment of mucus-propelling cilia may be unnecessary, a random orientation of cilia would exclude coordinated activity.

About half the cases in all subgroups have situs inversus.

Cilia from different types of epithelia of the same patient usually have the same ultrastructure indicating that the defect is a generalized one.[44,46,75,76] It is possible, however, that focal abnormalities may make the diagnosis uncertain; it is hence recommended that cilia from two or more sites are evaluated. A case has been reported where cilia at one site of the bronchi had microtubular transposition to a high percentage and at other sites were close to normal.[77] Chronic nasal obstruction may reduce the number of ciliated cells.[78] Also, in acute viral airway infections the number of ciliated cells and the mucociliary clearance are reduced.[79,80] In studies where repeated biopsies were taken from the same patient the cilia usually were found to have the same ultrastructure,[81] but in one case

an anomaly (short dynein arms) was found in a first but not a second biopsy.[55]

Cilia and sperm tails also tend to display the same type of defect in the same patient, although the cilia may have a few dynein arms in those men who have spermatozoa which are completely devoid of dynein arms.[3,75,82] There are also a few published cases with only the spermatozoa immotile and lacking dynein arms[54,83] or where only the cilia display these features.[84] The difference in axonemal ultrastructure between cilia and spermatozoa from the same patient could be due either to a mosaicism, to a separate genetic control of their structural component, or to a variable penetrance.

Some of the ciliary abnormalities listed above, and in particular defects other than the listed ones, have been described in patients with infections, allergies, or chemical treatment.[55,85,86] These include the clumping of several axonemes within a common limiting membrane (into what have been called compound cilia or multicilia), the presence of supernumerary microtubular doublets or singlets, or a deficiency in their number.[85-88] These latter types of ciliary defects therefore are not diagnostic of the immotile-cilia syndrome.

Motility of Cilia and Sperm Tails

The immotile-cilia syndrome is due to the cilia being completely immotile,[43,44,89] feebly motile,[54] or displaying erratic movements.[90-92] Because a good correlation usually exists between ciliary motility and spermatozoal motility, an examination of the spermatozoa can be made for diagnostic purposes,[75] as they are more easily examined than are epithelial cilia. The correlation is not 100 percent, however, as remarked above. Moreover sperm immotility may be due to other factors than an inborn error of cilia and sperm tails: exposure of the ejaculate to cold, immobilization by antibodies, necrospermia (i.e., dead spermatozoa), and certain disorders in which the spermatozoa are grossly abnormal.[75]

In order to directly observe the motility or immotility of cilia, ciliated cells have to be removed and observed in vitro. Cilia from persons with the immotile-cilia syndrome may be immotile or have an abnormal and inefficient motility. Several variants of abnormal motility have been described: reduced beat frequency, hyperfrequent low amplitude vibrations, "windscreen wiper-movement," multiplanar "egg-beater-like rotations," "corkscrewlike rotation," slow-grabbing movements of the distal portion, and flagellalike undulation.[90-94]

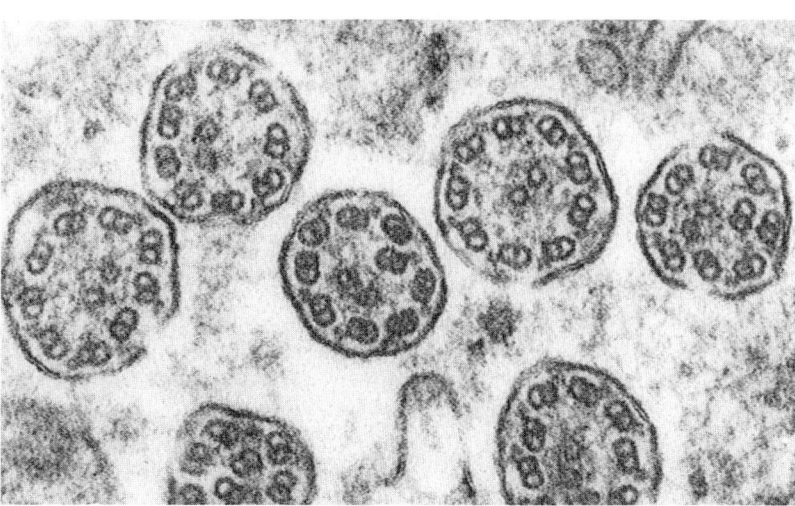

Fig. 112-7 Cilia from the nasal epithelium of a woman with the immotile-cilia syndrome. The inner microtubules are off-center presumably because of defective spokes.

Certain dysmotilities can be correlated to specific ultrastructural defects.[95] However, the functional capacity of the cilia measured as mucociliary clearance is absent; this is a hallmark of the syndrome.[96–99]

Biopsies or brushings from a ciliated epithelium can be examined with phase contrast or interference contrast microscope.[89,90,93,100] It is difficult, however, to distinguish between normal and erratic types of ciliary beatings with an unaided eye, and the analysis has to be performed either with an oscillographic technique[91,92,101] or by making videorecordings which can be studied in slow motion.[102]

A complete motility study should include three parameters: ciliary beat frequency, ciliary beat coordination, and ciliary beat amplitude.[102] There is, however, a possibility that even such a complete study will not be enough. In one patient with a reduced number of dynein arms ciliary motility in vitro was unaffected although mucociliary clearance in vivo was, possibly because of the increased load of mucus in vivo.[54] It was noticed that cilia started beating properly in vitro only after the mucus had been washed away.

Some investigators have objected to the term *immotile-cilia syndrome* for patients who have some degree of ciliary motility[90–92] or who evidently lack cilia and have suggested terms such as *primary ciliary dyskinesia*, the *diskinetic cilia syndrome*, or the *acilia syndrome*. A clinical investigation will not distinguish between immotile, dysmotile, or lacking cilia, however, and hence it is impractical to have different names for different subgroups. Ciliary motility, when present, is ineffective and represents a functionally immotile state, therefore the term *immotile-cilia syndrome* seems appropriate. In a clinical context the disease is an entity. The syndrome could logically be given the code number 748W in the International Classification of Diseases.

Situs Inversus and Embryonic Cilia

The following explanation has been suggested for the association between ciliary immotility and situs inversus.[3] Embryonic epithelia often carry a single cilium per cell. In the normal course of events these cilia are assumed to beat and, by their beatings, cause the heart to be moved to the left side and the liver to the right side of the body. With no ciliary work, chance alone will decide whether the visceral asymmetry will be normal or reversed. The validity of this hypothesis can be tested only when suitable animal models are examined, such as the mouse strain described by Layton.[103] Layton assumes that the action of the mutated gene for his animal model or for the immotile-cilia syndrome is due to a loss of the developmental control of the entire cytoskeleton.[104]

GENETIC CONSIDERATIONS

An examination of published pedigrees[9–21] indicates that the immotile-cilia syndrome is inherited as an autosomal recessive trait. Heterozygotes have a normal ciliary ultrastructure as was shown by Eavey et al.[105] who examined eight parents of children with the immotile-cilia syndrome. On average half the affected persons have situs inversus. As a consequence, the offspring of a mating between two heterozygotes each has a one-eighth chance of having situs inversus. Careful segregation

analyses of proband sibships in cases of situs inversus[106] or of the immotile-cilia syndrome[61] have been consistent with this mode of inheritance. Sturgess has further shown that there is no evidence of an increased risk of having a child with the immotile-cilia syndrome with higher age of the mother. Approximately 1 in 60 among the population would be a heterozygous carrier if the syndrome were genetically homogeneous.[61] One of the pedigrees published by Katsuhara is more consistent with a dominant mode of inheritance than with the recessive one.[17] It shows a woman, her daughter, and a granddaughter, but none of her sibs, with immotile-cilia syndrome (complete and incomplete Kartagener syndrome). Presumably a dominant mode of inheritance of this disease also exists, although it is rare.

The primary gene products may be those proteins that are seen to be missing in the cilia: dyneins, nexins, spoke proteins, etc.[29] Alternatively, they may be proteins that are responsible for the binding of the dyneins (nexin, etc.) to the microtubules or for their transport from the site of synthesis to the site of action.

Nearly 200 different polypeptides have been identified within the ciliary axoneme of lower organisms.[29] It is likely that various genes responsible for different subgroups of the immotile-cilia syndrome are located on most chromosomes in humans. Previous attempts to localize the (assumed single) gene for Kartagener syndrome have been completely unsuccessful. Conclusive results will probably be obtained only when studies are restricted to one family, and these results may not necessarily be valid in other families.

Chromosomal studies on several patients have almost always disclosed a normal karyotype.[6] Richer et al.[107] reported a man with the immotile-cilia syndrome and trisomy 12 mosaicism.

Males and females are equally affected. Most males with the syndrome have immotile spermatozoa and are sterile. Male sterility can also be observed in most, but not all[21,108] published pedigrees. In rare cases the Kartagener patient may have normally motile spermatozoa and be capable of fathering a healthy child.[84]

In a Norwegian population 5 percent of all children with Kartagener syndrome had parents that were first cousins, and 16 percent had parents that were second cousins.[109] Among the population in general 0.5 percent of parents are first cousins. Parents of patients with the immotile-cilia syndrome have normal cilia, and hence it is impossible to screen for carriers of the disease.[110]

CLINICAL FEATURES

Diagnosis

Diagnosis of the immotile-cilia syndrome can be performed by electron microscopy, if specific ultrastructural defects of cilia or sperm tails are found in persons with a clinical picture compatible with the syndrome. Alternatively diagnosis requires the demonstration of immotility or severe dysmotility of cilia or spermatozoa. Possibly with the exception of sperm motility investigations, such tests are too complicated to be suited as a first-line screening. Measurements of airway mucociliary clearance may be valuable in excluding the diagnosis, since an absence of mucociliary clearance is a hallmark of the syndrome.[96,111] The measurement of the tracheobronchial clearance of inhaled, radioactively tagged test particles is also a complicated and expensive method, which moreover has to be interpreted with caution since coughing will often obscure the impaired mucociliary clearance in these patients.[99,111] As a first-line screening method the saccharin test investigating nasal mucociliary clearance is much more applicable.[112,113] Saccharin particles are placed on the inferior nasal tubinate about 10 mm from its anterior end, and the time taken for the sweet taste to appear is recorded. This time is greatly prolonged—usually to more than 60 min—in patients with non-functioning cilia. A reduced mucociliary clearance is, however, found in a multitude of diseases and may thus be an acquired condition.

Samples of ciliated cells are easily obtained from the inferior nasal turbinate by gentle scraping with a curette or better still with a cytology brush, a procedure not even requiring anesthesia.[90,93,100] Alternatively, mucosal biopsies may be obtained by bronchoscopy. Ciliary motility may then be analyzed in vitro, by light microscopy and oscillometry or videoscreen recording, by which methods the characteristic immotility or dysmotility may be accurately assessed.[66,91,97,114] The ciliary material may be prepared also for electron microscopy, which is diagnostic in typical cases, such as those with a severe deficiency of dynein arms.[5] In cases with more discrete types of defects, the electron-microscopical evaluation is more problematic and may require quantitative analysis.[115]

The demonstration of specific defects of ciliary ultrastructure and/or motility is not necessary for purely clinical purposes. The diagnosis may be regarded as established with a sufficient degree of reliability in the following situations: (1) patients with complete Kartagener syndrome, (2) men with the typical clinical signs (chronic bronchitis and rhinitis since early childhood) having immotile or poorly motile but otherwise normal spermatozoa, (3) patients with the same clinical signs concerning airway disease having a sib fulfilling the criteria of (1) or (2). It should be kept in mind that most persons with *situs inversus* do not have chronic respiratory tract disease and thus do not have the immotile-cilia syndrome, and cases with *situs inversus* accompanied by other types of respiratory tract disease, such as asthma and atopic rhinitis, should not be confused with the immotile-cilia syndrome. Cases fulfilling the criteria of Kartagener syndrome but without any ciliary defects whatsoever have been described,[116] which is expected since causes of chronic respiratory disease other than ciliary defects must occasionally occur in persons with situs inversus. However, such cases probably are rare.

The immotile-cilia syndrome has many features in common with cystic fibrosis, for instance, male infertility. Mucociliary clearance may be retarded in cystic fibrosis but is often present in spite of the airway disease; this disease nevertheless has a more serious prognosis than in the immotile-cilia syndrome, and the cilia have a normal ultrastructure.[117] Patients with immunoglobulin deficiency may also have a rather similar clinical profile, with mucociliary clearance retarded secondary to the chronic infections; again ciliary ultrastructure has been found normal.[118] Another differential diagnosis is Young syndrome, defined as obstructive azoospermia and chronic sinopulmonary infections;[119,120] this condition is the most common cause of the combination of male infertility and chronic airway infections. The respiratory tract disease seems to be generally less severe here than in the immotile-cilia syndrome.[120]

Respiratory Tract

Although the immotile-cilia syndrome is a heterogeneous condition with regard to ultrastructure, and hence genetics, the clinical profile seems to be fairly or even remarkably uniform—perhaps not surprising when one considers the absence of mucociliary clearance as a common denominator. Characteristically, the respiratory tract disease can be traced back to early childhood or even infancy—often to the very day of birth.[50,52,66,99,121] Neonatal respiratory distress is not uncommon.[121,122] Chronic cough and expectoration of mucoid, mucopurulent, or at times purulent sputum is generally present and often tends to increase during the day rather than being most prominent in the morning as in smoker's chronic bronchitis. Atelectasis and pneumonia are fairly common.

Rhinitis with discharge of a mostly rather thin secretion is also almost universally present, and is not infrequently complicated by nasal polyposis.[52,73,121] Chronic or recurrent sinusitis is present, affecting both maxillary and ethmoidal sinuses, and the frontal sinuses often fail to develop. The mastoid cells are poorly aerated. Chronic secretory otitis media is constantly present in childhood, with bouts of more acute otitis superimposed;[18,52,73,76,123,124] in most patients there is a conductive hearing loss of moderate degree, e.g., 10 to 40 dB.[18,73,123] The ear and nose symptoms usually peak in childhood and adolescence, often with numerous surgical interventions, with a considerable improvement in adult age.[18]

Common colds do not seem to have a much more severe course in the immotile-cilia syndrome than in normals. When there is no apparent acute infection, sedimentation rate and serum immunoglobulins are usually normal.[99] Sputum cultures may fail to reveal specific pathogens; when such are found, *Haemophilus influenzae* is a common finding.[66,76]

Bronchiectasis is probably never present at birth but often develops during childhood and adolescence (Figs. 112-8 and 112-9). It occurs in dependent parts of the lungs, may be cylindrical or saccular, and on histologic examination shows nonspecific inflammation. The changes are identical to bronchiectasis from other causes.[125,126] When bronchiectasis develops, there may be a marked worsening of the previously often rather discrete endobronchial symptoms, with increased expectoration, infectious episodes with fever, hemoptysis, and development of finger clubbing. The respiratory tract disease of Kartagener syndrome has traditionally been described in terms of bronchiectasis and sinusitis, but by now it appears clear that a generalized bronchitis and rhinitis are the more primary features.

Lung function evaluated by spirometry may be normal or show an obstructive impairment of ventilation; in a few cases there may be a restrictive impairment as well, attributable to resectional surgery for bronchiectasis or to generally stiff lungs.[99,127] When obstruction occurs, it is usually of moderate degree and does not seem to progress much over the years.[50,52,99,121,128] In spite of this, there seems to be a tendency to slight arterial desaturation.[50] At times, there may be severe airflow obstruction with effort dyspnea by the third decade, and it seems that smokers are at a particular risk.[121] Usually there is little reversibility of airflow obstruction, although significant bronchospasm is occasionally present.[76,99,121,127] In a series of 35 adult persons with the syndrome (age range 19 to 65 years), forced expiratory volume in 1 s (FEV_1) averaged 67 $\pm$ 21 percent (mean $\pm$ SD) of predicted normal value, range 24 to 112 percent, with no correlation to age. Corresponding

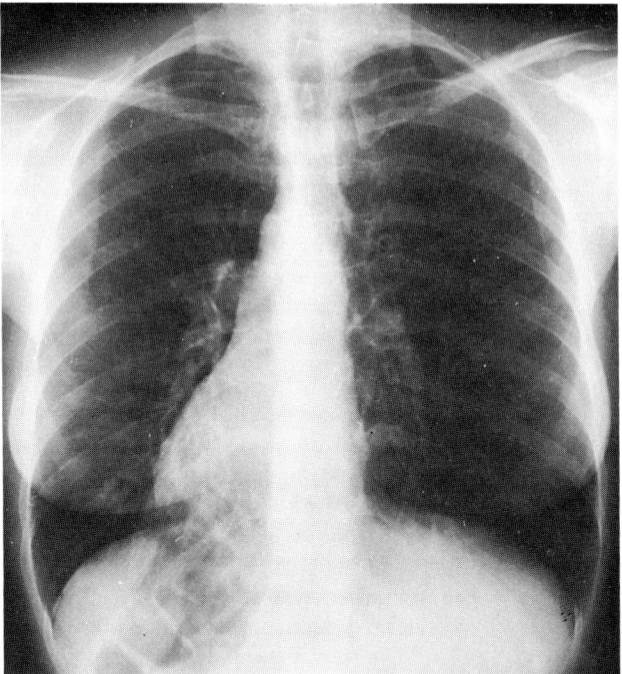

Fig. 112-8 Chest radiograph of a 32-year-old woman with Kartagener syndrome. Changes suggesting bronchiectasis are seen behind the heart. Note the transposition of the heart and also of the abdominal viscera, with part of the colon to the right and the liver to the left.

values for vital capacity were 79 ± 14 percent, range 47 to 116 percent.[128]

When significant airways obstruction is present, it is usually expressed as effort dyspnea; asthmatic attacks are not a prominent feature.[121,128] On lung auscultation crackles are usually heard, wheezing to a lesser extent. On chest radiographs a moderate degree of hyperinflation is often observable, in children as well as in adults.[52,129]

Sensory Organs

For otologic aspects of the immotile-cilia syndrome, see the discussion above. The sense of balance seems not to be affected in the majority of cases,[4] although about 10 percent claim that they have a less than good sense of balance.

Examination of the eyes of 10 patients with the syndrome showed corneal abnormalities in 9[130] but no other consistent abnormalities. These abnormalities may be secondary to a developmental disturbance. It may be remembered that the corneal endothelium is a monociliated epithelium.

Some patients have been described who suffer from both Kartagener syndrome and either retinitis pigmentosa[131] or a pigmented degeneration of the retina.[132] This is interesting because Fox et al.[133] have claimed that abnormalities in the ultrastructure of human nasal cilia are found in persons suffering from retinitis pigmentosa.

Most subjects with inborn ciliary immotility are anosmic or have a decreased sense of smell.[5,123]

Central Nervous System

In the literature on this syndrome one often notes that some of the patients suffer from dull headaches, endogenous depression,[5] or schizophrenia.[134] In the Swedish case reports two-

thirds of the patients complained of chronic headaches, and many had sought medical advice for this complaint. The headaches persisted even during periods free of sinusitis or other infections. Schizophrenia was not seen to be more common than in the general population.

It may be that patients with the immotile-cilia syndrome run a higher-than-normal risk of hydrocephalus. Occasional patients with Kartagener syndrome have died from hydrocephalus.[131,135] One baby developed hydrocephalus at an age of 2 weeks due to exit foramina obstruction, but was treated by a ventricular atrial shunt followed by a ventricular peritoneal shunt and grew up with normal intelligence.[136] It may be that ependymal cilia normally keep the aqueduct patent and that the risk of stenosis is increased with ciliary immotility.

The brains of seven persons with the immotile-cilia syndrome have been examined by means of computer tomography. In two or three of these a slight enlargement of the ventricular system and also the sulci was found.[5] The brain does not seem to mirror the situs inversus in persons having Kartagener syndrome; only 3 of 36 patients (8 percent) were left-handed.[5]

Reproductive Organs

It has already been remarked that nearly all men with the immotile-cilia syndrome are sterile because of an immotility or a poor motility of their spermatozoa, but that some men have motile spermatozoa and are fertile. In typical cases the volume of the ejaculate and the values for sperm number are within normal range. Similarly, sperm morphology evaluated by light microscopy is normal. The question arises: Will the spermatozoa be capable of fertilization in an in vitro fertilization test? The answer seems to be in the negative, although immotile human spermatozoa are capable of entering zona-less hamster eggs.[137] The zona pellucida of a human egg seems, however, to form a barrier to the immotile spermatozoa.[138]

Some patients are reported to have a hydrocele[139] or to be oligospermic.[59,91] In one patient the amount of carboxylmethylase has been measured in spermatozoa and found to be decreased.[140] This enzyme plays a role in chemotactic responses in bacteria and may also be involved in animal cell motility.

Women with the immotile-cilia syndrome may or may not be fertile.[128,141] In a Swedish series 9 of 19 women had been unsuccessful in their attempts to become pregnant, 5 had conceived, and 4 had not attempted to become pregnant.[128] The fertility of a woman with immotile cilia in the oviduct has been demonstrated by Bleau et al.,[142] whereas in another case a woman who had never conceived had oviductal cilia that were completely immotile.[143] It has been suggested that female fertility varies in the different subgroups of the immotile-cilia syndrome,[143] but evidence for this hypothesis has not yet been provided.

A priori it would seem likely that women with the immotile-cilia syndrome experience a greater than normal risk of ectopic pregnancies, but no evidence of this has been found.[5,6,142,144] Likewise, there does not seem to be an increased risk of salpingitis.

Cardiovascular System

As mentioned above, half the number of persons with the immotile-cilia syndrome have situs inversus, and may be classi-

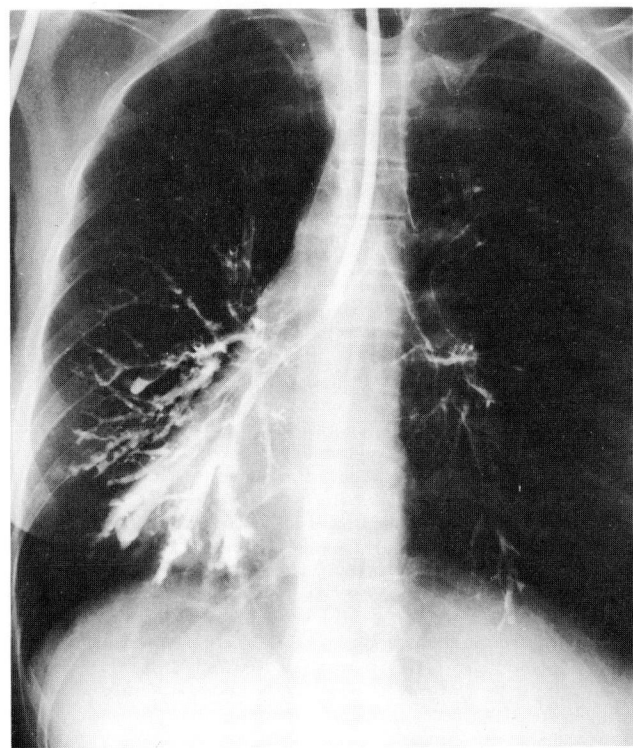

A.

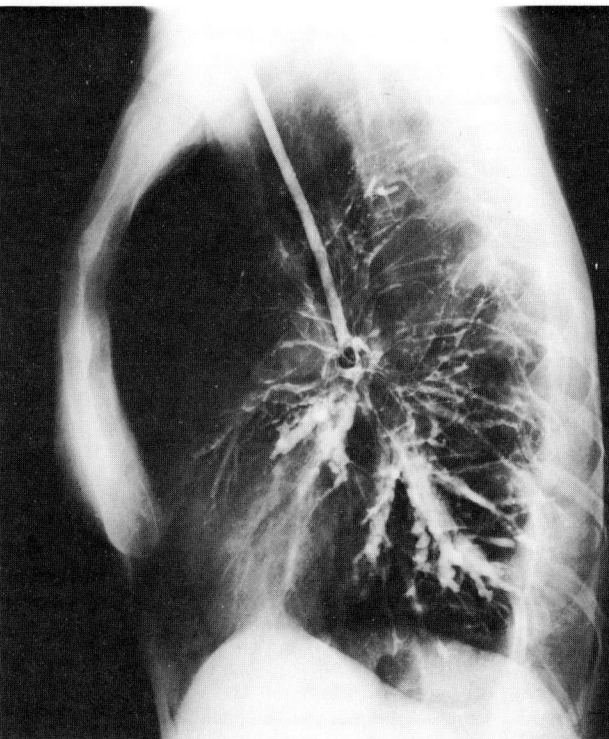

B.

Fig. 112-9 *A and B. Bronchography of the right lung from the same patient as in Fig. 112-7. Large bronchiectasis is seen in the lower lobe and in the right-sided lingula segment of the upper lobe.*

fied as having Kartagener syndrome. Most of these cases have a complete transposition of the thoracic and abdominal viscera that form a mirror-image of the normal condition. Usually no other congenital malformations of the heart or other organs are apparent in Kartaganer syndrome, as is common in cases of isolated dextrocardia.[145,146] Occasional malformations of the

heart have been recorded in Kartagener syndrome, as well as cases of incomplete situs inversus.[6,66]

Leukocytes

The capacity of the leukocytes to orient and to migrate in a chemotactic gradient has been examined in an attempt to find out whether defects in cell motility are restricted to spermatozoa and ciliated cells or have a more general occurrence. It has then been reported that the chemotactic migration indeed is significantly reduced in some, but not all, persons investigated, and also, that the capacity to orient is hampered.[147–150] Whether this decreased motility is a primary phenomenon, or whether it is a consequence of the chronic infections is at present unknown. Most persons with the immotile-cilia syndrome do not appear to have an increased incidence of infections at sites outside the airways.

Developmental Anomalies

An extensive list of malformations and diseases that have been observed in patients suffering from Kartagener syndrome is found in Ref. 6. It is likely that the simultaneous occurrence of a certain disease and the syndrome in many cases is purely coincidental. In other instances a disease or an anomaly may be a direct or indirect consequence of the ciliary malfunction. If so, one might expect to find the anomaly in several patients and a similar defect in the animal models. Some of the congenital cardiac malformations may belong to this category. So may polydactyly, which has been noted in some patients[151,152] and which is also characteristic of hpy/hpy mice, a strain in which cilia are abnormal.[28]

TREATMENT AND PROGNOSIS

Treatment is symptomatic and directed against complications in the upper and lower respiratory tract. There is no method available to restore ciliary and spermatozoal motility *in situ*.

Antibiotics or chemotherapeutic agents may be given when there are signs of bacterial infections, such as increased purulence of sputum or bouts of sinusitis or otitis. The value of mucolytics is uncertain, but they may be tried in selected cases with tenacious secretions. Bronchodilators (β-adrenergics, methylxanthines, or anticholinergics) may be valuable in cases when there is airway obstruction with a bronchospastic component.

Physiotherapy with postural drainage is often important and, if started early in life, might possibly prevent or delay the evolution of bronchiectasis and atelectasis. Abandonment of smoking is a most important preventive measure, since smoking probably accelerates deterioration of lung function.

Surgical interventions against maxillary sinusitis, nasal polyposis, and middle ear disease are often repeatedly performed in these patients (e.g., endonasal trepanation, Caldwell-Luc operation, polypectomy, tympanostomy). Such operations may doubtless be necessary in certain cases, but a certain amount of conservatism has been advocated in this context, as there often is a spontaneous remission in adult age.[18,123]

Thoracic surgical intervention against bronchiectasis is sometimes indicated, although the choice may be difficult in the individual case. In a series of 35 adult patients, bronchiectasis had been demonstrated by bronchography in 22 cases of whom 16 had been operated; half of these improved upon surgery.[128] The symptoms of chronic bronchitis are not to be expected to be cured by resectional surgery.

Without access to antibiotics the average life span may be somewhat reduced owing to severe respiratory tract infections particularly in childhood and adolescence. The rather frequent occurrence of chronic obstructive pulmonary disease with the risk of development of respiratory insufficiency probably also tends to somewhat reduce life span, although airways obstruction might not be very progressive in most cases. Whether there is an increased risk of lung cancer in the syndrome is not known.

Most persons with the syndrome seem to live an active life.[121] General physical and mental development is usually not retarded by the chronic disease. Situs inversus is usually not combined with congenital malformations. Kartagener syndrome has been described in old age.[153] With modern medical care and abstinence from smoking the prognosis may therefore be encouraging or even excellent.

REFERENCES

1. KARTAGENER M: Zur Pathogenese der Bronchiektasien: Bronchiektasien bei Situs viscerum inversus. *Beitr Klin Tuberk* 83:489, 1933.
2. SIEWERT AK: Ueber einen Fall von Bronchiektasie bei einem Patienten mit Situs inversus viscerum. *Berl Klin Wochenschr* 41:139, 1904.
3. AFZELIUS BA: A human syndrome caused by immotile cilia. *Science* 193:317, 1976.
4. ELIASSON R, MOSSBERG B, CAMNER P, AFZELIUS BA: The immotile-cilia syndrome. A congenital ciliary abnormality as an etiologic factor in chronic airway infections and male sterility. *N Engl J Med* 297:1, 1977.
5. AFZELIUS BA: The immotile-cilia syndrome and other ciliary diseases. *Intern Rev Exp Pathol* 19:1, 1979.
6. ROTT H-D: Kartagener's syndrome and the syndrome of immotile cilia. *Hum Genet* 46:249, 1979.
7. ADAMS R, CHURCHILL ED: Situs inversus, sinusitis and bronchiectasis. *J Thorac Surg* 7:206, 1937.
8. SVARTENGREN M, FLODERUS-MYRHED B, MOSSBERG B, CAMNER P: Defekta försvarsmekanismen i lungorna. *Hjärta Kärl Lungor (Stockh)* 3:81, 1983.
9. FALSER N: Anomalies of kinocilia in Kartagener's syndrome. *Laryngol Rhinol Otol* 62:128, 1983.
10. GIBNEY RTN, HERBERT FA: Kartagener's syndrome. *Irish Med J* 73:87, 1980.
11. MONNET P: Situs inversus and bronchopulmonary disease in the neonatal period. *Arch Fr Pediatr* 35:607, 1978.
12. KARTAGENER M, HORLACHER A: Zur Pathogenese der Bronchiektasien, Situs viscerum inversus and Polyposis nasi in einem Falle familiarer Bronchiektasien. *Beitr Klin Tuberk* 87:331, 1935.
13. WEINAUG P: Ein Fall von Kartagener-Syndrom bei Geschwistern. *Z Erkr Atmungsorgane* 134:454, 1971.
14. ROTT H-D, WARNATZ H, PASCH-HILGERS R, WEIKL A: Kartagener's syndrome in sibs. Clinical and immunological investigations. *Hum Genet* 43:1, 1978.
15. KNOX G, MURRAY S, STRANG L: A family with Kartagener's syndrome: Linkage data. *Ann Hum Genet* 24:137, 1960.
16. GUGGENHEIM F: Kartagener's syndrome in an Arab family. *Isr J Med Sci* 7:1079, 1971.
17. KATSUHARA K, KAWAMOTO S, WAKABAYASHI T, BELSKY JL: Situs inversus totalis and Kartageners syndrome in a Japanese population. *Chest* 61:56, 1972.
18. ERNSTSON S, AFZELIUS BA, MOSSBERG B: Otological manifestations of the immotile-cilia syndrome. *Acta Otolaryngol* 97:83, 1984.
19. PERONE PM: Situs viscerum inversus, bronchiettasie e sinusiti: Tre casi di sindrome di Kartagener. *Arch Ital Otolaryngol* 67:653, 1956.
20. OVERHOLT EL, BANMAN DF: Variants of Kartagener's syndrome in the same family. *Ann Intern Med* 48:547, 1958.
21. LOGAN WD, ABBOTT OA, HATCHER CR: Kartagener's triad. *Dis Chest* 48:613, 1965.
22. WAKEFIELD SJ, WAITE D: Abnormal cilia in Polynesians with bronchiectasis. *Am Rev Respir Dis* 121:1003, 1980.

23. AUGUST JR, TEER PA, BARTELS JE: Kartagener's syndrome in a dog. *J Am Anim Hosp Pract* 18:822, 1982.
24. EDWARDS DF, PATTON CS, BEMIS DA, KENNEDY JR, SELCER BA: Immotile cilia syndrome in three dogs from a litter. *J Am Vet Med Assoc* 183:667, 1983.
25. AFZELIUS BA, CARLSTEN J, KARLSSON S: Clinical, pathologic, and ultrastructural features of situs inversus and immotile-cilia syndrome in a dog. *J Am Vet Med Assoc* 184:560, 1984.
26. RANDOLPH JF, CASTLEMAN WL: Immotile cilia syndrome in 2 old-English sheepdog littermates. *J Small Anim Pract* 25:679, 1984.
27. WILSMAN NJ, MORRISON WB, FARNUM CE, FOX LE: Microtubular protofilaments and subunits of the outer dynein arm in cilia from dogs with primary ciliary dyskinesia. *Am Rev Respir Dis* 135:137, 1987.
28. BRYAN JHD: Abnormal cilia in male-sterile mutant mice. *Virchows Arch (A)* 400:77, 1983.
29. LUCK DJL, HUANG B, PIPERNO G: Genetic and biochemical analysis of the eukaryotic flagellum. *Soc Exp Biol Symp* 35:399, 1982.
30. JARVIK JW, CHOJNACKI B: Flagellar morphology in stumpy-flagella mutants of Chlamydomonas reinhardtii. *J Protozool* 32:649, 1985.
31. KAMIYA R, OKAMOTO M: A mutant of Chlamydomonas reinhardtii that lack the flagellar outer dynein arm but can swim. *J Cell Sci* 74:181, 1985.
32. AFZELIUS BA: Genetic disorders of cilia, in Schweiger HG (ed): *International Cell Biology 1980–1981*. Berlin, Springer-Verlag, 1981, p 440.
33. HARD R: Reactivation of outer-arm-depleted lung axonemes. *J Cell Biol* 99:47a, 1984.
34. SLEIGH M: The nature and action of respiratory tract cilia, in Brain JD, Procter DF, Reid LM (eds): *Respiratory Defence Mechanisms*, Monograph 3 of *Lung Biology in Health and Disease*. New York, Dekker, 1977, p 247.
35. SATIR P: Basis of flagellar motility in spermatozoa. Current status, in Fawcett DW, Bedford JM (eds): *The Spermatozoon*. Baltimore, Urban and Schwartzenberg, 1979, p 81.
36. STURGESS J: Mucous secretion in the respiratory tract. *Pediatr Clin North Am* 26:481, 1979.
37. WARNER FD: Structure-function relationships in cilia and flagella, in Harris JR (ed): *Electron microscopy of proteins*. London, New York, Academic, 1981, p 301.
38. DENTLER W, LE CLUYSE EL: Microtubule capping structures at the tip of tracheal cilia. *Cell Motil* 2:549, 1983.
39. GOODENOUGH UW, HEUSER JE: Outer and inner dynein arms of cilia and flagella. *Cell* 41:341, 1985.
40. FUJITA H: Fine structure of the thyroid gland. *Int Rev Cytol* 40:197, 1975.
41. SVEDBERGH B, BILL A: Scanning electron microscopic studies of the corneal epithelium in man and monkeys. *Acta Ophthalmol* 50:321, 1972.
42. ODOR DL, BLANDAU RJ: Observations on the solitary cilium of rabbit oviductal epithelium: Its motility and ultrastructure. *Am J Anat* 174:437, 1985.
43. GRIMFELD JA, TOURNIER G, JOUANNET P, BISSON JP, SALOMON JL, BACULARD A, GERBEAUX J: Immotile cilia syndrome in infants and children. *Thorax* 34:709, 1979.
44. JAHRSDOERFER R, FELDMAN PS, RUBEL EW, GUERRANT JL, EGGLESTON PA, SELDEN RF: Otitis media and the immotile cilia syndrome. *Laryngoscope* 89:769, 1979.
45. AFZELIUS BA, ELIASSON R: Flagellar mutants in man: On the heterogeneity of the immotile-cilia syndrome. *J Ultrastruct Res* 69:43, 1979.
46. STURGESS JM, CHAO J, WONG J, ASPIN N, TURNER JAP: Cilia with defective radial spokes. A cause of human respiratory disease. *N Engl J Med* 300:53, 1979.
47. STURGESS JM, CHAO J, TURNER JAP: Transposition of ciliary microtubules. Another cause of impaired ciliary motility. *N Engl J Med* 303:318, 1980.
48. SCHNEEBERGER EE, MCCORMACK J, ISSENBERG H, SCHUSTER SR, GERALD PS: Heterogeneity of ciliary morphology in the immotile-cilia syndrome in man. *J Ultrastruct Res* 73:34, 1980.
49. PEDERSEN H, REBBE H: Absence of arms in the axoneme of immobile human spermatozoa. *Biol Reprod* 12:541, 1975.
50. CORKEY CWB, LEVISON H, TURNER JAP: The immotile cilia syndrome—A longitudinal survey. *Am Rev Respir Dis* 124:544, 1981.
51. ESCALIER D, JOUANNET P, DAVID G: Abnormalities of the ciliary axonemal complex in children. *Biol Cell* 44:271, 1982.
52. LEVISON H, MINDORFF CM, CHAO J, TURNER JAP, STURGESS JM, STRINGER DA: Pathophysiology of the ciliary motility syndromes. *Eur J Respir Dis* 64, Suppl 127:102, 1983.
53. WHITE BL, CATLIN FI, STENBACK WA, HAWKINS ED, SEILHEIMER DK: The immotile cilia syndrome—One cause of persistent upper respiratory tract infection. *Int J Pediatr Otorhinolaryngol* 2:337, 1980.
54. WILTON LJ, TEICHTAHL H, TEMPLE-SMITH PD, DE KRETSER DM: Kartagener's syndrome with motile cilia and immotile spermatozoa. *Am Rev Respir Dis* 134:1233, 1986.

55. CORBEEL L, CORNILLE F, LAUWERYNS J, BOEL M, VAN DEN BERGHE G: Ultrastructural abnormalities of bronchial cilia in children with recurrent airway infections and bronchiectasis. *Arch Dis Child* 56:929, 1981.

56. DAVID G, SERRES C, ESCALIER D: Cinématique du spermatozoide humain. *Ann Endocrinol* 42:391, 1982.

57. WOODRING JH, ROYER JM, McDONAGH D: Kartagener's syndrome. *JAMA* 247:2814, 1982.

58. NIELSEN MH, PEDERSEN M, CHRISTENSEN B, MYGIND N: Blind quantitative electron microscopy of cilia from patients with primary ciliary dyskinesia and from normal subjects. *Eur J Respir Dis* 64, suppl 127:19, 1983.

59. ESCALIER D, DAVID G: Pathology of the cytoskeleton of the human sperm flagellum. *Biol Cell* 50:37, 1984.

60. CHABROLLE JP, EUZIERE P, BIGEL P, BLONDET P: Syndrome d'immotilité ciliaire chez un enfant de 10 ans. *Arch Fr Pediatr* 39:235, 1982.

61. STURGESS JM, THOMPSON MW, CZEGLEDY-NAGY E, TURNER JAP: Genetic aspects of immotile cilia syndrome. *Am J Med Genet* 25:149, 1986.

62. NEUSTEIN HB, NICKERSON B, O'NEIL M: Kartagener's syndrome with absence of inner dynein arms of respiratory cilia. *Am Rev Respir Dis* 122:979, 1980.

63. SALOMON JL, GRIMFELD A, TOURNIER G, BACULARD A, ESCALIER D, JOUANNET P, DAVID G: Ciliary disorders of the bronchi in children. *Rev Fr Malad Respir* 11:645, 1983.

64. HERZON FS, MURPHY S: Normal ciliary ultrastructure in children with Kartagener's syndrome. *Ann Otol Rhinol Laryngol* 89:81, 1980.

65. GREENSTONE MA, DEWAR A, COLE PJ: Ciliary dyskinesia with normal ultrastructure. *Thorax* 38:875, 1983.

66. PEDERSEN M, STAFANGER G: Bronchopulmonary symptoms in primary ciliary dyskinesia. *Eur J Respir Dis* 64, suppl 127:118, 1983.

67. AFZELIUS BA, GARGANI G, ROMANO C: Abnormal length of cilia as a cause of defective mucociliary clearance. *Eur J Respir Dis* 66:173, 1985.

68. DUDLEY JP, WAELCH MJ, CARNEY JM, STIEHM ER, SODERBER M: Scanning and transmission electron microscopic aspects of the nasal acilia syndrome. *Laryngoscope* 92:297, 1982.

69. FONZI L, LUNGARELLA G, PALATRESI R: Lack of kinocilia in the nasal mucosa. *Eur J Respir Dis* 63:558, 1982.

70. GÖTZ M, STOCKINGER L: Aplasia of respiratory tract cilia. *Lancet* 1:1283, 1983.

71. GORDON RE, KATTAN M: Absence of cilia and basal bodies with predominance of brush cells in the respiratory mucosa from a patient with immotile cilia syndrome. *Ultrastruct Pathol* 6:45, 1984.

72. CERESO L, PRICE G: Absence of cilia and basal bodies with predominance of brush cells in the respiratory mucosa from a patient with immotile cilia syndrome. *Ultrastruct Pathol* 8:381, 1985.

73. MYGIND NG, PEDERSEN M, TOREMALM NG: Lazy cilia make the otologist busy. *Clin Otolaryngol* 8:148, 1983.

74. HOLLEY MC, AFZELIUS BA: Alignment of cilia in immotile-cilia syndrome. *Tissue Cell* 18:521, 1986.

75. CAMNER P, AFZELIUS BA, ELIASSON R, MOSSBERG B: Relation between abnormalities of human sperm flagella and respiratory tract disease. *Int J Androl* 2:211, 1979.

76. TURNER JAP, CORKEY CWB, LEE JYC, LEVISON H, STURGESS JM: Clinical expression of immotile cilia syndrome. *Pediatrics* 67:805, 1981.

77. FOX B, BULL TB, MAKEY AR, RAWBONE R: The significance of ultrastructural abnormalities of human cilia. *Chest* 80, suppl:796,1981.

78. HILDING AC: The relation of ciliary insufficiency to death from asthma and other respiratory diseases. *Ann Otol Rhinol Laryngol* 52:5, 1943.

79. CAMNER P, JARSTRAND C, PHILIPSON K: Tracheobronchial clearance in patients with influenza. *Am Rev Respir Dis* 108:131, 1973.

80. PEDERSEN M, SAKAKURA Y, WINTHER B, BROFELDT S, MYGIND N: Nasal mucociliary transport, number of ciliated cells, and beating pattern in naturally acquired colds. *Eur J Respir Dis* 64, suppl 128:355, 1983.

81. PEDERSEN M: Specific types of abnormal ciliary motility in Kartagener's syndrome and analogous respiratory disorders. *Eur J Respir Dis* 64, suppl 127:78, 1983.

82. LUNGARELLA G, FONZI L, BURRINI AG: Ultrastructural abnormalities in respiratory cilia and sperm tails in a patient with Kartagener's syndrome. *Ultrastruct Pathol* 3:319, 1982.

83. WALT H, CAMPANA A, BALERNA M, DOMENIGHETTI G, HEDINGER C, JAKOB M, PESCIA G, SULMONI A: Mosaicism of dynein in spermatozoa and cilia and fibrous sheath aberrations in an infertile man. *Andrologia* 15:295, 1983.

84. JONSSON MS, McCORMICK JR, GILLIES CG, GONDOS B: Kartagener's syndrome with motile spermatozoa. *N Engl J Med* 307:1131, 1982.

85. AFZELIUS BA: Immotile-cilia syndrome and ciliary abnormalities induced by infection and injury. *Am Rev Respir Dis* 124:107, 1981.

86. CORNILLE FJ, LAUWERYNS JM, CORBEEL L: Atypical bronchial cilia in children with recurrent respiratory tract infections. *Pathol Res Pract* 178:595, 1984.

87. KONRADOVA V, HLOUSKOVA Z, TOMANEK A: Atypical kinocilia in human epithelium from large bronchus. *Folia Morphol (Praha)* 23:293, 1975.

88. TAKASAKA T, SATO M, ONODERA A: Atypical cilia in the human nasal mucosa. *Ann Otol Rhinol Laryngol* 89:37, 1980.

89. VEERMAN AJP, VANDELDEN L, FEENSTRA L, LEENE W: The immotile cilia syndrome—Phase contrast light microscopy, scanning and transmission electron microscopy. *Pediatrics* 65:698, 1980.

90. RUTLAND J, COLE PJ: Non-invasive sampling of nasal cilia for measurement of beat frequency and study of ultrastructure. *Lancet* 2:564, 1980.

91. ROSSMAN CM, FORREST JB, LEE RMKW, NEWHOUSE MT: The dyskinetic cilia syndrome—Ciliary motility in immotile cilia syndrome. *Chest* 78:580, 1980.

92. PEDERSEN M, MYGIND N: Ciliary motility in the immotile cilia syndrome. *Br J Dis Chest* 74:239, 1980.

93. STURGESS JM, TURNER JAP: Ultrastructural pathology of cilia in the immotile cilia syndrome. *Perspect Pediatr Pathol* 8:133, 1984.

94. ROSSMAN CM, FORREST JB, LEE RMKW, NEWHOUSE AF, NEWHOUSE MT: The dyskinetic cilia syndrome. *Chest* 80:860, 1981.

95. ROSSMAN CM, LEE RMKW, FORREST JB, NEWHOUSE MT: Nasal ciliary ultrastructure and function in patients with primary ciliary dyskinesia compared with that in normal subjects and in subjects with various respiratory diseases. *Am Rev Respir Dis* 129:161, 1984.

96. CAMNER P, MOSSBERG B, AFZELIUS BA: Evidence for congenitally nonfunctioning cilia in the tracheobronchial tract in two subjects. *Am Rev Respir Dis* 112:807, 1975.

97. PALMBLAD J, MOSSBERG B, AFZELIUS BA: Ultrastructural, cellular, and clinical features of the immotile-cilia syndrome. *Annu Rev Med* 35:481, 1984.

98. NUUTINEN J, KÄRJÄ J, KARJALAINEN P: Measurements of impaired mucociliary activity in children. *Eur J Respir Dis* 64:454, 1983.

99. MOSSBERG B, AFZELIUS BA, ELIASSON R, CAMNER P: On the pathogenesis of obstructive lung disease: A study in the immotile-cilia syndrome. *Scand J Respir Dis* 59:55, 1978.

100. BOAT TF, WOOD RE, TANDLER B, STERN RC, ORENSTEIN DM, DOERSHUK CF: A screening test for the immotile cilia syndrome. *Pediatr Res* 13:531, 1979.

101. PEDERSEN M, NIELSEN MH, MYGIND N: Primary ciliary dyskinesia. *Mod Probl Paediatr* 21:68, 1982.

102. VAN DER BAAN S, VEERMAN AJP, WULLFRAAT N, BEZEMER PD, FEENSTRA L: Primary ciliary dyskinesia. *Acta Otolaryngol* 102:274, 1986.

103. LAYTON WM: Random determination of a developmental process. *J Hered* 67:336, 1976.

104. LAYTON WM: Heart malformation in mice homozygous for a gene causing situs inversus, in Normal Morphogenesis of the Heart. *Birth Defects*, Washington, DC, The National Foundation, 1978, vol 14, p 277.

105. EAVEY RD, NADOL JB, HOLMES LB, LAIRD NM, LAPEY A, JOSEPH MP, STROME M: Kartagener's syndrome. A blinded, controlled study of cilia ultrastructure. *Arch Otol Head Neck Surg* 112:646, 1986.

106. MORENO A, MURPHY EA: Inheritance of Kartagener syndrome. *Am J Med Genet* 8:305, 1981.

107. RICHER C-L, BLEAU G, CHAPDELAINE A: Trisomy 12 mosaicism in an infertile man. *Can J Genet Cytol* 19:565, 1977.

108. HEUCKENKAMP PU, MARSHALL M, MEIER J, PARRISIUS G, ZÖLLNER N: Das Kartagener-syndrom. *Dtsch Med Wochenschr* 97:1458, 1972.

109. TORGERSEN J: Genic factors in visceral asymmetry and in the development and pathologic changes of lungs, heart and abdominal organs. *Arch Pathol* 47:566, 1949.

110. ANTONELLI M, MODESTI A, QUATTRINI A, DE ANGELIS M: Supernumerary microtubules in the respiratory cilia of two sibs. *Eur J Respir Dis* 64:607, 1983.

111. CAMNER P, MOSSBERG B, AFZELIUS BA: Measurements of tracheobronchial clearance in patients with immotile-cilia syndrome and its value in differential diagnosis. *Eur J Respir Dis* 64, suppl 127:57, 1983.

112. ANDERSEN I, PROCTOR DF: Measurement of nasal mucociliary clearance. *Eur J Respir Dis* 64, suppl 127:37, 1983.

113. STANLEY P, McWILLIAM L, GREENSTONE M, MACKAY I, COLE PJ: Efficacy of a saccharin test for screening to detect abnormal mucociliary clearance. *Br J Dis Chest* 78:62, 1984.

114. BURGERSDIJK FJA, DE GROOT JCMJ, GRAAMANS K, RADEMAKERS LHPM: Testing ciliary activity in patients with chronic and recurrent infections of the upper airways. *Laryngoscope* 96:1029, 1986.

115. NIELSEN MH, PEDERSEN M, CHRISTENSEN B, MYGIND N: Blind quantitative electron microscopy of cilia from patients with primary ciliary dyskinesia and from normal subjects. *Eur J Respir Dis* 64, suppl 127:19, 1983.

116. GREENSTONE M, RUTMAN A, PAVIA D, LAWRENCE D, COLE PJ: Normal

axonemal ultrastructure and function in Kartagener's syndrome: An explicable paradox. *Thorax* 40:956, 1985.

117. KOLLBERG H, MOSSBERG B, AFZELIUS BA, PHILIPSON K, CAMNER P: Cystic fibrosis compared with the immotile cilia syndrome. A study of mucociliary clearance, ciliary ultrastructure, clinical picture and ventilatory function. *Scand J Respir Dis* 59:297, 1978.

118. MOSSBERG B, BJÖRKANDER J, AFZELIUS BA, CAMNER P: Mucociliary clearance in patients with immunoglobulin deficiency. *Eur J Respir Dis* 63:570, 1982.

119. NEVILLE E, BREWIS R, YEATES WK, BURRIDGE A: Respiratory tract disease and obstructive azoospermia. *Thorax* 38:929, 1983.

120. HANDELSMAN DJ, CONWAY AJ, BOYLAN LM, TURTLE JR: Young's syndrome. Obstructive azoospermia and chronic sinopulmonary infections. *N Engl J Med* 310:3, 1984.

121. MOSSBERG B, CAMNER P, AFZELIUS BA: The immotile-cilia syndrome compared to other obstructive lung diseases: A clue to their pathogenesis. *Eur J Respir Dis* 64, *suppl* 127:129, 1983.

122. WHITELAW A, EVANS A, CORRIN B: Immotile cilia syndrome: A new cause of neonatal respiratory distress. *Arch Dis Child* 56:432, 1981.

123. MYGIND N, PEDERSEN M: Nose-, sinus-, and ear-symptoms in 27 patients with primary ciliary dyskinesia. *Eur J Respir Dis* 64, *suppl* 127:96, 1983.

124. PEDERSEN M, MYGIND N: Rhinitis, sinusitis and otitis media in Kartagener's syndrome. *Clin Otolaryngol* 7:373, 1983.

125. KARTAGENER M, STUCKI P: Bronchiectasis with situs inversus. *Arch Pediatr* 79:193, 1962.

126. MOSSBERG B, HANNGREN Å: Kartagener's syndrome—A ciliary immotility syndrome. *Mt Sinai J Med* 44:837, 1977.

127. EVANDER E, ARBORELIUS M, JONSON B, SIMONSSON BG, SVENSSON G: Lung function and bronchial reactivity in six patients with immotile cilia syndrome. *Eur J Respir Dis* 64, *suppl* 127:137, 1983.

128. MOSSBERG B, AFZELIUS BA, CAMNER P: Mucociliary clearance in obstructive lung diseases. Correlations to the immotile-cilia syndrome. *Eur J Respir Dis* 69, *suppl* 146:295, 1986.

129. NADEL HR, STRINGER DA, LEVISON H, TURNER JAP, STURGESS J: The immotile cilia syndrome: Radiological manifestations. *Radiology* 154:651, 1985.

130. SVEDBERGH B, JOHNSSON V, AFZELIUS BA: Immotile-cilia syndrome and the cilia of the eye. *Graefes Arch Klin Exp Ophthalmol* 215:265, 1981.

131. CHILD AH: Personal communication.

132. SEGAL P, KIKIELA M, MRZYGLOD B, ZEROMSKA-ZBIERSKA I: Kartagener's syndrome with familial eye changes. *Am J Ophthalmol* 55:1043, 1963.

133. FOX B, BULL TB, ARDEN GB: Variations in the ultrastructure of human nasal cilia including abnormalities found in retinitis pigmentosa. *J Clin Pathol* 33:327, 1980.

134. GLICK ID, GRAUBERT DN: Kartagener's syndrome and schizophrenia: A report of a case with chromosomal studies. *Am J Psychol* 121:603, 1964.

135. BERGSTROM WH, COOK CD, SCANNELL JG, BERENBERG W: Situs inversus, bronchiectasis and sinusitis. *Pediatrics* 6:573, 1950.

136. GREENSTONE MA, JONES RWA, DEWAR A, NEVILLE BGR: Hydrocephalus and primary ciliary dyskinesia. *Arch Dis Child* 59:481, 1984.

137. WILLIAMSON RA, KOEHLER JK, SMITH WD, KARP LE: Entry of immotile spermatozoa into zona-free hamster ova. *Gamete Res* 10:319, 1984.

138. AITKEN RJ, ROSS A, LEES MM: Analysis of sperm function in Kartagener's syndrome. *Fertil Steril* 40:693, 1983.

139. PELLNITZ D, HEYLAND S: Beitrag zur Kartagenerschen Trias (Situs inversus, Bronchiektasis und Nasenpolypen). *HNO* 3:41, 1952.

140. GAGNON C, SHERINS RJ, MANN T, BARDIN W, AMELAR RD, DUBIN L: Deficiency of protein carboxyl-methylase in spermatozoa of necrospermic patients, in Steinberger A, Steinberger E (eds): *Testicular Development, Structure, and Functions.* New York, Raven, 1980, p 491.

141. AFZELIUS BA, CAMNER P, MOSSBERG B: On the function of cilia in the female reproductive tract. *Fertil Steril* 29:72, 1978.

142. BLEAU G, RICHER C-L, BOUSQUET D: Absence of dynein arms in cilia of endocervical cells in a fertile woman. *Fertil Steril* 30:362, 1978.

143. MCCOMB P, LANGLEY L, VILLALON M, VERDUGO P: The oviductal cilia and Kartagener's syndrome. *Fertil Steril* 46:412, 1986.

144. MOURIQUAND P: Dyskinésie ciliaire primitive. Une revue générale. Conséquences sur la fertilité. *Thesis* University of Lyon, 1985.

145. COCKAYNE EA: The genetics of transposition of the viscera. *Q J Med* 7:479, 1938.

146. MILLER RD, DIVERTIE MB: Kartagener's syndrome. *Chest* 62:130, 1972.

147. AFZELIUS BA, EWETZ L, PALMBLAD J, UDEN A-M, VENIZELOS N: Structure and function of neutrophil leukocytes from patients with the immotile-cilia syndrome. *Acta Med Scand* 208:145, 1980.

148. WALTER RJ, MALECH HL, OLIVER JM: Cell motility and microtubules in cultured fibroblasts from patients with Kartagener's syndrome. *Cell Motil* 3:185, 1983.

149. VALERIUS NH, KNUDSEN BB, PEDERSEN M: Defective neutrophil motility in patients with primary ciliary dyskinesia. *Eur J Clin Invest* 13:489, 1983.

150. WOLBURG H, DOPFER R, SCHIEFERSTEIN G, THIEL E: Immotile cilia syndrome: Reduced chemotaxis and reduced number of intramembranous particles in granulocytes. *Klin Wochenschr* 62:1044, 1984.

151. CONWAY DJ: A congenital factor in bronchiectasis. *Arch Dis Child* 26:253, 1951.

152. SIELICKA-ZUBER L, FICER J: Zespól Kartagener. *Przegl Dermatol* 61:171, 1974.

153. AMJAD H, RICHBURG FD, ADLER E: Kartagener's syndrome. Case report in an elderly man. *JAMA* 227:1420, 1974.

CHAPTER 113

LEUKOCYTE ADHESION DEFICIENCY AND OTHER DISORDERS OF LEUKOCYTE MOTILITY

DONALD C. ANDERSON
C. WAYNE SMITH
TIMOTHY A. SPRINGER

1. *Recurrent bacterial or fungal infections of the skin or mucous membranes are prominent in patients with quantitative deficiencies of peripheral blood leukocytes. Such infections are also evident in patients with qualitative disorders resulting in insufficient accumulation of phagocytes at inflammatory sites. Among both patient groups, common pathogens such as* Staphylococcus aureus, Pseudomonas, *other gram-negative enteric species, or* Candida albicans *account for most infectious complications. Infected tissues in these patients are characteristically gangrenous or necrotic and devoid of pus and contain few granulocytes. Local inflammation may be minimal though the infection may lead to the destruction of cutaneous, subcutaneous, or submucosal tissues. A reliable interpretation of abnormal leukocyte functions assayed in vitro must take into consideration the clinical status of the individual patient. It is important to determine whether abnormal functions cause increased susceptibility to infection or simply reflect other factors surrounding the patient's condition such as pharmacologic agents, nutrition, infection, or underlying metabolic disease.*

2. *The molecular pathogenesis of a limited number of genetic or secondary disorders characterized by defective migration of leukocytes is known. Most notable is leukocyte adhesion deficiency, a heritable deficiency of the adherence proteins of the CD18 complex. This is a recently recognized autosomal recessive disorder characterized by recurrent bacterial infections, impaired pus formation and wound healing, and a wide spectrum of functional abnormalities in granulocytes, monocytes, and lymphoid cells. Superficial infections of body surfaces may invade locally or systemically. Typical small, erythematous, nonpustular skin lesions often progress to large, well-demarcated, ulcerative craters, or pyoderma gangrenosa, which heal slowly or with dysplastic eschars. Staphylococcal or gram-negative enteric bacterial organisms may be cultured from such lesions for up to several weeks despite antimicrobial therapy. Severe gingivitis and/or periodontitis is a major feature among all patients who survive infancy.*

3. *The recurrent infections observed in patients with leukocyte adhesion deficiency appear to reflect impairment of leukocyte mobilization into extravascular inflammatory sites. Infected tissues are devoid of neutrophils, even though marked peripheral blood leukocytosis (five- to twentyfold normal values) is a constant feature of this disorder. The severity of infectious complications appears to be directly related to the degree of glycoprotein deficiency. Two phenotypes, designated severe and moderate, have been identified. Severely deficient patients have essentially undetectable expression (<0.3 percent of normal amounts) of these glycoproteins on the surface of their leukocytes. Moderately deficient patients express 2.5 to 6 percent of normal levels. Patients with severe deficiency have either died in infancy or demonstrated a susceptibility to life-threatening*

systemic infections. In those with moderate deficiency (mean age 21 years, range 11 to 38 years) life-threatening infections have been infrequently observed.

4. *Abnormalities of adhesion-dependent functions in leukocytes including chemotaxis and aggregation have been observed among all patients studied. Phagocytosis of iC3b-opsonized particles is deficient since one of the deficient glycoproteins is the receptor for complement component C3. Abnormalities of antibody-dependent cellular cytotoxicity have also been observed in several patients. In contrast, adherence-independent cellular functions including f-Met-Leu-Phe receptor-ligand binding, oxidative metabolism, degranulation mediated by soluble stimuli, and intracellular microbicidal activity are relatively normal in most patients. Overall, more profound functional abnormalities have been observed among severely deficient as compared with moderately deficient patients.*

5. *The molecular basis of leukocyte adhesion deficiency has been found to involve a recently characterized family of structurally and functionally related glycoproteins on the surface of myeloid cells. These glycoproteins are involved in a wide array of functions dependent on adhesion. Each consists of noncovalently associated α and β subunits with $\alpha_1\beta_1$ stoichiometry. They share an identical β subunit ($M_r = 95,000$) and are distinguished immunologically by distinct α subunits whose relative molecular weights are as follows: $M_r = 165,000$ for Mac-1α (αM), $M_r = 177,000$ for LFA-1α (αL), and $M_r = 150,000$ for p150,95α (αX). The World Health Organization designation for these glycoproteins is CD18 for β; CD11a for αL; CD11b for αM; CD11c for αX. In studies of six unrelated patients and four related patients and other members of their kindred the following five distinct variations in the β subunit were identified. (1) The subunit was undetectable. (2) The quantities of β-subunit mRNA and protein precursor were low. (3) An aberrantly large β-subunit precursor likely due to an extra glycosylation site was found. (4) An aberrantly small β-subunit precursor due to a polypeptide chain defect was found. (5) No gross abnormality in the β-subunit precursor was found. In studies of one kindred including four related patients of the moderate phenotype, a β precursor of identically abnormal small size was identified in each case. Heterozygotes in this family show both a normal and an abnormally small β precursor, and noncarriers show only the normal β precursor. Cell lines from patients synthesize normal α-subunit precursors, but in the absence of a normal β subunit, this precursor cannot associate in an $\alpha\beta$ complex, does not undergo carbohydrate processing, and is not expressed on the cell surface. The α subunit is apparently degraded in the absence of the β subunit.*

6. *Bone marrow transplantation with successful engraftment rendered unnecessary any further treatment in two patients. In two other patients, successful engraftment was achieved, but recov-*

ery did not occur either because of graft-versus-host disease or infectious complications. Transplantation is recommended for severely deficient patients because of the high incidence of death before the age of 2. Moderately deficient patients live longer but may also be susceptible to life-threatening infections. Therapeutic guidelines for management of moderately deficient patients are not well defined.

HISTORICAL ACCOUNTS

The important role of phagocytic cells in host defense was recognized a century ago by Elie Metchnikoff. Historic findings by this jobless Russian zoologist in 1882 were among the first scientific evidence of phagocyte-host defense interactions. Several years later Metchnikoff described this conceptual breakthrough as follows[1]:

One day when the family had gone to a circus to see some extraordinary performing apes, I remained alone at my microscope, observing the life in the mobile cells of a transparent starfish larva, when a new thought suddenly flashed across my brain. It struck me that similar cells might serve in the defense of the organism against intruders. Feeling that there was in this something of surpassing interest, I felt so excited that I began striding up and down the room and even went to the seashore in order to collect my thoughts.

I said to myself that, if my supposition was true, a splinter introduced in to the body of a starfish larva, devoid of blood vessels or of a nervous system, should soon be surrounded by mobile cells as is to be observed in a man who runs a splinter into his finger. This was no sooner said than done.

I was too excited to sleep that night in the expectation of the result of my experiment, and very early the next morning I ascertained that it had fully succeeded.

That experiment formed the basis of the phagocyte theory, to the development of which I devoted the next twenty-five years of my life.

What Metchnikoff had described in the starfish experiment was not phagocytosis itself (i.e., the cellular ingestion of particles) but rather a more complex process involving the localized accumulation of cells at a point of injury. Further evidence that phagocytes undergo tropic migration was provided in 1888 by Theodore Leber, a German ophthalmologist.[2] He demonstrated for the first time migration of leukocytes toward chemical stimuli, a response later termed chemotaxis when observed in vitro. He wrote at that time[2]:

The property of the leukocyte to tropic migration by substances foreign to the organism is of the greatest importance in making possible an extensive counteraction of the organism against external factors, since only in this way is the accumulation of a large number of leukocytes at the site of noxa assured.

Since the time of these early landmark observations, the critical and multifaceted functions of phagocytes in inflammation have been described in a voluminous scientific literature. However, an understanding of the clinical relevance of these many observations largely awaited the recognition of pathologic disorders in the functions of human phagocytes. In 1954, Janeway and associates[3] described a group of patients with severe recurrent soft tissue infections. Approximately a decade life, Quie and coworkers[4] demonstrated a profound defect of intracellular microbicidal activity of phagocytic cells from these patients, and Holmes and coworkers[5] subsequently dem-

onstrated a defect of oxidative metabolism in this disorder, now termed *chronic granulomatous disease of childhood*. Subsequent to the recognition of this syndrome, a rapid succession of reports[6–11] described a heterogeneous group of patients with severe, recurrent sinopulmonary infections and/or staphylococcal soft tissue abscesses. Abnormal or diminished motility of neutrophils and/or monocytes was suggested as a major pathogenic mechanism accounting for these infectious complications. More recent investigations have successfully determined a molecular lesion accounting for or contributing to disturbed cellular adherence or motility in a limited number of clinical disorders. The scope of this chapter includes only those disorders for which molecular pathogenic mechanisms have been described or proposed. As background for these descriptions, selected aspects of the physiology of adherence and motility are discussed. Disorders of leukocyte killing are described in Chap. 114.

PHYSIOLOGY OF LEUKOCYTE LOCOMOTION

Definitions

The locomotion of leukocytes is regulated by a complex cellular apparatus responsive to many environmental stimuli. Among these are physical properties of substrates to which leukocytes adhere as well as chemical substances of host or microbial origin which influence the nature of migration.[12–15] Leukocytes demonstrate little movement in vitro in the absence of specific stimuli. Chemical substances, including chemotactic factors, may modify substantially the speed and direction of locomotion. Stimulated migration with no directional component is termed *chemokinesis* or *random locomotion*.[13] When under the influence of concentration gradients of chemotactic factors, the net direction as well as speed of a migrating cell population will be altered. The result is *chemotaxis*.[14–16] A positive chemotactic response results in the attraction of cells toward the stimulating agent with individual leukocytes, demonstrating a rather uniform orientation toward the origin of the chemotactic gradient.[17,18] It should be emphasized that the terms *random locomotion, chemokinesis,* or *chemotaxis* should be used only in cases where these forms of behavior have been demonstrated experimentally.

Methods to Evaluate the Motility of the Leukocytes In Vitro

A variety of techniques have been utilized to evaluate the migratory properties of myeloid or lymphoid cells. Evaluations of the kinetics and extent of the mobilization of leukocytes in various tissues of human subjects are limited to histopathologic assessments and applications of "skin window" techniques initially described by Rebuck and Crowley.[4,4a] Findings of large numbers of one or more types of leukocytes in tissue exudates does not exclude the possibility that these cells infiltrated too late to prevent the establishment of infections.[19] The skin window technique and several more quantitative modifications[20] have proved of limited value for several reasons. Difficulties encountered in creating uniform skin lesions in addition to the pain or possible infectious complications as-

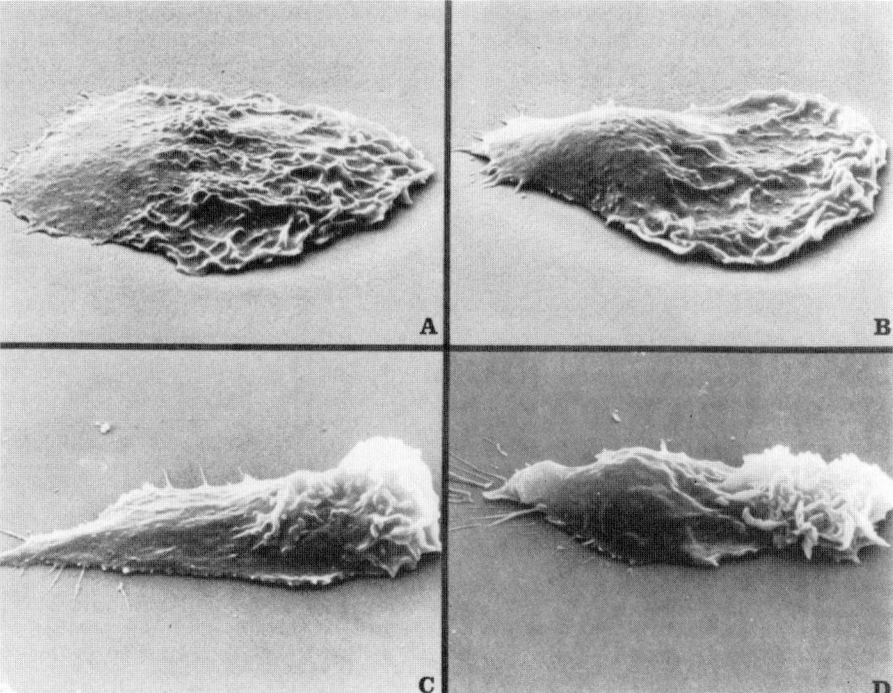

Fig. 113-1 Scanning electron micrographs of neutrophils responding to chemotactic factor. Human neutrophils were exposed to a gradient of the chemotactic factor, f-Met-Leu-Phe. Within 60 s of sensing the chemotactic factor, the cell spreads on the albumin-coated glass surface and ruffles on the side of the cell adjacent the higher concentration of the chemotactic factor (A), extends the lamellepodium forward and begins to develop a uropod with retraction fibers (B), elongates forming more pronounced ruffles within 2 to 3 min (C), and continues to migrate toward increasing concentrations of the chemotactic factor at a rate of between 5 and 15 μm/min (D). During migration the front of the cell is constantly ruffled and the tail of the cell (uropod) has a much smoother surface than the attached retraction fibers. (By permission of D.C. Anderson et al., Cell 31:719, 1982.)

sociated with the use of abrasive techniques limit their overall suitability for clinical application. Evaluations of the migratory functions of leukocytes in clinical samples are most commonly performed in vitro.

Visual Assays. Direct observations of individual cells undergoing locomotion in vitro can provide quantitative as well as descriptive information.[16,17,21] These assessments may be embellished by time-lapse photomicrographic recordings. Leukocytes, particularly neutrophils, are relatively fast moving cells compared, for instance, with fibroblasts. Most descriptions of the morphology of leukocytes during locomotion in vitro indicate that they assume a characteristic bipolar shape[17,17a] (Fig. 113-1). This involves the appearance of a veil-like, flattened membrane, or lamellipodium, at the anterior end of the cell. This pseudopod does not contain cytoplasmic organelles which remain in a more sharply delineated posterior portion of the cell. Migrating cells also generally demonstrate a uropod or taillike structure with retraction fibers developing as the cell migrates. During locomotion this oriented morphology is retained. Cells elongate as lamellipodia spread forward and cytoplasmic contents stream into the anterior portion of the cell. As they translocate, neutrophils continuously develop new lamellipodia which adhere to the surface upon which the cells crawl.

To study the effects of chemotactic factors on these events, it is necessary to establish experimental conditions which allow exposure of cells to stable and continuous chemical gradients. Under such conditions, effects on both the rate and direction of cell orientation or movement can be observed. Most investigators have used microbial point sources such as bacterial clumps or spores of yeast, or specially designed orientation chambers for applications in visual assays.[15–17,21]

The bipolar shape seen in migrating cells also occurs if neutrophils[22] and monocytes[23] are exposed to chemotactic stimuli in suspension. Thus, the cells need not be attached to a surface in order to assume a bipolar shape. Using this morphologic change as a sensitive indicator of chemotactic stimu-

lation, abnormal cellular responses have been identified in clinical conditions characterized by increased infections, and the inhibitory action of selected pharmacologic agents has been assessed.[24–26]

Micropore Filter and Agarose Assays. A second group of assays of chemotaxis include those in which the effect of chemoattractants on locomotion of a population of cells, or a sample of a population, is measured. In these assays, no attempt is made to follow the paths traveled by individual cells, and measurements are made generally after experimentally stopping cell migration. Each of these assays, in principle, represents modifications of the micropore filter method[22] originally described by Boyden[27] in which a test cell population migrates into or through a micropore filter toward a test reagent placed in an adjacent stimulant compartment. Since this assay was easy to use and gave reasonably quantitative measurements of the movement of cell populations, it rapidly gained widespread clinical applicability. It became possible to make comparisons between the chemotactic responses of cells from patients and those of control subjects. An important modification of the micropore filter method[17] distinguishes chemotaxis from chemokinesis. This is accomplished by the use of protocols in which a range of concentrations of a stimulant reagent is incorporated independently in the cell and stimulant compartments of a culture chamber.[28] A conceptually similar technique in which leukocytes migrate toward a chemoattractant source on plastic or glass under agarose[29] has also proved useful.

These various assays have advantages as well as disadvantages. Visual assays allow detailed examinations of the morphologic events of moving cells and the influences of attractants, inhibitors, or drugs. By analysis of the paths taken by individual cells, a detailed description of the influence of these agents on cellular velocity, direction of movement, turning behavior, adhesiveness, and other cellular properties can be obtained. A disadvantage of visual assays is the difficulty quantifying cell responses to a given agent, i.e., to obtain dose-response curves. In contrast, dose-response curves are easily obtained with filter assays which have proven useful for the study of the attractant or inhibitory activity of unknown factors. Since these assays give different types of information and neither gives a complete picture of the locomotion of leukocytes, it is reasonable to suggest the use of both techniques in parallel in studies of patients with suspected defects of locomotion.

Sensory Mechanisms of Cellular Locomotion

Early experimental observations of leukocytes undergoing chemotaxis suggested the existence of sensory mechanisms by which cells are able to detect differences in concentrations of chemotactic molecules in their environment. Identification of highly adaptive sensory mechanisms for neutrophils as well as other types of leukocytes resulted largely from investigations of the nature of chemotactic factors and the specific cellular receptors for these chemotactic moieties.[30]

Early studies documented that the activation of serum complement liberates highly active endogenous chemotactic factors for neutrophils and other leukocyte cell types and that this activation provides an important mechanism by which neutrophils and monocytes are mobilized into inflammatory lesions in vivo.[31-34] Other well defined chemoattractants more recently described include products of bacterial protein synthesis (e.g., N-formylated-methionyl peptides),[35,36] the arachidonate metabolite, leukotriene B_4 (5,12-dihydroxyeicosatetraenoic acid),[37] platelet-activating factor,[38] and a lymphokine, termed *lymphocyte-derived chemotactic factor*, produced by antigen or mitogen stimulated lymphocytes.[39] Mast cells contain tetrapeptides which are chemotactic for eosinophils and are released upon exposure of mast cells to specific antigen.[40] A cell-derived chemotactic factor produced by neutrophils after ingestion of crystalline materials such as monosodium urate or calcium pyrophosphate has been also described.[41]

The cellular nature of an inflammatory tissue exudate is thought to reflect the net influences of one or more chemotactic moieties (and/or inhibitors) of microbial and host origin generated locally at inflammatory sites. While mobilization of neutrophils is more frequently associated with non-IgE immune complexing or microbe-complement interactions, the eosinophil predominates in both the early and late cellular infiltrates of immediate-hypersensitivity reactions. While factors chemotactic for neutrophils are released by IgE-dependent activation of mast cells and mast cell-rich tissues, the predominant chemotactic activity of anaphylaxis favors eosinophils and is attributable to low molecular weight chemotactic factor.[40] Although delayed hypersensitivity reactions may manifest infiltrates containing multiple leukocyte populations, they are characteristically devoid of neutrophils. This may be related to potent inhibitors that are produced by immunologically stimulated lymphocytes and block accumulation of neutrophils.[42]

The binding of chemotactic factor to an appropriate receptor initiates a series of coordinated biochemical and cellular events, some of which contribute to cellular locomotion. These include alterations in ion fluxes[43,44] and transmembrane potential,[45] alterations of cell shape and adhesiveness,[22] secretion of enzymes from intracellular granules,[30] production of superoxide and other highly energized oxygen radicals,[30-46] and a stimulation of energy metabolism via enhancement of transmembrane glucose transport and anaerobic glycolysis.[47]

These various functions are probably sequentially activated and highly integrated in the inflammatory response. Secretory and oxidative functions in vitro are generally elicited by much higher concentrations of chemotactic factors than those optimal for chemotaxis. Thus, in a graded fashion, locomotion into a chemotactic gradient in vivo may precede secretory and oxidative events which ultimately contribute to microbicidal or cytotoxic functions required in localized inflammatory sites. Recent evidence suggests that the diverse functional responses of neutrophils to chemotactic stimuli reflect complex regulatory influences of the chemotactic factor receptors and the associated cellular transduction pathways.[30,48-53]

The peptides derived from the C5 component of complement, C5a and C5a$_{desarg}$, represent the most important of the complement-derived chemotactic factors.[31-34] C3a cleaved from C3 by the action of trypsin or C3 convertase was reported to be chemotactic for neutrophils in early studies, but later investigations failed to confirm these findings and indicated that the biologic activity of C3a was primarily anaphylatoxin. Human C5a is a 74-residue glycosylated peptide ($M_r = 9000$) produced by proteolysis of C5 by C5 convertase generated by activation of either the classic or alternate complement pathways or by intracellular granule associated proteases of neutrophils which act directly on C5.[54] The carboxyl terminal arginine residue of C5a formed in serum is rapidly hydrolyzed by carboxypeptidase N, to produce a less potent but more stable moiety, C5a$_{desarg}$.[34] C5a$_{desarg}$ lacks anaphylatoxin activity and is ten- to twentyfold less active than C5a as a chemoattractant for neutrophils. There is evidence that C5a$_{desarg}$ requires the presence of a naturally occurring anionic polypeptide (termed *C5a$_{desarg}$ cochemotaxin*) is serum or plasma, for full chemotactic activity.[55,56] Much of the chemotactic activity of zymosan activated serum is due to C5a$_{desarg}$ acting together with this cochemotaxin.

All C5a-mediated functions (including chemotaxis, degranulation, or superoxide generation) depend on binding of C5a peptides to a specific cell surface receptor in a rapid, specific, and saturable fashion.[57] Early studies employing [^{125}I]C5a showed that rapid and saturable binding of this moiety to neutrophils was essentially complete within 3 to 5 min. Approximately one-half saturation occurred at a C5a concentration of $3 \times 10^{-9} M$, and the number of binding sites per cell was estimated to be 1 to 3×10^5. Studies of the binding of radio-labeled C5a$_{desarg}$ to neutrophils have not been reported. However, C5a$_{desarg}$ has been shown to be approximately 400-fold less potent than C5a with respect to its ability to compete with radiolabeled C5a for the same binding site on neutrophils.[58] The critical importance of C5a and C5a$_{desarg}$ as chemotactic signals in vivo is related to the fact that theoretically these moieties may be generated continuously at the gradient source in inflammatory lesions. In fact, it has been demonstrated experimentally that renewable chemotactic gradients are established by suspending test microorganisms in serum.[21]

A group of N-formyl methionyl dipeptides was found to possess chemotactic activity for neutrophils.[35] Later studies[59] demonstrated that formyl tripeptides such as f-Met-Leu-Phe are extremely active, effecting maximum chemotactic responses at concentrations of 10^{-9} to $10^{-10} M$, and several investigators demonstrated specific saturable binding of these peptides to the surface of neutrophils or neutrophil membranes. The binding of formyl norleucyl-Leu-[^{3}H]Phe to rabbit peritoneal neutrophil membranes was found to have a K_d of $1.5 \times 10^{-9} M$, and there were approximately 10^5 binding sites per cell.[60] Later studies of human neutrophils indicated that N-formyl peptides bind with high affinity to a definable number (approximately 40,000 to 60,000) of receptors on the neutrophil surface.[61,62] Specific saturable receptors for N-formylated peptides have also been detected on the surface of human monocytes[63] and guinea pig peritoneal macrophages.[64] The ability of a series of synthetic N-formylated peptides to compete for f-Met-Leu-[³H]Phe neutrophil binding paralleled the potency of these peptides in eliciting biologic responses indicating that the N-formyl peptides share a common receptor.[59] Although the formyl peptides are synthetic molecules, they are thought to represent analogues of products of bacteria or other microorganisms. Bacteria such as *Escherichia coli* begin protein synthesis with formyl methionine which is later cleaved from the protein chain. Formyl-methionine is not used in eukaryotic protein synthesis except in mitochondria. Thus, the formyl-methionyl peptides likely represent a characteristic prokaryotic product which neutrophils can distinguish from products of host origin.[65] In a manner similar to other true chemotactic factors, formyl methionyl peptides elicit a wide spectrum of responses. Thus, they have proven to be ideal for studies of cellular physiology.[30,66]

Biochemical characterizations of formyl peptide receptors on leukocytes have utilized a variety of covalent cross-linking techniques and have demonstrated that the formyl peptide receptor is a glycosylated protein (M_r = 60,000 to 70,000).[67-69] The receptor has been purified from an immortal myeloid cell line (HL60) and reconstituted into phospholipid vesicles.[70] Removal of carbohydrate from the receptor yields a protein (M_r = 32,000) which maintains ligand binding capacity.[71] Following ligand binding to neutrophils, f-Met-Leu-Phe-receptor complexes are rapidly internalized and translocated to a Golgi-rich fraction.[30]

Many lipids and fatty acids have weak stimulatory effects on locomotion of neutrophils and mononuclear phagocytes, although in many cases these have not been shown convincingly to be chemotactic effects. Early studies indicated that oxidized derivatives of arachidonic acid, and later, 12-L-hydroxy-5,8,10,14-eicosatetraenoic acid attracted neutrophils into filters in chemotaxis chambers.[72] More recent studies demonstrated that other hydroxy products of lipoxygenase-modified arachidonic acid are chemoattractants. The most potent and well characterized of these is 5(S),12(R)-dihydroxyeicosa-6-14-cis-8,10-trans-tetraenoic acid (leukotriene B₄). Leukotriene B₄ is generated by the 5-lipoxygenase and related enzymes of neutrophils, macrophages, and mast cells and represents the major endogenous lipid chemoattractant secondarily released as a result of cellular activation by exogenous chemotactic factors.[52] At nanomolar concentrations, leukotriene B₄ elicits chemotactic and chemokinetic migration, and at much higher concentrations it stimulates release of lysosomal enzymes, superoxide production, enhancement of adherence, expression of C3b receptors, and complement-dependent cytotoxicity by neutrophils.[52,53,73,74] Stereospecific binding sites representing functional receptors for leukotriene B₄ have been identified on human neutrophils localized primarily in the plasma membrane.[53,74,75] Two classes of receptors for leukotriene B₄ are expressed. The high affinity (K_d = 0.4 nM) receptors appear to be coupled to chemotactic migration, and low affinity (K_d = 61 nM) receptors appear to be coupled to secretory functions such as enzyme release.[52]

Several lines of investigation indicate that receptors for chemotactic factors are qualitatively and quantitatively influenced by complex cellular regulatory processes which are op-

erative following receptor-ligand binding. Both high and low affinity receptors for f-Met-Leu-Phe and leukotriene B₄ on human neutrophils and macrophages have been characterized.[50,52,76,77] Increasing evidence suggests that at least a portion of high and low affinity receptors are interconvertible through processes functionally linked to a pertussis toxin-sensitive regulatory N protein and guanosine nucleotides.[50] Rapid internalization of f-Met-Leu-Phe-receptor complexes appears to represent one mechanism by which activated cells are functionally down-regulated upon exposure to high concentrations of chemotactic factors.[78,79] Conversely, treatment of neutrophils with f-Met-Leu-Phe or agents which induce exocytosis of specific granules may increase the number of f-Met-Leu-Phe receptors on the cell surface.[30,50,80-82] These additional receptors are derived from incompletely defined intracellular pools which may be associated with specific granules and may serve to replace internalized receptors during cell locomotion.[83] The physiological significance of modulations in chemotactic receptors in vivo is uncertain, but these events may allow for selective adaptive amplifications or attenuations of one or more cellular responses during inflammation.

Adhesive Determinants of Cellular Motility—Functional Studies

Adherence is of central importance in a wide spectrum of functions in granulocytes, monocytes, and lymphocytes.[84] For example, the precise nature of cellular interactions with various surfaces has been shown to influence the mobility of neutrophils and monocytes in vitro.[22,85] On a two-dimensional surface such as glass or plastic, the physical interactions with the substratum upon which leukocytes or other cell types crawl influence the extent and direction of cell migration.[22,85-87] The following evidence supports this concept: (1) A Mg^{2+}-deficient medium diminishes both cell migration and adherence, and neither effect is corrected by addition of exogenous Ca^{2+}.[43,90,91] (2) Substrates to which cells irreversibly adhere (e.g., neutrophils adhering to uncoated glass) or very minimally adhere (e.g., neutrophils on polypropylene plastic) effectively impair cell translocation even in the presence of chemotactic gradients. (3) Some cell types can crawl up a gradient of adhesiveness but cease to migrate when adherence becomes high.[89] (4) The chemokinetic influence of albumin, fibrinogen, or other serum proteins employed in visual chemotactic assays is linked to their reduction of cell-substrate adhesion.[92-94] Thus, cell migration on two-dimensional surfaces (as in the visual chemotaxis assays) requires adhesion that is sufficiently strong to allow attachment to a substratum but weak enough to permit continued locomotion. Enhancement of adherence to artificial substrates,[22,24,85] endothelial cells,[85-97] or other cell types[98-100] occurs when neutrophils are exposed to a chemotactic stimulus. With optimal levels of the stimulus, motility is augmented, but high concentrations may result in reduced motility, especially on artificial surfaces in vitro.[85,98,101]

Some investigators have presented experimental evidence that neutrophils can move relatively independently of adherence in certain instances.[102-105] Their results indicate that movement through three-dimensional matrices (e.g., cellulose filters used in the micropore filter assay for chemotaxis, or collagen gels) is largely adherence-independent. Though adherence-independent locomotion has received little study, it may well be important in migration of leukocytes through connective tissue after they leave the vascular system.[102,104]

Molecular Mechanisms in the Adhesiveness of Leukocytes

The molecular events contributing to cellular adherence are incompletely defined. Observations in vivo have revealed that neutrophils and monocytes adhere avidly and preferentially to vascular endothelium adjacent to a site of inflammation before their migration into tissues.[106] Since this adherence appears to be necessary for the localized recruitment of leukocytes into extravascular inflammatory sites, many investigators have examined the mechanisms by which the adhesiveness of neutrophils and monocytes are modulated by inflammatory stimuli.

A secretory mechanism by which adherence-promoting constituents are rapidly mobilized to cellular surfaces in response to chemotactic receptor occupancy represents one attractive explanation for rapid modulation of adherence. The process of extracellular release or exocytosis of specific granules or other secretory vesicles appears to be a highly integrated mechanism by which cell surface adherence properties are altered in response to inflammatory stimuli.[107] The perigranular membrane of specific granules seems to provide a source of new membrane required for morphologic alterations of motile cells.[108] Some experimental evidence suggests that specific granules also represent an intracellular pool from which the f-Met-Leu-Phe receptor[80,82] and glycoproteins with adhesive properties[109–114] are brought to cellular surfaces by chemotactic or secretory stimuli. The physiological and potential pathologic contributions of secretory-dependent functions of neutrophils have been emphasized by studies of patients with genetic deficiency of neutrophil specific granules.[83,115–117] Chemotactic factors also seem to stimulate a reduction in the negative surface charge of human neutrophils which has been at least temporally related to increased adhesiveness.[118–121]

Many different proteins on the leukocyte's surface participate in cellular functions dependent on adherence. Specific recognition of opsonized microorganisms is facilitated by membrane receptors for immunoglobulin G (IgG) and C3-derived ligands, which mediate adhesion of opsonized microorganisms before endocytosis is triggered.[122] Adhesion can be mediated by antibodies (IgG) bound to tissue cells through receptors on the surface of leukocytes for the Fc portion of the antibody molecule. This reaction activates killing of tissue cells to which the antibody is bound.[123] In addition, a recently characterized family of structurally and functionally related glycoproteins found on the surface of myeloid cells[124] is involved in a wide array of functions dependent on adhesion. The nomenclature, structure, cellular distribution and function of these glycoproteins are summarized in Table 113-1.[84,124,125] Each of these glycoproteins consists of noncovalently associated α and β subunits with $\alpha_1\beta_1$ stoichiometry. They share an identical β subunit (M_r = 95,000) and are distinguished immunologically by distinct α subunits whose relative molecular weights are as follows: M_r = 165,000 for Mac-1α(αM); M_r = 177,000 for LFA-1α(αL); and M_r = 150,000 for p150,95α(αX).[125] The World Health Organization designations for these glycoproteins are CD18 for β; CD11a for αL; CD11b for αM; and CD11c for αX.[126] That these glycoproteins function in cellular adhesion was initially shown by the ability of specific monoclonal antibodies to inhibit a wide variety of granulocyte, monocyte, and lymphocyte functions dependent on cell-substrate or cell-cell interactions.[84] Soon after this family of glycoproteins had been defined with monoclonal antibodies, an inherited deficiency was recognized in humans.

Mac-1, LFA-1, and p150,95 have different roles in adhesion. Mac-1 is a complement receptor (CR-3) which binds the ligand iC3b.[127,128] Monoclonal antibodies to Mac-1 inhibit binding and phagocytosis in iC3b opsonized particles by neutrophils and macrophages.[129,130] Purified Mac-1 binds iC3b,[127] and binding is dependent on Mg^{2+}. Mac-1 mediates adherence of neutrophils to endothelial cells and a variety of other substrates, and thus participates in numerous cellular functions including migration on surfaces to which leukocytes must attach in order to crawl, accumulation of neutrophils at sites of inflammation, phagocytosis of foreign particles such as latex beads, secretion of granule associate enzymes that results from

Table 113-1 The Mac-1, LFA-1, p150,95 Glycoprotein Family

Subunits	Mac-1		LFA-1		p150,95	
	αM	β	αL	β	αX	β
Molecular weight	170,000	95,000	180,000	95,000	150,000	95,000
WHO designation	CD11b	CD18	CD11a	CD18	CD11c	CD18
Cell distribution	Monocytes Macrophages Granulocytes Large granular lymphocytes		Lymphocytes Monocytes Granulocytes Large granular lymphocytes		Monocytes Macrophages Granulocytes	
Chemotactic or secretory stimulation increases surface expression	Yes		No		Yes	
Functions inhibited by monoclonal antibodies	Complement receptor type three function (iC3b binding, phagocytosis and intracellular killing of C3 opsonized microorganisms); granulocyte adherence, apreading, aggregation, ahemotaxis, and antibody-dependent cellular cytotoxicity		Cytolytic T lymphocyte-mediated killing and T-helper cell responses Natural killing Antibody-dependent cellular cytotoxicity Phorbol ester-stimulated lymphocyte aggregation		Granulocyte adherence and aggregation	
Common features	The β subunits appear identical. The α subunits αM and αL are 35% homologous in sequence. The α and β subunits are noncovalently associated in $\alpha_1\beta_1$ complexes. Both α and β subunits are glycosylated and expressed on cell surface. All functions shown require divalent cations.					

attachment of neutrophils to a surface, and cytotoxicity associated with attachment of neutrophils to other tissue cells.[86,123,129,131–133] LFA-1 participates primarily in lymphocyte and monocyte adhesion.[134,216,217] It can mediate antigen-independent adhesion and also appears to be required for T-lymphocyte antigen-dependent adhesion to and killing of some target cells. Similarly, LFA-1 has been demonstrated to be important in natural killing and antibody-dependent killing by lymphocytes and neutrophils, and in T-lymphocyte helper cell interactions.[123,133,135,136] As is true for Mac-1-dependent functions, all LFA-1-dependent cellular functions require Mg^{2+}.

The functional role of p150,95 has been demonstrated only recently. It serves as a receptor for the complement component iC3b on macrophages and neutrophils.[127,137,137a] On monocytes, p150,95 mediates adherence to endothelial cells, tumor cells, and other substrates.[138] Monocyte extravasation and differentiation into tissue macrophages is accompanied by increased p150,95 expression,[139] as is differentiation of myelomonocytic precursor cells in vitro.[140] On lymphoid cells, p150,95 is a marker of cell activation. Although most cytolytic T-lymphocyte clones express higher amounts of LFA-1 than p150,95, a subset expresses equal quantities, and functional studies show that both p150,95 and LFA-1 mediate attachment of lymphocytes to target cells.[141]

Biosynthesis of these glycoproteins has been studied both in the mouse and human,[124,142] and translation and glycosylation have been studied in the mouse in vitro.[143] Using cloned probes, the murine Mac-1 α-subunit mRNA of 6 kb[144] and the human β-subunit mRNA of 3.2 kb[145] have been defined. Thus, it now appears that each of the three α subunits and the common β subunit are encoded by a separate mRNA. These subunits are synthesized as precursors which are co-translationally glycosylated with N-linked high mannose carbohydrate groups. After α- and β-subunit association, which occurs 1 to 2 h after synthesis, most of the high mannose groups are converted to complex-type carbohydrates in the Golgi apparatus, and the subunits increase slightly in molecular weight. The mature glycoproteins are then transported to the cell surface or to storage sites in intracellular secretory vesicles.

In unstimulated neutrophils and monocytes, Mac-1 and p150,95 are present in one or more intracellular compartments as well as on the cell surface.[110,146] Inflammatory mediators including C5a and f-Met-Leu-Phe stimulate a four- to tenfold increase in Mac-1 and p150,95 (but not LFA-1) on neutrophil or monocyte surfaces.[131,132,147] Increased surface expression (as shown by monoclonal antibody binding in flow cytofluorography) is near maximal within 10 minutes at 37°C and is not impeded by protein synthesis inhibitors.[146] Intracellular pools of Mac-1 and p150,95 are associated with one or more types of cytoplasmic granules.[109,117,148] It is likely that the biosyntheses of Mac-1 and p150,95 destined for the cell surface and for intracellular storage sites are similar.

In recent studies, the individual contributions of Mac-1 subunits to adherence-dependent functions of neutrophils have been delineated utilizing normal neutrophils treated with monoclonal antibodies.[129] Phagocytosis of particles selectively opsonized with C3-derived ligands, and binding of iC3b opsonized sheep red blood cells are generally inhibitable by anti-αM but not by anti-β, -αL, or -αX. Monoclonal antibodies to αM, αX, and β inhibit adherence of neutrophils, and relatively more inhibition is observed when increased surface expression of αMβ and αXβ complexes is stimulated by in-

flammatory mediators. Both stimulated and baseline adherence is almost completely inhibited by monoclonal antibodies to the β subunit and the Mac-1α subunit. The general order of potency of inhibition is anti-β > anti-Mac-1α > anti-p150,95α > anti-LFA-α which reflects the relative amounts of each molecule expressed on the surface of neutrophils. Inhibition of chemotactic migration by anti-β, or anti-αM antibodies is observed in the subagarose assay (two dimensional) but not micropore filter assay (three dimensional) where adherence plays a relatively minor role. Inhibition is dependent on a continuous cell exposure to anti-Mac-1α or anti-β during the assay suggesting that recycled or new Mac-1 is required continuously for chemotaxis. These findings suggest that the Mac-1 molecule has adhesive properties in addition to a specific capacity to recognize and bind iC3b. Notably, none of the monoclonal antibodies to Mac-1 demonstrates inhibitory effects in assays of functions which do not depend on adherence such as enzyme release in response to chemotactic stimulation. Such functions are also normal in cells genetically deficient in these glycoproteins.

The Role of Chemotaxis in Inflammatory Reactions

The possibility that chemotaxis represents the principle mechanism for mobilizing leukocytes into inflamed tissues remains hypothetical. Most studies in vivo have failed to demonstrate directional migration of cells in extravascular loci.[149–151] Possibly this is true because most leukocytes exit vessels in or near the center of an inflammatory lesion and, therefore, in or near the center of any chemotactic gradient which may be operative.[152] Further, stable chemotactic gradients necessary for demonstration of directional migration in vitro may not occur in vivo or may exist over extremely small distances given the dynamic nature of the acute inflammatory response.

Though directional migration in vivo has not been clearly shown, considerable evidence indicates an important role for chemotactic factors in the recruitment of neutrophils, monocytes, or other leukocyte types into extravascular inflammatory sites. Studies of the physiological turnover of neutrophils indicate that very small numbers of cells are detectable in uninflamed tissues.[153–156] This is in striking contrast to the rapid and intense infiltration of neutrophils into tissues during acute inflammation. In animal models, $>10^7$ neutrophils per hour can accumulate in skin sites receiving an intradermal injection of a chemotactic factor; peak accumulation occurs within 1 to 4 h with an abrupt decline thereafter.[156] The entry of monocytes into inflamed rabbit skin parallels the kinetics of neutrophils for the first 4 to 6 h but is maintained thereafter for up to 20 h.[156–157] Injections of chemotactic factors including leukotriene B₄, platelet activating factor, C5a, or f-Met-Leu-Phe into rabbit skin elicit a significant neutrophil infiltration of the injection site.[157,158] Several other studies have documented a temporal association of chemotaxigenesis and the influx of neutrophils, monocytes, or macrophages into experimental inflammatory lesions mediated by immune complexes, glycogen, or chemotactic factors.[32,106,159,160]

Interactions of Leukocytes with Endothelium

Among the morphologic events that must be considered in order to understand the process of leukocyte migration in vivo are: (1) the margination of leukocytes occurring especially in the postcapillary venules, (2) the migration of leukocytes between endothelial cells, (3) the penetration of the vascular basement membrane by leukocytes, and (4) the migration into extravascular tissues. Although these events are incompletely understood, recent studies have provided considerable new insight into the molecular basis of at least the initial interactions of leukocytes with vascular endothelium.

A consistent observation in microscopic studies in vivo has been that marginated neutrophils roll along the endothelium of postcapillary venules for considerable distances before detaching, stopping, or emigrating through the blood vessel wall.[106,161-163] It appears that the endothelium becomes sticky[164,165] adjacent to a site of inflammation.[84,106,153,166] Localized adhesiveness of leukocytes to endothelium could occur as a result of: (1) local changes in the endothelium, (2) changes in the leukocyte, and/or (3) local changes in blood flow and, coincidentally, shear forces, shifting the balance in favor of intercellular adhesion. Since the endothelium is part of the permanent architecture of an inflamed tissue and the leukocyte only a passerby, many investigators have assumed that alterations of endothelial adherence play a primary role in the localized or directed attachment of leukocytes at these sites. Several lines of investigation, however, have shown that alterations in adhesiveness of circulating leukocytes resulting from systemic or localized exposure to chemotactic factors play an important active role. It seems likely that synergistic changes in both leukocytes and endothelial cells result from exposure to inflammatory stimuli.

Under steady-state conditions in the normal human adult, approximately 2.5×10^{10} circulating neutrophils and another 2.5×10^{10} marginated neutrophils are contained within the bloodstream. Although minor shifts between marginated and circulating pools represent physiological events, it has been recognized that rapid marked changes in the white blood cell count can be induced by major shifts between the circulating pool and the marginated pool in a number of pathologic states. Epinephrine induces neutrophilia by increasing the circulating pool at the expense of the marginal pool. This shift is associated with a transient decrease in the adhesiveness of neutrophils. A transient neutropenia can be induced experimentally by endotoxin, gelatin, dextran, cobra venom factor, or contact of blood with a foreign surface as during renal dialysis or continuous flow filtration by leukapheresis.[167-169] In each case there is some intravascular complement activation with generation of chemotactic factors (e.g., C5a). In animal models, infusion of complement or other chemotactic moieties induces a rapid transient neutropenia.[170] Neutropenia observed in clinical conditions characterized by intravascular complement activation (and/or the presence of other chemotactic factors) is thought to result from increased adherence of circulating neutrophils coincident with an increase in marginated pools and/or sequestration of leukocytes in target organs. Chemotactic factors elicit rapid alterations in adhesiveness of neutrophils and monocytes for endothelial cells in vitro, while no direct effects of chemotactic agents on endothelial adhesiveness have been observed in most studies.[22,95,96,171-177]

Blood flow may have several influences on leukocyte accumulation in inflammatory sites. Many vessels that are normally closed become open to flow in inflammation, and some evidence suggests that an initial slowing of flow in small vessels in inflamed tissues may reduce shear forces which normally diminish leukocyte-endothelial interactions. However, enhanced adherence of leukocytes to endothelium in inflamed sites has been observed without slowing of flow.[106] The well documented predilection of neutrophils to attach to high ven-

ular endothelium in postcapillary venules may, in fact, be related to reduced shear forces, since the postcapillary venule is the site of the first major decrease in vessel wall shear stress.[178,179] There is no direct evidence that neutrophils show a predilection for adherence to any particular endothelium. Preferential sequestration of neutrophils in the lung in complement activation states may reflect the fact that the lung is the initial capillary bed encountered by these activated cells within the venous circulation rather than a specific homing to pulmonary microvasculature. In contrast, circulating lymphocytes demonstrate considerable specificity with respect to high endothelial veins of peripheral or gut associated lymphoid tissues or other target organs. Recent observations indicate that specialized surface molecules of recirculating B or T lymphocytes are involved in this specificity.[180-185]

The important role of the CD18 complex of glycoproteins in the mediation of leukocyte-endothelial interactions in vivo has been emphasized by observations that neutrophils and monocytes which are genetically deficient in this complex fail to infiltrate into extravascular inflammatory sites despite the occurrence of profound granulocytosis in these patients.[131,132] The infusion of monoclonal antibodies to the β subunit into rabbits promotes a striking neutrophilia and severely inhibits exudation into experimental lesions (endotoxin coated sponges) in these animals.[186] These findings presumably reflect the same inhibitory effects of monoclonal antibodies to αM or β on stimulated adhesion of neutrophils or monocytes to endothelial monolayers in vitro.[174,187] The role of these glycoproteins in margination is uncertain since patients deficient in the CD18 complex demonstrate demargination responses to intravenous epinephrine, and experimental animals given intravenous infusions of monoclonal antibodies to the β subunit exhibit the same degree of marginating neutrophils rolling along venular endothelium as untreated animals.[188,189]

The role of one specific granule constituent in mediating adherence of neutrophils to endothelium has also been proposed. Purified lactoferrin, a prominent constituent of specific granules in neutrophils, promotes adherence of neutrophils to endothelial monolayers in vitro and, after intravenous infusion, produces neutrophil margination in rabbits.[111,112] Studies in some but not all patients with deficiency of specific granules and consequently lactoferrin have demonstrated abnormal leukocyte-endothelial interactions.[83,115,116]

The influences of a variety of inflammatory mediators on the adhesive and other properties of endothelium in vitro have been well documented in a number of laboratories.[190-193] Incubation of human umbilical vein endothelium with interleukin 1, bacterial endotoxin, or tumor necrosis factor in vitro stimulates production of extracellular matrix, production of procoagulant activity, and enhanced adherence for neutrophils or monocytes.[190-193] Indirect evidence indicates that transient biosynthesis of a factor on the surface of the endothelial cell mediates adherence of neutrophils and monocytes by a CD18-dependent mechanism.[190] Tumor necrosis factor also increases the expression of the CD18 complex on the leukocyte surface.[193] In addition to these stimuli, γ-interferon stimulates an increase in attachment of lymphocytes to endothelial cells.[185,194] The changes in the endothelium leading to the increased adherence of leukocytes are poorly understood. One glycoprotein (intercellular adherence molecule-1) of importance to the attachment of leukocytes to endothelial cells has been partially characterized.[195] It is expressed on surfaces of activated hematopoietic and nonhematopoietic cells and appears to represent the ligand for LFA-1. Expression of this molecule on vascular endothelium is most intense in inflamed tissues.[196]

Several types of endothelial injury can also enhance adherence of neutrophils to cultured endothelium. Neutrophils adhere more avidly to virally infected endothelial monolayers[197] or to those injured by exposure to excessive oxygen.[198] Proteolysis of fibronectin on the surface of endothelial cells by neutrophil-derived proteases promotes adherence of neutrophils,[199] and these adherent neutrophils may injure the endothelium.[200] Exposure of endothelial receptors for Fc and C3b have been reported following endothelial injury. These receptors could act to localize immune complexes and complement to the vessel wall and thereby increase adhesion by similar receptors present on the neutrophil.[201]

Secretory products of endothelium may also influence adherence. PGI_2, the major arachidonic acid metabolite of large vessel endothelium, has been found to inhibit neutrophil adherence to cultured endothelium.[201] Release of cyclic AMP by endothelial cells stimulated with epinephrine reduces adherence of neutrophils to cultured endothelium in vitro. This could contribute to the decrease in margination and the rise in circulating neutrophil counts observed following epinephrine administration in vivo.[202] Finally, evidence exists that endothelial cells synthesize platelet activating factor, a potent chemotactic factor for neutrophils.[203,204] Such findings support the concept that the endothelium is capable of actively generating mediators that secondarily influence the adhesiveness of neutrophils.

Locomotion into Extravascular Tissues

Electron-microscopic studies have shown that all leukocytes migrate out of vessels by passing between endothelial cells. Recent studies in vitro employing endothelial monolayers in chemotactic chambers indicate that neutrophils insert cytoplasmic processes into intercellular junctions. After penetrating the intercellular junction, the junctions reseal[205,206] and neutrophils appear to hesitate before migrating into the basal lamina.[175,205,207] The mechanisms involved in this emigration process are largely unknown. Specific neutrophil receptors for laminin, an extracellular endothelial matrix protein, may facilitate chemotaxis.[208] Penetration of the vessel wall may require that neutrophils literally digest their way through these cellular junctions as well as the matrix beneath the endothelium by limited release of enzymes. Leukocytes contain cathepsins, elastase, collagenase, and gelatinase, which, if secreted extracellularly, may break down the susceptible connective tissue.[83,107,209] For example, basement membrane destruction or fragmentation is an important feature of immune complex-mediated vascular injury.[207] Clearly, leukocytes are able to invade complex cellular and fibrous tissues. Leukocytes do not demonstrate contact paralysis of locomotion on contact with fibroblasts or endothelial cells in vitro.[210] In fact, contact guidance may contribute to the efficiency of leukocyte locomotion in vivo as suggested by findings of significantly biased cellular locomotion in three-dimensional aligned collagen gels.[211] Intrinsic hydraulic forces rather than adherence requirements may provide a mechanism for locomotion in three-dimensional matrices.[102] Thus, selected tissues may present the cell with a lattice to crawl through, but others, such as the serous lining of cavities or endothelium lining blood vessels, may be more like pain surfaces to which leukocytes must adhere in order to migrate.

CLINICAL DISORDERS OF LEUKOCYTE MOTILITY

General Considerations

The rapid localization of phagocytes to sites of microbial invasion or trauma represents a first-line defense mechanism of particular importance in nonimmune hosts. Quantitative or qualitative aberrations of either the cellular or humoral contributions to these adaptive responses may impair inflammatory defenses and, thus, increase infectious susceptibility. Early animal studies[19] demonstrated a critical 2- to 4-h period after cutaneous invasion by bacterial pathogens during which phagocytic cells must arrive at a site of invasion in order to prevent the establishment of an infectious process. Recurrent bacterial or fungal infections of the skin or mucous membranes are prominent in patients with quantitative deficiencies of peripheral blood leukocytes.[212] Such infections are also evident in patients with qualitative disorders resulting in insufficient accumulation of phagocytes at inflammatory sites, despite normal number of leukocytes in the peripheral blood.[133,213] Among both patient groups, common pathogens such as *Staphylococcus aureus*, *Pseudomonas*, other gram-negative enteric species, or *Candida albicans* account for most infectious complications. Infected tissues in these patients are characteristically gangrenous or necrotic and devoid of pus and contain few granulocytes when examined microscopically. Local inflammatory signs or symptoms in such patients may be minimal though the infection may lead to the destruction of cutaneous, subcutaneous, periodontal, or other submucosal tissues.

Among early reports of clinical disorders typified by susceptibility to recurrent soft tissue infections were patients with abnormalities of leukocyte migration in vitro and/or tissue mobilization in vivo.[6,8,9,214,215] In contrast to observations in patients with chronic granulomatous disease (Chap. 114), studies of granulocytes or monocytes in these patients demonstrated neither abnormalities of microbicidal functions nor granulomatous inflammation in infected tissues. Initially, at least for purposes of comparison of individual patients, a distinct subclassification of disorders of leukocyte motility or chemotaxis seemed justified. However, an explosion of literature followed in which defects of chemotaxis in vitro were associated with a vast array of clinical disorders or conditions. Such reports clearly implied but rarely documented that diminished chemotaxis in vitro was associated with diminished availability or delayed infiltration of phagocytes into inflamed tissues. Correlations between abnormalities of cellular motility in vitro and altered exudation in tissues of human subjects have been infrequent because of the imprecision of skin window techniques.

A reliable interpretation of leukocyte functions in vitro must take into consideration the clinical status of the individual patient, since it is important to determine whether abnormal functions result in increased susceptibility to infection or simply reflect other factors surrounding the patient's condition. Certain pharmacologic agents as well as the nutritional status of the patient may transiently influence selected functions tested in vitro.[25,216] Blood samples obtained for study during the course of infections may contain an increased percentage of immature myeloid cells which function suboptimally.[217] Also, many investigators have reported enhanced, diminished, or otherwise abnormal motility; phagocytosis; oxidative metabolism; and/or other functions of leukocytes in patients with clinical bacterial infections.[218-221] In most cases these abnormalities are found to be transient, probably reflecting cellular influences of inflammatory mediators[216,222-224] or products of the infecting organisms. Certain bacterial toxins exert significant inhibitory effects on cellular locomotion as well as other functions in vitro.[216] Some such as cholera toxin and certain enterotoxins of *E. coli* exert primarily intracellular effects (e.g., activate adenyl cyclase and elevate intracellular cyclic AMP levels).[225,226] Others preferentially perturb cell membrane properties and include streptolysin O, clostridial toxins (perfringolysin and phospholipase C), a diverse group of staphylococcal toxins (sphingomyelinase C and leukocidin), and proteases (alkaline protease and elastase) elaborated by pathogenic strains of *Pseudomonas aeruginosa*.[227,228] Suggested pathogenic mechanisms related to microbial toxin exposure include alteration of membrane fluidity, inhibition of cytoskeletal protein assemblage, and disruption of membrane receptors for chemotactic factors, complement ligands, or IgG Fc. Finally, certain microbial proteases or other products act directly on humoral mediators of cellular locomotion. For example, elastases elaborated by *P. aeruginosa* cleave C5 (as well as other serum complement proteins), thereby generating complement-derived chemotactic moieties in vitro or in vivo.[227]

The molecular pathogenesis of a limited number of genetic or secondary disorders characterized by defective migration of leukocytes has been defined. Most notable is the heritable deficiency of the adherence proteins of the CD18 complex. The discovery and characterization of this disorder probably best justifies the introduction into this text of a chapter on disorders of motility and adhesiveness in leukocytes. With respect to most of the other disorders to be considered here, a molecular pathogenesis is less clear.

Leukocyte Adhesion Deficiency

Leukocyte adhesion deficiency is a recently recognized autosomal recessive disorder characterized by recurrent bacterial infections, impaired pus formation and wound healing, and a wide spectrum of functional abnormalities in granulocytes, monocytes, and lymphoid cells. The features of this disease result from a deficiency of the CD18 complex of adhesive glycoproteins on the surface of leukocytes. Defective biosynthesis of the β chain common to each glycoprotein represents the fundamental molecular basis of this disease.

In 1980, a patient was reported with severe, widespread, and recurrent infections.[229] As demonstrated by sodium dodecyl sulfate–polyacrylamide gel electrophoresis (SDS-PAGE) analysis, lysates of whole neutrophils from this patient lacked a cell surface protein ($M_r = 110,000$) termed gp110. Subsequently, several similar patients were reported[230-232] with de-

ficiency of surface glycoproteins ($M_r = 130,000$ to $180,000$). Patients' neutrophils and monocytes failed to adhere to a variety of experimental surfaces, failed to undergo chemotaxis in vitro,[132,229,231] and failed to accumulate in artificial inflammatory skin lesions.[231] Receptor-mediated phagocytosis of complement opsonized particles in vitro was also found to be diminished.[132,230] In addition, there were deficiencies of aggregation and antibody-dependent cellular cytotoxicity in vitro.[132] The availability of monoclonal antibodies against the subunits of the CD18 complex of glycoproteins afforded the opportunity to define precisely the molecular deficiency of these patients and other similar patients subsequently identified. Both the α and β subunits of Mac-1, LFA-1, and p150,95 were found to be deficient on these patients' neutrophils, lymphocytes, and monocytes.[132,133,144,147,232-241] A selective deficiency in only one or two of the αβ complexes has thus far not been reported.[84] Patients' granulocytes and monocytes were also deficient in intracellular pools of αβ complexes as shown by SDS-PAGE of lysates of whole cells.[131,132,147,237] All types of these patients' leukocytes that have been studied were deficient including cultured cytolytic T lymphocytes, mitogen-stimulated T lymphocytes, and transformed B-lymphocyte cell lines.[136,147]

Clinical heterogeneity among patients with leukocyte adherence deficiency is related to quantitative differences in the extent of the molecular deficiency. To date, at least 30 reported patients with recurrent infections and defective adherence, mobility, and phagocytosis have been shown to lack partially or totally the glycoproteins of the CD18 complex.[84,131,132,238-248] Several patients demonstrating similar clinical features and/or functional deficits reported prior to the development of monoclonal antibodies represent presumptive examples of this disease.[246,249-254] One of the earliest patients with abnormal phagocytosis and motility was reported to have actin dysfunction,[246] but later evaluations indicated leukocyte adhesion deficiency.[254] Collectively, this group of patients sharing the same clinical syndrome and the same molecular defect has been referred to in the literature as *Mac-1, LFA-1 deficiency*,[132] *Mo-1 deficiency*,[236] or *deficiency of the CD18 glycoprotein complex*.[255] In the interest of brevity and comprehensiveness, we have suggested the name *leukocyte adhesion deficiency*.[84] Presumptive or confirmed cases reported to date are summarized in Table 113-2.

Clinical and Histopathologic Features of Leukocyte Adhesion Deficiency. Recurrent necrotic and indolent infections of soft tissues primarily involving skin, mucous membranes, and intestinal tract are the clinical hallmarks of this disease (see Fig. 113-2). Superficial infections of body surfaces may invade locally or systemically. Typical small, erythematous, nonpustular skin lesions often progress to large, well-demarcated, ulcerative craters, or pyoderma gangrenosa, which heal slowly or with dysplastic eschars.[84,132] Staphylococcal or gram-negative enteric bacterial organisms may be cultured from such

Table 113-2 Leukocyte Adhesion Deficiency Patients

References	Confirmed/presumed*	Female/male	Alive	Age†	Dead	Age†
84, 132, 229–231, 236, 238–246, 250–254, 257	33/26	25/33	28	9 (1–38)	29	1 (0–32)

*Confirmation of the disease requires assessment of leukocytes using monoclonal antibodies specific for CD11/CD18 subunits. Presumed cases exhibited a clinical course and functional abnormalities of leukocytes in vitro consistent with leukocyte adhesion deficiency.

†Age (years) last reported, median (age range).

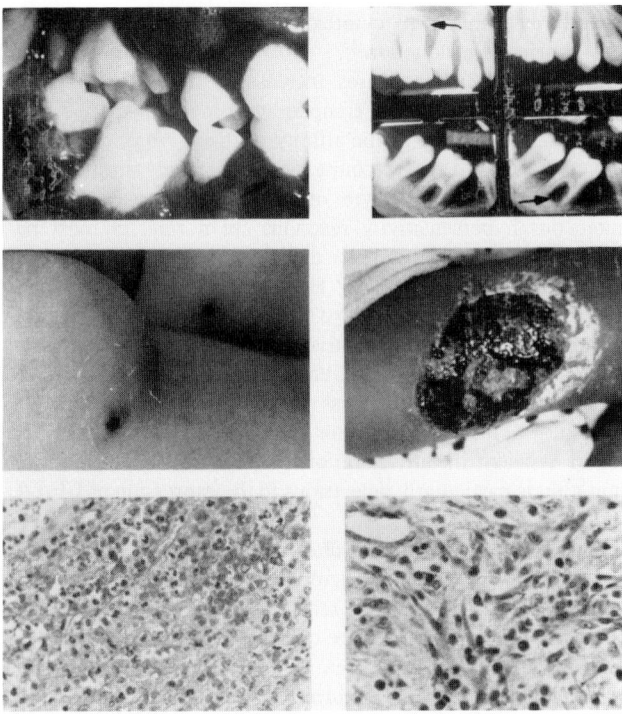

Fig. 113-2 Clinical examples of periodontitis and cutaneous infections in patients with leukocyte adherence deficiency. Severe gingivitis and periodontitis involving the permanent dentition of a 12-year-old-patient are shown at the *top left*. Gingivae exhibit acute inflammation, proliferation, recession, and periodontal pocket formation. All remaining teeth exhibit severe mobility. A radiograph of the same area is shown in the *top right* panel demonstrating >60 percent alveolar bone loss around molar teeth. Early erythematous cellulitic lesions with central ulcers from which *Pseudomonas maltophilia* was cultured are shown in the *middle left* panel. An ulcerative necrotic-gangrenous lesion (5 cm diameter) on volar surface of forearm is shown in the *middle right* panel. Sections of infected umbilical cord surgically resected at 18 days of life (hematoxylin and eosin, ×296) are shown at *bottom left* and *right*. A thrombus in an umbilical artery *(left)* contains numerous neutrophils. The inflammatory infiltrate of adjacent connective tissues *(right)* is totally devoid of neutrophils but does contain eosinophils in addition to macrophages, lymphocytes, and plasma cells. *(From D. C. Anderson et al.[132] Used by permission.)*

lesions for up to several weeks despite antimicrobial therapy. Fulminant progression of gas gangrene of soft tissues of a distal extremity in one patient prompted surgical amputation as a lifesaving measure.[231] Septicemia progressing from omphalitis associated with delayed umbilical cord severance has been observed in several families.[84,132,249,250] Perirectal abscess or cellulitis leading to peritonitis and/or septicemia has been reported in multiple patients, and facial or deep neck cellulitis has been observed to progress from ulcerative mucous membrane lesions of the oral cavity.[132,230,231] Recurrent invasive candidal esophagitis, erosive gastritis, acute appendicitis, and necrotizing enterocolitis have been reported in multiple patients.[84] Recurrent otitis media occurs commonly, and progression to mastoiditis and facial nerve paralysis has been reported. Other common respiratory infections include severe bacterial (pseudomonal) laryngotracheitis, recurrent pneumonitis, and sinusitis.[84] Severe gingivitis and/or periodontitis is a major feature among all patients who survive infancy. Acute gingivitis has appeared in all cases with eruption of the primary dentition. Subsequently, these patients develop characteristic features of progressive generalized prepubescent periodontitis, including gingival proliferation, defective recession,

mobility, pathologic migration, and advanced alveolar bone loss associated with periodontal pocket formation and partial or total loss of both the deciduous and permanent dentitions.[132,248]

The recurrent infections observed in affected patients appear to reflect a profound impairment of leukocyte mobilization into extravascular inflammatory sites. Skin windows as well as biopsies of infected tissues demonstrate inflammatory infiltrates totally devoid of neutrophils.[132,231,245] This histopathologic feature is particularly striking considering that marked peripheral blood leukocytosis (five- to twentyfold normal values) is a constant feature of this disorder. Transfusions of leukocytes result in the appearance of donor neutrophils and monocytes in skin windows and in skin chambers.[231] Impaired healing of traumatic or surgical wounds observed in several patients represents a clinical feature not generally observed in patients with neutropenia or dysfunctional neutrophils. Unusual paper-thin or dysplastic cutaneous scars have been found in some patients.[132,239] This may reflect the lack of monocyte infiltration and the lack of inflammatory contributions to healing such as the elaboration of angiogenesis factors.[132] The wide spectrum of gram-positive or gram-negative bacterial and fungal infectious microorganisms[84] is also characteristic of patients with primary neutropenia syndromes. These clinical models also demonstrate insufficient tissue leukocyte infiltration. However, deep-seated granulomatous infections typical of chronic granulomatous disease and other examples of oxidative or nonoxidative intracellular killing deficits have not been observed.

Some evidence suggests that patients with leukocyte adhesion deficiency have an increased susceptibility to viral infection. Most patients have demonstrated normal and self-limiting courses of varicella or other viral respiratory infections, and 5 of 10 patients in one report[132] demonstrated no untoward reactions to live viral vaccine administration. However, one patient died of an overwhelming infection with picornavirus involving oral pharynx, glottis, trachea, and lungs, and three patients of the same series had one or more episodes of aseptic (presumably viral) meningitis.[132]

The severity of clinical infectious complications among these patients appears to be directly related to the degree of glycoprotein deficiency. Two phenotypes, designated severe and moderate deficiency, have been identified (Table 113-3).[84,132] As measured by immunofluorescence flow cytometry

Table 113-3 Clinical Features of Mac-1, LFA-1, p150,95 Deficiency Syndrome in Texas Patients[84,132]

Clinical features	Severe*	Moderate†
Delayed umbilical cord severance	3/4	0/6
Persistent granulocytosis (15,000–161,000/mm³)	4/4	6/6
Recurrent infections:		
Cutaneous abscess or cellulitis	4/4	6/6
Perirectal cellulitis with sepsis	4/4	0/6
Stomatitis and facial cellulitis	4/4	3/6
Gingivitis and periodontitis	4/4	6/6
Pneumonitis necrotizing enterocolitis,	4/4	2/6
peritonitis	2/4	0/6
Impaired wound healing	3/4	2/6
Parental consanguinity	2/4	3/6
Age range (years)	1 to 6	11 to 38

*Leukocytes from these four patients had less than 0.3 percent normal amounts of Mac-1 on their surfaces.
†Leukocytes from these six patients had 2.5 to 6 percent normal amounts of Mac-1 on their surfaces.

and verified by radioimmunoassay and immunoprecipitation techniques, four severely deficient patients had essentially undetectable expression (<0.3 percent of normal amounts) of all three αβ complexes on their neutrophils. Six moderately deficient patients expressed 2.5 to 6 percent of all three αβ complexes. Patients with severe deficiency have either died in infancy or demonstrated a suceptibility to severe, life-threatening systemic infections (peritonitis, septicemia, pneumonitis, aseptic meningitis). In contrast, among the six patients with moderate deficiency (mean age 21 years, range 9 to 38 years) life-threatening infections have been infrequently observed despite a relatively prolonged survival.[132] Patients within a kindred demonstrate similar survival periods. For example, in one study, three patients with moderate disease died at ages 22, 19, and 32 years.[256] In other studies of patients with severe disease, five infants died in their first year and one died at 3 years of age.[250,252,253] In some moderately affected patients, skin lesions may disappear after the first few years of life, recurring only with occasional infections. Severe gingivitis is always observed in these patients and may be the presenting symptom.[248] Delayed umbilical cord separation occurs more frequently in patients with the severe phenotype, but it is not universally found.

Functional Abnormalities in Patients with Leukocyte Adhesion Deficiency. Some of the heterogeneity in functional abnormalities found among individual patients or kindreds may reflect methodologic differences among reporting laboratories.[84] However, abnormalities of adherence to substrates and adhesion-dependent functions including chemotaxis and aggregation have been observed among all patients studied.[132,133,229] Chemotaxis appears to be affected because it requires adhesion.[102,132] CR3-dependent binding and phagocytosis of iC3b-opsonized particles are deficient, in agreement with the identity of the CR3 with Mac-1.[128] In addition, since particles opsonized with iC3b are phagocytosed poorly, they fail to trigger the respiratory burst.[131,132,230,242,249,256,257] Abnormalities of antibody-dependent cellular cytotoxicity have also been observed in several patients.[123,132,133] In contrast, adherence-independent cellular functions including f-Met-Leu-Phe receptor-ligand binding and oxidative metabolism or degranulation mediated by soluble stimuli are generally normal.[131,132,231,238,239] Intracellular microbicidal activity (e.g., the ability to kill *S. aureus*) in most reported patients is relatively normal.[131,132,231,256] This indicates that receptors other than CR3 (e.g., Fcγ or CR1) are sufficient to promote a normal level of phagocytosis and intracellular killing in most instances.[117,131,132,147] Overall, more profound functional abnormalities have been observed among severely deficient as compared with moderately deficient patients.[84,132]

The predominance of recurrent bacterial (as opposed to viral or fungal) infections in patients with leukocyte adhesion deficiency implies that the functions of neutrophils or monocytes are more profoundly affected than those of lymphocytes. However, deficits of the LFA-1-dependent functions of lymphocytes have been observed in many patients. Furthermore, in cases where LFA-1-dependent functions are nearly normal, they are inhibited by much lower concentrations of monoclonal antibodies to LFA-1 than for normal cells. T lymphocyte-mediated killing, proliferative responses, natural killing, and antibody-dependent killing by patients' lymphocytes are deficient compared with that in adult controls.[123,133,136,238,245,249,251,258] In primary mixed lymphocyte culture, lymphocytes in several studies have demonstrated

profoundly diminished cytotoxic and proliferative responses and interferon production.[136,235,238,251] However, after further stimulation, these responses increase to nearly normal levels.[136] This may be due to compensatory mechanisms, perhaps involving an increase in the affinity of the T-lymphocyte antigen receptor, and may account for the relatively normal functions of B and T lymphocytes observed in most cases. Delayed cutaneous hypersensitivity reactions are normal in most patients tested, and most individuals demonstrate normal specific antibody synthesis.[132,244] However, T-lymphocyte-dependent antibody responses in vivo (for example, to repeated vaccination with tetanus, diphtheria toxoids, and polio virus) are impaired, and antibody production in vivo or in vitro in response to influenza virus was found to be abnormal in one patient.[259] Thus, responses of lymphocytes in vivo may be found deficient in only some of the patients whose β-subunit mutation is particularly deleterious to the expression of LFA-1.

Inheritance of Leukocyte Adhesion Deficiency. Several lines of evidence indicate that leukocyte adhesion deficiency is transmitted as an autosomal recessive disorder in most, if not all, cases. Individuals who are clinically unaffected but appear to be heterozygotes have been identified by expression of approximately 50 percent of normal amounts of Mac-1α/β subunits on the surface of their neutrophils following stimulation with chemotactic factors such as f-Met-Leu-Phe.[131,132] In three families, all the clinically unaffected mothers and fathers and some of the sibs were found to be heterozygotes.[132] In one family spanning three generations, an affected son was born to heterozygous parents. The affected son married a heterozygote, and the couple bore an affected son and daughter and two heterozygous daughters. These findings, together with the overall equal numbers of male and female patients recognized worldwide (Table 113-2)[132,241,242,250-252,256] and a frequent history of consanguineous marriages,[132,238,244,249,253,257] strongly suggests that leukocyte adhesion deficiency is inherited as a recessive trait on an autosomal chromosome. In one family, X-linked inheritance was suggested,[230,236] but there is no definitive evidence for an X-linked form of leukocyte adhesion deficiency.

The molecular basis of leukocyte adhesion deficiency has been studied at the protein, mRNA, and DNA levels. Biosynthesis has been studied using Epstein-Barr virus transformed B lymphocyte and mitogen-stimulated T-lymphocyte cell lines, and healthy individuals synthesize the LFA-1α subunit and the common β subunit and express the LFA-1 αβ complex on the cell surface. Cell lines from patients synthesize an apparently normal LFA-1α subunit precursor, but this precursor does not undergo carbohydrate processing, does not associate in an αβ complex, and is not expressed on the cell surface (Fig. 113-3). The LFA-1α subunit is apparently degraded in the absence of the β subunit.[147]

In hybrids of human and mouse lymphocytes, human LFA-1α and β subunits from healthy controls associate with mouse LFA-1α and β subunits to form interspecies hybrid αβ complexes.[260] In hybrids of patient and mouse lymphocytes, the α but not the β subunit was rescued by the formation of interspecies complexes that were expressed on the hybrid cell surfaces. These findings show that the LFA-1α subunit in genetically deficient cells is competent for surface expression in the presence of an appropriate mouse β subunit, suggesting indirectly that the genetic lesion affects the β subunit.

Recently, the β subunit polypeptide has been purified to homogeneity and the β subunit cDNA has been cloned and

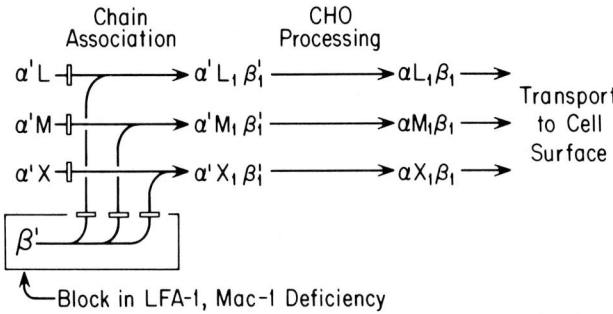

Fig. 113-3 Biosynthesis of the Mac-1, LFA-1 glycoprotein family. The biosynthetic pathway in normal cells is as described in Ref. 124. The evidence for a primary block in β-subunit synthesis, a secondary block in αL biosynthesis due to a lack of β-subunit association, and hypothetically similar blocks in αM and αX biosynthesis is discussed in the text. Precursors are indicated as α′ and β′, while mature subunits are indicated as α and β. *(From T. A. Springer et al.[147] Used by permission.)*

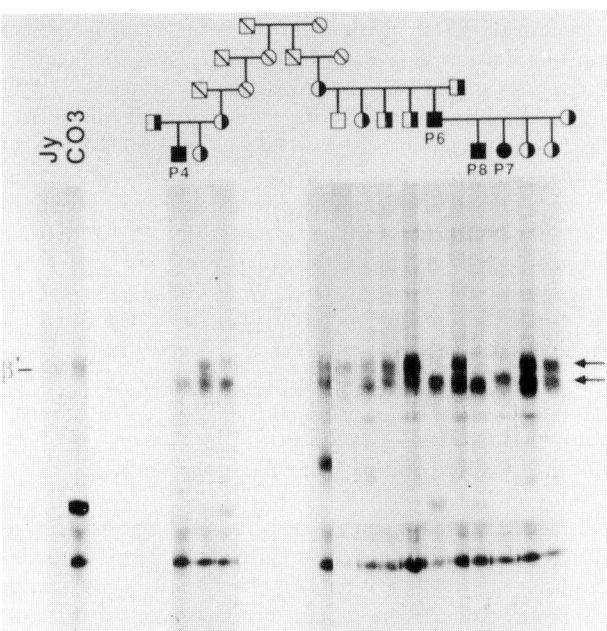

Fig. 113-4 Inheritance of an aberrantly small β precursor (β′) within a moderate kindred with leukocyte adhesion deficiency. Homozygous deficient patients (P4, 6, 7, and 8) (closed symbols), heterozygotes (half-filled symbols), or homozygous noncarriers (open symbols) demonstrate only abnormal β, abnormal and normal β precursor, or only normal β precursor, respectively (see Ref. 132). EBV-transformed cells from a control cell line (JY) and from patients with leukocyte adhesion deficiency and their kindred were pulse-labeled with [^{35}S]methionine. The β-subunit precursors were immunoprecipitated with rabbit anti-β-subunit serum and protein A-sepharose. Samples were subjected to SDS-PAGE and autoradiography with fluorography. The normal β precursor and the aberrantly small β precursor are indicated by arrows. *(From T. K. Kishimoto et al.[262] Used by permission.)*

sequenced.[145,261] Additionally, the development of rabbit antihuman β-subunit antibodies allows immunoprecipitation of β-subunit precursors in both healthy and deficient cell lines and permits their examination in SDS-PAGE.[262,263] Normal quantities of the β-subunit precursor and β-subunit mRNA were found in four unrelated patients.[263] However, the β-subunit precursors, as previously shown for LFA-1α subunit precursors,[147,264] did not undergo normal carbohydrate processing. In a study of six unrelated patients and four related patients and other members of their kindred the following five distinct variations in the β subunit were identified among the different mutant alleles:[262] (1) The subunit was undetectable. (2) The quantities of β-subunit mRNA and protein precursor were low. (3) An aberrantly large β-subunit precursor likely due to an extra glycosylation site was found. (4) An aberrantly small β-subunit precursor due to a polypeptide chain defect was found. (5) No gross abnormality in the β-subunit precursor was found. In studies of one kindred (see Fig. 113-4), including four related patients of the moderate phenotype, a β precursor of identically abnormal small size was identified in each case. Of 10 relatives within this family, nine have been typed as heterozygous carriers and one as a noncarrier.[132] All nine heterozygotes show both a normal and an abnormally small β precursor; the noncarrier shows only the normal β precursor. These studies provided conclusive evidence that the defect is in the gene for the β subunit.[262]

Differences in the β-subunit precursor between unrelated patients suggest distinct mutations in the β-subunit gene. This means that while the moderate and severe phenotypes are useful in a broad sense for categorizing patients, some heterogeneity in the severity or spectrum of clinical symptoms within each category is to be expected. While there is no obvious molecular explanation for the moderate and severe phenotypes, it is possible that mutant β subunits vary in their ability to complex with the α subunits and that this determines the amount of the αβ complex expressed on the cell surface. The β subunit and hence the genetic lesion has been mapped to chromosome 21 in somatic cell hybrids and by *in situ* hybridization (Ref. 260 and unpublished). This is in agreement with autosomal inheritance.

Therapeutic Considerations for Leukocyte Adhesion Deficiency. Bone marrow transplantation with successful engraftment rendered unnecessary any further treatment in two patients.[249] In two other patients, successful engraftment was achieved, but recovery did not occur either because of graft-versus-host disease or infectious complications. Transplantation is recommended for severely deficient patients because of the high incidence of death before age 2. Moderately deficient patients live longer but may also be susceptible to life-threatening infections. The occurrence of deaths at ages 19, 22, and 32 (Table 113-2) and the absence of any known patients older than 40 years shows that survival through adolescence is no guarantee of a long life. Therapeutic guidelines for management of moderately deficient patients are not well defined.

HLA-mismatched bone marrow transplantation has proven successful in many different diseases recently. This has been made possible in part by depletion of donor T cells thus preventing graft-versus-host disease. However, the incidence of rejection of the graft by the recipient has become more troublesome. It has been observed that LFA-1 deficient patients, none of whom mounted allogeneic mixed lymphocyte responses, did not reject grafts.[247] Since graft rejection can be mediated by both T and non-T cells, monoclonal antibodies against LFA-1 inhibit both T and natural killer immune functions in vitro,[134] and LFA-1 is not on hematopoietic stem cells,[265] graft recipients were treated with 0.1 mg/kg anti-LFA-1α subunit monoclonal antibodies for 3 days before and 5 days after transplantation. Recipients had a variety of inherited diseases such as Wiskott-Aldrich syndrome and osteopetrosis, and all received HLA-mismatched transplants. The use of monoclonal antibodies against LFA-1 resulted in seven of seven successful engraftments, a clear improvement over previous experience.

The fact that the genetic lesion occurs in the common β

subunit of the CD18 glycoprotein family opens the possibility that introduction of a normal β-subunit gene into hematopoietic cells should cure the disease. Since the mouse β subunit has been shown to complex with and rescue the surface expression of the human LFA-1α subunit in hybrids of patient and mouse lymphocytes,[260] it seems likely that introduction of a normal human β-subunit into patients' cells would result in expression of functional αβ complexes. Efforts are now being directed toward introducing the cloned β-subunit gene[145] into bone marrow cells using retroviral vectors. Thus, the feasibility of somatic gene therapy for this disease is now being explored.

Clinical Conditions Characterized by Abnormally Elevated Expression of CD18 Glycoproteins

Considering the many contributions of CD18 glycoproteins to cellular adherence and the importance of adherence in the inflammatory response, it is not surprising that abnormalities in this protein complex have been identified in other diseases. These include intrinsic cellular defects such as occur in neonatal leukocytes[266,267] as well as abnormalities secondary to extracellular inflammatory mediators.

High serum or tissue levels of biologically active complement fragments may pathologically elevate the adherence of circulating leukocytes and thereby promote leukocyte aggregation, sequestration, and an associated systemic leukopenia.[169] When infused into experimental animals, complement derived chemotactic factors activate peripheral blood phagocytes, which in turn, avidly adhere to one another or to endothelium of pulmonary vasculature.[268] These metabolically activated cells may obstruct blood flow as well as damage endothelial and pulmonary tissues through oxygen radical generation and lysosomal enzyme release.[167,269] This sequence of events is thought to contribute to acute respiratory symptoms, multiple organ injury, and leukopenia associated with gram-negative septicemia, endotoxemia, and other complement activation states, including hemodialysis, filtration leukapheresis, cardiopulmonary bypass, pancreatitis, and trauma.[101,167,169,268,270–272] Increasing evidence suggests that the CD18 glycoproteins play an important role in these events.

Pulmonary sequestration of leukocytes in patients undergoing hemodialysis has been correlated with increases in Mac-1 on circulating leukocytes.[273] In eight patients undergoing maintenance hemodialysis, there was a fivefold increase in the mean expression of Mac-1 on neutrophils within 15 min after the start of dialysis with a new cuprophane membrane. The peak increase coincided with the maximum drop in neutrophil count and with the peak rise in the plasma levels of the complement activation products $C5a_{desarg}$ and $C3a_{desarg}$. $C5a_{desarg}$ induced a comparable increase in Mac-1 expression on normal neutrophils in vitro at concentrations similar to those measured in vivo. Chemotactic peptides induced aggregation of normal neutrophils (a reflection of increased cell-cell adhesiveness), and the aggregation was specifically and totally blocked by mouse monoclonal antibodies to Mac-1 in vitro. Thus, it appears that increased expression of Mac-1 during complement activation by cuprophane membranes contributes to the onset of leukoaggregation and granulocytopenia in the hemodialysis model.

In other studies using isolated perfused rodent lungs,[274] monoclonal antibodies against Mac-1 attenuated sequestration, superoxide generation, lysozyme release, and lung injury

caused by infusion of human neutrophils stimulated by phorbol myristate acetate. In addition, lung injury was not observed in this experimental model following infusion of human neutrophils from a patient with leukocyte adhesion deficiency.

Another clinical syndrome with associated acute respiratory symptoms appears to involve the CD18 glycoproteins. Recent evidence indicates that the fungicidal polyene antibiotic amphotericin B promotes elevated expression of CR-1 and CR-3 and aggregation of human neutrophils in vitro.[275] This finding suggests that the acute pulmonary symptoms observed in hematologic patients simultaneously receiving amphotericin B and leukocyte transfusions are related to a CR-3-dependent pathogenic mechanism.[276]

Clinical Conditions Associated with Undefined Abnormalities of Cellular Adherence

Patients with poorly controlled diabetes mellitus exhibit impaired neutrophil adherence to nylon fibers or glass wool, reduced chemotaxis in vitro, and reduced leukocyte mobilization in vivo.[277] Improved metabolic control appears to correct the adhesive abnormalities.[278,279] Though these deficits are thought to contribute to infectious susceptibility in affected individuals, studies of neutrophil adherence under conditions of chemotactic activation or studies of leukocyte-endothelial interactions have not been reported. Thus, neither the extent of the abnormalities nor the mechanisms have been characterized.

Adhesive and migratory properties of phagocytic cells are influenced by a number of pharmacologic agents including β-adrenergic agonists, steroids, and nonsteroidal anti-inflammatory agents. The peripheral blood leukocytosis occurring in subjects receiving epinephrine is due to reduced adherence of neutrophils mediated through β receptors on endothelial cells.[202] Endothelial cells respond to catecholamine exposure in vitro by raising concentrations of cyclic AMP, a metabolic intermediate known to diminish leukocyte adherence.[280] Thus, cyclic nucleotides of endothelial origin appear to regulate physiological margination-demargination via secondary effects on adherence properties of circulating leukocytes.

Disorders Secondary to Abnormal Secretory Functions

Neutrophils contain multiple subpopulations of granules.[281] Azurophil or primary granules appear early in neutrophil development and contain lysosomal enzymes, including lysozyme and myeloperoxidase. Specific or secondary granules develop later. Though they lack myeloperoxidase and other hydrolases, specific granules are capable of extracellular release of a number of substances such as lactoferrin that may regulate inflammation.[83,282] The first example of a deficiency of specific granules was recognized in 1972.[283] Other cases have been subsequently reported by several laboratories.[115–117,284–289] One patient[283] appears to have had an acquired deficiency (associated with a myeloproliferative syndrome), while all others appeared to have genetically determined disease. Each has demonstrated susceptibility to recurrent and severe infections of the skin, mucous membranes, and lung, most commonly due to *S. aureus*, *P. aeruginosa*, other enteric pathogens, and *C. albicans*. Infections may progress from superficial sites; otitis media with associated mastoiditis was reported in one patient, and lung abscess formation due to *S.*

aureus followed the onset of pneumonia in another individual. The occurrence of necrotic oral lesions due to invasion by *E. coli* and species of *Pseudomonas* and *Klebsiella* was reported in another individual, but severe neutropenia recognized in that patient may have accounted for the development of these mucous membrane lesions.[285] Another patient[116] with severe scalp infections due to *Proteus mirabilia* and *S. aureus* required prolonged intravenous antibiotic therapy in addition to surgical debridement. Detailed descriptions of the histopathology of infected tissues in all patients are not reported, but skin window studies have demonstrated diminished pus formation in tissues of some individual who were not neutropenic.[115,116]

Neutrophils from each patient studied have demonstrated morphologic abnormalities, including a severe or total deficiency of specific granules and a variety of nuclear abnormalities including bilobed or multilobed nuclei or nuclear blebs, clefts, or pockets. Diminished or absent neutrophil lactoferrin content has been confirmed in only three cases, and the membrane marker alkaline phosphatase has been shown to be diminished or absent in neutrophils of all but one reported case. Total cellular content and/or release of the secondary granule markers (lactoferrin, B_{12} transport protein, cytochrome b, and lysozyme) have been shown to be diminished when assessed in selected patients, although levels of primary granule constituents (myeloperoxidase, β-glucuronidase) are generally normal.

Among recognized cases, somewhat heterogenous abnormalities in cellular functions have been observed. Chemotaxis and intracellular microbicidal activity represent the most consistently reported functional deficits. The basis of impaired leukocyte locomotion in vitro or diminished accumulation in skin windows in vivo is uncertain. However, in studies of two patients[115–117] defective cellular migration appeared to be functionally related to abnormalities of adherence. In one patient there was diminished adherence to nylon fibers and endothelial cells and impaired aggregation in response to f-Met-Leu-Phe.[115] In response to f-Met-Leu-Phe, another patient's neutrophils failed to enhance CR-3 expression although upregulation of CR-1 was normal. Immunoprecipitation experiments employing anti-CR-3 or anti-CR-1 and fractionated normal neutrophils showed that CR-3 was associated with plasma membrane and specific granule enriched fractions, while CR-1 was associated only with plasma membrane. Such findings are consistent with the hypothesis that CR-3 but not CR-1 is associated functionally and anatomically with the specific granules of neutrophils. Supporting data from two laboratories[117,290] demonstrate abnormal expression of Mac-1 on neutrophils deficient in specific granules.

Deficiency of specific granules is suggested by a history of recurrent cutaneous, subcutaneous, mucous membrane, or pulmonary infections due to *S. aureus*, virulent gram-negative enteric bacteria, or species of *Candida*. Findings of abnormal morphology and abnormally weak cytochemical reactions for alkaline phosphatase are highly suggestive of this disorder. Cytochemical and ultrastructural studies to confirm diminished numbers or abnormal morphology of specific granules and their specific constituents will establish a diagnosis. While most examples of specific granule deficiency recognized to date are probably genetic in origin, the mode of transmission of this disorder is uncertain. A prognosis is not well defined, but most individuals have survived the pediatric age group with antimicrobial and supportive therapy.

The molecular basis of the complex alterations of cellular functions in the syndromes associated with deficiency of specific granules remains undefined. Data presently available generally indicate that one or more specific granule constituents are required for or participate in neutrophil locomotion or oxidative metabolism in vitro. Considering the limited population of patients studied as well as the complex nature of functional or biochemical abnormalities, an interpretation of the precise pathogenic determinants of infectious suceptibility in these syndromes is not possible.

Functional Abnormalities in Neonatal Neutrophils

Since specific immunity is severely limited in the immediate postpartum period, the inflammatory functions of phagocytic cells are especially important for host defense against microbial invasion.[291] Both quantitative and qualitative abnormalities of phagocytic cells contribute to the enhanced infectious suceptibility of neonates. Neutropenia is commonly observed in systemically infected neonates, and studies in neonatal animals indicate that exhaustion of a limited reserve pool of bone marrow granulocytes contributes to a depletion of circulating or marginating pools when tissue demand is increased.[292] Among the most consistently observed functional abnormalities thought to contribute to impaired inflammation in neonates are those related to the motility of leukocytes.[24] As shown with skin windows, inflammatory responses in newborns differ from those in older children and adults in two respects: (1) the shift from the early granulocyte predominance to a predominance of mononuclear cells is slower and less pronounced, and (2) a marked eosinophilia is observed in some infants 2 to 21 days of age.[293,294] Strikingly diminished leukocyte mobilization in neonatal rats inoculated intraperitoneally with bacteria or chemotactic agents has been demonstrated.[295]

Neonatal neutrophils exhibit impaired chemotactic response to numerous chemotactic factors including those released by growing *S. aureus* and *E. coli* (e.g., f-Met-peptides) and those generated in plasma by antigen-antibody complexes (e.g., C5a).[24,296] Visual assays demonstrate that in addition to depressed migration, neonatal cells are significantly impaired in their ability to orient toward a gradient of chemotactic factors.[24,297] Depressed chemotaxis has been found in healthy neonates 1 to 5 days of age.[298,299] In addition, there is diminished generation of chemotactic activity (chemotaxigenesis) by virulent type III group B streptococci in neonatal sera related directly to diminished levels of both type-specific anticapsular antibody and serum complement activity.[300] Thus, impaired generation of chemotactic stimuli as well as abnormal cellular response appear to account for diminished inflammatory responses observed in even healthy term neonates.

Evidence exists that impaired chemotaxis of neonatal neutrophils is functionally linked to abnormalities in cellular adherence.[24,297,301,302] The modulation of adherence induced by chemotactic stimulation of adult neutrophils occurs to a very limited extent in neonatal neutrophils. Adherence is poorly enhanced by exposure of cells to C5a, f-Met-Leu-Phe, or bacterial chemotactic factors, and the movement of adhesion sites from front to tail of cells polarized by chemotactic stimulation is greatly reduced.[24,300] There is also impaired lateral mobility of lectin (concanavalin A) receptors on neonatal granulocyte surfaces most likely reflecting abnormal membrane fluidity.[217,303–307] Secretory abnormalities may also contribute to impaired adherence.[266,308] The following experimental observations support this possibility. Baseline expression of Mac-1 and receptors for f-Met-peptides on the surface of neonatal neutrophils has been found to be normal, but upregulation of these proteins following stimulation with chemotactic factors is significantly reduced compared to that in adult cells.[266] Ultrastructural assessments of neonatal neutrophils have demonstrated significantly less peroxidase-negative granule loss following chemotactic stimulation than adult cells. In addition, the release of lactoferrin, a marker of specific granules, following stimulation of neonatal neutrophils with secretagogues such as phorbol esters, is abnormal.[266,308] These studies suggest that abnormal expression of multiple surface determinants derived from peroxidase-negative (specific) granules or other intracellular pools may contribute to deficient chemotaxis and other inflammatory functions of neonatal granulocytes.[266]

Because multiple host defense mechanisms are defective or developmentally delayed in human neonates, a precise cause-and-effect relationship between impaired cellular migration and the occurrence of infectious complications cannot be established. However, neonates are particularly susceptible to the development of cutaneous inflammatory lesions or abscesses at sites of local trauma (for example, circumcision wounds, umbilicus, intertriginous areas, or sites of electrode-monitoring devices). Further, microorganisms such as *S. aureus*, gram-negative rods, and species of *Candida* represent the most common agents infecting cutaneous or mucous membrane lesions in human neonates. The propensity for systemic invasion and the development of neonatal septicemia by endogenous respiratory or gastrointestinal flora may also be related to insufficient infiltration of granulocytes or monocytes into submucosal tissues.[274,295,309]

Chediak-Higashi Syndrome

The Chediak-Higashi syndrome is an autosomal recessive disorder of mink, cattle, beige mice, and humans. This condition is characterized clinically by partial oculocutaneous albinism, the presence of giant lysosomal granules in all granular cell types, susceptibility to bacterial infection, variable occurrence of neutropenia and thrombocytopenia, and an accelerated lymphomalike proliferative phase generally occurring in the first decade of life.[310–312] Infectious complications are attributable to neutropenia as well as functional deficits of neutrophils, monocytes, and/or natural killer (NK) cells. A comprehensive review in 1972[310] documented the significance of infectious morbidity and mortality in this syndrome. Among 56 cases reviewed, 33 individuals died prior to 10 years of age; among 27 cases for whom a cause of death could be determined, infections represented the sole cause in 17 and a contributing factor in 9 additional cases. Pulmonary, cutaneous, subcutaneous, and upper respiratory infections were most commonly observed. *S. aureus* accounted for approximately 70 percent of all infections for which an etiologic agent was determined; group A *Streptococcus*, gram-negative enteric organisms (*Klebsiella, Pseudomonas, Proteus, Shigella* species), and *Aspergillus*, or species of *Candida* represented occasional etiologic agents.

Neutrophils, monocytes, and lymphocytes from these patients demonstrate large intracellular inclusions or granules, which represent the pathologic hallmark of the disease. Although they are most easily demonstrated in leukocytes, they are also present in renal tubular epithelium, gastric mucosa, pancreas, thyroid, neural tissue, and melanocytes.[310] In neutrophils, inclusions contain azurophilic granule markers (myeloperoxidase and acid phosphatase) and have been assumed to represent abnormal azurophilic granules. However, these abnormal granules contain both azurophilic and specific granule markers.[313] Normal appearing specific granules are present, but normal azurophilic granules have not been seen. Analaysis of bone marrow samples from patients with Chediak-Higashi syndrome suggest that abnormal granules are formed during granulocyte maturation by the progressive aggregation and fusion of azurophilic and specific granules. Such findings are consistent with a proposed membrane abnormality.[313,314]

Several functional abnormalities of neutrophils, monocytes, and natural killer cells of these patients have been identified. Neutrophils demonstrate delayed and diminished intracellular killing of both gram-positive and gram-negative bacterial organisms, despite a normal capacity to ingest these organisms and a normal or elevated oxidative burst.[310,315] Microbicidal abnormalities are attributed to impaired postphagocytic phagolysosomal fusion.[315] A rather selective impairment of the functions of natural killer cells (as opposed to other lymphocyte functions) has been reported.[316–319] Dysfunction of the natural killer cell system may account for the ultimate development of an aggressive lymphoproliferative syndrome in most patients.

Chemotaxis in vitro and leukocyte mobilization in vivo using the skin window technique are abnormal in patients with Chediak-Higashi syndrome.[311] In micropore filter assays employing a 5-μm pore size, the chemotactic activity of the patient's neutrophils was approximately 41.2 percent of that of controls. When the filter size was decreased to 1.2 μm, chemotaxis of the patient's cells was only 9.5 percent of that of the controls. These findings suggest that granular structures may mechanically impair migration through such small pores. A relationship of impaired leukocyte function to an underlying disorder of microtubule function and/or cyclic nucleotide metabolism has been suggested but not proven.[320–326]

A diagnosis of Chediak-Higashi syndrome can be ascertained by identifying characteristic phenotypic features of the disorder in addition to characteristic large cytoplasmic inclusions in all granular cells, including peripheral blood granulocytes. Giant melanosomes can be demonstrated from hair of patients. Neutropenia and thrombocytopenia are most characteristic during the accelerated phase of disease. Common abnormalities observed on examination of bone marrow aspirates include hypercellularity with extensive vacuolization and inclusions in myeloid precursors. Elevated serum lysozyme levels probably reflect intramedullary granulocyte destruction.[310] The accelerated phase of Chediak-Higashi syndrome is characterized by widespread tissue infiltrates of lymphoid and histiocytic cells usually without malignant histologic characteristics.[319,327] Splenomegaly and associated hypersplenism contribute to observed anemia and thrombocytopenia and may also contribute to the occurrence of neutropenia. Although viral agents and/or immunologic mechanisms may contribute to the pathogenesis of the accelerated phase, the precise mechanisms are undefined.

Most patients with Chediak-Higashi syndrome succumb to infectious or infiltrative complications within the first decade of life. Successful bone marrow transplantation with reversal of the defect in natural killer activity has been reported in one case.[328] Definitive preventive or therapeutic strategies await definition of its molecular pathogenesis.

Type 1b Glycogen Storage Disease

The association of neutropenia, impaired neutrophil migration, and recurrent infection in type 1b glycogen storage disease was first reported in 1980.[329] Most clinical features of type 1b glycogen storage disease are similar to those of type 1a glycogen storage disease, including hepatomegaly, fasting hypoglycemia, lactic acidosis, short stature, hyperlipidemia, and the occurrence of hepatomas with potential for malignant degeneration (see Chap. 12). Patients with type 1a glycogen storage disease demonstrate a deficiency of glucose-6-phosphatase activity in liver, kidney, and intestine. In contrast, type 1b glycogen storage disease patients demonstrate normal glucose-6-phosphatase activity.

A review of the clinical and laboratory features of 21 patients with type 1b glycogen storage disease[330] indicated that most suffered from a variety of moderate to severe bacterial infections including pneumonitis, recurrent otitis media, subcutaneous abscesses, generalized pyoderma, cellulitis, wound infections, and osteomyelitis, most commonly secondary to *S. aureus*. Most patients exhibited chronic neutropenia, which, in some patients, was associated with demonstrable serum inhibitors of myeloid stem cell proliferation, abnormalities of myeloid maturation, and/or decreased peripheral marginating pools. Functional abnormalities including diminished random or directed migration of neutrophils in vitro was documented in 8 of 11 patients tested, and deficient chemotactic modulation of adherence by chemotactic factors was observed in two patients.[26] In contrast, microbicidal activity of neutrophils and phagocytosis-associated oxidative metabolic activity have been shown to be normal in most patients with type 1b glycogen storage disease.[330]

The biochemical basis for quantitative or qualitative abnormalities of neutrophils or mononuclear leukocytes is uncertain. However, glucose-6-phosphatase activity in liver homogenates from patients with type 1b glycogen storage disease was normal only when assayed in the presence of detergents (e.g., triton X-100).[329,331] The high latency (90 percent) indicates that detection of this activity is dependent on detergent to disrupt microsomes. Further studies in one patient[332] identified a defect of glucose-6-phosphatase translocase, one of three integral membrane components of the hepatic microsomal glucose-6-phosphatase system (see Chap. 12). A physiological role of glucose-6-phosphate transport in neutrophils has not been defined, and thus a causal relationship between aberrant glucose-6-phosphate transport and impaired neutrophil migration cannot yet be established.

Mannosidosis

Mannosidosis is a lysosomal storage disease characterized clinically by psychomotor retardation, facial dysmorphology similar to that of Hurler syndrome, dysostosis multiplex, hepatosplenomegaly, hearing loss, and recurrent soft tissue infections (see Chap. 63). This autosomal recessive disease is due to a deficiency of acidic α-mannosidase activity resulting in mannose-rich oligosaccharide accumulation in lysosomes of circulating leukocytes and in neural and visceral tissues. A defect of neutrophil chemotaxis and phagocytosis in neutrophils and diminished lymphocyte transformation were described in one child with systemic mannosidosis.[333] It was suggested that these functional defects result from abnormal mannose catab-

olism and that partially degraded oligosaccharides, glycopeptides, glycoproteins, and terminal αD-mannose residues may bind to leukocyte plasma membranes as well as accumulate in lysosomal granules. In a review of 17 cases, 13 patients experienced significant or recurrent infections, including chronic otitis media, upper respiratory infections, severe or progressive pneumonia, and cutaneous inflammatory lesions. While the majority of documented infections were bacterial in origin, these individuals also were susceptible to viral infections, reflecting in part, impairment of cell-mediated immunity in this disease. One patient died of overwhelming adenoviral pneumonia.[333] A diagnosis of mannosidosis as suggested by typical clinical features can be confirmed by the demonstration of deficient acidic α-mannosidase activity in plasma, peripheral blood leukocytes, or cultured skin fibroblasts.

Periodontitis Syndromes

Experimental and clinical evidence has documented the important protective role of phagocytic cells, and in particular, neutrophils in tissues of the oral cavity.[334] The infiltration of neutrophils into gingival tissues early in the development of gingivitis is thought to provide a first-line defense against invasion by pathogenic oral microflora.[335] Individuals with developmental, genetic, or acquired disorders characterized by quantitative deficiencies of peripheral blood phagocytes or functional abnormalities of neutrophils commonly present with oral complications.[26,117,132,231,314,334–342] Primary or secondary agranulocytosis, and cyclic neutropenia syndromes are typified by severe ulceration, necrosis, or chronic inflammation of gingival or periodontal tissues.[337] Patients with severe leukocytopathies such as chronic granulomatous disease,[341] Chediak-Higashi syndrome,[339] and leukocyte adhesion deficiency[132] present with systemic as well as oral infections while those demonstrating less profound functional deficits such as in localized juvenile periodontitis, postlocalized juvenile periodontitis or generalized juvenile periodontitis present exclusively with periodontal manifestations.

Defective chemotactic responsiveness of neutrophils is thought to represent a major pathogenic mechanism in individuals with periodontitis syndromes.[248,334,340,343–349] Of 183 patients with localized juvenile periodontitis studied by multiple investigators[329,334,338,345,347,349–351] 132 (71 percent) have been reported to exhibit defective chemotaxis. Most patients exhibit intrinsic cellular defects, but cell-directed serum inhibitors, chemotactic factor inactivators, or abnormalities of chemotaxigenesis have been reported in a small proportion of patients tested. The pathogenic mechanisms accounting for impaired chemotaxis have not been defined. The epidemiologic or clinical associations of certain periodontopathic bacterial organisms with some periodontitis syndromes have suggested the possibility that cellular constituents or extracellular factors elaborated by these microorganisms may secondarily alter functions of leukocytes.[336,352–356] The pathogenic roles of gram-negative oral bacteria including *Actinobacillus actinomycetemcomitans*, species of *Bacteroides*, and species of *Capnocytophaga* have been increasingly appreciated.[352,356] Among the potentially pathogenic products of *A. actinomycetemcomitans*, a leukocytotoxin has been identified in vitro which may contribute to diminished chemotactic function.[357–360] Serum from selected juvenile periodontitis patients contains IgG antibodies which neutralize leukotoxic activity of *A. actinomycetemcomi-*

tans, and serum and gingival crevicular fluids from such patients contain high titers of antibodies to *A. actinomycetemcomitans* antigens.[360] While the molecular basis of leukotoxin production or toxicity remains undefined, the development of techniques to isolate leukotoxin from *A. actinomycetemcomitans*[361] and the availability of antileukotoxin monoclonal antibodies should facilitate and expand studies concerning its pathogenic role in localized juvenile periodontitis.[362] Other poorly defined inhibitors of chemotaxis have been found in culture filtrates or sonicates of *Bacteroides gingivalis*, *Fusobacterium nucleatum*, and species of *Capnocytophaga*.[336,354]

Despite intensive study, the prevalence, natural history, and etiology of juvenile periodontitis remain undefined. The familial aggregation in juvenile periodontitis has prompted a number of researchers to propose a possible genetic basis for this disease.[342,363] Defects of chemotaxis associated with juvenile periodontitis also appear to have a familial pattern of distribution, and in some cases both functional defects of leukocytes and clinical features of periodontitis are identified in multiple family members.[342] It has not, however, been determined if the familial occurrence of juvenile periodontitis results from a single major gene, multifactorial etiology, or environmental effects. Conflicting reports suggest an autosomal recessive or X-linked dominant mode of inheritance.[363–365] The mode of genetic transmission of specific periodontitis syndromes will await the identification of molecular markers for disease.

Schwachman-Diamond Syndrome

Clinical features of a syndrome first described by Schwachman and Diamond include exocrine pancreatic insufficiency, bone marrow hypoplasia with associated neutropenia, metaphyseal chondrodysplasia, growth retardation, and recurrent soft tissue infections.[366–369] In a series of 21 patients,[369] otitis media, bronchial pneumonia, osteomyelitis, dermatitis, and septicemia occurred in 17 (85 percent) of whom 3 (15 percent) died. Neutropenia was intermittent in most patients in this and other series.[370] Bone marrow aspirations in this disorder have demonstrated absent myeloid precursors or maturation arrest with variable degrees of hypoplasia.[368–370] Normal bone marrow aspirates in neutropenic patients have also been described, suggesting that marrow hypoplasia is patchy in distribution.[367] Diminished chemotaxis of neutrophils without other functional abnormalities was found in 12 of 14 patients with this syndrome.[366] Nine of these patients were neutropenic, and four demonstrated low levels of serum IgA or IgM without other immunologic abnormalities. Intermediate abnormalities of neutrophil chemotaxis were recognized in parents of some of these individuals suggesting that they were heterozygotes and that this abnormality is inherited as an autosomal recessive disorder. A pathogenic basis for hematologic as well as other features of this multisystem disease has not been determined, and the relative contributions of impaired cellular motility as opposed to neutropenia to infectious susceptibility in affected patients is uncertain.

Disorders Associated with Abnormal Generation of Chemotactic Factors

Abnormal chemotaxigenesis occurs in a number of genetic or acquired disorders, most importantly those associated with abnormalities of serum complement proteins.[213,371,372] (See Chap. 111 for detailed discussion of abnormalities of complement.) Diminished generation of complement-derived chemotactic factors (primarily C5a and C5a$_{desArg}$), has been demonstrated in association with a heritable deficiency of complement components C3 and C5,[373–376] and in a patient with Klinefelter syndrome who displayed a congenital absence of a C3 regulatory protein normally present in plasma.[373] Impaired generation of chemotactic activity in serum has also been described in a 19-year-old female patient with C5 deficiency and systemic lupus erythematosus.[377] Abnormal generation of complement-dependent chemotactic activity was found in sera of 10 of 23 patients with systemic lupus erythematosus, and this was thought to contribute to infectious susceptibility in some cases.[378] Two children with a clinical syndrome of dermatitis, diarrhea, wasting, dystrophy, and recurrent pyogenic infections (Leiner disease) were reported to have C5 dysfunction and reduced chemotactic activity.[379]

Individuals with these abnormalities of serum complement are susceptible to recurrent localized soft tissue infections as well as systemic episodes (septicemia, meningitis, septic arthritis) secondary to staphylococci, gram-negative enteric bacteria, *C. albicans*, and encapsulated pathogens, including *Streptococcus pneumonia*, and *Haemophilus influenzae* type b. Since they demonstrate severely diminished serum opsonic and/or serum bactericidal activities, the relative contributions of impaired chemotaxigenesis to their infectious susceptibility is uncertain. The preferential importance of complement components C3 and C5 for chemotaxigenesis is emphasized by the findings of normal generation of chemotactic activity in serum from patients with inherited deficiency of C6 or C8.[371] Early classic pathway complement components appear to be required for optimal chemotactic factor generation but only at limiting concentrations of serum. Moreover, individuals with heritable C2 or C4 deficiency generally do not demonstrate increased susceptibility to infectious diseases.[371]

Similar complex abnormalities of serum complement-mediated functions (including chemotaxigenesis) have been reported in human neonates,[296,300,380] and children with nephrotic syndrome who lose serum factor B in the urine.[381] Abnormal generation of chemotactic activity on incubation of serum with endotoxin has been reported in several patients with hypogammaglobulinemia,[371] although the basis for this defect is not elucidated. Abnormalities in the formation of the Hageman factor-dependent chemotactic agents kallikrein and plasminogen activator have also been demonstrated in plasma of patients with genetic deficiency of Hageman factor[213] or prekallikrein.[382] Normal serum contains inhibitors that are capable of destroying the biologic activity of a variety of chemotactic factors by enzymatic cleavage.[7] High levels of these inhibitors have been described in several groups of patients among whom the incidence of infections is increased. These include patients with renal diseases during chronic hemodialysis,[383] Hodgkin's disease,[384] lepromatous leprosy,[385] sarcoidosis,[386] and cirrhosis.[387]

Defects in Motility Associated with Immunologic Disorders

Primary immunodeficiency syndromes are described in Chaps. 109 and 110. In some of these disorders, abnormalities of cellular motility have been described. The contributions of these abnormalities to infectious susceptibility in each is uncertain. Possibly the first report of a clinical defect of chemotaxis[6] was a description of two female patients with fair skin, reddish hair, severe eczema, dystrophic fingernails, sinopulmonary infections, and recurrent staphylococcal abscesses (termed *Job syndrome*). Inflammatory lesions of soft tissues in these patients, despite their considerable size, demonstrated minimal erythema or tenderness. In 1972, two male patients with essentially the same syndrome were described.[9] The patients exhibited peculiar coarse facies, eczematoid rashes, cold abscesses, and recurrent sinopulmonary infections due to *S. aureus* or *H. influenzae*. Both demonstrated hyperimmunoglobulin E and a variety of additional subtle immunologic abnormalities. A summary of the clinical courses of 20 patients with hyperimmunoglobulin E revealed 13 males and 8 blacks, thus eliminating the concept that Job syndrome affects only red-haired females.[388] All had eczematoid dermatitis, and in seven instances a familial occurrence was noted. Serum IgE levels in unaffected relatives were normal. The patients consistently demonstrated poor delayed hypersensitivity responses as well as poor anamnestic responses to tetanus and diphtheria antigens. Almost all demonstrated diminished lymphocyte proliferation in vitro to specific antigens such as *C. albicans* or tetanus toxoid, but proliferative responses to lectins were generally normal. Other reports documented deficient suppressor T lymphocytes and increased IgE synthesis in culture.[389,390] Collectively, these reports suggest a defect of immune regulation as the primary pathogenic basis of this syndrome.[391] Heterogeneity with respect to the chemotactic functions of neutrophils or monocytes from patients with Job syndrome has lead to the consideration that these abnormalities do not reflect a primary dysfunction of neutrophils or monocytes.[11,392] Rather, these abnormalities may be related to high tissue levels of histamine. Histamine significantly inhibits the chemotactic response of normal neutrophils in vitro. Cytophilic IgE directed against invading bacteria could mediate a local release of histamine, thereby diminishing chemotaxis of circulating neutrophils. Patients with Job syndrome have been found to have high levels of serum IgE directed against antigens of *S. aureus* and *C. albicans*.[393,394]

One large patient group that must be carefully differentiated from individuals with Job syndrome includes those individuals with atopic eczema who are frequently colonized by *S. aureus* and later acquire secondary staphylococcal infections. These patients may demonstrate chemotactic defects,[395] but generally they do not demonstrate recurrent sinopulmonary infections and characteristic cold abscesses. Still other patients with a prominent allergic history develop recurrent infections that coincide with exacerbations of atopic symptoms.[396]

Defects in chemotaxis have also been described in selected patients with chronic mucocutaneous candidiasis, and these may accompany or occur in the absence of associated lymphocyte dysfunction.[10,214,397,398] Diminished chemotaxis of neutrophils associated with marked elevation of IgE was reported in one mother-daughter pair,[399] and abnormal mononuclear leukocyte chemotaxis associated with abnormal production of lymphocyte-derived chemotactic factor was reported in another patient.[214] A plasma inhibitor of neutrophil motility was detected in one patient with chronic mucocutaneous candidiasis. Partial characterization of this inhibitor revealed that it had several properties in common with IgG.[398]

A cellular defect of chemotaxis, phagocytosis, and intracellular bactericidal activity was reported in a 3-year-old male with agammaglobulinemia, recurrent cutaneous abscesses, and episodes of pneumonia. Similar defects were found in an adult with hypogammaglobulinemia and in another child with

gamma globulin deficiency associated with recurrent sinopulmonary infections.[213] Diminished chemotaxis occurred in 9 of 10 patients with serum IgA deficiency and 6 of 10 patients with hypogammaglobulinemia.[400,401] Diminished chemotaxis has also been observed in selected patients with severe combined immune deficiency disease.[402] The pathogenic basis and consequences of abnormal cellular motility described in these reports are uncertain.

In addition to complex immunologic abnormalities identified in patients with the Wiskott-Aldrich syndrome, diminished chemotaxis of monocytes has been reported in association with abnormal production of a lymphocyte-derived chemotactic factor.[403] These findings suggest that lymphocytes in Wiskott-Aldrich syndrome may release soluble factors that diminish the responsiveness of monocytes to chemotactic stimuli. The pathogenic significance of these limited findings is uncertain.

REFERENCES

1. METCHNIKOFF E: *Immunity in Infectious Diseases* (FG Binnie, trans.). London, Cambridge University Press, 1905.
2. LEBER T: Ueber die Entstehung der Entzundung die Wirkung der entzundungse-regendon Schadlichkeiten. *Fortschr Med* 6:460, 1888.
3. JANEWAY CA, CRAIG J, DAVIDSON M: Hypergammaglobulinemia associated with severe recurrent and chronic nonspecific infection. *Am J Dis Child* 88:388, 1954.
4. QUIE PG, WHITE JG, HOLMES B: *In vitro* bactericidal capacity of human polymorphonuclear leukocytes: Diminished activity in chronic granulomatous disease of childhood. *J Clin Invest* 46:668, 1967.
4a. REBUCK JW, CROWLEY JH: A method of studying leukocyte function *in vivo*. Ann NY Acad Sci 59:757, 1955.
5. HOLMES B, PAGE AR, GOOD RA: Studies of the metabolic activity of leukocytes from patients with a genetic abnormality of phagocytic function. *J Clin Invest* 46:1422, 1967.
6. DAVIS SD, SCHALLER J: Job's syndrome: Recurrent "cold" staphylococcal abscesses. *Lancet* 1:1013, 1966.
7. WARD PA, JOHNSON KJ, KREUTZER DL: Regulatory dysfunction leukotaxis. *Am J Pathol* 88:701, 1977.
8. MILLER ME, OSKI FA, HARRIS MB: Lazy-leukocyte syndrome: A new disorder of neutrophil function. *Lancet* 1:665, 1971.
9. BUCKLEY RH, WRAY BB, BELMAKER EZ: Extreme hyperimmunoglobulinemia E and undue susceptibility to infection. *Pediatrics* 49:59, 1972.
10. CLARK RA, ROOT RK, KIMBALL HR: Defective neutrophil chemotaxis in cellular immunity in a child with recurrent infections. *Ann Intern Med* 78:515, 1973.
11. HILL HR, QUIE PG: Raised serum IgE levels and defective neutrophil chemotaxis in three children with eczema and recurrent bacterial infections. *Lancet* 1:183, 1974.
12. WILKINSON PC: The locomotion of leukocytes: Definitions and descriptions, in Wilkinson PC (ed): *Chemotaxis and Inflammation*, 2d ed. Edinburgh, London, Melbourne, New York, Churchill Livingstone, 1982, p 1.
13. KELLER HU, WILKINSON PC, ABERCROMBIE M, BECKER EL, HIRSCH JG, MILLER ME, RAMSEY WS, ZIGMOND SH: A proposal for the definition of terms related to locomotion of leukocytes and other cells. *Clin Exp Immunol* 27:377, 1977.
14. KELLER HU, WILKINSON PC, ABERCROMBIE M, BECKER EL, HIRSCH JG, MILLER ME, RAMSEY WS, ZIGMOND SH, AUSTEN KF, BAUM J, BOREL JF, CURTIS ASG, DUNN GA, GALLIN JI, GOETZL EJ, HARRIS AK, HUMBERT JR, SORKIN E, TRINKAUS JP, VASILIEY JM, WEISS L, WISSLER JH: A proposal for the definition of terms related to locomotion of leukocytes and other cells. *Bull WHO* 58:505, 1980.
15. RAMSEY WS: Analysis of individual leukocyte behavior during chemotaxis. *Exp Cell Res* 70:129, 1972.
16. MCCUTCHEON M: Chemotaxis in leukocytes. *Physiol Rev* 26:319, 1946.
17. ZIGMOND SH, HIRSCH JG: Leukocyte locomotion and chemotaxis. New methods for evaluation and demonstration of a cell-derived chemotactic factor. *J Exp Med* 137:387, 197.
17a. ANDERSON DC, WIRLE LS, HUGHES BS, SMITH CW, BRINKLEY BR: Cytoplasmic microtubules in polymorphonuclear leukocytes: Effects of chemotactic stimulation. *Cell* 31:719, 1982.

18. ZIGMOND SH, LEVITSKY HI, KREEL BJ: Cell polarity: An examination of its behavioral expression and its consequences for polymorphonuclear leukocyte chemotaxis. *J Cell Biol* 89:585, 1981.

19. MILES AA, MILES EM, BURKE J: The value and duration of defense reactions of the skin to the primary lodgement of bacteria. *Br J Exp Pathol* 38:79, 1957.

20. SOLBERG CO, HALSTENSEN A, DIGRANES A, HELLUM KB: Penetration of antibiotics into human leukocytes and dermal suction blisters. *Rev Infect Dis* 5(3):S468, 1983.

21. ALLAN RB, WILKINSON PC: A visual analysis of chemotactic and chemokinetic locomotion of human neutrophil leukocytes. *Exp Cell Res* 111:191, 1978.

22. SMITH CW, HOLLERS JC, PATRICK RA, HASSETT C: Motility and adhesiveness in human neutrophils: Effects of chemotactic factors. *J Clin Invest* 63:221, 1979.

23. VERGHESE MW, SMITH CD, CHARLES LA, JAKOI L, SNYDERMAN RA: A guanine nucleotide regulatory protein controls polyphosphoinositide metabolism, Ca2+ mobilization and cellular responses to chemoattractants in human monocytes. *J Immunol* 137:271, 1986.

24. ANDERSON DC, HUGHES BJ, SMITH CW: Abnormal mobility of neonatal polymorphonuclear leukocytes. Relationship to impaired redistribution of surface adhesion sites by chemotactic factor of colchicine. *J Clin Invest* 68:863, 1981.

25. ANDERSON DC, KRISHNA GS, HUGHES BJ, MACE ML, SMITH CW, NICHOLS BL: Impaired polymorphonuclear leukocyte motility in malnourished infants: Relationship to functional abnormalities of cell adherence. *J Lab Clin Med* 101:881, 1983.

26. ANDERSON DC, MACE ML, MARTIN RR, SMITH CW: Recurrent infection in glycogenesis type 1b: Abnormal neutrophil motility related to impaired redistribution of adhesion sites. *J Infect Dis* 143:447, 1981.

27. BOYDEN S: The chemotactic effect of mixtures of antibody and antigen on polymorphonuclear leukocytes. *J Exp Med* 115:453, 1962.

28. WILKINSON PC, ALLAN RB: Assay systems for measuring leukocyte locomotion: An overview, in Gallin JI, Quie PG (eds): *Leukocyte Chemotaxis.* New York, Raven, 1978, p 1.

29. NELSON RD, QUIE PG, SIMMONS RL: Chemotaxis under agarose: A new and simple method for measuring chemotaxis and spontaneous migration of human polymorphonuclear leukocytes and monocytes. *J Immunol* 115:1650, 1975.

30. SNYDERMAN R, PIKE MC: Chemoattractant receptors on phagocytic cells. *Annu Rev Immunol* 2:257, 1984.

31. SNYDERMAN R, PHILLIPS JK, MERGENHAGEN SE: Polymorphonuclear leukocyte chemotactic activity in rabbit and guinea pig serum treated with immune complexes: Evidence of C5a as the major chemotactic factor. *Infect Immun* 1:521, 1970.

32. SNYDERMAN R, PHILLIPS JK, MERGENHAGEN SE: Biological activity of complement in vivo: Role of C5 in the accumulation of polymorphonuclear leukocytes in inflammatory exudates. *J Exp Med* 134:1131, 1971.

33. WARD PA, ZVAIFLER NJ: Complement derived leukotactic factors in inflammatory synovial fluids of humans. *J Clin Invest* 50:606, 1971.

34. FERNANDEZ HN, HUGLI TE: Partial characterization of human C5a anaphylatoxin. I. Chemical description of the carbohydrate and polypeptide portions of human C5a. *J Immunol* 117:1688, 1976.

35. SCHIFFMANN E, CORCORAN BA, WAHL SM: N-formylmethionyl peptides as chemoattractants for leukocytes. *Proc Natl Acad Sci USA* 72:1059, 1975.

36. SCHIFFMANN E, SHOWELL HL, CORCORAN BA, WARD PA, SMITH E, BECKER EL: The isolation and partial characterization of neutrophil chemotactic factors from *Escherichia coli. J Immunol* 114:1831, 1975.

37. FORD-HUTCHINSON AW, BRAY MA, DOIG MV, SHIPLEY ME, SMITH MJH: Leukotriene B$_4$, a potent chemokinetic and aggregating substance released from polymorphonuclear leukocytes. *Nature* 286:264, 1980.

38. DEUEL TF, SENIOR RM, CHANG D, GRIFFIN GL, HEINRIKSON RL, KAISER ET: Platelet factor 4 is chemotactic for neutrophils and monocytes. *Proc Natl Acad Sci USA* 78:4584, 1981.

39. POSTLETHWAITE A, SNYDERMAN R: Characterization of chemotactic activity produced in vivo by a cell mediated immune reaction in the guinea pig. *J Immunol* 114:274, 1975.

40. GOETZL EJ, AUSTEN KF: Purification and synthesis of eosinophilotactic tetrapeptides of human lung tissue: Identification of eosinophil chemotactic factor of anaphylaxis. *Proc Natl Acad Sci USA* 72:4123, 1975.

41. SPILBERG I, MEHTA J: Demonstration of a specific neutrophil receptor for a cell derived chemotactic factor. *J Clin Invest* 63:85, 1979.

42. GOETZL EJ: Regulation of the polymorphonuclear leukocyte chemotactic response by immunological reactions, in Gallin JI, Quie PG (eds): *Leukocyte Chemotaxis: Methods, Physiology, and Clinical Implications.* New York, Raven, 1978, p 161.

43. GALLIN JI, ROSENTHAL AS: The regulatory role of divalent cations in human granulocyte chemotaxis. *J Cell Biol* 62:594, 1974.

44. NACCACHE PH, SHOWELL HJ, BECKER EL, SHA'AFI RI: Transport of sodium, potassium, and calcium across rabbit polymorphonuclear leukocyte membranes: Effects of chemotactic factor. *J Cell Biol* 73:428, 1977.

45. GAIL MH, BOONE CW: The locomotion of mouse fibroblasts in tissue culture. *Biophys J* 10:980, 1970.

46. VANEPPS DE, GARCIA M: Enhancement of neutrophil function as a result of prior exposure to chemotactic factor. *J Clin Invest* 66:167, 1980.

47. BASS DA, DECHATELET LR, MCCALL CE: Independent stimulation of motility and the oxidative metabolic burst of human polymorphonuclear leukocytes. *J Immunol* 121:172, 1978.

48. LOHR KM, SNYDERMAN R: Amphotericin B alters the affinity and functional activity of the oligopeptide chemotactic factor receptor on human polymorphonuclear leukocytes. *J Immunol* 129:1594, 1982.

49. SNYDERMAN R: Characterization of the oligopeptide chemoattractant receptor on leukocytes: Binding affinity reflects signal transduction. *Fed Proc* 42:2855, 1983.

50. SNYDERMAN R, SMITH CD, VERGHESE MW: Model for leukocyte regulation by chemoattractant receptors: Roles of a guanine nucleotide regulatory protein and polyphosphoinositide metabolism. *J Leukocyte Biol* 40:785, 1986.

51. SNYDERMAN R, PIKE MC: Transductional mechanisms of chemoattractant receptors on leukocytes, in Snyderman R (ed): *Regulation of Leukocyte Function.* New York, Plenum, 1979, p 1.

52. GOLDMAN DW, GIFFORD LA, MAROTTI T, KOO CH, GOETZL EJ: Molecular and cellular properties of human polymorphonuclear leukocyte receptors for leukotriene B$_4$. *Fed Proc* 46:200, 1987.

53. GOLDMAN DW, GOETZL EJ: Heterogeneity of human polymorphonuclear leukocyte receptors for leukotriene B$_4$. *J Exp Med* 159:1027, 1984.

54. SNYDERMAN R, SHIN HS, DANNENBERG AM JR: Macrophage proteinase and inflammation: The production of chemotactic activity from the fifth component of complement by macrophage proteinase. *J Immunol* 109:896, 1972.

55. WISSLER JH, STECHER VJ, SORKIN E: Chemistry and biology of the anaphylatoxin related serum peptide system. III Evaluation of leukotactic activity as a property of a new peptide system with classical anaphylatoxin and cocytotaxin as components. *Eur J Immunol* 2:90, 1972.

56. PEREZ HD, GOLDSTEIN IM, CHERNOFF D, WEBSTER RO, HENSON PM: Chemotactic activity of C5a$_{desArg}$: Evidence of a requirement for an anionic peptide "helper factor" and inhibition by a cationic protein in serum from patients with systemic lupus erythematosus. *Mol Immunol* 17:163, 1980.

57. CHENOWETH DE, HUGLI TE: Demonstration of specific C5a receptor on intact human polymorphonuclear leukocytes. *Proc Natl Acad Sci USA* 75:3943, 1978.

58. GERARD C, CHENOWITH DE, MACKIN WM: Response of neutrophils to C5adesArg but not C5a in biologic activity. *J Immunol* 127:1978, 1981.

59. SHOWELL HJ, FREER RJ, ZIGMOND SH, SCHIFFMANN E, ASWANIKUMAR S, CORCORAN B, BECKER EL: The structure-activity relations of synthetic peptides as chemotactic factors and inducers of lysosomal enzyme secretion for neutrophils. *J Exp Med* 143:1154, 1976.

60. ASWANIKUMAR S, CORCORAN B, SCHIFFMAN E, DAY AR, FREER RJ, SHOWELL HJ, PERT CB: Demonstration of a receptor on rabbit neutrophils for chemotactic peptides. *Biochem Biophys Res Commun* 74:810, 1977.

61. WILLIAMS LT, SNYDERMAN R, PIKE MC, LEFKOWITZ RJ: Specific receptor sites for chemotactic peptides on human polymorphonuclear leukocytes. *Proc Natl Acad Sci USA* 74:1204, 1977.

62. NIEDEL JE, KAHANE I, CUATREEASAS P: Receptor-mediated uptake and degradation of ^{125}I chemotactic peptides by human neutrophils. *J Biol Chem* 254:10700, 1979.

63. WEINBERG JB, MUSCATO JJ, NIEDEL JE: Monocyte chemotactic peptide receptor. *J Clin Invest* 68:621, 1981.

64. SNYDERMAN R, FUDMAN EJ: Demonstration of a chemotactic factor receptor on macrophages. *J Immunol* 124:2754, 1980.

65. MARASCO WA, PHAN SH, KRUTZSCH H, SHOWELL HJ, FELTNER DE, NAIRN R, BECKER EL, WARD PA: Purification and identification of formyl-methionyl-leucyl-phenylalanine as the major peptide neutrophil chemotactic factor produced by *Escherichia coli. J Biol Chem* 259:5430, 1984.

66. WILKINSON PC: The physiology and biochemistry of leukocyte chemotaxis: I. Recognition, in Wilkinson PC (eds): *Chemotaxis and Inflammation,* 2d ed. Edinburgh, London, Melbourne, New York, Churchill Livingstone, 1982, p 63.

67. NIEDEL JE, DAVIS J, CUATRECASAS P: Covalent affinity labeling of the formyl peptide chemotactic receptor. *J Biol Chem* 255:7063, 1980.

68. PAINTER RG, SCHMITT M, JESAITIS AJ, SKYLAR LA, PREISSNER K, COCHRANE CG: Photoaffinity labeling of the N-formyl peptide receptor on human polymorphonuclear leukocytes. *J Cell Biochem* 20:203, 1982.

69. GOETZL EJ, FOSTER DW, GOLDMAN DW: Isolation and partial characterization of membrane protein constituents of human neutrophil receptors

for chemotactic formylmethionyl peptides. *Biochemistry* 20:5717, 1981.

70. HOYLE PC, FREER RJ: Isolation and reconstitution of the N-formyl peptide receptor for HL-60 derived neutrophil. *FEBS Lett* 167:277, 1984.

71. MALECH HL, GARDNER JP, HEIMAN DF, ROSENZWEIG SA: Asparagine-linked oligosaccharides on formyl peptide chemotactic receptors of human phagocytic cells. *J Biol Chem* 260:2509, 1985.

72. TURNER SR, TAINER JA, LYNN WS: Biogenesis of chemotactic molecules by the arachidonate lipoxygenase system of platelets. *Nature* 257:680, 1975.

73. GOETZL EJ, BRINDLEY LL, GOLDMAN SW: Enhancement of human neutrophil adherence by synthetic leukotriene constituents of the slow-reacting substance of anaphylaxis. *Immunology* 50:35, 1983.

74. GOLDMAN DW, GIFFORD LA, OLSON DM, GOETZL EJ: Transduction by leukotriene B$_4$ receptors of increases in cytosolic calcium in human polymorphonuclear leukocytes. *J Immunol* 135:525, 1985.

75. KREISLE RA, PARKER CW: Specific binding of leukotriene B$_4$ to a receptor on human polymorphonuclear leukocytes. *J Exp Med* 157:628, 1983.

76. KOO C, LEFKOWITZ RJ, SNYDERMAN R: The oligopeptide chemotactic factor receptor on human polymorphonuclear leukocyte membranes exists in two affinity states. *Biochem Biophys Res Commun* 106:442, 1982.

77. KOO C, LEFKOWITZ RJ, SNYDERMAN R: Guanine nucleotides modulate the binding affinity of the oligopeptide chemoattractant receptor on human polymorphonuclear leukocytes. *J Clin Invest* 72:748, 1983.

78. NIEDEL JE, KAHANE I, CUATRECASAS P: Receptor-mediated internalization of fluorescent chemotactic peptide by human neutrophils. *Science* 205:1412, 1979.

79. JESAITIS AJ, NAEMURA JR, SKLAR LA, COCHRANE CG, PAINTER RG: Rapid modulation of N-formyl chemotactic peptide receptors on the surface of human granulocytes: Formation of high-affinity ligand-receptor complexes in transient association with cell cytoskeleton. *J Cell Biol* 98:1378, 1984.

80. FLETCHER MP, GALLIN JI: Degranulating stimuli increase the availability of receptors on human neutrophils for the chemoattractant f-Met-Leu-Phe. *J Immunol* 124:1585, 1980.

81. FLETCHER MP, SELIGMANN BE, GALLIN JI: Correlation of human neutrophil secretion, chemoattractant receptor mobilization, and enhanced functional capacity. *J Immunol* 128:941, 1982.

82. FLETCHER MP, GALLIN JI: Human neutrophils contain an intracellular pool of putative receptors for the chemoattractant N-formylmethionylleucylphenylalanine. *Blood* 62:792, 1983.

83. GALLIN JI, FLETCHER MP, SELIGMANN BE: Human neutrophil-specific granules in the evolution of the inflammatory response. *Blood* 59:1317, 1982.

84. ANDERSON DC, SPRINGER TA: Leukocyte adhesion deficiency: An inherited defect in the Mac-1, LFA-1 and p150,95 glycoproteins. *Annu Rev Med* 38:175, 1987.

85. SMITH CW, HOLLERS JC: Motility and adhesiveness in human neutrophils. Redistribution of chemotactic factor induced adhesion sites. *J Clin Invest* 65:804, 1980.

86. GAIL MH, BOONE CW: Cell-substrate adhesivity. *Exp Cell Res* 70:33, 1972.

87. HARRIS A: Behavior of cultured cells on substrata of variable adhesiveness. *Exp Cell Res* 77:285, 1973.

88. REES DA, BADLEY RA, BAYLEY SA, COUCHMAN JR, SMITH CG, WOODS A: Surface components in fibroblast adhesion and movement, in Dingle JT, Gordon JL (eds): *Cellular Interactions.* Amsterdam, New York, Oxford, Elsevier/North-Holland, 1981, p 67.

89. CARTER SB: Principles of cell motility: The direction of cell movement and cancer invasion. *Nature* 208:1183, 1965.

90. BECKER EL, SHOWELL HJ: The effect of Ca^{++} and Mg^{++} on the chemotactic responsiveness and spontaneous motility of rabbit polymorphonuclear leukocytes. *Z Immunitaetsforsch Allerg Klin Immunol* 143:466, 1972.

91. BRYANT RE, DESPREZ RM, VANWAY MH, ROGERS DE: Studies on human leukocyte motility. I. Effects of alterations in pH, electrolyte concentration, and phagocytosis on leukocyte migration, adhesiveness, and aggregation. *J Exp Med* 124:483, 1966.

92. WILKINSON PC, ALLAN RB: Chemotaxis of neutrophil leukocytes towards substratum-bound protein attractants. *Exp Cell Res* 117:403, 1978.

93. WILKINSON PC, ALLAN RB: The locomotor behavior of human blood monocytes in chemotactic and chemokinetic environments and the role of the substratum in monocyte locomotion, in Van Furth R (eds): *Mononuclear Phagocytes, Functional Aspects.* The Hague, Martinus Nijhoff, 1980, p 475.

94. LACKIE JM, SMITH RPC: Interactions of leukocytes and endothelium, in Curtis ASG, Pitts JD (eds): *Cell Adhesion and Motility.* Cambridge, Cambridge University Press, 1980, p 235.

95. TONNESEN MG, SMEDLEY LA, HENSON PM: Neutrophil-endothelial cell interactions: Modulation of neutrophil adhesiveness induced by complement fragments C5a and C5a$_{desArg}$ and formyl-methionyl-leucyl-phenylalanine *in vitro.* *J Clin Invest* 74:1581, 1984.

96. HARLAN JM, KILLEN PD, SENECAL FM, SCHWARTZ BR, YEE EK, TAYLOR RF, BEATTY PG, PRICE TH, OCHS HD: The role of neutrophil membrane glycoprotein GP-150 in neutrophil adherence to endothelium *in vitro.* *Blood* 66:167, 1985.

97. HOOVER RL, FOLGER R, HAERING WA, WADE BR, KARNOVSKY MJ: Adhesion of leukocytes to endothelium: Roles of divalent actions, surface change, chemotactic agents and substrate. *J Cell Sci* 45:73, 1980.

98. O'FLAHERTY JT, KREUTZER DL, WARD PA: Chemotactic factor influences on the aggregation, swelling, and foreign surface adhesiveness of human leukocytes. *Am J Pathol* 90:537, 1978.

99. MCGILLIN JJ, PHAIR JP: Adherence augmented adherence and aggregation of polymorphonuclear leukocytes. *J Infect Dis* 139:69, 1979.

100. LENTNEK AL, SCHREIBER AD, MacGREGOR RR: The induction of augmented granulocyte adherence by inflammation. *J Clin Invest* 57:1098, 1976.

101. HAMMERSCHMIDT DE, WHITE JG, CRADDOCK PR, JACOB HS: Corticosteroids inhibit complement-induced granulocyte aggregation: A possible mechanism for their efficacy in shock states. *J Clin Invest* 63:798, 1979.

102. SCHMALSTIEG FC, RUDLOFF HE, HILLMAN GR, ANDERSON DC: Two dimensional and three dimensional movement of human polymorphonuclear leukocytes: Two fundamentally different mechanisms of location. *J Leukocyte Biol* 40:677, 1986.

103. BROWN AF: Neutrophil granulocytes: Adhesion and locomotion on collagen substrata in collagen matrices. *J Cell Sci* 58:455, 1982.

104. BROWN AF: Neutrophil and monocyte behavior in three-dimensional matrices. *Scan Electron Microsc* 2:747, 1984.

105. LACKIE JM, WILKINSON PC: Adhesion and locomotion of neutrophil leukocytes on 2-D substrata and in 3-D matrices, in Meiselman HJ, Lichtman MA, Lacelle PL (eds): *White Cell Mechanics: Basic Science and Clinical Aspects.* New York, AR Liss, 1984, p 237.

106. ATHERTON A, BORN GVR: Quantitative investigations of the adhesiveness of circulating polymorphonuclear leukocytes to blood vessel walls. *J Physiol* 222:447, 1972.

107. WRIGHT DG, GALLIN JI: Secretory responses of human neutrophils: Exocytosis of specific (secondary) granules by human neutrophils during adherence *in vitro* and during exudation *in vivo.* *J Immunol* 123:285, 1979.

108. HOFFSTEIN ST, FRIEDMAN RS, WEISSMANN G: Degranulation, membrane addition, and shape change during chemotactic factor-induced aggregation of human neutrophils. *J Cell Biol* 95:234, 1982.

109. JONES DH, ANDERSON DC, BURR BL, RUDLOFF HE, SMITH CW, SCHMALSTIEG FC: Subcellular location of Mac-1 (CR-3) in human neutrophils: Effects of chemotactic factors and PMA. *Pediatr Res* 21:312a, 1987.

110. TODD RF, ARNAOUT MA, ROSIN RE, CROWLEY CA, PETERS WA, BABIOR BM: Subcellular localization of the large subunit of Mol (Mol$_1$; formerly gp110), a surface glycoprotein associated with neutrophil adhesion. *J Clin Invest* 74:1280, 1984.

111. BOXER LA, HAAK RA, YANG H-H, WOLACH JB, WHITCOMB JA, BUTTERICK CH, BAEHNER RL: Membrane-bound lactoferrin alters the surface properties of polymorphonuclear leukocytes. *J Clin Invest* 70:1049, 1982.

112. OSEAS R, YANG H-H, BAEHNER RL, BOXER LA: Lactoferrin: A promoter of polymorphonuclear leukocyte adhesiveness. *Blood* 57:939, 1981.

113. BOCKENSTEDT LK, GOETZL EJ: Constituents of human neutrophils that mediate enhanced adherence to surfaces. *J Clin Invest* 65:1372, 1980.

114. OSEAS RS, ALLEN J, YANG H-H, BAEHNER RL, BOXER LA: Rabbit cationic protein enhances leukocyte adhesiveness. *Infect Immun* 33:523, 1981.

115. BOXER LA, COATES TD, HAAK RA, ET AL: Lactoferrin deficiency associated granulocyte function. *N Engl J Med* 307:404, 1982.

116. GALLIN JI, FLETCHER MD, SELIGMAN BE, HOFFSTEIN S, OCHURS K, MENNESSA N: Human neutrophil-specific granules deficiency: A method to access the role of neutrophil-specific granules in the evolution of the inflammatory response. *Blood* 59:1317, 1982.

117. O'SHEA JJ, BROWN EJ, SELIGMANN BE, METCALF JA, FRANK MM, GALLIN JI: Evidence for distinct intracellular pools of receptors for C3b and C3bi in human neutrophils. *J Immunol* 134:2580, 1985.

118. GALLIN JI, DUROCHER JR, KAPLAN AP: Interaction of leukocyte chemotactic factors with the cell surface. I. Chemotactic factor induced changes in human granulocyte surface charge. *J Clin Invest* 55:967, 1975.

119. GALLIN JI: Degranulating stimuli decrease the negative surface charge and increase the adhesiveness of human neutrophils. *J Clin Invest* 65:298, 1980.

120. SCHAAK TM, TAKEUCHI A, SPILBERG I, PERSELLIN RH: Alteration of polymorphonuclear leukocyte surface charge by endogenous and exogenous chemotactic factors. *Inflammation* 4:37, 1980.

121. MACGREGOR RR, SPAGNUOLO BE, LENTNEK AL: Inhibition of granulocyte adherence by ethanol, prednisone, and aspirin, measured with an *in vitro* assay system. *N Engl J Med* 291:642, 1974.

122. ARNAOUT MA, TODD RF III, DANA N, MELAMED J, SCHLOSSMAN SF, COLTEN HR: Inhibition of phagocytosis of complement C3—or immunoglobulin G—coated particles and of C3bi binding by monoclonal antibodies to a monocyte-granulocyte membrane glycoprotein (Mol). *J Clin Invest* 72:171, 1983.

123. KOHL S, SPRINGER TA, SCHMALSTIEG FC: Defective natural killer cytotoxicity and polymorphonuclear leukocyte antibody dependent cellular cytotoxicity in patients with LFA-1/OKM-1 deficiency. *J Immunol* 133:2942, 1984.

124. SANCHEZ-MADRID F, NAGY J, ROBBINS E, SIMON P, SPRINGER TA: A human leukocyte differentiation antigen family with distinct alpha subunits and a common beta subunit: The lymphocyte function associated antigen (LFA-1), the C3bi complement receptor (OKM1/Mac-1), and the p150,95 molecule. *J Exp Med* 158:1785, 1983.

125. SANCHEZ-MADRID F, SIMON P, THOMPSON S, SPRINGER TA: Mapping of antigenic and functional epitopes on the alpha and beta subunits of two related glycoproteins involved in cell interactions, LFA-1 and Mac-1. *J Exp Med* 158:586, 1983.

126. IUIS-WHO NOMENCLATURE SUBCOMMITTEE: Nomenclature for clusters of differentiation (CD) of antigens defined on human leukocyte populations. *Terminology* 62:809, 1984.

127. WRIGHT SD, RAO PE, VANVOORHIS WC, CRAIGMYLE LS, IIDA K, TALLE MA, WESTBERRY EF, GOLDSTEIN G, SILVERSTEIN SC: Identification of the C3bi receptor of human monocytes and macrophages with monoclonal antibodies. *Proc Natl Acad Sci USA* 80:5699, 1983.

128. BELLER DI, SPRINGER TA, SCHREIBER RD: Anti-Mac-1 selectively inhibits the mouse and human type three complement receptor. *J Exp Med* 156:1000, 1982.

129. ANDERSON DC, MILLER LJ, SCHMALSTIEG FC, ROTHLEIN R, SPRINGER TA: Contributions of the Mac-1 glycoprotein family to adherence-dependent granulocyte functions: Structure-function assessments employing subunit-specific monoclonal antibodies. *J Immunol* 137:15, 1986.

130. ROTHLEIN R, SPRINGER TA: Complement receptor type 3-dependent degradation of opsonized erythrocytes by mouse macrophage. *J Immunol* 135:2668, 1985.

131. ANDERSON DC, SCHMALSTIEG FC, KOHL S, ARNAOUT MA, HUGHES BJ, TOSI MF, BUFFONE GJ, BRINKLEY BR, DICKEY WD, ABRAMSON JS, SPRINGER TA, BOXER LA, HOLLERS JM, SMITH CW: Abnormalities of polymorphonuclear leukocyte function associated with a heritable deficiency of high molecular weight surface glycoproteins (GP138): Common relationship to diminished cell adherence. *J Clin Invest* 74:536, 1984.

132. ANDERSON DC, SCHMALSTIEG FC, GOLDMAN AS, SHEARER WT, SPRINGER TA: The severe and moderate phenotypes of heritable Mac-1, LFA-1, p150,95 deficiency: Their quantitative definition and relation to leukocyte dysfunction and clinical features. *J Infect Dis* 152:668, 1985.

133. KOHL S, LOO LS, SCHMALSTIEG FC, ANDERSON DC: The genetic deficiency of leukocyte surface glycoprotein Mac-1, LFA-1, p150,95 in humans is associated with defective antibody-dependent cellular cytotoxicity *in vitro* and defective protection against herpes simplex virus *in vivo*. *J Immunol* 137:1688, 1986.

134. SPRINGER TA, DUSTIN ML, KISHIMOTO TK, MARLIN SD: The lymphocyte function associated (LFA-1, CA2 & LFA-3) molecules: Cell adhesion receptors of the immune system. *Annu Rev Immunol* 5:223, 1986.

135. SPRINGER TA, DAVIGNON D, HO MK, KURZINGER K, MARTZ E, SANCHEZ-MADRID F: LFA-1 and Lyt-2,3, molecules associated with T lymphocyte-mediated killing; and Mac-1, an LFA-1 homologue associated with complement receptor function. *Immunol Rev* 68:111, 1982.

136. KRENSKY AM, MENTZER SJ, CLAYBERGER C, ANDERSON DC, SCHMALSTIEG FC, BURAKOFF SJ, SPRINGER TA: Heritable lymphocyte function-associated antigen-1 deficiency: Abnormalities of cytotoxicity and proliferation associated with abnormal expression of LFA-1. *J Immunol* 135:3102, 1985.

137. MYONES BL, DALZELL JG, HOGG N, ROSS GD: p150,95 has been shown on macrophages to be an iC3b receptor and termed the CR4. *Complement* 4:199, 1987.

137a. MYONES BL, DALZELL JG, HOGG N, ROSS GD: Neutrophil and monocyte cell surface p150,95 has iC3b-receptor (CR$_4$) activity resembling CR$_3$. *J Clin Invest* 82:640, 1988.

138. TEVELDE AA, KEIZER GD, FIGDOR CG: Differential function of LFA-1 family molecules (CD11 and CD18) in adhesion of human monocytes to melanoma and endothelial cells. *Immunology* 61:261, 1987.

139. SCHWARTING R, STEIN H, WANG CY: The monoclonal antibodies anti-S-HCL 1(anti Leu 14) and anti S-HCL(anti Leu M5) allow the diagnosis of hairy cell leukemia. *Blood* 65:974, 1985.

140. MILLER LJ, SCHWARTING R, SPRINGER TA: Regulated expression of the Mac-1, LFA-1, p150,95 glycoprotein family during leukocyte differentiation. *J Immunol* 137:2891, 1986.

141. KEIZER GD, BARST J, VISSER W, SCHWARTING R, DEVIRES JE, FIGDOR CG: Membrane glycoprotein p150,95 of human cytotoxic T cell clones is involved in conjugate formations with target cells. *J Immunol* 138:3130, 1987.

142. HO MK, SPRINGER TA: Biosynthesis and assembly of the alpha and beta subunits of Mac-1, a macrophage glycoprotein associated with complement receptor fraction. *J Biol Chem* 258:2766, 1983.

143. SASTRE L, KISHIMOTO TK, GEE C, ROBERTS T, SPRINGER TA: The mouse leukocyte adhesion proteins Mac-1 and LFA-1: Studies on mRNA translation and protein glycosylation. *J Immunol* 137:1060, 1986.

144. SASTRE L, ROMAN J, TEPLOW D, DREYER W, GEE C, LARSON R, ROBERTS T, SPRINGER TA: A partial genomic DNA clone for the alpha subunit of the mouse complement receptor type 3 and cellular adhesion molecule Mac-1. *Proc Natl Acad Sci USA*, in press.

145. KISHIMOTO TK, O'CONNOR K, LEE A, ROBERTS TM, SPRINGER TA: Cloning of the beta subunit of the leukocyte adhesion proteins: Homology to an extracellular matrix receptor defines a novel supergene family. *Cell* 48:681, 1987.

146. BERGER M, O'SHEA JJ, CROSS AS, FOLKS TM, CHUSED TM, BROWN EJ, FRANK MM: Human neutrophils increase expression of C3bi as well as C3b receptors upon activation. *J Clin Invest* 74:1566, 1984.

147. SPRINGER TA, THOMPSON WS, MILLER LJ, ANDERSON DC: Inherited deficiency of the Mac-1, LFA-1, p150,95 glycoprotein family and its molecular basis. *J Exp Med* 160:1901, 1984.

148. PETREQUIN PR, TODD RF, DEVALL LJ, BOXER LA, CURNUTTE JT: Association between gelatinase release and increased plasma membrane expression of the Mol glycoprotein. *Blood* 69:605, 1987.

149. ALLISON F, SMITH MR, WOOD WB: Studies on the pathogenesis of acute inflammation. *J Exp Med* 102:655, 1955.

150. CLIFF WJ: The acute inflammatory reaction in the rabbit ear chamber with particular reference to the phenomenon of leukocyte migration. *J Exp Med* 124:543, 1966.

151. WILKINSON PC: The role of chemotaxis in inflammatory reactions, in *Chemotaxis and Inflammation*, 2d ed. Edinburgh, London, Melbourne, New York, Churchill Livingstone, 1982, p 183.

152. KELLER HU, SORKIN E: Studies on chemotaxis. V. On the chemotactic effect of bacteria. *Int Arch Allergy Appl Immunol* 31:505, 1967.

153. COLDITZ IG, KERLIN RL, WATSON DL: Migration of neutrophils and their role in elaboration of host defense. *Crit Rev Physiol*, in press.

154. SMITH JB, MCINTOSH GH, MORRIS B: The traffic of cells through tissues: A study of peripheral lymph in sheep. *J Anat* 107:87, 1970.

155. HAY JB, CAHILL RNP: Lymphocyte migration patterns in sheep, in Hay JB (ed): *Animal Models of Immunological Processes*. London, Academic, 1987, p 97.

156. HALL JG, MORRIS B: The lymph-borne cells of the immune response. *Q J Exp Physiol* 48:235, 1963.

157. CYBULSKY MI, COLDITZ IG, MOVAT HZ: Interleukin 1 activity in the local recruitment of PMNs: Its potential role in endotoxin induced acute inflammation. *Fed Proc* 44:1260a, 1985.

158. COLDITZ IG, MOVAT HZ: Kinetics of neutrophil accumulation in acute inflammatory lesions induced by chemotaxins and chemotaxinigens. *J Immunol* 133:2168, 1984.

159. WILKINSON PC, O'NEILL GJ, MCINROY RJ, CATER JC, ROBERTS JA: Chemotaxis of macrophages: The role of a macrophage-specific cytotoxin from anaerobic corynebacteria and its relation to immunopotentiation in vivo. *Ciba Found Symp* 18:121, 1973.

160. DESHAZO CV, MCGRADE MT, HENSON PM, COCHRANE CG: The effect of complement depletion on neutrophil migration in acute immunologic arthritis. *J Immunol* 108:1414, 1972.

161. ATHERTON A, BORN GVR: Relationship between the velocity of rolling granulocytes and that of the blood flow in venules. *J Physiol* 233:157, 1973.

162. SCHMID-SCHOENBEIN GW, FUNG YC, ZWEIFACH BW: Vascular endothelium-leukocyte interaction: Sticking shear force in venules. *Circ Res* 36:173, 1975.

163. SCHMID-SCHOENBEIN GW, USAMI S, SKALAK R, CHIEN S: The interaction of leukocytes and erythrocytes in capillary and post-capillary vessels. *Microvasc Res* 19:45, 1980.

164. GRANT L: The sticking and emigration of white blood cells in inflammation, in Zweifach BW, Grant L, McCluskey RT (eds): *The Inflammatory Process*, 2d ed. New York, Academic, 1973, vol 2, p 205.

165. ZWEIFACH BW: Microvascular aspects of tissue injury, in Zweifach BW, Grant L, McCluskey RT (eds): *The Inflammatory Process*, 2d ed. New York, Academic, 1973, vol 2, p 3.

166. HARLAN JM: Leukocyte-endothelial cell interactions. *Blood* 65(3):513, 1985.

167. HAMMERSCHMIDT DE, CRADDOCK PR, MCCULLOUGH J: Complement activation and pulmonary leukostasis during nylon fiber filtration leukapheresis. *Blood* 51:721, 1978.

168. MCCALL CE, DECHATELET LR, BROWN D, LACHMANN P: New biological activity following intravascular activation of the complement cascade. *Nature* 249:841, 1974.

169. CRADDOCK PR, HAMMERSCHMIDT D, WHITE JG: Complement (C5a)-induced granulocyte aggregation in vitro: A possible mechanism of complement-mediated leukostasis and leukopenia. *J Clin Invest* 60:260, 1977.

170. O'FLAHERTY JT, CRADDOCK PR, JACOB HS: Effect of intravascular complement activation on granulocyte adhesiveness and distribution. *Blood* 51:731, 1978.

171. HOOVER RL, BRIGGS RT, KARNOVSKY MJ: The adhesive interaction between polymorphonuclear leukocytes and endothelial cells in vitro. *Cell* 14:423, 1978.

172. HOOVER RL, FOLGER R, HAERING WA, WADE BR, KARNOVSKY MJ: Adhesion of leukocytes to endothelium: Roles of divalent actions, surface change, chemotactic agents and substrate. *J Cell Sci* 45:73, 1980.

173. LACKIE JM, DEBONO D: Interactions of neutrophil granulocytes and endothelium *in vitro. Microvasc Res* 13:107, 1977.

174. TONNESEN MG, ANDERSON DC, SPRINGER TA, KNEDLER A, AVDI N, HENSON PM: Mac-1 glycoprotein family mediates adherence of neutrophils to endothelial cells stimulated by leukotriene B$_4$ and platelet activating factor. *Fed Proc* 45:379a, 1986.

175. TAYLOR RF, PRICE TH, SCHWARTZ SM, DALE DC: Neutrophil-endothelial cell interactions on endothelial monolayers grown on micropore filters. *J Clin Invest* 67:584, 1981.

176. BEESLEY JE, PEARSON JD, CARLETON JS, HUTCHINGS SA, GORDON JL: Interactions of leukocytes with vascular cells in culture. *J Cell Sci* 33:85, 1978.

177. HOOVER RL, KARNOVSKY MJ, AUSTEN KF, COREY EJ, LEWIS RA: Leukotriene B^4 action on endothelium mediates augmented neutrophil/endothelial adhesion. *Proc Natl Acad Sci USA* 81:2191, 1984.

178. MAYROVITZ H, WIEDEMAN M, TUMA R: Factors influencing leukocyte adherence in microvessels. *Thromb Haemost* 38:823, 1977.

179. WILKINSON PC, LACKIE JM: The adhesion, migration and chemotaxis of leukocytes in inflammation, in Movat HZ (ed): *Inflammatory Reaction.* Berlin, Springer-Verlag, 1979, p 47.

180. CHIN Y, CAREY GD, WOODRUFF JJ: Lymphocyte recognition of lymph node high endothelium. *J Immunol* 131:1368, 1983.

181. JALKANEN S, STEERE AC, FOX RI, BUTCHER EC: A distinct endothelial cell recognition system that controls lymphocyte traffic into inflamed synovium. *Science* 233:556, 1986.

182. BUTCHER EC, KRAAL G, STEVENS SK, WEISSMAN IL: A recognition function of endothelial cells: Directing lymphocyte traffic, in Nossel HL, Vogel HJ (eds): *Pathobiology of the Endothelial Cell.* Orlando, Academic, 1982, p 409.

183. HARRIS ED, KRANE SM: An endopeptidase from rheumatoid synovial tissue culture. *Biochim Biophys Acta* 258:566, 1972.

184. STOOLMAN LM, ROSEN SD: Possible role for cell-surface carbohydrate-binding molecules in lymphocyte recirculation. *J Cell Biol* 96:722, 1983.

185. JALKANEN S, WU N, BARTGATZE RF, BUTCHER EC: Human lymphocyte and lymphoma homing receptors. *Annu Rev Med* 38:467, 1987.

186. ARFORS KE, LUNDBERG CL, LINDBOM L, LUNDBERG K, BEATTY PG, HARLAN JM: A monoclonal antibody to the membrane glycoprotein complex CD18 inhibits polymorphonuclear leukocyte accumulation and plasma leakage in vivo. *Blood* 69:338, 1987.

187. WALLIS WJ, BEATTY PG, OCHS HD, HARLAN JM: Human monocyte adherence to cultured vascular endothelium: Monoclonal antibody-defined mechanisms. *J Immunol* 135(4):2323, 1985.

188. BUCHANAN MR, CROWLEY CA, ROSIN RE: Studies on the interaction between GP-180 deficient neutrophils and vascular endothelium. *Blood* 60:160, 1982.

189. PRICE TH, BEATTY PG, CORPUZ SR: In vivo inhibition of neutrophil function in the rabbit using monoclonal antibody to CD18. *J Immunol* 139:4174, 1987.

190. POHLMAN TH, STANNESS KA, BEATTY PG, OCHS HD, HARLAN JM: An endothelial cell surface factors(s) induced *in vitro* by lipopolysaccharide, interleukin-1, and tumor necrosis factor increases neutrophil adherence by a CDw18 (LFA)-dependent mechanism. *J Immunol* 136:4548, 1986.

191. POHLMAN TH, MUNFORD RS, HARLAN JM: Deacylated lipopolysaccharide inhibits neutrophil adherence to endothelium induced by lipopolysaccharide in vitro. *J Exp Med* 165:1393, 1987.

192. BEVILACQUA MP, POBER JS, MAJEAU GR, COTRAN RS, GIMBRONE MA: Interleukin I (IL-I) induces biosynthesis and cell surface expression of procoagulant activity in human vascular endothelial cell. *J Exp Med* 160:618, 1984.

193. GAMBLE JR, HARLAN JM, KLEBANOFF SJ, LOPEZ AF, VADAS MA: Stimulation of the adherence of neutrophils to umbilical vein endothelium by human recombinant tumor necrosis factor. *Proc Natl Acad Sci USA* 82:8667, 1985.

194. POBER JS, GIMBRONE MA, LAPIERRE LA, MENDRICK DL, FIERS W, ROTH-

195. LEIN R, SPRINGER TA: Activation of human endothelium by lymphokines: Overlapping patterns of antigenic modulation by interleukin 1, tumor necrosis factor and immune interferon. *J Immunol* 137:1893, 1986.

195. ROTHLEIN R, DUSTIN ML, MARLIN SD, SPRINGER TA: An intercellular adhesion molecule (ICAM-1) distinct from LFA-1. *J Immunol* 137:1, 1986.

196. DUSTIN ML, ROTHLEIN R, BHAN AK, DINARELLO CA, SPRINGER TA: Induction by IL-1 and interferon-gamma: Tissue distribution, biochemistry, and function of a natural adherence molecule (ICAM-1). *J Immunol* 137:245, 1986.

197. MACGREGOR R, FRIEDMAN H, MACARAK EJ, KEFALIDES NA: Virus infection of endothelial cells increases granulocyte adherence. *J Clin Invest* 65:1469, 1980.

198. BOWMAN C, BUTLER E, REPINE J: Hyperopia damages cultured endothelial cells causing increased neutrophil adherence. *Am Rev Respir Dis* 128:469, 1983.

199. VERCELLOTTI G, MCCARTHY J, FURCHT L, JACOB H, MOLDOW C: Inflamed fibronectin: An altered fibronectin enhances neutrophil adhesion. *Blood* 62:1063, 1983.

200. SMEDLEY LA, TONNESEN MG, SANDHAUS RA, HASLETT C, GUTHRIE LA, JOHNSTON RB, HENSON PM: Neutrophil mediated injury to endothelial cells, enhancement by endotoxin and essential role of neutrophil elastase. *J Clin Invest* 77:1233, 1986.

201. RYAN U, SCHULTZ D, RYAN J: Fc and C3b receptors on pulmonary endothelial cells: induction by injury. *Science* 214:557, 1981.

202. BOXER LA, ALLEN JM, BAEHNER RL, AMICK V: Diminished polymorphonuclear leukocyte adherence. *J Clin Invest* 66:268, 1980.

203. MERCANDETTI AJ, LANE TA, COLMERAUER MEM: Cultured human endothelial cells elaborate neutrophil chemoattractants. *J Lab Clin Med* 104:370, 1984.

204. PRESCOTT SM, ZIMMERMAN GA, MCINTYRE TM: Human endothelial cells in culture produce platelet-activating factor (1-alkyl-2-acetyl-sn-glycerol-3-phosphocholine) when stimulated with thrombin. *Proc Natl Acad Sci USA* 81:3534, 1984.

205. FURIE MB, CRAMER EV, NAPRSTEK BL, SILVERSTEIN SC: Cultured endothelial cell monolayers that restrict the transendothelial passage of macromolecules and electrical current. *J Cell Biol* 98:1033, 1984.

206. HURLEY JV: An electron microscopic study of leucocytic emigration and vascular permeability in rat skin. *Austr J Exp Biol Med Sci* 41:171, 1963.

207. COCHRANE CG, AIKIN BS: Polymorphonuclear leukocytes in immunologic reactions. The destruction of vascular basement membrane *in vivo* and *in vitro. J Exp Med* 124:733, 1966.

208. BRYANT G, RAO CN, BRENTANI M, MARTINS W, LOPES JD, MARTIN SE, LIOTTA LA, SCHIFFMANN E: A role for the laminin receptor in leukocyte chemotaxis. *J Leukocyte Biol* 41:220, 1987.

209. BAGGIOLINI M, BRETZ U, DEWALD B: Biochemical and structural properties of the vacuolar apparatus of polymorphonuclear leukocytes, in Rossi F, Patriarca PL, Romeo D (eds): *Mechanisms of Phagocytes.* Padua, Piccin, 1977, p 89.

210. ARMSTRONG PB, LACKIE JM: Studies on intercellular invasion *in vitro* using rabbit peritoneal neutrophil granulocytes (PMNs). I. Role of contact inhibition in locomotion. *J Cell Biol* 65:439, 1975.

211. ELSDALE T, BARD J: Collagen substrate for studies on cell behavior. *J Cell Biol* 54:626, 1972.

212. HOWARD MW, STRAUSS RG, JOHNSTON RB: Infections in patients with neutropenia. *Am J Dis Child* 131:788, 1977.

213. GALLIN JI: Abnormal phagocyte chemotaxis: Pathophysiology, clinical manifestations, and management of patients. *Rev Infect Dis* 3:1196, 1981.

214. SNYDERMAN R, ALTMAN LC, FRANKEL A: Defective mononuclear leukocyte chemotaxis: A previously unrecognized immune dysfunction. *Ann Intern Med* 78:509, 1973.

215. WARD PA, SCHLEGAL RJ: Impaired leukotactic responsiveness in a child with recurrent infections. *Lancet* 2:344, 1969.

216. WILKINSON PC: Leukocyte locomotion and chemotaxis: Effects of bacteria and viruses. *Rev Infect Dis* 2:293, 1980.

217. BONER A, ZELIGS BJ, BELLANTI JA: Chemotactic responses of various differentiational stages of neutrophils from human cord and adult blood. *Infect Immun* 35:921, 1982.

218. HILL HR, GERRARD JM, HOGAN NA: Hyperactivity of neutrophil leukotactic responses during active bacterial infections. *J Clin Invest* 53:996, 1974.

219. HILL HR, WARWICK WJ, DETTLOFF J: Neutrophil granulocyte function in patients with pulmonary infection. *J Pediatr* 84:55, 1974.

220. MCCALL CE, CAVES J, COOPER R: Functional characteristics of human toxic neutrophils. *J Infect Dis* 124:68, 1971.

221. MOVAT AG, BAUM J: Polymorphonuclear leukocyte chemotaxis in patients with bacterial infections. *Br Med J* 3:617, 1971.

222. GALLIN JI, BUESCHER ES: Abnormal regulation of inflammatory skin re-

sponses in male patients with chronic granulomatous disease. *Inflammation* 7:227, 1983.

223. GRINSBURG I, QUIE PG: Modulation of human polymorphonuclear leukocyte chemotaxis by leukocyte extracts, bacterial products, inflammatory exudates, and polyelectrolytes. *Inflammation* 4:301, 1980.

224. HILL HR: Clinical disorders of leukocyte functions. in Snyderman R (ed): *Current Topics in Immunology*, 14th ed. New York, Plenum, 1984, p 345.

225. BERGMAN M, GUERRANT F, MURAD R, ET AL: Interaction of polymorphonuclear neutrophils with E. coli: Effects of enterotoxin on phagocytosis, killing, chemotaxis and cyclic AMP. *J Clin Invest* 61:227, 1978.

226. BOURNE HR, LEHRER RI, LICHTENSTEIN LM: Effects of cholera enterotoxin on adenosine 3',5'-monophosphate and neutrophil function: Comparison with other compounds which stimulate leukocyte adenyl cyclase. *J Clin Invest* 52:698, 1973.

227. FICK RB, ROBBINS RA, SQUIER SU, SCHODERBEK WE, RUSS WD: Complement activation in cystic fibrosis respiratory fluids: In vivo and in vitro generation of C5a and chemotactic activity. *Pediatr Res* 20:1258, 1986.

228. BERGER M, DEARBORN D, LEGRIS G, DORING G, SORENSEN R: Complement receptor expression on neutrophils (PMN) in the lung in cystic fibrosis (CF). *Pediatr Res* 20:305a, 1986.

229. CROWLEY CA, CURNUTTE JT, ROSIN RE, ANDRE-SCHWARTZ J, GALLIN JI, KLEMPNER M, SNYDERMAN R, SOUTHWICK FS, STOSSEL TP, BABIOR BM: An inherited abnormality of neutrophil adhesion: Its genetic transmission and its association with a missing protein. *N Engl J Med* 302:1163, 1980.

230. ARNAOUT MA, PITT J, COHEN HJ, ET AL: Deficiency of a granulocyte-membrane glycoprotein (gp150) in a boy with recurrent bacterial infections. *N Engl J Med* 306:693, 1982.

231. BOWEN TJ, OCHS HD, ALTMAN LC: Severe recurrent bacterial infections associated with defective adherence and chemotaxis in two patients with neutrophils deficient in a cell-associated glycoprotein. *J Pediatr* 101:932, 1982.

232. SPRINGER TA, UNKELESS JC: Analysis of macrophage differentiation and function with monoclonal antibodies, in Adams DO, Hanna MG Jr (eds): *Contemporary Topics in Immunobiology* (14). New York, Plenum, 1984, p 135.

233. SPRINGER TA: The LFA-1, Mac-1 glycoprotein family and its deficiency in an inherited disease. *Fed Proc* 44:2660, 1985.

234. DANA N, TODD RF III, PITT J: Deficiency of a surface membrane glycoprotein (Mol) in man. *J Clin Invest* 73:153, 1983.

235. BEATTY PG, OCHS HD, HARLAN JM: Absence of a monoclonal antibody-defined protein complex in a boy with abnormal leukocyte function. *Lancet* 1:535, 1984.

236. ARNAOUT MA, SPITS H, TERHORST C, PITT J, TODD RF: Deficiency of a leukocyte surface glycoprotein (LFA-1) in two patients with Mol deficiency. *J Clin Invest* 74:1291, 1984.

237. SPRINGER TA, MILLER LJ, ANDERSON DC: p150,95, the third member of the Mac-1, LFA-1 human leukocyte adhesion glycoprotein family. *J Immunol* 136:240, 1986.

238. FISCHER A, SEGER R, DURANDY A, GROSPIERRE B, VIRELIZIER JL, LEDEIST F, GRISCELLI C, FISCHER E, KAZATCHKINE M, BOHLER MC, DESCAMPS-LATSCHA B, TRUNG PH, SPRINGER TA, OLIVER D, MAVAS C: Deficiency of the adhesive protein complex lymphocyte function antigen 1, complement receptor type 3, glycoprotein p150,95 in a girl with recurrent bacterial infections. *J Clin Invest* 76:2385, 1985.

239. ROSS GD, THOMPSON RA, WALPORT MJ, SPRINGER TA, WATSON JV, WARD RHR, LIDA J, NEWMAN SL, HARRISON RA, LACHMANN PJ: Characterization of patients with an increased susceptibility to bacterial infections and a genetic deficiency of leukocyte membrane complement receptor type 3 and the related membrane antigen LFA-1. *Blood* 66:882, 1985.

240. MIEDEMA F, TETTEROO PAT, TERPSTRA FG, KEIZER G, ROOS M, WEENING RS, WEEMAES CMR, ROOS D, MELIEF CJM: Immunologic studies with LFA-1 and Mol-deficient lymphocytes from a patient with recurrent bacterial infections. *J Immunol* 134:3075, 1985.

241. FUJITA K, KOBAYASHI K, UCHIDA M, KAJII T: Neutrophil adhesion abnormality with deficient surface membrane proteins (gp110 and p98): The effect of their antibodies on the function of normal neutrophils. *Pediatr Res* 20:361, 1986.

242. THOMPSON RA, CANDY DCA, MCNEISH AS: Familial defect of polymorph neutrophil phagocytosis associated with absence of a surface glycoprotein antigen (OKM1). *Clin Exp Immunol* 58:229, 1984.

243. ROSS GD: Characterization of phagocytic and cytotoxic abnormalities in patients who have an inherited deficiency of neutrophil complement receptor type three (CR3) and the related membrane antigens LFA-1 and p150,95, in Aiuti F, Rosen F, Cooper MD (eds): *Recent Advances in Primary and Acquired Immunodeficiencies*. New York, Raven, 1986, vol 28, p 530.

244. BUESCHER ES, GAITHER T, NATH J: Abnormal adherence-related functions

245. WEISMAN SJ, BERKOW RL, PLAUTZ G, TORRES M, MCGUIRE WA, COATES TD, HAAK RA, FLOYD A, JERSILD R, BAEHNER RL: Glycoprotein-180 deficiency: Genetics and abnormal neutrophil activation. *Blood* 65:696, 1985.

246. BOXER LA, HEDLEY-WHYTE T, STOSSEL TP: Neutrophil actin dysfunction and abnormal neutrophil behavior. *N Engl J Med* 291:1093, 1974.

247. FISCHER A, BLANCHE S, VEBER F, LEDEIST F, GEROTA I, LOPEZ M, DURANDY A, GRISCELLI C: Correction of immune disorders by HLA matched and mismatched bone marrow transplantation, in Gale RP (ed): *Recent Advances in Bone Marrow Transplantation*. New York, AR Liss, 1986, p 368.

248. WALDROP TC, ANDERSON DC, HALLMON WW, SCHMALSTIEG FC, JACOBS RL: Periodontal manifestations of the heritable Mac-1, LFA-1 deficiency syndrome—clinical, histopathologic and molecular characteristics. *J Periodontol* 58:400, 1987.

249. FISCHER A, PHAM HT, DESCAMPS-LATSCHA B: Bone marrow transplantation for inborn error of phagocytic cells associated with defective adherence, chemotaxis, and oxidative response during opsonized particle phagocytosis. *Lancet* 2:473, 1983.

250. HAYWARD AR, LEONARD J, WOOD CBS, HARVEY BAM, GREENWOOD MC, SOOTHILL JF: Delayed separation of the umbilical cord, widespread infections, and defective neutrophil mobility. *Lancet* 1:1099, 1979.

251. DAVIES EG, ISAACS D, LEVINSKY RJ: Defective immune interferon production and natural killer activity associated with poor neutrophil mobility and delayed umbilical cord separation. *Clin Exp Immunol* 50:454, 1982.

252. BISSENDEN JG, HAENEY MR, TARLOW MJ, THOMPSON RA: Delayed separation of the umbilical cord, severe widespread infections, and immunodeficiency. *Arch Dis Child* 56:397, 1981.

253. NIETHAMMER D, DIETERLE U, KLEIHAUER E, WILDFEUER A, HAFERKAMP O, HITZIG WH: An inherited defect in granulocyte function: Impaired chemotaxis, phagocytosis and intracellular killing of microorganisms. *Helv Paediatr Acta* 30:537, 1975.

254. SOUTHWICK FS, HOLBROOK T, HOWARD T, SPRINGER TA, STOSSEL TP, ARNAOUT MA: Neutrophil actin dysfunction is associated with a deficiency of Mol. *Clin Res* 34:533A, 1986.

255. SPRINGER TA, ANDERSON DC: Antibodies specific for the Mac-1, LFA-1, p150,95 glycoproteins or their family, or for other granulocyte proteins, in the 2nd International Workshop on Human Leukocyte Differentiation Antigens, in Reinherz EL, Haynes BF, Nadler LM, Bernstein ID (eds): *Leukocyte Typing II: Human Myeloid and Hematopoietic Cells*. New York, Springer-Verlag, 1986, vol 3, p 542.

256. WEENING RS, ROOS D, WEEMAES CMR, HOMAN-MULLER JWT, VANSCHAIK MLJ: Defective initiation of the metabolic stimulation of phagocytizing granulocytes: A new congenital defect. *J Lab Clin Med* 88:757, 1976.

257. HARVATH L, ANDERSEN BR: Defective initiation of oxidative metabolism in polymorphonuclear leukocyte. *N Engl J Med* 300:1130, 1979.

258. MENTZER SJ, BIERER BE, ANDERSON DC, SPRINGER TA, BURAKOFF SJ: Abnormal cytolytic activity of lymphocyte function-associated antigen-1-deficient human cytolytic T lymphocyte clones. *J Clin Invest* 78:1387, 1986.

259. FISCHER A, DURANDY A, STERKERS G, GRISCELLI C: Role of the LFA-1 molecule in cellular interactions required for antibody production in humans. *J Immunol* 136:3198, 1986.

260. MARLIN SD, MORTON CC, ANDERSON DC, SPRINGER TA: LFA-1 immunodeficiency disease: Definition of the genetic defect and chromosomal mapping of alpha and beta subunits by complementation in hybrid cells. *J Exp Med* 164:855, 1986.

261. LAW SKA, GAGNON J, HILDRETH JEF, WELLS CE, WILLIS AC, WONG AJ: The primary structure of the beta-subunit of the cell surface adhesion glycoproteins LFA-1, CR-3 and p150,95 and its relationship to the fibronectin receptor. *EMBO J* 6:915, 1987.

262. KISHIMOTO TK, HOLLANDER N, ROBERTS TM, ANDERSON DC, SPRINGER TA: Heterogenous mutations of the beta subunit common to the LFA-1, Mac-1, and p150,95 glycoproteins cause leukocyte adhesion deficiency. *Cell* 50:193, 1987.

263. DANA N, CLAYTON LK, TENNEN DG, PIERCE MW, LACHMANN PJ, LAW SA, ARANOUT MA: Leukocytes from four patients with complete or partial Leu-CAM deficiency contain the common beta-subunit precursor and beta-subunit messenger RNA. *J Clin Invest* 79:1010, 1987.

264. LISOWSKA-GROSPIERRE B, BOHLER MCH, FISCHER A, MAWAS C, SPRINGER TA, GRISCELLI C: Defective membrane expression of the LFA-1 complex may be secondary to the absence of the beta chain in a child with recurrent bacterial infections. *Eur J Immunol* 16:205, 1986.

265. MILLER BA, ANTOGNETTI G, SPRINGER TA: Identification of cell surface antigens present on murine hematopoietic stem cells. *J Immunol* 134:3286, 1985.

266. ANDERSON DC, FREEMAN KLB, HEERDT B, HUGHES BJ, JACK RM, SMITH

cw: Abnormal stimulated adherence of neonatal granulocytes: Impaired induction of surface Mac-1 by chemotactic factors or secretagogues. *Blood* 70:740, 1987.

267. BRUCE MC, BAILEY JE, MEDVIK K, BERGER M: Impaired surface membrane expression of C3bi, but not C3b receptors in neonatal neutrophils. *Pediatr Res* 21:306, 1987.

268. HAMMERSCHMIDT DE, HARRIS P, WAYLAND JH: Intravascular granulocyte (PMN) aggregation in live animals: A complement (C) mediated mechanism of ischemia. *Blood* 52(suppl):125, 1978.

269. SACKS T, MOLDOW CF, CRADDOCK PR: Oxygen radicals mediate endothelial cell damage by complement-stimulated granulocytes. An *in vitro* model of immune vascular damage. *J Clin Invest* 61:1161, 1978.

270. HAMMERSCHMIDT DE, WEAVER LJ, HUDSON LD: Association of complement activation and elevated plasma-C5a with adult respiratory distress syndrome. *Lancet* 1:947, 1980.

271. HAMMERSCHMIDT PE, BOWERS TK, KAMMI-KEPFE CJ, JACOB HS, CRADDOCK PR: Granulocyte aggregometry: A sensitive technique for the detection of C5a and complement activation. *Blood* 55:898, 1980.

272. CHENOWETH DE, COOPER SW, HUGLI TE, STEWART RW, BLACKSTONE EH, KIRKLIN JW: Complement activation during cardiopulmonary bypass: Evidence for generation of C3a and C5a anaphylotoxins. *N Engl J Med* 304:497, 1981.

273. ARNAOUT MA, HAKIM RM, TODD RF III, DANA N, COLTEN HR: Increased expression of an adhesion-promoting surface glycoprotein in the granulocytopenia of hemodialysis. *N Engl J Med* 312:457, 1985.

274. ISMAIL G, MORGANROTH ML, TODD RF, BOXER LA: Prevention of pulmonary injury in isolated perfused rat lungs by activated human neutrophils preincubated with anti-Mol monoclonal antibody. *Blood* 69:1167, 1987.

275. HECHT Y, TOSI M, BERGER M: Amphotericin B (AMB) causes neutrophil (PMN) aggregation by increasing complement receptor expression via A Ca^{++} mediated mechanism. *Clin Res* 35:477a, 1987.

276. WRIGHT DG, ROBICHAUD KJ, PIZZO PA: Lethal pulmonary reactions associated with the combined use of amphotericin b and leukocyte transfusions. *N Engl J Med* 304:1185, 1981.

277. MOWAT AG, BAUM J: Chemotaxis of polymorphonuclear leukocytes from patients with diabetes mellitus. *N Engl J Med* 284:621, 1971.

278. PETERSON CM, JONES RL, KOENIG RJ, MELVIN ET, LEHRMAN ML: Reversible hematologic sequelae of diabetes mellitus. *Ann Intern Med* 86:425, 1977.

279. BAGDADE JD, STEWART M, WALTERS E: Impaired granulocyte adherence: A reversible defect in host defense in patients with poorly controlled diabetes. *Diabetes* 27:677, 1978.

280. BUONASSISI V, VENTER JC: Hormone and neurotransmitter receptors in an established vascular endothelial cell line. *Proc Natl Acad Sci USA* 73:1612, 1976.

281. BAINTON DF: Sequential degranulation of the two types of polymorphonuclear leukocyte granules during phagocytosis of microorganisms. *J Cell Biol* 58:249, 1973.

282. GALLIN JI, WRIGHT DG, SCHIFFMANN E: Role of secretory events in modulating human neutrophil chemotaxis. *J Clin Invest* 62:1364, 1978.

283. SPITZNAGEL JK, COOPER MR, MCCALL AE: Selective deficiency of granules associated with lysozyme and lactoferrin in human polymorphs (PMN). *J Clin Invest* 51:93A, 1972.

284. GALLIN JI: Neutrophil specific granule deficiency. *Annu Rev Med* 36:263, 1985.

285. PARMLEY RT, OGAWA M, DARBY CP: Congenital neutropenia: Neutrophil proliferation with abnormal maturation. *Blood* 46:723, 1975.

286. KOMIYAMA A, MOROSAWA H, NAKAHATA T: Abnormal neutrophil maturation in a neutrophil defect with morphologic abnormality and impaired function. *J Pediatr* 94:19, 1979.

287. BRETON-GORIUS J, MASON DY, BURIOT D: Lactoferrin deficiency as a consequence of a lack of specific granules in neutrophils from a patient with recurrent infections. *Am J Pathol* 99:413, 1980.

288. STRAUSS RG, BOVE KE, JONES JF: An anomaly of neutrophil morphology with impaired function. *N Engl J Med* 290:478, 1974.

289. BORREGAARD N, BOXER LA, SMOLEN JE, TAUBER AI: Anomalous neutrophil granule distribution in a patient with lactoferrin deficiency: Pertinence to the respiratory burst. *Am J Hematol* 18:255, 1985.

290. PETREQUIN PR, TODD RF III, SMOLEN JE, BOXER LA: Expression of specific granule markers on the cell surface of neutrophil cytoblasts. *Blood* 67:1119, 1986.

291. WILSON CB: Immunologic basis for enhanced susceptibility of the neonate to infection. *J Pediatr* 108:1, 1986.

292. CHRISTENSEN RD, ROTHSTEIN G: Exhaustion of mature marrow neutrophils in neonates with sepsis. *J Pediatr* 97:316, 1980.

293. BULLOCK JD, ROBERTSON AF, BODENBENDER JG: Inflammatory response in the neonate re-examined. *Pediatrics* 44:58, 1969.

294. EITZMAN DV, SMITH RT: The nonspecific inflammatory cycle in neonatal infants. *Am J Dis Child* 97:326, 1974.

295. SCHUIT KE, HOMISCH L: Deficient *in vivo* neutrophil migration in neonatal rats. *J Leukocyte Biol* 35:583, 1984.

296. MILLER ME: Chemotactic function in the human neonate: Humoral and cellular aspects. *Pediatr Res* 5:487, 1971.

297. ANDERSON DC, HUGHES BJ, WIBLE LJ, ET AL: Impaired motility of neonatal PMN leukocytes: Relationship to abnormalities of cell orientation and assembly of microtubules in chemotactic gradients. *J Leukocyte Biol* 36:1, 1984.

298. PAHWA SG, PAHWA R, GRIMES E: Cellular and humoral components of monocyte and neutrophil chemotaxis in cord blood. *Pediatr Res* 11:677, 1977.

299. KLEIN RB, FISHER TJ, GARD SW: Decreased mononuclear and polymorphonuclear chemotaxis in human newborns, infants, and young children. *Pediatrics* 60:467, 1977.

300. ANDERSON DC, HUGHES BJ, EDWARDS MS, ET AL: Impaired chemotaxigenesis by Type III Group B streptococci in neonatal sera: Relationship to diminished concentrations of specific anticapsular antibody and abnormalities of serum complement. *Pediatr Res* 17:496, 1983.

301. KRAUSE PJ, MADERAZO EG, SCROGGS M: Abnormalities of neutrophil adherence in newborns. *Pediatrics* 69:184, 1982.

302. KRAUSE PJ, HERSON VC, BOUTIN-LEBOWITZ J, EISENFELD L: Polymorphonuclear leukocyte adherence and chemotaxis in stressed and healthy neonates. *Pediatr Res* 2:296, 1986.

303. OLIVER JM, BERLIN RD: Mechanisms that regulate the structural and functional architecture of cell surfaces. *Int Rev Cytol* 74:55, 1982.

304. KIMURA GM, MILLER ME, LEAKE RD, RAGHUNATHAN R, CHEUNG ATW: Reduced concanavalin A capping of neonatal polymorphonuclear leukocytes (PMNS). *Pediatr Res* 15:1271, 1981.

305. STRAUSS RG, HART MJ: Spontaneous and drug-induced concanavalin A capping of neutrophils from human infants and their mothers. *Pediatr Res* 15:1314, 1981.

306. MILLER ME: Developmental migration of human neutrophil motility and its relationship to membrane deformability, in Bellante JA, Dayton DH (eds): *The Phagocytic Cell in Host Resistance.* New York, Raven, 1975, p 295.

307. NEUFELD ND, CORBO LM: Membrane fluid properties of cord blood mononuclear leukocytes: Associated with increased insulin receptors. *Pediatr Res* 18:773, 1984.

308. AMBRUSO DR, BENTWOOD B, HENSON PM, JOHNSTON RB Jr: Oxidative metabolism of cord blood neutrophils: Relationship to content and degranulation of cytoplasmic granules. *Pediatr Res* 18:1148, 1984.

309. REGELMANN WE, MILLS EL, QUIE PG: Immunology of the newborn, in Feigin RD, Cherry JD (eds): *Textbook of Pediatric Infectious Diseases,* 2d ed. Philadelphia, Saunders, 1987, p 921.

310. BLUME RS, WOLFF SM: The Chediak-Higashi syndrome: Studies in four patients and a review of the literature. *Medicine* 51:247, 1972.

311. CLARK RA, KIMBALL HR: Defective granulocyte chemotaxis in the Chediak-Higashi syndrome. *J Clin Invest* 50:2645, 1971.

312. WOLFF SM, DALE DC, CLARK RA: The Chediak-Higashi syndrome: Studies of host defenses. *Ann Intern Med* 76:293, 1972.

313. RAUSCH PG, PRYZWANSKY KB, SPITZNAGEL JK: Immunocytochemical identification of azurophilic and specific granule markers in the giant granules of Chediak-Higashi neutrophils. *N Engl J Med* 298:693, 1978.

314. HAAK RA, INGRAHAM LM, BAEHNER RL, BOXER LA: Membrane fluidity in human and mouse Chediak-Higashi leukocytes. *J Clin Invest* 64:138, 1979.

315. ROOT RK, ROSENTHAL AS, BALESTRA DJ: Abnormal bactericidal, metabolic, and lysosomal functions of Chediak-Higashi syndrome leukocytes. *J Clin Invest* 51:649, 1972.

316. KLEIN M, RODER J, HALIOTIS T, KOTER J, JETT RB, HERBERMAN B, KATZ P, FAUCI AS: Chediak-Higashi gene in humans. II. The selectivity of the defect in natural-killer and antibody-dependent cell-mediator cytotoxicity function. *J Exp Med* 151:1049, 1980.

317. ABO T, RODER JC, ABO W, COOPER MD, BALCH CM: Natural killer (HNK-1$^+$) cells in Chediak-Higashi patients are present in normal numbers but are abnormal in functions and morphology. *J Clin Invest* 70:193, 1982.

318. KATZ P, ZAYTOUN AM, FAUCI AS: Deficiency of active natural killer cells in the Chediak-Higashi Syndrome. *J Clin Invest* 69:1231, 1982.

319. ARGYLE JC, KJELDSBERG CR, MARTY J, SHIGEOKA AO, HILL HR: T-cell lymphoma and the Chediak-Higashi Syndrome. *Blood* 60:672, 1982.

320. BOXER LA, RISTER M, ALLEN JM: Improvement of Chediak-Higashi leukocyte function by cyclic guanosine monophosphate. *Blood* 49:9, 1977.

321. BOXER LA, WATANABE AM, RISTER M: Correction of leukocyte function in Chediak-Higashi syndrome by ascorbate. *N Engl J Med* 295:1041, 1976.

322. OLIVER JM, ZURIER RB: Correction of characteristic abnormalities of mi-

crotubule function and granule morphology in Chediak-Higashi syndrome with cholinergic agonists. *J Clin Invest* 57:1239, 1976.

323. OLIVER JM, ZURIER RB, BERLIN RD: Concanavalin A cap formation on polymorphonuclear leukocytes of normal and beige (Chediak-Higashi) mice. *Nature* 253:471, 1975.

324. MALECH HL, ROOT RK, GALLIN JI: Structural analysis of human neutrophil migration: Centriole, microtubule, and microfilament orientation and function during chemotaxis. *J Cell Biol* 75:666, 1977.

325. ANDERSON DC, HUGHES BJ, WIBLE LJ, ET AL: Normal microtubule assembly of Chediak-Higashi PMNs. *Pediatr Res* 936:252a, 1984.

326. NATH J, FLAVIN M, GALLIN JI: Tubulin tyrosinolation in human polymorphonuclear leukocytes. Studies in normal subjects and in patients with the Chediak-Higashi syndrome. *J Cell Biol* 95:519, 1980.

327. KRUGER GRF, BEDOYA V, GRIMLEY PM: Lymphoreticular tissue lesions in Steinbrink-Chediak-Higashi Syndrome. *Virchows Arch (A)* 353:273, 1971.

328. VIRELIZIER JL, LAGRUE A, DURANDY A, ARENZANA F, OURY C, GRISCELLI C: Reversal of natural killer defect in a patient with Chediak-Higashi Syndrome after bone marrow transplantation. *N Engl J Med* 306:1055, 1982.

329. BEAUDET AL, ANDERSON DC, MICHELS VV, ET AL: Neutropenia and impaired neutrophil migration in type 1B glycogen storage disease. *J Pediatr* 97:906, 1980.

330. AMBRUSO DR, MCCABE ERB, ANDERSON DC, BEAUDET A, BRANDT IK, BROWN B, COLEMAN R, FRIEDMAN HS, HAYMOND MW, KEATING JP, KINNEY TR, LEONARD JV, MAHONEY DH, MATALON R, ROE TF, SIMMOND P, SLOMIN A: Infectious and bleeding complications in patients with glycogenesis 1b: Relationship to neutrophil and platelet function. *Am J Dis Child* 139:691, 1985.

331. NARISOWA K, IGARASHI Y, OTOMO H, TADA K: A new variant of glycogen storage disease type I probably due to a defect in the glucose-6-phosphate transport system. *Biochem Biophys Res Commun* 83:1360, 1978.

332. LANGE AJ, ARION WJ: Type 1b glycogen storage disease is caused by a defect in the glucose-6-phosphate translocase of the microsomal glucose-6-phosphatase system. *J Biol Chem* 255:8381, 1980.

333. DESNICK RJ, SHARP HL, GRABOWSKI GA: Mannosidosis: Clinical, morphologic, immunologic, and biochemical studies. *Pediatr Res* 10:985, 1976.

334. VAN DYKE TE, HOROSZEWICZ HU, CIANCIOLA LJ: Neutrophil chemotaxis dysfunction in human periodontitis. *Infect Immun* 27:124, 1980.

335. PAGE RC, SCHROEDER HE: *Periodontitis in Man and Other Animals*. Basel, S. Karger, 1982, p 1.

336. SHURIN SB, SOCRANSKY SS, SWEENEY E: A neutrophil disorder induced by capnocytophaga, a dental microorganism. *N Engl J Med* 301:849, 1979.

337. COHEN DW, MORRIS AL: Periodontal manifestations of cyclic neutropenia. *J Periodontol* 32:159, 1961.

338. VAN DYKE TE, HOROSZEWICZ HU, GENCO RJ: The polymorphonuclear leukocyte (PMNL) locomotor defect in juvenile periodontitis: Study of random migration, chemokinesis and chemotaxis. *J Periodontol* 53:682, 1982.

339. TEMPEL TR, KIMBALL HR, KAKENASHI S, AMEN CR: Host factors in periodontal disease: Periodontal manifestations of Chediak-Higashi Syndrome. *J Periodont Res* 7(suppl 10):26, 1972.

340. PAGE RC, BOWEN T, ALTMAN L, VANDESTEEN E, OCHS H, MACKENZIE P, OSTERBERG S, ENGLE LD, WILLIAMS BL: Prepubertal periodontitis, 1. Definition of a clinical disease entity. *J Periodontol* 54:257, 1983.

341. QUIE PG: Chronic granulomatous disease of childhood. *Adv Pediatr* 16:287, 1969.

342. VAN DYKE TE, SCHWEINEBRATEN I, CIANCIOLA LJ, OFFENBACHER S, GENCO RJ: Neutrophil chemotaxis in families with localized juvenile periodontitis. *J Periodontol Res* 20:503, 1985.

343. PAGE RC, SCHROEDER HE: Pathogenesis of inflammatory periodontal disease. *J Lab Invest* 33:234, 1976.

344. VAN DYKE TE: Role of the neutrophil in oral disease: Receptor deficiency in leukocytes from patients with juvenile periodontitis. *Rev Infect Dis* 7:419, 1985.

345. CLARK RA, PAGE RC, WILDE G: Defective neutrophil chemotaxis in juvenile periodontitis. *Infect Immun* 18:694, 1977.

346. CIANCIOLA LJ, GENCO RJ, PATTERS MR: Defective polymorphonuclear leukocyte function in a human periodontal disease. *Nature* 265:445, 1977.

347. LAVINE WS, MADERAZO EG, STOLMAN J: Impaired neutrophil chemotaxis in patients with juvenile and rapidly progressing periodontitis. *J Periodont Res* 14:10, 1979.

348. GENCO PS, VAN DYKE TE, PARK B: Neutrophil chemotaxis impairment in juvenile periodontitis: Evaluation of specificity, adherence, deformability and serum factors. *J Reticul Soc* 28:815, 1980.

349. CIANCIOLA LJ, GENCO RJ, PATTERS M, MACKENNA J: A family study of neutrophil chemotaxis in idiopathic juvenile periodontitis. *J Dent Res* 56B:B90, 1977.

350. RANNEY RR, DEBSKI BF, TEW JG: Pathogenesis of gingivitis and periodontal disease in children and young adults. *Pediatr Dent* 3:89, 1981.

351. SUZUKI JB, COLISON C, FALKER WF, NEWMAN RK: Immunologic profile of juvenile periodontitis. II. Neutrophil chemotaxis, phagocytosis and spore germination. *J Periodontol* 55:461, 1984.

352. ZAMBON JJ: *Actinobacillus actinomycetemcomitans* in human periodontal disease. *J Clin Periodontol* 12:1, 1985.

353. SLOTS J, GENCO RJ: Black-pigmented *Bacteroides sp.*, *Capnocytophage sp.*, *Actinobacillus actinomycetemcomitans* in human periodontol disease: Virulence factors in colonization, survival and tissue destruction. *J Dent Res* 63:412, 1984.

354. VAN DYKE TE, BARTHOLOMEW E, GENCO RJ, SLOTS J, LEVINE MJ: Inhibition of neutrophil chemotaxis by soluble bacterial products. *J Periodontol* 53:502, 1982.

355. ZAMBON JJ, CHRISTERSSON LA, SLOTS J: *Actinobacillus actinomycetemcomitans* in human periodontal disease: Prevalence in patient groups and distribution of biotypes and serotypes within families. *J Periodontol* 54:707, 1983.

356. GENCO RJ, SLOTS J, MAUTON J, MARRAN P: Systemic immune responses to oral anaerobic organisms, in Lambe DW, Genco RJ, Mayberry-Carson KJ (eds): *Anaerobic Bacteria: Selected Topics*. New York, Plenum, 1980, p 488.

357. WOOD DD, IHRIE EJ, DINARELLO CA, COHEN PL: Isolation of an interleukon-1-like factor from human joint effusions. *Arthritis Rheum* 26:975, 1983.

358. TSAI C-C, MCARTHUR WP, BAEHNI PC, HAMMOND BF, TAICHMAN NS: Extraction and partial characterization of a leukotoxin from a plaque-derived gram-negative microorganism. *Infect Immun* 25:427, 1979.

359. TSAI C-C, TAICHMAN NS: Dynamics of infection by leukotoxic strains of *Actinobacillus actinomycetemcomitans* in juvenile periodontitis. *J Clin Periodontol* 13:303, 1986.

360. TSAI C-C, MCARTHUR WP, BAEHNI PC, EVIAN C, GENCO RJ, TAICHMAN NS: Serum neutralizing activity against *Actinobacillus actinomycetemcomitans* leukotoxin in juvenile periodontitis. *J Clin Periodontol* 8:338, 1981.

361. TSAI C-C, SHENKER BJ, DIRIENZO JM, MALAMUD D, TAICHMAN NS: Extraction and isolation of a leukotoxin from *Actinobacillus actinomycetemcomitans* with polymyxin B. *Infect Immun* 43:700, 1984.

362. DIRIENZO JM, TSAI C-C, SHENKER BJ, TAICHMAN NS, LALLY ET: Monoclonal antibodies to leukotoxin of *Actinobacillus actinomycetemcomitans*. *Infect Immun* 47:31, 1985.

363. BEATY TH, BOUGHMAN JA, YANG P, ASTEMBORSKI JA, SUZUKI JB: Genetic analysis of juvenile periodontitis in families ascertained through an affected proband. *Am J Hum Genet* 40:443, 1987.

364. SAXEN L, NEVENALINNA HR: Autosomal recessive inheritance of juvenile periodontitis: Test of a hypothesis. *Clin Genet* 25:332, 1984.

365. MELNICK M, SHILDS ED, BIXLER D: Periodontitis: A phenotypic and genetic analysis. *Oral Surg Oral Med Oral Pathol* 42:32, 1976.

366. AGGET PJ, HARRIES JT, HARVEY BAM: An inherited defect of neutrophil mobility in Shwachman syndrome. *J Pediatr* 94:391, 1979.

367. BRUETON MJ, MAVROMICHALIS J, GOODCHILD MC: Hepatic dysfunction in association with pancreatic insufficiency and cyclical neutropenia. *Arch Dis Child* 52:76, 1977.

368. SHWACHMAN H, DIAMOND LK, OSKI FA: The syndrome of pancreatic insufficiency and bone marrow dysfunction. *J Pediatr* 65:645, 1964.

369. AGGETT PJ, CAVANAGH NPC, MATTHEW DJ, PINCOTT JR, SUTCLIFFE J, HARRIES JT: Shwachman's syndrome: A review of 21 cases. *Arch Dis Child* 55:331, 1980.

370. BURKE V, COLEBATCH JH, ANDERSON CM, SIMONS MJ: Association of pancreatic insufficiency and chronic neutropenia in childhood. *Arch Dis Child* 42:147, 1967.

371. CLARK RA: Disorders of granulocyte chemotaxis, in Gallin JI, Quie PG (eds): *Leukocyte Chemotaxis*. New York, Raven, 1978, p 329.

372. LEDDY JP, BAUM J, ROSENFIELD SI: Genetic deficiencies of complement-derived chemotactic factors, in Gallin JI, Quie PG (eds): *Leukocyte Chemotaxis*. New York, Raven, 1978, p 389.

373. ALPER CA, ABRAMSON N, JOHNSTON RB: Increased susceptibility to infection associated with abnormalities of complement-mediated functions and of the third component of complement (C3). *N Engl J Med* 282:349, 1970.

374. ALPER CA, COLTEN HR, ROSEN FS: Homozygous deficiency of C3 in a patient with repeated infections. *Lancet* 2:1179, 1972.

375. BALLOW M, SHIRA JE, HARDEN L: Complete absence of the third component of the complement in man. *J Clin Invest* 56:703, 1975.

376. ROSENFIELD SI, KELLY ME, LEDDY JP: Hereditary deficiency of the fifth component of complement in man. I. Clinical, immunochemical, and family studies. *J Clin Invest* 57:1626, 1976.

377. ROSENFIELD SI, BAUM J, STEIGBIGEL RT: Hereditary deficiency of the fifth component of complement in man. II. Biological properties of C5-deficient human serum. *J Clin Invest* 57:1635, 1976.

378. CLARK RA, KIMBALL HR, DECKER JL: Neutrophil chemotaxis in systemic lupus erythematosus. *Ann Rheum Dis* 33:167, 1974.

379. MILLER ME, NILSSON UR: A familial deficiency of the phagocytosis-enhancing activity of serum related to a dysfunction of the fifth component of complement (C5). *N Engl J Med* 282:354, 1970.

380. ADAMKIN P, STITZEL A, URSOM I, FARNETT ML, POST E, SPITZER R: Activity of the alternative pathway of complement in the newborn infant. *J Pediatr* 93:604, 1978.

381. ANDERSON DC, YORK TL, ROSE G, SMITH CW: Assessment of serum factor B, serum opsonins, granulocyte chemotaxis, and infection in nephrotic syndrome of children. *J Infect Dis* 140:1, 1979.

382. WEISS AS, GALLIN JI, KAPLAN AP: Fletcher factor deficiency: A diminished rate of Hageman factor activation caused by the absence of prekallikrein with abnormalities of coagulation, fibrinolysis, chemotactic activity and kinin generation. *J Clin Invest* 53:622, 1974.

383. GOLDBLUM SE, VANEPPS DE, REED WP: Serum inhibitor of C5 fragment-mediated polymorphonuclear leukocyte chemotaxis associated with chronic hemodialysis. *J Clin Invest* 64:255, 1979.

384. WARD PA, BERENBERG JL: Defective regulation of inflammatory mediators in Hodgkin's disease: Supernormal levels of chemotactic factor inactivator. *N Engl J Med* 290:76, 1974.

385. WARD PA, GORALNICK S, BULLOCK WE: Defective leukotaxis in patients with lepromatous leprosy. *J Lab Clin Med* 87:1025, 1976.

386. MADERAZO E, WARD PA, WORONICK CL, KUBIK J, DEGRAFF AC: Leukotactic dysfunction in sarcoidosis. *Ann Intern Med* 84:414, 1976.

387. MADERAZO E, WARD PA, QUINTILANI R: Defective regulation of chemotaxis in cirrhosis. *J Lab Clin Med* 85:621, 1974.

388. BUCKLEY RH, BECKER WG: Abnormalities in the regulation of human IgE synthesis. *Immunol Rev* 41:288, 1978.

389. CHURCH JA, FRENKEL LD, WRIGHT DG: T lymphocyte dysfunction, hyperimmunoglobulinemia E, recurrent bacterial infections, and defective neutrophil chemotaxis in a Negro child. *J Pediatr* 88:982, 1976.

390. GEHA RS, REINHERZ E, LEUNG D: Deficiency of suppressor T cells in the hyperimmunoglobulin E syndrome. *J Clin Invest* 68:783, 1981.

391. DONABEDIAN H, GALLIN JI: The hyperimmunoglobulin E recurrent infection (Job's) syndrome: A review of the NIH experience and literature. *Medicine* 62:195, 1983.

392. HILL HR, QUIE PG, PABST HF: Defect in neutrophil granulocyte chemotaxis in Job's syndrome of recurrent "cold" staphylococcal abscesses. *Lancet* 2:617, 1974.

393. SCHOPFER K, DOUGLAS SD, WILKINSON BJ: Immunoglobulin E antibodies against *Staphylococcus aureus* cell walls in the sera of patients with hyperimmunoglobulinemia E and recurrent staphylococcal infection. *Infect Immun* 27:563, 1980.

394. BERGER M, KIRKPATRICK H, GOLDSMITH PK: IgE antibodies to Staphylococcus aureus and Candida albicans in patients with the syndrome of hyperimmunoglobulin E and recurrent infections. *J Immunol* 125:2437, 1980.

395. RADERMECKER M, MALDAGUE MP: Depression of neutrophil chemotaxis in atopic individuals: An H_2 histamine receptor response. *Int Arch Allergy Appl Immunol* 65:144, 1981.

396. HILL HR, ESTENSEN RD, HOGAN NA: Severe staphylococcal disease associated with allergic manifestations, hyperimmunoglobulinemia E, and defective neutrophil chemotaxis. *J Lab Clin Med* 88:796, 1976.

397. FISCHER TJ, GARD SE, RACHELEFSKY GS: Monocyte chemotaxis under agarose: Defects in atopic disease, aspirin therapy, and mucocutaneous candidiasis. *Pediatr Res* 14:242, 1980.

398. TWOMEY JJ, WADDELL CC, KRANTZ S: Chronic mucocutaneous candidiasis with macrophage dysfunction, a plasma inhibitor, and co-existent aplastic anemia. *J Lab Clin Med* 85:968, 1975.

399. VANSCOY RE, HILL HR, RITTS RE: Familial neutrophil chemotaxis defect, recurrent bacterial infections, mucocutaneous candidiasis, and hyperimmunoglobulinemia E. *Ann Intern Med* 82:766, 1975.

400. D'AMELIO R, LEMOLI S, ROSSI P: Neutrophil chemotaxis defect in IgA deficiency evaluated by migration agarose method. *Scand J Immunol* 11:471, 1980.

401. D'AMELIO R, ROSSI P, LEMOLI S: Defective neutrophil chemotaxis in hypogammaglobulinemia and selective IgA deficiency. *Clin Immunol Immunopathol* 16:287, 1980.

402. AIUTI F, BUSINCO M, FIORILLI M: Fatal liver transplantation in two infants with severe combined immunodeficiency. *Transplant Proc* 11:230, 1979.

403. ALTMAN LC, SNYDERMAN R, BLAESE RM: Abnormalities of chemotactic lymphokine synthesis and mononuclear leukocyte chemotaxis in Wiskott-Aldrich syndrome. *J Clin Invest* 54:486, 1974.

CHAPTER 114

INHERITED DISORDERS OF PHAGOCYTE KILLING

JOHN R. FOREHAND
WILLIAM M. NAUSEEF
RICHARD B. JOHNSTON, JR.

1. *Phagocytic cells provide the body with a first line of defense against microbial infection. This protective capacity depends upon both oxygen-dependent and oxygen-independent killing mechanisms. The latter group includes the release of an array of hydrolytic enzymes from cytoplasmic granules into the phagolysosome. Oxygen-dependent microbial killing by phagocytes relies on a series of events initiated by phagocytosis, beginning with the generation of toxic oxygen products from molecular oxygen through a series of single electron transfers. This process is mediated by a plasma membrane-associated NADPH oxidase. Granules also release myeloperoxidase into the phagolysosome. In the presence of myeloperoxidase, H_2O_2 from the respiratory burst and chloride ions react to product hypochlorous acid, a potent microbicidal agent. These oxygen-dependent events do not occur normally in phagocytes from patients with chronic granulomatous disease, myeloperoxidase deficiency, or deficiency of the enzymes glucose-6-phosphate dehydrogenase, glutathione synthetase, or glutathione reductase.*

2. *Congenital absence of the NADPH oxidase or its activation mechanism in phagocytes results in the clinical syndrome of chronic granulomatous disease, associated with recurrent, pyogenic infections of the skin, soft tissues, mononuclear phagocyte system, and respiratory tract. Catalase-positive bacteria and fungi are the common pathogens. Phagocytes from these patients ingest organisms normally but display impaired microbial killing, which is the basis of the clinical syndrome. Chronic granulomatous disease is a heterogeneous disorder with regard to mode of inheritance, severity of disease, and defect in the NADPH oxidase system. Thus, the disease can result from one of several molecular defects of the respiratory burst apparatus in the phagocyte. In the most common form of chronic granulomatous disease, which is X-linked, the defective gene product is the β subunit of the cytochrome b component of NADPH oxidase. The gene is cloned and mapped to chromosome Xp21.*

3. *Severe glucose-6-phosphate dehydrogenase deficiency with impaired neutrophil hexose monophosphate shunt activity can mimic chronic granulomatous disease. Neutrophils with diminished glucose-6-phosphate dehydrogenase activity are unable to generate the NADPH required to sustain activity of the respiratory burst oxidase and as a result display a defect in intracellular killing.*

4. *Myeloperoxidase, a protein present in the azurophilic granule of mature neutrophils, catalyzes the oxidation of cellular halides by hydrogen peroxide to the potent microbicidal species, hypohalites. The partial or complete absence of MPO affects about 1 in 2000 apparently healthy individuals. Myeloperoxidase deficiency is usually not associated with clinically signifi-*

cant infections, with the exception of invasive fungal disease in individuals with concomitant diabetes mellitus.

5. *Glutathione synthetase and glutathione reductase activities are required to maintain adequate intracellular levels of reduced glutathione. This sulfhydryl-containing tripeptide protects the cell from oxidative injury. Deficiency of either of these enzymes permits auto-oxidative damage, which is associated with abnormal microbicidal activity.*

NORMAL MICROBICIDAL MECHANISMS OF PHAGOCYTIC CELLS

The role of phagocytes in host defense against invading microbes has been recognized since Metchnikoff reported his observations in 1883.[1-3] His pioneering studies were made with wandering mesothelial cells from starfish. In the human, phagocytosis is performed efficiently and rapidly by circulating polymorphonuclear neutrophils (PMNs), eosinophils, and monocytes, and by fixed tissue macrophages, which are the progeny of monocytes.[4] These professional phagocytes provide the body with a first line of defense against infection. When phagocytes, in response to chemotactic stimuli, migrate to sites of infection and contact invading microorganisms, ingestion ensues.

Once microorganisms are ingested, they are retained in intracellular vacuoles (phagosomes), where they are exposed to cell-generated antimicrobial factors and killed. Neutrophils use several methods to destroy invading microbes; these methods can be broadly classified as independent of or dependent on molecular oxygen.

Oxygen-Independent Mechanisms

It is difficult to determine the effectiveness of nonoxidative killing by neutrophils. However, several lines of evidence support a role for microbicidal activity that occurs in the absence of oxygen. First, the efficacy of oxygen-independent mechanisms can be demonstrated by the bactericidal activity of neutrophils in oxygen-depleted systems.[5-7] The inability to achieve complete anoxia in these systems precludes proof for nonoxidative killing. Secondly, neutrophils from patients with chronic granulomatous disease, which are unable to generate

---

Nonstandard abbreviations used in this chapter are: CGD = chronic granulomatous disease; f-Met-Leu-Phe = N-formylmethionylleucylphenylalanine; G-6-PD = glucose-6-phosphate dehydrogenase; MPO = myeloperoxidase; NBT = nitroblue tetrazolium; and PMA = phorbol myristate acetate.

microbicidal oxygen metabolites, can kill at least some of an inoculum of most bacteria.[8] Thirdly, constituents of neutrophil granules have bactericidal capacity.

Studies of fractions from disrupted neutrophils have localized the antibacterial protein activity to cytoplasmic granules.[9,10] Several antibacterial proteins have been described, a few of which merit mention (Table 114-1). They include 37,000- and 57,000-dalton cationic antibacterial proteins[11] and a 60,000-dalton bactericidal–permeability-increasing factor.[12] All are specific for gram-negative bacteria. Three low molecular weight peptides (<3500 dalton), the defensins, also derived from azurophilic granules, have both antibacterial and antifungal properties and require a pH of 7.0 to 8.0 for optimal activity.[13] Azurophil-derived bactericidal factor, a protein extracted from azurophilic granules, possesses in vitro bactericidal activity against virulent, clinical isolates of both gram-negative and gram-positive microorganisms at an optimal pH of 5.5 (approximately the pH that is thought to exist in the phagolysosome after the ingestion of microorganisms).[14] Further comparisons are difficult because of the unique isolation and purification techniques for each protein.

Studied in greater detail is the 14,500-dalton cationic protein lysozyme. This bacteriolytic agent is found in both azurophilic and specific granules of neutrophils and is secreted constitutively by monocytes and macrophages.[15] Lysozymes' bacteriolytic activity may be enhanced in the presence of complement.[16] It acts by cleaving the $\beta1\rightarrow4$ linkage between N-acetylmuramic acid and N-acetylglucosamine in the glycan backbone of the bacterial cell wall peptidoglycan.[9] The contribution of lysozymes to the microbicidal activity of the neutrophil is not clear. However, the digestion of bacteria within phagolysosomes correlates with their susceptibility to in vitro lysozyme activity.[9]

Optimal neutrophil antimicrobial activity is also likely to depend upon the intraphagolysosomal pH. Microorganisms often do not survive in a low pH environment,[17] and granule-associated antibacterial products that are released into the phagolysosome function within a narrow pH range.[9]

Oxygen-Dependent Mechanisms

Respiratory Burst. During phagocytosis, neutrophils undergo a burst of oxidative metabolism[18–23] that is summarized in Table 114-2. This impressive event begins with a marked increase in oxygen uptake, and includes increased utilization of glucose via the hexose monophosphate shunt and release of the bactericidal oxygen metabolites superoxide anion (O_2^-),[24,25] hydrogen peroxide (H_2O_2),[26] hydroxyl radical ($\cdot OH$),[25–29] and, perhaps, singlet oxygen.[30,31] This cyanide-insensitive[32] increase in oxidative metabolic activity is commonly termed the *respiratory burst*. Associated with this burst in oxidative metabolism is the phagocyte's ability to emit low levels of light (chemiluminescence).[30]

The enhanced oxygen consumption in response to phagocytosis was first described over 50 years ago but was felt to be associated with mitochondrial respiration normally required for energy-dependent cellular activity.[18] The observation that the phagocytosis-associated increase in oxygen consumption occurred in the presence of the inhibitor cyanide (CN^-) led to the conclusion in 1959 that mitochondrial energy metabolism was unnecessary for phagocytosis.[32] The significance of the enhanced oxygen uptake was unclear. Two years later it was observed that phagocytosing neutrophils produce H_2O_2, previously recognized for its toxicity to *E. coli*.[33] This finding provided a plausible basis for the microbicidal nature of phagocytosis. H_2O_2 was shown to interact with halide ions in the presence of the granule protein myeloperoxidase to generate microbicidal hypohalites, especially hypochlorite anion (OCl^-).[34] In 1973, phagocytosing neutrophils were reported to release O_2^-.[24]

O_2^-, now recognized to be the initial conversion product of the consumed oxygen, is generated through activity of a plasma membrane-associated enzyme or enzyme complex termed *NADPH oxidase*. This complex reduces oxygen univalently using NADPH as electron donor:[22]

$$2O_2 + NADPH \xrightarrow[\text{oxidase}]{\text{NADPH}} 2O_2^- + NADP^+ + H^+$$

Most of this O_2^- is thought to react with itself in a dismutation reaction (either spontaneously or more rapidly in the presence of superoxide dismutase) to form the second product of the respiratory burst, H_2O_2:

$$2O_2^- + 2H^+ \xrightarrow[\text{dismutase}]{\text{superoxide}} H_2O_2 + O_2$$

The list of oxygen metabolites generated in the phagocytosis-dependent respiratory burst now includes OCl^-[35] and hydroxyl radical ($\cdot OH$).[25,27–29] $\cdot OH$ is a highly potent oxidant formed by the interaction between O_2^- and H_2O_2 in the presence of iron or other metal (Haber-Weiss reactions), summarized as follows:

$$O_2^- + Fe^{3+} \longrightarrow Fe^{2+} + O_2$$
$$Fe^{2+} + H_2O_2 \longrightarrow Fe^{3+} + HO^- + \cdot OH$$

Table 114-1 Bactericidal Proteins of Human Neutrophils

Bactericidal protein	Subcellular location	Optimal pH	Susceptible species
1. Cationic antimicrobial proteins ($M_r = 37,000$ and $57,000$)	Mixed granules	5.6–7.4	Gram-negative bacteria
2. Bactericidal/permeability-increasing protein ($M_r = 60,000$)	Azurophilic granule	7.0	Gram-negative bacteria
3. Defensins ($M_r < 3500$)	Azurophilic granule	7.0–8.0	Gram-positive and gram-negative bacteria, *C. neoformans*, herpes simplex virus, type 1
4. Azurophil-derived bactericidal factor ($M_r = 29,000$)	Azurophilic granule	5.5	Gram-positive and gram-negative bacteria

Table 114-2 Components of the Respiratory Burst

1. Increased oxygen consumption
2. Enhanced glucose utilization through the hexose monophosphate shunt
3. Release of O_2^-, H_2O_2, and $\cdot OH$
4. Chemiluminescence
5. Turnover of NADPH and reduced glutathione

or by the interaction between H_2O_2 and iron (Fenton reaction).[22] This latter reaction is accelerated by the presence of O_2^-.[36] The physiological role of hydroxyl radical and control of its production are still being elucidated.[36-38] It is generally recognized that what is symbolized to exist as $\cdot OH$ may, in fact, exist at least partially as another potent oxidative radical (i.e., $\cdot OR$) formed in the above reactions.

More recently identified are chloramines, formed by the reactions of hypochlorite with ammonia or amines.[39] Other microbicidal products of the reduction of oxygen may be formed by phagocytes, but their role has not yet been substantiated.

That the respiratory burst is critical for killing of microorganisms by phagocytes was demonstrated convincingly by the occurrence of the inherited disorder chronic granulomatous disease (CGD). Neutrophils from patients with CGD lack a respiratory burst and exhibit markedly deficient killing of most bacteria,[40,41] which is manifested clinically as frequent and life-threatening infections with those bacteria.[42]

ACTIVATION. The onset of the respiratory burst requires that an appropriate signal be generated to activate the normally dormant NADPH oxidase. The burst of oxidative metabolic activity is initiated in a number of ways: by interaction between certain ligands and their specific plasma membrane receptors; by insertion into the plasma membrane of ionophores that mediate the movement of cations across the membrane; or, with phorbol esters, by direct activation of the Ca^{2+}- and phospholipid-dependent protein kinase C. Each of these broadly variable stimuli leads to transformation of the normally quiescent respiratory burst oxidase into an active state capable of catalyzing the conversion of oxygen to O_2^-.

Specific in vitro stimuli of the respiratory burst include phorbol esters, especially phorbol myristate acetate (PMA);[43] synthetic, bacteria-derived, and complement-derived chemotactic peptides;[44-48] calcium ionophores;[49,50] plant lectins;[51] inert particles;[25] opsonized zymosan;[52] fluoride ion;[53,54] immune complexes;[55] products of arachidonic acid metabolism;[56-58] structural analogues of inositol[59,60] and diacylglycerol, espe-

cially 1-oleoyl-2-acetyl-glycerol;[61] detergents;[62,63] antineutrophil antibodies;[64,65] the fungal alkaloid cytochalasin E;[66] phospholipase C;[67,68] platelet-activating factor;[69] and platelet-derived growth factor.[70] A typical time course of the release of O_2^- from neutrophils and monocytes exposed to PMA or opsonized yeast particles (zymosan) is shown in Fig. 114-1.

The respiratory burst associated with phagocytosis in normal neutrophils begins 30 to 60 s after initial contact is made between the microorganism (coated with IgG antibody or complement factor 3 or both) and the phagocytic cell membrane.[71] This delay, or "lag time" (Fig. 114-1), is presumably the result of the biochemical steps (signal transduction, stimulus-response coupling) required to link ligand-receptor interaction (stimulation) with modification of the NADPH oxidase to an active state (activation). These steps are summarized in schematic form in Fig. 114-2.

When signals are created by phagocytosis or binding of ligands such as the chemotactic peptide N-formylmethionyl-leucylphenylalanine (f-Met-Leu-Phe), occupancy of specific cell-surface receptors induces a rapid hydrolysis of plasma membrane phosphatidylinositol 4,5-bisphosphate (PIP_2) via the activation of the phosphodiesterase phospholipase C through an interaction with guanine nucleotide regulatory proteins (G proteins).[72-74] The hydrolytic breakdown products of phosphatidylinositol 4,5-bisphosphate (PIP_2), inositol 1,4,5-trisphosphate (IP_3) and 1,2-diacylglycerol, may serve as dual second messengers.[74-76] Inositol 1,4,5-trisphosphate (IP_3) triggers the release of nonmitochondrial stores of Ca^{2+},[77] which, in turn, may activate calmodulin and thereby stimulate calmodulin-dependent kinases.[78] An increase in intracellular free Ca^{2+} may activate Ca^{2+}-dependent K^+ channels in the plasma membrane, thereby triggering a change in a K^+-dependent membrane potential.[79,80] Diacylglycerol and Ca^{2+} activate the Ca^{2+}- and phospholipid-dependent protein kinase C.[78,81] Additional signal transduction pathways to stimulate the respiratory burst have been proposed.[82,83]

When neutrophils are stimulated by phorbol esters, multiple proteins are phosphorylated in association with O_2^- release.[84] That protein phosphorylation may play a role in stimulation of the respiratory burst is suggested by the atypical phosphorylation of specific proteins in neutrophils from individuals with CGD. These systems comprise the focus of intense research by cell biologists, and much remains to be defined.

Also associated with stimulation of the cell is the transfer of cellular constituents from intracellular storage sites to the

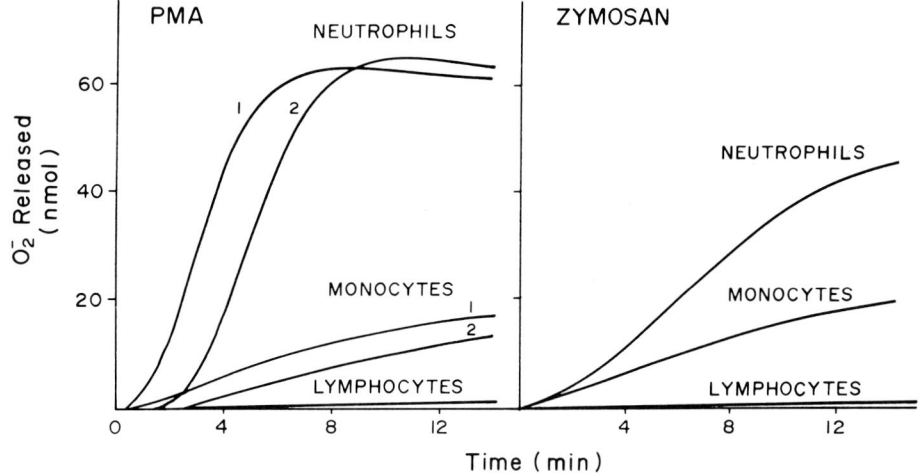

Fig. 114-1. Time course of O_2^- generation by 2.5×10^6 neutrophils, monocytes, or lymphocytes on contact with phorbol myristate acetate (PMA) at concentrations of 67 (1) or 33 (2) ng/ml (*left panel*) or with opsonized zymosan (*right*). Actual tracings of the recording spectrophotometer are represented. Note the typical, more vigorous respiratory burst in neutrophils compared to monocytes. (*Adapted from data of Johnston and Lehmeyer.[420] Used with permission.*)

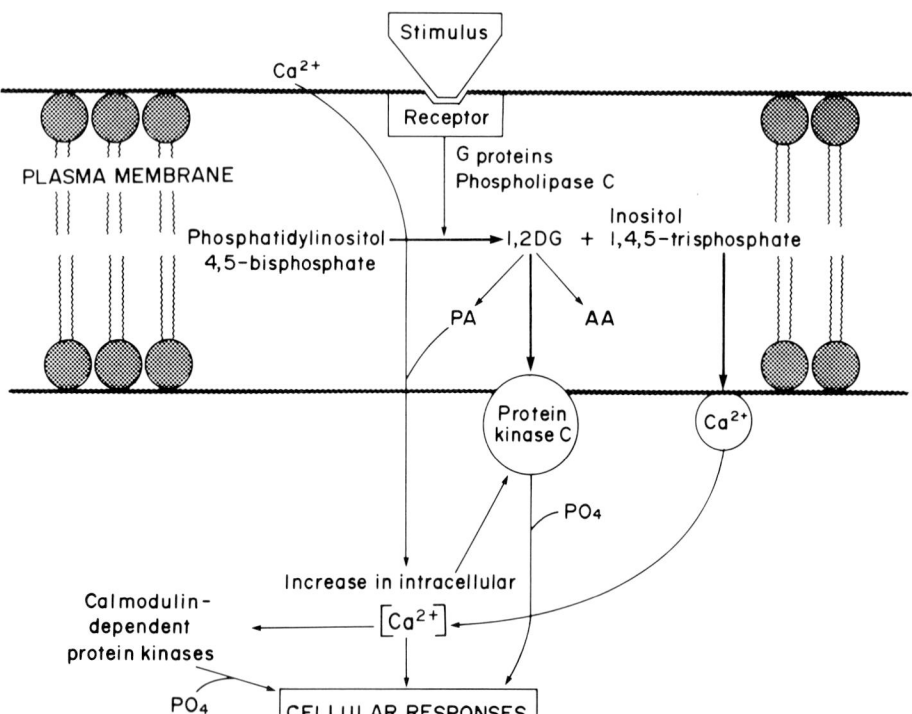

Fig. 114-2 Proposed pathway of transmembrane signal transduction induced by ligand-receptor interaction. DG = diacylglycerol; PA = phosphatidic acid.

plasma membrane (translocation). In particular, cytochrome b, thought to be a component of the NADPH oxidase, is found in the unstimulated cell primarily as an integral membrane protein of specific granules.[85,86] After stimulation, cytochrome b activity translocates to the plasma membrane[86,87] and to the membrane of the phagocytic vacuole.[88,89] Activity of protein kinase C also increases in the neutrophil plasma membrane after stimulation,[90] which could play a role in activation of the NADPH oxidase.

A greater understanding of the mechanisms by which the NADPH oxidase is activated has been gained from studying disrupted neutrophils that have not been stimulated. These preparations can generate O_2^- on the addition of NADPH in the presence of arachidonate or sodium dodecyl sulfate (SDS).[63,91–93] Activity in this system requires the cooperation of a cytosolic (soluble) fraction and a membrane-enriched (particulate) fraction. Stimulation prior to cell disruption partially removes the requirement for the cytosolic component,[63,91] implying that a cytosolic component has translocated to the membrane.

NADPH OXIDASE. The burst of oxidative activity associated with phagocytosis or with other appropriate stimuli is believed to be catalyzed by an NADPH oxidase (respiratory burst oxidase) first described over 30 years ago.[94,95] The respiratory burst oxidase is thought to be a multicomponent enzyme complex[86,96–98] analogous to that found in mitochondrial oxidative phosphorylation. However, because of its instability in vitro and its inactivity in unstimulated (resting) neutrophils, neither the molecular composition nor structure of the enzyme(s) is precisely known at present.

Several components of the oxidase complex have been proposed. Experimentation to date support well only two constituents, a flavoprotein that oxidizes NADPH and a unique low-potential cytochrome, probably the terminal electron carrier of the complex.

1. Flavoprotein. Its biochemical and electron transport properties make flavin adenine dinucleotide (FAD) a good candidate for the proximal electron carrier in the respiratory burst oxidase complex. Experimentally, FAD can accept reducing equivalents directly from NADPH, and a detergent-solubilized particulate fraction of disrupted neutrophils requires the addition of FAD to reestablish NADPH-dependent O_2^--generating activity, lost during the preparation.[99,100] The restoration of activity is specific for FAD rather than FMN or riboflavin. Too, FAD is undetectable in particulate fractions of neutrophils from some patients with either X-linked or autosomal recessive CGD.[101–104]

2. Cytochrome b$_{-245}$. Cytochrome b is a heme-containing glycoprotein with a molecular weight of 100,000 to 135,000.[105] The molecule is a heterodimer composed of a 22,000-dalton heme-associated protein (α subunit) and a 91,000-dalton glycoprotein (β subunit).[105,106] Cytochrome b$_{-245}$ has been detected only in neutrophils, monocytes, macrophages, and eosinophils.[107] Cloned cDNA for the β subunit[108] and for the α subunit[108a] have been obtained. The β subunit represents a 570-amino acid peptide which would be equivalent to 65,000 daltons.[109,110] The protein is glycosylated to explain the fact that the mature protein is 91,000 daltons. The glycosylation is consistent with the membrane localization of the protein. The predicted primary translation product of the α subunit is a nonglycosylated protein of 195 amino acids and 20,900 daltons. The sequence of a α subunit shows no overt similarities to known cytochromes, but there is a 31-residue region with a 39 percent identity to a region of polypeptide I of mitochondrial cytochrome oxidase. There is evidence for tight association between the two subunits. Expression of the mRNA for the β subunit is restricted to the phagocytic cell lineage, whereas mRNA for the α subunit appears to be constitutively expressed in a variety of cell types. These observations suggest that the large subunit may play a role in regulating the assembly of the heterodimer. It is unclear if the heme is bound to a single subunit or requires both subunits for binding. As will be discussed below, the β subunit is the product of the defective gene in X-linked CGD.[109,110]

The initial detection of cytochrome b in neutrophils led to investigation of its significance.[108] Unique redox properties make cytochrome b a good candidate for an electron carrier, particularly in a reaction expressly involving oxygen such as the respiratory burst.[111,112] To verify a role for cytochrome b in the conversion of oxygen to O_2^- during the respiratory burst, one should be able to demonstrate its reduction and oxidation (the transfer of electrons) during the exposure of whole cells to an appropriate stimulus. The stimulation of neutrophils with the potent trigger PMA in the absence of oxygen resulted in the reduction of cytochrome b.[113] The anaerobic exposure of a plasma membrane–enriched fraction of disrupted neutrophils to NADPH (thought to be the physiological substrate of the respiratory burst oxidase complex) also led to a reduction of cytochrome b.[114] Both experiments provided evidence that cytochrome b could participate in the enzymatic reduction of oxygen to O_2^-. The iron-containing heme component of oxidized cytochrome b is unable to accept directly both electrons donated by NADPH, whereas FAD can; thus, it is unlikely that cytochrome b can serve as the initial component of the enzyme complex. On the other hand, reduced cytochrome binds reversibly with carbon monoxide and is quickly reoxidized in the presence of oxygen.[111,115] These findings with cytochrome b are characteristic of an enzyme that catalyzes a reaction involving oxygen, and suggest that cytochrome b can serve as the terminal component, interacting directly with oxygen.

The absence of the characteristic reduced-minus-oxidized spectral pattern of cytochrome b in neutrophils from patients with classic X-linked CGD further supports the concept that it is an essential component of the respiratory burst.[116]

The current concept of the composition of the respiratory burst oxidase and the flow of electrons from NADPH to oxygen is illustrated in Fig. 114-3.

3. Other proposed components. Other components of the respiratory burst electron transport process have been proposed. Ubiquinone-10 is postulated to be part of the NADPH oxidase chain.[117] The extramitochondrial ubiquinone-10 content is disproportionately high in neutrophils.[118] Ubiquinone-10 copurifies with NADPH oxidase activity when neutrophils are disrupted and the cellular components are separated, and the addition of soluble ubiquinone-10 analogues to these preparations augments the NADPH-dependent O_2^--generating activity.[117] In vitro studies have demonstrated coupling of electron carrier function between FAD and ubiquinone-10 and between ubiquinone-10 and cytochrome b.[97] Another prosthetic group, an iron-sulfur complex like that in oxidative phosphorylation, has also been reported to function as a car-

rier in the transfer of electrons from NADPH to oxygen.[119] Others have not found this complex,[115] and its importance is unclear at the present time.

LOCATION. Once activated, the NADPH oxidase appears to sit in the plasma membrane with the NADPH-binding site oriented toward the cytoplasm, and the oxygen-binding and O_2^--releasing component situated toward the exterior (or toward the phagocytic vacuole).[120,121] Treatment of neutrophils with a nonpenetrating, protein-inactivating agent inhibited the production of superoxide in response to some stimuli but not others, suggesting that the NADPH oxidase was not readily accessible on the cell surface.[122] Although the enzyme appears to be anchored in the plasma membrane, electrons could be passed from the cytosolic electron donor, NADPH, into the interior of the membrane, to reduce oxygen in contact with the external surface of the intact cell or inner surface of the phagosome. Cytochrome b may be particularly suited to serve as a carrier of electrons through the plasma membrane, as the 91,000-dalton β subunit has a marked hydrophobic region that could represent a transmembrane segment.[108] The β subunit appears to be an integral membrane protein, and it is likely that the glycosylated domains extend to the external surface.

TERMINATION OF THE BURST. The duration of the respiratory burst is brief and depends upon the stimulus. Neutrophils prepared free of endotoxin and stimulated with 1 μM f-Met-Leu-Phe will cease to release O_2^- in 2 to 3 min.[123,124] Respiratory burst activity resulting from the ingestion of opsonized particles or exposure to PMA may last up to 10 min or longer (Fig. 114-1).[125]

Termination of the respiratory burst may result from inactivation of the NADPH oxidase by the oxygen-dependent or oxygen-independent bactericidal systems.[126–128] NADPH oxidase–rich fractions from neutrophils activated in the absence of oxygen or fractions exposed to inhibitors of myeloperoxidase (MPO) retained greater O_2^--generating capabilities than fractions activated in the presence of oxygen and myeloperoxidase.[126] This increased activity was also observed in neutrophils from individuals with myeloperoxidase deficiency.[127,128] Thus, it appears that an oxygen-dependent myeloperoxidase system inactivates the O_2^--forming enzyme.

ANTIOXIDANT MECHANISMS. Products of the respiratory burst are released into the phagolysosome where they participate in the destruction of the ingested particle. Figure 114-4 illustrates the metabolic pathways of the respiratory burst and the enzymes required to catalyze the reactions. As toxic oxygen metabolites can harm other circulating cells and adjacent tissues as well as the stimulated phagocyte, it is important that the site of action be concentrated in the phagolysosome. Neutrophils possess protective mechanisms to neutralize and rid the cell of oxygen metabolites not consumed in the microbicidal process.

Superoxide dismutase, which is found in the cytoplasm as a copper-zinc-containing enzyme and in the nucleus as a manganoprotein, is the principal scavenger of O_2^-.[129–131] This enzyme catalyzes the conversion (dismutation) of two O_2^- molecules to H_2O_2 and oxygen. The copper-containing plasma protein ceruloplasmin may also aid in the removal of O_2^- at sites of inflammation.[132]

Two well-described cytoplasmic systems exist in the neutro-

Fig. 114-3 Proposed sequence of electron transport in the respiratory burst oxidase.

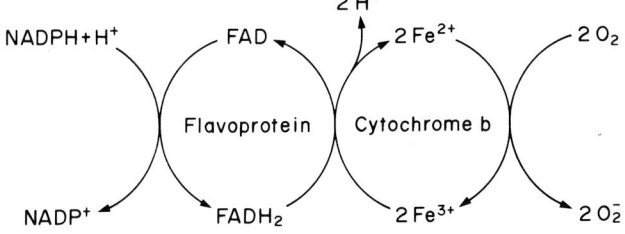

$$2 H^+$$

NADPH + H$^+$ → FAD → 2 Fe^{2+} → 2 O$_2$

Flavoprotein   Cytochrome b

NADP$^+$ ← FADH$_2$ ← 2 Fe^{3+} ← 2 O$_2^-$

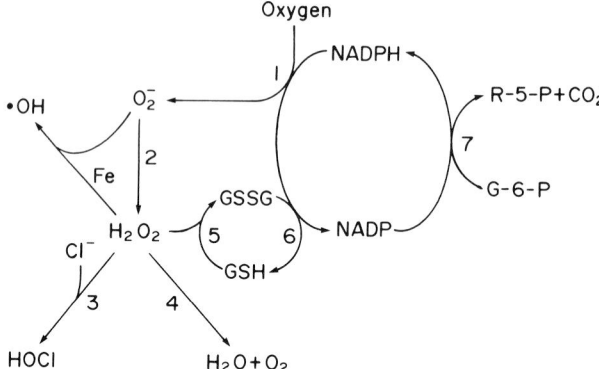

Fig. 114-4 The respiratory burst. Enzymes active in the burst or in protection against its toxic products are indicated by numerals, as follows: 1 = NADPH oxidase; 2 = superoxide dismutase; 3 = myeloperoxidase; 4 = catalase; 5 = glutathione peroxidase; 6 = glutathione reductase; 7 = glucose-6-phosphate dehydrogenase and 6-phosphogluconate dehydrogenase.

phil to protect against the potential oxidative injury of H_2O_2. *Glutathione* is a tripeptide found in all tissues and serves as a substrate for H_2O_2 in a reaction catalyzed by glutathione peroxidase.[133] *Catalase* enzymatically converts H_2O_2 to H_2O and oxygen.[134,135] Additionally, *pyruvate*, a product of aerobic glycolysis, has been proposed as an H_2O_2 scavenger.[136] Pyruvate reacts rapidly with H_2O_2 and increases survival of cells in tissue culture.

Other low molecular weight compounds found in cells or plasma can serve as detoxifying agents of harmful oxidants produced by the respiratory burst. *Vitamin E* (α-tocopherol) reacts with toxic oxygen radicals and preserves cell membranes from oxidative damage.[137,138] In an infant with a defect in the glutathione redox cycle, feeding vitamin E protected neutrophil membrane-dependent function against auto-oxidative damage.[139] *Vitamin C* (ascorbic acid) combines with oxygen free radicals to form harmless by-products[138,140] and can react with vitamin E radicals to regenerate vitamin E.[141] The nonessential amino acid *taurine* is a scavenger of hypochlorous acid (HOCl), with the formation of innocuous monochloramine taurine.[138,142,143]

Myeloperoxidase-Catalyzed System. Since Agner first described MPO in 1941,[144] numerous investigators have characterized the function and structure of this enzyme.[145-147] MPO is located in the azurophilic granules of neutrophils and the primary lysosomes of monocytes and is biochemically and immunologically distinct from eosinophil peroxidase.[148]

Oxygen-dependent killing of microorganisms[34,149-151] and tumor cells[152,153] can be mediated by the MPO-dependent system. Stimulated neutrophils release the products of the respiratory burst and the contents of the granules, including MPO, into the phagolysosome or the extracellular space. The combination of MPO, H_2O_2, and halide ions (the MPO-H_2O_2-halide system) results in the production of hypohalous acid and other intermediates that produce cytotoxicity. Hypochlorous acid and the monochloramines, the long-lived oxidants derived from HOCl, have been best studied in this regard.[154-165] The actual mechanisms for the cytocidal activity have not been established, but likely possibilities include destruction of bacterial electron transport,[166] ablation of the bacterial adenine nucleotide pool,[166] or oxidation of iron and sulfur centers critical for bacterial viability.[167,168]

MPO could modify the neutrophil-mediated inflammatory response in other ways. MPO-deficient neutrophils or mon-

ocytes produce larger amounts of oxygen-derived reactive species than do phagocytes with normal amounts of MPO.[127,128,169-175] Analysis of the kinetics of the response of these cells suggests a role for MPO in terminating the burst, as described above.

MPO also influences several features of the inflammatory response not directly related to the respiratory burst. For example, the MPO-dependent system inactivates a number of biologically important proteins,[176] including secreted granule products from neutrophils,[177-179] chemotaxins,[180-184] and α_1-antitrypsin.[185-187] In addition, the MPO-H_2O_2-halide system decreases the binding of chemotactic peptides to chemotactic factor receptors[188] and down-regulates natural killer cell activity.[189] Each of these activities could modulate the intensity or duration of the inflammatory response.

Each molecule of MPO (156,000 daltons) is composed of two large α subunits (59,000 daltons) and two smaller β subunits (13,000 daltons).[190-195] Native MPO can be cleaved by reduction and alkylation into a 78,000-dalton product that contains one α and one β subunit. This cleavage product, hemi-MPO, retains the same specific activity as native MPO, indicating that the intact molecule is composed of a pair of α-β complexes. Analytic ultracentrifugation of native and hemi-MPO indicates that the α and β subunits are linked along their long axes, most likely by a disulfide bond between the two α chains[191] or the two β chains.[192]

The presence and significance of various forms of MPO is an unsettled issue. Early studies suggested there were as many as 10 isozymes,[196-199] but more recent studies have failed to identify any isozymic variation.[190,200] Using cation-exchange chromatography during purification, a number of investigators have identified multiple forms of mature MPO that differ in the size of the α chain[195,201-204] or in the susceptibility to inhibition with 3-aminotriazole,[203] or in both. Three forms of MPO have been recovered from crystalline MPO[202]; they may represent biosynthetic intermediates distributed in different subcellular organelles or artifacts produced during isolation.[190,205]

There are two iron molecules in each molecule of MPO, each iron bound to the α subunit. Recent studies using electron spin resonance[206-208] have demonstrated that the peroxidative site of MPO is a chlorin group on each monomer and that the two chlorins are indistinguishable spectrally. These findings are consistent with earlier reports that the isolated α-β subunits (hemi-MPO) function peroxidatively with the same specific activity as the native molecule.[209]

INHERITED DISORDERS OF PHAGOCYTIC KILLING

Chronic Granulomatous Disease

Definition and History. Chronic granulomatous disease (CGD) is a heterogeneous group of genetic disorders characterized by recurrent, severe bacterial and fungal infections usually involving the skin, soft tissues, respiratory tract, lymph nodes, liver, and spleen.[111,138,210-214] CGD can be inherited in either an X-linked or an autosomal recessive fashion. Infectious episodes can be fatal, and therapy may require weeks to months of parenteral antibiotics in order to clear a deep-seated infection. Phagocytes from individuals with CGD can ingest normally, but they do not have to undergo a phagocytosis-associated respiratory burst, which is the basis for the defect in bactericidal activity. This defect has been demonstrated in neutrophils,[215] monocytes,[216,217] and eosinophils.[218]

CGD was first reported independently by Good and colleagues and by Landing and Shirkey in 1957.[219,220] The former report described four boys with suppurative granulomas in biopsy and necropsy specimens. In the latter paper, recurrent suppurative infections in two boys were associated with infiltration of viscera by pigmented lipid-laden histiocytes. The pathogenesis remained in question until the abnormal phagocytosis-associated metabolic and bactericidal defects of patients' neutrophils were described a decade later.[40,41,215] The metabolic defects were found to be accompanied by a failure of neutrophils to reduce the redox dye nitroblue tetrazolium (NBT), which led to the widespread use of phagocytic NBT dye reduction as an aid in diagnosing CGD.[40]

All the initially reported cases were male, suggesting an X-linked pattern of inheritance. However, in 1968, two papers appeared describing CGD in females.[221,222] One report noted the lack of abnormalities in parents, and an autosomal recessive mode of inheritance was proposed.[221] Defective O_2^- generation by CGD phagocytes was reported in 1974,[223] followed by evidence that the basic abnormality was a defect in NADPH-dependent O_2^- generation.[224–226] Cytochrome b activity in neutrophils, and its absence in CGD was described in 1978,[88] and the link between the lack of cytochrome b and X-linked CGD was reported in 1983.[227] The gene that is abnormal in X-linked CGD was cloned in 1986[108] and was subsequently determined to code for the β subunit of cytochrome b.[109,110]

Clinical Presentation. CGD should be considered in any individual with recurrent purulent infections caused by fungi or catalase-positive bacteria. The most frequent presentation is a male infant with a history of fever, infected dermatitis, pneumonia, lymphadenitis, and hepatosplenomegaly (Table 114-3). Since the condition is congenital, CGD is usually recognized in the affected individual before the first birthday, and the disease has been identified as early as the first week of life. Suspected cases, in families with a history of CGD, have been

Table 114-3 Clinical Findings in 168 Patients with Chronic Granulomatous Disease

Finding	Number of patients involved
Marked lymphadenopathy	137
Pneumonitis	134
Dermatitis	120
Hepatomegaly	114
Onset by age 1 year	109
Suppuration of nodes	104
Splenomegaly	95
Hepatic-perihepatic abscess	69
Osteomyelitis	54
Onset with dermatitis	42
Onset with lymphadenitis	38
Facial periorificial dermatitis	35
Persistent diarrhea	34
Septicemia or meningitis	29
Perianal abscess	28
Conjunctivitis	27
Death from pneumonitis	26
Persistent rhinitis	26
Ulcerative stomatitis	26

SOURCE: Johnston and Newman.[210] Used with permission.

diagnosed in utero with fetal blood.[228–230] In those patients with X-linked CGD whose diagnosis is made after age 1 year, a typical history of early onset recurrent infections can usually be obtained. Patients with certain variant forms of CGD, and perhaps those with the autosomally inherited form,[231] may have less severe symptoms and onset later in life.

Any organ system can be affected. However, cutaneous and mucous membrane surfaces are sites that are normally colonized with bacteria and fungi, making these structures and their underlying tissues a common target of microbial invasion. Therefore, skin and soft tissues, and the respiratory and gastrointestinal tracts are frequently involved. Patients occasionally have recurrent infections at the same anatomic sites.[213] Acute invasion and dissemination lead to suppurative complications and abscess formation, and chronic infections result in the development of characteristic noncaseating granulomas.

The most frequent sites of serious infection are in the mononuclear phagocyte system (spleen, liver, lymph nodes, lung).[210,212] This reflects the accumulation of infecting microorganisms by phagocytic cells that cannot kill them.[210] Cervical and other lymph node groups can become enlarged early in the course of the disease; spontaneous rupture and drainage can follow. *Staphylococcus aureus* and enteric bacteria are the organisms most often cultured from material taken from these sites (Table 114-4).[210,212] Chronically inflamed lymph nodes become infiltrated with lipid-laden pigmented macrophages and granulomas.

Hepatomegaly and splenomegaly are prominent, and liver involvement may progress to abscess formation (most commonly with *S. aureus*) requiring surgical intervention.[210] The occurrence of such abscesses, rare in children, should suggest CGD.[232]

Recurrent skin and soft tissue infections often occur and include pyogenic dermatitis, furunculosis, and subcutaneous abscesses.[210,212,233] An eczematoid dermatitis involving the eyelids and the area around the nares and mouth may be seen early in the course of the illness.[210] Granulomatous skin lesions have also been described.[232] Dermatologic findings can be prominent in adults with otherwise mild disease.[234] The cutaneous involvement may provide the first clue of an underlying immunodeficiency in a patient with CGD. Discoid lupus has been recognized in patients with autosomal recessive CGD[235,236] and in carriers of X-linked CGD.[237–241]

Infections of the lower respiratory tract with *S. aureus*, enteric bacteria, and *Aspergillus* species are common. Pulmonary infections with aspergillus may invade bone or soft tissues of the chest wall.[232] The pattern of pneumonia may be lobar, bronchial, or diffuse and generalized (Fig. 114-5) and may be accompanied by consolidation and by hilar lymphadenopathy.[138,232,242,243] Abscess formation is not common. Repeated infections may result in chronic lung disease with granulomatous infiltration of the lung and pulmonary fibrosis.[232,244] This has been noted both in adult and pediatric patients. In the upper airway, persistent rhinitis and otitis media are also common.

The oropharynx[245] and gastrointestinal tract[246] are frequent sites of infectious complications. Ulcerative stomatitis and gingivitis can be recurrent, and esophagitis may result in strictures and regurgitation.[210,247] Involvement of the gastrointestinal tract may mimic pyloric stenosis, eosinophilic gastroenteritis, or inflammatory bowel disease. Granulomatous inflammation of the stomach can lead to a characteristic luminal narrowing of the gastric antrum, as shown in Fig. 114-6, with persistent vomiting.[248–250] Similar lesions in the

Table 114-4 Infecting Organisms in 168 Patients with Chronic Granulomatous Disease*

Organism	Number of patients involved*
Staphylococcus aureus	87
Klebsiella-Aerobacter organisms	29
Escherichia coli	26
Serratia marcescens	16
Pseudomonas organisms	15
Staphylococcus albus	13
Aspergillus organisms	13
Candida albicans	12
Salmonella organisms	10
Proteus organisms	9
Streptococci	9
Nocardia organisms	4
Mycobacteria	4
Paracolobactrum organisms	4
Actinomyces organisms	2
Other enteric bacteria	9

*The number of patients from whom each organism was cultured from blood, cerebrospinal fluid, or purulent focus is shown.
SOURCE: Johnston and Newman.[210] Used with permission.

small or large bowel may result in diarrhea, malabsorption, or frank obstruction, and may require surgical intervention.[246,251] Rectal abscesses, perianal abscesses, and fistulas are not uncommon.[246]

Osteomyelitis has been described in about one-third of patients;[210,212,252] there is a peculiar predilection for the metacarpals and metatarsals. *Serratia marcescens, S. aureus,* and *Aspergillus* species are the most commonly isolated organisms.

Urinary tract infections are less common, occurring in only 7 percent of one large series of 168 patients.[210] Cystitis or obstructive uropathy may result from granulomatous involvement of the bladder wall (Fig. 114-7).[138,212,248,253–255] Amyloidosis,[138] glomerulonephritis,[256,257] renal abscesses,[258] and granulomatous inflammation of the kidney parenchyma have also been reported.[259] Gonadal involvement has been noted with tubo-ovarian abscesses in girls and testicular granulomas reported in a boy.[232]

Disseminated infection, with bacteremia or meningitis (or both), was reported in 29 (17 percent) of 168 cases described

Fig. 114-5 Lower respiratory tract involvement in a boy with CGD. The chest x-ray shows a diffuse reticulonodular interstitial pattern with superimposed alveolar densities in the left midlung field.

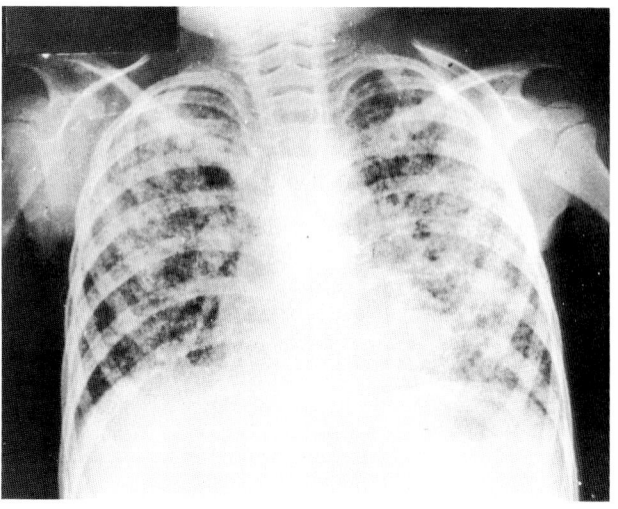

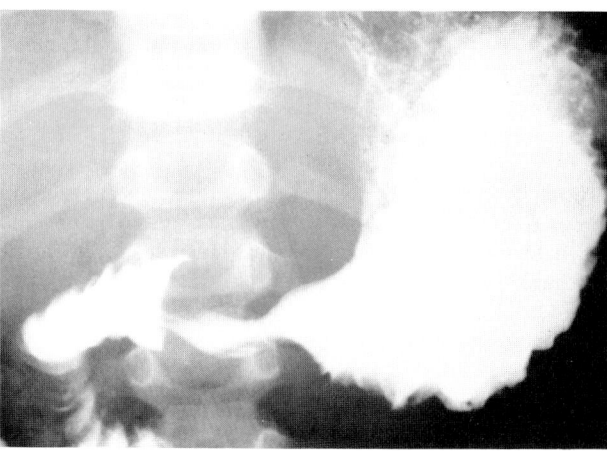

Fig. 114-6 Gastrointestinal involvement in CGD. A 5-year-old boy with X-linked CGD experienced the gradual onset of recurrent vomiting and weight loss. An upper gastrointestinal series showed annular narrowing of the antral lumen, nodular irregularities of the distal greater curvature of the stomach, and delayed gastric emptying.

in clinical detail.[210,260] *Salmonella* was the most commonly isolated organism both from the blood and in fatal infectious episodes.[261] Other complications include destructive chorioretinitis,[262] conjunctivitis,[210] thyroiditis,[263] pericarditis,[210] brain abscess,[210] and granulomatous involvement of the brain or spinal cord granuloma.[232,264]

In early surveys of children with CGD (1971 and 1977), one-half to three-fourths of patients had died before the age of 7.[42,210] Although there is still no specific cure for CGD, prophylactic antibiotics and the aggressive management of suppurative complications have greatly reduced deaths from infectious complications. A more recent review of 19 patients disclosed an overall mortality of 5 percent.[248] Although these 19 patients experienced no serious staphylococcal infections once they began antibiotic prophylaxis, the number of gram-negative isolates did not change while on antibiotic coverage.

Typical carriers of X-linked CGD are not unduly susceptible to infection, since about one-half of their phagocytes function normally; but there is an association with discoid lupus erythematosus and aphthous stomatitis.[237–241] Infiltrative and plaquelike lesions involving the face and distal extremities occur in these individuals. Of 14 carriers of X-linked CGD with discoid lupus erythematosus, none had serologic or clinical evidence of systemic lupus erythematosus.[237–241] One carrier mother was chronically infected with salmonella.[265]

Pathologic Findings. The infectious complications of CGD result in characteristic pathology. Specimens from acutely infected sites show a necrotic inflammatory process associated with suppuration. If the infection has been prolonged, granulomas are present, with multinucleated giant cells, macrophages, lymphocytes, and plasma cells.[212] The formation of these granulomas appears to be secondary to the prolonged intracellular residence of microorganisms.[266]

The abundance of mononuclear phagocytes in the liver, spleen, lungs, and lymph nodes makes these organs particularly susceptible to the formation of granulomatous lesions. When multiplying organisms are released from one phagocyte, they are ingested by another. This process recruits additional phagocytes with the eventual formation of granulomatous masses. Pigmented lipid-laden macrophages are also com-

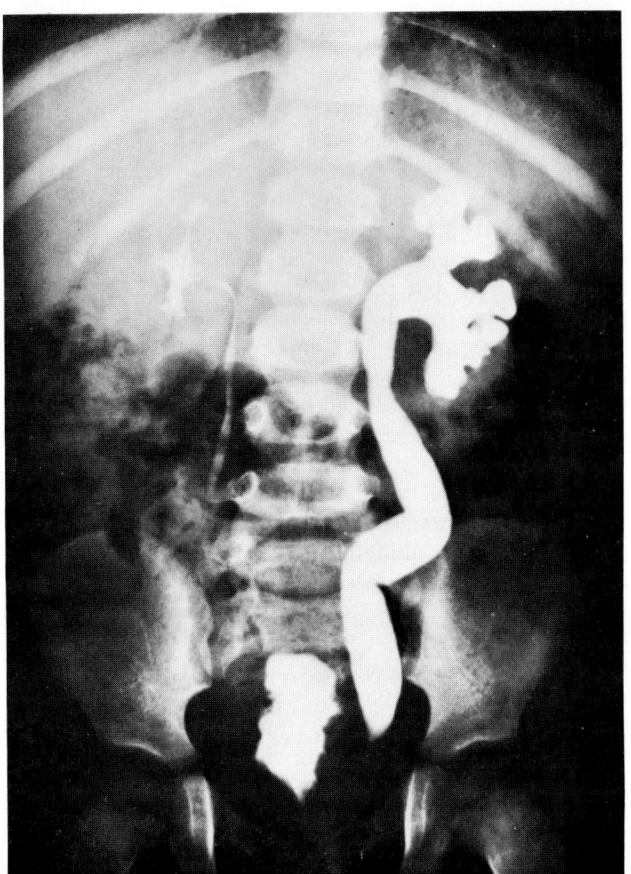

Fig. 114-7 Obstructive uropathy in a patient with CGD. Intravenous pyelogram of a boy with X-linked CGD demonstrating hydronephrosis and hydroureter on the left side. The obstruction was due to compression by a large inflammatory mass in the pelvis between the rectum and the bladder.

monly seen. The lipid material is yellow or tan in color (hematoxylin and eosin stain) and may result from incomplete degradative processes of phagocytes.[212]

Laboratory Findings. Except for studies of phagocyte function, laboratory findings reflect the presence of a chronic inflammatory disorder. During infections, a neutrophilic leukocytosis is frequent and may be associated with an elevated erythrocyte sedimentation rate. Anemia appears to be secondary to chronic infections; resolution usually occurs during disease-free intervals, and patients may benefit from iron therapy.[210,248] A polyclonal hypergammaglobulinemia is present, with elevated serum concentrations of IgG, IgM, and IgA.[42,138] Other tests of immune function are normal,[138] with the rare exception of abnormal lymphocyte transformation or chemotaxis, thought to be due to serum inhibitors.[267,268] If the phagocytic load is large, ingestion may be even greater in CGD than normal neutrophils that undergo auto-oxidation and subsequent decline in function.[269]

Five consecutively examined patients with X-linked CGD were found to lack the K_x (formerly K15) Kell blood group precursor antigen on the surface of their neutrophils.[270,271] A similar association had been previously reported between CGD and the rare McLeod phenotype (absence of K_x on red blood cell membranes) or the K_o phenotype (presence of K_x and absence of Kell antigens on red blood cell membranes).[272] Although the probability that the two events (CGD and the ab-

sence of K_x on neutrophils from five consecutively studied subjects) could occur independently was $<10^6$, it now seems certain that the absence of K_x does not lead to CGD. In one large kindred having four children with X-linked CGD, one unaffected male also had no detectable K_x on his neutrophils.[273] Other reports describe individuals with the McLeod phenotype and normal neutrophil bactericidal activity[274] and CGD in association with normal Kell antigens on neutrophils.[275]

It is not possible to explain the Kell data satisfactorily at this time, and perhaps not all of the reports will prove to be correct. The association with the McLeod phenotype appears to be satisfactorily explained by the presence of a separate McLeod locus which is near the locus for X-linked CGD. One male with a cytogenetically detectable deletion in Xp21 was affected with CGD, the McLeod phenotype, X-linked retinitis pigmentosa, and Duchenne muscular dystrophy.[275a] Other individuals with the concurrent occurrence of CGD and McLeod phenotype based on gene deletion have been identified.[276] Present evidence suggests that almost all patients with X-linked CGD are normal at the McLeod locus, and those who are not are affected with a gene deletion which includes the X-linked CGD locus and the McLeod locus.

Infecting Organisms. Individuals with CGD are susceptible to infections with catalase-producing organisms,[277] including bacteria, *Candida, Aspergillus,*[278] *Nocardia,*[279–281] and mycobacteria species.[282,283] The relative frequency of the various species isolated is shown in Table 114-4. The most frequent species associated with infection at almost any site are *S. aureus,* enteric bacteria, and aspergillus. Conspicuously absent are the encapsulated streptococcal and *Hemophilus* species, common pathogens in pediatric pyogenic infections. These latter species do not produce catalase, the heme-containing enzyme that catalyzes the degradation of H_2O_2. Therefore, they fall victim to the microbicidal effects of their endogenously produced H_2O_2 that is released into the phagocytic vacuole and converted to HOCl in the presence of MPO or to $\cdot$OH in the presence of iron.

Defect in CGD. The basis of the killing abnormality noted in neutrophils from patients with CGD is the near or complete absence of a respiratory burst. Since CGD is a heterogeneous disorder, with a dual mode of inheritance (X-linked and autosomal recessive), more than a single molecular defect exists. In fact, several defects have been described, and each results in the impaired generation of toxic oxygen species in response to phagocytosis. This concept has been further supported through in vitro studies in which the respiratory burst mechanism is reconstructed by combining whole cells or subcellular components of disrupted cells from different patients. Hybrid monocytes, created by the in vitro fusion of cells from X-linked and autosomal recessive individuals, demonstrated *de novo* respiratory burst activity (NBT reduction).[284,285] In analogous fashion, respiratory burst activity can be generated in a cell-free system by combining subcellular fractions of disrupted cells.[63,91–93] Neutrophils from CGD patients have deficient activity in either the cytosolic fraction (most cases of autosomal recessive CGD) or in the membrane-enriched fraction (X-linked CGD). Substituting a normal fraction from control neutrophils for the abnormal fraction results in normal respiratory burst activity.[214]

Because the basis of deficient phagocytic killing in CGD is

the absence of a normal respiratory burst, the fundamental underlying defect in the disease has been presumed to involve the catalytic activity of the oxidase or a step in the transmission of the signal that activates the NADPH oxidase. Chemotaxis, degranulation, and phagocytosis proceed normally in CGD, and, not surprisingly, early steps in the activation process (signal transduction) such as Ca^{2+} mobilization[286] and arachidonic acid metabolism[287-289] have been found to be normal in CGD neutrophils.

A change in membrane potential $(\Delta\psi)$ is seen in response to stimulation and is thought to precede respiratory burst activity.[290] Alteration in $\Delta\psi$ in response to some stimuli is markedly depressed in CGD, which has led to the conclusion that this alteration may be an important step in activation of the NADPH oxidase.[291] However, the change in $\Delta\psi$ in response to the Ca^{2+} ionophore A23187 is nearly normal in CGD neutrophils,[292] and the change in $\Delta\psi$ can be dissociated from the respiratory burst in normal neutrophils,[124,293] suggesting that a change in $\Delta\psi$ is not responsible for triggering the NADPH oxidase. That the extent of alteration in $\Delta\psi$ is abnormal in CGD could imply that the alteration (as measured) is, in part, secondary to the respiratory burst or that an abnormality exists prior to this event in the activation pathway.[138]

Acidification of the cytoplasm occurs normally in neutrophils in response to stimulation. This acidification does not take place effectively in CGD.[294] Artificially stimulating the production of acid equivalents in CGD neutrophils by activating the hexose monophosphate shunt did not correct the respiratory burst, demonstrating that the abnormality in cytoplasmic acidification is the result of an abnormal respiratory burst and not the cause.[294] Since oxidation of NADPH results in release of protons,[295] failure of this event in CGD might explain abnormal acidification.

Phosphorylation, which may be required for NADPH oxidase activation, is abnormal in CGD neutrophils after stimulation of the cell's respiratory burst.[296-298] Stimulated neutrophils from four patients with autosomal recessive CGD, in response to PMA, failed to phosphorylate a 44,000-dalton cell protein that was phosphorylated in neutrophils from normals and patients with X-linked CGD.[296] The substrate protein was present, and thus a kinase or a phosphorylase did not function normally, which suggests that this step in activation may be critical in triggering the NADPH oxidase. Neutrophils from patients with typical X-linked CGD failed to phosphorylate a 48,000-dalton protein in response to PMA.[299]

The structures for the subunits of the cytochrome b component of NADPH oxidase were presented above. The β subunit of cytochrome b is the defective gene product in X-linked CGD. Present evidence indicates that the defective respiratory burst in various forms of CGD results from the absence of the NADPH oxidase or one of its components. NADPH-dependent O_2^- release by membranes prepared from neutrophils of individuals with X-linked CGD is undetectable in the presence of physiological concentrations of NADPH.[224-226] In these experiments, cells were stimulated prior to disruption, so a defect in activation could not be clearly excluded. However, using a cell-free system capable of NADPH-dependent O_2^- production in the presence of arachidonate or SDS, stimulation of the intact cells is not required, and activity can be measured in preparations from normal unstimulated neutrophils. Studies of neutrophils prepared in this fashion from patients with X-linked CGD still show no NADPH-dependent O_2^- production,[92] which is consistent with the evidence that

the defect in X-linked CGD resides in the NADPH oxidase itself.

Cytochrome b and a flavoprotein are thought to be components of the NADPH oxidase, and each has been reported missing in CGD neutrophils. Cytochrome b has been found to be absent in cells from those with classic X-linked CGD, based upon the absence of the characteristic reduced-minus-oxidized absorbance spectrum.[227] Once it was concluded that cytochrome b consisted of two subunits, further analysis of neutrophils from nine patients with X-linked CGD and from three individuals with the uncommon autosomal recessive, cytochrome b–negative form of CGD revealed that neither the 22,000-dalton α-protein subunit nor the 91,000-dalton β-glycoprotein subunit of the cytochrome b heterodimer was detectable in any preparation.[105,106]

The 91,000-dalton β subunit of cytochrome b is the product of the X-linked CGD gene, which is located on the p21.1 region of the X chromosome.[109,110] Examination of this "X-CGD" gene region, using the 3' half of the specific complementary DNA probe, revealed no detectable alterations or deletions of genomic DNA in cells from 27 of 28 unrelated X-linked CGD patients.[108,276] However, in four patients with X-linked CGD who were examined, the X-CGD gene-encoded mRNA was absent in monocytes from three and structurally abnormal in the fourth.[108] The structurally abnormal mRNA was produced from a gene with an interstitial deletion. Although the genetic basis of X-linked CGD is a failure to synthesize normal β subunit of cytochrome b, the phenotypic defect is expressed as the absence of _both_ subunits of cytochrome b. The α-subunit of cytochrome b is thought to be unstable in the absence of the β-subunit.[108a] It is unclear if the heme is bound to one of the subunits of cytochrome b or if its binding might require the presence of both subunits.

A deficiency of FAD has been reported in particulate fractions of neutrophils from both X-linked CGD[87,103,104,300,301] and autosomal recessive CGD.[87,103] Twenty-three (68 percent) of 34 individuals with cytochrome b–negative X-linked CGD had decreased levels of FAD. Only 2 of 28 patients with autosomal recessive CGD had decreased amounts of FAD. One of these two had decreased amounts of cytochrome b. All other patients with autosomal recessive CGD had normal amounts of cytochrome b.[87,103] Thus, the FAD content of neutrophils may be normal or low in X-linked CGD, and changes in FAD content in this condition appear to be a secondary effect. Typical patients with X-linked CGD lack the cytochrome b protein and have mutations in the same locus at Xp21.

The cytochrome b spectrum is present in neutrophils from most patients with autosomal recessive CGD.[104,106,227,302] Both subunits of the protein were present in neutrophils from the few individuals examined with this form of the disease.[106,303] However, cytochrome b in neutrophils from individuals with autosomal recessive CGD was not reduced upon stimulation with PMA under anaerobic conditions,[304] in agreement with the concept that the defect in autosomal recessive CGD is in a step of activation or in a component of the respiratory burst oxidase that binds electrons prior to binding by cytochrome b. Examples of X-linked CGD with normal amounts of cytochrome b[104,301,305,306] and autosomal recessive CGD with absent cytochrome b have also been reported.[284,301,306]

In autosomal recessive CGD patients with normal amounts of cytochrome b, the basis of the defective respiratory burst may be an abnormal soluble, cytosolic activation factor of the respiratory burst oxidase,[214,307] based on mixing experiments with particulate and cytosolic fractions from disrupted normal and CGD neutrophils. Membrane-enriched fractions of disrupted neutrophils from patients with cytochrome b–positive autosomal recessive CGD, combined with a cytosolic factor derived from neutrophils of the same patients, did not initiate NADPH-dependent O_2^- production. Replacing the patients' cytosolic factor with cytosolic factor from normal individuals resulted in normal activity.

Neutrophils from some patients with a variant CGD phenotype are capable of producing small amounts of O_2^- and weakly reducing NBT.[102,285,305,308–313] In the histochemical NBT test in which 100 percent of normal neutrophils reduce NBT vigorously, 16 to 100 percent of PMNs from X-linked variants reduced NBT faintly.[305,309–313] Heterozygous carriers expressed two populations of neutrophils: those normally reducing NBT to formazan and those with a few grains of formazan (weakly positive).[314] From 4 to 85 percent of neutrophils from autosomal recessive CGD variants reduced NBT weakly.[284,311]

The lack of NADPH oxidase activity in CGD could indicate absence of the respiratory burst enzyme or the presence of a functionally defective enzyme protein. Membrane-enriched fractions of disrupted neutrophils from certain of the patients with variant CGD were found to have a decreased affinity for NADPH (high K_m) and diminished catalytic activity (less than 5 percent of normal) in the presence of physiological concentrations of NADPH.[309–313] Presumably the biochemical variations in patients with X-linked CGD represent allelic heterogeneity at the locus for the β subunit. The "high K_m" variant of CGD has been noted in both X-linked (with detectable cytochrome b)[309,310,313] and autosomal recessive (absent cytochrome b)[311] forms of the disease and is manifested as measurable, albeit diminished, stimulated O_2^- release in patients' neutrophils (3 to 30 percent of normal).

A partial deficiency of leukocyte glutathione peroxidase has been reported in association with the CGD phenotype.[315,316] This abnormality has not been consistent in any form of CGD, however,[306,317] and it does not seem likely at present that this deficiency causes the functional defect of CGD.

Glucose-6-Phosphate Dehydrogenase (G-6-PD) Deficiency

G6PD deficiency is associated with a bactericidal defect as the result of a subnormal respiratory burst, and this clinical presentation can mimic CGD.[318–321] Patients with erythrocyte G-6-PD deficiency suffer bouts of hemolytic anemia as a result of exposure to certain drugs and foods (see Chap. 91). G-6-PD catalyzes the first step in the hexose monophosphate shunt, which is necessary to maintain normal amounts of cellular NADPH. Cells, particularly erythrocytes, that lack adequate levels of NADPH are unable to maintain glutathione in a reduced state (GSH) and, thus, are susceptible to oxidative damage upon exposure to oxidants in drugs or foods. The disorder is inherited in an X-linked fashion, and affected individuals are male. G-6-PD activity is present in normal neutrophils and appears to be required to generate the NADPH used as a substrate for the respiratory burst oxidase.[318] Patients whose neutrophils are severely deficient in G-6-PD (with less than 5 percent activity) do not undergo a respiratory burst and suffer recurrent and sometimes fatal bacterial infections.[318–321] On the other hand, individuals with as little as 25 percent of nor-

mal G-6-PD activity have not shown an unusual susceptibility to infection.[318] Like neutrophils from individuals with CGD, G-6-PD-deficient neutrophils are unable to reduce NBT and demonstrate an in vitro killing defect against catalase-producing microorganisms. CGD and G-6-PD deficiency can be distinguished by exposing neutrophils to methylene blue, an oxidizing agent that converts NADPH to $NADP^+$, thereby activating the hexose monophosphate shunt in CGD but not in G-6-PD deficiency.

Inheritance. The syndrome of CGD can be inherited in an X-linked or an autosomal recessive pattern. Approximately 80 percent of reported cases are thought to be X-linked.[215] These conclusions are based on reports of pedigree analyses from multiple kindreds in which the identity of both hemizygotes and heterozygotes was based upon neutrophil function assays.

Initial reports suggested that CGD was an X-linked disorder. The first 32 cases described in the literature were male.[42] Furthermore, CGD had been described in maternal male cousins and half-brothers with different fathers. Neutrophils from some mothers and sisters, but not fathers, of these patients demonstrated intermediate values on functional assays, especially NBT slide tests, in which two populations of cells could be detected: One population of cells reduced the NBT dye normally, while the other set was incapable of converting the dye to the insoluble, blue formazan. This finding is explained by the random inactivation of one X chromosome in females.

Females with X-linked CGD have been recognized.[322–324] In these instances, the mother, but not the father, was found to be the heterozygous carrier through phagocytic functional assays. Results of the patients' NBT tests showed two populations of neutrophils, with as few as 4 to 8 percent showing normal reduction. Thus, these individuals could represent examples of extreme lyonization and a form of the illness clinically indistinguishable from classic X-linked CGD.

CGD also presents in an autosomal form. It has been reported in sisters and in siblings of both sexes,[308,317,325,326] in offspring of consanguineous marriages,[221,285,327] and in boys without demonstrable leukocyte defects in either parent.[221,308,325] Transmission by an autosomal recessive gene seemed most likely in these patients. As described elsewhere in this chapter, there may be more than one gene defect in this group.

Diagnosis. The diagnosis of CGD begins with the clinician's suspicion in examining an individual with recurrent bacterial abscess formation, frequently involving the skin and subcutaneous tissues, lymph nodes, and the respiratory tract. Any individual whose course is compatible with a phagocytic killing defect should have in vitro tests of neutrophil bactericidal and respiratory burst activity. The histochemical NBT test remains a reliable screening test for CGD (Fig. 114-8).[42,308] A positive NBT test occurs when yellow, soluble NBT is reduced by O_2^- to blue, insoluble formazan. The assay should be performed so that 100 percent of the control cells on the coverslip reduce the NBT.[324] This method will better ensure that "variants" with minimal respiratory burst activity and carriers of X-linked CGD can be identified.[314,324] An abnormal result in the NBT test should be substantiated by measurement of phagocytic bactericidal activity (Fig. 114-9)[41] and quantitative assay of the respiratory burst, e.g., by measurement of O_2^-,[328,329] chemiluminescence,[25] oxygen consump-

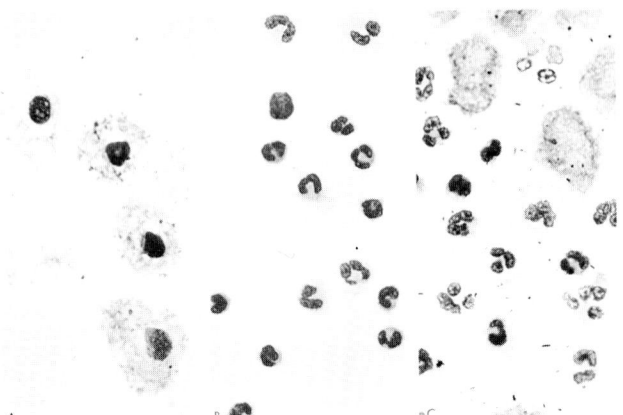

Fig. 114-8 NBT slide test for the diagnosis of CGD. A drop of blood is placed on an endotoxin-coated coverslip and incubated to allow the granulocytes and monocytes to adhere to the glass surface. The coverslip is then incubated with a solution of serum, PMA, and NBT dye; then washed, fixed, counterstained, and mounted. A. Normal control; all the granulocytes are NBT-positive and appear as large, degenerated cells with pale-blue cytoplasm. B. CGD patient; none of the granulocytes are NBT-positive. The neutrophils retain their typical morphologic appearance and contain no blue (reduced) dye. C. Carrier of CGD. Two populations of cells coexist. Some granulocytes are NBT-positive and others are negative.

tion,[330] or hydrogen peroxide production.[331] Prenatal diagnosis can be achieved with the NBT test using fetal blood obtained by percutaneous umbilical or placental vessel puncture.[228–230] This procedure is deemed relatively safe if performed after 17 weeks of gestation.[332] Prenatal diagnosis by DNA analysis also is possible now using restriction fragment length polymorphisms (RFLPs).[332a]

The level of red cell G-6-PD activity should be determined to rule out leukocyte G-6-PD deficiency.

Treatment. Patients with CGD are at risk of developing severe, protracted infections with catalase-positive organisms, most frequently *S. aureus* and enteric bacteria (Table 114-4). Thus, early diagnosis of purulent complications with surgical drainage, a culture to identify and assess the antibiotic susceptibility pattern of the organism, and long-term administration of appropriate antibiotics are crucial in order to minimize morbidity and mortality.

In the infection-free patient, treatment is aimed at preventing the onset of an infectious process. Prophylaxis can be successful with the use of a systemic penicillinase-resistant penicillin,[333] sulfonamide,[334] or trimethoprim-sulfamethoxazole[335] taken on a daily basis. In a retrospective study of 18 patients, treatment with trimethoprim-sulfamethoxazole, 5 mg (kg/day), led to increased infection-free periods (3.7 months before therapy, 10.7 months during therapy), primarily by eliminating *S. aureus* infections.[248] The improvement of patients on trimethoprim-sulfamethoxazole may be the result of the cell's ability to concentrate the agents in the phagocytic vacuole.[334–336]

Bone marrow transplantation has been attempted with mixed results.[337–342] A 5-month-old boy was transplanted because of recurrent infections despite trimethoprim-sulfamethoxazole prophylaxis; he has continued to show chimerism (presence of NBT-positive neutrophils) and has remained asymptomatic for 5 years (Ref. 341, and personal communication). However, failure to engraft is common. Several recipients experienced transplant rejection after initial engraft-

ment;[337–339] one of these individuals demonstrated chimerism and freedom from infection for 7 years prior to rejection (Prof. J. R. Hobbs, personal communication). One 15-year-old boy succumbed to graft-versus-host disease and sepsis 3 months after transplantation.[340] In every case, bone marrow transplantation was attempted as a result of failure of antibiotic prophylaxis. Yet to be studied is the efficacy of bone marrow transplantation performed prior to the onset of recurrent infections.

Granulocyte transfusions have been administered to patients with serious systemic infections, including pneumonia, liver abscesses, and an intramural ileal abscess, all apparently refractory to prolonged administration of parenteral antibiotics.[343–350] Transfusions were given as daily infusions of approximately 10^9 to 10^{10} granulocytes, and recipients tolerated up to 8 weeks of granulocyte therapy without untoward reactions. The efficacy of granulocyte transfusions is still in question, as the majority of patients were also receiving parenteral antibiotics or were recovering from surgical intervention, and controls studied were not adequate.

Patients with CGD and the K_o or McLeod phenotypes are susceptible to sensitization by Kell antigens when given blood. One patient with the McLeod phenotype experienced a hemolytic reaction after the sixth leukocyte transfusion.[344]

Incubation of normal monocytes with γ-interferon, a polypeptide cytokine secreted by activated T lymphocytes, enhances respiratory burst activity and content of mRNA coding for the β subunit of cytochrome b. Incubation of γ-interferon with monocytes from three patients with X-linked CGD gave similar results.[351] These results raise the possibility that patients with some alleles for X-linked CGD might be treated by administration of γ-interferon, and clinical trials of such treatment have been started.[351a,351b]

In most cases, prolonged antibiotic therapy clears the obstruction created by inflammatory granulomatous lesions of the gastrointestinal or genitourinary tract. In two patients with X-linked, cytochrome b–negative CGD and protracted severe narrowing of the gastric antrum, esophagus, and urinary tract, corticosteroids in conjunction with antibiotics reversed the ob-

Fig. 114-9 Bactericidal activity against *S. aureus* in neutrophils from a normal individual, a patient with myeloperoxidase deficiency, and a patient with chronic granulomatous disease.

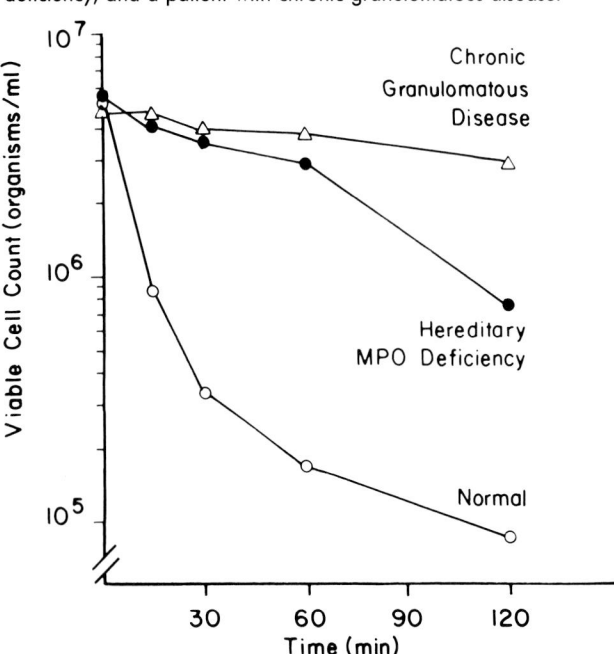

struction.[352] The responses were prompt, each lesion resolving within 2 weeks. In neither case were there complications of further immunosuppression.

Myeloperoxidase Deficiency

Description. Until the late 1970s hereditary deficiency of MPO had been infrequently reported; there were descriptions in the literature of only 15 patients from 12 families.[126,353–359] However, the diagnosis became common with the widespread application in clinical hematology laboratories of automated flow cytochemistry to quantitate peroxidase activity as a means to enumerate neutrophils in peripheral blood. Application of this technique revealed the true prevalence of MPO deficiency to be approximately 1 in 2000 apparently healthy individuals.[171,360] Histochemical studies of peripheral blood from such individuals revealed an absence of peroxidase staining in neutrophils and monocytes, whereas there was normal staining of the peroxidase in eosinophils, consistent with previous understanding that eosinophil peroxidase is a different protein. Other prominent neutrophil granule proteins, including β-glucuronidase, elastase, vitamin B_{12}–binding protein, and lysozyme, are present in normal amounts in MPO-deficient cells.

Clinical Course. Most individuals with MPO deficiency are healthy. In accord with the inability of MPO-deficient neutrophils to kill species of *Candida*, however, four of the six reported patients with MPO deficiency who have had significant infection had disseminated or visceral candidiasis.[353,357,358,360] Of these four patients, three[353,357,360] had concomitant diabetes mellitus. In some cases MPO deficiency has been part of more complex clinical pictures; some of these have included associated defects in chemotaxis,[361] normal chemotaxis but recurrent and severe skin infection,[362] acne vulgaris,[174] and pustular psoriasis.[363] The contribution of the deficiency of MPO to the clinical syndrome is not clear in these cases. Although MPO-deficient phagocytes lack an important system for oxygen-dependent killing, there are numerous additional systems that adequately protect the cell in most situations. In the absence of MPO, more subtle defects in host defense, such as those present in the antifungal defenses of some diabetics, become clinically significant.

In addition to the inherited form of MPO deficiency, there are numerous causes of acquired MPO deficiency. These include pregnancy,[364] lead poisoning,[365] Hodgkin's disease,[366] sepsis,[367] megaloblastic anemia,[368–370] ceroid lipofuscinosis,[371,372] and acute nonlymphocytic leukemias, particularly of the M2 to M4 types.[373–379] The last cause of MPO deficiency is especially noteworthy in that some patients have acquired MPO deficiency in the preleukemic phase of the disease.[380,381]

Laboratory Diagnosis. Neutrophils and monocytes from individuals with MPO deficiency appear completely normal under the microscope. Thus, the clinician must consider the possibility of MPO deficiency in order to alert the hematology laboratory to do the appropriate studies. Recurrent, invasive, or disseminated fungal disease in the absence of clearly identifiable risk factors should suggest the possibility of MPO deficiency.

The diagnosis can be easily made by quantitation of the peroxidase activity of isolated cells or by histochemical analysis of peroxidase activity of neutrophils or monocytes in peripheral blood smears. Peroxidase activity can be quantitated using a

variety of different substrates,[382–384] but none differentiate eosinophil from neutrophil-monocyte peroxidase. If MPO is quantitated in a population of leukocytes, the presence of a disproportionate number of eosinophils could obscure the diagnosis of MPO deficiency,[385] since eosinophils contain fourfold more peroxidase than do neutrophils,[386] and eosinophil peroxidase is more active than MPO.[387] The diagnosis can be established simply and directly by examining peripheral blood smears stained for peroxidase activity. Currently, substrates such as 3-amino-9-carbazole[388] and 4-chloro-1-naphthol[389] are recommended over the previous standard benzidine dihydrochloride, which is carcinogenic.[390]

Numerous investigators have characterized the in vitro behavior of MPO-deficient neutrophils and monocytes. These cells have an exuberant respiratory burst, manifested by greater than normal oxygen consumption, O_2^- and H_2O_2 release (Fig. 114-10), and hexose monophosphate shunt activity.[35,128,169,361] MPO-deficient neutrophils have normal amounts of catalase and glutathione peroxidase,[127] indicating that the detection of supernormal amounts of oxygen products is due to increased production and not decreased catabolism. In addition, the increase in production is due to a failure in termination of the oxygen burst (see above and Fig. 114-10).

Phagocytosis by MPO-deficient neutrophils of a variety of particles has been normal.[169,357,360,391] Release of granule products to a variety of stimuli has been reported to be normal or increased.[392] There is increased recovery of granule products from MPO-deficient neutrophils,[177–179] since the proteins are not oxidized and inactivated by the MPO-H_2O_2-halide system. Thus, accurate assessment of degranulation in such cells will

Fig. 114-10 The time course of O_2^- production by neutrophils from a patient with myeloperoxidase deficiency.

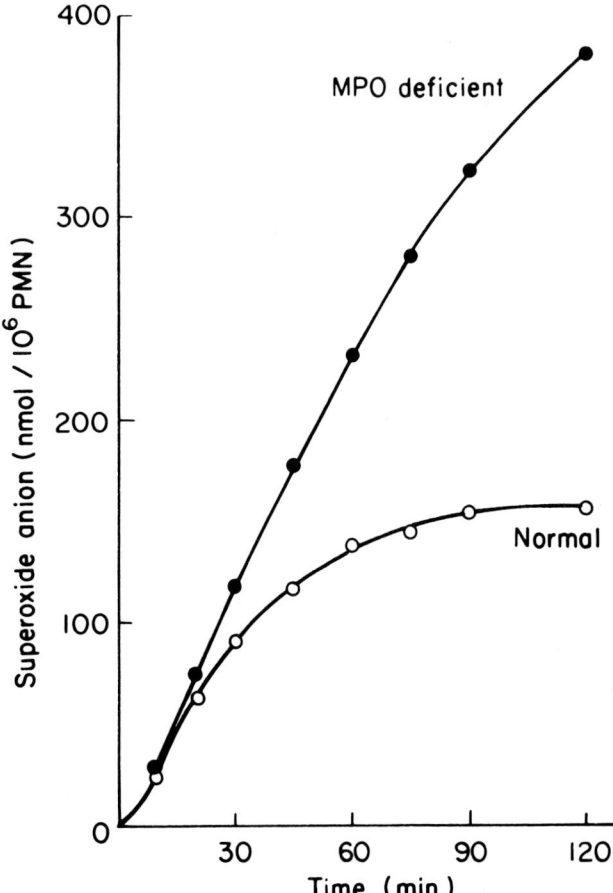

require careful measurement of degranulation in continuous on-line assays.

The microbicidal activity of MPO-deficient cells is defective (Fig. 114-9). MPO-deficient cells kill *S. aureus*,[169,171,357,360,391,393,394] *Serratia*,[357] and *E. coli*[170,395] significantly more slowly than do normal cells. However, after 1 h of incubation, MPO-deficient cells have killed the same number of organisms as have normal cells. This may reflect the sustained respiratory burst present in MPO-deficient cells and the amplified systems that compensate for the microbicidal defect in MPO deficiency.[393]

Most striking in vitro is the inability of MPO-deficient cells to kill a variety of species of fungi, including the clinically significant *Candida albicans* and *Candida tropicalis*[169,357,358,360,391,396] and hyphal forms of *Aspergillus fumigatus*.[397,398] In contrast *T. glabrata*,[361] *Candida parapsilosis*,[399] *Candida pseudotropicalis*,[400] and the spores of *A. fumigatus* and of *R. oryzae*[401] are killed normally by MPO-deficient cell.

Defect in Myeloperoxidase Deficiency. The biochemical defect in MPO deficiency is the lack of peroxidatively active proteins in the azurophilic granules of neutrophils and in the primary lysosomes of monocytes. Analysis of neutrophils from affected individuals using western blotting and monospecific antiserum directed against the enzymatically active MPO found in neutrophils reveals that the cells lack subunits of native MPO.[193] However, both MPO-deficient and normal neutrophils contain an immunochemically related protein of a higher molecular weight. This larger protein has a number of characteristics suggesting that it is the precursor of MPO (proMPO). The larger protein is extremely cationic, like MPO; it is identified by monoclonal antibodies generated to purified mature MPO; it cosediments with light subcellular organelles such as Golgi and endoplasmic reticulum; and it is the same size as proMPO identified in bone marrow and HL-60 cells.

MPO synthesis is under the control of a single gene. Recent studies using the human promyelocytic cell line HL-60 have provided a great deal of information regarding the biosynthesis, processing, and intracellular transport of MPO.[402–406] There is a single primary translation product of approximately 80,000 daltons which undergoes cotranslational glycosylation by the addition of five oligosaccharide sidechains to asparagines.[407] Recent studies have demonstrated incorporation of the chlorin iron into this proMPO very early in MPO biosynthesis.[408] The resultant species, approximately 92,000 daltons, is rapidly modified by the actions of glucosidases I and II in the endoplasmic reticulum to produce an 89,000-dalton protein. The action of these glucosidases is so rapid that the 92,000-dalton intermediate is identified only in the presence of inhibitors of glucosidases.

At this point, the proMPO appears to exit from the distal endoplasmic reticulum or proximal Golgi, since inhibitors of the Golgi mannosidases do not modify the size or behavior of proMPO. Cytochemical studies demonstrate a lack of peroxidase staining of the Golgi of HL-60 cells, whereas the endoplasmic reticulum shows intense staining for peroxidase.[409] In addition, mature MPO retains high mannose side chains and lacks the complex mannose sidechains acquired during transport through the Golgi. The mechanism by which proMPO enters this prelysosomal compartment is not understood at this time, but current attempts to characterize the lysosomal membranes and the prosequences of MPO may lead to a greater understanding of biosynthesis and transport of lysosomal proteins in myeloid cells and of the basis for hereditary MPO deficiency.

Although the genetic basis for MPO deficiency has not been defined, it has been proposed, based on the findings described above, that the underlying abnormality in MPO deficiency is defective posttranslational processing of proMPO. This could result from a mutation in the prosequences of the MPO gene. Such a change would be akin to that seen in the Z-variant of α_1-antitrypsin deficiency (Chap. 96).[410] In that disorder, single base changes result in proproteins that are not processed normally into mature proteins. Preliminary data to support this hypothesis include the presence of normal amounts and size of mRNA encoding for MPO in bone marrow isolated from an MPO-deficient subject.[411] Restriction endonuclease digests of genomic DNA of affected individuals show consistent differences from normal genomic DNA digests. Definition of the nature of the defect awaits sequencing of an additional fragment found in affected subjects.

Genetics. The gene for MPO is located on chromosome 17, at q22-q23,[412] near the breakpoint for the 15,17 translocation of promyelocytic leukemia.[413] Preliminary studies of genomic clones reveal that the gene includes 12 exons and 11 introns and spans approximately 14 kb. The full-length cDNA has an open reading frame of approximately 2.2 kb (745 amino acids). Northern blots of RNA from HL-60 cells or from normal human or murine bone marrow cells demonstrate species of mRNA for MPO at 3.0 to 3.3 kb and 3.5 to 4.0 kb. The significance of these two species is not known at this time. As would be predicted, expression of the MPO gene is restricted to cells of neutrophil and monocyte lineage and, in myeloid development, is limited to the promyelocytic stage of myeloid development. Differentiation of HL-60 cells into more mature myeloid cells is associated with decreased expression of the MPO gene.

The genetics of the clinical disorder are not established at this time. Although a number of family studies have suggested an autosomal recessive mode of inheritance,[169,170,357,385,391,414] other studies have suggested variable expression of the gene[171] or defects in structural as well as regulatory genes.[360] The recent availability of cDNA probes for MPO should clarify this question.

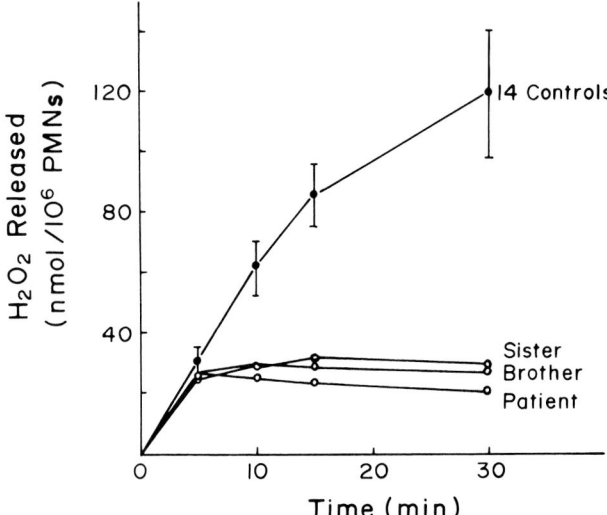

Fig. 114-11 The time course of zymosan-triggered H_2O_2 release by neutrophils from 14 controls and 3 individuals with glutathione reductase deficiency. (From Roos et al.[133] Used with permission.)

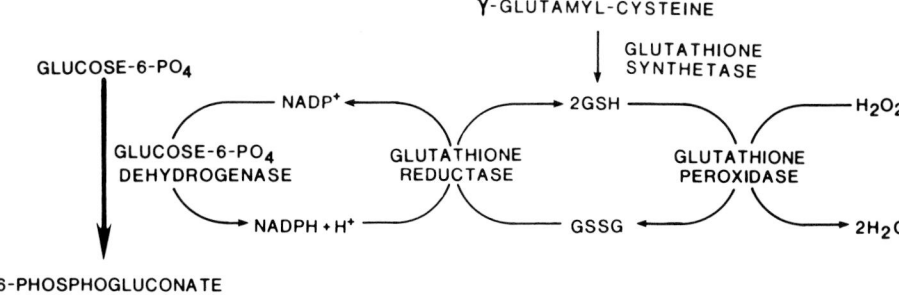

Fig. 114-12 Schematic representation of the glutathione oxidation-reduction cycle. GSH = reduced glutathione; GSSG = oxidized glutathione. (From Johnston.[419] Used with permission.)

Treatment. There is no specific therapy for MPO deficiency. Given the predilection of diabetics with MPO deficiency for severe fungal infections, it would be prudent to avoid factors that increase the risk of fungal superinfection (e.g., prolonged broad spectrum antibiotic therapy) and to treat possible fungal infections more quickly in such patients.

Glutathione Synthetase Deficiency

Glutathione is a sulfhydryl-containing tripeptide (L-γ-glutamyl-L-cysteinylglycine) found in many tissues. The ratio of GSH (reduced glutathione) to GSSG (oxidized glutathione) in normal cells is approximately 500:1.[415,416] Its biosynthesis from γ-glutamylcysteine and glycine is catalyzed by the enzyme glutathione synthetase. In the neutrophil, glutathione protects cellular structures from the harmful effects of H_2O_2 and, perhaps, other oxidizing radicals generated during the phagocytosis-associated respiratory burst. A reduction in the synthesis or regeneration of glutathione in the phagocyte leads to increased oxidative stress and loss of function.[133,417]

Glutathione synthetase deficiency with 5-oxoprolinuria has been described in a 2-year-old boy with two episodes of neutropenia associated with otitis media (see Chap. 31).[417] Hemolytic anemia had been noted at birth. Erythrocytes, leukocytes, and cultured skin fibroblasts had diminished glutathione synthetase activity (5 to 10 percent of normal) and intracellular glutathione content (10 to 20 percent of normal). There was no history of unusual infections. Neutrophil chemotaxis, phagocytosis, and NBT reduction all occurred normally. However, neutrophil bactericidal capacity and iodination were impaired. These defects were thought to be due to deficiency of glutathione, which would be expected to permit accumulation of H_2O_2 intracellularly after stimulation. The resultant increase in oxidative stress was shown to damage the patient's neutrophil membranes and microtubules and to impair phagolysosomal formation.[417]

Vitamin E (α-tocopherol), 400 IU/day, increased red cell survival, corrected both the bactericidal and iodination defects, and eliminated the neutropenia that had accompanied certain intercurrent illnesses.[139]

Congenital glutathione synthetase deficiency appears to be inherited in an autosomal recessive fashion.

Glutathione Reductase Deficiency

A 22-year-old female of first cousin parents suffered bouts of hemolysis in association with eating fava beans (see also Chap. 94). Diminished glutathione reductase activity was noted in her erythrocytes and granulocytes. Two siblings with an identical defect of glutathione metabolism were also identified.

However, there was no history of repeated infections in any of the three.[418] Chemotaxis, phagocytosis of opsonized *S. aureus*, and degranulation proceeded normally.[133] Intracellular killing appeared normal at low bacteria-to-phagocyte ratios, but higher ratios gave defective bacterial killing. The patient's neutrophils phagocytosed opsonized zymosan normally, and oxygen consumption and H_2O_2 production occurred at a normal rate for 5 to 10 min. However, this was followed by complete cessation of respiratory burst activity (Fig. 114-11). Hexose monophosphate shunt activity stopped after 10 min of phagocytosis with a subnormal initial rate.

Glutathione reductase catalyzes the reduction of glutathione disulfide to reduced glutathione, using electrons from NADPH (Fig. 114-12). Absence of glutathione reductase leads to defective generation of reduced glutathione, which permits oxidative damage to the stimulated neutrophil, as described above in "Glutathione Synthetase Deficiency." In contrast to other aspects of the respiratory burst, the release of O_2^-, measured as the reduction of cytochrome c, proceeded normally. Cytochrome c added in vitro scavenges the electrons from O_2^-, which prevents H_2O_2 formation from the dismutation reaction, protecting the cell from oxidative damage.

There is no specific therapy for glutathione reductase deficiency, but avoiding foods and drugs containing potent oxidants will lessen the chance of depleting cellular levels of glutathione. The pattern of inheritance is unknown.

Supported in part by USPHS grants AI 24748 and HL 34327, and a grant from the Veterans' Administration (Merit Review).

REFERENCES

1. METCHNIKOFF E: Untersuchungen über die intracelluläre Verdauung bei wirbellosen Thieren. *Arb Zool Inst Univ Wien* 5:141, 1883.
2. METCHNIKOFF E: Ueber die Beziehung der Phagocyten zu Milzbrandbacillen. *Virchows Arch (A)* 97:502, 1884.
3. METCHNIKOFF E: *Immunity in Infective Diseases.* New York, Cambridge University Press, 1905.
4. JOHNSTON RB JR: Current concepts: Immunology—Monocytes and macrophages. *N Engl J Med*, 318:747, 1988.
5. MANDELL GL: Bactericidal activity of aerobic and anaerobic polymorphonuclear neutrophils. *Infect Immun* 9:337, 1974.
6. OKAMURA N, SPITZNAGEL JK: Outer membrane mutants of *Salmonella typhimurium* LT2 have lipopolysaccharide resistance to the bactericidal activity of anaerobic human neutrophils. *Infect Immun* 36:1086, 1982.
7. VEL WA, NAMAVAR F, VERWEIJ AM, PUBBEN AN, MacLAREN DM: Killing capacity of human polymorphonuclear leukocytes in aerobic and anaerobic conditions. *J Med Microbiol* 62:65, 1984.
8. WEISS J, VICTOR M, STENDAHL O, ELSBACH P: Killing of Gram-negative bacteria by polymorphonuclear leukocytes. *J Clin Invest* 69:959, 1982.
9. SPITZNAGEL JK: Nonoxidative antimicrobial reactions of leukocytes, in Snyderman R (ed): *Contemporary Topics in Immunobiology.* New York, Plenum, 1984, vol 14, p 283.
10. SPITZNAGEL JK, SHAFER WM: Neutrophil killing of bacteria by oxygen-

independent mechanisms: A historical summary. *Rev Infect Dis* 7:398, 1985.

11. SHAFER WM, MARTIN LE, SPITZNAGEL JK: Cationic antimicrobial proteins isolated from human neutrophil granulocytes in the presence of diisopropylfluorophosphate. *Infect Immun* 49:29, 1984.

12. WEISS J, ELSBACH P, OLSSON I, ODEBERG H: Purification and characterization of a potent bactericidal and membrane active protein from the granules of human polymorphonuclear leukocytes. *J Biol Chem* 253:2664, 1978.

13. GANZ T, SELSTED ME, SZKLAREK D, HARWIG SSL, DAHER K, BAINTON DF, LEHRER RI: Defensins, natural peptide antibiotics of human neutrophils. *J Clin Invest* 76:1427, 1985.

14. GABAY JE, HEIPLE JM, COHN ZA, NATHAN CF: Subcellular location and properties of bactericidal factors from human neutrophils. *J Exp Med* 164:1407, 1986.

15. STROMINGER JL, GHUYSEN JM: Mechanisms of enzymatic bacteriolysis. *Science* 156:213, 1967.

16. WILSON LA, SPITZNAGEL JK: Molecular and structural damage of *Escherichia coli* produced by antibody, complement and lysozyme systems. *J Bacteriol* 96:1339, 1968.

17. AVERY OT, CULLEN GE: Hydrogen ion concentration of cultures of pneumococci of the different types of carbohydrate media. *J Exp Med* 30:359, 1919.

18. BALDRIDGE CW, GERALD RW: The extra respiration of phagocytosis. *Am J Physiol* 103:235, 1933.

19. KARNOVSKY ML: Metabolic basis of phagocytic activity. *Physiol Rev* 42:143, 1962.

20. BADWEY JA, KARNOVSKY ML: Active oxygen species and the functions of phagocytic leukocytes. *Annu Rev Biochem* 49:695, 1980.

21. KLEBANOFF SJ: Oxygen metabolism and the toxic properties of phagocytes. *Ann Intern Med* 93:480, 1980.

22. BABIOR BM: The respiratory burst of phagocytes. *J Clin Invest* 73:599, 1984.

23. KARNOVSKY ML, BADWEY JA: Respiratory burst during phagocytosis: An overview. *Methods Enzymol* 132:353, 1986.

24. BABIOR BM, KIPNES RS, CURNUTTE JT: Biological defense mechanisms: The production by leukocytes of superoxide, a potential bactericidal agent. *J Clin Invest* 52:741, 1973.

25. JOHNSTON RB JR, KEELE BB, MISRA HP, LEHMEYER JE, WEBB LS, BAEHNER RL, RAJAGOPALAN KV: The role of superoxide anion generation in phagocytic bactericidal activity: Studies with normal and chronic granulomatous disease leukocytes. *J Clin Invest* 55:1357, 1975.

26. KLEBANOFF SJ: Antimicrobial mechanisms in neutrophilic polymorphonuclear leukocytes. *Semin Hematol* 12:117, 1975.

27. TAUBER AI, BABIOR BM: Evidence for hydroxyl radical production by human neutrophils. *J Clin Invest* 60:374, 1977.

28. WEISS SJ, KING GW, LOBUGLIO AF: Evidence for hydroxyl radical generation by human monocytes. *J Clin Invest* 60:370, 1977.

29. WEISS SJ, RUSTAGI PK, LOBUGLIO AF: Human granulocyte generation of hydroxyl radical. *J Exp Med* 147:316, 1978.

30. ALLEN RC, STJERNHOLM RL, STEELE RH: Evidence for the generation of an electronic excitation state(s) in human polymorphonuclear leukocytes and its participation in bactericidal activity. *Biochem Biophys Res Commun* 47:679, 1972.

31. KRINSKY NI: Singlet excited oxygen as a mediator of the antibacterial action of leukocytes. *Science* 186:363, 1974.

32. SBARRA AJ, KARNOVSKY ML: The biochemical basis of phagocytosis. I. Metabolic changes during the ingestion of particles by polymorphonuclear leukocytes. *J Biol Chem* 234:1355, 1959.

33. IYER GYN, ISLAM MF, QUASTEL JH: Biochemical aspects of phagocytosis. *Nature* 192:535, 1961.

34. KLEBANOFF SJ: A peroxidase-mediated antimicrobial system in leukocytes. *J Clin Invest* 46:1078, 1967.

35. KLEBANOFF SJ, HAMON CB: Role of myeloperoxidase-mediated antimicrobial systems in intact leukocytes. *J Reticuloendothel Soc* 12:170, 1972.

36. HALLIWELL B: Oxidants and human disease: Some new concepts. *FASEB J* 1:358, 1987.

37. BRITIGAN BE, ROSEN GM, THOMPSON BY, CHAN Y, COHEN MS: Stimulated human neutrophils limit iron-catalyzed hydroxyl radical formation as determined by spin-trapping techniques. *J Biol Chem* 261:17026, 1986.

38. COHEN MS, BRITIGAN BE, HASSETT DJ, ROSEN GM: Do human neutrophils form hydroxyl radicals? Evaluation of an unresolved controversy. *J Free Radic Biol Med*, 5:81, 1988.

39. THOMAS EL: Myeloperoxidase, hydrogen peroxide, chloride antimicrobial system: Nitrogen-chlorine derivatives of bacterial components in bactericidal action against *Escherichia coli*. *Infect Immun* 23:522, 1979.

40. BAEHNER RL, NATHAN DG: Leukocyte oxidase: Defective activity in chronic granulomatous disease. *Science* 155:835, 1967.

41. QUIE PG, WHITE JG, HOLMES B, GOOD RA: In vitro bactericidal capacity of human polymorphonuclear leukocytes: Diminished activity in chronic granulomatous disease of childhood. *J Clin Invest* 46:668, 1967.

42. JOHNSTON RB JR, BAEHNER RL: Chronic granulomatous disease: Correlation between pathogenesis and clinical findings. *Pediatrics* 48:730, 1971.

43. DECHATELET LR, SHIRLEY PS, JOHNSTON RB JR: Effect of phorbol myristate acetate on the oxidative metabolism of human polymorphonuclear leukocytes. *Blood* 47:545, 1976.

44. GOLDSTEIN IM, ROOS D, KAPLAN HB, WEISSMANN G: Complement and immunoglobulins stimulate superoxide production by human leukocytes independently of phagocytosis. *J Clin Invest* 56:1155, 1975.

45. BOXER LA, YODER M, BONSIB S, SCHMIDT M, HO P, JERSILD R, BAEHNER R: Effects of a chemotactic factor, N-formylmethionyl peptide, on adherence, superoxide anion generation, phagocytosis, and microtubule assembly of human polymorphonuclear leukocytes. *J Lab Clin Med* 93:506, 1979.

46. LEHMEYER JE, SNYDERMAN R, JOHNSTON RB JR: Stimulation of neutrophil oxidative metabolism by chemotactic peptides: Influence of calcium ion concentration and cytochalasin B and comparison with stimulation by phorbol myristate acetate. *Blood* 54:35, 1979.

47. SIMCHOWITZ L, ATKINSON JP, SPILBERG I: Stimulus-specific deactivation of chemotactic factor-induced cyclic AMP response and superoxide generation by human neutrophils. *J Clin Invest* 66:736, 1980.

48. WEBSTER RO, HONG SR, JOHNSTON RB, HENSON PM: Biological effects of the human complement fragments C5a and C5a$_{des\ Arg}$ on neutrophil function. *Immunopharmacology* 2:201, 1980.

49. POZZAN T, LEW DP, WOLLHEIM CB, TSIEN RY: Is cytosolic ionized calcium regulation neutrophil activation? *Science* 221:1413, 1983.

50. KITAGAWA S, OHTA M, NOJIRI H, KAKINUMA K, SAITO M, TAKAKU F, MIURA Y: Functional maturation of membrane potential changes and superoxide-producing capacity during differentiation of human granulocytes. *J Clin Invest* 73:1062, 1984.

51. COHEN HJ, WHITIN JC, CHOVANIEC ME, TAPE E, SIMONS E: Is activation of the granulocyte by concanavalin A a reversible process? *Blood* 63:114, 1984.

52. ROOS D, BOT AAM, van SCHAIK MLJ, DE BOER M, DAHA MR: Interaction between human neutrophils and zymosan particles: The role of opsonins and divalent cation. *J Immunol* 126:433, 1981.

53. CURNUTTE JT, BABIOR BM, KARNOVSKY ML: Fluoride-mediated activation of the respiratory burst in human neutrophils. *J Clin Invest* 63:637, 1979.

54. GABLER WL, CREAMER HR, BULLOCK WW: Modulation of the kinetics of induced neutrophil superoxide generation by fluoride. *J Dent Res* 65:1159, 1986.

55. JOHNSTON RB JR, LEHMEYER JE: Elaboration of toxic oxygen by-products by neutrophils in a model of immune complex disease. *J Clin Invest* 57:836, 1976.

56. SERHAN CN, RADIN A, SMOLEN JE, KORCHAK H, SAMUELSSON B, WEISSMANN G: Leukotriene B$_4$ is a complete secretagogue in human neutrophils: A kinetic analysis. *Biochem Biophys Res Commun* 107:1006, 1982.

57. SAMUELSSON B: Leukotrienes: Mediators of immediate hypersensitivity reactions and inflammation. *Science* 20:568, 1983.

58. CURNUTTE JT, BADWEY JA, ROBINSON JM, KARNOVSKY MJ, KARNOVSKY ML: Studies on the mechanism of superoxide release from human neutrophils stimulated with arachidonate. *J Biol Chem* 259:11851, 1984.

59. ENGLISH D, SCHELL M, SIAKOTOS A, GABIG TG: Reversible activation of the neutrophil superoxide generation system by hexachlorocyclohexane: Correlation with effects on a subcellular superoxide-generation fraction. *J Immunol* 137:283, 1986.

60. KUHNS DB, KAPLAN SS, BASFORD RE: Hexachlorocyclohexanes, potent stimuli of O$_2^-$ production and calcium release in human polymorphonuclear leukocytes. *Blood* 68:535, 1986.

61. PENFIELD A, DALE MM: Synergism between A23187 and 1-oleoyl-2-acetylglycerol in superoxide preduction by human neutrophils. *Biochem Biophys Res Commun* 125:332, 1984.

62. GRAHAM RC, KARNOVSKY MJ, SHAFER AW, GLASS EA, KARNOVSKY ML: Metabolic and morphological observations on the effect of surface-active agents on leukocytes. *J Cell Biol* 32:629, 1967.

63. BROMBERG Y, PICK E: Activation of NADPH-dependent superoxide production in a cell-free system by sodium dodecyl sulfate. *J Biol Chem* 260:13539, 1985.

64. ROSSI F, ZATTI M, PARTIARCA P, CRAMER R: Stimulation of the respiration of polymorphonuclear leucocytes by anti-leucocyte antibodies. *Experientia* 26:491, 1970.

65. BOXER LA, STOSSEL TP: Effects of anti-human neutrophil antibodies in vitro. Quantitative studies. *J Clin Invest* 53:1534, 1974.

66. NAKAGAWARA A, MINAKAMI S: Generation of superoxide anions by leukocytes treated with cytochalasin E. *Biochem Biophys Res Commun* 64:760, 1975.

67. PATRIARCA P, ZATTI M, CRAMER R, ROSSI F: Stimulation of the respiration of polymorphonuclear leucocytes by phospholipase C. *Life Sci* 9:841, 1970.

68. PATRIARCA P, CRAMER R, MARUSSI M, MONCALVO S, ROSSI F: Phospholipid splitting and metabolic stimulation in polymorphonuclear leukocytes. *J Reticuloendothel Soc* 10:251, 1971.

69. INGRAHAM LM, COATES TD, ALLEN JM, HIGGINS CP, BAEHNER RL, BOXER LA: Metabolic, membrane and functional responses of human polymorphonuclear leukocytes to platelet-activation factor. *Blood* 59:1259, 1982.

70. TZENG DY, DEUEL TF, HUANG JS, SENIOR RM, BOXER LA, BAEHNER RL: Platelet-derived growth factor promotes polymorphonuclear leukocyte activation. *Blood* 64:1123, 1984.

71. NEWMAN SL, JOHNSTON RB JR: Role of binding through C3b and IgG in polymorphonuclear neutrophil function: Studies with trypsin-generated C3b. *J Immunol* 123:1839, 1979.

72. KOO C, LEFKOWITZ RJ, SNYDERMAN R: Guanine nucleotides modulate the binding affinity of the oligopeptide chemoattractant receptor on human polymorphonuclear leukocytes. *J Clin Invest* 72:748, 1983.

73. SMITH CD, LANE BC, KUSAKA I, VERGHESE MW, SNYDERMAN R: Chemoattractant receptor-induced hydrolysis of phosphatidylinositol 4,5-bisphosphate in human polymorphonuclear leukocyte membranes. *J Biol Chem* 260:5875, 1985.

74. SKLAR LA: Ligand-receptor dynamics and signal amplification in the neutrophil. *Adv Immunol* 39:95, 1986.

75. BERRIDGE MJ: Inositol trisphosphate and diacylglycerol as second messengers. *Biochem J* 220:345, 1984.

76. BERRIDGE MJ, IRVINE RF: Inositol trisphosphate, a novel second messenger in cellular signal transduction. *Nature* 312:315, 1984.

77. KRAUSE K-H, LEW PD: Subcellular distribution of Ca^{2+} pumping sites in human neutrophils. J Clin Invest 80:107, 1987.

78. RASMUSSEN H: The calcium messenger system. *N Engl J Med* 314:1094, 1986.

79. GALLIN EK: Calcium- and voltage-activated potassium channels in human macrophages. *Biophys J* 46:821, 1984.

80. PETERSON OH, MARUYAMA Y: Calcium-activated potassium channels and their role in secretion. *Nature* 307:693, 1984.

81. NISHIZUKA Y: The role of protein kinase C in cell surface signal transduction and tumour promotion. *Nature* 308:693, 1984.

82. MARIDONNEAR-PARINI I, TRINGALE SM, TAUBER AI: Identification of distinct activation pathways of the human neutrophil NADPH-oxidase. *J Immunol* 137:2925, 1986.

83. AGWU DE, MCPHAIL LC, DANIEL LW, MCCALL CE: A novel FMLP-activated phospholipase C hydrolyzed 1-0-alkyl-2-acyl-GPC in human neutrophils. *Fed Proc* 46:605, 1987.

84. ANDREWS PC, BABIOR BM: Phosphorylation of cytosolic proteins by resting and activated human neutrophils. *Blood* 64:883, 1984.

85. SEGAL AW, JONES OTC: The subcellular distribution and some properties of the cytochrome b component of the microbicidal oxidase system in human neutrophils. *Biochem J* 182:181, 1979.

86. BORREGAARD N: The respiratory burst of phagocytosis: Biochemistry and subcellular localization. *Immunol Lett* 11:165, 1985.

87. BORREGAARD N, TAUBER AI: Subcellular localization of the human neutrophil NADPH oxidase: b-cytochrome and associated flavoprotein. *J Biol Chem* 259:47, 1984.

88. SEGAL AW, JONES OTG: Novel cytochrome b system in phagocytic vacuoles of human granulocytes. *Nature* 276:515, 1978.

89. SEGAL AW, JONES OTC: Rapid incorporation of the human neutrophil plasma membrane cytochrome b into phagocytic vacuoles. *Biochem Biophys Res Commun* 92:710, 1980.

90. WOLFSON M, MCPHAIL LC, NASRALLAH VN, SNYDERMAN R: Phorbol myristate acetate mediates redistribution of protein kinase C in human neutrophils: Potential role in the activation of the respiratory burst enzyme. *J Immunol* 135:2057, 1985.

91. MCPHAIL LC, SHIRLEY PS, CLAYTON CC, SNYDERMAN R: Activation of the respiratory burst enzyme from human neutrophils in a cell-free system: Evidence for a soluble cofactor. *J Clin Invest* 75:1735, 1985.

92. CURNUTTE JT: Activation of human neutrophil nicotinamide adenine dinucleotide phosphate, reduced (triphosphopyridine nucleotide, reduced) oxidase by arachidonic acid in a cell-free system. *J Clin Invest* 75:1740, 1985.

93. CLARK RA, LEIDAL KG, PEARSON DW, NAUSEEF WM: NADPH oxidase of human neutrophils: Subcellular localization and characterization of an arachidonate-activatable superoxide-generating system. *J Biol Chem* 262:4065, 1987.

94. IYER GYN, QUASTREL JH: NADPH and NADH oxidation by guinea pig polymorphonuclear leucocytes. *Can J Biochem Physiol* 41:427, 1963.

95. ROSSI R, ZATTI M: Biochemical aspects of phagocytosis in polymorpho-

nuclear leucocytes. NADPH oxidation by the granules of resting and phagocytozing cells. *Experimentia* 20:21, 1964.

96. BABIOR BM: The nature of the NADPH oxidase, in Gallin JI, Fauci AS (eds): *Advances in Host Defense Mechanisms*. New York, Raven, 1983, p 91.

97. GABIG TG, LEFKER BA: Activation of the human neutrophil NADPH oxidase results in coupling of electron carrier function between ubiquinone-10 and cytochrome b_{559}. *J Biol Chem* 260:3991, 1985.

98. GABIG TG, LEFKER BA: NADPH oxidase from polymorphonuclear cells. *Methods Enzymol* 132:355, 1986.

99. BABIOR BM, KIPNES RS: Superoxide-forming enzyme from human neutrophils: Evidence for a flavin requirement. *Blood* 50:517, 1977.

100. BABIOR BM, PETERS WA: The O_2^--producing enzyme of human neutrophils: Further properties. *J Biol Chem* 256:2321, 1981.

101. CROSS AR, JONES OTG, GARCIA R, SEGAL AW: The association of FAD with the cytochrome b_{-245} of human neutrophils. *Biochem J* 208:759, 1982.

102. GABIG TG: The NADPH-dependent O_2^--generating oxidase from human neutrophils: Identification of a flavoprotein component that is deficient in a patient with chronic granulomatous disease. *J Biol Chem* 258:6352, 1983.

103. GABIG TG, LEFKER BA: Deficient flavoprotein component of the NADPH-dependent O_2^--generating oxidase in the neutrophils from three patients with chronic granulomatous disease. *J Clin Invest* 73:701, 1984.

104. BOHLER M-C, SEGER RA, MOUY R, VILMER E, FISCHER A, GRISCELLI C: A study of 25 patients with chronic granulomatous disease: A new classification by correlating respiratory burst, cytochrome b, and flavoprotein. *J Clin Immunol* 6:136, 1986.

105. PARKOS CA, ALLEN RA, COCHRANE CG, JESAITIS AJ: Purified cytochrome b from human granulocyte plasma membrane is comprised of two polypeptides with relative molecular weights of 91,000 and 22,000. *J Clin Invest* 80:732, 1987.

106. SEGAL AW: Absence of both cytochrome b_{-245} subunits from neutrophils in X-linked chronic granulomatous disease. *Nature* 326:88, 1987.

107. SEGAL AW, GARCIA R, GOLDSTONE AG, CROSS AR, JONES OTG: Cytochrome b_{-245} of neutrophils is also present in human monocytes, macrophages eosinophils. *Biochem J* 194:599, 1981.

108. ROYER-POKORA B, KUNKEL LM, MONACO AP, GOFF SC, NEWBURGER PE, BAEHNER RL, COLE FS, CURNUTTE JT, ORKIN SH: Cloning the gene for an inherited human disorder—chronic granulomatous disease—on the basis of its chromosomal location. *Nature* 322:32, 1986.

108a. PARKOS CA, DINAUER MC, WALKER LE, ALLEN RA, JESAITIS AJ, ORKIN SH: The primary structure and unique expression of the 22-kDa light chain of human neutrophil cytochrome b. *Proc Natl Acad Sci USA* 85:3319, 1988.

109. DINAUER MC, ORKIN SH, BROWN R, JESAITIS AJ, PARKOS CA: The glycoprotein encoded by the X-linked chronic granulomatous disease locus is a component of the neutrophil cytochrome b complex. *Nature* 327:717, 1987.

110. TEAHAN C, ROWE P, PARKER P, TOTTY N, SEGAL AW: The X-linked chronic granulomatous disease gene codes for the β-chain of cytochrome b_{-245}. *Nature* 327:720, 1987.

111. SEGAL AW: Superoxide generation, cytochrome b_{-245}, and chronic granulomatous disease, in Weissmann G (ed): *Advances in Inflammation Research*. New York, Raven, 1983, vol 8, p 55.

112. GABIG TG, SCHERVISH EW, SANTIAGA JT: Functional relationship of the cytochrome b to the superoxide-generating oxidase of human neutrophils. *J Biol Chem* 257:4114, 1982.

113. SEGAL AW, JONES OTG: Reduction and subsequent oxidation of a cytochrome *b* of human neutrophils after stimulation with phorbol myristate acetate. *Biochem Biophys Res Commun* 88:130, 1979.

114. CROSS AR, HIGSON FK, JONES OTG, HARPER AM, SEGAL AW: The enzymic reduction and kinetics of oxidation of cytochrome b_{-245} of neutrophils. *Biochem J* 204:479, 1982.

115. CROSS AR, JONES OTG, HARPER AM, SEGAL AW: Oxidation-reduction properties of the cytochrome b found in the plasma-membrane fraction of human neutrophils. *Biochem J* 194:599, 1981.

116. SEGAL AW, JONES OTG, WEBSTER D, ALLISON AC: Absence of a newly described cytochrome b from neutrophils of patients with chronic granulomatous disease. *Lancet* 2:446, 1978.

117. CRAWFORD DR, SCHNEIDER DL: Identification of ubiquinone-50 in human neutrophils and its role in microbicidal events. *J Biol Chem* 257:6662, 1982.

118. SLOAN EF, CRAWFORD DR, SCHNEIDER DL: Isolation of plasma membrane from human neutrophils and determination of cytochrome b and quinone content. *J Exp Med* 153:1316, 1981.

119. BELLAVITE P, CROSS AR, SERRA MC, DAVOLI A, JONES OTG, ROSSI F: The cytochrome b and flavin content properties of the O_2^--forming NADPH

oxidase solubilized from activated neutrophils. *Biochim Biophys Acta* 746:40, 1983.

120. DEWALD B, BAGGIOLINI M, CURNUTTE JT, BABIOR BM: Subcellular localization of the superoxide-forming enzyme in human neutrophils. *J Clin Invest* 63:21, 1979.

121. BABIOR GL, ROSIN RE, MCMURRICH BJ, PETERS WA, BABIOR BM: Arrangement of the respiratory burst oxidase in the plasma membrane of the neutrophil. *J Clin Invest* 67:1724, 1981.

122. MCPHAIL LC, HENSON PM, JOHNSTON RB JR: Respiratory burst enzyme in human neutrophils. *J Clin Invest* 67:710, 1981.

123. GUTHRIE LA, MCPHAIL LC, HENSON PM, JOHNSTON RB JR: Priming of neutrophils for enhanced release of oxygen metabolites by bacterial lipopolysaccharide: Evidence for increased activity of the superoxide-producing enzyme. *J Exp Med* 160:1656, 1984.

124. FOREHAND JR, PABST MJ, PHILLIPS WA, JOHNSTON RB JR: Lipopolysaccharide priming of human neutrophils for an enhanced respiratory burst: Role of cytosolic calcium. *Fed Proc* 46:2106, 1987.

125. JOHNSTON RB, LEHMEYER JE, GUTHRIE LA: Generation of superoxide anion and chemiluminescence by human monocytes during phagocytosis and on contact with surface-bound immunoglobulin G. *J Exp Med* 143:1551, 1976.

126. JANDL RC, ANDRE-SCHWARTZ J, BORGES-DUBOIS L, KIPNES RS, MCMURRICH BJ, BABIOR BM: Termination of the respiratory burst in human neutrophils. *J Clin Invest* 61:1176, 1978.

127. NAUSEEF WM, METCALF JA, ROOT RK: Role of myeloperoxidase in the respiratory burst of human neutrophils. *Blood* 61:483, 1983.

128. STENDAHL O, COBLE BI, DAHLGREN C, HED J, MOLIN L: Myeloperoxidase modulates the phagocytic activity of polymorphonuclear neutrophil leukocytes: Studies with cells from a myeloperoxidase-deficient patient. *J Clin Invest* 73:366, 1984.

129. MCCORD JM, FRIDOVICH I: Superoxide dismutase: An enzymic function for erythrocuprein (hemocuprein). *J Biol Chem* 244:6049, 1969.

130. DECHATELET LR, MCCALL CE, MCPHAIL LC, JOHNSTON RB JR: Superoxide dismutase activity in leukocytes. *J Clin Invest* 53:1197, 1974.

131. MICHELSON AM, MCCORD JM, FRIDOVICH I: *Superoxide and Superoxide Dismutases*. New York, Academic, 1977.

132. GOLDSTEIN IM, KAPLAN HB, EDELSON HS, WEISSMANN G: Ceruloplasmin: A scavenger of superoxide anion radicals. *J Biol Chem* 254:4040, 1979.

133. ROOS D, WEENING RS, VOETMAN AA, van SCHAIK MLJ, BOT AAM, MEERHOF LJ, LOOS JA: Protection of phagocytic leukocytes by endogenous glutathione: Studies in a family with glutathione reductase deficiency. *Blood* 53:851, 1979.

134. CHANCE B, SIES H, BOVERIS A: Hydroperoxide metabolism in mammalian organs. *Physiol Rev* 59:527, 1979.

135. ROOS D, WEENING RS, WYSS SR, AEBI HE: Protection of human neutrophils by endogenous catalase: Studies with cells from catalase-deficient individuals. *J Clin Invest* 65:1515, 1980.

136. O'DONNELL-TORMEY J, NATHAN CF, LANKS K, DEBOER CJ, de la HARPE J: Secretion of pyruvate: An antioxidant defense of mammalian cells. *J Exp Med* 165:500, 1987.

137. LUCY J: Functional and structural aspects of biological membranes: A suggested structural role of vitamin E in the control for membrane permeability and stability. *Ann NY Acad Sci* 203:4, 1972.

138. BABIOR BM, CROWLEY CA: Chronic granulomatous disease and other disorders of oxidative killing by phagocytes, in Stanbury JB, Wyngaarden JB, Fredrickson DS, Goldstein JL, Brown MS (eds): *Metabolic Basis of Inherited Diseases*, 5th ed. New York, McGraw-Hill, 1983, p 1956.

139. BOXER LA, OLIVER JM, SPIELBERG SP, ALLEN JM, SCHULMAN JD: Protection of granulocytes by vitamin E in glutathione synthetase deficiency. *N Engl J Med* 301:901, 1979.

140. BIGLEY RH, STANKOVA L: Uptake and reduction of oxidized and reduced ascorbate by human leukocytes. *J Exp Med* 139:1084, 1974.

141. PACKER JE, SLATER TJ, WILLSON RL: Direct observation of a free radical interaction between vitamin E and vitamin C. *Nature* 278:737, 1979.

142. NASKALSKI JW: Myeloperoxidase inactivation in the course of catalysis of chlorination of taurine. *Biochim Biophys Acta* 485:291, 1977.

143. GRISHAM MB, JEFFERSON MM, MELTON DF, THOMAS EL: Chlorination of endogenous amines by isolated neutrophils: Ammonia-dependent bactericidal, cytotoxic, and cytolytic activities of the chloramines. *J Biol Chem* 259:10404, 1984.

144. AGNER K: Verdoperoxidase: A ferment isolated from leukocytes. *Acta Physiol Scand (suppl)* 2:1, 1941.

145. SCHULTZ J: Myeloperoxidase, in Sbarra AJ, Strauss RR (eds): *The Reticuloendothelial System, Biochemistry and Metabolism*. New York, Plenum, 1980, vol 2, p 231.

146. NAUSEEF WM, OLSSON I, STROMBERG-ARNLJOTS K: Biosynthesis and processing of myeloperoxidase: A marker for myeloid cell differentiation. *Eur J Haematol*, 40:97, 1988.

147. ZGLICZYNSKI JM: Characteristics of MPO from neutrophils and other peroxidases from different cells, in Sabarra AJ, Strauss RR (eds): *The Reticuloendothelial System*. New York, Plenum, 1980, vol 2, p 255.

148. SALMON SE, CLINE MJ, SCHULTZ J, LEHRER RI: Myeloperoxidase deficiency: Immunologic study of a genetic leukocyte defect. *N Engl J Med* 282:250, 1970.

149. KLEBANOFF SJ: Myeloperoxidase-halide-hydrogen peroxide antibacterial system. *J Clin Invest* 50:2226, 1971.

150. LEHRER RI: Antifungal effects of peroxidase systems. *J Bacteriol* 95:2131, 1968.

151. BELDING ME, KLEBANOFF SJ, RAY CG: Peroxidase-mediated viricidal systems. *Science* 167:195, 1970.

152. CLARK RA, KLEBANOFF SJ: Neutrophil-mediated tumor cell cytotoxicity: Role of the preoxidase system. *J Exp Med* 141:1442, 1975.

153. CLARK RA, KLEBANOFF SJ, EINSTEIN AB: Peroxidase-H_2O_2-halide system: Cytotoxic effect on mammalian tumor cells. *Blood* 45:161, 1975.

154. GRISHAM MB, JEFFERSON MM, THOMAS EL: Role of monochloramines in the oxidation of erythrocyte hemoglobin by stimulated neutrophils. *J Biol Chem* 259:6757, 1984.

155. THOMAS EL, FISHMAN M: Oxidation of chloride and thiocyanate by isolated leukocytes. *J Biol Chem* 261:9694, 1986.

156. THOMAS EL, JEFFERSON MM, GRISHAM M: Myeloperoxidase-catalyzed incorporation of amino acids into proteins: Role of hypochlorous acid and chloramines. *Biochemistry* 21:6299, 1982.

157. THOMAS EL: Myeloperoxidase-hydrogen peroxide-chloride antimicrobial system: Effect of exogenous amines on antibacterial action against *Escherichia coli*. *Infect Immun* 25:110, 1979.

158. TEST ST, LAMPERT MB, OSSANNA PJ, THOENE JG, WEISS SJ: Generation of nitrogen-chlorine oxidants by human phagocytes. *J Clin Invest* 74:1341, 1984.

159. WEISS SJ, PEPPIN G, ORTIZ X, RAGSDALE C, TEST ST: Oxidative autoactivation of latent collagenase by human neutrophils. *Science* 227:747, 1985.

160. WEISS SJ, REGIANI S: Neutrophils degrade subendothelial matrices in the presence of alpha-$_1$-protease inhibitor. *J Clin Invest* 73:1297, 1984.

161. WEISS SJ, KLEIN R, SLIVKA A, WEI M: Chlorination of taurine by human neutrophils. *J Clin Invest* 70:598, 1982.

162. WEISS SJ, SLIVKA A: Monocyte and granulocyte-mediated tumor cell destruction. *J Clin Invest* 69:225, 1982.

163. ZGLICZYNSKI JM, STELMASZYNSKA T: Chlorinating ability of human phagocytosing leucocytes. *Eur J Biochem* 56:157, 1975.

164. ZGLICZYNSKI JM, STELMASZYNSKA T, DOMANSKI J, OSTROWSKI W: Chloramines as intermediates of oxidation reaction of amino acids by myeloperoxidase. *Biochim Biophys Acta* 235:419, 1974.

165. HARRISON JE, SCHULTZ J: Studies on the chlorinating activity of myeloperoxidase. *J Biol Chem* 251:1371, 1976.

166. ALBRICH JM, MCCARTHY CA, HURST JK: Biological reactivity of hypochlorous acid and implications for microbicidal mechanism of leukocyte myeloperoxidase. *Proc Natl Acad Sci USA* 78:210, 1981.

167. ROSEN H, KLEBANOFF SJ: Oxidation of microbial iron-sulfur centers by the MPO-H_2O_2-halide antimicrobial system. *Infect Immun* 47:613, 1985.

168. ROSEN H, KLEBANOFF SJ: Oxidation of *Escherichia coli* iron centers by the myeloperoxidase-mediated microbicidal system. *J Biol Chem* 257:13731, 1982.

169. CECH P, PAPATHANASSIOU A, BOREAUX G, ROTH P, MIESCHER PA: Hereditary myeloperoxidase deficiency. *Blood* 53:403, 1979.

170. CRANER R, SORANZO MR, DRI P, ROTTINI GD, BRAMEZZA M, CIRIELLI S: Incidence of myeloperoxidase deficiency in an area of northern Italy: Histochemical, biochemical, and functional studis. *Br J Haematol* 51:81, 1982.

171. KITAHARA M, EYRE HJ, SIMONIAN Y, ATKIN CL, HASSTEDT SJ: Hereditary myeloperoxidase deficiency. *Blood* 57:888, 1981.

172. KLEBANOFF SJ, PINCUS SH: Hydrogen proxide utilization in myeloperoxidase-deficient leukocytes: A possible microbicidal control mechanism. *J Clin Invest* 50:2226, 1971.

173. PATRIARCA P, CRAMER R, TEDESCO F, KUKINUMA K: Studies on the mechanism of metabolic stimulation in polymorphonuclear leukocytes during phagocytosis. *Biochim Biophys Acta* 385:387, 1975.

174. ROSEN H, KLEBANOFF SJ: Chemiluminescence and superoxide production by myeloperoxidase-deficient leukocytes. *J Clin Invest* 58:50, 1976.

175. LOCKSLEY RM, WILSON CB, KLEBANOFF SJ: Increased respiratory burst in myeloperoxidase-deficient monocytes. *Blood* 62:902, 1983.

176. CLARK RA: Extracellular effect of the myeloperoxidase–hydrogen peroxide–halide system, in Weissmann G (ed): *Advances in Infection Research*. New York, Raven, 1983, vol 5, p 107.

177. CLARK RA, BORREGAARD N: Neutrophils autoinactivate secretory products by myeloperoxidase-catalyzed oxidation. *Blood* 65:375, 1985.

178. KOBAYASHI M, TANAKA T, USUI T: Inactivation of lysosomal enzymes by the respiratory burst of polymorphonuclear leukocytes: Possible involve-

ment of myeloperoxidase-H$_2$O$_2$-halide system. *J Lab Clin Med* 100:896, 1982.

179. VOETMAN AA, WEENING RS, HAMERS MN, MEERHOF LJ, BOT AAAM, ROOS D: Phagocytosing human neutrophils inactivate their own granular enzymes. *J Clin Invest* 67:1541, 1981.

180. CLARK RA, SZOT S: Chemotactic factor inactivation by stimulated human neutrophils mediated by myeloperoxidase-catalyzed methionine oxidation. *J Immunol* 128:1507, 1982.

181. CLARK RA: Chemotactic factors trigger their own oxidative inactivation by human neutrophils. *J Immunol* 129:2725, 1982.

182. CLARK RA, SZOT S, VENKATASUBRAMANIAN K, SCHIFFMANN E: Chemotactic factor inactivation by myeloperoxidase-mediated oxidation of methionine. *J Immunol* 124:2020, 1980.

183. CLARK RA, KLEBANOFF SJ: Chemotactic factor inactivation by the myeloperoxidase–hydrogen peroxide–halide system. *J Clin Invest* 64:913, 1979.

184. TSAN M-F, DENISON RC: Oxidation of n-formyl methionyl chemotactic peptide by human neutrophils. *J Immunol* 126:1387, 1981.

185. CLARK RA, STONE P, EL-HAG A, CALORE JD, FRANZBLAU C: Myeloproxidase-catalyzed inactivation of α$_1$-protease inhibitor by human neutrophils. *J Biol Chem* 256:3348, 1981.

186. MATHESON NR, WONG PS, SCHUYLER M, TRAVIS J: Interaction of human alpha-1-proteinase inhibitor with neutrophil myeloperoxidase. *Biochemistry* 20:331, 1981.

187. MATHESON NR, WONG PS, TRAVIS J: Enzymatic inactivation of human alpha-1-proteinase inhibitor by neutrophil myeloperoxidase. *Biochem Biophys Res Commun* 88:402, 1979.

188. LANE TA, LAMKIN GE: Myeloperoxidase-mediated modulation of chemotactic peptide binding to human neutrophils. *Blood* 61:1203, 1983.

189. EL-HAG A, CLARK RA: Down-regulation of human natural killer activity against tumors by the neutrophil myeloperoxidase system and hydrogen peroxide. *J Immunol* 133:3291, 1984.

190. ANDERSEN M, ATKIN CL, EYRE HJ: Intact form of myeloperoxidase from normal human neutrophils. *Arch Biochem Biophys* 214:273, 1982.

191. ANDREWS PC, KRINSKY NI: The reductive cleavage of myeloperoxidase in half, producing enzymatically active hemi-myeloperoxidase. *J Biol Chem* 256:4211, 1981.

192. HARRISON JE, PABALAN S, SCHULTZ J: The subunit structure of crystalline canine myeloperoxidase. *Biochim Biophys Acta* 493:247, 1977.

193. NAUSEEF WM, ROOT RK, MALECH HL: Biochemical and immunologic analysis of hereditary myeloperoxidase deficiency. *J Clin Invest* 71:1297, 1983.

194. OLSSON I, OLOFSSON T, ODEBER H: Myeloperoxidase-mediated iodination in granulocytes. *Scand J Haematol* 9:483, 1972.

195. YAMADA M, MORI M, SUGIMURA T: Purification and characterization of small molecular weight myeloperoxidase forms from human promyelocytic leukemia HL-60 cells. *Biochemistry* 20:766, 1981.

196. FELDBERG NT, SCHULTZ J: Evidence that myeloperoxidase is composed of isoenzymes. *Arch Biochem Biophys* 148:407, 1972.

197. HIMMELHOCK SR, EVANS WH, MAGE MG, PETERSON EA: Purification of myeloperoxidases from the bone marrow of the guinea pig. *Biochemistry* 8:914, 1969.

198. SCHULTZ J, FELDBERG J, JOHN S: Myeloperoxidase. VIII. Separation into ten components by free-flow electrophoresis. *Biochem Biophys Res Commun* 28:543, 1967.

199. STRAUVEN TA, ARMSTRONG D, JAMES GT, AUSTIN JH: Separation of leukocyte peroxidase isoenzymes by agarose-acrylamide disc electrophoresis. *Age* 1:111, 1978.

200. NAUSEEF WM, MALECH HL: Immunochemical analysis of myeloperoxidase in normal and MPO-deficient neutrophils and a human promyelocytic cell line. *Clin Res* 30:560A, 1982.

201. MIYASAKI KT, WILSON ME, COHEN E, JONES PC, GENCO RJ: Evidence for and partial characterization of three major and three minor chromatographic forms of human neutrophil myeloperoxidase. *Arch Biochem Biophys* 246:751, 1986.

202. MORITA Y, IWAMOTO H, AIBARA S, KOBAYASHI T, HASEGAWA E: Crystallization and properties of myeloperoxidase from normal human leukocytes. *J Biochem* 99:761, 1986.

203. PEMBER SO, FUHRER-KRSI SM, BARNES KC, KINKADE JM: Isolation of three native forms of myeloperoxidase from human polymorphonuclear leukocytes. *FEBS Lett* 140:103, 1982.

204. SUZUKI K, OTA H, SASAGAWA S, SAKATANI T, FUJIKURA T: Assay method for myeloperoxidase in human polymorphonuclear leukocytes. *Anal Biochem* 132:345, 1983.

205. ATKIN CL, ANDERSEN MR, EYRE HJ: Abnormal neutrophil myeloperoxidase from a patient with chronic myelogenous leukemia. *Arch Biochem Biophys* 214:284, 1982.

206. BABCOCK GT, INGLE RT, OERTLING WA, DAVIS JC, AVERILL BA, HULSE CL, STUFKENS DJ, BOLSCHER BGJM, WEVER R: Raman characterization of human leukocyte myeloperoxidase and bovine spleen haemoprotein: Insight into chromophore structure and evidence that the chromophores of myeloperoxidase are equivalent. *Biochim Biophys Acta* 828:58, 1985.

207. IKEDO-SAITO M, ARGADE PV, ROUSSEAU DL: Resonance evidence of chloride binding to the heme iron in myeloperoxidase. *FEBS Lett* 1884:52, 1985.

208. SIBBETT S, HURST JK: Structural analysis of myeloperoxidase by resonance Raman spectroscopy. *Biochemistry* 23:3007, 1984.

209. ANDREWS PC, PARNES C, KRINSKY NI: Comparison of myeloperoxidase and hemi-myeloperoxidase with regard to catalysis, regulation, and bactericidal activity. *Arch Biochem Biophys* 228:439, 1984.

210. JOHNSTON RB JR, NEWMAN SL: Chronic granulomatous disease. *Pediatr Clin North Am* 24:365, 1977.

211. KLEBANOFF SJ, CLARK RA: Chronic granulomatous disease, in *The Neutrophil: Function and Clinical Disorders*. Amsterdam, North Holland, 1978, p 641.

212. TAUBER AI, BORREGAARD N, SIMONS E, WRIGHT J: Chronic granulomatous disease: A syndrome of phagocyte oxidase deficiencies. *Medicine* 62:286, 1983.

213. GALLIN JI, BUESCHER ES, SELIGMANN BE, NATH J, GAITHER T, KATZ P: Recent advances in chronic granulomatous disease. *Ann Intern Med* 99:657, 1983.

214. CURNUTTE JT, BABIOR BM: Chronic granulomatous disease. *Adv Hum Genet* 16:229, 1987.

215. HOLMES B, PAGE AR, GOOD RA: Studies of the metabolic activity of leukocytes from patients with a genetic abnormality of phagocytic function. *J Clin Invest* 46:1422, 1967.

216. DAVIS WC, HUBER H, DOUGLAS SD, FUDENBERG HH: A defect in circulating mononuclear phagocytes in chronic granulomatous disease of childhood. *J Immunol* 101:1093, 1968.

217. RODEY GE, PARK BH, WINDHORST DB, GOOD RA: Defective bactericidal activity of monocytes in fatal granulomatous disease. *Blood* 33:813, 1969.

218. LEHRER RI: Measurement of candidacidal activity of specific leukocyte types in mixed cell populations. II Normal and chronic granulomatous disease eosinophils. *Infect Immun* 3:800, 1971.

219. BERENDES H, BRIDGES RA, GOOD RA: Fatal granulomatosus of childhood: clinical study of new syndrome. *Minn Med* 40:309, 1957.

220. LANDING BH, SHIRKEY HS: Syndrome of recurrent infection and infiltration of viscera by pigmented lipid histiocytes. *Pediatrics* 20:431, 1957.

221. BAEHNER RL, NATHAN DG: Quantitative nitroblue tetrazolium test in chronic granulomatous disease. *N Engl J Med* 278:971, 1968.

222. QUIE PG, KAPLAN EL, PAGE AR, GRUSKAY FL, MALAWISTA SE: Defective polymorphonuclear-leukocyte function and chronic granulomatous disease in two female children. *N Engl J Med* 278:976, 1968.

223. CURNUTTE JT, WHITTEN DM, BABIOR BM: Defective superoxide production by granulocytes from patients with chronic granulomatous disease. *N Engl J Med* 290:593, 1974.

224. CURNUTTE JT, KIPNES RS, BABIOR BM: Defect in pyridine nucleotide-dependent superoxide production by a particulate fraction from the granulocytes of patients with chronic granulomatous disease. *N Engl J Med* 293:628, 1975.

225. HOHN DC, LEHRER RI: NADPH oxidase deficiency in X-linked chronic granulomatous disease. *J Clin Invest* 55:707, 1975.

226. MCPHAIL LC, DeCHATALET LR, SHIRLEY PS, WILFERT C, JOHNSTON RB JR, MCCALL CE: Deficiency of NADPH oxidase activity in chronic granulomatous disease. *J Pediatr* 90:213, 1977.

227. SEGAL AW, CROSS AR, GARCIA RC, BORREGAARD N, VALERIUS NH, SOOTHILL JF, JONES OTG: Absence of cytochrome b$_{-245}$ in chronic granulomatous disease: A multicenter European evaluation of its incidence and relevance. *N Engl J Med* 308:245, 1983.

228. NEWBURGER PE, COHEN HJ, ROTHCHILD SB, HIBBINS JC, MALAWISTA SE, MAHONEY MJ: Prenatal diagnosis of chronic granulomatous disease. *N Engl J Med* 300:178, 1979.

229. MATTHAY KK, GOLBUS MS, WARA DW, MENTZER WC: Prenatal diagnosis of chronic granulomatous disease. *Am J Med Genet* 17:731, 1984.

230. LEVINSKY R, HARVEY B, NICOLAIDES K, RODECK C: Antenatal diagnosis of chronic granulomatous disease. *Lancet* 1:504, 1986.

231. WEENING RS, ADRIAANSZ LH, WEEMAES CMR, LUTTER R, ROOS D: Clinical differences in chronic granulomatous disease in patients with cytochrome b-negative or cytochrome b-positive neutrophils. *J Pediatr* 107:102, 1985.

232. DONOWITZ GR, MANDELL GL: Clinical presentation and unusual infections in chronic granulomatous disease, in Gallin JI, Fauci AS (eds): *Advances in Host Defense Mechanisms*. New York, Raven, 1983, vol 3, p 55.

233. WINDHORST DG, GOOD RA: Dermatologic manifestations of fatal granulomatous disease of childhood. *Arch Dermatol* 103:351, 1971.

234. BARRIERE H, LITOUX P, STALDER JF, BURIOT C, HAKIM J: Chronic granulomatous disease: Late onset of skin lesions only, in two siblings. *Arch Dermatol* 17:683, 1981.

235. STALDER JF, DRENO B, BUREAU B, HAKIM J: Discoid lupus erythematosus-like lesions in an autosomal form of chronic granulomatous disease. *Br J Dermatol* 114:251, 1986.

236. STRATE M, BRANDRUP F, WAND P: Discoid lupus erythematosus like skin lesions in a patient with autosomal recessive chronic granulomatous disease. *Clin Genet* 30:184, 1986.

237. THOMPSON EN, SOOTHILL JF: Chronic granulomatous disease: Quantitative clinicopathological relationships. *Arch Dis Child* 45:24, 1970.

238. SCHALLER J: Illness resembling lupus erythematosus in mothers of boys with chronic granulomatous disease. *Ann Intern Med* 76:747, 1972.

239. HUMBERT JR, FISHMAN CB, WESTON WL, DEARMEY PA, THOREN CH: Frequency of the carrier state for X-linked chronic granulomatous disease among females with lupus erythematosus. *Clin Genet* 10:16, 1976.

240. KRAGBALLE D, BORREGAARD N, BRANDRUP F, KOCH C, JOHANSEN KS: Relation of monocyte and neutrophil oxidative metabolism to skin and oral lesions in carriers of chronic granulomatous disease. *Clin Exp Immunol* 43:390, 1981.

241. BARTON LL, JOHNSON CR: Discoid lupus erythematosus and X-linked chronic granulomatous disease. *Pediatr Dermatol* 3:376, 1986.

242. WOLFSON JJ, QUIE PG, LAXDAL SD, GOOD RA: Roentgenologic manifestations in children with a genetic defect of polymorphonuclear leukocyte function. *Radiology* 91:37, 1968.

243. GOLD RH, DOUGLAS SD, PREGER L, STEINBACH HL, FUDENBERG HH: Roentgenographic features of the neutrophil dysfunction syndrome. *Radiology* 92:1045, 1969.

244. DILWORTH JA, MANDELL GL: Adults with chronic granulomatous disease of "childhood." *Am J Med* 63:233, 1977.

245. KELLEHER D, BLOOMFIELD FJ, LENEHAN T, GRIFFIN M, GEIGHERY C, MCCANN SR: Chronic granulomatous disease presenting as an oculomucocutaneous syndrome mimicking Behcet's syndrome. *Postgrad Med J* 62:489, 1986.

246. AMENT ME, OCHS HD: Gastrointestinal manifestations of chronic granulomatous disease. *N Engl J Med* 288:382, 1974.

247. COHEN MS: Phagocytic cells in periodontal defense. Periodontal status of patients with chronic granulomatous disease of childhood. *J Periodontol* 56:611, 1985.

248. FORREST CB, FOREHAND JR, AXTELL RA, ROBERTS RL, JOHNSTON RB: Clinical features and current management of chronic granulomatous disease. *Hematol Oncol Clin North Am* 2:253, 1988.

249. GRISCOM NT, KIRKPATRICK JA, GIRDANY BR, BERSON WE, GRAND RJ, MACKIE GG: Gastric antral narrowing in chronic granulomatous disease of childhood. *Pediatrics* 54:456, 1974.

250. BOWEN A III, GIBSON MD: Chronic granulomatous disease with gastric antral narrowing. *Pediatr Radiol* 10:119, 1980.

251. STY JR, CHUSID MJ, BABBITT DP, WERLIN SL: Involvement of the colon in chronic granulomatous disease of childhood. *Radiology* 132:618, 1979.

252. WOLFSON JJ, KANE WJ, LAXDAL SD, GOOD RA, QUIE PG: Bone findings in chronic granulomatous disease of childhood. *J Bone Joint Surg* 51-A:1573, 1969.

253. CYR WL, JOHNSON H, BALFOUR J: Granulomatous cystitis as a manifestation of chronic granulomatous disease of childhood. *J Urol* 110:3537, 1973.

254. YOUNG AK, MIDDLETON RG: Urologic manifestations of chronic granulomatous disease of infancy. *J Urol* 123:119, 1980.

255. KONTRAS SB, BODENBENDER JG, MCCLAVE CR, SMITH JP: Interstitial cystitis as a manifestation of chronic granulomatous disease. *Clin Exp Immunol* 43:390, 1981.

256. VAN RHENEN DJ, KOOLEN MI, FELTKAMP-VROOM TM, WEENING RS: Immune complex glomerulonephritis in chronic granulomatous disease. *Acta Med Scand* 206:233, 1979.

257. FRIFELT JJ, SCHONHEYDER H, VALERIUS NH, STRATE M, STARKLINT H: Chronic granulomatous disease associated with chronic glomerulonephritis. *Acta Paediatr Scand* 74:152, 1985.

258. FORBES GS, HARTMAN GW, BURKE EC, SEGURA JW: Genitourinary involvement in chronic granulomatous disease of childhood. *Am J Roentgenol* 127:683, 1976.

259. BLOOMBERG SD, NEU HC, EHRLICH RM, BLANC WA: Chronic granulomatous disease of childhood with renal involvement. *Urology* 4:193, 1974.

260. FLEISCHMANN J, CHURCH JA, LEHRER RI: Case report: Primary candida meningitis and chronic granulomatous disease. *Am J Med Sci* 291:334, 1986.

261. LAZARUS GM, HEU HC: Agents responsible for infection in chronic granulomatous disease of childhood. *J Pediatr* 86:415, 1975.

262. MARTYN LJ, LISCHNER HW, PILAGGI AJ, HARLEY RD: Chorioretinal lesions in familial chronic granulomatous disease of childhood. *Am J Ophthalmol* 73:403, 1972.

263. HALAZUN JF, LUKENS JN: Thyrotoxicosis associated with aspergillus thyroiditis in chronic granulomatous disease. *J Pediatr* 80:106, 1972.

264. WALKER DH, OKIYE G: Chronic granulomatous disease involving the central nervous system. *Pediatr Pathol* 1:159, 1983.

265. MOELLERING RC, WEINBERG AN: Persistent salmonella infection in a female carrier for chronic granulomatous disease. *Ann Intern Med* 73:595, 1970.

266. JOHNSTON RB JR: Unusual forms of an uncommon disease (chronic granulomatous disease). *J Pediatr* 88:172, 1976.

267. WARD PA, SCHLEGEL RJ: Impaired leucotactic responsiveness in a child with recurrent infections. *Lancet* 2:344, 1969.

268. CLARK RA, KLEBANOFF SJ: Chronic granulomatous disease: Studies of a family with impaired neutrophil chemotactic, metabolic and bactericidal function. *Am J Med* 65:941, 1978.

269. BAEHNER RL, BOXER LA, DAVIS J: The biochemical basis of nitroblue tetrazolium reduction in normal human and chronic granulomatous disease polymorphonuclear leukocytes. *Blood* 48:309, 1976.

270. MARSH WL, OYEN R, NICHOLDS ME, ALLEN FH: Chronic granulomatous disease and the kell blood groups. *Br J Haematol* 29:247, 1975.

271. MARSH WL, URETSKY SC, DOUGLAS SD: Antigens of the kell blood group system on neutrophils and monocytes: Their relation to chronic granulomatous disease. *J Pediatr* 87:1117, 1975.

272. GIBLETT ER, KLEBANOFF SJ, PINCUS SH, SWANSON J, PARK BH, MCCULLOUGH J: Kell phenotypes in chronic granulomatous disease: A potential transfusion hazard. *Lancet* 1:1235, 1971.

273. DENSEN P, WILKINSON-KROOVAND S, MANDELL GL, SULLIVAN G, OYEN R, MARSH WL: K_x: Its relationship to chronic granulomatous disease and genetic linkage with Xg. *Blood* 58:34, 1981.

274. MARSH WL, MARSH NJ, MOORE A, SYMMANS WA, JOHNSON CL, REDMAN CM: Elevated serum creatine phosphokinase in subjects with McLeod syndrome. *Vox Sang* 40:403, 1981.

275. ITO K, MUKAMOTO Y, KONISHI H, SAKURA N, USUI T: Kell phenoptypes in 15 Japanese patients with chronic granulomatous disease. *Vox Sang* 37:39, 1979.

275a. FRANCKE U, OCHS HD, DE MARTINVILLE B, GIACALONE J, LINDGREN V, DISTECHE C, PAGON RA, HOFKER MH, VAN OMMEN G-JB, PEARSON PL, WEDGWOOD RJ: Minor Xp21 chromosome deletion in a male associated with expression of Duchenne muscular dystrophy, chronic granulomatous disease, retinitis pigmentosa, and McLeod syndrome. *Am J Hum Genet* 37:250, 1985.

276. FREY D, MACHLER M, SEGER R, SCHMID W, ORKIN SH: Gene deletion in a patient with chronic granulomatous disease and McLeod Syndrome: Fine mapping of the Xk gene locus. *Blood* 71:252, 1988.

277. MANDELL GL, HOOK EW: Leukocyte bactericidal activity in chronic granulomatous disease: Correlation of bacterial hydrogen peroxide production and susceptibility to intracellular killing. *J Bacteriol* 100:531, 1969.

278. KELLY JK, PINTO AR, WHITELAW WA, RORSTAD OP, BOWEN TJ, MATHESON DS: Fatal aspergillus pneumonia in chronic granulomatous disease. *Am J Clin Pathol* 86:668, 1986.

279. BUJAK JS, OTTESEN EA, DINARELLO CA, BRENNER VJ: Nocardiosis in a child with chronic granulomatous disease. *J Pediatr* 83:98, 1973.

280. CURRY WA: Human nocardiosis: A clinical review with selected case reports. *Arch Intern Med* 140:818, 1980.

281. CASALE TB, MACHER AM, FAUCI AS: Concomitant pulmonary aspergillosis and nocardiosis in a patient with a chronic granulomatous disease of childhood. *South Med J* 77:274, 1984.

282. CHUSID MJ, PARRILLO JE, FAUCI AS: Chronic granulomatous disease: Diagnosis in a 27-year old man with *Mycobacterium fortuitum*. *JAMA* 233:1295, 1975.

283. KOBAYASHI Y, KOMAZAWA Y, KOBAYASHI M, MATSUMOTO T, SAKURA N, ISHIKAWA K, USUI T: Presumed BCG infection in a boy with chronic granulomatous disease. A report of a case and a review of the literature. *Clin Pediatr* 23:586, 1984.

284. HAMERS MN, DE BOER M, MEERHOF LJ, WEENING RS, ROOS D: Complementation in monocyte hybrids revealing genetic heterogeneity in chronic granulomatous disease. *Nature* 307:553, 1984.

285. WEENING RS, CORBEEL L, DE BOER M, LUTTER R, VAN ZWIETEN R, HAMERS MN, ROOS D: Cytochrome b deficiency in an autosomal form of chronic granulomatous disease: A third form of chronic granulomatous disease recognized by monocyte hybridization. *J Clin Invest* 75:915, 1985.

286. LEW PD, WOLHEIM C, SEGER RA, POZZAN T: Cytosolic free calcium changes induced by chemotactic peptide in neutrophils from patients with chronic granulomatous disease. *Blood* 63:231, 1984.

287. FEINMARK SJ, UDN AM, PALMBLAD J, MALMSTEM C: Leukotriene biosynthesis by polymorphonuclear leukocytes from two patients with chronic granulomatous disease. *J Clin Invest* 72:1839, 1983.

288. HENDERSON WR, KLEBANOFF SJ: Leukotriene production and inactivation by normal, chronic granulomatous disease and myeloperoxidase-deficient neutrophils. *J Biol Chem* 258:13522, 1983.

289. SMITH DM, WALSH CE, DECHATELET LR, WAITE M: Arachidonic acid me-

tabolism in polymorphonuclear leukocytes from patients with chronic granulomatous disease. *Infect Immun* 40:1230, 1983.

290. KORCHAK HM, WEISSMANN G: Changes in membrane potential of human granulocytes antecede the metabolic responses to surface stimulation. *Proc Natl Acad Sci USA* 75:3818, 1978.

291. WHITIN JC, CHAPMAN CE, SIMONS ER, CHOVANIEC ME, COHEN HJ: Correlation between membrane potential changes and superoxide production in human granulocytes stimulated by phorbol byristate acetate. Evidence for defective activation in chronic granulomatous disease. *J Biol Chem* 255:1874, 1980.

292. SELIGMAN B, GALLIN JI: Abnormality in elicited membrane potential changes in neutrophils from patients with chronic granulomatous disease, in Gallin JI, Fauci AS (eds): *Advances in Host Defense Mechanisms*. New York, Raven, 1983, vol 3, p 195.

293. KUROKI M, NAOKI K, KOBATAKE Y, OKIMASU E, UTSUMI K: Measurement of membrane potential in polymorphonuclear leukocytes and its change during surface stimulation. *Biochim Biophys Acta* 693:326, 1982.

294. GRINSTEIN S, FURUYA W, BIGGAR WD: Cytoplasmic pH regulation in normal and abnormal neutrophils. Role of superoxide generation and Na^+/H^+ exchange. *J Biol Chem* 261:512, 1986.

295. GABIG TG, LEFKER BA, OSSANNA PJ, WEISS SJ: Proton stoichiometry associated with human neutrophil respiratory-burst reactions. *J Biol Chem* 259:13166, 1984.

296. SEGAL AW, HEYWORTH PG, COCKCROFT S, BARROWMAN MM: Stimulated neutrophils from patients with autosomal recessive chronic granulomatous disease fail to phosphorylate a M_r-44,000 protein. *Nature* 316:547, 1985.

297. HAYAKAWA T, SUZUKI K, SUZUKI S, ANDREWS PC, BABIOR BM: A possible role for protein phosphorylation in the activation of the respiratory burst in human neutrophils: Evidence from studies with cells from patients with chronic granulomatous disease. *J Biol Chem* 261:9109, 1986.

298. ISHII E, IRITA K, FUJITA I, TAKESHIGE K, KOBAYSHI M, USUI T, UEDA K: Protein phosphorylation of neutrophils from normal children and patients with chronic granulomatous disease. *Eur J Pediatr* 145:22, 1986.

299. BABIOR BM, OKAMURA N, CURNUTTE JT: The 48K phosphoprotein family of human neutrophils. *Blood* 70:83a, 1987.

300. RICCARDI S, GIORDANO D, SCHETTINI F, DEMATTIA D, LOVECCHIO T, SANTORO N, FUMARULO R: Cytochrome b and FAD content in polymorphonuclear leukocytes in a family with X-linked chronic granulomatous disease. *Scand J Haematol* 37:333, 1986.

301. OHNO Y, BUESCHER ES, ROBERTS R, METCALF JA, GALLIN JI: Reevaluation of cytochrome b and flavin adenine dinucleotide in neutrophils from patients with chronic granulomatous disease and description of a family with probable autosomal recessive inheritance of cytochrome b deficiency. *Blood* 67:1132, 1986.

302. SEGAL AW, JONES OTG: Neutrophil cytochrome b in chronic granulomatous disease. *Lancet* 1:1036, 1979.

303. PARKOS C, DINAUER M, JESAITIS A, ORKIN S, CURNUTTE J: Absence of both the 91K and 22K subunits of cytochrome b_{558} in two genetic forms of chronic granulomatous disease. *Blood* 70:93a, 1987.

304. SEGAL AW, JONES OTG: Absence of cytochrome b reduction in stimulated neutrophils from both female and male patients with chronic granulomatous disease. *FEBS Lett* 110:111, 1980b.

305. BORREGAARD N, CROSS AR, HERLIN T, JONES OTG, SEGAL AW, VALERIUS NH: A variant form of X-linked chronic granulomatous disease with normal nitro-blue tetrazolium slide test and cytochrome b. *Eur J Clin Invest* 13:243, 1983.

306. CURNUTTE JT: The classification of chronic granulomatous disease. *Hematol Oncol Clin North Am*, 2:241, 1988.

307. CURNUTTE JT, KUVER R, SCOTT PJ: Activation of neutrophil NADPH oxidase in a cell-free system. *J Biol Chem* 262:5563, 1987.

308. OCHS HD, IGO RP: The NBT slide test: A simple screening method for detecting chronic granulomatous disease and female carriers. *J Pediatr* 83:77, 1973.

309. LEW PD, SOUTHWICK FS, STOSSEL TP, WHITIN JC, SIMONS E, COHEN HJ: A variant of chronic granulomatous disease: Deficient oxidative metabolism due to a low-affinity NADPH oxidase. *N Engl J Med* 305:1329, 1981.

310. SEGER RA, TIEFENAUER L, MATSUNAGE T, WILDFEUER A, NEWBURGER PE: Chronic granulomatous disease due to granulocytes with abnormal NADPH oxidase activity and deficient cytochrome b. *Blood* 61:423, 1983.

311. SHURIN SB, COHEN HJ, WHITIEN JC, NEWBURGER PE: Impaired granulocyte superoxide production and prolongation of the respiratory burst due to a low-affinity NADPH-dependent oxidase. *Blood* 62:564, 1983.

312. STYRT B, KLEMPNER MS: Late-presenting variant of chronic granulomatous disease. *Pediatr Infect Dis* 3:556, 1984.

313. NEWBURGER PE, LUSCINSKAS FW, RYAN T, BEARD CJ, WRIGHT J, PLATT

OS, SIMONS ER, TAUBER AI: Variant chronic granulomatous disease: Modulation of the neutrophil defect by severe infection. *Blood* 68:914, 1986.

314. MEERHOF J, ROOS D: Heterogeneity in chronic granulomatous disease detected with an improved nitroblue tetrazolium slide test. *J Leukocyte Biol* 39:699, 1986.

315. HOLMES B, PARK PH, MALAWISTA SE, QUIE PG, NELSON DL, GOOD RA: Chronic granulomatous disease in females: A deficiency of leukocyte glutathione peroxidase. *N Engl J Med* 283:217, 1970.

316. MATSUDA I, OKA Y, TANIGUCHI N, FURUYAMA M, KODAMAS, ARASHIMA S, MITSUYAMA T: Leukocyte glutathione peroxidase deficiency in a male patient with chronic granulomatous disease. *J Pediatr* 88:581, 1976.

317. DECHATELET LR, SHIRLEY PS, MCPHAIL LC: Normal glutathione peroxidase activity in patients with chronic granulomatous disease. *J Pediatr* 89:598, 1976.

318. BAEHNER RL, JOHNSTON RB, NATHAN DG: Comparative study of the metabolic and bactericidal characteristics of severely glucose-6-phosphate dehydrogenase deficient polymorphonuclear leukocytes from children with chronic granulomatous disease. *J Reticuloendothel Soc* 12:150, 1972.

319. COOPER MR, DECHATELET LR, MCCALL CE, LAVIA MF, SPURR CL, BAEHNER RL: Complete deficiency of leukocyte glucose-6-phosphate dehydrogenase with defective bactericidal activity. *J Clin Invest* 51:769, 1972.

320. GRAY GR, KLEBANOFF SJ, STAMATAYANNOPOULOS G, AUSTIN T, NAIMAN SC, YOSHIDA A, KLIMAN MR, ROBINSON GC: Neutrophil dysfunction, chronic granulomatous disease and non-spherocytic haemolytic anaemia caused by complete deficiency of glucose-6-phosphate dehydrogenase. *Lancet* 2:530, 1973.

321. MAMLOK RJ, MAMLOK V, MILLS GC, DAESCHNER CW, SCHMALSTIEG FC, ANDERSON DC: Glucose-6-phosphate dehydrogenase deficiency, neutrophil dysfunction and *Chromobacterium violaceum* sepsis. *J Pediatr* 111:852, 1987.

322. MIYAZAKI S, SHIN H, GOYA N, NAKAGAWARE A: Identification of a carrier mother of a female patient with chronic granulomatous disease. *J Pediatr* 89:784, 1976.

323. MILLS EL, RHOLL KS, QUIE PG: X-linked inheritance in females with chronic granulomatous disease. *J Clin Invest* 66:332, 1980.

324. JOHNSTON RB III, HARBECK RJ, JOHNSTON RB JR: Recurrent severe infections in a girl with apparently variable expression of mosaicism for chronic granulomatous disease. *J Pediatr* 106:50, 1985.

325. AZIMI PH, BODENBENDER JG, HINTZ RL, KONTRAS SB: Chronic granulomatous disease in three female siblings. *JAMA* 206:2865, 1968.

326. ELGEFORS B, OLLING S, PELIRSON H: Chronic granulomatous disease in three siblings. *Scand J Infect Dis* 10:79, 1978.

327. D'AMELIO R, BELLAVITE P, BIANCE P, DE SOLE P, LE MOLI S, LIPPA S, SEMINARA R, VERCELLI B, ROSSE F, TOCCHE G, AIUTI F: Chronic granulomatous disease in two sisters. *J Clin Immunol* 4:220, 1984.

328. JOHNSTON RB JR: Measurement of O_2^- secreted by monocytes and macrophages. *Methods Enzymol* 105:365, 1984.

329. MARKET M, ANDREWS PC, BABIOR BM: Measurement of O_2^- production by human neutrophils. The preparation and assay of NADPH oxidase-containing particles from human neutrophils. *Methods Enzymol* 105:358, 1984.

330. ABSOLOM DR: Basic methods for the study of phagocytosis. *Methods Enzymol* 132:147, 1987.

331. BAGGIOLINI M, RUCH W, COOPER PH: Measurement of hydrogen peroxide production by phagocytes using homovanillic acid and horseradish peroxidase. *Methods Enzymol* 132:395, 1987.

332. DAFFOS F, CAPELLA-PAVLOVSKY M, FORESTIER F: Fetal blood sampling during pregnancy with use of a needle guided by ultrasound: A study of 606 consecutive cases. *Am J Obstet Gynecol* 153:655, 1985.

332a. LINDLOF M, KERE J, RISTOLA M, REPO H, LEIRISALO-REPO M, VON KOSKULL H, AMMALA P, DE LA CHAPELLE A: Prenatal diagnosis of X-linked chronic granulomatous disease using restriction fragment length polymorphism analysis. *Genomics* 1:87, 1987.

333. PHILIPPART AI, COLODNY AH, BAEHNER RL: Continuous antibiotic therapy in chronic granulomatous disease: Preliminary communication. *Pediatrics* 50:923, 1972.

334. JOHNSTON RB, WILFERT CM, BUCKLEY RH, WEBB LS, DECHATELET LR, MCCALL CE: Enhanced bactericidal activity of phagocytes from patients with chronic granulomatous disease in the presence of sulphisoxazole. *Lancet* 1:824, 1975.

335. GMÜNDER FK, SEGER RA: Chronic granulomatous disease: Mode of action of sulfamethoxazole/trimethoprim. *Pediatr Res* 15:1533, 1981.

336. EZER G, SOOTHILL JF: Intracellular bactericidal effects of refampicin in both normal and chronic granulomatous disease polymorphs. *Arch Dis Child* 49:463, 1974.

337. GOUDEMAND J, AUSSENS R, DELAMS-MARSALET Y, FARRIAUX JP, FONTAINE D: Attempt to treat a case of chronic familial granulomatous dis-

ease by allogeneic bone marrow transplantation. *Arch Fr Pediatr* 33:121, 1976.

338. WESTMINSTER HOSPITAL BONE-MARROW TRANSPLANT TEAM: Bone-marrow transplant from an unrelated donor for chronic granulomatous disease. *Lancet* 1:210, 1977.

339. ANDERSON IM, BARRETT AJ, BYROM N, FOROOZANFAR N, GABRIEL C, HENRY K, HOBBS JR, HIGH-JONES K, HUMBLE JG, JAMES DCO, MAWLE A, SELWYN S, WATSON G, YAMAMURA M: Clinical results of bone marrow transplantation in SCID and other immunodeficiency states. *Pathol Biol* 26:23, 1978.

340. RAPPEPORT JM, NEWBURGER PE, GOLDBLUM RM, GOLDMAN AS, NATHAN DG, PARKMAN R: Allogeneic bone marrow transplantation for chronic granulomatous disease. *J Pediatr* 101:952, 1982.

341. KAMANI N, AUGUST CS, DOUGLAS SD, BURKEY E, ETZIONI A, LISCHNER HW: Bone marrow transplantation in chronic granulomatous disease. *J Pediatr* 105:42, 1984.

342. KAMANI N, AUGUST CS, RAUSEN AR, D'ANGIO G, DOUGLAS SD: Marrow transplantation (BMT) form a heterozygous carrier donor in chronic granulomatous disease (CGD). *Pediatr Res* 19:276A, 1985.

343. RAUBITSCHEK AA, LEVIN AS, STITES DP, SHAW EB, FUDENBERG HH: Normal granulocyte infusion therapy for aspergillosis in chronic granulomatous disease. *Pediatrics* 51:230, 1973.

344. BRZICA SM, RHODES KH, PINEDA AA, TASWELL HF: Chronic granulomatous disease and the McLeod phenotype: Successful treatment of infection with granulocyte transfusions resulting in subsequent hemolytic transfusion reaction. *Mayo Clin Proc* 52:153, 1977.

345. CHUSID MJ, TOMASULO PA: Survival of transfused normal granulocytes in a patient with chronic granulomatous disease. *Pediatrics* 61:556, 1978.

346. PEDERSEN FK, JOHANSEN KS, ROSENKVIST J, TYGSTRUP I, VALERIUS NH: Refractory *Pneumocystis carinii* infection in chronic granulomatous disease: Successful treatment with granulocytes. *Pediatrics* 64:935, 1979.

347. CHUSID MJ, SHEA ML, SARFF LD: Determination of posttransfusion granulocyte kinetics by chemiluminescence in chronic granulomatous disease. *J Lab Clin Med* 95:168, 1980.

348. TOMTOVIAN R, ABRAMSON J, QUIE P, MCCULLOUGH J: Granulocyte transfusion therapy in chronic granulomatous disease: Report of a patient and review of the literature. *Transfusion* 21:739, 1981.

349. BUESCHER ES, GALLIN JI: Leukocyte transfusions in chronic granulomatous disease. Persistence of transfused leukogyres in sputum. *N Engl J Med* 307:800, 1982.

350. ELLIOT GR, CLAY ME, MILLS EL, ABRAMSON JS, MCCULLOUGH J, QUIE PG: Granulocyte transfusion kinetics measured by chemiluminescence, nitro-blue tetrazolium reduction, and recovery of Indium-111-labeled granulocytes. *Transfusion* 27:23, 1987.

351. EZEKOWITZ AF, ORKIN SH, NEWBURGER PE: Recombinant interferon gamma augments phagocyte superoxide production and X-linked chronic granulomatous disease gene expression in X-linked variant chronic granulomatous disease. *J Clin Invest* 80:1009, 1987.

351a. EZEKOWITZ RA, DINAUER MC, JAFFE HS, ORKIN SH, NEWBERGER PE: Partial correction of the phagocyte defect in patients with X-linked chronic granulomatous disease by subcutaneous interferon gamma. *N Engl J Med* 319:146, 1988.

351b. SECHLER JMG, MALECH HL, WHITE CJ, GALLIN JI: Recombinant human interferon-γ reconstitutes defective phagocyte function in patients with chronic granulomatous disease of childhood. *Proc Natl Acad Sci USA* 85:4874, 1988.

352. CHIN TW, STEIM ER, FALLOON J, GALLIN JI: Corticosteroids in treatment of obstructive lesions of chronic granulomatous disease. *J Pediatr* 111:349, 1987.

353. CECH P, STALDER H, WIDMANN J, ROHNER A, MIESCHER PA: Leukocyte myeloperoxidase deficiency and diabetes mellitus associated with Candida albicans liver abscess. *Am J Med* 66:149, 1979.

354. GRIGNASCHI VJ, SPERPERATO AM, ETCHEVERRY MJ, MACARIO AJ: An nuevo cuadio cito guimico: negativad espontanea de las reacciones de per-oxidas, oxidas y lipido en la progenia neutrophila y en los monocitos de dos hermanos. *Rev Assoc Med Argent* 77:218, 1963.

355. HUHN D, BELOHRADSKY BH, HAAS R: Familiärer myeloperoxidasedefekt und akute myeloische leukämie. *Acta Haematol (Basel)* 59:129, 1978.

356. KITAHARA M, STIMONIAN Y, EYRE HJ: Neutrophil myeloperoxidase: A simple reproducible technique to determine activity. *J Lab Clin Med* 93:232, 1979.

357. LEHRER RI, CLINE MJ: Leukocyte myeloperoxidase deficiency and disseminated candidiasis: The role of myeloperoxidase in resistance to Candida infection. *J Clin Invest* 48:14788, 1969.

358. MOOSMANN K, BOJANOWSKY A: Rezidivierende Candidiosis bei myeloperoxydase-mangel. *Monatsschr Kinderheilkd* 123:408, 1975.

359. UNDRITZ E: Die Alius-Grignaschi-anomalie: der erblich konstitutionelle peroxydasedefekt der neutrophilen und monocyten. *Blut* 14:129, 1966.

360. PARRY MF, ROOT RK, METCALF JA, DELANEY KK, KAPLOW LS, RICHAR WJ: Myeloperoxidase deficiency: Prevalence and clinical significance. *Ann Intern Med* 95:293, 1981.

361. ROBERTSON CF, THONG YH, HODGE GL, CHENEY K: Primary myeloperoxidase deficiency associated with impaired neutrophil margination and chemotaxis. *Acta Paediatr Scand* 68:915, 1979.

362. KUSSENBACH G, RISTER M: Der Myeloperoxidase-Mangel als Ursache rezidivierende Infektionen. *Klin Padiatr* 197:443, 1985.

363. STENDAHL O, LINDGREN S: Function of granulocytes with deficiency of myeloperoxidase-mediated iodination in a patient with generalized pustular psoriasis. *Scand J Haematol* 16:144, 1976.

364. EL-MAALLEM H, FLETCHER J: Impaired neutrophil function and myeloperoxidase deficiency in pregnancy. *Br J Haematol* 44:375, 1980.

365. CALDWELL KC, TADDEINI L, WOODBURN, ANDERSON GL, LOBELL M: Induction of myeloperoxidase deficiency in granulocytes in lead-intoxicated dogs. *Blood* 53:588, 1979.

366. LEHRER RI, CLINE MJ: Leukocyte candidacidal activity and resistance to system candidiasis in patients with cancer. *Cancer* 27:1211, 1971.

367. GRAHAM GS: The neutrophilic granules of the circulating blood in health and in disease: A preliminary report. *NY State J Med* 20:46, 1920.

368. ARAKAWA T, WADA Y, HAYASHI T, KAKIZAKI R, CHIBA N, CHIDA R, KONNO T: Uracil-uric refractory anemia with peroxidase negative neutrophils. *Tohuku J Exp Med* 87:52, 1965.

369. HIGASHI O, KATSUYAMA N, SATODATE R: A case with hematological abnormalities characterized by the absence of peroxidase activity in blood polymorphonuclear leukocytes. *Tohuku J Exp Med* 87:77, 1965.

370. LEHRER RI, GOLDBERG LS, APPLE MA, ROSENTHAL NP: Refractory megaloblastic anemia with myeloperoxidase-deficient neutrophils. *Ann Intern Med* 76:447, 1972.

371. ARMSTRONG D, DIMMITT S, van WORMER DE: Studies in Batten disease I: Peroxidase deficiency in granulocytes. *Arch Neurol* 30:144, 1974.

372. BOZDECH MJ, BAINTON DF, MUSTACCHI P: Partial peroxidase deficiency in neutrophils and eosinophils associated with neurological disease. *Am J Clin Pathol* 73:409, 1980.

373. BENDIX-HANSEN K: Myeloproxidase-deficient polymorphonuclear leukocytes (VII): Incidence in untreated myeloproliferative disorders. *Scand J Haematol* 36:8, 1986.

374. BENDIX-HANSEN K: Myeloproxidase-deficient polymorphonuclear leukocytes. Longitudinal study during preremission—and the remission phase in acute myeloid leukemia. *Blut* 52:237, 1986.

375. BENDIX-HANSEN K, KERNDRUP G, PEDERSEN B: Myeloperoxidase-deficient polymorphonuclear leukocytes (VI): Relation to cytogenetic abnormalities in primary myelodysplastic syndromes. *Scand J Haematol* 36:3, 1986.

376. BENDIX-HANSEN K, KERNDRUP G: Myeloperoxidase-deficient polymorphonuclear leukocytes (V): Relation to FAB classification and neutrophil alkaline phosphatase activity in primary myelodysplastic syndromes. *Scand J Haematol* 35:197, 1985.

377. BENDIX-HANSEN K, NIELSEN HK: Myeloperoxidase-deficient polymorphonuclear leukocytes (I): Incidence in unreated myeloid leukemia, lymphoid leukemia, and normal humans. *Scand J Haematol* 30:415, 1983.

378. BENDIX-HANSEN K, NIELSEN HK: Myeloproxidase-deficient polymorphonuclear leukocytes (II): Longitudinal study in acute myeloid leukemia, untreated, in remission, and in relapse. *Scand J Haematol* 31:5, 1983.

379. BENDIX-HANSEN K, NIELSEN HK: Myeloperoxidase-deficient polymorphonuclear leukocytes (IV): Relation to FAB classification in acute myeloid leukemia. *Scand J Haematol* 35:174, 1985.

380. CECH P, SCHNEIDER P, BACHMANN F: Partial myeloperoxidase deficiency. *Acta Haematol (Basel)* 67:180, 1982.

381. CECH P, MARKERT M, PERRIN LH: Partial myeloperoxidase deficiency in preleukemia. *Blut* 47:21, 1983.

382. BAGGIOLINI M, HIRSCH JG, DEDUVE C: Resolution of granules from rabbit heterophil leukocytes into distinct populations by zonal sedimentation. *J Cell Biol* 40:529, 1969.

383. CHANCE B, MAHELY AC: Assay of catalases and peroxidases, in Colowick SP, Kaplan NO (eds): *Methods in Enzymology*. New York, Academic, 1955, vol 2, p 764.

384. *Worthington Enzyme Manual*. Freehold, NJ, Worthington Biochem Corp, 1972, p 43.

385. DRI P, CRAMER R, SORANZO MR, COMIN A, MIOTTI V, PATRIARCA P: New approaches to the detection of myeloperoxidase deficiency. *Blood* 60:323, 1982.

386. WEVER R, HAMERS MN, WEENING RS, ROOS D: Characterization of the peroxidase in human eosinophils. *Eur J Biochem* 108:491, 1980.

387. BOS AJ, WEVER R, HAMERS MN, ROOS D: Some enzymatic characteristics of eosinophil peroxidase from patients with eosinophilia and from healthy donors. *Infect Immun* 32:427, 1981.

388. KAPLOW LS: Substitute for benzidine in myeloperoxidase staining. *Am J Clin Pathol* 63:451, 1975.

389. ELIAS JM: A rapid, sensitive myeloproxidase stain using 4-chloro-1-naphthol. *Am J Clin Pathol* 73:797, 1980.

390. Simplified myeloperoxidase stain using benzidine dihydrochloride. *Blood* 26:215, 1965.

391. LARROCHA C, FERNANDEZ DE CASTRO M, FONTAN G, VILORIA A, FERNANDEZ-CHACON JL, JIMENEZ C: Hereditary myeloperoxidase deficiency: Study of 12 cases. *Scand J Haematol* 29:389, 1982.

392. DRI P, CRAMER R, MENAGAZZI R, PATRIARCA P: Increased degranulation of human myeloperoxidase-deficient polymorphonuclear leukocytes. *Br J Haematol* 59:115, 1985.

393. KLEBANOFF SJ: Myeloperoxidase: Contribution to the microbicidal activity of intact leukocytes. *Science* 169:1095, 1970.

394. LEHRER RI, HANIFIN J, CLINE MJ: Defective bactericidal activity in myeloperoxidase-deficient human neutrophils. *Nature* 223:78, 1969.

395. BOS AJ, WEENING, HAMERS MN, WEVER R, BEHRENDT H, ROOS D: Characterization of hereditary partial myeloperoxidase deficiency. *J Lab Clin Med* 99:589, 1982.

396. ROOT RK, METCALF JA: The role of iodide versus chloride-dependent reactions in myeloperoxidase-mediated microbicidal activity of human neutrophils. *Clin Res* 29:534A, 1981.

397. DIAMOND RD, KRZESICKI R: Mechanisms of attachment of neutrophils to *Candida albicans* pseudohyphae in the absence of serum, and of subsequent damage to pseudohyphae by microbicidal processes in neutrophils in vitro. *J Clin Invest* 61:360, 1978.

398. DIAMOND RD, CLARK RA, HAUDENSCHILD CC: Damage to *Candida albicans* hyphae and pseudohyphae by the myeloperoxidase system and oxidative products of neutrophil metabolism in vitro. *J Clin Invest* 66:908, 1980.

399. LEHRER RI, LADRA KM, HAKE RB: Nonoxidative fungicidal mechanisms of mammalian granulocytes: Demonstration of components with candidacidal activity in human, rabbit, and guinea pig leukocytes. *Infect Immun* 11:1226, 1975.

400. LEHRER RI: Functional aspects of a second mechanism of candidacidal activity by human neutrophils. *J Clin Invest* 51:2566, 1972.

401. LEVITZ SM, DIAMOND RD: Killing of *Aspergillus fumigatus* spores and *Candida albicans* yeast phase by the iron-H_2O_2-I_2 cytotoxic system: Comparison with MPO-H_2O_2-halide system. *Infect Immun* 43:1100, 1984.

402. HASILIK A, POHLMANN R, OLSEN RL, VON FIGURA K: Myeloperoxidase is synthesized as a larger phosphorylated precursor. *EMBO J* 3:2671, 1984.

403. KOEFFLER HP, RANYARD J, PERTCHECK M: Myeloperoxidase: Its structure and control of its gene expression during myeloid differentiation. *Blood* 65:484, 1984.

404. NAUSEEF WM: Myeloperoxidase biosynthesis by a human promyelocytic leukemia cell line: Insight into myeloperoxidase deficiency. *Blood* 67:865, 1986.

405. STRÖMBERG K, PERSSON AM, OLSSON I: The processing and intracellular transport of myeloperoxidase. *Eur J Cell Biol* 39:424, 1986.

406. YAMADA M: Myeloproxidase precursors in human myeloid leukemia HL-60 cells. *J Biol Chem* 257:5980, 1982.

407. NAUSEEF WM: Posttranslational processing of a human myeloid lysosomal protein, myeloperoxidase. *Blood* 70:1143, 1987.

408. STRÖMBERG K, OLSSON I: Myeloperoxidase precursors incorporate heme. *J Biol Chem* 262;10430, 1987.

409. PARMLEY RT, AKIN DT, BARTON JC, GILBERT CS, KINKADE JM: Cytochemistry and ultrastructural morphometry of cultured HL-60 myeloid leukemia cells. *Cancer Res* 47:4932, 1987.

410. VERBANEC KM, HEATH EC: Biosynthesis, processing, and secretion of M and Z variant human α_1-antitrypsin. *J Biol Chem* 261:9979, 1986.

411. NAUSEEF WM: Genetic basis for hereditary myeloproxidase deficiency. *Clin Res* 35:484A, 1987.

412. VAN TUINEN P, JOHNSON KR, LEDBETTER SA, NUSSBAUM RL, MERRY DE, ROVERA G, LEDBETTER DH: Localization of myeloperoxidase to the long arm of human chromosome 17: Relationship to the 15,17 translocation of acute promyelocytic leukemia. *Oncogene* 1:319, 1987.

413. CHANG KS, SCHROEDER W, SICILIANO MJ, THOMPSON LH, MCCREDIE K, BERAN M, FREIREICH EJ, LIANG JC, TRUJILLO JM, STASS SA: The localization of the human myeloperoxidase gene is in close proximity to the translocation breakpoint in acute promyelocytic leukemia. *Leukemia* 1:458, 1987.

414. SALMON SE, CLINE MJ, SCHULTZ J, LEHRER RI: Myeloperoxidase deficiency. *N Engl J Med* 282:250, 1970.

415. MEISTER A: Biochemistry of glutathione, in Greenberg DM (ed): *Metabolism of Sulfur Compounds*. New York, Academic, 1975, pp 101–288.

416. MEISTER A, TATE SS: Glutathione and related gamma-glutamyl compounds: Biosynthesis and utilization. *Annu Rev Biochem* 45:559, 1976.

417. SPIELBERG SP, BOXER LA, OLIVER JM, ALLEN JM, SCHULMAN JD: Oxidative damage to neutrophils in glutathione synthetase deficiency. *Br J Haematol* 42:215, 1979.

418. LOOS JA, ROOS D, WEENING RS, HOUWERZIJL J: Familial deficiency of glutathione reductase in human blood cells. *Blood* 48:53, 1976.

419. JOHNSTON RB JR: Biochemical defects of polymorphonuclear and mononuclear phagocytes associated with disease, in Sbarra AJ, Strauss R (eds): *The Reticuloendothelial System*. New York, Plenum, 1980, vol 2, p 397.

420. JOHNSTON RB JR, LEHMEYER JE: The involvement of oxygen metabolites from phagocytic cells in bactericidal activity and inflammation, in Michelson AM, McCord JM, Fridovich I (eds): *Superoxide and Superoxide Dismutases*. New York, Academic, 1977, p 291.

PART 17

CONNECTIVE TISSUES

Amino acid
sequence —GLY—PRO—HYP—GLY—PRO—HYLYS—GLY—X—Y—

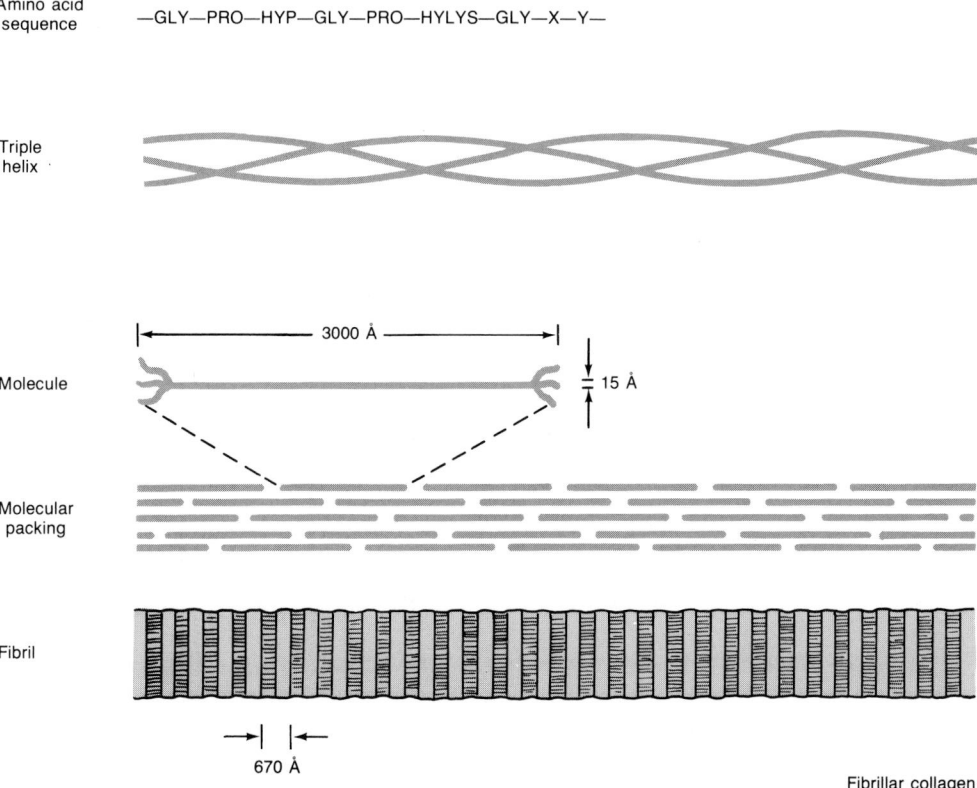

Triple
helix

Molecule

Molecular
packing

Fibril

Fibrillar collagen

CHAPTER 115

DISORDERS OF COLLAGEN BIOSYNTHESIS AND STRUCTURE

PETER H. BYERS

1. *Collagen is the most abundant protein family in the mammalian body. More than 20 dispersed genes encode the protein products that form the more than 11 different types of collagen that are distributed in a characteristic fashion among tissues.*

2. *Collagens are proteins that contain three chains wound in a triple helix. The biosynthesis is complex. Individual precursor chains are synthesized on membrane-bound polyribosomes. During transfer of the growing chain into the lumen of the rough endoplasmic reticulum, certain prolyl and lysyl residues in the triple-helical domain are hydroxylated and some hydroxylysyl residues are glycosylated. Assembly of the three chains in the rough endoplasmic reticulum is mediated by structures in the carboxyl-terminal propeptide domains of each chain, and folding of the triple helix occurs from the carboxyl-terminal end of the molecule. Transport through the Golgi apparatus is accompanied by modification of oligosaccharide groups. Following secretion, limited proteolysis leads to removal of the amino- and carboxyl-terminal propeptide extensions. Collagen molecules are stabilized in fibrillar structures or other meshworks through lysine-derived covalent intermolecular cross-links.*

3. *Virtually all disorders presently known to result from alterations in the structure and function of collagens involve the genes of type I collagen or the enzymes involved in the posttranslational modification of collagens.*

4. *The clinical heterogeneity apparent in the osteogenesis imperfecta phenotypes is a reflection of the underlying molecular heterogeneity. Mutations that affect the synthesis of the proα1(I) chains of type I collagen generally result in the relatively mild osteogenesis imperfecta type I phenotype. Multiexon deletions or insertions in the COL1A1 and COL1A2 genes that encode the chains of type I collagen and point mutations that result in substitutions for glycine residues in the triple-helical domain of proα1(I) chains generally result in the lethal osteogenesis imperfecta type II phenotype. Point mutations in the COL1A1 and COL1A2 genes may result in the osteogenesis imperfecta type III phenotypes if substitutions for glycine residues are located in appropriate domains or involve certain residues. Alternatively, homozygosity for a mutation which alters incorporation of proα2(I) chains into collagen molecules can produce the same phenotype. The moderately severe osteogenesis imperfecta type IV phenotype usually results from point mutations in the COL1A2 gene that result in substitutions for glycine residues in the carboxy-terminal 700 residues of the triple helix.*

5. *The molecular basis of the Ehlers-Danlos syndrome is heterogeneous. Ehlers-Danlos type IV results from mutations that affect the synthesis, structure, or secretion of type III collagen. Ehlers-Danlos type VI is a recessively inherited disorder that results from lack of lysyl hydroxylation. Ehlers-Danlos type VII usually results from loss of the substrate sequence for the amino-terminal procollagen protease in one of the chains of type I procollagen. Although ultrastructural studies suggest that many of the other forms of Ehlers-Danlos syndrome result from mutations that affect collagen aggregation in tissue, the molecular basis of most forms is not known.*

6. *Mutations that affect other collagens may give rise to such diverse phenotypes as spondyloepiphyseal dysplasia, achondrogenesis, and Stickler syndrome (type II collagen), and forms of epidermolysis bullosa (type VII) collagen. The phenotypic consequences of mutations in most collagen genes are not known.*

7. *The phenotypic effects of mutations result from alterations in one component of a multicomponent matrix.*

The collagens are a multigene family with more than 20 members, which are known to be dispersed to at least nine chromosomes (Table 115-1). The products of these genes share important structural properties: they all form trimeric structures that have a triple-helical domain characterized by the repeating amino acid sequence $(Gly-X-Y)_n$; they have an abundance of the special amino acids hydroxyproline and hydroxylysine; and they play a structural role in tissues.[1–4] Some other proteins, including acetylcholinesterase,[5] the Clq component of the complement cascade,[6] and a pulmonary surfactant protein,[7] have appropriated short stretches of the triple-helical structure, perhaps as a structural domain. Since the chapter for the last edition of this book,[8] the genes that encode most human collagens have been isolated and partially characterized. The emphasis in studying the inherited disorders of collagen structure, biosynthesis, and degradation has shifted from identification of alterations in the processing enzymes to characterization of mutations in the genes that encode the collagen proteins.[9–13] To date, molecular analysis of mutations has been limited to the genes that encode the chains of type I collagen, the most abundant collagen in the body. However, our understanding of mutations in these genes will serve as a model for determining the molecular basis of diseases that affect other collagen genes. The molecular basis of several forms of osteogenesis imperfecta[14,15] and the Ehlers-Danlos syndrome[16] is now understood, and there is partial understanding of some disorders that involve other fibrillar collagens.

As a family, the collagens are the most abundant proteins in the body. The vast majority of collagen in the body is type I collagen (Table 115-1) which is ubiquitously distributed. It is the major protein in bone, skin, tendon, ligament, sclera, cornea, blood vessels, and hollow organs. Mutations that affect the structure or processing of the chains of type I collagen are often expressed as generalized connective tissue disorders,

---

Nonstandard abbreviations used in this chapter are: CNBr = cyanogen bromide; EDS = Ehlers-Danlos syndrome; OI = osteogenesis imperfecta; and RER = rough endoplasmic reticulum.

Table 115-1 Collagen Types, Tissue Distribution, Molecular Structure, and Gene Location

Collagen type	Chains	Genes	Chromosomal location	Molecules	Tissue distribution
Fibrillar collagens					
I	α1(I)	COL1A1	17q21-q22	$[\alpha1(I)]_2\alpha2(I)$	Skin, tendon, bone, arteries
	α2(I)	COL1A2	7q21-q22		
				$[\alpha1(I)]_3$	Above and tumors, amniotic fluid
II	α1(II)	COL2A1	12q13-q14	$[\alpha1(II)]_3$	Cartilage, vitreous humor
III	α1(III)	COL3A1	2q31-q32	$[\alpha1(III)]_3$	Skin, arteries, uterus
V	α1(V)	COL5A1		$[\alpha1(V)]_3$	Skin, placenta, vessels, chorion, uterus
	α2(V)	COL5A2	2q31-q32	$[\alpha2(V)]_3$	
	α3(V)	COL5A3		$[\alpha1(V)]_2\alpha2(V)$ $\alpha1(V)\alpha2(V)\alpha3(V)$	
XI	α1(XI)	COL11A1	1p21	$\alpha1(XI)\alpha2(XI)\alpha1(II)$	Cartilage
	α2(XI)	COL11A2			
Long chain/interrupted					
IV	α1(IV)	COL4A1	13q33-q34	$[\alpha1(IV)]_2\alpha2(IV)$	Basal laminae
	α2(IV)	COL4A2	13q33-q34	$[\alpha1(IV)]_3$ $[\alpha2(IV)]_3$	
Short chain/interrupted					
VI	α1(VI)	COL6A1	21q223	Uncertain	Ubiquitous
	α2(VI)	COL6A2	21q223		
	α3(VI)	COL6A3	2q37		
VIII	α1(VIII)	COL8A1			
IX	α1(IX)	COL9A1		$\alpha1(IX)\alpha2(IX)\alpha3(IX)$	Cartilage
	α2(IX)	COL9A2			
	α3(IX)	COL9A3			
X	α1(X)	COL10A1			Cartilage
Extended chain/interrupted					
VII	α1(VII)	COL7A1		$\alpha1(VII)_3$	Epithelial-mesenchymal junctions

NOTE: The nomenclature for collagens is as follows: The individual chain of each molecule is referred to as an α chain. The type of collagen is designated by a Roman numeral in parentheses, e.g., (I), and the chains of a collagen type are numbered in Arabic numerals from 1 upward. The chains of type I collagen were originally numbered by their chromatographic elution during CM-cellulose column chromatography, α1(I) and α2(I), respectively. This convention no longer applies, and the numbering is dependent on priority of identification. The precursor chains are designated as pre-pro-α chains (with the signal sequence intact) and pro-α chains once the signal sequence has been removed. Pro-α chains from which the carboxyl-terminal, non-triple-helical precursor specific domain has been removed are called pNα chains and those from which the amino-terminal precursor specific extension has been removed are called pCα chains. β-Components (sometimes referred to as chains in the older literature) contain two α chains, generally cross-linked by lysine-derived covalent cross-links; γ components are three α chains similarly linked. These terms do not refer to individual, genetically distinct chains as they often do in other protein families. The genes encoding collagen chains are referred to in the following manner: COL1A2 indicates the gene that encodes the α2 (A2) chain of type I collagen (COL1).

although the specific tissue in which the major effect is seen may determine the clinical phenotype (e.g., osteogenesis imperfecta, Ehlers-Danlos syndrome, and the Marfan syndrome may all result from mutations in the genes that encode the chains of type I collagen). With the exception of types III, V, and VI collagen, which are also distributed in virtually all tissues (little type III collagen is found in bone and cartilage), most other collagens have a tissue-specific or structure-specific distribution. Types II, IX, X, and XI collagens are found in hyaline cartilage and the vitreous humor of the eye.[17–21] Type IV collagen is found in basement membranes,[22,23] and type VII collagen is found at some epithelial-mesenchymal junctions in anchoring fibril structures.[24] With the exception of collagen types I, III, V, and VI, most collagens are expressed in a limited array of fully differentiated cell types, but many cells synthesize a group of collagen types. For example, chondrocytes may express types II, IX, X, and XI but little or no types I and III. The mechanisms of tissue-specific regulation are of great interest but are poorly understood at present.

As a consequence of differences in structure, in quantitative expression, and in tissue distribution, the collagens perform different functions. In fact, the same collagen may perform different functions in different tissues. For example, type I collagen provides tensile strength in bone, skin, and tendon but normally is mineralized only in bone. It provides or facilitates transparency of the cornea (in part as a consequence of its fibril structure), while the sclera is opaque. It forms hollow tubes as part of blood vessels but solid structures as part of tendons. Type IV collagen provides the major structural protein of basement membrane, does not form fibril structures, and acts as a filtration barrier in the kidney and at the dermal-epidermal junction. The functions of types II, IX, X, and XI collagens in cartilage are less clear, although in the absence of type II collagen, bone does not grow normally. Similarly, the functions of the fibrillar collagens, types III and V, are not clear. However, analysis of the phenotypic effects of mutations in type III collagens indicates its essential role in the formation of intact tissues. Thus, collagens function in a number of ways. They provide tensile strength, facilitate transparency, and provide form during embryonic and fetal development. They interact with other proteins to build tissues and organs, to separate cell layers during and after development, and to provide filtration barriers between spaces. It is likely that some of the functions depend directly on the structure of collagen while others depend on interactions with additional matrix macromolecules.

This chapter details the molecular basis of various forms of osteogenesis imperfecta, the Ehlers-Danlos syndrome, and the Marfan syndrome and outlines studies of additional disorders in which gene structure or processing of gene products has been shown to be abnormal. To provide a framework, it begins with a review of the nature of the collagen gene family and of the biosynthesis of collagens, using type I collagen as the example. This is followed by a detailed review of the clinical phenotype, natural history, genetics, and molecular basis of each disorder.

THE COLLAGENS

Gene Structure

On the basis of protein structure and sequence it has become clear that there are at least four classes of collagen molecules: (1) the fibrillar collagens, (2) the nonfibrillar collagens with interrupted triple-helical sequences of about the same size as those of fibrillar collagens, (3) short-chain collagens in which the triple helix is about half the size of that in fibrillar collagens and may be interrupted, and (4) the long-chain collagen of anchoring fibrils with an interrupted triple helix.[25]

Genes That Encode the Fibrillar Collagens. The genes that encode the chains of collagen types I, II, III, V, and XI—a total of 10 distinct genes—constitute the family of fibrillar collagen genes (Table 115-1).[26–31] Each protein is characterized by an unbroken triple-helical domain (Gly-X-Y) containing approximately 1000 amino acids, and the genes encode this

structure with a set of 42 exons that contain 45, 54, 99, 108, or 162 base pairs (bp) (Fig. 115-1). There are transition exons at both ends of the triple-helical domains that encode the regions which contain the sites of proteolytic cleavage at the amino-terminal and carboxyl-terminal ends of the triple helix. The triple-helical domain of the amino-terminal propeptide extension is contained in a single exon. All the exons in the triple-helical domain begin with a glycine codon and thus end with the codon for the Y-position amino acid; exons in non-triple-helical domains may contain interrupted codons.

The organization of the genes for each of the fibrillar collagens is similar. The intron-exon structure is maintained, and the differences in the sizes of the genes are accounted for by differences in intron size. The gene encoding the α1(I) chain (COL1A1) contains about 18 kilobases (kb), while those encoding the α2(I) chain (COL1A2), the α1(II) chains (COL2A1), the α1(III) chain (COL3A1), and the α1(V) chain (COL5A1) are about 40 kb in size. The similar gene structure and homologies in amino acid sequence (see Table 115-1 for a compilation of collagen types, their constituent chains, and collagen gene size, chromosomal locations) provide strong evidence for the divergence of collagen types from an ancestral gene. The fibrillar collagen gene structure is present in birds and mammals, which dates the emergence of the structure of the fibrillar collagen genes prior to the radiation of those two groups, more than 50 million years ago. This concept is supported by analysis of deletion and insertion mutations that affect the genes of type I collagen. These mutations are lethal when only a single allele is involved (see "Osteogenesis Imperfecta" and "The Marfan Syndrome," below).

The genes that encode the chains of the fibrillar collagens are widely dispersed among the chromosomes: COL1A1 is on chromosome 17,[33,34] COL1A2 is on 7,[32,35] COL2A1 is on chromosome 12,[36] COL3A1 is on chromosome 2,[37,38] and COL5A2 is on chromosome 2 (in the same domain as COL3A1).[35,36]

Genes That Encode the Nonfibrillar Collagens. The genes that encode the nonfibrillar collagens are similar in size to those that encode fibrillar collagens, but their organization is different.[39,40] The exons that encode the largely triple-helical domains are of much more variable sizes, and they do not always begin with a glycine codon nor end with a codon for a Y-position amino acid. Furthermore, in contrast to the fibrillar collagen genes, there is frequent splitting of codons be-

Fig. 115-1 Fibrillar collagen gene structure. The intron-exon structure of the prototype fibrillar collagen genes [COL1A1 and COL1A2 which encode the proα1(I) and proα2(I) chains of type I procollagen, respectively] are represented. The exons are designated by the solid boxes or vertical lines. All the exons that encode sequences in the triple-helical domain (exons 7–48) contain 45, 54, 99, 108 or 162 nucleotides, start with a glycine codon, and end with the codon for the Y-position amino acid. The organization of the other fibrillar collagen genes is similar and intron-exon

boundaries and exon sizes are maintained throughout. The structure of the genes that encode the nonfibrillar collagens differs considerably. The domains in the polypeptide chains (see also Fig. 115-2) are: A = signal sequence; B = amino-terminal propeptide globular domain; C = amino-terminal propeptide triple-helical domain; D = amino-terminal telopeptide; E = triple helix; F = carboxyl-terminal telopeptide; and G = carboxyl-terminal propeptide. (*Adapted and redrawn from Ramirez et al., Ann NY Acad Sci 460:117, 1985, with permission.*)

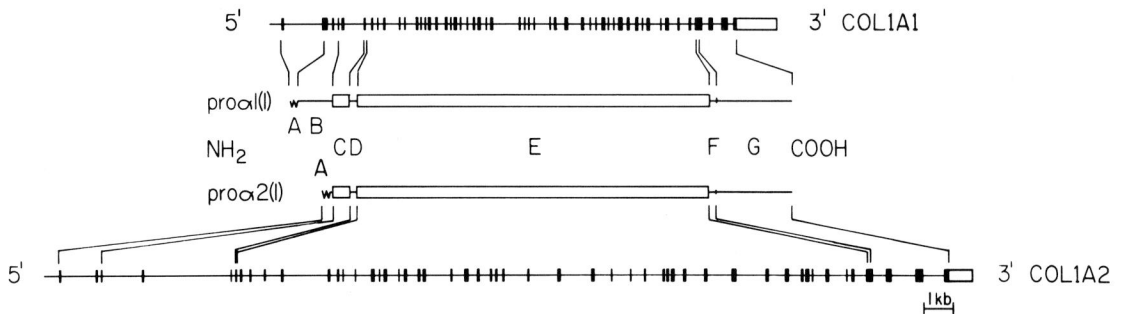

tween exons, even for residues within the triple-helical domains. Some of the interruptions of triple-helical sequence can be explained by point mutations, although many result from additional coding material. The genes for at least two type IV collagen chains, α1(IV) and α2(IV), have been isolated and partially characterized. Both are located on chromosome 13 within about 400 kb (the closest known linkage between two collagen genes).[41–43] It is likely that the genes for type IV collagen diverged from those for the fibrillar collagens prior to the radiation of the fibrillar gene types.

The genes for human collagens type VI[44] have been isolated, partially characterized, and their chromosomal location determined.[45] At least one of the human type XI collagen genes[46] has been isolated and partially characterized. Those for type VIII, IX, or X have not yet been characterized. The three genes that encode the chains of type IX collagen in chickens have been characterized.[47,48] Type IX collagen is unusual in that one of the chains contains a covalently linked sulfated glycosaminoglycan chain. This attachment appears to mediate some of the interactions with type II collagen in tissues.[49] The genes for type X collagen from chickens have been isolated and characterized and differ from the fibrillar collagen genes in having no intervening sequences.[50]

No information is yet available concerning the structure of the gene for type VII collagen, the long-chain collagen.

Collagen Protein Structure

Domain Structure of Type I Procollagen. Type I procollagen, a heterotrimer that contains two proα1(I) chains (encoded by COL1A1) and one proα2(I) chain (encoded by COL1A2), contains seven distinct domains, each of which has one or more functions (Fig. 115-2). Each prepoα chain is synthesized with a signal sequence of approximately 20 residues that facilitates passage across the rough endoplasmic reticulum (RER) membrane and is cleaved during transit.[51] The proα1(I) chain contains a cysteine-rich globular extension of 86 residues, the function of which is not known; a similar sequence is missing from the proα2(I) chain. Both chains contain a 36-residue domain (of repeating Gly-X-Y triplets) that forms a triple helix in the intact procollagen molecule. This short triple helix has a relatively high denaturation temperature and may stabilize the amino-terminal end of the molecule. There is a short, non-triple-helical domain that contains the site of proteolytic cleavage of the amino-terminal propeptide extension and lysyl residues that become involved in intermolecular cross-link formation. The major triple-helical domain of both chains is 1014 residues long and is characterized by glycine in every third position (Gly-X-Y)$_{338}$; hydroxyproline occupies the Y position in about a third of the triplets and is often preceded by proline. Some lysyl residues in the Y position are also hydroxylated, but the extent of this modification is highly dependent on the type of collagen. Hydroxyproline and hydroxylysine are found only in the Y position of the triple helix. All phenylalanine residues and virtually all leucine residues (with one exception) are found in the X position, apparently because of severe steric hindrance to the formation of triple helix when these residues occur in the Y position.[52] The basic residue arginine occurs preferentially in the Y position, while the acid residue glutamic acid is found usually in the X position, a distribution that may facilitate charge-charge interactions that increase the thermal stability of the triple helix. A 28-residue telopeptide at the carboxy-terminal end of the triple

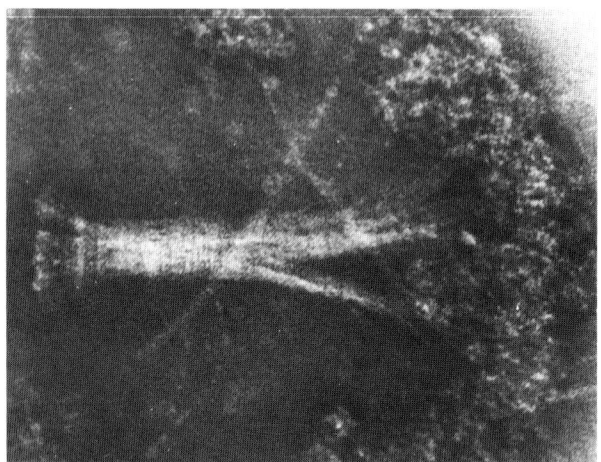

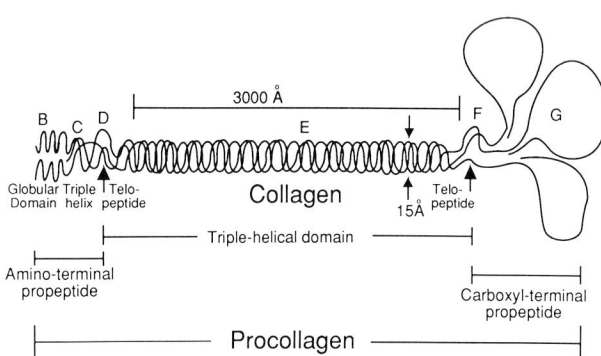

Fig. 115-2 Electron micrograph of segment-long-spacing (SLS) aggregates of type I procollagen *(top)* and a model of a type I procollagen molecule *(bottom)*. SLS aggregates were made by lateral aggregation of procollagen molecules that had been synthesized and secreted into culture medium by normal fibroblasts. Arrayed in a side-to-side orientation, the molecules are precipitated, stained, and then examined in the electron microscope. The model of type I procollagen represents the major domains of the molecule. B = amino-terminal propeptide extension; C = minor triple helix of the amino-terminal propeptide extension; D = amino-terminal telopeptide which terminates with the amino-terminal protease cleavage site; E = triple helix; F = carboxyl-terminal telopeptide; G = carboxyl-terminal propeptide extension. The signal sequence is not shown for either chain.

helix contains a lysyl residue in proα1(I), which is absent from proα2(I), and is involved in interchain cross-link formation. The carboxyl-terminal procollagen peptidase cleaves in the telopeptide. The final 220 residues of the proα chains form globular structures that contain intra- and interchain disulfide bonds. This domain facilitates chain assembly, determines the chain specificity of the type I procollagen molecule, and provides intracellular solubility.

Structure of the Collagen Triple Helix

By virtue of the triple-helical structure, collagen has a number of unique features. The primary sequence of the α chains can be written (Gly-X-Y)$_{338}$, where X and Y can be most amino acids except for tryptophan and cysteine, which are excluded from the triple helix in both chains of type I collagen; tyrosine is excluded from the triple helix of α1(I) but there is one residue in α2(I). Hydroxyproline and hydroxylysine are found only in the Y position as a consequence of enzymatic posttranslational modification (see below). The individual α chains assume a left-handed extended polyproline-like helical structure (minor helix) that has a distance of approximately 9.5 Å between residues in equivalent position (pitch). Three chains associate in parallel with two other chains to form a right-handed triple-helical structure (major helix) that has a pitch of approximately 100 Å (Fig. 115-3). Glycine as the smallest amino acid with no side chains is required in every third position of each chain because space does not exist in the structure for side chains. The side chains on any substituting residue would point toward the center of the helix and disrupt the triple helix (see below, "Osteogenesis Imperfecta"). The side chains of residues in the X and Y positions are arrayed toward the external surface of the molecule. The chains are associated in such a way that the glycine residues are staggered by one residue with respect to the next chain. The stability of the triple helix is provided by interchain hydrogen bonds between the amide group of glycine and the oxygen of the carbonyl group of an X-position residue on an adjacent chain.[53] Additional hydrogen bonds that involve the hydroxyl group of hydroxyproline and the carbonyl backbone of the chain further stabilize the molecule. In the absence of hydroxylation, the triple helix of type I collagen denatures at about 27°C[54,55]; with complete hydroxylation the denaturation temperature is about 42°C (the precise denaturation temperature depends on the manner in which it is measured). Triple-helical structure is one of the requirements for transport of type I collagen beyond the rough endoplasmic reticulum[56,57]; thus, in its absence little or no normal collagen is secreted at normal body temperatures. It is likely that other factors, especially charge-charge interactions, contribute to the stability of the triple helix, and their importance is often overlooked, although it has been recognized for some time.

The triple-helical structure of collagen provides resistance to degradation by most proteases, the exceptions being the specific collagenases synthesized by mesenchymal (and some epithelial) cells and collagenases synthesized by a number of microorganisms.[58,59] The resistance of the triple helix to proteases allows collagens to provide an extremely stable structure in the extracellular environment. Once denatured, the chains are exquisitely sensitive to most proteases, thus ensuring normal turnover.

Biosynthesis of Collagen

The biosynthesis, processing, and secretion of collagens is remarkably complex, beginning with coordinated transcription of genes for multiple chains, through posttranslational modifications, to secretion and degradation[60] (Table 115-2).

Control of Collagen Biosynthesis. Collagen biosynthesis is controlled at many levels, and the mechanisms by which control is exerted are not completely understood. The genes of type I collagen (COL1A1 and COL1A2) are located on different chromosomes, and their physical relationship during the cell cycle is not known. They are present in equal numbers (one copy per haploid genome) but are transcribed with different efficiencies; COL1A1 produces twice the steady state mRNA levels as COL1A2.[61] The difference results from transcriptional efficiency, not mRNA stability, and is probably not accounted for by the size of the genes. The expression of the genes is almost always coordinated and ultimately results in the synthesis of two proα1(I) chains for each proα2(I) chain. Nucleotide sequences in the first intron of the COL1A1 and COL1A2 genes of type I collagen provide enhancers and direct tissue-specific expression of the genes.[62–65] Upstream regions also provide positive control regions, and there is emerging evidence that those regions and regions in the first intron may provide negative control.[66,67] The expression of collagen genes can be altered by a variety of growth factors[68,69] and by the presence or absence of ascorbic acid.[70] Sequences between the transcription start sites and the first translated domain of the mRNA can form stem-loop structures which appear to influence the efficiency of translation.[71,72] Under some circumstances, for example, in chondrocytes placed in culture, the mRNA for proα2(I) chains is transcribed but inefficiently translated, apparently as a result of translational arrest.[73] Efficiency of translation may be regulated by the availability of the appropriate charged tRNA species.[74] There is evidence that control of translation of some collagen messages can be influenced by peptides derived from the amino-terminal extension of type I procollagen chains[75,76] and by sequences derived from the carboxyl-terminal propeptide extension.[77] An additional level of control is provided once the proα chains are synthesized. For heterotrimeric molecules, like type I procollagen, the relative ratios of the two chains determines the amount of the correct molecule available. Because molecular stability is determined, at least in part, by prolyl hydroxylation, the activity of the enzyme can affect the rate of synthesis of collagen. Finally, there is a constant level of intracellular degradation of collagenous proteins, and this appears to serve the function of editing out abnormal molecules.[78,79] Thus, there are controls of collagen production at many levels, some of which function in an "on-off" fashion, while others provide a more delicate range of variation.

Nuclear Events. Like virtually all eukaryotic mRNAs that encode secreted proteins, those encoding collagen chains are synthesized as precursors that are then spliced to remove intervening sequences,[80] capped, polyadenylated, and transported to the cytoplasm.

Fig. 115-3 The hierarchical structure and organization of fibrillar collagens. The α chains of fibrillar collagens contain a core triple-helical domain of slightly more than 1000 residues that is characterized by the repeating triplet, Gly-X-Y (top), and in which each chain forms a left-handed helix with a pitch of 3.6 nm. Three chains form a triple-helical molecule in which they are wound in a right-handed spiral. Molecules in the matrix aggregate in an ordered fashion staggered by about a quarter of the length of the triple-helical domain. The staggered order contributes an ordered pattern of electron dense and electron lucent regions in fibrils as seen in the electron microscope and reflected in the 670 Ångstrom repeating band pattern (bottom).

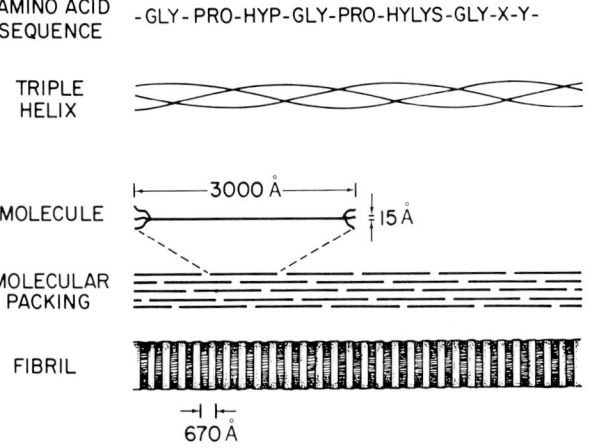

AMINO ACID SEQUENCE   - GLY - PRO - HYP - GLY - PRO - HYLYS - GLY - X - Y -

TRIPLE HELIX

MOLECULE   3000 Å   15 Å

MOLECULAR PACKING

FIBRIL

670 Å

Table 115-2 Nature and Location of Events During Collagen Biosynthesis

Event	Enzyme	Location*
Transcription	Many	Nucleus
Splicing	"Splicesome-complex"	Nucleus
Transport	Unknown	Nucleus-cytoplasm
Translation	Many	Cytoplasm/RER
Signal cleavage	Signal peptidase	RER membrane
Prolyl hydroxylation	Proline 4-hydroxylase	RER lumen
	Proline 3-hydroxylase	RER lumen
Lysyl hydroxylation	Lysyl hydroxylase	RER lumen
Hydroxylysyl glycosylation	Collagen glucosyltransferase	RER lumen
	Collagen galactosyltransferase	RER lumen
Heterosaccharide addition and modification	Many	RER lumen
Intrachain disulfide bond formation	Disulfide isomerase	RER lumen
Chain assembly	Not known	RER lumen
Interchain disulfide bond formation	Disulfide isomerase	RER lumen
Triple-helix propagation	Prolyl cis-trans isomerase	RER lumen
Transport to Golgi	Many (unknown)	RER/Golgi
Modification of heterosaccharide	Many	Golgi
Sulfation	Sulfotransferase	Golgi
Exocytosis	Many	Cell surface
Amino-terminal processing	Procollagen aminoprotease	ECM
Carboxyl-terminal processing	Procollagen carboxyprotease	ECM
Fibril formation	Nonenzymatic	ECM
Cross-link formation	Lysyl oxidase	ECM

*RER = rough endoplasmic reticulum; ECM = extracellular matrix.

Translation. Little is known about the control of translation of collagen mRNA species. As indicated above, the formation of stem-loop structures in mRNAs for some collagens may influence the efficiency of translation. In addition, translational arrest under some circumstances can influence the rate of synthesis of the chains of type I collagen.[73] The observation that cells from patients and animals with defects in cleavage of the amino-terminal propeptide of type I procollagen[81,82] synthesized less type I procollagen than control cells led to attempts to determine if the decrease in synthesis resulted from feedback regulation. Isolated amino-terminal propeptide extension from proα1(I) decreased the translational efficiency of proα1(I), proα2(I), and proα1(II) mRNA in vitro.[75] A short peptide from the pN domain of proα1(I) can virtually abolish translation at relatively high concentrations of proα1(I) chains but also blocks translation of all messages.[76] Evidence has also been presented suggesting that peptides derived from the carboxyl-terminal propeptide may also affect the efficiency of translation.[77]

Posttranslational Modification and Events in the RER.

SIGNAL SEQUENCE. The mRNA is translated on ribosomes that become membrane-bound. The signal sequences of preproα1(I) and preproα2(I) are cleaved during elongation of the chains as they are transported through the membrane into the lumen of the rough endoplasmic reticulum.

HYDROXYLATION OF PROLYL AND LYSYL RESIDUES. During translation, lagging about 300 residues behind assembly, prolyl and lysyl residues amino-terminal to glycyl residues in the major and minor triple-helical sequences are hydroxylated by the enzymes prolyl 4-hydroxylase and lysyl hydroxylase, respectively.[83,84] In addition, some prolyl residues in the sequence -Gly-Pro-4Hypro-Gly- are hydroxylated in the 3 position by the distinct enzyme prolyl 3-hydroxylase.[85] The usual

substrates for these reactions are the nascent chain and the free proα chains. For prolyl 4-hydroxylase, the minimum sequence requirement is an -X-Pro-Gly- triplet. The extent of hydroxylation is regulated, in part, by substrate availability because the fully hydroxylated triple helix has a melting temperature of 42°C, and chains in triple-helical conformation are not substrates for the hydroxylases.[86] Prolyl 4-hydroxylase, located either in the lumen of the rough endoplasmic reticulum or in the inner membrane,[87] is a tetramer that contains two α subunits and two β subunits.[88] The subunits have molecular weights of 64,000 (α) and 60,000 (β) and are the products of different genes. A cDNA for the β subunit has been isolated, and the sequence demonstrated that the protein is identical to protein disulfide isomerase,[89] an enzyme that facilitates disulfide exchange in folding proteins.[90] Like some other molecules that reside in the lumen of the rough endoplasmic reticulum (RER), the β subunit has the carboxyterminal amino acid sequence Lys-Asp-Glu-Leu (KDEL). In some proteins, this sequence appears to confer the ability to reside permanently in the RER.[91] Lysyl hydroxylase is a homodimer, the monomer of which has a molecular weight of 85,000.[92] Prolyl 3-hydroxylase has a molecular weight of about 160,000, but the subunit composition has not been determined.[93] It is likely that there are not collagen type-specific modifying enzymes, although the extent of posttranslational modification of prolyl and lysyl residues in different collagen types does differ substantially. For example, the relative degree of lysyl hydroxylation in type IV collagen is very high (more than 90 percent of the residues in the Y position are hydroxylated), while in types I and III about 15 percent of such lysyl residues are hydroxylated. The amount of 3-hydroxyproline differs markedly among collagen types, and the mechanisms that control the extent of modification have not been determined.

The three collagen hydroxylases require Fe^{2+}, 2-oxoglutarate, molecular oxygen (O_2), and ascorbate. The 2-oxoglutarate is decarboxylated and oxidized to succinate;[94] the other member of the oxygen molecule is incorporated into the prolyl residue at the 3 or 4 position or into the lysyl residue at the 5 position. The function of the ascorbate is not clear.[95] It can be replaced by some other reducing agents,[96] and it is thought that ascorbate may keep the Fe^{2+} atom reduced. Ascorbate is not used stoichiometrically during reactions, and there is evidence that it is important during noncoupled oxidation of 2-oxoglutarate. The role of ascorbate in providing a reducing agent for the disulfide exchange portion of prolyl 4-hydroxylase is not known.

The hydroxylation of proline in the 4 position is essential to provide thermal stability to the triple helix. The modification of the chains occurs during elongation and terminates with the formation of a stable triple helix. Hydroxylation of lysyl residues provides substrates for glycosylation and, in addition, the hydroxylysyl residues form more stable covalent cross-links than lysyl residues and are important determinants of tissue tensile strength.[97] The function of 3-hydroxyproline is unknown.

ASSEMBLY OF THE MOLECULE. The hydroxylation reactions begin while the chains are being synthesized and are completed when the molecule is assembled and the triple helix is stable. Following completion of synthesis, the globular domains of the proα chains fold and are stabilized by intrachain disulfide bonds.[98] This process is facilitated by a disulfide exchange enzyme, probably the β subunit of prolyl 4-hydroxylase. Once intrachain disulfide bonding is completed, the two proα1(I) chains and single proα2(I) chain associate through domains created by the correct folding of the carboxyl-terminal propeptide sequences,[99] and this interaction is stabilized by the formation of interchain disulfide bonds. Triple-helix formation begins at the carboxyl-terminal end of the molecule and is propagated toward the amino-terminal end.[100] There is a random distribution of cis and trans peptide bonds involving the prolyl residues along the chains in random coil configuration. The propagation of the triple-helical structure requires isomerization to the trans form, and it is likely that this is accomplished, in part, by enzymatic means (a prolyl cis-trans isomerase).[101]

HYDROXYLYSYL GLYCOSYLATION. The glycosylation of hydroxylysyl residues in collagen requires two enzymes, hydroxylysyl galactosyltransferase and galactosylhydroxylysyl glucosyltransferase.[102] The former transfers UDPgalactose to the oxygen on the 5 carbon of hydroxylysine in peptide linkage; Mn^{2+} is probably a cofactor for the enzyme. The latter transfers UDPglucose, also in the presence of the metal cofactor. The distribution of mono- and disaccharide is influenced by collagen type, probably via the amino acid sequence in the region of the hydroxylysyl residue. The reaction is carried out only on a non-triple-helical substrate. The functions of the carbohydrate on collagens are unknown. Carbohydrate modification may influence fibril formation, may affect collagen-cell interaction and collagen interactions with other macromolecules, and protects modified hydroxylysyl residues from oxidation to cross-link precursors.

GLYCOSYLATION OF ASPARAGINE RESIDUES IN THE PROPEPTIDE EXTENSIONS. Type I procollagen contains a single asparagine-linked carbohydrate group on the carboxy-terminal propeptide of each chain.[103,104] Other procollagens may contain more units, and they may be located in both non-triple-helical extension regions.[105] The carbohydrate units are synthesized on a dolichol lipid intermediate in the membrane of the RER and

transferred intact to the proα chains.[106–108] There is initial cleavage of the terminal sugar units while the chains are in the RER and additional trimming and resynthesis of the structure in the Golgi apparatus that results in a high mannose unit.[109]

Modifications Beyond the RER and Secretion. Procollagen molecules are translocated to the Golgi and then packaged in secretory vesicles that fuse with the cell membrane and release their contents into the extracellular environment. The manner in which the molecule is transported from the RER to the Golgi and the structural determinants of that movement are unclear. The importance of triple-helical conformation has been known for many years, but the mechanism by which a cell senses this structure and the nature of the structure that is recognized is not known. Agents that disrupt microtubule function interfere with secretion of procollagen, but this may result from general disruption of cell structure rather than collagen-specific mechanisms.[110–112]

In the Golgi, heterosaccharide is trimmed to yield a high mannose structure on each chain of type I procollagen. In addition, some collagens, notably type V, probably type III, and possibly type I, undergo sulfation of some tyrosine residues in the amino-terminal propeptide extension[113,114] and phosphorylation of certain serine residues of the extension of proα1(I) in bone.[115] The function of the glycosylation, sulfation, and phosphorylation is not known. Inhibition of glycosylation with tunicamycin does not appear to alter the efficiency of secretion of type I procollagen, as it does with some other matrix macromolecules (notably fibronectin).

Extracellular Events. Once outside the cell, procollagens undergo proteolytic conversion to collagen, form fibrils, interact with noncollagenous and collagenous proteins, are stabilized by intermolecular cross-links, and are degraded.

CLEAVAGE OF THE AMINO-TERMINAL AND CARBOXYL-TERMINAL PROPEPTIDES. The conversion of procollagen to collagen occurs in the extracellular space. The peptides are removed by two enzymes, procollagen N-proteinase and procollagen C-proteinase.[116–118] The N-proteinases are probably collagen type-specific, and there is evidence that those which cleave types I and III procollagen are distinct enzymes.[119] In type I collagen, the enzyme cleaves a Pro-Gln bond in the proα1(I) chains and a Ala-Gln bond in the proα2(I) chain; in both cases cyclization of the glutamine forms the amino-terminal residue, pyroglutamic acid. The enzyme is an endopeptidase that requires all three chains of type I procollagen to be in register to form the substrate.[120] The propeptide is removed as a block without further degradation. Some propeptide is detectable in plasma, but the site of further degradation and the half-life of the molecule in plasma are not known. In the procollagen molecule the propeptide probably acts to prevent or delay fibril formation, and the minor triple helix may stabilize the amino-terminal end of the major triple helix. The enzyme functions in the extracellular environment, probably close to the cell surface. The activity is maximal at neutral pH, and the enzyme requires a divalent cation for function. Cleavage is sequential in chains without apparent specificity as to the first reaction.

Cleavage at the carboxyl-terminal site occurs at an Ala-Asp bond in both proα1(I) and proα2(I).[121] In contrast to cleavage at the amino-terminal site, this reaction does not require an intact trimer. The enzyme requires a divalent cation, such as Ca^{2+}. There does not appear to be a preferred order for cleavage of the termini, and intermediates that contain either end intact can be found in tissues and in cultured cells. Some collagens are probably not processed in tissues, and some may be cleaved only at one end.

FIBRIL FORMATION. Once cleaved, collagen molecules rapidly aggregate into ordered structures. Aggregation occurs in concert with proteolytic processing of the propeptide extensions very close to the cell membrane in invaginations of the cell surface.[122] Under these conditions the high concentration of collagen molecules would drive the formation of fibrils. It has been proposed, on the basis of electron micrographs of cultured cells and of cells in tissues, that procollagen molecules aggregate in an ordered fashion in secretory vesicles and are then reordered following secretion and cleavage of the propeptides.[123] However, this concept is not widely accepted. Fibril formation results from aggregation of molecules. The interaction of molecules is determined largely by the distribution of charged and hydrophobic groups at the surface.[124] Collagen molecules aggregate in an ordered parallel, overlapping lateral array such that adjacent molecules are staggered by lengths slightly less than a quarter of a molecule (see Fig. 115-3). Fibril formation is a nonenzymatic process, and the nature of the interactions that govern fibril diameter is not completely understood. Interactions with collagens other than type I collagen (e.g., types III and V) or with proteoglycans or other glycoproteins are thought to control the rate of fibrillogenesis and ultimate fibril diameter.[125] That is certainly true of collagens in cartilage.[126] The absence of fibrils in basement membrane is accounted for in part by the absence of conversion of procollagen to collagen, by the interactions of type IV collagen with other components of the basement membrane, and by the interrupted nature of the triple helix.

CROSS-LINK FORMATION, STRUCTURE, AND FUNCTION. Collagen molecules in fibrillar array become substrates for the enzyme lysyl oxidase that oxidatively deaminates certain lysyl and hydroxylysyl residues in collagen and elastin[127,128] (see Fig. 115-4). There are four principal cross-linking loci in molecules of type I, II, and III collagens: (1) a lysyl residue located nine residues from the amino-terminal end of the triple helix of the chain in the telopeptide, (2) a hydroxylysyl residue (usually glycosylated) at triple-helical residue 87, (3) a glycosylated hydroxylysl residue at triple-helical position 930, and (4) a hydroxylysyl residue 16 amino acids from the carboxyl-terminal end of the triple helix in carboxy-terminal telopeptide.[97] The two non-triple-helical sites are the substrate positions of the enzymes. Because the sequences around the triple-helical residues are highly conserved among species and are virtually identical at the two sites, this may represent the attachment site for the enzyme and explain the need for the fibrillar substrate. The relative positioning of the triple-helical residues and those in the telopeptide extensions in the collagen fibril place the relevant lysyl or hydroxylysyl residues in appropriate proximity. Lysyl oxidase activity results in formation of a reactive aldehyde (allysine or hydroxyallysine if the substrate residues are lysine or hydroxylysine, respectively) that condenses with lysyl or hydroxylysyl residues in adjacent molecules to form divalent cross-links. The enzyme does not recognize the glycosylated hydroxylysyl residues as substrate, explaining one possible function of that modification. Although divalent cross-links are formed at first, there is rapid formation of more complex cross-links which stabilize collagen structures in tissues. The complex products may involve histidine or additional lysyl and hydroxylysyl residues to form

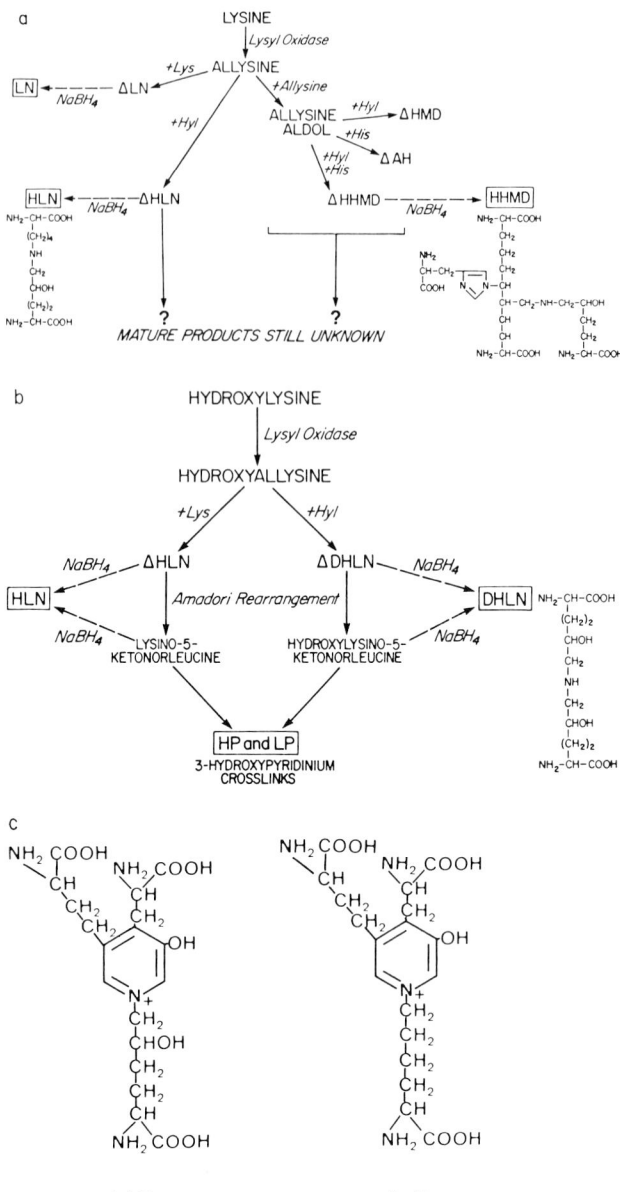

Fig. 115-4 Collagen cross-links. A. Cross-links derived from oxidation of lysyl residues by lysyl oxidase. The oxidation of lysyl residues in collagen peptide linkage begins the minor cross-link pathway. The first product is allysine, which may condense with a lysyl group, an additional allysine, or hydroxylysyl to form bivalent compounds that go on to form other more complex products by addition of histidine or other residues. The structures of some compounds are known; others have not yet been identified. The intermediates can be trapped by reduction with borohydride to produce the stable products indicated. B. The major pathway of cross-link formation begins with the oxidation of hydroxylysyl residues in peptide linkage by lysyl oxidase to form hydroxyallysine, which may condense with lysyl or hydroxylysyl residues on other chains, rearrange, and then, C., add a third group to form the fluorescent 3-hydroxypyridinium (HP) and lysyl pyridinium (LP) cross-links. LN = lysinonorleucine; HLN = hydroxylysinonorleucine; HMD = hydroxymerodesmosine; HHMD = histidinylhydroxymerodesmosine; DHLN = dehydrolysinonorleucine. (Courtesy of Dr. David Eyre, University of Washington.)

three-membered cross-links of amino acids that stabilize interactions among three chains. Lysyl oxidase functions as a monomeric enzyme that is a glycoprotein with a molecular weight of approximately 32,000.[129,130] It requires pyridoxal and copper as cofactors, the latter probably for stability.[131,132] Cross-linking is vitally important for the provision of tissue tensile strength to tissues. Several defects that affect cross-link formation demonstrate the importance of this aspect of collagen metabolism. Indeed, virtually any mutation that alters the ability of collagens to form fibrils probably affects stabilization of collagens and thus interferes with normal tissue function.

Collagen Degradation

In tissues, collagens are highly stable molecules. In adult animals the half-life is several months in skin and may be longer in bone.[133] However, connective tissues are dynamic and are constantly being remodeled in response to mechanical stress (in bones, for example), to growth, and to injury. The normal thermal stability, cross-linking, and interactions of multiple other molecules with collagens in tissues mitigate against ready recycling from the extracellular matrix.

Collagenases are a family of enzymes that recognize collagenous sequences and cleave intact molecules that are in fibrillar array.[134] The best studied of the enzymes are those which cleave the fibrillar collagens and generally result in a three-quarter–one-quarter cleavage with the site about one-quarter of the way from the carboxyl end of the triple helix. The enzymes generally recognize a specific Gly-Leu or Gly-Ile bond; both fibrillar and soluble molecules as well as procollagens are substrates.[135,136] In part, these proteases facilitate further degradation because of the lower melting temperature of the collagenous products. The two products, the A (large) and B (small) fragments of type I collagen, have melting temperatures several degrees below that of the intact molecule.[137] This suggests that these molecules in the matrix are thermally unstable, denature, and become substrate for other circulating proteases. Presumably these fragments are engulfed by phagocytes and further degraded within lysosomes to amino acids that are recycled (except for hydroxylated residues that cannot be used for protein synthesis).

Multiple cells of both mesenchymal and epithelial origin synthesize apparently distinct collagenases capable of degrading fibrillar collagens and other collagens.[138–140]

INHERITED DISORDERS OF COLLAGEN BIOSYNTHESIS AND STRUCTURE

Inheritance

Because of the complexity of collagen processing and the stringent requirements for maintenance of many structural motifs in collagen molecules, a variety of mutations that affect collagen structure or modifications result in recognizable phenotypic alterations.[141] Most mutations in the processing enzymes result in clinically apparent phenotypes only when the defect is present in the homozygous state, as is true of most other enzymatic disorders. In contrast, most mutations that affect the structural collagen genes are phenotypically apparent in the heterozygous state. Because collagens are polymeric proteins, the effect of mutations in one allele may be amplified. For example, a mutation in a single $\alpha2(I)$ allele would be represented in 50 percent of all type I collagen molecules synthesized (assuming that the defective chains are incorporated into

molecules with normal efficiency); a mutation in a single $\alpha1(I)$ allele would be represented in 75 percent of all type I collagen molecules synthesized; but a mutation in a $\alpha1(II)$ or $\alpha1(III)$ allele would be represented in 87.5 percent of all molecules produced. These differences result from the stoichiometry of the chains in affected molecules. Finally, if trimers with one, two, or three abnormal chains are all dysfunctional, then the effect of having a polymer becomes clear. In contrast, the effect of having a nonfunctional (or nonexpressed) allele is far less deleterious and would be expected to have fewer clinical consequences (see "Osteogenesis Imperfecta Type I," below, for example).

Tissue-Specific Expression

The phenotypic effects of mutations in collagen genes are often restricted to certain tissues. For example, mutations in type I collagen are generally expressed phenotypically either in skin or in bone (the nature of the mutation affects the tissue of expression); mutations in type III collagen are expressed phenotypically as abnormalities in skin, hollow viscera, and vessels; and mutations in type II collagen are expressed as abnormalities in cartilage and vitreous humor. As a result, knowledge of the tissue distribution of abnormalities can help to identify reasonable candidate genes for a disorder.

Screening and Methods of Analysis

The first disorders of collagen processing were identified almost 20 years ago and were recognized because of the differences in the size of collagen chains in skin (dermatosparaxis in cattle[142]) or because of altered posttranslational modification of collagen in skin (lysyl hydroxylase deficiency in Ehlers-Danlos syndrome type VI[143]). Measurements of the relative amounts of collagens in skin led to the suggestion that decreased production of type I collagen could result in the phenotypes of osteogenesis imperfecta (OI).[144] Ultrastructural examination of tissues from individuals with Ehlers-Danlos syndrome (EDS) type IV, in particular the observation of markedly dilated RER in dermal fibroblasts,[145] suggested that structural mutations which affect secretion of collagens could produce disease.

Characterization of macromolecules synthesized by cultured dermal fibroblastic cells became the method of choice to identify mutations that affected collagen molecules synthesized by those cells. This has demonstrated utility in some of the EDS phenotypes and many of the OI phenotypes, because skin fibroblasts synthesize type I and type III collagens in abundance. The ease with which mutations can be identified depends on the effect they have on molecular structure and processing. For example, large rearrangements in the genes that result in longer than normal or shorter than normal chains are readily apparent when radiolabeled proteins are examined (see below). Certain single amino acid substitutions can also be identified in this manner, either by specific labeling (e.g., with cysteine to identify substitutions within the triple-helical domain of type I collagen) or by their effect on posttranslational modification. Cultured dermal fibroblasts are less valuable in screening for some processing mutations (e.g., mutations that affect extracellular processing—cleavage of the amino- and carboxyl-terminal propeptides and cross-linking—and some varieties of intracellular modification) unless specific tests for those defects are used. Fibroblasts cannot be used to identify mutations in genes that are not expressed in those cells.

For disorders that affect genes not expressed in fibroblastic cells and to determine which type I collagen gene carries a mutation in dominantly inherited disorders, genetic linkage studies have been extremely valuable. Linkage studies with polymorphic markers in the genes for type I collagen have confirmed that mutations in both genes of type I collagen, COL1A1 and COL1A2, can account for dominantly inherited forms of osteogenesis imperfecta. Linkage studies have excluded candidate genes in certain disorders. For example, studies of inheritance of polymorphic markers in the COL2A1 gene have excluded mutations in type II collagen in families with dominantly inherited achondroplasia.[146] Chromosomal localization of collagen genes has, in some cases, excluded genes as candidates in disorders for which they might reasonably be considered, e.g., type IV collagen in Alport syndrome, a disorder affecting the basement membranes of the ear and the kidney. Localization of the genes for two type IV collagens on chromosome 13 has excluded them as candidates in the X-linked form of the disorder.

Linkage studies in dominantly inherited disorders of type I and type III collagen genes (in OI types I and IV and in EDS type IV) have identified the genes affected and have facilitated prenatal diagnosis and gene isolation. More recently, linkage studies have also excluded mutations in both type I collagen genes in some of the rare families with autosomal recessive forms of severe osteogenesis imperfecta.[147,148]

Although linkage studies can identify the gene responsible for the phenotype, direct analyses of the genes of type I and type III collagen have not identified any mutation in those genes in individuals with any of the inherited disorders of connective tissue without prior analysis of the proteins synthesized by their cells in culture.

OSTEOGENESIS IMPERFECTA

Osteogenesis imperfecta is a heterogeneous group of inherited disorders characterized by bone fragility that is accompanied by other evidence of connective tissue malfunction including abnormalities in teeth (dentinogenesis imperfecta), hearing loss, alterations in scleral hue, and evidence of soft tissue dysplasia[149] (Table 115-3). The vast majority of individuals with OI have mutations that affect the structure of genes encoding the chains of type I collagen.[150] The clinical heterogeneity is extensive and includes death in the perinatal period, survival with marked short stature and severe bone deformity, and normal life span with only mild decrease in bone mass.[151] This heterogeneity has led to many efforts to devise a classification of osteogenesis imperfecta that would predict natural history (with the attendant needs for medical intervention), determine the mode of genetic transmission, and facilitate a biochemical approach to this group of disorders. An initial attempt to classify osteogenesis imperfecta divided affected individuals into those with fractures and/or deformity at birth (OI congenita) and those who did not develop fractures or deformity until later (OI tarda).[152] This scheme was later amended to add a second tarda group to distinguish between patients with a severe and often lethal form and patients who survived.[153] Although this classification was often helpful in predicting long-term morbidity, it could be difficult, several years later, to distinguish some individuals initially classified in the tarda group from those in the congenita group. Nonetheless, this classification became the standard nomenclature for most physicians. Ibsen[154] and his colleagues in Denmark expanded the classification to include the additional criterion of the mode of inheritance. Beginning in the late 1970s Sillence and his colleagues used radiographic, genetic, and clinical criteria to develop the classification currently in use.[155] Al-

Table 115-3 Clinical Heterogeneity and Biochemical Defects in Osteogenesis Imperfecta

OI type	Clinical features	Inheritance*	Biochemical defects
I	Normal stature, little or no deformity, blue scleras, hearing loss in about 50 percent of individuals; dentinogenesis imperfecta is rare and may distinguish a subset.	AD	Decreased production of type I procollagen Substitution for residue other than glycine in triple helix of $\alpha 1(I)$
II	Lethal in the perinatal period, minimal calvarial mineralization, beaded ribs, compressed femurs, marked long bone deformity, platyspondyly.	AD (new mutation)	Rearrangements in the COL1A1 and COL1A2 genes Substitutions for glycyl residues in the triple-helical domain of the $\alpha 1(I)$ or $\alpha 2(I)$ chain
		AR (rare)	Small deletion in $\alpha 2(I)$ on the background of a null allele
III	Progressively deforming bones, usually with moderate deformity at birth. Scleras variable in hue, often lighten with age. Dentinogenesis common, hearing loss common. Stature very short.	AR	Frameshift mutation that prevents incorporation of pro$\alpha 2(I)$ into molecules (Noncollagenous defects)
		AD	Point mutations in the $\alpha 1(I)$ or $\alpha 2(I)$ chain
IV	Normal scleras, mild to moderate bone deformity and variable short stature, dentinogenesis is common, and hearing loss occurs in some.	AD	Point mutations in the $\alpha 2(I)$ chain Rarely, point mutations in the $\alpha 1(I)$ chain Small deletions in the $\alpha 2(I)$ chain

*AD = autosomal dominant; AR = autosomal recessive.

though this classification of OI into four major types (I to IV) was rapidly adopted by geneticists, it has not achieved similar popularity with orthopedic surgeons because of the difficulty in classifying many patients and because of the concern that natural history was not a major determinant in developing the classification. The Sillence modification of the Danish classification has been used to categorize most of the patients who have been investigated at the biochemical and genetic levels. The biochemical studies themselves and the recent linkage studies generally support the validity of the classification but emphasize that it is, in some respects, incomplete. Ultimately the biochemical and genetic studies will provide the basis of the most rational classification. It is likely, however, that even the biochemical classification will never be entirely adequate for prediction of natural history because of the confounding effects of other matrix components in regulating the phenotypic expression of the primary mutation.

Despite these limitations, the Sillence classification of OI is used in this chapter to categorize the phenotypic correlations of mutations in the structure and synthesis of type I collagen and to provide the background for a more extensive biochemical classification. As currently understood, osteogenesis imperfecta can be divided into four major groups (types I, II, III, and IV) that differ in clinical presentation, in mode of inheritance, in radiographic picture, and usually in the biochemical basis of the connective tissue disorder.

Osteogenesis Imperfecta Type I (Dominant Inheritance with Blue Sclerae)

Genetics and Natural History. OI type I is inherited in an autosomal dominant fashion and, typically, affected individuals have blue sclerae, normal teeth, and normal or near-normal stature and may experience a few or more than 50 fractures (usually of long bones) prior to puberty.[156] It has been suggested that this group of patients could be subdivided on the basis of the absence (IA) or presence (IB) of dentinogenesis imperfecta.[157]

Individuals with this type of OI rarely have fractures in the perinatal period. Fractures may occur first within the weeks following birth associated with diaper changing but more commonly occur as children begin to walk. The most frequent bones broken are the long bones of the arms and legs, the ribs, and the small bones of the hands and feet. The fracture frequency remains steady through childhood and then decreases following the onset of puberty, suggesting that hormonal changes improve bone strength, increase bone mass, or both. Fractures heal rapidly with evidence of good callus formation, and without deformity.

The frequency of this form of OI has been estimated at between 1 in 15,000 and 1 in 20,000, but because of the relatively mild phenotype, it may be more frequent. There appears to be no decrease in fertility or longevity in affected individuals. At birth blue sclerae are readily apparent and may be darkly colored, lightening gradually to the blue-gray present in affected adults. Radiographic bone morphology is generally normal, although mild osteopenia may be present on radiographs and can be documented by densitometry. Height of affected individuals is usually within the normal range, although affected individuals may be shorter than their unaffected family members. Vertebral body morphology in the adult is normal initially but often develops the classic "codfish" appearance which is accompanied by loss of height in the

later decades. Fracture frequency often increases following the menopause in women and in the sixth to eighth decades for men. In about half the families with OI type I, affected individuals have early onset hearing loss, beginning in the late teens and leading, gradually, to profound loss by the end of the fourth to fifth decades.[158–160] Although the hearing loss is mixed in type, recent advances in design and replacement of the fractured and fused bones of the middle ear have provided significant restoration of hearing for many affected individuals.[161] Early hearing loss is typically of high frequencies, and tympanometry results in a characteristic bifid compliance curve. Additional clinical findings often include mild joint hypermobility and increased bruising. A variety of nonskeletal problems have been identified in individuals with OI type I, including mitral valve and aortic valvular problems, but it is likely that these are not significantly more frequent than in the general population; however, a small group of patients has been identified that have slightly larger than normal aortic root diameters, without the risk of dissection.[162]

Biochemical Basis of OI Type I. Several forms of OI were among the earliest of the inherited disorders of collagen biosynthesis and structure to be studied using cultured dermal fibroblasts from affected individuals.[163] Cells cultured from patients who would be considered to have OI type I synthesized less type I procollagen than did controls. Skin from a number of individuals with mild, dominantly inherited OI and blue sclerae had a low ratio of type I to type III collagen, which suggested that decreased production of type I collagen rather than increased production of type III collagen by dermal cells accounted for the finding.[163] Subsequent studies of the synthesis of type I procollagen by cells cultured from three unrelated individuals with OI type I determined that the production of type I procollagen was about half the normal level, while that of type III procollagen was normal. The structure of the secreted type I procollagen was entirely normal as judged by peptide mapping. The decrease in type I procollagen production resulted from synthesis of only half the usual amount of the proα1(I) chains of type I procollagen.[164] Although the synthesis of proα2(I) chains was normal, about half of the chains could not be incorporated into intact molecules [presumably because the excess proα2(I) chains could not associate into trimeric molecules or because such molecules were unstable] and were degraded. The decreased production of proα1(I) by cells from some individuals with OI type I results from about half-normal steady state levels of the mRNA.[165] Examination of genomic DNA from 15 cell strains has demonstrated no evidence of change in size or copy number of the COL1A1 gene in most individuals.[166] Further, linkage studies of more than 10 additional families has demonstrated no evidence of deletion of those regions of the COL1A1 gene used for linkage analysis.[167] Thus, although a variety of mutations, including promoter and enhancer mutations, splicing mutations, premature termination, and inability of chains to assemble into molecules, could presumably result in the same phenotype, the precise molecular basis of this form of OI is only beginning to be understood and may commonly involve mutations that affect splicing.[168]

Analyses in families with OI type I have demonstrated linkage of the phenotype to polymorphic endonuclease restriction sites within the COL1A1 gene in most families and to sites in the COL1A2 gene in the minority.[167,169] Few clinical details and no biochemical data are included in these studies, so it is not clear whether the phenotypes of the families that map to different genes are identical or whether a minor feature (such as blue sclerae) might distinguish the phenotypes. Decreased production of proα1(I) is not the only way to decrease the secretion of type I procollagen without secreting abnormal molecules. For example, synthesis of a proα2(I) chain that is incorporated into molecules normally but results in rapid and complete degradation of all such molecules might have a similar effect.

Studies of type I collagen molecules synthesized by cells from two additional patients described as having OI type I phenotypes illustrate that structural mutations can also produce the phenotype. One such patient had blue scleras, was 4 ft. 10 in. tall, had deformity only as a result of a poor orthopedic result, had hearing loss, and was the only affected member of her family. Biochemical studies of collagens synthesized by cultured dermal fibroblasts identified a deletion of approximately 30 amino acid residues from the triple-helical domain of about half the α2(I) chains synthesized.[170] The deletion was localized in the domain bordered by residues 6 to 327 but not further defined. In a second family, cells cultured from an affected mother and son synthesized α1(I) chains bearing a cysteine residue within the protease-resistant domain of the collagen molecule (largely triple helix), a region from which that residue is normally absent.[171] The secreted molecules were normally stable, and it was proposed that the substitution was for an amino acid other than glycine in the triple helix or in the protease-resistant domains of the carboxyl-terminal telopeptide.[172] OI type I due to mutations that affect the structure of the chains of type I procollagen appears to be rare, and in most instances, the phenotype results from mutations that affect the synthesis of the proα1(I) chain (Fig. 115-5).

Diagnosis, Treatment, and Prenatal Diagnosis. The diagnosis of OI type I is first suspected clinically, usually because of the presence of a dominant family history, the observation of blue scleras in the patient, and bone fractures; the diagnosis is confirmed by measuring the production of type I procollagen by dermal fibroblasts in culture. Ordinarily, about 85 percent of the collagen synthesized by these cells is type I procollagen, and most of the remainder is type III procollagen. Cells from patients with OI type I synthesize about half the normal amount of type I procollagen but a normal amount of other proteins. In rare families (see above) other types of mutations may be found. Biochemical diagnosis is particularly important in the newly affected infant for whom there is no family history, because the results can facilitate genetic counseling and help to reassure the family about prognosis. Early diagnosis also can remove the concern of child abuse, and it may be important for families to have a letter from the child's physician stating the diagnosis.

There is currently no treatment for OI type I that reliably and predictably decreases the frequency of bone fracture or increases bone density. From a theoretical point of view, agents which increase the production of type I collagen have therapeutic potential, but none has yet been proved effective in controlled tests.

Prenatal identification of affected fetuses has not been attempted. Linkage analysis in appropriate families would provide early diagnosis if chorionic villus sampling were done. Alternatively, analysis of the amount of type I procollagen synthesized by cells cultured from chorionic villus samples taken at 9 to 10 weeks' gestation might provide a means for detecting affected infants, but no studies have been done yet.

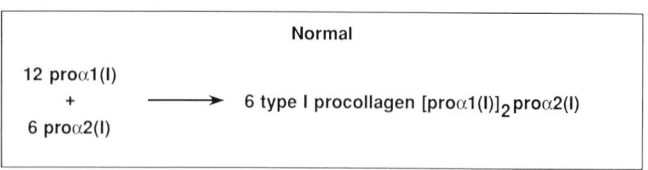

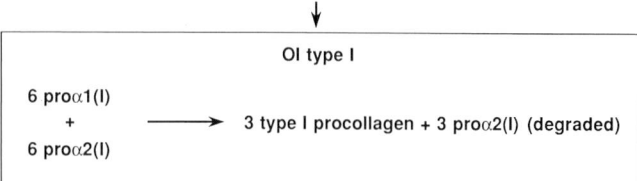

Fig. 115-5 Molecular basis of OI type I. Several defects in the structure of the COL1A1 gene can lead to a decrease in the synthesis of proα1(I) chains and thus to production of less than normal amounts of type I procollagen. In addition, rapid intracellular degradation of half the assembled type I procollagen molecules as a result of a destabilizing mutation in half the proα2(I) chains synthesized might produce the same biochemical phenotype and have similar clinical consequences to the listed mutations in the COL1A1 gene.

Amniotic fluid cells are not useful in establishing the diagnosis because the major population of cells that grows out does not synthesize normal type I procollagen.[173,174]

Osteogenesis Imperfecta Type II (Perinatal Lethal)

Genetics and Natural History. OI type II, the perinatal lethal form of OI, affects between 1 in 20,000 and 1 in 60,000 infants.[175,176] Prematurity and low birth weight are common. Affected infants have a characteristic facial appearance with dark scleras, beaked nose, and extremely soft calvarium (Fig. 115-6). The extremities are short, the legs are bowed, and the hips are usually in a flexed and abducted (frog-leg) position; the thoracic cavity is generally very small. The radiologic picture is characteristic but exhibits some heterogeneity.[177] All infants have markedly telescoped femurs, bowed tibias, and virtual absence of calvarial mineralization. The ribs are generally beaded, although they may be broad throughout; frank fractures are rare in the newborn period, and the vertebral bodies may be flattened. Death usually results from respiratory failure and frequently occurs during the first few hours following birth (Fig. 115-7). More than 60 percent of infants with OI type II die during the first day, 80 percent die within the first month, and survival beyond a year must be extremely rare. With the increasing use of routine early gestational ultrasound, first affected infants in families are being detected during the second trimester of pregnancy.[178–180]

There has been considerable confusion and controversy concerning the mode of inheritance of OI type II. The identification of a number of families that have produced multiple sibs who died with severe OI in the perinatal period, and consanguinity in some of these families, prompted geneticists to suggest that OI type II is a recessively inherited disorder.[181] Reexamination of the radiological phenotype of some of these infants suggests that they probably belong more appropriately in the recessive OI type III group (see, for example, Refs. 182, 183). Recent analysis of more than 100 families into which

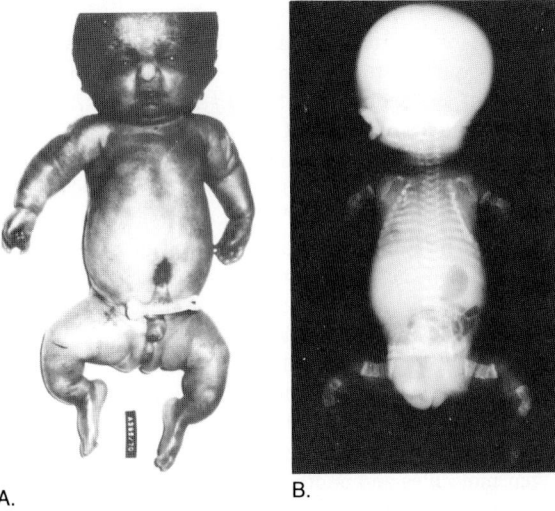

A.   B.

Fig. 115-6 *A.* Clinical and *B.* radiographic appearance of an infant with the perinatal lethal form of osteogenesis imperfecta (OI type II). Infants with OI type II have large soft calvaria, a small thoracic cavity, short extremities with marked angulation of the lower legs, and generally have their legs in a flexed and abducted position. The x-rays demonstrate virtual absence of calvarial mineralization, shortened and markedly undermineralized bones, block shaped femurs and bowed tibias, with markedly flattened vertebral bodies.

infants with OI type II were born[177,184] was compatible with the idea that the vast majority of affected infants arose as a result of new dominant mutations. There was a small group for which recessive inheritance could not be excluded, and another group in which both biochemical analysis and the structure of the families suggested that germline mosaicism for a mutation in an allele of one of the genes encoding a chain of type I collagen was the best explanation for recurrence of the phenotype within a family. It is now generally accepted that the OI type II phenotype results from new dominant mutations in the genes encoding the chains of type I collagen, but that there is a small recurrence risk, estimated to be 5 to 10 percent overall, which is explained largely by germ-cell mosaicism.[185] The option of prenatal diagnosis in subsequent pregnancies should be offered to all individuals who have had a child with OI type II.

OI type II needs to be differentiated from other lethal skeletal dysplasias and hypophosphatasia.[186,187] An experienced

Fig. 115-7 Survival data for 45 probands with OI type II. *(From Byers et al.[177] by permission of the American Journal of Human Genetics.)*

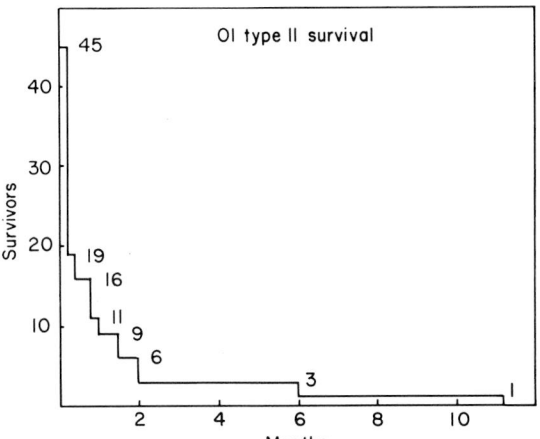

pediatric radiologist can help with this distinction, and the diagnosis can be confirmed by examination of the collagens synthesized by cultured fibroblastic cells.

Management and Prenatal Diagnosis. OI type II is a lethal condition with a life expectancy ranging from minutes to months. Death may result from pulmonary insufficiency, congestive heart failure, or infection. The most difficult management decisions occur at the birth of an affected infant when the diagnosis may not be clear and the infant has marked pulmonary insufficiency. Ordinarily, when the diagnosis is known, infants are offered supportive care, and parental bonding is encouraged. Many affected infants can leave the hospital, and supportive care in the home is essential. Bedding that contains soft foam can decrease the fracture frequency. Because of the respiratory insufficiency, many of these infants have feeding problems, and it is often difficult to maintain adequate caloric intake.

Prenatal diagnosis of OI type II has been accomplished by ultrasound screening of fetuses between 14 and 18 weeks' gestation (see above). By that age femurs are short, the thoracic cage is small, and calvarial mineralization is minimal. Analysis of chorionic villi for the presence of abnormal collagens and of collagens synthesized by cells grown from chorionic villi can be used to exclude the diagnosis and to identify an affected fetus.[188]

Biochemical Basis of OI Type II. OI type II is the best studied of all the inherited disorders of collagen metabolism. Collagens synthesized by cells or present in tissues from more than 100 infants have been partially characterized,[177,189–191] and the precise molecular defect has now been identified in at least seven infants (see below). OI type II is biochemically heterogeneous. Three classes of mutations that lead to the phenotype have been identified: (1) point mutations (probably largely in the COL1A1 gene), (2) multiexon deletions or insertions, and (3) in the only well-described example of compound heterozygosity, the presence of a small deletion in the triple-helical domain of one COL1A2 allele on the background of a "null" COL1A2 allele.

REARRANGEMENTS. The first detailed biochemical studies of collagens synthesized by cells cultured from individuals with OI included one cell strain from an infant with OI type II.[163] It was recognized then that the amount of type I procollagen secreted into the medium by cells from that infant was markedly decreased compared to controls. Subsequent studies of the same cell strain led to the recognition that decreased secretion was a reflection of intracellular retention of molecules that contained a proα1(I) chain from which a segment had been deleted.[192–194] The shortened chain resulted from an intron-to-intron deletion of approximately 650 bp in one COL1A1 allele that removed the three exons encoding triple-helical residues 327 to 411 of the proα1(I) chain.[195,196] There was a short inverted repeat at the end of the deleted fragment that may have facilitated deletion by a "looping-out" mechanism during replication of one strand. Because the deletion endpoints were within introns, the resulting proα1(I) chain was predicted to have an intact Gly-X-Y triplet structure, 84 residues shorter than the product of the normal allele. Cells from this infant synthesized a small proportion of apparently normal molecules and molecules which contained either one or two of the abnormal chains. Molecules that contained the shortened chain had a very low melting temperature (about 32°C), and virtually none of these molecules were secreted. Although the deletion from the COL1A1 allele is probably sufficient to explain the clinical phenotype, it has been noted that this cell strain excessively modified other collagens, notably type III. It is not clear whether the increased modification resulted from prolonged residence in the RER or whether there was an additional mutation in the cell strain.

Examination of collagens synthesized by cells from almost 100 additional infants with perinatal lethal OI has revealed only two additional examples of rearrangements in the genes encoding type I collagen. The first was a 600 bp insertion within one COL1A1 allele[197] that resulted in duplication of a sequence of about 60 amino acids just carboxyl-terminal to triple-helical residue 123 in proα1(I). Cells from the infant made three classes of molecules: normal, those with one abnormal chain, and those with two abnormal chains. The abnormal molecules were secreted only slightly less efficiently than the normal molecules and had decreased thermal stability. The lethal effect of this mutation was thought to be the result of having in the matrix half (or more) of the molecules that contained the inserted segment. These molecules probably could not form normal fibrils, and their presence in tissues would interfere with mineralization and cross-link formation.

The second rearrangement was a 4.5 kb deletion containing seven exons from one COL1A2 allele that resulted in the absence of 180 amino acids (triple-helical residues 586 to 765) in about half the proα2(I) chains.[198] Molecules that contained the shortened chain were secreted very inefficiently and remained in the lumen of the rough endoplasmic reticulum. The extent of posttranslational modification was markedly increased amino-terminal to the deletion junction, which suggested that although the triple-helical structure was maintained, the stability of the triple helix was compromised. The secretion of only a small amount of the abnormal molecule was apparently sufficient, on the background of secretion of less than the normal amount of normal type I procollagen, to result in the OI type II phenotype.

POINT MUTATIONS. It soon became clear that among infants with OI type II, large rearrangements in genes encoding the chains of type I collagen were rare. Instead, the majority of cells from infants with OI type II have either point mutations or interruptions in the structure of either the proα1(I) or proα2(I) chain that lead to disturbance in the triple-helix stability, interfere with secretion, and affect the formation of fibrils in the extracellular matrix. To date, five of these mutations have been characterized at the sequence level. In the first, tissue and collagens synthesized by cells from an infant with OI type II were shown to have a cysteine residue within the triple-helical domain of the α1(I) chain [cysteine is excluded from the triple-helical domain of the normal α1(I) and α2(I) chains].[199] All molecules that contained either one or two copies of the mutant chain were less efficiently secreted than the normal molecules, had undergone increased posttranslational modification (lysyl hydroxylation and hydroxylysyl glycosylation) along the entire length of the molecule, and were less stable to thermal denaturation (they melted at 38°C instead of the normal 42°C). A portion of both COL1A1 alleles was isolated and sequenced to show that the cysteine had substituted for the glycine at position 988 in the triple helix as a result of a single nucleotide substitution.[200] Because of the importance of glycine in every third position for the propagation of the triple helix, it was postulated that substitution for most glycyl residues in the triple-helical domain of the α1(I) chain would

result in the same phenotype, provided they interfered sufficiently with stability. Initial confirmation of this hypothesis derives from sequence studies of collagens isolated from tissue from one infant and sequence determination of cDNA or genomic DNA isolated from cells of three other affected infants. These studies have shown that substitution of an arginine for glycine 391 in α1(I),[201] cysteine for glycines 748 and 904,[202,203] and aspartic acid for glycine 883[185] each results in the OI type II phenotype. The relatively high frequency of cysteine-for-glycine substitutions observed initially was not seen in a larger sample. Of the 100 or more cell strains from these infants that have been studied, only five are known to have cysteine substitutions in the α1(I) chain. Cell strains from those infants with known single amino acid substitutions in proα1(I) and from virtually all other infants with OI type II (except those with rearrangements) synthesize a population of normal type I procollagen molecules and another population that is secreted less efficiently than normal, is overmodified along all or part of the molecule, and has a lower than normal thermal stability (Fig. 115-8). The mutation in one COL1A1 allele results in the production of three classes of molecules: those with no abnormal proα1(I) chains (25 percent), those with one abnormal chain (50 percent), and those with two abnormal chains (25 percent). In many cell strains there is little difference in the manner in which the abnormal molecules are handled, despite their different composition. Those abnormal molecules are subject to rapid degradation and, when secreted, probably cannot be efficiently incorporated into the matrix but do interfere with mineralization (in bone) and cross-link formation. The reason for the decreased thermal stability is not clear, but its effect is to allow the molecule to be further modified and to be retained in the cell longer than normal (Fig. 115-9). Evidence is emerging that point mutations that result in substitutions for glycyl residues in the triple helical domain of α2(I) can also produce OI type II.[204]

COMPOUND HETEROZYGOSITY FOR TWO MUTATIONS IN THE COL1A2 GENE. In one instance the OI type II phenotype has been shown to result from compound heterozygosity for mutations that affect the two COL1A2 alleles.[205] The first mutation, new in the family, results in shortened mRNA due to defective splicing of exon 28.[206,207] In addition, the infant apparently received a second defective COL1A2 allele from one parent that resulted in lack of synthesis of proα2(I) chains. As a result, all the proα2(I) chains synthesized (half the normal amount) were abnormal; furthermore, the cells also secreted a trimer of proα2(I) chains.

Biochemical-Pathologic Correlation. Not yet clear is how such mutations result in lethal disease and why such diverse mutations result in a similar phenotype. From a pathologic perspective, bone is markedly undermineralized,[208] osteoblastic cells with dilated rough endoplasmic reticulum are common, and increased osteoid is observed. Fibril diameter of collagen molecules is small, and fibers in skin are small and sparse.[180]

The known point mutations in COL1A1 are all between residues 391 and 1014 of the triple helix. (Fig. 115-10). In each case, assembly of the triple helix appears to be normal to the point of the mutation, but the stability of the molecule between the mutation and the amino-terminal end of the triple helix is decreased. Further, this portion of the molecule is subjected to increased posttranslational modification. In all known point mutations and in the rearrangements, overmodi-

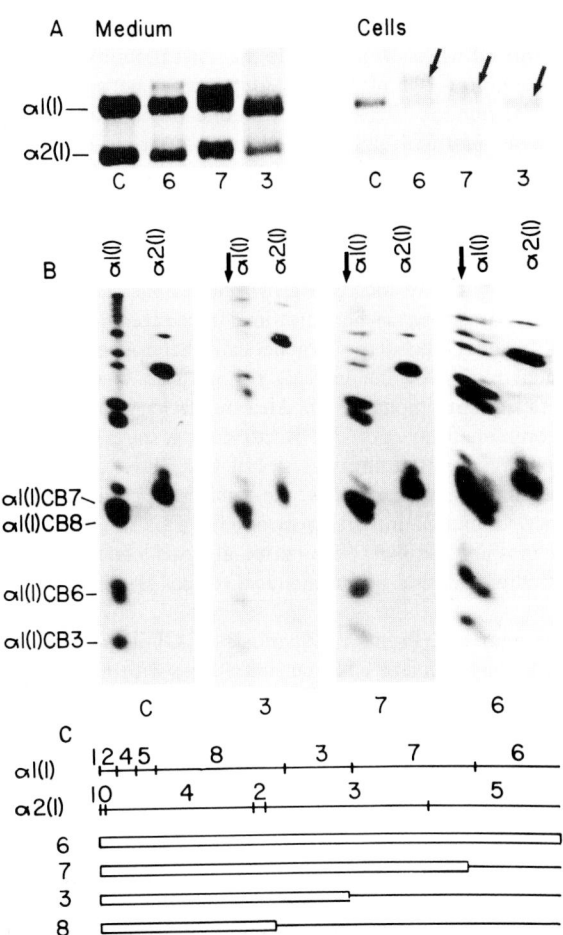

Fig. 115-8 Altered electrophoretic mobility of the chains of type I collagen synthesized by cells from infants with OI type II. *A.* Chains of type I collagen secreted into the medium or retained with the cells were separated by sodium dodecyl sulfate polyacrylamide gel electrophoresis under nonreducing conditions following treatment with pepsin to remove the non-triple-helical domains of procollagen. The arrows in the cell portion of the figure indicate the abnormal, slowly migrating α1(I) chains. Lane marker C designates control; 6, 7, and 3 indicate cell strains in which overmodification begins in α1(I)CB6, α1(I)CB7, and α1(I)CB3, respectively. *B.* Cyanogen bromide peptide maps of normal and abnormal type I collagen chains. The section of the gel represented in part A was resected; the chains in the gel were treated with cyanogen bromide, which cleaves proteins at methionyl residues; and the resultant peptides were then separated in a second dimension gel on top of which the gel fragment had been placed. The arrow at the top of each panel indicates the position of the abnormal, slowly migrating α1(I) chain indicated in part A. In panel 3 the mobilities of α1(I)CB8 and α1(I)CB3 from the abnormal chain are slow; in panel 7 the mobilities of α1(I)CB8, α1(I)CB3 and α1(I)CB7 are slow; and in panel 6 the mobilities of each of the CNBr peptides is slow. The delay in electrophoretic mobility results from increased posttranslational modification along all (panel 6) or part (panels 3 and 7) of the chain. *C.* Diagrammatic representation of the extent of increased posttranslational modification along the type I collagen molecule with the triple-helical domain of each α chain. Vertical lines = positions of methyionyl residues; numbers = CNBr peptides; open bars indicate the extent of increased posttranslational modification along the molecule. *(From Byers et al.[177] by permission of the American Journal of Human Genetics.)*

fication occurs amino-terminal to the defect, but modification is generally normal carboxyl-terminal to the site. It has been proposed that propagation of the triple-helical structure is very slow through the domain carrying the mutation and that, as a result, the chains remain accessible for further modification. Alternatively, the structure of the triple helix formed may not

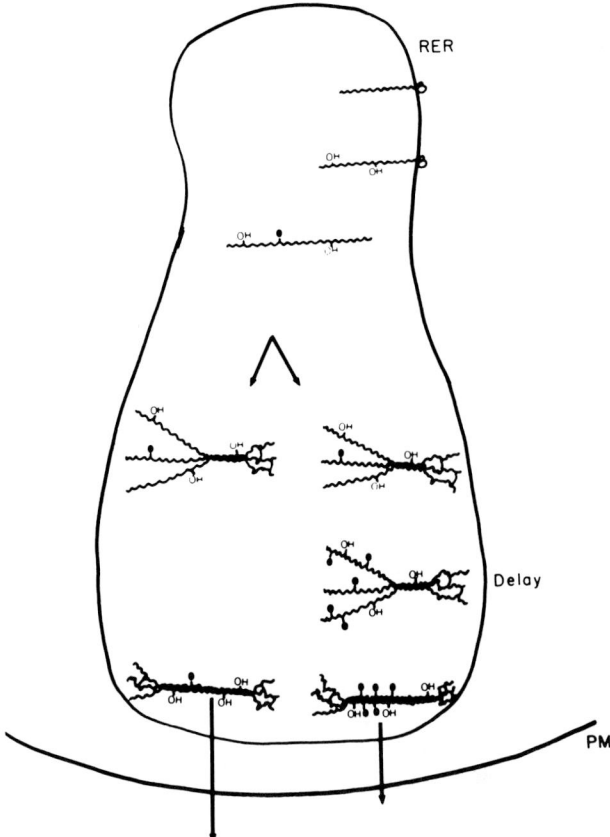

Fig. 115-9 Assembly, modification and secretion of normal and abnormal type I procollagen molecules synthesized by cells from infants with OI type II. Molecules that contain only normal chains are assembled and secreted within about 20 minutes of synthesis. Molecules that contain one or more abnormal chains are assembled normally, but the propagation of stable triple helix beyond the site of mutation in a chain is slowed and allows extensive posttranslational modification to occur amino-terminal to the mutant sequence. Overmodified molecules are slowly secreted and accumulated within the cell, often in the rough endoplasmic reticulum (RER) and may interfere with the secretion of other matrix proteins. PM = plasma membrane.

be as stable as the normal structure [a concept supported by the findings in collagens synthesized with the large deletion from proα2(I) described above]. The amount of the abnormal molecule needed in the matrix to produce the phenotype is not clear, but on the basis of studies of some of the cell strains described here and animal models (see below), it may be surprisingly small.

Osteogenesis Imperfecta Type III

Natural History and Genetics. OI type III, the progressive deforming variety, is usually recognized at birth because of short stature and deformities resulting from in utero fractures (Fig. 115-11). There are well-documented autosomal recessive and autosomal dominant forms of OI type III, although the recessive form is rare in most populations.[209–211] Radiologically, at birth the calvarium is undermineralized, the ribs are thin, long bones are thin with evidence of fracture, and the skeleton is osteopenic. If no fractures are present at birth, they usually occur during the first year of life, and deformity becomes apparent during that period. Beginning between 2 and 5 years of age, unusual "cystic" structures form in the epiphyseal region of some of the long bones, especially of the fe-

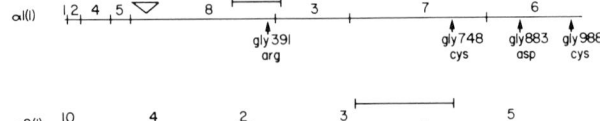

Fig. 115-10 Summary of known mutations that result in the OI type II phenotype. Only the triple-helical portions of each of the chains of type I collagen are indicated. Vertical bars = position of methionyl residues in the triple-helical domains; numbers = CNBr peptides. The methionyl residues are at positions 3, 39, 86, 123, 402, 551, and 816 in the α1(I) chain and at positions 3, 6, 327, 357, and 694 in the α2(I) chain. Horizontal bars = deletions; ▽ = insertions; ↑ = point mutations. Insertions and deletions are drawn to scale. The presence of point mutations only in the α1(I) chain and the identification of point mutations that result in substitutions of glycyl residues by cysteine or charged amino acids is a result of biased ascertainment because of the ease with which such mutations are found and characterized.

murs.[212] These are areas in which the growth plate is markedly disrupted, probably by recurrent microfractures. As a result, bone growth is poor, and marked shortening of stature results. Because of very thin cortex, fracture of long bones is frequent. Angulation deformities of the tibias and the femurs reduce the efficiency of weight bearing and increase the likelihood of fracture. Treatment is directed toward providing a more functional anatomy, and these are the children who benefit from placement of intramedullary rods in long bones, which improves prognosis and perhaps facilitates walking in some.[213,214] For some children, bone fragility makes independent ambu-

Fig. 115-11 Radiographic features of the progressive deforming OI type III phenotype in the newborn period. Calvarial mineralization is adequate; there is deformity of the long bones and rare fractures of the thin ribs. The infant pictured in this radiograph was heterozygous for mutation that resulted in substitution of cysteine for glycine at position 526 in the COL1A1 gene. (X-ray courtesy of Dr. Lester Weiss, Henry Ford Hospital, Detroit, MI.)

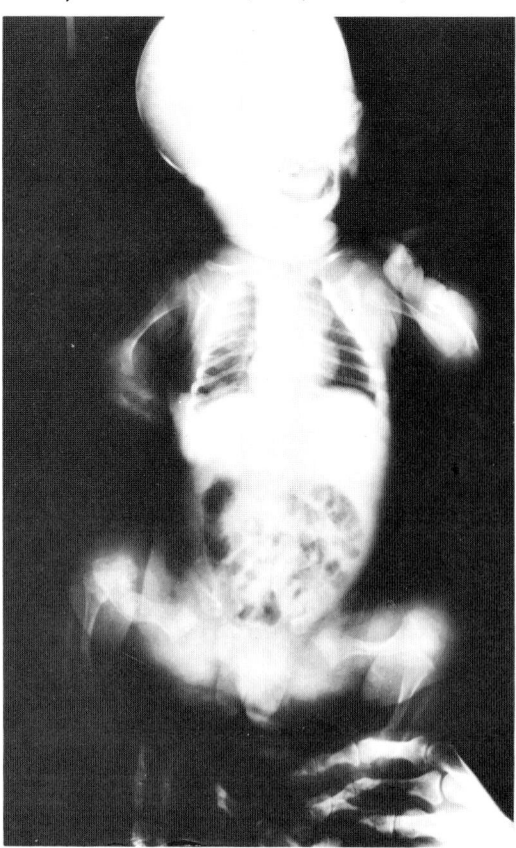

lation difficult in all but the most restricted circumstances, and motorized wheelchairs provide the most mobility. Growth in these children is limited, and adult height between 3 and 4½ feet is common. Because of the bone fragility and deformity, many of these children develop significant kyphoscoliosis and may progress to pulmonary insufficiency. Scleras are often pale blue at birth and become nearly normal by puberty. Dentinogenesis imperfecta is common; the frequency of hearing loss is not known. No medical therapy reliably decreases fracture frequency or increases growth and bone density.[215]

Initially described as an autosomal recessive condition,[151] the OI type III phenotype is genetically heterogeneous. The autosomal recessive phenotype is the unusual form in most populations, but among South African blacks it may be the most common form of OI.[211] Recurrence is rare in families with the severe deforming varieties of OI. Thus, while there may be some recessive families, the condition probably results from new dominant mutations in others. This has been confirmed in some families by birth of affected children to affected individuals and by biochemical studies (see below).

Management and Prenatal Diagnosis of OI Type III. The clinical management of children and adults with OI type III represents the most difficult challenge to physicians and others caring for individuals with OI. The primary objectives of therapy should always be to provide an affected individual with the maximum likelihood of enjoying a satisfying and productive life. The major complications are marked short stature, severe bone fragility and deformity, and severe, progressive scoliosis which may result in life-threatening cardiopulmonary decompensation. The bone fractures and deformity can be managed by a combination of splinting, usual orthopedic treatment of fractures, and use of intramedullary rods to provide anatomical positioning of extremities. Because of fragility, independent ambulation may be beyond the capabilities of some affected individuals. If that is the case, then efforts to provide mobility within the home and independence outside the home should be the thrust of therapy. Scoliosis may be difficult to treat because of the compliant nature of bones of the ribs and their deformation with external bracing. In some instances surgical intervention can ameliorate scoliosis, while in others it is of little long-term benefit.

Prenatal diagnosis of OI type III by ultrasound examination of fetuses during the second trimester has been documented.[216,217] If the specific biochemical defect is known in an individual hoping to have children (in the case of the dominantly inherited forms) or in a child in a family seeking to have additional children (with recessively inherited forms or with dominantly inherited forms), the mutations can be detected in collagens synthesized by chorionic villus cells or in the DNA isolated from the tissue directly. If families so choose, prenatal diagnosis by direct analysis of gene structure or by analysis of collagen synthesized by cultured cells can be achieved within 2 to 3 weeks of chorionic villus sampling. Because ultrasound diagnosis may not be feasible until considerably later (20 to 22 weeks), direct diagnosis is probably preferable when it is known that the mutation or the effects of the mutation can be detected.

Biochemical and Molecular Genetic Studies. OI type III has been a particularly difficult disorder to characterize biochemically, because cultured cells appear to synthesize only normal type I procollagen molecules in many instances. There are several plausible explanations for these findings. First, the primary mutations may occur in noncollagenous proteins; second, the mutations in type I collagen genes may be difficult to detect by the screening studies normally used; and third, mutations may occur in collagen genes other than those that encode the chains of type I collagen. It is likely that all these explanations are correct.

AUTOSOMAL RECESSIVE OI TYPE III. The molecular basis of recessively inherited OI type III has been determined in only one family. The proband was born to phenotypically normal first-cousin parents and recognized to have OI at birth. He had marked bone fragility, short stature, decreased calvarial mineralization, and moderate bone deformity which increased as he grew older.[218,219] Type I collagen isolated from the skin of the proband was composed solely of $\alpha1(I)$ chains. Cells cultured from the child secreted type I procollagen molecules that contained only $pro\alpha1(I)$ chains; the cells synthesized $pro\alpha2(I)$ chains that were not incorporated into procollagen molecules.[220,221] Both COL1A2 alleles contained the same 4-bp deletion near the end of the exon that encodes the carboxyl-terminal end of the $pro\alpha2(I)$ chain.[222,223] The frameshift changed the sequence of the final 33 residues of the chain. In addition to changing the composition, this mutation resulted in the loss of a cysteine in carboxyl-terminal propeptide position 245, which normally bonds with a cysteine at position 80 to stabilize the structure of the peptide. The change in sequence and the presumed change in tertiary structure of the carboxyl-terminal propeptide extension of the $pro\alpha2(I)$ chain alters the ability of the chain to be recognized and incorporated in a type I procollagen molecule. Although formation of $pro\alpha1(I)$ homotrimers is less favored than that of heterotrimers which contain $pro\alpha1(I)$ and $pro\alpha2(I)$ chains, homotrimers form in the absence of the normal $pro\alpha2(I)$ chains. The chains in these molecules are overmodified along their entire length (although their thermal stability is normal), and they are secreted more slowly than the normal type I procollagen. About two-thirds of the normal amount of type I procollagen would be synthesized and secreted (if the stability of the molecules is normal). It is not clear if the relatively severe phenotype results from the presence in the matrix of molecules that are overmodified, from the absence of the $\alpha2(I)$ chain, or from the presence of only abnormal molecules. This mutation demonstrates that, surprisingly, the absence of $\alpha2(I)$ chains in type I collagen can be tolerated.

AUTOSOMAL DOMINANT OI TYPE III. The OI type III phenotype can result from mutations in both COL1A1 and COL1A2 genes. The first evidence of alterations in type I collagen leading to the phenotype came from studies of skin and bone collagen taken from an infant that died within 2 months of birth and had a radiologic phenotype compatible with OI type III.[224] Protease digestion of collagen isolated from skin and bone cleaved about 120 residues from the amino-terminal end of the triple helix of some of the $\alpha1(I)$ chains. Such instability probably resulted from a mutation that destabilized the triple-helical domain of the type I collagen in that region.

Cells from several patients with OI type III synthesized type I procollagen molecules with an unstable triple helix. In one, a new point mutation resulted in substitution of cysteine for glycine at position 526 of the triple helix in the products of one COL1A1 allele.[225] Molecules that contained one or two abnormal $pro\alpha1(I)$ chains were assembled and secreted; both species were less stable than the normal molecules, had lowered melting temperatures, and were overmodified amino-ter-

minal to the site of the mutation. Cells from a second patient synthesized $pro\alpha2(I)$ chains about half of which contained a cysteine residue in the triple-helical domain.[226] Overmodification of the chains in molecules that contained the abnormal chain suggested that the residue substituted was a glycine. These two patients provide convincing evidence that mutations in either of the genes that encodes the chains of type I collagen may lead to the OI type III phenotype, and that the nature of the substitution, the residue substituted, and the location of the mutation in the chain may all contribute to the phenotypic effect.

Osteogenesis Imperfecta Type IV

Natural History and Genetics. OI type IV is a dominantly inherited disorder characterized by normal or grayish sclerae, mild to moderate deformity, and variable stature which may be short[227] (Fig. 115-12). Dentinogenesis imperfecta is common, but fewer than half of the affected individuals have hearing loss. When present, both features are familial, although, like the stature of affected individuals, they may vary considerably in expression. Some infants with OI type IV have fractures and deformity at birth, while others have only mild to moderate femoral bowing. Birth length is usually normal, but by the age of 2 years, height is generally at or below the 25th percentile (frequently below the 10th percentile), and growth is generally along the lower percentiles thereafter. As in the other forms of OI, fracture frequency decreases at the time of puberty only to increase in the older age group, especially in postmenopausal women. Progressive scoliosis is seen in about one-third of individuals with OI type IV and may compromise pulmonary function if severe.

Although thought to be rare initially,[151] OI type IV may be one of the more common varieties of OI. Both sporadically affected individuals and large families are seen, and there is significant intrafamilial and interfamilial variation. The intrafamilial variation probably results from variation in the genetic background on which the primary mutation is expressed (none of the other genes that account for the variability have yet been identified), and the interfamilial variation represents molecular heterogeneity within the phenotype. The intrafamilial variability can be striking (such that it may be difficult to decide whether the family is most appropriately classified on clinical grounds as OI type III, OI type IV, or OI type I). We have identified two families in which affected parents with OI type IV have had children with a lethal OI phenotype (Ref. 177 and unpublished observations). Such extreme variability is rare but must be considered in counseling.

Treatment and Prenatal Diagnosis. The objectives of treatment and management of the complications of OI type IV are to provide maximum independence and mobility. Fracture and excessive wear of very fragile teeth are the major complications of dentinogenesis imperfecta, and these problems can be treated by capping teeth with more solid materials. Advances in the use of hard polymers to coat and shape teeth may facilitate the treatment of dentinogenesis imperfecta. Hearing loss can be managed initially by aids but frequently requires surgery to replace the ossicular structures.

Prenatal diagnosis by linkage analysis in the dominant families has been reported using DNA obtained by chorionic villus sampling to exclude the presence of the mutant allele.[228] Analysis of the collagens synthesized by the mesenchymal cells

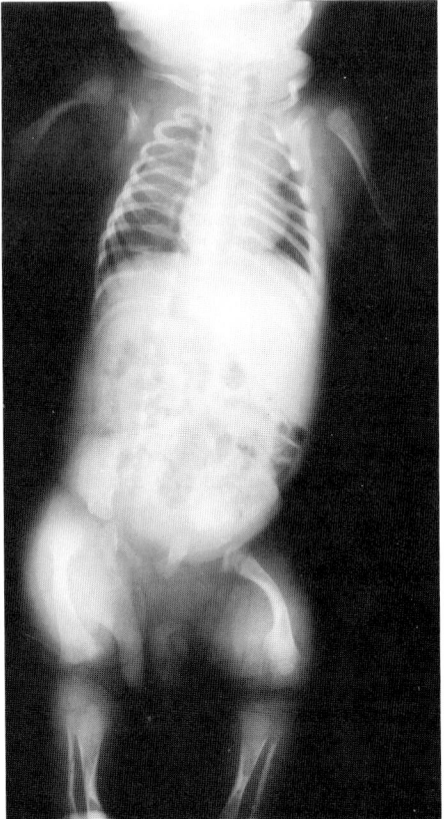

A.

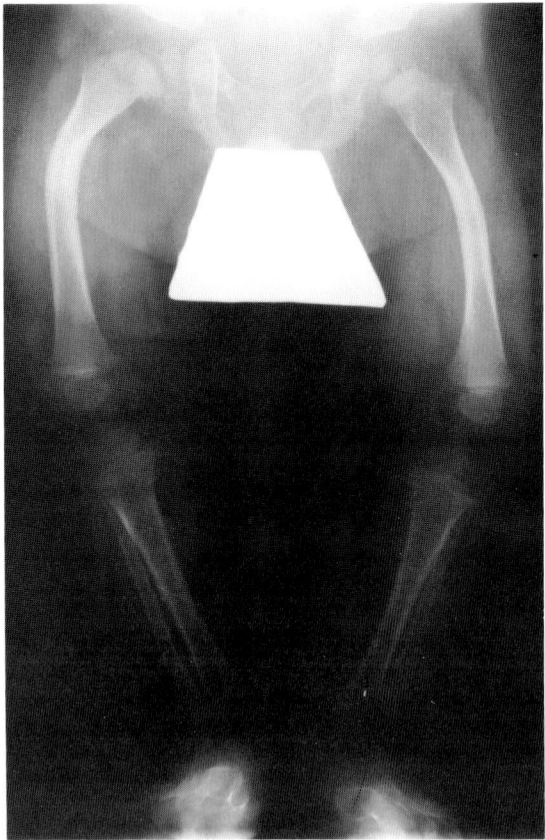

B.

Fig. 115-12 Radiographic features of OI type IV, *A.,* in the newborn period and, *B.,* at 8 months. The most notable feature is the bowing of femurs which gradually lessens during the first year. *(This patient is described in detail by Wenstrup et al., Hum Genet 74:47, 1986; x-rays courtesy of Dr. Alasdair Hunter, Ottawa.)*

grown from the biopsy can provide diagnostic information for small families in which the linkage phase cannot be determined and for sporadic affected individuals wishing to have unaffected children.

Biochemical and Molecular Genetic Studies. OI type IV was the first of the OI phenotypes to be studied by linkage analysis, and the initial studies demonstrated that the phenotype usually resulted from mutations in or near the COL1A2 gene.[229] Subsequently, linkage heterogeneity was recognized within the dominant OI phenotypes.[167,169,230] Although OI type IV was usually linked to COL1A2 polymorphic markers and OI type I to COL1A1, there are some OI type IV families in which linkage to COL1A1 is found, and, conversely, some OI type I families in which linkage to COL1A2 is seen. Unfortunately, the clinical phenotypes of these families are not clearly presented in some studies, and the differentiation of the two phenotypes may rest solely on the presence of minor features (subtlety of scleral hue) rather than major features of bone deformity and stature.

Linkage studies have been used to guide biochemical and molecular genetic studies in some families with OI type IV. In the first family in which linkage to COL1A2 could be demonstrated, cells from affected individuals synthesized and secreted normal type I procollagen and synthesized a population of molecules that was retained within cells.[231] These molecules became overmodified asymmetrically within the triple-helical domain and were then degraded. The retained molecules contained a proα2(I) chain that carried a small deletion (10 to 20 amino acids) in the triple-helical domain. Molecules that contained the abnormal chain had a markedly lowered thermal stability. The precise nature of the deletion has not been determined. Although the defect is difficult to detect, it seems likely either that the cells secrete some of the abnormal molecules or that the intracellular accumulation affects the manner in which the cell facilitates fibril formation.

In an additional family with OI type IV, cells from the affected members synthesized and secreted normal type I procollagen molecules and molecules that were overmodified along the entire length of the triple helix. The abnormal molecules incorporated a proα2(I) chain that, as the result of a single nucleotide change, substituted arginine for glycine 1012, the last of the triple-helical glycine residues.[232] Subsequently three families have been identified in which the appearance of cysteine within the triple-helical domain of the α2(I) chain (from which it is normally excluded) results in the OI type IV phenotype.[226] Because the molecules that contain the abnormal α2(I) chains are overmodified along a portion of their length, it is likely that the residue substitutes for a glycine. There is marked clinical variation within these families; an affected male fathered two children with a lethal phenotype in one family.

The linkage heterogeneity identified in OI type IV is reflected in the biochemical studies. For example, at least three families have been identified in which the appearance of cysteine in the triple-helical domain of α1(I), between residues 123 and 400 of the triple helix, lead to a phenotype compatible with OI type IV (Ref. 233; Byers et al., unpublished).

Other Forms of OI

The Silence classification does not adequately describe all individuals with OI, a point that has become increasingly clear

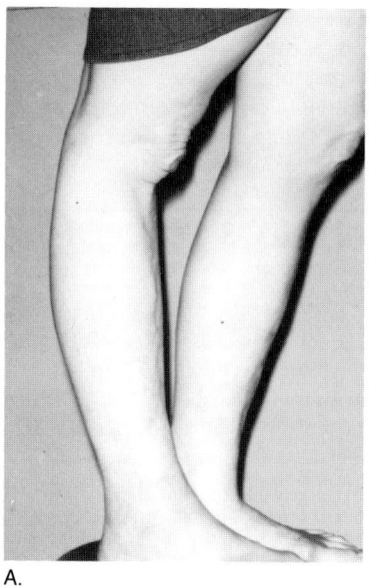 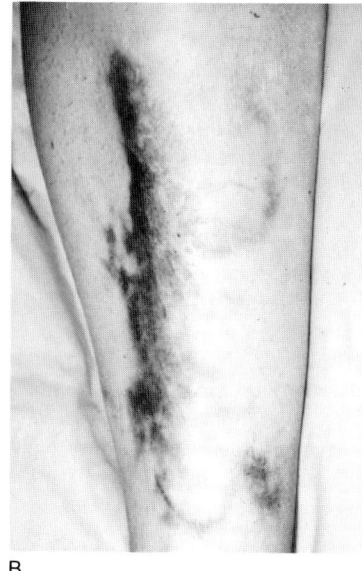 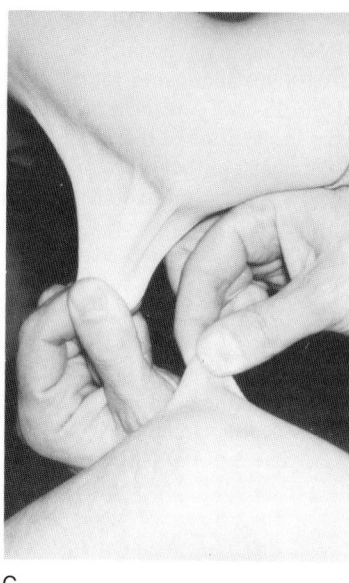

A.   B.   C.

Fig. 115-13 Clinical features of Ehlers-Danlos syndrome type I.
A., large joint hypermobility; B., cigarette paper scars and pigment
accumulation in areas of repeated trauma; C., skin hyperextensibility
(top) with control (bottom). *(From P Bornstein and PH Byers,
Collagen Metabolism, Upjohn, Kalamazoo, 1980.)*

with the sophisticated biochemical and molecular genetic testing done to identify the molecular basis for brittle bone diseases. For example, in one family affected individuals presented with clinical findings that represent a combination of features of OI and EDS.[234] The demonstration of the absence of amino acid residues encoded by exon 11 from about half the proα2(I) chains, as a result of a 19 bp deletion that removed a splice junction, appeared to account for some of the phenotypic findings.[235] The deletion removed one of the lysyl residues involved in intermolecular cross-link formation, affected the structure of the amino-terminal end of the triple helix, where interaction with matrix mineralizing elements may occur, and changed the organization of the amino-terminal propeptidase cleavage site.[236] Thus, a small deletion of protein sequence affected multiple functions of the molecule, and the clinical phenotype that resulted reflects, to some extent, the disruption of several functional domains of the type I procollagen molecule.

Other clinical phenotypes that have similarities to OI include the osteoporosis-glioma syndrome,[237–239] which has been described as a variant of OI, juvenile osteoporosis,[240] and maturity onset osteoporosis. In each instance, these disorders are characterized by marked osteopenia of unknown cause. There are no biochemical studies that provide clues about the nature of the mutations that result in these conditions.

Isolated dentinogenesis imperfecta is genetically distinct from the dentinogenesis imperfecta that accompanies some forms of OI.[241] Linkage studies have confirmed that the mutant gene is in close proximity to the Gc locus on chromosome 4,[242] a region devoid of fibrillar collagen genes. Teeth from individuals with isolated dentinogenesis imperfecta have been shown to lack a glycoprotein in dentin.[243] Although the molecular mechanism by which dentinogenesis imperfecta is produced is not known, identification of a candidate protein distinct from a collagen suggests that mutations that affect the interaction of the two proteins could result in the phenotype. Thus, mutations that alter collagen structure may produce OI and dentinogenesis imperfecta, while mutations that affect the

glycoprotein could produce dentinogenesis imperfecta but not interfere with other functions of the collagen molecule.

Animal Models

Three naturally occurring animal models of OI are known, and, in addition, recent experiments in transgenic mice and in mice that are homozygous for retroviral inserts in genomic DNA have demonstrated two further mechanisms for the production of OI in animals.

Two herds of cattle, one first isolated in Australia[244] and a second identified in New Zealand,[245] produced calves with a severe form of OI that was lethal in the first few weeks of life. In each herd, it was clear that the affected animals were sired by a single (separate) bull. In the Australian herd, about 45 percent of calves born as a result of insemination of cows with sperm from the bull had OI, although the bull was phenotypically normal. Outbreeding to different herds confirmed that there was not a high frequency recessive allele that gave rise to the phenotype and indicated clearly that the bull was mosaic in the germline for the mutation. Analysis of bone collagen from one of the calves[246] was compatible with the mutation being in a collagen gene because of the presence of normal collagen molecules and collagen molecules that were overmodified; the presence of the two populations of molecules was also consistent with heterozygosity for a mutation in a collagen gene. No molecular genetic studies have been published. In the second herd there were also multiple recurrences of the moderately severe phenotype among calves sired by a single phenotypically normal bull. No biochemical studies have yet been completed.

A mouse with a recessively inherited phenotype of fragile bones (the fragilitis ossium mouse) has been described.[247] Preliminary studies of the collagens synthesized by fibroblastic cells cultured from the mouse suggest that there are no easily recognized structural differences between those molecules and the collagens synthesized by cells from normal mice (Bonadio and Byers, unpublished observations).

A strain of mice has been created in which a retrovirus fortuitously inserted into the first intron of one COL1A1 allele.[248,249] Mice heterozygous for the insertion, known as the Mov-13 mutation, are apparently asymptomatic, although tissues contain about half the normal amount of COL1A1 mRNA. Embryos homozygous for the insertion die at about 12 days gestation from rupture of the heart and arterial vessels.[250] Tissues contain no demonstrable type I collagen, and it has been surmised that death results from mechanical failure of the organs. Attempts to rescue the homozygous embryos by insertion of the normal COL1A1 mouse gene into fertilized eggs have not yet proved successful. Transfection of the normal COL1A1 gene into cells grown from the embryos homozygous for the Mov-13 mutation rescues proα2(I) chains which are otherwise rapidly degraded following synthesis.[251] Transfection into Mov-13 cells of a gene that contained a point mutation which resulted in substitution for a single glycine resulted in rescue of proα2(I) chains but overmodification of all the molecules synthesized.[252] Introduction of the mutant collagen gene into normal fertilized mouse eggs resulted in a lethal phenotype characterized by bone deformity similar to that seen in the OI type II phenotype.[252] This experiment demonstrated that a point mutation in one collagen allele was sufficient to produce the lethal phenotype, even when the amount of mRNA from that gene was less than 10 percent of the total collagen mRNA.

Integrating Mechanisms

The genetic, biochemical, and clinical heterogeneity of OI is striking both among families and, on occasion, within families. Despite the diversity of mutations encountered to date among individuals with different forms of OI, there is a reasonably good correlation between the clinical phenotype and the effects that the underlying molecular defect has on the structure and processing of type I procollagen molecules. First, mutations that affect the "expression" of the COL1A1 gene are milder in their phenotypic effects than those which affect the structure of the protein. The former generally result in the OI type I phenotype, the latter in the deforming varieties of OI. Mutations which affect the "expression" of the COL1A2 gene may be silent, at least in early life. Second, point mutations in the COL1A1 gene that result in substitutions for glycine residues in the triple-helical domain are, in general, much more severe in their phenotypic outcome than those that affect the COL1A2 gene. Mutations in COL1A1 generally produce the OI type II phenotype, while those in COL1A2 generally produce OI type IV. There are two features of the type I collagen molecule that explain this discrepancy: the roles of the α1(I) and α2(I) chains in the molecule are not identical, and the relative proportion of abnormal molecules is much greater with mutation in a COL1A1 allele. Third, there appears to be a gradient in the effect of mutation in the COL1A1 gene: the clinical phenotype is mildest for mutations that occur near the amino-terminal end of the triple helix and most severe if they occur near the carboxyl terminus. Mutation in the COL1A2 gene may not follow the same "end rule." The effect of the location of the mutation may be modulated by the nature of the mutation and, in the case of point mutations, the nature of the residue that substitutes for glycine. Fourth, large rearrangements (multiexon insertions and deletions) have proved to be lethal when expressed in chains that are incorporated into molecules. Fifth, the genetic background on which a mutation occurs may be very important in determining the phenotypic outcome. Finally, virtually all structural mutations and mutations that affect the "expression" of the COL1A1 gene result in recognizable phenotypes

in the heterozygous state. These generalizations suggest that the continuum of the OI clinical phenotype reflects the molecular lesions that underlie the disorder and imply that, although not always clear, there are rules that govern the genotype-phenotype relationships.

EHLERS-DANLOS SYNDROME

The Ehlers-Danlos syndrome (EDS) is a heterogeneous group of generalized connective tissue disorders, the major manifestations of which are skin fragility, skin hyperextensibility, and joint hypermobility (Table 115-4).[253,254] During the last several years, genetic and biochemical studies have defined more than 10 types of EDS, and the molecular bases of several of them have been identified. It is important to identify correctly the type of EDS with which a patient is affected, because the natural history and mode of inheritance differ among the types. For example, EDS type IV is often complicated by bowel and arterial rupture leading to a shortened life expectancy, while most other types are generally benign. Unfortunately, much of the older literature does not differentiate clearly among the types, and the complications of EDS type IV often are cited as characteristic of the syndrome as a whole.

This group of disorders has been recognized for many years, but the first formal medical descriptions appeared near the turn of the last century.[255–257] The early reports concentrated on the unusual features of the skin and on ocular abnormalities. The heterogeneity began to be appreciated about 30 years ago, and the modern classification was developed by Barabas[258] and Beighton in the late 1960s[259] on the basis of analysis of patients with these phenotypes. On clinical and genetic grounds, five separate groupings of patients were identified. Subsequent biochemical studies identified a sixth[143] and seventh type,[81] and further clinical and biochemical studies identified additional families with diverse findings, prompting the expansion of the syndrome.

EDS type VI, identified by Pinnell and his colleagues,[143] was the first of the human disorders of the structure or modification of collagen molecules to have the biochemical defect identified and is one of the few that affects, primarily, the posttranslational modification of the molecule.

Ehlers-Danlos Syndrome Type I (Gravis Variety), Ehlers-Danlos Syndrome Type II (Mitis Variety), and Ehlers-Danlos Syndrome Type III (Familial Hypermobility)

Clinical Presentations, Natural History, and Genetics. EDS type I is inherited in an autosomal dominant fashion, and affected individuals have markedly soft, velvety hyperextensible skin, impressive joint hypermobility, and easy bruising. They form thin, atrophic, "cigarette-paper" scars following trauma (Fig. 115-13). Trauma often results in gaping wounds which bleed less than expected. Areas of repeated trauma (elbows, knees, and shins) generally have pigment deposition in addition to scarring. Molluscoid pseudotumors, small accumulations of connective tissue, form in the skin, and some individuals have palpable subcutaneous calcified nodules. Varicose veins are common. As many as half the infants with EDS type I are born 4 to 8 weeks prematurely,[260] usually because of premature rupture of the membranes. The diagnosis of

Table 115-4 Clinical Features, Mode of Inheritance, and Biochemical Defects in the Ehlers-Danlos Syndrome

Type	Clinical features	Inheritance*	Biochemical defect
I, gravis	Soft, velvety, hyperextensible skin; easy bruising; "cigarette paper" scars; hypermobile joints; varicose veins; prematurity.	AD	Not known
II, mitis	Similar to EDS type I but less severe.	AD	Not known
III, familial hypermobility	Soft skin, no scarring, marked large and small joint hypermobility.	AD	Not known
IV, arterial	Thin, translucent skin with visible veins; marked bruising; skin and joints have normal extensibility; arterial, bowel, and uterine rupture.	AD	Abnormal type III collagen synthesis, secretion, or structure; deletions, and point mutations in the gene
		(AR)	(Not known)
V, X-linked	Similar to EDS type II.	XLR	Not known
VI, ocular	Soft, velvety, hyperextensible skin; hypermobile joints; scoliosis; ocular fragility and keratoconus.	AR	Lysyl hydroxylase deficiency
VII, arthrochalasis multiplex congenita	Congenital hip dislocation, joint hypermobility, soft skin with normal scarring.	AD	Deletion of exons from COL1A1 and COL1A2 genes that encode the amino-terminal conversion sites
VIII, periodontal	Generalized periodontitis, skin similar to EDS type II.	AD	Not known
IX, cutis laxa, bladder diverticula, occipital horns	Soft, extensible, lax skin; bladder diverticula and rupture; short arms with limited pronation and supination; broad clavicles; occipital horns.	XLR	Abnormal copper utilization with defect in lysyl oxidase
X, fibronectin defect	Similar to EDS type II.	AR	Defect in fibronectin

*AD = autosomal dominant; AR = autosomal recessive; XLR = X-linked recessive.

EDS type I can be made in newborns but more often is not considered until children begin to crawl and stand. At that time, joint hypermobility may become apparent and lead to concern about delay in motor development in some children because of a delay in walking. Early trauma from falling characteristically leads to scars on the forehead, shins, knees, elbows, and chin. Because of repeated trauma, easy bruising, and skin fragility, the families of children with EDS type I (and several other forms of EDS and OI) may be evaluated by social service agencies for evidence of child abuse. Many individuals with EDS type I have evidence of mitral prolapse, and a few may be symptomatic.[261] Structural cardiac defects are probably not more common than in the general population. Scoliosis is uncommon and usually limited to the lumbar spine. The increased joint mobility is often associated with early degenerative joint disease, apparently because of the alteration in the joint mechanics; the most effective therapy for this is non-weight-bearing exercises and mild anti-inflammatory agents.

Surgery in individuals with EDS type I may be complicated by increase in tissue friability and bleeding. Sutures should be left in about twice as long as usual to facilitate healing and decrease the likelihood of abnormal scar formation. The precise incidence of EDS type I is not known; estimates are on the order of 1 in 20,000. The life expectancy for individuals with EDS type I is normal.

EDS type II, also a dominantly inherited disorder, is characterized by joint laxity and by soft, hyperextensible, fragile skin. The phenotypic presentation is generally less severe than in EDS type I. Prematurity is rare, varicose veins are less frequent, and the skin is less fragile. Mitral valve prolapse is common, and some individuals with EDS type II develop premature degenerative arthritis. The biochemical basis of this disorder is not understood, but the morphologic alterations in dermal collagen fibers and fibrils are similar to those seen in EDS type I. It is not clear whether EDS types I and II are allelic mutations or mutations in different genes (for example, mutations in COL1A1 and COL1A2 that interfere with carboxyl-terminal propeptide cleavage). Linkage studies and additional biochemical investigations will be necessary before the molecular basis of these disorders can be elucidated.

EDS type III is a dominantly inherited disorder characterized by marked joint hypermobility, recurrent joint dislocation, and soft but not hyperextensible or fragile skin. Affected infants may be slow to walk because of joint laxity. The major complications of EDS type III are recurrent joint dislocation, which may require surgery for stabilization, and early onset degenerative joint disease. Mitral valve prolapse is seen frequently. EDS type III is probably the most common type of EDS, but precise figures are lacking, and discrimination from variants of normal is often difficult.

Treatment. There is no specific therapy for these three types of EDS. Dietary supplementation with ascorbic acid has been recommended with anecdotal reports of decreased bruising and a trend toward normalization of joint hypermobility. However, because joint mobility usually decreases with age, these reports are difficult to evaluate.

The major differential diagnosis for EDS types I and II includes EDS types V, VI, VIII, and X (see below). Perhaps there is a continuum of EDS type III phenotypes with variants of normal, and this distinction can be difficult.

Biochemical, Genetic, and Structural Studies. The biochemical bases of EDS types I, II, and III are not known. Genetic linkage studies using polymorphic endonuclease restriction sites in COL1A1, COL1A2, and COL2A1 have excluded those genes as sites of mutations in some families.[262] Nonetheless, biomechanical studies of skin fragments are suggestive of abnormal collagen in dermis.[263] Electron-microscopic studies of dermis have demonstrated larger than normal collagen fibrils, frequent composite fibrils, and smaller than normal bundles[264,265] (Fig. 115-14). While these studies indicate an abnormality in the formation of the usual dermal collagen structures, they do not identify the specific biochemical abnormality.

Cells from one patient with EDS type I were found to have abnormalities in the biosynthesis of proteoglycans and in the conversion of type I procollagen to collagen.[266] We have identified several individuals with EDS whose cultured dermal fibroblastic cells do not efficiently cleave the carboxyl-terminal

Fig. 115-14 Morphological appearance of collagen fibrils in skin of an individual with Ehlers-Danlos syndrome type I. Fibrils are larger than control and there are frequent "composite" structures (arrows). The morphological appearance of collagen in skin from individuals with EDS types II, III, VI and X is similar to that shown here. The abnormal fibrils may be seen in other conditions. (*Courtesy of Dr. Karen A. Holbrook, University of Washington.*)

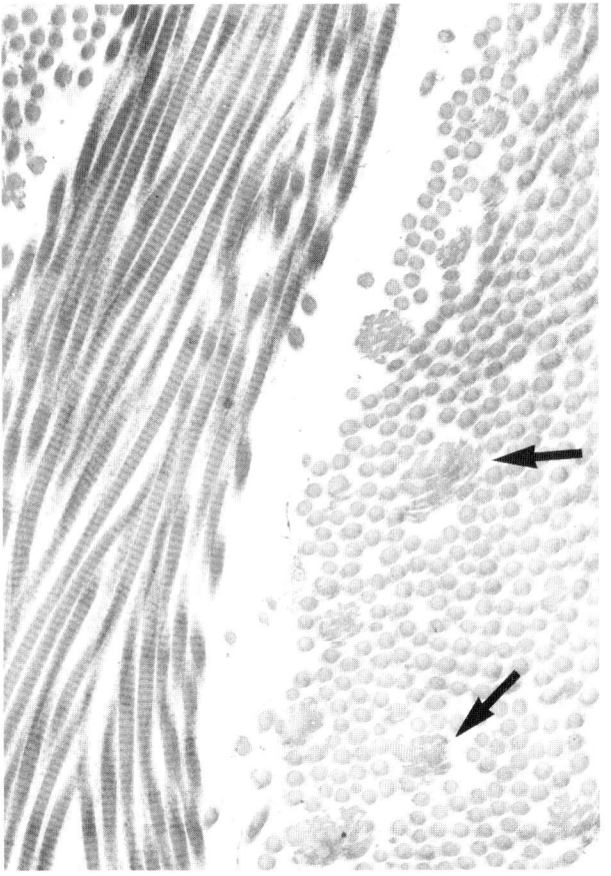

propeptide extension from the type I procollagen molecule (unpublished observations). However, it is not clear whether failure of cleavage is the result of an abnormal enzyme, a defective substrate, or biologic variation. Recently one man has been described who has joint hypermobility, hyperextensible skin, and aortic root dilatation whose cultured dermal fibroblasts failed to synthesize $proα2(I)$ chains, and, as a result, the cells secreted type I procollagen that contained only $proα1(I)$ chains.[267] This is a particularly intriguing patient because of the previous description of a child with OI type III and a similar molecular phenotype.[220] The cells from the man with a form of EDS did not synthesize any $proα2(I)$ chains, whereas those from the boy with OI type III synthesized chains that were not incorporated into molecules. Failure to synthesize $proα2(I)$ chains appears to be rare among individuals with EDS types I and II; the presence of aortic dilatation suggests that this clinical entity may be better considered as a variety of the Marfan syndrome (see below).

The ultrastructural appearance of dermal collagen from individuals with EDS types II and III is similar to that from patients with EDS type I. There are no biochemical or linkage studies that provide further clues to the nature of the biochemical defects in these disorders.

Ehlers-Danlos Syndrome Type IV, Vascular or Ecchymotic Type

Clinical Presentation, Natural History, and Genetics. EDS type IV was recognized as a distinct entity by Barabas in 1967,[261] although Sack[268] and Gottron[269] had probably described the same entity a quarter of a century previously. The biochemical basis of the disorder was first recognized in 1975.[270] This is a rare form of EDS and estimates of its prevalence range from 1 in 100,000 to less than 1 in 1 million.[271] The disorder is generally inherited in an autosomal dominant fashion,[272] but frequently there may be single affected individuals in families; it has been proposed that autosomal recessive forms also exist.[273,274] Affected individuals have thin, translucent skin through which the venous pattern over the trunk, abdomen, and extremities is visible (Fig. 115-15). They also have marked bruising and minimal joint hypermobility which may be limited to the small joints of the hands and feet. The skin over the face often has a parchmentlike appearance, and in some individuals there is an aged or acrogeric character to the hands and feet (in the older European literature some individuals with acrogeria probably have EDS type IV). There is an "EDS type IV facies" that is characterized by a "stare," a very thin nose, and the tight-skinned appearance.[274] Venous varicosities are frequent, may be severe, and appear at a young age. Even in families in which children are known to be at 50 percent risk, it is often difficult to make the diagnosis on clinical grounds in childhood unless bruising is severe or the venous pattern is particularly noticeable. Many individuals with EDS type IV are first thought to have disorders of coagulation because of the marked bruising.

The major clinical complications of EDS type IV are arterial rupture, spontaneous rupture of the colon, and rupture of the gravid uterus;[275] some individuals may experience all three. There does not appear to be a familial predilection for gastrointestinal complications, arterial rupture, or uterine tears. The age of first involvement may vary from late childhood to the seventh decade, although death from complications in the third and fourth decade is most common.

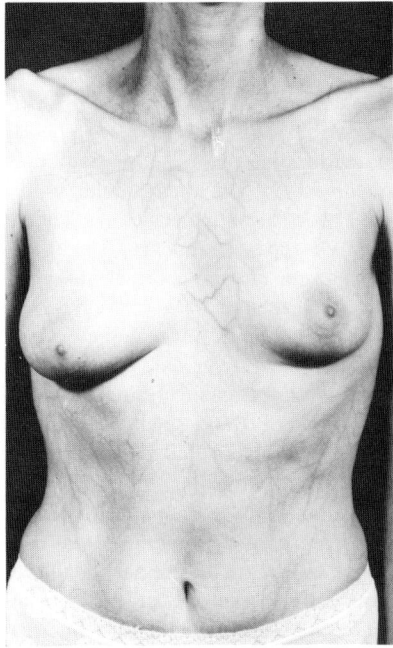

A.

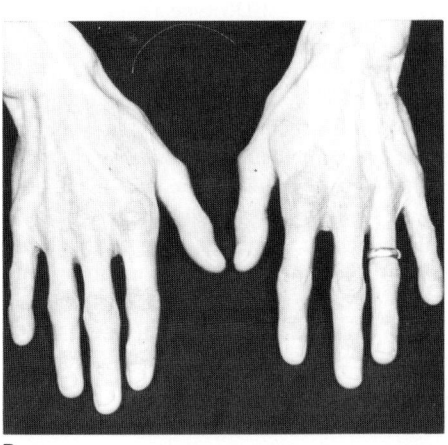

B.

Fig. 115-15 Clinical features of Ehlers-Danlos syndrome type IV. *A.* The venous vasculature of the chest and abdomen is remarkably apparent in this 26-year-old woman with EDS type IV. *B.* Her hands have the aged appearance of acrogeria. (*From Byers et al.*[281] *with permission of Human Genetics.*)

The location of arterial hemorrhage determines the presenting symptoms: stroke, intra-abdominal or intrathoracic bleeding, or limb compartment syndrome. The most common locations of arterial bleeding are in the abdominal cavity and involve the smaller arteries rather than the aorta itself. In some individuals there is evidence of aneurysm formation, while in others the vessels appear normal by angiography. Arterial rupture accounts for most deaths in EDS type IV because: it is frequent, hemorrhage from the involved vessels is rapid, and repair is difficult due to the markedly friable tissues. Surgical repair is possible but depends on early recognition of the cause of hypotension, the rapid ability to distinguish arterial bleeding from rupture of the gastrointestinal tract, and rapid and appropriate intervention.

Several individuals with EDS type IV have been described with carotid–cavernous sinus fistula formation and resultant unilateral exophthalmos.[276,277] Surgical repair or embolization has been attempted with success in some.

Rupture of the distal colon, usually in the sigmoid, is the

most common of the bowel problems. In some individuals it has been possible to identify diverticula opposite the mesenteric border, but the bowel surface appears normal in most. The clinical presentation of bowel rupture is similar to that in individuals without EDS type IV, and the surgical approach should be the same. Tissue friability and soiling of the peritoneal space are the major impediments to repair and rapid recovery. The degree of tissue friability differs among individuals and even in the same individual with aging. Descriptions of tissues with the physical characteristics of wet blotting paper are not uncommon in surgical reports. Assiduous attention to surgical technique and lavage of the peritoneal cavity with instillation of antibiotics and parenteral antibiotic therapy frequently permit rapid recovery. Following repair, recurrence of bowel rupture has been seen in some individuals. The likelihood of repeated episodes can be minimized by removal of the distal two-thirds of the colon.

Rupture of the small bowel is very rare, but recurrent abdominal pain during childhood, adolescence, and adult life may result from mural hemorrhage. Bowel function is generally not compromised by these episodes, although occasionally regions of mural fibrosis are observed at surgery or at autopsy in individuals with EDS type IV.

Uterine rupture is a relatively rare complication of EDS type IV and generally occurs in the last 2 months of pregnancy or during labor.[275] Uterine rupture in labor is accompanied by marked increase in abdominal pain, rapid loss of vascular volume, virtual cessation of labor, and loss of fetal heart tones. Prompt surgical intervention is the only lifesaving technique, and rapid recognition of the condition is necessary. More commonly, uterine rupture is not recognized and leads to maternal and infant death. Although infrequent, the possibility of this occurrence warrants close following of all pregnancies in women with EDS type IV. Delivery should be in a tertiary care medical center with careful monitoring during labor. The complications of pregnancy, in addition to vascular rupture and uterine rupture, include tearing of vaginal tissues during delivery. In one series,[275] the risk of life-threatening or lethal complications during pregnancy was nearly 15 percent, and almost 20 percent of the women in that series died as a result of complications of pregnancy. The absence of such complications in another series suggested that complications of pregnancy may vary in frequency in different populations.[278]

Other complications of EDS type IV include keratoconus (identified in three families)[279] and periodontal disease.

The life span of individuals with EDS type IV is generally shorter than that of their unaffected sibs. Deaths in the third through the fifth decades are the rule, with survival beyond 50 years of age being rare. We have documented the condition in a man who died at age 60 during attempted coronary artery bypass surgery.

Although initially thought to be an autosomal recessive disorder,[273] Ehlers-Danlos syndrome type IV is generally inherited in an autosomal dominant fashion. Of the more than two dozen individuals we have identified through biochemical testing, about half have had family histories compatible with EDS type IV, and the remainder are the first affected individuals in their families. The range of biochemical abnormalities in the two groups is similar. Because of the autosomal dominant mode of transmission, linkage analysis using polymorphic restriction sites in the COL3A1 gene can be used to identify individuals with the affected allele and has the potential for use in prenatal diagnosis.[275] Analysis of the type III collagen synthesized and secreted by cells from chorionic villus biopsies may facilitate prenatal diagnosis in pregnancies in which linkage studies are not informative.

Clinical Management. When suspected, the diagnosis of EDS type IV can be confirmed by measuring the amount of type III collagen in skin or by examining the biosynthesis of type III procollagen by cultured dermal fibroblasts. The differentiation of this type of EDS from others is important because of the nature of the complications and the importance of prompt surgical intervention. It is unfortunate that the complications that characterize EDS type IV are sometimes cited in texts as characteristic of other types of EDS. No medical treatment is available currently to increase the production of normal type III collagen. The important elements of clinical management are prompt recognition of the major complications of the disorder, patient education, and clear communication between the patient and physician. We often provide patients with a letter that summarizes the important complications and urge them to carry the letter on extended travel out of their local area.

Biochemical, Ultrastructural, and Genetic Studies. EDS type IV results from abnormalities in the structure, synthesis, or secretion of type III procollagen.[254] At the ultrastructural level, tissues (especially dermis and vessels) from most individuals with EDS type IV have abnormal collagen fibrils and fiber bundles.[280] The dermis is often thin, collagen fiber bundles are small, and fibril diameters are either uniformly small or have marked variation in diameter.[281] Elastic fibers are abundant because of the decreased amount of collagen in the dermis. In many patients, dermal fibroblasts have markedly dilated rough endoplasmic reticulum[281,282] (Fig. 115-16).

Fig. 115-16 Morphological appearance of fibroblasts in skin of the woman with EDS type IV shown in Fig. 115-15. There is marked dilatation of the rough endoplasmic reticulum with a form of type III procollagen that cannot be secreted. *(Courtesy of Dr. Karen A. Holbrook, University of Washington.)*

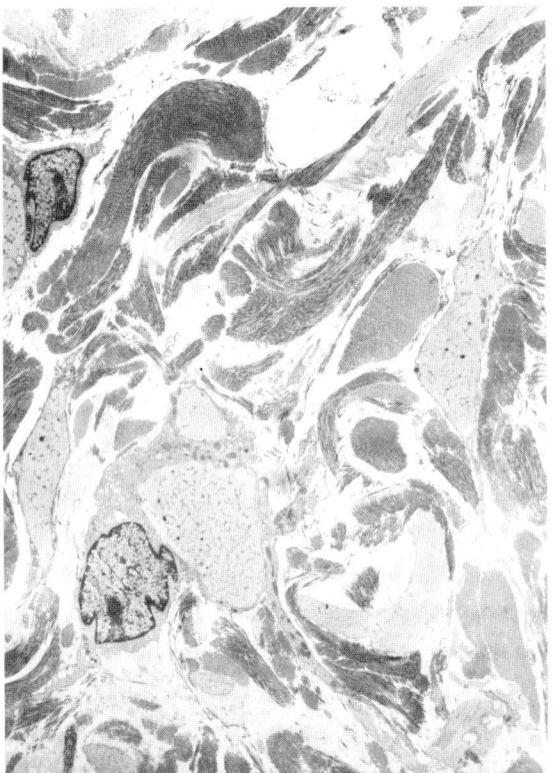

In the autosomal dominant forms of EDS type IV, the biochemical abnormalities are heterogeneous. Cells from some individuals in some families synthesize an apparently normal amount of type III procollagen but secrete about 10 to 15 percent of the normal amount.[283,284] The nonsecreted type III procollagen is sequestered within the rough endoplasmic reticulum, where it is overmodified (in a manner similar to the handling of abnormal type I procollagen molecules synthesized by cells from infants with OI type II) and very slowly degraded. There is virtual exclusion of the abnormal molecules from the extracellular space, and the abnormal molecules have a decreased thermal stability. Although none of these molecules has been more extensively characterized, it now seems likely that point mutations (that result in substitutions for glycine residues within the triple helix) and small deletions or insertions that interrupt the triple helix could all result in the same biochemical phenotype.

In other families, multiexon deletions from one COL3A1 allele result in inefficient secretion of the molecules that contain the shortened chain and a decrease in thermal stability of those molecules.[285,286] Incubation of the cells at 30°C can increase the secretion of molecules that contain the abnormal chain for some, but not all, mutations.[286]

In another family in which the EDS type IV phenotype is inherited in an autosomal dominant fashion, cultured cells from one individual synthesized type III procollagen molecules that contained chains with a small insertion in one domain.[287] In contrast to some other cell strains, these cells secreted the molecules that contained the abnormal chains as efficiently as those that contained only normal chains.

Studies of additional cell strains[288] demonstrate a marked reduction in the extracellular accumulation of type III collagen and procollagen but little accumulation of abnormal procollagen within the cells. A plausible explanation for such findings is the instability of the molecules that contain one or more mutant chains and their rapid intracellular degradation. Because type III procollagen is a homotrimer, such a mechanism would result in loss of 85 percent of the newly synthesized protein if all molecules that contained at least one mutant chain were degraded.

The molecular findings in EDS type IV parallel those in the several forms of OI. Because of difficulty in quantitating the synthesis and secretion of type III procollagen, it is not clear that the EDS type IV phenotype can result from mutations that result in "functional deletion" of one COL3A1 allele. In other respects, however, it is remarkable that many different types of mutations in the COL3A1 gene result in a single phenotype that exhibits little clinical variability. This contrasts with the wide range of variability seen in OI with different mutations in the COL1A1 and COL1A2 genes. It is possible that certain mutations in the COL3A1 genes are not clinically apparent early in life and lead to mild phenotypes that are difficult to delineate.

Ehlers-Danlos Syndrome Type V

Clinical Features, Natural History, and Genetics. EDS type V is an X-linked disorder clinically similar to EDS type II except that intramuscular hemorrhage is a common finding.[289,290] The disorder is apparently rare; the life span is probably normal, and female carriers are asymptomatic. As indicated above, genetic counseling for an isolated case of EDS in a moderately affected male should include the possibility of an X-linked disorder. In general, if EDS type VI can be excluded (see below), then the most likely diagnosis is EDS type II, given the apparent rarity of EDS type V.

Biochemical Studies. There has been considerable confusion surrounding the molecular basis of this disorder, which is not currently known. In one family, thought to have a variant of EDS type V, lysyl oxidase activity in the medium of cultured dermal fibroblasts from two of the patients was found to be decreased;[291] however, the methods used to measure the enzyme were probably not reliable.[127] In studies of cells from members of the two original families with EDS type V, the activity of lysyl oxidase in the medium was normal.[292] No studies of copper or ceruloplasmin levels have been reported, so it is not clear if this condition could be allelic with EDS type IX or Menkes disease (see "EDS Type IX," below).

Ehlers-Danlos Syndrome Type VI

Clinical Features, Natural History, and Genetics. Individuals with EDS type VI, an autosomal recessive condition,[143,293] have soft and hyperextensible skin, joint hypermobility, scoliosis, ocular fragility, and a marfanoid habitus (Fig. 115-17). Microcornea and recurrent intraocular bleeding with resultant blindness are major features in some patients. Some children have been identified because of delay in reaching major motor milestones, the result of marked joint laxity. Others have been identified by screening of sporadically affected individuals with EDS for decreased amounts of hydroxylysine in skin. The disorder is rare, and about a dozen families have been identified.[143,294–300]

Because of the relatively small number of affected individuals identified so far, the natural history of the disorder is not well understood. Three major complications have been identified: severe kyphoscoliosis which may be resistant to external bracing or surgical intervention, blindness from repeated retinal hemorrhage or rupture of the globe, and death from aortic

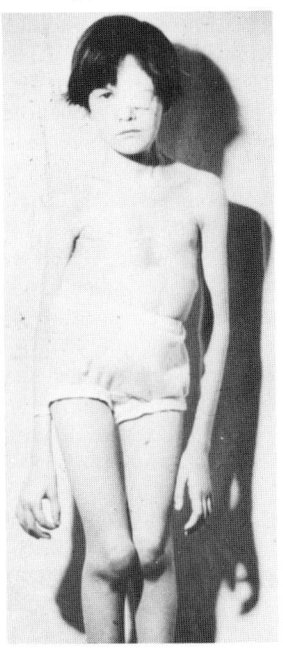

Fig. 115-17 Clinical appearance of the index patient with Ehlers-Danlos syndrome type VI. (*Courtesy of Dr. Sheldon Pinnell, Duke University.*)

rupture. Kyphoscoliosis is common among children identified because of developmental delay, but it is not clear that it represents a universal accompaniment of the biochemical disorder. When severe, the kyphoscoliosis can lead to cardiopulmonary failure, and death has been reported in the third decade.[298] The index patient with EDS type VI suffered rupture of the ocular globe from minimal trauma,[144] and retinal hemorrhage and gastrointestinal hemorrhage have been known to affect others with EDS type VI. The proband in the second family identified with EDS type VI died in her sixth decade as a result of intra-abdominal arterial rupture.[301]

The phenotype may be genetically heterogeneous because one family has been identified in which two affected male sibs with normal parents have skin and joint manifestations of EDS and are blind from retinal hemorrhage, yet both have normal levels of lysyl hydroxylation in skin collagen and normal levels of lysyl hydroxylase enzyme in cultured cells.[302]

Clinical Management and Prenatal Diagnosis. Because of the apparent frequency of severe kyphoscoliosis and accompanying cardiorespiratory complications, the complications of retinal hemorrhage and fragility of the ocular globe, and the autosomal recessive mode of inheritance of EDS type VI, it is important that this diagnosis be considered in all sporadic individuals with a compatible phenotype (e.g., in EDS types II, V, and X) and that appropriate testing be undertaken. The orthopedic management of scoliosis should follow accepted orthopedic practice. The efficacy of bracing and of surgical intervention is not yet established. Routine eye examination should be recommended because of the relatively high incidence of intraocular bleeding, keratoconus, and fragility of the globe. While no specific therapy has been demonstrated to be effective, the use of pharmacologic doses of ascorbic acid, a cofactor for lysyl hydroxylase, has been advocated, and an increase in urinary excretion of hydroxylysine has been found following long-term treatment with the vitamin.[295]

Prenatal diagnosis by measurement of lysyl hydroxylase enzyme activity in amniotic fluid cells has been attempted in one family at risk, and the birth of an unaffected but heterozygous infant was correctly predicted.[296] Amniotic fluid cells synthesize amounts of lysyl hydroxylase that are similar to those synthesized by dermal fibroblasts.[296]

Biochemical Studies. The EDS type VI phenotype results from markedly decreased activity of the enzyme lysyl hydroxylase.[143] The posttranslational hydroxylation of lysyl residues in types I and III collagens in skin is markedly reduced, but that of type II collagen in cartilage is normal or near normal in tissues from affected individuals in which it has been measured.[143] The residual enzyme appears to be almost normally efficient in the hydroxylation of lysyl residues in type IV collagen.[303] Differential lysyl hydroxylation of collagen types in individuals with EDS type VI could be explained by different affinities of a single enzyme for the specific collagens or by the presence of collagen type-specific lysyl hydroxylases. Isolation and characterization of the gene that encodes the mutant enzyme should determine whether there is more than a single enzyme.

Residual enzyme activity in the cells of affected individuals ranges from virtually unmeasurable to 10 to 15 percent of normal.[298,304] Enzyme levels in cells from obligate heterozygotes range from about 40 to 70 percent of control levels. Levels of lysyl hydroxylation of skin collagen also vary. In most individuals, fewer than 5 percent of available hydroxylatable lysyl residues are modified, but almost 50 percent are modified in some.[294] The range of enzyme activities in the cells from affected individuals and the range of substrate modifications in skin suggest that the mutations in the disorder are heterogeneous. Furthermore, because consanguinity is not a common feature of families with EDS type VI, it is likely that many or most affected individuals are compound heterozygotes for mutations in the gene that encodes lysyl hydroxylase. The nature of the defect in the enzyme is not yet understood, although biochemical studies suggest that abnormalities of substrate binding and of cofactor binding or utilization may be present in different individuals.

Decreased hydroxylation of lysyl residues in type I collagen interferes with the formation of normal cross-links among collagen molecules.[305] Although cross-links form in the absence of lysyl hydroxylation, the lysine-derived cross-links are not as stable as those derived from hydroxylysine and do not mature as readily to the multicomponent intermolecular links that stabilize molecular interactions on a larger scale.[97] Presumably, the clinical phenotype results from the absence of the more complex cross-links.

The diagnosis of EDS type VI is established by demonstration of a decreased content of hydroxylysine in dermal collagen and confirmed by assay of lysyl hydroxylase in cultured dermal fibroblasts. It is very difficult to demonstrate a decrease in hydroxylation of lysyl residues by cultured fibroblasts, because the level of collagen hydroxylation in cultured cells is higher than that in vivo. The lack of collagen hydroxylation does not appear to affect the stability or the transport of procollagen through the cell machinery or into the extracellular space. There is no effect on prolyl hydroxylation, although the enzymes have similar substrate requirements. The defective hydroxylation does appear to affect the normal incorporation of type I collagen into fibrils which, in skin, have a bizarre branching organization similar to that seen in EDS type I.

Ehlers-Danlos Syndrome Type VII

Natural History and Genetics. EDS type VII, also known as *arthrochalasis multiplex congenita*, is characterized by marked joint hypermobility, multiple joint dislocations, and congenital hip dislocation, usually bilateral (Fig. 115-18). The hip dislocation is often difficult to reduce, even with surgery. Mild to moderate short stature is seen in some individuals in whom mild midface hypoplasia is present. The precise prevalence of the condition is not known, but it is probably rare. Bilateral hip dislocation is one of the more frequent birth defects in the general population (with an incidence of approximately 1 in 500 live births), but only a small proportion of those infants have EDS type VII. All but one of the described individuals is an isolated case; there is one example of autosomal dominant inheritance,[306] but the biochemical studies in all the studied individuals are entirely compatible with the disorder being the result of dominant mutations (see below).

The major complications of EDS type VII are those which result from long-term instability of joints and failure to make a normal hip joint. There is insufficient follow-up of those children known to be affected to determine if the degenerative joint disease is sufficient to warrant early hip replacement.

Biochemical Abnormalities and Molecular Genetics. Initially, EDS type VII was thought to result from abnormalities

in the enzyme which cleaves the amino-terminal propeptide extension from type I procollagen,[81] analogous to a recessively inherited disorder in cattle, sheep, and cats.[143, 307–309] Restudy of some of the original patients and detailed study of collagens synthesized by cells from several new patients have demonstrated that, instead, the mutations involve the cleavage sites of the substrate proα1(I) and proα2(I) chains.[310–313] In two patients, the exon which contains the amino-terminal cleavage site in proα2(I) is not represented in the protein derived from one allele;[310–313] a similar defect in the proα1(I) chain has been characterized.[312] In cultured cells, it is possible to recognize both a defect in the rate of conversion of procollagen to collagen and retention of molecules that contain amino-terminal propeptide extensions. In order to identify such an abnormality, it is generally necessary to add agents such as polyethylene glycol to the culture medium to concentrate the procollagen and increase the normal rate of conversion. The mutations which delete the exon that contains the substrate site have an anomalous effect on the protein when treated with pepsin, because the deletion fuses the minor and major triple helices and removes the pepsin-sensitive site, preventing cleavage of the chain.

In four patients, the mutation has been identified at the genomic level and shown to result in the efficient excision from the mRNA of the sequence of the entire exon that contains the propeptide cleavage site.[314] In three individuals, the mutation changes a single nucleotide at the splice junction site near the 3' end of the exon. In contrast to mutations in some other genes which result in "leaky" read-through of the mutant sequence, those that involve the collagen sequence appear to be very "tight." In most families, a single individual is affected with EDS type VII; there is at least one family in which the condition is inherited in an autosomal dominant fashion. The biochemical nature of the defect in other families predicts that it would be inherited in an autosomal dominant fashion as well. Search for a recessively inherited form of EDS type VII, presumably due to mutations in the enzyme responsible for cleavage of the amino-terminal propeptide extension of type I procollagen, has been inconclusive.[315] It has been suggested that the condition in cattle, dermatosparaxis, may result from a more generalized defect in processing of proteins destined for extracellular transport, the amino-terminal propeptidase among them, so that the severity of the condition may not result only from a defect in the enzyme.[316] The human condition EDS type VII is much less severe than dermatosparaxis, in which skin fragility is very pronounced and affected calves generally die from infection of skin tears.

Deletion of the exon that encodes the amino-terminal procollagen peptidase cleavage site has several effects on the molecule: it deletes the site of cleavage in one chain, it throws into disarray the amino-terminal cleavage site in molecules which incorporate the abnormal chain, and it removes a lysyl residue in the telopeptide extension that is frequently hydroxylated and involved in intermolecular cross-links. When the mutation occurs in the COL1A2 gene, there appears to be relatively little effect on fibril formation in the dermis. In contrast, a mutation in the COL1A1 gene results in formation of irregular fibrils[317] reminiscent of the bizarre fibrils seen in tissues from dermatosparaxic animals. It is likely that the phenotypic effect of the mutations derives from alterations in cross-link formation and fibrillogenesis that result in decreased tensile strength of most tissues made up principally of type I collagen.

A.

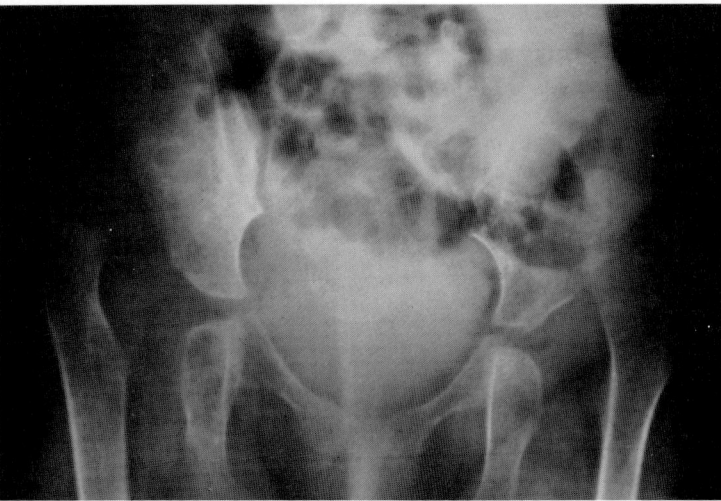

B.

C.

Fig. 115-18 Ehlers-Danlos syndrome type VII. *A.* Clinical features of young girl with EDS type VII that results from heterozygous deletion of the amino acid sequences encoded by exon 6 of the COL1A1 gene; the deletion removes the amino-terminal procollagen protease cleavage site. She has mild midface hypoplasia and markedly lax ligaments. *B.* Radiograph of bilateral hip dislocation. *C.* Morphologic appearance of collagen fibrils in the child's skin. Note the unusual structure. *(Courtesy of Dr. William Cole, Royal Children's Hospital, Melbourne.)*

Prenatal diagnosis has not been attempted, but the ready demonstration that the abnormal collagen can be detected in molecules synthesized by cells from affected individuals suggests that analysis of collagen synthesized by chorionic villus cells from fetuses at risk for the condition would yield diagnostic findings. Alternatively, in families in which the condition is inherited in an autosomal dominant fashion, linkage analysis could be of diagnostic value.

Ehlers-Danlos Syndrome Type VIII

EDS type VIII is characterized by soft and hyperextensible skin, bruising, hypermobile joints, and periodontal disease.[318,319] The disorder is inherited in an autosomal dominant fashion. Loss of teeth, as a result of marked periodontal involvement, is common by the third decade. EDS type VIII is rare, but no prevalence figures are available; only a few families have been described. No biochemical defects have been identified.

Ehlers-Danlos Syndrome Type IX

Natural History and Genetics. EDS type IX is a rare X-linked recessive disorder characterized by lax and soft skin at birth, development of bladder diverticula during childhood (which may be complicated by hydronephrosis and hydroureter) (Fig. 115-19), and appearance of bony occipital horns during adolescence.[320–322] The bladder diverticula may rupture, and some patients have required low pressure drainage to maintain bladder integrity. Although the males with this disorder are of normal height, skeletal deformities, including short humeri, partial radioulnar synostosis which limits pronation and supination, and short, broad clavicles are apparent on clinical and radiologic examination. Most affected males have a mild chronic diarrhea which appears to result from a defect in bowel motility, and some have orthostatic hypotension, which may be symptomatic. Intellectual function is generally normal when measured, but some of the affected males have required educational assistance, and moderate mental retardation was apparent in at least one male.[323] Carrier

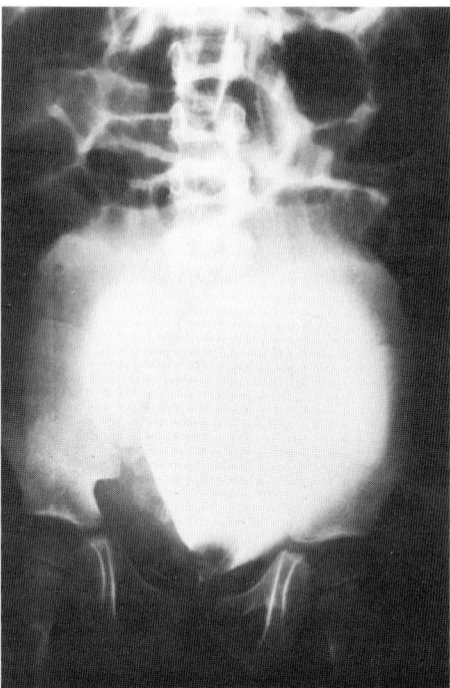

Fig. 115-19 Bladder diverticula in a 6-year-old child with Ehlers-Danlos syndrome type IX.

females have, so far, been unaffected by any of the phenotypic manifestations of the condition. Life span is probably normal.

Biochemical Findings. The basic defect in EDS type IX has not been determined but, like infants with the Menkes kinky hair syndrome, affected males have a defect in distribution of the intracellular copper to the apoenzymes into which it is integrated.[324–326] In EDS type IX, the major effect of this defect is a decrease in the activity of the copper-dependent enzyme lysyl oxidase.[321,326] Lysyl oxidase catalyzes the oxidation of lysyl residues in collagen (and elastin) to form cross-link precursors. Cells from these patients have a normal rate of copper uptake, but have very high intracellular levels and do not permit the normal efflux of copper bound to copper enzymes. Lysyl oxidase levels and activity in extracellular fluid are extremely low, and the formation of cross-links in collagen and elastin is correspondingly decreased. The virtually unmeasurable lysyl oxidase in tissue from some patients may reflect the marked instability of the apoenzyme in the absence of copper.[132] No other enzymes have been measured in cells or tissues of affected individuals, but it is likely that defects in other copper-dependent enzymes will be found to account for the altered bowel motility and the orthostatic hypotension.

The diagnosis of EDS type IX is generally suspected on clinical grounds and confirmed when serum copper and ceruloplasmin levels are found to be well below the normal range.

There have been no studies on therapeutic intervention, but all attempts in the Menkes syndrome, with which EDS type IX may be allelic, have been unsuccessful (see Chap. 54). Prenatal diagnosis in candidate families can probably be achieved by measurement of copper uptake and release by amniotic fluid cells, and the potential exists for linkage analysis in some families.

Ehlers-Danlos Syndrome Type X

EDS type X is inherited in an autosomal recessive fashion and is characterized by mild joint hypermobility and easy bruising. The disorder appears to result from an alteration in fibronectin which interferes with normal platelet aggregation.[327] Only one family has been identified to date.

Approach to Patients with EDS

Many patients with EDS-like clinical findings do not fit the general classification scheme. As more biochemical studies are completed, it is likely that the classification will expand. From the clinical point of view, the important considerations are whether the patient has a condition inherited in an autosomal dominant, autosomal recessive, or X-linked recessive fashion, and whether the natural history can be predicted from family studies or biochemical studies. It is vital to distinguish the known, well-characterized recessively inherited disorder EDS type VI, because prenatal diagnosis is avaliable and because orthopedic and ophthalmologic management differ from those in other varieties. It is important to identify patients with EDS type IV so that clear discussion of pregnancy risks and of problems in surgery can take place before an emergency arises. Biochemical studies of collagens synthesized by fibroblastic cells cultured from dermal punch biopsies can identify patients with EDS type IV and EDS type VI and some patients with EDS type VII. Low serum copper and ceruloplasmin levels identify patients with EDS type IX. In the near future, it is likely that defects in collagen processing or abnormalities of the structure or synthesis of other matrix macromolecules will be identified in patients with EDS types I and II. Research in these areas is underway.

Animal Models of EDS

Mink, cats, and dogs with clinical features of the EDS type I phenotype have been identified and studied in several laboratories.[328–330] These animals have lax joints and hyperextensible skin. Fibril structure in dermal collagen is similar to that in people with EDS type I in that mean fibril diameter is large, most fibrils are irregular, and there is an abundance of composite fibrils.[328] The disorder is inherited in an autosomal dominant fashion in those species, but the molecular basis of the disorder is not known in any.

Dermatosparaxis, an autosomal recessive disorder of the conversion of type I procollagen to collagen, has been identified in cattle, sheep, and cats. In each group, the amino-terminal processing of type I procollagen is abnormal as a result of an abnormal enzyme. The disorder has been studied most extensively in cattle and sheep. In cattle the disorder was long thought to result from a defect in procollagen amino-protease, but recent studies have suggested that a more generalized disorder of glycosylation may interfere with the secretion of the enzyme and result in accumulation of type I procollagen that retains amino-terminal extensions (pN-collagen).[316] Dermatosparaxis in cattle was the first disorder of collagen processing that was identified, and this disease has provided numerous lessons: (1) it was recognized that collagens were initially synthesized as precursors; (2) study of the disease led to the isolation, characterization, and sequence determination of the amino-terminal propeptide extensions of proα1(I) and proα2(I) chains; and (3) observations suggest that the propeptides may be involved in feedback regulation of collagen synthesis.[81] Neither the sheep nor the cats have been as extensively characterized. The clinical features of animals with dermatosparaxis differ from those of people with EDS type VII. Animals do have lax joints, but the fragility of their skin is striking, and a similar phenotype has not been characterized among humans with forms of EDS. It is possible that the human clinical counterpart of dermatosparaxis would not be considered as a variant of EDS.

Mice with several alleles at the X-chromosomal *mottled* locus have defects in copper metabolism and connective tissue abnormalities.[331,332] One group dies within a few days of birth as a result of severe central nervous system abnormalities and appears to be similar to infants with the Menkes syndrome.[333] In others, there is a gradient of connective tissue abnormalities that is similar to those identified in individuals with EDS type IX.[334,335] Lysyl oxidase deficiency and alteration in collagen cross-link formation have been demonstrated in mice with the *viable brindle* and *tortoise* alleles.[332] In all mice there are defects in the redistribution of copper from cells, and the different phenotypes probaby reflect the efficiency with which copper is provided to the various apoenzymes.[336] The phenotypic diversity probably reflects the clinical spectrum seen in EDS type IX and Menkes syndrome.

Integrating Mechanisms

The clinical heterogeneity within the Ehlers-Danlos syndrome is explained, in part, by the nature of the mutation and the molecules in which mutations occur. EDS type IV is readily distinguished from all the other varieties by the clinical presentation and natural history, and is the only type that results from mutations in the genes that encode the chains of type III collagen. In contrast to the different forms of OI, the nature and location of the mutations in the COL3A1 gene are not reflected as clearly in clinical heterogeneity. Although included among the EDS phenotypes for historical reasons, the involvement of a gene other than those that encode the chains of type I collagen clearly distinguishes EDS type IV from some other forms.

The clinical phenotypes of EDS types VI, VII, and IX reflect the disruption in formation of intermolecular cross-links in isolation or in conjunction with alterations in other functional domains of type I and other collagens or effects on other gene products. In EDS type VI the phenotype reflects the differential stability of cross-links that contain hydroxylysine instead of lysine in addition to a collagen-specific effect of the deficiency of lysyl hydroxylase enzyme activity. In EDS type VII, deletion of a lysyl residue involved in cross-link formation is additive with deletion of the propeptide cleavage sequence, and both contribute to a phenotype. Finally, in EDS type IX, defective cross-link formation because of aberrant enzyme activity (which results from lack of available copper) occurs on the background of other enzymatic deficiencies (in copper-dependent enzymes).

In all other forms of EDS, the underlying abnormalities are unknown, but the physical properties of tissues suggest that there are alterations in the effective formation of normal cross-links. It is likely that mutations in genes that encode the chains of type I collagen and in those that encode proteins that interact with collagens in tissues will result in similar phenotypes.

Because of the heterogeneity of the molecular species that are important to normal fibril formation and the production of normal tissue tensile strength, it is not possible to derive "molecular rules" in the same way as for OI.

OTHER CANDIDATES FOR DISORDERS OF TYPE I COLLAGEN METABOLISM

Marfan Syndrome

The only heritable disorder of connective tissue metabolism that has been identified as a possible additional example of disease caused by mutations in the genes of type I collagen is the Marfan syndrome.[337]

Clinical Features, Natural History, and Genetics. Marfan syndrome is a clinically and biochemically heterogeneous disorder characterized by ocular abnormalities (myopia and lens dislocation), skeletal disproportion (tall stature, dolichostenomelia, arachnodactyly, scoliosis, and pectus deformities), cardiovascular abnormalities (mitral valve prolapse and aortic aneurysm and dissection), and autosomal dominant inheritance. About 80 percent of individuals documented to have the Marfan syndrome by reasonably strict criteria inherited the gene from a parent; in the remaining 20 percent the condition arises as a result of new mutations.

The condition was first identified by Marfan in the late nineteenth century,[338] although Hecht and Beals[339] have suggested that he may have identified a condition now known as *contractural arachnodactyly*. The orthopedic complications were identified early, the ocular abnormalities were identified in the 1940s,[340] and the cardiovascular complications began to receive attention when studied by McKusick in the 1950s.[341] Since that time a number of conditions have been recognized that share features with the Marfan syndrome but appear to have different natural histories. These include homocystinuria, a recessively inherited disorder of amino acid metabolism first identified in 1962[342,343] (see Chap. 23); contractural arachnodactyly,[344] distinguished by tight joints rather than joint laxity and lacking the high likelihood of aortic dissection; and the mitral valve prolapse syndrome,[345] which has many of the skeletal characteristics of the syndrome but lacks the ocular findings and the complications of aortic dissection.

From a clinical point of view, the major concern in the Marfan syndrome is the premature death that results from aortic dissection and circulatory collapse. The median age of death in the Marfan syndrome in the only detailed study[346] was the mid-40s, and more than 95 percent of the deaths results from cardiovascular complications. During the last 10 years, the clinical approach to these catastrophic complications has changed. Two forms of intervention have been proposed, prophylactic replacement of the aneurysmal aorta and medical treatment designed to decrease the force of cardiac contraction, potentially sparing the ascending aorta.

Potential for Therapeutic Intervention. Both the surgical technique and the timing of replacement have changed during the last several years such that surgery is being recommended when the aortic diameter has reached 55 to 60 mm; the usual upper limit of normal, with normal body habitus, is 37 to 40 mm.[347] This strategy is predicated on the assumption that the longevity of those with aortic diameters of 55 to 60 mm is shorter than that of those receiving an aortic graft, a hypothesis that has not been fully tested. Currently, surgical technique in uncomplicated aneurysm replacement has yielded a low surgical mortality and known survival of at least 8 years. The preferred technique is replacement of the ascending aorta and aortic valve with a composite graft to prevent the post-surgical dilation of the residual aorta with associated development of aortic valvular incompetence, a common feature of earlier surgery.

Medical therapy of the cardiac complications of the Marfan syndrome remains controversial because of the lack of published data concerning the treatment protocols, outcome, the patient population, and the natural history of the treated and untreated individuals. Trials of treatment of individuals with the Marfan syndrome with β-adrenergic blockers (initially propanolol and more recently more selective agents) has been claimed to decrease the rate of increase in aortic diameter, to decrease the rate of aortic dissection, and to decrease the death rate.[348,349] These results have been published only in abstract form, and details are not currently available. Although the results appear encouraging, it is probably premature to propose treatment of all individuals with the Marfan syndrome until more information is available.

Molecular Basis of the Marfan Syndrome. Because collagens provide tensile strength to many tissues, including the aorta, the proposal that alterations in the structure or processing of collagens could lead to the Marfan syndrome has always seemed reasonable. Early studies of aortic pathology did not support this concept but, instead, revealed fractured elastic laminae and pools of mucopolysaccharide in the aortic media.[350] Subsequently, it was shown that dermal fibroblasts accumulated more hyaluronic acid in culture than did control cells,[351] that the accumulation was the result of increased synthesis rather than decreased degradation,[352] and that the activity of the hyaluronate synthetase system was increased.[353] This was examined in a total of less than half a dozen individuals, and in two generations in only one family, so the generality of the finding is still not clear.

Investigations of the role of defects in collagen structure have continued, stimulated by findings of decreased cross-link components in aorta[354] and by the identification of a single individual with a Marfan-like disorder in whom heterozygosity for an apparent insertion in the products of one COL1A2 allele was identified.[355,356] The effect of the mutation on the behavior of the affected molecules was far less dramatic than that of an insertion in the COL1A1 gene (which resulted in the lethal OI type II phenotype). The nature of the mutation in the cells from the woman with the Marfan-like disorder has not yet been characterized, and the finding of an insertion in a noncoding domain[357] has been ascribed to a polymorphism.[358]

The finding of an abnormal collagen synthesized by cells from the one patient did suggest that mutations which result in alterations in the structure of collagens and which interfere with normal cross-link formation could be candidates for the defects in the Marfan syndrome.[359,360] The recent observation of absent synthesis of proα2(I) chains by cells from some in-

dividuals with a form of EDS accompanied by aortic dilatation is also compatible with the concept that collagen mutations could produce a Marfan-like phenotype in some individuals (see above, "EDS Type I"). Convincing evidence against the involvement of collagen mutations in generation of the phenotype comes from linkage studies which, in a small number of families, have excluded COL1A1, COL1A2, and COL3A1 and candidate genes.[361–363] More recent studies have suggested that a high molecular weight matrix component, fibrillin, may be a candidate protein, and work is underway to test the hypothesis.[364]

DISORDERS OF OTHER COLLAGEN GENES

Type II Collagen

Type II collagen is found in articular and other cartilage and in the ocular vitreous, where it is the major protein constituent. Genetic linkage studies, using polymorphic sites in the COL2A1 gene, and direct examination of the collagenous proteins of articular or growth plate cartilage have identified three forms of skeletal dysplasia which are caused by mutations affecting type II collagen.

The Stickler syndrome, hereditary arthroophthalmopathy, is characterized by autosomal dominant inheritance, vitreal degeneration, skeletal dysplasia, and early degenerative joint disease.[365] Linkage studies in three families with the condition are compatible with the mutation being in the COL2A1 gene.[366] There are no data about the nature of the mutation.

Direct analyses of tissues from infants with a lethal form of achondrogenesis[367] and with several forms of spondyloepiphyseal dysplasia[368] have demonstrated the presence of abnormal, overmodified type II collagen in tissues, compatible with the presence of a mutation that destabilizes the triple helix. In another form of achondrogenesis, no type II collagen could be isolated from cartilage.[369] Analysis of these mutations is now underway.

Type IV Collagen

Type IV collagen is distributed in basement membranes. A number of disorders involving these structures (e.g., heritable renal disease, some forms of deafness, disorders of the dermal-epidermal junction) are candidates for abnormalities of type IV collagen, but no disorders have yet been confirmed to result from mutation in any of the genes that encode chains of type IV collgen.

Type VII Collagen

The limitation of type VII collagen to the epidermal-dermal junction in anchoring fibrils has suggested that some forms of epidermolysis bullosa result from mutations in the genes encoding this protein. Although anchoring fibrils are apparently absent in some forms of epidermolysis bullosa,[370] definitive proof of involvement of this protein is not yet available.

SUMMARY COMMENTS

As in many other fields, the investigation of the genetic disorders of collagen metabolism has been revolutionized by the introduction of molecular genetic techniques. These techniques have facilitated the analysis of mutations, brought an understanding of gene structure, and revealed the consequences of mutations in the evolutionary context. However, it is striking that our understanding of the molecular pathogenesis of these disorders remains virtually unexplored. That is, although we can in many instances document the mutation to the nucleotide level, we are unable to explain why the amino acid substitution affects molecular assembly, why the molecules may be poorly secreted, and why the presence of a small amount of abnormal molecule in the matrix results in the devastating clinical disease. In part the difficulty arises because of the complexity of the extracellular matrix, an entity in which many molecules interact to form a functional biologic unit.[371,372] It is likely that as we accumulate more information about the molecular genetics of these disorders, the absence of understanding of molecular interactions will become more apparent and will stimulate a detailed investigation of the molecular pathogenesis of the inherited disorders of collagen metabolism.

The original investigations were supported in part by grants (AR 21557 and GM 15253) from the National Institutes of Health and a Clinical Research Grant (6-298) from the March of Dimes Birth Defects Foundation.

REFERENCES

1. BORNSTEIN P, TRAUB W: Collagen, in Neurath HG, Hill RL (eds): *The Proteins*, 3d ed. New York, Academic, 1979, p 411.

2. MAYNE R, BURGESON RE (eds): *Structure and Function of Collagen Types*. Orlando, Academic, 1987.

3. BORNSTEIN P, SAGE H: Structurally distinct collagen types. *Annu Rev Biochem* 49:957, 1980.

4. FLEISCHMAJER R, OLSEN BR, KUHN K (eds): Biology, chemistry and pathology of collagen. *Ann NY Acad Sci* 460:1, 1985.

5. MAYS C, ROSENBERRY TL: Characterization of pepsin-resistant collagen-like tail subunit fragments of 18S and 14S acetylcholinesterase from *Electrophorus electricus*. *Biochemistry* 20:2810, 1981.

6. REID KBM: Complete amino acid sequences of the three collagen-like regions present in subcomponent Clq of the first component of human complement. *Biochem J* 179:367, 1979.

7. BHATTACHARYYA SN, PASSERO MA, DIAUGUSTINE RP, LYNN WS: Isolation and characterization of two hydroxyproline-containing glycoproteins from normal animal lung lavage and lamellar bodies. *J Clin Invest* 55:914, 1975.

8. PINNELL SR, MURAD S: Disorders of collagen, in Stanbury JB, Wyngaarden JB, Fredrickson DS, Goldstein JL, Brown MS (eds); *The Metabolic Basis of Inherited Disease*, 5th ed. New York, McGraw-Hill, 1983, p 1425.

9. PROCKOP DJ, KIVIRIKKO KI: Heritable diseases of collagen. *N Engl J Med* 311:376, 1984.

10. BYERS PH, BONADIO JF: The molecular basis of clinical heterogeneity in osteogenesis imperfecta: Mutations in type I collagen genes have different effects on collagen processing, in Lloyd JK, Scriver CR (eds): *Metabolic and Genetic Disease in Pediatrics*. London, Butterworths, 1985, p 56.

11. CHEAH KSE: Collagen genes and inherited connective tissue disease. *Biochem J* 229:287, 1985.

12. TSIPOURAS P, RAMIREZ F: Genetic disorders of collagen. *J Med Genet* 24:2, 1987.

13. SYKES B: Genetics cracks bone disease. *Nature* 330:607, 1987.

14. BYERS PH, BONADIO JF, COHN DH, STARMAN BJ, WENSTRUP RJ, WILLING

MC: Osteogenesis imperfecta: The molecular basis of clinical heterogeneity. *Ann NY Acad Sci*, 543:117, 1988.

15. BYERS PH, BONADIO JF: The nature, characterization and phenotypic effects of mutations that affect collagen structure and processing, in Olsen BR, Nimni M (eds): *Collagen: Biochemistry, Biotechnology, and Molecular Biology*. Boca Raton, CRC Press, in press, 1988, vol 4.

16. BYERS PH, HOLBROOK KA: Molecular basis of clinical heterogeneity in the Ehlers-Danlos syndrome. *Ann NY Acad Sci* 460:298, 1985.

17. MILLER EJ, MATUKAS VJ: Chick cartilage collagen: A new type of α1 chain not present in bone or skin of the species. *Proc Natl Acad Sci USA* 64:1264, 1969.

18. KUHN K: The classical collagens, in Mayne R, Burgeson RE (eds): *Structure and Function of Collagen Types*. Orlando, Academic, 1987, p 1.

19. VAN DER REST M, MAYNE R: Type IX collagen, in Mayne R, Burgeson RE (eds): *Structure and Function of Collagen Types*. Orlando, Academic, 1987, p 195.

20. SCHMID TM, LINSENMAYER TF: Type X collagen, in Mayne R, Burgeson RE (eds): *Structure and Function of Collagen Types*. Orlando, Academic, 1987, p 223.

21. EYRE D, WU J-J: Type XI or 1α2α3α collagen, in Mayne R, Burgeson RE (eds): *Structure and Function of Collagen Types*.Orlando, Academic, 1987, p 261.

22. KEFALIDES NA, ALPER R, CLARK CC: Biochemistry and metabolism of basement membranes. *Int Rev Cytol* 61:167, 1979.

23. GLANVILLE R: Type IV collagen, in Mayne R, Burgeson RE, (eds): *Structure and Function of Collagen Types*. Orlando, Academic, 1987, p 43.

24. BURGESON RE: Type VII collagen, in Mayne R, Burgeson RE (eds): *Structure and Function of Collagen Types*. Orlando, Academic, 1987, p 145.

25. MILLER EJ: The structure of fibril-forming collagen. *Ann NY Acad Sci* 460:1, 1985.

26. DE WET W, BERNARD M, BENSON-CHANDA V, CHU M-L, DICKSON L, WEIL D, RAMIREZ F: Organization of the human pro-α2(I) collagen gene. *J Biol Chem* 262:16032, 1987.

27. BARSH GS, ROUSH CL, GELINAS RE: DNA and chromatin structure of the human α1(I) collagen gene. *J Biol Chem* 259:14906, 1984.

28. CHU M-L, DE WET W, BERNARD M, DING J-F, MORABITO M, MYERS J, WILLIAMS C, RAMIREZ F: Human proα1(I) collagen gene structure reveals evolutionary conservation of a pattern of introns and exons. *Nature* 310:337, 1984.

29. SANGIORGI FO, BENSON-CHANDA V, DE WET WJ, SOBEL ME, TSIPOURAS P, RAMIREZ F: Isolation and partial characterization of the entire human proα1(II) collagen gene. *Nucleic Acids Res* 13:2207, 1985.

30. CHEAH KSE, STOKER NG, GRIFFIN JR, GROSVELD FG, SOLOMON E: Identification and characterization of the human type II collagen gene (COL2A1). *Proc Natl Acad Sci USA* 82:2555, 1985.

31. CHU M-L, WEIL D, DE WET W, BERNARD M, SIPPOLA M, RAMIREZ F: Isolation of cDNA and genomic clones encoding human proα1(III) collagen. *J Biol Chem* 260:4357, 1985.

32. MYERS JC, LOIDL HR, STOLLE CA, SEYER JM: Partial covalent structure of the human α2 type V collagen chain. *J Biol Chem* 260:5533, 1985.

33. SUNDERRAJ CV, CHURCH RL, KLOBUCHER LA, RUDDLE RH: Assignment of the gene for human type I procollagen to chromosome 17 by analysis of cell hybrids and microcell hybrids. *Proc Natl Acad Sci USA* 74:4444, 1977.

34. HUERRE C, JUNIEN C, WEIL D, CHU M-L, MORABITO M, VAN CONG M, MYERS JC, FOUBERT C, GROSS M-S, PROCKOP DJ, VOVE A, KAPLAN J-C, DE LA CHAPELLE A, RAMIREZ F: Human type I procollagen genes are located on different chromosomes. *Proc Natl Acad Sci USA* 79:6627, 1982.

35. SOLOMON E, HIORNE L, DALGLEISH R, TOLSTOSHEV P, CRYSTAL R, SYKES B: Regional localization of the human α2(I) collagen gene on chromosome 7 by molecular hybridization. *Cytogenet Cell Genet* 35:64, 1983.

36. STROM CM, EDDY RL, SHOWS TB: Localization of human type II procollagen gene (COL2A1) to chromosome 12. *Somatic Cell Mol Genet* 10:651, 1984.

37. EMANUEL BS, CANNIZZARO LA, SEYER JM, MYERS JC: Human α1(III) and α2(V) procollagen genes are located on the long arm of chromosome 2. *Proc Natl Acad Sci USA* 82:3385, 1985.

38. HUERRE-JEANPIERE C, HENRY I, BERNARD M, GALLANO P, WEIL D, GRZESCHIK K-H, RAMIREZ F, JUNIEN C: The pro α2(V) collagen (COL5A2) maps to 2q14.2q32, syntenic to the pro α1(III) collagen locus (COL3A1). *Hum Genet* 73:64, 1986.

39. KURKINEN M, BERNARD MP, BARLOW DP, CHOW LT: Characterization of 64-, 123- and 182-base-pair exons in the mouse α2(IV) collagen gene. *Nature* 317:177, 1985.

40. SAKURAI Y, SULLIVAN M, YAMADA Y: α1 type IV collagen gene evolved differently from fibrillar collagen genes. *J Biol Chem* 261:6654, 1986.

41. SOLOMON E, HALL V, KURKINEN M: The human α2(IV) collagen gene, COL4A2, is syntenic with the α1(IV) gene, COL4A1, on chromosome 13. *Ann Hum Genet* 51:125, 1987.

42. BOYD CD, TOTH-FEJEL S, GADI IK, LITT M, CONDON MR, KOLBE M, HAGEN IK, KURKINEN M, MacKENZIE JW, MAGENIS E: The genes coding for human pro α1(IV) collagen and pro α2(IV) collagen are both located at the end of the long arm of chromosome 13. *Am J Hum Genet* 42:309, 1988.

43. CUTTING GR, KAZAZIAN HH JR, ANTONARAKIS SE, KILLEN PD, YAMADA Y, FRANCOMANO CA: Macrorestriction analysis maps COL4A1 and COL4A2 collagen genes within a 400kb region on chromosome 13q34. *Am J Hum Genet* 41:A163, 1987.

44. CHU M-L, MANN K, DEUTZMANN R, PRIBULA-CONWAY D, HSU-CHEN CC, BERNARD MP, TIMPL R: Characterization of three constituent chains of collagen type VI by peptide sequences and cDNA clones. *Eur J Biochem* 168:309, 1987.

45. WEIL D, MATTEI M-G, PASSAGE E, VAN CON N'G, PRIBULA-CONWAY D, MANN K, DEUTZMANN R, TIMPL R, CHU M-L: Cloning and chromosomal localization of human genes encoding the three chains of type VI collagen. *Am J Hum Genet* 42:435, 1988.

46. RAMIREZ F: Personal communication.

47. LOZANO G, NINOMIYA Y, THOMPSON H, OLSEN BR: A distinct class of vertebrate collagen genes encodes chicken type IX collagen polypeptides. *Proc Natl Acad Sci USA* 82:4050, 1985.

48. OLSEN BR, NINOMIYA Y, LOZANO G, KONOMI H, GORDON M, GREEN G, PARSONS J, SEYER J, THOMPSON H, VASIOS G: Short-chain collagen genes and their expression in cartilage. *Ann NY Acad Sci* 460:141, 1985.

49. VAN DER REST M, MAYNE R: Type IX collagen proteoglycan from cartilage is covalently cross-linked to type II collagen. *J Biol Chem* 263:1615, 1988.

50. NINOMAYA Y, GORDON M, VAN DER REST M, SCHMID T, LINSENMAYER T, OLSEN BR: The developmentally regulated type X collagen gene contains a long open reading frame without introns. *J Biol Chem* 261:5041, 1986.

51. PALMITER RD, DAVIDSON JM, GAGNON J, ROWE DW, BORNSTEIN P: NH₂-terminal sequence of the chick proα1(I) chain synthesized in the reticulocyte lysate system. *J Biol Chem* 254:1433, 1979.

52. SALEM G, TRAUB W: Conformational implications of amino acid sequence regularities in collagen. *FEBS Lett* 51:94, 1975.

53. RAMACHANDRAN GH: Structure of collagen at the molecular level, in Ramachandran GN (ed): *Treatise on Collagen.* New York, Academic, 1967, vol 1, p 103.

54. BERG RA, PROCKOP DJ: The thermal transition of a nonhydroxylated form of collagen. Evidence for a role for hydroxyproline in stabilizing the triple-helix of collagen. *Biochem Biophys Res Commun* 52:115, 1973.

55. ROSENBLOOM J, HARSCH M, JIMENEZ S: Hydroxyproline content determines the denaturation temperature of chick tendon collagen. *Arch Biochem Biophys* 158:478, 1973.

56. JIMENEZ SA, DEHM P, OLSEN BR, PROCKOP DJ: Intracellular collagen and protocollagen from embryonic tendon cells. *J Biol Chem* 248:720, 1973.

57. HARWOOD R, GRANT ME, JACKSON DS: The route of secretion of procollagen. The influence of α,α'-bipyridyl, colchicine and antimycin A on the secretory process in embryonic-chick tendon and cartilage cells. *Biochem J* 156:81, 1976.

58. WOOLLEY DE: Mammalian collagenases, in Piez KA, Reddi AH (eds): *Extracellular Matrix Biochemistry.* New York, Elsevier, 1984, p 119.

59. HARPER E: Collagenases. *Annu Rev Biochem* 49:1063, 1980.

60. FESSLER JH, FESSLER LI: Biosynthesis of procollagen. *Annu Rev Biochem* 47:129, 1978.

61. DE WET WJ, CHU M-L, PROCKOP DJ: The mRNAs for the proα1(I) and pro-α2(I) chains of type I procollagen are translated at the same rate in normal human fibroblasts and in fibroblasts from two variants of osteogenesis imperfecta with altered steady state ratios of the two mRNAs. *J Biol Chem* 258:14385, 1983.

62. ROSSI P, DE CROMBRUGGHE B: Identification of a cell-specific transcriptional enhancer in the first intron of the mouse α2 (type I) collagen gene. *Proc Natl Acad Sci USA* 84:5590, 1987.

63. LIAU G, SZAPARY D, SETOYAMA C, DE CROMBRUGGHE B: Restriction enzyme digestions identify discrete domains in the chromatin around the promoter of the mouse α2(I) collagen gene. *J Biol Chem* 261:11362, 1986.

64. HATAMOCHI A, PATERSON B, DE CROMBRUGGHE B: Differential binding of a CCAAT DNA binding factor to the promoters of the mouse α2(I) and α1(III) collagen genes. *J Biol Chem* 261:11310, 1986.

65. BORNSTEIN P, McKAY J, MORISHIMA J, DEVARAYALU S, GELINAS RE: Regulatory elements in the first intron contribute to transcriptional control of the human α1(I) collagen gene. *Proc Natl Acad Sci USA* 84:8869, 1987.

66. SCHMIDT A, ROSSI P, DE CROMBRUGGHE B: Transcriptional control of the mouse α2(I) collagen gene: Functional deletion analysis of the promoter and evidence for cell-specific expression. *Mol Cell Biol* 6:347, 1986.

67. BORNSTEIN P, McKAY J: The first intron of the α1(I) collagen gene con-

tains several transcriptional regulatory elements. *J Biol Chem* 263:1603, 1988.

68. ROBERTS AB, SPORN MB, ASSOIAN RK, SMITH JM, ROCHE NS, WAKEFIELD LM, HEINE UI, LIOTTA LA, FALANGA VA, KEHRL JH, FAUCI AS: Transforming growth factory type-β: Rapid induction of fibrosis and angiogenesis *in vivo* and stimulation of collagen formation *in vitro.* *Proc Natl Acad Sci USA* 83:4167, 1986.

69. RAGHOW R, POSTLETHWAITE AE, KESKI-OJA J, MOSES HL, KANG AH: Transforming growth factor-β increases steady state levels of type I procollagen and fibronectin messenger RNAs posttranscriptionally in cultured human dermal fibroblasts. *J Clin Invest* 79:1285, 1987.

70. MURAD S, GROVE D, LINDBERG KA, REYNOLDS G, SIVARAJAH A, PINNELL SR: Regulation of collagen synthesis by ascorbic acid. *Proc Natl Acad Sci USA* 78:2879, 1981.

71. YAMADA Y, MUDRYJ M, DE CROMBRUGGHE B: A uniquely conserved regulatory signal is found around the translation initiation site in three different collagen genes. *J Biol Chem* 258:14914, 1983.

72. SCHMIDT A, YAMADA Y, DE CROMBRUGGHE B: DNA sequence comparison of the regulatory signals at the 5' end of the mouse and chick α2 type I collagen genes. *J Biol Chem* 259:7411, 1984.

73. BENNETT VC, ADAMS SL: Characterization of the translational control mechanism preventing synthesis of α2(I) collagen in chicken vertebral chondroblasts. *J Biol Chem* 262:14806, 1987.

74. CARPOUSIS A, CHRISTNER P, ROSENBLOOM J: Preferential usage of glycyl-tRNA isoaccepting species in collagen synthesis. *J Biol Chem* 252:2447, 1977.

75. PAGLIA LM, WILCZEK J, DE LEON LD, MARTIN GR, HÖRLEIN D, MÜLLER P: Inhibition of procollagen cell-free synthesis by amino-terminal extension peptides. *Biochemistry* 18:5030, 1979.

76. HORLEIN D, McPHERSON J, GOH SH, BORNSTEIN P: Regulation of protein synthesis: Translational control by procollagen-derived fragments. *Proc Natl Acad Sci USA* 78:6163, 1981.

77. AYCOCK RS, RAGHOW R, STRIKLIN GP, SEYER JM, KANG AH: Post-transcriptional inhibition of collagen and fibronectin synthesis by a synthetic homolog of a portion of the carboxyl-terminal propeptide of human type I collgen. *J Biol Chem* 261:14355, 1986.

78. BIENKOWSKI RS, CURRAN SF, BERG RA: Kinetics of intracellular degradation of newly synthesized collagen. *Biochemistry* 25:2455, 1986.

79. BERG RA, SCHWARTZ ML, ROME LH, CRYSTAL RG: Lysosomal function in the degradation of defective collagen in cultured lung fibroblasts. *Biochemistry* 23:2134, 1984.

80. AVVEDIMENTO VE, VOGELI G, YAMADA Y, MAIZEL JV Jr, PASTAN I, DE CROMBRUGGHE B: Correlation between splicing sites within an intron and their sequence complementarity with U1 RNA. *Cell* 21:689, 1980.

81. LICHTENSTEIN JR, MARTIN GR, KOHN L, BYERS PH, McKUSICK VA: Defect in conversion of procollagen to collagen in a form of Ehlers-Danlos syndrome. *Science* 182:298, 1973.

82. WIESTNER M, RODHE H, HELLE O, KRIEG T, TIMPL R, MÜLLER PK: Low rate of procollagen conversion in dermatosparactic sheep fibroblasts is paralleled by increased synthesis of type I and type III collagens. *EMBO J* 1:513, 1982.

83. KIVIRIKKO KI, MYLLYLÄ R: Posttranslational enzymes in the biosynthesis of collagen: Intracellular enzymes. *Methods Enzymol* 82A:245, 1982.

84. PUISTOLA U, TURPEENNIEMI-HUJANEN TM, MYLLYLÄ R, KIVIRIKKO KI: Studies on the lysyl hydroxylase reaction. II. Inhibition kinetics and the reaction mechanism. *Biochim Biophys Acta* 611:51, 1980.

85. RISTELI J, TRYGGVASON K, KIVIRIKKO KI: A rapid assay for prolyl 3-hydroxylase activity. *Anal Biochem* 84:423, 1978.

86. KIVIRIKKO KI, MYLLYLÄ R: Biosynthesis of the collagens, in Piez KA, Reddi AH (eds): *Extracellular Matrix Biochemistry.* New York, Elsevier, 1984, p 83.

87. OLSEN BR, BERG RA, KISHIDA Y, PROCKOP DJ: Collagen synthesis: Localization of prolyl hydrolase in tendon cells detected with ferritin-labeled antibodies. *Science* 182:825, 1973.

88. BERG RA, KEDERSAH NL, GUZMAN NA: Purification and partial characterization of the two nonidentical subunits of prolyl hydroxylase. *J Biol Chem* 254:311, 1979.

89. PIHLAJANIEMI T, HELAAKOSKI T, TASANEN K, MYLLYLÄ R, HUHTALA M-L, KOIVU J, KIVIRIKKO KI: Molecular cloning of the β-subunit of human prolyl 4-hydroxylase. This subunit and protein disulphide isomerase are products of the same gene. *EMBO J* 6:643, 1987.

90. CREIGHTON TE, HILLSON DA, FREEDMAN RB: Catalysis by protein-disulphide isomerase of the unfolding and refolding of proteins with disulphide bonds. *J Mol Biol* 142:43, 1980.

91. MUNRO S, PELHAM HRB: A C-terminal signal prevents secretion of luminal ER proteins. *Cell* 48:899, 1987.

92. TURPEENNIEMI-HUJANEN TM, PUISTOLA U, KIVIRIKKO KI: Isolation of ly-

syl hydroxylase, an enzyme of collagen synthesis, from chick embryos as a homogenous protein. *Biochem J* 189:247, 1980.

93. RISTELI J, TRYGGVASON K, KIVIRIKKO KI: Prolyl 3-hydroxylase: Partial characterization of the enzyme from rat kidney cortex. *Eur J Biochem* 73:485, 1977.

94. RAO NV, ADAMS E: Partial reaction of prolyl hydroxylase. (GLY-PRO-ALA)$_n$ stimulates α-ketoglutarate decarboxylation without prolyl hydroxylation. *J Biol Chem* 253:6327, 1978.

95. MYLLYLÄ R, KUUTTI-SAVOLAINEN E-R, KIVIRIKKO KI: The role of ascorbate in the prolyl hydroxylase reaction. *Biochem Biophys Res Commun* 83:441, 1978.

96. PETERKOFSKY B, KALWINSKY D, ASSAD R: Substance in L-929 cell extracts which replaces the ascorbate requirement for prolyl hydroxylase in a tritium release assay for reducing cofactor; correlation of its concentration with the extent of ascorbate-independent proline hydroxylation and the level of prolyl hydroxylase activity in these cells. *Arch Biochem Biophys* 199:362, 1980.

97. EYRE DR, PAZ MA, GALLOP PM: Cross-linking in collagen and elastin. *Annu Rev Biochem* 53:717, 1984.

98. DOEGE KJ, FESSLER JH: Folding of carboxyl domain and assembly of procollagen I. *J Biol Chem* 261:8924, 1986.

99. KOIVU J: Identification of disulfide bonds in carboxy-terminal propeptides of human type I procollagen. *FEBS Lett* 212:229, 1987.

100. BÄCHINGER HP, BRUCKNER P, TIMPL R, ENGEL J: The role of *cis-trans* isomerization of peptide bonds in the coil-triple helix conversion of collagen. *Eur J Biochem* 90:605, 1978.

101. BÄCHINGER HP: The influence of peptidyl-prolyl cis-trans isomerase on the *in vitro* folding of type III collagen. *J Biol Chem* 262:17144, 1987.

102. KIVIRIKKO KI, MYLLYLÄ R: Collagen glycosyltransferases. *Int Rev Connect Tissue Res* 8:23, 1979.

103. CLARK CC: The distribution and initial characterization of oligosaccharide units on the COOH-terminal propeptide extensions of the proα1 and proα2 chains of type I procollagen. *J Biol Chem* 254:10798, 1979.

104. ANTTINEN H, OIKARINEN A, RYHANEN L, KIVIRIKKO KI: Evidence for the transfer of mannose to the extension peptides of procollagen within the cisternae of the rough endoplasmic reticulum. *FEBS Lett* 87:222, 1978.

105. GUZMAN NA, GRAVES PN, PROCKOP DJ: Addition of mannose to both the amino- and carboxy-terminal propeptides of type II procollagen occurs without formation of a triple helix. *Biochem Biophys Res Commun* 84:691, 1978.

106. KORNFELD R, KORNFELD S: Assembly of asparagine-linked oligosaccharides. *Annu Rev Biochem* 54:631, 1985.

107. DUKSIN D, BORNSTEIN P: Impaired conversion of procollagen to collagen by fibroblasts and bone treated with tunicamycin, an inhibitor of protein glycosylation. *J Biol Chem* 252:955, 1977.

108. HOUSLEY TJ, ROWLAND FN, LEDGER PW, KAPLAN J, TANZER ML: Effects of tunicamycin on the biosynthesis of procollagen by human fibroblasts. *J Biol Chem* 255:121, 1980.

109. CLARK CC: Asparagine-linked glycosides. *Methods Enzymol* 82A:346, 1982.

110. DEHM P, PROCKOP DJ: Time lag in the secretion of collagen by matrix-free tendon cells and inhibition of the secretory process by colchicine and vinblastine. *Biochim Biophys Acta* 264:375, 1972.

111. DIEGELMANN RF, PETERKOFSKY B: Inhibition of collagen secretion from bone and cultured fibroblasts by microtubular disruptive drugs. *Proc Natl Acad Sci USA* 69:892, 1972.

112. EHRLICH HP, ROSS R, BORNSTEIN P: Effects of antimicrotubular agents on the secretion of collagen. *J Cell Biol* 62:390, 1974.

113. FESSLER LI, BROSH S, CHAPIN S, FESSLER JH: Tyrosine sulfation in precursors of collagen V. *J Biol Chem* 261:5034, 1986.

114. FESSLER LI, CHAPIN S, BROSH S, FESSLER JH: Intracellular transport and tyrosine sulfation of procollagens V. *Eur J Biochem* 158:511, 1986.

115. FISHER LW, ROBEY PG, TUROSS N, OTSUKA AS, TEPEN DA, ESCH FS, SHIMASAKI S, TERMINE JD: The M$_r$ 24,000 phosphoprotein from developing bone is the NH$_2$-terminal propeptide of the α1 chain of type I collagen. *J Biol Chem* 262:13457, 1987.

116. LAPIERE CM, LENAERS A, KOHN LD: Procollagen peptidase: An enzyme excising the coordination peptides of procollagen. *Proc Natl Acad Sci USA* 68:3054, 1971.

117. TUDERMAN L, PROCKOP DJ: Procollagen N-proteinase: Properties of the enzyme purified from chick embryo tendons. *Eur J Biochem* 125:545, 1982.

118. MORRIS NP, FESSLER LI, FESSLER JH: Procollagen peptide release by procollagen peptidases and bacterial collagenase. *J Biol Chem* 254:11024, 1979.

119. HAILILA R, PELTONEN L: Neutral protease cleaving the N-terminal propeptide of type III procollagen: Partial purification and characterization

120. TUDERMAN L, KIVIRIKKO KI, PROCKOP DJ: Partial purification and characterization of a neutral protease which cleaves the N-terminal propeptides from procollagen. *Biochemistry* 17:2948, 1978.

121. HOJIMA Y, VAN DER REST M, PROCKOP DJ: Type I procollagen carboxyl-terminal proteinase from chick embryo tendons: Purification and characterization. *J Biol Chem* 260:15996, 1985.

122. BIRK DE, TRELSTAD RL: Extracellular compartments in tendon morphogenesis: Collagen fibril, bundle, and macroaggregate formation. *J Cel Biol* 103:231, 1986.

123. TRELSTAD RL: Multistep assembly of type I collagen fibrils. *Cell* 28:197, 1982.

124. PIEZ KA, TRUS BL: Sequence regularities and packing of collagen molecules. *J Mol Biol* 122:419, 1978.

125. VOGEL KG, PAULSSON, HEINEGARD D: Specific inhibition of type I and type II collagen fibrillogenesis by the small proteoglycan of tendon. *Biochem J* 223:587, 1984.

126. PIEZ KA: Molecular and aggregate structures of the collagens, in Piez KA, Reddi AH (eds): *Extracellular Matrix Biochemistry*. New York, Elsevier, 1984, p 1.

127. SIEGEL RC: Lysyl oxidase. *Int Rev Connect Tissue Res* 8:73, 1979.

128. KAGAN HM: Lysyl oxidase, in Mecham RP (ed): *Biology of Extracellular Matrix*. Orlando, Academic, 1985, vol 1, p 321.

129. CRONLUND AL, KAGAN HM: Comparison of lysyl oxidase from bovine lung and aorta. *Connect Tissue Res* 15:173, 1986.

130. KUIVANIEMI H, ALA-KOKKO L, KIVIRIKKO KI: Secretion of lysyl oxidase by cultured human skin fibroblasts and effects of monensin, nigericin, tunicamycin and colchicine. *Biochim Biophys Acta* 883:326, 1986.

131. WILLIAMSON PR, MOOG RS, DOOLEY DM, KAGAN HM: Evidence for pyrroloquinolinequinone as the carbonyl cofactor in lysyl oxidase by absorption and resonance Raman spectroscopy. *J Biol Chem* 261:16302, 1986.

132. HARRIS ED: Copper-induced activation of aortic lysyl oxidase *in vivo*. *Proc Natl Acad Sci USA* 73:371, 1973.

133. MOLNAR JA, ALPERT N, BURKE JF, YOUNG VR: Synthesis and degradation rates of collagens *in vivo* in whole skin or rats, studied with ^{18}O$_2$ labelling. *Biochem J* 240:431, 1986.

134. BIRKEDAHL-HANSEN H: Catabolism and turnover of collagens-collagenases. *Methods Enzymol* 144D:140, 1987.

135. MILLER EJ, HARRIS ED JR, CHUNG E, FINCH JE JR, MCCROSKERY PA, BUTLER WT: Cleavage of type II and III collagens with mammalian collagenase: Site of cleavage and primary structure at the NH$_2$-terminal portion of the smaller fragment released from both collagens. *Biochemistry* 15:787, 1976.

136. FIELDS GB, VAN WART HE, BIRKEDAL-HANSEN H: Sequence specificity of human skin fibroblast collagenase. Evidence for the role of collagen structure in determining the collagenase cleavage site. *J Biol Chem* 262:6221, 1987.

137. CONSTANTINOU CD, VOGEL BE, JEFFREY JJ, PROCKOP DJ: The A and B fragments of normal type I procollagen have a similar thermal stability to proteinase digestion but are selectively destabilized by structural mutations. *Eur J Biochem* 163:247, 1987.

138. HOROWITZ AL, HANCE AJ, CRYSTAL RG: Granulocyte collagenase: Selective digestion of type I relative to type III collagen. *Proc Natl Acad Sci USA* 74:897, 1977.

139. HASTY KA, JEFFREY JJ, HIBBS MS, WELGUS HG: The collagen substrate specificity of human neutrophil collagenase. *J Biol Chem* 262:10048, 1987.

140. LIOTTA LA, ABE S, ROBEY PG, MARTIN GR: Preferential digestion of basement membrane collagen by an enzyme derived from a metastatic murine tumor. *Proc Natl Acad Sci USA* 76:2268, 1979.

141. MCKUSICK VA: *Heritable Disorders of Connective Tissue*, 4th ed. St Louis, Mosby, 1972.

142. LENAERS A, ANSAY M, NUSGENS BV, LAPIERE CM: Collagen made of extended α-chains, procollagen, in genetically-defective dermatosparaxic calves. *Eur J Biochem* 23:533, 1971.

143. PINNELL SR, KRANE SM, KENZORA JE, GLIMCHER MJ: A heritable disorder of connective tissue: Hydroxylysine-deficient collagen disease. *N Engl J Med* 266:1013, 1972.

144. SYKES B, FRANCIS MJO, SMITH R: Altered relation of two collagen types in osteogenesis imperfecta. *N Engl J Med* 296:1200, 1977.

145. HOLBROOK KA, BYERS PH: Ultrastructural characteristics of the skin in a form of the Ehlers-Danlos syndrome type IV: Storage in the rough endoplasmic reticulum. *Lab Invest* 44:342, 1981.

146. OGILVIE D, WORDSWORTH P, THOMPSON E, SYKES B: Evidence against the structural gene encoding type II collagen (COL2A1) as the mutant locus in achondroplasia. *J Med Genet* 23:19, 1986.

147. WALLIS G, VERSFELD J, SYKES B, MATHEW CG, BEIGHTON P: Osteogenesis imperfecta type III—Mutations in the type I collagen structural genes are not necessarily responsible. Submitted for publication.

148. AITCHISON K, OGILVIE D, HONEYMAN M, THOMPSON E, SYKES B: Homozygous osteogenesis imperfecta unlinked to collagen I genes. *Hum Genet*, 78:233, 1988.

149. SMITH R, FRANCIS MJO, HOUGHTON GR: *The Brittle Bone Syndrome: Osteogenesis Imperfect.* London, Butterworths, 1983.

150. BYERS PH: Inherited disorders of collagen gene structure and expression. *Am J Med Genet*, in press, 1988.

151. SILLENCE DO, SENN AS, DANKS DM: Genetic heterogeneity in osteogenesis imperfecta. *J Med Genet* 16:101, 1979.

152. SEEDORF KS: Osteogenesis imperfecta: A study of clinical features and heredity based on 55 Danish families comprising 180 affected members. Copenhagen, Universitetsforlaget I Arhus, 1949.

153. WYNNE-DAVIES R, GORMLEY J: Clinical and genetic patterns in osteogenesis imperfecta. *Clin Orthop* 159:26, 1981.

154. IBSEN KH: Distinct varieties of osteogenesis imperfecta. *Clin Orthop* 50:279, 1967.

155. SILLENCE D: Osteogenesis imperfecta: An expanding panorama of variants. *Clin Orthop* 159:11, 1981.

156. PATERSON CR, MCALLION S, MILLER R: Heterogeneity of osteogenesis imperfecta type I. *J Med Genet* 20:203, 1983.

157. LEVIN LS, SALINAS CF, JORGENSON RJ: Classification of osteogenesis imperfecta by dental characteristics. *Lancet* 1:332, 1978.

158. SHAPIRO JR, PIKUS A, WEISS G, ROWE DW: Hearing and middle ear function in osteogenesis imperfecta. *JAMA* 247:2120, 1982.

159. QUISLING RW, MOORE GR, JAHRSDOERFER RA, CANTRELL RW: Osteogenesis imperfecta; a study of 160 family members. *Arch Otolaryngol* 105:207, 1979.

160. PEDERSON U: Hearing loss in patients with osteogenesis imperfecta: A clinical and audiological study of 201 patients. *Scand Audiol* 13:67, 1984.

161. ARMSTRONG BW: Stapes surgery in patients with osteogenesis imperfecta. *Ann Otology Rhinol Laryngol* 93:634, 1984.

162. HORTOP J, TSIPOURAS P, HANLEY JA, MARON BJ, SHAPIRO JR: Cardiovascular involvement in osteogenesis imperfecta. *Circulation* 73:54, 1986.

163. PENTTINEN RP, LICHTENSTEIN JR, MARTIN GR, MCKUSICK VA: Abnormal collagen metabolism in cultured cells in osteogenesis imperfecta. *Proc Natl Acad Sci USA* 72:586, 1975.

164. BARSH GS, DAVID KE, BYERS PH: Type I osteogenesis imperfecta: A nonfunctional allele for proα1(I) chains of type I procollagen. *Proc Natl Acad Sci USA* 79:3838, 1982.

165. ROWE DW, SHAPIRO JR, POIRIER M, SCHLESINGER S: Diminished type I collagen synthesis and reduced alpha 1(I) collagen messenger RNA in cultured fibroblasts from patients with dominantly inherited (type I) osteogenesis imperfecta. *J Clin Invest* 76:604, 1985.

166. WILLING MC, COHN DH, BYERS PH: manuscript in preparation.

167. SYKES B, OGLIVIE D, WORDSWORTH P, ANDERSON J, JONES N: Osteogenesis imperfecta is linked to both type I collagen structural genes. *Lancet* 2:69, 1986.

168. GENOVESE C, ROWE D: Analysis of cytoplasmic and nuclear messenger RNA in fibroblasts from patients with type I osteogenesis imperfecta. *Methods Enzymol* 145:223, 1987.

169. WALLIS G, BEIGHTON P, BOYD C, MATHEW CG: Mutations linked to the proα2(I) collagen gene are responsible for several cases of osteogenesis imperfecta type I. *J Med Genet* 23:411, 1986.

170. BYERS PH, SHAPIRO JR, ROWE DW, DAVID KE, HOLBROOK KA: Abnormal α2-chain in type I collagen from a patient with a form of osteogenesis imperfecta. *J Clin Invest* 71:689, 1983.

171. NICHOLLS AC, POPE FM, CRAIG D: An abnormal collagen α chain containing cysteine in autosomal dominant osteogenesis imperfecta. *Br Med J* 288:112, 1984.

172. STEINMANN B, NICHOLLS A, POPE FM: Clinical variability of osteogenesis imperfecta reflecting molecular heterogeneity: Cysteine substitutions in the α1(I) collagen chain producing lethal and mild forms. *J Biol Chem* 261:8958, 1986.

173. CROUCH E, BORNSTEIN P: Collagen synthesis by human amniotic fluid cells in culture: Characterization of a procollagen with three identical pro alpha-1(I) chains. *Biochemistry* 17:5499, 1978.

174. BYERS PH, WENSTRUP RJ, BONADIO JF, STARMAN B, COHN DH: Molecular basis of inherited disorders of collagen biosynthesis: Implications for prenatal diagnosis, in Gedde-Dahl T, Wuepper KD (eds): *Prenatal Diagnosis of Heritable Skin Disease.* Basel, Karger, 1987, p 158.

175. ORIOLI IM, CASTILLA EE, BARBOSA-NETO JG: The birth prevalence rates for the skeletal dysplasias. *J Med Genet* 23:328, 1986.

176. CONNOR JM, CONNOR RA, SWEET EM, GIBSON AA, PATRICK WJ, MCNAY MB, REFORD DH: Lethal neonatal chondrodysplasias in the West of Scotland 1970–1983 with a description of a thanatophoric, dysplasialike, au-tosomal recessive disorder, Glasgow variant. *Am J Med Genet* 22:243, 1985.

177. BYERS PH, TSIPOURAS P, BONADIO JF, STARMAN BJ, SCHWARTZ RC: Perinatal lethal osteogenesis imperfecta (OI type II): A biochemically heterogeneous disorder usually due to new mutations in the genes for type I collagen. *Am J Hum Genet* 42:237, 1988.

178. SHAPIRO JE, PHILLIPS JA III, BYERS PH, SANDERS R, HOLBROOK KA, LEVIN LS, DORST J, BARSH GS, PETERSON KE, GOLDSTEIN P: Prenatal diagnosis of lethal perinatal osteogenesis imperfecta (OI type II). *J Pediatr* 100:127, 1982.

179. CHERVENAK FA, ROMERO R, BERKOWITZ RL, MAHONEY MJ, TORTORA M, MAYDEN K, HOBBINS JC: Antenatal sonographic findings of osteogenesis imperfecta. *Am J Obstet Gynecol* 143:228, 1982.

180. ELEJALDE BR, ELEJALDE MM: Prenatal diagnosis of perinatally lethal osteogenesis imperfecta. *Am J Med Genet* 14:353, 1983.

181. SILLENCE DO, BARLOW KK, GARBER AP, HALL JG, RIMOIN DL: Osteogenesis imperfecta type II. Delineation of the phenotype with reference to genetic heterogeneity. *Am J Med Genet* 17:407, 1984.

182. CHAWLA S: Intrauterine osteogenesis imperfecta in four siblings. *Br Med J* 1:99, 1964.

183. BRAGA S, PASSARGE E: Congenital osteogenesis imperfecta in three sibs. *Hum Genet* 58:441, 1981.

184. THOMPSON EM, YOUNG ID, HALL CM, PEMBERY ME: Osteogenesis imperfecta type IIA: Evidence for dominant inheritance. *J Med Genet* 24:386, 1987.

185. COHN DH, STARMAN BJ, BLUMBERG B, BYERS PH: Germinal mosaicism for a type I collagen gene mutations in lethal osteogenesis imperfecta. Submitted for publication.

186. RIMOIN DL: The chondrodystrophies. *Adv Hum Genet* 5:1, 1975.

187. WYNNE-DAVIES R, HALL CM, APLEY AG: *Atlas of Skeletal Dysplasias.* Edinburgh, Churchill Livingstone, 1985.

188. BYERS PH, COHN DH, STARMAN BJ: Unpublished observations.

189. BATEMAN JF, MASCARA T, CHAN D, COLE WG: Abnormal type I collagen metabolism by cultured fibroblasts in lethal perinatal osteogenesis imperfecta. *Biochem J* 217:103, 1984.

190. BONADIO J, BYERS PH: Subtle structural alterations in the chains of type I procollagen produce osteogenesis imperfecta type II. *Nature* 316:363, 1985.

191. BATEMAN J, CHAN D, MASCARA T, ROGERS JG, COLE WG: Collagen defects in lethal perinatal osteogenesis imperfecta. *Biochem J* 240:699, 1986.

192. BARSH GS, BYERS PH: Reduced secretion of structurally abnormal type I procollagen in a form of osteogenesis imperfecta. *Proc Natl Acad Sci USA* 78:5142, 1981.

193. WILLIAMS CJ, PROCKOP DJ: Synthesis and processing of a type I procollagen containing shortened proα1(I) chains by fibroblasts from a patient with osteogenesis imperfecta. *J Biol Chem* 258:5915, 1983.

194. CHU M-L, WILLIAMS CJ, PEPE G, HIRSCH JL, PROCKOP DJ, RAMIREZ F: Internal deletion in a collagen gene in a perinatal lethal form of osteogenesis imperfecta. *Nature* 304:78, 1983.

195. CHU M-L, GARGIULO V, WILLIAMS CJ, RAMIREZ F: Multiexon deletion in an osteogenesis imperfecta variant with increased type III collagen mRNA. *J Biol Chem* 260:691, 1985.

196. BARSH GS, ROUSH CL, BONADIO J, BYERS PH, GELINAS RE: Intron mediated recombination causes an α1(I) collagen deletion in a lethal form of osteogenesis imperfecta. *Proc Natl Acad Sci USA* 82:2870, 1985.

197. BYERS PH, STARMAN PH, COHN DH, HORWITZ AL: A novel mutation causes a perinatal lethal form of osteogenesis imperfecta: An insertion in one α1(I) collagen allele (COL1A1). *J Biol Chem* 263:7855, 1988.

198. WILLING MC, COHN DH, STARMAN BJ, HOLBROOK KA, GREENBERG CR, BYERS PH: Heterozygosity for a large deletion in the α2(I) collagen gene (COL1A2) has a dramatic effect on type I collagen secretion and produces perinatal lethal osteogenesis imperfecta. *J Biol Chem* 263:8398, 1988.

199. STEINMANN B, RAO VH, BRUCKNER P, GITZELMANN R, BYERS PH: Cysteine in the triple-helical domain of one allelic product of the α1(I) gene of type I collagen produces a lethal form of osteogenesis imperfecta. *J Biol Chem* 259:11129, 1984.

200. COHN DH, BYERS PH, STEINMANN B, GELINAS RE: Lethal osteogenesis imperfecta resulting from a single nucleotide change in one human proα1(I) collagen allele. *Proc Natl Acad Sci USA* 83:6045, 1986.

201. BATEMAN JF, CHAN D, WALKER ID, ROGERS JG, COLE WG: Lethal perinatal osteogenesis imperfecta due to the substitution of arginine for glycine at residue 391 of the α1(I) chains of type I collagen. *J Biol Chem* 262:7021, 1987.

202. VOGEL BE, MINOR RR, FREUND M, PROCKOP DJ: A point mutation in a type I procollagen gene converts glycine 748 of the α1 chain to cysteine and destabilizes the triple helix in a lethal variant of osteogenesis imperfecta. *J Biol Chem* 262:14737, 1987.

203. CONSTANTINOU CD, NIELSEN KB, PROCKOP DJ: The molecular defect in a

lethal variant of osteogenesis imperfecta is a single base mutation that substitutes cysteine for glycine 904 of the α1(I) chains of type I procollagen. *J Clin Invest*, in press.

204. BALDWIN CT, CONSTANTINOU CD, PROCKOP DJ: A single base mutation that converts the codon for glycine 907 of the α2(I) chain of type I procollagen to aspartate. The single amino acid substitution in itself destabilizes the triple helix. *Coll Relat Res*, in press, 1988.

205. DEWET WJ, PIHLAJANIEMI T, MYERS J, KELLY TE, PROCKOP DJ: Synthesis of a shortened proα2(I) chain and decreased synthesis of proα2(I) chains in a proband with osteogenesis imperfecta. *J Biol Chem* 258:7721, 1983.

206. DE WET W, SIPPOLA M, BERNARD M, PROCKOP D, CHU M-L, RAMIREZ F: Electromicroscopic localization of deletions in the human proα2(I) collagen gene. *Ann NY Acad Sci* 460:415, 1985.

207. TROMP G, PROCKOP DJ: Single base mutation in the proα2(I) gene of type I procollagen that causes efficient splicing of RNA from exon 27 to exon 29 and synthesis of a shortened in-frame proα2(I) protein in a lethal variant of osteogenesis imperfecta. *Proc Natl Acad Sci USA* 85:5254, 1988.

208. FOLLIS RH Jr: Maldevelopment of the corium in the osteogenesis imperfecta syndrome. *Bull Johns Hopkins Hosp* 93:225, 1953.

209. THOMPSON EM, YOUNG ID, HALL CM, PEMBREY ME: Recurrence risks and prognosis in severe sporadic osteogenesis imperfecta. *J Med Genet* 24:390, 1987.

210. SILLENCE DO, BARLOW KK, COLE WG, DIETRICH S, GARBER AP, RIMOIN DL: Osteogenesis imperfecta type III: Delineation of the phenotype with reference to genetic heterogeneity. *Am J Med Genet* 23:821, 1986.

211. BEIGHTON P, VERSFELD GA: On the paradoxically high relative prevalence of osteogenesis imperfecta type III in the Black population of South Africa. *Clin Genet* 27:398, 1985.

212. GOLDMAN AV, DAVIDSON D, PAVLOV H, BULLOUGH PG: "Popcorn" calcification: A prognostic sign in osteogenesis imperfecta. *Radiology* 136:351, 1980.

213. SOFIELD HA, MILLAR EA: Fragmentation, realignment and intramedullary rod fixation of deformities of the long bones in children: a ten year appraisal. *J Bone Joint Surg [Am]* 41A:1371, 1959.

214. MOOREFIELD WG Jr, MILLER GR: Aftermath of osteogenesis imperfecta: The disease in adulthood. *J Bone Joint Surg [Am]* 62A:113, 1980.

215. ALBRIGHT JA: Systemic treatment of osteogenesis imperfecta. *Clin Orthop* 159:88, 1981.

216. AYLSWORTH AS, SEED JW, BUILFORD WB, BURNS CB, WASHBURN DB: Prenatal diagnosis of a severe deforming type of osteogenesis imperfecta. *Am J Med Genet* 19:707, 1984.

217. ROBINSON LP, WORTHEN NJ, LACHMAN RS, ADOMIAN GE, RIMOIN DL: Prenatal diagnosis of osteogenesis imperfecta type III. *Prenat Diagn* 7:7, 1987.

218. NICHOLLS AC, POPE FM, SCHLOON H: Biochemical heterogeneity of osteogenesis imperfecta: A new variant. *Lancet* 1:1193, 1979.

219. NICHOLLS AC, OSSE G, SCHLOON HG, LENARD HG, DEAK S, MYERS JC, PROCKOP DJ, WEIGEL WRF, FRYER P, POPE FM: The clinical features of homozygous α2(I) collagen deficient osteogenesis imperfecta. *J Med Genet* 21:257, 1984.

220. DEAK SB, NICHOLLS AC, POPE FM, PROCKOP DJ: The molecular defect in a non-lethal variant of osteogenesis imperfecta. *J Biol Chem* 258:15192, 1983.

221. CHU M-L, ROWE D, NICHOLLS AC, POPE FM, PROCKOP DJ: Presence of translatable mRNA for proα2(I) chains in fibroblasts from a patient with osteogenesis imperfecta whose type I collagen does not contain α1(I) chains. *Coll Relat Res* 4:389, 1984.

222. DICKSON LA, PIHLAJANIEMI T, DEAK S, POPE FM, NICHOLLS A, PROCKOP DJ, MYERS JC: Nuclease S₁ mapping of a homozygous mutation in the carboxy-propeptide coding region of the proα2(I) collagen gene in a patient with osteogenesis imperfecta. *Proc Natl Acad Sci USA* 81:4524, 1984.

223. PIHLAJANIEMI T, DICKSON LA, POPE FM, KORHONEN VR, NICHOLLS A, PROCKOP DJ, MYERS JC: Osteogenesis imperfecta: Cloning of a proα2(I) collagen gene with a frameshift mutation. *J Biol Chem* 259:12941, 1984.

224. VAN DER REST M, HAYES A, MARIE P, DESBARATS M, KAPLAN P, GLORIEUX FH: Lethal osteogenesis imperfecta with amniotic band lesions: Collagen studies. *Am J Med Genet* 24:433, 1986.

225. STARMAN BJ, COHN DH, APONE S, EYRE D, WEISS L, BYERS PH: Substitution of cysteine for glycine at position 526 in the triple-helical domain of the proα1(I) chain of type I collagen results in a non-lethal form of osteogenesis imperfecta. Manuscript in preparation.

226. COHN DH, BYERS PH: manuscript in preparation.

227. PATERSON CR, MCALLION S, MILLER R: Osteogenesis imperfecta with dominant inheritance and normal sclerae. *J Bone Joint Surg [Br]* 65B:35, 1983.

228. TSIPOURAS P, SCHWARTZ RC, GOLDBERG JD, BERKOWITZ RL, RAMIREZ F: Prenatal prediction of osteogenesis imperfecta (OI type IV): Exclusion of inheritance using a collagen gene probe. *J Med Genet* 24:406, 1987.

229. TSIPOURAS P, MYERS JC, RAMIREZ F, PROCKOP DJ: Restriction fragment length polymorphisms associated with the proα2(I) gene of human type I procollagen. *J Clin Invest* 72:1262, 1983.

230. TSIPOURAS P, BORRESEN A-L, DICKSON LA, BERG K, PROCKOP DJ, RAMIREZ F: Molecular heterogeneity in the mild autosomal dominant forms of osteogenesis imperfecta. *Am J Hum Genet* 36:1172, 1984.

231. WENSTRUP RJ, TSIPOURAS P, BYERS PH: Osteogenesis imperfecta type IV: Biochemical confirmation of genetic linkage to the proα2(I) gene of type I collagen. *J Clin Invest* 78:1449, 1986.

232. WENSTRUP RJ, COHN DH, COHEN T, BYERS PH: Arginine for glycine substitution in the triple helical domain of the products of one α2(I) collagen allele (COL1A2) produces the osteogenesis imperfecta type IV phenotype. *J Biol Chem* 263:7734, 1988.

233. DE VRIES WN, DE WET WJ: The molecular defect in an autosomal dominant form of osteogenesis imperfecta. Synthesis of type I procollagen containing cysteine in the triple-helical domain of pro-α1(I) chains. *J Biol Chem* 261:9056, 1986.

234. SIPPOLA M, KAFFE S, PROCKOP DJ: A heterozygous defect for structurally altered pro-α2 chain of type I procollagen in a mild variant of osteogenesis imperfecta. *J Biol Chem* 259:14094, 1984.

235. KUIVANIEMI H, SABOL C, TROMP G, SIPPOLA-THIELE M, PROCKOP DJ: A 19-base pair deletion in the proα2(I) gene of type I procollagen that causes in-frame RNA splicing from exon 10 to exon 12 in a proband with atypical osteogenesis imperfecta and in his asymptomatic mother. *J Biol Chem* 263:11407, 1988.

236. MINOR RR, SIPPOLA-THIELE M, MCKEON J, BERGER J, PROCKOP DJ: Defects in the processing of procollagen to collagen are demonstrable in cultured fibroblasts from patients with the Ehlers-Danlos and osteogenesis imperfecta syndromes. *J Biol Chem* 261:10006, 1986.

237. SARAUX H, FRANZAL J, ROY C, ARON JJ, HAYAT B, LAMY M: Pseudogliome et fragilite osseuse hereditaire a transmission autosomal recessive. *Ann Oculist* 200:1241, 1967.

238. BIANCHINE JW, MURDOCK JL: Juvenile osteoporosis (?) in a boy with bilateral enucleation of the eyes for pseudoglioma. *Birth Defects* 5(4):225, 1969.

239. BEIGHTON P, WINSHIP I, BEHARI D: The ocular form of osteogenesis imperfecta: A new autosomal recessive syndrome. *Clin Genet* 28:69, 1985.

240. DENT CE, FRIEDMAN M: Idiopathic juvenile osteoporosis. *Q J Med* 34:177, 1965.

241. SHIELDS ED, BIXLER D, EL-KAFRAWY AM: A proposed classification for heritable human dentine defects with a description of a new entity. *Arch Oral Biol* 18:543, 1973.

242. BALL SP, COOK PJL, MARS M, BUCKTON KE: Linkage between dentinogenesis imperfecta and Gc. *Ann Hum Genet* 46:35, 1982.

243. TAKAGI Y, VEIS A, SAUK JJ: Relation of mineralization defects in collagen matrices to non-collagenous protein components. Identification of a molecular defect in dentinogenesis imperfecta. *Clin Orthop* 176:282, 1983.

244. DENHOLM LJ, COLE WG: Heritable bone fragility, joint laxity and dysplastic dentin in Friesian calves: A bovine syndrome of osteogenesis imperfecta. *Aust Vet J* 60:9, 1983.

245. THOMPSON K: Personal communication.

246. FISHER LW, DENHOLM LJ, CONN KM, TERMINE JD: Mineralized tissue protein profiles in the Australian form of bovine osteogenesis imperfecta. *Calcif Tissue Int* 38:16, 1986.

247. GUENET JL, STANESCU R, MAROTEAUX P, STANESCU V: Fragilitas ossium: A new autosomal recessive mutation in the mouse. *J Hered* 72:440, 1981.

248. SCHNIEKE A, HARBERS K, JAENISCH R: Embryonic lethal mutation in mice induced by retrovirus insertion into the α1(I) collagen gene. *Nature* 304:315, 1983.

249. HARBERS K, KUEHN M, DELIUS H, JAENISCH R: Insertion of retrovirus into the first intron of α1(I) collagen gene leads to embryonic lethal mutation in mice. *Proc Natl Acad Sci USA* 81:1504, 1984.

250. LÖHLER J, TIMPL R, JAENISCH R: Embryonic lethal mutation in mouse collagen I gene causes rupture of blood vessels and is associated with erythropoietic and mesenchymal cell death. *Cell* 38:597, 1984.

251. SCHNIEKE A, DZIADEK M, BATEMAN J, MASCARA T, HARBERS K, GELINAS R, JAENISCH R: Introduction of the human proα1(I) collagen gene into proα1(I)-deficient Mov-13 mouse cells leads to formation of functional mouse-human hybrid type I collagen. *Proc Natl Acad Sci USA* 84:764, 1987.

252. STACEY A, BATEMAN J, CHOI T, MASCARA T, COLE W, JAENISCH R: Perinatal lethal osteogenesis imperfecta in transgenic mice bearing an engineered mutant pro-α1(I) collagen gene. *Nature* 332:131, 1988.

253. BEIGHTON P: *The Ehlers-Danlos Syndrome*. London, Heinemann, 1970.

254. BYERS PH, HOLBROOK KA: Molecular basis of clinical heterogeneity in the Ehlers-Danlos syndrome. *Ann NY Acad Sci* 460:298, 1985.

255. TSCHERNOGOBOW A: Ein fall von cutis laxa. *Jahrb Ges Med* 27:562, 1892.

256. EHLERS E: Cutis laxa, niegung zu haemorrhagien in der haut, lockerung mehrerer artikulatinonen. *Dermatol Z* 8:173, 1901.

257. DANLOS M: Un cas de cutis laxa avec tumeurs par contusion chronique des coudes et des genoux (xanthome juvenile pseudodiabetique de MM Hallopeau et Mace de Lepinay). *Bull Soc Fr Dermatol Syph* 19:70, 1908.

258. BARABAS AP: Heterogeneity of the Ehlers-Danlos syndrome: Description of three clinical types and a hypothesis to explain the basic defect. *Br Med J* 2:612, 1967.

259. BEIGHTON P, PRICE A, LORD J, DICKSON E: Variants of the Ehlers-Danlos syndrome. *Ann Rheum Dis* 28:228, 1969.

260. BARABAS AP: Ehlers-Danlos syndrome associated with prematurity and premature rupture of foetal membranes: Possible increase in incidence. *Br Med J* 2:682, 1966.

261. LEIER CV, CALL TD, FULDERSON PK, WOOLEY CF: The spectrum of cardiac defects in the Ehlers-Danlos syndrome type I and III. *Ann Intern Med* 92:171, 1980.

262. SYKES B: Personal communication.

263. GRAHAME R: Physical properties of the skin in the Ehlers-Danlos syndrome, in Beighton P: *The Ehlers-Danlos Syndrome.* London, Heinemann, 1970, p.

264. VOGEL A, HOLBROOK KA, STEINMANN B, GITZELMANN R, BYERS PH: Abnormal collagen fibril structure in the gravis form (type I) of the Ehlers-Danlos syndrome. *Lab Invest* 40:201, 1979.

265. SEVENICH M, SCHULTZ-EHRENBURG U, ORFANOS CE: Ehlers-Danlos syndrome: A disease of fibroblasts and collagen fibrils. *Arch Dermatol Res* 267:237, 1980.

266. SHINKAI H, HIRABAYASHI O, TAMEKI A, MATSUBAYASHI S, SENO S: Connective tissue metabolism in cultured fibroblasts of a patient with Ehlers-Danlos syndrome type I. *Arch Dermatol Res* 257:113, 1976.

267. SASAKI T, ARAI K, ONO M, YAMAGUCHI T, FURUTA S, NAGAI Y: Ehlers-Danlos syndrome. A variant characterized by the deficiency of proα2 chain of type I procollagen. *Arch Dermatol* 123:76, 1987.

268. SACK G: Status dysvascularis; ein fall von besonderer zerreisslichkeit dev blutgefasse. *Dtsch Arch Klin Med* 178:663, 1936.

269. GOTTRON F: Familiare acrogeria. *Arch Dermatol Res* 181:571, 1940.

270. POPE FM, MARTIN GR, LICHTENSTEIN JR, PENTTINEN RP, GERSON G, ROWE DW, MCKUSICK VA: Patients with Ehlers-Danlos syndrome type IV lack type III collagen. *Proc Natl Acad Sci USA* 72:1314, 1975.

271. POPE FM, NICHOLLS AC, JONES PM, WELLS RS, LAWRENCE D: EDS IV (acrogeria): New autosomal dominant and recessive types. *JR Soc Med* 73:180, 1980.

272. TSIPOURAS P, BYERS PH, SCHWARTZ RC, CHU M-L, WEIL D, PEPE G, CASSIDY SB, RAMIREZ F: Ehlers-Danlos syndrome type IV: Cosegregation of the phenotype to a COL3A1 allele of type III procollagen. *Hum Genet* 74:41, 1986.

273. POPE FM, MARTIN GR, MCKUSICK VA: Inheritance of Ehlers-Danlos type IV syndrome. *J Med Genet* 14:200, 1977.

274. SULH HMB, STEINMANN B, RAO VH, DUDIN G, ZEID A, SLIM M, DER KALOUSTIAN VM: Ehlers-Danlos syndrome type IVD: An autosomal recessive disorder. *Clin Genet* 25:278, 1984.

275. RUDD NL, NIMROD C, HOLBROOK KA, BYERS PH: Pregnancy complications in type IV Ehlers-Danlos syndrome. *Lancet* 1:50, 1983.

276. IMAHORI S, BANNERMAN RM, GRAF CJ, BRENNAN JC: Ehlers-Danlos syndrome with multiple arterial lesions. *Am J Med* 47:967, 1969.

277. LACH B, NAIR SG, RUSSELL NA, BENOIT BG: Spontaneous carotid-cavennous fistula and multiple arterial dissections in type IV Ehlers-Danlos syndrome. *J Neurosurg* 66:462, 1987.

278. POPE FM, NICHOLLS AC: Pregnancy and Ehlers-Danlos syndrome type IV. *Lancet* 1:249, 1983.

279. KUMING BS, JOFFE L: Ehlers-Danlos syndrome associated with keratoconus. *S Afr Med J* 52:403, 1977.

280. HOLBROOK KA, BYERS PH: Diseases of the Extracellular matrix: Structural alterations of collagen fibrils in skin, in Uitto J, Perejda AJ (eds): *Connective Tissue Disease: Molecular Pathology of the Extracellular Matrix,* New York, Marcel Dekker, 1987, p 101.

281. BYERS PH, HOLBROOK KA, MCGILLIVRAY B, MacLEOD PM, LOWRY RB: Clinical and ultrastructural heterogeneity of type IV Ehlers-Danlos syndrome. *Hum Genet* 47:141, 1979.

282. LAURENT R, AGACHE P: L'acrogeria est-elle une maladie du fibroblaste? *Dermatologica* 148:28, 1974.

283. BYERS PH, HOLBROOK KA, BARSH GS, SMITH LT, BORNSTEIN P: Altered secretion of type III procollagen in a form of type IV Ehlers-Danlos syndrome: Biochemical studies in cultured fibroblasts. *Lab Invest* 44:336, 1981.

284. AUMAILLEY M, KRIEG T, DESSAU W, MÜLLER PK, TIMPL R, BRICAUD H: Biochemical and immunological studies of fibroblasts derived from a patient with Ehlers-Danlos syndrome type IV demonstrate reduced type III collagen synthesis. *Arch Dermatol Res* 269:169, 1980.

285. SUPERTI-FURGA A, GUGLER E, GITZELMANN R, STEINMANN B: Ehlers-Danlos syndrome type IV: A multi-exon deletion in one of the two COL3A1 alleles affecting structure, stability, and processing of type III procollagen. *J Biol Chem* 263: 6226, 1988.

286. SUPERTI-FURGA A, STEINMANN B: Impaired secretion of type III procollagen in Ehlers-Danlos syndrome type IV fibroblasts: Correction of the defect by incubation at reduced temperature and demonstration of subtle alterations in the triple-helical region of the molecule. *Biochem Biophys Res Commun* 150:140, 1988.

287. STOLLE CA, PYERITZ RE, MYERS JC, PROCKOP DJ: Synthesis of an altered type III procollagen in a patient with type IV Ehlers-Danlos syndrome. *J Biol Chem* 260:1937, 1985.

288. CLARK JG, KUHN C III, UITTO J: Lung collagen in type IV Ehlers-Danlos syndrome: Ultrastructural and biochemical studies. *Am Rev Resp Dis* 122:971, 1980.

289. BEIGHTON P: X-linked recessive inheritance of the Ehlers-Danlos syndrome. *Br Med J* 2:409, 1968.

290. BEIGHTON P, CURTIS D: X-linked Ehlers-Danlos syndrome type V; the next generation. *Clin Genet* 27:472, 1985.

291. DIFERRANTE N, LEACHMAN RD, ANGELINI D, DONNELLY PW, FRANCIS G, ALMAZAN A: Lysyl oxidase deficiency in Ehlers-Danlos type V. *Connect Tissue Res* 3:49, 1975.

292. SIEGEL RC, BLACK C, BAILEY AJ: Cross-linking of collagen in the X-linked Ehlers-Danlos type V. *Biochem Biophys Res Commun* 88:281, 1979.

293. SUSSMAN M, LICHTENSTEIN JR, NIGRA TP, MARTIN GR, MCKUSICK VA: Hydroxylysine-deficient collagen in a patient with a form of the Ehlers-Danlos syndrome. *J Bone Joint Surg [Am]* 56A:1228, 1974.

294. STEINMANN B, GITZELMANN R, VOGEL A, GRANT ME, HARWOOD R, SEAR CHJ: Ehlers-Danlos syndrome in two siblings with deficient lysyl hydroxylase activity in cultured skin fibroblasts but only mild dydroxylysine deficient skin. *Helv Paediatr Acta* 30:255, 1975.

295. ELSAS LJ, MILLER RL, PINNELL SR: Inherited human collagen lysyl hydroxylase deficiency: Ascorbic acid response. *Pediatrics* 92:378, 1978.

296. DEMBURE PP, PRIEST JH, SNODDY SC, ELSAS LJ: Genotyping and prenatal assessment of collagen lysyl hydroxylase deficiency in a family with Ehlers-Danlos syndrome, type VI. *Am J Hum Genet* 36:783, 1984.

297. IHME A, KRIEG T, NERLICH A, FELDMANN U, RAUTERBERG J, GLANVILLE RW, EDEL G, MÜLLER PK: Ehlers-Danlos syndrome type VI: Collagen type specificity of defective lysyl hydroylation in various tissues. *J Invest Dermatol* 83:161, 1984.

298. IHME A, RISTELI L, KRIEG T, RISTELI J, FELDMANN U, KUUSE K, MÜLLER PK: Biochemical characterization of variants of the Ehlers-Danlos syndrome type VI. *Eur J Clin Invest* 13:357, 1983.

299. KRIEG T, FELDMANN U, KESSLER W, MÜLLER PK: Biochemical characteristics of Ehlers-Danlos syndrome type VI in a family with one affected infant. *Hum Genet* 46:41, 1979.

300. DEMBURE PP, JANKO AR, PRIEST JH, ELSAS LJ: Ascorbate regulation of collagen biosynthesis in Ehlers-Danlos syndrome, type VI. *Metabolism* 36:687, 1987.

301. MCKUSICK VA: *Mendelian Inheritance in Man. Catalogs of Autosomal Dominant, Autosomal Recessive, and X-Linked Phenotypes,* 7th ed. Baltimore, Johns Hopkins University Press, 1986, p 949.

302. JUDISCH GF, WAZIRI M, KRACHMER JH: Ocular Ehlers-Danlos syndrome with normal lysyl hydroxylase activity. *Arch Ophthalmol* 94:1489, 1976.

303. RISTELI L, RISTELI J, IHME A, KRIEG T, MÜLLER PK: Preferential hydroxylation of type IV collagen by lysyl hydroxylase from Ehlers-Danlos syndrome type VI fibroblasts. *Biochem Biophys Res Commun* 96:1778, 1980.

304. QUINN RS, KRANE SM: Abnormal properties of collagen lysyl hydroxylase from skin fibroblasts of siblings with hydroxylysine-deficient collagen. *J Clin Invest* 57:83, 1976.

305. EYRE DR, GLIMCHER MJ: Reducible cross-links in hydroxylysine-deficient collagens of a heritable disorder of connective tissue. *Proc Natl Acad Sci USA* 69:2594, 1972.

306. ROBINOW M, DUVIC M, BYERS PH: Unpublished observations.

307. FJOLSTED M, HELLE O: A hereditary dysplasia of collagen tissues in sheep. *J Pathol* 112:183, 1974.

308. COUNTS DR, BYERS PH, HOLBROOK KA, HEGREBERG GA: Dermatosparaxis in the Himalayan cat: Biochemical studies of dermal collagen. *J Invest Dermatol* 74:96, 1980.

309. HOLBROOK KA, BYERS PH, COUNTS DF, HEGREBERG GA: Dermatosparaxis in a Himalayan cat: Ultrastructural studies of dermal collagen. *J Invest Dermatol* 74:100, 1980.

310. STEINMANN B, TUDERMAN L, PELTONEN L, MARTIN GR, MCKUSICK VA, PROCKOP DJ: Evidence for a structural mutation of procollagen type I in

a patient with the Ehlers-Danlos syndrome type VII. *J Biol Chem* 255:8887, 1980.

311. EYRE DR, SHAPIRO FD, ALDRIDGE JF: Heterozygous collagen defect in a variant of the Ehlers-Danlos syndrome type VII: Evidence for a deleted amino telopeptide domain in the proα2(I) chain. *J Biol Chem* 260:11322, 1985.

312. COLE WG, CHAN D, CHAMBERS GW, WALKER ID, BATEMAN JF: Deletion of 24 amino acids from the proα1(I) chain of type I procollagen in a patient with the Ehlers-Danlos syndrome type VII. *J Biol Chem* 261:5496, 1986.

313. WIRTZ MK, GLANVILLE RW, STEINMANN B, RAO VH, HOLLISTER DW: Ehlers-Danlos syndrome type VIIB. *J Biol Chem* 262:16376, 1987.

314. WEIL D, BERNARD M, COMBATA N, WIRTZ MK, HOLLISTER DW, STEINMANN B, RAMIREZ F: Identification of a mutation that causes exon-skipping during collagen pre-mRNA splicing in an Ehlers-Danlos syndrome variant. *J Biol Chem* 263:8561, 1988.

315. HALILA R, STEINMANN B, PELTONEN L: Processing of types I and III procollagen in Ehlers-Danlos syndrome type VII. *Am J Hum Genet* 39:222, 1986.

316. MAUCH C, AUMAILLEY M, PAYE M, LAPIERE CM, TIMPL R, KRIEG T: Defective attachment of dermatosparactic fibroblasts to collagen I and IV. *Exp Cell Res* 163:294, 1986.

317. COLE WG, EVANS R, SILLENCE DO: The clinical features of Ehlers-Danlos syndrome type VII due to a deletion of 24 amino acids from the proα1(I) chain of type I procollagen. *J Med Genet* 24:698, 1987.

318. STEWART RD, HOLLISTER DW, RIMOIN DL: A new variant of the Ehlers-Danlos syndrome: An autosomal dominant disorder of fragile skin, abnormal scarring, and generalized periodontitis. *Birth Defects* 13(3B):85, 1977.

319. LINCH DC, ACTON CHC: Ehlers-Danlos syndrome presenting with juvenile destructive periodontis. *Br Dent J* 147:95, 1979.

320. LAZOFF SG, RYBAK JJ, PARKER BR, LUZZATTI L: Skeletal dysplasia, occipital horns, diarrhea and obstructive uropathy—A new hereditary syndrome. *Birth Defects* 11(2): 71, 1975.

321. BYERS PH, SIEGEL RC, HOLBROOK KA, NARAYANAN AS, BORNSTEIN P, HALL JG: X-linked cutis laza: Defective collagen crosslink formation due to decreased lysyl oxidase activity. *N Engl J Med* 303:61, 1980.

322. SARTORIS DJ, LUZZATTI L, WEAVER DD, MacFARLANE JD, HOLLISTER DW, PARKER BR: Type IX Ehlers-Danlos syndrome: A new variant with pathognomonic radiographic features. *Radiology* 152:665, 1984.

323. BLACKSTON RD, HIRSCHHORN K, ELSAS LJ: Ehlers-Danlos syndrome (EDS), type IX: Biochemical evidence of X-linkage. *Am J Hum Genet* 41:A49, 1987.

324. KUIVANIEMI H, PELTONEN L, PALOTIE A, KAITILA I, KIVIRIKKO KI: Abnormal copper metabolism and deficient lysyl oxidase activity in a heritable connective tissue disorder. *J Clin Invest* 69:730, 1982.

325. PELTONEN L, KUIVANIEMI H, PALOTIE A, HORN N, KAITILA I, KIVIRIKKO KI: Alterations in copper and collagen metabolism in the Menkes syndrome and a new subtype of the Ehlers-Danlos syndrome. *Biochemistry* 22:6156, 1983.

326. KUIVANIEMI H, PELTONEN L, KIVIRIKKO KI: Type IX Ehlers-Danlos syndrome and Menkes syndrome: The decrease in lysyl oxidase activity is associated with a corresponding deficiency in the enzyme protein. *Am J Hum Genet* 37:798, 1985.

327. ARNESON MA, HAMMERSCHMIDT DE, FURCHT LT, KING RA: A new form of Ehlers-Danlos syndrome: Fibronectin corrects defective platelet function. *JAMA* 244:144, 1980.

328. HEGREBERG GA, PADGETT GA, GORHAM JR, HENSON JB: A connective tissue disease of dogs and mink resembling the Ehlers-Danlos syndrome of man. II. Mode of inheritance. *J Hered* 60:249, 1969.

329. MINOR RR: Collagen metabolism. *Am J Pathol* 98:227, 1980.

330. COUNTS DF: Isolation of collagen from the skins of Ehlers-Danlos syndrome-affected dogs by acetic acid extraction and pepsin digestion. *Biochem Biophys Acta* 626:208, 1980.

331. ROWE DW, McGOODWIN EB, MARTIN GR, SUSSMAN MD, GRAHN D, FARIS B, FRANZBLAU C: A sex linked defect in the cross-linking of collagen and elastin associated with the mottled locus in mice. *J Exp Med* 139:180, 1974.

332. ROWE DW, McGOODWIN EB, MARTIN GR, GRAHN D: Lysyl oxidase activity in the aneurysm-prone mottled mouse. *J Biol Chem* 252:939, 1977.

333. HUNT DM: Primary defect in copper transport underlies mottled mutants in the mouse. *Nature* 249:852, 1974.

334. HUNT DM: A study of copper treatment and tissue copper levels in the murine congenital copper deficiency, mottled. *Life Sci* 19:1913, 1976.

335. PORT AE, HUNT DM: A study of the copper-binding proteins in liver and kidney tissue of neonatal normal and mottled mutant mice. *Biochem J* 183:721, 1979.

336. PACKMAN S, CHIN P, O'TOOLE C: Copper utilization in cultured skin fibroblasts of the mottled mouse, an animal model for Menkes' kinky hair syndrome. *J Inherited Metab Dis* 7:168, 1984.

337. PYERITZ RE, McKUSICK VA: The Marfan syndrome: Diagnosis and management. *N Engl J Med* 300:772, 1979.

338. MARFAN AB: Un cas de deformation congenitale des quatre membres plus prononcee aux extremities characterisee par l'allongement des os avec un certain degre d'amincissement. *Bull Mem Soc Med Hop Paris* 13:220, 1896.

339. HECHT F, BEALS RK: "New" syndrome of congenital contractural arachnodactyly originally described by Marfan in 1896. *Pediatrics* 49:574, 1972.

340. MAUMENEE IH: The eye in the Marfan syndrome. *Trans Am Ophthalmol Soc* 79:684, 1981.

341. McKUSICK VA: The cardiovascular aspects of Marfan's syndrome. *Circulation* 11:321, 1955.

342. CARSON NAJ, NEILL DW: Metabolic abnormalities detected in a survey of mentally backward individuals in Northern Ireland. *Arch Dis Child* 37:505, 1962.

343. GERRITSEN T, VAUGHN JG, WAISMAN HA: The identification of homocystine in the urine. *Biochem Biophys Res Commun* 9:493, 1962.

344. BEALS RK, HECHT F: Contractural arachnodactyly, a heritable disorder of connective tissue. *J Bone Joint Surg* 53A:987, 1971.

345. DEVEREAUX RB, BROWN WT: Genetics of mitral valve prolapse. *Prog Med Genet* 5:139, 1983.

346. MURDOCK JL, WALKER BA, HALPERN BL, KUSMA JW, McKUSICK VA: Life expectancy and causes of death in the Marfan syndrome. *N Engl J Med* 286:804, 1972.

347. GOTT VL, PYERITZ RE, MAGOVERN GJ, CAMERON DE, McKUSICK VA: Surgical treatment of aneurysms of the ascending aorta in the Marfan syndrome: Results of composite-graft repair in 50 patients. *N Engl J Med* 314:1070, 1986.

348. PYERITZ RE: Propranolol retards aortic root dilatation in the Marfan syndrome. *Circulation* 68 (Supplement III):365, 1983.

349. PYERITZ RE: Protection of the aortic root by propranolol in Marfan syndrome. *J Med Genet* 23:469, 1986.

350. BOLANDE RP: The nature of the connective tissue abiotrophy in the Marfan syndrome. *Lab Invest* 12:1087, 1963.

351. MATALON R, DORFMAN A: The accumulation of hyaluronic acid in cultured fibroblasts of the Marfan syndrome. *Biochem Biophys Res Commun* 32:150, 1968.

352. LAMBERG SI, DORFMAN A: Synthesis and degradation of hyaluronic acid in the cultured fibroblasts of Marfan's disease. *J Clin Invest* 52:2428, 1973.

353. APPEL A, HORWITZ AL, DORFMAN A: Cell-free synthesis of hyaluronic acid in Marfan syndrome. *J Biol Chem* 254:12199, 1979.

354. BOUCEK RJ, NOBLE NL, GUNJA-SMITH Z, BUTLER WT: The Marfan syndrome: A deficiency in chemically stable collagen cross-links. *N Engl J Med* 305:988, 1981.

355. SCHECK M, SIEGEL RC, PARKER J, CHANG Y-H, FU JCC: Aortic aneurysm in Marfan's syndrome: Changes in the ultrastructure and composition of collagen. *J Anat* 129:645, 1979.

356. BYERS PH, SIEGEL RC, PETERSON KE, ROWE DW, HOLBROOK KA, SMITH LT, CHANG Y, FU JCC: Marfan syndrome; an abnormal α2 chain in type I collagen. *Proc Natl Acad Sci USA* 78:7745, 1981.

357. HENKE E, LEADER M, TAJIMA S, PINNELL S, KAUFMAN R: A 38 base pair insertion in the pro α2(I) collagen gene of a patient with Marfan syndrome. *J Cell Biochem* 27:161, 1985.

358. DALGLEISH R, WILLIAMS G, HAWKINS JR: Length polymorphism in the pro α2(I) collagen gene: An alternative explanation in a case of Marfan syndrome. *Hum Genet* 73:91, 1986.

359. BYERS PH, SIEGEL RC, HOLBROOK KA: Biochemical approaches to the Marfan syndrome: A review, in Akeson W, Glimcher MJ, Bornstein P (eds): *Proceedings of Symposium on Inherited Disease of Connective Tissue.* New York, Elsevier, 1982, p 122.

360. PYERITZ RE, McKUSICK VA: Basic defects in the Marfan syndrome. *N Engl J Med* 305:1011, 1981.

361. OGILVIE DJ, WORDSWORTH BP, PRIESTLEY LM, DALGLEISH R, SCHMIDTKE J, ZOLL B, SYKES BC: Segregation of all four major fibrillar collagen genes in the Marfan syndrome. *Am J Hum Genet* 41:1071, 1987.

362. TSIPOURAS P, BORRESEN A-L, BAMFORTH S, HARPER PS, BERG K: Marfan syndrome: Exclusion of genetic linkage to the COL1A2 gene. *Clin Genet* 30:428, 1986.

363. DALGLEISH R, HAWKINS JR, KESTON M: Exclusion of the α2(I) and α1(III) collagen genes as the mutant loci in a Marfan syndrome family. *J Med Genet* 24:148, 1987.

364. HOLLISTER DW, SAKAI LY, PYERITZ RE: Abnormalities of the microfibrillar fiber system in Marfan syndrome. *Am J Hum Genet* 41:A7, 1987.

365. STICKER GB, BELAU PG, FARRELL FJ, JONES JD, PUGH DG, STEINBERG AG, WARD LE: Hereditary progressive arthro-ophthalmopathy. *Proc Staff Meet Mayo Clin* 40:433, 1965.

366. FRANCOMANO CA, LIBERFARB R, HIROSE T, MAUMENEE I, STREETER E, MEYERS D, PYERITZ RE: The Stickler syndrome: Evidence for close linkage to the structural gene of type II collagen. *Genomics* 1:293, 1987.

367. MURRAY LW, RIMOIN DL: Type II collagen abnormalities in the spondyloepi- and spondyloepimetaphyseal dysplasias. *Am J Hum Genet* 37:A13, 1985.

368. GODFREY M, KEENE DR, BLANK E, HORI H, SAKAI LY, SHERWIN LA, HOLLISTER DW: Achondrogenesis type II: A dominant disorder of type II collagen? *Am J Hum Genet* 41:A5, 1987.

369. EYRE DR, UPTON MP, SHAPIRO FD, WILKINSON RH, VAWTER GF: Non-expression of cartilage type II collagen in a case of Langer-Saldino achondrogenesis. *Am J Hum Genet* 39:52, 1986.

370. BRIGGAMAN RA, WHEELER CE JR: Epidermolysys bullosa dystrophica-recessiva: A possible role of anchoring fibrils in the pathogenesis. *J Invest Dermatol* 65:203, 1975.

371. BORNSTEIN P, BYERS PH: Disorders of collagen metabolism, in Bondy PK, Rosenberg LE (eds): *Metabolic Control and Disease*, Philadelphia, Saunders, 1980, chap 15, p 1089.

372. AMENTA PS, GAY S, VAHERI A, MARTINEZ-HERNANDEZ A: The extracellular matrix is an integrated unit: Ultrastructural localization of collagen types I, III, IV, V, VI, fibronectin, and laminin in human term placenta. *Coll Relat Res* 6:125, 1986.

CHAPTER 116

HYPOPHOSPHATASIA

MICHAEL P. WHYTE

1. Hypophosphatasia (McKusick 14630, 24150, 24151) is a heritable metabolic bone disease that reveals the importance of alkaline phosphatase for mineralization of the skeleton and formation of the teeth. Subnormal serum alkaline phosphatase activity is the biochemical hallmark of hypophosphatasia. The reduction reflects a generalized deficiency of activity of the tissue-nonspecific (liver, bone, kidney) alkaline phosphatase isoenzyme. Activities of the intestinal and placental alkaline phosphatase isoenzymes are normal. Tissue-nonspecific alkaline phosphatase is a glycoprotein that has recently been found to be bound to the extracellular surface of plasma membranes by glycosylphosphatidylinositol linkage. Its gene has been localized to the short arm of chromosome 1.

2. In hypophosphatasia, defective skeletal mineralization causes rickets in infants and children and osteomalacia in adults. Clinical expressivity is extremely variable. Stillbirth can occur from in utero onset of the lethal perinatal form. The infantile type is associated with nephrocalcinosis from hypercalcemia and is often fatal. Premature loss of teeth is the cardinal clinical feature of childhood hypophosphatasia. Adults suffer from recurrent fractures and pseudofractures.

3. Three phosphocompounds—phosphoethanolamine, inorganic pyrophosphate, and pyridoxal-5'-phosphate—accumulate in hypophosphatasia and are inferred to be natural substrates for tissue-nonspecific alkaline phosphatase. Pyridoxal-5'-phosphate collects extracellularly; intracellular levels are normal. This observation explains the absence of symptoms of vitamin B_6 deficiency or toxicity and indicates that tissue-nonspecific alkaline phosphatase functions as an ectoenzyme. Accumulation of inorganic pyrophosphate, an inhibitor of mineralization, seems to account for the abnormalities of bone and teeth.

4. Severely affected individuals with hypophosphatasia are homozygous for an autosomal defect(s) that may be clinically manifest in some mildly affected heterozygous subjects. Although the molecular basis is unknown, there is evidence in some cases for a regulatory abnormality in the biosynthesis of tissue-nonspecific alkaline phosphatase.

5. There is no effective medical treatment.

6. Early prenatal diagnosis of severe hypophosphatasia is possible by ultrasonography and assay of alkaline phosphatase activity in amniotic fluid cells.

BIOCHEMISTRY OF ALKALINE PHOSPHATASE

Alkaline phosphatase (ALP) (orthophosphoric-monoester phosphohydrolase, alkaline optimum, EC 3.1.3.1) is present in nearly all plants and animals.[1] In human beings ALPs are ubiquitous plasma membrane–bound glycoproteins encoded by at least three gene loci.[2] Two isoenzymes are expressed in a tissue-specific manner, intestinal and placental ALP. The third isoenzyme is abundant in liver, bone, and kidney, and some is found in most tissues.[2] Accordingly, this "liver, bone, kidney" ALP is also called *tissue-nonspecific ALP*. The official symbol for its gene is ALPL,[3] although it is not a liver-specific isoenzyme, and ALPL will be used throughout this chapter to refer to the tissue-nonspecific ALP isoenzyme.

Each ALP isoenzyme can be distinguished immunologically and by its physicochemical properties, including sensitivity to a variety of stereospecific noncompetitive inhibitors.[1,2,4] The distinct electrophoretic characteristics of the ALPLs purified from liver, bone, and kidney are lost following digestion with glycosidases.[5] These ALPLs differ, therefore, in posttranslational modifications involving carbohydrate residues and are not products of separate structural genes.[6]

Genes for intestinal and placental ALP have been localized to the long arm of chromosome 2, and for ALPL to the short arm of chromosome 1.[7,8] The cDNA for each gene has been cloned and sequenced.[9–11] Intestinal ALP appears to exist in a soluble form in the fetus and in a plasma membrane–bound form in the adult; the two forms may be encoded at different gene loci.[12] Placental ALP is highly polymorphic with three common and several rare alleles.[6] Its expression in placenta is controlled by the fetal genome. No allelic variation at the protein level has been found for the ALPL isoenzyme.[2,11]

ALPs are Zn^{2+} metalloenzymes that are generally regarded as dimers.[1,2] In the plasma membrane, however, ALPs probably exist as tetramers.[13] The molecular mass of the monomeric subunits ranges from 40 to 75 kDa.[2] The primary structure of the active site appears to be well conserved. Catalytic activity requires binding of both Zn^{2+} and Mg^{2+}. Each isoenzyme has broad substrate specificity and their pH optima depend upon the type and concentration of substrate.[1] Catalysis involves phosphorylation-dephosphorylation of serine residues; dissociation of covalently linked phosphate appears to be the rate-limiting step. Inorganic phosphate (Pi) is a potent competitive inhibitor.[1]

Little is known about the biosynthesis of ALPs in higher organisms. Analysis of cDNA sequences indicates that the nascent human ALP polypeptides have a hydrophobic domain at their carboxy termini.[9–11] However, in the plasma membrane, ALPs appear to be anchored to the polar head group of phosphatidylinositol, since they can be liberated by phosphatidylinositol-specific phospholipase.[13,14] The nature of the interaction with phosphatidylinositol may differ among the ALPs.[14] Although lipid-free ALP is present in serum, the mechanism of its release from plasma membranes is not understood. The site of clearance of ALP from the circulation appears to be the liver.[15]

Nonstandard abbreviations used in this chapter are: ALP = alkaline phosphatase; ALPL = tissue-nonspecific (liver, bone, kidney) alkaline phosphatase isoenzyme; Pi = inorganic phosphate; PPi = inorganic pyrophosphate; PEA = phosphoethanolamine; and PLP = pyridoxal-5'-phosphate.

Assays which use stereospecific inhibitors, heat denaturation, and retardation of ALP by antibody on electrophoresis have shown approximately equal amounts of ALPL from liver and bone in the sera of normal adults.[16] In infants and children, and particularly during the growth spurt of adolescence, serum is especially rich in bone ALPL.[1] Intestinal isoenzyme usually represents a few percent of the total serum ALP.[4] Some individuals (with specific blood types and secretor status) increase their circulating intestinal ALP levels after ingesting a fatty meal.[1,17] Placental ALP normally circulates only during pregnancy. However, placental-like ALPs have been reported in the sera of patients with various malignancies.[2]

PHYSIOLOGY OF SKELETAL FORMATION

The skeleton serves two important physiological purposes. It functions throughout life as both the framework for the body and a reservoir for calcium and other ions.

Skeletal development is a complex process that involves growth, modeling (shaping), and remodeling (formation and resorption) of individual bones. Lengthening of the extremities occurs by endochondral bone formation. In the growth plates, there is orderly proliferation of cartilage cells, deposition of skeletal matrix, degeneration of chondrocytes, and then mineralization until just after puberty. Skeletal remodeling continues lifelong in all bones and is the basis for the skeleton's metabolic role.[18] Skeletal remodeling is mediated by osteoblasts and osteoclasts. These two cell types are rich in alkaline and acid phosphatase, respectively. Osteoblasts synthesize bone matrix (osteoid) which subsequently calcifies; osteoclasts resorb the skeleton by degrading both bone mineral and matrix.[18]

Histologic studies suggest that the earliest site of skeletal mineralization is within extracellular membrane-bound structures called matrix vesicles.[19] Matrix vesicles were first identified as buds of chondrocyte plasma membrane, but have since been found in membranous and cortical bone and in fracture callus. They are rich in ALPL, pyrophosphatase, and ATPase activity and may contain polysaccharide, phospholipid, and glycolipid.[19] During endochondral bone formation, crystals of hydroxyapatite are first observed within matrix vesicles; subsequently, extravesicular crystal growth is noted.[19,20] Accordingly, two types of skeletal mineralization occur: primary, which begins in matrix vesicles, and secondary, where there is extravesicular nucleation and enlargement of hydroxyapatite crystals.[20]

For skeletal mineralization to occur properly, there must be adequate circulating levels of ionized calcium and Pi. Generalized impairment of skeletal mineralization in infants or children causes rickets. Rickets is characterized by defective endochondral ossification. In adults, whose growth plates have fused, impaired skeletal mineralization is manifested as osteo-

Table 116-1 Suggested Roles for ALP in Mineralization

1. Increases local Pi levels
2. Destroys inhibitors of hydroxyapatite crystal growth
3. Transports Pi
4. Ca^{2+}-binding protein
5. Ca^{2+}, Mg^{2+}-ATPase
6. Tyrosine-specific phosphoprotein phosphatase

malacia. Extracellular levels of calcium and/or Pi are subnormal in nearly all forms of rickets or osteomalacia (see Chaps. 79, 80, and 103 to 105). Hypophosphatasia is an exception.

PHYSIOLOGICAL ROLE OF ALKALINE PHOSPHATASE

In 1923, Robison discovered that ossifying cartilage from young rats and rabbits was rich in phosphatase activity. He suggested that this phosphatase conditioned skeletal mineralization by hydrolyzing some unknown phosphate ester(s) to produce free Pi.[21] In 1924, Robison and Soames reported that this phosphatase had an alkaline pH optimum and that it precipitated calcium and Pi from solutions in which organic phosphate esters were the only source of Pi.[22]

Soon thereafter, ALP activity was also found to be abundant in tissues that do not mineralize (e.g., intestine and placenta). This finding raised questions about the specificity of ALP in the process of mineralization.[1] Furthermore, ALP activity was noted to be especially rich in the plasma membranes of some fetal tissues and in a variety of mature cell types actively involved in ion transport.[1] These observations suggested that ALP acts more globally; e.g., in transport processes or in signal transduction. Other general physiological roles for ALP have been suggested,[1,23] including hydrolysis of phosphate esters to supply the nonphosphate moiety, synthesis of phosphate esters with ALP acting as a transferase, and regulation of a variety of cellular processes, perhaps with ALP acting as a phosphoprotein phosphatase. The function of ALPL in skeletal mineralization is still unclear,[23] though a variety of mechanisms of action of ALPL for this purpose have been proposed (Table 116-1).

Robison's suggestion that ALP conditions mineralization by raising the concentration of Pi locally remains a viable hypothesis. Nucleoside phosphate liberated by degenerating cells could be the substrate source of Pi.[24] However, it has also been suggested that ALPL might hydrolyze an inhibitor of mineralization.[1,23] The discovery that inorganic pyrophosphate (PPi) can impair hydroxyapatite crystal deposition[25] and the finding that plasma levels of PPi are increased in hypophosphatasia[26] presented a plausible explanation for the defective mineralization in this disorder (see below). Indeed, as first reported by Moss and colleagues in 1967,[27] ALP can function as an inorganic pyrophosphatase. Other roles for ALP in mineralization have been proposed. It has been suggested that ALP might function as a plasma membrane transport protein for Pi,[23] as an extracellular Ca^{2+}-binding protein that promotes calcium phosphate formation and orients its deposition into osteoid,[28] as a Ca^{2+}, Mg^{2+}-ATPase, or as a phosphoprotein phosphatase that conditions the skeletal matrix for mineralization.[29]

The methods used to assay ALP activity reflect our ignorance of the physiological function(s) of this enzyme.[1] In both the clinical and research laboratory, ALP activity is generally assayed with high concentrations (mM) of artificial substrates at nonphysiological (alkaline) pH. With certain substrates at lower concentration, the pH optimum of ALP is less alkaline, but the hydrolytic rate is reduced. The physiological significance of this observation has been unclear.[1] In the author's opinion, it was characterization of hypophosphatasia as an inborn error of metabolism that has best elucidated the physiological role of ALPL.

HYPOPHOSPHATASIA

History

J. C. Rathbun coined the term *hypophosphatasia* in 1948 when he described an infant boy who died from severe rickets, weight loss, and seizures and whose ALP activity in serum, bone, lung, kidney, and bowel was subnormal.[30] Several excellent historical reviews recount probable cases that were described several decades earlier, and summaries of early progress in understanding this disorder are available.[31–33] In 1950, Schneider and Corcoran provided evidence that hypophosphatasia was a heritable condition.[34] Sobel and coworkers noted in 1953 that premature loss of deciduous teeth was an integral part of the clinical expression.[35] By 1980, 278 cases had been described.[36]

Among the observations that clarified the metabolic basis for hypophosphatasia and the physiological role of ALPL were the discoveries of increased endogenous levels of three phosphocompounds (Fig. 116-1). In 1955, Fraser, Yendt, and Christie[37] and McCance, Morrison, and Dent[38] reported increased urinary levels of a substance that proved to be phosphoethanolamine (PEA). This discovery provided a useful biochemical marker for the disorder. In 1965 and 1971, Russell found high levels of PPi in urine[39] and in blood,[26] respectively, thus presenting an explanation for the defective mineralization. In 1985, Whyte and colleagues[40] reported that plasma levels of pyridoxal-5′-phosphate (PLP) were elevated—a finding which suggested that ALPL functions as an ectoenzyme (see below).

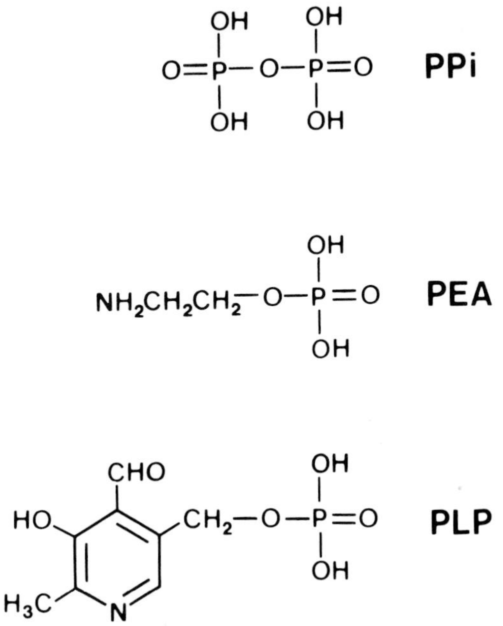

Clinical Features

Hypophosphatasia occurs in all races. The incidence in Toronto was estimated by Fraser to be 1 in 100,000 live births.[32] Consanguinity has been reported in some families with severely affected cases.[32,41]

Despite the presence of at least some ALPL in most normal tissues, the clinical consequences of hypophosphatasia involve predominantly the skeleton and dentition. Severity of clinical expression is remarkably variable and ranges from death in utero to onset of recurrent fractures late in adult life.[32,36,41–43] Some individuals with characteristic biochemical abnormalities may never become symptomatic.[42,43]

Since the precise molecular genetic defects are unknown for hypophosphatasia, the classification of patients remains a clinical one. Several schemes have been proposed; each emphasizes the clinical heterogeneity.[32,41] In general, four forms—perinatal or lethal, infantile, childhood, and adult—are distinguished depending primarily upon the age at which skeletal lesions develop.[32,36] The prognosis depends upon the severity of the skeletal disease which, in turn, correlates with the age at presentation. The earlier a patient becomes symptomatic, the more severe the disorder. Subjects who have only dental manifestations are regarded as having "odontohypophosphatasia." Although the following nosology is useful clinically, it is clear that distinct separation of the clinical forms is not possible.

Perinatal (lethal) hypophosphatasia, the most severe form, is expressed in utero and can result in stillbirth. The pregnancy may be complicated by polyhydramnios. *Caput membraneceum* and almost complete lack of mineralization of the skeleton may be present at birth. Limbs are shortened and deformed, and unusual spurs may occur on the long bones.[44] Some subjects live a few days but suffer increasing respiratory compromise from rachitic disease of the chest. Failure to gain weight, a high-pitched cry, irritability, periodic apnea with cyanosis and bradycardia, unexplained fever, myelophthisic anemia (perhaps from encroachment on the marrow space by excess osteoid), intracranial hemorrhage, and idiopathic seizures may occur.[36,41]

Radiographic survey of the skeleton enables this form of hypophosphatasia to be readily distinguished from even the most severe types of osteogenesis imperfecta and congenital dwarfism. Indeed, the radiologic changes may be considered diagnostic.[44] In some cases, the skeleton may appear to be almost completely unmineralized (Fig. 116-2). In others, there is marked bony undermineralization and severe rachitic changes that are most obvious at the metaphyses of the wrist, knees, and costochondral junctions. Epiphyses may be poorly ossified, and irregular extensions of growth plate cartilage and unmineralized osteoid protrude into the metaphyses. In some cases, separate diaphyseal defects occur as well. Fractures are often present. The cranial bones may show ossification only at their central portions. The unossified membranous bone gives the illusion that the sutures are widely separated, although they are functionally closed.[44]

Hypophosphatasemia is present in cord blood at birth.[45] Histologic abnormalities are found primarily in the skeleton where an extreme excess of osteoid can be demonstrated in undecalcified sections of bone.[20] Extramedullary hematopoiesis is occasionally noted in the liver.

Infantile hypophosphatasia presents before age 6 months.[32] Postnatal development often seems normal until poor feeding and inadequate weight gain are observed at several months of age.[45,46] In retrospect, hypotonia and wide fontanelles may have been noted earlier. Rachitic deformities develop and may progress; cranial sutures remain wide. Flail chest with predisposition to pneumonia is common. Ophthalmologic findings

Fig. 116-1 Three phosphocompounds appear to be natural substrates for tissue-nonspecific alkaline phosphatase (ALPL) since each accumulates endogenously in hypophosphatasia: inorganic pyrophosphate (PPi), phosphoethanolamine (PEA), and pyridoxal-5′-phosphate (PLP).

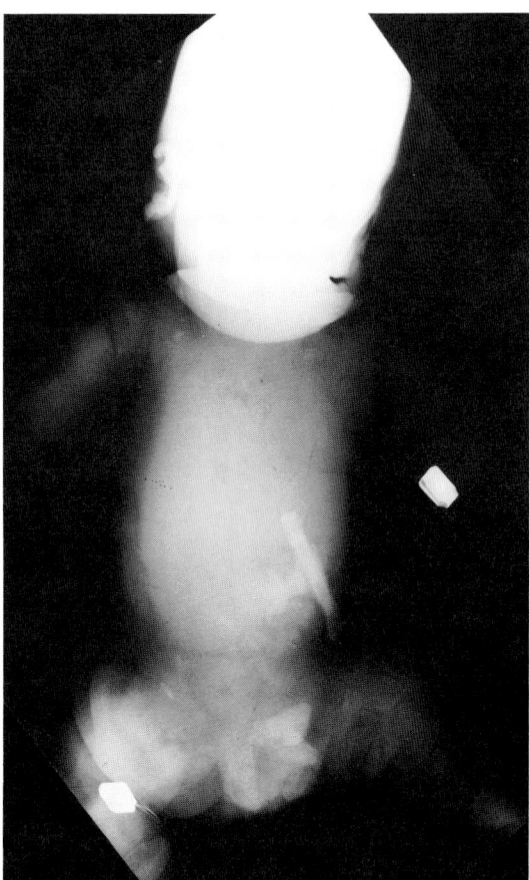

Fig. 116-2 Perinatal hypophosphatasia. Radiologic study of a stillborn with severe hypophosphatasia reveals profound skeletal hypomineralization, a finding that enables the perinatal (lethal) form to be readily distinguished from other congenital bone disorders.

may include blue sclerae.[47] Hypercalcemia and hypercalciuria develop in some patients, resulting in recurrent vomiting, nephrocalcinosis, and renal compromise.[32,45,46] Premature synostosis of the cranial sutures is the rule.[44] There may be bulging of the anterior fontanelle. Patients can develop raised intracranial pressure with papilledema, proptosis, mild hypertelorism, and brachycephaly.

The radiologic changes are characteristic and severe, resembling those of the perinatal form, though less marked.[44] In some subjects, abrupt transition from an uncalcified metaphysis to a relatively normal diaphysis can occur and suggests a sudden metabolic change.[32] Sequential radiologic studies may disclose not only a persistent defect in bone mineralization, but progressive skeletal demineralization as well.[46] Histopathologic findings reveal severe rickets with defects in membranous and endochondral bone formation and skeletal remodeling.[48]

Childhood hypophosphatasia is highly variable in its clinical expression.[32,45,48] Premature loss of deciduous teeth (i.e., earlier than 5 years of age) from aplasia or hypoplasia of dental cementum[49] may be the only clinical abnormality, and radiographic studies may show no sign of rickets. These patients with odontohypophosphatasia generally have milder biochemical features compared to children with skeletal disease (see below). Premature loss of deciduous teeth occurs without inflammatory periodontal disease and with only minimal root resorption. Dental radiographs may show enlarged pulp chambers and root canals ("shell teeth"). The incisors are frequently lost first, but nearly the entire dentition may be

disturbed. Alveolar bone attrition may occur from lack of mechanical stimulation, since aplasia of the cementum prevents periodontal ligaments from connecting teeth and jaw.[50] Odontohypophosphatasia may be the actual etiology of many cases of "early onset periodontitis,"[51] although hereditary leukocyte abnormalities (see Chap. 113) and other factors account for juvenile periodontitis.

When rickets is apparent radiologically in addition to premature loss of teeth, there often is short stature, delayed walking, and a characteristic waddling gait.[32,45] Rachitic deformities include a dolichocephalic skull with frontal bossing, beading of the costochondral junctions, either bowed legs or knock-knee deformity, and enlargement of the wrists, knees, and ankles. Recurrent nephrotic syndrome, probably coincidental, has been reported in one child.[52] Radiographs of the metaphyseal regions of long bones may reveal characteristic focal defects; i.e., "tongues" of radiolucency that project from the rachitic growth plate into the metaphysis (Fig. 116-3). This feature, if present, permits distinction of hypophosphatasia from other forms of rickets and metaphyseal dysplasias.[44] Epiphyseal centers of ossification may be well-preserved. Functional synostosis of cranial sutures can occur in affected infants and young children despite widely "open" fontanelles and hypomineralized areas of calvarium. Later, true premature bony fusion of cranial sutures may cause proptosis, raised intracranial pressure, and brain damage. Here, the skull may have a "beaten-copper" appearance on radiologic study.[44]

Fig. 116-3 Childhood hypophosphatasia. Posteroanterior radiograph of the knee of a 5-year-old boy with hypophosphatasia reveals growth plates that are not greatly widened, yet defective endochondral bone formation is revealed by irregular radiolucencies (arrows) that project into the metaphyses. This finding is characteristic of the childhood form of hypophosphatasia.

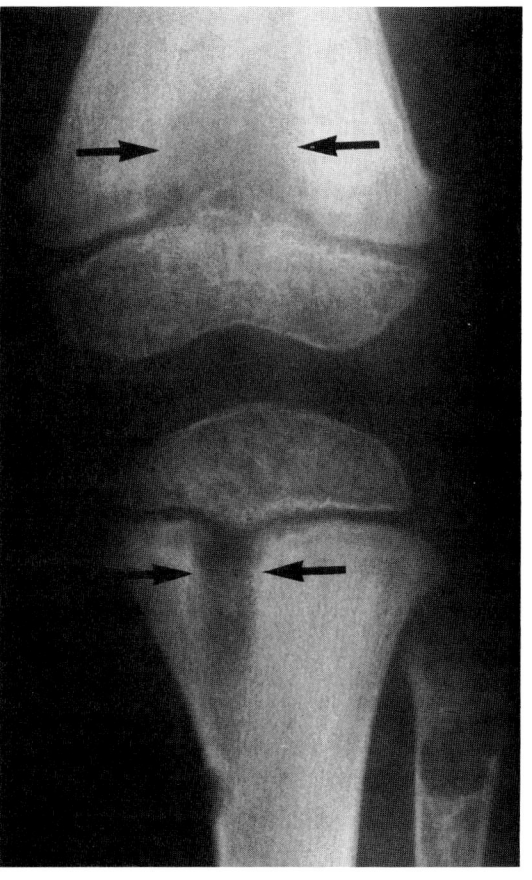

Adult hypophosphatasia usually presents during middle age.[42,43] Some patients recall a history of rickets and premature exfoliation of deciduous teeth; early loss or extraction of adult teeth is also common.[42,43,53] Osteomalacia may cause pain in the feet from recurrent metatarsal stress fractures and/or discomfort in the thighs or hips from femoral pseudofractures (Fig. 116-4). Chondrocalcinosis and calcium pyrophosphate deposition disease, sometimes with attacks of arthritis, occur in some patients, apparently from the increased endogenous levels of PPi.[43,54] Family screening may reveal symptomatic or asymptomatic adults.[42,43]

Radiologic study of adult hypophosphatasia may detect osteopenia.[42] Pseudofractures (Looser zones), a hallmark of defective bone mineralization, occur most often laterally in the proximal femora rather than medially as in most other types of osteomalacia.[55] Analysis of cartilage from the pubic symphysis of one adult with chondrocalcinosis has documented calcium-pyrophosphate crystal deposition.[54]

Pseudohypophosphatasia has been documented convincingly in one subject.[56] In this disorder, circulating ALPL activity is consistently normal or increased, yet the clinical, radiologic, and biochemical findings are otherwise typical of subjects who survive infantile hypophosphatasia.[56,57] The enzymatic defect may involve a mutant ALPL that retains its enzymatic activity toward artificial substrates at alkaline pH but is catalytically defective toward natural substrates at physiological pH.[57,58] Other reports of pseudohypophosphatasia are less convincing[59–61] and probably describe individuals with transient increases in circulating ALP activity or misinterpretation of reference ranges for serum ALP activity and/or urinary phosphoethanolamine (PEA) levels (see below).

Fig. 116-4   Adult hypophosphatasia. The femur of a middle-aged woman reveals a pseudofracture or Looser zone (arrow) which has been unhealed for several years. Characteristically, these cortical bone defects form on the lateral aspect of the femur in adult hypophosphatasia rather than medially as in most other forms of osteomalacia.

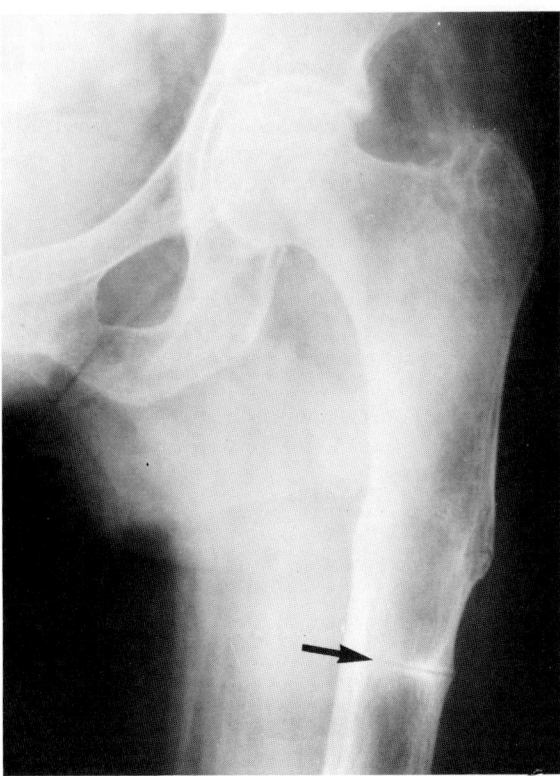

Laboratory Diagnosis

Hypophosphatasia can usually be diagnosed with confidence in subjects with a consistent clinical history and physical findings in whom serum ALP activity is clearly subnormal. However, a variety of diagnostic pitfalls must be avoided.[62] First, blood specimens must be obtained correctly. Chelation of Mg^{2+} or Zn^{2+} by EDTA, etc., in collection tubes will destroy ALP activity.[1] Circulating ALP activity varies according to age and sex; e.g., normal infants and children have considerably higher serum ALP levels due to bone ALPL enzyme than do adults, and these levels increase during the growth spurt of adolescence.[1] Unless serum ALP activity is assayed at a pediatric hospital, the normal values provided by most laboratories are usually those for adults. Therefore, infants or children with hypophosphatasia may incorrectly be regarded as having normal serum ALP activity or "pseudohypophosphatasia." Although a variety of conditions (hypothyroidism, starvation, scurvy, severe anemia, celiac disease, Wilson disease, hypomagnesemia, Zn^{2+} deficiency) and drugs (glucocorticoids, clofibrate, intoxication levels of vitamin D, milk-alkali syndrome) as well as radioactive heavy metals or massive transfusion of blood may cause hypophosphatasemia,[62] each of these sources should be readily discerned. Finally, occasional reports describe transient increases in serum ALP activity (probably bone enzyme) in hypophosphatasia after fracture or orthopedic surgery.[42] Conditions that increase circulating activity of any of the other forms of ALP (e.g., pregnancy, liver disease) could also mask the diagnosis.[45,63] Determination of serum ALP activity on more than one occasion is therefore advisable to establish the diagnosis. Quantitation of the individual ALP isoenzymes in serum[4] may be helpful in puzzling cases.

In one kindred with adult hypophosphatasia, hypophosphatasemic subjects consistently showed a reduction of bone ALPL and often had reduced liver ALPL in serum.[16] ALP activity in intestinal tissue has occasionally also been reported to be low.[30,64] Leukocyte ALP activity, first noted to be absent in an affected adult,[65] is a form of ALPL and can be subnormal in any clinical form of hypophosphatasia.[48]

Subjects with the adult and childhood forms of hypophosphatasia have serum Pi levels that are above the mean value for normal controls; indeed, about 50 percent of these individuals are hyperphosphatemic. Enhanced renal reclamation of Pi (increased tubular maximum for Pi/glomerular filtration rate) accounts for this finding.[66] However, rare patients have been reported with a disorder characterized by hypophosphatasemia and renal Pi wasting.[67,68]

Hypercalciuria and hypercalcemia occur frequently in infantile hypophosphatasia;[32,36,41] severely affected children may have hypercalciuria without hypercalcemia. Circulating levels of the bioactivated forms of vitamin D (25-hydroxyvitamin D and 1.25-dihydroxyvitamin D) and immunoreactive parathyroid hormone are usually unremarkable.[69,70] Several patients have been reported to have elevated immunoreactive parathyroid hormone levels,[71] but concomitant hypercalcemia with renal compromise and attendant retention of immunoreactive fragments of parathyroid hormone may have explained this finding in some of them. Low circulating levels of parathyroid hormone and the possibility of an abnormality in the Ca^{2+}–parathyroid hormone feedback system have also been described.[72]

Other routine laboratory tests, including liver function studies and assay of muscle enzymes in serum (e.g., bilirubin, aspartate aminotransferase, lactate dehydrogenase, creatine kinase, aldolase), are generally unremarkable in all forms of hypophosphatasia. These normal findings emphasize the selective involvement of the skeleton and dentition despite the deficiency of ALPL in all tissues. Increased levels of proline in blood and urine have been reported in a few subjects, but the significance of this observation is not known.[73] Serum acid phosphatase activity is generally normal,[74] but was elevated in one adult case.[75]

Documentation of increased PEA levels in a 24-h urine collection supports the diagnosis, but is not specific for hypophosphatasia. Phosphoethanolaminuria has been noted in a variety of other disorders, including several metabolic bone diseases.[76] Furthermore, urinary PEA levels are importantly influenced by age in normal subjects. Licata and coworkers report the following normal ranges for urine PEA: less than age 15 years, 83 to 222 μmol PEA per gram of creatinine; age 15 to 30 years, 42 to 146; age 31 to 41 years, 38 to 155; and greater than age 45 years, 48 to 93.[76] Urinary PEA levels also depend upon diet and follow a circadian rhythm; they have been described as normal in several mild cases of hypophosphatasia.[41,77]

Increased plasma level of pyridoxal-5-phosphate (PLP) is a sensitive and specific marker for hypophosphatasia[40,57,78] (Fig. 116-5). Subjects should not, however, be taking vitamin supplements when tested.[78] Even patients with odontohypophosphatasia demonstrate this abnormality.[40] In general, the more severe the disorder, the greater the elevation in plasma PLP level, although overlap among plasma PLP levels for the clinical forms of hypophosphatasia helps to illustrate the clinical spectrum of this condition.

Fig. 116-5 Plasma pyridoxal-5′-phosphate (PLP) levels in hypophosphatasia. Plasma PLP levels have been elevated in all of 33 probands tested to date. In general, the plasma PLP level reflects the clinical severity of the skeletal disease. Log scale; hatched area is the normal range, mean ± 2 SD, for normal adults.[40]
(*Reproduced from Coburn and Whyte.[78] Used by permission of Alan R. Liss, Inc.*)

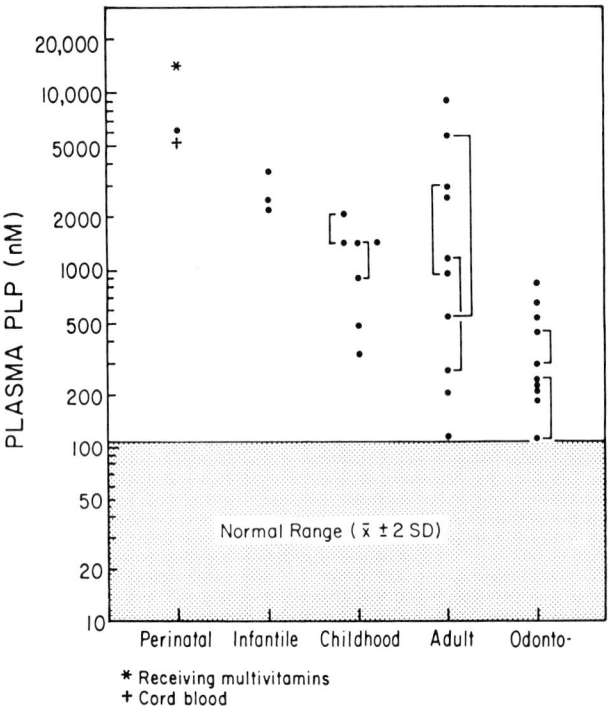

* Receiving multivitamins
\+ Cord blood
] Sibs

Radiologic studies of the skeleton, if not diagnostic, are often characteristic in severely affected subjects (see various clinical types). Skeletal scintigraphy can reveal premature closure of cranial sutures although they may appear "widened" on conventional radiographs.[79]

In all but the mildest cases of hypophosphatasia,[42] histopathologic study of nondecalcified sections of bone reveals defective skeletal mineralization.[20,48] To diagnose rickets or osteomalacia by bone biopsy, thin, nondecalcified sections should be examined.[48] Patients should receive in vivo tetracycline labeling prior to biopsy to demonstrate that excess osteoid is due to defective skeletal mineralization, not rapid matrix formation. In severe cases of hypophosphatasia, even the bony structures of the middle ear may be poorly ossified.[80] The severity of the mineralization defect reflects the clinical severity.[48] Cases reported as pseudohypophosphatasia based on skeletal symptoms, dental caries, elevated urinary PEA levels, and excess osteoid in the absence of deficient serum ALP activity[81] are inadequately documented because information from tetracycline labeling of bone is lacking.

In growth plates, characteristic features of rickets are present. The zones of provisional calcification are widened, there is disruption of the normal columnar arrangement of chondrocytes, and degenerating cartilage fails to calcify. The tissue sources of bone ALPL (osteoblasts, chondrocytes, and matrix vesicles) are present but have reduced levels of ALPL activity.[20,48] Evidence of secondary hyperparathyroidism is generally absent. Cranial "sutures" that are widened are not fibrous tissue, but uncalcified osteoid.[32]

Unless histochemical studies of ALP activity are performed with appropriate controls, the histopathologic changes of hypophosphatasia are like those of other forms of rickets or osteomalacia.[48] However, the numbers and morphology of osteoblasts and osteoclasts vary from case to case, as does the appearance of unmineralized osteoid. Woven bone, a finding that can reflect defective skeletal formation or repair, may be present.[48]

Electron microscopy of bone from cases of infantile hypophosphatasia has revealed that the distribution of proteoglycan granules, collagen fibers, and matrix vesicles is normal in the extracellular chondroid space.[20,48] However, the matrix vesicles are deficient in ALP activity and do not contain hydroxyapatite crystals. Instead, isolated or small groups of crystals, frequently not associated with matrix vesicles, are noted.[20]

Histopathologic study of exfoliated teeth, demonstrating aplasia or hypoplasia of cementum, is an excellent means for diagnosing hypophosphatasia (Fig. 116-6). Dessicated teeth that were exfoliated years earlier may still be useful for examination. Premature loss of deciduous teeth occurs in a variety of conditions including toxicities, metabolic errors, malignancies, and primary dental diseases.[50] However, in hypophosphatasia, a paucity of cementum is observed in prematurely lost teeth despite the presence of connective tissue cells that look like cementoblasts.[50,82] The degree of hypoplasia of the cementum generally reflects the severity of the disease, but does vary from tooth to tooth.[82] Incisors are the most severely affected. Enamel is not abnormal.[50,82] Dental tubules may be enlarged, but reduced in number. Big pulp chambers suggest retarded dentinogenesis. There may also be evidence of delayed calcification. The excessive width of predentin, increased amounts of interglobular dentin, and impaired calcification of cementum are analogous to the excess osteoid observed in bone.

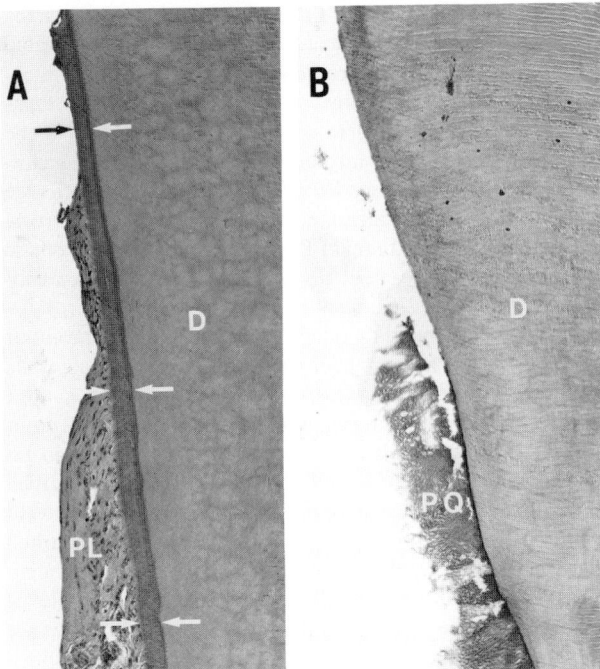

Fig. 116-6 Dental findings in hypophosphatasia. A. Decalcified section of part of the root of a maxillary incisor from a child with sex-linked hypophosphatemic rickets (see Chap. 105) is essentially normal and shows primary cementum (delineated by arrows) at the surface. B. In hypophosphatasia, cementum is absent. X150. PL = periodontal ligament; PQ = plaque; D = dentin.

Biochemical and Genetic Defect

ALPL Deficiency. The molecular defect(s) that causes hypophosphatasia is unknown. There is no animal model. The cardinal biochemical feature, hypophosphatasemia, is explained by deficiency of circulating liver and bone ALPL activity.[16] This deficiency does not appear to be due to enhanced loss, degradation, or inhibition of the enzyme in the circulation. Urinary levels of ALP activity are not increased in affected adults, and the level of ALP in the bile of infantile cases is low.[42,83] Homologous bone ALPL (obtained by plasmapheresis of patients with Paget bone disease) seems to have a normal half-life when infused into the circulation of affected infants in attempted enzyme-replacement therapy.[46] Coincubation experiments, using mixtures of serum from patients and control subjects, and heterokaryon studies, using fused patient and control fibroblasts, failed to indicate absence of an activator or presence of an inhibitor of ALPL in patient serum or tissues.[32,42,54,84] Instead, the hypophosphatasemia of hypophosphatasia seems to reflect a failure of especially liver and bone tissue to contribute normal levels of ALPL activity to the circulation.

Autopsy studies of subjects with the perinatal and infantile forms have been especially important in clarifying the enzymatic and genetic abnormalities in hypophosphatasia. Profound deficiency of ALP activity has been documented in liver, bone, and kidney, but ALP activity is normal in intestine or placenta (fetal trophoblast).[85,86] This observation indicates that the severe forms are due to a defect that diminishes the enzymatic activity of all of the secondary isoenzymes of the ALPL family, whereas placental and intestinal ALP are unaffected.

Autopsy studies of children or adults with hypophosphatasia

have not been reported. However, a variety of indirect evidence suggests that these clinically milder forms are also due to a defect(s) that diminishes the activity of the family of ALPs encoded by the ALPL gene. In adult hypophosphatasia, serum levels of both liver and bone ALPL activity are decreased.[16] Furthermore, in affected children and adults, ALPL activity can be deficient in circulating granulocytes and in bone obtained by biopsy.[48] Finally, ALP in dermal fibroblasts from control subjects is primarily an ALPL, and cultivated skin fibroblasts from individuals with all clinical forms of hypophosphatasia have been found to be low in ALPL activity in comparison to age-matched controls.[87] Each of the four clinical forms of hypophosphatasia appear, therefore, to be due to some heritable defect that selectively diminishes ALPL activity. In one study, monoclonal antibodies to ALPL were used successfully in prenatal diagnosis to document low levels of ALPL in a fetus with severe hypophosphatasia (see below).[88] This is the only report to date in which the ALPL defect has been studied immunologically for cross-reacting material.

Inheritance. Schneider and Corcoran described affected sibs in 1950 and thereby provided the first evidence that hypophosphatasia was inherited.[34] Early family studies, which generally concerned a severely affected infant or child proband, indicated that hypophosphatasia was transmitted as an autosomal recessive trait.[31–36,60,61,89–91] Here, carriers were generally identified by assay of total ALP activity in serum and semiquantitative measurement of urinary PEA levels. The parents of severe cases demonstrated low or low-normal levels of serum ALP activity and modest phosphoethanolaminuria.[31,32] More recent investigations, using quantitative studies of PEA excretion, confirm that the severe perinatal and infantile forms of hypophosphatasia are indeed transmitted as autosomal recessive traits.

The inheritance pattern for the milder forms of hypophosphatasia is less clear. Odontohypophosphatasia had been considered to be an autosomal recessive condition[89] but, like adult-onset cases of hypophosphatasia, may reflect clinical expression of an autosomal dominant trait.[42,43,64,92–96] Some mildly affected patients appear to be heterozygotes for the defect that causes severe disease in homozygotes.[42,95,96] Others could represent a spectrum of homozygotes and compound heterozygotes with defective alleles of varying severity. In this regard, it is interesting that the clinical expression tends to run true to form in affected sibs in all forms of hypophosphatasia, and vertical transmission of clinically apparent disease seems to be unusual.[42,43] Further studies of the inheritance pattern of the mild forms of hypophosphatasia are necessary, but will require sensitive means to detect carriers. Sørensen and colleagues emphasize the need to quantitate several biochemical parameters to identify heterozygotes.[97] Quantitation of PPi levels in blood and urine, isoenzyme forms of ALP in serum, and PLP levels in plasma are likely to be helpful in this regard. Pyridoxine loading, followed by assay of plasma PLP levels, also seems promising for carrier detection.[78] Identification of restriction fragment length polymorphisms in the ALPL gene should facilitate linkage studies.[98]

Gene Defect. Recent characterization of the cDNA and gene for human ALPL should help to clarify the molecular basis for hypophosphatasia.[11] However, at this time, the precise defect remains unknown for any clinical form of the disorder.

As reviewed briefly below, a variety of evidence supports the hypothesis that the basis for at least one form of hypophosphatasia may be a regulatory defect in the biosynthesis of ALPL.

Our clinical observations of one subject with infantile hypophosphatasia indicated that the structural gene for ALPL was intact. After a series of intravenous infusions of pooled normal plasma in attempted enzyme replacement therapy, a 4-month correction of hypophosphatasemia was observed where the heat lability and electrophoretic properties of the ALP in serum were consistent with normal bone ALPL.[99] Remarkable skeletal remineralization was demonstrated both radiologically and histologically during this time. These observations could not be attributed to ALP in the plasma infusions. The findings were consistent with the possibility that in this patient hypophosphatasia was due to deficiency of an ALPL activator that could be supplied in normal plasma.[99]

Some patients with adult hypophosphatasia suffer premature loss of deciduous teeth and/or rickets in childhood[42] but then feel well until middle age. This observation suggests that clinical remission may occur. Indeed, children with hypophosphatasia have somewhat higher levels of serum ALP activity than classic adult cases, yet develop clinically overt bone disease earlier.[48] The degree of ALPL deficiency relative to the serum ALP level that is normal for age is similar in affected children and adults. These observations are also consistent with a regulatory defect in ALPL biosynthesis.

Some ALP activity is detectable by sensitive methods in liver, bone, and kidney tissue from infants with hypophosphatasia.[100] In most, but not all, of these subjects where the ALP has been partially characterized, it appears to differ from the ALPL present in control specimens.[100] In one case of infantile hypophosphatasia, enzyme inhibition and isoelectric focusing studies showed that the small amount of ALP activity detected in liver, bone, and kidney was intestinal ALP.[86] This observation was interpreted to reflect compensatory expression of an intestinal ALP gene. Indeed, in one study of homogenates of small bowel mucosa from a family with a clinically mild childhood-adult form of hypophosphatasia, affected individuals had increased intestinal ALP activity.[93] Infantile hypophosphatasia fibroblasts in culture, however, seem to produce some ALPL-like enzyme.[100]

Chromosomal defects have been reported rarely in hypophosphatasia. A D/D translocation was found in one adult patient, but was not present in other affected family members, and this common translocation was presumably unrelated to the disorder.[54] Phenylketonuria has been noted in one infant with hypophosphatasemia, phosphoethanolaminuria, and generalized skeletal demineralization.[101] A report of Morquio syndrome and hypophosphatasia in a Canadian Hutterite kindred probably reflects the coincidental occurrence of two autosomal recessive conditions.[102]

Genetic complementation studies, using cultured skin fibroblasts from 11 individuals from 10 families with perinatal or infantile hypophosphatasia, failed to show correction of ALPL activity.[84] This suggested that the defect for hypophosphatasia in these subjects was at the same gene locus.

Treatment

There is no established medical therapy for hypophosphatasia, although a variety of treatments have been studied.[32,42,71,99] If extracellular accumulation of PPi is a key pathogenetic factor (see below), reduction in endogenous PPi levels might enable skeletal mineralization to proceed normally.[26] Indeed, an attempt to promote renal PPi excretion with oral Pi supplementation was reported to increase urinary PPi levels and to be followed by radiographic improvement in three affected children.[103] However, feeding Pi does not significantly change plasma PPi levels, and increased urinary PPi levels after oral Pi may reflect enhanced renal PPi synthesis.[26] This therapeutic approach has been repeated, but its efficacy has not been confirmed.[44,104]

Enzyme replacement therapy, attempted with intravenous infusions of plasma from patients with *hyper*phosphatasemia from Paget bone disease, was of no clinical benefit to four subjects affected with the infantile form.[105] Intravenous infusions of fresh normal plasma was followed by clinical and radiographic improvement in one such patient.[106] As described previously, pooled plasma infusions were followed by well-documented correction of hypophosphatasemia and marked temporary clinical, radiographic, and histologic improvement in one subject with the infantile form.[99] A subsequent trial of pooled plasma infusions in a different patient did not produce this response.[107] The reason for the different outcomes is presently unclear.

If hypophosphatasia is due to a regulatory defect of the ALPL gene, treatment with agents that can stimulate biosynthesis or enhance available activity of ALPL may be helpful. Prolonged challenge with cortisone in a few patients with severe hypophosphatasia has been reported to be followed by periods of normalization of circulating ALP activity and radiologic improvement,[32,108,109] but this is not a consistent finding.[32] Brief treatment with an active fragment of parathyroid hormone to stimulate ALP activity has been unsuccessful.[99] In other metabolic bone diseases, sodium fluoride will stimulate osteoblasts and increase serum bone ALPL activity,[110] but this compound has not been rigorously tested in hypophosphatasia.

Traditional therapies for rickets and osteomalacia (vitamin D and mineral supplements) are important to avoid in hypophosphatasia, since circulating levels of calcium, Pi, and the vitamin D metabolites are not reduced. Indeed, in infantile cases, excess vitamin D promotes absorption of calcium without enhancing skeletal formation. Accordingly, in hypophosphatasia, vitamin D therapy is especially predisposing to hypercalcemia and hypercalciuria.[32] However, complete restriction of vitamin D intake or exposure to sunshine should also be avoided, since superimposed vitamin D–deficiency rickets can occur.[70] Hypercalcemia in infantile hypophosphatasia can be corrected by glucocorticoid therapy and/or restriction of dietary calcium.[45] Nevertheless, progressive skeletal demineralization may occur.[46,105]

Affected infants and children should be followed carefully for increased intracranial pressure from premature cranial synostosis. Anatomic (functional) synostosis may occur prior to characteristic radiographic changes. Therefore, craniotomy may be necessary before craniostenosis is recognized radiologically.[44]

Fractures in children do mend, although delayed healing after femoral osteotomy with casting has been reported.[111] In adult patients, orthopedic management is a mainstay of treatment. Pseudofractures may remain stable for years, but will not heal unless they first progress to completion, or are treated orthopedically.[42] Use of intramedullary rods rather than load-sparing devices like plates is best for the prophylactic or acute orthopedic management of femoral fractures and pseudofractures.[55] Expert dental care is important for affected children and adults.

Prognosis

Perinatal (lethal) hypophosphatasia is uniformly fatal. The author is unaware of any case with prolonged survival. Infantile hypophosphatasia can have a somewhat cyclical clinical course characterized by a period of deterioration followed by improvement, but is fatal in at least 50 percent of patients.[32] The prognosis appears to become more favorable in those patients who survive infancy. Childhood hypophosphatasia may also spontaneously improve,[32] but recurrence of symptoms in adulthood seems possible.[32,42,112] Adult hypophosphatasia causes chronic orthopedic problems after onset of skeletal symptomatology.[42,43] Exacerbation of the osteopenia and fractures seems to occur in women at menopause, but estrogen replacement therapy has not prevented worsening of osteomalacia in two cases (personal observation).

Prenatal Diagnosis

In two fetuses at risk for mild hypophosphatasia, whose ultrasonography was reportedly normal in early pregnancy, low ALP activity in cord blood sampled at birth suggested that the newborns were affected (personal observation). Only the severe forms of hypophosphatasia have been diagnosed prenatally. A variety of techniques have been studied. Assay of total ALP activity in amniotic fluid and cord blood obtained by fetoscopy at 16 weeks' gestation has not been helpful.[113] Indeed, at 14 to 18 weeks' gestation, most of the ALP activity in amniotic fluid is intestinal isoenzyme.[114] Ultrasound examination at 16 weeks' gestation can reveal an abnormal fetal head. An ultrasound study, however, was judged to be normal at 16 to 19 weeks' gestation in three cases of the perinatal hypophosphatasia in which radiographic study at 38 weeks' gestation showed absence of a fetal skeleton.[115,116] Amniocentesis for assay of α-fetoprotein in amniotic fluid and ALP activity in cultivated amniotic fluid cells will help to differentiate anencephaly from severe hypophosphatasia. Successful early prenatal diagnosis of a severely affected fetus has been reported with a chorionic villus sample using monoclonal antibodies against ALPL and placental ALP.[88] However, combined techniques—using serial ultrasonography (with attention to the limbs as well as skull), radiologic study of the fetus, and, importantly, assay of ALP activity in amniotic fluid cells by an experienced laboratory—now allow very reliable early prenatal diagnosis of severe cases.[117]

PHYSIOLOGICAL ROLE OF TISSUE-NONSPECIFIC ALKALINE PHOSPHATASE (ALPL) EXPLORED IN HYPOPHOSPHATASIA

Although the molecular defect(s) in hypophosphatasia is unknown and much needs to be learned concerning the biosynthesis and cellular processing of ALPL, this inborn error of metabolism is a valuable model to explore the physiological role of ALPL.[118] Subjects with the perinatal and infantile forms of hypophosphatasia are profoundly deficient in ALPL activity in all organs. Affected children and adults, who may be heterozygotes for this disorder, appear to have the same selective isoenzyme deficiency, but one that is quantitatively less severe.

The clinical presentation of hypophosphatasia makes clear that, in some way, ALPL functions importantly in mineralization of the skeleton and formation of the teeth, yet it also suggests that ALPL is less important in other tissues. Although the liver and kidneys are normally rich in ALPL activity, hepatic and renal dysfunction are not significant problems in hypophosphatasia. Recurrent pulmonary atelectasis and infection in affected infants suggest that ALPL deficiency might condition an abnormality in the biosynthesis of surfactant (a phospholipid).[45] However, the respiratory problems are likely to be, in large part, from the rib cage deformities.

In hypophosphatasia, the level of ALP activity in bone tissue correlates somewhat with the circulating ALP activity, but reflects better the degree of osteoid accumulation.[48] The observation that some hydroxyapatite crystals are found in specimens of bone tissue from severely affected patients with hypophosphatasia, but not within matrix vesicles, indicates that the process of primary mineralization is especially disturbed in this disorder.[20] The defects in dentin and cementum are histologically similar to those in bone and appear to reflect a severe disturbance in calcification from ALPL deficiency in the dentition.[50]

The discovery that PEA levels are increased in blood and urine in hypophosphatasia provided a useful biochemical marker for the disorder and gave the first evidence from this inborn error for a natural substrate for ALPL. Despite the detailed studies by Rasmussen[33] of renal handling of PEA in normal subjects and in hypophosphatasia patients, relatively little insight into the physiological role of ALPL resulted from these investigations. PEA normally appears in small amounts in urine when plasma levels are scarcely detectable; i.e., there appears to be no renal threshold.[33] Although its metabolic origin is unclear, PEA is thought not to be a derivative of phosphatidylethanolamine; the major source of PEA is reported to be the liver.[119] Mammalian liver also degrades PEA to ammonia, acetaldehyde, and Pi in a reaction catalyzed by O-phosphorylethanolamine phospholyase, which requires PLP (see below) as a cofactor.[120] Indeed, it has been proposed that pseudohypophosphatasia might be due to a deficiency of this enzyme. Urinary levels of PEA were found to correlate inversely with the activity of liver ALPL (but not bone ALPL) in the serum of hypophosphatasemic adults in one family with adult hypophosphatasia.[16] This finding is consistent with altered hepatic metabolism accounting for the endogenous accumulation of PEA in hypophosphatasia.

Discovery that PPi levels are increased in the urine[39] and plasma[26] in hypophosphatasia not only indicated that PPi is a natural substrate for ALPL, but suggested a mechanism for the associated rickets and osteomalacia:[26,34] PPi is known to inhibit calcium and Pi precipitation from solution by binding strongly to hydroxyapatite crystals and impairing their growth and dissolution.[25] However, as discussed, the precise mechanism for skeletal mineralization is unclear,[23] and several roles for ALPL in calcification have been proposed (Table 116-1).

Studies using cultivated ALPL-deficient infantile hypophosphatasia fibroblasts demonstrate that extracellular generation of PPi by these cells from ATP is normal.[121] Their level of nucleoside triphosphate pyrophosphatase activity is unremarkable, and this enzyme appears to be different from ALPL. Accordingly, accumulation of PPi in hypophosphatasia seems to be the result of defective degradation rather than increased synthesis of PPi.[121]

A variety of somewhat indirect studies of ALP action have suggested that ALPL may function in cell growth and differentiation. However, cultivated ALPL-deficient infantile hypophosphatasia dermal fibroblasts grow normally.[122]

Our recent discovery that circulating levels of PLP (a cofactor form of vitamin B_6) are markedly increased in hypophosphatasia provided evidence for a third natural substrate for ALPL and also helped clarify the physiological role of this isoenzyme.[40] As reviewed in Fig. 116-7, the metabolism of vitamin B_6 normally involves the conversion of a variety of dietary forms of vitamin B_6—including pyridoxine, pyridoxal, and pyridoxamine and their phosphorylated derivatives—to the cofactor form PLP in the liver.[123] Organ ablation studies show that the liver is the major source of PLP in plasma. Apparently, PLP is secreted from the liver into plasma bound to albumin.[123] Although some PLP circulates freely in plasma (approximately 5 percent), it cannot traverse plasma membranes and must first be dephosphorylated to pyridoxal before it enters tissues. Once pyridoxal crosses the plasma membrane, it is rephosphorylated to PLP or converted to pyridoxamine-5′-phosphate; each acts intracellularly as a cofactor for a variety of enzymatic reactions. Ultimately, vitamin B_6 is de-

Fig. 116-7 Role of tissue-nonspecific alkaline phosphatase (ALPL) in vitamin B_6 metabolism. The various vitameric forms of vitamin B_6 in the diet—pyridoxal (PL), pyridoxine (PN), and pyridoxamine (PM), and their phosphorylated derivatives—are absorbed as soluble compounds into the hepatic portal circulation. In the liver, each is converted to PLP, which is secreted bound to albumin into the plasma. To enter tissues, the small amount of unbound PLP in plasma must be dephosphorylated to PL, which can traverse membranes. Rephosphorylation of PL within cells produces PLP, a cofactor form of vitamin B_6. 4-Pyridoxic acid (4-PA), the major degradation product of vitamin B_6, is excreted in the urine. The high plasma level of PLP in hypophosphatasia is consistent with an ectoenzyme role for ALPL in the extracellular dephosphorylation of PLP to PL.

VITAMIN B₆ METABOLISM

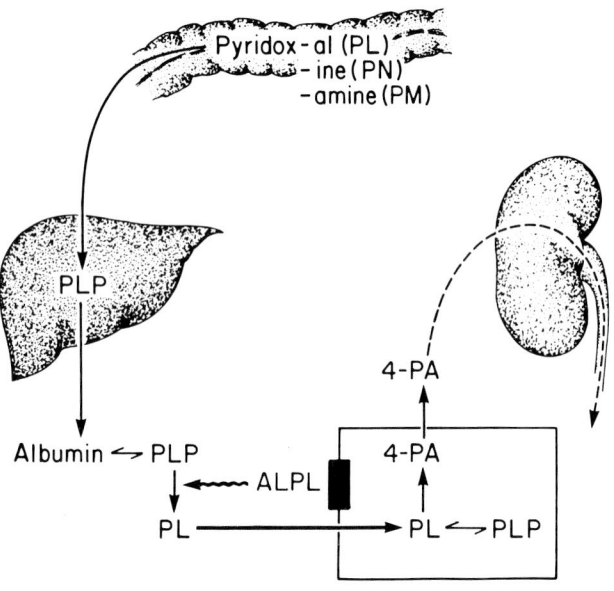

graded to 4-pyridoxic acid, primarily in the liver, and is then excreted into the urine.[123]

Marked increases in the plasma levels of PLP in hypophosphatasia indicate that ALPL acts in the dephosphorylation of PLP.[40,78] Since plasma membranes are impermeable to PLP, the increased plasma PLP levels in hypophosphatasia appear to result from failure of PLP hydrolysis by plasma membrane–bound ALPL; accordingly, ALPL must function as an *ecto*enzyme.[40,78] Consonant with this conclusion is the clinical observation that subjects with hypophosphatasia do not have symptoms of vitamin B_6 deficiency or toxicity. Dermatitis, stomatitis, peripheral neuritis, depression, or anemia—clinical hallmarks of vitamin B_6 deficiency[123]—are not present. Similarly, peripheral neuropathy, a sign of vitamin B_6 toxicity,[123] is not a feature of hypophosphatasia. Vitamin B_6 deficiency has been associated with two findings reported in hypophosphatasia—renal stone disease and epilepsy. However, the nephrocalcinosis in infants with hypophosphatasia is readily explained by the attendant hypercalciuria and hypercalcemia rather than altered oxalate metabolism.[123] The epilepsy in these patients may be related to their cranial deformity and periodic apnea. Recent observations in one infant with hypophosphatasia who received intravenous infusions of PEA indicate that the high endogenous levels of PEA may be epileptogenic.[124]

Other observations indicate that intracellular vitamin B_6 status is normal in hypophosphatasia. Urinary levels of 4-pyridoxic acid were normal in all of four subjects examined with the childhood form of hypophosphatasia.[40] Our autopsy study of three perinatal cases in which plasma PLP concentrations were 50- to 900-fold elevated revealed tissue levels of PLP, pyridoxal, and total forms of vitamin B_6 that were essentially unremarkable.[107] Levels of PLP and total B_6 in homogenates of ALPL-deficient fibroblasts obtained from subjects with infantile hypophosphatasia are the same as those from controls.[125] Finally, children with hypophosphatasia respond normally to an L-tryptophan load (M. P. Whyte and S. P. Coburn, unpublished observation).

Since ALPL appears to be the phosphatase that dephosphorylates PLP to pyridoxal in the extracellular space, pyridoxal in the circulation could be low in hypophosphatasia. However, subjects with all but the perinatal form of hypophosphatasia[107] have had somewhat elevated plasma pyridoxal levels.[40,118] Plasma pyridoxal levels were below assay sensitivity in two subjects with perinatal hypophosphatasia.[107] Yet, in all forms of hypophosphatasia there appears to be sufficient extracellular dephosphorylation of PLP to pyridoxal by some mechanism to account for the normal vitamin B_6 status.

The clinical and biochemical observations concerning vitamin B_6 metabolism in hypophosphatasia indicate an ectoenzyme role for ALPL.[78,118] Characterization of ALPL as a plasma membrane–bound glycoprotein[5] that is covalently linked to the polar head group of phosphatidylinositol[13,14,126] supports this conclusion. Studies using cultivated dermal fibroblasts from patients with infantile hypophosphatasia[127] and human osteogenic sarcoma cells[128] show that ALPL is plasma membrane–associated with ectotopography and capable of dephosphorylating physiological concentrations of PLP and PEA at physiological pH. Indeed, in disorders in which serum levels of liver and bone ALPL are increased by organ-specific increments in ALPL activity (e.g., other skeletal and hepatic diseases), plasma PLP levels are decreased.[78,129]

A variety of evidence, however, indicates that *circulating* ALP is physiologically inactive.[118] For example, infants with hypophosphatasia who received intravenous infusions of bone ALP–rich plasma obtained from patients with Paget bone disease or plasma from normal donors had progressive skeletal disease.[105] Furthermore, this therapy failed to reduce urinary PEA or PPi levels.[46] Accordingly, deficiency of ALPL activity in the skeleton itself appears to account for the rickets and osteomalacia of hypophosphatasia. In fact, Fraser and Yendt reported in 1955 that rachitic rat cartilage would calcify in serum obtained from an infant with hypophosphatasia, yet slices of the patient's costochondral junction would not mineralize in synthetic calcifying medium or in the pooled serum of healthy children.[130]

A Model for ALPL Function

Observations from studies of subjects with hypophosphatasia can be formulated into an overview of how ALPL functions physiologically (Fig. 116-8). Increased endogeneous levels of PEA, PPi, and PLP in this disorder indicate that ALPL is catalytically active toward a variety of phosphocompounds of fairly variable chemical structure (Fig. 116-1) at physiological pH. Since PEA, PPi, and PLP are normally present in extracellular fluid at nanomolar or micromolar concentrations, ALPL has physiological activity at substrate concentrations and pH which are much lower than those used for artificial substrates in routine biochemical assays for ALP activity.[128] In this sense, "alkaline phosphatase" is a misnomer for ALPL.

Clinical and biochemical observations of vitamin B_6 metabolism in hypophosphatasia are consistent with cell membrane studies[126] which reveal that ALPL is an ectoenzyme. Extracellular accumulation of PEA, PPi, and PLP in hypophosphatasia is a consequence of deficient ecto-ALPL activity. Accu-

mulation of membrane-impermeable PLP in plasma, but not in tissues, explains the absence of vitamin B_6 deficiency or toxicity. The source of PEA is unclear, but it might be related to the metabolism of lipid membranes. Generation of extracellular PPi, perhaps from ATP, occurs normally in hypophosphatasia by the action of nucleoside triphosphate pyrophosphatase. Rickets and osteomalacia develop in hypophosphatasia from local extracellular accumulation of PPi, an inhibitor of the process of primary skeletal mineralization, which goes unhydrolyzed because of deficient ecto-ALPL activity.

ADDENDUM

Recently, genetic linkage of infantile hypophosphatasia in six inbred Canadian kindreds to the Rh blood group has provided evidence that this disorder results from a defect at the ALPL gene locus (Chodirker BN, et al.: *Genomics* 1:280, 1987). Furthermore, a missense mutation in the ALPL locus has been identified as the cause of perinatal hypophosphatasia in a different Canadian family (Weiss MJ, et al.: *Proc Natl Acad Sci USA* 85:7666, 1988).

REFERENCES

1. MCCOMB RB, BOWERS GN JR, POSEN S: *Alkaline Phosphatase.* New York, Plenum, 1979.
2. STINGBRAND T, FISHMAN WH: *Human Alkaline Phosphatases.* New York, AR Liss, 1984.
3. Human Gene Mapping 8 (1985): Eighth International Workshop On Human Gene Mapping. *Cytogenet Cell Genet* 40, Nos 1–4, 1985. Simultaneous publication in Birth Defects: Original Article, Series vol 21, no 4, 1985, March of Dimes Birth Defects Foundation, White Plains, NY.
4. MULIVOR RA, BOCCELLI D, HARRIS H: Quantitative analysis of alkaline phosphatases in serum and amniotic fluid: Comparison of biochemical and immunologic assays. *J Lab Clin Med* 105:342, 1985.
5. MOSS DW, WHITAKER KB: Modification of alkaline phosphatases by treatment with glycosidases. *Enzyme* 34:212, 1985.
6. HARRIS H: *The Principles of Human Biochemical Genetics,* 3d ed. Amsterdam, Elsevier/North Holland, 1980.
7. GRIFFIN CA, SMITH M, HENTHORN PS, HARRIS H, WEISS MJ, RADUCHA M, EMANUEL BS: Human placental and intestinal alkaline phosphatase genes map to 2q34-q37. *Am J Hum Genet* 41:1025, 1987.
8. SMITH M, WEISS MJ, GRIFFIN CA, MURRAY JC, BUETOW KH, EMANUEL BS, HENTHORN PS, HARRIS H: Regional assignment of the gene for human liver/bone/kidney alkaline phosphatase to human chromosome 1p34-1p36.1. *Genomics* 2:139, 1988.
9. BERGER J, GARATTINI E, HUA J-C, UDENFRIEND S: Cloning and sequencing of human intestinal alkaline phosphatase cDNA. *Proc Natl Acad Sci USA* 84:695, 1987.
10. HENTHORN PS, RADUCHA M, EDWARDS YH, WEISS MJ, SLAUGHTER C, LAFFERTY MA, HARRIS H: Nucleotide and amino acid sequences of human intestinal alkaline phosphatase: Close homology to placental alkaline phosphatase. *Proc Natl Acad Sci USA* 84:1234, 1987.
11. WEISS MJ, RAY K, HENTHORN PS, LAMB B, KADESCH T, HARRIS H: Structure of the human liver/bone/kidney alkaline phosphatase gene. *Proc Natl Acad Sci USA* 263:12002, 1988.
12. MUELLER HD, LEUNG H, STINSON RA: Different genes code for alkaline phosphatase from human fetal and adult intestine. *Biochem Biophys Res Commun* 126:427, 1985.
13. HAWRYLAK K, STINSON RA: Tetrameric alkaline phosphatase from human liver is converted to dimers by phosphatidylinositol phospholipase C. *FEBS Lett* 212:289, 1987.
14. SEETHARAM B, TIRUPPATHI C, ALPERS DH: Hydrophobic interactions of brush border alkaline phosphatases: The role of phosphatidyl inositol. *Arch Biochem Biophys* 253:189, 1987.
15. YOUNG GP, ROSE IS, CROPPER S, SEETHARAM S, ALPERS DH: Hepatic clearance of rat plasma intestinal alkaline phosphatase. *Am J Physiol* 247:G419, 1984.
16. MILLAN JL, WHYTE MP, AVIOLI LV, FISHMAN WH: Hypophosphatasia (adult form): Quantitation of serum alkaline phosphatase isoenzyme activity in a large kindred. *Clin Chem* 26:840, 1980.

Fig. 116-8 Metabolic basis for hypophosphatasia (hypothesis). Extracellular generation of PPi, presumably by the action of nucleoside triphosphate pyrophosphatase (NTP-PPiase) on ATP, is normal in hypophosphatasia, but extracellular hydrolysis of PPi, PEA, and PLP is diminished because of deficient ecto-ALPL activity. Accumulation of PPi (an endogenous inhibitor of skeletal mineralization) extracellularly accounts for the characteristic rickets and osteomalacia. Increased PEA may account for seizures in severe cases. PLP accumulation is inconsequential because extracellular levels of PL are not subnormal.

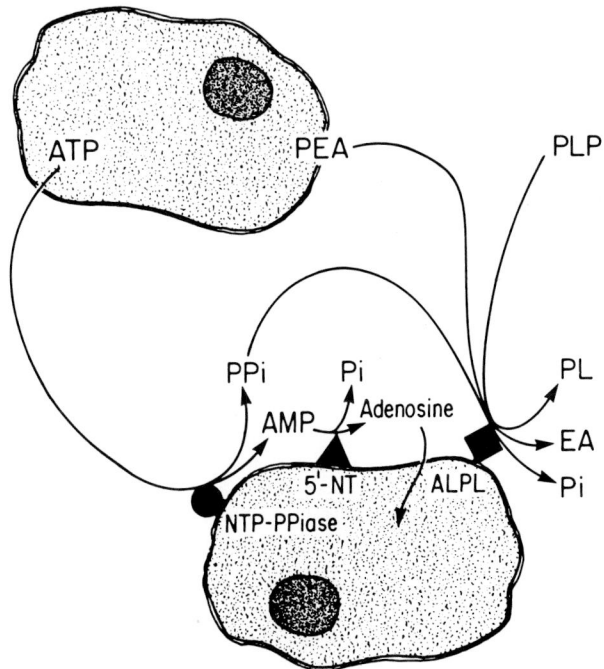

17. LANGMAN MJS, LEUTHOLD E, ROBSON EB, HARRIS J, LUFFMAN JE, HARRIS H: Influence of diet on "intestinal" component of serum alkaline phosphatase in people of different ABO blood groups and secretory status. *Nature* 212:41, 1966.

18. RAISZ LG, KREAM BE: Regulation of bone formation. *N Engl J Med* 309:29, 83, 1983.

19. ALI SY: *Cell Mediated Calcification and Matrix Vesicles.* New York, Elsevier, 1986.

20. ORNOY A, ADOMIAN GE, RIMOIN DL: Histologic and ultrastructural studies on the mineralization process in hypophosphatasia. *Am J Med Genet* 22:743, 1985.

21. ROBISON R: The possible significance of hexosephosphoric esters in ossification. *Biochem J* 17:286, 1923.

22. ROBISON R, SOAMES KM: The possible significance of hexosephosphoric esters in ossification. II. The phosphoric esterase of ossifying cartilage. *Biochem J* 18:740, 1924.

23. WUTHIER RE, REGISTER TC: Role of alkaline phosphatase, a polyfunctional enzyme, in mineralizing tissues, in Butler WT (ed): *The Chemistry and Biology of Mineralized Tissues.* Burmingham, EBSCO Media, 1985, p 113.

24. MAJESKA RJ, WUTHIER RE: Studies on matrix vesicles isolated from chick epiphyseal cartilage. Association of pyrophosphatase and ATP-ase activities with alkaline phosphatase. *Biochim Biophys Acta* 391:51, 1975.

25. FLEISCH H, RUSSELL RGG, STRAUMANN F: Effect of pyrophosphate on hydroxyapatite and its implications in calcium homeostasis. *Nature* 212:901, 1966.

26. RUSSELL RGG, BISAZ S, DONATH A, MORGAN DB, FLEISCH H: Inorganic pyrophosphate in plasma in normal persons and in patients with hypophosphatasia, osteogenesis imperfecta, and other disorders of bone. *J Clin Invest* 50:961, 1971.

27. MOSS DW, EATON RH, SMITH JK, WHITBY LG: Association of inorganic pyrophosphatase activity with human alkaline phosphatase preparations. *Biochem J* 102:53, 1967.

28. DeBERNARD B, BIANCO P, BONUCCI E, COSTANTINI M, LUNAZZI GC, MARTINUZZI P, MODRICKY C, MORO L, PANFILI E, POLLESELLO P, STAGNI N, VITTOR F: Biochemical and immunohistochemical evidence that in cartilage an alkaline phosphatase is a Ca^{2+}-binding glycoprotein. *J Cell Biol* 103:1615, 1986.

29. LAU KH, FARLEY JR, BAYLINK DJ: Phosphotyrosyl-specific protein phosphatase activity of a bovine skeletal acid phosphatase isoenzyme. Comparison with the phosphotyrosyl protein phosphatase activity of skeletal alkaline phosphatase. *J Biol Chem* 260:4653, 1985.

30. RATHBUN JC: Hypophosphatasia, a new developmental anomaly. *Am J Dis Child* 71:822, 1948.

31. CURRARINO G, NEUHAUSER E, REYERSBACK G, SOBEL E: Hypophosphatasia. *Am J Roentgenol* 78:392, 1957.

32. FRASER D: Hypophosphatasia. *Am J Med* 22:730, 1957.

33. RASMUSSEN K: Phosphorylethanolamine and hypophosphatasia. Studies on urinary excretion, renal handling and elimination of endogenous and exogenous phosphorylethanolamine in healthy persons, carriers, and in patients with hypophosphatasia. *Dan Med Bull* 15 (suppl II):1, 1968.

34. SCHNEIDER RW, CORCORAN AC: Familial nephrogenic osteopathy due to excessive tubular reabsorption of inorganic phosphate: A new syndrome and a novel mode of relief. *J Lab Clin Med* 36:985, 1950.

35. SOBEL EH, CLARK LC, FOX RP, ROBINOW M: Rickets, deficiency of "alkaline" phosphatase activity and premature loss of teeth in childhood. *Pediatrics* 11:309, 1953.

36. TERHEGGEN HG, WISCHERMANN A: Congenital hypophosphatasia. *Monatsschr Kinderheilkd* 132:512, 1984.

37. FRAZER D, YENDT ER, CHRISTIE FHE: Metabolic abnormalities in hypophosphatasia. *Lancet* 1:286, 1955.

38. MCCANCE RA, MORRISON AB, DENT CE: The excretion of phosphoethanolamine and hypophosphatasia. *Lancet* 1:131, 1955.

39. RUSSELL RGG: Excretion of inorganic pyrophosphate in hypophosphatasia. *Lancet* 2:461, 1965.

40. WHYTE MP, MAHUREN JD, VRABEL LA, COBURN SP: Markedly increased circulating pyridoxal-5'-phosphate concentrations in hypophosphatasia (alkaline phosphatase acts in vitamin B6 metabolism). *J Clin Invest* 76:752, 1985.

41. TAILLARD F, DESBOIS JC, DELEPINE N, GRETILLAT F, ALLANEAU C, HERRAULT A: L'hypophosphatsie affection polymorphe de frequence peutetre sous estimee. *Med Inf (Lond)* 91:559, 1984.

42. WHYTE MP, TEITELBAUM SL, MURPHY WA, BERGFELD M, AVIOLI LV: Adult hypophosphatasia: Clinical, laboratory, and genetic investigation of a large kindred with review of the literature. *Medicine (Baltimore)* 58:329, 1979.

43. WHYTE MP, FALLON MD, MURPHY WA: Adult hypophosphatasia with chondrocalcinosis and arthropathy: Variable penetrance of hypophosphatasemia in a large Oklahoma kindred. *Am J Med* 72:631, 1982.

44. KOZLOWSKI K, SUTCLIFFE J, BARYLAK A, HARRINGTON G, KEMPERDICK H, NOLTE K, RHEINWEIN H, THOMAS PS, UNIECKA W: Hypophosphatasia: Review of 24 cases. *Pediatr Radiol* 5:103, 1976.

45. TEREE TM, KLEIN L: Hypophosphatasia: Clinical and metabolic studies. *J Pediatr* 72:41, 1968.

46. WHYTE MP, VALDES R JR, RYAN LM, MCALISTER WH: Infantile hypophosphatasia: Enzyme replacement therapy by intravenous infusion of alkaline phosphatase-rich plasma from patients with Paget's bone disease. *J Pediatr* 101:379, 1982.

47. BRENNER RL, SMITH JL, CLEVELAND WW, BEJAR RL, LOCKHART WS: Eye signs in hypophosphatasia. *Arch Ophthalmol* 81:614, 1969.

48. FALLON MD, TEITELBAUM SL, WEINSTEIN RS, GOLDFISCHER S, BROWN DM, WHYTE MP: Hypophosphatasia: Clinicopathologic comparison of the infantile, childhood, and adult forms. *Medicine (Baltimore)* 63:12, 1984.

49. KJELLMAN M, OLDFELT V, NORDENRAM A, OLOW-NORDENRAM M: Five cases of hypophosphatasia with dental findings. *Int J Oral Surg* 2:152, 1973.

50. BIXLER D: Heritable disorders affecting cementum and the peridontal ligament, in Stewart RE, Prescott GH (eds): *Oral Facial Genetics.* St Louis, MO, CV Mosby, 1976, p 262.

51. PAGE RC, BAAB DA: New look at the etiology and pathogenesis of early onset periodontitis. *J Periodontology* 56:748, 1985.

52. MEURMAN JH, HAKALA PE: Cranial manifestations of hypophosphatasia in childhood nephrotic syndrome. *Int J Oral Surg* 13:249, 1984.

53. WENDLING D, CASSOU M, GUIDET M: Hypophosphatasia in adults. Apropos of 2 cases. *Rev Rhum Mal Osteoartic* 52:43, 1985.

54. O'DUFFY JD: Hypophosphatasia associated with calcium pyrophosphate dihydrate deposits in cartilage. *Arthritis Rheum* 13:381, 1970.

55. COE JD, MURPHY WA, WHYTE MP: Management of femoral fractures and pseudofractures in adult hypophosphatasia. *J Bone Joint Surg* 68-A:981, 1986.

56. SCRIVER CR, CAMERON D: Pseudohypophosphatasia. *N Engl J Med* 281:604, 1969.

57. COLE DEC, STINSON RA, COBURN SP, RYAN LM, WHYTE MP: Increased serum pyridoxal-5'-phosphate in pseudohypophosphatasia (letter). *N Engl J Med* 314:992, 1986.

58. FEDDE KN, OAKLEY LM, COLE DEC, WHYTE MP: Pseudohypophosphatasia: Identification of defective pyridoxal-5'-phosphate phosphatase in cultured fibroblasts. *Am J Hum Genet* 39:A-10, 1986.

59. HEATON BW, MCCLENDON JL: Childhood pseudohypophosphatasia. Clinical and laboratory study of two cases. *Tex Dent J* 103:4, 1986.

60. MEHES K, KLUJBER L, LASSU G, KAJTAR P: Hypophosphatasia: Screening and family investigation in an endogamous Hungarian village. *Clin Genet* 3:60, 1972.

61. RUBECZ I, MEHES K, KLUJBER L, BOZZAY L, WEISENBACH J, FENYVESI J: Hypophosphatasia: Screening and family investigation. *Clin Genet* 6:155, 1974.

62. WEINSTEIN RS, WHYTE MP: Heterogeneity of adult hypophosphatasia: Report of severe and mild cases. *Arch Intern Med* 141:727, 1981.

63. PILLANS PI, BERMAN P, SAUNDERS SJ: Cholestatic jaundice with a normal serum alkaline phosphatase level: Another case of hypophosphatasia in an adult. *Gastroenterology* 84:175, 1983.

64. EBERLE F, HARTENFELS S, PRALLE H, KABISCH A: Adult hypophosphatasia without apparent skeletal disease: "Odontohypophosphatasia" in four heterozygote members of a family. *Klin Wochenschr* 62:371, 1984.

65. BEISEL WR, AUSTERN KF, ROSEN H, HERNDON EG: Metabolic observations in adult hypophosphatasia. *Am J Med* 29:369, 1960.

66. WHYTE MP, RETTINGER SD: Hyperphosphatemia due to enhanced renal reclamation of phosphate in hypophosphatasia. *J Bone Min Res* 2(suppl 1):abstract 399, 1987.

67. NUSYNOWITZ ML: Low serum alkaline phosphatase level, hypophosphatemia, and aching extremities (letter). *JAMA* 242:2800, 1979.

68. JUAN D, LAMBERT PW: Vitamin D. Metabolism and phosphorus absorption studies in a case of coexistent vitamin D resistant rickets and hypophosphatasia, in Cohn DV, Talmage RV, Matthews JL (eds): *Hormonal Control of Calcium Metabolism.* Amsterdam, International Congress Series 511, Excerpta Medica, 1981.

69. WHYTE MP, SEINO Y: Circulating vitamin D metabolite levels in hypophosphatasia. *J Clin Endocrinol Metab* 55:178, 1982.

70. OPSHAUG O, MAURSETH K, HOWLID H, AKSNES L, AARSKOG D: Vitamin D metabolism in hypophosphatasia. *Acta Pediatr Scand* 71:517, 1982.

71. WOLFISH NM, HEICK H: Hyperparathyroidism and infantile hypophosphatasia: Effect of prednisone and vitamin D therapy. *J Pediatr* 95:1079, 1979.

72. TAILLARD F, DESBOIS J-C, GUERIS J, DELEPINE N, LACOUR B, GRETILLAT F, WYART D: Pyrophosphates inorganiques et parathormone dans l'hypophosphatasie. Étude d'une famille. *Biomed Pharmacother* 39:236, 1985.

73. DE-VRIES HR, DURAN M, DeBREE PK, WADMAN SK: A patient with hypophosphatasia and hyperprolinaemia. *Neth J Med* 21:28, 1978.

74. RETTINGER SD, WHYTE MP: Normal circulating acid phosphatase activity in hypophosphatasia. *J Inherited Metab Dis* 8:161, 1985.

75. IQBAL SJ, TAYLOR WH, ROBERTS NB, DARLOW JM: Raised serum acid phosphatase activity in an adult with hypophosphatasia. *J Inherited Metab Dis* 6:103, 1983.

76. LICATA AA, RADFOR N, BARTTER FC, BOU E: The urinary excretion of phosphoethanolamine in diseases other than hypophosphatasia. *Am J Med* 64:133, 1978.

77. TECZA S, PRANDOTA J, MORAWSKA Z, RUDZKA M, PANKOW-PRANDOTA L: Hypophosphatasia with normal urinary phosphoethanolamine in a 22-month old girl. *Pediatr Pol* 55:791, 1980.

78. COBURN SP, WHYTE MP: Role of phosphatases in the regulation of vitamin B6 metabolism in hypophosphatasia and other disorders, in Leklem JE, Reynolds RD (eds): *Clinical and Physiological Applications of Vitamin B6.* New York, AR Liss, 1988, pp 65–93.

79. STY JR, BOEDECKER RA, BABBITT DP: Skull scintigraphy in infantile hypophosphatasia. *J Nucl Med* 20:305, 1979.

80. NOMURA Y, MORI W: Hypophosphatasia: Histopathology of human temporal bones. *J Laryngol Otol* 82:1129, 1982.

81. MANICOURT D, ORLOFF S, TAVERNE-VERBANCK J: Osteomalacia in hyperphosphoethanolaminuria without hypophosphatasia. *Ann Endocrinol* 40:167, 1979.

82. BEUMER J III, TROWBRIDGE HO, SILVERMAN S JR, EISENBERG E: Childhood hypophosphatasia and the premature loss of teeth: A clinical and laboratory study of seven cases. *Oral Surg Oral Med Oral Pathol* 35:631, 1973.

83. GORODISCHER R, DAVIDSON RG, MOSOVICH LL, YAFFE SJ: Hypophosphatasia: A developmental anomaly of alkaline phosphatase? *Pediatr Res* 10:650, 1976.

84. WHYTE MP, VRABEL LA: Infantile hypophosphatasia: Genetic complementation analyses with skin fibroblast heterokaryons suggest a defect(s) at a single gene locus. *Clin Res* 33:332-A, 1985.

85. VANNEUVILLE FJ, LEROY LG: Enzymatic diagnosis of congenital lethal hypophosphatasia in tissues, plasma, and diploid skin fibroblasts. *J Inherited Metab Dis* 4:129, 1981.

86. MUELLER HD, STINSON RA, MOHYUDDIN F, MILNE JK: Isoenzymes of alkaline phosphatase in infantile hypophosphatasia. *J Lab Clin Med* 102:24, 1983.

87. WHYTE MP, VRABEL LA, SCHWARTZ TD: Alkaline phosphatase deficiency in cultured skin fibroblasts from patients with hypophosphatasia: Comparison of the infantile, childhood, and adult forms. *J Clin Endocrinol Metab* 57:831, 1983.

88. WARREN RC, MCKENZIE CF, RODECK CH, MOSCOSO G, BROCK DJH, BARRON L: First trimester diagnosis of hypophosphatasia with a monoclonal antibody to liver/bone/kidney isoenzyme of alkaline phosphatase. *Lancet* 2:856, 1985.

89. PIMSTONE B, EISENBERG E, SILVERMAN S: Hypophosphatasia: Genetic and dental studies. *Ann Intern Med* 65:722, 1966.

90. HARRIS B, ROBSON EB: A genetical study of ethanolamine phosphate excretion in hypophosphatasia. *Hum Genet* 23:421, 1959.

91. MCCANCE RA, FAIRWEATHER DVI, BARRETT AM, MORRISON AB: Genetic, clinical, biochemical and pathological features of hypophosphatasia. *Q J Med* 25:523, 1956.

92. SILVERMAN JL: Apparent dominant inheritance of hypophosphatasia. *Arch Intern Med* 110:191, 1962.

93. DANOVITCH SH, BAER PN, LASTER L: Intestinal alkaline phosphatase activity in familial hypophosphatasia. *N Engl J Med* 278:1253, 1968.

94. EISENBERG E, PIMSTONE B: Hypophosphatasia in an adult. *Clin Orthop* 52:199, 1967.

95. EASTMAN J, BIXLER D: Lethal and mild hypophosphatasia in half-sibs. *J Craniofac Genet Dev Biol* 2:35, 1982.

96. EASTMAN JR, BIXLER D: Clinical, laboratory and genetic investigations of hypophosphatasia: Support for autosomal dominant inheritance with homozygous lethality. *J Craniofac Genet Dev Biol* 3:213, 1983.

97. SØRENSEN SA, FLODGAARD H, SØRENSEN E: Serum alkaline phosphatase, serum pyrophosphatase, phosphorylethanolamine and inorganic pyrophosphate in plasma and urine: A genetic and clinical study of hypophosphatasia. *Monogr Hum Genet* 10:66, 1978.

98. RAY KP, WEISS MJ, DRACOPOLI NC, HARRIS H: Probe 8B/ES' detects a second RFLP at the human liver/bone/kidney alkaline phosphatase locus. *Nucleic Acids Res* 16:2361, 1988.

99. WHYTE MP, MAGILL HL, FALLON MD, HERROD HG: Infantile hypophosphatasia: Normalization of circulating bone alkaline phosphatase activity followed by skeletal remineralization (evidence for an intact structural gene for tissue nonspecific alkaline phosphatase). *J Pediatr* 108:82, 1986.

100. WHYTE MP, RETTINGER SD, VRABEL LA: Infantile hypophosphatasia: Enzymatic defect explored with alkaline phosphatase deficient patient dermal fibroblasts in culture. *Calcif Tissue Int* 40:244, 1987.

101. BLASKOVICS ME, SHAW KNF: Hypophosphatasia with phenylketonuria. *Z Kinderheilkd* 117:265, 1974.

102. LOWRY RB, SNYDER FF, WESENBERG RL, MACHIN GA, APPLEGARTH DA, MORGAN K, CARTER RJ, TOONE JR, HOLMES RM, DEWAR RD: Morquio syndrome (MPS IVA) and hypophosphatasia in a Hutterite kindred. *Am J Med Genet* 22:463, 1985.

103. BONGIOVANNI AM, ALBUM MM, ROOT AW, HOPE JW, MARINO J, SPENCER DM: Studies on hypophosphatasia and response to high phosphate intake. *Am J Med Sci* 255:163, 1968.

104. MAESAKA H, NIITSU N, SUWA S, FUJITA T: Neonatal hypophosphatasia with elevated serum parathyroid hormone. *Eur J Pediatr* 125:71, 1977.

105. WHYTE MP, MCALISTER WH, PATTON LS, MAGILL HL, FALLON MD, LORENTZ WB, HERROD HG: Enzyme replacement therapy for infantile hypophosphatasia attempted by intravenous infusions of alkaline phosphatase-rich Paget plasma: Results in three additional patients. *J Pediatr* 105:926, 1984.

106. ALBEGGIANI A, CATALDO F: Infantile hypophosphatasia diagnosed at 4 months and surviving 2 years. *Helv Paediatr Acta* 37:49, 1982.

107. WHYTE MP, MAHUREN JD, FEDDE KN, COLE FS, MCCABE ERB, COBURN SP: Perinatal hypophosphatasia: Tissue levels of vitamin B6 are unremarkable despite markedly increased circulating concentrations of pyridoxal-5'-phosphate (evidence for an ectoenzyme role for tissue nonspecific alkaline phosphatase). *J Clin Invest* 81:1234, 1988.

108. SCAGLIONE PR, LUCEY JF: Further observations on hypophosphatasia. *Am J Dis Child* 92:493, 1956.

109. FRASER D, LAIDLAW JC: Treatment of hypophosphatasia with cortisone, preliminary communication. *Lancet* 1:553, 1956.

110. RIGGS BL, SEEMAN E, HODGSON SF, TAVES DR, O'FALLON WM: The effect of the fluoride/calcium regimen on vertebral fracture occurrence in postmenopausal osteoporosis: Comparison with conventional therapy. *N Engl J Med* 306:446, 1982.

111. JACOBSON DP, MCCLAIN EJ: Hypophosphatasia in monozygotic twins. *J Bone Joint Surg* 49-A:377, 1967.

112. WEINSTEIN RS, WHYTE MP: Fifty year follow-up of hypophosphatasia (letter). *Arch Intern Med* 141:1720, 1981.

113. RUDD NL, MISKIN M, HOAR DI, BENZIE R, DORAN TA: Prenatal diagnosis of hypophosphatasia. *N Engl J Med* 295:146, 1976.

114. MULIVOR RA, MENNUTI M, ZACKAI EH, HARRIS H: Prenatal diagnosis of hypophosphatasia: Genetic, biochemical, and clinical studies. *Am J Hum Genet* 30:271, 1978.

115. HAUSSER C, HABIB R, POITRAS P: Hypophosphatasia: A complete absence of the fetal skeleton. *Union Med Can* 113:978, 1984.

116. GARBER AP, SILLENCE DO, LACHMAN RS, WORTHEN NJ, RIMOIN DL, KABACK MM, MULIVOR RA: Discordance between ultrasound and radiographic/biochemical findings in the prenatal diagnosis of congenital lethal hypophosphatasia. The National Foundation March of Dimes Birth Defects Conference, 1979, p 61.

117. KOUSSEFF BG, MULIVOR RA: Prenatal diagnosis of hypophosphatasia. *Obstet Gynecol* 57:6(suppl):9S, 1981.

118. WHYTE MP: Alkaline phosphatase: Physiologic role explored in hypophosphatasia, in Peck WA (ed): *Bone and Mineral Research,* vol 6. Amsterdam, Elsevier (in press).

119. BENKE PJ, FLESHOOD HL, PITAT HC: Osteoporotic bone disease in the pyridoxine deficient rat. *Biochem Med* 6:526, 1972.

120. GRON IH: Mammalian O-phosphorylethanolamine phospholyase activity and its inhibition. *Scand J Clin Lab Invest* 38:107, 1978.

121. CASWELL AM, WHYTE MP, RUSSELL RGG: Normal activity of nucleoside-triphosphate pyrophosphatase in alkaline phosphatase-deficient fibroblasts from patients with infantile hypophosphatasia. *J Clin Endocrinol Metab* 63:1237, 1986.

122. WHYTE MP, VRABEL LA: Infantile hypophosphatasia fibroblasts grow normally in culture: Evidence against a role for constitutive alkaline phosphatase in the regulation of cell growth and differentiation. *Calcif Tissue Int* 40:1, 1987.

123. DOLPHIN D, POULSON R, AVRAMOVIC O: *Vitamin B6 Pyridoxal Phosphate: Clinical, Biochemical, and Medical Aspects:* Part B. New York, Wiley, 1986.

124. TAKAHASHI T, IWANTANTI A, MIZUNO S, MORISHITA Y, NISHIO H, KODAMA S, MATSUO T: The relationship between phosphoethanolamine level in serum and intractable seizure on hypophosphatasia infantile form, in Cohn DV, Fugita T, Potts JT Jr, Talmage RV (eds): *Endocrine Control of Bone and Calcium Metabolism.* Amsterdam, Excerpta Medica, 1984, vol 8-B, pp 93–94.

125. WHYTE MP, MAHUREN JD, SCOTT MJ, COBURN SP: Hypophosphatasia: Pyridoxal-5'-phosphate levels are markedly increased in hypophosphatasemic

plasma but normal in alkaline phosphatase-deficient fibroblasts (evidence for an ectoenzyme role for alkaline phosphatase in vitamin B6 metabolism). *J Bone Min Res* 1:92, 1986.

126. LOW MG, SALTIEL AR: Structural and functional roles of glycosyl-phosphatidylinositol in membranes. *Science* 239:268, 1988.

127. FEDDE KN, SCOTT MJ, WHYTE MP: Alkaline phosphatase: Identity with pyridoxal-5'-phosphate demonstrated with normal and hypophosphatasia fibroblasts in culture. *J Bone Min Res* 1:60-A, 1986.

128. FEDDE KN, LANE CC, WHYTE MP: Alkaline phosphatase is an ectoenzyme that acts on micromolar concentration of natural substrates at physiologic pH in human osteosarcoma (SAOS-2) cells. *Arch Biochem Biophys* 264:400, 1988.

129. ANDERSON BB, O'BRIEN H, GRIFFIN GE, MOLLIN DL: Hydrolysis of pyridoxal-5'-phosphate in plasma in conditions with raised alkaline phosphatase. *Gut* 21:192, 1980.

130. FRASER D, YENDT ER: Metabolic abnormalities in hypophosphatasia. *Am J Dis Child* 90:552, 1955.

CHAPTER 117

THE CARBONIC ANHYDRASE II DEFICIENCY SYNDROME: Osteopetrosis with Renal Tubular Acidosis and Cerebral Calcification

WILLIAM S. SLY

1. The carbonic anhydrase II deficiency syndrome is an autosomal recessive disorder which produces osteopetrosis, renal tubular acidosis, and cerebral calcification. Other features include mental retardation (seen in over 90 percent of reported cases), growth failure, and dental malocclusion.

2. Complications of osteopetrosis include increased susceptibility to fractures (which do, however, heal normally) and cranial nerve compression symptoms. Anemia and other hematological manifestations of osteopetrosis are absent.

3. The renal tubular acidosis is usually a mixed type. A distal component is evident from inability to acidify the urine, and a proximal component evident from a lowered transport maximum for bicarbonate.

4. Thirty patients have been reported, all of whom have a quantitative deficiency of carbonic anhydrase II activity and immunoreactivity in erythrocytes. Heterozygous carriers can be identified by simple tests, but prenatal diagnosis is not yet feasible.

5. A structural gene mutation at the CA II locus on chromosome 8 is suspected. Although the CA II cDNA has been cloned, the mutational basis for the syndrome has not yet been established.

6. Symptoms of metabolic acidosis improve with treatment, but no specific treatment is available.

HISTORY

Osteopetrosis (marble bone disease) was first described in 1904 by Albers-Schönberg.[1] Subsequently, over 300 cases have been reported.[2] Among these, two principal types were distinguished. An autosomal dominant form was called the adult, benign form because of the relatively few symptoms and the benign course, which is compatible with normal life span. The diagnosis is often made incidentally in adults evaluated for other complaints. At the other extreme is the clinically severe, autosomal recessive form which has its onset in infancy and produces anemia, leukopenia, hepatomegaly, failure to thrive, cranial nerve symptoms, and early death. This form is often referred to as the infantile, malignant, or lethal form. Beighton and colleagues have pointed out the existence of clinically intermediate forms of osteopetrosis.[3] Although this genetic heterogeneity indicates that multiple genetic causes produce osteopetrosis, the common mechanism underlying all forms is thought to be failure of bone resorption.[4]

The association of renal tubular acidosis with osteopetrosis was reported independently from three different countries—France,[5] Belgium,[6] and the United States[7]—in 1972. These initial pedigrees suggested that the pattern of inheritance is autosomal recessive. The clinical course began with onset in infancy or early childhood. Though not entirely benign, it was much milder than the course of the recessive lethal form and was compatible with long survival. The hematologic abnormalities associated with the recessive lethal form of osteopetrosis were mild or absent. In 1980, Ohlsson et al.[8] reported the additional finding of cerebral calcification, documented by CT scans, in four children from Saudi Arabia with osteopetrosis and renal tubular acidosis. Calcification of the basal ganglia in the original American kindred was reported independently by Whyte et al. the same year.[9]

In 1983, Sly et al.[10] reported that the three sisters from the original American kindred with this syndrome (Fig. 117-1) lacked carbonic anhydrase II (CA II) in their erythrocytes, and that their normal-appearing parents and many first-degree relatives had half-normal levels of CA II in erythrocyte lysates. These observations, coupled with the fact that CA II was the only known soluble isozyme of CA in kidney and brain, led them to propose that CA II deficiency is the primary defect in this newly recognized metabolic disorder of bone, kidney, and brain.

In a subsequent report, Sly et al.[11] extended these studies to 18 additional patients in 11 unrelated families of different geographical and ethnic origins. Subsequently, Ohlsson et al.[12] reported four additional Saudi Arabian patients, including the first affected neonate, and summarized the clinical features of 21 reported patients. Recently, Cochat et al.[13] added an additional case and provided an excellent review of the clinical findings of the 30 patients reported to date, including a few who have not been completely described clinically. Deficiency of CA II was found in erythrocyte lysates of every patient identified with this syndrome.

NOMENCLATURE

The syndrome of osteopetrosis with renal tubular acidosis (McKusick catalogue no. 25973[14]) was recognized as a distinct entity in 1972.[5–7] In 1980, when Ohlsson et al.[8] pointed out that cerebral calcification was part of the syndrome, they suggested that it be referred to as *marble brain disease* by analogy with marble bone disease, the name given earlier to inherited forms of osteopetrosis that did not involve the brain.[2] However, since the enzymatic basis for the disorder was estab-

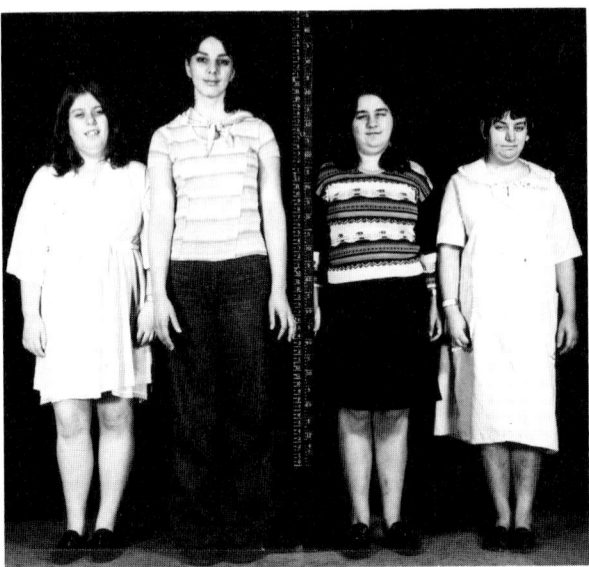

Fig. 117-1 American family reported by Whyte et al. with the CA II deficiency syndrome. From left are patient 3, unaffected sister, patient 2, and patient 1 (proposita). This picture was taken in 1978 when the proposita was 29. Osteopetrosis had been diagnosed at age 2 following a pathologic fracture. Note short stature, unusual facial features, and squint in the three affected sisters. Patients 2 and 3 had limited vision and were considered legally blind. Vision was nearly normal in patient 1. (*From Whyte et al.*[9])

lished,[10,11] it has been referred to as the *carbonic anhydrase II deficiency syndrome.*[12,14] It has also been called the *Guibaud-Vainsel syndrome* after the authors of the first two full reports on the disorder.[14]

CLINICAL MANIFESTATIONS

There is considerable variability in the age of onset and the severity of clinical manifestations among the 30 reported cases.[13] All have renal tubular acidosis and eventually develop osteopetrosis and cerebral calcification. Additional features include growth failure, mental retardation, and dental malocclusion. In some patients, bone fractures and other complications of osteopetrosis have dominated the clinical picture.[6,9] In others, symptoms of metabolic acidosis including failure to thrive, developmental retardation, and growth retardation have been more prominent.[5,8,13]

Osteopetrosis

The osteopetrosis results from a generalized accumulation of bone mass that is secondary to a defect in bone resorption.[4] This defect prevents the normal development of marrow cavities, the normal tubulation of long bones, and the enlargement of osseous foramina. The clinical manifestations of osteopetrosis in the CA II deficiency syndrome tend to be milder than in the recessive, lethal form of osteopetrosis. They appear later,[12,13] and they also tend to improve over time.[9]

Anemia is rarely profound in patients with CA II deficiency, though two patients had sufficient anemia to be referred for bone marrow transplantation. In fact, the first reported bone marrow transplantation for osteopetrosis was done on a patient who very likely had the CA II deficiency syndrome,[15] and not the recessive lethal form of osteopetrosis, for which bone mar-

row transplantation has become an accepted form of therapy.[16] This patient was reported to have a favorable hematologic response, but to have been unimproved in terms of the metabolic acidosis following bone marrow transplantation.[13]

The radiologic findings in patients with CA II deficiency syndrome are not distinguishable from those in patients with other forms of osteopetrosis.[9,13] Increased bone density (Fig. 117-2), abnormal modeling, delay or failure of normal tubulation of long bones, transverse banding of metaphyses, fractures, and "bone in bone" appearance are all seen, as in other forms of osteopetrosis. However, the changes can vary with age. In the only neonate studied to date, the radiologic features were too subtle to justify the diagnosis at 23 days of age,[12] even though the hyperchloremic metabolic acidosis and alkaline urine were already prominent findings. This observation suggests that the osteopetrosis is a postpartum developmental abnormality which appears over the first year of life. The first patients reported by Guibaud[5,13] also had no osteopetrosis at age 4 months, but typical findings evolved and progressed over the first 3 years of life before stabilizing. In at least some patients followed into adulthood, the radiologic features of osteopetrosis, which were fully developed in childhood, improved substantially after puberty (Fig. 117-3). The radiographs may become nearly normal as the patients move into adulthood.[9]

Bone fractures are common in childhood in many patients, with some reporting 15 to 30 fractures by midadolescence.[6,9,17] After puberty, the frequency of bone fractures decreases. Fractures were the most prominent symptoms in the Ameri-

Fig. 117-2 Anteroposterior radiographs of right tibia and fibula of patient 2 at 2 years of age and left tibia and fibula of patient 3 at age 6. Features of osteopetrosis include diffuse osteosclerosis with absence of medullary cavities and flared metaphyses containing transverse lines. Despite the increased bone density, healing fractures are evident in both radiographs.

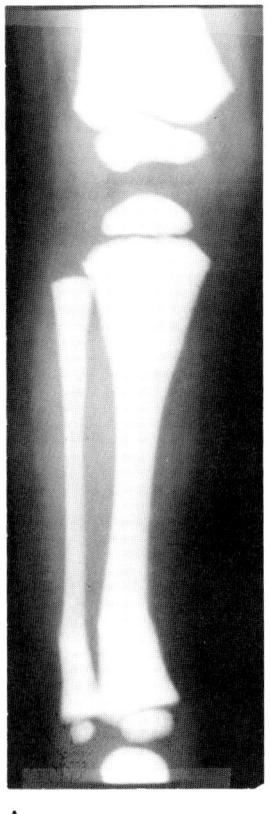

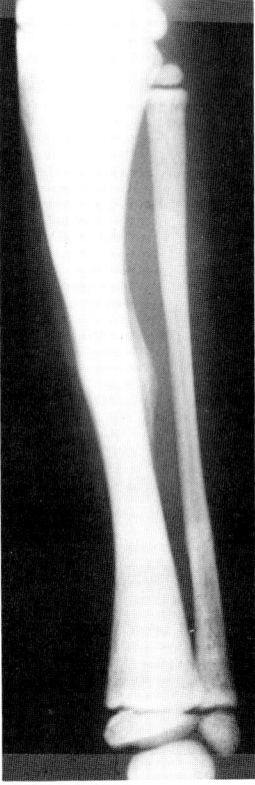

A   B

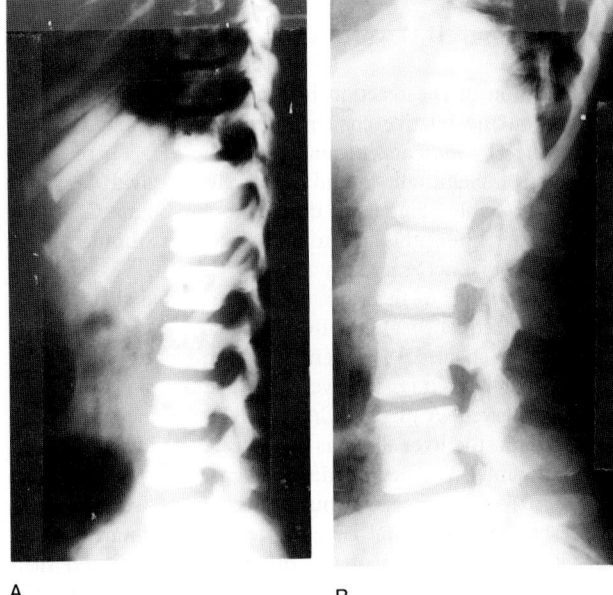

Fig. 117-3 Patient 1, lumbar spine (lateral roentgenograms). *A.* Age 8 years. *B.* Age 25 years. Osteosclerosis diminished greatly. Persistent osteosclerosis at the vertebral end plates characterizes the "sandwich vertebrae" of osteopetrosis. (*From Whyte et al.*[9])

can patients[7] and in the Belgian patient[6] in whom mental retardation was not present (Fig. 117-2). Fractures were not seen in Guibaud's patient.[5]

The symptoms of cranial nerve compression secondary to osteopetrosis are milder than in the recessive, lethal form of osteopetrosis. However, the cranial nerve symptoms appear in 60 percent of reported patients.[13] Optic nerve pallor is common, but frank optic nerve atrophy is less frequent. Strabismus is also common, as is hearing impairment. Facial weakness has been noted in two reports.

Renal Tubular Acidosis

Patients typically have metabolic acidosis which varies considerably in type and severity in different pedigrees.[13] Metabolic acidosis was already present at 23 days of age in the first affected neonate.[12] Although one of the first patients reported had only proximal renal tubular acidosis, evidenced by low bicarbonate threshold, and had normal distal acidification,[5,13] most of the patients have a combination of proximal and distal renal tubular acidosis.[6,9,15,18,19] Of 21 patients in whom the renal lesion was characterized, 4 were felt to have proximal renal tubular acidosis, 6 distal, and 11 to have both proximal and distal components to their renal tubular acidosis.[12] Most patients had hyperchloremia, a normal anion gap, and inappropriately alkaline urine pH (>6.0). These findings are consistent with distal renal tubular acidosis. Symptomatic hyperkalemia has been observed in four patients.[9,13] However, unlike other patients with distal renal tubular acidosis, in these patients there is neither hypercalciuria nor nephrocalcinosis. Glomerular filtration rate is not reduced, and serum creatinine and blood urea nitrogen are not elevated.

Most patients also have a reduced tubular maximum for bicarbonate. Although they usually have no bicarbonaturia when acidotic, they lose bicarbonate when plasma bicarbonate levels are raised to normal levels by loading. They do not have amino aciduria, glycosuria, or any other manifestations of the Fanconi syndrome.

Mental Retardation

The frequency and severity of mental retardation were not fully appreciated initially, because affected patients in two of the first four families recognized with this syndrome were not retarded.[6,7,9] However, over 90 percent of the patients reported to date have had significant mental retardation.[12,15] Even in the two families where intelligence was not below the normal range, some learning disabilities were observed. In most families, the mental retardation in affected patients has been severe enough to preclude education in regular schools.[15]

Cerebral Calcification

Cerebral calcifications, evident by computed tomography (CT) scans, were first reported by Ohlsson.[8] They were not present at birth, but appeared some time during the first decade (in one case, by 18 months).[5,8a,11,13] Calcifications involved the caudate nucleus, putamen, and globus pallidus, and also appeared peripherally in the periventricular and subcortical white matter (Fig. 117-4). The rate of progression of cerebral calcification has been documented in very few patients.

Growth Failure

Growth retardation is nearly a constant finding. Almost all reported patients had short stature, and many were underweight. Bone age was retarded and corresponded to height age. Genu valgum is a common finding in older patients. At least part of the growth retardation is due to the chronic metabolic acidosis. Guibaud reported acceleration of growth following correction of the acidosis,[5] but later noted that growth retardation persisted even after treatment.[13] The final height achieved by the patient who responded initially to correction of the acidosis was still nearly 4 SD below normal.[5,13]

Fig. 117-4 CT scan of the head of patient 3 at 33 years of age. Scattered dense cerebral calcifications are especially prominent in the basal ganglia. (*With permission from* The New England Journal of Medicine 313:139, 1985.)

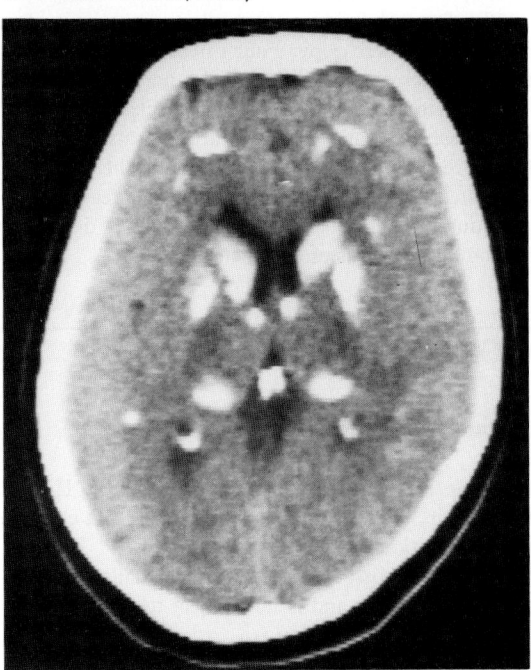

Dental Malocclusion

Dentition was typically delayed, and dental malocclusion was a prominent finding in affected patients from several families. Dental malalignment and malocclusion complicate dental hygiene, and dental caries may be severe.[9,12] Enamel hypoplasia has also been noted.[8,12]

Other Features

Ohlsson[8,12] has reported a characteristic facies in the patients from Saudi Arabia that is present in many patients from other ethnic groups as well. These features include craniofacial disproportion with a prominent forehead and a large cranial vault relative to the size of the face. The mouth is small, and there is micrognathia. The nose is narrow, but prominent. The philtrum is short, the upper lip thin, and the lower lip thick. Squint is common and contributes to the unusual facies (Fig. 117-1).

Ohlsson et al.[12] recently reported findings of restrictive lung disease in two patients. Chest films showed no signs of parenchymal lung disease, but the rib cages were very dense.

Optic atrophy has been found in patients in whom the optic foramina were of normal size.[13] The mechanism of optic atrophy in these patients is unclear.

PATHOLOGY

No autopsies have been reported on patients with the CA II deficiency syndrome. However, bone biopsies from iliac crest have been analyzed, and showed histologic features typical of osteopetrosis.[5,9,12] The cortical bone showed small Haversian systems widely separated from dense bone. The separation of cortical and cancellous was generally indistinct. Trabeculae were broad and irregular. Osteoid and normal-appearing osteoblasts were seen lining trabecular bone in several areas. On routine microscopy, osteoclast morphology was unremarkable. A minute sample of femoral cortex was obtained during open reduction of a femoral fracture. Osteoclasts were normal in appearance on light microscopy. Four osteoclasts were identified on electron microscopy, and showed a normal rim of cytoplasm adjacent to the bone surface. This "clear zone" was free of organelles. The osteoclasts appeared normal, although no "ruffled borders" were seen. In summary, the histologic findings of osteopetrosis were present, but no features appeared to distinguish the osteopetrosis of the CA II deficiency syndrome from other forms of osteopetrosis.

PATHOGENESIS

The Carbonic Anhydrase Gene Family

All three soluble isozymes of CA in humans (CA I, II, and III) are monomeric, 29-kDa zinc metalloenzymes that catalyze the reversible hydration of CO_2 (reaction I, below).[20] Reaction II involves an ionic dissociation, occurs virtually instantaneously nonenzymatically, and is not subject to enzymatic acceleration.

$$CO_2 + H_2O \overset{I}{\rightleftharpoons} H_2CO_3 \overset{II}{\rightleftharpoons} H^+ + HCO_3^- \quad (117\text{-}1)$$

The direction of the reaction in a given tissue or body fluid depends on the relative concentrations of CO_2 and HCO_3^-, and on the H^+ ion concentration, i.e., the pH. There is also a distinctive membrane-bound CA in lung called CA IV,[21] which is probably identical to the membrane-bound CA in the brush border lining the lumen of the proximal tubules of the kidney.[22] A distinct, secretory form of CA (CA VI) has been described in saliva of the rat,[23] the human,[24] and sheep.[25] The amino acid sequence of the ovine salivary CA was recently reported and showed 33 percent sequence identity with ovine CA II, though residues involved in the active site were more highly conserved. A distinct CA has also been reported in mitochondria in the liver that has been designated CA V.[26]

Genetic and structural evidence suggests that at least the soluble isozymes comprise a multilocus enzyme family derived from a common ancestral gene by gene duplications.[27] However, kinetic parameters of the different isozymes and their sensitivities to different inhibitors, as well as their tissue distributions, can differ markedly, indicating different physiological roles for the different isozymes.[28,29]

The human CA II isozyme, whose turnover number for CO_2 hydration (1.3 to 1.9 × 10^6 s^{-1}) is the highest known for any enzyme,[30,31] is widely distributed. It has been identified in erythrocytes, brain, eye, kidney, cartilage, liver, lung, skeletal muscle, pancreas, gastric mucosa, and anterior pituitary body.[20,32] The other isozymes, whose activities are lower than those of CA II, in the order CA II > CA IV > CA I > CA III, appear to have a more limited distribution.[21,28,29] CA I is found primarily in erythrocytes. CA III is found mainly in red skeletal muscle, and CA IV has been found primarily in lung and kidney.

The Biochemical Defect

In 1983, the three affected sisters reported initially by Sly et al.[7] and described in detail by Whyte et al.[9] were shown to have no detectable CA II activity in their erythrocytes.[10] CA I was present in near-normal levels. No immunoreactivity was detectable with specific antibody to CA II. The obligate heterozygote parents and several additional family members were found to have half-normal levels of CA II activity. These findings were subsequently extended to 18 similarly affected patients from 11 unrelated families of different geographic and ethnic origins.[11] Every patient with osteopetrosis and renal tubular acidosis since tested has had nondetectable levels of CA II activity.[15] Thus, there has been no exception to the finding of a quantitative defect in CA II in erythrocytes of patients with this syndrome.

There is presently no definitive evidence on the mutational alteration which produces the inherited deficiency of CA II. In addition, the deficiency has not yet been demonstrated directly in bone and kidney. However, the deficiency in these tissues can be inferred from the fact that CA II is the only soluble isozyme present in these tissues, and the fact that the observed metabolic abnormalities in the affected patients can readily be explained by the CA II deficiency in these two organs.[33]

Although the complete absence of CA II activity and immunoreactivity in erythrocytes have been consistent findings in affected patients, it should be stressed that the residual activity in cells that continue to synthesize protein (such as osteoclasts in bone and cells in the proximal and distal tubules of the kidney) might be significantly higher than in erythrocytes. In fact, we suspect that some of the clinical heterogeneity in this syndrome may be explained by differences in residual CA II activity in bone and kidney in patients with different mutations in the structural gene for CA II.

Pathophysiology

The finding of a quantitative defect in CA II in these patients provided an unusual opportunity to assess the function of this enzyme and to understand its importance for bone, brain, and kidney metabolism.

Bone Metabolism. All known forms of osteopetrosis involve the failure to resorb bone.[4] Studies showing inhibition of PTH-induced release of Ca^{2+} from bone by CA inhibitors had suggested a role for CA in bone resorption.[34-36] Also, CA had been demonstrated histochemically in chick and hen osteoclasts,[37] and CA II demonstrated immunohistochemically in rat[38] and human[34] osteoclasts. The osteopetrosis seen in patients with CA II deficiency provided genetic evidence for a role for CA in bone resorption, and specifically implicated the CA II isozyme.[10]

It has been suggested that CA aids the resorptive process by mediating the secretion of H^+.[35,38] We have proposed that the role of CA II in acidifying the bone-resorbing component is an indirect one, analogous to its role in supporting the acidification of the lumen in the distal tubule of the kidney. It has been suggested recently that the acidification of the bone-resorbing compartment is mediated by a proton-translocating ATPase,[40] that secretes protons into the lumen. This reaction would simultaneously generate an OH^- in the cytoplasm for each H^+ translocated to the lumen. Titration of the OH^- ions produced in the cytosol by CA II might be required for the proton translocation ATPase to maintain the pH gradient between the cytosol of the osteoclast (~pH 7.0) and the bone-resorbing compartment (~pH 4.5). This could explain the pharmacologic evidence for a requirement for CA in bone resorption.[34-36] Since CA II is the only CA isozyme known to be expressed in osteoclasts,[39,40] it could also explain the osseous manifestations of CA II deficiency.

Renal Tubular Acidosis. Three things need explanation with regard to renal metabolism in these patients. First, most CA II–deficient patients have both a proximal and a distal component to their renal tubular acidosis.[15] Second, in some patients proximal renal tubular acidosis predominates, while in others, the distal renal tubular acidosis predominates.[15] Third, CA II–deficient patients have a nearly normal bicarbonaturia following ingestion or infusion of carbonic anhydrase inhibitors.[33] These observations can be explained by a model in which the functions of CA II in the proximal and distal tubules are physiologically and biochemically distinct, and the major role of CA in bicarbonate reclamation is assigned not to CA II, but to CA IV, the luminal CA in the brush border of the proximal tubule.[41,42] CA IV is biochemically and immunologically distinct from CA II, and appears to be normal in CA II–deficient patients.[33]

First, the explanation for the proximal renal tubular acidosis. There is general agreement that renal reabsorption of bicarbonate is a major factor in acid-base homeostasis. Most of the bicarbonate reclamation takes place in the proximal tubule and is blocked by inhibitors of CA. However, two distinct CAs participate in bicarbonate reclamation by the proximal tubule, and they play separate roles in bicarbonate reclamation.

Bicarbonate reclamation depends on H^+ secretion, which is mediated by Na^+-H^+ exchange in the proximal tubule. The H^+ secreted into the lumen of the proximal tubule is titrated by the HCO_3^- in the glomerular filtrate to produce H_2CO_3 which is in contact with the membrane-bound CA IV. The luminal CA IV catalyzes the dehydration of H_2CO_3 to H_2O and CO_2.[43,44] The bicarbonaturia seen in already acidotic CA II–deficient patients in response to infused acetazolamide is attributed to inhibition of this luminal CA IV.[33]

The CO_2 produced by the CA IV–catalyzed reaction in the lumen diffuses freely into the cytosol of the proximal tubule. Here in the cytoplasm CO_2 encounters CA II, which acts to hydrate the CO_2 to produce H_2CO_3, which then dissociates spontaneously to HCO_3^- and H^+. The HCO_3^- generated from CO_2 in the cytosol is transported from the cytosol to the interstitial fluid or peritubular capillary, completing the reclamation of the filtered bicarbonate. The H^+ regenerated in the cytosol by the CA II–catalyzed reaction can be secreted in exchange for Na^+ to initiate another round of HCO_3^- reclamation.[44]

Thus, both the luminal CA IV and the cytosolic CA II participate in the reclamation of HCO_3^- in the proximal tubule. The fact that CA II–deficient patients do not spill HCO_3^- when acidotic suggests that CA II is not required for HCO_3^- reclamation when patients have low bicarbonate loads, i.e., are acidotic. However, they have a lowered tubular maximum for bicarbonate and lose bicarbonate when the filtered load is increased by bicarbonate infusion or ingestion, indicating that CA II is required to regenerate H^+ for bicarbonate reclamation under normal bicarbonate loads. This requirement explains the proximal component of the renal tubular acidosis in CA II–deficient patients (Fig. 117-5A).

The prominent distal component of the renal tubular acidosis in most CA II–deficient patients, evidenced by inappropriately high urine pH values when patients are acidotic, suggests a need for CA II for distal acidification as well. This is consistent with the immunohistochemical evidence showing a much more intense reaction for CA II in the distal tubule and the intercalated cells of the collecting ducts than in the proximal tubules.[42] Why is there normally such an abundance of CA II in the distal tubules, when most of the HCO_3^- reclamation takes place in the proximal tubule? We suggested[33] that the explanation may be inferred from the analogous situation in the distal nephron and collecting system in the amphibian. In the turtle bladder, for example, the "CA-rich cells" are specialized cells that secrete H^+ and are capable of generating a steep pH gradient.[45,46] However, the acidification of the lumen is sensitive to inhibition by acetazolamide. In the amphibian, it has been proposed that CA is needed to titrate the OH^- produced in the cytosol by the proton-translocating Mg^{2+}-ATPase. We have suggested a similar role for CA II in the distal tubule of the human kidney, i.e., catalyzing the conversion of OH^- and CO_2 to HCO_3^-.[33] Unless the OH^- is titrated by CO_2, the proton-translocating ATPase cannot generate a pH gradient and acidify the lumen. The absence of CA II for this reaction in CA II–deficient patients can explain their defect in distal tubular acidification (Fig. 117-5B).

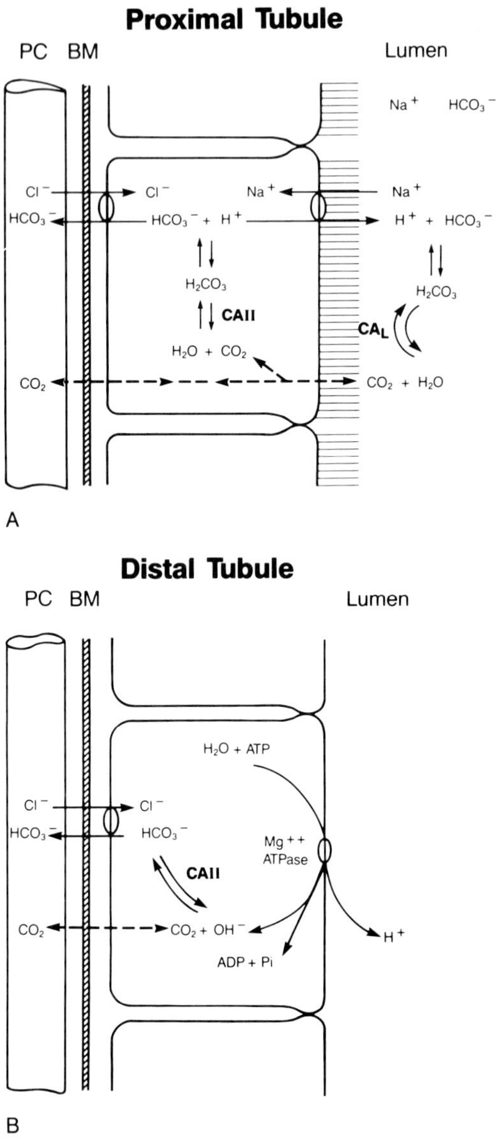

Proximal Tubule

A

Distal Tubule

B

Fig. 117-5 A. Proposed roles of carbonic anhydrases in bicarbonate reclamation in the proximal tubule. Na^+ and HCO_3^- enter the lumen of the proximal tubule. H^+ is secreted in exchange for Na^+, and H^+ and HCO_3^- are converted to CO_2 and H_2O in a reaction catalyzed by the luminal CA (CA IV). We propose that this enzyme functions normally in CA II–deficient patients and that its inhibition explains the positive response to acetazolamide (normal bicarbonate diuresis). CO_2 diffuses freely into the proximal tubular cell [and across the basement membrane (BM) and into the peritubular capillary (PC)] and is exposed to cytosolic CA II, which catalyzes its rehydration to form HCO_3^- and H^+. The HCO_3^- is transported from the contraluminal surface of the proximal tubular cell (possibly in exchange for Cl^-, though the mechanism is unclear), and the H^+ generated by CA II is secreted in exchange for Na^+ to initiate another cycle of HCO_3^- reabsorption. Loss of CA II–mediated regeneration of H^+ is suggested as the cause of HCO_3^- wasting in CA II–deficient patients. B. Proposed role of CA II in distal urinary acidification. We propose that H^+ is secreted into the lumen by a proton-translocating Mg^{2+}-ATPase, as in amphibians, which produces OH^- in the cytosol. CO_2 can condense with OH^- to form HCO_3^- in a CA II–catalyzed reaction, and HCO_3^- can be transported across the basement membrane and into the peritubular capillary. We suggest that failure to titrate the OH^- limits the ability to secrete H^+ and acidify the urine appropriately in CA II–deficient patients. (*From Sly et al.*[33])

We still have the third point to address. The basis for heterogeneity in the renal lesion in CA II deficiency still requires explanation. Why is there variability in prominence of the proximal and distal lesions in different pedigrees? The explanation for this heterogeneity is presently speculative, since the mutational basis for CA II deficiency has not been demonstrated in a single patient. However, if one assumes that different structural gene mutations produce CA II deficiency in the different pedigrees of patients with the CA II deficiency syndrome, it is plausible that different mutations could lead to this heterogeneity in at last two ways. First, different mutations could affect the rate of enzyme turnover in proximal and distal tubular cells differentially, resulting in different levels of residual enzyme activity in the two different locations. Second, different structural gene mutations could affect the two different enzymatic activities in the two locations differentially. Thus, hydration of CO_2 to produce H^+ and HCO_3^- in the proximal tubule and the condensation of OH^- and CO_2 to produce HCO_3^- in the distal tubule might be differentially affected by different mutations in the CA II gene. Delineation of the mutations in different CA II–deficient patients, and studies of the enzyme produced after expression of the cloned mutant enzymes in prokaryotic and eukaryotic cells, should soon be feasible and allow one to test this hypothesis.

Brain Calcification and Cerebral Function. The mechanism of the cerebral calcification is unclear. Carbonic anhydrase II is primarily a glial enzyme that occurs predominantly in oligodendrocytes.[47] It is the only soluble carbonic anhydrase in brain homogenates. As much as 50 percent of the total carbonic anhydrase II activity occurs in a membrane-bound or myelin-associated form.[48] Its function in the brain is not known. Whether the cerebral calcification in carbonic anhydrase II deficiency is a direct effect of the deficiency of CA II in the brain or an indirect effect—for example, of carbonic anhydrase deficiency in erythrocytes, or of chronic systemic acidosis—is not clear.

While brain development and central nervous system function are not profoundly deranged in patients with this syndrome, psychomotor delay, learning disabilities, and even mental retardation are evident in most affected patients.[15] The mental retardation was not so obvious in the initial reports of patients with CA II deficiency syndrome, but it is now clear that over 90 percent of the reported patients have mental retardation severe enough to prevent adequate performance in regular schools. Whether this is a direct consequence of the CA II deficiency or an indirect effect is not clear.

Growth Failure. Growth failure appears to result from the combined effects of the osteopetrosis on bone elongation and the chronic metabolic acidosis on general health. Correction of the acidosis has been followed by a growth spurt in one patient,[15] but the dramatic reduction in final height achieved makes it clear that the growth retardation is not due to the acidosis alone.

GENETICS

Inheritance

The CA II deficiency syndrome is inherited as an autosomal recessive trait. Affected patients are offspring of normal-appearing heterozygote carrier parents who have half-normal levels of CA II in their erythrocyte lysates. Heterozygotes have no symptoms and no signs of the disorder. Males and females are affected with equal frequency and severity. Consanguinity is very common (87 percent) in parents of affected offspring.[15]

The geographical distribution of this syndrome is striking, with more than half the known cases observed in families from Kuwait, Saudi Arabia, and North Africa.[11] This probably results from both an increased frequency of the carbonic anhydrase II deficiency allele in these regions and an increased frequency of consanguineous marriages, particularly in the Bedouin tribes from which many of these patients originated.

Molecular Genetics

The gene encoding CA II is located at chromosome 8q22.[49] The genes for CA I and CA II are closely linked in this chromosomal region.[50,51] The genomic organization of the CA II gene in the mouse has been defined. The entire mouse gene (strain YBR) was 38 kb, and was composed of seven exons and six introns.[52] The human genomic organization is thought to be similar, based on analysis of the 3.8-kb genomic clone at the 5' end containing the regulatory region and the first two exons of the human gene.[52a,53,54] However, the organization of the rest of the human gene has not been reported. The 5' regulatory sequences of the mouse and human CA II genes have been sequenced and compared.[54] The nucleotide sequences of the 5' regions of the CA II genes of humans and mice show a high degree of homology from 200 bases 5' of the start codon through at least 60 base pairs 5' of the second intron, and are also highly G + C–rich. The presence of individual features characteristic of both housekeeping genes (high G + C content, and 9 CCGCCC or GGGCGG boxes) and highly regulated genes (TATA box, β-globin-like tandem repeats, and limited cell type expression of the human CA II gene) suggested that this is an intermediate-type promoter. Deletion experiments indicated that the direct repeat elements were necessary for optimum transcription. Because the human CA II 5' region has similarities to other documented Sp1-responsive promoters, it is likely that human CA II transcription is modulated by the transcription factor Sp1 in human cell lines.

The cDNA sequences for CA I, CA II, and CA III have all been reported.[55–58] The complete human cDNA for CA II was cloned from a kidney λgt10 library.[54] Expression of the cDNA insert in COS-7 cells produced active CA enzymatic activity and an immunoprecipitable product. The cDNA insert is 1551 bp in length and encodes a 260-amino acid polypeptide. The deduced amino acid sequence was identical with that determined by amino acid sequencing of the protein.[59] The protein-coding region of this DNA showed 81 and 71 percent nucleotide identity with cDNAs for CA II from the mouse and chick, respectively. Even the long 3' untranslated region of the human cDNA for CA II (703 bp) showed 64 and 42 percent identity with those from the mouse and chick, demonstrating remarkable conservation of the CA II cDNAs in amniotes. The nucleotide sequence of the protein coding region of the human CA II cDNA is 64% and 65% identical with those of human CA I and CA III, which are thought to have arisen from a common precursor by gene duplication. The identity at the amino acid level is 60% and 58%, respectively.

To date, hemolysates from over 50,000 individuals from different populations have been screened for electrophoretic variants of CA I and CA II isozymes.[32] Three amino acid substitutions have been detected. Each can be explained by a single base change in the coding sequence of the cDNA.[55]

There is no direct evidence that the mutation underlying CA II deficiency is in the structural gene, or even that it maps to chromosome 8. A restriction fragment length polymorphism associated with the CA II gene has been reported in which the absence or presence of a *Taq*I site approximately 1.0 kb 5' to the initiation codon produces either 5.4 kb or 4.0 + 1.4 kb *Taq*I fragments.[60] Segregation analysis shows that these alleles are inherited in a Mendelian fashion, with a frequency of around 50 percent. To date, no polymorphism has been linked to the CA II deficiency allele, but few families with this disorder have been examined.

DIAGNOSIS

Clinically, CA II deficiency should be suspected in any newborn infant with metabolic acidosis and failure to thrive, especially if the urine pH is alkaline. Osteopetrosis may not be present initially, but usually develops over the first year of life. If osteopetrosis and renal tubular acidosis coexist, the diagnosis is virtually certain. No patient with this combination has yet been found who did not have CA II deficiency. Cerebral calcification, evident by CT scan, is usually present by the end of the first decade.

Enzymatic confirmation can be made by quantitating the CA II level in erythrocyte lysates.[61,62] A relatively easy assay has been described which allows one to quantitate both CA I and CA II levels in erythrocyte lysates. This method takes advantage of the large difference in sensitivity of CA I and CA II to inhibition by sodium iodide. Normally CA I and CA II each contribute about 50 percent of the total activity, and the CA I activity is virtually completely abolished by inclusion of 8 mM sodium iodide in the assay. One simply measures the total activity (CA I + CA II) and also the activity seen in the presence of 8 mM sodium iodide (CA II). Patients with CA II deficiency have no iodide-resistant enzyme (i.e., no CA II). Obligate heterozygotes have about half-normal levels of iodide-resistant activity. Other assays have been described including staining of individual isozymes following electrophoresis, quantitation of CA I/CA II ratios by high pressure liquid chromatography, and immunologic identification of the isozymes on immunodiffusion with specific antiserums.[10]

GENETIC COUNSELING

The appropriate counseling for an autosomal recessive trait is indicated. First-degree relatives can be tested for heterozygosity. Prenatal diagnosis is currently not available. The osteopetrosis does not appear prenatally. Carbonic anhydrase levels in erythrocytes are normally extremely low at birth, and it is not clear that CA II deficiency could be diagnosed by measuring CA II activity in samples of fetal blood. No disease-associated DNA markers are available. Although the cDNA probe for CA II is available, the disease has not yet been linked to the structural gene for CA II, and it is not yet certain that the mutation underlying CA II deficiency involves a structural gene locus.

TREATMENT

No specific treatment for CA II deficiency is available. Treatment for the metabolic acidosis is recommended, at least until after adolescence. It appears that the renal tubular acidosis may stabilize at a milder level after puberty. Frequent fractures require conventional orthopedic management. Bone healing is usually normal. Most patients require special education because of serious mental retardation. There is no specific treatment for the cranial nerve abnormalities, which may lead to impaired vision, hearing deficits, and facial nerve weakness. Attention to dental hygiene is important because of the susceptibility to caries.

In the early course of the American family, treatment with bicarbonate was withheld for fear that the acidosis might be compensating for the osteopetrosis and that treatment of the acidosis might aggravate the osteopetrosis with further loss of vision and hearing. However, prolonged treatment of several patients by Dr. Guibaud and colleagues appeared to have a beneficial effect on general health without any marked progression of the osteopetrosis and with no aggravation of cranial nerve symptoms.[15] It is not clear whether the development of cerebral calcification is influenced favorably, unfavorably, or not at all by correction of the acidosis.

Bone marrow transplantation is not indicated, since the hematologic manifestations for which this is usually considered appropriate in the infantile, recessive, lethal form of osteopetrosis[16] are not present in the CA II deficiency syndrome. Although the bone manifestations might improve following bone marrow transplantation, since CA II–containing osteoclasts would be provided by stem cells from the donor marrow, the renal insufficiency would not improve. This was actually the observation reported in the first patient transplanted for osteopetrosis.[15]

We had the opportunity to replace the CA II–deficient red cells with CA II–replete blood cells following severe uterine hemorrhage in one of the patients we followed.[63] Raising the circulating erythrocyte levels of CA II to the heterozygote range by transfusion with replete erythrocytes had no effect on plasma pH or urine pH. These observations supported the proposal that the metabolic acidosis is due to the renal CA II deficiency, and is not a secondary consequence of CA II deficiency in erythrocytes.

FUTURE PROSPECTS

Several laboratories are attempting to identify the molecular defect in the CA II deficiency syndrome. Delineation of the molecular defect may make prenatal diagnosis possible.

Another important development is the recent description of a mouse with CA II deficiency.[64] The mutation was produced intentionally by exposing mice that were heterozygotes for electrophoretically distinguishable CA II gene products to a powerful mutagen and then screening their progeny electrophoretically for loss of one of the alleles. A null mutation was found, and a breeding colony established. The affected mouse has severe acidosis but has not been found to have osteopetrosis or cerebral calcification. Although this may not prove to be an animal model that has all the components of the human CA II deficiency syndrome, it is certain to be a profitable model for studying many facets of CO_2 and HCO_3^- metabo-lism and for studying certain experimental therapies like bone marrow replacement and gene therapy.

Finally, the remarkable utility of this human disease in shedding light on the physiological roles of the various carbonic anhydrases should stimulate clinical research aimed at identifying disorders due to deficiencies of other members of the CA gene family.[32] An inherited deficiency of CA I has already been found and proved to have no clinical consequences.[32] Presumably, this reflects that facts that (1) CA I is expressed primarily in the erythrocytes and (2) CA II, which is also expressed in erythrocytes, is present in normal levels in CA I–deficient patients. CA II could more than handle the requirements for CA activity in the erythrocytes.[31] It seems likely that deficiencies for CA III or CA IV would produce significant clinical abnormalities. Such experiments of nature probably exist, and once they are identified, they will likely add greatly to our understanding of why we have evolved so many isozymes to catalyze a reaction as simple as the reversible hydration of CO_2.

IMPLICATIONS FOR OSTEOPETROSIS

By now, there is considerable histochemical, pharmacologic, and genetic evidence that CA II is a major enzyme required for the generation of hydrogen ion gradients and for the normal function of osteoclasts in bone resorption. Although osteopetrosis results from a defect in bone resorption, there are other metabolic disorders in which the reverse is true, and accelerated bone loss is the problem. Can one take advantage of the dependence on CA in the process of bone resorption to inhibit accelerated bone loss? A number of organ culture systems have been developed to study bone resorption.[31,65,66] In organ culture, Ca^{2+} release from bones was shown to be hormone responsive (to parathormone and dibutyryl cyclic AMP) and sensitive to inhibition by acetazolamide and other inhibitors of CA.[66-68] Animal studies have suggested that bone loss associated with disuse can be partially prevented by CA inhibitors.[69] This observation raises hope that CA inhibitors might have a role in treating common causes of bone loss like osteoporosis. One problem, however, is that chronic administration of currently available agents produces a systemic acidosis due to their actions on the kidney, and systemic acidosis itself can lead to calcium mobilization from bone. It has been suggested[66] that development of effective inhibitors that might be useful in metabolic bone disease may require development of agents that act selectively on CA II in bone or that can be selectively targeted to bone-resorbing osteoclasts to avoid inhibition of CA II in kidney and other sites.

REFERENCES

1. ALBERS-SCHONBERG H: Röntgenbilder einr seltenen. Knochenerkrankung. *Muench Med Wochenschr* 51:365, 1904.
2. JOHNSTON CC JR, LAVY N, LORD T, VELLIOS F, MERRITT AD, DEISS WP JR: Osteopetrosis: A clinical, genetic, metabolic, and morphologic study of the dominantly inherited, benign form. *Medicine (Baltimore)* 47:149, 1968.
3. BEIGHTON P, HAMERSMA H, CREMIN BJ: Osteopetrosis in South Africa: The benign, lethal and intermediate forms. *S Afr Med J* 55:659, 1979.
4. MARKS SC JR: Morphological evidence of reduced bone resorption in osteopetrotic (op) mice. *Am J Anat* 163:157, 1982.
5. GUIBAUD P, LARBRE F, FREYCON M-T, GENOUD J: Osteopetrose et acidose

renale tubulaire: Deux cas de cette association dans une fratrie. *Arch Fr Pediatr* 29:269, 1972.

6. VAINSEL M, FONDU P, CADRANEL S, ROCHMANS C, GEPTS W: Osteopetrosis associated with proximal and distal tubular acidosis. *Acta Paediatr Scand* 61:429, 1972.

7. SLY WS, LANG R, AVIOLI L, HADDAD J, LUBOWITZ H, MCALISTER W: Recessive osteopetrosis: New clinical phenotype. *Am J Hum Genet* 24(suppl):34a, 1972.

8. OHLSSON A, STARK G, SAKATI N: Marble brain disease: Recessive osteopetrosis, renal tubular acidosis and cerebral calcification in three Saudi Arabian families. *Dev Med Child Neurol* 22:72, 1980.

8a. CUMMINGS WA, OHLSSON A: Intracranial calcification in children with osteopetrosis caused by carbonic anhydrase II deficiency. *Radiology* 157:325, 1985.

9. WHYTE MP, MURPHY WA, FALLON MD, SLY WS, TEITELBAUM SL, MACALISTER WH, AVIOLI LV: Osteopetrosis, renal tubular acidosis and basal ganglia calcification in three sisters. *Am J Med* 69:65, 1980.

10. SLY WS, HEWETT-EMMETT D, WHYTE MP, YU Y-SL, TASHIAN RE: Carbonic anhydrase II deficiency identified as the primary defect in the autosomal recessive syndrome of osteopetrosis with renal tubular acidosis and cerebral calcification. *Proc Natl Acad Sci USA* 80:2752, 1983.

11. SLY WS, WHYTE P, SUNDARAM V, TASHIAN RE, HEWETT-EMMETT D, GUIBAUD P, VAINSEL M, BALUARTE HJ, GRUSKIN A, AL-MOSAWI M, SAKATI N, OHLSSON A: Carbonic anhydrase II deficiency in 12 families with the autosomal recessive syndrome of osteopetrosis with renal tubular acidosis and cerebral calcification. *N Engl J Med* 313:139, 1985.

12. OHLSSON A, CUMMING WA, PAUL A, SLY WS: Carbonic anhydrase II deficiency syndrome: Recessive osteopetrosis with renal tubular acidosis and cerebral calcification. *Pediatrics* 77:371, 1986.

13. COCHAT P, LORAS-DUCLAUX I, GUIBAUD P: Deficit en anhydrase carbonique II: Osteopetrose, acidose renale tubulaire et calcifications intracraniennes. Revue de la literature a partir de trois observations. *Pediatrie* 42:121, 1987.

14. MCKUSICK VA: *Mendelian Inheritance in Man*, 7th ed. Baltimore, Johns Hopkins University Press, 1986, p 1183.

15. BALLET JP, GRISCELLI C, COUTRI SG, MILHAUD G, MAROTEAUX P: Bone marrow transplantation in osteopetrosis. *Lancet* 2:1137, 1977.

16. COCCIA PF, KRIVIT W, CERVENKA J, CLAWSON C, KERSEY JH, KIM TH, NESBIT ME, RAMSAY NK, WARKENTIN PI, TEITELBAUM SL, KAHN AJ, BROWN DM: Successful bone-marrow transplantation for infantile malignant osteopetrosis. *N Engl J Med* 302:701, 1980.

17. LEONE G: Osteopetrosis recessive con calcificazioni cerebrali: Studio di 3 sogetti adulti in due famiglie consanguine. *Radiol Med* 68:373, 1982.

18. BALUARTE J, HINER L, ROOT A, GRUSKIN A: Osteopetrosis and renal tubular acidosis. *Pediatr Res* 7:412, 1973.

19. BREGMAN H, BROWN J, ROGERS A, BOURKE E: Osteopetrosis with combined proximal and distal tubular acidosis. *Am J Kidney Dis* 2:357, 1982.

20. TASHIAN RE: Evolution and regulation of the carbonic anhydrase isozymes, in Rattazzi MC, Scandalios JG, Whitt GS (eds): *Isozymes: Current Topics in Biological Research*. New York, AR Liss, 1977, vol 2, p 21.

21. WHITNEY PL, BRIGGLE TV: Membrane-associated carbonic anhydrase purified from bovine lung. *J Biol Chem* 257:12056, 1982.

22. WISTRAND PJ: Properties of membrane-bound carbonic anhydrase. *Ann NY Acad Sci* 429:195, 1984.

23. FELDSTEIN JB, SILVERMAN DN: Purification and characterization of carbonic anhydrase from the saliva of the rat. *J Biol Chem* 259:5447, 1984.

24. MURAKAMI H, SLY WS: Purification and characterization of human salivary carbonic anhydrase. *J Biol Chem* 262:1382, 1987.

25. FERNLEY RT, WRIGHT RD, COGHLAN JP: Complete amino acid sequence of ovine salivary carbonic anhydrase. *Biochemistry* 27:2815, 1988.

26. STOREY BT, DODGSON SJ, FORSTER RE II: Mitochondrial carbonic anhydrase: The purified enzyme. *Ann NY Acad Sci* 429:210, 1984.

27. TASHIAN RE, HEWETT-EMMETT D, GOODMAN M: On the evolution and genetics of carbonic anhydrases I, II, and III, in Rattazzi MC, Scandalios JG, Whitt GS (eds): *Isozymes: Current Topics in Biological and Medical Research*. New York, AR Liss, 1983, p 79.

28. KOESTER MK, PULLAN LM, NOLTMANN EA: The *p*-nitrophenyl phosphatase activity of muscle carbonic anhydrase. *Arch Biochem Biophys* 211:632, 1981.

29. SANYAL G, SWENSON ER, PESSAH NI, MAREN TH: The carbon dioxide hydration activity of skeletal muscle carbonic anhydrase: Inhibition by sulfonamides and anions. *Mol Pharmacol* 22:211, 1982.

30. SANYAL G, MAREN TH: Thermodymamics of carbonic anhydrase catalysis: A comparison between isozymes B and C. *J Biol Chem* 256:608, 1981.

31. WISTRAND PJ: The importance of carbonic anhydrase B and C for the unloading of CO_2 by the human erythrocyte. *Acta Physiol Scand* 113:417, 1981.

32. TASHIAN RE, HEWETT-EMMETT D, DODGSON SJ, FORSTER RE, SLY WS: The value of inherited deficiencies of human carbonic anhydrase isoenzymes in understanding their cellular roles. *Ann NY Acad Sci* 429:262, 1984.

33. SLY WS, WHYTE MP, KRUPIN T, SUNDARAN V: Positive renal response to intravenous acetazolamide in patients with carbonic anhydrase II deficiency. *Pediatr Res* 19:1033, 1985.

34. WAITE LC, VOLKERT WA, KENNY AD: Inhibition of bone resorption by acetazolamide in the rat. *Endocrinology* 87:1129, 1970.

35. WAITE LC: Carbonic anhydrase inhibitors, parathyroid hormone and calcium metabolism. *Endocrinology* 91:1160, 1972.

36. MINKIN C, JENNINGS J: Carbonic anhydrase and bone remodeling: Sulfonamide inhibition of bone resorption in organ culture. *Science* 176:1031, 1972.

37. GAY CV, MUELLER WJ: Carbonic anhydrase and osteoclasts: Localization by labelled inhibitor autoradiography. *Science* 183:432, 1974.

38. VAANANEN HK, PARVINEN E-K: High activity isoenzyme of carbonic anhydrase in rat calvaria osteoclasts: Immunohistochemical study. *Histochemistry* 78:481, 1983.

39. VAANANEN HK: Immunohistochemical localization of carbonic anhydrase isoenzymes I and II in human bone, cartilage, and giant cell tumor. *Histochemistry* 81:485, 1984.

40. BARON R, NEFF L, LOUVARD D, COURTOY PJ: Cell-mediated extracellular acidification and bone resorption: Evidence for a low pH in resorbing lacunae and localization of a 100-kD lysosomal membrane protein at the osteoclast ruffled border. *J Cell Biol* 101:2210, 1985.

41. LONNERHOLM G: Histochemical locations of carbonic anhydrase in mammalian tissues. *Ann NY Acad Sci* 429:369, 1984.

42. SPICER SS, SENS MA, TASHIAN RE: Immunocytochemical demonstration of carbonic anhydrase in human epithelial cells. *J Histochem Cytochem* 30:864, 1982.

43. LUCCI MS, TINKER JP, WEINER IM, DUBOSE TD JR: Function of proximal tubule carbonic anhydrase defined by selective inhibition. *Am J Physiol* F245:443, 1983.

44. DUBOSE TD, PUCACCO LR, CARTER NW: Determination of disequilibrium pH in the rat kidney in vivo: Evidence for hydrogen secretion. *Am J Physiol* 240:F138, 1981.

45. SCHWARTZ JH, ROSEN S, STEINMETZ PR: Carbonic anhydrase function and the epithelium organization of H^+ secretion in turtle urinary bladder. *J Clin Invest* 51:2653, 1972.

46. GLUCK S, KELLY S, AL-AWQATI Q: The proton-translocating ATPase responsible for urinary acidification. *J Biol Chem* 257:9230, 1982.

47. KUMPULAINEN T: Immunohistochemical localization of human carbonic anhydrase isozymes. *Ann NY Acad Sci* 429:359, 1984.

48. LEES MB, SAPIRSTEIN VS, REISS DS, KOLODNY EH: Carbonic anhydrase and 2',3' cyclic nucleotide 3'-phosphohydrolase activity in normal human brain and in demyelinating diseases. *Neurology (NY)* 30:719, 1980.

49. NAKAI H, BYERS MG, VENTA PJ, TASHIAN RE, SHOWS TB: The gene for human carbonic anhydrase II (CA 2) is located at chromosome 8q22. *Cytogenet Cell Genet* 44:234, 1987.

50. VENTA PJ, MONTGOMERY JC, TASHIAN RE: Molecular genetics of carbonic anhydrase isozymes, in Rattazzi MC, Scandalios JG, White GS (eds): *Isozymes: Current Topics in Biological and Medical Research*. New York, AR Liss, 1987, vol 14, p 59.

51. EDWARDS YH, LLOYD J, PARKAR M, POVEY S: The gene for human muscle specific carbonic anhydrase (CA III) is assigned to chromosome 8. *Ann Hum Genet* 90:44, 1986.

52. EDWARDS YH, BARLOW JH, KONIALIS CP, POVEY S, BUTTERWORTH PHW: Assignment of the gene determining human carbonic anhydrase, CA I, to chromosome 8. *Ann Hum Genet* 50:123, 1986.

52a. VENTA PJ, MONTGOMERY JC, HEWETT-EMMETT D, TASHIAN RE: Structure and exon to protein domain relationships of the mouse carbonic anhydrase II gene. *J Biol Chem* 260:12130, 1985.

53. VENTA PJ, MONTGOMERY JC, WIEBAUER K, HEWETT-EMMETT D, TASHIAN RE: Organization of the mouse and human carbonic anhydrase II genes. *Ann NY Acad Sci* 429:309, 1984.

54. VENTA PJ, MONTGOMERY JC, HEWETT-EMMETT D, TASHIAN RE: Comparison of the 5' regions of human and mouse carbonic anhydrase II genes and identification of possible regulatory elements. *Biochim Biophys Acta* 826, 195, 1985.

55. MURAKAMI H, MARELICH GP, GRUBB JH, KYLE JW, SLY WS: Cloning, expression and sequence homologies of the cDNA for human carbonic anhydrase II. *Genomics* 1:159, 1987.

56. BARLOW JH, LOWE N, EDWARDS YH, BUTTERWORTH PHW: Human carbonic anhydrase I cDNA. *Nucleic Acids Res* 15:2386, 1987.

57. WADE R, GUNNING P, EDDY R, SHOWS T, KEDES L: Nucleotide sequence, tissue specific expression, and chromosome location of human carbonic anhydrase III: The human CA III gene is located on the same chromo-

some as the closely linked CA I and CA II gene. *Proc Natl Acad Sci USA* 83:9571, 1986.

58. LLOYD H, MCMILLAN S, HOPKINSON D, EDWARDS YH: Nucleotide sequence and derived amino acid sequence of a cDNA encoding human muscle carbonic anhydrase. *Gene* 41:233, 1986.

59. HENDERSON LE, HENDERSON D, NYMAN PO: Primary structure of human carbonic anhydrase C. *J Biol Chem* 251:5457, 1976.

60. VENTA PJ, SHOWS TB, CURTIS PH, TASHIAN RE: Polymorphic gene for human carbonic anhydrase II: A molecular disease marker located on chromosome 8. *Proc Natl Acad Sci USA* 80:4437, 1983.

61. SUNDARAM V, RUMBOLO P, GRUBB J, STRISCIUGLIO P, SLY WS: Carbonic anhydrase deficiency: Diagnosis and carrier detection using differential enzyme inhibition and inactivation. *Am J Hum Genet* 38:125, 1986.

62. CONROY CW, MAREN TH: The determination of osteopetrotic phenotypes by selective inactivation of red cell carbonic anhydrase isoenzymes. *Clin Chim Acta* 152:347, 1985.

63. WHYTE MP, HAMM LL, SLY WS: Transfusion of carbonic anhydrase-replete erythrocytes fails to correct the acidification defect in the syndrome of osteopetrosis, renal tubular acidosis, and cerebral calcification (carbonic anhydrase-II deficiency). *J Bone Miner Res* 3:385, 1988.

64. LEWIS SE, ERICKSON RP, BARNETT LB, VENTA PJ, TASHIAN RE: *N*-Ethyl-*N*-nitrosourea-induced null mutation at the mouse *Car-2* locus: An animal model for human carbonic anhydrase II deficiency syndrome. *Proc Natl Acad Sci USA* 85:1962, 1988.

65. BUSHINSKY DA, GOLDRING JM, COE FL: Cellular contribution to pH-mediated calcium flux in neonatal mouse calvariae. *Am J Physiol* 248:F785, 1985.

66. RAISZ LG, SIMMONS HA, THOMPSON WJ, SHEPARD KL, ANDERSON PS, RODAN GA: Effects of a potent carbonic anhydrase inhibitor on bone resorption in organ culture. *Endocrinology* 122:1083, 1988.

67. ANDERSON RE, JEE WSS, WOODBURY DM: Stimulation of carbonic anhydrase in osteoclasts by parathyroid hormone. *Calcif Tissue Int* 37:646, 1985.

68. HALL GE, KENNY AD: Bone resorption induced by parathyroid hormone and dibutyryl cyclic AMP: Role of carbonic anhydrase. *J Pharmacol Exp Ther* 238:778, 1986.

69. KENNY AD: Role of carbonic anhydrase in bone: Partial inhibition of disuse atrophy of bone by parenteral acetazolamide. *Calcif Tissue Int* 37:126, 1985.

PART 18

MUSCLE

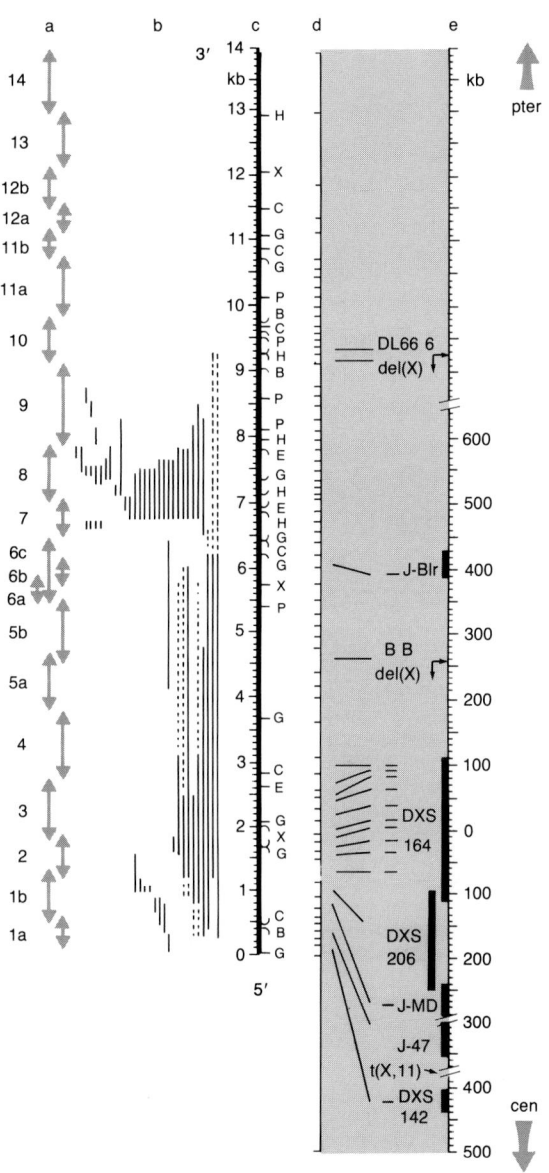

Duchenne muscular dystrophy

CHAPTER 118

THE MUSCULAR DYSTROPHIES

PETER S. HARPER

1. The muscular dystrophies form a group of genetically determined, progressive, primary disorders of muscle, whose principal members can be distinguished by a combination of clinical, genetic and pathologic criteria. These include the X-linked Duchenne and Becker muscular dystrophies, determined by a single locus, Emery Dreifuss muscular dystrophy, also inherited on the X chromosome, and the autosomal dominant myotonic and facioscapulohumeral dystrophies.

2. In none of the major muscular dystrophies has biochemical study of muscle or other tissue led to identification of a primary protein defect. However, molecular genetic analysis of the X chromosome has led to localization and isolation of the gene for Duchenne and Becker muscular dystrophies through a combination of approaches based on analysis of chromosomal deletions and translocations affecting the p21 region, complemented by genetic linkage analysis with neighboring DNA sequences.

3. The Duchenne/Becker gene is now known to be the largest human gene so far characterized ($\approx 2 \times 10^6$ bp). The gene contains at least 60 exons, corresponds to a 14-kb RNA transcript, and codes for a protein, dystrophin, whose properties and distribution suggest a key role in maintaining the integrity of myofibrillar structure and function. The mouse mutant mdx appears to be homologous, confirming its value as an experimental model.

4. The molecular pathology of Duchenne and Becker muscular dystrophies shows a wide variety of underlying mutational defects, with partial or complete gene deletion as a prominent cause. Molecular analysis of deletions and of restriction fragment length polymorphisms can now be used effectively in carrier detection and prenatal diagnosis in a high proportion of families.

5. Emery-Dreifuss muscular dystrophy is a clinically distinct disorder determined by a separate genetic locus on the distal long arm of the X chromosome.

6. Myotonic dystrophy, the commonest autosomal dystrophy, shows an exceptionally variable phenotype, with multisystem involvement outside muscle including ocular, endocrine, and central nervous system abnormalities. The myotonia represents a specific electrophysiological defect whose mechanism is likely to differ from that producing myotonia in the rare nonprogressive myotonic syndromes including myotonia congenita. The gene for myotonic dystrophy is localized to chromosome 19, with DNA sequences sufficiently close for prenatal and presymptomatic prediction, but the gene itself remains to be isolated.

7. Among the other autosomal muscular dystrophies, facioscapulohumeral dystrophy is the most frequent, though it is often benign in its course. The gene has not yet been localized. Autosomal recessive "limb girdle dystrophies" are rare, and many such cases may in fact be X-linked.

8. No effective therapy currently exists for any of the major muscular dystrophies. However, this is now likely to change, as identification of the specific gene product and the range of molecular pathology allows new therapeutic strategies to be devised.

The muscular dystrophies represent some of the most serious human genetic diseases and, as a group, rank among the most frequent of those disorders following Mendelian inheritance. The major forms, notably Duchenne muscular dystrophy, have been studied clinically and pathologically for the past century. Their hereditary nature has been recognized during most of this time. We thus possess a wealth of clinical information, supplemented by numerous detailed studies of muscle pathology and physiology and, more recently, by biochemical studies of normal and dystrophic muscle. Yet, despite this, the fundamental nature of the defect has remained unknown for all the major forms of muscular dystrophy, with consequent limitations for therapy and for genetic prediction.

This unhappy and, for investigators and clinicians, intensely frustrating situation, is changing rapidly, thanks largely to work done during the past 5 years and published almost entirely since the previous edition of this text. This work relates directly to the genes determining the major muscular dystrophies, their localization, identification, and characterization. It has proceeded in large part independently to the previous work based on muscle biochemistry and physiology, though it has in no sense made such work redundant. Indeed, we are likely to see the pendulum swing back to the protein defects as the genes themselves become more clearly defined.

Since the work of the past 5 years on muscular dystrophies has been so radically different from that undertaken previously, the form and approach of this chapter has also been completely recast, giving what some may consider an inappropriate emphasis to the genetic and molecular approach at the expense of classical biochemical and neuromuscular investigations. Nevertheless, it has already become clear that the muscular dystrophies can be regarded as a prototype for applying the approach which has become known as *reverse genetics* to those numerous genetic disorders where even less is known in phenotypic terms than has been the case for the muscular dystrophies. Most of these disorders, including many serious genetic conditions of the nervous system, have so far not warranted inclusion in this text, since their metabolic basis has been totally obscure. Application of the approaches outlined here for muscular dystrophies, however, is allowing progress to be made in these other disorders.

No attempt is made in this chapter to explain the basic tech-

---

Nonstandard abbreviations used in this chapter are: DMD = Duchenne muscular dystrophy; DX = DNA segment X chromosome; pERT = phenol enhanced reassociation technique; BMD = Becker muscular dystrophy.

niques of molecular genetics on which the recent advances have been founded; these have been covered fully in Chap. 2 and are in no sense unique to the area of muscular dystrophies. It must be stressed, though, that the success of these techniques has depended largely on their use in close conjunction with careful clinical and formal genetic studies and that advances have depended almost entirely on the collaborative efforts of groups of workers able to contribute their different skills to the field.

CLASSIFICATION OF THE MUSCULAR DYSTROPHIES

The list of major human muscular dystrophies (Table 118-1) is one that has changed little in recent years.[1] Based primarily on clinical and genetic considerations, but supported by results of muscle pathology and electrophysiology, this classification now finds general support, though there are inevitably disagreements as to the extent of heterogeneity and which disorders should be regarded as major forms.

These disorders, the subjects of the present chapter, show the fundamental attributes of the muscular dystrophies, which may be defined as a group of genetically determined, progressive, and degenerative primary disorders of muscle. This definition excludes a number of other important forms of muscle disease, in particular those disorders of anterior born cell origin (e.g., spinal muscular atrophies), inflammatory muscle disease (e.g., polymyositis), nonprogressive metabolic myopathies (e.g., glycogenoses, disorders of carnitine metabolism), and the heterogeneous group of congenital myopathies. These disorders are covered in detail in the recent works of Engel and Banker[2] and Walton[3] and are summarized briefly at the end of this chapter.

DUCHENNE MUSCULAR DYSTROPHY

The best known, most serious, and common of the muscular dystrophies, Duchenne muscular dystrophy (DMD), was also the first to be clearly recognized. Although Meryon[4] had reported cases in 1852, the studies of Duchenne,[5,6] published in 1861 and 1868, gave considerable details of a number of cases, while by the time of Gowers' monograph in 1879,[7] an extensive body of information was in existence. The clinical descriptions and illustrations (Fig. 118-1) of these early workers were lucid and detailed, while the investigative approaches, including electrophysiology and muscle histology obtained by

Table 118-1 Major Forms of Human Muscular Dystrophy

X-linked
  Duchenne muscular dystrophy
  Becker muscular dystrophy
  Emery-Dreifuss dystrophy
Autosomal recessive
  Autosomal recessive childhood muscular dystrophy
  Adult limb girdle dystrophy
  Congenital muscular dystrophy
Autosomal dominant
  Myotonic dystrophy
  Facioscapulohumeral dystrophy
  Oculopharyngeal muscular dystrophy

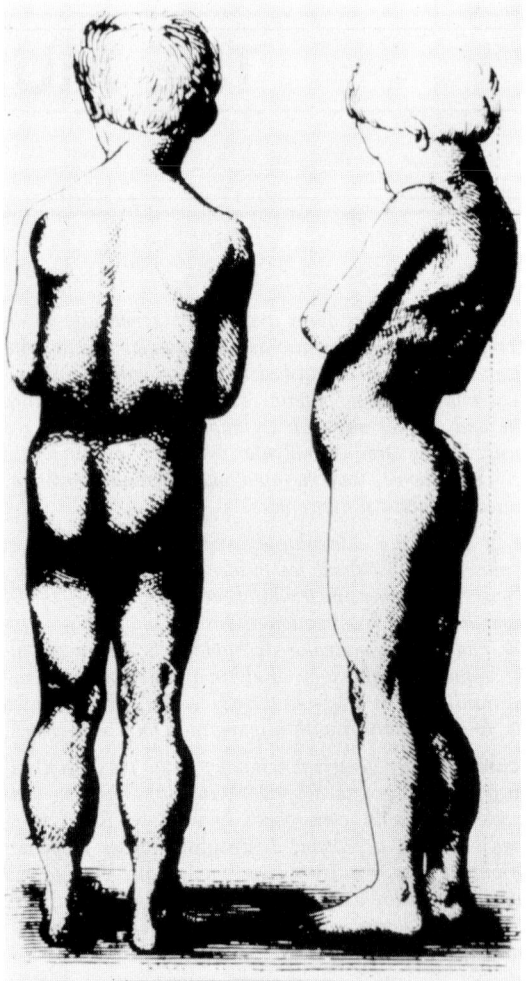

A.

B.

Fig. 118-1 Early illustrations of Duchenne muscular dystrophy. A. From Duchenne[6]; the increased lumbar lordosis and calf hypertrophy are clearly shown. B. From Gowers[7] showing the characteristic method of rising from the ground to the upright position (Gowers sign).

"harpoon" biopsy, were remarkably advanced for their time. Considering the amount of work done over the subsequent century, it is surprising that no subsequent monographs specifically devoted to the disorder have been written. This deficiency has fortunately now been filled by a recent monograph by Emery,[8] which combines valuable clinical descriptions with much investigative data, including a synthesis of recent molecular developments.

The clinical features of Duchenne muscular dystrophy are summarized in Table 118-2 and illustrated in Fig. 118-2; their relative importance is largely age-related. The affected neonate is entirely healthy; a normal course is common throughout the first year of life, which in no way excludes the condition, as seen in those asymptomatic boys diagnosed in early infancy on account of their family history. Motor delay of some form is an important feature;[9] over half fail to walk alone by 18 months, while routine developmental screening may suggest delay in other motor skills. Some affected boys show a more general delay in development, including speech, so that a high

Table 118-2 Clinical Features of Duchenne Muscular Dystrophy

Early
  Slow walking
  Delayed speech
  General developmental delay
Intermediate
  Unusual gait
  Proximal muscle weakness
  Pseudohypertrophy of calves
Late
  Generalized weakness
  Achilles tendon contractures
  Cardiac involvement

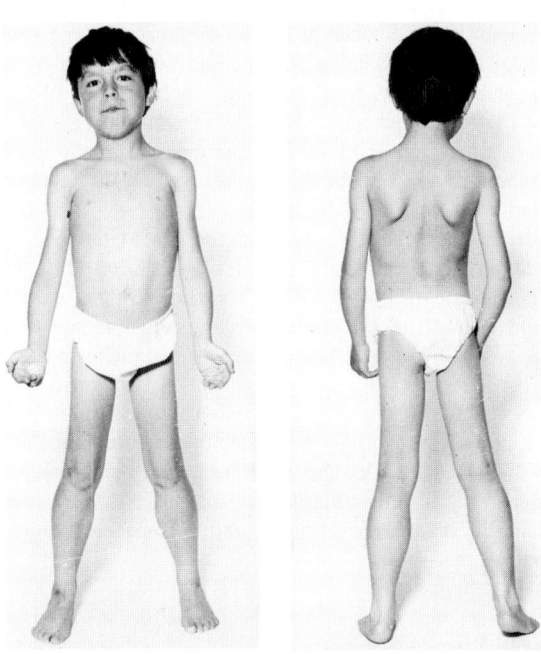

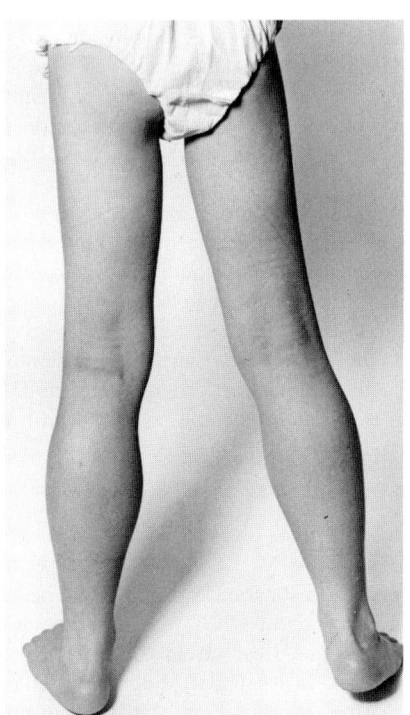

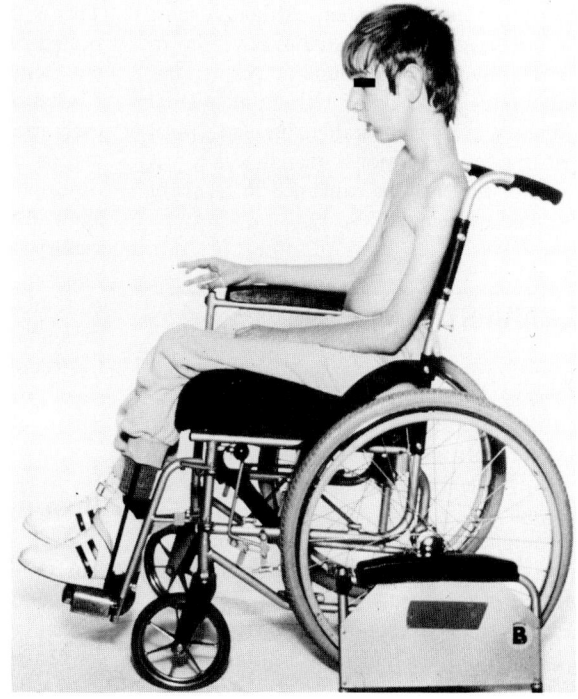

A.

B.

C.

Fig. 118-2 Clinical features of Duchenne muscular dystrophy. *A* and *B.* Nine-year-old boy showing proximal muscle weakness, typical posture, and calf hypertrophy. *C.* Fifteen-year-old boy with advanced DMD; note straight spine and good foot position.

index of suspicion is important for any male child showing developmental delay, whether or not there are features to suggest a neuromuscular problem.

As walking becomes established, an abnormal or unusual gait, clumsiness, and features suggestive of large muscle weakness may be noted by the parents. Mothers frequently find it difficult to articulate the precise nature of the problem but are often fully aware that something is not as it should be. All too often they are reassured without Duchenne muscular dystrophy being excluded, when a serum creatine kinase would have given a conclusive result at any stage after 3 months of age.

By the age of 4 or 5 years the typical waddling gait will be apparent with more general signs of proximal weakness, including Gower's sign (Fig. 118-1B), while calf pseudohypertrophy may be obvious. Steady deterioration then predominates over the natural tendency for the child to acquire new skills, so that increasing physical disability results in more than 90 percent of boys being chair-bound by the age of 11 years. Achilles tendon contractures and scoliosis may, if not carefully watched for, prevented, and where necessary corrected, become serious complications at this time.

While a number of patients survive into their early or even mid-twenties, the mean age of death of affected boys is close to 17 years according to a recent large study,[10] an age noted by Emery[8] to differ by less than 2 years from that found by Gowers a century before. Cardiorespiratory problems, related to diminished respiratory capacity, intercurrent chest infection, and in some cases cardiac arrhythmias are the principal direct causes of death.

Involvement of cardiac muscle is almost universal in advanced DMD, even though cardiac symptoms are often minimized by the inactivity of wheelchair-bound patients. Cardiac failure may be a contributary or even principal cause of breathlessness, while fatal arrythmias may occur in the absence of previous respiratory problems. However, cardiac problems are rarely significant in mobile patients, in contrast with Emery Dreifuss and myotonic dystrophies.

Apart from skeletal and cardiac muscle involvement, the only other system that is significantly and primarily affected by the disease is the central nervous system. Although most patients have normal intelligence, several studies have shown an overall decrease in IQ equivalent to around 20 points, and some patients (around one-fifth) have a significant mental handicap.[11,12] The contrast with comparably disabled spinal muscular atrophy patients leaves no doubt that this is a primary effect, but it cannot currently be explained in terms of pathogenesis or even brain pathology.

DIAGNOSTIC INVESTIGATIONS

Although the diagnosis of Duchenne muscular dystrophy is often beyond doubt on clinical grounds when a family history of the disorder exists, the gravity of the prognosis is such that the diagnosis must always be confirmed. Where there is no family history, the diagnosis becomes even more important because of the genetic implications to other family members.

The most important single diagnostic investigation is the serum level of the muscle enzyme creatine kinase (CK). First noted to be elevated by Ebashi et al.[13] and by Dreyfus et al.,[14] this enzyme rapidly became and has remained the mainstay of diagnosis, both for the affected male and for the carrier fe-

male. Although a wide variety of soluble enzymes present in the sarcoplasm are elevated in DMD and other muscular dystrophies, none, whether alone or in combination, has been shown to be superior to CK in diagnosis or carrier detection.

Creatine kinase levels in the male with DMD are not merely elevated, but grossly increased, usually 50 to 100 times the upper limit of normal. Levels are elevated at birth, but the frequency of high levels in normal neonates makes it unwise to use cord blood for diagnosis in infants known to be at risk.[15] By the end of the first week of life, the normal range is less variable, so that DMD can be clearly distinguished even by the semiquantitative methods used for mass screening on filter paper blood samples (see below). In the presymptomatic stages and throughout early childhood, the extreme elevation of CK is shared by very few other disorders, the principal exceptions being Becker muscular dystrophy, some cases of polymyositis and rhabdomyolysis, and occasionally hypothyroidism. Conversely, not only does a normal level of CK exclude the future development of DMD, but also a slightly or moderately raised level in conjunction with neuromuscular symptoms should lead to the diagnosis of DMD being reconsidered.

The discovery of CK levels in the DMD range in a girl should be interpreted with considerable caution. The finding could indicate true DMD if a sex chromosome anomaly is present, while the extremely rare autosomal recessive childhood dystrophy should be considered, especially in the presence of consanguinity or in a child of North African origin. Some DMD heterozygotes may show extreme elevation, and a proportion of these may later become "manifesting carriers" (see below). The use of CK in carrier detection generally depends on interpretation of minor elevations, not the extreme increase seen in males, and is considered more fully later.

Muscle Biopsy

This is the other essential diagnostic investigation in the suspected case of DMD. As with CK, specific changes are present from infancy, even in the total absence of symptoms or clinical signs. Figure 118-3 shows typical appearances from an early case: there are active degenerative changes with phagocytosis, along with fatty infiltration. The appearance in Becker dystrophy is similar, but the other major muscular dystrophies show distinctive differences. Needle biopsy now allows satisfactory samples to be taken from children of all ages for a full range of studies. Fuller details of muscle biopsy appearances and interpretation in the different myopathies are given in the monograph by Dubowitz,[16] while Engel[17] has reviewed the ultrastructural changes seen in the various stages of DMD. A small proportion of the biopsy should be kept deep frozen for dystrophin analysis.[125]

DNA Analysis

The third diagnostic investigation that must now be regarded as essential is the isolation of DNA, which can be done conveniently using white blood cells from the same sample used for serum CK analysis. In particular, the recognition of a molecular deletion (currently around two-thirds of cases using all

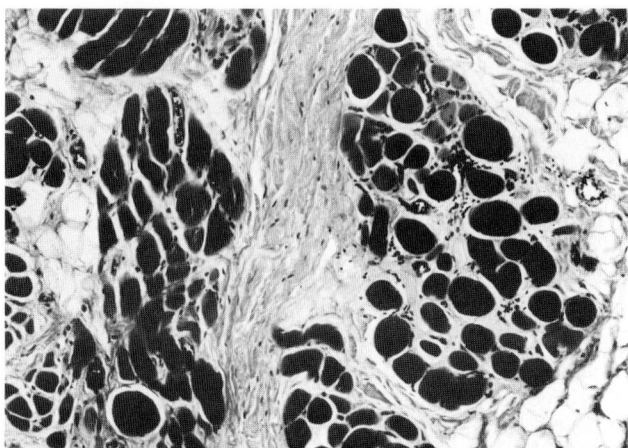

Fig. 118-3 Muscle histology in Duchenne muscular dystrophy. The fibers vary in size and many show hyaline change. Basophilic fibers are present, and there is an increase in connective tissue (×220). (*Courtesy of Dr. G. Cole, Cardiff.*)

available DNA probes) has profound consequences for prediction within the family, as discussed later. It is essential that, even if full molecular analysis may not be available in a center, clinicians come to regard the taking of a sample for DNA isolation and storage as an integral part of the initial study of any patient with DMD. Likewise, the taking of a full and thorough pedigree is included here as an essential investigation. This is not something that should be "left to the geneticists," since the discovery of an affected male relative in a previous generation will radically alter the interpretation of all other investigations in a suspected case of DMD.

The other investigations listed in Table 118-3 are of less critical importance in the author's view. Electromyography[18] is helpful in distinguishing myopathies from neurogenic disorders, but this is rarely relevant in the child with a greatly raised CK. Electrocardiography shows rather characteristic changes in DMD,[19] in particular abnormally tall R waves in the anterior precordial leads, but is principally helpful as a serial investigation in older children where the risk of arrhythmia or cardiomyopahy is higher; it should always be done prior to any surgical procedure. Ultrasound of skeletal muscles has been studied extensively[20] but is not specific enough to be of real use in DMD. Chromosomes should always be determined in a female but are not required in the suspected male case unless other disorders are present or mental retardation is marked.

The Manifesting Carrier for DMD

The occurrence of apparent DMD in a girl is rare and should prompt a search for a sex chromosome anomaly, as well as consideration of the autosomal recessive childhood muscular dystrophy, discussed later. A somewhat different problem re-

lating to DMD in females is posed by those heterozygotes who show clinical features and whose recognition is of particular importance for correct genetic counseling.

The expression of some degree of muscle disease in a proportion of female heterozygotes is to be expected on the basis of variation in X-chromosome inactivation. The proportion in whom it is found varies according to the criteria used; Moser and Emery[21] found significant muscle weakness in 10 percent of adult females, some having symptoms causing serious disability. Table 118-4 shows the features most commonly seen; onset is usually in adult life, not childhood; weakness and wasting are frequently asymmetric, whereas progression is generally slow.

When occurring in the context of a well established family history of DMD in males, the recognition of this situation is not difficult. In the absence of an affected male in the family, however, this is far from the case, and there is a real possibility that such a patient will be misdiagnosed as having an autosomal recessive adult limb girdle dystrophy, with potentially disastrous consequences for genetic counseling. Since in most populations the autosomal recessive form is now recognized to be exceedingly rare (see later), adult onset limb girdle dystrophy in a female with no family history of muscle disease is at least as likely as an autosomal disorder[22] to represent heterozygosity for DMD.

Apart from the clinical features of asymmetry and calf hypertrophy, helpful diagnostic features are the level of creatine kinase (greatly elevated in the DMD manifesting carrier), the occurrence of Duchenne-like electrocardiogram changes, and the muscle biopsy changes, which resemble those of DMD, though often patchy in nature. The finding of CK elevation in other female relatives also suggests DMD, while a careful family study may reveal likely DMD in a deceased male relative. Dystrophin analysis may prove to be helpful in the distinction[218] (see below).

THE GENETICS OF DUCHENNE MUSCULAR DYSTROPHY

The X-linked pattern of inheritance, with the disorder confined to males but transmitted through healthy females, was recognized even in the earliest reports—in fact, well before Mendel's principles were rediscovered. The only factor absent to give formal proof of this mode of inheritance was the failure of males to reproduce, so that lack of male-to-male transmission could not be demonstrated. In the milder Becker form no male-to-male transmission has occurred despite abundant opportunities. The occurrence of the disorder in 45X (Turner syndrome) females and, more rarely, in girls with a balanced X-autosome translocation gives further confirmation of the X-linked nature of the disease, which has now been placed be-

Table 118-3 Diagnostic Investigations in Duchenne Muscular Dystrophy

Pedigree documentation
Serum creatine kinase
Muscle biopsy (including dystrophin assay)
DNA analysis

Electromyography
Electrocardiography

Table 118-4 Manifesting Carriers of Duchenne Muscular Dystrophy

Onset usually in middle life
Proximal muscle weakness
Asymmetry of weakness and wasting common
Calf hypertrophy usual
Slowly progressive; disability rarely severe
Creatine kinase often greatly elevated
Muscle biopsy suggestive of DMD; often patchy

yond doubt by its linkage with X-chromosome DNA polymorphisms and by direct molecular studies.

Despite occasional suggestions of subclinical forms of DMD or of increased fetal loss representing affected males,[23] these have not been substantiated,[24] and it is clear that in the hemizygous male the gene shows full penetrance with a rather uniform expression as regards onset and severity in the great majority of families.

The incidence of Duchenne muscular dystrophy has been studied in numerous surveys, most retrospective, but including some that have continued over many years, as well as some based on neonatal screening. The results show a remarkable uniformity in comparison with many genetic disorders, with variation as likely to reflect incomplete ascertainment as real differences in incidence. Most studies[8] give an incidence of 1 in 5000 to 1 in 4000 male births (20 to 25 $\times$ 10^{-5}), with a figure of 27 $\times$ 10^{-5} for the most extensive and systematic newborn screening program in West Germany.[25] Thus, a true incidence of 1 in 3500 to 1 in 4000 male births seems likely in most populations.

It might be expected that with increasingly effective genetic counseling and carrier detection the incidence is declining. There is some evidence that this is so for familial cases in both western Australia[26] and Wales,[27] but not in Scotland, where the frequency of isolated cases showed no significant change over a 20-year period.[28]

A major factor in this temporal and geographic constancy is the high mutation rate in DMD, a subject which has produced considerable debate over the years. The problem of a genetically lethal X-linked recessive disorder at equilibrium in the population was first addressed by Haldane in 1935.[29] He pointed out that, where reproductive fitness is given by f and incidence by I, the mutation rate is

$$1/3\ I(1 - f)$$

so that where $f = 0$, the result becomes simply $1/3I$.

For DMD, with an incidence rate of around 25 $\times$ 10^{-5}, this gives a mutation rate of around 8 $\times$ 10^{-5}, an extremely high value. Until recently it has been a matter of speculation of whether this is due to genetic instability of the region or to other factors, but it now seems clear (see below) that it reflects the remarkably large size of the DMD gene itself.

The issue, both theoretical and practical, about new mutations in DMD cases, which has produced such controversy, is that, until recently, it has been impossible to be certain whether an individual case really results from a new mutation or not. The lack of any definitive test that will exclude carrier status in the mother with certainty, together with an abundance of tests that have at various times been considered indicative of the carrier state, has led to suggestions that almost all mothers of DMD boys are in fact carriers.[30] While most, though not all systemic studies have shown a proportion close to that expected from the original Haldane formula,[28,31–33] it is only now becoming possible to recognize new mutations directly by molecular studies, as discussed later, but preliminary results suggest approximately equal mutation rates in the two sexes; it is indeed likely that this will vary for different loci, as is already known for hemophilia A, where the proportion of isolated cases representing new mutants is much less than expected theoretically.

The risk for a female relative carrying the DMD gene will depend not only on the likelihood of the index case representing a new mutation but also on other factors in the pedigree structure,[34] which may influence the level of risk greatly, as shown in Fig. 118-4. Although these pedigree risks will be modified by information from creatine kinase and DNA analysis, as discussed later, they must not be ignored;[35] the level of prior risk is frequently a major factor in whether the end result of carrier detection studies is definitive or not.

Genetic heterogeneity has proved to be of considerable importance in relation to DMD and to other X-linked muscular dystrophies. Emery et al.[36] suggested that boys with marked mental retardation might form a separate subgroup, but others have not found evidence for this. The question has again been examined in the light of recent molecular developments. O'Brien et al.[37] found no difference in recombination fraction for linked markers between families where an affected boy had mental retardation and those where this was absent. Nor has any clear difference in phenotype emerged from separation of those showing a molecular deletion, an aspect discussed later. The rare cases with a large cytogenetically visible deletion, usually accompanied by severe retardation, form a clearly distinct group which illustrates the value of searching for unusual phenotypes in a disorder such as DMD.

Fig. 118-4 *X:21 balanced translocation in a girl with muscular dystrophy. (Courtesy of Dr. Ron Worton, Toronto.)*

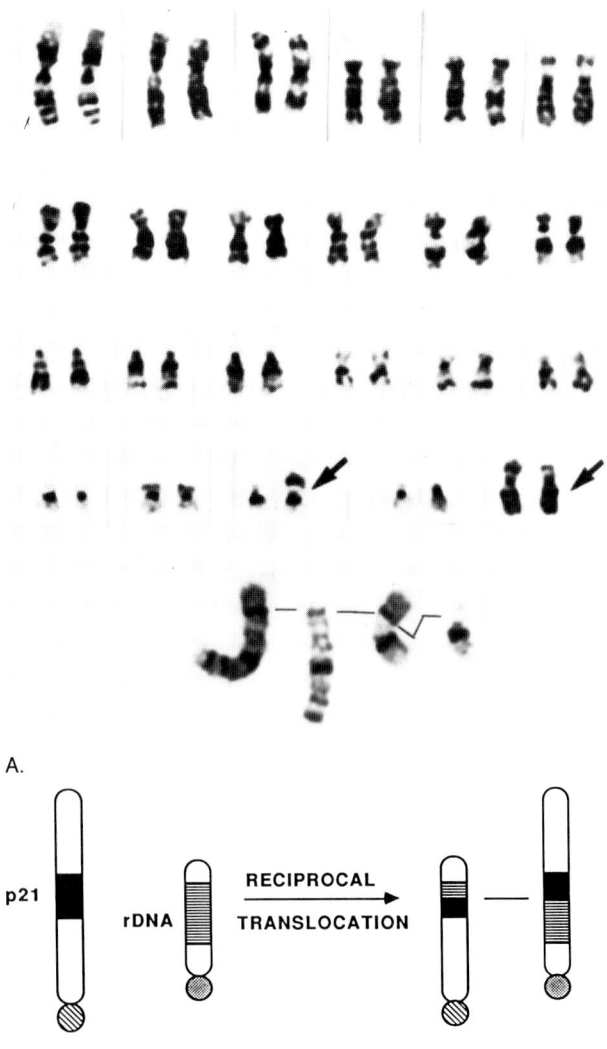

A.

B.

THE MOLECULAR BASIS FOR DUCHENNE MUSCULAR DYSTROPHY

Duchenne muscular dystrophy is the first human genetic disorder for which the strategy of reverse genetics has been successful; that is, the identification of the gene and the analysis of changes in it responsible for the disorder have been accomplished without any knowledge of the primary gene product. Since this approach is likely to be fruitful for many other genetic disorders that are currently poorly understood, the steps leading to isolation of the gene are described in some detail, even though some of these steps are already mainly of historical interest. They provide a striking example of how the new techniques of molecular genetics can, when used in combination with classic cytogenetic and clinical genetic methods, provide solutions to a problem that had previously resisted half a century of classic biochemical research. Table 118-5 indicates some of the landmarks in our progress, to be discussed below.

Mapping the DMD Locus

Until 10 years ago, the only firm information on the localization of the DMD gene was that it was on the X chromosome, a fact made clear by its inheritance pattern. The only available marker loci, those for the Xg blood group and for red-green color blindness, had shown no evidence of genetic linkage with DMD,[38,39] though comparable studies had suggested linkage of Becker muscular dystrophy with color blindness and G-6-PD,[40] now known to be located terminally on the long arm of the X chromosome. In the absence of further polymorphic markers, the prospects for progress appeared poor, but two independent lines of research were to change the situation dramatically.

The first of these was the recognition that, while most DMD boys showed no detectable cytogenetic abnormality, a small number of girls with a disorder similar to DMD (or sometimes BMD) showed a balanced translocation between the X chromosome and an autosome, and that the breakpoint on the X chromosome was not random. The second development was the isolation of cloned DNA sequences specific for the X chromosome which showed restriction fragment length polymorphisms (RFLPs) and could be used as markers in ge-

netic linkage studies in the same way as had the classic phenotypic markers. Each of these approaches in isolation could probably have provided a firm localization for the DMD gene; used in combination, the results were conclusive.

The first report of an X-autosome translocation associated with DMD came in the form of two brief abstracts in 1977,[41,42] and these were followed by two separate and more detailed case reports in 1979.[43,44] The suggestion made in these papers, which in time proved to be correct, was that the breakage of the X chromosome had somehow affected the function of the DMD gene and that the site of the breakpoint reflected the actual localization of the gene. The relative lack of interest that these observations produced at the time reflected in part the fact that they were isolated case reports and that the association with DMD could be fortuitous; also at that time the possible localization of the gene did not provide an obvious basis for further research that might increase our understanding of DMD.

More than 20 cases of X-autosomal translocation with DMD cases are now documented,[45,46] and some of the principal features are summarized in Table 118-6. Figure 118-4 shows the X:21 translocation which has proved to be of special importance in the light of subsequent experimental work.[47,48] As the reports appeared, it became quite clear that they had one factor in common: the X-chromosome breakpoint was constantly located at p21, the dark staining band located approximately half-way along the short arm of the chromosome (see Fig. 118-5). There was debate as to whether the breakpoint was identical in all cases (a point to be discussed below) but there was an undoubted constancy about the X chromosome compared with the diverse autosomes that were involved.

Another fact that became apparent only as the published series increased were that all cases were *de novo*, with no other affected cases in the family and no evidence of the carrier state in mothers. (Elevated creatine kinase levels in one case were not confirmed on reassessment.)[47] A further point of relevance was the clinical variability in severity; although the distribution of muscle involvement and the histologic appearance were similar in all cases, several, including the first to be recorded (by Verellen et al.[41] in 1977) showed prolonged survival and mobility that should more appropriately have been classified as BMD.

As is often the case, a number of puzzling and contradictory features of the DMD girls with X-autosomal translocations became apparent only after molecular understanding of the locus had progressed; the resolution of some of these points is discussed below, but the second line of evidence for localizing the DMD gene, that arising from DNA polymorphisms, now requires description.

In 1980, when this work began, there were no DNA markers on the X chromosome, though human genes had already been cloned and the significance of RFLPs for mapping the human genome was beginning to be appreciated.[49] A human gene library for total human DNA had been produced,[50] but there was no specific source for isolating sequences located on

Table 118-5 Landmarks in Isolation of the Duchenne Muscular Dystrophy Gene

1979	First full report of affected girl with X-autosome translocation
1981	First X chromosome DNA library
1982	First linked DNA marker for DMD
1983	Flanking DNA markers Similar linkage found for BMD
1984	Multiple flanking markers
1985	First prenatal diagnosis and first systematic carrier detection using flanking markers Deletions recognized using pERT sequences XJ sequence isolated from X:21 translocation patient
1986	RNA transcript isolated; exons corresponding to part of gene identified; partial sequence of gene determined
1987	Size and limits of DMD gene defined; extensive sequence data; gene product, "dystrophin," isolated
1988	Information on tissue and subcellular localization of dystrophin; alteration and deficiency of dystrophin correlated with clinical phenotype

Table 118-6 X-Autosome Translocations and Duchenne Muscular Dystrophy

X breakpoint consistently in band p21
Autosomal breakpoint variable
Translocations all balanced; no detectable loss of genetic material
All cases *de novo*; no evidence of carrier state in relatives
Severity variable; some cases closer to Becker phenotype

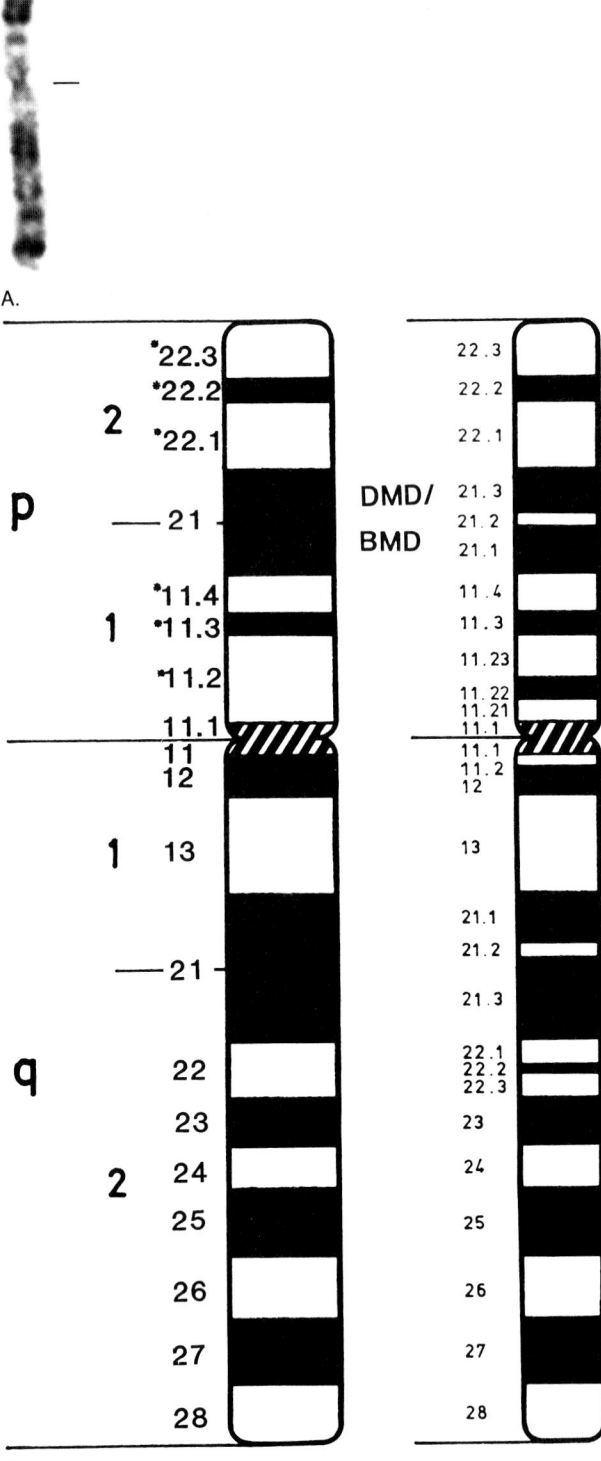

A.

B.

Fig. 118-5 A. Prometaphase cytogenetic preparation of normal X chromosome, to show banding pattern. *(Courtesy of Selwyn Roberts, Cardiff.)* B. Schematic diagram of the X chromosome, following ISCN classification, showing in more detail the p21 region containing the DMD locus.

the X chromosome. Two techniques resolved this deficiency; the use of flow cytometry to sort chromosomes based on their size and staining properties[51] and the use of human-rodent hybrid cell lines which contained only a few (or ideally one) human chromosomes.

The first flow-sorted DNA library relatively specific for the

human X chromosome was produced in 1981 by Davies et al.[52] and the first attempt to use a polymorphic sequence from it for linkage was a study of the X-linked thyroxine binding globulin (TBG) deficiency using a sequence on the long arm of the X chromosome.[53] At this stage the possibility of DMD being on the short arm was already suspected from the first X-autosome translocations, so the first available short arm sequence showing a polymorphism was tested for linkage with DMD families.

The detection of linkage between DMD and this sequence (RC8)[54] not only confirmed the cytogenetic localization by independent means but also provided the first demonstration that RFLPs identified by recombinant DNA techniques could be used to map genes in the same way as had previously been done using conventional markers, with the potential for practical applications in prediction and for possible identification of the gene itself. In retrospect, as seen from the viewpoint of one personally involved, the ability of this marker to detect the linkage at all was surprising; it was not highly polymorphic, the probe was not easy to use, and interpretation of the band pattern on Southern blotting was often difficult, while the structure of the initial series of families used was not always ideal. It is fortunate that all these problems, so clear in retrospect, did not deter the investigators from actually undertaking the work!

The initial detection of genetic linkage between DMD and RC8 was rapidly followed by a second linkage[55] with a probe, L.128, that had been derived not from a specific source of X-chromosome sequences but from the total human DNA library of Maniatis et al.[50] This probe, located more proximally on the short arm when tested against a panel of somatic hybrid cell lines with partial deletions of the X chromosome, showed a higher degree of polymorphism than RC8, and it was soon possible to show clear linkage with DMD, both markers showing a distance of 15 to 20 cm from DMD but with free recombination between the two markers themselves. It was thus clear from both linkage and physical mapping that the marker loci "flanked" or "bridged" the DMD locus, considerably increasing the potential for practical use in prediction.

At this stage an unexpected finding occurred which demonstrated the power of even loosely linked DNA markers in resolving heterogeneity as well as the rashness of relying too heavily on preconceived ideas based on earlier work. The possible linkage of Becker muscular dystrophy with color blindness and G-6-PD on the long arm of the X chromosome has already been mentioned, but when Kingston et al.[56] tested a series of BMD families with the short arm sequences L128 and RC8, there was clear evidence of linkage, with distances comparable to those found for DMD. These observations, since confirmed and extended, made it likely that BMD and DMD are alleles, or at least closely linked, and suggested that, as had earlier been suggested by clinical studies, the two disorders are a single entity rather than resulting from entirely separate causes.

The initial two bridging markers were rapidly supplemented by further polymorphic DNA sequences in and around the X p21 region. Some of these were derived from the flow sorted DNA libraries of Kunkel et al.[57] and Hofker et al.[58] while the OTC probe was derived from the gene specific cDNA clone from this enzyme.[59] The closest sequences to the DMD locus were C7(DXS) on the distal side and p754 (DXS) proximally. Together these markers formed a framework with which the short arm of the X chromosome could be mapped as a whole,[60] as well as providing a series of markers on each side of DMD for use in prediction.[61]

The copious information derived from the numerous DNA polymorphisms linked to DMD highlighted one apparent anomaly: all the linked markers showed relatively frequent recombination with the disorder, even the probe 754 which, from cytogenetic evidence, mapped within band p21[62] and might have been expected to show negligible recombination. This looseness of linkage not only suggested that the existing markers were too distant from the DMD locus to be used as a starting point for direct molecular analysis in the identification of the DMD gene itself; it also posed questions as to the nature of the p21 region, in particular whether there might be some inherent instability responsible for the frequency of crossing over. It also produced obvious limitations to the use of these markers in prediction.

The resolution of this problem resulted largely from an entirely different approach taken by Kunkel et al. based on the existence of rare patients with DMD who show visible cytogenetic deletions. The importance of such patients is now recognized as being crucial in the fine mapping of many genetic disorders, and they require some description.

The prototype of this group of deletions was the patient "BB" reported by Francke et al.[63] who had a visible deletion in the p21 region of his X chromosome and who suffered not only from DMD but also from mental retardation, chronic granulomatous disease, the McLeod red blood cell phenotype, and (possibly) retinitis pigmentosa. This combination of disorders not only suggested that they were determined by a closely linked series of genes that had been lost in this particular patient but also provided the basis for the detailed molecular study of the deleted region.

Recognition of the importance of these minor deletions prompted a search for further instances in patients known to have both DMD and other X-linked disorders; several such cases have now been recognized, the most frequent showing a combination of DMD with congenital adrenal hypoplasia and glyceroluria due to glycerol kinase deficiency.[64,65] The chromosomes of one such patient[66] are shown in Fig. 118-6 and by combining the extent of cytogenetic deletion with DNA probe data and the overlapping clinical combination of disorders, a map can be constructed of the relative position of the different disease loci in relation to each other, as shown in Fig. 118-7 and discussed more fully later.

The approach of Kunkel et al.[67] was to isolate DNA from the deletion patient BB and to mix random sheared fragments of this DNA with restriction enzyme digested DNA from a nondeleted cell line containing multiple X chromosomes, the DNA from BB being in excess. This double-stranded DNA mixture was separated into single strands by heating and allowed to reassociate in the presence of phenol. Most of the normal DNA would be expected to hybridize with the large excess of homologous DNA from BB under these conditions, except for those normal sequences corresponding to DNA from the deleted region, which would have no counterpart in BB and thus would hybridize with each other. By ensuring that only these particular double-stranded sequences had ends allowing them to be cloned in a specific plasmid vector, they could be preferentially isolated from the bulk of remaining DNA.

The result of this experiment was that seven DNA clones given the acronym pERT (phenol-enhanced reassociation technique) were isolated that mapped to band p21 and were located in the deleted region. These were then tested against a

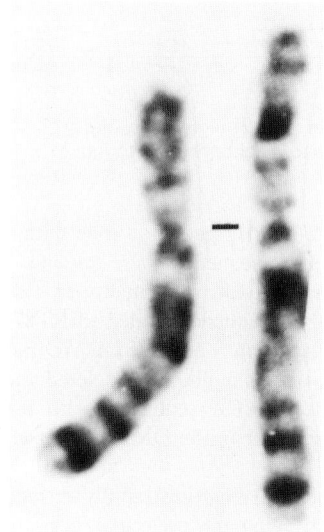

A.

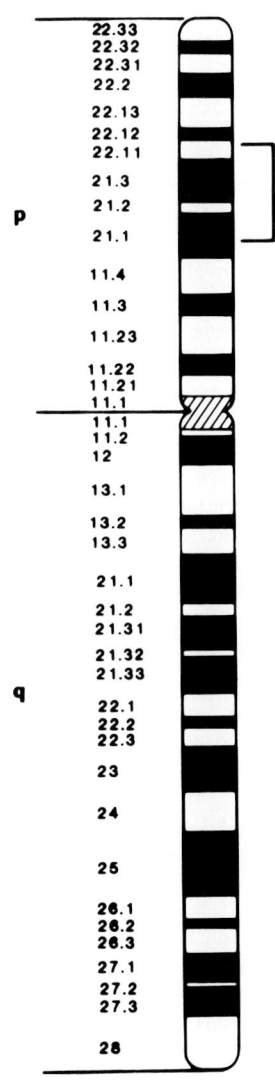

B.

Fig. 118-6 *A.* X chromosomes of the mother of a male patient with DMD, congenital adrenal hypoplasia, mental retardation, and glycerol kinase deficiency, showing an interstitial deletion of region p21 in one of her X chromosomes. *(From Clarke et al., 1986.) B.* Diagram to show region of X chromosome involved by the deletion.

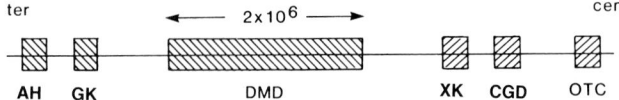

Fig. 118-7 Diagrammatic map of the p21 region, showing the relative localization of the DMD and neighboring genes (not to scale).

panel of DNA samples from 57 DMD patients (none with a visible deletion) to see if any of the sequences were missing.

Most of the clones tested showed no abnormality in this group of patients, but one 200-bp sequence, coded pERT87, showed an absence of hybridization in 5 of the 57 DMD patients, suggesting that these patients might have deleted the gene for DMD along with the pERT87 sequence, with the corollary that pERT87 must be either in the DMD gene itself or very close to it.

An intensive and remarkable collaboration rapidly ensued between the various groups studying the molecular basis of DMD, which soon confirmed the original finding.[68] Around 7 percent of almost 1000 DMD patients tested showed deletion for pERT87 (Fig. 118-8) with no obvious correlation between the existence of a deletion and clinical features. Two of one hundred BMD patients also showed a deletion, confirming the essential allelism of the two conditions. No deletions for pERT87 were found in normal males.

The results of the pERT87 study provided the first firm evidence for DNA sequences that could be related directly to the disorder, rather than acting merely as markers with no functional relationship to the disease. The study also gave the first direct evidence of the nature of at least some DMD mutations, the finding of gene deletions providing a parallel with those other genetic disorders which have been thoroughly analyzed at the DNA level, such as the thalassemias and hemophilias.

Concurrently with this work Worton and colleagues in Toronto were approaching the isolation of the DMD gene by utilizing one of the X-autosome translocations discussed earlier. This female patient, whose phenotype was actually closer to that of BMD, showed a X:21 translocation (Fig. 118-4), the autosomal breakpoint being through the satellited region of the short arm of chromosome 21, known to consist principally of DNA coding for ribosomal RNA. Since the molecular structure of this ribosomal DNA locus was already partially understood, it was argued that sequences in the X:21 translocated chromosome immediately adjacent to the repetitive ribosomal DNA should represent DNA from the X chromosome at or close to the translocation breakpoint and thus be closely related to the DMD/BMD gene.[69]

This prediction proved to be correct, and when the junctional sequences were cloned,[70] one (XJ1) proved not only to map physically in the p21 region but also to show deletions in

Fig. 118-8 DNA hybridization showing deletion of intragenic probes pERT87 or XJ in a series of unrelated DMD patients; note that in this series the deletions do not extend across the region of both probes. (Courtesy of Dr. N.S.T. Thomas, Cardiff.)

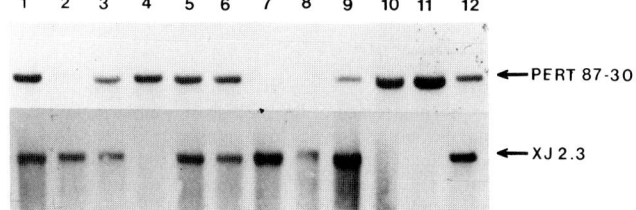

a proportion of DMD patients (Fig. 118-9), not all of whom also showed deletion of pERT87. XJ was localized centromeric to pERT87 and thus gave a separate point from which to explore the detailed structure of the DMD gene.

These studies with the pERT and XJ sequences had thus provided our first understanding of the DMD locus at the molecular level. They had shown that at least 8 percent of DMD patients had a gene deletion, that DMD and BMD were determined by essentially the same locus, and that they provided the starting points for detailed molecular analysis of the DMD gene itself. Despite this, there remained until the later part of 1986 some very real uncertainties and problems, both theoretical and practical, some of which are still in the process of resolution.

The principal problem to be resolved followed the use of

Fig. 118-9 Structure of the DMD gene. (From Koenig et al., 1987.) A. Regions of gene covered by individual cDNA clones. B. Extent and distribution of deletions in affected DMD males. C. cDNA restriction map. D. Map of Hind III fragments relating cDNA to genomic DNA. E. Genomic DNA map. (Courtesy of Dr. L. Kunkel.)

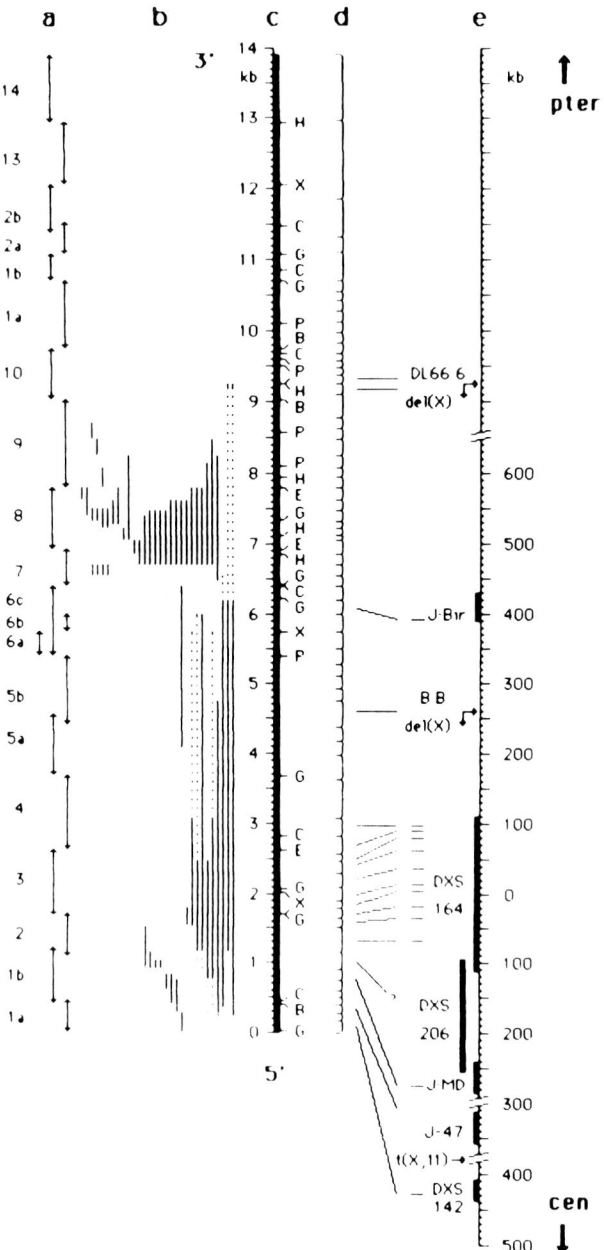

the pERT87 and XJ clones in family studies of those patients (the majority) not showing evidence of deletion. Both these probes, and various subclones derived from them, show RFLPs with a number of restriction enzymes, and the number of these has been increased by the use of adjoining sequences. If, as seemed likely, these probes were integrally related to the DMD gene itself, negligible recombination might be expected between marker and disease, and a high degree of accuracy in prediction would be anticipated. This proved to be far from the case, and family studies have consistently shown a recombination rate of around 5 percent with both pERT87 and XJ[71–73] giving a potential error rate in prediction at least as great as that already obtainable by flanking markers in some cases. This raised again the question as to whether this region of the X chromosome was particularly unstable, or whether the high frequency of recombination reflected the fact that mutations producing the DMD phenotype could be produced over an unusually extensive length of DNA. Whatever the precise explanation, it clearly suggested that the DMD gene was a most unusual one and that assumptions based on other cloned genes would not necessarily hold true for DMD.

Evidence suggesting that mutations resulting in an identical clinical phenotype of DMD could be produced by changes in widely separated regions of DNA has come from the detailed study of those patients identified as having molecular deletions for pERT87. Kunkel and his colleagues have mapped in detail the extent of the DMD deletions detected by deletions of pERT87[74,75] and have used this to define the boundaries of the DMD gene. Direct gene walking allowed the original 200-bp sequence to be extended in both directions to 200 kb. Some deletions fall entirely within this region; in other patients the deletion extends across the entire region. The construction of DNA libraries from patients in whom one end of the deletion extended out of the region then allowed these more distant junction fragments to be identified, both distally in the direction of the adrenal hypoplasia and glycerol kinase loci and proximally in the direction of probe 754 and chronic granulomatous disease. Comparable studies were also undertaken by Worton and colleagues using the XJ clones. They sequenced a considerable length of DNA around this and overlapped distally the region sequenced by Kunkel's group who proceeded proximally from the original pERT87 clone. This work suggested that the deletions extend over a considerable length of DNA and, apart from those involving other adjacent genes, showed no obvious correlation between extent of deletion and phenotype.

This evidence has been complemented by detailed studies on the various X-autosome translocation cases.[46] Boyd et al., have reviewed 20 reported cases and have performed molecular studies on six of them; the molecular analyses indicate a minimum distance of 175 kb between the breakpoints, while the more extensive cytogenetic data suggest an area of over 10^6 bp over which a breakpoint can produce DMD. A complementary approach to analysis of the DMD region of the X chromosome has been provided by techniques for separation of large DNA fragments, based on pulsed or alternating field gel electrophoresis. This technique allows DNA fragments of up to several million base pairs in length, produced by digestion with rare cutting restriction enzymes such as Not1 or sfi1, to be separated in a comparable way to that previously achieved by conventional gel electrophoresis for fragments of several thousand base pairs. Several groups[76–78] have produced physical maps of the p21 region based on large, overlapping DNA fragments identified by this technique.

A further piece of evidence comes from the study of Bertelson et al.,[79] who analyzed the meiotic exchange points across p21 in 25 families with DMD who were informative for multiple DNA markers. They found no evidence of an increased recombination rate in this region overall and concluded that the observed frequency of recombination between DMD and probes in p21 reflected the extent of the region involved, rather than instability.

From the above brief account it can be seen that the application of a number of genetic techniques and the exploitation of various types of unusual defect seen in patients with DMD have given us a reasonably detailed picture of this region of the X chromosome. The p21 band emerges as a region containing relatively few specific genes, which can now be related physically to each other and to that for DMD. The gap between those probes originally identified as close to DMD by linkage studies and those integrally related to the disorder has been bridged, and the occurrence of translocations and deletions in association with DMD is satisfactorily explained.

These studies thus all point to the length of DNA in which a genetic change can produce DMD being extremely large, possibly around 2×10^6 bp. They do not, however, immediately answer the question as to whether there is one exceptionally large DMD gene or several separate genes or whether the function of the gene might be unusually susceptible to changes in neighboring DNA regions.

A definitive answer to these questions has now been provided by further work of Kunkel and colleagues.[75,80] After extending the pERT87 region of DNA by chromosome walking to a total of 220 kb, a search was made for highly conserved regions of DNA that might correspond to sequences showing transcription. Two subclones of pERT87 showing such conservation across numerous species were identified, corresponding sequences in mouse DNA were cloned, and nucleotide sequencing of both human and mouse sequences was carried out to identify open reading frames surrounded by conserved DNA. These were found in both subclones (pERT87-25 and pERT87-4), and these clones were used to search for transcribed sequences by hybridizing with messenger RNA derived from fetal muscle. A large 16-kb MRNA transcript was found to hybridize with 87-25, but no corresponding transcript was identified for 87-4.

Fetal muscle mRNA was also used to construct a complementary DNA (cDNA) library that was screened with pERT 87-25. Several cDNA clones containing inserts of up to 3 kb in size were isolated, and one of these cDNA clones was used for characterization. When this cDNA probe was hybridized to genomic DNA digested with Hind III, it identified eight bands from 2.0 to 8.0 kb in size. These bands represent some of the exons of the DMD gene, though they constitute only some 10 percent of the total gene. Analysis of these transcripts has shown that the gene is orientated with its 3' end distally and its 5' end located toward the centromere. The groups of Worton and Davies have also isolated cDNA clones from the XJ and adjacent HIP25 regions.[81–83]

Because these new cDNA probes identify much larger regions of the Duchenne locus, as they hybridize to exons which are separated by large nonhybridizing intronic regions, they are extremely useful for detecting molecular deletions in DMD and BMD patients and significantly increase the overall rate of detection of such defects. Preliminary studies suggest that around two-thirds of DMD and BMD patients show identifiable exon deletions,[84] a proportion much higher than suspected from previous studies using genomic probes but agreeing with the evidence of altered fragment size seen in pulsed field gel electrophoresis studies of affected patients. This high proportion of deletions will considerably increase the number of families where a specific prenatal diagnosis can be offered and will be especially helpful for those families whose pedigree structure is unsuitable for linkage prediction. It will also be of great interest to see to what extent the deletion of particular exons can be related to clinical phenotype. The occurrence of deletions within the gene appears to be nonrandom, 80 percent occurring in a region corresponding to only 2 kb of cDNA,[85] which can also be identified by a genomic probe.[86]

Koenig et al.[84] have now reported the isolation of the entire length of the cDNA corresponding to the DMD gene. This represents 14 kb of DNA, with at least 60 exons of average size 200 bp, contrasting with introns averaging 35,000 bp. The 3′ and 5′ ends have been sequenced and defined in relation to the various adjoining probes, and a restriction map of the entire region has been produced. Figure 118-9 shows how the cDNA data relate to the deletions observed and to the genomic DNA.

Mechanisms of Mutation in DMD

Our understanding of the molecular basis of DMD is now sufficient to permit some appreciation of the variety of mechanisms involved. Table 118-7 lists some of those for which firm evidence already exists. Deletions, ranging from the rare visible ones affecting several genes to the more frequent purely molecular deletions, have already been discussed; their frequency is remarkably high in comparison with most other known genetic disorders, though less than the 90 percent seen in X-linked ichthyosis due to steroid sulfatase deficiency, the gene for which is located more distally on Xp close to the pseudoautosomal region. A less familiar and, at present, less common, category is that of gene duplication,[85,87] recognized in only a few cases but easy to miss on a Southern blot in comparison with a deletion. The origin of both deletions and duplications could be related, though it is less easy to explain the relationship of gene duplication to loss of gene function than it is for gene deletion.

An observation of considerable interest, which may well be more frequent than originally thought likely, is the occurrence of multiple affected or carrier children showing a molecular deletion from a parent showing no evidence of such a deletion.[88] Such families probably result from germinal mosaicism in the parent and will have important practical consequences in genetic counseling.

A glimpse of an unusual postzygotic event resulting in DMD comes from a report of monozygous twin girls discordant for DMD[89]; the most likely explanation of this is that both twins were heterozygous for DMD but that one embryo received the active X carrying the normal DMD allele, while

Table 118-7 Possible Mutational Basis for Duchenne (and Becker) Muscular Dystrophy

Gene deletion (at least 60 percent of cases)
Visible chromosome deletion (rare)
X-autosome translocation in female (rare)
Gene duplication (probably rare)
Postzygotic segregation of inactive X (in monozygotic twin female)
Germinal mosaicism

in the affected twin this had already been permanently inactivated.

Most of our understanding of the mutational basis of human genetic disorders at the DNA level has so far come from conditions such as hemoglobinopathies where the actual mutational event has usually occurred many generations ago. DMD offers a particularly valuable situation of new mutations actually occurring; it is likely that not only will the variety of mechanisms be great, but also that some of them will be novel, at least for humans.

A tentative explanation can also now be given of why an X-autosome translocation at p21 should produce DMD in girls. It was noted earlier that all cases were de novo, with no evidence of the carrier state in other family members. It thus might seem surprising that, with one presumably normal X chromosome, these girls are clinically affected. The explanation appears to be that normal X-chromosome inactivation requires the process to spread physically from an inactivation center on the proximal long arm;[90] any physical discontinuity prevents inactivation, so that in these individuals only the translocated X, containing the disrupted DMD gene, is active.

So far, none of the molecular studies has given a clear association between the type of gene defect observed and the clinical phenotype. As mentioned earlier, the extent of the observed deletion (apart from the rare visible chromosomal deletions) does not appear to be a critical factor; whether specific exons will prove to be affected in association with particular clinical features (such as severity of muscle disease and occurrence of mental retardation) is now under study. There appears to be a particular concentration of small deletions at a specific site in BMD, and there is now direct evidence that whether a mutation results in a classic Duchenne or Becker phenotype may depend on the occurrence of frame shift.[91]

The debate over possible differences in mutation rate between the sexes has now been largely resolved by studies of isolated cases of patients with DMD and their parents. Although the numbers analyzed are still small, there seems to be no significant departure from the classic Haldane ratio; even more importantly, the proportion of mutations representing deletions also appears to be similar in cases of maternal and paternal mutational origin.

DMD in Relation to Surrounding Loci

The molecular studies of DMD described above have also shed light on neighboring disorders on the X chromosome, especially those loci involved in complex deletion syndromes. As shown in Fig. 118-7, the order of loci can be deduced from the combination of clinical phenotypes and the patterns of molecular deletion. Thus, the glycerol kinase locus is located closer to DMD than that for adrenal hypoplasia,[92] while for those disorders located proximal to DMD, the McLeod red cell phenotype is closer than the chronic granulomatous disease locus.[93] Interestingly, patients with McLeod syndrome also show a mild myopathy with elevated creatine kinase, but this has been shown to be present in those patients where the DMD gene is intact.

Chronic granulomatous disease (CGD) has benefited even more directly from these studies, since one of the pERT clones outside the DMD locus (pERT 379) was recognized as a sequence transcribed in phagocytic cells. This has allowed the identification of the CGD gene and its protein,[94] another example of the success of "reverse genetics."

Applied Molecular Genetics

Prenatal Diagnosis and Carrier Detection. The molecular work outlined above is recent, but this has not prevented rapid application to practical diagnostic problems in both Duchenne and Becker muscular dystrophies. Indeed, one of the most fruitful aspects of the work has been the close involvement of clinical geneticists, who have been able to ensure that families receive the benefits of the new techniques with minimal delay. Already it is recognized that DNA analysis is an essential part of the investigation of these disorders; services are currently being set up on a national or regional basis to cope with the demand produced by the developments. At the same time it is clear that even those aspects which can be considered as forming a diagnostic service are not fixed but will certainly need to be modified in the light of future developments.[95] Although the discussion here is placed in the context of Duchenne muscular dystrophy, the recognition that the Becker form is allelic makes the approach equally applicable to this disorder.

Prenatal Diagnosis. Until the advent of linked DNA markers for the DMD gene, there was no proven method for prenatal diagnosis of this disorder. Attempts to utilize fetal blood creatine kinase levels obtained by fetoscopy[96] had proven unreliable[97] so that fetal sexing by amniocentesis was the only option until 1982. At this stage the development of first trimester prenatal diagnosis[98] provided an important step forward in terms of acceptability of fetal sexing, with both DNA-based and cytogenetic determination of sex allowing an early decision to be made for those requesting termination of a male pregnancy.[99,100]

Although the first linked DNA markers (RC8 and L128) were too distant to warrant their use for prenatal diagnosis in most circumstances, it was immediately clear from the initial studies that DNA polymorphisms could in principle be used prenatally. Their use in chorionic villus material was validated experimentally[101] and in conjunction with diagnostic fetal sexing, while the recognition that a family informative for flanking markers could enable accurate prediction even with relatively loose linkage[102] prompted the search for more such families. The development of multiple flanking probes considerably increased the proportion of informative families,[103] one of which provided the first relatively specific DNA prenatal prediction for DMD in 1985.[104] The critical advance which made the possibility of prenatal diagnosis the rule rather than the exception was the recognition of pERT and XJ probes within the DMD gene itself and the identification of specific molecular deletions in affected patients. The recognition of a deletion within a family is of particular practical importance since it allows a specific diagnosis or exclusion to be made in the first trimester with near certainty, even if the rest of the family is unavailable for study or uninformative. Figure 118-10A shows one such example, and several others have been reported.[105,106] The same approach is feasible for those rare families showing a chromosomally visible deletion.[107] Until recently only around 10 percent of DMD cases could be shown to result from a deletion (the proportion was initially less for BMD). However, as further and more selective probes covering the entire DMD gene have been developed, in particular the cDNA clones mentioned earlier, the proportion of deletions has risen markedly and is likely to represent around two-thirds of all cases.[84]

The recognition of this high frequency of deletions adds ex-

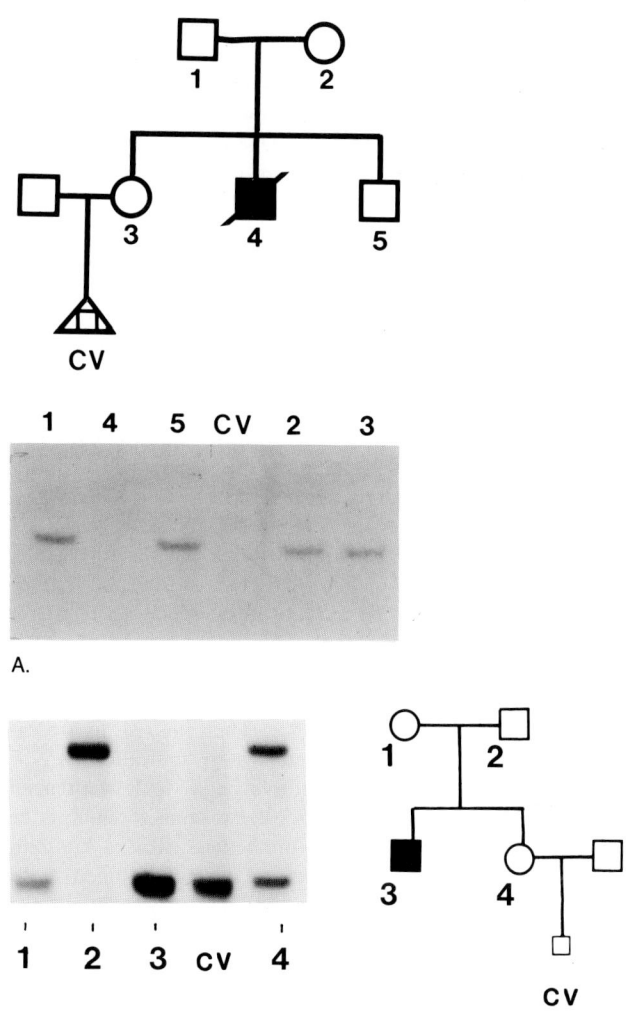

Fig. 118-10 Molecular prediction in DMD. *A.* Deletion of probe pERT87 in a pregnancy at risk for DMD. The chorion villus sample (CV) from the pregnancy at risk shows the same deletion as the affected uncle (4). Note that this individual was already deceased, but DNA had been stored, allowing its later use for this prediction. *B.* Prenatal prediction using DNA polymorphisms (intragenic probe P20; Msp polymorphism). The male fetus, studied by chorion villus sampling (CV), has received the grandmaternal allele from its mother (4) who is heterozygous for the marker, and is thus likely to be affected assuming no recombination has occurred. N.B.: Both mother and grandmother were identified as carriers on basis of very high CK levels. The molecular analysis shown does not determine their carrier status since the case is an isolated one and the grandmother is homozygous for this polymorphism.

tra weight to the importance of ensuring that DNA is isolated and stored on all affected individuals and it should considerably reduce the proportion of families in which prediction is dependent on analysis of the whole kindred.

For those families (still a considerable proportion) where no deletion can be detected or where affected males are dead, a family-based approach to prenatal diagnosis, based on the analysis of linked RFLPs, remains essential.[108,109] Here again the pERT and XJ clones and their successors have provided considerable help, being the most accurate markers available (recombination rate around 5 percent) and showing a considerable number of polymorphisms so that most families can now be offered prenatal diagnosis with 95 percent accuracy (see Fig. 118-10B). Where it is possible to show that probes flanking the gene, such as C7 and 754, have not recombined, a still greater accuracy (around 1 percent) can be achieved, but only a minority of such families will both be informative and show no recombination. In most situations 95 percent accuracy is the greatest that can be anticipated in the absence of a deletion. Now that the ends of the gene have been recognized, these will provide more accurate and probably more informative flanking markers that should reduce error to a minimum.[241]

The rapid development of new probes and new data on recombination poses logistic problems when prenatal diagnosis is being considered as a service. Any laboratory providing such a service needs to have a defined plan of investigation[95,108] that needs to be kept under review because of the rapid pace of development. While it was possible that identification of the gene product might have swung emphasis away from DNA based techniques, this seems unlikely now that it is known to be a muscle-specific protein.

DMD and other disorders where diagnosis is based on DNA techniques need advance planning wherever possible. Not only is it essential to know whether an existing case of DMD is due to a deletion but also in many cases analysis of the complete kindred is essential for interpretation of a prenatal result. Although it may be possible to undertake such studies in an emergency, it is much more satisfactory to analyze the family situation in advance. Then the risk to a pregnancy is known beforehand, and a clear indication can be given before a pregnancy is undertaken as to how prenatal testing will modify this risk. Prenatal diagnosis can thus be seen as an integral part of risk prediction within a kindred, which also involves careful clinical and genetic documentation, carrier detection studies, and combined analysis of all the available information.[95,109]

Carrier Detection. As stated above, the identification of carriers now has to be seen as part of an integrated system of genetic analysis, and linked DNA polymorphisms are currently an essential part of this. However, unlike prenatal diagnosis, carrier detection for DMD antedates the DNA era and has existed for many years in a moderately effective, though often misused, form. The use of serum creatine kinase levels, in particular, has proved effective in carrier detection, around two-thirds of carrier women showing values above 95th percentile of the normal range, while the use of likelihood ratios between values for obligatory carriers and normal individuals allows further discrimination of levels within the normal range.[110]

Despite considerable effort to develop new carrier tests based on phenotype (considered briefly later), none has supplanted or even effectively supplemented the careful use of CK. Such a failure is not surprising, seeing that the gene product has until recently been undefined and that the X-linked nature of DMD, with its expression in heterozygotes subject to X-chromosome inactivation, inevitably makes some carriers close to undetectable at the phenotypic level. The irrelevance of X inactivation is thus a particular advantage of DNA-based tests for the heterozygous state and allows them to be applied as effectively in heterozygote detection as in prenatal diagnosis.

The potential for linked markers, especially flanking markers, being used in carrier detection was apparent from the outset, and the first report[102] gave examples of the use of the linked probes singly, when flanking, and in conjunction with existing creatine kinase data. This last point has occasionally been overlooked in the application of DNA polymorphisms,

but it is now generally agreed that carrier risks need to be based on the accurate integration of all available information—pedigree, CK, and molecular. In fact, it is reassuring that the two approaches can be shown to be in close agreement,[103,111] the effect of the combined analysis being to allow more definitive risk estimates (whether high or low) and rarely resulting in conflict. In general, CK remains the more powerful technique when levels are markedly elevated, whereas DNA results are especially helpful when CK is in the normal range.

A special group of carriers is that where the index case shows a molecular deletion. Here it may be possible to show that a potential carrier has "lost" an allele that she should have inherited, i.e., that she is effectively hemizygous and thus clearly a carrier. Exclusion of carrier state in this way can be less easy, especially when dependent on dosage of a particular probe allele. In rare cases, both cytogenetic and molecular data may be of help. The possibility of germinal mosaicism makes it wise for all pregnancies of a mother who has had an affected boy with a deletion to be at risk, even when she herself does not appear to carry the deletion.[88]

In carrier detection, as with prenatal diagnosis, careful organization and planning is essential for efficient carrier detection in a population. There is no real substitute[103] for a comprehensive register covering a specific geographic region,[109] and it is for this reason that the clinical geneticist, rather than the neurologist, pediatrician, or clinical biochemist, is proving to be the main coordinator of these services. This is likely to remain the case even should specific tests in future permit an individual diagnosis in most patients; the very complexity of many X-linked families extending across geographic, age-related, and specialty boundaries has made the prevention of Duchenne muscular dystrophy an undertaking that requires a long-term and kindred-based approach.

Population Prevention of DMD

Once DMD has been diagnosed in a family, a combination of genetic counseling, carrier detection, and early prenatal diagnosis can provide highly effective measures for the prevention of further cases, while allowing most potential carriers the possibility of having children free from the disorder. This process is, though, totally dependent on recognition of the initial case, and it is here that our current approaches to prevention remain inadequate. The fact that about one-third of cases represent new mutations, with a further one-third occurring as mutations in the carrier mother, further highlights the limitations of our current preventive methods. The only way in which the disorder might be entirely avoided in the absence of therapy would be a combination of mass screening for heterozygotes and universal screening of pregnancies, neither of which is currently feasible, even were it seen as desirable.

Early Detection and Screening for DMD

The early detection of the first case of DMD in a family remains an area where there is much room for improvement. Despite publicity from lay societies and intense interest among many professionals, the diagnosis of DMD remains lamentably late in many cases. O'Brien et al.[112] showed that most instances of multiple affected sibs would have been avoided if the diagnosis had been made at the time when the mother first expressed concern. Because of such problems, there has been considerable pressure for early screening for affected boys, based on the elevated CK levels that are a feature of the disorder from the neonatal period onward.

Estimation of CK semiquantitatively using a filter-paper dried blood sample comparable to that used for phenylketonuria screening has been shown to be feasible by a number of methods.[113] False positives are low because of the marked separation of the DMD male and normal ranges, and several programs have been introduced on a pilot basis in Germany,[114] France,[115] and Scotland.[116] However, long-term results, in particular false positives, cases missed, and other disorders identified, have not yet been sufficiently evaluated to assess the effectiveness of such programs. An alternative approach, based on the observation that less than half of DMD boys are walking independently at 18 months, is to screen only those males not walking at this age.[117] Such a project is currently being evaluated in Wales by the author and his colleagues and has the advantage of requiring many fewer tests to be undertaken, with reduced risk of false positives and of causing serious concern to mothers of apparently healthy newborn infants. The limitations are that up to half of the cases are likely to be undetected unless a more efficient index of motor delay related to DMD can be determined.

It is now feasible to undertake DNA analysis on a filter paper blood sample,[118] so that it is possible that the future may see DNA-based screening developments. In particular, if therapy becomes available that modifies the course of the disorder, the case for early population screening will become overwhelming. Until then population prevention will remain an elusive goal, with the burden of effort still falling on thorough family-based measures.

The Protein Defect in DMD

DMD has proved to be the prototype for reverse genetics and is the first disorder where the sequence of analysis proceeding from mapping of the gene, through its identification and the characterization of RNA and cDNA, to the recognition of the protein has run its full course.

As a result of the large size of the DMD gene shown by molecular studies, attention was initially focused on correspondingly large protein molecules in muscle, including titin and nebulin. Nebulin in particular has received attention as a candidate protein,[119,120] being localized predominantly in the I band and having a molecular weight of around 500 kDa. Preliminary studies suggested it may be absent or diminished in DMD muscle, but antibodies raised against this protein have shown it to be present in DMD patients,[121] and to be at normal levels in the mdx mouse. In addition, there is no evidence for an X-linked gene determining its production, so that any abnormality involving nebulin in DMD is likely to be a secondary phenomenon.

More positive and specific evidence has recently come from the work of Hoffman et al.[122-125] in a series of papers which mark the beginning of our real understanding of DMD at the protein level. Their initial experiments[122] showed a marked conservation in both cDNA structure and pattern of expression between human and mouse for the DMD gene, with 88 percent homology of DNA sequence and 87 percent for amino acid sequence; there was also a similar hydropathicity profile of amino acids. Transcription was present in a wide variety of normal skeletal and cardiac muscle samples, with a low degree of expression in smooth muscle.

Hoffman et al. proceeded to raise antibodies to fusion proteins derived from cDNA for the DMD gene and bacterial DNA. Antibodies in rabbits and sheep detected a 400 kDa protein, whose size was that expected from the 14-kb transcript. The distribution was also similar, occurring principally in skeletal and cardiac muscle, at a much lower level in smooth muscle, and interestingly at a minimal level in brain. Both protein and RNA composed only a small fraction of the totals in muscle, representing 0.001 to 0.01 percent of total RNA and around 0.02 percent of total muscle protein. The protein was absent in muscle from boys with DMD and in the mdx mouse.

Since this protein does not correspond precisely to any previously recognized muscle protein, Hoffman et al.[123] have named it *dystrophin*, a name which also recognizes the fact that it was isolated and characterized as a result of studying patients with muscular dystrophy. The detailed study of dystrophin is now in progress, but preliminary findings can be summarized as follows.

Fractionation studies[124] show dystrophin to be located in the heavy microsomal fraction of muscle, which also contains the triadic junctional region and the ryanodine receptor. The triads are structures consisting of t tubules between areas of junctional sarcoplasmic reticulum; they are located at the A-1 junction ultrastructurally and are critical for myofibrillar contraction, being sites of Ca^{2+} release from sarcoplasmic reticulum, as well as of uptake of intracellular Ca^{2+} by Ca^{2+}, Mg^{2+}-ATPase and the extrinsic Ca^{2+} binding protein. Dystrophin could act as an anchor between triads and the myofibrillar cytoskeleton, and a defect in dystrophin would fit with the observed disruption of this region in DMD muscle.

Sequence data suggest a strong homology between the amino-terminal 200 amino acids of dystrophin and the actin filament-binding domain of the cytoskeletal protein α-actinin as determined in the chicken.[126]

Worton and his colleagues[238] have recently reported data that do not entirely agree with the above findings. They have independently identified a protein from cDNA at the DMD locus that appears to be identical with the dystrophin characterized by Kunkel and colleagues. However, they find a localization to the sarcolemma rather than to the triadic regions and also do not find any close homology with α-actinin. Data from other groups[239,240] indicate that there is no consensus yet.

The first clinical investigations using dystrophin analysis are now emerging. Hoffmann et al.[125] have reported a series of 103 patients with various neuromuscular disorders, showing that dystrophin was minimal or absent in muscle biopsy material of almost all classic DMD patients, while in patients with a phenotype intermediate between DMD and BMD, a reduced level of dystrophin was seen. In more typical Becker patients, by contrast, there were normal levels of a protein of abnormal size. These findings fit well with the original suggestion put forward, and now confirmed, that in classic DMD the mutation results in frameshift, with no significant production of protein, while in BMD there is no frameshift, so that protein can be synthesized, even though missing some exons and defective in structure and function. It is most interesting to note that a few patients were found with anomalous results, including some with other diagnoses but with abnormal dystrophin assay suggesting involvement of the DMD locus; one patient with apparently typical DMD had normal dystrophin and may represent a separate disorder. Thus dystrophin assay, along with DNA analysis, is likely to become a valuable diagnostic tool in distinguishing heterogeneity, particularly in atypical patients.

The preliminary studies outlined above will undoubtedly be the subject of much further work in the coming months and will also necessitate the reassessment of much of the older experimental work on DMD. The confirmation of the mdx mouse as a true homologue of the disorder[122] should be of great value for experimental studies and for therapeutic approaches. It is of particular interest that the phenotype is relatively mild, suggesting that a proportion, perhaps considerable, of the muscle pathology in DMD is secondary and thus perhaps preventable by appropriate strategies.

Other Experimental Studies in DMD

The wealth of investigations in the disorder over a period of several decades has been the subject of numerous reviews, most recently those of Emery[8] and of Engel and Banker,[2] as well as the previous edition of this text. The brief account given here outlines the principal hypotheses explored and, in most cases, abandoned in connection with the fundamental defect in DMD. While requiring complete reassessment in the light of our new understanding of the molecular basis, the data should not be irrelevant.

Contractile Proteins of Muscle. While these are clearly disrupted and affected by degenerative changes as shown by both classic histology and ultrastructural changes, no specific primary abnormality has been found in the morphology or biochemistry of actin and myosin[127] or in the energy transfer process involved in muscle contraction.[128] The molecular characterization of the known contractile proteins has shown no defect at the gene level, nor is this expected, since they are autosomally determined.[129] The high molecular weight proteins titin and nebulin have already been mentioned in this respect and appear unlikely to be responsible. Homology of dystrophin with the protein α-actinin has already been suggested, and much more information should soon be available on the precise relationship of dystrophin with other important muscle proteins.

Muscle Enzymes. A variety of enzymes characteristic of muscle has been studied for qualitative and quantitative changes, with an equal variety of findings, often contradictory;[130] a pattern of enzyme activity characteristic of immature or fetal muscle is seen,[131] but it is not clear how this might relate to pathogenesis. Key glycocytic enzymes are reduced, but this is thought to be secondary.[132]

Neurogenic Hypothesis. The possibility that the primary defect might arise in the motor nerve rather than in the muscle itself was raised by the electrophysiological work of McComas and colleagues[133] and caused a lively debate, but the techniques underlying these findings have been questioned[134] and few would now question that DMD is a primary myopathy, even though neural tissue may show a degree of involvement.

Vascular Hypothesis. The suggestion that the muscle changes might result from defects in the microvasculature followed ultrastructural work of W. K. Engel and others and also studies on the effects of microembolism in experimental animals.[135] Further detailed studies in early cases have shown blood vessels to be essentially normal.[136]

Membrane Hypothesis. A considerable number of studies have examined the plasmolemma membrane for morphologic changes using freeze fracture and other techniques. Although initial reports suggested altered particle density in DMD,[137] these have not been sustained.[138] Suggestions of a membrane defect detectable in other cell types such as fibroblasts, erythrocytes, and white blood cells[139–141] arose from comparable studies on myotonic dystrophy and are fully discussed in the previous edition of this text. There has been great difficulty in obtaining reproducibility of these studies, and at present there does not seem to be firm evidence to suggest a defect outside muscle, while even for muscle itself no specific change has been identified that incriminates membranes as the primary site of any defect in DMD. The situation for myotonic dystrophy may prove to be different.

Animal Models and DMD. The dystrophic (dy) mouse, first recognized by Michelson et al.[142] has been the subject of much work aimed at throwing light on DMD, but its autosomal nature could have readily been predicted to be strongly against any true homology, in view of the conservation of X-linked traits throughout placental mammals. The discovery by Bulfield et al.[143] of an X-linked mouse dystrophy (mdx) raised hopes that here indeed might be a true model for DMD; however, genetic evidence was debatable. Although mdx is linked to markers that are located on the X-chromosome long arm in humans, suggesting a possible homology with Emery Dreifuss dystrophy, recent work by two groups on the localization of sequences homologous to the human DMD gene on the mouse X chromosome shows that these are close to the site of the mdx gene[144,145] and have not ruled out the two being identical.

Now that the DMD cDNA has been completely isolated for both the human mouse DMD gene, with homology approaching 90 percent shown between the two, it has become possible to test the mdx mouse more directly for presence of the RNA and protein. Preliminary analysis suggests that these are absent in the mdx mouse confirming it as a true homologue of DMD.[122] Its relative mildness may reflect a considerably lower expression of the gene in normal mouse muscle and has considerable implications for future therapy. The availability of a true homologue should prove a most valuable tool in therapeutic trials.

BECKER MUSCULAR DYSTROPHY

The existence of a disorder similar to DMD but with a later onset and milder course was first recognized by Becker and Kiener in 1955,[146] and the disorder was subsequently delineated further by Becker[147] and by others.[148,149] Extensive studies by Emery and Skinner[150] and recently by Kingston[151] have given further definition to the disorder, while molecular studies have thrown new light on its relationship to Duchenne dystrophy.

Figure 118-11 illustrates a typical patient with Becker muscular dystrophy, while Table 118-8 summarizes some of the principal features of BMD and compares them to those seen in DMD. The pattern of muscle involvement is essentially similar, as is the frequent occurrence of calf pseudohypertrophy. Onset is later (but with overlap) and the course milder, the study of Emery and Skinner finding 96 percent of BMD males to be still walking at 12 years, by which age 96 percent of Duchenne males were chair-bound. The age at death is cor-

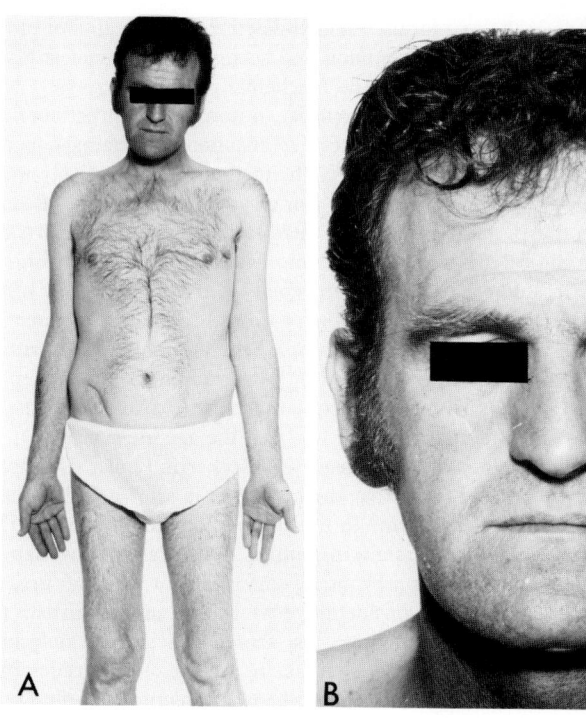

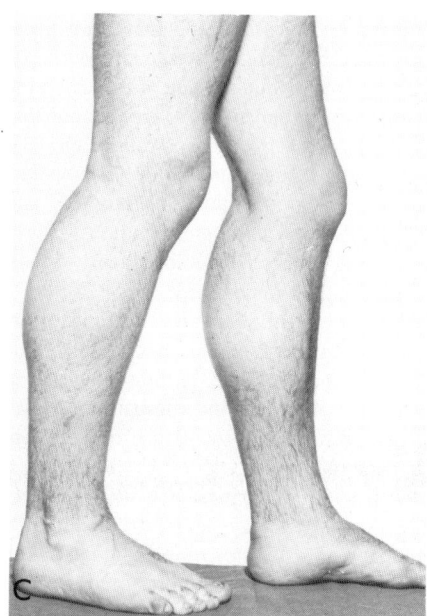

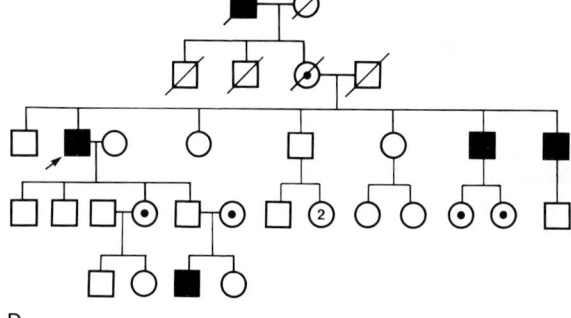

Fig. 118-11 Becker muscular dystrophy, to show typical clinical features, in particular: A. Proximal muscle involvement. B. Lack of facial weakness. C. Calf hypertrophy. D. Typical X-linked pedigree pattern, showing male transmission through obligatory carrier daughter.

D.

respondingly delayed, with 94 percent of Becker males living beyond the age of 21 years. A markedly greater variability of the course in Becker compared with Duchenne muscular dystrophy was confirmed by Kingston's finding in 104 patients of an age range of 18 to 75 years at death, with a mean of 52 years. Among the other clinical problems—slow motor development, cardiomyopathy, and mental retardation—all occurred in the BMD series, though less frequently than in Duchenne patients.

Occasional families where one member has a phenotype fitting the criteria for BMD while another more resembles DMD have been recorded,[152] but in general there is relatively close correlation of severity within a kindred.

One of the major differences between Becker and Duchenne dystrophies is that Becker patients survive to reproduce, though with diminished fertility. The fertility of affected males was 67 percent in the study of Emery and Skinner, 62.5 percent in that of Kingston. All daughters of affected males will be obligatory heterozygotes, so that it is possible to analyze carrier data from a much earlier age than in DMD.

Manifesting carriers are distinctly uncommon in BMD, and none of the 59 obligatory carriers in the study of Kingston showed significant muscle weakness. One sister in a sibship of three affected males is the only manifesting BMD carrier observed personally by the author, with moderate proximal

Table 118-8 Becker and Duchenne Muscular Dystrophies: Similarities and Differences

	BMD	DMD
Onset	Variable; commonly midchildhood to early adult life	2–4 yr
Age in wheelchair	Variable; >95% after 1½ years	>95% before 12 yr
Age at death	Rare before 30 years	Commonly 15–25 yr
Mental retardation	May occur	Frequent
Cardiac involvement	Uncommon	Usual
Calf hypertrophy	Usual; often very marked	Usual
Creatine kinase levels	Greatly raised in childhood	Greatly raised

weakness developing at age 40, greatly elevated CK, and typical electromyographic and muscle biopsy changes.

Carrier detection in BMD has been radically changed by the demonstration that BMD and DMD are allelic. The molecular aspects of carrier detection have already been discussed in the context of DMD, but the use of creatine kinase requires caution, since the proportion of carriers showing abnormal levels is less than for DMD and is strongly age-related.[153] The derivation of age-related likelihood ratios is fully discussed by Kingston,[151] who also illustrates how CK and DNA data can be integrated for risk determination.[154] While more closely linked DNA probes have subsequently become available, the principles remain unchanged.

For a number of years the relationship of BMD to DMD has been debated. Whether they are allelic or are determined by separate loci on the X chromosome is clearly fundamental to the molecular basis and the pathogenesis of the two disorders, but until recently evidence bearing directly on this has been inadequate.

The general similarities in distribution of muscle involvement, muscle histology, and extreme elevation in creatine kinase, together with the common mode of inheritance, generally inclined early investigators to consider the two disorders as likely to be fundamentally the same, but this view appeared to become untenable when genetic linkage data became available suggesting different loci for DMD and BMD. Study of classic linkage markers on the X chromosome, notably color blindness and the Xg blood group, had been shown to be convincingly negative for DMD,[38,39] but in 1969 Emery et al. reported linkage between BMD and color blindness,[40] data for Xg and BMD being negative; further data were added subsequently.[155] Although the linkage was not close (25 percent recombination) and the results not fully conclusive (maximum lod score 1.25), further support was given by evidence of Zatz et al.[156] showing positive lod scores between BMD and G-6-PD, which was already known to be linked to color blindness. In addition, it was suggested that a previously studied family[157] with a scapuloperoneal syndrome showing linkage to color blindness might have BMD. This combined evidence thus suggested that Becker and Duchenne muscular dystrophies were not alleles and must therefore have essentially different gene products and pathogenesis.

The development of DNA markers showing clear evidence of linkage with Duchenne muscular dystrophy gave an opportunity to resolve this question, and in 1983 Kingston et al.[158] reported results that clearly contradicted the earlier linkage data. The DNA polymorphism L1.28 (DXS7) showed clear evidence of linkage with BMD, the maximum lod score being 3.6 at a recombination fraction of 19 percent, similar to that already found for DMD. Any doubts that the localization of the two disorders was essentially the same came from a study of both disorders with seven linked DNA markers which showed essentially similar distances for BMD and DMD, firmly placing both in the p21 region.[159] Data from other groups confirmed the localization,[160] and no suggestion of heterogeneity within the BMD data was obtained.

These results strongly suggested but did not formally prove allelism of DMD and BMD. Evidence for this has now come from molecular deletion analysis of the pERT87 region, discussed in full earlier. At least two BMD patients in the collaborative series reported by Kunkel et al. showed molecular evidence of deletion, indicating that mutational change in the same region of DNA may cause each disorder. The analysis of cDNA probes has now shown a comparable incidence of dele-

tions in the two forms. A small deletion in the region of probe P20 is particularly common and seems to be characteristic of the Becker rather than the Duchenne phenotype.

Viewing the data in retrospect, it now seems surprising how ready workers were in general to abandon the original concept of BMD and DMD being allelic in the face of relatively weak early linkage data to the contrary. The eventual outcome should perhaps encourage others to recognize the importance of clinical and other phenotypic data in conjunction with genetic studies, so that heterogeneity can be recognized when likely to be present but not overstressed in the face of essential clinical similarities. For example, the original patient with a balanced X-autosome (X:21) translocation was persistently described as having Duchenne muscular dystrophy when she was still walking when she was past the age of 20 years.

Should the separate category of Becker muscular dystrophy be maintained, now that the condition is known to be allelic to the Duchenne form? In the author's opinion it should. The disorders run separately in families, with minimal overlap of phenotype. The problems of management and of genetic counseling differ considerably, while the natural history remains strikingly different. The shared genetic and molecular basis should help the patients in each group considerably. Becker families will be able to benefit directly from the DNA markers and the large body of research concentrated on DMD. For Duchenne patients the existence of a relatively mild disorder is evidence that a change in the mutant gene need not always be associated with an inexorably fatal phenotype, and could be relevant to formulating therapeutic strategies in the future.

EMERY-DREIFUSS MUSCULAR DYSTROPHY

In 1961 Dreifuss and Hogan[161] described a kindred with relatively mild X-linked muscular dystrophy living in the Appalachian region of Virginia. They considered it to be essentially a variant of Duchenne dystrophy, but when the family was restudied by Emery and Dreifuss,[162] it was clear that there were significant differences, notably the high frequency of cardiac complications and the early and widespread contractures. In the United States[163,164] and in Europe[165] a number of similar families have since been described which have defined the phenotype more clearly and have shown clear differences from both Duchenne and Becker dystrophies, establishing it as a third distinct X-linked muscular dystrophy.

The clinical features of Emery-Dreifuss muscular dystrophy are illustrated in Fig. 118-12A and are summarized in Table 118-9, while Table 118-10 compares them with those of Becker muscular dystrophy, the form with which it is most likely to be confused. Most important is the cardiac defect, which in the Emery-Dreifuss type is early in onset and regular

Table 118-9 Emery-Dreifuss Muscular Dystrophy

Inheritance X-linked
Onset commonly in teens; slowly progressive
Scapulo- or humeroperoneal distribution common
No calf pseudohypertrophy
Early contractures in upper and lower limbs
Creatine kinase only moderately raised
Consistent and often life-threatening cardiac involvement (usually AV conduction defects)

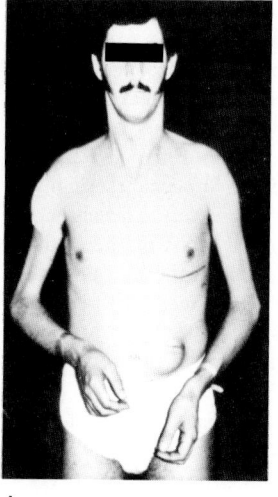
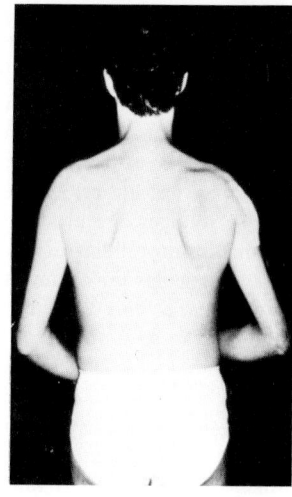

A.

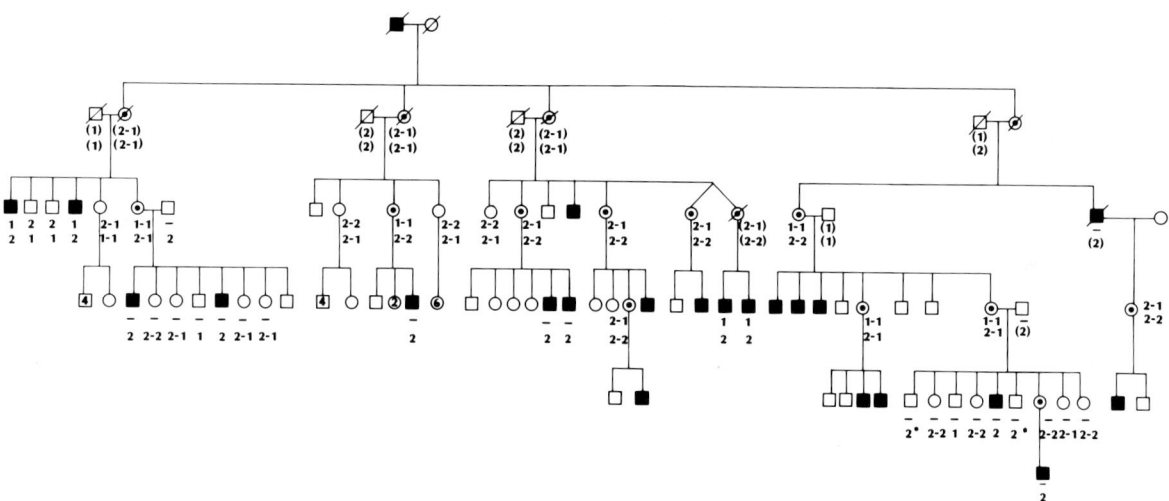

B.

Fig. 118-12 Emery-Dreifuss muscular dystrophy. A. Affected male, showing elbow contractures. (Courtesy of Dr. L. Rowland.) B. Pedigree of a large Appalachian kindred, showing X-linked pattern and segregation with DNA markers (factor VIII, *upper*; DX13, *lower*) on distal Xq. (*From Thomas et al.*[168] Family previously studied by Hopkins et al.[164])

in occurrence. Cardiac conduction defects are prominent, and unless treated may lead to sudden death. Presymptomatic detection of heart involvement by means of regular electrocardiograms and the insertion of a cardiac pacemaker at an early stage may be lifesaving; widespread cardiomyopathy leading to heart failure is uncommon.

The neuromuscular features are often mild and only slowly progressive, with onset commonly in adolescence, but with significant disability rare until well into adult life. The upper girdle is involved early, but in the lower limbs weakness and wasting may be more distal, giving a humeroperoneal distribution. It is likely that a number of families of this type, originally thought to have separate disorders, in fact have Emery-Dreifuss dystrophy, including the family originally reported by Thomas et al.[157] and found to show genetic linkage with color blindness. Early contractures, particularly in the upper limbs, further distinguishes this from Becker muscular dystrophy (Fig. 118-12A).

Serum creatine kinase is only moderately raised in Emery-Dreifuss dystrophy, while both electromyography and muscle

Table 118-10 Emery-Dreifuss and Becker Muscular Dystrophies: Comparative Features

Symptom	Emery-Dreifuss	Becker
Muscle involvement	Upper limbs often involved early; distal weakness in lower limbs	Proximal; mainly lower limb in early stages
Calf hypertrophy	Usually absent	Prominent from early stage
Contractions	Early, widespread; upper and lower limbs	Late or absent, except Achilles tendons
Creatine kinase	Moderately elevated	Greatly raised, especially in early and preclinical stage
Cardiac involvement	Regular, early, may be life threatening	Uncommon, usually but not always mild
Gene location	Xq27–28	Xp21

histology may show some features considered as neuropathic, adding to the difficulty in diagnosing the isolated male case. Further confusion has come from reports of autosomal dominant inheritance in some families,[166] so it is clear that the phenotype has yet to be fully defined and that further heterogeneity may exist. Heterozygote detection in Emery-Dreifuss dystrophy has hitherto been an uncertain process, especially in the younger age group. Creatine kinase serum levels are normal in most obligatory carriers, so that DNA markers will be of particular importance (see below). Identification of heterozygotes is also of clinical importance since prospective study of the large American kindreds suggests that some heterozygotes are at risk of cardiac conduction defects in later life.

Genetically there is no doubt about X linkage in most of the large kindreds reported (Fig. 118-12B), and there is now clear linkage data on several kindreds which supports an entirely different localization of the gene to that shown for DMD and BMD. Boswinkel et al.[167] showed in 1985 that there appeared to be frequent recombination with markers in the p21 region, while the author and his colleagues[168] were able to study one of the two large kindreds reported by Hopkins et al.[164] and to show clear evidence of linkage with the three distal long arm markers factor 8, DX13 (DXS15), and St14 (DXS52). Similar results were obtained by Yates et al.[169] and by Merlini et al.[170]

Combining these studies leaves no doubt that the Emery-Dreifuss gene has a distal long arm localization. Although its precise relationship to the marker loci in terms of order is still uncertain, the data should soon be sufficient to allow prenatal and heterozygote prediction with reasonable accuracy. A further valuable development of particular interest in the light of the original color blindness linkage data of P.K. Thomas et al.[157] is the cloning of the genes underlying red-green color blindness[171]; polymorphisms have been detected in relation to these probes which should prove to be a powerful genetic marker in this region of the X chromosome.[172]

Now that a clear, though approximate, localization of the Emery-Dreifuss gene has been achieved, isolation of the gene itself can proceed. This region of the X chromosome is already known to be the site of numerous other genetic disorders, including hemophilia A, Hunter syndrome, and spondyloepiphyseal dysplasia tarda. The techniques of large fragment DNA electrophoresis using pulsed or alternating field techniques,[173] the development of overlapping cosmid clones for the region, and the identification of "HTF islands" denoting probable genes will all be resources that can be used in the isolation of the genes in this region.

OTHER X-LINKED MUSCULAR DYSTROPHIES

In addition to the three major forms of X-linked muscular dystrophy (at two separate loci) discussed above, the possibility remains of further heterogeneity. Given the marked variation of both the Becker and Emery-Dreifuss phenotypes it will not be easy to delineate these with certainty; none of the previously reported families warrant a separate status at present. The family reported by Mabry et al.[174] has previously been considered separate but showed features suggestive of the Emery-Dreifuss phenotype, notably cardiac involvement.

One X-linked myopathy deserving mention, though not strictly a muscular dystrophy, is the X-linked "lethal" myotu-bular myopathy.[175] This disorder commonly presents with unexplained male perinatal deaths, though survival has been recorded. In the family shown in Fig. 118-13, a considerable number of such deaths had been recorded before full neuropathologic study showed the true cause. Muscle biopsy of heterozygotes in the kindred showed distinctive abnormalities, while study of other tissues in an affected male suggested that the disorder may be a generalized metabolic defect. Preliminary gene mapping linkage studies suggest a distal long arm localization on the X chromosome,[176] but further work is required for definitive mapping of the gene.

A new X-linked myopathy has recently been described in a large Finnish kindred.[177] This relatively benign condition is characterized histologically by a marked degree of autophagy of muscle fibers and seems likely to be located on the distal long arm of the X chromosome.

MYOTONIC DYSTROPHY (DYSTROPHIA MYOTONICA: STEINERT'S DISEASE)

Myotonic dystrophy, uniquely among the muscular dystrophies, is characterized by myotonia, an electrophysiological disturbance resulting in delayed muscle relaxation. Although a number of nonprogressive disorders may also result in myotonia (Table 118-11), none of them show the progressive weakness and wasting that place them in the group of muscular dystrophies, so that the combination of myotonia and a progressive muscular dystrophy is specific for myotonic dystrophy.

Myotonic dystrophy was first recognized as a clinical entity more than 70 years ago by Steinert[178] and has since then been the subject of a considerable amount of study. Much of this work is summarized in the monographs of Caughey and Myrianthopoulos[179] and of Harper,[180] while details of subsequent work are given in several recent reviews.[181,182] The account given here concentrates on developments in molecular genetics which, as with the X-linked dystrophies, promise to be the key for a true understanding of the metabolic basis.

Clinical Features

Myotonic dystrophy is one of the most variable disorders known and has presenting features that are often nonneurologic ones. The condition must be considered in a framework much broader than that of the other muscular dystrophies.

Table 118-11 The Myotonic Disorders

Disorder	Inheritance
Myotonic dystrophy	Autosomal dominant
Myotonia congenita	
Thomsen's disease	Autosomal dominant
Recessive generalized myotonia	Autosomal recessive
Paramyotonia congenita	Autosomal dominant
	Autosomal dominant
Periodic paralysis	
Hypokalemic	Autosomal dominant
Normo-hyperkalemic (adynamia episodica)	Autosomal dominant
Chondrodystrophic myotonia	Autosomal recessive
(Schwartz-Jampel syndrome)	
Acquired myotonia	
Drug-induced	
Associated with malignancy	

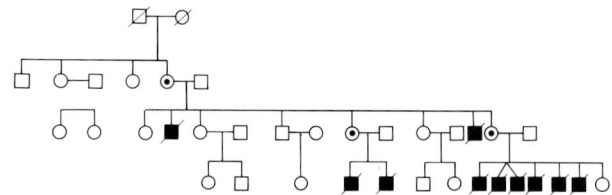

A.

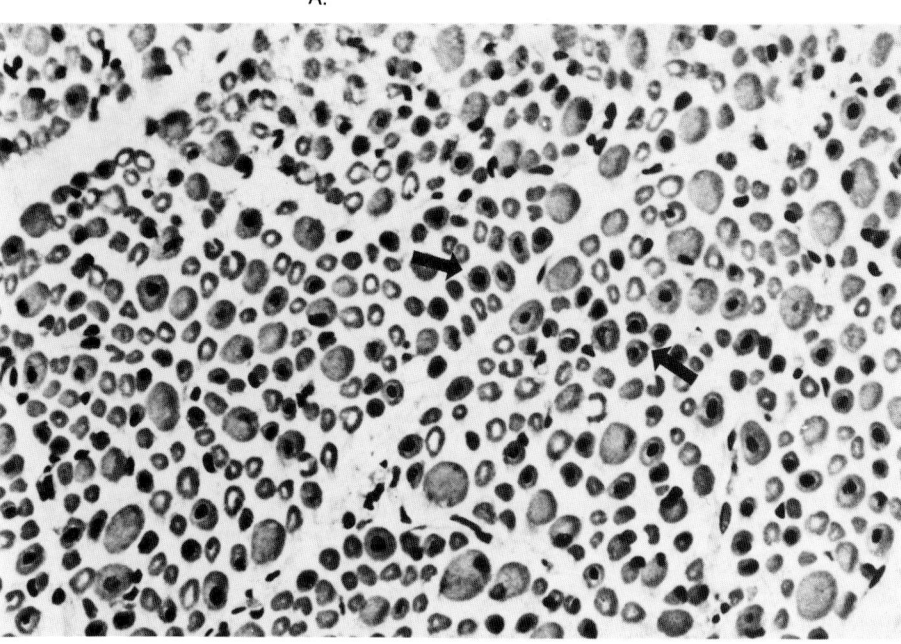

Fig. 118-13 X-linked myotubular myopathy. *A.* Pedigree showing numerous male perinatal deaths, mostly undiagnosed. *B.* Transverse section of muscle from affected male. Note many small muscle fibers with centrally placed nuclei (× 400). (Courtesy of Dr. G. Cole, Cardiff.)

B.

Nonetheless, the commonest symptoms are neuromuscular, principally related to muscle weakness and to myotonia, the latter being most commonly interpreted as stiffness. Table 118-12 shows the most frequent presenting symptoms, while Table 118-13 gives the predominant muscle distribution. It can be seen that the muscles involved contrast strikingly with Duchenne and Becker dystrophies, the only other major dystrophy with somewhat similar muscle groups involved being facioscapulohumeral dystrophy. The mainly distal limb involvement can cause confusion with neuropathic conditions such as Charcot-Marie-Tooth disease, but the recognition of myotonia allows a specific clinical diagnosis of myotonic dystrophy to be made immediately. Involvement of facial and jaw muscles is almost invariable in myotonic dystrophy; ptosis can be marked, while weakness and wasting of sternomastoid muscles is seen selectively in the neck. Figure 118-14 illustrates some of these features.

Myotonia can most readily be recognized by direct percussion of the muscle (in particular the thenar eminence) or by testing for rapid relaxation (especially of grip or, less commonly, eye closure). While most patients complain of stiffness in relation to their myotonia, this is frequently not mentioned unless directly inquired about. Some patients seems genuinely unaware that their myotonia is abnormal, while others may deliberately minimize their symptoms. The end result is that diagnosis is delayed in many patients, even when myotonia is obvious if actually sought.

The extramuscular features of myotonic dystrophy are of special importance, both in the diagnosis of relatives at risk and in terms of prognosis and management of the affected individual. Some of these can be related to smooth or cardiac

Table 118-12 Presenting Symptoms in Myotonic Dystrophy (Data on 170 Patients)

Symptom	N
Muscle weakness	60
Myotonia	36
Asymptomatic (family study)	31
Mental retardation	20
Cataract	9
Neonatal problems	5
Other	9

Table 118-13 Muscular Involvement in Myotonic Dystrophy

Muscles most prominently affected
  Superficial facial muscles
  Levator palpebrae superioris
  Temporalis
  Sternomastoids
  Distal muscles of forearm
  Dorsiflexors of foot
Other muscles commonly affected
  Quadriceps
  Diaphragm and intercostals
  Intrinsic muscles of hands and feet
  Palate and pharyngeal muscles
  Tongue
  External ocular muscles
Muscles frequently spared
  Pelvic girdle
  Hamstrings
  Soleus and gastrocnemius

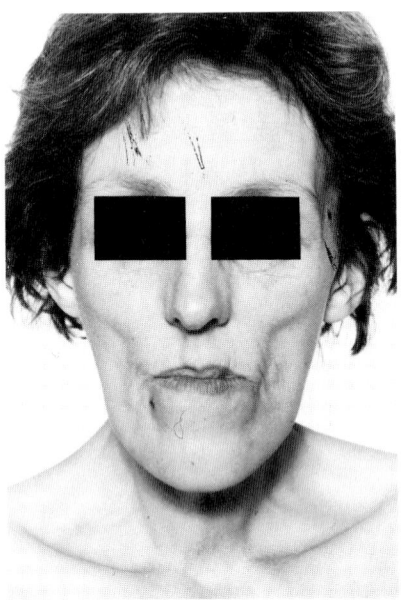 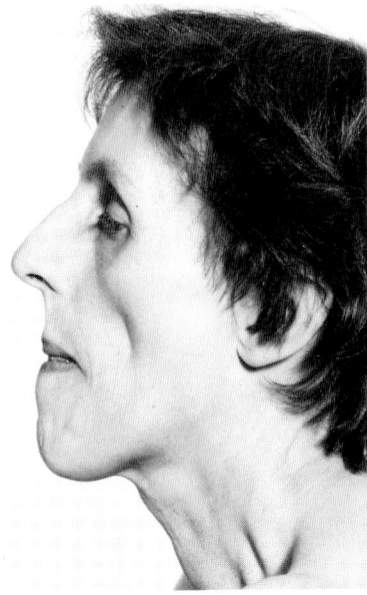 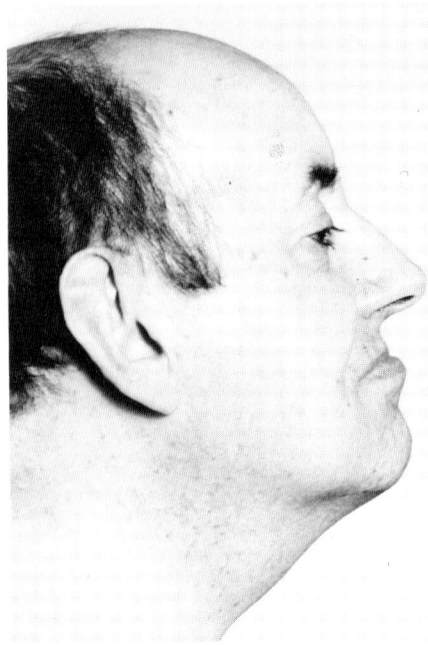

A.   B.

Fig. 118-14 Myotonic dystrophy in adults showing *(A)* facial and jaw weakness and wasting of sternomastoid muscles and *(B)* ptosis and marked balding.

muscle dysfunction (Table 118-14), while others involve entirely different systems (Table 118-15). Among these are cataracts, characterized by highly distinctive multicolored subcortical lens opacities when viewed with the slit lamp; a variety of endocrine changes, of which testicular tubular atrophy in males is most prominent; and varying degrees of central nervous system involvement ranging from increased somnolence, apathy, and mild personality deterioration in some adults to severe mental retardation in a proportion of congenitally affected patients. Some patients presenting with these systemic features (notably cataract) may have only minimal or occasionally no detectable muscle abnormality, even on careful investigation.

Diagnostic tests in myotonic dystrophy are summarized in Table 118-16. It should be emphasized that these are not always necessary in patients with clear-cut clinical features, while no single test can be considered pathognomic. However, the combined use of these tests, together with a careful clinical study of family members, will allow most diagnostic problems to be resolved.[183,184] Of particular note are the ophthalmologic assessment, where the lens changes (mentioned above) are highly specific, especially before established cataract has developed, while associated retinal changes may also be found.

Table 118-14 Smooth and Cardiac Muscle Involvement in Myotonic Dystrophy

Gastrointestinal tract	Widespread involvement, particularly of pharynx and esophagus
Gallbladder	Delayed emptying; high incidence of stones
Urinary bladder	Probably unaffected
Ureter	Isolated instances of dilatation
Uterus	Incoordinate contraction in labor and in vitro
Eye	Ciliary body affected; low intraocular tension
Heart	Conduction defects, in particular heart block, atrial arrhythmias; less commonly, cardiomyopathy

Electromyography will confirm the presence of the myotonia and is of particular importance in distinguishing other syndromes with muscle stiffness, including various familial cramping disorders (generally electrically silent) and disorders of presynaptic origin (generally showing persistent electrical activity at rest). While the presence of myotonia will not distinguish other myotonic disorders such as myotonia congenita, the finding of myotonia together with "dystrophic" changes such as diminished amplitude of action potentials and polyphasic potentials, in the context of a progressive neuromuscular disorder, is conclusive.

Further clinical investigations—such as electrocardiography, glucose tolerance and other endocrine studies, and gastrointestinal radiology—are all frequently helpful in management but are less definitive in diagnosis of myotonic dystrophy. The most important diagnostic aid is awareness of the disorder and of its variable and often unexpected methods of presentation.

Table 118-15 Other Systems Involved in Myotonic Dystrophy

System	*Symptom*
Eye	Cataract, retinal degeneration, ocular hypotonia, ptosis, extraocular weakness
Endocrine	Testicular tubular atrophy; diabetes (rarely clinically significant); sometimes abnormalities of growth hormone and other pituitary functions
Brain	Severe involvement in congenital form; mild mental deterioration frequent in adults; hypersomnia
Peripheral nerve	Variable and rarely clinically significant; minor sensory loss may occur
Skeletal	Cranial hyperostosis, air sinus enlargement; jaw and palate involvement; talipes (childhood cases); scoliosis (uncommon)
Skin	Premature balding; calcifying epithelioma
Lungs	Aspiration pneumonia from esophageal and diaphragmatic involvement; hypoventilation

Table 118-16 Diagnostic Tests in Myotonic Dystrophy

Electromyography	Myotonic potentials
Slit-lamp examination	Multicolored lens opacities
Creatine kinase	Moderate elevation frequent
Glucose and insulin tolerance	Impaired glucose tolerance; hyperinsulinism
Electrocardiogram	Conduction defects; prolonged PR interval

Congenital Myotonic Dystrophy

First recognized by Vanier in 1960,[185] it has since become clear that this form of myotonic dystrophy is distinctive, frequently fatal, and far from rare.[186] It is seen only in off-spring of women who are themselves affected with myotonic dystrophy, often mildly,[187] and its genetic relationship to the commoner form of the disease is still not fully re-solved.[188]

Table 118-17 lists the main characteristics of congenital myotonic dystrophy; the features at different ages are shown in Fig. 118-15. The facial appearance is highly distinctive, largely due to the combination of bilateral facial palsy with marked jaw weakness. The early, often intrauterine onset of muscle weakness helps to mold the facial features by giving the characteristic tented upper lip. Decreased intrauterine muscle action plays a role in many of the other features, such as the high incidence of respiratory inadequacy and pulmonary hypoplasia (due to underdeveloped diaphragm and inter-costal muscles), the occurrence of talipes and other joint contractures, the development of polyhydramnios (lack of intrauterine swallowing), and the generally poor fetal movements. By contrast to the adult disorder, myotonia is inconspicuous or absent in affected infants, though it be-comes more prominent as affected individuals reach later child-hood.

The differential diagnosis of congenital myotonic dystrophy in the neonate relates not so much to other muscular dystro-phies as to the broader group of congenital myopathies. These are not discussed in detail in this chapter but are listed in Table 118-18. Many patients die rapidly from respiratory in-adequacy before the diagnosis can be made, but with the in-creasing success of neonatal intensive care, a higher proportion survive to be diagnosed. The relationship to adult myotonic dystrophy is important since the discovery of a typical adult case in the family, usually the mother or maternal relatives, will confirm the diagnosis in the infant. Even more important is for the risk of the severe congenital form to be fully appre-ciated by all women with myotonic dystrophy who are consid-ering child-bearing.

Table 118-17
Congenital Myotonic Dystrophy: Major Clinical Features

Bilateral facial weakness
Hypotonia
Delayed motor development
Mental retardation
Neonatal respiratory distress
Feeding difficulties
Talipes
Hydramnios in later pregnancy
Reduced fetal movements

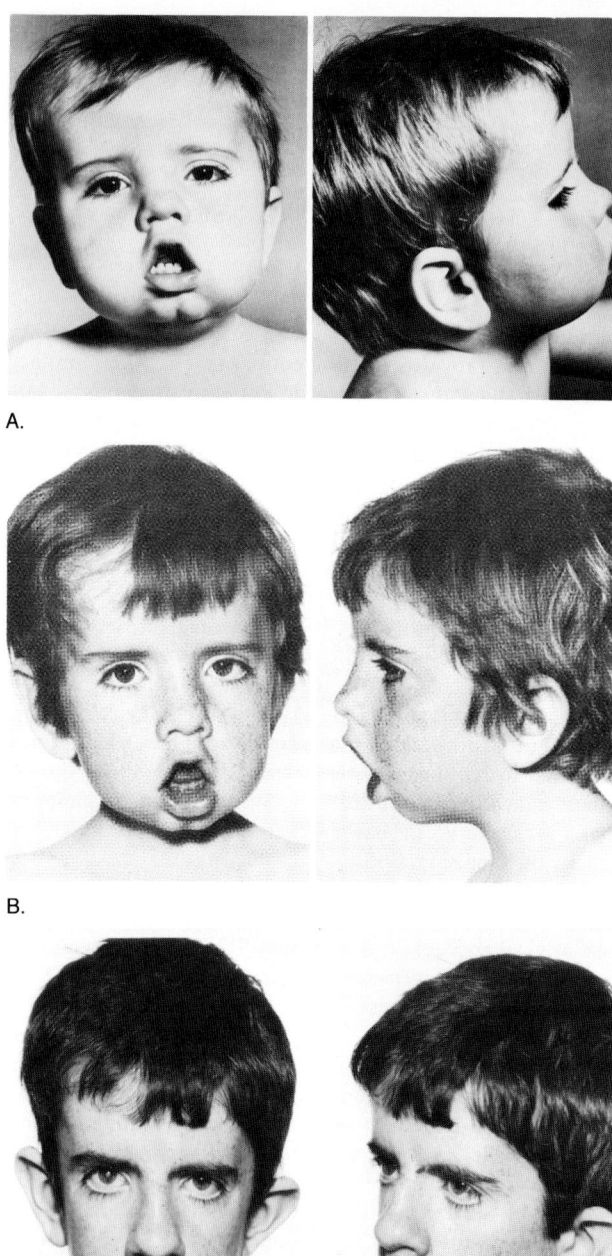

Fig. 118-15 Congenital myotonic dystrophy, showing facial features in same patient at different ages. *A.* Age 2 years. *B.* Age 6 years. *C.* Age 12 years. Note facial diplegia, tented upper lip, and open mouth due to jaw muscle weakness.

Genetics of Myotonic Dystrophy

Myotonic dystrophy has been recognized as an autosomal dominant disorder for more than 50 years. A series of family and population studies suggests a rather uniform prevalence over most of the world, though in some areas such as the iso-lated Saguenay region of Quebec, Canada,[189] the "founder ef-fect" has resulted in local concentrations. Both sexes transmit and develop the disorder equally. Although the congenital form is confined to the offspring of affected females, the pro-

Table 118-18 Congenital Myopathies

Disorder	Inheritance
Central core disease	Autosomal dominant
Nemaline myopathy	Autosomal dominant; variable
Congenital myotubular (centronuclear) myopathy	X-linked recessive; also autosomal recessive
Congenital fiber-type disproportion	Uncertain
Fingerprint body myopathy	Uncertain
Multicore myopathy	Autosomal dominant?

portion of affected offspring is close to 50 percent for parents of either sex, provided that the entire range is taken into account. Variation in expression and severity is extreme, but nonpenetrance of the gene is rare in that skipped generations are exceptional in thoroughly investigated families. A reduced fertility of both sexes to around 70 percent of normal has been shown, which is perhaps surprising in view of the relative rarity of new mutation in the disorder. Such estimates are likely to ignore the numerous mildly affected individuals who do not come to ascertainment.

Genetic heterogeneity has been suggested on the basis of familial correlation of age at onset,[190] but even within a single kindred the extremes can be seen, so that no clear separation of clinical phenotype can be defined such as is seen with Duchenne and Becker muscular dystrophies. Occasional kindreds, such as one reported from Labrador,[191] may show a concentration of unusual features, but the author's opinion is that a satisfactory case has not been made for genetic heterogeneity on clinical grounds.

Various hypotheses have been proposed to account for the remarkable phenotypic variability seen in myotonic dystrophy. The original concept of "anticipation" postulated a deterioration in successive generations, but it was pointed out by Penrose[192] that the inevitable bias of ascertainment would favor the observation and recording of those multigeneration families with mild features in the oldest generation and early onset in the youngest. The recognition of congenital myotonic dystrophy as a distinctive syndrome showing intrauterine onset and the necessity for an affected mother help further in explaining the range of variation. Nevertheless, the extreme mildness of the disorder in some late onset individuals, along with the recognition that some kindreds can be connected by near-asymptomatic individuals, suggests that further factors could be acting, possibly requiring some premutational event comparable to that postulated for the fragile X phenotype. This difficulty in defining the minimum phenotype makes an accurate estimate of the proportion of new mutations unreliable, quite apart from giving uncertainty in reassuring apparently normal relatives that they are indeed free from the gene.

A recently recognized factor which could be relevant for the maternal transmission of the congenital form is the phenomenon of *genetic imprinting*, by which differences in DNA methylation may result in a selective effect of the parental genotype.[193] Already well documented in the mouse, this may also occur in the human genome and deserves consideration as a possible explanation for those disorders showing a differential phenotype according to the sex of the transmitting parent.

Gene Mapping and Molecular Studies

Myotonic dystrophy was one of the first autosomal disorders for which genetic linkage data became available. In Mohr's classic work, "A study of linkage in man,"[194] in which genetic linkage between the Lutheran blood group and secretor loci was first demonstrated, some data on families from the earlier Danish study of Thomasen with myotonic dystrophy were also analyzed and suggested the possibility of linkage with Lutheran blood group. Further work by Renwick et al.[195] and Harper et al.[196] confirmed that the secretor, Lutheran, and myotonic dystrophy loci were indeed all linked. In 1982 this linkage group, along with the locus for complement C3, was assigned to chromosome 19 by somatic cell hybrid studies.[197] This assignment opened the way for a detailed molecular analysis comparable to that pioneered for Duchenne muscular dystrophy on the X chromosome, and the past 5 years have seen considerable progress in the mapping of the myotonic dystrophy gene on chromosome 19.[198,199]

A considerable number of genetic markers are now available as markers on chromosome 19,[200,201] some of which are listed in Table 118-19. Some of these markers are protein polymorphisms, including a number of blood group systems and the enzyme peptidase D; others are cell surface antigens or receptor sites that are not polymorphic but which can be analyzed in cultured fibroblasts or hybrid cell lines. Among the increasing number of DNA polymorphisms are several specific gene loci as well as anonymous DNA sequences from various sources.

Sources of chromosome 19 DNA probes have included flow-sorted DNA libraries of varying degrees of refinement, as well as hybrid cell lines in which chromosome 19 is the principal human chromosome. The first anonymous polymorphic DNA sequence, 1J2 (D19S6),[198] was isolated from a flow-sorted DNA library enriched for chromosomes 19 and 20, while further linked probes such as LDR152 (D19S19) have come from a more 19-specific flow-sorted library.[202] Hybrid cell lines have provided a number of other probes, while specific genes on chromosome 19, such as apo C-2 and the LDL and insulin receptors, have also been available for testing.

Figure 118-16 shows the approximate relationship of some of these DNA markers to myotonic dystrophy on chromosome 19. While genetic linkage analysis has been partly responsible for the mapping,[199] the use of hybrid cell lines with breakpoints at differing sites on chromosome 19 has also been a major resource and has allowed a physical ordering and localization on the chromosome.[198,203] As a result of these combined approaches, the orientation of the linkage group of loci is now established, while it is clear that the myotonic dystrophy locus is on the long arm of the chromosome.[201]

Precise mapping of the gene has so far been hindered by lack of several of the vital factors that contributed to identification of the DMD gene. Chromosome 19 is somewhat featureless in its banding structure, with few clearly defined re-

Table 118-19 Genetic Markers on Chromosome 19 Linked to Myotonic Dystrophy

DNA polymorphisms
  Apo C-2 (several polymorphisms)
  LDR152
  1J2
  Creatine kinase (muscle specific)
  Na$^+$ K$^+$-ATPase
Protein polymorphisms
  Secretor status
  Lutheran blood group
  Peptidase D
  Complement C3

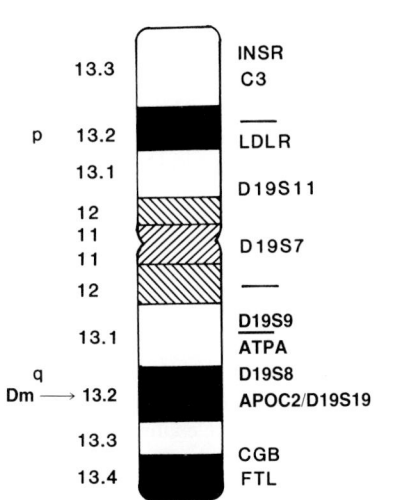

Fig. 118-16 Diagrammatic map of chromosome 19 based on cell hybrid studies, showing localization of principal markers and approximate site of myotonic dystrophy gene.

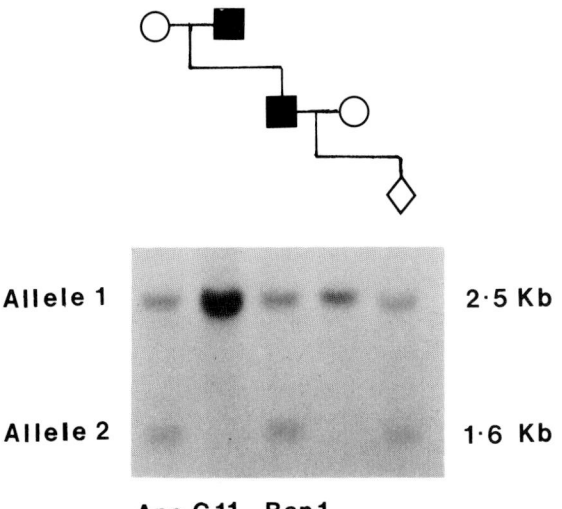

Fig. 118-17. Use of a closely linked gene marker (apo C-2) for prenatal prediction of myotonic dystrophy (after Meredith et al., 1987). The father of the fetus, having inherited allele 1 and myotonic dystrophy from his nonaffected father, has transmitted allele 2 to the fetus, which is thus predicted to be unaffected in the absence of recombination.

gions apart from the centromere, which makes accurate characterization of breakpoints difficult. No patients with visible deletions or balanced translocations involving chromosome 19 have been associated with myotonic dystrophy, so that experiments analogous to those done for DMD on the X chromosome have not so far been possible. Even precise linkage analysis is hindered by the marked difference in recombination frequency between the sexes (recombination at female meiosis is three times that of male meiosis for this chromosome[204]).

Linkage markers are nonetheless now sufficiently close for some to be of practical use in prediction. At present the marker that is both close and the most informative is the gene apo C-2,[205,206] which shows no more than 4 percent recombination with myotonic dystrophy on pooled data and which detects a variety of polymorphisms allowing application in the majority of families requiring prediction. Apo C-2 has now been used both for prenatal prediction (using DNA from chorion villus sampling) and for prediction of genotype in relatives at risk.[207] Figure 118-17 shows an example of prenatal exclusion; in less satisfactory pedigree structures the existence of several polymorphisms can allow a haplotype which may provide a more specific prediction to be defined. At present the only clear recognized "flanking" probes are too distant to add useful practical information, but classification of order of a series of closely linked markers currently under study by several groups should allow a series of DNA markers to be used in a comparable manner to that done for DMD. In particular the probe LDR 152 appears to be close to myotonic dystrophy,[202] though it is less informative than apo C-2 and the relative order in relation to the disease gene is undetermined.

In the absence of specific chromosomal rearrangements, isolation of the myotonic dystrophy gene is being approached by a combination of other techniques. Pulsed field electrophoresis has already allowed a preliminary map of fragments around the apo C-2 gene, the closest marker to myotonic dystrophy, to be constructed while a comparable map of the more distal region should bracket the myotonic dystrophy gene. Whether molecular deletions, comparable to those defined by the pERT probes in DMD, will also be seen for myotonic dystrophy re-

mains to be seen. If, indeed, the number of independent new mutations is relatively small, such deletions might be rare. However, in this case probes close to the gene should show marked allelic association.

Already our available molecular genetic map of chromosome 19 allows specific candidate genes to be tested. Such an opportunity was first provided when the insulin receptor gene was located on chromosome 19.[208] The known association of myotonic dystrophy with hyperinsulinism and a consistent abnormality in glucose tolerance made a defect in this gene an attractive hypothesis. However, this was rapidly disproved by the finding that not only was there recombination between the insulin receptor gene polymorphisms and myotonic dystrophy but also the insulin receptor gene was located on the distal short arm of the chromosome, distant from those markers showing close linkage with myotonic dystrophy.[209] The gene for the muscle specific form of creatine kinase, also now known to be chromosome 19,[210] should be testable as a candidate gene in the same way. The recently isolated gene for Na,K-ATPase is of special interest in view of the disturbance of ion transport occurring in mytonia and the suggestion from previous work that an abnormality of this group of enzymes might exist.[211] Following cloning of the mouse gene for Na,K-ATPase, the corresponding human gene has been isolated and shown to map to chromosome 19 in the region containing the closest known markers for myotonic dystrophy.[212] However, recombination has been shown, making it unlikely that this form of ATPase is in fact the myotonic dystrophy gene, and genetic linkage data suggest[213] that the Na,K-ATPase locus is further from myotonic dystrophy than is apo C-2.

Other Experimental Studies in Myotonic Dystrophy

In this chapter, for both myotonic dystrophy and the X-linked muscular dystrophies, the genetic and molecular evidence has been considered first, and in most detail, with the more abundant and historically preceding phenotypic experimental data considered second and in considerably less detail. This deliberate reversal of the conventional sequence may partly result from personal preference but also reflects the growing view, illustrated particularly well by the muscular dystrophies, that the key to disordered gene function may well come initially from studies of the gene itself. Whether this will prove as true for myotonic dystrophy as it already has on the X chromosome remains to be seen, but it is certainly true that conventional biochemical studies have not yet given a clear idea as to the primary gene product involved in this disorder, though they have given strong hints as to its general nature.

Most of this experimental work, notably that involving membrane proteins, was fully and authoritatively reviewed by Appel and Roses in the previous edition of this text and is not repeated here. Much early work is similarly summarized in the author's monograph[180] and will likewise be mentioned only if it seems relevant to current thought concerning the nature of the disorder. It is likely that identification of the gene, even if it precedes recognition of the gene product, will result immediately in a return to experimental work involving protein biochemistry, much of which seems to have gone into temporary abeyance in the expectation that the gene will "emerge" from the current intense study of the genetic basis.

General and Clinical Considerations. In considering the possible nature of the myotonic dystrophy gene and its product, several general points can be learned from the disease itself. First, its autosomal dominant inheritance makes a classic inborn error of metabolism a rather unlikely possibility. A key rate-limiting enzyme, or one located in the cell membrane where spatial orientation is crucial, could certainly be compatible with such inheritance, but the disorder is essentially one of heterozygotes. (The author has made numerous attempts, so far in vain, to secure precise documentation of and samples from possible homozygotes.)

Second, a general consideration recognized by all those involved clinically with this disorder is its multisystemic nature. Muscle is indeed prominently involved in most patients, but the widespread defects in lens, retina, central nervous system, and endocrine organs all suggest that the disordered primary processes are not confined to muscle. On the other hand, it would be perverse to ignore muscle, particularly as it is the seat of the most specific abnormality found in the disorder myotonia.

Third, the disorder is progressive, albeit often only very slowly, contrasting in this respect with the other inherited myotonic disorders (mentioned briefly below) and resembling in this respect other muscular dystrophies. Fourth, the remarkable congenital form of myotonic dystrophy, in which genetically affected offspring of affected mothers appear to sustain a passive intrauterine inhibition of muscle development, suggests that some factor, possibly humoral, may be acting on predisposed fetal muscle.

Muscle Pathology. Detailed studies of muscle histology, histochemistry, and electron microscopy have given a clear picture of the changes that occur in myotonic dystrophy,[214] changes which are distinctive, though not totally specific. Figure 118-18 shows some of the more charateristic changes, notably increased internal nuclei, often in chains, together with ringed fibers and sarcoplasmic masses. Histochemistry shows a relative loss of type 1 fibers, while electron-microscopic changes include degeneration of microfilaments and proliferation of the sarcotubular system. More important from the viewpoint of pathogenesis are the negative ultrastructural findings, in particular absence of marked change in small blood vessels and nerve endings, perhaps secondary to prolonged myotonic contractions.

Study of muscle from cases of congenital myotonic dystrophy shows several changes not present in adult patients.[215] The muscles are hypoplastic and the fibers have an immature rounded appearance, with numerous central nuclei; there are abundant satellite cells, suggesting arrested development rather than degeneration.[216] Histochemical studies show a peripheral area deficient of mitochondrial enzymes.[217]

More detailed experimental studies of muscle have examined the sarcolemmal membrane using freeze-fracture techniques[218] and have also involved cultured muscle cells.[219] No clear morphologic defects have so far been identified by either approach, and as with Duchenne dystrophy, there have been different conclusions reached by different investigators. A recent observation of interest, not yet confirmed independently, is the presence of receptors for the bee venom toxin apamin in muscle from myotonic dystrophy patients.[220] Unfortunately, neither the toxin nor the receptor site has been sufficiently characterized to allow it to be localized cytogenetically or tested as a candidate defect.

The possibility that a generalized membrane defect might exist in myotonic dystrophy led to an extensive series of studies not only on muscle cell membranes but also on those of cultured fibroblasts and red blood cells. Ultrastructural,[221] biophysical,[222] and biochemical[223] approaches have all been used, but despite a variety of initially positive results, no consistent and reproducible abnormalities to suggest a primary defect have been found in either myotonic or Duchenne muscular dystrophy. Since this field remains in a somewhat unresolved state, readers may wish to consult reviews giving different overall opinions.[224,225]

The Biochemical Basis of Myotonia

Since myotonia is one of the most distinctive features of myotonic dystrophy, it is not surprising that considerable effort has gone into the study of its physiological and biochemical basis. So far this work has proved more valuable in understanding the nonprogressive myotonic disorders, such as myotonia congenita and myotonic periodic paralysis. An excellent and detailed account of this work is given by Rudel,[226] but the main aspects are summarized below.

Electrophysiologically, myotonia is seen as a repetitive series of action potentials occurring following a mechanical or electrical stimulus, usually showing a rapid increase and slow decrease in amplitude and frequency. Experimentally this may be produced by an increased membrane resistance or by decreased resting potential across the membrane, which may have various causes. The best studied animal model for myotonia, the myotonic goat, probably homologous with human myotonia congenita, shows an increased membrane resistance, due to lowered chloride conductance[227]; a defect in the chloride ion channel or some related molecule appears likely and should be identifiable as these processes become more fully understood. However, the myotonia in myotonic dystrophy does not appear to result from this mechanism showing no constant change in chloride conductance, but rather a reduced membrane potential with increased sodium conductance.[228] No definite animal homologue exists for myotonic dystrophy.

A number of chemicals exist that can produce myotonia, notably hypocholesterolemic agents and a group of monocarboxylic acids. The former act by replacing membrane choles-

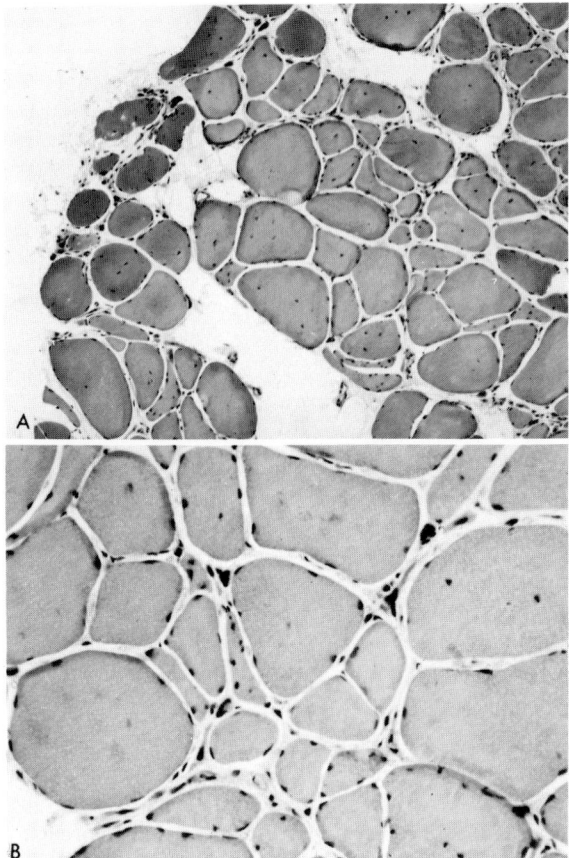

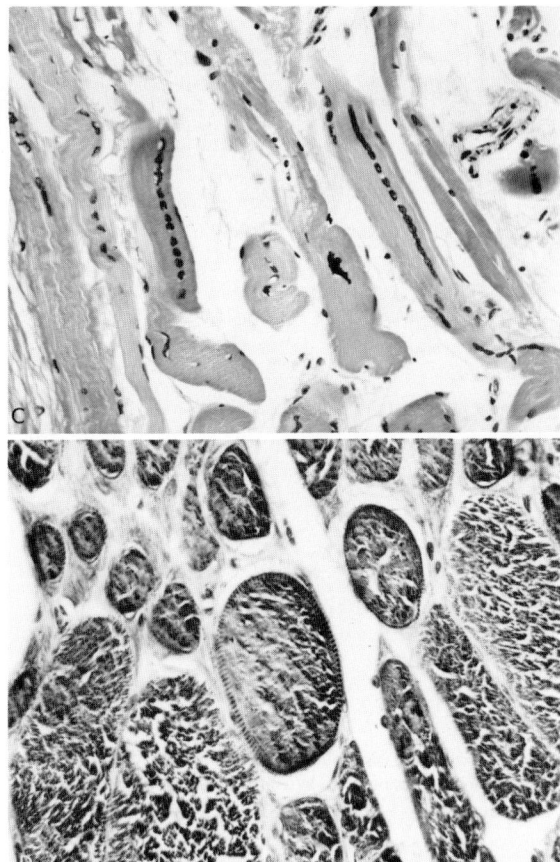

Fig. 118-18 Changes in muscle histology in adult myotonic dystrophy. *A.* Transverse section showing variation in fiber size and numerous internal nuclei. *B.* Higher power transverse section showing atrophic fibers with clumped nuclei. *C.* Longitudinal section showing long chains of internal nuclei. *D.* Transverse section showing ringed fibers. (*From Harper.*[180])

terol by its precursor desmosterol, while the latter act more directly. Again, the myotonia produced is more analogous to that seen in myotonia congenita and the myotonic goat than to that of myotonic dystrophy, though it should be noted that some hypocholesterolemic drugs also produce cataract.

Despite our current inability to relate myotonia to myotonic dystrophy in molecular terms, this field should become increasingly relevant as the various membrane components and other molecules involved in ion transport become identified and cloned. They will then become candidate genes that can immediately be tested for an appropriate localization on chromosome 19, which should determine their relevance to myotonic dystrophy.

FACIOSCAPULOHUMERAL MUSCULAR DYSTROPHY

This is one of the most benign forms of muscular dystrophy, as well as one of the most common. Recent thorough studies by Padberg[229] in Holland and Lunt[230] in Britain have clarified the range of severity, showing that about 20 percent of affected adults have minimal symptoms and only 10 percent become wheelchair bound. The main muscles to be involved are, as the name implies, the facial muscles, along with those of the neck, shoulder girdle, and upper arms. In the lower limbs the peroneal muscles may be as affected as the proximal groups. (See Fig. 118-19.)

Cardiac and other complications are not seen, while mental function is normal. A suggestion that a characteristic retinal vascular degeneration, Coates disease, might form an integral part of the disorder[231] has not been confirmed; certainly ocular problems were not frequent in the major studies of Padberg and of Lunt.

Inheritance is clearly autosomal dominant, though careful examination is required to exclude the disorder. Creatine kinase levels are moderately raised; an elevated level is useful in confirming the disorder in a young person at risk with equivocal muscle weakness. Muscle histology is not highly specific, but biopsy is useful to distinguish the rarer but somewhat similar neurogenic conditions which may present as upper girdle syndromes.

Gene mapping data are still at an early stage, though protein polymorphisms were studied by Padberg,[229] while a preliminary exclusion map based on a large panel of families has been drawn up by Lunt and colleagues.[232] Molecular studies on a large Utah kindred are also in progress (M. Leppert, personal communication), so progress should be rapid.

AUTOSOMAL RECESSIVE "LIMB GIRDLE" MUSCULAR DYSTROPHIES

Duchenne-Like Autosomal Recessive Childhood Dystrophy

Although some cases of apparent DMD in girls result from sex chromosome anomalies, a small number of cases is likely

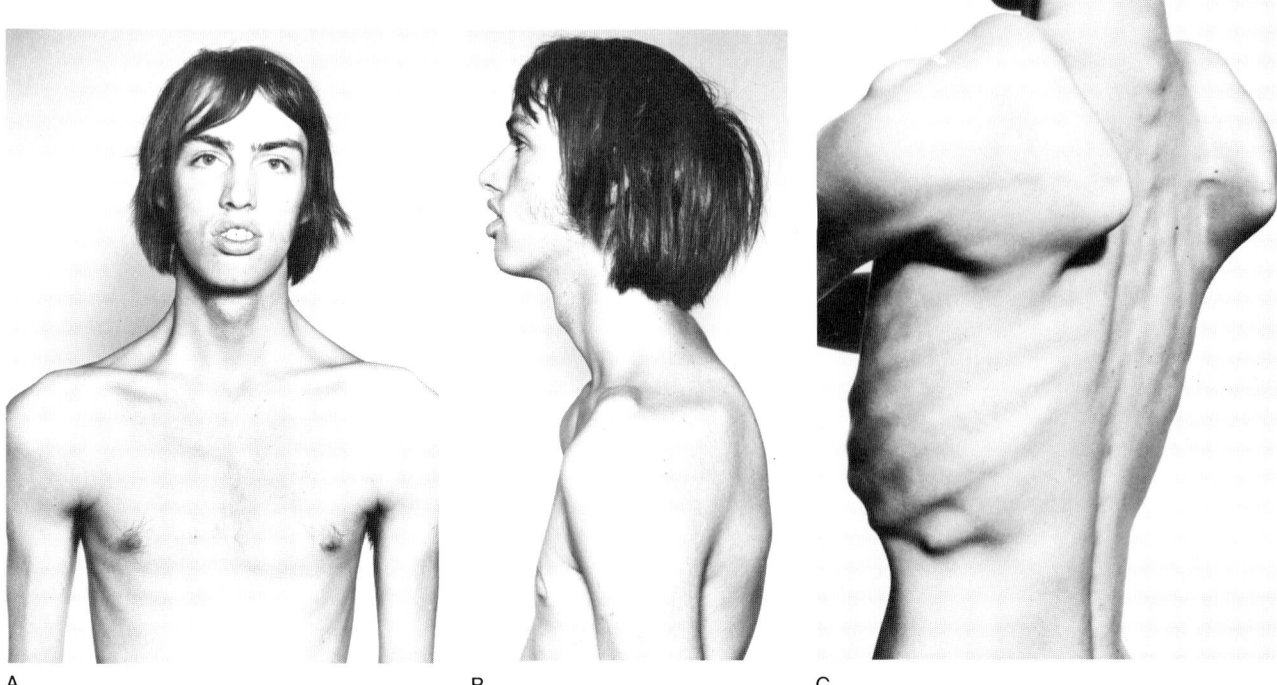

A.   B.   C.

Fig. 118-19 *A. and B. Facioscapulohumeral muscular dystrophy showing typical facial weakness. C. Wasting of shoulder girdle muscles in another affected male.*

to result from autosomal recessive inheritance.[233] While exceptionally rare in most of Europe and North America, this form appears to be more frequent in North Africa[234] and possibly in Switzerland.[235] Differences from true DMD are slight, but include lack of characteristic electrocardiographic changes and a somewhat milder course. Although too rare to affect genetic counseling significantly for DMD as a whole, the possibility should be borne in mind when there is parental consanguinity or when multiple recombinations are observed with X-chromosome DNA markers and the disorder is confined to a single sibship.

Adult Onset Autosomal Recessive Limb Girdle Dystrophy

This disorder, although recognized in all the major population surveys and classifications of the muscular dystrophies, is becoming more rarely diagnosed. Older studies probably included cases that would now be recognized as chronic spinal muscular atrophy, specific metabolic myopathies, and some nongenetic causes. Incidence values of between 1 and 3 per 100,000 have been recorded, but a careful recent study in Scotland[236] showed a most likely maximum incidence of 0.3 per 100,000 when the excess of male cases thought likely to represent Becker muscular dystrophy was removed.

Particular care must be taken not to confuse affected females with manifesting carriers for DMD, the genetic risk for offspring being profoundly different. Equally important (and just as difficult) is to distinguish the isolated male case from Becker muscular dystrophy. Distinguishing points include calf hypertrophy, electrocardiographic changes, and Duchenne-like biopsy changes in BMD. The occurrence of a markedly

raised CK level in the mother would also favor this diagnosis, but a good working rule is never to accept the diagnosis of "autosomal recessive limb girdle dystrophy" unless both genetic and neuromuscular studies have been thorough and to give genetic counseling as for X-linked inheritance if there is any doubt. DNA analysis for deletion in the p21 region of the X chromosome should be undertaken in all affected males, and with a high proportion of BMD cases now showing specific exon deletions this should be helpful in an increasing proportion of cases. Analysis of dystrophin from muscle biopsy also seems valuable in identifying which cases result from mutations at DMD locus.[125]

CONGENITAL AND METABOLIC MYOPATHIES

These two important groups of muscle disorders are not discussed in this chapter. Congenital myopathies are referred to above in relation to congenital myotonic dystrophy and the X-linked form of myotubular myopathy, and the main members of the group are summarized in Table 118-18. Clinical features vary, but hypotonia from birth, delayed motor development, and a tendency to gradual improvement during childhood are prominent features which contrast with those of the muscular dystrophies. Their classification is currently mainly on histologic grounds, in particular the electron microscopic and histochemical features, and it must be regarded as provisional. The inheritance of most forms is far from clear and no primary biochemical defect has yet been recognized in any member of the group.

The extensive group of metabolic myopathies[237] is summarized in Table 118-20. Several of these disorders are considered fully in other chapters and muscle involvement is not always the predominant feature. Exercise-related muscle cramps and myoglobinuria are characteristic features of several members. As to be expected from enzyme defects of interme-

Table 118-20 Metabolic Myopathies with a Known Enzyme Defect

Disorder	Inheritance	Principal features
Myophosphorylase deficiency (McArdle syndrome)	Autosomal recessive	Exercise-related cramps
Phosphofructokinase deficiency	Autosomal recessive	Cramps; myoglobinuria
Acid maltase deficiency	Autosomal recessive	Progressive, fatal cardiomyopathy and neurodegeneration (infantile type; Pompe disease); slowly progressive limb girdle dystrophy (adult type)
Glycogen debranching enzyme deficiency	Autosomal recessive	Mild myopathy; hepatomegaly, hypoglycaemia
Phosphoglycerate kinase deficiency	X-linked recessive	Hemolytic anemia and CNS involvement (infantile type) myopathy with myoglobinuria (later childhood)
Phosphoglyceromutase deficiency	Autosomal recessive	Cramps; myoglobinuria
Lactate dehydrogenase deficiency	Autosomal recessive	Weakness, myoglobinuria, lipid accumulation in muscle
Carnitine palmitoyl transerase deficiency	Autosomal recessive	Myoglobinuria, lipid accumulation

diary metabolism, most follow recessive inheritance, all except phosphoglycerate kinase deficiency being autosomally determined.

Management and Therapy

For none of the human muscular dystrophies do we have any curative treatment, nor is there currently any measure that significantly alters the natural history of the disorders. With the identification of the gene product achieved for Duchenne and Becker muscular dystrophy, and likely in the foreseeable future for myotonic dystrophy, this situation may change. The therapeutic implications of dystrophin are the subject of intensive study. Already treatment trials have been established to ensure that any drug or other measure claimed to have significant effect is rigorously tested. Meanwhile, there are numerous aspects of management which are of the utmost importance to patients and their families, even though they may appear inadequate by scientific standards. The following brief notes are based on the author's own experience of jointly managing a muscular dystrophy clinic that spans all age ranges and covers the different forms of dystrophy.

For Duchenne muscular dystrophy in early childhood, the most valuable measure is to help the parents to come to terms with a distressing diagnosis and to provide support for them as they cope with the inevitable stresses that this poses. Support is also required during the wider and essential family studies that may place other family members at risk, with resulting fear and guilt. Careful application of the preventive genetic measures already discussed may be of considerable help. For the affected boy, careful forward planning of educational facilities is vital to take into account the progressive physical disability to be expected but to avoid isolation from his healthy peers as far as is possible. Early recognition of learning difficulties and low IQ is important.

Contractures of Achilles tendons can be delayed by teaching stretching exercises and by using light molded night splints. Surgery is often helpful as the child begins to use a wheelchair. Scoliosis must be detected at the earliest opportunity; by the use of carefully fitted orthotic jackets and braces this can usually be prevented. Radical surgery to correct scoliosis, while often successful, should not be necessary except in a small minority of DMD patients.

The use of a wheelchair, particularly with electrical power, should be regarded as a step forward in enhancing mobility, not as a sign of defeat. Children achieve a remarkable dexterity and mobility in this way even when severely disabled; par-

adoxically it is often the later onset Becker patients who may refuse to recognize the extent of their disability and how a wheelchair can help. All patients require a careful assessment of how physical aids and adaptations in the home or at work may improve their mobility and independence.

Measures to prolong walking must be looked at critically in the light of whether they really enhance mobility. Swivel walkers for DMD patients and lightweight flexible callipers for adults may give some years of useful, independent walking but should not be persisted with unless they are truly improving function. Patients with foot drop from distal weakness, as may be seen in myotonic and facioscapulohumeral dystrophies, may benefit from toe springs or occasionally from tendon transplant surgery. Prevention of obesity by careful attention to diet from an early stage is a further measure in maintaining mobility.

The recognition of cardiac involvement is of major importance in Emery-Dreifuss dystrophy, where early implantation of a pacemaker may be lifesaving. Conduction problems are common also in myotonic dystrophy, and the recognition of potential cardiac complications is essential if surgical or anaesthetic measures are to be taken in any of the major muscular dystrophies.

Drug therapy is currently relevant only for the control of myotonia in myotonic dystrophy; even here it is often not well tolerated by patients, who may prefer to keep their muscle stiffness. Phenytoin, procainamide, and quinine are all effective drugs for the small number of patients with severe myotonia, as well as for those suffering from nonprogressive myotonic disorders, whose myotonia may be more disabling.

Specific drug therapy to alter the natural history of DMD has been attempted using several membrane stabilizing drugs whose actions include reduction of calcium entry into muscle. While these have a rational basis in view of the role of calcium in causing secondary muscle damage, no clear benefit has been shown. Emery gives a clear recount of the use of these and numerous other agents in treatment trials and describes clearly the pitfalls that must be taken into account in designing and interpreting such trials.

So far none of the molecular or other work described in the major section of this chapter has had direct therapeutic applications. However, there can now be no doubt that the characterization of the genes for the different muscular dystrophies and their corresponding proteins will allow planned therapeutic strategies that have been impossible until now. Whether such therapy operates at the gene level or will take the form of replacing or modifying deficient or defective proteins is too early to determine; by the time that the next edition of this text is published, we should have a clear indication of which approaches to therapy are likely to be fruitful.

ACKNOWLEDGEMENTS

The critical help of Drs. Nick Thomas, Andrew Norman, and Duncan Shaw in reviewing this chapter is gratefully acknowledged, as is the financial support of the Muscular Dystrophy Group of Great Britain, the Muscular Dystrophy Association of America, the Medical Research Council, and the Wolfson Trust.

REFERENCES

1. WALTON JN: On the inheritance of muscular dystrophy. *Ann Hum Genet* 20:1, 1955.
2. ENGEL AG, BANKER BQ: *Myology*. New York, McGraw-Hill, 1986.
3. WALTON JN: *Disorders of voluntary muscle*, 4th ed. Churchill Livingstone, 1988.
4. MERYON E: On granular and fatty degeneration of the voluntary muscles. *Med Chir Trans* 35:73, 1852.
5. DUCHENNE GBA: *De l'electrisation localisee et son application a la pathologie et a la therapeutique*, 2d ed. Paris, Bailliere et fils, 1861.
6. DUCHENNE GBA: Recherches sur la paralysie musculaire pseudohypertrophique ou paralysie myo-sclerosique. *Arch Gen Med* 11:5, 1868.
7. GOWERS WR: *Pseudo-hypertrophic Muscular Paralysis—A Clinical Lecture*. London, J and A Churchill, 1879.
8. EMERY AEH: *Duchenne Muscular Dystrophy*. New York, Oxford University Press, 1987.
9. DUBOWITZ V: Myopathic changes in a muscular dystrophy carrier. *J Neurol Neurosurg Psychiatry* 26:322.
10. GARDNER-MEDWIN D: The natural history of Duchenne muscular dystrophy, in Wise, GB, Blaw ME, Procopid PG (eds): *Topics in Child Neurology*. New York, London, SP Medical and Scientific Books, Spectrum Publications, vol 2, pp 17–29.
11. WORDEN DK, VIGNOS PJ: Intellectual function in childhood progressive muscular dystrophy. *Pediatrics* 29:968, 1962.
12. DUBOWITZ V: Intellectual impairment in muscular dystrophy. *Arch Dis Child* 40:296, 1965.
13. EBASHI S, TOYOKURA Y, MOMOI H, SUGITA H: High creatine phosphokinase activity of sera of progressive muscular dystrophy. *J Biochem, Tokyo* 46:103, 1959.
14. DREYFUS JC, SCHAPIRA G, DEMOS J: Étude de la creatine-kinase serique chez les myopathes et leurs familles. *Rev Fr Etud Clin Biol* 5:384, 1960.
15. BLUM D, BRAUMAN J: Serum enzymes in the neonatal period. *Biol Neonate* 26:53, 1975.
16. DUBOWITZ V: *Muscle Biopsy—A Practical Approach*, 2d ed. London, Bailliere Tindall, 1985.
17. ENGEL AG: Duchenne dystrophy, in Engel AG, Banker BQ (eds): *Myology*. McGraw-Hill, 1986, p 1185.
18. DAUBE JR: Electrodiagnosis of muscle disorders, in Engel AG, Banker BQ (eds): *Myology*. New York, McGraw-Hill, 1986, p 1081.
19. EMERY AEH: Abnormalities of the electrocardiogram in hereditary myopathies. *J Med Genet* 9:8, 1972.
20. HECKMATT JZ, LEEMAN S, DUBOWITZ V: Ultrasound imaging in the diagnosis of muscle disease. *J Pediatr* 101:656, 1982.
21. MOSER H, EMERY AEH: The manifesting carrier in Duchenne muscular dystrophy. *Clin Genet* 5:271, 1974.
22. ZELLWEGER H, IONASESCU V, SIMPSON J: Sporadic Duchenne muscular dystrophy in females; genetic counseling of women with pelvifemoral muscular dystrophy. *Helv Paediatr Acta* 35:343, 1980.
23. EMERY AEH, SPIKESMAN AM: The existence of a subclinical form of Duchenne muscular dystrophy? in *Muscle Diseases*. Walton JN, Canal N, Scarlato G (eds): Amsterdam, Excepta Medica, 1970, p 424.
24. EMERY AEH: Evidence against the existence of a subclinical form of X-linked Duchenne muscular dystrophy. *J Neurol Sci* 10:523, 1970.
25. SCHEUERBRANDT G, LUNDIN A, LOVGREN T, MORTIER W: Screening for Duchenne muscular dystrophy: An improved screening test for creatine kinase and its application in an infant screening program. *Muscle Nerve* 9:11, 1986.
26. HURSE PV, KAKULAS BA: Genetic counselling in neuromuscular disease in Western Australia. *Proc Austral Assoc Neurol* 11:145, 1974.
27. HARPER PS: Carrier detection in Duchenne muscular dystrophy: A critical

assessment, in Schotland DL (ed): *Disorders of the Motor Unit*. Chichester, NY, Wiley, 1982, p 821.
28. DAVIE AM, EMERY AEH: Estimation of proportion of new mutants among cases of Duchenne muscular dystrophy. *J Med Genet* 15:339, 1978.
29. HALDANE JBS: The rate of spontaneous mutation of a human gene. *J Genet* 31:317, 1935.
30. ROSES AD, ROSES MJ, METCALF BS, HULL KL, NICHOLSON GA, HARTWIG GB, ROE CR: Pedigree testing in Duchenne muscular dystrophy. *Ann Neurol* 2:270, 1977.
31. YASUDA N, KONDO K: No sex difference in mutation rates of Duchenne muscular dystrophy. *J Med Genet* 17:106, 1980.
32. DANIELI GA, PILOTTO G, ANGELINI C, BONFANTE A: Duchenne muscular dystrophy—Data from family studies. *Hum Genet* 54:63, 1980.
33. CASKEY CT, NUSSBAUM RL, COHAN LC, POLLACK L: Sporadic occurrence of Duchenne muscular dystrophy: Evidence for new mutation. *Clin Genet* 18:329, 1980.
34. MURPHY EA, MUTALIK GS: The application of Bayesian methods in genetic counselling. *Hum Hered* 19:126, 1969.
35. BUNDEY S: Calculation of genetic risks in Duchenne muscular dystrophy by geneticists in the United Kingdom. *J Med Genet* 15:249, 1978.
36. EMERY AEH, SKINNER R, HOLLWAY S: A study of possible heterogeneity in Duchenne muscular dystrophy. *Clin Genet* 15:444, 1979.
37. O'BRIEN TA, HARPER PS, DAVIES K, MURRAY JM, SARFARAZI M, WILLIAMSON R: Lack of heterogeneity in Duchenne muscular dystrophy. *J Med Genet* 20:249, 1983.
38. BLYTH H, CARTER CO, DUBOWITZ V, EMERY AEH, GAVIN J, JOHNSON HA, MCKUSICK VA, RACE RR, SANGER R, TIPPETT P: Duchenne's muscular dystrophy and the Xg blood groups: A search for linkage. *J Med Genet* 2:157, 1965.
39. EMERY AEH: Genetic linkage between the loci for colour blindness and Duchenne type muscular dystrophy. *J Med Genet* 3:92, 1966.
40. SKINNER R, SMITH C, EMERY AEH: Linkage between the loci for benign (Becker-type) X-borne muscular dystrophy and deutan colour blindness. *J Med Genet* 11:317, 1974.
41. VERELLEN C, DE MEYER R, FREUND M, LATERRE C, SCHOLBERG B, FREDERIC J: Progressive muscular dystrophy of the Duchenne type in a young girl associated with an aberration of chromosome X, in *Proc 5th Internat Congr Birth Defects*. Amsterdam, Excerpta Medica, 1977, p 42.
42. GREENSTEIN RM, REARDON MP, CHAN TS: An X/autosome translocation in a girl with Duchenne muscular dystrophy (DMD); evidence for DMD gene localization. *Pediatr Res* 11:457, 1977.
43. CANKI N, DUTRILLAUX B, TIVADAR I: Dystrophie musculaire de Duchenne chez une petite fille porteuse d'une translocation t(X;3) (p21;q13) de novo. *Ann Genet* 22:35, 1979.
44. LINDENBAUM RH, CLARKE G, PATEL C, MONCRIEFF M, HUGHES JT: Muscular dystrophy in an X;1 translocation female suggests that Duchenne locus is on X chromosome short arm. *J Med Genet* 16:389, 1979.
45. BOYD Y, BUCKLE VJ: Cytogenetic heterogeneity of translocation associated with Duchenne muscular dystrophy. *Clin Genet* 29:108, 1986.
46. BOYD Y, BUCKLE V, HOLT S, MUNRO E, HUNTER D, CRAIG I: Muscular dystrophy in girls with X; autosome translocations. *J Med Genet* 23:484, 1986.
47. VERELLEN-DUMOULIN CH, FREUND M, DEMEYER R, et al: Expression of an X-linked muscular dystrophy in a female due to translocation involving Xp21 and non-random inactivation of the normal X chromosome. *Hum Genet* 67:115, 1984.
48. RAY PN, BELFALL B, DUFF C, LOGAN C, KEAN V, THOMPSON MW, SYLVESTER JE, GORSKI JL, SCHMICKEL RD, WORTON RG: Cloning of the breakpoint of an X;21 translocation associated with Duchenne muscular dystrophy. *Nature* 318:671, 1985.
49. BOTSTEIN D, WHITE RL, SKOLNICK M, DAVIS RW: Construction of a genetic linkage map in man using restriction fragment length polymorphisms. *Am J Hum Genet* 32:314, 1980.
50. MANIATIS T, HARDISON EC, LACY E, LAUER J, O'CONNELL C, QUON D, SIM DK, EFSTRATIADIA: The isolation of structural genes from libraries of eucaryotic DNA. *Cell* 15:687, 1978.
51. YOUNG BD: Human chromosome analysis by flow cytometry, in KE Davies (ed): *Human Genetic Disease. A Practical Approach*. Oxford, IRL Press, 1986, p 101.
52. DAVIES KE, YOUNG BD, ELLES RG, HILL ME, WILLIAMSON R: Cloning of a representative genomic library of the human X-chromosome after sorting by flow cytometry. *Nature* 293:374, 1981.
53. HILL MEE, DAVIES KE, HARPER PS, WILLIAMSON R: The Mendelian inheritance of a human X chromosome-specific DNA sequence polymorphism and its use in linkage studies of genetic disease. *Hum Genet* 60:222, 1982.
54. MURRAY JM, DAVIES KE, HARPER PS, MEREDITH L, MUELLER CR, WILLIAMSON R: Linkage relationship of a cloned DNA sequence on the short arm of the X chromosome to Duchenne muscular dystrophy. *Nature* 300:69, 1982.

55. DAVIES KE, PEARSON PL, HARPER PS, MURRAY JM, O'BRIEN T, SARFARAZI M, WILLIAMSON R: Linkage analysis of two cloned DNA sequences flanking the Duchenne muscular dystrophy locus on the short arm of the human X-chromosome. *Nucl Acids Res* 11:2303, 1983.

56. KINGSTON HM, SARFARAZI M, THOMAS NST, HARPER PS: Localisation of the Becker muscular dystrophy gene on the short arm of the X chromosome by linkage to cloned DNA sequences. *Hum Genet* 67:6, 1984.

57. KUNKEL LM, TANTRAVAHI U, EISENHARD M, LATT SA: Regional localisation on the human X of DNA sequences cloned from flow sorted chromosomes. *Nucleic Acids Res* 10:1557, 1982.

58. HOFKER MH, WAPENAAR MC, GOOR N, BAKKER B, VAN OMMEN GJB, PEARSON PL: Isolation of probes detecting restriction fragment length polymorphisms from X chromosome specific libraries: Potential use for diagnosis of Duchenne muscular dystrophy. *Hum Genet* 70:148, 1985.

59. DAVIES KE, BRIAND P, IONASESCU V, et al: Gene for OTC: Characterization and linkage to Duchenne muscular dystrophy. *Nucleic Acids Res* 1:155, 1985.

60. DRAYNA D, WHITE R: The genetic linkage map of the human X chromosome. *Science* 230:753, 1985.

61. BROWN CS, THOMAS NST, SARFARAZI M, DAVIES KE, KUNKEL LM, PEARSON PL, KINGSTON HM, SHAW DJ, HARPER PS: Genetic linkage relationships of seven DNA probes with Duchenne and Becker muscular dystrophies. *Hum Genet* 71:62, 1985.

62. DE MARTINVILLE B, KUNKEL LM, BRUNS G, MORLE F, KOENIG M, MANDELL JL, HORWICH A, LATT SA, GUSELLA JF, HOUSMAN D, FRANCKE U: Localisation of DNA sequences in region Xp21 of the human X chromosome: Search for molecular markers close to the Duchenne muscular dystrophy locus. *Am J Hum Genet* 37:235, 1985.

63. FRANCKE U, OCHS HD, DE MARTINVILLE B, GIACALONE J, LINDGREN V, DISTECKE C, PAGON RA, HOFKER MH, VAN OMMEN GJB, PEARSON PL, WEDGEWOOD RJ: Minor Xp21 chromosome deletion in a male associated with expression of Duchenne Muscular dystrophy, Chronic granulomatous disease, Retinitis pigmentosa and McLeod syndrome. *Am J Hum Genet* 37:250, 1985.

64. GUGGENHEIM MA, MCCABE ERB, ROIG M, et al: Glycerol kinase deficiency with neuromuscular, skeletal and adrenal abnormalities. *Ann Neurol* 7:441, 1980.

65. FRANCKE U, HARPER JF, DARRAS BT, COWAN JM, MCCABE ERB, KOHLSCHUTTER A, SELTZER WK, SAITO F, GOTO J, HARPEY JP, WISE JE: Congenital adrenal hypoplasia, myopathy, and glycerol kinase deficiency: Molecular genetic evidence for deletions. *Am J Hum Genet* 40:212, 1987.

66. CLARKE A, ROBERTS SH, THOMAS NST, WHITFIELD A, WILLIAMS J, HARPER PS: Duchenne muscular dystrophy with adrenal insufficiency and glycerol kinase deficiency: High resolution cytogenetic analysis with molecular, biochemical and clinical studies. *J Med Genet* 23:501, 1986.

67. KUNKEL LM, MONACO AP, MIDDLESWORTH W, OCHS HD, LATT SA: Specific cloning of DNA fragments absent from the DNA of a male patient with an X chromosome deletion. *Proc Natl Acad Sci USA* 82:4778, 1985.

68. MONACO AP, BERTELSON CJ, MIDDLESWORTH W, COLLETTI CA, ALDRIDGE J, FISCHBECK KH, BARTLETT R, PERICAK-VANCE MA, ROSES AD, KUNKEL LM: Detection of deletions spanning the Duchenne muscular dystrophy locus using a tightly linked DNA segment. *Nature* 316:842, 1985.

69. WORTON RG, DUFF C, SYLVESTER JE, SCHMICKEL RD, WILLARD HF: Duchenne muscular dystrophy involving translocation of the DMD gene next to ribosomal RNA genes. *Science* 224:1447, 1984.

70. RAY PN, BELFALL B, DUFF C, LOGAN C, KEAN V, THOMPSON MW, SYLVESTER JE, GORSKI JL, SCHMICKEL RD, WORTON RG: Cloning of the breakpoint of an X;21 translocation associated with Duchenne muscular dystrophy. *Nature* 318:672, 1985.

71. THOMPSON MW, RAY PN, BELFALL B, DUFF C, LOGAN C, OSS I, WORTON RG: Linkage analysis of polymorphisms within the DNA fragment XJ cloned from the breakpoint of an X;21 translocation associated with X linked muscular dystrophy. *J Med Genet* 23:548, 1986.

72. WALKER A, HART K, COLE C, HODGSON S, JOHNSON L, DUBOWITZ V, BOBROW M: Linkage studies in Duchenne and Becker muscular dystrophies. *J Med Genet* 23:538, 1986.

73. FISCHBECK K, RITTER AW, TIRSCHWELL DL, et al: Recombination with PERT 87 (DXS 164) in families with X-linked muscular dystrophy. *Lancet* 2:104, 1986.

74. KUNKEL LM, HEJTMANCIK JF, CASKEY CT, et al: Analysis of deletions in DNA from patients with Becker and Duchenne muscular dystrophy. *Nature* 322:73, 1986.

75. MONACO AP, BERTELSON CJ, COLLETTI-FEENER C, KUNKEL LM: Localization and cloning of Xp21 deletion breakpoints involved in muscular dystrophy. *Hum Genet* 75:221, 1987.

76. MONACO AP, NEVE RL, COLLETTI-FEENER C, BERTELSON CJ, KURNIT DM, KUNKEL LM: Isolation of candidate cDNAs for portions of the Duchenne muscular dystrophy gene. *Nature* 323:646, 1986.

77. VAN OMMEN GJB, VERKERK JMH, HOFKER MH, MONACO AP, KUNKEL LM, RAY P, WORTON R, WIERINGA B, BAKKER E, PEARSON PL: A physical map of 4 million bp around the Duchenne muscular dystrophy gene on the human X-chromosome. *Cell* 47:499, 1986.

78. KENWRICK S, PATTERSON M, SPEER A, FISCHBECK K, DAVIES K: Molecular analysis of the Duchenne muscular dystrophy region using pulsed field gel electrophoresis. *Cell* 48:351, 1987.

79. BERTELSON CJ, BARTLEY JA, MONACO AP, COLLETTI-FEENER C, FISCHBECK K, KUNKEL LM: Localisation of Xp21 meiotic exchange points in Duchenne muscular dystrophy families. *J Med Genet* 23:531, 1986.

80. MONACO AP, KUNKEL LM: A giant locus for the Duchenne and Becker muscular dystrophy gene. *Trends Genet* 3:33, 1987.

81. SMITH TJ, WILSON L, KENWRICK SJ, FORREST SM, SPEER A, COUTELLE C, DAVIES KE: Isolation of a conserved sequence deleted in Duchenne muscular dystrophy patients. *Nucleic Aids Res* 15:2167, 1987.

82. BURGHES AHM, LOGAN C, XIUYAN HU, BELFALL B, WORTON R, RAY PN: A cDNA clone from the Duchenne/Becker muscular dystrophy gene. *Nature* 328:434, 1987.

83. FORREST SM, CROSS GS, SPEER A, GARDNER-MEDWIN D, BURN J, DAVIES KE: Preferential deletion of exons in Duchenne and Becker muscular dystrophies. *Nature* 329:630, 1987.

84. FORREST SM, CROSS GS, THOMAS NST, HARPER PS, SMITH TJ, READ AP, MOUNTFORD RC, GEIRSSON RT, DAVIES KE: Effective strategy for prenatal prediction of Duchenne and Becker muscular dystrophy. *Lancet* ii:1294, 1987.

85. KOENIG M, HOFFMAN EP, BERTELSON CJ, MONACO AP, FEENER C, KUNKEL LM: Complete cloning of the Duchenne muscular dystrophy (DMD) cDNA and preliminary genomic organization of the DMD gene in normal and affected individuals. *Cell* 50:509, 1987.

86. WAPENAAR MC, KIEVITS T, HART KA, ABBS S, BLONDEN LAJ, DEN DUNNEN JT, GROOTSCHOLTEN PM, BAKKER E, VERELLEN-DUMOULIN CH, BOBROW M, VAN OMMEN GJB, PEARSON PJ: A deletion hot spot in the Duchenne muscular dystrophy gene. *Genomics* 2:101, 1988.

87. XIUYAN HU, BURGHES AHM, RAY PN, THOMPSON MW, MURPHY EG, WORTON RG: Partial gene duplication in Duchenne and Becker muscular dystrophies. *J Med Genet* 25:369, 1988.

88. BAKKER E, VAN BROECKHOVEN C, BONTEN EJ, VAN DE VOOREN MJ, VEENEMA H, VAN HUL W, VAN OMMEN GJB, VANDENBERGHE A, PEARSON PL: Germline mosaicism and Duchenne muscular dystrophy mutations. *Nature* 329:554, 1987.

89. BURN J, POVEY S, BOYD Y, MUNRO EA, WEST L, HARPER K, THOMAS D: Duchenne muscular dystrophy in one of monozygotic twin girls. *J Med Genet* 23:494, 1986.

90. LYON MF: X-chromosome inactivation and the location and expression of X-linked genes. *Am J Hum Genet* 42:8, 1988.

91. MONACO AP, BERTELSON CCJ, LEICHTI-GALLATI S, MOSER H, KUNKEL LM: An explanation for the phenotypic differences between patients bearing partial deletions of the Duchenne muscular dystrophy locus. *Genomics* 2:90, 1988.

92. KATES JRW, GILLARD EF, COOKE A, COLGAN JM, EVANS TJ, FERGUSON-SMITH MA: A deletion of Xp21 maps congenital adrenal hypoplasia distal to glycerol kinase deficiency. *Cytogenet Cell Genet* 46:723, 1987.

93. BERTELSON CJ, POGO AO, CHAUDHURI A, MARSH WL, REDMAN CM, BANERJEE DD, SYMMANS WA, SIMON T, FREY D, KUNKEL LM: Localization of the Mcleod locus (XK) within XP21 by deletion analysis. *Am J Hum Genet* 42:703, 1988.

94. ROYER-POKORA B, KUNKEL LM, MONACO AP, GOFF SC, NEWBURGER PE, BAEHNER RL, COLE FS, CURRNUTTE JT, ORKIN SH: Cloning the gene for an inherited human disorder (chronic granulomatous disease) on the basis of its chromosomal localisation. *Nature* 332:32, 1986.

95. HARPER PS, THOMAS NST: A molecular approach to genetic counseling in the X-linked muscular dystrophies. *Am J Med Genet* 25:687, 1986.

96. RODECK CH, CAMPBELL S: Sampling pure fetal blood by fetoscopy in the second trimester of pregnancy. *Br Med J* 2:728, 1978.

97. GOLBUS MS, STEPHENS JD, MAHONEY MJ, HOBBINS JC, HASELTINE FP, CASKEY CT, BANKER BQ: Failure of fetal creatine phosphokinase as a diagnostic indicator of Duchenne muscular dystrophy. *N Engl J Med* 300:860, 1979.

98. BRAMBATI B, SIMONI G, FALRO S (eds): *Chorionic Villus Sampling.* New York, Dekker, 1986.

99. GOSDEN JR, MITCHELL AR, GOSDEN CM, RODECK CH, MORSMAN JM: Direct vision chorion biopsy and chromosome-specific DNA probes for determination of fetal sex in first-trimester prenatal diagnosis. *Lancet* 2:1416, 1982.

100. SIMONI G, BRAMBATI B, DANESINO C, ROSELLA F, TERZOLI GL, FRACCARO M: *Hum Genet* 63:349, 1983.

101. ELLES RG, WILLIAMSON R, NIAZI M, COLEMAN DV, HORWELL D: Absence

of maternal contamination of chorionic villi for fetal-gene analysis. *N Engl J Med* 308:1433, 1983.

102. HARPER PS, O'BRIEN T, MURRAY JM, DAVIES KM, PEARSON P, WILLIAMSON R: The use of linked DNA polymorhisms for genotype prediction in families with Duchenne muscular dystrophy. *J Med Genet* 20:252, 1983.

103. WILLIAMS H, SARFARAZI M, BROWN C, THOMAS N, HARPER PS: The use of flanking markers in prediction for Duchenne muscular dystrophy. *Arch Dis Child* 61:218, 1986.

104. BAKKER E, HOFKER MH, GOOR N, MANDEL JL, WROGEMANN K, DAVIES KE, KUNKEL LM, WILLARD HJ, FENTON WA, SANDKUYL L, MAJOOR-KRAKAUER D, VAN ESSEN AJ, JAHODA MGJ, SACHS ES, van OMMEN GJB, PEARSON PL: Prenatal diagnosis and carrier detection of Duchenne muscular dystrophy with closely linked RFLPs. *Lancet* i:655, 1985.

105. OLD JM, DAVIES KE: Prenatal diagnosis of Duchenne muscular dystrophy by DNA analysis. *J Med Genet* 23:556, 1986.

106. LINDOF M, KAARIAINEN H, DAVIES KE, De la CHAPELLE A: Carrier detection and prenatal diagnosis in X linked muscular dystrophy using restriction fragment length polymorphisms. *J Med Genet* 23:560, 1986.

107. CLARKE A, ROBERTS SH, THOMAS NST, WHITFIELD A, WILLIAMS J, HARPER PS: Duchenne muscular dystrophy with adrenal insufficiency and glycerol kinase deficiency: High resolution cytogenetic analysis with molecular, biochemical and clinical studies. *J Med Genet* 23:501, 1986.

108. COLE CG, COYNE A, HART KA, SHERIDAN R, WALKER A, JOHNSON L, HODGSON S, BOBROW M: Prenatal testing for Duchenne and Becker muscular dystrophy. *Lancet* i:262, 1988.

109. DARRAS BT, HARPER JF, FRANCKE U: Prenatal diagnosis and detection of carriers with DNA probes in Duchenne's muscular dystrophy. *New Engl J Med* 316:985, 1987.

110. SIBERT JR, HARPER PS, THOMPSON RJ, NEWCOMBE RG: Carrier detection in Duchenne muscular dystrophy. *Arch Dis Child* 54:534, 1979.

111. HODGSON S, WALKER A, COLE C, HART K, JOHNSON L, HECKMATT J, DUBOWITZ V, BOBROW M: The application of linkage analysis to genetic counselling in families with Duchenne of Becker muscular dystrophy. *J Med Genet* 24:152, 1987.

112. O'BRIEN T, SIBERT JR, HARPER PS: Implications of diagnostic delay in Duchenne muscular dystrophy. *Br Med J* 287:1106, 1983.

113. ZELLWEGER H, ANTONIK A: Newborn screening for Duchenne muscular dystrophy. *Pediatrics* 55:30, 1975.

114. SCHEUERBRANDT G, MORTIER W: Voluntary newborn screening for Duchenne muscular dystrophy: A nationwide pilot program in West Germany, in Serratrice G, Cros D, Desnuelle C, Gastaut J-L, Pellissier J-F, Pouget J, Schiano A (eds): *Neuromuscular Diseases.* New York, Raven, 1984, p 33.

115. DELLAMONICA C, COLLOMBEL C, COTTS J, ADDIS P: Screening for neonatal Duchenne muscular by bioluminescence measurement of creatine kinase in a blood sample spotted on paper. *Clin Chem* 29:161, 1983.

116. SKINNER R, EMERY AEH, SCHEUERBRANDT G, SYME J: Feasibility of neonatal screening for Duchenne muscular dystrophy. *J Med Genet* 19:1, 1982.

117. GARDNER-MEDWIN D: Controversies about Duchenne muscular dystrophy. 1. Neonatal screening. *Dev Med Child Neurol* 21:390, 1979.

118. MCCABE ERB, HUANG S-Z, SELTZER WK, LAW ML: DNA microextraction from dried blood spots on filter paper blotters: Potential applications to newborn screening. *Hum Gen* 75:213, 1987.

119. HOROWITS R, KEMPNER ES, BISHER ME, PODOLSKY RJ: A physiological role for titin and nebulin in skeletal muscle. *Nature* 323:160, 1986.

120. WOOD DS, ZEVIANI M, PRELLE A, BONILLA E, SALVIATI G, MIRANDA AF, DiMAURO S, ROWLAND LP: Is nebulin the defective gene product in Duchenne muscular dystrophy? *N Engl J Med* 316:107, 1987.

121. NAVE R, OSBORN M: Nebulin and titin expression in Duchenne muscular dystrophy appears normal. *Febs Lett*, 224/1:49, 1987.

122. HOFFMAN EP, MONACO AP, FEENER CC, KUNKEL LM: Conservation of the Duchenne muscular dystrophy gene in mice and humans. *Science* 239:347, 1987.

123. HOFFMAN EP, BROWN RH, KUNKEL LM: Dystrophin: The protein product of the Duchenne muscular dystrophy locus. *Cell* 51:919, 1987.

124. HOFFMAN EP, KNUDSON CM, CAMPBELL KP, KUNKEL LM: Subcellular fractionation of dystrophin to the triads of skeletal muscle. *Nature* 330:754, 1987.

125. HOFFMAN EP, FISCHBECK HK, BROWN MD, JOHNSON M, MEDORI R, LOIKE JD, HARRIS JB, WATERSON R, BROOKE M, SPECHT L, KUPSKY W, CHAMBERLAIN J, CASKEY CT, SHAPIRO R, KUNKEL LM: Characterization of dystrophin in muscle-biopsy specimens from patients with Duchenne's or Becker's Muscular dystrophy. *New Engl J Med* 318:1363, 1988.

126. HAMMONDS RG: Protein sequence of DMD gene is related to actin-binding domain of α-actinin. *Cell* 51:1, 1987.

127. SAMAHA FJ: Actomyosin alterations in Duchenne muscular dystrophy. *Arch Neurol* 28:385, 1973.

128. EDWARDS RHT: Energy metabolism in normal and dystrophic human muscle, in Rowland LP (ed): *Pathogenesis of Human Muscular Dystrophies.* Amsterdam, Oxford, Excerpta Medica, 1977, pp 415–428.

129. EDWARDS YH, PARKAR M, POVEY S, WEST LF, PARRINGTON JM, SOLOMON E: Human myosin heavy chain genes assigned to chromosome 17 using a human cDNA clone as probe. *Ann Hum Genet* 49:101, 1985.

130. PENNINGTON RJT: Clinical biochemistry of muscular dystrophy. *Br Med Bull* 36:123, 1980.

131. EMERY AEH: Muscle lactate dehydrogenase isoenzymes in hereditary myopathies. *J Neurol Sci* 7:137, 1968.

132. ELLIS DA: Changes in muscle enzymes in Duchenne dystrophy and their possible relations to functional disturbance, in Lunt GG, Marchbanks RM (eds): *The Biochemistry of Myasthenia Gravis and Muscular Dystrophy.* London, Academic, 1978, pp 245–265.

133. MCCOMAS AJ, SICA REP, CURRIE S: Muscular dystrophy: Evidence for a neural factor. *Nature* 226:1263, 1970.

134. BRADLEY WG, JENKISON M, MONTGOMERY A: The significance of neural abnormalities in muscular dystrophy, in Bradley WG, Gardner-Medwin D, Walton JN (eds): *Recent Advances in Myology.* Amsterdam, Excerpta Medica, 1975, pp. 116–124.

135. ENGEL WK: The vascular hypothesis, in Bradley WG, Gardner-Medwin D, Walton JN (eds): *Recent Advances in Myology.* Amsterdam, Excerpta Medica, 1975, pp 166–173.

136. KOEHLER J: Blood vessel structure in Duchenne muscular dystrophy. I. Light and electron microscopic observations in resting muscle. *Neurology* 27:861, 1977.

137. SCHOTLAND DL, BONILLA E, WAKAYAMA Y: Freeze fracture studies of muscle plasma membrane in human muscular dystrophy. *Acta Neuropathol (Berl)* 54:189, 1981.

138. LLOYD SJ, BROWN JN: Erythrocyte membrane studies. *Neurology* 31:1371, 1981.

139. ROSES AD, APPEL SH: Erythrocyte spectrin peak. II. Phosphorylation in Duchenne muscular dystrophy. *J Neurol Sci* 29:185, 1976.

140. PICKARD NA, GRUEMER HD, VERRILL HL, ISSACS ER, ROBINOW M, NANCE WE, MYERS EC, GOLDSMITH B: Systemic membrane defect in the proximal muscular dystrophies. *N Engl J Med* 229:841, 1978.

141. ROWLAND LP: Biochemistry of muscle membranes in Duchenne muscular dystrophy. *Muscle Nerve* 3:3, 1980.

142. MICHELSON AM, RUSSELL ES, HARMAN PJ: Dystrophia muscularis: A hereditary primary myopathy in the house mouse. *Proc Natl Acad Sci USA* 41:1079, 1955.

143. BULFIELD G, SILLER WG, WIGHT PAL, MOORE KJ: X chromosome-linked muscular dystrophy (mdx) in the mouse. *Proc Natl Acad Sci USA* 81:1189, 1984.

144. AVNER PD, ARNAUD L, AMAR A, HANAUER, CAMBROU J: Detailed ordering of markers localising to the Xq26-Xqter region of the human X chromosome by the use of an interspecific Mus spretus mouse cross. *Proc Natl Acad Sci* 84:1629, 1987.

145. BROCKDORFF N, CROSS GS, CANANNA JS, FISHER EM, LYON MF, DAVIES KE, BROWN SDM: The mapping of a cDNA from the human X-linked Duchenne muscular dystrophy gene to the mouse X chromosome. *Nature* 328, 166, 1987.

146. BECKER PE, KIENER F: Eine neue X-chromosomale Muskeldystrophie. *Arch Psychiatr Neurol* 193:427, 1955.

147. BECKER PE: Two new families of benign sex-linked recessive muscular dystrophy. *Rev Can Biol* 21:551, 1962.

148. BLYTH H, PUGH RJ: Muscular dystrophy in childhood: The genetic aspect. *Ann Hum Genet* 23:127, 1959.

149. ZELLWEGER H, HANSON JW: Slowly progressive X-linked recessive muscular dystrophy (Type IIIb). *Arch Intern Med* 120:525, 1967.

150. EMERY AEH, SKINNER R: Clinical studies in benign (Becker type) X-linked muscular dystrophy. *Clin Genet* 10:189, 1976.

151. KINGSTON HM: Clinical and genetic studies of Becker muscular dystrophy. M.D. Thesis. University of Manchester, 1983.

152. HAUSMANOWA-PETRUSEWICZ I, BORKOWSKA J: Intrafamilial variability of X-linked progressive muscular dystrophy. Mild and acute form of X-linked muscular dystrophy in the same family. *J Neurol* 218:43, 1978.

153. SKINNER R, EMERY AEH, ANDERSON AJB, FOXALL C: The detection on carriers of benign (Becker type) X-linked muscular dystrophy. *J Med Genet* 19:1, 1975.

154. KINGSTON HM, SARFARAZI M, NEWCOMBE RG, WILLIS N, HARPER PS: Carrier detection in Becker muscular dystrophy using creatine kinase estimation and DNA analysis. *Clin Genet* 27:383, 1985.

155. SKINNER R, SMITH C, EMERY AEH: Linkage between the loci for benign (Becker-type) X-borne muscular dystrophy and deutan colour blindess. *J Med Genet* 11:317, 1974.

156. ZATZ M, ITSKAN SB, SANGER R, FROTA-PESSOA O, SALDANHA PH: New linkage data for the X-linked types of muscular dystrophy and G6PD

variants, color blindness and Xg blood groups. *J Med Genet* 11:321, 1974.

157. THOMAS PK, CALNE DB, ELLIOT CF: X linked scapuloperoneal syndrome. *J Neurol Neurosurg Psychiatr* 35:208, 1972.

158. KINGSTON HM, THOMAS NST, PEARSON PL, SARFARAZI M, HARPER PS: Genetic linkage between Becker muscular dystrophy and a polymorphic DNA sequence on the short arm of the X chromosome. *J Med Genet* 20:255, 1983.

159. KINGSTON HM, SARFARAZI M, THOMAS NST, HARPER PS: Localisation of the Becker muscular dystrophy gene on the short arm of the X chromosome by linkage to cloned DNA sequences. *Hum Genet* 67:6, 1984.

160. FADDA S, MOCHI M, RONCUZZI L, et al.: Definitive localisation of Becker muscular dystrophy in Xp by linkage to a cluster of DNA polymorphisms (DXS43 and DXS9). *Hum Gen* 71:33, 1985.

161. DREIFUSS FH, HOGAN GR: Survival in X-chromosomal muscular dystrophy. *Neurology (Minneap)* 11:734, 1961.

162. EMERY AEH, DREIFUSS FE: Unusual type of benign X-linked muscular dystrophy. *J Neurol Neurosurg Psychiatry* 29:338, 1966.

163. ROWLAND LP, FETELL M, OLARTE M, HAYS A, SINGH N, WANAT FE: Emery-Dreifuss muscular dystrophy. *Ann Neurol* 5:111, 1979.

164. HOPKINS LC, JACKSON JA, ELSAS LJ: Emery-Dreifuss humeroperoneal muscular dystrophy: An X-linked myopathy with unusual contractures and bradycardia. *Ann Neurol* 10:230, 1981.

165. ROTTHAUWE HW, MORTIER W, BEYER H: Neuer Typ einer recessiv X-chromosomal vererbten Muskeldystrophie: Scapulo-humero-distale Muskeldystrophie mit fruhzeitigen Kontrakturen und Herzrhythmusstorungen. *Hamangenetik* 16:181, 1972.

166. FENICHEL GM, SUL YC, KILROY AW, BLOUIN R: An autosomal dominant dystrophy with hymeropelvic distribution and cardiomyopathy. *Neurology* 32:1399, 1982.

167. BOSWINKEL E, WALKER A, HODGSON S, et al: Linkage analysis using eight DNA polymorphisms along the length of the X chromosome locates the gene for Emery-Dreifuss muscular dystrophy to distal Xq. *Cytogenet Cell Genet* 40:586, 1985.

168. THOMAS NST, WILLIAMS H, ELSAS LJ, HOPKINS LC, SARFARAZI M, HARPER PS: Localisation of the gene for Emery-Dreifuss muscular dystrophy to the distal long arm of the X chromosome. *J Med Genet* 23:596, 1986.

169. YATES JRW, AFFARA NA, JAMIESON DM, FERGUSON-SMITH MA, HAUSMANOWA-PETRUSEWICZ I, ZAREMBA J, BORKOWSKA J, JOHNSON AW, KELLY K: Emery-Dreifuss muscular dystrophy: Localisation to Xq27.3→qter confirmed by linkage to the factor VIII gene. *J Med Genet* 23:587, 1986.

170. MERLINI L, GRANATA C, DOMINICI P, BONFIGLIOLI S: Emery-Dreifuss muscular dystrophy: Report of five cases in a family and review of the literature. *Muscle Nerve* 9:481, 1986.

171. NATHANS J, THOMAS D, HOGNESS DS: Molecular genetics of human color vision: The genes encoding blue, green, and red pigments. *Science* 232:193, 1986.

172. MOTULSKY AG: Normal and abnormal color-vision genes. *Am J Hum Genet* 42:405, 1988.

173. SHAW DJ: A new strategy for mapping the human genome. *J Med Genet* 23:421, 1986.

174. MABRY CC, ROECKEL IE, MUNICH RL, ROBERTSON D: X-linked pseudohypertrophic muscular dystrophy with a late onset and slow progression. *N Engl J Med* 273:1062, 1965.

175. BARTH PG, van WIJNGAARDEN GK, BETHLEM J: X-linked myotubular myopathy with fatal neonatal asphyxia. *Neurology* 25:531, 1975.

176. THOMAS NST, SARFARAZI M, ROBERTS K, WILLIAMS H, COLE G, LIECHTI-GALLATI S, HARPER PS: X-linked myotubular myopathy (MTMI): Evidence for linkage to Xq28 markers. *Cytogenet and Cell Genet* 46:704, 1987.

177. KALIMO H, SAVONTAUS M-L, LANG H, PALJARVI L, SONNINEN V, DEAN PB, KATEVUO K, SALMINEN A: X-linked myopathy with excessive autophagy (XMEA): A new hereditary muscle disease. *Ann Neurol* (in press).

178. STEINERT H: Uber das klinische und anatomische Bild des Muskelschwundes der Myotoniker. *Dtsch Z Nervenhlk* 37:38, 1909.

179. CAUGHEY JE, MYRIANTHOPOULOS NC: *Dystrophia Myotonica and Related Disorders.* Springfield, Ill., Charles C Thomas, 1963.

180. HARPER PS: *Myotonic Dystrophy.* Philadelphia, Saunders, 1979 (2d ed, 1989).

181. HARPER PS: Myotonic disorders, in Engel AG, Banker BQ (eds): *Myology.* New York, McGraw-Hill, 1986, p 1267.

182. HARPER PS: The Myotonic disorders, in Emery AEA, Rimoin DL (eds): *Principles and Practice of Medical Genetics,* 2d ed. Edinburgh, Churchill Livingstone, 1989.

183. BUNDEY S, CARTER CO, SOTHILL JF: Early recognition of heterozygotes for the gene of dystrophia myotonica. *J Neurol Neurosurg Psychiatry* 33:279, 1970.

184. HARPER PS: Presymptomatic detection and genetic counselling in myotonic dystrophy. *Clin Genet* 4:134, 1973.

185. VANIER TM: Dystrophia myotonia in childhood. *Br Med J* 2:1284, 1960.

186. HARPER PS: Congenital myotonic dystrophy in Britain. *Arch Dis Child* 50:505, 1975.

187. HARPER PS, DYKEN PR: Early onset dystrophia myotonica—Evidence supporting a maternal environmental factor. *Lancet* 2:53, 1972.

188. HARPER PS: Congenital myotonic dystrophy in Britain. II. Genetic basis. *Arch Dis Child* 50:514, 1975.

189. VEILLETTE S, PERRON M, DESBIENS F: *La dystrophie myotonique: Etude epidemiologique et socio-geographique au Saguenay-Lac-Saint-Jean,* Quebec, 1986. Personal communication.

190. BUNDEY S, CARTER CO: Genetic heterogeneity for dystrophia myotonica. *J Med Genet* 9:311, 1972.

191. PRYSE-PHILLIPS W, JOHNSON GJ, LASSEN B: A "partial syndrome" of myotonic dystrophy. *Can J Neurol Sci* 6:388, 1979.

192. PENROSE LS: The problem of anticipation in pedigrees of dystrophia myotonica. *Ann Eugen (London)* 14:125, 1948.

193. REIK W, COLLICK A, NORRIS ML, BARTON SC, SURANI MA: Genomic imprinting determines methylation of parental alleles in transgenic mice. *Nature* 328:248, 1987.

194. MOHR J: *A Study of Linkage in Man.* Copenhagen, Munskgaard, 1954.

195. RENWICK JH, BUNDEY SE, FERGUSON-SMITH MA, IZATT MM: Confirmation of the linkage of the loci for myotonic dystrophy and ABH secretion. *J Med Genet* 8:407, 1971.

196. HARPER PS, RIVAS ML, BIAS WBM, HUTCHINSON JR, DYKEN PR, MCKUSICK VA: Genetic linkage confirmed between the loci for myotonic dystrophy, ABH secretion and Lutheran Blood Group. *Am J Hum Genet* 24:310, 1972.

197. WHITEHEAD AS, SOLOMON E, CHAMBERS S, BODMER WF, POVEY S, FEY G: Assignment of the structural gene for the third component of human complement to chromosome 19. *Proc Natl Acad Sci USA* 79:5021, 1982.

198. BROOK JD, SHAW DJ, MEREDITH L, BRUNS GAP, HARPER PS: Localisation of genetic markers and orientation of the linkage group on chromosome 19. *Hum Genet* 68:282, 1984.

199. SHAW DJ, MEREDITH AL, SARFARAZI M, HARLEY HG, HUSON SM, BROOK JD, BUFTON L, LITT L, MOHANDAS T, HARPER PS: Regional localisations and linkage relationships of seven RFLPs and myotonic dystrophy on chromosome 19. *Hum Genet* 74:262, 1986.

200. NAYLOR S, LALOUEL JM, SHAW DJ: Report of the committee on the genetic constitution of chromosomes 17, 18 and 19. *Human Gene Mapping* 8. Basel, Karger, 1985, p 242.

201. SHAW DJ, EIBERG H: Report of the committee on the genetic constitution of chromosomes 17, 18 and 19. *Human Gene Mapping* 9. Basel, Karger, 1987, p. 242.

202. BARTLETT RJ, PERICAK-VANCE MA, YAMAOKA L, GILBERT J, HERBSTREITH M, HUNG W-Y, LEE JE, MOHANDAS T, BRUNS G, LABERGE C, THIABULT M-C, ROSS D, ROSES AD: A new probe for the diagnosis of myotonic muscular dystrophy. *Science* 235:1641, 1987.

203. BROOK JD, SHAW DJ, THOMAS NST, MEREDITH AL, COWELL J, HARPER PS: Mapping genetic markers on human chromosome 19 using subchromosomal fragments in somatic cell hybrids. *Cytogenet Cell Genet* 41:30, 1986.

204. SHERMAN SL, BALL SP, ROBSON EB: A genetic map of chromosome 19 based on family linkage data. *Ann Hum Genet* 49:181, 1985.

205. SHAW DJ, MEREDITH AL, SARFARAZI M, HUSON SM, BROOK JD, MYKLEBOST O, HARPER PS: The apolipoprotein CII gene: Sub-chromosomal localisation and linkage to the myotonic dystrophy locus. *Hum Genet* 70:271, 1985.

206. MYKLEBOST O, ROGNE S: A physical map of the apolipoprotein gene cluster on human chromosome 19. *Hum Genet* 78:244, 1988.

207. MEREDITH AL, HUSON SM, LUNT PW, SARFARAZI M, HARLEY HG, BROOK JD, SHAW DJ, HARPER PS: Application of a closely linked polymorphism of restriction fragment length to counselling and prenatal testing in families with myotonic dystrophy. *BMJ* 293:1353, 1986.

208. YANG-FENG TL, FRANCKE U, ULLRICH A: Gene for human insulin receptor: Localisation to site on chromosome 19 involved in pre-B-cell leukemia. *Science* 228:728, 1985.

209. SHAW DJ, MEREDITH AL, BROOK JD, SARFARAZI M, HARLEY HG, HUSON SM, BELL BI, HARPER PS: Linkage relationships of the insulin receptor gene with the complement component 3, LDL receptor, apolipoprotein C2 and myotonic dystrophy loci on chromosome 19. *Hum Genet* 74:267, 1986.

210. NIGRO JM, SCHWEINFEST CW, RAJKOVIC A, PAVLOVIC J, JAMAL S, DOTTIN RP, HART JT, KAMARCK ME, RAE PMM, CARTY MD, MARTIN-DeLEON P: cDNA cloning and mapping of the human creatine kinase M gene to 19q13. *Am J Hum Genet* 40:115, 1987.

211. HULL KR, ROSES AD: Stoichiometry of sodium and potassium transport of

erythrocytes from patients with muscular dystrophy. *J Physiol* 254:169, 1976.

212. YANG-FENG TL, SCHNEIDER JW, UNDGREN V, SHULL MM, BENZ EJ, LINGREL JB, FRANCKE U: Localisation of Human Na⁺, K⁺-ATPase α- and β-subunit genes. *Genomics* 2:128, 1988.

213. HARLEY HG, BROOK JD, JACKSON C, GLASER T, WALSH KV, SARFARAZI M, KENT R, LAGER M, KOCH M, HARPER PS: Localisation of human Na⁺, K⁺-ATPase subunit gene to chromosome 19q12-q13.2 and linkage to the myotonic dystrophy locus. *Genomics* (in press).

214. CASANOVA G, JERUSALEM F: Myopathology of myotonic dystrophy: A morphometric study. *Acta Neuropathal* 45:231, 1979.

215. KARPATI G, CARPENTER S, WATTERS GV, EISEN AE, ANDERMANN F: Infantile myotonic dystrophy: Histochemical and electron microscopic features in skeletal muscle. *Neurology* 23:1066, 1973.

216. SARNAT HB, SILBERT SW: Maturational arrest of fetal muscle in neonatal myotonic dystrophy. *Arch Neurol* 33:466,1976.

217. FARKAS E, TOME FMS, FARDEAU M, ARSENIO-NUNES ML, DREYFUS P, DIEBLER MF: Histochemical and ultrastructural study of muscle biopsies in 3 cases of dystrophia myotonica in the newborn child. *J Neurol Sci* 21:273, 1974.

218. SCHOTLAND DL, BONILLA E, VAN METER M: Alteration in muscle plasma membrane structure. *Science* 196:1005, 1977.

219. MERICKEL M, GRAY R, CHAUVIN P, APPEL S: Cultured muscle from myotonic muscular dystrophy patients: Altered membrane electrical properties. *Proc Natl Acad Sci* 78:648, 1981.

220. RENAUD J-F, DESNUELLE C, SCHMID-ANTOMARCHI H, HUGHES M, SERRATRICE G, LAZDUNSKI M: Expression of apamin receptor in muscles of patients with myotonic muscular dystrophy. *Nature* 319:678, 1986.

221. MILLER SE, ROSES AD, APPEL SH: Scanning electron microscopy studies in muscular dystrophy. *Arch Neurol* 33:172, 1976.

222. BUTTERFIELD DA, CHESTNUT DB, APPEL SH, ROSES AD: Spin label study of erythrocyte membrane fluidity in myotonic and Duchenne dystrophy and congenital myotonia. *Nature* 263:159, 1976.

223. ROSES AD, APPEL SH: Protein kinase activity in erythrocyte ghosts of patients with myotonic muscular dystrophy. *Proc Natl Acad Sci USA* 70:1855, 1973.

224. LUCY JA: Is there a membrane defect in muscle and other cells? *Br Med Bull* 36:187, 1980.

225. APPEL SH, ROSES AD: The muscular dystrophies, in Stanbury JB, Wyngaarden JB, Fredrickson DS, Goldstein JL, Brown MS (eds): *The Metabolic Basis of Inherited Disease*, 5th ed. New York, McGraw-Hill, 1983, p 1470.

226. RUDEL R: The pathophysiologic basis of the myotonias and the periodic paralyses, in Engel AG, Banker BQ (eds): *Myology*. New York, McGraw-Hill, 1986.

227. BRYANT SH: Cable properties of external intercostal muscle fibers from myotonic and non myotonic goats. *J Physiol (Lond)* 204:539, 1969.

228. BRETAG AH: Muscle chloride channels. *Physiol Rev* 67:618, 1987.

229. PADBERG G: Facioscapulohumeral disease. (Thesis) University of Leiden, 1982.

230. LUNT PW, HARPER PS: A genetic study of facioscapulohumeral muscular dystrophy. *J Med Genet*, in press.

231. FITZSIMMONS RB, GURWIN EB, BIRD AC: Retinal vascular abnormalities in FSH. A general association with genetic and therapeutic implications. *Brain* 110:631, 1987.

232. LUNT PW, UPADHYAYA M, NOADES J, SARFARAZI M, HARPER PS: An exclusion map for facioscapulohumeral muscular dystrophy. *Cytogenet and Cell Genet* 46:652, 1987.

233. SOMER H, VOUTILAINEN A, KNUUTILA S, KAITILA I, RAPOLA J, LEINONEN H: Duchenne-like muscular dystrophy in two sisters with normal karyotypes: Evidence for autosomal recessive inheritance. *Clin Genet* 28:151, 1985.

234. BEN HAMIDA M, FARDEAU M, ATTIA N: Severe childhood muscular dystrophy affecting both sexes and frequent in Tunisia. *Muscle Nerve* 6:469, 1983.

235. MOSER H: Progressive Muskeldystrophie. VII Haufigdeit, Klinik und Genetik der Typen I and II. *Schweitz Med Wochenschr* 96:169, 1966.

236. YATES JRW, EMERY AEH: A population study of adult onset limb-girdle muscular dystrophy. *J Med Genet* 22:250, 1985.

237. DiMAURO S, BRESOLIN N: Phosphorylase deficiency, in Engel AG, Banker BQ (eds): *Myology*, New York, McGraw-Hill, 1986, Chap 52, p 1585. See subsequent chapters for description of other metabolic myopathies.

238. ZUBRZYCKA-GAARN EE, BULMAN DE, KARPATI G, BURGHES AHM, BELFAST B, KLAMUT HJ, TALBOT J, HODGES RS, RAY PN, WORTON RG: The Duchenne muscular dystrophy gene product is localised in sarcolemma of human skeletal muscle. *Nature* 333:466, 1988.

239. NUDEL U, ROBZYK K, YAFFE D: Expression of the putative Duchenne muscular dystrophy gene in differentiated myogenic cell cultures and in the brain. *Nature* 331:635, 1987.

240. SUGITA H, ARAHATA K, ISHIGURO T, SUHARA Y, TSUKAHARA T, ISHIURA S, EGUCHI C, NONAKA I, OZAWA E: Negative immunostaining of Duchenne muscular dystrophy (DMD) and mdx muscle surface membranes with antibody against synthetic peptide fragment predicted from DMD cDNA. *Proc Japan Acad* 64:37, 1988.

241. VAN OMMEN GJB, BERTELSON C, GINJAAR HD, et al.: Long range genomic map of the Duchenne muscular dystrophy (DMD) gene: Isolation and use of J66(DXS268), a distal intragenic marker. *Genomics* 1:329, 1987.

PART 19

SKIN

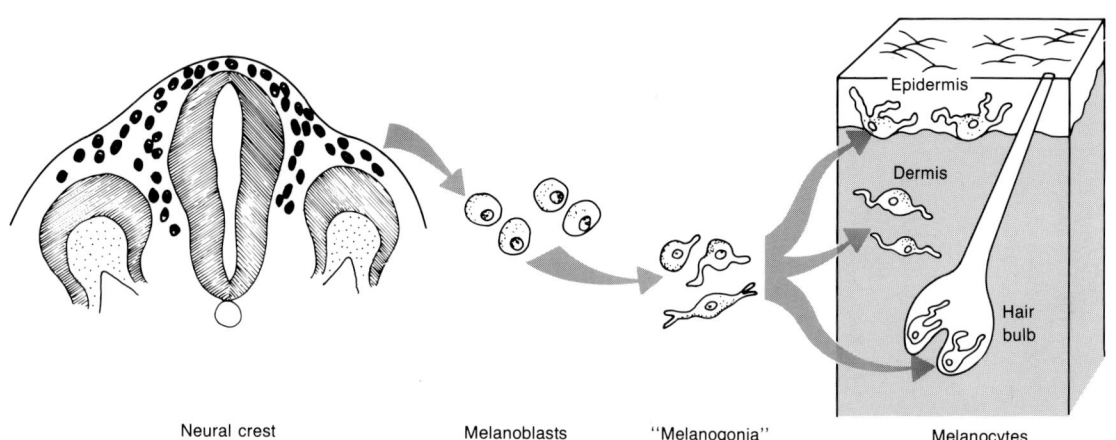

Neural crest Melanoblasts "Melanogonia" Melanocytes

Epidermis

Dermis

Hair bulb

CHAPTER 119

ALBINISM

CARL J. WITKOP, JR.
WALTER C. QUEVEDO, JR.
THOMAS B. FITZPATRICK
RICHARD A. KING

1. Albinism is a generic designation covering a variety of clinical syndromes exhibiting hypomelanosis based on congenital, heritable metabolic defects in the pigment cell (melanocyte) system of the eye and integument. In human albinos, melanocytes appear to be normally distributed throughout the eye and integument but fail to synthesize adequate amounts of melanin.

2. Classically two general forms of albinism have been recognized: oculocutaneous albinism (OCA) and ocular albinism (OA). Abnormalities of melanogenesis in integument of OA albinos indicate that OA is a form of OCA. As the major clinical manifestations in OA involve the eye, the designations OA and OCA will be retained in the clinical context.

3. Ten types of OCA have been described in humans. They have in common hypopigmentation of skin, hair, and eyes; hypoplasia of the ocular fovea; nystagmus; diaphanous irides; photophobia; decreased visual acuity; and decussation defects at the optic chiasm. All but one are autosomal recessive traits. It is not certain whether all autosomal recessive types represent the homozygous state of identical genes or are genetic compounds of allelic genes. The 10 types described have been designated: IA, tyrosinase-negative albinism; IB, yellow mutant albinism; IC, platinum albinism; II, tyrosinase-positive albinism; III, minimal pigment albinism; IV, brown albinism; V, rufous albinism; VIA, Hermansky-Pudlak syndrome; VIB, Chédiak-Higashi syndrome; VII, autosomal dominant albinism.

4. Four types of ocular albinism (OA) have been described: X-linked of Nettleship-Falls (XOAN); an X-linked form with deafness (XOAD); autosomal recessive (AROA); and an autosomal dominant form with lentigines and deafness (ADOA). OA occurs as an autosomal recessive trait at least as frequently as it occurs as an X-linked trait. XOAN and XOAD albinos and heterozygotes have melanin macroglobules in the melanocytes of skin. Melanin macroglobules occur in the lentigines of ADOA but not in normal skin. They have not been observed in the autosomal recessive form. The retinas of females heterozygous for XOAN and XOAD show a mosaic pattern of pigment distribution due to random X-chromosome inactivation early in development. The metabolic defects leading to hypo-melanosis of the retinal and uveal tracts in the various forms of OA are unknown. Skin pigmentation appears to be slightly altered.

5. All 10 forms of OCA can be distinguished from one another on the basis of their clinical, biochemical, ultrastructural, and genetic characteristics as well as their prevalence in different populations.

6. Tyrosinase-negative (ty-neg) albinos have a constant phenotype that does not vary with ethnic background. The phenotype is characterized by a complete absence of visible pigment. Hair bulbs have no tyrosinase activity, and when incubated in L-tyrosine do not form pigment. Melanocytes contain only stage I and stage II unpigmented melanosomes. It is the second most frequent type of OCA. Heterozygotes are detected by their near-zero tyrosinase activity by the method of King.

7. Yellow mutant albinos (ym) phenotypically have yellow to yellow-red hair. Hair bulbs do not form black eumelanin upon incubation with L-tyrosine. There is an intensification of the yellow-red (pheomelanin) color when hair bulbs are incubated with L-tyrosine plus L-cysteine, and an increase in unevenly pigmented stage III melanosomes. Ym albinos develop a slight tan on exposure to sunlight. Tyrosinase activity is present but low and appears to cause a shift to rapid pheomelanogenesis rather than to slow eumelanogenesis. It appears to be allelic with ty-neg albinism.

8. Platinum (pt) albinos develop slight amounts of pigment in eyes and hair in late childhood. The hair is a metallic-cream-platinum color and not stark white as in the ty-neg albino. Hair bulbs of older children and adults have faint amounts of pigment, which increases slightly upon incubation in L-tyrosine. Melanosomes are mostly round early stage III with faint linear pigmentation of the matrix. Plantinum appears allelic with ty-neg OCA. It is not certain whether platinum and minimal pigment albinism represent different genetic entities.

9. Tyrosinase-positive (ty-pos) albinos have some visible pigment, although in infancy this may not be clinically apparent in Caucasoids. Hair color is usually white-yellow to yellow-

Nonstandard abbreviations used in this chapter include: ADOA = autosomal dominant ocular albinism with lentigines and deafness; AHP = aminohydroxyphenylalanine; AROA = autosomal recessive ocular albinism; ASA = acetylsalicylic acid; BADS = black locks, albinism, sensorineural deafness syndrome; CHS = Chédiak-Higashi syndrome; DC = dopachrome; DCF = dopachrome conversion factor; DCOR = dopachrome oxidoreductase; DHI = 5,6-dihydroxyindole; DHICA = 5,6-dihydroxyindole-2-carboxylic acid; DOPA = L-β-3,4-dihydroxyphenylalanine; ERG = electroretinogram; HPS = Hermansky-Pudlak syndrome; 5-HT = 5-hydroxytryptamine; MSH = melanocyte-stimulating hormone; OA = ocular albinism; OCA = oculocutaneous albinism; pt = platinum oculocutaneous albinism; PTCA = pyrrole-2,3,5-tricarboxylic acid; RER = rough endoplasmic reticulum; SDS = sodium dodecyl sulfate; SER = smooth endoplasmic reticulum; ty-neg = tyrosinase-negative oculocutaneous albinism; ty-pos = tyrosinase-positive oculocutaneous albinism; T1 = glycosylated T3; T2 = artifactually deaminated T3; T3 = the native, soluble, nonglycosylated form of mouse tyrosinase; T4 = insoluble, membrane-bound mouse tyrosinase; UVR = ultraviolet radiation; XOAD = X-linked ocular albinism with deafness; XOAN = X-linked ocular albinism of Nettleship-Falls.

Table 119-1 Comparison of the Characteristics of Hypomelanotic Diseases with Features of Oculocutaneous Albinism

Characteristic	Type IA, ty-neg	Type IB, ym	Type IC, Pt	Type II, ty-pos	Type III, minimal pigment
Hair color	White throughout life	White at birth; yellow red by 6 months	White at birth; develops metalic off-white color in late childhood	White, yellow tan; darkens with age	White at birth to white or very slight yellow in adults
Skin color	Pink to red	White at birth; cream, slight tan on exposed skin	Pink to red; no tan	Pink-white to cream, lentigines but no tan	Pink-white, no tan
Pigmented nevi and freckles	Absent	Present	Absent to faint pigment	May be present and numerous	Absent
Susceptibility to skin neoplasia	+ + + +	+ +	+ + + +	+ + + +	Unknown, probably + + + +
Eye color	Gray to blue	Blue in infancy; darkens with age	Gray to blue	Blue, yellow-brown; age- and race-dependent	Gray to blue
Transillumination of iris	No pigment	Cartwheel in adults	Pigment in center of iris or cartwheel in late childhood	Pigment at pupil and limbus or cartwheel	Pigment in pupil, clumps at limbus
Red reflex	Present	Present	Present	May be absent in dark-race adults	Present
Fundal pigment	0	0 to + in adults	0	0 to + in adults	0 to ? in adults
Nystagmus	+ + + +	+ to + +	+ + + +	+ + to + + +	+ + + +
Photophobia	+ + + +	+ to + +	+ + + +	+ + to + + +	+ + + +
Visual acuity	Most legally blind; constant or wors with age; 20/200 to 20/400 +	20/90 to 20/400	20/200 to 20/400	Children, severe defect; adults, same or better; 20/60 to 20/400 +	20/160 to 20/200
Serum tyrosine levels	Normal	Normal	Normal	Low normal to normal	Unknown
β-Melanocyte stimulating hormone levels	Normal	Unknown	Unknown	Normal	Unknown
Melanosomes in hair bulbs	Stages I and II only	To stage III pheomelanosomes	Round and eliptical up to early stage III	To stage III, eumelanosomes	Late stage II, some with melanin
Incubation of hair bulbs in tyrosine	No pigmentation	None to questionable	Slight increase in stage III melanosomes	Pigmentation marked	Unknown
Other	Heterozygotes have near zero tyrosinase activity	Hair bulb test shows increased red or yellow with tyrosine-cysteine incubation	Heterozygotes have zero to normal tyrosinase activity. May be same as minimal pigment OCA	[3]Tyrosinase assay suggests heterogeneity	Heterozygotes have from zero to normal tyrosinase activity may be same as pt

tan, and lightly pigmented nevi may be present. Hair bulb melanocytes may contain up to early stage III, lightly pigmented melanosomes. Hair bulbs incubated in L-tyrosine form black eumelanin, and melanosomes are converted to stage IV melanosomes. It is the most frequent type of albinism.

10. Minimal pigment albinos develop some pigment in irides in late childhood. They have white hair or hair with slightly yellow tints and white skin that does not tan. Hair bulb melanocytes contain stage I and II melanosomes and do not form pigment upon incubation in L-dopa. In contrast to ty-neg heterozygotes, one parent of these albinos may have tyrosinase activity normal for hair color. It is thought that minimal pigment albinos represent genetic compounds of allelic genes.

11. Brown oculocutaneous albinos have been identified in Africans, New Guineans, and in Afro-Americans. The phenotype has not been recognized in other racial groups. Brown albinos have light-brown skin and hair and ocular features of albinism. They have slight erythema and tan moderately on exposure to sunlight. Hair bulbs contain eumelanosomes with reduced pigment usually only up to stage III. Skin melanosomes are round and incompletely melanized. Tyrosinase activity is normal.

12. Rufous albinism has been seen most frequently among New Guineans and Africans. The skin and irides have a red tinge and the hair color varies but most frequently has a mahogany-red color. Nystagmus, iris transillumination, and visual defects are slight.

13. The Hermansky-Pudlak syndrome (HPS) is a triad of tyrosinase-positive OCA, a mild bleeding diathesis due to storage pool–deficient platelets lacking dense bodies, and ceroid storage disease. The storage pool–deficient platelets lack normal levels of nonmetabolic adenine nucleotides, calcium, and serotonin. The aggregation defect can be corrected by epinephrine stimulation of the membrane-modulated aggregation pathway. The pigment phenotype is variable. HPS albinos may resemble any type of OCA or OA. Ceroid in HPS resembles that

Type IV, brown OCA	Type V, rufous OCA	Type VIA, HPS	Type VIB, CHS	Type VII, autosomal dominant OCA
Beige to light brown in Africans	Mahogany red to deep red	White, red, brown	Blond to dark brown; steel-gray tint	White to cream with reddish tint
Cream to light tan on exposed skin; tans lightly	Reddish brown	Cream-gray to light normal	Pink to pink-white	White to cream
Uncommon	May be present	Present	Present	May be present
Similar to Caucasians in Africa +	Low	+ + +	+ +	Unknown
Hazel to light tan	Reddish brown to brown	Blue-gray to brown; age- and race-dependent	Blue to dark brown	Gray to blue
Cartwheel effect	Slight	None to cartwheel effect	Cartwheel effect to normal	Translucent to cartwheel effect
Present in children; may be absent in adults	Unknown	Present in light Caucasians; not in dark races	Present, less after 5 years	Present in children
+ to + + + in adults	+ to + + +	0 to + in adults	+ to + + +	0 to +
+ to + +	0 to + +	+ to + + +	0 to + +	+ + to + + +
+ to + +	0 to + +	+ to + + + +	0 to + +	+ + to + + +
20/30 to 20/150	Normal to 20/100, most 20/30	20/70 to 20/400	Normal to moderate decrease	20/70 to 20/200
Unknown	Unknown	Normal	Normal	Unknown
Unknown	Unknown	Unknown	Unknown	Unknown
Stage I to stage III, some lightly pigmented stage IV	Unknown	To stage III, pheomelanosomes and eumelanosomes	Macromelanosomes and normal to stage IV	Stage I to early stage III; no structural abnormality
Slight to no pigment increase	Pigmentation	Pigmentation slight increase	Pigmentation	Pigmentation; increased tyrosinase activity in Golgi
Tyrosinase activity normal	Seen in New Guineans and Africans	Lysosomal disease, platelet dense bodies absent; ceroid storage; heterozygotes detected by low thioredoxin reductase	Lysosomal disease; susceptibility to infection; giant lysosomal granules; lymphoreticular malignancy	

in neuronal ceroid-lipofuscinosis and does not originate from polyunsaturated fats. Patients variably develop fibrotic restrictive lung disease, granulomatous colitis and gingivitis, kidney failure, and cardiomyopathy. HPS patients with ceroid in urine sediment also excrete high levels of dolichols, which are constituents of lysosomal membranes. HPS patients appear to have a defect in processing lysosomal membranes. Skin and hair bulb melanocytes contain round, unevenly pigmented pheomelanosomes. The pigment defect appears to be secondary to a metabolic defect suppressing tyrosinase activity. Thioredoxin-reductase activity, which regulates tyrosinase activity, is low in skin of HPS albinos. The most consistent and diagnostic feature of HPS is lack of platelet dense bodies. Carriers can be detected by low levels of thioredoxin reductase in skin biopsies.

14. The Chédiak-Higashi syndrome (CHS), usually fatal in childhood, is characterized by pigment dilution, the presence of giant peroxidase-positive secondary lysosomal granules in leukocytes which do not degranulate and which impede che-

motaxis, and a marked susceptibility to infection. Children surviving early infections frequently develop a terminal lymphoreticular malignancy. The reduced hair, skin, and eye color is associated with giant melanosomes in melanocytes and keratinocytes. The number of melanosomes within keratinocytes is reduced. The giant melanosomes appear to be degraded by lysosomal hydrolases within melanocytes. Melanosomes of more normal size are transferred to keratinocytes, where they form unusually large phagolysosomes. The cutaneous hypopigmentation of CHS appears to result from the reduced number of melanosomes within keratinocytes and possibly from the grouping of melanosomes into aggregates of abnormal size. A defect in killer cell function is found in CHS lymphocytes.

15. Autosomal dominant oculocutaneous albinism is rare. The patients resemble ty-pos albinos. A defect in melanosomal membranes has been postulated but not demonstrated.

16. All human and animal albinos tested have abnormal decussation of the optic neuronal tracts such that neurons from the

temporal retina, which normally course to the same side of the brain as the eye of origin, cross to the contralateral side in albinos. Albinos lack the internal mechanism for binocular vision, and hence, use one eye for reading. To compensate for this defect at the chiasm, the geniculocortical projections are arranged in different patterns. These defects result from any mutation which suppresses melanogenesis in the developing optic stalk. The defect can be demonstrated in vivo by asymmetrical monocular stimulated visually evoked potentials.

17. Melanin normally occurs in the inner ear and protects the inner ear from noise trauma. Pigment in the inner ear is absent or reduced in OCA. OCA albinos have evidence for a neuronal decussation defect in the otic neurons at the level of the superior olive. In contrast to the optic system defect, this results in only mild functional defects.

18. OCA albinos, especially in tropical settings, have a high prevalence of solar keratoses and squamous cell carcinoma, but the prevalence of melanomas has been low.

HISTORICAL INTRODUCTION

Albinism comprises a heterogeneous group of heritable disorders of the melanin pigmentary system, found throughout the animal kingdom. In humans, all forms of albinism are characterized by hypoplasia of the fovea, translucent irides, photophobia, nystagmus, decreased visual acuity, and absence of binocular vision due to abnormal decussation of optic neurons at the chiasma, in addition to generalized decreased melanotic pigment in skin, hair, and eyes (oculocutaneous albinism, OCA) or eye (ocular albinism, OA). The term *albinoidism* refers to hypomelanotic conditions without nystagmus, photophobia, and decreased visual acuity.[1,2] Ten disorders with the

clinical features of OCA (Table 119-1) and four with features of OA (Table 119-2) have been described. These disorders can be identified by their clinical, genetic, and ultrastructural features,[2-7] by the response of anagen hair bulbs incubated in L-tyrosine concerning their ability to produce pigment,[8,9] and by their tyrosinase activity.[10]

Historical reviews of albinism can be found in the comprehensive monograph by Pearson et al.[11] and in more recent summaries by Froggatt,[12,13] Witkop,[9,14] and Kinnear et al.[15] The term *albino* is derived from the Latin adjective *albus*, "white," and was first applied by Balthazar Tellez to certain "white" Negroes whom he observed in Africa.[11] Recognizable accounts of albinism dating from the first century A.D. are to be found in Pliny[16] and Gellius.[17] According to Sorsby,[18] the pseudepigraphic descriptions of the birth of Noah in the Book of Enoch the Prophet and the Dead Sea Scrolls indicate that he was possibly an albino, and Revelation 1:14 describes an albino phenotype. The essential clinical features of albinism are well-summarized in the following description, published in 1699 by Lionel Wafer,[19] of albinos among the Cuna Indians of the San Blas Islands of Panama.

There is one complexion so singular . . . that I never saw nor heard of any like them in any part of the world. . . . They are white . . . tis rather a milk-white, lighter than the colour of any (*Europeans*), and much like that of a white horse. . . . From their seeing so clear as they do in a moon-shiny night, we us'd to call them mooney'd. For they see not very well in the sun, poring in the clearest Day; their eyes being but weak, and running with water if the sun shine towards them; so that in the day-time they care not to go abroad. . . . When moon-shiny night's come, they are all life and activity, running abroad, and into the woods, skipping about like wild-bucks, and running as fast by moon-light, even in the gloom and shade of the woods, as the other (*Indians*) by Day, being as

Table 119-2 Comparison of the Characteristics of the Various Forms of Ocular Albinism

Characteristic	X-linked (Nettleship)	X-linked with deafness	Autosomal recessive ocular albinism	OA-lentigines-deafness
Hair color	Normal to slight lightening	Normal to slight lightening	Normal to slight lightening	Normal
Skin color	Normal to mottled	Normal to mottled	Normal to light	Normal
Pigmented nevi and freckles	Present	Present	Present	Lentigines
Susceptibility to skin neoplasia	No	No	No	Unknown
Eye color	Normal range	Normal range	Normal range	Normal range
Transillumination of iris	Cartwheel, males; diaphanous, females	Cartwheel, males; diaphanous, females	Cartwheel to diphanous	Cartwheel to diaphanous
Red reflex	Present, males	Present, males	Present, males and females	Present
Fundal pigment	Males, 0; females, mosaic fundus	Males, 0; females, mosaic fundus	Males and females, 0 to +	0
Nystagmus	+ + to + + + +	+ + to + + + +	+ + to + + + +	+ + +
Photophobia	+ + to + + +	+ + to + + +	+ + to + + +	+ + +
Visual acuity	Moderate to severe decrease; 20/50 to 20/400	Moderate to severe decrease; 20/50 to 20/400	Moderate to severe decrease; 20/100 to 20/400	20/200
Serum tyrosine levels	Unknown	Unknown	Unknown	Unknown
β-Melanocyte-stimulating hormone levels	Unknown	Unknown	Unknown	Unknown
Melanosomes	Melanin macroglobules in skin of hemi/heterozygotes	Melanin macroglobules in skin of hemi/heterozygotes	Normal	Melanin macroglobules in lentigines
Incubation of hair bulbs in tyrosine	Pigmentation	Pigmentation	Pigmentation	Unknown
Other	Carrier females, mosaic retina	High frequency hearing loss; onset puberty to 40 yrs	Males and females equally affected	Sensorineural deafness autosomal dominant

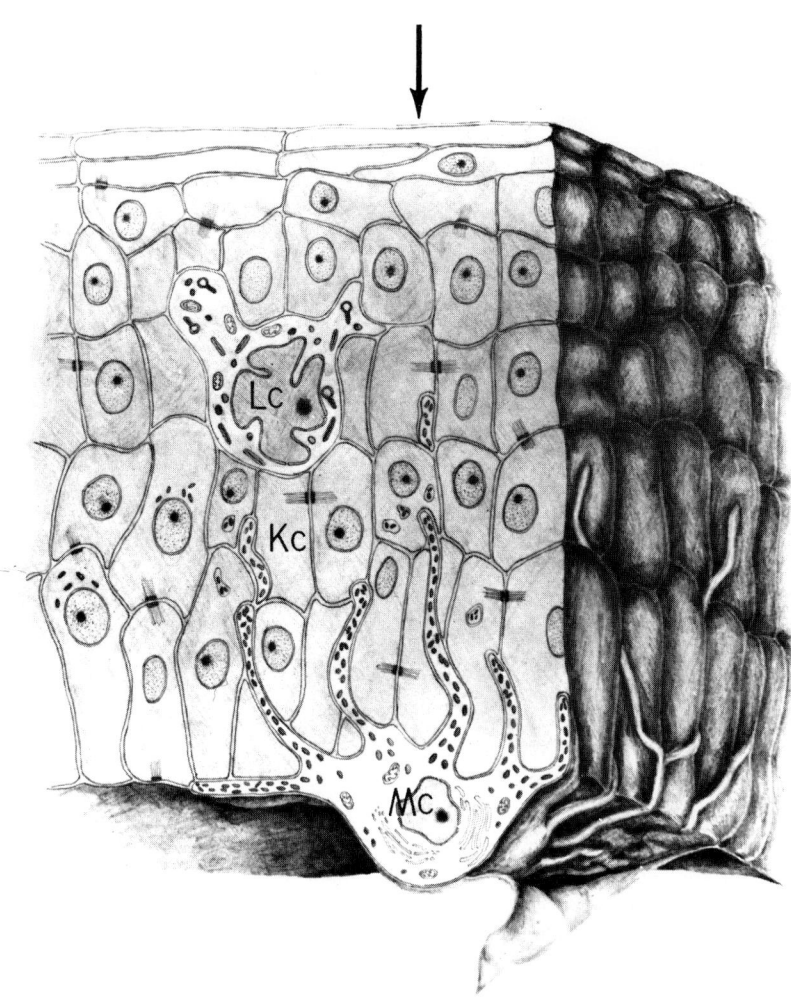

Fig. 119-1 Epidermal melanin unit consisting of a melanocyte and associate pool of keratinocytes. Langerhans cell is located among the suprabasal keratinocytes. Mc = melanocyte; Kc = keratinocyte; Lc = Langerhans cell.

nimble as they, tho' not so strong and lusty. . . . Neither is the child of a man and a woman of these white (*Indians*), white like the parents, but copper-colour'd as their parents were. . . . They were but short-lived.

The outstanding characteristics are the "milk-white" color and photophobia. The recessive inheritance is suggested by the fact that "neither is the child of a man and woman of these white (Indians), white like the parents, but copper-color'd." The striking contrast of albino skin with the normal darkly pigmented skin of Indians and Negroes sets them apart, and many myths were conjured up about these strange "moon-ey'd" people.

By 1913, the general outlines of what we now know about albinism and melanin production had been established or predicted. Albinism was one of the first inherited anomalies in humans to be investigated statistically on the basis of a population ascertainment by Raseri in 1879.[20] Ehrmann[21] demonstrated that melanin was formed intracellularly by "melanoblasts" (now called *melanocytes*) and transferred to epithelial cells by "protoplasmic threads" which connected melanoblasts to epithelial cells (keratinocytes). He indicated that light was necessary to stimulate pigment production. Florence Durham,[22] in 1904, demonstrated that tyrosinase activity could be found in the skin of pigmented animals but was absent in albino animals. Considerable experimental evidence on the nature of the defect in albinism led Sir Archibald Garrod,[23] in 1908, to speculate that albinism, among other disorders, was an inborn error of metabolism. In 1927, Raper[24] elucidated the

chemical intermediates in the conversion of tyrosine to melanin.

Pearson et al.[11] and Stannus[25] reported in 1913 their results of a worldwide survey of albinism and hypomelanotic disorders and proposed that albinism was ascribable to either the absence of "melanoblasts" or to the absence of tyrosinase activity, but they favored the theory that albinism was due to a structural defect. As will be seen, most forms of albinism result from either a primary or a secondary intracellular block in melanogenesis in conditions in which melanocytes are present in integument and eye.

Albinism is found in insects, fishes, amphibians, reptiles, and birds, as well as in humans and other mammals.[26–31]

MELANIN AND NORMAL MELANIN PIGMENTATION

Melanocytes are distinctive, specialized dendritic cells in which the biosynthesis of melanin takes place (Fig. 119-1). During embryonic development in mammals, precursor melanocytes, except in the retinal pigment epithelium, arise in the neural crest and actively migrate to peripheral sites. The melanocytes of the retinal pigment epithelium are derived from the outer layer of the optic cup and differ morphologically from the melanocytes in other sites. In humans, mature melanocytes are normally present in certain characteristic regions: *skin* (hair bulbs, dermis, and the dermoepidermal junc-

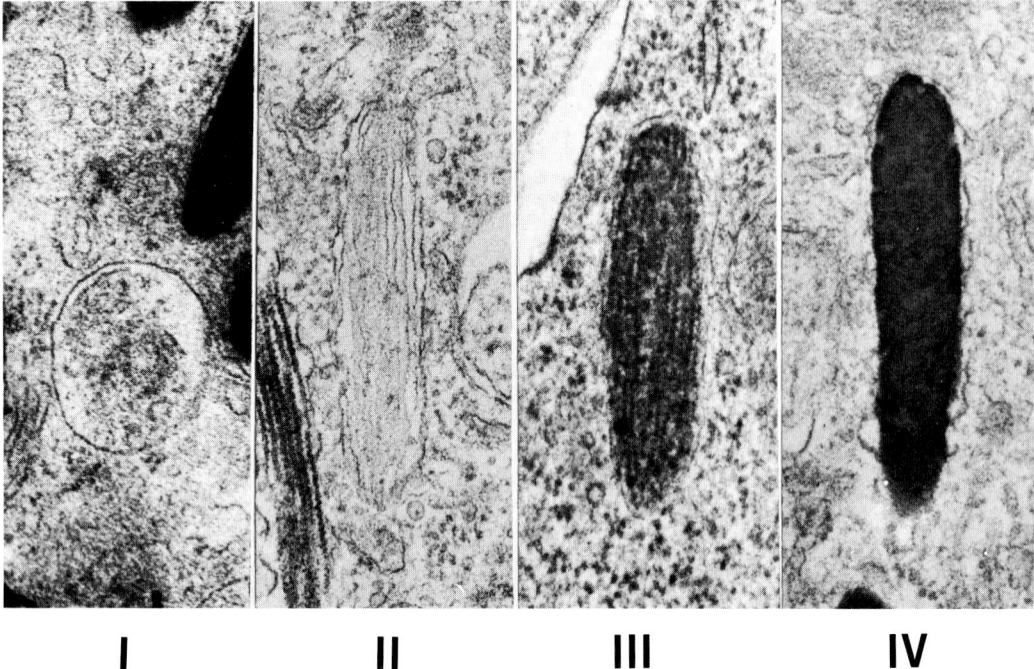

| I | II | III | IV |

Fig. 119-2 Stages in the development of the eumelanosome (see text for detailed description).

tion), *mucous membranes, nervous system* (pia-arachnoid), *eye* (uveal tract and retinal pigment epithelium), *inner ear, cochlea* (wall of the modiolus, spiral lamina, Reissner's membrane, and stria vascularis), and *vestibular system* (saccule, utricle, and ampullae).[32] Melanin pigment is synthesized in specialized cytoplasmic organelles called *melanosomes* (Fig. 119-2). Within the melanosome, the enzymatic conversion of the amino acid tyrosine to melanin is catalyzed by the aerobic oxidase *tyrosinase* (EC 1.14.18.1) (Fig. 119-3). All melanocytes, with the exception of those in the hair bulbs, retinal pigment epithelium, and inner ear, appear to have the ability to form malignant melanomas.

Epidermal Melanin Unit and Skin Color

The number of melanocytes in skin from any one anatomic location is relatively constant regardless of the intensity of pigmentation.[33,34] The number of melanocytes varies with anatomic location. Large numbers are found in hair bulbs, skin of the genitalia and face, and in oral and nasal mucosa, whereas they are relatively scanty in abdominal skin. The concentration of melanocytes from comparable anatomic locations by race shows that there is relatively little variation in the number of melanocytes. Thus, racial pigmentation differences do not depend upon the number of melanocytes but on the intensity of pigment produced by these cells.[35]

Color variation in human skin derives chiefly from the pres-

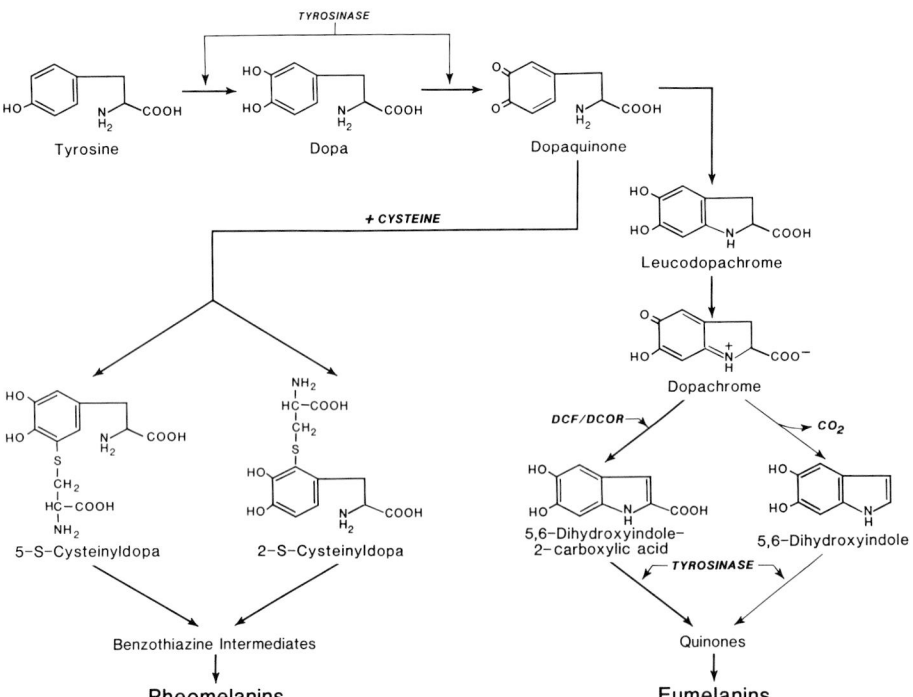

Fig. 119-3 The melanin pathway. DCF–DCOR = dopachrome conversion factor–dopachrome oxidoreductase.

ence within the epidermis of specialized melanin-bearing organelles, the melanosomes. Tanning of human skin on exposure to ultraviolet radiation (UVR) results from the presence of increased amounts of melanin within the epidermis. Melanosomes synthesized by melanocytes are passed to keratinocytes and transported within them to the epidermal surface. *Melanin must be present in keratinocytes* to impart a brown color, as viewed in the living skin. In some cases, the melanosomes are catabolized en route. The multicellular *epidermal melanin unit* (melanocyte and associated pool of keratinocytes) is the focal point for the control of melanin metabolism within mammalian epidermis[36] (Fig. 119-1).

Melanin pigmentation of human skin is divisible into two components: (1) *constitutive skin color* designates the cutaneous melanin pigmentation generated in accordance with cellular genetic programs in the absence of direct influences by UVR and is generally taken to be the level of pigmentation in those parts of the body habitually shielded from light; (2) *facultative (inducible) skin color,* or "tan," characterizes the immediate and delayed tanning reactions elicited by direct exposure of the skin to UVR. Facultative color change is reversible in that the hyperpigmentation of the skin tends to decline toward the constitutive level when exposure to UVR is discontinued. Skin hyperpigmentation induced by endocrine changes, as in pregnancy and Addison disease, also represents a type of facultative color change. Alterations in endocrine balance may significantly influence the response of human skin to UVR.

Fig. 119-4 A molecular model for the defense against free radical attack and control of melanin biosynthesis by the thioredoxin reductase–thioredoxin system. *Light reaction:* Electrons from central metabolism (i.e., NADPH) primarily flow in the direction of free radical reduction at the surface of the plasma membrane (i.e., $2O_2^- + 3\ NADPH + 3H^+ \xrightarrow{TR} 2H_2O + H_2O_2$). This causes an increase in concentration of oxidized thioredoxin-promoting melanin biosynthesis. *Dark reaction:* Electrons from central metabolism primarily flow in the direction of reduction of oxidized thioredoxin in the cytosol

$$\text{(i.e., } T\!\begin{array}{c}S\\|\\S\end{array} + NADPH + \longrightarrow T\begin{array}{c}SH\\\\SH\end{array} + NADP^+\text{).}$$

This increases the concentration of reduced thioredoxin, which inhibits tyrosinase. (*From Schallreuter et al.*[149] *By permission of the Journal of Investigative Dermatology.*)

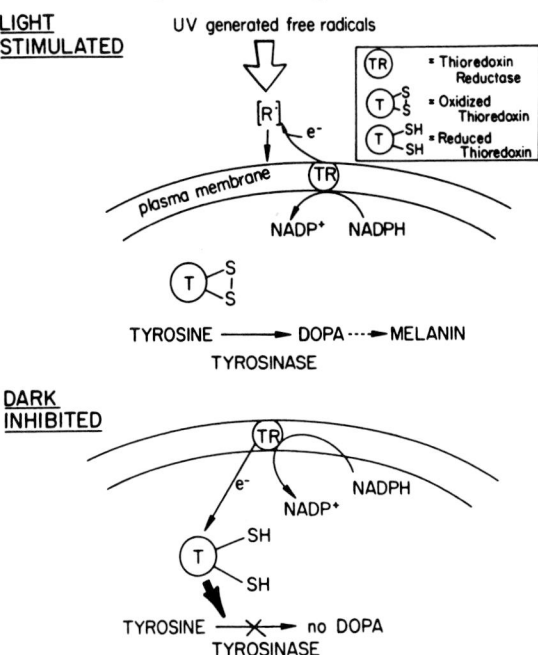

Accordingly, facultative color changes in humans arise from the complex interplay of light, hormones, and the "tanning potential" set by the individual's genetic constitution.

The capacity for facultative color change is broadly related to levels of constitutive skin color. The full extent of genetic involvement in facultative color change is not known, but studies indicate that melanogenesis induced by UVR is regulated by the thioredoxin–thioredoxin reductase system acting on tyrosinase, as subsequently described (Fig. 119-4).

Constitutive Melanin Pigmentation

It has been estimated that the additive interaction of genes at three or four loci (i.e., three to four gene pairs) is sufficient to account for the variation in skin color between black and white Americans.[37] Reasons for believing that the actual situation may be considerably more complicated have been advanced by Harrison.[38] In addition to the polygenic series that through additive interactions determines the level of cutaneous pigmentation, other genes are known, as in albinism, to act "individually in partly or completely deleting melanin pigmentation." In mice, more than 147 genes at approximately 62 loci affect skin and hair color.[31] Genetic influences on human melanin pigmentation may be equally complex.

Melanin Biosynthesis

Two types of melanin can be synthesized (Fig. 119-3), the yellow-red pheomelanins and the brown-black eumelanins. Melanin is synthesized by melanocytes in membrane-bound particles, the melanosomes, which in epidermal structures are then transferred to keratinocytes[39] (Fig. 119-2). Electron-microscopically fully formed melanosomes from brown- and black-pigmented hair are ellipsoid structures (that may appear round in cross section) on which pigment is evenly distributed; they are recognized as *eumelanosomes.* Melanosomes from red or yellow hair are round and show an uneven distribution of pigment in a spotty fashion; they are recognized as *pheomelanosomes.*

Pheomelanosomes and eumelanosomes of follicular melanocytes at their earliest stage of development (stage I) are identical, i.e., multivesicular body–like structures, round in shape, with a limiting membrane surrounding microvesicles (globulovesicular bodies) and filaments.[40] The filaments have a periodicity of approximately 100 Å. In eumelanogenesis, the stage II melanosome is oval in shape and has numerous filaments aligned parallel to the long axis of the melanosome. Melanin is subsequently deposited within the melanosome (stage III), ultimately producing a more or less homogeneous darkening of its interior (stage IV). Round, membrane-limited microvesicles (vesiculoglobular bodies) may be found within eumelanosomes at all stages of development. Electron-lucent spherical bodies are frequently found in the stage IV melanosome.[40,41] One interpretation is that the electron-lucent bodies of stage IV melanosomes are microvesicles that are embedded in eumelanin that has been deposited on their surfaces but not within their interiors. It is possible that microvesicles are related to the incorporation of tyrosinase into the developing melanosome.[42]

The pheomelanosomes of human red hair parallel eumelanosomes in their development but have pheomelanin deposited in irregular or granular patches on the filamentous matrix.[43–46] Chemical analysis shows that some human red hair contains varying proportions of both eumelanin and pheomelanin, and these proportions are reflected by the proportions of eumelanosomes and pheomelanosomes seen electron-microscopically.[46]

The filamentous structural matrix proteins of the melanosomes are synthesized on the rough endoplasmic reticulum (RER) and packaged in membranes in the RER or smooth endoplasmic reticulum (SER).[41,42,47–49] In turn, tyrosinase synthesized on the RER is enclosed in membrane-limited microvesicles at one or more sites in the Golgi complex. The tyrosinase-bearing microvesicles fuse with the structural premelanosomes of RER/SER origin, yielding a melanosome fully equipped with tyrosinase.[41,42] Biochemical and cytochemical studies indicate that tyrosinase may be located in the limiting membrane as well as in the matrix of the melanosome.[50,51]

Biochemistry of Melanin Biosynthesis

The synthesis of melanin, involving the conversion of the amino acid tyrosine to black-brown eumelanin and red-yellow pheomelanin, is limited to the melanosome within the melanocyte[52–54] (Fig. 119-3). The initial steps of the melanin pathway are the hydroxylation of tyrosine to L-3,4-dihydroxyphenylalanine (dopa) and the oxidation of dopa to dopaquinone, both steps being catalyzed by tyrosinase (EC 1.14.18.1).[54–57] Dopaquinone then enters the pheomelanin, the eumelanin, or both pathways, but the mechanism for controlling the pathway into which dopaquinone enters has not been fully defined. Prota and others have suggested that the switch between pathways is controlled by the concentration of sulhydryl groups at the site of melanin synthesis.[54,55,58] In support of this hypothesis is the finding that in the formation of pheomelanin, dopaquinone combines with cysteine residues containing the reactive SH group in a very fast reaction, whereas the conversion of dopaquinone to leukodopachrome is not as fast.[54,59–61] The effect of this is to make the affinity of the pheomalanin pathway for dopaquinone greater than that of the eumelanin pathway, and the significance of this is discussed below.[54,59–61]

The classic Raper-Mason scheme for the eumelanin pathway involves the conversion of leukodopachrome (cyclodopa) to dopachrome (DC), to 5,6-dihydroxyindole (DHI), to indole-5,6-quinone, to melanin.[54,62,63] Recent studies suggest that the actual pathway is more complex. The conversion of leukodopachrome to DC is coupled with the conversion of dopaquinone to dopa, and half of the dopaquinone is recycled to dopa.[64–68] Raper identified 5,6-dihydroxyindole-2-carboxylic acid (DHICA) as an intermediate in the pathway,[24] but suggested that DHI is the major contributor to melanin.[67] Both DHI and DHICA form in the conversion of DC to melanin,[66–70] and studies now suggest that DHICA is the major precursor in the formation of eumelanin in vivo.[70] This is consistent with the enzymatic and melanin structural studies discussed below. In the pheomelanin pathway, dopaquinone combines with cysteine or glutathione to form cysteinyldopas (5-S-, 2-S-, 2,5-diS-, and 6-S-cysteinyldopa) which are converted into the corresponding benzothiazines by oxidative cyclization of the cysteinyl residues.[54] The benzothiazine intermediates then polymerize to pheomelanin. Pure eumelanin or pheomelanin may form, but a mixed type of melanin forms as the usual product of the melanin pathway.[54]

Tyrosinase is a copper-containing enzyme that is active in the oxidation of tyrosine, dopa, and DHI,[54,56,71] although the biologic role of tyrosinase at the step involving DHI is unknown. Dopa is the cofactor for the hydroxylation of tyrosine and the dehydrogenation of DHI.[71,72] There are two atoms of copper per molecule of tyrosinase, each bound to histidine residues.[73] Mammalian tyrosinase has not been purified to homogenicity. *Neurospora* tyrosinase has been purified and sequenced, revealing four histidine residues in the active site of the enzyme.[74,75] Several laboratories recently have reported isolation of putative mammalian tyrosinase cDNAs.[76,76a,77] The most convincing reports are those by Kwon and his colleagues, who isolated a candidate human tyrosinase cDNA which encodes a protein recognized by antityrosinase antibodies.[76a] The murine equivalent to this clone is deleted in albino mice known to have deletions at the *c*-locus. Furthermore, using the human cDNA as a probe, these same investigators isolated a putative murine tyrosinase cDNA which conferred tyrosinase enzyme activity to tyrosinase-negative recipient cells.[77a,77b] The murine gene structure has been determined, and evidence of multiple transcripts generated by alternative splicing has been obtained.[77b]

Mammalian tyrosinasae has a characteristic electrophoretic pattern of isozymes that are the result of posttranslational glycosylation. Electrophoretic, kinetic, and amino acid compositional analyses suggest that there is a single common nascent polypeptide.[51,78–83] For mouse tyrosinase, it is thought that the native soluble enzyme (T3) has an M_r of approximately 54,000 when synthesized in the endoplasmic reticulum. T3 undergoes glycosylation in the Golgi to soluble T1 with an approximate M_r of 72,000 through the addition of neutral sugars (mannose and galactose) and sialic acid. T1 is then transported by the vesiculoglobular body to the melanosome, where it becomes membrane-bound T4.[84–86] T4 is insoluble and is the form of the enzyme responsible for melanin synthesis in the melanosome in vivo, although soluble enzyme extracted from the melanocyte is active in vitro.[51,83,87,88] Another form of the enzyme T2 appears to be an artifact of polyacrylamide gel electrophoresis, resulting from deamination of T3 with the heating and high pH of the gel.[83] The mechanism for inhibiting melanin synthesis outside of the melanosome is unknown. The glycosylation does not affect activity of extracted enzyme, and all isozymic forms are fully active.[51,83] Polyclonal antityrosinase antibodies cross-react with all isozymic forms,[89–91] whereas monoclonal antityrosinase antibody, raised against T4 that had been solubilized by trypsinization, is specific for T4 and does not cross-react with the T1 or the T2 form of the enzyme.[92] Tyrosinase from lower eukaryotic organisms is polymeric, but mammalian tyrosinase has generally been thought to exist as a monomer, with the different molecular weight estimates accounted for on the basis of differences in glycosylation rather than polymer formation. This view must be reexamined because mammalian tyrosinase has a strong tendency to aggregate, and aggregate forms of the enzyme are resistant to dissociation by urea or sodium dodecyl sulfate (SDS).[93] Polymeric forms of the enzyme may exist in vivo. Maturation and translocation of tyrosinase from the ribosomes of the endoplasmic reticulum to the premelanosomes are regulated by the glycosylation of the tyrosinase and the premelanosomes.[94–98] The glycosylation inhibitors glucosamine and tunicamycin produce a loss of pigment in cultured B-16 mouse melanoma cells associated with the loss of T3 tyrosinase and with the formation of melanosomes having an altered internal architecture.[93,98] Tyrosinase has four asparagine-linked sugar chains, and 25 to 34 percent are high mannose types, with the remaining being complex-type sugar chains.[96] The melanosomal carbohydrates have not been identified, but it is suggested that they play a role in the acceptance of tyrosinase by this organelle.[98] Tyrosinase does not appear to have a direct structural role in the internal matrix of the melanosome.[99]

The conversion of dopachrome has been undergoing intensive investigation, and data now support the role of an enzyme at this step in the eumelanin pathway. The first evidence for a second pigment pathway enzyme was provided in 1980 by Logan and Weatherhead, who found that tyrosinase activity did not directly correlate with melanin production.[58,100] They found that tyrosinase activity in the hair follicles of Siberian hamsters was high during the spring and the autumn molts but that the hair produced following the latter molt was unpigmented. At about the same time, Pawelek and coworkers reported three melanogenic regulatory factors that acted on the eumelanin pathway after dopaquinone: (1) dopachrome conversion factor (DCF), which promoted the conversion of DC to DHI; (2) indole-blocking factor, which inhibited the conversion of DHI to indolequinone; and (3) indole conversion factor, which promoted the conversion of DHI to indolequinone.[101–104] Subsequent work has shown that part of the indole conversion factor activity is provided by tyrosinase.[71] Barber et al. subsequently provided evidence that the dopachrome conversion factor activity is due to a new enzyme in the pigment pathway that they called dopachrome oxidoreductase (DCOR).[105] The evidence that this activity was an enzyme included protease sensitivity, pH stability, heat lability of a crude preparation of the material, and the estimated molecular weight of approximately 34,000.

DCF-DCOR has not been purified, and precise biochemical characterization is lacking; however, several important properties of this enzyme have been established. The distribution of DCF-DCOR is similar to that of tyrosinase within the melanocyte.[105] DCF-DCOR activity can be demonstrated in albino melanocytes devoid of tyrosinase activity,[104,105] and activity increases in hair follicle melanocytes after melanocyte-stimulating hormone (MSH) treatment of mice[106] but not in cultured Cloudman melanoma cells known to be MSH-sensitive.[102] The activity of skin, hair follicles, and eye DCF-DCOR varies in mice of different genotypes, affecting coat color, and the lowest hair follicle activity in pigmented mice is found with those having a yellow coat.[104,106,107] Recessive yellow (e/e) mice have no DCF-DCOR acvtivity in their hair follicles,[106] although activity is present in their eumelanin-containing eye.[108] Incubation of the orange substrate DC with DCF-DCOR, in the absence of tyrosinase activity, leads to a colorless compound which has been identified as 5,6-dihydroxyindole-2-carboxylic acid (DHICA).[69] Incubation of DC with DCF-DCOR, when followed over a 30-min period, leads to a rapid increase in DHICA and only a minimal increase in DHI.[70] These experiments imply that DHICA is the major intermediate in the eumelanin pathway and is produced under enzyme control, while DHI is a minor intermediate. Metal ions may also play a role in promoting the conversion of DC to DHICA and DHI. Prota has suggested that metal ions are sufficient for controlling this step of the eumelanin pathway.[109,110] The DCF-DCOR–catalyzed conversion of DC to DHICA can be demonstrated in the presence of a metal ion chelator; however, the biologic role of ion-controlled DC conversion has not been fully established.[70]

The knowledge of the melanin pathway can be used to explain the phenotype of the different types of oculocutaneous albinism. The total absence of tyrosinase activity leads to no eumelanin or pheomelanin synthesis, because there is no formation of dopaquinone. A partial loss of tyrosinase activity should produce a pheomelanogenic phenotype, because the reduced amount of dopaquinone will preferentially enter the high affinity pheomelanin pathway. Inhibition of a conversion step in the eumelanin pathway will produce a similar pheomelanogenic phenotype. If the inhibition of the eumelanin step is not complete, then there will be some eumelanin synthesis with a predominance of pheomelanin synthesis. In support of this concept of pathway activity is the fact that most pigment types of oculocutaneous albinism produce a predominance of pheomelanin, as discussed below.

Melanin Structure

The final structure of melanin is complex, and is important in its function. In general, eumelanin is a dark-brown to black high molecular weight material that is insoluble in acid and alkali and contains 6 to 9 percent nitrogen and 0 to 1 percent sulfur, whereas pheomelanin is a reddish-brown high molecular weight material that is soluble in alkali and contains 8 to 11 percent nitrogen and 9 to 12 percent sulfur.[111] Isolation of melanin from human tissue usually yields a material that is not purely eumelanin or pheomelanin, suggesting that a mixed type of melanin is the usual product of the melanin pathway.[112,113] Melanin in the pigmented retinal epithelium in the eye is black and is found in eumelanosomes, yet analysis of this pigment shows that it contains derivatives of cysteinyldopa.[114] There is no relationship between the ocular and the epidermal melanin, however, and this is consistent with the different embryonic origins of the melanocytes for these tissues.[114,115] The actual structure of melanin has been difficult to determine, primarily because it is dense, has a tendency to aggregation and absorption, and is poorly soluble. Eumelanin is primarily a copolymer of DHI and DHICA, with the latter compound the predominant indole,[116] but all of the eumelanin intermediates participate in the polymerization to some degree.[54] The structure of pheomelanin is not as well defined, and primarily involves polymerization of the 1,4-benzothiazine intermediates derived from the 5-S-cysteinyldopa.[54] Interestingly, the same pathway through the benzothiazines can also produce the low molecular weight trichrome pigments, which are epidermal pigments found in certain types of red and yellow hair and feathers.[45] The role of trichrome pigments in human skin, hair, or eye pigmentation is largely unexplored.

The quantity of eumelanin and pheomelanin can be determined in various tissues, using methods developed by Ito.[111,117] Permanganate oxidation of eumelanin produces pyrrole-2,3,5-tricarboxylic acid (PTCA), and hydriodic acid hydrolysis of pheomelanin produces aminohydroxyphenylalanine (AHP). PTCA and AHP are quantitated by high performance liquid chromatography, providing an exact melanin content of a sample of hair or tissue such as melanoma.[111]

Melanin performs a variety of different functions, and it is important to consider these in relation to its location in different tissues.[118] Epidermal melanin is synthesized in the melanocyte and passed in the dendrites of the melanocyte to the keratinocyte. After transfer, the keratinocyte migrates to the skin surface and degenerates to form the stratum corneum, while the melanosome is degraded into melanin dust.[119] The melanocytes in the pigmented retinal epithelium do not transfer their melanosomes to other cells, and this melanin remains in these organelles. Most of the functions of melanin relate to pigment in the melanosome, and the function of melanin dust is unknown.[119] Melanin is present in all animal species, fungi, bacteria, and higher plants, and it appears to have many functions.[54]

A primary function of melanin is photoprotection.[54,118] In the skin, melanin protects against the adverse effects of ultraviolet radiation by dissipating light energy as heat or in a chemical reaction which consumes molecular oxygen, or by acting as a scavenger for reactive oxygen species such as superoxide and singlet oxygen.[120–123] The reaction of superoxide with melanin (in this case, dopa melanin) is associated with a reduction of superoxide to hydrogen peroxide and an oxidation of superoxide to molecular oxygen,[121] and melanin itself may have superoxide dismutase–like activity.[120] Melanins are known to contain free radicals.[123] It is also known that photooxidation of melanin produces reactive species such as superoxide,[124–127] and these may damage the cell. This is a particular problem with pheomelanin and may be related to the increased risk of cancer in people with increased levels of this melanin in their skin.[125] The photoprotection provided by melanin is a complex process that has a biologic cost, and if the damage to the cell exceeds the protection provided by the melanin, then phototoxicity results. Other functions of melanin include a camouflage agent, a thermoregulator through heat absorption, and a protector of essential metabolites from photodestruction.[118,128] The latter function may include protection from ultraviolet-mediated destruction of folic acid and other vitamins, and this protection could have had a significant selective advantage in areas of relative folate deficiency.[129] Melanin may provide intracellular detoxification of highly reactive quinones. Quinones are converted into melanin that has the property of being an insoluble, relatively inert polymer which cannot diffuse out of the cell.[54] The quinones are generated in melanin synthesis by the melanocyte when it is stimulated to make pigment, and this mechanism may be important in protecting the melanocyte from self-injury when it is metabolically active.[54]

Transfer and Fate of Melanosomes within Keratinocytes

Melanosomes synthesized by melanocytes are transferred to keratinocytes of the skin and hair by means of dendritic processes.[40] The melanocytes of the epidermal-dermal interface and of the matrix of the hair bulb project their dendrites between each keratinocyte. In the epidermis, each melanocyte supplies melanosomes to a group of approximately 36 keratinocytes. This partnership of a single melanocyte and its constellation of keratinocytes is expressed in the term *epidermal melanin unit*[130] (Fig. 119-1).

Melanosomes within keratinocytes occur as discrete particles (nonaggregated) or as aggregates of two or more melanosomes within membrane-limited organelles (Fig. 119-1). These melanosome-containing organelles, previously termed *melanosome complexes*, resemble the membrane-limited, melanosome-containing organelles identified as phagolysosomes within macrophages. Aggregated melanosomes in keratinocytes appear to undergo gradual degradation into small electron-dense particles. This phenomenon of aggregation of melanosomes into complexes or, alternatively, occurring as single melanosomes in keratinocytes is variable, and the factors that determine it are not completely understood.[131] Aggregation appears to be a size-dependent phenomenon,[132] inasmuch as small el-

lipsoidal melanosomes aggregate in the form of a secondary lysosome and undergo degradation. Larger ellipsoidal melanosomes do not appear to aggregate within keratinocytes. Each phagocytized large melanosome forms part of a secondary lysosome and is possibly less prone to degradation than are melanosomes forming complexes. While there is a general tendency for large melanosomes to exist as single nonaggregated melanosomes in keratinocytes and for small melanosomes to aggregate into phagolysosomes,[131,132] there is no agreement as to the critical size above which melanosomes are arranged singly within keratinocytes. Estimates range from 0.4 to 1 μm.[133] Further, while melanosomes in keratinocytes of unexposed skin from Australian aborigines and African blacks tend to occur as single large melanosomes whereas those from Caucasians, Orientals, and Amerindians are smaller and predominantly aggregated in phagolysosomes,[131–134] this difference is not absolute and the pattern can be altered by trauma, UVR, and other factors.[135,136] The biosynthesis of melanosomes within melanocytes depends on cues arising in the dermis and throughout the complex levels of biologic organization that characterize the epidermal melanin unit.[137] The reported changes in lysosomes alone suggest that the metabolic activity of keratinocytes is significantly altered by the arrival of melanosomes from melanocytes. These metabolic changes possibly extend beyond those associated with lysosomes and, by feedback control, affect the melanocytes in which the melanosomes originated. Products derived from melanosome degradation or from other sources within keratinocytes can conceivably pass downward by way of the dendrites or the intercellular spaces[137,138] to regulate melanocyte function.

Facultative Melanin Pigmentation; Action of Light

Physiological Responses. Solar radiation profoundly influences facultative skin color. The increase in melanin pigmentation after exposure of human skin to sunlight or to UVR from artificial sources is familiarly known as "tanning." Tanning involves two distinct biologic phenomena: (1) immediate tanning and (2) delayed tanning. Immediate tanning is optimally produced by both long UVR (320 to 380 nm) and visible (400 to 700 nm) light, and delayed tanning is optimally stimulated by exposure to the so-called sunburn spectrum (290 to 320 nm) and to a lesser extent by exposure to long-wave UVR and visible radiation.

Immediate Tanning can best be seen in moderately to heavily pigmented individuals or in the previously exposed (tanned) areas of fair-skinned individuals. The skin begins to become hyperpigmented within 5 to 10 min on exposure to the midday summer sun and is maximally pigmented after 1 h of irradiation. The hyperpigmented areas, when withdrawn from exposure to light, fade rapidly within the first 30 min, and thereafter the color usually fades gradually, so that after 3 to 4 h, the irradiated areas are barely hyperpigmented. Sometimes, after prolonged sun exposure (90 to 120 min), residual hyperpigmentation may be visible for as long as 24 to 36 h, after which time, newly synthesized melanin (delayed tanning) begins to pigment the skin.

Delayed tanning involves new production of melanosomes and therefore appears slowly over a period of days after exposure to UVR. An increased tyrosinase reaction is demonstrable histochemically at 48 to 72 h following exposure. No increased tyrosinase reaction is evident in immediate tanning because new melanosomes are not synthesized.

Light Exposure and the Epidermal Melanin Unit. The immediate tanning reaction appears to be based on a passive, acellular, photochemical reaction of preformed melanin that does not involve the synthesis of new melanosomes, the passing of preformed melanosomes to keratinocytes, or ultrastructural changes in keratinocytes.[139,140] Production of immediate pigment darkening does not depend upon the structural and functional integrity of the melanocyte cytoskeletal apparatus and is not confined to viable skin, whereas its reversibility is.[139] Immediate tanning provides no photoprotection.[141]

Hyperpigmentation of the skin in delayed tanning is due to the following seven changes in the normal process of melanin pigmentation: (1) an increase in the number of functional melanocytes as the result of proliferation of melanocytes and also possibly the activaiton of dormant or resting melanocytes; (2) hypertrophy of melanocytes and increased arborization of their dendrites; (3) augmentation of melanosomal synthesis manifested by an increase in the number of melanosomes in stages I to IV; (4) an increase in the rate of melanization in melanosomes; (5) an increase in the transfer of melanosomes from melanocytes to keratinocytes as the result of increased turnover of keratinocytes; (6) most notably in Caucasoids and Mongoloids, an increase in the size of melanosome complexes and possibly altered melanosome degradation within keratinocytes; and (7) activation of tyrosinase as a result of the direct effect of radiation on the tyrosinase-inhibiting sulfhydryl compounds of the epidermis.[142]

There is marked variability in the response of human skin to UVR. A working classification of six types of human skin has been made based upon their erythema and delayed tanning abilities[143] (Table 119-3).

The thioredoxin–thioredoxin reductase system has been proposed as a regulatory mechanism of UVR-generated pigmentation[143,144] (Fig. 119-4). Thioredoxin is a small dithiol protein with an M_r of 12,000 present in the plasma membrane of keratinocytes and melanocytes.[146,147] It is the natural electron acceptor for thioredoxin reductase, while NADPH is the electron donor for the enzyme.[148] Membrane-associated thioredoxin reductase is a free radical scavenger at the cell surface of live epidermis.[144] The model proposes that when skin is exposed to sunlight, UV-generated free radicals are trapped by thioredoxin reductase at the cell surface leaving thioredoxin in an oxidized state preventing the inhibition of tyrosinase by this thioprotein, while in the absence of UVR, thioredoxin reductase reduces thioredoxin, which can consequently inhibit tyrosinase (Fig. 119-4). Oxidized thioredoxin has no effect on tyrosinase activity, while reduced thioredoxin strongly inhibits

the enzyme.[144] Thioredoxin reductase activity in the epidermis of normal subjects was found to show a linear relationship with skin type as classified by Fitzpatrick.[143] The lowest activity was found in type I skin and the highest activity in type VI skin.[144] Thioredoxin reductase activity was found to be reduced in vitiliginous human skin[145] and in HPS.[149] Increased extracellular calcium (Ca^{2+}) has been shown to affect thioredoxin reductase directly by allosteric inhibition of extracellular free radical reduction using intracellular NADPH as electron donor. However, this reaction with Ca^{2+} outside the cell does not affect the transfer of electrons from NADPH through thioredoxin reductase to thioredoxin in the cytosol, an intracellular reaction, which is controlled by the internal Ca^{2+} concentration.[146,150]

DEFINITION AND CLASSIFICATION OF TYPES OF ALBINISM IN HUMANS

Classically, two major forms of albinism have been recognized in humans, oculocutaneous albinism (OCA) and ocular albinism (OA). OCA was thought to involve the entire melanocytic system of integument and eyes, while OA was thought to involve only melanocytes of the eye.[151] Present evidence indicates that in X-linked OA described by Nettleship[152] and Falls[153] (XOAN), alterations are present in dermal melanosomes[154,155] as well as in those in the eye[156] and that most patients with autosomal recessive OA (AROA) have lighter skin than their unaffected siblings; thus, strictly speaking, these are forms of OCA. However, as the major clinical features of OA are limited to the eye, this classification is retained in a clinical context.

In general, the term *albinism* should be restricted to inherited, congenital, generalized hypomelanotic conditions in which melanocytes are present in integument and eye, and in which hypopigmentation of the ocular fundus, hypoplasia of the ocular fovea, nystagmus, abnormal decussation of the optic neurons at the chiasm, decreased pigment in the iris, frequently with photophobia, and decreased visual acuity are also present. Clinically, these conditions may primarily affect the eye (OA) or the integument and eye (OCA). Strabismus is often present in all forms of albinism, but the prevalence varies according to the specific type of albinism.[3,14]

This definition of albinism is imprecise in defining the boundaries between albinism and other hypopigmented conditions in all instances. Within sibships of individuals who are undoubtedly albinos, we have observed other siblings who lack some feature of the criteria for albinism. Among 23 brown albinos tested in Africa, one did not have clinical nystagmus even after dark adaptation.[157] In several instances, we have seen sibs of oculocutaneous albinos whose integumentary features, hair bulb tyrosinase activities, diaphanous irides, depigmented ocular fundi lacking a foveal reflex visually or on fundal photographs, and abnormal visual evoked responses were identical to those of their albino siblings, but who had no nystagmus and had 20/25 vision.

Nearly all albinos, including ty-neg, ty-pos, ym, pt, brown, HPS, CHS, XOAN, and AROA albinos tested to date, have evidence for decussation defects of the optic tract.[15,158–173] However, optic tract misrouting also occurs in hypopigmented persons with Prader-Willi syndrome who have strabismus but do not have nystagmus or hypoplasia of the fovea,[174] and de-

Table 119-3 Working Classification of Sun-Reactive Skin Types

Skin type*	Erythema and tanning reactions to first exposure in summer to 3 minimum erythema doses (MED)†
I	Always burn, never tan
II	Usually burn, tan less than average (with difficulty)
III	Sometimes mild burn, tan about average
IV	Rarely burn, tan more than average (with ease)
V	Brown skin, unexposed skin brown, rarely burn, profuse, immediate pigment-darkening reaction
VI	Dark-skinned (black), unexposed skin black, generally never burn, tan profusely

*Type I and II persons all have pale skin color and often but not always blue eyes, red or red-blond scalp hair; they may or may not have freckling. Some persons with dark-brown hair and blue or green eyes, notably people of Irish extraction, have types I and II sun-reactive skin.
†1 MED = 15 to 30 min of noon sun, or 30 mJ/cm².

Table 119-4 Hair Bulb Tyrosinase Activity

| Type | No. | Tyrosinase activity,* pmol tyrosine oxidized per 120 min per hair bulb | |
		Mean ± SD	Range
Controls	No.		
Brown hair	22	1.49 ± 0.79	0.27–3.31
Black hair	10	1.68 ± 0.67	0.94–3.06
Blond hair	13	1.50 ± 0.85	0.19–2.66
Red hair	12	2.72 ± 1.26	0.78–4.99
Oculocutaneous albinos			
IA, tyrosinase-negative	32	0.02 ± 0.03	0.00–0.12
IA heterozygote	31	0.08 ± 0.12	0.00–0.42
IB, yellow	5	0.03 ± 0.04	0.00–0.10
IB heterozygote	4	0.04 ± 0.04	0.00–0.09
II, tyrosinase-positive	17	1.04 ± 0.84	0.03–3.09
II heterozygote	28	1.28 ± 0.80	0.44–3.90
III, minimal pigment	5	0.02 ± 0.03	0.00–0.07
III heterozygote			
High	6	1.20 ± 0.61	0.42–2.05
Low	7	0.06 ± 0.07	0.00–0.18
IV, brown	1	1.75	
VI, Hermansky-Pudlak	24	0.29 ± 0.35	0.00–1.18
VI heterozygote	6	1.06 ± 0.70	0.17–2.02
Ocular albinos			
XROA†	5	0.37 ± 0.55	0.00–1.33
XROA heterozygote	5	0.84 ± 0.76	0.15–2.02
AROA†	5	0.32 ± 0.20	0.04–0.60
AROA heterozygote	3	0.71	0.28–1.01

*Tritiated tyrosine assay.[177]
†XROA = X-linked recessive ocular albinism; AROA = autosomal recessive ocular albinism.

cussation defects have been found in pigmented cats heterozygous for *c*-locus (tyrosinase) OCA.[175] We do not consider these latter two conditions, which share some features of albinism, examples of albinism.

Ten disorders can be distinguished from one another on the basis of clinical, ultrastructural, and biochemical criteria[3–10,157,176–182]; by their tyrosinase activity (Table 119-4); by their genetic characteristics as determined by matings of albinos of different genotypes[9,14,182–187a] (Table 119-5); and by distribution in various populations[2,4,9,11–14,149,157,176,188–200] (Table 119-6). Diagnosis of any particular type of albinism depends upon both the clinical and biochemical features of the patient

and in some instances, the ultrastructural features of melanosomes.

Tyrosinase-negative OCA (ty-neg OCA), yellow mutant OCA (ym OCA), and platinum OCA (pt OCA) are thought to be allelic mutations at the tyrosinase locus. It is not known whether the pt albino as described by Witkop[9] is the same or different from the "minimal pigment" albino described by King et al.[6] They will be described here separately. Ty-neg OCA is the second most frequent type of albinism in both Africans and Caucasians.

Tyrosinase-positive OCA (ty-pos OCA) is thought to be due to an intrinsic defect in the pathway involving a step distal to the tyrosinase controlled step and is not allelic with ty-neg OCA (Table 119-5).[4,14,182] It is the most frequent form of albinism.

Brown OCA has been recognized in Africans,[157] natives of New Guinea,[201] and in Afro-Americans[5] who have light-brown skin, brown hair, and yellow-brown eyes with slight to moderate nystagmus and decreased visual acuity. It is not known whether brown OCA as described in blacks is the same as autosomal recessive ocular albinism (AROA) described in Caucasians or whether it is a separate condition.

Red or rufus OCA has been observed in natives of New Guinea, in Africans, and in Afro-Americans.[3,9,25] Most patients have red-tinged skin and dark-mahogany-red hair.

Hermansky-Pudlak syndrome (HPS) is a triad of tyrosinase-positive OCA, a bleeding diathesis due to storage pool–deficient platelets, and storage of ceroid in tissues. It is the third most frequent form of albinism.

Chédiak-Higashi syndrome (CHS) is also a tyrosinase-positive form of OCA and is included as an example of albinism as most, but not all, patients show the cardinal features of albinism, including decussation defects in the optic tracts.[168] Both HPS and CHS have defects in lysosomes or lysosomal-like organelles. The pigmentation defects in HPS and CHS are most likely due to factors extrinsic to the tyrosine-melanin pathway which secondarily involve the biosynthetic pathway.

Autosomal dominant OCA possibly represents a defect in structural protein of the melanosomal matrix.

Patients with the black locks, albinism, and deafness of the sensorineural-type syndrome (BADS) and Cross syndrome have clinical phenotypes resembling oculocutaneous albinos, but as the melanocytes are absent or reduced in these conditions, they are not, strictly speaking, forms of albinism.

As will be discussed later, we are not certain whether some of the types listed in Table 119-1 are due to the homozygous

Table 119-5 Types of Matings Showing Complementation or Allelism*

Father	Mother	Nonallelic (complementary)	Allelic (noncomplementary)
Ty-neg	X Ty-pos	Daughter normal	
Ty-pos	X Ym	Two sons and daughter normal	
Ym	X Ty-pos	Son and daughter normal	
Ty-pos	X HPS	Son and daughter normal	
XOAN	X Ty-neg	Son normal	
XOAN	X Ym	Daughters XOAN het†	
XOAN	X AROA	Daughters XOAN het, son normal	
AROA	X Ty-neg	Daughter normal	
Ym het	X Ty-neg het		3 daughters ym/ty-neg
Ty-neg het	X Pt		3 daughters ty-neg/pt
Ty-neg het	X Pt het		1 daughter ty-neg/pt

*Matings of various types indicate that ty-neg OCA is allelic with platinum and yellow mutant oculocutaneous albinism, and nonallelic with tyrosinase-positive OCA and autosomal recessive ocular albinism.
†Abbreviation: het = heterozygote.

Table 119-6 Estimated Prevalence of Albinism in Various Populations

Population	Reference	Type	Prevalence
World survey	11	All types	1 in 20,000
Ireland	12, 13	All types	1 in 10,000
Ireland	12, 13	Ty-neg	1 in 15,000
U.S.A.:	1, 14,* 176	All types	1 in 16,000*
Caucasians	1, 14, 176	All types	1 in 18,000
U.S.A.	1, 14, 176	Ty-neg	1 in 39,000
U.S.A.	1, 14, 176	Ty-pos	1 in 36,000
U.S.A.	1, 14, 176	XOAN and AROA	1 in 180,000
Afro-Americans	1, 14, 176	All types	1 in 10,000
U.S.A.	1, 14, 176	Ty-neg	1 in 28,000
U.S.A.	1, 14, 176	Ty-pos	1 in 15,000
Africans:			
Nigeria	191	All types	1 in 15,000
Ibo, Nigeria	191	Ty-pos	1 in 1,100
Ibo, Nigeria	157, 191	Brown	1 in 10,000
Transekei, South Africa	193	All types	1 in 3,000
Soweto, South Africa	196	Ty-pos	1 in 3,900
Bamileke, Cameroon	197	Ty-pos	1 in 3,800
Amerindians:			
Jimez, U.S.A.	188	Ty-pos	1 in 140
Tele Cuna, Panama	133, 192	Ty-pos	1 in 143
Hopi, U.S.A.	188	Ty-pos	1 in 227
Zuni, U.S.A.	188, 190	Ty-pos	1 in 240
Queche-Maya, Guatemala	14	Ty-pos	1 in 6,500
Puerto Rico	4, 149	HPS	1 in 2,000
Northwest (Arecibo, Hatillo, Aguada, Aguadilla, Rincon-combined)	149	HPS	1 in 946
Isolates:			
Brandywine, Md., U.S.A.	189, 190	Ty-pos	1 in 85
Nahual (Aztec), Santa Catarine Iztatlan, Mexico	195	Ty-pos	1 in 92
Lençois Island, Brazil	194, 195	Ty-pos	1 in 300
Blind schools, U.S.A.†	176	All types	1 in 11
Blind school, Puerto Rico		All types	1 in 3

*Corrected for 88 percent Caucasian and 12 percent Afro-Americans, disregarding other racial components.
†Prevalence figures revised from Witkop et al.[176] based on recent data.

state of identical genes or whether they represent compounds of allelic genes[6] as has been recognized for the allelic tyrosinase-negative–yellow mutant genes[179] (Table 119-5).

Albinoidism is used to designate inherited hypomelanotic conditions lacking nystagmus, photophobia, and decreased visual acuity.[2,9,176] Albinoidism may occur in oculocutaneous forms[202,203] associated with deafness,[204] secondary to a metabolic error, as in Menkes syndrome,[205] as an inconsistent feature in Apert syndrome,[206] and in a Waardenburg-like condition.[207]

Piebaldism[208] (leukism[30]), heterochromia irides, and white hair locks[13,209] are conditions in which portions of the skin, hair, and eyes are congenitally hypopigmented. Many of these "spotty" forms of depigmentation are associated with deafness. Vitiligo, in which the skin is normally pigmented at birth but becomes depigmented later in life, often shows a distinct inheritance pattern compatible with an autosomal dominant trait.[210,211] All these conditions and those metabolic conditions in which the patient is normally pigmented at birth but may later become depigmented (e.g., Menkes syndrome,[205] phenylketonuria,[212–214] and kwashiorkor[14]) are not considered to be forms of albinism and will not be included here. (See Refs. 9,30,215–217 for reviews of hypomelanotic disorders.)

Oculocutaneous Albinism

Tyrosinase-Negative (Ty-Neg) OCA (OCA IA).[8,182,218] This

autosomal recessively inherited form of albinism (approximate synonyms: *complete perfect albinism*,[11,219–221] *albinism*,[22,222] and *albinism IA*[177,223,224]) may be considered the classic Garrodian type of albinism in that there is no clinically detectable pigment in skin, hair, or eyes, nor is there evidence of tyrosinase activity in tissues incubated in L-tyrosine or L-dopa.[9,14,181,182,218] Hair bulbs from patients with this type of albinism do not have pigment discernible by light [Fig. 119-5A(1)] or by electron microscopy (Fig. 119-6A). Melanocytes are present in skin, hair, and eyes, but they contain only stage I and stage II melanosomes, with no evidence of pigment accumulation on the melanosomal matrix (Fig. 119-6A). Hair bulbs incubated in L-tyrosine or L-dopa by the method of Kugelman and van Scott[8] or in tyrosine plus cysteine do not form pigment discernible visually [Fig. 119-5B(1) and C(1)] or by electron-microscopic means (Fig. 119-6B). (See "Differential Diagnosis and Hair Bulb Incubation Test" below.)

Ty-neg OCA is the second most prevalent type of albinism in both Caucasian and African populations. It has not been reported in Amerindians (Table 119-5). Ty-neg albinos from various pigmentary (racial) backgrounds have similar phenotypic characteristics. All have snow-white hair; pink-white skin; gray to blue-gray irides in tangenital illumination; a prominent red reflex from a completely unmelanized fundus (giving a "pink-eye" appearance); very diaphanous irides with no cartwheel effect on transillumination and through which the lens is visible[3,14,176,225]; severe nystagmus and photophobia[3,14,15,176]; and a markedly decrease visual acuity.[3,15,176,226] Hypoplasia of the fovea is always present, and the normal foveolar light reflex is not seen.[15] There is absence of pigment in the macula lutea, and the normal hyperpigmenta-

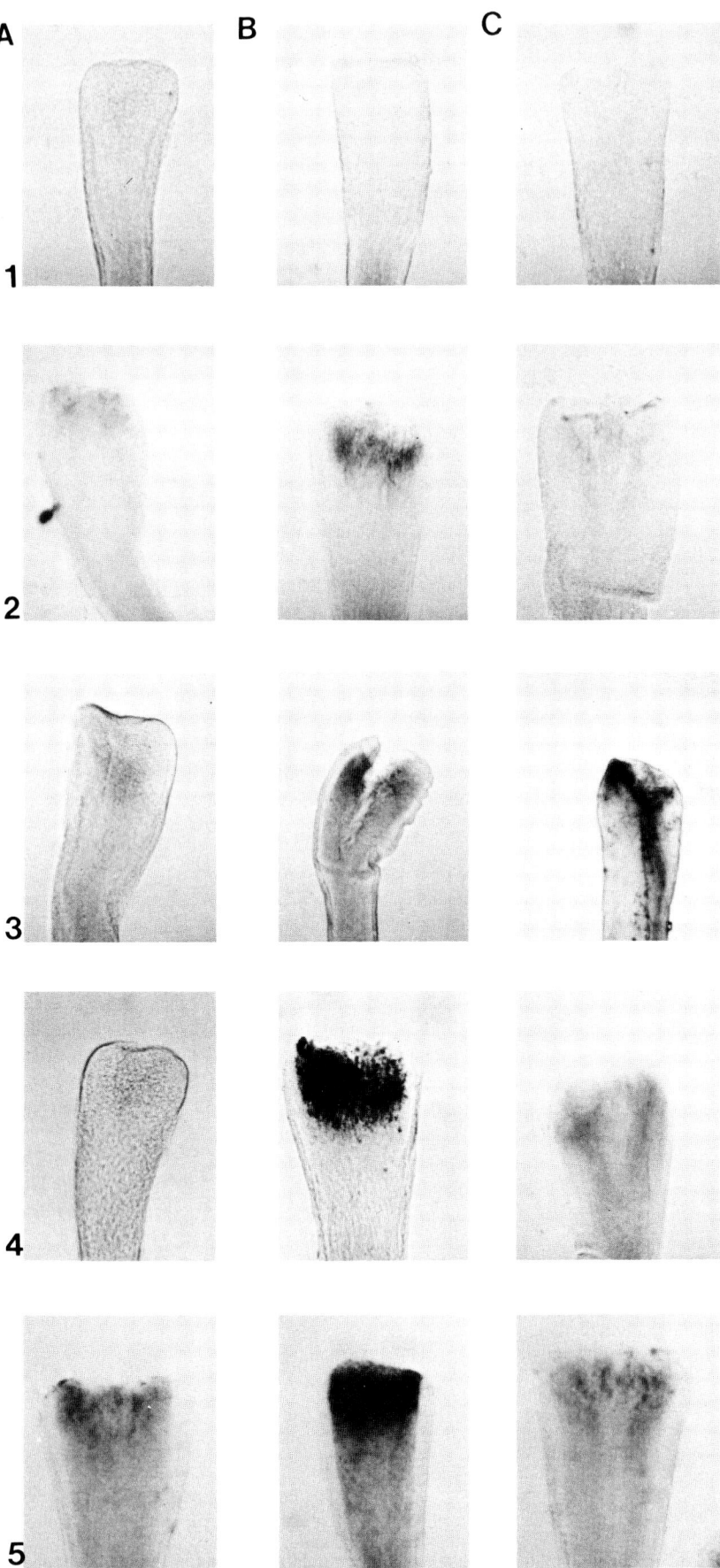

Fig. 119-5 Appearance of (A) freshly epilated hair bulbs and hair bulbs incubated in either a solution containing (B) 80 mg of L-tyrosine in 1 dl of 0.1 M phosphate buffer, pH 6.8, or (C) 40 mg of L-tyrosine plus 40 mg L-cysteine in the same buffer. (1) Tyrosinase-negative OCA, (2) platinum OCA, (3) yellow mutant OCA, (4) tyrosinase-positive OCA compared to (5) a normal blond individual. The yellow mutant has yellow pigment in the fresh hair bulbs that does not change in the tyrosine-incubated specimens. Intensification of yellow-red pigment occurs in the tyrosine-cysteine-incubated specimen. Cysteine inhibits the formation of pigment in platinum OCA, tyrosinase-positive OCA, and normal blond hair; the amount of pigment in the tyrosine-plus-cysteine—incubated specimens is not greater than that initially present in the freshly epilated hair bulbs. Freshly epilated ty-pos hair bulbs may resemble fresh ty-neg hair bulbs [A(4)] or have traces of pigment as seen in the platinum [A(2)]. (See Fig. 3, Ref. 9 for color reactions.)

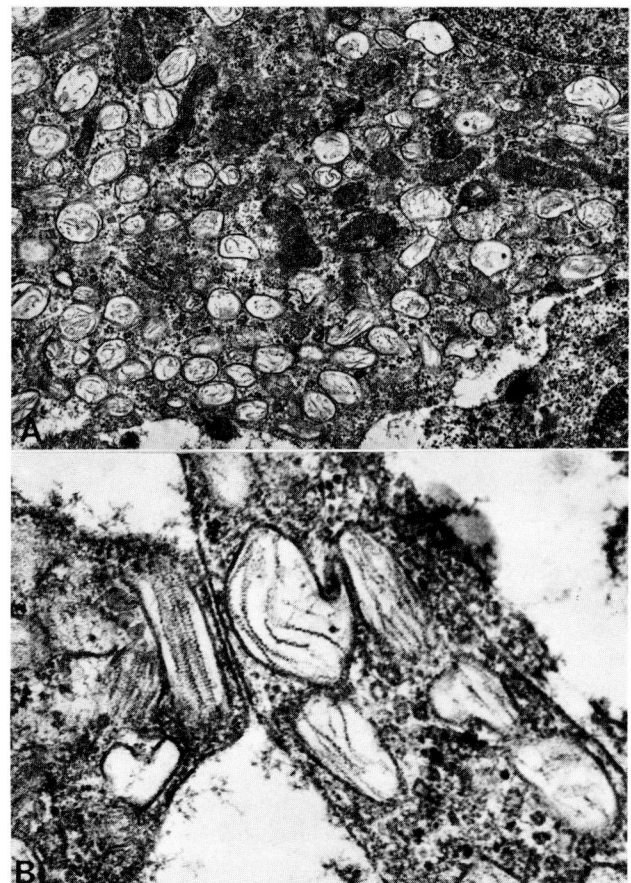

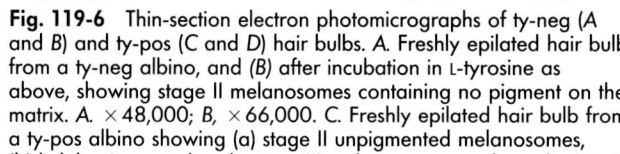

Fig. 119-6 Thin-section electron photomicrographs of ty-neg (A and B) and ty-pos (C and D) hair bulbs. A. Freshly epilated hair bulb from a ty-neg albino, and (B) after incubation in L-tyrosine as above, showing stage II melanosomes containing no pigment on the matrix. A. ×48,000; B, ×66,000. C. Freshly epilated hair bulb from a ty-pos albino showing (a) stage II unpigmented melanosomes, (b) lightly pigmented early stage III melanosomes, and, rarely, (c) pigmented stage IV melanosomes. ×27,500. D. After incubation in L-tyrosine, nearly all melanosomes have been converted to stage IV melanosomes. ×10,250. (From Witkop et al.[182])

tion surrounding the fovea is lacking.[15,156] After prolonged exposure to sunlight, the hair tips may turn a light yellow, which has been interpreted as a change in the keratin configuration. Brown-pigmented nevi are not found on the skin, but accumulations of nevus cells are detectable as small reddish or purplish-red spots on the skin. The two most important clinical signs of ty-neg OCA are lack of pigment in the irides and absence of pigment in skin and hair.

Approximately 90 percent of ty-neg albinos have a moderate to severe strabismus.[14] Most frequent is esotropia (80 percent); the remainder are exotropic. Exposure of the patient to bright sunlight will accentuate both the nystagmus and the strabismus. The visual acuity of most ty-neg albinos has been 20/200 or poorer, with most patients remaining the same or becoming worse with age.[3]

Electron photomicrographs of ty-neg albino hair bulbs show that they contain numerous melanocytes filled with stage I intermediate vesicles, and stage II early melanosomes, in which the unmelanized matrix is plainly visible.[4,182,227,228] In this unmelanized stage, a prominent melanosomal matrix may be distinguished. The cross-linked fibers of the melanosomal matrix closely resemble the matrix found in stage II melanosomes from normal hair types. Following incubation in L-tyrosine or L-dopa, there is no evidence of any increased pigmentation in the stage II melanosomes, nor is there any evidence of enzyme

activity in the Golgi apparatus, endoplasmic reticulum, or vesicular bodies[14,182,228] (Fig. 119-6B). Melanosomes do not develop past stage II in this disease. Premelanosomes are found lying in the cytoplasm of the melanocyte or packed onto its dendrites and are passed into keratinocytes.[4]

Serum levels of L-tyrosine, copper, and β-MSH in ty-neg albinos are within normal limits. There is no evidence of a pigment inhibitor in the serum of ty-neg albinos.[14,180] Hair bulbs from normal red-haired individuals and from ty-pos albinos incubated in serum of ty-neg albinos readily form pigment.[180]

All available evidence indicates a mutation of the tyrosinase locus such that no active tyrosinase is synthesized,[14,180,182] and further, there is no evidence of the synthesis of an inactive tyrosinase protein. Ty-neg human albinism resembles c-locus albinism in mice in this respect. Tyrosinase isolated from various c-locus mutants in mice appears to be identical in structure and function but varies in amount.[87]

Caucasian ty-neg heterozygotes may have detectable clinical differences in iris translucency from normal.[3,229] While abnormal iris translucency is found in some ty-neg Caucasian heterozygotes, it is rarely encountered in Negro heterozygotes.[3,176] Even among Caucasians, this sign is not sufficiently precise to make it a reliable indicator of the carrier state.[3,225] Chemical detection of the heterozygote state of ty-neg albinism has been developed by King and Witkop,[181,230] utilizing a micromethod adapted from Pomerantz[231] which depends upon the detection of [³H]OH production from a tritiated tyrosine substrate. The test utilizes anagen hair bulbs as the tissue source of enzyme activity. Ty-neg albino hair bulbs produce no increase in [³H]OH when incubated in [³H]tyrosine (Table 119-4). The obligate heterozygotes of ty-neg albinism have little or no tyrosinase activity with this test.[230] This test determines the free unbound tyrosinase (T1, T3). Because the heterozygotes are normally pigmented, it is postulated that T1 tyrosinase is immediately bound to the melanosome matrix as T4 in the heterozygote, leaving no excess unbound, soluble enzyme. Hence the test indicates little or no enzymatic activity in the heterozygote rather than the 50 percent activity expected theoretically in carriers of the gene.

Matings of ty-neg OCA with ty-pos OCA albinos show complementation,[182] and kindreds in which ym OCA and ty-neg OCA segregate[179] and in which pt OCA and ty-neg OCA segregate (Table 119-5) indicate that ty-neg OCA, pt OCA, and ym OCA are allelic. Unpublished studies by Kwon suggest that some carriers of ty-neg OCA represent small deletions, while others have point mutations. Ty-neg albinism in humans appears to be the homologue of the *c*-locus albinism in animals. Tissues from *c/c* mice show essentially the same ultrastructural features of melanocytes and melanosomes found in humans, react to L-tyrosine and L-dopa incubation, and have enzyme activity similar to that of human ty-neg tissue. Linkage studies in mice and rats show that the albinism (*c*-locus) and β-hemoglobin loci are linked.[232,233] What may have been

Fig. 119-7 Melanosomes from a patient with genotype ym/ty-neg. A. Freshly epilated hair bulb has mostly round lightly pigmented stage II and a few unevenly pigmented early stage III pheomelanosomes. After incubation in tyrosine there was no change in their ultrastructural appearance. B. Hair bulbs from the same patient after incubation in a solution of 40 mg tyrosine and 40 mg cysteine for 12 h shows numerous stage III to stage IV pheomelanosomes. ×11,000. (*From Hu et al.[179] By permission of American Journal of Human Genetics.*)

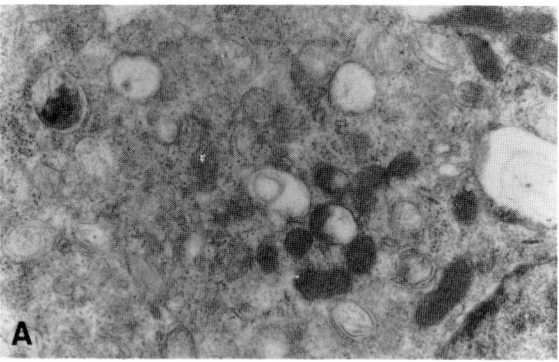

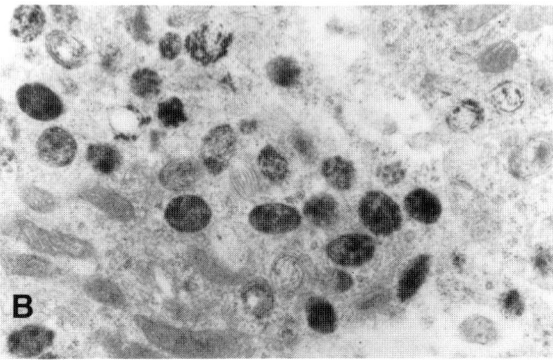

ty-neg albinism and sickle-cell hemoglobin have been observed to segregate in the same human kindred.[234] Ty-pos albinism and sickle-cell hemoglobin show no evidence for linkage.[14]

Yellow Mutant (ym) OCA (OCA IB).[144,199] Approximate synonyms for this type of autosomal recessively inherited albinism are *OCA IB, Amish albinism,*[199] and *xanthous albinism.*[25,222] The yellow type of albino has yellow to yellow-red or yellow-brown hair and a slight tanning effect in skin exposed to sunlight. The result of the hair bulb test of Kugelman and van Scott[8] is either negative or equivocal [Fig. 119-5B(3)]. Melanocytes are present in skin, hair, and eyes, but melanosomes are round rather than ellipsoid, are of the pheomelanosomal type, develop only to early stage III, and show an uneven pigmentation of the melanosomal matrix (Fig. 119-7A).

The phenotypic expression of the ym gene varies with the ethnic origin of the patient. Caucasian ym albinos at birth appear to have no visible pigment and resemble ty-neg albino infants. The hair is dead-white but gradually turns a bright-yellow between the ages of 6 weeks and 6 years. In addition, at approximatley the same time, the skin turns a very light cream color and shows a minimal but distinct tanning effect when exposed to sunlight.[14] In Negro patients with the ym mutation, the skin has a definite dark-cream color, frequently with numerous pigmented nevi, and the hair may vary from dark-yellow to yellow-brown. By midinfancy, the irides usually have some detectable pigment, and by 3 years of age there is a distinct, easily detectable cartwheel effect on transillumination of the ocular bulb. Photophobia and nystagmus, although always present and distinctive features of the condition, are in general less severe than those seen in the ty-pos type of albino[3] (see Table 15-6, Ref. 176). A slight amount of retinal pigment may be detected on funduscopic examination of Negro ym albinos but may be absent in Caucasian ym albinos. The macular reflex is absent or markedly diminished.

The main feature distinguishing ty-pos from ym albinos is in the response of the latter to hair bulb incubation tests.[9] In the ym albinos, there are nearly always microscopically distinguishable pigment granules in the hair bulb and often in the hair shaft [Fig. 119-5A(3)], but the result of incubating hair bulbs in response is equivocal or negative [Fig. 119-5B(3)]. In the freshly epilated hair bulbs from Caucasian ym albinos, the pigment has a definite golden tint, and the color of the hair shaft varies from light to bright-yellow. In Negro ym albinos, the hair bulbs range from bright-yellow to yellow-brown, frequently with reddish tints. Hair bulbs from the ym albino do not form black eumelanin on incubation in L-tyrosine or L-dopa, or an occasional hair bulb will show some slight darkening. Frequently those showing slight darkening are from ym albinos from more deeply pigmented families, but they lack the definite black pigmentation seen in the ty-pos type of albino.[9] Hair bulbs from ym subjects show intensification of the yellow-red pheomelanin when incubated in a solution of 40 mg L-tyrosine and 40 mg L-cysteine per deciliter of a 0.1 *M* phosphate buffer at pH 6.8 (see Fig. 3, Ref. 9 for color reactions) [Fig. 119-5C(3)]. Hair bulbs of ty-pos and normal blond subjects incubated in the serum of ym albinos form increased pigment.[180] Thus the ym albino serum does not contain inhibitors for pigment formation.[180] The melanocytes appear to be packed with abnormal numbers of melanosomes in various stages of development. Many small, round, unevenly pigmented forms and elongated forms showing partial pigmentation of the matrix resembling the pheomelanosomes of red hair are present in melanocytes and in phagolysosomes in keratinocytes.[4] Specimens incubated in tyrosine and viewed with the electron microscope do not show an increased density of melanosomes, as in the ty-pos type,[4,14,179] but melanosomes become darker in an unevenly distributed pattern following tyrosine-cysteine incubation[179] (Fig. 119-7B). An occasional keratinocyte has been observed containing round melanosomes with a dense core, surrounded by a fibrous cortex that is separated from the organellar membrane by a space[235] (see Figs. 11-40 and 11-41, Ref. 4 and Figs. 15-24 and 15-25, Ref. 176), resembling the rhodomelanochrome-containing melanosomes described by Bagnara and coworkers[236–238] in *Agalychnis dancicolor* and related leaf frog species.

The tyrosinase activity of hair bulbs of ym albinos is low compared with normal yellow or red hair (Table 119-4). Most subjects have had values ranging from 0 to 0.200 pmol tyrosine oxidized per 120 min per anagen hair bulb.

The ym OCA gene is most likely allelic with the gene for ty-neg OCA[179] (Table 119-5). Hu et al.[179] reported a kindred in which the unaffected mother was a first cousin of a biochemically proven ty-neg albino. She had three daughters with clinical, chemical, and ultrastructural features of ym albinism. It was postulated that the father was genotypically ym/+ and the mother ty-neg/+. The children, who appear to have the genotype ym/ty-neg, show typical ty-neg stage II melanosomes in freshly epilated hair bulbs. Following incubation in tyrosine-cysteine solutions, the small, round melanosomes showed a pheomelanin spotty type of pigment accumulation. Subsequent study of this family by the author showed that the tyrosinase activity in the hair bulbs of the mother was essentially zero, as has been found in obligate heterozygotes for ty-neg OCA.[230] The father, who was presumed to be an obligate heterozygote for ym albinism, had low tyrosinase activity, which has been observed in this laboratory in obligate heterozygotes for ym OCA (Table 119-4).

Platinum (pt) OCA (OCA IC).[9,15] Platinum autosomal recessively inherited OCA, described by Witkop,[9] is a tentative classification and is possibly identical with minimal pigment OCA described by King et al.[6] Pt OCA albinos resemble tyrosinase-negative albinos in infancy and early childhood. By midchildhood, they have accumulated small amounts of pigment in irides and hair. The hair is a metallic-cream-platinum color rather than the stark white found in the ty-neg albino, which may not be obvious on clinical examination unless the patient is examined beside a ty-neg albino (see Figs. 2 and 4, Ref. 9). By 10 to 14 years of age, small amounts of pigment accumulate in the midportion of the irides detectable by transillumination of the globe, or, rarely, a cartwheel distribution of pigment is found. Approximately 60 percent have strabismus, and uncorrected visual acuities have ranged from 20/200 to 20/400. Pt patients do not tan.

Freshly epilated hair bulbs from adult patients have faint amounts of pigment in dendrites [Fig. 119-5A(2)]. After incubation in L-tyrosine a slight increase of pigment occurs [Fig. 119-5B(2)], but incubation in L-tyrosine and L-cysteine mixture does not elicit pigmentation [Fig. 119-5C(2)] (see Fig. 3, Ref. 9 for color reaction). Ultrastructurally, hair bulb melanocytes contain mostly unpigmented stage II melanosomes and a few early stage III melanosomes (Fig. 119-8A). An increase in early stage III melanosomes occurs after incubation in L-tyrosine (Fig. 119-8B). Hair bulb tyrosinase activities have ranged from 0 to 0.149 pmol tyrosine oxidized per 120 min per anagen hair bulb in pt albinos.

Obligate heterozygotes have had tyrosinase activities within the normal range for hair color, or one parent has had normal tyrosinase activity while the other has had from 0 to 100 pmol tyrosine oxidized per 120 min per anagen hair bulb. Pt OCA may represent an allele at the ty-neg locus, or it may represent a compound type. Pt albinos appear phenotypically different than ty-neg/ym compound albinos.[9,179] Evidence that pt OCA may be allelic with ty-neg OCA and ym OCA comes from a family with three platinum sisters aged 62 to 72 years. One sister had two ty-neg daughters tested at ages 40 and 47 years. The father had a tyrosinase activity of 0.120 pmol tyrosine oxidized per 120 min per anagen hair bulb and was presumed to be a carrier for the ty-neg gene (Table 119-5). Pt OCA may respresent a homologue of platinum *c*-locus gene in mice.[27,29]

Minimal Pigment OCA (OCA III).[6] A new type of albinism has been described in a small number of Caucasian families that appears to be the expression of a genetic compound of two alleles affecting tyrosinase function.[6] A first individual to be recognized with this type of OCA was initially thought to have ty-neg OCA (type IA). Toward the end of her first decade of life, however, she developed easily identified pigment in her iris which could be seen with iris transillumination. Evaluation of the proband and her sister has shown that the phenotype can be variable.

At birth, affected individuals had no skin, hair, or eye pigment. At the age of 7, the proband developed a thin ring of iris pigment at the pupillary border, which increased slightly over the next 4 years. At age 11, the iris pigment included a ring of pigment at the pupillary border and small clumps at

Fig. 119-8 Hair bulb melanocyte from a pt albino. A. Freshly epilated hair bulb has mostly round to ellipsoid stage II melanosomes with a few very early stage III melanosomes showing a linear pigmentation of the matrix. B. After incubation in L-tyrosine for 12 h there is an increase in early and midstage type III melanosomes, but no stage IV melanosomes are seen. There was no change in pigmentation when hair bulbs were incubated in a solution of L-tyrosine and L-cysteine. ×12,000.

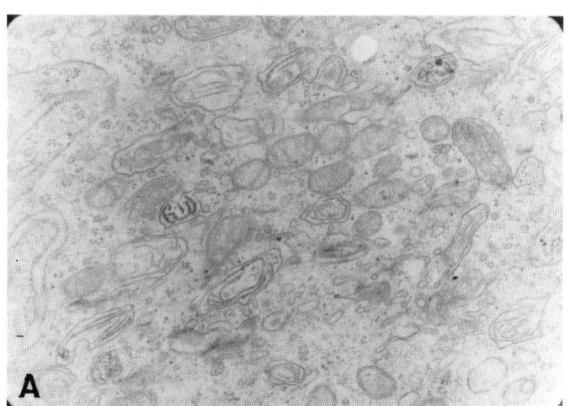

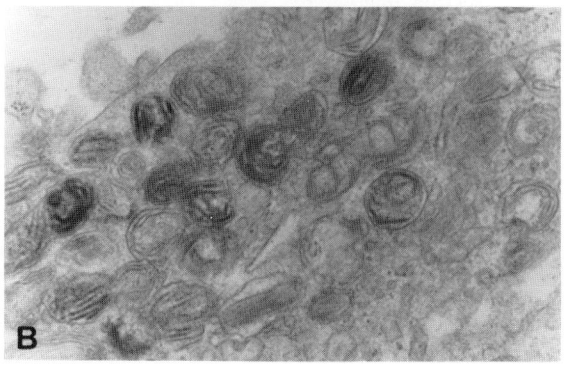

the periphery of the iris. The proband's affected sister developed similar iris pigment by 3½ years. Both sisters have white skin which does not tan and no cutaneous pigment. Their hair was white at birth and has remained white (proband) or has developed a slight yellow tint (sister). All ocular features of albinism are present with nystagmus, photophobia, strabismus, reduced visual acuity, and foveal hypoplasia. The choroidal vessels were not visualized in the macular region but were clearly seen in peripheral areas.

The hair bulb melanocyte and melanosome architecture was normal. In the proband, the melanocyte contained many stage I premelanosomes, scattered stage II premelanosomes, and no stage III premelanosomes or stage IV melanized melanosomes. Most of the premelanosomes were elliptical pre-eumelanosomes. There was no increase in melanin with dopa incubation. There was no measurable tyrosinase activity in the hair bulbs of affected individuals. Most importantly, the parents' hair bulb tyrosinase activity is different from that found in other types of OCA. In five families examined, one parent had no measurable tyrosinase activity, consistent with being a heterozygote for ty-neg OCA, while the other parent had normal tyrosinase activity for his or her hair color. It is presumed that the parent with low activity has one normal allele that codes for normal tyrosinase and one deficient allele that codes for a deficient amount or activity of tyrosinase. The fact that the hair bulb tyrosinase activity is zero is thought to be related to the method of assay, which involves the determination of the activity of tyrosinase which has been solubilized from the melanocyte (that is, soluble enzyme). The melanosome-bound enzyme is unavailable for assay with this method. In the tyrosinase-negative heterozygote, the normal enzyme is packaged in the melanosome for pigment synthesis and is unavailable for assay. The parent with the high activity also has one normal allele which codes for normal tyrosinase as well as one deficient allele which codes for a deficient amount or activity of tyrosinase but which has more residual activity than the tyrosinase-negative allele. As a result, there is soluble enzyme available in the hair bulb melanocyte for assay. The affected individual has both deficiency alleles and is a genetic compound.

Tyrosinase-Positive (Ty-Pos) OCA (OCA II).[4,8,14,182,218] Adults with this form of autosomal recessively inherited albinism (approximate synonyms: *complete imperfect albinism,*[219,220] *albinoidism,*[14] and *albinism II*[137,223,224]) usually have some clinically detectable pigment. Patients have evidence of tyrosinase activity when tissues such as hair bulbs are incubated in L-tyrosine or L-dopa.[3,8,14] Hair bulbs from patients with ty-pos albinism frequently have a few pigment granules discernible with the light microscope [Fig. 119-5A(4)], and lightly pigmented stage III melanosomes can be observed in thin-section electron micrographs (Fig. 119-6C). Hair bulbs incubated by the method of Kugelman and van Scott[8] form increased amounts of pigment discernible with a light microscope [Fig. 119-5B(4)], but do not form eumelanin in tyrosine plus cysteine [Fig. 119-5C(4)]. Increased pigmentation of melanosomes can be seen with the electron microscope (Fig. 119-6D). (See "Differential Diagnosis and Hair Bulb Incubation Test" below.) Ty-pos OCA is the most frequent type of albinism in Caucasians, Africans, and Amerindians. All Amerindians reported have had ty-pos OCA (Table 119-6).

The major clinical feature distinguishing ty-pos albinism from ty-neg albinism is that some melanin pigment is formed in skin, hair, and eyes in ty-pos albinos. The onset of visible pigment formation is delayed, so that infants with this form of albinism, regardless of their ethnic (pigmentary) background, may phenotypically resemble the ty-neg albino infant. The ty-pos albino accumulates small amounts of pigment with age. The intensity of the pigment accumulated depends upon the pigmentary (racial) background of the patient. Phenotypically, the clinical characteristics of the ty-pos albino overlap those of both the ty-neg albino and normal lightly pigmented individuals. Many ty-pos Caucasian albino infants and some adults may phenotypically resemble ty-neg Caucasian albinos. Some ty-pos Negro adults have been observed to have skin color darker than that of some normal blond Caucasians. Although most ty-pos albinos of all racial backgrounds have white hair in infancy, they frequently gradually accumulate pigment, so that the hair color turns to yellow or light tan with age (see color figures in Refs. 9,14,15).

A history is frequently obtained of a change in eye color from light gray to blue or yellow, hazel, or even light brown and a change in hair color from white to cream, tan, or light yellow-brown. A red eye reflex is usually easily elicited in all infants, but in children and adults among American Indian and African ty-pos albinos it may be absent or diminished. It is usually retained in adult Caucasian ty-pos albinos. Adult Caucasian albinos usually have a lighter retina than do adult Negro and Indian albinos of this type, but even in these individuals some darkening can be noted with age. The foveal reflex is usually absent or markedly diminished. Among 52 ty-pos albinos from the Brandywine isolate, approximately 10 percent had questionable macular reflexes.[14] Mesodermal remnants on the anterior surface of the iris and the posterior surface of the cornea were seen on slit-lamp examination in 25 percent of this group (see "Defects Associated with Albinism" below). Strabismus, usually esotropic, was found in 60 percent. The irides are diaphanous on transillumination, with a prominent cartwheel effect showing pigment accumulation, particularly at the pupillary border and the limbus of the iris.[9,14,15] The irides are less diaphanous in the ty-pos type than in the ty-neg type of albino.[3,156,176,184] Horizontal or pendular nystagmus and photophobia have been observed in all subjects but appears to be less severe than in the ty-neg type of albino.[3,176] Some subjects have maintained that photophobia and nystagmus have decreased with age.[14,221]

Visual acuity shows a greater range among ty-pos albinos, but in general the mean acuity value is better than among ty-neg albinos[3,176] and nystagmus is less severe.[3,176] Ty-pos albino adults may have better visual acuity and less severe nystagmus than they had as children,[3] while ty-neg albinos tend to have the same defects as adults that they had as children, or more severe ones. The prognosis for vision is slightly better for a ty-pos than for a ty-neg albino.

The central nervous system of ty-pos albinos is normally pigmented.[159] Brain tissue shows normal pigmentation of the locus ceruleus and substantia nigra. Thus, neuromelanin is present in these structures, as noted in HPS albinos[7] and in albinos of unknown type.[239,240]

Thin-section electron photomicrographs of freshly epilated ty-pos hair bulb and skin melanocytes show numerous stage I intermediate vesicles, stage II melanosomes, and partially pigmented stage III melanosomes. Fully pigmented stage IV melanosomes are rarely seen[3,4,182,190] (Fig. 119-6C).

Melanocytes from ty-pos albinos frequently contain one or more polyphagosome complexes in which aggregates of melanosomes, at various stages of development, and strands of endoplasmic reticulum are observed undergoing destruction in the cytoplasm of the melanocyte.[3,4,190] Partially pigmented, early stage III melanosomes are found in dendrites of the ty-pos melanocytes, and melanosomes in various stages of development are passed to keratinocytes, where they occupy a normal position over the nucleus.[4,190]

Hair bulbs from ty-pos albinos prefixed in 1% glutaraldehyde and incubated in 80 mg L-tyrosine per deciliter of phosphate buffer (pH 6.8) for 10 h and then stained in 1% osmic acid and 1% glutaraldehyde show that nearly all melanosomes have been converted to the fully pigmented stage IV condition[4,176,190] (Fig. 119-6D). This incubation procedure often results in staining of the terminal layers of the Golgi cisternae (GERL) and indicates that tyrosine uncomplexed in melanosomes is present in this structure, just as it is in the GERL from normally pigmented subjects and animals.[4,241,242] Stage II to stage IV melanosomes are passed to keratinocytes, where they lie individually or in phagolysosomes over the nucleus of the keratinocyte.

The basic defect in ty-pos albinism is unknown. Serum copper levels and serum β-MSH levels have been found normal in ty-pos albinos.[180,182] The serum levels of the substrate amino acids tyrosine and phenylalanine are within the normal range.[4,180] The uptake of tyrosine by hair bulbs from ty-pos albinos correlates with tyrosinase activity as it does in hair bulbs of variously colored hair from normal subjects with no evidence of a defect in the uptake of the substrate by hair bulb melanocytes.[243] Inhibitors of pigmentation are not present in ty-pos serum since hair bulbs from ty-pos albinos will pigment in vitro in their own serum without added substrate, as will normal blond hair bulbs.[180] Hair bulb incubation studies show that the minimum substrate concentration needed to induce visible or microscopic pigment formation in 12 h is no different from that for normally colored hair.[14,180] The tyrosinase activities of hair bulbs assayed in vitro range from normal to a fourfold increase compared with hair bulbs from patients with normally colored hair,[181,230] and enzyme kinetic studies indicate that tyrosinase from ty-pos hair bulbs is identical to normal enzyme.[10] Prolonged oral administration of L-dopa and UVR does not increase pigment in vivo. Pigmentation can be induced in vivo in the skin of ty-pos albinos by stripping the skin with cellulose tape to minute bleeding points and packing the area with wet gauze strips containing a solution of L-tyrosine and L-dopa for 1 week, followed by UVR.[244]

Tyrosinase activities in ty-pos albino hair bulbs fall roughly within three groups, those with high activity (3.87 to 2.56 pmol tyrosine oxidized per 120 min per anagen hair bulb), those with intermediate activity (2.05 to 1.43), and those with low activity (0.95 to 0.11),[177] with no correlation with the degree of pigmentation. These groupings of tyrosinase activity suggest that type II OCA is heterogeneous. The block in type II OCA appears to be in the distal eumelanin pathway. Studies of Pawelek et al.,[102] Korner and Pawelek,[71,101] and Barber et al.[105] suggest sites where the block could be located. The block results in an inhibition of eumelanin formation and a tendency for ty-pos albinos to produce yellow pheomelanin-containing hair. There are two studies with somewhat conflicting results concerning pheomelanin intermediate 5-S-cysteinyldopa in ty-neg and ty-pos albinos. Nimmo et al.[245] found no differences in the plasma concentration of 5-S-cysteinyldopa in Caucasian ty-neg and ty-pos OCA albinos when compared with normally pigmented Caucasian subjects, while Aquaron et al.[246] found significantly elevated urinary 5-S-cysteinyldopa excretion in both ty-neg and ty-pos Negro albinos compared with normally pigmented Camaroon subjects.

Heterozygotes for ty-pos albinism have not been identifiable by clinical or biochemical tests that have an acceptable reliability. Estimates of iris translucency in ty-pos obligate heterozygotes fall within the range of values of normally pigmented subjects.[3,176,225] Tyrosinase activity as measured by the conversion of [³H]tyrosine to L-dopa and [³H]OH in hair bulbs of ty-pos obligate heterozygotes is indistinguishable from normal.[10,181,177,190] The basic biochemical defect is unknown.

Brown OCA (OCA IV).[157] Brown OCA was first described in the Nigerian population and had been noted in previous reports of albinism in Africa.[157] The clinical, ophthalmologic, and biochemical characterization of affected individuals in the United States has been published.[5] Brown OCA has an autosomal recessive pattern of inheritance that is independent of the more common tyrosinase-positive OCA in the black population.[247] All affected individuals have been from Negroid populations, and the phenotype has not been recognized in other racial groups. The prevalence of brown OCA is unknown in the United States but affects approximately 1 in 10,000 Ibos in Nigeria (Table 119-6).

The phenotype of an affected individual is characterized by light-brown skin and hair and the ocular features of albinism, which include nystagmus, strabismus, reduced visual acuity, and foveal hypoplasia. At birth, the skin and hair are light brown and the irides gray to tan. There is some increase in hair and iris pigment with time, but this is not marked. The skin remains light brown. A slight tan develops on sun exposure, and the skin is resistant to the acute effects of sun exposure such that little erythema develops after ultraviolet radiation. Pigmented freckles, nevi, or lentigines are uncommon. Best corrected visual acuity is in the range of 20/60 to 20/150. Monocular stimulated visual-evoked potentials (VEPs) are asymmetrical with an albino pattern.[157]

The melanocyte structure is normal in the hair bulbs and the skin. The hair bulb melanosomes are elliptical eumelanosomes, and the normal progression of melanosomal development is absent. Some of the melanosomes are fully melanized (stage IV), but many have a reduced amount of melanin, as if there was an arrest in melanosomal development at the stage I or II premelanosome. Incubation in dopa has no effect on the melanization of the melanosomes, but a slight dopa reaction in the Golgi can be seen. The skin melanosomes have a different architecture. The melanosomes are generally round with irregular and incomplete melanization. Many are small with a granular internal pattern. Elliptical melanosomes are present, but the typical internal banding pattern is replaced by an irregular granular pattern. Most melanosomes are stage II or III premelanosomes, but some stage IV fully melanized melanosomes are present. Large single stage IV eumelanosomes, typical of black skin, are absent. Hair bulb tyrosinase activity and urinary cysteinyldopa excretion are normal in brown OCA. The phenotype, the morphology of the melanosome, and the normal tyrosinase activity suggest that this type of OCA is the result of a block in the eumelanin pathway. The enzymatic abnormality has not been described. It is possible that autosomal recessive ocular albinism is the equivalent condition in the white population.

Red or Rufous OCA (OCA V). This autosomal recessively inherited type of OCA was mentioned by Person et al.,[11] and Stannus[25] described "red albinos" in Africa, terming the condition "xanthous" albinism, which included yellow-haired subjects as well as those with red hair and red-tinted skin.

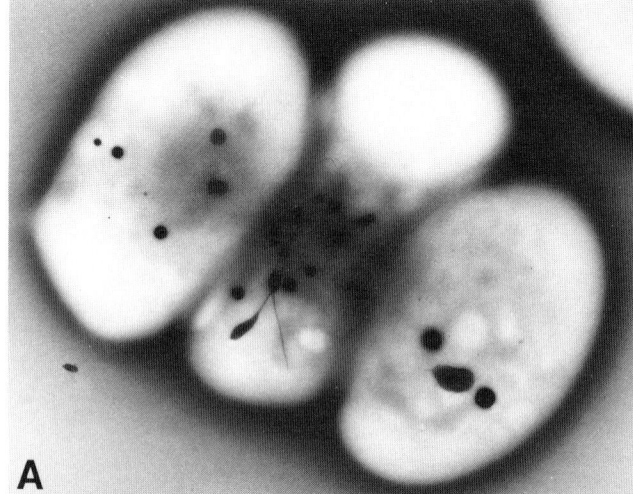

Fig. 119-9 Platelet whole mounts. A. Platelets from a normal individual left in contact with a formvar-coated grid for 1 min and air-dried contain a total of 23 dense bodies. On the average, 4 to 8 dense bodies per platelet can be visualized in normal platelets by this method. B. Platelets from an HPS patient using the same technique contain no dense bodies. ×15,000. *(From Witkop et al.[269] By permission of the American Journal of Hematology.)*

Walsh,[248] Harvey,[249] and Hornabrook et al.[250] described red-skinned subjects among New Guineans. Patients with similar phenotypic features have been observed in Africans[25,246] and in Afro-Americans.[9] The skin color is a mahogany reddish brown, and the hair color is most frequently a deep mahogany red to a sandy red but has ranged from white to black. The irides are reddish brown to brown with slight translucency on transillumination. About 66 percent of the patients have very mild nystagmus that is elicited primarily on lateral gaze or after dark adaptation. Only a mild photophobia is present. The fundus shows a definite light-reddish-brown pigment. Visual acuity ranges from 20/20 to 20/100. Most with nystagmus have visual acuities of 20/40 or better. The hair bulb test is positive.

The Hermansky-Pudlak Syndrome (HPS) (OCA VIA).[251] The approximate synonym is *albinism with hemorrhagic diathesis.*[251] HPS is an autosomal recessively inherited triad of ty-pos OCA,[3,4] a mild bleeding diathesis due to storage pool–deficient platelets,[3,4,7,252–259] and accumulation of ceroid in tissues.[3,4,7,9,260–268] HPS patients have developed fibrotic, restric-

tive lung disease, granulomatous colitis and gingivitis, kidney failure, and cardiomyopathy.[4,7,9] As will be discussed later, some components of the triad are variable, particularly the phenotypic expression of the pigmentary defect, the manifestations of ceroid storage disease, and nephelometric evidence of storage pool–deficient platelets. The most consistent diagnostic feature of HPS is reduced or absent platelet dense bodies[269] (Fig. 119-9).

Hermansky and Pudlak[251] first described the essential features of the syndrome in two 33-year-old albino patients who throughout life had suffered episodes of epistaxis, bruising, or prolonged bleeding following tooth extraction. The reports of Firth[270] of red-headed albinos with bleeding diathesis and of Horler and Witts[271] and Larsen et al.[272] may represent examples of the disorder, but details on these patients are insufficient to warrant their inclusion as definite examples.

HPS is the third most common occurring type of albinism. HPS has been reported in diverse ethnic populations.[1,4] Reports have included Japanese,[268,273–277] Argentinians,[278] Czechs,[251,279] Belgians,[280] Italians,[281,248] Swiss,[283,284] Dutch,[285,286] Germans,[287] Irish,[255] English,[15,252,254,257,282,288] Indians from Madras,[9] Mexicans,[289] and Puerto Ricans.[3,5,7,9,226–230,290–296] The authors have studied patients of Finnish, Hasidic, and Ashkenazic Jewish, and Ukrainian extraction. The condition is most prevalent among Puerto Ricans, especially from the towns of Rincon, Aguada, Aguadilla, Hatillo, and Arecibo. On the basis of an incomplete ascertainment, 67 HPS patients were identified among the combined population of these five cities of 63,350 persons for a prevalence of at least 1 in 946 persons in these cities.[269]

CLINICAL FEATURES OF HPS. The pigmentary phenotype of Puerto Rican patients[7,9,290,292] as well as those of non-Puerto Rican patients[9,15,286] is extremely variable. Some resemble ty-neg OCA albinos with no clinically detectable pigment in integument and eyes.[4,9,15,286,291,292] Most have some pigment and resemble ty-pos OCA albinos.[7,9,15,251,263,266,267,275,292,294] A few have had deeply pigmented skin and hair, but depigmented ocular fundi and resemble ocular albinos.[9,149,285,291] However all phenotypes have nystagmus, hypoplasia of the fovea, albinotic fundi, and decreased visual acuity.[4,7,9,285–295a] Patients of Northern European ancestry may closely resemble the ty-neg phenotype, while those from India and Puerto Rico resemble normal Northern Europeans in their pigmentary features. It is only when patients from deeply pigmented stocks are compared with their parents and nystagmus and photophobia are also noted that the essential depigmented condition of the HPS patient is recognized. The pigmentary features alone, without the findings of nystagmus, photophobia, and bleeding defect in some families, are insufficient to raise a high degree of clinical suspicion that these patients are unusual. The color of skin, hair, and eyes of HPS patients ranges from that seen in ty-neg albinos to a color only slightly lighter than the color of normally pigmented subjects from their population.[109] Most HPS patients have diaphanous irides detectable on slit-lamp examination or transillumination of the globe.[295a] Some have no detectable pigment in irides, but most show definite accumulations ranging from pigment at the limbus and pupillary border to hypopigmented slits.[291,294,295a] The severity of photophobia is variable. While the best corrected visual acuities of HPS patients have ranged from 20/60 to 20/400,[3,136,291,294,295a] 85 percent have had best corrected visual acuities of 20/200 or poorer. All 18 HPS albinos tested by the authors have had abnormal monocular visually evoked potentials of the albino pattern compatible with a decussation defect in the optic tract.[158,162,295a] Fagadau et al.[294] found abnormal electroretinographic (ERG) patterns with reduced rod and cone responses in two Puerto Rican HPS patients and suggested that these may have been caused by ceroid accumulation within the retina. The ERGs were found to be normal in four HPS patients, two of English extraction and two of Italian extraction tested by Kinnear and Tuddenham.[282] Patient 3 had ceroid in bone marrow, and a few granules were found in patient 4. Evidence that the two studies may not be incompatible is that ceroid in tissues is variable and that the urines of the two English patients were tested by one of the authors (C.J.W.) and only the urine of patient 4 contained a few ceroid granules.

Mild hemorrhagic episodes are a cardinal feature of the syndrome. Most patients have a history of mild bleeding events, but in a few, massive fatal bleeding has occurred.[4,287] Most frequently reported is ease of bruisability, epistaxis, gingival bleeding, prolonged bleeding following tooth extraction and circumcision, postpartum bleeding, and hemoptysis.[4,7,290,292] Some women with the disorder have had massive bleeding following delivery,[4,285,286] while most have had uneventful deliveries.[293] The kindred of the patient of Muniz and associates[263] was reinvestigated by Witkop et al.[4] An affected sister of the propositus married an unaffected cousin and had an affected daughter. The sister died of massive hemorrhage following the birth of her affected daughter. The daughter developed gastric symptoms at age 26 and died after taking a proprietary antacid which contained large amounts of acetylsalicylic acid. Other examples have been observed in which administration of acetylsalicylic acid may have intensified the hemorrhagic defect, resulting in fatal bleeding.[287] Among the first 39 patients reported with HPS, 31 had prolonged bleeding following tooth extraction. In a current study (C.J.W.), among 42 Puerto Rican deceased HPS subjects 7 have died of hemorrhagic episodes. Four were infants who died at deliveries complicated by maternal hemorrhage. Two mothers died with hemorrhage at delivery, and one died from gastric hemorrhage.[296a] Platelet counts are within the normal range.[4,7,290,292,293] Bleeding times are variable even at different times in the same patient and may be normal[7,289,293] or prolonged.[7,268,289,290,293]

The clinical manifestations of ceroid storage disease are variable. Ceroid storage disease has been associated with the development of restrictive lung diseaes in Puerto Rican,[7,176,263,266,290,296,296a] European,[176,251,280,288] and Japanese[268,275–277] patients, as well as granulomatous colitis[7,275] and kidney failure.[9,176] However, not all HPS patients develop these disorders. Among 156 HPS patients examined (C.J.W., R.A.K.), the youngest patient with clinical storage disease was a 6-year-old boy with restrictive lung disease and granulomatous colitis. The oldest patient without clinical storage disease was 55 years of age. Ceroid in bone marrow or urine may be absent in infants, children,[4,176,255,296] and even some adults,[276,296] which suggests that the accumulation of ceroid is partially age dependent.

The most frequent and serious complication of ceroid storage is fibrotic, restrictive lung disease.[7,9,251,260,266,268,275–277,280,290,293,296–298] The clinical onset of restrictive lung disease in most patients has been in the fourth decade, when they note dyspnea on mild exertion, and most patients develop severe manifestations during the fourth and fifth decades.[7,251,266,268,275–277,289,290,293,298] Pulmonary function tests frequently show changes at puberty[296] with a gradual worsening of lung function with reduced vital capacities, decreased diffusing capacity (DL_{CO}, resting hypoxemia which worsens with

exercise, and maximum expiratory flow volume curves with contours typical of restrictive interstitial lung disease.[7,266,288] Detectable radiographic changes in the lung usually occur later than moderate changes detectable by pulmonary function studies.[290] Radiographs show a diffuse, bilateral, interstitial, reticular pattern, symmetrically involving both lungs.[7,299] Some patients with advanced disease have shown bullous emphysema and bronchiectasis with broad fibrotic bands.[299] Pulmonary fibrosis is the leading cause of death among HPS patients surviving the neonatal period. Among 36 deceased Puerto Rican HPS patients surviving past 1 year of age, 21 died from restrictive lung disease between the ages of 35 and 48 years.[296a] Some HPS patients have developed tuberculosis. The problem of diagnosing tuberculosis is confounded by granulomas containing ceroid that is acid-fast that occur in the lung as well as in the gastrointestinal tract.[7,290,298,299]

Granulomatous colitis is the second most frequent manifestation of ceroid storage disease in HPS patients.[7,267,296] It may first appear in childhood, but more frequently involves patients in the second and third decades.[7,267] Patients complain of abdominal pain and have bloody stools. Nonnecrotizing granulomatous plaques and ulcerative lesions extending into the muscularis most frequently involve the colon, rectum, and transverse colon.[7,267,299] Melanosis coli may be present.[268] The condition is refractive to medical treatment and is best treated surgically. Patients have a high recurrence of granulomatous fistulas in the surgical site.[7] Among 36 deceased Puerto Rican HPS patients surviving past 1 year of age, two have died from sequellae of granulomatous colitis.[296a]

Kidney failure has also been observed in HPS patients.[9,297] Massive amounts of ceroid material deposit in the epithelium of proximal tubules, but not in glomeruli[9,260,268,276] (Fig. 119-10). One patient developed a cardiomyopathy with deposits of ceroid in cardiac muscle.[9]

THE PIGMENT DEFECT IN HPS. The hair bulb incubation test of Kugelman and van Scott[8] shows a minimal increased pigmentation after incubation in L-tyrosine or L-dopa.[3,4] Electron photomicrographs of thin sections of freshly epilated hair bulbs from HPS patients show numerous atypical, irregularly pigmented pheomelanosomes with an "onionskin" matrix resembling those seen in normal red-haired patients.[4,176] Melanosomes up to stage II are abundant, but fully formed stage IV melanosomes are rare.[3,4,7,265,283] Atypical large melanosomes with matrix fibers running at various angles are also encountered. Melanosomes in dermal melanocytes and in keratinocytes appear reduced in number, and are round with un-

Fig. 119-10 Freshly deparaffinized unstained section of kidney from an HPS patient who died of kidney failure with autofluorescent ceroid material in tubular epithelium. × 500, UV fluorescence.

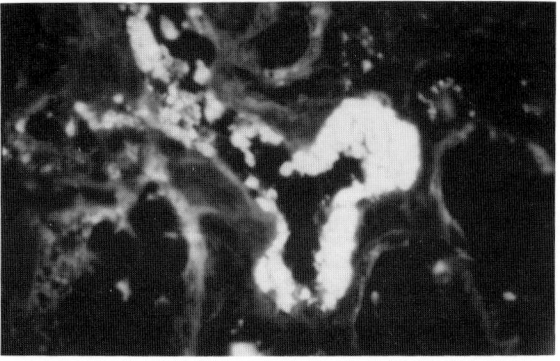

even pigmentation.[7] The melanosomes in keratinocytes occur as individual organelles and in membrane-bound aggregates, within which they are found in varying stages of formation.[3,4,7,176,283]

After hair bulbs are incubated in L-tyrosine, nearly all the early melanosomes are converted to fully pigmented melanosomes. Microassay of tyrosinase activity usually ranges from zero to low normal values.[149,300] Thus these cells have the ability to form mature melanosomes, and the tyrosinase step is intact but reduced in activity. Pigmentation of the terminal cisterna layer of the Golgi apparatus after incubation in L-tyrosine[4,176] indicates the presence of tyrosinase uncomplexed with melanosomal matrix in this structure.[241]

An occasional melanocyte may contain vacuoles resembling the lipid inclusion vacuoles seen in bone marrow macrophages and epithelial cells in this disease.[4,176] Normal melanosomes from the skin of HPS patients are greatly reduced or absent. The melanocytes are weakly dopa-positive but increase in pigment after tyrosine-cysteine and dopa-cysteine incubation.[3,283] Melanin macroglobules (macromelanosomes) similar to those observed in XOAN and neurofibromatosis (Fig. 119-11) have been observed in skin from Swiss HPS patients[283,284] but have not been observed by one of us (C.J.W.) in biopsies from 20 Puerto Rican patients nor by Schinella et al.[7]

The locus ceruleus and substantia nigra were normally pigmented in the patients examined at autopsy by Schinella et al.,[7] and the meninges contained ceroid.

THE PLATELET DEFECT IN HPS. The most consistent and diagnostic finding in HPS is absence or marked reduction in the number of platelet dense bodies[269,284,296a] (Fig. 119-9). Platelets from patients with HPS have morphologic, chemical, and functional defects.[4,252–259,301,302] Normal platelets in thin sections have an average of 1.1 to 1.4 dense bodies per platelet.[303–305] Dense bodies are the storage organelles for seroto-

nin (5-hydroxytryptamine, or 5-HT), adenine nucleotides (ADP and ATP), and calcium. Platelets from HPS patients have a marked decrease in the number of dense bodies[253–259,269,296a,301,302,305] and contain 10 percent or less of normal levels of 5-HT.[253,254,257,259,284,301,305–309] Analysis of nucleotides by high pressure liquid chromatography shows a marked reduction of ADP in the HPS platelet, while AMP is unchanged and ATP falls within the range of low normal to deficient values.[307–309] Accordingly, the HPS platelet shows a striking elevation of the ATP/ADP ratio.[257,258,273,274,281,301,308–310] HPS platelets thus meet the requirements of storage pool–deficient platelets. When HPS platelets are exposed to 5-HT–rich plasma, the initial uptake of 5-HT is normal,[257,258,307] but it rapidly diverges from the uptake curve of normal platelets,[257–259,274,281,284] and significant numbers of dense bodies do not form. Platelets from HPS patients also show a decrease in calcium content.[311] The morphologic abnormality of absent dense bodies in HPS platelets thus correlates with the observed chemical deficiencies of 5-HT, ADP, and calcium. Functional studies of HPS patients show that they have abnormal responses to potent aggregating agents such as ADP, epinephrine, thrombin, collagen, or bacteria. In these assays, the platelets of normal subjects undergo an initial change in shape followed, if the stimulus is sufficiently strong, by massive irreversible aggregation (Fig. 119-12). The normal secondary wave depends upon the release by platelets of nucleotides, serotonin, and calcium stored in the platelet organelles. Platelets from HPS patients show the initial shape change but usually do not proceed to irreversible aggregation when challenged by concentrations of agents sufficient to elicit this response in normal platelets[252,255,256,263,302] (Fig. 119-12).

However, exceptions have been noted in about 10 percent of HPS patients whose platelets have normal nephelometric tracings or a variable response to a particular agonist.[7,269] With this variation noted, the platelets from the typical acetylsalicylic acid (ASA)–free HPS patient usually will not have a secondary wave of irreversible aggregation when stimulated by dilute solutions of collagen, epinephrine, and ADP but will aggregate with arachidonic acid (AA) and variably with thrombin. The addition of only 10 percent of normal platelets to platelet-rich HPS plasma is sufficient to restore the collagen-induced aggregation curve to normal.[4,176,302] This indicates that when sufficient storage pool constituents are present, HPS platelets will aggregate.

Fig. 119-11 Melanin macroglobules from the skin of a woman heterozygous for X-linked OA. Melanin macroglobules have been reported in skin biopsies of patients with HPS and ocular albinism-lentigines-deafness syndrome. They differ from macromelanosomes from CHS patients. (*Courtesy of Dr. Francis E. O'Donnell Jr.*)

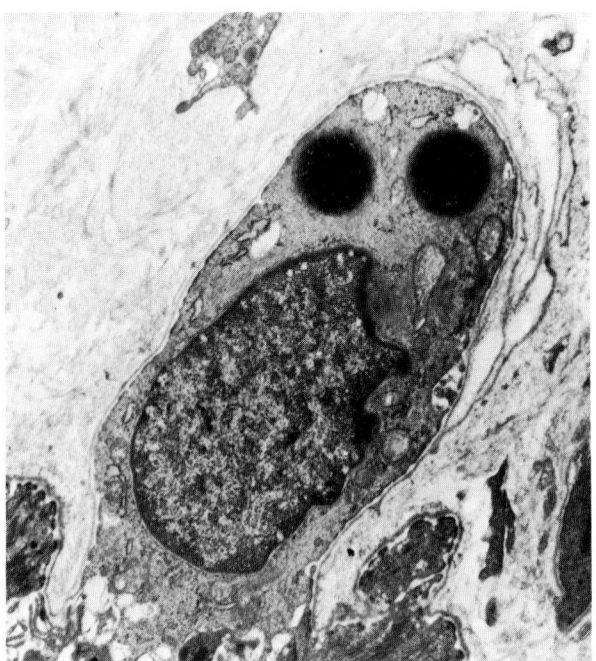

Fig. 119-12 The aggregometer response of a patient's citrated platelet-rich plasma (C-PRP) to the addition of collagen in tracing 1 is compared with the response of a normal sample of C-PRP to the same agent shown in tracing 2. Narrowing of the baseline in both samples indicates that the HPS platelet, like the normal platelet, undergoes an initial shape change. However, the HPS tracing did not reach a maximal decrease in optical density, suggesting inadequate availability of secretory products essential for rapid development of irreversible aggregation. ΔT, change in light transmission. (*From White et al.[255] By permission of the American Journal of Pathology.*)

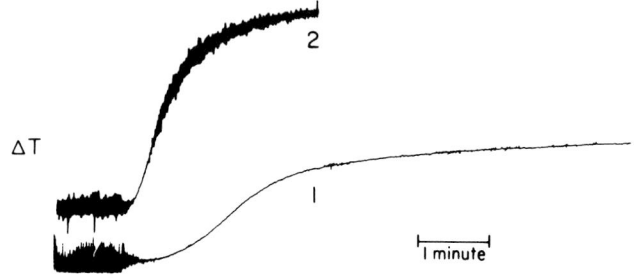

In addition to aggregation induced by release of ADP from platelet storage organelles, normal platelets can aggregate via the prostaglandin-arachidonic acid–thromboxane–generating system and by the β-adrenergic membrane modulation system. These latter two systems are intact in HPS platelets. Nephelometric tracings similar to those of HPS platelet-rich plasma are obtained from ASA-treated normal platelets[312–317] (Fig. 119-12). The ASA-treated normal platelet differs from the HPS platelet in that it has normal dense bodies and contains a normal storage pool, but the effect of ASA is to block the platelet cyclo-oxygenase that converts arachidonic acid to cyclic endoperoxide intermediates in the thromboxane-generating pathway.[318–320] The ASA-treated platelet defect and the HPS platelet defect are mutually correctable. If 30 percent ASA-treated normal platelet-rich plasma is added to 70 percent HPS platelet-rich plasma, the aggregation curve is indistinguishable from normal.[176,302] These experiments indicate that a mechanism is intact in the HPS platelet that can overcome the block imposed by ASA in the normal platelet.[317] Gerrard et al.[310] demonstrated that the microsomal fraction of HPS platelets is a potent source of prostaglandin endoperoxides that overcome the ASA-blocking effect in collagen aggregation of ASA-treated normal cells. The addition of arachidonic acid or the enzyme prostaglandin synthetase (cyclo-oxygenase) from HPS platelets alone did not correct the defect. Further, the HPS microsomal fraction added to ASA-treated normal platelets was sufficient to overcome the ASA block and was accompanied by a release of serotonin from the ASA-treated platelets without collagen.[310] The action of HPS platelet endoperoxide is identical to that derived from normal platelets and causes a direct stimulation of the platelet contractile mechanism.[305] A series of experiments by Rao and associates[321–325] defined the β-adrenergic membrane modulation system in HPS platelets. Addition of aggregating agents to HPS platelet-rich plasma in high concentrations, arachidonate (1.2 μM), thrombin (0.5 μ/ml), and collagen (100 ng/ml), causes irreversible aggregation.[324] Addition of arachidonate at low concentration (0.45 μM), which induces aggregation in normal platelets, causes irreversible aggregation in HPS platelets but no secretion of ADP. HPS platelets do not respond with aggregation to any concentration of epinephrine and develop only primary waves to the action of threshold concentrations of thrombin (0.2 μg/ml) and ADP (2.0 μM). Pretreatment of HPS platelets with 2.5 μM of epinephrine and subsequent exposure to threshold concentrations of thrombin and ADP produce irreversible aggregation. ASA-treated storage pool–deficient HPS platelets, which cannot form thromboxane A_2 or undergo release reaction on stimulation by arachidonic acid, can still undergo irreversible aggregation in response to thrombin and ADP if treated first with epinephrine.[324] On the other hand, ASA-treated HPS platelets do not aggregate with arachidonic acid following treatment with epinephrine, while ASA-treated normal platelets do.

These findings indicate that HPS platelets, as well as normal platelets, possess the mechanism of intrinsic membrane modulation that is capable of restoring sensitivity to refractory cells and securing irreversible aggregation, even when prostaglandin synthesis is blocked and secretion cannot and does not take place. They further suggest that the receptor site for arachidonic acid bypasses the membrane modulation system, and that some portion of the system may be altered in HPS. The findings are in accord with the concept of Huang and Detwiler,[326] who have suggested that secretion is the result of irreversible aggregation, not its cause. These findings may also explain why some HPS patients have had no indications of unusual bleeding episodes or only mild consequences of their platelet problem unless they have ingested ASA or other cyclo-oxygenase inhibitors.

STORAGE DEFECT IN HPS. A granular, yellow, autofluorescent material that resembles ceroid-lipofuscin histochemically[7,265] and ultrastructurally[7,264,265,268] accumulates in tissues of HPS patients (Figs. 119-10, 119-13, and 119-16). The amount of accumulation is age dependent and the tissues in which it accumulates are variable in different patients.[4,7,9,260–268,275–277,296]

The organs most frequently affected and in which the largest amounts of material accumulates initially are the kidney,[7,9,261,268,276] bone marrow,[4,7,176,261,262,264,268] spleen,[7,261,268] and liver.[7,261,268] Ceroid accumulates in the proximal tubules of the kidney, in macrophages of the bone marrow and spleen, and in the portal area and Kupffer cells of the liver. Ceroid accumulation in large bowel may be massive[268,296a] or scanty.[7,296a] Schinella et al.[7] found in one patient small pigment aggregates in the lamina propria of villi throughout the gastrointestinal tract from stomach to colon in the absence of ulcerations. Ceroid occurs in oral epithelial cells in

Fig. 119-13 Bone marrow macrophages from a patient with HPS. *A.* Early stages of erythrocyte (E) digestion and globular electron-dense, lipidlike material with included vacuoles (L). ×11,500. *B.* Late stage showing the macrophage cytoplasm filled with many clear vacuoles (L), resembling those seen in lipid storage diseases, and numerous electron-dense inclusions (C) resembling ceroid. ×14,500. (*From White et al.[264] By permission of the* American Journal of Pathology.)

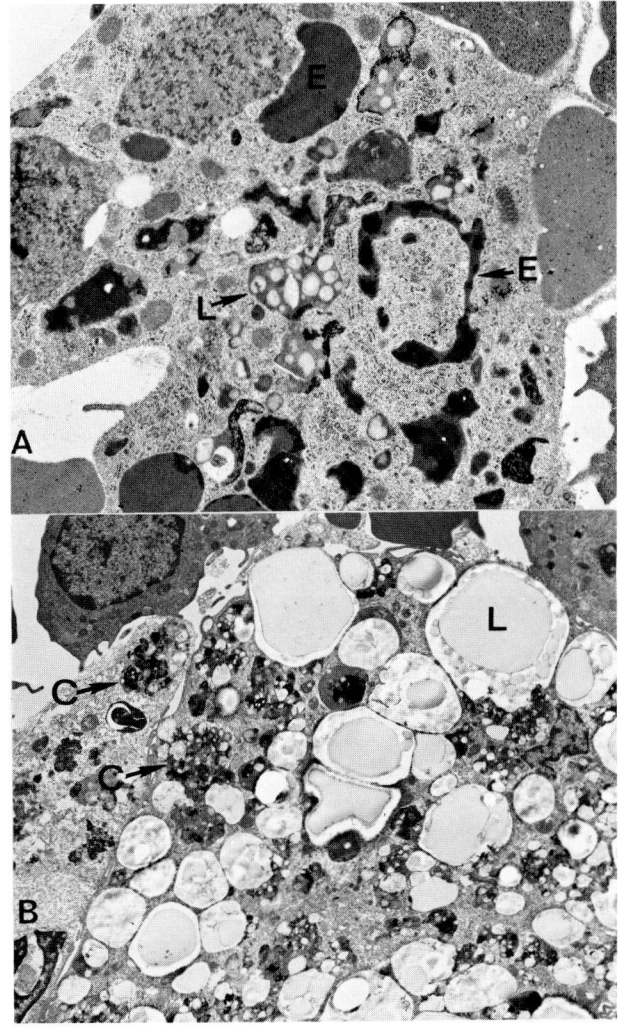

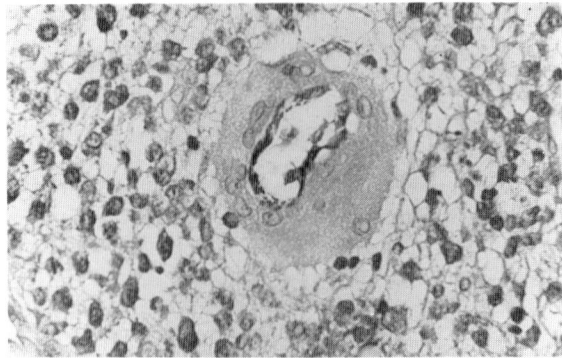

Fig. 119-14 Multinucleated giant cell containing AFIP-lipofuscin stain–positive material surrounded by foamy macrophages. From granulomatous gingival lesion of patient in Fig. 119-15. Similar lesions are found in granulomas of the colon in HPS patients. × 200, AFIP lipofuscin stain.

many HPS patients[4,7,176,265] and in urinary sediment[4,7,9,176,296] and can be identified by its autofluorescent characteristic utilizing ultraviolet microscopy. Moderate a-mounts of ceroid have been found in lung,[7,261,266,268,275,296,298] cardiac muscle,[7,9,261,268] and lymph nodes.[7,261] Lesser amounts of ceroid have been identified in dermal macrophages subjacent to freckles,[7] in circulating leukocytes,[4,176,235] in brain,[261] and in adrenal, pancreas, testis, esophagus, prostate, and urinary bladder.[268]

Patients with pulmonary fibrosis have a diffuse thickening of septa, frequently with honeycomb cystic changes, often with a superimposed lobular pneumonia.[7,268,277] Aggregates of ceroid-containing alveolar macrophages are often associated with deposits of anthracotic material in fibrotic septa.[7,296] Lavage studies show macrophages containing ceroid material, increased immunoglobulins and IgG- and IgA-secreting cells, and normal percentages of putative helper and supressor T cells.[298]

Ceroid deposits may occur throughout the entire gastrointestinal tract, from the mouth to the rectum.[4,7,268] Ceroid deposits in the gastrointestinal tract may be associated with isolated plaquelike deposits in the lamina propria or with granulomatous ulcerations.[7,296a] Multinucleated giant cells containing deposits of ceroid (Fig. 119-14) are surrounded by inflammatory cells and ballooned vacuolated macrophages. These lesions histologically resemble those found in Crohn regional ileitis, and many HPS patients are diagnosed as having

Fig. 119-15 HPS patient with granulomatous gingivitis which regrew to this size 1 month after gingivectomy. A similar granulomatous gingivitis occurs in some patients with Crohn disease.

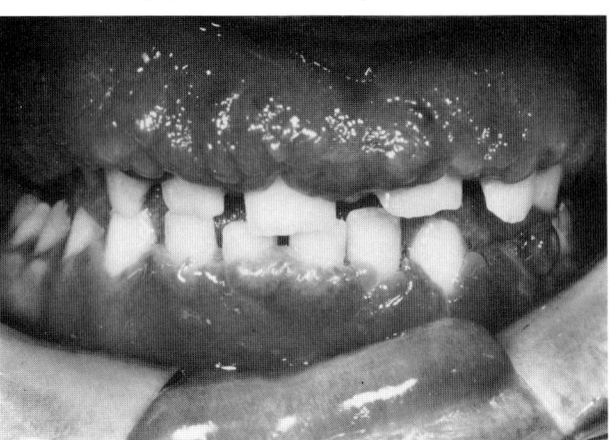

Crohn disease. Chronic granulomatous gingivitis also occurs in some patients with Crohn disease. Figure 119-15 illustrates the appearance of the gingiva of an HPS patient which had enlarged to this size 1 month following a gingivectomy. Histologically and ultrastructurally the gingival and colonic lesions are identical and resemble lesions from Crohn disease.[296a] Oral epithelium frequently contains ceroid granules, and some patients develop palatal lesions resembling gouty tophi[4,265] (see Fig. 15-8, Ref. 176).

Bone marrow contains pigment-laden macrophages that stain a sea-blue color with azure dyes.[3,4,251,260,262,286] As a result, HPS has been reported as an example of the sea-blue histiocyte syndrome.[327] Two types of storage material accumulate in reticuloendothelial, oral mucosal, and other cells and can be found in urine sediment.[4,265,296] One fraction is soluble in chloroform-methanol and consists primarily of neutral fats, fatty acids, cholesterol, and cholesterol esters.[265] The other fraction, insoluble in chloroform-methanol, consists of clumps of golden-yellow pigmented, granular autofluorescent material that resembles ceroid-lipofuscin ultrastructurally[7,296a] and histochemically.[265,268] The staining qualities of the ceroid-lipid complex vary somewhat depending upon the source of the material. In bone marrow macrophages, there is a close association of the golden-yellow granular ceroid material and lipid-filled vacuoles (Fig. 119-13). Tissues in which this association occurs (liver, spleen, lung, oral epithelium) show histochemical reactions for fatty acids, neutral lipids, and ceroid-lipofuscin. Where the ceroid material is separated from the lipid, such as in urinary sediment, the fat stains are less intense or absent. Fresh unextracted specimens of bone marrow, buccal mucosa, liver, and lung give histochemical reactions characteristic of neutral lipids, take lipofuscin stains, and have a bright-yellow to yellow-orange fluorescence in UVR.[228] After removal of soluble lipids by chloroform-methanol extraction, the material no longer stains with simple fat stains but retains its fluorescent characteristics and ceroid-lipofuscin-staining qualities.[263,265]

Ultrastructurally, the tissues show deposits of granular electron-dense material frequently associated with numerous electron-lucent vacuoles characteristic of lipid deposits (Fig. 119-13). The small clumps of electron-dense material, often surrounded by a thin limiting membrane consistent with lysosomes, often lie adjacent to each other and appear to coalesce at their periphery.[4,7,264,268,296a] Most of the electron-dense material has a granular or amorphous appearance but occasionally shows a distinct fingerprint pattern of concentric, alternating light and dark bands with a periodicity of approximately 20 mm (Fig. 119-16). The granular pattern resembles that seen in the adult form of neuronal ceroid-lipofuscinosis (Batten-Kufs disease), while the fingerprint pattern resembles that seen in the juvenile (Spielmeyer-Voght-Sjögren) type of neuronal ceroid-lipofuscinosis.

INCLUSIONS IN CIRCULATING LEUKOCYTES. Two types of inclusions have been noted in the cytoplasm of peripheral leukocytes. One type resembles the ceroid-lipid complex observed in bone marrow macrophages, and the other is a membrane-bound particle with an electron-dense core and peripheral fibrillar material (see Figs. 15-20, 15-21, 15-24, Ref. 176).

Halon and Mitus[262] found small vesicles and vacuoles in the peripheral lymphocytes of their patient. White et al.[235] described ceroid-lipid complexes in circulating monocytes which were not observed in bone marrow monocytes. A second type of inclusion was also noted in circulating monocytes but not

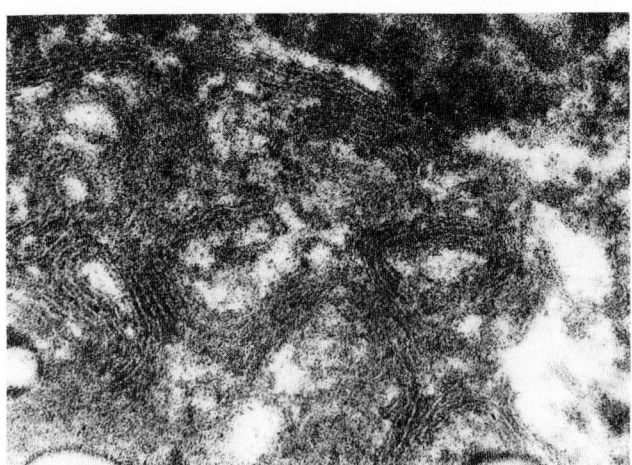

Fig. 119-16 Granular area of ceroid from HPS patient showing a laminated fingerprint pattern with a periodicity of approximately 20 nm resembling ceroid from patients with the juvenile form of neuronal ceroid-lipofuscinosis. ×100,000. (Courtesy of Dr. Roger A. Schinella.)

in bone marrow cells.[176,235] No cells were observed to contain both types of inclusions. These membrane-bound particles have an electron-dense core with peripherally arranged, electron-dense fibrils that resemble apatite crystals. These inclusion bodies closely resemble structures found in melanocytes of leaf frogs. In frogs, these structures were believed to represent a type of melanosome producing a red pigment, a pteridine-containing rhodomelanochrome.[236,238]

THE BASIC DEFECT IN HPS. The basic defect in HPS is unknown. A large number of enzymes and metabolic products are normal in HPS patients (see Tables 15-10 to 15-13, Ref. 176). Gerritsen et al.[329] determined the activities of 10 lysosomal-associated enzymes in leukocytes of patients with HPS and found no significant differences from those of control subjects. However, on the basis of the ultrastructural and histochemical changes seen in tissues from HPS patients,[7,267,268] the finding of increased acid phosphatase and esterase in macrophages,[260] and a deficiency of phospholipose A,[330] a number of investigators have suggested that there is an abnormality of lysosomal function in this disorder.

The chemical nature of the ceroid-lipofuscin pigment which accumulates in HPS is uncertain. However, the autofluorescence and histochemical reactions of the storage material in the syndrome[4,7,9,265–268] appear quite similar to the reactions of material stored in patients with infantile, late infantile, and juvenile forms of neuronal ceroid-lipofuscinosis.[331] The autofluorescent ceroid-lipofuscin pigments were initially thought to be derived from peroxidation of polyunsaturated fats with coupling of released malondialdehyde to amines and protein.[332–336] Wolfe et al.[337–339] and Ng Ying Kin and coworkers[340] have shown that the lipid-soluble fraction of the isolated storage material from infantile, late infantile, and juvenile forms of neuronal ceroid-lipofuscinosis contains elevated levels of long-chain (C_{90}–C_{105}) polyisoprenoid alcohols (dolichols) and that the lipid solvent–insoluble, autofluorescent fraction contains a highly insoluble protein associated with a fluorophore with properties suggestive of a retinoid structure.[337,341] Investigations by Palmer et al.[342,343] of sheep affected with neuronal ceroid-lipofuscinosis confirm the protein nature of the ceroid, show that it does not involve lipid-peroxidation, and document its association with lysosomal constituents. Further, Wolfe et al.[341,344–346] and Ng Ying Kin

et al.[340] demonstrated that the levels of dolichols in tissue are moderately increased with age in human and rat brain cortex and are highly elevated in the brain of patients with Alzheimer disease,[340,344] Down syndrome,[345] and neuronal ceroid-lipofuscinosis.[338,340,346] Elevated urinary dolichols were found in patients with neuronal ceroid-lipofuscinosis,[338,339,347] a condition in which ceroid-lipofuscin accumulates in kidney.[348] However, elevated dolichols were not found in the urine of patients with Alzheimer disease or Down syndrome.[345,346]

Wong, Decker, and Lennarz[349] demonstrated that the major fraction of dolichol and dolichol esters is located in the lysosomes and that they are constituents of the membrane. There is no known degradative pathway for dolichols. It is postulated that dolichols are eliminated from the cell by exocytosis and that in the inherited neuronal ceroid-lipofuscin diseases and in acquired defects such as aging and Alzheimer disease the processing of membranes of lysosomal-like organelles is defective.[340,350] Witkop et al.[296] studied 49 HPS patients and found that the excretion of urinary dolichols was highly significantly elevated when patients had excretion of ceroid in the urine, but not when evidence of ceroid accumulation in the kidney was lacking. Further, HPS patients fed a 60 percent polyunsaturated fat diet for 8 days and immediately switched to a 60 percent saturated fat diet for 12 days showed no significant variation in the quantity of ceroid excreted in the urine.[296] Thus, available evidence indicates that HPS is a ceroid storage disease in which the major manifestations are nonneuronal in contrast to the neuronal ceroid-lipofuscinoses, in which the major symptoms involve neurologic parameters. It further indicates that the ceroid material is not derived from polyunsaturated fat and suggests that the processing of lysosomal and lysosomal-like membranes may be defective in HPS.[350] Fibrosis and granulomas occur in tissues which normally have a large macrophage component, gingiva, gut, and lung. There is no evidence of a cellular immunological defect in HPS. Whether the granulomatous lesions are a direct result of either the postulated lysosomal membrane defect or the accumulation of ceroid is open to question. The material accumulates in large amounts in kidney, but granulomas have not been observed in the organ. Further, in colonic tissue from several patients studied with numerous granulomatous and ulcerative lesions, ceroid, while present, did not occur in massive quantities. Dolichols from lysosomal membranes and ceroid are eliminated from cells by exocytosis. The exocytic process is thought to involve thioendoproteinase enzymes. Pale ear and wild type mice injected intraperitoneally with the thioendoproteinase inhibitor leupeptin accumulate ceroid in the same sequence in organs as that seen in HPS.[296a] It appears that tissue lesions result from either a defect in macrophage function or an overloading of macrophages with ceroid with subsequent degeneration of macrophages.[7,296a]

The pigment defect in HPS albinos possibly involves suppression of tyrosinase activity and hence melanogenesis via reduced thioredoxin controlled by the thioredoxin–thioredoxin reductase system[144–150] (Fig. 119-4). Schallreuter and Witkop[149] found that the thioredoxin reductase activity in skin of HPS patients was markedly reduced, which would make them susceptible to damage by UV-generated free radicals and to cause inhibition of tyrosinase activity.

HPS heterozygotes have a statistically significant lowered 5-HT content in platelets compared to normal subjects, but the range of values for the HPS heterozygotes overlaps the lower range of normal values sufficiently to make this an unreliable test for the carrier.[306] In a study of 45 individuals from seven kindreds Schallreuter and Witkop[149] found that obligate heterozygotes showed significantly lower thioredoxin reductase activities in skin than noncarriers, which permitted the identification of putative heterozygotes. The assay involves the determination of thioredoxin reductase activity in 3-mm punch biopsies from sun-unexposed skin measured as a decrease in amplitude of the nitroxide radical signal detected by electron spin resonance spectroscopy.[146] Reports of increased chromosomal breakage in HPS patients[301] have not been substantiated by other investigators.[7,351]

Chédiak-Higashi Syndrome (CHS)(OCA VIB). [352–356] Approximate synonyms are *Beguez Cesar-Steinbrinck-Chédiak-Higashi syndrome, congenital giantism of peroxidase granules, granulation anomaly of leukocytes,* and *hereditary giantism of cytoplasmic organelles.* This autosomal recessively inherited, often fatal, disease of childhood is characterized by an imperfect OCA (pigment dilution) with giant melanosomes,[357–359] giant peroxidase-positive lysosomal granules in leukocytes,[352,360–368] and giant granules in Schwann cells[358–363] and other tissues, and a marked susceptibility to infections.[352,356,364–367] During the course of the disease, children may develop a peripheral neuropathy.[358,366,368] Children surviving the early infectious episodes, i.e., children of ages 8 to 18 years, most frequently develop a terminal lymphoreticular malignancy.[352,358,363,369,370,377] A few patients have survived to age 35.[370–372]

The color of the hair may vary from light-blond to brunette, but it has an unusually striking, metallic, frosted gray sheen.[14] The skin color varies from light cream to slate gray.[15] The skin usually burns easily, even after moderate exposure to sunlight. Pigmented and papillary lesions of the skin occur in high frequency. The eyes are unusually pigmented and vary from a pale blue-violet to brown, the latter especially if the parents are also dark-eyed. In contrast to what is seen in the ty-neg type of albinism transillumination of the ocular bulb shows definite accumulation of pigment in the iris. Most patients show a moderate photophobia, squint, and nystagmus, but in dark-eyed patients these may be absent.[357] Funduscopic examination may show a moderate to markedly decreased pigmentation of the retina,[357,373,374] the optic nerve head may be elevated by edema,[372,373] the ERG negative and positive responses are abnormal,[375] and visually evoked potentials and auditory evoked potentials showed abnormal responses indicating optic and otic neuronal tract misrouting.[168,376]

Young children have repeated infections, usually with gram-positive organisms of the staphylococcal and streptococcal type.[372] At about 5 years of age a progressive neuropathy frequently develops, manifested by cranial and peripheral neuropathy, and a wide-based, stamping gait[366,368,376] accompanied by muscle weakness, foot drop, decreased muscle stretch reflexes, sensory loss, diffusely abnormal electroencephalogram, abnormal electromyogram, decreased motor nerve conduction velocity, and occasionally convulsions.[377] Neurologic changes in adults may resemble spinocerebellar degeneration and parkinsonism.[336,378]

The accelerated phase of the disease is a lymphohistiocytic proliferation of unknown origin that has occurred in a majority of cases and has been likened to the virus-associated hemophagocytic syndrome.[378] As the disease progresses, anemia, thrombocytopenia, and absolute neutropenia develop. Poor prognostic signs of the lymphoreticular malignancy are mediastinal and hilar lymphadenopathy, jaundice, marked splenomegaly, moderate hepatomegaly, a leukemic type of gingivitis, and pseudomembranous sloughing of the buccal mucosa.[368,377,379,386] Previously normal tests of liver function, coagulation immunoglobulins, and cellular immunity may become abnormal. At autopsy, infiltration of mature lymphocytes and histiocytes without significant numbers of plasma cells, eosinophils, or neutrophils may involve the perivascular architecture of nearly all tissues. A majority of patients have had bruising, epistaxis, gastrointestinal bleeding, and prolonged bleeding times not always accompanied by the thrombocytopenia of the accelerated phase. Platelets from some patients with or without bleeding may have a storage pool deficiency of nucleotides, serotonin, and releasable divalent cations.[380–383] Platelet dense bodies may be reduced.[381–384] Platelet-associated diadenosine $5',5'''-p^1,p^4$-tetraphosphate is deficient in CHS human and bovine platelets.[385] ADP is decreased, the ATP/ADP ratio is increased, and the uptake and retention of 5-HT are impaired.[382–384,386] Giant granulation of platelets may be absent or may be present in as many as 5 percent of platelets.[380]

Melanocytes from CHS patients appear normal in number, and they have tyrosinase activity. The hair bulb test of Kugelman and van Scott[8,387] gives a positive result and produces fully pigmented stage IV melanosomes.[4,14,357,368] The microassay for tyrosinase[181] shows high activity of the enzyme in hair bulbs. The majority of the melanosomes are abnormally large structures that can be passed only with difficulty to the keratinocyte,[176,357,358,362,388] but some normal-sized melanosomes are formed.[388] The giant granules found in this disease were first studied in leukocytes, which stain for acid phosphatase and peroxidase,[361–363] known to be localized in lysosomes. Abnormal membrane-bound lysosomal-like organelles may appear in infancy and have been found in Schwann cells, in cells of the buccal mucosa, pancreas, liver, gastric and duodenal mucosa, adrenal, pituitary, spleen, kidney, bone marrow, hair, skin, iris, and conjunctiva.[358,363,365,377,388] Many of these organelles show fragility of their limiting membranes and undergo fragmentation and degeneration within leukocytes, Schwann cells, melanocytes, and keratinocytes.[358,370,388]

Neutrophils from CHS patients contain a few giant (up to 4 μm)[176] azurophilic-staining granules. Neutrophils show reduced migration into inflammatory sites in vivo and defective chemotaxis in vitro.[372,389–393] The leukotaxis defect has been attributed to an imbalance of cyclic nucleotides[391,392] and a consequent inability to assemble microtubules, correctable in vitro and in vivo by ascorbic acid.[393,394] The effect of filter pore size on migration in the standard Boyden chamber using zymosan-activated serum or an arachidonic acid gradient showed that CHS neutrophils had a significant reduction in migratory response when 5-μm filters were used, but the difference from normal neutrophil migration was eliminated when 8-μm filters were employed.[395] This study indicated that the chemotactic defect was largely due to a mechanical impediment provided by the giant cytoplasmic granules and that the surface receptor and motility systems of the CHS neutrophil are intact.[395] Following bacterial ingestion there is delayed degranulation of leukocytes, accompanied by an absence of peroxidase activity and reduced bactericidal activity.[373,389,390,396–398] Lysosomal enzymes (alkaline phosphatase, β-glucuronidase, and myeloperoxidase)[373] are reduced, and the cell is unable to deliver them to normal phagocytic vacuoles. The giant granules resemble the normal granules of the specific cell type in both fine structure and cytochemic reactions[399–409] but may show morphologic variability from one cell type to another.[410] The variability in the intensity of cytochemic stains of the giant inclusions, even within the same cell, suggests that most giant granules undergo transformation to secondary lysosomes, which are unable to participate in the degranulation process.[409] The giant granules result from fusion of small primary granules which begins in the neutrophil precursors within the bone marrow and continues during cell maturation.[411] Present evidence indicates that the underlying defect in the CHS neutrophil involves an organelle membrane abnormality which fosters the giant granule formation.[380,411] Abnormalities of cyclic nucleotide metabolism and microtubule assembly were postulated when it was observed that concanavalin A–induced capping took place spontaneously in the beige mouse leukocytes, a phenomenon that occurs in normal mouse cells only after treatment with microtubule poisons, such as colchicine.[412–415] The capping defect in the beige mouse cells could be corrected by treating cells in vitro with agents such as ascorbic acid and carbamylcholine, which elevated cellular levels of cyclic guanosine monophosphate (cGMP).[391–394,413] Human leukocytes were found to have normal levels of cGMP, however, and elevated levels of cyclic adenosine monophosphate (cAMP), which fell to normal values with ascorbic acid treatment.[393] Support for a microtubule defect came from studies on human CHS monocytes in tissue culture,[391] human CHS fibroblasts in culture,[415] and human platelets.[416] The concept that microtubule formation underlies the defect present in all cell systems known to be abnormal in this disorder has been challenged. While platelets from CHS patients are functionally defective, share the cyclic nucleotide abnormality reported in CHS leukocytes, and possess giant granules,[382,383,416,417] the number of microtubules in platelets and their reassembly after depolymerization were identical to those of normal human platelets.[417] Microtubules associated with the centriole in CHS lymphocytes and monocytes were found to be numerically identical to those in normal cells.[418] Frankel et al.[419] were unable to detect differences from normal in the beige mouse in microtubule number and distribution using indirect immunofluorescence in peritoneal macrophages and fibroblasts. Ostlund et al.[420] found the cytoplasmic microtubular network of cultured CHS fibroblasts quantitatively and qualitatively similar to normal human cultured fibroblasts. Further, there is no known defect in cell division in any organ system in CHS patients,[421] a process that requires assembly of microtubules into mitotic spindles. At present, the role of a microtubule defect in CHS is unclear.

Patients with CHS may have a defect in cellular immunity. Roder[422] described a marked impairment in splenic natural killing function and antibody-dependent, cell-mediated cytolysis of tumor cells in beige mice. Other forms of cell-mediated lysis were normal.[423] Extension of this work to humans with CHS showed that the natural killing activity was profoundly impaired and did not result from alteration of an antitarget selectivity pattern, the kinetics of lysis, or suppressor cells; from a lack of ability to respond to interferon; or from a lack of target cell recognition.[424] Lymphocyte-mediated antibody-dependent, cell-mediated cytolysis against tumor cell targets was also defective in the human cells, whereas antibody-dependent, cell-mediated cytolysis mediated by mononuclear and polymorphonuclear leukocytes against erythrocyte targets was normal.[425] Thus, CHS shares a defect of the immune system with another pigment anomaly, the Griscelli syndrome.[426,427]

The pathognomonic feature of CHS is the presence of giant peroxidase-positive lysosomal granules in granulocytes of the peripheral blood. An occasional patient will have these changes in leukocytes but will not show repeated infections,

will not have evidence of a platelet storage defect until the third decade, may present with neurologic problems and not have obvious oculocutaneous defects, yet have abnormal visually evoked potentials and abnormal brainstem auditory evoked potentials of the albino type.[376,428] Giant granules that resemble those of CHS by light microscopy occur occasionally in chronic myelogenous leukemia and acute myeloid leukemias.[429–431] Electron-microscopically, these giant granules are formed by fusion of azurophilic granules, as in CHS, but contain numerous microcrystalline structures resembling Auer bodies but with a different periodicity.[431]

Treatment with high doses of ascorbic acid (200 mg in infants to 6 g in adults per day) has been advocated as a long-term regimen for patients with CHS. Boxer et al.[393] reported clinical improvement as well as improved functions of cells in vitro in an infant on ascorbic acid, but Gallin et al.[432] found no clinical improvement in two adult patients placed on ascorbic acid for 8 months. Griscelli and Virelizier[433] found ascorbic acid given over several weeks or months to three patients was unable to prevent the accelerated phase of the disease. There was no improvement in phagocytic cell chemotaxis, bactericidal activity, or lymphocyte function after ascorbic acid administered in vivo, nor were the investigators able to demonstrate an effect in vitro on leukocyte chemotaxis or bactericidal activity. Their studies on the beige mouse, however, showed that ascorbic acid significantly protected both normal and CHS mice from a challenge lethal infection with *Candida albicans*, but the survival rate of beige mice was significantly less than that of controls. The ascorbic acid–treated beige mice had improved chemotaxis and bactericidal activity but no morphologic changes in giant lysosomal granules in polymorphonuclear leukocytes. No abnormality in cAMP or cGMP was found in the beige mouse leukocytes.[432] Griscelli and Virelizer[433] reported a successful bone marrow transplantation in a 3-year-old Laotian child from his HLA-A,B, and D compatible, mixed leukocyte reaction–negative sister. Twenty months following transplant the patient was clinically and immunologically normal, with 100 percent of leukocytes showing female markers and absence of abnormal granules.

Heterozygotes for CHS occasionally show giant lysosomal granules in peripheral leukocytes, but not with sufficient frequency to make this a reliable test for the carrier.

Approximately 200 examples of CHS have been described in the literature, mostly among persons of Spanish descent,[352,354,364,386] in a Venezuelan isolate,[434] among persons of European ancestry,[353,357,360,365] Japanese,[355,356] blacks,[435–437] Laotians,[433] and Indonesians.[438] A defect similar to that seen in CHS human patients has been observed in Aleutian mink,[390,439,440] Hereford cattle,[440,441] killer whales,[442] cats,[443] and beige mice.[441] The primary gene product defect in CHS in unknown.

Autosomal Dominant OCA (OCA VII). Frenk and Calme[444] reported a Swiss kindred of three generations in which patients had the clinical criteria of OCA and which was similar to a four-generation kindred observed by the authors.[2] In these families hair color varied from white to white with slight red tints. Skin color ranged from white to light cream with pigmented nevi. The irides were gray to gray-blue in color, with marked translucency on transillumination. Nystagmus and photophobia were present in all cases and were about equal in severity to those in the ty-pos albino. Visual acuity ranged from 20/70 to 20/200. Ultrastructurally, the skin and hair contained normal numbers of melanocytes, and no structural abnormality of the melanosomes was observed. Frenk and Calme[444] believed that the activity of tyrosinase was increased in the regions of the Golgi and in premelanosomes in stage I.

Ocular Albinism (OA)

Patients with OA usually fall within the range of normal regarding pigmentation of hair and skin, but relatively mild cutaneous manifestations of pigmentary dilution are frequently found in all types of OA when the affected individuals are compared with their sibs, and in some forms, such as XOAN,[152] there is histologic evidence of abnormalities in melanogenesis in skin[15,154–156] as well as eyes.[154,156] Classically, OA has been recognized as an X-linked trait,[152–154] wherein the obligate heterozygotes show a mosaic pigment pattern of their fundi[153,445–447] compatible with a lyonization effect of genes on the X chromosome. A review of our clinic admissions and a study of a population of albinos at Moorfield's Eye Hospital indicate that the autosomal recessive form of ocular albinism (AROA) is at least as frequent as XOAN[15,187] (Table 119-6).

X-linked Ocular Albinism of Nettleship-Falls (XOAN).[152,153]

XOAN[152,153,446] has also been described as hereditary sex-linked nystagmus,[448,449] and patients with nystagmus have not been recognized as having ocular albinism and are often misdiagnosed as having motor-defect congenital nystagmus.[450] Pigmentation other than in the eyes is slightly reduced[156,223,451] and may show macular hypopigmented spots especially on the chest of hemizygous blacks.[452] Hemizygous males are severely affected, while heterozygous females generally show minor pigmentary changes in the irides and retina. Giant, round, abnormal, melanin macroglobules (macromelanosomes) are found in fundal and epidermal melanocytes of both hemizygous males and heterozygous females[15,154–156,445–447] (Fig. 119-11).

Affected males have reduced pigmentation in the irides, which may vary from pale blue to light green, with an occasional patient showing brown pigment most prominent at the pupillary border. Eye color frequently becomes darker with age. The irides are diaphanous in approximately 80 percent of affected males.[445] Pigment is usually detectable in the iris by slit-lamp examination or transillumination of the globe. Nystagmus is nearly always present in the primary position and is most frequently either a combined rotary and horizontal or a horizontal type. Nystagmus has been reported to diminish with age, this improvement being accompanied by increased darkening of the iris color.[453] Head nodding and heat tilt are prominent in about half the affected males.[453] Photophobia is usually severe, and nystagmus becomes prominent on exposure to light after dark adaption. Visual acuity is usually 20/50 or worse, seldom being worse than 20/300 in whites, but it may be as good as 20/25 in blacks, and does not improve with age.[156] Near vision is relatively better; most patients can read N5 or N6 type at 4 to 5 in. Refraction anomalies are common. Strabismus is found in about 60 percent of patients, with extropia being about four times more frequent than estropia.[453]

The background color of the fundus is pale yellow to pale yellow-orange, not dead white, as in choroideremia.[223,453] The choroidal vessels are easily visualized and the perifoveal vessels may have a normal,[454] or more frequently, an abnormal coursing across the macula-foveal area with abnormal wreathing.[455]

The ERG is usually normal,[456–457] but occasionally a supernormal scotopic ERG[456] and the electro-oculogram may show a supernormal ratio of "light peak to dark trough," the frequencies of these findings being greater in the ty-neg OCA than in the XOAN patients.[458] The most constant clinical diagnostic features are ophthalmologic evidence of foveal hypoplasia and melanin macroglobules in skin. This is especially helpful in diagnosing XOAN in blacks, in whom the irides often do not transilluminate and the fundus is moderately pigmented.[156,452]

Females heterozygous for XOAN usually show a mosaic pattern of pigment distribution in the fundus and occasionally translucent irides.[15,153–156,445,446,452,453,459–463] The mosaic appearance of the fundus has been described as tigroid, pigment dusting, or "splashes of mud"[153,460,461] and is attributed to lyonization. Occasionally a female within a kindred may be affected as severely as a male, with nystagmus and photophobia in addition to severe iris and fundal hypopigmentation.[459,463,464] These examples probably represent the chance selection by nearly all progenitor optic pigment cells of the X chromosome that bears the mutant gene as the active X. Linkage between XOAN and the Xg blood group from combined kindreds has led to estimates of a recombination fraction of 0.15.[465–467]

X-Linked Ocular Albinism with Sensorineural Deafness.

Winship et al.[468] described an extensive family in which ocular albinism and late onset sensorineural deafness were inherited as an X-linked trait. Hemizygous males had all of the clinical features of XOAN but in addition had a 50 db or greater hearing loss in frequencies above 4000 Hz. Subjective hearing loss began at an average age of 45 years. Heterozygous females had normal vision and hearing, and fundal pigment varied from normal to tigroid in appearance. Affected males and carrier females had melanin macroglobules in dermal melanocytes (Fig. 119-11). Two additional families with similar findings have come to our attention in whom the hearing loss subjectively began in late childhood and was slowly progressive.

Autosomal Recessive Ocular Albinism (AROA).[151,469]

AROA was initially described by Witkop et al.[151] in four families in which females were as severely affected as males, and the pedigrees were compatible with an autosomal recessive inheritance. Similarly affected females with no familial or chromosomal evidence of X linkage were described by Scialfa[470] and Thomson.[471] Studies by O'Donnell et al.[469] showed that the patients had all the features of OA, including decreased visual acuity, prominent red reflex, hypoplasia of the fovea, photophobia, nystagmus, strabismus, diaphanous irides, light-yellow fundi, and asymmetric monocular stimulated visually evoked potentials. Three patients had a mildly subnormal scotopic ERG but were myopic. Visual acuity ranged from 20/100 to 20/400.

Pigmentation of the skin and hair is within normal limits, but affected patients generally have slightly lighter skin and hair color than their unaffected sibs. Reticulated macular hypopigmentation of the skin seen in XOAN males has not been observed. The hair bulb tyrosine incubation test is positive. Electron-microscopic features of hair bulbs and skin are not unusual, and melanin macroglobules that occur in the skin of XOAN patients have not been found.

AROA is not allelic with ty-neg OCA,[9] and matings of a XOAN man and an AROA woman produced a daughter with the typical fundus features of a XOAN heterozygote but did not show additive effects of the two genes[9,15,186,187] (Table

119-5). It is not known whether AROA as seen in Caucasians represents the same or a different genetic defect as the brown OCA seen in blacks.

Autosomal Dominant Ocular Albinism with Lentigines and Deafness Syndrome (ADOA).[472]

Seven affected males and five affected females were found by Lewis[472] in three consecutive generations of a Caucasian family in a pattern compatible with autosomal dominant inheritance. Affected patients had reduced visual acuity, photophobia, congenital nystagmus, translucent irides, strabismus, hypermetropic refractive errors, and albinotic fundi with hypoplasia of the fovea. In addition, the patients had multiple cutaneous lentigines which histologically contained melanin macroglobules that were absent in normal skin. The patients had congenital sensorineural deafness and vestibular abnormalities.

X-Linked Åland Island Eye Disease.

This condition, described by Forsius and Eriksson,[473] is no longer considered a type of albinism. O'Donnell et al.[474] found that skin melanosomes were normal and that the eye changes were most likely due to a high grade axial myopia and stretching of the retinal pigment epithelium. Further, van Dorp et al.[475] found no electrophysiological evidence of misrouting of the optic pathways and that the optokinetic nystagmus did not resemble that of a majority of albinos.

Other Conditions with Clinical Features of OCA

The Cross syndrome[14,176,476–481] and black locks albinism and deafness of the sensorineural type (BADS)[176] have clinical features of OCA, but there is evidence that melanocytes are absent or reduced in integument, and thus these are not strictly speaking examples of albinism (see fifth edition of this text).[176]

Albinoidism

Oculocutaneous and ocular forms of albinoidism are distinguished clinically from various types of albinism by the absence of hypoplasia of the fovea, nystagmus, photophobia, and, with rare exceptions, a lack of decreased visual acuity.[2,176] For discussions of various forms of albinoidism and other pigment disorders, readers are referred to general texts[9,15,176,443] and previous editions of this text.[176]

DEFECTS ASSOCIATED WITH ALBINISM

Ocular defects that have been found with various types of albinism include minor abnormalities of color vision[483–490] and anterior chamber defects of the Axenfeld type.[491–498] They occur in both OCA and OA albinos with sufficient frequency to be more than a chance association.

Edmonds[483] noted a mild red defect in one of 16 albino patients. Investigations by Pickford,[484,485] Taylor,[486] Pickford and Taylor,[487] Krill,[488] and Krill and Fishman[489] reported a red defect consistent with mild forms of protonomaly in some but not all patients.[488] Lourenço et al.[490] tested 10 black ty-pos albinos utilizing the Farnsworth-Munsell 100-hue test and Nagel anomaloscope and found that as a group albinos showed an increased number of errors on the 100-hue test and a widening into the red end of the Rayleigh equation.

Axenfeld's anomaly has been described in OCA,[14,176,491,494,496,497] in both ty-neg[494] and ty-pos patients,[14,176] and in OA.[492,495,497,498] Witkop[14] found that 25 percent of the ty-pos OCA albinos in the Brandywine isolate had mesodermal remnants on the anterior surface of the iris and posterior surface of the cornea. Van Dorp et al.[497] found Axenfeld's anomaly in 7 percent of an albino population and concluded that the association of Axenfeld's anomaly and albinism is causally related.

The Central Nervous System in Albinos

Optic Neurologic Defects in Albinos. In vertebrates with laterally placed eyes and panoramic vision, such as most fish, amphibians, reptiles, and birds,[499] there is a complete decussation of optic fibers at the chiasma. As the eyes shift to a frontal position and develop stereoscopic vision, the proportion of optic fibers that originates in the temporal retina and does not decussate increases (rat, 10 percent; dog and horse, 20 percent; cat, 30 to 40 percent).[499–501] Primates and humans have from 45 to 50 percent uncrossed fibers.[502]

Albino humans with all types of OCA (ty-neg, ty-pos, ym, HPS, brown) and OA (XOAN, AROA)[157–174] have abnormal optic neuronal pathways, as do albino animals,[503–513] in that most fibers from the temporal retina, which in normally pigmented animals course to the same side of the brain as the eye of origin, cross to the opposite side (Fig. 119-17). These anatomic abnormalities in the albino optic neuronal pathway result in behavioral[514] and electrophysiological abnormalities.[500,515,516] These are detectable in humans as asymmetric monocular stimulated visually evoked potentials most consistently asymmetric in the P2 peak at about 100 to 120 ms latency.[158,165,166,169] As a result of this defect at the chiasm, albinos lack the internal mechanism for binocular vision. The defect is independent of species and has been demonstrated in various animals with mutations at the c-locus (tyrosinase locus), including the albino (c/c) guinea pig,[500,512,518] rat,[503,508,514–517] rabbit,[504,512,518] mink,[512,513] ferret,[507,527] Siamese (c^s/c^s),[505,506,519–521,524–526,528,529] and albino (c/c) cats,[531] monkey,[522,523] and chinchilla (c^{ch}/c^{ch}) white tiger.[510]

Initially, it was postulated that the neuronal defect resulted from a nonpigmentary function of tyrosinase, which is defective or deficient in these animals, but the defect is not confined to animals or humans with mutations at the c-locus. Anatomic studies of the brains of two ty-pos and one ty-neg human albinos showed evidence of disorganization of the retinogeniculate tracts[159,530] (Fig. 119-18). Witkop et al.[4] and Creel et al.[158,162] postulated that the optic defect is associated with any defect which results in the absence of pigment in the developing optic cup during the critical developmental stage specifying growth of optic cup neurons to their brain targets regardless of the underlying genetic mechanism affecting pigment formation. In animals with binocular visual systems, the line of the retina defining whether cells send axons contralaterally or ipsilaterally corresponds to the representation of the vertical meridian, which receives images projected directly in front of the animal. When pigment in the developing optic cup and stalk absent in normally binocular system animals, the visual system reverts to the more primitive panoramic system. Evidence from Siamese cats suggests that the midportions of the temporal retina are most susceptible to the anomaly[520,521] (Fig. 119-17).

The pathways from the lateral geniculate ganglion to the

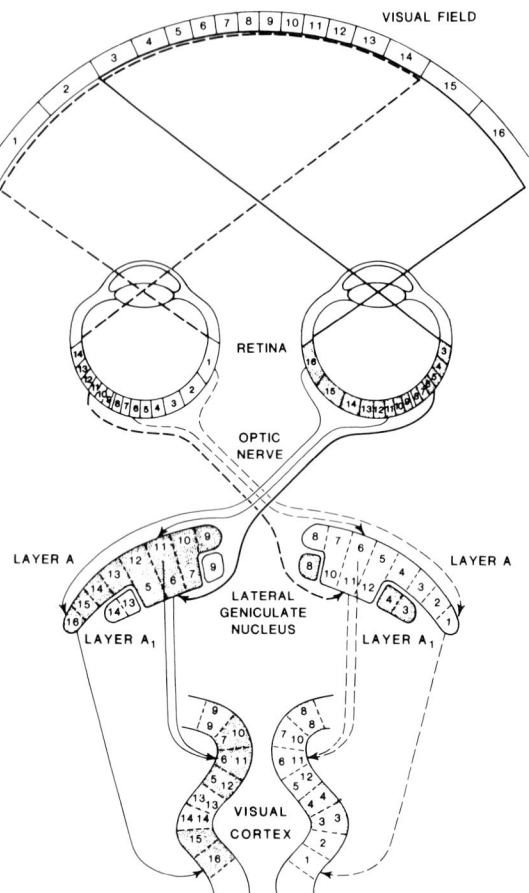

Fig. 119-17 Schematic representation of abnormal pathways (heavy arrows) to the lateral geniculate nuclei in the Siamese cat. If the connections from the lateral geniculate nuclei were normal, then the effects shown in the visual cortex would be expected. Projections from the two layers of the lateral geniculate would conflict, so that neural activity at a single point in the cortex would be interpreted as stimuli in two parts of the visual field, such as in segments 5 and 12. *(From Guillery.[526] By permission of Scientific American.)*

not associated with a particular type of ty-pos or ty-neg albinism, but both patterns were found in various mutants. Further, a single patient had different patterns in the right and left cortex. Cooper and Blasdel[528] suggested that the two patterns, Boston and Midwestern, may represent ends of a continuum.

During embryonic development the ipsilateral retinogeniculate projections in Siamese cats are delayed and appear several days later than in normal cats.[529] The anomalous connections in the geniculocortical pathways are secondary to the chiasmic misrouting.[530] The number of misrouted neurons at the chiasm correlates with the amount of retinal pigment in the animal. The number of misrouted temporal retinal fibers in the Siamese is less than in the (c/c) albino cat.[530,531] Three patterns of geniculocortical projection have been recognized. Two in Siamese cats, the Midwestern and Boston patterns (Fig. 119-19), and the albino pattern in (c/c) cats.[531] In Siamese cats, the proportion of misrouted temporal fibers is smaller than in the albino cat, and competition of both types of fibers results in mixed hemifield domains (Boston) or supression (Midwestern) patterns.[530,531] In albino cats, most fibers are crossed at the chiasm. In visual cortex in areas 17 and 18, the two hemifields are grouped into a system of alternating retinotopically organized domains.[531] These patterns are thought to be influenced by two developmental processes. One is retinal, and the other is nonretinal.[530,532] A roughly normal geniculocortical projection has been shown to develop when the retinal afferents were removed in fetal ferrets.[532]

Investigations concerning the possible role of melanin in di-

Fig. 119-18 Drawings of frontal sections taken at comparable levels through the lateral geniculate nuclei of a normal (1) and a ty-pos albino (2) brain. The most rostral sections (level a) pass through the zone in which the six-layered and the four-layered segments are fusing. The magnocellular layers are shown in black, and the conventional numbering is indicated where six layers are evident. The bilaminar part of the nucleus is indicated by unlabeled arrows. Notice the small size of the albino nucleus, absence of the swelling adjacent to the tip, and disruption and fusion of layers compared with the normal. Scale = 2 mm. *(From Guillery et al.[159] By permission of Brain Research.)*

visual cortex, the geniculocortical tracts, are also anomalous in albinos.[505,520,521,524] Guillery and coworkers[525,526] reasoned that given the initial decussation defect of the retinogeniculate pathway and normal connections from the lateral geniculate nucleus to the cortex, there would be a disruption of the order of the visual field segments, an inversion of a portion of the visual field as a reversal of normal such that there would be an ascending sequence in one layer of the cortex and a descending sequence in the same layer, and a noncorrespondence or mismatching of two adjacent layers (Fig. 119-17). It was found that partial compensation for these abnormalities was achieved in two ways in cats from different regions and in ferrets.[527] In the "Midwestern" pattern the input to the cortex from the A_1 layer of the lateral geniculate nucleus (normally, temporal retinal nondecussated input) was suppressed. In the "Boston" pattern a rerouting of axons occurred, reversing the order of the misdirected mid-half-field segments[525,526] (Fig. 119-19). While both patterns partially correct the order of the field projection in the cortex, they are incompatible with a binocular visual mechanism. Carroll and associates,[163,164] utilizing visually evoked potentials simultaneously recorded from multiple electrodes over the visual cortex area of human albinos, found two patterns of response which were suggestive of a Boston or a Midwestern model. The particular pattern was

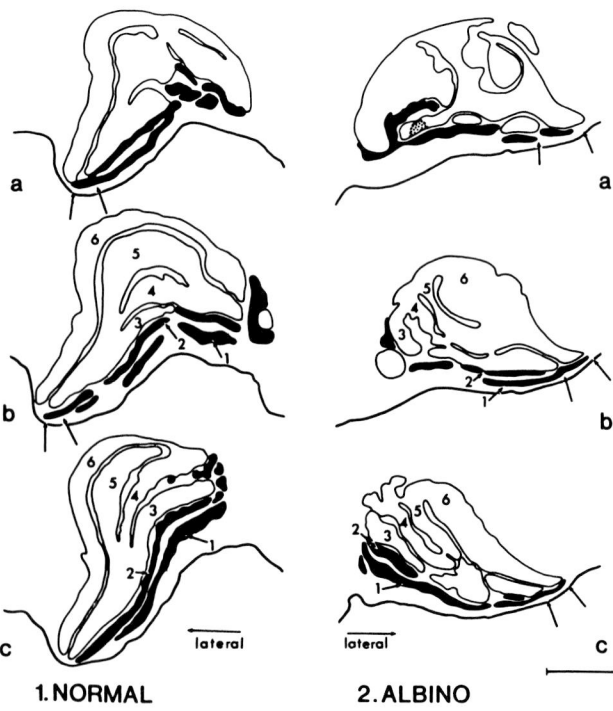

1. NORMAL   **2. ALBINO**

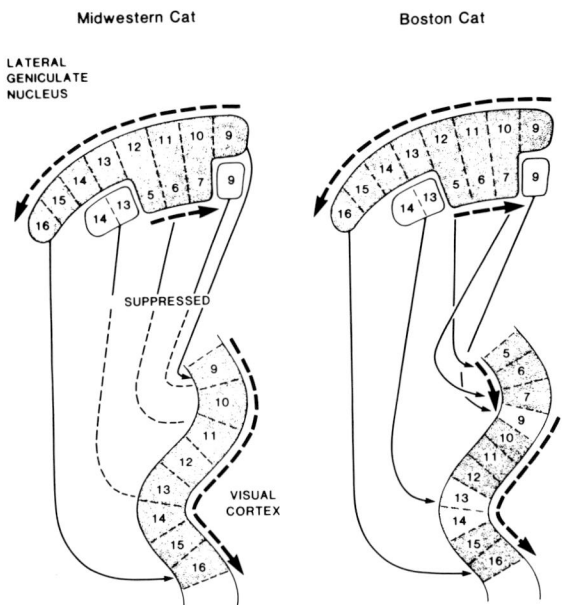

Midwestern Cat   Boston Cat

LATERAL
GENICULATE
NUCLEUS

SUPPRESSED

VISUAL
CORTEX

Fig. 119-19 Schematic representation of two types of patterns in the geniculocortical projections in Siamese cats which compensate for the disrupted projections in the lateral geniculate nucleus, illustrated here for the left side of the brain. In a "Midwestern" cat the input to the cortex from layer A is largely suppressed, eliminating the misdirected segments 5 to 7. Thus, the misdirected part of the visual field, although projected to the wrong cortex, "reads" correctly as a more or less continuous picture of the outside world. (From Guillery.[526] By permission of Scientific American.)

recting normal retinogeniculate innervation have concentrated on the transient accumulation of melanin in the developing optic stalk.[533–535] The early optic cup consists of a layer of retinal ganglion cells surrounded by a layer of pigment cells on a stalk connecting this structure to the brain.

Retinofugal neurons grow from the retinal ganglion cells through the stalk to the brain.[533] Strongin and Guillery[533] showed that there was no difference in degenerative cellular changes within the cup of albino and pigmented mouse, hamster, ferret, and human embryos. However in the stalk, concentrations of melanocytes showed lysis of melanosomes in pigmented animals but not in albinos, and neuronal cells were found to contain electron-dense granules at this point, which suggested that melanin played a role in directing optic neurons. Silver and Sapiro[534] showed that in pigmented animals the upper wall of the distal half of the eye stalk is transiently pigmented prior to the migration of pioneer optic axons. Outgrowing neurites avoid this melanotic stretch of neurons and preferentially grow through extracellular tunnels in the pigment-free zones of the distal stalk. Pigment is absent from the midpoint of the stalk to the brain. At the pigment–pigment-free margin many axons shift upward. In albino animals, some pioneering axons invade all nonpigmented areas, both the upper (normally pigmented) and lower wall. Thus, the normal topographic arrangement of pioneer optic neurons is altered in the albino (see Fig. 8, Ref. 534). Dräger[535] found high affinity for binding ^{45}Ca was localized to melaninized areas of the eye. She suggested that melanin binding of calcium may reduce calcium in cells affecting gap junction formation. Absence of a melanin-calcium sink could alter gap junction formation, resulting in a temporal coordination defect in developing neurons in albinos.

Altered retinal afferent projections in albino animals have been implicated in alterations in the efferent oculomotor sys-

tem affecting nystagmus and strabismus in albinos.[536–538] Collewijn et al.[536] found that in albino rabbits restricting visual contrast to the anterior sector of the visual field—this sector being binocular in pigmented rabbits and somewhat homologous to the temporal retina in humans—resulted in a dramatically increased nystagmus. When a target was moved, horizontal optokinetic eye movements were inverted and the direction of pursuit by the eye was opposite to that of the stimulus. The researchers postulated that the optokinetic inversion could be causally associated with nystagmus in mammals, particularly cats and humans, in which species large proportions of temporal neurons remain ipsilateral in normal pigmented subjects but are rerouted to the contralateral side in the albino. Subsequent studies[536–537] showed that the defect most likely resided in miswiring of neuronal connections at the retina such that some cells have their directional selectivity inverted 180°. Stimulation of the nasal retina in hypopigmented subjects results in normal following movements, but stimulation of the temporal retina results in movement of the eye in a direction opposite and sometimes oblique to the motion of the stimulus. The effect is destabilization of the image on the retina, a misdirection of ocular motor reflexes, a deterioration of binocular coordination, and a tendency of the motor reflexes to drive the eyes in different directions. It is thought that this miscoordination accounts for the high prevalence of strabismus in albino patients.

Otic Neurologic Defects in Albinos. The auditory system in mammals, while more complex, is somewhat analogous to the optic system in that pigment is normally found in the inner ear[539] and there are both decussated and nondecussated neuronal paths in the brain.[540] The amount of pigment in the inner ear is correlated with the amount of pigment in the iris[541] and is absent or reduced in albinos.[539] Evidence that an analogous decussation defect may exist in the auditory system of human ty-neg, ty-pos, and HPS albinos was presented by Creel et al.[542] Subsequent studies by this group of investigators showed that CHS patients[168] and albino cats[543,544] had similar defects in auditory brainstem neuronal tracts. Brainstem auditorily evoked potentials in human albinos indicated a significant hemispheric asymmetry symptomatic of differences between decussated and nondecussated auditory pathways approximately at the level of the superior olivary nuclei, and most likely at the medial superior olive (Fig. 119-20). In albino c-locus cats, neurons in the medial superior olivary nucleus were, on average, 40 percent smaller than in pigmented animals, with no overlap in neuronal size distributions for the two groups of animals.[544]

A number of investigations have been conducted concerning the possible role of melanin in the inner ear as a mechanism for attenuating noise trauma.[545–548] Hood et al.,[545] on the basis of temporary threshold shift (TTS) following intense noise challenge, postulated that melanin in the inner ear acts as a protective mechanism for noise trauma. Carlin and McCroskey,[546] utilizing eye color as an indicator of the amount of pigment in the inner ear, found significant differences in permanent threshold shift in industrial employees that correlated with eye color. Garber et al.[547] showed that ty-pos, ty-neg, and HPS albinos had significantly greater TTS following 100- and 110-dB challenges than did blue- or brown-eyed normal subjects. Further, albinos had significant differences from pigmented subjects in dichotic hearing tasks that were compatible with a possible decussation defect in the auditory tract. Conlee et al.[548] showed that albino guinea pigs had a greater suscep-

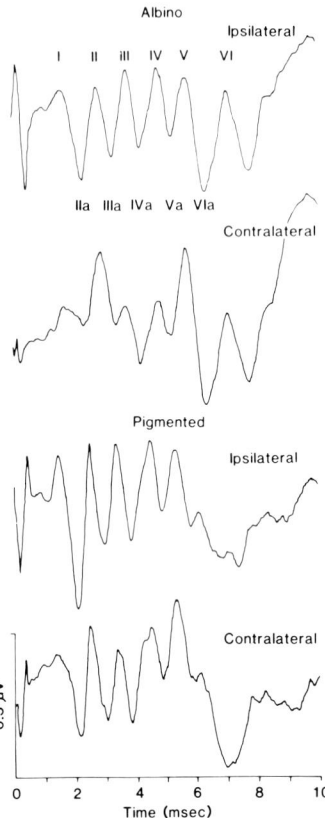

Fig. 119-20 Brainstem auditorily evoked potentials recorded from hemispheres ipsilateral and contralateral to the stimulated ear in a human ty-neg albino and a pigmented subject showing over 50 percent attenuation of component III in the contralateral potential in the albino. The medial superior olive is most likely the primary generator of component III. *(From Creel et al.[542] By permission of Science.)*

tibility to noise-induced permanent threshold shift than pigmented guinea pigs. Possibly melanin in the inner ear acts through its role as a semiconductor with high redox potential,[549] attenuating sound energy peaks by converting them to thermal energy.[550] Certain drugs preferentially bind to malanin and may be involved in ototoxicity. Many show different anatomic distributions in pigmented and albino animals, and albino animals have different reactions to certain drugs than pigmented animals.[551-555]

The locus ceruleus and substantia nigra in albinos contain neuromelanin,[7,159,240] which is synthesized by tyrosine hydroxylase rather than tyrosinase.

An occasional albino will have both mental retardation and some type of albinism. This probably results by chance association, particularly in kindreds in which parents are consanguineous, or secondary to severe visual and auditory defects, as in BADS. Albinos in general have the same range of IQ scores as normally pigmented persons.[556,557]

CARCINOMA IN ALBINOS

Patients with OCA, especially from tropical climates, are susceptible to neoplastic skin lesions.[191,197,200,558,559] The primary lesions are found almost exclusively on sun-exposed sites, such as the head, neck, and arms, with a predilection for the malar ridges, cheek, scalp, ear, and neck. Ty-pos and HPS albinos develop goose foot–shaped lentigines, solar keratoses, and

squamous cell carcinoma.[191,197,200] While albinos have been reported with melanomas,[558,560-569] and we have observed HPS and ty-pos patients with melanomas,[282] these tumors are probably less frequent in albinos than in normally pigmented persons. Skin carcinomas in albinos are primarily squamous cell tumors arising from solar keratoses.[191,200] Among 512 albinos studied in Nigeria, 50 percent had developed solar keratoses by 14 years of age and 50 percent had developed squamous-cell carcinoma by 26 years of age. No patient beyond 40 years of age was found in this albino population, nearly all having died of their malignancies prior to that age. Among 1286 albinos residing in tropical climates, none had melanomas, and basal cell carcinoma was rare.[191,200] The carcinomas tend to be well-differentiated histologically and to metastasize late. Ty-pos and HPS albinos did not show an increased frequency of chromosomal abnormalities in their lymphocytes or fibroblasts.[3,7,351] CHS patients have a predilection for pigmentary and papillary lesions of the skin,[355,360,364,570,571] but lymphoreticular malignancy is their major neoplastic problem.

DIFFERENTIAL DIAGNOSIS AND THE HAIR BULB INCUBATION TEST

The diagnosis of any particular type of albinism is made on the basis of both clinical and laboratory features. The ocular findings are the most important clinical signs and symptoms in making a diagnosis of any form of albinism. In order of constancy, they are: hypoplasia of the fovea; nystagmus; transillumination of the irides; depigmentation of the fundi; photophobia; and decreased visual acuity. Asymmetric monocular visually evoked potentials are of value in confirming the albinic pattern of the optic decussation defect.[165,166,170] In addition, hypopigmentation of the hair, skin, and eyes, particularly when the patient is compared with parents or persons of similar ethnic background, should be present in order to make a diagnosis of OCA. The clinical, histologic, and chemical features of the various forms of albinism appear in Tables 119-1 and 119-2.

The hair bulb tyrosine incubation test is of value in distinguishing ty-neg from ty-pos types of OCA. The original test solution used by Kugelman and van Scott[8] contained 80 mg L-tyrosine in 100 ml 0.1 M phosphate buffer at pH 6.8. The problem with this solution is the difficulty in solubilizing this amount of tyrosine at pH 6.8. The buffer is prepared from two stock solutions. Solution A contains 28.392 g/liter Na_2HPO_4, and solution B contains 27.598 g/liter NaH_2PO_4. The working solution is made by combining 24.5 ml of solution A and 25.5 ml of solution B and bringing the volume to 1 dl with distilled water. Eighty milligrams of L-tyrosine is added to 85 ml of the working buffer. The solution is heated and mixed with a few drops of concentrated HCl until all the tyrosine is in solution. The pH is adjusted to 6.8 with dilute NaOH, and sufficient working buffer is added to bring the volume up to 1 dl. The solution has a working life of 2 weeks. Hair bulbs are also incubated in a mixture of 40 mg L-tyrosine and 40 mg L-cysteine in the above buffer. Hairs are plucked from the scalp to obtain those with well-developed anagen bulbs (Fig. 119-5). From 8 to 10 hair bulbs are incubated at 37°C for 12 to 24 h and compared for pigment formation with fresh or formalin-fixed controls from the patient (see Fig. 3, Ref. 9 for color reactions). The pigment system in Caucasian infants and young children may not mature until 2 to 3 years of age. We recommend that the test be delayed until the child is 3 years of age, and, if negative, repeated at older ages or combined with electron microscopy. Ty-neg melanocytes contain only up to stage II melanosomes, while other types have stage III and stage IV melanosomes. As methods are available for testing the carriers for ty-neg OCA using an assay of tyrosinase activity in hair bulbs,[10] parents of young children can be tested to see if they are carriers of the ty-neg gene or are whether they are within the normal range of tyrosinase activity for hair color and hence are carriers of one of the tyrosinase-positive types of albinism.

Ty-neg albinos have no visible pigment in skin, hair, and eyes, and hair bulbs incubated in L-tyrosine do not form pigment. Ty-pos albinos have visible pigment, pigment in irides seen on transillumination of the globe or by slit-lamp examination, pigmented nevi, and freckles, and the hair bulb test is positive. Ym albinos have pigment in hair, skin, and eyes, and exhibit a slight tanning effect. They have a negative or faintly positive reaction to the tyrosine hair bulb test, but show an intensification of yellow, yellow-brown, or red pigment when incubated in a solution of 40 mg L-tyrosine and 40 mg L-cysteine.[9] Electron-microscopically, ym melanocytes contain many small, round melanosomes with uneven distribution of pigment on the matrix. The pigment phenotype of HPS patients may resemble that of any other type of OCA or OA. Usually, HPS patients have a history of mild bleeding and evidence of bruising. They have abnormal platelet aggregation, and may have ceroid material in bone marrow, buccal epithelial cells, and urine sediment that can be identified by UV microscopy. The most reliable method of diagnosis of an HPS patient is the absence or marked reduction of platelet-dense bodies.[269] ASA does not interfere with this test. Platelet-rich plasma is prepared, and either fresh whole mounts (Fig. 119-9) or glutaraldehyde-fixed buttons of centrifuged platelets can be examined electron-microscopically in thin sections.[269]

CHS patients have repeated infections, giant peroxidase-positive granules in leukocytes, steel-gray sheen to the hair, and in some older children, neurologic findings. The Cross syndrome comprises severe oligophrenia, athetosis, gingival fibromatosis, and microphthalmos. Patients with BADS have profound sensorineural deafness and black locks.

The mothers of X-linked OA males usually have mosaic pigment patterns in their ocular fundi, and melanin macroglobules are present in skin biopsy specimens of both hemizygous males and heterozygous females. Autosomal recessive OA affects males and females with equal severity. Consanguinity may be present in the parents, mosaic fundi are absent in female heterozygotes, and melanin macroglobules are not found in skin melanocytes.

CLINICAL MANAGEMENT OF ALBINISM

All types of albinos, OCA and OA, should avoid ASA and ASA-like drugs until it is determined that they do not have HPS. The three major problems encountered by patients with albinism are their sensitivity to sunlight, with susceptibility to skin cancers,[191,197,200] their visual acuity defect, which limits most to public transportation,[572–574] and their psychosocial difficulties.[15,575] Patients with HPS and CHS have additional problems.[3,4,7,290,293]

Albinos in the Northern hemisphere should avoid direct sunlight whenever possible, especially during the 3 h before and after solar noon during summer months. Sunscreen lotions, with a solar blocking factor of at least 20, should be applied to areas of skin exposed to the sun.[143] The skin of albinos should be inspected at yearly intervals for premalignant and malignant lesions. Protective clothing, such as denim, should be worn. It is important to realize that not all materials are as effective as others in blocking damaging radiation. The structure of the material is more important than the weight.[576] Carcinoma of the skin occurs in albinos who also have carotenemia and high serum levels of β-carotene. It does not appear that oral administration of β-carotene offers significant protection against the genesis of squamous cell carcinoma.[200,577]

Tinted glasses may be helpful in reducing photophobia. Photochromatic lenses have met with variable acceptance by our patients and those of Taylor.[572] The peripheral parts of the retina in albinos seem to be most sensitive to the dazzling effects of light. Our patients have preferred sunglasses with wide, dark-tinted temporal bows and dark-tinted "flippers" mounted on the superior rim of the glasses, which they find more effective than tinted lenses alone. Haptic contact lenses with opaque scleral portions and tinted irides have been tried with questionable success.[572–574] Near vision is functionally better than far vision in most albinos, who have little difficulty reading N10 or N8 print or better. While telescopic spectacles increase contrast sensitivity in the peripheral retina in albinos,[578] the degree of magnification is limited by hypoplasia of central vision receptors. Telescopic spectacles and contact lenses have offered distinct advantages over conventional lenses in lecture hall–type situations.[572,573] A few states permit driving with telescopic lenses, if the correction permits 20/40 vision or better. Print contact magnifiers and low vision–correcting reading glasses have enabled over 90 percent of albinos to read 6-point type, with most being able to read 4-point type.[574] In several large series, no albinos had defects of a severity that required Braille after corrections were made for astigmatic and refractive errors.[572,573,578] Operations for strabismus can be done for cosmetic purposes, but because of the decussation anomaly in the optic tract, binocular vision will not improve. Since near vision is functionally better than far vision, most albinos do quite well in a public school setting with the judicious use of special assistance. In general, albinos educated in public school settings do better socially as adults than those in special institutions for the partially sighted provided special educational assistance is available in the public schools, especially in the first 3 years of school.[3,572] Albinos should avoid noise trauma.

As near vision is functionally better than distant vision, albinos tend to enter academic vocations.[574,579] Adult albinos tend to reach higher socioeconomic levels than their pigmented sibs.[579] A disproportionally large number have professional careers in teaching, social work, medicine, nursing, computer science, independent business, and engineering.[574,579] However many albinos have been told by misinformed academic counselors that these professions were not appropriate academic goals for albinos.

HPS patients should avoid ASA or ASA-like drugs. Platelet transfusion may be necessary in the event of major surgery or massive bleeding. Cryoprecipitate alone or in conjunction with platelet transfusion has been used effectively to control bleeding.[7,580,581] The peak effect on bleeding time is 2 to 4 h posttransfusion with a duration of action of 24 h or less.[290] Vitamin E administration has been recommended to decrease bleeding symptoms,[290] but the authors have found it ineffective in vivo or in vitro as measured by aggregation tests. Steroids are ineffective in controlling the lung and the bowel disease.[7,267] The bowel disease is refractory to medical treatment, often requiring surgical treatment.[7,267] Lung biopsy is contraindicated because of the bleeding problem. HPS patients should avoid breathing dust, smoke, and organic solvents. Portable oxygen alleviates dyspnea and improves exercise tolerance in advanced lung involvement.

Prenatal diagnosis has been used successfully only in cases of ty-neg OCA. Affected fetuses were identified by scalp biopsies at 20 weeks of gestational age. Skin and hair bulb melanocytes containing only up to stage II melanosomes as seen by electron microscopy identified the affected fetuses.[582,583]

Genetic counseling for prevention can be used in all forms of albinism with tests for the carrier available for ty-neg OCA,[10] HPS,[149] and XOAN.[154–156]

Supplemented by National Institutes of Health grants GM 22167 and Clinical Research Centers Programs, PR 400.

REFERENCES

1. FITZPATRICK TB, QUEVEDO WC JR: Albinism, in Stanbury JB, Wyngaarden JB, Fredrickson DS (eds): *The Metabolic Basis of Inherited Disease*, 3d ed. New York, McGraw-Hill, 1972, p 326.

2. WITKOP CJ JR: Depigmentations of the general and oral tissues and their genetic foundations. *Ala J Med Sci* 16:331, 1979.

3. WITKOP CJ JR, HILL CW, DESNICK SJ, THIES JK, THORN HL, JENKINS M, WHITE JG: Ophthalmologic, biochemical, platelet, and ultrastructural defects in the various types of oculocutaneous albinism. *J Invest Dermatol* 60:443, 1973.

4. WITKOP CJ JR, WHITE JG, KING RA: Oculocutaneous albinism, in Nyhan WL (ed): *Heritable Disorders of Amino Acid Metabolism Patterns of Clinical Expression and Genetic Variation*. New York, Wiley, 1974, pp 177–261.

5. KING RA, LEWIS RA, TOWNSEND D, ZELICKSON A, OLDS DP, BRUMBAUGH J: Brown oculocutaneous albinism. Clinical, ophthalmological, and biochemical characterization. *Ophthalmology* 92:1496, 1985.

6. KING RA, WIRTSCHAFTER JD, OLDS DP, BRUMBAUGH J: Minimal pigment: A new type of oculocutaneous albinism. *Clin Genet* 29:42, 1986.

7. SCHINELLA RA, GRECO MA, GARAY SM, LACKNER H, WOLMAN SR, FAZZINI EP: Hermansky-Pudlak syndrome: A clinicopathologic study. *Hum Pathol* 16:366, 1985.

8. KUGELMAN TP, VAN SCOTT EJ: Tyrosinase activity in melanocytes of human albinos. *J Invest Dermatol* 37:73, 1961.

9. WITKOP CJ JR: Inherited disorders of pigmentation. *Clin Dermatol* 3:70, 1985.

10. KING RA, OLDS DP, WITKOP CJ JR: Characterization of human hairbulb tyrosinase: Properties of normal and albino enzyme. *J Invest Dermatol* 71:136, 1978.

11. PEARSON K, NETTLESHIP E, USHER CH: *A Monograph on Albinism in Man*. Draper's Company Research Memoirs, Biometric Series 6,8,9: parts 1,2,4 London, Dulau, 1911–1913.

12. FROGGATT P: Albinism: A Statistical, Genetical and Clinical Appraisal Based upon a Complete Ascertainment of the Condition in Northern Ireland, thesis. Trinity College, Dublin, 1957.

13. FROGGATT P: Albinism in northern Ireland. *Ann Hum Genet* 24:213, 1960.

14. WITKOP CJ JR: Albinism, in Harris H, Hirschhorn K (eds): *Advances in Human Genetics*. New York, Plenum, 1971, vol 2, p 61.

15. KINNEAR PE, JAY B, WITKOP CJ JR: Albinism. *Surv Ophthalmol* 30:75, 1985.

16. PLINIUS SECUNDUS THE ELDER: *The Natural History of Pliny*, Rackman H (trans). London, William Heineman, book 7, 1942.

17. GELLIUS A: *The Attic Nights*, Rolfe JC (trans). London, William Heinemann, book 9, 1952.

18. SORSBY A: Noah-an albino. *Br Med J* 2:1587, 1958.

19. WAFER L: *New Voyage and Description of the Isthmus of America. Giving an Account of the Author's Abode There*. London, 1699, p 134 (cited by Pearson et al,[11] part I, p 17.

20. RASERI E: Materiali per d'etinologia Italiana. *Arch l'antropol Florence* 9:259, 1879.

21. EHRMANN S: Das melanotische Pigment und die pigmentbildenden Zellen

des Menschen und der Wirbeltiere in ihrer Entwickelung nebst Bemerkungen über Blutbildung und Haarwechsel. Cassel, TG Fisher, 1896.

22. DURHAM FM: On the presence of tyrosinases in the skin of some pigmented vertebrates. *Proc R Soc Lond* 74:310, 1904.

23. GARROD AE: Inborn errors of metabolism. Croonian Lectures, Lecture I. *Lancet* 2:1, 1908.

24. RAPER HS: XIV. The tyrosinase-tyrosine reaction. VI. Production from tyrosine of 5,6-dihydroxyindole and 5:6-dihydroxyindole-2-carboxylic acid the precursors of melanin. *Biochem J* 21:89, 1927.

25. STANNUS HS: Anomalies of pigmentation among natives of Nyasaland: A contribution to the study of albinism. *Biometrika* 9:333, 1913.

26. SHUFELDT RW: Albinism in American animals. *Proc Zool Soc Lond* 86:540, 1916.

27. LITTLE CC: Coat color genes in rodents and carnivores. *Q Rev Biol* 33:103, 1958.

28. NOBLE GK: *The Biology of the Amphibia*. New York, Dover, 1954, p 577.

29. SEARLE AG: *Comparative Genetics of Coat Colour in Mammals*. New York, Academic, 1968.

30. WAARDENBURG PJ: *Remarkable Facts in Human Albinism and Leukism*. The Netherlands, Assen, Van Gorcum, 1970.

31. SILVERS WK: *The Coat Colors of Mice. A Model for Mammalian Gene Action and Interaction*. New York, Springer-Verlag, 1979.

32. LAFERRIERE KA, ARENBERG IK, HAWKINS JE JR, JOHNSSON LG: Melanocytes of the vestibular labyrinth and their relationship to the microvasculature. *Ann Otol* 83:685, 1974.

33. SZABO G: Quantitative histological investigations on the melanocyte system of human epidermis, in Gordon M (ed): *Pigment Cell Biology*. New York, Academic, 1959.

34. SZABO G: The regional anatomy of the human integument with special reference to the distribution of hair follicles, sweat glands, and melanocytes. *Trans R Soc Lond* B252:447, 1967.

35. SZABO G, GERALD AB, PATHAK MA, FITZPATRICK TB: The ultrastructure of racial color differences in man, in Riley V (ed): *Pigmentation: Its Genesis and Biologic Control*. New York, Appleton-Century-Crofts, 1972, p 23.

36. QUEVEDO WC JR, FITZPATRICK TB, PATHAK MA, JIMBOW K: Role of light in human skin color variation. *Am J Phys Anthropol* 43:393, 1975.

37. STERN C: Model estimates of the number of gene pairs involved in pigmentation variability of the Negro-American. *Hum Hered* 20:165, 1970.

38. HARRISON GA: Differences in human pigmentation: Measurement, geographic variation, and causes. *J Invest Dermatol* 60:418, 1973.

39. SEIJI M, FITZPATRICK TB, SIMPSON RT, BIRBECK MSC: Chemical composition and terminology of specialized organelles (melanosomes and melanin granules) in mammalian melanocytes. *Nature* 197:1082, 1963.

40. FITZPATRICK TB, SZABO G, SEIJI M, QUEVEDO WC JR: Biology of the melanin pigmentary system, in Fitzpatrick TB, Eisen AZ, Wolff K, Freedberg IM, Austen KF (eds): *Dermatology in General Medicine*, 2d ed. New York, McGraw-Hill, 1979, p 131.

41. JIMBOW K, QUEVEDO WC JR, FITZPATRICK TB, SZABO G: Some aspects of melanin biology: 1950–1975. *J Invest Dermatol* 67:72, 1976.

42. VARGA JM, MOELLMANN G, FRITSCH P, GODAWSKA E, LERNER AB: Association of cell surface receptors for melanotropin with the Golgi region in mouse melanoma cells. *Proc Natl Acad Sci USA* 73:559, 1976.

43. MOTTAZ JH, ZELICKSON AS: Ultrastructure of hair pigment, in Montagna W, Dobson RL (eds): *Advances in Biology of Skin, Hair Growth*. Oxford, Pergamon, 1969, p 471.

44. STANKA P: Ultrastructural study of pigment cells of human red hair. *Cell Tissue Res* 150:167, 1974.

45. BIRBECK MSC, BARNICOT NA: Electron microscope studies on pigment formation in human hair follicles, in Gordon M (ed): *Pigment Cell Biology*. New York, Academic, 1959.

46. JIMBOW K, ISHIDA O, ITO S, HORI Y, WITKOP CJ JR, KING RA: Combined chemical and electron microscopic studies of pheomelanosomes in human red hair. *J Invest Dermatol* 81:506, 1983.

47. QUEVEDO WC JR: Genetic control of melanin metabolism within the melanin unit of mammalian epidermis. *J Invest Dermatol* 60:407, 1973.

48. SUKURAI T, OCHIAI H, TAKEUCHI T: Ultrastructural change of melanosomes associated with agouti pattern formation in mouse hair. *Dev Biol* 47:466, 1975.

49. QUEVEDO WC JR: Normal pigmentation: Histology, cellular biology, and chemistry. *Ala J Med Sci* 16:305, 1980.

50. TODA K, FITZPATRICK TB: Ultrastructural and biochemical studies of the formation of melanosomes in the embryonic chick retinal pigment epithelium, in Riley V (ed): *Pigmentation: Its Genesis and Biologic Control*. New York, Appleton-Century-Crofts, 1972, p 125.

51. HEARING VJ, NICHOLSON JM, MONTAGUE PM, EKEL TM, TOMECKI KJ: Mammalian tyrosinase. Structural and functional interrelationships of isozymes. *Biochim Biophys Acta* 522:327, 1978.

52. CLEFFMAN G: Function specific changes in the metabolism of agouti pigment cells. *Exp Cell Res* 35:590, 1964.

53. LERNER AB: Metabolism of phenylalanine and tyrosine. *Adv Enzymol* 14:73, 1953.

54. PROTA G: Recent advances in the chemistry of melanogenesis in mammals. *J Invest Dermatol* 75:122, 1980.

55. PROTA G, THOMSON RH: Melanin pigmentation in mammals. *Endeavour* 35:32, 1976.

56. LERNER AB, FITZPATRICK TB: Biochemistry of melanin formation. *Physiol Rev* 30:91, 1950.

57. RILEY PA: The mechanism of melanogenesis. *Symp Zool Soc Lond* 39:77, 1977.

58. LOGAN A, WEATHERHEAD B: Pelage color changes and hairfollicle tyrosinase activity in the Siberian hamster. *J Invest Dermatol* 71:295, 1978.

59. JIMENEZ M, GARCIA-CANOVAS F, GARCIA-CARMONA F, IBORRA JL, LOZANO JA: Kinetic and stoichiometry of cysteinyldopa formation in the first steps of melanogenesis. *Int J Biochem* 18:161, 1986.

60. JERGIL B, LINDBLADH C, RORSMAN H, ROSENGREN E: Tyrosinase activity in the medium of human melanoma cell culture. *Acta Derm Venereol (Stockh)* 63:205, 1983.

61. THOMPSON A, LAND EJ, CHEDEKEL MR, SUBBARAO KV, TRUSCOTT TG: A pulse radiolysis investigation of the oxidation of the melanin precursors 3,4-dihydroxyphenylalanine (dopa) and the cysteinyldopas. *Biochim Biophys Acta* 843:49, 1985.

62. RAPER HS: The aerobic oxidases. *Physiol Rev* 8:245, 1928.

63. MASON HS: The chemistry of melanin. III. The mechanism of the oxidation of dihydroxyphenylalanine by tyrosinase. *J Biol Chem* 172:83, 1948.

64. CANOVAS FG, GARCIA-CARMONA F, SANCHEZ JV, PASTOR JLI, TERUEL JAL: The role of pH in the melanin biosynthetic pathway. *J Biol Chem* 257:8738, 1982.

65. GARCIA-CARMONA F, GARCIA-CANOVAS F, IBORRA JL, LOZANO JA: Kinetic studies of the pathway of melanization between 1-dopa and dopachrome. *Biochim Biophys Acta* 717:124, 1982.

66. PROTA G: Some new aspects of eumelanin chemistry, in Baghara JT (ed): *Advances in Pigment Cell Research.* New York, AR Liss, 1988, p 101.

67. NICOLAUS RA: The process of melanogenesis from tyrosine. I. Precursors, in *Melanins.* Paris, Hermann, 1968, p 43.

68. PROTA G: XIII International Pigment Cell Conference. Tucson, AZ, 1986.

69. KORNER AM, GETTINS P: Synthesis in vitro of 5,6-dihydroxyindole-2-carboxylic acid by dopachrome conversion factor from Cloudman S91 melanoma cells. *J Invest Dermatol* 85:229, 1985.

70. LEONARD LJ, TOWNSEND D, KING RA: Enzyme control of conversion of dopachrome to 5,6-dihydroxyindole-2-carboxylic acid in eumelanin pathway. *Clin Res* 35:699A, 1987.

71. KORNER A, PAWELEK J: Mammalian tyrosinase catalyzes three reactions in the biosynthesis of melanin. *Science* 217:1163, 1982.

72. POMERANTZ SH, WARNER MC: 3,4-Dihydroxy-1-phenylalanine as the tyrosinase cofactor. Occurrence in melanoma and binding constant. *J Biol Chem* 242:5308, 1967.

73. MARTINEZ JH, SOLANO F, GARCIA-BORRON JC, IBORRA JL, LOZANO JA: The involvement of histidine at the active site of Harding-Passey mouse melanoma tyrosinase. *Biochem Int* 11:729, 1985.

74. LERCH K: Neurospora tyrosinase: Structural, spectroscopic and catalytic properties. *Mol Cell Biochem* 52:125, 1983.

75. LERCH K, HUBER M, SCHNEIDER J-J, DREXEL R, LINZEN B: Different properties of metal binding sites in binuclear copper proteins, tyrosinase and hemocyanin. *J Inorg Biochem* 26:213, 1986.

76. SHIBAHARA S, TOMITA Y, SAKAKURA T, NAGER C, CHAUDURI B, MULLER R: Cloning and expression of cDNA encoding mouse tyrosinase. *Nucleic Acids Res* 14:2413, 1986.

76a. KWON BS, HAQ AK, POMERANTZ SH, HALABAN R: Isolation and sequence of a cDNA clone for human tyrosinase that maps at the mouse c-albino locus. *Proc Natl Acad Sci USA* 84:7473, 1987.

77. KWON BS, HAQ AK, KIM GS, POMERANTZ SH, HALABAN R: Cloning and characterization of a human tyrosinase cDNA, in Bagnara JT (ed): *Advances in Pigment Cell Research.* New York, AR Liss, 1988, p 273.

77a. RUPPERT S, MULLER G, KWON B, SCHUTZ G: Multiple transcripts of the mouse tyrosinase gene are generated by alternative splicing. *EMBO J* 7:2715, 1988.

77b. MULLER G, RUPPERT S, SCHMID E, SCHUTZ G: Functional analysis of alternatively spliced tyrosinase gene transcripts. *EMBO J* 7:2723, 1988.

78. YAMAMOTO H, BRUMBAUGH JA: Purification and isoelectric heterogeneity of chicken tyrosinase. *Biochim Biophys Acta* 800:282, 1984.

79. BURNETT JB, SEILER H, BROWN IV: Separation and characterization of multiple forms of tyrosinase from mouse melanoma. *Cancer Res* 27:880, 1967.

80. HOLSTEIN TJ, BURNETT JB, QUEVEDO WC JR: Genetic regulation of multi-

81. BURNETT JB, HOLSTEIN TJ, QUEVEDO WC JR: Electrophoretic variations of tyrosinase in follicular melanocytes during the hair growth cycle. *J Exp Zool* 171:369, 1969.

82. POMERANTZ SH, LI JPC: Purification and properties of tyrosinase isoenzymes from hamster melanoma. *Yale J Biol Med* 46:541, 1973.

83. HEARING VJ, EKEL TM, MONTAGUE PM: Mammalian tyrosinase: Isozymic forms of the enzyme. *Int J Biochem* 13:99, 1981.

84. JIMBOW K, FITZPATRICK TB: Characterization of a new melanosomal structural component—the vesicular body. *J Ultrastruct Res* 48:269, 1974.

85. MAUL GG, BRUMBAUGH JA: On the possible function of coated vesicles in melanogenesis of the regenerating fowl feather. *J Cell Biol* 48:41, 1971.

86. JIMBOW K, OIKAWA O, SUGIYAMA S, TAKEVICHI T: Comparison of eumelanogenesis and pheomelanogenesis in retinal and follicular melanocytes: Role of vesiculoglobular bodies in melanosome differentiation. *J Invest Dermatol* 73:278, 1979.

87. TOWNSEND D, WITKOP CJ, MATTSON J: Tyrosinase subcellular distribution and kinetic parameters in wild type and c-locus mutant C57BL/6J mice. *J Exp Zool* 216:113, 1981.

88. NISHIOKA K: Particulate tyrosinase of human malignant melanoma. Solubilization, purification following trypsin treatment, and characterization. *Eur J Biochem* 85:137, 1978.

89. OHTAKI N, MIYAZAKI K: Immunologic homogeneity and electrophoretic heterogeneity of mouse melanoma tyrosinase. *J Invest Dermatol* 61:339, 1973.

90. MIYAZAKI K, OHTAKI N: Tyrosinase as glycoprotein. *Arch Dermatol Forsch* 252:211, 1975.

91. HALABAN R, POMERANTZ SH, MARSHALL S, LERNER AB: Tyrosinase activity and abundance in Cloudman melanoma cells. *Arch Biochem Biophys* 230:383, 1984.

92. TOMITA Y, MONTAGUE PM, HEARING VJ: Anti-T4-tyrosinase monoclonal antibodies—Specific markers for pigmented melanocytes. *J Invest Dermatol* 85:426, 1985.

93. GARCIA-BORRON JC, SOLANO F, IBORRA JL, LOZANO JA: Aggregation equilibrium of tyrosinase of Harding-Passey mouse melanoma. *Biochem J* 228:95, 1985.

94. IMOKAWA G, MISHIMA Y: Loss of melanogenic properties in tyrosinase induced by glycosylation inhibitors within malignant melanoma cells. *Cancer Res* 42:1994, 1982.

95. MISHIMA Y, IMOKAWA G: Selective aberration and pigment loss in melanosomes of malignant melanoma cells in vitro by glycosylation inhibitors: Premelanosomes as glycoprotein. *J Invest Dermatol* 81:106, 1983.

96. OHKURA T, YAMASHITA K, MISHIMA Y, KOBATA A: Purification of hamster melanoma tyrosinases and structural studies of their asparagine-linked sugar chains. *Arch Biochem Biophys* 235:63, 1984.

97. IMOKAWA G, MISHIMA Y: Functional analysis of tyrosinase isozymes of cultured malignant melanoma cells during the recovery period following interrupted melanogenesis induced by glycosylation inhibitors. *J Invest Dermatol* 83:196, 1984.

98. IMOKAWA G, MISHIMA Y: Importance of glycoprotein in the initiation of melanogenesis: An electron microscopic study of B-16 melanoma cells after release from inhibition of glycosylation. *J Invest Dermatol* 87:319, 1986.

99. JIMBOW K, JIMBOW M, CHIBA M: Characterization of structural properties for morphological differentiation of melanosomes: I. Purification of tyrosinase by tyrosine affinity chromatography and its characterization in B16 and Harding Passey melanoma. *J Invest Dermatol* 77:213, 1981.

100. LOGAN A, WEATHERHEAD B: Post-tyrosinase inhibition of melanogenesis by melatonin in hairfollicles in vitro. *J Invest Dermatol* 74:47, 1980.

101. KORNER AM, PAWELEK J: Dopachrome conversion: A possible control point in melanin biosynthesis. *J Invest Dermatol* 75:192, 1980.

102. PAWELEK J, KORNER A, BERGSTROM A, BOLOGNA J: New regulators of melanin biosynthesis and the autodestruction of melanoma cells. *Nature* 286:617, 1980.

103. HEARING VJ, KORNER AW, PAWELEK JW: New regulators of melanogenesis are associated with purified tyrosinase isozymes. *J Invest Dermatol* 79:16, 1982.

104. MURRAY M, PAWELEK JM, LAMOREUX ML: New regulatory factors for melanogenesis: Developmental changes in neonatal mice of various genotypes. *Dev Biol* 100:120, 1983.

105. BARBER JI, TOWNSEND D, OLDS DP, KING RA: Dopachrome oxidoreductase: A new enzyme in the pigment pathway. *J Invest Dermatol* 83:145, 1984.

106. BARBER JI, TOWNSEND D, OLDS DP, KING RA: Decreased dopachrome oxidoreductase in yellow mice. *J Hered* 76:59, 1985.

107. LAGESON JR, TOWNSEND D, KING RA: Dopachrome oxidoreductase activ-

ity in mouse ocular tissue: Effect of coat color mutations. *Clin Res* 35:698A, 1987.

108. LAMOREUX ML: Dopachrome conversion and dopa oxidase activities in recessive yellow mice. Catalytic activities of extracts from pheomelanic and eumelanic tissues. *J Hered* 77:337, 1986.

109. NAPOLITANO A, CHIOCCARA F, PROTA G: A reexamination of the zinc catalyzed rearrangement of dopachrome using immobilized tyrosinase. *Gazz Chim Ital* 115:357, 1985.

110. PROTA G: Personal communication.

111. ITO S, FUJITA K: Microanalysis of eumelanin and pheomelanin in hair and melanosomes by chemical degradation and liquid chromatography. *Anal Biochem* 144:527, 1985.

112. ITO S, NOVELLINO E, CHIOCCARA F, MISURACA G, PROTA G: Co-polymerization of dopa and cysteinyldopa in melanogenesis in vitro. *Experientia* 36:822, 1980.

113. PROTA G, RORSMAN H, ROSENGREN A-M, ROSENGREN E: Pheomelanin pigments from a human melanoma. *Experientia* 32:970, 1976.

114. NOVELLINO E, ORTONNE JP, VOULOT C, CHIOCCARA F, MISURACA G, PROTA G: Identification of cysteinyldopa-derived units in eumelanins from mammalian eyes. *FEBS Lett* 125:101, 1981.

115. DRYJA TP, O'NEIL-DRYJA M, ALBERT DM: Elemental analysis of melanin from bovine hair, iris, choroid, and retinal pigment epithelium. *Invest Ophthalmol Vis Sci* 18:231, 1979.

116. ITO S: Reexamination of the structure of eumelanin. *Biochim Biophys Acta* 883:155, 1986.

117. ITO S, JIMBOW K: Quantitative analysis of eumelanin and pheomelanin in hair and melanomas. *J Invest Dermatol* 80:268, 1983.

118. QUEVEDO WC JR: Physiology of vertebrate dermal pigmentation, in Fitzpatrick TB, Morikawa F, Seiji M, Sober AJ, Toda K (eds): *Biology and Diseases of Dermal Pigmentation.* Tokyo, University of Tokyo Press, 1981, p 39.

119. KLEIN LE, NORDLUND JJ: Genetic basis of pigmentation and its disorders. *Int J Dermatol* 20:621, 1981.

120. KORYTOWSKI W, KALYANARAMAN B, MENON IA, SARNA T, SEALY RC: Reaction of superoxide anions with melanin: Electron spin resonance and spin trapping studies. *Biochim Biophys Acta* 882:145, 1986.

121. KORYTOWSKI W, HINTZ P, SEALY RC, KALYANARAMAN B: Mechanism of dismutation of superoxide produced during autooxidation of melanin pigments. *Biochem Biophys Res Commun* 131:659, 1985.

122. SARNA T, SEALY RC: Photoinduced oxygen consumption in melanin systems. Action spectra and quantum yields for eumelanin and synthetic melanin. *Photochem Photobiol* 39:69, 1984.

123. SEALY RC, PUZYNA W, KALYANARAMAN B, FELIX CC: Identification by electron spin resonance spectroscopy of free radicals produced during autoxidative melanogenesis. *Biochim Biophys Acta* 800:269, 1984.

124. FELIX CC, HYDE JS, SARNA T, SEALY RC: Melanin photoreactions in areated media: Electron spin resonance evidence for production of superoxide and hydrogen peroxide. *Biochem Biophys Res Commun* 84:335, 1978.

125. CHEDEKEL MR, SMITH SK, POST PW, POKORA A, VESSELL DL: Photodestruction of pheomelanin: Role of oxygen. *Proc Natl Acad Sci USA* 75:5395, 1978.

126. MENON A, PERSAD S, RANADIVE S, HABERMAN HF: Effects of ultraviolet-visible irradiation in the presence of melanin isolated from human black or red hair upon Ehlich ascites carcinoma cells. *Cancer Res* 43:3165, 1983.

127. PERSAD S, MENON IA, HABERMAN JF: Comparison of the effects of UV-visible irradiation of melanin and melanin-hematoporphyrin complexes from human black and red hair. *Photochem Photobiol* 37:63, 1983.

128. MORISON WL: What is the function of melanin? *Arch Dermatol* 121:1160, 1985.

129. BRANDA RF, EATON JW: Skin color and nutrient photolysis: An evolutionary hypothesis. *Science* 201:625, 1978.

130. FITZPATRICK TB, BREATHNACH AS: Das epidermale Melanin-Enheit-System. *Dermatol Wochenschr* 147:481, 1963.

131. SZABO G, GERALD AB, PATHAK MA, FITZPATRICK TB: Racial differences in the fate of melanosomes in human epidermis. *Nature* 222:1081, 1969.

132. TODA K, PATHAK MA, PARRISH JA, FITZPATRICK TB, QUEVEDO WC JR: Alteration of racial differences in melanosome distribution in human epidermis after exposure to ultraviolet light. *Nature* 236:143, 1972.

133. OLSON RL, GAYLOR J, EVERETT MA: Skin color, melanin, and erythema. *Arch Dermatol* 108:541, 1973.

134. KONRAD K, WOLFF K: Hyperpigmentation, melanosome size, and distribution patterns of melanosomes. *Arch Dermatol* 107:853, 1973.

135. OLSON RL, EVERETT MA: Alterations in epidermal lysosomes following ultraviolet light exposure, in Urbach F (ed): *The Biologic Effects of Ultraviolet Radiation.* Oxford, Pergamon, 1969, p 473.

136. MOTTAZ JH, THORNE EG, ZELICKSON AS: Response of the epidermal melanocyte to minor trauma. *Arch Dermatol* 104:611, 1971.

137. QUEVEDO WC JR: Genetic regulation of pigmentation in mammals, in Kawamura T, Fitzpatrick TB, Seiji M (eds): *Biology of Normal and Abnormal Melanocytes.* Tokyo, University of Tokyo Press, 1971, p 99.

138. WOLFF K, HONIGSMANN H: Permeability of the epidermis and the phagocytic activity of keratinocytes: Ultrastructural studies with thorotrast as a marker. *J Ultrastruct Res* 36:176, 1971.

139. HONIGSMANN H, SCHULER G, ABERER W, ROMANI N, WOLFF K: Immediate pigment darkening phenomenon. A reevaluation of its mechanism. *J Invest Dermatol* 87:648, 1986.

140. BEITNER H, WENNERSTEN G: A qualitative and quantitative transmission electron microscopic study of the immediate pigment darkening reaction. *Photodermatology* 2:273, 1985.

141. BLACK G, MATZINGER E, GANGE RW: Lack of photoprotection against UVB-induced erythema by immediate pigmentation induced by 382nm radiation. *J Invest Dermatol* 85:448, 1985.

142. PATHAK MA, HORI Y, SZABO G, FITZPATRICK TB: The photobiology of melanin pigmentation in human skin, in Kawamura T, Fitzpatrick TB, Seiji M (eds): *Biology of Normal and Abnormal Melanocytes.* Tokyo, University of Tokyo Press, 1971, p 149.

143. PATHAK MA, FITZPATRICK TB, GREITER F, KRAUS EW: Preventive treatment of sunburn, dermatoheliosis, and skin cancer with sun-protective agents, in Fitzpatrick TB, Eizen AZ, Wolff K, Freeberg IM, Austen KF (eds): *Dermatology in General Medicine,* 3d ed. New York, McGraw-Hill, 1987, p 1507.

144. SCHALLREUTER KU, WOOD JM: The tole of thioredoxin reductase in the reduction of free radicals at the surface of the epidermis. *Biochem Biophys Res Commun* 136:630, 1986.

145. SCHALLREUTER KU, HORDINSKY MK, WOOD JM: Thioredoxin reductase for free radical reduction on the skin in different hypopigmented disorders. *Arch Dermatol* 123:615, 1987.

146. SCHALLREUTER KU, PITTELKOW MR, WOOD JM: Free radical reduction by thioredoxin reductase at the surface of normal and vitiliginous human keratinocytes. *J Invest Dermatol* 87:728, 1986.

147. SCHALLREUTER KU, WOOD JM: Oxygen biochemistry at the surface of the skin, in Hagedorn S, Hanson RS (eds): *S. Dagley Retirement Symposium.* London, Gordon-Breach, 1987.

148. HOLMGREN A: Thioredoxin. *Am Rev Biochem* 54:237, 1985.

149. SCHALLREUTER KU, KING BA, WITKOP CJ: Thioredoxin reductase activity in Hermansky-Pudlak syndrome. A method for identification of putative heterozygotes. *J Invest Dermatol* 90:372, 1988.

150. SCHALLREUTER KU, PITTELKOW MR, GLEASON FK, WOOD JM: The role of calcium in the regulation of free radical reduction by thioredoxin reductase at the surface of the skin. *J Inorg Biochem* 28:277, 1986.

151. WITKOP CJ JR, QUEVEDO WC JR, FITZPATRICK TB: Albinism, in Stanbury JB, Wyngaarden JB, Fredrickson DS (eds): *The Metabolic Basis of Inherited Disease,* 4th ed. New York, McGraw-Hill, 1978, p 283.

152. NETTLESHIP E: On some hereditary diseases of the eye. *Trans Ophthalmol Soc UK* 29:59, 1909.

153. FALLS HF: Sex-linked ocular albinism displaying typical fundus changes in the female heterozygote. *Am J Ophthalmol* 34:41, 1951.

154. O'DONNELL FE JR, HAMBRICK GW, GREEN WR, ILIFF WJ, STONE DL: X-linked ocular albinism. An oculocutaneous macromelanosomal disorder. *Arch Ophthalmol* 94:1883, 1976.

155. GARNER A, JAY BS: Macromelanosomes in X-linked ocular albinism. *Histopathology* 4:243, 1980.

156. O'DONNELL FE JR, GREEN WR: The eye in albinism, in Duane TD (ed): *Clinical Ophthalmology.* Hagerstown, MD, Harper & Row, 1979.

157. KING RA, CREEL D, CERVENKA J, OKORO AN, WITKOP CJ: Albinism in Nigeria with delineation of a new recessive oculocutaneous type. *Clin Genet* 17:259, 1980.

158. CREEL D, WITKOP CJ JR, KING RA: Asymmetric visually evoked potentials in human albinos. Evidence for visual system anomalies. *Invest Ophthalmol* 13:430, 1974.

159. GUILLERY RW, OKORO AN, WITKOP CJ JR: Abnormal visual pathways in the brain of a human albino. *Brain Res* 96:373, 1975.

160. CREEL D, O'DONNELL FE JR, WITKOP CJ JR: Visual system anomalies in human ocular albinos. *Science* 201:931, 1978.

161. COLEMAN J, SYDNOR CF, WOLBARSHT ML, BESSLER M: Abnormal visual pathways in human albinos studied with visually evoked potentials. *Exp Neurol* 65:667, 1979.

162. CREEL D, KING RA, WITKOP CJ JR, OKORO AN: Visual system anomalies in human albinos, in Klaus SN (ed): *Pigment Cell, Pathophysiology of Melanocytes.* New Haven, Karger, 1979, p 21.

163. CARROLL WM, JAY BS, MCDONALD WI, HALLIDAY AM: Two distinct pat-

terns of visual evoked response asymmetry in human albinism. *Nature* 286:604, 1980.

164. CARROLL WM, JAY BS, MCDONALD WI, HALLIDAY AM: Pattern evoked potentials in human albinism. *J Neurol Sci* 48:265, 1980.

165. CREEL D, SPEKREIJSE H, REITS D: Evoked potentials in albinos: Efficacy of pattern stimuli in detecting misrouted optic fibers. *Electroencephalogr Clin Neurophysiol* 52:595, 1981.

166. CREEL D, SPEKREIJSE H, REITS D: Visual evoked potential methods of detecting misrouted optic projections. *Doc Ophthalmol Proc Ser* 27:157, 1981.

167. WITKOP CJ JR, JAY B, CREEL D, GUILLERY RW: Optic and otic neurologic abnormalities in oculocutaneous and ocular albinism. *Birth Defects* 18(6):299, 1982.

168. CREEL D, BOXER LA, FAUCI AS: Visual and auditory anomalies in Chediak-Higashi syndrome. *Electroencephalogr Clin Neurophysiol* 55:252, 1983.

169. BOYLAN C, HARDING GFA: Investigation of visual pathway abnormalities in human albinos. *Ophthalmic Physiol Opt* 3:273, 1983.

170. APKARIAN P, REITS D, SPEKREIJSE H, VAN DOORP D: A decisive electrophysiological test for human albinism. *Electroencephalogr Clin Neurophysiol* 55:513, 1983.

171. APKARIAN P, REITS D, SPEKREIJSE H: Component specificity in albino VEP asymmetry: Maturation of the visual pathway anomaly. *Exp Brain Res* 53:285, 1984.

172. BOYLAN C, CLEMENT RA, HARDING GFA: Lateralization of the flash visual evoked cortical potential in human albinos. *Invest Ophthalmol Vis Sci* 25:1448, 1984.

173. CREEL D: Problems of ocular miswiring in albinism, Duane's syndrome, and Marcus Gunn phenomenon. *Int Ophthalmol Clin* 24:165, 1984.

174. CREEL DJ, BENDEL CM, WIESNER GL, WIRTSCHAFTER JD, ARTHUR DC, KING RA: Abnormalities of the central visual pathways in Prader-Willi syndrome associated with hypopigmentation. *N Engl J Med* 314:1606, 1986.

175. LEVENTHAL AG, VITEK D, CREEL DJ: Abnormal visual pathways in normally pigmented cats that are heterozygous for albinism. *Science* 229:1395, 1985.

176. WITKOP CJ JR, QUEVEDO WC JR, FITZPATRICK TB: Albinism and other disorders of pigment metabolism, in Stanbury JB, Wyngaarden JB, Fredrickson DS, Goldstein JL, Brown MS (eds): *The Metabolic Basis of Inherited Disease*, 5th ed. New York, McGraw-Hill, 1983, p 301.

177. KING RA, OLDS DP: Hairbulb tyrosinase activity in oculocutaneous albinism: Suggestions for pathway control and block location. *Am J Med Genet* 20:49, 1985.

178. KING RA: Albinism, in Demis DJ, Dobson RL, McGuire JM (eds): *Clinical Dermatology*. Philadelphia, Harper & Row, 1982, p 1.

179. HU F, HANIFIN JM, PRESCOTT GH, TONGUE AC: Yellow mutant albinism: Cytochemical, ultrastructural, and genetic characterization suggesting multiple allelism. *Am J Hum Genet* 32:387, 1980.

180. WITKOP CJ JR, WHITE JC, NANCE WE, UMBER RE: Mutations in the melanin pigment system in man resulting in features of oculocutaneous albinism, in Riley V (ed): *Pigmentation: Its Genesis and Biologic Control*. New York, Appleton-Century-Crofts, 1972, p 359.

181. KING RA, WITKOP CJ JR: Hairbulb tyrosinase activity in oculocutaneous albinism. *Nature* 263:69, 1976.

182. WITKOP CJ JR, NANCE WE, RAWLS RF, WHITE JG: Autosomal recessive oculocutaneous albinism in man: evidence for genetic heterogeneity. *Am J Hum Genet* 22:55, 1970.

183. TREVOR-ROPER PD: Marriage of two complete albinos with normally pigmented offspring. *Br J Ophthalmol* 36:107, 1952.

184. TREVOR-ROPER PD: Albinism. *Proc R Soc Med Sec Ophthalmol* 56:21, 1963.

185. GRAGG GW: Albinoidism and albinism. *Birth Defects* 7(3):203, 1971.

186. JAEGER C, JAY B: X-linked ocular albinism. A family containing a manifesting heterozygote, and an affected male married to a female with autosomal recessive ocular albinism. *Hum Genet* 56:299, 1981.

187. JAY B, WITKOP CJ, KING RA: Albinism in England. *Birth Defects* 18(6):319, 1982.

187a. WITKOP CJ JR, KING RA, TOWNSEND D: Human albinism and animal models of albinism. *Pigment Cell Res* (suppl 1):88, 1988.

188. WOOLF CM: Albinism among Indians in Arizona and New Mexico. *Am J Hum Genet* 17:23, 1965.

189. WITKOP CJ JR, MACLEAN CJ, SCHMIDT PJ, HENRY JL: Medical and dental findings in the Brandywine isolate. *Ala J Med Sci* 3:382, 1966.

190. WITKOP CJ JR, NISWANDER JP, BERGSMA DR, WORKMAN PL, WHITE JG: Tyrosinase-positive oculocutaneous albinism among the Zuni and the Brandywine triracial isolate: Biochemical and clinical characteristics and fertility. *Am J Phys Anthropol* 36:397, 1972.

191. OKORO AN: Albinism in Nigeria. *Br J Dermatol* 92:485, 1975.

192. KEELER CE: The Caribe Cuna moon-child and its heredity. *J Hered* 44:163, 1953.

193. ROSE EF: Pigment anomalies encountered in the Transkei. *S Afr Med J* 48:2345, 1974.

194. FREIRE-MAIA N, CAVALLI IJ: Genetic investigations in a Northern Brazilian island. 1. Population structure. *Hum Hered* 28:386, 1978.

195. WINTER MC: The albinos of Santa Catarina Iztatlan. *Am Anthropol* 84:885, 1982.

196. KROMBERG JGR, JENKINS T: Prevalence of albinism in the South African Negro. *S Afr Med J* 61:383, 1982.

197. AQUARON R: L'albinisme oculo-cutané au Cameroun. A propos de 216 observations. *Rev Epidemiol Sante Publique* 28:81, 1980.

198. FREIRE-MAIA N, et al: Medical and genetic studies of the population of Lençois Island, Maranhao. Twenty-fourth Annual Meeting, Brazilian Society of Advances in Science and Culture 180 (suppl):24, 1972.

199. NANCE WE, JACKSON CE, WITKOP CJ JR: Amish albinism: A distinctive autosomal recessive phenotype. *Am J Hum Genet* 22:579, 1970.

200. WITKOP CJ JR: Epidemiology of skin cancer in man. Genetic factors, in Laerum D, Iverson OH (eds): *Biology of Skin Cancer*. Geneva, International Union against Cancer, Tech Report Series 63(15):67, 1981.

201. HALL AJ, SESBE T, CARDOZO RL, NURSE GT: A high-frequency albinism variant on the gulf coast of Papua. *Papua New Guinea Med J* 24:35, 1981.

202. BERGSMA DR, KAISER-KUPFER M: A new form of albinism. *Am J Ophthalmol* 77:837, 1974.

203. DONALDSON DD: Transillumination of the iris. *Am Ophthalmol Soc* 72:89, 1974.

204. TIETZ W: A syndrome of deaf-mutism associated with albinism showing dominant autosomal inheritance. *Am J Hum Genet* 15:259, 1963.

205. MENKES JH, ALTER M, STEIGLEDER GK, WEAKLEY DR, SUNG JS: A sex-linked recessive disorder with retardation of growth, peculiar hair and focal cerebral and cerebellar degeneration. *Pediatrics* 29:764, 1962.

206. MARGOLIS S, SIEGEL IM, CHOY A, BREINING M: Depigmentation of hair, skin, and eyes associated with the Apert syndrome. *Birth Defects* 14(6-C):341, 1978.

207. BARD LA: Heterogeneity in Waardenburg's syndrome. *Arch Ophthalmol* 96:1193, 1978.

208. COMINGS DE, ODLAND GF: Partial albinism. *JAMA* 195:510, 1966.

209. FRANCOIS J, VERRIEST G: Anomalies of pigmentation, in Francois J (ed): *Heredity in Ophthalmology*. St Louis, CV Mosby, 1961, p 519.

210. MERENLENDER J, RYWLIN JA: A propos de l'hérédité du vitiligo acquis (vitiligo dans 3 générations). *Acta Derm Venereol (Stockh)* 21:583, 1940.

211. LERNER AB: Vitiligo. *J Invest Dermatol* 32:285, 1959.

212. COWIE V, PENROSE LS: Dilution of hair colour in phenylketonuria. *Ann Eugen* 15:297, 1951.

213. SYNDERMAN SE, NORTON P, HOLT EL: "Effect" of tyrosine administration in phenylketonuria. *Fed Proc* 14:450, 1955.

214. MIYAMOTO M, FITZPATRICK TB: Competitive inhibition of mammalian tyrosinase by phenylalanine and its relationship to hair pigmentation in phenylketonuria. *Nature* 179:199, 1957.

215. WITKOP CJ JR: Abnormalities of pigmentation, in Emery AEH, Rimoin DL (eds): *The Principles and Practice of Medical Genetics*. Edinburgh, Churchill Livingstone, 1982, p 622.

216. ORTONNE J-P, MOSHER DB, FITZPATRICK TB: *Vitiligo and Other Hypomelanoses of Hair and Skin*. New York, Plenum, 1983.

217. MOSHER DB, FITZPATRICK TB, ORTONNE JP, HORI Y: Disorders of pigmentation, in Fitzpatrick TB, Eisen AZ, Wolff K, Freeberg IM, Austen KF (eds): *Dermatology in General Medicine*, 3d ed. New York, McGraw-Hill, 1987, p 794.

218. WITKOP CJ JR, VAN SCOTT EJ, JACOBY GA: Evidence for two forms of autosomal recessive albinism in man, in *Proceedings of the Second International Congress of Human Genetics*. Rome, Institute Gregor Mendel, 1961, p 1064.

219. SAINT HILAIRE IG: Histoire générale et particulière des anomalies de l'organisation chez l'homme et les animaux. Paris, JB Ballière, 1832–1836.

220. SAINT HILAIRE IG: Sur l'albinisme et le mélanisme. *La Lancette Française Gazette des Hôpitaux Civils et Militaires* 9:128,509, 1839.

221. NIEDELMAN ML: Abnormalities of pigmentation in the Negro. *Arch Dermatol Syphilol* 51:1, 1945.

222. KLEIN D: Les diverse formes hereditaries de l'albinisme. *Bull Schweitz Akad Med Wiss* 17:351, 1961.

223. WAARDENBURG PJ: in Waardenburg PJ, Franschetti A, Klein D (eds): *Genetics and Ophthalmology*. Springfield, IL, Charles C Thomas, 1961, vol 1, p 704.

224. MCKUSICK VA: *Mendelian Inheritance in Man: Catalogs of Autosomal Dominant, Autosomal Recessive and X-linked Phenotypes*, 7th ed. Baltimore, Johns Hopkins University Press, 1986, p 812.

225. WIRTSCHAFTER JD, DENSLOW GT, SHINE IB: Quantification of iris translucency in albinism. *Arch Ophthalmol* 90:274, 1973.

226. JAY B, CARRUTHERS J, TREPLIN MCW, WINDER AF: Human albinism. *Birth Defects* 12(3):415, 1976.

227. BIRBECK MSC, BARNICOT NA: Electron microscope studies on pigment formation in human hair follicles, in Gordon M (ed): *Pigment Cell Biology*. New York, Academic, 1959, p 549.

228. JUNG EG, ANTON-LAMPRECHT I: Investigation of a case of oculocutaneous albinism. *Birth Defects* 7(8):26, 1971.

229. WAARDENBURG PJ: Herkenbaarheid van latente overdragers van albinismus universalis en albinismus oculi. *Ned Tijdschr Geneeskd* 91:1963, 1947.

230. KING RA, WITKOP CJ: Detection of heterozygotes for tyrosinase-negative oculocutaneous albinism by hairbulb tyrosinase assay. *Am J Hum Genet* 29:164, 1977.

231. POMERANTZ SH: L-Tyrosine-3,5-^{3} H assay for tyrosinase development in skin of newborn hamsters. *Science* 164:838, 1969.

232. POPP RA: Studies of the mouse hemoglobin locus. II. Position of the hemoglobin locus with respect to albinism and shaker-1 loci. *J Hered* 53:73, 1962.

233. BRDICKA R: Evidence for linkage between hemoglobin and chromagen loci. *Folia Biol (Praha)* 12:305, 1966.

234. MASSIE RW, HARTMAN RC: Albinism and sicklemia in a Negro family. *Am J Hum Genet* 9:127, 1957.

235. WHITE JG, WITKOP CJ JR, GERRITSEN SM: The Hermansky-Pudlak syndrome: Inclusions in circulating leucocytes. *Br J Haematol* 24:761, 1973.

236. BAGNARA JT, TAYLOR JD, PROTA G: Color changes, unusual melanosomes, and a new pigment from leaf frogs. *Science* 182:1034, 1973.

237. MISURACA G, PROTA G, BAGNARA JT, FROST SK: Identification of the leaf-frog melanophore pigment, rhodomelanochrome, as pterorhodin. *Comp Biochem Physiol* 57B:41, 1977.

238. BAGNARA JT, FERRIS W, TAYLOR JD: The comparative biology of a new melanophore pigment from leaf frogs, in Riley V (ed): *Pigment Cell. Unique Properties of Melanocytes*. Basel, Karger, 1976, vol 3, p 53.

239. FOLEY JH, BAXTER D: On the nature of pigment granules in the cells of the locus caeruleus and substantia nigra. *J Neuropathol* 17:586, 1958.

240. KENNEDY BJ, ZELICKSON AS: Melanoma in an albino. *JAMA* 186:839, 1963.

241. BRUMBAUGH JA, ZIEG RH: The ultrastructural effects of the dopa reaction upon developing retinal and epidermal melanocytes in the fowl, in Riley V (ed): *Pigmentation: Its Genesis and Biologic Control*, New York, Appleton-Century-Crofts, 1972, p 107.

242. MISHMA Y, TAKAHASHI M, COOPER M: Intracytoplasmic activities in malignant melanoma: Viral, melanogenic and anti-melanogenic, in Kawamura T, Fitzpatrick TB, Seiji M (eds): *Biology of Normal and Abnormal Melanocytes*. Baltimore, University Park Press, 1971, p 279.

243. KING RA, OLDS DP: Tyrosine uptake in normal and albino hairbulbs. *Arch Dermatol Res* 276:313, 1984.

244. WITKOP CJ JR, WHITE JG, NANCE WE, JACKSON CE, DESNICK S: Classification of albinism in man. *Birth Defects* 7(8):13, 1971.

245. NIMMO JE, HUNTER JAA, PERCY-ROBB IW, JAY B, PHILLIPS CI, TAYLOR WOG: Plasma 5-S-cysteinyldopa concentrations in oculocutaneous albinism. *Acta Derm Venereol (Stockh)* 65:169, 1985.

246. AQUARON RR, ROUGE F, AUBERT CH: Pheomelanin in albino Negros: Urinary excretion of 5-S-cysteinyldopa in Cameroonian subjects, in Seiji M (ed): *Pigment Cell*. Tokyo, University of Tokyo Press, 1981, p 97.

247. KING RA, RICH SS: Segregation analysis of brown oculocutaneous albinism. *Clin Genet* 29:496, 1986.

248. WALSH JR: A distinctive pigment of the skin in New Guinea indigenes. *Ann Hum Genet* 34:379, 1971.

249. HARVEY RG: The "redskins" of Lufa sub-district: Further observations on the distinctive skin pigmentation of some New Guinea indigenes. *Hum Biol Oceania* 1:103, 1971.

250. HOMABROOK RW, MCDONALD WI, CARROLL RL: Congenital nystagmus among the redskins of the highlands of Papua New Guinea. *Br J Ophthalmol* 64:375, 1980.

251. HERMANSKY F, PUDLAK P: Albinism associated with hemorrhagic diathesis and unusual pigmented reticular cells in the bone marrow: Report of two cases with histochemical studies. *Blood* 14:162, 1959.

252. HARDISTY RM, HUTTON RA: Bleeding tendency associated with "new" abnormality of platelet behavior. *Lancet* 1:983, 1967.

253. MAURER HM, WOLFF JA, BUCKINGHAM S, HOROWITZ HI, SPIELVOGEL A, SITARZ A: Heterogeneous hemostatic defect in albinism. *Abstr Soc Pediatr Res* 102, 1967.

254. MILLS DCB, HARDISTY RM: The nature of the platelet defect in albinos with a bleeding tendency. *Proceedings of the 13th Congress, International Society of Hematology,* Munich, 1970, p 31.

255. WHITE JG, EDSON JR, DESNICK SJ, WITKOP CJ JR: Studies of platelets in a variant of the Hermansky-Pudlak syndrome. *Am J Pathol* 63:319, 1971.

256. LOGAN LJ, RAPAPORT SI, MAHER I: Albinism and abnormal platelet function. *N Engl J Med* 284:1340, 1971.

257. HARDISTY RM, MILLS DCB: The platelet defect associated with albinism. *Ann NY Acad Sci* 201:429, 1972.

258. HARDISTY RM, MILLS DCB, KETSA-ARD K: The platelet defect associated with albinism. *Br J Haematol* 23:679, 1972.

259. MAURER HM, WOLFF JA, BUCKINGHAM S, SPIELVOGEL AR: "Impotent" platelets in albinos with prolonged bleeding times. *Blood* 39:490, 1972.

260. BEDNAR B, HERMANSKY F, LOJDA Z: Vascular pseudohemophilia associated with ceroid pigmentophagia in albinos. *Am J Pathol* 45:283, 1964.

261. BEDNAR B, JIRASEK A: Cerebral ceroidosis in albinos. *Pathol Eur* 3:341, 1968.

262. HALON PJ, MITUS WJ: Ceroid storage in albinism. *Proceedings of the 13th Congress, International Society of Hematology*, Munich, 1970, p 322.

263. MUÑIZ FJ, FRADERA J, MALDONADO N, PEREZ-SANTIAGO E: Albinism, bleeding tendency and abnormal pigmented cells in the bone marrow: A case report. *Tex Rep Biol Med* 28:167, 1970.

264. WHITE JG, WITKOP CJ JR, GERRITSEN SM: The Hermansky-Pudlak syndrome: Ultrastructure of bone marrow macrophages. *Am J Pathol* 70:329, 1973.

265. WITKOP CJ JR, WHITE JG, GERRITSEN SM, TOWNSEND D, KING RA: Hermansky-Pudlak syndrome (HPS): A proposed block in glutathione peroxidase. *Oral Surg* 35:790, 1973.

266. GARAY SM, GARDELLA JE, FAZZINI EP, GOLDRING RM: Hermansky-Pudlak syndrome. Pulmonary manifestations of a ceroid storage disease. *Am J Med* 66:737, 1979.

267. SCHINELLA RA, GRECO MA, COLBERT BL, DENMARK LW, COX RP: Hermansky-Pudlak syndrome with granulomatous colitis. *Ann Intern Med* 92:20, 1980.

268. TAKAHASHI A, YOKOYAMA T: Hermansky-Pudlak syndrome with special reference to lysosomal dysfunction: A case report and review of the literature. *Virchows Arch (A)* 402:247, 1984.

269. WITKOP CJ, KRUMWIEDE M, SEDANO H, WHITE JG: The reliability of absent platelet dense bodies as a diagnostic criterion for Hermansky-Pudlak syndrome. *Am J Hematol* 26:305, 1987.

270. FIRTH D: Red-headed albinos. *Proc R Soc Med* 17:25, 1924.

271. HORLER AR, WITTS LJ: Hereditary capillary purpura (Von Willebrand's disease). *Q J Med* 27:173, 1958.

272. LARSEN MC, LEY AB, ZUCKER MB, LOSEKE LE: The association of albinism with pseudohemophilia. *Ann Intern Med* 56:504, 1962.

273. MORI K, YODA B, SAKAI H, GOTO Y: A case of "storage-pool disease" associated with albinism (Hermansky-Pudlak syndrome). *Acta Haematol Jap* 41:992, 1978.

274. TANOUE K: Defective platelet functions in a patient with albinism and storage pool disease. *Acta Haematol Jap* 41:1000, 1978.

275. CHIJMATSU Y, YAMAGUCHI T, SUZUKI M, IKEMOTO H, HONMA K, SAIKI S: A case of interstitial pneumonia associated with Hermansky-Pudlak syndrome. *Nippon Kyobu Shikkan Gakkai Zasshi* 22:708, 1984.

276. MATSUMOTO S, NISHIKAWA A, SUGITA H, KAWABATA Y, IWAI K: An autopsy case of Hermansky-Pudlak syndrome with diffuse interstitial pneumonia (Davies-Tuddenham syndrome)—Marked ceroid-like granule deposition in the renal proximal tubular epithelia. *Nippon Kyobu Shikkan Gakkai Zasshi* 22:932, 1984.

277. NISHIMURA K, KITAICHI M, IZUMI T, NAGAI S, CHIHARA J, MATSUI Y, KADO M, KINO T, OSHIMA S, KANAJI K, OKUMA M, YAMAKAWA R: A case of Hermansky-Pudlak syndrome associated with diffuse interstitial pneumonia. *Nippon Naika Gakkai Zasshi* 73:1497, 1984.

278. KLEIMANS M, SASSETTI B, KORDICH L: Disfunción plaquetaria y albinismo. Presentación de dos casos. *Sangre* 21:181, 1976.

279. HERMANSKY F, CIESLAR P: Thrombopathies héréditaires par trouble de libération. *Rev Fr Hematol* 16:413, 1976.

280. HOSTE P, WILLEMS J, DEVRIENDT J, LAMONT H, VAN DER STRAETEN M: Familial diffuse interstitial pulmonary fibrosis associated with oculocutaneous albinism: Report of two cases with a family study. *Scand J Respir Dis* 60:128, 1979.

281. LOREZ HP, RICHARDS JG, DAPRADA M, PICOTTI GB, PARETI FL, CAPITANIO A, MANNUCCI PM: Storage pool disease: Comparative fluorescence microscopical, cytochemical and biochemical studies on amine-storing organelles of human blood platelets. *Br J Haematol* 43:297, 1979.

282. KINNEAR PE, TUDDENHAM EGD: Albinism with haemorrhagic diathesis: Hermansky-Pudlak syndrome. *Br J Ophthalmol* 69:904, 1985.

283. FRENK E, LATTION F: The melanin pigmentary disorder in a family with Hermansky-Pudlak syndrome. *J Invest Dermatol* 78:141, 1982.

284. LATTION F, SCHNEIDER PH, DAPRADA M, LOREZ HP, RICHARDS JG, PICOTTI GB, FRENCK E: Syndrome d'Hermansky-Pudlak dans un village valaisan. *Helv Paediatr Acta* 38:495, 1983.

285. GERRITSEN SM: The Hermansky-Pudlak Syndrome, Proefschrift, Rijksu-

niversiteit Te Utrecht, Drukkerij Biblo BV—s'Hertogenbosch, Utrecht, June 6, 1978.

286. VERLOOP MCV, WIERINGEN A, VUYLSTEKE J, HART HC, HUIZINGA J: Albinismus, haemorrhagische Diathese und anomale Pigmentzellen im Knochenmark. *Med Klin* 59:408, 1964.

287. THEURING F, FIEDLER J: Fatal bleeding following tooth extraction. Hermansky-Pudlak syndrome. *Dtsch Stomatol* 23:52, 1973.

288. DAVIES BH, TUDDENHAM GD: Familial pulmonary fibrosis associated with oculocutaneous albinism and platelet function defect: A new syndrome. *Q J Med* 45:219, 1976.

289. GAMBOA-MARRUFO JD, LOPERENA L, BELLO-GONZALEZ A: Albinismo y enfermedad hemorrágica. Síndrome de Hermansky y Pudlak. *Bol Med Hosp Infant Mex* 41:53, 1984.

290. DEPINHO RA, KAPLAN KL: The Hermansky-Pudlak syndrome: Report of three cases and review of pathophysiology and management considerations. *Medicine (Baltimore)* 64:192, 1985.

291. SIMON JW, ADAMS RJ, CALHOUN JH, SHAPIRO SS, INGERMAN CM: Ophthalmic manifestations of the Hermansky-Pudlak syndrome (oculocutaneous albinism and hemorrhagic diathesis). *Am J Ophthalmol* 93:71, 1982.

292. PALMER DJ, MILLER MT, RAO S: Hermansky-Pudlak oculocutaneous albinism: Clinical and genetic observations in six patients. *Ophthal Paediatr Genet* 3:147, 1983.

293. REISS RE, COPEL JA, ROBERTS NS, HOBBINS JC: Hermansky-Pudlak syndrome in pregnancy: Two case studies. *Am J Obstet Gynecol* 153:564, 1985.

294. FAGADAU WR, HEINEMANN MH, COTLIER E: Hermansky-Pudlak syndrome: Albinism with lipofuscin storage. *Int Ophthalmol* 4:113, 1981.

295. TAYLOR WOG: Albinos who bleed (Hermansky-Pudlak syndrome): The Gypsy's warning? *Trans Ophthalmol Soc UK* 101:223, 1981.

295a. SUMMERS CG, KNOBLOCH WH, WITKOP CJ JR, KING RA: Hermansky-Pudlak syndrome: Ophthalmic findings. *Ophthalmology* 95:545, 1988.

296. WITKOP CJ JR, WOLFE LS, CAL SX, WHITE JG, TOWNSEND D, KEENAN KM: Elevated urinary dolichol excretion in the Hermansky-Pudlak syndrome: Indicator of lysosomal dysfunction. *Am J Med* 82:463, 1987.

296a. WITKOP CJ, WHITE JG, TOWNSEND D, SEDANO HO, CAL SX, BABCOCK M, KRUMWIEDE M, KEENAN K, LOVE JE, WOLFE LS: Ceroid storage disease in Hermansky-Pudlak syndrome: Induction in animal models, in Zs.-NASY I (ed): *Lipofuscin—1987: State of the Art.* Amsterdam, Elsevier, 1988, p 413.

297. BOMALSKI JS, GREEN D, CARONE F: Oculocutaneous albinism, platelet storage pool disease, and progressive lupus nephritis. *Arch Intern Med* 143:809, 1983.

298. WHITE DA, SMITH GJW, COOPER JAD JR, GLICKSTEIN M, RANKIN JA: Hermansky-Pudlak syndrome and interstitial lung disease: Report of a case with lavage findings. *Am Rev Respir Dis* 130:138, 1984.

299. LEITMAN BS, BALTHAZAR EJ, GARAY SM, NAIDICH DP, MCCAULEY DI: The Hermansky-Pudlak syndrome: Radiographic features. *J Can Assoc Radiol* 37:42, 1986.

300. KING RA, OLDS DP, WITKOP CJ JR: Enzyme studies in human oculocutaneous albinism, in Klaus SN (ed): *Pigment Cell Pathophysiology of Melanocytes.* Basel, Karger, 1979, vol 5, p 16.

301. MAURER HM, BUCKINGHAM S, MCGILVRAY E, SPIELVOGEL A, WOLFF JA: Prolonged bleeding time, abnormal binding of platelet serotonin (5-HT), absent platelet "dark body," defective platelet factor-3 activation, bone marrow inclusions and chromosome breaks in albinism. Twelfth Congress, International Society of Hematology, New York, 1968, p 198.

302. WHITE JG, WITKOP CJ JR: Effects of normal and aspirin platelets on defective secondary aggregation in the Hermansky-Pudlak syndrome: A test for storage pool deficient platelets. *Am J Pathol* 68:57, 1972.

303. WHITE JG: Fine structure alterations induced in platelets by adenosine diphosphate. *Blood* 31:604, 1968.

304. WHITE JG: Dense bodies in human platelets: Inherent electron opacity of serotonin storage organelles. *Blood* 33:598, 1969.

305. GERRARD JM, WHITE JG: The influence of prostaglandin endoperoxides on platelet ultrastructure. *Am J Pathol* 80:189, 1975.

306. GERRITSEN SM, AKKERMAN JWN, NIJMEIJER B, SIXMA JJ, WITKOP CJ, WHITE J: The Hermansky-Pudlak syndrome. Evidence for a lowered 5-hydroxytryptamine content in platelets of heterozygotes. *Scand J Haematol* 18:249, 1977.

307. WEISS HJ, TSCHOPP TB, ROGERS J, BRAND H: Studies of platelet 5-hydroxytryptamine (serotonin) in storage pool disease and albinism. *Clin Invest* 54:421, 1974.

308. RAO GHR, WHITE JG, JACHIMOWICZ AA, WITKOP CJ JR: Nucleotide profiles of normal and abnormal platelets by high-pressure liquid chromatography. *J Lab Clin Med* 84:839, 1974.

309. RAO GHR, WHITE JG, JACHIMOWICZ AA, WITKOP CJ JR: An improved method for the extraction of endogenous platelet serotonin. *J Lab Clin Med* 87:129, 1976.

310. GERRARD JM, WHITE JG, RAO GHR, KRIVIT W, WITKOP CJ JR: Labile aggregation stimulating substance (LASS): The factor from storage pool deficient platelets correcting defective aggregation and release of aspirin treated normal platelets. *Br J Haematol* 29:657, 1975.

311. DAY HF, HOLMSEN H, SCRUTTON MC, WEISS HJ: Metal content of platelets obtained from patients with storage pool deficiency. Fourth International Congress of Thrombosis and Hemostasis. Vienna, G Gistel, 1973, p 297.

312. O'BRIEN JR: Effects of salicylates on human platelets. *Lancet* 1:779, 1968.

313. WEISS HJ, ALEDORT LM: Impaired platelet connective tissue reaction in man after aspirin ingestion. *Lancet* 2:495, 1967.

314. WEISS HJ, ALEDORT LM, KOCHWA S: The effect of salicylates on the hemostatic properties of platelets in man. *J Clin Invest* 47:2169, 1968.

315. ZUCKER MB, PETERSON J: Inhibition of adenosine diphosphate-induced secondary aggregation and other platelet functions by acetylsalicylic acid ingestion. *Proc Soc Exp Biol Med* 127:547, 1967.

316. EVANS G, NISHIZAWA EE, PACKHAM MA, MUSTARD JF: The effect of acetylsalicylic acid (aspirin) on platelet function. *Blood* 30:550, 1967.

317. GERRARD JM, WHITE JG: The influence of aspirin and indomethacin on the platelet contractile wave. *Am J Pathol* 82:513, 1976.

318. SMITH JB, WILLIS AL: Formation and release of prostaglandins in response to thrombin. *Br J Pharmacol* 40:545, 1970.

319. SILVER MJ, HERNANDOVICH J, INGERMAN C, KOCSIS JJ, SMITH JB: Persistent inhibition by aspirin of collagen-induced platelet prostaglandin formation, in Scriabine A, Sherry S (eds): *Platelets and Thrombosis.* Baltimore, University Park Press, 1974, p 91.

320. COHEN I: Platelet structure and function. Role of prostaglandins. *Ann Clin Lab Sci* 19:187, 1980.

321. RAO GHR, REDDY KR, WHITE JG: The influence of epinephrine on prostacyclin (PGI2) induced dissociation of ADP aggregated platelets. *Prostagland Med* 4:385, 1980.

322. RAO GHR, REDDY KR, WHITE JG: Influence of trifluoperazine on platelet aggregation and disaggregation. *Prostagland Med* 5:221, 1980.

323. RAO GHR, JOHNSON GJ, WHITE JG: Influence of epinephrine on the aggregation response of aspirin-treated platelets. *Prostagland Med* 5:45, 1980.

324. RAO GHR, GERRARD JM, WITKOP CJ, WHITE JG: Platelet aggregation independent of ADP release or prostaglandin synthesis in patients with Hermansky-Pudlak syndrome. *Prostagland Med* 6:459, 1981.

325. RAO GHR, REDDY KR, WHITE JG: Modification of human platelet response to sodium arachidonate by membrane modulation. *Prostagland Med* 6:75, 1981.

326. HUANG EM, DETWILER TC: Reassessment of the evidence for the role of secreted ADP in biphasic platelet aggregation. *J Lab Clin Med* 95:59, 1980.

327. SAWITSKY A, ROSNER F, CHADSKY S: The sea-blue histiocyte syndrome, a review: Genetic and biochemical studies. *Semin Hematol* 9:285, 1972.

328. CIESLAR P, HERMANSKY F, SMETANAK K, PROKES J: Platelet functions and ultrastructure in the Hermansky-Pudlak syndrome. *Folia Haematol (Leipz)* 101:553, 1974.

329. GERRITSEN SM, AKKERMAN JWN, STAAL G, ROELOFSEN B, KOSTER JF, SIXMA JJ: Biochemical studies in Hermansky-Pudlak syndrome. *Scand J Haematol* 23:161, 1979.

330. RENDU F, BRETON-GORIUS J, TRUGNAN G, CASTRO-MALASPINA H, ANDRIEV J-M, BEREZIAT G, LEBRET M, CAEN JP: Studies on a new variant of the Hermansky-Pudlak syndrome: Qualitative, ultrastructural and functional abnormalities of the platelet dense bodies associated with a phospholipase A defect. *Am J Hematol* 4:387, 1978.

331. WITKOP CJ JR, CUTLER B, LOCKMAN LA: Diagnosis of late infantile neuronal "ceroid-lipofuscinosis" from histochemical and ultrastructural changes in dental pulp. *Oral Surg* 57:294, 1984.

332. ENDICOTT KM: Similarity of the acid-fast pigment ceroid and oxidized unsaturated fat. *AMA Arch Pathol* 37:49, 1944.

333. HARTROFT WS, PORTA EA: Ceroid. *Am J Med Sci* 250:324, 1965.

334. PORTA EA, HARTROFT WS: Lipid pigments in relation to aging and dietary factors (lipofuscin), in Wolman M (ed): *Pigments in Pathology.* New York, Academic, 1969, p 192.

335. TAPPEL A: Lipid peroxidation and fluorescent molecular damage to membranes, in Trumps B, Arstilla A (eds): *Pathobiology of Cell Membranes.* New York, Academic, 1975, p 145.

336. DONATO H JR: Lipid peroxidation, cross-linking reactions, and aging, in Sohol RS (ed): *Age Pigments.* Amsterdam, Elsevier/North Holland, 1981, p 63.

337. WOLFE LS, NG YING KIN NMK, BAKER RR: Batten disease and related disorders: New findings on the chemistry of the storage material, in Callahan WJ, Lowden JA (eds): *Lysosomes and Lysosomal Storage Disease.* New York, Raven, 1981, p 315.

338. WOLFE LS, NG YING KIN NMK, PALO J, HALTIA M: Dolichols in brain and

urinary sediment in neuronal ceroid lipofuscinosis. *Neurology (NY)* 33:103, 1983.

339. WOLFE LS, PALO J, SANTAVUORI P, ANDERMANN F, ANDERMANN E, JACOB JC, KOLODNY E: Urinary sediment dolichols in the diagnosis of neuronal ceroid-lipofuscinosis. *Ann Neurol* 19:270, 1986.

340. NG YING KIN NMK, PALO J, HALTIA M, WOLFE LS: High levels of brain dolichols in neuronal ceroid-lipofuscinosis and senescence. *J Neurochem* 40:1465, 1983.

341. WOLFE LS, NG YING KIN NMK, BAKER RR, CARPENTER S, ANDERMANN F: Identification of retinoyl complexes as the autofluorescent component of the neuronal storage material in Batten disease. *Science* 195:1360, 1977.

342. PALMER DN, HUSBANDS DR, WINTER PJ, BLUNT JW, JOLLY RD: Ceroid lipofuscinosis in sheep. I Bis (monocylglycero) phosphate, dolichol, ubiquinone, phospholipids, fatty acids, and fluorescence in liver lipopigment lipids. *J Biol Chem* 261:1766, 1986.

343. PALMER DN, BARNES G, HUSBANDS DR, JOLLY RD: Ceroid lipofuscinosis in sheep. II The major component of the lipopigment in liver, kidney, pancreas, and brain is low molecular weight protein. *J Biol Chem* 261:1773, 1986.

344. WOLFE LS, NG YING KIN NMK, PALO J, HALTIA M: Raised levels of cerebral cortex dolichols in Alzheimer's disease (letter). *Lancet* 2:99, 1982.

345. WOLFE LS, PALO J, BERGERON C, KOTILA N, VARONEN S: Elevation of dolichols in brain in Alzheimer's disease but normal in Alzheimer's and Downs urinary sediment. *Neurochem Pathol* 3:213, 1985.

346. WOLFE LS, GOLD RJM, NG YING KIN NMK: Dolichols in ceroid-lipofuscinosis, Alzheimer's disease and aging. *Trans Am Soc Neurochem* 15:1020, 1984.

347. NG YING KIN NMK, WOLFE LS: Presence of abnormal amounts of dolichols in the urinary sediment of Batten disease patients. *Pediatr Res* 16:530, 1982.

348. DE BALEQUE M, POLLACK MA, SUZUKI K: Late infantile neuronal storage disease with curvilinear bodies. Systemic pathologic features. *Arch Pathol Lab Med* 100:139, 1976.

349. WONG TK, DECKER GL, LENNARZ WJ: Localization of dolichol in the lysosomal fraction of rat liver. *J Biol Chem* 257:6614, 1982.

350. WOLFE LS, IVY GO, WITKOP CJ: Dolichols, lysosomal membrane turnover and relationships to the accumulation of ceroid and lipofuscin in inherited diseases, Alzheimer's disease and aging, in Twelfth Nobel Conference: Structure, Biosynthesis and Function of Isoprenoid Compounds in Eucaryotic Cells, Sodergarn, Sweden. May 25–28, 1986. *Chim Scripta* 27:79, 1987.

351. CERVENKA J, WITKOP CJ JR, OKORO AN, KING RA: Chromosome breaks and sister chromatid exchanges in albinos in Nigeria. *Clin Genet* 15:17, 1979.

352. BÉGUEZ-CESAR A: Neutropénia crónica maligna familiare con granulaciones atípicas de los leucocitos. *Bol Soc Cubana Pediatr* 15:900, 1943.

353. STEINBRINCK W: Über eine neue Granulationsanomalie der Leukocyten. *Dtsch Arch Klin Med* 193:577, 1948.

354. CHÉDIAK M: Nouvelle anomalie leucocytaire de caractère constitutionnel et familial. *Rev Hematol* 7:362, 1952.

355. HIGASHI O: Congenital gigantism of peroxidase granules. *Tohoku J Exp Med* 59:315, 1954.

356. SATO A: Chediak and Higashi's disease. Probable identity of "a new leucocytal anomaly (Chediak)" and "congenital gigantism of peroxidase granules (Higashi)." *Tohoku J Exp Med* 61:201, 1955.

357. WINDHORST DB, ZELICKSON AS, GOOD RA: A human pigmentary dilution based on a heritable subcellular structural defect—The Chédiak-Higashi syndrome. *J Invest Dermatol* 50:9, 1968.

358. LOCKMAN LA, KENNEDY WR, WHITE JG: The Chediak-Higashi syndrome: Electrophysiologic and electron microscopic observations on the peripheral neuropathy. *J Pediatr* 70:942, 1967.

359. DONOHUE WL, BAIN HW: Chediak-Higashi syndrome—A lethal familial disease with anomalous inclusions in the leucocytes and constitutional stigmata-report of a case with necropsy. *Pediatrics* 20:416, 1957.

360. BERNARD J, BESSIS M, SELIGMANN M, CHASSIGNEUX J, CHOME J: Un cas de maladie de Chediak-Steinbrinck-Higashi: Étude clinique et cytologique. *Presse Med* 68:563, 1960.

361. BESSIS M, BERNARD J, SELIGMANN M: Étude cytologique d'un cas de maladie de Chediak, *Nouv Rev Fr Hematol* 1:422, 1961.

362. WHITE JG: The Chediak-Higashi syndrome: A possible lysosomal disease. *Blood* 28:143, 1966.

363. MYERS JP, SUNG JH, COWAN D, WOLFF A: Pathological findings in the central and peripheral nervous systems in Chediak-Higashi's disease and the finding of cytoplasmic neuronal inclusions. *J Neuropathol Exp Neurol* 22:357, 1963.

364. MAGGI R, GUTIERRIZ E, PENALBER J, DI MENNA A, ROCCATAGLIAT M, MATERA F, ETCHEGARAY E, MILLAN J: Sindrome de Beguez Cesar-Chediak-Higashi. Presentación de dos casos. *Arch Argent Pediatr* 48:323, 1957.

365. SCHNEIDER LA: Chediak-Higashi syndrome, in *Proceedings of the Seventh Congress, Society of International Hematology.* Rome, 1958, p 430.

366. KRITZLER RA, TERNER JY, LINDENBAUM J, MAGIDSON J, WILLIAMS R, PREISIG R, PHILIPS GB: Chediak-Higashi syndrome—Cytologic and serum lipid observations in a case and family. *Am J Med* 36:583, 1964.

367. PADGETT GA, REIQUAM CW, HENSON JB, GORHAM JR: Comparative studies of susceptibility to infection in Chediak-Higashi syndrome. *J Pathol Bacteriol* 95:509, 1968.

368. WITKOP CJ JR: The face and oral structures, in Rubin A (ed): *Handbook of Congenital Malformations.* Philadelphia, Saunders, 1967, p 103.

369. EFRATI P, JONAS W: Chediak's anomaly of leucocytes in malignant lymphoma associated with leukemic manifestations: Case report with necropsy. *Blood* 13:1063, 1958.

370. DENT PB, FISH LA, WHITE JG, GOOD RA: Chediak-Higashi syndrome: Observations on the nature of the associated malignancy. *Lab Invest* 15:1634, 1966.

371. LASCANO FD, FERREYRA ME, SEOANE MR: Enfermedad de Chediak-Higashi. *Rev Clin Esp* 110:329, 1968.

372. WOLFF SM, DALE DC, CLARK RA, ROOT RK, KIMBALL HR: The Chediak-Higashi syndrome: Studies of host defenses. *Ann Intern Med* 76:293, 1972.

373. BREGEAT P, EHERMY P, HAMMARD H: Manifestations oculaires du syndrome de Chediak-Higashi. *Arch Ophthalmol (Paris)* 23:661, 1966.

374. JOHNSON DL, JACKOBSON LW, TOYAMA R, MONAHAN RH: Histopathy of eyes in Chediak-Higashi syndrome. *Arch Ophthalmol* 75:84, 1966.

375. BENEZRA D, MENGISTU F, CIVIDALLI G, WEIZMAN Z, MERIN S, AUERBACH E: Chediak-Higashi syndrome: Ocular findings. *J Pediatr Ophthalmol Strabismus* 17:68, 1980.

376. PETTIT RE, BERDAL KG: Chédiak-Higashi syndrome: Neurologic appearance. *Arch Neurol* 41:1001, 1984.

377. BLUME RS, WOLFF SM: The Chediak-Higashi syndrome: Studies in four patients and a review of the literature. *Medicine* 51:247, 1972.

378. RUBIN CM, BURKE BA, MCKENNA RW, MCCLAIN KL, WHITE JG, NESBITT ME JR, FILIPOVICH AH: The accelerated phase of Chediak-Higashi syndrome. An expression of the virus-associated hemophagocytic syndrome? *Cancer* 56:524, 1985.

379. MCLELLAND R, ESTEVEZ JM: The Chediak-Higashi syndrome. *J Assoc Can Radiol* 19:78, 1968.

380. CLAWSON CC, WHITE JG: Chediak-Higashi syndrome, in Buyse M (ed): *Birth Defects Compendium,* 3d ed. New York, AR Liss, 1982.

381. BUCHANAN GR, HANDIN RI: Platelet function in the Chediak-Higashi syndrome. *Blood* 47:941, 1976.

382. BELL TG, MEYERS KM, PRIEUR DJ, FAUCI AS, WOLFF SM, PADGETT GA: Decreased nucleotide and serotonin storage associated with defective function in Chediak-Higashi syndrome cattle and human platelets. *Blood* 48:175, 1976.

383. BOXER GJ, HOLMSEN H, ROBKIN L, BANG NU, BOXER LA, BAEHNER RL: Abnormal platelet function in Chediak-Higashi syndrome. *Br J Haematol* 35:521, 1977.

384. RENDU T, BRETON-GORIUS J, LEBRET M, KLEBANOFF C, BURIOT D, GRISCELLI C, LEVY-TOLEDANO S, CAEN JP: Evidence that abnormal platelet functions in human Chédiak-Higashi syndrome are the result of a lack of dense bodies. *Am J Pathol* 111:301, 1983.

385. KIM BK, CHAO FC, LEAVITT R, FAUCI AS, MEYERS KM, ZAMECNIK PC: Diadenosine 5′,5‴-p1,p4-tetraphosphate deficiency in blood platelets of Chédiak-Higashi syndrome. *Blood* 66:735, 1985.

386. APITZ-CASTRO R, CRUZ MR, LEDEZMA E, MERINO F, RAMIREZ-DUQUE P, DANGELMEIER C, HOLMSEN H: The storage pool deficiency in platelets from humans with the Chediak-Higashi syndrome: Study of six patients. *Br J Haematol* 59:471, 1985.

387. STEGMAIER OC, SCHNEIDER LA: Chediak-Higashi syndrome: Dermatologic manifestations. *Arch Dermatol* 91:1, 1965.

388. WINDHORST DB, WHITE JG, ZELICKSON AS, CLAWSON CC, DENT PB, POLLARA B, GOOD RA: The Chediak-Higashi anomaly and the Aleutian trait in mink: Homologous defects of lysosomal structure. *Ann NY Acad Sci* 155:818, 1968.

389. CLARK RA, KIMBALL HR: Defective granulocyte chemotaxis in the Chediak-Higashi syndrome. *J Clin Invest* 50:2645, 1971.

390. CLARK RA, KIMBALL HR, PADGETT GA: Granulocyte chemotaxis in the Chediak-Higashi syndrome of mink. *Blood* 39:644, 1972.

391. OLIVER JM: Impaired microtubule function correctable by cyclic GMP and cholinergic agonist in the Chediak-Higashi syndrome. *Am J Pathol* 85:395, 1976.

392. ZURIER RB: Cyclic nucleotides and the Chediak-Higashi syndrome, in Hamet P, Sands H (eds): *Advances in Cyclic Nucleotide Research.* New York, Raven, 1980, vol 12, p 173.

393. BOXER LA, WATANABE AM, RISTER M, BESCH HR, ALLEN J, BAEHNER RL:

Correction of leukocyte function in Chediak-Higashi syndrome by ascorbate. *N Engl J Med* 295:1041, 1976.

394. OLIVER JM, ZURIER RB: Correction of characteristic abnormalities of microtubule function and granule morphology in Chédiak-Higashi syndrome with cholinergic agents. *J Clin Invest* 57:1239, 1976.

395. CLAWSON CC, WHITE JG, REPINE JE: The Chediak-Higashi syndrome. Evidence that defective leukotaxis is primarily due to an impediment by giant granules. *Am J Pathol* 92:745, 1978.

396. CLAWSON CC, REPINE JE, WHITE JG: Chediak-Higashi syndrome: Quantitation defect in bactericidal capacity. *Blood* 38:814, 1971.

397. CLAWSON CC, REPINE JE, WHITE JG: Quantitation of bactericidal capacity in normal and abnormal human neutrophils. *Pediatr Res* 6:367, 1972.

398. CLAWSON CC, REPINE JE, WHITE JG: The Chediak-Higashi syndrome. Quantitation of a deficiency in maximal bactericidal capacity. *Am J Pathol* 94:539, 1979.

399. BLUME RS, BENNETT JM, YANKEE RA, WOLFF SM: Defective granulocyte regulation in the Chediak-Higashi syndrome. *N Engl J Med* 279:1009, 1968.

400. MAURI C, SILINGARDI V: A cytological and cytochemical study of Chediak's leukocytic anomaly. *Acta Haematol* 32:114, 1964.

401. PAGE AR, BERENDES H, WARNER J, GOOD RA: The Chediak-Higashi syndrome. *Blood* 20:330, 1962.

402. SADAN N, YAFFEE D, ROZENSZAN L, ADAR H, SOROKER B, EFRATI R: Cytochemical and genetic studies in four cases of Chediak-Higashi-Steinbrinck syndrome. *Acta Haematol* 34:20, 1965.

403. WHITE JG: Virus-like particles in the peripheral blood cells of two patients with Chediak-Higashi syndrome. *Cancer* 19:877, 1966.

404. WINDHORST DB, ZELICKSON AS, GOOD RA: Chediak-Higashi syndrome, hereditary giantism of cytoplasmic organelles. *Science* 151:81, 1966.

405. ASH P, LOUTIT JF, TOWNSEND KMS: Giant lysosomes, a cytoplasmic marker in osteoclasts of beige mice. *Am J Pathol* 130:237, 1980.

406. RAUSCH PG, PRYZWANSKY KB, SPITZNAGEL JK: Immunocytochemical identification of azurophilic and specific granule markers in the giant granules of Chediak-Higashi neutrophiles. *N Engl J Med* 298:693, 1978.

407. PARMLEY RT, POON M-C, CHRIST WM, MALLUH A: Giant platelet granules in a child with the Chediak-Higashi syndrome. *Am J Hematol* 6:51, 1979.

408. WHITE JG, CLAWSON CC: The Chediak-Higashi syndrome: Spectrum of giant organelles in peripheral blood cells. *Henry Ford Hosp Med J* 27:286, 1979.

409. WHITE JG, CLAWSON CC: Chediak-Higashi syndrome: Variable cytochemical reactivity of giant inclusions in polymorphonuclear leukocytes. *Ultrastruct Pathol* 1:223, 1980.

410. WHITE JG, CLAWSON CC: The Chediak-Higashi syndrome. Ring-shaped lysosomes in circulating monocytes. *Am J Pathol* 96:781, 1979.

411. WHITE JG, CLAWSON CC: The Chediak-Higashi syndrome: The nature of the giant neutrophile granules and their interactions with cytoplasm and foreign particulates. *Am J Pathol* 98:151, 1980.

412. OLIVER JM, ZURIER RB, BERLIN RD: Concanavalin A cap formation on polymorphonuclear leukocytes of normal and beige (Chediak-Higashi) mice. *Nature* 253:471, 1975.

413. BOXER LA, RISTER M, ALLEN JM, BAEHNER RL: Improvement of Chediak-Higashi leukocyte function by cyclic guanosine monophosphate. *Blood* 49:9, 1977.

414. BOXER LA, ALBERTINI DF, BAEHNER RL, OLIVER JM: Impaired microtubule assembly and polymorphonuclear leukocyte function in Chediak-Higashi syndrome correctable by ascorbic acid. *Br J Haematol* 43:207, 1979.

415. HINDS K, DANES BS: Microtubular defects in Chediak-Higashi syndrome. *Lancet* 2:146, 1976.

416. BUCHANAN GR, HANDIN RI: Platelet function in the Chediak-Higashi syndrome. *Blood* 47:941, 1976.

417. WHITE JG: Platelet microtubules and giant granules in the Chediak-Higashi syndrome. *Am J Med Tech* 44:273, 1978.

418. WHITE JG, CLAWSON CC: The Chediak-Higashi syndrome: Microtubules in monocytes and lymphocytes. *Am J Hematol* 7:349, 1979.

419. FRANNKEL FR, TUCKER RW, BRUCE J, STENBERG R: Fibroblasts and macrophages of mice with the Chediak-Higashi-like syndrome have microtubules and actin cables. *J Cell Biol* 79:401, 1978.

420. OSTLUND RE, LEUNG JT, TUCKER RW: Abnormal lysosome-microtubule interaction in Chediak-Higashi syndrome. *Clin Res* 27:303A, 1979.

421. KLEBANOFF SJ, CLARK RA: *The Neutrophil: Function and Clinical Disorders.* New York, Elsevier North-Holland, 1978, p 735.

422. RODER JC: The beige mutation in the mouse 1. A stem cell predetermined impairment in natural killer cells. *J Immunol* 123:2168, 1979.

423. RODER JC, LOHMANN-MATTHES M-L, DOMZIG W, WIGZELL H: The beige mutation in the mouse. II. Selectivity of the natural killer (NK) cell defect. *J Immunol* 123:2174, 1979.

424. HALIOTIS T, RODER J, KLEIN M, ORTALDO J, FAUCI AS, HERBERMAN RB:

Chédiak-Higashi gene in humans 1. Impairment of natural-killer function. *J Exp Med* 151:1039, 1980.

425. KLEIN M, RODER J, HALIOTIS T, KOREC S, JETT JR, HERBERMAN RB, KATZ P, FAUCI AS: Chédiak-Higashi gene in humans II. The selectivity of the defect in natural-killer and antibody-dependent cell-mediated cytotoxicity function. *J Exp Med* 151:1049, 1980.

426. GRISCELLI C, DURANDY A, GUY-GRAND D, DAGUILLARD F, HERTZOG C, PRUNIERAS MA: A syndrome associating partial albinism and immunodeficiency. *Am J Med* 65:691, 1978.

427. VIRELIZIER J-L, LIPINSKI M, TURSZ T, GRISCELLI C: Defects of immune interferon secretion and natural killer activity in patients with immunological disorders. *Lancet* 2:696, 1979.

428. GALE PF, PARKIN JL, QUIE PG, PETTIT RE, NELSON RP, BRUNNING RD: Leukocyte granulation abnormality associated with normal neutrophile function and neurologic impairment. *Am J Clin Pathol* 86:33, 1986.

429. VAN SLYCK EJ, REBUCK JW: Pseudo-Chediak-Higashi anomaly in acute leukemia. *Am J Clin Pathol* 62:673, 1974.

430. GORMAN AM, O'CONNELL LG: Letter to the editor. Pseudo-Chediak-Higashi anomaly in acute leukemia. *Am J Clin Pathol* 65:1030, 1976.

431. TULLIEZ M, VERNANT JP, BRENTON-GORIUS J, IMBERT M, SULTAN C: Pseudo-Chediak-Higashi anomaly in a case of acute myeloid leukemia: Electron microscopic studies. *Blood* 54:863, 1979.

432. GALLIN JI, ELIN RJ, HUBERT RT, FAUCI AS, KALINER MA, WOLFF SM: Efficacy of ascorbic acid in Chediak-Higashi syndrome (CHS): Studies in humans and mice. *Blood* 53:226, 1979.

433. GRISCELLI C, VIRELIZIER J-L: Bone marrow transplantation in a patient with Chédiak-Higashi syndrome. *Birth Defects* 19(3):333, 1983.

434. RAMÍREZ-DUQUE P, ARENDS T, MERINO F: Chédiak-Higashi syndrome: Description of a cluster in a Venezuelan-Andean isolated region. *J Med* 13:431, 1982.

435. DEBEER HA, ANDERSON R, FINDLAY GH: Chediak-Higashi syndrome in a "black" child. *S Afr Med J* 60:108, 1981.

436. VALENZUELA R, AIKAWA M, O'REAGAN S, MAKKER S: Chédiak-Higashi syndrome in a black infant: A light and electron microscopic study with special emphasis on erythrophagocytosis. *Am J Clin Pathol* 65:483, 1976.

437. LEAL I, MERINO F, SOTO H, GOIHMAN-YAHR M, DASALVO L, AMESTY C, BRETAÑA A: Chediak-Higashi syndrome in a Venezuelan black child. *J Am Acad Dermatol* 13:337, 1985.

438. ABDULSALAM M, MUSLICHAN S, WAHIDIYAT I, GATOT D, GINTING B: Chediak-Higashi syndrome in an Indonesian infant. *Paediatr Indones* 25:159, 1985.

439. LUTZNER MA, TIERNEY JH, BENDITT EP: Giant granules and widespread cytoplasmic inclusions in a genetic syndrome of Aleutian mink. *Lab Invest* 14:2063, 1965.

440. PADGETT GA, LEADER RW, GORHAM JR, O'MARY CC: The familial occurrence of the Chediak-Higashi syndrome in mink and cattle. *Genetics* 49:505, 1965.

441. PADGETT GA: The Chediak-Higashi syndrome. *Adv Vet Sci Comp Med* 12:239, 1968.

442. TAYLOR RE, FARRELL RK: Light and electron microscopy of peripheral blood neutrophiles in a killer whale affected with Chediak-Higashi syndrome. *Fed Proc* 32:822, 1973.

443. KRAMER JW, DAVIS WC, PRIEUR DJ: Chediak-Higashi syndrome of cats. *Lab Invest* 36:554, 1977.

444. FRENK E, CALME A: Hypopigmentation oculo-cutanée familiar à transmission dominante due à un trouble de la formation des mélanosomes. *Schweiz Med Wochenschr* 107:1964, 1977.

445. CORTIN P, TREMBLAY M, LEMAGNE JM: X-linked ocular albinism: Relative value of skin biopsy, iris transillumination and funduscopy in identifying affected males and carriers. *Can J Ophthalmol* 16:121, 1981.

446. SZYMANSKI KA, BOUGHMAN JA, NANCE WE, OLANSKY DC, WEINBERG RS: Genetic studies of ocular albinism in a large Virginia kindred. *Ann Ophthalmol* 16:183, 1984.

447. YOSHIIKE T, MANABE M, HAYAKAWA M, OGAWA H: Macromelanosomes in X-linked ocular albinism (XLOA). *Acta Derm Venereol (Stockh)* 65:66, 1985.

448. ENGELHARD CF: Eine Familie mit hereditarem Nystagmus. *Zentralbl Gesamte Neurol Psychiatr* 28:319, 1915.

449. LEIN JN, SITWART CT, MALL FC: Sex-linked hereditary nystagmus. *Pediatrics* 18:214, 1956.

450. SIMON JW, KANDEL GL, KROHEL GB, NELSON PT: Albonotic characteristics in congenital nystagmus. *Am J Ophthalmol* 97:320, 1984.

451. WALKER BA, MARTYN LJ, COFFMAN T: X-linked ocular albinism. *Birth Defects* 7(3):200, 1971.

452. O'DONNELL FE JR, GREEN WR, FLEISCHMAN JA, HAMBRICK GW: X-linked ocular albinism in blacks: Ocular albinism cum pigmento. *Arch Ophthalmol* 96:1189, 1978.

453. JOHNSON GJ, GILLAN JG, PEARCE WG: Ocular albinism in Newfoundland. *Can J Ophthalmol* 6:237, 1971.

454. GREGOR Z: The perifoveal vasculature in albinism. *Br J Ophthalmol* 62:554, 1978.

455. SPEDICK MG, BEAUCHAMP GR: Retinal vascular and optic nerve abnormalities in albinism. *J Pediatr Ophthalmol Strabismus* 23:58, 1986.

456. KRILL AE, LEE GB: The electroretinogram in albinos and carriers of the ocular albino trait. *Arch Ophthalmol* 69:32, 1963.

457. TOMEI F, WIRTH A: Letter to Editors. The electroretinogram of albinos. *Vision Res* 18:1465, 1978.

458. RESSER F, WEINSTEIN GW, FEIOCK KB: Electrooculography as a test of retinal function. *Am J Ophthalmol* 70:505, 1970.

459. WAARDENBURG PJ, VAN DEN BOSCH J: X-chromosomal ocular albinism in a Dutch family. *Ann Hum Genet* 21:101, 1956.

460. GILLESPIE FD, COVELLI B: Carriers of ocular albinism with and without ocular changes. *Am Ophthalmol Soc Trans* 67:535, 1969.

461. KRILL AE: X-chromosomal-linked disease affecting the eye. Status of the heterozygous female. *Ophthalmol Soc* 67:535, 1969.

462. FRANÇOIS J, DEWEER JP: Albinisme oculaire lié au sexe et altérations caractéristiques du fond d'oeil chez les femmes hétérozygotes. *Ophthalmologia* 126:209, 1953.

463. GILLESPIE FD: Ocular albinism with report of a family with female carriers. *Arch Ophthalmol* 66:774, 1961.

464. PEARCE WG, JOHNSON GJ, GILLAN JG: Nystagmus in a female carrier of ocular albinism. *J Med Genet* 9:126, 1972.

465. PEARCE WG, JOHNSON GJ, SANGER R: Ocular albinism and Xg (letter). *Lancet* 1:1072, 1971.

466. FIALKOW PJ, GIBLETT ER, MOTULSKY AG: Measurable linkage between ocular albinism and Xg. *Am J Hum Genet* 19:63, 1967.

467. PEARCE WG, SANGER R, RACE RR: Ocular albinism and Xg. *Lancet* 1:1282, 1968.

468. WINSHIP I, GERICKE G, BEIGHTON P: X-linked inheritance of ocular albinism with late-onset sensorineural deafness. *Am J Med Genet* 19:797, 1984.

469. O'DONNELL FE, KING RA, GREEN WR, WITKOP CJ JR: Autosomal recessively inherited ocular albinism. *Arch Ophthalmol* 96:1621, 1978.

470. SCIALFA AC: Ocular albinism in a female. *Am J Ophthalmol* 73:943, 1972.

471. THOMSON E: Note on a dark haired girl with ocular albinism. *Ophthalmoscope* 8:884, 1910.

472. LEWIS RA: Ocular albinism and deafness. Twenty-ninth Annual Meeting. American Society of Human Genetics. Vancouver, 1978, p 57A.

473. FORSIUS H, ERIKSSON AW: Ein neues Augensyndrom mit X-chromosomaler Transmission. Eine Sippe mit Fundusalbinismus, Fovealhypoplacie, Nystagmus, Myopie, Astigmatismus und Dyschromatopsie. *Klin Monatsbl Augenheilkd* 144:447, 1964.

474. O'DONNELL FE, GREEN WR, MCKUSICK VA, FORSIUS H, ERIKSSON AW: Forsius-Eriksson syndrome: Its relation to Nettleship-Falls X-linked ocular albinism. *Clin Genet* 17:403, 1980.

475. VAN DORP DB, ERIKSSON AW, DELLEMAN JW, VAN VLIET AGM, COLLEWIJN H, VAN BALEN THM, FORSIUS HR: Åland eye disease: No albino misrouting. *Clin Genet* 28:526, 1985.

476. CROSS HE, MCKUSICK VA, BREEN WA: A new oculocerebral syndrome with hypopigmentation. *J Pediatr* 70:398, 1967.

477. WITKOP CJ JR: Heterogeneity in gingival fibromatosis. *Birth Defects* 7(7):210, 1971.

478. WITKOP CJ JR: Heterogeneity in inherited dental traits: Gingival fibromatosis and amelogenesis imperfecta. *South Med J (suppl)* 64:16, 1971.

479. WITKOP CJ JR, CROSS HE: Gingival fibromatosis, hypopigmentation, microphthalmaia, oligophrenia and athetosis, in Bergsma D (ed): *Birth Defects Atlas and Compendium*. Baltimore, Williams & Wilkins, 1973, p 434.

480. PREUS M, FRASER FC, WIGGLESWORTH FW: An oculocutaneous hypopigmentation syndrome. *J Genet Hum* 31:323, 1983.

481. PASSARGE E, FUCHS-MENKE S: Oculocerebral syndrome with hypopigmentation. *Birth Defects* 11(2):466, 1975.

482. FITZPATRICK TB, EISEN AZ, WOLFF K, FREEDBERG IM, AUSTEN KF (eds): *Dermatology in General Medicine*, 3d ed. New York, McGraw-Hill, 1987.

483. EDMUNDS RT: Vision of albinos. *Arch Ophthalmol* 42:755, 1949.

484. PICKFORD RW: Colour vision of an albino. *Nature* 168:954, 1951.

485. PICKFORD RW: Colour vision of three albinos. *Nature* 181:361, 1958.

486. PICKFORD RW, TAYLOR WOG: Colour vision of two albinos. *Br J Ophthalmol* 52:640, 1968.

487. TAYLOR WOG: Albinism and colour defects. *Mod Prob Ophthalmol* 17:292, 1976.

488. KRILL AE: Total color blindness and albinism. *Postgrad Med* 37:279, 1965.

489. KRILL AE, FISHMAN GA: Acquired color vision defects. *Trans Am Acad Ophthalmol Otolaryngol* 75:1095, 1971.

490. LOURENCO PE, FISCHMAN GA, ANDERSON RJ: Color vision in albino subjects. *Doc Ophthalmol* 55:341, 1983.

491. HALES RH: Albinism with Axenfeld's syndrome. *Rocky Mt Med J* 65:51, 1968.

492. ALKEMADE P: *Dysgenesis Mesodermalis of the Iris and the Cornea*. Assen, The Netherlands, Van Gorcum, 1969.

493. BRADLEY WF, RICHARDSON J, FREW IJC: The familial association of neurofibromatosis, peroneal muscular atrophy, congenital deafness, partial albinism and Axenfeld's defect. *Brain* 97:521, 1974.

494. LUBIN JR: Oculocutaneous albinism associated with corneal mesodermal dysgenesis. *Am J Ophthalmol* 91:437, 1981.

495. RICCI B, LACERRA F, LUBINS JR: Letter to the editor. Mesodermal dysgenesis. *Am J Ophthalmol* 92:587, 1981.

496. BENSON W: Oculocutaneous albinism with Axenfeld's anomaly. Letter to the editor. *Am J Ophthalmol* 92:133, 1981.

497. VAN DORP DB, DELLEMAN JW, LOEWER-SIEGER DH: Oculocutaneous albinism and anterior chambre cleavage malformations: Not a coincidence. *Clin Genet* 26:440, 1984.

498. HAYAKAWA M, KATO K, NAKAJIMA A, YOSHIIKE T, OGAWA H: Nettleship-Falls X-linked ocular albinism with Axenfeld's anomaly: A case report. *Ophthalmol Paediatr Genet* 7:109, 1986.

499. POLYAK S, in Klüver H (ed): *The Vertebrate Visual System*. Chicago, University of Chicago Press, 1957.

500. CREEL DJ, GIOLLI RA: Retinogeniculostriate projections in guinea pigs: Albino and pigmented strains compared. *Exp Neurol* 36:411, 1972.

501. HAYHOW WR, WEBB C, JERVIE A: The accessory optic fiber system of the rat. *J Comp Neurol* 115:187, 1960.

502. KUPFER C, CHUMBLEY L, DOWNER JC: Quantitative histology of optic nerve, optic tract, and lateral geniculate nucleus of man. *J Anat* 101:393, 1967.

503. LUND RD: Uncrossed visual pathways of hooded and albino rats. *Science* 149:1506, 1965.

504. GIOLLI RA, GUTHRIE MD: The primary optic projections in the rabbit: An experimental degeneration study. *J Comp Neurol* 136:99, 1969.

505. GUILLERY RW: An abnormal retinogeniculate projection in Siamese cats. *Brain Res* 14:739, 1969.

506. CREEL DJ: Visual system anomaly associated with albinism in the cat. *Nature* 231:465, 1971.

507. GUILLERY RW: An abnormal retinogeniculate projection in the albino ferret *(Mustela furo)*. *Brain Res* 33:482, 1971.

508. GUILLERY RW, SITTHI AMORN C, EIGHMY BB: Mutants with abnormal visual pathways: An explanation of anomalous geniculate laminae. *Science* 174:831, 1971.

509. GIOLLI RA, CREEL DJ: The primary optic projections in pigmented and albino guinea pigs: An experimental degeneration study. *Brain Res* 55:25, 1973.

510. GUILLERY RW, KAAS JH: Genetic abnormality of the visual pathways in a "white" tiger. *Science* 180:1287, 1973.

511. GUILLERY RW, SCOTT GL, CATTANACH BM, DEOL MS: Genetic mechanisms determining the central visual pathways of mice. *Science* 179:1014, 1973.

512. SANDERSON KJ: Normal and abnormal retinogeniculate pathways in rabbits and mink. *Anat Rec* 172:398, 1972.

513. SANDERSON KJ, GUILLERY RW, SHACKLEFORD RM: Congenitally abnormal visual pathways in mink *(Mustela vision)* with reduced retinal pigment. *J Comp Neurol* 154:225, 1974.

514. CREEL DJ, SHERIDAN CL: Monocular acquisition and interocular transfer in albino rats with unilateral striate ablations. *Psychonomic Sci* 6:89, 1966.

515. MONTERO VM, BRUGGE JF, BEITEL RE: Relation of the visual field to the lateral geniculate body of the albino rat. *J Neurophysiol* 31:221, 1968.

516. CREEL DJ, DUSTMAN RE, BECK EC: Differences in visually evoked responses in albinos versus hooded rats. *Exp Neurol* 29:298, 1970.

517. CUNNINGHAM TJ, LUND RD: Laminar patterns in the dorsal division of the lateral geniculate nucleus of the rat. *Brain Res* 34:394, 1971.

518. GIOLLI RA, GUTHRIE MD: Organization of subcortical projections of visual areas I and II in the rabbit: An experimental degeneration study. *J Comp Neurol* 142:351, 1971.

519. CREEL DJ: Differences of ipsilateral and contralateral visually evoked responses in the cat: Strains compared. *J Comp Physiol Psychol* 77:161, 1971.

520. GUILLERY RW, KAAS JH: A study of normal and congenitally abnormal retinogeniculate projections in cats. *J Comp Neurol* 143:73, 1971.

521. KAAS JH, GUILLERY RW: The transfer of abnormal visual field representation from the dorsal-lateral geniculate nucleus to the visual cortex in Siamese cats. *Brain Res* 59:61, 1973.

522. GROSS KJ, HICKEY TL: Abnormal laminar patterns in the lateral geniculate nucleus of an albino monkey. *Brain Res* 190:231, 1980.

523. GUILLERY RW, HICKEY TL, KAAS JH, FELLERMAN DJ, DEBRUYN EJ, SPARKS DL: Abnormal central visual pathways in the brain of an albino green monkey *(Cercopithecus aethiops)*. *J Comp Neurol* 226:165, 1984.

524. HUBEL DH, WIESEL TN: Aberrant visual projections in the Siamese cat. *J Physiol* 218:33, 1971.

525. GUILLERY RW, CASAGRANDE VA, OBERDORFER MD: Congenitally abnormal vision in Siamese cats. *Nature* 252:195, 1974.

526. GUILLERY RW: Visual pathways in albinos. *Sci Am* 230:44, 1974.

527. HUANG K, GUILLERY RW: A demonstration of two distinct geniculocortical projection patterns in albino ferrets. *Dev Brain Res* 20:231, 1985.

528. COOPER ML, BLASDEL GG: Regional variation in the representation of the visual field in the visual cortex of the Siamese cat. *J Comp Neurol* 193:237, 1980.

529. KLIOT M, SHATZ CJ: Abnormal development of the retinogeniculate projection in Siamese cats. *J Neurosci* 5:2641, 1985.

530. GUILLERY RW: Neuronal abnormalities of albinos. *Trend Neurosci* 9:364, 1986.

531. LEVENTHAL AG, CREEL DJ: Retinal projections and functional architecture of cortical areas 17 and 18 in the tyrosinase-negative cat. *J Neurosci* 5:795, 1985.

532. GUILLERY RW, OMBRELLARO M, LAMANTIA AL: The organization of the lateral geniculate nucleus and of the geniculocortical pathway that develops without retinal afferents. *Dev Brain Res* 20:221, 1985.

533. STRONGIN AC, GUILLERY RW: The distribution of melanin in the developing optic cup and stalk and its relation to cellular degeneration. *J Neurosci* 1:1193, 1981.

534. SILVER J, SAPIRO J: Axonal guidance during development of the optic nerve: The role of pigmented epithelia and other extrinsic factors. *J Comp Neurol* 202:521, 1981.

535. DRÄGER VC: Calcium binding in pigmented and albino eyes. *Proc Natl Acad Sci USA* 82:6716, 1985.

536. COLLEWIJN H, WINTERSON BJ, DUBOIS MFW: Optokinetic eye movement in albino rabbits: Inversion in anterior visual field. *Science* 199:1351, 1977.

537. WINTERSON BJ, COLLEWIJN H: Inversion of direction-selectivity to anterior fields in neurons of nucleus of optic tract in rabbits with ocular albinism. *Brain Res* 220:31, 1981.

538. MANGINI NJ, VANABLE JW JR, WILLIAMS MA, PINTO LH: The optokinetic nystagmus and ocular pigmentation of hypopigmented mouse mutants. *J Comp Neurol* 241:191, 1985.

539. WOLFF D: Melanin in the inner ear. *Arch Otolaryngol* 14:195, 1931.

540. HARRISON JM, HOWE ME: Auditory system. Anatomy, physiology (ear), in Keidel W, Neff W (eds): *Handbook of Sensory Physiology*. New York, Springer-Verlag, 1974, vol 5, p 284.

541. BONACCORSI P: Il colore dell'iride come "test" di valutazione qualitativa, nell'uomo, della concentrazione de melanina nella stria vascolare. *Ann Laringol Otol Rinol Faringol* 64:725, 1965.

542. CREEL D, GARBER SR, KING RA, WITKOP CJ JR: Auditory brainstem anomalies in human albinos. *Science* 209:1253, 1980.

543. CREEL D, CONLEE JW, PARKS TN: Auditory brainstem anomalies in albino cats. I. Evoked potential studies. *Brain Res* 260:1, 1983.

544. CONLEE JW, PARKS TN, ROMERO C, CREEL DJ: Auditory brainstem anomalies in albino cats: II. Neuronal atrophy in the superior olive. *J Comp Neurol* 225:141, 1984.

545. HOOD J, POOLE J, GREEDMAN L: Eye color and susceptibility to TTS. *J Acoust Soc Am* 59:706, 1976.

546. CARLIN MF, MCCROSKEY RL: Is eye color a predictor of noise-induced hearing loss? *Ear Hear* 1:191, 1980.

547. GARBER SR, TURNER CW, CREEL D, WITKOP CJ JR: Auditory system abnormalities in human albinos. *Ear Hear* 3:207, 1982.

548. CONLEE JW, ABDUL-BAQI KJ, MCCANDLESS GA, CREEL DJ: Differential susceptibility to noise-induced permanent threshold shift between albino and pigmented guinea pigs. *Hear Res* 23:81, 1986.

549. MCGINNESS J, CORRY P, PROCTOR P: Amorphous semiconductor switching in melanins. *Science* 183:853, 1974.

550. LYTTKENS L, LARSSON B, GOLLER H, ENGLESSON S, STAHLE J: Melanin capacity to accumulate drugs in the inner ear. A study on lidocaine, bupivacaine and chlorpromazine. *Acta Otolaryngol (Stockh)* 80:61, 1979.

551. WITKOP CJ JR, KING RA, CREEL DJ: The abnormal albino animal, in Riley V (ed): *Pigment Cell*, Basel, Karger, 1976, vol 3, p 201.

552. CREEL D: Review, Inappropriate use of albino animals as models in research. *Pharmacol Biochem Behav* 12:969, 1980.

553. LOCKARD RB: The albino rat: A defensable choice or a bad habit? *Am Psychol* 23:734, 1968.

554. LINDQUIST NG: Accumulation of drugs on melanin. *Acta Radiol* 325(suppl):5, 1973.

555. BARZA M, KANE A, BAUM J: Marked differences between pigmented and albino rabbits in the concentration of Clindamycin in iris and choroid-retina. *J Infect Dis* 139:203, 1979.

556. BECKMAN AS: Albinism in Negro children. *J Genet Psychol* 69:199, 1946.

557. STEWART HF JR, KEELER CE: A comparison of the intelligence and personality of moon-child albino and control Cuna Indians. *J Genet Psychol* 106:319, 1965.

558. OETTLE AG: Skin cancer in Africa, National Cancer Institute (USA) Monograph 10, 1963, p 197.

559. KEELER CE: Albinism, xeroderma pigmentosum, and skin cancer. National Cancer Institute (USA) Monograph 10, 1963, p 349.

560. BHENDE YM: Malignant amelanotic melanoma of skin in albino. *Indian J Med Sci* 6:755, 1952.

561. YOUNG TE: Malignant melanoma in an albino. *Arch Pathol* 64:186, 1957.

562. LEONARDI R, GRASSO S: Melanoblastoma in albino: Histological findings. *Minerva Dermatol* 33:24, 1958.

563. DURON RA: Malignant melanoma in albinos. *Rev Med Hondur* 33:149, 1965.

564. GARRINGTON GE, SCOFIELD HH, CORNYN J, LACY GR: Intraoral malignant melanoma in a human albino. *Oral Surg* 24:224, 1967.

565. ALPERT LI, DAMJANOV I: Malignant melanoma in an albino: Diagnosis supported by ultrastructure. *Mt Sinai J Med* 45:447, 1978.

566. STOLL DB, RUSCHAK P, KAUH Y, MARTIN J, LUSCOMBE H: Lentigo maligna in a woman with oculocutaneous albinism. *Arch Dermatol* 117:360, 1981.

567. WOOD C, GRAHAM D, WILLSEN J, STREFLING A: Albinism and amelanotic melanoma: Occurrence in a child with positive test results for tyrosinase. *Arch Dermatol* 118:283, 1982.

568. SCOTT MJ JR, GIACOBETTI R, ZUGERMAN C: Correspondence. Malignant melanoma with oculocutaneous albinism. *J Am Acad Dermatol* 7:684, 1982.

569. PEHAMBERGER H, HONINGSMANN H, WOLFF K: Dysplastic nevus syndrome with multiple primary amelanotic melanomas in oculocutaneous albinism. *J Am Acad Dermatol* 11:731, 1984.

570. DOS SANTOS SOBINHO BJ, MOURAO OG: Chediak-Higashi syndrome-presentation of two cases. *J Pediatr (Rio de Janeiro)* 24:341, 1959.

571. PIERINI DO, ABULAFIA J: Manifestaciones cutáneas del sindrome de Chédiak-Higashi. *Arch Argent Dermatol* 8:23, 1958.

572. TAYLOR WOG: Eldridge-Green Lecture, 1978. Visual disabilities of oculocutaneous albinism and their alleviation. *Trans Ophthalmol Soc UK* 98:423, 1978.

573. FONDA G: Characteristics and low-vision corrections in albinism. *Arch Ophthalmol* 68:754, 1962.

574. FONDA G, THOMAS H, GORE GV III: Educational and vocational placement, and low-vision corrections in albinism: A report based on 253 patients. *Sight-saving Rev* 41:29, 1971.

575. CAMERON D: On being an albino: A personal account. *Br Med J* 1:28, 1979.

576. BERNE B, FISCHER T: Protective effects of various types of clothes against UV radiation. *Acta Derm Venereol (Stockh)* 60:459, 1980.

577. AQUARON R, LE FRANCOIS P, KAMDEN L, GUEGUEN R: Carotenoides et vitamine A seriques au Cameroun chez des sujets melanodermes et albinos. *Int J Vitam Nutr Res* 48:105, 1978.

578. LASKIN DS, BROWNING RA: Contrast sensitivity in albinotic patients. *Am J Optom Physiol Opt* 6:158, 1983.

579. WITKOP C: Careers achieved by albinos. *NOAH News* 2:2, 1984.

580. GERRITSEN SW, AKKERMAN J-WN, SIXMA JJ: Correction of the bleeding time in patients with storage pool deficiency by infusion of cryoprecipitate. *Br J Haematol* 40:153, 1978.

581. MACKIE J, BULL H, BROZIVIÉ M, HUSSEIN M: Correspondence: Hermansky-Pudlak syndrome and factor VIII ristocetin cofactor. *Br J Haematol* 41:499, 1979.

582. EADY RAJ, GUNNER DB, GARDNER A, RODECK CH: Prenatal diagnosis of oculocutaneous albinism by electron microscopy of fetal skin. *J Invest Dermatol* 80:210, 1983.

583. EADY RAJ: Prenatal diagnosis of oculocutaneous albinism: Implications for other hereditary disorders of pigmentation. *Semin Dermatol* 3:241, 1984.

CHAPTER 120

XERODERMA PIGMENTOSUM

JAMES E. CLEAVER
KENNETH H. KRAEMER

1. Xeroderma pigmentosum (XP) is a rare autosomal recessive disease in which patients show a greater than 2000-fold increased frequency of sunlight-induced skin cancers. Two major clinical forms are seen. One form involves progressive degenerative changes of the skin and eyes. The other form includes, in addition, progressive neurologic degeneration. Together, these diseases occur at a frequency of about 1 in 250,000 in the United States.

2. Within these two clinical forms of XP, complementation analysis has allowed a further classification into at least nine groups with defective excision repair of DNA. The nonneurologic forms of XP involve most patients in groups C, E, and F, plus a "variant" form with normal excision repair; the neurologic forms consist of most patients in groups A, B, D, G, H, and I. Cultured cells from patients in each group restore DNA repair processes when fused with cells from any of the other groups, suggesting that at least nine different gene products are defective.

3. Patients with XP groups A through I are deficient in gene products that are required for the initial step of excision of damaged DNA.

4. Patients with the variant form of XP are deficient in a gene product that in normal cells permits semiconservative replication past damaged sites in DNA.

5. Cells from different complementation groups of XP show characteristic ranges of hypersensitivity to killing and mutagenesis by ultraviolent (UV) radiation and by certain chemical carcinogens such as benzo[a]pyrene and nitroquinoline oxide. The types of mutations observed in UV-treated DNA replicated in XP-A and XP-D cells are restricted in comparison with those replicated in normal cells. The predominant base substitution mutation observed is the $G:C$ to $A:T$ transition.

Several kinds of skin disease are caused by alterations in the normal resistance of the skin to sunlight. These occur because of either (1) a loss in the shielding afforded by melanin, exemplified by albinism (Chap. 119)[1]; (2) the deposition of sensitizing compounds in the skin, exemplifed by porphyria[2]; or (3) a decrease in the capacity of cells to repair or replicate damage induced by sunlight, exemplified by xeroderma pigmentosum (XP).[3,4] In albinism and the porphyrias, the amount of sunlight-induced DNA damage is increased; in XP the amount of damage is unchanged, but DNA repair and DNA replication are diminished or altered (Fig. 120-1).[3,4] The major clinical feature that results is a high incidence of sunlight-induced skin cancers (Fig. 120-2).[3–8]

An important distinction should be made between the concepts of hypersensitivity of DNA-damaging agents and of defects in repair of damaged DNA.[3] A large group of diseases are known in which cells or tissues exhibit abnormal sensitivity to one or more kinds of DNA-damaging agents.[3] In only a few of these diseases, including the various forms of XP, is the hypersensitivity caused by a defect in the repair of damaged DNA.[5,6] In other hypersensitivity diseases there may be more complex abnormalities, such as alterations in both semiconservative replication[9] and repair[10,11] as seen in ataxia-telangiectasia after x-irradiation, and alteration in the recovery of DNA replication after irradiation by ultraviolet (UV) light as seen in Cockayne syndrome.[12] These are discussed in more detail below.

DNA REPAIR PATHWAYS

At least three different biochemical repair systems operate in damaged cells to safeguard DNA from permanent damage.[3,4] These are (1) photoreactivation, (2) excision repair, and (3) postreplication repair (Fig. 120-1). All three exist in most cell types. They are especially important in the skin, where they mend damage to DNA caused by the UV rays (>290 nm) present in sunlight. Some of the repair systems can mend damage to DNA caused by chemical carcinogens.[13] These systems protect internal tissues against the carcinogenic and mutagenic consequences of exposure to chemicals that damage DNA.

Photoreactivation simply reverts the damaged DNA to the normal chemical state without removing or exchanging any material from DNA. The photoreactivation system is specific for one form of damage induced by UV light, the cyclobutane pyrimidine dimer. Photoreactivation cleaves these dimers, but has no ability to modify other damaged sites. The existence and importance of this system in human tissue is controversial. Its demonstration in cell culture[14–18] is difficult, although it has been demonstrated directly in human skin.[19]

Excision repair, in contrast, is extremely versatile and can mend a large variety of UV-light, x-ray, and chemically induced forms of damage to DNA.[13] This system excises damaged single strands of DNA and replaces them with a new sequence of bases using as a template for base pairing the intact strand of DNA opposite the original damaged site. Excision repair is of central importance in the recovery of cells from radiation damage. It employs a wide variety of enzymes with different specificities and mechanisms for removal of damage.

The third system is exceedingly complex and is less easily defined as a specific system for handling damage in DNA. It involves multiple mechanisms by which semiconservative DNA replication can take place despite the presence of damage or incomplete excision repair in one strand of DNA.[3,4,20] Part of this set of mechanisms is known as postreplication repair, which may be nothing more than an operational term for a particular type of DNA replication by which intact new strands of DNA can be synthesized despite the presence of unexcised damage on the parental template strands.[20]

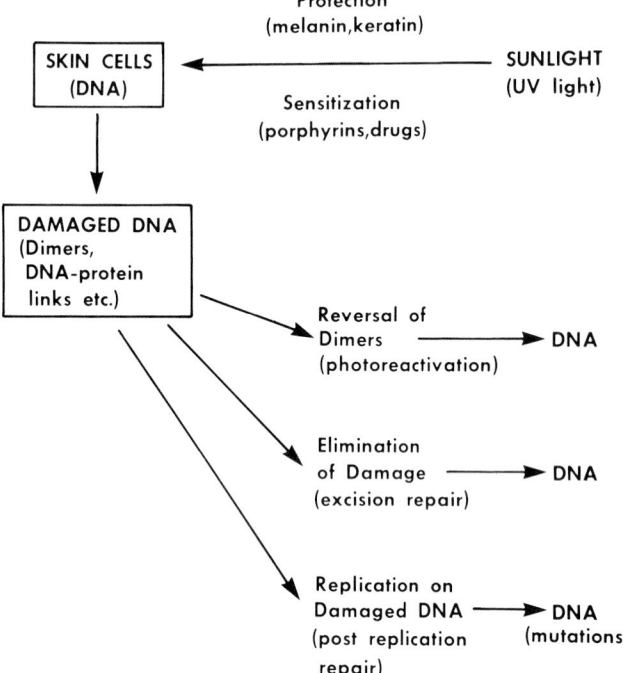

Fig. 120-1 Schematic diagram of processes leading to damaged DNA in skin cells and three processes that repair damaged DNA. Damage to DNA of skin cells is caused by absorption of UV light; increased damage results if protection afforded by melanin is lost (e.g., in albinism) or if photosensitizers are present in the skin (e.g., in porphyrias). Damage is repaired by direct reversal (photoreactivation) or by excision and replacement (excision repair). Semiconservative replication of damaged templates may introduce errors (mutations) by a variety of mechanisms.

At one time XP was thought to be a disease involving a single defect in one of the repair systems.[5] However, it now appears that the three main repair systems may be interrelated or may have enzymes in common,[3,6] and several may be altered in patients with XP. Consequently, a full understanding of the biochemistry of XP and its relationship to the clinical symptoms may be more complicated than was first suspected. Because the outstanding clinical characteristic of XP is marked predisposition to develop skin cancers after exposure to sunlight, the disease comprises a unique conjunction of environmental, genetic, and biochemical factors in the etiology of cancer.[8,21,22] The elucidation of its biochemical basis should thus provide clues to understanding the genetic changes involved in carcinogenesis by many physical and chemical agents.

CLINICAL FEATURES OF XP

XP is a rare autosomal recessive disease. Affected patients (homozygotes) have sun sensitivity resulting in progressive degenerative changes of sun-exposed portions of the skin and eyes, often leading to neoplasia. Some XP patients have, in addition, progressive neurologic degeneration. Obligate heterozygotes (parents) are generally asymptomatic.

History. Xeroderma, or parchment skin, was the term given by Moritz Kaposi to the condition he observed in a patient in 1863 and reported in the dermatology textbook he wrote with Ferdinand von Hebra in 1870.[23] In 1882 the term *pigmentosum* was added to emphasize the striking pigmentary abnormalities. Eye involvement, including cloudiness of the cornea, was recognized by Kaposi. In 1883, Neisser reported two brothers with cutaneous xeroderma pigmentosum and neurologic degeneration beginning in the second decade.[24] De Sanctis and Cacchione (1932)[25] described three siblings with cutaneous XP associated with microcephaly, progressive mental deterioration, dwarfism, and immature sexual development, the *De Sanctis–Cacchione syndrome.*

Defective DNA excision repair in ultraviolet-irradiated cultured skin fibroblasts from some XP patients was reported by Cleaver in 1968,[5] and in skin in vivo by Epstein et al.[26] The form of the disease in the first XP patient with normal excision repair described by Burk et al.[27] was subsequently named the *variant* form of XP[28] and was found to have an abnormality in another DNA repair system, postreplication repair.[29,30] In 1972, De Weerd-Kastelein et al.,[31] by using cell fusion techniques, demonstrated genetic heterogeneity in the DNA excision repair defect of XP.

Epidemiology. Xeroderma pigmentosum has been found in all races worldwide. The frequency is about 1 in 250,000 in the United States and Europe but is considerably higher in Japan (1 in 40,000) and Egypt. In a literature survey of more than

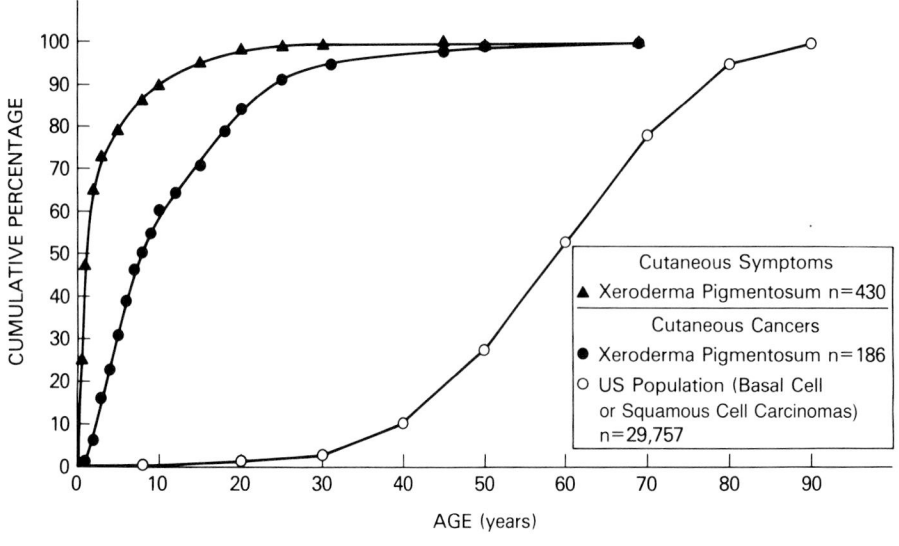

Fig. 120-2 Age at onset of XP symptoms. Age at onset of cutaneous symptoms (generally sun sensitivity or pigmentation) was reported for 430 patients. Age at first skin cancer was reported for 186 patients and is compared with age distribution for 29,757 patients with basal cell carcinoma or squamous cell carcinoma in the United States general population. (*From Kraemer et al.*[32] *Used by permission.*)

800 patients[32] there were nearly equal numbers of males (54 percent) and females (46 percent). Consanguinity of the patients' parents was reported in 31 percent, an elevated frequency often seen in recessive disorders. Nearly 20 percent of the patients, including a high proportion of Japanese patients, had neurologic abnormalities.

Symptomatology. The median age of onset of symptoms was between 1 and 2 years. In 5 percent of the patients, onset of symptoms was delayed until after 14 years (Fig. 120-2).[32] Initial symptoms included abnormal reaction to sun exposure in 19 percent (including severe sunburn with blistering and persistent erythema on minimal sun exposure; see Table 120-1). However, many patients sunburned normally. Freckling occurred by 2 years of age in most of the patients. The cutaneous abnormalities were usually strikingly limited to sun-exposed areas of the body. At an early age, the skin appears similar to that seen in farmers and sailors after many years of sun exposure: areas of increased pigment alternating with areas of decreased pigment, with atrophy and telangiectasia. A few patients who exhibit a wide spectrum of characteristic cutaneous and ocular findings have been unambiguously diagnosed as having XP, even though the erythematous response was normal.[33] This may be a distinctive feature of the form of XP known as *variant* or *pigmented xerodermoid*,[29,30,33,34] but this form can be diagnosed fully only by biochemical tests.[29,30]

Patients developed premalignant actinic keratoses and malignant and benign neoplasms.[32] The neoplasms were predominantly basal cell or squamous cell carcinomas (at least 45 percent of patients, many with multiple primary neoplasms) but also included melanomas (5 percent of patients), sarcomas, keratoacanthomas, and angiomas.[32] About 97 percent of the basal cell and squamous cell carcinomas occurred on the face, head, and neck, the sites of greatest ultraviolet exposure. The median age of onset of first skin neoplasm was 8 years, nearly 50 years younger than that in the general population of the United States (Fig. 120-2). This may be the largest reduction in age of onset of neoplasia documented for any recessive human genetic disease. The frequency of basal cell carcinomas, squamous cell carcinomas, or melanoma of the skin was 2000 times greater than in the general population for patients under 20 years of age.[35] There was an approximate 30-year reduction in survival, with a 70 percent probability of surviving to age 40 years.[32] Many patients died of neoplasia.

Ocular abnormalities found include photophobia, which may vary among patients from severe to absent; conjunctivitis of the interpalpebral (sun-exposed) area; ectropion due to atrophy of the skin of the eyelids; exposure keratitis; and be-

Table 120-1 Cutaneous Manifestations of XP

Erythema and bullae (acute sun sensitivity in infancy)
Freckles
Xerosis (dryness) and scaling
Areas of hypopigmentation alternating with areas of
 hyperpigmentation
Telangiectasia
Atrophy
Tumors
Actinic keratoses
Basal and squamous cell carcinomas
Malignant melanomas
Others (keratocanthomas, angiomas, fibromas, sarcomas)

SOURCE: From Robbins et al.[21] Used by permission.

Table 120-2 Ocular Abnormalities Associated with XP

Lids
 Blepharitis
 Erythema, pigmentation, keratoses
 Atrophy leading to entropion, ectropion, loss of cilia, and loss
  of lower lid
 Neoplasms
  Papillomas
  Epitheliomas of free border of lid
  Basal and squamous cell carcinomas
Conjunctiva
 Conjunctivitis with photophobia, lacrimation, edema
 Pigmentation, telangiectasia
 Dryness
 Symblepharon
 Inflammatory nodules
 Neoplasms
  Intraepithelial epitheliomas
  Squamous cell carcinomas
Cornea
 Exposure keratitis with edema, cellular invasion, vascularization
 Dryness
 Opacification
 Ulceration and scarring
 Neoplasms
Iris
 Iritis
 Synechiae
 Atrophy
 Neoplasms

SOURCE: From Robbins et al.[21] Used by permission.

nign and malignant neoplasms of the lids, conjunctiva, and limbus (Table 120-2). The distribution of ocular damage and neoplasms closely corresponds with the sites of ultraviolet exposure. The ocular neoplasms involved the anterior portion of the eye (lids, cornea, conjunctiva) almost exclusively.[32] This portion of the eye shields the posterior eye (uveal tract, retina) from ultraviolet radiation; visible light is the only radiation that reaches the photosensitive cells of the retina. The frequency of ocular neoplasms was increased 2000-fold in patients under 20 years.[35] There was also a greater than 10,000-fold increase in squamous cell carcinoma of the tip of the tongue,[35] another sun-exposed portion of the body (Fig. 120-3).

The 18 percent of XP patients who had neurologic abnormalities had a sex ratio, reported age, frequency of ocular abnormalities, and frequency of cutaneous neoplasms similar to

Fig. 120-3 Pedunculated lingual neoplasm in patient of complementation group C (patient is described in Ref. 186). (Photograph kindly supplied by Dr. J. German, New York Blood Center.)

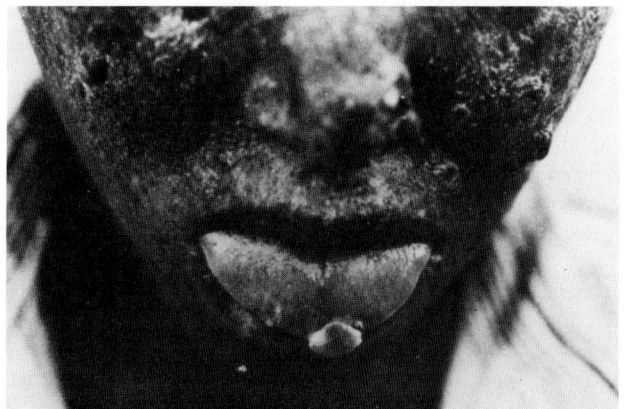

Table 120-3 Neurologic
Abnormalities Associated with XP

Microcephaly
Higher cortical dysfunction
  Progressive mental deterioration
  Low intelligence
  Emotional lability
  Abnormal electroencephalogram
Basal ganglia and cerebellar involvement
  Choreoathetosis
  Ataxia
Extrapyramidal and pyramidal involvement
  Spasticity
  Extensor plantar responses
  Achilles tendon shortening
Cranial nerve involvement
  Sensorineural deafness
Lower motor neuron involvement
  Hyporeflexia or areflexia
  Neuropathic electromyogram and muscle biopsy

SOURCE: From Robbins et al.[21] Used by permission.

those of patients with only skin and eye involvement.[32] The neurologic symptoms varied in age of onset and severity, but were all characterized by progressive deterioration (Table 120-3).[36] Diminished deep tendon reflexes and sensorineural deafness were frequent early abnormalities. In some patients progressive mental retardation became evident only in the second decade of life. Patients with the De Sanctis–Cacchione syndrome had neurologic and somatic abnormalities beginning in the first years of life.[25] They had microcephaly, intellectual deterioration with loss of the ability to talk, and increasing spasticity with loss of ability to walk leading to quadraparesis, in addition to dwarfism and immature sexual development. Among the few autopsies reported, the major finding was loss (or absence) of neurons, particularly in the cerebral cortex and cerebellum, without evidence of a storage process or inflammatory changes.[21,37] The severity of neurologic disease has been reported to correlate with the degree of sensitivity of cultured skin fibroblasts to ultraviolet inhibition of colony-forming ability.[38]

Two patients have been reported with clinical features of both XP and a second recessive disorder, Cockayne syndrome.[21,39] These patients had the cutaneous pigmentary and neoplastic features of XP with the dwarfism, mental retardation, increased reflexes, and retinal degeneration typical of Cockayne syndrome. Fibroblasts from Cockayne syndrome patients are also hypersensitive to killing by ultraviolet radiation but have normal excision repair.[40–43] Complementation studies have revealed that these patients each have unique excision repair defects; they are the sole members of complementation groups B[21] and H.[39]

Xeroderma pigmentosum patients have a 10- to 20-fold increase in frequency of internal neoplasms.[35] There were reports of four patients with primary brain tumors (including two sarcomas), two with leukemia, two with lung tumors (including one patient who died at age 34 years after smoking a pack of cigarettes a day for 16 years), and three with gastric carcinomas.[32,44,45] Chemical carcinogens are suspected to play a role in these neoplasms, since cultured cells from XP patients are hypersensitive to certain DNA-binding chemical carcinogens that produce damaged DNA which is normally acted on by the ultraviolet excision repair system. These include benzo[a]pyrene derivatives (found in cigarette smoke) and tryptophan pyrolysis products (found in charred food).[46,47]

Treatment. Management of XP patients is a multifaceted process involving early diagnosis, genetic counseling, patient and family education, and regular monitoring of the skin.[48] The diagnosis is suspected in cases with marked sun sensitivity, photophobia, and/or early onset of freckling. Laboratory tests of ultraviolet sensitivity of fibroblasts and of excision repair confirm the diagnosis. Genetic counseling is directed toward acquainting the patients and their parents with the inherited aspects of the disease and its rarity, with the increased risk in cases of familial relationship between the two parents, with the 25 percent probability that the disease will appear among subsequent offspring, and with the improbability of the patient's having affected children.[22,32,49]

Patients should be shielded from sunlight by protective measures including wearing two layers of clothing, using long hairstyles, wearing broad-brimmed hats and ultraviolet-absorbing sunglasses with side shields, and use of chemical sunscreens with high SPF (sun protective factor) numbers, i.e., SPF 15 or higher. Patients should avoid direct exposure to sunlight, especially during the peak UV hours (about 10 A.M. to 3 P.M. in the continental United States), and indirect UV reflected from snow or water. Window glass and many plastic shields for fluorescent lamps will absorb ultraviolet radiation indoors. Known chemical carcinogens such as tobacco smoke should be avoided. Patients and their families should be taught to examine the skin and to recognize and bring to medical attention any lesions suspected of malignancy. Color photographs are often useful for follow-up.

Malignant skin neoplasms are treated as in patients who do not have XP by excision, electrodesiccation and curettage, cryosurgery, or chemosurgery. Xeroderma pigmentosum patients have received x-ray therapy for malignant skin tumors and had normal response.[48] Dermabrasion or dermatome shaving has been used in cases with multiple tumors, permitting the epidermis to be repopulated by cells from the hair follicles, which are relatively shielded from sunlight.[48] Total removal of the skin of the face with grafting of skin from sunshielded areas has been used in extreme cases. Clinical trials of skin cancer prevention with oral retinoids are in progress.

PRODUCTION OF CELLULAR DAMAGE BY SUNLIGHT

Sunlight is the major environmental agent that precipitates the clinical symptoms of XP; it does so by damaging cutaneous cells. An understanding of the biochemical defects in XP requires knowledge of the way the damaging wavelengths in sunlight are absorbed by macromolecules and of the nature of the damage that is produced.

The wavelengths of sunlight extend into the near-UV region, the shortest detectable being about 290 nm. This lower limit slightly overlaps the upper region of the absorption spectra of nucleic acids and proteins. Energy in this region of overlap is absorbed by macromolecules in the skin, producing harmful effects that include erythema, burns, and actinic carcinogenesis.[50–52] Comparisons between direct sunlight and shortwave UV light (254 nm) indicate that sunlight in the Midwestern United States is equivalent in germicidal activity to about 0.1 to 0.2 J per square meter of surface per minute [J/(m²·min)] of 254-nm ultraviolet light.[53,54] Since normal human cells in culture have a D_{37} of only about 3 to 5 J/m² of radiation at 254 nm, the direct exposure of human proliferating cells to sunlight can result in significant amounts of cell killing.*

Light at the UV end of the sun's spectrum produces its biologic effects through absorption of quanta in molecules that have unsaturated chemical bonds, such as aromatic amino acids in proteins and purine and pyrimidine components of DNA and RNA. The action spectra for production of DNA damage (pyrimidine photoproducts),[56] cell killing,[57,58] production of aberrant chromosomes,[59] and induction of unscheduled DNA synthesis (i.e., DNA synthesis not associated with the normal cell cycle[60]) are all similar, exhibiting maximum efficiency in wavelengths from 260 to 280 nm. Although there is negligible energy in this region of the sun's spectrum, there is sufficient overlap of the shortest end of the sun's spectrum with the longer-wavelength side of the absorption spectrum of DNA for significant photochemical reaction to occur.

Two kinds of pyrimidine photoproducts are formed in DNA by absorption of UV light. The more frequent is the cyclobutane pyrimidine dimer (Fig. 120-4). This is formed between adjacent pyrimidines in the same strand of DNA by the formation of new bonds between the 5 positions and between the 6 positions on the pyrmidine rings. At least four possible isomers (forms I to IV)[61] can be formed by irradiating frozen solutions of pyrimidines; the form I (meso) dimer corresponds to the one formed in DNA and can be isolated from sunlight and UV-irradiated cells and skin.[54,62–64] An alternative pyrimidine dimer is the [6-4] pyrimidine-pyrimidone product consisting of 5'TC or 5'CC (Fig. 120-4), which is formed at lower rates than the cyclobutane dimer but is also important biologically. Various estimates suggest that the [6-4] photoproduct is formed at 10 to 50 percent of the frequency of cyclobutane dimers by low doses of 254-nm light but there is a strong influence of local base sequences on dimer yields.[65] This lesion has been shown to be important in production of mutations in bacteria[65] and has recently been associated with mutagenic sites in shuttle vector plasmids replicated in XP cells, although structural features of chromatin strongly affect mutant yields.[66] Numerous biologic effects, such as cell killing, production of chromosome aberrations, mutagenesis, and carcinogenesis, can be attributed to these photoproducts in DNA.[56–60,62,67] Other photoproducts have biologic effects in some circumstances. These include the unstable cytosine hydrate, purine photoproducts, and, at relatively high doses, locally denatured regions, DNA-protein cross-links, and single strand breaks.[67]

In addition to damaging DNA directly, sunlight can also produce chemical carcinogens by photochemical alteration of low–molecular weight compounds.[68] Such chemical carcinogens can damage DNA. Repair of this chemically induced damage is accomplished by systems similar to those that repair UV-induced damage,[13,69] which are discussed above.

CELLULAR CHARACTERISTICS OF XP

Most studies that have contributed to delineation of the cellular and biochemical aspects of XP have been based on fibroblast cultures from the skin. For an inherited disease such as

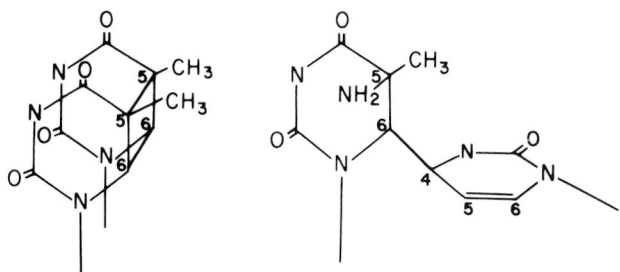

T <> T   TC (6-4) PHOTOPRODUCT

Fig. 120-4 Cyclobutane pyrimidine dimer (type I, meso) and [6-4] pyrimidine-pyrimidone products formed by UV light in DNA. *Top.* Cyclobutane dimer between adjacent thymines on the same strand of DNA with 5-5 and 6-6 bonds produced by irradiation. *Bottom.* [6-4] Photoproduct between adjacent thymine and cytosine on same strand of DNA. Structures shown are schematic. In DNA, the structures consist of pyrimidine bases stacked one above the other with considerable distortion of the phosphodiester backbone of DNA. *(Illustration provided by D. E. Brash.)*

XP, the results obtained are assumed to be typical of most somatic cells.

Fibroblast cultures can be obtained from XP patients by punch biopsy or by surgical removal of small pieces of skin. Cells are established in culture by routine procedures.[70]† XP cultures have no special nutritional requirements and have lifetimes and growth rates in vitro similar to those from normal individuals.[71] Occasionally, cultures grow slowly in the initial period after biopsy. This refractoriness to culture may be a result of the atrophied state of the biopsied skin rather than a feature of XP itself.

Chromosomal Features

Cultured cells from most XP patients have a normal karyotype. Distinctive karyotypic changes characteristic for some diseases with a high cancer incidence, such as Down syndrome, ataxia-telangiectasia, Fanconi anemia, and Bloom syndrome,[22] are not seen in XP, although karyotypic changes have occasionally been reported in XP cells. For example, two sisters with the De Sanctis–Cacchione syndrome had different karyotypes, one normal and the other with an extra chromosome, but these karyotypic changes seem unrelated to the disease.[72] In another patient, reciprocal exchanges were identified in a small percentage of the cells,[73] but this may have been related to the treatment the patient had been undergoing. In one instance, a sib of an affected patient appeared to have a small proportion of normal cells and milder clinical symptoms.[74]

Spontaneous and induced sister chromatid exchanges (SCEs) can be visualized in human fibroblasts by a combination of growth in bromodeoxyuridine and staining with a photochemical reaction plus Giemsa (Fig. 120-5).[75,76] XP cells show a normal frequency of spontaneous SCEs,[77] but a greater than normal frequency after exposure to UV light and most chemical carcinogens (Fig. 120-4).[78,79] Similarly, XP cells

---

*The D_{37} is the dose required to reduce survival to 0.37 from the initial value of 1.0, and in target theory[55] corresponds to the dose required to produce an average of one lethal hit on the sensitive target of an irradiated organism when the survival curve is exponential.

†Representative cultures are available from cell banks in both the American Type Culture Collection, 12301 Parkway Drive, Rockville, Md., and the Mammalian Genetic Mutant Cell Repository, Institute for Medical Research, Copewood Street, Camden, N.J. In comparative studies, the nomenclature adopted to identify XP cell lines is the following form: "XP number letter designation of laboratory or city of origin." Thus, cell lines from Rotterdam are XP1RO, XP2RO, etc.; those from San Francisco are XP1SF, XP2SF, etc.; those from Bethesda are XP1BE, XP2BE, etc. Other letters are chosen as appropriate. Heterozygotes are correspondingly identified as XPH1SF, XPH2SF, etc.

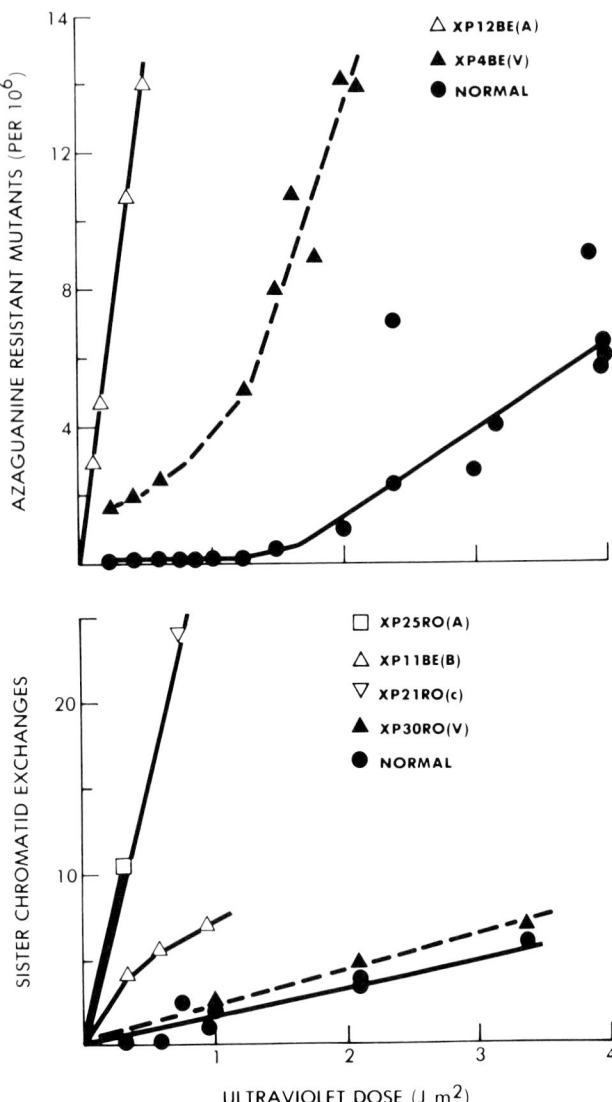

Fig. 120-5 Relative frequencies of UV-induced mutations to 8-azaguanine (20 μM) resistance or of sister chromatid exchanges in normal (●), excision-defective XP (□, △, ▼), and XP variant (▲) cells as a function of ultraviolet dose. *Top.* Mutation frequencies. *(Redrawn from Maher et al.[104,105] Used by permission.) Bottom.* SCE frequencies. *(Redrawn from de Weerd-Kastelein et al.[79] Used by permission.)*

show more chromosome aberrations than normal cells after exposure to UV light and chemical carcinogens.[80,81]

Sensitivity of Colony Formation to DNA Damage

The number of cells in culture that can grow into colonies after UV irradiation can be used as an in vitro measurement of sensitivity. Fibroblast cultures from patients who exhibit neurologic abnormalities are generally the most sensitive (Figs. 120-6 and 120-7).[86] The colony-forming ability of cells from subjects with most forms of XP is much more sensitive than that of normal cells to UV light and some chemicals; the sensitivity increase corresponds to a dose-modifying factor between 3 and 10.[38,82–88] XP cells are also more sensitive to 4-nitroquinoline-1-oxide, benz[a]anthracene, and a variety of aromatic amides, but are normal in response to N-methyl-N'-nitro-N-nitrosoguanidine.[84,85,87,88]

Fibroblasts from some variant XP patients without neuro-

logic complications do not exhibit a great increase in UV sensitivity (e.g., XP7TA and XP30RO in Fig. 120-6).[27,28,38,89] However, if caffeine is added to the medium after irradiation, the amount of cell killing is increased in fibroblasts from these XP patients. Those from normal individuals and from most XP patients are unaffected (Fig. 120-6).[89] Caffeine at high concentrations alters the regulation of semiconservative DNA replication,[90] which then acts synergistically with the biochemical defect in these variant XP cells.

Host Cell Reactivation

The ability of UV-damaged viruses to undergo DNA repair and undergo replication in infected cells is dependent on the genetic constitution of the cells. This is because most viruses depend on cellular enzymes for their repair and reproduction. The degree of dependence is greater for the smaller viruses (e.g., simian virus 40, or SV40) than for the larger ones (e.g., herpes simplex, cytomegalovirus).[91–100] Ultraviolet treatment of a virus suspension before it is used to infect host cells damages the viral DNA and inactivates a certain fraction of the viruses. The fraction inactivated depends on the ability of the host cell to repair the damaged DNA in the infecting virus. The extent of this "host cell reactivation" by various cell types often parallels the cells' ability to survive UV damage. Host cell reactivation therefore is an important assay of the func-

Fig. 120-6 UV inactivation curves for normal and XP fibroblasts irradiated and grown in medium with or without 1 μM caffeine. The dose is expressed in both J/m² and the estimated number of pyrimidine dimers per 10⁸ daltons DNA. *A.* Normal human fibroblasts, stains 1BR, 2B1, 4BR, 19BR, grown without (○, □, △, Ⴟ, respectively) or with (●, ■, ▲, Ⴟ, respectively) 1 μM caffeine. *B.* XP fibroblasts, strains XP7TA and XP30RO (XP variants) and XP4LO (a De Sanctis–Cacchione syndrome patient). Cells grown without (○, □, △, respectively) or with (●, ■, ▲, respectively) 1 μM caffeine. *(From Arlett et al.[89] Used by permission.)*

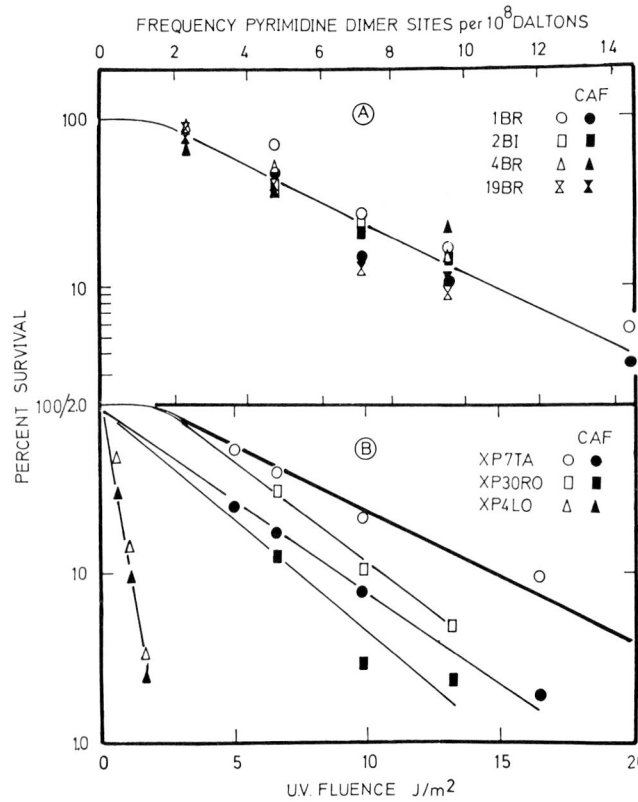

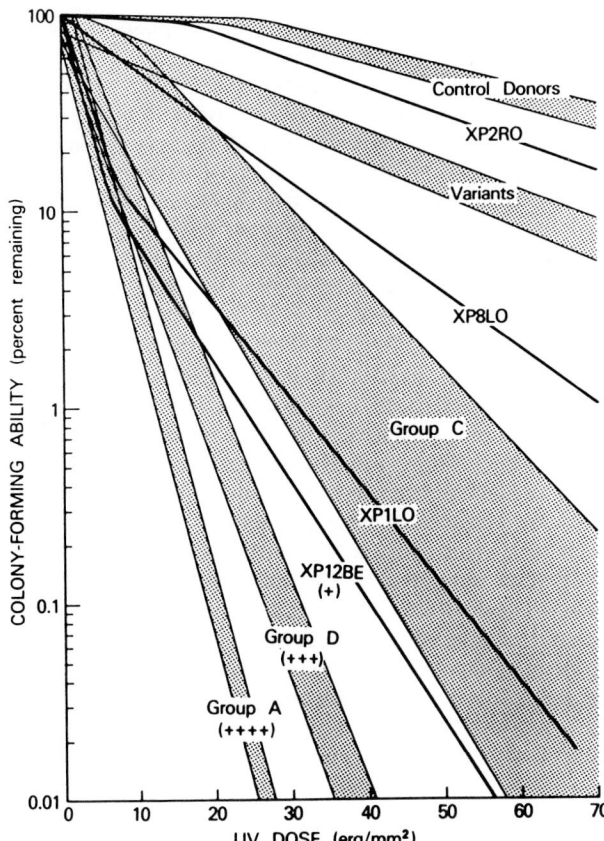

Fig. 120-7 UV (254 nm) inactivation curve for fibroblasts from normal and various XP patients. Each complementation group (A–E, variant) is represented either by a range encompassing data from several patients in that group or as a single line for data from a single patient (i.e., the exceptional group A patients with little neurologic involvement—XP1LO, XP8LO, and XP12BE—and, in group E, XP2RO). The severity of neurologic abnormalities is indicated by: + + + +, numerous clinical manifestations by age 7; + + +, numerous clinical manifestations between ages 7 and 12; +, areflexia and abnormal electroencephalogram at age 10. (*From Andrews et al.*[38] *Used by permission.*)

tional capacity of the DNA repair system. The survival of various UV-damaged viruses, including vaccinia,[91,92] herpes simplex virus,[92,93] adenovirus,[94,95] SV40,[96] and Epstein-Barr virus (EBV)[97,98] is less in XP cells than in normal cells. All of these are DNA viruses that replicate in the cell nucleus.

The D_{37} of irradiated viruses grown in XP complementation group A cells is about 20 times less than in normal cell strains for adenovirus[94,95] and about 3 times less for herpes virus.[92,93] The D_{37} for adenovirus in XP cells corresponds to the production of about one pyrimidine dimer per viral genome. Irradiated adenoviruses grown in XP variant cells show reductions in survival of a factor of only about 2, compared with those grown in normal cells.[99] This may be the only assay that consistently demonstrates an abnormality in every form of XP. Ultraviolet-damaged adenovirus grown in fused, complementing XP-A and XP-D cells show normal survival,[100] indicating that fusion results in complementation of the functional activity of DNA repair in vivo.

Host cell reactivation has recently been utilized to measure effects of the cellular repair system in the absence of replication, using UV-damaged nonreplicating expression vector plasmids.[101,102] The plasmids contain a bacterial enzyme, chloramphenicol acetyltransferase (CAT), in a construction that permits expression of this novel activity upon transfection

into mammalian cells. Expression of transfected CAT activity following UV damage is much less in XP group A and D cells than in normal cells (Fig. 120-8). The unrepaired DNA damage appears to block transcription efficiently. In fact, with the XP-A and XP-D cells, about one cyclobutane pyrimidine dimer in the gene results in its inactivation. Removal of 99 percent of the cyclobutane dimers by treatment of UV-damaged plasmid with photolyase prior to transfection did not completely restore CAT expression to normal levels. This implies that nondimer photoproducts are also poorly repaired by these XP cells.[102]

Induction of Mutations by UV Light

A small proportion of the cells that recover from irradiation carry mutations in the form of base-pair changes or deletions in the DNA. These are thought to arise from faulty replication of DNA that contains damaged bases. Some mutations can be detected through the cells' gain of drug resistance—i.e., by growing cells in drugs that are lethal analogues of normal metabolites (e.g., 8-azaguanine or 6-thioguanine as analogues of purines) and observing the growth of mutant cells that have acquired resistance. In human cells in culture, only a few gene loci are amenable to quantitative study of mutagenesis. One that has been studied extensively is the defective gene in the Lesch-Nyhan syndrome.[103] The key step in this pathway consists of an enzyme, hypoxanthine–guanine phosphoribosyltransferase (HGPRT), that attaches a phosphoribosyl group to

Fig. 120-8 Transient expression of CAT gene in SV40-transformed xeroderma pigmentosum, ataxia-telangiectasia (GM 5849), retinoblastoma (GM 3022), Lesch-Nyhan (GM 0847), and normal human cells (GM 0637) and primary human skin fibroblasts (GM 1652-1°) transfected with UV-treated pSV2catSVgpt DNA. Cell types and designations indicated in figure. (*Reproduced from Protic-Sablijic,*[101] *with permission.*)

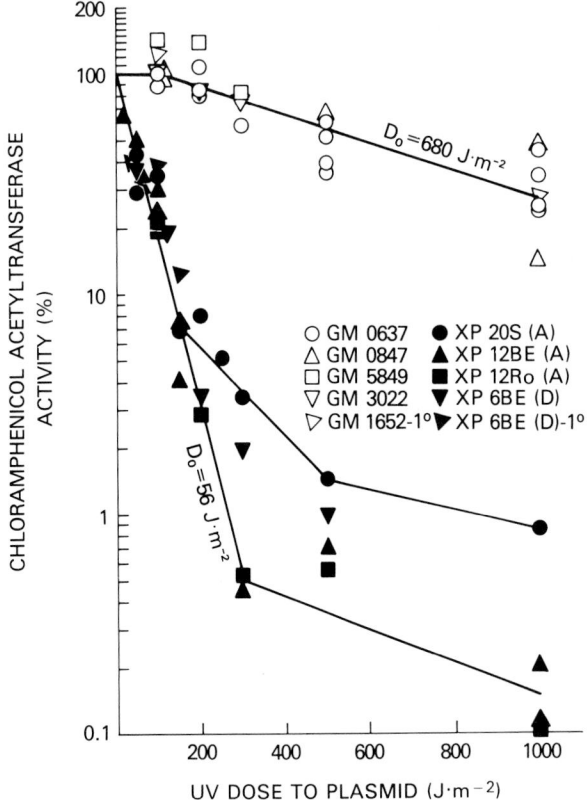

8-azaguanine or 6-thioguanine so that it can be incorporated into DNA. Resistant mutants produced by irradiation can survive high concentrations of these analogues because HGPRT activity has been lost. Other gene loci amenable to study are those that regulate binding of toxic chemicals to membrane proteins such as the ouabain resistance locus or the diphtheria toxin resistance locus.

The frequency with which cells resistant to 6-thioguanine, ouabain, diphtheria toxin, or other toxic chemicals are produced by irradiation with UV light or artificial sunlight, or by exposure to chemical carcinogens, is greater in all XP cells, including XP variants, than in normal cells (Fig. 120-5).[104-108] In addition, XP cells are more easily transformed to anchorage independence,[109] a step on the path to malignant transformation. This implies that the genetic defects in XP cells confer increased mutability. The similar responses of all the XP cells in this mutagenesis assay contrast with the variability in their responses in the UV-light toxicity assay (Figs. 120-5, 120-6, and 120-8). This observation implies that the hypersensitive XP cells (later to be defined as the excision-defective groups A through I) have lost a system that normally repairs UV-induced damage in such a way as to avoid the errors that lead to mutations. In the XP variant, the damage is repaired in such a way as to allow cell survival. However, the repair system has lost fidelity and so produces a high frequency of mutations.

A newly developed host cell reactivation assay using a replicating plasmid has been used to measure UV-induced base substitution mutagenesis in XP and normal cells.[66,110,111] The "shuttle vector" plasmid, pZ189, contains SV40 sequences that permit replication in some mammalian cells, plasmid sequences facilitating replication in bacteria, and a 150–base pair marker gene (a bacterial suppressor tRNA) that serves as the target for mutations. The UV-damaged plasmid is transfected into the XP or normal cells where DNA repair, replication, and mutation occur. The replicated plasmids are harvested and then used to transform an indicator strain of *Escherichia coli* containing a suppressible (amber) mutation in the β-galactosidase gene. Plasmid survival and mutations are reflected in the number and color of bacterial colonies obtained by plating the bacteria on selective agar plates containing ampicillin and an indicator dye (X-gal), which is metabolized by β-galactosidase. Mutations that inactivate the suppressor tRNA function will result in white or light-blue colonies, while an active marker gene gives blue colonies. The mutant plasmids are purified and the DNA sequence is determined.

The mutational spectrum found with pZ189 replicated in XP-A cells was restricted in comparison with that found with the normal cells (Table 120-4).[110] There were significantly fewer plasmids with multiple base substitution mutations and with single or tandem transversion mutations. With both cell lines, the predominant base substitution mutation was the G:C to A:T transition. Thus, with these human cells, the major UV photoproduct, the TT dimer, is not the major premutagenic lesion. This finding is consistent with observations made in bacteria more than 20 years ago, and more recently explained by the "A" rule: a tendency of polymerases to insert adenines opposite noninstructional lesions.[65] Thus, insertion of A opposite TT dimers results in the correct pairing, while insertion of A opposite a C involved in photoproducts results in G:C to A:T transitions. A similar restricted mutagenic spectrum was found with an XP-D line. The G:C to A:T mutations common to the XP and normal cells may be particularly important in somatic mutagenesis by UV radiation.

Both cyclobutane dimers (mainly 5′TC and 5′CC) and nondimer photoproducts, such as the [6-4] pyrimidine-pyrimidone photoproduct, have been shown to be mutagenic in monkey[111] and XP[66] cells by use of UV-exposed shuttle vector plasmids treated with photoreactivating enzyme prior to transfection.

Table 120-4 Mutations Observed in Shuttle Vector pZ189 Replicated in Xeroderma Pigmentosum or Repair-Proficient Cells

	Number of plasmids with base changes†	
Mutations	*Xeroderma pigmentosum*	*Normal*
Independent plasmids sequenced‡	61 (100%)	89 (100%)
Point mutations		
Single base substitution	47★ (77%)	48 (53%)
Tandem base substitutions§	12 (20%)	16 (18%)
Multiple base substitutions¶	1★ (2%)	24 (28%)
Base insertions and deletions		
Single base insertion	0	2
Single or tandem base deletions	1	3

Types of single or tandem base substitutions and number of changes

Transitions	67★ (94%)	61 (75%)
G:C to A:T	66★ (93%)	59 (73%)
A:T to G:C	1 (1%)	2 (2%)
Transversions	4★ (6%)	20 (25%)
G:C to T:A	0★	8 (10%)
G:C to C:G	1 (1%)	5 (6%)
A:T to T:A	3 (4%)	6 (8%)
A:T to C:G	0	1 (1%)

★$p < .01$ versus normal.
†Fifty to 300 J/m² with xeroderma pigmentosum, 100 to 5000 J/m² with normal.
‡From separate transfections or different mutations in the same transfection including all experiments.
§Two base substitutions 0 to 2 bases apart, or 3 adjacent base substitutions.
¶At least two base substitutions more than 3 bases apart.
SOURCE: Modified from Bredberg et al.,[110] by permission.

BIOCHEMICAL CHARACTERISTICS OF XP

Excision Repair Pathways

The first studies of cultured fibroblasts from patients with the common and the neurologic forms of XP[5,112] showed that both classes of patients are defective to varying degrees in their ability to perform excision repair of damaged DNA. This normally is accomplished by several different repair enzyme systems with different mechanisms and efficiencies for removing various kinds of damaged DNA bases.[3,4,113] The sites of damage and rates of repair are influenced by the organization of DNA in the nucleus, which consists of histone particles around which 200 base pairs of DNA are wrapped to form each structural unit, or nucleosome (see Fig. 120-9).[114–117]

Two major pathways of excision repair, the nucleotide and base excision repair pathways, operate on different kinds of damage in DNA.[3,4,113] In prokaryotes, the nucleotide pathway removes pyrimidine dimers and large chemical adducts to DNA (e.g., benzo[a]anathracene adducts, methoxypsoralen monoadducts, acetoxyacetylaminofluorene adducts) and replaces the damaged site with a newly synthesized polynucleotide patch approximately 10 to 50 bases in length.[118,119] The base excision pathway removes DNA bases that have undergone relatively small degrees of modification, such as alkylation or deamination, by a glycosylase and an apurinic endonuclease and replaces them with a patch that may be smaller than in nucleotide repair.[118,119] Another type of repair has been found in human cells that is specific for damage in the form of O^6-alkylguanine produced by alkylating agents. Some human tumor cell strains are defective in this repair,[120] which operates by direct removal of the alkyl group itself with its transfer to the protein.[118,119,120]

Detailed analysis of the enzymes responsible for the first step in removal of pyrimidine dimers in various bacteria—the UV endonucleases—has demonstrated two distinct mechanisms. Ultraviolet endonucleases from *Micrococcus luteus* and T4 phage–infected *E. coli* catalyze a glycosyl cleavage of the thymine deoxyribose bond on the 5′-thymine of the dimer.[121,122] This mechanism does not occur in *E. coli* itself, however, where a true endonucleolytic cleavage occurs on either side of the damage to release a 12- or 13-base oligonucleotide.[123] The mechanism that occurs in human cells is currently unknown, but may be similar to that in *E. coli* (Fig. 120-10).

The polymerization step of excision repair of UV damage is catalyzed predominantly by DNA polymerase α[124] or δ,[125] although polymerase β may also be involved.[126] The final step of repair is the sealing of the 5′,3′ gap, a reaction catalyzed by polynucleotide ligase. Two forms of ligase are known (ligases I and II), and defects in ligase I have been reported in Bloom disease.[127,128] Excision repair requires a temporary relaxation of nucleosomal structure so that repaired regions are more accessible to exogenous nucleases (Fig. 120-8).[113,115–117]

The process by which new bases are inserted into DNA during repair has been given various names according to the methods used for study, and a full description of methods is available elsewhere.[4,129] Autoradiographic methods of detection gave rise to the term *unscheduled synthesis*.[130] Cesium chloride isopyknic gradient methods led to the term *repair replication*,[131] which is also used in the bromouracil photolysis method.[132] The term *radiation-stimulated [³H]thymidine incorporation*[27] describes an increase in total radioactivity incorporated into DNA by excision repair in cells in which normal DNA synthesis is naturally low (e.g., lymphocytes, plateau-phase tissue cultures), or is depressed by inhibitors of semiconservative DNA synthesis. These various terms all describe the same biochemical process and are essentially equivalent. The different methods are chosen according to the cells or tissues under study. A conclusion derived from the use of each of the methods is that the patches that replace excised dimers

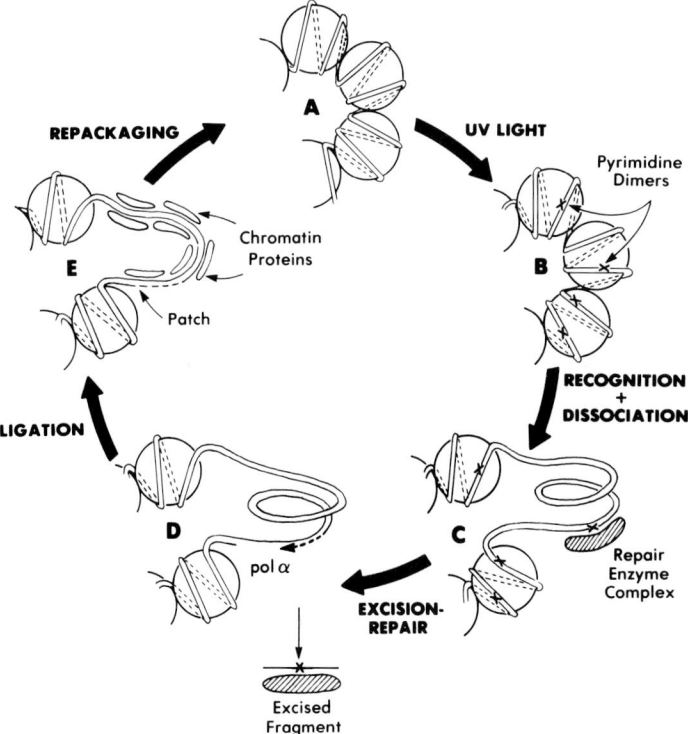

Fig. 120-9 Heuristic scheme for excision repair of damaged sites on DNA in mammalian chromatin. The first step involves mechanisms that recognize damage and dissociate nucleoproteins to make the DNA accessible to repair enzymes. This is followed by sequential incision by a DNA polymerase, sealing of the patch by a polynucleotide ligase, and final reassembly and repackaging of nucleoprotein. (*Reproduced from Cleaver,[117a] by permission.*)

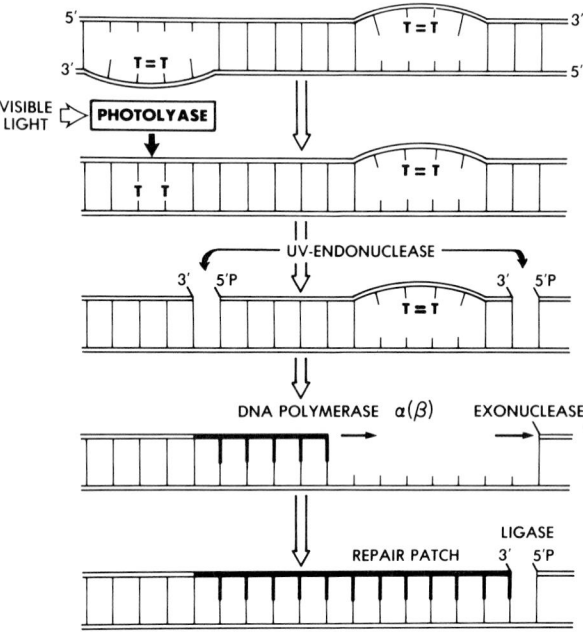

PHOTOREACTIVATION AND NUCLEOTIDE EXCISION REPAIR

Fig. 120-10 Biochemical steps for excision repair of pyrimidine dimers (nucleotide excision repair) in DNA prokaryotes showing biochemical details of events represented schematically in Fig. 120-9. The initial step of nucleotide excision occurs when a UV-specific endonuclease makes an incision on the 5' and 3' sides. Excision and subsequent polymerization releases a small oligonucleotide containing the dimer.

are relatively large, 10 to 50 bases long,[4,5,14,133] and contain both purines and pyrimidines.[13] These patches are probably formed through exonucleolytic degradation of DNA strands beyond the site of the dimer initially excised.

The continuous excision of dimers (Figs. 120-9, 120-10) and insertion of the bases (Figs. 120-11, 120-12) is associated with a very low net frequency of DNA strand breaks.[4,134–141] This suggests that during excision repair a dynamic balance is established between strand breakage and rejoining. The actual number of sites involved in excision repair at any instant is small, no more than about 1 in 2×10^8 daltons of DNA. Only about 1 percent of the dimers produced in DNA by a dose of 10 J/m^2 is undergoing excision at any instant. The excision rate must therefore be dictated by the enzymes involved in the early steps of repair, which presumably move from site to site repairing different sites in sequence.

DEFECTIVE REPAIR IN XP

Cells from patients with XP excise pyrimidine dimers and carry out repair replication at rates that are between 0 and 90 percent of normal (Figs. 120-10, 120-12).[142,143] Cells from affected sibs usually carry out these processes at similar rates. Those XP cell lines that do not excise a detectable number of dimers also have low levels of repair replication, and those that excise at only a slightly reduced level also show only slightly reduced rates of repair replication. The reductions are similar in all tissues thus far investigated, including skin in vivo,[26] peripheral lymphocytes,[27] fibroblasts,[5] liver cell cultures,[144] and tumor cells.[48] Patients with the XP variant ex-

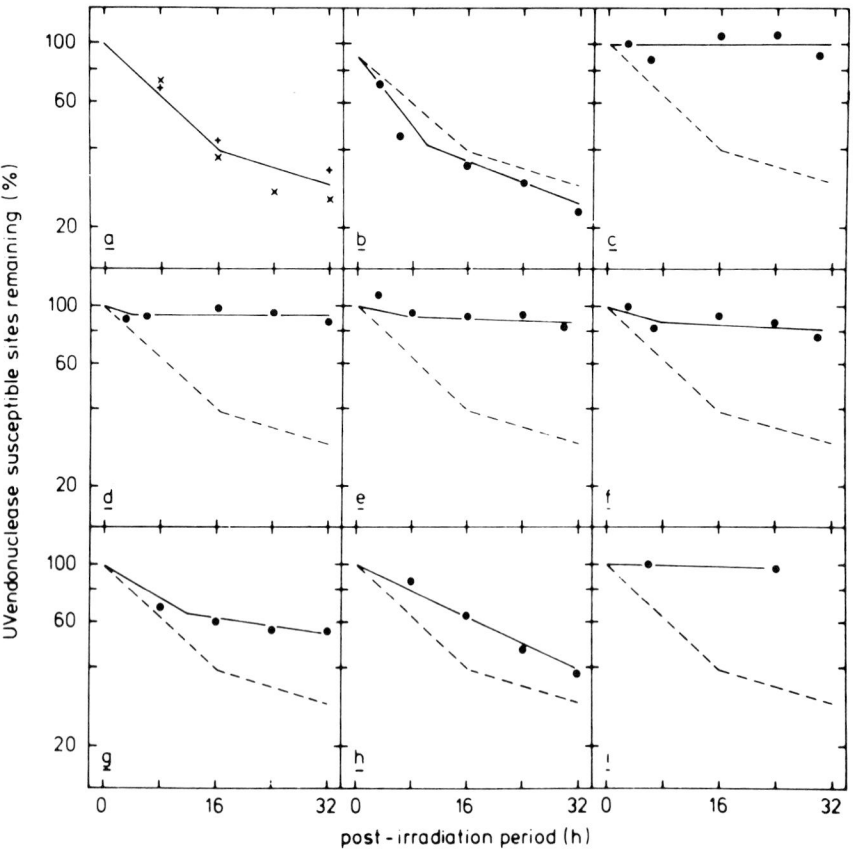

Fig. 120-11 Time course of disappearance of UV endonuclease–susceptible sites (pyrimidine dimers) from the DNA of normal human cells and cells from each complementation group of XP after radiation at 254 nm. After specified periods of post-UV incubation, cell samples were assayed to determine the number of dimers remaining in the extracted DNA. The percentages shown for the incubated samples are relative to those found for the parallel nonincubated ones, and normalized to 100 percent for the number of dimers present immediately after irradiation. *Panel a,* two normal cell lines. The other panels give data for one patient from each XP group; *b,* XP variant; *c,* group A; *d,* group B; *e,* group C; *f,* group D; *g,* group E; *h,* group F; *i,* group G. The dashed lines indicate the mean response of normal cells. *(Reproduced from Zelle and Lohman[143] by permission of Elsevier Press.)*

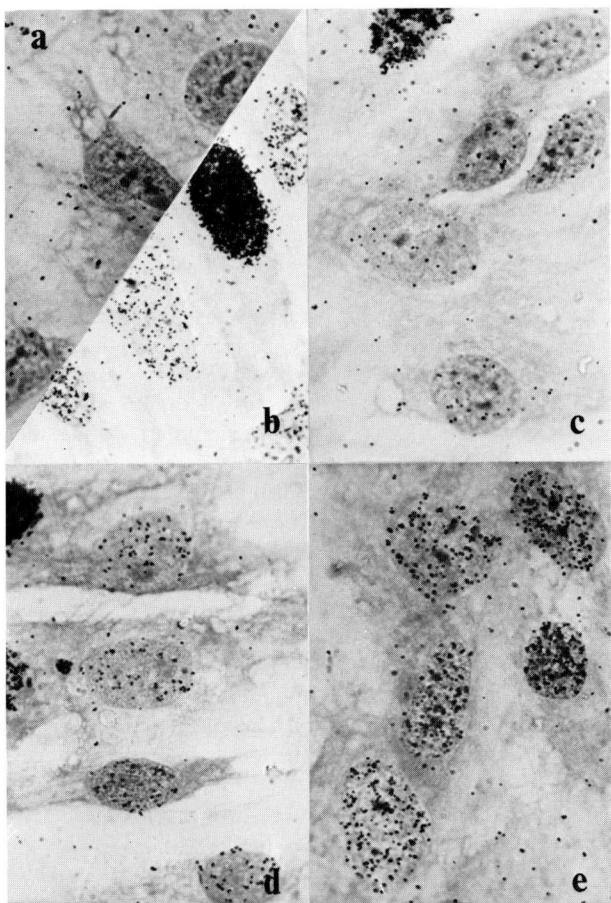

Fig. 120-12 Autoradiographs of normal and XP cells irradiated with 30 J/m² of UV light and labeled for 3 h with [³H]thymidine (10 μCi/ml, 21.9 Ci/mmol). *A.* Normal (JEC) cells, nonirradiated. *B.* Normal (JEC) cells, irradiated. *C.* Repair-deficient XP23SF cells, irradiated. *D.* Partially repair-deficient XP20SF cells, irradiated. *E.* XP variants, irradiated. (*From J. E. Cleaver, unpublished data, 1975.*)

hibit normal levels of both dimer excision and repair replication.[27–30]

Photoreactivation in XP

Photoreactivation is a DNA repair system that is absolutely specific for pyrimidine dimers, and is therefore important only in repair of UV damage. It involves a single enzyme that binds to dimers and, on subsequent exposure to light between 300 and 600 nm, cleaves them.[14–19,145–149] The monomerized thymines remain in DNA, and no material is excised from DNA by this process. The cellular effect of photoreactivation is observed as the mitigation by visible light of many UV-induced effects caused by dimers in DNA, such as cell killing, mutagenesis, and production of chromosome aberrations.[4,146] Most cell culture experiments have given little evidence for an active photoreactivation system in mammalian cells, including human cells.[4,14,18,147–149] A weakly active enzyme was isolated from human cells that had properties in vitro resembling those of photoreactivating enzymes, although it could monomerize only a small fraction of dimers.[15–17]

To this day, demonstration of efficient photoreactivation has been reported by only one research group,[15–17,19] and attempts to demonstrate this repair system by several other groups have

been unsuccessful or ambiguous.[18,148,149] The role of this system in the resistance to UV-induced skin changes in humans thus remains controversial.

Repair of Damage from Chemical Mutagens and Carcinogens in XP

Most chemical mutagens and carcinogens damage many cellular components, but the damage they cause to DNA is the most serious. XP cells show differential sensitivity to different agents. In response to damage from some mutagens and carcinogens, XP cells perform the same amounts of excision repair and have the same sensitivity to killing as do normal cells.[13,85,150,151] However, in response to damage from other carcinogens, XP cells perform less excision repair and have greater sensitivity than normal cells.[13,84–88,152–154] Since XP cells also respond normally to x-ray-induced damage, but not to UV-induced damage, the chemicals to which XP cells respond normally can be considered "x-ray-like" and those to which XP cells are sensitive, "UV-like" (Table 120-5).[13] The patch sizes synthesized in response to damage from x-ray-like chemicals may be smaller than those synthesized in response to UV-like chemicals.[4,154,155]

The impaired response of XP cells to various carcinogens and mutagens appears to depend on the type of damage to DNA and the extent to which repair of the damage requires enzymes that are deficient in XP cells. Damage is caused by the reaction between cellular components and electrophilic carcinogens or mutagens ("ultimate carcinogens").[156] Some carcinogenic and mutagenic chemicals are electrophilic in their native state (e.g., alkylating agents such as methyl methanesulfonate, propane sulfone, methyl nitrosourea), whereas others require metabolic conversion by cellular enzymes before becoming electrophilic (e.g., 4-nitroquinoline-1-oxide, acetylaminofluorene, benz[a]anthracene). Reactions between chemical carcinogens and DNA produce three types of damage: alkylated bases and phosphate groups, covalent adducts between bases and carcinogens, and strand breaks. The relative proportions of these three classes of damage depend on the carcinogen in question. Many chemical carcinogens induce several kinds of DNA damage, each of which might be repaired

Table 120-5 Classification of Carcinogens and Mutagens on the Basis of the Total Amount of DNA Repair in XP Cells

Agents causing damage that is repaired defectively in XP cells	Agents causing damage that is repaired normally in XP cells
UV light	X-rays
Methoxypsoralen adduct	Bromouracil photoproducts
4-Nitroquinoline-1-oxide	Dimethyl sulfate
Bromobenz[a]anthracene	Methyl methanesulfonate
Benz[a]anthracene epoxide	N-methyl-N'-nitro-N-nitrosoguanidine
1-Nitropyridine-1-oxide	Methyl nitrosourea
Acetylaminofluorene	ICR 170
Aromatic amides	
Benzo[a]pyrene	

NOTE: The measurements of repair are biased toward those lesions in DNA that predominate and that are repaired more rapidly with larger patches. Therefore, quantitatively minor lesions, such as those from x-rays that are defectively repaired or from 4NQO that are normally repaired, will not be resolved in measurements of the total amount of repair. For references to specific chemicals, see text.

by different types of excision repair. For example, ethylnitrosourea produces a variety of alkylated bases in DNA, including N-7 and N-3 ethyladenine, which are repaired by an *N*-glycosylase (base excision pathway). It also produces phosphotriesters that are not repaired at all and O^6-ethylguanine, which is repaired by an alkyltransferase.[118–120,157,158] The classification of agents with respect to repair refers to the predominant response to the quantitatively most frequent repairable lesions.

Damage that does not involve a strand break requires different recognition and endonucleolytic action for initiating excision than does strand break damage, which may not even require a specific endonuclease. Breaks may be produced directly as a part of the damage (as in x-ray-induced damage) or may appear as a result of enzymatic action on damaged (alkylated) bases in which a base is removed by an *N*-glycosylase reaction, as for example on N-7 and N-3 ethyladenine.[158] Other damage, which does not involve breaks or alkylated bases, tends to involve several bases (e.g., pyrimidine dimers) or adducts between bases and relatively large chemical groups (e.g., 4-nitroquinoline-1-oxide adducts to purines). The classification of carcinogens as UV-like therefore implies that excision repair of damage induced by UV-like carcinogens involves the enzyme(s) of UV repair that are defective in XP cells. Excision repair of x-ray-like damage or damage from alkylating agents bypasses those defects. The biologic significance of the classification into x-ray-like and UV-like carcinogens for carcinogenesis is unclear at present, although the two categories correspond approximately to nucleotide and base repair or to large patch and small patch repair.[13,154] Both cat-

egories include strong and weak carcinogens. The categories do not appear to correlate in any simple manner with the mutagenic and carcinogenic potential of a chemical.

GENETICS

Genetic Heterogeneity in XP

Genetic heterogeneity in XP patients whose cells are defective in excision repair is suggested by the different residual activities of dimer excision (Fig. 120-11) and repair replication (Fig. 120-12), and by the different clinical patterns. In addition to these quantitative differences are genetic differences between patients that can be analyzed by somatic cell hybridization. Cells from different XP patients can be hybridized in culture using as cell fusing agents inactivated Sendai virus or polyethylene glycol (Fig. 120-13). Cell fusion produces multinucleated cells with nuclei from each XP patient (heterokaryons). Heterokaryons from some combination of XP patients exhibit complementation and increased repair, whereas other combinations remain repair-deficient.[6,21,31,159–163] If complementation occurs, it is an indication that the cell types contain defects in different genes and each supplies what the other is lacking. Numerous studies in which cells from many patients were hybridized in pairs have demonstrated at least nine complementation groups among patients who are deficient in excision repair (Table 120-6, Fig. 120-11).[6,21,31,159–163] This implies that the initial step of pyrimidine dimer excision, which

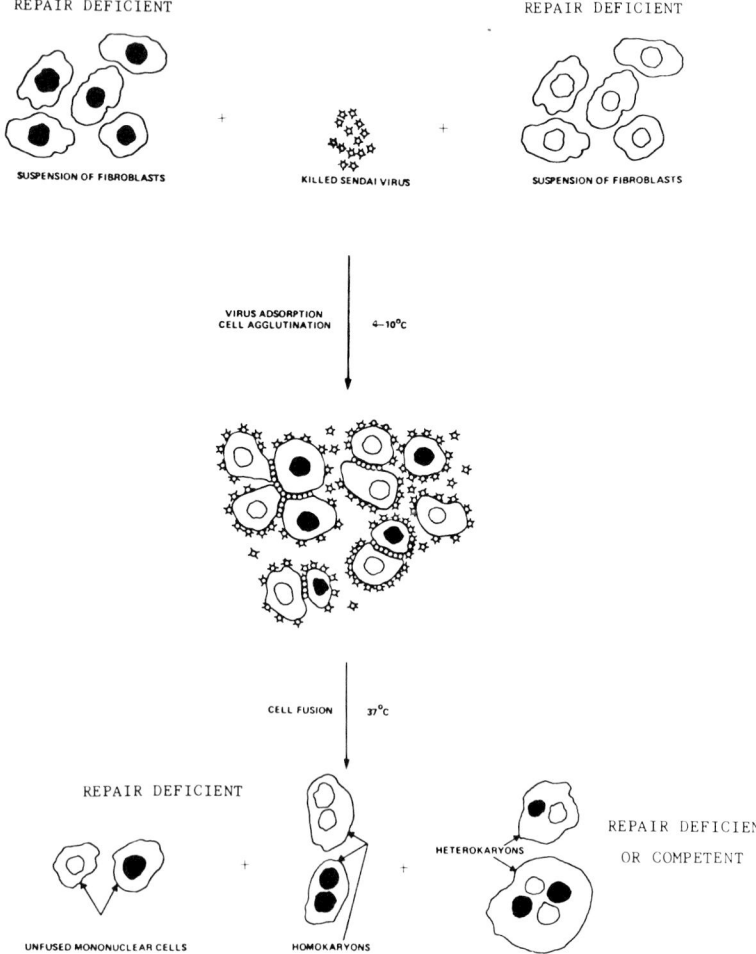

Fig. 120-13 Schematic representation of cell fusion under the influence of inactivated Sendai virus as it is employed to detect complementation between different genetic defects. Fibroblasts from two XP patients who are both repair-deficient (denoted by dark and light nuclei) are allowed to agglutinate in the cold and fuse at 37°C to form multinucleate cells. Multinucleate cells with nuclei from the same cell line (homokaryons) will exhibit a repair defect similar to that of the original mononuclear cells. Multinucleate cells with nuclei from each cell line (heterokaryons) will be either repair-deficient or repair-competent, depending on whether the repair defects in the original cell lines are in the same or different complementation groups. One complementation group will usually comprise XP patients with defects in a single gene that codes for an enzyme, an enzyme subunit, or a single polypeptide.

Table 120-6 Levels of Unscheduled DNA Synthesis and Clinical Symptoms in the Complementation Groups of XP

Complementation groups	Clinical form	Percent of normal repair	Representative cell lines
A	Neurologic form	2–5	XPPKSF, XP25RO, XP1LO, XP17SF, XP12BE
B	Neurologic form (and Cockayne syndrome)	3–7	XP11BE
C	Classic form	10–20 5–15	XP4RO, XP12SF XP1BE
D	Neurologic form*	25–50	XP5BE, XP6BE, XP2NE, XP3NE
E	Classic form	40–50	XP2RO, XP3RO
F	Classic form	18	XP3YO
G	Neurologic form	<2	XP3BR, XP2B1
H	Neurologic form (and Cockayne syndrome)	30	XPSC8
I	Neurologic form	15–40	XP3MA, XP20MA

*Sometimes associated with trichothiodystrophy.

appears to be the action of a single UV endonuclease, actually requires the cooperative function of at least nine distinct gene products. The number of patients from each complementation group observed so far in four populations is shown in Table 120-7. There are two major groups, A and C. The next most frequent are group D and variant, with the remaining groups represented by only one or two families.

The existence of nine complementation groups in XP probably indicates intergenic, rather than intragenic, complementation. The affected genes may play a role as both structural and regulatory genes in the formation of one or more enzymes mediating the early steps in excision repair. One hypothesis consistent with the observed kinetics of excision and strand breakage is that the excision, replication, and ligation enzymes act in a coordinated way by means of an enzyme complex, as first suggested by Haynes.[164] This complex might contain nine different peptides. A defect in any one of the peptides might interfere with the action of the complex. Isolation of repair enzyme activity[165] and estimates of its apparent molecular weight in excess of 10^6 (Refs. 166,167) support the idea of an enzyme complex.

Interspecies Comparison in DNA Repair

Ultraviolet-sensitive mutant cell lines have been isolated from Chinese hamster ovary (CHO) cells[168] and mouse cells,[169] and both species demonstrate multiple complementation groups. Seven groups (I to VII) have thus far been identified in rodent cell lines. These mutants are also sensitive to an alkylating agent that cross-links DNA, mitomycin C. This property is exhibited by human cell lines from patients with Fanconi anemia but not from patients with XP.[170] The rodent and human (XP) mutants represent different complementation groups, because interspecies cell hybrids complement one another.[171]

If each complementation group represents a gene with a corresponding gene product, and if the human and rodent genes are involved in the same pathway of excision repair, then about 15 genes are involved in the initial step of dimer excision. The difference between XP and rodent cell mutants may lie in the way these are identified, one set from patients and the other set from cells in culture. It may be that the CHO mutants represent gene products whose functions are essential in embryogenesis and development; defects in these gene products would then be lethal and so would not be found in patients. On the other hand, the human XP mutants might represent defects that are compatible with life but are much less commonly identified by the cell culture procedure.

One CHO complementation group has been used in gene cloning and chromosomal transfer experiments, and can be corrected by a human gene on chromosome 19.[172] This chromosome restores dimer excision and repair to one group of UV-sensitive CHO cells.[173] This gene, however, has not been shown to correct any XP cell lines.

Cloning XP Genes and Reversion of the XP Phenotype

The increased UV sensitivity of XP cells should provide a strong selective system for use in cloning the XP gene. A conventional approach would be to transfect XP cells with ge-

Table 120-7 Relative Frequencies of Various XP Complementation Groups among Different Populations

Population	Complementation group (number of patients)										Total cases
	A	B	C	D	E	F	G	H	I	Var	
North America	9	1	11	8	0	0	0	0	0	5	34
Europe	12	0	26	16	2	0	2	1	2	19	80
Japan	30	0	5	4	3	11	1	0	0	21	75
Egypt	7	0	12	0	0	0	0	0	0	5	24
Other	5	0	6	0	0	0	0	0	0	4	15
Total cases	63	1	60	28	5	11	3	1	2	54	228

SOURCE: Kraemer et al.,[32] Cleaver et al.,[186] and Hashem et al.[217] (used by permission); and personal communication from Dr. H. Takebe.

nomic DNA or with a genomic library, and to select for the transfer and expression of UV resistance. Such an approach has identified a DNA repair gene on human chromosome 19 (ERCC 1), which complements the UV and mitomycin C sensitivity of one complementation group of UV-sensitive hamster cells.[173–176] This gene, however, appears to be unrelated to the XP defects, since the hamster UV-sensitive mutants differ significantly from XP and the respective cells appear mutually complementary.[171] Such an approach to cloning the genes relevant to XP, however, has been a consistent failure[177–179] despite an early report to the contrary,[180] although transfer of a chromosomal fragment that corrects XP group A has been achieved.[181]

One of the problems encountered in attempts to clone the XP gene results from the masking of any successful gene transfer by the reversion of the XP phenotype to UV resistance.[178,179] This reversion process appears to involve either second-site mutations or other changes in gene expression that suppress the original UV-sensitive phenotype. Detailed analysis of one XP revertant has indicated that acquisition of resistance to UV light is associated with repair of [6-4] photoproduct only.[182] Evidence from this cell line suggests that the [6-4] photoproduct plays a major role in cell killing, mutagenesis, and sister chromatid exchange production. The complexity of XP and the unexpected phenomenon of reversion clearly represent serious difficulties to the problem of cloning the XP genes.

Characteristics of Complementation Groups

Group A. Group A usually corresponds to the most severe clinical form of XP, in which there are both skin symptoms and central nervous system disorders. Most patients exhibit disorders from birth and correspond to the clinical category of the De Sanctis–Cacchione syndrome and xerodermic idiocy.[25,32,183–186] Excision repair is very low in these cells, which are about 10 times more sensitive than normal to killing by UV light and many carcinogens (Figs. 120-6 and 120-7). They are also about 4 times more sensitive to methyl methanesulfonate[187] and have slightly reduced levels of apurinic endonuclease.[188]

There are exceptions to these general characteristics of group A cells. In one British case, XP8LO, the cells exhibited about 30 percent of normal excision repair and higher survival after UV than other group A cells. The patient is without CNS disorders.[189]

Cells from one 35-year-old Egyptian male (XP13CA) had a low level of unscheduled synthesis typical of most group A cells, but the patient was neurologically normal, had normal stature, and was fertile (Fig. 120-14).[186] Two other group A patients, XP12BE and XP1LO, also show minimal neurologic abnormalities, and the cells have higher survival after UV irradiation than the majority in group A.[21,38] In one Italian family, group A sibs exhibited different clinical symptoms, only one having disorders of the CNS.[74] In cell cultures, it appeared that the sib without CNS disorder had higher repair on average due to a subpopulation of cells with normal repair mixed with typical group A cells.

Therefore, although group A patients usually have the associated neurologic abnormalities of the De Sanctis–Cacchione syndrome, several are known who are neurologically normal.

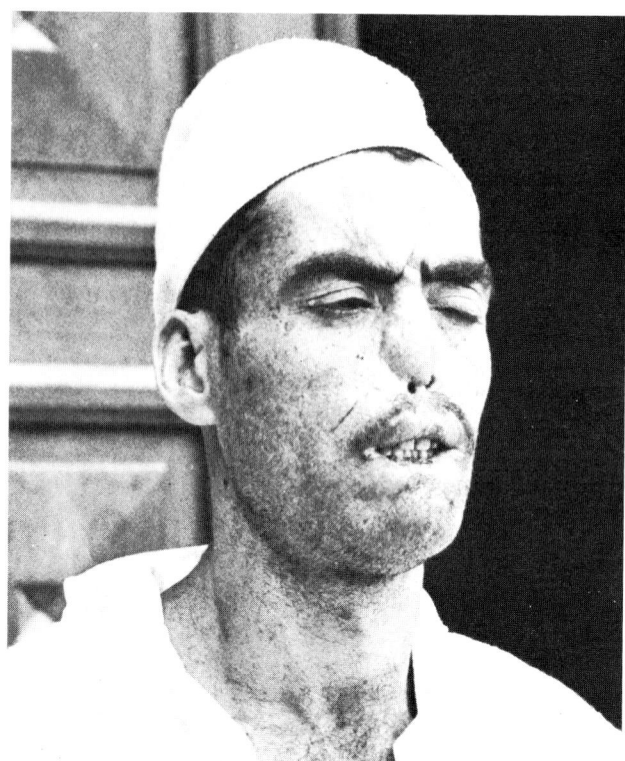

Fig. 120-14 Exceptional group A patient (XP13CA) from complementation group A exhibiting skin abnormalities, including the consequences of invasive skin carcinoma of the nose, but with normal neurologic status, unlike most group A patients. (Photograph kindly supplied by Dr. J. German, New York Blood Center.)

Thus, skin manifestations in group A patients may occur alone—depending on the mutation at the presumed locus.

Group B. There is only one reported patient (Fig. 120-15) in group B (XP11BE). The patient died of acute hypertension at age 33; she remains perplexing because she had symptoms of both XP and Cockayne syndrome.[21] She had reduced stature, deafness and mental retardation, immature sexual development, premature senility, absence of subcutaneous fat, and optic nerve and retinal pigment degeneration characteristic of Cockayne syndrome. She exhibited acute sun sensitivity, ocular changes, and cutaneous malignancy at age 18, all typical of XP. The conjunction of two extremely rare disorders in one patient is statistically unlikely, so that this constellation of symptoms may be regarded as characteristic of this group unless or until other cases are identified. Cells from this patient have low levels of excision repair and are very sensitive to killing by UV light.

Group C. Group C is one of the largest groups (Fig. 120-3) and is often referred to as the *common* or *classic form* of XP. The patients show only skin disorders. These vary considerably in severity, depending on the climate. Tumors of the tongue have been observed in several patients (Fig. 120-3).[32,186] Cells have low but heterogeneous levels of excision repair (10 to 20 percent of normal) and are less sensitive to killing by UV light and chemical carcinogens than in groups A and D.[21,86] One characteristic of repair unique to this group is that in nonproliferating cells, repair occurs in clusters rather than randomly.[191–193]

One exceptional patient (XP1M1) exhibited symptoms of XP, systemic lupus erythematosus, microcephaly, and a marginal degree of mental retardation.[194] Cells from this patient had typical DNA repair levels but were the most UV-sensitive of any in group C.[38] Two reported instances of central nervous system tumors in XP patients, XP106LO[195] and a Hawaiian patient,[196] are in this group.

Group D. Patients in group D resemble those in group A in exhibiting both skin and CNS disorders, although the latter usually develop later in life than in patients in group A.[185,195] Patients have been reported in both the United States and Europe with trichothiodystrophy, a sulfur deficiency of the hair, suggesting a relationship of group D to another genetic disorder.[197] Representatives of this group are slightly more common in Britain than elsewhere, but their distribution is not as restricted as that of groups B, F, and G. Excision repair is low (10 to 20 percent), as in group C cells, but functionally poorer. Some evidence suggests that the amount of unscheduled DNA synthesis is higher than expected from the low amount of dimer excision observed in these cells.[143] Cells are almost as sensitive to cell killing as are group A cells.[21,86] Cells in this group were claimed in one study to have reduced levels of apurinic endonuclease,[198] but this was not confirmed in another study.[199]

Group E. Patients in the rare group E exhibit mild degrees of skin symptoms, and are neurologically normal.[21] The level of excision repair is high (greater than 50 percent of normal), and the level relative to normal cells increases with increasing UV dose. The cells are only slightly more sensitive than normal to UV damage. Patients have been reported from Europe and Japan.[200–202]

Group F. The only representatives of group F have been described in Japan (XP230S and XP2Y0).[162,203] The skin symptoms were relatively mild, and the patients had no neurological abnormalities. Excision repair was 10 to 15 percent of normal but increased to 60 percent with time of incubation. The cells appear to be more defective in a component of excision repair that occurs at rapid rates and at early times after irradiation.[203] The cells showed an intermediate sensitivity to killing by UV light and a high degree of excision of pyrimidine dimers.

Group G. Two representatives of group G have been described in England (XP3BR, XP2B1)[163,204] and one in Japan (XP31KO).[205] The European patients had mental retardation, microcephaly, and sun sensitivity, but no neoplasms. The cells had extremely low levels of dimer excision and unscheduled synthesis and were as sensitive as groups A and D to killing by UV light. XP3BR is unusual in having a slightly increased sensitivity to killing by x-rays.[204,206] There is heterogeneity within this group: the Japanese patient was 37 years old with no neurological abnormalities, normal skin phototest reaction, and a basal cell carcinoma. Unscheduled DNA synthesis of XP31KO was 25 percent, a level much higher than in the other group G cells.

XP Group H. The one representative of group H (XP-SC-8) has been described—like the patient in group B—as presenting symptoms including the neurological dysfunction of Cock-

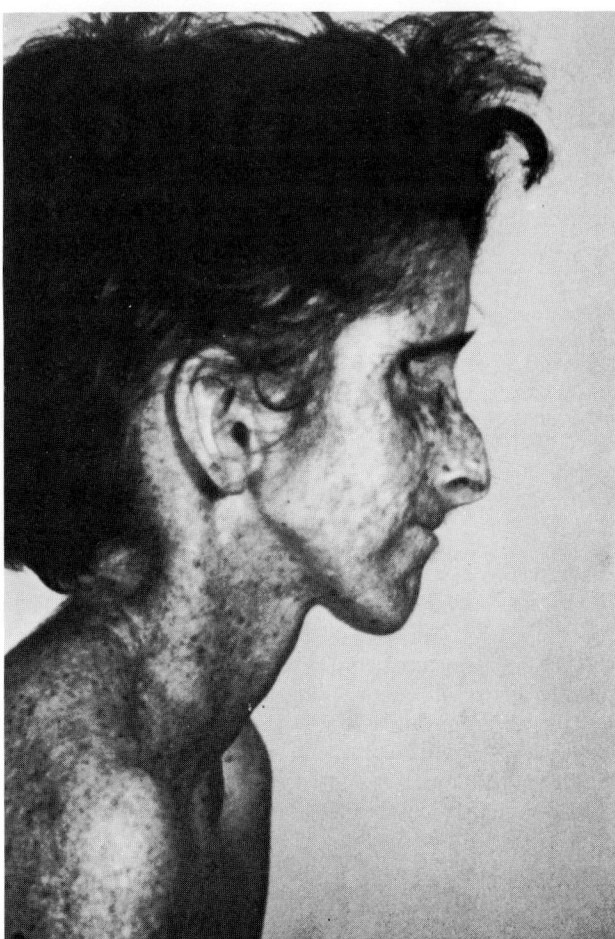

Fig. 120-15 XP patient (XP11BE) from complementation group B exhibiting skin, ocular, and neurologic characteristics that have been ascribed to both XP and Cockayne syndrome. *(From Kraemer.[190] Used with permission.)*

ayne syndrome, as well as XP. Unscheduled synthesis was 30 percent of normal.[207,208] A recent study suggests that this patient may not represent a distinct group but may be from group D.[208a]

XP Group I. The two patients in group I were a 13-year-old girl (XP3MA) and her 24-year-old brother (XP20MA) described in Germany.[209,210] They had sun sensitivity; severe ocular abnormalities, including atrophy of the lower eyelids; retarded intellectual development; and multiple skin carcinomas and a malignant melanoma. Post-UV colony-forming ability was 27 percent of normal, unscheduled DNA synthesis was 15 percent of normal, and DNA incising ability measured by alkaline elution was 38 percent of normal.

XP Variant. Patients in the variant group (Fig. 120-16) have mild to severe skin symptoms and normal CNS. The variant form is found worldwide and is a frequently occurring group distinct from all the other XP groups, even though it cannot often be clinically discriminated without cell culture studies. Originally defined as a clinically recognized XP without any biochemical defect in excision repair,[27,28] it was also described earlier under the clinical designation *pigmented xerodermoid*.[29,34] With careful clinical investigation, patients in this group may be recognized by relatively mild symptoms and the

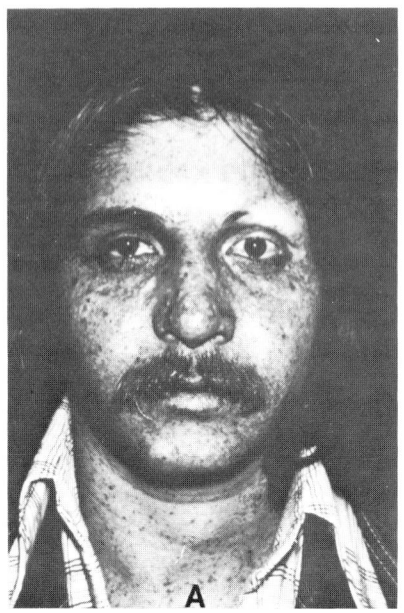
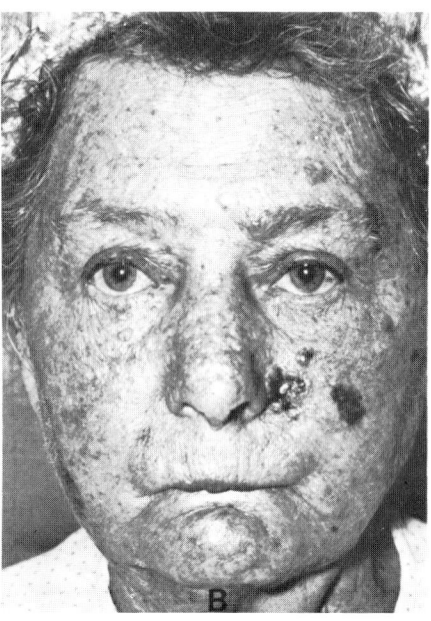

Fig. 120-16 XP variants (A, XP115LO; B, XP5MA) exhibiting skin symptoms characteristic of XP and normal neurologic status. [Photographs kindly provided by Drs. H. Hoffmann and E. G. Jung (A) and Dr. F. Gianelli (B).]

absence of an enhanced erythematous response, but this is insufficient for unambiguous diagnosis.

Slight alterations in late stages of excision repair have been reported,[140,141] but these are of unknown importance. The high level of mutagenesis[104,107,211] with near-normal levels of cell survival after UV irradiation[38] could be interpreted as indicating that an inherited disorder in excision repair has made this system error-prone. The outstanding feature of this form of XP is that after UV irradiation, replication forks appear to stop or to be interrupted during semiconservative replication at every site of DNA damage. This radiation effect on replication is exaggerated by growth in 1 mM caffeine,[29,30,89,212] which stimulates many new replication forks,[90] and survival is concomitantly diminished.[89,213] These observations can be explained if it is assumed that normal cells and cells from XP groups A through I have gene product(s) that normally facilitate replication without interruption at damaged sites, and that XP variant cells have lost one or more of these gene product(s).[29,30] This is correlated with a reduced rate of recovery of DNA replication after UV irradiation.[212]

Whether the variant group is homogeneous or will have multiple subgroups is not known, but the clinical heterogeneity is suggestive.[27-30,33,34,214] The pigmented xerodermoid family of Jung et al.[34,214] although biochemically identical to other XP variants, is unusual because no clinical symptoms were evident until after the age of 40, and patients lived into their eighties. These mild symptoms contrast with other variant families from comparable environments in whom the disease is quite severe.[29,195] One attempt at studying complementation between cells from different XP variant patients indicated a single XP variant group.[215]

XP Heterozygotes

Clinical and laboratory investigations of XP heterozygotes have failed to uncover consistent clinical or cellular abnormalities.[25,26,28,186] In a study of XP cases in the United States,[216] the majority of XP heterozygotes were asymptomatic, although a few families in one geographical location had nonmelanoma skin cancers. In Egypt no skin abnormalities were seen in nearly 100 heterozygotes, despite the intense sunlight and the severe skin abnormalities seen in homozygotes.[186,217]

Studies of DNA repair in cell cultures from heterozygotes also fail to detect any consistent DNA repair defects, although slight reductions in repair have been reported in occasional studies at high UV doses.[218,219] In one study, fusion of heterozygote with homozygote cells produced multinucleated cells, each of which contained many repair-deficient nuclei and one heterozygous XP nucleus.[219] Slight reductions in repair were then evident in comparison with normal cells.[219] Also, a slightly lower rate of dimer excision from DNA of heterozygote as compared to normal cells has been observed at high UV doses.[219]

Measurements of host cell reactivation of irradiated adenovirus[94] or herpes virus[220] did not show any differences between normal hosts and XP heterozygotes. However, measurements of the rate of production of viral antigen from irradiated adenovirus did show lower rates in heterozygotes.[221]

The XP gene therefore appears to have a significant effect on clinical symptoms and DNA repair only when present in the homozygous state.

ISOLATION OF EXCISION REPAIR ENZYMES

Enzymes for the first step of repair would be expected to have unique properties related to their action on UV photoproducts. The enzymes for the later stages of excision repair (polymerases and a ligase) probably do not have unique properties, because they operate on molecules in which specific damage has been excised. The later stages of repair may be performed by some of the polymerases[222] and the ligases[223] already identified and characterized in animal tissues. The situation may resemble that in *E. coli*, where several different polymerases can play a role in excision repair, depending on the genetic and physiological state of the cell, although the preferred mode involves polymerase I.[224]

Identification of a UV-specific endonuclease involved in an early step of repair in human cells has been much more difficult than anticipated, mainly because of uncertainty in defining precisely the activity of the enzyme to be measured in any assay in crude or partially purified extracts. The most obvious function, and one that proved successful in isolating bacterial enzymes, is the ability of a UV-specific endonuclease to make nicks in UV-irradiated supercoiled DNA.[225,226] Experiments based on this kind of substrate have identified enzyme activity that nicks UV-irradiated DNA in HeLa cells,[226,227] embryonic lung,[225] adult skin fibroblasts,[225,227] rat liver,[228] numerous XP fibroblast cell lines,[225,227] and calf thymus.[229] This nicking activity does not appear to be involved in the repair of pyrimidine dimers, because it nicks only about 1 percent of the dimers present in the UV-irradiated substrates,[225,226,229] and because specific monomerization of dimers by photoreactivation in vitro does not alter the nicking activity of these extracts on the substrate.[225] Thus this enzyme activity does not have one of the properties required of a UV-specific endonuclease—that of nicking specifically close to dimers in DNA. It is therefore either an enzyme involved in repair of other kinds of lesions than dimers or is a less specific endonuclease. Examples of enzymes that will make nicks at a low frequency in UV-irradiated DNA in a manner similar to that seen with animal cell extracts include the S1 nuclease from *Aspergillus oryzae*[230] and a nuclease from *Neurospora crassa*.[231]

Because nicking activity has not proved to be a satisfactory assay system, a more specific one has been devised that is closely related to the enzyme's function in vivo—the ability of a cell extract to excise pyrimidine dimers in vitro.[232–234] This assay measures the function of several enzymes together (at least a UV endonuclease and a UV exonuclease) and is therefore not an assay for UV endonuclease alone. Extracts from normal human cells have the capacity to excise dimers from DNA in vitro, but this activity is easily destroyed by freezing and thawing or excessive sonication during preparation of the extracts.[235]

Unfrozen extracts from both normal and XP cells (complementation groups A and C) can excise dimers from UV-irradiated *E. coli* DNA.[233] On this basis, even XP cells that cannot perform excision repair in vivo still perform repair in vitro.[233,234] This suggests either that the defect is more complex than first envisaged and is not simply a missing UV-specific endonuclease[112] or that the excision observed in vitro is mediated by other enzymes that do not serve this function in the cell. When cell extracts were compared for their ability to excise dimers from both exogenous purified DNA and their own DNA still associated with nucleoprotein, extracts from XP cells (complementation groups A and C) excised dimers only from exogenous DNA and not from DNA in chromatin. Thus the defect in these XP cells may lie in some factor that governs the accessibility of dimers in the DNA.

PRENATAL DIAGNOSIS OF XP

Once the main biochemical features of XP were delineated, the assays were adapted for use in prenatal diagnosis. Cell suspensions can be obtained from amniotic fluid by transabdominal puncture during the second half of the first trimester of pregnancy and used to grow fibroblasts in tissue culture representative of the fetus. Fibroblasts from normal fetuses have normal capacities for excision repair,[82] whereas those from XP fetuses are expected to be defective.

It is possible to identify a family at risk for the XP genotype only when one homozygous child has already appeared in the family. Prenatal diagnosis was first achieved in such a family by Ramsay et al.[236]

Speed is paramount in tests for DNA repair in amniocentesis specimens. One of the main purposes is to provide a family with reliable information on which to base a decision whether to interrupt pregnancy within the time period allowed by law. Autoradiographic analysis of DNA repair and many other assays for excision repair deficiency or postreplication repair deficiency can be completed in a few days. The longest delay is due to the time required for fibroblast cultures to develop from amniocentesis cell suspensions (about 1 week or longer). Autoradiographic analysis can be done on smaller cultures and is technically easier than most other assays. In the first successful prenatal diagnosis of XP,[236] fibroblast cultures were ready to assay for unscheduled synthesis 6 days after amniocentesis, and autoradiography was completed in 3 days.

One potential problem in all amniocentetic tests is that of an error in diagnosis because of contamination of a sample with unrepresentative cells (e.g., nonviable or maternal cells). Usually, the presence of nonviable cells can be excluded because they will be lost from cultures during the first days of growth. The probability of contamination with maternal cells is low (of the order of 0.5 percent or less) and can be excluded for male fetuses by observing sex chromatin in interphase or karyotypic analysis. The risk of false diagnosis should be less than 1 in 500.

OTHER HYPERSENSITIVITY DISEASES

XP is only one of a large number of human disorders in which cells (fibroblasts, lymphocytes, etc.) are more sensitive than normal (i.e., hypersensitive) to DNA-damaging agents (Table 120-8). Only for XP, however, is there a clear correlation between the hypersensitivity to UV light, the biochemical defect in DNA repair, and the etiology of the disease. In several of the hypersensitive diseases, abnormalities have been found in DNA replication rather than repair. Other diseases in which there is only about twice as much sensitivity as normal appear more difficult to attribute to specific defects in repair or replication of DNA; secondary or more subtle defects may be involved.

Ataxia-telangiectasia (AT) is a disorder associated with neurologic symptoms, vascular telangiectasia, and eventual development of lymphoreticular malignancy.[10,237] This disorder involves a complex spectrum of defects in repair of lesions in DNA caused by ionizing radiation[11,237,239] or chemical agents.[238,239] In addition, DNA replication is resistant to inhibition by x-rays.[9,10,240] A small fraction of x-ray-induced chromosomal breaks appear to remain unrejoined in AT cells in comparison with normal cells.[241]

Cockayne syndrome is a premature aging syndrome that includes sensitivity to UV light and some chemicals.[40–42] Repair of UV damage is normal,[43] but DNA replication and RNA synthesis fail to recover from inhibition by UV damage.[12]

Fanconi anemia is a disease involving a deficiency in bone development and bone marrow function. Although cells are markedly hypersensitive to DNA-DNA cross-linking agents,[170] the biochemical defect is poorly understood and results have thus far been quite variable.[170,242–244]

Table 120-8 Hypersensitivity Diseases

Disease	Agent	D_0 ratios[*]	References
Xeroderma pigmentosum (A, C, D)	UV (and chemical carcinogens)	5–10	21, 38
XP variant	UV	1.6	21, 38
Ataxia-telangiectasia	X-rays	2.9–3.5	10, 239
AT heterozygotes	X-rays	0.9–1.2	237
Fanconi anemia	Mitomycin C;	4–15	170
	X-rays	1–2	253, 254
Cockayne syndrome	UV	4.6	40–42
Cockayne heterozygotes	UV	1.8	40–42
Chediak-Higashi syndrome	UV	2.2	255
Retinoblastoma (hereditary)	X-rays	1.2–1.5	256
Huntington's disease	X-rays	1.25–2.0	254
Partial trisomy 13	X-rays	1.6–2.0	253
Progeria	X-rays	1.1–1.6	253, 254
Werner syndrome	X-rays	1.1–1.6	254
Gardner syndrome (hereditary polyposis coli)	X-rays	1–2	257

[*]This is the ratio of the losses required to reduce the survival of normal and affected cell lines to 37 percent as estimated from the exponential portion of survival curves.

Patients with Bloom syndrome have high spontaneous frequencies of lymphatic and other malignancies,[73] high baseline levels of sister chromatid exchanges,[245] and a high frequency of somatic cell mutation.[246] Neither consistent hypersensitivity, other than that involving SCEs,[247] nor any defect in DNA repair has been demonstrated in Bloom syndrome.[43,248] DNA ligase I is reported to have reduced activity and increased heat sensitivity in cells from patients with this syndrome.[127,128]

DNA REPAIR AND CARCINOGENESIS IN XP

One theory of carcinogenesis[249] invokes an accumulation of genetic damage as part of the underlying mechanism. Environmental mutagens are postulated to damage some critical region(s) of the genome of somatic cells.[250,251] If the damage is not repaired before DNA replication occurs, then that region becomes the site of a somatic mutation or of chromosomal rearrangements and amplifications. If these changes occur in genes involved in growth control, then they might become early events in carcinogenesis. Incomplete, inefficient, or inaccurate repair in some hereditary diseases should therefore be correlated with increased carcinogenesis. Carcinogenesis induced by radiation or chemicals in normal individuals would then be due to the normal amount of inaccuracy present in repair, or perhaps to inhibition of repair by the damaging agents themselves, or replication of a damaged region before repair was complete. XP would be an example of increased damage remaining in DNA during replication, with a resultant accumulation of mutations.

Carcinogenesis often appears to proceed by a multistep process, the first step being an initiation event and the later steps, which can often occur much later, being promotional events. One theory of carcinogenesis would correlate initiation with the induction of somatic mutations, and promotion with an alteration in the expression of the mutations (e.g., by induction of aneuploidy, which produces haploid cells which can express recessive mutations generated by the initiating carcinogenic event).

Substantial evidence from microorganisms and mammalian cells supports a theory in which initiating events in carcino-genesis are akin to mutagenic events caused by damage to DNA. Generally there is a high correlation between the mutagenic activity of a chemical and its carcinogenic activity.[250,251] In XP there is a correlation between high levels of carcinogenesis and susceptibility to UV-induced mutagenesis[3,8,21,104–110] in all forms of the disease, both excision repair–defective and variant, although UV-induced rearrangements of DNA in the form of SCEs are elevated only in excision-defective XPs. In other diseases, however, the correlations are weaker. In AT cells, mutagenesis from x-rays appears normal in spite of the hypersensitivity to x-rays.[252]

These kinds of results suggest that the various cellular factors studied experimentally, such as DNA damage, repair, mutation, and transformation, are but a few of the complex mechanisms involved in carcinogenesis. Further elucidation of details of the biochemical, cellular, and clinical characteristics of XP should provide a better understanding of one kind of carcinogenesis, but might have implications for carcinogenesis in general.

This work was supported by the Office of Health and Environmental Research, U.S. Department of Energy, contract no. DE-AC03-76-SF01012, and by the National Cancer Institute. We are especially grateful to Ms. S. Brekhus for preparing the manuscript.

REFERENCES

1. WITKOP CJ JR, QUEVEDO WC JR, FIZPATRICK TB: Albinism, in Stanbury JB, Wyngaarden JB, Fredrickson DS, Goldstein JL, Brown MS (eds): *The Metabolic Basis of Inherited Disease,* 5th ed. New York, McGraw-Hill, 1983, chap 15.

2. KAPPAS A, SASSA S, ANDERSON KE: The porphyrias, in Stanbury JB, Wyngaarden JB, Fredrickson DS, Goldstein JL, Brown MS (eds): *The Metabolic Basis of Inherited Disease,* 5th ed. New York, McGraw-Hill, 1983, chap 60.

3. CLEAVER JE: DNA damage, repair systems and human hypersensitive diseases. *J Environ Pathol Toxicol* 3:53, 1980.

4. CLEAVER JE: Repair processes for photochemical damage in mammalian cells, in Lett JT, Adler H, Zelle M (eds): *Advances in Radiation Biology.* New York, Academic, 1974, vol 4, p 1.

5. CLEAVER JE: Defective repair replication of DNA in xeroderma pigmentosum. *Nature* 218:652, 1968.

6. CLEAVER JE, BOOTSMA D: Xeroderma pigmentosum: Biochemical and genetic characteristics. *Annu Rev Genet* 9:19, 1975.

7. CLEAVER JE: DNA damage and repair in light-sensitive human skin disease. *J Invest Dermatol* 54:181, 1970.

8. ROOK A, WILKINSON DS, EBLING FJG (eds): *Textbook of Dermatology.* Oxford, Blackwell, 1968, vol 1.

9. PAINTER RB, YOUNG B: Radiosensitivity in ataxia telangiectasia: A new explanation. *Proc Natl Acad Sci USA* 77:7315, 1980.

10. PATERSON MC, SMITH BP, LOHMAN PHM, ANDERSON AK, FISHMAN L: Defective excision repair of γ-ray-damaged DNA in human (ataxia-telangiectasia) fibroblasts. *Nature* 260:444, 1976.

11. TAYLOR AMR, HARNDEN DG, ARLETT CF, HARCOURT SA, LEHMANN AR, STEVENS S, BRIDGES BA: Ataxia telangiectasia: A human mutation with abnormal radiation sensitivity. *Nature* 258:427, 1975.

12. LEHMANN AR, KIRK-BELL S, MAYNE L: Abnormal kinetics of DNA synthesis in ultraviolet light irradiated cells from patients with Cockayne's syndrome. *Cancer Res* 3:4237, 1979.

13. CLEAVER JE: DNA repair with purines and pyrimidines in radiation- and carcinogen-damaged normal and xeroderma pigmentosum human cells. *Cancer Res* 33:362, 1973.

14. CLEAVER JE: Photoreactivation: A radiation repair mechanism absent from mammalian cells. *Biochem Biophys Res Commun* 24:569, 1966.

15. SUTHERLAND BM: Photoreactivating enzyme from human leukocytes. *Nature* 248:109, 1974.

16. SUTHERLAND BM, RICE M, WAGNER EK: Xeroderma pigmentosum cells contain low levels of photoreactivating enzyme. *Proc Natl Acad Sci USA* 72:103, 1975.

17. SUTHERLAND JC, SUTHERLAND BM: Human photoreactivating enzyme. Action spectrum and safelight conditions. *Biophys J* 15:435, 1975.

18. MORTELMANS K, CLEAVER JE, FRIEDBERG EC, PATERSON MC, SMITH BP, THOMAS GH: Photoreactivation of thymine dimers in UV-irradiated human cells: Unique dependence on culture conditions. *Mutat Res* 44:433, 1977.

19. SUTHERLAND BM, HARBER LC, KOCHEVAR IE: Pyrimidine dimer formation and repair in human skin. *Cancer Res* 40:3181, 1980.

20. PARK SD, CLEAVER JE: Postreplication repair: Questions of its definition and possible alteration in xeroderma pigmentosum cell strains. *Proc Natl Acad Sci USA* 76:3927, 1979.

21. ROBBINS JH, KRAEMER KH, LUTZNER MA, FESTOFF BW, COON HG: Xeroderma pigmentosum. An inherited disease with sun sensitivity, multiple cutaneous neoplasms, and abnormal DNA repair. *Ann Intern Med* 80:221, 1974.

22. MCKUSICK VA: *Mendelian Inheritance in Man. Catalogs of Autosomal Dominant, Autosomal Recessive, and X-Linked Phenotypes,* 7th ed. Baltimore, Johns Hopkins Press, 1986.

23. HEBRA F, KAPOSI M: *On Diseases of the Skin, Including the Exanthemata.* Tay W (trans). London, New Sydenham Society, 1874, vol 3, p 252.

24. NEISSER A: Ueber das "Xeroderma pigmentosum" (Kaposi) Lioderma essentailis cum melanosi et telangiectasia. *Viertel Dermatol Syphil* 47–62, 1883.

25. DE SANCTIS C, CACCHIONE A: L'idiozia xerodermica. *Riv Sper Freniatr* 56:269, 1932.

26. EPSTEIN JH, FUKUYAMA K, REED WB, et al: Defect in DNA synthesis in skin of patients with xeroderma pigmentosum demonstrated in vivo. *Science* 168:1477, 1970.

27. BURK PG, LUTZNER MA, CLARKE DD, ROBBINS JH: Ultraviolet-stimulated thymidine incorporation in xeroderma pigmentosum lymphocytes. *J Lab Clin Med* 77:759, 1971.

28. CLEAVER JE: Xeroderma pigmentosum: Variants with normal DNA repair and normal sensitivity to ultraviolet light. *J Invest Dermatol* 58:124, 1972.

29. CLEAVER JE, ARUTYUNYAN RM, SARKISIAN T, KAUFMANN WK, GREENE AE, CORIELL L: Similar defects in DNA repair and replication in the pigmented xerodermoid and the xeroderma pigmentosum variants. *Carcinogenesis* 1:647, 1980.

30. LEHMANN AR, KIRK-BELL S, ARLETT CF, PATERSON MC, LOHMAN PHM, DE WEERD-KASTELEIN EA, BOOTSMA D: Xeroderma pigmentosum cells with normal levels of excision repair have a defect in DNA synthesis after UV-irradiation. *Proc Natl Acad Sci USA* 72:219, 1975.

31. DE WEERD-KASTELEIN EA, KLEIJZER W, BOOTSMA D: Genetic heterogeneity of xeroderma pigmentosum demonstrated by somatic cell hybridization. *Nature* 238:80, 1972.

32. KRAEMER KH, LEE MM, SCOTTO J: Xeroderma pigmentosum: Cutaneous, ocular and neurologic abnormalities in 830 published cases. *Arch Dermatol* 123:241, 1987.

33. RAMSAY CA, GIANNELLI F: The erythemal action spectrum and deoxyribonucleic acid repair synthesis in xeroderma pigmentosum. *Br J Dermatol* 92:49, 1975.

34. JUNG EG: New form of molecular defect in xeroderma pigmentosum. *Nature* 228:361, 1970.

35. KRAEMER KH, LEE MM, SCOTTO J: DNA repair protects against cutaneous and internal neoplasia: Evidence from xeroderma pigmentosum. *Carcinogenesis* 5:511, 1984.

36. MIMAKI T, ITOH N, ABE J, TAGAWA T, SATO K, YABUUCHI H, TAKEBE H: Neurological manifestations of xeroderma pigmentosum. *Ann Neurol* 20:70, 1986.

37. ROYTTA M, ANTTINEN A: Xeroderma pigmentosum with neurological abnormalities. A clinical and neuropathological study. *Acta Neurol Scand* 73:191, 1986.

38. ANDREWS AD, BARRETT SF, ROBBINS JH: Xeroderma pigmentosum neurological abnormalities correlate with colony-forming ability after ultraviolet radiation. *Pro Natl Acad Sci USA* 75:1984, 1978.

39. MOSHELL AN, GANGES MB, LUTZNER MA, et al: A new patient with both xeroderma pigmentosum and Cockayne syndrome establishes the new xeroderma pigmentosum complementation group H, in Friedberg E, Bridges B (eds): *Cellular Responses to DNA Damage.* New York, AR Liss, 1983, p 209.

40. SCHMICKEL RD, CHU EHY, TROSKO JE, CHANG CC: Cockayne syndrome: A cellular sensitivity to ultraviolet light. *Pediatrics* 60:135, 1977.

41. WADE MH, CHU EHY: Effects of DNA damaging agents on cultured fibroblasts derived from patients with Cockayne syndrome. *Mutat Res* 59:49, 1979.

42. CHANG WS, TARONE RE, ANDREWS AD, WHANG-PENG JS, ROBBINS JH: Ultraviolet light-induced sister chromatid exchanges in xeroderma pigmentosum and in Cockayne syndrome lymphocyte cell lines. *Cancer Res* 38:1601, 1978.

43. AHMED FE, SETLOW RB: Excision repair in ataxia telangiectasia, Fanconi's anemia, Cockayne syndrome, and Bloom's syndrome after treatment with ultraviolet radiation and *N*-acetoxy-2-acetylaminofluorene. *Biochim Biophys Acta* 521:805, 1978.

44. PUIG L, MARTI R, MATIAS-GUIU X, LECHA M, GUIX M: Gastric adenocarcinoma in a patient with xeroderma pigmentosum. *Br J Dermatol* 113:632, 1985.

45. TAKEBE H, TATSUMI K, SATOH Y: DNA repair and its possible involvement in the origin of multiple cancer. *Jpn J Clin Oncol* 15(suppl 1):299, 1985.

46. OKUI T, FUJIWARA Y: Defective repair of tryptophan pyrolysate (Trp P-1 and Trp P-2) and aflatoxin B1 damage in xeroderma pigmentosum cells. *J Radiat Res* 24:356, 1983.

47. PROTIC-SABLJIC M, WHYTE DB, KRAEMER KH: Hypersensitivity of xeroderma pigmentosum cells to dietary carcinogens. *Mutat Res* 145:89, 1985.

48. KRAEMER KH, SLOR H: Xeroderma pigmentosum. *Clin Dermatol* 3:33, 1985.

49. LYNCH HT, ANDERSON DE, SMITH JL, HOWELL JB, KRUSH AJ: Xeroderma pigmentosum, malignant melanoma, and congenital ichthyosis. *Arch Dermatol* 96:625, 1967.

50. SETLOW RB: The wavelengths in sunlight effective in producing skin cancer: A theoretical analysis. *Proc Natl Acad Sci USA* 71:3363, 1974.

51. EPSTEIN JH: Ultraviolet carcinogenesis. *Photophysiology* 5:235, 1970.

52. BLUM HF: *Carcinogenesis by Ultraviolet Light.* Princeton, NJ, Princeton University Press, 1959.

53. HARM W: Use of an *E. coli uvr rec* mutant for monitoring the germicidal activity of sunlight. *Radiat Res* 39:517, 1969.

54. TROSKO JE, KRAUSE D, ISOUN M: Sunlight-induced pyrimidine dimers in human cells *in vitro. Nature* 228:358, 1970.

55. ZIMMER KG: *Studies on Quantitative Radiation Biology* (Griffith HD, trans). New York, Hafner, 1961.

56. ROTHMAN RH, SETLOW RB: An action spectrum for cell killing and pyrimidine dimer formation in Chinese hamster V-79 cells. *Photochem Photobiol* 29:57, 1979.

57. TODD P, COOHILL TP, MAHONEY JA: Responses of cultured Chinese hamster cells to ultraviolet light of different wavelengths. *Radiat Res* 35:390, 1968.

58. KANTOR GJ, SUTHERLAND JC, SETLOW RB: Action spectra for killing nondividing normal human and xeroderma pigmentosum cells. *Photochem Photobiol* 31:459, 1980.

59. CHU EHY: Effects of ultraviolet radiation on mammalian cells. I. Induction of chromosome aberrations. *Mutat Res* 2:75, 1965.

60. ICHIHASHI M, RAMSAY CA: The action spectrum and dose response studies of unscheduled DNA synthesis in normal human fibroblasts. *Photochem Photobiol* 23:103, 1975.

61. SMITH KC: An isomer of the cyclobutane-type thymine dimer produced in the presence of adenine. *Biochem Biophys Res Commun* 25:426, 1966.

62. PATHAK MA, KRAMER DM, GUNGERICH U: Formation of thymine dimers in mammalian skin by ultraviolet radiation *in vivo. Photochem Photobiol* 15:177, 1972.

63. SETLOW RB: Molecular changes responsible for ultraviolet inactivation of the biological activity of NDA, in Pavan C, Chagas C, Frota-Pessoa O,

Caldas LR (eds): *Mammalian Cytogenetics and Related Problems in Radiology*. New York, Macmillan, 1964, p 379.

64. SETLOW RB: Cyclobutane-type pyrimidine dimers in polynucleotides. *Science* 153:379, 1966.

65. BRASH DE, HASELTINE WA: UV-induced mutation hotspots occur at DNA damage hotspots. *Nature* 298:189, 1982.

66. BRASH DE, SEETHARAM S, KRAEMER KH, SEIDMAN MM, BREDBERG A: Photoproduct frequency is not the major determinant of UV base substitution hotspots or coldspots in human cells. *Proc Natl Acad Sci USA* 84:3782, 1987.

67. SITH KC, HANAWALT PC: *Molecular Photobiology: Inactivation and Recovery*. New York, Academic, 1969.

68. BLACK HS, LO WB: Formation of a carcinogen in human skin irradiated with ultraviolet light. *Nature* 234:306, 1971.

69. BROWN AJ, FICKEL TH, CLEAVER JE, LOHMAN PHM, WADE MH, WATERS R: Overlapping pathways for repair of damage from ultraviolet light and chemical carcinogens in human fibroblasts. *Cancer Res* 39:2522, 1979.

70. HARRIS M: *Cell Culture and Somatic Variation*. New York, Holt, 1964.

71. CLEAVER JE: DNA repair deficiencies and cellular senescence are unrelated in xeroderma pigmentosum cell lines. *Mech Ageing Dev* 27:189, 1984.

72. WALTIMO O, IIVANAINEN M, HOKKANEN E: Xeroderma pigmentosum with neurological manifestations. Family studies of two affected sisters, one of them with a chromosome abnormality, and report of one separate case. *Acta Neurol Scand* 43:(suppl 31)66, 1967.

73. GERMAN J: Genes which increase chromosomal instability in somatic cells and predispose to cancer. *Prog Med Genet* 8:61, 1972.

74. STEFANINI M, KLEIJER W, DALPRA L, ELLI R, PORRO MN, NICOLETTI B, NUZZO F: Differences in the levels of UV repair and in clinical symptoms in two sibs affected by xeroderma pigmentosum. *Hum Genet* 634:1, 1980.

75. KATO H: Spontaneous sister chromatid exchanges detected by a BUdR-labeling method. *Nature* 251:70, 1974.

76. PERRY P, WOLFF S: New Giemsa method for the differential staining of sister chromatids. *Nature* 251:156, 1974.

77. WOLFF S, BODYCOTE J, THOMAS GH, CLEAVER JE: Sister chromatid exchange in xeroderma pigmentosum cells that are defective in DNA excision repair or post-replication repair. *Genetics* 81:349, 1975.

78. WOLFF S, RODIN B, CLEAVER JE: Sister chromatid exchanges induced by mutagenic carcinogens in normal and xeroderma pigmentosum cells. *Nature* 265:347, 1977.

79. DE WEERD-KASTELEIN EA, KEIJZER W, RAINALDI G, BOOTSMA D: Induction of sister chromatid exchanges in xeroderma pigmentosum cells after exposure to ultraviolet light. *Mutat Res* 45:253, 1977.

80. PARRINGTON JM, DELHANTY JDA, BADEN HP: Unscheduled DNA synthesis, UV-induced chromosome aberrations and SV40 transformation in cultured cells from xeroderma pigmentosum. *Ann Hum Genet* 35:149, 1971.

81. SASAKI MS: DNA repair capacity and susceptibility to chromosome breakage in xeroderma pigmentosum cells. *Mutat Res* 20:41, 1973.

82. CLEAVER JE: DNA repair and radiation sensitivity in human (xeroderma pigmentosum) cells. *Int J Radiat Biol* 18:557, 1970.

83. GOLDSTEIN S: The role of DNA repair in aging and cultured fibroblasts from xeroderma pigmentosum and normals. *Proc Soc Exp Biol Med* 137:730, 1971.

84. TAKEBE H, FURUYAMA JI, MIKI Y, KONDO S: High sensitivity of xeroderma pigmentosum cells to the carcinogen 4-nitroquinoline-1-oxide. *Mutat Res*

85. STICH HF, SAN RHC, KAWAZOE Y: Increased sensitivity of xeroderma pigmentosum cells to some chemical carcinogens and mutagens. *Mutat Res* 17:127, 1973.

86. HOFFMAN ME, MENIGHINI R: Action of hydrogen perioxide on human fibroblasts in culture. *Photochem Photobiol* 30:151, 1979.

87. STICH HF, SAN RHC: DNA repair synthesis and survival of repair deficient human cells exposed to the K-region epoxide of benz(a)anthracene. *Proc Soc Exp Biol Med* 142:155, 1973.

88. MAHER VM, BIRCH N, OTTO JR, MCCORMICK JJ: Cytotoxicity of carcinogenic aromatic amides in normal and xeroderma pigmentosum fibroblasts with different DNA repair capabilities. *J Natl Cancer Inst* 54:1287, 1975.

89. ARLETT CF, HARCOURT SA, BROUGHTON BC: The influence of caffeine on cell survival in excision proficient and excision deficient xeroderma pigmentosum and normal human cell strains following ultraviolet light irradiation. *Mutat Res* 33:341, 1975.

90. PAINTER RB: Effect of caffeine on DNA synthesis in irradiated and unirradiated mammalian cells. *J Mol Biol* 143:289, 1980.

91. ZAVADOVA Z: Host-cell repair of vaccinia virus and of double stranded RNA of encephalomyocarditis virus. *Nature New Biol* 233:123, 1971.

92. LYTLE CD, AARONSON SA, HARVEY E: Host-cell reactivation in mammalian cells. II. Survival by herpes simplex virus and vaccinia virus in normal

93. RABSON AS, TYRRELL SA, LEGALLAIS FY: Growth of ultraviolet-damaged herpes virus in xeroderma pigmentosum cells. *Proc Soc Exp Biol Med* 132:802, 1969.

94. DAY RS III: Studies on repair of adenovirus 2 by human fibroblasts using normal, xeroderma pigmentosum, and xerodema pigmentosum heterozygous strains. *Cancer Res* 34:1965, 1974.

95. DAY RS III: Cellular reactivation of ultraviolet-irradiated human adenovirus 2 in normal and xeroderma pigmentosum fibroblasts. *Photochem Photobiol* 19:9, 1974.

96. AARONSON SA, LYTLE CD: Decreased host-cell reactivation of irradiated SV40 virus in xeroderma pigmentosum. *Nature* 228:359, 1970.

97. HENDERSON EE: Host cell reactivation of Epstein-Barr virus in normal and repair defective leukocytes. *Cancer Res* 38:3256, 1978.

98. HENDERSON EE, LONG WK: Host cell reactivation of UV- and X-ray damaged herpes simplex virus by Epstein-Barr (EBV)-transformed lymphoblastoid cells. *Virology* 115:237, 1981.

99. DAY RS III: Xeroderma pigmentosum variants have decreased repair of UV-damaged DNA. *Nature* 253:748, 1975.

100. DAY RS III, KRAEMER KH, ROBBINS JH: Complementing xeroderma pigmentosum fibroblasts restore biological activity to UV damaged DNA. *Mutat Res* 28:251, 1975.

101. PROTIC-SABLJIC M, KRAEMER KH: One pyrimidine dimer inactivates expression of a transfected gene in xeroderma pigmentosum cells. *Proc Natl Acad Sci USA* 82:6622, 1985.

102. PROTIC-SABLJIC M, KRAEMER KH: Reduced repair of non-dimer photoproducts in a gene transfected into xeroderma pigmentosum cells. *Photochem Photobiol* 43:509, 1986.

103. KELLEY WN, WYNGAARDEN JB: The Lesch-Nyhan syndrome, in Stanbury JB, Wyngaarden, JB, Fredrickson DS, Goldstein JL, Brown MS (eds): *The Metabolic Basis of Inherited Disease*, 5th ed. New York, McGraw-Hill, 1983, p 1115.

104. MAHER VM, OUELETTE LM, CURREN RD, MCCORMICK JJ: Frequency of ultraviolet light-induced mutations is higher in xeroderma pigmentosum variant cells. *Nature* 261:593, 1976.

105. MAHER VM, DORNEY DJ, MENDRALA AL, KONZE-THOMAS B, MCCORMICK JJ: DNA excision-repair processes in human cells can eliminate the cytotoxic and mutagenic consequences of ultraviolet irradiation. *Mutat Res* 62:311, 1979.

106. GLOVER TW, CHANG CC, TROSKO JE, LI SS: Ultraviolet light induction of diphtheria toxin-resistant mutants of normal and xeroderma pigmentosum human fibroblasts. *Proc Natl Acad Sci USA* 76:3982, 1979.

107. PATTON JD, ROWAN LA, MENDRALA AL, HOWELL JN, MAHER VM, MCCORMICK JJ: Xeroderma pigmentosum fibroblasts including cells from XP variants are abnormally sensitive to the mutagenic and cytotoxic action of broad spectrum simulated sunlight. *Photochem Photobiol* 39:37, 1984.

108. DELUCA JG, KADEN DA, KOMIVES EA, THILLY WG: Mutation of xeroderma pigmentosum lymphoblasts by far-ultraviolet light. *Mutat Res* 128:47, 1984.

109. MCCORMICK JJ, KATELEY-KOHLER S, WATANABE M, MAHER VM: Abnormal sensitivity of human fibroblasts from xeroderma pigmentosum variants to transformation to anchorage independence by ultraviolet radiation. *Cancer Res* 46:489, 1986.

110. BREDBERG A, KRAEMER KH, SEIDMAN M: Restricted ultraviolet mutational spectrum in a shuttle vector propagated in xeroderma pigmentosum cells. *Proc Natl Acad Sci USA* 83:8273, 1986.

111. PROTIC-SABLJIC M, TUTEJA N, MUNSON PJ, HAUSER J, KRAEMER KH, DIXON K: UV light-induced cyclobutane dimers are mutagenic in mammalian cells. *Mol Cell Biol* 6:3349, 1986.

112. CLEAVER JE: Xeroderma pigmentosum: A human disease in which an initial stage of DNA repair is defective. *Proc Natl Acad Sci USA* 63:428, 1969.

113. CLEAVER JE: DNA repair and its coupling to DNA replication in eukaryotic cells. *Biochim Biophys Acta* 516:489, 1978.

114. MCGHEE JD, FELSENFELD G: Nucleosome structure. *Annu Rev Biochem* 49:115, 1980.

115. BODELL WJ: Nonuniform distribution of DNA repair in chromatin after treatment with methylmethane sulfonate. *Nucleic Acids Res* 4:2619, 1977.

116. CLEAVER JE: Nucleosome structure controls rates of excision repair in DNA of human cells. *Nature* 270:451, 1977.

117. SMERDON MJ, TLSTY TD, LIEBERMAN MW: Distribution of ultraviolet-induced DNA repair synthesis in nuclease sensitive and resistant regions of human chromatin. *Biochemistry* 17:2377, 1978.

118. STRAUSS B, TATSUMI K, KARRAN P, HIGGINS NP, BEN-ASHER E, ALTAMIRANO-DIMAS M, ROSENBLATT L, BOSE K: Mechanisms of DNA excision repair in human cells, in *Polycyclic Hydrocarbons and Cancer*.

Gelboin HV, Ts'o POP (eds): New York, Academic, 1978, p 177.

119. HANAWALT PC, COOPER PK, GANESAN AK, SMITH CA; DNA repair in bacteria and mammalian cells. *Annu Rev Biochem* 48:783, 1979.

120. DAY RS III, ZIOLKOWSKI CH, SCUDIERO DA, MEYER A, MATTERN MR: Human tumor cell strains defective in the repair of alkylation damage. *Carcinogenesis* 1:21, 1980.

121. HASELTINE WA, GORDON LK, LINDAN CP, GRAFSTROM RH, SHAPER NL, GROSSMAN L: Cleavage of pyrimidine dimers in specific DNA sequences by a pyrimidine dimer DNA glycosylase of *M. luteus*. *Nature* 285:634, 1980.

122. DEMPLE B, LINN S: DNA N-glycosylases and UV repair. *Nature* 287:203, 1980.

123. SANCAR A, RUPP WD: A novel repair enzyme: UVRABC excision nuclease of Escherichia coli cuts a DNA strand on both sides of the damaged region. *Cell* 33:249, 1983.

124. HUBSCHER U, KUENZLE CC, SPADARI S: Functional roles of DNA polymerases β and α. *Proc Natl Acad Sci USA* 76:2316, 1979.

125. DRESLER SL, FRATTINI MG: DNA replication and UV-induced DNA repair synthesis in human fibroblasts are much less sensitive than DNA polymerase alpha to inhibition of butylphenyl-deoxyguanosine triphosphate. *Nucleic Acids Res* 14:7093, 1986.

126. CIARROCCHI G, JOSE JG, LINN S: Further characterization of a cell-free system for measuring replicative and repair DNA synthesis with cultured human fibroblasts and evidence for the involvement of DNA polymerase α in DNA repair. *Nucleic Acids Res* 7:1205, 1979.

127. WILLIS AE, LINDAHL T: DNA ligase I deficiency in Bloom's syndrome. *Nature* 325:357, 1987.

128. CHAN JYH, BECKER FF, GERMAN J, RAY JH: Altered DNA ligase I activity in Bloom's syndrome cells. *Nature* 325:357, 1987.

129. CLEAVER JE: Methods for studying repair of DNA damaged by physical and chemical carcinogens, in Busch H (ed): *Methods in Cancer Research*. New York, Academic, 1975, vol II, p 123.

130. DJORDJEVIC B, TOLMACH LJ: Responses of synchronous population of HeLa cells to ultraviolet irradiation at selected stages of the generation cycle. *Radiat Res* 32:327, 1967.

131. PETTIJOHN D, HANAWALT PC: Evidence for repair-replication of ultraviolet damaged DNA in bacteria. *J Mol Biol* 9:395, 1964.

132. REGAN JD, SETLOW RB, LEY RD: Normal and defective repair of damaged DNA in human cells: A sensitive assay utilizing the photolysis of bromodeoxyuridine. *Proc Natl Acad Sci USA* 68:708, 1971.

133. EDENBERG H, HANAWALT PC: Size of repair patches in the DNA of ultraviolet-irradiated HeLa cells. *Biochim Biophys Acta* 272:361, 1972.

134. SETLOW RB, REGAN JD, GERMAN J, CARRIER WL: Evidence that xeroderma pigmentosum cells do not perform the first step in the repair of ultraviolet damage to their DNA. *Proc Natl Acad Sci USA* 64:1035, 1969.

135. CLEAVER JE: Sedimentation of DNA from human fibroblasts irradiated with ultraviolet light: Possible detection of excision breaks in normal and repair-deficient xeroderma pigmentosum cells. *Radiat Res* 57:207, 1974.

136. CLEAVER JE, THOMAS GH, TROSKO JE, LETT JT: Excision repair (dimer excision, strand breakage and repair replication) in primary cultures of eukaryotic (bovine) cells. *Exp Cell Res* 74:67, 1972.

137. KLEIJZER WJ, HOEKSEMA JL, SLUYTER ML, BOOTSMA D: Effects of inhibitors on repair of DNA in normal human and xeroderma pigmentosum cells after exposure to X rays and ultraviolet irradiation. *Mutat Res* 17:385, 1973.

138. BEN-HUR E, BEN-ISHAI R: DNA repair in ultraviolet light irradiated HeLa cells and its reversible inhibition by hydroxyurea. *Photochem Photobiol* 13:337, 1971.

139. FORNACE AJ JR, KOHN KW, KANN HE JR: DNA single-stranded breaks during repair of UV damage in human fibroblasts and abnormalities of repair in xeroderma pigmentosum. *Proc Natl Acad Sci USA* 73:39, 1976.

140. DINGMAN CW, KAKUNAGA T: DNA strand breaking and rejoining in response to ultraviolet light in normal human and xeroderma pigmentosum cells. *Int J Radiat Biol* 30:55, 1976.

141. DUNN WC, REGAN JD: Inhibition of DNA excision repair in human cells by arabinofuranosyl cytosine: Effects on normal and xeroderma pigmentosum cells. *Mol Pharmacol* 15:367, 1976.

142. BOOTSMA D, MULDER MP, POT F, COHEN JA: Different inherited levels of DNA repair replication in xeroderma pigmentosum cell strains after exposure to ultraviolet irradiation. *Mutat Res* 9:507, 1970.

143. ZELLE B, LOHMAN PHM: Repair of UV-endonuclease-susceptible sites in the 7 complementation groups of xeroderma pigmentosum A through G. *Mutat Res* 62:363, 1979.

144. DUPUY JM, LAFFORET D, RACHMAN F: Xeroderma pigmentosum with liver involvement. *Helv Paediatr Acta* 29:213, 1975.

145. HARM W, RUPERT CS, HARM H: Photoenzymatic repair of DNA. I. Investigation of the reaction by flash illumination, in Beers RF Jr, Herriott RM, Tilghman RC (eds): *Molecular and Cellular Repair Processes*. Baltimore, Johns Hopkins University Press, 1972, p 53.

146. COOK JS: Photoenzymatic repair in animal cells, in Beers RF Jr, Herriott RM, Tilghman RC (eds): *Molecular and Cellular Repair Processes*. Baltimore, Johns Hopkins University Press, 1972, p 79.

147. COOK JS, MCGRATH JR: Photoreactivating-enzyme activity in Metazoa. *Proc Natl Acad Sci USA* 58:1359, 1967.

148. LYTLE CD, BENANE SG, STAFFORD JE: Host cell reactivation in mammalian cells. V. Photoreactivation studies with herpes virus in marsupial and human cells. *Photochem Photobiol* 23:331, 1975.

149. HARM H: Damage and repair in mammalian cells after exposure to nonionizing radiations. III. Ultraviolet and visible light irradiation of cells of placental mammals, including humans, and determination of photorepairable damage *in vitro*. *Mutat Res* 69:167, 1980.

150. CLEAVER JE: Repair of alkylation damage in ultraviolet sensitive (xeroderma pigmentosum) human cells. *Mutat Res* 12:453, 1971.

151. KLEIJER WJ, LOHMAN PHM, MULDER MP, BOOTSMA D: Repair of X-ray damage in DNA of cultivated cells from patients having xeroderma pigmentosum. *Mutat Res* 9:517, 1970.

152. SETLOW RB, REGAN JD: Defective repair of N-acetoxy-2-acetylaminofluorene-induced lesions in the DNA of xeroderma pigmentosum cells. *Biochem Biophys Res Commun* 16:1019, 1972.

153. STICH HF, SAN RHC, MILLER JA, MILLER EC: Various levels of DNA repair synthesis in xeroderma pigmentosum cells exposed to the carcinogens N-hydroxy and N-acetoxy-2-acetyl-aminofluorene. *Nature* 238:9, 1972.

154. REGAN JD, SETLOW RB: Two forms of repair in the DNA of human cells damaged by chemical carcinogens and mutagens. *Cancer Res* 34:3318, 1974.

155. PAINTER RB, YOUNG BR: Repair replication in mammalian cells after X-irradiation. *Mutat Res* 14:225, 1972.

156. MILLER EC, MILLER JA: Biochemical mechanisms of chemical carcinogenesis, in Busch H (ed): *The Molecular Biology of Cancer*. New York, Academic, 1974, p 377.

157. BODELL WJ, SINGER B, THOMAS GH, CLEAVER JE: Evidence for removal at different rates of O-ethylphosphotriesters in two human fibroblast cell lines. *Nucleic Acids Res* 6:2819, 1979.

158. SINGER B, BRENT TP: Human lymphoblasts contain glycosylase activity excising N-3 and N-7 methyl and ethyl purines but not O-6-alkylguanine or 1-alkylguanine. *Proc Natl Acad Sci USA* 78:856, 1981.

159. KRAEMER KH, COON HG, PETTIGA RA, BARRETT SF, RASH AE, ROBBINS JH: Genetic heterogeneity in xeroderma pigmentosum. Complementation groups and their relationship to DNA repair rates. *Proc Natl Acad Sci USA* 72:59, 1975.

160. DE WEERD-KASTELEIN DA, KEIJZER W, BOOTSMA D: A third complementation group in xeroderma pigmentosum. *Mutat Res* 22:87, 1974.

161. KRAEMER KH, DE WEERD-KASTELEIN EA, ROBBINS JH, KEIJZER W, BARRETT SF, PETINGA RA, BOOTSMA D: Five complementation groups in xeroderma pigmentosum. *Mutat Res* 33:327, 1975.

162. ARASE S, KOZUKA T, TANAKA K, IKENAGA M, TAKEBE H: A sixth complementation group in xeroderma pigmentosum. *Mutat Res* 59:143, 1979.

163. KEIJZER W, JASPERS NGJ, ABRAHAMS PJ, TAYLOR AMR, ARLETT CF, ZELLE B, TAKEBE H, KANMONT PDS, BOOTSMA D: A seventh complementation group in excision deficient xeroderma pigmentosum. *Mutat Res* 62:183, 1979.

164. HAYNES RH: General discussion. *Radiat Res Suppl* 6:232, 1966.

165. WALDSTEIN EA, PELLER S, SETLOW RB: UV-endonuclease from calf thymus with specificity towards pyrimidine dimers in DNA. *Proc Natl Acad Sci USA* 76:3746, 1978.

166. GRUENERT DC, CLEAVER JE: Repair of ultraviolet damage in human cells also exposed to agents that cause strand breaks, crosslinks, monoadducts and alkylations. *Chem Biol Interact* 33:153, 1981.

167. PARK SD, CHOI KH, HONG SW, CLEAVER JE: Inhibition of excision repair of ultraviolet damage in human cells by exposure to methylmethane sulfonate. *Mutat Res* 82:365, 1981.

168. THOMPSON LH, BUSCH DB, BROOKMAN K, MOONEY CL, GLASER DA: Genetic diversity of UV-sensitive DNA repair mutants of Chinese hamster ovary cells. *Proc Natl Acad Sci USA* 78:3734, 1981.

169. HORI TA, SHIOMI T, SATO K: Human chromosome 13 compensates a DNA repair defect in UV sensitive cells by mouse-human cell by hybridization. *Proc Natl Acad Sci USA* 80:5655, 1983.

170. FUJIWARA Y, TATSUMI M, SASAKI MS: Cross-link repair in human cells and its possible defect in Fanconi's anemia cells. *J Mol Biol* 113:635, 1977.

171. STEFANINI H, KEIJZER W, WESTERVELD A, BOOTSMA D: Interspecies complementation analysis of xeroderma pigmentosum and UV-sensitive Chinese hamster cells. *Exp Cell Res* 161:373, 1985.

172. THOMPSON LH, MOONEY CL, BURKHART-SCHULTZ K, CARRANO AV, SICI-

LIANO MJ: Correction of a nucleotide-excision repair mutation by human chromosome 19 in hamster-human hybrid cells. *Somat Cell Genet* 11:87, 1985.

173. ZDZIENICKA MZ, ROZA L, WESTERVELD A, BOOTSMA D, SIMONS JWIM: Biological and biochemical consequences of the human *ERCC-1* repair gene after transfection into a repair-deficient CHO cell line. *Mutat Res* 183:69, 1987.

174. RUBIN JS, JOYNER AL, BERNSTEIN A, WHITEMORE GF: Molecular identification of a human DNA repair gene following DNA-mediated gene transfer. *Nature* 306:206, 1983.

175. WESTERVELD A, HOEIJMAKERS JHJ, VAN DUIN M, DE VIT J, OKIJK H, PASTINK A, WOOD RD, BOOTSMA D: Molecular cloning of a human DNA repair gene. *Nature* 310:425, 1983.

176. VAN DUIN M, DE WIT J, ODIJK H, WESTERVELD A, YASUI A, KOKEN MHM, HOEIJMAKERS JHJ, BOOTSMA D: Molecular characterization of the human excision repair gene *ERCC1*: cDNA cloning and amino acid homology with the yeast DNA repair gene *RAD10*. *Cell* 44:913, 1986.

177. LEHMANN AR: Use of recombinant techniques in cloning DNA repair and in the study of mutagenesis in mammalian cells. *Mutat Res* 150:61, 1985.

178. ROYER-POKORA B, HASELTINE WA: Isolation of UV-resistant revertants from a xeroderma pigmentosum group A line. *Nature* 311:390, 1984.

179. SCHULTZ RA, BARBIS DP, FRIEDBERG EC: Studies on gene transfer and reversion to UV resistance in xeroderma pigmentosum cells. *Somatic Cell Genet* 11:617, 1985.

180. TAKANO T, NODA M, TAMURA TA: Transfection of cells from a xeroderma pigmentosum patient with normal human DNA converts UV resistance. *Nature* 269:270, 1982.

181. KARENTZ D, CLEAVER JE: Repair deficient xeroderma pigmentosum cells made UV light resistant by fusion with X-ray-inactivated Chinese hamster cells. *Mol Cell Biol* 6:3428, 1986.

182. CLEAVER JE, CORTES F, LUTZE LH, MORGAN WF, PLAYER AN, MITCHELL DL: Unique DNA repair properties in a xeroderma pigmentosum revertant. *Mol Cell Biol*, 7:3353, 1987.

183. REED WB, MAY SB, NICKEL WR: Xeroderma pigmentosum with neurological complications: The deSanctis Cacchione syndrome. *Arch Dermatol* 91:224, 1965.

184. REED WB, LANDING B, SUGARMAN G, CLEAVER JE, MELNYK J: Xeroderma pigmentosum. Clinical and laboratory investigation of its defect. *JAMA* 207:2073, 1969.

185. THRUSH DC, HOLTI G, BRADLEY WG, CAMPBELL MI, WALTON JN: Neurological manifestations of xeroderma pigmentosum in two siblings. *J Neurol Sci* 22:91, 1974.

186. CLEAVER JE, ZELLE B, HASHEM N, GERMAN J: Xeroderma pigmentosum in Egypt. II. Epidemiology, clinical symptoms and molecular biology. *J Invest Dermatol* 77:96, 1981.

187. THILLMANN HW, WITTE J: Correlation of the colony-forming abilities of xeroderma pigmentosum fibroblasts with repair-specific DNA incision reactions catalyzed by cell-free extracts. *Arch Toxicol* 44:197, 1980.

188. KUHNLEIN U, PENHOET EE, LINN S: An altered apurinic endonuclease activity in group A and group D xeroderma pigmentosum fibroblasts. *Proc Natl Acad Sci USA* 73:1169, 1976.

189. DE WEERD-KASTELEIN EA, KEIJZER W, SABOUR M, PARKINGTON JM, BOOTSMA D: A xeroderma pigmentosum patient having a high residual activity of unscheduled DNA synthesis after UV is assigned to complementation group A. *Mutat Res* 37:307, 1976.

190. KRAEMER KH: Xeroderma pigmentosum, in Demis DJ, Dobson RL, McGuire J (eds): *Clinical Dermatology*. 4:unit 19-7, 1980, p 1.

191. MANSBRIDGE JN, HANAWALT PC: Domain-limited repair of DNA in ultraviolet irradiated fibroblasts from xeroderma pigmentosum complementation group C, in Friedberg EC, Bridges BR (eds): *Cellular Responses to DNA Damage*. New York, AR Liss, 1983, p 195.

192. KARENTZ D, CLEAVER JE: Excision repair in xeroderma pigmentosum group C but not group D is clustered in a small fraction of the total genome. *Mutat Res* 165:165, 1986.

193. CLEAVER JE: DNA repair in human xeroderma pigmentosum group C cells involves a different distribution of damaged sites in confluent and growing cells. *Nucleic Acids Res* 14:8155, 1986.

194. HANANIAN J, CLEAVER JE: Xeroderma pigmentosum exhibiting neurological disorders and systemic lupus erythematosus. *Clin Genet* 17:39, 1980.

195. PAWSEY SA, MAGNUS IA, RAMSAY CA, BENSON PF, GIANELLI F: Clinical, genetic and DNA repair studies on a consecutive series of patients with xeroderma pigmentosum. *Q J Med* 48:179, 1979.

196. GOLDSTEIN N, HAY-ROE V: Prevention of skin cancer with a PABA in alcohol sunscreen in xeroderma pigmentosum. *Cutis* (Jan) 61, 1975.

197. STEFANINI M, LOGOMARSINI P, ARLETT CF, MARINONI S, BORRONE C, CROVATO F, TREVISAN G, CORDONE G, NUZZO F: Xeroderma pigmentosum (complementation group D) mutation is present in patients affected by trichothiodystrophy with photosensitivity. *Hum Genet* 74:107, 1986.

198. KUHNLEUN U, LEL B, PENHOET E, LINN E: Xeroderma pigmentosum fibroblasts of the group D lack an apurinic DNA endonuclease species with a low apparent K_m. *Nucleic Acids Res* 5:951, 1978.

199. MOSES RE, BEAUDET AL: Apurinic endonuclease activities in repair-deficient human cell lines. *Nucleic Acids Res* 5:463, 1978.

200. FISCHER E, SCHNYDER UW, JUNG EG: Report of three sisters with XP-E, a rare xeroderma pigmentosum complementation group. *Photodermatology* 1:232, 1984.

201. KAWADA A, SATOH Y, FUJIWARA Y: Xeroderma pigmentosum complementation group E: A case report. *Photodermatology* 3:233, 1986.

202. FUJIWARA Y, UEHARA Y, ICHIHASHI M, YAMAMOTO Y, NISHIOKA K: Assignment of 2 patients with xeroderma pigmentosum to complementation group E. *Mutat Res* 145:55, 1985.

203. FUJIWARA Y, UEHARA Y, ICHIHASHI M, NISHIOKA K: Xeroderma pigmentosum complementation group F: More assignments and repair characteristics. *Photochem Photobiol* 41:629, 1985.

204. ARLETT CF, HARCOURT SA, LEHMANN AR, STEVENS S, FERGUSON-SMITH MA, MOSLEY WN: Studies on a new case of xeroderma pigmentosum (XP3BR) from complementation group G with a cellular sensitivity to ionizing radiation. *Carcinogenesis* 1:745, 1980.

205. ICHIHASHI M, FUJIWARA Y, UEHARA Y, MATSUMOTO A: A mild form of xeroderma pigmentosum assigned to complementation group G and its repair heterogeneity. *J Invest Dermatol* 85:284, 1985.

206. COX R, MASSON WK: Radiosensitivity in cultured human fibroblasts. *Int J Radiat Biol* 38:575, 1980.

207. ROBBINS JH, MOSHELL AN, LUTZNER MA, GANGES MB, DUPUY JM: A new patient with both xeroderma pigmentosum and Cockayne syndrome is in a new complementation group. *J Invest Dermatol* 80:331A, 1983.

208. DUPUY JM, MOSHELL AN, LUTZNER MA, ROBBINS JH: A new patient with both xeroderma pigmentosum and Cockayne syndrome is not in complementation group B. *J Invest Dermatol* 78:356, 1982.

208a JOHNSON RT, ELLIOT GC, SQUIRES S, JOYSEY VC: Lack of complementation between xeroderma pigmentosum groups D and H. *Mutat Res*, in press.

209. FISCHER E, KEIJZER W, THIELMANN HW, POPANDA O, BAHNERT E, ELDER L, JUNG EG, BOTTSMA D: A ninth complementation group in xeroderma pigmentosum, XPI. *Mutat Res* 145:217, 1985.

210. JUNG EG, BOHNERT E, FISCHER E: Heterogeneity of xeroderma pigmentosum (XP); variability and stability within and between the complementation groups C, D, E, I, and variants. *Photodermatology* 3:125, 1986.

211. MYHR BC, TURNBULL D, DIPAOLO JA: Ultraviolet mutagenesis of normal and xeroderma pigmentosum variant fibroblasts. *Mutat Res* 62:341, 1979.

212. CLEAVER JE, THOMAS GH, PARK SD: Xeroderma pigmentosum variants have a slow recovery of DNA synthesis after irradiation with ultraviolet light. *Biochim Biophys Acta* 564:122, 1979.

213. CLEAVER JE, CARTER DM: Xeroderma pigmentosum variants: Influence of temperature on DNA repair. *J Invest Dermatol* 60:29, 1973.

214. HOFMANN H, JUNG EG, SCHNYDER UW: Pigmented xerodermoid: First report of a family. *Bull Cancer* 65:347, 1978.

215. JASPERS NGJ, JANSEN VD, KUILEN G, BOOTSMA D: Complementation analysis of xeroderma pigmentosum variants. *Exp Cell Res* 136:81, 1981.

216. SWIFT M, CHASE C: Cancer in families with xeroderma pigmentosum. *J Natl Cancer Inst* 62:1415, 1979.

217. HASHEM N, BOOTSMA D, KEIJZER W, GREENE AE, CORIELL L, THOMAS GH, CLEAVER JE: Clinical characteristics, DNA repair, and complementation groups in xeroderma pigmentosum patients from Egypt. *Cancer Res* 40:13, 1980.

218. GIANELLI F, PAWSLEY SA: DNA repair synthesis in human heterokaryons. II. A test for heterozygosity in xeroderma pigmentosum and some insight into the structure of the defective enzyme. *J Cell Sci* 15:163, 1974.

219. RITTER MA: Reduced DNA repair in xeroderma pigmentosum (XP) heterozygotes, in *Sixth International Congress of Radiation Research*. Tokyo, Japan, Toppan Printing Co, 1979, p 264.

220. SELSKY CA, GREER S: Host-cell reactivation of ultraviolet irradiated and chemically treated herpes simplex virus 1 by xeroderma pigmentosum, xeroderma pigmentosum heterozygotes and normal skin fibroblasts. *Mutat Res* 50:395, 1978.

221. RAINBOW AJ: Reduced capacity to repair irradiated adenovirus in fibroblasts from xeroderma pigmentosum heterozygotes. *Cancer Res* 40:3945, 1980.

222. WEISSBACH A: DNA polymerases. *Cell* 5:101, 1975.

223. LINDAHL T, EDELMAN GM: Polynucleotide ligase from myeloid and lymphoid tissues. *Proc Natl Acad Sci USA* 61:680, 1968.

224. GROSSMAN L: Enzymes involved in the repair of DNA, in Lett JT, Adler H, Zelle M (eds): *Advances in Radiation Biology*. New York, Academic, 1974, vol 4, p 77.

225. BACCHETTI S, VAN DER PLAS A, VELDHUISEN G: A UV-specific endonu-

cleolytic activity present in human cell extracts. *Biochem Biophys Res Commun* 48:662, 1972.

226. BRENT TP: Repair enzyme suggested by mammalian endonuclease activity specific for ultraviolet-irradiated DNA. *Nature* 239:172, 1972.

227. DUKER NJ, TEEBOR GW: Different ultraviolet DNA endonuclease activity in human cells. *Nature* 255:82, 1975.

228. VAN LANCKER JL, TOMURA T: Purification and some properties of a mammalian repair endonuclease. *Biochim Biophys Acta* 353:99, 1974.

229. BACCHETTI S, BENNE R: Purification and characterization of an endonuclease from calf thymus acting on irradiated DNA. *Biochim Biophys Acta* 390:285, 1975.

230. SHISHIDO K, ANDO T: Cleavage of ultraviolet light-irradiated DNA by single strand–specific S1 endonuclease. *Biochem Biophys Res Commun* 59:1380, 1974.

231. KATO AC, FRASER MJ: Action of single-strand specific *Neurospora crassa* endonuclease on ultraviolet light-irradiated native DNA. *Biochim Biophys Acta* 312:645, 1973.

232. COOK K, FRIEDBERG EC, SLOR H, CLEAVER JE: Excision of thymine dimers from specifically increased DNA by extracts of xeroderma pigmentosum cells. *Nature* 256:235, 1975.

233. MORTELMANS K, FRIEDBERG EC, SLOR H, THOMAS G, CLEAVER JE: Defective thymine dimer excision by cell-free extracts of xeroderma pigmentosum cells. *Proc Natl Acad Sci USA* 73:2757, 1976.

234. KANO Y, FUJIWARA Y: Defective thymine dimer excision from xeroderma pigmentosum chromatin and its characteristic catalysis by cell-free extracts. *Carcinogenesis* 4:1419, 1983.

235. SLOR H, LEV-SOBE T, FRIEDBERG EC: Evidence for inactivation of DNA repair in frozen and thawed mammalian cells. *Mutat Res* 45:137, 1947.

236. RAMSAY CA, COLTART TM, BLUMT S, PAWSEY SA, GIANNELLI F: Prenatal diagnosis of xeroderma pigmentosum. Report of the first successful case. *Lancet* 2:1109, 1974.

237. PATERSON MC, ANDERSON AK, SMITH BP, SMITH PJ: Enhanced radiosensitivity of cultured fibroblasts from ataxia telangiectasia heterozygotes manifested by defective colony-forming ability and reduced DNA repair replication after hypoxic γ-irradiation. *Cancer Res* 39:3725, 1979.

238. SCUDIERO DA: Decreased DNA repair synthesized defective colony forming ability of ataxia telangiectasia fibroblast cell strains treated with N-methyl-N′-nitro-N-nitrosoguanidine. *Cancer Res* 40:984, 1980.

239. SMITH PJ, PATERSON MC: Defective DNA repair and increased lethality in ataxia telangiectasia cells following γ-ray irradiation. *Nature* 287:745, 1980.

240. EDWARDS MJ, TAYLOR AMR: Unusual levels of $(ADP-ribose)_n$ and DNA synthesis in ataxia telangiectasia cells following γ-ray irradiation. *Nature* 287:745, 1980.

241. CORNFORTH MN, BEDFORD JS: On the nature of the defect in cells from individuals with ataxia telangiectasia. *Science* 227:1589, 1985.

242. FORNACE AJ, LITTLE JB, WEICHSELBAUM RR: DNA repair in a Fanconi's anemia fibroblast cell strain. *Biochim Biophys Acta* 561:99, 1979.

243. KAYE J, SMITH CA, HANAWALT PC: DNA repair in human cells containing photoadducts of 8-methoxypsoralen or angelicin. *Cancer Res* 40:696, 1980.

244. POON PK, O'BRIEN RL, PARKER JW: Defective DNA repair in Fanconi's anemia. *Nature* 250:223, 1974.

245. CHAGANTI RSK, SCHONBERG S, GERMAN J: A manyfold increase in sister chromatid exchanges in Bloom's syndrome lymphocytes. *Proc Natl Acad Sci USA* 71:4508, 1974.

246. WARREN ST, SCHULTZ RA, CHANG CC, TROSKO JE: Elevated spontaneous mutation rate in Bloom's syndrome fibroblasts. *Proceedings of the 31st Meeting of the American Society of Human Genetics*, New York, 1980, p 161A.

247. KREPINSKY AB, RAINBOW AJ, HEDDLE JA: Studies on the ultraviolet light sensitivity of Bloom's syndrome fibroblasts. *Mutat Res* 69:357, 1980.

248. REMSEN JF: Repair of damage by *N*-acetoxy-2-acetylaminofluorene in Bloom's syndrome. *Mutat Res* 72:151, 1980.

249. BURNET M: Cancer—A biological approach. I. The processes of control. *Br Med J* 779, 1957.

250. AMES BN: The detection of chemical mutagens with enteric bacteria, in *Chemical Mutagens, Principles and Methods for Their Detection.* New York, Plenum, 1971, vol 1, p 267.

251. AMES BN: Dietary carcinogens and anticarcinogens, oxygen radicals and degenerative diseases. *Science* 221:1256, 1983.

252. ARLETT CF: Survival and mutation in gamma-irradiated human cell strains from normal or cancer prone individuals, in Okada S, Imamura M, Terashima T, Yamaguchi H (eds): *Radiation Research.* Japan, Japanese Association for Radiation Research, 1980, p 596.

253. WEICHSELBAUM RR, NOVE J, LITTLE JB: X-ray sensitivity of fifty-three human diploid fibroblast cell strains from patients with characterized genetic disorders. *Cancer Res* 40:926, 1980.

254. ARLETT CF, HARCOURT SA: Survey of radiosensitivity in a variety of cell strains. *Cancer Res* 40:920, 1980.

255. TANAKA H, ORI T: High sensitivity but normal DNA-repair activity after UV irradiation in Epstein-Barr virus-transformed lymphoblastoid cell lines from Chediak-Higashi syndrome. *Mutat Res* 72:143, 1980.

256. WEICHSELBAUM RR, NOVE J, LITTLE JB: X-ray sensitivity of diploid fibroblasts from patients with hereditary or sporadic retinoblastoma. *Proc Natl Acad Sci USA* 75:3962, 1978.

257. LITTLE JB, NOVE J, WEICHSELBAUM RR: Abnormal sensitivity of diploid skin fibroblasts from a family with Garner's syndrome to the lethal effects of X-irradiation, ultraviolet light and mitomycin-C. *Mutat Res* 70:241, 1980.

PART 20

INTESTINE

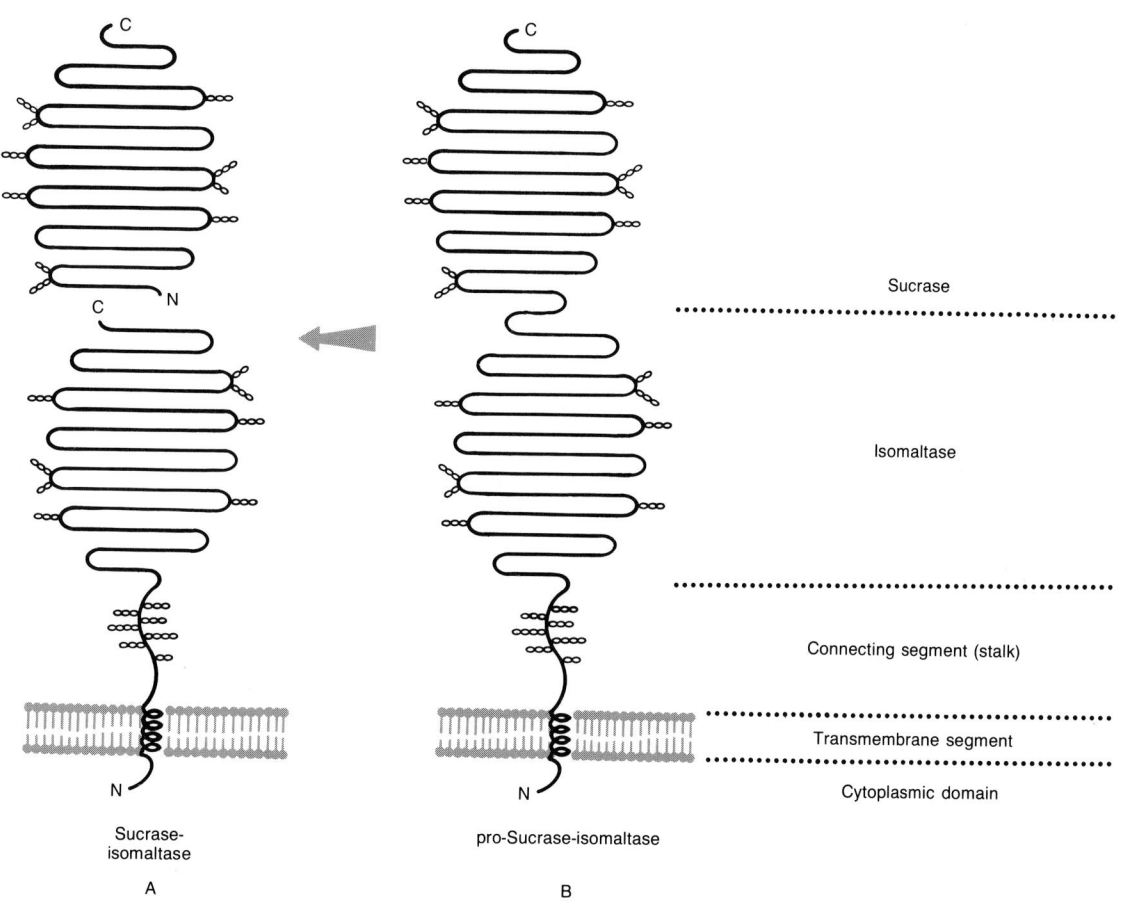

Sucrase

Isomaltase

Connecting segment (stalk)

Transmembrane segment

Cytoplasmic domain

Sucrase-
isomaltase

A

pro-Sucrase-isomaltase

B

CHAPTER 121

SMALL-INTESTINAL DISACCHARIDASES*

GIORGIO SEMENZA
SALVATORE AURICCHIO

1. *The brush border membrane of the human small intestine is endowed with a total of seven glycosidases, which give rise to free monosaccharides by splitting dietary disaccharides and oligosaccharides that arise in the intestinal lumen from the α amylolysis of starch. The four "maltases" occur as two heterodimers (i.e., the glucoamylase complex and the sucrase-isomaltase complex); the β-glycosidase complex, which is composed of a single type of polypeptide, has two catalytic sites (lactase and glycosylceramidase). Trehalase is composed of a single type of subunit(s) (Table 121-1). These glycosidases are "stalked" intrinsic proteins of the membrane; the "body" of the protein mass, including the catalytic sites, protrudes toward the small-intestinal lumen.*

2. *The glycosidases (with the possible exception of trehalase, the synthesis of which is still little known) are synthesized as large polypeptide chains, each of which has an apparent molecular weight in the range 200,000 to 250,000. These "pro" forms are each split into the final forms either extracellularly (as are the α-glucosidase complexes) or intracellularly (the β-glycosidase complex; see Table 121-2). Since the two catalytic domains in each of these complexes belong to a single translational unit, they are subjected to the same biologic control mechanism(s).*

3. *Mammals other than humans are equipped at birth with the β-glycosidase and the glucoamylase complexes. They develop sucrase-isomaltase and trehalase at the time of weaning, when the β-glycosidase complex begins to decline, eventually reaching a level as low as 5 to 10 percent of that at birth. In contrast, human beings develop the brush border disaccharidases before birth, beginning prior to the tenth week of gestation, with a developmental "burst" (particularly in the β-glycosidase complex) a few weeks before birth. The level of the β-glycosidase complex—in effect, the level of lactase activity—remains high throughout adulthood in most white people and a few other races.*

4. *The primary site of control in the spontaneous physiological development of sucrase-isomaltase is in all likelihood at the level of transcription. Dietary and hormonal factors also control the levels of disaccharidase activities.*

5. *Both secondary and primary (genetic) disaccharidase deficiencies are known, which may lead to malabsorption and intolerance of the corresponding disaccharide(s), but not of the constituent monosaccharides. Diagnosis depends on determination of enzyme activities through small-intestinal biopsies and/or on oral tolerance tests with the corresponding disaccharides; among the latter the breath hydrogen test is particularly reliable.*

6. *All genetic defects of intestinal disaccharidases are monofactorial, autosomal, and recessive. The most common of them (indeed, perhaps the most common of all genetic disturbances in humans, affecting one-third to one-half of the human race) is adult hypolactasia: in this condition intestinal lactase declines in childhood or shortly thereafter (as it does in mammals other than human beings) to 10 percent or less of the level at birth. (See Chap. 122 for further details.)*

7. *Sucrase-isomaltase deficiency is much rarer and is genetically heterogeneous. Congenital lactase deficiency and trehalase deficiency are extremely rare, and virtually nothing is known about their molecular basis.*

LUMINAL HYDROLYSIS OF STARCH

In the average Western diet, starch provides approximately 50 percent of absorbable carbohydrates, but disaccharides (mainly sucrose and lactose) are also important nutrients. In addition, small amounts of free fructose, of the disaccharide trehalose (which is hydrolyzed into two molecules of glucose), and of nonabsorbable carbohydrates including dietary fiber, stachyose, and raffinose are ingested.[1-3]

Starch is a mixture of two types of polysaccharides, amylose and amylopectin. Amylose has a linear structure and is made up of 1-4-α-linked glucose units. Amylopectin has a branched structure: the majority of the glucose residues are connected by 1,4-α-glucosidic bonds (the linear chains); the branch points are made by 1,6-α-glucosidic linkages. In the digestive tract, starch is eventually hydrolyzed to yield free glucose by the cumulative action of both the salivary and pancreatic α-amylases, the latter being present in solution in the intestinal lumen (but also adsorbed at the surface of the brush border membrane), and of the α-glucosidases of the intestinal mucosa.

The hydrolysis in vitro of amylose by salivary or pancreatic α-amylase starts as a random hydrolysis of the internal 1,4 bonds. As it proceeds, it becomes more and more selective, as a result of the greater resistance to enzymatic attack of the last and next-to-last 1,4-α-glucopyranosyl bonds at the nonreducing end of the small linear 1,4-α-glucans and of the 1,4-α bond adjacent to the reducing end.[4-10] The final (limit) products resulting from amylose hydrolysis in vitro are maltose and maltotriose;[11] those from amylopectin are glucose (in small amounts), maltose, maltotriose, and branched dextrins (Fig. 121-1).[12-16]

In humans older than 1 year, the α-amylase activity of duodenal juice after a test meal is very high; the intestinal hydro-

*In the present chapter we will use the term *disaccharidases* to refer to the enzymes in Tables 121-1 and 121-2. The term will be used even in those cases where the substrates of interest are oligosaccharides or glycosides other than disaccharides.

Table 121-1 Types of Major Intestinal Disaccharidases

Enzyme or complex	Representative data on substrate specificities
Glucoamylase complex (EC 3.2.1.20; the "heat-stable" maltases): glucoamylase-(maltase)-1 + glucoamylase-(maltase)-2	The two subunits have similar but probably not quite identical substrate specificities.[36,41] They split 1,4-α-glucopyranosidic bonds from the nonreducing ends of amylose, amylopectin, glycogen, and straight-chain 1,4-α-glucopyranosyl oligomers, including maltose.[40,42] Minor 1,6-α-glucopyranosidase activity.[39,42–44]
Sucrase-isomaltase complex (the "heat-labile" maltases): sucrase-(maltase) (EC 3.2.1.48) + isomaltase-(maltase) (EC 3.2.1.10)	Both subunits split maltose (see, for example, Refs. 43, 44, and 56), maltotriose,[46] maltitol (G. Semenza and A. K. Balthazar, unpublished), α-F-glucopyranoside,[47] and (less well) aryl-α-glucopyranosides.[48] In addition, the sucrase subunit splits sucrose and turanose;[49] the isomaltase subunit splits the 1,6-α-glucopyranosyl bonds in isomaltose, isomaltulose (palatinose), and panose and in a number of branched limit α-dextrins.[38,43–45,50,51]
Trehalase (EC 3.2.1.28)	α,α'-Trehalose and 6,6'-dideoxy-α-α'-trehalose;[52] α- and β-F-glucopyranoside (tested on renal trehalase)[53]
β-Glycosidase complex: lactase (EC 3.2.1.23) + glycosylceramidase (EC 3.2.1.45–46; also called phlorizin hydrolase, EC 3.2.1.62)	A number of β-glycosides: α- and β-lactose, 3-(β-D-galactosido)-D-glucose, 6-(β-D-galactosido)-D-glucose, aryl-β-galactopyranosides, aryl-β-glucopyranosides, methyl-β-galactopyranoside.[54,55] The "lactase" site preferentially splits β-glycosides with hydrophilic aglycons (typically lactose, but also cellobiose,[56–59] cellotriose, and cellotetrose, and also, but much less, cellulose[59]), whereas the "glycosylceramidase" site preferentially splits β-glycosides with a large, hydrophobic aglycon (typically, galactosyl- and glycosyl-β-ceramides,[58] phlorizin,[60] and other aryl-β-glycosides.[55,61]

Table 121-2 Molecular Forms of the Small-Intestinal Heterodimeric Glycosidases During Biosynthesis

Enzyme	Species	$10^{-3} \times M_r$ of: Primary translation product, nonglycosylated form	Transient form	Endoglycosidase H sensitivity	Mature form* ($10^{-3} \times M_r$)	Transport time, min	References
Sucrase-isomaltase complex	Rabbit	200	230	+	275† (120 + 140†‡§)		86, 94, 101, 106
	Pig	225	240	+	265 (140 + 150)	60–90	95, 107
	Human	210	217	+	231 (145 + 151)	60–90	93, 97
Maltase-glucoamylase (glucoamylase complex)	Pig	200	225	+	245† (125 + 135)	60–90	91, 107
Lactase–phlorizin hydrolase (β-glycosidase complex)	Pig	210	225	+	245 (160)¶	60–90	92
	Rat	220			130		93b
	Human	200	214	+	262 (156)¶	60–90	93, 93a, 97
		216.393**			120.068**		93d
	Rabbit	215.629**			121.221**		93d

*Values in parentheses indicate the M_r of proteolytically cleaved mature forms.
†Strong evidence for anchoring via the N-terminal region is available (i.e., change in the N-terminal amino acid residue during proteolytic solubilization and/or sizable hydrophobic sequence in the N-terminal region), although not necessarily for the species indicated in the second column.
‡Evidence for the nonparticipation of the C-terminal regions in the anchoring is available.[79,80]
§The M_r of the unglycosylated pro-sucrase-isomaltase, as deduced from cDNA cloning and sequencing, is 203,000.[80]
¶The proteolytic processing leading to the final form with $M_r = 160,000$ takes place intracellularly.
**Calculated from the cDNA-deduced amino acid sequence of pro-lactase-phlorizin hydrolase (i.e., residue 20–1927 of human or residue 20–1926 of rabbit pre-pro-lactase-phlorizin hydrolase; and residue 869–1927 of human or residue 867–1926 of rabbit pre-pro-lactase-phlorizin hydrolase). The mature lactase-phlorizin hydrolase "complex" appearing in the brush border membrane consists of a single polypeptide chain and is anchored via a hydrophobic segment at the C-terminal region. It is synthesized as a pre-pro form, i.e., with a cleavable signal. It is subjected to extensive processing; only the C-terminal 60% of pre-pro-lactase-phlorizin hydrolase appears in the brush border membrane.[93d]
NOTE: Most apparent M_r values listed were estimated from SDS-PAGE. They thus occasionally differ somewhat from those calculated from hydrodynamic parameters (see, Ref. 86).

lysis of starch in vivo is thus very rapid. The amylopectin of a test meal consisting of more than 5000 glucose units is digested at the end of the duodenum into oligosaccharides composed of an average of three glucose units.[17] The major components of this carbohydrate mixture are maltose, maltotriose, and branched dextrins with both 1,4-α and one or more 1,6-α branching links. (Isomaltose is not produced in the digestion of starch by α-amylase.[17]) Maltose, maltotriose, and at least some of these branched dextrins must be considered limit products of the α-amylolysis in vivo, which are further hydrolyzed into free glucose by brush border α-glucosidases; see "Intestinal (Membrane Surface) Hydrolysis of Oligosaccharides," below.

Although the intraluminal hydrolysis of free starch does proceed rapidly in vivo, the starch in most staple foods (wheat, corn, oats, potatoes) may escape *complete* digestion and absorption in the small intestine, and thus some may reach the colon.[18,19] From the amount of hydrogen excreted in the breath[20] (see "Diagnosis of Disaccharidase Deficiency, Carbohydrate Malabsorption, and Carbohydrate Intolerance") after an oral load of 100 g of flours from different sources, the proportion of starch not absorbed by the healthy small bowel was estimated to be 5 to 20 percent.[18,19] These values were recently confirmed by measuring directly the ileal recovery of carbohydrates after ingestion of starch.[21,22] The type of starch and the protein content of the flours appear to be important, because starch from all-purpose wheat flour and from potato is absorbed by the small intestine less completely than that from rice flour or low-gluten wheat flour.[18,19] With other foods, such as legumes or rices rich in amyloses,[23] the percentage of carbohydrates reaching the colon may be even higher. It has been calculated that a substantial amount of dietary starch, perhaps as much as 40 g/day, may reach the colon.[21]

The diarrhea that would otherwise ensue from the delivery of such large quantities of carbohydrates to the large intestine is prevented by the action of the colonic flora. Inadequately absorbed carbohydrates are in fact salvaged through fermentation to gases (hydrogen, methane, and carbon dioxide) and to acetic, propionic, and butyric acids; these acids are readily absorbed from and/or metabolized in the colon. This organ, therefore, makes an important contribution to the absorption of carbohydrates escaping small-intestinal digestion,[24] so that, as a rule, sugars are absent from the stool. As a matter of fact, children after the first year of life are able to absorb, almost completely, 170 g/m² body surface of cooked wheat or potato starch, administered in biscuits and macaroni.[25] The human colon is able to metabolize anaerobically up to 50 g unprocessed wheat starch without changing the stool content of volatile fatty acids and lactic acid or its bacterial mass.[26,27]

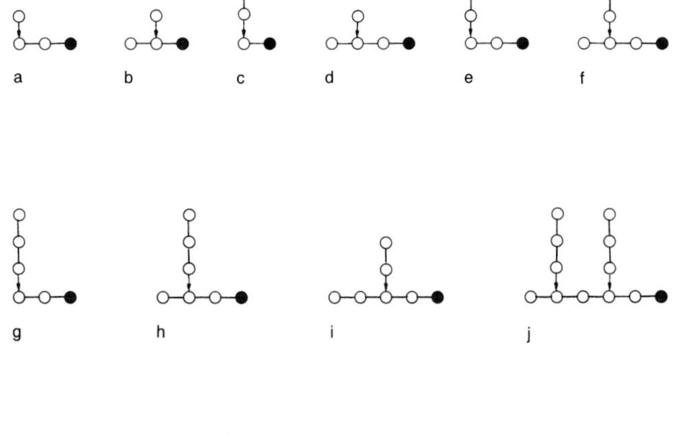

DIGESTION OF STARCH AND GLUCOSE POLYMERS IN HUMAN INFANTS

α-Amylase activity in the duodenal lumen does not reach normal adult levels until well after birth.[17] There is practically no α-amylase activity in the duodenal fluid of premature and term infants at birth.[28] After the first month of life, amylase activity can be increased upon stimulation by pancreozymin and secretin and in response to ingested starch.[29] As a consequence of the low levels of α-amylase activity in duodenal juice, in most infants younger than 6 months of age the duodenal hydrolysis of amylopectin is incomplete, with large amounts of dextrin composed of more than 30 glucose units and, in comparison with older infants, less maltose and more maltotetrose in the luminal fluid; maltotetrose accounts for only 1 to 3 percent of total carbohydrates in the duodenal juice by the end of the first year of life.[17]

This does not mean that young infants may not absorb even sizable quantities of starch and glucose polymers almost completely.[25,30–32] One-month-old infants may tolerate up to 110 g/m² of rice starch per day, whereas larger quantities cause fermentative diarrhea.[25] However, healthy young infants do not absorb glucose polymers longer than 43 glucose units as completely as short-chain glucose polymers (e.g., 3 to 8 glucose units).[33] The capability of young infants to digest limited amounts of starches and glucose polymers in spite of low levels of pancreatic α-amylase may depend on various factors. First of all, the low levels of salivary[34] and of pancreatic α-amylase activity in duodenal juice may still be sufficient if the quantities of starch or glucose polymers are small. Furthermore, the glucoamylase of the small-intestinal mucosa probably plays an important role in digestion of dextrins and glucose polymers during the first few months of life, even if this enzyme is best suited for the hydrolysis of oligomers smaller than 10 glucose residues.[35,36] Finally, at this age also the colonic flora undoubtedly plays a significant role in salvaging unabsorbed starch and glucose polymers.[31]

INTESTINAL (MEMBRANE SURFACE) HYDROLYSIS OF OLIGOSACCHARIDES

The elaborate structure of the brush border greatly expands the surface area of the apical plasma membrane (to some 200 m² in a normal adult man!), making it better suited to carry out the final steps in digestion and to absorb the resulting products. The tight packing of microvilli, however, also results in thick, unstirred layers, to which mucus also contributes. The limiting factor in membrane digestion in vivo is often the diffusion of the substrate from the lumen to the membrane surface. It seems very appropriate, therefore, that large molecules such as starch and glycogen are first split by enzymes present in solution in the lumen (through "cavital digestion") and that their smaller, partial degradation prod-

Fig. 121-1 Branched limit dextrins from the α amylolysis of amylopectin in vitro. ○ = nonreducing glucose unit; ● = reducing glucose unit; — = 1,4-α-glucopyranosidic bond; → = 1,6-α-glucopyranosidic bond. (*From Auricchio et al.[155] Used by permission.*)

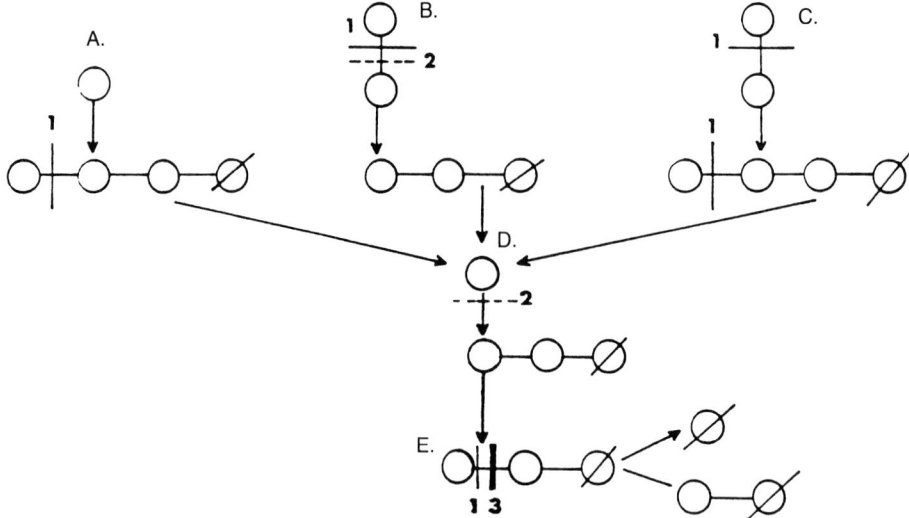

Fig. 121-2 Hydrolysis by glucoamylase and by the sucrase-isomaltase complex of the shortest limit dextrins resulting from exhaustive digestion of starch by α-amylase. ○ = nonreducing glucose unit; ø = reducing glucose unit; — = 1,4-α-glucopyranosidic bond; → = 1,6-α-glucopyranosidic bond. *A.* 6-α-D-Glucopyranosyl-maltotetrose. *B.* 6-α-D-Maltopyranosyl-maltotriose. *C.* 6-α-D-Maltopyranosyl-maltotetrose. *D.* 6-α-D-Glucopyranosyl-maltotriose. *E.* Maltotriose. 1 — = bond hydrolyzed by glucoamylase; 2 - - - - = bond hydrolyzed by isomaltase; 3 — = bond hydrolyzed by sucrase. Hence glucoamylase hydrolyzes the pentasaccharides (*A* and *B*) and hexasaccharide (*C*) to the tetrasaccharide (*D*). Isomaltase is also able to split the second of the pentasaccharides (*B*) into the tetrasaccharide (*D*). The further degradation of 6-α-D-glucopyranosyl-maltotriose is accomplished mainly by the sucrase-isomaltase complex, with the isomaltase subunit converting it into glucose and maltotriose and the sucrase subunit (assisted by glucoamylase) converting maltotriose into maltose and glucose. *(From Auricchio.[156] Used by permission.)*

ucts diffuse onto the brush border membrane to be split further ("membrane digestion"[37]).

Table 121-1 reports the essentials of the substrate specificities of brush border glycosidases (more can be found in the original literature cited). Considering only the digestion of the oligo- and disaccharides commonly occurring as such in the diet, or arising during the digestion of starch and glycogen, the β-glycosidase complex accounts for all the lactase activity; trehalase for all the trehalase activity; the sucrase-isomaltase complex for all the sucrase activity, for almost all or all of the isomaltase (1,6-α-oligosaccharidase) activity, and for about 80 percent of the maltase activity; and the maltase-glucoamylase complex for a few percent (if any) of the isomaltase activity, for about 20 percent of the maltase activity, and for all the glucoamylase activity.*

Hence, the limit dextrins arising from the α amylolysis of starch in the lumen are completely split to free glucose by the combined action of the glucoamylase and the sucrase-isomaltase complexes (Fig. 121-2).[38–40] The linear 1,4-α-glucans are split, with different V_{max} and K_m values, by the four maltases listed in Table 121-1. The 1,6-α-branched dextrins are split almost exclusively by the isomaltase subunit of the sucrase-isomaltase complex. It should be noted that these branched dextrins can be as much as 25 percent of the original starch.

In adult human small intestine, lactase-glycosylceramidase and sucrase-isomaltase activities are highest in the jejunum and lower at the proximal and distal ends. In contrast, glucoamylase activity increases along the small intestine and reaches maximal values in the ileum, or distal end.[62,63] Similar distribution patterns have been demonstrated in the intestine of the human newborn.[64,65]

The capacity for digestion of most oligosaccharides of α-glucose exceeds the capacity for absorption of the component monosaccharides. The anatomic structure of the brush border region provides a diffusion barrier to the movement of monosaccharides (liberated by the disaccharidases) back from the outer surface of the brush border membrane into the intestinal lumen. It thus favors the absorption of monosaccharides originating from the disaccharides.[66–70] In spite of this, some of the monosaccharides liberated do appear in the intestinal lumen[71,72]; i.e., for most oligosaccharides, hydrolysis is not rate-limiting. However, the glucose itself inhibits intestinal maltases somewhat.[73]

In contrast to the hydrolysis of other oligosaccharides, that of lactose is the rate-limiting step for the absorption of this sugar.[74] Even in apparently normal individuals, mucosal lactase activity is the lowest of all disaccharidase activities. (Indeed, the capacity of this enzyme can be exceeded easily, which results in the presence of unsplit lactose in the lumen.) The monosaccharides arising from the hydrolysis of lactose never appear in significant amounts at the luminal side of the brush border, indicating that the transport system or systems for its component monosaccharides, glucose and galactose, are capable of completely absorbing the hydrolysis products presented to them.[75]

MEMBRANE ANCHORING AND BIOSYNTHESIS OF DISACCHARIDASES

The mode of anchoring and the biosynthesis of brush border glycosidases have been the object of recent reviews,[76–78a] to which the reader is referred for details. See also Table 121-2.

*Pancreatic α-amylase and brush border glucoamylase hydrolyze only 1,4-α-glucopyranosidic bonds, as they occur, for example, in starch and other 1,4-α glucans. They differ, however, in several respects. α-Amylase prefers long chains, and does not split maltose; glucoamylase prefers short chains and does split maltose. The end products of the action of α-amylase on linear chains are maltose and maltotriose, whereas the end product of glucoamylase is glucose only. (It is set free progressively from the nonreducing ends.) Finally, different compounds are known which activate or inhibit either α-amylase or glucoamylase without affecting the other; they allow the quantitative determination of either enzyme in the presence of the other (see, for example, Refs. 46 and 57).

The Sucrase-Isomaltase, Maltase-Glucoamylase, and β-Glycosidase (Lactase–Phlorizin Hydrolase) Complexes*

The α-glucosidase complexes are heterodimers, each composed of two similar but not identical subunits; each subunit consists of a single glycosylated polypeptide chain with an apparent molecular weight in the 120,000 to 160,000 range (Table 121-2). The sucrase-isomaltase[79,80] and the glucoamylase[81,82] complexes are anchored to the membrane via one subunit only. The anchoring segment in the transmembranal subunit is located not far from the N terminus of the subunit.

The positioning of the sucrase-isomaltase complex is now known in a fair amount of detail (reviewed in Refs. 76–78); (see Fig. 121-3A). The N terminus of the isomaltase subunit is located at the *cytosolic* side of the membrane;[80] a number of positive charges occur in the first four amino acid residues; an extremely hydrophobic stretch of approximately 20 residues[80,82a] crosses the membrane once[80] in a helical configuration;[82b] and most of the protein mass of isomaltase, including the C terminus, protrudes to the outer, luminal side of the membrane. The sucrase subunit has a peripheral positioning,

*The β-glycosidase activity which is associated with lactase was initially described as phlorizin-hydrolase (β-glucosidase).[60] It was later recognized[58] that the "natural" substrates of β-glycosidase are β-glucosyl and β-galactosyl ceramides. These substrates, however, are costly and are so little soluble in water that they are impractical in routine determinations. In the present chapter we will refer interchangeably to this β-glycosidase activity as *phlorizin hydrolase activity* or *glycosylceramidase activity.*

interacting with the membrane fabric solely via isomaltase;[79] the only hydrophobic segment present in the whole complex is the one which occurs at the N-terminal region of the isomaltase subunit[80] and accounts for approximately 1 percent of the total protein mass.

In the glucoamylase complex, also, the "anchor" is confined to one subunit only;[81,82] it is located not far from the N-terminal region of that subunit.[83]

Both the sucrase-isomaltase[84] and the glucoamylase[83] complexes dimerize further, thus forming homo-heterotetramers of the type $(\alpha, \beta)_2$.

As to the β-glycosidase (lactase–phlorizin hydrolase) complex, conclusive evidence on its subunit composition, mode of anchoring, number of catalytic sites, etc., is now available.[93d] It occurs in the brush border membrane and is composed of a single polypeptide chain with a molecular weight of approximately 121,000, which carries the two hydrolytic sites for β-glycosides with a hydrophilic ("lactase") or a hydrophobic ("phlorizin hydrolase") aglycone (see Table 121-1). Contrary to the α-glucosidase complexes, it is anchored to the membrane via a highly hydrophobic sequence of some 19 amino acids long, which is located near the C-terminal end. This anchoring segment crosses the membrane bilayer only once, in a direction opposite to those of the α-glucosidase complexes, i.e., N_{out}-C_{in}, the C terminus being located at the cytosolic side of the membrane.

The major lines in the biosynthesis of these heterodimers have been established in some detail for sucrase-isomaltase, but again, they seem to hold true for the other α-glucosidase complex as well.

Fig. 121-3 Positioning of sucrase-isomaltase (A) and of prosucrase-isomaltase (B) in the small-intestinal brush border membrane. The (unspecified) interactions within and between the sucrase and isomaltase domains (or subunits) are not indicated. ooo = sugar chains. (From Semenza.[77] Used by permission.) C. Positioning of the lactase–phlorizin hydrolase (β-glycosidase) complex. Note the opposite direction of the polypeptide chain spanning the brush border membrane, and also that this "complex" is composed of a *single* polypeptide chain, with the two catalytic activities associated with different domains. (Adapted from Mantei et al.[93d]

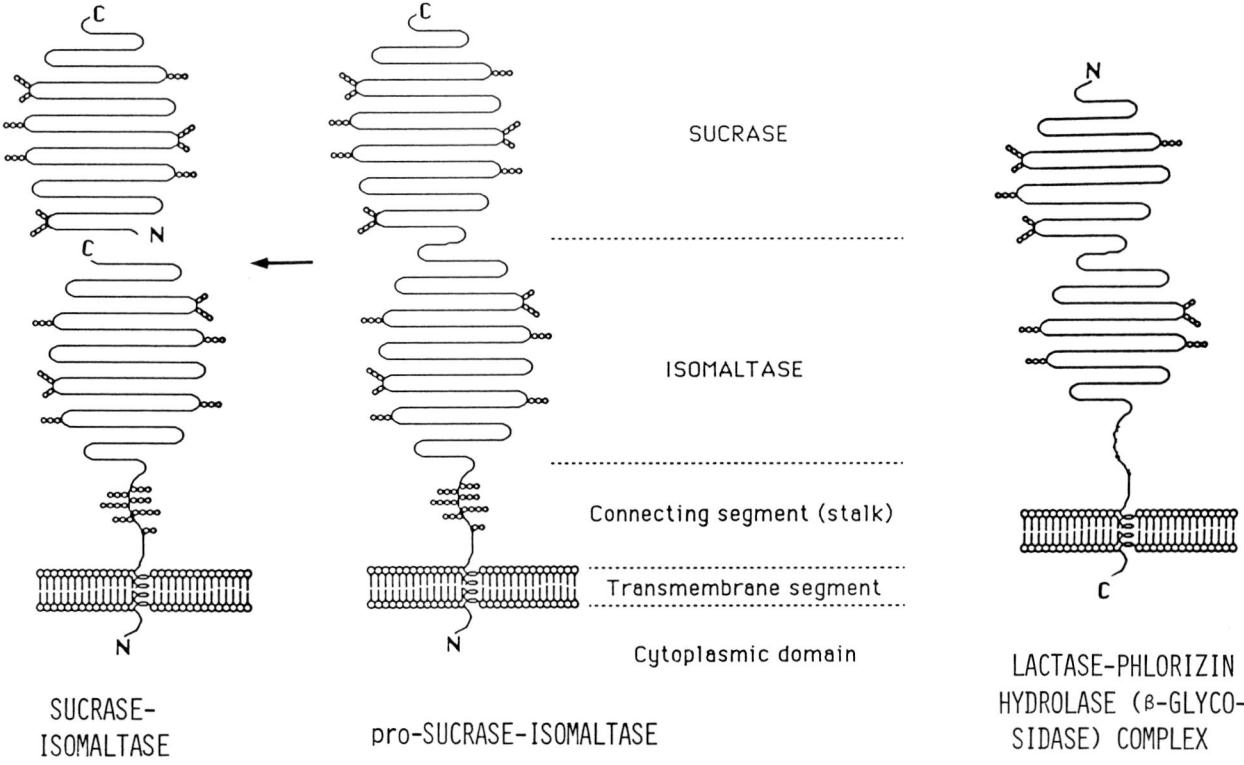

SUCRASE

ISOMALTASE

Connecting segment (stalk)

Transmembrane segment

Cytoplasmic domain

SUCRASE-ISOMALTASE

A.

pro-SUCRASE-ISOMALTASE

B.

LACTASE-PHLORIZIN HYDROLASE (β-GLYCOSIDASE) COMPLEX

C.

As discussed in later sections, sucrase and isomaltase activities develop simultaneously, respond identically to hormonal and dietary stimuli, and in most cases are equally affected by genetic defects. Their identical or closely related biologic control mechanism(s), *plus* a very close similarity in the functional (and, where known, structural) properties of the two subunits,[77,85-87] *plus* the mode of membrane insertion of sucrase-isomaltase (in Fig. 121-3A, notice the peripheral positioning of sucrase and the anchoring of isomaltase via the N-terminal region) prompted one of us to formulate the "one polypeptide chain, two active sites" precursor hypothesis,[88-90] as follows: (1) An ancestral gene existed, coding for a one–polypeptide chain, one–active site enzyme that split both maltose and isomaltose (a simple isomaltase). (2) The gene was partially duplicated, resulting in a gene coding for a long single polypeptide chain with two identical active sites (a double isomaltase). (3) Point mutation(s) and/or deletion(s) changed one of these active sites from an isomaltase-maltase into a sucrase-maltase. Thereby a long polypeptide chain was formed, carrying two similar, but not identical, active sites (the pro-sucrase-isomaltase). (4) Posttranslational modification of this single long polypeptide chain by pancreatic proteases leads to the two subunits that make up the final sucrase-isomaltase complex. The subunits remain associated with one another via interactions formed during the folding of the original single-chain pro-sucrase-isomaltase.

When sucrase-isomaltase is synthesized unexposed to pancreatic juice—whether in vivo or in vitro, whether produced in cultivated tissue or cells or translated in a cell-free system—it is always in the form of a 260,000-dalton single-chain polypeptide, i.e., of pro-sucrase-isomaltase.[76,77]* Furthermore, the total sequencing of the 1827 amino acid residues of this pro-sucrase-isomaltase (by cDNA cloning and sequencing[80]) has revealed a 41 percent identity between the isomaltase and sucrase portions, with another 40 percent of nonidentical but conservative changes, 28 percent of which result from single-base mutations of the codons. This has brought final evidence, therefore, for the partial gene duplication postulated by the "one polypeptide chain, two active sites" mechanism. Finally, the characteristics and mode of membrane insertion of fowl (pro-) sucrase-isomaltase, which are very similar to those of the mammalian enzyme, strongly suggest that the mutation of double isomaltase into pro-sucrase-isomaltase took place prior to the separation of mammals from reptiles and birds, i.e., more than 350 million years ago.[82]

This phylogenetic pedigree of sucrase-isomaltase has recently been enriched by two observations. The membrane-spanning domains of (1) pro-sucrase-isomaltase, maltase-glucoamylase, and endopeptidase 24.11[90a] (all three are brush border enzymes) and (2) the asialoglycoprotein receptors (proteins of the basolateral membrane)[90b] show significant homology to one another and have apparently evolved from an exon

unrelated to those of the glucosidase portions. Furthermore, lysosomal α-glucosidase (the enzyme whose absence leads to glycogenosis type II, Pompe's disease) is reported to have a highly significant homology with brush border sucrase and isomaltase.[90c] The lysosomal enzyme lacks both the stalk and the N-terminal hydrophobic anchor of pro-sucrase-isomaltase and is synthesized with an N-terminal *cleavable* signal. Lysosomal α-glucosidase is thus likely to have evolved from the same ancestral gene as brush border isomaltase before it acquired the hydrophobic anchor and the stalk portion.

As for the maltase-glucoamylase and β-glycosidase complexes, each of them is also synthesized as a single large polypeptide chain of 220,000 daltons or more which is split into the final forms either by pancreatic proteases (the glucoamylase complex[42,82,91]) or intracellularly (the lactase–phlorizin hydrolase complex[92-93a-c]). Thus, in each of the three complexes in Table 121-1, the two catalytic domains belong to a single translational unit, which is the obvious basis for the close relationship in the biologic control of the two catalytic sites in each complex, i.e., of sucrase and isomaltase activities and also of lactase and phlorizin hydrolase activities. (More information is given in later sections.)

The individual steps in biosynthesis and membrane insertion of these polypeptides are less well understood. It is clear, however, that pro-sucrase-isomaltase, and presumably the maltase-glucoamylase complex also, are synthesized *without* a cleavable signal, i.e., that the hydrophobic stretch at the N-terminal region of isomaltase has a dual function: that of the signal ("leading sequence") during biosynthesis and insertion into the membrane of the endoplasmic reticulum, and that of the anchor in the final protein (Fig. 121-4). This was demonstrated by the pro-sucrase-isomaltase cDNA sequence, which showed no signal prior to the N terminus of the final polypeptide.[80] Also, the N-terminal sequence of the primary translation product (in vitro, in a cell-free system, without microsomal membranes) corresponded exactly to that of "mature" pro-sucrase-isomaltase.[94]

The complete primary structure of the β-glycosidase complex (lactase-phlorizin hydrolase) and of its pre-pro form has recently been established.[93d] It shows no homology with the

Fig. 121-4 Suggested minimum mechanism for the synthesis and membrane assembly of pro-sucrase-isomaltase. The highly hydrophobic stretch between positions 12 and 31 is suggested to play a dual role of (uncleaved) signal during biosynthesis and of membrane anchor in the final pro-sucrase-isomaltase. ER = endoplasmic reticulum. SRP = signal recognition particle. DP = docking protein. The sugar chains in pro-sucrase-isomaltase are shown as branches. *(From Semenza.[77] Used by permission.)*

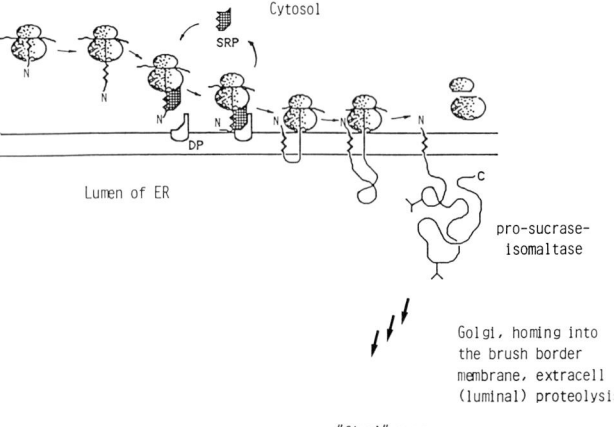

*This pro-sucrase-isomaltase should not be confused with the enzymatically inactive protein cross-reacting with sucrase-isomaltase which has been obtained in homogeneous or highly purified form from the intestine of baby rats[347] or rabbits.[109] The kind and amount of information on these cross-reacting proteins is somewhat different for the two species, but perhaps what is known for one species complements what is known for the other. The protein from rabbit intestine appears at about the sixth day of life, reaches a maximum at about the eightieth day, and decreases thereafter, still remaining detectable in adult life, particularly at the apical pole of crypt cells. It has a somewhat larger molecular weight ($s_{20,w}$ = 9.8 S) than sucrase-isomaltase ($s_{20,w}$ = 9.2 S). The cross-reacting proteins from the rat are, unlike sucrase-isomaltase, periodic Schiff-negative. These proteins may derive from endocytosed, partially degraded sucrase-isomaltase or from incompletely or nonglycosylated (pro-) sucrase-isomaltase, or they may have another origin.

α-glucosidase complexes. The long pre-pro-lactase phlorizin hydrolase (1927 amino acid residues in human enzyme; 1926 amino acids in rabbit homologue) comprises five domains: (1) a cleaved signal sequence of 19 amino acids; (2) a larger "pro" portion of 847 amino acids (in the rabbit), none of which appears in the mature brush border lactase-phlorizin hydrolase; (3) the mature enzyme, which contains both catalytic sites in a single polypeptide chain; (4) a membrane-spanning hydrophobic segment near the C terminus, which serves as the membrane anchor; and (5) a short hydrophilic segment at the C terminus, which must be cytosolic. Whereas pro-sucrase-isomaltase shows a twofold internal homology, pre-pro-lactase-phlorizin hydrolase shows a fourfold internal homology (which naturally indicates that a partial gene duplication has occurred twice), two of the homologous regions occurring in the "pro" portion and two in mature lactase-phlorizin hydrolase. Pre-pro-lactase-phlorizin hydrolase therefore differs in several respects from the α-glucosidase complexes: The degree of internal homology is different; its mode of anchoring to the membrane is different; accordingly, its mode of biosynthesis is also different, since it is endowed with a cleavable, rather than uncleavable, signal.

From the endoplasmic reticulum membranes, where they are *N*-glycosylated, the primary translation products proceed through the series of stacks of the Golgi membranes, where most or all of them are trimmed, complex-glycosylated, and *O*-glycosylated. In tissue cultures, movement from the endoplasmic reticulum to the Golgi membrane and glycosylation into the "high mannose" forms takes 60 to 90 min (Table 121-2).[95–97] (The sugar chains are often responsible for the blood group specificity of these enzymes,[98,99] and also for their microheterogeneity; for lactase, for example, see Ref. 100.)

Intracellular rather than extracellular proteolytic processing of prolactase is far more impressive than that of sucrase-isomaltase: of the 1900–odd amino acid residues of pre-pro-lactase-phlorizin hydrolase, not more than 60% at the C-terminal end appear as the "final" enzyme in the brush border membrane. The destiny and role, if any, of the "pro" portion (847 amino acids) are still unclear. Since it lacks a hydrophobic sequence of any length, it is unlikely to be targeted to a membrane. It could be secreted into the intestinal lumen (indeed, a "soluble" lactase occurs in the "succus entericus" (see Ref. 94a), but this may or may not be solubilized brush border lactase); secreted into the blood; targeted to some intracellular compartment, e.g., to lysosomes, or to the cytosol (known to be endowed with a soluble β-galactosidase); or rapidly degraded.

From the trans-most Golgi membranes the "pro" forms of these complexes are passed to the brush border on the luminal pole of the enterocyte. Contrary to what was suggested at one time,[101] these enzymes probably do not pass into the basolateral membrane en route to their final destination.[102,102a]

Very recently, the cDNA for human sucrase-isomaltase has also been partially cloned.[120b] The gene could be assigned to chromosome 3q25–26.[102c] That of the β-glycosidase (lactase-phlorizin hydrolase) complex has been localized on chromosome 2.[102d]

Trehalase

Trehalase is unique among the intestinal glycosidases in several respects. First of all, it is a minor component (accounting for about 0.1 percent of the intrinsic protein[103]). It occurs either as a monomer or as a homooligomer.[103,104] The apparent molecular weight of this polypeptide chain is approximately 75,000 daltons,[103,104] i.e., considerably smaller than those of the other glycosidases (Table 121-2). Finally, trehalase is most likely anchored to the brush border membrane via phosphatidylinositol, as shown by its selective solubilization by phosphatidylinositol-specific phospholipase C.[105] Virtually nothing is known of its biosynthesis.

DEVELOPMENT AND REGULATION OF THE DISACCHARIDASES

In Mammals Other Than Humans

At birth the small intestinal brush border membrane of most mammals is endowed with the β-glucosidase and the glucoamylase complexes only. The other α-glucosidase activities (Table 121-1) develop during extrauterine life—in the rat (see, for example, Ref. 108) and the rabbit (Ref. 109) from day 15–18 to approximately day 25–30, i.e., at the time of weaning. At the same time, lactase (and also phlorizin hydrolase[110]) activities begin to decline. Their levels in adulthood are eventually 10% or less of those at birth. Initiation of the postnatal ontogenic events in the (rat) gastrointestinal tract is probably determined by the genetic program,[111,112] while the terminal phase of intestinal development seems to be influenced by environmental factors such as nutrients and hormones.[113–115]

Enterocytes arising in the crypts acquire the ability to digest and absorb nutrients during subsequent migration along intestinal villi. The basic program describing this differentiation is carried within each enterocyte, but the signal to differentiate depends upon interactions taking place between crypts, enterocytes, and underlying fibroblasts.[116,117] At weaning, in the suckling rat, an active sucrase-isomaltase complex first appears in crypt cells and then progresses gradually to uniform distribution along the villus.[118–120a]

Little is known about the location of the primary site of control of spontaneous development of most brush border glycosidases. The development of (pro-) sucrase-isomaltase at the time of weaning (in rabbits) is likely to be regulated at the level of transcription, since enzyme activities appear concordantly with sucrase-isomaltase mRNA (Fig. 121-5).[121]

The appearance of α-glucosidase activities is subjected to hormonal control: cortisonelike steroids,[119,122–125] thyroxine,[122] insulin,[126] and epidermal growth factor[127] can induce their appearance (in rats, rabbits, and mice) if administered approximately 1 week before the time of their normal development. Glucocorticoid-induced precocious development of rat intestinal epithelium and increased turnover rate (see below) may be mediated, at least in part, through alterations in the synthesis of extracellular matrix proteins by differential regulation of their gene expression.[128] The response of sucrase-isomaltase mRNA to hydrocortisone administration is parallel to that of the enzyme activity.[125,128a]

The reader will find a discussion of this complicated topic and of the equally complicated dietary regulation of disaccharidases in recent reviews.[114,129–130]

Parallel to the appearance and increase of sucrase activity and to the decline of lactase activity taking place at the time of weaning, the life span of the enterocytes also decreases, as shown by cytokinetic measurements.[115,131–134] Indeed, the correlation between the decline in intestinal lactase and shortened

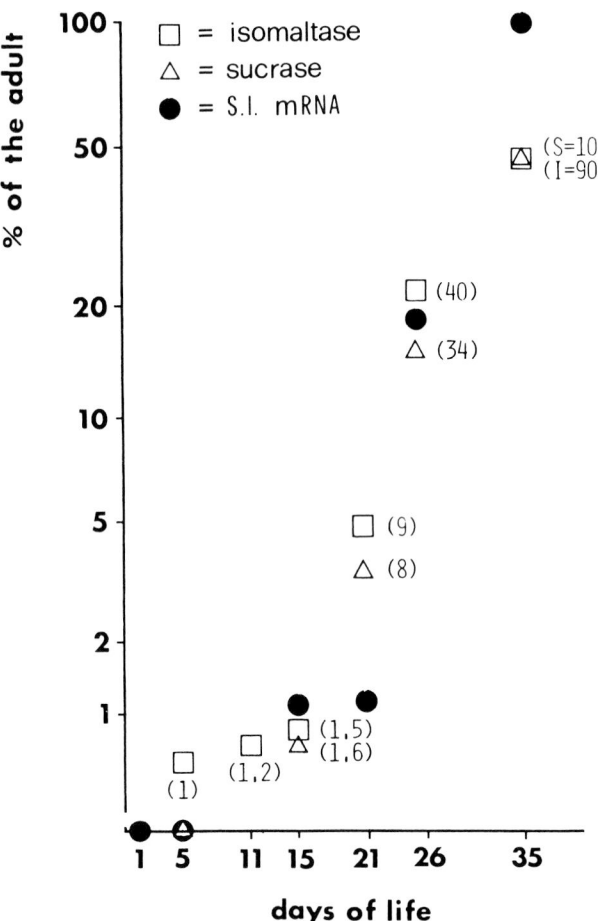

Fig. 121-5 Development of sucrase-isomaltase activities and of sucrase-isomaltase mRNA in baby rabbits. Homogenates of small intestine were assayed for sucrase (△) and isomaltase (□) activities at the various time points after birth. The enzyme activity is expressed as percent of adult value and reported on a semilogarithmic scale. In parentheses the sucrase and isomaltase activities at different ages, expressed in units per gram of protein, are shown. The corresponding adult values were 220 for sucrase and 190 for isomaltase. Sucrase-isomaltase mRNA levels (●), detected by dot blot and measured by a densitometer, are also reported as percent of adult level. (From Sebastio et al.[121] Used by permission.)

life span of enterocytes is reported to be so close[133,133a] that the former has been suggested to derive from the latter: in the adult rat, lactase appears fairly late in the life of the enterocyte, i.e., when it has already proceeded halfway along the length of the villus. In baby rats, lactase appears soon after the enterocyte has left the crypt.[118,120]

Some[134] maintain a different view, i.e., that a decreased rate of synthesis is the reason for the decline in lactase after weaning, because the rate of incorporation of leucine into lactase (relative to the total microvillar protein synthesized) is found to be much smaller in adult than in baby rats.

However, very recent work[134a] has shown that both mechanisms are likely to contribute to the postweaning decline of lactase.

The enterocytes of adult rats are rich in a high mannose, high fucose 300,000-dalton polypeptide, which is present only in traces in the suckling animals. (The opposite is true, of course, for the lactase-glycosylceramidase complex.) This 300,000-dalton polypeptide, which is devoid of lactase activity, immunologically cross-reacts with lactase and may well be

identical with pro-β-glycosidase. These observations, plus those on the effect of thyroxine on baby rats (sharp decline of lactase activity and increase of the 300,000-dalton polypeptide), suggest that the processing of pro-β-glycosidase into "final" β-glycosidase complex may be involved in the physiological decline of lactase-glycosylceramidase after weaning.[93c]

Actually, a combined effect of glucocorticosteroids and thyroxine on the decline of lactase has been known for some time.[135–137] Thyroxine accelerates the decline of lactase,[138] and thyroidectomy at 6 days in the suckling rat results in persistence of high lactase activity.[137]

Many findings in the literature argue against adaptation to dietary lactose or to other β-glycosides as a controlling factor in influencing lactase levels at weaning.[57,139–143]

In Humans

The developmental pattern of disaccharidases is different in humans. This species develops α- and β-glycosidase activities during fetal life. The newborn is therefore able to digest not only lactose, but also α-glucosides, and thus, with due precautions, can be precociously weaned. This contrasts with other mammalian species, which survive after birth on mother's milk only. Some humans also retain high intestinal lactase activity after weaning (see the section "Types of Hereditary Carbohydrate Intolerance" and Chap. 122).

Intestinal lactase activity is detectable in the human fetal intestine by the eighth week of gestation. Mucosal enzyme activity rises gradually between the eighth and thirty-fourth weeks of gestation and more rapidly shortly before birth, so that lactase activity in term neonates is two to four times higher than that in infants 2 to 11 months of age (Fig. 121-6A).[65,144–147] Within the first week of life, enterally fed preterm infants show a rapid postnatal rise in lactase activity.[65,148] Nevertheless, most premature infants do not seem to experience lactose intolerance. Although the absorption of this disaccharide in the small bowel is incomplete in both preterm and term infants, adequate colonic salvage of malabsorbed carbohydrates is achieved by colonic flora.[149–154]

α-Glucosidase activities appear between the eighth and tenth weeks of gestation, remain thereafter at levels comparable to adult levels, and increase greatly at term (Fig. 121-6A).[144,145] The primary site of control is likely to be at the level of transcription, since the appearance of sucrase-isomaltase mRNA parallels that of the enzymatic activities (Fig. 120-6B,C).[125]

Established cell lines derived from human colonic cancer show an "enterocytelike" differentiation similar to that which occurs in fetal colon. Glucose regulates the levels of sucrase-isomaltase in these cells via impaired glycosylation and rapid degradation[156a] and at the level of the mRNA.[156b]

Glycosylation of Disaccharidases and Development

Fetal and preweaning brush border disaccharidases have different sugar moieties from those of the adult forms, and different electrophoretic mobilities.[157–161a]

In the rat, the incorporation of monosaccharide precursor into glycoproteins and the proportion of newly synthesized galactosylated or fucosylated glycoproteins transported to the brush border membrane increase during postnatal development.[162]

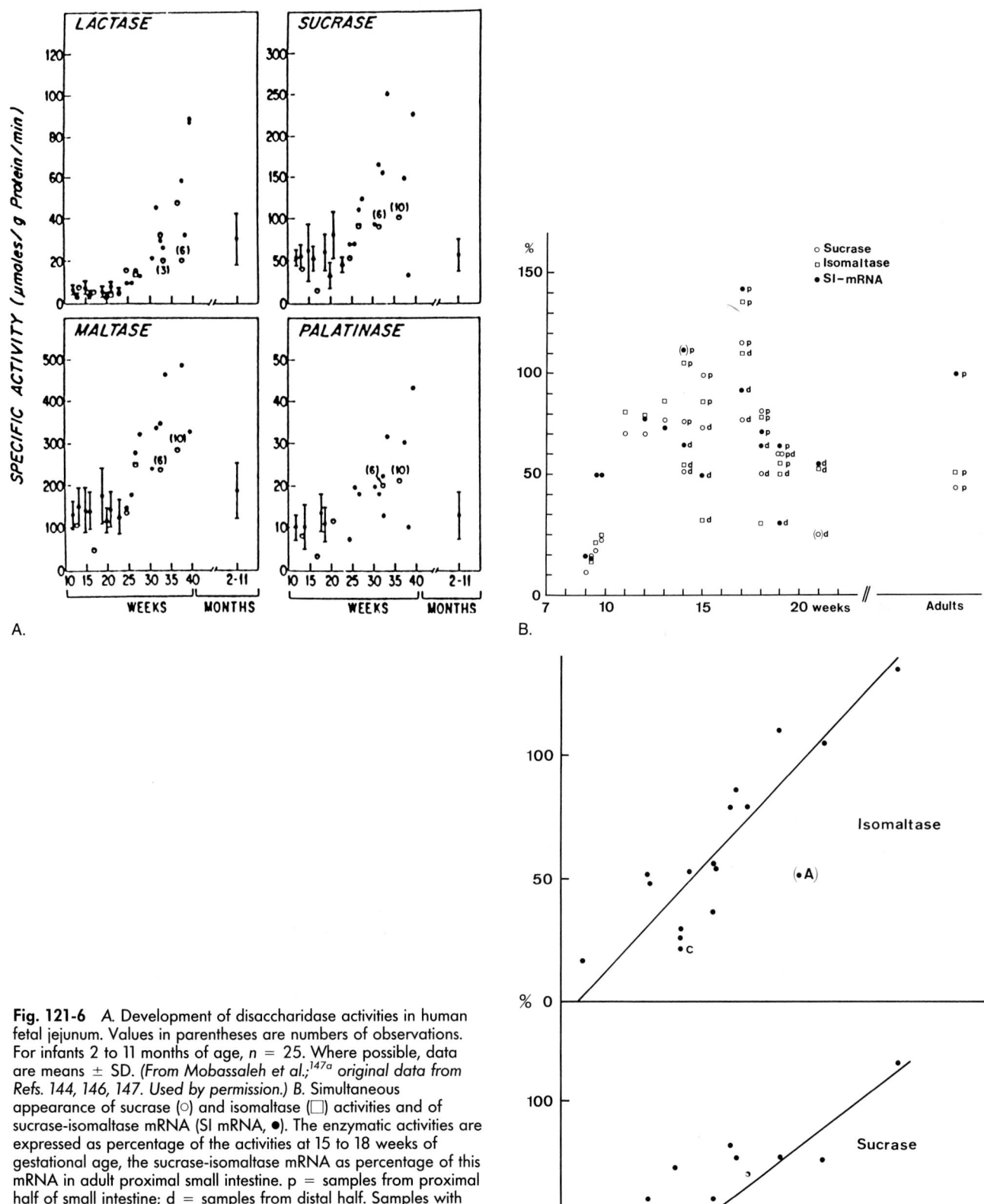

Fig. 121-6   *A.* Development of disaccharidase activities in human fetal jejunum. Values in parentheses are numbers of observations. For infants 2 to 11 months of age, n = 25. Where possible, data are means ± SD. *(From Mobassaleh et al.;[147a] original data from Refs. 144, 146, 147. Used by permission.) B.* Simultaneous appearance of sucrase (○) and isomaltase (□) activities and of sucrase-isomaltase mRNA (SI mRNA, ●). The enzymatic activities are expressed as percentage of the activities at 15 to 18 weeks of gestational age, the sucrase-isomaltase mRNA as percentage of this mRNA in adult proximal small intestine. p = samples from proximal half of small intestine; d = samples from distal half. Samples with neither p nor d were from total intestine. *(From Sebastio et al.[125] Used by permission.) C.* Correlation between isomaltase activity *(top panel),* sucrase activity *(bottom panel),* and sucrase-isomaltase mRNA in the samples of Fig. 121-6B. c = sample of colon (18 weeks old); A = sample from proximal part of small intestine from a healthy human individual. The correlation coefficients r (= 0.889 for isomaltase; = 0.812 for sucrase) and the lines were calculated utilizing all points with the exception of A. The slopes of the lines are not different from 1, and their intercepts are not different from the origin *(From Sebastio et al.[125] Used by permission.)*

CHANGES OF DISACCHARIDASES IN ACQUIRED DISEASES

Several factors such as dietary components, hormones, and endoluminal enzymes may alter the activity of brush border oligosaccharidases by varying the rates of their synthesis, their degradation, or both, and may also lead to a change in their covalent structure. The turnover of disaccharidases is much faster than cell turnover. In fact, rather than being simply synthesized once and for all by an intestinal cell, a particular membrane protein is turned over repeatedly during the cell's life cycle: whereas the life of rat intestinal villus is about 36 h, that of sucrase can vary from 2.5 to 14 h, depending on the experimental conditions.[163,164] Turnover of brush border proteins is also heterogeneous. Large-molecular-weight proteins, including disaccharidases, have a more rapid turnover than lower-molecular-weight proteins.[165,166] The sucrase and the isomaltase parts of the sucrase-isomaltase complex appear to be degraded at different rates (see below), and the carbohydrate moiety may be selectively removed at least in part while the protein core remains attached to the membrane.[167] Altered degradation rate is an important mechanism controlling levels of brush border enzymes in various pathologic and physiological conditions.

In the following, we briefly discuss three representative conditions in which changes of disaccharidase activities are brought about by a variety of mechanisms.

Diabetes

Diabetes, either in humans or in experimental animals, is accompanied by an increase in activity of membrane transport systems (for a review, see Ref. 167a) and in hydrolytic enzyme activities including those of disaccharidases; the enhanced sucrase in diabetic animals reflects a selective increase in sucrase-isomaltase *protein* which is due (mainly) to a decreased rate of degradation,[164] perhaps related to altered glycosylation of intestinal microvillus.[167b] The turnover of brush border proteins as a whole and of the enterocyte is either normal or increased.

The increased disaccharidase activity in diabetic rats appears to be the result of insulin deficiency: it is independent of intraluminal factors, such as food intake or pancreatobiliary secretions.[168] (For a review, see Ref. 130.)

Exocrine Pancreatic Insufficiency

In addition to processing some "pro" forms to the final heterodimers (see the earlier section on biosynthesis of disaccharidases), luminal proteases, particularly pancreatic, seem to play an important role in the degradation and inactivation of intestinal microvillus membrane proteins. In distal rat small intestine, the sucrase part of the sucrase-isomaltase complex is (preferentially) broken down by pancreatic enzymes.[169] Reduction of pancreatic enzymes in intestinal lumen in rats[170,171] and genetic exocrine pancreatic insufficiency in mice[172] cause decreased degradation rates and thereby enhance the activity of several disaccharidases (maltase, sucrase, lactase). Administration of elastase restores to normal the enzyme activity levels and the turnover rates.[170] In humans, pancreatic insufficiency caused by chronic pancreatitis or by cystic fibrosis also leads to increased levels of sucrase and maltase, which are also ascribed to a decrease in degradation of these enzymes. Oral administration of pancreatic proteases in patients causes a decrease in sucrase, maltase, and lactase activities.[173]

Secondary Generalized Glycosidase Deficiency

In a number of intestinal diseases with various degrees of mucosal atrophy of the small intestine, there is a generalized decrease in glycosidase activity of varying severity. In atrophic intestinal mucosa from proximal small intestine of children with active celiac disease or cow's milk protein intolerance[174] or of patients with infectious diarrheas (particularly those accompanied by malnutrition and/or small-intestinal lesion[175]), glycosidase activities are significantly reduced compared with those of normal controls. In all these conditions, lactase is usually the first glycosidase affected, is the one to reach the lowest level, and is the last to recover. Glucoamylase activity is only slightly reduced.[176–180] Various mechanisms may underlie this decrease in disaccharidase activity: atrophy of small-intestinal mucosa, with reduced surface; reduced microvillus surface area;[181] presence on the villi of immature enterocytes with low levels of digestive enzymes;[182] or increased degradation of proteins of the brush border membrane by luminal enzymes of bacterial origin, either proteases or deglycosylating enzymes, with partially deglycosylated disaccharidases then becoming more susceptible to luminal proteolysis.[183] The last mechanism could be the cause of decreased disaccharidase activity in contaminated small bowel syndrome[184] or in giardiasis.[185]

DIAGNOSIS OF DISACCHARIDASE DEFICIENCY, CARBOHYDRATE MALABSORPTION, AND CARBOHYDRATE INTOLERANCE

Disaccharidase Deficiency

Disaccharidase activity is usually measured in homogenates of small-intestinal biopsies obtained only from the proximal small intestine and therefore gives little information on the ability of the total bowel mucosa to hydrolyze disaccharide.*

Assay of disaccharidases in biopsies involves use of D-glucose-oxidase[186,187] or D-glucose-dehydrogenase[188] to measure glucose released from the substrate. Lactase activity should be assayed in the presence of p-chloromercurybenzoate, so that only the relevant brush border enzyme is measured.[189] Alternatively, brush border lactase can be selectively determined by using cellobiose as the substrate,[190] since cellobiose is not hydrolyzed by the other β-galactosidases present in the cell homogenate. For the assay of glucoamylase with glycogen or high-molecular-weight soluble starch as the substrate, it is necessary to inactivate (e.g., with chelating agents) the pancreatic α-amylase which is adsorbed on the small-intestinal mucosa; with maltose as the substrate, the sucrase-isomaltase complex must first be heat-inactivated.[43,191,192]

Disaccharidases may also be measured by quantitative immunoelectrophoresis of proteins from individual small-intestinal biopsies using specific antisera.[193]

Enzymatic activity is usually expressed either in units per

---

*One source of error, often not recognized, is the circadian rhythm in disaccharidase activities. Activity may vary by a factor of 2 between minimum and maximum (for a review, see Ref. 130).

gram of wet mucosa or in units per gram of protein (1 g wet weight of mucosa contains approximately 100 mg protein). There are no advantages in one way of expressing the results over another. (For a discussion on this point see also Ref. 167a.)

Most papers agree satisfactorily on the mean values and the standard deviations of normal α-glucosidase activities (e.g., Refs. 186, 187, 193a, 194, and 195). Normal enzymatic values are usually defined as those of histologically normal small-intestinal mucosa.[196–198] Disaccharidase "deficiency" is defined as the reduction of an enzyme activity to levels lower than the normal mean by at least 2 standard deviations.[195,198]

In congenital sucrase-isomaltase deficiency, sucrase activity is absent or nearly so, isomaltase activity is either absent or heavily reduced, and maltase activity is severely reduced (see the section "Molecular Defects," below).[199]

In heterozygotes for congenital sucrase-isomaltase deficiency, sucrase and isomaltase levels are intermediate between those of affected patients and normal controls,[199,200] and the sucrase/lactase ratio is abnormal (the normal value for the ratio having been determined for subjects with persistent high lactase activity in adult life.)[201] Heterozygotes are best identified by comparing their activity of the relevant enzyme with a weighted averaged of other enzymatic activities in their own brush border membrane.[202]

In normal humans, lactase activity varies widely according to age and ethnic group (see Chap. 122). It is conventional to regard levels of lactase activity less than 8 units per gram of protein or 0.7 units per gram wet weight as diagnostic of primary adult hypolactasia.[203–205]

Carbohydrate Malabsorption

Sugar malabsorption is the failure to digest and absorb carbohydrates adequately, with or without signs of clinical intolerance. *Intolerance* and *malabsorption* should thus not be used as synonyms.

The oral absorption tests used routinely in humans are based either on the extent of the blood glucose increase following oral administration of the sugar,* on the appearance of gases (mainly hydrogen) in the expired air, or on the presence in feces of the malabsorbed carbohydrates and/or of their fermentation products created by the colonic flora. The first two tests measure the capacity of the small bowel to digest and absorb a carbohydrate load; the third one provides additional information on the efficiency of colonic mechanisms to compensate for small-bowel failure.

The amount of sugar administered in oral tolerance tests is usually much larger than that present in a physiologically balanced diet.

Blood samples are obtained at chosen times after ingestion of the load (2 g sugar per kilogram of body weight, maximum 50 g). After sucrose and lactose are administered, a peak rise in serum glucose of less than 20 to 25 mg/dl (during the first 90 min) is diagnostic of sugar malabsorption.[187,203,206] The rise in blood glucose following administration of the disaccharide is best compared with that observed after administration of the component monosaccharides.[187,203]

*Mention should also be made of the oral tolerance test with 3-O-methyl-lactose. This substituted disaccharide is split by small-intestinal lactase to yield galactose and 3-O-methylglucose. The latter is absorbed in the small intestine (but not in the colon), and is not metabolized to any significant extent. Hence, the appearance of 3-O-methyl-glucose in urine following oral administration of 3-O-methyl-lactose is an indirect measure of total small-intestinal lactase activity.[205a]

Whereas this oral load test is reliable in adults, it is not so in children, for whom both false positive and false negative results are reported with either lactose or sucrose in 20 to 30 percent of cases.[207] It is imperative that the child have no diarrhea at the time of the test.

The extent of rise in blood glucose following oral administration of a sugar provides no information, however, as to whether the sugar has been absorbed *completely* or not. Incomplete absorption can be deduced only by measuring parameters directly related to the carbohydrates reaching the colon, such as the increase in breath hydrogen after ingesting a sugar load.

The breath hydrogen test is the most reliable and also the least invasive procedure for measuring carbohydrate malabsorption, even in children.[208–211] A peak rise in breath hydrogen greater than 20 parts per million (10, according to Kneepkens et al.[212]) over the fasting baseline value after ingestion of a carbohydrate load or a carbohydrate-containing meal indicates sugar malabsorption. When the test meal consists of solids, breath hydrogen collection should be continued for 8 h in recognition of the delayed orocaecal transit of solids as compared to liquids.[213] No antibiotic should be given before or during the test. False negative hydrogen breath tests due to inability of colonic bacterial flora to produce hydrogen from unabsorbed carbohydrates amount to 2 to 9 percent.[214–217] Excretion of hydrogen in breath after a test meal may be quantitated by comparing it with hydrogen excretion after a dose of lactulose, which is not split by lactase[18,19] and can thus be used as a reference for totally nonabsorbable sugar. This method has recently been validated in vivo in humans.[26] The lactose breath hydrogen test gives the best discrimination between lactose absorbers and malabsorbers.[194,205]

Acetate is another product of the bacterial colonic fermentation of unabsorbed carbohydrate. Venous blood acetate in the nonfasting state can be quantitatively related to carbohydrate breakdown in the colon, although the concentration of acetate in blood may vary with different types of malabsorbed carbohydrates. Breath hydrogen and blood acetate correlate with one another.[24]

When the colon fails to compensate fully for the carbohydrate malabsorption in the small intestine, the sugars themselves and the products of their bacterial breakdown (such as lactic acid or volatile fatty acids) appear in a liquid stool. Detection of reducing substances in feces using copper sulfate tablets (Clinitest)[218] is useful as a screening test for lactose malabsorption in infants after a milk-containing meal or after administration of an oral lactose load but is relatively unreliable in the newborn period[219] and in adults.[220]

Malabsorbed carbohydrates can be also detected in feces by chromatographic methods,[220a] or by measuring fecal excretion of ^{13}C-enriched sugars.[32,33]

Carbohydrate Intolerance

Sugar intolerance refers to abdominal symptoms that result from sugar malabsorption, such as flatulence, borborygmus, abdominal distension, pain, and diarrhea. Final confirmation of the role of disaccharide intolerance in producing these symptoms in an individual patient requires resolution of symptoms following elimination from the diet of the foods containing the offending disaccharide.

Clinical intolerance of lactose may correlate poorly with the levels of intestinal lactase activity[221] or with the results of oral tolerance tests[221a] or of the breath hydrogen test; see the next section.[222,233]

PATHOGENESIS OF CARBOHYDRATE INTOLERANCE

General

Whether or not sugar malabsorption produces symptoms[18,26,224–226] depends not only on the intestinal digestive and absorptive capacity, but also on additional factors, such as the quantity of the ingested sugar, the rate of gastric emptying, the response of the small intestine to the osmotic load, the metabolic activity of colonic bacteria, and the absorptive capacities of the colon, mainly for water and short-chain fatty acids (Fig. 121-7).[227] We will discuss some of these factors, one at a time.

Gastric emptying is delayed and duodenal-ileal transit is accelerated by the insufficient digestion of the sugar itself: the unabsorbed carbohydrate, when present in the distal small intestine, inhibits gastric emptying by an ill-defined mechanism; at the same time, it stimulates duodenal-ileal transit, because of the decreased water and sodium absorption.[27,228–232] (The delayed gastric emptying thus partially compensates for the effects of the high sugar in the intestine.[207])

As a consequence, the reduced digestion per se, the delayed gastric emptying, and the accelerated duodenal-ileal transit all concur in reducing monosaccharide absorption.[27,233] The ensuing flattened blood glucose profile elicits, in turn, little or no increase in the plasma levels of insulin, C peptide, and GIP.

Accelerated duodenal-ileal transit may entail the malabsorption of unrelated nutrients, such as starch or fat.[234–236] Furthermore, ileal flow rates may exceed the critical values above which the right colon propels fluid onward.[237–239]

The colonic bacterial flora salvages some of the dietary carbohydrate not digested and absorbed by the small bowel,[20] and in so doing limits both colonic wastage and diarrhea. In normal adults it has been calculated that the colon may salvage up to 20 to 25 g lactose (or lactulose) and up to 50 g starch.[26,240,241] Adaptation of the colonic flora to a particular dietary carbohydrate may further increase this salvaging capacity.[242–244] Diarrhea ensues either when this capacity is exceeded because the amount of unsplit carbohydrates is excessive, or when it is reduced for one reason or another. The latter mechanism has been suggested as the cause of lactose intolerance in milk-fed infants treated with antibiotics.[245]

The diarrhea which is due to carbohydrate malabsorption is brought about in the colon by the osmotic effect both of the unabsorbed sugars and of the short-chain fatty acids and lactic acid arising therefrom in quantities exceeding the absorptive capacity of the colon itself.

In Sucrase-Isomaltase Deficiency

The intolerance of sugars in congenital sucrase-isomaltase deficiency deserves a special comment. The clinical symptoms are mainly those of intolerance of ingested sucrose—abdominal distension, and osmotic-fermentative diarrhea with liquid feces containing sucrose and glucose (see for example, Ref. 220a). This correlates well with the lack of sucrase activity in this disease.

The situation with respect to 1,6-α-glucopyranosides is more complex. The oral tolerance of substrates of isomaltase (e.g., palatinose, i.e., 1,6-α-glucopyranosylfructose; and 1,6-α-glucose oligomers) may be as poor as that of sucrose;[246] that of dextrins, amylopectin, or starch may also be reduced.[246] When present in the diet, the latter glucans may nevertheless elicit diarrhea to a much milder degree than sucrose, particularly during the first year of life.[206,220a,246] The milder symptoms are due to the low content of 1,6-α-glucosyl bonds in these glucans (compared with the oligosaccharides used in the oral tolerance tests just mentioned); to the reduced, but not necessarily absent, 1,6-α-glucosidase (isomaltase) activity (see "Molecular Defects," below); to the salvaging role of colonic flora; and to a sufficient residual capacity to hydrolyze 1,4-α-glucopyranosidic bonds.

The last point must be specified further. The hydrolysis of

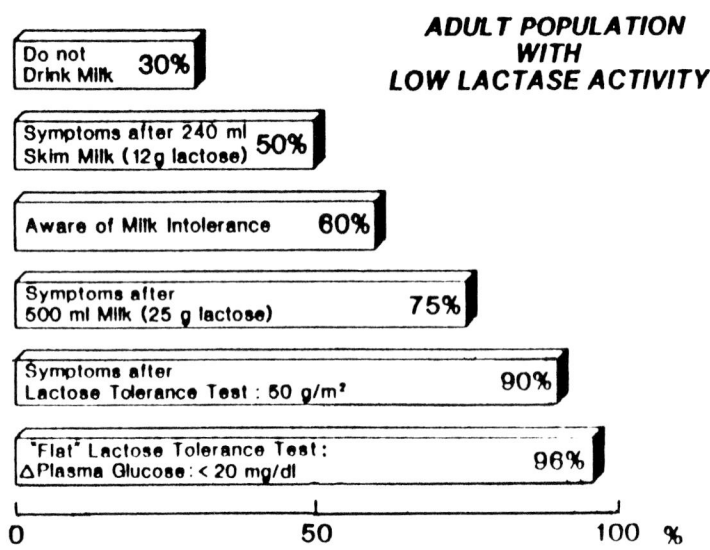

Fig. 121-7 Factors determining symptoms in lactose intolerance. They include not only small-intestinal lactase activity, but also the size of the ingested lactose load, the rate of gastric emptying, the rate of transit, and the colonic handling of the nonabsorbed sugar load. These factors are also involved in the symptomatic response to malabsorption of other sugars. *(From Ravich and Bayless.[227] Used by permission.)*

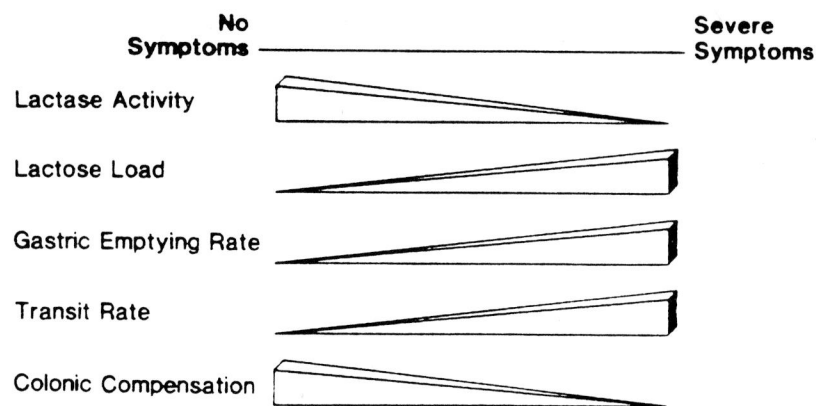

Fig. 121-8 Consequences of low intestinal lactase activity in adults, given as frequency of responses to varying amounts of milk and lactose. (From Ravich and Bayless.[227] Used by permission.)

amylopectin and of starch by α-amylase(s) is, as a rule, normal in these patients (but see below).[247] The capacity to hydrolyze completely the 1,4-α-glucans arising from α-amylolysis is severely reduced in patients with sucrose-isomaltose malabsorption, yet the level is still sufficient to ensure adequate digestion. This level is mainly due to the glucoamylase complex (Table 121-1), which is generally unaffected (but see Refs. 248–250: in some cases of sucrase-isomaltase deficiency, glucoamylase also is affected, which can lead to reduced starch tolerance); also, the maltase activity of the "residual, altered isomaltase" present in some patients with sucrase-isomaltase deficiency (see under "Molecular Defects") may contribute an adequate digestion of 1,4-α-glucopyranosidic bonds.

Finally, as mentioned in the section "Digestion of Starch and Glucose Polymers in Human Infants," in *normal* infants younger than 6 months of age the α-amylolytic digestion of starch in the lumen is either nil (during the first month of life) or incomplete. Infants of this age, if affected by sucrase-isomaltase deficiency, therefore show a very poor tolerance to starch.[221,247]

TYPES OF HEREDITARY CARBOHYDRATE INTOLERANCE

Primary Adult-Type Hypolactasia

Primary adult-type hypolactasia is the most common form of genetically determined disaccharidase deficiency (see also Chap. 122). Isolated low lactase activity in adults was first described in Europe[251] and the United States[252] in individuals from populations which typically have persistent high lactase activity in adult life. The latter phenotype was considered "normal" until it was realized that, in the great majority of the world's human populations, intestinal lactase declines during childhood and adolescence to about 5 to 10 percent of the level at birth,[253] as it does in most mammals after weaning.

Subjects with primary adult hypolactasia have no feeding problems during infancy, since the enzyme deficiency is not present at birth. The "postweaning" decline in intestinal lactase activity may start at different ages in the different ethnic groups: by age 3 years in blacks and Mexicans, later on in North European and American white groups.[201,205,254–257] In the Finnish population, hypolactasia manifests itself between 10 and 20 years of age.[258] Evidence of sugar malabsorption by oral tolerance test or breath hydrogen test suggests increasing prevalence of malabsorption with age in these populations, with a substantial percentage of individuals demonstrating abnormal responses to the tests only as teenagers.[259–262] Intolerance to consumption of 250 ml milk is rare in preadolescents.

Clinical and Nutritional Consequences of Hypolactasia. Shortly after drinking milk, lactose malabsorbers usually suffer from borborygmus, abdominal symptoms, such as meteorism, abdominal fullness, loose stools or diarrhea, and abdominal pain.[224,263–266] The clinical effects of lactose ingestion are related to dose, with a wide variation in response among individuals.[255,264,267] The relationship of symptoms to milk ingestion may even go unrecognized by some patients. The conventional lactose load used in the tolerance test, 50 g, will produce symptoms in 70 to 90 percent of malabsorbers, whereas 10 to 15 g lactose or half a pint of milk will produce abdominal symptoms in only 30 to 60 percent (see Fig. 121-8).[225,267,268]

Lactose intolerance due to lactase deficiency should be considered as the possible cause of gastrointestinal complaints in a number of patients with "idiopathic" diarrhea, irritable bowel syndrome, or recurrent abdominal pain, particularly in children[212] and in gastrectomized adults. A coincident lactose intolerance may modify the pattern of clinical presentation of gastrointestinal or other disease, and a period on a lactose-free diet may often be of diagnostic value in patients with abdominal complaints.[269]

Intolerance to lactose may also have nutritional consequences. Most lactose malabsorbers drink less milk than do lactose tolerants[225,270]; this behavior may decrease the intake of calcium. An increased incidence of intestinal lactase deficiency has been reported in subjects with osteoporosis,[271,271a] which has been attributed to the avoidance of dairy products because of symptoms induced by lactose malabsorption and/or to a deleterious effect of lactose malabsorption on calcium absorption.[272–276]

It is not clear whether consumption of moderate quantities of milk may be dangerous to lactose malabsorbers. It certainly induces loss of calories and nutrients in feces; but this may become a problem only if the overall intake is only marginally adequate.[276a,277] It is probably inadvisable to encourage the consumption of lactose-rich food, e.g., fresh milk, in populations with a high frequency of lactose malabsorbers, since in these very populations the caloric and nutritional intake is often deficient.[277,278]

There is also no answer to the opposite question, i.e., whether a lactose-rich diet in adult life may be dangerous in subjects with persistent *high* lactase activity. Simoons[278a] has noted a high incidence of senile cataract in some groups of people who consume large quantities of milk and lactose-rich dairy products and who in addition have a high frequency of persistent lactase activity in adult life. Furthermore, a high frequency of lactose absorbers has been found among adults with idiopathic senile and presenile cataract, when compared with controls, in a population with a high prevalence of primary adult-type hypolactasia;[279] this suggests that adults able to absorb galactose from a lactose-containing diet are especially susceptible to cataract.

Diagnosis. The diagnosis of lactose intolerance relies first of all on objective measurements of the clinical effects of the withdrawal and reintroduction of lactose. If the symptoms are solely due to lactose intolerance, response to a lactose-poor diet is excellent. Partial resolution of symptoms may suggest a coincidental problem of lactose malabsorption with another disorder, most often irritable bowel syndrome.[269] When gastrointestinal symptoms occur after ingestion of cow's milk, they need not be due to late-onset lactase deficiency: they may relate to a secondary lactase deficiency resulting from some gastrointestinal disease, to malabsorption of the monosaccharides deriving from the intestinal hydrolysis of lactose (glucose and galactose), to an allergic reaction to cow's milk protein,[280,281] or to some other cause.

Thus, the diagnosis of lactose malabsorption and lactase deficiency should be secured by appropriate tests (i.e., an oral tolerance test, a breath hydrogen test, and/or an assay of lactase in a jejunal biopsy specimen); see the section on diagnosis of malabsorption and intolerance, above.

Genetics and the Geographic Hypothesis. Lactase activity in human jejunum after infancy is genetically determined (see Chap. 122). The two adult human lactase phenotypes (either high or low activity) are attributable to different alleles at one autosomal locus. The effect of the allele responsible for the persistence of lactase after childhood is dominant to that of the allele causing decline of lactase activity.[252,283] Accordingly, lactase deficiency of adulthood (called *low lactase digestion capacity* by Flatz in Chap. 122) is the recessive phenotype. By calculating the lactase/maltase or lactase/sucrase ratio[283,284] in small-intestinal biopsies, a trimodal distribution was found, indicating a homozygous lactase-deficient phenotype, and heterozygous or homozygous lactase-persistent phenotypes (see Chap. 122 and Ref. 288).[278,282,285–287]

Simoons has pointed out the striking similarity between the geographic areas of persistent high lactase activity and the traditional areas of milking. According to this *geographic hypothesis*,[253] humans in the Paleolithic period, like other land mammals, underwent a normal decline in intestinal lactase activity after weaning. With the appearance of milkable domesticated animals, a mutated human being with persistent high lactase activity would have a significant selective advantage, probably because of facilitated access to calories and nutrients, particularly calcium,[289] provided by milk. That advantage would occur within groups, especially pastoral and semipastoral ones, living under marginal nutritional conditions and consuming substantial amounts of lactose-rich dairy products. This hypothesis suggests, therefore, that the genetic change causing persistent high lactase activity may have taken place under the influence of the spread of agriculture, when humans, during

the last few thousand years, ceased being food collectors (hunter-gatherers) and became food producers, thanks to the domestication of plants and animals.[290]

Therapy. In most cases it is sufficient to avoid foods rich in lactose (fresh milk, powdered milk, and milk puddings), whereas foods containing small amounts of lactose are usually well tolerated. Some individuals with hypolactasia can even drink small amounts of milk without symptoms.

Lactose malabsorbers do not have symptoms when they ingest appreciable quantities of lactose in yogurt, since the lactase of the yogurt microorganism itself markedly contributes to the digestion of the disaccharide in vivo.[291] Furthermore, the calcium in the yogurt is absorbed normally by lactose malabsorbers. Thus, yogurt is an excellent source of dietary calcium for them.[292]

Pretreatment of milk with β-galactosidase makes it well tolerated. In some countries milk previously percolated through immobilized β-galactosidase, and thus made poor in lactose, is available to the general public. The addition of microbial β-galactosidase directly to milk at mealtime also represents an effective enzyme replacement therapy.[293]

Congenital Lactase Deficiency

Congenital lactase deficiency is a very rare disease.[294–297] It is relatively more frequent in Finland, where 16 cases have recently been described.[298] Not more than 40 cases have been reported altogether.

A severe diarrhea starts during the first hours or days of life, with dehydration, malnutrition, and large amounts of lactose in the feces. On a lactose-free diet, children show good growth and psychomotor development. The disease appears in sibs and seems to have an autosomal recessive inheritance mode.[298] On a lactose-free diet, jejunal biopsies are morphologically normal; lactase activity is the only one affected. Lactase was originally thought to be totally absent in this disease,[299,300] even when a very sensitive assay method was used,[301] but most probably lactase is present, albeit at trace levels,[298,302] much lower than in adult hypolactasia.

Congenital lactase deficiency should not be confused with severe infantile lactose intolerance, first described by Durand;[303] in the latter disease the infant is critically ill, suffering from vomiting and failure to thrive on a lactose-containing diet, with lactosuria, aminoaciduria, and acidosis.[304–307] Cataract may also be present.[304,305,307] This disorder is not a mucosal enzyme deficiency, because substantial evidence exists that jejunal lactase activity is normal. It is probably due to an abnormal permeability of the gastric mucosa.[306]

Congenital Sucrase-Isomaltase Deficiency

Hereditary sucrose malabsorption was first described by Weijers et al.[308] in 1960. Shortly thereafter it was realized that in this condition isomaltose malabsorption is also present,[220a,246,309] because of an absence of or severe reduction in not only sucrase but also isomaltase activity.[199,310–312] The disease occurs in families and is inherited as an autosomal recessive trait.[200,312]

Symptoms appear when sucrose or starch dextins are added to the diet. Breast-fed infants or infants fed formulas containing only lactose remain well. The clinical manifestations are watery, osmotic-fermentative diarrhea, which may lead to dehydration and malnutrition, and even to occasional vomiting and mild steatorrhea. Failure to thrive and other symptoms are severe in the young child, but there is a tendency toward spontaneous improvement of symptoms with age; starch tolerance improves after the first years of life.[313] Symptoms, if persisting in adult life, may be limited to some increase in frequency of bowel movement and to minor abdominal distension, although episodes of diarrhea associated with large sucrose intake may still occur. In spite of this spontaneous favorable evolution, it is important that this condition be recognized as early as possible, so that the normal development of the child can be secured by removal of sucrose from the diet.[314]

The diagnosis can be missed in children with chronic diarrhea,[314,315] particularly in older children with a mild clinical presentation and normal growth and development.[316] In adults, the disease is a possible cause of refractory diarrhea or gastrointestinal complaints.[317] Many adults with this disorder have symptoms dating back to childhood, but occasionally the symptoms may appear as late as the time of puberty.[226,318–321]

Hereditary sucrase-isomaltase deficiency is probably rare in most human populations; only some 200 cases were reported up to 1984.[322] Welsh et al. found a 2 percent frequency of heterozygotes in a large series of small-intestinal biopsies from white American subjects.[201] The disease is more common among Greenland and Canadian Eskimos and in Canadian Indians, the reported incidence of homozygotes varying between 4 and 10 percent.[283,284,323] It is not known whether the high frequency of the disease in these populations is the result of the high degree of inbreeding or whether this mutation produced an unidentified biologic advantage in populations that do not traditionally eat foods containing sucrose. Such an advantage might be related to some role of sucrase-isomaltase other than its digestive function. In the rabbit, the sucrase-isomaltase complex may serve as an intestinal receptor for an enteropathogenic *Escherichia coli*.[324]

The diagnosis is based on the demonstration that osmotic-fermentative diarrhea, with increased fecal excretion of lactic acid, is elicited by sucrose and starch dextrins in the diet. A sucrose tolerance test will produce a flat blood glucose curve and will result in acid watery diarrhea and presence of sucrose in the feces, whereas the absorption of a mixture of glucose and fructose will be normal. The sucrose hydrogen breath test consistently demonstrates excessive H_2 excretion in the breath.[210,325,326] The final diagnosis is based on the demonstration of deficiencies of α-glucosidase enzymes which are typical of the disease.

Treatment in the first years of life consists in the elimination of sucrose, glucose polymers, and starch from the diet: symptoms subside within a few days. Restriction of starch intake is usually unnecessary after 2 to 3 years of age, though excessive amounts should be avoided.

Trehalase Deficiency

Trehalose is a disaccharide which occurs mainly in insects and in mushrooms.[327] In practice, the only dietary source of trehalase for humans is mushrooms.

Isolated trehalose malabsorption was reported in an elderly woman[328] and in a family.[329] In the latter case, a 24-year-old man presented diarrhea and vomiting after ingestion of a large amount of *edible* mushrooms. Peroral biopsies of the patient

and of his father showed lack of trehalase activity: both subjects presented trehalose malabsorption on oral tolerance test with the disaccharide. Trehalase deficiency appears to be an autosomal recessive phenotype.[329]

Trehalase deficiency is likely to go undetected, since ingestion of large quantities of foods containing trehalose is not common; therefore its real frequency is unknown. Studies on disaccharidase activities in intestinal biopsies suggest that this defect in adult white Americans is rare,[201] whereas it is very frequent (10 to 15 percent) in Greenland Eskimos.[322,330]

MOLECULAR DEFECTS

Congenital Sucrase-Isomaltase Deficiency

In the complex chain of events coding for the expression and hormonal regulation of a polypeptide chain of nearly 2000 amino acid residues, its membrane insertion, its glycosylation, its homing to the brush border membrane, and so on (see the section on disscharidase biosynthesis and anchoring, above), many steps can conceivably be affected by mutations. The result may be a lack of sucrase-isomaltase, or the appearance of an abnormal sucrase-isomaltase. Indeed, it was realized fairly early that sucrose-isomaltose malabsorption is a heterogeneous condition: whereas all patients lack sucrase, some have only traces of isomaltase activity while others have reduced but still conspicuous isomaltase activity.[199,249,302,331–334] The reports on the molecular defects in cases of sucrose-isomaltose malabsorption differ widely; they certainly agree with the concept that this condition has molecular genetic heterogeneity. But it is unfortunate that most of the papers dealing with this infrequent condition have investigated only a few patients (mostly belonging to a single pedigree) and have considered only a few properties. What follows is a list of reported and/or potential molecular defects.

1. Absence of sucrase-isomaltase activity and of immunologically cross-reacting material in total homogenates of jejunal biopsies was reported by Gray's group.[332] These conditions could be the consequence of mutations in the sucrase-isomaltase gene, in its promotor, or in a regulatory gene.

2. Absence of sucrase-isomaltase activity and of the corresponding protein band in SDS-PAGE of brush border *membranes* was reported by Crane's group[335] and by others.[331,333,334] This finding would be compatible with the finding in item (1) above and also with a defective homing mechanism of pro-sucrase-isomaltase into the brush border.

3. Defective homing of pro-sucrase-isomaltase between Golgi and brush border membranes has been reported by Hauri's group in cases with reduced but still fairly high isomaltase activity.[336] At least three phenotypes could be identified by the combined use of electrophoretic mobility and monoclonal antibodies: in one, the sucrase-isomaltase protein accumulated probably in the endoplasmic reticulum as a high-mannose precursor; in another, the intracellular transport was apparently blocked in the Golgi apparatus; and in a third, a catalytically altered enzyme was transported to the cell surface. The block of the high-mannose form in the endoplasmic reticulum was corroborated by in vitro pulse-chase experiments using peroral biopsies.[337,338] It should be noted that the high-mannose form of pro-sucrase-isomaltase has about one-half of the enzyme activity of the fully processed "ripe" form (at least in the pig; see Ref. 339). Furthermore, the high-mannose form in patients with defective homing is reported to be more easily degraded.[338]

4. Absence of the sucrase and isomaltase bands in SDS-PAGE of the brush border membranes and presence of abnormal band(s) have been reported. In one case a high-molecular-weight single-chain isomaltase was found which cross-reacted with anti-sucrase-isomaltase antisera.[340] Is it a "back-mutated" protease-resistant double isomaltase? (See the section on disaccharide biosynthesis, above, for the "one polypeptide chain, two active sites" hypothesis.) Is it a mutated pro-sucrase-isomaltase with enzymatically inactive sucrase portion and with resistance to proteolytic processing?

5. Absence of the sucrase subunit and presence of a low-activity isomaltase subunit was reported.[333,334] This finding may be related to that in item 3, above, or if this isomaltase is located in the brush border membrane, it may indicate a mutated isomaltase subunit with (evidently) lower enzymatic activity and impaired capacity to interact normally with sucrase. It may be due, also, to a stop in the expression of the pro-sucrase-isomaltase polypeptide chain somewhere near the end of the isomaltase portion, which prevents synthesis of the sucrase portion (and hence of the sucrase subunit).

6. Presence of an immunologically cross-reacting, enzymatically inactive protein was reported by Dubs et al.[341] in patients with nonzero isomaltase activity.

7. Reduction in the amount[249,331,333,334] and/or change in the sedimentation properties[248] of the maltase-glucoamylase complex, present in some cases of sucrose-isomaltose malabsorption, may indicate that the biologic regulation of mechanisms of the two α-glucosidase heterodimeric complexes are related—a likely possibility, in view of the close similarities between the two complexes.

8. A possible regulatory gene controlling the expression of sucrase-isomaltase and its response to diet has been demonstrated in mice,[342] which may indicate that mutations in the regulatory gene are potentially responsible for (human) sucrose-isomaltose malabsorption: the sucrase and isomaltase activities in the brush border membranes can indeed be equally and severely reduced.[343] The regulatory gene demonstrated in mice does not influence either maltase-glucoamylase or trehalase.

Primary Adult-Type Hypolactasia

The β-glycosidase complex present in the small intestine of subjects affected with primary adult-type hypolactasia seems to be identical with that present in lactose digesters: it has the same electrophoretic mobility,[202,344] the same immunological properties,[344,345] and the same specific lactase[344,345] and phlorizin hydrolase activities.[346] The difference between lactose digesters and malabsorbers must therefore be sought in the *regulation* of biosynthesis, processing, homing and/or of degradation of the β-glycosidase complex.

In all likelihood, human "primary adult-type hypolactasia" is to be equated with the decline in lactase that is universally found in mammals other than humans after weaning: the stage in life at onset is the same, and in humans and other mammals alike "baby" lactase and the reduced adult enzyme are indistinguishable. In other words, the "abnormal" allele in the regulation of lactase biosynthesis (or degradation) is the one leading to *persistence* of the enzyme in adulthood in many white peoples and other human populations.

As discussed in the section "Development and Regulation of the Disaccharidases," there is unfortunately very little agreement on the mechanism of decline in intestinal lactase in the experimental animal at weaning. For some, the major factor is the accelerated cell kinetics (e.g., Refs. 133 and 133a); for others, it is a decreased rate of synthesis (e.g., Ref. 134). One must also add to these factors the enhanced proteolytic degradation of lactase when it is already in decline, both in normal postweaning experimental mammals and in human adult malabsorbers.[173] The very interesting suggestion that the decline of lactase at the time of weaning may be related to the processing of pro-β-glycosidase to "final" lactase-glycosylceramidase has been mentioned in a previous section.[93c] A similar mechanism may be operative in adult-type hypolactasia also. Whatever the mechanism of the decline or of the persistence of lactase in adulthood, all attempts at "reinducing" the enzyme's activity or at preventing its decline by administering lactose have been singularly unsuccessful.

REFERENCES

1. MCMICHAEL HB: Disorders of carbohydrate digestion and absorption. *Clin Endocrinol Metab* 5:627, 1976.

2. GRAY GM: Carbohydrate absorption and malabsorption, in Johnson LR (ed): *Gastrointestinal Disease*. New York, Raven, 1981, p. 1063.

3. GITZELMANN R, AURICCHIO S: The handling of soya α-galactosides by a normal and a galactosemic child. *Pediatrics* 36:231, 1965.

4. PAZUR JH, FRENCH D, KNAPP DW: Mechanism of salivary amylase action. *Proc Iowa Acad Sci* 57:203, 1950.

5. PAZUR JH: The hydrolysis of amylotriose and amylotetraose by salivary amylase. *J Biol Chem* 205:75, 1953.

6. PAZUR JH, BUDOVICH T: Hydrolysis of amylotriose by cristalline salivary amylase. *Science* 121:702, 1955.

7. PAZUR JH: Radioisotopes and enzymatic transformation of oligosaccharides. *Abstr 134th Am Chem Soc Meeting* 6D New York, 1958.

8. NORDIN PH: Action pattern of salivary amylase. Thesis, Iowa State College, 1953.

9. BIRD R, HOPKINS RH: The action of some α-amylases on amylose. *Biochem J* 56:86, 1954.

10. WALKER GJ, WHELAN WJ: The action patterns of alfa-amylases. *Stärke* 12:358, 1960.

11. WHELAN WJ, ROBERTS PJP: The mechanism of carbohydrase action. Part II, Alfa-amylolysis of linear substrate. *J Chem Soc* 1928, 1953.

12. WHELAN WJ: The action patterns of α-amylases. *Stärke* 12:358, 1960.

13. ROBERTS PJP, WHELAN WJ: The mechanism of carbohydrase action. 5. Action of human salivary α-amylase on amylopectin and glycogen. *Biochem J* 76:246, 1960.

14. BINES J, WHELAN WJ: The mechanism of carbohydrase action. 6. Structure of a salivary α-amylase limit dextrin from amylopectin. *Biochem J* 76:253, 1960.

15. HELLER J, SCHRAMM M: α-amylase limit dextrins of high molecular weight obtained from glycogen. *Biochim Biophys Acta* 81:96, 1964.

16. NORDIN PH, FRENCH D: 1-Phenyl-flavazole derivates of starch dextrins. *J Am Chem Soc* 80:1445, 1958.

17. AURICCHIO S, DELLA PIETRA D, VEGNENTE A: Studies on intestinal digestion of starch in man. II. Intestinal hydrolysis of amylopectin in infants and children. *Pediatrics* 39:853, 1967.

18. ANDERSON IH, LEVINE AS, LEVITT MD: Incomplete absorption of the carbohydrate in all-purpose wheat flour. *N Engl J Med* 304:891, 1981.

19. LEVINE AS, LEVITT MD: Malabsorption of starch moiety of oats, corn, and potatoes. *Gastroenterology* 80:1209, 1981.

20. BOND JH, LEVITT MD: Use of pulmonary hydrogen (H2) measurements to quantitate carbohydrate absorption. Study of partially gastrectomized patients. *J Clin Invest* 51:1219, 1972.

21. STEPHEN AM, HADDAD AC, PHILLIPS SF: Passage of carbohydrate into the colon. *Gastroenterology* 85:589, 1983.

22. CHAPMAN RW, SILLERY JK, GRAHAM MM, SAUNDERS DR: Absorption of starch by healthy ileostomates: Effect of transit time and carbohydrate load. *Am J Clin Nutr* 41:1244, 1985.

23. GODDARD MS, YOUNG G, MARCUS R: The effect of amylose content on insulin and glucose responses to ingested rice. *Am J Clin Nutr* 39:388, 1984.

24. POMARE EW, BRANCH WJ, CUNNINGS JH: Carbohydrate fermentation in the human colon and its relation to acetate concentration in venous blood. *J Clin Invest* 75:1448, 1985.

25. DE VIZIA B, CICCIMARRA F, DE CICCO N, AURICCHIO S: Digestibility of starches in infants and children. *J Pediatr* 86:50, 1975.

26. FLOURIE B, FLORENT C, JOUANY JP, THIVEND P, ETANCHAUD F, RAMBAUD JC: Colonic metabolism of wheat starch in healthy humans. *Gastroenterology* 90:111, 1986.

27. LAYER P, ZINSMEISTER AR, DI MAGNO E: Effects of decreasing intraluminal amylase activity on starch digestion and postprandial gastrointestinal function in humans. *Gastroenterology* 91:41, 1986.

28. LEBENTHAL E, LEE PC: Development of functional response in human exocrine pancreas. *Pediatrics* 66:556, 1980.

29. ZOPPI G, ANDREOTTI G, PAJNO-FERRARA F, NJAI DM, GABURRO D: Exocrine pancreas function in premature and fullterm neonates. *Pediatr Res* 6:880, 1972.

30. SENTERRE J: Net absorption of starch in low birth weight infants. *Acta Paediatr Scand* 69:653, 1980.

31. SHULMAN RJ, WONG WW, IRVING CS, NICHOLS BL, KLEIN PD: Utilization of dietary cereal by young infants. *J Pediatr* 103:23, 1983.

32. KLEIN PD, KLEIN ER: Application of stable isotopes to pediatric nutrition and gastroenterology: Measurement of nutrient absorption and digestion using 13C. *J Pediatr Gastroenterol Nutr* 4:19, 1985.

33. SHULMAN RJ, KERZNER B, SLOAN HR, BOUTTON TW, WONG WW, NICHOLS BL, KLEIN PD: Absorption and oxidation of glucose polymers of different lengths in young infants. *Pediatr Res* 20:740, 1986.

34. MURRAY RD, KERZNER B, SLOAN HR, MCCLUNG J, GILBERT M, AILABOUNI A: The contribution of salivary amylase to glucose polymers hydrolysis in premature infants. *Pediatr Res* 20:186, 1986.

35. KERZNER B, SLOAN HR, MCCLUNG HJ, AILABOUNI A: The jejunal absorption of glucose oligomers in the absence of pancreatic enzymes. *Pediatr Res* 15:250, 1981.

36. KELLY JJ, ALPERS DH: Properties of human intestinal glucoamylase. *Biochem Biophys Acta* 315:113, 1981.

37. UGOLEV AM: Membrane (contact) digestion. *Physiol Rev* 45:555, 1965.

38. GRAY GM, LALLY BC, CONKLIN KA: Action of intestinal sucrase-isomaltase and its monomers on an α-limit dextrin. *J Biol Chem* 254:6038, 1979.

39. TARAVEL FR, DATEMA R, WOLOSZCZUK W, MARSHALL JJ, WHELAN WJ: Purification and characterization of a pig intestinal α-limit dextrinase. *Eur J Biochem* 130:147, 1983.

40. RODRIGUEZ IR, TARAVEL FR, WHELAN WJ: Characterization and function of pig intestinal sucrase isomaltase and its separate subunits. *Eur J Biochem* 143:575, 1984.

41. SJÖSTRÖM H, NORÉN O, DANIELSEN EM, SKOVBJERG H: Structure of microvillar enzymes in different phases of their life cycles, in Porter R, Collins G (eds): *Brush Border Membranes.* Ciba Foundation Symposium 95, London, Pitman, 1983, p 95.

42. SÖRENSEN SH, NORÉN O, SJÖSTRÖM H, DANIELSEN EM: Amphiphilic pig intestinal microvillus maltase/glucoamylase. Structure and specificity. *Eur J Biochem* 126:559, 1982.

43. DAHLQVIST A: Specificity of the human intestinal disaccharidases and implications for hereditary disaccharide intolerance. *J Clin Invest* 41:463, 1962.

44. AURICCHIO S, SEMENZA G, RUBINO A: Multiplicity of human intestinal disaccharidases. II. Characterization of the individual maltases. *Biochim Biophys Acta* 96:498, 1965.

45. KOLÍNSKÁ J, SEMENZA G: Studies on intestinal sucrase and on intestinal sugar transport. V. Isolation and properties of sucrase-isomaltase from rabbit small intestine. *Biochim Biophys Acta* 146:181, 1967.

46. MESSER M, KERRY KR: Intestinal digestion of maltotriose in man. *Biochim Biophys Acta* 132:432, 1967.

47. BARNETT JEG, JARVIS WTS, MUNDAY KA: Enzymic hydrolysis of the carbon-fluorine bond of a α-D-glucosyl fluoride by rat intestinal mucosa. *Biochem J* 103:699, 1967.

48. COGOLI A, SEMENZA G: A probable oxocarbonium ion in the reaction mechanism of small intestinal sucrase and isomaltase. *J Biol Chem* 250:7802, 1975.

49. DAHLQVIST A: Characterization of hog intestinal invertase as a glucosido-invertase. III. Specificity of purified invertase. *Acta Chem Scand* 14:63, 1960.

50. LARNER J, MCNICKLE CM: Gastrointestinal digestion of starch. I. The action of oligo-1,6-glucosidase on branched saccharides. *J Biol Chem* 215:723, 1955.

51. SEIJI M: Studies on digestion of starch by α-limit-dextrinase. *J Biochem* 40:519, 1953.

52. LABAT-ROBERT J, BAUMANN FC, BAR-GUILLOUX E, ROBIC D: Comparative specificities of trehalases from various species. *Comp Biochem Physiol* 61B:111, 1978.

53. HEHRE EJ, SAWAI T, BREWER CF, NAKANO M, KANDA T: Trehalase: stereocomplementary hydrolytic and glucosyl transfer reactions with α- and β-D-glucosyl fluoride. *Biochemistry* 21:3090, 1982.

54. WALLENFELS K, FISCHER J: Untersuchungen über milchzuckerspaltende Enzyme. X. Die Laktase des Kälberdarms. *Z Physiol Chem* 321:223, 1960.

55. KRAML J, KOLÍNSKÁ J, ELLEDÉROVÁ H, HIRŠOVÁ D: β-Glucosidase (phlorizin hydrolase) activity of the lactase fraction isolated from the small intestinal mucosa of infant rat and the relationship between β-glucosidases and β-galactosidases. *Biochim Biophys Acta* 258:520, 1972.

56. SEMENZA G, AURICCHIO S, RUBINO A: Multiplicity of human intestinal disaccharidases. 1. Chromatographic separation of maltases and of two lactases. *Biochim Biophys Acta* 96:487, 1965.

57. SCHLEGEL-HAUETER S, HORE P, KERRY KR, SEMENZA G: The preparation of lactase and glucoamylase of rat small intestine. *Biochim Biophys Acta* 258:506, 1971.

58. LEESE HJ, SEMENZA G: On the identity between the small-intestinal enzymes phlorizin-hydrolase and glycosylceramidase. *J Biol Chem* 248:8170, 1973.

59. SKOVBJERG H, NORÉN O, SJÖSTRÖM H, DANIELSEN EM, ENEVOLDSEN BS: Further characterization of intestinal lactase/phlorizin hydrolase. *Biochim Biophys Acta* 707:89, 1982.

60. MALATHI P, CRANE RK: Phlorizin hydrolase: A β-glucosidase of hamster intestinal brush border membrane. *Biochim Biophys Acta* 173:245, 1969.

61. COLOMBO V, LORENZ-MEYER H, SEMENZA G: Small-intestinal phlorizin hydrolase: The β-glycosidase complex. *Biochim Biophys Acta* 327:412, 1973.

62. SKOVBJERG H: Immunoelectrophoretic studies on human small intestinal brush border proteins. The longitudinal distribution of peptidases and disaccharidases. *Clin Chim Acta* 112:205, 1981.

63. TRIADOU N, BATAILLE J, SCHMITZ J: Longitudinal study of the human intestinal brush border membrane proteins. Distribution of the main disaccharidases and peptidases. *Gastroenterology* 85:1326, 1983.

64. RAUL F, LACROIX B, APRAHAMIAN M: Longitudinal distribution of brush border hydrolases and morphological maturation in the intestine of the preterm infant. *Early Hum Dev* 13:225, 1986.

65. AURICCHIO S, RUBINO A, MÜRSET G: Intestinal glycosidase activities in the human embryo, fetus and newborn. *Pediatrics* 35:944, 1965.

66. MILLER D, CRANE RK: The digestive function of the epithelium of the small intestine. 1. An intracellular locus of disaccharide and sugar phosphate ester hydrolysis. *Biochim Biophys Acta* 52:281, 1961.

67. PARSON DS, PRITCHARD JS: Hydrolysis of disaccharides during absorption by the perfused small intestine of amphibia. *Nature* 208:1097, 1965.

68. HAMILTON JD, MCMICHAEL HB: Role of microvillous in the absorption of disaccharides. *Lancet* 2:154, 1968.

69. MALATHI P, RAMASWAMY K, CASPARY WF, CRANE RK: Studies on the transport of glucose from disaccharides by hamster small intestine in vitro. 1. Evidence for a disaccharidase-related transport system. *Biochim Biophys Acta* 307:613, 1973.

70. RAMASWAMY K, MALATHI P, CASPARY WF, CRANE RK: Studies on the transport of glucose from disaccharides by hamster small intestine in vitro. II: Characteristic of the disaccharidase-related transport system. *Biochim Biophys Acta* 345:39, 1974.

71. GRAY GM, INGELFINGER FJ: Intestinal absorption of sucrose in man: The site of hydrolysis and absorption. *J Clin Invest* 44:390, 1965.

72. MCMICHAEL HB, WEBB J, DOWSON AM: The absorption of maltose and lactose in man. *Clin Sci* 33:135, 1967.

73. ALPERS DH, COTE MN: Inhibition of lactose hydrolysis by dietary sugars. *Am J Physiol* 221:865, 1971.

74. DAWSON DJ, LOBLEY RW, BURROWS PC, MILLER W, HOLMES R: Lactose digestion by human jejunal biopsies: The relationship between hydrolysis and absorption. *Gut* 27:521, 1986.

75. GRAY GM, SANTIAGO N: Disaccharide absorption in normal and diseased human intestine. *Gastroenterology* 51:489, 1966.

76. SEMENZA G: A unifying concept in the phylogenesis, biosynthesis, membrane insertion and physiopathology of sucrase-isomaltase and other brush border proteins, in Alvarado F, van Os CH (eds): *Ion Gradient-Coupled Transport.* Amsterdam, Elsevier, 1986, p 41.

77. SEMENZA G: Anchoring and biosynthesis of stalked brush border membrane proteins: Glycosidases and peptidases of enterocytes and renal tubuli. *Annu Rev Cell Biol* 2:255, 1986.

78. SPIESS M, HUNZIKER W, LODISH HF, SEMENZA G: Molecular cell biology of brush border hydrolases: Sucrase isomaltase and γ-glutamyl transpeptidase, in Kenny AJ, Turner AJ (eds): *Ectoenzymes.* Amsterdam, Elsevier, 1987, p 87.

78a. SEMENZA G: The insertion of stalked proteins of the brush border membranes: The state of the art in 1988. *Biochem Int*, in press.

79. BRUNNER J, HAUSER H, BRAUN H, WILSON KJ, WACKER H, O'NEILL B, SEMENZA G: The mode of association of the enzyme complex sucrase-iso-

maltase with the intestinal brush border membrane. *J Biol Chem* 254:1821, 1979.

80. HUNZIKER W, SPIESS M, SEMENZA G, LODISH H: The sucrase-isomaltase complex: Primary structure, membrane orientation and evolution of a stalked intrinsic brush border protein. *Cell* 46:227, 1986.

81. LEE L, FORSTNER G: Hydrophobic binding domains of rat intestinal maltase-glucoamylase. *Biochem Cell Biol* 64:782, 1986.

82. HU C, SPIESS M, SEMENZA G: The mode of anchoring and precursor forms of sucrase-isomaltase and maltase-glucoamylase in chicken intestinal brush border membrane. Phylogenetic implications. *Biochim Biophys Acta* 896:275, 1987.

82a. SJÖSTRÖM H, NORÉN O, CHRISTIANSEN LA, WACKER H, SPIESS M, BIGLER-MEIER B, RICKLI EE, SEMENZA G: N-terminal sequences of pig intestinal sucrase-isomaltase and pro-sucrase-isomaltase. Implications for the biosynthesis and membrane insertion of pro-sucrase-isomaltase. *FEBS Lett* 148:321, 1982.

82b. SPIESS M, BRUNNER J, SEMENZA G: Hydrophobic labeling, isolation and partial characterization of the NH₂-terminal membranous segment of sucrase-isomaltase complex. *J Biol Chem* 257:2370, 1982.

83. NORÉN O, SJÖSTRÖM H, COWELL G, TRANUM-JENSEN J, HANSEN OC, WELINDER KG: Pig intestinal microvillar maltase-glucoamylase. Structure and membrane insertion. *J Biol Chem* 261:12306, 1986.

84. COWELL GM, SJÖSTRÖM H, NORÉN O, TRANUM-JENSEN J: Topology and quaternary structure of pro-sucrase-isomaltase and final forms of sucrase-isomaltase. *Biochem J* 237:455, 1986.

85. SEMENZA G: Intestinal oligo- and disaccharides, in Randle PJ, Steiner DF (eds): *Carbohydrate Metabolism and Its Disorders*. London, Academic, 1981, p 425.

86. HAUSER H, SEMENZA G: Sucrase-isomaltase: A stalked intrinsic protein of the brush border membrane. *CRC Crit Rev Biochem* 14:319, 1983.

87. SEMENZA G: Glycosidases, in Kenny AJ, Turner AJ (eds): *Ectoenzymes*. Amsterdam, Elsevier, 1987, p 265.

88. SEMENZA G: The sucrase-isomaltase complex, a large dimeric amphipathic protein from the small intestinal brush border membrane: Emerging structure-function relationships, in Ahlberg P, Sundelöf LO (eds): *Structure and Dynamics of Chemistry*. Symp 500th Jubilee Univ Uppsala, Sweden, 1977, p 226.

89. SEMENZA G: Mode of insertion of the sucrase-isomaltase complex in the intestinal brush border membrane: Implications for the biosynthesis of this stalked intrinsic membrane protein, in Elliot K, Whelan WJ (eds): *Development of Mammalian Absorptive Processes, Ciba Foundation Symp*, Amsterdam, Excerpta Medica, 1979, 70, p 133.

90. SEMENZA G: The mode of anchoring of sucrase-isomaltase to the small-intestinal brush border membrane and its biosynthetic implications, in Rapoport S, Schewe T (eds): *Proc 12th FEBS Meeting, Dresden*. Oxford/New York, Pergamon, 1978, vol 53, p 21.

90a. FULCHER IS, PAPPIN JC, KENNY AJ: The N-terminal amino acid sequence of pig kidney endopeptidase 24.11 shows homology with pro-sucrase-isomaltase. *Biochem J* 240:305, 1986.

90b. SPIESS M, MANTEI N, SEMENZA G: Unpublished observations, 1989.

90c. HOEFSLOOT LH, HOOGEVEEN-WESTERVELD M, KROOS MA, VAN BEUMEN J, REUSER AJJ, OOSTRA BA: Primary structure and processing of lysosomal α-glucosidase; homology with the intestinal sucrase-isomaltase complex. *EMBO J* 7:1697, 1988.

91. DANIELSEN EM, SJÖSTRÖM H, NORÉN O: Biosynthesis of microvillar proteins. Pulse-chase labeling studies on maltase-glucoamylase, aminopeptidase A and dipeptidyl peptidase IV. *Biochem J* 210:389, 1983.

92. DANIELSEN EM, SKOVBJERG H, NORÉN O, SJÖSTRÖM H: Biosynthesis of intestinal microvillar proteins. Intracellular processing of lactase-phlorizin hydrolase. *Biochem Biophys Res Commun* 122:82, 1984.

93. SKOVBJERG H, DANIELSEN EM, NORÉN O, SJÖSTRÖM H: Evidence for biosynthesis of lactase-phlorizin hydrolase as a single-chain high-molecular weight precursor. *Biochim Biophys Acta* 789:247, 1984.

93a. NAIM HY, STERCHI EE, LENTZE MJ: Biosynthesis and maturation of lactase-phlorizin hydrolase in the human small intestinal epithelial cells. *Biochem J* 241:427, 1987.

93b. BÜLLER HA, MONTGOMERY RK, SASAK WV, GRAND RJ: Biosynthesis, glycosylation and intracellular transport of intestinal lactase-phlorizin hydrolase in rat. *J Biol Chem* 262:17206, 1987.

93c. NSI-EMVO E, LAUNAY JF, RAUL F: Is adult-type hypolactasia in the intestine of mammals related to changes in the intracellular processing of lactase? *Cell Mol Biol* 33:335, 1987.

93d. MANTEI N, VILLA M ENZLER T, WACKER H, BOLL W, JAMES P, HUNZIKER H, SEMENZA G: Complete primary structure of human and rabbit lactase-phlorizin hydrolase: Implications for biosynthesis, membrane anchoring and evolution of the enzyme. *EMBO J* 7:2705, 1988.

94. GHERSA P, HUBER P, SEMENZA G, WACKER H: Cell-free synthesis, membrane integration and glycosylation of pro-sucrase-isomaltase. *J Biol Chem* 261:7969, 1986.

94a. ARAMAYO LA, DE SILVA DGH, HUGHES CA, BROWN GA, MCNEISH AS: Disaccharidase activities in jejunal fluid. *Arch Dis Child* 58:686, 1983.

95. DANIELSEN EM: Biosynthesis of intestinal microvillar proteins. Pulse-chase labeling studies on aminopeptidase N and sucrase-isomaltase. *Biochem J* 204:639, 1982.

96. DANIELSEN EM, COWELL GM, NORÉN O, SJÖSTRÖM H: Biosynthesis of microvillar proteins. *Biochem J* 221:1, 1984.

97. HAURI HP, STERCHI EE, BIENZ D, FRANSEN JAM, MARXER A: Expression and intracellular transport of microvillus membrane hydrolases in human intestinal epithelial cells. *J Cell Biol* 101:838, 1985.

98. KELLY JJ, ALPERS DH: Blood group antigenicity of purified human intestinal disaccharidases. *J Biol Chem* 248:8216, 1973.

99. FERACCI H, RIGAL A, MAROUX S: Biosynthesis and intracellular pool of aminopeptidase N in rabbit enterocytes. *J Membr Biol* 83:139, 1985.

100. COUSINEAU J, GREEN JR: Isolation and characterization of the proximal and distal forms of lactase-phlorizin-hydrolase from the small intestine of the suckling rat. *Biochim Biophys Acta* 615:147, 1980.

101. HAURI HP, QUARONI A, ISSELBACHER K: Biogenesis of intestinal plasma membrane: Posttranslational route and cleavage of sucrase-isomaltase. *Proc Natl Acad Sci USA* 76:5183, 1979.

102. DANIELSEN EM, COWELL GM: Biosynthesis of intestinal microvillar proteins. Evidence for an intracellular sorting taking place in, or shortly after, exit from the Golgi complex. *Eur J Biochem* 152:493, 1985.

102a. HANSEN G, DABELSTEEN E, SJÖSTRÖM H, NORÉN O: Immunomicroscopic localization of aminopeptidase N in the pig enterocyte. Implication for the route of intracellular transport. *Eur J Cell Biol* 43:53, 1987.

102b. GREEN F, EDWARDS Y, HAURI HP, POVEY S, HO WM, PINTO M, SWALLOW D: Isolation of a cDNA probe for a human jejunum brush-border hydrolase, sucrase-isomaltase, and assignment of the gene locus to chromosome 3. *Gene* 57:101, 1987.

102c. WEST LF, DAVIS MB, GREEN FR, LINDENBAUM RH, SWALLOW D: Regional assignment of the gene coding for human sucrase-isomaltase (SI) to chromosome 3q25-26. *Ann Hum Genet* 52:57, 1988.

102d. KRUSE TA, BOLUND L, GRZESCHIK KH, ROPERS HH, SJÖSTRÖM H, NORÉN O, MANTEI N, SEMENZA G: The human lactase-phlorizin hydrolase gene is located on chromosome 2. *FEBS Lett* 240:123, 1988.

103. GALAND G: Purification and characterization of kidney and intestinal brush-border membrane trehalases from the rabbit. *Biochim Biophys Acta* 789:10, 1984.

104. YOKOTA K, NISHI Y, TAKESUE Y: Purification and characterization of amphiphilic trehalase from rabbit small intestine. *Biochim Biophys Acta* 881:405, 1986.

105. TAKESUE Y, YOKOTA K, NISHI Y, TAGUCHI R, IKESAWA H: Solubilization of trehalase from rabbit renal and intestinal brush-border membranes by a phosphoinositol-specific phospholipase C. *FEBS Lett* 201:5, 1986.

106. WACKER H, JAUSSI R, SONDEREGGER O, DOKOW M, GHERSA P, HAURI HP, CHRISTEN PH, SEMENZA G: Cell-free synthesis of the one-chain precursor of a major intrinsic protein complex of the small-intestinal brush border membrane (pro-sucrase-isomaltase). *FEBS Lett* 136:329, 1981.

107. DANIELSEN EM, COWELL GM: Biosynthesis of intestinal microvillar proteins. Further characterization of the intracellular processing and transport. *FEBS Lett* 166:28, 1984.

108. RUBINO A, ZIMBALATTI F, AURICCHIO S: Intestinal disaccharidase activities in adult and suckling rats. *Biochim Biophys Acta* 92:305, 1964.

109. DUBS R, GITZELMAN R, STEINMANN B, LINDENMANN J: Catalytically inactive sucrase antigen of rabbit small intestine: The enzyme precursor. *Helv Paediatr Acta* 30:89, 1975.

110. COLOMBO V, LORENZ-MEYER H, SEMENZA G: Small-intestinal phlorizin hydrolase: The "β-glycosidase complex." *Biochim Biophys Acta* 327:412, 1973.

111. LEE PC, LEBENTHAL E: Early weaning and precocious development of small intestine in rats: Genetic, dietary or hormonal control. *Pediatr Res* 17:645, 1983.

112. YEH KJ, HALT PR: Ontogenic timing mechanism initiates the expression of rat intestinal sucrase activity. *Gastroenterology* 90:520, 1986.

113. HENNING SJ: Postnatal development: Coordination of feeding, digestion and metabolism. *Am J Physiol* 241:G199, 1981.

114. HENNING SJ: Ontogeny of enzymes in the small intestine. *Annu Rev Physiol* 47:231, 1985.

115. KLEIN RM, MCKENZIE JC: The role of cell renewal in the ontogeny of the intestine. I. Cell proliferation patterns in adult, fetal and neonatal intestine. *J Pediatr Gastroenterol Nutr* 2:204, 1983.

116. KEDINGER M, SIMON PM, GRENIER JF, HAFFEN K: Role of epithelial mesenchymal interactions in the ontogenesis of intestinal brush border enzymes. *Dev Biol* 86:339, 1981.

117. HAFFEN K, LACROIX B, KEDINGER M, SIMON-ASSMANN PM: Inductive properties of fibroblastic cell cultures derived from rat intestinal mucosa on epithelial differentiation. *Differentiation* 23:226, 1983.

118. SIMON PM, KEDINGER M, RAUL F, GRENIER JF, HAFFEN K: Developmental pattern of rat intestinal brush border enzymic proteins along the villous-crypt axis. *Biochem J* 178:407, 1979.

119. DOELL RG, KRETCHMER N: Intestinal invertase: Precocious development of activity after injection of hydrocortisone. *Science* 143:42, 1964.

120. BOYLE JT, KOKONOS M, KOLDOVSKÝ O: Developmental profile of jejunal lactase and sucrase activity along the villous-crypt in the rat. *Pediatr Res* 16:157A, 1982.

120a. LUND EK, SMITH MW: Rat jejunal disaccharidase activity increases biphasically during early development. *J Physiol* 391:487, 1987.

121. SEBASTIO G, HUNZIKER W, BALLABIO A, AURICCHIO S, SEMENZA G: On the primary site of control in the spontaneous development of small intestinal sucrase isomaltase after birth. *FEBS Lett* 208:460, 1986.

122. MALO CH, MÉNARD D: Hormonal control of intestinal glucoamylase activity in suckling and adult mice. *Comp Biochem Physiol* 65B:169, 1980.

123. KEDINGER M, SIMON PM, RAUL F, GRENIER JF, HAFFEN K: The effect of dexamethasone on the development of rat intestinal brush border enzymes in organ culture. *Dev Biol* 74:9, 1980.

124. BEAULIEU JF, CALVERT R: Influences of dexamethasone on the maturation of fetal mouse intestinal mucosa in organ culture. *Comp Biochem Physiol* 82A:91, 1985.

125. SEBASTIO G, HUNZIKER W, O'NEILL B, MALO C, MÉNARD D, AURICCHIO S, SEMENZA G: The biosynthesis of intestinal sucrase-isomaltase in human embryo is most likely controlled at the level of transcription. *Biochem Biophys Res Commun* 149:830, 1987.

126. MÉNARD D, MALO CH, CALVERT R: Insulin accelerates the development of intestinal brush border hydrolytic activities of suckling mice. *Dev Biol* 85:150, 1981.

127. MALO CH, MÉNARD D: Influence of epidermal growth factor on the development of suckling mouse intestinal mucosa. *Gastroenterology* 83:28, 1982.

128. WALSH MJ, LELEIKO NS, STERLING KM: Glucocorticoid-induced development of the rat small intestine is associated with differential regulation of intestinal and basement membrane collagen in RNA synthesis. *Gastroenterology* 90:1683(A), 1986.

128a. SEBASTIO G, HUNZIKER W, BALLABIO A, MAIURI S, AURICCHIO S, SEMENZA G: On the primary site of control in spontaneous and glucocorticoid-triggered precocious development of small-intestinal sucrase-isomaltase complex. 20th Annual Meeting of the European Society for Paediatric Gastroenterology and Nutrition.

129. KEDINGER M, HAFFEN K, SIMON-ASSMAN P: Control mechanisms in the ontogenesis of villus cells, in Desnuelle P, Sjöström H, Norén O (eds): *Molecular and Cellular Biology of Digestion.* Amsterdam, Elsevier, 1986, p 323.

129a. MOOG F: Perinatal development of the enzymes of the brush border membrane, in Lebenthal E (ed): *Textbook of Gastroenterology and Nutrition.* New York, Raven, 1981, p 139.

130. KOLDOVSKÝ O: Developmental, dietary and hormonal control of intestinal disaccharidases in mammals (including man), in Randle PJ, Steiner DF, Whelan WJ (eds): *Carbohydrate Metabolism and Its Disorders.* London, Academic, 1981, vol 3, p 418.

131. BUTS JP, DE MEYER R: Postnatal proximodistal development of the small bowel mucosal mass in growing rats. *Biol Neonate* 40:62, 1981.

132. BUTS JP, DE MEYER R: Intestinal development in the suckling rat: Effects of weaning, diet composition and glucocorticoids on thymidine kinase activity and DNA synthesis. *Pediatr Res* 18:145, 1984.

133. TSUBOI KK, KWONG LK, NEU J, SUNSHINE P: A proposed mechanism of normal intestinal lactase decline in the postweaned mammal. *Biochim Biophys Res Commun* 101:645, 1981.

133a. TSUBOI KK, KWONG LK, D'HARLINGUE AE, STEVENSON DK, KERNER JA, SUNSHINE P: The nature of maturational decline of intestinal lactase activity. *Biochim Biophys Acta* 840:69, 1985.

134. JONAS MM, MONTGOMERY RK, GRAND RJ: Intestinal lactase synthesis during postnatal development in the rat. *Pediatr Res* 19:956, 1985.

134a. SMITH MW, JAMES PS: Cellular origin of lactase decline in postweaning rats. *Biochim Biophys Acta* 905:503, 1987.

135. MOOG F: The functional differentiation of the small intestine. II. The differentiation of alkaline phosphomonoesterases in the duodenum of the mouse. *J Exp Zool* 118:187, 1951.

136. MOOG F: The functional differentiation of the small intestine. III. The influence of the pituitary-adrenal system on the differentiation of phosphatase in the duodenum of the suckling mouse. *J Exp Zool* 124:329, 1953.

137. YEH K, MOOG F: Intestinal lactase activity in the suckling rat: Influence of hypophysectomy and thyroidectomy. *Science* 183:77, 1974.

138. MALO CH, MÉNARD D: Opposite effects of one and three injections of cortisone or thyroxine on intestinal lactase activity in suckling mice. *Experientia* 35:493, 1979.

139. LEICHTER J: Effect of dietary lactose on intestinal lactase activity in young rats. *J Nutr* 103:392, 1973.

140. FERGUSON A, GERSKOWITCH VP, RUSSELL RI: Pre- and postweaning disaccharidase patterns in isografts of fetal mouse intestine. *Gastroenterology* 64:292, 1973.

141. BOLIN TD, MCKERN A, DAVIS AE: The effect of diet on lactase activity in the rat. *Gastroenterology* 60:432, 1971.

142. BOLIN TD, PIROLA RC, DAVIS AE: Adaptation of intestinal lactase in the rat. *Gastroenterology* 57:406, 1969.

143. MONTGOMERY RK, SYBICKI MA, GRAND RJ: Autonomous biochemical and morphological differentiation in the fetal rat intestine transplanted at 17 and 20 days of gestation. *Dev Biol* 87:76, 1981.

144. ANTONOVICZ I, CHANG SK, GRAND RJ: Development and distribution of lysosomal enzymes and disaccharidases in human fetal intestine. *Gastroenterology* 67:51, 1974.

145. ANTONOVICZ I, LEBENTHAL E: Development pattern of small intestinal enterokinase and disaccharidase activity in the human fetus. *Gastroenterology* 72:1299, 1977.

146. DAHLQVIST A, LINDBERG T: Fetal development of the small intestinal disaccharidase and alkaline phosphatase activities in the human. *Biol Neonate* 9:24, 1965.

147. JIŘŠOVÁ V, KOLDOVSKÝ O, HERINGOVÁ A, UHER J, JODL J: Development of invertase activity in the intestines of human fetuses, appearance of jejunoileal differences. *Biol Neonate* 13:143, 1968.

147a. MOBASSALEH M, MONTGOMERY RK, BILLER JA, GRAND RJ: Development of carbohydrate absorption in the fetus and neonate. *Pediatrics* 75 *(suppl)*:160, 1985.

148. MAYNE A, HUGHES CA, SULE D, BROWN GA, MCNEISH AS: Development of intestinal disaccharidases in preterm infants. *Lancet* 2:622, 1983.

149. MacLEAN WC JR, FINK BB: Lactose malabsorption by premature infants: Magnitude and clinical significance. *J Pediatr* 97:383, 1980.

150. MacLEAN WC, FINK BB, SCHOELLER DA, WONG W, KLEIN PD: Lactose assimilation by full-term infants: Relations of (13C) and H2 breath test with fecal (13C) excretion. *Pediatr Res* 17:629, 1983.

151. SCHOELLER DA, KELIN PD, MacLEAN WC, WATKINS JB, VANSANTEN E: Fecal 13C analysis for the detection and quantitation of intestinal malabsorption. Limits of detection to disorders of intestinal cholylglycine metabolism. *J Lab Clin Med* 97:439, 1981.

152. LIFSHITZ CH, O'BRIAN SMITH E, GARZA C: Delayed complete functional lactase sufficiency in breast-fed infants. *J Pediatr Gastroenterol Nutr* 2:478, 1983.

153. CHILES C, WATKINS JB, BARR RG, TSAJ PY, GOLDMAN DA: Lactose utilization in the newborn: Role of colonic flora. *Pediatr Res* 13:365, 1979.

154. BOND JH, CURRIER BE, BUCHWALD H, LEVITT MD: Colonic conservation of malabsorbed carbohydrate. *Gastroenterology* 78:444, 1980.

155. AURICCHIO S, CICCIMARRA F, DELLA PIETRA D, VEGNENTE A: Intestinal hydrolysis of starch. *Mod Probl Pediatr* 11:23, 1968.

156. AURICCHIO S: Brush border enzymes, in Anderson CM, Burke V, Gracey M (eds): *Paediatric Gastroenterology,* 2d ed. Australia, Blackwell, chap 5, part III, 1986, p 185.

156a. TRUGNAN G, ROUSSET M, CHANTRET I, BARBAT A, ZWEIBAUM A: The post-translational processing of sucrase-isomaltase in HT-29 cells is a function of their state of enterocytic differentiation. *J Cell Biol* 104:1199, 1987.

157. KRAML J, KOLÍNSKÁ J, KADLECOVÁ L, ZÁKOSTELECKÁ M, LOJDA Z: Analytical isoelectric focusing of rat intestinal brush border enzymes: Postnatal changes and effect of neuraminidase in vitro. *FEBS Lett* 151:193, 1983.

158. AURICCHIO S: "Fetal" forms of brush border enzymes in the intestine and meconium. *J Pediatr Gastroenterol Nutr* 2(suppl):164, 1983.

159. AURICCHIO S, CAPORALE C, SANTAMARIA F, SKOVBJERG H: Fetal forms of oligoaminopeptidase, dipeptidylaminopeptidase IV and sucrase in human intestine and meconium. *J Pediatr Gastroenterol Nutr* 3:28, 1984.

160. KRAML J, KOLÍNSKÁ J, KADLECOVÁ L, ZÁKOSTELECKÁ M, LOJDA Z: Effect of hydrocortisone on the desialylation of intestinal brush border enzymes of the rat during postnatal development. *FEBS Lett* 172:25, 1984.

161. TRIADOU N, ZWEIBAUM A: Maturation of sucrase-isomaltase complex in human fetal small and large intestine during gestation. *Pediatr Res* 19:136, 1985.

161a. KRAML J, KOLÍNSKÁ J: Sialylated forms of intestinal brush-border enzymes. Lecture presented at the 14th International Congress of Biochemistry, Prague, 1988, Abstract No. TU:C18-3.

162. YEH K, MOOG F: Biosynthesis and transport of glycoproteins in the small

intestinal epithelium of rats. I. Developmental change and effect of hypophysectomy. *Dev Biol* 101:446, 1984.

163. JAMES WPT, ALPERS DH, GERBER JE, ISSELBACHER KJ: The turnover of disaccharidases and brush border proteins in rat intestine. *Biochim Biophys Acta* 230:194, 1971.

164. OLSEN WA, KORSMO H: The intestinal brush border membrane in diabetes. Studies of sucrase-isomaltase metabolism in rats with streptozotocin diabetes. *J Clin Invest* 60:181, 1977.

165. ALPERS DH: The relation of size to the relative rates of degradation of intestinal brush border proteins. *J Clin Invest* 51:2621, 1972.

166. FORSTNER G, GALAND G: The influence of hydrocortisone on the synthesis and turnover of microvillus membrane glycoproteins in suckling rat intestine. *Can J Biochem* 54:224, 1976.

167. AHNEN DJ, SANTIAGO NA, YOSHIOKA C, GRAY GM: Intestinal sucrase-α-dextrinase: Differential degradation of its protein and carbohydrate components in vivo. *Gastroenterology* 82:1006, 1982.

167a. KARASOV WH, DIAMOND JM: Adaptive regulation of sugar and amino acid transport by vertebrate intestine. *Am J Physiol* 245:G443, 1983.

167b. JACOBS LR: Alterations in labeling of cell-surface glycoproteins from normal and diabetic rat intestinal microvillus membranes. *Biochim Biophys Acta* 649:155, 1981.

168. SCHEDL HP, AL-JURF AS, WILSON DH: Elevated intestinal disaccharidase activity in the streptozotocin diabetic rat is independent of enteral feeding. *Gastroenterology* 82:1171, 1982.

169. GODA T, KOLDOVSKY O: Evidence of degradation process of sucrase-isomaltase in jejunum of adult rats. *Biochem J* 229:751, 1985.

170. ALPERS DH, TEDESCO FJ: The possible role of pancreatic proteases in the turnover of the intestinal brush border proteins. *Biochim Biophys Acta* 401:28, 1975.

171. RIBY JE, KRETCHMER N: Participation of pancreatic enzymes in the degradation of intestinal sucrase-isomaltase. *J Pediatr Gastroenterol Nutr* 4:971, 1985.

172. KWONG WKL, SEETHARAM B, ALPERS DH: Effect of exocrine pancreatic insufficiency on small intestine in the mouse. *Gastroenterology* 74:1277, 1978.

173. SEETHARAM B, PERRILLO R, ALPERS DH: Effect of pancreatic proteases on intestinal lactase activity. *Gastroenterology* 79:827, 1980.

174. SMITH MW, PHILLIPS AD, WALKER-SMITH JA: Selective inhibition of brush border hydrolase development in coeliac disease and cow's milk protein intolerance. 19th Meeting of the European Society for Pediatric Gastroenterology and Nutrition, Edinburgh, June 1986.

175. LIFSHITZ F: Perspectives of carbohydrate intolerance in infants with diarrhea, in Lifshitz F (ed): *Carbohydrate Intolerance in Infancy.* New York, Marcel Dekker, 1982, p 3.

176. SHMERLING DH, AURICCHIO S, RUBINO A, HADORN B, PRADER A: Der sekundäre Mangel an intestinalen Disaccharidaseakvität bei der Coeliakie. Quantitative Bestimmung der Enzymaktivität und klinische Beurteilung. *Helv Paediatr Acta* 19:507, 1964.

177. LEBENTHAL E, LEE P: Possible alternative pathway for starch digestion in infants and mucosal glucamylase activity in small intestinal atrophy. *Pediatr Res* 29:504, 1980.

178. GRAY GM, WILLIAM MW JR, EUGENE H: Persistent deficiency of intestinal lactase in apparently cured tropical sprue. *Gastroenterology* 54:552, 1968.

179. ROMER H, URBACH R, GOMEZ MA, LOPEZ A, PEROZO-RUGGERI G, VEGAS ME: Moderate and severe protein energy malnutrition in childhood: Effects of jejunal mucosae morphology and disaccharidase activities. *J Pediatr Gastroenterol Nutr* 2:459, 1983.

180. GREENE HL, MCCABE DR, MERENSTEIN GB: Protracted diarrhea and malnutrition in infancy: Changes in intestinal morphology and disaccharidase activities during treatment with total intravenous nutrition or oral elemental diets. *J Pediatr* 87:695, 1975.

181. PHILLIPS AD, AVIGAD S, SACKS J, RICE SJ, FRANCE NE, WALKER-SMITH SA: Microvillous surface area in secondary disaccharidase deficiency. *Gut* 21:44, 1980.

182. BOYLE JT, CELANO R, KOLDOVSKÝ O: Demonstration of a difference in expression of maximal lactase and sucrase activity along the villus in the adult rat jejunum. *Gastroenterology* 79:503, 1980.

183. ALPERS DH, SEETHARAM B: Pathophysiology of diseases involving intestinal brush border proteins. *N Engl J Med* 296:1047, 1977.

184. SHERMAN P, WESLEY A, FORSTNER G: Sequential disaccharidase loss in rat intestinal blind loops: Impact of malnutrition. *Am J Physiol* 248:626, 1985.

185. WELSH JD, POLEY JR, HENSLEY J, BATHIA M: Intestinal disaccharidase and alkaline phosphatase activity in Giardiasis. *J Pediatr Gastroenterol Nutr* 3:37, 1984.

186. DAHLQVIST A: Method for assay of intestinal disaccharidases. *Anal Biochem* 7:18, 1964.

187. AURICCHIO S, RUBINO A, TOSI R, SEMENZA G, LANDOLT M, KISTLER HJ,

188. PRADER A: Disaccharidase activities in human intestinal mucosa. *Enzymol Biol Clin* 3:193, 1963.

188. BANAUCH D, BRUMMER W, EBELING W, METZ H, RINDFREY M, LAND H: Eine Glucose-Dehydrogenase für die Glucose-Bestimmung in Körperflüssigkeiten. *Z Klin Chem Klin Biochem* 13:101, 1975.

189. ASP NG, DAHLQVIST A: Human small-intestinal β-galactosidases specific assay of three different enzymes. *Anal Biochem* 47:527, 1972.

190. TSUBOI KK, SCHWARZ SM, BURRILL PH, KWONG LK, SUNSHINE P: Sugar hydrolases of the infant rat intestine and their arrangement on the brush border membrane. *Biochim Biophys Acta* 554:234, 1979.

191. EGGERMONT E: The hydrolysis of the naturally occurring alpha-glucosides by the human intestinal mucosa. *Eur J Biochem* 9:483, 1969.

192. AURICCHIO S, CICCIMARRA F, STARACE E, VEGNENTE A, GILIBERTI P, PROVENZALE L: Glucamylase activity of human intestinal mucosa. *Rend Gastroenterol* 3:1, 1971.

193. SKOVBJERG H, SJÖSTROM A, NORÉN O, GUDMAND-HØYER E: Immunoelectrophoretic studies on human small intestinal brush border proteins. A quantitative study from single, small intestinal biopsies. *Clin Chim Acta* 92:315, 1979.

193a. LEBENTHAL E, ANTONOWICZ I, SHWACHMAN H: Correlation of lactase activity, lactose tolerance and milk consumption in different age groups. *Am Clin Nutr* 28:595, 1975.

194. NEWCOMER AD, MCGILL DB, THOMAS PM, HOFMANN AF: Prospective comparison of indirect methods for detecting lactase deficiency. *N Engl J Med* 293:1232, 1975.

195. EGGERMONT E, CARCHON H, EECKELS R: Centile values of small intestinal mucosal enzymatic activities in Caucasian children. *Pediatr Res* 15:1205A, 1981.

196. NIESSEN KH, SCHMIDT K, BRUGGMANN G: Disaccharidasen der Dünndarmschleimhaut bei Säuglingen und Kindern. *Z Gastroenterol* 13:565, 1975.

197. MCMICHAEL WB, WEBB J, DAWSON AM: Jejunal disaccharidases and some observations on the cause of lactase deficiency. *Br Med J* 2:1037, 1966.

198. CALVIN RT, KLISH WJ, NICHOLS BL: Disaccharidase activities, jejunal morphology, and carbohydrate tolerance in children with chronic diarrhea. *J Pediatr Gastroenterol Nutr* 4:949, 1985.

199. AURICCHIO S, RUBINO A, PRADER A, REY J, JOS J, FRÉZAL J, DAVIDSON M: Intestinal glycosidase activities in congenital malabsorption of disaccharides. *J Pediatr* 66:555, 1965.

200. KERRY KR, TOWNLEY RRW: Genetic aspects of intestinal sucrase-isomaltase deficiency. *Aust Pediatr J* 1:223, 1965.

201. WELSH JD, POLEY JR, BHATIA M, STEVENSON DE: Intestinal disaccharidase activities in relation to age, race, and mucosal damage. *Gastroenterology* 75:855, 1978.

202. CRANE RK, MÉNARD D, PREISER H, CERDA J: The molecular basis of brush border membrane disease, in Bolis L, Hoffman JF, Leaf A (eds): *Membranes and Disease.* New York, Raven, 1976, p 229.

203. HAEMMERLI UP, KISTLER HJ, AMMANN R, MARTHALER T, SEMENZA G, AURICCHIO S, PRADER A: Acquired milk intolerance in the adult caused by lactose malabsorption due to a selective deficiency of intestinal lactase activity. *Am J Med* 38:7, 1965.

204. NEWCOMER AD, MCGILL DB: Disaccharidase activity in the small intestine: Prevalence of lactase deficiency in 100 healthy subjects. *Gastroenterology* 53:881, 1967.

205. FORGET P, LAMBET J, GRANDFILS C, DANDRIFOSSE G, GENBELLE F: Lactase insufficiency revisited. *J Pediatr Gastroenterol Nutr* 4:868, 1985.

205a. MARTINEZ-PARDO M, MONTES PG, MARTIN-LOMAS M, SOLS A: Intestinal lactase evaluation in vivo with 3-methyllactose. *FEBS Lett* 98:99, 1979.

206. WEIJERS HA, VAN DE KAMER JH, DICKE WK, IJSSELING J: Diarrhoea caused by deficiency of sugar-splitting enzymes. I. *Acta Paediatr* 50:55, 1961.

207. KRASILNIKOFF PA, GUDMANN-HØYER E, MOLTKE HH: Diagnostic value of disaccharide tolerance tests to children. *Acta Paediatr Scand* 64:693, 1975.

208. FERNANDES J, VOS CE, DOUWES AC, SLOTEMA E, DEGENHART HJ: Respiratory hydrogen excretion as a parameter for lactose malabsorption in children. *Am J Clin Nutr* 31:597, 1978.

209. MAFFEI HVL, METZ G, BAMPOE V, SHINER M, HERMAN S, BROOK CGD: Lactose intolerance, detected by breath hydrogen test in infants and children with chronic diarrhoea. *Arch Dis Child* 52:766, 1977.

210. PERMAN JA, BARR RG, WATKINS JB: Sucrose malabsorption in children: Non-invasive diagnosis by interval breath hydrogen determination. *J Pediatr* 93:17, 1978.

211. ROBB TA, DAVIDSON GP: Advances in breath hydrogen quantitation in paediatrics: Sample collection and normalization to constant oxygen and nitrogen levels. *Clin Chim Acta* 111:281, 1981.

212. KNEEPKENS CMF, BIJLEVELD CMA, VONK RJ, FERNANDES J: The daytime breath hydrogen profile in children with abdominal symptoms and diarrhoea. *Acta Paediatr Scand* 75:632, 1986.

213. KERLIN P, PHILLIPS SF: Differential transit of liquids and solid residue through the ileum of man. *Am J Physiol* 245:G38, 1983.

214. DOUWES AC, SCHAAP C, VAN DER KEI VAN MOORSEL JM: Hydrogen breath test in schoolchildren. *Arch Dis Child* 60:333, 1985.

215. LEVITT MD, DONALDSON RM: Use of respiratory hydrogen to detect carbohydrate malabsorption. *J Lab Clin Med* 75:937, 1970.

216. BJORNEKLETT A, JENSSEN E: Relationship between hydrogen (H₂) and methane (CH₄) in man. *Scand J Gastroenterol* 17:985, 1982.

217. GARDINER AJ, TARLOW MJ, SYMONDS J, HUTCHINSON GJP, SHUTERLAND JT: Failure of the hydrogen breath test to detect primary sugar malabsorption. *Arch Dis Child* 56:368, 1981.

218. KERRY KR, ANDERSON CM: A ward test for sugar in faeces. *Lancet* 1:981, 1964.

219. DAVIDSON AGF, MULLINGER M: Reducing substances in neonatal stool detected by Clinitest. *Pediatrics* 46:632, 1970.

220. MCMICHAEL HB, WEBB J, DAWSON AM: Lactase deficiency in adult: A cause of functional diarrhoea. *Lancet* 1:717, 1965.

220a. AURICCHIO S, PRADER A, MÜRSET G, WITT G: Saccharoseintoleranz: Durchfall infolge hereditären Mangels an intestinaler Saccharaseaktivität. *Helv Paediatr Acta* 16:483, 1961.

221. HARRISON M, WALKER-SMITH JA: Reinvestigation of lactose intolerant children: Lack of correlation between continuing lactose intolerance and small intestinal morphology, disaccharidase activity and lactose tolerance tests. *Gut* 18:48, 1977.

221a. DAWSON DJ, NEWCOMER AD, MCGILL DB: Lactose tolerance tests in adults with normal lactase activity. *Gastroenterology* 50:340, 1966.

222. DAVIDSON GP, ROBB TA: Value of breath hydrogen analysis in management of diarrheal illness in childhood: Comparison with duodenal biopsy. *J Pediatr Gastroenterol Nutr* 4:381, 1985.

223. LIFSHITZ CH, BAUTISTA A, GAPALACHRISHNA GS, STUFF J, GARZA C: Absorption and tolerance of lactose in infants recovering from diarrhea. *J Pediatr Gastroenterol Nutr* 4:942, 1985.

224. WELSH JD: Isolated lactase deficiency in humans: Reports on 100 patients. *Medicine (Baltimore)* 49:257, 1970.

225. BAYLESS TM, ROTHFELD B, MASSA C, WISE L, PAIGE D, BEDINE MS: Lactose and milk intolerance: Clinical implications. *N Engl J Med* 292:1156, 1975.

226. RINGROSE RE, PREISER H, WELSH JD: Sucrase-isomaltase (Palatinase) deficiency diagnosed during adulthood. *Dig Dis Sci* 25:384, 1980.

227. RAVICH WJ, BAYLESS TM: Carbohydrate absorption and malabsorption. *Clin Gastroenterol* 12:335, 1983.

228. LAUNIALA K: The effect of unabsorbed sucrose and mannitol on small intestinal flow rate and mean transit time. *Scand J Gastroenterol* 3:665, 1968.

229. LAUNIALA K: The effect of unabsorbed sucrose- or mannitol-induced accelerated transit on absorption in the human small intestine. *Scand J Gastroenterol* 4:25, 1969.

230. GODA T, BUSTAMANTE S, EDMOND J, GRIMES J, KOLDOVSKÝ O: Precocious increase of sucrase activity by carbohydrates in the small intestine of suckling rats. II. Role of digestibility of sugars, osmolality, and stomach evacuation in producing diarrhea. *J Pediatr Gastroenterol Nutr* 4:634, 1985.

231. CASPARY WF, KALISH H: Effect of alpha-glucosedehydrolase inhibition on intestinal absorption of sucrose, water, and sodium in man. *Gut* 20:750, 1979.

232. AZPIROZ F, MALAGELADA JR: Luminal nutrients in the proximal and distal small intestine elicit gastric relaxation. *Dig Dis Sci* 29:564, 1984.

233. JENKINS DFA, TAYLOR RH, GOFF WD: Scope and specificity of acarbose in slowing carbohydrate absorption in man. *Diabetes* 31:951, 1981.

234. HOLGATE AM, READ NW: Relationship between small bowel transit time and absorption of a solid meal. *Dig Dis Sci* 28:812, 1983.

235. CHAPMAN RW, GRAHAM MM: Absorption of starch by healthy ileostomatoses: Effect of transit time and of carbohydrate load. *Am J Clin Nutr* 41:1244, 1985.

236. AURICCHIO S, CICCIMARRA F, DE VIZIA B: *Starch Malabsorption.* XIII International Congress of Pediatrics, Vienna, Aug 29–Sept 4, 1971, p 139.

237. CHAUVE A, DEVROEDE G, BASTIN E: Intraluminal pressures during perfusion of the human colon in situ. *Gastroenterology* 70:336, 1976.

238. DEBONGNIE JC, PHILIPS FS: Capacity of the human colon to absorb fluid. *Gastroenterology* 74:698, 1978.

239. PALMA R, VIDON N, BERNIER JJ: Maximal capacity for fluid absorption in human bowel. *Dig Dis Sci* 26:929, 1981.

240. NEWCOMER AD, MCGILL DB, THOMAS PM, HOFFMAN AF: Tolerance to lactose among lactase deficient American Indians. *Gastroenterology* 74:44, 1978.

241. SAUNDERS DR, WIGGINS HS: Conservation of mannitol, lactulose and raffinose by the human colon. *Am J Physiol* 241:G387, 1981.

242. ARGENZIO RA, SOUTHWORTH M: Sites of organic acid production and absorption in gastrointestinal tract of the pig. *Am J Physiol* 228:454, 1975.

243. ORSKOV ER, FRASE C, MASON WC, MANN SO: Influence of starch digestion in the large intestine of sheep on caecal fermentation, caecal microflora and faecal nitrogen excretion. *Br J Nutr* 24:671, 1970.

244. FLORENT CH, FLOURIE B, LEBLOND A, RAUTUREAU M, BERNIER JJ, RAMBAUD JC: Influence of chronic lactulose ingestion on the colonic metabolism of lactulose in man (an in vivo study). *J Clin Invest* 75:608, 1985.

245. BHATIA J, PRIHODA AR, RICHARDSON CJ: Parenteral antibiotics and carbohydrate intolerance in term neonates. *Am J Dis Child* 149:111, 1986.

246. AURICCHIO S, DAHLQVIST A, MÜRSET G, PRADER A: Isomaltose intolerance causing decreased ability to utilize dietary starch. *J Pediatr* 62:165, 1963.

247. AURICCHIO S, CICCIMARRA F, MOAURO L, REY F, JOS J, REY J: Intraluminal and mucosal starch digestion in congenital deficiency of intestinal sucrase and isomaltase activities. *Pediatr Res* 6:832, 1972.

248. EGGERMONT E, HERS HG: The sedimentation properties of the intestinal alpha-glucosidases of normal human subjects and of patients with sucrose intolerance. *Eur J Biochem* 9:488, 1969.

249. HADORN B, GREEN JR, STERCHI EE, HAURI HP: Biochemical mechanism in congenital enzyme deficiencies of the small intestine. *Clin Gastroenterol* 10:671, 1981.

250. SKOVBJERG H, KRASILNIKOFF PA: Maltase-glucoamylase and residual isomaltase in sucrose intolerant patients. *J Pediatr Gastroenterol Nutr* 5:365, 1986.

251. AURICCHIO S, RUBINO A, LANDOLT M, SEMENZA G, PRADER A: Isolated intestinal lactase deficiency in the adult. *Lancet* 2:324, 1963.

252. DAHLQVIST A, HAMMOND JD, CRANE RK, DUNPHY JV, LITTMAN A: Intestinal lactase deficiency and lactose intolerance in adults: Preliminary report. *Gastroenterology* 45:488, 1963.

253. SIMOONS FJ: The geographic hypothesis and lactose malabsorption. A weighing of the evidence. *Dig Dis* 23:963, 1980.

254. COOK GC: Lactase activity in newborn and infant Baganda. *Br Med J* 1:527, 1967.

255. KEUSCH GT, TRONCALE FJ, MILLER LH, PROMADHAT V, ANDERSON PR: Acquired lactose malabsorption in Thai children. *Pediatrics* 43:540, 1969.

256. SAHI T, ISOKOSKI M, JUSSILA J, LAUNIALA K: Lactose malabsorption in Finnish children of school age. *Acta Paediatr Scand* 61:11, 1972.

257. SAHI T, LAUNIALA K: Manifestation and occurrence of selective adult-type lactose malabsorption in Finnish teenagers. *Am J Dig Dis* 23:699, 1978.

258. SAHI T, LAUNIALA K, LAITINEN H: Hypolactasia in a fixed cohort of young Finnish adults: A follow-up study. *Scand J Gastroenterol* 18:865, 1983.

259. PAIGE DM: Lactose malabsorption in children: Prevalence, symptoms, and nutritional considerations, in Paige DM, Bayless TM (eds): *Lactose Digestion: Clinical and Nutrition Implications.* Baltimore, Johns Hopkins University Press, 1981, p 151.

260. NEWCOMER AD, THOMAS PT, MCGILL D, HOFMANN AF: Lactase deficiency: A common genetic trait of the American Indian. *Gastroenterology* 72:234, 1977.

261. CASKEY DA, PAYNE-BOSE D, WELSH JD, GEARHART HI, NANCE RD, MORRISON RD: Effect of age on lactose malabsorption in Oklahoma native Americans as determined by breath hydrogen analysis. *Am J Dig Dis* 22:113, 1977.

262. ROGGERO P, OFFREDI ML, MOSCA F, PERAZZANI M, MANGIATERRA B, GHISLANZONI P, MARENGHI L, CAREDDU P: Lactose absorption and malabsorption in healthy Italian children: Do the quantity of malabsorbed sugar and the small bowel transit time play roles in symptoms production? *J Pediatr Gastroenterol Nutr* 4:82, 1985.

263. JUSSILA J, LAUNIALA K, GORBATOW O: Lactase deficiency and a lactose-free diet in patients with "unspecific abdominal complaints." *Acta Med Scand* 186:217, 1969.

264. GUDMAND-HØYER E, DAHLQVIST A, JARNUM S: The clinical significance of lactose malabsorption. *Am J Gastroenterol* 53:460, 1970.

265. MITCHELL KJ, BAYLESS TM, HUANG SS, PAIGE DM, GOODGAME RW, ROTHFELD B: Intolerance of a glass of milk in healthy teenagers. *Gastroenterology* 64:773, 1973.

266. SAHI T: Dietary lactose and aetiology of human small intestinal hypolactasia. *Gut* 19:1074, 1978.

267. BEDINE MS, BAYLESS TM: Intolerance of small amount of lactose by individuals with low lactase levels. *Gastroenterology* 65:735, 1973.

268. JONES DW, LATHAM MC, KOSIKOWSKI FW, WOODWARD G: Symptom response to lactose-reduced milk in lactose-intolerant adults. *Am J Clin Nutr* 29:633, 1976.

269. FERGUSON A: Diagnosis and treatment of lactose intolerance. *Br Med J* 283:1423, 1981.

270. FOWKES FGR, FERGUSON A: Prevalence of self-diagnosed irritable bowel syndrome and cows' milk intolerance in white and non white doctors. *Scott Med J* 26:41, 1980.

271. BIRGE SJ JR, KEUTMANN HT, CUATRECASAS P, WHEATON GD: Osteopo-

rosis, intestinal lactase deficiency and low dietary calcium intake. *N Engl J Med* 276:445, 1967.

271a. NEWCOMER AD, HODGSON SF, MCGILL DB, THOMAS BJ: Lactase deficiency prevalence in osteoporosis. *Ann Intern Med* 89:218, 1978.

272. CONDON JR, NASSIM JR, MILLARD JC, HILBE A, STAINTHORPE EM: Calcium and phosphorus metabolism in relation to lactose tolerance. *Lancet* 1:1027, 1970.

273. KOCIAN J, SKALA I, BAKOS K: Calcium absorption from milk and lactose free milk in healthy subjects and patients with lactose intolerance. *Digestion* 9:317, 1973.

274. EDITORIAL: Lactase deficiency in osteoporosis. *Lancet* 1:86, 1979.

275. EDITORIAL: Lactose malabsorption and lactose intolerance. *Lancet* 2:831, 1979.

276. COCHET BA, JUNG M, GRIESSEN P, SCHALLER P, DONATH A: Effects of lactose on intestinal calcium absorption in normal and lactase-deficient subjects. *Gastroenterology* 84:935, 1983.

276a. SAHI T, JUSSILA J, PENTTILA IM, SARNA S, ISOKOSKI M: Serum lipids and protein in lactose malabsorption. *Am J Clin Nutr* 30:476, 1977.

277. SIMOONS FJ, JOHNSSON JB, KRETCHMER N: Perspective on milk-drinking and malabsorption of lactose. *Pediatrics* 59:98, 1977.

278. FLATZ G, ROTTHAUWE HW: The human lactase polymorphism: Physiology and genetics of lactose absorption and malabsorption. *Prog Med Genet* 2:205, 1977.

278a. SIMOONS FJ: A geographic approach to senile cataracts: Possible links with milk consumption, lactase activity and galactose metabolism. *Dig Dis Sci* 27:257, 1982.

279. RINALDI E, ALBINI L, COSTAGLIOLA C, DE ROSA G, AURICCHIO G, DE VIZIA B, AURICCHIO S: High frequency of lactose absorbers among adults with idiopathic senile and presenile cataract in a population with a high prevalence of primary adult lactose malabsorption. *Lancet* 1:357, 1984.

280. JACKSON W: Clinical manifestations, in Jackson W (ed): *Proceedings of the First Food Allergy Workshop.* Oxford, Medical Education Service, 1980, p 41.

281. LESSOFF MH, WRAITH DG, MERRETT TG, MERRETT J, BUISSERET PD: Food allergy and intolerance in 100 patients—Local and systemic effects. *Q J Med* 49:259, 1980.

282. SAHI T: The inheritance of selective adult-type lactose malabsorption. *Scand J Gastroenterol* 9(suppl 30):1, 1974.

283. ELLESTEAD-SAYED JJ, HAYWORTH JC, HILDES JA: Disaccharide consumption and malabsorption in Canadian Indians. *Am J Clin Nutr* 30:698, 1977.

284. ELLESTEAD-SAYED JJ, HAWORTH JC, HILDES JA: Disaccharide malabsorption and dietary patterns in two Canadian Eskimo communities. *Am J Clin Nutr* 31:1473, 1978.

285. ROSENZWEIG NS, HUANG SS, BAYLESS TM: Transmission of lactose intolerance. *Lancet* 2:777, 1967.

286. HO MW, POLEY S, SWALLOW D: Lactase polymorphism in adult British natives: Estimating allele frequences by enzyme assays in autopsy samples. *Am J Hum Genet* 34:650, 1982.

287. FLATZ G: Gene-dosage effect of intestinal lactase activity demonstrated in vivo. *Am J Hum Genet* 36:306, 1984.

288. KRETCHMER N: Memorial lecture: Lactose and lactase—A historical perspective. *Gastroenterology* 61:805, 1971.

289. FLATZ G, ROTTHAUWE HW: Lactose nutrition and natural selection. *Lancet* 2:76, 1973.

290. SIMOONS FJ: Celiac disease as a geographic problem, in Walcker DN, Kretchmer N (eds): *Food, Nutrition and Evolution.* Masson, 1981, p 179.

291. KOLARS JC, LEVITT MD, AOUJI M, SAVAIANO DA: Yoghurt—An autodigesting source of lactose. *N Engl J Med* 310:1, 1984.

292. SMITH TM, KOLARS JC, SAVAIANO DA: Absorption of calcium from milk and yoghurt. *Am J Clin Nutr* 42:1197, 1985.

293. ROSADO JL, SOLOMONS NW, LISKER R, BOURGES H, ANRUBIO G, GARCIA A, PEREZ-BRICENO R, AIZUPURU E: Enzyme replacement therapy for primary adult lactase deficiency. Effective reduction of lactose malabsorption and milk intolerance by direct addition of beta-galactosidase to milk at mealtime. *Gastroenterology* 87:1072, 1984.

294. HOLZEL A, SCHWARZ V, SUTCLIFFE KW: Defective lactose absorption causing malnutrition in infancy. *Lancet* 1:1126, 1959.

295. LIFSHITZ F: Congenital lactase deficiency. *J Pediatr* 69:229, 1966.

296. LAUNIALA K, KUITUNEN P, VISAKORPI J: Disaccharidases and histology of duodenal mucosa in congenital lactose malabsorption. *Acta Paediatr Scand* 55:257, 1966.

297. LEVIN B, ABRAHAM JM, BURGESS EA, WALLIS PG: Congenital lactose malabsorption. *Arch Dis Child* 45:173, 1975.

298. SAVILATHI E, LAUNIALA K, KUITUNEN P: Congenital lactase deficiency: A clinical study on 16 patients. *Arch Dis Child* 58:246, 1983.

299. ASP NG, DAHLQVIST A: Intestinal β-galactosidases in adult low lactase activity and in congenital lactase deficiency. *Enzyme* 18:84, 1974.

300. ASP NG, DAHLQVIST A, KUIUNEN P, LAUNIALA K, VISAKORPI JK: Complete deficiency of brush border lactase in congenital lactose malabsorption. *Lancet* 2:329, 1973.

301. DAHLQVIST A, ASP NG: Accurate assay of low intestinal lactase activity with a fluorimetric method. *Anal Biochem* 44:654, 1971.

302. FREIBURGHAUS AU, SCHMITZ J, SCHINDLER M, ROTTHAUWE HW, KUITUNEN P, LAUNIALA K, HADORN B: Protein patterns of brush border fragments in congenital lactose malabsorption and in specific hypolactasia of the adult. *N Engl J Med* 294:1030, 1976.

303. DURAND P: Lattosuria idiopatica in una paziente con diarrea cronica ed acidosi. *Minerva Pediatr* 1:706, 1958.

304. RUSSO G, MOLICA F, MAZZONE D, SANTONOCITO B: Congenital lactose intolerance of gastrogen origin associated with cataracts. *Acta Paediatr Scand* 63:457, 1974.

305. HIRASHIMA Y, SHINOZUKA S, IEIRI T, MATSUDA I, ONO Y, MURATA T: Lactose intolerance associated with cataracts. *Eur J Pediatr* 130:41, 1979.

306. BERG NO, DAHLQVIST A, LINDBERG T: A boy with severe infantile gastrogen lactose intolerance and acquired lactase deficiency. *Acta Paediatr Scand* 68:751, 1979.

307. HOSKOVA A, SABACKY J, MRSKOS A, POSPISIL R: Severe lactose intolerance with lactosuria and vomiting. *Arch Dis Child* 55:304, 1980.

308. WEIJERS HA, VAN DE KAMER JH, MOSEL DAA, DICK WK: Diarrhoea caused by deficiency of sugar splitting enzymes. *Lancet* 2:296, 1960.

309. PRADER A, AURICCHIO S, MÜRSET G: Durchfall infolge hereditären Mangels an intestinaler Saccharaseaktivität (Saccharoseintoleranz). *Schweiz Med Wochenschr* 91:465, 1961.

310. ANDERSON CM, MESSER M, TOWNLEY RRW, FREEMAN M, ROBINSON RJ: Intestinal isomaltase deficiency in patients with hereditary sucrose and starch intolerance. *Lancet* 2:556, 1962.

311. ANDERSON CM, MESSER M, TOWNLEY RRW, FREEMAN M: Intestinal sucrase and isomaltase deficiency in two siblings. *Pediatrics* 31:1003, 1963.

312. BURGESS EA, LEVIN B, MAHALANABIS D, TONGE RE: Hereditary sucrose intolerance. Levels of sucrase activity in jejunal mucosa. *Arch Dis Child* 39:431, 1964.

313. PRADER A, AURICCHIO S: Defects of intestinal disaccharide absorption. *Annu Rev Med* 1965.

314. GUDMAND-HOYER E, KRASILNIKOFF PA: The effect of sucrose malabsorption on the growth pattern in children. *Scand J Gastroenterol* 12:103, 1977.

315. AMENT ME, PERERA DR, ESTHER LJ: Sucrase-isomaltase deficiency, a frequently misdiagnosed disease. *J Pediatr* 83:721, 1973.

316. ANTONOVICZ I, LLOYD JD, KHAW KT, SHWACHMAN H: Congenital sucrase isomaltase deficiency. Observation over a period of 6 years. *Pediatrics* 49:847, 1972.

317. SONNTAG WM, BRILL ML, TROYER WE, WELSH JD, SEMENZA G, PRADER A: Sucrose-isomaltose malabsorption in an adult female. *Gastroenterology* 47:18, 1964.

318. NEALE G, CLARK M, LEVIN B: Intestinal sucrase deficiency presenting as sucrose intolerance in adult life. *Br Med J* 2:1223, 1965.

319. STARNES CW, WELSH JD: Intestinal sucrase-isomaltase deficiency and renal calculi. *N Engl J Med* 202:1023, 1970.

320. JANSEN W, QUE CS, VEEGER W: Primary combined saccharase and isomaltase deficiency. *Arch Intern Med* 116:1125, 1972.

321. COOPER BT, SCOTT J, HOPKINS J, PETERS TJ: Adult onset sucrase-isomaltase deficiency with secondary disaccharidase deficiency resulting from severe dietary carbohydrate restriction. *Dig Dis Sci* 28:473, 1983.

322. GUDMAND-HØYER E, KRASILNIKOFF PA, SKOVBJERG H: Sucrose-isomaltose malabsorption, in Draper H (ed): *Advances in Nutritional Research.* New York, London, Plenum, 1984, vol 6, p 233.

323. GUDMAND-HØYER E: Sucrose malabsorption in children: A report of thirty-one Greenlanders. *J Pediatr Gastroenterol Nutr* 4:873, 1985.

324. CHENEY CP, BOEDEKER EC: Evidence that the sucrase/isomaltase complex may serve as an intestinal receptor for an enteropathogenic "Escherichia coli." *Gastroenterology* 82:1032, 1982.

325. METZ G, JENKINS DJA, NEWMAN A, BLENDIS LM: Breath hydrogen in hyposucrasia. *Lancet* 1:119, 1976.

326. DOUWES AC, FERNANDES J, JONGBLOED AA: Diagnostic value of sucrose tolerance test in children evaluated by breath hydrogen measurement. *Acta Paediatr Scand* 69:79, 1980.

327. BIRCH JB: Trehalose. *Adv Carbohydr Chem* 18:201, 1963.

328. BERGOZ R: Trehalose malabsorption causing intolerance to mushrooms. *Gastroenterology* 5:909, 1971.

329. MADZAROVOVA-NOHEJILOVÁ J: Trehalase deficiency in a family. *Gastroenterology* 65:130, 1973.

330. MCNAIR A, GUDMAND-HØYER E, JARNUM S, ORRILD L: Sucrose malabsorption in Greenland. *Br Med J* 2:19, 1972.

331. SCHMITZ J, BRESSON JL, TRIADOU N, BATAILLE J, REY J: Analyse en electrophorèse sur gel de polyacrylamide des protéines de la membrane mi-

crovillositaire et d'une fraction cytoplasmique dans 8 cas d'intolérance congénitale au saccharose. *Gastroenterol Clin Biol* 4:251, 1980.

332. GRAY GM, CONKLIN KA, TOWNLEY RRW: Sucrase-isomaltase deficiency. Absence of an inactive enzyme variant. *N Engl J Med* 294:750, 1976.

333. SKOVBJERG H, KRASILNIKOFF PA: Maltase-glucoamylase and residual isomaltase in sucrose intolerant patients. *J Pediatr Gastroenterol Nutr* 3:365, 1986.

334. SKOVBJERG H, KRASILNIKOFF PA: Immunoelectrophoretic studies on human small intestinal brush border protein. The residual isomaltase in sucrose intolerant patients. *Pediatr Res* 15:214, 1981.

335. PREISER H, MÉNARD D, CRANE RK, CERDA JJ: Deletion of enzyme protein from brush border membrane in sucrase-isomaltase deficiency. *Biochim Biophys Acta* 363:279, 1974.

336. NAIM HY, ROTH J, STERCHI EE, LENTZE M, MILLA P, SCHMITZ J, HAURI HP: Sucrase-isomaltase deficiency in humans. Different mutations disrupt intracellular transport, processing and function of an intestinal brush border enzyme. *J Clin Invest* 82:667, 1988.

337. NAIM HY, STERCHI EE, HAURI HP, SCHMITZ J, LENTZE MJ: Defective post-translational processing of sucrase-isomaltase (SI) in congenital sucrase-isomaltase deficiency. Abstract 26 in XIX Annual Meeting of the European Society for Paediatric Gastroenterology and Nutrition (ESPAGN) Edinburgh, June 25–27, 1986.

338. LLOYD ML, OLSEN WA: A study of the molecular pathology of sucrase-isomaltase deficiency. A defect in the intracellular processing of the enzyme. *N Engl J Med* 316:438, 1987.

339. SJÖSTRÖM H, NORÉN O, DANIELSEN EM: The enzymatic activity of "high-mannose" glycosylated forms of intestinal microvillar hydrolases. *J Paediatr Gastroenterol Nutr* 4:980, 1985.

340. FREIBURGHAUS AU, DUBS R, HADORN B, GAZE H, HAURI HO, GITZELMANN R: The brush border membrane in hereditary sucrase-isomaltase deficiency: Abnormal protein pattern and presence of immunoreactive enzyme. *Eur J Clin Invest* 7:455, 1977.

341. DUBS R, STEINMANN B, GITZELMANN R: Demonstration of an inactive enzyme antigen in sucrase-isomaltase deficiency. *Helv Paediatr Acta* 28:187, 1973.

342. JAMES PS, SMITH MW, BUTCHER GW, BROWN D, LUND EK: Evidence for a possible regulatory gene (Suc-1) controlling sucrase expression in mouse intestine. *Biochem Genet* 24:169, 1986.

343. COOPER BT, CANDY DCA, HARRIES JT, PETERS TJ: Subcellular fractionation studies of the intestinal mucosa in congenital sucrase-isomaltase deficiency. *Clin Sci Mol Med* 57:181, 1979.

344. SKOVBJERG H, GUDMAND-HÓYER E, FENGER HJ: Immunoelectrophoretic studies on human small intestinal brush border proteins. The amount of lactase protein in adult-free hypolactasia. *Gut* 21:360, 1980.

345. POTTER J, HO M-W, BOLTON H, FURTH AJ, SWALLOW DM, GRIFFITH B: Human lactase and the molecular basis of lactase persistence. *Biochem Genet* 23:432, 1985.

346. LORENZ-MEYER H, BLUM AL, HAEMMERLI HP, SEMENZA G: A second enzyme defect in acquired lactase deficency. Lack of small-intestinal phlorizin-hydrolase. *Eur J Clin Invest* 2:326, 1972.

347. KOLÍNSKÁ J, KRAML J, ZÁKOSTELECKÁ M, LOJDA Z: Low molecular weight antigens of sucrase-isomaltase in the intestinal mucosa of suckling rats. *Mol Physiol* 5:133, 1984.

CHAPTER 122

THE GENETIC POLYMORPHISM OF INTESTINAL LACTASE ACTIVITY IN ADULT HUMANS

GEBHARD FLATZ

1. The utilization of lactose for human nutrition requires the hydrolysis of this disaccharide in the intestinal tract. This is achieved by the enzyme lactase, a β-galactosidase located in the brush border of small intestinal epithelial cells. Lactase activity is high during infancy when milk is the main nutrient. As in most other mammals, lactase activity normally declines in a majority of humans after the weaning phase and remains low throughout life (phenotype: lactase restriction). In other healthy humans, lactase activity persists at a level not much lower than in infants (phenotype: lactase persistence). Subjects with lactase restriction have a low lactose digestion capacity (low LDC); those with lactose persistence can hydrolyze large amounts of lactose (high LDC). The adult lactose phenotypes can be diagnosed through small-intestinal biopsy or lactose tolerance tests.

2. Family studies, measurement of relative lactase activity, and a study of lactose digestion in twins prove that the lactose phenotypes are genetically determined. The observed segregation is satisfactorily explained by a mendelian system of two autosomal alleles: the globally more frequent lactase restriction gene LAC⋆R, and the lactose persistence gene LAC⋆P. Multiple allelism at the lactase locus is possible but not definitely proved. LAC⋆P is dominant over the recessive allele LAC⋆R, which means that of the three genotypes LAC⋆P/LAC⋆P, LAC⋆P/LAC⋆R, and LAC⋆R/LAC⋆R only the last causes the phenotype lactase restriction (low LDC).

3. The distribution of the lactase phenotypes in human populations is highly variable. In most tropical and subtropical countries and in all East Asian populations, lactase restriction is predominant. According to the Hardy-Weinberg rule, the frequency of the gene LAC⋆P is higher than that of LAC⋆R in populations with less than 25 percent lactase restriction. In the Old World, there are only two human population groups in which the lactase persistence gene predominates: Northwestern Europeans, and milk-dependent nomads of the Afro-Arabian desert zone. Natural selection in favor of the lactase persistence gene due to improved utilization of animal milk in the nutrition of older children and adults with high LDC is the most likely cause of the unusual lactase phenotype distribution in Europeans and Afro-Arabian nomads.

4. In self-chosen nutritional conditions, the disease potential of lactase restriction is low. In countries where animal milk is part of the usual diet, most people seem to adjust milk consumption to their individual lactose tolerance threshold. The role of lactase restriction in the causation of recurrent abdominal pain in children, irritable bowel syndrome in adults, and osteoporosis in postmenopausal women and the role of lactase persistence in promoting coronary heart disease and premature cataract are controversial.

A difference in lactase activity between suckling and adult animals has been known since 1895, when Röhmann and Lappe[1] showed that cows and adult dogs have a much lower small-intestinal lactose digestion capacity than calves and puppies. The developmental rule derived from this observation was not applied to humans for a long time, probably because medical research was most active in countries where the majority of the population retain high small-intestinal lactase activity throughout life. Constitutionally low lactase activity in healthy adult humans was discovered independently by two groups of researchers in 1963.[2,3] The term *lactase deficiency* for this type of enzymatic variation is not preferred by the present author, because it seems inappropriate to speak of a trait which is present in the majority of adult humans as a pathological or abnormal condition. It is important to realize that both high and low lactase activity in healthy adult humans are normal and should be seen on the same level as similar genetically determined variations, e.g., the human blood groups. This is increasingly supported by current nomenclature: genetic variability of lactase activity is listed in McKusick's catalog[4] as "22310 Disaccharide Intolerance III (Adult Lactase Deficiency; lactase persistence, included; hereditary persistence of intestinal lactase, included)." The biochemical, physiological, and nutritional implications of genetically determined "lactase deficiency" have been treated in Chap. 121. The main objective of this chapter is to stress the formal and population genetic aspects of lactase variability in adults.

Only 3 years after the discovery of constitutionally low lactase activity in healthy adult humans,[2,3] the idea that the variability of lactase activity represents a genetic polymorphism was clearly expressed by Bayless and Rosensweig.[5] According to Ford,[6] "genetic polymorphism is a type of variation in which individuals with sharply distinct qualities co-exist as normal members of a population" and is defined as "the occurrence together in the same habitat of two or more discontinuous forms, or 'phases,' of a species in such proportions that the rarest of them cannot be maintained by recurrent mutation." Therefore, the prerequisites for designating an observed variability as genetic polymorphism are: (1) the demonstration that the phases of a trait in the population are distinct, i.e., that the expression of the traits is discontinuous;

Nonstandard abbreviation used in this chapter is: LDC = lactose digestion capacity.

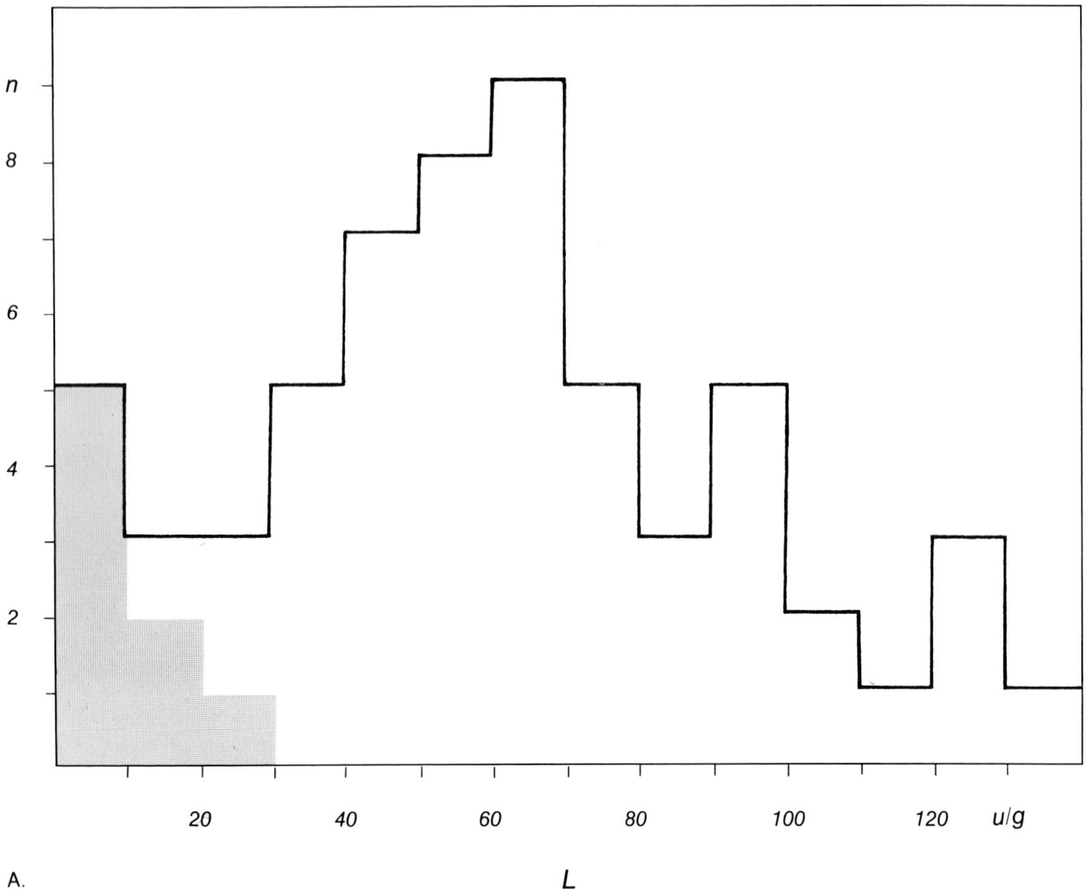

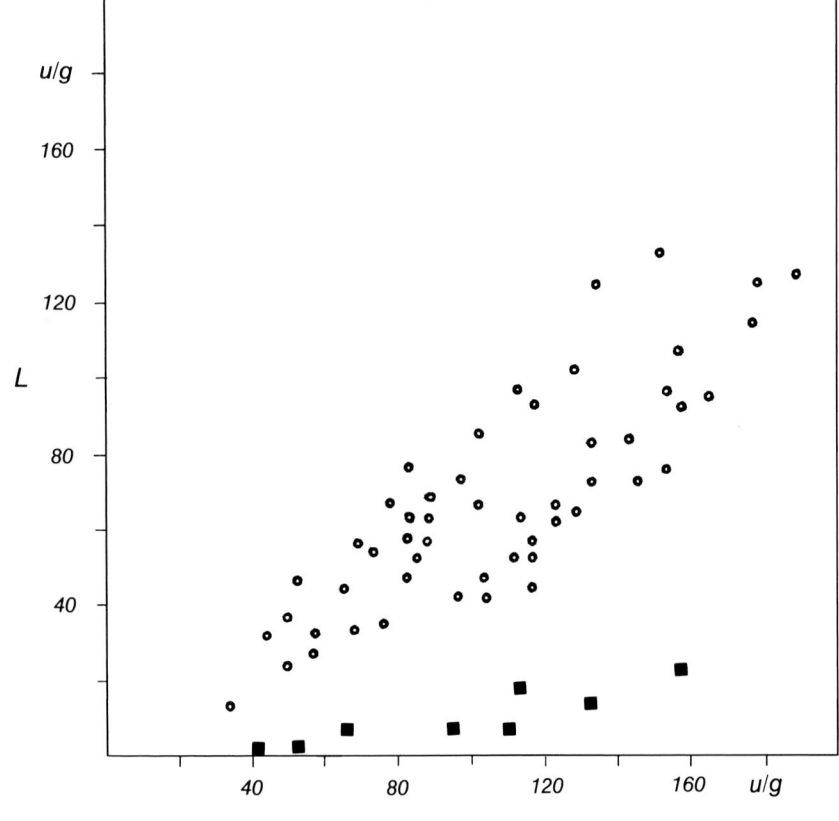

A.

B.

Fig. 122-1 Lactase activity (L, in units per gram protein in intestinal biopsy homogenates) and lactase/sucrase activity ratios (L/S) in 60 healthy adult male Germans (age 20–53 years). Screen (A) and squares (B) represent subjects with low lactose digestion capacity, as determined by two independent lactose tolerance tests. n = number of subjects.

(2) that the variable expression of the trait is genetically determined; and (3) that the rarest of the phases has a frequency of more than approximately 1 percent (thus precluding recurrent mutation as the cause of the variability). It will be shown that these three characteristics of a genetic polymorphism apply to the variability of lactase activity in healthy adult humans.

LOW AND HIGH ADULT LACTASE ACTIVITY AS PHYSIOLOGICAL TRAITS

When lactase activity is determined in biopsies of morphologically normal small intestine, a bimodal distribution is obtained in most human populations. In Central and Northern Europeans and their overseas descendants, the average lactase activity is not much lower than that of normal infants of the same population. Some individuals, however, exhibit a distinctly low lactase activity. Depending on the conditions of analysis, the two modes of lactase activity may be separated or overlapping. The fact that any of no less than three reference parameters—wet weight of the biopsy specimen, protein concentration, or DNA content of the homogenate—are recommended in disaccharidase activity determinations attests to the difficulties in defining a reliable base for the calculation of intestinal enzyme activities. The overlapping of low and high lactase activities is probably caused in part by variations of the reference parameters. In contrast to activities of a single enzyme, the ratios of disaccharidase activities are fairly constant in a given individual, and maltase/lactase or sucrase/lactase ratios are superior to simple lactase activities in resolving two distinct groups of adults with high and low lactase activity (Fig. 122-1).[7] It is convenient to designate these two groups of differing lactase activity as *physiological lactase phenotypes.*

That these two groups are biologically different is proved by the result of lactose tolerance tests. Subjects with high lactase activity can completely digest the usual test dose of 50 g lactose. They have a significant rise in blood glucose concentration within 15 to 45 min following lactose administration, and since no undigested lactose reaches the colon, they lack colonic hydrogen formation and hydrogen excretion in the breath. In contrast, the lactose digestion capacity of subjects in the group with low lactase activity is usually overtaxed by a single dose of 50 g lactose. There is no increase or only a small increase in blood glucose concentration; lactose reaching the colon is fermented by colonic bacteria; the hydrogen produced in this process is partially excreted in the expired air; and the osmotic effects of undigested lactose, the acidification of the colonic contents by short-chain fatty acids, and the formation of copious amounts of gas cause symptoms of lactose intolerance, such as nausea, meteorism, flatulence, borborygmi, and diarrhea. Comparative studies have shown that the lactose tolerance test with breath hydrogen determination and the lactose-ethanol test with blood galactose determination reliably separate the two phenotypic groups of adults with high and low lactase activity.[8,9]

Phylogenetically, low lactase activity in adult mammals is normal.[10] In all lactose-producing mammals, a characteristic developmental pattern of lactase activity has been observed. Lactase activity is high in the newborn and suckling period, declines regularly after the species-specific weaning phase, and remains low in adolescent and adult animals. The concept that humans are an exception to this rule is no longer tenable.

Worldwide studies have shown that the majority of adult humans belong to the phenotypic group with low lactase activity and low lactose digestion capacity. In analogy to the ontogenetic development in other mammals, mature human newborns and normal human infants have high lactase activity. In subjects who develop physiological low adult lactase activity, the decrease occurs during childhood. The decline of lactase activity begins between 2 and 3 years, and is usually complete by the age of 5 to 6 years.[11] Rare exceptions to this developmental pattern with a conversion from high to low lactase activity during adolescence have been observed in Finland.[12] In other healthy subjects this decline of lactase activity does not take place; lactase activity and lactose digestion capacity remain high throughout life. There is ample evidence of the independence of these development patterns and the resulting phenotypes from nutritional factors, such as the amount of milk in the diet.[13–15] The usual terms for the two distinct lactase phenotypes fail to recognize that the difference between them is not a matter of lactose absorption but rather one of lactose digestion. Therefore, the terms *high lactose digestion capacity (high LDC)* and *low lactose digestion capacity (low LDC)* seem more appropriate.

GENETIC DETERMINATION OF THE LACTASE PHENOTYPES

A genetic basis of the two physiological adult lactose phenotypes was suspected soon after the discovery of low lactase activity ("lactase deficiency") as a common trait among healthy adult humans.[16] Different genetic models were proposed, but experimental evidence of a simple mode of inheritance of the lactase phenotypes was lacking. Sahi[17] summarized earlier segregation studies and showed that insufficient numbers and/or unreliable methods—e.g., the lactose tolerance test with blood glucose determination (which gives particularly poor results in children[18]—precluded proof of Mendelian inheritance of the two adult lactase phenotypes. It was not before 1973 that the classical methods of segregation analysis and reliable methods of lactase phenotype diagnosis were applied in a family study.[19]

This work was facilitated by the relatively high frequency of low lactase activity among Finns, but also by the fact that the Finnish study group was the first to apply a reliable diagnostic procedure, the lactose-ethanol tolerance test with blood galactose determination[20,21] to a sufficiently large number of informative families. They proved convincingly that healthy adult subjects with low lactase activity are homozygous for a recessive autosomal allele causing the physiological postweaning decline of lactase activity, whereas subjects with high adult lactase activity are either heterozygous or homozygous for a dominant allele preventing the normal decline of lactase activity. The results of this study were soon confirmed by independent segregation analyses in different populations.[22,23] The postweaning decrease in lactase activity can thus be described as a regular genetic switch and a developmental program which is characteristic of almost all species of mammals. At present, the molecular mechanisms of this ontogenetic switch (restriction of lactase activity during childhood) and its failure (persistence of lactase activity throughout life) are unknown. Since the physicochemical, immunologic, and kinetic properties of lactase in infants and adults—and in individuals with lactase restriction and those with lactase persistence—are identical (see Chap. 121), it is clear that the difference between the physiological adult lactase phenotypes is regulatory and not structural. In this respect, lactase restriction differs fundamentally from enzyme deficiencies due to gene deletions or structural mutations. At the present state of knowledge, it seems advisable to use a system of neutral descriptive terms and to avoid expressions implying definite genetic mechanisms, such as *lactase repression*. The suggested nomenclature for the physiological adult lactase phenotypes and the underlying genotypes is listed in Table 122-1. With respect to gene symbols, the abbreviation LAC is introduced for the lactase locus. LAC⋆R is the allele causing lactase restriction in childhood, and LAC⋆P the allele determining lactase persistence. If the rare gene responsible for congenital lactase deficiency should prove to be allelic, it could be incorporated into this system as LAC⋆C, and other alleles (e.g., genes with different timing of the switch) can be distinguished by the addition of numerals.

Although the genetic etiology of low and high adult lactase activity and their Mendelian segregation is now generally recognized, it is rarely appreciated that additional independent evidence for the formal genetic model of the two alleles (or group of alleles) LAC⋆R and LAC⋆P has accumulated. The first type of evidence concerns the relationship between lactase phenotype and genotype. If there is a correlation between lactase gene dosage and lactase activity, a trimodal distribution of lactase activity would be expected in populations possessing the lactase alleles LAC⋆R and LAC⋆P. Such a trimodality has not been convincingly demonstrated using conventional lactase activity determination. Only disaccharidase activity ratios determined with optimized methods have uncovered a trimodal distribution of sucrase/lactase or maltase/lactase activity ratios compatible with Hardy-Weinberg expectations of the distribution of the three genotypes LAC⋆R/LAC⋆R, LAC⋆R/ LAC⋆P, and LAC⋆P/LAC⋆P.[24,25] Additional proof of monogenic inheritance of the lactase phenotypes was obtained in a study of lactose digestion in twins, using two independent methods of assessing LDC. Concordance of the lactose phenotypes among monozygous twins was complete, and the distribution of dizygous twin pairs concordant for low LDC, discordant pairs, and pairs concordant for high LDC corresponded with Hardy-Weinberg expectations.[9]

In view of occcasional doubts concerning the simple genetic etiology of the lactase phenotypes, it is important to note that their diagnosis requires the administration of unphysiological doses of lactose. Therefore, *low LDC* and *lactase restriction* are not synonymous with *lactose intolerance*. Many healthy subjects with low lactase activity experience no symptoms or only minimal symptoms with ordinary amounts of milk or other lactose-containing foods. Many genetic and nutritional factors influence lactose tolerance in a single individual.[26] Therefore, it is expected that familial aggregation, but not Mendelian seg-

regation, will be found in family studies if lactose tolerance is ascertained by personal nutritional history and the lactase phenotype is not determined using biochemical methods.[27]

DISTRIBUTION OF THE LACTASE PHENOTYPES IN HUMAN POPULATIONS: THE LACTASE POLYMORPHISM

The data on the distribution of the lactase phenotypes in the world population are not as reliable as those of other monogenic traits. This is mainly due to the difficulties in performing lactose tolerance tests (in comparison with serological or electrophoretic studies on single blood samples), and to the inadequacy of the methods of lactose testing in earlier studies. Even if specific enzymatic methods for the glucose assay are used, the lactose tolerance test based solely on blood glucose determination is unreliable and prone to overestimate the number of subjects with high LDC.[8,9,18] Despite these limitations, the available data of lactose tests in approximately 23,000 subjects permit a sufficiently precise description of the distribution of the lactase phenotypes in the world population. Detailed summaries of the lactase phenotype distribution have already been published.[28,29]

As is evident from the distribution data summarized in Table 122-2, lactase restriction is predominant and often the ubiquitous lactase phenotype in the native populations of Australia and Oceania, East and Southeast Asia, tropical Africa, and the Americas. The opposite distribution, predominance of the lactase persistence alelle, is found in two separate groups of populations: (1) Central and Northern Europeans (the Scandinavian countries, Germany, Austria, Switzerland, northern France, Belgium, the Netherlands, Britain, and Ireland), and (2) nomadic, milk-dependent populations in the arid zones of North Africa and Arabia (Tuareg, Fulbe, Beja, and Bedouin people). In these populations the lactase persistence allele LAC⋆P is more frequent than LAC⋆R. According to the Hardy-Weinberg rule, this means that less than 25 percent of the population have low LDC. Contrary to common opinion, lactase persistence is obviously not predominant in all European populations. The two regions of high prevalence of lactase persistence are separated by a wide peri-Mediterranean belt inhabited by peoples with predominant lactase restriction. This includes the littoral of North Africa, the Near East, Turkey, the Balkans, Italy, and southern France—areas were the frequency of low LDC is between 45 and 95 percent. In the eastern part of Central Europe (Hungary, Poland), 30 to 40 percent of the people have low LDC, and there may be a continuous west-east gradient extending from this region to the Far East, where 76 percent of the Kazakhs of northwestern China, 88 percent of Mongols in China, and 95 to 100 percent of southern Chinese have low lactase activity. Lactase restriction is also predominant in Southeast Asia and in South Asia (Iran, Afghanistan, Pakistan, India, and Sri Lanka). As expected, intermediate frequencies of the lactase phenotypes are found in populations originating from recent mixing of peoples with high and low frequencies of low LDC. In some of these, e.g., American Indians[30] and Eskimos,[31] the frequency of lactase persistence is correlated with the number of European ancestors. Figure 122-2 shows the distribution of the lac-

Table 122-1 Relation between Enzymatic and Digestive Adult Lactase Phenotypes and Genotypes

Enzymatic phenotype	Digestive phenotype	Genotype
Lactase restriction	Low lactose digestion capacity (low LDC)	LAC⋆R/LAC⋆R
Lactase persistence	High lactose digestion capacity (high LDC)	LAC⋆R/LAC⋆P, LAC⋆P/LAC⋆P

tase phenotypes in the Old World, the region where lactase polymorphism evolved.

The distinctness of the two lactase phenotypes, their proven genetic determination, and the highly variable distribution in human populations leave no doubt that the variability of intestinal lactase activity in healthy adults represents a genetic polymorphism. It is also clear that lactase restriction in childhood or adolescence occurs in the majority of humans. Postweaning lactase restriction conforms to the developmental pattern in most of the mammalian species. Lactase persistence is the "unusual" or even "abnormal" condition, and its high prevalence in some populations requires explanation.[32] Therefore the rationale in calling genetically determined low lactase activity in healthy adults "lactase deficiency" is to be questioned. Are individuals lacking the Rhesus blood group factor D "Rhesus factor–deficient"? Would one designate blood group O as "combined sphingolipid H–N-acetylgalactosamyl–galactosyl transferase deficiency"?

Table 122-2 Distribution of the Adult Lactase Phenotyes in Human Populations

Population or country	Subgroup	Number of subjects	High LDC	Low LDC	Percent low LDC	Population or country	Subgroup	Number of subjects	High LDC	Low LDC	Percent low LDC
Finland	Finns	449	371	78	17	Jordan	Agricultural	204	43	161	79
	Lapps	521	305	216	41		Bedouins	162	123	39	24
	Swedes	91	84	7	8	Saudi Arabia	Bedouins	22	17	5	23
Sweden	Swedes	400	396	4	1		Other Arabs	18	8	10	56
Denmark	Danes	761	743	18	3	Lebanon		225	48	177	79
Britain	British	96	90	6	6	Syria		75	7	68	91
Ireland	Irish	50	48	2	4	Arabs	Mixed groups	30	5	25	83
Netherlands	Dutch	14	14	0	0	Iran	Iranians	40	7	33	83
Germany	Germans	1872	1596	276	15	Afghanistan	Afghans	270	47	223	83
France	North	73	56	17	23	Pakistan		467	195	272	58
	South	82	47	35	43	India	North	264	194	70	27
Spain	Spaniards	265	225	40	15		Central	125	46	79	63
Switzerland	Swiss	64	54	10	16		South	60	20	40	67
Austria	Austrians	528	422	106	20	Indians	Overseas	87	22	65	75
Italy	North	565	301	264	47	Sri Lanka	Sinhalese	200	55	145	73
	South	128	41	78	68	Thailand	Thai	428	8	420	98
	Sicily	100	29	71	71	Vietnamese	In U.S.A.	31	0	31	100
Yugoslavia	Slovenians	153	99	54	35	China	Han North	641	49	592	93
	South	51	25	26	51		Han South	405	17	388	96
Hungary	Hungarians	707	446	61	37		Mongols	198	24	174	88
Czechoslovakia	Czechs	217	189	28	13		Kazakhs	195	46	149	76
Poland	Poles	296	187	109	37		Uighurs	202	37	165	82
Soviet Union	Leningrad	248	210	38	15		Hui	177	24	153	86
	Estonians	650	467	183	28		Koreans	198	12	186	94
Greece	Greeks	972	452	520	53		Hakka	202	22	180	89
Cyprus	Greeks	67	19	48	72		Bai/Zhuang	359	27	332	93
Gypsies	European	253	83	170	67		Taiwan	71	0	71	100
Turkey	Turks	470	135	335	71	Chinese	Overseas	94	23	71	76
Morocco	Maghrebi	55	12	43	78	Japan	Japanese	66	10	56	85
Egypt		584	157	427	73	Indonesia	Javanese	53	5	48	91
Sudan	Arabs	387	179	208	54	Papua New Guinea	Tribals	123	12	111	90
	Beja	303	252	51	17	Fiji	Fijians	12	0	12	100
	Other nomads	61	42	19	31	Australia	Whites	133	127	6	5
	South	366	92	274	75		Aborigines	145	48	97	67
Ethiopia		58	6	52	90	Greenland	Eskimo	119	18	101	85
Somalia		244	58	186	76		Mixed	108	67	41	38
Kenya	Bantu	71	19	52	73	Canada	Whites	16	15	1	6
Uganda, Rwanda	Bantu	114	14	100	88		Indians	30	11	19	63
	Hima, Tussi	70	65	5	7	U.S.A.	Alaska	36	6	30	83
	Mixed	75	38	37	49		Indians	221	11	210	95
Central Africa	Bantu	112	6	106	95		Whites	1101	887	214	19
South Africa	Bantu	57	3	54	95		Blacks	390	138	252	65
	Bushmen	65	3	62	95		Mexicans	305	147	158	52
	Mixed	152	26	126	83	Mexico	Mexicans	401	69	332	83
Nigeria	Ibo, Yoruba	113	12	101	89	Colombia	Mestizos	45	30	15	33
	Hausa	48	9	39	81		Chami Indians	24	0	24	100
	Fulani (Fulbe)	9	7	2	22	Peru	Mestizos	94	26	68	72
Niger	Tuareg	118	103	15	13	Bolivia	Aymara	31	7	24	77
Senegal	Agricultural	131	85	46	35	Brazil	Whites	53	27	26	49
	Peuhl (Fulbe)	29	29	0	0		Nonwhites	31	8	23	74
Israel	Israeli	272	92	180	66		Japanese	20	0	20	100
	Arabs	67	13	54	80						

For references see Tables IV and V and Addenda in Ref. 29.
LDC = lactose digestion capacity.

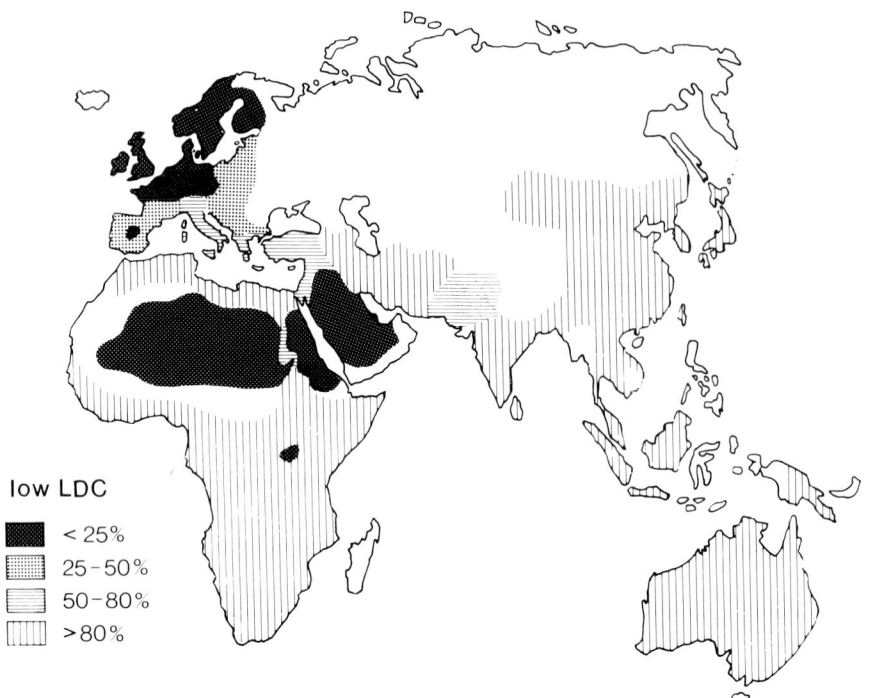

low LDC

▓ < 25%

▒ 25−50%

▤ 50−80%

▥ >80%

Fig. 122-2 Distribution of the lactase phenotypes [shown as percent lactose digestion capacity (see key)] in the native populations of the Old World. *Blank areas:* insufficient data.

EXPLANATIONS FOR THE VARIABLE DISTRIBUTION OF THE LACTASE PHENOTYPES IN HUMAN POPULATIONS

High frequencies of adult lactase persistence are found only in populations with a tradition of substantial production and consumption of animal milk. It is generally assumed that the allele LAC⋆P has reached high frequencies by natural selection in pastoralist populations that developed dairying during the Neolithic period. On the individual level, however, people adjust their dietary intake of milk and milk products consciously or unconsciously to their individual lactose tolerance threshold. Even in populations with generally high milk intake, subjects with low LDC rarely experience severe symptoms of lactose intolerance. This observation may also be relevant on the population level, and the question must be raised whether peoples adopted dairying and milk consumption because the majorities among them were lactase-persistent. Most writers addressing this problem assume a selective advantage of subjects with high LDC, but an opposite, neutralistic hypothesis has been advanced. On the basis of the observation that the lactase persistence gene seems to be present in variable frequencies in most human populations, Nei and Saitou[33] reason that this gene originated before the separation of the major human races; i.e., long before the domestication of milking animals. Populations in which the lactase persistence gene attained high frequencies by chance (genetic drift) are presumed to have been able to utilize the benefit of animal milk in adult nutrition. Subsequent selection in favor of the lactase persistence gene is held possible but not essential for the present distribution of the lactase phenotypes.

The validity of this hypothesis must be questioned for two reasons: (1) as mentioned before, the usual field tests for lactose digestion tend to overestimate the frequency of lactase persistence, and lactase restriction may be ubiquitous in many populations for which frequencies of low LDC in excess of 95 percent have been reported; and (2) there is evidence for migration of nomadic pastoralist peoples with a presumably high

frequency of lactase persistence to economically more promising agricultural areas with absent or low milk production.[34,35] If these factors are taken into consideration, natural selection in favor of LAC⋆P is a more likely cause of the high prevalence of lactase persistence in Afro-Arabian nomads and in the populations of Central and Northern Europe. Johnson, Kretchmer, and Simoons[36] have aptly described the appropriate environmental conditions: "Such selective advantage would only develop among peoples, whether farmers or pastoralists, who had a plentiful milk supply, who did not process their milk into products that were low in lactose and for whom milk provided essential nutrients that could not be readily obtained in the other foods available." This statement is the salient argument of the "culture historical hypothesis," first advanced by Simoons in 1970.[37] Such environmental conditions, conveniently described as "milk dependence," are present in the arid desert areas of North Africa and Arabia,[34] and therefore the culture historical hypothesis plausibly explains the high frequency of lactase persistence among all examined nomadic populations of this area.

Assuming nutritional milk dependence as a selective factor in populations other than nomadic pastoralists raises difficulties. In most agricultural populations of the Old World except tropical Africa and East Asia, animal milk is used in moderate amounts in the nutrition of older children and adults. The frequency of low LDC in milk-using populations of the Mediterranean area and the Near East varies between 50 and 100 percent, and there is no correlation between present and traditional milk use on the one hand, and the frequency of lactase persistence, on the other. Moderate milk consumption does not seem to result in selection in favor of LAC⋆P, and the adaptation of milk by fermentation is a procedure permitting innocuous consumption of relatively large amounts of milk products by subjects with low LDC. The variable lactase phenotype distribution in agricultural populations in the Mediterranean area and in Southwest Asia is more likely due to migrations of pastoralist populations with presumably high frequencies of LAC⋆P than to differences in selective pressure in favor of lactase persistence.[38]

The application of the culture historical hypothesis to European populations is even more problematic. The frequency of LAC*P does not correspond to the known genetic gradient caused by the migratory settlement of Europe from the Near East in the postglacial period.[39] On the contrary, the highest frequency of LAC*P is found in southern Scandinavia, an area where agriculture and dairying were introduced late, probably not more than 4000 years ago.[40] This means that the period available for selection in favor of LAC*P was only about half as long as that in the Afro-Arabian arid zone. It seems likely, therefore, that European lactase persistence developed independently of that in nomadic pastoralists. This view is strenghtened by the fact that Northern European populations are and were characterized by a mixed economy of farming and dairying which is not conducive to milk dependence. To explain the relatively rapid establishment of high frequencies of a lactase persistence allele in Northern Europe in the absence of milk dependence, Flatz and Rotthauwe advanced the "calcium absorption hypothesis."[41] This is based on the observation that lactose increases the absorption of calcium in subjects with high LDC in the absence of monosaccharides,[42] and on the assumption that rickets and osteomalacia were potent selective factors in the conditions of low solar irradiation that are characteristic of Northwestern Europe.[43,44] Notwithstanding the difficulties in obtaining experimental evidence for the calcium absorption hypothesis, the wide geographic distance between the two population groups with predominance of LAC*P suggests an independent origin of the lactase persistence gene in these groups, and legitimates the proposition of differing selective mechanisms in the two areas. Modern methods of DNA analysis may soon permit the localization of the lactase gene. The molecular structure of the chromosomal segment containing the LAC locus may tell us whether Afro-Arabian and European lactase persistence have a common or a separate mutational origin.

NUTRITIONAL AND MEDICAL IMPLICATIONS

The majority of humans with genetically determined low LDC live in countries where animal milk is not used in the normal diet. Consequently, lactose intolerance is not likely to occur. Even in milk-consuming societies, lactose intolerance is not a frequent medical problem, because individuals with lactase restriction seem to adjust milk intake to their individual tolerance level. This is exemplified by the observation that the diet manuals in 58 percent of 323 American hospitals did not contain instructions with respect to lactose intolerance.[45] Lactose intolerance is most likely to develop when people with low LDC change their dietary habits—e.g., following the move from a country with low milk consumption to an area where milk use is high, or when nutrients with high lactose concentration, such as powdered milk, are distributed during relief programs in communities where the majority of people have low LDC. In these cases, the pharmacological action of lactose in subjects with lactase restriction should be kept in mind. Personal communications from several professionals from Southern European or tropical countries indicate that a glass of cold milk is a convenient and inexpensive laxative in subjects with low lactase activity.

Several associations between the adult lactase phenotypes and diseases have been reported, but the evidence is controversial. A role of low LDC in recurrent abdominal pain in children[46–48] and in "irritable bowel syndrome" in adults[49–55] has been claimed, but there are other reports which do not support this association.[56–61] Only a few studies are satisfactory with respect to matching in ethnicity between the patient and control groups, which seems mandatory in view of the great variation in the distribution of the lactase phenotypes. The possible placebo effect of milk withdrawal must also be taken into consideration.[62] Lactase persistence is not devoid of possible disease associations. There is some evidence for a role of milk consumption by lactase-persistent subjects in the causation of hyperlipidemia,[63] coronary heart disease,[64] and cataract.[65] A study in Italy demonstrated a high frequency of premature cataract in milk-consuming subjects with high LDC,[66] but a similar survey in Sweden was negative.[67] Since the cataracts observed in genetic disorders of galactose metabolism are attributed to galactitol, it may be advisable to determine the galactose tolerance of subjects with premature cataracts in further studies of this association.

An even more controversial subject is the role of lactase restriction in presenile osteoporosis. It is not possible to fully discuss this aspect of the association between lactase phenotypes and disease in the context of this chapter. Several reports describe a significantly higher frequency of lactase restriction in osteoporotic women in comparison with control groups,[68–71] and a reduction of calcium availability by milk avoidance and by reduced absorption is claimed to be a causative factor. However, there are doubts[72] that a high calcium intake can prevent osteoporosis, and the recommendations for daily adult calcium intake vary considerably.[73–75] No ill effects have been observed following prolonged restriction of calcium intake to less than 200 mg/day,[76] an amount easily supplied by a milk-free diet. Furthermore, in contrast to osteomalacia, osteoporosis is not primarily due to calcium deficiency. It is rather a defect of bone matrix formation which is influenced by several other factors, e.g., physical activity, exposure to sunshine, hormonal status, and vitamin and protein nutrition. At present, one can hardly say more about the role of lactase restriction in osteoporosis of the elderly than that it may be a contributory factor in milk-consuming societies where a large part of the daily protein and calcium requirement is covered by milk and milk products.

REFERENCES

1. RÖHMANN F, LAPPE J: Über die Lactase des Dünndarms. *Dtsch Chem Ges* 28:2506, 1895.
2. AURICCHIO S, RUBINO A, SEMENZA G, LANDOLT M, PRADER A: Isolated intestinal lactase deficiency in the adult. *Lancet* 2:324, 1963.
3. DAHLQVIST A, HAMMOND B, CRANE RK, DUNPHY JV, LITTMAN A: Intestinal lactase deficiency and lactose intolerance in adults: Preliminary report. *Gastroenterology* 45:488, 1963.
4. MCKUSICK V: *Mendelian Inheritance in Man. Catalogs of Autosomal Dominant, Autosomal Recessive, and X-linked Phenotypes*, 7th ed. Baltimore, Johns Hopkins University Press, 1986.
5. BAYLESS TM, ROSENSWEIG NS: A racial difference in the incidence of lactase deficiency. A survey of milk intolerance and lactase deficiency in healthy adult males. *JAMA* 197:968, 1966.
6. FORD EB: *Genetic Polymorphism*. London, Faber & Faber, 1965.
7. NEWCOMER AD, MCGILL DB: Distribution of disaccharidase activity in the small bowel of normal and lactase-deficient subjects. *Gastroenterology* 51:481, 1966.
8. NEWCOMER AD, MCGILL DB, THOMAS PJ, HOFMANN AF: Prospective comparison of indirect methods for detecting lactase deficiency. *N Engl J Med* 293:1232, 1975.
9. METNEKI J, CZEIZEL A, FLATZ SD, FLATZ G: A study of lactose absorption capacity in twins. *Hum Genet* 67:296, 1984.

10. BLAXTER KL: Lactation and the growth of the young, in Kow SK, Cowie AT (eds): *The Mammary Gland and Its Secretion.* New York, Academic, 1961.

11. SIMOONS FJ: Age of onset of lactose malabsorption. *Pediatrics* 66:646, 1980.

12. SAHI T, LAUNIALA K, LAITINEN H: Hypolactasia in a fixed cohort of young Finnish adults. A follow-up study. *Scand J Gastroenterol* 18:865, 1983.

13. FLATZ G, ROTTHAUWE HW: Evidence against nutritional adaptation of tolerance to lactose. *Hum Genet* 13:118, 1971.

14. KNUDSEN KB, WELSH MD, KRONENBERG RS, VANDERVEEN JE, HEIDELBAUCH ND: Effect of a nonlactose diet on human intestinal disaccharidase activity. *Am J Dig Dis* 13:593, 1968.

15. LEBENTHAL E, SUNSHINE P, KRETCHMER N: Effect of prolonged nursing on the activity of intestinal lactase. *Gastroenterology* 64:1136, 1973.

16. CUATRECASAS PD, LOXKWOOD H, CALDWELL J: Lactase deficiency in the adult: A common occurrence. *Lancet* 1:14, 1965.

17. SAHI T: The inheritance of selective adult-type lactose malabsorption. *Scand J Gastroenterol* 9 (Suppl 30), 1974.

18. KRASILNIKOFF PA, GUDMAND-HOYER E, MOLTKE HH: Diagnostic value of disaccharide tolerance tests in children. *Acta Paediatr Scand* 64:693, 1975.

19. SAHI T, ISOKOSKI M, JUSSILA J, LAUNIALA K, PYÖRÄLÄ K: Recessive inheritance of adult-type lactose malabsorption. *Lancet* 2:823, 1973.

20. FISCHER W, ZAPF J: Zur erworbenen Laktoseintoleranz. *Klin Wochenschr* 43:1243, 1965.

21. ISOKOSKI M, JUSSILA J, SARNA S: A simple screening method for lactose malabsorption. *Gastroenterology* 62:28, 1972.

22. LISKER R, GONZALEZ B, DALTABUIT M: Recessive inheritance of the adult type of intestinal lactase deficiency. *Am J Hum Genet* 27:662, 1975.

23. RANSOME-KUTI O, KRETCHMER N, JOHNSON JD, GRIBBLE JT: A genetic study of lactose digestion in Nigerian families. *Gastroenterology* 68:431, 1975.

24. HO MW, POVEY S, SWALLOW D: Lactase polymorphism in adult British natives: Estimating allele frequencies by enzyme assays in autopsy samples. *Am J Hum Genet* 34:650, 1982.

25. FLATZ G: Gene dosage effect on lactase activity demonstrated in vivo. *Am J Hum Genet* 36:306, 1984.

26. FLATZ G, ROTTHAUWE HW: The human lactase polymorphism: Physiology and genetics of lactose absorption and malabsorption. *Prog Med Genet* 2:205, 1977.

27. JOHNSON RC, SCHWITTERS SY, COLE RE, AHERN FM, AU K: A family study of lactose intolerance. *Behav Genet* 67:296, 1981.

28. SIMOONS FJ: The geographic hypothesis and lactose malabsorption: A weighing of the evidence. *Am J Dig Dis* 23:963, 1978.

29. FLATZ G: The genetics of lactose digestion in humans. *Adv Hum Genet* 16:1, 1987.

30. NEWCOMER AD, THOMAS PJ, MCGILL DB, HOFMANN AF: Lactase deficiency: A common trait of the American Indian. *Gastroenterology* 72:234, 1977.

31. GUDMAND-HOYER E, MCNAIR A, JARNUM S, BROERSMA L, MCNAIR J: Lactose-malabsorption in Vestgronland. *Ugeskr Laeger* 135:169, 1973.

32. DAHLQVIST A: The basic aspects of the chemical background of lactase deficiency. *Postgrad Med J* 53:57, 1977.

33. NEI M, SAITOU N: Genetic relationship of human populations and ethnic differences in relation to drugs and food, in Kalow W, Goedde HW, Agarwal DP (eds): *Ethnic Differences in Reactions to Drugs and Other Xenobiotics.* New York, AR Liss, 1986.

34. BAYOUMI RAL, FLATZ SD, KÜHNAU W, FLATZ G: Beja and Nilotes: Nomadic pastoralist groups in the Sudan with opposite distributions of the adult lactase phenotypes. *Am J Phys Anthropol* 58:173, 1982.

35. HIJAZI SS, ABULABAN A, AMMARIN Z, FLATZ G: Distribution of adult lactase phenotypes in Bedouins and in urban and agricultural populations of Jordan. *Trop Geogr Med* 35:157, 1983.

36. JOHNSON JD, KRETCHMER N, SIMOONS FJ: Lactose malabsorption: Its biology and history. *Adv Pediatr* 21:197, 1974.

37. SIMOONS FJ: Primary adult lactose intolerance and the milking habit: A problem in biological and cultural interrelations. II. A culture historical hypothesis. *Am J Dig Dis* 15:695, 1970.

38. FLATZ G: Laktase-Phänotypen in sesshaften und nomadischen Bevölkerungsgruppen des Nahen Ostens. *Homo* 35:173, 1984.

39. PIAZZA A, MENOZZI P, CAVALLI-SFORZA LL: The HLA-A, B frequencies in the world: Migration or selection? *Hum Immunol* 4:297, 1980.

40. AMMERMANN AJ, CAVALLI-SFORZA LL: Measuring the rate of spread of early farming in Europe. *Man* 6:674, 1971.

41. FLATZ G, ROTTHAUWE HW: Lactose nutrition and natural selection. *Lancet* 2:76, 1973.

42. COCHET B, JUNG A, GRIESSEN M, BARTHOLDI P, SCHALLER P, DONATH A: Effects of lactose on intestinal calcium absorption in normal and lactose deficient subjects. *Gastroenterology* 84:935, 1983.

43. JONXIS JHP: Some investigations on rickets. *J Pediatr* 59:607, 1961.

44. LOOMIS WF: Skin-pigment regulation of Vitamin-D biosynthesis in man. *Science* 157:501, 1967.

45. WELSH, JD: Diet therapy in adult lactose malabsorption: Present practices. *Am J Clin Nutr* 31:592, 1978.

46. BAYLESS TM, HUANG SS: Recurrent abdominal pain due to milk and lactose intolerance in school-aged children. *Pediatrics* 47:1029, 1971.

47. BARR RG, LEVINE MD, WATKINS JD: Recurrent abdominal pain of childhood due to lactose intolerance: A prospective study. *N Engl J Med* 300:1449, 1979.

48. LIEBMAN WM: Recurrent abdominal pain in children: Lactose and sucrose intolerance. A prospective study. *Pediatrics* 64:43, 1979.

49. MCMICHAEL HB, WEBB J, DAWSON AM: Lactase deficiency in adults: A cause of "functional" diarrhoea. *Lancet* 1:717, 1965.

50. WESER E, RUBIN W, ROSS L, SLEISINGER MH: Lactase deficiency in patients with the "irritable-colon syndrome." *N Engl J Med* 273:1070, 1965.

51. MCDONAUGH TJ: Lactose intolerance: A newly recognized cause of gastrointestinal symptoms seen in the practice of occupational medicine. *J Occup Med* 11:57, 1969.

52. FUNG WP, KHO KM: The importance of milk intolerance in patients presenting with chronic (nervous) diarrhoea. *Aust NZ J Med* 1:374, 1971.

53. PENA AS, TRUELOVE SC: Hypolactasia and the irritable colon syndrome. *Scand J Gastroenterol* 7:433, 1972.

54. GUDMAND-HOYER E, RIIS P, WULFF HR: The significance of lactose malabsorption in the irritable colon syndrome. *Scand J Gastroenterol* 8:273, 1973.

55. PORRO GB, PERTRILLO N, PARENTE F, SANGALETTI O, DELLA VEDOVA G: Recurrent abdominal pain and lactose intolerance. *Br Med J* 283:501, 1981.

56. NEWCOMER AD, MCGILL DB: Irritable bowel syndrome: Role of lactase deficiency. *Mayo Clin Proc* 58:339, 1983.

57. BLUMENTHAL I, KELLEHER J, LITTLEWOOD JM: Recurrent abdominal pain and lactose intolerance in childhood. *Br Med J* 282:2013, 1980.

58. CHRISTENSEN MF: Prevalence of lactose malabsorption in children with recurrent abdominal pain. *Pediatrics* 65:681, 1980.

59. LEBENTHAL E, ROSSI TM, NORD KS, BRANSKI D: Recurrent abdominal pain and lactose absorption in children. *Pediatrics* 67:828, 1981.

60. DEARLOVE J, DEARLOVE B, PEARL K, PRIMAVESI R: Dietary lactose and the child with abdominal pain. *Br Med J* 286:1936, 1983.

61. WALD A, CHANDRA R, FISHER SE: Lactose malabsorption in recurrent abdominal pain of childhood. *J Pediatr* 100:65, 1982.

62. MACLEAN WC: Lactose intolerance. *N Engl J Med* 302:177, 1980.

63. SAHI T, JUSSILA J, PENTTILÄ I, SARNA S, ISOKOSKI M: Serum lipids and proteins in lactose malabsorption. *Am J Clin Nutr* 30:476, 1977.

64. SEGALL JJ: Hypothesis: Is lactose a dietary risk factor for ischaemic heart disease? *Int J Epidemiol* 9:271, 1980.

65. SIMOONS FJ: A geographic approach to senile cataracts: Possible links with milk consumption, lactase activity and galactose metabolism. *Dig Dis Sci* 27:257, 1982.

66. RINALDI E, ALBINI L, COSTAGLIOLA C, DEROSA G, AURICCHIO G, DEVIZIA B, AURICCHIO S: High frequency of lactose absorbers among adults with idiopathic senile and presenile cataract in a population with high prevalence of primary adult lactose malabsorption. *Lancet* 1:355, 1984.

67. BENGTSON G, STEEN B, DAHLQVIST A, JÄGERSTAD M: Does lactose intake induce cataract in man? *Lancet* 1:1293, 1984.

68. BIRGE SJ, KEUTMANN HT, CUATRECASAS P, WHEDON GD: Osteoporosis, intestinal lactase deficit and low dietary calcium intake. *N Engl J Med* 276:445, 1967.

69. NEWCOMER AD, HODGSON SF, MCGILL DB, THOMAS PJ: Lactase deficiency: Prevalence in osteoporosis. *Ann Intern Med* 89:218, 1978.

70. VELEBIT L, COCHET B, COURVOISIER B: Incidence de l'intolerance au lactose dans l'osteoporose postmenopausique. *Schweiz Med Wochenschr* 108:2061, 1978.

71. KOCIAN J, VULTERINOVA M, BEJBLOVA O, SKALA I: Influence of lactose intolerance on the bones of patients with partial gastrectomy. *Digestion* 8:324, 1973.

72. ALHAVA EM, JUSSILA J, KARJALAINEN P, VUOJOLAHTI P: Lactose malabsorption and bone mineral content. *Acta Med Scand* 201:281, 1977.

73. FOOD AND NUTRITION BOARD: *Recommended Dietary Allowances.* Washington DC, National Academy of Science, 1968, p 233.

74. WALKER ARP: The human requirement of calcium. Should low intakes be supplemented? *Am J Clin Nutr* 25:518, 1972.

75. PASSMORE R, NICOL BM, RAC MN: *Handbook on Human Nutritional Requirements.* Geneva, World Health Organization, 1974, p 453.

76. HEGSTEDT DM, MOSCOSCO I, COLLAZOS C: A study of the minimum calcium requirement of adult men. *J Nutr* 44:181, 1952.

INDEX

Page references in *italic* indicate tables; page references in **boldface** indicate illustrations.

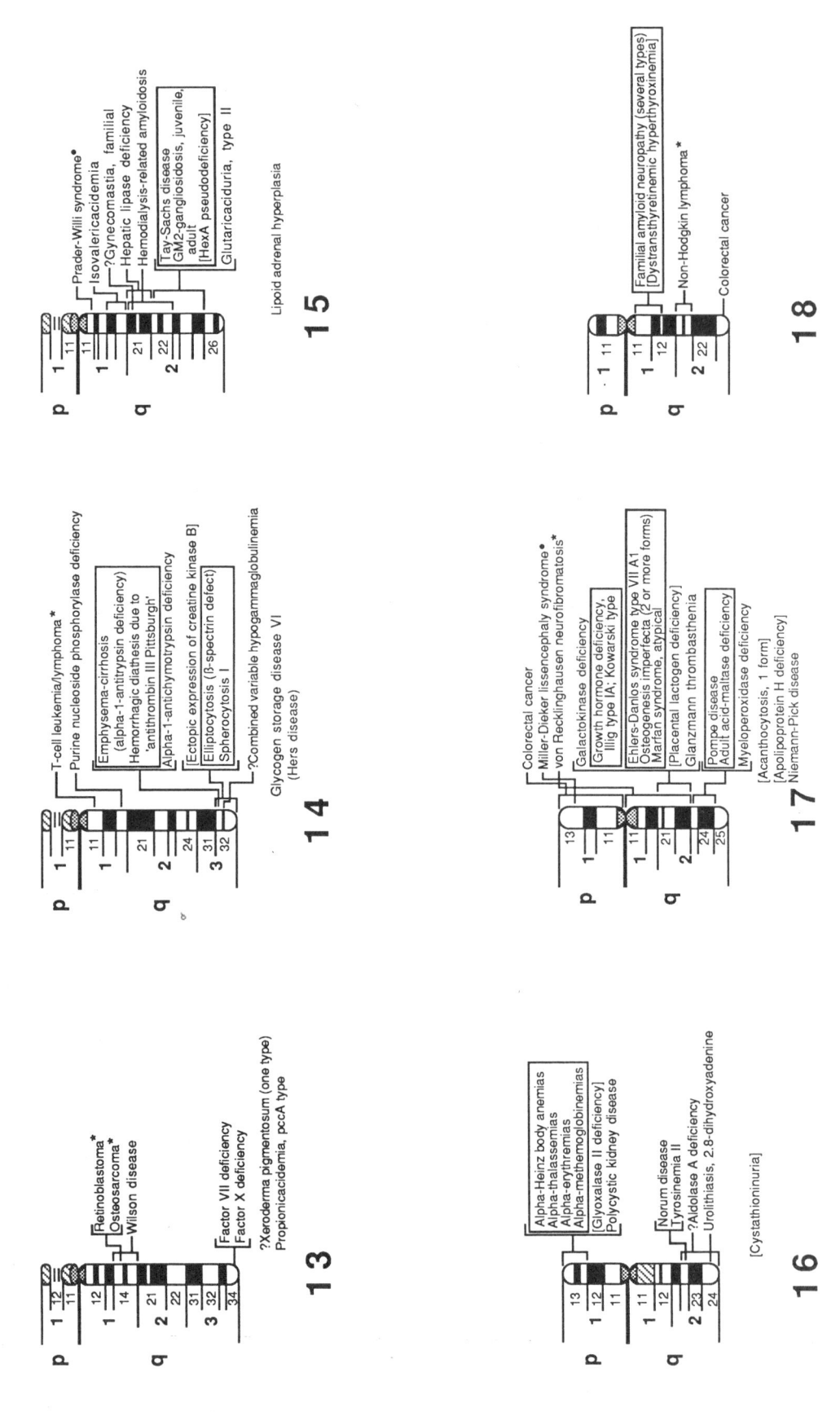

13

Retinoblastoma *
Osteosarcoma *
Wilson disease

Factor VII deficiency
Factor X deficiency

?Xeroderma pigmentosum (one type)
Propionicacidemia, pccA type

14

T-cell leukemia/lymphoma *
Purine nucleoside phosphorylase deficiency

Emphysema-cirrhosis
(alpha-1-antitrypsin deficiency)
Hemorrhagic diathesis due to
'antithrombin III Pittsburgh'
Alpha-1-antichymotrypsin deficiency

Ectopic expression of creatine kinase B]
Elliptocytosis (β-spectrin defect)
Spherocytosis I

?Combined variable hypogammaglobulinemia

Glycogen storage disease VI
(Hers disease)

15

Prader-Willi syndrome •
Isovalericacidemia
?Gynecomastia, familial
Hepatic lipase deficiency
Hemodialysis-related amyloidosis

Tay-Sachs disease
GM2-gangliosidosis, juvenile,
adult
[HexA pseudodeficiency]
Glutaricaciduria, type II

Lipoid adrenal hyperplasia

16

Alpha-Heinz body anemias
Alpha-thalassemias
Alpha-erythremias
Alpha-methemoglobinemias
[Glyoxalase II deficiency]
Polycystic kidney disease

Norum disease
Tyrosinemia II
?Aldolase A deficiency
Urolithiasis, 2,8-dihydroxyadenine

[Cystathioninuria]

17

Colorectal cancer
Miller-Dieker lissencephaly syndrome •
von Recklinghausen neurofibromatosis *

Galactokinase deficiency

Growth hormone deficiency,
Illig type IA; Kowarski type
Ehlers-Danlos syndrome type VII A1
Osteogenesis imperfecta (2 or more forms)
Marfan syndrome, atypical
[Placental lactogen deficiency]
Glanzmann thrombasthenia

Pompe disease
Adult acid-maltase deficiency
Myeloperoxidase deficiency

[Acanthocytosis, 1 form]
[Apolipoprotein H deficiency]
Niemann-Pick disease

18

Familial amyloid neuropathy (several types)
[Dystransthyretinemic hyperthyroxinemia]

Non-Hodgkin lymphoma *

Colorectal cancer

(Continued)